1999 Standard Postage Stamp Catalogue

ONE HUNDRED AND FIFTY-FIFTH EDITION IN SIX VOLUMES

VOLUME 4

COUNTRIES OF THE WORLD

J-O

VICE PRESIDENT/PUBLISHER	Stuart J. Morrissey
EDITOR	James E. Kloetzel
ASSOCIATE EDITOR	William W. Cummings
VALUING EDITOR	Martin J. Frankevicz
NEW ISSUES EDITOR	David C. Akin
COMPUTER CONTROL COORDINATOR	Denise Oder
EDITORIAL ASSISTANTS	Judith E. Bertrand, Beth Brown
ART/PRODUCTION DIRECTOR	Janine C. S. Apple
PRODUCTION COORDINATOR	Nancy S. Martin
MARKETING/SALES DIRECTOR	William Fay
ADVERTISING	Sabrina D. Morton
CIRCULATION/PRODUCT PROMOTION MANAGER	Tim Wagner

Released July 1998

Includes New Stamp Listings through the June, 1998 *Scott Stamp Monthly* Catalogue Update

Copyright© 1998 by

Scott Publishing Co.

911 Vandemark Road, Sidney, OH 45365-0828

A division of AMOS PRESS, INC., publishers of *Linn's Stamp News, Coin World, Cars & Parts* magazine, *Moneycard Collector* and *The Sidney Daily News.*

Table of Contents

See Volume 1 for United States, United Nations and Countries of the World A-B.
See Volumes 2, 3, 5, 6 for Countries of the World C-I, P-Z.

Volume 2: C-F
Volume 3: G-I
Volume 5: P-Sl
Volume 6: So-Z

Scott Publishing Mission Statement

The Scott Publishing Team exists to serve the recreational, educational and commercial hobby needs of stamp collectors and dealers.

We strive to set the industry standard for philatelic information and products by developing and providing goods that help collectors identify, value, organize and present their collections.

Quality customer service is, and will continue to be, our highest priority. We aspire toward achieving total customer satisfaction.

Copyright Notice

The contents of this book are owned exclusively by Scott Publishing Co. and all rights thereto are reserved under the Pan American and Universal Copyright Conventions.

Copyright @1998 by Scott Publishing Co., Sidney, OH. Printed in U.S.A.

COPYRIGHT NOTE
Permission is hereby given for the use of material in this book and covered by copyright if:

(a) The material is used in advertising matter, circulars or price lists for the purpose of offering stamps for sale or purchase at the prices listed therein; and

(b) Such use is incidental to the business of buying and selling stamps and is limited in scope and length, i.e., it does not cover a substantial portion of the total number of stamps issued by any country or of any special category of stamps of any country; and

(c) Such material is not used as part of any catalogue, stamp album or computerized or other system based upon the Scott catalogue numbers, or in any updated valuations of stamps not offered for sale or purchase; and

(d) Such use is not competitive with the business of the copyright owner; and

(e) Such use is for editorial purposes in publications in the form of articles or commentary, except for computer software or the serialization of books in such publications, for which separate written permission is required.

Any use of the material in this book which does not satisfy all the foregoing conditions is forbidden in any form unless permission in each instance is given in writing by the copyright owner.

Trademark Notice

The terms SCOTT, SCOTT'S, SCOTT CATALOGUE NUMBERING SYSTEM, SCOTT CATALOGUE NUMBER, SCOTT NUMBER and abbreviations thereof, are trademarks of Scott Publishing Co., used to identify its publications and its copyrighted system for identifying and classifying postage stamps for dealers and collectors. These trademarks are to be used only with the prior consent of Scott Publishing Co.

No part of this work may be reproduced in any form or by any means, electronic or mechanical, including photocopying, without permission in writing from Scott Publishing Co., P.O. Box 828, Sidney, OH 45365-0828.

ISBN 0-89487-243-5

Library of Congress Card No. 2-3301

Scott Publishing Co.

SCOTT

911 VANDEMARK ROAD, P. O. Box 828, SIDNEY, OHIO 45365-0828 937-498-0802

Dear Catalogue User,

Robust stamp buying activity continues with new levels of support arising from many quarters. Since the previous edition of this volume there has been increased competition at auctions, an ever-diminishing supply of good material coming to market and the emergence of a whole new world of philatelic commerce on the Internet.

More than 15,500 values have changed in Volume 4 of the *1999 Scott Standard Postage Stamp Catalogue.* Value changes appear across the board with many revisions in Macao, Liechenstein and Korea. This volume contains listings for countries of the world J-O.

As faithful readers of this letter page already know, I have the curious habit of asking myself questions. Here goes:

Where is Macao?

Near the same spot Hong Kong used to be, but not for long.

Values for Macao, which will be returned to the People's Republic of China in December 1999, are again up sharply. Many of the classic issues are twice the 1998 levels in the unused column. Scott 1-15, the 1884-85 Portuguese Crown set, soars to $822 unused and $304 used, from the 1998 levels of $432 unused and $275 used. The 1887 surcharges, Scott 24-28, zip to $295 unused and $101 used, from $147 unused and $90 used. The King Carlos set of 1898-1903 leaps to $755 unused from $298. The 1951 Sampan and Junk jump to $552 mint never hinged and $17 used, from $410 mint never hinged and $14 used.

Have any Asian countries from Volume 4 been affected by the economic crisis?

Not when it comes to stamps. In Korea the 1954 definitives, Scott 196-199, rise to $175 mint never hinged from $150. The 1956 Syngman Rhee inauguration set, Scott 227-228, hops to $80 mint never hinged from $70.

Malaysia shows many strong increases. The 1965 Birds set, Scott 20-27, climbs to $79 mint never hinged from $61, and the 1970 Butterflies, Scott 66-73, shoot to $33 mint never hinged from $24. Another 300 values were changed in the predecessor Malayan issues. Most changes are found in the listings for the various states. In Johore's 1884-86 overprints on Straits Settlements stamps, the 2c rose with 17 1/2x2 3/4mm overprint, Scott 4, scoots to $1,500 unused from $1,300. Kelantan's 1937-40 Sultan Ismail set, Scott 29-43, leaps to $525 unused and $629 used, from $475 unused and $509 used.

What about British Empire?

Most of the first 50 stamps of Malta show modest increases. Scott 8-13, the 1885 Queen Victoria set, ascends to $75 unused and $14 used, from $62 unused and $10 used. Many stamps issued from 1950 to about 1982 record moderate decreases. However most of the 1983-1994 issues show moderate increases.

Anything else?

With the exception of a few decreases found mostly in 19th century issues, Liberia records plenty of increases. Scott 9, the 1864 24c "Liberia" with single frame line on medium to thick paper, charges to $82.50 unused and $95 used, from $62.50 unused and $77 used. The 1979 Norman Rockwell sheet of 50, Scott 857a, bounds to $20 mint never hinged from $12.

In the Netherlands, the 1928 four-sided type B syncopated perfs, Scott 164a-193a, ascend to $298 hinged and $220 used, from $271 hinged and $205 used. The 1949 Queen Juliana high values, Scott 319-322, shoot to $978 mint never hinged and $400 hinged, from $853 mint never hinged and $375 hinged.

Manchukuo continues to be on the move. The 1932 definitives, Scott 1-18, zip to $183 hinged and $61 used, from $151 hinged and $49 used. Newly added for this set is a never hinged value of $250.

What about editorial changes?

Totals for sets with three and four stamps have been added for all countries in Volume 4.

Four minors have been added to Northern Rhodesia's 1963 Arms set. Two are on Scott 78, the 3p value. Scott 78c, valued at $900 mint never hinged, has the orange eagle omitted, and Scott 78d, valued at $125 mint never hinged, has the value and the orange eagle omitted. An item similar to Scott 78d has been added to the 9p value, as Scott 81b, valued at $250 mint never hinged, and an item similar to Scott 78c has been added to the 5sh value as Scott 86a, valued at $1,400 mint never hinged. Minors for se-tenant multiples have been added in Jamaica, Korea, Laos, Malawi, Mali, Marshall Islands, Mauritania, Monaco, Montserrat, Morocco, Netherlands, Netherlands Antilles, Nicaragua and Niger.

Korea Scott 1451, the 1986 Peace Year 400w, has been renumbered as Scott C45, and the souvenir sheet containing this item has been footnoted. Number changes also affect Kenya's 1996 Red Cross issue, Mali's 1997 Transportation strips and Niue's 1997 Humpback Whale set.

In Nepal, a footnote has been added stating that the used values for Nos. 9-49 are for telegraph cancels.

Anything big brewing for 1999?

Yes. IBRA 99, the international show to be held in Nuremberg, Germany from April 27 to May 4, 1999 promises to be a blockbuster. This is the first big international stamp show to be held in Germany since World War II. Attendance should be huge and the selection of material promises to be awe inspiring. Start making your travel plans now.

Are you still having your share of collecting fun?

If you've peaked in your specialty, have only the expensive stamps to buy in France, or if the mania surrounding gum condition is getting you down, maybe you need a new area to collect. Perhaps you're the type that just likes to dream. If so I would highly recommend the Scott Product Guide. There is no other wishbook like it in the hobby. The Product Guide is chockfull of collecting ideas and it is absolutely free. Just call 1-800-572-6885.

Happy collecting,

Stuart Morrissey

Stuart Morrissey/ Publisher

Acknowledgments

Our appreciation and gratitude go to the following individuals who have assisted us in preparing information included in the 1999 Scott Catalogues. Some helpers prefer anonymity. These individuals have generously shared their stamp knowledge with others through the medium of the Scott Catalogue.

Those who follow provided information that is in addition to the hundreds of dealer price lists and advertisements and scores of auction catalogues and realizations which were used in producing the catalogue values. It is from those noted here that we have been able to obtain information on items not normally seen in published lists and advertisements. Support from these people goes beyond data leading to catalogue values, for they also are key to editorial changes.

A.R. Allison (Orange Free State Study Circle)
B. J. Ammel (The Nile Post)
Mike Armus
Robert Ausubel
Jack Hagop Barsoumian (International Stamp Co.)
Jules K. Beck
John Birkinbine II
John R. Boker, Jr.
Victor Bove
Jeff Brasor (Honduras Collectors Club, Associated Collectors of El Salvador)
George W. Brett
Roger S. Brody
Lawrence A. Bustillo
Nathan Carlin
Richard A. Champagne
Charlie Chesloe (Tribuna Stamp Co.)
Henry Chlanda
Laurie Conrad
Frank D. Correl
Andrew Cronin (Canadian Society of Russian Philately)
William T. Crowe
Bob Dumaine (Sam Houston Duck Company)
William S. Dunn
Leon Finik (Loral Stamps)
Henry Fisher
Geoffrey Flack
Joseph E. Foley (Eire Philatelic Association)
Marvin Frey
Huguette Gagnon (Ethiopian Philatelic Society)
Bob Genisol (Sultan Stamp Center)
Richard B. Graham
Gary Griffith
Harry Hagendorf
Calvet M. Hahn
Rudolf Hamar (Estonian Philatelic Society)
John B. Head
Robert R. Hegland
Erich E. Hamm (Philactica)
Dale S. Hendricks (Dale Enterprises, Inc.)
Clifford O. Herrick (Fidelity Trading Company)
Lee H. Hill, Jr.
Dr. Eugene H. Holmok (Tatra Stamps, Reg'd.)
Jack R. Hughes (Fellowship of Samoa Specialists)
Wilson Hulme (U.S. Philatelic Classics Society)
Eric Jackson
Peter C. Jeannopoulos
Clyde Jennings
Stanford M. Katz
Lewis Kaufman
Dr. James W. Kerr
Charles Kezbers
Ken Lawrence
Pedro Llach (Filatelia Llach S.L.)
David MacDonnell
F. Brian Marshall (Sarawak Specialists' Society)
Marilyn R. Mattke
Dr. Hector R. Mena (Society of Costa Rica Collectors)
Robert Meyersburg
Jack E. Molesworth (Jack E. Molesworth, Inc.)
William E. Mooz
Gary M. Morris (Pacific Midwest Co.)
Peter Mosiondz, Jr.
Bruce M. Moyer
Richard H. Muller (Richard's Stamps)
Victor Ostolaza
Souren V. Panirian
John E. Pearson (Pittwater Philatelic Service)
Otto Peetoom (Ormskirk Stamps)
Donald J. Peterson
Stanley Piller (Stanley M. Piller & Associates)
Stephen Radin (Albany Stamp Co.)
Siddique Mahmudur Rahman (Bangladesh Institute of Philatelic Studies)
Jon W. Rose
Frans H. A. Rummens (American Society for Netherlands Philately)
Richard H. Salz
Theodosios Sampson (Superior Stamp & Coin)
Jacques C. Schiff, Jr. (Jacques C. Schiff, Jr., Inc.)
Bernard Seckler (Fine Arts Philatelists)
F. Burton Sellers
Michael Shamilzadeh
Jeff Siddiqui (Pakistan Study Circle)
Richard Simchak
Sergio & Liane Sismondo (The Classic Collector)
Dr. Russell V. Skavaril (St. Helena, Ascension & Tristan da Cunha Philatelic Society)
Dr. Hubert C. Skinner
Roger D. Skinner
Jay Smith
Ekrem Spahich (Croatian Philatelic Society)
Richard Stambaugh
Glenn Tjia (Quality Philatelics)
Scott R. Trepel (Siegel Auction Galleries, Inc.)
Ming W. Tsang (Hong Kong Stamp Society)
Jerome S. Wagshal
Richard A. Washburn
Giana Wayman
Raymond H. Weill
Dr. Gary B. Weiss
Hans A. Westphal
John M. Wilson
Robert F. Yacano (K-Line Philippines)
Val Zabijaka

A special acknowledgment to Liane and Sergio Sismondo of The Classic Collector for their extraordinary assistance and knowledge sharing that has aided in the preparation of this year's Standard and Classic Specialized Catalogues.

Addresses, Telephone Numbers, Web Sites, E-Mail Addresses of General & Specialized Philatelic Societies

Collectors can contact the following groups for information about the philately of the areas within the scope of these societies, or inquire about membership in these groups. Aside from the general societies, we limit this list to groups that specialize in particular fields of philately, particular areas covered by the Scott Standard Postage Stamp Catalogue, and topical groups. Many more specialized philatelic societies exist than those listed below. These addresses were compiled in January 1998, and are, to the best of our knowledge, correct and current. Groups should inform the editors of address changes whenever they occur. The editors also want to hear from other such specialized groups not listed.

General "Umbrella" Societies

American Philatelic Society
PO Box 8000
State College PA 16803
Ph: (814) 237-3803
http://www.west.net/~stamps1/aps.html
E-mail: relamb@stamps.org

American Stamp Dealers' Association
Joseph Savarese
3 School St.
Glen Cove NY 11542
Ph: (516) 759-7000
http://www.amerstampdlrs.com
E-mail: asda@inx.net

International Society of Worldwide Stamp Collectors
Carol Cervenka
2502 Second St.
Caddo Mills TX 75135-9704
Ph: (903) 527-3957
http://www.frontiernet/~stamptmf/iswsc.html
E-mail: iswsc@webwide.net

Junior Philatelists of America
Ellie Chapman
PO Box 850
Boalsburg PA 16827-0850
http://www.jpastamps.org
E-mail: jpaellie@aol.com

Royal Philatelic Society
41 Devonshire Place
London, United Kingdom W1N 1PE

Royal Philatelic Society of Canada
PO Box 929, Station Q
Toronto, ON, Canada M4T 2P1
http://www.interlog.com/~rspc
E-mail: rpsc@interlog.com

Groups focusing on fields or aspects found in world-wide philately (some may cover U.S. area only)

American Air Mail Society
Stephen Reinhard
PO Box 110
Mineola NY 11501
http://ourworld.compuserve.com/homepages/aams/
E-mail: sr1501@aol.com

American First Day Cover Society
Douglas Kelsey
PO Box 65960
Tucson AZ 85728-5960
E-mail: afdcs@aol.com

American Revenue Association
Bruce Miller
Suite 332, 701 South First Ave.
Arcadia CA 91006

American Topical Association
Douglas Kelsey
PO Box 65749
Tucson AZ 85728
Ph: (520) 321-9292
E-mail: ataoffice@aol.com

Errors, Freaks and Oddities Collectors Club
Jim McDevitt
138 Lakemont Dr. East
Kingsland GA 31548
Ph: (912) 729-1573
E-mail: cwouscg@aol.com

National Duck Stamp Collectors Society
Anthony J. Monico
PO Box 43
Harleysville PA 19438-0043

No Value Identified Club
Albert Sauvanet
Le Clos Royal B, Boulevard des Pas Enchantes
St. Sebastien-sur Loire, France 44230
E-mail: alain.vailly@irin.univ_nantes.fr

The Perfins Club
Kurt Ottenheimer
462 West Walnut St.
Long Beach NY 11561

Post Mark Collectors Club
Larry Boing
2351 Grandview Road
Crest Hill IL 60435-1951

Postal History Society
Kalman V. Illyefalvi
8207 Daren Court
Pikesville MD 21208-2211
Ph: (410) 653-0665

Precancel Stamp Society
1750 Skippack Pk. #1603
Center Square PA 19422
Ph: (610) 279-6014

United Postal Stationery Society
Joann Thomas
PO Box 48
Redlands CA 92373
http://www.uh.edu/~lib19/upss.htm

Groups focusing on U.S. area philately as covered in the Standard Catalogue

Bureau Issues Association
David G. Lee
PO Box 2641
Reston VA 20195-0641

Canal Zone Study Group
Richard H. Salz
60 27th Ave.
San Francisco CA 94121

Carriers and Locals Society
Steven M. Roth
PO Box 57160
Washington DC 20036
Ph: (202) 293-6813
E-mail: smroth@wizard.net

Confederate Stamp Alliance
Richard L. Calhoun
PO Box 581
Mt. Prospect IL 60056-0581

Hawaiian Philatelic Society
Kay H. Hoke
PO Box 10115
Honolulu HI 96816-0115
Ph: (808) 521-5721
http://www.stampshows.com/hps.html

Plate Number Coil Collectors Club
Gene C. Trinks
3603 Bellows Court
Troy MI 48083
http://www.geocities.com/Heartland/Hills/6283
E-mail: gctrinks@tir.com

United Nations Philatelists
Alex Bereson
18 Portola Drive
San Francisco CA 94131-1518
E-mail: bereson@ix.netcom.com

U.S. Philatelic Classics Society
Mark D. Rogers
PO Box 80708
Austin TX 78708-0708
http://www.scruz.net/~eho/uspcs
E-mail: mdr3@swbell.net

U.S. Possessions Philatelic Society
David S. Durbin
1608 S. 22nd St.
Blue Springs MO 64015

Groups focusing on philately of foreign countries or regions

American Society of Polar Philatelists (Antarctic areas)
Richard Julian
1153 Fairview Dr.
York PA 17403
E-mail: rajulian@netrax.net

American Belgian Philatelic Society
Kenneth L. Costilow
621 Virginius Dr.
Virginia Beach VA 23452-4417
Ph: (757) 463-6081
E-mail: ken_costilow@prodigy.com

Bermuda Collectors Society
Thomas J. McMahon
364 Nash Road
North Salem NY 10560

Brazil Philatelic Association
Kurt Ottenheimer
462 West Walnut St.
Long Beach NY 11561

British Caribbean Philatelic Study Group
Gale J. Raymond
Bali-Hai, PO Box 228
Sugar Land TX 77478-0228

British North America Philatelic Society (Canada & Provinces)
Jerome C. Jarnick
108 Duncan Drive
Troy MI 48098
Ph: (248) 689-1966
http://www.compusmart.ab.ca/stalbert/bnaps.htm
E-mail: jarnick@compuserve.com

Burma Philatelic Study Circle
A. Meech
7208 91st Ave.
Edmonton, AB, Canada T6B 0R8
E-mail: alan.meech@ualberta.ca

China Stamp Society
Paul H. Gault
120 West 18th Ave.
Columbus OH 43210
http://www.azstarnet.com/~gersten/China.Stamp.Society.html
E-mail: gault.1@osu.edu

Colombia/Panama Philatelic Study Group
PO Box 2245
El Cajon CA 92021
E-mail: jimacross@juno.com

Society of Costa Rica Collectors
Dr. Hector R. Mena
PO Box 14831
Baton Rouge LA 70808
http://www.intersurf.com/~hrmena
E-mail: hrmena@intersurf.com

Croatian Philatelic Society (Croatia & other Balkan areas)
Ekrem Spahich
502 Romero, PO Box 696
Fritch TX 79036-0696
Ph: (806) 857-0129
http://www.hrnet.org/cps
E-mail: ou812@arn.net

Society for Czechoslovak Philately
Robert T. Cossaboom
PO Box 25332
Scott AFB IL 62225-0332
http://www.erols.com/sibpost
E-mail: klfck1@aol.com

Estonian Philatelic Society
Rudolf Hamar
1912 Nugget Drive
Felton CA 95018

Ethiopian Philatelic Society
Huguette Gagnon
PO Box 8110-45
Blaine WA 98231-8110
Ph: (604) 584-1701

Falkland Islands Philatelic Study Group
Carl J. Faulkner
Williams Inn, On-the-Green
Williamstown MA 01267-2620

France & Colonies Philatelic Society
Walter Parshall
103 Spruce St.
Bloomfield NJ 07003-3514

Germany Philatelic Society
PO Box 779
Arnold MD 21012-4779

Great Britain Collectors Club
Frank J. Koch
PO Box 309
Batavia OH 45103-0309
http://www.netxpress.com/users/winphins/gbcc/gbcc_hp.html
E-mail: koch.fj@pg.com

Hellenic Philatelic Society of America (Greece and related areas)
Dr. Nicholas Asimakopulos
541 Cedar Hill Ave.
Wyckoff NJ 07481
Ph: (201) 447-6262

International Society of Guatemala Collectors
Mrs. Mae Vignola
105 22nd Ave.
San Francisco CA 94121

Haiti Philatelic Society
Ubaldo Del Toro
5709 Marble Archway
Alexandria VA 22310

Honduras Collectors Club
Jeff Brasor
PO Box 173
Coconut Creek FL 33097

Hong Kong Stamp Society
Dr. An-Min Chung
120 Deerfield Rd.
Broomall PA 19008
Ph: (215) 576-6850

Hungary Philatelic Society
Thomas Phillips
PO Box 1162
Fairfield CT 06432-1162

India Study Circle
John Warren
PO Box 70775
Washington DC 20024
Ph: (202) 260-9464
E-mail: warren.john@epamail.epa.gov

Society of Indochina Philatelists
Paul Blake
1466 Hamilton Way
San Jose CA 95125

Iran Philatelic Study Circle
David J. Armacost
PO Box 33381
Phoenix AZ 85067

Eire Philatelic Association (Ireland)
Michael J. Conway
19 Pine Needle Drive
Shelton CT 06484
http://ourworld.compuserve.com/homepages/aranman/epa.htm
E-mail: brennan704@aol.com

Society of Israel Philatelists
Paul S. Aufrichtig
300 East 42nd St.
New York NY 10017

International Society for Japanese Philately
Kenneth Kamholz
PO Box 1283
Haddonfield NJ 08033
http://www.west.net/~lmevans/isjp.html
E-mail: kamholz@mosquito.com

Korea Stamp Society
William M. Collyer
PO Box 4158
Saticoy CA 93007-0158

Latin American Philatelic Society
Piet Steen
197 Pembina Ave.
Hinton, AB, Canada T7V 2B2

Cuyahoga Latvian Philatelist Club
Arturs Rubenis
1460 West Clifton Blvd.
Lakewood OH 44107-3309

Latvian Philatelic Society
J. Ronis
7 Lowes Ave.
Brampton, ON, Canada L6X 1R8

Liberian Philatelic Society
William Thomas Lockard
PO Box 267
Wellston OH 45692
Ph: (614) 384-2020

Liechtenstudy USA (Liechtenstein)
Ralph Schneider
PO Box 23049
Belleville IL 62223
Ph: (618) 277-8543
http://www.rschneiderstamps.com/info.html
E-mail: rschneider@aol.com

Lithuanian Philatelic Society
Fred Baumgartner
446 S. 6th Ave.
La Grange IL 60525
Ph: (708) 354-5909

Lithuanian Philatelic Society of New York
Vincent M. Alones
217 McKee St.
Floral Park NY 11001-1314

Mexico-Elmhurst Philatelic Society International
Juan Jose Cabuto-Vidrio
PO Box 435360
San Ysidro CA 92143-5360

Nepal & Tibet Philatelic Study Group
Roger D. Skinner
1020 Covington Road
Los Altos CA 94022-5003
Ph: (415) 968-4163

American Society of Netherlands Philately
Jan Enthoven
W6428 Riverview Drive
Onalaska WI 54650
Ph: (608) 781-8612
http://www.cs.cornell.edu/Info/People/aswin/NL/neth

Society of Australasian Specialists / Oceania
Henry Bateman
PO Box 4862
Monroe LA 71211
Ph: (800) 571-0293
E-mail: ck100@iamerica.net

Orange Free State Study Circle
J. R. Stroud
28 Oxford St.
Burnham-on-sea, Somerset, United Kingdom TA8 1LQ

Pakistan Study Circle
Jeff Siddiqui
PO Box 7002
Lynnwood WA 98046
E-mail: jeffsiddiqui@msn.com

Papuan Philatelic Society
Steven Zirinsky
PO Box 49, Ansonia Station
New York NY 10023
Ph: (212) 665-0765
E-mail: szirinsky@compuserve.com

International Philippine Philatelic Society
Robert F. Yacano
PO Box 94
Eden NY 14057
Ph: (716) 992-9665

Pitcairn Islands Study Group
Nelson A. L. Weller
2940 Wesleyan Lane
Winston-Salem NC 27106
Ph: (910) 724-6398
E-mail: nalweller@juno.com

Plebiscite-Memel-Saar Study Group
Clay Wallace
100 Lark Court
Alamo CA 94507

Polonus Philatelic Society (Poland)
PO Box 458
Berwyn IL 60402

International Society for Portuguese Philately
Clyde Homen
1491 Bonnieview
Hollister CA 95023-5117
E-mail: cjh@hollinet.com

Rhodesian Study Circle
William R. Wallace
PO Box 16381
San Francisco CA 94116

Romanian Chapter of Croatian Philatelic Society
Dan Demetriade
PO Box 09700
Detroit MI 48209

Canadian Society of Russian Philately
Andrew Cronin
PO Box 5722, Station A
Toronto, ON, Canada M5W 1P2
Fax: (905) 764-8968

Rossica Society of Russian Philately
George G. Werbizky
409 Jones Rd.
Vestal NY 13850

Ryukyu Philatelic Specialist Society
Carmine J. DiVincenzo
PO Box 381
Clayton CA 94517-0381

St. Helena, Ascension & Tristan Da Cunha Philatelic Society
Dr. Russell V. Skavaril
222 East Torrance Road
Columbus OH 43214-3834
Ph: (614) 262-3046
http://ourworld.compuserve.com/homepages/st_helena_ascen_tdc

St. Pierre & Miquelon Study Group
David Salovey
PO Box 464
New York NY 10014-0464

Associated Collectors of El Salvador
Jeff Brasor
PO Box 173
Coconut Creek FL 33097

Fellowship of Samoa Specialists
Jack R. Hughes
1541 Wellington St.
Oakland CA 94602-1751

Sarawak Specialists' Society
Art Bunce
PO Box 2516
Escondido CA 92033

Arabian Philatelic Association (Saudi Arabia)
ARAMCO, Box 1929
Dhahran, Saudi Arabia 31311

Scandinavian Collectors Club
Donald B. Brent
PO Box 13196
El Cajon CA 92020
http://www.nb.net/~downs/scc/scc.htm
E-mail: dbrent47@sprynet.com

Slovakia Stamp Society
Jack Benchik
PO Box 555
Notre Dame IN 46556

Philatelic Society for Greater Southern Africa
William C. Brooks VI
PO Box 2698
San Bernardino CA 92406-2698

Spanish Philatelic Society
Robert H. Penn
3021 Valley View Dr.
Bangor PA 18013
Ph: (610) 588-5627

American Helvetia Philatelic Society (Switzerland, Liechtenstein)
Richard T. Hall
PO Box 666
Manhattan Beach CA 90267-0666
E-mail: rtavish@pacbell.net

Tannu Tuva Collectors Society
Ken Simon
513 Sixth Ave. So.
Lake Worth FL 33460-4507
Ph: (561) 588-5954
http://www.blarg.net/~brad/ttcs.htm
E-mail: p003115b@pb.seflin.org

Society for Thai Philately
H. R. Blakeney
PO Box 25644
Oklahoma City OK 73125

Tonga/Tin Can Mail Study Circle
Tom Jackson
121 Mullingar Ct., #1A
Schaumburg IL 60193
http://members.aol.com/tongajan/ttcmsc.html
E-mail: tjackso3@ix.netcom.com

Turkish and Ottoman Philatelic Society
Gary F. Paiste
4249 Berritt St.
Fairfax VA 22030

Ukrainian Philatelic & Numismatic Society
Bohdan O. Pauk
PO Box 11184
Chicago IL 60611-0184
Ph: (773) 276-0355

Yugoslavia Study Group
Michael Lenard
1514 North 3rd Ave.
Wausau WI 54401

Topical Groups

American Indian Philatelic Society
Charles Eson
128 Western Ave. Altamont NY 12009

Americana Unit
Dennis Dengel
17 Peckham Rd.
Poughkeepsie NY 12603-2018
http://www.philately.com/society_news/americana_unit.htm
E-mail: 70363.3621@compuserve.com

Astronomy Study Unit
George Young
PO Box 632
Tewksbury MA 01876-0632
Ph: (978) 851-8283
http://www.fandm.edu/departments/astronomy/miscell/astunit.html
E-mail: george-young@msn.com

Bicycle Stamp Club
Norman Batho
358 Iverson Place
East Windsor NJ 08520
Ph: (609) 448-9547
E-mail: normbatho@worldnet.att.net

Canadiana Study Unit
John Peebles
PO Box 3262, Station "A"
London, ON, Canada N6A 4K3
E-mail: john.peebles@odyssey.on.ca

Captain Cook Study Unit
Brian P. Sandford
173 Minuteman Dr.
Concord MA 01742-1923
http://freespace.virgin.net/chris.jones/index.htm
E-mail: borehami@wcg.co.uk

Casey Jones Railroad Unit
Oliver Atchison
PO Box 31631
San Francisco CA 94131-0631
Ph: (415) 648-8057
E-mail: casey_jones@gowebway.com

Cats on Stamps Study Unit
Mary Ann Brown
3006 Wade Rd.
Durham NC 27705

Chess on Stamps Study Unit
Anne Kasonic
7624 County Road #153
Interlaken NY 14847
http://www.iglobal.net/home/reott/stamps1.htm#cossu
E-mail: akasonic@epix.net

Christopher Columbus Philatelic Society
Donald R. Ager
PO Box 71
Hillsboro NH 03244
Ph: (603) 464-5379
E-mail: don_ager@conknet.com

Dogs on Stamps Study Unit
Morris Raskin
202A Newport Rd.
Cranbury NJ 08512
Ph: (609) 655-7411
E-mail: mraskin@worldnet.att.net

Earth's Physical Features Study Group
Fred Klein
515 Magdalena Ave.
Los Altos CA 94024
http://www.philately.com/society_news/earths_physical.htm

Embroidery, Stitchery, Textile Unit
Helen N. Cushman
1001 Genter St., Apt. 9H
La Jolla CA 92037
Ph: (619) 459-1194

Europa Study Unit
Hank Klos
PO Box 611
Bensenville IL 60106
E-mail: hank@bensenville.lib.il.us

Fine & Performing Arts
Ruth Richards
10393 Derby Dr.
Laurel MD 20723
E-mail: bersec@aol.com

Gay & Lesbian History Stamp Club
Joe Petronie
PO Box 515981
Dallas TX 75251-5981

Gems, Minerals & Jewelry Study Group
George Young
PO Box 632
Tewksbury MA 01876-0632
Ph: (978) 851-8283
http://www.rockhounds.com/rockshop/gmjsuapp.txt
E-mail: george-young@msn.com

Graphics Philately Association
Dulcie Apgar
PO Box 1513
Thousand Oaks CA 91358

Lighthouse Stamp Society
Dalene Thomas
8612 West Warren Lane
Lakewood CO 80227-2352
Ph: (303) 986-6620
http://www.nyx.net/~dathomas
E-mail: dathomas@nyx.net

Mask Study Unit
Carolyn Weber
PO Box 2542
Oxnard CA 93034
http://www.philately.com/society_news/masks.htm

Mathematical Study Unit
Estelle Buccino
5615 Glenwood Rd.
Bethesda MD 20817
Ph: (301) 718-8898

Medical Subjects Unit
Dr. Frederick C. Skvara
PO Box 6228
Bridgewater NJ 08807

Mesoamerican Archeology Study Unit
Chris Moser
PO Box 1442, Riverside CA 92502

Napoleonic Age Philatelists
Ken Berry
7513 Clayton Dr.
Oklahoma City OK 73132-5636
Ph: (405) 721-0044

Petroleum Philatelic Society International
Feitze Papa
922 Meander Dr.
Walnut Creek CA 94598-4239

Philatelic Music Circle
Cathleen Osborne
PO Box 1781
Sequim WA 98382

Rainbow Study Unit
Shirley Sutton
PO Box 37
Lone Pine, AB, Canada T0G 1M0
Ph: (304) 584-2268
E-mail: george-young@msn.com

Rotary on Stamps Unit
Donald Fiery
PO Box 333, Hanover PA 17331
Ph: (717) 632-8921

Scouts on Stamps Society International
Carl Schauer
PO Box 526
Belen NM 87002
Ph: (505) 864-0098

Ships on Stamps Unit
Robert Stuckert
2750 Highway 21 East
Paint Lick KY 40461
Ph: (606) 925-4901

Sports Philatelists International
Margaret Jones
5310 Lindenwood Ave.
St. Louis MO 63109-1758
http://www.concentric.net/~laimins/spi.html

Stamps on Stamps/Centenary Unit
William Critzer
13385 Country Way
Los Altos Hills CA 94022
Ph: (650) 941-1567
E-mail: willcrit@aol.com

Windmill Study Unit
Walter J. Hollien
PO Box 346
Long Valley NJ 07853-0346

Wine on Stamps Study Unit
James Crum
5132 Sepulveda
San Bernardino CA 92404-1134
Ph: (909) 886-3186

Women on Stamps Study Unit
Phebe Quattrucci
259 Middle Road
Falmouth ME 04105

Expertizing Services

The following organizations will, for a fee, provide expert opinions about stamps submitted to them. Collectors should contact these organizations to find out about their fees and requirements before submitting philatelic material to them. The listing of these groups here is not intended as an endorsement by Scott Publishing Co.

American Philatelic Expertizing Service
PO Box 8000
State College PA 16803

Philatelic Foundation
501 Fifth Ave., Rm. 1901
New York NY 10017

Professional Stamp Experts
1 Datran Center, Suite 1149
9100 South Dadeland Blvd.
Miami FL 33156

Confederate Stamp Alliance Authentication Service
10833 Greencrest Dr.
Baton Rouge LA 70811

Ukrainian Philatelic & Numismatic Society Expertizing Service
30552 Dell Lane
Warren MI 48092-1862

Information on Catalogue Values, Grade and Condition

Catalogue Value

The Scott Catalogue value is a retail value; that is, an amount you could expect to pay for a stamp in the grade of Very Fine with no faults. Any exceptions to the grade valued will be noted in the text. The general introduction on the following pages and the individual section introductions further explain the type of material that is valued. The value listed for any given stamp is a reference that reflects recent actual dealer selling prices for that item.

Dealer retail price lists, public auction results, published prices in advertising and individual solicitation of retail prices from dealers, collectors and specialty organizations have been used in establishing the values found in this catalogue. Scott Publishing Co. values stamps, but Scott is not a company engaged in the business of buying and selling stamps as a dealer.

Use this catalogue as a guide for buying and selling. The actual price you pay for a stamp may be higher or lower than the catalogue value because of many different factors, including the amount of personal service a dealer offers, or increased or decreased interest in the country or topic represented by a stamp or set. An item may occasionally be offered at a lower price as a "loss leader," or as part of a special sale. You also may obtain an item inexpensively at public auction because of little interest at that time or as part of a large lot.

Stamps that are of a lesser grade than Very Fine, or those with condition problems, generally trade at lower prices than those given in this catalogue. Stamps of exceptional quality in both grade and condition often command higher prices than those listed.

Values for pre-1900 unused issues are for stamps with approximately half or more of their original gum. Stamps with most or all of their original gum may be expected to sell for more, and stamps with less than half of their original gum may be expected to sell for somewhat less than the values listed. On rarer stamps, it may be expected that the original gum will be somewhat more disturbed than it will be on more common issues. Post-1900 unused issues are assumed to have full original gum. From breakpoints in most countries' listings, stamps are valued as never hinged, due to the wide availability of stamps in that condition. These notations are prominently placed in the listings and in the country information preceding the listings. Some countries also feature listings with dual values for hinged and never-hinged stamps.

Grade

A stamp's grade and condition are crucial to its value. The accompanying illustrations show examples of Very Fine stamps from different time periods, along with examples of stamps in Fine to Very Fine and Extremely Fine grades as points of reference.

FINE stamps (illustrations not shown) have designs that are noticeably off center on two sides. Imperforate stamps may have small margins, and earlier issues may show the design touching one edge of the stamp design. For perforated stamps, perfs may barely clear the design on one side, and very early issues normally will have the perforations slightly cutting into the design. Used stamps may have heavier than usual cancellations.

FINE-VERY FINE stamps may be somewhat off center on one side, or slightly off center on two sides. Imperforate stamps will have two margins of at least normal size, and the design will not touch any edge. For perforated stamps, the perfs are well clear of the design, but are still noticeably off center. *However, early issues of a country may be printed in such a way that the design naturally is very close to the edges. In these cases, the perforations may cut into the design very slightly.* Used stamps will not have a cancellation that detracts from the design.

VERY FINE stamps may be slightly off center on one side, but the design will be well clear of the edge. The stamp will present a nice, balanced appearance. Imperforate stamps will have three normal-sized margins. *However, early issues of many countries may be printed in such a way that the perforations may touch the design on one or more sides. Where this is the case, a boxed note will be found defining the centering and margins of the stamps being valued.* Used stamps will have light or otherwise neat cancellations. This is the grade used to establish Scott Catalogue values.

EXTREMELY FINE stamps are close to being perfectly centered. Imperforate stamps will have even margins that are larger than normal. Even the earliest perforated issues will have perforations clear of the design on all sides.

Condition

Grade addresses only centering and (for used stamps) cancellation. *Condition* refers to factors other than grade that affect a stamp's desirability.

Factors that can increase the value of a stamp include exceptionally wide margins, particularly fresh color, the presence of selvage, and plate or die varieties. Unusual cancels on used stamps (particularly those of the 19th century) can greatly enhance their value as well.

Factors other than faults that decrease the value of a stamp include loss of original gum, regumming, a hinge remnant or foreign object adhering to the gum, natural inclusions, straight edges, and markings or notations applied by collectors or dealers.

Faults include missing pieces, tears, pin or other holes, surface scuffs, thin spots, creases, toning, short or pulled perforations, clipped perforations, oxidation or other forms of color changelings, soiling, stains, and such man-made changes as reperforations or the chemical removal or lightening of a cancellation.

Scott Publishing Co. recognizes that there is no formally enforced grading scheme for postage stamps, and that the final price you pay or obtain for a stamp will be determined by individual agreement at the time of transaction.

On the following two pages are illustrations of various stamps from countries appearing in this volume. These stamps are arranged by country, and they represent early or important issues that are often found in widely different grades in the marketplace. The editors believe the illustrations will prove useful in showing the margin size and centering that will be seen on the various issues.

In addition to the matters of margin size and centering, collectors are reminded that the very fine stamps valued in the Scott catalogues also will possess fresh color and intact perforations, and they will be free from defects.

Most examples shown are computer – manipulated images made from single digitized master illustrations.

Fine-Very Fine
SCOTT CATALOGUES VALUE STAMPS IN THIS GRADE
Very Fine
Extremely Fine
Fine-Very Fine
SCOTT CATALOGUES VALUE STAMPS IN THIS GRADE
Very Fine
Extremely Fine

Fine-Very Fine
SCOTT CATALOGUES VALUE STAMPS IN THIS GRADE
Very Fine
Extremely Fine
MAURITIUS
ONE SHILLING
CORREOS MEJICO
DOS REALES
PRINCIPAUTE DE MONACO
1F POSTES 1F
POST ZEGEL
POSTZEGEL
Fine-Very Fine
SCOTT CATALOGUES VALUE STAMPS IN THIS GRADE
Very Fine
Extremely Fine
NEDERLAND
20 CENT.
10 CENT
NEDERL INDIE
POST ZEGEL
NEW ZEALAND
POSTAGE
TWO PENCE
2 TO SKILLING 2

For purposes of helping to determine the gum condition and value of an unused stamp, Scott Publishing Co. presents the following chart which details different gum conditions and indicates how the conditions correlate with the Scott values for unused stamps. Used together, the Illustrated Grading Chart on the previous pages and this Illustrated Gum Chart should allow catalogue users to better understand the grade and gum condition of stamps valued in the Scott catalogues.

Gum Categories:	MINT N.H.	ORIGINAL GUM (O.G.)				NO GUM
	Mint Never Hinged *Free from any disturbance*	**Lightly Hinged** *Faint impression of a removed hinge over a small area*	**Hinge Mark or Remnant** *Prominent hinged spot with part or all of the hinge remaining*	**Large part o.g.** *Approximately half or more of the gum intact*	**Small part o.g.** *Approximately less than half of the gum intact*	**No gum** *Only if issued with gum*
Commonly Used Symbol:	★★	★	★	★	★	(★)
Pre-1900 Issues (Pre-1890 for U.S.)	*Very fine pre-1900 stamps in these categories trade at a premium over Scott value*			Scott Value for "Unused"		Scott "No Gum" listings for selected unused classic stamps
From 1900 to break-points for listings of never-hinged stamps	Scott "Never Hinged" listings for selected unused stamps	Scott Value for "Unused" (Actual value will be affected by the degree of hinging of the full o.g.)				
From breakpoints noted for many countries	Scott Value for "Unused"					

Never Hinged (NH; ★★): A never-hinged stamp will have full original gum that will have no hinge mark or disturbance. The presence of an expertizer's mark does not disqualify a stamp from this designation.

Original Gum (OG; ★): Pre-1900 stamps should have approximately half or more of their original gum. On rarer stamps, it may be expected that the original gum will be somewhat more disturbed that it will be on more common issues. Post-1900 stamps should have full original gum. Original gum will show some disturbance caused by a previous hinge(s) which may be present or entirely removed. The actual value of a post-1900 stamp will be affected by the degree of hinging of the full original gum.

Disturbed Original Gum: Gum showing noticeable effects of humidity, climate or hinging over more than half of the gum. The significance of gum disturbance in valuing a stamp in any of the Original Gum categories depends on the degree of disturbance, the rarity and normal gum condition of the issue and other variables affecting quality.

Regummed (RG; (★)): A regummed stamp is a stamp without gum that has had some type of gum privately applied at a time after it was issued. This normally is done to deceive collectors and/or dealers into thinking that the stamp has original gum and therefore has a higher value. A regummed stamp is considered the same as a stamp with none of its original gum for purposes of grading.

ScottMounts

For stamp presentation unequaled in beauty and clarity, insist on ScottMounts. Made of 100% inert polystyrol foil, ScottMounts protect your stamps from the harmful effects of dust and moisture. Available in your choice of clear or black backs, ScottMounts are center-split across the back for easy insertion of stamps and feature crystal clear mount faces. Double layers of gum assure stay-put bonding on the album page. Discover the quality and value ScottMounts have to offer.

ScottMounts are available from your favorite stamp dealer or direct from:

Scott Publishing Co.
P.O. Box 828 Sidney OH 45365-0828

Discover the quality and value ScottMounts have to offer.

For a complete list of ScottMount sizes or a free sample pack call or write Scott Publishing Co.

SCOTT

1-800-572-6885

Catalogue Listing Policy

It is the intent of Scott Publishing Co. to list all postage stamps of the world in the *Scott Standard Postage Stamp Catalogue*. The only strict criteria for listing is that stamps be decreed legal for postage by the issuing country. Whether the primary intent of issuing a given stamp or set was for sale to postal patrons or to stamp collectors is not part of our listing criteria. Scott's role is to provide basic comprehensive postage stamp information. It is up to each stamp collector to choose which items to include in a collection.

It is Scott's objective to seek reasons why a stamp should be listed, rather than why it should not. Nevertheless, there are certain types of items that will not be listed. These include the following:

1. Unissued items that are not officially distributed or released by the issuing postal authority. Even if such a stamp is "accidentally" distributed to the philatelic or even postal market, it remains unissued. If such items are officially issued at a later date by the country, they will be listed. Unissued items consist of those that have been printed and then held from sale for reasons such as change in government, errors found on stamps or something deemed objectionable about a stamp subject or design.
2. Stamps "issued" by non-existent postal entities or fantasy countries, such as Nagaland, Occusi-Ambeno, Staffa, Sedang, Torres Straits and others.
3. Semi-official or unofficial items not required for postage. Examples include items issued by private agencies for their own express services. When such items are required for delivery, or are valid as prepayment of postage, they are listed.
4. Local stamps issued for local use only. Postage stamps issued by governments specifically for "domestic" use, such as Haiti Scott 219-228, or the United States non-denominated stamps, are not considered to be locals, since they are valid for postage throughout the country of origin.
5. Items not valid for postal use. For example, a few countries have issued souvenir sheets that are not valid for postage. This area also includes a number of worldwide charity labels (some denominated) that do not pay postage.
6. Intentional varieties, such as imperforate stamps that look like their perforated counterparts and are issued in very small quantities. These are often controlled issues intended for speculation.
7. Items distributed by the issuing government only to a limited group, such as a stamp club, philatelic exhibition or a single stamp dealer, and later brought to market at inflated prices. These items normally will be included in a footnote.

The fact that a stamp has been used successfully as postage, even on international mail, is not in itself sufficient proof that it was legitimately issued. Numerous examples of so-called stamps from non-existent countries are known to have been used to post letters that have successfully passed through the international mail system.

There are certain items that are subject to interpretation. When a stamp falls outside our specifications, it may be listed along with a cautionary footnote.

A number of factors are considered in our approach to analyzing how a stamp is listed. The following list of factors is presented to share with you, the catalogue user, the complexity of the listing process.

Additional printings — "Additional printings" of a previously issued stamp may range from an item that is totally different to cases where it is impossible to differentiate from the original. At least a minor number (a small-letter suffix) is assigned if there is a distinct change in stamp shade, noticeably redrawn design, or a significantly different perforation measurement. A major number (numeral or numeral and capital-letter combination) is assigned if the editors feel the "additional printing" is sufficiently different from the original that it constitutes a different issue.

Commemoratives — Where practical, commemoratives with the same theme are placed in a set. For example, the U.S. Civil War Centenniel set of 1961-65 and the Constitution Bicentennial series of 1989-90 appear as sets. Countries such as Japan and Korea issue such material on a regular basis, with an announced, or at least predictable, number of stamps known in advance. Occasionally, however, stamp sets that were released over a period of years have been separated. Appropriately placed footnotes will guide you to each set's continuation.

Definitive sets — Blocks of numbers generally have been reserved for definitive sets, based on previous experience with any given country. If a few more stamps were issued in a set than originally expected, they often have been inserted into the original set with a capital-letter suffix, such as U.S. Scott 1059A. If it appears that many more stamps than the originally allotted block will be released before the set is completed, a new block of numbers will be reserved, with the original one being closed off. In some cases, such as the British Machin Head series or the U.S. Transportation and Great Americans series, several blocks of numbers exist. Appropriately placed footnotes will guide you to each set's continuation.

New country — Membership in the Universal Postal Union is not a consideration for listing status or order of placement within the catalogue. The index will tell you in what volume or page number the listings begin.

"No release date" items — The amount of information available for any given stamp issue varies greatly from country to country and even from time to time. Extremely comprehensive information about new stamps is available from some countries well before the stamps are released. By contrast some countries do not provide information about stamps or release dates. Most countries, however, fall between these extremes. A country may provide denominations or subjects of stamps from upcoming issues that are not issued as planned. Sometimes, philatelic agencies, those private firms hired to represent countries, add these later-issued items to sets well after the formal release date. This time period can range from weeks to years. If these items were officially released by the country, they will be added to the appropriate spot in the set. In many cases, the specific release date of a stamp or set of stamps may never be known.

Overprints — The color of an overprint is always noted if it is other than black. Where more than one color of ink has been used on overprints of a single set, the color used is noted. Early overprint and surcharge illustrations were altered to prevent their use by forgers.

Se-tenants — Connected stamps of differing features (se-tenants) will be listed in the format most commonly collected. This includes pairs, blocks or larger multiples. Se-tenant units are not always symmetrical. An example is Australia Scott 508, which is a block of seven stamps. If the stamps are primarily collected as a unit, the major number may be assigned to the multiple, with minors going to each component stamp. In cases where continuous-design or other unit se-tenants will receive significant postal use, each stamp is given a major Scott number listing. This includes issues from the United States, Canada, Germany and Great Britain, for example.

Understanding the Listings

On the opposite page is an enlarged "typical" listing from this catalogue. Below are detailed explanations of each of the highlighted parts of the listing.

1 Scott number — Scott catalogue numbers are used to identify specific items when buying, selling or trading stamps. Each listed postage stamp from every country has a unique Scott catalogue number. Therefore, Germany Scott 99, for example, can only refer to a single stamp. Although the Scott catalogue usually lists stamps in chronological order by date of issue, there are exceptions. When a country has issued a set of stamps over a period of time, those stamps within the set are kept together without regard to date of issue. This follows the normal collecting approach of keeping stamps in their natural sets.

When a country issues a set of stamps over a period of time, a group of consecutive catalogue numbers is reserved for the stamps in that set, as issued. If that group of numbers proves to be too few, capital-letter suffixes, such as "A" or "B," may be added to existing numbers to create enough catalogue numbers to cover all items in the set. A capital-letter suffix indicates a major Scott catalogue number listing. Scott uses a suffix letter only once. Therefore, a catalogue number listing with a capital-letter prefix will not also be found with the same letter (lower case) used as a minor-letter listing. If there is a Scott 16A in a set, for example, there will not also be a Scott 16a.

Suffix letters are not cumulative. A minor variety of Scott 16A would be Scott 16b, not Scott 16Ab. Any exceptions, such as Great Britain Scott 358cp, are clearly indicated.

There are times when a reserved block of Scott catalogue numbers is too large for a set, leaving some numbers unused. Such gaps in the numbering sequence also occur when the catalogue editors move an item's listing elsewhere or have removed it entirely from the catalogue. Scott does not attempt to account for every possible number, but rather attempts to assure that each stamp is assigned its own number.

Scott numbers designating regular postage normally are only numerals. Scott numbers for other types of stamps, such as air post, semi-postal, postal tax, postage due, occupation and others have a prefix consisting of one or more capital letters or a combination of numerals and capital letters.

2 Illustration number — Illustration or design-type numbers are used to identify each catalogue illustration. For most sets, the lowest face-value stamp is shown. It then serves as an example of the basic design approach for other stamps not illustrated. Where more than one stamp use the same illustration number, but have differences in design, the design paragraph or the description line clearly indicates the design on each stamp not illustrated. Where there are both vertical and horizontal designs in a set, a single illustration may be used, with the exceptions noted in the design paragraph or description line.

When an illustration is followed by a lower-case letter in parentheses, such as "A2(b)," the trailing letter indicates which overprint or surcharge illustration applies.

Illustrations normally are 75 percent of the original size of the stamp. An effort has been made to note all illustrations not illustrated at that percentage. Virtually all souvenir sheet illustrations are reduced even more. Overprints and surcharges are shown at 100 percent of their original size, unless otherwise noted. In some cases, the illustration will be placed above the set, between listings or omitted completely. Overprint and surcharge illustrations are not placed in this catalogue for purposes of expertizing stamps.

3 Paper color — The color of a stamp's paper is noted in italic type when the paper used is not white.

4 Listing styles — There are two principal types of catalogue listings: major and minor.

Major listings are in a larger type style than minor listings. The catalogue number is a numeral that can be found with or without a capital-letter suffix, and with or without a prefix.

Minor listings are in a smaller type style and have a small-letter suffix or (if the listing immediately follows that of the major number) may show only the letter. These listings identify a variety of the major item. Examples include perforation, color, watermark or printing method differences, multiples (some souvenir sheets, booklet panes and se-tenant combinations), and singles of multiples.

Examples of major number listings include 16, 28A, B97, C13A, 10N5, and 10N6A. Examples of minor numbers are 16a and C13b.

5 Basic information about a stamp or set — Introducing each stamp issue is a small section (usually a line listing) of basic information about a stamp or set. This section normally includes the date of issue, method of printing, perforation, watermark and, sometimes, some additional information of note. *Printing method, perforation and watermark apply to the following sets until a change is noted.* Stamps created by overprinting or surcharging previous issues are assumed to have the same perforation, watermark and printing method as the original. Dates of issue are as precise as Scott is able to confirm and often reflect the dates on first-day covers, rather than the actual date of release.

6 Denomination — This normally refers to the face value of the stamp; that is, the cost of the unused stamp at the post office at the time of issue. When a denomination is shown in parentheses, it does not appear on the stamp. This includes the non-denominated stamps of the United States, Brazil and Great Britain, for example.

7 Color or other description — This area provides information to solidify identification of a stamp. In many recent cases, a description of the stamp design appears in this space, rather than a listing of colors.

8 Year of issue — In stamp sets that have been released in a period that spans more than a year, the number shown in parentheses is the year that stamp first appeared. Stamps without a date appeared during the first year of the issue. Dates are not always given for minor varieties.

9 Value unused and Value used — The Scott catalogue values are based on stamps that are in a grade of Very Fine unless stated otherwise. Unused values refer to items that have not seen postal, revenue or any other duty for which they were intended. Pre-1900 unused stamps that were issued with gum must have at least most of their original gum. Later issues are assumed to have full original gum. From breakpoints specified in most countries' listings, stamps are valued as never hinged. Stamps issued without gum are noted. Modern issues with PVA or other synthetic adhesives may appear ungummed. Self-adhesive stamps are valued as appearing undisturbed on their original backing paper. For a more detailed explanation of these values, please see the "Catalogue Value," "Condition" and "Understanding Valuing Notations" elsewhere in this introduction.

In some cases, where used stamps are more valuable than unused stamps, the value is for an example with a contemporaneous cancel, rather than a modern cancel or a smudge or other unclear marking. For those stamps that were released for postal and fiscal purposes, the used value represents a postally used stamp. Stamps with revenue cancels generally sell for less.

10 Changes in basic set information — Bold type is used to show any changes in the basic data given for a set of stamps. This includes perforation differences from one stamp to the next or a different paper, printing method or watermark.

11 Total value of a set — The total value of sets of three or more stamps issued after 1900 are shown. The set line also notes the range of Scott numbers and total number of stamps included in the grouping. *Set value* is the term used to indicate the value of a stamp set when its combined total is less than the sum of the individual stamps. This happens when some of the stamps in a set have the minimum catalogue value.

NYASALAND
King George VI and Leopard – A6
TWO SHILLINGS
2/- 2/-
POSTAGE REVENUE
NYASALAND PROTECTORATE
King George VI
A7
1938-44 Engr. Perf. 12½
54 A6 ½p green .15 .30
54A A6 ½p dk brown ('42) .15 .40
55 A6 1p dark brown .15 .15
55A A6 1p green ('42) .15 .20
56 A6 1½p dark carmine .65 1.90
56A A6 1½p gray ('42) .15 1.25
57 A6 2p gray 1.25 .40
57A A6 2p dark car ('42) .15 .30
58 A6 3p blue .30 .15
59 A6 4p rose lilac .80 .30
60 A6 6p dark violet .85 .25
61 A6 9p olive bister 1.40 1.40
62 A6 1sh orange & blk 1.40 .55
Typo.
Perf. 14
Chalky Paper
63 A7 2sh ultra & dl vio, bl 5.50 4.50
64 A7 2sh6p red & blk, bl 6.50 4.50
65 A7 5sh red & grn, yel 22.50 11.00
a. 5sh dk red & dp grn, yel ('44) 50.00 37.50
66 A7 10sh red & grn, grn 32.50 14.00
Wmk. 3
67 A7 £1 blk & vio, red 16.00 15.00
Nos. 54-67 (18) 90.55 56.55
1 SCOTT NUMBER
2 ILLUS. NUMBER
3 PAPER COLOR
4 LISTING STYLES
MAJORS
MINORS
5 BASIC INFORMATION ON STAMP OR SET
6 DENOMINATION
7 COLOR OR OTHER DESCRIPTION
8 YEAR OF ISSUE
UNUSED
9 CATALOGUE VALUES
USED
10 CHANGES IN BASIC SET INFORMATION
11 TOTAL VALUE OF SET

Special Notices

Classification of stamps

The *Scott Standard Postage Stamp Catalogue* lists stamps by country of issue. The next level of organization is a listing by section on the basis of the function of the stamps. The principal sections cover regular postage, semi-postal, air post, special delivery, registration, postage due and other categories. Except for regular postage, catalogue numbers for all sections include a prefix letter (or number-letter combination) denoting the class to which a given stamp belongs.

The following is a listing of the most commonly used catalogue prefixes.

Prefix....Category
C ....Air Post
M..........Military
P...........Newspaper
N ....Occupation - Regular Issues
O ....Official
Q ....Parcel Post
J............Postage Due
RA ....Postal Tax
B............Semi-Postal
E............Special Delivery
MR ....War Tax

Other prefixes used by more than one country include the following:
H ....Acknowledgment of Receipt
CO.........Air Post Official
CQ.........Air Post Parcel Post
RAC.......Air Post Postal Tax
CF..........Air Post Registration
CB ....Air Post Semi-Postal
CBO.......Air Post Semi-Postal Official
CE ....Air Post Special Delivery
EY..........Authorized Delivery
S ....Franchise
G ....Insured Letter
GY ....Marine Insurance
MC ....Military Air Post
MQ........Military Parcel Post
NC.........Occupation - Air Post
NO.........Occupation - Official
NJ ....Occupation - Postage Due
NRA.......Occupation - Postal Tax
NB ....Occupation - Semi-Postal
NE ....Occupation - Special Delivery
QY ....Parcel Post Authorized Delivery
AR ....Postal-fiscal
RAJ ....Postal Tax Due
RAB ....Postal Tax Semi-Postal
F............Registration
EB..........Semi-Postal Special Delivery
EO ....Special Delivery Official
QE ....Special Handling

New issue listings

Updates to this catalogue appear each month in the *Scott Stamp Monthly* magazine. Included in this update are additions to the listings of countries found in the *Scott Standard Postage Stamp Catalogue* and the *Specialized Catalogue of United States Stamps*, as well as corrections and updates to current editions of this catalogue.

From time to time there will be changes in the final listings of stamps from the *Scott Stamp Monthly* to the next edition of the catalogue. This occurs as more information about certain stamps or sets becomes available.

The catalogue update section of the *Scott Stamp Monthly* is the most timely presentation of this material available. Annual subscriptions to the *Scott Stamp Monthly* are available from Scott Publishing Co., Box 828, Sidney, OH 45365-0828.

Number additions, deletions and changes

A listing of catalogue number additions, deletions and changes from the previous edition of the catalogue appears in each volume. See Volume 1 Catalogue Number Additions, Deletions, & Changes in the table of contents for the location of this list.

Understanding valuing notations

The *minimum catalogue value* of an individual stamp or set is 15 cents. This represents a portion of the cost incurred by a dealer when he prepares an individual stamp for resale. As a point of philatelic-economic fact, the lower the value shown for an item in this catalogue, the greater the percentage of that value is attributed to dealer mark up and profit margin. In many cases, such as the 15-cent minimum value, that price does not cover the labor or other costs involved with stocking it as an individual stamp. The sum of minimum values in a set does not properly represent the value of a complete set primarily composed of a number of minimum-value stamps, nor does the sum represent the actual value of a packet made up of minimum-value stamps. Thus a packet of 1,000 different common stamps — each of which has a catalogue value of 15 cents — normally sells for considerably less than 150 dollars!

The *absence of a retail value* for a stamp does not necessarily suggest that a stamp is scarce or rare. In the U.S. listings, a dash in the value column means that the stamp is known in a stated form or variety, but information is either lacking or insufficient for purposes of establishing a usable catalogue value.

Stamp values in *italics* generally refer to items that are difficult to value accurately. For expensive items, such as those priced at $1,000 or higher, a value in italics indicates that the affected item trades very seldom. For inexpensive items, a value in italics represents a warning. One example is a "blocked" issue where the issuing postal administration may have controlled one stamp in a set in an attempt to make the whole set more valuable. Another example is an item that sold at an extreme multiple of face value in the marketplace at the time of its issue.

One type of warning to collectors that appears in the catalogue is illustrated by a stamp that is valued considerably higher in used condition than it is as unused. In this case, collectors are cautioned to be certain the used version has a genuine and contemporaneous cancellation. The type of cancellation on a stamp can be an important factor in determining its sale price. Catalogue values do not apply to fiscal or telegraph cancels, unless otherwise noted.

Some countries have released back issues of stamps in canceled-to-order form, sometimes covering as much as a 10-year period. The Scott Catalogue values for used stamps reflect canceled-to-order material when such stamps are found to predominate in the marketplace for the issue involved. Notes frequently appear in the stamp listings to specify which items are valued as canceled-to-order, or if there is a premium for postally used examples.

Many countries sell canceled-to-order stamps at a marked reduction of face value. Countries that sell or have sold canceled-to-order stamps at *full* face value include Australia, Netherlands, France and Switzerland. It may be almost impossible to identify such stamps if the gum has been removed, because official government canceling devices are used. Postally used copies of these items on cover, however, are usually worth more than the canceled-to-order stamps with original gum.

Abbreviations

Scott Publishing Co. uses a consistent set of abbreviations throughout this catalogue to conserve space, while still providing necessary information.

COLOR ABBREVIATIONS

amb .....amber
anil ......aniline
ap ....apple
aqua.....aquamarine
az ....azure
bis........bister
bl ....blue
bld ....blood
blk ....black
bril.......brilliant
brn........brown
brnsh ...brownish
brnz.....bronze
brt ......bright
brnt .....burnt
car ....carmine
cer ....cerise
chlky....chalky
cham ...chamois
chnt.....chestnut
choc.....chocolate
chr.......chrome
cit........citron
cl ....claret
cob ......cobalt
cop ......copper
crim.....crimson
cr.........cream
dk........dark
dl.........dull
dp........deep
db........drab
emer....emerald
gldn .....golden
grysh....grayish
grn........green
grnsh ...greenish
hel ....heliotrope
hn........henna
ind.......indigo
int........intense
lav ....lavender
lem ......lemon
lil.........lilac
lt..........light
mag .....magenta
man .....manila
mar......maroon
mv........mauve
multi ....multicolored
mlky ....milky
myr......myrtle
ol ....olive
olvn .....olivine
org.......orange
pck ......peacock
pnksh...pinkish
Prus .....Prussian
pur.......purple
redsh ...reddish
res ....reseda
ros ....rosine
ryl........royal
sal........salmon
saph.....sapphire
scar......scarlet
sep.......sepia
sien......sienna
sil ....silver
sl ....slate
stl ....steel
turq .....turquoise
ultra.....ultramarine
Ven......Venetian
ver.......vermilion
vio ....violet
yel ....yellow
yelsh....yellowish

When no color is given for an overprint or surcharge, black is the color used. Abbreviations for colors used for overprints and surcharges include: "(B)" or "(Blk)," black; "(Bl)," blue; "(R)," red; and "(G)," green.

Additional abbreviations in this catalogue are shown below:

Adm. ....Administration
AFL ....American Federation of Labor
Anniv. ....Anniversary
APS ....American Philatelic Society
Assoc. ....Association
ASSR. ....Autonomous Soviet Socialist Republic
b......................Born
BEP ....Bureau of Engraving and Printing
Bicent. ....Bicentennial
Bklt.................Booklet
Brit. ....British
btwn................Between
Bur. ....Bureau
c. or ca............Circa
Cat. ....Catalogue
Cent. ....Centennial, century, centenary
CIO ....Congress of Industrial Organizations
Conf. ....Conference
Cong................Congress
Cpl. ....Corporal
CTO ....Canceled to order
d......................Died
Dbl. ....Double
EKU.................Earliest known use
Engr.................Engraved
Exhib...............Exhibition
Expo................Exposition
Fed. ....Federation
GB...................Great Britain
Gen. ....General
GPO ....General post office
Horiz. ....Horizontal
Imperf..............Imperforate
Impt. ....Imprint
Intl. ....International
Invtd................Inverted
L.......................Left
Lieut., lt. ....Lieutenant
Litho................Lithographed
LL.....................Lower left
LR ....Lower right
mm..................Millimeter
Ms. ....Manuscript
Natl. ....National
No. ....Number
NY....................New York
NYC ....New York City
Ovpt. ....Overprint
Ovptd. ....Overprinted
P.......................Plate number
Perf..................Perforated, perforation
Phil...................Philatelic
Photo...............Photogravure
PO....................Post office
Pr. ....Pair
P.R. ....Puerto Rico
Prec..................Precancel, precanceled
Pres. ....President
PTT ....Post, Telephone and Telegraph
Rio...................Rio de Janeiro
Sgt. ....Sergeant
Soc. ....Society
Souv. ....Souvenir
SSR..................Soviet Socialist Republic, see ASSR
St......................Saint, street
Surch................Surcharge
Typo. ....Typographed
UL ....Upper left
Unwmkd. ....Unwatermarked
UPU ....Universal Postal Union
UR....................Upper Right
US ....United States
USPOD ....United States Post Office Department
USSR ....Union of Soviet Socialist Republics
Vert. ....Vertical
VP ....Vice president
Wmk. ....Watermark
Wmkd. ....Watermarked
WWI ....World War I
WWII ....World War II

Examination

Scott Publishing Co. will not comment upon the genuineness, grade or condition of stamps, because of the time and responsibility involved. Rather, there are several expertizing groups that undertake this work for both collectors and dealers. Neither will Scott Publishing Co. appraise or identify philatelic material. The company cannot take responsibility for unsolicited stamps or covers sent by individuals.

How to order from your dealer

When ordering stamps from a dealer, it is not necessary to write the full description of a stamp as listed in this catalogue. All you need is the name of the country, the Scott catalogue number and whether the desired item is unused or used. For example, "Japan Scott 422 unused" is sufficient to identify the unused stamp of Japan listed as "422 A206 5y brown."

Basic Stamp Information

A stamp collector's knowledge of the combined elements that make a given stamp issue unique determines his or her ability to identify stamps. These elements include paper, watermark, method of separation, printing, design and gum. On the following pages each of these important areas is briefly described.

Paper

Paper is an organic material composed of a compacted weave of cellulose fibers and generally formed into sheets. Paper used to print stamps may be manufactured in sheets, or it may have been part of a large roll (called a web) before being cut to size. The fibers most often used to create paper on which stamps are printed include bark, wood, straw and certain grasses. In many cases, linen or cotton rags have been added for greater strength and durability. Grinding, bleaching, cooking and rinsing these raw fibers reduces them to a slushy pulp, referred to by paper makers as "stuff." Sizing and, sometimes, coloring matter is added to the pulp to make different types of finished paper.

After the stuff is prepared, it is poured onto sieve-like frames that allow the water to run off, while retaining the matted pulp. As fibers fall onto the screen and are held by gravity, they form a natural weave that will later hold the paper together. If the screen has metal bits that are formed into letters or images attached, it leaves slightly thinned areas on the paper. These are called watermarks.

When the stuff is almost dry, it is passed under pressure through smooth or engraved rollers - dandy rolls - or placed between cloth in a press to be flattened and dried.

Stamp paper falls broadly into two types: wove and laid. The nature of the surface of the frame onto which the pulp is first deposited causes the differences in appearance between the two. If the surface is smooth and even, the paper will be of fairly uniform texture throughout. This is known as *wove paper.* Early papermaking machines poured the pulp onto a continuously circulating web of felt, but modern machines feed the pulp onto a cloth-like screen made of closely interwoven fine wires. This paper, when held to a light, will show little dots or points very close together. The proper name for this is "wire wove," but the type is still considered wove. Any U.S. or British stamp printed after 1880 will serve as an example of wire wove paper.

Closely spaced parallel wires, with cross wires at wider intervals, make up the frames used for what is known as *laid paper.* A greater thickness of the pulp will settle between the wires. The paper, when held to a light, will show alternate light and dark lines. The spacing and the thickness of the lines may vary, but on any one sheet of paper they are all alike. See Russia Scott 31-38 for examples of laid paper.

Batonne, from the French word meaning "a staff," is a term used if the lines in the paper are spaced quite far apart, like the printed ruling on a writing tablet. Batonne paper may be either wove or laid. If laid, fine laid lines can be seen between the batons. The laid lines, which are a form of watermark, may be geometrical figures such as squares, diamonds, rectangles or wavy lines.

Quadrille is the term used when the lines in the paper form little squares. *Oblong quadrille* is the term used when rectangles, rather than squares, are formed. See Mexico-Guadalajara Scott 35-37 for examples of oblong quadrille paper.

Paper also is classified as thick or thin, hard or soft, and by color if dye is added during manufacture. Such colors may include yellowish, greenish, bluish and reddish.

Brief explanations of other types of paper used for printing stamps, as well as examples, follow.

Pelure — Pelure paper is a very thin, hard and often brittle paper that is sometimes bluish or grayish in appearance. See Serbia Scott 169-170.

Native — This is a term applied to handmade papers used to produce some of the early stamps of the Indian states. Stamps printed on native paper may be expected to display various natural inclusions that are normal and do not negatively affect value. Japanese paper, originally made of mulberry fibers and rice flour, is part of this group. See Japan Scott 1-18.

Manila — This type of paper is often used to make stamped envelopes and wrappers. It is a coarse-textured stock, usually smooth on one side and rough on the other. A variety of colors of manila paper exist, but the most common range is yellowish-brown.

Silk — Introduced by the British in 1847 as a safeguard against counterfeiting, silk paper contains bits of colored silk thread scattered throughout. The density of these fibers varies greatly and can include as few as one fiber per stamp or hundreds. U.S. revenue Scott R152 is a good example of an easy-to-identify silk paper stamp.

Silk-thread paper has uninterrupted threads of colored silk arranged so that one or more threads run through the stamp or postal stationery. See Great Britain Scott 5-6 and Switzerland Scott 14-19.

Granite — Filled with minute cloth or colored paper fibers of various colors and lengths, granite paper should not be confused with either type of silk paper. Austria Scott 172-175 and a number of Swiss stamps are examples of granite paper.

Chalky — A chalk-like substance coats the surface of chalky paper to discourage the cleaning and reuse of canceled stamps, as well as to provide a smoother, more acceptable printing surface. Because the designs of stamps printed on chalky paper are imprinted on what is often a water-soluble coating, any attempt to remove a cancellation will destroy the stamp. *Do not soak these stamps in any fluid.* To remove a stamp printed on chalky paper from an envelope, wet the paper from underneath the stamp until the gum dissolves enough to release the stamp from the paper. See St. Kitts-Nevis Scott 89-90 for examples of stamps printed on this type of chalky paper.

India — Another name for this paper, originally introduced from China about 1750, is "China Paper." It is a thin, opaque paper often used for plate and die proofs by many countries.

Double — In philately, the term double paper has two distinct meanings. The first is a two-ply paper, usually a combination of a thick and a thin sheet, joined during manufacture. This type was used experimentally as a means to discourage the reuse of stamps.

The design is printed on the thin paper. Any attempt to remove a cancellation would destroy the design. U.S. Scott 158 and other Banknote-era stamps exist on this form of double paper.

The second type of double paper occurs on a rotary press, when the end of one paper roll, or web, is affixed to the next roll to save time feeding the paper through the press. Stamp designs are printed over the joined paper and, if overlooked by inspectors, may get into post office stocks.

Goldbeater's Skin — This type of paper was used for the 1866 issue of Prussia, and was a tough, translucent paper. The design was printed in reverse on the back of the stamp, and the gum applied over the printing. It is impossible to remove stamps printed on this type of paper from the paper to which they are affixed without destroying the design.

Ribbed — Ribbed paper has an uneven, corrugated surface made by passing the paper through ridged rollers. This type exists on some copies of U.S. Scott 156-165.

Various other substances, or substrates, have been used for stamp manufacture, including wood, aluminum, copper, silver and gold foil, plastic, and silk and cotton fabrics.

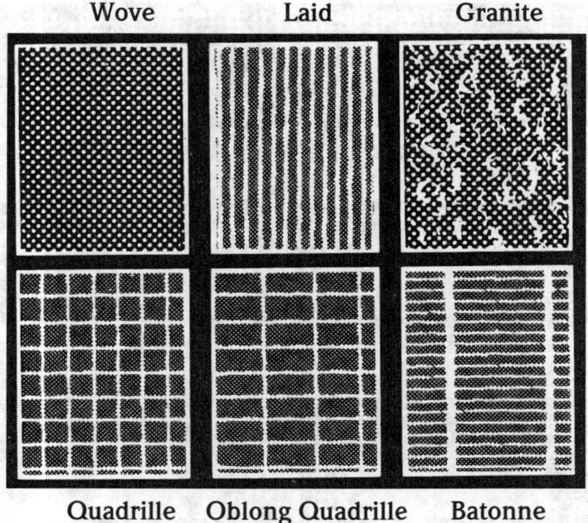

Watermarks

Watermarks are an integral part of some papers. They are formed in the process of paper manufacture. Watermarks consist of small designs, formed of wire or cut from metal and soldered to the surface of the mold or, sometimes, on the dandy roll. The designs may be in the form of crowns, stars, anchors, letters or other characters or symbols. These pieces of metal - known in the paper-making industry as "bits" - impress a design into the paper. The design sometimes may be seen by holding the stamp to the light. Some are more easily seen with a watermark detector. This important tool is a small black tray into which a stamp is placed face down and dampened with a fast-evaporating watermark detection fluid that brings up the watermark image in the form of dark lines against a lighter background. These dark lines are the thinner areas of the paper known as the watermark. Some watermarks are extremely difficult to locate, due to either a faint impression, watermark location or the color of the stamp. There also are electric watermark detectors that come with plastic filter disks of various colors. The disks neutralize the color of the stamp, permitting the watermark to be seen more easily.

Multiple watermarks of Crown Agents and Burma

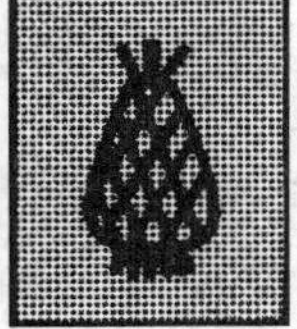

Watermarks of Uruguay, Vatican City and Jamaica

WARNING: Some inks used in the photogravure process dissolve in watermark fluids (Please see the section on Soluble Printing Inks). Also, see "chalky paper."

Watermarks may be found normal, reversed, inverted, reversed and inverted, sideways or diagonal, as seen from the back of the stamp. The relationship of watermark to stamp design depends on the position of the printing plates or how paper is fed through the press. On machine-made paper, watermarks normally are read from right to left. The design is repeated closely throughout the sheet in a "multiple-watermark design." In a "sheet watermark," the design appears only once on the sheet, but extends over many stamps. Individual stamps may carry only a small fraction or none of the watermark.

"Marginal watermarks" occur in the margins of sheets or panes of stamps. They occur on the outside border of paper (ostensibly outside the area where stamps are to be printed). A large row of letters may spell the name of the country or the manufacturer of the paper, or a border of lines may appear. Careless press feeding may cause parts of these letters and/or lines to show on stamps of the outer row of a pane.

Soluble Printing Inks

WARNING: Most stamp colors are permanent; that is, they are not seriously affected by short-term exposure to light or water. Many colors, especially of modern inks, fade from excessive exposure to light. There are stamps printed with inks that dissolve easily in water or in fluids used to detect watermarks. Use of these inks was intentional to prevent the removal of cancellations. Water affects all aniline inks, those on so-called safety paper and some photogravure printings - all such inks are known as *fugitive colors. Removal from paper of such stamps requires care and alternatives to traditional soaking.*

Separation

"Separation" is the general term used to describe methods used to separate stamps. The three standard forms currently in use are perforating, rouletting and die-cutting. These methods are done during the stamp production process, after printing. Sometimes these methods are done on-press or sometimes as a separate step. The earliest issues, such as the 1840 Penny Black of Great Britain (Scott 1), did not have any means provided for separation. It was expected the stamps would be cut apart with scissors or folded and torn. These are examples of imperforate stamps. Many stamps were first issued in imperforate formats and were later issued with perforations. Therefore, care must be observed in buying single imperforate stamps to be certain they were issued imperforate and are not perforated copies that have been altered by having the perforations trimmed away. Stamps issued imperforate usually are valued as singles. However, imperforate varieties of normally perforated stamps should be collected in pairs or larger pieces as indisputable evidence of their imperforate character.

PERFORATION

The chief style of separation of stamps, and the one that is in almost universal use today, is perforating. By this process, paper between the stamps is cut away in a line of holes, usually round, leaving little bridges of paper between the stamps to hold them together. Some types of perforation, such as hyphen-hole perfs, can be confused with roulettes, but a close visual inspection reveals that paper has been removed. The little perforation bridges, which project from the stamp when it is torn from the pane, are called the teeth of the perforation.

As the size of the perforation is sometimes the only way to differentiate between two otherwise identical stamps, it is necessary to be able to accurately measure and describe them. This is done with a perforation gauge, usually a ruler-like device that has dots or graduated lines to show how many perforations may be counted in the space of two centimeters. Two centimeters is the space universally adopted in which to measure perforations.

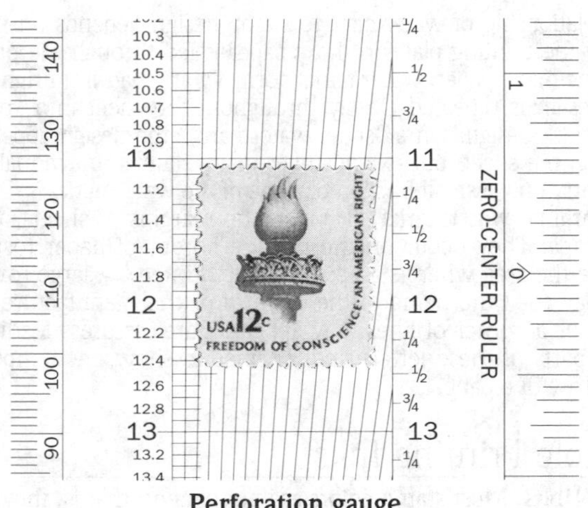

Perforation gauge

To measure a stamp, run it along the gauge until the dots on it fit exactly into the perforations of the stamp. If you are using a graduated-line perforation gauge, simply slide the stamp along the surface until the lines on the gauge perfectly project from the center of the bridges or holes. The number to the side of the line of dots or lines that fit the stamp's perforation is the measurement. For example, an "11" means that 11 perforations fit between two centimeters. The description of the stamp therefore is "perf. 11." If the gauge of the perforations on the top and bottom of a stamp differs from that on the sides, the result is what is known as *compound perforations.* In measuring compound perforations, the gauge at top and bottom is always given first, then the sides. Thus, a stamp that measures 11 at top and bottom and 10 1/2 at the sides is "perf. 11 x 10 1/2." See U.S. Scott 632-642 for examples of compound perforations.

Stamps also are known with perforations different on three or all four sides. Descriptions of such items are clockwise, beginning with the top of the stamp.

A perforation with small holes and teeth close together is a "fine perforation." One with large holes and teeth far apart is a "coarse perforation." Holes that are jagged, rather than clean-cut, are "rough perforations." *Blind perforations* are the slight impressions left by the perforating pins if they fail to puncture the paper. Multiples of stamps showing blind perforations may command a slight premium over normally perforated stamps.

The term *syncopated perfs* describes intentional irregularities in the perforations. The earliest form was used by the Netherlands from 1925-33, where holes were omitted to create distinctive patterns. Beginning in 1992, Great Britain has used an oval perforation to help prevent counterfeiting. Several other countries have started using the oval perfs.

A new type of perforation, still primarily used for postal stationery, is known as microperfs. Microperfs are tiny perforations (in some cases hundreds of holes per two centimeters) that allows items to be intentionally separated very easily, while not accidentally breaking apart as easily as standard perforations. These are not currently measured or differentiated by size, as are standard perforations.

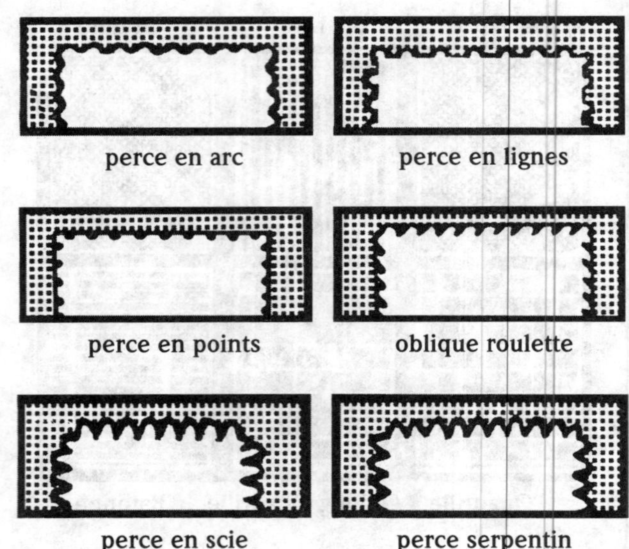

ROULETTING

In rouletting, the stamp paper is cut partly or wholly through, with no paper removed. In perforating, some paper is removed. Rouletting derives its name from the French roulette, a spur-like wheel. As the wheel is rolled over the paper, each point makes a small cut. The number of cuts made in a two-centimeter space determines the gauge of the roulette, just as the number of perforations in two centimeters determines the gauge of the perforation.

The shape and arrangement of the teeth on the wheels varies. Various roulette types generally carry French names:

Perce en lignes - rouletted in lines. The paper receives short, straight cuts in lines. This is the most common type of rouletting. See Mexico Scott 500.

Perce en points - pin-rouletted. This differs from a small perforation because no paper is removed, although round, equidistant holes are pricked through the paper. See Mexico Scott 242-256.

Perce en arc and *perce en scie* - pierced in an arc or saw-toothed designs, forming half circles or small triangles. See Hanover (German States) Scott 25-29.

Perce en serpentin - serpentine roulettes. The cuts form a serpentine or wavy line. See Brunswick (German States) Scott 13-18.

Once again, no paper is removed by these processes, leaving the stamps easily separated, but closely attached.

DIE-CUTTING

The third major form of stamp separation is die-cutting. This is a method where a die in the pattern of separation is created that later cuts the stamp paper in a stroke motion. Although some standard stamps bear die-cut perforations, this process is primarily used for self-adhesive postage stamps. Die-cutting can appear in straight lines, such as U.S. Scott 2522, shapes, such as U.S. Scott 1551, or imitating the appearance of perforations, such as New Zealand Scott 935A and 935B.

Printing Processes

ENGRAVING (Intaglio, Line-engraving, Etching)

Master die — The initial operation in the process of line engraving is making the master die. The die is a small, flat block of softened steel upon which the stamp design is recess engraved in reverse.

Master die

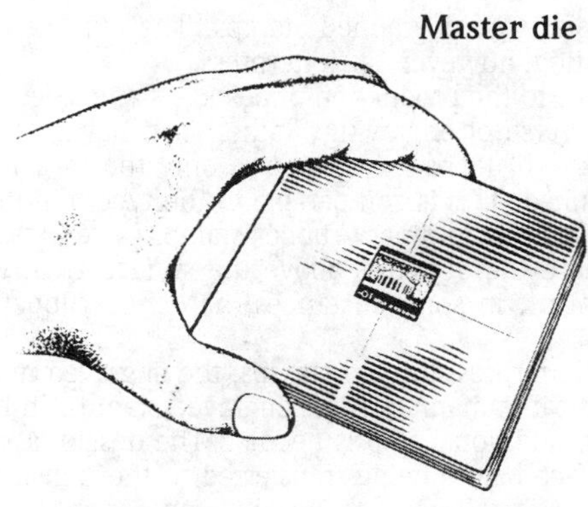

Photographic reduction of the original art is made to the appropriate size. It then serves as a tracing guide for the initial outline of the design. The engraver lightly traces the design on the steel with his graver, then slowly works the design until it is completed. At various points during the engraving process, the engraver hand-inks the die and makes an impression to check his progress. These are known as progressive die proofs. After completion of the engraving, the die is hardened to withstand the stress and pressures of later transfer operations.

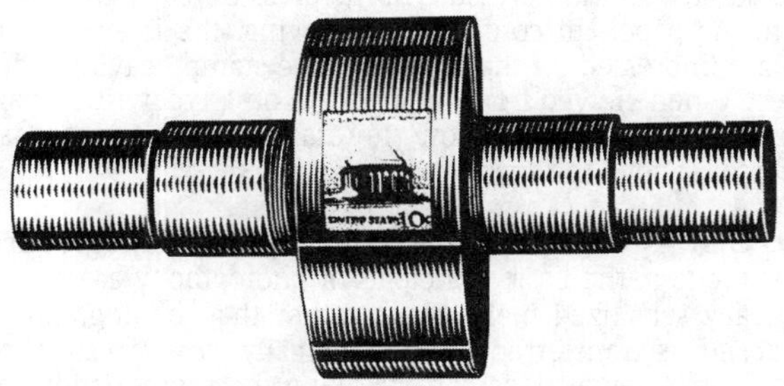

Transfer roll

Transfer roll — Next is production of the transfer roll that, as the name implies, is the medium used to transfer the subject from the master die to the printing plate. A blank roll of soft steel, mounted on a mandrel, is placed under the bearers of the transfer press to allow it to roll freely on its axis. The hardened die is placed on the bed of the press and the face of the transfer roll is applied to the die, under pressure. The bed or the roll is then rocked back and forth under increasing pressure, until the soft steel of the roll is forced into every engraved line of the die. The resulting impression on the roll is known as a "relief" or a "relief transfer." The engraved image is now positive in appearance and stands out from the steel. After the required number of reliefs are "rocked in," the soft steel transfer roll is hardened.

Different flaws may occur during the relief process. A defective relief may occur during the rocking in process because of a minute piece of foreign material lodging on the die, or some other cause. Imperfections in the steel of the transfer roll may result in a breaking away of parts of the design. This is known as a relief break, which will show up on finished stamps as small, unprinted areas. If a damaged relief remains in use, it will transfer a repeating defect to the plate. Deliberate alterations of reliefs sometimes occur. "Altered reliefs" designate these changed conditions.

Plate — The final step in pre-printing production is the making of the printing plate. A flat piece of soft steel replaces the die on the bed of the transfer press. One of the reliefs on the transfer roll is positioned over this soft steel. Position, or layout, dots determine the correct position on the plate. The dots have been lightly marked on the plate in advance. After the correct position of the relief is determined, the design is rocked in by following the same method used in making the transfer roll. The difference is that this time the image is being transferred from the transfer roll, rather than to it. Once the design is entered on the plate, it appears in reverse and is recessed. There are as many transfers entered on the plate as there are subjects printed on the sheet of stamps. It is during this process that double and shifted transfers occur, as well as re-entries. These are the result of improperly entered images that have not been properly burnished out prior to rocking in a new image.

Modern siderography processes, such as those used by the U.S. Bureau of Engraving and Printing, involve an automated form of rocking designs in on preformed cylindrical printing sleeves. The same process also allows for easier removal and re-entry of worn images right on the sleeve.

Transferring the design to the plate

Following the entering of the required transfers on the plate, the position dots, layout dots and lines, scratches and other markings generally are burnished out. Added at this time by the siderographer are any required *guide lines, plate numbers* or other *marginal markings*. The plate is then hand-inked and a proof impression is taken. This is known as a plate proof. If the impression is approved, the plate is machined for fitting onto the press, is hardened and sent to the plate vault ready for use.

On press, the plate is inked and the surface is automatically wiped clean, leaving ink only in the recessed lines. Paper is then forced under pressure into the engraved recessed lines, thereby receiving the ink. Thus, the ink lines on engraved stamps are slightly raised, and slight depressions (debossing) occur on the back of the stamp. Prior to the advent of modern high-speed presses and more advanced ink formulations, paper had to be dampened before receiving the ink. This sometimes led to uneven shrinkage by the time the stamps were perforated, resulting in improperly perforated stamps, or misperfs. Newer presses use drier paper, thus both *wet* and *dry printings* exist on some stamps.

Rotary Press — Until 1914, only flat plates were used to print engraved stamps. Rotary press printing was introduced in 1914, and slowly spread. Some countries still use flat-plate printing.

After approval of the plate proof, older *rotary press plates* require additional machining. They are curved to fit the press cylinder. "Gripper slots" are cut into the back of each plate to receive the "grippers," which hold the plate securely on the press. The plate is then hardened. Stamps printed from these bent rotary press plates are longer or wider than the same stamps printed from flat-plate presses. The stretching of the plate during the curving process is what causes this distortion.

Re-entry — To execute a re-entry on a flat plate, the transfer roll is re-applied to the plate, often at some time after its first use on the press. Worn-out designs can be resharpened by carefully burnishing out the original image and re-entering it from the transfer roll. If the original impression has not been sufficiently removed and the transfer roll is not precisely in line with the remaining impression, the resulting double transfer will make the re-entry obvious. If the registration is true, a re-entry may be difficult or impossible to distinguish. Sometimes a stamp printed from a successful re-entry is identified by having a much sharper and clearer impression than its neighbors. With the advent of rotary presses, post-press re-entries were not possible. After a plate was curved for the rotary press, it was impossible to make a re-entry. This is because the plate had already been bent once (with the design distorted).

However, with the introduction of the previously mentioned modern-style siderography machines, entries are made to the pre-formed cylindrical printing sleeve. Such sleeves are dechromed and softened. This allows individual images to be burnished out and re-entered on the curved sleeve. The sleeve is then rechromed, resulting in longer press life.

Double Transfer — This is a description of the condition of a transfer on a plate that shows evidence of a duplication of all, or a portion of the design. It usually is the result of the changing of the registration between the transfer roll and the plate during the rocking in of the original entry. Double transfers also occur when only a portion of the design has been rocked in and improper positioning is noted. If the worker elected not to burnish out the partial or completed design, a strong double transfer will occur for part or all of the design.

It sometimes is necessary to remove the original transfer from a plate and repeat the process a second time. If the finished reworked image shows traces of the original impression, attributable to incomplete burnishing, the result is a partial double transfer.

With the modern automatic machines mentioned previously, double transfers are all but impossible to create. Those partially doubled images on stamps printed from such sleeves are more than likely re-entries, rather than true double transfers.

Re-engraved — Alterations to a stamp design are sometimes necessary after some stamps have been printed. In some cases, either the original die or the actual printing plate may have its "temper" drawn (softened), and the design will be re-cut. The resulting impressions from such a re-engraved die or plate may differ slightly from the original issue, and are known as "re-engraved." If the alteration was made to the master die, all future printings will be consistently different from the original. If alterations were made to the printing plate, each altered stamp on the plate will be slightly different from each other, allowing specialists to reconstruct a complete printing plate.

Dropped Transfers — If an impression from the transfer roll has not been properly placed, a dropped transfer may occur. The final stamp image will appear obviously out of line with its neighbors.

Short Transfer — Sometimes a transfer roll is not rocked its entire length when entering a transfer onto a plate. As a result, the finished transfer on the plate fails to show the complete design, and the finished stamp will have an incomplete design printed. This is known as a "short transfer." U.S. Scott No. 8 is a good example of a short transfer.

TYPOGRAPHY (Letterpress, Surface Printing, Flexography, Dry Offset, High Etch)

Although the word "Typography" is obsolete as a term describing a printing method, it was the accepted term throughout the first century of postage stamps. Therefore, appropriate Scott listings in this catalogue refer to typographed stamps. The current term for this form of printing, however, is "letterpress."

As it relates to the production of postage stamps, letterpress printing is the reverse of engraving. Rather than having recessed areas trap the ink and deposit it on paper, only the raised areas of the design are inked. This is comparable to the type of printing seen by inking and using an ordinary rubber stamp. Letterpress includes all printing where the design is above the surface area, whether it is wood, metal or, in some instances, hardened rubber or polymer plastic.

For most letterpress-printed stamps, the engraved master is made in much the same manner as for engraved stamps. In this instance, however, an additional step is needed. The design is transferred to another surface before being transferred to the transfer roll. In this way, the transfer roll has a recessed stamp design, rather than one done in relief. This makes the printing areas on the final plate raised, or relief areas.

For less-detailed stamps of the 19th century, the area on the die not used as a printing surface was cut away, leaving the surface area raised. The original die was then reproduced by stereotyping or electrotyping. The resulting electrotypes were assembled in the required number and format of the desired sheet of stamps. The plate used in printing the stamps was an electroplate of these assembled electrotypes.

Once the final letterpress plates are created, ink is applied to the raised surface and the pressure of the press transfers the ink impression to the paper. In contrast to engraving, the fine lines of letterpress are impressed on the surface of the stamp, leaving a debossed surface. When viewed from the back (as on a typewritten page), the corresponding line work on the stamp will be raised slightly (embossed) above the surface.

PHOTOGRAVURE (Gravure, Rotogravure, Heliogravure)

In this process, the basic principles of photography are applied to a chemically sensitized metal plate, rather than photographic paper. The design is transferred photographically to the plate through a halftone, or dot-matrix screen, breaking the reproduction into tiny dots. The plate is treated chemically and the dots form depressions, called cells, of varying depths and diameters, depending on the degrees of shade in the design. Then, like engraving, ink is applied to the plate and the surface is wiped clean. This leaves ink in the tiny cells that is lifted out and deposited on the paper when it is pressed against the plate.

Gravure is most often used for multicolored stamps, generally using the three primary colors (red, yellow and blue) and black. By varying the dot matrix pattern and density of these colors, virtually any color can be reproduced. A typical full-color gravure stamp will be created from four printing cylinders (one for each color). The original multicolored image will have been photographically separated into its component colors.

For examples of the first photogravure stamps printed (1914), see Bavaria Scott 94-114.

LITHOGRAPHY (Offset Lithography, Stone Lithography, Dilitho, Planography, Collotype)

The principle that oil and water do not mix is the basis for lithography. The stamp design is drawn by hand or transferred from engraving to the surface of a lithographic stone or metal plate in a greasy (oily) substance. This oily substance holds the ink, which will later be transferred to the paper. The stone (or plate) is wet with an acid fluid, causing it to repel the printing ink in all areas not covered by the greasy substance.

Transfer paper is used to transfer the design from the original stone or plate. A series of duplicate transfers are grouped and, in turn, transferred to the final printing plate.

Photolithography — The application of photographic processes to lithography. This process allows greater flexibility of design, related to use of halftone screens combined with line work. Unlike photogravure or engraving, this process can allow large, solid areas to be printed.

Offset — A refinement of the lithographic process. A rubber-covered blanket cylinder takes the impression from the inked lithographic plate. From the "blanket" the impression is *offset* or transferred to the paper. Greater flexibility and speed are the principal reasons offset printing has largely displaced lithography. The term "lithography" covers both processes, and results are almost identical.

EMBOSSED (Relief) Printing

Embossing, not considered one of the four main printing types, is a method in which the design first is sunk into the metal of the die. Printing is done against a yielding platen, such as leather or linoleum. The platen is forced into the depression of the die, thus forming the design on the paper in relief. This process is often used for metallic inks.

Embossing may be done without color (see Sardinia Scott 4-6); with color printed around the embossed area (see Great Britain Scott 5 and most U.S. envelopes); and with color in exact registration with the embossed subject (see Canada Scott 656-657).

COMBINATION PRINTINGS

Sometimes two or even three printing methods are combined in producing stamps. In these cases, such as Austria Scott 933, the stamp's dual printing technique can be determined by studying the individual characteristics of each printing type (intaglio and offset). A few stamps, such as Singapore Scott 684-684A, combine as many as three of the four major printing types (offset, intaglio and letterpress). When this is done it often indicates the incorporation of security devices against counterfeiting.

INK COLORS

Inks or colored papers used in stamp printing often are of mineral origin, although there are numerous examples of organic-based pigments. As a general rule, organic-based pigments are far more subject to varieties and change than those of mineral-based origin.

The appearance of any given color on a stamp may be affected by many aspects, including printing variations, light, color of paper, aging and chemical alterations.

Numerous printing variations may be observed. Heavier pressure or inking will cause a more intense color, while slight interruptions in the ink feed or lighter impressions will cause a lighter appearance. Stamps printed in the same color by water-based and solvent-based inks can differ significantly in appearance. This affects several stamps in the U.S. Prominent Americans series. Hand-mixed ink formulas (primarily from the 19th century) produced under different conditions (humidity and temperature) account for notable color variations in early printings of the same stamp (see U.S. Scott 248-250, 279B, for example). Different sources of pigment can also result in significant differences in color.

Light exposure and aging are closely related in the way they affect stamp color. Both eventually break down the ink and fade colors, so that a carefully kept stamp may differ significantly in color from an identical copy that has been exposed to light. If stamps are exposed to light either intentionally or accidentally, their colors can be faded or completely changed in some cases.

Papers of different quality and consistency used for the same stamp printing may affect color appearance. Most pelure papers, for example, show a richer color when compared with wove or laid papers. See Russia Scott 181a, for an example of this effect.

The very nature of the printing processes can cause a variety of differences in shades or hues of the same stamp. Some of these shades are scarcer than others, and are of particular interest to the advanced collector.

Luminescence

All forms of tagged stamps fall under the general category of luminescence. Within this broad category is fluorescence, dealing with forms of tagging visible under longwave ultraviolet light, and phosphorescence, which deals with tagging visible only under shortwave light. Phosphorescence leaves an afterglow and fluorescence does not. These treated stamps show up in a range of different colors when exposed to UV light. The differing wavelengths of the light activates the tagging material, making it glow in various colors that usually serve different mail processing purposes.

Intentional tagging is a post-World War II phenomenon, brought about by the increased literacy rate and rapidly growing mail volume. It was one of several answers to the problem of the need for more automated mail processes. Early tagged stamps served the purpose of triggering machines to separate different types of mail. A natural outgrowth was to also use the signal to trigger machines that faced all envelopes the same way and canceled them.

Tagged stamps come in many different forms. Some tagged stamps have luminescent shapes or images imprinted on them as a form of security device. Others have blocks (United States), stripes, frames (South Africa and Canada), overall coatings (United States), bars (Great Britain and Canada) and many other types. Some types of tagging are even mixed in with the pigmented printing ink (Australia Scott 366, Netherlands Scott 478 and U.S. Scott 1359 and 2443).

The means of applying taggant to stamps differs as much as the intended purposes for the stamps. The most common form of tagging is a coating applied to the surface of the printed stamp. Since the taggant ink is frequently invisible except under UV light, it does not interfere with the appearance of the stamp. Another common application is the use of phosphored papers. In this case the paper itself either has a coating of taggant applied before the stamp is printed or has taggant applied during the papermaking process, incorporating it into the fibers. This is currently in use in the United States. A similar form is the application of a fluorescent coating either to the finished paper or during the papermaking process. This type of tagging has been extensively used by Australia and Germany.

Many countries now use tagging in various forms to either expedite mail handling or to serve as a printing security device against counterfeiting. Following the introduction of tagged stamps for public use in 1959 by Great Britain, other countries have steadily joined the parade. Among those are Germany (1961); Canada and Denmark (1962); United States, Australia, France and Switzerland (1963); Belgium and Japan (1966); Sweden and Norway (1967); Italy (1968); and Russia (1969). Since then, many other countries have begun using forms of tagging, including Brazil, China, Czechoslovakia, Hong Kong, Guatemala, Indonesia, Israel, Lithuania, Luxembourg, Netherlands, Penrhyn Islands, Portugal, St. Vincent, Singapore, South Africa, Spain and Sweden to name a few.

In some cases, including United States, Canada, Great Britain and Switzerland, stamps were released both with and without tagging. Many of these were released during each country's experimental period. Tagged and untagged versions are listed for the aforementioned countries and are noted in some other countries' listings. For at least a few stamps, the experimentally tagged version is worth far more than its untagged counterpart, such as the 1963 experimental tagged version of France Scott 1024.

In some cases, luminescent varieties of stamps were inadvertently created. Several Russian stamps, for example, sport highly fluorescent ink that was not intended as a form of tagging. Older stamps, such as early U.S. postage dues, can be positively identified by the use of UV light, since the organic ink used has become slightly fluorescent over time. Other stamps, such as Austria Scott 70a-82a (varnish bars) and Obock Scott 46-64 (printed quadrille lines), have become fluorescent over time.

Various fluorescent substances have been added to paper to make it appear brighter. These optical brightners, as they are known, greatly affect the appearance of the stamp under UV light. The brightest of these is known as Hi-Brite paper. These paper varieties are beyond the scope of the Scott Catalogue.

Shortwave UV light also is used extensively in expertizing, since each form of paper has its own fluorescent characteristics that are impossible to perfectly match. It is therefore a simple matter to detect filled thins, added perforation teeth and other alterations that involve the addition of paper. UV light also is used to examine stamps that have had cancels chemically removed and for other purposes as well.

Gum

The Illustrated Gum Chart in the first part of this introduction shows and defines various types of gum condition. Because gum condition has an important impact on the value of unused stamps, we recommend studying this chart and the accompanying text carefully.

The gum on the back of a stamp may be shiny, dull, smooth, rough, dark, white, colored or tinted. Most stamp gumming adhesives use gum arabic or dextrine as a base. Certain polymers such as polyvinyl alcohol (PVA) have been used extensively since World War II.

The *Scott Standard Postage Stamp Catalogue* does not list items by types of gum. The *Scott Specialized Catalogue of United States Stamps* does differentiate among some types of gum for certain issues.

Reprints of stamps may have gum differing from the original issues. In addition, some countries have used different gum formulas for different seasons. These adhesives have different properties that may become more apparent over time.

Many stamps have been issued without gum, and the catalogue will note this fact. See United States Scott PR33-PR56. Sometimes, gum may have been removed to preserve the stamp. Germany Scott B68, for example, has a highly acidic gum that eventually destroys the stamps. This item is valued in the catalogue with gum removed.

Reprints and Reissues

These are impressions of stamps (usually obsolete) made from the original plates or stones. If they are valid for postage and reproduce obsolete issues (such as U.S. Scott 102-111), the stamps are *reissues.* If they are from current issues, they are designated as *second, third,* etc., *printing.* If designated for a particular purpose, they are called *special printings.*

When special printings are not valid for postage, but are made from original dies and plates by authorized persons, they are *official reprints. Private reprints* are made from the original plates and dies by private hands. An example of a private reprint is that of the 1871-1932 reprints made from the original die of the 1845 New Haven, Conn., postmaster's provisional. *Official reproductions* or imitations are made from new dies and plates by government authorization. Scott will list those reissues that are valid for postage if they differ significantly from the original printing.

The U.S. government made special printings of its first postage stamps in 1875. Produced were official imitations of the first two stamps (listed as Scott 3-4), reprints of the demonetized pre-1861 issues (Scott 40-47) and reissues of the 1861 stamps, the 1869 stamps and the then-current 1875 denominations. Even though the official imitations and the reprints were not valid for postage, Scott lists all of these U.S. special printings.

Most reprints or reissues differ slightly from the original stamp in some characteristic, such as gum, paper, perforation, color or watermark. Sometimes the details are followed so meticulously that only a student of that specific stamp is able to distinguish the reprint or reissue from the original.

Remainders and Canceled to Order

Some countries sell their stock of old stamps when a new issue replaces them. To avoid postal use, the *remainders* usually are canceled with a punch hole, a heavy line or bar, or a more-or-less regular-looking cancellation. The most famous merchant of remainders was Nicholas F. Seebeck. In the 1880s and 1890s, he arranged printing contracts between the Hamilton Bank Note Co., of which he was a director, and several Central and South American countries. The contracts provided that the plates and all remainders of the yearly issues became the property of Hamilton. Seebeck saw to it that ample stock remained. The "Seebecks," both remainders and reprints, were standard packet fillers for decades.

Some countries also issue stamps *canceled-to-order (CTO),* either in sheets with original gum or stuck onto pieces of paper or envelopes and canceled. Such CTO items generally are worth less than postally used stamps. In cases where the CTO material is far more prevalent in the marketplace than postally used examples, the catalogue value relates to the CTO examples, with postally used examples noted as premium items. Most CTOs can be detected by the presence of gum. However, as the CTO practice goes back at least to 1885, the gum inevitably has been soaked off some stamps so they could pass as postally used. The normally applied postmarks usually differ slightly from standard postmarks, and specialists are able to tell the difference. When applied individually to envelopes by philatelically minded persons, CTO material is known as *favor canceled* and generally sells at large discounts.

Cinderellas and Facsimiles

Cinderella is a catch-all term used by stamp collectors to describe phantoms, fantasies, bogus items, municipal issues, exhibition seals, local revenues, transportation stamps, labels, poster stamps and many other types of items. Some cinderella collectors include in their collections local postage issues, telegraph stamps, essays and proofs, forgeries and counterfeits.

A *fantasy* is an adhesive created for a nonexistent stamp-issuing authority. Fantasy items range from imaginary countries (Occusi-Ambeno, Kingdom of Sedang, Principality of Trinidad or Torres Straits), to non-existent locals (Winans City Post), or nonexistent transportation lines (McRobish & Co.'s Acapulco-San Francisco Line).

On the other hand, if the entity exists and could have issued stamps (but did not) or was known to have issued other stamps, the items are considered *bogus* stamps. These would include the Mormon postage stamps of Utah, S. Allan Taylor's Guatemala and Paraguay inventions, the propaganda issues for the South Moluccas and the adhesives of the Page & Keyes local post of Boston.

Phantoms is another term for both fantasy and bogus issues.

Facsimiles are copies or imitations made to represent original stamps, but which do not pretend to be originals. A catalogue illustration is such a facsimile. Illustrations from the Moens catalogue of the last century were occasionally colored and passed off as stamps. Since the beginning of stamp collecting, facsimiles have been made for collectors as space fillers or for reference. They often carry the word "facsimile," "falsch" (German), "sanko" or "mozo" (Japanese), or "faux" (French) overprinted on the face or stamped on the back. Unfortunately, over the years a number of these items have had fake cancels applied over the facsimile notation and have been passed off as genuine.

Forgeries and Counterfeits

Forgeries and counterfeits have been with philately virtually from the beginning of stamp production. Over time, the terminology for the two has been used interchangeably. Although both forgeries and counterfeits are reproductions of stamps, the purposes behind their creation differ considerably.

Among specialists there is an increasing movement to more specifically define such items. Although there is no universally accepted terminology, we feel the following definitions most closely mirror the items and their purposes as they are currently defined.

Forgeries (also often referred to as *Counterfeits*) are reproductions of genuine stamps that have been created to defraud collectors. Such spurious items first appeared on the market around 1860, and most old-time collections contain one or more. Many are crude and easily spotted, but some can deceive experts.

An important supplier of these early philatelic forgeries was the Hamburg printer Gebruder Spiro. Many others with reputations in this craft included S. Allan Taylor, George Hussey, James Chute, George Forune, Benjamin & Sarpy, Julius Goldner, E. Oneglia and L.H. Mercier. Among the noted 20th-century forgers were Francois Fournier, Jean Sperati and the prolific Raoul DeThuin.

Forgeries may be complete replications, or they may be genuine stamps altered to resemble a scarcer (and more valuable) type. Most forgeries, particularly those of rare stamps, are worth only a small fraction of the value of a genuine example, but a few types, created by some of the most notable forgers, such as Sperati, can be worth as much or more than the genuine. Fraudulently produced copies are known of most classic rarities and many medium-priced stamps.

In addition to rare stamps, large numbers of common 19th- and early 20th-century stamps were forged to supply stamps to the early packet trade. Many can still be easily found. Few new philatelic forgeries have appeared in recent decades. Successful imitation of well-engraved work is virtually impossible. It has proven far easier to produce a fake by altering a genuine stamp than to duplicate a stamp completely.

Counterfeit (also often referred to as *Postal Counterfeit* or *Postal Forgery*) is the term generally applied to reproductions of stamps that have been created to defraud the government of revenue. Such items usually are created at the time a stamp is current and, in some cases, are hard to detect. Because most counterfeits are seized when the perpetrator is captured, postal counterfeits, particularly used on cover, are usually worth much more than a genuine example to specialists. The first postal counterfeit was of Spain's 4-cuarto carmine of 1854 (the real one is Scott 25). Apparently, the counterfeiters were not satisfied with their first version, which is now very scarce, and they soon created an engraved counterfeit, which is common. Postal counterfeits quickly followed in Austria, Naples, Sardinia and the Roman States. They have since been created in many other countries as well, including the United States.

An infamous counterfeit to defraud the government is the 1-shilling Great Britain "Stock Exchange" forgery of 1872, used on telegraph forms at the exchange that year. The stamp escaped detection until a stamp dealer noticed it in 1898.

Fakes

Fakes are genuine stamps altered in some way to make them more desirable. One student of this part of stamp collecting has estimated that by the 1950s more than 30,000 varieties of fakes were known. That number has grown greatly since then. The widespread existence of fakes makes it important for stamp collectors to study their philatelic holdings and use relevant literature. Likewise, collectors should buy from reputable dealers who guarantee their stamps and make full and prompt refunds should a purchased item be declared faked or altered by some mutually agreed-upon authority. Because fakes always have some genuine characteristics, it is not always possible to obtain unanimous agreement among experts regarding specific items. These students may change their opinions as philatelic knowledge increases. More than 80 percent of all fakes on the philatelic market today are regummed, reperforated (or perforated for the first time), or bear forged overprints, surcharges or cancellations.

Stamps can be chemically treated to alter or eliminate colors. For example, a pale rose stamp can be re-colored to resemble a blue shade of high market value. In other cases, treated stamps can be made to resemble missing color varieties. Designs may be changed by painting, or a stroke or a dot added or bleached out to turn an ordinary variety into a seemingly scarcer stamp. Part of a stamp can be bleached and reprinted in a different version, achieving an inverted center or frame. Margins can be added or repairs done so deceptively that the stamps move from the "repaired" into the "fake" category.

Fakers have not left the backs of the stamps untouched either. They may create false watermarks, add fake grills or press out genuine grills. A thin India paper proof may be glued onto a thicker backing to create the appearance an issued stamp, or a proof printed on cardboard may be shaved down and perforated to resemble a stamp. Silk threads are impressed into paper and stamps have been split so that a rare paper variety is added to an otherwise inexpensive stamp. The most common treatment to the back of a stamp, however, is regumming.

Some in the business of faking stamps have openly advertised fool-proof application of "original gum" to stamps that lack it, although most publications now ban such ads from their pages. It is believed that very few early stamps have survived without being hinged. The large number of never-hinged examples of such earlier material offered for sale thus suggests the widespread extent of regumming activity. Regumming also may be used to hide repairs or thin spots. Dipping the stamp into watermark fluid, or examining it under longwave ultraviolet light often will reveal these flaws.

Fakers also tamper with separations. Ingenious ways to add margins are known. Perforated wide-margin stamps may be falsely represented as imperforate when trimmed. Reperforating is commonly done to create scarce coil or perforation varieties, and to eliminate the naturally occurring straight-edge stamps found in sheet margin positions of many earlier issues. Custom has made straight-edged stamps less desirable. Fakers have obliged by perforating straight-edged stamps so that many are now uncommon, if not rare.

Another fertile field for the faker is that of overprints, surcharges and cancellations. The forging of rare surcharges or overprints began in the 1880s or 1890s. These forgeries are sometimes difficult to detect, but experts have identified almost all. Occasionally, overprints or cancellations are removed to create non-overprinted stamps or seemingly unused items. This is most commonly done by removing a manuscript cancel to make a stamp resemble an unused example. "SPECIMEN" overprints may be removed by scraping and repainting to create non-overprinted varieties. Fakers use inexpensive revenues or pen-canceled stamps to generate unused stamps for further faking by adding other markings. The quartz lamp or UV lamp and a high-powered magnifying glass help to easily detect removed cancellations.

The bigger problem, however, is the addition of overprints, surcharges or cancellations - many with such precision that they are very difficult to ascertain. Plating of the stamps or the overprint can be an important method of detection.

Fake postmarks may range from many spurious fancy cancellations to a host of markings applied to transatlantic covers, to adding normally appearing postmarks to definitives of some countries with stamps that are valued far higher used than unused. With the increased popularity of cover collecting, and the widespread interest in postal history, a fertile new field for fakers has come about. Some have tried to create entire covers. Others specialize in adding stamps, tied by fake cancellations, to genuine stampless covers, or replacing less expensive or damaged stamps with more valuable ones. Detailed study of postal rates in effect at the time a cover in question was mailed, including the analysis of each handstamp used during the period, ink analysis and similar techniques, usually will unmask the fraud.

Restoration and Repairs

Scott Publishing Co. bases its catalogue values on stamps that are free of defects and otherwise meet the standards set forth earlier in this introduction. Most stamp collectors desire to have the finest copy of an item possible. Even within given grading categories there are variances. This leads to a controversial practice that is not defined in any universal manner: stamp *restoration.*

There are broad differences of opinion about what is permissible when it comes to restoration. Carefully applying a soft eraser to a stamp or cover to remove light soiling is one form of restoration, as is washing a stamp in mild soap and water to clean it. These are fairly accepted forms of restoration. More severe forms of restoration include pressing out creases or removing stains caused by tape. To what degree each of these is acceptable is dependent upon the individual situation. Further along the spectrum is the freshening of a stamp's color by removing oxide build-up or the effects of wax paper left next to stamps shipped to the tropics.

At some point in this spectrum the concept of *repair* replaces that of restoration. Repairs include filling thin spots, mending tears by reweaving or adding a missing perforation tooth. Regumming stamps may have been acceptable as a restoration or repair technique many decades ago, but today it is considered a form of fakery.

Restored stamps may or may not sell at a discount, and it is possible that the value of individual restored items may be enhanced over that of their pre-restoration state. Specific situations dictate the resultant value of such an item. Repaired stamps sell at substantial discounts from the value of sound stamps.

Terminology

Booklets — Many countries have issued stamps in small booklets for the convenience of users. This idea continues to become increasingly popular in many countries. Booklets have been issued in many sizes and forms, often with advertising on the covers, the panes of stamps or on the interleaving.

The panes used in booklets may be printed from special plates or made from regular sheets. All panes from booklets issued by the United States and many from those of other countries contain stamps that are straight edged on the sides, but perforated between. Others are distinguished by orientation of watermark or other identifying features. Any stamp-like unit in the pane, either printed or blank, that is not a postage stamp, is considered to be a *label* in the catalogue listings.

Scott lists and values booklet panes only. Complete booklets are listed and valued in only a few cases, such as Grenada Scott 1055 and some forms of British prestige booklets. Individual booklet panes are listed only when they are not fashioned from existing sheet stamps and, therefore, are identifiable from their sheet stamp counterparts.

Panes usually do not have a used value assigned to them because there is little market activity for used booklet panes, even though many exist used and there is some demand for them.

Cancellations — The marks or obliterations put on stamps by postal authorities to show that they have performed service and to prevent their reuse are known as cancellations. If the marking is made with a pen, it is considered a "pen cancel." When the location of the post office appears in the marking, it is a "town cancellation." A "postmark" is technically any postal marking, but in practice the term generally is applied to a town cancellation with a date. When calling attention to a cause or celebration, the marking is known as a "slogan cancellation." Many other types and styles of cancellations exist, such as duplex, numerals, targets, fancy and others. See also "precancels," below.

Coil Stamps — These are stamps that are issued in rolls for use in dispensers, affixing and vending machines. Those coils of the United States, Canada, Sweden and some other countries are perforated horizontally or vertically only, with the outer edges imperforate. Coil stamps of some countries, such as Great Britain and Germany, are perforated on all four sides and may in some cases be distinguished from their sheet stamp counterparts by watermarks, counting numbers on the reverse or other means.

Covers — Entire envelopes, with or without adhesive postage stamps, that have passed through the mail and bear postal or other markings of philatelic interest are known as covers. Before the introduction of envelopes in about 1840, people folded letters and wrote the address on the outside. Some people covered their letters with an extra sheet of paper on the outside for the address, producing the term "cover." Used airletter sheets, stamped envelopes and other items of postal stationery also are considered covers.

Errors — Stamps that have some major, consistent, unintentional deviation from the normal are considered errors. Errors include, but are not limited to, missing or wrong colors, wrong paper, wrong watermarks, inverted centers or frames on multicolor printing, inverted or missing surcharges or overprints, double impressions, missing perforations and others. Factually wrong or misspelled information, if it appears on all examples of a stamp, are not considered errors in the true sense of the word. They are errors of design. Inconsistent or randomly appearing items, such as misperfs or color shifts, are classified as freaks.

Overprints and Surcharges — Overprinting involves applying wording or design elements over an already existing stamp. Overprints can be used to alter the place of use (such as "Canal Zone" on U.S. stamps), to adapt them for a special purpose ("Porto" on Denmark's 1913-20 regular issues for use as postage due stamps, Scott J1-J7) or to commemorate a special occasion (United States Scott 647-648).

A *surcharge* is a form of overprint that changes or restates the face value of a stamp or piece of postal stationery.

Surcharges and overprints may be handstamped, typeset or, occasionally, lithographed or engraved. A few hand-written overprints and surcharges are known.

Precancels — Stamps that are canceled before they are placed in the mail are known as precancels. Precanceling usually is done to expedite the handling of large mailings and generally allow the affected mail pieces to skip certain phases of mail handling.

In the United States, precancellations generally identified the point of origin; that is, the city and state. This information appeared across the face of the stamp, usually centered between parallel lines. More recently, bureau precancels retained the parallel lines, but the city and state designations were dropped. Recent coils have a service inscription that is present on the original printing plate. These show the mail service paid for by the stamp. Since these stamps are not intended to receive further cancellations when used as intended, they are considered precancels. Such items often do not have parallel lines as part of the precancellation.

In France, the abbreviation *Affranchts* in a semicircle together with the word *Postes* is the general form of precancel in use. Belgian precancellations usually appear in a box in which the name of the city appears. Netherlands precancels have the name of the city enclosed between concentric circles, sometimes called a "lifesaver." Precancellations of other countries usually follow these patterns, but may be any arrangement of bars, boxes and city names.

Precancels are listed in the Scott catalogues only if the precancel changes the denomination (Belgium Scott 477-478); if the precanceled stamp is different from the non-precanceled version (such as untagged U.S. precancels); or if the stamp exists only precanceled (France Scott 1096-1099, U.S. Scott 2265).

Proofs and Essays — Proofs are impressions taken from an approved die, plate or stone in which the design and color are the same as the stamp issued to the public. Trial color proofs are impressions taken from approved dies, plates or stones in colors that vary from the final version. An essay is the impression of a design that differs in some way from the issued stamp. "Progressive die proofs" generally are considered to be essays.

Provisionals — These are stamps that are issued on short notice and intended for temporary use pending the arrival of regular issues. They usually are issued to meet such contingencies as changes in government or currency, shortage of necessary postage values or military occupation.

During the 1840s, postmasters in certain American cities issued stamps that were valid only at specific post offices. In 1861, postmasters of the Confederate States also issued stamps with limited validity. Both of these examples are known as "postmaster's provisionals."

Se-tenant — This term refers to an unsevered pair, strip or block of stamps that differ in design, denomination or overprint.

Unless the se-tenant item has a continuous design (see U.S. Scott 1451a, 1694a) the stamps do not have to be in the same order as shown in the catalogue (see U.S. Scott 2158a).

Specimens — The Universal Postal Union required member nations to send samples of all stamps they released into service to the International Bureau in Switzerland. Member nations of the UPU received these specimens as samples of what stamps were valid for postage. Many are overprinted, handstamped or initial-perforated "Specimen," "Canceled" or "Muestra." Some are marked with bars across the denominations (China-Taiwan), punched holes (Czechoslovakia) or back inscriptions (Mongolia).

Stamps distributed to government officials or for publicity purposes, and stamps submitted by private security printers for official approval, also may receive such defacements.

The previously described defacement markings prevent postal use, and all such items generally are known as "specimens."

Tete Beche — This term describes a pair of stamps in which one is upside down in relation to the other. Some of these are the result of intentional sheet arrangements, such as Morocco Scott B10-B11. Others occurred when one or more electrotypes accidentally were placed upside down on the plate, such as Colombia Scott 57a. Separation of the tete-beche stamps, of course, destroys the tete beche variety.

Currency Conversion

Country	Dollar	Pound	S Franc	Guilder	Yen	Lira	HK Dollar	D-Mark	Fr Franc	Cdn Dollar	Aust Dollar
Australia	1.4818	2.4967	0.9960	0.7225	0.0115	0.0008	0.1913	0.8140	0.2429	1.0474	....
Canada	1.4148	2.3838	0.9510	0.6898	0.0109	0.0008	0.1826	0.7772	0.2319	....	0.9548
France	6.1012	10.279	4.1011	2.9749	0.0472	0.0034	0.7875	3.3516	....	4.3124	4.1174
Germany	1.8204	3.0672	1.2236	0.8876	0.0141	0.0010	0.2350	....	0.2984	1.2867	1.2285
Hong Kong	7.7471	13.053	5.2074	3.7774	0.0599	0.0043	....	4.2557	1.2698	5.4758	5.2282
Italy	1795.	3024.4	1206.56	875.23	13.885	....	231.70	986.05	294.20	1268.73	1211.36
Japan	129.28	217.82	86.896	63.033	....	0.0720	16.687	71.015	21.188	91.373	87.242
Netherlands	2.0509	3.4556	1.3786	....	0.0159	0.0011	0.2647	1.1266	0.3361	1.4496	1.3841
Switzerland	1.4877	2.5066	....	0.7254	0.0115	0.0008	0.1920	0.8172	0.2438	1.0515	1.0040
U.K.	0.5935	....	0.3989	0.2894	0.0046	0.0003	0.0766	0.3260	0.0973	0.4195	0.4005
U.S.	....	1.6849	0.6722	0.4876	0.0077	0.0006	0.1291	0.5493	0.1639	0.7068	0.6749

Country	Currency	U.S. $ Equiv.
Jamaica	dollar	.0278
Japan	yen	.0077
Jordan	dinar	1.41
Kenya	shilling	.0167
Kiribati	Australian dollar	.6749
Korea (South)	won	.0007
Kuwait	dinar	3.277
Laos	kip	.0005
Latvia	lat	1.697
Lebanon	pound	.0007
Lesotho	maloti	.2015
Liberia	U.S. dollar	1.00
Liechtenstein	Swiss franc	.6722
Lithuania	litas	.25
Luxembourg	franc	.0267
Macao	pataca	.125
Madagascar	franc	.0002
Malawi	kwacha	.04
Malaysia	dollar	.2791
Maldive Islands	rafiyaa	.0849
Mali	CFA franc	.0016
Malta	pound	2.5357
Marshall Islands	U.S. dollar	1.00
Mauritania	ouguiya	.0057
Mauritius	rupee	.0426
Mexico	peso	.1175
Micronesia	U.S. dollar	1.00
Monaco	French franc	.1639
Mongolia	tugrik	.0012
Montserrat	East Caribbean dollar	.3704
Morocco	dirham	.1018
Mozambique	metical	.00009
Namibia	rand	.201
Nauru	Australian dollar	.6749
Nepal	rupee	.0164
Netherlands	guilder	.4876
Netherlands Antilles	guilder	.5587
Nevis	East Caribbean dollar	.3704
New Caledonia	CFP franc	.009
New Zealand	dollar	.5632
Nicaragua	gold cordoba	.0974
Niger	CFA franc	.0016
Nigeria	naira	.0457
Niue	New Zealand dollar	.5632
Norfolk Island	Australian dollar	.6749
Norway	krone	.1331
Oman	rial	2.597

Source: ***Wall Street Journal*** *Mar. 30, 1998. Figures reflect values as of Mar. 27, 1998.*

Specialty Series

Scott produces album pages for more than 160 different countries. Scott Specialty pages are renowned for their quality and detail. There are spaces for every major variety of postage stamp within each country or specialty area. Each space is identified by Scott number and many of the spaces are illustrated. Pages are printed on one side only on chemically neutral paper that will not harm your stamps.
Below is complete list of the entire line of foriegn pages produced by Scott. Albums are updated annually. For page and price breakouts see your favorite dealer or call Scott Publishing Co. direct.

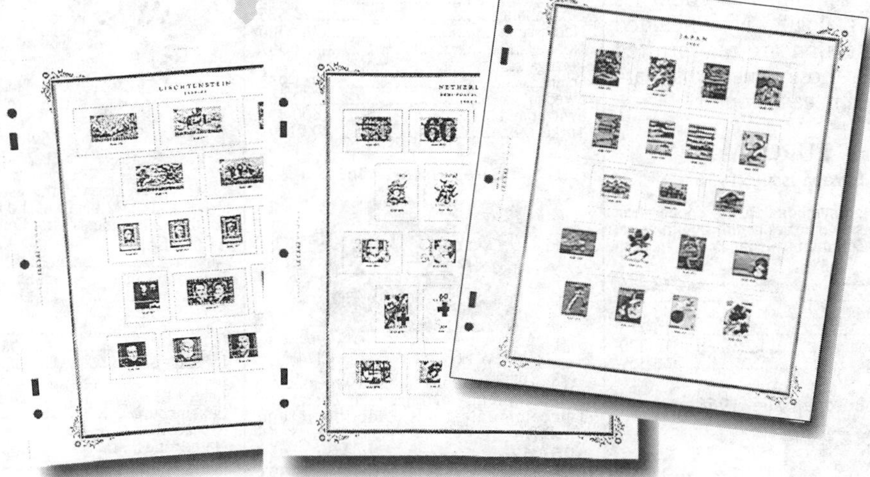

Scott Produces Album Pages for more than 160 countries.

ADEN
AFGHANISTAN
ALBANIA
ALGERIA
ANTIGUA
AUSTRALIA
AUSTRALIA DEPENDENCIES
AUSTRIA
BAHAMAS
BAHRAIN
BALTIC STATES
BANGLADESH
BARBADOS
BELGIUM
BELIZE
BERMUDA
BHUTAN
BOLIVIA
BOTSWANA
BRAZIL
BRITISH AFRICA
BRITISH ANTARCTIC TERRITORIES
BRITISH EUROPE
BRITISH HONDURAS
BRITISH ORIENT
BRITISH SOUTH ATLANTIC
BRUNEI
BULGARIA
BURKINA FASO
BURMA
BURUNDI
CANADA
CAYMAN ISLANDS
CENTRAL AFRICA
CHANNEL ISLANDS
CHILE
CHINA
COLOMBIA
COM. OF INDEPENDENT STATES
COMORO ISLANDS
CONGO
COSTA RICA
CROATIA
CZECHOSLOVAKIA
DENMARK
DOMINICA
DOMINICAN REPUBLIC
ECUADOR
EGYPT

EQUATORIAL GUINEA
ERITREA
ETHIOPIA
FALKLAND ISLANDS
FAROE ISLANDS
FIJI
FINLAND & ALAND ISLANDS
FRANCE
FRENCH OFFICES ABROAD
FRENCH POLYNESIA
FRENCH SOUTH. & ANTARCTIC TERRIT.
GABON
GAMBIA
GERMANY
EAST GERMANY
GHANA
GILBERT & ELLICE ISLANDS
GREAT BRITAIN
GREAT BRITAIN OFFICES ABROAD
GREECE
GREENLAND
GRENADA
GUATEMALA
GUINEA
GUINEA-BISSAU
HAITI
HONDURAS
HUNGARY
ICELAND
INDIA
INDONESIA
IRELAND
ISRAEL
ISRAEL TABS
ITALIAN COLONIES
ITALY
IVORY COAST
JAMAICA
JAPAN
JORDAN
KENYA
KIRIBATI
KOREA
KUWAIT
LAOS

LEBANON
LESOTHO
LIBERIA
LIECHTENSTEIN
LUXEMBOURG
MACEDONIA
MADAGASCAR
MALAWI
MALAYSIA
MALDIVE ISLANDS
MALI
MAURITIUS
MEXICO
MONACO & FRENCH ANDORRA
MONTSERRAT
MOROCCO
NAMIBIA
NAURU
NEPAL
NEW CALEDONIA
NEW HEBRIDES (BRITISH)
NEW HEBRIDES (FRENCH)
NEW ZEALAND
NEW ZEALAND DEPENDENCIES
NEVIS/ST KITTS
NICARAGUA
NIGER
NIGERIA
NORWAY
OMAN
PAKISTAN
PANAMA
PARAGUAY
PAKISTAN
PANAMA
PARAGUAY
PEOPLE'S REPUBLIC OF CHINA
PERU
PHILIPPINES
PITCAIRN ISLANDS
POLAND
PORTUGAL
PORTUGUESE COLONIES
QATAR
ROMANIA

RUSSIA
SALVADOR
SAMOA
SAN MARINO
SAUDI ARABIA
SENEGAL
SEYCHELLES
SIERRA LEONE
SLOVENIA
SOLOMON ISLANDS
SOUTH AFRICA
SPAIN & SPANISH ANDORRA
SRI LANKA
ST LUCIA
ST PIERRE & MIQUELON
ST THOMAS & PRINCE ISLANDS
ST VINCENT
SUDAN
SWAZILAND
SWEDEN
SWITZERLAND
SYRIA
TAIWAN
TANZANIA
THAILAND
TOGO
TONGA
TRINIDAD
TUNISIA
TURKEY
TURKS & CAICOS ISLANDS
TUVALU
UGANDA
UNITED ARAB EMIRATES
URUGUAY
VANUATU
VATICAN CITY
VENEZUELA
VIRGIN ISLANDS
WALLIS & FUTUNA
YEMEN
YUGOSLAVIA
ZAIRE
ZAMBIA
ZIMBABWE

SCOTT

1-800-572-6885

Common Design Types

Pictured in this section are issues where one illustration has been used for a number of countries in the Catalogue. Not included in this section are overprinted stamps or those issues which are illustrated in each country.

EUROPA

Europa Issue, 1956

The design symbolizing the cooperation among the six countries comprising the Coal and Steel Community is illustrated in each country.

Belgium 496-497
France 805-806
Germany 748-749
Italy 715-716
Luxembourg 318-320
Netherlands 368-369

Europa Issue, 1958

"E" and Dove CD1

European Postal Union at the service of European integration.

1958, Sept. 13

Belgium 527-528
France 889-890
Germany 790-791
Italy 750-751
Luxembourg 341-343
Netherlands 375-376
Saar 317-318

Europa Issue, 1959

6-Link Endless Chain – CD2

1959, Sept. 19

Belgium 536-537
France 929-930
Germany 805-806
Italy 791-792
Luxembourg 354-355
Netherlands 379-380

Europa Issue, 1960

19-Spoke Wheel – CD3

First anniverary of the establishment of C.E.P.T. (Conference Europeenne des Administrations des Postes et des Telecommunications.)

The spokes symbolize the 19 founding members of the Conference.

1960, Sept.

Belgium 553-554
Denmark 379
Finland 376-377
France 970-971
Germany 818-820
Great Britain 377-378
Greece 688
Iceland 327-328
Ireland 175-176
Italy 809-810
Luxembourg 374-375
Netherlands 385-386
Norway 387
Portugal 866-867
Spain 941-942
Sweden 562-563
Switzerland 400-401
Turkey 1493-1494

Europa Issue, 1961

19 Doves Flying as One – CD4

The 19 doves represent the 19 members of the Conference of European Postal and Telecommunications Administrations C.E.P.T.

1961-62

Belgium 572-573
Cyprus 201-203
France 1005-1006
Germany 844-845
Great Britain 383-384
Greece 718-719
Iceland 340-341
Italy 845-846
Luxembourg 382-383
Netherlands 387-388
Spain 1010-1011
Switzerland 410-411
Turkey 1518-1520

Europa Issue 1962

Young Tree with 19 Leaves CD5

The 19 leaves represent the 19 original members of C.E.P.T.

1962-63

Belgium 582-583
Cyprus 219-221
France 1045-1046
Germany 852-853
Greece 739-740
Iceland 348-349
Ireland 184-185
Italy 860-861
Luxembourg 386-387
Netherlands 394-395
Norway 414-415
Switzerland 416-417
Turkey 1553-1555

Europa Issue, 1963

Stylized Links, Symbolizing Unity – CD6

1963, Sept.

Belgium 598-599
Cyprus 229-231
Finland 419
France 1074-1075
Germany 867-868
Greece 768-769
Iceland 357-358
Ireland 188-189
Italy 880-881
Luxembourg 403-404
Netherlands 416-417
Norway 441-442
Switzerland 429
Turkey 1602-1603

Europa Issue, 1964

Symbolic Daisy – CD7

5th anniversary of the establishment of C.E.P.T. The 22 petals of the flower symbolize the 22 members of the Conference.

1964, Sept.

Austria 738
Belgium 614-615
Cyprus 244-246
France 1109-1110
Germany 897-898
Greece 801-802
Iceland 367-368
Ireland 196-197
Italy 894-895
Luxembourg 411-412
Monaco 590-591
Netherlands 428-429
Norway 458
Portugal 931-933
Spain 1262-1263
Switzerland 438-439
Turkey 1628-1629

Europa Issue, 1965

Leaves and "Fruit" CD8

1965

Belgium 636-637
Cyprus 262-264
Finland 437
France 1131-1132
Germany 934-935
Greece 833-834
Iceland 375-376
Ireland 204-205
Italy 915-916
Luxembourg 432-433
Monaco 616-617
Netherlands 438-439
Norway 475-476
Portugal 958-960
Switzerland 469
Turkey 1665-1666

Europa Issue, 1966

Symbolic Sailboat – CD9

1966, Sept.

Andorra, French 172
Belgium 675-676
Cyprus 275-277
France 1163-1164
Germany 963-964
Greece 862-863
Iceland 384-385
Ireland 216-217
Italy 942-943
Liechtenstein 415
Luxembourg 440-441
Monaco 639-640
Netherlands 441-442
Norway 496-497
Portugal 980-982
Switzerland 477-478
Turkey 1718-1719

Europa Issue, 1967

Cogwheels CD10

1967

Andorra, French 174-175
Belgium 688-689
Cyprus 297-299
France 1178-1179
Greece 891-892
Germany 969-970
Iceland 389-390
Ireland 232-233
Italy 951-952
Liechtenstein 420
Luxembourg 449-450
Monaco 669-670
Netherlands 444-447
Norway 504-505
Portugal 994-996
Spain 1465-1466
Switzerland 482
Turkey B120-B121

Europa Issue, 1968

Golden Key with C.E.P.T. Emblem CD11

1968

Andorra, French 182-183
Belgium 705-706
Cyprus 314-316
France 1209-1210
Germany 983-984
Greece 916-917
Iceland 395-396
Ireland 242-243
Italy 979-980
Liechtenstein 442
Luxembourg 466-467
Monaco 689-691
Netherlands 452-453
Portugal 1019-1021
San Marino 687
Spain 1526
Turkey 1775-1776

Europa Issue, 1969

"EUROPA" and "CEPT" – CD12

Tenth anniversary of C.E.P.T.

1969

Andorra, French 188-189
Austria 837
Belgium 718-719
Cyprus 326-328
Denmark 458
Finland 483
France 1245-1246
Germany 996-997
Great Britain 585
Greece 947-948
Iceland 406-407
Ireland 270-271
Italy 1000-1001
Liechtenstein 453
Luxembourg 474-475
Monaco 722-724
Netherlands 475-476
Norway 533-534
Portugal 1038-1040
San Marino 701-702
Spain 1567

Sweden 814-816
Switzerland 500-501
Turkey 1799-1800
Vatican 470-472
Yugoslavia 1003-1004

Europa Issue, 1970

Interwoven Threads CD13

1970
Andorra, French 196-197
Belgium 741-742
Cyprus 340-342
France 1271-1272
Germany 1018-1019
Greece 985, 987
Iceland 420-421
Ireland 279-281
Italy 1013-1014
Liechtenstein 470
Luxembourg 489-490
Monaco 768-770
Netherlands 483-484
Portugal 1060-1062
San Marino 729-730
Spain 1607
Switzerland 515-516
Turkey 1848-1849
Yugoslavia 1024-1025

Europa Issue, 1971

"Fraternity, Cooperation, Common Effort" – CD14

1971
Andorra, French 205-206
Belgium 803-804
Cyprus 365-367
Finland 504
France 1304
Germany 1064-1065
Greece 1029-1030
Iceland 429-430
Ireland 305-306
Italy 1038-1039
Liechtenstein 485
Luxembourg 500-501
Malta 425-427
Monaco 797-799
Netherlands 488-489
Portugal 1094-1096
San Marino 749-750
Spain 1675-1676
Switzerland 531-532
Turkey 1876-1877
Yugoslavia 1052-1053

Europa Issue, 1972

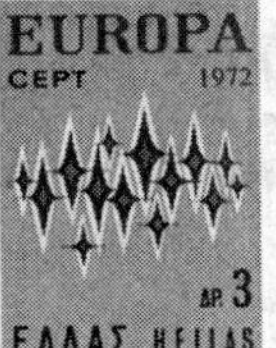

Sparkles, Symbolic of Communications CD15

1972
Andorra, French 210-211
Andorra, Spanish 62
Belgium 825-826
Cyprus 380-382
Finland 512-513
France 1341
Germany 1089-1090
Greece 1049-1050
Iceland 439-440
Ireland 316-317
Italy 1065-1066
Liechtenstein 504
Luxembourg 512-513
Malta 450-453
Monaco 831-832
Netherlands 494-495
Portugal 1141-1143
San Marino 771-772
Spain 1718
Switzerland 544-545
Turkey 1907-1908
Yugoslavia 1100-1101

Europa Issue, 1973

Post Horn and Arrows CD16

1973
Andorra, French 319-320
Andorra, Spanish 76
Belgium 839-840
Cyprus 396-398
Finland 526
France 1367
Germany 1114-1115
Greece 1090-1092
Iceland 447-448
Ireland 329-330
Italy 1108-1109
Liechtenstein 528-529
Luxembourg 523-524
Malta 469-471
Monaco 866-867
Netherlands 504-505
Norway 604-605
Portugal 1170-1172
San Marino 802-803
Spain 1753
Switzerland 580-581
Turkey 1935-1936
Yugoslavia 1138-1139

PORTUGAL & COLONIES

Vasco da Gama Issue

Fleet Departing CD20

Fleet Arriving at Calicut CD21

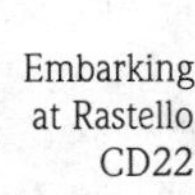

Embarking at Rastello CD22

Muse of History – CD23

San Gabriel, da Gama and Camoens – CD24

Archangel Gabriel, the Patron Saint CD25

Flagship San Gabriel CD26

Vasco da Gama CD27

Fourth centenary of Vasco da Gama's discovery of the route to India.

1898
Azores 93-100
Macao 67-74
Madeira 37-44
Portugal 147-154
Port. Africa 1-8
Port. india 189-196
Timor 45-52

Pombal Issue

POSTAL TAX

Marquis de Pombal CD28

Planning Reconstruction of Lisbon, 1755 CD29

Pombal Monument, Lisbon CD30

Sebastiao Jose de Carvalho e Mello, Marquis de Pombal (1699-1782), statesman, rebuilt Lisbon after earthquake of 1755. Tax was for the erection of Pombal monument. Obligatory on all mail on certain days throughout the year.

Postal Tax Dues are inscribed "Multa."

1925
Angola RA1-RA3, RAJ1-RAJ3
Azores RA9-RA11, RAJ2-RAJ4
Cape Verde RA1-RA3, RAJ1-RAJ3
Macao RA1-RA3, RAJ1-RAJ3
Madeira RA1-RA3, RAJ1-RAJ3
Mozambique RA1-RA3, RAJ1-RAJ3
Nyassa RA1-RA3, RAJ1-RAJ3
Portugal RA11-RA13, RAJ2-RAJ4
Port. Guinea RA1-RA3, RAJ1-RAJ3
Port. India RA1-RA3, RAJ1-RAJ3
St. Thomas & Prince Islands RA1-RA3, RAJ1-RAJ3
Timor RA1-RA3, RAJ1-RAJ3

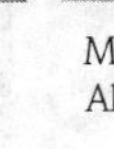

Vasco da Gama CD34

Mousinho de Albuquerque CD35

Dam CD36

Prince Henry the Navigator – CD37

Affonso de Albuquerque CD38

Plane over Globe CD39

1938-39
Angola 274-291
Cape Verde 234-251
Macao 289-305
Mozambique 270-287
Port. Guinea 233-250
Port. India 439-453
St. Thomas & Prince Islands 302-319, 323-340
Timor 223-239

1938-39
Angola C1-C9
Cape Verde C1-C9
Macao C7-C15
Mozambique C1-C9
Port. Guinea C1-C9
Port. India C1-C8
St. Thomas & Prince Islands C1-C18
Timor C1-C9

Lady of Fatima Issue

Our Lady of the Rosary, Fatima, Portugal CD40

1948-49
Angola 315-318
Cape Verde 266
Macao 336
Mozambique 325-328
Port. Guinea 271
Port. India 480
St. Thomas & Prince Islands 351
Timor 254

A souvenir sheet of 9 stamps was issued in 1951 to mark the extension of the 1950 Holy Year. The sheet contains: Angola No. 316, Cape Verde No. 266, Macao No. 336, Mozambique No. 325, Portuguese Guinea No. 271, Portugese India Nos. 480, 485, St. Thomas & Prince Islands No. 351, Timor No. 254.

The sheet also contains a portrait of Pope Pius XII and is inscribed "Encerramento do Ano Santo, Fatima 1951." It was sold for 11 escudos.

Holy Year Issue

Church Bells and Dove CD41 — Angel Holding Candelabra CD42

Holy Year, 1950.

1950-51

Angola 331-332
Cape Verde 268-269
Macao 339-340
Mozambique 330-331
Port. Guinea 273-274
Port. India 490-491, 496-503
St. Thomas & Prince Islands 353-354
Timor 258-259

A souvenir sheet of 8 stamps was issued in 1951 to mark the extension of the Holy Year. The sheet contains: Angola No. 331, Cape Verde No. 269, Macao No. 340, Mozambique No. 331, Portuguese Guinea No. 275, Portuguese India No. 490, St. Thomas & Prince Islands No. 354, Timor No. 258, some with colors changed. The sheet contains doves and is inscribed "Encerramento do Ano Santo, Fatima 1951." It was sold for 17 escudos.

Holy Year Conclusion Issue

Our Lady of Fatima CD43

Conclusion of Holy Year. Sheets contain alternate vertical rows of stamps and labels bearing quotation from Pope Pius XII, different for each colony.

1951

Angola 357
Cape Verde 270
Macao 352
Mozambique 356
Port. Guinea 275
Port. India 506
St. Thomas & Prince Islands 355
Timor 270

Medical Congress Issue

CD44

First National Congress of Tropical Medicine, Lisbon, 1952.

Each stamp has a different design.

1952

Angola 358
Cape Verde 287
Macao 364
Mozambique 359
Port. Guinea 276
Port. India 516
St. Thomas & Prince Islands 356
Timor 271

POSTAGE DUE STAMPS

CD45

1952

Angola J37-J42
Cape Verde J31-J36
Macao J53-J58
Mozambique J51-J56
Port. Guinea J40-J45
Port. India J47-J52
St. Thomas & Prince Islands J52-J57
Timor J31-J36

Sao Paulo Issue

Father Manuel de Nobrega and View of Sao Paulo CD46

Founding of Sao Paulo, Brazil, 400th anniv.

1954

Angola 385
Cape Verde 297
Macao 382
Mozambique 395
Port. Guinea 291
Port. India 530
St. Thomas & Prince Islands 369
Timor 279

Tropical Medicine Congress Issue

CD47

Sixth International Congress for Tropical Medicine and Malaria, Lisbon, Sept. 1958.

Each stamp shows a different plant.

1958

Angola 409
Cape Verde 303
Macao 392
Mozambique 404
Port. Guinea 295
Port. India 569
St. Thomas & Prince Islands 371
Timor 289

Sports Issue

CD48

Each stamp shows a different sport.

1962

Angola 433-438
Cape Verde 320-325
Macao 394-399
Mozambique 424-429
Port. Guinea 299-304
St. Thomas & Prince Islands 374-379
Timor 313-318

Anti-Malaria Issue

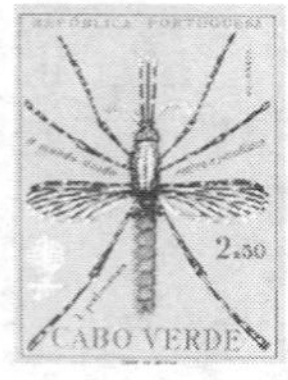

Anopheles Funestus and Malaria Eradication Symbol CD49

World Health Organization drive to eradicate malaria.

1962

Angola 439
Cape Verde 326
Macao 400
Mozambique 430
Port. Guinea 305
St. Thomas & Prince Islands 380
Timor 319

Airline Anniversary Issue

Map of Africa, Super Constellation and Jet Liner CD50

Tenth anniversary of Transportes Aereos Portugueses (TAP).

1963

Angola 490
Cape Verde 327
Mozambique 434
Port. Guinea 318
St. Thomas & Prince Islands 381

National Overseas Bank Issue

Antonio Teixeira de Sousa CD51

Centenary of the National Overseas Bank of Portugal.

1964, May 16

Angola 509
Cape Verde 328
Port. Guinea 319
St. Thomas & Prince Islands 382
Timor 320

ITU Issue

ITU Emblem and the archangel Gabriel CD52

International Communications Union, Cent.

1965, May 17

Angola 511
Cape Verde 329
Macao 402
Mozambique 464
Port. Guinea 320
St. Thomas & Prince Islands 383
Timor 321

National Revolution Issue

CD53

40th anniv. of the National Revolution.

Different buildings on each stamp.

1966, May 28

Angola 525
Cape Verde 338
Macao 403
Mozambique 465
Port. Guinea 329
St. Thomas & Prince Islands 392
Timor 322

Navy Club Issue

CD54

Centenary of Portugal's Navy Club.

Each stamp has a different design.

1967, Jan. 31

Angola 527-528
Cape Verde 339-340
Macao 412-413
Mozambique 478-479
Port. Guinea 330-331
St. Thomas & Prince Islands 393-394
Timor 323-324

Admiral Coutinho Issue

CD55

Centenary of the birth of Admiral Carlos Viegas Gago Coutinho (1869-1959), explorer and aviation pioneer.

Each stamp has a different design.

1969, Feb. 17

Angola 547
Cape Verde 355
Macao 417
Mozambique 484
Port. Guinea 335
St. Thomas & Prince Islands 397
Timor 335

Administration Reform Issue

Luiz Augusto Rebello da Silva – CD56

Centenary of the administration reforms of the overseas territories.

1969, Sept. 25

Angola 549
Cape Verde 357
Macao 419
Mozambique 491
Port. Guinea 337
St. Thomas & Prince Islands 399
Timor 338

Marshal Carmona Issue

CD57

Birth centenary of Marshal Antonio Oscar Carmona de Fragoso (1869-1951), President of Portugal.

Each stamp has a different design.

1970, Nov. 15

Angola	563
Cape Verde	359
Macao	422
Mozambique	493
Port. Guinea	340
St. Thomas & Prince Islands	403
Timor	341

Olympic Games Issue

CD59

20th Olympic Games, Munich, Aug. 26-Sept. 11.

Each stamp shows a different sport.

1972, June 20

Angola	569
Cape Verde	361
Macao	426
Mozambique	504
Port. Guinea	342
St. Thomas & Prince Islands	408
Timor	343

Lisbon-Rio de Janeiro Flight Issue

CD60

50th anniversary of the Lisbon to Rio de Janeiro flight by Arturo de Sacadura and Coutinho, March 30-June 5, 1922.

Each stamp shows a different stage of the flight.

1972, Sept. 20

Angola	570
Cape Verde	362
Macao	427
Mozambique	505
Port. Guinea	343
St. Thomas & Prince Islands	409
Timor	344

WMO Centenary Issue

WMO Emblem – CD61

Centenary of international meterological cooperation.

1973, Dec. 15

Angola	571
Cape Verde	363
Macao	429
Mozambique	509
Port. Guinea	344
St. Thomas & Prince Islands	410
Timor	345

FRENCH COMMUNITY

Upper Volta can be found under Burkina Faso in Vol. 1

Colonial Exposition Issue

People of French Empire CD70

Women's Heads CD71

France Showing Way to Civilization CD72

"Colonial Commerce" CD73

International Colonial Exposition, Paris.

1931

Cameroun	213-216
Chad	60-63
Dahomey	97-100
Fr. Guiana	152-155
Fr. Guinea	116-119
Fr. India	100-103
Fr. Polynesia	76-79
Fr. Sudan	102-105
Gabon	120-123
Guadeloupe	138-141
Indo-China	140-142
Ivory Coast	92-95
Madagascar	169-172
Martinique	129-132
Mauritania	65-68
Middle Congo	61-64
New Caledonia	176-179
Niger	73-76
Reunion	122-125
St. Pierre & Miquelon	132-135
Senegal	138-141
Somali Coast	135-138
Togo	254-257
Ubangi-Shari	82-85
Upper Volta	66-69
Wallis & Futuna Isls.	85-88

Paris International Exposition Issue

Colonial Arts Exposition Issue

"Colonial Resources"

CD74 CD77

Overseas Commerce – CD75

Exposition Building and Women CD76

"France and the Empire" CD78

Cultural Treasures of the Colonies CD79

Souvenir sheets contain one imperf. stamp.

1937

Cameroun	217-222A
Dahomey	101-107
Fr. Equatorial Africa	27-32, 73
Fr. Guiana	162-168
Fr. Guinea	120-126
Fr. India	104-110
Fr. Polynesia	117-123
Fr. Sudan	106-112
Guadeloupe	148-154
Indo-China	193-199
Inini	41
Ivory Coast	152-158
Kwangchowan	132
Madagascar	191-197
Martinique	179-185
Mauritania	69-75
New Caledonia	208-214
Niger	72-83
Reunion	167-173
St. Pierre & Miquelon	165-171
Senegal	172-178
Somali Coast	139-145
Togo	258-264
Wallis & Futuna Isls.	89

Curie Issue

Pierre and Marie Curie CD80

40th anniversary of the discovery of radium. The surtax was for the benefit of the Intl. Union for the Control of Cancer.

1938

Cameroun	B1
Cuba	B1-B2
Dahomey	B2
France	B76
Fr. Equatorial Africa	B1
Fr. Guiana	B3
Fr. Guinea	B2
Fr. India	B6
Fr. Polynesia	B5
Fr. Sudan	B1
Guadeloupe	B3
Indo-China	B14
Ivory Coast	B2
Madagascar	B2
Martinique	B2
Mauritania	B3
New Caledonia	B4
Niger	B1
Reunion	B4
St. Pierre & Miquelon	B3
Senegal	B3
Somali Coast	B2
Togo	B1

Caillie Issue

Rene Caille and Map of Northwestern Africa - CD81

Death centenary of Rene Caillie (1799-1838), French explorer.

All three denominations exist with colony name omitted.

1939

Dahomey	108-110
Fr. Guinea	161-163
Fr. Sudan	113-115
Ivory Coast	160-162
Mauritania	109-111
Niger	84-86
Senegal	188-190
Togo	265-267

New York World's Fair Issue

Natives and New York Skyline CD82

1939

Cameroun	223-224
Dahomey	111-112
Fr. Equatorial Africa	78-79
Fr. Guiana	169-170
Fr. Guinea	164-165
Fr. India	111-112
Fr. Polynesia	124-125
Fr. Sudan	116-117
Guadeloupe	155-156
Indo-China	203-204
Inini	42-43
Ivory Coast	163-164
Kwangchowan	121-122
Madagascar	209-210
Martinique	186-187
Mauritania	112-113
New Caledonia	215-216
Niger	87-88
Reunion	174-175
St. Pierre & Miquelon	205-206
Senegal	191-192
Somali Coast	179-180
Togo	268-269
Wallis & Futuna Isls.	90-91

French Revolution Issue

Storming of the Bastille – CD83

French Revolution, 150th anniv. The surtax was for the defense of the colonies.

1939

Cameroun	B2-B6
Dahomey	B3-B7
Fr. Equatorial Africa	B4-B8, CB1
Fr. Guiana	B4-B8, CB1
Fr. Guinea	B3-B7
Fr. India	B7-B11
Fr. Polynesia	B6-B10, CB1
Fr. Sudan	B2-B6
Guadeloupe	B4-B8
Indo-China	B15-B19, CB1
Inini	B1-B5
Ivory Coast	B3-B7
Kwangchowan	B1-B5
Madagascar	B3-B7, CB1
Martinique	B3-B7
Mauritania	B4-B8
New Caledonia	B5-B9, CB1
Niger	B2-B6
Reunion	B5-B9, CB1
St. Pierre & Miquelon	B4-B8
Senegal	B4-B8, CB1
Somali Coast	B3-B7
Togo	B2-B6
Wallis & Futuna Isls.	B1-B5

Plane over Coastal Area CD85

All five denominations exist with colony name omitted.

1940	
Dahomey	C1-C5
Fr. Guinea	C1-C5
Fr. Sudan	C1-C5
Ivory Coast	C1-C5
Mauritania	C1-C5
Niger	C1-C5
Senegal	C12-C16
Togo	C1-C5

Colonial Infantryman CD86

1941	
Cameroun	B13B
Dahomey	B13
Fr. Equatorial Africa	B8B
Fr. Guiana	B10
Fr. Guinea	B13
Fr. India	B13
Fr. Polynesia	B12
Fr. Sudan	B12
Guadeloupe	B10
Indo-China	B19B
Inini	B7
Ivory Coast	B13
Kwangchowan	B7
Madagascar	B9
Martinique	B9
Mauritania	B14
New Caledonia	B11
Niger	B12
Reunion	B11
St. Pierre & Miquelon	B8B
Senegal	B14
Somali Coast	B9
Togo	B10B
Wallis & Futuna Isls.	B7

Cross of Lorraine & Four-motor Plane CD87

1941-5	
Cameroun	C1-C7
Fr. Equatorial Africa	C17-C23
Fr. Guiana	C9-C10
Fr. India	C1-C6
Fr. Polynesia	C3-C9
Fr. West Africa	C1-C3
Guadeloupe	C1-C2
Madagascar	C37-C43
Martinique	C1-C2
New Caledonia	C7-C13
Reunion	C18-C24
St. Pierre & Miquelon	C1-C7
Somali Coast	C1-C7

Transport Plane CD88

Caravan and Plane CD89

1942	
Dahomey	C6-C13
Fr. Guinea	C6-C13
Fr. Sudan	C6-C13
Ivory Coast	C6-C13
Mauritania	C6-C13
Niger	C6-C13
Senegal	C17-C25
Togo	C6-C13

Red Cross Issue

Marianne CD90

The surtax was for the French Red Cross and national relief.

1944	
Cameroun	B28
Fr. Equatorial Africa	B38
Fr. Guiana	B12
Fr. India	B14
Fr. Polynesia	B13
Fr. West Africa	B1
Guadeloupe	B12
Madagascar	B15
Martinique	B11
New Caledonia	B13
Reunion	B15
St. Pierre & Miquelon	B13
Somali Coast	B13
Wallis & Futuna Isls.	B9

Eboue Issue

CD91

Felix Eboue, first French colonial administrator to proclaim resistance to Germany after French surrender in World War II.

1945	
Cameroun	296-297
Fr. Equatorial Africa	156-157
Fr. Guiana	171-172
Fr. India	210-211
Fr. Polynesia	150-151
Fr. West Africa	15-16
Guadeloupe	187-188
Madagascar	259-260
Martinique	196-197
New Caledonia	274-275
Reunion	238-239
St. Pierre & Miquelon	322-323
Somali Coast	238-239

Victory Issue

Victory – CD92

European victory of the Allied Nations in World War II.

1946, May 8	
Cameroun	C8
Fr. Equatorial Africa	C24
Fr. Guiana	C11
Fr. India	C7
Fr. Polynesia	C10
Fr. West Africa	C4
Guadeloupe	C3
Indo-China	C19
Madagascar	C44
Martinique	C3
New Caledonia	C14
Reunion	C25
St. Pierre & Miquelon	C8
Somali Coast	C8
Wallis & Futuna Isls.	C1

Chad to Rhine Issue

Leclerc's Departure from Chad – CD93

Battle at Cufra Oasis – CD94

Tanks in Action, Mareth – CD95

Normandy Invasion – CD96

Entering Paris – CD97

Liberation of Strasbourg – CD98

"Chad to the Rhine" march, 1942-44, by Gen. Jacques Leclerc's column, later French 2nd Armored Division.

1946, June 6	
Cameroun	C9-C14
Fr. Equatorial Africa	C25-C30
Fr. Guiana	C12-C17
Fr. India	C8-C13
Fr. Polynesia	C11-C16
Fr. West Africa	C5-C10
Guadeloupe	C4-C9
Indo-China	C20-C25
Madagascar	C45-C50
Martinique	C4-C9
New Caledonia	C15-C20
Reunion	C26-C31
St. Pierre & Miquelon	C9-C14
Somali Coast	C9-C14
Wallis & Futuna Isls.	C2-C7

UPU Issue

French Colonials, Globe and Plane CD99

Universal Postal Union, 75th anniv.

1949, July 4	
Cameroun	C29
Fr. Equatorial Africa	C34
Fr. India	C17
Fr. Polynesia	C20
Fr. West Africa	C15
Indo-China	C26
Madagascar	C55
New Caledonia	C24
St. Pierre & Miquelon	C18
Somali Coast	C18
Togo	C18
Wallis & Futuna Isls.	C10

Tropical Medicine Issue

Doctor Treating Infant CD100

The surtax was for charitable work.

1950	
Cameroun	B29
Fr. Equatorial Africa	B39
Fr. India	B15
Fr. Polynesia	B14
Fr. West Africa	B3
Madagascar	B17
New Caledonia	B14
St. Pierre & Miquelon	B14
Somali Coast	B14
Togo	B11

Military Medal Issue

Medal, Early Marine and Colonial Soldier CD101

Centenary of the creation of the French Military Medal.

1952	
Cameroun	332
Comoro Isls.	39
Fr. Equatorial Africa	186
Fr. India	233
Fr. Polynesia	179
Fr. West Africa	57
Madagascar	286
New Caledonia	295
St. Pierre & Miquelon	345
Somali Coast	267
Togo	327
Wallis & Futuna Isls.	149

Liberation Issue

Allied Landing, Victory Sign and Cross of Lorraine – CD102

Lberation of France, 10th anniv.

1954, June 6

Cameroun.....C32
Comoro Isls.....C4
Fr. Equatorial Africa.....C38
Fr. India.....C18
Fr. Polynesia.....C22
Fr. West Africa.....C17
Madagascar.....C57
New Caledonia.....C25
St. Pierre & Miquelon.....C19
Somali Coast.....C19
Togo.....C19
Wallis & Futuna Isls.....C11

FIDES Issue

Plowmen
CD103

Efforts of FIDES, the Economic and Social Development Fund for Overseas Possessions (Fonds d' Investissement pour le Developpement Economique et Social).

Each stamp has a different design.

1956

Cameroun.....326-329
Comoro Isls.....43
Fr. Polynesia.....181
Madagascar.....292-295
New Caledonia.....303
Somali Coast.....268
Togo.....331

Flower Issue

CD104

Each stamp shows a different flower.

1958-9

Cameroun.....333
Comoro Isls.....45
Fr. Equatorial Africa.....200-201
Fr. Polynesia.....192
Fr. So. & Antarctic Terr.....11
Fr. West Africa.....79-83
Madagascar.....301-302
New Caledonia.....304-305
St. Pierre & Miquelon.....357
Somali Coast.....270
Togo.....348-349
Wallis & Futuna Isls.....152

Human Rights Issue

Sun, Dove and U.N. Emblem – CD105

10th anniversary of the signing of the Universal Declaration of Human Rights.

1958

Comoro Isls.....44
Fr. Equatorial Africa.....202
Fr. Polynesia.....191
Fr. West Africa.....85
Madagascar.....300
New Caledonia.....306
St. Pierre & Miquelon.....356
Somali Coast.....274
Wallis & Futuna Isls.....153

C.C.T.A. Issue

CD106

Commission for Technical Cooperation in Africa south of the Sahara, 10th anniv.

1960

Cameroun.....335
Cent. African Rep.....3
Chad.....66
Congo, P.R.....90
Dahomey.....138
Gabon.....150
Ivory Coast.....180
Madagascar.....317
Mali.....9
Mauritania.....117
Niger.....104
Upper Volta.....89

Air Afrique Issue, 1961

Modern and Ancient Africa, Map and Planes – CD107

Founding of Air Afrique (African Airlines).

1961-62

Cameroun.....C37
Cent. African Rep.....C5
Chad.....C7
Congo, P.R.....C5
Dahomey.....C17
Gabon.....C5
Ivory Coast.....C18
Mauritania.....C17
Niger.....C22
Senegal.....C31
Upper Volta.....C4

Anti-Malaria Issue

CD108

World Health Organization drive to eradicate malaria.

1962, Apr. 7

Cameroun.....B36
Cent. African Rep.....B1
Chad.....B1
Comoro Isls.....B1
Congo, P.R.....B3
Dahomey.....B15
Gabon.....B4
Ivory Coast.....B15
Madagascar.....B19
Mali.....B1
Mauritania.....B16
Niger.....B14
Senegal.....B16
Somali Coast.....B15
Upper Volta.....B1

Abidjan Games Issue

CD109

Abidjan Games, Ivory Coast, Dec. 24-31, 1961.

Each stamp shows a different sport.

1962

Chad.....83-84
Cent. African Rep.....19-20
Congo, P.R.....103-104
Gabon.....163-164, C6
Niger.....109-111
Upper Volta.....103-105

African and Malagasy Union Issue

Flag of Union
CD110

First anniversary of the Union.

1962, Sept. 8

Cameroun.....373
Cent. African Rep.....21
Chad.....85
Congo, P.R.....105
Dahomey.....155
Gabon.....165
Ivory Coast.....198
Madagascar.....332
Mauritania.....170
Niger.....112
Senegal.....211
Upper Volta.....106

Telstar Issue

Telstar and Globe Showing Andover and Pleumeur-Bodou – CD111

First television connection of the United States and Europe through the Telstar satellite, July 11-12, 1962.

1962-63

Andorra, French.....154
Comoro Isls.....C7
Fr. Polynesia.....C29
Fr. So. & Antarctic Terr.....C5
New Caledonia.....C33
Somali Coast.....C31
St. Pierre & Miquelon.....C26
Wallis & Futuna Isls.....C17

Freedom From Hunger Issue

World Map and Wheat Emblem
CD112

U.N. Food and Agriculture Organization's "Freedom from Hunger" campaign.

1963, Mar. 21

Cameroun.....B37-B38
Cent. African Rep.....B2
Chad.....B2
Congo, P.R.....B4
Dahomey.....B16
Gabon.....B5
Ivory Coast.....B16
Madagascar.....B21
Mauritania.....B17
Niger.....B15
Senegal.....B17
Upper Volta.....B2

Red Cross Centenary Issue

CD113

Centenary of the International Red Cross.

1963, Sept. 2

Comoro Isls.....55
Fr. Polynesia.....205
New Caledonia.....328
St. Pierre & Miquelon.....367
Somali Coast.....297
Wallis & Futuna Isls.....165

African Postal Union Issue

UAMPT Emblem, Radio Masts, Plane and Mail
CD114

Establishment of the African and Malagasy Posts and Telecommunications Union.

1963, Sept. 8

Cameroun.....C47
Cent. African Rep.....C10
Chad.....C9
Congo, P.R.....C13
Dahomey.....C19
Gabon.....C13
Ivory Coast.....C25
Madagascar.....C75
Mauritania.....C22
Niger.....C27
Rwanda.....36
Senegal.....C32
Upper Volta.....C9

Air Afrique Issue, 1963

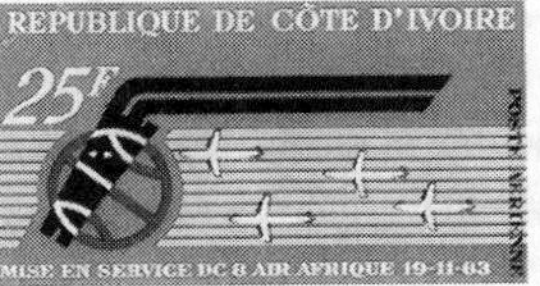

Symbols of Flight – CD115

First anniversary of Air Afrique and inauguration of DC-8 service.

1963, Nov. 19

Cameroun.....C48
Chad.....C10
Congo, P.R.....C14
Gabon.....C18
Ivory Coast.....C26
Mauritania.....C26
Niger.....C35
Senegal.....C33

Europafrica Issue

Europe and Africa Linked
CD116

Signing of an economic agreement between the European Economic Community and the African and Malagasy Union, Yaounde, Cameroun, July 20, 1963.

1963-64

Cameroun 402
Chad C11
Cent. African Rep. C12
Congo, P.R. C16
Gabon C19
Ivory Coast 217
Niger C43
Upper Volta C11

Human Rights Issue

Scales of Justice and Globe CD117

15th anniversary of the Universal Declaration of Human Rights.

1963, Dec. 10

Comoro Isls. 58
Fr. Polynesia 206
New Caledonia 329
St. Pierre & Miquelon 368
Somali Coast 300
Wallis & Futuna Isls. 166

PHILATEC Issue

Stamp Album, Champs Elysees Palace and Horses of Marly – CD118

Intl. Philatelic and Postal Techniques Exhibition, Paris, June 5-21, 1964.

1963-64

Comoro Isls. 60
France 1078
Fr. Polynesia 207
New Caledonia 341
St. Pierre & Miquelon 369
Somali Coast 301
Wallis & Futuna Isls. 167

Cooperation Issue

CD119

Cooperation between France and the French-speaking countries of Africa and Madagascar.

1964

Cameroun 409-410
Cent. African Rep. 39
Chad 103
Congo, P.R. 121
Dahomey 193
France 1111
Gabon 175
Ivory Coast 221
Madagascar 360
Mauritania 181
Niger 143
Senegal 236
Togo 495

ITU Issue

Telegraph, Syncom Satellite and ITU Emblem CD120

Intl. Telecommunication Union, Cent.

1965, May 17

Comoro Isls. C14
Fr. Polynesia C33
Fr. So. & Antarctic Terr. C8
New Caledonia C40
New Hebrides 124-125
St. Pierre & Miquelon C29
Somali Coast C36
Wallis & Futuna Isls. C20

French Satellite A-1 Issue

Diamant Rocket and Launching Installation – CD121

Launching of France's first satellite, Nov. 26, 1965.

1965-66

Comoro Isls. C15-C16
France 1137-1138
Fr. Polynesia C40-C41
Fr. So. & Antarctic Terr. C9-C10
New Caledonia C44-C45
St. Pierre & Miquelon C30-C31
Somali Coast C39-C40
Wallis & Futuna Isls. C22-C23

French Satellite D-1 Issue

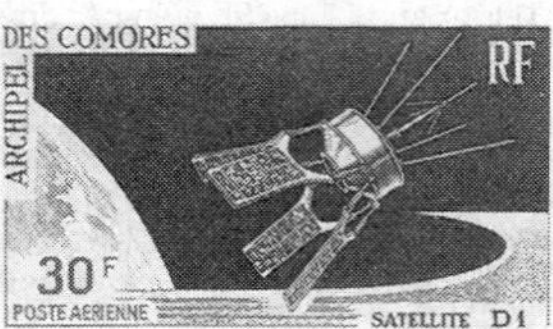

D-1 Satellite in Orbit – CD122

Launching of the D-1 satellite at Hammaguir, Algeria, Feb. 17, 1966.

1966

Comoro Isls. C17
France 1148
Fr. Polynesia C42
Fr. So. & Antarctic Terr. C11
New Caledonia C46
St. Pierre & Miquelon C32
Somali Coast C49
Wallis & Futuna Isls. C24

Air Afrique Issue, 1966

Planes and Air Afrique Emblem – CD123

Introduction of DC-8F planes by Air Afrique.

1966

Cameroun C79
Cent. African Rep. C35
Chad C26
Congo, P.R. C42
Dahomey C42
Gabon C47
Ivory Coast C32
Mauritania C57
Niger C63
Senegal C47
Togo C54
Upper Volta C31

African Postal Union, 1967

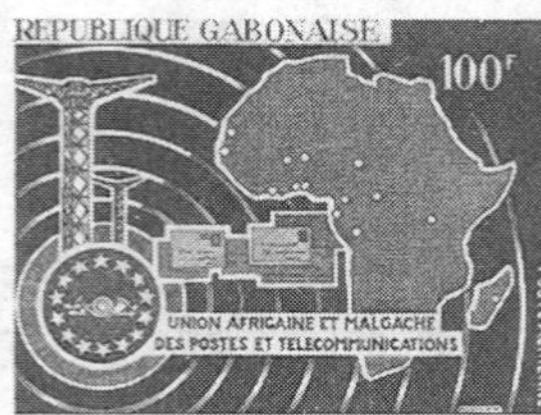

Telecommunications Symbols and Map of Africa – CD124

Fifth anniversary of the establishment of the African and Malagasy Union of Posts and Telecommunications, UAMPT.

1967

Cameroun C90
Cent. African Rep. C46
Chad C37
Congo, P.R. C57
Dahomey C61
Gabon C58
Ivory Coast C34
Madagascar C85
Mauritania C65
Niger C75
Rwanda C1-C3
Senegal C60
Togo C81
Upper Volta C50

Monetary Union Issue

Gold Token of the Ashantis, 17-18th Centuries – CD125

West African Monetary Union, 5th anniv.

1967, Nov. 4

Dahomey 244
Ivory Coast 259
Mauritania 238
Niger 204
Senegal 294
Togo 623
Upper Volta 181

WHO Anniversary Issue

Sun, Flowers and WHO Emblem CD126

World Health Organization, 20th anniv.

1968, May 4

Afars & Issas 317
Comoro Isls. 73
Fr. Polynesia 241-242
Fr. So. & Antarctic Terr. 31
New Caledonia 367
St. Pierre & Miquelon 377
Wallis & Futuna Isls. 169

Human Rights Year Issue

Human Rights Flame CD127

1968, Aug. 10

Afars & Issas 322-323
Comoro Isls. 76
Fr. Polynesia 243-244
Fr. So. & Antarctic Terr. 32
New Caledonia 369
St. Pierre & Miquelon 382
Wallis & Futuna Isls. 170

2nd PHILEXAFRIQUE Issue

CD128

Opening of PHILEXAFRIQUE, Abidjan, Feb. 14. Each stamp shows a local scene and stamp.

1969, Feb. 14

Cameroun C118
Cent. African Rep. C65
Chad C48
Congo, P.R. C77
Dahomey C94
Gabon C82
Ivory Coast C38-C40
Madagascar C92
Mali C65
Mauritania C80
Niger C104
Senegal C68
Togo C104
Upper Volta C62

Concorde Issue

Concorde in Flight CD129

First flight of the prototpye Concorde super-sonic plane at Toulouse, Mar. 1, 1969.

1969

Afars & Issas C56
Comoro Isls. C29
France C42
Fr. Polynesia C50
Fr. So. & Antarctic Terr. C18
New Caledonia C63
St. Pierre & Miquelon C40
Wallis & Futuna Isls. C30

Development Bank Issue

Bank Emblem CD130

African Development Bank, fifth anniv.

1969

Cameroun 499

Chad 217
Congo, P.R. 181-182
Ivory Coast 281
Mali 127-128
Mauritania 267
Niger 220
Senegal 317-318
Upper Volta 201

ILO Issue

ILO Headquarters, Geneva, and Emblem – CD131

Intl. Labor Organization, 50th anniv.

1969-70
Afars & Issas 337
Comoro Isls. 83
Fr. Polynesia 251-252
Fr. So. & Antarctic Terr. 35
New Caledonia 379
St. Pierre & Miquelon 396
Wallis & Futuna Isls. 172

ASECNA Issue

Map of Africa, Plane and Airport – CD132

10th anniversary of the Agency for the Security of Aerial Navigation in Africa and Madagascar (ASECNA, Agence pour la Securite de la Navigation Aerienne en Afrique et a Madagascar).

1969-70
Cameroun 500
Cent. African Rep. 119
Chad 222
Congo, P.R. 197
Dahomey 269
Gabon 260
Ivory Coast 287
Mali 130
Niger 221
Senegal 321
Upper Volta 204

U.P.U. Headquarters Issue

CD133

New Universal Postal Union headquarters, Bern, Switzerland.

1970
Afars & Issas 342
Algeria 443
Cameroun 503-504
Cent. African Rep. 125
Chad 225
Comoro Isls. 84
Congo, P.R. 216
Fr. Polynesia 261-262
Fr. So. & Antarctic Terr. 36
Gabon 258
Ivory Coast 295
Madagascar 444
Mali 134-135
Mauritania 283
New Caledonia 382
Niger 231-232
St. Pierre & Miquelon 397-398
Senegal 328-329
Tunisia 535
Wallis & Futuna Isls. 173

De Gaulle Issue

CD134

First anniversary of the death of Charles de Gaulle, (1890-1970), President of France.

1971-72
Afars & Issas 356-357
Comoro Isls. 104-105
France 1322-1325
Fr. Polynesia 270-271
Fr. So. & Antarctic Terr. 52-53
New Caledonia 393-394
Reunion 377, 380
St. Pierre & Miquelon 417-418
Wallis & Futuna Isls. 177-178

African Postal Union Issue, 1971

UAMPT Building, Brazzaville, Congo – CD135

10th anniversary of the establishment of the African and Malagasy Posts and Telecommunications Union, UAMPT.

Each stamp has a different native design.

1971, Nov. 13
Cameroun C177
Cent. African Rep. C89
Chad C94
Congo, P.R. C136
Dahomey C146
Gabon C120
Ivory Coast C47
Mauritania C113
Niger C164
Rwanda C8
Senegal C105
Togo C166
Upper Volta C97

West African Monetary Union Issue

African Couple, City, Village and Commemorative Coin – CD136

West African Monetary Union, 10th anniv.

1972, Nov. 2
Dahomey 300
Ivory Coast 331
Mauritania 299
Niger 258
Senegal 374
Togo 825
Upper Volta 280

African Postal Union Issue, 1973

Telecommunications Symbols and Map of Africa – CD137

11th anniversary of the African and Malagasy Posts and Telecommunications Union (UAMPT).

1973, Sept. 12
Cameroun 574
Cent. African Rep. 194
Chad 294
Congo, P.R. 289
Dahomey 311
Gabon 320
Ivory Coast 361
Madagascar 500
Mauritania 304
Niger 287
Rwanda 540
Senegal 393
Togo 849
Upper Volta 297

Philexafrique II — Essen Issue

CD138

CD139

Designs: Indigenous fauna, local and German stamps.

Types CD138-CD139 printed horizontally and vertically se-tenant in sheets of 10 (2x5). Label between horizontal pairs alternately commemoratives Philexafrique II, Libreville, Gabon, June 1978, and 2nd International Stamp Fair, Essen, Germany, Nov. 1-5.

1978-1979
Benin C285-C286
Central Africa C200-C201
Chad C238-C239
Congo Republic C245-C246
Djibouti C121-C122
Gabon C215-C216
Ivory Coast C64-C65
Mali C356-C357
Mauritania C185-C186
Niger C291-C292
Rwanda C12-C13
Senegal C146-C147
Togo C363-C364
Upper Volta C253-C254

BRITISH COMMONWEALTH OF NATIONS

The listings follow established trade practices when these issues are offered as units by dealers. The Peace issue, for example, includes only one stamp from the Indian state of Hyderabad. The U.P.U. issue includes the Egypt set. Pairs are included for those varieties issues with bilingual designs se-tenant.

Silver Jubilee Issue

Windsor Castle and King George V CD301

Reign of King George V, 25th anniv.

1935
Antigua 77-80
Ascension 33-36
Bahamas 92-95
Barbados 186-189
Basutoland 11-14
Bechuanaland Protectorate 117-120
Bermuda 100-103
British Guiana 223-226
British Honduras 108-111
Cayman Islands 81-84
Ceylon 260-263
Cyprus 136-139
Dominica 90-93
Falkland Islands 77-80
Fiji 110-113
Gambia 125-128
Gibraltar 100-103
Gilbert & Ellice Islands 33-36
Gold Coast 108-111
Grenada 124-127
Hong Kong 147-150
Jamaica 109-112
Kenya, Uganda, Tanganyika 42-45
Leeward Islands 96-99
Malta 184-187
Mauritius 204-207
Montserrat 85-88
Newfoundland 226-229
Nigeria 34-37
Northern Rhodesia 18-21
Nyasaland Protectorate 47-50
St. Helena 111-114
St. Kitts-Nevis 72-75
St. Lucia 91-94
St. Vincent 134-137
Seychelles 118-121
Sierra Leone 166-169
Solomon Islands 60-63
Somaliland Protectorate 77-80
Straits Settlements 213-216
Swaziland 20-23
Trinidad & Tobago 43-46
Turks & Caicos Islands 71-74
Virgin Islands 69-72

The following have different designs but are included in the omnibus set:

Great Britain 226-229
Offices in Morocco 67-70, 226-229, 422-425, 508-510
Australia 152-154
Canada 211-216
Cook Islands 98-100
India 142-148
Nauru 31-34
New Guinea 46-47
New Zealand 199-201
Niue 67-69
Papua 114-117
Samoa 163-165
South Africa 68-71
Southern Rhodesia 33-36
South-West Africa 121-124
249 stamps, Never Hinged $975.

Coronation Issue

Queen Elizabeth and King George VI CD302

1937
Aden 13-15
Antigua 81-83
Ascension 37-39
Bahamas 97-99
Barbados 190-192
Basutoland 15-17
Bechuanaland Protectorate 121-123

Bermuda ... 115-117
British Guiana ... 227-229
British Honduras ... 112-114
Cayman Islands ... 97-99
Ceylon ... 275-277
Cyprus ... 140-142
Dominica ... 94-96
Falkland Islands ... 81-83
Fiji ... 114-116
Gambia ... 129-131
Gibraltar ... 104-106
Gilbert & Ellice Islands ... 37-39
Gold Coast ... 112-114
Grenada ... 128-130
Hong Kong ... 151-153
Jamaica ... 113-115
Kenya, Uganda, Tanganyika ... 60-62
Leeward Islands ... 100-102
Malta ... 188-190
Mauritius ... 208-210
Montserrat ... 89-91
Newfoundland ... 230-232
Nigeria ... 50-52
Northern Rhodesia ... 22-24
Nyasaland Protectorate ... 51-53
St. Helena ... 115-117
St. Kitts-Nevis ... 76-78
St. Lucia ... 107-109
St. Vincent ... 138-140
Seychelles ... 122-124
Sierra Leone ... 170-172
Solomon Islands ... 64-66
Somaliland Protectorate ... 81-83
Straits Settlements ... 235-237
Swaziland ... 24-26
Trinidad & Tobago ... 47-49
Turks & Caicos Islands ... 75-77
Virgin Islands ... 73-75

The following have different designs but are included in the omnibus set:

Great Britain ... 234
Offices in Morocco ... 82, 439, 514
Canada ... 237
Cook Islands ... 109-111
Nauru ... 35-38
Newfoundland ... 233-243
New Guinea ... 48-51
New Zealand ... 223-225
Niue ... 70-72
Papua ... 118-121
South Africa ... 74-78
Southern Rhodesia ... 38-41
South-West Africa ... 125-132

202 stamps, Never Hinged $80.

Peace Issue

King George VI and Parliament Buildings, London – CD303

Return to peace at the close of World War II.

1945-46

Aden ... 28-29
Antigua ... 96-97
Ascension ... 50-51
Bahamas ... 130-131
Barbados ... 207-208
Bermuda ... 131-132
British Guiana ... 242-243
British Honduras ... 127-128
Cayman Islands ... 112-113
Ceylon ... 293-294
Cyprus ... 156-157
Dominica ... 112-113
Falkland Islands ... 97-98
Falkland Islands Dep. ... 1L9-1L10
Fiji ... 137-138
Gambia ... 144-145
Gibraltar ... 119-120
Gilbert & Ellice Islands ... 52-53
Gold Coast ... 128-129
Grenada ... 143-144
Jamaica ... 136-137
Kenya, Uganda, Tanganyika ... 90-91
Leeward Islands ... 116-117
Malta ... 206-207
Mauritius ... 223-224
Montserrat ... 104-105
Nigeria ... 71-72
Northern Rhodesia ... 46-47
Nyasaland Protectorate ... 82-83
Pitcairn Island ... 9-10
St. Helena ... 128-129
St. Kitts-Nevis ... 91-92
St. Lucia ... 127-128
St. Vincent ... 152-153
Seychelles ... 149-150
Sierra Leone ... 186-187
Solomon Islands ... 80-81
Somaliland Protectorate ... 108-109
Trinidad & Tobago ... 62-63
Turks & Caicos Islands ... 90-91
Virgin Islands ... 88-89

The following have different designs but are included in the omnibus set:

Great Britain ... 264-265
Offices in Morocco ... 523-524
Aden
Kathiri State of Seiyun ... 12-13
Qu'aiti State of Shihr and Mukalla ... 12-13
Australia ... 200-202
Basutoland ... 29-31
Bechuanaland Protectorate ... 137-139
Burma ... 66-69
Cook Islands ... 127-130
Hong Kong ... 174-175
India ... 195-198
Hyderabad ... 51
New Zealand ... 247-257
Niue ... 90-93
Pakistan-Bahawalpur ... O16
Samoa ... 191-194
South Africa ... 100-102
Southern Rhodesia ... 67-70
South-West Africa ... 153-155
Swaziland ... 38-40
Zanzibar ... 222-223

164 stamps, Never Hinged $42.50

Silver Wedding Issue

King George VI and Queen Elizabeth
CD304 CD305

1948-49

Aden ... 30-31
Kathiri State of Seiyun ... 14-15
Qu'aiti State of Shihr and Mukalla ... 14-15
Antigua ... 98-99
Ascension ... 52-53
Bahamas ... 148-149
Barbados ... 210-211
Basutoland ... 39-40
Bechuanaland Protectorate ... 147-148
Bermuda ... 133-134
British Guiana ... 244-245
British Honduras ... 129-130
Cayman Islands ... 116-117
Cyprus ... 158-159
Dominica ... 114-115
Falkland Islands ... 99-100
Falkland Islands Dep. ... 1L11-1L12
Fiji ... 139-140
Gambia ... 146-147
Gibraltar ... 121-122
Gilbert & Ellice Islands ... 54-55
Gold Coast ... 142-143
Grenada ... 145-146
Hong Kong ... 178-179
Jamaica ... 138-139
Kenya, Uganda, Tanganyika ... 92-93
Leeward Islands ... 118-119
Malaya
Johore ... 128-129
Kedah ... 55-56
Kelantan ... 44-45
Malacca ... 1-2
Negri Sembilan ... 36-37
Pahang ... 44-45
Penang ... 1-2
Perak ... 99-100
Perlis ... 1-2
Selangor ... 74-75
Trengganu ... 47-48
Malta ... 223-224
Mauritius ... 229-230
Montserrat ... 106-107
Nigeria ... 73-74
North Borneo ... 238-239
Northern Rhodesia ... 48-49
Nyasaland Protectorate ... 85-86
Pitcairn Island ... 11-12
St. Helena ... 130-131
St. Kitts-Nevis ... 93-94
St. Lucia ... 129-130
St. Vincent ... 154-155
Sarawak ... 174-175
Seychelles ... 151-152
Sierra Leone ... 188-189
Singapore ... 21-22
Solomon Islands ... 82-83
Somaliland Protectorate ... 110-111
Swaziland ... 48-49
Trinidad & Tobago ... 64-65
Turks & Caicos Islands ... 92-93
Virgin Islands ... 90-91
Zanzibar ... 224-225

The following have different designs but are included in the omnibus set:

Great Britain ... 267-268
Offices in Morocco ... 93-94, 525-526
Bahrain ... 62-63
Kuwait ... 82-83
Oman ... 25-26
South Africa ... 106
South-West Africa ... 159

138 stamps, Never Hinged $1,600.

U.P.U. Issue

Mercury and Symbols of Communications – CD306

Plane, Ship and Hemispheres – CD307

Mercury Scattering Letters over Globe CD308

U.P.U. Monument, Bern – CD309

Universal Postal Union, 75th anniversary.

1949

Aden ... 32-35
Kathiri State of Seiyun ... 16-19
Qu'aiti State of Shihr and Mukalla ... 16-19
Antigua ... 100-103
Ascension ... 57-60
Bahamas ... 150-153
Barbados ... 212-215
Basutoland ... 41-44
Bechuanaland Protectorate ... 149-152
Bermuda ... 138-141
British Guiana ... 246-249
British Honduras ... 137-140
Brunei ... 79-82
Cayman Islands ... 118-121
Cyprus ... 160-163
Dominica ... 116-119
Falkland Islands ... 103-106
Falkland Islands Dep. ... 1L14-1L17
Fiji ... 141-144
Gambia ... 148-151
Gibraltar ... 123-126
Gilbert & Ellice Islands ... 56-59
Gold Coast ... 144-147
Grenada ... 147-150
Hong Kong ... 180-183
Jamaica ... 142-145
Kenya, Uganda, Tanganyika ... 94-97
Leeward Islands ... 126-129
Malaya
Johore ... 151-154
Kedah ... 57-60
Kelantan ... 46-49
Malacca ... 18-21
Negri Sembilan ... 59-62
Pahang ... 46-49
Penang ... 23-26
Perak ... 101-104
Perlis ... 3-6
Selangor ... 76-79
Trengganu ... 49-52
Malta ... 225-228
Mauritius ... 231-234
Montserrat ... 108-111
New Hebrides ... 62-65
Nigeria ... 75-78
North Borneo ... 240-243
Northern Rhodesia ... 50-53
Nyasaland Protectorate ... 87-90
Pitcairn Islands ... 13-16
St. Helena ... 132-135
St. Kitts-Nevis ... 95-98
St. Lucia ... 131-134
St. Vincent ... 170-173
Sarawak ... 176-179
Seychelles ... 153-156
Sierra Leone ... 190-193
Singapore ... 23-26
Solomon Islands ... 84-87
Somaliland Protectorate ... 112-115
Southern Rhodesia ... 71-72
Swaziland ... 50-53
Tonga ... 87-90
Trinidad & Tobago ... 66-69
Turks & Caicos Islands ... 101-104
Virgin Islands ... 92-95
Zanzibar ... 226-229

The following have different designs but are included in the omnibus set:

Great Britain ... 276-279
Offices in Morocco ... 546-549
Australia ... 223
Bahrain ... 68-71
Burma ... 116-121
Ceylon ... 304-306
Egypt ... 281-283
India ... 223-226
Kuwait ... 89-92
Oman ... 31-34
Pakistan-Bahawalpur ... 26-29, O25-O28
South Africa ... 109-111
South-West Africa ... 160-162

315 stamps, Never Hinged $325.

University Issue

Arms of University College CD310

Alice, Princess of Athlone CD311

1948 opening of University College of the West Indies at Jamaica.

1951

Antigua ... 104-105
Barbados ... 228-229
British Guiana ... 250-251
British Honduras ... 141-142
Dominica ... 120-121
Grenada ... 164-165
Jamaica ... 146-147
Leeward Islands ... 130-131
Montserrat ... 112-113
St. Kitts-Nevis ... 105-106
St. Lucia ... 149-150
St. Vincent ... 174-175

Trinidad & Tobago 70-71
Virgin Islands 96-97
28 stamps

Coronation Issue

Queen Elizabeth II CD312

1953

Aden 47
Kathiri State of Seiyun 28
Qu'aiti State of Shihr and Mukalla 28
Antigua 106
Ascension 61
Bahamas 157
Barbados 234
Basutoland 45
Bechuanaland Protectorate 153
Bermuda 142
British Guiana 252
British Honduras 143
Cayman Islands 150
Cyprus 167
Dominica 141
Falkland Islands 121
Falkland Islands Dependencies 1L18
Fiji 145
Gambia 152
Gibraltar 131
Gilbert & Ellice Islands 60
Gold Coast 160
Grenada 170
Hong Kong 184
Jamaica 153
Kenya, Uganda, Tanganyika 101
Leeward Islands 132
Malaya
Johore 155
Kedah 82
Kelantan 71
Malacca 27
Negri Sembilan 63
Pahang 71
Penang 27
Perak 126
Perlis 28
Selangor 101
Trengganu 74
Malta 241
Mauritius 250
Montserrat 127
New Hebrides 77
Nigeria 79
North Borneo 260
Northern Rhodesia 60
Nyasaland Protectorate 96
Pitcairn 19
St. Helena 139
St. Kitts-Nevis 119
St. Lucia 156
St. Vincent 185
Sarawak 196
Seychelles 172
Sierra Leone 194
Singapore 27
Solomon Islands 88
Somaliland Protectorate 127
Swaziland 54
Trinidad & Tobago 84
Tristan da Cunha 13
Turks & Caicos Islands 118
Virgin Islands 114

The following have different designs but are included in the omnibus set:

Great Britain 313-316
Offices in Morocco 579-582
Australia 259-261
Bahrain 92-95
Canada 330
Ceylon 317
Cook Islands 145-146
Kuwait 113-116
New Zealand 280-284
Niue 104-105
Oman 52-55
Samoa 214-215
South Africa 192
Southern Rhodesia 80
South-West Africa 244-248
Tokelau Islands 4
106 stamps, Never Hinged $70.

Royal Visit 1953

Separate designs for each country for the visit of Queen Elizabeth II and the Duke of Edinburgh.

1953

Aden 62
Australia 267-269
Bermuda 163
Ceylon 318
Fiji 146
Gibraltar 146
Jamaica 154
Kenya, Uganda, Tanganyika 102
Malta 242
New Zealand 286-287
13 stamps

West Indies Federation

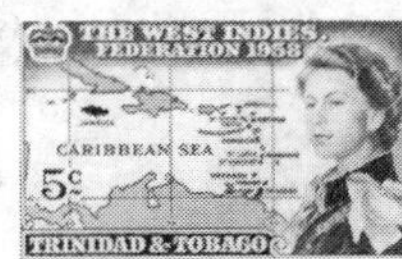

Map of the Caribbean – CD313

Federation of the West Indies, April 22, 1958.

1958

Antigua 122-124
Barbados 248-250
Dominica 161-163
Grenada 184-186
Jamaica 175-177
Montserrat 143-145
St. Kitts-Nevis 136-138
St. Lucia 170-172
St. Vincent 198-200
Trinidad & Tobago 86-88
30 stamps, Never Hinged $6.

Freedom from Hunger Issue

Protein Food CD314

U.N. Food and Agricultural Organization's "Freedom from Hunger" campaign.

1963

Aden 65
Antigua 133
Ascension 89
Bahamas 180
Basutoland 83
Bechuanaland Protectorate 194
Bermuda 192
British Guiana 271
British Honduras 179
Brunei 100
Cayman Islands 168
Dominica 181
Falkland Islands 146
Fiji 198
Gambia 172
Gibraltar 161
Gilbert & Ellice Islands 76
Grenada 190
Hong Kong 218
Malta 291
Mauritius 270
Montserrat 150
New Hebrides 93
North Borneo 296
Pitcairn 35
St. Helena 173
St. Lucia 179
St. Vincent 201
Sarawak 212
Seychelles 213
Solomon Islands 109
Swaziland 108
Tonga 127
Tristan da Cunha 68
Turks & Caicos Islands 138
Virgin Islands 140
Zanzibar 280
37 stamps

Red Cross Centenary Issue

Red Cross and Elizabeth II – CD315

1963

Antigua 134-135
Ascension 90-91
Bahamas 183-184
Basutoland 84-85
Bechuanaland Protectorate 195-196
Bermuda 193-194
British Guiana 272-273
British Honduras 180-181
Cayman Islands 169-170
Dominica 182-183
Falkland Islands 147-148
Fiji 203-204
Gambia 173-174
Gibraltar 162-163
Gilbert & Ellice Islands 77-78
Grenada 191-192
Hong Kong 219-220
Jamaica 203-204
Malta 292-293
Mauritius 271-272
Montserrat 151-152
New Hebrides 94-95
Pitcairn Islands 36-37
St. Helena 174-175
St. Kitts-Nevis 143-144
St. Lucia 180-181
St. Vincent 202-203
Seychelles 214-215
Solomon Islands 110-111
South Arabia 1-2
Swaziland 109-110
Tonga 134-135
Tristan da Cunha 69-70
Turks & Caicos Islands 139-140
Virgin Islands 141-142
70 stamps

Shakespeare Issue

Shakespeare Memorial Theatre, Stratford-on-Avon – CD316

400th anniversary of the birth of William Shakespeare.

1964

Antigua 151
Bahamas 201
Bechuanaland Protectorate 197
Cayman Islands 171
Dominica 184
Falkland Islands 149
Gambia 192
Gibraltar 164
Montserrat 153
St. Lucia 196
Turks & Caicos Islands 141
Virgin Islands 143
12 stamps

ITU ISSUE

ITU Emblem CD317

Intl. Telecommunication Union, cent.

1965

Antigua 153-154
Ascension 92-93
Bahamas 219-220
Barbados 265-266
Basutoland 101-102
Bechuanaland Protectorate 202-203
Bermuda 196-197
British Guiana 293-294
British Honduras 187-188
Brunei 116-117
Cayman Islands 172-173
Dominica 185-186
Falkland Islands 154-155
Fiji 211-212
Gibraltar 167-168
Gilbert & Ellice Islands 87-88
Grenada 205-206
Hong Kong 221-222
Mauritius 291-292
Montserrat 157-158
New Hebrides 108-109
Pitcairn Islands 52-53
St. Helena 180-181
St. Kitts-Nevis 163-164
St. Lucia 197-198
St. Vincent 224-225
Seychelles 218-219
Solomon Islands 126-127
Swaziland 115-116
Tristan da Cunha 85-86
Turks & Caicos Islands 142-143
Virgin Islands 159-160
64 stamps, Never Hinged $50.

Intl. Cooperation Year Issue

ICY Emblem – CD318

1965

Antigua 155-156
Ascension 94-95
Bahamas 222-223
Basutoland 103-104
Bechuanaland Protectorate 204-205
Bermuda 199-200
British Guiana 295-296
British Honduras 189-190
Brunei 118-119
Cayman Islands 174-175
Dominica 187-188
Falkland Islands 156-157
Fiji 213-214
Gibraltar 169-170
Gilbert & Ellice Islands 104-105
Grenada 207-208
Hong Kong 223-224
Mauritius 293-294
Montserrat 176-177
New Hebrides 110-111
Pitcairn Islands 54-55
St. Helena 182-183
St. Kitts-Nevis 165-166
St. Lucia 199-200
Seychelles 220-221
Solomon Islands 143-144
South Arabia 17-18
Swaziland 117-118
Tristan da Cunha 87-88
Turks & Caicos Islands 144-145
Virgin Islands 161-162
62 stamps

Churchill Memorial Issue

Winston Churchill and St. Paul's, London, During Air Attack – CD319

1966

Antigua 157-160
Ascension 96-99
Bahamas 224-227
Barbados 281-284
Basutoland 105-108
Bechuanaland Protectorate 206-209
Bermuda 201-204
British Antarctic Territory 16-19
British Honduras 191-194
Brunei 120-123
Cayman Islands 176-179
Dominica 189-192
Falkland Islands 158-161

Fiji 215-218
Gibraltar 171-174
Gilbert & Ellice Islands 106-109
Grenada 209-212
Hong Kong 225-228
Mauritius 295-298
Montserrat 178-181
New Hebrides 112-115
Pitcairn Islands 56-59
St. Helena 184-187
St. Kitts-Nevis 167-170
St. Lucia 201-204
St. Vincent 241-244
Seychelles 222-225
Solomon Islands 145-148
South Arabia 19-22
Swaziland 119-122
Tristan da Cunha 89-92
Turks & Caicos Islands 146-149
Virgin Islands 163-166
132 stamps

Royal Visit Issue, 1966

Queen Elizabeth II and Prince Philip
CD320

Caribbean visit, Feb. 4 - Mar. 6, 1966.

1966

Antigua 161-162
Bahamas 228-229
Barbados 285-286
British Guiana 299-300
Cayman Islands 180-181
Dominica 193-194
Grenada 213-214
Montserrat 182-183
St. Kitts-Nevis 171-172
St. Lucia 205-206
St. Vincent 245-246
Turks & Caicos Islands 150-151
Virgin Islands 167-168
26 stamps

World Cup Soccer Issue

Soccer Player and Jules Rimet Cup
CD321

World Cup Soccer Championship, Wembley, England, July 11-30.

1966

Antigua 163-164
Ascension 100-101
Bahamas 245-246
Bermuda 205-206
Brunei 124-125
Cayman Islands 182-183
Dominica 195-196
Fiji 219-220
Gibraltar 175-176
Gilbert & Ellice Islands 125-126
Grenada 230-231
New Hebrides 116-117
Pitcairn Islands 60-61
St. Helena 188-189
St. Kitts-Nevis 173-174
St. Lucia 207-208
Seychelles 226-227
Solomon Islands 167-168
South Arabia 23-24
Tristan da Cunha 93-94
40 stamps

WHO Headquarters Issue

World Health Organization Headquarters, Geneva – CD322

1966

Antigua 165-166
Ascension 102-103
Bahamas 247-248
Brunei 126-127
Cayman Islands 184-185
Dominica 197-198
Fiji 224-225
Gibraltar 180-181
Gilbert & Ellice Islands 127-128
Grenada 232-233
Hong Kong 229-230
Montserrat 184-185
New Hebrides 118-119
Pitcairn Islands 62-63
St. Helena 190-191
St. Kitts-Nevis 177-178
St. Lucia 209-210
St. Vincent 247-248
Seychelles 228-229
Solomon Islands 169-170
South Arabia 25-26
Tristan da Cunha 99-100
44 stamps

UNESCO Anniversary Issue

"Education" – CD323

"Science" (Wheat ears & flask enclosing globe). "Culture" (lyre & columns).
20th anniversary of the UNESCO.

1966-67

Antigua 183-185
Ascension 108-110
Bahamas 249-251
Barbados 287-289
Bermuda 207-209
Brunei 128-130
Cayman Islands 186-188
Dominica 199-201
Gibraltar 183-185
Gilbert & Ellice Islands 129-131
Grenada 234-236
Hong Kong 231-233
Mauritius 299-301
Montserrat 186-188
New Hebrides 120-122
Pitcairn Islands 64-66
St. Helena 192-194
St. Kitts-Nevis 179-181
St. Lucia 211-213
St. Vincent 249-251
Seychelles 230-232
Solomon Islands 171-173
South Arabia 27-29
Swaziland 123-125
Tristan da Cunha 101-103
Turks & Caicos Islands 155-157
Virgin Islands 176-178
81 stamps

Silver Wedding Issue, 1972

Queen Elizabeth II and Prince Philip
CD324

Designs: borders differ for each country.

1972

Anguilla 161-162
Antigua 295-296
Ascension 164-165
Bahamas 344-345
Bermuda 296-297
British Antarctic Territory 43-44
British Honduras 306-307
British Indian Ocean Territory 48-49
Brunei 186-187
Cayman Islands 304-305
Dominica 352-353
Falkland Islands 223-224
Fiji 328-329
Gibraltar 292-293
Gilbert & Ellice Islands 206-207
Grenada 466-467
Hong Kong 271-272
Montserrat 286-287
New Hebrides 169-170
Pitcairn Islands 127-128
St. Helena 271-272
St. Kitts-Nevis 257-258
St. Lucia 328-329
St.Vincent 344-345
Seychelles 309-310
Solomon Islands 248-249
South Georgia 35-36
Tristan da Cunha 178-179
Turks & Caicos Islands 257-258
Virgin Islands 241-242
60 stamps

Princess Anne's Wedding Issue

Princess Anne and Mark Phillips
CD325

Wedding of Princess Anne and Mark Phillips, Nov. 14, 1973.

1973

Anguilla 179-180
Ascension 177-178
Belize 325-326
Bermuda 302-303
British Antarctic Territory 60-61
Cayman Islands 320-321
Falkland Islands 225-226
Gibraltar 305-306
Gilbert & Ellice Islands 216-217
Hong Kong 289-290
Montserrat 300-301
Pitcairn Island 135-136
St. Helena 277-278
St. Kitts-Nevis 274-275
St. Lucia 349-350
St. Vincent 358-359
St. Vincent Grenadines 1-2
Seychelles 311-312
Solomon Islands 259-260
South Georgia 37-38
Tristan da Cunha 189-190
Turks & Caicos Islands 286-287
Virgin Islands 260-261
44 stamps

Elizabeth II Coronation Anniversary Issue

CD326

CD327

CD328

Designs: Royal and local beasts in heraldic form and simulated stonework. Portrait of Elizabeth II by Peter Grugeon.
25th anniversary of coronation of Queen Elizabeth II.

1978

Ascension 229
Barbados 474
Belize 397
British Antarctic Territory 71
Cayman Islands 404
Christmas Island 87
Falkland Islands 275
Fiji 384
Gambia 380
Gilbert Islands 312
Mauritius 464
New Hebrides 258
St. Helena 317
St. Kitts-Nevis 354
Samoa 472
Solomon Islands 368
South Georgia 51
Swaziland 302
Tristan da Cunha 238
Virgin Islands 337
20 sheets

Queen Mother Elizabeth's 80th Birthday

CD330

Designs: Photographs of Queen Mother Elizabeth. Falkland Islands issued in sheets of 50; others in sheets of 9.

1980

Ascension 261
Bermuda 401
Cayman Islands 443
Falkland Islands 305
Gambia 412
Gibraltar 393
Hong Kong 364
Pitcairn Islands 193
St. Helena 341
Samoa 532
Solomon Islands 426
Tristan da Cunha 277
12 stamps

Royal Wedding Issue, 1981

Prince Charles and Lady Diana
CD331

Wedding of Charles, Prince of Wales, and Lady Diana Spencer, St. Paul's Cathedral, London, July 29, 1981.

1981

Antigua 623-625
Ascension 294-296
Barbados 547-549
Barbuda 497-499
Bermuda 412-414
Brunei 268-270
Cayman Islands 471-473
Dominica 701-703
Falkland Islands 324-326
Falkland Islands Dep. 1L59-1L61
Fiji 442-444
Gambia 426-428
Ghana 759-761
Grenada 1051-1053
Grenada Grenadines 440-443
Hong Kong 373-375
Jamaica 500-503
Lesotho 335-337
Maldive Islands 906-908
Mauritius 520-522
Norfolk Island 280-282
Pitcairn Islands 206-208
St. Helena 353-355
St. Lucia 543-545
Samoa 558-560
Sierra Leone 509-517
Solomon Islands 450-452
Swaziland 382-384

Tristan da Cunha....294-296
Turks & Caicos Islands....486-488
Caicos Island....8-10
Uganda....314-316
Vanuatu....308-310
Virgin Islands....406-408

Princess Diana

CD332 CD333

Designs: Photographs and portrait of Princess Diana, wedding or honeymoon photographs, royal residences, arms of issuing country. Portrait photograph by Clive Friend. Souvenir sheet margins show family tree, various people related to the princess. 21st birthday of Princess Diana of Wales, July 1.

1982

Antigua....663-666
Ascension....313-316
Bahamas....510-513
Barbados....585-588
Barbuda....544-546
British Antarctic Territory....92-95
Cayman Islands....486-489
Dominica....773-776
Falkland Islands....348-351
Falkland Islands Dep.....1L72-1L75
Fiji....470-473
Gambia....447-450
Grenada....1101A-1105
Grenada Grenadines....485-491
Lesotho....372-375
Maldive Islands....952-955
Mauritius....548-551
Pitcairn Islands....213-216
St. Helena....372-375
St. Lucia....591-594
Sierra Leone....531-534
Solomon Islands....471-474
Swaziland....406-409
Tristan da Cunha....310-313
Turks and Caicos Islands....530A-534
Virgin Islands....430-433

250th anniv. of first edition of Lloyd's List (shipping news publication) and of Lloyd's marine insurance.

CD335

Designs: First page of early edition of the list; historical ships, modern transportation or harbor scenes.

1984

Ascension....351-354
Bahamas....555-558
Barbados....627-630
Cayes of Belize....10-13
Cayman Islands....522-525
Falkland Islands....404-407
Fiji....509-512
Gambia....519-522
Mauritius....587-590
Nauru....280-283
St. Helena....412-415
Samoa....624-627
Seychelles....538-541
Solomon Islands....521-524
Vanuatu....368-371
Virgin Islands....466-469

Queen Mother 85th Birthday

CD336

Designs: Photographs tracing the life of the Queen Mother, Elizabeth. The high value in each set pictures the same photograph taken of the Queen Mother holding the infant Prince Henry.

1985

Ascension....372-376
Bahamas....580-584
Barbados....660-664
Bermuda....469-473
Falkland Islands....420-424
Falkland Islands Dep.....1L92-1L96
Fiji....531-535
Hong Kong....447-450
Jamaica....599-603
Mauritius....604-608
Norfolk Island....364-368
Pitcairn Islands....253-257
St. Helena....428-432
Samoa....649-653
Seychelles....567-571
Solomon Islands....543-547
Swaziland....476-480
Tristan da Cunha....372-376
Vanuatu....392-396
Zil Elwannyen Sesel....101-105

Queen Elizabeth II, 60th Birthday

CD337

1986, April 21

Ascension....389-393
Bahamas....592-596
Barbados....675-679
Bermuda....499-503
Cayman Islands....555-559
Falkland Islands....441-445
Fiji....544-548
Hong Kong....465-469
Jamaica....620-624
Kiribati....470-474
Mauritius....629-633
Papua New Guinea....640-644
Pitcairn Islands....270-274
St. Helena....451-455
Samoa....670-674
Seychelles....592-596
Solomon Islands....562-566
South Georgia....101-105
Swaziland....490-494
Tristan da Cunha....388-392
Vanuatu....414-418
Zambia....343-347
Zil Elwannyen Sesel....114-118

Royal Wedding

Marriage of Prince Andrew and Sarah Ferguson CD338

1986, July 23

Ascension....399-400
Bahamas....602-603
Barbados....687-688
Cayman Islands....560-561
Jamaica....629-630
Pitcairn Islands....275-276
St. Helena....460-461
St. Kitts....181-182
Seychelles....602-603
Solomon Islands....567-568
Tristan da Cunha....397-398
Zambia....348-349
Zil Elwannyen Sesel....119-120

Queen Elizabeth II, 60th Birthday

Queen Elizabeth II Inspecting Guard, 1946 CD339

Designs: Photographs tracing the life of Queen Elizabeth II.

1986

Anguilla....674-677
Antigua....925-928
Barbuda....783-786
Dominica....950-953
Gambia....611-614
Grenada....1371-1374
Grenada Grenadines....749-752
Lesotho....531-534
Maldive Islands....1172-1175
Sierra Leone....760-763
Uganda....495-498

Royal Wedding Issue, 1986

CD340

Designs: Photographs of Prince Andrew and Sarah Ferguson during courtship, engagement and marriage.

1986

Antigua....939-942
Barbuda....809-812
Dominica....970-973
Gambia....635-638
Grenada....1385-1388
Grenada Grenadines....758-761
Lesotho....545-548
Maldive Islands....1181-1184
Sierra Leone....769-772
Uganda....510-513

Lloyds of London, 300th Anniv.

CD341

Designs: 17th century aspects of Lloyds, representations of each country's individual connections with Lloyds and publicized disasters insured by the organization.

1986

Ascension....454-457
Bahamas....655-658
Barbados....731-734
Bermuda....541-544
Falkland Islands....481-484
Liberia....1101-1104
Malawi....534-537
Nevis....571-574
St. Helena....501-504
St. Lucia....923-926
Seychelles....649-652
Solomon Islands....627-630
South Georgia....131-134
Trinidad & Tobago....484-487
Tristan da Cunha....439-442
Vanuatu....485-488
Zil Elwannyen Sesel....146-149

Moon Landing, 20th Anniv.

CD342

Designs: Equipment, crew photographs, spacecraft, official emblems and report profiles created for the Apollo Missions. Two stamps in each set are square in format rather than like the stamp shown; see individual country listings for more information.

1989

Ascension Is.....468-472
Bahamas....674-678
Belize....916-920
Kiribati....517-521
Liberia....1125-1129
Nevis....586-590
St. Kitts....248-252
Samoa....760-764
Seychelles....676-680
Solomon Islands....643-647
Vanuatu....507-511
Zil Elwannyen Sesel....154-158

Queen Mother, 90th Birthday

CD343 CD344

Designs: Portraits of Queen Elizabeth, the Queen Mother. See individual country listings for more information.

1990

Ascension Is.....491-492
Bahamas....698-699
Barbados....782-783
British Antarctic Territory....170-171
British Indian Ocean Territory....106-107
Cayman Islands....622-623
Falkland Islands....524-525
Kenya....527-528
Kiribati....555-556
Liberia....1145-1146
Pitcairn Islands....336-337
St. Helena....532-533
St. Lucia....969-970
Seychelles....710-711
Solomon Islands....671-672
South Georgia....143-144
Swaziland....565-566
Tristan da Cunha....480-481
Zil Elwannyen Sesel....171-172

Queen Elizabeth II, 65th Birthday, and Prince Philip, 70th Birthday

CD345 CD346

Designs: Portraits of Queen Elizabeth II and Prince Philip differ for each country. Printed in sheets of 10 + 5 labels (3 different) between. Stamps alternate, producing 5 different triptychs.

1991

Ascension Is....505-506
Bahamas....730-731
Belize....969-970
Bermuda....617-618
Kiribati....571-572
Mauritius....733-734
Pitcairn Islands....348-349
St. Helena....554-555
St. Kitts....318-319
Samoa....790-791
Seychelles....723-724
Solomon Islands....688-689
South Georgia....149-150
Swaziland....586-587
Vanuatu....540-541
Zil Elwannyen Sesel....177-178

Royal Family Birthday, Anniversary

CD347

Queen Elizabeth II, 65th birthday, Charles and Diana, 10th wedding anniversary: Various photographs of Queen Elizabeth II, Prince Philip, Prince Charles, Princess Diana and their sons William and Henry.

1991

Antigua....1446-1455
Barbuda....1229-1238
Dominica....1328-1337
Gambia....1080-1089
Grenada....2006-2015
Grenada Grenadines....1331-1340
Guyana....2440-2451
Lesotho....871-875
Maldive Islands....1533-1542
Nevis....666-675
St. Vincent....1485-1494
St. Vincent Grenadines....769-778
Sierra Leone....1387-1396
Turks & Caicos Islands....913-922
Uganda....918-927

Queen Elizabeth II's Accession to the Throne 40th Anniversary

CD348

CD349

Various photographs of Queen Elizabeth II with local Scenes.

1992 - CD348

Antigua....1513-1518
Barbuda....1306-1309
Dominica....1414-1419
Gambia....1172-1177
Grenada....2047-2052
Grenada Grenadines....1368-1373
Lesotho....881-885
Maldive Islands....1637-1642
Nevis....702-707
St. Vincent....1582-1587
St. Vincent Grenadines....829-834
Sierra Leone....1482-1487
Turks and Caicos Islands....978-987
Uganda....990-995
Virgin Islands....742-746

1992 - CD349

Ascension Islands....531-535
Bahamas....744-748
Bermuda....623-627
British Indian Ocean Territory....119-123
Cayman Islands....648-652
Falkland Islands....549-553
Gibraltar....605-609
Hong Kong....619-623
Kenya....563-567
Kiribati....582-586
Pitcairn Islands....362-366
St. Helena....570-574
St. Kitts....332-336
Samoa....805-809
Seychelles....734-738
Soloman Islands....708-712
South Georgia....157-161
Tristan da Cunha....508-512
Vanuatu....555-559
Zambia....561-565
Zil Elwannyen Sesel....183-187

Royal Air Force, 75th Anniversary

CD350

1993

Ascension....557-561
Bahamas....771-775
Barbados....842-846
Belize....1003-1008
Bermuda....648-651
British Indian Ocean Territory....136-140
Falkland Is....573-577
Fiji....687-691
Montserrat....830-834
St. Kitts....351-355

End of World War II, 50th Anniv.

CD351

CD352

1995

Ascension....613-617
Bahamas....824-828
Barbados....891-895
Belize....1047-1050
British Indian Ocean Territory....163-167
Cayman Islands....704-708
Falkland Islands....634-638
Fiji....720-724
Kiribati....662-668
Liberia....1175-1179
Mauritius....803-805
St. Helena....646-654
St. Kitts....389-393
St. Lucia....1018-1022
Samoa....890-894
Solomon Islands....799-803
South Georgia & S. Sandwich Is....198-200
Tristan da Cunha....562-566

UN, 50th Anniv.

CD353

1995

Bahamas....839-842
Barbados....901-904
Belize....1055-1058
Jamaica....847-851
Liberia....1187-1190
Mauritius....813-816
Pitcairn Islands....436-439
St. Kitts....398-401
St. Lucia....1023-1026
Samoa....900-903
Tristan da Cunha....568-571
Virgin Islands....807-810

Queen Elizabeth, 70th Birthday

CD354

1996

Ascension....632-635
British Antarctic Territory....240-243
British Indian Ocean Territory....176-180
Falkland Islands....653-657
Pitcairn Islands....446-449
St. Helena....672-676
Samoa....912-916
Tokelau....223-227
Tristan da Cunha....576-579
Virgin Islands....824-828

JAMAICA

jə-'mā-kə

LOCATION — Caribbean Sea, about 90 miles south of Cuba
GOVT. — Independent state in the British Commonwealth
AREA — 4,411 sq. mi.
POP. — 2,230,000 (est. 1982)
CAPITAL — Kingston

Jamaica became an independent state in the British Commonwealth in August 1962. As a colony, it administered two dependencies: Cayman Islands and Turks and Caicos Islands.

12 Pence = 1 Shilling
20 Shillings = 1 Pound
100 Cents = 1 Dollar (1969)

Catalogue values for unused stamps in this country are for Never Hinged items, beginning with Scott 129 in the regular postage section and Scott B4 in the semi-postal section.

Watermarks

Wmk. 45- Pineapple

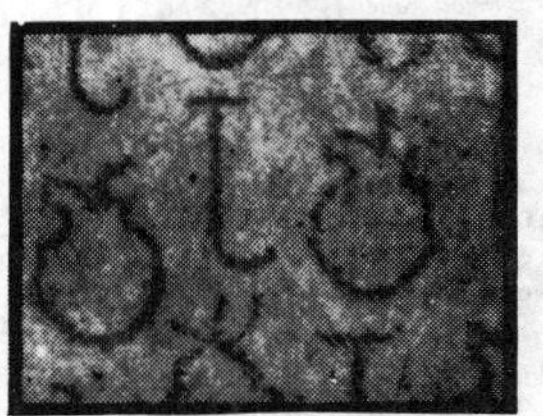

Wmk. 352- J and Pineapple, Multiple

Values for unused stamps are for examples with original gum as defined in the catalogue introduction. Very fine examples of Nos. 1-12 will have perforations touching the design on at least one side due to the narrow spacing of the stamps on the plates. Stamps with perfs clear on all four sides are scarce and will command higher prices.

Queen Victoria
A1 A2

A3 A4

A5 A6

1860-63 Typo. Wmk. 45 *Perf. 14*
1 A1 1p blue 55.00 12.50
a. Diagonal half used as ½p on cover 850.00
b. 1p deep blue 90.00 27.50
c. 1p pale blue 60.00 14.50
d. 1p pale greenish blue 65.00 17.50
2 A2 2p rose 125.00 45.00
a. 2p deep rose 175.00 45.00
3 A3 3p green ('63) 140.00 37.50
4 A4 4p brown org 200.00 40.00
a. 4p orange 225.00 25.00
5 A5 6p lilac 225.00 22.50
a. 6p deep lilac 850.00 60.00
b. 6p gray lilac 250.00 35.00
6 A6 1sh brown 200.00 32.50
a. 1sh lilac brown 550.00 27.50
b. 1sh yellow brown 525.00 27.50

All except No. 3 exist imperforate.

1870-71 Wmk. 1
7 A1 1p blue 50.00 1.25
8 A2 2p rose 60.00 .85
a. 2p brownish rose 75.00 1.00
9 A3 3p green 90.00 8.00
10 A4 4p brown org ('72) 165.00 10.00
a. 4p red orange 500.00 6.50
11 A5 6p lilac ('71) 60.00 6.00
12 A6 1sh brown ('73) 27.50 9.00
Nos. 7-12 (6) 452.50 35.10

The 1p and 4p exist imperf.
See Nos. 17-23, 40, 43, 47-53.

A7

A8

A9

A10

1872, Oct. 29
13 A7 ½p claret 12.50 3.50
a. ½p deep claret 13.50 3.50

Exists imperf. See No. 16.

1875, Aug. 27 *Perf. 12½*
14 A8 2sh red brown 42.50 22.50
15 A9 5sh violet 100.00 135.00

Exist imperf.
See Nos. 29-30, 44, 54.

1883-90 Wmk. 2 *Perf. 14*
16 A7 ½p blue green ('85) 2.25 .65
a. ½p gray green 1.00 .15
17 A1 1p blue ('84) 300.00 6.75
18 A1 1p carmine ('85) 25.00 .75
a. 1p rose 50.00 .75
19 A2 2p rose ('84) 165.00 5.00
20 A2 2p slate ('85) 47.50 .50
a. 2p gray 65.00 1.75
21 A3 3p ol green ('86) 2.50 1.00
22 A4 4p red brown 2.25 .40
a. 4p orange brown 375.00 22.50
23 A5 6p orange yel ('90) 7.50 5.50
a. 6p yellow 20.00 9.00
Nos. 16-23 (8) 552.00 20.55

Nos. 18 and 20 exist imperf. Perf. 12 stamps are considered to be proofs.
For surcharge, see No. 27.

1889-91
24 A10 1p lilac & red vio 2.00 .15
25 A10 2p green 5.00 6.00
26 A10 2½p lilac & ultra ('91) 5.00 .90
Nos. 24-26 (3) 12.00 7.05

No. 22a Surcharged in Black **TWO PENCE HALF-PENNY**

1890, June
27 A4 2½p on 4p org brn 27.50 9.00
b. Double surcharge 350.00 250.00
d. "PFNNY" 100.00 70.00
f. As "d," double surcharge

Three settings of surcharge.

1897
28 A6 1sh brown 5.50 5.00
29 A8 2sh red brown 27.50 18.00
30 A9 5sh violet 50.00 *55.00*
Nos. 28-30 (3) 83.00 *78.00*

The 2sh exists imperf.

Llandovery Falls
A12

Arms of Jamaica
A13

1900, May 1 Engr. Wmk. 1
31 A12 1p red 1.25 .25

1901, Sept. 25
32 A12 1p red & black 1.75 .20
a. Pair, imperf. horiz. 6,000.
b. Bluish paper 175.00 125.00

1903-04 Typo. Wmk. 2
33 A13 ½p green & black 1.50 .15
b. "SERv ET" for "SERVIET" 40.00 42.50
34 A13 1p car & black ('04) 1.50 .15
b. "SERv ET" for "SERVIET" 35.00 35.00
35 A13 2½p ultra & black 2.50 .45
a. "SERv ET" for "SERVIET" 60.00 70.00
36 A13 5p yel & black ('04) 15.00 *22.50*
a. "SERv ET" for "SERVIET" 600.00 *650.00*
Nos. 33-36 (4) 20.50 *23.25*

1905-11 Chalky Paper Wmk. 3
37 A13 ½p green & black 3.50 .20
b. "SERv ET" for "SERVIET" 35.00 35.00
38 A13 1p car & black 12.50 .15
39 A13 2½p ultra & blk ('07) 2.00 .65
40 A4 4p black, *yel* ('10) 8.50 *22.50*
41 A13 5p yel & black ('07) 22.50 25.00
a. "SERv ET" for "SERVIET" 600.00 700.00
42 A13 6p red vio & vio ('11) 10.00 10.00
43 A6 1sh black, *green* ('10) 3.00 *6.00*
44 A8 2sh vio, *blue* ('10) 5.00 3.00
45 A13 5sh vio & black 35.00 27.50
Nos. 37-45 (9) 102.00 95.00

1905-11 Ordinary Paper
46 A13 2½p ultra ('10) 1.75 1.00
47 A3 3p olive green 3.00 1.10
48 A3 3p vio, *yel* ('10) 3.00 2.00
49 A4 4p red brn ('08) 55.00 32.50
50 A4 4p red, *yel* ('11) 1.25 *4.00*
51 A5 6p dull vio ('09) 10.00 11.00
52 A5 6p org yel ('09) 17.50 *22.50*
a. 6p orange ('06) 15.00 17.50
53 A6 1sh brown ('06) 15.00 10.00
54 A8 2sh red brn ('08) 100.00 *125.00*
Nos. 46-54 (9) 206.50 *209.10*

Nos. 48 and 51 also come on chalky paper.

A14

A15

1906
58 A14 ½p green 4.50 .25
a. Booklet pane of 6
59 A15 1p carmine 1.00 .15

For overprints see Nos. MR1, MR4, MR7, MR10.

Edward VII
A16

George V
A17

1911, Feb. 3
60 A16 2p gray 2.00 *7.75*

1912-20
61 A17 1p scarlet ('16) .55 .15
a. 1p carmine ('12) .40 .15
b. Booklet pane of 6
62 A17 1½p brown org ('16) .75 .15
a. 1½p yellow orange 7.00 .75
63 A17 2p gray .75 1.25
64 A17 2½p ultra ('13) .50 .15

Chalky Paper
65 A17 3p violet, *yel* .45 .15
66 A17 4p scar & blk, *yel* ('13) .40 1.65
67 A17 6p red vio & dl vio 3.25 6.00
68 A17 1sh black, *green* 1.65 1.50
a. 1sh blk, *bl grn, olive back* ('20) 1.65 3.00
69 A17 2sh ultra & vio, *blue* ('19) 7.75 15.00
70 A17 5sh scar & green, *yel* ('19) 27.50 45.00

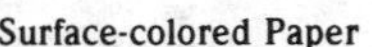

Surface-colored Paper
71 A17 3p violet, *yel* ('13) .45 .35
72 A17 4p scar & black, *yel* ('14) .85 1.75
73 A17 1sh black, *green* ('15) 1.75 3.00
Nos. 61-73 (13) 46.60 76.10

See Nos. 101-102. For overprints see Nos. MR2-MR3, MR5-MR6, MR8-MR9, MR11.

Exhibition Buildings of 1891 — A18

Arawak Woman Preparing Cassava — A19

World War I Contingent Embarking for Overseas Duty — A20

King's House, Spanish Town — A21

Return of Overseas Contingent, 1919 — A22

Columbus Landing in Jamaica — A23

Cathedral in Spanish Town — A24

Statue of Queen Victoria — A26

Memorial to Admiral Rodney — A27

Monument to Sir Charles Metcalfe — A28

Woodland Scene — A29

King George V — A30

1919-21 Typo. Wmk. 3 *Perf. 14*
Chalky Paper
75 A18 ½p ol grn & dk grn ('20) .20 .15
76 A19 1p org & car ('21) 2.00 .15

Engr.
Ordinary Paper

77	A20	1½p green	.20	.15
78	A21	2p grn & bl ('21)	1.00	1.50
79	A22	2½p blue & dk blue ('21)	1.00	1.00
80	A23	3p blue & grn ('21)	1.25	1.00
81	A24	4p green & dk brown ('21)	2.00	*5.00*
83	A26	1sh brt org & org ('20)	3.00	3.75
a.		Frame inverted	*18,500.*	*12,000.*
		As "a," revenue cancel		*2,500.*
84	A27	2sh brn & bl ('20)	12.50	17.00
85	A28	3sh org & violet ('20)	15.00	*45.00*
86	A29	5sh ocher & blue ('21)	40.00	42.50
87	A30	10sh dk myrtle grn ('20)	75.00	*110.00*
		Nos. 75-87 (12)	153.15	*227.20*

See note after No. 100.

A 6p stamp depicting the abolition of slavery was sent to the Colony but was not issued. "Specimen" copies exist with wmk. 3 or 4. Value $1,250 each. Without "Specimen," value $20,000.

Port Royal in 1853 A31

1921-23 Typo. Wmk. 4 *Perf. 14*
Chalky Paper

88	A18	½p ol grn & dk grn ('22)	.80	.15
a.		Booklet pane of 4		
89	A19	1p orange & car ('22)	.50	.15
a.		Booklet pane of 6		

Engr.
Ordinary Paper

90	A20	1½p green	2.00	.15
91	A21	2p grn & blue	1.25	.20
92	A22	2½p bl & dk bl	.70	.20
93	A23	3p bl & grn ('22)	.40	.15
94	A24	4p grn & dk brn	.55	.15
95	A31	6p bl & blk ('22)	9.00	1.50
96	A26	1sh brn org & dl org	1.50	.25
97	A27	2sh brn & bl ('22)	2.00	1.10
98	A28	3sh org & violet	12.50	14.00
99	A29	5sh ocher & bl ('23)	15.00	14.00
a.		5sh orange & blue	19.00	15.00
100	A30	10sh dk myrtle green ('22)	55.00	55.00
		Nos. 88-100 (13)	101.20	87.00

No. 89 differs from No. 76 in having the words "Postage and Revenue" at the bottom.

On No. 79 the horizontal bar of the flag at the left has a broad white line below the colored line. On No. 92 this has been corrected and the broad white line placed above the colored line.

Watermark is sideways on #76-77, 87, 89-90.

Type of 1912-19 Issue

1921-27 Typo. Wmk. 4

101	A17	½p green ('27)	.15	.15
a.		Booklet pane of 6		
102	A17	6p red vio & dl vio	8.50	3.25

No. 102 is on chalky paper.

A32

Type I

Type II

Type II - Cross shading beneath "Jamaica."

1929-32 Engr. *Perf. 13½x14, 14*

103	A32	1p red, type I	.25	.15
a.		1p red, type II ('32)	.15	.15
b.		Booklet pane of 6, type II		
104	A32	1½p brown	1.75	.15
105	A32	9p violet brown	3.75	1.40
		Nos. 103-105 (3)	5.75	1.70

The frames on Nos. 103 to 105 differ.

Coco Palms at Columbus Cove — A33

Scene near Castleton, St. Andrew — A34

Priestman's River, Portland Parish — A35

1932 *Perf. 12½*

106	A33	2p grn & gray blk	4.00	.45
a.		Vertical pair, imperf. between	*3,500.*	
107	A34	2½p ultra & sl blue	2.00	.60
a.		Vertical pair, imperf. between	*4,000.*	*4,000.*
108	A35	6p red vio & gray black	3.00	1.65
		Nos. 106-108 (3)	9.00	2.70

Common Design Types pictured following the introduction.

Silver Jubilee Issue
Common Design Type

1935, May 6 *Perf. 11x12*

109	CD301	1p car & blue	.20	.15
a.		Booklet pane of 6	*150.00*	
110	CD301	1½p black & ultra	.35	.40
111	CD301	6p indigo & grn	2.00	2.50
112	CD301	1sh brn vio & ind	2.50	3.00
		Nos. 109-112 (4)	5.05	6.05

Coronation Issue
Common Design Type

1937, May 12 *Perf. 13½x14*

113	CD302	1p carmine	.15	.15
114	CD302	1½p gray black	.15	.15
115	CD302	2½p bright ultra	.35	.40
		Nos. 113-115 (3)	.65	
		Set, never hinged	1.10	
		Set value		.55

King George VI — A36

Coco Palms at Columbus Cove — A37

Scene near Castleton, St. Andrew — A38

Bananas A39

Citrus Grove A40

Priestman's River, Portland Parish — A41

Kingston Harbor A42

Sugar Industry A43

Bamboo Walk — A44

Woodland Scene — A45

King George VI — A46

1938-51 *Perf. 13½x14*

116	A36	½p dk blue grn	.15	.15
a.		Booklet pane of 6	6.75	
b.		Wmkd. sideways		
117	A36	1p carmine	.15	.15
a.		Booklet pane of 6	11.00	
118	A36	1½p brown	.15	.15

Perf. 12½, 13x13½, 13½x13, 12½x13

119	A37	2p grn & gray blk, perf. 12½	.15	.15
a.		Perf. 13x13½ ('39)	.15	.15
b.		Perf. 12½x13 ('51)	.15	.15
120	A38	2½p ultra & sl bl	1.50	1.25
121	A39	3p grn & lt ultra	.15	.15
122	A40	4p grn & yel brn	.15	.15
123	A41	6p red vio & gray blk, perf. 13½x13 ('50)	.15	.15
a.		Perf. 12½	.15	.15
124	A42	9p rose lake	.30	.30
125	A43	1sh dk brn & brt grn	.30	.15
126	A44	2sh brn & brt bl	1.10	.60

Perf. 13, 14

127	A45	5sh ocher & bl, perf. 13 ('50)	2.00	1.25
a.		Bluish paper, perf. 13 ('49)	5.00	5.00
b.		Perf. 14	1.50	1.10
128	A46	10sh dk myrtle grn, perf. 14	4.00	3.25
a.		Perf. 13 ('50)	3.50	2.50
		Nos. 116-128 (13)	10.25	7.85
		Set, never hinged	30.00	

See Nos. 140, 148, 149, 152.

Catalogue values for unused stamps in this section, from this point to the end of the section, are for Never Hinged items.

Courthouse, Falmouth — A47

Kings Charles II and George VI — A48

House of Assembly, 1762-1869 A50

Institute of Jamaica — A49

Allegory of Labor and Learning — A51

Constitution and Flag of Jamaica — A52

Perf. 12½

1945, Aug. 20 Engr. Wmk. 4

129	A47	1½p brown	.15	.15
a.		Booklet pane of 4	27.50	
b.		Perf. 12½x13½ ('46)	.15	.15
130	A48	2p dp grn, perf. 12½x13½	.15	.15
a.		Perf. 12½	.95	.50
131	A49	3p bright ultra	.20	.20
a.		Perf. 13 ('46)	.30	.80
132	A50	4½p slate black	.25	.25
a.		Perf. 13 ('46)	.40	.40
133	A51	2s chocolate	.80	.80
134	A52	5s deep blue	1.00	1.25
135	A49	10s green	2.25	2.50
		Nos. 129-135 (7)	4.80	5.30

Granting of a new Constitution in 1944.

Peace Issue
Common Design Type

1946, Oct. 14 Wmk. 4 *Perf. 13½*

136	CD303	1½p black brown	.15	.15
a.		Perf. 13½x14	.15	.15

Perf. 13½x14

137	CD303	3p deep blue	.20	.20
a.		Perf. 13½	.35	.35

Silver Wedding Issue
Common Design Types

1948, Dec. 1 Photo. *Perf. 14x14½*

138	CD304	1½p red brown	.25	.25

Engr.; Name Typo.
Perf. 11½x11

139	CD305	£1 red	22.50	25.00

Type of 1938 and

Tobacco Industry A53

1949, Aug. 15 Engr. *Perf. 12½*

140	A39	3p ultra & slate blue	1.10	.40
141	A53	£1 purple & brown	27.50	27.50

UPU Issue
Common Design Types
Perf. 13½, 11x11½

1949, Oct. 10 Wmk. 4

142	CD306	1½p red brown	.30	.15
143	CD307	2p dark green	.40	.25
144	CD308	3p indigo	.75	.50
145	CD309	6p rose violet	1.90	1.25
		Nos. 142-145 (4)	3.35	2.15

University Issue
Common Design Types

1951, Feb. 16 *Perf. 14x14½*

146	CD310	2p brown & gray blk	.20	.15
147	CD311	6p rose lilac & gray blk	.50	.35

George VI Type of 1938

1951, Oct. 25 *Perf. 13½x14*

148	A36	½p orange	.15	.15
a.		Booklet pane of 6	5.00	
149	A36	1p blue green	.20	.15
a.		Booklet pane of 6	11.00	
		Set value	.25	.15

Boy Scout Emblem with Map — A54

Map and Emblem — A55

Perf. 13½x13, 13x13½

1952, Mar. 5 Typo. Wmk. 4

150 A54 2p blk, yel grn & blue .30 .15
151 A55 6p blk, yel grn & dk red .50 .40

1st Caribbean Boy Scout Jamboree, 1952.

Banana Type of 1938

1952, July 1 Engr. *Perf. 12½*

152 A39 3p rose red & green .50 .40

Coronation Issue

Common Design Type

1953, June 2 *Perf. 13½x13*

153 CD312 2p dk green & black .20 .15

Type of 1938 with Portrait of Queen Elizabeth II and Inscription: "ROYAL VISIT 1953"

1953, Nov. 25 *Perf. 13*

154 A37 2p green & gray black .15 .15

Visit of Queen Elizabeth II and the Duke of Edinburgh, 1953.

Warship off Port Royal A56

Designs: 2½p, Old Montego Bay. 3p, Old Kingston. 6p, Proclaiming abolition of slavery.

1955, May 10 Engr. *Perf. 12x12½*

Center in Black

155 A56 2p olive green .15 .15
156 A56 2½p light ultra .20 .15
157 A56 3p deep plum .20 .15
158 A56 6p rose red .30 .25
Nos. 155-158 (4) .85 .70

300th anniv. of Jamaica's establishment as a British territory.

Palm Trees — A57

Blue Mountain Peak — A58

Arms of Jamaica — A59

Arms of Jamaica — A60

Designs: 1p, Sugar cane. 2p, Pineapple. 2½p, Bananas. 3p, Mahoe flower. 4p, Breadfruit. 5p, Ackee fruit. 6p, Streamer (hummingbird). 1sh, Royal Botanic Gardens, Hope. 1sh6p, Rafting on the Rio Grande. 2sh, Fort Charles.

1956 Wmk. 4 *Perf. 12½*

159 A57 ½p org ver & black .15 .15
a. Booklet pane of 6 .30
160 A57 1p emerald & black .15 15
a. Booklet pane of 6 .50
161 A57 2p rose red & black .15 .15
a. Booklet pane of 6 .80
162 A57 2½p lt ultra & black .15 .15
a. Booklet pane of 6 1.65
163 A57 3p brown & green .15 .15
164 A57 4p dk blue & ol grn .15 .15
165 A57 5p ol green & car .20 .15
166 A57 6p carmine & black .25 .15

Perf. 13½

167 A58 8p red org & brt ultra .25 .15
168 A58 1sh blue & yel grn .30 .15
169 A58 1sh6p dp cl & ultra .60 .20
170 A58 2sh ol grn & ultra 2.00 .40

Perf. 11½

171 A59 3sh blue & black 1.90 .90
172 A59 5sh carmine & blk 2.75 1.25
173 A60 10sh blue grn & blk 6.50 4.00
174 A60 £1 purple & blk 12.00 6.50
Nos. 159-174 (16) 27.65 14.75

For overprints see Nos. 185-196. For types overprinted see Nos. 208-216.

West Indies Federation

Common Design Type

Perf. 11½x11

1958, Apr. 22 Engr. Wmk. 314

175 CD313 2p green .15 .15
176 CD313 5p blue .30 .30
177 CD313 6p carmine rose .45 .30
Nos. 175-177 (3) .90 .75

Britannia Plane over 1860 Packet Boat — A61

1sh Stamps of 1860 and 1956 — A62

Design: 6p, Victorian post cart and mail truck.

1960, Jan. 4 *Perf. 13x13½*

178 A61 2p lilac & blue .15 .15
179 A61 6p ol grn & car rose .30 .20

Perf. 13

180 A62 1sh blue, yel grn & brn .50 .50
Nos. 178-180 (3) .95 .85

Centenary of Jamaican postal service.

Independent State

Zouave Bugler and Map of Jamaica A63

Designs: 1sh6p, Gordon House (Legislature) and hands of three races holding banner. 5sh, Map and symbols of agriculture and industry.

1962, Aug. 8 Photo. *Perf. 13*

181 A63 2p multicolored .15 .15
182 A63 4p multicolored .15 .15
a. Yellow omitted
183 A63 1sh6p red, black & brn .40 .20
184 A63 5sh multicolored 1.40 1.40
Nos. 181-184 (4) 2.10 1.90

Issue of 1956 Overprinted:

1 9 6 2 INDEPENDENCE — a

1 9 6 2 INDEPENDENCE 1962 — b

Perf. 12½

1962, Aug. 8 Wmk. 4 Engr.

185 A57(a) ½p org ver & blk .15 .15
186 A57(a) 1p emer & black .15 .15
187 A57(a) 2½p lt ultra & blk .15 .15
188 A57(b) 3p brown & green .15 .15
189 A57(b) 5p ol green & car .15 .15
190 A57(b) 6p car & black .15 .15

Perf. 13½

191 A58(b) 8p red org & brt ultra .30 .15
192 A58(b) 1sh blue & yel grn .35 .30
193 A58(b) 2sh ol green & ultra 1.00 .65

Perf. 11½

194 A59(a) 3sh blue & blk 1.50 1.65
195 A60(a) 10sh bl grn & blk 4.00 4.50
196 A60(a) £1 pur & black 7.75 9.00
Nos. 185-196 (12) 15.80 17.15

Nos. 181-196 issued to commemorate Jamaica's independence.

"Independence" measures 17½x1½mm on #185-187; 18x1mm on #194-196.

See Nos. 208-216.

Weight Lifting, Soccer, Boxing and Cycling A64

Designs: 6p, Various water sports. 8p, Running and jumping. 2sh, Arms and runner.

Perf. 14½x14

1962, Aug. 11 Photo. Wmk. 314

197 A64 1p car & dk brown .15 .15
198 A64 6p blue & brown .15 .15
199 A64 8p olive & dk brown .20 .15
200 A64 2sh multicolored .70 .70
Nos. 197-200 (4) 1.20 1.15

IX Central American and Caribbean Games, Kingston, Aug. 11-25.

A souvenir sheet containing one each of Nos. 197-200, imperf., was sold exclusively by National Sports, Ltd., at 5sh (face 3sh3p). The Jamaican Post Office sold the entire issue of this sheet to National Sports at face value, plus the printing cost. The stamps are postally valid. The sheet has marginal inscriptions and simulated perforations in ultramarine. Value $3.25.

Freedom from Hunger Issue

Man Planting Mango Tree and Produce A65

Perf. 12½

1963, June 4 Unwmk. Litho.

201 A65 1p blue & multi .15 .15
202 A65 8p rose & multi .60 .60

See note after CD314, Common Design section.

Red Cross Centenary Issue

Common Design Type

1963, Sept. 2 Wmk. 314 *Perf. 13*

203 CD315 2p black & red .15 .15
204 CD315 1sh6p ultra & red .60 .50
Set value .55

Carole Joan Crawford — A66

Unwmk.

1964, Feb. 14 Photo. *Perf. 13*

205 A66 3p multicolored .15 .15
206 A66 1sh olive & multi .30 .25
207 A66 1sh6p multicolored .40 .40
a. Souvenir sheet of 3 .90 .90
Nos. 205-207 (3) .85 .80

Carole Joan Crawford, Miss World, 1963.

No. 207a contains one each of Nos. 205-207 with simulated perforations. Issued May 25. Sold for 4sh.

Types of 1956 Overprinted like 1962 Independence Issue

Perf. 12½

1963-64 Wmk. 314 Engr.

208 A57(a) ½p org ver & blk .15 .15
209 A57(a) 1p emer & blk ('64) .15 .15
210 A57(a) 2½p lt ultra & blk ('64) .20 .15
211 A57(b) 3p brown & green .30 .15
212 A57(b) 5p ol grn & car ('64) .60 .55

Perf. 13½

213 A58(b) 8p red org & brt ultra ('64) .75 .65
214 A58(b) 1sh bl & yel grn 1.75 1.65
215 A58(b) 2sh ol grn & ultra ('64) 2.50 2.50

Perf. 11½

216 A59(a) 3sh bl & blk ('64) 3.50 3.50
Nos. 208-216 (9) 9.90 9.45

Overprint is at bottom on Nos. 214-215, at top on Nos. 192-193.

Lignum Vitae, National Flower, and Map — A67

1½p, Ackee, national fruit, and map. 2p, Blue Mahoe, national tree, and map, vert. 2½p, Land shells (snails). 3p, Flag over map. 4p, Murex antillarum, sea shell. 6p, Papilio homerus. 8p, Streamer (hummingbird). 9p, Gypsum industry. 1sh, Stadium and statue of runner. 1sh6p, Palisadoes International Airport. 2sh, Bauxite mining. 3sh, Blue marlin and boat. 5sh, Port Royal exploration of sunken city, map, ship and artifacts. 10sh, Coat of arms, vert. £1, Flag and Queen Elizabeth II.

Perf. 14½, 14x14½

1964, May 4 Photo. Wmk. 352

Size: 26x22mm, 22x26mm

217 A67 1p bis, vio bl & green .15 .15
a. Booklet pane of 6 .35
218 A67 1½p multicolored .15 .15
219 A67 2p multicolored .15 .15
a. Booklet pane of 6 .85
220 A67 2½p multicolored .15 .15
221 A67 3p emer, yel & black .15 .15
a. Booklet pane of 6 1.10
222 A67 4p violet & buff .15 .15
223 A67 6p multicolored .15 .15
a. Ultramarine omitted 30.00
224 A67 8p multicolored .20 .15
a. Red omitted

Perf. 14½x14, 13½x14½, 14x14½

Size: 32x26mm, 26x32mm

225 A67 9p blue & yel .25 .15
226 A67 1sh yel brn & blk .30 .15
a. Yellow brown omitted 200.00
b. Black omitted 550.00
227 A67 1sh6p sl, buff & bl .40 .15
228 A67 2sh bl, brn red & black .65 .35
229 A67 3sh grn, saph & dk bl, perf. 14½x14 1.10 .65
a. Perf. 14x14½ 1.90 1.25
230 A67 5sh bl, blk & bis 1.50 .85
231 A67 10sh multicolored 2.00 1.75
a. Blue ("Jamaica" etc.) omitted 150.00
232 A67 £1 multicolored 4.75 3.25
Nos. 217-232 (16) 12.20 8.50

See Nos. 306-318. For overprints & surcharges see Nos. 248-251, 279-291, 305.

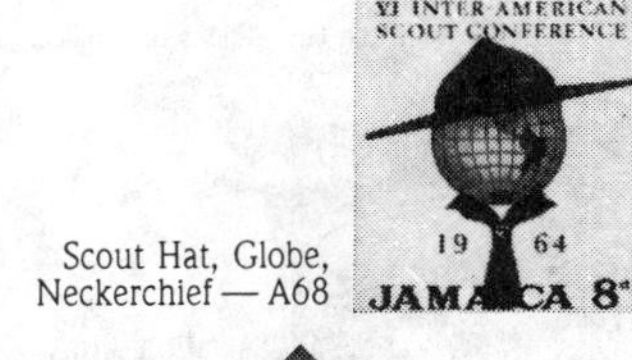

Scout Hat, Globe, Neckerchief — A68

Scout Emblem, American Crocodile — A69

Design: 3p, Scout belt buckle.

Perf. 14½x14, 14

1964, Aug. 27 Wmk. 352

233 A68 3p pink, black & red .15 .15
234 A68 8p ultra, black & olive .20 .20
235 A69 1sh ultra & gold .35 .35
Nos. 233-235 (3) .70 .70

6th Inter-American Scout Conference, Kingston, Aug. 25-29.

Gordon House, Kingston, and Commonwealth Parliamentary Association Emblem — A70

Designs: 6p, Headquarters House, Kingston. 1sh6p, House of Assembly, Spanish Town.

1964, Nov. 16 Photo. ***Perf. 14½x14***

236 A70 3p yel green & blk .15 .15
237 A70 6p red & black .15 .15
238 A70 1sh6p ultra & black .30 .35
Nos. 236-238 (3) .60
Set value .50

10th Commonwealth Parliamentary Conf.

Eleanor Roosevelt — A71

1964, Dec. 10 Wmk. 352

239 A71 1sh lt green, blk & red .25 .20

Eleanor Roosevelt (1884-1962) on the 16th anniv. of the Universal Declaration of Human Rights.

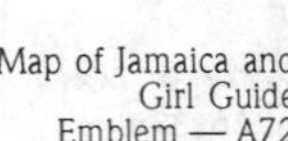

Map of Jamaica and Girl Guide Emblem — A72

Girl Guide Emblems — A73

Perf. 14x14½, 14

1965, May 17 Photo. Wmk. 352

240 A72 3p lt blue, yel & yel grn .15 .15
241 A73 1sh lt yel grn, blk & bis .30 .30
Set value .35

50th anniv. of the Girl Guides of Jamaica.

Salvation Army Cap — A74

1sh6p, Flag bearer, drummer and globe, vert.

Perf. 14x14½, 14½x14

1965, Aug. 23 Photo. Wmk. 352

242 A74 3p dp blue, yel, mar & blk .15 .15
243 A74 1sh6p emerald & multi .40 .40
Set value .45

Centenary of the Salvation Army.

Paul Bogle, William Gordon and Morant Bay Court House A75

1965, Dec. 29 Unwmk. ***Perf. 14x13***

244 A75 3p vio blue, blk & brn .15 .15
245 A75 1sh6p yel green, blk & brn .30 .30
246 A75 3sh pink & brown .60 .60
Nos. 244-246 (3) 1.05 1.05

Cent. of the Morant Bay rebellion against governor John Eyre.

ITU Emblem, Telstar, Telegraph Key and Man Blowing Horn — A76

Perf. 14x14½

1965, Dec. 29 Photo. Wmk. 352

247 A76 1sh gray, black & red .45 .45

Cent. of the ITU.

Nos. 221, 223, 226-227 Overprinted: "ROYAL VISIT / MARCH 1966"

Perf. 14½, 14½x14

1966, Mar. 3 Photo. Wmk. 352

Size: 26x22mm

248 A67 3p emer, yel & black .15 .15
249 A67 6p multicolored .25 .20

Size: 32x26mm

250 A67 1sh yel brown & blk .40 .35
251 A67 1sh6p slate, buff & blue .65 .65
Nos. 248-251 (4) 1.45 1.35

See note after Antigua No. 162.

Winston Churchill A77

1966, Apr. 18 ***Perf. 14, 14x14½***

252 A77 6p olive green & gray .30 .25
253 A77 1sh violet & sepia .60 .50

Sir Winston Leonard Spencer Churchill (1874-1965), statesman and WWII leader.

Runner, Flags of Jamaica, Great Britain and Games' Emblem A78

Designs: 6p, Bicyclists and waterfall. 1sh, Stadium. 3sh, Games' Emblem.

Perf. 14½x14

1966, Aug. 4 Photo. Wmk. 352

254 A78 3p multicolored .15 .15
255 A78 6p multicolored .15 .15
256 A78 1sh multicolored .25 .25
257 A78 3sh gold & dk vio blue .60 .60
a. Souvenir sheet of 4 2.75 2.75
Nos. 254-257 (4) 1.15 1.15

8th British Empire and Commonwealth Games, Aug. 4-13, 1966.

No. 257a contains 4 imperf. stamps with simulated perforations similar to Nos. 254-257. Issued Aug. 25, 1966.

Bolivar Statue, Kingston, Flags of Jamaica and Venezuela — A79

1966, Dec. 5 ***Perf. 14x14½***

258 A79 8p multicolored .25 .25

150th anniv. of the "Bolivar Letter," written by Simon Bolivar, while in exile in Jamaica.

Jamaican Pavilion A80

1967, Apr. 28 ***Perf. 14½x14***

259 A80 6p multicolored .15 .15
260 A80 1sh multicolored .30 .30

EXPO '67 Intl. Exhibition, Montreal, Apr. 28-Oct. 27.

Donald Burns Sangster — A81

Perf. 13x13½

1967, Aug. 28 Unwmk.

261 A81 3p multicolored .15 .15
262 A81 1sh6p multicolored .30 .30
Set value .35 .35

Sir Donald Burns Sangster (1911-1967), Prime Minister.

Traffic Police and Post Office A82

Designs: 1sh, Officers representing various branches of police force in front of Police Headquarters. 1sh6p, Constable, 1867, Old House of Assembly, and 1967 constable with New House of Assembly.

Perf. 13½x14

1967, Nov. 28 Photo. Wmk. 352

Size: 42x25mm

263 A82 3p red brown & multi .15 .15

Size: 56½x20½mm

Perf. 13½x14½

264 A82 1sh yellow & multi .30 .30

Size: 42x25mm

Perf. 13½x14

265 A82 1sh6p gray & multi .50 .50
Nos. 263-265 (3) .95 .95

Centenary of the Constabulary Force.

> A Human Rights set of three (3p, 1sh, 3sh) was prepared and announced for release on Jan. 2, 1968. The Crown Agents distributed sample sets, but the stamps were not issued. On Dec. 3, Nos. 271-273 were issued instead. Designs of the unissued set show bowls of food, an abacus and praying hands. Value, $75.

Wicketkeeper, Emblem of West Indies Cricket Team — A82a

Designs: No. 266, Wicketkeeper and emblem of West Indies Cricket Team. No. 267, Batsman and emblem of Marylebone Cricket Club. No. 268, Bowler and emblem of West Indies Cricket Team.

1968, Feb. 8 Photo. ***Perf. 14***

266 A82a 6p multicolored .25 .25
267 A82a 6p multicolored .25 .25
268 A82a 6p multicolored .25 .25
a. Horiz. strip of 3, #266-268 .75
Nos. 266-268 (3) .75 .75

Visit of the Marylebone Cricket Club to the West Indies, Jan.-Feb. 1968.

Sir Alexander and Lady Bustamante A83

1968, May 23 ***Perf. 14½***

269 A83 3p brt rose & black .15 .15
270 A83 1sh olive green & black .25 .25
Set value .30 .30

Labor Day, May 23, 1968.

Human Rights Flame and Map of Jamaica A84

Designs: 1sh, Hands shielding Human Rights flame, vert. 3sh, Man kneeling on Map of Jamaica, and Human Rights flame.

1968, Dec. 3 Wmk. 352 ***Perf. 14½***

271 A84 3p multicolored .15 .15
a. Gold (flame) omitted 110.00
272 A84 1sh multicolored .20 .20
273 A84 3sh multicolored .70 .70
a. Gold (flame) omitted 110.00
Nos. 271-273 (3) 1.05 1.05

International Human Rights Year.

ILO Emblem A85

Unwmk.

1969, May 23 Litho. ***Perf. 14***

274 A85 6p black & orange yel .15 .15
275 A85 3sh black & brt green .60 .60

50th anniv. of the ILO.

WHO Emblem, Children and Nurse — A86

Designs: 1sh, Malaria eradication, horiz. 3sh, Student nurses.

1969, May 30 Photo. ***Perf. 14***

276 A86 6p org, black & brown .15 .15
277 A86 1sh blue grn, blk & brn .20 .20
278 A86 3sh ultra, black & brn .60 .60
Nos. 276-278 (3) .95 .95

WHO, 20th anniv.

Nos. 217-219, 221-223, 225-232 Surcharged with New Value and: "C-DAY 8th SEPTEMBER 1969"

1969, Sept. 8 Wmk. 352 ***Perf. 14½***

Size: 26x22mm, 22x26mm

279 A67 1c on 1p multi .15 .15
280 A67 2c on 2p multi .15 .15
281 A67 3c on 3p multi .15 .15
282 A67 4c on 4p multi .15 .15
283 A67 5c on 6p multi .15 .15
a. Blue (wing dots) omitted 40.00

Perf. 14½x14, 13½x14½, 14x14½

Size: 32x26mm, 26x32mm

284 A67 8c on 9p multi .20 .15
285 A67 10c on 1sh multi .25 .20
286 A67 15c on 1sh6p multi .40 .30

287 A67 20c on 2sh multi .60 .50
288 A67 30c on 3sh multi .75 .65
289 A67 50c on 5sh multi .90 .85
290 A67 $1 on 10sh multi 1.75 1.65
291 A67 $2 on £1 multi 4.25 3.50
Nos. 279-291 (13) 9.85 8.55

Introduction of decimal currency.

The old denomination is obliterated by groups of small rectangles on the 1c and 3c, and with a square on the 2c, 4c and 8c; old denominations not obliterated on others.

Madonna and Child with St. John, by Raphael — A87

Christmas (Paintings): 2c, The Adoration of the Kings, by Vincenzo Foppa. 8c, The Adoration of the Kings, by Dosso Dossi.

1969, Oct. 25 Litho. *Perf. 13*

292 A87 2c vermilion & multi .15 .15
293 A87 5c multicolored .15 .15
294 A87 8c orange & multi .30 .30
Set value .50 .50

First Jamaica Penny — A88

Design: 3c, First Jamaica halfpenny.

1969, Oct. 27 *Perf. 12x12½*

295 A88 3c brt pink, blk & silver .15 .15
296 A88 15c emerald, blk & silver .30 .30
Set value .35 .35

Centenary of the first Jamaican coinage.

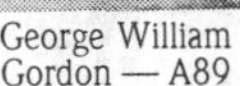

George William Gordon — A89

Crucifixion, by Antonello da Messina — A90

Portraits: 3c, Sir Alexander Bustamante (1884-1977). 5c, Norman W. Manley (1893-1969). 10c, Marcus M. Garvey (1887-1940). 15c, Paul Bogle (1820-1865).

Perf. 12x12½

1970, Mar. 11 Photo. Unwmk.

297 A89 1c lt violet & multi .15 .15
298 A89 3c lt blue & multi .15 .15
299 A89 5c lt gray & multi .15 .15
300 A89 10c pale rose & multi .25 .25
301 A89 15c pale green & multi .45 .45
Set value .95 .95

National heroes connected with Jamaica's independence.

1970, Mar. 23

Easter: 3c, Christ Appearing to St. Peter, by Annibale Carracci. 20c, Easter lily.

302 A90 3c pink & multi .15 .15
303 A90 10c gray green & multi .30 .30
304 A90 20c gray & multi .60 .60
Nos. 302-304 (3) 1.05 1.05

No. 219 Surcharged **2c** ■

1970, July 16 Wmk. 352 *Perf. 14½*

305 A67 2c on 2p multicolored .15 .15

Type of Regular Issue, 1964
Values in Cents and Dollars

Designs: 1c, Lignum vitae and map. 2c, Blue mahoe and map, vert. 3c, Flag over map. 4c, Murex antillarum, sea shell. 5c, Papilio homerus. 8c, Gypsum industry. 10c, Stadium and statue of runner. 15c, Palisadoes International Airport. 20c, Bauxite mining. 30c, Blue marlin and boat. 50c, Port Royal exploration of sunken city, map, ship and artifacts. $1, Coat of arms, vert. $2, Flag and Queen Elizabeth II.

1970 Wmk. 352 Photo. *Perf. 14½*
Size: 26x22mm, 22x26mm

306 A67 1c bister & multi .15 .15
307 A67 2c gray green & multi .15 .15
308 A67 3c emer, yel & black .15 .15
309 A67 4c violet & buff .15 .15
310 A67 5c green & multi .15 .15

Perf. 14½x14, 13½x14½, 14x14½
Size: 32x26mm, 26x32mm

311 A67 8c blue & yellow .25 .15
312 A67 10c yel brn & black .35 .15
313 A67 15c multicolored .55 .25
314 A67 20c multicolored .70 .45
315 A67 30c multicolored .80 .60
316 A67 50c multicolored 1.25 1.00
317 A67 $1 multicolored 2.50 1.75
318 A67 $2 multicolored 5.00 3.75
Nos. 306-318 (13) 12.15 8.85

Issued: #306-312, 9/7; #313-318, 11/2.

Bright's Cable Gear on "Dacia" A91

Designs: 3c, Telegraph cable ship "Dacia." 50c, Double current Morse key, 1870, and map of Jamaica.

1970, Oct. 12 Litho. *Perf. 14½*

319 A91 3c red orange & multi .15 .15
320 A91 10c blue green & multi .35 .15
321 A91 50c emerald & multi 1.50 1.50
Nos. 319-321 (3) 2.00 1.80

Centenary of telegraph service.

Bananas, Citrus Fruit, Sugar Cane and Tobacco — A92

1970, Nov. 2 Wmk. 352 *Perf. 14*

322 A92 2c brown & multi .15 .15
323 A92 10c black & multi .35 .35
Set value .45 .45

Jamaica Agricultural Society, 75th anniv.

"The Projector," 1845 — A93

Locomotives: 15c, Engine 54, 1944. 50c, Engine 102, 1967.

1970, Nov. 21 Litho. *Perf. 13½*

324 A93 3c green & multi .15 .15
325 A93 15c org brown & multi 1.00 1.00
326 A93 50c multicolored 3.50 3.50
Nos. 324-326 (3) 4.65 4.65

125th anniv. of the Jamaican railroad.

Kingston Cathedral — A94

30c, Arms of Jamaica Bishopric. 10c, 20c, like 3c.

1971, Feb. 22 *Perf. 14½*

327 A94 3c lt green & multi .15 .15
328 A94 10c dull orange & multi .20 .20
329 A94 20c ultra & multi .40 .40
330 A94 30c gray & multi .60 .60
Nos. 327-330 (4) 1.35 1.35

Centenary of the disestablishment of the Church of England.

Henry Morgan, Ships in Port Royal Harbor A95

Designs: 15c, Mary Read, Anne Bonny and pamphlet on their trial. 30c, 18th century merchantman surrendering to pirate schooner.

1971, May 10 Litho. Wmk. 352

331 A95 3c red brown & multi .15 .15
332 A95 15c gray & multi .75 .75
333 A95 30c lilac & multi 1.75 1.75
Nos. 331-333 (3) 2.65 2.65

Pirates and buccaneers.

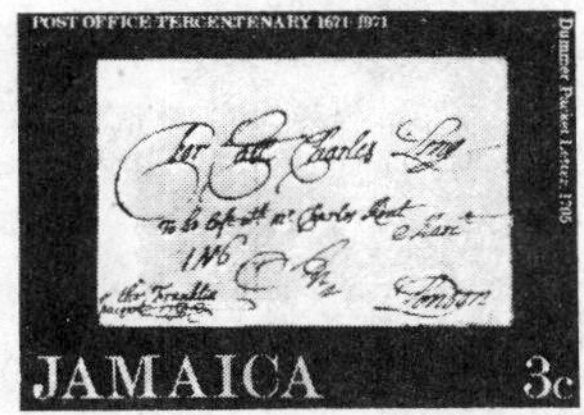

Dummer Packet Letter, 1705 — A96

Designs: 5c, Stampless cover, 1793. 8c, Post office, Kingston, 1820. 10c, Modern date cancellation on No. 312. 20c, Cover with stamps of Great Britain and Jamaica cancellations, 1859. 50c, Jamaica No. 83a, vert.

1971, Oct. 30 *Perf. 13½*

334 A96 3c dk carmine & black .15 .15
335 A96 5c lt ol grn & black .20 .20
336 A96 8c purple & black .30 .30
337 A96 10c slate, black & brn .35 .35
338 A96 20c multicolored .70 .70
339 A96 50c dk gray, blk & org 1.75 1.75
Nos. 334-339 (6) 3.45 3.45

Tercentenary of Jamaica Post Office.

Earth Station and Satellite — A97

1972, Feb. 17 *Perf. 14x13½*

340 A97 3c red & multi .15 .15
341 A97 15c gray & multi .55 .55
342 A97 50c multicolored 1.65 1.65
Nos. 340-342 (3) 2.35 2.35

Jamaica's earth satellite station.

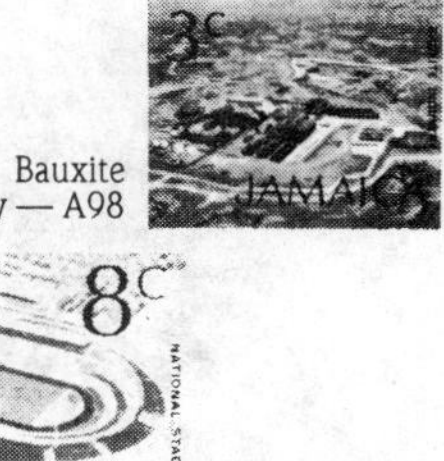

Bauxite Industry — A98

National Stadium — A99

Perf. 14½x14, 14x14½

1972-79 Litho. Wmk. 352

343 A98 1c Pimento, vert. .15 .15
344 A98 2c Red ginger, vert. .15 .15
345 A98 3c shown .15 .15
346 A98 4c Kingston harbor .15 .15
347 A98 5c Oil refinery .15 .15
348 A98 6c Senate Building, Univ. of the West Indies .15 .15

Perf. 13½

349 A99 8c shown .15 .15
350 A99 9c Devon House, Hope Road .15 .15
351 A99 10c Stewardess and Air Jamaica plane .15 .15
352 A99 15c Old Iron Bridge, vert. .15 .15
353 A99 20c College of Arts, Science & Technology .20 .15
354 A99 30c Dunn's River Falls, vert. .25 .20
355 A99 50c River raft .45 .40
356 A99 $1 Jamaica House .85 .85
357 A99 $2 Kings House 1.25 1.25

Perf. 14½x14
Size: 37x26½mm

358 A99 $5 Map and arms of Jamaica ('79) 3.00 3.00
Nos. 343-358 (16) 7.50 7.35

For overprints see Nos. 360-362, 451.

Nos. 345, 351, 355 Overprinted: "TENTH ANNIVERSARY INDEPENDENCE 1962-1972"

1972, Aug. 8 *Perf. 14½x14, 13½*

360 A98 3c multicolored .15 .15
361 A99 10c multicolored .28 .28
362 A99 50c multicolored 1.40 1.40
Nos. 360-362 (3) 1.83 1.83

Arms of Kingston — A100

Design: 5c, 30c, Arms of Kingston, vert.

1972, Dec. 4 *Perf. 13½x14, 14x13½*

363 A100 5c pink & multi .15 .15
364 A100 30c lemon & multi .65 .65
365 A100 50c lt blue & multi 1.10 1.10
Nos. 363-365 (3) 1.90 1.90

Centenary of Kingston as capital.

Mongoose and Map of Jamaica A101

40c, Mongoose & rat. 60c, Mongoose & chicken.

Perf. 14x14½

1973, Apr. 9 Litho. Wmk. 352

366 A101 8c yel green & blk .20 .20
367 A101 40c blue & black .95 .95
368 A101 60c salmon & black 1.75 1.75
a. Souvenir sheet of 3, #366-368 4.00 4.00
Nos. 366-368 (3) 2.90 2.90

Centenary of the introduction of the mongoose to Jamaica.

Euphorbia Punicea — A102

Flowers: 6c, Hylocereus triangularis. 9c, Columnea argentea. 15c, Portlandia grandiflora. 30c, Samyda pubescens. 50c, Cordia sebestena.

1973, July 9 *Perf. 14*

369 A102 1c dp green & multi .15 .15
370 A102 6c vio blue & multi .20 .20
371 A102 9c orange & multi .30 .30
372 A102 15c brown & multi .50 .50
373 A102 30c olive & multi 1.00 1.00
374 A102 50c multicolored 1.75 1.75
Nos. 369-374 (6) 3.90 3.90

Broughtonia Sanguinea A103

Orchids: 10c, Arpophyllum jamaicense, vert. 20c, Oncidium pulchellum, vert. $1, Brassia maculata.

1973, Oct. 8 *Perf. 14x13½, 13½x14*

375 A103 5c multicolored .25 .25
376 A103 10c multicolored .45 .45
377 A103 20c slate & multi .90 .90
378 A103 $1 ultra & multi 4.50 4.50
a. Souv. sheet of 4, #375-378, perf 12 6.25 6.25
Nos. 375-378 (4) 6.10 6.10

Mailboat "Mary" (1808-1815) — A104

Designs: Mailboats.

Perf. 13½ (5c, 50c), 14½ (10c, 15c)
1974, Apr. 8 **Wmk. 352**

379 A104 5c shown .20 .15
a. Perf. 14½ 7.50 1.25
380 A104 10c "Queensbury" (1814-27) .45 .35
381 A104 15c "Sheldrake" (1829-34) .75 .55
382 A104 50c "Thames" (1842) 2.25 1.90
a. Souv. sheet of 4, #379-382, perf 13½ 5.00 3.50
Nos. 379-382 (4) 3.65 2.95

Jamaican Dancers — A105

Designs: Dancers.

1974, Aug. 1 **Litho.** *Perf. 13½*

383 A105 5c green & multi .15 .15
384 A105 10c black & multi .20 .20
385 A105 30c brown & multi .60 .60
386 A105 50c lilac & multi 1.00 1.00
a. Souvenir sheet of 4, #383-386 2.75 2.75
Nos. 383-386 (4) 1.95 1.95

National Dance Theatre.

Globe, Letter, UPU Emblem A106

1974, Oct. 9 *Perf. 14*

387 A106 5c plum & multi .15 .15
388 A106 9c olive & multi .25 .25
389 A106 50c multicolored 1.25 1.25
Nos. 387-389 (3) 1.65 1.65

Centenary of Universal Postal Union.

Senate Building and Sir Hugh Wooding A107

10c, 50c, Chapel & Princess Alice. 30c, like 5c.

1975, Jan. 13 **Wmk. 352**

390 A107 5c yellow & multi .15 .15
391 A107 10c salmon & multi .20 .20
392 A107 30c dull orange & multi .55 .55
393 A107 50c multicolored 1.00 1.00
Nos. 390-393 (4) 1.90 1.90

University College of the West Indies, 25th anniversary.

Commonwealth Symbol — A108

Commonwealth Symbol and: 10c, Arms of Jamaica. 30c, Dove of peace. 50c, Jamaican flag.

1975, Apr. 29 **Litho.** *Perf. 13½*

394 A108 5c buff & multi .15 .15
395 A108 10c rose & multi .20 .20
396 A108 30c violet blue & multi .65 .65
397 A108 50c multicolored 1.00 1.00
Nos. 394-397 (4) 2.00 2.00

Commonwealth Heads of Government Conference, Jamaica, Apr.-May.

Graphium Marcellinus A109

Koo Koo, "Actor-boy" A110

Butterflies: 20c, Papilio thoas melonius. 25c, Papilio thersites. 30c, Papilio homerus.

1975, Aug. 25 **Litho.** *Perf. 14*

398 A109 10c lt green & multi .75 .40
399 A109 20c lt green & multi 1.50 .85
400 A109 25c lt green & multi 2.25 1.25
401 A109 30c lt green & multi 2.50 1.50
a. Souvenir sheet of 4, #398-401 7.00 4.50
Nos. 398-401 (4) 7.00 4.00

See Nos. 423-426, 435-438.

1975, Nov. 3 **Litho.** **Wmk. 352**

Christmas: 10c, Red "set-girls." 20c, French "set-girls." 50c, Jawbone or "House John Canoe." Festival dancers drawn by I. M. Belisario in Kingston, 1837.

402 A110 8c multicolored .15 .15
403 A110 10c olive & multi .20 .20
404 A110 20c ultra & multi .40 .40
405 A110 50c multicolored 1.25 1.25
a. Souv. sheet of 4, #402-405, perf. 13½ 3.25 3.25
Nos. 402-405 (4) 2.00 2.00

See Nos. 416-418.

Map of Jamaica, by Benedetto Bordone, 1528 — A111

Maps of Jamaica by: 20c, Tommaso Porcacchi, 1576. 30c, Theodor DeBry, 1594. 50c, Barent Langenes, 1598.

1976, Mar. 12 *Perf. 13½x14*

406 A111 10c brown, buff & red .20 .20
407 A111 20c bister & multi .40 .40
408 A111 30c lt blue & multi .65 .65
409 A111 50c multicolored 1.25 1.25
Nos. 406-409 (4) 2.50 2.50

See Nos. 419-422.

Olympic Rings A112

1976, June 14 **Litho.** *Perf. 13½x14*

410 A112 10c black & multi .20 .20
411 A112 20c blue & multi .40 .40
412 A112 25c red & multi .50 .50
413 A112 50c green & multi 1.00 1.00
Nos. 410-413 (4) 2.10 2.10

21st Olympic Games, Montreal, Canada, July 17-Aug. 1.

Map of West Indies, Bats, Wicket and Ball A112a

Prudential Cup — A112b

1976, Aug. 9 **Unwmk.** *Perf. 14*

414 A112a 10c lt blue & multi .30 .30
415 A112b 25c lilac rose & blk .75 .75

World Cricket Cup, won by West Indies Team, 1975.

Christmas Type of 1975

Belisario Prints, 1837: 10c, Queen of the "set-girls." 20c, Band of Jawbone John Canoe. 50c, Koo Koo, "actor-boy."

1976, Nov. 8 **Wmk. 352** *Perf. 13½*

416 A110 10c brick red & multi .20 .20
417 A110 20c bister & multi .40 .40
418 A110 50c tan & multi 1.00 1.00
a. Souv. sheet of 3, #416-418, perf. 14 2.50 2.50
Nos. 416-418 (3) 1.60 1.60

Christmas.

Map Type of 1976

Maps of Jamaica by: 9c, Edmund Hickeringill, 1661. 10c, John Ogilby, 1671. 25c, House of Visscher, 1680. 40c, John Thornton, 1689.

1977, Feb. 28 **Litho.** *Perf. 13*

419 A111 9c lt blue & multi .20 .20
420 A111 10c buff & multi .25 .25
421 A111 25c multicolored .60 .60
422 A111 40c multicolored 1.00 1.00
Nos. 419-422 (4) 2.05 2.05

Butterfly Type of 1975

10c, Eurema elathea. 20c, Dynamine egaea. 25c, Atlantea pantoni. 40c, Hypolimnas misippus.

1977, May 9 **Wmk. 352** *Perf. 13½*

423 A109 10c black & multi .60 .60
424 A109 20c black & multi 1.25 1.25
425 A109 25c black & multi 1.50 1.50
426 A109 40c black & multi 2.50 2.50
a. Souv. sheet of 4, #423-426, perf. 14½ 6.25 6.25
Nos. 423-426 (4) 5.85 5.85

Scout Emblem, Doctor Bird, Outline of Jamaica — A113

1977, Aug. 5 **Litho.** *Perf. 14*

427 A113 10c multicolored .20 .15
428 A113 20c multicolored .35 .30
429 A113 25c multicolored .55 .40
430 A113 50c multicolored 1.10 .85
Nos. 427-430 (4) 2.20 1.70

6th Caribbean Jamboree, Hope Gardens, Kingston, Aug. 3-17.

Trumpeter A114

Designs: 10c, 3 clarinetists. 20c, 2 kettle drummers, vert. 25c, Cellist and trumpeter, vert.

1977, Dec. 19 **Litho.** *Perf. 14*

431 A114 9c multicolored .25 .20
432 A114 10c multicolored .30 .25
433 A114 20c multicolored .65 .50
434 A114 25c multicolored .80 .65
a. Souvenir sheet of 4, #431-434 3.00 2.25
Nos. 431-434 (4) 2.00 1.60

Jamaica Military Band, 50th anniversary.

Butterfly Type of 1975

Butterflies: 10c, Callophrys crethona. 20c, Siproeta stelenes. 25c, Urbanus proteus. 50c, Anaea troglodyta.

1978, Apr. 17 **Litho.** *Perf. 14½*

435 A109 10c black & multi .40 .40
436 A109 20c black & multi .85 .85
437 A109 25c black & multi 1.10 1.10
438 A109 50c black & multi 2.00 2.00
a. Souvenir sheet of 4, #435-438 5.75 4.50
Nos. 435-438 (4) 4.35 4.35

Half Figure with Canopy — A115

Norman Manley Statue — A116

Arawak Artifacts, found 1792: 20c, Standing figure. 50c, Birdman.

1978, July 10 **Litho.** *Perf. 13½x13*

439 A115 10c multicolored .15 .15
440 A115 20c multicolored .35 .35
441 A115 50c multicolored .90 .90
a. Souv. sheet of 3, #439-441, perf. 14 1.75 1.75
Nos. 439-441 (3) 1.40 1.40

1978, Sept. 25 **Litho.** **Wmk. 352**

Designs: 20c, Alexander Bustamante statue. 25c, Kingston coat of arms. 40c, Gordon House Chamber, House of Representatives.

442 A116 10c multicolored .15 .15
443 A116 20c multicolored .25 .25
444 A116 25c multicolored .30 .30
445 A116 40c multicolored .45 .45
Nos. 442-445 (4) 1.15 1.15

24th Commonwealth Parliamentary Conf.

Salvation Army Band A117

Designs: 20c, Trumpeter. 25c, "S" and Cross entwined on pole of Army flag. 50c, William Booth and Salvation Army shield.

1978, Dec. 4 *Perf. 14*

446 A117 10c multicolored .15 .15
447 A117 20c multicolored .30 .30
448 A117 25c multicolored .35 .35
449 A117 50c multicolored .70 .70
Nos. 446-449 (4) 1.50 1.50

Christmas; Salvation Army centenary.

"Negro Aroused," by Edna Manley — A118

Arawak Grinding Stone, c. 400 B.C. — A119

1978, Dec. 11 *Perf. 13*

450 A118 10c multicolored .20 .20

International Anti-Apartheid Year.

No. 351 Overprinted: "TENTH / ANNIVERSARY / AIR JAMAICA / 1st APRIL 1979"

1979, Apr. 2 Litho. *Perf. 13½*

451 A99 10c multicolored .20 .20

1979, Apr. 23 *Perf. 14*

Arawak Artifacts (all A.D.): 10c, Stone implements, c. 500, horiz. 20c, Cooking pot, c. 300, horiz. 25c, Serving boat, c. 300, horiz. 50c, Storage jar fragment, c. 300.

452 A119 5c multicolored .15 .15
453 A119 10c multicolored .15 .15
454 A119 20c multicolored .20 .20
455 A119 25c multicolored .25 .25
456 A119 50c multicolored .50 .50
Nos. 452-456 (5) 1.25 1.25

Jamaica No. 183, Hill Statue A120

Hill Statue and Stamps of Jamaica: 20c, No. 83a. 25c, No. 5. 50c, No. 271.

1979, Aug. 13 Litho. *Perf. 14*

457 A120 10c multicolored .15 .15
458 A120 20c multicolored .15 .15
a. Souvenir sheet of 1 .35 .35
459 A120 25c multicolored .20 .20
460 A120 50c multicolored .45 .45
Nos. 457-460 (4) .95 .95

Sir Rowland Hill (1795-1879), originator of penny postage.

Children, IYC Emblem A121

International Year of the Child: 20c, Doll, vert. 25c, "The Family." 25c, "House on the Hill." 25c, 50c are children's drawings.

1979, Oct. 1

461 A121 10c multicolored .15 .15
462 A121 20c multicolored .15 .15
463 A121 25c multicolored .20 .20
464 A121 50c multicolored .45 .45
Nos. 461-464 (4) .95 .95

Tennis, Montego Bay — A122

Jamaican Tody — A123

Designs: 2c, Golfing, Tryall Hanover. 4c, Horseback riding, Negril Beach. 5c, Old Waterwheel, Tryall Hanover. 6c, Fern Gully, Ocho Rios. 7c, Dunn's River Falls, Ocho Rios.

10c, Doctorbird. 12c, Yellow-billed parrot. 15c, Hummingbird. 35c, White-chinned thrush. 50c, Jamaican woodpecker. 65c, Rafting Martha Brae Trelawny. 75c, Blue marlin fishing, Port Antonio. $1, Scuba diving. Ocho Rios. $2, Sail boats, Montego Bay.

Perf. 13½

1979-80 Litho. Wmk. 352

465 A122 1c multicolored .15 .15
466 A122 2c multicolored .15 .15
467 A122 4c multicolored .15 .15
468 A122 5c multicolored .15 .15
469 A122 6c multicolored .15 .15
470 A122 7c multicolored .15 .15
472 A123 8c multicolored .15 .15
473 A123 10c multicolored .15 .15
474 A123 12c multicolored .15 .15
475 A123 15c multicolored .15 .15
476 A123 35c multicolored .30 .30
477 A123 50c multicolored .40 .40
478 A122 65c multicolored .50 .50
479 A122 75c multicolored .60 .60
480 A122 $1 multicolored .75 .75
481 A122 $2 multicolored 1.65 1.65
Set value 5.00 5.00

Issued: #465-470, 11/26/79; #472-481, 5/80.
For surcharges see Nos. 581-582, 665-666.

Institute of Jamaica Centenary — A124

1980, Feb. 25 Litho. *Perf. 13½*

484 A124 5c shown .15 .15
485 A124 15c Institute building, 1980 .15 .15
486 A124 35c "The Ascension" on microfilm reader, vert. .40 .40
487 A124 50c Hawksbill and green turtles .50 .50
488 A124 75c Jamaican owl, vert. .80 .80
Nos. 484-488 (5) 2.00 2.00

Don Quarrie, 1976 Gold Medalist, 200-Meter Race, Moscow '80 Emblem A125

1952 4x400-meter Relay Team: a, Arthur Wint. b, Leslie Laing. c, Herbert McKenley. d, George Rhoden.

1980, July 21 Litho. *Perf. 13*

489 A125 15c shown .15 .15
490 Strip of 4 2.50 2.50
a.-d. A125 35c any single .60 .60

22nd Summer Olympic Games, Moscow, July 19-Aug. 3.

Parish Church, Kingston A126

1980, Nov. 24 Litho. *Perf. 14*

491 A126 15c shown .15 .15
492 A126 20c Coke Memorial .15 .15
493 A126 25c Church of the Redeemer .20 .20
494 A126 $5 Holy Trinity Cathedral 3.50 3.50
a. Souvenir sheet of 4, #491-494 4.25 4.25
Nos. 491-494 (4) 4.00 4.00

Christmas.

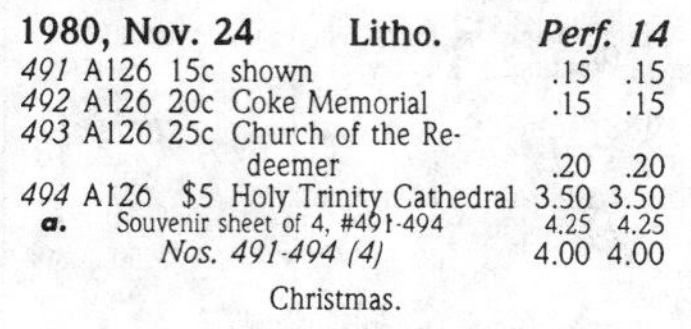

Tube Sponge A127

1981, Feb. 27 Wmk. 352 *Perf. 14*

495 A127 20c Blood cup sponge, vert. .20 .20
496 A127 45c shown .40 .40
497 A127 60c Black coral, vert. .50 .50
498 A127 75c Tire reef .65 .65
Nos. 495-498 (4) 1.75 1.75

See Nos. 523-527.

Indian Coney A128

Designs: b, Facing left. c, Eating. d, Family.

1981, May 25 Wmk. 352 *Perf. 14*

499 Strip of 4 1.25 1.25
a.-d. A128 20c any single .30 .30

Royal Wedding Issue
Common Design Type

1981, July 29 Litho. *Perf. 15*

500 CD331 20c White orchid .15 .15
501 CD331 45c Royal coach .30 .30
502 CD331 60c Couple .40 .40

Perf. 13½

503 CD331 $5 St. James' Palace 3.50 3.50
a. Souvenir sheet of 1 3.50 3.50
b. Booklet pane of 4, perf. 14x14½ 7.00
Nos. 500-503 (4) 4.35 4.35

Also issued in sheets of 5 + label, perf. 13½.

Intl. Year of the Disabled A129

1981, Sept. 14 Wmk. 352 *Perf. 13½*

504 A129 20c Blind weaver .20 .20
505 A129 45c Artist .40 .40
506 A129 60c Learning sign language .50 .50
507 A129 1.50 Basketball players 1.25 1.25
Nos. 504-507 (4) 2.35 2.35

World Food Day A130

Perf. 13x13½, 13½x13

1981, Oct. 16 Litho. Wmk. 352

508 A130 20c No. 218 .20 .20
509 A130 45c No. 76, vert. .40 .40
510 A130 $2 No. 121 1.75 1.75
511 A130 $4 No. 125 3.50 3.50
Nos. 508-511 (4) 5.85 5.85

Bob Marley (1945-1981), Reggae Musician — A131

Designs: Portraits of Bob Marley and song titles.

1981, Oct. 20 Wmk. 373 *Perf. 14½*

512 A131 1c multicolored .15 .15
513 A131 2c multicolored .15 .15
514 A131 3c multicolored .15 .15
515 A131 15c multicolored .35 .35
516 A131 20c multicolored .45 .45
517 A131 60c multicolored 1.25 1.25
518 A131 $3 multicolored 6.50 6.50
Nos. 512-518 (7) 9.00 9.00

Souvenir Sheet

519 A131 $5.25 multicolored 6.50 6.50

Christmas A132

1981, Dec. 11 Wmk. 352 *Perf. 14*

520 A132 10c Webb Memorial Baptist Church .15 .15
521 A132 45c Church of God .35 .35
522 A132 $5 Bryce United Church 3.75 3.75
a. Souvenir sheet of 3, #520-522, perf. 12½x12 4.25 4.25
Nos. 520-522 (3) 4.25 4.25

See Nos. 547-549.

Marine Life Type of 1981

1982, Feb. 22 Litho. *Perf. 14*

523 A127 20c Gorgonian coral, vert. .20 .20
524 A127 45c Hard sponge .40 .40
525 A127 60c Sea cow .50 .50
526 A127 75c Plume worm .65 .65
527 A127 $3 Coral-banded shrimp 2.75 2.75
Nos. 523-527 (5) 4.50 4.50

Scouting Year — A133

Princess Diana, 21st Birthday — A134

20c, 45c, 60c, Various scouts. $2, Baden-Powell.

1982, July 12 Litho. *Perf. 13½*

528 A133 20c multicolored .20 .20
529 A133 45c multicolored .40 .40
530 A133 60c multicolored .50 .50
531 A133 $2 multicolored 1.75 1.75
a. Souvenir sheet of 4, #528-531 3.00 3.00
Nos. 528-531 (4) 2.85 2.85

1982, Sept. 1 *Perf. 14½*

532 A134 20c Lignum vitae .15 .15
533 A134 45c Couple in coach .40 .40
534 A134 60c Wedding portrait .50 .50
a. Booklet pane of 3, #532-534 1.25
535 A134 75c Saxifraga longifolia .60 .60
536 A134 $2 Diana 1.75 1.75
537 A134 $3 Viola gracilis major 2.50 2.50
a. Booklet pane of 3, #535-537 5.50
Nos. 532-537 (6) 5.90 5.90

Souvenir Sheet

538 A134 $5 Honeymoon 4.00 4.00

Nos. 535, 537 in sheets of 5.

Nos. 532-538 Overprinted: "ROYAL BABY / 21.6.82"

1982, Sept. 13

539 A134 20c multicolored .15 .15
540 A134 45c multicolored .40 .40
541 A134 60c multicolored .50 .50
a. Booklet pane of 3, #539-541 1.25
542 A134 75c multicolored .60 .60
543 A134 $2 multicolored 1.75 1.75

544 A134 $3 multicolored 2.50 2.50
a. Booklet pane of 3, #542-544 5.50
Nos. 539-544 (6) 5.90 5.90

Souvenir Sheet

545 A134 $5 multicolored 5.00 5.00

Birth of Prince William of Wales, June 21.

Lizard Cuckoo Capturing Prey — A135

Designs: b, Searching for prey. c, Calling. d, Landing. e, Flying.

1982, Oct. 25
546 Strip of 5 4.50 4.50
a.-e. A135 $1 any single .90 .90

Christmas Type of 1981
Perf. 13x13½

1982, Dec. 8 Wmk. 352
547 A132 20c United Pentecostal Church .25 .25
548 A132 45c Disciples of Christ Church .45 .45
549 A132 75c Open Bible Church .75 .75
Nos. 547-549 (3) 1.45 1.45

Visit of Queen Elizabeth II — A136

1983, Feb. 14 Litho. *Perf. 14*
550 A136 $2 Queen Elizabeth II 1.90 1.90
551 A136 $3 Arms 2.75 2.75

A136a

1983, Mar. 14 Litho. Wmk. 352
552 A136a 20c Dancers .20 .20
553 A136a 45c Bauxite mining .35 .35
554 A136a 75c Map .60 .60
555 A136a $2 Arms, citizens 1.65 1.65
Nos. 552-555 (4) 2.80 2.80

Commonwealth Day.

25th Anniv. of Intl. Maritime Org. A137

1983, Mar. 17 Litho. *Perf. 14*
556 A137 15c Cargo ship .30 .30
557 A137 20c Cruise liner .40 .40
558 A137 45c Container vessel .80 .80
559 A137 $1 Intl. Seabed Headquarters 1.90 1.90
Nos. 556-559 (4) 3.40 3.40

21st Anniv. of Independence A138

Prime Ministers Alexander Bustamante and Norman Washington Manley.

1983, July 25 Litho. *Perf. 14*
560 A138 15c blue & multi .15 .15
561 A138 20c lt green & multi .20 .20
562 A138 45c yellow & multi .45 .45
Nos. 560-562 (3) .80 .80

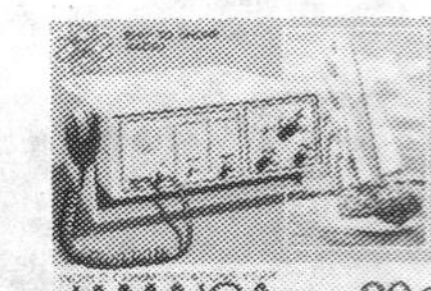

World Communications Year — A139

1983, Oct. 18 Wmk. 352 *Perf. 14*
563 A139 20c Ship-to-shore radio .20 .20
564 A139 45c Postal services .40 .40
565 A139 75c Telephone communication .70 .70
566 A139 $1 TV satellite .95 .95
Nos. 563-566 (4) 2.25 2.25

Christmas 1983 A140

Paintings: 15c, Racing at Caymanas, by Sidney McLaren. 20c, Seated Figures, by Karl Parboosingh. 75c, The Petitioner, by Henry Daley, vert. $2, Banana Plantation, by John Dunkley, vert.

1983, Dec. 12 Litho. *Perf. 13½*
567 A140 15c multicolored .15 .15
568 A140 20c multicolored .15 .15
569 A140 75c multicolored .35 .35
570 A140 $2 multicolored .85 .85
Nos. 567-570 (4) 1.50 1.50

Alexander Bustamante (1884-1977), First Prime Minister
A141 A141a

1984, Feb. 24 Litho. *Perf. 14*
571 A141 20c Portrait .15 .15
572 A141 20c Blenheim (birthplace) .15 .15
a. Pair, #571-572 .30 .30

Sea Planes A142

1984, June 11 Litho. *Perf. 14*
573 A142 25c Gypsy Moth .30 .30
574 A142 55c Consolidated Commodore .70 .70
575 A142 $1.50 Sikorsky S-38 1.65 1.65
576 A142 $3 Sikorsky S-40 3.25 3.25
Nos. 573-576 (4) 5.90 5.90

1984 Summer Olympics A143

1984, July 11
577 A143 25c Bicycling .15 .15
578 A143 55c Relay race .25 .25
579 A143 $1.50 Running .85 .85
580 A143 $3 Women's running 1.75 1.75
a. Souvenir sheet of 4, #577-580 3.25 3.25
Nos. 577-580 (4) 3.00 3.00

Nos. 469, 474 Surcharged

1984, Aug. 7 Litho. *Perf. 13½*
581 A122 5c on 6c #469 .15 .15
582 A123 10c on 12c #474 .15 .15
Set value .15 .15

Early Steam Engines A144

1984, Nov. 16 Litho. *Perf. 13½*
583 A144 25c Enterprise, 1845 .25 .25
584 A144 55c Tank Locomotive, 1880 .50 .50
585 A144 $1.50 Kitson-Meyer Tank, 1904 1.25 1.25
586 A144 $3 Superheater, 1916 2.50 2.50
Nos. 583-586 (4) 4.50 4.50

See Nos. 608-611.

Christmas — A145

Local sculptures: 20c, Accompong Madonna, by Namba Roy. 25c, Head, by Alvin Marriott. 55c, Moon, by Edna Manley. $1.50, All Women are Five Women, by Mallica Reynolds.

1984, Dec. 6 Wmk. 352 *Perf. 14*
587 A145 20c multicolored .15 .15
588 A145 25c multicolored .20 .20
589 A145 55c multicolored .40 .40
590 A145 $1.50 multicolored 1.10 1.10
Nos. 587-590 (4) 1.85 1.85

Jamaican Boas A146

1984, Oct. 22 Litho. *Perf. 14½*
591 A146 25c Head of boa *1.10 1.10*
592 A146 55c Boa over water *2.75 2.75*
593 A146 70c Boa with young *3.50 3.50*
594 A146 $1 Boa on branch *5.50 5.50*
a. Souvenir sheet of 4, #591-594 *6.50 6.50*
Nos. 591-594 (4) *12.85 12.85*

Stamps in #594a do not have WWF emblem.

Brown Pelicans — A147

1985, Apr. 15 Wmk. 352 *Perf. 13*
595 A147 20c multicolored .15 .15
596 A147 55c multicolored .35 .35
597 A147 $2 multicolored 1.00 1.00
598 A147 $5 multicolored 2.50 2.50
a. Souvenir sheet of 4, #595-598 4.00 4.00
Nos. 595-598 (4) 4.00 4.00

Birth bicentenary of artist and naturalist John J. Audubon (1785-1851).

Queen Mother 85th Birthday
Common Design Type

1985, June 7 Litho. *Perf. 14½x14*
599 CD336 25c Holding photograph album, 1963 .15 .15
600 CD336 55c With Prince Charles, Windsor Castle, 1983 .25 .25
601 CD336 $1.50 At Belfast University .60 .60
602 CD336 $3 Holding Prince Henry 1.10 1.10
Nos. 599-602 (4) 2.10 2.10

Souvenir Sheet

603 CD336 $5 With limousine 1.90 1.90

Maps of Americas and Jamaica, IYY and Jamboree Emblems A148

1985, July 30 Litho. *Perf. 14*
604 A148 25c multicolored .15 .15
605 A148 55c multicolored .30 .30
606 A148 70c multicolored .35 .35
607 A148 $4 multicolored 1.90 1.90
Nos. 604-607 (4) 2.70 2.70

Intl. Youth Year and 5th Pan-American Scouting Jamboree.

Locomotives Type of 1984

1985, Sept. 30 Size: 39x25mm
608 A144 25c Baldwin .15 .15
609 A144 55c Rogers .35 .35
610 A144 $1.50 Projector .90 .90
611 A144 $4 Diesel 2.25 2.25
Nos. 608-611 (4) 3.65 3.65

The Old Settlement, by Ralph Campbell A149

Christmas (Paintings by local artists): 55c, The Vendor, by Albert Hiue, vert. 75c, Road Menders, by Gaston Tabois. $4, Woman, Must I Not Be About My Father's Business? by Carl Abrahams, vert.

1985, Dec. 9
612 A149 20c multicolored .15 .15
613 A149 55c multicolored .20 .20
614 A149 75c multicolored .25 .25
615 A149 $4 multicolored 1.40 1.40
Nos. 612-615 (4) 2.00 2.00

Birds — A150

A151

1986, Feb. 10 Litho. *Perf. 14*
616 A150 25c Chestnut-bellied cuckoo .15 .15
617 A150 55c Jamaican becard .25 .25
618 A150 $1.50 White-eyed thrush .75 .75
619 A150 $5 Rufous-tailed flycatcher 2.50 2.50
Nos. 616-619 (4) 3.65 3.65

Queen Elizabeth II 60th Birthday
Common Design Type

Designs: 20c, With Princess Margaret, 1939. 25c, Leaving Liverpool Street Station for Sandringham with Princes Charles and Andrew, 1962. 70c, Visiting the Montego Bay war memorial, Jamaica, 1983. $3, State visit to Luxembourg, 1976. $5, Visiting Crown Agents' offices, 1983.

1986, Apr. 21 *Perf. 14½*
620 CD337 20c scar, blk & sil .15 .15
621 CD337 25c ultra & multi .15 .15
622 CD337 70c green & multi .20 .20
623 CD337 $3 violet & multi .90 .90
624 CD337 $5 rose vio & multi 1.50 1.50
Nos. 620-624 (5) 2.90 2.90

1986, May 19

AMERIPEX '86: 25c, Bustamante Childrens Hospital. 55c, Vacation cities. $3, Norman Manley Law School. $5, Exports.

625 A151 25c multicolored .15 .15
626 A151 55c multicolored .30 .30
627 A151 $3 multicolored 1.40 1.40
628 A151 $5 multicolored 2.50 2.50
a. Souvenir sheet of 4, #625-628 4.50 4.50
Nos. 625-628 (4) 4.35 4.35

Royal Wedding Issue, 1986
Common Design Type

Designs: 30c, At the races. $4, Andrew addressing the press.

Perf. 14½x14

1986, July 23 **Wmk. 352**

629 CD338 20c multicolored .15 .15
630 CD338 $5 multicolored 1.90 1.90

Boxing Champions — A152

Champions: 45c, Richard "Shrimpy" Clarke, 1986 Commonwealth flyweight. 70c, Michael McCallum, 1984 WBA junior middleweight. $2, Trevor Berbick, 1986 WBC heavyweight. $4, Clarke, McCallum and Berbick.

1986, Oct. 27 **Litho.** ***Perf. 14***

631 A152 45c multicolored .20 .20
632 A152 70c multicolored .30 .30
633 A152 $2 multicolored .75 .75
634 A152 $4 multicolored 1.50 1.50
Nos. 631-634 (4) 2.75 2.75

Flowers A153

1986, Dec. 1 ***Perf. 14***

635 A153 20c Heliconia wagneriana, vert. .15 .15
636 A153 25c Heliconia psittacorum .15 .15
637 A153 55c Heliconia rostrata, vert. .30 .30
638 A153 $5 Strelitzia reginae 2.50 2.50
Nos. 635-638 (4) 3.10 3.10

Christmas. See Nos. 675-678, 706-709.

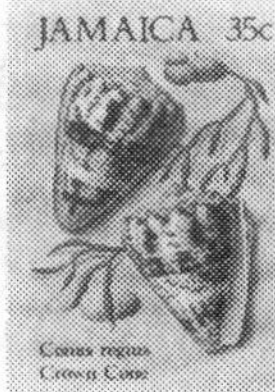

Shells — A154

1987, Feb. 23 **Litho.** ***Perf. 15***

639 A154 35c Crown cone .15 .15
640 A154 75c Measled cowrie .30 .30
641 A154 $1 Trumpet triton .45 .45
642 A154 $5 Rooster-tail conch 2.25 2.25
Nos. 639-642 (4) 3.15 3.15

Prime Ministers A155

Natl. Coat of Arms A156

Designs: 1c-9c, Norman Washington Manley. 10c-90c, Sir Alexander Bustamante.

1987-91 ***Perf. 12½x13***

643 A155 1c dull red .15 .15
644 A155 2c rose pink .15 .15
645 A155 3c light olive .15 .15
646 A155 4c dull green .15 .15
647 A155 5c slate blue .15 .15
648 A155 6c ultramarine .15 .15
649 A155 7c dull magenta .15 .15
650 A155 8c red lilac .15 .15
651 A155 9c brown olive .15 .15
652 A155 10c deep rose .15 .15
653 A155 20c bright orange .15 .15
654 A155 30c emerald .15 .15
655 A155 40c lt blue green .15 .15
656 A155 50c gray olive .18 .18
657 A155 60c light ultra .22 .22
658 A155 70c pale violet .26 .26
659 A155 80c violet .30 .30
660 A155 90c light brown .32 .32
661 A156 $1 dull brn & buff .35 .35
662 A156 $2 orange .75 .75
663 A156 $5 gray olive & greenish buff 1.75 1.75
664 A156 $10 royal blue & pale blue 3.50 3.50

Perf. 13x13½

664A A156 $25 vio & pale vio 4.75 4.75
664B A156 $50 lilac & pale lilac 9.50 9.50
Nos. 643-664B (24) 23.83 23.83

Issued: $25, $50, 10/9/91; others, 5/18/87.

Nos. 647, 653 reissued inscribed "1988," Nos. 655-656 "1991." Nos. 653, 655-656, 660-661 "1992." Nos. 652-653, 656, 660-661 "1993." Nos. 652-656 "1994." Nos. 661-663 "1997."

Nos. 477-478 Surcharged

1986, Nov. 3 ***Perf. 13½***

665 A123 5c on 50c multicolored .15 .15
666 A122 10c on 65c multicolored .15 .15
Set value .15

A157

A158

Wmk. 352

1987, July 27 **Litho.** ***Perf. 14***

667 A157 55c Flag, sunset .20 .20
668 A157 70c Flag, horiz. .25 .25

Natl. Independence, 25th anniv.

1987, Aug. 17

669 A158 25c Portrait .20 .15
670 A158 25c Statue .20 .15
a. Pair, #669-670 .40 .20

Marcus Mosiah Garvey (1887-1940), natl. hero. No. 670a has a continuous design.

Salvation Army in Jamaica, Cent. — A159

Designs: 25c, School for the Blind. 55c, Col. Mary Booth, Bramwell-Booth Memorial Hall. $3, "War Chariot," 1929. $5, Arrival of col. Abram Davey on the S.S. Alene, 1887.

1987, Oct. 8 ***Perf. 13***

671 A159 25c multicolored .15 .15
672 A159 55c multicolored .30 .30
673 A159 $3 multicolored 1.90 1.90
674 A159 $5 multicolored 3.00 3.00
a. Souvenir sheet of 4, #671-674 5.50 5.50
Nos. 671-674 (4) 5.35 5.35

Flower Type of 1986

1987, Nov. 30 **Litho.** ***Perf. 14½***

675 A153 20c Hibiscus hybrid .15 .15
676 A153 25c Hibiscus elatus .15 .15
677 A153 $4 Hibiscus cannabinus 1.50 1.50
678 A153 $5 Hibiscus rosa sinensis 1.90 1.90
Nos. 675-678 (4) 3.70 3.70

Christmas. Nos. 675-678 vert.

Birds — A160

Designs: No. 679, Chestnut-bellied cuckoo, black-billed parrot, Jamaican euphonia. No. 680, Jamaican white-eyed vireo, rufous-throated solitaire, yellow-crowned elaenia. No. 681, Snowy plover, little blue heron, great white heron. No. 682, Common stilt, snowy egret, black-crowned night heron.

1988, Jan. 22 **Litho.** ***Perf. 14***

679 A160 45c multicolored .35 .35
680 A160 45c multicolored .35 .35
a. Pair, #679-680 .70 .70
681 A160 $5 multicolored 3.25 3.25
682 A160 $5 multicolored 3.25 3.25
a. Pair, #681-682 6.50 6.50
Nos. 679-682 (4) 7.20 7.20

Nos. 680a, 682a have continuous designs.

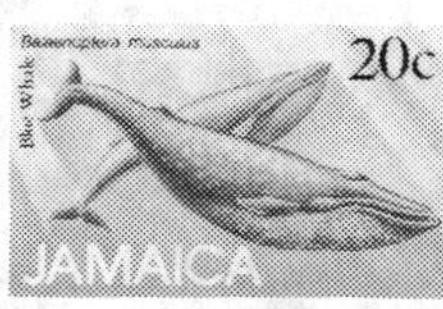

Marine Mammals A161

1988, Apr. 14 **Litho.** ***Perf. 14***

683 A161 20c Blue whales .15 .15
684 A161 25c Gervais's whales .25 .25
685 A161 55c Killer whales .50 .50
686 A161 $5 Common dolphins 5.25 5.25
Nos. 683-686 (4) 6.15 6.15

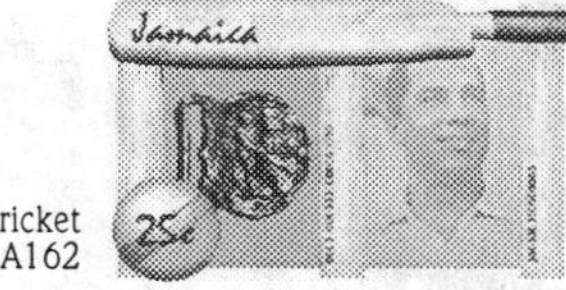

Cricket A162

Bat, wicket posts, ball, 18th cent. belt buckle and batsmen: 25c, Jackie Hendriks. 55c, George Headley. $2, Michael Holding. $3, R.K. Nunes. $4, Allan Rae.

1988, June 6 **Litho.** ***Perf. 14***

687 A162 25c multicolored .15 .15
688 A162 55c multicolored .35 .35
689 A162 $2 multicolored 1.25 1.25
690 A162 $3 multicolored 2.00 2.00
691 A162 $4 multicolored 2.75 2.75
Nos. 687-691 (5) 6.50 6.50

Intl. Red Cross and Red Crescent Organizations, 125th Annivs. — A163

Anniversary emblem, Jamaica Red Cross emblem and: 55c, Ambulances. $5, Jean-Henri Dunant, 1828-1910, treating the wounded after the Battle of Solferino, 1859.

1988, Aug. 8 **Litho.** ***Perf. 14½***

692 A163 55c multicolored .20 .20
693 A163 $5 multicolored 1.90 1.90

1988 Summer Olympics, Seoul A164

1988, Aug. 24 **Wmk. 352** ***Perf. 14***

694 A164 25c Boxing .15 .15
695 A164 45c Cycling .20 .20
696 A164 $4 Women's running 1.50 1.50
697 A164 $5 Hurdling 1.90 1.90
a. Souvenir sheet of 4, #694-697 3.75 3.75
Nos. 694-697 (4) 3.75 3.75

No. 697a sold for $9.90. For surcharges see Nos. B4-B7.

Natl. Olympic Bobsled Team A165

1988, Nov. 4 **Litho.** ***Perf. 14***

698 A165 25c Team members .15 .15
699 A165 25c Two-man bobsled .15 .15
a. Pair, #698-699 .20 .20
700 A165 $5 Team members, diff. 1.50 1.50
701 A165 $5 Four-man bobsled 1.50 1.50
a. Pair, #700-701 3.00 3.00
Nos. 698-701 (4) 3.30 3.30

Nos. 699a, 701a have continuous designs.

Labor Year — A166

Perf. 14½x14

1988, Nov. 24 **Wmk. 352**

702 A166 25c Medicine, fire fighting .15 .15
703 A166 55c Handicrafts .20 .20
704 A166 $3 Garment industry 1.10 1.10
705 A166 $5 Fishing 1.90 1.90
Nos. 702-705 (4) 3.35 3.35

Flower Type of 1986

1988, Dec. 15

706 A153 25c Euphorbia pulcherrima, vert. .15 .15
707 A153 55c Spathodea campanulata .20 .20
708 A153 $3 Hylocereus triangularis, vert. 1.10 1.10
709 A153 $4 Broughtonia sanguinea 1.50 1.50
Nos. 706-709 (4) 2.95 2.95

Christmas.

Methodist Church in Jamaica, Bicent. A167

Designs: 25c, Old York Castle School. 45c, Parade Chapel, Kingston, and Rev. Thomas Coke. $5, Fr. Hugh Sherlock and St. John's Church.

1989, Jan. 19 ***Perf. 13½***

710 A167 25c multicolored .15 .15
711 A167 45c multicolored .15 .15
712 A167 $5 multicolored 1.65 1.65
Nos. 710-712 (3) 1.95 1.95

Indigenous Moths — A168

Wmk. 352

1989, Aug. 30 **Litho.** ***Perf. 14***

713 A168 25c *Syntomidopsis variegata* .15 .15
714 A168 55c *Himantoides undataperkinsi* .30 .30
715 A168 $3 *Hypercompe nigriplaga* 1.75 1.75
716 A168 $5 *Sthenognatha toddi* 2.75 2.75
Nos. 713-716 (4) 4.95 4.95

See Nos. 725-728, 752-755. For surcharges and overprints see Nos. 729-732, 756-759.

A169

A171

Discovery of America, 500th Anniv. (in 1992): 25c, Arawak spear fisherman. 70c, Smoking tobacco. $5, Ferdinand and Isabella inspecting caravels. $10, Columbus studying chart.

1989, Dec. 22 *Perf. 13½*
717 A169 25c multicolored .15 .15
718 A169 70c multicolored .25 .25
719 A169 $5 multicolored 1.90 1.90
720 A169 $10 multicolored 3.75 3.75
a. Souvenir sheet of 4, #717-720, perf. 12½ 6.00 6.00
Nos. 717-720 (4) 6.05 6.05

No. 720a exists imperf.

Wmk. 352

1990, June 28 Litho. *Perf. 14*
721 A171 45c multicolored .20 .20
722 A171 55c multi, diff. .20 .20
723 A171 $5 multi, diff. 3.00 3.00
Nos. 721-723 (3) 3.40 3.40

Girl Guides of Jamaica, 75th anniv.

Indigenous Moths Type of 1989

Wmk. 352

1990, Sept. 12 Litho. *Perf. 14*
725 A168 25c Eunomia rubripunctata .15 .15
726 A168 55c Perigonia jamaicensis .15 .15
727 A168 $4 Uraga haemorrhoa 1.65 1.65
728 A168 $5 Empyreuma pugione 2.50 2.50
Nos. 725-728 (4) 4.45 4.45

Nos. 725-728 Ovptd. in Black 

1990, Sept. 12
729 A168 25c No. 725 .15 .15
730 A168 55c No. 726 .15 .15
731 A168 $4 No. 727 1.50 1.50
732 A168 $5 No. 728 2.00 2.00
Nos. 729-732 (4) 3.80 3.80

Expo '90, International Garden and Greenery Exposition, Osaka, Japan.

Intl. Literacy Year A172

Wmk. 352

1990, Oct. 10 Litho. *Perf. 14*
733 A172 55c shown .15 .15
734 A172 $5 Mathematics class 2.00 2.00

Christmas — A173

Children's art.

Perf. 13½x14

1990, Dec. 7 Litho. Wmk. 352
735 A173 20c To the market .15 .15
736 A173 25c Untitled (houses) .15 .15
737 A173 55c Jack and Jill .15 .15
738 A173 70c Untitled (market) .20 .20
739 A173 $1.50 Lonely (beach) .45 .45
740 A173 $5 Market woman, vert. 1.40 1.40
Nos. 735-740 (6) 2.50 2.50

See Nos. 760-763.

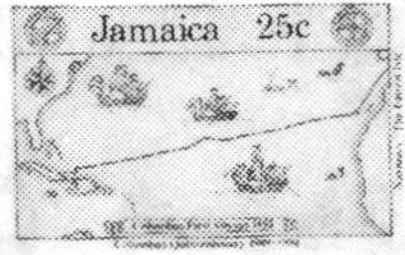

Discovery of America, 500th Anniv. (in 1992) — A174

Maps of Columbus' voyages.

1990, Dec. 19 *Perf. 14*
741 A174 25c First, 1492 .15 .15
742 A174 45c Second, 1493 .15 .15
743 A174 $5 Third, 1498 1.50 1.50
744 A174 $10 Fourth, 1502 3.00 3.00
Nos. 741-744 (4) 4.80 4.80

Souvenir Sheet

745 Sheet of 4 9.00 9.00
a. A174 25c Cuba, Jamaica .15 .15
b. A174 45c Hispaniola, Puerto Rico .15 .15
c. A174 $5 Central America 2.75 2.75
d. A174 $10 Venezuela 5.75 5.75

See Nos. 764-767.

Natl. Meteorological Service — A175

1991, May 20 Litho. Wmk. 352
746 A175 50c multicolored .15 .15
747 A175 $10 multicolored 1.90 1.90

11th World Meteorological Congress.

Intl. Council of Nurses Council of Natl. Representatives, Jamaica — A176

Perf. 13½

1991, June 24 Litho. Wmk. 352
748 A176 50c Mary Seacole .15 .15
749 A176 $1.10 Mary Seacole House .25 .25

Souvenir Sheet

750 A176 $8 Hospital at Scutari 2.00 2.00

Cyclura Collei (Jamaican Iguana) — A177

Designs: a, Head pointed to UR. b, Facing right. c, Climbing rock. d, Facing left. e, Head pointed to UL.

Wmk. 352

1991, July 29 Litho. *Perf. 13*
751 A177 $1.10 Strip of 5, #a.-e. 2.25 2.25

Natural History Soc. of Jamaica, 50th anniv.

Moths Type of 1989

1991, Aug. 12 *Perf. 14*
752 A168 50c Urania sloanus .15 .15
753 A168 $1.10 Phoenicoprocta jamaicensis .30 .30
754 A168 $1.40 Horama grotei .40 .40
755 A168 $8 Amplypterus gannascus 2.50 2.50
Nos. 752-755 (4) 3.35 3.35

Nos. 752-755 Overprinted 

1991, Sept. 23
756 A168 50c on No. 752 .15 .15
757 A168 $1.10 on No. 753 .30 .30
758 A168 $1.40 on No. 754 .40 .40
759 A168 $8 on No. 755 2.50 2.50
Nos. 756-759 (4) 3.35 3.35

Children's Christmas Art Type

Children's drawings.

1991, Nov. 27 *Perf. 14x15*
760 A173 50c Doctor bird .15 .15
761 A173 $1.10 Road scene .20 .20
762 A173 $5 House, people .90 .90
763 A173 $10 Cows grazing 1.75 1.75
Nos. 760-763 (4) 3.00 3.00

Christmas.

Discovery of America Type of 1990

Designs: 50c, Explorers did not land at Santa Gloria because of hostile Indians. $1.10, Fierce dog used to subdue the Indians. $1.40, Indians brought gifts of fruit. $25, Columbus describes Jamaica with crumpled paper.

1991, Dec. 16 *Perf. 13½x14*
764 A174 50c multicolored .15 .15
765 A174 $1.10 multicolored .15 .15
766 A174 $1.40 multicolored .15 .15
767 A174 $25 multicolored 2.50 2.50
a. Souvenir sheet of 4, #764-767 3.00 3.00
Nos. 764-767 (4) 2.95 2.95

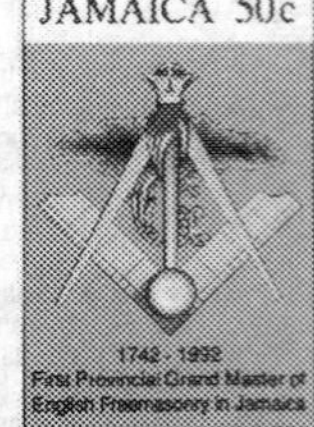

First Provincial Grand Master of English Freemasonry in Jamaica, 250th Anniv. — A178

Masonic symbols: 50c, Square and compass. $1.10, Stained glass window. $1.40, Square and compass on Bible. $25, Seeing eye.

1992, May 1 *Perf. 13½*
768 A178 50c multicolored .15 .15
769 A178 $1.10 multicolored .15 .15
770 A178 $1.40 multicolored .15 .15
771 A178 $25 multicolored 3.50 3.50
a. Souvenir sheet of 4, #768-771 3.75 3.75
Nos. 768-771 (4) 3.95 3.95

Destruction of Port Royal by Earthquake, 300th Anniv. A179

Scenes of destruction: 50c, Ship in harbor. $1.10, Homes, church. $1.40, Homes toppling. $5, Port Royal from contemporary broadsheet. $25, Fissure in street.

1992, June 7 *Perf. 14x13½*
772 A179 50c multicolored .15 .15
773 A179 $1.10 multicolored .15 .15
774 A179 $1.40 multicolored .15 .15
775 A179 $25 multicolored 2.50 2.50
Nos. 772-775 (4) 2.95 2.95

Souvenir Sheet

Perf. 13x12

776 A179 $5 multicolored .50 .50

No. 776 inscribed on reverse.

Independence, 30th Anniv. — A180

1992, Aug. 6 *Perf. 13½*
777 A180 50c black & multi .15 .15
778 A180 $1.10 green & multi .15 .15
779 A180 $25 yellow & multi 2.25 2.25
Nos. 777-779 (3) 2.55 2.55

Credit Union Movement in Jamaica, 50th Anniv. — A181

1992, Aug. 24 *Perf. 14x15*
780 A181 50c Emblem .15 .15
781 A181 $1.40 Emblem, O'Hare Hall .15 .15
Set value .20 .20

Pottery — A182

Designs: 50c, "Rainbow" vase, by Cecil Baugh O.D. $1.10, "Yabba Pot," by Louisa Jones (MaLou) O.D. $1.40, "Sculptured Vase," by Gene Pearson. $25, "Lidded Form," by Norma Rodney Harrack.

1993, Apr. 26 *Perf. 13½*
782 A182 50c multicolored .15 .15
783 A182 $1.10 multicolored .15 .15
784 A182 $1.40 multicolored .15 .15
785 A182 $25 multicolored 2.25 2.25
Nos. 782-785 (4) 2.70 2.70

Girls' Brigade, Cent. A183

1993, Aug. 9 *Perf. 14x13½*
786 A183 50c Parade .15 .15
787 A183 $1.10 Brigade members .15 .15
Set value .20 .20

Jamaica Combined Cadet Force, 50th Anniv. A184

Designs: 50c, Tank, cadet, vert. $1.10, Airplane, female cadet. $1.40, Ships, female cadet, vert. $3, Cap badge, cadet.

1993, Nov. 8 *Perf. 14*
788 A184 50c multicolored .15 .15
789 A184 $1.10 multicolored .15 .15
790 A184 $1.40 multicolored .15 .15
791 A184 $3 multicolored .30 .30
Set value .55 .55

Golf Courses A185

50c, $1.10, Constant Spring. $1.40, $2, Half Moon. $3, $10, Jamaica Jamaica. $25, Tryall, vert.

1993-94 Litho. Wmk. 352 *Perf. 14*
792 A185 50c yellow & multi .15 .15
793 A185 $1.10 blue & multi .15 .15
794 A185 $1.40 brn org & multi .15 .15
795 A185 $2 lilac & multi .20 .20
796 A185 $3 dark blue & multi .30 .30
797 A185 $10 tan & multi 1.00 1.00
Set value 1.20 1.20

Souvenir Sheets

798 A185 $25 green & multi 2.25 2.25
799 A185 $25 #798 inscribed with Hong Kong '94 emblem 2.50 2.50

Issue dates: Nos. 792-797, Dec. 21, 1993. No. 798, Dec. 16, 1993. No. 799, Feb. 18, 1994.

A186 A187

1994, Jan. 12 *Perf. 14x15*
800 A186 $25 Portrait 1.65 1.65
801 A186 $50 Portrait, diff. 3.50 3.50
a. Pair, #800-801 5.25 5.25

Norman Washington Manley, birth cent.

1994, Mar. 1 *Perf. 14*

Royal Visit: $1.10, Jamaican, United Kingdom flags. $1.40, Royal yacht Britannia. $25, Queen Elizabeth II. $50, Prince Philip, Queen.

802 A187 $1.10 multicolored .15 .15
803 A187 $1.40 multicolored .15 .15
804 A187 $25 multicolored 1.65 1.65
805 A187 $50 multicolored 3.50 3.50
Nos. 802-805 (4) 5.45 5.45

Air Jamaica, 25th Anniv. — A188

Wmk. 352

1994, Apr. 26 Litho. *Perf. 14*

806 A188 50c Douglas DC9 .15 .15
807 A188 $1.10 Douglas DC8 .15 .15
808 A188 $5 Boeing 727 .30 .30
809 A188 $50 Airbus A300 3.00 3.00
Nos. 806-809 (4) 3.60 3.60

Giant Swallowtail — A189

Various views of the butterfly.

Perf. 14x13½

1994, Aug. 18 Litho. Wmk. 352

810 A189 50c multicolored .15 .15
811 A189 $1.10 multicolored .15 .15
812 A189 $10 multicolored .60 .60
813 A189 $25 multicolored 1.60 1.60
Nos. 810-813 (4) 2.50 2.50

Souvenir Sheet

814 189 $50 multicolored 3.25 3.25

A190

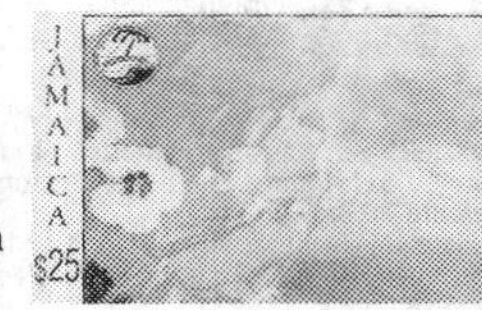

Tourism A191

Designs: 50c, Royal Botanical Gardens, by Sidney McClaren. $1.10, Blue Mountains, coffee beans, leaves. $5, Woman in hammock, waterfalls.

Tourist poster: No. 818a, Flowers, birds (c). b, Diver (d). c, Vegetation, coastline (a, d). d, Guide, tourists on raft.

Wmk. 352

1994, Sept. 7 Litho. *Perf. 14*

815 A190 50c multicolored .15 .15
816 A190 $1.10 multicolored .15 .15
817 A190 $5 multicolored .30 .30
Set value .40 .40

Souvenir Sheet

818 A191 $25 Sheet of 4, #a.-d. 6.00 6.00

Caribbean Tourism Conf. (#818).

Red Poll Cattle — A192

1994, Nov. 16 *Perf. 14x13½*

819 A192 50c Calf .15 .15
820 A192 $1.10 Heifer .15 .15
821 A192 $25 Cow 1.50 1.50
822 A192 $50 Bull 3.00 3.00
Nos. 819-822 (4) 4.80 4.80

Christmas — A193

Paintings by Children: 50c, Clean-up crew. 90c, Hospital Room. $1.10, House. $50, Meadow.

1994, Dec. 1 *Perf. 14x14½*

823 A193 50c multicolored .15 .15
824 A193 90c multicolored .15 .15
825 A193 $1.10 multicolored .15 .15
826 A193 $50 multicolored 3.25 3.25
Nos. 823-826 (4) 3.70 3.70

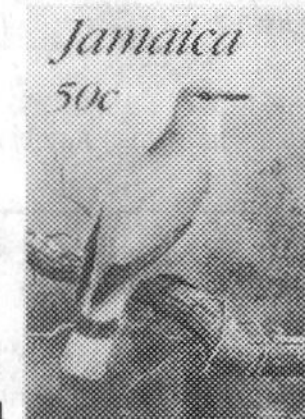

Birds — A194

Wmk. 384

1995, Apr. 24 Litho. *Perf. 14*

827 A194 50c Ring-tailed pigeon .15 .15
828 A194 90c Yellow-billed parrot .15 .15
829 A194 $1.10 Black-billed parrot .15 .15
830 A194 $50 Brown owl 3.25 3.25
Nos. 827-830 (4) 3.70 3.70

Souvenir Sheet

831 A194 $50 Streamertail 3.25 3.25
a. Ovptd. in sheet margin 3.25 3.25

No. 831 is a continuous design.

No. 831a ovptd. with Singapore '95 emblem. Issued: 9/1/95.

Caribbean Development Bank, 25th Anniv. — A195

Anniversary emblem and: 50c, $1, Jamaican flag, graph, vert. $1.10, Industries, agriculture. $50, Bank notes, coins.

Perf. 13½

1995, May 11 Litho. Wmk. 352

832 A195 50c green & multi .15 .15
833 A195 $1 black & multi .15 .15
834 A195 $1.10 multicolored .15 .15
835 A195 $50 multicolored 3.25 3.25
Nos. 832-835 (4) 3.70 3.70

Bob Marley (1945-81), Reggae Musician — A196

Marley performing songs: 50c, Songs of Freedom, by Adrian Boot. $1.10, Fire, by Neville Garrick. $1.40, Time Will Tell, by Peter Murphy. $3, Natural Mystic, by Boot. $10, Live at Lyceum, by Boot.

$100, Legend, by Boot.

Wmk. 352

1995, July 31 Litho. *Perf. 14*

836 A196 50c multicolored .15 .15
837 A196 $1.10 multicolored .15 .15
838 A196 $1.40 multicolored .15 .15
839 A196 $3 multicolored .20 .20
840 A196 $10 multicolored .60 .60
Set value 1.00 1.00

Souvenir Sheet

841 A196 $100 multicolored 6.00 6.00

Souvenir Sheet

Queen Mother, 95th Birthday — A197

Illustration reduced.

1995, Aug. 4 *Perf. 14x13½*

842 A197 $75 multicolored 4.50 4.50

Order of the Caribbean Community — A198

Designs: 50c, Michael Manley, former prime minister, Jamaica. $1.10, Sir Alister McIntyre, Vice Chancellor, UWI, Jamaica. $1.40, P. Telford Georges, former Chief Justice, Bahamas. $50, Dame Nita Barrow, Governor General, Barbados.

1995, Aug. 23 *Perf. 14x14½*

843 A198 50c multicolored .15 .15
844 A198 $1.10 multicolored .15 .15
845 A198 $1.40 multicolored .15 .15
846 A198 $50 multicolored 3.00 3.00
Nos. 843-846 (4) 3.45 3.45

UN, 50th Anniv.

Common Design Type

Designs: 50c, Signals Land Rover. $1.10, Antonov AN-32. $3, Bedford Articulated Tanker. $5, Fairchild DC-119 Flying Boxcar. $50, Observation vehicles.

Wn.k. 352

1995, Oct. 24 Litho. *Perf. 14*

847 CD353 50c multicolored .15 .15
848 CD353 $1.10 multicolored .15 .15
849 CD353 $3 multicolored .20 .20
850 CD353 $5 multicolored .30 .30
Nos. 847-850 (4) .80 .80

Souvenir Sheet

851 CD353 $50 multicolored 3.00 3.00

No. 851 has continuous design.

Arrival of East Indians in Jamaica, 150th Anniv. A199

Wmk. 352

1996, May 22 Litho. *Perf. 14*

852 A199 $2.50 Coming ashore .15 .15
853 A199 $10 Musicians, dancers .60 .60

UNICEF, 50th Anniv. — A200

1996, Sept. 2 *Perf. 14½x14*

854 A200 $2.50 multicolored .15 .15
855 A200 $8 multicolored .45 .45
856 A200 $10 multicolored .60 .60
Nos. 854-856 (3) 1.20 1.20

Jamaican Hutia (Indian Coney) A201

Designs: $2.50, Two in den. $10, One on ledge. $12.50, Mother, young. $25, One up close.

1996, Sept. 23 *Perf. 13½x14*

857 A201 $2.50 multicolored .15 .15
858 A201 $10 multicolored .60 .60
859 A201 $12.50 multicolored .70 .70
860 A201 $25 multicolored 1.40 1.40
Nos. 857-860 (4) 2.85 2.85

World Wildlife Fund.

Kingston Parish Church of St. Thomas the Apostle, 300th Anniv. A202

Designs: $2, High altar. $8, Exterior view. $12.50, Carving, "The Angel," by Edna Manley, vert.

$60, Exterior view at sunset.

Unwmk.

1996, Feb. 7 Litho. *Perf. 14*

861 A202 $2 multicolored .15 .15
862 A202 $8 multicolored .50 .50
863 A202 $12.50 multicolored .75 .75
Nos. 861-863 (3) 1.40 1.40

Souvenir Sheet

864 A202 $60 multicolored 3.60 3.60

No. 864 contains one 42x56mm stamp.

Chernobyl's Children — A203

Perf. 13½x14

1997, Apr. 7 Litho. Unwmk.

865 A203 $55 multicolored 3.30 3.30

Orchids A204

$1, Coelia triptera, vert. $2, Oncidium pulchellum. $2.50, Oncidium triquetrum, vert. $3, Broughtonia negrilensis, vert. $5, Enclyclia frangrans.

Wmk. 352

1997, Oct. 6 Litho. *Perf. 14*

866 A204 $1 multicolored .15 .15
867 A204 $2 multicolored .15 .15
868 A204 $2.50 multicolored .20 .20
869 A204 $3 multicolored .25 .25
870 A204 $5 multicolored .40 .40
Nos. 866-870 (5) 1.15 1.15

Jamaica stamps can be mounted in the Scott British North and West Caribbean album.

Diana, Princess of Wales (1961-97) — A205

Unwmk.

1998, Feb. 24 Litho. *Perf. 14*

871 A205 $20 Portrait 1.25 1.25

Souvenir Sheet

872 A205 $80 With Mother Teresa 4.75 4.75

No. 871 was issued in sheets of 6. No. 872 contains one 42x56mm stamp.

SEMI-POSTAL STAMPS

Native Girl — SP1

Native Boy — SP2

Native Boy and Girl — SP3

1923, Nov. 1 Engr. *Perf. 12*

B1 SP1 ½p green & black 2.00 *4.00*
B2 SP2 1p car & black 4.00 *9.00*
B3 SP3 2½p blue & black 11.00 *22.50*
Nos. J1-J3 (3) 17.00 *35.50*

Each stamp was sold for ½p over face value. The surtax benefited the Child Saving League of Jamaica.

Catalogue values for unused stamps in this section, from this point to the end of the section, are for Never Hinged items.

Nos. 694-697 Surcharged "HURRICANE GILBERT RELIEF FUND" and New Value in Black

Wmk. 352

1988, Nov. 11 Litho. *Perf. 14*

B4 A164 25c +25c multi .18 .18
B5 A164 45c +45c multi .32 .32
B6 A164 $4 +$4 multi 2.90 2.90
B7 A164 $5 +$5 multi 3.60 3.60
Nos. J4-J7 (4) 7.00 7.00

Red Surcharge

B4a A164 25c + 25c .18 .18
B5a A164 45c + 45c .32 .32
B6a A164 $4 + $4 2.90 2.90
B7a A164 $5 + $5 3.60 3.60
Nos. J4a-J7a (4) 7.00 7.00

WAR TAX STAMPS

Regular Issues of 1906-19 Overprinted **WAR STAMP.**

1916 Wmk. 3 *Perf. 14*

MR1 A14 ½p green .15 .15
a. Without period 11.00 *15.00*
b. Double overprint 200.00 200.00
c. Inverted overprint 95.00 95.00
d. As "c," without period 350.00
MR2 A17 3p violet, *yel* 5.50 8.25
a. Without period 21.00 30.00

Surface-colored Paper

MR3 A17 3p violet, *yel* 1.40 1.50
Nos. MR1-MR3 (3) 7.05 9.90

Regular Issues of 1906-18 Overprinted **WAR STAMP.**

MR4 A14 ½p green .18 .15
a. Without period 11.00 11.00
b. Pair, one without ovpt. 475.00 375.00
c. "R" inserted by hand 300.00 210.00
d. "WAR" only 125.00
MR5 A17 1½p orange .16 .15
a. Without period 6.75 6.50
b. "TAMP" 90.00 90.00
c. "S" inserted by hand 225.00
d. "R" omitted 400.00 350.00
e. "R" inserted by hand 250.00 200.00
MR6 A17 3p violet, *yel* .38 .40
a. Without period 17.00 18.00
b. "TAMP" 225.00 140.00
c. "S" inserted by hand 150.00 140.00
d. Inverted overprint 500.00 175.00
e. As "a," inverted
Nos. MR4-MR6 (3) .72
Set value .56

Regular Issues of 1906-19 Overprinted **WAR STAMP.**

1917, Mar.

MR7 A14 ½p green .15 .15
a. Without period 7.50 6.00
b. Overprinted on back instead of face 125.00
c. Inverted overprint 13.00 10.00
MR8 A17 1½p orange .15 .15
a. Without period 7.00 5.25
b. Double overprint 90.00 90.00
c. Inverted overprint 90.00 90.00
d. As "a," inverted
MR9 A17 3p violet, *yel* .22 .22
a. Without period 13.00 12.00
b. Vertical overprint 400.00 400.00
c. Inverted overprint 150.00
d. As "a," inverted
Set value .40 .35

There are many minor varieties of Nos. MR1-MR9.

Regular Issues of 1906-19 Overprinted in Red **WAR STAMP**

1919, Oct. 4

MR10 A14 ½p green .15 .15
MR11 A17 3p violet, *yel* .22 .18
Set value .30 .22

OFFICIAL STAMPS

No. 16 Overprinted in Black **OFFICIAL**

Type I - Word 15 to 16mm long.
Type II - Word 17 to 17½mm long.

1890 Wmk. 2 *Perf. 14*

O1 A7 ½p green (II) 7.50 1.25
a. Type I 25.00 25.00
b. Inverted overprint (II) 75.00 80.00
c. Double overprint (II) 80.00 90.00
d. Dbl. ovpt., one invtd. (II) 375.00 375.00
e. Dbl. ovpt., one vert. (II) 1,100.
f. Double overprint (I) 575.00

Missing "O," "L" or one or both "I's" known.

No. 16 and Type of 1889 Overprinted **OFFICIAL**

1890-91

O2 A7 ½p green 4.50 .50
O3 A10 1p carmine rose 4.50 .75
O4 A10 2p slate 5.50 1.25
Nos. O2-O4 (3) 14.50 2.50

JAPAN

jə-'pan

LOCATION — North Pacific Ocean, east of China
GOVT. — Constitutional monarchy
AREA — 142,726 sq. mi.
POP. — 120,020,000 (est. 1984)
CAPITAL — Tokyo

1000 Mon = 10 Sen
100 Sen = 1 Yen (or En)
10 Rin = 1 Sen

Catalogue values for unused stamps in this country are for Never Hinged items, beginning with Scott 375 in the regular postage section, Scott B8 in the semi-postal section, and Scott C9 in the airpost section.

Watermarks

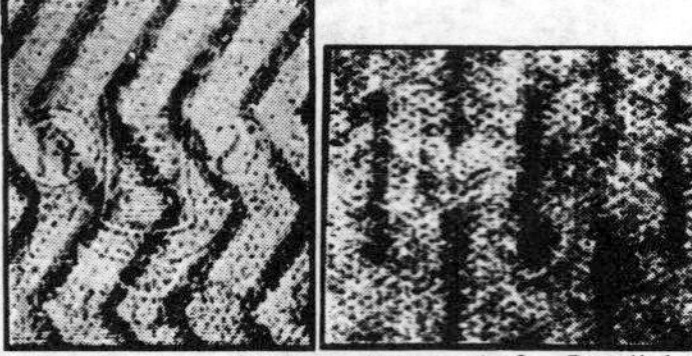

Wmk. 141 - Zigzag Lines   Wmk. 142 - Parallel Lines

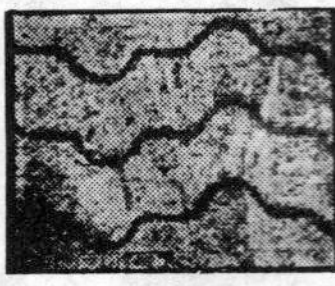

Wmk. 257 - Curved Wavy Lines

After 1945, Wmk. 257 exists also in a narrow spacing on a small number of issues.

Counterfeits of Nos. 1-71 are plentiful. Some are excellent and deceive many collectors.

Nos. 1-54A were printed from plates of 40 with individually engraved subjects. Each stamp in the sheet is slightly different.

Pair of Dragons Facing Characters of Value — A1

Plate I

Plate II

48 mon:
Plate I - Solid dots in inner border.
Plate II - Tiny circles replace dots.

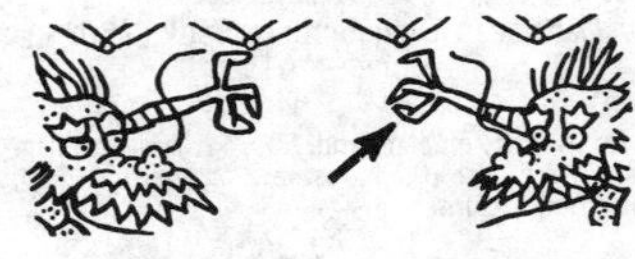

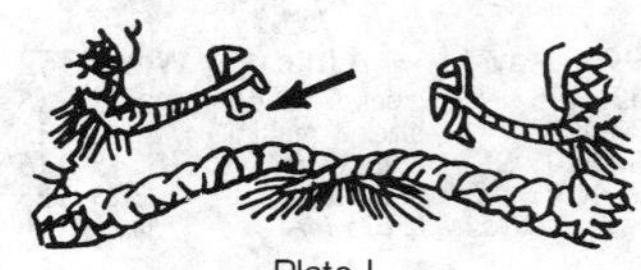

Plate I

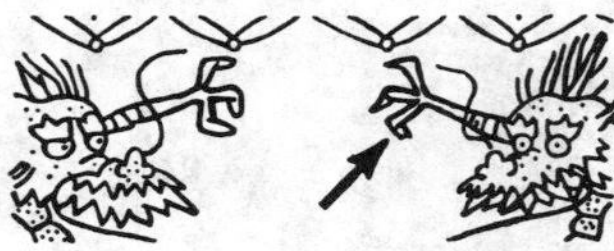

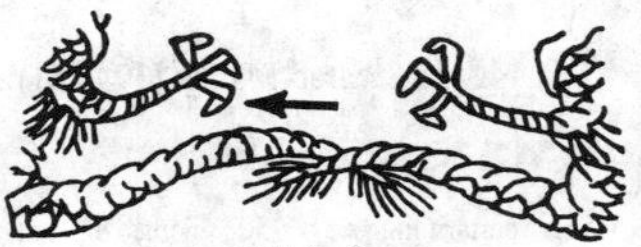

Plate II

100 mon:
Plate I - Lowest dragon claw at upper right and at lower left point upward.
Plate II - Same two claws point downward.

Plate I

Plate II

200 mon:
Plate I - Dot in upper left corner.
Plate II - No dot. (Some Plate I copies show dot faintly; these can be mistaken for Plate II.)

Plate I

Plate II

500 mon:
Plate I - Lower right corner of Greek-type border incomplete
Plate II - Short horizontal line completes corner border pattern.

Unwmk.

1871, Apr. 20 Engr. *Imperf.*

Native Laid Paper Without Gum

Denomination in Black

1 A1 48m brown (I) 275. 300.
a. 48m red brown (I) 275. 300.
b. Wove paper (I) 275. 300.
c. 48m brown (II) 300. 325.
d. Wove paper (II) 300. 325.
2 A1 100m blue (I) 250. 250.
a. Wove paper (I) 300. 300.
b. Plate II 550. 525.
c. Wove paper (II) 725. 725.
3 A1 200m vermilion (I) 400. 350.
a. Wove paper (I) 450. 400.
b. Plate II 2,000. 2,000.
c. Wove paper (II) *3,500.*
4 A1 500m blue green (I) 500. 500.
a. 500m greenish blue (I) 550. 525.
b. 500m green (I) 1,150. 1,150.
c. 500m yellow green (I) 1,250. 1,250.
d. Wove paper (I) 600. 550.
e. 500m blue green (II) 550. *3,000.*
f. 500m greenish blue (II) 550. *3,000.*
g. Wove paper (II) 2,000. *4,000.*
h. Denomination inverted (I) *95,000.*

Perforations, Nos. 5-8

Perforations on Nos. 5-8 generally are rough and irregular due to the perforating equipment used and the quality of the paper. Values are for stamps with rough perfs that touch the frameline on one or more sides.

Dragons and Denomination — A1a

½ sen:
Plate I - Same as 48m Plate II. Measures not less than 19.8x19.8mm. Some subjects on this plate measure 20.3x20.2mm.
Plate II - Same as 48m Plate II. Measures not more than 19.7x19.3mm. Some subjects measure 19.3x18.7mm.

Plates I & II

Plate III

1 sen:
Plate I - Same as 100m Plate I. Narrow space between frameline and Greek-type border.
Plate II - Same as 100m Plate II. Same narrow space between frameline and border.
Plate III - Space between frameline and border is much wider. Frameline thinner. Shading on dragon heads heavier than on Plates I and II.

Native Laid Paper With or Without Gum

1872 *Perf. 9-12 & compound*

Denomination in Black

5 A1a ½s brown (II) 90.00 100.00
a. ½s red brown (II) 90.00 100.00
b. ½s gray brown (II) 90.00 100.00
c. Wove paper (II) 850.00 750.00
d. ½s brown (I) 125.00 175.00
e. ½s red brown (I) 125.00 175.00
f. ½s gray brown (I) 125.00 175.00
g. Wove paper (I) 175.00 250.00
6 A1a 1s blue (II) 275.00 275.00
a. Wove paper (II) 525.00 550.00
b. Plate I 1,050. *2,250.*
c. Wove paper (I) *5,000.*
d. Plate III *8,000.* 1,750.
e. Wove paper (III) *4,750.*
7 A1a 2s vermilion 450.00 450.00
a. Wove paper 475.00 475.00
8 A1a 5s blue green 575.00 550.00
a. 5s yellow green 575.00 550.00
b. Wove paper 775.00 775.00

In 1896 the government made imperforate imitations of Nos. 6-7 to include in a presentation book.

Expect perforations on Nos. 9-71 to be rough and irregular.

Imperial Crest and Branches of Kiri Tree — A2

Dragons and Chrysanthemum Crest — A3

Imperial Chrysanthemum Crest — A4

Imperial Crest and Branches of Kiri Tree — A5

1872-73 ***Perf. 9 to 13 and Compound***

Native Wove or Laid Paper of Varying Thickness

No.	Type	Description	Unused	Used
9	A2	½s brown, *wove*	25.00	25.00
a.		Upper character in left label has 2 diagonal top strokes missing	1,900.	1,500.
b.		Laid paper	70.00	—
c.		As "a," laid paper	2,250.	—

Nos. 9, 9a are on stiff, brittle wove paper. Nos. 9b, 9c on a soft, fibrous paper. Nos. 9b and 9c probably were never put in use.

No.	Type	Description	Unused	Used
10	A2	1s blue, *wove*	45.00	27.50
a.		Laid paper	55.00	30.00
11	A2	2s ver, *wove*	125.00	52.50
12	A2	2s dull rose, *laid*	87.50	37.50
a.		Wove paper	125.00	50.00
13	A2	2s yel, *laid* ('73)	87.50	22.50
a.		Wove paper ('73)	210.00	27.50
14	A2	4s rose, *laid* ('73)	75.00	25.00
a.		Wove paper ('73)	250.00	35.00
15	A3	10s blue grn, *wove*	300.00	200.00
16	A3	10s yel grn, *laid*	550.00	400.00
a.		Wove paper ('73)	600.00	550.00
17	A4	20s lilac, *wove*	425.00	350.00
a.		20s violet, *wove*	425.00	350.00
b.		20s red violet, *laid*		—
18	A5	30s gray, *wove*	525.00	425.00

See Nos. 24-25, 30-31, 37-39, 51-52.

1874

Foreign Wove Paper

No.	Type	Description	Unused	Used
24	A2	4s rose	675.	225.
25	A5	30s gray	—	*6,250.*

A6

A7

A8

Type A6 differs from A2 by the addition of a syllabic character in a box covering crossed kiri branches above SEN. Stamps of type A6 differ for each value in border and spandrel designs.

In type A7, the syllabic character appears just below the buckle. In type A8, it appears in an oval frame at bottom center below SE of SEN.

With Syllabic Characters

イ	ロ	ハ	ニ	ホ	ヘ	ト	チ
i	ro	ha	ni	ho	he	to	chi
1	2	3	4	5	6	7	8
リ	ヌ	ル	ヲ	ワ	カ	ヨ	タ
ri	nu	ru	wo	wa	ka	yo	ta
9	10	11	12	13	14	15	16
レ	ソ	ツ	子	ナ	ラ	ム	
re	so	tsu	ne	na	ra	mu	
17	18	19	20	21	22	23	

Perf. 9½ to 12½ and Compound

1874

Native Laid or Wove Paper

No.	Type	Description	Unused	Used
28	A6	2s yellow	225.	325.

Unused value is for copies with syll. 16, used value for copies with syll. 1.

No.	Type	Description	Unused	Used
29	A7	6s vio brn (Syll. 1)	1,150.	375.
		Syllabic 2	1,500.	400.
		Syllabic 3		1,000.
		Syllabic 4,5,7		500.
		Syllabic 6		625.
		Syllabic 8		475.
		Syllabic 9		550.
		Syllabic 10		3,250.
		Syllabic 11		3,000.
		Syllabic 12		1,750.
30	A4	20s red vio (Syll. 3)	*7,750.*	
		Syllabic 2	*8,000.*	
31	A5	30s gray (Syll. 1)	2,750.	3,250.
a.		Very thin laid paper	2,750.	3,250.

No. 30, syll. 1, comes only with specimen dot. Value $22,500.

Perf. 11 to 12½ and Compound

1874

Foreign Wove Paper

No.	Type	Description	Unused	Used
32	A6	½s brown (Syll. 1)	21.00	17.50
		Syllabic 2	37.50	37.50
33	A6	1s blue (Syll. 4,6,9)	150.00	30.00
		Syllabic 1,2,3	175.00	30.00
		Syllabic 5	500.00	120.00
		Syllabic 7	225.00	30.00
		Syllabic 8	150.00	30.00
		Syllabic 10	175.00	45.00
		Syllabic 11	175.00	45.00
		Syllabic 12	190.00	45.00
34	A6	2s yel (Syll. 2-4, 9, 15, 17, 20)	140.00	27.50
		Syllabic 1	275.00	27.50
		Syllabic 5	350.00	27.50
		Syllabic 6	2,000.	40.00
		Syllabic 7	2,000.	22.50
		Syllabic 8	140.00	30.00
		Syllabic 10	*2,750.*	42.50
		Syllabic 11	140.00	22.50
		Syllabic 12,22	*2,750.*	22.50
		Syllabic 13	*2,250.*	22.50
		Syllabic 14	*2,750.*	30.00
		Syllabic 16	*2,250.*	22.50
		Syllabic 18,19	140.00	22.50
		Syllabic 21	225.00	22.50
		Syllabic 23	240.00	22.50
35	A6	4s rose (Syll. 1)	2,250.	350.00
36	A7	6s vio brn (Syll. 16)	140.00	47.50
		Syllabic 10	525.00	550.00
		Syllabic 11	450.00	
		Syllabic 13		*5,250.*
		Syllabic 14	275.00	225.00
		Syllabic 15		*2,750.*
		Syllabic 17	175.00	72.50
		Syllabic 18	250.00	100.00
37	A3	10s yel grn (Syll. 2)	85.00	50.00
		Syllabic 1	275.00	90.00
		Syllabic 3	625.00	350.00
38	A4	20s violet (Syll. 5)	240.00	67.50
		Syllabic 4	240.00	67.50
39	A5	30s gray (Syll. 1)	225.00	65.00

1875 ***Perf. 9 to 13 and Compound***

No.	Type	Description	Unused	Used
40	A6	½s gray (Syll. 2, 3)	17.50	16.50
		Syllabic 4	32.50	
41	A6	1s brn (Syll. 15-17)	32.50	17.50
		Syllabic 5	350.00	45.00
		Syllabic 7		275.00
		Syllabic 8	*15,000.*	250.00
		Syllabic 12	575.00	175.00
		Syllabic 13	42.50	17.50
		Syllabic 14	45.00	17.50
42	A6	4s green (Syll. 1)	100.00	20.00
		Syllabic 2	160.00	20.00
		Syllabic 3	140.00	20.00
43	A7	6s orange (Syll. 16,17)	80.00	17.50
		Syllabic 10	175.00	45.00
		Syllabic 11	150.00	35.00
		Syllabic 13	150.00	30.00
		Syllabic 14	200.00	35.00
		Syllabic 15		
44	A8	6s orange (Syll. 20)	80.00	17.50
		Syllabic 19	90.00	16.00
		Syllabic 21	110.00	20.00
		Syllabic 22	4,250.	1,750.

Dragons — A9

Wild Goose — A10

Wagtail — A11

Imperial Crest — A11a

DESPERATELY NEEDED...
JAPAN #1-71

Mint, Used, Damaged, Counterfeits... We Buy It All!
SEND BY REGISTERED OR INSURED MAIL
FOR OUR FREE EVALUATION

GET TOKYO PRICES FOR YOUR JAPANESE STAMPS!
Call or Write
"The Japanese Specialists"

GARY TANAKA & CO.
1139 Bal Harbor Blvd., Punta Gorda, FL 33950
TOLL FREE 1-800-218-5140 • Fax: 1-941-639-4272

JAPAN
stamps & Postal History
Classic & Modern Issues
Buying & Selling
JACK & CAROL YAO
P.O.Box 416, Hinsdale, IL 60522
(630) 323-8471 Fax (630) 323-7373

Kiri Branches — A11b

Goshawk — A12

No.	Type	Description	Unused	Used
45	A9	10s ultra (Syll. 4)	125.00	18.00
		Syllabic 5	4,000.	350.00
46	A10	12s rose (Syll. 1)	250.00	125.00
		Syllabic 2	260.00	150.00
		Syllabic 3	3,750.	475.00
47	A11	15s lilac (Syll. 1)	240.00	175.00
		Syllabic 2	250.00	150.00
		Syllabic 3	275.00	160.00
48	A11a	20s rose (Syll. 8)	65.00	16.00
49	A11b	30s vio (Syll. 2-4)	125.00	50.00
50	A12	45s lake (Syll. 1)	275.00	150.00
		Syllabic 2	1,500.	500.00
		Syllabic 3	1,400.	425.00

Issue dates: No. 46, syll. 2, 1882. No. 46, syll. 3, 1883. Others, 1875.

The 1s brown on laid paper, type A6, formerly listed as No. 50A, is one of several stamps of the preceding issue which exist on a laid type paper. They are difficult to identify and mainly of interest to specialists.

Without Syllabic Characters

1875

No.	Type	Description	Unused	Used
51	A2	1s brown	6,000.	650.00
52	A2	4s green	300.00	67.50

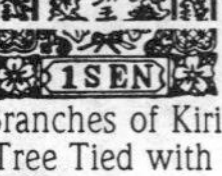

Branches of Kiri Tree Tied with Ribbon — A13

Imperial Crest and Kiri Branches — A14

1875-76

No.	Type	Description	Unused	Used
53	A13	1s brown	55.00	15.00
54	A13	2s yellow	110.00	15.00
54A	A14	5s green ('76)	225.00	110.00
		Nos. 53-54A (3)	390.00	140.00

A15

A16

Imperial Crest, Star and Kiri Branches — A17

Sun, Kikumon and Kiri Branches — A18

Imperial Crest and Kiri Branches — A19

Kikumon — A20

Perf. 8 to 14 and Compound

1876-77 **Typo.**

No.	Type	Description	Unused	Used
55	A15	5r slate	19.00	14.00
56	A16	1s black	42.50	5.00
a.		Horiz. pair, imperf. btwn.		
57	A16	2s brown ol	60.00	3.50
58	A16	4s blue grn	50.00	4.50
a.		4s green	50.00	4.50
59	A17	5s brown	72.50	27.50
60	A17	6s orange ('77)	200.00	60.00
61	A17	8s vio brn ('77)	75.00	6.75
62	A17	10s blue ('77)	60.00	2.75
63	A17	12s rose ('77)	275.00	175.00
64	A18	15s yel grn ('77)	175.00	3.50
65	A18	20s dk blue ('77)	200.00	14.00
66	A18	30s violet ('77)	250.00	140.00
a.		30s red violet	250.00	140.00
67	A18	45s carmine ('77)	725.00	600.00

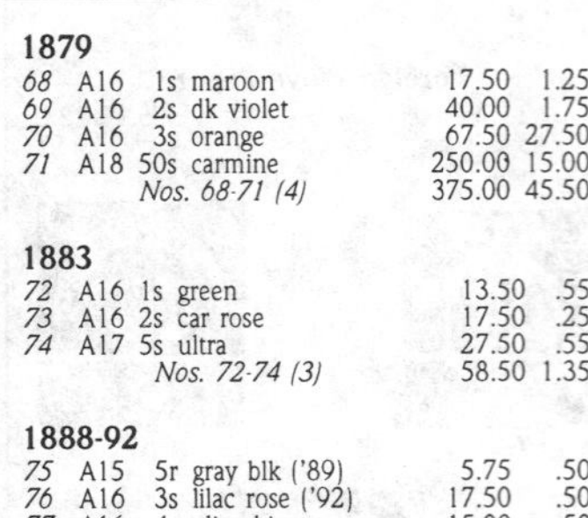

1879

No.	Type	Description	Unused	Used
68	A16	1s maroon	17.50	1.25
69	A16	2s dk violet	40.00	1.75
70	A16	3s orange	67.50	27.50
71	A18	50s carmine	250.00	15.00
		Nos. 68-71 (4)	375.00	45.50

1883

No.	Type	Description	Unused	Used
72	A16	1s green	13.50	.55
73	A16	2s car rose	17.50	.25
74	A17	5s ultra	27.50	.55
		Nos. 72-74 (3)	58.50	1.35

1888-92

No.	Type	Description	Unused	Used
75	A15	5r gray blk ('89)	5.75	.50
76	A16	3s lilac rose ('92)	17.50	.50
77	A16	4s olive bis	15.00	.50
78	A17	8s blue lilac	22.50	1.90
79	A17	10s brown org	20.00	.50
80	A18	15s purple	65.00	.55
81	A18	20s orange	87.50	1.90
a.		20s yellow	87.50	1.90
82	A19	25s blue green	175.00	2.00
83	A18	50s brown	125.00	4.00
84	A20	1y carmine	200.00	5.00
		Nos. 75-84 (10)	733.25	17.35

Stamps of types A16-A18 differ for each value, in backgrounds and ornaments.

Nos. 58, 61-62, 64-65, 71-84 are found with telegraph or telephone office cancellations. These sell at considerably lower prices than postally used copies.

Cranes and Imperial Crest — A21

Perf. 11½ to 13 and Compound

1894, Mar. 9

No.	Type	Description	Unused	Used
85	A21	2s carmine	25.00	3.25
86	A21	5s ultra	42.50	14.00

25th wedding anniv. of Emperor Meiji (Mutsuhito) and Empress Haru.

Gen. Yoshihisa Kitashirakawa
A22 A23

Field Marshal Akihito Arisugawa
A24 A25

1896, Aug. 1 **Engr.**

No.	Type	Description	Unused	Used
87	A22	2s rose	30.00	3.00
88	A23	5s deep ultra	60.00	2.75
89	A24	2s rose	30.00	3.00
90	A25	5s deep ultra	60.00	2.75
		Nos. 87-90 (4)	180.00	11.50

Victory in Chinese-Japanese War (1894-95).

A26

A27

A28

A29

Perf. 11½ to 14 and Compound

1899-1907 **Typo.**

No.	Type	Description	Unused	Used
91	A26	5r gray	6.00	.70
92	A26	½s gray ('01)	3.25	.20
93	A26	1s lt red brn	4.00	.20
94	A26	1½s ultra ('00)	14.00	1.00
95	A26	1½s violet ('06)	10.00	.25
96	A26	2s lt green	10.00	.20
97	A26	3s violet brn	10.00	.25
a.		Double impression		
98	A26	3s rose ('06)	5.75	.25
99	A26	4s rose	6.25	1.10
a.		4s pink ('06)	6.25	1.25
100	A26	5s orange yel	20.00	.25
101	A27	6s maroon ('07)	32.50	4.00
102	A27	8s olive grn	35.00	4.25
103	A27	10s deep blue	13.00	.20
104	A27	15s purple	47.50	1.60
105	A27	20s red orange	25.00	.20
106	A28	25s blue green	67.50	1.00
107	A28	50s red brown	67.50	1.25
108	A29	1y carmine	77.50	1.40
		Nos. 91-108 (18)	454.75	18.30

For overprints see Nos. M1, Offices in China, 1-18, Offices in Korea, 1-14.

Boxes for Rice Cakes and Marriage Certificates — A30

Symbols of Korea and Japan — A31

Perf. 11½ to 12½ and Compound

1900, May 10

No.	Type	Description	Unused	Used
109	A30	3s carmine	35.00	.75

Wedding of the Crown Prince Yoshihito and Princess Sadako.

For overprints see Offices in China No. 19, Offices in Korea, 15.

1905, July 1

No.	Type	Description	Unused	Used
110	A31	3s rose red	90.00	20.00

Issued to commemorate the amalgamation of the postal services of Japan and Korea. Korean stamps were withdrawn from sale June 30, 1905, but remained valid until Aug. 31. No. 110 was used in the Korea and China Offices of Japan, as well as in Japan proper.

Field-piece and Japanese Flag — A32

Empress Jingo — A33

1906, Apr. 29

No.	Type	Description	Unused	Used
111	A32	1½s blue	30.00	3.75
112	A32	3s carmine rose	62.50	17.50

Triumphal military review following the Russo-Japanese War.

1908 **Engr.**

No.	Type	Description	Unused	Used
113	A33	5y green	850.00	3.50
114	A33	10y dark violet	1,100.	5.75

The frame of No. 114 differs slightly from the illustration.

For overprints see Offices in China Nos. 20-21, 48-49.

A34

A35

A36

Perf. 12, 12x13, 13x13½

1913 **Typo.** **Unwmk.**

No.	Type	Description	Unused	Used
115	A34	½s brown	7.00	1.00
116	A34	1s orange	14.00	1.00
117	A34	1½s lt blue	19.00	1.50
a.		Booklet pane of 6	210.00	
118	A34	2s green	20.00	1.00
119	A34	3s rose	27.50	.50
a.		Booklet pane of 6	210.00	
120	A35	4s red	30.00	12.00
121	A35	5s violet	35.00	1.50
122	A35	10s deep blue	110.00	.75
123	A35	20s claret	110.00	1.50

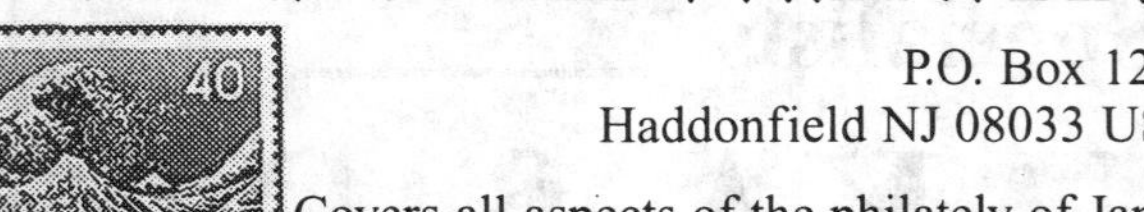
INTERNATIONAL SOCIETY FOR JAPANESE PHILATELY
P.O. Box 1283
Haddonfield NJ 08033 USA
Covers all aspects of the philately of Japan
Expertization services and sales circuits
Suitable for beginning and advanced collectors
Award-winning illustrated journal Japanese Philately
Journal runs over 250 pages annually in 8½ x 11 format
Sample back issue of journal $1.00
Free prospectus and application form
Annual dues just $12.00

124 A35 25s olive green 110.00 3.00
125 A36 1y yel grn & mar 750.00 25.00
Nos. 115-125 (11) 1,232. 48.75

1914-25 Wmk. 141 Granite Paper
Size: 19x22½mm ("Old Die")

127 A34 ½s brown 3.00 .15
128 A34 1s orange 3.00 .15
129 A34 1½s blue 3.00 .15
a. Booklet pane of 6 85.00
d. As "a," imperf.
130 A34 2s green 5.00 .15
a. Booklet pane of 6 85.00
131 A34 3s rose 2.00 .15
a. Booklet pane of 6 72.50
132 A35 4s red 16.00 1.25
a. Booklet pane of 6 85.00
133 A35 5s violet 14.00 .50
134 A35 6s brown ('19) 21.00 2.75
136 A35 8s gray ('19) 18.00 10.50
137 A35 10s deep blue 18.00 .15
a. Booklet pane of 6 85.00
138 A35 13s olive brn ('25) 42.50 2.25
139 A35 20s claret 85.00 .70
140 A35 25s olive grn 14.00 1.00
141 A36 30s orange brn ('19) 21.00 .60
143 A36 50s dk brown ('19) 30.00 1.00
145 A36 1y yel grn & mar 165.00 1.00
b. Imperf., pair
146 A33 5y green 500.00 2.75
147 A33 10y violet 700.00 5.25
Nos. 127-147 (18) 1,660. 30.45

1924-33
"New Die" Size: 18½x22mm (Flat Plate)
or 18½x22½mm (Rotary)

127a A34 ½s brown 2.00 1.00
128a A34 1s orange 2.00 1.00
129b A34 1½s blue 3.25 .30
c. Bklt. pane of 6 ('30) 21.00
131b A34 3s rose 1.40 .15
c. Bklt. pane of 6 ('28) 50.00
133a A35 5s violet 17.50 .15
135 A35 7s red org ('30) 8.75 .15
138a A35 13s bister brn ('25) 7.00 .15
140a A35 25s olive green 50.00 .20
142 A36 30s org & grn ('29) 19.00 .30
144 A36 50s yel brn & dk bl ('29) 13.00 .55
145a A36 1y yel grn & mar 80.00 .60
Nos. 127a-145a (11) 203.90 4.55

See Nos. 212-213, 239-241, 243, 245, 249-252, 255. For overprints see Nos. C1-C2, M2-M5, Offices in China, 22-47.

Ceremonial Cap — A37

Imperial Throne — A38

Enthronement Hall, Kyoto — A39

Perf. 12½
1915, Nov. 10 Typo. Unwmk.

148 A37 1½s red & blk 2.25 .50
149 A38 3s orange & vio 2.25 .60

Engr.
Perf. 12x12½

150 A39 4s carmine rose 13.00 10.00
151 A39 10s ultra 25.00 20.00
Nos. 148-151 (4) 42.50 31.10

Enthronement of Emperor Yoshihito.

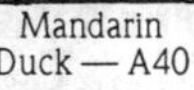
Mandarin Duck — A40

Ceremonial Cap — A41

1916, Nov. 3 Typo. *Perf. 12½*

152 A40 1½s green, red & yel 2.25 .90
153 A40 3s red & yellow 4.25 1.25
154 A41 10s ultra & dk blue 750.00 275.00

Nomination of the Prince Heir Apparent, later Emperor Hirohito.

Dove and Olive Branch
A42 A43

Perf. 12, 12½, 13½x13
1919, July 1 Engr.

155 A42 1½s dark brown 2.00 .65
156 A43 3s gray green 2.50 .95
157 A42 4s rose 6.00 4.00
158 A43 10s dark blue 25.00 14.00
Nos. 155-158 (4) 35.50 19.60

Restoration of peace after World War I.

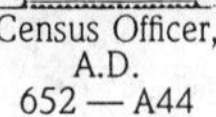
Census Officer, A.D. 652 — A44

Meiji Shrine, Tokyo — A45

Perf. 12½
1920, Sept. 25 Typo. Unwmk.

159 A44 1½s red violet 7.00 3.00
160 A44 3s vermilion 7.75 3.00

Taking of the 1st modern census in Japan. Not available for foreign postage except to China.

1920, Nov. 1 Engr.

161 A45 1½s dull violet 2.50 1.25
162 A45 3s rose 2.50 1.25

Dedication of the Meiji Shrine. Not available for foreign postage except to China.

National and Postal Flags — A46

Ministry of Communications Building, Tokyo — A47

Typographed (A46), Engraved (A47)
1921, Apr. 20 *Perf. 12½, 13x13½*

163 A46 1½s gray grn & red 2.00 .90
164 A47 3s violet brn 2.50 1.10
165 A46 4s rose & red 40.00 20.00
166 A47 10s dark blue 225.00 150.00
Nos. 163-166 (4) 269.50 172.00

50th anniv. of the establishment of postal service and Japanese postage stamps.

Battleships "Katori" and "Kashima" — A48

1921, Sept. 3 Litho. *Perf. 12½*

167 A48 1½s violet 2.00 .90
168 A48 3s olive green 2.75 .90
169 A48 4s rose red 37.50 18.00
170 A48 10s deep blue 42.50 21.00
Nos. 167-170 (4) 84.75 40.80

Return of Crown Prince Hirohito from his European visit.

Mount Fuji — A49

Mt. Niitaka, Taiwan — A50

Perf. 13x13½
1930-37 Typo. Wmk. 141
Granite Paper
Size: 18½x22mm ("New Die")

171 A49 4s green ('37) 2.75 .35
172 A49 4s orange 6.50 .25
174 A49 8s olive green 10.00 .15
175a A49 20s blue ('37) 20.00 25.00
176 A49 20s brown violet 30.00 .20
Nos. 171-176 (5) 69.25 25.95

1922-29
Size: 19x22½mm ("Old Die")

171a A49 4s green 9.00 3.00
172a A49 4s orange ('29) 90.00 9.00
173 A49 8s rose 18.00 6.00
174a A49 8s olive green ('29) 250.00 80.00
175 A49 20s deep blue 20.00 .60
176a A49 20s brown vio ('29) 90.00 1.50
Nos. 171a-176a (6) 477.00 100.10

See Nos. 242, 246, 248.

Perf. 12½
1923, Apr. 16 Unwmk. Engr.

177 A50 1½s orange 10.00 8.00
178 A50 3s dark violet 15.00 7.00

1st visit of Crown Prince Hirohito to Taiwan. The stamps were sold only in Taiwan, but were valid throughout the empire.

Cherry Blossoms A51

Sun and Dragonflies A52

Empress Jingo — A53

1923 Wmk. 142 Litho. *Imperf.*
Without Gum; Granite Paper

179 A51 ½s gray 5.00 2.00
180 A51 1½s lt blue 6.00 1.00
181 A51 2s red brown 5.25 1.00
182 A51 3s brt rose 4.00 .70
183 A51 4s gray green 37.50 14.00
184 A51 5s dull violet 18.00 1.00
185 A51 8s red orange 65.00 25.00
186 A52 10s deep brown 40.00 1.00
187 A52 20s deep blue 42.50 1.40
Nos. 179-187 (9) 223.25 47.10

#179-187 exist rouletted and with various perforations. These were made privately.

WANTED
JAPAN
AND ALL WORLDWIDE STAMPS & COVERS
Mint & Used
Send your material for our CASH OFFER!
Be sure to include your phone number for our immediate response.
R.E. "Bob" Wilson
ISJP APS
P.O. Box 1084
Thousand Oaks, CA 91358-0084
(805) 495-4744

Perf. 12, 13x13½
1924 Engr. Wmk. 141
Granite Paper

188 A53 5y gray green 250.00 3.00
189 A53 10y dull violet 400.00 2.25

See Nos. 253-254.

Cranes — A54

Phoenix — A55

Paying Top Dollar
Japan • Manchukuo Occupations
Mint • Used • Covers
Collections • Accumulations
Topical & Worldwide Collections Needed
Call, Write or Send for our no-nonsense offer
Frederic S. Boatwright

P.O. Box 695 Sullivan, MO 63080
Phone /Fax 573-860-4057
APS

Buying & Selling Stamps and Covers of...
Japan ★ All China ★ Macao
Hong Kong ★ Korea ★ Thailand
Vietnam ★ Cambodia ★ Laos

Buying Worldwide!
Write, Call or Send Insured For Our Top Offer!

PACIFIC MIDWEST CO.
(Our 33rd year)
P.O. Box 1696, Daly City, CA 94014
Ph. 650-994-1117 • FAX 650-994-7439
E-mail: Garyucb@concentric.net
• We accept Visa, MasterCard •
China Stamp Soc.
Hong Kong Stamp Soc

Perf. 10½ to 13½ and Compound

1925, May 10 Litho. Unwmk.

190 A54 1½s gray violet 1.75 .90
191 A55 3s silver & brn org 3.00 1.75
a. Vert. pair, imperf. btwn. 500.00
192 A54 8s light red 27.50 12.50
193 A55 20s silver & gray grn 60.00 37.50
Nos. 190-193 (4) 92.25 52.65

25th wedding anniv. of the Emperor Yoshihito (Taisho) and Empress Sadako.

Mt. Fuji — A56

Yomei Gate, Nikko — A57

Nagoya Castle — A58

Perf. 13½x13

1926-37 Typo. Wmk. 141

Granite Paper

194 A56 2s green 1.90 .15
195 A57 6s carmine 6.75 .15
196 A58 10s dark blue 8.25 .15
197 A58 10s carmine ('37) 9.00 8.50
Nos. 194-197 (4) 25.90 8.95

See Nos. 244, 247. For surcharges see People's Republic of China No. 2L5-2L6.

WANTED JAPAN

MINT & USED STAMPS, COVERS, CANCELLATIONS, REVENUES, COLLECTIONS, ACCUMULATIONS AND EVERYTHING!

Sell your Japanese philatelic holdings to a Japanese dealer, living in North America, who knows, thoroughly, the Japanese market and the value of your Japanese collection. Expert in Japanese philately, national exhibiter; able to communicate with clients in either English or Japanese. Your satisfaction is guaranteed! Call or write to us soon!

SEND YOUR STAMPS FOR OUR CASH OFFER!

STEPHEN J. HASEGAWA
P.O. Box 40610 San Francisco, CA 94140-0610
Phone 415-648-0116 • FAX 415-821-9657 (24 Hours)

Member ISJP

Baron Hisoka Maejima — A59

Map of World on Mollweide's Projection — A60

Perf. 12½, 13x13½

1927, June 20 Unwmk.

198 A59 1½s lilac 2.50 .90
199 A59 3s olive green 2.50 .90
200 A60 6s carmine rose 75.00 50.00
201 A60 10s blue 90.00 50.00
Nos. 198-201 (4) 170.00 101.80

50th anniv. of Japan's joining the UPU. Baron Maejima (1835-1919) organized Japan's modern postal system and was postmaster general.

Phoenix — A61

Enthronement Hall, Kyoto — A62

1928, Nov. 10 Engr. ***Perf. 12½***

Yellow Paper

202 A61 1½s deep green .90 .50
203 A62 3s red violet .90 .50
204 A61 6s carmine rose 2.75 2.00
205 A62 10s deep blue 3.50 2.50
Nos. 202-205 (4) 8.05 5.50

Enthronement of Emperor Hirohito.

Great Shrines of Ise — A63

Map of Japanese Empire — A64

1929, Oct. 2 ***Perf. 12½***

206 A63 1½s gray violet 1.25 1.00
207 A63 3s carmine 1.75 1.25

58th rebuilding of the Ise Shrines.

1930, Sept. 25 Unwmk.

208 A64 1½s deep violet 2.25 1.25
209 A64 3s deep red 2.50 1.65

2nd census in the Japanese Empire.

Meiji Shrine — A65

1930, Nov. 1 Litho.

210 A65 1½s green 1.75 1.00
211 A65 3s brown org 2.25 1.25

10th anniv. of dedication of Meiji Shrine.

Coil Stamps

Wmk. Zigzag Lines (141)

1933 Typo. ***Perf. 13 Horiz.***

212 A34 1½s light blue 13.00 18.00
213 A34 3s rose 15.00 22.00

Japanese Red Cross Badge — A66

Red Cross Building, Tokyo — A67

Perf. 12½

1934, Oct. 1 Engr. Unwmk.

214 A66 1½s green & red 1.65 1.10
215 A67 3s dull vio & red 1.90 1.25
216 A66 6s dk car & red 9.00 5.50
217 A67 10s blue & red 12.00 8.50
Nos. 214-217 (4) 24.55 16.35

15th International Red Cross Congress. Sheets of 20 with commemorative marginal inscription. One side of sheet is perf. 13.

White Tower of Liaoyang and Warship "Hiei" — A68

Akasaka Detached Palace, Tokyo — A69

1935, Apr. 2

218 A68 1½s olive green 1.10 .75
219 A69 3s red brown 1.65 1.00
220 A68 6s carmine 7.25 3.75
221 A69 10s blue 10.00 6.00
Nos. 218-221 (4) 20.00 11.50

Visit of Emperor Kang Teh of Manchukuo (Henry Pu-yi) to Tokyo, April 6, 1935. Sheets of 20 with commemorative marginal inscription. One side of sheet is perf. 13.

Mt. Fuji — A70

Perf. 13x13½

1935 Typo. Granite Paper

222 A70 1½s rose carmine 10.00 .25
a. Miniature sheet of 20 650.00 550.00

Issued to pay postage on New Year's cards from Dec. 1-31, 1935. After Jan. 1, 1936, used for ordinary letter postage. No. 222 was issued in sheets of 100.

Mt. Fuji — A71

Fuji from Lake Ashi A72

Fuji from Lake Kawaguchi A73

Fuji from Mishima A74

1936, July 10 Photo. Wmk. 141

Granite Paper

223	A71	1 1/2s red brown	2.50	2.25
224	A72	3s dark green	4.75	3.75
225	A73	6s carmine rose	10.50	9.00
226	A74	10s dark blue	12.50	11.00
		Nos. 223-226 (4)	30.25	26.00

Fuji-Hakone National Park.

Dove, Map of Manchuria and Kwantung — A75

Shinto Shrine, Port Arthur — A76

Headquarters of Kwantung Government — A77

1936, Sept. 1 Litho. *Perf. 12 1/2*

Granite Paper

227	A75	1 1/2s gray violet	20.00	12.00
228	A76	3s red brown	15.00	12.50
229	A77	10s dull green	175.00	165.00
		Nos. 227-229 (3)	210.00	189.50

30th anniv. of Japanese administration of Kwangtung Leased Territory and the South Manchuria Railway Zone.

Imperial Diet Building A78

Grand Staircase A79

1936, Nov. 7 Engr. *Perf. 13*

230	A78	1 1/2s green	2.00	1.00
231	A79	3s brown vio	2.25	1.25
232	A79	6s carmine	6.25	4.00
233	A78	10s blue	10.00	5.25
		Nos. 230-233 (4)	20.50	11.50

Opening of the new Diet Building, Tokyo.

"Wedded Rocks," Futamigaura — A80

1936, Dec. 10 Photo.

234	A80	1 1/2s rose carmine	4.25	.20

Issued to pay postage on New Year's greeting cards.

Types of 1913-26

Perf. 13 1/2x13, 13x13 1/2

1937 Typo. Wmk. 257

239	A34	1/2s brown	2.25	1.10
240	A34	1s orange yel	3.25	1.50
241	A34	3s rose	1.25	.15
242	A49	4s green	4.50	.20
243	A35	5s violet	5.75	.15
244	A57	6s crimson	9.50	1.10
245	A35	7s red org	9.50	.15
246	A49	8s olive bister	10.00	.55
247	A58	10s carmine	8.00	.15
248	A49	20s blue	14.00	.30
249	A35	25s olive grn	40.00	1.25
250	A36	30s org & grn	24.00	.25
251	A36	50s brn org & dk bl	125.00	1.10
252	A36	1y yel grn & mar	67.50	.45
		Nos. 239-252 (14)	324.50	8.40

Engr.

253	A53	5y gray green	325.00	4.00
254	A53	10y dull violet	450.00	3.50

For overprint see People's Republic of China No. 2L6.

Coil Stamp

1938 Typo. *Perf. 13 Horiz.*

255	A34	3s rose	3.75	3.75

New Year's Decoration — A81

1937, Dec. 15 Photo. *Perf. 13*

256	A81	2s scarlet	8.00	.20

Issued to pay postage on New Year's cards, later for ordinary use.

Trading Ship — A82

Rice Harvest — A83

Gen. Maresuke Nogi — A84

Power Plant — A85

Admiral Heihachiro Togo — A86

Mount Hodaka — A87

Garambi Lighthouse, Taiwan — A88

Diamond Mountains, Korea — A89

Meiji Shrine, Tokyo — A90

Yomei Gate, Nikko — A91

Plane and Map of Japan — A92

Kasuga Shrine, Nara — A93

Mount Fuji and Cherry Blossoms — A94

Horyu Temple, Nara — A95

WE BUY...
JAPAN • THAILAND
KOREA • RYUKYU
MANCHUKO • CHINA
stamps, covers, collections.

• AUCTIONS IN JAPAN •

Sell your stamps in the richest country.
WE ARE ACCEPTING CONSIGNMENTS FOR OUR AUCTIONS IN TOKYO!

Written in Japanese language, with most items photographed, our auction catalogs reach collectors all over Japan as well as other Asian countries. GET THE MAXIMUM FOR YOUR STAMPS!

Communication and rapport with collectors are VERY IMPORTANT! Because of our long business experience and excellent reputation with our clients, we can be more helpful to you.

Contact HARUYO (Mrs. Baker) concerning consignments.
Postal cancellations are in high demand.
Please call before shipping.

For Buying & Consignments call Toll Free 1-888-696-6996

Wanted: POSTAL HISTORY OF JAPAN, CHINAS, KOREA
paying top prices for the following commercial covers of Japan. Cancellation must be clear.
#82, 84, 106, 107, 108, 124, 125, 173, 185, 273, 274, 275, 279, 325-342, 351-361, 432, 435, 436, 509, 510, 517, 518, 609, 623, C9, C10, C11, C12, C13, C19, C20, C24, C32, C42, C43, M1-5, offices in China & Korea

Also wanted: English cancellations on stamps up to 1955:
Kumamoto, Sapporo, Tochigi, Hirosima, Sendai, Okayama, Fukuoka, Kokura, Nagasaki, Otaru, Shimonoseki, Niigata

Please sent us a copy (xerox) of your covers for our top price.

DIRECT PIPELINE TO COLLECTIONS IN JAPAN & ASIA
for sample auction catalogs, contact our office.

Call or write to us soon...

RISING SUN STAMPS

APS **Box 716, Marshalls Creek, PA 18335**
Phone (717) 421-6043 • Fax (717) 421-5758

Miyajima Torii, Itsukushima Shrine — A96

Golden Pavilion, Kyoto — A97

Great Buddha, Kamakura — A98

Kamatari Fujiwara — A99

Plum Blossoms — A100

Typographed or Engraved

1937-45 Wmk. 257 *Perf. 13*

257 A82 ½s purple .60 .30
258 A83 1s fawn 1.75 .25
259 A84 2s crimson .40 .15
a. Booklet pane of 20 50.00
b. 2s pink, perf. 12 ('45) 1.50 1.00
c. 2s vermilion ('44) 2.50 2.00
260 A85 3s green ('39) .40 .15
261 A86 4s dark green .90 .15
a. Booklet pane of 20 15.00
262 A87 5s dark ultra ('39) .90 .15
263 A88 6s orange ('39) 1.75 .70
264 A89 7s deep green ('39) .55 .15
265 A90 8s dk pur & pale vio ('39) .50 .20
266 A91 10s lake ('38) 2.75 .15
267 A92 12s indigo ('39) .55 .35
268 A93 14s rose lake & pale rose ('38) .55 .25
269 A94 20s ultra ('40) .55 .15
270 A95 25s dk brn & pale brn ('38) .55 .15
271 A96 30s pck blue ('39) 1.40 .15
a. Imperf., pair 375.00
272 A97 50s ol & pale ol ('39) .70 .15
a. Pale olive (forest) omitted
273 A98 1y brn & pale brn ('39) 2.75 .35
274 A99 5y dp gray grn ('39) 20.00 1.40
275 A100 10y dk brn vio ('39) 13.00 1.00
Nos. 257-275 (19) 50.55 6.30

Nos. 257 to 261, 265, 268, 270, 272 and 273 are typographed; the others are engraved.

Coil Stamps

1938-39 Typo. *Perf. 13 Horiz.*

276 A82 ½s purple ('39) 3.00 4.50
277 A84 2s crimson 3.25 4.75
278 A86 4s dark green 3.25 4.75
279 A93 14s rose lake & pale rose 85.00 67.50
Nos. 276-279 (4) 94.50 81.50

See Nos. 329, 331, 333, 341, 351, 360 and 361. For surcharges see Nos. B4-B5, Burma 2N4-2N27, China-Taiwan, 8-9, People's Republic of China 2L3, 2L7, 2L9-2L10, 2L39, Korea 55-56. For overprints see Ryukyu Islands (US Specialized) Nos. 2X1-2X2, 2X4-2X7, 2X10, 2X13-2X14, 2X17, 2X20, 2X23, 2X27, 2X29, 2X33-2X34, 3X2-3X7, 3X10-3X11, 3X14, 3X17, 3X19, 3X21, 3X23, 3X26-3X30, 5X1-5X3, 5X5-5X8, 5X10.

Mount Nantai — A101

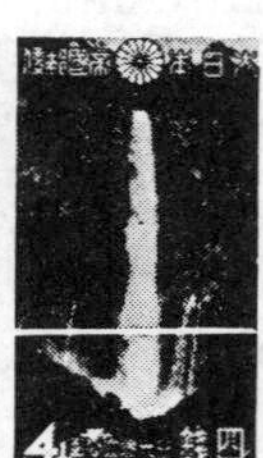
Kegon Falls — A102

Sacred Bridge, Nikko A103

Mount Hiuchi A104

Unwmk.

1938, Dec. 25 Photo. *Perf. 13*

280 A101 2s brown orange .85 .60
281 A102 4s olive green .85 .60
282 A103 10s deep rose 6.75 4.50
283 A104 20s dark blue 6.75 4.50
a. Souvenir sheet of 4, #280-283 70.00 70.00
Nos. 280-283 (4) 15.20 10.20
Set, never hinged 32.50

Nikko National Park.
No. 283a sold for 50s.

Many souvenir sheets were sold in folders. Values are for sheets without folders.

Mount Daisen A106

Yashima Plateau, Inland Sea A107

Abuto Kwannon Temple A108

Tomo Bay, Inland Sea — A109

1939, Apr. 20

285 A106 2s lt brown .95 .60
286 A107 4s yellow grn 1.90 1.25
287 A108 10s dull rose 8.50 4.75
288 A109 20s blue 8.50 4.75
a. Souvenir sheet of 4, #285-288 30.00 32.50
Nos. 285-288 (4) 19.85 11.35
Set, never hinged 40.00

Daisen and Inland Sea National Parks.
No. 288a sold for 50s.

View from Kuju Village, Kyushu A111

Mount Naka A112

Crater of Mount Naka A113

Volcanic Cones of Mt. Aso A114

1939, Aug. 15

290 A111 2s olive brown .85 .50
291 A112 4s yellow green 2.75 1.90
292 A113 10s carmine 17.50 10.00
293 A114 20s sapphire 25.00 11.00
a. Souvenir sheet of 4, #290-293 95.00 90.00
Nos. 290-293 (4) 46.10 23.40
Set, never hinged 100.00

Aso National Park. No. 293a sold for 50s.

Globe — A116

Tsunetami Sano — A117

1939, Nov. 15 *Perf. 12½*

Cross in Carmine

295 A116 2s brown 1.40 .90
296 A117 4s yellow green 1.50 1.00
297 A116 10s crimson 9.00 7.75
298 A117 20s sapphire 9.00 7.75
Nos. 295-298 (4) 20.90 17.40
Set, never hinged 40.00

Intl. Red Cross Society founding, 75th anniv.

Sacred Golden Kite — A118

Mount Takachiho — A119

Five Ayu Fish and Sake Jar — A120

Kashiwara Shrine — A121

1940 Engr. *Perf. 12*

299 A118 2s brown orange .80 .80
300 A119 4s dark green .60 .48
301 A120 10s dark carmine 3.75 3.50
302 A121 20s dark ultra .80 .80
Nos. 299-302 (4) 5.95 5.58
Set, never hinged 7.00

2,600th anniv. of the legendary date of the founding of Japan.

Mt. Hokuchin, Hokkaido A122

Mt. Asahi, Hokkaido A123

Sounkyo Gorge — A124

Tokachi Mountain Range A125

1940, Apr. 20 Photo. *Perf. 13*

303 A122 2s brown .85 .75
304 A123 4s yellow green 3.00 2.00
305 A124 10s carmine 8.25 6.00
306 A125 20s sapphire 8.25 6.50
a. Souvenir sheet of 4, #303-306 250.00 250.00
Nos. 303-306 (4) 20.35 15.25
Set, never hinged 40.00

Daisetsuzan National Park. No. 306a sold for 50s.

Mt. Karakuni, Kyushu A127

Mt. Takachiho A128

Torii of Kirishima Shrine A129

Lake of the Six Kwannon A130

1940, Aug. 21

308 A127 2s brown .80 .55
309 A128 4s green 1.75 1.40
310 A129 10s carmine 6.00 4.50
311 A130 20s deep ultra 7.25 5.50
a. Souvenir sheet of 4, #308-311 200.00 200.00
Nos. 308-311 (4) 15.80 11.95
Set, never hinged 35.00

Kirishima National Park.
No. 311a sold for 50s.

Education Minister with Rescript on Education A132

Characters Signifying Loyalty and Filial Piety A133

1940, Oct. 25 Engr. *Perf. 12½*

313 A132 2s purple .75 .75
314 A133 4s green .90 .90
Set, never hinged 2.00

50th anniv. of the imperial rescript on education, given by Emperor Meiji to clarify Japan's educational policy.

Mt. Daiton, Taiwan A134

Central Peak of Mt. Niitaka A135

Buddhist Temple on Mt. Kwannon A136

View from Mt. Niitaka A137

1941, Mar. 10 Photo. *Perf. 13*

315 A134	2s	brown	1.00	.75
316 A135	4s	brt green	1.75	1.00
317 A136	10s	rose red	6.00	3.00
318 A137	20s	brilliant ultra	7.50	4.00
a.		Souvenir sheet of 4, #315-318	70.00	60.00
		Nos. 315-318 (4)	16.25	8.75
		Set, never hinged	35.00	

Daiton and Niitaka-Arisan National Parks. #318a sold with #323a in same folder for 90s.

Seisui Precipice, East Taiwan Coast — A139

Taroko Gorge — A141

Mt. Tsugitaka A140

Upper River Takkiri District A142

1941, Mar. 10

320 A139	2s	brown	1.10	.75
321 A140	4s	brt green	1.65	1.00
322 A141	10s	rose red	5.50	2.00
323 A142	20s	bril ultra	7.50	3.50
a.		Souvenir sheet of 4, #320-323	75.00	60.00
		Nos. 320-323 (4)	15.75	7.25
		Set, never hinged	35.00	

Tsugitaka-Taroko National Park. See note after No. 318.

War Factory Girl — A144

Building of Wooden Ship — A145

Hyuga Monument and Mt. Fuji — A146

War Worker and Planes — A147

Palms and Map of "Greater East Asia" — A148

"Enemy Country Surrender" — A149

Aviator Saluting and Japanese Flag — A150

Torii of Yasukuni Shrine — A151

Mt. Fuji and Cherry Blossoms — A152

Torii of Miyajima — A153

Garambi Lighthouse, Taiwan — A154

Typographed; Engraved

1942-45 Wmk. 257 *Perf. 13*

325 A144	1s	orange brn ('43)	.15	.15
328 A145	2s	green	.35	.25
329 A84	3s	brown ('44)	.45	.20
330 A146	4s	emerald	.15	.15
331 A86	5s	brown lake	.20	.15
332 A147	6s	lt ultra ('44)	.35	.25
a.		Imperf., pair		
333 A86	7s	org ver ('44)	.20	.15
334 A148	10s	crim & dl rose	.35	.15
a.		Dull rose (map) omitted	350.00	350.00
335 A149	10s	lt gray ('45)	2.00	2.00
336 A150	15s	dull blue	1.40	.85
337 A151	17s	gray vio ('43)	.45	.35
338 A152	20s	blue ('44)	.45	.15
339 A151	27s	rose brn ('45)	.45	.35
340 A153	30s	bluish grn ('44)	1.40	.55
341 A88	40s	dull violet	.35	.15
342 A154	40s	dk violet ('44)	1.00	.85
		Nos. 325,328-342 (16)	9.70	6.70

Nos. 325-335, 337-340 and 342 are typo. Nos. 336 and 341 are engr.

Nos. 329, 331, 333-334, 342 issued with and without gum. No. 335 issued only without gum. These are valued without gum.

#328, 342 exist with watermark sideways. #328 exists printed on gummed side.

Most stamps of the above series exist in numerous shades.

For overprints and surcharges see North Borneo Nos. N34, N37, N41-N42, People's Republic of China 2L4, 2L8, Korea 57-60, Ryukyu Islands (US Specialized) Nos. 2X3, 2X9, 2X12, 2X15-2X16, 2X18-2X19, 2X21-2X22, 2X24-2X26, 2X28, 3X1, 3X8-3X9, 3X12-3X13, 3X15-3X16, 3X18, 3X20, 3X25, 3X31, 4X1-4X2, 5X4.

Kenkoku Shrine, Hsinking — A155

Boys of Japan and Manchukuo A156

Orchid Crest of Manchukuo A157

1942 Unwmk. Engr. *Perf. 12*

343 A155	2s	brown	.85	.85
344 A156	5s	olive	.50	.50
345 A155	10s	red	.75	.75
346 A157	20s	dark blue	1.90	1.90
		Nos. 343-346 (4)	4.00	4.00
		Set, never hinged	5.00	

The 2s and 10s were issued Mar. 1 for the 10th anniv. of the creation of Manchukuo; 5s and 20s on Sept. 15 for the 10th anniv. of Japanese diplomatic recognition of Manchukuo.

C-59 Locomotive — A158

Yasukuni Shrine, Tokyo — A159

1942, Oct. 14 Photo.

347 A158	5s	Prus green	3.50	3.50
		Never hinged	4.00	

70th anniv. of Japan's 1st railway.

1944, June 29 *Perf. 13*

348 A159	7s	Prus green	.60	.60
		Never hinged	1.00	

75th anniversary of Yasukuni Shrine.

Kwantung Shrine and Map of Kwantung Peninsula — A160

1944, Oct. 1

349 A160	3s	red brown	3.00	5.25
350 A160	7s	gray violet	3.25	5.25
		Set, never hinged	8.00	

Dedication of Kwantung Shrine, Port Arthur.

Sun and Cherry Blossoms — A161

Sunrise at Sea and Plane — A162

Coal Miners — A163

Yasukuni Shrine — A164

Lithographed, Typographed

1945-47 Wmk. 257 *Imperf.*

Without Gum

351 A84	2s	rose red	.35	.35
352 A161	3s	rose carmine	.20	.30
353 A162	5s	green	.20	.20
a.		5s blue	8.00	8.00
354 A149	10s	lt gray	9.00	9.00
354A A149	10s	blue	22.50	
355 A152	10s	red orange	.20	.15
356 A152	20s	ultra ('46)	.40	.15
357 A153	30s	brt blue ('46)	1.50	.90
358 A163	50s	dark brown ('46)	.30	.15
a.		Souvenir sheet of 5 ('47)	11.00	13.00
359 A164	1y	dp ol grn ('46)	.90	.90
360 A99	5y	dp gray grn	5.00	.80
361 A100	10y	dk brown vio	35.00	.90
		Nos. 351-354,355-361 (11)	53.05	13.80

Nos. 351 and 354 are typographed. The other stamps in this set are printed by offset lithography.

No. 358a was issued with marginal inscriptions to commemorate the Sapporo (Hokkaido) Philatelic Exhibition, Nov., 1947.

Nos. 351 to 361 are on grayish paper, and Nos. 355 to 361 also exist on white paper.

Most stamps of the above series exist in numerous shades and with private perforation or roulette.

See No. 404. For overprints see Ryukyu Islands (US Specialized) Nos. 2X8, 2X11, 2X30, 3X22, 4X3, 5X9.

Baron Hisoka Maejima — A165

Horyu Temple Pagoda — A166

"Thunderstorm below Fuji," by Hokusai — A167

"First Geese," Print by Hokusai — A168

Kintai Bridge, Iwakuni — A169

Kiyomizu Temple, Kyoto — A170

Goldfish — A171

Noh Mask — A172

Plum Blossoms — A173

Characters Read Right to Left

1946-47 Wmk. 257 Litho. *Imperf.*

Without Gum

362 A165	15s	dark green	.38	.25
363 A166	30s	dull lilac	.50	.15
364 A167	1y	ultra	.65	.18
a.		1y deep ultramarine	1.90	.15
b.		1y light blue	.75	.15
365 A168	1.30y	olive bister	2.25	.52
366 A169	1.50y	dark gray	2.25	.38
367 A170	2y	vermilion	2.00	.15
a.		Souvenir sheet of 5 ('47)	22.50	21.00
368 A171	5y	lilac rose	7.25	.48
		Nos. 362-368 (7)	15.28	2.11

Engr.

369 A172	50y	bister brn	70.00	.75
370 A173	100y	brn car ('47)	70.00	.75

Perf. 13

371 A172	50y	bis brn, with gum ('47)	70.00	.75
372 A173	100y	brn car, with gum ('47)	70.00	.38

Litho.

Perf. 13x13½, 12, 12x12½

373 A166	30s	dull lilac	2.75	2.75

Rouletted in Colored Lines

Typo. Unwmk.

With Gum

374 A166	30s	deep lilac	1.00	1.50

Nos. 363, 368, 373 exist with and without gum, valued without gum, as are Nos. 371-372, 374.

No. 367a for the "Know Your Stamps" exhibition, Kyoto, Aug. 19-24, 1947. Size: 113x71mm

#362, 369 exist with watermark horizontal.

See Nos. 384-387, 512A. For overprints see Ryukyu Islands (US Specialized) Nos. 2X32, 3X24, 4X4.

Catalogue values for unused stamps in this section, from this point to the end of the section, are for Never Hinged items.

Medieval Postman's Bell A175

Baron Hisoka Maejima A176

Design of First Japanese Stamp — A177

Communication Symbols — A178

Perf. 12½, 13½x13

1946, Dec. 12 Engr. Unwmk.

With Gum

375 A175 15s orange 5.75 3.25
376 A176 30s deep green 6.75 4.25
377 A177 50s carmine 3.00 2.25
378 A178 1y deep blue 3.00 2.25
a. Souvenir sheet of 4, #375-378, imperf. 175.00 175.00
Nos. 375-378 (4) 18.50 12.00

Government postal service in Japan, 75th anniv.

No. 378a measures 183x125mm and is ungummed. There were 2 printings: I - The 4 colors were printed simultaneously. Arched top inscription in high relief (2,000 sheets). II - Stamps were printed in one step, sheet inscriptions in another. Top inscription flat, almost level with paper's surface (49,000 sheets). 1st printing value $950.

Mother and Child, Diet Building
A180

Bouquet of Japanese May Flowers
A181

Perf. 12½

1947, May 3 Litho. Wmk. 257

380 A180 50s rose brown .25 .30
381 A181 1y brt ultra .52 .42
a. Souv. sheet of 2, #380-381, imperf. 11.00 6.00
b. As "a," 50s stamp omitted 1,000.
c. As "a," 1y stamp omitted 1,000.

Inauguration of the constitution of May 3, 1947.

A182

1947, Aug. 15 Photo. *Perf. 12½*

382 A182 1.20y brown 2.25 1.10
383 A182 4y brt ultra 4.50 1.50

Reopening of foreign trade on a private basis.

The ornaments on No. 383 differ from those shown in the illustration.

Types of 1946 Redrawn
Characters Read Left to Right

1947-48 Wmk. 257 Typo. *Perf. 13*

384 A166 30s deep lilac 1.65 1.40
385 A166 1.20y lt olive grn 1.10 .35
a. Souvenir sheet of 15 200.00 140.00
386 A170 2y vermilion ('48) 4.25 .20
387 A168 4y lt ultra 2.75 .28
Nos. 384-387 (4) 9.75 2.23

No. 385a was issued with marginal inscriptions to commemorate the "Know Your Stamps" Exhibition, Tokyo, May, 1947.

On No. 386, the chrysanthemum crest has been eliminated and the top inscription centered.

Plum Blossoms — A183

1947 Typo. *Imperf.*

388 A183 10y dk brown vio 35.00 .80

This stamp is similar to type A100 but with new inscription "Nippon Yubin" (Japan Post), reading from left to right. The characters for the denomination are likewise transposed.

A184

A185

Baron Hisoka Maejima
A186

Whaling
A187

National Art, Imperial Treasure House, Nara — A188

1947 Typo. *Perf. 13x13½*

389 A184 35s green .45 .30

Litho.

390 A185 45s lilac rose .65 .55
a. Imperf., pair 700.00
b. Perf. 11x13½ 4.50 4.50
391 A186 1y dull brown 2.75 .40

Typo.

392 A187 5y blue 6.75 .15
a. Imperf., pair 600.00
b. Perf. 11x13½ 22.50 2.75

Engr.

Perf. 13½x13

393 A188 10y lilac 18.00 .15
a. Imperf., pair
Nos. 389-393 (5) 28.60 1.55

No. 389 was produced on both rotary and flat press. Sheets of the rotary press printing have a border. Those of the flat press printing have none.

Lily of the Valley — A188a

1947, Sept. 13 Unwmk. *Perf. 12½*

394 A188a 2y dk Prus green 3.25 1.40

Relief of Ex-convicts Day, Sept. 13, 1947.

Souvenir Sheet

A189

1947 Wmk. 257 Litho. *Imperf.*

Without Gum

395 A189 Sheet of 5, ultra 2.75 3.00

Stamp Hobby Week, Nov. 1-7, 1947. Sheet size: 113½x71½mm, on white or grayish paper.

"Benkei," 1880 Locomotive — A190

1947, Oct. 14 Unwmk. Engr.

396 A190 4y deep ultra 15.00 15.00

75th anniv. of railway service in Japan.

Hurdling
A191

Diving
A192

Discus Throwing
A193

Volleyball
A194

1947, Oct. 25 Photo. *Perf. 12½*

With Gum

397 A191 1.20y red violet 10.00 6.50
398 A192 1.20y red violet 10.00 6.50
399 A193 1.20y red violet 10.00 6.50
400 A194 1.20y red violet 10.00 6.50
a. Block of 4, #397-400 55.00 30.00

2nd Natl. Athletic Meet, held in Kanazawa, Oct. 30-Nov. 3.

Souvenir Sheets

A195

1948 Wmk. 257 Litho. *Imperf.*

Without Gum

401 A195 Sheet of 2, #368 14.00 14.00

Same, Inscribed with Three instead of Two Japanese Characters at Bottom Center

402 A195 Sheet of 2, #368 16.00 14.00

Philatelic exhibitions at Osaka (No. 401) and Nagoya (No. 402).

Stylized Tree — A196

National Art Treasure, Nara — A197

Perf. 12½

1948, Apr. 1 Unwmk. Photo.

403 A196 1.20y dp yellow grn .70 .60

Forestation movement. Sheets of 30, marginal inscription.

Coal Miners Type of 1946, and Type A197

Wmk. 257

1948 Litho. With Gum *Perf. 13*

404 A163 50s dark brown 1.00 .50

Typo.

405 A197 10y rose violet 17.00 .15
a. Imperf., pair

See No. 515A.

School Children — A198

Perf. 12½

1948, May 3 Unwmk. Photo.

406 A198 1.20y dark carmine .75 .60

Reorganization of Japan's educational system. Sheets of 30, marginal inscription.

Souvenir Sheets
No. 402 Overprinted at Top, Bottom and Sides with Japanese Characters and Flowers in Green

1948, Apr. 3 Wmk. 257 *Imperf.*

407 A195 Sheet of 2 70.00 35.00
a. Overprint inverted 250.00
b. Overprint on No. 401 175.00

Mishima Philatelic Exhibition, Apr. 3-9.

No. 395 Overprinted at Top and Bottom With Japanese Characters in Plum

1948, Apr. 18

408 A189 Sheet of 5, ultra 25.00 21.00

Centenary of the death of Katsushika Hokusai, painter.

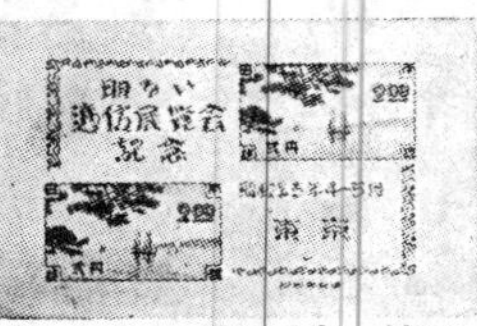
Sampans on Inland Sea, Near Suma — A199

Engr. & Litho.

1948, Apr. 22 Unwmk. *Imperf.*

Without Gum

409 A199 Sheet of 2 10.50 5.50

Communications Exhib., Tokyo, Apr. 27-May 3, 1948. Sheet contains two 2y deep carmine stamps.

Sheet exists with green border omitted.

1948, May 20

With Gum

410 A199 Sheet of 2, ultra border 18.00 12.00

Aomori Newspaper and Stamp Exhibition. Border design of apples and apple blossoms.

Type A199 With Altered Border and Inscriptions

1948, May 23

With Gum

411 A199 Sheet of 2, blue border 18.00 12.00

Fukushima Stamp Exhibition. Border design of cherries and crossed lines.

Horse Race — A200

1948, June 6 Photo. *Perf. 12½*

With Gum

412 A200 5y brown 2.25 .60

25th anniv. of the enforcement of Japan's horse racing laws. Each sheet contains 30 stamps and 2 labels, with marginal inscription.

A201

A202

Wmk. 257

1948, Sept. 10 Litho. *Perf. 13*

413 A201 1.50y blue 1.40 .45
414 A202 3.80y lt brown 5.50 3.50

Souvenir Sheet

Imperf

415 Sheet of 4 35.00 22.50

Kumamoto Stamp Exhibition, Sept. 20. Souvenir sheet, issued Sept. 20, contains two each of 1.50y deep blue (A201) and 3.80y brown (A202).

Rectifying Tower — A203

Perf. 12½

1948, Sept. 14 Photo. Unwmk.

416 A203 5y dark olive bister 2.50 1.25

Government alcohol monopoly.

Swimmer — A204

Runner — A205

Designs: No. 419, High jumper. No. 420, Baseball players. No. 421, Bicycle racers.

1948

417 A204 5y blue 3.50 1.50
418 A205 5y green 8.00 3.00
419 A205 5y green 8.00 3.00
420 A205 5y green 8.00 3.00
421 A205 5y green 8.00 3.00
a. Block of 4, #418-421 47.50 15.00
Nos. 417-421 (5) 35.50 13.50

3rd Natl. Athletic Meet. Swimming matches held at Yawata, Sept. 16-19, field events, Fukuoka, Oct. 29-Nov. 3.

"Beauty Looking Back," Print by Moronobu — A206

1948, Nov. 29 *Perf. 13*

422 A206 5y brown 90.00 40.00
a. Sheet of 5 500.00 300.00
Hinged 325.00

Philatelic Week, Nov. 29-Dec. 5.
See Nos. 2418-2419.

Souvenir Sheet

1948, Dec. 3 *Imperf.*

Without Gum

423 A206 5y brown, sheet of 1 45.00 25.00

Kanazawa and Takaoka stamp exhibitions.

Child Playing Hane-tsuki — A207

1948, Dec. 13 **Litho.** *Perf. 13*

424 A207 2y scarlet 3.50 2.00

Issued to pay postage on New Year's cards, later for ordinary use.

Farm Woman A208

Whaling A209

Miner A210

Tea Picking A211

Girl Printer A212

Factory Girl with Cotton Bobbin A213

Mt. Hodaka A214

Planting A215

Postman A216

Blast Furnace A217

Locomotive Assembly A218

Typographed, Engraved

1948-49 **Wmk. 257** *Perf. 13x13½*

425 A208 2y green 1.25 .15
a. Overprinted with 4 characters in frame .50 .60
b. As "a," overprint inverted 150.00
426 A209 3y lt grnsh bl ('49) 6.50 .15
427 A210 5y olive bis 14.00 .15
a. Booklet pane of 20
428 A211 5y blue grn ('49) 37.50 4.50
429 A212 6y red org ('49) 7.25 .15
430 A210 8y brown org ('49) 7.25 .15
a. Booklet pane of 20
431 A213 15y blue 3.00 .15
432 A214 16y ultra ('49) 8.00 3.00
433 A215 20y dk green ('49) 30.00 .15
434 A216 30y violet bl ('49) 40.00 .15
435 A217 100y car lake ('49) 450.00 .80
436 A218 500y deep blue ('49) 425.00 1.40
Nos. 425-436 (12) 1,029. 10.90
Set, hinged 750.00

No. 425a has a red control overprint of four characters ("Senkyo Jimu," or "Election Business") arranged vertically in a rectangular frame. Each candidate received 1,000 copies.

Nos. 432, 435-436 are engraved.

See Nos. 511-512, 514-515, 518, 520, 521A-521B.

Souvenir Sheets

Typo. and Litho.

1948, Oct. 16 *Imperf.*

437 A213 15y blue, sheet of 1 42.50 25.00

Nagano Stamp Exhibition, Oct. 16.

1948, Nov. 2 *Imperf.*

438 A210 5y ol bis, sheet of 2 45.00 32.50

Shikoku Traveling Stamp Exhib., Nov. 1948.

Sampans on Inland Sea A219

Perf. 13x13½

1949 **Wmk. 257** **Engr.**

439 A219 10y rose lake 40.00 13.00
440 A219 10y car rose 30.00 11.00
441 A219 10y orange ver 27.50 12.00
442 A214 16y brt blue 12.50 5.00
Nos. 439-442 (4) 110.00 41.00
Set, hinged 80.00

Issued in sheets of 20 stamps with marginal inscription publicizing expositions at Takamatsu (#439), Okayama (#440) and Matsuyama (#441), Nagano Peace Exposition, Apr. 1-May 31, 1949 (#442).

Ice Skater — A221

Ski Jumper — A222

1949 **Unwmk.** **Photo.** *Perf. 12*

444 A221 5y violet 1.90 1.00
445 A222 5y ultra 2.25 1.00

Issued for the winter events of the 4th National Athletic Meet - skating at Suwa Jan. 27-30 and skiing at Sapporo Mar. 3-6. Issue dates: No. 444, Jan. 27; No. 445, Mar. 3.

Steamer in Beppu Bay — A223

1949, Mar. 10 **Engr.** *Perf. 13x13½*

446 A223 2y carmine & ultra .85 .60
447 A223 5y green & ultra 3.25 .80

Scene at Fair — A224

Stylized Trees — A225

1949, Mar. 15 **Photo.** *Imperf.*

448 A224 5y brt rose 2.00 .90
a. Perf. 13 2.50 1.00
b. Sheet of 20, imperf. 55.00 55.00

Issued to publicize the Japan Foreign Trade Fair, Yokohama, 1949.

No. 448a was printed in sheets of 50 (10x5); No. 448 in sheets of 20 (4x5) with marginal inscriptions (No. 448b).

1949, Apr. 1 **Unwmk.** *Perf. 12*

449 A225 5y bright green 8.00 .90

Issued to publicize the forestation movement.

Lion Rock A226

Daiho-zan (Mt. Ohmine) A227

Doro Gorge A228

Bridge Pier Rocks A229

1949, Apr. 10 **Photo.** *Perf. 13*

450 A226 2y brown 1.50 .50
451 A227 5y yellow grn 4.25 1.00
452 A228 10y scarlet 18.00 4.00
453 A229 16y blue 8.50 1.50
a. Souv. sheet of 4, #450-453, no gum 40.00 32.50
b. As "a," 10y stamp omitted
Nos. 450-453 (4) 32.25 7.00

Yoshino-Kumano National Park.
No. 453a sold for 40y.

Boy — A230

Radio Tower and Star — A231

1949, May 5 *Perf. 12*

455 A230 5y rose brn & org 4.00 1.25
a. Orange omitted 450.00

Children's Day, May 5, 1949.

Souvenir Sheets

1949, May 5 *Imperf.*

456 A230 5y rose brn & org, sheet of 10 325.00 250.00
Hinged 250.00

Children's Exhib., Inuyama, Apr. 1-May 31.

1949, May 11 *Perf. 13*

457 A231 20y dp blue, sheet of 1 140.00 100.00
Hinged 75.00

Electrical Communication Week, May 11-18.

Symbols of Communication A232

Central Meteorological Observatory, Tokyo A233

Wmk. 257

1949, June 1 **Engr.** *Perf. 12*

458 A232 8y brt ultra 3.50 1.10

Establishment of the Post Ministry and the Ministry of Electricity and Communication.

1949, June 1 **Unwmk.** *Perf. 12½*

459 A233 8y deep green 3.50 1.10

75th anniv. of the establishment of the Central Meteorological Observatory.

Mt. Fuji in Autumn A234

Lake Kawaguchi A235

Fuji from Mt. Shichimen A236

Shinobuno Village and Mt. Fuji A237

1949, July 15 **Photo.** *Perf. 13*

460 A234 2y yellow brown 2.50 .65
461 A235 8y yellow green 5.00 1.00
462 A236 14y carmine lake 2.50 .40
463 A237 24y blue 4.00 .60
a. Souvenir sheet of 4, #460-463 50.00 30.00
Nos. 460-463 (4) 14.00 2.65

Fuji-Hakone National Park.
No. 463a sold for 55y.

Allegory of Peace
A238

Doves over Nagasaki — A239

Perf. 13x13½, 13½x13

1949 Photo. Unwmk.

465 A238 8y yellow brown	5.75	1.50
466 A239 8y green	4.25	1.25

Establishment of Hiroshima as the City of Eternal Peace and of Nagasaki as the International City of Culture. Issued: #465, Aug. 6; #466, Aug. 9.

Boy Scout — A240

Pen Nib of Newspaper Stereotype Matrix — A241

1949, Sept. 22 *Perf. 13x13½*

467 A240 8y brown	5.25	2.00

Natl. Boy Scout Jamboree.

1949, Oct. 1 *Perf. 13½x13*

468 A241 8y deep blue	4.00	1.50

Natl. Newspaper Week.

Racing Swimmer Poised for Dive — A242

Javelin Thrower — A243

1949 *Perf. 13½*

469 A242 8y dull blue	2.50	1.10

Perf. 12

470 A243 8y shown	3.75	1.90
471 A243 8y Yacht Racing	3.75	1.90
472 A243 8y Relay Race	3.75	1.90
473 A243 8y Tennis	3.75	1.90
a. Block of 4, #470-473	27.50	9.50
Nos. 469-473 (5)	17.50	8.70

4th Natl. Athletic Meet. The swimming matches were held at Yokohama, Sept. 15-18 and the fall events at Tokyo, Oct. 30.

Issued: #469, Sept. 15; #470-473, Oct. 30.

Map and Envelopes Forming "75" — A244

Symbols of UPU — A245

1949, Oct. 10 Engr. *Perf. 12, 13½*

474 A244 2y dull green	1.90	.50
475 A245 8y maroon	2.25	.50
a. Souv. sheet of 2, #474-475, imperf.	4.00	4.00
476 A244 14y carmine	7.25	2.50
477 A245 24y aqua	11.00	2.50
a. Imperf., pair		
Nos. 474-477 (4)	22.40	6.00

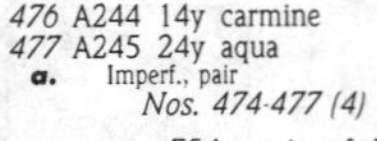

75th anniv. of the UPU.

Floating Zenith Telescope
A246

"Moon and Geese," Print by Hiroshige
A247

1949, Oct. 30 Photo. *Perf. 12*

478 A246 8y dk blue grn	2.50	1.00

50th anniv. of the Mizusawa Latitudinal Observatory.

1949, Nov. 1 *Perf. 13x13½*

479 A247 8y purple	110.00	30.00
a. Sheet of 5	650.00	400.00
Sheet, hinged	450.00	

Postal Week, Nov. 1-7. See #2420-2421.

Dr. Hideyo Noguchi
A248

Yukichi Fukuzawa
A249

Soseki Natsume
A250

Shoyo Tsubouchi
A251

Danjuro Ichikawa
A252

Joseph Hardy Niijima
A253

Hogai Kano
A254

Kanzo Uchimura
A255

Ichiyo Higuchi — A256

Ogai Mori — A257

Shiki Masaoka — A258

Shunso Hishida — A259

Amane Nishi — A260

Kenjiro Ume — A261

Hisashi Kimura — A262

Inazo Nitobe — A263

Torahiko Terada — A264

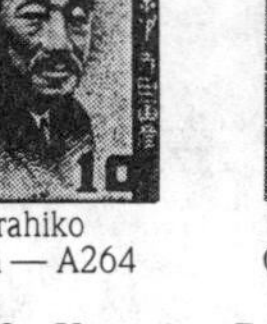

Tenshin Okakura — A265

1949-52 Unwmk. Engr. *Perf. 12½*

480 A248 8y green	9.00	.80
a. Imperf., pair		
481 A249 8y deep olive ('50)	4.00	.80
a. Imperf., pair		
482 A250 8y dk Prus grn ('50)	4.00	.80
483 A251 8y Prus grn ('50)	4.00	.80
a. Imperf., pair		
484 A252 8y dk violet ('50)	10.00	2.25
485 A253 8y vio brn ('50)	4.00	.80
486 A254 8y dk green ('51)	7.50	1.50
487 A255 8y dp purple ('51)	7.50	1.50
488 A256 8y carmine ('51)	13.50	2.00
489 A257 8y vio brn ('51)	22.50	2.50
490 A258 8y choc ('51)	13.50	2.50
491 A259 8y dk blue ('51)	11.00	2.50
492 A260 10y dk green ('52)	60.00	4.00
493 A261 10y brn vio ('52)	11.00	1.00
494 A262 10y carmine ('52)	4.00	1.00
495 A263 10y dk grn ('52)	4.75	1.00
496 A264 10y choc ('52)	4.25	1.25
497 A265 10y dk blue ('52)	5.50	1.00
Nos. 480-497 (18)	200.00	28.00
Set, hinged	140.00	

Tiger — A266

Microphones of 1925 and 1950 — A267

1950, Feb. 1 Photo. *Perf. 12*

498 A266 2y dark red	5.00	1.25

6th prize (lottery), sheet of 5, value $140.

1950, Mar. 21 *Perf. 13*

499 A267 8y ultra	2.75	1.00

25th anniversary of broadcasting in Japan. Sheets of 20 with marginal inscription.

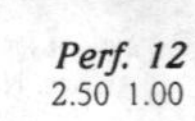

Dove and Olive Twig on Letter Box — A268

1950, Apr. 20 *Perf. 12*

500 A268 8y dp yellow grn	2.50	1.00

Day of Posts, Apr. 20.

Lake Akan and Mt. Akan
A269

Lake Kutcharo, Hokkaido
A270

Mt. Akan-Fuji
A271

Lake Mashu
A272

1950, July 15 Unwmk. *Perf. 13*

501 A269 2y yellow brn	2.00	.50
502 A270 8y dp yellow grn	2.50	1.00
503 A271 14y rose car	11.00	3.00
504 A272 24y brt blue	14.00	4.00
a. Souvenir sheet of 4, #501-504	55.00	32.50

Akan National Park.
No. 504a sold for 55y.

Gymnast on Rings — A273

Designs: No. 506, Pole vault. No. 507, Soccer. No. 508, Equestrian.

1950, Oct. 28 *Perf. 13½x13*

505 A273 8y rose brown	25.00	6.00
506 A273 8y rose brown	25.00	6.00
507 A273 8y rose brown	25.00	6.00
508 A273 8y rose brown	25.00	6.00
a. Strip of 4, #505-508	110.00	
b. Block of 4, #505-508	190.00	
As "b," hinged	125.00	

5th National Athletic Meet. Sheets of 20 stamps in which each horizontal row contains all four designs.

Types of 1947-49 and

Ishiyama-dera Pagoda — A274

Hisoka Maejima — A275

Long-tailed Cock of Tosa — A276

Goddess Kannon — A277

Himeji Castle — A278

Nyoirin Kannon of Chuguji — A280

Phoenix Hall, Byodoin Temple A279

Perf. 13x13½, 13½x13 (14y)

1950-52 Typo. Unwmk.

509	A274 80s carmine ('51)		1.25	1.25
a.	Sheet of 1		6.00	6.50
	Photo.			
510	A275 1y dk brown ('51)		2.00	.30
a.	Souvenir sheet of 4		10.00	9.00
	Typo.			
511	A208 2y green ('51)		1.65	.15
512	A209 3y lt grnsh bl ('51)		45.00	1.00
512A	A168 4y lt ultra ('52)		32.50	.80
513	A276 5y dp grn & org brn ('51)		4.75	.15
a.	Orange brown omitted		250.00	
514	A212 6y red org ('51)		5.00	.25
515	A210 8y dk org brn ('51)		40.00	.40
515A	A197 10y rose vio ('51)		72.50	4.50
516	A277 10y red brn & lil ('51)		18.00	.15
	Engr.			
517	A278 14y brn & car ('51)		50.00	20.00
a.	Sheet of 1		70.00	50.00
	Typo.			
518	A215 20y dk green ('51)		65.00	.70
	Engr.			
519	A279 24y dp ultra		30.00	10.00
a.	Sheet of 1		35.00	32.50
	Typo.			
520	A216 30y vio bl ('52)		165.00	1.00
	Photo.			
521	A280 50y dk brown ('51)		140.00	.90
	Hinged		110.00	
c.	Sheet of 1		275.00	225.00
	Hinged		165.00	
	Engr.			
521A	A217 100y car lake ('52)		400.00	1.00
521B	A218 500y dp blue ('52)		375.00	1.50
	Nos. 509-521B (17)		1,447.	44.05

No. 510a for the 80th anniv. of Japan's postal service. On No. 512A, characters read from left to right.

Compare designs: A274 with A314c; A275 with A314a, A447, A563a; A277 with A332a; A279 with A385a; A280 with A565f.

Girl and Rabbit — A281

1951, Jan. 1 Photo. *Perf. 12*

522	A281 2y rose pink	4.25	.60

9th prize (lottery), sheet of 5, value $45.

Scenic Spots Issue

Skiers on Mt. Zao A282 A283

1951, Feb. 15 *Perf. 13*

523	A282 8y olive	16.00	1.40
524	A283 24y blue	19.00	3.50

Tea Picking — A284

Mt. Fuji Seen from Nihon Plateau — A285

Nihon-daira Plateau.

1951, Apr. 2

525	A284 8y olive green	19.00	3.00
526	A285 24y bright blue	80.00	12.00

Hot Springs, Hakone — A286

Lake Ashi, Hakone — A287

1951, May 25

527	A286 8y chestnut brown	9.00	1.75
528	A287 24y deep blue	7.00	2.00

Senju Waterfall A288

Ninai Waterfall A289

Akame 48 Waterfalls.

1951, June 1

529	A288 8y deep green	7.75	2.00
530	A289 24y deep blue	11.00	1.40

Pavilion, Wakanoura Bay — A290

Wakanoura Bay — A291

Wakanoura & Tomogashima.

1951, June 25

531	A290 8y brown	6.75	1.10
532	A291 24y brt blue	6.25	1.25

Uji River — A292

View from Uji Bridge — A293

Perf. 13x13½, 13½x13

1951, Aug. 1 Engr.

533	A292 8y brown	7.25	1.50
534	A293 24y deep blue	6.75	1.75

Oura Catholic Church, Nagasaki A294

Sofuku Temple A295

1951, Sept. 15 Photo. *Perf. 13½*

535	A294 8y carmine rose	9.00	.90
536	A295 24y dull blue	7.00	1.50

Marunuma A296

Sugenuma A297

1951, Oct. 1

537	A296 8y rose violet	11.00	1.00
a.	Imperf., pair		
538	A297 24y dull blue grn	5.75	1.25

Kakuenpo (peak) — A298

Nagatoro Bridge — A299

Shosenkyo Gorge.

1951, Oct. 15

539	A298 8y brown red	10.50	1.00
540	A299 24y dp Prus grn	10.00	1.25
	Nos. 523-540 (18)	249.00	39.55

Boy's Head and Seedling — A300

1951, May 5 *Perf. 13½*

541	A300 8y orange brown	25.00	1.75

Issued to publicize Children's Day, May 5, 1951.

Oirase River A301

Lake Towada A302

View from Kankodai A303

Mt. Hakkoda from Mt. Yokodake A304

1951, July 20 Photo. *Perf. 13x13½*

542	A301 2y brown	2.50	.50
543	A302 8y green	10.50	.85
544	A303 14y dark red	7.50	2.00
545	A304 24y blue	8.25	3.00
a.	Souvenir sheet of 4, #542-545	50.00	30.00
	Nos. 542-545 (4)	28.75	6.35

Towada Natl. Park. No. 545a sold for 55y.

Chrysanthemum A305

National Flag A306

1951, Sept. 9 *Perf. 13½*

546	A305 2y orange brown	2.75	.60
547	A306 8y slate blue & red	6.50	1.25
548	A305 24y blue green	15.00	3.25
	Nos. 546-548 (3)	24.25	5.10

Signing of the peace treaty of 1951.

Putting the Shot A307

Hockey A308

1951, Oct. 27

549	A307 2y orange brown	3.25	1.25
550	A308 2y gray blue	3.25	1.25
a.	Pair, #549-550	7.00	3.00

6th Natl. Athletic Meet, Hiroshima, Oct. 27-31.

Okina Mask — A309

1952, Jan. 16 Photo. *Perf. 13½x13*

551	A309 5y crimson rose	9.25	.40

Sheets reproducing four of these stamps with Japanese inscriptions and floral ornament at left were awarded as sixth prize in the national lottery. Value $85.

Southern Cross from Ship — A310

Earth and Big Dipper — A311

1952, Feb. 19

552	A310 5y purple	7.00	.60
553	A311 10y dark green	14.00	1.25

75th anniv. of Japan's admission to the UPU.

Red Cross and Lilies — A312

Red Cross Nurse — A313

1952, May 1

554 A312 5y rose red & dk red 5.00 .65
555 A313 10y dk green & red 11.00 1.25
a. Red cross omitted
b. Imperf., pair

75th anniv. of the formation of the Japanese Red Cross Society.

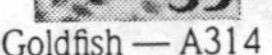

Goldfish — A314

A314a

A314b

A314c

Japanese Serow — A315

1952 *Perf. 13x13½*

556 A314 35y red orange 13.00 .15
a. Imperf., pair

Types of 1951
Redrawn; Zeros Omitted
Unwmk.

557 A314a 1y dark brown .25 .15
558 A314b 50y dark brown 5.75 .15

Typo.

559 A314c 4y dp cl & pale rose 1.75 .15
a. Background (pale rose) omitted

Ornamental frame and background added, denomination at upper left, Japanese characters at upper right.

Photo.

560 A315 8y brown .25 .15
Nos. 556-560 (5) 21.00
Set value .25

Mt. Yari — A316

Kurobe Valley — A317

Mt. Shirouma A318

Mt. Norikura A319

1952, July 5 *Perf. 13½x13, 13x13½*

561 A316 5y brown 5.25 .32
562 A317 10y blue green 24.00 1.25
563 A318 14y bright red 7.75 1.10
564 A319 24y bright blue 16.00 2.00
a. Souv. sheet of 4, #561-564, imperf. 85.00 65.00
Nos. 561-564 (4) 53.00 4.67

Japan Alps (Chubu-Sangaku) National Park.
No. 564a sold for 60y.

Yasuda Hall, Tokyo University A320

Yomei Gate, Nikko A321

1952, Oct. 1 **Engr.** *Perf. 13*

565 A320 10y dull green 17.00 1.25

75th anniversary of the founding of Tokyo University.

1952, Oct. 15 **Photo.** *Perf. 13x13½*

566 A321 45y blue 4.00 .15

Mountain Climber — A322

1952, Oct. 18
Dated "1952"

567 A322 5y shown 5.00 1.50
568 A322 5y Wrestlers 5.00 1.50
a. Pair, #567-568 20.00 4.00

7th Nat.l Athletic Meet, Fukushima, Oct. 18-22.

Mt. Azuma A323

Mt. Asahi A324

Mt. Bandai A325

Mt. Gatsun A326

Unwmk.
1952, Oct. 18 **Photo.** *Perf. 13*

569 A323 5y brown 3.25 .45
570 A324 10y olive grn 14.00 1.25
571 A325 14y rose red 7.00 1.65
572 A326 24y blue 11.00 3.25
a. Souv. sheet of 4, #569-572, imperf. 90.00 65.00
Nos. 569-572 (4) 35.25 6.60

Bandai-Asahi National Park.
No. 572a sold for 60y.

Kirin — A327

Flag of Crown Prince — A328

Engr. and Photo.
1952, Nov. 10 *Perf. 13½*

573 A327 5y red org & pur 2.50 .32
574 A327 10y red org & dk grn 3.25 .50
575 A328 24y deep blue 12.00 4.00
a. Souv. sheet of 3, #573-575, imperf. 90.00 125.00
Nos. 573-575 (3) 17.75 4.82

Issued to commemorate the nomination of Crown Prince Akihito as Heir Apparent.

No. 575a measures 130x129mm, and has a background design of phoenix and clouds in violet brown and blue. Sold for 50y.

Sambaso Doll — A329

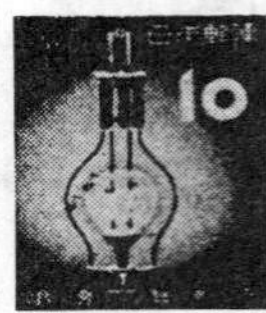

First Electric Lamp in Japan — A330

Perf. 13½x13
1953, Jan. 1 **Photo.** **Unwmk.**

576 A329 5y carmine 7.00 .40

For postage on New Year's cards, later for ordinary use.
Sheets of 4 were awarded as 6th prize in the natl. lottery. Value $70.

1953, Mar. 25

577 A330 10y brown 7.00 1.25

75th anniv. of electric lighting in Japan.

"Kintai Bridge," Print by Hiroshige A331

Kintai Bridge as Rebuilt in 1953 A332

1953, May 3 *Perf. 13*

578 A331 10y chestnut 6.00 2.00
579 A332 24y blue 6.00 2.25

Kannon Type of 1951
Redrawn; Zeros Omitted

A332a

1953-54 **Typo.**

580 A332a 10y red brn & lilac 4.50 .15
a. Booklet pane 10 + 2 labels (souvenir) ('54) 190.00 175.00
b. Bklt. pane 10 + 2 labels ('54) 95.00

No. 580a was issued in honor of Philatelic Week 1954. The inscriptions on the two labels are arranged in two rows of boldface characters.
On No. 580b, the label inscriptions are arranged in three rows of mixed heavy and thin characters.
See Nos. 611a-611b and 672.

Lake Shikotsu, Hokkaido A333

Mt. Yotei A334

1953, July 25 **Photo.** *Perf. 13*

581 A333 5y ultra 2.25 .45
582 A334 10y green 6.25 1.00
a. Souv. sheet of 2, #581-582, imperf., no gum 45.00 35.00

Shikotsu-Toya National Park.
No. 582a sold for 20 yen.

Akita Dog — A335

Cormorant Fishing — A336

1953 **Unwmk.**

583 A335 2y gray .25 .15

Engr.

584 A336 100y dark red 32.50 .15
a. Imperf., pair 600.00
Set value .15

See No. 1622.

Futamigaura Beach A337

Namikiri Coast A338

1953, Oct. 2 **Photo.**

585 A337 5y red 1.50 .50
586 A338 10y blue 3.50 .75
a. Souv. sheet of 2, #585-586, imperf., no gum 27.50 25.00

Ise-Shima National Park.

Phoenix — A339

Design: 10y, Japanese crane in flight.

1953, Oct. 12 **Engr.** *Perf. 12½*

587 A339 5y brown carmine 3.00 1.00

Photo.

588 A339 10y dark blue 7.00 1.75

Nos. 587-588 were issued on the occasion of the return of Crown Prince Akihito from his visit to Europe and America. Issued in sheets of 20 with marginal inscription.

Rugby Match — A340

Judo — A341

1953, Oct. 22 *Perf. 13½*

589 A340 5y black 6.00 1.00
590 A341 5y blue green 6.00 1.00
a. Pair, #589-590 16.00 3.00

8th Natl. Athletic Meet, Matsuyama, Oct. 22-26.

Sky and Top of Observatory — A342

1953, Oct. 29

591 A342 10y dk gray blue 10.00 1.00

75th anniversary of the Tokyo Astronomical Observatory.

Mt. Unzen from Golf Course A343

Mt. Unzen from Chijiwa Beach
A344

1953, Nov. 20 *Perf. 13*

592 A343	5y red	1.50	.32
593 A344	10y blue	3.75	.50
a.	Souv. sheet of 2, #592-593, imperf., no gum	26.00	25.00

Unzen National Park.

Toy Horse — A345

Racing Skaters — A346

1953, Dec. 25 *Perf. 13½x13*

594 A345	5y rose	5.50	.40

Issued to pay postage on New Year's cards, later for ordinary use. A sheet reproducing four of these stamps was awarded as sixth prize in the national lottery. Value $50.

1954, Jan. 16

595 A346	10y blue	4.00	1.00

World Speed Skating Matches for Men, Sapporo City, Jan. 16-17, 1954.

Golden Hall, Chusonji Temple — A347

Thread, Pearls, Gears, Buttons and Globe — A348

1954, Jan. 20

596 A347	20y olive green	.85	.15

1954, Apr. 10

597 A348	10y dark red	3.00	.65

International Trade Fair, Osaka, Apr. 10-23.

Little Cuckoo
A349

Wrestlers
A350

1954, May 10 *Perf. 13x13½*

598 A349	3y blue green	.15	.15
a.	Imperf., pair	350.00	

1954, May 22 **Engr.**

599 A350	10y deep green	2.25	.65

World Free Style Wrestling Championship Matches, Tokyo, 1954.

Mt. Asama
A351

Mt. Tanikawa
A352

1954, June 25 *Perf. 13*

600 A351	5y dk gray brn	1.65	.40
601 A352	10y dk blue grn	3.25	.90
a.	Souvenir sheet of 2, #600-601, no gum	26.00	25.00

Jo-Shin-etsu National Park.

Table Tennis — A353

Archery — A354

1954, Aug. 22 **Engr.** *Perf. 12*

602 A353	5y dull brown	3.50	.70
603 A354	5y gray green	3.50	.70
a.	Pair, #602-603	8.00	

9th Natl. Athletic Meet, Sapporo, Aug. 22-26.

Morse Telegraph Instrument
A355

ITU Monument
A356

Perf. 13x13½, 13½x13

1954, Oct. 13

604 A355	5y dark purple brown	2.25	.35
605 A356	10y deep blue	5.50	.60

75th anniv. of Japanese membership in the ITU.

Daruma Doll — A357

1954, Dec. 20 **Photo.** *Perf. 13½x13*

606 A357	5y black & red	4.50	.35

Sheets reproducing four of these stamps with Japanese inscriptions and ornaments were awarded as fifth prize in the national lottery. Value $50.

Mountain Stream, Tama Gorge — A358

Chichibu Mountains
A359

1955, Mar. 1 **Engr.** *Perf. 13*

607 A358	5y blue	1.90	.35
608 A359	10y red brown	2.50	.42
a.	Souv. sheet of 2, #607-608, imperf., no gum	25.00	20.00

Chichibu-Tama National Park.

Bridge and Iris — A360

1955, Mar. 15 *Perf. 13x13½*

609 A360	500y deep plum	100.00	.25

Paper Carp as Flown on Boys' Day
A361

Mandarin Ducks
A362

Unwmk.

1955, May 16 **Photo.** *Perf. 13*

610 A361	10y multicolored	3.75	.70

15th congress of the International Chamber of Commerce, Tokyo, May 16-21, 1955.

1955-64

611 A362	5y lt bl & red brn	.45	.15
a.	Bklt. pane, 4 #611, 8 #580 ('59)	26.00	
b.	Bklt. pane, 4 #611, 8 #725 ('63)	25.00	
c.	Bklt. pane of 4 ('64)	11.00	
d.	Imperf., pair	650.00	

See Nos. 738, 881d, 914b.

Benten Cape — A363

Jodo Beach
A364

1955, Sept. 30

612 A363	5y deep green	1.75	.22
613 A364	10y rose lake	2.50	.40
a.	Souv. sheet of 2, #612-613, imperf., no gum	26.00	20.00

Rikuchu-Kaigan National Park.
No. 613a sold for 20y.

Girl Athletes
A365

Runners
A366

1955, Oct. 30 **Engr.**

614 A365	5y brown lake	1.50	.40
615 A366	5y bluish black	1.50	.40
a.	Pair, #614-615	4.25	

10th National Athletic Meet, Kanagawa Prefecture.
See Nos. 639-640, 657.

"A Girl Blowing Glass Toy," by Utamaro
A367

1955, Nov. 1 **Photo.**

616 A367	10y multicolored	10.00	4.00

150th anniv. of the death of Utamaro, woodcut artist, and to publicize Philatelic Week, Nov. 1955. Issued in sheets of 10.

Kokeshi Dolls — A368

Table Tennis — A369

1955, Dec. 30 **Unwmk.** *Perf. 13*

617 A368	5y olive grn & red	2.50	.18

Sheets reproducing four of these stamps, were awarded as fifth prize in the New Year's lottery. Value $30.

1956, Apr. 2 *Perf. 13x13½*

618 A369	10y red brown	1.50	.35

Intl. Table Tennis Championship, Tokyo, 4/2-11.

Judo — A370

1956, May 2 *Perf. 13*

619 A370	10y green & lilac	1.75	.35

Issued to publicize the first World Judo Championship Meet, Tokyo, May 3, 1956.

Boy and Girl with Paper Carp
A371

1956, May 5

620 A371	5y lt blue & blk	1.25	.25

Establishment of World Children's Day, 5/5/56.

Water Plants, Lake Akan
A372

Big Purple Butterfly
A373

1956 **Unwmk.** *Perf. 13*

621 A372	55y lt blue, grn & blk	15.00	.15
622 A373	75y multicolored	7.75	.25

See Nos. 887A, 917.

Castle Type of 1951
Redrawn; Zeros Omitted

A373a

1956 **Engr.** *Perf. 13½x13*

623 A373a	14y gray olive	5.50	1.65

Osezaki Promontory
A374

Kujuku Island
A375

1956, Oct. 1 **Photo.**

624 A374	5y red brown	.85	.30

Engr. & Photo.

625 A375 10y lt blue & indigo 1.10 .40
  a. Souv. sheet of 2, #624-625, imperf., no gum 20.00 19.00

Saikai National Park.
No. 625a sold for 20y.

Palace Moat and Modern Tokyo
A376

1956, Oct. 1 **Engr.**
626 A376 10y dull purple 3.00 .40

500th anniv. of the founding of Tokyo.

Sakuma Dam — A377

1956, Oct. 15 **Unwmk.** ***Perf. 13***
627 A377 10y dark blue 2.50 .50

Completion of Sakuma Dam.

Long Jump
A378

Basketball
A379

1956, Oct. 28 ***Perf. 13½x13***
628 A378 5y brown violet .85 .30
629 A379 5y steel blue .85 .30
  a. Pair, #628-629 2.50

11th Natl. Athletic Meet, Hyogo Prefecture.
See No. 658.

Kabuki Actor Ebizo Ichikawa by Sharaku — A380

1956, Nov. 1 **Photo.** ***Perf. 13***
630 A380 10y multicolored 9.00 4.25

Stamp Week. Sheets of 10.

Mount Manaslu
A381

1956, Nov. 3
631 A381 10y multicolored 3.00 1.25

Japanese expedition which climbed Mount Manaslu in the Himalayas on May 9 and 11, 1956.

Electric Locomotive and Hiroshige's "Yui Stage"
A382

1956, Nov. 19 **Unwmk.** ***Perf. 13***
632 A382 10y dk ol bis, blk & grn 4.00 1.00

Electrification of Tokaido Line.

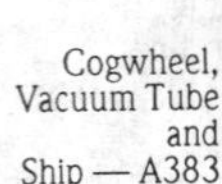

Cogwheel, Vacuum Tube and Ship — A383

1956, Dec. 18 **Engr.**
633 A383 10y ultra 1.25 .35

Japanese Machinery Floating Fair.

Toy Whale — A384

United Nations Emblem — A385

1956, Dec. 20 **Photo.**
634 A384 5y multicolored 1.50 .15
  a. Imperf., pair

Sheets reproducing four of these stamps, with inscriptions and ornaments, were awarded as sixth prize in the national lottery. Value $15.

Photogravure and Engraved

1957, Mar. 8 **Unwmk.** ***Perf. 13½x13***
635 A385 10y lt blue & dk car .75 .40

Japan's admission to the UN, Dec. 18, 1956.

Temple Type of 1950
Redrawn; Zeros Omitted

A385a

1957-59 **Engr.** ***Perf. 13x13½***
636 A385a 24y violet 20.00 2.00
636A A385a 30y rose lilac ('59) 40.00 .35
  b. Imperf., pair

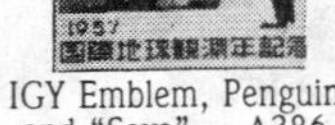

IGY Emblem, Penguin and "Soya" — A386

Atomic Reactor — A387

1957, July 1 **Photo.** ***Perf. 13***
637 A386 10y blue, yel & blk 1.10 .35

International Geophysical Year.

1957, Sept. 18 **Engr.** ***Perf. 13***
638 A387 10y dark purple .70 .15

Completion of Japan's atomic reactor at Tokai-Mura, Ibaraki Prefecture.

Sports Type of 1955

Designs: No. 639, Girl on parallel bars. No. 640, Boxers.

1957, Oct. 26 **Unwmk.** ***Perf. 13***
639 A366 5y ultra .70 .15
640 A366 5y dark red .70 .15
  a. Pair, #639-640 2.00
  Set value .20

12th Natl. Athletic Meet, Shizuoka Prefecture.

"Girl Bouncing Ball," by Suzuki Harunobu
A388

1957, Nov. 1 **Photo.**
641 A388 10y multicolored 2.25 1.00

1957 Stamp Week. Issued in sheets of 10. See Nos. 646, 671, 728, 757.

Lake Okutama and Ogochi Dam — A389

1957, Nov. 26 **Engr.** ***Perf. 13½***
642 A389 10y ultra .30 .15

Completion of Ogochi Dam, part of the Tokyo water supply system.

Modern and First Japanese Blast Furnaces
A390

Toy Dog (Inu-hariko)
A391

1957, Dec. 1 **Photo.** **Unwmk.**
643 A390 10y orange & dk pur .25 .15

Centenary of Japan's iron industry.

1957, Dec. 20 ***Perf. 13½x13***
644 A391 5y multicolored .30 .15

New Year 1958. Sheets reproducing 4 #644, with inscriptions and ornaments, were awarded as 5th prize in the New Year lottery. Value $6.

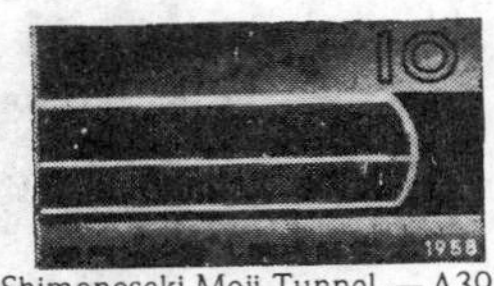

Shimonoseki-Moji Tunnel — A392

1958, Mar. 9 ***Perf. 13x13½***
645 A392 10y multicolored .35 .15

Completion of the Kan-Mon Underwater Highway connecting Honshu and Kyushu Islands.

Stamp Week Type of 1957

Design: 10y, Woman with Umbrella, woodcut by Kiyonaga.

1958, Apr. 20 **Unwmk.** ***Perf. 13***
646 A388 10y multicolored .80 .20

Stamp Week, 1958. Sheets of 10.

Statue of Ii Naosuke and Harbor
A393

Unwmk.

1958, May 10 **Engr.** ***Perf. 13***
647 A393 10y gray blue & car .25 .15

Cent. of the opening of the ports of Yokohama, Nagasaki and Hakodate to foreign powers.

National Stadium — A394

3rd Asian Games, Tokyo: 10y, Torch and emblem. 14y, Runner. 24y, Woman diver.

1958, May 24 **Photo.**
648 A394 5y bl grn, bis & pink .15 .15
649 A394 10y multicolored .25 .15
650 A394 14y multicolored .35 .15
651 A394 24y multicolored .40 .15
  Nos. 648-651 (4) 1.15
  Set value .45

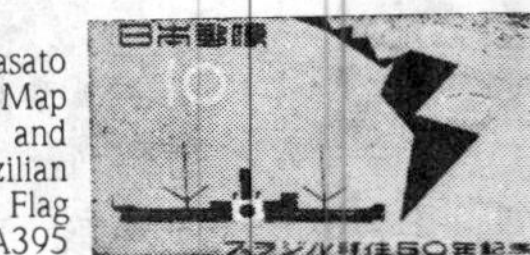

Kasato Maru, Map and Brazilian Flag
A395

1958, June 18
652 A395 10y multicolored .25 .15

50 years of Japanese emigration to Brazil.

Sado Island and Local Dancer — A396

Mt. Yahiko and Echigo Plain — A397

1958, Aug. 20 **Unwmk.** ***Perf. 13***
653 A396 10y multicolored .70 .15
654 A397 10y multicolored .70 .15
  Set value .24

Sado-Yahiko Quasi-National Park.

Stethoscope
A398

1958, Sept. 7 **Photo.** ***Perf. 13***
655 A398 10y Prussian green .30 .15

5th Intl. Cong. on Diseases of the Chest and the 7th Intl. Cong. of Bronchoesophagology.

"Kyoto" (Sanjo Bridge), Print by Hiroshige
A399

1958, Oct. 5
656 A399 24y multicolored 3.25 .40

Issued for International Letter Writing Week, Oct. 5-11. See No. 679.

Sports Types of 1955-56

Designs: No. 657, Weight lifter. No. 658, Girl badminton player.

1958, Oct. 19 **Engr.**
657 A365 5y gray blue .35 .15
658 A379 5y claret .35 .15
  a. Pair, #657-658 1.10

13th Natl. Athletic Meet, Toyama Prefecture.

Keio University and Yukichi Fukuzawa — A400

1958, Nov. 8 Engr. *Perf. 13½*

659 A400 10y magenta .45 .15

Centenary of Keio University.

Globe and Playing Children A401

1958, Nov. 23 Photo. *Perf. 13*

660 A401 10y deep green .40 .15

9th Intl. Conf. of Social Work and the 2nd Intl. Study Conf. on Child Welfare.

Flame: Symbol of Human Rights — A402

1958, Dec. 10 Unwmk. *Perf. 13*

661 A402 10y multicolored .40 .15

10th anniv. of the signing of the Universal Declaration of Human Rights.

Toy of Takamatsu (Tai-Ebisu) A403

Tractor and Map of Kojima Bay A404

1958, Dec. 20 *Perf. 13½*

662 A403 5y multicolored .70 .15

New Year 1959. Sheets reproducing 4 #662, with inscriptions and ornaments, were awarded as prizes in the New Year lottery. Size: 103x89mm. Value $6.

1959, Feb. 1 *Perf. 12½*

663 A404 10y claret & bister brn .30 .15

Completion of the embankment closing Kojima Bay for reclamation.

Karst Plateau — A405

Akiyoshi Cave — A406

1959, Mar. 16 Photo. *Perf. 13½*

664 A405 10y green, bl & ocher 1.40 .15

665 A406 10y multicolored 2.25 .15

Set value .25

Akiyoshidai Quasi-National Park.

Map of Southeast Asia — A407

1959, Mar. 27

666 A407 10y deep carmine .40 .15

Asian Cultural Cong., Tokyo, Mar. 27-31, marking the 2,500th anniv. of the death of Buddha.

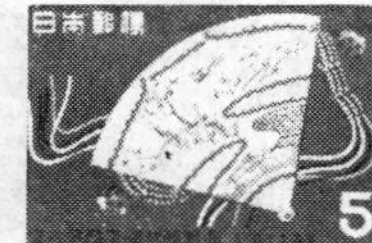

Ceremonial Fan — A408

Prince Akihito and Princess Michiko — A409

Photogravure; Portraits Engraved

1959, Apr. 10

667 A408 5y magenta & violet .30 .15

668 A409 10y red brn & dull pur .70 .15

a. Souv. sheet of 2, #667-668, imperf. 6.00 6.00

669 A408 20y org brn & brn 1.00 .15

670 A409 30y yel grn & dk grn 2.00 .25

Nos. 667-670 (4) 4.00 .70

Wedding of Crown Prince Akihito and Princess Michiko, Apr. 10, 1959.

Type of 1957

Women Reading Poetry, print by Eishi Fujiwara.

1959, May 20 Photo. *Perf. 13*

671 A388 10y multicolored 3.75 1.25

Stamp Week. Issued in sheets of 10.

Redrawn Kannon Type of 1953
Coil Stamp
Perf. 13 Horiz.

1959, Jan. 20 Typo. Unwmk.

672 A332a 10y red brn & lilac 25.00 22.50

Measuring Glass, Tape Measure and Scales — A410

Nurses Carrying Stretcher — A411

1959, June 5 Photo. *Perf. 13*

673 A410 10y lt blue & blk .30 .15

Adoption of the metric system.

1959, June 24

674 A411 10y olive grn & red .40 .15

Centenary of the Red Cross idea.

Mt. Fuji and Lake Motosu — A412

1959, July 21 Engr. *Perf. 13*

675 A412 10y green, bl & sepia .60 .15

Establishment of Natural Park Day and 1st Natural Park Convention, Yumoto, Nikko, July 21, 1959.

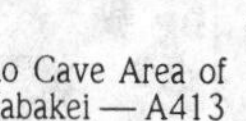

Ao Cave Area of Yabakei — A413

Hita, Mt. Hiko and Great Cormorant A414

1959, Sept. 25 Photo. *Perf. 13*

676 A413 10y multicolored 1.50 .15

677 A414 10y multicolored 1.50 .15

Yaba-Hita-Hiko Quasi National Park.

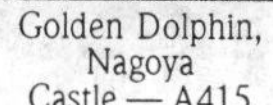

Golden Dolphin, Nagoya Castle — A415

Japanese Crane, IATA Emblem — A416

1959, Oct. 1

678 A415 10y brt bl, gold & blk .80 .15

350th anniversary of Nagoya.

Hiroshige Type of 1958

Design: 30y, "Kuwana," the 7-ri Crossing Point, print by Hiroshige.

1959, Oct. 4 Unwmk.

679 A399 30y multicolored 5.25 1.00

Intl. Letter Writing Week, Oct. 4-10.

1959, Oct. 12 Engr.

680 A416 10y brt grnsh blue .45 .15

15th General Meeting of the International Air Transport Association.

Shoin Yoshida and PTA Symbol — A417

Throwing the Hammer — A418

1959, Oct. 27 Photo. *Perf. 13*

681 A417 10y brown .45 .15

Centenary of the death of Shoin Yoshida, educator, and in connection with the Parent-Teachers Association convention.

1959, Oct. 25 Engr.

Design: No. 683, Woman Fencer.

682 A418 5y gray blue .70 .15

683 A418 5y olive bister .70 .15

a. Pair, #682-683 1.75

Set value .25

14th National Athletic Meet, Tokyo.

Globes — A419

1959, Nov. 2 Photo.

684 A419 5y brown red .45 .15

15th session of GATT (General Agreement on Tariffs & Trade), Tokyo, Oct. 12-Nov. 21.

Toy Mouse of Kanazawa — A420

1959, Dec. 19 Unwmk. *Perf. 13½*

685 A420 5y gold, red, grn & blk 1.00 .15

New Year 1960. Sheets reproducing 4 #685, with marginal inscription and ornaments, were awarded as prizes in natl. lottery. Value $6.

Yukio Ozaki and Clock Tower, Ozaki Memorial Hall — A421

Nara Period Artwork, Shosoin Treasure House — A422

1960, Feb. 25 Photo. *Perf. 13½*

686 A421 10y red brn & dk brn .40 .15

Completion of Ozaki Memorial Hall, erected in memory of Yukio Ozaki (1858-1954), statesman.

1960, Mar. 10

687 A422 10y olive gray .50 .15

Transfer of the capital to Nara, 1250th anniv.

Scenic Trio Issue

Bay of Matsushima A423

Ama-no-hashidate (Heavenly Bridge) — A424

Miyajima from the Sea — A425

1960 Engr.

688 A423 10y maroon & bl grn 1.65 .40

689 A424 5y green & lt bl 1.90 .40

690 A425 10y vio blk & bl grn 1.90 .40

Nos. 688-690 (3) 5.45 1.20

Issued: #688, 3/15; #689, 7/15; #690, 11/15.

Takeshima, off Gamagori A426

1960, Mar. 20 Photo. *Perf. 13½*

691 A426 10y multicolored 1.10 .15

Mikawa Bay Quasi-National Park.

Poetess Isé, 13th Century Painting — A427

1960, Apr. 20 Unwmk. *Perf. 13*
692 A427 10y multicolored 3.00 1.25

Stamp Week, 1960.

Kanrin Maru — A428

Design: 30y, Pres. Buchanan receiving first Japanese diplomatic mission.

1960, May 17 **Engr.**
693 A428 10y bl grn & brn .75 .20
694 A428 30y car & indigo 1.25 .20

Cent. of the Japan-US Treaty of Amity and Commerce. Nos. 694 and 693 form pages of an open book when placed next to each other. Souvenir sheet is No. 703.

Crested Ibis (Toki) — A429

Radio Waves Encircling Globe — A430

1960, May 24 Photo. *Perf. 13½*
695 A429 10y gray, pink & red .60 .20

12th Intl. Congress for Bird Preservation.

1960, June 1 **Engr.**
696 A430 10y carmine rose .40 .15

25th anniv. of the Intl. Radio Program by the Japanese Broadcasting Corporation.

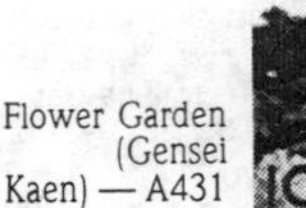

Flower Garden (Gensei Kaen) — A431

1960, June 15 **Photo.**
697 A431 10y multicolored 1.25 .20

Abashiri Quasi-National Park.

Cape Ashizuri — A432

1960, Aug. 1 **Unwmk.**
698 A432 10y multicolored 1.25 .20

Ashizuri Quasi-National Park.

The Scott editorial staff regrettably cannot accept requests to identify, authenticate or appraise stamps and postal markings.

Rainbow Spanning Pacific, Cherry Blossoms and Pineapples — A433

Henri Farman's Biplane and Jet — A434

1960, Aug. 20 *Perf. 13½*
699 A433 10y multicolored .75 .25

75th anniversary of Japanese contract emigration to Hawaii.

1960, Sept. 20 *Perf. 13*
700 A434 10y brn & chlky bl .60 .15

50th anniversary of Japanese aviation.

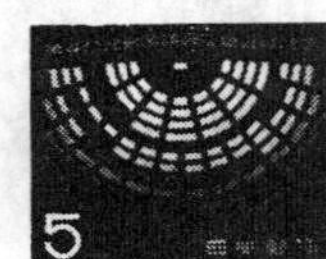
Seat Plan of Diet — A435

"Red Fuji" by Hokusai and Diet Building — A436

1960, Sept. 27
701 A435 5y indigo & org .35 .15
702 A436 10y blue & red brn .80 .15
Set value .25

49th Inter-Parliamentary Conference.

Souvenir Sheet
Type A428

1960, Sept. 27 **Engr.**
703 Sheet of 2, #693-694 22.50 22.50

Visit of Prince Akihito and Princess Michiko to the US.

"Night Snow at Kambara," by Hiroshige A437

1960, Oct. 9 **Photo.**
704 A437 30y multicolored 11.00 2.00

Issued for International Letter Writing Week, Oct. 9-15. See Nos. 735, 769.

Japanese Fencing (Kendo) — A438

Okayama Astrophysical Observatory — A439

No. 706, Girl gymnast and vaulting horse.

1960, Oct. 23 Engr. *Perf. 13½*
705 A438 5y dull blue .55 .15
706 A438 5y rose violet .55 .15
a. Pair, #705-706 1.25

15th National Athletic Meet, Kumamoto.

1960, Oct. 19
707 A439 10y brt violet .75 .15

Opening of the Okayama Astrophysical Observatory.

Lt. Naoshi Shirase and Map of Antarctica — A440

Little Red Calf of Aizu, Gold Calf of Iwate — A441

1960, Nov. 29 **Photo.**
708 A440 10y fawn & black .65 .15

50th anniv. of the 1st Japanese Antarctic expedition.

1960, Dec. 20 Unwmk. *Perf. 13½*
709 A441 5y multicolored .80 .15

New Year 1961. Sheets reproducing 4 #709 were awarded as prizes in the New Year lottery. Size: 102x89mm. Value $7.

Diet Building at Night — A442

Opening of First Session — A443

1960, Dec. 24 Photo.; Engr. (10y)
710 A442 5y gray & dk bl .60 .15
711 A443 10y carmine .60 .15
Set value .25

70th anniversary of the Japanese Diet.

Narcissus A444

Nojima Cape Lighthouse and Fisherwomen A445

#713, Plum blossoms. #714, Camellia japonica. #715, Cherry blossoms. #716, Peony. #717, Iris. #718, Lily. #719, Morning glory. #720, Bellflower. #721, Gentian. #722, Chrysanthemum. #723, Camellia sasanqua.

1961 Photo. *Perf. 13½*
712 A444 10y lilac, yel & grn 2.50 .60
713 A444 10y brown, grn & yel 1.65 .60
714 A444 10y lem, grn, pink & yel 1.25 .50
715 A444 10y gray, brn, pink, yel & blk 1.25 .65
716 A444 10y blk, grn, pink & yel 1.25 .65
717 A444 10y gray, pur, grn & yel .85 .45
718 A444 10y gray grn, yel & brn .60 .25
719 A444 10y lt bl, grn & lil .60 .25
720 A444 10y lt yel grn, vio & grn .60 .25
721 A444 10y org, vio bl & grn .60 .25
722 A444 10y blue, yel & grn .60 .25
723 A444 10y sl, pink, yel & grn .60 .25
Nos. 712-723 (12) 12.35 4.95

1961, Mar. 15
724 A445 10y multicolored .70 .15

South Boso Quasi-National Park.

Cherry Blossoms A446

Hisoka Maejima A447

Unwmk.
1961, Apr. 1 Photo. *Perf. 13*
725 A446 10y lilac rose & gray .40 .15
a. Lilac rose omitted 350.00
b. Imperf., pair 500.00
c. Booklet pane of 4 8.00
d. Gray omitted 300.00

See No. 611b.

Coil Stamp

1961, Apr. 25 *Perf. 13 Horiz.*
726 A446 10y lil rose & gray 5.00 1.65

1961, Apr. 20 *Perf. 13*
727 A447 10y olive & black .90 .15

90th anniv. of Japan's modern postal service from Tokyo to Osaka, inaugurated by Deputy Postmaster General Hisoka Maejima.

Type of 1957

"Dancing Girl" from a "Screen of Dancers."

1961, Apr. 20 *Perf. 13½*
728 A388 10y multicolored 1.50 .65

Stamp Week, 1961. Sheets of 10 (5x2).

Lake Biwa — A448

1961, Apr. 25
729 A448 10y blk, dk bl & yel grn .75 .15

Lake Biwa Quasi-National Park.

Rotary Emblem and People of Various Races — A449

1961, May 29 Engr. *Perf. 13*
730 A449 10y gray & orange .30 .15

52nd convention of Rotary Intl., Tokyo, May 29-June 1, 1961.

Faucet, Wheat, Insulator & Cogwheel A450

Sun, Earth and Meridian A451

1961, July 7 Photo. *Perf. 13½*
731 A450 10y violet & aqua .35 .15

Aichi irrigation system, Kiso river.

1961, July 12
732 A451 10y yellow, red & blk .35 .15

75th anniv. of Japanese standard time.

Parasol Dance on Dunes of Tottori — A452

1961, Aug. 15
733 A452 10y multicolored .85 .20

San'in Kaigan Quasi-National Park.

Onuma Lake and Komagatake Volcano — A453

Gymnast on Horizontal Bar — A454

1961, Sept. 15
734 A453 10y grn, red brn & bl .85 .20

Onuma Quasi-National Park.

Hiroshige Type of 1960

1961, Oct. 8 ***Perf. 13***

Design: 30y, "Hakone," print by Hiroshige from the 53 Stages of the Tokaido.

735	A437	30y multicolored	6.00	2.25

Intl. Letter Writing Week, Oct. 8-14.

1961, Oct. 8 **Engr.** ***Perf. 13½***

Design: No. 737, Women rowing.

736	A454	5y blue green	.50	.15
737	A454	5y ultra	.50	.15
a.		Pair, #736-737	1.10	
		Set value		.25

16th National Athletic Meet, Akita.

See Nos. 770-771, 816-817, 852-853.

Duck Type of 1955
Coil Stamp

1961, Oct. 2 **Photo.** ***Perf. 13 Horiz.***

738	A362	5y lt bl & red brn	3.50	3.00

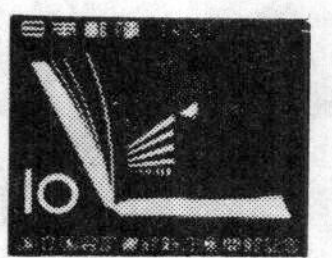
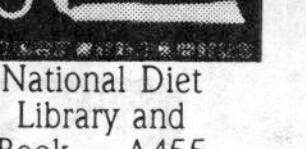

National Diet Library and Book — A455

Papier Maché Tiger — A456

1961, Nov. 1 ***Perf. 13½***

739	A455	10y dp ultra & gold	.35	.15

Opening of the new Natl. Diet Library, Tokyo.

1961, Dec. 15 ***Perf. 13½***

740	A456	5y multicolored	.55	.15

New Year 1962. Sheets reproducing 4 #740 were awarded as 5th prize in the New Year lottery. Size: 102x90, Value $6.

Mt. Fuji from Lake Ashi — A457

Minokake-Iwa at Irozaki — A458

Mt. Fuji from Mitsu Pass — A459

Mt. Fuji from Cape of Ose — A460

1962, Jan. 16 **Unwmk.** **Photo.**

741	A457	5y deep green	.70	.15
742	A458	5y dark blue	.45	.15
743	A459	10y red brown	1.75	.20
744	A460	10y black	1.50	.25
		Nos. 741-744 (4)	4.40	.75

Fuji-Hakone-Izu National Park.

Omishima A461

1962, Feb. 15 ***Perf. 13½***

745	A461	10y ultra, red & yel	.50	.15

Kitanagato-Kaigan Quasi-National Park.

Perotrochus Hirasei — A462

Sacred Bamboo — A463

Shari-den of Engakuji — A464

Yomei Gate, Nikko — A465

Noh Mask — A466

Copper Pheasant — A466a

Wind God, Fujin, by Sotatsu — A467

Japanese Crane — A468

Mythical Winged Woman, Chusonji — A469

1962-65 **Unwmk.** ***Perf. 13***

746	A462	4y dk brn & red ('63)	.15	.15
747	A463	6y gray grn & car	.15	.15
748	A464	30y violet black	3.25	.15
749	A465	40y rose red	3.25	.15
750	A466	70y yel brn & blk ('65)	1.95	.15
751	A466a	80y crim & brn ('65)	1.25	.15
752	A467	90y brt blue grn	30.00	.20
753	A468	100y pink & blk ('63)	8.75	.15
754	A469	120y purple	7.75	.15
		Nos. 746-754 (9)	56.50	
		Set value		.90

See Nos. 888, 888A, 890, 1076, 1079, 1257.

Coil Stamp
Perf. 13 Horiz.

755	A464	30y dull violet ('63)	3.50	1.25

Hinamatsuri, Doll Festival — A470

1962, Mar. 3 ***Perf. 13½***

756	A470	10y brn, blk, bl & car	1.25	.35

The Doll Festival is celebrated Mar. 3 in honor of young girls.

Type of 1957

Design: Dancer from "Flower Viewing Party" by Naganobu Kano.

1962, Apr. 20 **Photo.** ***Perf. 13½***

757	A388	10y multicolored	1.40	.90

Stamp Week, 1962. Sheets of 10.

Sakurajima Volcano and Kagoshima Bay — A471

1962, Apr. 30

758	A471	10y multicolored	.40	.15

Kinkowan Quasi-National Park.

Mount Kongo — A472

1962, May 15 ***Perf. 13½***

759	A472	10y gray bl, dk grn & sal	.40	.15

Kongo-Ikoma Quasi-National Park.

Suigo Park Scene and Iris — A473

1962, June 1 ***Perf. 13½***

760	A473	10y multicolored	.50	.15

Suigo Quasi-National Park.

Train Emerging from Hokuriku Tunnel — A474

1962, June 10 **Photo.**

761	A474	10y olive gray	.80	.15

Opening of Hokuriku Tunnel between Tsuruga and Imajo, Fukui Prefecture.

Star Festival (Tanabata Matsuri) A475

Boy Scout Hat on Map of Southeast Asia A476

1962, July 7 **Unwmk.** ***Perf. 13½***

762	A475	10y multicolored	.40	.15

The Tanabata festival is celebrated on the evening of July 7.

1962, Aug. 3

763	A476	10y red org, blk & bis	.25	.15

Asian Boy Scout Jamboree, Mt. Fuji, Aug. 3-7.

Ozegahara Swampland and Mt. Shibutsu A477

Fumes on Mt. Chausu, Nasu — A478

Lake Chuzenji and Mt. Nantai — A479

Senryu-kyo Narrows, Shiobara A480

1962, Sept. 1

764	A477	5y greenish blue	.25	.15
765	A478	5y maroon	.25	.15
766	A479	10y purple	.40	.15
767	A480	10y olive	.40	.15
		Nos. 764-767 (4)	1.30	
		Set value		.50

Nikko National Park.

Wakato Suspension Bridge — A481

Perf. 13½x13

1962, Sept. 26 **Engr.** **Unwmk.**

768	A481	10y rose red	.75	.25

Opening of Wakato Bridge over Dokai Bay in North Kyushu.

Hiroshige Type of 1960

Design: 40y, "Nihonbashi," print by Hiroshige from the 53 Stages of the Tokaido.

1962, Oct. 7 **Photo.** ***Perf. 13***

769	A437	40y multicolored	5.00	1.65

Intl. Letter Writing Week, Oct. 7-13.

Sports Type of 1961

Design: No. 770, Woman softball pitcher. No. 771, Rifle shooting.

1962, Oct. 21 **Engr.** ***Perf. 13½***

770	A454	5y bluish black	.25	.15
771	A454	5y brown violet	.25	.15
a.		Pair, #770-771	.60	
		Set value		.15

17th National Athletic Meeting, Okayama.

Shichi-go-san Festival A482

Rabbit Bell A483

1962, Nov. 15 **Photo.** ***Perf. 13½***

772	A482	10y multicolored	.40	.15

This festival for 7 and 3-year-old girls and 5-year-old boys is celebrated on Nov. 15.

1962, Dec. 15

773	A483	5y multicolored	.35	.15

New Year 1963. Sheets reproducing 4 #773 were awarded as prizes in the New Year lottery. Value $7.

Mt. Ishizuchi A484

1963, Jan. 11 **Unwmk.** ***Perf. 13½***

774	A484	10y multicolored	.30	.15

Ishizuchi Quasi-National Park.

Setsubun, Spring Festival, Bean Scattering Ceremony — A485

Map of City, Birds, Ship and Factory — A486

1963, Feb. 3 **Photo.**
775 A485 10y multicolored .30 .15

1963, Feb. 10
776 A486 10y chocolate .25 .15

Consolidation of the communities of Moji, Kokura, Wakamatsu, Yawata and Tobata into Kita-Kyushu City.

"Frost Flowers" on Mt. Fugen — A487

Amakusa Island and Mt. Unzen — A488

1963, Feb. 15
777 A487 5y gray blue .25 .15
778 A488 10y carmine rose .25 .15
Set value .20

Unzen-Amakusa National Park.

Green Pond, Midorigaike A489

Hakusan Range — A490

Perf. 13½
1963, Mar. 1 **Unwmk.** **Photo.**
779 A489 5y violet brown .20 .15
780 A490 10y dark green .20 .15
Set value .20

Hakusan National Park.

Keya-no-Oto Rock — A491

1963, Mar. 15
781 A491 10y multicolored .25 .15

Genkai Quasi-National Park.

Wheat Emblem and Globe — A492

1963, Mar. 21
782 A492 10y dark green .20 .15

FAO "Freedom from Hunger" campaign.

"Girl Reading Letter," Yedo Screen — A493

1963, Apr. 20 ***Perf. 13½***
783 A493 10y multicolored .65 .65

Issued to publicize Stamp Week, 1963.

World Map and Centenary Emblem — A494

1963, May 8
784 A494 10y multicolored .15 .15

Centenary of the International Red Cross.

Globe and Leaf with Symbolic River System — A495

1963, May 15 **Photo.**
785 A495 10y blue .15 .15

5th Congress of the Intl. Commission on Irrigation and Drainage.

Ito-dake, Asahi Range — A496

Lake Hibara and Mt. Bandai — A497

1963, May 25 **Unwmk.** ***Perf. 13½***
786 A496 5y green .20 .15
787 A497 10y red brown .20 .15
Set value .20

Bandai-Asahi National Park.

Lidth's Jay — A498

#789, Rock ptarmigan. #790, Eastern turtle dove. #791, Japanese white stork. #792, Bush warbler. #792A, Meadow bunting.

1963-64 ***Perf. 13½***
Design and Inscription

788	A498	10y lt green	.85	.55
789	A498	10y blue	.25	.15
790	A498	10y pale yellow	.25	.15
791	A498	10y grnsh blue ('64)	.25	.15
792	A498	10y green ('64)	.25	.15
792A	A498	10y lt rose brn ('64)	.20	.15
		Nos. 788-792A (6)	2.05	
		Set value		.95

Intersection at Ritto, Shiga — A499

Girl Scout and Flag — A500

1963, July 15 **Unwmk.** ***Perf. 13½***
793 A499 10y bl grn, blk & org .20 .15

Opening of the Nagoya-Kobe expressway, linking Nagoya with Kyoto, Osaka and Kobe.

1963, Aug. 1 **Photo.**
794 A500 10y multicolored .20 .15

Asian Girl Scout and Girl Guides Camp, Togakushi Heights, Nagano, Aug. 1-7.

View of Nashu — A501

Whirlpool at Naruto — A502

1963, Aug. 20
795 A501 5y olive bister .20 .15
796 A502 10y dark green .20 .15
Set value .20

Inland Sea National Park.

Lake Shikaribetsu, Hokkaido A503

Mt. Kurodake from Sounkyo Valley — A504

1963, Sept. 1 **Unwmk.** ***Perf. 13½***
797 A503 5y deep Prus blue .20 .15
798 A504 10y rose violet .20 .15
Set value .20

Daisetsuzan National Park.

Parabolic Antenna for Space Communications A505

1963, Sept. 9 **Photo.**
799 A505 10y multicolored .15 .15

14th General Assembly of the International Scientific Radio Union, Tokyo.

"Great Wave off Kanagawa," by Hokusai A506

1963, Oct. 10 ***Perf. 13***
800 A506 40y gray, dk bl & yel 2.50 .55

Issued for International Letter Writing Week, Oct. 6-12. Design from Hokusai's "36 Views of Fuji." Printed in sheets of 10 (5x2).

Diver, Pole Vaulter and Relay Runner — A507

Woman Gymnast — A508

1963, Oct. 11 ***Perf. 13½***
801 A507 10y bl, ocher, blk & red .15 .15

Tokyo Intl. (Pre-Olympic) Sports Meet, Tokyo, Oct. 11-16.

Perf. 13½
1963, Oct. 27 **Unwmk.** **Engr.**

Design: #803, Japanese wrestling (sumo).

802 A508 5y slate green .15 .15
803 A508 5y brown .15 .15
a. Pair, #802-803 .40
Set value .15

18th National Athletic Meet, Yamaguchi.

Phoenix Tree and Hachijo Island A509

Toy Dragons of Tottori and Yamanashi A510

1963, Dec. 10 **Photo.**
804 A509 10y multicolored .20 .15

Izu Islands Quasi-National Park.

1963, Dec. 16
805 A510 5y gold, pink, aqua, indigo & red .15 .15
a. Aqua omitted

New Year 1964. Sheets containing 4 #805 were awarded as 5th prize in the New Year lottery. Value $4.25.

Wakasa-Fuji from Takahama A511

1964, Jan 25 ***Perf. 13½***
806 A511 10y multicolored .20 .15

Wakasa Bay Quasi-National Park.

Agave and View from Horikiri Pass — A512

1964, Feb. 20 **Unwmk.**
807 A512 10y multicolored .20 .15

Nichinan-Kaigan Quasi-National Park.

Uji Bridge — A513

View of Toba — A514

1964, Mar. 15 **Photo.**
808 A513 5y sepia .15 .15
809 A514 10y red lilac .15 .15
Set value .15

Ise-Shima National Park.

Takayama Festival Float and Mt. Norikura — A515

#811, Yamaboko floats & Gion Shrine, Kyoto.

1964 **Photo.** ***Perf. 13½***
810 A515 10y lt green & multi .20 .15
811 A515 10y grnsh blue & multi .20 .15
Set value .15

No. 810 issued for the annual Takayama spring and autumn festivals, Takayama City, Gifu Prefecture. No. 811 for the annual Gion festival of Kyoto, July 10-30.

Issue dates: #810, Apr. 15. #811, July 15.

Yadorigi Scene from Genji Monogatari Scroll — A516

1964, Apr. 20
814 A516 10y multicolored .32 .15

Stamp Week, 1964. Sheets of 10 (2x5).

Himeji Castle — A517

1964, June 1 ***Perf. 13½***
815 A517 10y dark brown .15 .15

Restoration of Himeji Castle.

Sports Type of 1961

1964, June 6 ***Perf. 13½***
816 A454 5y Handball .15 .15
817 A454 5y Woman on beam .15 .15
a. Pair, #816-817 .40
Set value .24 .20

19th National Athletic Meeting, Niigata.

Cable Cross Section, Map of Pacific Ocean A518

Tokyo Expressway Crossing Nihonbashi A519

1964, June 19
818 A518 10y gray grn, dp mag & yel .15 .15

Opening of the transpacific cable.

1964, Aug. 1 **Photo.**
819 A519 10y green, silver & blk .15 .15

Opening of the Tokyo Expressway.

Coin-like Emblems A520

1964, Sept. 7 **Unwmk.** ***Perf. 13½***
820 A520 10y scarlet, gold & blk .15 .15

Annual general meeting of the Intl. Monetary Fund, Intl. Bank for Reconstruction and Development, Intl. Financial Corporation and the Intl. Development Assoc., Tokyo, Sept. 7-11.

Athletes, Olympic Flame and Rings — A521

National Stadium, Tokyo — A522

30y, Nippon Bodokan (fencing hall). 40y, Natl. Gymnasium. 50y, Komazawa Gymnasium.

1964
821 A521 5y multicolored .15 .15
822 A522 10y multicolored .15 .15
823 A522 30y multicolored .40 .15
824 A522 40y multicolored .40 .15
825 A522 50y multicolored .52 .18
a. Souvenir sheet of 5, #821-825 2.75 3.00
Nos. 821-825 (5) 1.62
Set value .45

18th Olympic Games, Tokyo, Oct. 10-25. Issue dates: 5y, Sept. 9. Others, Oct. 10.

Hand with Grain, Cow and Fruit — A523

Express Train — A524

1964, Sept. 15 ***Perf. 13½***
826 A523 10y violet brn & gold .15 .15

Draining of Hachirogata Lagoon, providing new farmland for the future.

1964, Oct. 1
827 A524 10y blue & black .20 .15

Opening of the new Tokaido railroad line.

Mt. Fuji Seen from Tokaido, by Hokusai A525

1964, Oct. 4 ***Perf. 13***
828 A525 40y multicolored 1.25 .35

Issued for International Letter Writing Week, Oct. 4-10. Issued in sheets of 10 (5x2). See Nos. 850, 896, 932, 971, 1016.

"Straw Snake" Mascot — A526

1964, Dec. 15 **Photo.** ***Perf. 13½***
829 A526 5y crimson, blk & yel .15 .15

New Year 1965. Sheets containing 4 #829 were awarded as prizes in the New Year lottery (issued Jan. 20, 1965). Value $2.

Mt. Daisen — A527

Paradise Cove, Oki Islands — A528

1965, Jan. 20 **Unwmk.** ***Perf. 13½***
830 A527 5y dark blue .15 .15
831 A528 10y brown orange .15 .15
Set value .15

Daisen-Oki National Park.

Niseko-Annupuri A529

1965, Feb. 15 **Photo.**
832 A529 10y multicolored .15 .15

Niseko-Shakotan-Otarukaigan Quasi-Natl. Park.

Meteorological Radar Station on Mt. Fuji — A530

1965, Mar. 10 **Photo.** ***Perf. 13½***
833 A530 10y multicolored .15 .15

Completion of the Meteorological Radar Station on Kengamine Heights of Mt. Fuji.

Kiyotsu Gorge — A531

Lake Nojiri and Mt. Myoko — A532

1965, Mar. 15
834 A531 5y brown .15 .15
835 A532 10y magenta .15 .15
Set value .15

Jo-Shin-etsu Kogen National Park.

Communications Museum, Tokyo — A533

1965, Mar. 25 **Unwmk.** ***Perf. 13½***
836 A533 10y green .15 .15

Philatelic Exhibition celebrating the completion of the Communications Museum.

Japan stamps can be mounted in the annually supplemented Scott Japan album.

"The Prelude" by Shoen Uemura A534

1965, Apr. 20 **Photo.**
837 A534 10y gray & multi .35 .15

Issued for Stamp Week, 1965.

Playing Children, Cows and Swan — A535

Stylized Tree and Sun — A536

1965, May 5 **Unwmk.** ***Perf. 13½***
838 A535 10y pink & multi .15 .15

Opening of the National Garden for Children, Tokyo-Yokohama.

1965, May 9
839 A536 10y multicolored .15 .15

Issued to publicize the forestation movement and the forestation ceremony, Tottori Prefecture.

Globe, Old and New Communication Equipment A537

1965, May 17
840 A537 10y brt blue, yel & blk .15 .15

Cent. of the ITU.

Crater of Mt. Naka, Kyushu — A538

Five Central Peaks of Aso and Mountain Road — A539

1965, June 15 **Photo.** ***Perf. 13½***
841 A538 5y carmine rose .15 .15
842 A539 10y deep green .15 .15
Set value .15

Aso National Park.

ICY Emblem and Doves — A540

1965, June 26 **Unwmk.**
843 A540 40y multicolored .50 .15

Intl. Cooperation Year, 1965, and 20th anniv. of the UN.

Horse Chase, Soma A541

Chichibu Festival Scene A542

1965 Photo. *Perf. 13x13½*

844 A541 10y multicolored .18 .15
845 A542 10y multicolored .20 .15
Set value .20

No. 844 issued to publicize the ancient Soma Nomaoi Festival, Fukushima Prefecture; No. 845, to publicize the festival dedicated to the Chichibu Myoken Shrine (built 1584).

Issue dates: #844, July 16. #845, Dec. 3.

Meiji Maru, Black-tailed Gulls — A543

1965, July 20 *Perf. 13½*

846 A543 10y grn, gray, blk & yel .15 .15

25th Maritime Day, July 20.

Drop of Blood, Girl's Face and Bloodmobile A544

1965, Sept. 1 *Perf. 13½*

847 A544 10y yel, grn, blk & red .15 .15

Issued to publicize the national campaign for blood donations, Sept. 1-30.

Tokai Atomic Power Station and Structure of Alpha Uranium — A545

1965, Sept. 21 Photo.

848 A545 10y multicolored .15 .15

9th General Conf. of the Intl. Atomic Energy Agency, IAEA, Tokyo, Sept. 21-30.

People and Flag — A546

1965, Oct. 1

849 A546 10y multicolored .15 .15

Tenth national census.

Hokusai Type of 1964

Design: No. 850, "Waters at Misaka" by Hokusai (Mt. Fuji seen across Lake Kawaguchi).

1965, Oct. 6 Unwmk. *Perf. 13*

850 A525 40y multicolored .75 .20

Issued for International Letter Writing Week, Oct. 6-12. Issued in sheets of 10 (5x2).

Emblems and Diagram of Seats in National Diet — A547

1965, Oct. 15 *Perf. 13½*

851 A547 10y multicolored .15 .15

75th anniv. of natl. suffrage, 40th anniv. of universal suffrage and 20th anniv. of women's suffrage.

Sports Type of 1961

Designs: No. 852, Gymnast on vaulting horse. No. 853, Walking race.

1965, Oct. 24 Engr. *Perf. 13½*

852 A454 5y red brown .15 .15
853 A454 5y yellow green .15 .15
a. Pair, #852-853 .30 .20

20th National Athletic Meeting, Gifu.

Profile and Infant — A548

1965, Oct. 30 Photo. *Perf. 13*

854 A548 30y car lake, yel & lt bl .35 .15

8th Intl. Conf. of Otorhinolaryngology and the 11th Intl. Conf. of Pediatrics.

Mt. Iwo from Shari Coast, Hokkaido A549

Rausu Lake and Mt. Rausu A550

1965, Nov. 15 *Perf. 13½*

855 A549 5y Prus green .15 .15
856 A550 10y bright blue .15 .15
Set value .15

Shiretoko National Park.

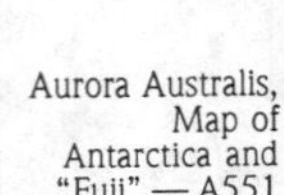

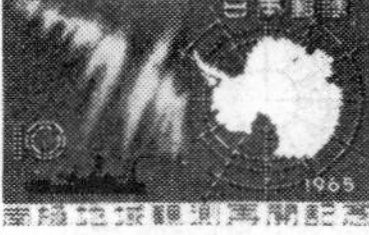

Aurora Australis, Map of Antarctica and "Fuji" — A551

1965, Nov. 20

857 A551 10y bl, yel & dk bl .15 .15

Issued to publicize the Antarctic expedition, which left on the observation ship "Fuji," Nov. 20, 1965.

"Secret Horse" Straw Toy, Iwate Prefecture A552

Telephone Dial and 1890 Switchboard A553

1965, Dec. 10

858 A552 5y lt blue & multi .20 .15

Issued for New Year 1966. Sheets containing four of No. 858 were awarded as prizes in the New Year lottery (issued Jan. 20, 1966). Value $2.

1965, Dec. 16

859 A553 10y multicolored .15 .15

75th anniversary of telephone service in Japan.

Japanese Spiny Lobster A554

Carp — A555

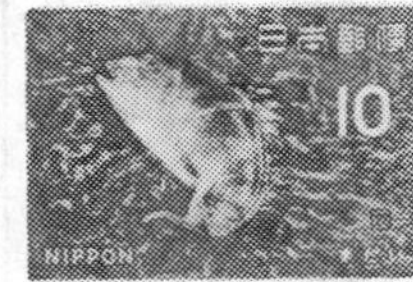

Bream A555a

Skipjack Tuna — A555b

Ayu — A555c

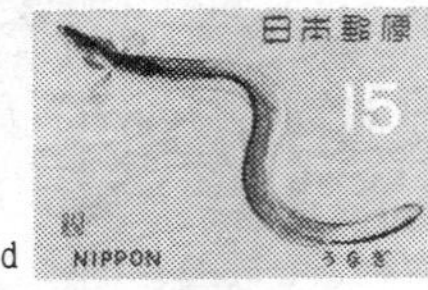

Eel — A555d

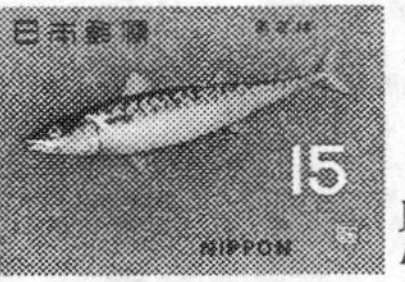

Jack Mackeral A555e

Chum Salmon A555f

Yellowtail A555g

Tiger Puffer A555h

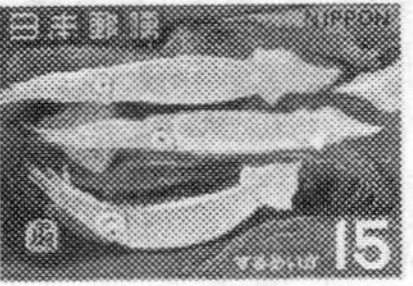

Squid — A555i

Turbo Cornutus A555j

1966-67 Photo. *Perf. 13*

Multicolored; Background in Colors Indicated

860 A554 10y green & ultra .16 .15
861 A555 10y blue green .16 .15
862 A555a 10y dk blue .16 .15
863 A555b 10y dk ultra .16 .15
864 A555c 10y bis & dk grn .16 .15
865 A555d 15y grnsh bl & yel .25 .15
866 A555e 15y brt grn .25 .15
867 A555f 15y brt grn & bl .25 .15
868 A555g 15y lt bl grn ('67) .30 .15
869 A555h 15y brt grn ('67) .32 .15
870 A555i 15y ultra & grn ('67) .42 .15
871 A555j 15y chlky bl ('67) .42 .15
Nos. 860-871 (12) 3.01
Set value 1.00

Famous Gardens Issue

Kobuntei Pavilion and Plum Blossoms, Kairakuen Garden, Ibaragi — A556

Japanese Cranes and Okayama Castle, Korakuen Garden, Okayama — A557

Kenrokuen Garden in the Snow — A558

1966-67 *Perf. 13½*

872 A556 10y gold, blk & grn .20 .15
873 A557 15y blue, blk & mag .22 .15
874 A558 15y silver, grn & dk brn .22 .15
Nos. 872-874 (3) .64
Set value .24

Issued: 10y, 2/25; #873, 11/3; #874, 1/25/67.

Crater Lake, Zao — A559

1966, Mar. 15

875 A559 10y multicolored .16 .15

Zao Quasi-National Park.

Muroto Cape — A560

Senba Cliffs, Anan Coast — A561

1966, Mar. 22 *Perf. 13½*

876 A560 10y multicolored .16 .15
877 A561 10y multicolored .16 .15
Set value .15

Muroto-Anan Coast Quasi-National Park.

AIPPI Emblem A562

1966, Apr. 11 *Perf. 13*

878 A562 40y multicolored .50 .15

26th General Assembly of the Intl. Association for the Protection of Industrial Properties, Tokyo, Apr. 11-16.

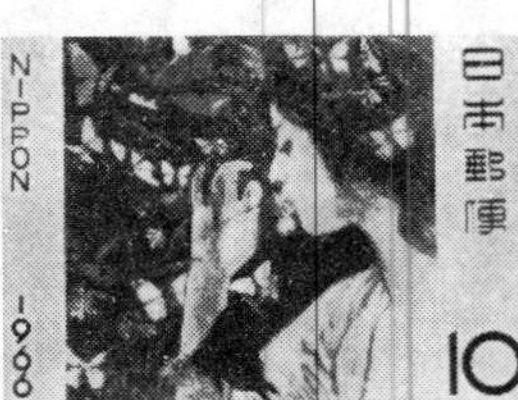

"Butterflies" by Takeji Fujishima — A563

Photogravure and Engraved

1966, Apr. 20 *Perf. 13½*

879 A563 10y gray & multi .32 .15

Stamp Week, 1966. Sheets of 10 (2x5).
See No. 907.

Hisoka Maejima — A563a

Goldfish — A564

Chrysanthemums A565

Wisteria A565a

Hydrangea A565b

Golden Hall, Chusonji A565c

Yomei Gate, Nikko — A565d

Nyoirin Kannon of Chuguji — A565f

Central Hall, Enryakuji Temple — A566

Ancient Clay Horse (Haniwa) — A567

A567a

A567b

A567c

Katsura Palace Garden — A568

A569

Bodhisattva Playing Flute (from Todaiji Lantern) — A570

Designs: 20y, Wisteria. 25y, Hydrangea. 35y, Luminescent squid. 45y, Lysichiton camtschatsense (white flowers). 500y, Deva King statue, South Gate, Todaiji.

1966-69 **Photo.** *Perf. 13*

879A A563a 1y olive bis ('68) .15 .15
880 A564 7y ol & dp org 1.00 .15
881 A565 15y bl & yel (bl "15") .90 .15
b. Bklt. pane of 2 + label ('67) 3.25
c. Bklt. pane of 4 ('67) 2.25
d. Bklt. pane of 4 (2 #881 + 2 #611) ('67) 6.00
e. Imperf., pair 350.00
881A A565a 20y vio & multi ('67) 1.65 1.00
882 A565b 25y grn & lt ultra .50 .15
882A A565c 30y dp ultra & gold ('68) .60 .15
883 A564 35y blue, gray & blk .85 .15
883A A565d 40y bl grn & brn ('68) .60 .15
884 A565 45y blue & multi ('67) .60 .15
885 A565f 50y dk car rose 10.50 .15

Engr.

886 A566 60y slate green 1.40 .15

Photo.

887 A567 65y orange brown 13.00 .15
887A A567a 75y rose, blk, yel & pur 1.40 .15
888 A567b 90y gold & brown 2.50 .15
888A A567c 100y ver & blk ('68) 1.65 .15

Engr.

889 A568 110y brown 1.90 .15
890 A569 120y red 3.25 .15
891 A570 200y Prus grn (22x33mm) 6.50 .15
891A A570 500y dull pur ('69) 9.50 .15
Nos. 879A-891A (19) 58.45
Set value 1.60

Nos. 880-881 were also issued with fluorescent frame on July 18, 1966.
See Nos. 913-916, 918, 926, 1072, 1081, 1244, 1256.

UNESCO Emblem A571

Map of Pacific Ocean A572

1966, July 2 **Photo.** *Perf. 13*

892 A571 15y multicolored .22 .15

20th anniv. of UNESCO.

1966, Aug. 22 *Perf. 13*

893 A572 15y bis brn, dl bl & rose .22 .15

11th Pacific Science Congress, Tokyo, Aug. 22-Sept. 10.

Amakusa Bridges, Kyushu — A573

Emblem of Post Office Life Insurance and Family — A574

1966, Sept. 24 **Photo.** *Perf. 13*

894 A573 15y multicolored .22 .15

Completion of five bridges linking Misumi Harbor, Kyushu, with Amakusa islands.

1966, Oct. 1

895 A574 15y yellow grn & multi .22 .15

Post office life insurance service, 50th anniv.

Hokusai Type of 1964

50y, "Sekiya on the Sumida" (horseback riders and Mt. Fuji) from Hokusai's "36 Views of Fuji."

1966, Oct. 6

896 A525 50y multicolored 1.00 .40

Intl. Letter Writing Week, Oct. 6-12. Printed in sheets of 10 (5x2).

Sharpshooter — A575

Design: No. 898, Hop, skip and jump.

1966, Oct. 23 **Engr.** *Perf. 13½*

897 A575 7y ultra .15 .15
898 A575 7y carmine rose .15 .15
a. Pair, #897-898 .40
Set value .15

21st Natl. Athletic Meet, Oita, Oct. 23-28.

National Theater A576

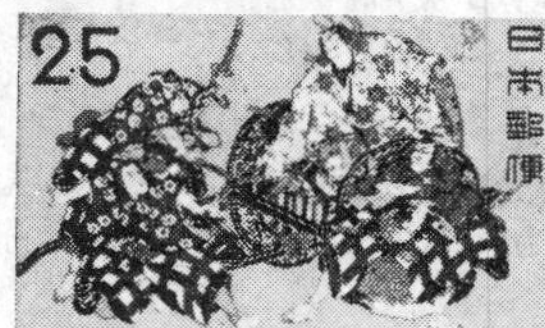
Kabuki Scene — A577

Bunraku Puppet Show — A578

1966, Nov. 1 *Perf. 13, 13½*

899 A576 15y multicolored .20 .15
900 A577 25y multicolored .52 .20
901 A578 50y multicolored .52 .25
Nos. 899-901 (3) 1.24
Set value .50

Inauguration of first National Theater in Japan. Nos. 900-901 issued in sheets of 10.

Rice Year Emblem A579

Ittobori Carved Sheep, Nara Prefecture A580

1966, Nov. 21 *Perf. 13½*

902 A579 15y red, blk & ocher .15 .15

FAO International Rice Year.

1966, Dec. 10 **Photo.** *Perf. 13½*

903 A580 7y bl, gold, blk & pink .20 .15

New Year 1967. Sheets containing 4 #903 were awarded as prizes in the New Year lottery. Value $1.50.

International Communications Satellite, Lani Bird 2 — A581

1967, Jan. 27 *Perf. 13½*

904 A581 15y dk Prus bl & sepia .20 .15

Inauguration in Japan of Intl. commercial communications service via satellite.

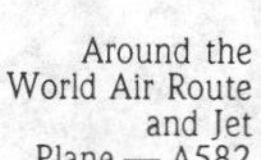

Around the World Air Route and Jet Plane — A582

1967, Mar. 6 **Photo.** *Perf. 13½*

905 A582 15y multicolored .20 .15

Issued to publicize the inauguration of Japan Air Lines Tokyo-London service via New York, which completes the around the world air route.

Library of Modern Japanese Literature A583

1967, Apr. 11

906 A583 15y grnsh bl, lt & dk brn .20 .15

Opening of the Library of Modern Japanese Literature, Komaba Park, Meguro-ku, Tokyo.

Painting Type of 1966

Design: 15y, Lakeside (seated woman), by Seiki (Kiyoteru) Kuroda.

1967, Apr. 20

907 A563 15y multicolored .60 .20

Stamp Week, 1967. Sheets of 10 (2x5).

Kobe Harbor A584

1967, May 8 **Photo.** *Perf. 13x13½*

908 A584 50y multicolored .70 .18

5th Cong. of the Intl. Association of Ports and Harbors, Tokyo, May 8-13.

Welfare Commissioner's Emblem — A585

Traffic Light, Automobile and Children — A586

1967, May 12 *Perf. 13½*

909 A585 15y dk brown & gold .18 .15

50th anniversary of the Welfare Commissioner System.

1967, May 22 *Perf. 13x13½*

910 A586 15y emer, red, blk & yel .18 .15

Issued to publicize traffic safety.

Kita and Kai-Koma Mountains A587

Akaishi and Hijiri Mountains A588

1967, July 10

911 A587 7y Prus blue .15 .15
912 A588 15y rose lilac .24 .15
Set value .15

South Japan Alps National Park.

Types of 1966-69 Redrawn and

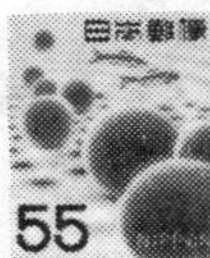
A588a

Original 20y No. 881A

Redrawn 20y No. 915

1967-69 **Photo.** ***Perf. 13***

913 A564 7y brt yel grn & dp org .22 .15
914 A565 15y bl & yel (white "15") .35 .15
a. Pane of 10 (5x2) ('68) 2.75
b. Bklt. panes of 4 with gutter (6 #914 + 2 #611) ('68) 3.25
c. Imperf., pair 225.00
d. Blue shading omitted
e. Bklt. panes of 2 & 4 with gutter ('68) 17.50
915 A565a 20y vio & multi ('69) 1.50 .15
916 A565f 50y brt carmine 1.10 .15
917 A588a 55y lt bl, grn & blk ('69) 1.25 .15
918 A567 65y deep orange 1.50 .15
Nos. 913-918 (6) 5.92
Set value .30

Issued for use in facer-canceling machines. Issue dates: 7y, Aug. 1; 15y, 50y, July 1; 65y, July 20, 1967; 20y, Apr. 1, 1969; 55y, Sept. 1, 1969.

On No. 913 the background has been lightened and a frame line of shading added at top and right side.

No. 914a is imperf. on four sides.

The two panes of Nos. 914b and 914e are connected by a vertical creased gutter 21mm wide. The left pane of No. 914b consists of 2 No. 914 and 2 No. 611; the right pane, 4 of No. 914. The left pane of 2 of No. 914e includes a 4-line inscription.

On No. 915 the wisteria leaves do not touch frame at left and top. On No. 881A they do.

Coil Stamp

1968, Jan. 9 ***Perf. 13 Horiz.***

926 A565 15y bl & yel (white "15") .80 .45

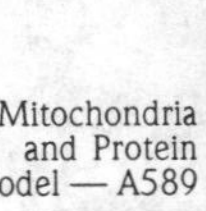
Mitochondria and Protein Model — A589

1967, Aug. 19 **Photo.** ***Perf. 13***

927 A589 15y gray & multi .20 .15

7th Intl. Biochemistry Cong., Tokyo, Aug. 19-25.

Gymnast on Horizontal Bar — A590

Universiade Emblem — A591

1967, Aug. 26

928 A590 15y red & multi .24 .15
929 A591 50y yellow & multi .65 .24
Set value .28

World University Games, Universiade 1967, Tokyo, Aug. 26-Sept. 4.

Paper Lantern, ITY Emblem — A592

"Sacred Mt. Fuji" by Taikan Yokoyama — A593

1967, Oct. 2 **Photo.** ***Perf. 13***

930 A592 15y ultra & multi .22 .15
931 A593 50y multicolored 1.75 1.10

International Tourist Year, 1967. No. 931 issued in sheets of 10.

Hokusai Type of 1964

Design: 50y, "Kajikazawa, Koshu" (fisherman and waves) from Hokusai's "36 Views of Fuji."

1967, Oct. 6

932 A525 50y multicolored 1.75 .50

Issued for International Letter Writing Week, Oct. 6-12. Sheets of 10 (5x2).

Athlete, Wild Primrose and Chichibu Mountains — A594

1967, Oct. 22 **Photo.** ***Perf. 13***

933 A594 15y gold & multi .30 .15

22nd Natl. Athletic Meet, Saitama, Oct. 22-27.

Miroku Bosatsu, Koryuji Temple, Kyoto — A595

Kudara Kannon, Horyuji Temple, Nara — A596

Golden Hall and Pagoda, Horyuji Temple, Nara — A597

1967, Nov. 1 **Photo.**

934 A595 15y multicolored .32 .25

Engr.

935 A596 15y pale grn, blk & red .32 .25

Photo. & Engr.

936 A597 50y multicolored 2.00 .65
Nos. 934-936 (3) 2.64 1.15

National treasures of Asuka Period (6th-7th centuries). No. 936 issued in sheets of 10.

Highway and Congress Emblem A598

1967, Nov. 5 **Photo.** ***Perf. 13***

937 A598 50y multicolored .65 .15

13th World Road Cong., Tokyo, Nov. 5-11.

Mt. Kumotori A599

Lake Chichibu A600

1967, Nov. 27

938 A599 7y olive .15 .15
939 A600 15y red lilac .25 .15
Set value .15

Chichibu-Tama National Park

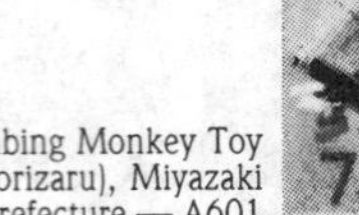
Climbing Monkey Toy (Noborizaru), Miyazaki Prefecture — A601

1967, Dec. 11 **Photo.** ***Perf. 13***

940 A601 7y multicolored .20 .15

New Year 1968. Sheets containing 4 #940 were awarded as prizes in the New Year lottery. Value $1.50.

Mt. Sobo — A602

Takachiho Gorge — A603

1967, Dec. 20

941 A602 15y multicolored .22 .15
942 A603 15y multicolored .22 .15
Set value .20

Sobo Katamuki Quasi-National Park.

Girl, Boy and Sakura Maru — A604

1968, Jan. 19 **Photo.** ***Perf. 13***

943 A604 15y ultra, ocher & blk .18 .15

Cent. of the Meiji Era, and 1st Japanese Youth Good Will Cruise in celebration of the centenary.

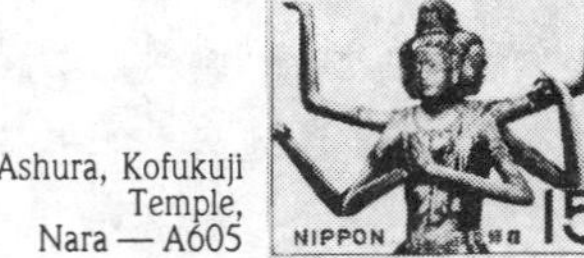
Ashura, Kofukuji Temple, Nara — A605

Gakko Bosatsu, Todaiji Temple, Nara — A606

Kichijo Ten, Yakushiji Temple, Nara — A607

1968, Feb. 1 **Engr.** ***Perf. 13***

944 A605 15y sepia & car .28 .30

Engr. & Photo.

945 A606 15y dk brn, pale grn & org .50 .35

Photo.

946 A607 50y multicolored 1.50 .70
Nos. 944-946 (3) 2.28 1.35

Issued to show National Treasures of the Nara Period (710-784).

Grazing Cows and Mt. Yatsugatake A608

Mt. Tateshina A609

1968, Mar. 21 **Photo.** ***Perf. 13***

947 A608 15y multicolored .24 .15
948 A609 15y multicolored .24 .15
Set value .24

Yatsugatake-Chushin-Kogen Quasi-Natl. Park.

Young Dancer (Maiko) in Tenjuan Garden, by Bakusen Tsuchida — A610

1968, Apr. 20 **Photo.** ***Perf. 13***

949 A610 15y multicolored .45 .15

Stamp Week, 1968. Sheets of 10 (5x2).

Rishiri Isl. Seen from Rebun Isl. — A611

1968, May 10 **Photo.** ***Perf. 13***

950 A611 15y multicolored .18 .15

Rishiri-Rebun Quasi-National Park.

Gold Lacquer and Mother-of-Pearl Box — A612

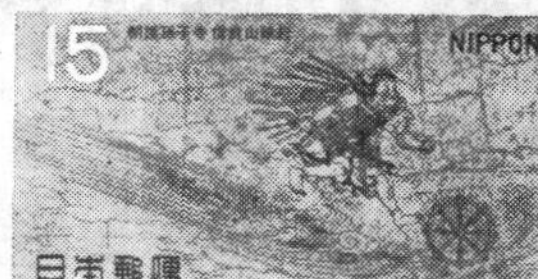

"The Origin of Shigisan" Painting from Chogo-sonshiji, Nara — A613

Bodhisattva Samantabhadra A614

1968, June 1 **Engr. & Photo.**

951 A612 15y lt blue & multi .45 .20

Photo.

952 A613 15y tan & multi .45 .35
953 A614 50y sepia & multi 3.25 1.00
Nos. 951-953 (3) 4.15 1.55

Issued to show national treasures of the Heian Period (8-12th centuries).

Memorial Tower and Badge of Hokkaido — A615

1968, June 14

954 A615 15y grn, vio bl, bis & red .22 .15

Centenary of development of Hokkaido.

Sunrise over Pacific and Fan Palms — A616

1968, June 26 **Photo.** ***Perf. 13***

955 A616 15y blk, org & red org .22 .15

Return of Bonin Islands to Japan by US.

Map of Japan Showing Postal Codes — A617

Two types of inscription:
Type I (enlarged)

あなたの住所にも郵便番号を

"Postal code also on your address"

Type II (enlarged)

あて名に郵便番号を

"Don't omit postal code on the address"

1968, July 1

956 A617 7y yel grn & red (I) 1.40 .35
957 A617 7y yel grn & red (II) 1.40 .35
a. Pair, #956-957 4.50
958 A617 15y sky bl & car (I) 1.00 .15
a. Bklt. panes of 4 with gutter (3 #958 + 3 #959 + 2 #611) 35.00
959 A617 15y sky bl & car (II) 1.00 .15
d. Pair, #958-959 3.00
Nos. 956-959 (4) 4.80 1.00

Introduction of the postal code system.

The double booklet pane, No. 958a, comes in two forms, the positions of the Postal Code types being transposed.

Coil Stamps
Perf. 13 Horiz.

959A A617 15y sky blue & car (I) 1.10 .65
959B A617 15y sky blue & car (II) 1.10 .65
c. Pair, #959A-959B 2.25 1.50

Kiso River — A618

Inuyama Castle — A619

1968, July 20 ***Perf. 13½***

960 A618 15y multicolored .20 .15
961 A619 15y multicolored .20 .15
Set value .15

Hida-Kisogawa Quasi-National Park.

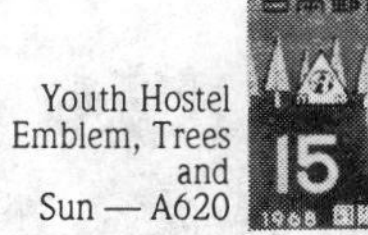

Youth Hostel Emblem, Trees and Sun — A620

1968, Aug. 6 **Photo.** ***Perf. 13***

962 A620 15y citron & multi .22 .15

Issued to publicize the 27th International Youth Hostel Congress, Tokyo, Aug. 6-20.

Boys Forming Tournament Emblem — A621

Pitcher and Tournament Flag — A622

1968, Aug. 9

963 A621 15y yel grn, yel, blk & red .30 .15
964 A622 15y red, yellow & blk .30 .15
a. Pair, #963-964 .65 .30

50th All-Japan High School Baseball Championship Tournament, Koshi-en Baseball Grounds, Aug. 9. Nos. 963-964 printed checkerwise.

Minamoto Yoritomo, Jingoji, Kyoto — A623

Heiji Monogatari Scroll Painting — A624

Red-threaded Armor, Kasuga Shrine, Nara — A625

1968, Sept. 16 **Photo.** ***Perf. 13***

965 A623 15y black & multi .55 .30
966 A624 15y tan & multi .65 .35

Photo. & Engr.

967 A625 50y multicolored 2.00 1.35
Nos. 965-967 (3) 3.20 2.00

National treasures of Kamakura period (1180-1192 to 1333).

Mt. Iwate, seen from Hachimantai A626

Lake Towada, seen from Mt. Ohanabe A627

1968, Sept. 16 **Photo.**

968 A626 7y red brown .15 .15
969 A627 15y green .24 .15
Set value .15

Towada-Hachimantai National Park.

Gymnast, Tojimbo Cliff and Narcissus — A628

1968, Oct. 1 **Photo.** ***Perf. 13***

970 A628 15y multicolored .30 .15

23rd National Athletic Meet, Fukui Prefecture, Oct. 1-6.

Hokusai Type of 1964

Design: 50y, "Fujimihara in Owari Province" (cooper working on a barrel) from Hokusai's "36 Views of Fuji."

1968, Oct. 7

971 A525 50y multicolored 1.25 .45

Issued for International Letter Writing Week, Oct. 7-13. Sheets of 10 (5x2).

Centenary Emblem, Sun and First Western Style Warship — A629

Imperial Carriage Arriving in Tokyo (1868), by Tomone Kobori A630

1968, Oct. 23

972 A629 15y vio bl, red, gold & gray .20 .15
973 A630 15y multicolored .24 .15
a. Imperf., pair
Set value .15

Meiji Centenary Festival.

Old and New Lighthouses — A631

1968, Nov. 1 **Photo.** ***Perf. 13***

974 A631 15y multicolored .22 .15

Centenary of the first western style lighthouse in Japan.

Ryo'o Court Dance and State Hall, Imperial Palace — A632

1968, Nov. 14

975 A632 15y multicolored .22 .15

Completion of the new Imperial Palace.

Mt. Takachiho A633

Mt. Motobu, Yaku Island — A634

1968, Nov. 20

976 A633 7y purple .15 .15
977 A634 15y orange .24 .15
Set value .15

Kirishima-Yaku National Park.

Carved Toy Cock of Yonezawa, Yamagata Prefecture — A635

Human Rights Flame, Dancing Children and Globe — A636

1968, Dec. 5 **Photo.** ***Perf. 13***

978 A635 7y lt blue & multi .20 .15

New Year 1969. Sheets containing 4 #978 were awarded as prizes in the New Year lottery. Value $1.50.

1968, Dec. 10

979 A636 50y orange & multi .75 .15

International Human Rights Year.

Set Values

A 15-cent minimum now applies to individual stamps and sets. Where the 15-cent minimum per stamp would increase the value of a set beyond retail, there is a "Set Value" notation giving the retail value of the set.

Striped Squirrel A637

Kochomon Cave and Road A638

1968, Dec. 14
980 A637 15y emerald & blk .30 .15
Issued to promote saving.

1969, Jan. 27 **Photo.**
981 A638 15y multicolored .30 .15
Echizen-Kaga-Kaigan Quasi-National Park.

Silver Pavilion, Jishoji Temple, Kyoto — A639

Pagoda, Anrakuji Temple, Nagano — A640

Winter Landscape by Sesshu — A641

1969, Feb. 10 **Photo.** ***Perf. 13***
982 A639 15y multicolored .30 .15

Photo. & Engr.
983 A640 15y lt green & multi .30 .15

Photo.
984 A641 50y tan, blk & ver 1.50 1.20
Nos. 982-984 (3) 2.10 1.50

Issued to show national treasures of the Muromachi Period (1333-1572).

Mt. Chokai, seen from Tobishima Island — A642

1969, Feb. 25 **Photo.**
985 A642 15y brt blue & multi .22 .15
Chokai Quasi-National Park.

Mt. Koya Seen from Jinnogamine A643

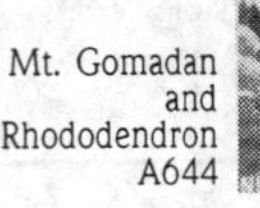

Mt. Gomadan and Rhododendron A644

1969, Mar. 25 **Photo.** ***Perf. 13***
986 A643 15y multicolored .20 .15
987 A644 15y multicolored .20 .15
Set value .15

Koya-Ryujin Quasi-National Park.

Hair (Kami), by Kokei Kobayashi A645

1969, Apr. 20 **Photo.** ***Perf. 13***
988 A645 15y multicolored .40 .22
Issued for Philatelic Week.

Mother, Son Crossing Street — A646

Tokyo-Nagoya Expressway and Sakawagawa Bridge — A647

1969, May 10 **Photo.** ***Perf. 13***
989 A646 15y lt blue, red & grn .22 .15
National traffic safety campaign.

1969, May 26
990 A647 15y multicolored .22 .15
Completion of Tokyo-Nagoya Expressway.

Nuclear Ship Mutsu and Atom Diagram A648

1969, June 12
991 A648 15y gray, blk, pink & bl .22 .15
Issued to publicize the launching of the first Japanese nuclear ship, Mutsu.

Museum of Modern Art and Palette — A649

1969, June 11 **Photo.** ***Perf. 13½***
992 A649 15y lt bl, brn, yel & blk .22 .15
Opening of the new National Museum of Modern Art, Tokyo.

Cable Ship KKD Maru and Map of Japan Sea — A650

1969, June 25
993 A650 15y lt bl, blk & ocher .22 .15
Completion of the Japan sea cable between Naoetsu, Japan, and Nakhodka, Russia.

Postcards, Postal Code Symbol — A651

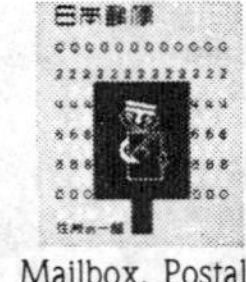
Mailbox, Postal Code Symbol — A652

1969, July 1 **Photo.** ***Perf. 13***
997 A651 7y yellow grn & car .40 .15
998 A652 15y sky blue & car .40 .15
Set value .24

1st anniv. of the postal code system and to promote its use.

Lions Emblem and Rose — A653

1969, July 2
999 A653 15y bl, blk, rose & gold .22 .15
52nd Convention of Lions Intl., Tokyo, July 2-5.

Hotoke-ga-ura on Shimokita Peninsula, Northern Honshu — A654

1969, July 15
1000 A654 15y multicolored .22 .15
Shimokita Hanto Quasi-National Park.

Himeji Castle, Hyogo Prefecture A655

"Pine Forest" (Detail), by Tohaku Hasegawa — A656

"Cypresses," Attributed to Eitoku Kano — A657

1969, July 21 **Photo. & Engr.**
1001 A655 15y lt blue & multi .28 .20

Photo.
1002 A656 15y pale brown & blk .28 .20
1003 A657 50y gold & multi 1.25 .80
Nos. 1001-1003 (3) 1.81 1.20

Issued to show national treasures of the Momoyama period (1573-1614). The 50y is in sheets of 10 (2x5); Nos. 1001-1002 in sheets of 20 (5x4).

Harano-fudo Waterfall A658

Mt. Nagisan A659

1969, Aug. 20
1004 A658 15y multicolored .20 .15
1005 A659 15y multicolored .20 .15
Set value .15

Hyobosen-Ushiroyama-Nagisan Quasi-Natl. Park.

Mt. O-akan, Hokkaido A660

Mt. Iwo A661

1969, Aug. 25 **Photo.** ***Perf. 13***
1006 A660 7y bright blue .15 .15
1007 A661 15y sepia .20 .15
Set value .15

Akan National Park.

Angling, by Taiga Ikeno — A662

The Red Plum, by Korin Ogata — A663

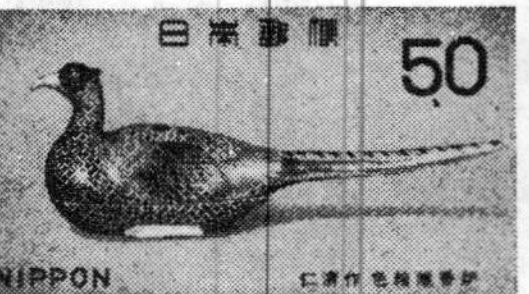
Pheasant-shaped Incense Burner — A664

No. 1010, The White Plum, by Korin Ogata.

1969, Sept. 25 **Photo.** ***Perf. 13x13½***
1008 A662 15y multicolored .30 .15

Perf. 13
1009 A663 15y gold & multi .35 .15
1010 A663 15y gold & multi .35 .15
a. Pair, #1009-1010 .75 .25

Photo. & Engr.
1011 A664 50y multicolored 1.00 .35
Nos. 1008-1011 (4) 2.00
Set value .58

Natl. treasures, Edo Period (1615-1867).

Birds Circling Globe and UPU Congress Emblem — A665

Woman Reading Letter, by Utamaro A666

Designs (UPU Congress Emblem and): 50y, Two Women Reading a Letter, by Harunobu. 60y, Man Reading a Letter (Miyako Dennai), by Sharaku.

1969, Oct. 1 **Photo.** ***Perf. 13***
1012 A665 15y red & multi .22 .15
1013 A666 30y multicolored .55 .38
1014 A666 50y multicolored .65 .48
1015 A666 60y multicolored .95 .65
Nos. 1012-1015 (4) 2.37 1.66

16th UPU Congress, Tokyo, Oct. 1-Nov. 16. 15y issued in sheets of 20, others in sheets of 10.

Hokusai Type of 1964

Design: 50y, "Passing through Koshu down to Mishima" from Hokusai's 36 Views of Fuji.

1969, Oct. 7 **Photo.** ***Perf. 13***
1016 A525 50y multicolored 1.00 .55

Issued for International Letter Writing Week Oct. 7-13. Sheets of 10 (5x2).

Rugby Player, Camellia and Oura Catholic Church — A667

1969, Oct. 26
1017 A667 15y lt ultra & multi .22 .15

24th Natl. Athletic Meet, Nagasaki, Oct. 26-31.

Cape Kitayama A668 Goishi Coast A669

1969, Nov. 20 **Photo.** ***Perf. 13***
1018 A668 7y gray & dk blue .15 .15
1019 A669 15y salmon & dk red .24 .15
Set value .32 .15

Rikuchu Coast National Park.

Worker in Hard Hat — A670 Dog Amulet, Hokkeji, Nara — A671

1969, Nov. 26
1020 A670 15y ultra, blk yel & brn .22 .15

50th anniv. of the ILO.

1969, Dec. 10
1021 A671 7y orange & multi .20 .15

New Year 1970. Sheets containing 4 #1021 were awarded as prizes in the New Year lottery. Value $1.50.

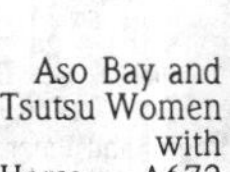

Aso Bay and Tsutsu Women with Horse — A672

1970, Feb. 25 **Photo.** ***Perf. 13***
1022 A672 15y multicolored .22 .15

Iki-Tsushima Quasi-National Park.

Fireworks over EXPO '70 — A673 Cherry Blossoms Around Globe — A674

Irises, by Korin Ogata (1658-1716) — A675

1970, Mar. 14 **Photo.** ***Perf. 13***
1023 A673 7y red & multi .15 .15
1024 A674 15y gold & multi .15 .15
1025 A675 50y gold & multi .65 .65
a. Souv. sheet of 3, #1023-1025 1.75 1.40
b. Bklt. pane of 4 & 3 with gutter 3.00
Nos. 1023-1025 (3) .95
Set value .75

EXPO '70 Intl. Exposition, Senri, Osaka, Mar. 15-Sept. 13.

No. 1025b contains a pane of 4 No. 1023 and a pane with Nos. 1023-1025. A 35mm gutter separates the panes.

Woman with Hand Drum, by Saburosuke Okada — A676

1970, Apr. 20 **Photo.** ***Perf. 13***
1026 A676 15y multicolored .45 .15

Issued for Stamp Week, Apr. 20-26.

Mt. Yoshino — A677 Nachi Waterfall — A678

1970, Apr. 30 **Photo.** ***Perf. 13***
1027 A677 7y gray & pink .15 .15
1028 A678 15y pale blue & grn .24 .15
Set value .32 .15

Yoshino-Kumano National Park.

Pole Lanterns at EXPO — A679 View of EXPO Within Globe — A680

Grass in Autumn Wind, by Hoitsu Sakai (1761-1828) — A681

1970, June 15 **Photo.** ***Perf. 13***
1029 A679 7y red & multi .15 .15
1030 A680 15y blue & multi .25 .15
1031 A681 50y silver & multi .60 .15
a. Souv. sheet of 3, #1029-1031 1.75
b. Bklt. panes of 4 & 3 with gutter 3.00
Nos. 1029-1031 (3) 1.00
Set value .20

EXPO '70, 2nd issue.

No. 1031b contains a pane of 4 No. 1029 and a pane with Nos. 1029-1031. A 35mm gutter separates the panes.

Buildings and Postal Code Symbol — A682

1970, July 1 **Photo.** ***Perf. 13***
1032 A682 7y emerald & vio .35 .15
1033 A682 15y brt blue & choc .48 .15
Set value .20

Postal code system.

"Maiden at Dojo Temple" A683 Scene from "Sukeroku" A684

"The Subscription List" (Kanjincho) — A685

1970, July 10
1034 A683 15y multicolored .24 .15
1035 A684 15y multicolored .24 .16
1036 A685 50y multicolored .65 .40
Nos. 1034-1036 (3) 1.13 .71

Issued to publicize the Kabuki Theater.

Girl Scout — A686

1970, July 26
1037 A686 15y multicolored .18 .15

50th anniversary of Japanese Girl Scouts.

Kinoura Coast and Festival Drum — A687

Tate Mountains Seen from Himi Coast — A688

1970, Aug. 1
1038 A687 15y multicolored .20 .15
1039 A688 15y multicolored .20 .15
Set value .15

Noto Hanto Quasi-National Park.

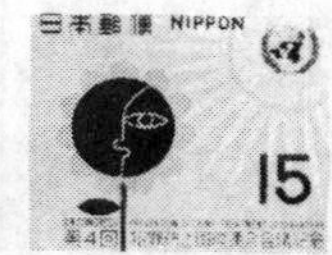

Sunflower and UN Emblem — A689

1970, Aug. 17
1040 A689 15y lt blue & multi .22 .15

Issued to publicize the 4th United Nations Congress on the Prevention of Crime and the Treatment of Offenders, Kyoto, Aug. 17-26.

Mt. Myogi — A690

Mt. Arafune — A691

1970, Sept. 11 **Photo.** ***Perf. 13***
1041 A690 15y multicolored .20 .15
1042 A691 15y multicolored .20 .15
Set value .15

Myogi-Arafune-Sakukogen Quasi-Natl. Park.

G.P.O., Tokyo, by Hiroshige III — A692 Equestrian, Mt. Iwate and Paulownia — A693

1970, Oct. 6
1043 A692 50y multicolored .70 .30

Intl. Letter Writing Week, Oct. 6-12. Sheets of 10 (5x2). Design from wood block series, "Noted Places in Tokyo."

1970, Oct. 10 **Photo.** ***Perf. 13***
1044 A693 15y silver & multi .22 .15

25th Natl. Athletic Meet, Morioka, Oct. 10-16.

Hodogaya Stage, by Hiroshige III — A694 Tree and UN Emblem — A695

1970, Oct. 20
1045 A694 15y silver & multi .22 .15

Centenary of telegraph service in Japan.

1970, Oct. 24

50y, UN emblem and Headquarters with flags.

1046 A695 15y olive, ap grn & gold .20 .15
1047 A695 50y multicolored .60 .15
Set value .20

25th anniversary of United Nations.

Vocational Training Competition Emblem A696

Diet Building and Doves A697

1970, Nov. 10 Photo. *Perf. 13*

1048 A696 15y multicolored .22 .15

The 19th International Vocational Training Competition, Chiba City, Nov. 10-19.

1970, Nov. 29

1049 A697 15y multicolored .22 .15

80th anniversary of Japanese Diet.

Wild Boar, Folk Art, Arai City, Niigata Prefecture — A698

1970, Dec. 10

1050 A698 7y multicolored .20 .15

New Year 1971. Sheets containing 4 #1050 were awarded as prizes in the New Year lottery. Value $1.50.

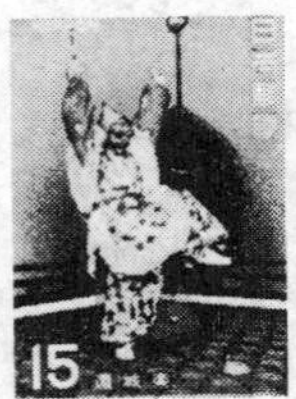

Gen-jo-raku A699

Ko-cho A700

Tai-hei-raku — A701

1971, Apr. 1 Photo. *Perf. 13*

1051 A699 15y multicolored .24 .15
1052 A700 15y multicolored .24 .15
1053 A701 50y multicolored .65 .15
Nos. 1051-1053 (3) 1.13
Set value .24

Gagaku, classical Japanese court entertainment.

Woman Voter and Parliament A702

Pines and Maple Leaves A703

1971, Apr. 10 Photo. *Perf. 13*

1054 A702 15y orange & multi .22 .15

25th anniversary of woman suffrage.

1971, Apr. 18

1055 A703 7y emerald & violet .15 .15

National forestation campaign.

Woman of Tokyo, by Kiyokata Kaburagi — A704

1971, Apr. 19

1056 A704 15y gray & multi .32 .15

Philatelic Week, Apr. 19-25.

Mailman A705

Mailbox A706

Railroad Post Office — A707

1971, Apr. 20

1057 A705 15y blk & org brn .20 .15
1058 A706 15y multicolored .20 .15
1059 A707 15y multicolored .20 .15
Nos. 1057-1059 (3) .60
Set value .15

Centenary of Japanese postage stamps.

Titmouse A708

Penguins A709

1971, May 10 Photo. *Perf. 13*

1060 A708 15y emer, blk & bis .22 .15

25th Bird Week.

1971, June 23 Photo. *Perf. 13*

1061 A709 15y dk blue, yel & grn .25 .15

Antarctic Treaty pledging peaceful uses of and scientific co-operation in Antarctica, 10th anniv.

Goto Wakamatsu Seto Region — A710

Kujukushima ("99 Islands"), Kyushu — A711

1971, June 26 Photo. *Perf. 13*

1062 A710 7y dark green .15 .15
1063 A711 15y deep brown .22 .15
Set value .15

Saikai National Park.

Arabic Numerals and Postal Code Symbol — A712

1971, July 1

1064 A712 7y emerald & red .20 .15
1065 A712 15y blue & carmine .28 .15
Set value .22

Promotion for postal code system.

Inscribed "NIPPON" Types of 1962-67 and

Little Cuckoo — A713

Mute Swan — A714

Sika Deer — A715

Beetle — A716

Pine — A717

Noh Mask — A717a

Pheasant — A717b

Golden Eagle — A717c

Bronze Phoenix, Uji — A718

Burial Statue of Warrior, Ota — A718a

Buddha, Sculpture, 685 — A718b

Tentoki Sculpture, 11th Century — A718c

Bazara-Taisho, c. 710-794 — A718d

Goddess Kissho — A718e

1971-75 Photo. *Perf. 13*

1067 A713 3y emerald .15 .15
a. Bklt. pane of 20 ('72) 2.00
1068 A714 5y bright blue .15 .15
1069 A715 10y yel grn & sep ('72) .16 .15
a. Bklt. pane of 6 (2 #1069, 4 #1071 with gutter btwn.) ('72) 1.40
1070 A716 12y deep brown .16 .15
1071 A717 20y grn & sep ('72) .25 .15
a. Pane of 10 (5x2) ('72) 2.75
1072 A565b 25y emer & lt ultra ('72) .30 .15
1074 A717a 70y dp org & blk 1.00 .15
1075 A717b 80y crimson & brn 1.25 .15
1076 A467 90y org & dk brn 1.50 .15
1077 A717c 90y org & brn ('73) 1.50 .15
1079 A469 120y dk brn & lt grn ('72) 1.75 .15
1080 A718 150y lt & dk green 2.00 .15
1081 A570 200y dp car (18x22mm; '72) 3.25 .15
1082 A718a 200y red brn ('74) 3.25 .15
1083 A718b 300y dk blue ('74) 4.00 .15
1084 A718c 400y car rose ('74) 5.50 .15
1085 A718d 500y green ('74) 6.50 .25
1087 A718e 1000y multi ('75) 15.00 1.00
a. Miniature sheet of 1 15.00 9.00
Nos. 1067-1087 (18) 47.67
Set value 2.25

No. 1071a is imperf. on four sides.
See #1249-1250, 1254, 1631, design A1200.

Coil Stamp
Perf. 13 Horiz.

1088 A717 20y green & sep ('72) .42 .30

Boy Scout Bugler — A719

Rose and Rings — A720

1971, Aug. 2

1090 A719 15y lt blue & multi .22 .15

13th World Boy Scout Jamboree, Asagiri Plain, Aug. 2-10.

1971, Oct. 1

1091 A720 15y ultra & multi .22 .15

50th anniv. of Japanese Conciliation System.

Tokyo Horsedrawn Streetcar, by Yoshimura A721

1971, Oct. 6

1092 A721 50y multicolored .75 .30

Intl. Letter Writing Week. Sheets of 10 (5x2).

Emperor's Flag, Chrysanthemums and Phoenix — A722

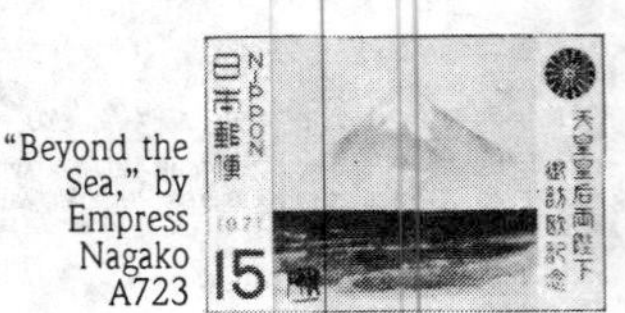

"Beyond the Sea," by Empress Nagako A723

1971, Oct. 14

1093 A722 15y gold, vio, red & bl .24 .15
1094 A723 15y gold, vio, red & bl .24 .15
a. Souv. sheet of 2, #1093-1094, imperf. .85 .85
b. Pair, #1093-1094 .50 .25

European trip of Emperor Hirohito and Empress Nagako, Sept. 28-Oct. 15. No. 1094a has violet map of Asia, Africa and Europe in background.

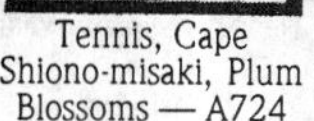

Tennis, Cape Shiono-misaki, Plum Blossoms — A724

Child's Face and "100" — A725

1971, Oct. 24 **Photo.** ***Perf. 13***

1095 A724 15y orange & multi .22 .15

26th National Athletic Meet, Wakayama Prefecture, Oct. 24-29.

1971, Oct. 27

1096 A725 15y pink, car & blk .22 .15

Centenary of Japanese Family Registration System.

Tiger, by Gaho Hashimoto A726

Design: No. 1098, Dragon, from "Dragon and Tiger," by Gaho Hashimoto.

1971, Nov. 1 **Engr.** ***Perf. 13***

1097 A726 15y olive & multi .28 .15
1098 A726 15y olive & multi .28 .15
a. Pair, #1097-1098 .75
Set value .15

Centenary of Government Printing Works. Nos. 1097-1098 printed checkerwise.

Mt. Yotei from Lake Toya — A727

Mt. Showa-Shinzan — A728

Treasure Ship — A729

1971, Dec. 6

1099 A727 7y slate grn & yel .15 .15
1100 A728 15y pink & vio bl .24 .15
Set value .16

Shikotsu-Toya National Park.

1971-72

1101 A729 7y emerald, gold & org .15 .15
1102 A729 10y lt blue, org & gold .16 .15
Set value .16

New Year 1972. Sheets containing 3 #1102 were awarded as prizes in the New Year lottery. Value $1.75.

Issued: 7y, Dec. 10; 10y, Jan. 11, 1972.

Downhill Skiing — A730

#1104, Bobsledding. 50y, Figure skating, pairs.

1972, Feb. 3 **Photo.** ***Perf. 13***

Size: 24x34mm

1103 A730 20y ultra & multi .25 .15
1104 A730 20y ultra & multi .25 .15

Size: 49x34mm

1105 A730 50y ultra & multi .65 .22
a. Souv. sheet of 3, #1103-1105 1.50 1.40
Nos. 1103-1105 (3) 1.15
Set value .34

11th Winter Olympic Games, Sapporo, Feb. 3-13. No. 1105a has continuous design extending into margin.

Bunraku, Ningyo Jyoruri Puppet Theater

A731 A732

A733

1972, Mar. 1 **Photo.** ***Perf. 13½***

1106 A731 20y gray & multi .32 .15

Perf. 12½x13

1107 A732 20y multicolored .32 .15

Lithographed and Engraved

Perf. 13½x13

1108 A733 50y multicolored .65 .18
Set value .28

Japanese classical entertainment.

Express Train on New Sanyo Line — A734

Taishaku-kyo Valley — A735

Hiba Mountains Seen from Mt. Dogo — A736

1972, Mar. 15 **Photo.** ***Perf. 13***

1109 A734 20y multicolored .30 .15

Centenary of first Japanese railroad.

1972, Mar. 24

1110 A735 20y gray & multi .25 .15
1111 A736 20y green & multi .25 .15
Set value .15

Hiba-Dogo-Taishaku Quasi-National Park.

Heart and UN Emblem — A737

1972, Apr. 15

1112 A737 20y gray, red & black .30 .15

"Your heart is your health," World Health Day.

"A Balloon Rising," by Gakuryo Nakamura — A738

1972, Apr. 20

1113 A738 20y violet bl & multi .32 .15

Philatelic Week, Apr. 20-26.

Shurei Gate, Okinawa A739

Camellia A740

1972, May 15

1114 A739 20y ultra & multi .30 .15

Ratification of the Reversion Agreement with US under which the Ryukyu Islands were returned to Japan.

1972, May 20

1115 A740 20y brt grn, vio bl & yel .30 .15

National forestation campaign and 23rd Arbor Day, May 21.

Mt. Kurikoma and Kijiyama Kokeshi Doll — A741

Naruko-kyo Gorge and Naruko Kokeshi Doll — A742

1972, June 20 **Photo.** ***Perf. 13***

1116 A741 20y blue & multi .25 .15
1117 A742 20y red & multi .25 .15
Set value .24

Kurikoma Quasi-National Park.

Envelope, Postal Code Symbol — A743

Mailbox, Postal Code Symbol — A744

1972, July 1

1118 A743 10y blue, blk & gray .22 .15
1119 A744 20y emerald & org .40 .15
Set value .20

Publicity for the postal code system.

Mt. Hodaka — A745

Mt. Tate — A746

1972, Aug. 10 **Photo.** ***Perf. 13***

1120 A745 10y rose & violet .15 .15
1121 A746 20y blue & buff .28 .15
Set value .20

Chubu Sangaku National Park.

Ghost in "Tamura" A747

Lady Rokujo in "Lady Hollyhock" A748

"Hagoromo" (Feather Robe) — A749

1972, Sept. 20 **Engr.**

1122 A747 20y multicolored .30 .15

Photo.

1123 A748 20y multicolored .30 .15

Perf. 13½x13

1124 A749 50y multicolored .75 .15
Nos. 1122-1124 (3) 1.35
Set value .30

Noh, classical public entertainment.

School Children A750

Eitai Bridge, Tokyo, by Hiroshige III A751

1972, Oct. 5 **Photo.** ***Perf. 13***

1125 A750 20y lt ultra, vio bl & car .28 .15

Centenary of modern education system.

1972, Oct. 9

1126 A751 50y multicolored .70 .15

Intl. Letter Writing Week, Oct. 9-15.

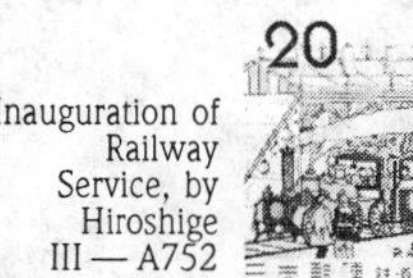

Inauguration of Railway Service, by Hiroshige III — A752

Locomotive, Class C62 — A753

1972, Oct. 14

1127 A752 20y multicolored .32 .15
1128 A753 20y multicolored .32 .15
Set value .15

Centenary of Japanese railroad system.

Kendo (Fencing) and Sakurajima Volcano — A754

1972, Oct. 22

1129 A754 10y yellow & multi .18 .15

27th National Athletic Meet, Kagoshima Prefecture, Oct. 22-27.

Boy Scout Shaking Hand of Cub Scout — A755

1972, Nov. 4

1130 A755 20y yellow & multi .28 .15

50th anniversary of the Boy Scouts of Japan.

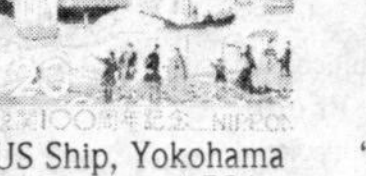

US Ship, Yokohama Harbor — A756

"Clay Plate with Plum Blossoms" — A757

1972, Nov. 28 Photo. *Perf. 13*

1131 A756 20y multicolored .30 .15

Centenary of Japanese customs. Wood block by Hiroshige III (d. 1896).

1972, Dec. 11

1132 A757 10y blue & multi .15 .15

New Year 1973. Art work by Kenzan Ogata (1663-1743). Sheets containing 3 #1132 were awarded as prizes in the New Year lottery. Value $1.75.

Mt. Tsurugi — A758

Oboke Valley — A759

1973, Feb. 20 Photo. *Perf. 13*

1133 A758 20y multicolored .25 .15

1134 A759 20y multicolored .25 .15

Set value .15

Mt. Tsurugi Quasi-National Park.

Mt. Takao — A760

Minoo Falls — A761

1973, Mar. 12 Photo. *Perf. 13*

1135 A760 20y multicolored .25 .15

1136 A761 20y multicolored .25 .15

Set value .15

Meiji Forests Quasi-National Park.

Phoenix Tree — A762

Sumiyoshi Shrine Visitor — A763

1973, Apr. 7 Photo. *Perf. 13*

1137 A762 20y brt grn, yel & dk bl .30 .15

National forestation campaign.

1973, Apr. 20

1138 A763 20y multicolored .30 .15

Philatelic Week, Apr. 20-26. Design from painting by Ryusei Kishida (1891-1929) of his daughter, "A Portrait of Reiko Visiting Sumiyoshi Shrine."

Mt. Kamagatake A764

Mt. Haguro — A765

1973, May 25 Photo. *Perf. 13*

1139 A764 20y multicolored .25 .15

1140 A765 20y multicolored .25 .15

Set value .20

Suzuka Quasi-National Park.

Chichijima Beach — A766

Coral Reef on Minami Island — A767

1973, June 26

1141 A766 10y grnsh bl & Prus bl .16 .15

1142 A767 20y lilac & dk pur .24 .15

Set value .15

Ogasawara National Park.

5th anniversary of the return of the Bonin (Ogasawara Islands) to Japan.

Tree, Postal Code Symbol — A768

Mailman, Postal Code Symbol — A769

1973, July 1 Photo. *Perf. 13*

1143 A768 10y brt green & gold .20 .15

1144 A769 20y blue, purple & car .30 .15

Set value .20

Postal code system, 5th anniversary.

Sandan Gorge — A770

Mt. Shinnyu — A771

1973, Aug. 28 Photo. *Perf. 13*

1145 A770 20y multicolored .25 .15

1146 A771 20y multicolored .25 .15

Set value .15

Nishi-Chugoku-Sanchi Quasi-National Park.

Tenryu Valley — A772

Mt. Horaiji — A773

1973, Sept. 18 Photo. *Perf. 13*

1147 A772 20y lilac & multi .25 .15

1148 A773 20y vio bl, lt bl & sil .25 .15

Set value .15

Tenryu-Okumikawa Quasi-National Park.

Cock, by Jakuchu Ito (1716-1800) — A774

Woman Runner at Start — A775

1973, Oct. 6

1149 A774 50y gold & multi .70 .25

International Letter Writing Week, Oct. 7-13. Sheets of 10.

1973, Oct. 14

1150 A775 10y silver & multi .20 .15

28th National Athletic Meet, Chiba Prefecture, Oct. 14-19.

Kan Mon Bridge A776

1973, Nov. 14 Engr. *Perf. 13*

1151 A776 20y black, rose & yel .28 .15

Opening of Kan Mon Bridge connecting Honshu and Kyushu.

Old Man and Dog — A777

Designs: No. 1153, Old man and wife pounding rice mortar, which yields gold. No. 1154, Old man sitting in tree and landlord admiring tree.

1973, Nov. 20 Photo.

1152 A777 20y multicolored .24 .15

1153 A777 20y multicolored .25 .15

1154 A777 20y multicolored .25 .15

Nos. 1152-1154 (3) .74

Set value .15

Folk tale "Hanasaka-jijii" (The Old Man Who Made Trees Bloom).

Bronze Lantern, Muromachi Period — A778

1973, Dec. 10

1155 A778 10y emerald, blk & org .20 .15

New Year 1974. Sheets containing 3 #1155 were awarded as prizes in the New Year lottery. Value $1.50.

Nijubashi, Tokyo — A779

Imperial Palace, Tokyo — A780

1974, Jan. 26 Photo. *Perf. 13*

1156 A779 20y gold & multi .25 .15

1157 A780 20y gold & multi .25 .15

a. Souv. sheet of 2, #1156-1157 .90 .40

Set value .15

50th anniversary of the wedding of Emperor Hirohito and Empress Nagako.

Young Wife — A781

Crane Weaving A782

Cranes in Flight — A783

1974, Feb. 20 Photo. *Perf. 13*

1158 A781 20y multicolored .25 .15

1159 A782 20y multicolored .25 .15

1160 A783 20y multicolored .25 .15

Nos. 1158-1160 (3) .75

Set value .15

Folk tale "Tsuru-nyobo" (Crane becomes wife of peasant).

Marudu Falls — A784

Marine Scene — A785

1974, Mar. 15

1161 A784 20y multicolored .25 .15

1162 A785 20y multicolored .25 .15

Set value .15

Iriomote National Park.

"Finger," by Ito Shinsui — A786

Nambu Red Pine Sapling & Mt. Iwate — A787

1974, Apr. 20 Photo. *Perf. 13*

1163 A786 20y multicolored .30 .15

Philatelic Week, Apr. 20-27.

1974, May 18

1164 A787 20y multicolored .30 .15

National forestation campaign.

Supreme Court Building A788

1974, May 23 Engr.

1165 A788 20y redsh brown .30 .15

Completion of Supreme Court Building, Tokyo.

Midget Using Bowl as Boat — A789

Designs: No. 1167, Midget fighting demon. No. 1168, Princess and midget changed into prince with magic hammer.

1974, June 10 Photo. *Perf. 13*

1166 A789 20y yellow & multi .25 .15
1167 A789 20y bister & multi .25 .15
1168 A789 20y bister & multi .25 .15
Nos. 1166-1168 (3) .75
Set value .15

Folk tale "Issun Hoschi" (The Story of the Mini-mini Boy).

"Police," by Kunimasa Baido — A790

1974, June 17 *Perf. 13*

1169 A790 20y multicolored .30 .15

Centenary of the Tokyo Metropolitan Police Department.

Japanese Otter — A791

Litho. and Engr.; Photo. and Engr. (Nos. 1172-1173)

1974

1170 A791 20y Mayailurus iriomotensis .30 .15
1171 A791 20y shown .30 .15
1172 A791 20y Pentalagus furnessi .30 .15
1173 A791 20y Pteropus pselaphon .30 .15
Nos. 1170-1173 (4) 1.20
Set value .40

Nature conservation.
Issue dates: #1170, Mar. 25; #1171, June 25; #1172, Aug. 30; #1173, Nov. 15.

Transfusion Bottle, Globe, Doves — A794

1974, July 1 Photo.

1174 A794 20y brt blue & multi .30 .15

Intl. Red Cross Blood Donations Year.

Discovery of Kaguya Hime in Shining Bamboo A795

Kaguya Hime as Grown-up Beauty — A796

Kaguya Hime and Escorts Returning to Moon — A797

1974, July 29 Photo. *Perf. 13*

1175 A795 20y multicolored .25 .15
1176 A796 20y multicolored .25 .15
1177 A797 20y multicolored .25 .15
Nos. 1175-1177 (3) .75
Set value .15

Folk tale "Kaguya Hime" or "Tale of the Bamboo Cutter."

Rich and Poor Men with Wens — A798

Poor Man Dancing With Spirits A798a

Design: No. 1180, Rich man with two wens, poor man without wen, spirits.

1974, Sept. 9 Photo. *Perf. 13*

1178 A798 20y multicolored .25 .15
1179 A798a 20y multicolored .25 .15
1180 A798 20y multicolored .25 .15
Nos. 1178-1180 (3) .75
Set value .15

Folk tale "Kobutori Jiisan," or "The Old Man who had his Wen Taken by Spirits."

Goode's Projection and Diet — A799

"Aizen" by Ryushi Kawabata — A800

1974, Oct. 1 Photo. *Perf. 13*

1181 A799 20y multicolored .25 .15
1182 A800 50y multicolored .60 .15
Set value .24

Interparliamentary Union, 61st Meeting, Tokyo, Nov. 2-11.

Pine and Hawk, by Sesson A801

UPU Emblem A802

Tending Cow, Fan by Sotatsu Tawaraya — A803

1974, Oct. 7

1183 A801 50y sepia, blk & dk brn .65 .15

Intl. Letter Writing Week, Oct. 6-12.

1974, Oct. 9

1184 A802 20y multicolored .25 .15
1185 A803 50y multicolored .60 .15
Set value .15

Centenary of Universal Postal Union.

Soccer Players and Sailboat A804

Various Mushrooms A805

1974, Oct. 20 Photo.

1186 A804 10y multicolored .18 .15

29th National Athletic Meet, Ibaraki Prefecture, Oct. 20-25.

1974, Nov. 2

1187 A805 20y multicolored .30 .15

9th International Congress on the Cultivation of Edible Fungi, Japan, Nov. 4-13.

Steam Locomotive Class D51 — A806

Class C57 — A807

Class 8620 — A808

Class C11 — A809

Designs: Steam locomotives.

1974, Nov. 26 Photo. *Perf. 13*

1188 A806 20y shown .40 .15
1189 A807 20y shown .40 .15
a. Pair, #1188-1189 .80 .15

1975, Feb. 25

1190 A806 20y Class D52 .40 .15
1191 A807 20y Class C58 .40 .15
a. Pair, #1190-1191 .80 .15

1975, Apr. 3

1192 A808 20y shown .40 .15
1193 A809 20y shown .40 .15
a. Pair, #1192-1193 .80 .15

1975, May 15

1194 A806 20y Class 9600 .40 .15
1195 A807 20y Class C51 .40 .15
a. Pair, #1194-1195 .80 .15

1975, June 10 Photo. & Engr.

1196 A806 20y Class 7100 .40 .15
1197 A806 20y Class 150 .40 .15
a. Pair, #1196-1197 .80 .15
Nos. 1188-1197 (10) 4.00
Set value .50

Japanese National Railways.

Ornamental Nail Cover, Katsura Palace — A810

1974, Dec. 10

1198 A810 10y blue & multi .20 .15

New Year 1975. Sheets containing 3 #1198 were awarded as prizes in the New Year Lottery. Value $1.50.

Short-tailed Albatrosses — A811

Bonin Island Honey-eater A812

Temminck's Robin — A813

Ryukyu-Yamagame Tortoise — A814

Design: No. 1200, Japanese cranes.

1975-76 Photo. & Engr. *Perf. 13*

1199 A811 20y multicolored .28 .15
1200 A811 20y multicolored .28 .15
1201 A812 20y multicolored .28 .15

1202 A813 50y multicolored .65 .15
1203 A814 50y multicolored .65 .15
Nos. 1199-1203 (5) 2.14
Set value .35

Nature conservation.
Issued: #1199, 1/16; #1200, 2/13; #1201, 8/8; #1202, 2/27/76; #1203, 3/25/76.

Taro Urashima Releasing Turtle — A815

Palace of the Sea God and Fish — A816

Smoke from Casket Making Taro an Old Man — A817

1975, Jan. 28 Photo. *Perf. 13*
1204 A815 20y multicolored .25 .15
1205 A816 20y multicolored .25 .15
1206 A817 20y multicolored .25 .15
Nos. 1204-1206 (3) .75
Set value .15

Folk tale "Legend of Taro Urashima."

Kan-mon-sho (Seeing and Hearing), by Shiko Munakata — A818

1975, Mar. 20 Photo. *Perf. 13*
1207 A818 20y brown & multi .30 .15

Japan Broadcasting Corp., 50th anniv.

Old Man Feeding Mouse A819

Man Following Mouse Underground A820

Mice Entertaining and Bringing Gifts — A821

1975, Apr. 15 Photo. *Perf. 13*
1208 A819 20y multicolored .25 .15
1209 A820 20y multicolored .25 .15
1210 A821 20y multicolored .25 .15
Nos. 1208-1210 (3) .75
Set value .15

Folk tale "Paradise for the Mice."

Matsuura Screen (detail), 16th Century
A822 A823

1975, Apr. 21
1211 A822 20y gold & multi .30 .15
1212 A823 20y gold & multi .30 .15
a. Pair, #1211-1212 .60 .15

Philatelic Week, Apr. 21-27.

Oil Derricks, Congress Emblem — A824

1975, May 10 Photo. *Perf. 13*
1213 A824 20y multicolored .30 .15

9th World Petroleum Cong., Tokyo, May 11-16.

Trees and River — A825

IWY Emblem, Sun and Woman — A826

1975, May 24
1214 A825 20y green & multi .30 .15

National forestation campaign.

1975, June 23
1215 A826 20y orange & multi .30 .15

International Women's Year 1975.

Okinawan Dancer, EXPO 75 Emblem A827

Birds in Flight (Bingata) A828

Aquapolis and Globe — A829

1975, July 19 Photo. *Perf. 13*
1216 A827 20y ultra & multi .25 .15
1217 A828 30y blue grn & multi .35 .15
1218 A829 50y ultra & multi .60 .15
a. Souv. sheet of 3, #1216-1218 1.50 .90
Nos. 1216-1218 (3) 1.20
Set value .24

Oceanexpo 75, 1st Intl. Ocean Exposition, Okinawa, July 20, 1975-Jan. 18, 1976.

Historic Ship Issue

Kentoshi-sen 7th-9th Centuries A830

Ships: No. 1220, Kenmin-sen, 7th-9th centuries. No. 1221, Goshuin-sen, merchant ship, 16th-17th centuries. No. 1222, Tenchi-maru, state barge, built 1630. No. 1223, Sengoku-bune (cargo ship) and fishing vessel. No. 1224, Shoheimaru, 1852, European-type sailing ship. No. 1225, Taisei-maru, four-mast bark training ship, 1903. No. 1226, Tenyomaru, first Japanese passenger liner, 1907. No. 1227, Asama-maru, passenger liner. No. 1228, Kinai-maru, transpacific freighter and Statue of Liberty. No. 1229, Container ship. No. 1230, Tanker.

1975-76 Engr. *Perf. 13*
1219 A830 20y rose red .28 .15
1220 A830 20y sepia .28 .15
a. Pair, #1219-1220 .56 .15
1221 A830 20y lt olive .28 .15
1222 A830 20y dark blue .28 .15
a. Pair, #1221-1222 .56 .15
1223 A830 50y violet blue .65 .15
1224 A830 50y lilac .65 .15
a. Pair, #1223-1224 1.30 .25
1225 A830 50y gray .65 .15
1226 A830 50y dark brown .65 .15
a. Pair, #1225-1226 1.30 .25
1227 A830 50y olive green .65 .15
1228 A830 50y olive brown .65 .15
a. Pair, #1227-1228 1.30 .25
1229 A830 50y ultra .65 .15
1230 A830 50y violet blue .65 .15
a. Pair, #1229-1230 1.30 .25
Nos. 1219-1230 (12) 6.32
Set value 1.00

Printed checkerwise in sheets of 20.
Issued: #1219-1220, Aug. 30; #1221-1222, Sept. 25, 1975; #1223-1224, Mar. 11; #1225-1226, Apr. 12; #1227-1228, June 1, 1976; #1229-1230, Aug. 18, 1976.

Apple and Apple Tree — A831

Peacock, by Korin Ogata — A832

1975, Sept. 17 Photo. *Perf. 13*
1231 A831 20y gray, black & red .30 .15

Centenary of apple cultivation in Japan.

1975, Oct. 6 Photo. *Perf. 13*
1232 A832 50y gold & multi .70 .15

Intl. Letter Writing Week, Oct. 6-12.

American Flag and Cherry Blossoms A833

Japanese Flag and Dogwood A834

1975, Oct. 14
1233 A833 20y ultra & multi .25 .15
1234 A834 20y green & multi .25 .15
a. Souv. sheet of 2, #1233-1234 .90 .60
Set value .15

Visit of Emperor Hirohito and Empress Nagako to the United States, Oct. 1-14.

Savings Box and Coins — A835

Weight Lifter — A836

1975, Oct. 24
1235 A835 20y multicolored .30 .15

Japan's Postal Savings System, centenary.

1975, Oct. 25
1236 A836 10y multicolored .20 .15

30th National Athletic Meet, Mie Prefecture, Oct. 26-31.

Papier-mache Dragon, Fukushima Prefecture — A837

1975, Dec. 13 Photo. *Perf. 13*
1237 A837 10y multicolored .18 .15

New Year 1976. Sheets containing 3 #1237 were awarded as prizes in the New Year Lottery. Value $1.50.

Inscribed "NIPPON"
Types of 1963-1974 and

Japanese Narcissus — A841

Noh Mask, Old Man — A843

Guardian Dog, Katori Shrine — A845

Sho-Kannon, Yakushiji Temple — A846

Designs: 50y, Nyoirin Kannon, Chuguji Temple. 150y, Bronze phoenix, Uji. 200y, Clay burial figure of warrior, Ota.

1976-79 Photo. *Perf. 13*
1244 A565f 50y emerald .80 .15
a. Bklt. panes of 2 & 4 with gutter 5.00
1245 A841 60y multicolored 1.00 .15
1248 A843 140y lil rose & lil 2.00 .15
1249 A718 150y red org & brn 2.00 .15
1250 A718a 200y red orange 2.75 .15
1251 A845 250y blue 3.50 .15
1253 A846 350y dk violet brn 4.25 .15
Nos. 1244-1253 (7) 16.30
Set value .50

Coil Stamps
Perf. 13 Horiz.
1254 A715 10y yel grn & sep ('79) .20 .15
1256 A565f 50y emerald 1.25 .15
1257 A468 100y ver & blk ('79) 1.50 .30
Nos. 1254-1256 (2) 1.45
Set value .50

See No. 1631.

Hikone Folding Screen (detail), 17th Century
A850 A851

1976, Apr. 20 **Photo.** ***Perf. 13***

1258 A850 50y gold & multi .75 .15
1259 A851 50y gold & multi .75 .15
a. Pair, #1258-1259 1.75
Set value .20

Philatelic Week, Apr. 20-26.

Plum Blossoms, Cedars, Mt. Tsukuba — A852

1976, May 22

1260 A852 50y multicolored .70 .15

National forestation campaign.

Green Tree Frog — A853

Bitterlings A854

Sticklebacks A855

1976 **Photo. & Engr.** ***Perf. 13***

1261 A853 50y multicolored .60 .15
1262 A854 50y multicolored .60 .15
1263 A855 50y multicolored .60 .15
Nos. 1261-1263 (3) 1.80
Set value .30

Nature conservation.
Issue dates: No. 1261, July 20; No. 1262, Aug. 26; No. 1263, Sept. 16.

Crows, by Yosa Buson — A856

Gymnasts and Stadium — A857

1976, Oct. 6 **Photo.** ***Perf. 13***

1264 A856 100y gray, blk & buff 1.25 .20

Intl. Letter Writing Week, Oct. 6-12.

1976, Oct. 23 **Photo.** ***Perf. 13***

1265 A857 20y multicolored .30 .15

31st National Athletic Meet, Saga Prefecture, Oct. 24-29.

Cable, Cable Ship, Map of East China Sea — A858

1976, Oct. 25

1266 A858 50y blue, blk & silver .65 .15

Opening of Sino-Japanese cable between Shanghai and Reihoku-cho, Kumamoto Prefecture.

Classical Court Dance A859

Imperial Coach A860

1976, Nov. 10 **Photo.** ***Perf. 13***

1267 A859 50y multicolored .65 .15
1268 A860 50y multicolored .65 .15
a. Souv. sheet of 2, #1267-1268 1.40 .80
Set value .20

Emperor Hirohito's accession to the throne, 50th anniversary.

Kindergarten Class — A861

1976, Nov. 16

1269 A861 50y multicolored .60 .15

Centenary of first kindergarten in Japan.

Healthy Family A862

Bamboo Toy Snake A863

1976, Nov. 24

1270 A862 50y multicolored .60 .15

Natl. Health Insurance, 50th anniv.

1976, Dec. 1 **Photo.** ***Perf. 13***

1271 A863 20y multicolored .30 .15

New Year 1977. Sheets containing 2 #1271 were awarded as prizes in the New Year lottery. Value $1.65.

National Treasures

East Pagoda, Yakushiji Temple, c. 730 — A864

Deva King in Armor Holding Spear, Nara Period — A865

1976, Dec. 9 **Photo.** ***Perf. 13***

1272 A864 50y multicolored .60 .15

Engr.

1273 A865 100y green & multi 1.25 .20

Golden Pavilion, Toshodai-ji Temple, 8th Century — A866

Praying Women, from Heike Nokyo Sutra, 12th Century — A867

Photogravure and Engraved

1977, Jan. 20 ***Perf. 13***

1274 A866 50y multicolored .65 .15

Photo.

1275 A867 100y multicolored 1.40 .20

Comic Picture Scroll, Attributed to Toba Sojo Kakuyu (1053-1140) — A868

Saint on Cloud, 11th Century Wood Carving, Byodoin Temple A869

1977, Mar. 25 **Photo.** ***Perf. 13***

1276 A868 50y multicolored .65 .15

Engr.

1277 A869 100y multicolored 1.40 .20

Noblemen on Way to Court, from Picture Scroll, Heian Period — A870

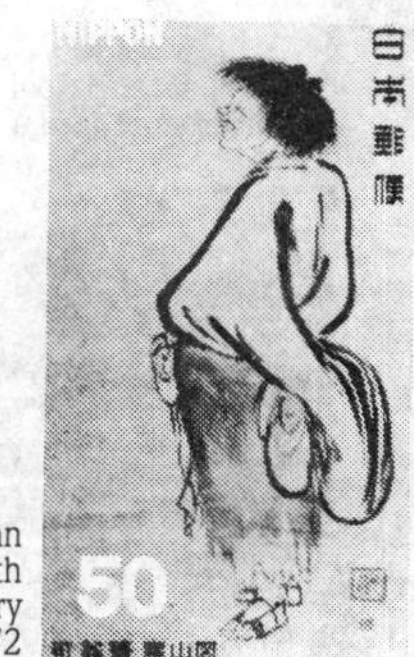

Statue of Seitaka-doji, Messenger, Kamakura Period — A871

1977, June 27 **Photo.** ***Perf. 13***

1278 A870 50y multicolored .65 .15

Engr.

1279 A871 100y multicolored 1.40 .20

The Recluse Han Shan, 14th Century Painting — A872

Tower, Matsumoto Castle, 16th Century — A873

1977, Aug. 25 **Photo.** ***Perf. 13***

1280 A872 50y multicolored .65 .15

Photogravure and Engraved

1281 A873 100y black & multi 1.40 .20

Pine and Flowers, Chishakuin Temple, Kyoto, 1591 — A874

Main Hall, Kiyomizu Temple, 1633 — A875

1977, Nov. 16 **Photo.** ***Perf. 13***

1282 A874 50y multicolored .65 .15

Engr.

1283 A875 100y multicolored 1.40 .20

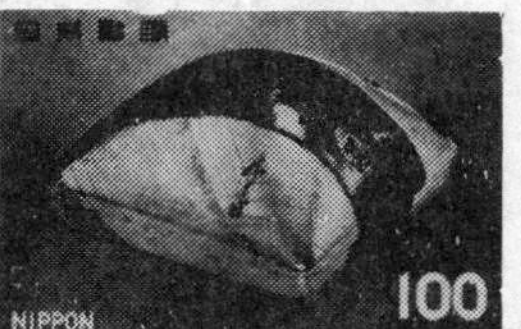

Scene from Tale of Genji, by Sotatsu Tawaraya — A876

Inkstone Case, by Koetsu Honami — A877

1978, Jan. 26 **Photo.** ***Perf. 13***

1284 A876 50y multicolored .65 .15

Photogravure and Engraved

1285 A877 100y black & multi 1.40 .25

Family Enjoying Cool Evening, by Morikage Kusumi — A878

Yomeimon, Toshogu Shrine, 1636 — A879

1978, Mar. 3 Photo. *Perf. 13*

1286 A878 50y gray & multi .65 .15

Photogravure and Engraved

1287 A879 100y multicolored 1.40 .25

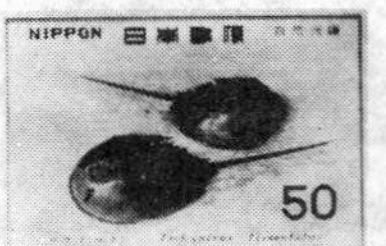
Horseshoe Crabs — A884

Graphium Doson Aibidum — A885

Firefly — A886

Cicada — A887

Dragonfly — A888

1977 Photo. *Perf. 13*

1292 A884 50y multicolored .60 .15

Photogravure and Engraved

1293 A885 50y multicolored .60 .15
1294 A886 50y multicolored .60 .15
1295 A887 50y multicolored .60 .15

Photo.

1296 A888 50y multicolored .60 .15
Nos. 1292-1296 (5) 3.00
Set value .50

Issued: #1292, 2/18; #1293, 5/18; #1294, 7/22; #1295, 8/15; #1296, 9/14.

Figure Skating — A889

Figure Skating Pair — A890

1977, Mar. 1

1297 A889 50y silver & multi .65 .15
1298 A890 50y silver & multi .65 .15
Set value .20

World Figure Skating Championships, National Yoyogi Stadium, March 1-6.

Sun Shining on Forest — A891

1977, Apr. 16 Photo. *Perf. 13*

1299 A891 50y green & multi .65 .15

National forestation campaign.

Weavers and Dyers (Detail from Folding Screen)
A892 A893

1977, Apr. 20

1300 A892 50y gold & multi .65 .15
1301 A893 50y gold & multi .65 .15
a. Pair, #1300-1301 1.50
Set value .20

Philatelic Week, Apr. 20-26.

Nurses — A894

1977, May 30 Photo. *Perf. 13*

1302 A894 50y multicolored .65 .15

16th Quadrennial Congress of the Intl. Council of Nurses, Tokyo, May 30-June 3.

Fast Breeder Reactor, Central Part — A895

1977, June 6

1303 A895 50y multicolored .65 .15

Experimental fast breeder reactor "Joyo," which began operating Apr. 24, 1977.

Workers and Safety Emblems A896

Work on High-rise Buildings A897

Cargo Unloading A898

Machinery Work A899

1977, July 1

1304 A896 50y multicolored .70 .15
1305 A897 50y multicolored .70 .15
1306 A898 50y multicolored .70 .15
1307 A899 50y multicolored .70 .15
a. Block or strip of 4, #1304-1307 3.00
Set value .40

National Safety Week, July 1-July 7.

Carrier Pigeons, Mail Box, UPU Emblem — A900

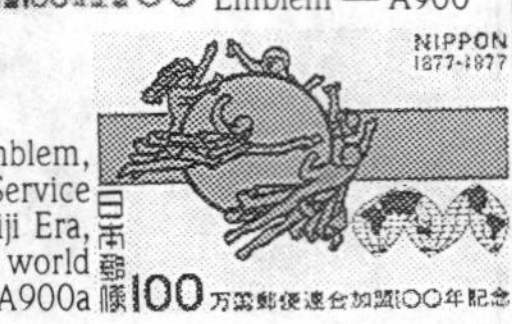
UPU Emblem, Postal Service Flag of Meiji Era, world Map — A900a

1977, June 20 Photo. *Perf. 13*

1308 A900 50y multicolored .60 .15
1309 A900a 100y multicolored 1.25 .20
a. Souv. sheet of 2, #1308-1309 2.00 1.00

Cent. of Japan's admission to the UPU.

Surgeon in Operating Room — A901

1977, Sept. 3 Photo. *Perf. 13*

1310 A901 50y multicolored .65 .15

27th Cong. of the Intl. Surgeon's Society on the 75th anniv. of its founding, Kyoto, Sept. 3-8.

Child Using Telephone, Map of New Cable Route — A902

1977, Aug. 26

1311 A902 50y multicolored .65 .15

Inauguration of underwater telephone cable linking Okinawa, Luzon and Hong Kong.

Early Speaker, Waves and Telegraph Key — A903

1977, Sept. 24 Photo. *Perf. 13*

1312 A903 50y multicolored .65 .15

50th anniversary of amateur radio in Japan.

Bicyclist, Mt. Iwaki and Iwaki River — A904

Flowers and Ducks, Attributed to Hasegawa Tohaku — A905

1977, Oct. 1

1313 A904 20y multicolored .30 .15

32nd National Athletic Meet, Aomori Prefecture, Oct. 2-7.

1977, Oct. 6

1314 A905 100y multicolored 1.40 .20

Intl. Letter Writing Week, Oct. 6-12.

Dinosaur, Stars, Museum A906

1977, Nov. 2 Photo. *Perf. 13*

1315 A906 50y multicolored .65 .15

Centenary of National Science Museum.

Decorated Horse, Fushimi Toy — A907

Tokyo Subway, 1927 — A908

1977, Dec. 1 Photo. *Perf. 13*

1316 A907 20y multicolored .30 .15

New Year 1978. Sheets containing 2 #1316 were awarded as prizes in the New Year lottery. Value $1.50.

1977, Dec. 6

1317 A908 50y shown .65 .15
1318 A908 50y Subway, 1977 .65 .15
a. Pair, #1317-1318 1.50
Set value .20

Tokyo Subway, 50th anniversary.

Primrose — A909

Pinguicula Ramosa — A910

Dicentra — A911

1978 Photo. & Engr. *Perf. 13*

1319 A909 50y multicolored .65 .15
1320 A910 50y multicolored .65 .15
1321 A911 50y multicolored .65 .15
Nos. 1319-1321 (3) 1.95
Set value .36

Nature protection.
Issued: #1319, 4/12; #1320, 6/8; #1321, 7/25.

Kanbun Bijinzu Folding Screen, Edo Period
A912 A913

1978, Apr. 20 Photo. *Perf. 13*

1322 A912 50y multicolored .65 .15
1323 A913 50y multicolored .65 .15
a. Pair, #1322-1323 1.50
Set value .24

Philatelic Week, Apr. 16-22.

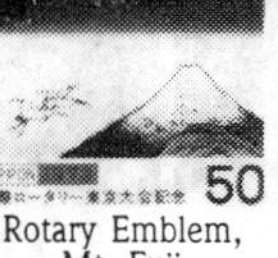

Rotary Emblem, Mt. Fuji
A914

Congress Emblem, by Taro Okamoto
A915

1978, May 13 Photo. *Perf. 13*

1324 A914 50y multicolored .65 .15

69th Rotary International Convention, Tokyo, May 14-18.

1978, May 15

1325 A915 50y multicolored .65 .15

23rd International Ophthalmological Congress, Kyoto, May 14-20.

Narita International Airport, Tokyo — A916

1978, May 20

1326 A916 50y multicolored .65 .15

Opening of Tokyo International Airport.

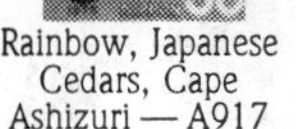

Rainbow, Japanese Cedars, Cape Ashizuri — A917

Lion, by Sotatsu Tawaraya, Lions Emblem — A918

1978, May 20

1327 A917 50y multicolored .65 .15

National forestation campaign.

1978, June 21 Photo. *Perf. 13*

1328 A918 50y multicolored .65 .15

61st Lions Intl. Convention, Tokyo, June 21-24.

Sumo Print Issues

Grand Champion Hidenoyama with Sword Bearer and Herald, by Kunisada I (Toyokuni III)
A919 A920

Ekoin Drum Tower, Ryogoku, by Hiroshige — A921

Photogravure and Engraved

1978, July 1 *Perf. 13*

1329 A919 50y multicolored .70 .15
1330 A920 50y multicolored .70 .15
a. Pair, #1329-1330 1.40 .30

Photo.

1331 A921 50y multicolored .70 .15
Nos. 1329-1331 (3) 2.10
Set value .36

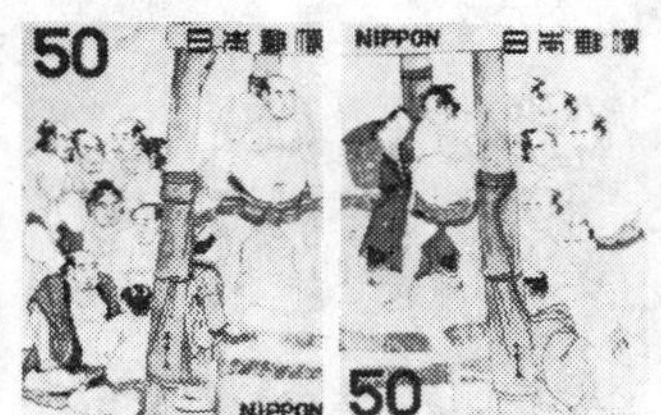

Champions Tanikaze and Onogawa in Ring-entry Ceremony, 1782, by Shunsho
A922 A923

Jimmaku, Raiden and Referee Shonosuke, 1791 Bout, by Shun'ei — A924

Photogravure and Engraved

1978, Sept. 9 *Perf. 13*

1332 A922 50y multicolored .70 .15
1333 A923 50y multicolored .70 .15
a. Pair, #1332-1333 1.40 .30
1334 A924 50y multicolored .70 .15
Nos. 1332-1334 (3) 2.10
Set value .36

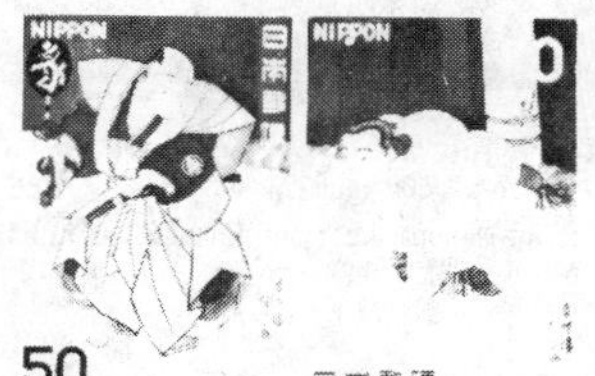

Referee Shonosuke and Champion Onomatsu, by Kunisada I
A925 A926

Children's Sumo Play, by Utamaro — A927

1978, Nov. 11 *Perf. 13*

1335 A925 50y multicolored .70 .15
1336 A926 50y multicolored .70 .15
a. Pair, #1335-1336 1.40 .30
1337 A927 50y multicolored .70 .15
Nos. 1335-1337 (3) 2.10
Set value .36

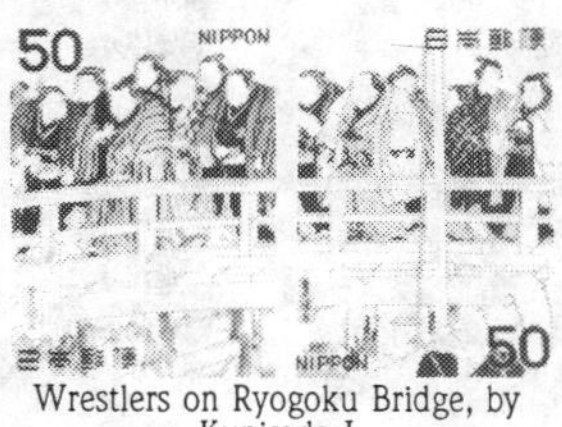

Wrestlers on Ryogoku Bridge, by Kunisada I
A928 A929

Bow-receiving Ceremony at Tournament, by Kunisada II — A930

1979, Jan. 13 *Perf. 13*

1338 A928 50y multicolored .70 .15
1339 A929 50y multicolored .70 .15
a. Pair, #1338-1339 1.40 .30
1340 A930 50y multicolored .70 .15
Nos. 1338-1340 (3) 2.10
Set value .36

Takekuma and Iwamigata (Hidenoyama) Wrestling, by Kuniyoshi
A931 A932

Daidozan (Great Child Mountain) in Ring-entry Ceremony, by Sharaku — A933

1979, Mar. 10 *Perf. 13*

1341 A931 50y multicolored .70 .15
1342 A932 50y multicolored .70 .15
a. Pair, #1341-1342 1.40 .30
1343 A933 50y multicolored .70 .15
Nos. 1341-1343 (3) 2.10
Set value .36

Radio Gymnastics Emblem — A934

1978, Aug. 1 Photo. *Perf. 13*

1344 A934 50y multicolored .65 .15

Radio gymnastics program exercises, 50th anniversary.

Chamber of Commerce and Industry
A935

1978, Aug. 28 Photo. *Perf. 13*

1345 A935 50y multicolored .65 .15

Tokyo Chamber of Commerce, centenary.

Symbolic Sculptures, Tokyo Stock Exchange — A936

Flowering Plum with Pheasant, from Screen, Tenkyuin Temple — A937

1978, Sept. 14 Engr. *Perf. 13*

1346 A936 50y lilac, grn & brn .65 .15

Centenary of the Tokyo and Osaka Stock Exchanges.

1978, Oct. 6 Photo. *Perf. 13*

1347 A937 100y multicolored 1.40 .25

Intl. Letter Writing Week, Oct. 6-12.

Softball and Mt. Yarigatake
A938

Artificial Hip, Orthopedists' Emblem
A939

1978, Oct. 14

1348 A938 20y multicolored .30 .15

33rd National Athletic Meet, Nagano Prefecture, Oct. 15-20.

1978, Oct. 16

1349 A939 50y multicolored .65 .15

14th World Cong. of Intl. Soc. of Orthopedic Surgeons (50th anniv.), Kyoto, Oct. 15-20.

Telescope and Stars — A940

Sheep Bell, Nakayama Toy — A941

1978, Dec. 1 Photo.

1350 A940 50y multicolored .65 .15

Tokyo Astronomical Observatory, cent.

1978, Dec. 4

1351 A941 20y multicolored .30 .15

New Year 1979. Sheets containing 2 #1351 were awarded as prizes in the New Year Lottery. Value $1.50.

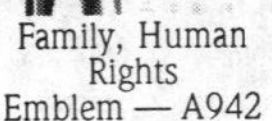

Family, Human Rights Emblem — A942

Hands Shielding Children — A943

1978, Dec. 4

1352 A942 50y multicolored .65 .15

Human Rights Week, Dec. 4-10.

1979, Feb. 16 Photo. *Perf. 13*

1353 A943 50y multicolored .65 .15

Education of the handicapped, centenary.

Telephone Dials — A944

Sketch of Man, by Leonardo da Vinci — A945

1979, Mar. 14 Photo. *Perf. 13*

1354 A944 50y multicolored .65 .15

Completion of nation-wide telephone automatization.

Photogravure and Engraved

1979, Apr. 7 *Perf. 13*

1355 A945 50y multicolored .65 .15

Centenary of, promulgation of State Medical Act, initiating modern medicine.

Standing Beauties, Middle Edo Period
A946 A947

1979, Apr. 20 Photo.

1356 A946 50y multicolored .65 .15
1357 A947 50y multicolored .65 .15
a. Pair, #1356-1357 1.50
Set value .24

Philatelic Week, Apr. 16-22.

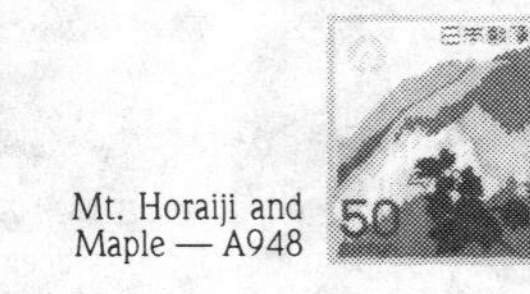

Mt. Horaiji and Maple — A948

1979, May 26 Photo. *Perf. 13*

1358 A948 50y multicolored .65 .15

National forestation campaign.

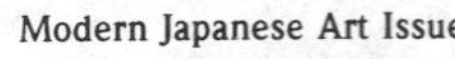

Modern Japanese Art Issue

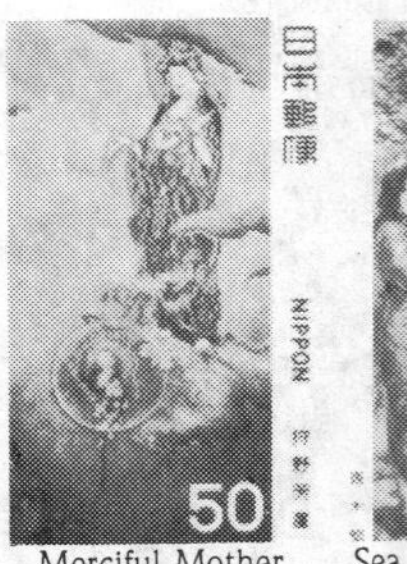

Merciful Mother Goddess, by Kano Hogai — A949

Sea God's Princess, by Aoki Shigeru — A950

1979, May 30 Photo. *Perf. 13*

1359 A949 50y multicolored .70 .15
1360 A950 50y multicolored .70 .15
Set value .24

Fire Dance, by Gyoshu Hayami — A951

Leaning Figure, by Tetsugoro Yorozu — A952

1979, June 25 Photo. *Perf. 13*

1361 A951 50y red & multi .65 .15

Photogravure and Engraved

1362 A952 50y red & multi .65 .15
Set value .24

The Black Cat, by Shunso Hishida — A953

Kinyo, by Sotaro Yasui — A954

1979, Sept. 21 Photo. *Perf. 13*

1363 A953 50y multicolored .65 .15
1364 A954 50y multicolored .65 .15
Set value .24

Nude, by Kagaku Murakami — A955

Harvest, by Asai Chu — A956

Photogravure and Engraved

1979, Nov. 22 *Perf. 13*

1365 A955 50y multicolored .65 .15
1366 A956 50y multicolored .65 .15
Set value .24

Salmon — A956a

Hall of the Supreme Buddha — A956b

Photogravure and Engraved

1980, Feb. 22 *Perf. 13½*

1367 A956a 50y multicolored .65 .15

Photo.

1368 A956b 50y multicolored .65 .15
Set value .24

Quarantine Officers, Ships, Plane, Microscope A957

1979, July 14 Photo.

1369 A957 50y multicolored .65 .15

Centenary of Japanese Quarantine system.

Girl Mailing Letter A958

Hakata Doll with Letter-paper Roll A959

1979, July 23

1370 A958 20y multicolored .32 .15
1371 A959 50y multicolored .65 .15
Set value .17

Letter Writing Day.

Pitcher, Baseball with Black Lion Emblem — A960

1979, July 27

1372 A960 50y multicolored .65 .15

50th National Inter-city Amateur Baseball Tournament, Tokyo, August.

Girl Floating in Space — A961

Design: No. 1374, Boy floating in space.

1979, Aug. 1

1373 A961 50y magenta & multi .65 .15
1374 A961 50y blue & multi .65 .15
a. Souv. sheet of 2, #1373-1374 1.50
Set value .24

International Year of the Child.

Japanese Song Issue

Moon over Castle, by Rentaro Taki — A962

Evening Glow, by Shin Kusakawa — A963

Maple Leaves, by Teiichi Okano — A964

The Birthplace, by Teiichi Okano — A965

Winter Landscape A966

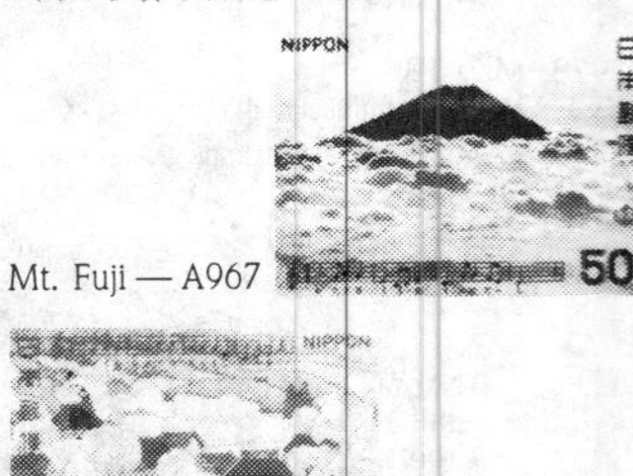

Mt. Fuji — A967

Spring Brook — A968

Cherry Blossoms A969

1979, Aug. 24 Photo. & Engr.

1375 A962 50y multicolored .65 .15
1376 A963 50y multicolored .65 .15
Set value .24

1979, Nov. 26

1377 A964 50y multicolored .65 .15
1378 A965 50y multicolored .65 .15
Set value .24

1980, Jan. 28 *Perf. 13*

1379 A966 50y multicolored .65 .15
1380 A967 50y multicolored .65 .15
Set value .24

1980, Mar. 21 *Perf. 13*

1381 A968 50y multicolored .65 .15
1382 A969 50y multicolored .65 .15
Set value .24
Nos. 1375-1382 (8) 5.20

Great Owl, by Okyo Maruyama — A970

1979, Oct. 8 **Photo.** *Perf. 13*
1383 A970 100y multicolored 1.25 .25

Intl. Letter Writing Week, Oct. 8-14.

Runner — A971

"ITU," Globe — A972

1979, Oct. 13
1384 A971 20y multicolored .32 .15

34th National Athletic Meet, Miyazaki, Oct. 4-19.

1979, Oct. 13 **Litho.** *Perf. 13½*
1385 A972 50y multicolored .65 .15

Admission to ITU, cent.

Woman and Fetus — A973

1979, Nov. 12 **Photo.**
1386 A973 50y multicolored .65 .15

9th World Congress of Gynecology and Obstetrics, Tokyo, Oct. 25-31.

Happy Monkeys, Osaka Toy — A974

Government Auditing Centenary — A975

1979, Dec. 1 **Photo.** *Perf. 13x13½*
1387 A974 20y multicolored .30 .15

New Year 1980. Sheets of 2 #1387 were New Year Lottery prizes. Value $1.50.

1980, Mar. 5 **Photo.** *Perf. 13½*
1388 A975 50y multicolored .65 .15

Scenes of Outdoor Play in Spring, by Sukenobu Nishikawa
A976 A977

1980, Apr. 21 **Photo.** *Perf. 13½*
1389 A976 50y multicolored .65 .15
1390 A977 50y multicolored .65 .15
a. Pair, #1389-1390 1.30 .50
Set value .24

Philatelic Week, Apr. 21-27. Sheets of 10.

Japanese Song Issue

The Sea — A978

The Night of the Hazy Moon — A979

Memories of Summer — A981

The Sun Flag — A980

1980 **Photo. & Engr.** *Perf. 13*
1391 A978 50y multicolored .70 .15
1392 A979 50y multicolored .70 .15
1393 A980 50y multicolored .70 .15
1394 A981 50y multicolored .70 .15
Nos. 1391-1394 (4) 2.80
Set value .48

Issued: #1391-1392, 4/28; #1393-1394, 6/16.

Song by the Sea — A982

The Red Dragonfly — A983

1980, Sept. 18 *Perf. 13*
1395 A982 50y multicolored .65 .15
1396 A983 50y multicolored .65 .15
Set value .24

Lullaby — A984

Coconut, by Toraji Ohnaka — A985

1981, Feb. 9 *Perf. 13*
1397 A984 60y multicolored .70 .15
1398 A985 60y multicolored .70 .15
Set value .20

Spring Has Come, by Tatsuyuki Takano — A986

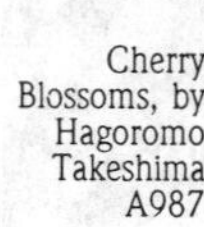

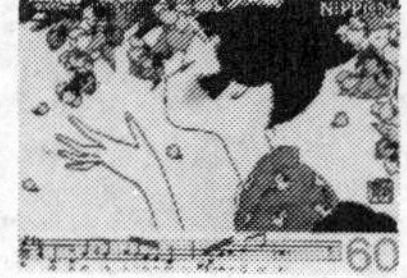
Cherry Blossoms, by Hagoromo Takeshima A987

1981, Mar. 10 *Perf. 13*
1399 A986 60y multicolored .70 .15
1400 A987 60y multicolored .70 .15
Set value .20

Modern Japanese Art Issue

Dancers, by Seiki Kuroda — A988

Mother and Child, by Shoen Uemura — A989

1980, May 12 **Photo.** *Perf. 13½*
1401 A988 50y multicolored .70 .15
1402 A989 50y multicolored .70 .15
Set value .24

The Black Fan, by Takeji Fujishima — A990

Dear Me . . . It's a Shower, by Seiho Takeuchi — A991

1980, July 7 **Photo.** *Perf. 13½*
1403 A990 50y multicolored .70 .15
1404 A991 50y multicolored .70 .15
Set value .24

Woman, by Morie Ogiwara — A992

Kurofuneya, by Yumeji Takehisa — A993

1980, Oct. 27 **Photo.** *Perf. 13½*
1405 A992 50y multicolored .70 .15
1406 A993 50y multicolored .70 .15
Set value .24

Nippon Maru, Institute Emblem — A994

1980, May 17
1407 A994 50y multicolored .65 .15

Institute for Nautical Training, training ships Nippon Maru and Kaio Maru, 50th anniversary.

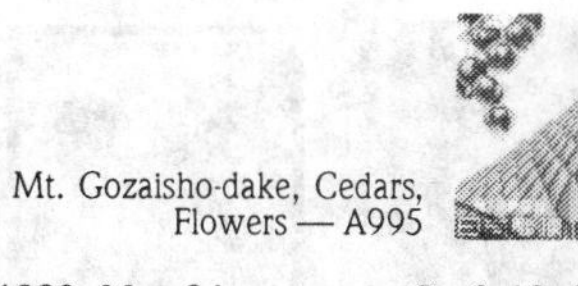
Mt. Gozaisho-dake, Cedars, Flowers — A995

1980, May 24 *Perf. 13x13½*
1408 A995 50y multicolored .65 .15

National forestation campaign.

Yayosu Fire Brigade Review, by Hiroshige III — A996

1980, May 31
1409 A996 50y multicolored .65 .15

Fire fighting centenary.

A997

A997a

Perf. 13x13½, 13½x13

1980, July 23

Letter Writing Day: 20y, Teddy Bear holding letter. 50y, Folded and tied letter of good wishes, horiz.

1410 A997 20y multicolored .30 .15
1411 A997a 50y multicolored .60 .15
Set value .18

Lühdorfla Japonica A998

1980, Aug. 2 *Perf. 13½*
1412 A998 50y multicolored .65 .15

16th Intl. Cong. of Entomology, Kyoto, Aug. 3-9.

Three-dimensional World Map — A999

1980, Aug. 25 **Photo.**
1413 A999 50y multicolored .65 .15

24th Intl. Geographic Cong. and 10th Intl. Cartographic Conf., Tokyo, August.

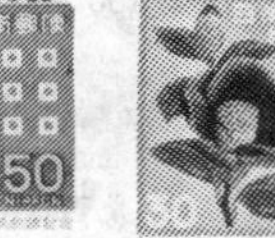

Integrated Circuit A1000 — Camellia A1001

1980, Sept. 29
1414 A1000 50y multicolored .65 .15

Intl. Federation for Information Processing Cong. '80, Tokyo, Oct. 6-9 and World Conf. on Medical Informatics '80, Tokyo, Sept. 29-Oct. 4.

1980, Oct. 1
1415 A1001 30y shown .42 .15
1416 A1001 40y Rape flower, cabbage butterflies .50 .15
1417 A1001 50y Cherry blossoms .70 .15
Nos. 1415-1417 (3) 1.62
Set value .24

See No. 1437.

Cranes, by Motooki Watanabe A1002 — Archery, Mt. Nantai A1003

1980, Oct. 6 ***Perf. 13***
1418 A1002 100y multicolored 1.25 .24

24th Intl. Letter Writing Week, Oct. 6-12.

1980, Oct. 11
1419 A1003 20y multicolored .32 .15

35th Natonal Athletic Meet, Tochigi, Oct.

Globe, Jaycee Emblem — A1004 — Diet Building and Doves — A1005

1980, Nov. 8 ***Perf. 13***
1420 A1004 50y multicolored .65 .24

35th Jaycee (Intl. Junior Chamber of Commerce) World Congress, Osaka, Nov. 9-15.

1980, Nov. 29 ***Perf. 13½***
1421 A1005 50y multicolored .65 .15

90th anniversary of Japanese Diet.

Type of 1980 and:

Amur Adonis — A1006 — White Trumpet Lily — A1007

Hanging Bell, Byodoin Temple — A1008 — Bronze Buddhist Ornament, 7th Century — A1009

Writing Box Cover — A1010 — Mirror with Figures — A1011

Heart-shaped Figurine — A1012 — Silver Crane — A1013

Maitreya, Horyuji Temple — A1014 — Ichiji Kinrin, Chusonji Temple — A1015

Komokuten, Todaiji Temple — A1016 — Lady Maya — A1017

Enamel Jar, by Ninsei Nonomura A1018 — Miroku Bosatsu, Koryuji Temple A1019

1980-82 **Photo.** ***Perf. 13x13½***
1422 A1006 10y multicolored .25 .15
1423 A1007 20y multicolored .30 .15
1424 A1008 60y multicolored .90 .15
a. Bklt. pane (#1424, 4 #1424 with gutter btwn.) ('81) 4.00
1425 A1009 70y multicolored 1.10 .20
1426 A1010 70y multicolored 1.10 .15
1427 A1011 80y multicolored 1.25 .15
1428 A1012 90y multicolored 1.40 .16
1429 A1013 100y multicolored 1.50 .18
1430 A1014 170y multicolored 2.50 .25
1431 A1015 260y multicolored 3.75 .40
1432 A1016 310y multicolored 4.50 .65
1433 A1017 410y multicolored 5.75 1.15
1434 A1018 410y multicolored 5.75 1.15
1435 A1019 600y multicolored 8.50 1.40
Nos. 1422-1435 (14) 38.55 6.29

Coil Stamps

Perf. 13 Horiz.

1436 A1006 10y multi ('82) .25 .15
1437 A1001 40y as #1416 .60 .15
1438 A1008 60y multi ('82) .90 .15
1439 A1013 100y multi ('82) 1.50 .18
Nos. 1436-1439 (4) 3.25
Set value .42

See Nos. 1627, 1629.

Clay Chicken, Folk Toy — A1026

1980, Dec. 1 ***Perf. 13 Horiz.***
1442 A1026 20y multicolored .30 .15

New Year 1981.

Sheets of two were New Year Lottery Prizes. Value $1.50.

Modern Japanese Art Issue

Snow-Covered Power Station, by Shikanosuke Oka — A1027

NuKada-no-Ohkimi and Nara in Spring, by Yukihiko Yasuda — A1028

1981, Feb. 26 ***Perf. 13½***
1443 A1027 60y multicolored .75 .15

Photo.

1444 A1028 60y multicolored .75 .15
Set value .20

Artist's Family, by Narashige Koide — A1029

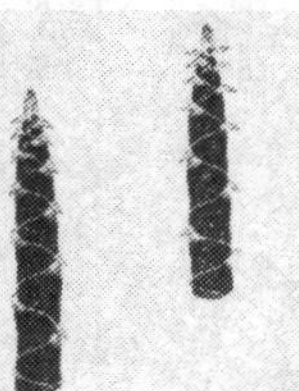

Bamboo Shoots, by Heihachiro Fukuda — A1030

Photo. & Engr., Photo.

1981, June 18 ***Perf. 13½***
1445 A1029 60y multicolored .75 .15
1446 A1030 60y multicolored .75 .15
Set value .20

Portrait of Ichiyo, by Kiyokata Kaburagi (1878-1972) A1031

Portrait of Reiko, by Ryusei Kishida (1891-1929) A1032

Photo., Photo. and Engr.

1981, Nov. 27 **Engr.** ***Perf. 13½***
1447 A1031 60y multicolored .75 .15
1448 A1032 60y multicolored .75 .15
Set value .20

Yoritomo in a Cave, by Seison Maeda — A1033

Advertisement of a Terrace, by Yuzo Saeki — A1034

1982, Feb. 25 **Photo.** ***Perf. 13½***
1449 A1033 60y multicolored .75 .15
1450 A1034 60y multicolored .75 .15
Set value .20

Emblem, Port Island A1035

1981, Mar. 20 ***Perf. 13***
1451 A1035 60y multicolored .70 .15

Portopia '81, Kobe Port Island Exhibition, Mar. 20-Sept. 15.

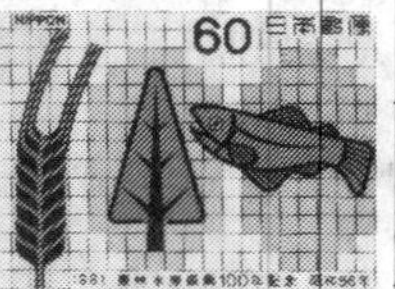

Agriculture, Forestry and Fishery Promotion Centenary A1036

1981, Apr. 7
1452 A1036 60y multicolored .70 .15

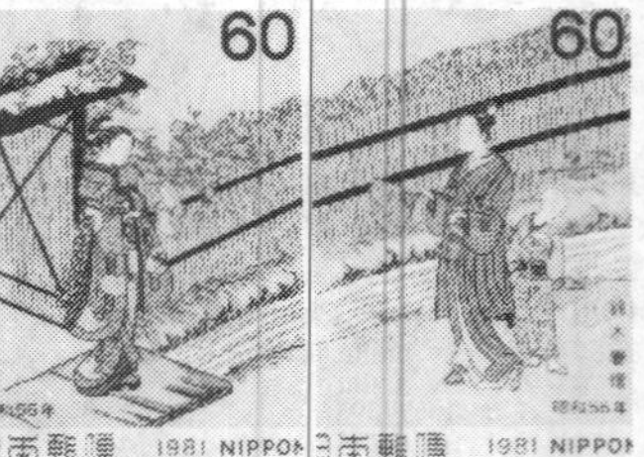

Moonflower, by Harunobu Suzuki A1037 A1038

1981, Apr. 20 **Photo.** ***Perf. 13½***
1453 A1037 60y multicolored .75 .15
1454 A1038 60y multicolored .75 .15
a. Pair, #1453-1454 1.50 .30

Philatelic Week, Apr. 21-27.

Cherry Blossoms A1039

Cargo Ship and Crane A1040

1981, May 23 Photo. *Perf. 13x13½*
1455 A1039 60y multicolored .70 .15

1981, May 25 *Perf. 13*
1456 A1040 60y multicolored .70 .15

International Port and Harbor Association, 12th Convention, Nagoya, May 23-30.

Land Erosion Control Cent. — A1041

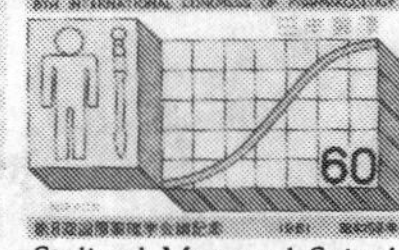

Stylized Man and Spinal Cord Dose Response Curve — A1042

1981, June 27 *Perf. 13½*
1457 A1041 60y multicolored .70 .15

1981, July 18 Photo. *Perf. 13*
1458 A1042 60y multicolored .70 .15

8th Intl. Pharmacology Cong., Tokyo, July 19-24.

Girl Writing Letter A1043

Japanese Crested Ibis A1044

1981, July 23
1459 A1043 40y shown .48 .15
1460 A1043 60y Boy, stamp .70 .15
Set value .16

Letter Writing Day (23rd of each month).

1981, July 27 Litho.
1461 A1044 60y multicolored .70 .15

Energy Conservation — A1045

1981, Aug. 1 Photo.
1462 A1045 40y Plug, faucet .48 .15
1463 A1045 60y shown .70 .15
Set value .16

Western Architecture Issue

Oura Cathedral — A1046

Hyokei Hall, Tokyo A1047

Photogravure and Engraved

1981, Aug. 22
1464 A1046 60y multicolored .70 .15
1465 A1047 60y multicolored .70 .15
Set value .20

Old Kaichi School, Nagano A1048

Doshisha University Chapel, Kyoto A1049

1981, Nov. 9 *Perf. 13*
1466 A1048 60y multicolored .70 .15
1467 A1049 60y multicolored .70 .15
Set value .20

St. John's Church, Meiji-mura — A1050

Military Exercise Hall (Former Sapporo Agricultural School), Sapporo A1051

1982, Jan. 29 *Perf. 13*
1468 A1050 60y multicolored .70 .15
1469 A1051 60y multicolored .70 .15
Set value .20

Former Kyoto Branch of Bank of Japan A1052

Main Building, Former Saiseikan Hospital — A1053

1982, Mar. 10 *Perf. 13*
1470 A1052 60y multicolored .70 .15
1471 A1053 60y multicolored .70 .15
Set value .20

Oyama Shrine Gate, Kanazawa — A1054

Former Iwasaki Family Residence, Tokyo A1055

1982, June 12 *Perf. 13*
1472 A1054 60y multicolored .70 .15
1473 A1055 60y multicolored .70 .15
Set value .20

Hokkaido Prefectural Govt. Building, Sapporo A1056

Former Residence of Tsugumichi Saigo A1057

1982, Sept. 10 *Perf. 13*
1474 A1056 60y multicolored .70 .15
1475 A1057 60y multicolored .70 .15
Set value .20

Old Mutsuzawa School — A1058

Sakuranomiya Public Hall — A1059

1983, Feb. 15
1476 A1058 60y multicolored .70 .15
1477 A1059 60y multicolored .70 .15
Set value .20

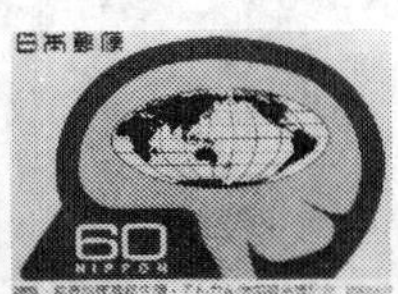

Globe on Brain — A1060

1981, Sept. 12 Photo.
1478 A1060 60y multicolored .70 .15

Intl. medical conferences, Kyoto: 12th Neurology, Sept. 20-25; 10th Brainwaves and Clinical Neurophysiology, Sept. 13-17; 1981 Intl. Epilepsy Conference, Sept. 17-21.

Congress Emblem — A1061

Plum Trees and Fowl, by Sanraku Kano — A1062

1981, Sept. 16
1479 A1061 60y multicolored .70 .15

24th World PTTI (Post, Telegraph and Telephone Intl. Labor Federation) Cong., Tokyo, Sept. 16-22.

1981, Oct. 6 Photo.
1480 A1062 130y multicolored 1.75 .18

25th Intl. Letter Writing Week, Oct. 6-12.

A1063

A1064

1981, Oct. 9 Photo. & Engr.
1481 A1063 60y No. 1 .85 .15
1482 A1063 60y No. 2 .85 .15
1483 A1063 60y No. 3 .85 .15
1484 A1063 60y No. 4 .85 .15
a. Strip or block of 4, #1481-1484 3.50 1.00

Philatokyo '81 Intl. Stamp Exhibition, Tokyo, Oct. 9-18.

1981, Oct. 13 Photo.
1485 A1064 40y multicolored .50 .15

36th Natl. Athletic Meet, Oct. 13-18.

New Year of 1982 (Year of the Dog) — A1065

1981, Dec. 1 Photo. *Perf. 13x13½*
1486 A1065 40y multicolored .48 .15

Sheets of 2 were lottery prizes. Value $1.50.

Ueno Zoo Centenary — A1066

Designs: a, Gorilla, flamingo. b, Penguins, lion. c, Panda, elephants. d, Zebras, giraffe.

1982, Mar. 20 Photo.
1487 Strip of 4 3.25 1.40
a.-d. A1066 60y any single .70 .32

Views of the Snow on Matsuchiyama, by Kiyonago Torii
A1067 A1068

1982, Apr. 20 Photo. *Perf. 13½*

1488 A1067 60y multicolored .75 .35
1489 A1068 60y multicolored .75 .35
a. Pair, #1488-1489 1.50 .70

Philatelic Week.

Shisa (Lion-shaped Guard Dog) A1069

Natl. Forestation Campaign A1070

1982, May 15 Photo.

1490 A1069 60y multicolored .70 .32

10th anniv. of Reversion Agreement returning Ryukyu Islands.

1982, May 22 *Perf. 13x13½*

1491 A1070 60y multicolored .70 .32

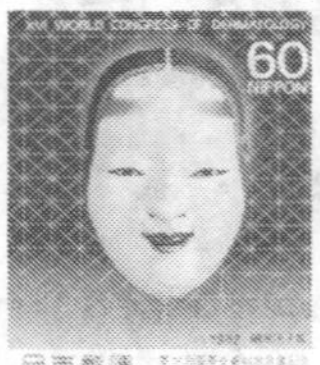

16th Intl. Dermatology Conference Tokyo, May 23-28 — A1071

1982, May 24 *Perf. 13*

1492 A1071 60y Noh mask .70 .32

Tohoku-Shinkansen Railroad Line Opening — A1072

1982, June 23

1493 A1072 60y Diesel locomotive .70 .32
1494 A1072 60y Steam model 1290 .70 .32
a. Pair, #1493-1494 1.50

Letter Writing Day — A1073

Perf. 13x13½, 13½x13

1982, July 23

1495 A1073 40y Sea gull, letter .50 .15
1496 A1073 60y Fairy, letter, horiz. .75 .35

Modern Japanese Art Issue

Kimono Patterned with Irises, by Saburosuke Okada (1869-1939) A1074

Bodhisattva Kuan-yin on Potalaka Island, by Tessai Tomioka (1837-1924) A1075

1982, Aug. 5 Photo. *Perf. 13½*

1497 A1074 60y multicolored .70 .32
1498 A1075 60y multicolored .70 .32

The Sarasvati, by Shiko Munakata (1903-1975) A1076

Saltim- banque, by Seiji Togo (1897-1978) A1077

1982, Nov. 24

1499 A1076 60y multicolored .70 .32
1500 A1077 60y multicolored .70 .32

Snowstorm, by Shinsui Ito — A1078

Spiraeas and Callas with Persian Pot, by Zenzaburo Kojima — A1079

1983, Jan. 24 Photo.

1501 A1078 60y multicolored .70 .32
1502 A1079 60y multicolored .70 .32

Muga, by Taikan Yokoyama (1868-1958) A1080

Roen, by Koun Takamura (1852-1934) A1081

Photo., Photo. and Engr.

1983, Mar. 10 *Perf. 13½*

1503 A1080 60y multicolored .70 .32
1504 A1081 60y multicolored .70 .32

A1082 A1083 A1084

1982, Aug. 23 *Perf. 13x13½*

1505 A1082 60y Wreath .75 .35
1506 A1083 60y Crane .75 .35
1507 A1084 70y Tortoise .85 .38
Nos. 1505-1507 (3) 2.35 1.08

For use on greeting (Nos. 1506-1507) and condolence (No. 1505) cards.

See Nos. 1555-1556, 1836-1839, 2227-2230 and footnote after No. 1765.

400th Anniv. of Boys' Delegation to Europe, Tensho Era — A1085

1982, Sept. 20 Photo. *Perf. 13*

1508 A1085 60y 16th cent. ship, map .70 .32

10th Anniv. of Japanese-Chinese Relations Normalization — A1086

Design: Hall of Prayer for Good Harvests, Temple of Heaven, Peking, by Ryuzaburo Umehara.

1982, Sept. 29

1509 A1086 60y multicolored .70 .32

Table Tennis — A1087

"Amusement," Doll by Goyo Hirata — A1088

1982, Oct. 2

1510 A1087 40y multicolored .50 .25

37th Natl. Athletic Meet, Matsue, Oct. 3-8.

1982, Oct. 6

1511 A1088 130y multicolored 1.65 .60

Intl. Letter Writing Week, Oct. 6-12.

Central Bank System Centenary A1089

Design: The Bank of Japan near Eitaibashi in Snow, by Yasuji Inoue.

Photogravure and Engraved

1982, Oct. 12 *Perf. 13½*

1512 A1089 60y multicolored .70 .32

A1090

A1091

Opening of Joetsu Shinkansen Railroad Line

1982, Nov. 15

1513 A1090 60y Locomotive, 1982 .70 .32
1514 A1091 60y Locomotive, 1931 .70 .32
a. Pair, #1513-1514 1.50 .70

New Year 1983 A1092

Natl. Museum of History and Folklore Opening A1093

1982, Dec. 1 *Perf. 13x13½*

1515 A1092 40y Kintaro on Wild Boar .50 .15

Sheets of 2 were lottery prizes. Value, $1.50.

1983, Mar. 16 Photo. *Perf. 13½x13*

1516 A1093 60y multicolored .70 .32

Women Working in the Kitchen, by Utamaro Kitagawa (1753-1806)

A1094 A1095

1983, Apr. 20 Photo. *Perf. 13*

1517 A1094 60y multicolored .70 .32
1518 A1095 60y multicolored .70 .32
a. Pair, #1517-1518 1.40 .70

Philatelic Week.

Natl. Forestation Campaign — A1096

50th Nippon Derby — A1097

1983, May 21 *Perf. 13*

1519 A1096 60y Hakusan Mountains, black lily, forest .70 .32

1983, May 28

1520 A1097 60y Colt, racing horse .70 .32

Islands Cleanup Campaign — A1098

1983, June 13 Photo. *Perf. 13½*

1521 A1098 60y multicolored .70 .32

Western Architecture Series

Hohei Hall Sapporo A1099

Old Glover House, Nagasaki A1100

Gojyuku Bank, Hirosaki
A1101

Gakushuin Elementary School, Tokyo
A1102

Bank of Japan, Tokyo
A1103

Old Hunter House, Kobe
A1104

Photogravure and Engraved

1983, June 23 *Perf. 13*
1522 A1099 60y multicolored .75 .35
1523 A1100 60y multicolored .75 .35

1983, Aug. 15 *Perf. 13*
1524 A1101 60y multicolored .75 .35
1525 A1102 60y multicolored .75 .35

1984, Feb. 16 *Perf. 13*
1526 A1103 60y multicolored .75 .35
1527 A1104 60y multicolored .75 .35
Nos. 1522-1527 (6) 4.50 2.10

Official Gazette Centenary
A1107

Letter Writing Day
A1108

Design: First issue, Drawing of the Government Bulletin Board at Nihonbashi, by Hiroshige Ando III.

1983, July 2 **Photo.** *Perf. 13*
1530 A1107 60y multicolored .70 .32

Perf. 13x13½, 13½x13

1983, July 23
1531 A1108 40y Boy writing letter .50 .22
1532 A1108 60y Fairy bringing letter, horiz. .75 .35

Opening of Natl. Noh Theater, Tokyo — A1109

1983, Sept. 14 **Photo.** *Perf. 13*
1533 A1109 60y Masked actor, theater .70 .32

Endangered Birds Issue

Rallus Okinawae — A1110

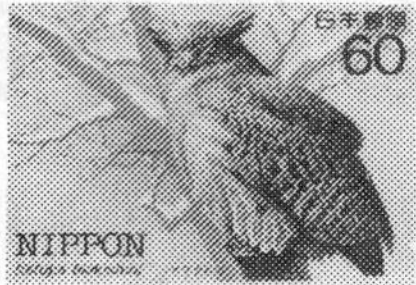
Ketupa Blakistoni
A1111

Photo. and Engr., Photo.

1983, Sept. 22 *Perf. 13*
1534 A1110 60y multicolored .75 .35
1535 A1111 60y multicolored .75 .35

Photo., Photo. & Engr.

1983, Nov. 25 *Perf. 13*
1536 A1110 60y Sapheopipo noguchii .75 .35
1537 A1111 60y Branta canadensis leucopareia .75 .35

Photo., Photo. and Engr.

1984, Jan. 26 *Perf. 13*
1538 A1111 60y Megalurus pryeri pryeri .75 .35
1539 A1110 60y Spilornis cheela perplexus .75 .35

1984, Mar. 15 **Photo.** *Perf. 13*
1540 A1110 60y Columba janthina nitens .75 .35
1541 A1111 60y Tringa guttifer .75 .35

1984, June 22 **Photo.** *Perf. 13*
1542 A1110 60y Falco peregrinus frutti .75 .35

Photo. and Engr.

1543 A1111 60y Dendrocopus leucutus austoni .75 .35
Nos. 1534-1543 (10) 7.50 3.50

Souvenir Sheet

1984, Dec. 10 **Photo. & Engr.**
1544 Sheet of 3 2.75 1.10
a. A1111 60y Prus grn, engr., #1535 .80 .35
b. A1110 60y vio brn, engr., #1539 .80 .35
c. A1110 60y ol blk, engr., #1542 .80 .35

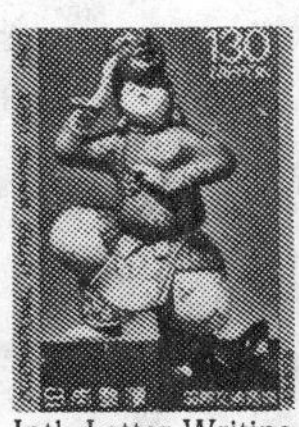
Intl. Letter Writing Week — A1124

38th Natl. Athletic Meet — A1125

Chikyu Doll by Juzo Kagoshima (1898-1982).

1983, Oct. 6 **Photo.** *Perf. 13*
1548 A1124 130y multicolored 1.75 .70

1983, Oct. 15 *Perf. 13*
1549 A1125 40y Naginata event .50 .26

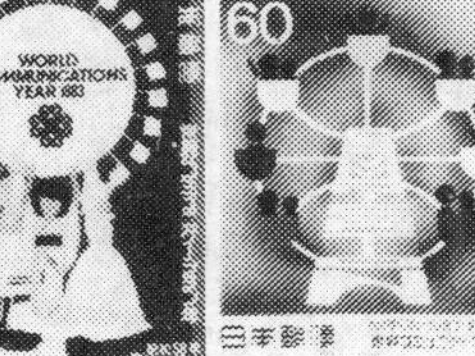
World Communications Year
A1126 A1127

1983, Oct. 17 **Photo.** *Perf. 13*
1550 A1126 60y multicolored .70 .32
1551 A1127 60y multicolored .70 .32

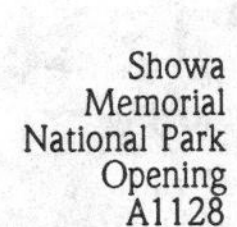

Showa Memorial National Park Opening
A1128

1983, Oct. 26 **Photo.** *Perf. 13*
1552 A1128 60y multicolored .70 .32

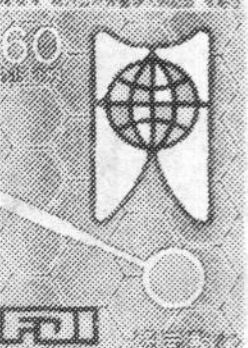
A1129

A1130

1983, Nov. 14 **Photo.**
1553 A1129 60y multicolored .70 .32

71st World Dentistry Congress.

1983, Nov. 14 **Photo.** *Perf. 13*
1554 A1130 60y multicolored .70 .32

Shirase, Antarctic observation ship, maiden voyage.

Type of 1982

1983, Nov. 22 **Photo.** *Perf. 12½*
1555 A1082 40y Wreath .60 .26
1556 A1083 40y Crane .60 .26

For use on condolence and greeting cards.

New Year 1984 — A1131

1983, Dec. 1 **Photo.** *Perf. 13x13½*
1557 A1131 40y Rat riding hammer .50 .25

Sheets of 2 were lottery prizes. Value, $1.50.

Universal Declaration of Human Rights, 35th Anniv. — A1132

1983, Dec. 5 **Photo.** *Perf. 13½*
1558 A1132 60y Emblem .70 .32

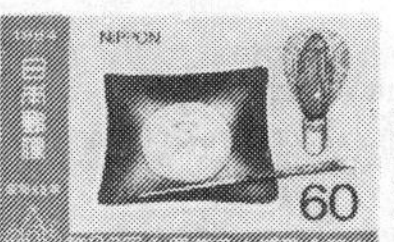
20th Grand Confectionery Fair, Tokyo, Feb. 24-Mar. 12 — A1133

1984, Feb. 24 **Photo.**
1559 A1133 60y Confection, tea whisk .70 .32

Natl. Bunraku Theater Opening, Osaka — A1134

1984, Apr. 6 **Photo.** *Perf. 13*
1560 A1134 60y Bunraku puppet .70 .32

A1135

A1136

Philatelic Week (Sharaku Prints): No. 1561, Hanshiro Iwai IV Playing Shigenoi. No. 1562, Oniji Otani Playing Edobe.

Photogravure and Engraved

1984, Apr. 20 *Perf. 13½*
1561 A1135 60y multicolored .70 .32
1562 A1136 60y multicolored .70 .32
a. Pair, #1561-1562 1.40 .70

Natl. Forestation Campaign
A1137

Weather Forecasting Centenary
A1138

1984, May 19 **Photo.**
1563 A1137 60y Cedar Forest, Sakurajima .70 .32

1984, June 1 *Perf. 13x13½*
1564 A1138 60y Himawari satellite, map .70 .32

UNESCO Emblem, Doves
A1139

Letter Writing Day
A1140

1984, July 16 **Photo.**
1565 A1139 60y multicolored .70 .32

UNESCO Clubs and Associations World Congress, July 16-24.

Perf. 13x13½, 13½x13

1984, July 23
1566 A1140 40y Birds in tree .48 .20
1567 A1140 60y Bird holding letter, horiz. .70 .32

Disaster Relief — A1141

Perf. 13x12½, 12½x13

1984, Aug. 23 **Photo.**
1568 A1141 40y Fire, wind .48 .20
1569 A1141 60y Mother, child, vert. .70 .32

Alpine Plant Series

Leontopodium Fauriei — A1142

Lagotis Glauca A1143

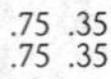

Photogravure and Engraved
Perf. 12½x13, 13x12½

1984, Aug. 27
1570 A1142 60y multicolored .75 .35
1571 A1143 60y multicolored .75 .35

Trollius Riederianus A1144

Primula Cuneifolia A1145

1984, Sept. 21 ***Perf. 13***
1572 A1144 60y multicolored .75 .35
1573 A1145 60y multicolored .75 .35

Rhododendron Aureum — A1146

Oxytropis Nigrescens Var. Japonica A1147

1985, Jan. 25 ***Perf. 13***
1574 A1146 60y multicolored .75 .35
1575 A1147 60y multicolored .75 .35

Draba Japonica — A1148

Dryas Octopetala A1149

1985, Feb. 28
1576 A1148 60y multicolored .75 .35
1577 A1149 60y multicolored .75 .35

Callianthemum Insigne Var. Miyabeanum A1150

Gentiana Nipponica A1151

1985, July 31 ***Perf. 13***
1578 A1150 60y multicolored .75 .35
1579 A1151 60y multicolored .75 .35

Campanula Chamissonis — A1152

Viola Crassa A1153

1985, Sept. 27
1580 A1152 60y multicolored .75 .35
1581 A1153 60y multicolored .75 .35

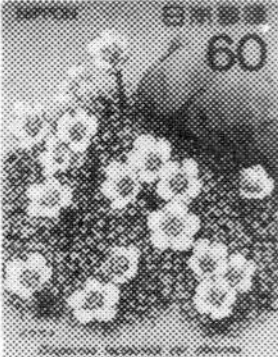
Deapensia Lapponica A1154

Pedicularis Apodochila A1155

1986, Feb. 13 ***Perf. 13***
1582 A1154 60y multicolored .75 .35
1583 A1155 60y multicolored .75 .35
Nos. 1582-1583 (2) 1.50 .70

Basho's Street, Sendai — A1156

1984, Sept. 1 **Photo.** ***Perf. 13***
1584 A1156 60y multicolored .70 .32

Intl. Microbiological Association's 6th Intl. Congress of Virology, Sendai, Sept. 1-7.

Electronic Mail — A1157

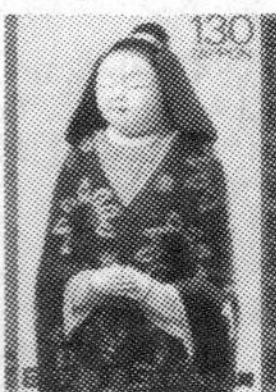
28th Intl. Letter Writing Week, Oct. 6-12 — A1158

1984, Oct. 1 **Photo.**
1585 A1157 500y multicolored 10.00 4.00

1984, Oct. 6
1586 A1158 130y Wooden doll 1.65 .70

17th Intl. Internal Medicine Congress, Kyoto, Oct. 7-12 — A1159

1984, Oct. 8
1587 A1159 60y Ginkakuji Temple .70 .32

39th Natl. Athletic Meet, Nara City, Oct. 12-17 — A1160

1984, Oct. 12
1588 A1160 40y Field hockey .50 .25

Traditional Crafts Series

Kutaniyaki Plates
A1161 A1162

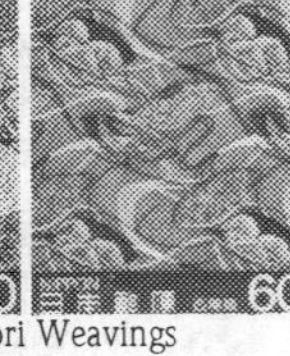
Nishijinori Weavings
A1163 A1164

1984, Nov. 2 **Photo.** ***Perf. 12½x13***
1589 A1161 60y Birds .80 .35
1590 A1162 60y Flowers .80 .35
a. Pair, #1589-1590 1.65 .75
1591 A1163 60y Flowers .80 .35
1592 A1164 60y Leaves .80 .35
a. Pair, #1591-1592 1.65 .75

Edokimekomi Dolls
A1165 A1166

Ryukyubingata Cloth
A1167 A1168

1985, Feb. 15 **Photo.** ***Perf. 13***
1593 A1165 60y Adult figures .80 .35
1594 A1166 60y Child and pet .80 .35
a. Pair, #1593-1594 1.65 .75
1595 A1167 60y Bird and branch .80 .35
1596 A1168 60y Birds .80 .35
a. Pair, #1595-1596 1.65 .75

Ichii-ittobori Carved Birds
A1169 A1170

Imariyaki & Aritayaki Ceramic Ware
A1171 A1172

Kamakurabori Wood Carvings
A1173 A1174

Ojiyachijimi Weavings
A1175 A1176

Hakata Ningyo Clay Figures
A1177 A1178

Nanbu Tekki Iron Ware
A1179 A1180

1985, May 23 **Photo.** ***Perf. 13***
1597 A1169 60y Bird .80 .35
1598 A1170 60y Birds .80 .35
a. Pair, #1597-1598 1.65 .75
1599 A1171 60y Bowl .80 .35
1600 A1172 60y Plate .80 .35
a. Pair, #1599-1600 1.65 .75

1985, June 24 **Photo. & Engr.**
1601 A1173 60y Bird and flower panel .80 .35
1602 A1174 60y Round flower panel .80 .35
a. Pair, #1601-1602 1.65 .75

Litho.
1603 A1175 60y Hemp star pattern .80 .35
1604 A1176 60y Hemp linear pattern .80 .35
a. Pair, #1603-1604 1.65 .75

1985, Aug. 8 **Photo.**
1605 A1177 60y Man .80 .38
1606 A1178 60y Woman and child .80 .38
a. Pair, #1605-1606 1.65 .80

Photogravure and Engraved
1607 A1179 60y Silver kettle .80 .38
1608 A1180 60y Black kettle .80 .38
a. Pair, #1607-1608 1.65 .80

Wajimanuri Lacquerware
A1181 A1182

Izumo-ishidoro Sandstone Sculptures
A1183 A1184

Photo., Photo. & Engr. (#1611-1612)

1985, Nov. 15

1609 A1181 60y Bowl on table .80 .38
1610 A1182 60y Bowl .80 .38
a. Pair, #1609-1610 1.65 .80
1611 A1183 60y Columnar lantern .80 .38
1612 A1184 60y Lantern on four legs .80 .38
a. Pair, #1611-1612 1.65 .80

Kyo-sensu Silk Fans
A1185 A1186

Tobeyaki Porcelain
A1187 A1188

1986, Mar. 13 Photo. *Perf. 13*

1613 A1185 60y Flower bouquets .80 .38
1614 A1186 60y Sun and trees .80 .38
a. Pair, #1613-1614 1.65 .80
1615 A1187 60y Jug .80 .38
1616 A1188 60y Jar .80 .38
a. Pair, #1615-1616 1.65 .80
Nos. 1613-1616 (4) 3.20 1.52

Japanese Professional Baseball, 50th Anniv. — A1189

1984, Nov. 15 *Perf. 13½*

1617 A1189 60y Batter .80 .35
1618 A1189 60y Pitcher .80 .35
a. Pair, #1617-1618 1.65 .80
1619 A1189 60y Matsutaro Shoriki .80 .35
Nos. 1617-1619 (3) 2.40 1.05

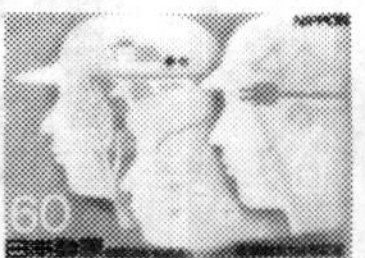

Industrial Education Centenary — A1190

New Year 1984 — A1191

1984, Nov. 20 *Perf. 13x12½*

1620 A1190 60y Workers, symbols .70 .32

1984, Dec. 1 Photo. *Perf. 13½x13*

1621 A1191 40y Sakushu Cattle Folk Toy .50 .25

Sheets of 2 were lottery prizes. Value, $1.50.

A1200

Ivory Shell — A1201

Hiougi-gai (Bivalve) — A1202

Rinbo Shell — A1203

Ooitokake-gai (Conch) — A1204

A1205

A1206

A1207

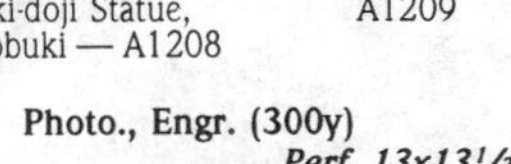

Keiki-doji Statue, Kongobuki — A1208

A1209

Photo., Engr. (300y)

1984-89 *Perf. 13x13½*

1622 A1200 2y turq blue ('89) .15 .15
1623 A1201 40y multi ('88) .52 .15
1624 A1202 41y multi ('89) .62 .15
b. Imperf., self-adhesive .62 .15
1625 A1203 60y multi ('88) .80 .15
a. Bklt. pane, 5 each #1623, 1625 6.75
1626 A1204 62y multi ('89) .92 .15
a. Bklt. pane, 2 #1624, 4 #1626 5.00
b. Imperf., self-adhesive .92 .15
c. Bklt. pane, 2 #1624b, 4 #1626b ('89) 5.00
1627 A1205 72y dark vio, blk & org yel ('89) 1.10 .20
1628 A1206 175y multi ('89) 2.65 .25
1629 A1207 210y multi ('89) 3.15 .30
1630 A1208 300y dk red brown 5.25 1.40
1631 A1209 360y dull pink & brn ('89) 5.50 .80
Nos. 1622-1631 (10) 20.66
Set value 3.10

Coil Stamps

Perf. 13 Horiz.

1636 A1202 41y multi ('89) .62 .15
1637 A1204 62y multi ('89) .92 .15
Set value .15

No. 1622 inscribed "Nippon," unlike No. 583.

No. 1626c is adhered to the booklet cover, made of peelable paper, folded in half and rouletted down the center fold.

Issued: 40y, 60y, 4/1; 300y, 4/3; 2y, 72y, 4/1; 42y, #1626, 1626a, 41y, #1637, 3/24; 175y, 210y, 360y, 6/1; #1626d, 7/3.

A1210

EXPO '85 — A1211

1985, Mar. 16 Photo. *Perf. 13*

1640 A1210 40y multicolored .50 .22
1641 A1211 60y multicolored .75 .35
a. Souv. sheet of 2, #1640-1641 1.65

University of the Air — A1212

1985, Apr. 1 Photo. *Perf. 13½*

1642 A1212 60y University broadcast tower .70 .35

Inauguration of adult education through broadcasting.

Nippon Telegraph & Telephone Co. — A1213

1985, Apr. 1

1643 A1213 60y Satellite receiver .70 .35

Inauguration of Japan's new telecommunications system.

World Import Fair, Nagoya A1214

1985, Apr. 5 Photo. *Perf. 13*

1644 A1214 60y 16th century map of Japan .70 .35

Industrial Proprietary System Cent. — A1215

Design: Portrait of Korekiyo Takashashi, system promulgator, inscriptions in English.

1985, Apr. 18 Photo. *Perf. 13½*

1645 A1215 60y multicolored .70 .35

Winter in the North — A1216

To the Morning Light — A1217

Paintings by Yumeji Takehisa (1884-1934).

1985, Apr. 20 *Perf. 13*

1646 A1216 60y multicolored .70 .35
1647 A1217 60y multicolored .70 .35
a. Pair, #1646-1647 1.50 .75

Philatelic Week. Printed in sheets of 10.

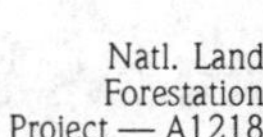

Natl. Land Forestation Project — A1218

Intl. Year of the Forest: Autumn bellflower, camphor tree, cattle and Mt. Aso.

1985, May 10 *Perf. 13½*

1648 A1218 60y multicolored .70 .35

Radio Japan, 50th Anniv. — A1219

Painting: Cherry Blossoms at Night, by Taikan Yokoyama.

1985, June 1 Photo. *Perf. 13*

1649 A1219 60y multi (Left) .75 .35
1650 A1219 60y multi (Right) .75 .35
a. Pair, #1649-1650 1.60 .70

Hisoko Maejima, 1st Postmaster General — A1220

1985, June 5 Photo. *Perf. 13*

1651 A1220 60y Portrait, former P.O. building .70 .35

Oonaruto Bridge Opening A1221

1985, June 7 *Perf. 13½*

1652 A1221 60y multicolored .70 .35

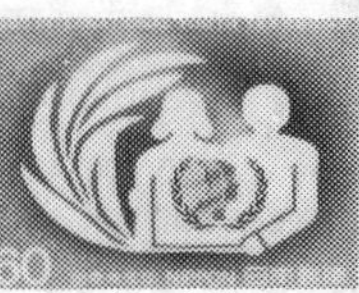

Intl. Youth Year A1222

Owl Carrying Letter A1223

1985, July 20 Photo. *Perf. 13*

1653 A1222 60y Emblem, silhouette .70 .35

Perf. 13½x13, 13x13½

1985, July 23 Photo.

1654 A1223 40y shown .60 .28
1655 A1223 60y Girl, cat, bird, letter .75 .45

Letter Writing Day (23rd of each month).

Electronic Mail — A1224

Meson Theory, 50th Anniv. — A1225

1985, Aug. 1 Photo. *Perf. 13x13½*

1656 A1224 500y multicolored 7.00 3.00

1985, Aug. 15 Photo. *Perf. 13*
1657 A1225 60y Portrait, nuclear particles .70 .35

Dr. Hideki Yukawa was presented the Nobel Prize for Physics for the Meson Theory in 1949, which is the foundation for high-energy physics.

A1226

A1227

1985, Aug. 24 Photo. *Perf. 13½*
1658 A1226 60y Gymnast, horse .70 .35

Universiade 1985, Kobe.

1985, Sept. 13 Photo.
1659 A1227 40y Emblem, competitor .50 .25

28th Intl. Vocational Training Competition, Oct. 21-27.

Normalization of Diplomatic Relations Between Japan and the Republic of Korea, 20th Anniv. — A1228

1985, Sept. 18
1660 A1228 60y Rose of Sharon .70 .30

Kan-Etsu Tunnel Opening A1229

1985, Oct. 2 *Perf. 13*
1661 A1229 60y Mountains, diagram, cross sections .70 .35

Seisen Doll by Goyo Hirata (1903-1981) — A1230

1985, Oct. 7
1662 A1230 130y multicolored 1.75 .85

Intl. Letter Writing Week, Oct. 6-12.

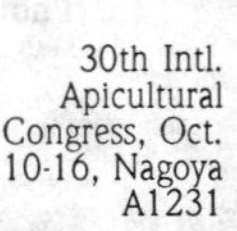
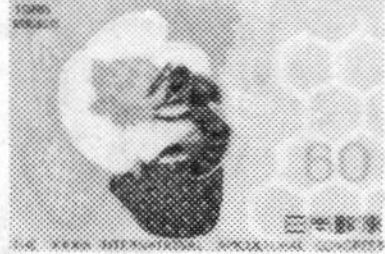
30th Intl. Apicultural Congress, Oct. 10-16, Nagoya A1231

1985, Oct. 9
1663 A1231 60y Honeybee, strawberry plants .70 .35

Japanese Overseas Cooperation Volunteers, 20th Anniv. A1232

1985, Oct. 9 Litho.
1664 A1232 60y Planting crop .70 .35

40th Natl. Athletic Meet, Oct. 20-25, Tottori City Sports Arena — A1233

1985, Oct. 19 Photo.
1665 A1233 40y Handball player, Mt. Daisen .50 .25

New Year 1986 A1234

Natl. Ministerial System of Government, Cent. A1235

1985, Dec. 2 Photo. *Perf. 13x13½*
1666 A1234 40y Shinno papier-mache tiger .50 .25

Sheets of 2 were lottery prizes. Value, $1.40.

1985, Dec. 20 Litho. *Perf. 13½*
1667 A1235 60y Official seal, Cabinet emblem .70 .35

Building Institute, Cent. — A1236

Philately Week — A1237

1986, Apr. 9 Photo. *Perf. 13*
1668 A1236 60y multicolored .70 .42

1986, Apr. 15

Southern Hateroma (details), by Keigetsu Kikuchi.

1669 A1237 60y Woman standing .75 .42
1670 A1237 60y Seated woman .75 .42
a. Pair, #1669-1670 1.60 .85

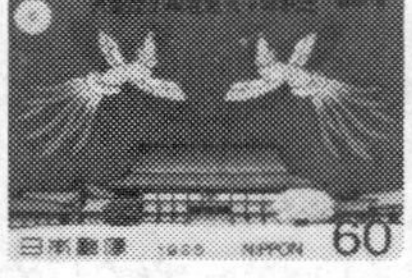
Kyoto Imperial Palace, Phoenix A1238

#1672, Imperial chrysanthemum crest & partridges.

1986, Apr. 28
1671 A1238 60y multicolored .75 .42
1672 A1238 60y multicolored .75 .42
a. Souv. sheet of 2, #1671-1672 1.65 1.25

Reign of Emperor Hirohito, 60th anniv.

6th Intl. Summit, Tokyo — A1239

1986, May 2
1673 A1239 60y Mt. Fuji .70 .42

Shrike on Reed, Emperor Nintoku's Mausoleum A1240

1986, May 9 *Perf. 13½*
1674 A1240 60y multicolored .70 .42

Natl. Land Afforestation Campaign.

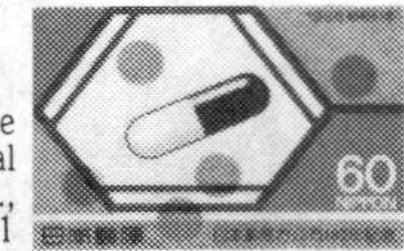
Japanese Pharmaceutical Regulatory Syst., Cent. — A1241

1986, June 25 Photo. *Perf. 13½*
1675 A1241 60y multicolored .70 .45

Japanese Standard Time, Cent. A1242

Letter Writing Day A1243

1986, July 11 Litho. *Perf. 13*
1676 A1242 60y Meridian, clock .70 .45

1986, July 23 Photo. *Perf. 13x13½*
1677 A1243 40y Bird .55 .35
1678 A1243 60y Girl, rabbit, birds .80 .52
a. Bklt. pane, 5 each #1677-1678 7.50

Sheets of 2 were lottery prizes. Value, *$60.*

Merchant Marine Education, 110th Anniv. A1244

Training ship Nihonmaru & navigation training institute founders Makoto Kondo, Yataro Iwasaki.

1986, July 26 *Perf. 13*
1679 A1244 60y multicolored .75 .48

CTO's exist for Nos. 1680-1681, 1684-1685, 1688-1689, 1694-1695, 1696-1697. They read "Japan" between two arcs in a corner.

Insects

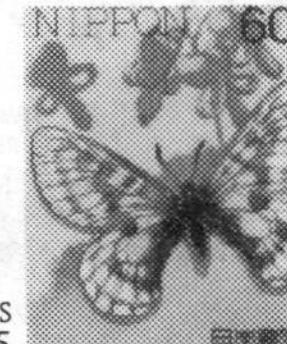
Parnassius Eversmanni — A1245

Photogravure and Engraved

1986, July 30 *Perf. 13*
1680 A1245 60y shown .80 .48
1681 A1245 60y Poecilocoris lewisi .80 .48
a. Pair, #1680-1681 1.60 1.00
1682 A1245 60y Rasalia batesi .80 .48
1683 A1245 60y Epiophlebia superstes .80 .48
a. Pair, #1682-1683 1.60 1.00

1986, Sept. 26 *Perf. 13*
1684 A1245 60y Dorcus hopei .80 .55
1685 A1245 60y Thermo- zephyrus ataxus .80 .55
a. Pair, #1684-1685 1.60 1.10
1686 A1245 60y Sympetrum pedemontanum .80 .55
1687 A1245 60y Damaster blaptoides .80 .55
a. Pair, #1686-1687 1.60 1.10

1986, Nov. 21 *Perf. 13*
1688 A1245 60y Elcysma westwoodii .80 .52
1689 A1245 60y Rhyothemis variegata .80 .52
a. Pair, #1688-1689 1.60 1.10
1690 A1245 60y Tibicen japonicus .80 .52
1691 A1245 60y Chrysochroa holstii .80 .52
a. Pair, #1690-1691 1.60 1.10

1987, Jan. 23 *Perf. 13*
1692 A1245 60y Parantica sita .80 .55
1693 A1245 60y Cheirotonus jambar .80 .55
a. Pair, #1692-1693 1.60 1.10
1694 A1245 60y Lucanus maculifemoratus .80 .55
1695 A1245 60y Anotogaster sieboldii .80 .55
a. Pair, #1694-1695 1.60 1.10

1987, Mar. 12 *Perf. 13*
1696 A1245 60y Ascaraphus ramburi .80 .55
1697 A1245 60y Polyphylla laticollis .80 .55
a. Pair, #1696-1697 1.60 1.10
1698 A1245 60y Kallima inachus .80 .55
1699 A1245 60y Calopteryx cornelia .80 .55
a. Pair, #1698-1699 1.60 1.10
Nos. 1680-1699 (20) 16.00 10.60

Miniature Sheet

1699A Sheet of 4 (#1680, 1692, 1699b-1699c) 3.50 2.75
b. A1245 40y Anthocaris cardamines .75 .55
c. A1245 40y Sasakia charonda .75 .55
d. Bklt. pane, 5 #1680, 5 #1699b 8.50
e. Bklt. pane, 5 #1692, 5 #1699c 8.50

Booklet panes are perf. 13x13½ on 2 or 3 sides.

Folkways in Twelve Months (Detail), by Shunsho Katsukawa A1265

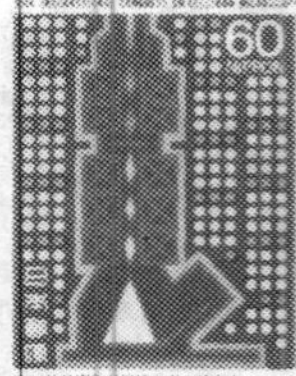
Electron Microscope A1266

1986, Aug. 23 Photo. *Perf. 13*
1700 A1265 60y multicolored .70 .48

52nd conference of the Intl. Federation of Library Associations, Tokyo, Aug. 24-29.

1986, Aug. 30
1701 A1266 60y multicolored .70 .48

11th Int. Congress of Electron Microscopy, Kyoto, Aug. 31-Sept. 7.

23rd Intl. Conference on Social Welfare, Tokyo, Aug. 31-Sept. 5 — A1267

1986, Aug. 30 Litho.
1702 A1267 60y multicolored .70 .48

Ohmorimiyage Doll, by Juzoh Kagoshima A1268

41st Natl. Athletic Meet, Oct. 12-17, Kofu A1269

1986, Oct. 6 Photo.
1703 A1268 130y multicolored 1.75 1.10

Intl. Letter Writing Week.

1986, Oct. 9
1704 A1269 40y multicolored .52 .38

5th World Ikebana Convention A1270

Painting: Flower in Autumn and a Girl in Rakuhoku.

1986, Oct. 17 Photo. *Perf. 13½x13*
1705 A1270 60y multicolored .70 .48

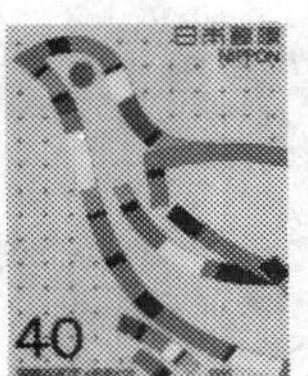

A1271

Intl. Peace Year — A1272

Lithographed, Photogravure (#1707)

1986, Nov. 28
1706 A1271 40y multicolored .55 .35
1707 A1272 60y multicolored .80 .52

New Year 1987 (Year of the Hare) — A1273

Design: A Couple of Rabbits Making Rice Cake, Nagoya clay figurine.

1986, Dec. 1 Photo. *Perf. 13x13½*
1708 A1273 40y multicolored .52 .32

Sheets of two containing Nos. 1506 and 1708 were lottery prizes. Value, $1.75.

Real Estate Registry System, Cent. — A1274

1987, Jan. 30 Photo. *Perf. 13½*
1709 A1274 60y multicolored .70 .48

Literature Series

Basho — A1275

Verse from Basho's Haiku — A1276

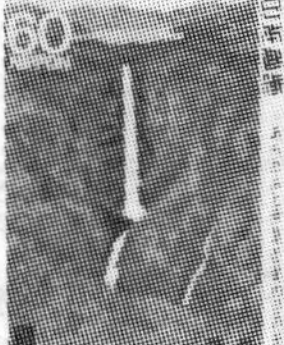

Kegon Falls — A1277

Haiku Verse — A1278

Cuckoo — A1279

Horse and Verse — A1280

Willow Tree — A1281

Rice Paddy and Verse — A1282

Chestnut Tree in Bloom — A1283

Chestnut Leaves and Verse — A1284

Planting Rice Paddy — A1285

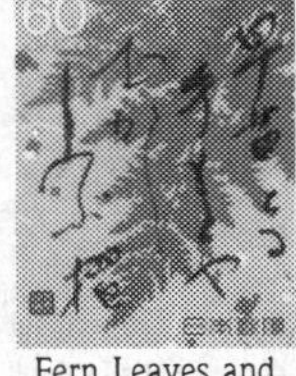

Fern Leaves and Verse — A1286

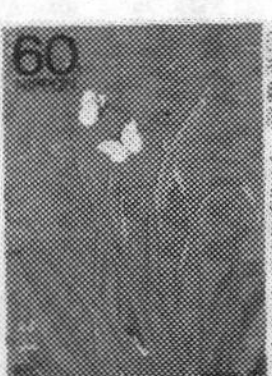

Sweetflags — A1287

Sweetflags and Verse — A1288

Prosperous Man, 17th Cent. — A1289

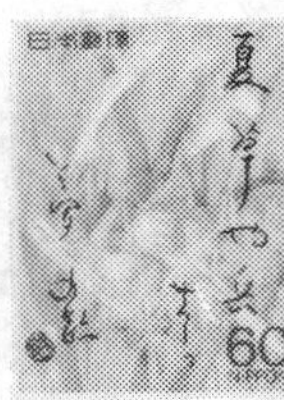

Summer Grass and Verse — A1290

Safflowers in Bloom — A1291

Verse — A1292

Yamadera (Temple) — A1293

Forest and Verse — A1294

1987-89 Photo. *Perf. 13x13½*

1710 A1275 60y multicolored .90 .60
1711 A1276 60y multicolored .90 .60
a. Sheet of 2, #1710-1711, imperf. ('89) 2.50
b. Pair, #1710-1711 1.80 1.25
1712 A1277 60y multicolored .90 .60
1713 A1278 60y multicolored .90 .60
a. Sheet of 2, #1712-1713, imperf. ('89) 2.50
b. Pair, #1712-1713 1.80 1.25
1714 A1279 60y multicolored .90 .60
1715 A1280 60y multicolored .90 .60
a. Sheet of 2, #1714-1715, imperf. ('89) 2.50
b. Pair, #1714-1715 1.80 1.25
1716 A1281 60y multicolored .90 .60
1717 A1282 60y multicolored .90 .60
a. Sheet of 2, #1716-1717, imperf. ('89) 2.50
b. Pair, #1716-1717 1.80 1.25
1718 A1283 60y multicolored .90 .60
1719 A1284 60y multicolored .90 .60
a. Sheet of 2, #1718-1719, imperf. ('89) 2.50
b. Pair, #1718-1719 1.80 1.25
1720 A1285 60y multicolored .90 .60
1721 A1286 60y multicolored .90 .60
a. Sheet of 2, #1720-1721, imperf. ('89) 2.50
b. Pair, #1720-1721 1.80 1.25
1722 A1287 60y multi ('88) .90 .60
1723 A1288 60y multi ('88) .90 .60
a. Sheet of 2, #1722-1723, imperf. ('89) 2.50
b. Pair, #1722-1723 1.80 1.25
1724 A1289 60y multi ('88) .90 .60
1725 A1290 60y multi ('88) .90 .60
a. Sheet of 2, #1724-1725, imperf. ('89) 2.50
b. Pair, #1724-1725 1.80 1.25
1726 A1291 60y multi ('88) .90 .60
1727 A1292 60y multi ('88) .90 .60
a. Sheet of 2, #1726-1727, imperf. ('89) 2.50
b. Pair, #1726-1727 1.80 1.25
1728 A1293 60y multi ('88) .90 .60
1729 A1294 60y multi ('88) .90 .60
a. Sheet of 2, #1728-1729, imperf. ('89) 2.50
b. Pair, #1728-1729 1.80 1.25
Nos. 1710-1729 (20) 18.00 12.00

Illustrations and text from Oku-no hosomichi, 1694, a travel description haiku written by Munefus "Basho" Matsuo (1644-1694), poet.

Issue dates: #1710-1713, Feb. 26. #1714-1717, June 23. #1718-1721, Aug. 25. #1722-1725, Jan. 3. #1726-1729, Mar. 26.

12th World Orchid Congress, Tokyo
A1295 A1296

1987, Mar. 19 Photo. *Perf. 13*
1730 A1295 60y multicolored .80 .60
1731 A1296 60y multicolored .80 .60

Railway Post Office Termination, Oct. 1, 1986 — A1297

1987, Mar. 26 Litho. *Perf. 13½*
1732 A1297 60y Mail car .80 .60
1733 A1297 60y Loading mail on car .80 .60
a. Pair, #1732-1733 1.60 1.25

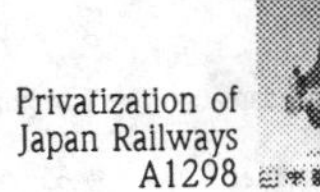

Privatization of Japan Railways A1298

1987, Apr. 1 Photo. *Perf. 13½*
1734 A1298 60y Locomotive No. 137, c. 1900 .80 .60
1735 A1298 60y Linear induction train, 1987 .80 .60

Natl. Marine Biology Research, Cent. — A1299

1987, Apr. 2 *Perf. 13*
1736 A1299 60y Sea slugs .80 .60

Philately Week
A1300 A1301

1987, Apr. 14
1737 A1300 60y multicolored .80 .60
1738 A1301 60y multicolored .80 .60
a. Pair, #1737-1738 1.60 1.25

Map of Asia and Oceania A1302

1987, Apr. 27 Photo. *Perf. 13½*
1739 A1302 60y multicolored .80 .60

20th annual meeting of the Asian Development Bank.

Nat'l. Land Afforestation Campaign — A1303

1987, May 23
1740 A1303 60y Magpie, seashore .80 .60

National Treasures Series

A1304

A1305

Golden Turtle Sharito — A1306

Imuyama Castle Donjon, 1469 — A1307

Kongo Sanmai in Tahotoh Temple, Kamakura Era — A1308

Wood Ekoh-Dohji Statue in the Likeness of Kongobuji Fudodo, Kamakura Era, by Unkei — A1309

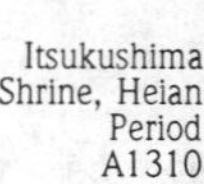

Itsukushima Shrine, Heian Period A1310

Kozakura-gawa, Braided Armor Worn by Minamoto-no-Yoshimitsu, Heian Period War Lord, Kai Province — A1311

Statue of *Nakatsu-hime-no-mikoto,* a Hachiman Goddess, Heian Period, Yakushiji Temple — A1312

Murou-ji Temple Pagoda, 9th Cent. — A1313

Designs: No. 1741, Yatuhashi gold inkstone box, by Kohrin Ogata. No. 1742, Donjon of Hikone Castle, c. 1573-1592.

1987, May 26 Photo. *Perf. 13*
1741 A1304 60y multicolored .90 .60

Photo. & Engr.
Perf. 13½
1742 A1305 110y multicolored 1.65 1.15

1987, July 17 Photo. *Perf. 13*
1743 A1306 60y multicolored .90 .62

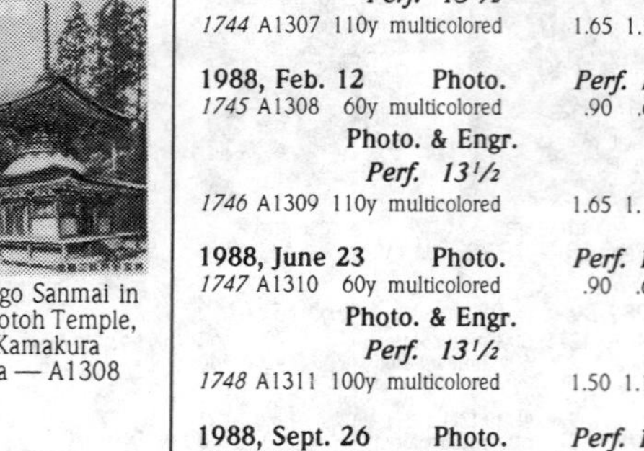

Photo. & Engr.
Perf. 13½
1744 A1307 110y multicolored 1.65 1.15

1988, Feb. 12 Photo. *Perf. 13*
1745 A1308 60y multicolored .90 .62

Photo. & Engr.
Perf. 13½
1746 A1309 110y multicolored 1.65 1.15

1988, June 23 Photo. *Perf. 13*
1747 A1310 60y multicolored .90 .68

Photo. & Engr.
Perf. 13½
1748 A1311 100y multicolored 1.50 1.15

1988, Sept. 26 Photo. *Perf. 13*
1749 A1312 60y multicolored .92 .70

Photo. & Engr.
Perf. 13½
1750 A1313 100y multicolored 1.50 1.15
Nos. 1741-1750 (10) 12.47 8.97

Letter Writing Day — A1314

1987, July 23 Photo. *Perf. 13x13½*
1751 A1314 40y Flowers, envelope .55 .42
1752 A1314 60y Elephant .82 .62
a. Bklt. pane, 5 each #1751-1752 7.00

Sheets of 2, Nos. 1751-1752, were lottery prizes. Value, *$20.*

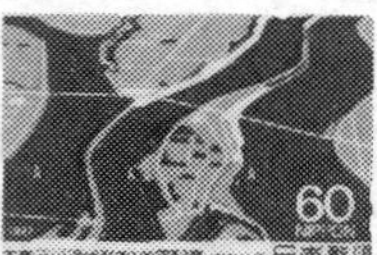
Kiso Three Rivers Flood Control, Cent. — A1315

1987, Aug. 7 Photo. *Perf. 13½*
1753 A1315 60y Kiso, Nagara and Ibi Rivers .82 .62

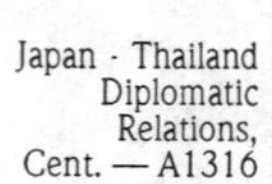
Japan - Thailand Diplomatic Relations, Cent. — A1316

Design: Temple of the Emerald Buddha and cherry blossoms.

1987, Sept. 26 *Perf. 13*
1754 A1316 60y multicolored .85 .65

Intl. Letter Writing Week — A1317

13th World Congress of Certified Public Accountants, Tokyo, Oct. 11-15 — A1318

Dolls by Goyo Hirata: 130y, Gensho Kanto, by Royojo Hori (1898-1984). 150y, Utage-no-Hana (Fair Woman at the Party).

1987, Oct. 6 Photo. *Perf. 13*
1755 A1317 130y multicolored 1.85 1.40
1756 A1317 150y multicolored 2.10 1.60

1987, Oct. 9 *Perf. 13*

Design: Three Beauties (adaptation), by Toyokuni Utagawa (1769-1825).

1757 A1318 60y multicolored .85 .65

Modern Waterworks, Cent. — A1319

Shurei Gate, Okinawa, Basketball Players — A1320

Design: Lion's head public fountain, 1887, Waterworks Museum, Yokohama.

1987, Oct. 16 Engr.
1758 A1319 60y multicolored .88 .65

1987, Oct. 24 Photo.
1759 A1320 40y multicolored .88 .65

42nd Natl. Athletic Meet, Okinawa.

6th World Cong. on Smoking & Health, Nov. 9-12, Tokyo — A1321

World Telecommunications Conf., Nov. 15-18, Tokyo — A1322

1987, Nov. 9
1760 A1321 60y multicolored .90 .68

1987, Nov. 13 *Perf. 13½*

Design: Microwave dish antenna at Kashima Station Radio Research Laboratory.

1761 A1322 60y multicolored .90 .68

World Conference on Large Historic Cities, Nov. 18-21, Kyoto A1323

Design: Nijo Castle guardhouse roof and Ninomaru Hall, 17th cent.

1987, Nov. 18 *Perf. 13*
1762 A1323 60y multicolored .90 .68

Intl. Year of Shelter for the Homeless A1324

Prize-winning illustrations by: 40y, Takahiro Nahahama. 60y, Yoko Sasaki.

1987, Nov. 25
1763 A1324 40y multicolored .60 .45
1764 A1324 60y multicolored .90 .68

New Year 1988 (Year of the Dragon) — A1325

Design: Kurashiki papier-mache dragon, 1869, by Tajuro Omizu.

1987, Dec. 1 *Perf. 13x13½*
1765 A1325 40y multicolored .60 .45

Sheets of 2, Nos. 1506, 1765, were lottery prizes. Value, $2.25.

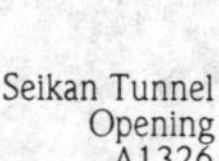
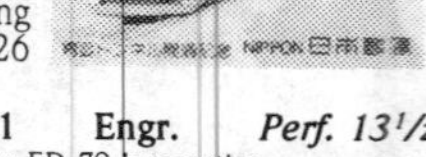
Seikan Tunnel Opening A1326

1988, Mar. 11 Engr. *Perf. 13½*
1766 A1326 60y ED 79 locomotive, map .95 .70

Opening of Seto-Oohashi Bridge

Kagawa Side
A1327 A1328

Okayama Side
A1329 A1330

1988, Apr. 8 Engr. *Perf. 13½*
1767 A1327 60y multicolored 1.00 .75
1768 A1328 60y multicolored 1.00 .75
1769 A1329 60y multicolored 1.00 .75
1770 A1330 60y multicolored 1.00 .75
a. Strip of 4, #1767-1770 4.00 3.00

Nos. 1767-1768 and 1769-1770 have continuous designs.

Philately Week
A1331 A1332

Prints by Kotondo Torii (b. 1900): No. 1771, Long Undergarment. No. 1772, Kimono Sash.

1988, Apr. 19 Photo. *Perf. 13*
1771 A1331 60y multicolored 1.00 .75
1772 A1332 60y multicolored 1.00 .75
a. Pair, #1771-1772 2.00

Souv. sheet of 2 exists. Value $12.

Silk Road Exposition, Apr. 24-Oct. 23, Nara — A1333

Design: Plectrum guard playing the biwa, detail of Raden-Shitan-no-Gogen-Biwa, a five-panel work of gold lacquer nacre on sandalwood preserved at Shosoin.

1988, Apr. 23 Photo. & Engr.
1773 A1333 60y multicolored .95 .75

Natl. Afforestation Campaign — A1334

Design: Yahsima, site of the Genji-Heike war, and cuckoo on olive tree branch.

1988, May 20 Photo. *Perf. 13½*
1774 A1334 60y multicolored .95 .75

Literature Series

Mogami River — A1335

Verse and Flower — A1336

Mt. Gassan A1337

Verse and Mountain A1338

Mimosa in Bloom — A1339

Verse, Birds, Kisagata Inlet — A1340

Ocean Waves — A1341

Verse and Current — A1342

Rice — A1343

Birds in Flight, Verse — A1344

Sun Glow — A1345

Rice, Verse — A1346

Nata-dera Temple — A1347

Verse, White Grass — A1348

Trees — A1349

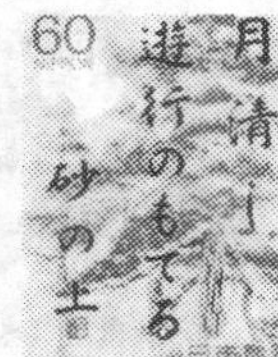

Verse, Moonlit Forest — A1350

Autumn on the Beach — A1351

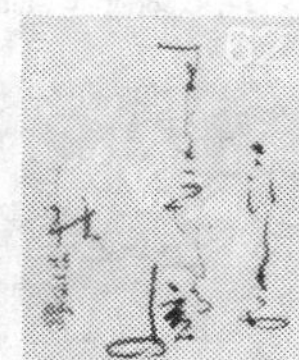

Verse — A1352

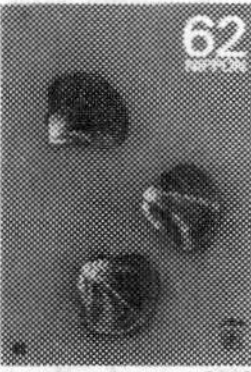

Clams — A1353

Verse — A1354

1988, May 30 Photo. *Perf. 13x13½*
1775 A1335 60y multicolored .95 .75
1776 A1336 60y multicolored .95 .75
a. Souv. sheet of 2, #1775-1776, imperf. ('89) 2.00
b. Pair, #1775-1776 1.90 1.50
1777 A1337 60y multicolored .95 .75
1778 A1338 60y multicolored .95 .75
a. Souv. sheet of 2, #1777-1778, imperf. ('89) 2.00
b. Pair, #1777-1778 1.90 1.50

1988, Aug. 23
1779 A1339 60y multicolored .95 .70
1780 A1340 60y multicolored .95 .70
a. Souv. sheet of 2, #1779-1780, imperf ('89) 2.00
b. Pair, #1779-1780 1.90 1.50
1781 A1341 60y multicolored .95 .70
1782 A1342 60y multicolored .95 .70
a. Souv. sheet of 2, #1781-1782, imperf. ('89) 2.00
b. Pair, #1781-1782 1.90 1.50

1988, Nov. 11
1783 A1343 60y multicolored .95 .70
1784 A1344 60y multicolored .95 .70
a. Souv. sheet of 2, #1783-1784, imperf. ('89) 2.00
b. Pair, #1783-1784 1.90 1.50
1785 A1345 60y multicolored .95 .70
1786 A1346 60y multicolored .95 .70
a. Souv. sheet of 2, #1785-1786, imperf. ('89) 2.00
b. Pair, #1785-1786 1.90 1.50

1989, Feb. 13
1787 A1347 60y multicolored .95 .70
1788 A1348 60y multicolored .95 .70
a. Souv. sheet of 2, #1787-1788, imperf. 2.00
b. Pair, #1787-1788 2.00 1.50
1789 A1349 60y multicolored .95 .70
1790 A1350 60y multicolored .95 .70
a. Souv. sheet of 2, #1789-1790, imperf. 2.00
b. Pair, #1789-1790 2.00 1.50

1989, May 12
1791 A1351 62y multicolored .95 .70
1792 A1352 62y multicolored .95 .70
a. Souv. sheet of 2, #1791-1792, imperf. 2.00
b. Pair, #1791-1792 1.90 1.40
1793 A1353 62y multicolored .95 .70
1794 A1354 62y multicolored .95 .70
a. Souv. sheet of 2, #1793-1794, imperf. 2.00
b. Pair, #1793-1794 1.90 1.40
Nos. 1791-1794 (4) 3.80 2.80

Illustrations and text from *Oku-no-hosomichi,* "Narrow Road to a Far Province," 1694, a travel description written in haiku by Munefus "Basho" Matsuo (1644-94), poet.

Issue date: Nos. 1776a-1794a, Aug. 1, 1989.

Intl. Conference on Volcanoes, Kagoshima A1355

1988, July 19 Photo. *Perf. 14*
1795 A1355 60y multicolored .90 .70

A1356

A1357

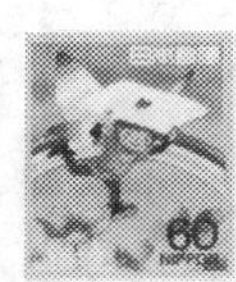

A1358

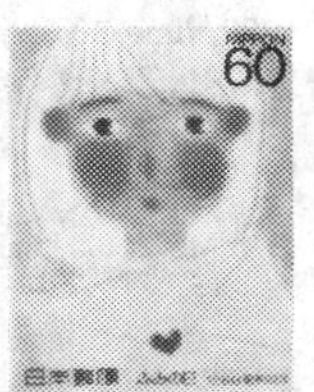

Letter Writing Day, 10th Anniv. — A1359

Designs and contest-winning children's drawings: No. 1796, Cat and letter. No. 1797, *Crab and Letter,* by Katsuyuki Yamada. No. 1798, Fairy and letter. No. 1799, *Girl and Letter,* by Takashi Ukai.

Photo., Litho. (Nos. 1797, 1799)
1988, July 23 *Perf. 13x13½*
1796 A1356 40y multicolored .65 .50
a. Imperf., self-adhesive .65 .50
1797 A1357 40y multicolored .65 .50
1798 A1358 60y multicolored .95 .70
a. Bklt. pane, 5 each #1796, 1798 9.00
b. Imperf., self-adhesive .95 .70
c. Bklt. pane, 3 each #1796a, 1798b 6.00
1799 A1359 60y multicolored .95 .70
Nos. 1796-1798 (3) 2.25 1.70

No. 1798c is adhered to the booklet cover, made of peelable paper, folded in half and rouletted down the center fold, with No. 1796a at left and No. 1798b at right of the roulette.

Sheets of 2 containing Nos. 1796, 1798 were lottery prizes. Value, $12.

A1360 A1361

A1362 A1363

15th World Puppetry Festival, July 27-Aug. 11

Puppets: No. 1800, *Ohana,* string puppet from the film *Spring and Fall in the Meiji Era,* by Kinosuke Takeda (1923-1979), Japan. No. 1801, Girl, stick puppet from the Natl. Radost Puppet Theater, Brno, Czechoslovakia. No. 1802, Woman, shadow puppet from China. No. 1803, Knight, a marionette from Sicily.

1988, July 27 Photo. *Perf. 13*
1800 A1360 60y multicolored .90 .70
1801 A1361 60y multicolored .90 .70
1802 A1362 60y multicolored .90 .70
1803 A1363 60y multicolored .90 .70
a. Block or strip of 4, #1800-1803 3.75 3.00

Japan-China Treaty, 10th Anniv.
A1364 A1365

1988, Aug. 12 Photo.
1804 A1364 60y Peony .90 .70
1805 A1365 60y Panda .90 .70

18th World Poultry Congress, Nagoya, Sept. 4-9 — A1366

1988, Sept. 3 *Perf. 13½*
1806 A1366 60y multicolored .90 .70

Rehabilitation Intl. 16th World Congress, Tokyo, Sept. 5-9 — A1367

Photo. & Embossed
1988, Sept. 5 *Perf. 13*
1807 A1367 60y multicolored .90 .70

A1368 A1369

Prints: 80y, *Kumesaburo Iwai as Chiyo,* by Kunimasa Utagawa (1773-1810), late Edo Period. 120y, *Komazo Ichikawa III as Ganryu Sasaki,* by Toyokuni Utagawa (1769-1825).

1988, Oct. 6 Photo.
1808 A1368 80y multicolored 1.25 1.00
1809 A1368 120y multicolored 2.00 1.50

Intl. Letter-Writing Week.

1988, Oct. 14

Design: Gymnast on parallel bars and "Kinkakuji," Temple of the Golden Pavilion.

1810 A1369 40y multicolored .65 .50

43rd Natl. Athletic Meet, Kyoto.

Japan-Mexico Trade Agreement, Cent. A1370

New Year 1989 (Year of the Snake) A1371

1988, Nov. 30 Photo.
1811 A1370 60y multicolored .95 .75

1988, Dec. 1

Design: Clay bell snake by Masanobu Ogawa.

1812 A1371 40y multicolored .65 .50

Sheets of two containing Nos. 1506, 1812 were lottery prizes. Value, $2.50.

UN Declaration of Human Rights, 40th Anniv. — A1372

1988, Dec. 5 Litho. *Perf. 13½*
1813 A1372 60y multicolored .95 .75

National Treasures Series

Votive Silver Lidded Bowl Used in Todai-ji Temple Ground-Breaking Ceremony, 8th Cent. — A1373

Bronze Yakusi-nyorai Buddha, Asuka Period, 7th Cent. — A1374

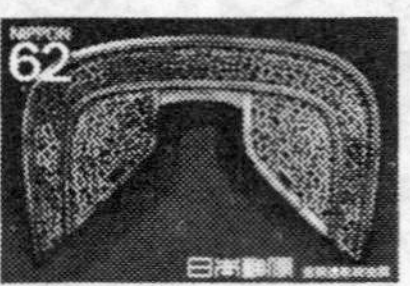

Kondo-Sukashibori-Kurakanagu, Bronze Saddle from Ohjin Imperial Mausoleum — A1375

Tamamushi-no-Zushi, Buddhist Altar in Lacquered Cypress from the Azuka Era — A1376

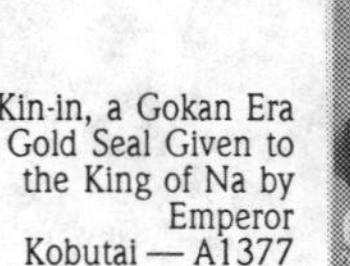

Kin-in, a Gokan Era Gold Seal Given to the King of Na by Emperor Kobutai — A1377

Shinninshaba-gazokyo, a 5th Cent. European Bronze Plate — A1378

Photo., Photo & Engr. (100y)

1989, Jan. 20 *Perf. 13, 13½ (100y)*
1814 A1373 60y multicolored .95 .75
1815 A1374 100y multicolored 1.60 1.25

1989, June 30
1816 A1375 62y multicolored .90 .65
1817 A1376 100y multicolored 1.40 1.00

1989, Aug. 15
1818 A1377 62y multicolored .90 .65
1819 A1378 100y multicolored 1.40 1.00
Nos. 1814-1819 (6) 7.15 5.30

Asian-Pacific Expo, Fukuoka, Mar. 17-Sept. 3 — A1383

1989 Photo. *Perf. 13*
1822 A1383 60y multicolored .95 .70
1823 A1383 62y multicolored 1.25 .95

Issue dates: 60y, Mar. 16. 62y, Apr. 18.

Yokohama Exposition (Space and Children), Yokohama City, Mar. 25 to Oct. 1 — A1384

Design: Detail of *Russian Lady Sight-seeing at the Port,* by Yoshitora, and entrance to the Yokohama City Art Museum.

1989, Mar. 24 Litho.
1824 A1384 60y multicolored .95 .70
1825 A1384 62y multicolored .95 .70

World Bonsai Convention, Omiya, Apr. 6-9 — A1385

1989, Apr. 6 Photo. *Perf. 13*
1826 A1385 62y multicolored .90 .65

Awa-odori, by Tsunetomi Kitano (b. 1880)

A1386 A1387

1989, Apr. 18 *Perf. 13*
1827 A1386 62y multicolored .90 .65
1828 A1387 62y multicolored .90 .65
a. Pair, #1827-1828 2.00

Philately Week. Sheets of 2 containing #1827-1828 were lottery prizes. Value, $5.

Holland Festival 1989 — A1388

1989, Apr. 19 *Perf. 13½*
1829 A1388 62y Ship .90 .65

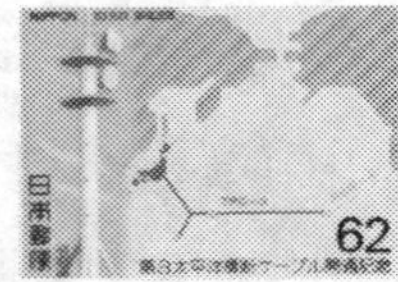

Fiber-optic Cable, the 3rd Transpacific Line Relay Linking Japan and the US — A1389

1989, May 10 *Perf. 13½x13*
1830 A1389 62y Station tower, map .90 .65

Natl. Afforestation Campaign — A1390

1989, May 19 *Perf. 13½*
1831 A1390 62y Bayberry, lime, Mt. Tsurugi .90 .65

World Design Exposition, Nagoya, July 15-Nov. 26

A1391 A1392

1989, July 14
1832 A1391 41y multicolored .55 .40
1833 A1392 62y multicolored .85 .65

Letter Writing Day

A1393 A1394

1989, July 21 *Perf. 13x13½*
1834 A1393 41y multicolored .55 .40
1835 A1394 62y multicolored .85 .65
a. Bklt. pane, 5 each #1834-1835 7.25

Sheets of 2 containing Nos. 1834-1835 were lottery prizes. Value, $5.25.

Congratulations and Condolences Types of 1982

1989, Aug. 10 Photo. *Perf. 13x13½*
1836 A1082 41y Wreath .55 .40
1837 A1083 41y Crane .55 .40
1838 A1083 62y Crane .85 .65
1839 A1084 72y Tortoise 1.00 .75
Nos. 1836-1839 (4) 2.95 2.20

6th Interflora World Congress, Tokyo, Aug. 27-30 — A1395

1989, Aug. 25 Photo. *Perf. 13½*
1840 A1395 62y multicolored .85 .65

Prefecture Issues

Nos. 1841-1990, 2246-2400 have been reserved for issues for Japan's 47 prefectures (political subdivisions). These stamps were available only in the prefecture for which they were issued, except for No. 1909a, which was available nationwide. All of the stamps were valid throughout Japan. Prefecture stamps are distinguishable from other Japanese issues by the calligraphic style of the four characters which represent the country name.

Monkeys (Nagano) A1396

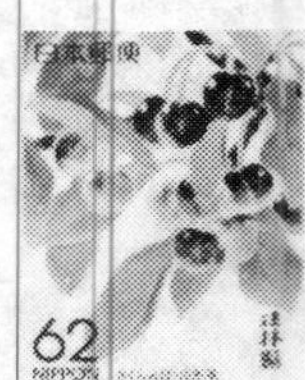

Cherries on Tree (Yamagata) A1397

Shurei-mon, Gate of Courtesy (Okinawa) A1398

Dogo Hot Spa (Ehime) A1399

Blue-eyed Doll (Kanagawa) — A1400

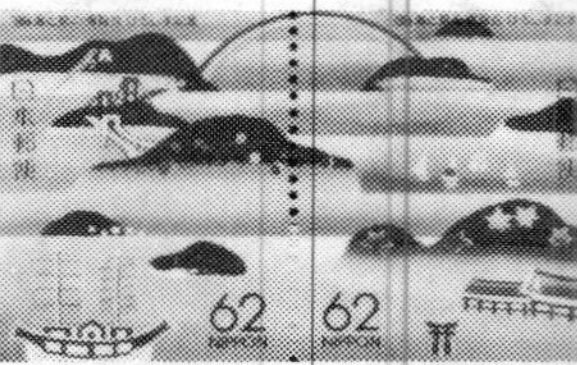

Seto Inland Sea (Hiroshima)

A1401 A1402

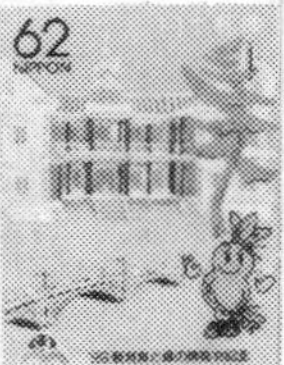

Memorial Hall and Mandai Bridge (Niigata) — A1403

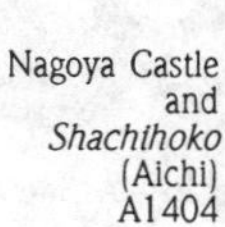

Nagoya Castle and *Shachihoko* (Aichi) A1404

Mt. Takasaki Monkey Holding Perilla Leaf, Fruit (Oita) — A1405

City Hall, 1888 (Hokkaido) — A1406

Runner, Flower (Hokkaido) A1407

Kumamoto Castle (Kumamoto) A1408

Stone Lantern, Kenroku-en Park (Ishikawa) A1409

Bunraku Puppets and Theater (Osaka) A1410

Shigaraki Ware Raccoon Dog and Lake Biwa (Shiga) A1411

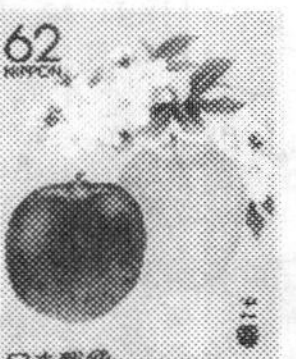
Apples and Blossoms (Aomori) — A1412

Raccoon Dogs Dancing (Chiba) — A1413

Blowfish Lanterns (Yamaguchi) A1414

Tokyo Station (Tokyo) A1415

2nd Asian Winter Olympics (Hokkaido) A1416

Waterfalls (Toyama) A1417

Perf. 13, 13½ (#1844, 1851, 1860), 13x13½ (#1852-1859)

1989-90 Photo., Litho. (#1856-1857)

1841	A1396	62y	multicolored	.85	.65
1842	A1397	62y	multicolored	.85	.65
1843	A1398	62y	multicolored	.85	.65
1844	A1399	62y	multicolored	.85	.65
1845	A1400	62y	multicolored	.85	.65
1846	A1401	62y	multicolored	.85	.65
1847	A1402	62y	multicolored	.85	.65
a.			Pair, #1846-1847	2.00	1.50
1848	A1403	62y	multicolored	.85	.65
1849	A1404	62y	multicolored	.85	.65
1850	A1405	62y	multicolored	.85	.65
1851	A1406	62y	multicolored	.85	.65
1852	A1407	62y	multicolored	.85	.65
1853	A1408	62y	multicolored	.85	.65
1854	A1409	62y	multicolored	.85	.65
1855	A1410	62y	multicolored	.85	.65
1856	A1411	62y	multicolored	.85	.65
1857	A1412	62y	multicolored	.85	.65
1858	A1413	62y	multicolored	.85	.65
1859	A1414	62y	multicolored	.85	.65
1860	A1415	62y	multicolored	.85	.65
1861	A1416	62y	multicolored	.85	.65
1862	A1417	62y	multicolored	.80	.60

Sheets containing 4 #1841, 1842, 1844, 1851 or 3 #1854 + label, 3 #1859 + label were lottery prizes.

Issued: #1841-1842, Apr. 1; #1843, May 15; #1844, June 1; #1845, June 2; #1846-1847, July 7; #1848, July 14. #1849, Aug. 1; #1850-1851, Aug. 15. #1852, Sept. 1; #1853, Sept. 29; #1854-1857, Oct. 2; #1858, Oct. 27; #1859-1860, Nov. 1; #1861, Mar. 1, 1990; #1862, Apr. 18, 1990.

Nos. 1863-1909 were issued as one set. It is broken into sections for ease of reference.

Hokkaido A1418

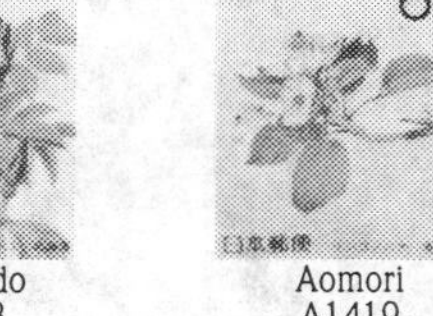
Aomori A1419

Iwate — A1420

Miyagi — A1421

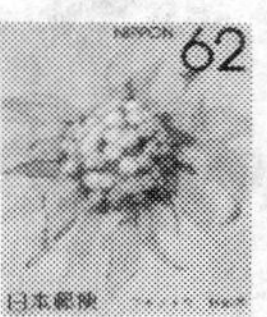
Akita A1422

Yamagata A1423

Fukushima A1424

Ibaraki A1425

Flowers of the Prefectures.

1990, Apr. 27 Litho. *Perf. 13½*

1863	A1418	62y	Sweet briar	.80	.60
1864	A1419	62y	Apple blossom	.80	.60
1865	A1420	62y	Paulowina	.80	.60
1866	A1421	62y	Japanese bush clover	.80	.60
1867	A1422	62y	Butterbur flower	.80	.60
1868	A1423	62y	Safflower	.80	.60
1869	A1424	62y	Alpine rose	.80	.60
1870	A1425	62y	Rose	.80	.60

See No. 2285.

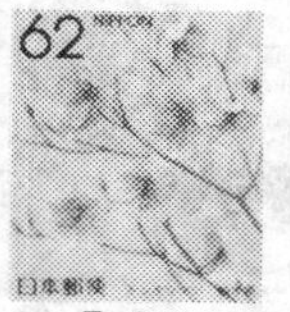
Tochigi A1426

Gunma A1427

Saitama A1428

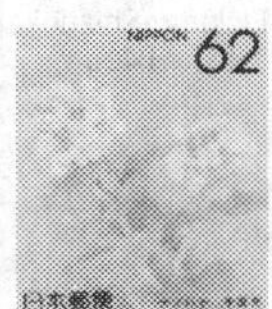
Chiba A1429

Kanagawa A1430

Yamanashi A1431

Tokyo A1432

Nagano A1433

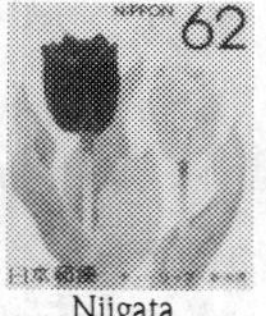
Niigata A1434

Toyama A1435

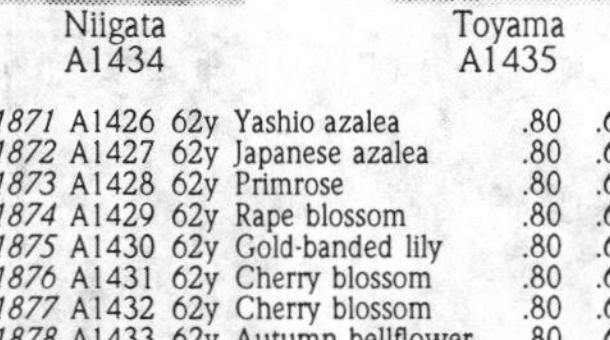

1871	A1426	62y	Yashio azalea	.80	.60
1872	A1427	62y	Japanese azalea	.80	.60
1873	A1428	62y	Primrose	.80	.60
1874	A1429	62y	Rape blossom	.80	.60
1875	A1430	62y	Gold-banded lily	.80	.60
1876	A1431	62y	Cherry blossom	.80	.60
1877	A1432	62y	Cherry blossom	.80	.60
1878	A1433	62y	Autumn bellflower	.80	.60
1879	A1434	62y	Tulip	.80	.60
1880	A1435	62y	Tulip	.80	.60

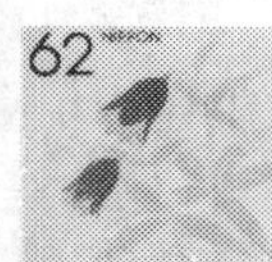
Ishikawa A1436

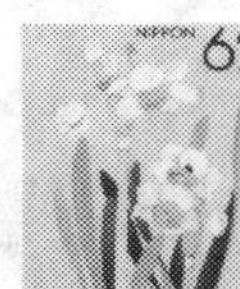
Fukui A1437

Gifu A1438

Shizuoka A1439

Aichi — A1440

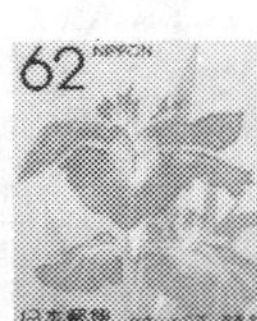
Mie — A1441

Shiga — A1442

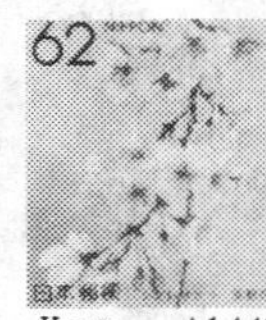
Kyoto — A1443

Osaka — A1444

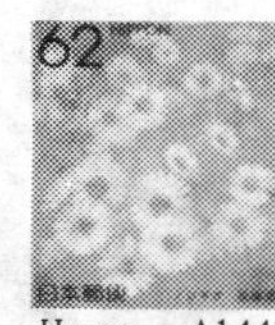
Hyogo — A1445

1881	A1436	62y	Black lily	.80	.60
1882	A1437	62y	Daffodil	.80	.60
1883	A1438	62y	Chinese milk vetch	.80	.60
1884	A1439	62y	Azalea	.80	.60
1885	A1440	62y	Rabbit-ear iris	.80	.60
1886	A1441	62y	Iris	.80	.60
1887	A1442	62y	Alpine rose	.80	.60
1888	A1443	62y	Drooping cherry blossom	.80	.60
1889	A1444	62y	Japanese apricot and primrose	.80	.60
1890	A1445	62y	Chrysanthemum	.80	.60

Nara A1446

Wakayama A1447

Tottori A1448

Shimane A1449

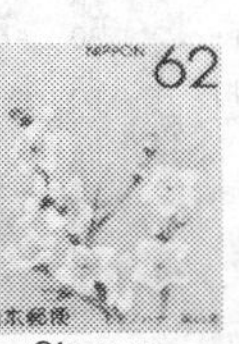
Okayama A1450

Hiroshima A1451

Yamaguchi A1452

Tokushima A1453

Kagawa A1454

Ehime A1455

1891	A1446	62y	Double cherry blossom	.80	.60
1892	A1447	62y	Japanese apricot	.80	.60
1893	A1448	62y	Pear blossom	.80	.60
1894	A1449	62y	Peony	.80	.60
1895	A1450	62y	Peach blossom	.80	.60
1896	A1451	62y	Japanese Mmple	.80	.60
1897	A1452	62y	Summer orange blossom	.80	.60
1898	A1453	62y	Sudachi orange blossom	.80	.60
1899	A1454	62y	Olive blossom	.80	.60
1900	A1455	62y	Mandarin orange blossom	.80	.60

Kochi
A1456

Fukuoka
A1457

Saga
A1458

Nagasaki
A1459

Kumamoto
A1460

Oita
A1461

Miyazaki
A1462

Kagoshima
A1463

Okinawa — A1464

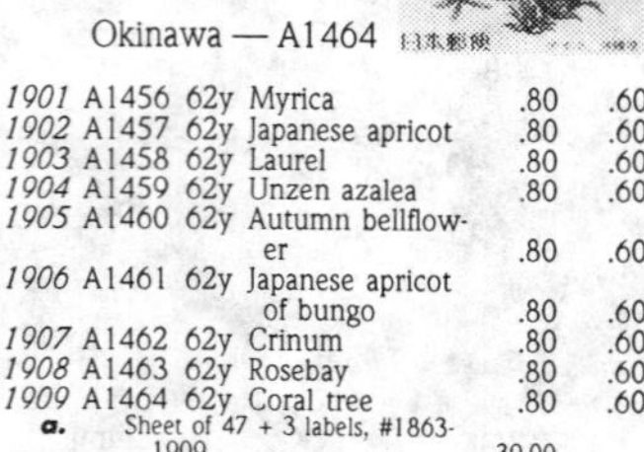

1901	A1456	62y	Myrica	.80	.60
1902	A1457	62y	Japanese apricot	.80	.60
1903	A1458	62y	Laurel	.80	.60
1904	A1459	62y	Unzen azalea	.80	.60
1905	A1460	62y	Autumn bellflower	.80	.60
1906	A1461	62y	Japanese apricot of bungo	.80	.60
1907	A1462	62y	Crinum	.80	.60
1908	A1463	62y	Rosebay	.80	.60
1909	A1464	62y	Coral tree	.80	.60
a.			Sheet of 47 + 3 labels, #1863-1909	39.00	

Nos. 1863-1909 were issued in sheets of 20.

Seven Baby Crows (Ibaraki) — A1465

Inns of Tsumago & Magome (Nagano)
A1466 A1467

Mt. Fuji and Tea Picking (Shizuoka)
A1468

Two Peaches (Fukushima)
A1469

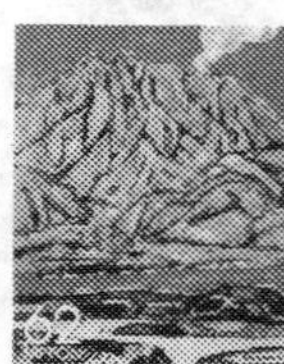

Mt. Sakurajima (Kagoshima)
A1470

Fireworks Festival of Omagari (Akita)
A1471

Travel Expo '90, Nagasaki (Nagasaki) — A1472

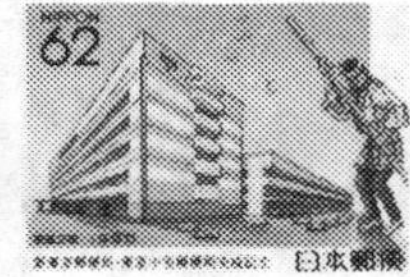

Tokyo Shin Post Office (Tokyo)
A1473

Yasukibushi Folk Song (Shimane)
A1474

Ryukyu Dancer (Okinawa)
A1475

Litho., Litho. & Engr. (#1911-1912)

1990 *Perf. 13*

1910	A1465	62y	multicolored	.80	.60
1911	A1466	62y	blk & buff	.80	.60
1912	A1467	62y	blk & pale grn	.80	.60
a.			Pair, #1911-1912	1.65	1.25
1913	A1468	62y	multicolored	.80	.60
1914	A1469	62y	multicolored	.95	.70
1915	A1470	62y	multicolored	.95	.70
1916	A1471	62y	multicolored	.95	.70
1917	A1472	62y	multicolored	.95	.70
1918	A1473	62y	multicolored	.95	.70
1919	A1474	62y	multicolored	.95	.70
1920	A1475	62y	multicolored	.95	.70

Issued: #1910-1912, May 1; #1913, May 2; #1914, June 1; #1915-1916, July 2; #1917, Aug. 1; #1918, Aug. 6; #1919-1920, Aug. 15.

Sheets of 3 + label of #1910, 1913, 1920 were lottery prizes. Value, each $3.25.

Dancing Girl (Kyoto)
A1476

Old Path of Kumano (Wakayama)
A1477

45th Natl. Athletic Meet (Fukuoka)
A1478

Izu Swamp, Swans (Miyagi)
A1479

Spring (Gifu) — A1480

Summer (Gifu) — A1481

Autumn (Gifu) — A1482

Winter (Gifu) — A1483

Nursery Rhyme, Toryanse (Saitama) — A1484

Japanese Cranes (Hokkaido)
A1485

1990

1921	A1476	62y	multicolored	.95	.70
1922	A1477	62y	multicolored	.95	.70
1923	A1478	62y	multicolored	.95	.70
1924	A1479	62y	multicolored	1.00	.75
1925	A1480	62y	multicolored	1.00	.75
1926	A1481	62y	multicolored	1.00	.75
1927	A1482	62y	multicolored	1.00	.75
1928	A1483	62y	multicolored	1.00	.75
a.			Strip of 4, #1925-1928	4.00	3.00
1929	A1484	62y	multicolored	1.00	.75
1930	A1485	62y	multicolored	1.00	.75

Issued: #1921-1923, 9/3; #1924, 10/1; #1925-1928, 10/9; #1929, 10/12; #1930, 10/30.

Sheets of 3 #1922 + label were lottery prizes. Value, $3.25.

Bizen Ware (Okayama)
A1487 A1488

Battle of Yashima (Kagawa) — A1486

Yoshinogari Ruins (Saga) — A1489

Bride Under Cherry Blossoms (Yamanashi)
A1490

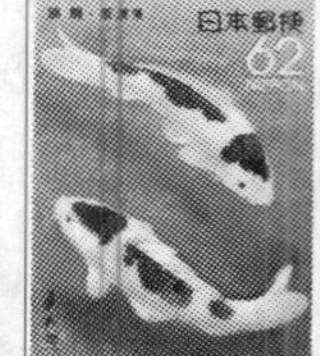

Carp (Niigata)
A1491

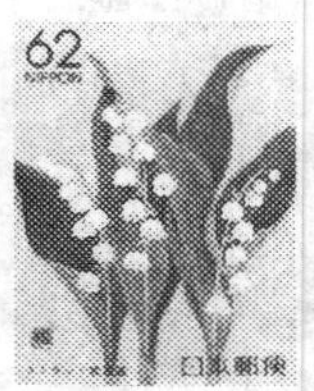

Lily Bell (Hokkaido)
A1492

Lilac (Hokkaido)
A1493

Day Lily (Hokkaido)
A1494

Rowanberry (Hokkaido)
A1495

Litho., Photo. (#1934-1935)

1991 *Perf. 13*

1931	A1486	62y	multicolored	1.00	.75
1932	A1487	62y	multicolored	.95	.70
1933	A1488	62y	multicolored	.95	.70
a.			Pair, #1932-1933	1.90	1.50
1934	A1489	62y	multicolored	.95	.70
1935	A1490	62y	multicolored	.95	.70
1936	A1491	62y	multicolored	.95	.70
1937	A1492	62y	multicolored	.95	.70
1938	A1493	62y	multicolored	.95	.70
1939	A1494	62y	multicolored	.95	.70
1940	A1495	62y	multicolored	.95	.70
a.			Strip of 4, #1937-1940	3.80	2.50

Issued: #1931, Feb. 19; #1932-1933, Apr. 5; #1934, Apr. 12; #1935, Apr. 18; #1936, May 1; #1937-1940, May 31.

Nikkou Mountains (Tochigi) — A1496

Mt. Iwate by Yaoji Hashimoto (Iwate) — A1497

Wooden Puppet (Tokushima) A1498

Whales (Kochi) A1499

Fringed Orchids (Tokyo) A1500

Cape Toi, Horses (Miyazaki) A1501

Black Pearls of Kabira Bay (Okinawa) A1502

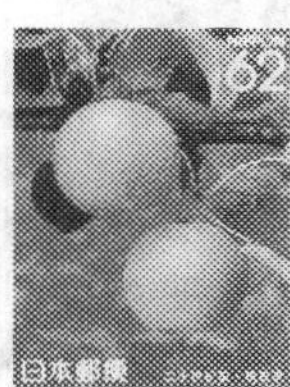
Japanese Pears (Tottori) A1504

Tsujun-kyo Bridge (Kumamoto) A1503

1991 **Photo.**

1941	A1496	62y multicolored	.95	.70
1942	A1497	62y multicolored	.95	.70
a.		Booklet pane of 10	9.50	
1943	A1498	62y multicolored	.95	.70
a.		Pane of 10	9.50	
1944	A1499	62y multicolored	.95	.70
a.		Pane of 10	9.50	
1945	A1500	41y multicolored	.68	.50
a.		Booklet pane of 10	15.00	
1946	A1501	62y multicolored	.95	.70
a.		Booklet pane of 10	15.00	
1947	A1502	41y multicolored	.68	.50
1948	A1503	62y multicolored	.95	.70
a.		Bklt. pane of 10	15.00	
1949	A1504	62y multicolored	.95	.70

Issued: #1941, May 29; #1942, June 10; #1943-1944, June 26; #1945-1946, July 1; #1947-1948, Aug. 1; #1949, Aug. 26.

Sheets of 3 #1946 + label were lottery prizes. Value, $3.

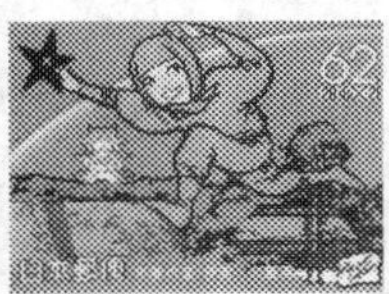
Ninja, Iga Ueno Castle (Mie) — A1506

46th Natl. Athletic Meet (Ishikawa) — A1505

Eyeglass Industry (Fukui) — A1507

Nursery Rhyme, Tortoise and the Hare — A1508

Kobe City Weathervane (Hyogo) — A1509

Spring (Nara) — A1510

Autumn (Nara) (Gunma) — A1511

Litho., Photo. (#1950, 1952)

1991 ***Perf. 13, 13½ (#1950)***

1950	A1505	41y multicolored	.68	.50
a.		Booklet pane of 10	6.80	
1951	A1506	62y multicolored	.95	.70
a.		Booklet pane of 10	14.00	
1952	A1507	62y multicolored	1.00	.75
a.		Booklet pane of 10	14.00	10.50
1953	A1508	62y multicolored	1.00	.75
a.		Booklet pane of 10	14.00	
1954	A1509	62y multicolored	1.00	.75
a.		Booklet pane of 10	14.00	
1955	A1510	62y multicolored	1.00	.75
1956	A1511	62y multicolored	1.00	.75
a.		Pair, #1955-1956	2.00	1.50
b.		Bklt. pane of 5 #1956a	14.00	

Issued: #1950, Sept. 2; #1951, Sept. 10; #1952, Oct. 1; #1953, Oct. 23; #1954, Oct. 25; #1955-1956, Oct.

See Nos. 2272-2273.

Gogo-An Temple, Sea of Japan (Niigata) — A1512

Natl. Land Afforestation Campaign (Fukuoka) — A1513

Arctic Fox (Hokkaido) A1514

Tateyama Mountain Range (Toyama) A1515

Rikuchu Coast (Iwate) A1516

Kurushima Strait (Ehime) A1517

Tsurusaki Dance (Oita) A1518

Tanabata Lantern Festival (Yamaguchi) A1519

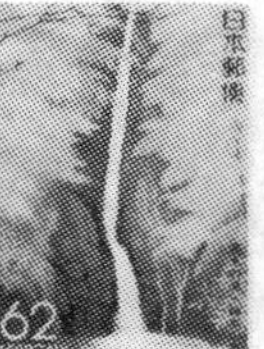
Shasui-no-taki Waterfall (Kanagawa) A1520

Kurodabushi Dance (Fukuoka) A1521

Boat Race (Okinawa) A1522

Osaka Castle, Business Park (Osaka) A1523

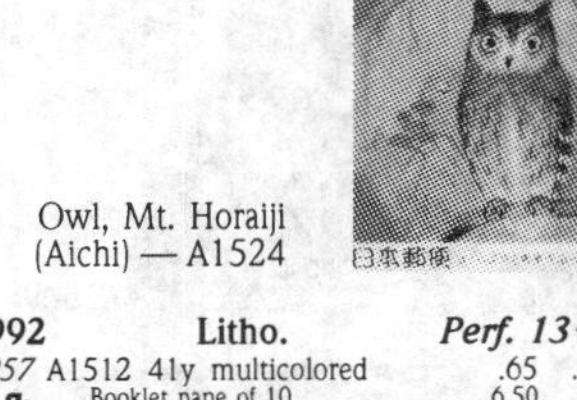
Owl, Mt. Horaiji (Aichi) — A1524

1992 **Litho.** ***Perf. 13½***

1957	A1512	41y multicolored	.65	.50
a.		Booklet pane of 10	6.50	
		Photo.		
1958	A1513	41y multicolored	.65	.50
1959	A1514	62y multicolored	1.00	.75
a.		Souvenir sheet of 3	3.00	2.25
		Litho.		
1960	A1515	62y multicolored	1.00	.75
a.		Booklet pane of 10	10.00	
		Photo.		
1961	A1516	62y multicolored	1.00	.75
a.		Booklet pane of 10	10.00	
1962	A1517	62y multicolored	1.00	.75
a.		Booklet pane of 10	10.00	
1963	A1518	62y multicolored	1.05	.80
1964	A1519	62y multicolored	1.05	.80
1965	A1520	62y multicolored	1.00	.75
a.		Booklet pane of 10	10.00	
b.		Souvenir sheet of 3	3.00	2.25
		Litho.		
1966	A1521	62y multicolored	1.00	.75
1967	A1522	62y multicolored	1.00	.75
1968	A1523	41y multicolored	.70	.50
		Photo.		
1969	A1524	62y multicolored	1.00	.75
a.		Souvenir sheet of 3	3.00	2.25
b.		Booklet pane of 10	10.00	

Issued: #1957, May 1; #1958, May 8; #1961-1962, June 23; #1959, May 29; #1963, July 23; #1964, July 7; #1965, July 24; #1967, Aug. 17; #1969, Oct. 15; #1966, Aug. 3.

Oga Peninsula (Akita) A1525

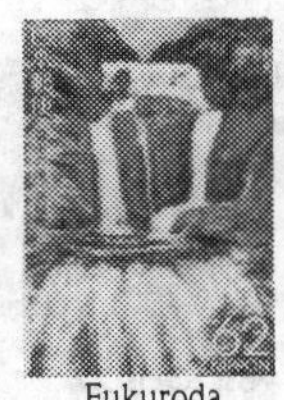
Fukuroda Waterfall (Ibaraki) A1526

Notojima Bridge, Nanao Bay (Ishikawa) A1527

Tama District Mountains (Metropolitan Tokyo) A1528

Harbor Seal (Hokkaido) — A1529

Peace Statue (Kagawa) A1530

Hana Ta'ue Rice Planting Festival (Hiroshima) A1531

Paradise Flycatcher and Mt. Fuji (Shizuoka) A1532

Sailboats on Lake Biwa (Shiga) — A1533

Matumoto Castle & Japan Alps (Nagano) — A1534

Ohara Festival (Kagoshima) A1535

Oirase Mountain Stream (Aomori) A1536

Yourou Valley (Chiba) — A1537

1993 **Litho.** ***Perf. 13½***

1970	A1525	41y multicolored	.70	.50
a.		Booklet pane of 10	7.00	
1971	A1526	62y multicolored	1.10	.80
a.		Booklet pane of 10	11.00	
		Photo.		
1972	A1527	62y multicolored	1.15	.85
a.		Booklet pane of 10	11.50	
1973	A1528	62y multicolored	1.15	.85
a.		Booklet pane of 10	11.50	
1974	A1529	62y multicolored	1.15	.85
1975	A1530	62y multicolored	1.15	.85
a.		Booklet pane of 10	11.50	
1976	A1531	62y multicolored	1.20	.90
1977	A1532	41y multicolored	.80	.60
a.		Booklet pane of 10	12.00	
1978	A1533	62y multicolored	1.20	.90
a.		Booklet pane of 10	12.00	
1979	A1534	62y multicolored	1.20	.90
a.		Booklet pane of 10	12.00	

1980 A1535 41y multicolored .80 .60
a. Booklet pane of 10 8.00

Perf. 13x13½

1981 A1536 62y multicolored 1.00 .75
a. Booklet pane of 10 10.00

Perf. 13½

1982 A1537 41y multicolored .70 .55
a. Booklet pane of 10 7.00

Issued: #1970, Feb. 12; #1971, Mar. 26; #1972, Apr. 2; #1973, Apr. 23; #1974, May 17; #1975, May 21; #1976, June 4; #1977, June 23; #1978, July 1; #1979, July 16; #1980, Sept. 1; #1981, Sept. 22; #1982, Oct. 1.

Dream Bridge (Metropolitan Tokyo) A1538

Kurobe Canyon & Dam (Toyama) A1539

Haiku, Storehouse of Poet Issa (1763-1827) (Nagano) A1540

Okuni, Izumo Great Shrine, Taisha (Shimane) A1541

Fukiwari Falls (Gunma) A1542

Ezoshika (Hokkaido) A1543

Watch Tower, Festival in Tajima (Hyogo) A1544

Wakura Coast (Wakayama) A1545

1994 Photo. *Perf. 13*

1983 A1538 50y multicolored .95 .70
a. Booklet pane of 10 9.50
1984 A1539 80y multicolored 1.50 1.10
a. Booklet pane of 10 15.00
1985 A1540 80y multicolored 1.50 1.25
a. Booklet pane of 10 15.00
1986 A1541 80y multicolored 1.50 1.25
a. Booklet pane of 10 15.00

Litho.

1987 A1542 80y multicolored 1.50 1.25
a. Booklet pane of 10 15.00
1988 A1543 50y multicolored 1.00 .75
a. Booklet pane of 10 10.00
1989 A1544 50y multicolored 1.00 .75
a. Booklet pane of 10 10.00
1990 A1545 80y multicolored 1.50 1.25
a. Booklet pane of 10 15.00

Issued: #1983, 3/23; #1984, 4/25; #1985-1986, 5/2; #1987, 6/6; #1988, 6/7; #1989, 6/23; #1990, 7/15.

See Nos. 2246-2400 for future Prefecture issues.

Far East and South Pacific Games for the Disabled (FESPIC), Kobe, Sept. 15-20 A1546

1989, Sept. 14 Photo. *Perf. 13½*

1991 A1546 62y multicolored .90 .65

Okuni Kabuki Screen
A1547 A1548

1989, Sept. 18 *Perf. 13*

1992 A1547 62y multicolored .90 .65
1993 A1548 70y multicolored 1.00 .75

EUROPALIA '89, Japan.

A1549

A1550

Scenes from the Yadori and Takekawa Chapters of the Tales of the Genji picture scroll, attributed to Fujiwara-no-Takeyoshi, late Heian Period (897-1185).

1989, Oct. 6 Photo. *Perf. 13½*

1994 A1549 80y multicolored 1.15 .90
1995 A1550 120y multicolored 1.70 1.25

Intl. Letter Writing Day.

Intl. Conference on Irrigation and Drainage A1551

100th Tenno Sho Horse Race A1552

1989, Oct. 13

1996 A1551 62y Rice .90 .70

1989, Oct. 27 *Perf. 13*

1997 A1552 62y Jockey riding Shinzan .90 .70

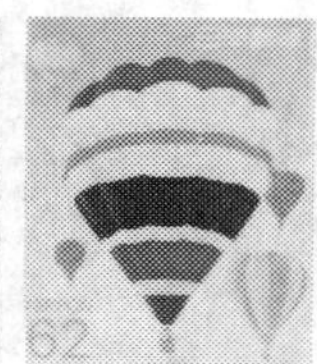

9th Hot Air Balloon World Championships, Saga — A1553

1989, Nov. 17 Photo. *Perf. 13x13½*

1998 A1553 62y multicolored .90 .65

Copyright Control System, 50th Anniv. A1554

1989, Nov. 17 *Perf. 13*

1999 A1554 62y Conductor .90 .65

New Year 1990 (Year of the Horse)
A1555 A1556

1989, Dec. 1 *Perf. 13x13½, 13½*

2000 A1555 41y *Yawata-Uma* festival horse .60 .40
2001 A1556 62y *Kazari-Uma,* Meiji Period .90 .65

No. 2001 was sold through Jan. 10, 1990, serving as a lottery ticket.

Sheets of two containing Nos. 1838, 2000 were lottery prizes. Value, $2.

Electric Locomotives

10,000 A1557

1990 Photo. & Engr., Photo. *Perf. 13*

2002 A1557 62y shown .90 .65
2003 A1557 62y EF58 .90 .65
2004 A1557 62y ED40 .90 .65
2005 A1557 62y EH10 .90 .65
2006 A1557 62y EF53 .90 .65
2007 A1557 62y ED70 .90 .65
2008 A1557 62y EF55 .80 .60
2009 A1557 62y ED61 .80 .60
2010 A1557 62y EF57 .80 .60
2011 A1557 62y EF30 .80 .60
Nos. 2002-2011 (10) 8.60 6.30

Issued two stamps at a time, the first photo. & engr., the second photo.

Issue dates: Nos. 2002-2003, Jan. 31; Nos. 2004-2005, Feb. 28; Nos. 2006-2007, Apr. 23; Nos. 2008-2009, May 23; Nos. 2010-2011, July 18.

Intl. Garden and Greenery Exposition, Osaka A1558

1990, Mar. 30 Photo. *Perf. 13*

2021 A1558 62y multicolored .90 .65

See No. B45.

A1559 A1560

Painting: *Women Gazing at the Stars,* by Chou Ohta.

1990, Apr. 20 Photo. *Perf. 13*

2022 A1559 62y multicolored .90 .65
a. Souvenir sheet of 1 .90 .65

Philately Week.

1990, May 18 Photo. *Perf. 13½*

2023 A1560 62y Azalea, Mt. Unzen .80 .60

Natl. Land Afforestation Campaign.

Flower, Butterfly A1561

Designs: 70y, Abstract art.

1990, June 1 Photo. *Perf. 13*

2024 A1561 62y multicolored .80 .60
2025 A1561 70y multicolored .90 .65

Japan-Turkey Relations, Cent. — A1562

1990, June 13

2026 A1562 62y multicolored .80 .60

Horses Series

Horse at Stable from Umaya-zu Byobu — A1563

Ponies — A1564

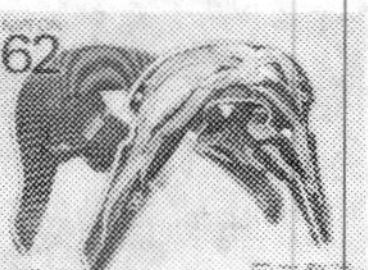

Lacquered Saddle, 16th Cent. — A1565

Lacquered Stirrups, 16th Cent. — A1566

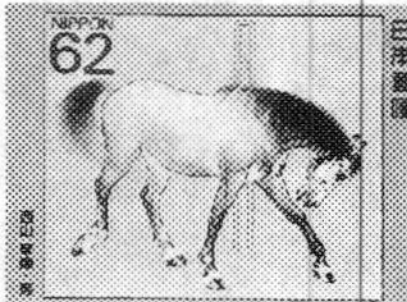

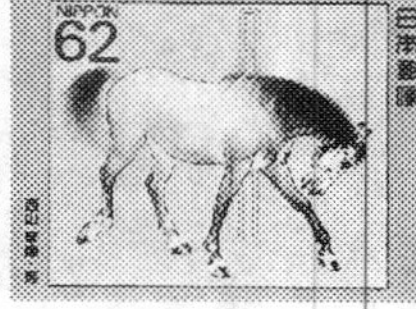

Horse by S. Nishiyama A1567

"Kamo-Kurabeuma-Monyo-Kosode" A1568

Kettei A1569

Postal Carriages
A1569a A1569b

Inkstone Case "Sano-no-Watashi" — A1570

"Bushu-Senju-zu" by Hokusai — A1571

"Shudan" by Kogetsu Saigo A1571a

#2027-2031 each show a panel of folding screen with a different horse tied up at a stable.

Perf. 13x13½, 13

1990 Litho. & Engr.

Color of Horse

2027 A1563 62y red brown .80 .60
2028 A1563 62y gray .80 .60
2029 A1563 62y beige .80 .60
2030 A1563 62y tan .80 .60
2031 A1563 62y mottled .80 .60
a. Strip of 5, #2027-2031 4.10

Photo.

2032 A1564 62y shown .80 .60

Photo. & Engr.

2033 A1565 62y shown .80 .60
2034 A1566 62y shown .80 .60
a. Pair, #2033-2034 1.65 1.25

Photo.

2035 A1567 62y multicolored .80 .60
2036 A1568 62y multicolored .80 .60
2037 A1569 62y multicolored .80 .60

Photo. & Engr., photo. (#2040, 2042)

1991 *Perf. 12½x13*

2038 A1569a 62y multicolored 1.00 .75
2039 A1569b 62y multicolored 1.00 .75
a. Pair, #2038-2039 2.00 1.50

Perf. 13½x13

2040 A1570 62y multicolored 1.00 .75
2041 A1571 62y multicolored 1.00 .75
2042 A1571a 62y multicolored 1.00 .75
Nos. 2027-2037 (11) 8.80 6.60

Issued: #202702032, 6/20; #2033-2035, 7/31; #2036-2037, 9/27; #2038-2040, Jan. 31. Nos. 2041-2042, Feb. 28.

38th Intl. Youth Hostel Fed. Conference — A1573

1990, June 25 Litho. *Perf. 13*

2057 A1573 62y multicolored .80 .60

Letter Writing Day
A1574 A1575

1990, July 23 Photo. *Perf. 13½*

2058 A1574 41y multicolored .55 .40
2059 A1575 62y multicolored .80 .60
a. Souv. sheet of 1 .90 .70
b. Bklt. pane, 5 each #2058-2059 7.50

See No. 2117.

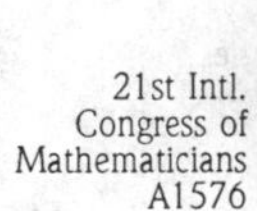

21st Intl. Congress of Mathematicians A1576

1990, Aug. 17 Photo. *Perf. 13*

2060 A1576 62y multicolored .80 .60

World Cycling Championships A1577

1990, Aug. 20 Litho. *Perf. 13½*

2061 A1577 62y multicolored .80 .60

Ogai Mori, Educator A1578

1990, Aug. 27 Photo.

2062 A1578 62y multicolored .80 .60

Intl. Assoc. for Germanic Studies (IVG), 8th Congress.

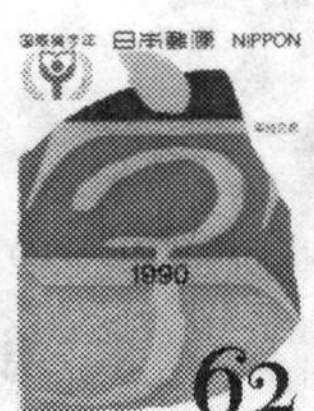

Character "Ji" in Shape of Rosetta Stone — A1579

1990, Sept. 7 *Perf. 13*

2063 A1579 62y multicolored .80 .60

Intl. Literacy Year.

Decade for Natural Disaster Reduction A1580

1990, Sept. 27 Photo.

2064 A1580 62y multicolored .80 .60

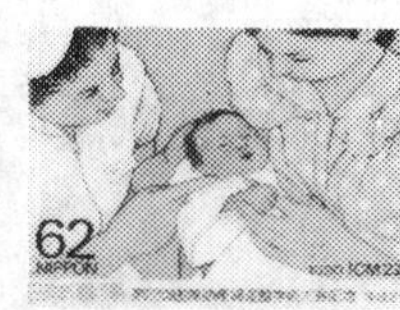

Intl. Confederation of Midwives, 22nd Congress A1581

1990, Oct. 5 Photo.

2065 A1581 62y multicolored .90 .65

A1582

"Choju-Jinbutsu-Giga" — A1583

Photo. & Engr.

1990, Oct. 5 *Perf. 13½*

2066 A1582 80y multicolored 1.15 .90
2067 A1583 120y multicolored 1.75 1.30

Intl. Letter Writing Week.

"Fumizukai-zu" by Harunobu Suiendo — A1584

1990, Oct. 16 Photo.

2068 A1584 100y multicolored 1.45 1.10
a. Souv. sheet of 1 1.45 1.10

No. 2068a exists with surcharge which paid admission to PHILANIPPON '91. These were not sold by the post office.

Court System, Cent. — A1585

1990, Nov. 1 Photo. *Perf. 13x13½*

2069 A1585 62y "Justice" .90 .65

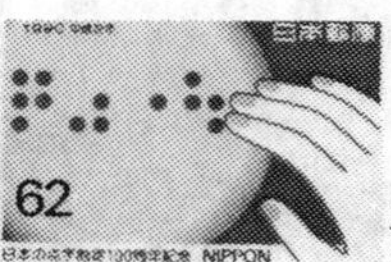

Japanese Braille, Cent. — A1586

Photo & Embossed

1990, Nov. 1 *Perf. 13½*

2070 A1586 62y multicolored .90 .65

Enthronement of Akihito A1587

Designs: No. 2071, Chinese phoenix depicted on Emperor's chair. No. 2072, Diamond pattern for costume worn at banquet ceremony.

1990, Nov. 9 Photo. *Perf. 13*

2071 A1587 62y multicolored .90 .65
2072 A1587 62y multicolored .90 .65
a. Souv. sheet of 2, #2071-2072 1.80 1.30

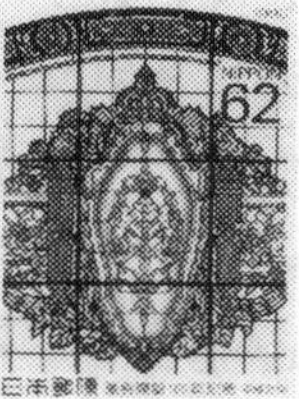

Japanese Diet, Cent. — A1588

1990, Nov. 29 Litho.

2073 A1588 62y multicolored .90 .65

New Year 1991 (Year of the Sheep)
A1589 A1590

1990, Dec. 3 Photo. *Perf. 13x13½*

2074 A1589 41y multicolored .60 .40

Photo. & Engr.

Perf. 13½

2075 A1590 41y multicolored .60 .40
2076 A1590 62y multi, diff. .90 .65
Nos. 2074-2076 (3) 2.10 1.45

Sheets of 2 No. 2074 were lottery prizes. Value, $1.50.

Dr. Yoshio Nishina, Physicist — A1591

Telephone Service, Cent. — A1592

1990, Dec. 6 Photo. *Perf. 13*

2077 A1591 62y multicolored .90 .65

Use of radio isotopes in Japan, 50th anniv.

1990, Dec. 14

2078 A1592 62y multicolored .90 .65

A1593 A1594

1991, Mar. 1 Photo. *Perf. 13½*

2079 A1593 41y Figure skating .60 .45

Perf. 13½x13

2080 A1593 62y Speed skating, horiz. 1.00 .75

1991 Winter Universiade.

1991, Apr. 1 Photo. *Perf. 13*

2081 A1594 62y multicolored .95 .70

Postal Life Insurance System.

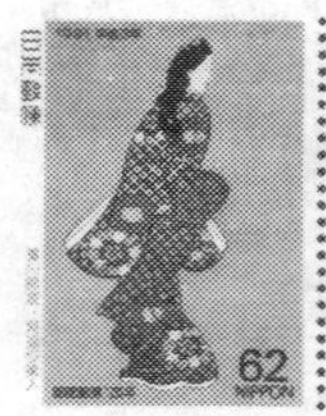

Philately Week

A1595 A1596

#2082, Beauty Looking Back by Moronobu. #2083, Opening Dance by Shuho Yamakawa.

1991, Apr. 19

2082 A1595 62y multicolored .95 .70
2083 A1596 62y multicolored .95 .70
a. Souv. sheet of 2, #2082-2083 1.90 1.50

Postal Service, 120th anniv.

Pairs of Nos. 2082-2083 with label between are available from sheets of 20.

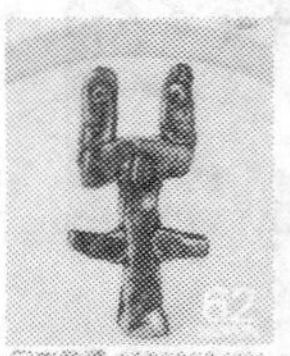

A1597 A1598

1991, Apr. 19 *Perf. 13½*

2084 A1597 62y multicolored .95 .70

Ceramic World Shigaraki '91.

1991, May 24 Photo. *Perf. 13½*

2085 A1598 41y multicolored .65 .50

Natl. Land Afforestation Campaign.

Standard Datum of Leveling, Cent. — A1599

1991, May 30 Photo. *Perf. 13*

2086 A1599 62y mutlicolored .95 .70

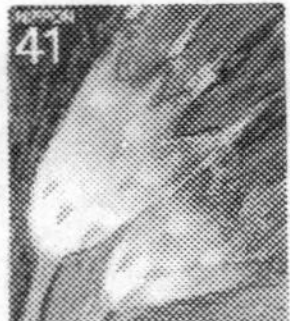

Flowers — A1600

Couple in Ethnic Dress — A1601

1991, May 31 Photo. *Perf. 13*

2087 A1600 41y shown .60 .30
2088 A1601 62y shown .95 .70
2089 A1600 70y World peace 1.05 .80
2090 A1601 100y Butterfly 1.50 1.15
Nos. 2087-2090 (4) 4.10 2.95

Intl. Stamp Design Contest winning entries.

Kabuki Series

Kagamijishi A1602 Yaegakihime A1603

Koshiro Matsumoto VII A1604 Danjuro Ichikawa XI A1605

Baigyoku Nakamura III A1606 Ganjiro Nakamura II A1607

Kichiemon Nakamura I — A1608 Nizaemon Kataoka XIII — A1609

Enjaku Jitsukawa II A1610 Hakuo Matsumoto I A1611

Fuji-Musume A1612 Kotobuki-Soganotaimen A1613

Perf. 13 (62y), 13½ (100y)

1991-92 Photo.

2091 A1602 62y dp bl grn & gold .95 .70
2092 A1603 100y multicolored 1.50 1.15
2093 A1604 62y multicolored 1.00 .75
2094 A1605 100y multicolored 1.60 1.20
2095 A1606 62y multicolored 1.00 .75
2096 A1607 100y multicolored 1.60 1.20
2097 A1608 62y multicolored 1.00 .75
2098 A1609 100y multicolored 1.55 1.15
2099 A1610 62y multicolored 1.00 .75
2100 A1611 100y multicolored 1.60 1.20
2101 A1612 62y multicolored 1.05 .80
2102 A1613 100y multicolored 1.60 1.20
Nos. 2091-2102 (12) 15.45 11.60

Issue dates: #2091-2092, June 28; #2093-2094, Sept. 27; #2095-2096, Nov. 20; #2097-2098, Feb. 20, 1992; #2099-2100, Apr. 10, 1992; #2101-2102, June 30, 1992.

Waterbird Series

Gallinago Hardwickii (Latham's Snipe) A1614

1991-93 Photo. *Perf. 13½*

2103 A1614 62y shown .95 .70
2104 A1614 62y Sula leucogaster .95 .70
2105 A1614 62y Larus crassirostris 1.00 .75
2106 A1614 62y Podiceps ruficollis 1.00 .75
2107 A1614 62y Lunda cirrhata 1.00 .75
2108 A1614 62y Grus monacha 1.00 .75
2109 A1614 62y Cygnus cygnus 1.00 .75
2110 A1614 62y Rostratula benghalensis 1.00 .75
2111 A1614 62y Calonectris leucomelas 1.00 .75
2112 A1614 62y Halcyon coromanda 1.00 .75
2113 A1614 62y Alcedo atthis 1.00 .75
2114 A1614 62y Bubulcus ibis 1.00 .75
Nos. 2103-2114 (12) 11.90 8.90

#2103-2104 printed in blocks of 12 with gutter between in sheet of 24.

Issued: #2103-2104, June 28. #2105-2106, Sept. 27. #2107-2108, Jan. 30, 1992. #2109-2110, Mar. 25, 1992. #2111-2112, Aug. 31, 1992. #2113-2114, Jan. 29, 1993.

See Nos. 2192-2195.

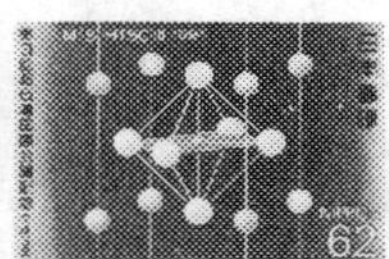

Intl. Conf. on Superconductivity — A1620

1991, July 19 Litho. *Perf. 13½*

2115 A1620 62y multicolored .95 .70

Type of Letter Writing Day of 1990 and

A1621

1991, July 23 Photo. *Perf. 13x13½*

2116 A1621 41y multicolored .70 .50
2117 A1575 62y multicolored .95 .70
a. Souvenir sheet of 1 .95 .70
b. Bklt. pane, 5 each #2116-2117 8.00

Nos. 2117, 2117a have light blue frameline and inscription and violet denomination.

3rd IAAF World Track & Field Championships, Tokyo — A1622

1991, Aug. 23 *Perf. 13*

2118 A1622 41y High jump .70 .50
2119 A1622 62y Shot put .95 .70

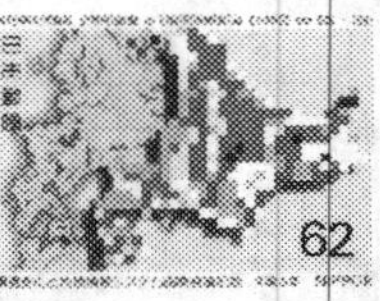

Intl. Symposium on Environmental Change and Geographical Information Systems A1623

1991, Aug. 23

2120 A1623 62y multicolored .95 .70

Intl. Letter Writing Week A1624

Bandainagon-emaki picture scroll probably by Mitsunaga Tokiwa: 80y, Crowd of people. 120y, People, house.

Photo. & Engr.

1991, Oct. 7 *Perf. 13½*

2121 A1624 80y multicolored 1.30 .95
2122 A1624 120y multicolored 2.00 1.50

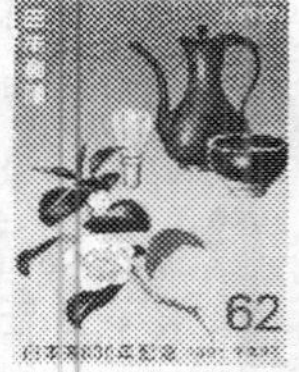

A1625 A1626

Design: 62y, Breezy Fine Weather by Hokusai.

1991, Oct. 8 Photo. *Perf. 13*

2123 A1625 62y multicolored 1.00 .75

Summit Conf. on Earthquake and Natural Disasters Countermeasures.

1991, Oct. 31 Litho. *Perf. 13*

2124 A1626 62y multicolored 1.00 .75

Japanese Green Tea, 800th anniv.

A1627 A1628

Design: Koshaku-Musume by Kunisada Utagawa.

Photo. & Engr.

1991, Nov. 15 *Perf. 13*

2125 A1627 62y multicolored 1.05 .80
a. Sheet of 2 2.10 1.60

World Stamp Exhibition, Nippon '91.

1991, Nov. 20 **Photo.**

2126 A1628 62y multicolored 1.05 .80

Administrative Counselors System, 30th anniv.

A1629 A1630

New Year 1992 (Year of the Monkey)

A1631 A1632

1991, Dec. 2 **Photo.** *Perf. 13½*

2127 A1629 41y multicolored .70 .50
2128 A1630 62y multicolored 1.00 .75
2129 A1631 41y +3y, multi .75 .60
2130 A1632 62y +3y, multi 1.05 .80
Nos. 2127-2130 (4) 3.50 2.65

8th Conference on Intl. Trade in Endangered Species (CITES) A1633

1992, Mar. 2 **Photo.** *Perf. 13*

2131 A1633 62y multicolored 1.00 .75

A1634 A1635

Flowers on the Chair, by Hushum Yamaguchi.

1992, Apr. 20

2132 A1634 62y multicolored 1.00 .75

Philately Week.

1992, May 15

2133 A1635 62y multicolored 1.00 .75

Return of Ryukyu Islands to Japan, 20th anniv.

Intl. Space Year

A1636 A1637

1992, July 7 **Photo.** *Perf. 13*

2134 A1636 62y multicolored 1.05 .80
2135 A1637 62y multicolored 1.05 .80
a. Pair, #2134-2135 2.10 1.56

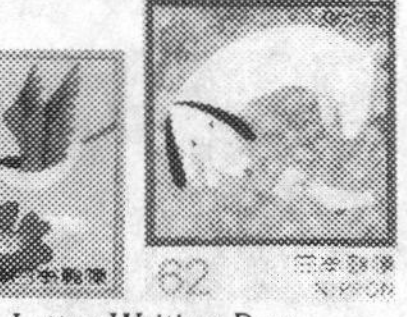

Letter Writing Day

A1638 A1639

1992, July 23 *Perf. 13x13½*

2136 A1638 41y multicolored .70 .50

Perf. 13½

2137 A1639 62y multicolored 1.05 .80
a. Souvenir sheet of 1 1.05 .80
b. Bklt. pane, 5 each #2136-2137 8.50

29th Intl. Geological Congress, Kyoto — A1640

1992, Aug. 24 **Photo.** *Perf. 13½x13*

2138 A1640 62y multicolored 1.00 .75

47th Natl. Athletic Meet, Yamagata Prefecture — A1641

1992, Sept. 4 *Perf. 13½*

2139 A1641 41y multicolored .70 .50

Normalization of Japanese-Chinese Relations, 20th Anniv.

A1642 A1643

Photo. & Engr.

1992, Sept. 29 *Perf. 13*

2140 A1642 62y multicolored 1.00 .75
2141 A1643 62y multicolored 1.00 .75
a. Pair, #2140-2141 2.00 1.50

Intl. Letter Writing Week — A1644

Heiji picture scroll: 80y, Nobles, servants in carriages by Taikenmon gate. 120y, Fujiwara-no Nobuyori seated before samurai.

Photo. & Engr.

1992, Oct. 6 *Perf. 13½*

2142 A1644 80y multicolored 1.35 1.00
2143 A1644 120y multicolored 2.00 1.50

Cat and Birds A1644a

Design: 70y, Santa Claus, snow scene.

Perf. 13½x13, 13x13½

1992, Oct. 9 **Photo.**

2144 A1644a 62y multicolored 1.00 .75
2145 A1644a 70y multicolored 1.15 .85

Winners of Third Postage Stamp Design contest.

30th Congress of Intl. Cooperative Alliance, Tokyo — A1644b

1992, Oct. 27 *Perf. 13x13½*

2146 A1644b 62y multicolored 1.00 .75

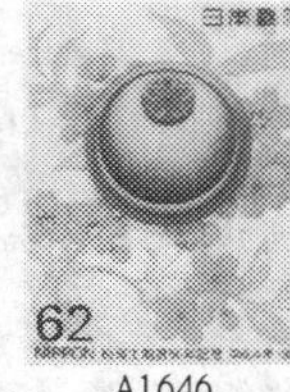

A1645 A1646

Cultural Pioneers: No. 2147, Takakazu Seki (1642?-1708), mathematician. No. 2148, Akiko Yosano (1878-1942), poet.

1992, Nov. 4 **Photo. & Engr.** *Perf. 13*

2147 A1645 62y multicolored 1.00 .75
2148 A1645 62y multicolored 1.00 .75

See Nos. 2217-2219.

1992, Nov. 9 **Photo.** *Perf. 13x13½*

2149 A1646 62y multicolored 1.00 .75

Certified Public Tax Accountant System, 50th anniv.

A1647 A1648

New Year 1993 (Year of the Rooster)

A1649 A1650

1992, Nov. 16 *Perf. 13x13½*

2150 A1647 41y multicolored .70 .50
2151 A1648 62y multicolored 1.00 .75
a. Souvenir sheet of 2, #2150-2151 2.00 1.50

Perf. 13½

2152 A1649 41y +3y multi .70 .50
2153 A1650 62y +3y multi 1.00 .75
Nos. 2150-2153 (4) 3.40 2.50

Surtax on Nos. 2152-2153 for lottery.

Flora and Fauna — A1651

1992-94 **Photo.** *Perf. 13x13½*

2154 A1651 9y Dragonfly .15 .15
2155 A1651 15y Swallowtail .30 .20
2156 A1651 18y Ladybug .30 .25
2157 A1651 41y Mandarin duck .70 .50
2158 A1651 50y Japanese white-eye .90 .65
2159 A1651 62y Rufous turtle dove 1.00 .75
a. Booklet pane, 5 #2157, 5 #2159 8.50
b. Booklet pane of 10 10.00
2160 A1651 72y Varied tit 1.20 .90
2161 A1651 80y Pied kingfisher 1.40 1.00
a. Miniature sheet, 5 #2158, 10 #2161 + 3 labels *40.00*
2162 A1651 90y Spotbill duck 1.65 1.10
2163 A1651 130y Bullfinch 2.50 1.90
2164 A1651 190y Fringed orchid 3.75 2.75
2165 A1651 270y Wild pink 4.75 3.50
2166 A1651 350y Adder's tongue lily 6.25 4.50
2167 A1651 420y Japanese iris 7.50 5.25
2167A A1651 430y Violet 8.25 6.25
Nos. 2154-2167A (15) 40.60 29.65

Coil Stamps

Perf. 13 Horiz.

2168 A1651 50y like #2156 .90 .65
2169 A1651 80y like #2161 1.40 1.00

Booklet Stamps

Self-Adhesive

Die Cut

2170 A1651 41y like #2157 .72 .55
2171 A1651 50y like #2158 .90 .65
2172 A1651 62y like #2159 1.00 .75
a. Bklt. pane, 2 #2170, 4 #2172 5.50
2173 A1651 80y like #2161 1.40 1.00
a. Bklt. pane, 4 #2171, 4 #2173 9.50

Issued: 41y, 62y, 72y, 11/30/92; 9y, 18y, #2158, 2161, 90y, 1/13/94; 270y, 350y, 420y, 1/24/94; 15y, 130y, 190y, 430y, 4/25/94.

Nos. 2172a, 2173a are adhered to the booklet cover, made of peelable paper, folded in half and rouletted down the center fold.

See Nos. 2475-2482.

World Alpine Skiing Championships, Morioka-Shizukuishi — A1657

1993, Feb. 3 **Photo.** *Perf. 13*

2174 A1657 41y shown .75 .60
2175 A1657 62y Skier, diff. 1.10 .80

Seasonal Flowers Series

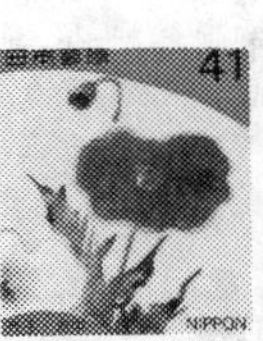

Poppy — A1658

Cherry Blossoms — A1659

Lily — A1660

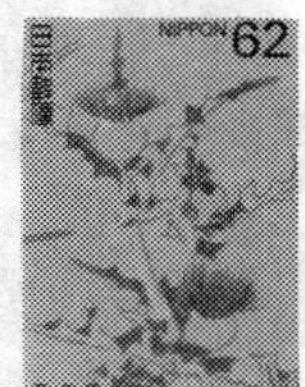

Thistle — A1661

Chinese Bellflowers A1662

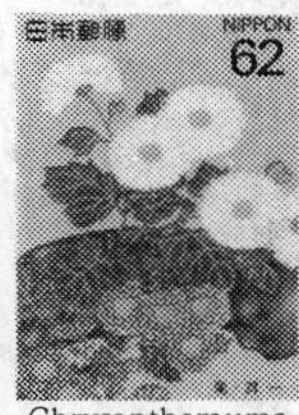

Chrysanthemums A1663

Plum Blossom — A1664 Winter Camellia — A1665

Perf. 13½ (41y, 50y), 13 (62y, 80y)

1993-94 **Photo.**

2176 A1658 41y multicolored .72 .55

Perf. 13

2177 A1659 62y multicolored 1.10 .80
2178 A1660 41y multicolored .80 .60

Perf. 13

2179 A1661 62y multicolored 1.20 .90
2180 A1662 41y multicolored .70 .55
2181 A1663 62y multicolored 1.00 .75
2182 A1664 50y multicolored .90 .65
2183 A1665 80y multicolored 1.40 1.00
Nos. 2176-2183 (8) 7.82 5.80

Issued: #2176-2177, 3/12; #2178-2179, 6/18; #2180-2181, 9/16; #2182-2183, 1/28/94.

Waterbird Type

1993 **Photo.** *Perf. 13½*

2192 A1614 62y Grus vipio 1.10 .80
2193 A1614 62y Ansner albifrons 1.10 .80
2194 A1614 62y Anas formosa 1.20 .90
2195 A1614 62y Haliaeetus albicilla 1.20 .90
Nos. 2192-2195 (4) 4.60 3.40

Issued: #2192-2193, 3/31; #2194-2195, 5/25.

Philately Week A1674 Natl. Land Afforestation Campaign A1675

Painting: In the Studio, by Nanpu Katayama.

1993, Apr. 20 **Photo.** *Perf. 13*

2196 A1674 62y multicolored 1.15 .85

1993, Apr. 23 *Perf. 13½*

2197 A1675 41y multicolored .75 .60

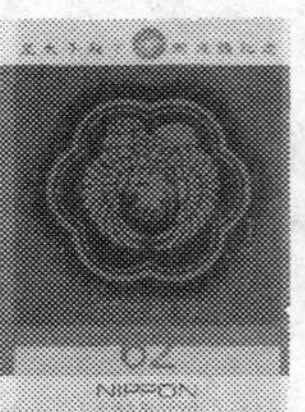

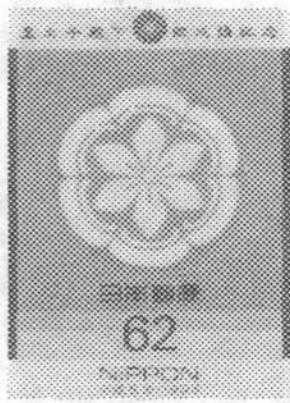

Mandarin Duck in the Nest — A1676 Gardenia in the Nest — A1677

Design: 70y, Mandarin Duck and Gardenia emblems, horiz.

1993, June 8 **Photo.** *Perf. 13*

2198 A1676 62y multicolored 1.25 .90
2199 A1677 62y multicolored 1.25 .90
a. Pair, #2198-2199 2.50 1.80
2200 A1676 70y multicolored 1.25 .95
Nos. 2198-2200 (3) 3.75 2.75

Royal Wedding of Crown Prince Naruhito and Masako Owada.

5th Meeting of Signatories to Ramsar, Iran Convention on Wetlands and Waterfowl Habitats A1678

1993, June 10 **Photo.** *Perf. 13½*

2201 A1678 62y Crane with young 1.20 .90
2202 A1678 62y Crane's head 1.20 .90
a. Pair, #2201-2202 2.40 1.80

Commercial Registration System, Cent. — A1679

1993, July 1 **Photo.** *Perf. 13x13½*

2203 A1679 62y multicolored 1.20 .90

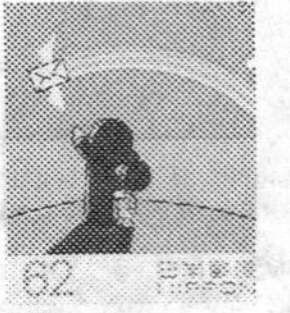

Letter Writing Day
A1680 A1681

1993, July 23 *Perf. 13x13½*

2204 A1680 41y multicolored .80 .60

Perf. 13½x13

2205 A1681 62y multicolored 1.20 .90
a. Souvenir sheet of 1 1.20 .90
b. Booklet pane, 5 each #2204-2205 10.00

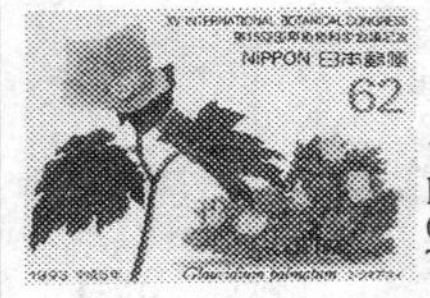

15th Intl. Botanical Congress, Tokyo — A1682

Designs: No. 2206, Glaucidium palmatum. No. 2207, Sciadopitys verticillata.

1993, Aug. 23 **Photo.** *Perf. 13½x13*

2206 A1682 62y multicolored 1.25 .90
2207 A1682 62y multicolored 1.25 .90
a. Pair, #2206-2207 2.50 1.80

World Federation for Mental Health Congress, Chiba City — A1683

1993, Aug. 23 *Perf. 13½x13*

2208 A1683 62y multicolored 1.25 .90

A1684 A1685

1993, Sept. 3 **Photo.** *Perf. 13½*

2209 A1684 41y Swimming .80 .60
2210 A1684 41y Karate .80 .60
a. Pair, #2209-2210 1.65 1.25

48th natl. athletic meet, Kagawa Prefecture.

1993, Sept. 22 **Photo.** *Perf. 13*

Japanese-Portuguese Relations, 450th Anniv.: No. 2211, Arrival of Portuguese, folding screen, c. 1560-1630. No. 2212, Mother-of-Pearl Host Box, Jesuit symbols and grape motif.

2211 A1685 62y multicolored 1.25 .90
2212 A1685 62y multicolored 1.25 .90
a. Pair, #2211-2212 2.50 1.90

Intl. Letter Writing Week A1686

Portraits from Picture Scrolls of the Thirty-Six Immortal Poets: 80y, Ki no Tsurayuki. 120y, Kodai no Kimi.

1993, Oct. 6 *Perf. 13½*

2213 A1686 80y multicolored 1.65 1.25
2214 A1686 120y multicolored 2.50 1.75

10th World Veterans' Track and Field Championships, Miyazaki Prefecture — A1687

1993, Oct. 7 *Perf. 14*

2215 A1687 62y multicolored 1.25 .90

Souvenir Sheet

Wedding of Crown Prince Naruhito and Princess Masako — A1688

1993, Oct. 13 **Photo.** *Perf. 13½*

2216 A1688 62y multicolored 1.25 .90

Cultural Pioneers Type of 1992

#2217, Kazan Watanabe (1793-1841), artist. #2218, Umetaro Suzuki (1874-1943), chemist. #2219, Toson Shimazaki (1872-1943), poet.

1993, Nov. 4 **Photo.** *Perf. 13*

2217 A1645 62y multicolored 1.10 .80

Photo. & Engr.

2218 A1645 62y multicolored 1.10 .80
2219 A1645 62y multicolored 1.10 .80
Nos. 2217-2219 (3) 3.30 2.40

Agricultural Research Center, Cent. — A1689

1993, Nov. 17 *Perf. 13½*

2220 A1689 62y multicolored 1.10 .85

A1690 A1691

New Year 1994 (Year of the Dog)
A1692 A1693

1993, Nov. 17 *Perf. 13x13½*

2221 A1690 41y multicolored .75 .55
2222 A1691 62y multicolored 1.10 .80
a. Souvenir sheet of 2, #2221-2222 2.25 1.60

Perf. 13½

2223 A1692 41y +3y multi .80 .60
2224 A1693 62y +3y multi 1.25 .90
Nos. 2221-2224 (4) 3.90 2.85

Declaration of Human Rights, 45th Anniv. — A1694

Designs: 62y, Man with bird perched on head. 70y, Globe, dove, person breaking chains, peace symbol.

1993, Dec. 10 **Photo.** *Perf. 13*

2225 A1694 62y multicolored 1.25 .90
2226 A1694 70y multicolored 1.40 1.00

Congratulations and Condolences Types of 1982

1994, Mar. 10 **Photo.** *Perf. 13x13½*

2227 A1082 50y Wreath .95 .70
2228 A1083 50y Crane .95 .70
2229 A1083 80y Crane 1.50 1.10
2230 A1084 90y Tortoise 1.65 1.25
Nos. 2227-2230 (4) 5.05 3.75

For use on condolence and greeting cards.

1994 World Figure Skating Championships, Tokyo A1695

1994, Mar. 17 **Photo.** *Perf. 13*

2231 A1695 50y Ice dancing .95 .70
2232 A1695 50y Women's singles .95 .70
a. Pair, #2231-2232 2.00 1.50
2233 A1695 80y Men's singles, vert. 1.50 1.10
2234 A1695 80y Pairs, vert. 1.50 1.10
a. Pair, #2233-2234 3.00 2.25
Nos. 2231-2234 (4) 4.90 3.60

Philately Week — A1696

1994, Apr. 20 **Photo.** *Perf. 13*

2235 A1696 80y Irises 1.50 1.25

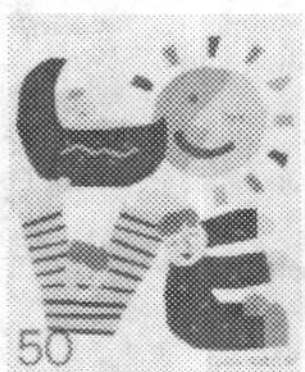

Intl. Year of the Family — A1697

Natl. Land Afforestation Campaign — A1698

Designs: No. 2236, "Love" spelled by people. No. 2237, Faces in flowers. No. 2238, Sun shining on people, homes. No. 2239, Family flying inside bird.

1994, May 13 Photo. *Perf. 13*

2236 A1697 50y multicolored 1.00 .75
2237 A1697 50y multicolored 1.00 .75
2238 A1697 80y multicolored 1.50 1.25
a. Pair, #2236, 2238 2.50 2.00
2239 A1697 80y multicolored 1.50 1.25
a. Pair, #2237, 2239 2.50 2.00
Nos. 2236-2239 (4) 5.00 4.00

1994, May 20

2240 A1698 50y multicolored 1.00 .75

Intl. Conference on Natural Disaster Reduction A1699

1994, May 23

2241 A1699 80y multicolored 1.50 1.25

No. 2241 printed in sheets of 16 with 4 labels.

A1700 A1701

1994, May 24

2242 A1700 80y multicolored 1.50 1.25

Prototype Fast Breeder Reactor, Monju.

1994, June 3 Photo. *Perf. 13*

2243 A1701 80y multicolored 1.50 1.25

Environment day.

Letter Writing Day
A1702 A1703

1994, July 22

2244 A1702 50y multicolored 1.00 .75
2245 A1703 80y multicolored 1.50 1.00
a. Souvenir sheet of 1 1.50 1.00
b. Bklt. pane, 5 each #2244-2245 12.50

Prefecture Issues

Nos. 1841-1990, 2246-2400 have been reserved for issues for Japan's 47 prefectures (political subdivisions). These stamps were available only in the prefecture for which they were issued, except for No. 1909a, which was available nationwide. All of the stamps were valid throughout Japan. Prefecture stamps are distinguishable from other Japanese issues by the calligraphic style of the four characters which represent the country name.

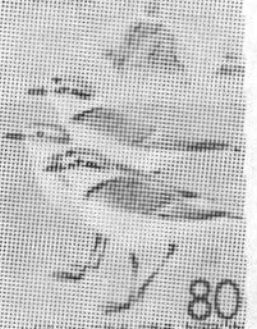

Kentish Plovers (Mie) A1704

Awaodori Dance (Tokushima) A1705

Tug-of-War (Okinawa) — A1706

Kehi Pine Wood (Fukui) — A1707

Matsushima (Miyagi) — A1708

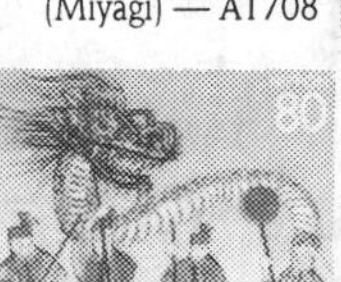

Kunchi Festival (Nagasaki) A1709

1994 Photo. *Perf. 13*

2246 A1704 80y multicolored 1.50 1.00
a. Booklet pane of 10 15.00
2247 A1705 50y multicolored 1.00 .75
a. Booklet pane of 10 10.00
2248 A1706 50y multicolored 1.00 .75
2249 A1707 50y multicolored 1.00 .75
a. Booklet pane of 10 10.00
2250 A1708 80y multicolored 1.65 1.25
a. Booklet pane of 10 16.50
2251 A1709 80y multicolored 1.65 1.25
a. Booklet pane of 10 16.50

Issued: #2246, 7/22; #2247, 2248, 7/1; #2249, 9/1; #2250, 9/20; #2251, 10/3.

Hokkaido Chipmunks (Hokkaido) — A1710

Ushiwakamaru and Benkei (Kyoto) A1711

Utopia Flower (Gifu) A1712

Jade Bead, Gyofu Soma (1883-1950), Lyricist (Niigata) A1713

Cape Ashizuri-Misaki Lighthouse (Kochi) A1714

Ishikawamon Gate, Kanazawa Castle (Ishikawa) A1715

Akamon Gate, University of Tokyo (Tokyo) A1716

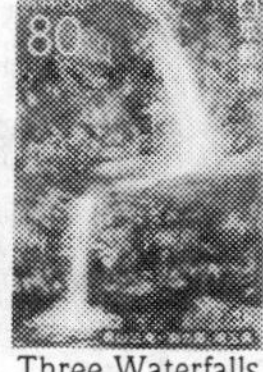

Three Waterfalls, Kuroyama (Saitama) A1717

Lady's Slipper, Rebun Island (Hokkaido) A1718

Street with Zelkova Trees (Miyagi) A1719

Eisa Festival (Okinawa) — A1720

Nos. 2272-2273, Taiheiki (Nara).

1995 Photo. *Perf. 13*

2252 A1710 80y multicolored 1.90 1.40
a. Booklet pane of 10 19.00

Perf. 13½

2253 A1711 80y multicolored 1.90 1.40
a. Booklet pane of 10 19.00
2254 A1712 80y multicolored 1.90 1.40
a. Booklet pane of 10 19.00
2255 A1713 80y multicolored 1.90 1.40
a. Booklet pane of 10 19.00
2256 A1714 80y multicolored 1.90 1.40
a. Booklet pane of 10 19.00
2257 A1715 80y multicolored 1.90 1.40
a. Booklet pane of 10 19.00
2258 A1716 50y multicolored 1.10 .80
a. Booklet pane of 10 11.00
2259 A1717 80y multicolored 1.75 1.25
a. Booklet pane of 10 17.50
2260 A1718 80y multicolored 1.75 1.25
a. Booklet pane of 10 17.50
2261 A1719 50y multicolored 1.00 .70
a. Booklet pane of 10 10.00
2262 A1720 80y multicolored 1.60 1.10

Issued: #2252, 3/3; #2253, 4/3; #2254, 4/26; #2255, 5/1; #2256-2257, 6/1; #2258-2260, 7/7; #2261-2262, 8/1.

Kishiwada Danjiri Festival (Osaka) A1721

Yamadera Temple (Yamagata) A1722

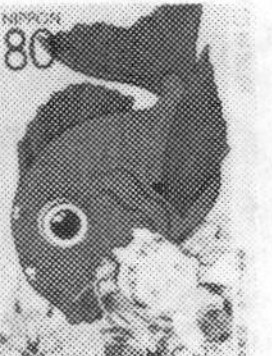

Karatsu Kunchi Festival (Saga) — A1723

Hida (Gifu) — A1724

Niimi-No-Shou Festival (Okayama) A1728

Kirifuri Waterfall (Tochigi) A1729

10th All-Japan Holstein Show (Chiba) — A1732

1995 Photo. *Perf. 13½*

2263 A1721 80y multicolored 1.60 1.10
a. Booklet pane of 10 16.00
2264 A1722 80y multicolored 1.60 1.10
a. Booklet pane of 10 16.00
2265 A1723 80y multicolored 1.60 1.10
a. Booklet pane of 10 16.00

Perf. 13

2266 A1724 80y Spring 1.60 1.10
2267 A1724 80y Summer 1.60 1.10
2268 A1724 80y Autumn 1.60 1.10
2269 A1724 80y Winter 1.60 1.10
a. Strip of 4, #2266-2269 6.50 4.50

Perf. 13½

2270 A1728 80y multicolored 1.60 1.10
2271 A1729 50y multicolored 1.00 .70
a. Booklet pane of 10 10.00
2272 A1511 80y like #1956 1.50 1.00
2273 A1510 80y like #1955 1.50 1.00
a. Pair, #2272-2273 3.00 2.00
2274 A1732 80y multicolored 1.60 1.10
a. Booklet pane of 10 15.00

Issued: #2263, 9/1; #2264, 9/15; #2265-2269, 10/2; #2270, 10/13; #2271, 10/27; #2272-2273, 11/6/95; #2274, 11/21/95.

Clione Limancia (Hokkaido) A1733

Ushibuka Haiya Festival (Kumamoto) A1734

Peony of Sukagawa (Fukushima) A1735

Hamayu (Mie) A1736

Ama Divers (Mie) — A1737

World Ceramics Expo '96 (Saga) — A1738

Shosenkyo Gorge (Yamanashi) A1739

Murasaki Shikibu of Takefu (Fukui) A1740

1996 Litho. *Perf. 13½x13*

2275 A1733 80y multicolored 1.50 1.00
 a. Booklet pane of 10 11.50

Photo.

2276 A1734 80y multicolored 1.50 1.00
 a. Booklet pane of 10 15.00
2277 A1735 80y multicolored 1.50 1.00
 a. Booklet pane of 10 15.00
2278 A1736 80y multicolored 1.50 1.00
2279 A1737 80y multicolored 1.50 1.00
 a. Pair, #2278-2279 3.00 2.00
 b. Booklet pane, 5 #2279a 15.00
2280 A1738 80y multicolored 1.50 1.00

Perf. 13½

2281 A1739 50y multicolored .90 .60
 a. Booklet pane of 10 9.00
2282 A1740 80y multicolored 1.50 1.00
 a. Booklet pane of 10 15.00

Issued: #2275, 2/6; #2276, 4/1; #2277, 4/26; #2278-2279, 5/1; #2280, 5/17; #2281, 6/3; #2282, 6/24.

A1741

A1742

A1744

A1746

A1745

A1747

A1748

A1749

#2283, Ancient Trees, Kompon-chudo of Mt. Hiei (Shiga). #2284, Nishiumi Marine Park (Ehime). #2285, Sweetbriar (Hokkaido). #2286, Nebuta Festival (Aomori). #2287, Shimozuru Usudaiko Odori Folk Dance (Miyazaki). #2288, Main Palace, Shuri Castle (Okinawa). #2289, Asakusa Kaminarimon Gate (Metropolitan Tokyo). #2290, Tottori Shanshan Festival (Tottori). #2291, Saito Kinen Festival Matsumoto (Nagano). #2292, Automn bellflower (gentian) (Nagano).

1996 Photo. *Perf. 13½*

2283 A1741 80y multicolored 1.50 1.00
 a. Booklet pane of 10 15.00
2284 A1742 80y multicolored 1.50 1.00
 a. Booklet pane of 10 15.00
2285 A1418 80y like #1863 1.50 1.00
2286 A1744 80y multicolored 1.50 1.00
 a. Booklet pane of 10 15.00
2287 A1745 80y multicolored 1.50 1.00
 a. Booklet pane of 10 15.00
2288 A1746 80y multicolored 1.50 1.00
2289 A1747 80y multicolored 1.50 1.00
 a. Booklet pane of 10 15.00
2290 A1748 80y multicolored 1.50 1.00
2291 A1749 80y multicolored 1.50 1.00
 a. Booklet pane of 10 15.00
2292 A1433 80y like #1878 1.50 1.00

Issued: #2283, 2284, 7/1; #2285, 7/5; #2286, 7/23; #2287-2288, 8/1; #2289, 8/8; #2290, 8/16; #2291-2292, 8/22.

Sengokubara Marsh (Kanagawa) — A1751

Nagoya Festival (Aichi)
A1752 A1753

Grass-burning Rite on Mt. Wakakusa (Nara) A1754

1997 Men's Handball World Championships (Kumamoto) A1755

Tea Picking (Shizuoka) A1756

Dahurian Rhododendron (Hokkaido) A1757

Mt. Fuji (Shizuoka)
A1758 A1759

1996-97 Photo. *Perf. 13½*

2293 A1751 80y multicolored 1.40 .90
 a. Booklet pane of 10 14.00
2294 A1752 80y multicolored 1.40 .90
2295 A1753 80y multicolored 1.40 .90
 a. Pair, #2294-2295 2.80 1.80
 b. Booklet pane, 5 #2295a 14.00
2296 A1754 50y multicolored .90 .60
 a. Booklet pane of 10 9.00
2297 A1755 80y multicolored 1.25 .90
 a. Booklet pane of 10 12.50
2298 A1756 50y multicolored .80 .55
 a. Booklet pane of 10 8.00
2299 A1757 80y multicolored 1.25 .90
 a. Booklet pane of 10 12.50
2300 A1758 80y multicolored 1.25 .90
2301 A1759 80y multicolored 1.25 .90
 a. Pair, #2300-2301 2.50 1.80
 b. Booklet pane, 5 #2301a 12.50

Issued: #2293, 9/6; #2294-2295, 10/1; #2296, 11/15; #2297, 4/17/97; #2298-2301, 4/25/97.

Marugame Castle (Kagawa) A1760

Hokkaido Ermine (Hokkaido) A1761

Okayama Castle (Okayama) — A1762

Okinawan Fruits (Okinawa)
A1763 A1764

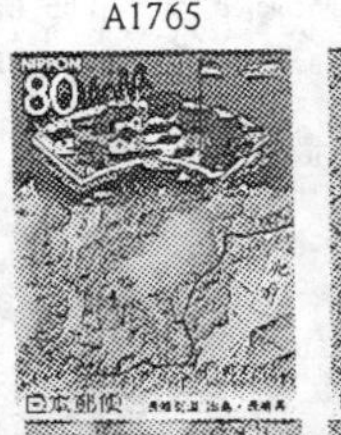

A1765

A1766

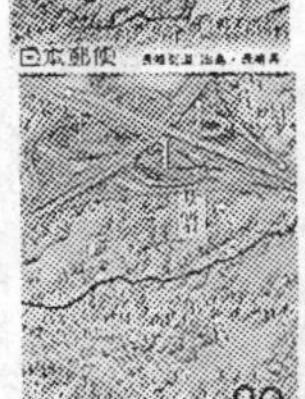

A1767 A1768

Nagasaki Kaido Highway (Nagasaki, Saga, Fukuoka)

Fukiya Koji's Hanayome Ningyo, Doll of Bride (Nigata) A1769

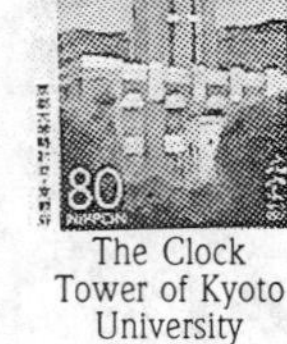

The Clock Tower of Kyoto University (Kyoto) A1770

1997 Photo. *Perf. 13½*

2302 A1760 80y multicolored 1.40 1.00
 a. Pane of 10 14.00
2303 A1761 50y multicolored .85 .60
 a. Pane of 10 8.50
2304 A1762 80y multicolored 1.40 1.00
 a. Pane of 10 14.00

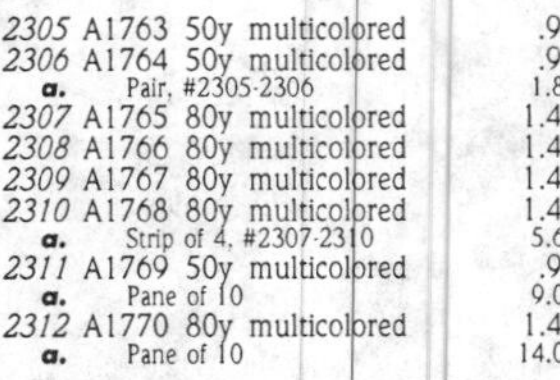

2305 A1763 50y multicolored .90 .70
2306 A1764 50y multicolored .90 .70
 a. Pair, #2305-2306 1.80 1.40
2307 A1765 80y multicolored 1.40 1.00
2308 A1766 80y multicolored 1.40 1.00
2309 A1767 80y multicolored 1.40 1.00
2310 A1768 80y multicolored 1.40 1.00
 a. Strip of 4, #2307-2310 5.60 4.00
2311 A1769 50y multicolored .90 .70
 a. Pane of 10 9.00
2312 A1770 80y multicolored 1.40 1.00
 a. Pane of 10 14.00

Issued: #2302, 5/15; #2303-2304, 5/30; #2305-2306, 6/2; #2307-2310, 6/3; #2311-2312, 6/18.

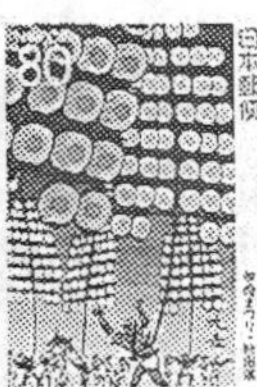

Kanto Festival (Akita) A1771

San-in Yume Minato Exposition (Tottori) A1772

Waterwheel Plant, Hozoji-numa Pond (Saitama) A1773

Lake Kasumigaura (Ibaragi) A1776

Bon Wind Festival, Owara (Toyama)
A1774 A1775

A1777

A1778

A1779

A1780

Sites in Tokyo (Tokyo) A1781

First World Walking Festival (Saitama) A1782

1997 Photo. *Perf. 13½*

2313 A1771 80y multicolored 1.30 1.00
a. Pane of 10 13.00
2314 A1772 80y multicolored 1.30 1.00
a. Pane of 10 13.00
2315 A1773 50y multicolored .85 .60
a. Pane of 10 8.50
2316 A1774 80y multicolored 1.40 1.00
2317 A1775 80y multicolored 1.40 1.00
a. Pair, #2316-2317 2.80 2.00
b. Pane of 5, #2317a 14.00
2318 A1776 80y multicolored 1.40 1.00
a. Pane of 10 14.00
2319 A1777 80y multicolored 1.30 1.00
2320 A1778 80y multicolored 1.30 1.00
2321 A1779 80y multicolored 1.30 1.00
2322 A1780 80y multicolored 1.30 1.00
2323 A1781 80y multicolored 1.30 1.00
a. Strip of 5, #2319-2323 6.50 5.00
b. Pane of 2 each, #2319-2323 13.00
2324 A1782 80y multicolored 1.30 1.00
a. Pane of 10 13.00

Issued: #2313, 7/7; #2314, 7/11; #2315, 8/1; #2316-2317, 8/20; #2318, 9/1; #2319-2323, 10/1; #2324, 10/28.

Kanagawa-Chiba Bridge Tunnel (Chiba, Kanagawa)
A1783 A1784

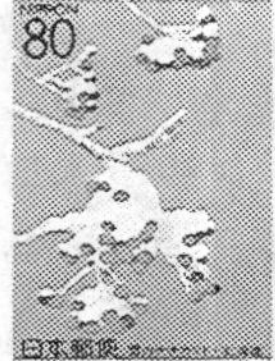

Snow-Covered Tree (Hokkaido) A1785

Flower in a Dream (Hokkaido) A1786

1997-98 Litho. *Perf. 13½*

2325 A1783 80y multicolored 1.25 .95
2326 A1784 80y multicolored 1.25 .95
a. Pair, #2325-2326 2.50 1.90
b. Pane of 5 each, #2325-2326 12.50
2327 A1785 80y multicolored 1.25 .95
2328 A1786 80y multicolored 1.25 .95
a. Pair, #2327-2328 1.50 1.90
b. Pane of 5 each, #2327-2328 7.50

Issued: #2325-2326, 12/18; #2327-2328, 2/5/98.

This is an expanding set. Format and numbers will change if necessary.

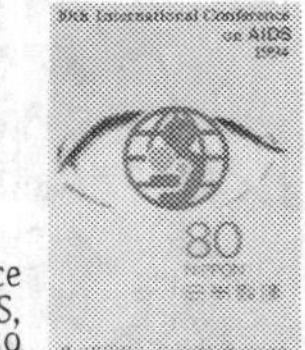

10th Intl. Conference on AIDS, Yokohama — A1859

1994, Aug. 5 Photo. *Perf. 13*

2401 A1859 80y multicolored 1.50 1.00

Postal History Series

A1860 A1861

A1862

A1863 A1864

First Japanese stamps (Baron Hisoka Maejima and): No. 2402, #1. No. 2403, #2. No. 2404, #3. No. 2405, #4.

CTO's exist for Nos. 2402-2405. They read "Japan" between two arcs in a corner.

Photo. & Engr.

1994, Aug. 10 *Perf. 13*

2402 A1860 80y brown & black 1.50 1.00
2403 A1860 80y blue & black 1.50 1.00
2404 A1860 80y vermilion & black 1.50 1.00
2405 A1860 80y olive green & black 1.50 1.00
a. Strip of 4, #2402-2405 6.00 4.00

Photo. & Engr.

1994, Nov. 18 *Perf. 13½*

Early Japanese stamps (Edoardo Chiossone and): No. 2406, #55. No. 2407, Type A16. No. 2408, #63. No. 2409, #65.

2406 A1861 80y buff, slate & black 1.65 1.25
2407 A1861 80y gray & dk brown 1.65 1.25
2408 A1861 80y gray lilac & rose 1.65 1.25
2409 A1861 80y lt blue & dk blue 1.65 1.25
a. Strip of 4, #2406-2409 6.50 5.00

Photo. & Engr.

1995, Jan. 25 *Perf. 13½*

Designs: No. 2410, #85, transporting mail by ricksha. No. 2411, #86, transporting mail by horse-drawn carriage.

2410 A1862 80y multicolored 1.65 1.25
2411 A1862 80y multicolored 1.65 1.25
Nos. 2402-2411 (10) 15.90 11.50

Photo. & Engr.

1995, May 25 *Perf. 13½*

Designs: No. 2412, #C3, First Osaka-Tokyo airmail flight. No. 2413, #C6, Workers loading freight onto airplane.

2412 A1863 110y multicolored 2.50 1.90
2413 A1863 110y multicolored 2.50 1.90

Nos. 2412-2413 printed in blocks of 10 with gutter between in sheets of 20.

Photo. & Engr.

1995, Sept. 19 *Perf. 13½*

Designs: No. 2414, Light mail van, #436. No. 2415, Cherub commemorative mail box, #428. No. 2416, Mail box, #435. No. 2417, Van, #433.

2414 A1864 80y multicolored 1.60 1.10
2415 A1864 80y multicolored 1.60 1.10
2416 A1864 80y multicolored 1.60 1.10
2417 A1864 80y multicolored 1.60 1.10
a. Block of 4, #2414-2417 6.50 4.50

Postal History Series
Types of 1948-49 With "NIPPON" Inscribed at Bottom

Photo. & Engr.

1996, June 3 *Perf. 13½*

Size: 22x47mm

2418 A206 80y like #422, brown 1.50 1.00
2419 A206 80y like #422, multi 1.50 1.00
2420 A246 80y like #479, purple 1.50 1.00
2421 A246 80y like #479, multi 1.50 1.00
a. Strip of 4, #2418-2421 6.00 4.00

Opening of Kansai Intl. Airport — A1877

Designs: No. 2422, Airport, part of plane's vertical stabilizer. No. 2423, Aft section of airplane. No. 2424, Airport, jet.

1994, Sept. 2 Photo. *Perf. 13*

2422 A1877 80y multicolored 1.65 1.25
2423 A1877 80y multicolored 1.65 1.25
a. Vert. pair, #2422-2423 3.30 2.50
b. Vert. strip of 3, #2422-2424 5.00 3.75
2424 A1877 80y multicolored 1.65 1.25
Nos. 2422-2424 (3) 4.95 3.75

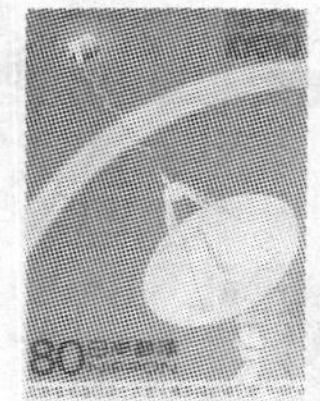

A1878 A1879

1994, Sept. 19

2425 A1878 80y multicolored 1.65 1.25

ITU Plenipotentiary Conference, Kyoto.

1994, Sept. 30

2426 A1879 50y Kick volleyball 1.00 .75
2427 A1879 80y Steeplechase 1.65 1.25
2428 A1879 80y Synchronized swimming 1.65 1.25
a. Pair, #2427-2428 3.30 2.50
Nos. 2426-2428 (3) 4.30 3.25

12th Asian Games, Hiroshima.

Intl. Letter Writing Week A1880

Screen paintings of popular indoor games, Momoyama, Edo periods: 90y, Sugoroku. 110y, Japanese chess. 130y, Go.

1994, Oct. 6 Photo. *Perf. 13x13½*

2429 A1880 90y multicolored 1.90 1.40
2430 A1880 110y multicolored 2.25 1.65
2431 A1880 130y multicolored 2.75 2.00
Nos. 2429-2431 (3) 6.90 5.05

49th Natl. Athletic Meet, Aichi Prefecture — A1881

1994, Oct. 28 *Perf. 13½*

2432 A1881 50y multicolored 1.00 .75

A1882 A1883

1994, Nov. 4 Photo. *Perf. 13*

2433 A1882 80y multicolored 1.65 1.25

Intl. Diabetes Federation, 15th Congress, Kobe.

1994, Nov. 4 Photo. & Engr.

Cultural pioneers: No. 2434, Michio Miyagi (1894-1956), Musician. No. 2435, Gyoshu Hayami (1894-1935), artist.

2434 A1883 80y multicolored 1.65 1.25
2435 A1883 80y multicolored 1.65 1.25

Heiankyo (Kyoto), 1200th Anniv.
A1884 A1885

Kanpuzu, by Hideyori Kano, Momoyama period depicts autumn scene on Kiyotakigawa River: No. 2436, People seated, white birds. No. 2437, Bridge, people. No. 2438, Bridge, birds flying. No. 2439, People, Jingoji Temple, Atago-Jinja Shrine. No. 2440, People seated, tree.

No. 2441, Painting of Dry Garden (Sekitei), Ryoanji Temple, by Eizo Kato. No. 2442, Painting of artificial pond, Shugakuin Rikyu, by Kanji Kawai, horiz.

1994, Nov. 8 Photo. *Perf. 13x13½*

2436 A1884 80y multicolored 1.65 1.25
2437 A1884 80y multicolored 1.65 1.25
2438 A1884 80y multicolored 1.65 1.25
2439 A1884 80y multicolored 1.65 1.25
2440 A1884 80y multicolored 1.65 1.25
a. Strip of 5, #2436-2440 8.25 6.25
2441 A1885 80y multicolored 1.65 1.25

Perf. 13½x13

2442 A1885 80y multicolored 1.65 1.25
Nos. 2436-2442 (7) 11.55 8.75

A1886 A1887

New Year 1995 (Year of the Boar)
A1888 A1889

1994, Nov. 15 *Perf. 13x13½*

2443 A1886 50y multicolored 1.00 .75
2444 A1887 80y multicolored 1.65 1.25

Perf. 13½

2445 A1888 50y +3y multi 1.10 .80
2446 A1889 80y +3y multi 1.65 1.25
Nos. 2443-2446 (4) 5.40 4.05

World Heritage Series

Himeji Castle
A1890 A1891

A1892

Horyuji Temple
A1893

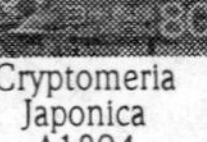

Cryptomeria Japonica
A1894

Cervus Nippon Yakushimae
A1895

Virgin Beech Forest
A1896

Black Woodpecker
A1897

1994, Dec. 14 Photo. *Perf. 13*

2447	A1890	80y multicolored	1.65	1.25
2448	A1891	80y multicolored	1.65	1.25

1995, Feb. 22

Designs: 80y, Goddess Kannon from inner temple wall. 110y, Temple exterior.

2449	A1892	80y multicolored	1.65	1.25
2450	A1893	110y multicolored	2.25	1.65

1995, July 28

2451	A1894	80y multicolored	1.75	1.25
2452	A1895	80y multicolored	1.75	1.25

1995, Nov. 21 Photo. *Perf. 13*

2453	A1896	80y multicolored	1.60	1.10
2454	A1897	80y multicolored	1.60	1.10
		Nos. 2447-2454 (8)	13.90	10.10

Japan-Brazil Friendship, Cent. — A1898

Designs: No. 2455, Natl. emblems, flowers. No. 2456, Soccer players.

1995, Mar. 3 Photo. *Perf. 13½*

2455	A1898	80y multicolored	1.90	1.40
2456	A1898	80y multicolored	1.90	1.40

Fujiwara-Kyo Palace, 1300th Anniv.
A1899 A1900

Designs: 50y, Unebiyama, Nijozan Mountains, roofing tile from palace. 80y, Portrait of a Woman, in Asuka and Hakuho era style, by Okada, 1925.

1995, Mar. 28

2457	A1899	50y multicolored	1.25	.95
2458	A1900	80y multicolored	1.90	1.40

Modern Anatomical Education
A1901

1995, Mar. 31 *Perf. 13*

2459	A1901	80y multicolored	1.90	1.40

A1902 A1903

1995, Apr. 12 Photo. *Perf. 13*

2460	A1902	80y multicolored	1.90	1.40

1995 Census.

1995, Apr. 20

2461	A1903	80y multicolored	1.90	1.40

Japanese Overseas Cooperation Volunteers, 30th anniv.

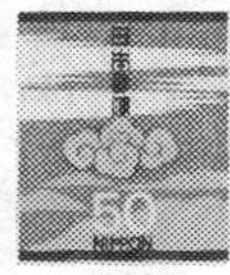

A1904 A1905

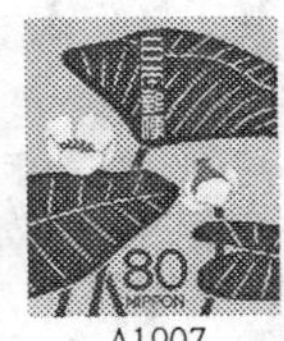

A1906 A1907

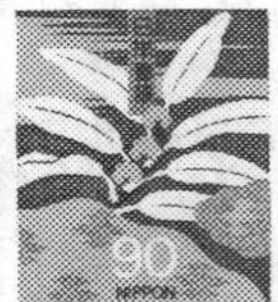

A1908

1995, Apr. 25 *Perf. 13x13½*

2462	A1904	50y multicolored	1.25	.95
2463	A1905	50y multicolored	1.25	.95
2464	A1906	80y multicolored	1.90	1.40
2465	A1907	80y multicolored	1.90	1.40
2466	A1908	90y multicolored	2.25	1.65
		Nos. 2462-2466 (5)	8.55	6.35

For use on condolence and greeting cards.

A1909 A1910

1995, May 19 Photo. *Perf. 13½x13*

2467	A1909	50y multicolored	1.10	.90

Natl. land afforestation campaign.

1995, June 1 *Die Cut Perf. 13½*

Greetings: No. 2468, Rainbow, hearts. No. 2469, Girl holding heart-shaped balloon. No. 2470, Flower holding pencil, sign. No. 2471, Star, sun, moon as flowers, fauna. No. 2472, Person, dog with flowers, butterfly in hair.

Self-Adhesive

2468	A1910	80y multicolored	1.90	1.40
2469	A1910	80y multicolored	1.90	1.40
2470	A1910	80y multicolored	1.90	1.40
2471	A1910	80y multicolored	1.90	1.40
2472	A1910	80y multicolored	1.90	1.40
a.		Miniature sheet, #2468-2472 + 5 labels	9.50	

Letter Writing Day
A1911 A1912

1995, July 21 Photo. *Perf. 13½*

2473	A1911	50y multicolored	1.10	.80
2474	A1912	80y multicolored	1.75	1.25
a.		Souvenir sheet of 1	1.75	1.25
b.		Booklet pane, 5 each #2473-2474	15.00	
		Complete booklet, #2474b	15.00	

Flora & Fauna Type of 1992 and

Shikikacho-zu
A1926

Matsutaka-Zu
A1926a

1997-98 Photo. *Perf. 13½*

2475	A1651	10y Scarab, dandelions	.15	.15
2475A	A1651	20y Honey bee, flower	.30	.25
2475B	A1651	30y Hairstreak, flowers	.50	.35
2476	A1651	70y Great tit	1.20	.90
2479	A1651	110y Plover	1.90	1.40
2480	A1651	120y Shrike	1.90	1.40
2481	A1651	140y Japanese grosbeak	2.20	1.65
2481A	A1651	160y Jay	2.50	1.90
		Perf. 13x13½		
2482	A1651	390y Dayflower	7.50	5.25
		Perf. 13½		
2488	A1926	700y multicolored	15.00	11.50
		Photo. & Engr.		
2488A	A1926a	1000y multicolored	19.00	14.50
		Nos. 2475-2488A (3)	41.50	31.25

Issued: 700y, 7/4/95; 390y, 1000y, 3/28/96; 70y, 110y, 7/22/97; 10y, 20y, 30y, 11/28/97; 120y, 140y, 2/16/98 160y, 2/23/98.

This is an expanding set. Numbers may change.

End of World War II, 50th Anniv.
A1937 A1938

Design: No. 2491, Children holding hands behind stained glass window, peace dove, earth from space.

1995, Aug. 1 Photo. *Perf. 13*

2489	A1937	50y multicolored	1.00	.70
2490	A1938	80y multicolored	1.60	1.10
2491	A1938	80y multicolored	1.60	1.10
		Nos. 2489-2491 (3)	4.20	2.90

A1939 A1940

1995, Aug. 23

2492	A1939	80y multicolored	1.60	1.10

18th Universiade, Fukuoka.

1995, Aug. 25

50y, Radio controlled plane, transmitter. 80y, Radio controlled helicopter, competitor, assistant.

2493	A1940	50y multicolored	1.00	.70
2494	A1940	80y multicolored	1.60	1.10

1995 Aeromodel World Championships, Okayama Prefecture.

World Veterinary Congress, Yokohama
A1941

World Sports Championships
A1942

1995, Sept. 1 Photo. *Perf. 13*

2495	A1941	80y Dog, cow & horse	1.60	1.10

1995, Sept. 28

#2496, 1995 World Judo Championships, Chiba Prefecture. #2497, 1995 World Gymnastics Championships, Sabae, Fukui Prefecture.

1995, Sept. 28

2496	A1942	80y multicolored	1.60	1.10
2497	A1942	80y multicolored	1.60	1.10

Letter Writing Week
A1943

Screen paintings: 90y, Shell-matching game. 110y, Battledore and shuttlecock. 130y, Playing cards.

1995, Oct. 6 *Perf. 13½*

2498	A1943	90y multicolored	1.75	1.25
2499	A1943	110y multicolored	2.25	1.50
2500	A1943	130y multicolored	2.50	1.75
		Nos. 2498-2500 (3)	6.50	4.50

A1944

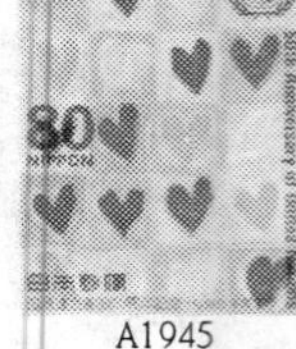

A1945

1995, Oct. 13 *Perf. 13x13½*

2501	A1944	50y multicolored	1.00	.70

50th Natl. athletic meet, Fukushima prefecture.

1995, Oct. 24 ***Perf. 13***

2502 A1945 80y UN, hearts 1.60 1.10
2503 A1945 80y UNESCO, children 1.60 1.10

UN, UNESCO, 50th anniv.

Cultural Pioneers — A1946

#2504, Tadataka Ino (1745-1818), cartographer. #2505, Kitaro Nishida (1870-1945), philosopher.

1995, Nov. 6 Photo. & Engr. ***Perf. 13***

2504 A1946 80y multicolored 1.60 1.10
2505 A1946 80y multicolored 1.60 1.10

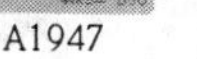

A1947 A1948

New Year 1996 (Year of the Rat)
A1949 A1950

1995, Oct. 15 Photo. ***Perf. 13x13½***

2506 A1947 50y multicolored 1.00 .70
2507 A1948 80y multicolored 1.60 1.10

Perf. 13½

2508 A1949 50y +3y multi 1.10 .75
2509 A1950 80y +3y multi 1.65 1.15

Japanese-Korean Diplomatic Relations, 30th Anniv. — A1951

1995, Dec. 18 ***Perf. 13***

2510 A1951 80y multicolored 1.60 1.10

Nos. 2511-2512 are unassigned.

A1952 A1953

1996, Feb. 16 Photo. ***Perf. 13***

2513 A1952 80y multicolored 1.50 1.00

Philippe Franz von Siebold (1796-1866), naturalist.

1996, Mar. 1

2514 A1953 80y multicolored 1.50 1.00

Labor Relations Commissions, 50th anniv.

Senior Citizens — A1954

1996, Mar. 21 ***Perf. 13½***

2515 A1954 80y multicolored 1.50 1.00

No. 2515 issued in sheets of 5.

50th Postwar Memorial Year
A1955 A1956

#2516, Crowd, Emperor's limosine approaching Diet. #2517, Prime Minister Shigeru signing Peace Treaty, San Francisco, 9/8/51. . #2518, Women performing traditional Okinawan dance.

1996, Apr. 1 Photo. ***Perf. 13***

2516 A1955 80y multicolored 1.50 1.00
2517 A1955 80y multicolored 1.50 1.00
a. Pair, Nos. 2516-2517 3.00 2.00
2518 A1956 80y multicolored 1.50 1.00

Promulgation of the the Constitution, 11/7/46 (#2176). Return of Okinawa, 5/15/72 (#2518).

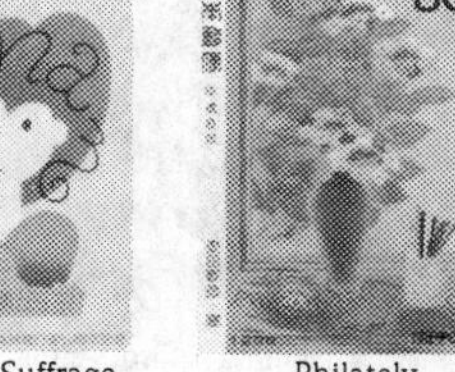

Woman Suffrage, 50th Anniv. — A1957

Philately Week — A1958

1996, Apr. 10 ***Perf. 13½***

2519 A1957 80y multicolored 1.50 1.00

1996, Apr. 19 ***Perf. 13***

2520 A1958 80y multicolored 1.50 1.00

UNICEF, 50th Anniv. — A1959

Child Welfare Week, 50th Anniv. — A1960

1996, May 1 Photo. ***Perf. 13***

2521 A1959 80y multicolored 1.50 1.00

1996, May 1

2522 A1960 80y multicolored 1.50 1.00

Bird Week, 50th Anniv.
A1961 A1962

1996, May 10

2523 A1961 80y multicolored 1.50 1.00
2524 A1962 80y multicolored 1.50 1.00
a. Pair, #2523-2524 3.00 2.00

JAPAN MNH COMMEMORATIVE YEAR SETS

1957 .... $6.90	1965 .... $8.60	1973 .... $9.80	1981 .... 38.80	1988 .... 65.00
1958..........11.50	1966..........12.10	1974..........18.40	1982 .... 38.15	1989 .... 90.00
1959 .... 26.45	1967..........16.35	1975 .... 20.50	1983 .... 36.50	1990........166.00
1960 .... 38.25	1968 .... 31.10	1976..........12.20	1984 .... 42.60	1991 .... 82.80
1961 .... 33.25	1969 .... 21.85	1977..........44.85	1985 .... 59.50	1992 .... 63.25
1962 .... 27.10	1970..........12.25	1978 .... 30.50	1986 .... 42.55	1993 .... 79.35
1963..........16.40	1971..........10.35	1979 .... 31.80	1987 ...... $60.40	1994........109.00
1964 .... 8.90	1972..........14.50	1980 ...... $31.10		

DISCOUNT SCHEDULE
10 Years 1957-66, Reg. $189.45, Net $178.
10 Years 1967-76, Reg. $167.30, Net $159.
10 Years 1977-86, Reg. $396.35, Net $376.
8 Years 1987-94, Reg. $715.80, Net $688.

TERMS: Cash with order. Satisfaction guaranteed. Please send Stamped Envelope for **FREE** Japan Price List. Visa and MasterCard accepted. Please send all raised information.

SWAMY IYER
Phone 310-378-9207 Email:SIyer20303@aol.com
P.O. Box 848, Redondo Beach, CA 90277

Natl. Afforestation Campaign — A1963

1996, May 17

2525 A1963 50y multicolored .90 .60

50th Postwar Memorial Year
A1964 A1965

#2526, 1964 Olympic Games, Tokyo. #2527, Japan Intl. Exposition.

1996, June 24 Photo. ***Perf. 13***

2526 A1964 80y multicolored 1.50 1.00
2527 A1965 80y multicolored 1.50 1.00

We're Buying
Japan
1870-date Manchukuo & Ryukyus

WANTED:
All NH, Hinged or Used sets and singles.
• Good Collections & Accumulations
• Large quantities okay
• Classics
• Booklets
• Souvenir Sheets

For our retail clients we also need mint classics and rarities like the 1923 unissued Earthquake set. All other Asian material wanted including China, Hong Kong and Macau! We sell better Japan. Want lists invited!

Highest Prices Paid!
Immediate payment to any amount!
For selling Asia call
1-800-9-4-STAMP (1-800-947-8267)

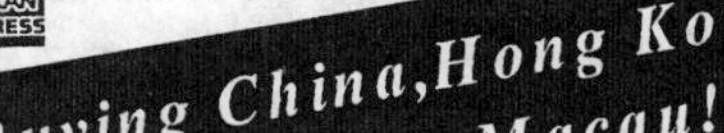

Also Buying China, Hong Kong & Macau!

Henry Gitner Philatelists, Inc.
Philately - The Quiet Excitement! P.O. Box 3077-S, Middletown, NY 10940
Tel: 914-343-5151 Fax: 914-343-0068
Email:hgitner@hgitner.com http://www.hgitner.com
Toll Free: 1-800-947-8267

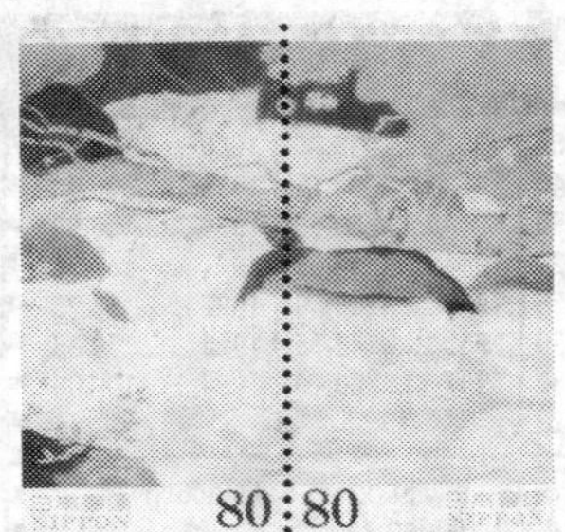

River Administration System, Cent.
A1966 A1967

1996, July 5 Photo. *Perf. 13½*

2528 A1966 80y multicolored	1.50	1.00
2529 A1967 80y multicolored	1.50	1.00
a. Pair, #2528-2529	3.00	2.00

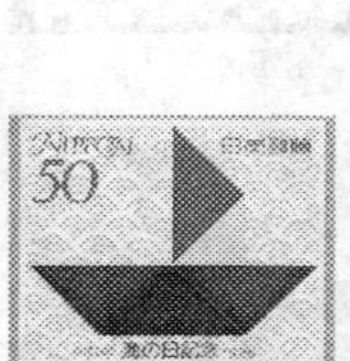

Marine Day's Establishment
A1968 A1969

1996, July 19

2530 A1968 50y multicolored	.90	.60
2531 A1969 80y multicolored	1.50	1.00

Letter Writing Day
A1970 A1971

1996, July 23

2532 A1970 50y multicolored	.90	.60
2533 A1971 80y multicolored	1.50	1.00
a. Souvenir sheet of 1	1.50	1.00
b. Booklet pane, 5 each #2532-2533	12.00	
Complete booklet	12.00	

Miyazawa Kenji (1896-1933) A1972

Hanawa Hokiichi (1746-1821) A1973

Photo. & Engr.

1996, Aug. 27 *Perf. 13*

2534 A1972 80y multicolored	1.50	1.00
2535 A1973 80y multicolored	1.50	1.00

A1974 A1975

Designs: No. 2536, Advances of women in society, diffusion of home electrical products. No. 2537, Modern highway, railway systems.

1996, Aug. 27 Photo. *Perf. 13*

2536 A1974 80y multicolored	1.50	1.00
2537 A1975 80y multicolored	1.50	1.00

51st Natl. Athletic Meet — A1976

Community Chest, 50th Anniv. — A1977

1996, Sept. 6 Photo. *Perf. 13½*

2538 A1976 50y Archery	.90	.60

1996, Sept. 30

2539 A1977 80y multicolored	1.40	.90

Intl. Music Day — A1978

1996, Oct. 1 *Perf. 13*

2540 A1978 80y multicolored	1.40	.90

A1979

Intl. Letter Writing Week A1980

Paintings: #2541, Water wheel, Mt. Fuji. #2542, Flowers. #2543, Mt. Fuji in Clear Weather (Red Fuji), by Hokusai. #2544, Flowers, diff. #2545, Mt. Fuji, lake. #2546, Flowers, diff.

1996, Oct. 7 *Perf. 13½*

2541 A1979 90y multicolored	1.60	1.10
2542 A1980 90y multicolored	1.60	1.10
a. Pair, #2541-2542	3.25	2.25
2543 A1979 110y multicolored	1.90	1.25
2544 A1980 110y multicolored	1.90	1.25
a. Pair, #2543-2544	4.00	2.50
2545 A1979 130y multicolored	2.25	1.50
2546 A1980 130y multicolored	2.25	1.50
a. Pair, #2545-2546	4.50	3.00
Nos. 2541-2546 (6)	11.50	7.70

18th World Congress of Savings Banks — A1981

1996, Oct. 23 *Perf. 13*

2547 A1981 80y multicolored	1.40	.90

50th Postwar Memorial Year
A1982 A1983

#2548, Earth from space. #2549, Cellular telephone, fiber optic cable, satellite in orbit.

1996, Nov. 8 Photo. *Perf. 13*

2548 A1982 80y multicolored	1.50	1.00
2549 A1983 80y multicolored	1.50	1.00

A1984 A1985

New Year 1997 (Year of the Ox)
A1986 A1987

1996, Nov. 15 Photo. *Perf. 13x13½*

2550 A1984 50y multicolored	.90	.60
2551 A1985 80y multicolored	1.50	1.00

Perf. 13½

2552 A1986 50y +3y multi	.95	.65
2553 A1987 80y +3y multi	1.50	1.00

Ishihara Yujiro, Actor
A1988 A1989

Misora Hibari, Entertainer
A1990 A1991

Tezuka Osamu, Cartoonist
A1992 A1993

1997, Jan. 28 Photo. *Perf. 13*

2554 A1988 80y multicolored	1.30	.90
2555 A1989 80y multicolored	1.30	.90
a. Pair, #2554-2555	2.60	1.80
2556 A1990 80y multicolored	1.30	.90
2557 A1991 80y multicolored	1.30	.90
a. Pair, #2556-2557	2.60	1.80
2558 A1992 80y multicolored	1.30	.90
2559 A1993 80y multicolored	1.30	.90
a. Pair, #2558-2559	2.60	1.80
Nos. 2554-2559 (6)	7.80	5.40

Daigo, by Okumura Togyu (1889-1990) A1996

1997, Apr. 18 Litho. *Perf. 13½*

2562 A1996 80y multicolored	1.30	.90

Philately Week.

Supreme Court, 50th Anniv. A1997

Doraemon A1998

1997, May 2 Photo. *Perf. 13*

2563 A1997 80y Main court room	1.40	1.00

Serpentine Die Cut 13½

1997, May 2

Designs: No. 2564, With parachute. No. 2565, Shown. No. 2566, Standing on hand. No. 2567, With propeller. No. 2568, In love.

Self-Adhesive
Booklet Stamps

2564 A1998 80y multicolored	1.40	1.00
2565 A1998 80y multicolored	1.40	1.00
2566 A1998 80y multicolored	1.40	1.00
2567 A1998 80y multicolored	1.40	1.00
2568 A1998 80y multicolored	1.40	1.00
a. Pane of 5, #2564-2568	7.00	

Japanese Migration to Mexico, Cent. — A1999

1997, May 12 *Perf. 13*

2569 A1999 80y multicolored	1.40	1.00

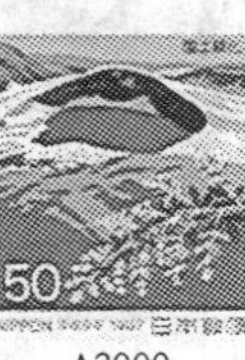

A2000 A2001

1997, May 16 *Perf. 13½*

2570 A2000 50y Miyagi bush clover	.85	.60

Natl. afforestation campaign.

1997, May 20 *Perf. 13*

2571 A2001 80y Natl. Diet	1.40	1.00

Natl. House of Councilors, 50th anniv.

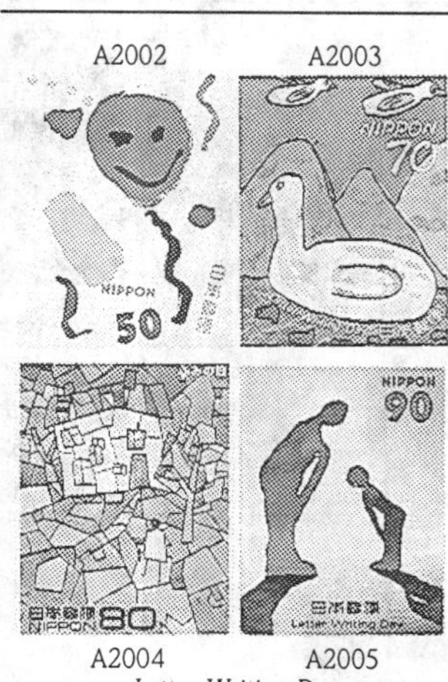

A2002 A2003

A2004 A2005

Letter Writing Day

1997, July 23 Photo. *Perf. 13*

2572 A2002 50y multicolored	.85	.60
2573 A2003 70y multicolored	1.20	.90
2574 A2004 80y multicolored	1.40	1.00
a. Souvenir sheet of 1	1.40	1.00
b. Booklet pane, 5 each #2572, 2574	11.50	
Complete booklet, #2574b	11.50	
2575 A2005 90y multicolored	1.50	1.15
Nos. 2572-2575 (4)	4.95	3.65

Part-time and Correspondence Education at Upper Secondary Schools, 50th Anniv. — A2006

Labor Standards Law, 50th Anniv. — A2007

1997, Aug. 11 Photo. *Perf. 13*

2576 A2006 50y multicolored .85 .60

1997, Sept. 1

2577 A2007 80y multicolored 1.40 1.00

Friendship Between Japan and Chile, Cent. — A2008

52nd Natl. Sports Festival — A2009

1997, Sept. 1 *Perf. 13½*

2578 A2008 80y multicolored 1.40 1.00

See Chile No. 1217.

1997, Sept. 12

2579 A2009 50y multicolored .85 .60

Intl. Letter Writing Week A2010

Paintings of Tokaido's 53 Stations by Hiroshige: No. 2580, Hodogaya (bridge over waterway). No. 2582, Kameyama snow-coverered mountain slope). No. 2584, Sumida Riverbank Snowscape (woman in traditional attire beside river), by Hiroshige

From Scrolls of Flowers and Birds of the Four Seasons by Hoitsu Sakai: No. 2581, Bird on tree. No. 2583, Leaves and berries. No. 2585, Bird on tree branch of blossoms.

1997, Oct. 6 Photo. *Perf. 13½*

2580 A2010 90y multicolored	1.40	1.00
2581 A2010 90y multicolored	1.40	1.00
a. Pair, #2580-2581	2.80	2.00
2582 A2010 110y multicolored	1.75	1.30
2583 A2010 110y multicolored	1.75	1.30
a. Pair, #2582-2583	3.50	2.60
2584 A2010 130y multicolored	2.00	1.60
2585 A2010 130y multicolored	2.00	1.60
a. Pair, #2584-2585	4.00	3.20
Nos. 2580-2585 (6)	10.30	7.80

Grand Opening of the Natl. Theater of Tokyo — A2011

1997, Oct. 9 *Perf. 13*

2586 A2011 80y multicolored 1.30 1.00

Favorite Songs

A2012 A2013

50y Departure on a Fine Day, by Tanimura Shinji. 80y, Desert Under the Moon, by Kato Masao & Sakasi Suguru.

1997, Oct. 24

2587 A2012 50y multicolored	.80	.60
2588 A2013 80y multicolored	1.30	1.00

Kouda Rohan (1867-1947), Writer — A2014

Ando Hiroshige (1797-1858), Artist — A2015

1997, Nov. 4

2589 A2014 80y multicolored	1.30	1.00
2590 A2015 80y multicolored	1.30	1.00

A2016

A2017

New Year 1997 (Year of the Tiger)

A2018 A2019

1997, Nov. 14 *Perf. 13x13½*

2591 A2016 50y multicolored	.80	.60
2592 A2017 80y multicolored	1.30	1.00

Perf. 13½

2593 A2018 50y +3y multi	.85	.65
2594 A2019 80y +3y multi	1.35	1.00

Return of Okinawa to Japan, 25th Anniv. — A2020

1997, Nov. 21 *Perf. 13*

2595 A2020 80y multicolored 1.30 1.00

Shibuya Family's House A2021

Tomizawa Family's House A2022

Photo. & Engr.

1997, Nov. 28 *Perf. 13½*

2596 A2021 80y multicolored	1.30	1.00
2597 A2022 80y multicolored	1.30	1.00

A2023 A2024

Woodprints: No. 2598, Mother Sea. No. 2599, Mother Earth.

1997, Dec. 1 Photo. *Perf. 13*

2598 A2023 80y multicolored	1.25	.95
2599 A2023 80y multicolored	1.25	.95
a. Pair, #2598-2599	2.50	1.90

3rd Conference of the Parties to the UN Framework Convention on Climate Change, Kyoto.

1997, Dec. 2

2600 A2024 80y multicolored 1.25 .95

Agricultural Insurance System, 50th anniv.

Favorite Songs

A2025 A2026

1997, Dec. 8

2601 A2025 50y Sunayama	.80	.60
2602 A2026 80y Jingle Bells	1.25	.95

A2027

A2028

1998, Jan. 26 Photo. *Perf. 13*

2603 A2027 50y Shabondama	.80	.60
2604 A2028 80y Kitaguni no Haru	1.25	.95

1998 Winter Olympic & Paralympic Games, Nagano

A2029 A2030

Paralympic logo and: No. 2605, Glaucidium palmatum. No. 2606, Ice hockey.

Olympic rings and: No. 2607: a, Gentiana nipponica. b, Caltha palustris. c, Fritillaria camtschatcensis. d, Paeonia japonica. e, Erythronium japonicum. f, Snowboarding. g, Curling. h, Speed skating. i, Cross-country skiing. j, Downhill skiing.

1998, Feb. 5

2605 A2029 50y multicolored	.80	.60
2606 A2030 80y multicolored	1.25	.95
a. Pair, #2605-2606	2.05	1.50
2607 Sheet of 10	10.50	7.75
a.-e. A2029 50y Any single	.80	.60
f.-j. A2030 80y Any single	1.25	.95

A2031

Historic Houses A2032

Photo. & Engr.

1998, Feb. 23 *Perf. 13½*

2608 A2031 80y multicolored	1.25	.95
2609 A2032 80y multicolored	1.25	.95

SEMI-POSTAL STAMPS

Douglas Plane over Japan Alps — SP1

Wmk. Zigzag Lines (141)

1937, June 1 Photo. *Perf. 13*

B1	SP1	2s + 2s rose carmine	1.75	.80
B2	SP1	3s + 2s purple	1.75	1.40
B3	SP1	4s + 2s green	2.75	1.15
		Nos. B1-B3 (3)	6.25	3.35
		Set, never hinged	7.75	

The surtax was for the Patriotic Aviation Fund to build civil airports.

Nos. 259 and 261 Surcharged in Blue or Red

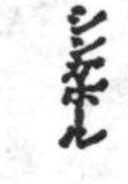

1942, Feb. 16 Wmk. 257 *Perf. 13*

B4	A84	2s + 1s crimson (Bl)	1.00	1.00
B5	A86	4s + 2s dk grn (R)	1.50	1.50
		Set, never hinged	3.00	

Fall of Singapore to Japanese forces.

Tank Corps Attack, Bataan — SP2

Pearl Harbor under Japanese Attack — SP3

Unwmk.

1942, Dec. 8 Photo. *Perf. 12*

B6	SP2	2s + 1s rose brown	1.50	1.10
B7	SP3	5s + 2s sapphire	2.00	1.65
		Set, never hinged	5.00	

1st anniv. of the "Greater East Asia War." The surtax was for national defense.

Catalogue values for unused stamps in this section, from this point to the end of the section, are for Never Hinged items.

SP4

1947, Nov. 25 Wmk. 257 *Perf. 12½*

B8	SP4	1.20y + 80s dk rose red	1.25	1.00

Japan's 1st Community Chest drive. The surtax was for charitable purposes.

Nurse — SP5

Bird Feeding Young — SP6

1948, Oct. 1 Unwmk. *Perf. 12½*

B9	SP5	5y + 2.50y bright red	8.50	8.50
B10	SP6	5y + 2.50y emerald	8.50	8.50

Souvenir Sheet

Wmk. 257

Imperf

B11	SP7	Sheet of 2	57.50	52.50

The surtax on Nos. B9-B11 was divided between the Red Cross and Community Chest organizations.

No. B11 contains Nos. B9-B10, imperf.

Javelin Thrower SP8

Designs: No. B13, Wrestlers. No. B14, Diver. No. B15, Water polo. No. B16, Woman gymnast. No. B17, Judo. No. B18, Fencing. No. B19, Basketball. No. B20, Rowing. No. B21, Sailing. No. B22, Boxing. No. B23, Volleyball. No. B24, Bicyclist. No. B25, Equestrian. No. B26, Field hockey. No. B27, Pistol shooting. No. B28, Modern pentathlon. No. B29, Weight lifter. No. B30, Women's kayak doubles. No. B31, Soccer.

Perf. 13½

1961, Oct. 11 Unwmk. Engr.

B12	SP8	5y + 5y bister	1.00	.52
B13	SP8	5y + 5y dk green	1.00	.52
B14	SP8	5y + 5y carmine	1.00	.52
a.		Souvenir sheet of 3 ('64)	4.50	5.00

1962, June 23

B15	SP8	5y + 5y green	.52	.28
B16	SP8	5y + 5y dk purple	.52	.28
B17	SP8	5y + 5y dk carmine	.52	.28
a.		Souvenir sheet of 3 ('64)	3.00	3.50

1962, Oct. 10

B18	SP8	5y + 5y brick red	.35	.28
B19	SP8	5y + 5y slate grn	.35	.28
B20	SP8	5y + 5y violet	.35	.28
a.		Souvenir sheet of 3 ('64)	2.50	2.75

1963, June 23

B21	SP8	5y + 5y blue	.45	.28
B22	SP8	5y + 5y dk brown	.45	.28
B23	SP8	5y + 5y brown	.45	.28
a.		Souvenir sheet of 3 ('64)	4.00	4.25

1963, Nov. 11

B24	SP8	5y + 5y dk blue	.20	.15
B25	SP8	5y + 5y olive	.20	.15
B26	SP8	5y + 5y black	.20	.15
B27	SP8	5y + 5y claret	.20	.15
a.		Souvenir sheet of 4 ('64)	4.00	4.25

1964, June 23

B28	SP8	5y + 5y bluish vio	.24	.15
B29	SP8	5y + 5y dp olive	.24	.15
B30	SP8	5y + 5y grnsh blue	.24	.15
B31	SP8	5y + 5y rose claret	.24	.15
a.		Souvenir sheet of 4 ('64)	4.00	4.25
		Nos. B12-B31 (20)	8.72	5.28

Issued to raise funds for the 1964 Olympic Games in Tokyo.

The souvenir sheets were issued Aug. 20, 1964. Each contains one each of the stamps in the set it follows. Nos. B14a, B20a, B23a and B27a, exist imperf.

Cobalt Treatment Unit — SP9

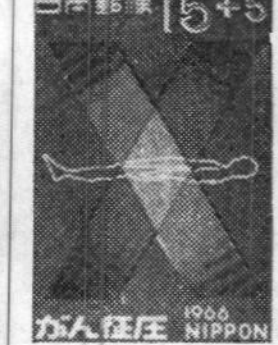

Early Cancer Detection with X-rays — SP10

1966, Oct. 21 Photo. *Perf. 13*

B32	SP9	7y + 3y yel org & blk	.22	.15
B33	SP10	15y + 5y multicolored	.42	.20

9th Intl. Anticancer Congress, Tokyo, Oct. 23-29. The surtax was for the fight against cancer and for research.

EXPO '70 Emblem and Globe — SP11

Cherry Blossoms, Screen, Chishakuin Temple — SP12

1969, Mar. 15 Photo. *Perf. 13*

B34	SP11	15y + 5y bl, ocher & ver	.80	.80
B35	SP12	50y + 10y gold, brn & grn	1.50	1.50

Issued to publicize EXPO '70, International Exhibition, Osaka, 1970.

DESPERATELY NEEDED

JAPAN

DESPERATELY NEEDED

CANCELLATIONS • COVERS • COLLECTIONS • MINT • USED
FROM CLASSICS TO PACKET MATERIAL, WE BUY IT ALL!

HOW TO SELL:
1. Ship material by registered or insured mail.
2. We will immediately send you a check as our offer.

OR

for Larger Accumulations
Just Give Us A Call...
WE WILL TRAVEL TO BUY YOUR STAMPS

GET TOKYO PRICES FOR YOUR JAPANESE STAMPS!
Call or Write
"The Japanese Specialists"

GARY TANAKA & CO.
1139 Bal Harbor Blvd., Punta Gorda, FL 33950
TOLL FREE 1-800-218-5140 • Fax: 1-941-639-4272

Ice Hockey, Sapporo Olympic Emblem SP13

Design: No. B37, Ski jump and Sapporo Olympic Games emblem, vert.

1971, Feb. 6 Photo. *Perf. 13*

B36	SP13	15y + 5y multi	.35	.15
B37	SP13	15y + 5y multi	.35	.15

To promote the 11th Winter Olympic Games, Sapporo, Japan, 1972.

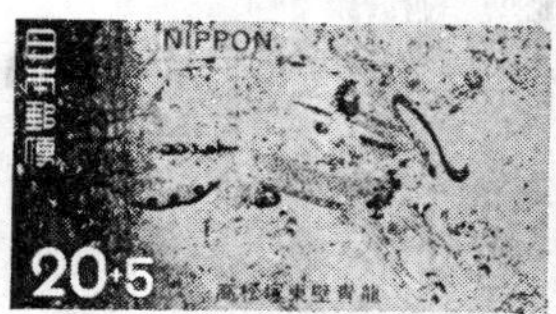

Blue Dragon, East Wall — SP14

Murals from ancient tomb mound: No. B39, Two men, east wall, vert. 50y+10y, Four women, west wall, vert.

1973, Mar. 26 Photo. *Perf. 13*
Size: 48x27mm, 27x48mm

B38	SP14	20y + 5y multi	.35	.15
B39	SP14	20y + 5y multi	.35	.15

Photogravure and Engraved
Size: 33x48mm

B40	SP14	50y + 10y multi	.75	.25
		Nos. B38-B40 (3)	1.45	.55

Surtax was for restoration work on the murals of the Takamatsu-zuka tomb mound, discovered in March, 1972, and excavated in Nara Prefecture.

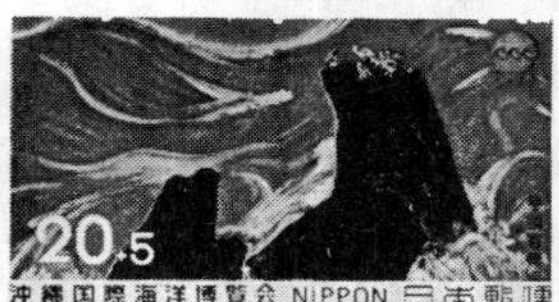

Reefs, by Hyakusui Hirafuku — SP15

1974, Mar. 2 Photo. *Perf. 13*

B41	SP15	20y + 5y multi	.30	.15

The surtax was for the International Ocean Exposition, Okinawa, 1975.

Intl. Year of the Disabled — SP16

Photogravure and Embossed
1981, Sept. 1 *Perf. 13½*

B42	SP16	60y + 10y multi	1.00	.20

Surtax was for education of the disabled.

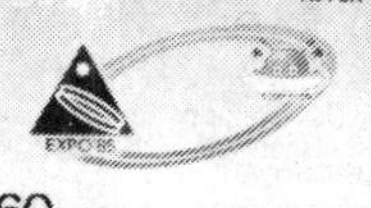

TSUKUBA '85 Intl. Exposition, Mar. 17-Sept. 16, 1985 — SP17

1984, Feb. 19 Photo. *Perf. 13½*

B43	SP17	60y + 10y multi	1.10	.45

Intl. Garden and Greenery Exposition, Osaka — SP18

1989, June 1 Photo. *Perf. 13*

B44	SP18	62y +10y multi	1.10	.82

Surtax for the preparation and management of the exposition.

Intl. Garden and Greenery Exposition, Osaka — SP19

1990, Mar. 30

B45	SP19	41y +4y multi	.60	.45

SP20

SP21

1991, July 5 Photo. *Perf. 13*

B46	SP20	62y +10y multi	1.20	.90

11th World Congress of the World Federation of the Deaf.

1995, Apr. 20 Photo. *Perf. 13*

B47	SP21	80y +20y multi	2.50	1.90

Philately week. Surtax for benefit of victims of Kobe earthquake.

1998 Winter Olympic Games, Nagano — SP22

1997, Feb. 7 Photo. *Perf. 13*

B48	SP22	80y +10y shown	1.50	1.10
B49	SP22	80y +10y Stylized owls	1.55	1.10
a.		Pair, #B48-B49	3.00	2.25

AIR POST STAMPS

Regular Issue of 1914 Overprinted in Red or Blue

Wmk. Zigzag Lines (141)
1919, Oct. 3 *Perf. 13x13½*
Granite Paper

C1	A34	1½s blue (R)	300.00	85.00
C2	A34	3s rose (Bl)	525.00	250.00

Excellent counterfeits exist.

Passenger Plane over Lake Ashi — AP1

1929-34 Engr. *Perf. 13½x13*
Granite Paper

C3	AP1	8½s orange brn	32.50	13.50
C4	AP1	9½s rose	10.00	3.50
C5	AP1	16½s yellow grn	11.00	4.25
C6	AP1	18s ultra	12.00	3.50
C7	AP1	33s gray	22.50	3.00
		Nos. C3-C7 (5)	88.00	27.75
		Set, never hinged	190.00	

Souvenir Sheet

C8	AP1	Sheet of 4, #C4-C7	1,400.	1,500.
		Never hinged	2,000.	

Issue dates: 9½s, Mar. 1, 1934; No. C8, Apr. 20, 1934; others, Oct. 6, 1929. No. C8 for Communications Commemoration Day (1st observance of establishment of the postal service and issuance of Nos. 1-4). Sold only at Phil. Exhib. p.o., Tokyo, Apr. 20-27. Size: 110x100mm.

Catalogue values for unused stamps in this section, from this point to the end of the section, are for Never Hinged items.

Southern Green Pheasant AP3

Perf. 13x13½
1950, Jan. 10 Engr. Unwmk.

C9	AP3	16y gray	35.00	5.50
C10	AP3	34y brown violet	50.00	10.00
C11	AP3	59y carmine	75.00	8.00
C12	AP3	103y orange yellow	55.00	14.00
C13	AP3	144y olive	65.00	14.00
		Nos. C9-C13 (5)	280.00	51.50
		Set, hinged	190.00	

Pagoda and Plane — AP4

Plane and Mt. Tsurugi-dake — AP5

1951-52 Photo.

C14	AP4	15y purple	4.00	2.75
C15	AP4	20y blue	32.50	.90
C16	AP4	25y yellow grn	30.00	.32
C17	AP4	30y brown red	22.50	.32
C18	AP4	40y gray blk	8.50	.40
C19	AP5	55y brt blue	250.00	42.50
C20	AP5	75y brnsh red	175.00	17.00
C21	AP5	80y magenta	24.00	3.00
C22	AP5	85y black	30.00	6.00
C23	AP5	125y olive bis	15.00	3.50
C24	AP5	160y Prus green	32.50	4.25
		Nos. C14-C24 (11)	624.00	80.94
		Set, hinged	425.00	

Issue dates: 25y, 30y, Dec. 20. 15y, 20y, 40y, Sept. 1. 55y-160y, Feb. 11, 1952.

Redrawn; Underlined Zeros Omitted

1952-62

C25	AP4	15y purple ('62)	2.00	.60
C26	AP4	20y blue	67.50	.70
C27	AP4	25y yel grn ('53)	1.25	.15
C28	AP4	30y brown red	8.50	.15
C29	AP4	40y gray blk ('53)	5.75	.15
C30	AP5	55y brt blue	85.00	4.00
C32	AP5	75y brnsh red	175.00	10.00
C33	AP5	80y magenta	125.00	4.00
C34	AP5	85y black	6.75	1.40
C36	AP5	125y olive bis	10.50	1.50
C38	AP5	160y Prus green	42.50	2.00
		Nos. C25-C38 (11)	529.75	24.65
		Set, hinged	275.00	

See No. C43.

Great Buddha of Kamakura — AP6

1953, Aug. 15 *Perf. 13½*

C39	AP6	70y red brown	4.25	.15
C40	AP6	80y blue	6.50	.15
C41	AP6	115y olive green	4.00	.40
C42	AP6	145y Prus green	16.00	1.40
		Nos. C39-C42 (4)	30.75	2.10

Coil Stamp
Redrawn Type of 1952-62

1961, Oct. 2 *Perf. 13 Horiz.*

C43	AP4	30y brown red	40.00	22.50

MILITARY STAMPS

Nos. 98, 119, 131 Overprinted

Perf. 11½ to 13½
1910-14 Unwmk.

M1	A26	3s rose	250.00	35.00
M2	A34	3s rose ('13)	400.00	160.00

Wmk. 141

M3	A34	3s rose ('14)	30.00	17.50
		Nos. M1-M3 (3)	680.00	212.50

Nos. M1-M3 overprint type I has 3.85mm between characters; type II, 4-4.5mm (movable type).

1921 On Offices in China No. 37

M4	A34	3s rose	*6,000.*	*5,000.*

No. M4 is a provisional military stamp issued at the Japanese Post Office, Tsingtao, China. The overprint differs from the illustration, being 12mm high with thicker characters. Counterfeits are plentiful.

Overprint 16mm High

1924 On No. 131

M5	A34	3s rose	100.00	70.00
a.		3s rose (#131b)	110.00	75.00

Excellent forgeries exist of Nos. M1-M5.

JAPANESE OFFICES ABROAD

Offices in China

Regular Issues of Japan Overprinted in Red or Black 郵支

Perf. 11½, 12, 12½, 13½, 13x13½
1900-06 Unwmk.

1	A26	5r gray (R)	4.25	3.25
2	A26	½s gray (R) ('01)	2.50	.85
3	A26	1s lt red brn (R)	2.50	.85
4	A26	1½s ultra	11.00	2.50
5	A26	1½s vio ('06)	6.00	1.15
6	A26	2s lt grn (R)	6.00	.85
7	A26	3s violet brn	6.75	.85
8	A26	3s rose ('06)	5.00	.60
9	A26	4s rose	5.50	1.50
10	A26	5s org yel (R)	11.00	1.50
11	A27	6s maroon ('06)	19.00	12.00
12	A27	8s ol grn (R)	10.00	7.00
13	A27	10s deep blue	10.00	.70
14	A27	15s purple	22.50	1.50
15	A27	20s red org	20.00	.70
16	A28	25s blue grn (R)	42.50	4.00
17	A28	50s red brown	45.00	2.25
18	A29	1y carmine	67.50	2.25
		Nos. 1-18 (18)	297.00	44.30

No. 6 with black overprint is bogus.

1900

19	A30	3s carmine	30.00	16.00

Wedding of Crown Prince Yoshihito and Princess Sadako.

1908

20	A33	5y green	450.00	55.00
21	A33	10y dark violet	750.00	140.00

On #20-21 the space between characters of the overprint is 6½mm instead of 1½mm.

1913 *Perf. 12, 12x13, 13x13½*

22	A34	½s brown	18.00	18.00
23	A34	1s orange	19.00	19.00
24	A34	1½s lt blue	50.00	22.50
a.		Bklt. pane of 6	450.00	

No.	Type	Description	Unused	Used
25	A34	2s green	57.50	25.00
26	A34	3s rose	27.50	9.50
a.		Bklt. pane of 6	450.00	
27	A35	4s red	77.50	77.50
28	A35	5s violet	77.50	57.50
29	A35	10s deep blue	77.50	22.50
30	A35	20s claret	300.00	165.00
31	A35	25s olive green	110.00	25.00
32	A36	1y yel grn & mar	950.00	625.00
		Nos. 22-32 (11)	1,764.	1,066.

1914-21 Wmk. 141

Granite Paper

No.	Type	Description	Unused	Used
33	A34	½s brown	3.50	.85
34	A34	1s orange	4.00	.85
35	A34	1½s blue	4.50	.85
a.		Booklet pane of 6	250.00	
36	A34	2s green	3.00	1.00
a.		Booklet pane of 6	375.00	
37	A34	3s rose	2.50	.85
a.		Booklet pane of 6	375.00	
38	A35	4s red	11.00	5.00
a.		Booklet pane of 6	375.00	
39	A35	5s violet	20.00	1.85
40	A35	6s brown ('20)	35.00	20.00
41	A35	8s gray ('20)	42.50	22.50
42	A35	10s dp blue	14.00	1.40
a.		Booklet pane of 6		
43	A35	20s claret	47.50	3.50
44	A35	25s olive grn	57.50	3.75
45	A36	30s org brn ('20)	100.00	30.00
46	A36	50s dk brn ('20)	110.00	35.00
47	A36	1y yel grn & mar ('18)	165.00	7.00
48	A33	5y green	2,250.	650.00
49	A33	10y violet ('21)	3,000.	2,000.
		Nos. 33-49 (17)	5,870.	2,784.

On Nos. 48-49 the space between characters of overprint is 4½mm, instead of 6½mm on Nos. 20-21 and 1½mm on all lower values. See No. M4.

Counterfeit overprints exist of Nos. 1-49.

Offices in Korea

Regular Issue of Japan Overprinted in Red or Black 鮮 朝

1900 Unwmk. *Perf. 11½, 12, 12½*

No.	Type	Description	Unused	Used
1	A26	5r gray (R)	21.00	10.00
2	A26	1s lt red brn (R)	22.50	5.50
3	A26	1½s ultra	275.00	160.00
4	A26	2s lt green (R)	21.00	11.00
5	A26	3s violet brn	19.00	5.00
6	A26	4s rose	72.50	30.00
7	A26	5s org yel (R)	75.00	30.00
8	A27	8s ol grn (R)	275.00	160.00
9	A27	10s deep blue	37.50	10.00
10	A27	15s purple	95.00	6.50
11	A27	20s red orange	95.00	5.50
12	A28	25s blue grn (R)	250.00	60.00
13	A28	50s red brown	190.00	20.00
14	A29	1y carmine	525.00	15.00
		Nos. 1-14 (14)	1,973.	528.50

1900

No.	Type	Description	Unused	Used
15	A30	3s carmine	125.00	65.00

Wedding of Crown Prince Yoshihito and Princess Sadako.

Counterfeit overprints exist of Nos. 1-15.

Taiwan (Formosa)

Numeral of Value and Imperial Crest — A1

1945 Unwmk. Litho. *Imperf.*

Without Gum

No.	Type	Description	Unused	Used
1	A1	3s carmine	27.50	27.50
2	A1	5s blue green	22.50	22.50
3	A1	10s pale blue	35.00	35.00
		Nos. 1-3 (3)	85.00	85.00

Additional values, prepared, but not issued, were: 30s, 40s, 50s, 1y, 5y and 10y. The entire set of nine was overprinted by Chinese authorities after World War II and issued for use in Taiwan.

For overprints see China-Taiwan Nos. 1-7.

JORDAN

ˈjȯr-dᵊn

Trans-Jordan

LOCATION — In the Near East, separated from the Mediterranean Sea by Israel
GOVT. — Kingdom
AREA — 38,400 sq. mi.
POP. — 3,750,000 (est. 1982)
CAPITAL — Amman

The former Turkish territory was mandated to Great Britain following World War I. It became an independent state in 1946.

10 Milliemes = 1 Piaster
1000 Mils = 1 Palestine Pound (1930)
1000 Fils = 1 Jordan Dinar (1951)

Catalogue values for unused stamps in this country are for Never Hinged items, beginning with Scott 221 in the regular postage section, Scott B13 in the semi-postal section, Scott C1 in the air post section, Scott J47 in the postage due section, Scott RA1 in the postal tax section, Scott N1 in the occupation section, Scott NJ1 in the occupation postage due section, and Scott NRA1 in the occupation postal tax section.

Watermarks

Wmk. 305- Roman and Arabic Initials

Wmk. 328- UAR

British Mandate

Stamps and Type of Palestine 1918 Overprinted in Black or Silver

شرقي الاردن

1920, Nov. Wmk. 33 *Perf. 14, 15x14*

No.	Type	Description	Unused	Used
1	A1	1m dark brown	.30	.40
a.		Inverted overprint	125.00	
b.		Perf. 15x14	.35	.50
c.		As "b," inverted overprint	110.00	
2	A1	2m blue green	.30	.40
a.		Perf. 15x14	5.50	6.25
3	A1	3m light brown	.50	.70
a.		Perf. 14	11.00	11.00
4	A1	4m scarlet	.65	.75
a.		Perf. 14	12.00	15.00
5	A1	5m orange	.85	.50
a.		Perf. 15x14	1.00	1.25
6	A1	1pi dark blue (S)	.75	1.10
a.		Perf. 15x14		
7	A1	2pi olive green	1.75	1.90
a.		Perf. 15x14	1.50	1.65
8	A1	5pi plum	1.40	4.00
a.		Perf. 15x14	7.50	10.00
9	A1	9pi bister	3.00	12.50
a.		Perf. 15x14	875.00	875.00
10	A1	10pi ultramarine	3.50	14.00
11	A1	20pi gray	7.50	25.00
		Nos. 1-11 (11)	20.50	61.25

The overprint reads "Sharqi al-ardan" (East of Jordan).

For overprints see Nos. 12-63, 83A.

Stamps of 1920 Issue Handstamp Surcharged "Ashir el qirsh" (tenth of piaster) and numeral in Black, Red or Violet

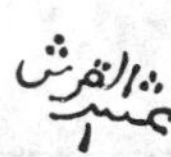

1922

No.	Type	Description	Unused	Used
12	A1	1/10pi on 1m dk brn	18.00	22.50
13	A1	1/10pi on 1m dk brn (R)	67.50	67.50
13A	A1	1/10pi on 1m dk brn (V)	67.50	67.50
14	A1	2/10pi on 2m bl grn	22.50	22.50
a.		3/10pi on 2m bl grn (error)	85.00	85.00
15	A1	2/10pi on 2m bl grn (R)	75.00	75.00
16	A1	2/10pi on 2m bl grn (V)	75.00	75.00
17	A1	3/10pi on 3m lt brn	8.00	8.00
17A	A1	3/10pi on 3m lt brn (V)	165.00	165.00
18	A1	4/10pi on 4m scar	45.00	45.00
19	A1	5/10pi on 5m org	150.00	95.00
c.		Perf. 15x14	165.00	150.00
19A	A1	5/10pi on 5m dp org (R)	225.00	
19B	A1	5/10pi on 5m org (V)	250.00	

For overprint see No. 83B.

Handstamp Surcharged "El qirsh" (piaster) and numeral in Black, Red or Violet

No.	Type	Description	Unused	Used
20	A1	1pi dk bl (R)	140.00	50.00
20A	A1	1pi dk bl (V)	350.00	
21	A1	2pi ol grn (Bk)	225.00	60.00
22	A1	2pi ol grn (R)	250.00	65.00
22A	A1	2pi ol grn (V)	250.00	75.00
23	A1	5pi plum (Bk)	40.00	60.00
23A	A1	5pi plum (V)	250.00	
24	A1	9pi bister (Bk)	225.00	250.00
25	A1	9pi bister (R)	110.00	125.00
a.		Perf. 14	400.00	400.00
26	A1	10pi ultra (Bk)	850.00	900.00
27	A1	20pi gray (Bk)	600.00	750.00
27A	A1	20pi gray (V)	800.00	850.00

Same Surcharge in Black on Palestine Nos. 13-14

No.	Type	Description	Unused	Used
28	A1	10pi on 10pi ultra	1,750.	
29	A1	20pi on 20pi gray	2,250.	

For overprints see Nos. 86, 88, 94, 97, 98.

Stamps of 1920 Handstamped in Violet, Black or Red

1922, Dec. *Perf. 15x14, 14*

No.	Type	Description	Unused	Used
30	A1	1m dk brn (V)	20.00	18.00
31	A1	1m dk brn (Bk)	16.00	16.00
32	A1	1m dk brn (R)	10.00	13.00
33	A1	2m bl grn (V)	6.50	6.50
34	A1	2m bl grn (Bk)	8.50	8.50
35	A1	2m bl grn (R)	20.00	20.00
36	A1	3m lt brn (V)	6.00	6.00
37	A1	3m lt brn (Bk)	7.00	7.00
38	A1	3m lt brn (R)	22.50	22.50
39	A1	4m scar (V)	40.00	40.00
39A	A1	4m scar (Bk)	40.00	40.00
40	A1	4m scar (R)	40.00	40.00
41	A1	5m orange (V)	20.00	15.00
42	A1	5m orange (R)	70.00	85.00
a.		Perf. 14	250.00	65.00
43	A1	1pi dk blue (V)	13.00	8.00
44	A1	1pi dk blue (R)	20.00	14.00
45	A1	2pi ol grn (V)	18.00	13.00
a.		Perf. 14	70.00	70.00
46	A1	2pi ol grn (Bk)	11.00	9.00
47	A1	2pi ol grn (R)	50.00	40.00
48	A1	5pi plum (V)	50.00	70.00
a.		Perf. 14	80.00	90.00
49	A1	5pi plum (R)	70.00	85.00
50	A1	9pi bister (V)	175.00	200.00
50A	A1	9pi bister (Bk)	60.00	70.00
50B	A1	9pi bister (R)	350.00	400.00
51	A1	10pi ultra (V)	1,250.	1,350.
51A	A1	10pi ultra (R)	1,750.	1,750.
52	A1	20pi gray (V)	1,300.	1,400.
52A	A1	20pi gray (R)	2,000.	2,000.

The overprint reads "Hukumat al Sharqi al Arabia" (Arab Government of the East) and date, 1923. The surcharges or overprints on Nos. 12 to 52A inclusive are handstamped and, as usual, are found inverted and double.

Ink pads of several colors were in use at the same time and the surcharges and overprints frequently show a mixture of two colors.

For overprints see #84, 87, 89, 92-93, 95-96.

Stamps of 1920 Overprinted in Gold

حكومة الشرق العربية نيسان سنة ٩٢١

1923, Mar. 1 *Perf. 14, 15x14*

No.	Type	Description	Unused	Used
53	A1	1m dark brn (G)	15.00	20.00
a.		Perf. 15x14	1,600.	1,750.
54	A1	2m blue grn (G)	14.00	17.00
a.		Double overprint	240.00	
b.		Inverted overprint	300.00	
55	A1	3m lt brn (G)	10.00	13.00
a.		Black overprint	70.00	75.00
56	A1	4m scarlet (Bk)	8.50	10.00
57	A1	5m orange (Bk)	10.00	10.00
a.		Perf. 15x14	45.00	40.00
58	A1	1pi dk blue (G)	11.00	13.00
a.		Double overprint	400.00	450.00
b.		Black overprint	650.00	750.00
59	A1	2pi ol grn (G)	12.50	13.00
a.		Black overprint	250.00	
b.		Overprint on back	175.00	
60	A1	5pi plum (G)	50.00	70.00
a.		Inverted overprint	250.00	
b.		"922" for "921"		
61	A1	9pi bister (Bk)	65.00	90.00
a.		Perf. 15x14	200.00	200.00
62	A1	10pi ultra (G)	70.00	90.00
63	A1	20pi gray (G)	70.00	90.00
a.		Inverted overprint	425.00	
b.		Double overprint	400.00	
c.		Double ovpt., one inverted	450.00	

The overprint reads "Hukumat al Sharqi al Arabia, Nissan Sanat 921" (Arab Government of the East, April, 1921).

For overprints see Nos. 85, 99, 100, 102.

Stamps of Hejaz, 1922, Overprinted in Black

Coat of Arms (Hejaz A7)

حكومة الشرق العربية ٩ شعبان ١٣٤١

1923, Apr. Unwmk. *Perf. 11½*

No.	Type	Description	Unused	Used
64	A7	1/8pi orange brn	1.40	1.50
a.		Double overprint	100.00	
65	A7	½pi red	1.40	.50
a.		Inverted overprint	100.00	
66	A7	1pi dark blue	.28	.28
a.		Inverted overprint	105.00	
67	A7	1½pi violet	.45	.50
a.		Double overprint	125.00	
68	A7	2pi orange	.45	.50
a.		Inverted overprint		
b.		Pair, one without overprint		
69	A7	3pi olive brn	1.10	1.40
a.		Inverted overprint	125.00	
b.		Double overprint	150.00	
c.		Pair, one without overprint	300.00	
70	A7	5pi olive green	1.90	2.25
		Nos. 64-70 (7)	6.98	6.93

The overprint is similar to that on the preceding group but is differently arranged. There are numerous varieties in the Arabic letters.

For overprints see Nos. 71-72, 91, J1-J5.

With Additional Surcharge of New Value in Arabic:

a b

No.	Type	Description	Unused	Used
71	A7(a)	¼pi on 1/8pi	2.50	2.75
a.		Inverted surcharge	175.00	
72	A7(b)	10pi on 5pi	5.00	6.25

Independence Issue

Palestine Stamps and Type of 1918 Overprinted Vertically in Black or Gold

1923, May Wmk. 33 *Perf. 15x14*

No.	Type	Description	Unused	Used
73	A1	1m dark brn (Bk)	7.00	8.00
a.		Double ovpt., one reversed	425.00	425.00
73B	A1	1m dark brn (G)	225.00	225.00
c.		Double ovpt., one reversed	625.00	625.00
74	A1	2m blue grn	22.50	24.50
75	A1	3m lt brown	5.00	5.50
76	A1	4m scarlet	5.00	5.50
77	A1	5m orange	37.50	40.00
78	A1	1pi dk blue (G)	37.50	40.00
a.		Double overprint	550.00	550.00
79	A1	2pi olive grn	37.50	40.00
80	A1	5pi plum (G)	37.50	40.00
a.		Double overprint	360.00	
81	A1	9pi bis, perf. 14	37.50	40.00
82	A1	10pi ultra, perf. 14	37.50	40.00
83	A1	20pi gray	37.50	40.00
		Nos. 73-83 (12)	527.00	548.50

The overprint reads, "Arab Government of the East (abbreviated), Souvenir of Independence, 25th, May, 1923 ('923')."

There were printed 480 complete sets and a larger number of the 1, 2, 3 and 4m. A large number of these sets were distributed to high officials. The overprint was in a setting of twenty-four and the error "933" instead of "923" occurs once in the setting.

The overprint exists reading downward on all values, as illustrated, and reading upward on all except the 5m and 2pi.

Forged overprints exist.

For overprint see No. 101.

Stamps of Preceding Issues, Handstamp Surcharged

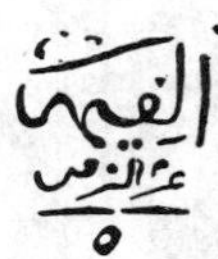

83A A1 2½ /10pi on 5m dp org 175.00 190.00
83B A1 5/10pi on 3m (#17) *8,000.*
84 A1 5/10pi on 3m (#36) 20.00 20.00
85 A1 5/10pi on 3m (#55) 8.75 8.75
86 A1 5/10pi on 5pi (#23) 42.50 42.50
87 A1 5/10pi on 5pi (#48) 4.00 4.00
88 A1 1pi on 5pi (#23) 42.50 42.50
89 A1 1pi on 5pi (#48) *1,900.*

Same Surcharge on Palestine Stamp of 1918

90 A1 5/10pi on 3m lt brn *8,500.*

As is usual with handstamped surcharges these are found double, inverted, etc.

No. 67 Surcharged by Handstamp نصف قرش

Unwmk. *Perf. 11½*

91 A7 ½pi on 1½pi vio 3.50 3.75
a. Surcharge typographed 30.00 32.50

The surcharge reads: "Nusf el qirsh" (half piastre). See note after No. 90.

Stamps of Preceding Issues Surcharged by Handstamp

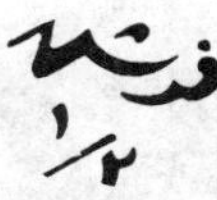

1923, Nov. Wmk. 33 *Perf. 14, 15x14*

92 A1 ½pi on 2pi (#45) 45.00 45.00
93 A1 ½pi on 2pi (#47) 87.50 87.50
94 A1 ½pi on 5pi (#23) 27.50 27.50
95 A1 ½pi on 5pi (#48) 2,250. 2,000.
96 A1 ½pi on 5pi (#49) 1,800. 1,750.
97 A1 ½pi on 9pi (#24) *6,500.*
98 A1 ½pi on 9pi (#25) 87.50 87.50
99 A1 ½pi on 9pi (#61) 165.00 165.00

Surcharged by Handstamp

100 A1 1pi on 10pi (#62) *2,000. 2,000.*
101 A1 1pi on 10pi (#82) *3,000. 3,000.*
102 A1 2pi on 20pi (#63) 22.50 24.00

Of the 25 copies made of No. 100, a few were handstamped in violet.

Stamp of Hejaz, 1922, Overprinted by Handstamp

1923, Dec. Unwmk. *Perf. 11½*

103 A7 ½pi red 3.00 3.25

Stamp of Hejaz, 1922, Overprinted

1924

104 A7 ½pi red 3.25 3.75

King Hussein Issue

Stamps of Hejaz, 1922, Overprinted مالك العرب

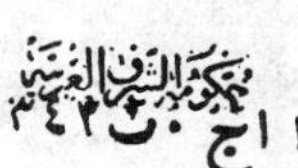

1924

Gold Overprint

105 A7 ½pi red 1.25 1.25
106 A7 1pi dark blue 1.75 1.75
107 A7 1½pi violet 1.50 1.50
108 A7 2pi orange 2.00 2.00

Black Overprint

109 A7 ½pi red .65 .65
110 A7 1pi dark blue .75 .75
111 A7 1½pi violet .90 .90
112 A7 2pi orange 1.00 1.00
Nos. 105-112 (8) 9.80 9.80

The overprint reads: "Arab Government of the East. In commemoration of the visit of H. M. the King of the Arabs, 11 Jemad el Than i 1342 (17th Jan. 1924)." The overprint was in a setting of thirty-six and the error "432" instead of "342" occurs once in the setting and is found on all values.

Stamps of Hejaz, 1922-24, Overprinted in Black or Red

Coat of Arms (Hejaz A8)

حكومة الشرق العربي ١٣٤٢

1924

113 A7 ⅛pi red brown .30 .15
114 A7 ¼pi yellow green .15 .15
a. Tête bêche pair 2.00 2.00
115 A7 ½pi red .15 .15
116 A7 1pi dark blue 2.50 2.50
117 A7 1½pi violet 2.25 2.25
118 A7 2pi orange 2.00 2.00
119 A7 3pi red brown 1.40 1.40
120 A7 5pi olive green 1.75 2.25
121 A8 10pi vio & dk brn (R) 4.00 4.50
a. Pair, one without overprint
Nos. 113-121 (9) 14.50 15.35

The overprint reads: "Hukumat al Sharqi al Arabia, 1342." (Arab Government of the East, 1924).

Stamps of Hejaz, 1925, Overprinted in Black or Red

(Hejaz A9)

(Hejaz A10)

(Hejaz A11)

1925, Aug.

122 A9 ⅛pi chocolate .30 .30
123 A9 ¼pi ultramarine .30 .30
124 A9 ½pi carmine rose .30 .20
125 A10 1pi yellow green .30 .20
126 A10 1½pi orange .70 1.25
127 A10 2pi deep blue 1.00 1.50
128 A11 3pi dark green (R) 1.25 2.25
129 A11 5pi orange brn 2.00 4.00
Nos. 122-129 (8) 6.15 10.00

The overprint reads: "Hukumat al Sharqi al Arabi. 1343 Sanat." (Arab Government of the East, 1925). Nos. 122-129 exist imperforate, and with overprint inverted or double.

Type of Palestine, 1918, Overprinted in Black شرق الاردن

1925, Nov. 1 Wmk. 4 *Perf. 14*

130 A1 1m dark brown .15 .15
131 A1 2m yellow .15 .15
132 A1 3m Prussian bl .15 .15
133 A1 4m rose .15 .15
134 A1 5m orange .15 .15
135 A1 6m blue green .15 .15
136 A1 7m yel brown .15 .15
137 A1 8m red .20 .20
138 A1 1pi gray .25 .25
139 A1 13m ultramarine .30 .50
140 A1 2pi olive green .50 .60
141 A1 5pi plum 2.50 3.00
142 A1 9pi bister 5.00 5.50
143 A1 10pi light blue 8.50 10.00
144 A1 20pi violet 18.00 19.00
Nos. 130-144 (15) 36.30 40.10

This overprint reads: "Sharqi al-ardan" (East of Jordan).

For overprints see Nos. J12-J23.

Perf. 15x14

142a A1 9pi 600.00 950.00
143a A1 10pi 70.00 75.00
144a A1 20pi 950.00 850.00
Nos. 142a-144a (3) 1,620. 1,875.

Amir Abdullah ibn Hussein
A1 A2

1927-29 Engr. *Perf. 14*

145 A1 2(m) Prus blue .15 .15
146 A1 3(m) rose .15 .15
147 A1 4(m) green .55 .65
148 A1 5(m) orange .15 .15
149 A1 10(m) red .55 .35
150 A1 15(m) ultra .55 .15
151 A1 20(m) olive grn .70 .70
152 A2 50(m) claret 2.75 3.00
153 A2 90(m) bister 6.00 8.00
154 A2 100(m) lt blue 7.00 6.00
155 A2 200(m) violet 16.00 20.00
156 A2 500(m) dp brn ('29) 55.00 80.00
157 A2 1000(m) gray ('29) 100.00 150.00
Nos. 145-157 (13) 189.55 269.30

For overprints see Nos. 158-168, B1-B12, J24-J29.

Stamps of 1927 Overprinted in Black دستور

1928, Sept. 1

158 A1 2(m) Prus blue .65 1.50
159 A1 3(m) rose .65 2.00
160 A1 4(m) green .65 2.00
161 A1 5(m) orange .65 1.10
162 A1 10(m) red 1.25 2.75
163 A1 15(m) ultra 1.25 1.00
164 A1 20(m) olive grn 3.00 6.50
165 A2 50(m) claret 4.75 6.50
166 A2 90(m) bister 12.00 12.00
167 A2 100(m) lt blue 21.00 37.50
168 A2 200(m) violet 65.00 95.00
Nos. 158-168 (11) 110.85 167.85

The overprint is the Arabic word "Dastour," meaning "Constitution." The stamps were in commemoration of the enactment of the law setting forth the Constitution.

A3

"MILS" or "L. P." at lower right and Arabic equivalents at upper left.

1930-36 Engr. *Perf. 14*

Size: 17¼x21mm

169 A3 1m red brn ('34) .15 .70
170 A3 2m Prus blue .15 .45
171 A3 3m rose .40 .60
172 A3 3m green ('34) .65 .90
173 A3 4m green .65 1.50
174 A3 4m rose ('34) 1.65 1.00
175 A3 5m orange .35 .20
a. Perf. 13½x14 (coil) ('36) 16.00 10.00
176 A3 10m red .70 .15
177 A3 15m ultra .70 .20
a. Perf. 13½x14 (coil) ('36) 16.00 10.00
178 A3 20m olive grn 1.25 .40

Size: 19¼x23½mm

179 A3 50m red violet 1.50 1.40
180 A3 90m bister 2.50 4.00
181 A3 100m light blue 3.25 3.50
182 A3 200m violet 8.00 13.00
183 A3 500m deep brown 19.00 35.00
184 A3 £1 gray 47.50 75.00
Nos. 169-184 (16) 88.40 138.00

See Nos. 199-220, 230-235. For overprint see No. N15a.

1939 *Perf. 13½x13*

Size: 17¼x21mm

169a A3 1m red brown 2.50 2.00
170a A3 2m Prussian blue 6.50 2.00
172a A3 3m green 11.00 4.00
174a A3 4m rose 47.50 13.00
175b A3 5m orange 50.00 3.00
176a A3 10m red 70.00 4.00
177b A3 15m ultramarine 27.50 3.50
178a A3 20m olive green 45.00 12.00
Nos. 169a-178a (8) 260.00 43.50

For overprint see No. N3a.

Mushetta — A4

Nymphaeum, Jerash — A5

Kasr Kharana — A6

Kerak Castle — A7

Temple of Artemis, Jerash — A8

Aijalon Castle — A9

Khazneh, Rock-hewn Temple, Petra — A10

Allenby Bridge, River Jordan — A11

Amir Abdullah ibn Hussein — A13

Ancient Threshing Floor — A12

1933, Feb. 1 *Perf. 12*

185 A4 1m dk brn & blk .35 .75
186 A5 2m claret & blk .35 .60
187 A6 3m blue green .40 1.00
188 A7 4m bister & blk .65 1.50
189 A8 5m orange & blk .70 1.00
190 A9 10m brown red 1.25 2.25
191 A10 15m dull blue 2.00 1.00
192 A11 20m ol grn & blk 2.75 3.50
193 A12 50m brn vio & blk 7.50 8.00
194 A6 90m yel & black 10.50 17.50
195 A8 100m blue & blk 10.50 17.50
196 A9 200m dk vio & blk 40.00 47.50
197 A10 500m brn & ver 110.00 125.00
198 A13 £1 green & blk 425.00 500.00
Nos. 185-198 (14) 611.95 727.10

Nos. 194-197 are larger than the lower values in the same designs.

Amir Abdullah ibn Hussein — A14

Perf. 13x13½

1942, May 18 Litho. Unwmk.

199	A14	1m dull red brn	.65	2.00
200	A14	2m dull green	1.40	1.00
201	A14	3m dp yel green	1.40	2.00
202	A14	4m rose pink	1.40	2.00
203	A14	5m orange yel	1.50	.75
204	A14	10m dull ver	1.75	1.75
205	A14	15m deep blue	2.00	1.50
206	A14	20m dull ol grn	6.00	6.00
		Nos. 199-206 (8)	16.10	17.00

Type A14 differs from A3 in the redrawn inscription above the head and in the form of the "millieme" character at upper left.

For overprint see No. N1.

Abdullah Type of 1930-39
White Paper

1943-44 Engr. Wmk. 4 *Perf. 12*

Size: 17¾x21½mm

207	A3	1m red brown	.15	.40
208	A3	2m Prussian grn	.40	.40
209	A3	3m blue green	.90	.50
210	A3	4m deep rose	.90	.50
211	A3	5m orange	.90	.15
212	A3	10m scarlet	2.00	.70
213	A3	15m blue	2.00	.15
214	A3	20m olive ('44)	2.00	.60

Size: 20x24mm

215	A3	50m red lil ('44)	2.00	.75
216	A3	90m ocher	4.00	3.00
217	A3	100m dp bl ('44)	5.00	1.10
218	A3	200m dk vio ('44)	8.00	4.50
219	A3	500m dk brn ('44)	12.00	10.00
220	A3	£1 black ('44)	20.00	18.00
		Nos. 207-220 (14)	60.25	40.75

See Nos. 230-235. For overprints see Nos. 255-256, 259, 264-269, RA23, N2-N4, N7, N12-N17.

Catalogue values for unused stamps in this section, from this point to the end of the section, are for Never Hinged items.

Independent Kingdom

Symbols of Peace and Liberty — A15

Perf. 11½

1946, May 25 Unwmk. Litho.

221	A15	1m sepia	.15	.15
222	A15	2m yel orange	.15	.15
223	A15	3m dl ol grn	.15	.15
224	A15	4m lt violet	.15	.15
225	A15	10m orange brn	.15	.15
226	A15	12m rose red	.15	.15
227	A15	20m dark blue	.15	.15
228	A15	50m ultra	.55	.45
229	A15	200m green	1.00	1.00
		Set value	2.15	2.00

Independence of the Kingdom of Trans-Jordan.

Nos. 221-229 exist imperforate.

Abdullah Type of 1930-39

1947 Wmk. 4 Engr. *Perf. 12*

230	A3	3m rose carmine	.15	.15
231	A3	4m deep yel green	.15	.15
232	A3	10m violet	.15	.15
233	A3	12m deep rose	.65	.65
234	A3	15m dull olive grn	.16	.16
235	A3	20m deep blue	.20	.20
		Set value	1.20	1.20

For overprints see Nos. 257-258, 260-263, RA24-RA25, N5-N6, N8-N11.

Parliament Building, Amman A16

1947, Nov. 1 Engr. Unwmk.

236	A16	1m purple	.15	.15
237	A16	3m red orange	.15	.15
238	A16	4m yel green	.15	.15
239	A16	10m dk vio brn	.15	.15
240	A16	12m carmine	.15	.15
241	A16	20m deep blue	.15	.15
242	A16	50m red vio	.20	.20
243	A16	100m rose	.35	.35
244	A16	200m dark green	.75	.75
		Set value	1.70	1.70

Founding of the new Trans-Jordan parliament, 1947.

Nos. 236-244 exist imperforate.

Symbols of the UPU — A17

King Abdullah ibn Hussein A18

1949, Aug. 1 Wmk. 4 *Perf. 13*

245	A17	1m brown	.15	.15
246	A17	4m green	.15	.15
247	A17	10m red	.15	.15
248	A17	20m ultramarine	.16	.16
249	A18	50m dull green	.28	.28
		Set value	.64	.62

UPU, 75th anniv. For overprints see #N18-N22.

Nos. 207-208, 211, 215-220, 230-235 Surcharged in Carmine, Black or Green

FILS

1952 Wmk. 4 *Perf. 12*

Size: 17¾x21½mm

255	A3	1f on 1m red brn (Bk)	.15	.15
256	A3	2f on 2m Prus grn	.15	.15
257	A3	3f on 3m rose car (Bk)	.15	.15
258	A3	4f on 4m dp yel grn	.20	.15
259	A3	5f on 5m org (G)	.65	.20
260	A3	10f on 10m vio	.48	.48
261	A3	12f on 12m dp rose (Bk)	.48	.48
262	A3	15f on 15m dl ol grn	.52	.30
263	A3	20f on 20m dp bl	.75	.45

Size: 20x24mm

264	A3	50f on 50m red lil (G)	1.10	.65
265	A3	90f on 90m ocher (G)	5.75	5.50
266	A3	100f on 100m dp bl	3.50	1.10
267	A3	200f on 200m dk vio	4.75	1.00
268	A3	500f on 500m dk brn	10.00	2.75
269	A3	1d on £1 black	21.00	4.75
		Nos. 255-269 (15)	49.63	18.26

This surcharge also exists on Nos. 199-203, 205, 209-210, 212-214. Numerous inverted, double and wrong color surcharges exist.

Relief Map — A19

Amir Abdullah ibn Hussein — A20

Perf. 13½x13

1952, Apr. 1 Engr. Wmk. 4

270	A19	1f red brn & yel grn	.15	.15
271	A19	2f dk bl grn & red	.15	.15
272	A19	3f car & gray blk	.15	.15
273	A19	4f green & orange	.15	.15
274	A19	5f choc & rose vio	.15	.15
275	A19	10f violet & brown	.15	.15
276	A19	20f dark bl & blk	.20	.20
277	A19	100f dp blue & brn	1.10	.80
278	A19	200f purple & orange	1.40	1.40
		Nos. 270-278 (9)	3.60	3.30

Unity of Jordan, Apr. 24, 1950.

For overprints see Nos. 297-305.

1952 Wmk. 4 *Perf. 11½*

279	A20	5f orange	.15	.15
280	A20	10f violet	.15	.15
281	A20	12f carmine	.35	.35
282	A20	15f olive	.15	.15
283	A20	20f deep blue	.20	.15

Size: 20x24½mm

Perf. 12x12½

284	A20	50f plum	.48	.48
285	A20	90f brn orange	1.40	1.10
286	A20	100f deep blue	1.10	.52
		Nos. 279-286 (8)	3.98	3.05

Nos. RA5-RA7 Overprinted in Black or Carmine

Perf. 11½x12½

1953 Unwmk. Engr.

286A	PT1	10m carmine	27.50	17.00
286B	PT1	15m gray (C)	2.75	1.25
286C	PT1	20m dark brown	35.00	17.00

Same Overprint on Nos. NRA4-NRA7

286D	PT1	5m plum	35.00	17.00
286E	PT1	10m carmine	35.00	17.00
286F	PT1	15m gray (C)	35.00	17.00
286G	PT1	20m dk brn (C)	35.00	17.00
		Nos. 286A-286G (7)	205.25	103.25

In addition a few sheets of Nos. RA9, NRA1, NRA3, NRA8-NRA9 and RA37-RA41 have been reported with this overprint. It is doubtful whether they were regularly issued. See Nos. 344-347.

Same Overprint on Nos. RA28-RA31 in Black or Carmine

1953 Wmk. 4 *Perf. 11½x12½*

287	PT1	5f plum	.15	.15
288	PT1	10f carmine	.18	.18
289	PT1	15f gray (C)	.35	.25
290	PT1	20f dark brown (C)	.55	.40
		Nos. 287-290 (4)	1.23	.98

King Hussein A21

1953, Oct. 1 Unwmk. Engr. *Perf. 12*

Portrait in Black

291	A21	1f dark green	.15	.15
292	A21	4f deep plum	.15	.15
293	A21	15f deep ultra	.20	.15
294	A21	20f dark purple	.24	.15
295	A21	50f dark blue grn	.75	.35
296	A21	100f dark blue	1.10	.70
		Nos. 291-296 (6)	2.59	
		Set value		1.40

Accession of King Hussein, May 2, 1953.

Nos. 270-278 Overprinted in Black with Two Bars Through Center Inscription

1953 Wmk. 4 *Perf. 13½x13*

297	A19	1f red brn & yel grn	.15	.15
298	A19	2f dk bl grn & red	.15	.15
299	A19	3f car & gray blk	.15	.15
300	A19	4f green & orange	.15	.15
301	A19	5f choc & rose vio	.18	.18
302	A19	10f violet & brown	.45	.20
303	A19	20f dark bl & blk	.45	.38
304	A19	100f dp blue & brn	2.00	1.00
305	A19	200f purple & org	3.75	1.65
		Nos. 297-305 (9)	7.43	4.01

Two main settings of the bars exist on Nos. 297-300 and 304—the "normal" 1½mm spacing, and the "narrow" ½mm spacing.

El Deir Temple, Petra — A22

Dome of the Rock — A23

Designs: 2f, 4f, 500f, 1d, King Hussein. 3f, 5f, Treasury Bldg., Petra. 12f, 50f, 100f, 200f, Al Aqsa Mosque. 20f, as 10f.

1954 Unwmk. Engr. *Perf. 12½*

306	A22	1f dk bl grn & red brn	.15	.15
307	A22	2f red & black	.15	.15
308	A22	3f dp plum & vio bl	.15	.15
309	A22	4f org brn & dk grn	.15	.15
310	A22	5f vio & dk grn	1.25	.15
311	A23	10f pur & dk grn	.25	.15
312	A23	12f car rose & sep	.60	.40
313	A23	20f dp bl & dk grn	.25	.15
314	A23	50f dk bl & dp rose	2.25	2.25
315	A23	100f dk grn & dp bl	1.10	.45
316	A23	200f dp cl & pck bl	3.50	.75
317	A22	500f choc & purple	9.00	4.50
318	A22	1d dk ol grn & rose brn	17.50	10.00
		Nos. 306-318 (13)	36.30	19.40

See Nos. 324-337. For overprint see No. 425.

Globe — A23a

Perf. 13½x13

1955, Jan. 1 Photo. Wmk. 195

319	A23a	15f green	.15	.15
320	A23a	20f violet	.15	.15
321	A23a	25f yellow brown	.18	.15
		Nos. 319-321 (3)	.48	
		Set value		.35

Founding of the APU, July 1, 1954.

Princess Dina Abdul Hamid and King Hussein — A24

1955, Apr. 19 *Perf. 11x11½*

322	A24	15f ultramarine	.18	.15
323	A24	100f rose brown	.75	.75

Marriage of King Hussein and Princess Dina Abdul Hamid.

Types of 1954

Design: 15f, Dome of the Rock.

Perf. 12½

1955-64 Engr. Wmk. 305

324	A22	1f dk bl grn & red brn ('57)	.15	.15
325	A22	2f red & blk ('57)	.15	.15
326	A22	3f dp plum & vio bl ('56)	.15	.15
327	A22	4f org brn & dk grn ('56)	.15	.15
328	A22	5f vio & dk grn ('56)	.15	.15
329	A23	10f pur & grn ('57)	.15	.15
330	A23	12f car rose & sep	.15	.15
331	A23	15f dp brn & rose red	.15	.15
332	A23	20f dp bl & dk grn ('57)	.15	.15
333	A23	50f dk bl & dp rose	.30	.18
334	A23	100f dk grn & dp bl ('62)	.60	.35
335	A23	200f dp cl & pck bl ('65)	2.00	.50
336	A22	500f choc & pur ('65)	7.50	3.00
337	A22	1d dk ol grn & rose brn ('65)	20.00	4.00
		Nos. 324-337 (14)	31.75	9.38

Envelope A25

Wmk. 305

1956, Jan. 15 Engr. *Perf. 14*

"Postmarks" in Black

338	A25	1f light brown	.15	.15
339	A25	4f dark car rose	.15	.15
340	A25	15f blue	.15	.15
341	A25	20f yellow olive	.15	.15
342	A25	50f slate blue	.38	.20
343	A25	100f vermilion	.65	.38
		Set value	1.40	.90

1st Arab Postal Congress in Amman.

Nos. RA1, RA3, RA8 and RA33 Overprinted in Carmine or Black

Perf. 11½x12½

1956, Jan. 5 **Unwmk.**

344 PT1 1m ultramarine .15 .15
345 PT1 3m emerald .15 .15
346 PT1 50m purple .30 .18

Wmk. 4

347 PT1 100f orange (Bk) 1.00 .55
Set value 1.40 .80

Numerous inverted, double and wrong color surcharges exist.

Torch of Liberty — A26

King Hussein — A27

1958 Wmk. 305 Engr. *Perf. 12½*

348 A26 5f blue & red brown .15 .15
349 A26 15f bister brn & blk .15 .15
350 A26 35f blue grn & plum .20 .16
351 A26 45f car & olive grn .28 .20
Set value .65 .55

10th anniv. of the Universal Declaration of Human Rights.

Perf. 12x11½

1959 Wmk. 305 Engr.

Centers in Black

352 A27 1f deep green .15 .15
353 A27 2f violet .15 .15
354 A27 3f deep carmine .15 .15
355 A27 4f brown black .15 .15
356 A27 7f dark green .15 .15
357 A27 12f deep carmine .15 .15
358 A27 15f dark red .15 .15
359 A27 21f green .32 .28
360 A27 25f ocher .20 .15
361 A27 35f dark blue .20 .15
362 A27 40f olive green .28 .15
363 A27 50f red .35 .16
364 A27 100f blue green .80 .20
365 A27 200f rose lake 1.20 .40
366 A27 500f gray blue 3.00 1.40
367 A27 1d dark purple 7.25 3.50
Nos. 352-367 (16) 14.65 7.44

For overprints see Nos. 423-424, 425a, 426-427.

Arab League Center, Cairo, and King Hussein A28

Perf. 13x13½

1960, Mar. 22 Photo. Wmk. 328

368 A28 15f dull green & blk .15 .15

Opening of the Arab League Center and the Arab Postal Museum in Cairo.

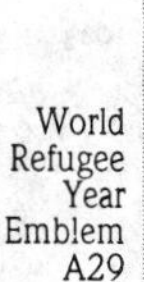

World Refugee Year Emblem A29

Perf. 13½

1960, Apr. 7 Wmk. 305 Litho.

369 A29 15f pale blue & red .16 .15
370 A29 35f bister & blue .26 .26

World Refugee Year, July 1, 1959-June 30, 1960.
For overprints see Nos. 377-378.

Shah of Iran, King Hussein and Flags A30

Perf. 13x13½

1960, May 15 Wmk. 305

Flags in Green, Red & Black

371 A30 15f yellow & black .15 .15
372 A30 35f blue & black .18 .15
373 A30 50f salmon & black .26 .15
Nos. 371-373 (3) .59
Set value .34

Visit of Mohammed Riza Pahlavi, Shah of Iran, to Jordan, Nov. 2, 1959.

Oil Refinery, Zarka A31

1961, May 1 Engr. *Perf. 14x13*

374 A31 15f dull vio & blue .15 .15
375 A31 35f dl vio & brick red .20 .15
Set value .21

Opening of oil refinery at Zarka.

Urban and Nomad Families and Chart — A32

Perf. 13x13½

1961, Oct. 15 Photo. Unwmk.

376 A32 15f orange brown .20 .15

First Jordanian census, 1961.

Nos. 369-370 Overprinted in English and Arabic, "In Memorial of Dag Hammarskjoeld 1904-1961," and Laurel Leaf Border

1961 Wmk. 305 Litho. *Perf. 13½*

377 A29 15f pale blue & red 2.75 1.40
378 A29 35f bister & blue 2.75 1.40

Dag Hammarskjold, Secretary General of the UN, 1953-1961.

Malaria Eradication Emblem — A33

Perf. 11x11½

1962, Apr. 15 Unwmk.

379 A33 15f bright pink .15 .15
380 A33 35f blue .22 .22

WHO drive to eradicate malaria. A souvenir sheet exists with one each of #379-380. Value $2.

Dial and Exchange Building, Amman A34

1962, Dec. 11 Engr. Wmk. 305

381 A34 15f blue & lilac .15 .15
382 A34 35f lilac & emer .22 .22

Telephone automation in Amman (in 1960).

Opening of the Port of 'Aqaba A35

1962, Dec. 11

383 A35 15f lilac & blk .16 .16
384 A35 35f violet bl & blk .25 .25
a. Souvenir sheet of 2, #383-384 .75 .75

No. 384a imperf., same value.

Dag Hammarskjold and UN Headquarters, NY — A36

Perf. 14x14½

1963, Jan. 24 Photo. Unwmk.

385 A36 15f ultra, ol grn & brn red .20 .16
386 A36 35f ol, brn red & ultra .42 .40
387 A36 50f brn red, ol & ultra .65 .65
Nos. 385-387 (3) 1.27 1.21

17th anniv. of the UN and in memory of Dag Hammarskjold, Secretary General of the UN, 1953-61. An imperf. souvenir sheet contains one each of #385-387 with simulated perforations. Value $5.

Imperforates

Starting with No. 385, imperforates exist of many Jordanian stamps.

Church of St. Virgin's Tomb, Jerusalem — A37

Arab League Building, Cairo — A38

Designs: No. 389, Basilica of the Agony, Gethsemane. No. 390, Church of the Holy Sepulcher, Jerusalem. No. 391, Church of the Nativity, Bethlehem. No. 392, Haram el-Khalil (tomb of Abraham), Hebron. No. 393, Dome of the Rock, Jerusalem. No. 394, Mosque of Omar el-Khatab, Jerusalem. No. 395, Al Aqsa Mosque, Jerusalem.

1963, Feb. 5 *Perf. 14½x14*

Center Multicolored

388 A37 50f blue .45 .38
389 A37 50f dull red .45 .38
390 A37 50f bright blue .45 .38
391 A37 50f olive green .45 .38
a. Vert. strip of 4, #388-391 1.90
392 A37 50f gray .60 .38
393 A37 50f purple .60 .38
394 A37 50f dull red .60 .38
395 A37 50f light purple .60 .38
a. Vert. strip of 4, #392-395 2.50
Nos. 388-395 (8) 4.20 3.04

1963, July 16 Photo. *Perf. 13½x13*

396 A38 15f slate blue .15 .15
397 A38 35f orange red .22 .15
Set value .20

Arab League.

Wheat and UN Emblem — A39

Perf. 11½x12½

1963, Sept. Litho. Wmk. 305

398 A39 15f lt bl, grn & black .15 .15
399 A39 35f lt grn, grn & blk .18 .15
a. Souvenir sheet of 2, #398-399 .75 .75
Set value .24

FAO "Freedom from Hunger" campaign. No. 399a imperf., same value.

East Ghor Canal, Pylon, Gear Wheel and Wheat A40

1963, Sept. 20 *Perf. 14½x14*

400 A40 1f dull yel & black .15 .15
401 A40 4f blue & black .15 .15
402 A40 5f lilac & black .15 .15
403 A40 10f brt yel grn & blk .15 .15
404 A40 35f orange & black .15 .15
Set value .35 .32

East Ghor Canal Project.

UNESCO Emblem, Scales and Globe — A41

Perf. 13½x13

1963, Dec. 10 Unwmk.

405 A41 50f pale vio bl & red .32 .32
406 A41 50f rose red & blue .32 .32

15th anniv. of the Universal Declaration of Human Rights.

Red Crescent and King Hussein — A42

1963, Dec. 24 Photo. *Perf. 14x14½*

407 A42 1f red & red lilac .15 .15
408 A42 2f red & bl green .15 .15
409 A42 3f red & dk blue .15 .15
410 A42 4f red & dk green .15 .15
411 A42 5f red & dk brown .15 .15
412 A42 85f red & dp green .95 .95

Design: Red Cross at right, no portrait

413 A42 1f red lilac & red .15 .15
414 A42 2f blue grn & red .15 .15
415 A42 3f dk blue & red .15 .15
416 A42 4f dk green & red .15 .15
417 A42 5f dk brown & red .15 .15
418 A42 85f dp green & red 3.75 3.75
Set value, #407-418 5.00 5.00

Centenary of the Intl. Red Cross. Two 100f imperf. souvenir sheets, red and red lilac, exist in the Red Crescent and Red Cross designs. Value $15.

Hussein ibn Ali and King Hussein A43

Perf. 11x11½

1963, Dec. 25 Litho. Unwmk.

419 A43 15f yellow & multi .15 .15
420 A43 25f multicolored .16 .15
421 A43 35f brt pink & multi .35 .28
422 A43 50f lt blue & multi .50 .50
Nos. 419-422 (4) 1.16 1.08

Arab Renaissance Day, June 10, 1916. Perf. and imperf. souvenir sheets exist containing one each of Nos. 419-422. Value for both, $3.

Nos. 359, 312, 357 and 361 Surcharged **1 Fils** ١ فلس

Perf. 12x11½, 12½

Wmk. 305, Unwmk.

1963, Dec. 16 Engr.

423 A27 1f on 21f grn & blk .15 .15
424 A27 2f on 21f grn & blk .15 *1.00*
425 A23 4f on 12f car rose & sepia .15 .15
a. 4f on 12f dp car & blk (#357) 6.50 5.00
426 A27 5f on 21f grn & blk .16 .15
427 A27 25f on 35f dk bl & blk .35 .15
Set value .75
Nos. 423-427 (5) *1.60*

Pope Paul VI, King Hussein and Al Aqsa Mosque, Jerusalem — A44

Portraits and: 35f, Dome of the Rock. 50f, Church of the Holy Sepulcher. 80f, Church of the Nativity, Bethlehem.

1964, Jan. 4 Litho. *Perf. 13x13½*

428 A44	15f emerald & blk		.15	.15
429 A44	35f car rose & blk		.25	.25
430 A44	50f brown & black		.45	.45
431 A44	80f vio bl & blk		.75	.75
	Nos. 428-431 (4)		1.60	1.60

Visit of Pope Paul VI to the Holy Land, Jan. 4-6. An imperf. souvenir sheet contains 4 stamps similar to Nos. 428-431. Value $3.

A45

Crown Prince Abdullah ben Al-Hussein — A46

Design: 5f, Crown Prince standing, vert.

1964, Mar. 30 Photo. *Perf. 14*

432 A46	5f multicolored	.15	.15
433 A45	10f multicolored	.15	.15
434 A46	35f multicolored	.25	.25
	Set value	.35	.35

2nd birthday of Crown Prince Abdullah ben Al-Hussein (b. Jan. 30, 1962).

A47

Mercury Astronauts, Spacecraft — A48

Designs: b, M. Scott Carpenter. c, Entering space. d, Alan Shepard. e, At launch pad. f, Virgil Grissom. g, After separation. h, Walter Schirra. i, Lift-off. j, John Glenn. Stamp has point down on b, d, f, h, j.

1964, Mar. 25 Photo. *Perf. 14*

435 A47	20f Block of 10, #a.-j.	5.00	5.00

Imperf

Size: 111x80mm

436 A48	100f multicolored	6.50	6.50

Table Tennis A49

Designs: 1f, 2f, 3f, 5f vertical.

Perf. 14½x14, 14x14½

1964, June 1 Litho. Unwmk.

446 A49	1f Basketball	.15	.15
447 A49	2f Volleyball	.15	.15
448 A49	3f Soccer	.15	.15
449 A49	4f shown	.15	.15
450 A49	5f Running	.15	.15
451 A49	35f Bicycling	.70	.70
452 A49	50f Fencing	1.00	1.00
453 A49	100f High jump	1.75	1.75
	Nos. 446-453 (8)	4.20	4.20

1964 Olympic Games, Tokyo, Oct. 10-25. An imperf. 200f greenish blue souvenir sheet in design of 100f exists. Value $6.

Mother and Child — A50

1964, June 1 Wmk. 305 *Perf. 14*

454 A50	5f multicolored	.15	.15
455 A50	10f multicolored	.15	.15
456 A50	25f multicolored	.16	.15
	Set value	.28	.20

Social Studies Seminar, fourth session.

Pres. John F. Kennedy — A51

1964, July 15 Unwmk.

457 A51	1f brt violet	.15	.15
458 A51	2f carmine rose	.15	.15
459 A51	3f ultramarine	.15	.15
460 A51	4f orange brown	.15	.15
461 A51	5f bright green	.15	.15
462 A51	85f rose red	2.50	2.50
	Set value	2.75	2.75

President John F. Kennedy (1917-1963). An imperf. 100f brown souvenir sheet exists. Size of stamp: 58x83mm. Value $5.

Ramses II A52

Perf. 14½x14

1964, July Litho. Wmk. 305

463 A52	4f lt blue & dark brn	.15	.15
464 A52	15f yellow & violet	.15	.15
465 A52	25f lt yel grn & dk red	.15	.15
	Set value	.28	.22

UNESCO world campaign to save historic monuments in Nubia.

King Hussein and Map of Jordan and Israel — A53

1964, Sept. 5 Unwmk. *Perf. 12*

466 A53	10f multicolored	.15	.15
467 A53	15f multicolored	.15	.15
468 A53	25f multicolored	.16	.15
469 A53	50f multicolored	.35	.26
470 A53	80f multicolored	.50	.45
	Set value	1.15	.90

Council of the Heads of State of the Arab League (Arab Summit Conference), Cairo, Jan. 13, 1964. An imperf. souvenir sheet contains Nos. 466-470 with simulated perforations. Value $1.

Pope Paul VI, King Hussein and Patriarch Athenagoras; Church of St. Savior, Church of the Holy Sepulcher and Dome of the Rock — A54

1964, Aug. 17 Litho.

471 A54	10f dk grn, sep & org	.15	.15
472 A54	15f claret, sep & org	.15	.15
473 A54	25f choc, sepia & org	.20	.18
474 A54	50f blue, sepia & org	.42	.38
475 A54	80f brt grn, sep & org	.60	.52
	Nos. 471-475 (5)	1.52	1.38

Meeting between Pope Paul VI and Patriarch Athenagoras of the Greek Orthodox Church in Jerusalem, Jan. 5, 1964. An imperf. souvenir sheet contains Nos. 471-475 with simulated perforations. Value $3.

A two-line bilingual overprint, "Papa Paulus VI World Peace Visit to United Nations 1965", was applied to Nos. 471-475 and the souvenir sheet. These overprints were issued Apr. 27, 1966.

Pagoda, Olympic Torch and Emblem — A55

1964, Nov. 21 Litho. *Perf. 14*

476 A55	1f dark red	.15	.15
477 A55	2f bright violet	.15	.15
478 A55	3f blue green	.15	.15
479 A55	4f brown	.15	.15
480 A55	5f henna brown	.15	.15
481 A55	35f indigo	.45	.45
482 A55	50f olive	.65	.65
483 A55	100f violet blue	1.40	1.40
	Set value	2.75	2.75

18th Olympic Games, Tokyo, Oct. 10-25. An imperf. 100f carmine rose souvenir sheet exists. Size of stamp: 82mm at the base. Value $7.

Scouts Crossing Stream on Log Bridge — A56

Designs: 2f, First aid. 3f, Calisthenics. 4f, Instruction in knot tying. 5f, Outdoor cooking. 35f, Sailing. 50f, Campfire.

1964, Dec. 7 Unwmk.

484 A56	1f brown	.25	.15
485 A56	2f bright violet	.25	.15
486 A56	3f ocher	.25	.15
487 A56	4f maroon	.25	.15
488 A56	5f yellow green	.25	.15
489 A56	35f bright blue	1.00	1.00
490 A56	50f dk slate green	1.75	1.50
	Nos. 484-490 (7)	4.00	3.25

Jordanian Boy Scouts. An imperf. 100f dark blue souvenir sheet in campfire design exists. Size of stamp: 104mm at the base. Value $8.

Yuri A. Gagarin — A57

Russian Cosmonauts: No. 492, Gherman Titov. No. 493, Andrian G. Nikolayev. No. 494, Pavel R. Popovich. No. 495, Valeri Bykovski. No. 496, Valentina Tereshkova.

1965, Jan. 20 Litho. *Perf. 14*

491 A57	40f sepia & vio bl	.40	.40
492 A57	40f pink & dk grn	.40	.40
493 A57	40f lt bl & vio blk	.40	.40
494 A57	40f olive & dk vio	.40	.40
495 A57	40f lt grn & red brn	.40	.40
496 A57	40f chlky bl & blk	.40	.40
	Nos. 491-496 (6)	2.40	2.40

Russian cosmonauts. A blue 100f souvenir sheet exists showing portraits of the 6 astronauts and space-ship circling globe. This sheet received later an additional overprint honoring the space flight of Komarov, Feoktistov and Yegorov. Value $10, each.

For overprints see Nos. 527-527E.

UN Headquarters and Emblem — A58

1965, Feb. 15 *Perf. 14x15*

497 A58	30f yel brn, pur & lt bl	.15	.15
498 A58	70f vio, lt bl & yel brn	.35	.35

19th anniv. of the UN (in 1964). A souvenir sheet contains Nos. 497-498, imperf. Value $9.

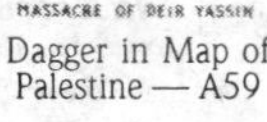

Dagger in Map of Palestine — A59

Volleyball Player and Cup — A60

1965, Apr. 9 Photo. *Perf. 11x11½*

499 A59	25f red & olive	.65	.20

Deir Yassin massacre, Apr. 9, 1948.

1965, June Litho. *Perf. 14½x14*

500 A60	15f lemon	.15	.15
501 A60	35f rose brown	.22	.18
502 A60	50f greenish blue	.32	.26
	Nos. 500-502 (3)	.69	.59

Arab Volleyball Championships. An imperf. 100f orange brown souvenir sheet exists. Size of stamp: 33x57mm. Value $7.

Cavalry Horsemanship — A61

Army Day: 10f, Tank. 35f, King Hussein and aides standing in army car.

1965, May 24

503 A61 5f green .15 .15
504 A61 10f violet blue .15 .15
505 A61 35f brown red .32 .24
Set value .42 .34

John F. Kennedy — A62

1965, June 1 Wmk. 305 Perf. 14

506 A62 10f black & brt green .15 .15
507 A62 15f violet & orange .30 .20
508 A62 25f brown & lt blue .30 .30
509 A62 50f deep claret & emer 1.00 .60
Nos. 506-509 (4) 1.75 1.25

John F. Kennedy (1917-63). An imperf. 50f salmon and dark blue souv. sheet exists. Value $8.

Pope Paul VI, King Hussein and Dome of the Rock — A63

Perf. 13½x14

1965, June 15 Litho. Wmk. 305

510 A63 5f brown & rose lil .15 .15
511 A63 10f vio brn & lt yel grn .22 .15
512 A63 15f ultra & salmon .22 .18
513 A63 50f black & rose .75 .52
Nos. 510-513 (4) 1.34 1.00

1st anniversary of the visit of Pope Paul VI to the Holy Land. An imperf. 50f violet and light blue souvenir sheet exists with simulated perforations. Value $7.50.

Jordan's Pavilion and Unisphere — A64

Perf. 14x13½

1965, Aug. Unwmk. Photo.

514 A64 15f silver & multi .15 .15
515 A64 25f bronze & multi .15 .15
516 A64 50f gold & multi .30 .26
a. Souvenir sheet of 1, 100f 1.00 1.00
Nos. 514-516 (3) .60
Set value .42

New York World's Fair, 1964-65.
No. 516a contains a 100f gold and multicolored stamp, type A64, imperf.

Library Aflame and Lamp A64a

1965, Aug. Wmk. 305 Perf. 11½x11

517 A64a 25f black, grn & red .15 .15

Burning of the Library of Algiers, June 2, 1962.

ITU Emblem, Old and New Telecommunication Equipment — A65

1965, Aug. Litho. Perf. 14x13½

518 A65 25f lt blue & dk bl .15 .15
519 A65 45f grnsh gray & blk .26 .22

ITU, centenary. An imperf. 100f salmon and carmine rose souvenir sheet exists with carmine rose border. Size of stamp: 39x32mm. Value $1.

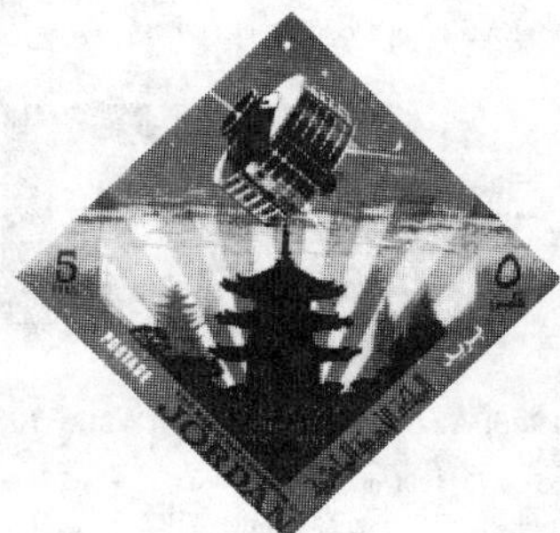

Syncom Satellite over Pagoda — A66

Designs: 10f, 20f, Rocket in space. 15f, Astronauts in cabin.

1965, Sept. Perf. 14

521 A66 5f multicolored .15 .15
521A A66 10f multicolored .20 .15
521B A66 15f multicolored .30 .25
521C A66 20f multicolored .38 .30
521D A66 50f multicolored 1.00 .75
Nos. 521-521D (5) 2.03
Set value 1.35

Achievements in space research. A 50f multicolored imperf. souvenir sheet shows earth and Syncom satellite. Value $5.

Dead Sea A66a

Designs: b, Qumran Caves. c, Dead Sea. d, Dead Sea Scrolls.

1965, Sept. 23 Photo. Perf. 14

522 A66a 35f Strip of 4, #a.-d.

Visit of King Hussein to France and US — A66b

Wmk. 305

1965, Oct. 5 Litho. Perf. 14

523 A66b 5f shown .15 .15
523A A66b 10f With Charles DeGaulle .18 .18
523B A66b 20f With Lyndon Johnson .35 .35
523C A66b 50f like #523 .90 .90
Nos. 523-523C (4) 1.58 1.58

No. 523C exists in a 50f imperf. souvenir sheet.

Intl. Cooperation Year — A66c

1965, Oct. 24 Perf. 14x13½

524 A66c 5f brt org & dk org .15 .15
524A A66c 10f brt bl & dk bl .22 .22
524B A66c 45f brt grn & dk violet 1.00 1.00
Nos. 524-524B (3) 1.37 1.37

Arab Postal Union, 10th Anniv. — A66d

1965, Nov. 5 Perf. 15x14

525 A66d 15f violet bl & blk .20 .20
525A A66d 25f brt yel grn & blk .35 .35

Dome of the Rock A66e

1965, Nov. 20 Perf. 14x15

526 A66e 15f multicolored
526A A66e 25f multicolored

Nos. 491-496 with Spaceship and Bilingual Ovpt. in Blue "Alexei Leonov / Pavel Belyaev / 18-3-65"

1966, Jan. 15 Litho. Perf. 14

527 A57 40f on No. 491 2.25 2.25
527A A57 40f on No. 492 2.25 2.25
527B A57 40f on No. 493 2.25 2.25
527C A57 40f on No. 494 2.25 2.25
527D A57 40f on No. 495 2.25 2.25
527E A57 40f on No. 496 2.25 2.25
Nos. 527-527E (6) 13.50 13.50

Both souvenir sheets mentioned after No. 496 exist overprinted in red violet.

King Hussein — A67

Perf. 14½x14

1966, Jan. 15 Photo. Unwmk.

Portrait in Slate Blue

528 A67 1f orange .15 .15
528A A67 2f ultramarine .15 .15
528B A67 3f dk purple .15 .15
528C A67 4f plum .15 .15
528D A67 7f brn orange .15 .15
528E A67 12f cerise .15 .15
528F A67 15f olive brn .15 .15

Portrait in Violet Brown

528G A67 21f green .22 .15
528H A67 25f greenish bl .26 .15
528I A67 35f yel bister .38 .22
528J A67 40f orange yel .45 .26
528K A67 50f olive grn .55 .15
528L A67 100f lt yel grn 1.10 .32
528M A67 150f violet 1.90 .75
Nos. 528-528M,C43-C45 (17) 18.66 9.55

Anti-tuberculosis Campaign — A67a

1966, May 17 Photo. Perf. 14x15

Blue Overprint

529 A67a 15f multicolored .25 .25
529A A67a 35f multicolored .60 .60
529B A67a 50f multicolored .85 .85
Nos. 529-529B (3) 1.70 1.70

Unissued Freedom from Hunger stamps overprinted. Two imperf. souvenir sheets exist, one with simulated perforations.

Nos. 529-529B with Added Surcharge Obliterated with Black Bars

1966, May 17 Photo. Perf. 14x15

530 A67a 15f on 15f + 15f .25 .25
530A A67a 35f on 35f + 35f .60 .60
530B A67a 50f on 50f + 50f .85 .85
Nos. 530-530B (3) 1.70 1.70

Stations of the Cross — A67b

Designs: Stations on Jesus' walk to Calvary along Via Dolorosa. Denominations expressed in Roman numerals.

1966, Sept. 14 Photo. Perf. 15x14

531 1f Condemned to death .15 .15
531A 2f Takes up cross .15 .15
531B 3f Falls the 1st time .16 .16
531C 4f Meets His mother .22 .22
531D 5f Simon helps carry cross .28 .28
531E 6f Woman wipes Jesus' brow .32 .32
531F 7f Falls 2nd time .38 .38
531G 8f Tells women not to weep .45 .45
531H 9f Falls 3rd time .50 .50
531I 10f Stripped of His garment .55 .55
531J 11f Nailed to cross .60 .60
531K 12f Death on cross .65 .65
531L 13f Removal from cross .70 .70
531M 14f Burial .75 .75
Nos. 531-531M (14) 5.86 5.86

Souvenir Sheet

Imperf

531N 100f like #551 13.00 13.00

Gemini Astronauts, Spacecraft — A67c

Astronauts and spacecraft from Gemini Missions 6-8.

1966, Nov. 15 Photo. Perf. 15x14

532 1f Walter M. Schirra .15 .15
532A 2f Thomas P. Stafford .15 .15
532B 3f Frank Borman .15 .15
532C 4f James A. Lovell .15 .15
532D 30f Neil Armstrong .60 .60
532E 60f David R. Scott 1.25 1.25
Set value 2.00 2.00

Imperf

Size: 119x89mm

532F 100f Gemini 6-8 astronauts 12.00 12.00

Christmas — A67d

Perf. 14x15, 15x14

1966, Dec. 21 **Photo.**

533 5f Magi following star .15 .15
533A 10f Adoration of the Magi .20 .20
533B 35f Flight to Egypt, vert. .70 .70
Nos. 533-533B (3) 1.05 1.05

Souvenir Sheet

Imperf

533C 50f like #533A *12.50 12.50*

King Hussein — A67e

Builders of World Peace: No. 534, Dag Hammarskjold. No. 534A, U Thant. No. 534B, Jawaharlal Nehru. No. 534C, Charles DeGaulle. No. 534D, John F. Kennedy. No. 534E, Lyndon B. Johnson. No. 534F, Pope John XXIII. No. 534G, Pope Paul VI. No. 534H, King Abdullah of Jordan.

1967, Jan. 5 **Photo.** ***Perf. 15x14***

Background Color

534 A67e 5f gray .15 .15
534A A67e 5f brt yel grn .15 .15
534B A67e 10f rose lilac .18 .18
534C A67e 10f red brown .18 .18
534D A67e 35f olive green .60 .60
534E A67e 35f orange .60 .60
534F A67e 50f rose claret .85 .85
534G A67e 50f yel bister .85 .85
534H A67e 100f brt blue 1.75 1.75
534I A67e 100f dull blue 1.75 1.75
Nos. 534-534I (10) 7.06 7.06

Imperf

Size: 99x64mm

534J A67e 100f Kennedy, etc. *12.50 12.50*
534K A67e 100f DeGaulle, etc. *12.50 12.50*

King Hussein A67f

Photo. & Embossed

1967, Feb. 7 ***Imperf.***

Gold Portrait and Border

Diameter: 50f, 100f, 48mm; 200f, 54mm

Portrait of King Hussein

535 A67f 5f dk bl & salmon .15 .15
535A A67f 10f purple & salmon .15 .15
535B A67f 50f blk brn & vio .75 .75
535C A67f 100f dk ol grn & pink 1.50 1.50
535D A67f 200f dp bl & bl 3.00 3.00

Portrait of Crown Prince Hassan

536 A67f 5f brt yel grn & blk .15 .15
536A A67f 10f vio & blk .15 .15
536B A67f 50f bl & blk .75 .75
536C A67f 100f bister & blk 1.50 1.50
536D A67f 200f brt pink & blk 3.00 3.00

Portrait of John F. Kennedy

537 A67f 5f brt bl & lt grn .15 .15
537A A67f 10f dp grn & pink .15 .15
537B A67f 50f brt rose & org yel .75 .75
537C A67f 100f brn & apple grn 1.50 1.50
537D A67f 200f dk purple & pale grn 3.00 3.00
Nos. 535-537D (15) 16.65 16.65

1968 Summer Olympic Games, Mexico — A67g

Olympic torch and: 1f, Natl. University Library with O'Gormans mosaics, statue, Mexico City. 2f, Fishermen on Lake Patzcuaro. 3f, Natl. University buildings. 4f, Paseo de la Reforma, Mexico City. 30f, Guadalajara Cathedral. 60f, 100f, Palace of Fine Arts, Mexico City.

Perf. 14x15

1967, Mar. **Photo.** **Unwmk.**

538 A67g 1f lake, dk bl vio & blk .15 .15
538A A67g 2f blk, lake & dk bl vio .15 .15
538B A67g 3f dark bl vio, blk & lake .15 .15
538C A67g 4f bl, grn & brn .15 .15
538D A67g 30f grn, brn & bl .45 .45
538E A67g 60f brn, bl & grn .90 .90
Set value 1.50 1.50

Souvenir Sheet

Imperf

538F A67g 100f brn, dark bl & grn

Symbolic Water Cycle A68

Perf. 14½x14

1967, Mar. 1 **Litho.** **Wmk. 305**

539 A68 10f dp org, blk & gray .15 .15
540 A68 15f grnsh bl, blk & gray .15 .15
541 A68 25f brt rose lil, blk & gray .18 .18
Set value .35 .35

Hydrological Decade (UNESCO), 1965-74.

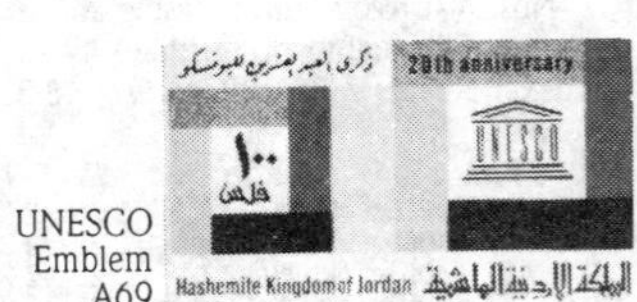

UNESCO Emblem A69

1967, Mar. 16

542 A69 100f multicolored .65 .65

20th anniv. of UNESCO.

Dromedary — A70

Animals: 2f, Karakul. 3f, Angora goat.

Perf. 14x15

1967, Feb. 11 **Photo.** **Unwmk.**

543 A70 1f dark brn & multi .15 .15
544 A70 2f yellow & multi .15 .15
545 A70 3f lt blue & multi .15 .15
Set value, #543-545, C46-C48 .85 .65

A souvenir sheet exists with a 100f in design and colors of No. C47, simulated perforation and marginal animal design. Value $6.

Inauguration of WHO Headquarters, Geneva — A71

1967, Apr. 7 **Wmk. 305**

546 A71 5f emerald & blk .15 .15
547 A71 45f dl orange & blk .32 .32
Set value .36 .36

Arab League Emblem and Hands Reaching for Knowledge — A72

1968, May 5 **Unwmk.** ***Perf. 11***

548 A72 20f org & slate grn .15 .15
549 A72 20f brt pink & dk bl .15 .15
Set value .20 .20

Issued to publicize the literacy campaign.

"20" and WHO Emblem A73

Perf. 14½x14

1968, Aug. 10 **Wmk. 305**

550 A73 30f multicolored .22 .18
551 A73 100f multicolored .75 .60

20th anniv. of the WHO.

European Goldfinch A74

Protected Game: 10f, Rock partridge, vert. 15f, Ostriches, vert. 20f, Sand partridge. 30f, Dorcas gazelle. 40f, Oryxes. 50f, Houbara bustard.

1968, Oct. 5 **Unwmk.** ***Perf. 13½***

552 A74 5f multicolored .15 .15
553 A74 10f multicolored .18 .15
554 A74 15f multicolored .20 .15
555 A74 20f multicolored .32 .15
556 A74 30f multicolored .45 .18
557 A74 40f multicolored .60 .25
558 A74 50f multicolored .85 .30
Nos. 552-558,C49-C50 (9) 4.90 3.48

Human Rights Flame — A75

1968, Dec. 10 **Litho.** ***Perf. 13***

559 A75 20f dp org, lt org & blk .18 .15
560 A75 60f grn, lt blue & blk .50 .45

International Human Rights Year.

Dome of the Rock, Jerusalem A76

5f, 45f, Holy Kaaba, Mecca, & Dome of the Rock.

1969, Oct. 8 **Photo.** ***Perf. 12***

Size: 56x25mm

561 A76 5f dull vio & multi .15 .15

Size: 36x25mm

562 A76 10f vio blue & multi .18 .15
563 A76 20f Prus bl & multi .38 .15

Size: 56x25mm

564 A76 45f Prus bl & multi .75 .22
Nos. 561-564 (4) 1.46
Set value .44

ILO Emblem — A77

1969, June 10 ***Perf. 13½x14***

565 A77 10f blue & black .15 .15
566 A77 20f bister brn & blk .15 .15
567 A77 25f lt olive & black .15 .15
568 A77 45f lil rose & black .26 .25
569 A77 60f orange & black .38 .32
Nos. 565-569 (5) 1.09
Set value .84

ILO, 50th anniversary.

Horses — A78

Designs: 20f, White stallion. 45f, Mare and foal.

1969, July 6 **Unwmk.** ***Perf. 13½***

570 A78 10f dark bl & multi .15 .15
571 A78 20f dl green & multi .18 .15
572 A78 45f red & multi .45 .30
Nos. 570-572 (3) .78
Set value .46

Prince Hassan and Princess Tharwat A79

Designs: 60f, 100f, Prince Hassan and bride in western bridal gown.

1969, Dec. 2 **Photo.** ***Perf. 12½***

573 A79 20f gold & multi .15 .15
573A A79 60f gold & multi .45 .38
573B A79 100f gold & multi .75 .75
c. Strip of 3, #573-573B 1.50

Wedding of Crown Prince Hassan, 11/14/68.

The Tragedy and the Flight of the Refugees A79a

Different design on each stamp. Each strip of 5 has five consecutive denominations.

Perf. 14½x13½

1969, Dec. 10 **Photo.**

574 A79a 1f-5f Strip of 5
574A A79a 6f-10f Strip of 5
574B A79a 11f-15f Strip of 5
574C A79a 16f-20f Strip of 5
574D A79a 21f-25f Strip of 5
574E A79a 26f-30f Strip of 5

For surcharges see Nos. 870-875.

Inscribed: Tragedy in the Holy Lands

Different design on each stamp. Each strip of 5 has five consecutive denominations.

Perf. 14½x13½

1969, Dec. 10 **Photo.**

575 A79a 1f-5f Strip of 5
575A A79a 6f-10f Strip of 5
575B A79a 11f-15f Strip of 5
575C A79a 16f-20f Strip of 5
575D A79a 21f-25f Strip of 5
575E A79a 26f-30f Strip of 5

For surcharges see Nos. 876-881.

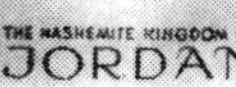

Pomegranate Flower (inscribed "Desert Scabius") — A80

Oranges — A81

Black Bush Robin — A82

Designs: 15f, Wattle flower ("Caper"). 20f, Melon. 25f, Caper flower ("Pomegranate"). 30f, Lemons. 35f, Morning glory. 40f, Grapes. 45f, Desert scabius ("Wattle"). 50f, Olive-laden branch. 75f, Black iris. 100f, Apples. 180f, Masked shrike. 200f, Palestine sunbird. (Inscriptions incorrect on 5f, 15f, 25f and 45f.)

Perf. 14x13½ (flowers), 12 (fruit), 13½x14 (birds)

1969-70 Photo.

576 A80 5f yel & multi ('70) .15 .15
577 A81 10f blue & multi .15 .15
578 A80 15f tan & multi ('70) .20 .15
579 A81 20f sepia & multi .30 .15
580 A80 25f multi ('70) .38 .15
581 A81 30f vio bl & multi .42 .15
582 A80 35f multi ('70) .45 .15
583 A81 40f dull yel & multi .52 .15
584 A80 45f gray & multi ('70) .55 .15
585 A81 50f car rose & multi .60 .15
586 A80 75f multi ('70) 1.00 .22
587 A81 100f dk gray & multi 1.25 .38
588 A82 120f org & multi ('70) 1.90 .45
589 A82 180f multi ('70) 2.25 1.00
590 A82 200f multi ('70) 2.75 1.25
Nos. 576-590 (15) 12.87
Set value 4.10

Issued: Fruits, 11/22; flowers, 3/21; birds, 9/1.

Soccer — A83

Designs: 10f, Diver. 15f, Boxers. 50f, Runner. 100f, Bicyclist, vert. 150f, Basketball, vert.

1970, Aug. ***Perf. 13½x14, 14x13½***

651 A83 5f green & multi .15 .15
652 A83 10f lt bl & multi .15 .15
653 A83 15f gray & multi .15 .15
654 A83 50f gray & multi .38 .30
655 A83 100f yellow & multi .75 .60
656 A83 150f multicolored 1.10 1.00
Nos. 651-656 (6) 2.68 2.35

Boy Fetching Water, UNICEF and Refugee Emblems — A84

Emblems and: 5f, Refugee children, horiz. 15f, Girl and tents. 20f, Boy in front of tent.

1970, Aug.

657 A84 5f multicolored .15 .15
658 A84 10f multicolored .30 .20
659 A84 15f multicolored .42 .20
660 A84 20f multicolored .60 .20
Nos. 657-660 (4) 1.47
Set value .65

Issued for Childhood Day.

Nativity Grotto, Bethlehem A85

Church of the Nativity, Bethlehem: 10f, Manger. 20f, Altar. 25f, Interior.

1970, Dec. 25 Photo. ***Perf. 13½***

661 A85 5f blue & multi .15 .15
662 A85 10f scarlet & multi .15 .15
663 A85 20f rose lilac & multi .15 .15
664 A85 25f green & multi .20 .15
Set value .45 .30

Christmas.

Flag and Map of Arab League Countries A85a

1971, May 10 Photo. ***Perf. 11½x11***

665 A85a 10f orange & multi .15 .15
666 A85a 20f lt blue & multi .15 .15
667 A85a 30f olive & multi .20 .15
Set value .40 .25

25th anniversary of the Arab League.

Emblem and Doves — A86

Designs: 5f, Emblem and 4 races, vert. 10f, Emblem as flower, vert.

1971, July

668 A86 5f green & multi .15 .15
669 A86 10f brick red & multi .15 .15
670 A86 15f dk blue & multi .20 .15
Set value .40 .18

Intl. Year Against Racial Discrimination.

Dead Sea — A87

Views of the Holy Land: 30f, Excavated building, Petra. 45f, Via Dolorosa, Jerusalem, vert. 60f, Jordan River. 100f, Christmas bell, Bethlehem, vert.

1971, Aug. ***Perf. 14x13½, 13½x14***

671 A87 5f blue & multi .15 .15
672 A87 30f pink & multi .38 .20
673 A87 45f blue & multi .50 .38
674 A87 60f gray & multi .75 .50
675 A87 100f gray & multi 1.25 .90
Nos. 671-675 (5) 3.03 2.13

Tourist publicity.

Opening of UPU Headquarters, Bern in 1970 — A88

1971, Oct. ***Perf. 11***

676 A88 10f brn, brn & yel grn .15 .15
677 A88 20f dk vio, grn & yel grn .28 .15
Set value .17

Avicenna (980-1037) — A89

Child Learning to Write — A90

Arab Scholars: 10f, Averroes (1126-1198). 20f, ibn-Khaldun (1332-1406). 25f, ibn-Tufail (?-1185). 30f, Alhazen (965?-1039?).

1971, Sept. ***Perf. 12***

678 A89 5f gold & multi .15 .15
679 A89 10f gold & multi .15 .15
680 A89 20f gold & multi .28 .15
681 A89 25f gold & multi .30 .15
682 A89 30f gold & multi .40 .20
Nos. 678-682 (5) 1.28
Set value .52

1972, Feb. 9 Photo. ***Perf. 11***

683 A90 5f ultra, brn & grn .15 .15
684 A90 15f mag, brn & blue .15 .15
685 A90 20f grn, brn & blue .20 .15
686 A90 30f org, brn & blue .30 .20
Nos. 683-686 (4) .80
Set value .50

International Education Year.

Mother and Child — A91

Pope Paul VI and Holy Sepulcher — A92

Mother's Day: 10f, Mothers and children, horiz. 30f, Arab mother and child.

1972, Mar. ***Perf. 14x13½***

687 A91 10f lt grn & multi .15 .15
688 A91 20f red brown & blk .16 .15
689 A91 30f blue, brn & blk .25 .16
Nos. 687-689 (3) .56
Set value .32

1972, Apr. Photo. ***Perf. 14x13½***

690 A92 30f black & multi .20 .15

Easter. See Nos. C51-C52.

UNICEF Emblem, Children A93

UNICEF Emblem and: 20f, Child playing with blocks spelling "UNICEF," vert. 30f, Mother and child.

1972, May ***Perf. 11½x11, 11x11½***

691 A93 10f bl, vio bl & blk .15 .15
692 A93 20f multicolored .16 .15
693 A93 30f blue & multi .25 .16
Nos. 691-693 (3) .56
Set value .30

25th anniv. (in 1971) of UNICEF.

UN Emblem, Dove and Grain — A94

1972, July ***Perf. 11x11½***

694 A94 5f vio & multi .15 .15
695 A94 10f multicolored .15 .15
696 A94 15f black & multi .16 .15
697 A94 20f green & multi .20 .15
698 A94 30f multicolored .35 .20
Nos. 694-698 (5) 1.01
Set value .50

25th anniv. (in 1970) of the UN.

Al Aqsa Mosque, Jerusalem A95

Designs: 60f, Al Aqsa Mosque on fire. 100f, Al Aqsa Mosque, interior.

1972, Aug. 21 Litho. ***Perf. 14½***

699 A95 30f green & multi .25 .20
700 A95 60f blue & multi .50 .35
701 A95 100f ocher & multi .80 .52
Nos. 699-701 (3) 1.55 1.07

3rd anniversary of the burning of Al Aqsa Mosque, Jerusalem.

House in Desert — A96

1972, Nov. ***Perf. 14x13½, 13½x14***

702 A96 5f Falconer, vert .15 .15
703 A96 10f shown .15 .15
704 A96 15f Man on camel .20 .15
705 A96 20f Pipe line construction .28 .15
706 A96 25f Shepherd .30 .15
707 A96 30f Camels at water trough .48 .20
708 A96 35f Chicken farm .52 .20
709 A96 45f Irrigation canal .75 .35
Nos. 702-709 (8) 2.83
Set value 1.15

Life in the Arab desert.

Wasfi el Tell and Dome of the Rock — A97

Wasfi el Tell, Map of Palestine and Jordan — A98

Perf. 13x13½, 13½x13

1972, Dec. Photo.

710 A97 5f citron & multi .15 .15
711 A98 10f red & multi .15 .15
712 A97 20f dl blue & multi .25 .18
713 A98 30f green & multi .45 .25
Set value .86 .52

In memory of Prime Minister Wasfi el Tell, who was assassinated in Cairo by Black September terrorists.

Trapshooting — A99

Designs: 75f, Trapshooter facing right, horiz. 120f, Trapshooter facing left, horiz.

1972, Dec. *Perf. 14x13½, 13½x14*

No.	Type	Description	Unused	Used
714	A99	25f multicolored	.15	.15
715	A99	75f multicolored	.42	.35
716	A99	120f multicolored	.75	.50
		Nos. 714-716 (3)	1.32	1.00

World Trapshooting Championships.

Aero Club Emblem A100

1973, Jan. **Photo.** *Perf. 13½x14*

No.	Type	Description	Unused	Used
717	A100	5f blue, blk & yel	.15	.15
718	A100	10f blue, blk & yel	.20	.15
		Nos. 717-718,C53-C55 (5)	1.06	
		Set value		.52

Royal Jordanian Aero Club.

Peace Dove and Jordanian Flag — A101

Designs: 10f, Emblem. 15f, King Hussein. 30f, Map of Jordan.

1973, Mar. *Perf. 11½*

No.	Type	Description	Unused	Used
719	A101	5f blue & multi	.15	.15
720	A101	10f pale grn & multi	.15	.15
721	A101	15f olive & multi	.18	.15
722	A101	30f yel grn & multi	.35	.30
		Set value	.70	.45

Hashemite Kingdom of Jordan, 50th anniv.

Battle, Flag and Map of Palestine — A102

Designs: 10f, Two soldiers in combat, map of Palestine. 15f, Map of Palestine, olive branch, soldier on tank.

1973, Apr. 10 **Photo.** *Perf. 11*

No.	Type	Description	Unused	Used
723	A102	5f crimson & multi	.16	.15
724	A102	10f crimson & multi	.30	.16
725	A102	15f grn, blue & brn	.50	.20
		Nos. 723-725 (3)	.96	
		Set value		.40

5th anniversary of Karama Battle.

Father and Child — A103

Father's Day: 20f, Father & infant. 30f, Family.

1973, Apr. 20 *Perf. 13½*

No.	Type	Description	Unused	Used
726	A103	10f citron & multi	.15	.15
727	A103	20f lt blue & multi	.15	.15
728	A103	30f multicolored	.22	.15
		Nos. 726-728 (3)	.52	
		Set value		.30

Phosphate Mine — A104

1973, June 25 **Litho.** *Perf. 13½x14*

No.	Type	Description	Unused	Used
729	A104	5f shown	.15	.15
730	A104	10f Cement factory	.16	.15
731	A104	15f Sharmasil Dam	.25	.15
732	A104	20f Kafrein Dam	.30	.20
		Nos. 729-732 (4)	.86	
		Set value		.50

Development projects.

Camel Racer — A105

Designs: Camel racing.

1973, July 21

No.	Type	Description	Unused	Used
733	A105	5f multicolored	.15	.15
734	A105	10f multicolored	.15	.15
735	A105	15f multicolored	.15	.15
736	A105	20f multicolored	.16	.15
		Set value	.35	.22

Book Year Emblem — A106

1973, Aug. 25 **Photo.** *Perf. 13x13½*

No.	Type	Description	Unused	Used
737	A106	30f dk grn & multi	.32	.15
738	A106	60f purple & multi	.65	.25

Intl. Book Year. For overprints see #781-782.

Family A107

Family Day: 30f, Family around fire. 60f, Large family outdoors.

1973, Sept. 18 **Litho.** *Perf. 13½*

No.	Type	Description	Unused	Used
739	A107	20f multicolored	.15	.15
740	A107	30f multicolored	.20	.15
741	A107	60f multicolored	.42	.25
		Nos. 739-741 (3)	.77	
		Set value		.46

Kings of Iran and Jordan, Tomb of Cyrus the Great and Mosque of Omar — A108

1973, Oct. **Litho.** *Perf. 13*

No.	Type	Description	Unused	Used
742	A108	5f ver & multi	.15	.15
743	A108	10f brown & multi	.20	.15
744	A108	15f gray & multi	.32	.18
745	A108	30f blue & multi	.60	.35
		Nos. 742-745 (4)	1.27	
		Set value		.70

2500th anniversary of the founding of the Persian Empire by Cyrus the Great.

Palestine Week Emblem A109

Palestine Week: 10f, Torch and laurel. 15f, Refugee family behind barbed wire, vert. 30f, Children, Map of Palestine, globe. Sizes: 5f, 10f, 30f; 38½x22mm. 15f, 25x46mm.

1973, Nov. 17 **Photo.** *Perf. 11*

No.	Type	Description	Unused	Used
746	A109	5f multicolored	.15	.15
747	A109	10f dl bl & multi	.25	.15
748	A109	15f yel grn & multi	.30	.15
749	A109	30f brt grn & multi	.65	.25
		Nos. 746-749 (4)	1.35	
		Set value		.50

Traditional Harvest A110

Traditional and modern agricultural methods.

1973, Dec. 25 *Perf. 13½*

No.	Type	Description	Unused	Used
750	A110	5f shown	.15	.15
751	A110	10f Harvesting machine	.15	.15
752	A110	15f Traditional seeding	.15	.15
753	A110	20f Seeding machine	.18	.15
754	A110	30f Ox plow	.25	.22
755	A110	35f Plowing machine	.30	.22
756	A110	45f Pest control	.38	.32
757	A110	60f Horticulture	.55	.50
		Nos. 750-757,C56 (9)	2.76	2.31

Red Sea Fish — A111

Designs: Various Red Sea fishes.

1974, Feb. 15 **Photo.** *Perf. 14*

No.	Type	Description	Unused	Used
758	A111	5f multicolored	.15	.15
759	A111	10f multicolored	.15	.15
760	A111	15f multicolored	.18	.15
761	A111	20f multicolored	.22	.15
762	A111	25f multicolored	.25	.15
763	A111	30f multicolored	.30	.18
764	A111	35f multicolored	.32	.22
765	A111	40f multicolored	.38	.25
766	A111	45f multicolored	.45	.30
767	A111	50f multicolored	.52	.38
768	A111	60f multicolored	.75	.48
		Nos. 758-768 (11)	3.67	2.56

Battle of Muta, 1250 A112

1974, Mar. 15 **Photo.** *Perf. 13½*

No.	Type	Description	Unused	Used
769	A112	10f shown	.30	.15
770	A112	20f Yarmouk Battle, 636	.60	.30
771	A112	30f Hitteen Battle, 1187	.90	.45

Clubfooted Boy, by Murillo — A113

Paintings: 10f, Praying Hands, by Dürer. 15f, St. George and the Dragon, by Paolo Uccello. 20f, Mona Lisa, by Da Vinci. 30f, Hope, by Frederic Watts. 40f, Angelus, by Jean F. Millet, horiz. 50f, The Artist and her Daughter, by Angelica Kauffmann. 60f, Portrait of my Mother, by James Whistler, horiz. 100f, Master Hare, by Reynolds.

Perf. 14x13½, 13½x14

1974, Apr. 15 **Litho.**

No.	Type	Description	Unused	Used
772	A113	5f black & multi	.15	.15
773	A113	10f black & gray	.15	.15
774	A113	15f black & multi	.15	.15
775	A113	20f black & multi	.15	.15
776	A113	30f black & multi	.20	.15
777	A113	40f black & multi	.25	.15
778	A113	50f black & multi	.32	.22
779	A113	60f black & multi	.42	.25
780	A113	100f black & multi	.65	.45
		Nos. 772-780 (9)	2.44	
		Set value		1.40

Nos. 737-738 Overprinted

المؤتمر الدولي لتاريخ بلاد الشام

٢٠ - ٢٥/٤/١٩٧٤

الجامعة الاردنية

1974, Apr. 20 **Photo.** *Perf. 13x13½*

No.	Type	Description	Unused	Used
781	A106	30f dk grn & multi	.35	.20
782	A106	60f purple & multi	.75	.50

Intl. Conf. for Damascus History, Apr. 20-25.

UPU Emblem — A114

1974 *Perf. 13x12½*

No.	Type	Description	Unused	Used
783	A114	10f yel grn & multi	.15	.15
784	A114	30f blue & multi	.30	.15
785	A114	60f multicolored	.60	.30
		Nos. 783-785 (3)	1.05	
		Set value		.48

Centenary of Universal Postal Union.

Camel Caravan at Sunset A115

Designs: 3f, 30f, Palm at shore of Dead Sea. 4f, 40f, Hotel at shore. 5f, 50f, Jars from Qumran Caves. 6f, 60f, Copper scrolls, vert. 10f, 100f, Cracked cistern steps, vert. 20f, like 2f.

1974, June 25 **Photo.** *Perf. 14*

No.	Type	Description	Unused	Used
786	A115	2f multicolored	.15	.15
787	A115	3f multicolored	.15	.15
788	A115	4f multicolored	.15	.15
789	A115	5f multicolored	.15	.15
790	A115	6f multicolored	.15	.15
791	A115	10f multicolored	.15	.15
792	A115	20f multicolored	.18	.15
793	A115	30f multicolored	.26	.15
794	A115	40f multicolored	.38	.18
795	A115	50f multicolored	.42	.25
796	A115	60f multicolored	.62	.32
797	A115	100f multicolored	1.00	.50
		Set value	3.10	1.70

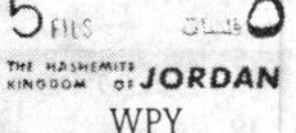

WPY Emblem — A116

Water Skiing — A117

1974, Aug. 20 **Photo.** *Perf. 11*

No.	Type	Description	Unused	Used
798	A116	5f lt green, blk & pur	.15	.15
799	A116	10f lt green, blk & car	.15	.15
800	A116	20f lt green, blk & org	.20	.15
		Set value	.35	.20

World Population Year.

Perf. 14x13½, 13½x14

1974, Sept. 20

Water Skiing: 10f, 100f, Side view, horiz. 20f, 200f, Turning, horiz. 50f, like 5f.

No.	Type	Description	Unused	Used
801	A117	5f multicolored	.15	.15
802	A117	10f multicolored	.15	.15
803	A117	20f multicolored	.15	.15
804	A117	50f multicolored	.35	.20
805	A117	100f multicolored	.65	.40
806	A117	200f multicolored	1.40	.80
		Nos. 801-806 (6)	2.85	
		Set value		1.55

Holy Kaaba, Mecca, and Pilgrims — A118

1974, Nov. Photo. *Perf. 11*

807 A118 10f blue & multi .15 .15
808 A118 20f yellow & multi .25 .15
Set value .20

Pilgrimage season.

Amrah Palace A119

Ruins: 20f, Hisham Palace. 30f, Kharraneh Castle.

1974, Nov. 25 Photo. *Perf. 14x13½*

809 A119 10f black & multi .25 .15
810 A119 20f black & multi .50 .30
811 A119 30f black & multi .75 .50
Nos. 809-811 (3) 1.50 .95

Jordanian Woman — A120

Designs: Various women's costumes.

1975, Feb. 1 Photo. *Perf. 12*

812 A120 5f lt green & multi .15 .15
813 A120 10f yellow & multi .15 .15
814 A120 15f lt blue & multi .15 .15
815 A120 20f ultra & multi .15 .15
816 A120 25f green & multi .18 .15
Set value .50 .35

Treasury, Petra — A121

Ommayyad Palace, Amman A122

Designs: 30f, Dome of the Rock, Jerusalem. 40f, Columns, Forum of Jerash.

Perf. 14x13½, 13½x14

1975, Mar. 1 Photo.

824 A121 15f lt blue & multi .15 .15
825 A122 20f pink & multi .18 .15
826 A122 30f yellow & multi .30 .15
827 A122 40f lt blue & multi .38 .18
Nos. 824-827,C59-C61 (7) 2.27 1.47

King Hussein — A123

1975, Apr. 8 Photo. *Perf. 14*
Size: 19x23mm

831 A123 5f green & ind .15 .15
832 A123 10f vio & indigo .15 .15
833 A123 15f car & indigo .15 .15
834 A123 20f brn ol & ind .15 .15
835 A123 25f vio bl & ind .15 .15
836 A123 30f brown & ind .15 .15
837 A123 35f vio & indigo .16 .15
838 A123 40f orange & ind .18 .15
839 A123 45f red lil & ind .20 .15
840 A123 50f bl green & ind .22 .15
Nos. 831-840,C62-C68 (17) 8.61 5.84

Globe, "alia" and Plane — A125

Designs: 30f, Boeing 727 connecting Jordan with world, horiz. 60f, Globe and "alia."

1975, June 15 Photo. *Perf. 11*

853 A125 10f multicolored .15 .15
854 A125 30f multicolored .26 .18
855 A125 60f multicolored .55 .38
Set value .85 .60

Royal Jordanian Airline, 30th anniversary.

Satellite Transmission System, Map of Mediterranean — A126

1975, Aug. 1 Photo. *Perf. 11*

856 A126 20f vio bl & multi .25 .15
857 A126 30f green & multi .32 .18

Opening of satellite earth station.

Chamber of Commerce Emblem — A127

1975, Oct. 15 Photo. *Perf. 11*

858 A127 10f yellow & blue .15 .15
859 A127 15f yel, red & blue .15 .15
860 A127 20f yel, grn & blue .16 .15
Set value .38 .18

Amman Chamber of Commerce, 50th anniv.

Hand Holding Wrench, Wall and Emblem — A128

1975, Nov. Photo. *Perf. 11½*

861 A128 5f green, car & blk .15 .15
862 A128 10f car, green & blk .15 .15
863 A128 20f blk, green & car .20 .15
Set value .35 .20

Three-year development plan.

Family and IWY Emblem A129

Salt Industry A130

IWY Emblem and: 25f, Woman scientist with microscope. 60f, Woman graduate.

1976, Apr. 27 Litho. *Perf. 14x13½*

864 A129 5f multicolored .15 .15
865 A129 25f multicolored .15 .15
866 A129 60f multicolored .38 .25
Set value .58 .40

International Women's Year.

1976, June 1 Litho. *Perf. 13½x14*

Arab Labor Organization Emblem and: 30f, Welders. 60f, Ship at 'Aqaba.

867 A130 10f gray & multi .15 .15
868 A130 30f bister & multi .18 .15
869 A130 60f brown & multi .38 .25
Set value .60 .40

Arab Labor Organization.

Nos. 574-574E Surcharged
Perf. 14½x13½

1976, July 18 Photo.
Strips of 5

870 A79a 25f on 1f-5f
871 A79a 25f on 6f-10f
872 A79a 40f on 11f-15f
873 A79a 50f on 16f-20f
874 A79a 75f on 21f-25f
875 A79a 125f on 26f-30f

Nos. 575-575E Surcharged

876 A79a 25f on 1f-5f
877 A79a 25f on 6f-10f
878 A79a 40f on 11f-15f
879 A79a 50f on 16f-20f
880 A79a 75f on 21f-25f
881 A79a 125f on 26f-30f

Tennis — A132

Designs: 10f, Athlete and wreath. 15f, Soccer. 20f, Equestrian and Jordanian flag. 30f, Weight lifting. 100f, Stadium, Amman.

1976, Nov. 1 Litho. *Perf. 14x13½*

990 A132 5f buff & multi .15 .15
991 A132 10f lt bl & multi .15 .15
992 A132 15f green & multi .15 .15
993 A132 20f green & multi .16 .15
994 A132 30f green & multi .25 .15
995 A132 100f multicolored .80 .48
Nos. 990-995 (6) 1.66
Set value .88

Sports and youth.

Dam — A133

Telephones, 1876 and 1976 — A134

Designs: Various dams.

1976, Dec. 7 Litho. *Perf. 14x13½*

996 A133 30f multicolored .22 .15
997 A133 60f multicolored .45 .32
998 A133 100f multicolored .75 .50

1977, Feb. 17 Litho. *Perf. 11½x12*

125f, 1876 telephone and 1976 receiver.

999 A134 75f rose & multi .60 .45
1000 A134 125f blue & multi .90 .75

Centenary of first telephone call by Alexander Graham Bell, Mar. 10, 1876.

Street Crossing, Traffic Light — A135

Designs: 75f, Traffic circle and light. 125f, Traffic light and signs, motorcycle policeman.

1977, May 4 Litho. *Perf. 11x12*

1001 A135 5f rose & multi .15 .15
1002 A135 75f black & multi .60 .45
1003 A135 125f yellow & multi 1.00 .75
Nos. 1001-1003 (3) 1.75 1.35

International Traffic Day.

Plane over Ship — A136

Child with Toy Bank — A137

Coat of Arms and: 25f, Factories and power lines. 40f, Fertilizer plant and trucks. 50f, Ground to air missile. 75f, Mosque and worshippers. 125f, Radar station and TV emblem.

1977, Aug. 11 Photo. *Perf. 11½x12*

1004 A136 10f sil & multi .15 .15
1005 A136 25f sil & multi .20 .15
1006 A136 40f sil & multi .30 .24
1007 A136 50f sil & multi .42 .30
1008 A136 75f sil & multi .60 .45
1009 A136 125f sil & multi 1.10 .75
Nos. 1004-1009 (6) 2.77 2.04

Imperf
Size: 100x70mm

1009A A136 100f multicolored

25th anniv. of the reign of King Hussein.

1977, Sept. 1 Litho. *Perf. 11½x12*

Postal Savings Bank: 25f, Boy with piggy bank. 50f, Postal Savings Bank emblem. 75f, Boy talking to teller.

1010 A137 10f multicolored .15 .15
1011 A137 25f multicolored .22 .15
1012 A137 50f multicolored .45 .30
1013 A137 75f multicolored .65 .45
Nos. 1010-1013 (4) 1.47 1.05

King Hussein and Queen Alia — A138

Queen Alia — A139

1977, Nov. 1 Litho. *Perf. 11½x12*

1014 A138 10f lt grn & multi .15 .15
1015 A138 25f rose & multi .15 .15
1016 A138 40f yellow & multi .28 .16
1017 A138 50f blue & multi .35 .20
Nos. 1014-1017 (4) .93
Set value .50

1977, Dec. 1 Litho. *Perf. 11½x12*

1018 A139 10f green & multi .15 .15
1019 A139 25f brown & multi .20 .15
1020 A139 40f blue & multi .35 .20
1021 A139 50f yellow & multi .42 .25
Nos. 1018-1021 (4) 1.12
Set value .60

Queen Alia, died in 1977 air crash.

Jinnah, Flags of Pakistan and Jordan — A140

APU Emblem, Members' Flags — A141

1977, Dec. 20 *Perf. 11½*
1022 A140 25f multicolored .20 .15
1023 A140 75f multicolored .60 .40

Mohammed Ali Jinnah (1876-1948), 1st Governor General of Pakistan.

1978, Apr. 12 Litho. *Perf. 12x11½*
1024 A141 25f yellow & multi .45 .30
1025 A141 40f buff & multi .75 .50

25th anniv. (in 1977), of Arab Postal Union.

Copper Coffee Set — A142

Roman Amphitheater, Jerash — A143

Handicraft: 40f, Porcelain plate and ashtray. 75f, Vase and jewelry. 125f, Pipe holder.

1978, May 30 Photo. *Perf. 11½x12*
1026 A142 25f olive & multi .20 .15
1027 A142 40f lilac & multi .32 .20
1028 A142 75f ultra & multi .60 .40
1029 A142 125f orange & multi 1.00 .65
Nos. 1026-1029 (4) 2.12 1.40

1978, July 30 Litho. *Perf. 12*

Tourist Views: 20f, Roman Columns, Jerash. 40f, Goat, grapes and man, Roman mosaic, Madaba. 75f, Rock formations, Rum, and camel rider.

1030 A143 5f multicolored .15 .15
1031 A143 20f multicolored .16 .15
1032 A143 40f multicolored .32 .20
1033 A143 75f multicolored .60 .40
Nos. 1030-1033 (4) 1.23
Set value .75

King Hussein and Pres. Sadat — A144

Designs: No. 1035, King Hussein and Pres. Assad, Jordanian and Syrian flags, horiz. No. 1036, King Hussein, King Khalid, Jordanian and Saudi Arabian flags, horiz.

1978, Aug. 20 *Perf. 11½x12*
1034 A144 40f multicolored .32 .20
1035 A144 40f multicolored .32 .20
1036 A144 40f multicolored .32 .20
Nos. 1034-1036 (3) .96 .60

Visits of Arab leaders to Jordan.

Cement Factory — A145

Designs: 10f, Science laboratory. 25f, Printing press. 75f, Artificial fertilizer plant.

1978, Sept. 25 Litho. *Perf. 12*
1037 A145 5f multicolored .15 .15
1038 A145 10f multicolored .15 .15
1039 A145 25f multicolored .30 .20
1040 A145 75f multicolored .90 .60
Nos. 1037-1040 (4) 1.50 1.10

Industrial development.

"UNESCO" Scales and Globe — A146

1978, Dec. 5 Litho. *Perf. 12x11½*
1041 A146 40f multicolored .40 .30
1042 A146 75f multicolored .90 .65

30th anniversary of UNESCO.

1976-1980 Development Plan — A147

1979, Oct. 25 Litho. *Perf. 12½x12*
1043 A147 25f multicolored .22 .15
1044 A147 40f multicolored .36 .24
1045 A147 50f multicolored .45 .25
Nos. 1043-1045 (3) 1.03 .64

IYC Emblem, Flag of Jordan — A148

1979, Nov. 15 Litho. *Perf. 12x12½*
1046 A148 25f multicolored .20 .15
1047 A148 40f multicolored .32 .20
1048 A148 50f multicolored .40 .24
Nos. 1046-1048 (3) .92 .59

International Year of the Child.

1979 Population and Housing Census — A149

1979, Dec. 25 Litho. *Perf. 12½x12*
1049 A149 25f multicolored .22 .15
1050 A149 40f multicolored .38 .24
1051 A149 50f multicolored .45 .30
Nos. 1049-1051 (3) 1.05 .69

King Hussein — A150

1980 Litho. *Perf. 13½x13*
1052 A150 5f multicolored .15 .15
1053 A150 10f multicolored .15 .15
1055 A150 20f multicolored .16 .15
1056 A150 25f multicolored .20 .15
a. Inscribed 1979 .20 .15
1058 A150 40f multicolored .32 .20
a. Inscribed 1979 .32 .20
1059 A150 50f multicolored .40 .25
1060 A150 75f multicolored .55 .32
1061 A150 125f multicolored 1.00 .65
Nos. 1052-1061 (8) 2.93
Set value 1.70

The 5, 10, 20, 25, 40f also come inscribed 1981.

International Nursing Day — A151

El Deir Temple, Petra — A152

1980, May 12 Litho. *Perf. 12x12½*
1062 A151 25f multicolored .22 .15
1063 A151 40f multicolored .35 .22
1064 A151 50f multicolored .40 .25
Nos. 1062-1064 (3) .97 .62

1980 Litho. *Perf. 14½*
1065 A152 25f multicolored .24 .16
1066 A152 40f multicolored .35 .24
1067 A152 50f multicolored .45 .30
Nos. 1065-1067 (3) 1.04 .70

World Tourism Conf., Manila, Sept. 27.

Hegira (Pilgrimage Year) — A153

1980, Nov. 11 Litho. *Perf. 14½*
1068 A153 25f multicolored .22 .15
1069 A153 40f multicolored .40 .22
1070 A153 50f multicolored .50 .28
1071 A153 75f multicolored .90 .42
1072 A153 100f multicolored .90 .55
Nos. 1068-1072 (5) 2.92 1.62

Souvenir Sheet

Imperf

1073 A153 290f multicolored 4.25 2.75

#1073 contains designs of #1068-1071.

11th Arab Summit Conference, Amman — A153a

1980, Nov. 25 Litho. *Perf. 14½*
1073A A153a 25f multi .20 .15
1073B A153a 40f multi .30 .25
1073C A153a 50f multi .45 .32
1073D A153a 75f multi .75 .45
1073E A153a 100f multi .90 .65
f. Souv. sheet of 5, #1073A-1073E, imperf. 4.00 4.00
Nos. 1073A-1073E (5) 2.60 1.82

A154

A155

1981, May 8 Litho. *Perf. 14½*
1074 A154 25f multicolored .25 .15
1075 A154 40f multicolored .40 .28
1076 A154 50f multicolored .45 .35
Nos. 1074-1076 (3) 1.10 .78

Red Crescent Society.

1981, June 17 Litho. *Perf. 14x14½*
1077 A155 25f multicolored .25 .15
1078 A155 40f multicolored .32 .28
1079 A155 50f multicolored .45 .32
Nos. 1077-1079 (3) 1.02 .75

13th World Telecommunications Day.

Nos. 174 and 832 — A156

Perf. 13½x14½, 14½x13½

1981, July 1 Litho.
1080 A156 25f shown .25 .18
1081 A156 40f Nos. 313, 189, vert. .45 .30
1082 A156 50f Nos. 272, 222 .50 .38
Nos. 1080-1082 (3) 1.20 .86

Postal Museum opening.

A157

A158

Arab Women: 25f, Khawla Bint El-Azwar, Ancient Warrior. 40f, El-Khansa (d.645), writer. 50f, Rabia El-Adawiyeh, religious leader.

1981, Aug. 25 Litho. *Perf. 14½x14*
1083 A157 25f multicolored .22 .15
1084 A157 40f multicolored .36 .24
1085 A157 50f multicolored .45 .30
Nos. 1083-1085 (3) 1.03 .69

1981, Oct. 16 Litho. *Perf. 14x14½*
1086 A158 25f multicolored .22 .15
1087 A158 40f multicolored .36 .24
1088 A158 50f multicolored .45 .30
Nos. 1086-1088 (3) 1.03 .69

World Food Day.

Intl. Year of the Disabled — A159

Hands Reading Braille — A160

1981, Nov. 14 Litho. *Perf. 14½x14*
1089 A159 25f multicolored .22 .15
1090 A159 40f multicolored .36 .24
1091 A159 50f multicolored .45 .30
Nos. 1089-1091 (3) 1.03 .69

1981, Nov. 14 *Perf. 14x14½*
1092 A160 25f multicolored .22 .15
1093 A160 40f multicolored .36 .24
1094 A160 50f multicolored .45 .30
Nos. 1092-1094 (3) 1.03 .69

A161

A162

Design: Hand holding jug and stone tablet.

1982, Mar. 10 Litho. *Perf. 14x14½*
1095 A161 25f multicolored .32 .22
1096 A161 40f multicolored .55 .35
1097 A161 50f multicolored .70 .45
Nos. 1095-1097 (3) 1.57 1.02

Nos. 1095-1097 inscribed 1981.

1982, Apr. 12 Litho. *Perf. 14x14½*
1098 A162 10f multicolored .15 .15
1099 A162 25f multicolored .22 .15
1100 A162 40f multicolored .36 .24
1101 A162 50f multicolored .45 .30
1102 A162 100f multicolored .90 .60
Nos. 1098-1102 (5) 2.08 1.44

30th anniv. of Arab Postal Union.

King Hussein and Rockets A163

1982, May 25 Litho. *Perf. 14½x14*

No.	Type	Description	Unused	Used
1103	A163	10f shown	.15	.15
1104	A163	25f Tanks crossing bridge	.22	.15
1105	A163	40f Jet	.36	.24
1106	A163	50f Tanks, diff.	.45	.30
1107	A163	100f Raising flag	.90	.60
		Nos. 1103-1107 (5)	2.08	1.44

Independence and Army Day; 30th anniv. of King Hussein's accession to the throne.

Salt Secondary School — A164

1982, Sept. 12 Litho. *Perf. 14½x14*

No.	Type	Description	Unused	Used
1108	A164	10f multicolored	.15	.15
1109	A164	25f multicolored	.22	.15
1110	A164	40f multicolored	.36	.24
1111	A164	50f multicolored	.45	.30
1112	A164	100f multicolored	.90	.60
		Nos. 1108-1112 (5)	2.08	1.44

International Heritage of Jerusalem — A165

1982, Nov. 14 Litho. *Perf. 14x14½*

No.	Type	Description	Unused	Used
1113	A165	10f Gate to Old City	.20	.15
1114	A165	25f Minaret	.55	.30
1115	A165	40f Al Aqsa	.90	.50
1116	A165	50f Dome of the Rock	1.10	.60
1117	A165	100f Dome of the Rock, diff.	2.25	1.25
		Nos. 1113-1117 (5)	5.00	2.80

Yarmouk Forces — A166

1982, Nov. 14 *Perf. 14½x14*

No.	Type	Description	Unused	Used
1118	A166	10f multicolored	.15	.15
1119	A166	25f multicolored	.30	.20
1120	A166	40f multicolored	.48	.30
1121	A166	50f multicolored	.60	.40
1122	A166	100f multicolored	1.20	.90

Size: 71x51mm

Imperf

No.	Type	Description	Unused	Used
1123	A166	100f Armed Forces emblem	11.50	11.50
		Nos. 1118-1123 (6)	14.23	13.45

2nd UN Conf. on Peaceful Uses of Outer Space, Vienna, Aug. 9-21 — A167

1982, Dec. 1 *Perf. 14½x14*

No.	Type	Description	Unused	Used
1124	A167	10f multicolored	.15	.15
1125	A167	25f multicolored	.22	.15
1126	A167	40f multicolored	.36	.24
1127	A167	50f multicolored	.45	.30
1128	A167	100f multicolored	.90	.60
		Nos. 1124-1128 (5)	2.08	1.44

Birth Centenary of Amir Abdullah ibn Hussein — A168

1982, Dec. 13 Litho. *Perf. 14½*

No.	Type	Description	Unused	Used
1129	A168	10f multicolored	.15	.15
1130	A168	25f multicolored	.25	.15
1131	A168	40f multicolored	.40	.30
1132	A168	50f multicolored	.60	.50
1133	A168	100f multicolored	1.40	.90
		Nos. 1129-1133 (5)	2.80	2.00

Roman Ruins of Jerash A169

1982, Dec. 29 Litho. *Perf. 15*

No.	Type	Description	Unused	Used
1134	A169	10f Temple colonnade	.15	.15
1135	A169	25f Arch	.22	.15
1136	A169	40f Columns	.36	.24
1137	A169	50f Ampitheater	.45	.30
1138	A169	100f Hippodrome	.90	.60
		Nos. 1134-1138 (5)	2.08	1.44

King Hussein — A170

1983 Litho. *Perf. 14½x14*

No.	Type	Description	Unused	Used
1139	A170	10f multicolored	.15	.15
1140	A170	25f multicolored	.25	.15
1141	A170	40f multicolored	.40	.30
1142	A170	60f multicolored	.60	.40
1143	A170	100f multicolored	1.00	.65
1144	A170	125f multicolored	1.25	.70
		Nos. 1139-1144 (6)	3.65	2.35

Issue dates: 10f, 60f, Feb. 1; 40f, Feb. 8; 25f, 100f, 125f, Mar. 3. Inscribed 1982.

Massacre at Shatilla and Sabra Palestinian Refugee Camps — A171

Designs: 10f, 25f, 50f, No. 1149, Various victims. 40f, Children. No. 1150, Wounded child.

1983, Apr. 9 Litho. *Perf. 14½*

No.	Type	Description	Unused	Used
1145	A171	10f multicolored	.25	.20
1146	A171	25f multicolored	.45	.40
1147	A171	40f multicolored	.70	.50
1148	A171	50f multicolored	.85	.70
1149	A171	100f multicolored	1.25	1.00
		Nos. 1145-1149 (5)	3.50	2.80

Souvenir Sheet

Imperf

No.	Type	Description	Unused	Used
1150	A171	100f multicolored	15.00	

Opening of Queen Alia Intl. Airport A172

1983, May 25 Litho. *Perf. 12½*

No.	Type	Description	Unused	Used
1151	A172	10f Aerial view	.15	.15
1152	A172	25f Terminal buildings	.22	.15
1153	A172	40f Hangar	.36	.24
1154	A172	50f Terminal buildings, diff.	.45	.30
1155	A172	100f Embarkation Bridge	.90	.60
		Nos. 1151-1155 (5)	2.08	1.44

Royal Jordanian Radio Amateurs' Society A173

1983, Aug. 11 Litho. *Perf. 12*

No.	Type	Description	Unused	Used
1156	A173	10f multicolored	.15	.15
1157	A173	25f multicolored	.22	.15
1158	A173	40f multicolored	.36	.24
1159	A173	50f multicolored	.45	.30
1160	A173	100f multicolored	.90	.60
		Nos. 1156-1160 (5)	2.08	1.44

Royal Academy for Islamic Cultural Research A174

1983, Sept. 16 Litho. *Perf. 12*

No.	Type	Description	Unused	Used
1161	A174	10f Academy Bldg.	.20	.16
1162	A174	25f Silk carpet	.45	.30
1163	A174	40f Mosque, Amman	.65	.45
1164	A174	50f Dome of the Rock	.85	.55
1165	A174	100f Islamic city views	1.75	1.10
		Nos. 1161-1165 (5)	3.90	2.56

A 100f souvenir sheet shows letter from Mohammed.

World Food Day — A175

1983, Oct. 16 Litho. *Perf. 12*

No.	Type	Description	Unused	Used
1166	A175	10f Irrigation canal	.15	.15
1167	A175	25f Greenhouses	.25	.15
1168	A175	40f Light-grown crops	.40	.24
1169	A175	50f Harvest	.50	.30
1170	A175	100f Sheep farm	1.00	.60
		Nos. 1166-1170 (5)	2.30	1.44

World Communications Year — A176

1983, Nov. 14

No.	Type	Description	Unused	Used
1171	A176	10f Radio switchboard operators	.15	.15
1172	A176	25f Earth satellite station	.28	.15
1173	A176	40f Symbols of communication	.42	.28
1174	A176	50f Emblems	.52	.32
1175	A176	100f Airmail letter	1.10	.65
		Nos. 1171-1175 (5)	2.47	1.55

Intl. Palestinian Solidarity Day — A177

Dome of the Rock, Jerusalem.

1983, Nov. 29 *Perf. 12*

No.	Type	Description	Unused	Used
1176	A177	5f multicolored	.35	.15
1177	A177	10f multicolored	.65	.30

35th Anniv. of UN Declaration of Human Rights — A178

1983, Dec. 10

No.	Type	Description	Unused	Used
1178	A178	10f multicolored	.15	.15
1179	A178	25f multicolored	.25	.15
1180	A178	40f multicolored	.32	.25
1181	A178	50f multicolored	.45	.30
1182	A178	100f multicolored	1.00	.60
		Nos. 1178-1182 (5)	2.17	1.45

Anti-Paralysis — A179

1984, Apr. 7 *Perf. 13½x11½*

No.	Type	Description	Unused	Used
1183	A179	40f multicolored	.40	.24
1184	A179	60f multicolored	.60	.36
1185	A179	100f multicolored	1.00	.60
		Nos. 1183-1185 (3)	2.00	1.20

Anti-Polio Campaign.

Israeli Bombing of Iraq Nuclear Reactor A180

Various designs.

1984, June 7 Litho. *Perf. 13½x11½*

No.	Type	Description	Unused	Used
1186	A180	40f multicolored	.60	.24
1187	A180	60f multicolored	.80	.35
1188	A180	100f multicolored	1.25	.60
		Nos. 1186-1188 (3)	2.65	1.19

Independence and Army Day — A181

King Hussein and various armed forces.

1984, June 10

No.	Type	Description	Unused	Used
1189	A181	10f multicolored	.15	.15
1190	A181	25f multicolored	.25	.15
1191	A181	40f multicolored	.40	.24
1192	A181	60f multicolored	.60	.35
1193	A181	100f multicolored	1.00	.60
		Nos. 1189-1193 (5)	2.40	1.49

1984 Summer Olympics, Los Angeles A182

1984, July 28

No.	Type	Description	Unused	Used
1194	A182	25f shown	.25	.15
1195	A182	40f Swimming	.40	.24
1196	A182	60f Shooting, archery	.60	.35
1197	A182	100f Gymnastics	1.00	.60
		Nos. 1194-1197 (4)	2.25	1.34

An imperf. 100f souvenir sheet exists picturing pole vaulting.

Water and Electricity Year A183

1984, Aug. 11

No.	Type	Description	Unused	Used
1198	A183	25f Power lines, factory	.25	.15
1199	A183	40f Amman Power Station	.40	.24
1200	A183	60f Irrigation	.60	.35
1201	A183	100f Hydro-electric dam	1.00	.60
		Nos. 1198-1201 (4)	2.25	1.34

Coins A184

1984, Sept. 26 Photo. *Perf. 13*

No.	Type	Description	Unused	Used
1202	A184	40f Omayyad gold dinar	.40	.24
1203	A184	60f Abbasid gold dinar	.60	.35
1204	A184	125f Hashemite silver dinar	1.25	.75
		Nos. 1202-1204 (3)	2.25	1.34

Royal Society for the Conservation of Nature — A185

1984, Oct. 18

1205 A185 25f Four antelopes .25 .15
1206 A185 40f Grazing .40 .24
1207 A185 60f Three antelopes .60 .35
1208 A185 100f King Hussein, Queen Alia, Duke of Edinburgh 1.00 .60
Nos. 1205-1208 (4) 2.25 1.34

Natl. Universities A186

Designs: 40f, Mu'ta Military University, Karak. 60f, Yarmouk University, Irbib. 125f, Jordan University, Amman.

1984, Nov. 14 ***Perf. 13x13½***

1209 A186 40f multicolored .40 .24
1210 A186 60f multicolored .60 .35
1211 A186 125f multicolored 1.25 .75
Nos. 1209-1211 (3) 2.25 1.34

Al Sahaba Tombs A187

Designs: 10f, El Harath bin Omier el-Azdi and Derer bin El-Azwar. 25f, Sharhabil bin Hasna and Abu Obaidah Amer bin el-Jarrah. 40f, Muath bin Jabal. 50f, Zaid bin Haretha and Abdullah bin Rawaha. 60f, Amer bin Abi Waqqas. 100f, Jafar bin Abi Taleb.

1984, Dec. 5 Litho. ***Perf. 13½x11½***

1212 A187 10f multicolored .15 .15
1213 A187 25f multicolored .25 .15
1214 A187 40f multicolored .40 .24
1215 A187 50f multicolored .50 .30
1216 A187 60f multicolored .60 .35
1217 A187 100f multicolored 1.00 .60
Nos. 1212-1217 (6) 2.90 1.79

Independence and Army Day — A188

Designs: 25f, King Hussein, soldier descending mountain. 40f, Hussein, Arab revolt flag, globe, King Abdullah. 60f, Flag, natl. arms, equestrian. 100f, Natl. flag, arms, King Abdullah.

1985, June 10 ***Perf. 13x13½***

1218 A188 25f multicolored .25 .15
1219 A188 40f multicolored .40 .24
1220 A188 60f multicolored .60 .35
1221 A188 100f multicolored 1.00 .60
Nos. 1218-1221 (4) 2.25 1.34

Men in Postal History A189

1985, July 1

1222 A189 40f Sir Rowland Hill .40 .24
1223 A189 60f Heinrich von Stephan .60 .35
1224 A189 125f Yacoub al-Sukkar 1.25 .75
Nos. 1222-1224 (3) 2.25 1.34

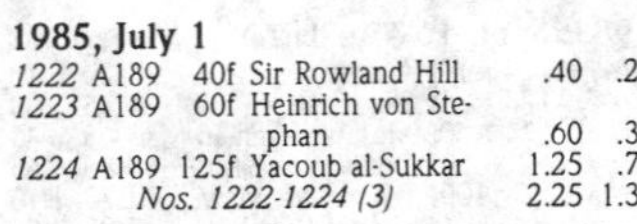

1st Convention of Jordanian Expatriates A190

Various designs.

1985, July 20 **Photo.**

1225 A190 40f multicolored .40 .24
1226 A190 60f multicolored .60 .35
1227 A190 125f multicolored 1.25 .75
Nos. 1225-1227 (3) 2.25 1.34

Intl. Youth Year — A191

Various designs.

1985, Aug. 11 Litho. ***Perf. 13½x13***

1228 A191 10f multicolored .15 .15
1229 A191 25f multicolored .25 .15
1230 A191 40f multicolored .40 .24
1231 A191 60f multicolored .60 .35
1232 A191 125f multicolored 1.25 .75
Nos. 1228-1232 (5) 2.65 1.64

World Tourism Organization, 10th Anniv. — A192

1985, Sept. 13 ***Perf. 13½x13***

1233 A192 10f Ruins of the Treasury, Petra .15 .15
1234 A192 25f Jerash Temple .25 .15
1235 A192 40f Roman baths .40 .24
1236 A192 50f Jordanian valley town .50 .30
1237 A192 60f Aqaba Bay .60 .35
1238 A192 125f Roman amphitheater 1.25 .75
Nos. 1233-1238 (6) 3.15 1.94

An imperf. 100f souvenir sheet exists picturing flower, 10 and natl. flag.

UN Child Survival Campaign — A193

Various designs.

1985, Oct. 7

1239 A193 25f multicolored .25 .15
1240 A193 40f multicolored .40 .24
1241 A193 60f multicolored .60 .35
1242 A193 125f multicolored 1.25 .75
Nos. 1239-1242 (4) 2.50 1.49

An imperf. 100f souvenir sheet exists picturing campaign emblem and the faces of healthy children.

5th Jerash Festival A194

1985, Oct. 21

1243 A194 10f Opening ceremony, 1980 .15 .15
1244 A194 25f Folk dancers .25 .15
1245 A194 40f Dancers .40 .24
1246 A194 60f Choir, Roman theater .60 .35
1247 A194 100f King and Queen 1.00 .60
Nos. 1243-1247 (5) 2.40 1.49

UN, 40th Anniv. A195

1985, Oct. 25 Photo. ***Perf. 13x13½***

1248 A195 60f multicolored .60 .35
1249 A195 125f multicolored 1.25 .75

King Hussein, 50th Birthday A196

Various photos of King.

1985, Nov. 14 Litho. ***Perf. 14½***

1250 A196 10f multicolored .15 .15
1251 A196 25f multicolored .25 .15
1252 A196 40f multicolored .40 .24
1253 A196 60f multicolored .60 .35
1254 A196 100f multicolored 1.00 .60
Nos. 1250-1254 (5) 2.40 1.49

An imperf. 200f souvenir sheet exists picturing flags, King Hussein and Dome of the Rock.

Restoration of Al Aqsa Mosque, Jerusalem A196a

1985, Nov. 25 Litho. ***Perf. 13x13½***

1254A A196a 5f multicolored *.65 .65*
1254B A196a 10f multicolored *1.40 1.00*

Police A197

1985, Dec. 18

1255 A197 40f Patrol car .30 .20
1256 A197 60f Crossing guard .42 .28
1257 A197 125f Police academy .90 .60
Nos. 1255-1257 (3) 1.62 1.08

Launch of ARABSAT-1, 1st Anniv. — A198

1986, Feb. 8 Litho. ***Perf. 13½x13***

1258 A198 60f Satellite in orbit .32 .20
1259 A198 100f Over map of Arab countries .55 .32

Arabization of the Army, 30th Anniv. — A199

40f, King Hussein presenting flag. 60f, Greeting army sergeant. 100f, Hussein addressing army.

1986, Mar. 1 ***Perf. 11½x12½***

1260 A199 40f multicolored .22 .15
1261 A199 60f multicolored .32 .20
1262 A199 100f multicolored .55 .32
Nos. 1260-1262 (3) 1.09 .67

An imperf. souvenir sheet exists with design of 100f.

Natl. Independence, 40th Anniv. — A200

Design: King Abdullah decorating soldier.

1986, May 25 ***Perf. 12½x11½***

1263 A200 160f multicolored .88 .52

Arab Revolt against Turkey, 70th Anniv. — A201

Unattributed paintings (details): 40f, The four sons of King Hussein, Prince of Mecca, vert. 60f, Abdullah, retainers and bodyguard. 160f, Abdullah and followers on horseback.

Perf. 12½x11½, 11½x12½

1986, June 10

1264 A201 40f multicolored .22 .15
1265 A201 60f multicolored .32 .20
1266 A201 160f multicolored .88 .52
Nos. 1264-1266 (3) 1.42 .87

An imperf. 200f souvenir sheet exists picturing the Arab Revolt flag, King Abdullah and text from independence declaration.

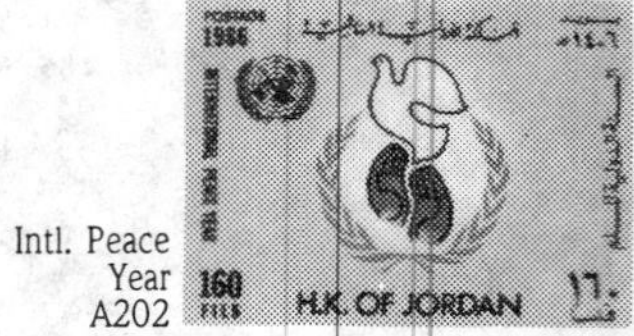

Intl. Peace Year A202

1986, July 1 Litho. ***Perf. 13½x13***

1267 A202 160f multicolored .90 .55
1268 A202 240f multicolored 1.35 .80

King Hussein Medical City Cardiac Center A203

1986, Aug. 11

1269 A203 40f Cardiac Center .22 .15
1270 A203 60f Surgery .35 .22
1271 A203 100f Surgery, diff. .55 .32
Nos. 1269-1271 (3) 1.12 .69

UN, 40th Anniv. — A204

Excerpts from King Hussein's speech: 40f, In Arabic. 80f, Arabic, diff. 100f, English.

1986, Sept. 27 *Perf. 12½x11½*

1272	A204	40f multicolored	.22	.15
1273	A204	80f multicolored	.45	.28
1274	A204	100f multicolored	.55	.32
		Nos. 1272-1274 (3)	1.22	.75

An imperf. 200f stamp 90x70mm exists picturing speech in Arabic and English, King Hussein at podium.

Arab Postal Union, 35th Anniv. A205

1987, Apr. 12 Litho. *Perf. 13½x13*

1275	A205	80f Old post office	.45	.28
1276	A205	160f New post office	.90	.55

Chemical Soc. Emblem and Chemists A206

Designs: 60f, Jaber ibn Hayyan al-Azdi (720-813). 80f, Abu-al-Qasem al-Majreeti (950-1007). 240f, Abu-Bakr al-Razi (864-932).

1987, Apr. 24

1277	A206	60f multicolored	.35	.22
1278	A206	80f multicolored	.45	.28
1279	A206	240f multicolored	1.35	.80
		Nos. 1277-1279 (3)	2.15	1.30

SOS Children's Village A207

1987, May 7

1280	A207	80f Village in Amman	.45	.28
1281	A207	240f Child, bird mural	1.35	.80

4th Brigade, 40th Anniv. A208

1987, June 10

1282	A208	60f shown	.35	.22
1283	A208	80f Soldiers in armored vehicle	.45	.28

Size: 70x91mm

Imperf

1284	A208	160f Four veterans	.90	.55
		Nos. 1282-1284 (3)	1.70	1.05

Indigenous Birds A209

1987, June 24

1285	A209	10f Hoopoe	.15	.15
1286	A209	40f Palestine sunbird	.30	.20
1287	A209	50f Black-headed bunting	.38	.25
1288	A209	60f Spur-winged plover	.45	.30
1289	A209	80f Greenfinch	.60	.40
1290	A209	100f Black-winged stilt	.75	.50
		Nos. 1285-1290 (6)	2.63	1.80

King Hussein — A210

1987, June 24 Litho. *Perf. 13x13½*

1291	A210	60f multicolored	.45	.30
1292	A210	80f multicolored	.60	.40
1293	A210	160f multicolored	1.20	.80
1294	A210	240f multicolored	1.80	1.20
		Nos. 1291-1294 (4)	4.05	2.70

Battle of Hittin, 800th Anniv. A211

Dome of the Rock and Saladin (1137-1193), Conqueror of Jerusalem — A212

1987, July 4

1295	A211	60f Battle, Jerusalem	.35	.24
1296	A211	80f Horseman, Jerusalem, Dome of the Rock	.45	.30
1297	A211	100f Saladin	.75	.50
		Nos. 1295-1297 (3)	1.55	1.04

Souvenir Sheet

Perf. 12x12½

1298	A212	100f shown	.75	.50

No. 1298 exists imperf.

Natl. Coat of Arms — A213

Perf. 11½x12½

1987, Aug. 11 **Litho.**

1299	A213	80f multicolored	.60	.40
1300	A213	160f multicolored	1.20	.80

Amman Industrial Park at Sahab A214

1987, Aug. 11 *Perf. 13½x13*

1301	A214	80f multicolored	.60	.40

University Crest A215

University Entrance — A216

Perf. 11½x11, 12½x11½

1987, Sept. 2

1302	A215	60f multicolored	.45	.30
1303	A216	80f multicolored	.60	.40

University of Jordan, 25th anniv.

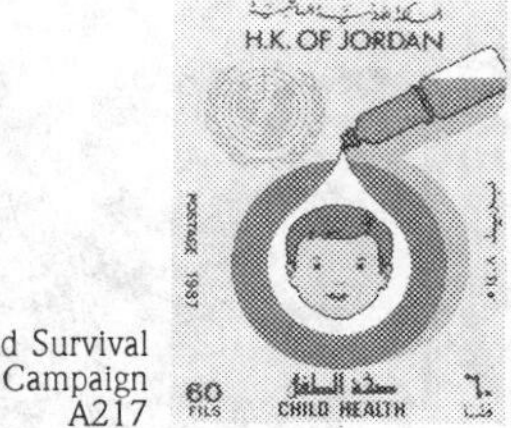

UN Child Survival Campaign A217

1987, Oct. 5 Litho. *Perf. 13x13½*

1304	A217	60f Oral vaccine	.45	.30
1305	A217	80f Natl. flag, child	.60	.40
1306	A217	160f Growth monitoring	1.20	.80
		Nos. 1304-1306 (3)	2.25	1.50

Parliament, 40th Anniv. — A218

1987, Oct. 20 *Perf. 13½x13*

1307	A218	60f Opening ceremony, 1947	.45	.30
1308	A218	80f In session, 1987	.60	.40

A219

Special Arab Summit Conference, Amman — A220

1987, Nov. 8

1309	A219	60f multicolored	.45	.30
1310	A219	80f multicolored	.60	.40
1311	A219	160f multicolored	1.20	.80
1312	A219	240f multicolored	1.80	1.20
		Nos. 1309-1312 (4)	4.05	2.70

Size: 90x66mm

Imperf

1313	A220	100f multicolored		

King Hussein, Dag Hammarskjold Peace Prize Winner for 1987 — A221

1988, Feb. 6 Litho. *Perf. 12½*

1314	A221	80f Hussein, woman, vert.	.60	.40
1315	A221	160f shown	1.20	.80

Natl. Victory at the 1987 Arab Military Basketball Championships — A222

1988, Mar. 1 *Perf. 13½x13*

1316	A222	60f Golden Sword Award	.45	.30
1317	A222	80f Hussein congratulating team	.60	.40
1318	A222	160f Jump ball	1.20	.80
		Nos. 1316-1318 (3)	2.25	1.50

WHO, 40th Anniv. — A223

1988, Apr. 7 Photo. *Perf. 13x13½*

1319	A223	60f multicolored	.55	.38
1320	A223	80f multicolored	.72	.48

Arab Scouts, 75th Anniv. — A224

1988, July 2 Litho. *Perf. 13x13½*

1321	A224	60f multicolored	.45	.35
1322	A224	80f multicolored	.60	.45

Birds A225

1988, July 21 Litho. *Perf. 11½x12*

1323	A225	10f Crested lark	.15	.15
1324	A225	20f Stone curlew	.15	.15
1325	A225	30f Redstart	.20	.15
1326	A225	40f Blackbird	.28	.22
1327	A225	50f Rock dove	.35	.28
1328	A225	160f Smyrna kingfisher	1.10	.82

Size: 71x90mm

Imperf

1328A	A225	310f Six species	3.75	2.75
		Nos. 1323-1328A (7)	5.98	4.52

Restoration of San'a, Yemen Arab Republic
A226

1988, Aug. 11 Litho. *Perf. 12x11½*
1329 A226 80f multicolored .60 .45
1330 A226 160f multicolored 1.20 .90

Historic Natl. Sites
A227

1988, Aug. 11 *Perf. 13½x13*
1331 A227 60f Umm Al-rasas .45 .35
1332 A227 80f Umm Oais .60 .45
1333 A227 160f Iraq Al-amir 1.20 .90
Nos. 1331-1333 (3) 2.25 1.70

An imperf. souvenir sheet of 3 exists containing one each Nos. 1331-1333.

1988 Summer Olympics, Seoul — A228

1988, Sept. 17 Litho. *Perf. 13x13½*
1334 A228 10f Tennis .15 .15
1335 A228 60f Character trademark .45 .35
1336 A228 80f Running, swimming .60 .45
1337 A228 120f Basketball .90 .68
1338 A228 160f Soccer 1.20 .90
Nos. 1334-1338 (5) 3.30 2.53

Size: 70x91mm

Imperf

1339 A228 100f Emblems

Royal Jordanian Airlines, 25th Anniv. — A229

1988, Dec. 15 Litho. *Perf. 11½x12*
1340 A229 60f Ruins of Petra .42 .32
1341 A229 80f Aircraft, world map .55 .42

UN Declaration of Human Rights, 40th Anniv. — A230

1988, Dec. 10
1342 A230 80f multicolored .55 .42
1343 A230 160f multicolored 1.10 .82

Arab Cooperation Council, Feb. 16 — A231

1989 Litho. *Perf. 13½x13*
1344 A231 10f shown .15 .15
1345 A231 30f multi, diff. .15 .15
1346 A231 40f multi, diff. .20 .15
1347 A231 60f multi, diff. .30 .22
Nos. 1344-1347 (4) .80
Set value .54

Martyrs of Palestine and Their Families
A232

1989 *Perf. 14½*
1348 A232 5f multi .15 .15
1349 A232 10f multi .15 .15
Set value .20 .16

Interparliamentary Union, Cent. — A233

1989 Litho. *Perf. 12*
1350 A233 40f multicolored .22 .16
1351 A233 60f multicolored .35 .25

Arab Housing Day and World Refuge Day
A234

Designs: 5f, Housing complex, emblems, vert. 60f, Housing complex, emblem.

1989
1352 A234 5f multicolored .15 .15
1353 A234 40f shown .22 .16
1354 A234 60f multicolored .35 .25
Set value .60 .55

Ministry of Agriculture, 50th Anniv.
A235

1989 Litho. *Perf. 12*
1355 A235 5f shown .15 .15
1356 A235 40f Tree, anniv. emblem .17 .15
1357 A235 60f Fruit tree, emblem, apiary .25 .16
Set value .46 .30

Arabian Horse Festival
A236

1989 *Perf. 12*
1358 A236 5f shown .15 .15
1359 A236 40f Horse, building facade .17 .15
1360 A236 60f Horse's head, vert. .25 .16
Nos. 1358-1360 (3) .57 .46

Size: 90x70mm

Imperf

1361 A236 100f Mare and foal 7.50 5.00

Natl. Library Assoc.
A237

1989 *Perf. 12*
1362 A237 40f multicolored .15 .15
1363 A237 60f multicolored .22 .15
Set value .24

Mosque of the Martyr King Abdullah — A238

1989 *Perf. 12*
1364 A238 40f multicolored .15 .15
1365 A238 60f multicolored .22 .15

Size: 90x70mm

Imperf

1366 A238 100f multicolored 5.25 5.25

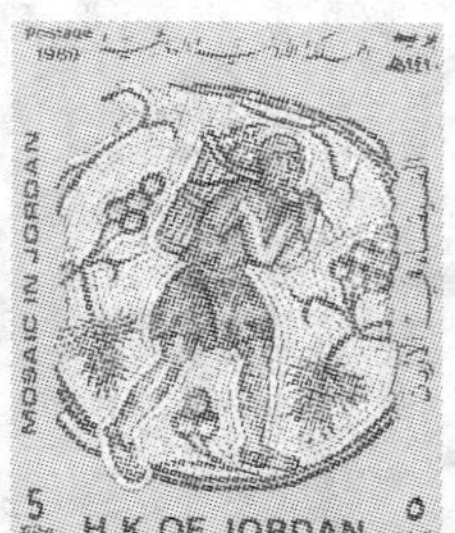

Mosaics
A239

1989, Dec. 23 Litho. *Perf. 12*
1367 A239 5f Man with Basket .15 .15
1368 A239 10f Building .15 .15
1369 A239 40f Deer .42 .28
1370 A239 60f shown .62 .40
1371 A239 80f Town, horiz. .82 .55
Nos. 1367-1371 (5) 2.16 1.53

Size: 90x70mm

Imperf

1372 A239 100f like #1371, horiz. 6.00 4.00

Arab Cooperation Council, 1st Anniv. — A240

1990, Feb. 16 *Perf. 13*
1373 A240 5f multicolored .15 .15
1374 A240 20f multicolored .18 .15
1375 A240 60f multicolored .55 .36
1376 A240 80f multicolored .72 .48
Nos. 1373-1376 (4) 1.60 1.14

Nature Conservation — A241

1990, Apr. 22
1377 A241 40f Horses .20 .15
1378 A241 60f Mountain .30 .15
1379 A241 80f Oasis .40 .25
Nos. 1377-1379 (3) .90 .55

Prince Abdullah's Arrival in Ma'an, 70th Anniv. — A243

1990 Litho. *Perf. 13½x13*
1382 A243 40f org & multi .15 .15
1383 A243 60f grn & multi .22 .15

Size: 90x70mm

Imperf

1384 A243 200f multicolored 2.75 1.80

UN Development Program, 40th Anniv.
A244

1990 *Perf. 13*
1385 A244 60f multicolored .22 .15
1386 A244 80f multicolored .30 .20

King Hussein — A245

1991 Litho. *Perf. 12x13½*
1387 A245 5f yel org & multi .15 .15
1391 A245 40f orange & multi .20 .15
1393 A245 60f blue & multi .30 .15
1395 A245 80f pink & multi .45 .22
1397 A245 240f brown & multi .70 .35
1398 A245 320f red lilac & multi .90 .45
1399 A245 1d yel green & multi 2.80 1.40
Nos. 1387-1399 (7) 5.50 2.87

This is an expanding set. Numbers will change if necessary.

Endangered Animals — A246

1991, Sept. 1 Litho. *Perf. 13x13½*
1401 A246 5f Nubian ibex .15 .15
1402 A246 40f Onager .18 .15
1403 A246 80f Arabian gazelle .35 .18
1404 A246 160f Arabian oryx .70 .25
Nos. 1401-1404 (4) 1.38
Set value .60

Energy Rationalization Program — A247

Designs: 5f, Light bulbs. 40f, Solar panels, sun, vert. 80f, Electric table lamp, vert.

Perf. 13½x13, 13x13½

1991, Oct. 3 **Litho.**

1405 A247 5f multicolored .15 .15
1406 A247 40f multicolored .18 .15
1407 A247 80f multicolored .35 .18
Set value .56 .28

Grain Production for Food Security A248

1991, Oct. 16 ***Perf. 13½x13***

1408 A248 5f Different grains .15 .15
1409 A248 40f shown .18 .15
1410 A248 80f Wheat stalk, kernels .35 .18
Set value .56 .28

Palestinian Uprising — A249

1991, Nov. 29 **Litho.** ***Perf. 11***

1411 A249 20f multicolored .68 .35

Blood Donation Campaign A250

1991, Nov. 14 **Litho.** ***Perf. 13½x13***

1412 A250 80f multicolored .30 .15
1413 A250 160f multicolored .60 .30

Expo '92, Seville A251

1992, Feb. 20

1414 A251 80f multicolored .30 .15
1415 A251 320f multicolored 1.20 .60

Healthy Hearts A252

80f, Man & woman, heart at center of scale, vert.

Perf. 13x13½, 13½x13

1992, Apr. 7 **Litho.**

1416 A252 80f multicolored .38 .20
1417 A252 125f multicolored .60 .30

SOS Children's Village, 'Aqaba A253

1992, Apr. 30 **Litho.** ***Perf. 13½x13***

1418 A253 80f shown .40 .20
1419 A253 125f Village .60 .30

1992 Summer Olympics, Barcelona A254

Stylized designs with Barcelona Olympic emblem: 5fr, Judo, 40f, Runner, vert. 80f, Diver. 125f, Flag, Cobi, map, vert. 160f, Table tennis.
100f, Incorporates all designs of set.

Perf. 13½x13, 13x13½

1992, July 25 **Litho.**

1420 A254 5f multicolored .15 .15
1421 A254 40f multicolored .16 .15
1422 A254 80f multicolored .32 .16
1423 A254 125f multicolored .50 .25
1424 A254 160f multicolored .65 .32
Nos. 1420-1424 (5) 1.78
Set value .82

Size: 70x90mm

Imperf

1425 A254 100f multicolored 11.00 5.50

King Hussein, 40th Anniv. of Accession A255

Designs: 40f, Flags, King in full dress uniform, vert. 125f, King wearing headdress, flags. 160f, King in business suit, crown. 200f, Portrait.

1992, Aug. 11 ***Perf. 13x13½***

1426 A255 40f multicolored .16 .15

Perf. 13½x13

1427 A255 80f shown .32 .16
1428 A255 125f multicolored .50 .25
1429 A255 160f multicolored .65 .32
Nos. 1426-1429 (4) 1.63 .88

Size: 90x70mm

Imperf

1430 A255 200f multicolored 6.00 3.00

Butterflies A256

5f, Danaus chrysippus. 40f, Aporia cartaegi. 80f, Papilio machaon. 160f, Pseudochazara telephassa. 200f, Same as #1431-1434.

1992, Dec. 20 **Litho.** ***Perf. 13½x13***

1431 A256 5f multicolored .15 .15
1432 A256 40f multicolored .15 .15
1433 A256 80f multicolored .32 .16
1434 A256 160f multicolored .65 .32
Nos. 1431-1434 (4) 1.27 .78

Imperf

Size: 90x70mm

1435 A256 200f multicolored 9.00 4.50

See Nos. 1448-1452.

Intl. Customs Day — A257

1993, Jan. 26 **Litho.** ***Perf. 13½x13***

1436 A257 80f green & multi .38 .18
1437 A257 125f pale orange & multi .58 .30

Royal Scientific Society A258

1993, June 10 **Litho.** ***Perf. 12½x13***

1438 A258 80f multicolored .35 .18

Es Salt Municipality, Cent. — A259

1993, Sept. 1 **Litho.** ***Perf. 12***

1439 A259 80f pink & multi .38 .18
1440 A259 125f green & multi .58 .28
a. Souvenir sheet of 2, #1439-1440, imperf. 4.50 4.50

No. 1440a sold for 200f.

Great Arab Revolt and Army Day A260

Designs: 5f, Rockets, planes, tank, King Hussein, 40f, King Hussein, military activities. 80f, Amir Abdullah ibn Hussein, Dome of the Rock, map, flags. 125f, Amir Abdullah ibn Hussein, Dome of the Rock, riders. 100f, King Hussein, flags.

1993, June 10

1441 A260 5f multicolored .15 .15
1442 A260 40f multicolored .16 .15
1443 A260 80f multicolored .32 .16
1444 A260 125f multicolored .50 .25
Nos. 1441-1444 (4) 1.13 .71

Size: 90x70mm

Imperf

1445 A260 100f multicolored 2.75 2.75

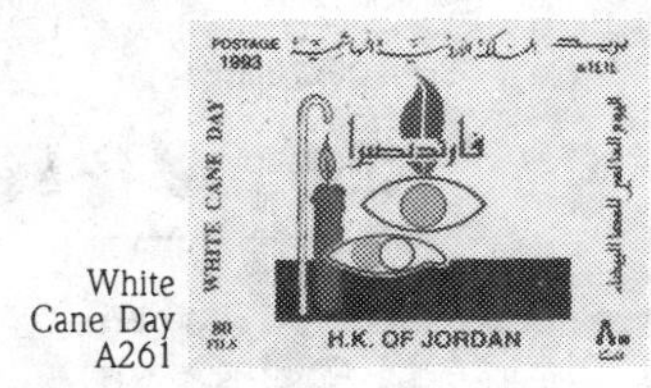

White Cane Day A261

Design: 125f, Lighted world, cane, eye, vert.

1993, Oct. 23 **Litho.** ***Perf. 12***

1446 A261 80f shown .40 .20
1447 A261 125f multicolored .60 .30

Butterfly Type of 1992

Designs: 5f, Lampides boeticus. 40f, Melanargria titea. 80f, Allancastria deyrollei. 160f, Gonepteryx cleopatra. 100f, Same designs as Nos. 1448-1451.

1993, Oct. 10 **Litho.** ***Perf. 12***

1448 A256 5f multicolored .15 .15
1449 A256 40f multicolored .18 .15
1450 A256 80f multicolored .35 .18
1451 A256 160f multicolored .70 .35
Nos. 1448-1451 (4) 1.38 .83

Size: 83x65mm

Imperf

1452 A256 100f multicolored 11.00 5.50

UN Declaration of Human Rights, 45th Anniv. — A262

1993, Dec. 10 ***Perf. 12***

1453 A262 40f yellow & multi .18 .15
1454 A262 160f red & multi .70 .35

Recovery & Homecoming, 1st Anniv. — A263

King Hussein: 80f, Crowd. 125f, Waving to people. 160f, Embracing woman. 100f, Standing on airplane ramp.

1993, Nov. 25

1455 A263 80f multicolored .35 .18
1456 A263 125f multicolored .55 .28
1457 A263 160f multicolored .70 .35
Nos. 1455-1457 (3) 1.60 .81

Size: 85x65

Imperf

1458 A263 100f multicolored 3.50 1.75

World AIDS Day — A264

1993, Dec. 1 ***Perf. 12***

1459 A264 80f red & multi .35 .18
1460 A264 125f green & multi .55 .28

Size: 83x70mm

Imperf

1461 A264 200f like #1459-1460 3.50 1.75

King Hussein A265

King Hussein wearing: 40f, Military uniform. 80f, Traditional costume. 125f, Business suit. 160f, 100f, Dress uniform in portrait with Queen Noor, horiz.

1993, Nov. 14 ***Perf. 12***

1462 A265 40f multi, horiz. .18 .15
1463 A265 80f multi, horiz. .35 .18
1464 A265 125f multi, horiz. .55 .28
1465 A265 160f multicolored .70 .35
Nos. 1462-1465 (4) 1.78 .96

Size: 82x68mm

Imperf

1466 A265 100f multicolored *4.75 2.50*

Assumption of Constitutional Powers by King Hussein, 40th anniv.

Saladin (1138-1193), Dome of the Rock — A266

1993, Nov. 25 ***Perf. 12***

1467 A266 40f blue & multi .18 .15
1468 A266 80f gray & multi .35 .18
1469 A266 125f yellow & multi .55 .28
Nos. 1467-1469 (3) 1.08 .61

Triumphal Arch, Jerash — A267

Perf. 12x13½ (#5f, 50f, 160f, 320f, 1d), 12 (#25f, 240f, 500f), 14 (#100f, 200f, 300f, 400f)

1993-96 **Litho.**

1470 A267 5f blue & multi
1471 A267 25f pale violet & multi
1472 A267 50f yellow & multi
1474 A267 100f apple green & multi
1476 A267 160f yellow & multi .70 .35
1476A A267 200f silver & multi
1477 A267 240f pink & multi
1477A A267 300f pink & multi
1478 A267 320f brown & multi
1478A A267 400f bright blue & multi
1479 A267 500f bister & multi
1480 A267 1d olive & multi

Issued: 5f, 320f, 1/13/93 (dated 1992); 25f, 1/18/96 (dated 1995); 100f, 200f, 300f, 5/15/96; 1d, 1/13/93; 160f, 1/13/93; 240f, 3/23/94; 50f, 1975; 400f, 5/15/96; 500f, 10/25/96.

This is an expanding set. Numbers may change. Numbers have been reserved for additional values in this set.

Hashemite Charity Organization — A268

Designs: 80f, Loading supplies into plane. 125f, People gathering at plane.

1994, Mar. 20 **Litho.** ***Perf. 12***

1481 A268 80f multicolored .35 .18
1482 A268 125f multicolored .55 .28

Third Hashemite Restoration of Al Aqsa Mosque, Dome of the Rock — A269

King Hussein with various scenes of restoration.

1994, Apr. 18 **Litho.** ***Perf. 12x12½***

1483 A269 80f yellow & multi .28 .15
1484 A269 125f lt orange & multi .45 .22
1485 A269 240f lilac & multi .85 .42
Nos. 1483-1485 (3) 1.58 .79

Imperf

Size: 90x70mm

1486 A269 100f green & multi *5.25 2.75*

ILO, 75th Anniv. A270

1994, June 13 **Litho.** ***Perf. 12***

1487 A270 80f yellow & multi .28 .15
1488 A270 125f brt pink & multi .45 .22

Intl. Red Cross and Red Crescent Societies, 75th Anniv. — A271

1994, May 8 ***Perf. 12***

1489 A271 80f shown .28 .15
1490 A271 160f Doves, emblems, vert .55 .28

Size: 61x78mm

Imperf

1491 A271 200f #1489-1490 *5.50 2.75*

Intl. Year of the Family A272

1994, Aug. 11 **Litho.** ***Perf. 12***

1492 A272 80f green & multi .32 .16
1493 A272 125f pink & multi .50 .25
1494 A272 160f yellow & multi .65 .32
Nos. 1492-1494 (3) 1.47 .73

Jordanian Participation in UN Peacekeeping Forces — A274

Designs: 80f, King Hussein greeting troops. 125f, King inspecting troops. 160f, Checkpoint.

Intl. Olympic Committee, Cent. — A273

Olympic rings and: 80f, Globe, venue symbols, vert. 100f, Jordanian colors. 125f, Venue symbols, diff., vert. 160f, shown. 240f, Torch.

1994, June 23

1495 A273 80f blue & multi .32 .16
1496 A273 125f multicolored .50 .25
1497 A273 160f multicolored .65 .32
1498 A273 240f multicolored 1.00 .50
Nos. 1495-1498 (4) 2.47 1.23

Size: 90x70mm

Imperf

1499 A273 100f multicolored *6.75 3.50*

1994, Aug. 11 **Litho.** ***Perf. 12***

1500 A274 80f multicolored .28 .15
1501 A274 125f multicolored .45 .22
1502 A274 160f multicolored .55 .28
Nos. 1500-1502 (3) 1.28 .65

Water Conservation Day — A275

Designs: 80f, Hands, water droplet. 125f, Water faucet, foods, factory. 160f, Child, rain drops.

1994, Nov. 14 **Litho.** ***Perf. 14***

1503 A275 80f multicolored .28 .15
1504 A275 125f multicolored .45 .22
1505 A275 160f multicolored .55 .28
Nos. 1503-1505 (3) 1.28 .65

ICAO, 50th Anniv. A276

1994, Oct. 25 ***Perf. 12***

1506 A276 80f green & multi .28 .15
1507 A276 125f red & multi .45 .22
1508 A276 160f blue & multi .55 .28
Nos. 1506-1508 (3) 1.28 .65

Crown Prince's Award, 10th Anniv. A277

1994, Dec. 11 **Litho.** ***Perf. 12***

1509 A277 80f yel grn & multi .28 .15
1510 A277 125f org brn & multi .42 .22
1511 A277 160f vio bl & multi .55 .28
Nos. 1509-1511 (3) 1.25 .65

UN, 50th Anniv. A278

1995, Apr. 1 **Litho.** ***Perf. 14***

1512 A278 80f green & multi .40 .20
1513 A278 125f pink & multi .60 .30

May Day A279

Designs: 80f, Emblem, workers, flag. 125f, Emblem, world map, worker. 160f, Hands holding wrench, torch, Jordanian map, emblem.

1995, May 1

1514 A279 80f multicolored .28 .15
1515 A279 125f multicolored .42 .22
1516 A279 160f multicolored .55 .28
Nos. 1514-1516 (3) 1.25 .65

Jordan Week in Japan A280

Globe in two hemishperes with olive branches and: 125f, Japanese, Jordanian flags. 160f, Flags above wall.

1995, May 22 **Litho.** ***Perf. 14***

1517 A280 80f green & multi .35 .20
1518 A280 125f pink & multi .55 .25
1519 A280 160f gray & multi .70 .35
Nos. 1517-1519 (3) 1.60 .80

Opening of Al al-Bayt University A281

1995, Feb. 8 **Litho.** ***Perf. 12***

1520 A281 80f green blue & multi .30 .15
1521 A281 125f olive green & multi .50 .25
a. Souvenir sheet, #1520-1521, imperf. .80 .40

No. 1521a sold for 200f. Nos. 1520-1521 are dated 1994.

Petra, the Rose City A282

Archaeological discoveries: 50f, Amphitheater. 75f, Facial carvings, bowl, pitcher. 80f, Columns of building, vert. 160f, Front of building with columns, vert. 200f, Building in side of mountain.

1995, Aug. 11 **Litho.** ***Perf. 14***

1524 A282 50f multicolored .20 .15
1525 A282 75f multicolored .25 .15
1526 A282 80f multicolored .30 .15
1527 A282 160f multicolored .60 .30
Nos. 1524-1527 (4) 1.35 .75

Size: 90x70mm

Imperf

1528 A282 200f multicolored *5.25 2.75*

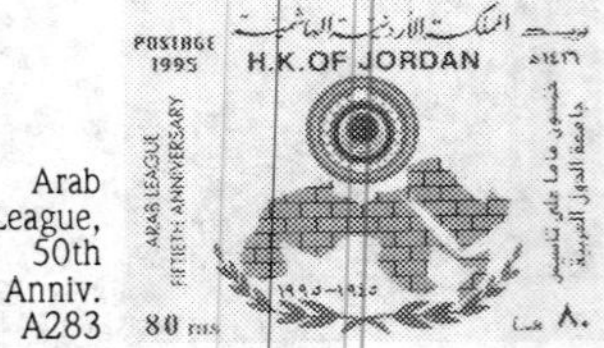

Arab League, 50th Anniv. A283

1995, Sept. 20 **Litho.** ***Perf. 14***

1529 A283 80f green & multi .25 .15
1530 A283 125f pink & multi .40 .20
1531 A283 160f gray & multi .50 .25
Nos. 1529-1531 (3) 1.15 .60

FAO, 50th Anniv. A284

Designs: 125f, "50," FAO emblem, shafts of grain. 160f, UN, FAO emblems, "50."

1995, Oct. 16 Litho. *Perf. 14*

1532 A284 80f shown .30 .15
1533 A284 125f multicolored .50 .25
1534 A284 160f multicolored .65 .30
Nos. 1532-1534 (3) 1.45 .70

Middle East and North Africa Economic Summit, Amman — A285

1995, Oct. 29 *Perf. 12*

1535 A285 80f brt pink & multi .30 .15
1536 A285 125f org yel & multi .50 .25

The Deaf A286

1995, Nov. 30 *Perf. 14*

1537 A286 80f shown .30 .15
1538 A286 125f Emblems, hand sign .50 .25

King Hussein, 60th Birthday A287

Designs: 40f, Crown over King's picture in business suit. 80f, Crown, flag, dove, ruins of Petra, King in traditional head wear, military uniform. 100f, King dress uniform, crown, "60." 125f, King in traditional head wear, business suit, crown, flag, olive branch. 160f, Flag, King in business suit. 200f, "60," Dome of the Rock, King in dress uniform, olive branch.

1995, Nov. 14

1539 A287 25f multicolored .15 .15
1540 A287 40f multicolored .15 .15
1541 A287 80f multicolored .30 .15
1542 A287 100f multicolored .40 .20
1543 A287 125f multicolored .50 .25
1544 A287 160f multicolored .65 .30
Nos. 1539-1544 (6) 2.15 1.20

Size: 83x63mm

Imperf

1545 A287 200f multicolored *5.25 2.75*

Independence, 50th Anniv. — A288

King Hussein and: No. 1547, Outline map of Jordan, crown, dove of peace, Amir Abdullah ibn Hussein. 300f, Jordanian monuments, flag.

No. 1549, Map of Jordan surrounded by wreath, dove, national flags.

1996, May 25 Litho. *Perf. 12*

1546 A288 100f multicolored .40 .20
1547 A288 200f multicolored .75 .40
1548 A288 300f multicolored 1.15 .60
Nos. 1546-1548 (3) 2.30 1.20

Size: 86x66mm

1549 A288 200f multicolored *2.60 1.30*

1996 Summer Olympic Games, Atlanta A289

1996 Olympic Games Emblem and: 50f, Natl. flag, Olympic rings, sports pictograms. 100f, Sports pictograms. 200f, Hands. 300f, Torch, Olympic rings, natl. flag.

1996, July 19 Litho. *Perf. 12*

1550 A289 50f multicolored .20 .15
1551 A289 100f multicolored .35 .20
1552 A289 200f multicolored .70 .35
1553 A289 300f multicolored 1.00 .50
Nos. 1550-1553 (4) 2.25 1.20

Protection of the Ozone Layer — A290

1996, Sept. 16

1554 A290 100f multicolored .35 .20

UNICEF, 50th Anniv. A291

1996, Dec. 11 Litho. *Perf. 12*

1555 A291 100f green & multi .35 .15
1556 A291 200f gray lilac & multi .70 .35

Crown Prince El-Hassan, 50th Birthday — A292

Designs: 50f, On horseback. 100f, Wearing suit & tie, vert. No. 1559, Natl. flag, wearing traditional attire.

No. 1560, Wearing graduation cap.

1997, Mar. 20 Litho. *Perf. 12*

1557 A292 50f multicolored .20 .15
1558 A292 100f multicolored .35 .20
1559 A292 200f multicolored .70 .35
Nos. 1557-1559 (3) 1.25 .70

Size: 84x64mm

Imperf

1560 A292 200f multicolored *3.75 1.90*

Heinrich von Stephan (1831-97) A293

1997, Apr. 8 Litho. *Perf. 12*

1561 A293 100f multicolored .35 .20
1562 A293 200f multicolored .70 .35

Discovery of the Madeba Mosaic Map, Cent. A294

1997, Apr. 7

1563 A294 100f Karak, vert. .35 .20
1564 A294 200f River Jordan .70 .35
1565 A294 300f Jerusalem, vert. 1.00 .50
Nos. 1563-1565 (3) 2.05 1.05

Size: 86x67mm

Imperf

1566 A294 100f Entire map *5.25 2.60*

Jordanian Rosefinch A295

1997, May 25 Litho. *Perf. 12*

1567 A295 50f multicolored .20 .15
1568 A295 100f multi, diff. .35 .20
1569 A295 150f multi, diff. .55 .25
1570 A295 200f multi, diff. .70 .35
Nos. 1567-1570 (4) 1.80 .95

Jerash Festival, 15th Anniv. A296

Designs: 50f, Couples in traditional costumes, ruins. 100f, Symphony orchestra, silhouettes of buildings. 150f, Pillars, parade of dignitaries. 200f, Women in traditional costumes, crowd, ruins.

15d, Queen Noor lighting torch.

1997 Litho. *Perf. 12*

1571 A296 50f multicolored .20 .15
1572 A296 100f multicolored .35 .20
1573 A296 150f multicolored .50 .25
1574 A296 200f multicolored .65 .35
Nos. 1571-1574 (4) 1.70 .95

Size: 90x70mm

Imperf

1575 A296 15d multicolored 5.25 2.60

Natl. Forum for Women A297

Emblem and: 50f, Women in tradtional and modern dress, vert. 100f, Natl. flag, flame, book. 150fr, Natl. flag, women seated at conference table.

1997 Litho. *Perf. 12*

1576 A297 50f multicolored .20 .15
1577 A297 100f multicolored .35 .20
1578 A297 150f multicolored .50 .25
Nos. 1576-1578 (3) 1.05 .60

Jordanian Team, 1997 Arab Soccer Champions — A298

Designs: 50f, Team parading in stadium. 75f, Team in red uniforms. 100f, Team in white uniforms, ceremony.

200f, Formal presentation to King Hussein, motorcade.

1997

1579 A298 50f multicolored .20 .15
1580 A298 75f multicolored .25 .15
1581 A298 100f multicolored .35 .20
Nos. 1579-1581 (3) .80 .50

Size: 91x70mm

Imperf

1582 A298 200f multicolored *3.75 1.80*

House of Parliament, 50th Anniv. — A299

100f, Outside view of building, drawing. 200f, Speaker, members assembled in chamber.

1997, Nov. 1 *Perf. 12½*

1583 A299 100f multicolored .35 .20
1584 A299 200f multicolored .70 .35

SEMI-POSTAL STAMPS

Locust Campaign Issue

Nos. 145-156 Overprinted

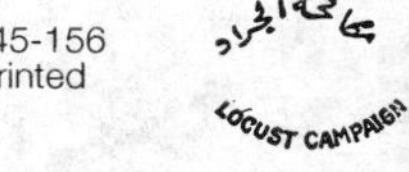

1930, Apr. 1 Wmk. 4 *Perf. 14*

B1 A1 2(m) Prus blue .60 2.00
a. Inverted overprint 200.00
B2 A1 3(m) rose .60 2.00
B3 A1 4(m) green .85 3.00
B4 A1 5(m) orange 10.00 12.00
a. Double overprint 350.00
B5 A1 10(m) red 1.00 2.00
B6 A1 15(m) ultra 1.00 2.00
a. Inverted overprint 225.00
B7 A1 20(m) olive grn 1.00 3.00
B8 A2 50(m) claret 4.50 7.00
B9 A2 90(m) bister 10.00 30.00
B10 A2 100(m) lt blue 13.00 32.50
B11 A2 200(m) violet 25.00 70.00
B12 A2 500(m) brown 70.00 110.00
a. "C" of "Locust" omitted 600.00
Nos. B1-B12 (12) 137.55 275.50

These stamps were issued to raise funds to help combat a plague of locusts.

Catalogue values for unused stamps in this section, from this point to the end of the section, are for Never Hinged items.

Jerusalem SP1

1997 Litho. *Perf. 13½x13*

B13 SP1 100f +10f bl & multi .35 .35
B14 SP1 200f +20f yel & multi .75 .75
B15 SP1 300f +30f bl grn & multi 1.10 1.10
Nos. B13-B15 (3) 2.20 2.20

AIR POST STAMPS

Catalogue values for unused stamps in this section are for Never Hinged items.

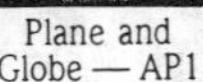

Plane and Globe — AP1

Temple of Artemis, Jerash — AP2

Perf. 13½x13

1950, Sept. 16 Engr. Wmk. 4

No.	Type	Description	Unused	Used
C1	AP1	5f org & red vio	.15	.15
C2	AP1	10f pur & brown	.16	.16
C3	AP1	15f ol grn & rose car	.20	.20
C4	AP1	20f deep blue & blk	.30	.30
C5	AP1	50f rose pink & dl grn	.40	.30
C6	AP1	100f blue & brown	.70	.70
C7	AP1	150f blk & red org	1.00	1.00
		Nos. C1-C7 (7)	2.91	2.81

1954 Unwmk. *Perf. 12*

No.	Type	Description	Unused	Used
C8	AP2	5f blue blk & org	.15	.15
C9	AP2	10f vio brn & ver	.15	.15
C10	AP2	25f bl grn & ultra	.15	.15
C11	AP2	35f dp plum & grnsh bl	.18	.15
C12	AP2	40f car rose & blk	.22	.15
C13	AP2	50f dp ultra & org yel	.25	.25
C14	AP2	100f dk bl & vio brn	.45	.45
C15	AP2	150f stl bl & red brn	.60	.60
		Nos. C8-C15 (8)	2.15	2.05

1958-59 Wmk. 305 *Perf. 12*

No.	Type	Description	Unused	Used
C16	AP2	5f blue blk & org	.15	.15
C17	AP2	10f vio brn & ver	.15	.15
C18	AP2	25f bl grn & ultra	.20	.15
C19	AP2	35f dp plum grnsh bl	.20	.20
C20	AP2	40f car rose & blk	.25	.25
C21	AP2	50f dp ultra & org yel ('59)	.60	.60
		Set value	1.30	1.25

Stadium and Torch — AP3

Perf. 11x11½

1964, July 12 Litho. Wmk. 305

No.	Type	Description	Unused	Used
C22	AP3	1f yellow & multi	.15	.15
C23	AP3	4f red & multi	.15	.15
C24	AP3	10f blue & multi	.15	.15
C25	AP3	35f yel grn & multi	.42	.42
a.		Souvenir sheet of 4, #C22-C25	1.00	1.00
		Set value	.65	.65

Opening of Hussein Sports City. No. C25a also exists imperf.

Gorgeous Bush-Shrike — AP4

Birds: 500f, Ornate hawk-eagle, vert. 1d, Gray-headed kingfisher, vert.

Perf. 14x14½

1964, Dec. 18 Photo. Unwmk.

Birds in Natural Colors

No.	Type	Description	Unused	Used
C26	AP4	150f lt grn, blk & car	1.65	.40
C27	AP4	500f brt bl, blk & grn	8.25	2.75
C28	AP4	1d lt ol grn & blk	16.00	8.25
		Nos. C26-C28 (3)	25.90	11.40

Buying Sets

It is often less expensive to purchase complete sets than individual stamps that make up the set. Set values are provided for many such sets.

Pagoda, Olympic Torch and Emblem — AP5

1965, Mar. 5 Litho. *Perf. 14*

No.	Type	Description	Unused	Used
C29	AP5	10f deep rose	.15	.15
C30	AP5	15f violet	.15	.15
C31	AP5	20f blue	.15	.15
C32	AP5	30f green	.18	.18
C33	AP5	40f brown	.25	.25
C34	AP5	60f carmine rose	.38	.38
		Set value	1.05	1.05

18th Olympic Games, Tokyo, Oct. 10-25, 1964. An imperf. 100f violet blue souvenir sheet exists. Size of stamp: 60x60mm. Value $9.

For overprints see Nos. C42A-C42F.

Forum, Jerash AP6

Antiquities of Jerash: No. C36, South Theater. No. C37, Triumphal arch. No. C38, Temple of Artemis. No. C39, Cathedral steps. No. C40, Artemis Temple, gate. No. C41, Columns. No. C42, Columns and niche, South Theater. Nos. C39-C42 are vertical.

1965, June 22 Photo. *Perf. 14x15*

Center Multicolored

No.	Type	Description	Unused	Used
C35	AP6	55f bright pink	.45	.45
C36	AP6	55f light blue	.45	.45
C37	AP6	55f green	.45	.45
C38	AP6	55f black	.45	.45
C39	AP6	55f light green	.45	.45
C40	AP6	55f carmine rose	.45	.45
C41	AP6	55f gray	.45	.45
C42	AP6	55f blue	.45	.45
		Nos. C35-C42 (8)	3.60	3.60

#C35-C38 are printed in horizontal rows of 4; #C39-C42 in vertical rows of 4; sheets of 16.

Nos. C29-C34 with Bilingual Ovpt. "James McDivitt / Edward White / 2-6-1965" and Rocket

1965, Sept. 25 Litho. *Perf. 14*

No.	Type	Description	Unused	Used
C42A	AP5	10f deep rose	.30	.30
C42B	AP5	15f violet	.45	.45
C42C	AP5	20f blue	.60	.60
C42D	AP5	30f green	.90	.90
C42E	AP5	40f brown	1.25	1.25
C42F	AP5	60f carmine rose	1.75	1.75
		Nos. C42A-C42F (6)	5.25	5.25

The imperf. 100f blue souvenir sheet exists overprinted.

King Hussein Type of Regular Issue

1966, Jan. 15 Photo. *Perf. 14½x14*

Portrait in Brown

No.	Type	Description	Unused	Used
C43	A67	200f brt blue grn	1.50	.75
C44	A67	500f light green	3.75	2.00
C45	A67	1d light ultra	7.50	3.75
		Nos. C43-C45 (3)	12.75	6.50

Animal Type of Regular Issue, 1967

Animals: 4f, Striped hyena. 30f, Arabian stallion. 60f, Persian gazelle.

1967, Feb. 11 Photo. *Perf. 14x15*

No.	Type	Description	Unused	Used
C46	A70	4f dk brn & multi	.15	.15
C47	A70	30f lt bl & multi	.22	.15
C48	A70	60f yellow & multi	.45	.30
		Set value	.70	.50

Game Type of Regular Issue, 1968

Protected Game: 60f, Nubian ibex, vert. 100f, Wild ducks.

1968, Oct. 5 Litho. *Perf. 13½*

No.	Type	Description	Unused	Used
C49	A74	60f multicolored	.75	.75
C50	A74	100f multicolored	1.40	1.40

Easter Type of Regular Issue

Designs: 60f, Altar, Holy Sepulcher. 100f, Feet Washing, Holy Gate, Jerusalem.

1972, Apr. Photo. *Perf. 14x13½*

No.	Type	Description	Unused	Used
C51	A92	60f dk bl & multi	.45	.45
C52	A92	100f multicolored	.75	.75

Aero Club Type of Regular Issue

15f, Two Piper 140s. 20f, R.J.A.C. Beechcraft. 40f, Aero Club emblem with winged horse.

1973, Jan. Photo. *Perf. 13½x14*

No.	Type	Description	Unused	Used
C53	A100	15f blue, blk & red	.15	.15
C54	A100	20f blue, blk & red	.18	.15
C55	A100	40f mag, blk & yel	.38	.22
		Nos. C53-C55 (3)	.71	
		Set value		.38

Agriculture Type of Regular Issue

Design: 100f, Soil conservation.

1973, Dec. 25 *Perf. 13½*

No.	Type	Description	Unused	Used
C56	A110	100f multicolored	.65	.45

King Hussein Driving Car — AP7

1974, Dec. 20 *Perf. 12*

No.	Type	Description	Unused	Used
C57	AP7	30f multicolored	.20	.15
C58	AP7	60f multicolored	.45	.32

Royal Jordanian Automobile Club.

Building Type of Regular Issue

Designs: 50f, Palms, Aqaba. 60f, Obelisk tomb. 80f, Fort of Wadi Rum.

1975, Mar. 1 Photo. *Perf. 13½x14*

No.	Type	Description	Unused	Used
C59	A121	50f pink & multi	.32	.22
C60	A121	60f lt bl & multi	.42	.30
C61	A121	80f yellow & multi	.52	.32
		Nos. C59-C61 (3)	1.26	.84

Hussein Type of Regular Issue

1975, Apr. 8 Photo. *Perf. 14x13½*

Size: 22x27mm

No.	Type	Description	Unused	Used
C62	A123	60f dk grn & brn	.28	.18
C63	A123	100f org brn & brn	.42	.30
C64	A123	120f dp bl & brn	.50	.36
C65	A123	180f brt mag & brn	.85	.50
C66	A123	200f grnsh bl & brn	.90	.50
C67	A123	400f pur & brown	1.75	1.10
C68	A123	500f orange & brn	2.25	1.40
		Nos. C62-C68 (7)	6.95	4.34

POSTAGE DUE STAMPS

Stamps of Regular Issue (Nos. 69, 66-68 Surcharged with New Value like No. 91) Overprinted

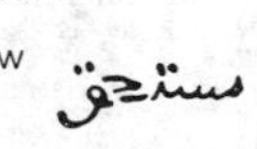

This overprint reads: "Mustahaq" (Tax or Due)

1923 Unwmk. *Perf. 11½*

Typo. Ovpt. "Mustahaq" 10mm long

No.	Type	Description	Unused	Used
J1	A7	½pi on 3pi ol brn	45.00	55.00
a.		Inverted overprint	175.00	175.00
b.		Double overprint	175.00	175.00

Handstamped Overprint 12mm long

No.	Type	Description	Unused	Used
J2	A7	½pi on 3pi ol brn	15.00	20.00
J3	A7	1pi dark blue	9.00	9.00
J4	A7	1½pi violet	9.00	10.00
J5	A7	2pi orange	10.00	10.00
		Nos. J1-J5 (5)	88.00	104.00

These overprints are found double, inverted, etc. as is usual with handstamps.

Stamps of Hejaz Handstamped

حكومة
الشرق العربية
مستحق
٩ نيسان ١٣٤١

No.	Type	Description	Unused	Used
J6	A7	½pi red	1.00	1.25
J7	A7	1pi dark blue	1.10	1.75
J8	A7	1½pi violet	1.40	2.25
J9	A7	2pi orange	2.00	3.00
J10	A7	3pi olive brown	3.00	5.50
J11	A7	5pi olive green	5.50	8.00
		Nos. J6-J11 (6)	14.00	21.75

Type of Palestine, 1918, Overprinted

مستحق
شرق الاردن

1925 Wmk. 4 *Perf. 14*

No.	Type	Description	Unused	Used
J12	A1	1m dark brown	1.10	3.00
J13	A1	2m yellow	1.50	2.00
J14	A1	4m rose	2.50	3.00
J15	A1	8m red	3.00	5.00
J16	A1	13m ultramarine	4.00	5.00
J17	A1	5pi plum	4.50	7.00
a.		Perf. 15x14	37.50	47.50
		Nos. J12-J17 (6)	16.60	25.00

The overprint reads: "Mustahaq. Sharqi al'Ardan." (Tax. Eastern Jordan).

Stamps of Palestine, 1918, Surcharged

مستحق
شرق
الاردن
٤ مليم

1926

No.	Type	Description	Unused	Used
J18	A1	1m on 1m dk brn	2.00	3.00
J19	A1	2m on 1m dk brn	2.00	3.00
J20	A1	4m on 3m Prus bl	2.00	4.00
J21	A1	8m on 3m Prus bl	2.25	4.50
J22	A1	13m on 13m ultra	2.25	5.00
J23	A1	5pi on 13m ultra	3.00	7.00
		Nos. J18-J23 (6)	13.50	26.50

The surcharge reads "Tax—Eastern Jordan" and New Value.

Stamps of Regular Issue, 1927, Overprinted

مستحق

1929

No.	Type	Description	Unused	Used
J24	A1	2m Prussian bl	.70	2.00
J25	A1	10m red	1.00	2.00
J26	A2	50m claret	4.00	8.50
		Nos. J24-J26 (3)	5.70	12.50

With Additional Surcharge

No.	Type	Description	Unused	Used
J27	A1	1(m) on 3(m) rose	.65	2.25
J28	A1	4(m) on 15(m) ultra	1.00	2.25
a.		Inverted surch. and ovpt.	95.00	
J29	A2	20(m) on 100(m) lt bl	3.00	7.00
		Nos. J27-J29 (3)	4.65	11.50

D1

1929 Engr. *Perf. 14*

Size: 17¼x21mm

No.	Type	Description	Unused	Used
J30	D1	1m brown	.40	1.75
a.		Perf. 13½x13	90.00	45.00
J31	D1	2m orange	.40	2.00
J32	D1	4m green	.40	2.25
J33	D1	10m carmine	1.00	2.50
J34	D1	20m olive green	4.00	8.00
J35	D1	50m blue	5.00	10.00
		Nos. J30-J35 (6)	11.20	26.50

See Nos. J39-J43 design with larger type. For surcharge see No. J52. For overprints see Nos. NJ1a, NJ3, NJ5a, NJ6-NJ7.

D2

1942 Unwmk. Litho. *Perf. 13x13½*

No.	Type	Description	Unused	Used
J36	D2	1m dull red brn	.15	.15
J37	D2	2m dl orange yel	.25	.25
J38	D2	10m dark carmine	.50	.50
		Nos. J36-J38 (3)	.90	.90

For overprints see Nos. NJ8-NJ10.

Type of 1929

1943-44 Engr. Wmk. 4 *Perf. 12*
Size: 17¾x21¼mm

No.	Type	Description	Unused	Used
J39	D1	1m orange brn	.15	.15
J40	D1	2m yel orange	.15	.15
J41	D1	4m yel green	.15	.15
J42	D1	10m rose carmine	.15	.15
J43	D1	20m olive green	4.50	4.50
		Nos. J39-J43 (5)	5.10	5.10

For overprints see Nos. J47-J51, NJ1-NJ2, NJ3a, NJ5, NJ6a.

Catalogue values for unused stamps in this section, from this point to the end of the section, are for Never Hinged items.

Nos. J39-J43, J35 Surcharged "FILS" and its Arabic Equivalent in Black, Green or Carmine

1952 Wmk. 4 *Perf. 12*

No.	Type	Description	Unused	Used
J47	D1	1f on 1m org brn (Bk)	.15	.15
J48	D1	2f on 2m yel org (G)	.15	.15
J49	D1	4f on 4m yel grn	.15	.15
J50	D1	10f on 10m rose car (Bk)	.40	.35
J51	D1	20f on 20m ol grn	.50	.50
		Perf. 14		
J52	D1	50f on 50m blue	.65	.65
		Nos. J47-J52 (6)	2.00	1.95

This overprint exists on Nos. J34, J36-J38. Exists inverted, double and in wrong color.

D3

Inscribed: "The Hashemite Kingdom of the Jordan"

1952 Engr. *Perf. 11½*

No.	Type	Description	Unused	Used
J53	D3	1f orange brown	.15	.15
J54	D3	2f yel orange	.15	.15
J55	D3	4f yel green	.15	.15
J56	D3	10f rose carmine	.15	.15
J57	D3	20f yel brown	.15	.15
J58	D3	50f blue	.52	.30
		Set value	.90	.60

Type of 1952 Redrawn

Inscribed: "The Hashemite Kingdom of Jordan"

1957 Wmk. 305 *Perf. 11½*

No.	Type	Description	Unused	Used
J59	D3	1f orange brown	.15	.15
J60	D3	2f yel orange	.15	.15
J61	D3	4f yel green	.15	.15
J62	D3	10f rose carmine	.18	.15
J63	D3	20f yel brown	.35	.25
		Set value	.70	.50

OFFICIAL STAMP

Saudi Arabia No. L34 Overprinted

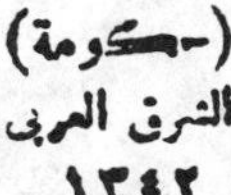

1924, Jan. Typo. *Perf. 11½*

No.	Type	Description	Unused	Used
O1	A7	½pi red	200.00	

Overprint reads: "(Government) the Arabian East 1342."

POSTAL TAX STAMPS

Catalogue values for unused stamps in this section are for Never Hinged items.

Mosque at Hebron — PT1

Designs: 10m, 15m, 20m, 50m, Dome of the Rock. 100m, 200m, 500m, £1, Acre.

Perf. 11½x12½

1947 Unwmk. Engr.

No.	Type	Description	Unused	Used
RA1	PT1	1m ultra	.22	.15
RA2	PT1	2m carmine	.22	.20
RA3	PT1	3m emerald	.30	.28
RA4	PT1	5m plum	.42	.20
RA5	PT1	10m carmine	.45	.30
RA6	PT1	15m gray	.65	.30
RA7	PT1	20m dk brown	.80	.45
RA8	PT1	50m purple	2.25	1.10
RA9	PT1	100m orange red	4.00	2.50
RA10	PT1	200m dp blue	10.00	7.50
RA11	PT1	500m green	16.00	12.50
RA12	PT1	£1 dk brown	27.50	27.50
		Nos. RA1-RA12 (12)	62.81	52.98

Issued to help the Welfare Fund for Arabs in Palestine. Required on foreign-bound letters to the amount of half the regular postage.

For overprints and surcharges see #286A-286C, 344-346, RA37-RA46, NRA1-NRA12.

Nos. 211, 232 and 234 Overprinted in Black

اعانة
Aid

1950 Wmk. 4 *Perf. 12*

No.	Type	Description	Unused	Used
RA23	A3	5m orange	6.50	
RA24	A3	10m violet	10.00	
RA25	A3	15m dull olive grn	12.00	
		Nos. RA23-RA25 (3)	28.50	

Arch and Colonnade, Palmyra, Syria — PT2

Two types of 5m:
Type I - "A" with serifs. Arabic ovpt. 8mm wide.
Type II - "A" without serifs. Arabic ovpt. 5mm wide.

Black or Carmine Overprint

1950-51 Engr. *Perf. 13½x13*

No.	Type	Description	Unused	Used
RA26	PT2	5m orange (I)	6.50	
a.		Type II ('51)	27.50	
RA27	PT2	10m violet (C)	6.50	

The overprint on No. RA27 is similar to that on RA23-RA25 but slightly bolder.

Type of 1947

Designs: 5f, Hebron Mosque. 10f, 15f, 20f, Dome of the Rock. 100f, Acre.

1951 Wmk. 4 *Perf. 11½x12½*

No.	Type	Description	Unused	Used
RA28	PT1	5f plum	.15	.15
RA29	PT1	10f carmine	.15	.15
RA30	PT1	15f gray	.16	.16
RA31	PT1	20f dk brown	.22	.22
RA33	PT1	100f orange	1.50	1.50
		Nos. RA28-RA33 (5)	2.18	2.18

The tax on Nos. RA1-RA33 was for Arab aid in Palestine.

For overprints see Nos. 287-290.

Postal Tax Stamps of 1947 Surcharged "FILS" or "J.D." and Their Arabic Equivalents and Bars in Carmine or Black

1952 Unwmk.

No.	Type	Description	Unused	Used
RA37	PT1	1f on 1m ultra	.38	.15
RA38	PT1	3f on 3m emer	.38	.15
RA39	PT1	10f on 10m car	.60	.42
RA40	PT1	15f on 15m gray	.80	.60
RA41	PT1	20f on 20m dk brown	1.25	.80
RA42	PT1	50f on 50m pur	3.00	2.00
RA43	PT1	100f on 100m org red	8.25	5.25
RA44	PT1	200f on 200m dp blue	21.00	6.50
RA45	PT1	500f on 500m grn	35.00	13.00
RA46	PT1	1d on £1 dk brn	55.00	32.50
		Nos. RA37-RA46 (10)	125.66	61.37

"J.D." stands for Jordanian Dinar.

OCCUPATION STAMPS

Catalogue values for unused stamps in this section are for Never Hinged items.

For Use in Palestine

Stamps of Jordan Overprinted in Red, Black, Dark Green, Green or Orange Red

فلسطين
PALESTINE

On No. 200

1948 Unwmk. *Perf. 13x13½*

No.	Type	Description	Unused	Used
N1	A14	2m dull green (R)	.75	.75

On #207-209, 211, 230-235, 215-220

1948 Wmk. 4 *Perf. 12, 13½x13, 14*

No.	Type	Description	Unused	Used
N2	A3	1m red brown	.20	.20
N3	A3	2m Prus green (R)	.30	.30
a.		2m Prussian blue, perf. 13½x13 (R) (#170a)	.30	.50
N4	A3	3m blue green (R)	.50	.50
N5	A3	3m rose carmine	.25	.25
N6	A3	4m dp yel grn (R)	.25	.25
N7	A3	5m orange (G)	.60	.25
N8	A3	10m violet (OR)	.75	.35
N9	A3	12m deep rose	.60	.60
N10	A3	15m dl ol grn (R)	.70	.50
N11	A3	20m dp blue (R)	.60	.60
N12	A3	50m red lil (Dk G)	1.25	1.25
N13	A3	90m ocher (Dk G)	4.00	3.50
N14	A3	100m dp blue (R)	4.50	4.00
N15	A3	200m dk vio (R)	8.00	7.00
a.		200m vio, perf. 14 (R) (#182)	15.00	15.00
N16	A3	500m dk brn (R)	13.00	5.00
N17	A3	£1 black (R)	20.00	10.00
		Nos. N2-N17 (16)	55.50	34.55

The first overprinting of these stamps include Nos. N1-N6, N9-N17. The second overprinting includes Nos. N1, N3, N5-N17, in inks differing in shade from the originals.

Many values exist with inverted or double overprint.

فلسطين

Jordan Nos. 245-249 Overprinted in Black or Red

PALESTINE

1949, Aug. Wmk. 4 *Perf. 13*

No.	Type	Description	Unused	Used
N18	A17	1m brown (Bk)	.15	.15
N19	A17	4m green	.18	.18
a.		"PLAESTINE"	20.00	
N20	A17	10m ultra	.28	.28
N21	A17	20m ultra	.28	.28
N22	A18	50m dull green	.70	.70
a.		"PLAESTINE"	20.00	
		Nos. N18-N22 (5)	1.59	1.59

The overprint is in one line on No. N22.
UPU, 75th anniversary.

OCCUPATION POSTAGE DUE STAMPS

Catalogue values for unused stamps in this section are for Never Hinged items.

فلسطين

Jordan Nos. J39, J30a, J40, J32, J41-J43, J34 and J35 Overprinted in Black, Red or Carmine

PALESTINE

1948-49 Wmk. 4 *Perf. 12, 14*

No.	Type	Description	Unused	Used
NJ1	D1	1m org brn, perf. 12	.15	.15
a.		Perf. 13½x13 (#J30a)	15.00	10.00
NJ2	D1	2m yel orange	.15	.15
NJ3	D1	4m grn (R) (#J32)	.50	.50
a.		4m yel grn (C) (#J41)	3.75	
NJ5	D1	10m rose car (#J42) ('49)	.80	.80
a.		Perf. 14 (#J33)	80.00	
NJ6	D1	20m ol grn (R), perf. 14	.50	.50
a.		Perf. 12 (R) (#J43)	20.00	
NJ7	D1	50m blue (R)	.50	.50
		Nos. NJ1-NJ3,NJ5-NJ7 (6)	2.60	2.60

The second overprinting of these stamps includes Nos. NJ1-NJ3, NJ3a and NJ5-NJ7, in inks differing in shade from the originals.

Double and inverted overprints exist.

Same Overprint in Black on Jordan Nos. J36-J38

1948-49 Unwmk. *Perf. 13x13½*

No.	Type	Description	Unused	Used
NJ8	D2	1m dl red brn	*100.00*	*100.00*
NJ9	D2	2m dl org yel ('49)	5.00	5.00
NJ10	D2	10m dark car	2.00	2.00

OCCUPATION POSTAL TAX STAMPS

Catalogue values for unused stamps in this section are for Never Hinged items.

Postal Tax Stamps of 1947 Overprinted in Red or Black

فلسطين
PALESTINE

1950

No.	Type	Description	Unused	Used
NRA1	PT1	1m ultra (R)	.24	.16
NRA2	PT1	2m carmine	.24	.16
NRA3	PT1	3m emerald (R)	.32	.20
NRA4	PT1	5m plum	.48	.28
NRA5	PT1	10m carmine	1.10	.40
NRA6	PT1	15m gray (R)	1.65	.60
NRA7	PT1	20m dk brown (R)	2.50	.75
NRA8	PT1	50m purple (R)	3.25	1.40
NRA9	PT1	100m org red	4.25	1.75
NRA10	PT1	200m dp blue (R)	12.00	4.00
NRA11	PT1	500m green (R)	24.00	10.00
NRA12	PT1	£1 dk brown (R)	45.00	20.00
		Nos. NRA1-NRA12 (12)	95.03	39.70

For overprints see Nos. 286D-286G.

KARELIA

kə-'rē-lə-ə

LOCATION — In northwestern Soviet Russia
GOVT. — An autonomous republic of the Soviet Union
AREA — 55,198 sq. mi. (approx.)
POP. — 270,000 (approx.)
CAPITAL — Petrozavodsk (Kalininsk)

In 1921 the Karelians rebelled and for a short period a form of sovereignty independent of Russia was maintained.

100 Pennia = 1 Markka

Bear — A1

1922 Unwmk. Litho. *Perf. 11½, 12*

No.	Type	Description	Unused	Used
1	A1	5p dark gray	10.00	*45.00*
2	A1	10p light blue	10.00	*45.00*
3	A1	20p rose red	10.00	*45.00*
4	A1	25p yellow brown	10.00	*45.00*
5	A1	40p magenta	10.00	*45.00*
6	A1	50p gray green	10.00	*45.00*
7	A1	75p orange yellow	10.00	*45.00*
8	A1	1m pink & gray	10.00	*45.00*
9	A1	2m yel grn & gray	22.50	*100.00*
10	A1	3m lt blue & gray	27.50	*125.00*
11	A1	5m red lil & gray	27.50	*150.00*
12	A1	10m lt brn & gray	27.50	*225.00*
13	A1	15m green & car	27.50	*225.00*
14	A1	20m rose & green	27.50	*225.00*
15	A1	25m yellow & blue	27.50	*225.00*
		Nos. 1-15 (15)	267.50	*1,635.*

Nos. 1-15 were valid Jan. 31-Feb. 16, 1922. Counterfeits abound.

OCCUPATION STAMPS

Issued under Finnish Occupation

Issued in the Russian territory of Eastern Karelia under Finnish military administration.

Types of Finland Stamps, 1930 Overprinted in Black:

ITÄ- KARJALA Sot.hallinto	ITÄ-KARJALA Sot.hallinto
On A26	On A27-A28

1941 Unwmk. *Perf. 14*

N1	A26	50p	brt yel grn	.40	*.85*
N2	A26	1.75m	dk gray	.75	*1.25*
N3	A26	2m	dp org	1.75	*2.25*
N4	A26	2.75m	yel org	.75	*1.25*
N5	A26	3½m	lt ultra	1.75	*2.25*
N6	A27	5m	rose vio	4.00	*7.00*
N7	A28	10m	pale brn	4.00	*8.00*
			Nos. N1-N7 (7)	13.40	*22.85*

Types of Finland Stamps, 1930 Overprinted in Green:

ITÄ-KARJALA Sot. hallinto On A26 — **ITÄ-KARJALA Sot. hallinto** On A27-A29

N8	A26	50p	brt yel grn	.45	*.65*
N9	A26	1.75m	dk gray	.65	*.70*
N10	A26	2m	dp org	.90	*1.10*
N11	A26	2.75m	yel org	.65	*.70*
N12	A26	3½m	lt ultra	.90	*1.25*
N13	A27	5m	rose vio	2.00	*3.25*
N14	A28	10m	pale brn	4.50	*6.00*
N15	A29	25m	green	4.50	*6.00*
			Nos. N8-N15 (8)	14.55	*19.65*

Mannerheim Type of Finland Overprinted **ITÄ-KARJALA Sot.hallinto**

1942

N16	A48	50p	dk yel grn	.90	*1.40*
N17	A48	1.75m	slate bl	.90	*1.40*
N18	A48	2m	red org	.90	*1.40*
N19	A48	2.75m	brn org	.70	*1.25*
N20	A48	3.50m	brt ultra	.70	*1.25*
N21	A48	5m	brn vio	.70	*1.25*
			Nos. N16-N21 (6)	4.80	*7.95*

Same Overprint on Ryti Type of Finland

N22	A49	50p	dk yel grn	.70	*1.25*
N23	A49	1.75m	slate bl	.70	*1.25*
N24	A49	2m	red org	.70	*1.25*
N25	A49	2.75m	brn org	.90	*1.40*
N26	A49	3.50m	brt ultra	.90	*1.40*
N27	A49	5m	brn vio	.90	*1.40*
			Nos. N22-N27 (6)	4.80	*7.95*

The overprint translates, "East Karelia Military Administration."

OCCUPATION SEMI-POSTAL STAMP

Arms of East Karelia — SP1

1943 Unwmk. Engr. *Perf. 14*

NB1	SP1	3.50m + 1.50m	dk ol	.60	*2.50*

This surtax aided war victims in East Karelia.

KATANGA

kə-'täŋ-gə

LOCATION — Central Africa
GOVT. — Republic
CAPITAL — Elisabethville

Katanga province seceded from the Congo (ex-Belgian) Republic in July, 1960, but established nations did not recognize it as an independent state. The UN declared the secession ended in Sept, 1961. The last troops surrendered Sept, 1963.

During the secession Katanga stamps were tolerated in the international mails, but the government authorizing them was not recognized.

100 Centimes = 1 Franc

Catalogue values for all unused stamps in this country are for Never Hinged items.

Belgian Congo Nos. 318-322 Overprinted "KATANGA"

Perf. 11½

1960, Sept. 12 Photo. Unwmk.

1	A94	50c golden brn, ocher & red brn	
2	A94	1fr dk bl, pur & red brn	
3	A94	2fr gray, brt bl & red brn	
		Nos. 1-3 (3)	75 75

Inscription in French

4	A95	3fr gray & red	5.00 5.00

Inscription in Flemish

5	A95	3fr gray & red	5.00 5.00

For surcharges see Nos. 50-51.

Animal Type of Belgian Congo, Nos. 306-317, Overprinted "KATANGA"

1960, Sept. 19

Granite Paper

6	A92	10c	bl & brn	
7	A93	20c	red org & slate	
8	A92	40c	brn & bl	
9	A93	50c	brt ultra, red & sep	
10	A92	1fr	brn, grn & blk	
11	A93	1.50fr	blk & org yel	
12	A92	2fr	crim, blk & brn	
13	A93	3fr	blk, gray & lil rose	
14	A92	5fr	brn, dk brn & brt grn	
15	A93	6.50fr	bl, brn & org yel	
16	A92	8fr	org brn, ol bis & lil	
17	A93	10fr	multi	
			Nos. 6-17(12)	30.00 20.00

Inverted overprints exist.

Flower Type of Belgian Congo, Nos. 263-271, 274-281, Overprinted "KATANGA"

1960, Sept. 22

Granite Paper

Flowers in Natural Colors

18	A86	10c	dp plum & ocher	
19	A86	15c	red & yel grn	
20	A86	20c	grn & gray	
21	A86	25c	dk grn & dl org	
22	A86	40c	grn & sal	
23	A86	50c	dk car & aqua	
24	A86	60c	bl grn & pink	
25	A86	75c	dp plum & gray	
26	A86	1fr	car & yel	
27	A86	2fr	ol grn & buff	
28	A86	3fr	ol grn & pink	
29	A86	4fr	choc & lil	
30	A86	5fr	dp plum & lt bl grn	
31	A86	6.50fr	dk car & lil	
32	A86	7fr	dk grn & fawn	
33	A86	8fr	grn & lt yel	
34	A86	10fr	dp plum & pale ol	
			Nos. 18-34(17)	35.00 22.50

Inverted overprints exist.

Carving and Mask Type of Belgian Congo, Nos. 241, 246, 254-256, Surcharged or Overprinted "KATANGA"

1960, Sept. 22 *Perf. 12½*

35	A82	1.50fr on 1.25fr	
36	A82	3.50fr on 2.50fr	
37	A82	20fr red org & vio brn	
38	A82	50fr dp org & blk	
39	A82	100fr crim & blk brn	
		Nos. 35-39(5)	45.00 30.00

Inverted surcharges and overprints exist.

Map Type of Congo Democratic Republic, Nos. 356-365, Overprinted "11 / JUILLET / DE / L'ETAT DU KATANGA"

1960, Oct. 26 *Perf. 11½*

Granite Paper

40	A93a	20c	brown	.15	.15
41	A93a	50c	rose red	.15	.15
42	A93a	1fr	green	.15	.15
43	A93a	1.50fr	red brn	.15	.15
44	A93a	2fr	rose car	.15	.15
45	A93a	3.50fr	lilac	.15	.15
46	A93a	5fr	brt bl	.20	.15
47	A93a	6.50fr	gray	.25	.15
48	A93a	10fr	orange	.35	.25
49	A93a	20fr	ultra	.65	.45
			Set value (10)	1.75	1.25

Belgian Congo Nos. 321-322 Surcharged

1961, Jan. 16

50	A95	3.50fr on 3fr #321	2.50 2.50
51	A95	3.50fr on 3fr #322	2.50 2.50

A1

A2

Katangan Wood Carvings: 3.50fr-8fr, Preparing meal. 10fr-100fr, Family group.

1961, Mar. 1 *Perf. 11½*

Granite Paper

52	A1	10c	grn & lt grn	.15	.15
53	A1	20c	purple & lil	.15	.15
54	A1	50c	blue & lt bl	.15	.15
55	A1	1.50fr	ol grn & lt ol grn	.15	.15
56	A1	2fr	red brn & lt brn	.15	.15
57	A1	3.50fr	dk blue & lt bl	.15	.15
58	A1	5fr	bl grn & lt bl grn	.15	.15
59	A1	6fr	org brn & tan	.15	.15
60	A1	6.50fr	bl vio & gray vio	.15	.15
61	A1	8fr	claret & pink	.15	.15
62	A1	10fr	dk brn & lt brn	.15	.15
63	A1	20fr	dk ol & lt grn	.25	.20
64	A1	50fr	brn & lt brn	.45	.35
65	A1	100fr	Prus bl & lt bl	.90	.75
			Nos. 52-65 (14)	3.25	
			Set value		2.00

1961, July 8 *Perf. 11½*

1fr, 5fr, Abstract vehicle. 2.50fr, 6.50fr, Gear.

Granite Paper

66	A2	50c	blk, grn & red	.20	.20
67	A2	1fr	blk & blue	.20	.20
68	A2	2.50fr	blk & yellow	.20	.20
69	A2	3.50fr	blk, brn & scar	.30	.30
70	A2	5fr	blk & purple	.50	.50
71	A2	6.50fr	blk & orange	.65	.65
			Nos. 66-71 (6)	*2.05*	*2.05*

Katanga International Fair.

Air Katanga A3

Design: 6.50fr, 10fr, Plane on ground.

1961, Aug. 1 *Perf. 11½*

Granite Paper

72	A3	3.50fr	multicolored	
73	A3	6.50fr	multicolored	
74	A3	8fr	multicolored	
75	A3	10fr	multicolored	
			Nos. 72-75(4)	5.00 5.00

Katanga Gendarmerie — A4

1962, Oct. 1 *Perf. 11½*

Granite Paper

76	A4	6fr	multicolored	
77	A4	8fr	multicolored	
78	A4	10fr	multicolored	
			Nos. 76-78(3)	4.00 4.00

SEMI-POSTAL STAMPS

Pres. Moise Tshombe — SP1

1961, July 11 *Perf. 11½*

Granite Paper

B1	SP1	6.50fr	+ 5fr multi	
B2	SP1	8fr	+ 5fr multi	
B3	SP1	10fr	+ 5fr multi	
			Nos. B1-B3(3)	4.00 3.00

POSTAGE DUE STAMPS

Belgian Congo Nos. J8a-J10a, J16-J19 Handstamped "KATANGA" in Blue

1960, Dec. 30 Unwmk. *Perf. 12½*

J1	D2	10c	olive green	
J2	D2	20c	dark ultra	
J3	D2	50c	green	

Perf. 11½

J4	D3	1fr	light blue	
J5	D3	2fr	vermilion	
J6	D3	4fr	purple	
J7	D3	6fr	violet blue	
			Nos. J1-J7 (7)	20.00 20.00

This overprint also exists on Belgian Congo Nos. J11a-J12a, J13-J15.

KAZAKHSTAN

,ka-(,)zak-'stan

(Kazahstan)

LOCATION — Bounded by southern Russia, Uzbekistan, Kyrgyzstan, and China.
GOVT. — Independent republic, member of the Commonwealth of Independent States.
AREA — 1,049,200 sq. mi.
POP. — 16,500,000 (1989)
CAPITAL — Alma Ata

With the breakup of the Soviet Union on Dec. 26, 1991, Kazakhstan and ten former Soviet republics established the Commonwealth of Independent States.

100 Kopecks = 1 Ruble
100 Tijn = 1 Tenge

Catalogue values for all unused stamps in this country are for Never Hinged items.

Overprinted Stamps

The Philatelic Club of Alma Ata, Kazakhstan, has announced that various overprinted stamps of the USSR were not generally available nor were they in values reflecting actual postal rates.

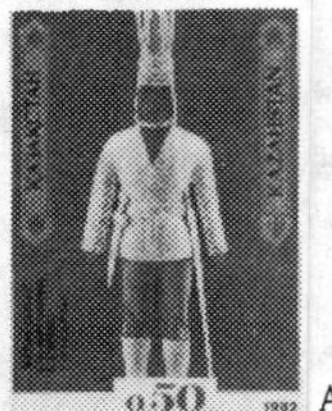

A1

Perf. 12x12½

1992, Mar. 23 Litho. Unwmk.

1	A1	50k multicolored	.75

Saiga Tatarica — A2

1992, Sept. 11 Litho. *Perf. 12*

2	A2	75k multicolored	1.10

Camels and Train, by K. Kasteev — A3

1992, Sept. 11 Litho. *Perf. 12½x12*

3	A3	1r multicolored	.35

Day of the Republic A3a

1992, Dec. 16 Litho. *Perf. 12*

4 A3a 5r multicolored .55

Space Ship and Yurt — A4

Natl. Flag — A5

1993, Jan. 24 Litho. *Perf. 13x12½*

22	A4	1r green	.15
23	A4	3r red	.15
24	A4	10r golden brown	.20
25	A4	25r purple	.50

Perf. 14

26	A5	50r multicolored	1.00
		Nos. 22-26 (5)	2.00

See Nos. 64, 69, 108-115.

Space Mail — A6

1993, Mar. 5 Litho. *Perf. 13½*

35 A6 100r multicolored 1.75

New Year 1993 (Year of the Rooster) — A7

1993, Mar. 22 Litho. *Perf. 13x13½*

36 A7 60r yellow, black & red 1.10

See Nos. 54, 98, 141, 187A.

Cosmonauts' Day — A8

1993, Apr. 12 *Perf. 13½x13*

37 A8 90r multicolored 1.40

Pres. Nursultan Nasarbajev — A9

1993, Aug. 2 Litho. *Perf. 14*

38 A9 50r multicolored .75

Bukar Zhirav Kalkaman (1668-1781), Poet — A10

1993, Aug. 18 *Perf. 13½x13*

39 A10 15r multicolored .25

Map, Pres. Nasarbajev — A11

1993, Sept. 24 Litho. *Perf. 13*

40 A11 100r multicolored .65

Wildlife — A12

Designs: 5ti, Selevinia betpakdalensis. 10ti, Hystrix leucura. 15ti, Vormela peregusna. 20ti, Equis hemionus onager. 25ti, Ovis orientalis. 30ti, Acinonyx jubatus venaticus.

1993, Nov. 11 *Perf. 12x12½*

41	A12	5ti multicolored	.15
42	A12	10ti multicolored	.15
43	A12	15ti multicolored	.20
44	A12	20ti multicolored	.25
45	A12	25ti multicolored	.30
46	A12	30ti multicolored	.35
		Nos. 41-46 (6)	1.40

1994 Winter Olympics, Lillehammer A13

1994, Jan. 24 Litho. *Perf. 13½x13*

47	A13	15ti Ice hockey	.20
48	A13	25ti Slalom skiing	.30
49	A13	90ti Ski jumping	1.10
50	A13	150ti Speed skating	1.90
		Nos. 47-50 (4)	3.50

1994 Winter Olympics, Lillehammer — A14

Designs: 2te, Skiers Vladimir Smirnov, Kazakhstan; Bjorn Daehlie, Norway. 6.80te, 12te, Smirnov.

1994, Feb. 19 Litho. *Perf. 13x13½*

51	A14	2te multicolored	.50
52	A14	6.80te multicolored	1.50
a.		Pair, #51-52	2.00
53	A14	12te like No. 52	2.75
		Nos. 51-53 (3)	4.75

No. 53 has an additional two line Cyrillic inscription.

New Year Type of 1993

Size: 26x38mm

1994, Mar. 22 *Perf. 12*

54 A7 30te green, black & blue .30

New Year 1994 (Year of the Dog).

Space Program A15

1994, Apr. 12 *Perf. 13½x13*

55 A15 2te multicolored .55

Souvenir Sheet

Russian Space Shuttle, Cosmonaut A16

1994, July 12 *Perf. 13*

56 A16 6.80te Sheet of 4 4.75

Space Ship and Yurt Type of 1993

1994, July 12 Litho. *Perf. 11½*

64	A4	15te blue	.15
69	A4	80te lake	.55

For surcharges see Nos. 70-76, 122.
This is an expanding set. Numbers may change.

Nos. 64, 69 Surcharged in Lake or Purple

1995 Litho. *Perf. 11½*

70	A4	1te on 15te #64	.15
71	A4	2te on 15te #64	.15
72	A4	3te on 80te #69 (P)	.20
73	A4	4te on 80te #69 (P)	.30
74	A4	6te on 80te #69 (P)	.40
75	A4	12te on 80te #69 (P)	.85
76	A4	20te on 80te #69 (P)	1.40
		Nos. 70-76 (7)	3.45

Issued: 1te, 2te, 12te, 2/2/95. 3te, 4te, 6te, 20te, 2/10/95.

Music Competition Festival — A18

Designs: 10te, Snow-covered mountain top. 15te, Aerial view of stadium at night.

1994, Aug. 1 *Perf. 13½*

81	A18	10te multicolored	1.00
82	A18	15te multicolored	1.50

Exist dated 1995.

Reptiles A19

Designs: 1te, Agrionemys horsfieldi. 1.20te, Phrynocephalus mystaceus. 2te, Agkistrodon halys. 3te, Teratoscincus scincus. 5te, Trapelus sanguinolenta. 7te, Ophisaurus apodus. 10te, Varanus griseus.

1994, Oct. 10 *Perf. 12½x12*

83	A19	1te multicolored	.15
84	A19	1.20te multicolored	.15
85	A19	2te multicolored	.25
86	A19	3te multicolored	.35
87	A19	5te multicolored	.60
88	A19	7te multicolored	.85
		Nos. 83-88 (6)	2.35

Souvenir Sheet

89 A19 10te multicolored 1.25

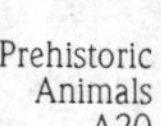

Prehistoric Animals A20

1994, Nov. 24 Litho. *Perf. 12½x12*

90	A20	1te Entelodon	.20
91	A20	1.20te Saurolophus	.20
92	A20	2te Plesiosaurus	.35
93	A20	3te Sordes pilosus	.50
94	A20	5te Mosasaurus	.90
95	A20	7te Megaloceros giganteum	1.25
		Nos. 90-95 (6)	3.40

Souvenir Sheet

96 A20 10te Koelodonta antiquitatis 1.75

Day of the Republic — A21

1994, Oct. 25 *Perf. 11½*

97 A21 2te multicolored .35

For surcharge see No. 160B.

New Year Type of 1993

1995, Mar. 22 Litho. *Perf. 14*

Size: 27x32mm

98 A7 10te blue, black & ultra .65

New Year 1995 (Year of the Boar).

Abai (Ibraghim) Kynanbaev (1845-1904), Poet — A22

1995, Mar. 31

99	A22	4te Portrait	.30
100	A22	9te Portrait, diff.	.65

Space Day A23

Designs: 10te, Cosmonauts Malenchenko, Musabaev and Merbold.

1995, Apr. 12 Litho. *Perf. 14*

101	A23	2te multicolored	*1.00*
102	A23	10te multicolored	*3.00*

Mahatma Gandhi (1869-1948) — A24

1995, Oct. 2

103	A24	9te multicolored	2.25
104	A24	22te multicolored	5.50

End of World War II, 50th Anniv. A25

Designs: 1te, Hero, battle scene. 3te, Heroine, tank. 5te, Dove, monument.

1995, May 9 Litho. *Perf. 14*

105 A25 1te multicolored .50
106 A25 3te multicolored 1.00
107 A25 5te multicolored 1.50
Nos. 105-107 (3) 3.00

Spaceship and Yurt Type of 1993

1995, Mar. 24 Litho. *Perf. 14x14½*

108 A4 20ti orange .15 .15
109 A4 25ti yellow brown .15 .15
110 A4 50ti gray .15 .15
111 A4 1te green .20 .20
112 A4 2te blue .35 .35
113 A4 4te bright pink .65 .65
114 A4 6te gray green 4.00 4.00
115 A4 12te lilac 2.00 2.00
Nos. 108-115 (8) 7.65 7.65

Nos. 108-115 are inscribed "1995."

Paintings — A26

Designs: 4te, "Springtime," by S. Mambeev. 9te, "Mountains," by Z. Shchardenov. 15te, "Kulash Baiseitova in role of Kyz Zhibek," by G. Ismailova, vert. 28te, "Kokpar," by K. Telzhanov.

1995, June 23 Litho. *Perf. 14*

116 A26 4te multicolored .40 .40
117 A26 9te multicolored .90 .90
118 A26 15te multicolored 1.50 1.50
119 A26 28te multicolored 2.75 2.75
Nos. 116-119 (4) 5.55 5.55

Dauletkerey (1820-87), Composer — A27

1995, Sept. 1 Litho. *Perf. 14*

120 A27 2te yellow & multi .50 .50
121 A27 28te lake & multi 6.50 6.50

No. 69 Surcharged in Purple

8.00

1995, Sept. 25 Litho. *Perf. 11½*

122 A4 8te on 80te 1.00 1.00

UN, 50th Anniv. — A28

1995, Nov. 24 Litho. *Perf. 14*

123 A28 10te multicolored 1.65 1.65

A number has been reserved for an additional value with this set.

Resurrection Cathedral — A29

Circus — A29a

Buildings in Alma-Ata: 2te, Culture Palace. 3te, Opera and Ballet House. 6te, Kazakh Science Academy. 48te, Dramatics Theatre.

Perf. 14, 13x12 (#126, 129)

1995-96 Litho.

125 A29 1te green .15 .15
126 A29a 1te green .15 .15
127 A29 2te blue .30 .30
128 A29 3te red .40 .40
129 A29a 6te olive .80 .80
130 A29 48te brown 6.75 6.75
Nos. 125-130 (6) 8.55 8.55

Issued: Nos. 125, 127-128, 130, 10/25/95; Nos. 126, 129, 7/5/96.

Raptors A30

1te, Haliaeetus albicilla. 3te, Pandion haliaetus. 5te, Gypaetus barbatus. 6te, Gyps himalayensis. 30te, Falco cherrug. 50te, Aquila chrysaetus.

1995, Dec. 20 Litho. *Perf. 14*

131 A30 1te multicolored .15 .15
132 A30 3te multicolored .30 .30
133 A30 5te multicolored .45 .45
134 A30 6te multicolored .55 .55
135 A30 30te multicolored 2.75 2.75
136 A30 50te multicolored 4.50 4.50
Nos. 131-136 (6) 8.70 8.70

New Year Type of 1993
Size: 27x32mm

1996, Mar. 21 Litho. *Perf. 14*

141 A7 25te lil, blk & red 1.50 1.50

New Year 1996 (Year of the Rat).

Space Day — A32

1996, Apr. 12

142 A32 6te Earth 1.25 1.25
143 A32 15te Cosomonaut 3.00 3.00
144 A32 20te Space station Mir 4.50 4.50
Nos. 142-144 (3) 8.75 8.75

Souvenir Sheet

Save the Aral Sea — A33

Designs: a, Felis caracal. b, Salmo trutta aralensis. c, Hyaena hyaena. d, Pseudoscaphirhynchus kaufmanni. e, Aspiolucius esocinus.

1996, Apr. 20 Litho. *Perf. 14*

145 A33 20te Sheet of 5, #a.-e. 6.75 6.75

See Kyrgyzstan No. 107, Tadjikistan No. 91, Turkmenistan No. 52, Uzbekistan No. 113.

1996 Summer Olympic Games, Atlanta — A34

1996, June 19 Litho. *Perf. 14*

146 A34 4te Cycling .35 .35
147 A34 6te Wrestling .50 .50
148 A34 30te Boxing 2.50 2.50
Nos. 146-148 (3) 3.35 3.35

Souvenir Sheet

149 A34 50te Hurdles 2.50 2.50

Issued: #146-148, 6/19/96; #149, 7/19/96.

Architectural Sites — A35

Designs: 1te, Tomb, 8-9th cent. 3te, Mausoleum, 11-12th cent. 6te, Mausoleum, 13th cent. 30te, Mosque, 14th cent.

1996, Sept. 27 Litho. *Perf. 14*

150 A35 1te multicolored .55 .55
151 A35 3te multicolored 1.65 1.65
152 A35 6te multicolored 3.25 3.25
Nos. 150-152 (3) 5.45 5.45

Souvenir Sheet

153 A35 30te multicolored 2.75 2.75

World Post Day — A37

1996, Oct. 9 Litho. *Perf. 14*

156 A37 9te shown .75 .75
157 A37 40te UPU emblem 4.00 4.00

A38

A39

1996, Aug. 21

158 A38 12te multicolored .50 .50

Schambyl Schabaev (1846-1945).

1996, Oct. 2

159 A39 46te Space station Mir 2.00 2.00
160 A39 46te T. Aubakirov 2.00 2.00
a. Pair, #159-160 4.00 4.00

T. Aubakirov, 1st Kazak cosmonaut.

No. 97 Surcharged 1.

1997, Oct. 25 Litho. *Perf. 11½*

160B A21 21te on 2te multi 1.10 1.10

Surcharge adds numeral 1 to existing value to appear as 21, obliterates original date and adds new date.

Butterflies — A40

4te, Saturnia schenki. 6te, Parnassius patricius. 12te, Parnassius ariadne. 46te, Colias draconis.

1996, Nov. 21 Litho. *Perf. 14*

161 A40 4te multicolored .20 .20
162 A40 6te multicolored .25 .25
163 A40 12te multicolored .50 .50
164 A40 46te multicolored 2.00 2.00
Nos. 161-164 (4) 2.95 2.95

Hunting Dogs A41

1996, Nov. 29

165 A41 5te multicolored .25 .25

Souvenir Sheet

166 A41 100te like #165 4.00 4.00

No. 166 is a continuous design.

A42

A43

Traditional Costumes, Furnishings: a, 10te, Woman outside tent. b, 16te, Man outside tent. c, 45te, Interior view of furnishings.

1996, Dec. 5

167 A42 Strip of 3, #a.-c. 10.50 10.50

1996, Dec. 24

Archives, Bicent.: 4te, Quill pen, candle, documents. 68te, Scroll, papers, book.

168 A43 4te brown .20 .20
169 A43 68te purple 3.25 3.25

Motion Pictures, Cent. — A44

Film scenes: a, Man in hat holding up fingers. b, Horse, woman, man. c, Two men, from "His Time Arrives." d, Woman holding paper, boy holding hat.

1996, Dec. 25 Litho. *Perf. 14*

170 A44 24te Sheet of 4, #a.-d. 3.75 3.75

Vormela Peregusna — A45

1997, Feb. 12 Litho. *Perf. 14*

171 A45 6te shown .25 .25
172 A45 10te Adult .40 .40
173 A45 32te Two young 1.25 1.25
174 A45 46te Adult, tail up 1.75 1.75
Nos. 171-174 (4) 3.65 3.65

World Wildlife Fund.

Zodiac Constellations A47

1997, Mar. 26 Litho. *Perf. 14*

176 A47 1te Aries .15 .15
177 A47 2te Taurus .15 .15
178 A47 3te Gemini .15 .15
179 A47 4te Cancer .15 .15
180 A47 5te Leo .20 .20
181 A47 6te Virgo .25 .25
182 A47 7te Libra .25 .25
183 A47 8te Scorpio .30 .30
184 A47 9te Sagittarius .35 .35
185 A47 10te Capricorn .35 .35
186 A47 12te Aquarius .45 .45
187 A47 20te Pisces .75 .75
Nos. 176-187 (12) 3.50 3.50

New Year Type of 1993 With Kazakhstan Inscribed in Both Cyrillic & Roman Letters

1997, Mar. 22 Litho. *Perf. 14*

187A A7 40te multicolored 3.00 3.00

New Year 1997 (Year of the Ox).

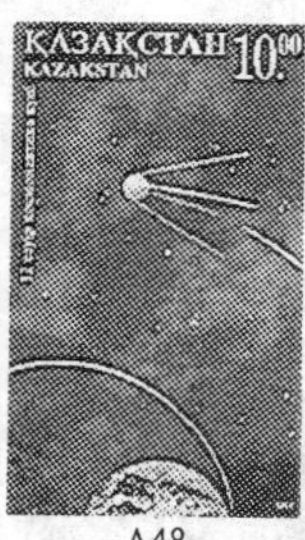

A48

A49

Cosmonauts' Day: a, Earth, Sputnik. b, Space vehicle, Saturn. c, Space shuttle, space station.

1997, Apr. 12

188 A48 10te Strip of 3, #a.-c. 1.40 1.40

1997, Apr. 23

189 A49 15te orange yellow & green .55 .55
190 A49 60te orange yellow & green 2.20 2.20

UNESCO World Book Day.

Mukhtar Auezov (1897-1961), Writer — A50

1997, May

191 A50 25te House 1.10 1.10
192 A50 40te Auezov at his desk 1.50 1.50

Orders and Medals — A51

Various medals.

1997, June 30 Litho. *Perf. 14*

193 A51 15te green & yellow ribbon .55 .55
194 A51 15te green, red & pink ribbon .55 .55
195 A51 20te grn bl & multi .75 .75
196 A51 30te grn yel & multi 1.10 1.10
Nos. 193-196 (4) 2.95 2.95

Tulips — A52

15te, Tulipa regelii. No. 198, Tulipa greigii. No. 199, Tulipa alberti.

1997, Aug. 7 Litho. *Perf. 13½*

197 A52 15te multicolored .55 .55
198 A52 35te multicolored 1.25 1.25
199 A52 35te multicolored 1.25 1.25
Nos. 197-199 (3) 3.05 3.05

Paintings — A53

Designs: No. 200, Two men on horseback chasing wild horse. No. 201, Man kneeling down beside animals, vert. No. 202, Abstract of cat, elephants, table, bowl of fruit, stars, vert.

1997, Sept. 10 Litho. *Perf. 14*

200 A53 25te multicolored .95 .95
201 A53 25te multicolored .95 .95
202 A53 25te multicolored .95 .95
Nos. 200-201 (2) 1.90 1.90

Agate — A54

Azurite — A55

1997, Oct. Litho. *Perf. 14*

203 A54 15te shown .60 .60
204 A54 15te Chalcedony .60 .60
205 A55 20te shown .80 .80
206 A55 20te Malachite .80 .80
a. Souvenir sheet, #203-206 2.75 2.75
Nos. 203-206 (4) 2.80 2.80

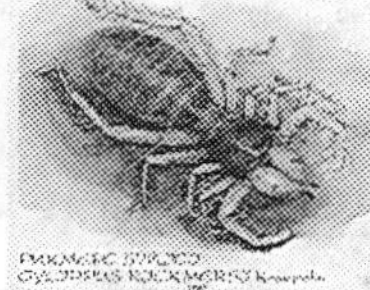

Desert Fauna — A56

Designs: No. 207, Gylippus rickmersi. No. 208, Anemelobathus rickmersi. No. 209, Latrodectus pallidus. No. 210, Oculicosa supermirabilis.

1997, Dec. Litho. *Perf. 14*

207 A56 30te multicolored 1.10 1.10
208 A56 30te multicolored 1.10 1.10
209 A56 30te multicolored 1.10 1.10
210 A56 30te multicolored 1.10 1.10
Nos. 207-210 (4) 4.40 4.40

Souvenir Sheet

Nature Park — A57

Designs: a, Mountain goat. b, Trees on side of mountain. c, Rock formations, wildflowers.

1997, Dec.

211 A57 30te Sheet of 3, #a.-c. 2.75 2.75

A58

Sports A59

Designs: No. 212, Woman, man riding horses. No. 213, Wrestling match. No. 214, Group of men on galloping horses.

1997, Dec. 30 Litho. *Perf. 14*

212 A58 20te multicolored .75 .75
213 A58 20te multicolored .75 .75
214 A58 20te multicolored .75 .75
215 A59 20te multicolored .75 .75
Nos. 212-215 (4) 3.00 3.00

SEMI-POSTAL STAMP

Christmas SP1

Designs: a, Nativity. b, Cow, rabbit. c, Horses.

1994, Nov. 3 Litho. *Perf. 12½x12*

B1 SP1 1te +30ti Block of 3 + label .50

KENYA

'ke–nyə

LOCATION — East Africa, bordering on the Indian Ocean
GOVT. — Republic
AREA — 224,960 sq. mi.
POP. — 18,750,000 (est. 1983)
CAPITAL — Nairobi

Formerly a part of the British colony of Kenya, Uganda, Tanganyika, Kenya gained independence Dec. 12, 1963.

100 Cents = 1 Shilling

Catalogue values for all unused stamps in this country are for Never Hinged items.

Treetop Hotel and Elephants A1

Designs: 5c, Cattle ranching. 10c, Wood carving. 15c, Riveter. 20c, Timber industry. 30c, Jomo Kenyatta facing Mt. Kenya. 40c, Fishing industry. 50c, Flag and emblem. 65c, Pyrethrum industry (daisies). 1sh, National Assembly bldg. 2sh, Harvesting coffee. 5sh, Harvesting tea. 10sh, Mombasa port. 20sh, Royal College, Nairobi.

Perf. 14x14½

1963, Dec. 12 Photo. Unwmk.

Size: 21x17½mm

1 A1 5c bl, buff & dk brn .15 .15
2 A1 10c brown .15 .15
a. Booklet pane of 4 .30
3 A1 15c deep magenta .15 .15
a. Booklet pane of 4 .30
4 A1 20c yel grn & dk brn .15 .15
a. Booklet pane of 4 .40
5 A1 30c yel & black .15 .15
a. Booklet pane of 4 .55
6 A1 40c blue & brown .20 .15
7 A1 50c grn, blk & dp car .20 .15
a. Booklet pane of 4 1.25
8 A1 65c steel blue & yel .35 .25

Perf. 14½

Size: 41½x25½mm

9 A1 1sh multicolored .45 .15
10 A1 1.30sh grn, brn & blk .50 .15
11 A1 2sh multicolored .70 .20
12 A1 5sh ultra, yel grn & brn 1.40 .40
13 A1 10sh brn & dark brn 3.50 1.25
14 A1 20sh pink & grnsh blk 7.00 2.50
Nos. 1-14 (14) 15.05
Set value 5.00

President Jomo Kenyatta and Flag of Kenya — A2

Flag and: 15c, Cockerel. 50c, African lion. 1.30sh, Hartlaub's touraco. 2.50sh, Nandi flame flower.

1964, Dec. 12 Photo. *Perf. 13x12½*

15 A2 15c lt violet & multi .20 .15
16 A2 30c dk blue & multi .40 .15
17 A2 50c dk brown & multi .60 .35
18 A2 1.30sh multicolored 1.90 .75
19 A2 2.50sh multicolored 4.75 3.75
Nos. 15-19 (5) 7.85 5.15

Establishment of the Republic of Kenya, Dec. 12, 1964.

Greater Kudu A3

Animals: 5c, Thomson's gazelle. 10c, Sable antelope. 15c, Aardvark. 20c, Senegal bush baby. 30c, Warthog. 40c, Zebra. 50c, Buffalo. 65c, Black rhinoceros. 70c, Ostrich. 1.30sh, Elephant. 1.50sh, Bat-eared fox. 2.50sh, Cheetah. 5sh, Vervet monkey. 10sh, Giant pangolin. 20sh, Lion.

1966-69 Unwmk. *Perf. 14x14½*

Size: 21x17mm

20 A3 5c gray, black & org .15 .15
21 A3 10c black & yel green .15 .15
22 A3 15c dp orange & black .15 .15
23 A3 20c ultra, lt brn & black .15 .15
24 A3 30c lt ultra & blk .15 .15
25 A3 40c ocher & blk .20 .15
26 A3 50c dp orange & blk .25 .15
27 A3 65c dp yel green & blk 1.40 .90
28 A3 70c rose lake & black 1.40 .70

Perf. 14½

Size: 41x25mm

29 A3 1sh gray bl, ol & blk .50 .15
30 A3 1.30sh yel grn & blk 1.40 .15
31 A3 1.50sh brn org, brn & black 1.75 .90
32 A3 2.50sh ol bis, yel & blk 2.50 .45
33 A3 5sh brt grn, ultra & black 2.25 .70
34 A3 10sh red brn, bis & black 4.50 1.40
35 A3 20sh ocher, bis, gold & black 9.00 3.00
Nos. 20-35 (16) 25.90 9.40

Issued: #28, 31, 9/15/69; others, 12/12/66.

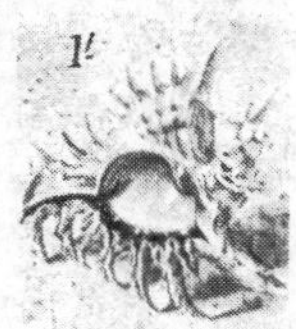

Branched Murex — A4

Sea shells: 5c, Morning pink. 10c, Episcopal miter. 15c, Strawberry-top shell. 20c, Humpback cowrie. 30c, variable abalone. 40c, Flame-top shell. 50c, Violet sailor. 60c, Bull's-mouth helmet. 70c, Pearly nautilus. 1.50sh, Neptune's trumpet. 2.50sh, Mediterranean tulip shell. 5sh, Fluctuating turban. 10sh, Textile cone. 20sh, Scorpion shell.

1971 Dec. 13 Photo. *Perf. 14½x14*

Size: 17x21mm

36 A4 5c bister & multi .15 .15
37 A4 10c dull grn & multi .15 .15
a. Booklet pane of 4 .40
38 A4 15c tan & multi .15 .15
a. Booklet pane of 4 .40
39 A4 20c tan & multi .15 .15
a. Booklet pane of 4 .50
40 A4 30c yellow & multi .20 .15
a. Booklet pane of 4 .80
41 A4 40c gray & multi .20 .15
a. Booklet pane of 4 .80
42 A4 50c buff & multi *(Janthina globosa)* .45 .15
a. Booklet pane of 4 1.80
43 A4 60c lilac & multi .45 .15
44 A4 70c gray grn & multi *(Nautilus pompileus)* .75 .15
a. Booklet pane of 4 2.50

Perf. 14½

Size: 25x41mm

45 A4 1sh ocher & multi .65 .15
46 A4 1.50sh pale grn & multi .90 .15
47 A4 2.50sh vio gray & multi 1.50 *.15*
48 A4 5sh lemon & multi 3.00 *.25*
49 A4 10sh multicolored 5.00 *.75*
50 A4 20sh gray & multi 12.50 *1.75*
Nos. 36-50 (15) 26.20
Set value *3.70*

Used values of Nos. 48-50 are for stamps with printed cancellations.

For surcharges see Nos. 53-55.

Revised Inscription

1974, Jan. 20 *Perf. 14½x14*

51	A4	50c *(Janthina janthina)*	5.00	.30
52	A4	70c *(Nautilus pompilius)*	9.00	1.40

Nos. 46-47, 50 Surcharged with New Value and 2 Bars

1975, Nov. 17 **Photo.** *Perf. 14½*

53	A4	2sh on 1.50sh multi	2.50	1.60
54	A4	3sh on 2.50sh multi	12.00	15.00
55	A4	40sh on 20sh multi	14.00	14.00
		Nos. 53-55 (3)	28.50	30.60

Microwave Tower — A5

Designs: 1sh, Cordless switchboard and operators, horiz. 2sh, Telephones of 1880, 1930 and 1976. 3sh, Message switching center, horiz.

1976, Apr. 15 **Litho.** *Perf. 14½*

56	A5	50c blue & multi	.15	.15
57	A5	1sh red & multi	.30	.20
58	A5	2sh yellow & multi	.50	.35
59	A5	3sh multicolored	.85	.60
a.		Souvenir sheet of 4	2.50	2.25
		Nos. 56-59 (4)	1.80	1.30

Telecommunication development in East Africa. No. 59a contains 4 stamps similar to Nos. 56-59 with simulated perforations.

Akii Bua, Ugandan Hurdler A6

Designs: 1sh, Filbert Bayi, Tanzanian runner. 2sh, Steve Muchoki, Kenyan boxer. 3sh, Olympic torch, flags of Kenya, Tanzania and Uganda.

1976, July 5 **Litho.** *Perf. 14½*

60	A6	50c blue & multi	.15	.15
61	A6	1sh red & multi	.20	.20
62	A6	2sh yellow & multi	.40	.40
63	A6	3sh blue & multi	.60	.60
a.		Souv. sheet of 4, #60-63, perf. 13	6.75	5.75
		Nos. 60-63 (4)	1.35	1.35

21st Olympic Games, Montreal, Canada, July 17-Aug. 1.

Tanzania-Zambia Railway — A7

Designs: 1sh, Nile Bridge, Uganda. 2sh, Nakuru Station, Kenya. 3sh, Class A locomotive, 1896.

1976, Oct. 4 **Litho.** *Perf. 14½*

64	A7	50c lilac & multi	.35	.15
65	A7	1sh emerald & multi	.65	.25
66	A7	2sh brt rose & multi	1.25	.50
67	A7	3sh yellow & multi	2.00	.70
a.		Souv. sheet of 4, #64-67, perf. 13	8.00	5.00
		Nos. 64-67 (4)	4.25	1.60

Rail transport in East Africa.

Nile Perch — A8

Game Fish: 1sh, Tilapia. 3sh, Sailfish. 5sh, Black marlin.

1977, Jan. 10 **Litho.** *Perf. 14½*

68	A8	50c multicolored	.20	.15
69	A8	1sh multicolored	.40	.20
70	A8	3sh multicolored	1.50	.50
71	A8	5sh multicolored	2.00	1.00
		Nos. 68-71 (4)	4.10	1.85
a.		Souvenir sheet of 4, #68-71	6.00	5.00

Festival Emblem and Masai Tribesmen Bleeding Cow — A9

Festival Emblem and: 1sh, Dancers from Uganda. 2sh, Makonde sculpture, Tanzania. 3sh, Tribesmen skinning hippopotamus.

1977, Jan. 15 *Perf. 13½x14*

72	A9	50c multicolored	.15	.15
73	A9	1sh multicolored	.25	.20
74	A9	2sh multicolored	1.00	.40
75	A9	3sh multicolored	1.10	.60
a.		Souvenir sheet of 4, #72-75	3.50	2.50
		Nos. 72-75 (4)	2.50	1.35

2nd World Black and African Festival, Lagos, Nigeria, Jan. 15-Feb. 12.

Automobile Passing through Village A10

Safari Rally Emblem and: 1sh, Winner at finish line. 2sh, Car going through washout. 5sh, Car, elephants and Mt. Kenya.

1977, Apr. 5 **Litho.** *Perf. 14*

76	A10	50c multicolored	.15	.15
77	A10	1sh multicolored	.25	.25
78	A10	2sh multicolored	.55	.50
79	A10	5sh multicolored	1.30	1.25
a.		Souvenir sheet of 4, #76-79	5.00	4.00
		Nos. 76-79 (4)	2.25	2.15

25th Safari Rally, Apr. 7-11.

Rev. Canon Apolo Kivebulaya — A11

1sh, Uganda Cathedral. 2sh, Early grass-topped Cathedral. 5sh, Early tent congregation, Kigezi.

1977, June 20 **Litho.** *Perf. 14*

80	A11	50c multicolored	.15	.15
81	A11	1sh multicolored	.20	.20
82	A11	2sh multicolored	.45	.45
83	A11	5sh multicolored	1.10	1.10
a.		Souvenir sheet of 4, #80-83	2.50	2.50
		Nos. 80-83 (4)	1.90	1.90

Church of Uganda, centenary.

Elizabeth II and Prince Philip at Sagana Lodge — A12

Designs: 5sh, "Treetops" observation hut, Aberdare Forest, and elephants, vert. 10sh, Pres. Jomo Kenyatta, Elizabeth II, crossed spears and shield. 15sh, Elizabeth II and Pres. Kenyatta in open automobile. 50sh, Elizabeth II and Prince Philip at window in Treetops.

1977, July 20 **Litho.** *Perf. 14*

84	A12	2sh multicolored	.35	.35
85	A12	5sh multicolored	.55	.55
86	A12	10sh multicolored	2.00	1.75
87	A12	15sh multicolored	2.50	2.25
a.		Souvenir sheet of 1	2.50	2.50
		Nos. 84-87 (4)	5.40	4.90

Souvenir Sheet

88	A12	50sh multicolored	7.50	7.50

Reign of Queen Elizabeth II, 25th anniv.

Pancake Tortoise A13

Wildlife Fund Emblem and; 1sh, Nile crocodile. 2sh, Hunter's hartebeest. 3sh, Red colobus monkey. 5sh, Dugong.

1977, Sept. 26 **Litho.** *Perf. 14x13½*

89	A13	50c multicolored	.25	.15
90	A13	1sh multicolored	.50	.25
91	A13	2sh multicolored	.95	.50
92	A13	3sh multicolored	1.60	.70
93	A13	5sh multicolored	2.50	1.20
a.		Souvenir sheet of 4, #90-93	7.50	3.00
		Nos. 89-93 (5)	5.80	2.80

Endangered species.

Kenya-Ethiopia Border Point — A14

Designs: 1sh, Station wagon at Archer's Post. 2sh, Thika overpass. 5sh, Marsabit Game Lodge and elephant.

1977, Nov. 10 **Litho.** *Perf. 14*

94	A14	50c multicolored	.20	.15
95	A14	1sh multicolored	.25	.20
96	A14	2sh multicolored	.55	.25
97	A14	5sh multicolored	1.50	.75
a.		Souvenir sheet of 4, #94-97	3.00	2.50
		Nos. 94-97 (4)	2.50	1.35

Opening of Nairobi-Addis Ababa highway.

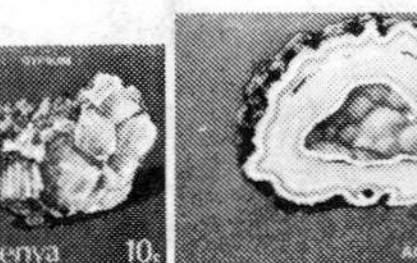

Minerals Found in Kenya
A15 A16

Perf. 14½x14, 14½ (A16)

1977, Dec. 13 **Photo.**

98	A15	10c Gypsum	.15	.15
99	A15	20c Trona	.15	.15
100	A15	30c Kyanite	.15	.15
101	A15	40c Amazonite	.15	.15
102	A15	50c Galena	.15	.15
103	A15	70c Silicified wood	.25	.15
104	A15	80c Fluorite	.30	.15
105	A16	1sh Amethyst	.35	.15
106	A16	1.50sh Agate	.55	.20
107	A16	2sh Tourmaline	.75	.30
108	A16	3sh Aquamarine	1.10	.45
109	A16	5sh Rhodolite garnet	1.90	.75
110	A16	10sh Sapphire	3.75	1.50
111	A16	20sh Ruby	7.50	3.00
112	A16	40sh Green grossular garnet	19.00	6.00
		Nos. 98-112 (15)	36.20	13.40

The 10c, 20c, 40c, 50c and 80c were also issued in booklet panes of 4. The 50c was also issued in a booklet pane of 2.

For surcharge see No. 242.

Soccer, Joe Kadenge and World Cup A17

World Cup and: 1sh, Mohammed Chuma receiving trophy, and his portrait. 2sh, Shot on goal and Omari S. Kidevu. 3sh, Backfield defense and Polly Ouma.

1978, Apr. 10 **Litho.** *Perf. 14x13½*

113	A17	50c green & multi	.15	.15
114	A17	1sh lt brown & multi	.30	.20
115	A17	2sh lilac & multi	.60	.35
116	A17	3sh dk blue & multi	1.00	.55
a.		Souvenir sheet of 4, #113-116	2.50	2.10
		Nos. 113-116 (4)	2.05	1.25

World Soccer Cup Championships, Argentina 78, June 1-25.

Boxing and Games' Emblem A18

Games Emblem and: 1sh, Pres. Kenyatta welcoming 1968 Olympic team. 3sh, Javelin. 5sh, Pres. Kenyatta, boxing team and trophy.

1978, July 15 **Photo.** *Perf. 13x14*

117	A18	50c multicolored	.15	.15
118	A18	1sh multicolored	.20	.15
119	A18	3sh multicolored	.60	.40
120	A18	5sh multicolored	1.00	.65
		Nos. 117-120 (4)	1.95	1.35

Commonwealth Games, Edmonton, Canada, Aug. 3-12.

Overloaded Truck — A19

Road Safety: 1sh, Observe speed limit. 1.50sh, Observe traffic lights. 2sh, School crossing. 3sh, Passing. 5sh, Railroad crossing.

1978, Sept. 18 **Litho.** *Perf. 13½x14*

121	A19	50c multicolored	.15	.15
122	A19	1sh multicolored	.35	.15
123	A19	1.50sh multicolored	.55	.25
124	A19	2sh multicolored	.65	.30
125	A19	3sh multicolored	1.00	.50
126	A19	5sh multicolored	1.60	.75
		Nos. 121-126 (6)	4.30	2.10

Pres. Kenyatta at Harambee Water Project Opening A20

Kenyatta Day: 1sh, Prince Philip handing over symbol of independence, 1963. 2sh, Pres. Jomo Kenyatta addressing independence rally. 3sh, Stage at 15th independence anniversary celebration. 5sh, Handcuffed Kenyatta led by soldiers, 1952.

1978, Oct. 16 **Litho.** *Perf. 14*

127	A20	50c multicolored	.15	.15
128	A20	1sh multicolored	.25	.15
129	A20	2sh multicolored	.40	.30
130	A20	3sh multicolored	.60	.40
131	A20	5sh multicolored	.90	.75
		Nos. 127-131 (5)	2.30	1.75

Soldiers and Emblem A21

Anti-Apartheid Emblem and: 1sh, Anti-Apartheid Conference. 2sh, Stephen Biko, South African Anti-Apartheid leader. 3sh, Nelson Mandela, jailed since 1961. 5sh, Bishop Lamont, expelled from Rhodesia in 1977.

1978, Dec. 11 **Litho.** *Perf. 14x14½*

132	A21	50c multicolored	.15	.15
133	A21	1sh multicolored	.25	.15
134	A21	2sh multicolored	.45	.30
135	A21	3sh multicolored	.70	.40
136	A21	5sh multicolored	1.25	.75
		Nos. 132-136 (5)	2.80	1.75

Anti-Apartheid Year and Namibia's struggle for independence.

Children on School Playground — A22

Children's Year Emblem and: 2sh, Boy catching fish. 3sh, Children dancing and singing. 5sh, Children and camel caravan.

1979, Feb. 5 Litho. *Perf. 14*

137	A22	50c multicolored	.15	.15
138	A22	2sh multicolored	.50	.25
139	A22	3sh multicolored	.70	.35
140	A22	5sh multicolored	1.25	.60
		Nos. 137-140 (4)	2.60	1.35

International Year of the Child.

"The Lion and the Jewel" A23

National Theater: 1sh, Dancers and drummers. 2sh, Programs of various productions. 3sh, View of National Theater. 5sh, "Genesis," performed by Nairobi City Players.

1979, Apr. 6 Litho. *Perf. 13½x14*

141	A23	50c multicolored	.15	.15
142	A23	1sh multicolored	.20	.15
143	A23	2sh multicolored	.40	.30
144	A23	3sh multicolored	.60	.50
145	A23	5sh multicolored	1.00	.80
		Nos. 141-145 (5)	2.35	1.90

Village Workshop — A24

Salvation Army Emblem and: 50c, Blind telephone operator, vert. 1sh, Care for the aged, vert. 5sh, Vocational training (nurse).

1979, June 4 *Perf. 13½x13, 13x13½*

146	A24	50c multicolored	.15	.15
147	A24	1sh multicolored	.30	.15
148	A24	3sh multicolored	.80	.40
149	A24	5sh multicolored	1.25	.75
		Nos. 146-149 (4)	2.50	1.45

Salvation Army Social Services, 50th anniv.

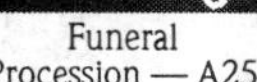

Funeral Procession — A25

British East Africa No. 2, Hill, Signature — A26

Kenyatta: 1sh, Taking oath of office. 3sh, Addressing crowd. 5sh, As young man with wooden trying plane.

1979, Aug. 22 Litho. *Perf. 13½x14*

150	A25	50c multicolored	.15	.15
151	A25	1sh multicolored	.25	.15
152	A25	3sh multicolored	.70	.45
153	A25	5sh multicolored	1.25	.70
		Nos. 150-153 (4)	2.35	1.45

Jomo Kenyatta (1893-1978), first president of Kenya.

1979, Nov. 27 Litho. *Perf. 14*

Hill, Signature and: 1sh, Kenya, Uganda and Tanzania #54. 2sh, Penny Black. 5sh, Kenya #19.

154	A26	50c multicolored	.15	.15
155	A26	1sh multicolored	.20	.15
156	A26	2sh multicolored	.40	.30
157	A26	5sh multicolored	.85	.65
		Nos. 154-157 (4)	1.60	1.25

Sir Rowland Hill (1795-1879), originator of penny postage.

Highways, Globe, Conference Emblem — A27

Conference Emblem and: 1sh, Truck at Athi River, New Weighbridge. 3sh, New Nyali Bridge, Mombasa. 5sh, Jomo Kenyatta Airport Highway.

1980, Jan. 10 Litho. *Perf. 14*

158	A27	50c multicolored	.15	.15
159	A27	1sh multicolored	.25	.20
160	A27	3sh multicolored	.70	.60
161	A27	5sh multicolored	1.25	1.00
		Nos. 158-161 (4)	2.35	1.95

4th IRF African Highway Conference, Nairobi, Jan. 20-25.

Patient Airlift A28

1980, Mar. 20 Litho. *Perf. 14½*

162	A28	50c Outdoor clinic	.15	.15
163	A28	1sh Mule transport of patient, vert.	.25	.20
164	A28	3sh Surgery, vert.	.60	.60
165	A28	5sh shown	.90	.90
a.		Souvenir sheet of 4, #162-165	2.50	2.00
		Nos. 162-165 (4)	1.90	1.85

Flying doctor service.

Hill Statue, Kidderminster and Mt. Kenya — A29

1980, May 6 Litho. *Perf. 14*

166	A29	25sh multicolored	5.25	4.00
a.		Souvenir sheet	6.00	4.50

London 1980 International Stamp Exhibition, May 6-14.

Pope John Paul II and Crowd A30

Visit of Pope John Paul II to Kenya: 1sh, Pope, Nairobi Cathedral, papal flag and arms, vert. 5sh, Pope, papal and Kenya flags, dove, vert. 10sh, Pres. Arap Moi of Kenya, Pope, flag of Kenya on map of Africa.

1980, May 8 *Perf. 13½*

167	A30	50c multicolored	.15	.15
168	A30	1sh multicolored	.25	.20
169	A30	5sh multicolored	1.10	.90
170	A30	10sh multicolored	2.25	1.75
		Nos. 167-170 (4)	3.75	3.00

Sting Ray — A31

1980, June 27 Litho. *Perf. 14½*

171	A31	50c shown	.15	.15
172	A31	2sh Alkit snapper	.55	.40
173	A31	3sh Sea slug	.85	.60
174	A31	5sh Hawksbill turtle	1.40	1.00
		Nos. 171-174 (4)	2.95	2.15

National Archives, 1904 A32

1980, Oct. 9 Litho. *Perf. 14*

175	A32	50c shown	.15	.15
176	A32	1sh Commissioner's Office, Nairobi, 1913	.20	.20
177	A32	1.50sh Nairobi House, 1913	.25	.25
178	A32	2sh Norfolk Hotel, 1904	.40	.40
179	A32	3sh McMillan Library, 1929	.60	.60
180	A32	5sh Kipande House, 1913	1.00	1.00
		Nos. 175-180 (6)	2.60	2.60

Woman in Wheelchair and Child A33

1981, Feb. 10 Litho. *Perf. 14x13½*

181	A33	50c shown	.15	.15
182	A33	1sh Pres. Arap Moi, team captain	.20	.20
183	A33	3sh Blind mountain climbers, Mt. Kenya, 1965	.70	.60
184	A33	5sh Disabled artist	1.10	.90
		Nos. 181-184 (4)	2.15	1.85

International Year of the Disabled.

Longonot Earth Station Complex — A34

1981, Apr. 4 Litho. *Perf. 14x14½*

185	A34	50c shown	.15	.15
186	A34	2sh Intelsat V	.45	.35
187	A34	3sh Longonot I	.75	.50
188	A34	5sh Longonot II	1.10	.90
		Nos. 185-188 (4)	2.45	1.90

Conference Center, OAU Flag — A35

18th Organization for African Unity Conference, Nairobi: 1sh, Map of Africa showing Panaftel earth stations. 3sh, Parliament Building, Nairobi. 5sh, Jomo Kenyatta Intl. Airport. 10sh, OAU flag.

1981, June 24 Wmk. 373 *Perf. 13½*

189	A35	50c multicolored	.15	.15
190	A35	1sh multicolored	.15	.15
191	A35	3sh multicolored	.50	.50
192	A35	5sh multicolored	.80	.80
193	A35	10sh multicolored	1.75	1.75
a.		Souvenir sheet of 1, perf. 14½	2.00	2.00
		Nos. 189-193 (5)	3.35	3.35

St. Paul's Cathedral — A36

Reticulated Giraffe — A37

1981, July 29 Litho. *Perf. 14*

194	A36	50c Charles, Pres. Arap Moi	.15	.15
195	A36	3sh shown	.60	.50
196	A36	5sh Britannia	1.00	.80
197	A36	10sh Charles	2.00	1.75
		Nos. 194-197 (4)	3.75	3.20

Souvenir Sheet

198	A36	25sh Couple	6.00	5.50

Royal Wedding.

1981, Aug. 31 Litho. *Perf. 14½*

199	A37	50c shown	.15	.15
200	A37	2sh Bongo	.45	.35
201	A37	5sh Roan antelope	1.10	.90
202	A37	10sh Mangabey	2.25	1.75
		Nos. 199-202 (4)	3.95	3.15

World Food Day — A38

Ceremonial Tribal Costumes — A39

1981, Oct. 16 Litho. *Perf. 14*

203	A38	50c Plowing	.15	.15
204	A38	1sh Rice field	.20	.20
205	A38	2sh Irrigation	.40	.35
206	A38	5sh Cattle	1.00	.80
		Nos. 203-206 (4)	1.75	1.50

Perf. 14½x13½

1981, Dec. 18 Litho.

207	A39	50c Kamba	.15	.15
208	A39	1sh Turkana	.30	.20
209	A39	2sh Giriama	.60	.40
210	A39	3sh Masai	.90	.60
211	A39	5sh Luo	1.90	1.00
		Nos. 207-211 (5)	3.85	2.35

Australopithecus Boisei — A40

1982, Jan. 16 Litho. *Perf. 14*

212	A40	50c shown	.20	.15
213	A40	2sh Homo erectus	1.25	.40
214	A40	3sh Homo habilis	2.00	.60
215	A40	5sh Proconsul africanus	3.25	.90
		Nos. 212-215 (4)	6.70	2.05

Scouting Year A41

1982, June 2 Litho. *Perf. 14½*

216	A41	70c Tree planting	.15	.15
217	A41	70c Paying homage	.15	.15
218	A41	3.50sh Be Prepared	.80	.50
219	A41	3.50sh Intl. friendship	.80	.50
220	A41	5sh Helping disabled	1.30	.75
221	A41	5sh Community service	1.30	.75

222 A41 6.50sh Paxtu Cottage 1.65 .90
223 A41 6.50sh Lady Baden-Powell 1.65 .90
Nos. 216-223 (8) 7.80 4.60

Souvenir Sheet

224 Sheet of 4 4.00 2.25
a. A41 70c like #216 .15 .15
b. A41 3.50sh like #218 .80 .45
c. A41 5sh like #220 1.25 .70
d. A41 6.50sh like #222 1.65 .85

Stamps of same denomination se-tenant.

1982 World Cup — A42

Designs: Various soccer players on world map.

1982, July 5 Litho. *Perf. 12½*

225 A42 70c multicolored .15 .15
226 A42 3.50sh multicolored .75 .60
227 A42 5sh multicolored 1.10 .80
228 A42 10sh multicolored 2.25 1.75
Nos. 225-228 (4) 4.25 3.30

Souvenir Sheet
Perf. 13½x14

229 A42 20sh multicolored 4.50 3.50

A43

A44

1982, Sept. 28 Litho. *Perf. 14½*

230 A43 70c Cattle judging .15 .15
231 A43 2.50sh Farm machinery 1.00 .40
232 A43 3.50sh Musical ride 1.25 .60
233 A43 6.50sh Emblem 2.75 1.25
Nos. 230-233 (4) 5.15 2.40

Agricultural Society, 80th anniv.

1982, Oct. 27 Photo. *Perf. 11½*
Granite Paper

234 A44 70c Microwave radio system .15 .15
235 A44 3.50sh Ship-to-shore communication 1.25 .50
236 A44 5sh Rural telecommunication 1.75 .75
237 A44 6.50sh Emblem 2.50 1.00
Nos. 234-237 (4) 5.65 2.40

ITU Plenipotentiaries Conf., Nairobi, Sept.

5th Anniv. of Kenya Ports Authority A45

1983, Jan. 20 Litho. *Perf. 14*

238 A45 70c Container cranes .20 .15
239 A45 2sh Cranes, diff. .90 .40
240 A45 3.50sh Cranes, diff. 1.50 .70
241 A45 5sh Mombasa Harbor map 2.25 .90
a. Souvenir sheet of 4, #238-241 7.00 3.00
Nos. 238-241 (4) 4.85 2.15

No. 104 Surcharged

1983, Jan. Photo. *Perf. 14½x14*

242 A15 70c on 80c multicolored 1.00 .15

A45a

1983, Mar. 14 Litho. *Perf. 14½*

243 A45a 70c Coffee picking, vert. .15 .15
244 A45a 2sh Pres. Arap Moi, vert. .35 .30
245 A45a 5sh Globe .80 .65
246 A45a 10sh Masai dance 1.60 1.40
Nos. 243-246 (4) 2.90 2.50

Commonwealth Day.

Dichrostachys Cinerea — A46 Dombeya Burgessiae — A47

Perf. 14½x14, 14x14½

1983, Feb. 15 Photo.

247 A46 10c shown .15 .15
248 A46 20c Rhamphicarpa montana .15 .15
249 A46 30c Barleria eranthemoides .15 .15
250 A46 40c Commelina .15 .15
251 A46 50c Canarina abyssinica .15 .15
252 A46 70c Aspilia mossambicensis .20 .15
253 A47 1sh Dombeya burgessiae .25 .20
254 A47 1.50sh Lantana trifolia .35 .30
255 A47 2sh Adenium obesum .45 .40
256 A47 2.50sh Terminalia orbicularis .60 .50
257 A47 3.50sh Ceropegia ballyana .75 .70
258 A47 5sh Ruttya fruticosa 1.10 .90
259 A47 10sh Pentanisia ouranogyne 1.75 1.50
260 A47 20sh Brillantaisia nyanzarum 3.00 2.75
261 A47 40sh Crotalaria axillaris 6.00 4.50
Nos. 247-261 (15) 15.20 12.65

See Nos. 350-354.

30th Anniv. of Customs Cooperation Council — A48

1983, May 11 Litho. *Perf. 14½*

262 A48 70c Parcel check .15 .15
263 A48 2.50sh Headquarters, Mombasa .50 .40
264 A48 3.50sh Headquarters, Brussels .65 .60
265 A48 10sh Patrol boat 2.00 1.75
Nos. 262-265 (4) 3.30 2.90

World Communications Year — A49

1983, July 4 Litho. *Perf. 14½*

266 A49 70c Satellite, dish antenna, vert. .15 .15
267 A49 2.50sh Mailbox, birthday card, telephone, vert. 1.00 .40
268 A49 3.50sh Jet, ship 1.25 .60
269 A49 5sh Railroad bridge, highway 2.00 .80
Nos. 266-269 (4) 4.40 1.95

Intl. Maritime Organization, 25th Anniv. — A50

1983, Sept. 22 Litho. *Perf. 14½*

270 A50 70c Kilindini Harbor .15 .15
271 A50 2.50sh Life preserver .95 .30
272 A50 3.50sh Mombasa Container Terminal 1.25 .40
273 A50 10sh Marine Park 3.75 1.25
Nos. 270-273 (4) 6.10 2.10

29th Commonwealth Parliamentary Conference — A51

1983, Oct. 31 Litho. *Perf. 14*

274 A51 70c shown .15 .15
275 A51 2.50sh Parliament Bldg., vert. .65 .30
276 A51 5sh State Opening, vert. 1.50 .60
a. Souv. sheet of 3, #274-276 + label 2.50 1.25
Nos. 274-276 (3) 2.30 1.05

Royal Visit — A52

1983, Nov. 10 Litho. *Perf. 14*

277 A52 70c Flags .15 .15
278 A52 3.50sh Sagana State Lodge .65 .50
279 A52 5sh Tree Tops Hotel .90 .75
280 A52 10sh Elizabeth II and Daniel Arap Moi 1.75 1.50
Nos. 277-280 (4) 3.45 2.90

Souvenir Sheet

281 A52 25sh multicolored 3.75 3.00

No. 281 contains Nos. 277-280 without denominations showing simulated perforations.

President Daniel Arap Moi, Monument — A53

1983, Dec. 9 Litho. *Perf. 14½*

282 A53 70c shown .15 .15
283 A53 2sh Tree planting .30 .25
284 A53 3.50sh Map, flag, emblem .52 .40
285 A53 5sh School, milk program .75 .60
286 A53 10sh People, flag, banner 1.50 1.20
Nos. 282-286 (5) 3.22 2.60

Souvenir Sheet
Imperf

287 A53 25sh multicolored 3.75 3.00

Independence, 20th Anniv. No. 287 contains Nos. 282-286 without denominations.

Rare Local Birds — A54

1984, Feb. 6 Litho. *Perf. 14½x13½*

288 A54 70c White-backed night heron .15 .15
289 A54 2.50sh Quail plover .90 .30
290 A54 3.50sh Heller's ground thrush 1.25 .40
291 A54 5sh Papyrus gonolek 1.75 .60
292 A54 10sh White-winged Apalis 3.50 1.20
Nos. 288-292 (5) 7.55 2.65

Intl. Civil Aviation Org., 40th Anniv. A55

1984, Apr. 2 Litho. *Perf. 14*

293 A55 70c Radar, vert. .15 .15
294 A55 2.50sh Kenya School of Aviation .40 .30
295 A55 3.50sh Jet, Moi Intl. Airport .50 .40
296 A55 5sh Air traffic control center .75 .60
Nos. 293-296 (4) 1.80 1.45

1984 Summer Olympics A56

1984, May 21 *Perf. 14½*

297 A56 70c Running .15 .15
298 A56 2.50sh Hurdles .40 .30
299 A56 5sh Boxing .80 .60
300 A56 10sh Field Hockey 1.65 1.20
Nos. 297-300 (4) 3.00 2.25

Souvenir Sheet
Imperf

301 A56 25sh Torch bearers 3.50 3.50

No. 301 contains designs of Nos. 297-300.

Bookmobile — A57

1984, Aug. 10 Litho. *Perf. 14½*

302 A57 70c Emblem .15 .15
303 A57 3.50sh shown .50 .40
304 A57 5sh Adult library .75 .60
305 A57 10sh Children's library 1.50 1.20
Nos. 302-305 (4) 2.90 2.35

Intl. Fed. of Library Associations, 50th Conf.

Kenya Export Year (KEY) A58

1984, Oct. 1 Litho. *Perf. 14*

306 A58 70c Emblem, vert. .15 .15
307 A58 3.50sh Airport 1.00 .40
308 A58 5sh Harbor, vert. 1.50 .60
309 A58 10sh Exports 3.00 1.25
Nos. 306-309 (4) 5.65 2.40

A59

Tribal Costumes — A60

1984, Aug. 23 Litho. *Perf. 14x14½*
310 A59 70c Doves, cross .15 .15
311 A59 2.50sh Doves, Hinduism symbol .75 .40
312 A59 3.50sh Doves, Sikhism symbol 1.00 .50
313 A59 6.50sh Doves, Islam symbol 2.25 1.10
Nos. 310-313 (4) 4.15 2.15

World Conference on Religion and Peace, Nairobi, Aug. 23-31, 1984.

1984, Nov. 5 Litho. *Perf. 14½x13½*
314 A60 70c Luhya .15 .15
315 A60 2sh Kikuyu .50 .20
316 A60 3.50sh Pokomo .90 .35
317 A60 5sh Nandi 1.25 .50
318 A60 10sh Rendile 2.50 1.10
Nos. 314-318 (5) 5.30 2.30

60th Anniv., World Chess Federation — A61

1984, Dec. 21 Litho. *Perf. 14½*
319 A61 70c Nyayo Stadium, knight .15 .15
320 A61 2.50sh Fort Jesus, rook .70 .30
321 A61 3.50sh National Monument, bishop 1.00 .40
322 A61 5sh Parliament, queen 1.40 .50
323 A61 10sh Nyayo Fountain, king 2.75 1.00
Nos. 319-323 (5) 6.00 2.35

Energy Conservation — A62

1985, Jan. 22 Litho. *Perf. 13½*
324 A62 70c Stove, fire pit .15 .15
325 A62 2sh Solar panel .30 .25
326 A62 3.50sh Biogas tank .50 .40
327 A62 10sh Plowing field 1.40 1.00

Imperf
328 A62 20sh Energy conservation 2.75 2.00
Nos. 324-328 (5) 5.10 3.80

No. 328 contains Nos. 324-327 without denominations.

Girl Guides, 75th Anniv. A63

1985, Mar. 27 Litho. *Perf. 13½*
329 A63 1sh Girl Guide, handicrafts .15 .15
330 A63 3sh Community service .80 .30
331 A63 5sh Lady Baden-Powell, Kenyan leader 1.25 .50
332 A63 7sh Food project 1.75 .70
Nos. 329-332 (4) 3.95 1.65

Intl. Red Cross Day A64

1985, May 8 *Perf. 14½*
333 A64 1sh Emblem .15 .15
334 A64 4sh First Aid 1.65 .45
335 A64 5sh Blood donation 2.00 .60
336 A64 7sh Famine relief, cornucopia 3.00 .75
Nos. 333-336 (4) 6.80 1.95

A65

A66

Diseases caused by microorganisms carried by insects.

1985, June 25
337 A65 1sh Malaria .15 .15
338 A65 3sh Leishmaniasis 1.25 .30
339 A65 5sh Trypanosomiasis 2.00 .55
340 A65 7sh Babesiosis 3.00 .75
Nos. 337-340 (4) 6.40 1.75

7th Intl. Congress on Protozoology, Nairobi, June 22-29.

1985, July 15
341 A66 1sh Repairing water pipes .15 .15
342 A66 3sh Traditional food processing .60 .30
343 A66 5sh Basket weaving 1.00 .50
344 A66 7sh Dress making 1.30 .70
Nos. 341-344 (4) 3.05 1.65

UN Decade for Women.

43rd Intl. Eucharistic Congress, Nairobi, Aug. 11-18 A67

1985, Aug. 15 *Perf. 13½*
345 A67 1sh The Last Supper .15 .15
346 A67 3sh Afro-Christian family .80 .30
347 A67 5sh Congress altar, Uhuru Park 1.25 .50
348 A67 7sh St. Peter Claver's Church 1.75 .70
Nos. 345-348 (4) 3.95 1.65

Souvenir Sheet
349 A67 25sh Pope John Paul II 5.00 2.50

Flower Types of 1983

1985 Photo. *Perf. 14½x14, 14½*
350 A46 80c like #250 .15 .15
351 A46 1sh Dombeya burgessiae .15 .15
352 A47 3sh Calotropis procera 1.25 .30
353 A47 4sh Momordica foetida 1.50 .40
354 A47 7sh Oncoba spinosa 2.50 .65
Nos. 350-354 (5) 5.55 1.65

Endangered Wildlife — A68

1985, Dec. 10 Litho. *Perf. 14½*
355 A68 1sh Diceros bicornis .40 .20
356 A68 3sh Acinonyx jubatus 1.25 .50
357 A68 5sh Cercopithecus neglectus 2.25 .75
358 A68 10sh Equus greyvi 4.50 1.50

Size: 130x122mm

Imperf
359 A68 25sh Hunter pursuing game 6.00 2.25
Nos. 355-359 (5) 14.40 5.20

Trees A69

1986, Jan. 24 *Perf. 14½*
360 A69 1sh Borassus aethiopum .15 .15
361 A69 3sh Acacia xanthophloea .90 .30
362 A69 5sh Ficus natalensis 1.50 .55
363 A69 7sh Spathodea nilotica 2.00 .75

Size: 117x97mm

Imperf
364 A69 25sh Glade 7.00 2.75
Nos. 360-364 (5) 11.55 4.50

Intl. Peace Year — A70

1986 World Cup Soccer Championships, Mexico — A71

1986, Apr. 17 *Perf. 14½*
365 A70 1sh Dove, UN emblem .15 .15
366 A70 3sh UN General Assembly, horiz. .65 .35
367 A70 7sh Mushroom cloud 1.50 .75
368 A70 10sh Isaiah 2:4, horiz. 2.25 1.10
Nos. 365-368 (4) 4.55 2.35

1986, May 9
369 A71 1sh Dribbling .15 .15
370 A71 3sh Penalty shot .60 .30
371 A71 5sh Tackling 1.00 .50
372 A71 7sh Champions 1.50 .70
373 A71 10sh Heading the ball 2.25 1.25

Size: 110x86mm

Imperf
374 A71 30sh Harambee Stars 6.00 3.25
Nos. 369-374 (6) 11.50 6.15

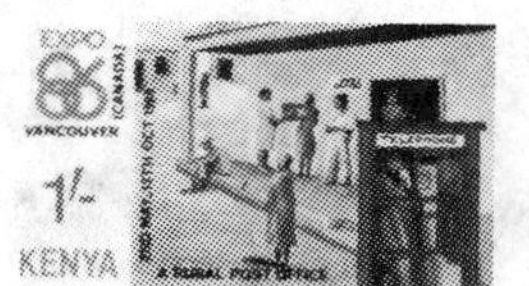

EXPO '86, Vancouver — A72

1986, June 11 *Perf. 13½x13*
375 A72 1sh Rural post office .15 .15
376 A72 3sh Container depot, Embakasi .90 .30
377 A72 5sh Plane landing 1.50 .50
378 A72 7sh Shipping exports 2.00 .75
379 A72 10sh Goods transport 2.75 1.10
Nos. 375-379 (5) 7.30 2.80

TELECOM '86, Nairobi, Sept. 16-23 — A73

1986, Sept. 16 Litho. *Perf. 14½*
380 A73 1sh Telephone-computer links .15 .15
381 A73 3sh Telephones, 1876-1986 .80 .30
382 A73 5sh Satellite communications 1.25 .45
383 A73 7sh Switchboards 1.75 .65
Nos. 380-383 (4) 3.95 1.55

A74

Dhows (Ships) A75

1986, Oct. 30 Litho. *Perf. 14½*
384 A74 1sh Mashua .15 .15
385 A74 3sh Mtepe .80 .25
386 A74 5sh Dau La Mwao 1.25 .50
387 A74 10sh Jahazi 2.75 1.00
Nos. 384-387 (4) 4.95 1.90

Souvenir Sheet
388 A75 25sh Lamu, map 5.00 2.50

Christmas A76

1986, Dec. 5 *Perf. 12*
389 A76 1sh Nativity, vert. .15 .15
390 A76 3sh Shepherd boy, vert. .80 .30
391 A76 5sh Angel, map 1.25 .45
392 A76 7sh Magi 1.75 .65
Nos. 389-392 (4) 3.95 1.55

UNICEF, 40th Anniv. — A77

Child Survival Campaign: 1sh, Universal immunization by 1990. 3sh, Food and nutrition. 4sh, Oral rehydration. 5sh, Family planning. 10sh, Literacy of women.

1987, Jan. 6 Litho. *Perf. 14½*
393 A77 1sh multicolored .15 .15
394 A77 3sh multicolored .65 .30
395 A77 4sh multicolored .90 .40
396 A77 5sh multicolored 1.10 .45
397 A77 10sh multicolored 2.00 .95
Nos. 393-397 (5) 4.80 2.25

A78

Tourism A79

1987, Mar. 25 Litho. *Perf. 14½*
398 A78 1sh Akamba carvers .15 .15
399 A78 3sh Beach 1.25 .30
400 A78 5sh Escarpment 1.90 .45
401 A78 7sh Pride of lions 2.75 .65
Nos. 398-401 (4) 6.05 1.55

Souvenir Sheet
402 A79 30sh Kenya geysers 7.00 3.00

Ceremonial Costumes — A80

1987, May 20 *Perf. 14½x13½*
403 A80 1sh Embu .15 .15
404 A80 3sh Kisii .70 .30
405 A80 5sh Samburu 1.25 .55
406 A80 7sh Taita 1.75 .80
407 A80 10sh Boran 2.50 1.10
Nos. 403-407 (5) 6.35 2.90

See Nos. 505-509.

Posts & Telecommunications Corp., 10th Anniv. — A81

1987, July 1 Litho. *Perf. 13½*

408	A81	1sh	Telecommunications satellite	.15	.15
409	A81	3sh	Rural post office, Kajiado	.60	.30
410	A81	4sh	Athletics	.85	.35
411	A81	5sh	Rural communication	1.00	.45
412	A81	7sh	Speedpost	1.50	.65
			Nos. 408-412 (5)	4.10	1.90

Souvenir Sheet

413	A81	25sh	Natl. Flag	3.25	2.50

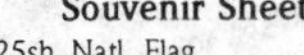

A82 A83

1987, Aug. 5 *Perf. 14½x14*

414	A82	1sh	Volleyball	.15	.15
415	A82	3sh	Cycling	.35	.30
416	A82	4sh	Boxing	.48	.35
417	A82	5sh	Swimming	.60	.45
418	A82	7sh	Steeple chase	.85	.65
			Nos. 414-418 (5)	2.43	1.90

Souvenir Sheet

Perf. 14x14½

419	A82	30sh	Kasarani Sports Complex	3.50	2.75

4th All Africa Games, Nairobi, Aug. 1-12. Nos. 414-418, vert.

1987, Oct. 27 Litho. *Perf. 13½x14*

Medicinal herbs.

420	A83	1sh	Aloe volkensii	.15	.15
421	A83	3sh	Cassia didymobotrya	.70	.30
422	A83	5sh	Erythrina abyssinica	1.25	.45
423	A83	7sh	Adenium obesum	1.75	.65
424	A83	10sh	Herbalist's clinic	2.25	.90
			Nos. 420-424 (5)	6.10	2.45

Butterflies — A84

1988-90 Photo. *Perf. 15x14*

424A	A84	10c	Cyrestis camillus	.15	.15
425	A84	20c	Iolaus sidus	.15	.15
426	A84	40c	Vanessa cardui	.15	.15
427	A84	50c	Colotis euippe omphale	.15	.15
428	A84	70c	Precis westermanni	.15	.15
429	A84	80c	Colias electo	.15	.15
430	A84	1sh	Eronia leda	.15	.15
430A	A84	1.50sh	Papilio dardanus planemoides	.15	.15

Size: 25x41mm

Perf. 14½

431	A84	2sh	Papilio rex	.25	.20
432	A84	2.50sh	Colotis phisadia	.30	.25
433	A84	3sh	Papilio desmondi teita	.35	.30
434	A84	3.50sh	Papilio demodocus	.40	.30
435	A84	4sh	Papilio phorcas	.50	.35
436	A84	5sh	Charaxes druceanus teita	.60	.45
437	A84	7sh	Cymothoe teita	.80	.60
438	A84	10sh	Charaxes zoolina	1.15	.90
439	A84	20sh	Papilio dardanus	2.35	1.75
440	A84	40sh	Charaxes cithaeron kennethi	4.65	3.50
			Nos. 424A-440 (18)	12.55	9.80

Issue dates: 10c, Sept. 1, 1989. 1.50sh, May 18, 1990. Others, Feb. 14, 1988.

Game Lodges A85

1988, May 31 Litho. *Perf. 14½*

441	A85	1sh	Samburu	.15	.15
442	A85	3sh	Naro Moru River	.60	.30
443	A85	4sh	Mara Serena	.75	.40
444	A85	5sh	Voi Safari	1.00	.50
445	A85	7sh	Kilimanjaro Buffalo Lodge	1.30	.70
446	A85	10sh	Meru Mulika	1.90	1.00
			Nos. 441-446 (6)	5.70	3.05

World Expo '88, Brisbane A86

EXPO '88 and Australia bicentennial emblems plus: 1sh, Stadium, site of the 1982 Commonwealth Games, and runners. 3sh, Flying Doctor Service aircraft. 4sh, HMS Sirius, a 19th cent. immigrant ship. 5sh, Ostrich and emu. 7sh, Pres. Daniel Arap Moi, Queen Elizabeth II and Robert Hawke, prime minister of Australia. 30sh, Kenya Pavilion at EXPO '88.

1988, June 10

447	A86	1sh	multicolored	.15	.15
448	A86	3sh	multicolored	.60	.30
449	A86	4sh	multicolored	.75	.40
450	A86	5sh	multicolored	1.00	.50
451	A86	7sh	multicolored	1.30	.70
			Nos. 447-451 (5)	3.80	2.05

Souvenir Sheet

452	A86	30sh	multicolored	3.25	2.50

World Health Organization, 40th Anniv. — A87

1988, July 1 Litho. *Perf. 14½*

453	A87	1sh	shown	.15	.15
454	A87	3sh	Nutrition	.80	.30
455	A87	5sh	Immunization	1.25	.50
456	A87	7sh	Water supply	1.75	.70
			Nos. 453-456 (4)	3.95	1.65

1988 Summer Olympics, Seoul — A88

1988, Aug. 1 Litho. *Perf. 14½x14*

457	A88	1sh	Handball	.15	.15
458	A88	3sh	Judo	.40	.30
459	A88	5sh	Weight lifting	.60	.50
460	A88	7sh	Javelin	.90	.65
461	A88	10sh	400-meter relay	1.25	.95
			Nos. 457-461 (5)	3.30	2.55

Souvenir Sheet

462	A88	30sh	Tennis	3.75	2.75

Utensils A89

Perf. 14½x14, 14x14½

1988, Sept. 20 Litho.

463	A89	1sh	Calabashes, vert.	.15	.15
464	A89	3sh	Milk gourds, vert.	.50	.25
465	A89	5sh	Cooking pots	.90	.45
466	A89	7sh	Winnowing trays	1.25	.65
467	A89	10sh	Reed baskets	1.75	.90
			Nos. 463-467 (5)	4.55	2.40

Souvenir Sheet

468	A89	25sh	Gourds, calabash, horn	3.25	2.40

10-Year Presidency of Daniel Arap Moi — A90

Designs: 1sh, Swearing-in ceremony, 1978. 3sh, Promoting soil conservation. 3.50sh, Public transportation (bus), Nairobi. 4sh, Jua Kali artisans at market. 5sh, Moi University, Eldoret, established in 1985. 7sh, Hospital ward expansion. 10sh, British Prime Minister Margaret Thatcher and Pres. Moi inaugurating the Kapsabet Telephone Exchange, Jan. 6, 1988.

Perf. 13½x14½

1988, Oct. 13 Litho.

469	A90	1sh	multicolored	.15	.15
470	A90	3sh	multicolored	.70	.30
471	A90	3.50sh	multicolored	.80	.30
472	A90	4sh	multicolored	1.00	.35
473	A90	5sh	multicolored	1.25	.45
474	A90	7sh	multicolored	1.75	.65
475	A90	10sh	multicolored	2.50	.90
			Nos. 469-475 (7)	8.15	3.10

Independence, 25th Anniv. — A91

1988, Dec. 9 Litho. *Perf. 11½*

476	A91	1sh	Natl. flag	.15	.15
477	A91	3sh	Coffee picking	.90	.30
478	A91	5sh	Model of postal hq.	1.25	.45
479	A91	7sh	Harambee Star Airbus A310-300	1.75	.65
480	A91	10sh	Locomotive 9401	2.50	.90
			Nos. 476-480 (5)	6.55	2.45

Natl. Monuments A92

1989, Mar. 15 Litho. *Perf. 14½*

481	A92	1.20sh	Gedi Ruins, Malindi	.15	.15
482	A92	3.40sh	Vasco Da Gama Pillar, Malindi, vert.	.60	.30
483	A92	4.40sh	Ishiakani Monument, Kiunga	.80	.40
484	A92	5.50sh	Ft. Jesus, Mombasa	1.00	.50
485	A92	7.70sh	She Burnan Omwe, Lamu, vert.	1.30	.70
			Nos. 481-485 (5)	3.85	2.05

Red Cross, 125th Anniv. A93

1989, May 8 Litho. *Perf. 14x13½*

486	A93	1.20sh	Anniv. and natl. soc. emblems	.15	.15
487	A93	3.40sh	First aid	.80	.40
488	A93	4.40sh	Disaster relief	1.00	.50
489	A93	5.50sh	Jean-Henri Dunant	1.25	.65
490	A93	7.70sh	Blood donation	1.80	.90
			Nos. 486-490 (5)	5.00	2.60

World Wildlife Fund — A94

Mushrooms — A95

Giraffes, Giraffa Camelopardalis Reticulata.

1989, July 12 Litho. *Perf. 14½*

491	A94	1.20sh	multicolored	.15	.15
492	A94	3.40sh	multicolored	.80	.40
493	A94	4.40sh	multicolored	1.00	.50
494	A94	5.50sh	multicolored	1.25	.65

Size: 80x110mm

Imperf

495	A94	30sh	multicolored	6.00	3.60
			Nos. 491-495 (5)	9.20	5.30

No. 495 contains four labels like Nos. 491-494, perf. 14½, without denominations or WWF emblem.

1989, Sept. 6 Litho. *Perf. 14½*

496	A95	1.20sh	Oyster	.15	.15
497	A95	3.40sh	Chestnut	1.25	.40
498	A95	4.40sh	White button	1.50	.50
499	A95	5.50sh	Termite	1.75	.60
500	A95	7.70sh	Shiitake	2.50	.85
			Nos. 496-500 (5)	7.15	2.50

Jawaharlal Nehru, 1st Prime Minister of Independent India — A96

1989, Nov. 9 Litho. *Perf. 13½x14*

501	A96	1.20sh	Independence struggle	.15	.15
502	A96	3.40sh	Education	1.10	.35
503	A96	5.50sh	Portrait	1.75	.60
504	A96	7.70sh	Industry	2.40	.80
			Nos. 501-504 (4)	5.40	1.90

Costume Type of 1980

1989, Dec. 8 Litho. *Perf. 14½x13½*

505	A80	1.20sh	Kipsigis	.15	.15
506	A80	3.40sh	Rabai	.90	.35
507	A80	5.50sh	Duruma	1.50	.60
508	A80	7.70sh	Kuria	2.00	.80
509	A80	10sh	Bajuni	2.60	1.10
			Nos. 505-509 (5)	7.15	3.00

Pan-African Postal Union, 10th Anniv. — A97

Perf. 14x13½, 13½x14

1990, Jan. 31 Litho.

510	A97	1.20sh	EMS Speedpost	.15	.15
511	A97	3.40sh	Mail runner	.35	.35
512	A97	5.50sh	Mandera P.O.	.60	.60
513	A97	7.70sh	EMS, diff., vert.	.80	.80
514	A97	10sh	PAPU emblem, vert.	1.05	1.05
			Nos. 510-514 (5)	2.95	2.95

Soccer Trophies — A98

1.50sh, Moi Golden Cup. 4.50sh, East & Central Africa Challenge Cup. 6.50sh, East & Central Africa Club Championship Cup. 9sh, World Cup.

1990, May 21 Litho. *Perf. 14½*

515 A98 1.50sh multicolored .15 .15
516 A98 4.50sh multicolored .90 .45
517 A98 6.50sh multicolored 1.25 .65
518 A98 9sh multicolored 1.75 .90
Nos. 515-518 (4) 4.05 2.15

Penny Black 150th Anniv., Stamp World London '90 — A99

1990, Apr. 27 Litho. *Perf. 11½*

519 A99 1.50sh shown .15 .15
520 A99 4.50sh Great Britain No. 1 1.00 .50
521 A99 6.50sh Early British cancellations 1.40 .70
522 A99 9sh Main P.O. 1.90 .95
a. Souvenir sheet of 4, #519-522 4.50 3.50
Nos. 519-522 (4) 4.45 2.30

No. 522a sold for 30 shillings.

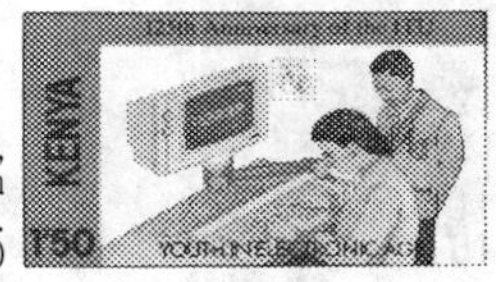

ITU, 125th Anniv. A100

4.50sh, Telephone assembly. 6.50sh, ITU Anniv. emblem. 9sh, Telecommunications development.

1990, July 12

523 A100 1.50sh multicolored .15 .15
524 A100 4.50sh multicolored .45 .45
525 A100 6.50sh multicolored .65 .65
526 A100 9sh multicolored .90 .90
Nos. 523-526 (4) 2.15 2.15

Queen Mother, 90th Birthday

Common Design Types

Perf. 14x15

1990, Aug. 4 Litho. Wmk. 384

527 CD343 10sh Queen Mother .95 .95

Perf. 14½

528 CD344 40sh At garden party, 1947 3.75 3.75

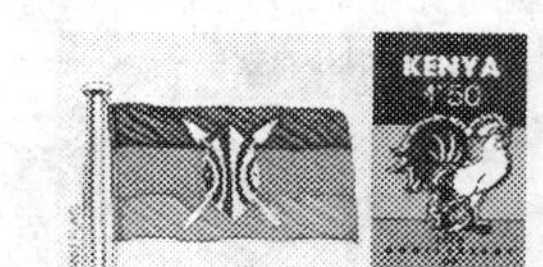

Kenya African National Union (KANU), 50th Anniv. A101

1990, June 11

529 A101 1.50sh KANU flag .15 .15
530 A101 2.50sh Nyayo Monument .25 .25
531 A101 4.50sh KICC Party Headquarters .45 .45
532 A101 5sh Jomo Kenyatta .50 .50
533 A101 6.50sh Daniel T. Arap Moi .65 .65
534 A101 9sh KANU mass meeting .90 .90
535 A101 10sh Voters 1.00 1.00
Nos. 529-535 (7) 3.90 3.90

Kenya Postage Stamps, Cent. — A102

Intl. Literacy Year — A103

Designs: 1.50sh, Kenya #431. 4.50sh, East Africa and Uganda Protectorates #2. 6.50sh, British East Africa #1. 9sh, Kenya and Uganda #25. 20sh, Kenya, Uganda, Tanzania #232.

1990, Sept. 5 Litho. *Perf. 14x14½*

536 A102 1.50sh multicolored .15 .15
537 A102 4.50sh multicolored .70 .45
538 A102 6.50sh multicolored 1.00 .65
539 A102 9sh multicolored 1.30 .90
540 A102 20sh multicolored 3.00 2.00
Nos. 536-540 (5) 6.15 4.15

1990, Nov. 30 Litho. *Perf. 13½x14*

541 A103 1.50sh Adult literacy class .15 .15
542 A103 4.50sh Radio teaching program .90 .45
543 A103 6.50sh Technical training 1.25 .65
544 A103 9sh Literacy year emblem 1.75 .90
Nos. 541-544 (4) 4.05 2.15

1992 Summer Olympics, Barcelona A106

1991, Nov. 29 Litho. *Perf. 14x13½*

554 A106 2sh National flag .15 .15
555 A106 6sh Basketball .90 .45
556 A106 7sh Field hockey 1.00 .50
557 A106 8.50sh Table tennis 1.25 .60
558 A106 11sh Boxing 1.75 .80
Nos. 554-558 (5) 5.05 2.50

Fight AIDS — A107

Wildlife — A108

1991, Oct. 31 Litho. *Perf. 13½x14*

559 A107 2sh You too can be infected .15 .15
560 A107 6sh Has no cure .90 .45
561 A107 8.50sh Casual sex is unsafe 1.25 .60
562 A107 11sh Sterilize syringe before use 1.75 .80
Nos. 559-562 (4) 4.05 2.00

Queen Elizabeth II's Accession to the Throne, 40th Anniv.

Common Design Type

1992, Feb. 6 Litho. *Perf. 14x13½*

563 CD349 3sh multicolored .20 .20
564 CD349 8sh multicolored .60 .60
565 CD349 11sh multicolored .80 .80
566 CD349 14sh multicolored 1.00 1.00
567 CD349 40sh multicolored 2.80 2.80
Nos. 563-567 (5) 5.40 5.40

1992, May 8 *Perf. 14½*

568 A108 3sh Leopard .20 .20
569 A108 8sh Lion 1.25 .60
570 A108 10sh Elephant 1.40 .70
571 A108 11sh Buffalo 1.60 .80
572 A108 14sh Rhinoceros 2.00 1.00
Nos. 568-572 (5) 6.45 3.30

Vintage Cars A109

Designs: 3sh, Intl. Harvester S.S. motor truck, 1926. 8sh, Fiat 509, 1924. 10sh, "R" Hupmobile, 1923. 11sh, Chevrolet Box Body, 1928. 14sh, Bentley Parkward, 1934.

1992, June 24 *Perf. 14½*

573 A109 3sh multicolored .20 .20
574 A109 8sh multicolored .90 .60
575 A109 10sh multicolored 1.00 .70
576 A109 11sh multicolored 1.25 .80
577 A109 14sh multicolored 1.50 1.00
Nos. 573-577 (5) 4.85 3.30

1992 Summer Olympics, Barcelona — A110

1992, July 24 Litho. *Perf. 14½*

578 A110 3sh Runners .15 .15
579 A110 8sh Judo .90 .45
580 A110 10sh Women's volleyball 1.10 .55
581 A110 11sh 4x100-meter relay 1.25 .60
582 A110 14sh 10,000-meter run 1.60 .80
Nos. 578-582 (5) 5.00 2.55

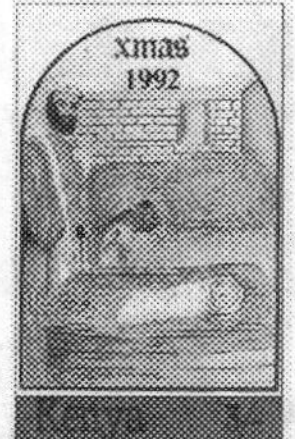

Christmas A111

Lighthouses A112

3sh, Joseph, Jesus & animals in stable. 8sh, Mary holding Jesus in stable. 11sh, Map of Kenya, Christmas tree. 14sh, Adoration of the Magi.

1992, Dec. 14 Litho. *Perf. 13½x14*

583 A111 3sh multicolored .20 .20
584 A111 8sh multicolored 1.00 .50
585 A111 11sh multicolored 1.40 .70
586 A111 14sh multicolored 1.75 .90
Nos. 583-586 (4) 4.35 2.30

1993, Jan. 25 *Perf. 14½*

Designs: 3sh, Asembo Bay, Lake Victoria. 8sh, Ras Serani, Mombasa. 11sh, Ras Serani, Mombasa, diff. 14sh, Gingira, Lake Victoria.

587 A112 3sh multicolored .40 .20
588 A112 8sh multicolored 1.00 .50
589 A112 11sh multicolored 1.40 .70
590 A112 14sh multicolored 1.75 .90
Nos. 587-590 (4) 4.55 2.30

Birds — A113

1993-94 Photo. *Perf. 15x14*

Granite Paper

594 A113 50c Superb starling .15 .15
597 A113 1sh Red & yellow barbet .15 .15
598 A113 1.50sh Ross's turaco .15 .15
600 A113 3sh Greater honeyguide .20 .20
601 A113 5sh African fish eagle .20 .20
602 A113 7sh Malachite kingfisher .45 .45
603 A113 8sh Speckled pigeon .50 .50
604 A113 10sh Cinnamon-chested bee-eater .65 .65
605 A113 11sh Scarlet-chested sunbird .70 .70
606 A113 14sh Reichenow's weaver .90 .90

Size: 25x42mm

Perf. 14½

608 A113 50sh Yellow-billed hornbill 3.25 3.25
609 A113 80sh Lesser flamingo 5.00 5.00
610 A113 100sh Hadada ibis 6.45 6.45
Nos. 594-610 (13) 18.75 18.75

Issued: 1.50sh, 5sh, 2/14/94; others, 2/22/93.
This is an expanding set. Numbers may change.

17th World Congress of Rehabilatation Intl. — A114

1993, July 1 Litho. *Perf. 14½*

611 A114 3sh Health care, vert. .15 .15
612 A114 8sh Recreation .50 .40
613 A114 10sh Vocational training .70 .55
614 A114 11sh Recreation & sports .75 .60
615 A114 14sh Emblem, vert. .90 .75
Nos. 611-615 (5) 3.00 2.45

Maendeleo ya Wanawake Organization, 42th Anniv. — A115

Designs: 3.50sh, Maendeleo House. 9sh, Planting trees. 11sh, Rural family planning services, vert. 12.50sh, Water nearer the people. 15.50sh, Maendeleo improved wood cookstove, vert.

Perf. 14x13½, 13½x14

1994, Mar. 17 Litho.

616 A115 3.50sh multicolored .20 .20
617 A115 9sh multicolored .55 .45
618 A115 11sh multicolored .65 .55
619 A115 12.50sh multicolored .75 .60
620 A115 15.50sh multicolored .90 .80
Nos. 616-620 (5) 3.05 2.60

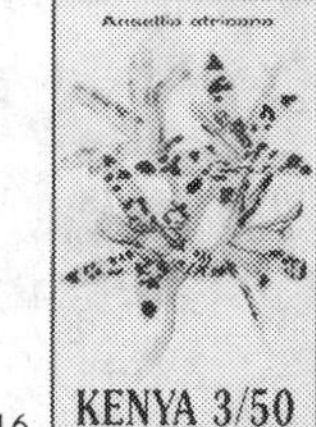

Orchids — A116

3.50sh, Ansellia africana. 9sh, Aerangis lutecalba. 12.50sh, Polystachya bella. 15.50sh, Brachycorythis kalbreyeri. 20sh, Eulophia guineensis.

1994, June 27 Litho. *Perf. 13½x14*

621 A116 3.50sh multicolored .15 .15
622 A116 9sh multicolored .70 .35
623 A116 12.50sh multicolored .90 .45
624 A116 15.50sh multicolored 1.10 .55
625 A116 20sh multicolored 1.50 .75
Nos. 621-625 (5) 4.35 2.25

African Development Bank, 30th Anniv. — A117

1994, Nov. 21 Litho. *Perf. 14½*

626 A117 6sh KICC, Nairobi .40 .25
627 A117 25sh Isinya, Kajiado 1.60 1.00

Intl. Year of the Family — A118

Rotary, 50th Anniv. — A119

1994, Dec. 22

628 A118 6sh Family planning .35 .25
629 A118 14.50sh Health .90 .60
630 A118 20sh Education, horiz. 1.25 .80
631 A118 25sh Emblem, horiz. 1.50 1.00
Nos. 628-631 (4) 4.00 2.65

1994, Dec. 29 *Perf. 13½x14*

Designs: 6sh, Paul P. Harris, founder. 14.50sh, Rotary Club of Mombasa. 17.50sh, Polio plus vaccine. 20sh, Water projects. 25sh, Emblem, motto.

632 A119 6sh multicolored .30 .25
633 A119 14.50sh multicolored .75 .60
634 A119 17.50sh multicolored .90 .70
635 A119 20sh multicolored 1.00 .80
636 A119 25sh multicolored 1.25 1.00
Nos. 632-636 (5) 4.20 3.35

SPCA — A120

Golf — A121

1995, Jan. 13 Litho. *Perf. 14½*

637 A120 6sh Donkey .30 .25
638 A120 14.50sh Cattle .75 .60
639 A120 17.50sh Sheep .90 .70
640 A120 20sh Dog 1.00 .80
641 A120 25sh Cat 1.25 1.00
Nos. 637-641 (5) 4.20 3.35

Kenya Society for Prevention of Cruelty to Animals.

1995, Feb. 28 Litho. *Perf. 14½*

642 A121 6sh Man in vest .50 .25
643 A121 17.50sh Woman 1.50 .75
644 A121 20sh Man in red shirt 1.75 .90
645 A121 25sh Golf club 2.25 1.10
Nos. 642-645 (4) 6.00 3.00

Traditional Crafts — A122

1995, Mar. 24 Litho. *Perf. 14x13½*

646 A122 6sh Perfume containers .35 .30
647 A122 14.50sh Basketry .75 .65
648 A122 17.50sh Preservation pots .90 .80
649 A122 20sh Gourds 1.00 .90
650 A122 25sh Wooden containers 1.25 1.10
Nos. 646-650 (5) 4.25 3.75

UN, 50th Anniv. A123

23sh, UN Headquarters, Nairobi. 26sh, People holding UN emblem. 32sh, UN Peacekeeper's helmet. 40sh, UN emblem.

1995, Oct. 24 Litho. *Perf. 13½*

651 A123 23sh multicolored 1.00 .90
652 A123 26sh multicolored 1.10 1.00
653 A123 32sh multicolored 1.50 1.30
654 A123 40sh multicolored 1.75 1.60
Nos. 651-654 (4) 5.35 4.80

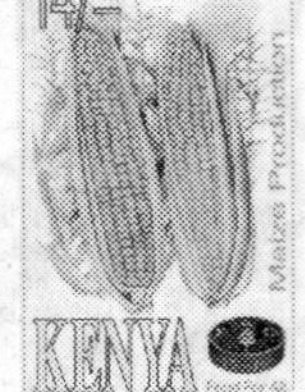

A124

A125

1995, Sept. 29 Litho. *Perf. 13½*

655 A124 14sh Tse-tse fly .55 .55
656 A124 26sh Tick 1.00 1.00
657 A124 32sh Wild silk moth 1.30 1.30
658 A124 33sh Maize borer 1.40 1.40
659 A124 40sh Locust 1.65 1.65
Nos. 655-659 (5) 5.90 5.90

ICIPE, 25th anniv.

1995, Oct. 16

660 A125 14sh Maize production .55 .55
661 A125 28sh Cattle rearing 1.00 1.00
662 A125 32sh Poultry keeping 1.30 1.30
663 A125 33sh Fishing 1.40 1.40
664 A125 40sh Fruits 1.65 1.65
Nos. 660-664 (5) 5.90 5.90

FAO, 50th anniv.

Miniature Sheets

1996 Summer Olympics, Atlanta — A126

No. 665: a, 14sh, Swimming. b, 20sh, Archery. c, 32sh, Javelin. d, 40sh, Fencing. e, 50sh, Discus. f, 20sh, Weight lifting.

No. 666: a, Pole vault. b, Equestrian. c, Diving. d, Track e, Torch bearer. f, Hurdles. g, Kayak. h, Boxing. i, Gymnastics.

Medal winers: No. 667: a, Greg Louganis, diving. b, Muhammed Ali, boxing. c, Nadia Comaneci, gymnastics. d, Daley Thompson, decathlon. e, Kipchoge "Kip" Keino, track and field. f, Kornelia Enders, swimming. g, Jackie Joyner-Kersee, track and field. h, Michael Jordan, basketball. i, Shun Fujimoto, gymnastics.

No. 668, Torch bearer. No. 669, Gold medalist.

1996, Jan. 5 Litho. *Perf. 14*

665 A126 Sheet of 6, #a.-f. 7.00 7.00
666 A126 20sh Sheet of 9, #a.-i. 7.25 7.25
667 A126 25sh Sheet of 9, #a.-i. 9.00 9.00

Souvenir Sheets

668-669 A126 100sh each 4.00 4.00

World Tourism Organization, 20th Anniv. — A127

1996, Jan. 31 Litho. *Perf. 13½*

670 A127 6sh Lions .25 .25
671 A127 14sh Mount Kenya .55 .55
672 A127 20sh Water sports .80 .80
673 A127 25sh Hippopotomus 1.00 1.00
674 A127 40sh Culture 1.65 1.65
Nos. 670-674 (5) 4.25 4.25

Perf. 13x13½

675 A127 50sh Giraffes, vert. 2.00 2.00

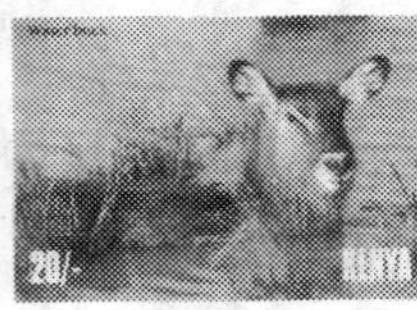

Wild Animals A128

1996 *Perf. 13x13½*

Booklet Stamps

676 A128 20sh Water buck .80 .80
677 A128 20sh Rhinoceros .80 .80
678 A128 20sh Cheetah .80 .80
679 A128 20sh Oryx .80 .80
680 A128 20sh Reticulated giraffe .80 .80
681 A128 20sh Bongo .80 .80
a. Booklet pane, Nos. 676-681 4.80
Complete booklet, 4 No. 681a 20.00

Nos. 676-681 appear in No. 681a in two different orders. Complete booklet contains 2 of each type of pane.

1996 Summer Olympic Games, Atlanta — A129

Red Cross — A130

1996, July 18 Litho. *Perf. 13½x14*

682 A129 6sh Woman running .25 .25
683 A129 14sh Steeple chase .55 .55
684 A129 20sh Victory lap .80 .80
685 A129 25sh Boxing 1.00 1.00
686 A129 40sh Man running 1.60 1.60
Nos. 682-686 (5) 4.20 4.20

1996, Aug. 30 Litho. *Perf. 14*

687 A130 6sh Emblem .25 .25
688 A130 14sh Blood donation .55 .55
689 A130 20sh Immunization .80 .80
690 A130 25sh Refugees 1.00 1.00
691 A130 40sh Clean environment 1.60 1.60
Nos. 687-691 (5) 4.20 4.20

A131

6/= LOGO KENYA

A132

1996, Sept. 10 Litho. *Perf. 14½*

693 A131 6sh Impala .25 .25
694 A131 20sh Colobus monkey .80 .80
695 A131 25sh Elephant 1.00 1.00
696 A131 40sh Black rhino 1.60 1.60
Nos. 693-696 (4) 3.65 3.65

East African Wildlife Society.

1996, Oct. 31 Litho. *Perf. 13½*

697 A132 6sh Logo .25 .25
698 A132 14sh Eye camps .55 .55
699 A132 20sh Wheel chair .80 .80
700 A132 25sh Ambulance 1.00 1.00
Nos. 697-700 (4) 2.60 2.60

Lions Club Intl.

COMESA (Common Market for Eastern and Southern Africa — A133

1997, Jan. 15 Litho. *Perf. 13½x14*

701 A133 6sh COMESA logo .20 .20
702 A133 20sh Natl. flag .75 .75

Fish of Lake Victoria A134

Haplochromis: #703, Orange rock hunter. #704, Chilotes. #705, Cinctus. #706, Nigricans.

1997, Jan. 31 *Perf. 14x13½*

703 A134 25sh multicolored .90 .90
704 A134 25sh multicolored .90 .90
705 A134 25sh multicolored .90 .90
706 A134 25sh multicolored .90 .90
Nos. 703-706 (4) 3.60 3.60

World Wildlife Fund.

Locomotives — A135

1997, Feb. 20 Litho. *Perf. 14x13½*

707 A135 6sh Class 94, 1981 .20 .20
708 A135 14sh Class 87, 1964 .50 .50
709 A135 20sh Class 59, 1955 .75 .75
710 A135 25sh Class 57, 1939 .90 .90
711 A135 30sh Class 23, 1923 1.10 1.10
712 A135 40sh Class 10, 1914 1.50 1.50
Nos. 707-712 (6) 4.95 4.95

Dated 1996.

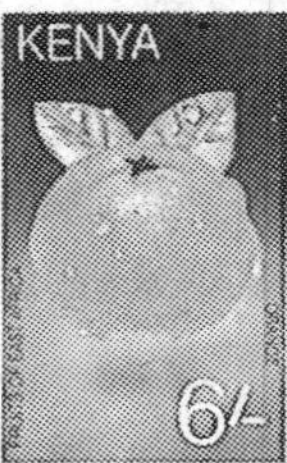

Fruits — A136

A137

1997, Feb. 28 *Perf. 14½*

713 A136 6sh Orange .20 .20
714 A136 14sh Pineapple .50 .50
715 A136 20sh Mango .75 .75
716 A136 25sh Papaya .90 .90
Nos. 713-716 (4) 2.35 2.35

1997, Sept. 1 Litho. *Perf. 14½*

Scouting Organizations: No. 717, Girl Guides, 75th anniv. No. 718, Lord Baden Powell. No. 719, Girl scouts hiking. No. 720, Girl Guides planting trees. No. 721, Boy Scouts first aid. No. 722, Boy Scouts camping. No. 723, Brownies entertaining aged.

717 A137 10sh multicolored .35 .35
718 A137 10sh multicolored .35 .35
a. Pair, #717-718 .70 .70
719 A137 27sh multicolored .85 .85
720 A137 27sh multicolored .85 .85
a. Pair, #719-720 1.70 1.70
721 A137 33sh multicolored 1.10 1.10
722 A137 33sh multicolored 1.10 1.10
a. Pair, #721-722 2.20 2.20
723 A137 42sh multicolored 1.40 1.40
724 A137 42sh multicolored 1.40 1.40
a. Pair, #723-724 2.80 2.80
Nos. 717-724 (8) 7.40 7.40

Tourist Attractions — A138

Designs: 10sh, Crocodile. 27sh, Hot Springs, Lake Bogoria. 30sh, Warthogs. 33sh, Wind surfing. 42sh, Traditional huts.

1997, Oct. 9 *Perf. 13½*

No.	Type	Description	Unused	Used
725	A138	10sh multicolored	.30	.30
726	A138	27sh multicolored	.85	.85
727	A138	30sh multicolored	1.00	1.00
728	A138	33sh multicolored	1.10	1.10
729	A138	42sh multicolored	1.40	1.40
		Nos. 725-729 (5)	4.65	4.65

POSTAGE DUE STAMPS

D1

Perf. 14x13½

1967-85 Litho. Unwmk.
"POSTAGE DUE" 12½mm long

No.	Type	Description	Unused	Used
J1	D1	5c dark red	.15	.15
J2	D1	10c green	.15	.15
J3	D1	20c dark blue	.15	.15
J4	D1	30c reddish brown	.15	.15
J5	D1	40c brt red lilac	.15	.15
		Perf. 14		
J6	D1	80c brick red	.35	.30
		Perf. 15x14		
J7	D1	1sh orange	1.75	*1.90*
		Perf. 14½x14		
J8	D1	2sh pale violet	.15	.15
		Set value	2.50	*2.75*

Issued: 80c, 1978. 2sh, 1985; others, 1/3/67.
See Nos. J9-J14.

1969-70 *Perf. 14*

No.	Type	Description	Unused	Used
J1a	D1	5c	.15	.15
J2a	D1	10c	.15	.15
J3a	D1	20c	.15	.15
J4a	D1	30c	.15	.15
J5a	D1	40c	.15	.15
J7a	D1	1sh	1.00	*2.50*
		Nos. J1a-J7a (6)	1.75	*3.25*

Issued: 1sh, 2/18/70; others, 12/16/69.

1971-73 *Perf. 14x15*

No.	Type	Description	Unused	Used
J1b	D1	5c	.50	.50
J2b	D1	10c	.50	.50
J3b	D1	20c	.50	.50
J4b	D1	30c	2.00	2.00
J5b	D1	40c	.50	.50
J7b	D1	1sh	1.00	1.25
		Nos. J1b-J7b (6)	5.00	5.25

Issued: 30c, 7/13/71; others, 2/20/73. The 10c, 20c, 1sh on chalky paper were issued 7/13/71.

1973, Dec. 12 *Perf. 15*

No.	Type	Description	Unused	Used
J1c	D1	5c	.15	.15
J2c	D1	10c	.15	.15
J3c	D1	20c	.15	.15
J4c	D1	30c	.15	.15
J5c	D1	40c	2.00	2.00
J7c	D1	1sh	1.00	1.25
		Nos. J1c-J7c (6)	3.60	3.85

1983 Wmk. 373 *Perf. 14x13½*

J2d D1 10c
J3d D1 20c
J5d D1 40c

Nos. J5, J7-J8 Redrawn

1987-93 Litho. Unwmk. *Perf. 15x14*

No.	Type	Description	Unused	Used
J9	D1	40c bright red lilac	.15	.15
J10	D1	50c dark green	.15	.15
J11	D1	1sh light orange	.80	.80
J12	D1	2sh pale violet	.15	.15
J13	D1	3sh dark blue	.15	.15
J14	D1	5sh red brown	.15	.15
		Nos. J9-J14 (6)	1.55	1.55

"KENYA" is 9mm wide and "POSTAGE DUE" is 11½mm wide on Nos. J9, J11. "CENTS" is 4½mm wide and "SHILLING" has cross bar on "G"; both are in a new font.

"KENYA" is 8½mm wide and "POSTAGE DUE" is 11½mm wide on No. J12.

Issued: 40c, 1sh, 1987; others, Dec. 6, 1993.

OFFICIAL STAMPS

Nos. 1-5 and 7 Overprinted **OFFICIAL**

Perf. 14x14½

1964, Oct. 1 Photo. Unwmk.
Size: 21x17½mm

No.	Type	Description	Unused	Used
O1	A1	5c blue, buff & dk brn	.15	.15
O2	A1	10c brown	.20	.20
O3	A1	15c dp magenta	.30	.30
O4	A1	20c yel green & dk brn	.45	.45
O5	A1	30c yellow & black	.65	.65
O6	A1	50c green, blk & dp car	1.10	1.10
		Nos. O1-O6 (6)	2.85	2.85

KENYA, UGANDA, TANZANIA

'ke–nyə, ü–'gan–də, ˌtan–zə–'nē–ə

LOCATION — East Africa, bordering on the Indian Ocean
GOVT. — States in British Commonwealth
AREA — 679,802 sq. mi.
POP. — 42,760,000 (est. 1977)
CAPITAL — Nairobi (Kenya), Kampala (Uganda), Dar es Salaam (Tanzania)

Kenya became a crown colony in 1906, including the former East Africa Protectorate leased from the Sultan of Zanzibar and known as the Kenya Protectorate. In 1963 the colony became independent. Its stamps are listed under "Kenya."

The inland Uganda Protectorate, lying west of Kenya Colony, was declared a British Protectorate in 1894. Uganda became independent in 1962.

Tanganyika, a trust territory larger than Kenya or Uganda, was grouped with them postally from 1935 under the East African Posts & Telecommunications Administration. Tanganyika became independent in 1961. When it merged with Zanzibar in 1964, "Zanzibar" was added to the inscriptions on stamps issued under the E.A.P. & T. Administration. In 1965 the multiple inscription was changed to "Kenya, Uganda, Tanzania," variously arranged.

Zanzibar withdrew its own stamps in 1968, and K., U. & T. stamps became valid Jan. 1, 1968.

100 Cents = 1 Rupee
100 Cents = 1 Shilling (1922)
20 Shillings = 1 Pound

Catalogue values for unused stamps in this country are for Never Hinged items, beginning with Scott 90.

East Africa and Uganda Protectorates

King George V
A1 A2

1921 Typo. Wmk. 4 *Perf. 14*
Ordinary Paper

No.	Type	Description	Unused	Used
1	A1	1c black	.90	.50
2	A1	3c green	1.25	1.25
3	A1	6c rose red	2.00	1.50
4	A1	10c orange	4.25	.20
5	A1	12c gray	4.25	*12.50*
6	A1	15c ultramarine	3.25	*10.00*
		Chalky Paper		
7	A1	50c gray lilac & blk	9.00	*45.00*
8	A2	2r blk & red, *blue*	45.00	*95.00*
9	A2	3r green & violet	70.00	*110.00*
10	A2	5r gray lil & ultra	75.00	*125.00*
11	A2	50r gray grn & red	2,100.	*2,500.*
		Nos. 1-10 (10)	214.90	*400.95*

The name of the colony was changed to Kenya in August, 1920, but stamps of the East Africa and Uganda types were continued in use. Stamps of types A1 and A2 watermarked Multiple Crown and C A (3) are listed under East Africa and Uganda Protectorates.

For stamps of Kenya and Uganda overprinted "G. E. A." used in parts of former German East Africa occupied by British forces, see Tanganyika Nos. 1-9.

Kenya, Uganda & Tanganyika stamps can be mounted in the Scott British Africa album.

Kenya and Uganda

King George V
A3 A4

1922-27 **Wmk. 4**

No.	Type	Description	Unused	Used
18	A3	1c brown	.50	*1.00*
19	A3	5c violet	1.25	.15
20	A3	5c green ('27)	1.65	.15
21	A3	10c green	1.65	.15
22	A3	10c black ('27)	1.50	.15
23	A3	12c black	1.50	*18.00*
24	A3	15c car rose	1.00	.15
25	A3	20c orange	1.50	.15
26	A3	30c ultra	1.00	.15
27	A3	50c gray	2.00	.15
28	A3	75c ol bister	2.75	*6.25*
29	A4	1sh green	2.75	1.65
30	A4	2sh gray lilac	7.00	6.50
31	A4	2sh50c brown ('25)	18.00	*50.00*
32	A4	3sh gray black	15.00	6.75
33	A4	4sh gray ('25)	20.00	*62.50*
34	A4	5sh carmine	22.50	15.00
35	A4	7sh50c org ('25)	60.00	*110.00*
36	A4	10sh ultra	45.00	40.00
37	A4	£1 org & blk	125.00	*165.00*
38	A4	£2 brn vio & grn ('25)	725.00	*1,000.*
39	A4	£3 yel & dl vio ('25)	1,000.	*1,250.*
40	A4	£4 rose lil & blk ('25)	1,600.	*2,500.*
41	A4	£5 blue & blk	2,100.	*3,000.*
		Revenue cancel		50.00
41A	A4	£10 grn & blk	*11,000.*	
41B	A4	£20 grn & red ('25)	*12,500.*	
41C	A4	£25 red & blk	*15,000.*	
41D	A4	£50 red & blk	*17,500.*	
41E	A4	£75 red & blk	*37,500.*	
41F	A4	£100 red & blk	*42,500.*	
		Nos. 18-37 (20)	331.55	*483.85*

High face value stamps are known with revenue cancellations removed and forged postal cancellations added.

Kenya, Uganda, Tanganyika Silver Jubilee Issue

Common Design Type

1935, May Engr. *Perf. 13½x14*

No.	Type	Description	Unused	Used
42	CD301	20c ol grn & lt bl	.30	.15
43	CD301	30c blue & brown	.75	.70
44	CD301	65c indigo & green	2.50	2.25
45	CD301	1sh brt vio & indigo	3.00	2.25
		Nos. 42-45 (4)	6.55	5.35

Kavirondo Cranes — A5 Dhow on Lake Victoria — A6

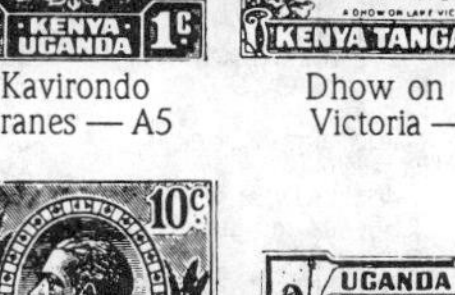

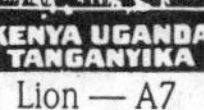

Lion — A7

Mount Kilimanjaro — A8

Jinja Bridge by Ripon Falls — A9

Mount Kenya — A10

Lake Naivasha — A11

FIVE CENTS
Type I - Left rope does not touch sail.
Type II - Left rope touches sail.

Perf. 13, 14, 11½x13, 13x11½

1935, May 1 Engr.; Typo. (10c, £1)

No.	Type	Description	Unused	Used
46	A5	1c red brn & blk	.15	.15
47	A6	5c grn & blk (I)	.15	.15
a.		Type II	*15.00*	1.50
b.		Perf. 13x11½ (I)	*1,000.*	*250.00*
c.		Perf. 13x11½ (II)	*375.00*	*95.00*
48	A7	10c black & yel	.30	.15
49	A8	15c red & black	.30	.15
50	A5	20c red org & blk	.15	.15
51	A9	30c dk ultra & blk	.20	.15
52	A6	50c blk & red vio	.50	.15
53	A10	65c yel brn & blk	1.00	1.50
54	A11	1sh grn & black	1.00	.40
a.		Perf. 13x11½ ('36)	*1,000.*	85.00
55	A8	2sh red vio & rose brn	4.50	2.25
56	A11	3sh blk & ultra	5.00	2.50
a.		Perf. 13x11½	*1,500.*	
57	A9	5sh car & black	15.00	*22.50*
58	A5	10sh ultra & red vio	37.50	37.50
59	A7	£1 blk & scar	125.00	125.00
		Nos. 46-59 (14)	190.75	192.70

Coronation Issue

Common Design Type

1937, May 12 Engr. *Perf. 13½x14*

No.	Type	Description	Unused	Used
60	CD302	5c deep green	.15	.15
61	CD302	20c deep orange	.15	.15
62	CD302	30c brt ultra	.25	.25
		Set value	.45	.45
		Set, never hinged	1.40	

Kavirondo Cranes — A12 Dhow on Lake Victoria — A13

Lake Naivasha — A14 Jinja Bridge, Ripon Falls — A16

Mt. Kilimanjaro — A15 Lion — A17

FIFTY CENTS:
Type I - Left rope does not touch sail.
Type II - Left rope touches sail.

1938-54 Engr. *Perf. 13*

No.	Type	Description	Unused	Used
66	A12	1c red brn & gray blk	.40	.20
a.		1c violet brown & black, perf. 13x13½ ('42)	.15	.15
		Perf. 13x11½		
67	A13	5c grn & blk	.40	.15
68	A13	5c red org & brn ('49)	.30	.15
a.		Perf. 13x12½ ('50)	.50	.15
69	A14	10c org & brn	.50	.15
a.		Perf. 14 ('41)	42.50	2.00
70	A14	10c green & black ('49)	.25	.15
a.		Perf. 13x12½ ('50)	.50	.15
		Perf. 13x12½		
71	A14	10c gray & red brn ('52)	.25	.15
		Perf. 13½x13, 13x13½		
72	A15	15c car & gray blk ('43)	.90	.15
a.		Booklet pane of 4	4.50	
b.		Perf. 13	2.50	.15
73	A15	15c green & black ('52)	.40	.15
74	A12	20c org & gray blk ('42)	1.25	.15
a.		Booklet pane of 4	8.00	
b.		Imperf., pair		
c.		Perf. 13	*4.00*	.15
d.		Perf. 14 ('41)	*12.50*	2.75
		Perf. 13x12½		
75	A13	25c car & black ('52)	.60	.30

Perf. 13x13½

76 A16 30c dp bl & gray blk ('42) .35 .15
a. Perf. 14 ('41) 75.00 10.00
b. Perf. 13 7.00 .15
77 A16 30c brown & pur ('52) .30 .15
78 A12 40c brt bl & gray blk ('52) .75 .20

Perf. 13x12½

79 A13 50c gray blk & red vio (II) ('49) 1.75 .15
a. Perf. 13x11½ (II) .25 .15
b. Perf. 13x11½ (I) 200.00 100.00
80 A14 1sh yel brn & gray blk ('49) 1.25 .15
a. Perf. 13x11½ .35 .15

Perf. 13½x13

81 A15 2sh red vio & org brn ('44) 3.25 .30
a. Perf. 13 20.00 1.00
b. Perf. 14 ('41) 20.00 3.00

Perf. 13x11½

82 A14 3sh gray blk & ultra 7.50 .50
a. Perf. 13x12½ ('50) 2.00 .60

Perf. 13x13½

83 A16 5sh car rose & gray blk ('44) 7.50 .65
a. Perf. 13 30.00 3.50
b. Perf. 14 ('41) 10.00 1.75
84 A12 10sh ultra & red vio ('44) 10.00 1.75
a. Perf. 13 35.00 6.50
b. Perf. 14 ('41) 27.50 10.00

Typo.

Perf. 14

85 A17 £1 blk & scar ('41) 7.50 4.75
a. Perf. 11½x13 125.00 55.00
b. Perf. 12½ ('54) 8.25 14.00
Nos. 66-85 (20) 45.40 10.45
Set, never hinged 75.00

See Nos. 98-99.

South Africa Nos. 48, 57, 60 and 62 Surcharged

5c
KENYA
TANGANYIKA
UGANDA

Basic stamps of Nos. 86-89 are inscribed alternately in English and Afrikaans.

1941-42 Wmk. 201 *Perf. 15x14, 14*

86 A6 5c on 1p car & gray, pair .30 .40
a. Single, English .15 .15
b. Single, Afrikaans .15 .15
87 A17 10c on 3p ultra, pair .40 .40
a. Single, English .15 .15
b. Single, Afrikaans .15 .15
88 A7 20c on 6p org & grn, pair .60 .60
a. Single, English .20 .15
b. Single, Afrikaans .20 .15
89 A11 70c on 1sh lt bl & ol brn, pair .90 .90
a. Single, English .30 .15
b. Single, Afrikaans .30 .15
Nos. 86-89 (4) 2.20 2.30
Set, never hinged 8.50

Issued: #86-88, 7/1/41; #89, 4/20/42.

Catalogue values for unused stamps in this section, from this point to the end of the section, are for Never Hinged items.

Peace Issue

Common Design Type

Perf. 13½x14

1946, Nov. 11 Engr. Wmk. 4

90 CD303 20c red orange .15 .15
91 CD303 30c deep blue .15 .15
Set value .25 .25

Silver Wedding Issue

Common Design Types

1948, Dec. 1 Photo. *Perf. 14x14½*

92 CD304 20c orange .20 .15

Engr.; Name Typo.

Perf. 11½x11

93 CD305 £1 red 27.50 27.50

UPU Issue

Common Design Types

Engr.; Typo. on Nos. 95 and 96

1949, Oct. 10 *Perf. 13, 11x11½*

94 CD306 20c red orange .30 .22
95 CD307 30c indigo .45 .36
96 CD308 50c gray .80 .80
97 CD309 1sh red brown 1.60 1.60
Nos. 94-97 (4) 3.15 2.98

Type of 1949 with Added Inscription: "Royal Visit 1952"

1952, Feb. 1 Engr. *Perf. 13x12½*

98 A14 10c green & black .15 .15
99 A14 1sh yel brown & gray blk .65 .65

Visit of Princess Elizabeth, Duchess of Edinburgh, and the Duke of Edinburgh, 1952.

Coronation Issue

Common Design Type

1953, June 2 *Perf. 13½x13*

101 CD312 20c red orange & blk .15 .15

Owen Falls Dam — A18

Giraffe — A19

Elizabeth II — A21

Mt. Kilimanjaro A20

1954, Apr. 28 *Perf. 12½x13*

102 A18 30c dp ultra & black .20 .20

Visit of Queen Elizabeth II and the Duke of Edinburgh, 1954.

1954-59 *Perf. 12½x13, 13x12½*

Designs: 5c, 30c, Owen Falls Dam (without "Royal Visit 1954"). 20c, 40c, 1sh, Lion. 15c, 1.30sh, 5sh, Elephants. 10sh, Royal Lodge, Sagana.

103 A18 5c choc & black .15 .15
a. Booklet pane of 4 .50
b. Dam inverted —
104 A19 10c carmine .15 .15
a. Booklet pane of 4 .60
105 A20 15c lt blue & blk (no period below "c") ('58) .35 .15
a. Booklet pane of 4 2.00
106 A20 15c lt blue & blk (period below "c") ('59) 1.25 .15
a. Booklet pane of 4 6.00
107 A19 20c org & black .20 .15
a. Booklet pane of 4 .80
b. Imperf., pair 800.00
108 A18 30c ultra & black .20 .15
a. Booklet pane of 4 1.00
109 A19 40c brown ('58) .35 .15
110 A19 50c dp red lilac .45 .15
a. Booklet pane of 4 2.00
111 A20 65c brn car & grn ('55) 1.75 .65
112 A19 1sh dp mag & blk .50 .15
113 A20 1.30sh pur & red org ('55) 1.50 .15
114 A20 2sh dp grn & gray 1.75 .30
115 A20 5sh black & org 5.00 .75
116 A20 10sh ultra & black 10.00 1.40
117 A21 £1 black & ver 15.00 3.25
Nos. 103-117 (15) 38.60 7.85

No. 103b is unique.

For "Official" overprints see Tanganyika Nos. O1-O12.

Map Showing Lakes Victoria and Tanganyika A22

Perf. 12½x13

1958, July 30 Engr. Wmk. 314

118 A22 40c green & blue .30 .30
119 A22 1.30sh violet & green .75 .70

Cent. of the discovery of Lakes Victoria and Tanganyika by Sir Richard F. Burton and Capt. J. H. Speke.

Sisal — A23

A25

Mount Kenya and Giant Plants A24

10c, Cotton. 15c, Coffee. 20c, Gnu. 25c, Ostriches. 30c, Thompson's gazelles. 40c, Manta ray. 50c, Zebras. 65c, Cheetah. 1.30sh, Murchison Falls & hippopotamuses. 2sh, Mt. Kilimanjaro & giraffes. 2.50sh, Candelabra tree & black rhinoceroses. 5sh, Crater Lake & Mountains of the Moon. 10sh, Ngorongoro Crater & buffaloes.

Perf. 14½x14

1960, Oct. 1 Photo. Wmk. 314

120 A23 5c dull blue .15 .15
121 A23 10c lt olive green .15 .15
a. Booklet pane of 4 .50
122 A23 15c dull purple .15 .15
a. Booklet pane of 4 .50
123 A23 20c brt lilac rose .15 .15
a. Booklet pane of 4 .70
124 A23 25c olive gray .65 .35
125 A23 30c brt vermilion .20 .20
a. Booklet pane of 4 .90
126 A23 40c bright blue .35 .20
127 A23 50c dull violet .40 .20
a. Booklet pane of 4 1.90
128 A23 65c lemon .95 1.25

Engr.

Perf. 14

129 A24 1sh vio & red lilac .50 .20
130 A24 1.30sh choc & dk car .95 .20
131 A24 2sh dk bl & dull bl 1.25 .35
132 A24 2.50sh ol grn & dull bl 1.65 .75
133 A24 5sh rose red & lilac 3.25 .75
134 A24 10sh sl bl & ol grn 6.50 1.50

Perf. 13½x13

135 A25 20sh lake & bluish violet 13.00 5.00
Nos. 120-135 (16) 30.25 11.55

Booklets issued in 1961.

On Nos. 120-134, positions of "Kenya," "Uganda" and "Tanganyika" are rotated.

For "Official" overprints see Tanganyika Nos. O13-O20.

Agricultural Development — A26

Design: 30c, 1.30sh, Farmer picking corn.

Unwmk.

1963, Mar. 21 Photo. *Perf. 14*

136 A26 15c lt ol green & ultra .15 .15
137 A26 30c yel & red brown .20 .15
138 A26 50c dp org & ultra .30 .15
139 A26 1.30sh lt blue & red brn .60 .40
Nos. 136-139 (4) 1.25 .85

FAO "Freedom from Hunger" campaign.

Scholars and Open Book A27

1963, June 28 Unwmk. *Perf. 14*

140 A27 30c multicolored .15 .15
141 A27 1.30sh multicolored .35 .35
Set value .40

Inauguration of University of East Africa.

Red Cross A28

1963, Sept. 2

142 A28 30c blue & red .40 .15
143 A28 50c bister brown & red 1.25 .30

Centenary of International Red Cross.

Kenya, Uganda, Tanganyika and Zanzibar

Issued by the East African Common Services Organization. Not used in Zanzibar.

Japanese Crest and Olympic Rings — A29

Olympic Rings and Banners A30

Unwmk.

1964, Oct. 25 Photo. *Perf. 14*

144 A29 30c orange & dk purple .15 .15
145 A29 50c dk purple & org .15 .15
146 A30 1.30sh blue, grn & org .30 .30
147 A30 2.50sh blue, vio & lil rose .60 .60
Nos. 144-147 (4) 1.20 1.20

18th Olympic Games, Tokyo, Oct. 10-25.

Kenya, Uganda, Tanzania

Issued by the East African Common Services Organization.

Safari Rally Emblem and Leopard — A31

Design: 1.30sh, Car on road through national park and emblem of the East African Safari Rally.

1965, Apr. 15 Unwmk. *Perf. 14*

148 A31 30c blue grn, yel & blk .15 .15
149 A31 50c brown, yel & blk .15 .15
150 A31 1.30sh lt ultra, ocher & green .35 .30
151 A31 2.50sh blue, dk grn & dull red .65 .65
Nos. 148-151 (4) 1.30 1.25

13th East African Safari Rally, Apr. 15-19, 1965.

ITU Emblem, Old and Modern Communication Equipment — A32

1965, May 17 **Photo.**
152 A32 30c lilac rose, gold & brn .15 .15
153 A32 50c gray, gold & brown .15 .15
154 A32 1.30sh lt vio bl, gold & brn .35 .30
155 A32 2.50sh brt bl grn, gold & brn .75 .75
Nos. 152-155 (4) 1.40 1.35

Cent. of the ITU.

ICY Emblem — A33

1965, Aug. 4 **Unwmk.** ***Perf. 14***
156 A33 30c green & gold .15 .15
157 A33 50c slate black & gold .15 .15
158 A33 1.30sh ultra & gold .40 .30
159 A33 2.50sh car & gold .80 .70
Nos. 156-159 (4) 1.50 1.30

International Cooperation Year.

Game Park Lodge A34

Tourist Publicity: 50c, Murchison Falls, Uganda. 1.30sh, Lake Nakuru, Kenya. 2.50sh, Deep-sea fishing, Tanzania.

1966, Apr. 4 **Photo.** ***Perf. 14***
160 A34 30c ocher & multi .15 .15
161 A34 50c green & multi .15 .15
a. Blue omitted
162 A34 1.30sh multicolored .90 .30
163 A34 2.50sh gray & multi 1.90 .75
Nos. 160-163 (4) 3.10 1.35

Javelin Thrower and Games' Emblem A35

1966, Aug. 2 **Unwmk.** ***Perf. 14***
164 A35 30c multicolored .15 .15
165 A35 50c multicolored .15 .15
166 A35 1.30sh multicolored .35 .30
167 A35 2.50sh multicolored .75 .75
Nos. 164-167 (4) 1.40 1.35

8th British Commonwealth and Empire Games, Jamaica, Aug. 4-13, 1966.

UNESCO Emblem A36

1966, Oct. 3 **Photo.** ***Perf. 14***
168 A36 30c rose red, brt grn & blk .15 .15
169 A36 50c lt brn, brt grn & blk .15 .15
170 A36 1.30sh gray, brt grn & blk .90 .30
171 A36 2.50sh yel, brt grn & blk 1.90 .70
Nos. 168-171 (4) 3.10 1.30

20th anniv. of UNESCO.

Dragon Rapide A37

Planes: 50c, Super VC10. 1.30sh, Comet 4. 2.50sh, F.27 Friendship.

1967, Jan. 23 **Unwmk.**
172 A37 30c multicolored .15 .15
173 A37 50c multicolored .25 .15
174 A37 1.30sh multicolored .60 .40
175 A37 2.50sh multicolored 1.75 1.50
Nos. 172-175 (4) 2.75 2.20

21st anniversary of East African Airways.

Pillar Tomb, East African Coast — A38

Designs: 50c, Man hunting elephant, petroglyph, Tanzania. 1.30sh, Clay head, Luzira, Uganda. 2.50sh, Proconsul skull, Rusinga Island, Kenya.

1967, May 2 **Photo.** ***Perf. 14***
176 A38 30c rose lake, blk & yel .15 .15
177 A38 50c gray, black & ver .15 .15
178 A38 1.30sh green, yel & blk .70 .30
179 A38 2.50sh cop red, yel & blk 1.40 .65
Nos. 176-179 (4) 2.40 1.25

Archaeological relics of East Africa.

Emblems of Kenya, Tanzania and Tanganyika — A39

Photo.; Gold Impressed

1967, Dec. 1 ***Perf. 14½x14***
180 A39 5sh gray, black & gold .75 .75

Establishment of East African Community.

Mount Kenya A40

Designs: 30c Mountain climber. 1.30sh, Mount Kilimanjaro. 2.50sh, Ruwenzori Mountains.

1968, Mar. 4 **Photo.** ***Perf. 14½***
181 A40 30c multicolored .15 .15
182 A40 50c multicolored .25 .15
183 A40 1.30sh multicolored .50 .35
184 A40 2.50sh multicolored 1.10 .90
Nos. 181-184 (4) 2.00 1.55

Family and Rural Hospital A41

Family and: 50c, Student nurse. 1.30sh, Microscope. 2.50sh, Mosquito and hand holding hypodermic.

1968, May 13 **Photo.** ***Perf. 13½***
185 A41 30c multicolored .15 .15
186 A41 50c rose vio, blk & brt pink .15 .15
187 A41 1.30sh brn org, blk & brt pink .25 .25
188 A41 2.50sh gray, blk & brt pink .50 .50
Nos. 185-188 (4) 1.05 1.05

20th anniv. of the WHO.

Stadium A42

Designs: 50c, Diving tower. 1.30sh, Pylons and tracks. 2.50sh, Boxing ring, vert.

Perf. 14½x14, 14x14½

1968, Oct. 14 **Photo.**
189 A42 30c dull pur & gray grn .15 .15
190 A42 50c brt grn, blk & gray .15 .15
191 A42 1.30sh gray grn, blk & dk car .35 .30
192 A42 2.50sh buff, brn org & brn blk .65 .65
Nos. 189-192 (4) 1.30 1.25

19th Olympic Games, Mexico City, Oct. 12-27.

Railroad Ferry MV Umoja A43

Water Transport: 50c, Transatlantic liner S.S. Harambee. 1.30sh, Lake motor vessel Victoria. 2.50sh, Ferry St. Michael.

1969, Jan. 20 **Photo.** ***Perf. 14***
193 A43 30c blue, gray & dk bl .15 .15
194 A43 50c blue, gray & scar .30 .20
195 A43 1.30sh bl, dk bl & dk green .70 .60
196 A43 2.50sh bl, dk bl & org 1.60 1.60
Nos. 193-196 (4) 2.75 2.55

Farm Workers and ILO Emblem A44

ILO Emblem and: 50c, Construction. 1.30sh, Industry. 2.50sh, Shipping.

1969, Apr. 14 **Photo.** ***Perf. 14***
197 A44 30c green, blk & yel .15 .15
198 A44 50c car rose, blk & car .15 .15
199 A44 1.30sh dp org, blk & org .30 .25
200 A44 2.50sh grnsh bl, blk & ultra .60 .60
Nos. 197-200 (4) 1.20 1.15

50th anniv. of the ILO.

Pope Paul VI, Mountains of the Moon, Papal Arms, Crested Crane — A45

Euphorbia Tree in Shape of Africa, Development Bank Emblem — A46

1969, July 31 **Photo.** ***Perf. 14***
201 A45 30c dk blue, blk & gold .15 .15
202 A45 70c plum, blk & gold .15 .15
203 A45 1.50sh gray bl, blk & gold .40 .35
204 A45 2.50sh dp vio, blk & gold .65 .65
Nos. 201-204 (4) 1.35 1.30

Visit of Pope Paul VI to Uganda, July 31-Aug. 2.

Perf. 14x13½

1969, Dec. 8 **Litho.** **Unwmk.**
205 A46 30c brt grn, dk grn & gold .15 .15
206 A46 70c plum, dk grn & gold .15 .15
207 A46 1.50sh grnsh bl, dk grn & gold .30 .30
208 A46 2.50sh brn org, dk grn & gold .50 .50
Nos. 205-208 (4) 1.10 1.10

African Development Bank, 5th anniv.

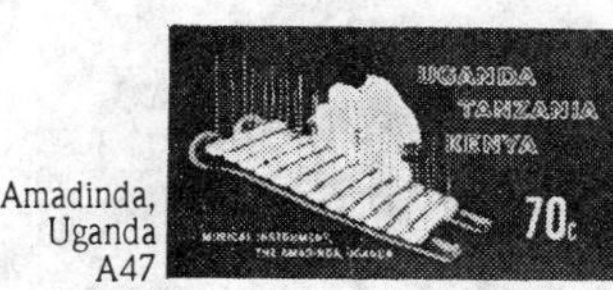

Amadinda, Uganda A47

Musical Instruments: 30c, Marimba, Tanzania. 1.50sh, Nzomari (trumpet), Kenya. 2.50sh, Adeudeu, Kenya.

1970, Feb. 16 **Litho.** ***Perf. 11x12***
209 A47 30c multicolored .15 .15
210 A47 70c multicolored .15 .15
211 A47 1.50sh dk rose brn & org .50 .30
212 A47 2.50sh multicolored .80 .65
Nos. 209-212 (4) 1.60 1.25

Satellite Earth Station A48

Designs: 70c, Radar station by day. 1.50sh, Radar station by night. 2.50sh, Satellite transmitting communications to and from earth.

1970, May 18 **Litho.** ***Perf. 14½***
213 A48 30c multicolored .15 .15
214 A48 70c multicolored .15 .15
215 A48 1.50sh org, blk & vio .45 .30
216 A48 2.50sh dull bl & multi .65 .65
Nos. 213-216 (4) 1.40 1.25

Opening of the East African Satellite Earth Station, Mt. Margaret, Kenya.

Runner — A49

1970, July 16 **Litho.** ***Perf. 14½***
217 A49 30c org brn, dk brn & blk .15 .15
218 A49 70c grn, dk brn & blk .15 .15
219 A49 1.50sh dull pur, dk brn & blk .30 .30
220 A49 2.50sh grnsh bl, dk brn & blk .50 .50
Nos. 217-220 (4) 1.10 1.10

9th British Commonwealth Games, Edinburgh, July 16-25.

UN Emblem and People A50

1970, Oct. 19 **Photo.** ***Perf. 14½***
221 A50 30c org brn, gold & black .15 .15
222 A50 70c bl grn, gold & black .15 .15
223 A50 1.50sh dull red brn, gold & blk .30 .30
224 A50 2.50sh olive, gold & blk .50 .50
Nos. 221-224 (4) 1.10 1.10

25th anniversary of the United Nations.

Conversion from Pounds to Kilograms A51

Designs: 70c, Conversion from Fahrenheit to centigrade. 1.50sh, Conversion from gallons to liters. 2.50sh, Conversion from miles to kilometers.

1971, Jan. 4 **Photo.** ***Perf. 14½***
225 A51 30c silver & multi .15 .15
226 A51 70c silver & multi .15 .15
227 A51 1.50sh silver & multi .30 .30
228 A51 2.50sh silver & multi .50 .50
Nos. 225-228 (4) 1.10 1.10

Conversion to metric system of weights and measures.

Locomotive — A52

Designs: Various locomotives.

1971, Apr. 19 Photo. *Perf. 14½*

229 A52 30c gold & multi .15 .15
230 A52 70c gold & multi .40 .25
231 A52 1.50sh gold & multi 1.00 1.00
232 A52 2.50sh gold & multi 2.25 2.25
a. Souvenir sheet of 4, #229-232 10.00 10.00
Nos. 229-232 (4) 3.80 3.65

70th anniversary of the completion of the Mombasa to Kisumu line.

Bull and Campaign Emblem A53

Designs: 30c, 1.50sh, Campaign emblem and cow. 2.50sh, like 70c.

1971, July 5 Photo. *Perf. 14½*

233 A53 30c yel grn, blk & bis .15 .15
234 A53 70c gray bl, blk & bis .15 .15
235 A53 1.50sh mag, blk & bis .30 .30
236 A53 2.50sh red org, blk & bis .50 .50
Nos. 233-236 (4) 1.10 1.10

Rinderpest campaign by the Organization for African Unity.

Meeting of Stanley and Livingstone — A54

1971, Oct. 28 Litho. *Perf. 14*

237 A54 5sh multicolored .60 .60

Centenary of the meeting at Ujiji of Dr. David Livingstone, missionary, and Henry M. Stanley, journalist, who had been sent to find Livingstone.

Modern Farming Village A55

Designs: 30c, Pres. Julius K. Nyerere carried in triumph, 1961, vert. 1.50sh, University of Dar es Salaam. 2.50sh, Kilimanjaro International Airport.

1971, Dec. 9 *Perf. 14*

238 A55 30c bister & multi .15 .15
239 A55 70c lt blue & multi .15 .15
240 A55 1.50sh lt green & multi .25 .25
241 A55 2.50sh yel & multi .55 .55
Nos. 238-241 (4) 1.10 1.10

10th anniv. of independence of Tanzania.

Flags of African Nations and Fair Emblem A56

1972, Feb. 23 *Perf. 13½x14*

242 A56 30c lt bl & multi .15 .15
243 A56 70c gray & multi .15 .15
244 A56 1.50sh yel & multi .25 .25
245 A56 2.50sh multicolored .50 .50
Nos. 242-245 (4) 1.05 1.05

First All-Africa Trade Fair, Nairobi, Kenya, Feb. 23-Mar. 5.

Child Drinking Milk, UNICEF Emblem A57

25th Anniv. (in 1971) of UNICEF: 70c, Children playing ball. 1.50sh, Child writing on blackboard. 2.50sh, Boy playing with tractor.

1972, Apr. 24 Litho. *Perf. 14½x14*

246 A57 30c brn org & multi .15 .15
247 A57 70c lt ultra & multi .15 .15
248 A57 1.50sh yel & multi .30 .30
249 A57 2.50sh green & multi .50 .50
Nos. 246-249 (4) 1.10 1.10

Hurdles, Olympic and Motion Emblems A58

1972, Aug. 28

250 A58 40c shown .15 .15
251 A58 70c Running .15 .15
252 A58 1.50sh Boxing .20 .20
253 A58 2.50sh Hockey .50 .50
a. Souvenir sheet of 4, #250-253 5.00 5.00
Nos. 250-253 (4) 1.00 1.00

20th Olympic Games, Munich, Aug. 26-Sept. 11.

Uganda Kob, Semliki Game Reserve A59

1972, Oct. 9 Litho. *Perf. 14*

254 A59 40c shown .15 .15
255 A59 70c Intl. Conf. Center .20 .20
256 A59 1.50sh Makerere Univ., Kampala .50 .50
257 A59 2.50sh Uganda arms 1.25 1.25
a. Souvenir sheet of 4, #254-257, perf. 13x14 5.00 5.00
Nos. 254-257 (4) 2.10 2.10

Uganda's independence, 10th anniv. #256 also for 50th anniv. of Makerere University, Kampala.

Flag of East Africa — A60

1972, Dec. 1 Litho. *Perf. 14½x14*

258 A60 5sh multicolored 1.50 1.50

5th anniv. of the East African Community.

Anemometer, Lake Victoria Station — A61

WMO Emblem and: 70c, Release of weather balloon, vert. 1.50sh, Hail suppression by meteorological rocket. 2.50sh, Meteorological satellite receiving antenna.

1973, Mar. 5 Litho. *Perf. 14*

259 A61 40c multicolored .15 .15
260 A61 70c ultra & multi .15 .15
261 A61 1.50sh emer & multi .35 .30
262 A61 2.50sh multicolored .65 .65
Nos. 259-262 (4) 1.30 1.25

Cent. of intl. meteorological cooperation.

Scouts Laying Bricks — A62

Designs: 70c, Baden-Powell's gravestone, Nyeri, Kenya. 1.50sh, World Scout emblem. 2.50sh, Lord Baden-Powell.

1973, July 16 Litho. *Perf. 14*

263 A62 40c ocher & multi .15 .15
264 A62 70c multicolored .30 .30
265 A62 1.50sh multicolored .60 .60
266 A62 2.50sh grn & ultra 1.65 1.50
Nos. 263-266 (4) 2.70 2.55

24th Boy Scout World Conference (1st in Africa), Nairobi, Kenya, July 16-21.

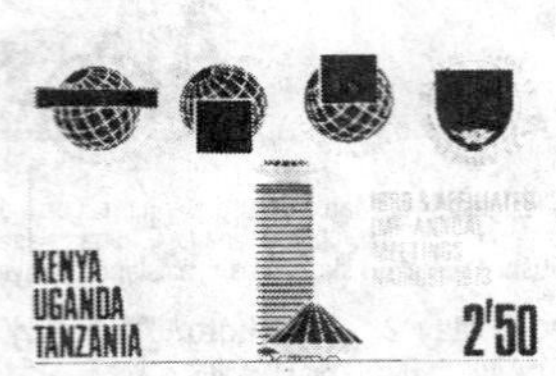

International Bank for Reconstruction and Development and Affiliates' Emblems — A63

Designs: 40c, Arrows dividing 4 bank affiliate emblems. 70c, Vert. lines dividing 4 emblems. 1.50sh, Kenyatta Conference Center, Nairobi, vert.

1973, Sept. 24 Litho. *Perf. 14x13½*

267 A63 40c gray, blk & grn .15 .15
268 A63 70c brn, gray & blk .20 .20
269 A63 1.50sh lem, gray & blk .50 .50
270 A63 2.50sh blk, org & gray .95 .95
a. Souvenir sheet of 4 2.50 2.50
Nos. 267-270 (4) 1.80 1.80

Intl. Bank for Reconstruction and Development and Affiliate Intl. Monetary Fund Meetings, Nairobi.

No. 270a contains stamps similar to Nos. 267-270 with simulated perforations.

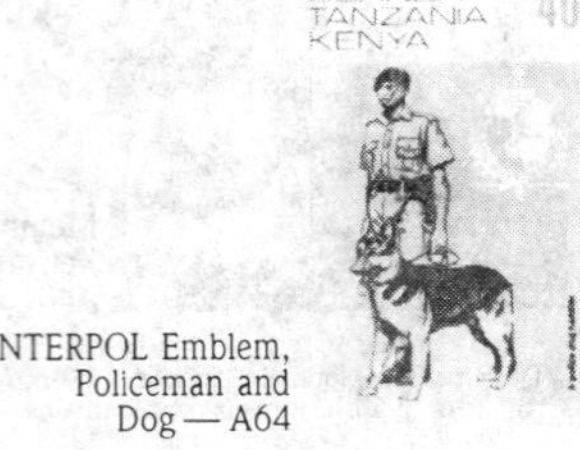

INTERPOL Emblem, Policeman and Dog — A64

Designs: 70c, East African policemen and emblem. 1.50sh, INTERPOL emblem. 2.50sh, INTERPOL Headquarters, St. Cloud, France.

1973-74 Litho. *Perf. 14x14½*

271 A64 40c yellow & multi .20 .15
272 A64 70c multicolored .40 .20
273 A64 1.50sh violet & multi .80 .70
274 A64 2.50sh lemon & multi *(St. Clans)* 1.90 1.90
275 A64 2.50sh lemon & multi *(St. Cloud)* ('74) 1.90 1.90
Nos. 271-275 (5) 5.20 4.85

50th anniv. of Intl. Criminal Police Org. Issued: Nos. 271-274, Oct. 24, 1973.

Tea Factory, Nandi Hills A65

1973, Dec. 12 Photo. *Perf. 13x14*

276 A65 40c shown .15 .15
277 A65 70c Kenyatta Hospital .15 .15
278 A65 1.50sh Nairobi Airport .35 .35
279 A65 2.50sh Kindaruma hydroelectric plant .65 .65
Nos. 276-279 (4) 1.30 1.30

10th anniversary of independence.

Afro-Shirazi Party Headquarters — A66

Designs: 70c, Michenzani housing development. 1.50sh, Map of East Africa and television screen with flower. 2.50sh, Amaan Stadium.

1974, Jan. 12 Litho. *Perf. 13½x14*

280 A66 40c multicolored .15 .15
281 A66 70c multicolored .15 .15
282 A66 1.50sh black & multi .35 .35
283 A66 2.50sh black & multi .65 .65
Nos. 280-283 (4) 1.30 1.30

10th anniversary of Zanzibar revolution.

Symbol of Union A67

Designs: 70c, Map of Tanganyika and Zanzibar, and handshake. 1.50sh, Map of Tanganyika and Zanzibar, and communications symbols. 2.50sh, Flags of Tanu, Tanzania and Afro-Shirazi Party.

1974, Apr. 24 Litho. *Perf. 14½*

284 A67 40c sepia & multi .15 .15
285 A67 70c blue grn & multi .15 .15
286 A67 1.50sh ultra & multi .40 .40
287 A67 2.50sh multicolored .90 .90
Nos. 284-287 (4) 1.60 1.60

Union of Tanganyika and Zanzibar, 10th anniv.

Family and Home A68

Designs: 70c, Drummer at dawn. 1.50sh, Family hoeing, and livestock. 2.50sh, Telephonist, train, plane, telegraph lines.

1974, July 15 Litho. *Perf. 14½*

288 A68 40c multicolored .15 .15
289 A68 70c multicolored .15 .15
290 A68 1.50sh multicolored .45 .45
291 A68 2.50sh multicolored .80 .80
Nos. 288-291 (4) 1.55 1.55

17th Intl. Conf. on Social Welfare, July 14-20.

Post and Telegraph Headquarters, Kampala — A69

Cent. of the UPU: 70c, Mail train and truck. 1.50sh, UPU Headquarters, Bern. 2.50sh, Loading mail on East African Airways VC-10.

1974, Oct. 9 Litho. *Perf. 14*

292 A69 40c lt green & multi .15 .15
293 A69 70c gray & multi .15 .15
294 A69 1.50sh yel & multi .45 .45
295 A69 2.50sh lt blue & multi .80 .80
Nos. 292-295 (4) 1.55 1.55

Family Planning Clinic A70

World Population Year: 70c, "Tug of War." 1.50sh, Scales and world population figures. 2.50sh, World Population Year emblem.

1974, Dec. 16 Litho. *Perf. 14½*

296 A70 40c multicolored .15 .15
297 A70 70c purple & multi .15 .15
298 A70 1.50sh multicolored .45 .45
299 A70 2.50sh blue blk & multi .80 .80
Nos. 296-299 (4) 1.55 1.55

Seronera Wild Life Lodge, Tanzania A71

Game lodges of East Africa: 70c, Mweya Safari Lodge, Uganda. 1.50sh, Ark-Aberdare Forest Lodge, Kenya. 2.50sh, Paraa Safari Lodge, Uganda.

1975, Feb. 24 Litho. *Perf. 14½*

No.	Type	Description	Unused	Used
300	A71	40c multicolored	.15	.15
301	A71	70c multicolored	.15	.15
302	A71	1.50sh multicolored	.45	.35
303	A71	2.50sh multicolored	.80	.80
		Nos. 300-303 (4)	1.55	1.45

Wooden Comb, Bajun, Kenya — A72

African Artifacts: 1sh, Earring, Chaga, Tanzania. 2sh, Armlet, Acholi, Uganda. 3sh, Kamba gourd, Kenya.

1975, May 5 Litho. *Perf. 13½*

No.	Type	Description	Unused	Used
304	A72	50c gray & multi	.15	.15
305	A72	1sh gray & multi	.20	.20
306	A72	2sh multicolored	.45	.45
307	A72	3sh multicolored	.75	.75
		Nos. 304-307 (4)	1.55	1.55

Map Showing OAU Members, Ugandan Flag — A73

Elephant, Kenya — A74

OAU Emblem and: 50c, Entebbe Airport, horiz. 2sh, Nile Hotel, Kampala, horiz. 3sh, Ugandan Martyrs' Shrine, Namugongo.

Perf. 11½x11, 11x11½

1975, July 28 Litho.

No.	Type	Description	Unused	Used
308	A73	50c multicolored	.15	.15
309	A73	1sh multicolored	.20	.20
310	A73	2sh multicolored	.45	.45
311	A73	3sh multicolored	.75	.75
		Nos. 308-311 (4)	1.55	1.55

Organization for African Unity (OAU), Summit Conf., Kampala, July 28 - Aug. 1.

1975, Sept. 11 Litho. *Perf. 11x11½*

Protected animals: 1sh, Albino buffalo, Uganda. 2sh, Elephant, exhibit in National Museum, Kenya. 3sh, Abbott's duiker, Tanzania.

No.	Type	Description	Unused	Used
312	A74	50c multicolored	.40	.30
313	A74	1sh brown & multi	.70	.60
314	A74	2sh yel green & multi	1.50	1.25
315	A74	3sh blue grn & multi	2.50	2.50
		Nos. 312-315 (4)	5.10	4.65

Masai Villagers Bleeding Cow, Masai, Kenya — A75

Festival Emblem and: 1sh, Ugandan dancers. 2sh, Family, Makonde sculpture, Tanzania. 3sh, Skinning hippopotamus, East Africa.

1975, Nov. 3 Litho. *Perf. 13½x14*

No.	Type	Description	Unused	Used
316	A75	50c org brown & multi	.15	.15
317	A75	1sh brt green & multi	.20	.20
318	A75	2sh dk blue & multi	.45	.45
319	A75	3sh lilac & multi	.75	.75
		Nos. 316-319 (4)	1.55	1.55

2nd World Black and African Festival of Arts and Culture, Lagos, Nigeria, Jan. 5 - Feb. 12.

Fokker Friendship, Nairobi Airport — A76

East African Airways, 30th anniv.: 1sh, DC-9 Kilimanjaro Airport. 2sh, Super VC10, Entebbe Airport. 3sh, East African Airways emblem.

1976, Jan. 2 Litho. *Perf. 11½*

No.	Type	Description	Unused	Used
320	A76	50c ultra & multi	.50	.25
321	A76	1sh rose & multi	.75	.40
322	A76	2sh orange & multi	2.00	1.00
323	A76	3sh black & multi	3.25	1.60
		Nos. 320-323 (4)	6.50	3.25

POSTAGE DUE STAMPS

Kenya and Uganda

D1

D2

Perf. 14½x14

1928-33 Typo. Wmk. 4

No.	Type	Description	Unused	Used
J1	D1	5c deep violet	1.00	1.25
J2	D1	10c orange red	1.00	1.25
J3	D1	20c yel green	1.00	1.65
J4	D1	30c ol brn ('31)	9.00	*7.00*
J5	D1	40c dull blue	4.50	*9.00*
J6	D1	1sh grnsh gray ('33)	35.00	*125.00*
		Nos. J1-J6 (6)	51.50	*145.15*

Kenya, Uganda, Tanganyika

1935, May 1 *Perf. 13½x14*

No.	Type	Description	Unused	Used
J7	D2	5c violet	.20	.25
J8	D2	10c red	.20	.20
J9	D2	20c green	.35	.30
J10	D2	30c brown	.55	*.90*
J11	D2	40c ultramarine	3.50	*6.00*
J12	D2	1sh gray	10.00	*14.00*
		Nos. J7-J12 (6)	14.80	*21.65*

OFFICIAL STAMPS

The 1959-60 "OFFICIAL" overprints on Nos. 103-104, 106-108, 110, 112-117, 120-123, 125, 127, 129, 133 are listed under Tanganyika, as they were used by the Tanganyika government.

KIAUCHAU

(Kiautschou)

LOCATION — A district of China on the south side of the Shantung peninsula.
GOVT. — German colony
AREA — 200 sq. mi.
POP. — 192,000 (approx. 1914).

The area was seized by Germany in 1897 and through negotiations that followed was leased to Germany by China.

100 Pfennig = 1 Mark
100 Cents = 1 Dollar (1905)

Tsingtau Issues

Stamps of Germany, Offices in China 1898, with Additional Surcharge:

5 Pfg. *a* **5 Pfg.** *b* **5 Pfg.** *c*

On Nos. 1-9, a blue or violet line is drawn through "PF. 10 PF." All exist without this line. All copies of Nos. 1b, 2b and 3b lack the colored line.

1900

"China" Overprint at 56 degree Angle

No.	Type	Description	Unused	Used
1	A10(a)	5pfg on 10pf car	40.00	40.00
c.		Dbl. surch., one inverted	300.00	
2	A10(b)	5pfg on 10pf car	40.00	40.00
c.		Dbl. surch., one inverted	300.00	
3	A10(c)	5pfg on 10pf car	42.50	45.00
c.		Dbl. surch., one inverted	350.00	
		Nos. 1-3 (3)	122.50	125.00

"China" Overprint at 48 degree Angle

No.	Type	Description	Unused	Used
1a	A10(a)	5pfg on 10pf car	110.00	125.00
b.		Double surcharge	450.00	575.00
2a	A10(b)	5pfg on 10pf car	110.00	125.00
b.		Double surcharge	450.00	575.00
3a	A10(c)	5pfg on 10pf car	125.00	140.00
b.		Double surcharge	500.00	600.00
		Nos. 1a-3a (3)	345.00	390.00

Surcharged:

5 Pf. *d* **5 Pf.** *e* **5 Pf.** *f*

"China" Overprint at 48 degree Angle on Nos. 4-9

No.	Type	Description	Unused	Used
4	A10(d)	5pf on 10pf car	*2,500.*	*3,250.*
a.		Double surcharge	*7,250.*	*14,000.*
5	A10(e)	5pf pn 10pf car	*2,500.*	*3,250.*
a.		Double surcharge	*7,250.*	*14,000.*
6	A10(f)	5pf on 10pf car	*2,500.*	*3,250.*
a.		Double surcharge	*7,250.*	*14,000.*
b.		5fP		*17,500.*
c.		As "b," double surcharge	—	—

With Additional Handstamp **5**

No.	Type	Description	Unused	Used
7	A10(d)	5pf on 10pf car	*37,500.*	*45,000.*
8	A10(f)	5pf on 10pf car	*37,500.*	*45,000.*
a.		On No. 6b	—	—

With Additional Handstamp **5 Pf.**

No.	Type	Description	Unused	Used
9	A10(f)	5pf on 10pf car	*7,500.*	*9,000.*
a.		Double surcharge		*32,500.*
b.		On No. 6a		
c.		On No. 6b		
d.		On No. 6c		

Kaiser's Yacht "Hohenzollern"
A1 A2

1901, Jan. Unwmk. Typo. *Perf. 14*

No.	Type	Description	Unused	Used
10	A1	3pf brown	2.00	2.00
11	A1	5pf green	2.00	1.50
12	A1	10pf carmine	2.75	2.00
13	A1	20pf ultra	7.50	9.50
14	A1	25pf org & blk, *yel*	15.00	19.00
15	A1	30pf org & blk, *sal*	15.00	17.00
16	A1	40pf lake & blk	17.50	22.50
17	A1	50pf pur & blk, *sal*	17.50	25.00
18	A1	80pf lake & blk, *rose*	30.00	52.50

Engr. *Perf. 14½x14*

No.	Type	Description	Unused	Used
19	A2	1m carmine	55.00	95.00
20	A2	2m blue	82.50	110.00
21	A2	3m black vio	82.50	*200.00*
22	A2	5m slate & car	275.00	*600.00*
		Nos. 10-22 (13)	604.25	*1,156.*

A3 A4

1905 Typo.

No.	Type	Description	Unused	Used
23	A3	1c brown	1.40	1.50
24	A3	2c green	2.25	1.25
25	A3	4c carmine	3.75	1.25
26	A3	10c ultra	11.00	5.25
27	A3	20c lake & blk	30.00	22.50
28	A3	40c lake & blk, *rose*	85.00	110.00

Engr.

No.	Type	Description	Unused	Used
29	A4	$½ carmine	60.00	90.00
30	A4	$1 blue	140.00	95.00
31	A4	$1½ black vio	1,100.	*1,750.*
32	A4	$2½ slate & car	1,400.	*3,250.*

1905-16 Wmk. 125 Typo.

No.	Type	Description	Unused	Used
33	A3	1c brown ('06)	1.10	1.40
a.		1c yellow brown ('16)	.50	—
34	A3	2c green ('09)	.75	.90
a.		2c dark green ('14)	.50	2.25
35	A3	4c carmine ('09)	1.00	1.25
36	A3	10c ultra ('09)	1.25	*3.25*
a.		10c blue	11.50	3.75
37	A3	20c lake & blk ('08)	2.75	*19.00*
38	A3	40c lake & blk, *rose*	3.75	*60.00*

Engr.

No.	Type	Description	Unused	Used
39	A4	$½ car ('07)	6.75	*67.50*
40	A4	$1 steel blue ('06)	7.50	*67.50*
41	A4	$1½ blk violet	7.00	*175.00*
42	A4	$2½ slate & car	19.00	*525.00*
		Nos. 33-42 (10)	50.85	

Four values of the design A3 and A4 stamps in recognizably different shades were printed and released in 1918, but by then Germany had lost control of Kiauchau, and these stamps are not known used. The four stamps and their unused values are: 20c red & black, $2; $½ pale rose, $4.50; $1 bright blue, $5.75; $1½ gray violet, $11.50.

KIONGA

'kyöŋ-gə

LOCATION — Southeast Africa and northeast Mozambique, on Indian Ocean south of Rovuma River
GOVT. — Formerly part of German East Africa
AREA — 400 sq. mi.

This territory, occupied by Portuguese troops during World War I was allotted to Portugal by the Treaty of Versailles. Later it became part of Mozambique.

100 Centavos = 1 Escudo

Lourenco Marques No. 149 Surcharged in Red

1916, May 29 Unwmk. *Perf. 11½*

No.	Type	Description	Unused	Used
1	A2	½c on 100r bl, *bl*	20.00	16.00
2	A2	1c on 100r bl, *bl*	20.00	16.00
3	A2	2½c on 100r bl, *bl*	20.00	16.00
4	A2	5c on 100r bl, *bl*	20.00	16.00
		Nos. 1-4 (4)	80.00	64.00

Most of the stock of Lourenço Marques No. 149 used for these surcharges lacked gum.

KIRIBATI

'kir-ə-,bas

LOCATION — A group of islands in the Pacific Ocean northeast of Australia
GOVT. — Republic
AREA — 264 sq. mi.
POP. — 60,302 (1982)
CAPITAL — Tarawa

Kiribati, former Gilbert Islands, consists of the Gilbert, Phoenix, Ocean and Line Islands.

Catalogue values for all unused stamps in this country are for Never Hinged items.

Watermark

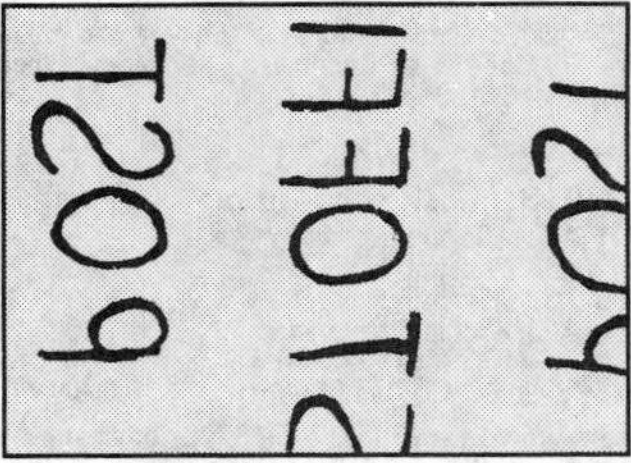

Wmk. 380- "POST OFFICE"

Kiribati Flag — A50

Parliament, London, Assembly, Tarawa A51

Wmk. 373

1979, July 12 Litho. ***Perf. 14***

325 A50 10c multicolored	.15	.15
326 A51 45c multicolored	.40	.40

Independence.

Training Ship Teraaka A52

Designs: 3c, Passenger launch Tautunu. 5c, Hibiscus. 7c, Cathedral, Tarawa. 10c, House of Assembly, Bikenibeu Island. 12c, Betio harbor. 15c, Reef egret. 20c, Flamboyant tree. 25c, Moorish idol (fish). 30c, Frangipani blossoms. 35c, Chapel, Tangintebu Island. 50c, Hypolimnas bolina elliciana (butterfly). $1, Tarawa Lagoon ferry, Tabakea. $2, Sunset over lagoon. $5, Natl. flag.

1979-80 Wmk. 373

327 A52 1c multicolored	.15	.15
328 A52 3c multicolored	.15	.15
329 A52 5c multicolored	.15	.15
330 A52 7c multicolored	.15	.15
331 A52 10c multicolored	.15	.15
332 A52 12c multicolored	.15	.15
333 A52 15c multicolored	.15	.15
334 A52 20c multicolored	.15	.15
335 A52 25c multicolored	.15	.15
336 A52 30c multicolored	.20	.20
337 A52 35c multicolored	.20	.20
338 A52 50c multicolored	.35	.35
339 A52 $1 multicolored	.65	.45
340 A52 $2 multicolored	1.10	.90
340A A52 $5 multicolored	2.50	2.75
Nos. 327-340A (15)	6.35	6.20

Issued: $5, Aug. 27, 1980; others, July 12, 1979.

1980-81 Unwmk.

327a A52 1c multi ('81)	.15	.15
328a A52 3c multi ('81)	.15	.15
329a A52 5c multi	.15	.15
330a A52 7c multi	.15	.15
331a A52 10c multi	.15	.15
332a A52 12c multi	.15	.15
333a A52 15c multi	.15	.15
334a A52 20c multi ('81)	.15	.15
335a A52 25c multi	.15	.15
336a A52 30c multi ('81)	.20	.20
337a A52 35c multi ('81)	.20	.25
338a A52 50c multi ('81)	.35	.35
339a A52 $1 multi	.55	.65
340b A52 $2 multi	1.40	1.40
340c A52 $5 multi ('80)	2.00	2.00
Nos. 327a-340c (15)	6.05	6.20

For overprints see Nos. O1-O15.

Gilbert and Ellice Islands No. 1 — A53

Simulated Cancel and: 20c, Gilbert and Ellice No. 70. 25c, Great Britain No. 139. 45c, Gilbert and Ellice No. 31.

Wmk. 373

1979, Sept. 27 Litho. ***Perf. 14***

341 A53 10c multicolored	.15	.15
342 A53 20c multicolored	.15	.15
343 A53 25c multicolored	.20	.20
344 A53 45c multicolored	.20	.20
a. Souvenir sheet of 4, #341-344	.90	.90
Nos. 341-344 (4)	.70	.70

Sir Rowland Hill (1795-1879), originator of penny postage.

Boy Climbing Coconut Palm, IYC Emblem — A54

IYC Emblem, Coat of Arms and: 10c, Boy and giant clam shell. 45c, Girl reading book. $1, Boy wearing garlands. All vert.

Perf. 14x13½, 13½x14

1979, Nov. 28 Litho.

345 A54 10c multicolored	.15	.15
346 A54 20c multicolored	.15	.15
347 A54 45c multicolored	.15	.15
348 A54 $1 multicolored	.40	.40
Nos. 345-348 (4)	.85	.85

International Year of the Child.

Downrange Station A55

National Space Development Agency of Japan (NASDA) Satellite Tracking: 45c, Experimental satellite trajectory (map). $1, Rocket launch, Tanegashima, Japan, vert.

1980, Feb. 20 Litho. ***Perf. 14½***

349 A55 25c multicolored	.15	.15
350 A55 45c multicolored	.30	.30
351 A55 $1 multicolored	.55	.55
Nos. 349-351 (3)	1.00	1.00

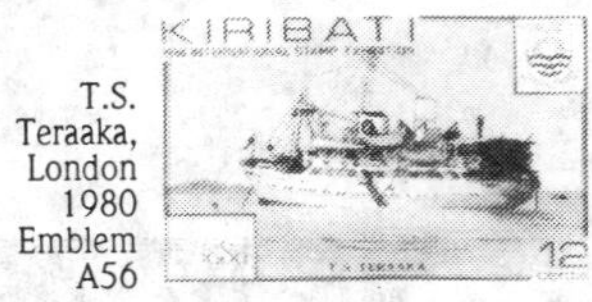

T.S. Teraaka, London 1980 Emblem A56

1980, Apr. 30 Litho. Unwmk.

352 A56 12c shown	.15	.15
353 A56 25c Air Tungaru plane, Bonriki Airport	.15	.15
354 A56 30c Radio operator	.15	.15
355 A56 $1 Bairiki post office	.40	.40
a. Souvenir sheet of 4, #352-355	1.00	1.00
Nos. 352-355 (4)	.85	.85

London 1980 Intl. Stamp Exhib., May 6-14.

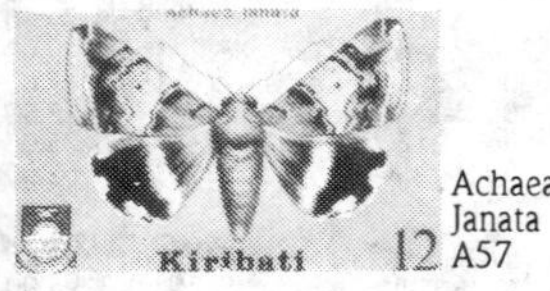

Achaea Janata A57

1980, Aug. 27 Litho. ***Perf. 14***

356 A57 12c shown	.15	.15
357 A57 25c Ethmia nigroapicella	.15	.15
358 A57 30c Utetheisa pulchelloides	.25	.25
359 A57 50c Anua coronata	.45	.45
Nos. 356-359 (4)	1.00	1.00

Capt. Cook Hotel A58

1980, Nov. 19 Wmk. 373 ***Perf. 13½***

360 A58 10c shown	.15	.15
361 A58 20c Stadium	.15	.15
362 A58 25c Intl. Airport, Bonriki	.15	.15
363 A58 35c National Library	.20	.20
364 A58 $1 Otintai Hotel	.40	.40
Nos. 360-364 (5)	1.05	1.05

Acalypha Godseffiana — A59

Perf. 14x13½

1981, Feb. 18 Litho. Wmk. 373

365 A59 12c shown	.15	.15
366 A59 30c Hibiscus schizopetalus	.15	.15
367 A59 35c Calotropis gigantea	.20	.20
368 A59 50c Euphorbia pulcherrima	.30	.30
Nos. 365-368 (4)	.80	.80

Abaiang and Marakei Islands, String Figures A60

Wmk. 380

1981, May 6 Litho. ***Perf. 14***

369 A60 12c shown	.15	.15
370 A60 30c Butaritari, Little Makin, house	.25	.25
371 A60 35c Maiana, Coral Road	.30	.30
372 A60 $1 Christmas Isld., Resolution	.60	.60
Nos. 369-372 (4)	1.30	1.30

Prince Charles, Lady Diana, Royal Yacht Charlotte A60a

Prince Charles and Lady Diana — A60b

Illustration A60b is greatly reduced.

Wmk. 380

1981, July 29 Litho. ***Perf. 14***

373 A60a 12c Couple, The Katherine	.15	.15
a. Bklt. pane of 4, perf. 12, unwmkd.	.50	
374 A60b 12c Couple	.15	.15
375 A60a 50c The Osborne	.40	.40
376 A60b 50c like #374	.40	.40
a. Bklt. pane of 2, perf. 12, unwmkd.	1.00	
377 A60a $2 Britannia	1.25	1.25
378 A60b $2 like #374	1.25	1.25
Nos. 373-378 (6)	3.60	3.60

Souvenir Sheet

Perf. 12

379 A60b $1.20 like #374	1.75	1.75

Royal wedding.

Bonriki Tuna Fish Bait Breeding Center A61

1981, Nov. 19

380 A61 12c shown	.15	.15
381 A61 30c Fishing boat	.25	.25
382 A61 35c Cold storage, Betio	.30	.30
383 A61 50c Nei Manganibuka	.45	.45
a. Souvenir sheet of 4, #380-383	1.25	1.25
Nos. 380-383 (4)	1.15	1.15

Pomarine Jaegers A62

1982-85 Litho. ***Perf. 14***

384 A62 1c shown	.15	.15
385 A62 2c Mallards	.15	.15
386 A62 4c Collared petrels	.15	.15
387 A62 5c Blue-faced boobies	.15	.15
388 A62 7c Friendly quail dove	.15	.15
389 A62 8c Shovelers	.15	.15
390 A62 12c Christmas Isld. warblers	.25	.25
391 A62 15c Pacific plovers	.30	.30
392 A62 20c Reef herons	.40	.40
392A A62 25c Brown noddies ('83)	2.50	1.25
393 A62 30c Brown boobies	.55	.55
394 A62 35c Audubon's shearwaters	.65	.65
395 A62 40c White-throated storm petrels, vert.	.75	.75
396 A62 50c Bristle-thighed curlews, vert.	1.00	1.00
396A A62 55c Fairy tern ('85)	9.00	9.00
397 A62 $1 Scarlet-breasted lorikeets, vert.	2.00	2.00
398 A62 $2 Long-tailed cuckoo, vert.	2.50	2.50
399 A62 $5 Great frigate birds, vert.	7.50	7.00
Nos. 384-399 (18)	28.30	26.55

Issued: 25c, 1/31/83; 55c, 11/19/85; others, 2/18/82.

For overprints see Nos. O16-O20.

Air Tungaru A63

1982, Feb. 18 Wmk. 380

400 A63 12c De Havilland DH114 Heron	.15	.15
401 A63 30c Britten-Norman Trislander	.20	.20
402 A63 35c Casa 212 Aviocar	.25	.25
403 A63 50c Boeing 727	.40	.40
Nos. 400-403 (4)	1.00	1.00

21st Birthday of Princess Diana, July 1 — A64

1982, May 19

404 A64 12c Mary of Teck, 1893	.15	.15
405 A64 50c Teck arms	.30	.30
406 A64 $1 Diana	.65	.65
Nos. 404-406 (3)	1.10	1.10

Overprinted: "ROYAL BABY"

1982, July 14

407 A64 12c multicolored	.15	.15
408 A64 50c multicolored	.30	.30
409 A64 $1 multicolored	.65	.65
Nos. 407-409 (3)	1.10	1.10

Birth of Prince William of Wales, June 21.

Scouting Year — A65

1982, Aug. 12

410 A65 12c First aid	.15	.15
411 A65 25c Repairing boat	.15	.15
412 A65 30c Saluting	.15	.15
413 A65 50c Gilbert Islds. #304	.30	.30
Nos. 410-413 (4)	.75	.75

Visit of Queen Elizabeth II and Prince Philip A66

Wmk. 380

1982, Oct. 23 Litho. ***Perf. 14***

414 A66 12c Couple, dancer	.15	.15
415 A66 25c Couple, boat	.20	.20
416 A66 35c Philatelic Bureau	.30	.30
Nos. 414-416 (3)	.65	.65

Souvenir Sheet

417 A66 50c Queen Elizabeth II, vert. 1.00 1.00

Nos. 414-416 also issued in sheets of 6.

A67

1983, Mar. 14 Wmk. 380 *Perf. 14*

418 A67 12c Obaia the Feathered legend .15 .15
419 A67 30c Robert Louis Stevenson Hotel, Abemama .20 .20
420 A67 50c Betio Harbor .30 .30
421 A67 $1 Map .60 .60
Nos. 418-421 (4) 1.25 1.25

Commonwealth day.

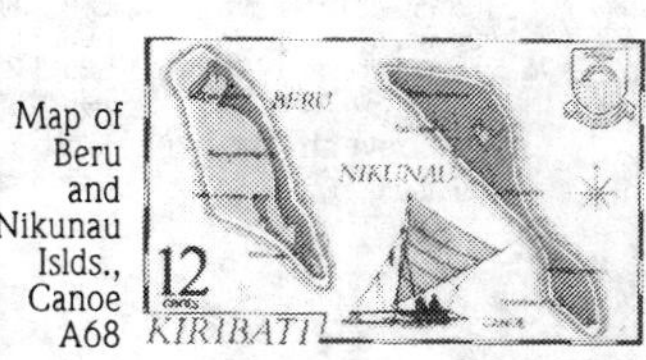

Map of Beru and Nikunau Islds., Canoe A68

1983, May 19 Litho. *Perf. 14*

422 A68 12c shown .15 .15
423 A68 25c Abemama, Kuria, Aranuka .20 .20
424 A68 35c Nonouti, vert. .30 .30
425 A68 50c Tarawa, vert. .45 .45
Nos. 422-425 (4) 1.10 1.10

See #436-439, 456-459, 475-479, 487-490.

Copra Industry A69

Designs: 12c, Collecting fallen Coconuts. 25c, Selecting Coconuts for Copra. 30c, Removing Husk from Coconuts. 35c, Drying Copra in the Sun. 50c, Loading Copra, Betio Harbor.

1983, Aug. 8 Litho. *Perf. 14*

426 A69 12c multicolored .15 .15
427 A69 25c multicolored .35 .35
428 A69 30c multicolored .40 .40
429 A69 35c multicolored .50 .50
430 A69 50c multicolored .75 .75
Nos. 426-430 (5) 2.15 2.15

Battle of Tarawa, 40th Anniv. A70

1983, Nov. 17 Litho. Wmk. 380

431 A70 12c War memorials .15 .15
432 A70 30c Battle map .15 .15
433 A70 35c Defense gun .20 .20
434 A70 50c Scenes, 1943, 1983 .30 .30
435 A70 $1 Aircraft carrier .65 .65
Nos. 431-435 (5) 1.45 1.45

Map Type of 1983

1984, Feb. 14 Wmk. 380 *Perf. 14*

436 A68 12c Teraina .15 .15
437 A68 30c Nikumaroro .35 .35
438 A68 35c Kanton .40 .40
439 A68 50c Banaba .60 .60
Nos. 436-439 (4) 1.50 1.50

Local Ships A71

1984, May 9 Litho. Wmk. 380

440 A71 12c Tug boat .20 .20
441 A71 35c Ferry landing craft .60 .60
442 A71 50c Ferry .85 .85
443 A71 $1 Cargo and passanger boat 1.75 1.75
a. Souvenir sheet of 4, #440-443, perf. 13½ 4.00 4.00
Nos. 440-443 (4) 3.40 3.40

Ausipex '84 A72

1984, Aug. 21 Litho. *Perf. 14*

444 A72 12c South Tarawa sewer & water system .15 .15
445 A72 30c Fishing boat Nouamake .25 .25
446 A72 35c Overseas communications training .30 .30
447 A72 50c Intl. telecommunications link .45 .45
Nos. 444-447 (4) 1.15 1.15

Legends A73

Designs: 12c, Tabakea supporting Banaba on his back. 30c, Nakaa, Judge of the Dead. 35c, Naareau and Tiku-Tiku-Tamoamoa. 50c, Whistling Ghosts.

1984, Nov. 21 Wmk. 380 *Perf. 14*

448 A73 12c multicolored .15 .15
449 A73 30c multicolored .25 .25
450 A73 35c multicolored .30 .30
451 A73 50c multicolored .45 .45
Nos. 448-451 (4) 1.15 1.15

See Nos. 464-467.

Reef Fish — A74

1985, Feb. 19 Litho. *Perf. 14*

452 A74 12c Tang .25 .25
453 A74 25c White-barred triggerfish .75 .75
454 A74 35c Surgeon fish 1.25 1.25
455 A74 80c Squirrel fish 2.50 2.50
a. Souvenir sheet of 4, #452-455 6.00 6.00
Nos. 452-455 (4) 4.75 4.75

See Nos. 540-554, 567.

Map Type of 1983

1985, May 9 Litho. *Perf. 13½*

456 A68 12c Tabuaeran, frigate bird .25 .25
457 A68 35c Rawaki, coconuts .75 .75
458 A68 50c Arorae, xanthid crab 1.00 1.00
459 A68 $1 Tamana, fish hook 2.00 2.00
Nos. 456-459 (4) 4.00 4.00

Intl. Youth Year — A76

1985, Aug. 5

460 A76 15c Boys playing soccer .30 .30
461 A76 35c Emblems .75 .75
462 A76 40c Girl processing fruit, vert. .85 .85
463 A76 55c Intl. youth exchange 1.25 1.25
Nos. 460-463 (4) 3.15 3.15

Legends Type of 1984

15c, Nang Kineia & the Tickling Ghosts. 35c, Myth of Auriaria & Tituabine. 40c, First Coming of Babai at Arorae. 55c, Riiki & the Milky Way.

1985, Nov. 19 Wmk. 380 *Perf. 14*

464 A73 15c multicolored .40 .40
465 A73 35c multicolored .85 .85
466 A73 40c multicolored 1.00 1.00
467 A73 55c multicolored 1.35 1.35
Nos. 464-467 (4) 3.60 3.60

Transport and Telecommunications Decade 1985-95 — A77

1985, Dec. 9 Litho. *Perf. 14*

468 A77 15c Satellite network 1.00 1.00
469 A77 40c Tarawa-Suva feeder service 2.00 2.00

Queen Elizabeth II 60th Birthday

Common Design Type

15c, Review of Girl Guides, Windsor Castle, 1938. 35c, Birthday parade, Buckingham Palace, 1980. 40c, With Prince Philip during royal tour, 1982. 55c, Banquet, Austrian embassy in London, 1966. $1, Visiting Crown Agents' offices, 1983.

1986, Apr. 21 *Perf. 14½x14*

470 CD337 15c scar, black & sil .15 .15
471 CD337 35c ultra & multi .30 .30
472 CD337 40c green & multi .35 .35
473 CD337 55c violet & multi .50 .50
474 CD337 $1 rose vio & multi 1.00 1.00
Nos. 470-474 (5) 2.30 2.30

For overprints see Nos. 495-499.

Map Type of 1983

1986, June 17 Wmk. 380 *Perf. 14*

475 A68 15c Manra .60 .60
476 A68 30c Birnie, McKean 1.25 1.25
477 A68 35c Orona 1.50 1.50
478 A68 40c Malden 1.75 1.75
479 A68 55c Vostok, Caroline, Flint 2.50 2.50
Nos. 475-479 (5) 7.60 7.60

Lizards A79

1986, Aug. 26 Unwmk. *Perf. 14*

480 A79 15c Lepidodactylus lugubris .60 .60
481 A79 35c Gehyra mutilata 1.50 1.50
482 A79 40c Hemidactylus frenatus 1.65 1.65
483 A79 55c Gehyra oceanica 2.25 2.25
Nos. 480-483 (4) 6.00 6.00

See Nos. 491-494.

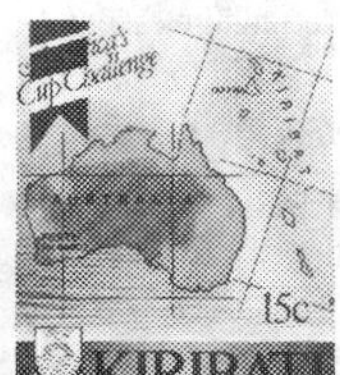

America's Cup — A80

Perf. 14x14½

1986, Dec. 29 Unwmk.

484 Strip of 3 2.75 2.75
a. A80 15c Map of Australia .20 .20
b. A80 55c Course, trophy .65 .65
c. A80 $1.50 Australia II 1.75 1.75

No. 484 has a continuous design.

Transport and Telecommunications Decade (1985-1995) — A81

Designs: 30c, Nei Moamoa, flagship of Kiribati overseas shipping line. 55c, Manual and electronic telephone switching systems.

1987, Mar. 31 Litho. *Perf. 14*

485 A81 30c multicolored 1.50 1.50
486 A81 55c multicolored 3.00 3.00

Map Type of 1983

1987, Sept. 22 Litho. Unwmk.

487 A68 15c Starbuck, red-tailed tropicbird .20 .20
488 A68 30c Enderbury, white tern .40 .40
489 A68 55c Tabiteuea, pandanus .70 .70
490 A68 $1 Onotoa, Okai house 1.25 1.25
Nos. 487-490 (4) 2.55 2.55

Nos. 487-490 vert.

Lizard Type of 1986

1987, Oct. 27 *Perf. 15*

491 A79 15c Emoia nigra .15 .15
492 A79 35c Cryptoblepharus .20 .20
493 A79 40c Emoia cyanura .25 .25
494 A79 $1 Lipinia noctua .75 .75
a. Souvenir sheet of 4, #491-494 2.25 2.25
Nos. 491-494 (4) 1.35 1.35

Nos. 470-474 Overprinted "40TH WEDDING ANNIVERSARY" in Silver

Perf. 14½x14

1987, Nov. 30 Litho. Unwmk.

495 CD337 15c scar, black & sil .15 .15
496 CD337 35c ultra & multi .35 .35
497 CD337 40c green & multi .40 .40
498 CD337 55c violet & multi .50 .50
499 CD337 $1 rose vio & multi .90 .90
Nos. 495-499 (5) 2.30 2.30

Intl. Red Cross and Red Crescent Organizations, 125th Annivs. — A83

15c, Jean Henri Dunant (1828-1910), founder. 35c, Red Cross volunteers on parade. 40c, Stretcher bearers. 55c, Gilbert and Ellice Islands #159.

Perf. 14½x14

1988, May 8 Litho. Unwmk.

500 A83 15c multicolored .35 .35
501 A83 35c multicolored .65 .65
502 A83 40c multicolored .75 .75
503 A83 55c multicolored 1.00 1.00
Nos. 500-503 (4) 2.75 2.75

A84

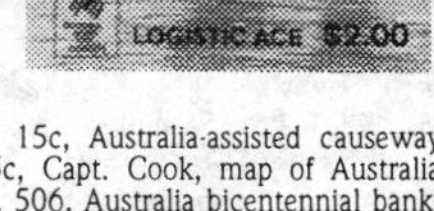

SYDPEX '88, Australia Bicentennial A85

Emblem and: 15c, Australia-assisted causeway construction. 35c, Capt. Cook, map of Australia and Kiribati. No. 506, Australia bicentennial banknote obverse. No. 507, Bank note reverse. $2, "Logistic Ace."

1988, July 30 Litho. *Perf. 14½*

504 A84 15c multicolored .25 .25
505 A84 35c multicolored .60 .60
506 A84 $1 multicolored 1.75 1.75
507 A84 $1 multicolored 1.75 1.75
a. Pair, #506-507 3.50 3.50
Nos. 504-507 (4) 4.35 4.35

Souvenir Sheet

Perf. 13½x14

508 A85 $2 multicolored 3.00 3.00

Robert F. Stockton, 1st propeller-driven steamship, 150th anniv.

Transport and Telecommunications Decade (1985-1995) — A86

Wmk. 373

1988, Dec. 28 Litho. *Perf. 14*

509 A86 35c Telephone operator, map .90 .90
510 A86 45c Betio-Bairiki Causeway 1.25 1.25

Ships A87

Perf. 14¹/₂

1989, May 26 Litho. Wmk. 384

511 A87 15c Brigantine Hound, 1835 .50 .50
512 A87 30c Brig Phantom, 1854 1.00 1.00
513 A87 40c HMS Alacrity, 1873 1.50 1.50
514 A87 $1 Whaler Charles W. Morgan, 1851 3.25 3.25
Nos. 511-514 (4) 6.25 6.25

See Nos. 557-561, 687-690.

A88

Birds — A89

Perf. 13¹/₂x14

1989, July 12 Litho. Wmk. 384

515 A88 15c House of Assembly .50 .50
516 A88 $1 Constitution 3.00 3.00

Natl. Independence, 10th anniv.

Moon Landing, 20th Anniv.

Common Design Type

Apollo 10: 20c, Service and command modules, launch escape system. 50c, Eugene A. Cernan, Thomas P. Stafford and John W. Young. 60c, Mission emblem. 75c, Splashdown, Honolulu. $2.50, Apollo 11 command module in space.

1989, July 20 *Perf. 14*

Size of Nos. 518-519: 29x29mm

517 CD342 20c multicolored .50 .50
518 CD342 50c multicolored 1.00 1.00
519 CD342 60c multicolored 1.25 1.25
520 CD342 75c multicolored 1.50 1.50
Nos. 517-520 (4) 4.25 4.25

Souvenir Sheet

521 CD342 $2.50 multicolored 5.25 5.25

Perf. 14¹/₂x14

1989, June 28 Litho. Wmk. 384

522 A89 15c Eastern reef heron .40 .40
523 A89 15c Brood in nest .40 .40
a. Pair, #522-523 .80 .80
524 A89 $1 White-tailed tropicbird in flight 2.50 2.50
525 A89 $1 Seated tropicbird 2.50 2.50
a. Pair, #524-525 5.00 5.00
Nos. 522-525 (4) 5.80 5.80

Nos. 523a, 525a have continuous designs.
For overprints see Nos. 534-535.

Souvenir Sheets

A90

A91

Perf. 14x13¹/₂

1989, Aug. 7 Litho. Wmk. 384

526 A90 $2 Gilbert & Ellice Isls. #58 3.25 3.25

Perf. 14x13¹/₂

1989, Sept. 25 Litho. Unwmk.

Workmen renovating the Statue of Liberty: a, Torch. b, Drilling copper sheeting. c, Glancing at a sketch of the statue.

527 Sheet of 3 3.50 3.50
a.-c. A91 35c any single 1.00 1.00

World Stamp Expo '89, Washington, DC, PHILEXFRANCE '89, Paris. No. 526 margin pictures #435, France #634 and US #2224.

Transport and Telecommunications Decade, 1985-95 — A92

1989, Oct. 16 Wmk. 384 *Perf. 14*

528 A92 30c shown 1.00 1.00
529 A92 75c MV *Mataburo* 2.50 2.50

Christmas — A93

Paintings: 10c, *Adoration of the Holy Child* (detail), by Denys Calvert. 15c, *Adoration of the Holy Child* (entire painting). 55c, *The Holy Family and St. Elizabeth*, by Rubens. $1, *Madonna with Child and Mary Magdalene*, School of Corregio.

1989, Dec. 1

530 A93 10c multicolored .40 .40
531 A93 15c multicolored .50 .50
532 A93 55c multicolored 1.75 1.75
533 A93 $1 multicolored 3.25 3.25
Nos. 530-533 (4) 5.90 5.90

Nos. 524-525 Ovptd.

1989, Oct. 21 Litho. *Perf. 14¹/₂x14*

534 A89 $1 on No. 524 2.50 2.50
535 A89 $1 on No. 525 2.50 2.50
a. Pair, #534-535 5.00 5.00

STAMPSHOW '89, Melbourne.

Penny Black 150th Anniv., Stamp World London '90 — A94

Stamps on stamps: 15c, Gilbert & Ellice #15, Great Britain #2. 50c, Gilbert & Ellice #8, Great Britain #1 canceled. 60c, Kiribati #384, Great Britain #58. $1, Gilbert Islands #269, Great Britain #3.

1990, May 1 Litho. *Perf. 14*

536 A94 15c multicolored .50 .50
537 A94 50c multicolored 1.50 1.50
538 A94 60c multicolored 2.00 2.00
539 A94 $1 multicolored 3.00 3.00
Nos. 536-539 (4) 7.00 7.00

Fish Type of 1985

Fish: 1c, Blue-barred orange parrotfish. 5c, Honeycomb rock cod. 10c, Bluefin jack. 15c, Paddle tail snapper. 20c, Variegated emperor. 25c, Rainbow runner. 30c, Black saddled coral trout. 35c, Great barracuda. 40c, Convict surgeonfish. 50c, Violet squirrelfish. 60c, Freckled hawkfish. 75c, Pennant coral fish. $1, Yellow and blue sea perch. $2, Pacific sailfish. $5, Whitetip reef shark.

Wmk. 373

1990, July 12 Litho. *Perf. 14*

540 A74 1c multicolored .15 .15
541 A74 5c multicolored .15 .15
542 A74 10c multicolored .15 .15
543 A74 15c multicolored .25 .25
544 A74 20c multicolored .35 .35
545 A74 25c multicolored .40 .40
546 A74 30c multicolored .45 .45
547 A74 35c multicolored .50 .50
548 A74 40c multicolored .60 .60
549 A74 50c multicolored .75 .75
550 A74 60c multicolored 1.00 1.00
551 A74 75c multicolored 1.25 1.25
552 A74 $1 multicolored 1.50 1.50
553 A74 $2 multicolored 3.00 3.00
554 A74 $5 multicolored 7.50 7.50
Nos. 540-554 (15) 18.00 18.00

Dated 1990. See No. 567. For overprints see Nos. 587-590.

Queen Mother 90th Birthday

Common Design Types

1990, Aug. 4 Wmk. 384 *Perf. 14x15*

555 CD343 75c Queen Mother 1.50 1.50

Perf. 14¹/₂

556 CD344 $2 King, Queen & WWII bombing victim, 1940 3.75 3.75

Ships Type of 1989

1990, Nov. 5 Litho. *Perf. 14¹/₂*

557 A87 15c Whaling ship Herald, 1851 .35 .35
558 A87 50c Bark Belle, 1849 1.10 1.10
559 A87 60c Schooner Supply, 1851 1.50 1.50
560 A87 75c Whaling ship Triton, 1848 1.75 1.75
Nos. 557-560 (4) 4.70 4.70

Souvenir Sheet

561 A87 $2 Convict transport Charlotte, 1789 6.25 6.25

Manta Ray — A95

1991, Jan. 17 Wmk. 373 *Perf. 14*

562 A95 15c shown 1.00 1.00
563 A95 20c Manta ray, diff. 1.25 1.25
564 A95 30c Whale shark 1.75 1.75
565 A95 35c Whale shark, diff. 2.25 2.25
Nos. 562-565 (4) 6.25 6.25

World Wildlife Fund.

Fish Type of 1985

Design: 23c, Bennett's pufferfish.

1991, Apr. 30 Wmk. 384

567 A74 23c multicolored .70 .70

For overprint see No. 587.

Elizabeth & Philip, Birthdays

Common Design Types

1991, June 17 *Perf. 14¹/₂*

571 CD345 65c multicolored 1.50 1.50
572 CD346 70c multicolored 1.50 1.50
a. Pair, #571-572 + label 3.00 3.00

Phila Nippon '91 A96

Opening of new Tungaru Central Hospital: 23c, Aerial view. 50c, Traditional dancers. 60c, Main entrance. 75c, Foundation stone, plaque. $5, Ambulance, nursing staff.

1991, Nov. 16 *Perf. 13¹/₂x14*

573 A96 23c multicolored .35 .35
574 A96 50c multicolored .80 .80
575 A96 60c multicolored 1.00 1.00
576 A96 75c multicolored 1.25 1.25
Nos. 573-576 (4) 3.40 3.40

Souvenir Sheet

577 A96 $5 multicolored 7.50 7.50

Christmas A97

Designs: 23c, Island mother and child. 50c, Family in island hut. 60c, Nativity Scene. 75c, Adoration of the Shepherds.

1991, Dec. 2 Wmk. 373

578 A97 23c multicolored .35 .35
579 A97 50c multicolored .80 .80
580 A97 60c multicolored 1.00 1.00
581 A97 75c multicolored 1.25 1.25
Nos. 578-581 (4) 3.40 3.40

Queen Elizabeth II's Accession to the Throne, 40th Anniv.

Common Design Type

Wmk. 373

1992, Feb. 6 Litho. *Perf. 14*

582 CD349 23c multicolored .35 .35
583 CD349 30c multicolored .50 .50
584 CD349 50c multicolored .75 .75
585 CD349 60c multicolored 1.00 1.00
586 CD349 75c multicolored 1.25 1.25
Nos. 582-586 (5) 3.85 3.85

Nos. 550-551, 553, & 567 Ovptd. EXPO'92

Wmk. 384, 373

1992, June 1 Litho. *Perf. 14*

587 A74 23c on No. 567 .50 .50
588 A74 60c on No. 550 1.25 1.25
589 A74 75c on No. 551 1.50 1.50
590 A74 $2 on No. 553 4.50 4.50
Nos. 587-590 (4) 7.75 7.75

Marine Training Center, 25th Anniv. A98

1992, Aug. 28 *Perf. 14*

591 A98 23c Entrance .35 .35
592 A98 50c Cadets at morning parade .75 .75
593 A98 60c Fire school 1.00 1.00
594 A98 75c Lifeboat training 1.25 1.25
Nos. 591-594 (4) 3.35 3.35

FAO, WHO A99

Wmk. 373

1992, Dec. 1 Litho. *Perf. 14*
595 A99 23c Children running .35 .35
596 A99 50c Night fishing .75 .75
597 A99 60c Fruit 1.00 1.00
598 A99 75c Ship 1.25 1.25
Nos. 595-598 (4) 3.35 3.35

Water Birds — A100

Perf. 14½
1993, May 28 Litho. Wmk. 373
599 A100 23c Phoenix petrel .40 .40
600 A100 23c Cooks petrel .40 .40
a. Pair, #599-600 .80 .80
601 A100 60c Northern pintail 1.00 1.00
602 A100 60c Eurasian widgeon 1.00 1.00
a. Pair, #601-602 2.00 2.00
603 A100 75c Spectacled tern 1.25 1.25
604 A100 75c Black naped tern 1.25 1.25
a. Pair, #603-604 2.50 2.50
605 A100 $1 Stilt wader 1.75 1.75
606 A100 $1 Wandering tattler 1.75 1.75
a. Pair, #605-606 3.50 3.50
Nos. 599-606 (8) 8.80 8.80

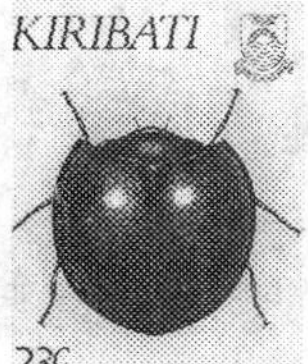

Insects — A101

Perf. 14½x14
1993, Aug. 23 Litho. Wmk. 373
607 A101 23c Chilocorus nigritus .50 .50
608 A101 60c Rodolia pumila 1.25 1.25
609 A101 75c Rodolia cardinalis 1.50 1.50
610 A101 $1 Cryptolaemus montrouzieri 2.25 2.25
Nos. 607-610 (4) 5.50 5.50

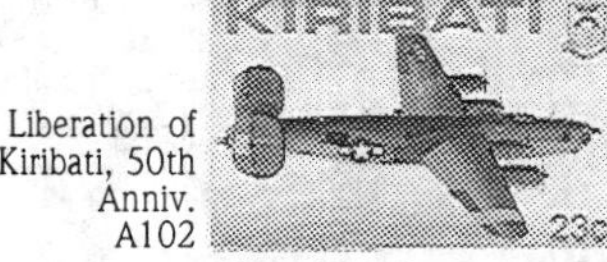

Liberation of Kiribati, 50th Anniv. A102

No. 611: a, Air reconnaissance of Tarawa Atoll. b, USS Nautilus surveys Tarawa. c, USS Indianapolis. d, USS Pursuit leads seaborne assault. e, Kingfisher spotter plane. f, Destroyers USS Ringgold and USS Dashiell. g, Sherman tank on seabed. h, Fighter plane in lagoon. i, Naval gun on seabed. j, First US aircraft to land on Betio Island.

No. 612: a, Transports disembark landing craft. b, Marines assault Betio Island. c, Sea and air assault of Betio. d, Marines pinned down in surf. e, USS Maryland firing broadside. f, Betio from the air. g, Memorial to US Navy dead. h, Memorial to expatriates. i, Memorial to Japanese dead. j, Battle map of Betio.

Wmk. 373
1993, Nov. 1 Litho. *Perf. 14*
Sheets of 10
611 A102 23c #a.-j. + label 4.00 4.00
612 A102 75c #a.-j. + label 12.50 12.50

Christmas — A103

Perf. 13½x14
1993, Dec. 1 Litho. Wmk. 373
613 A103 23c Shepherds .45 .45
614 A103 40c Three kings .80 .80
615 A103 60c Holy Family 1.25 1.25
616 A103 75c Mother, children 1.75 1.75
Nos. 613-616 (4) 4.25 4.25

Souvenir Sheet
617 A103 $3 Madonna and Child 5.25 5.25

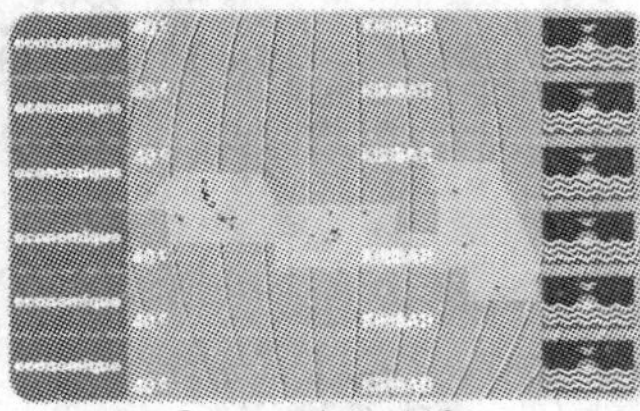
Stampcards — A104

Illustration reduced.

Rouletted 6 on 2 or 3 Sides
1993, Nov. 1 Litho.
Self-Adhesive
Cards of 6 + 6 labels
618 A104 40c #a.-f. *3.00*
619 A104 $1 #a.-f. *7.00*
620 A104 $1.20 #a.-f. *8.50*
621 A104 $1.60 #a.-f. *12.50*
Nos. 618-621 (4) *31.00*

Nos. 619-621 are airmail. Individual stamps measure 70x9mm and have a card backing. Se-tenant labels on No. 618 inscribed "economique." Se-tenant labels on Nos. 619-621 inscribed "prioritaire AIR MAIL."

Souvenir Sheet

New Year 1994 (Year of the Dog) — A105

Wmk. 373
1994, Feb. 18 Litho. *Perf. 14*
622 A105 $3 multicolored 6.00 6.00

Hong Kong '94.

Whales A106

Designs: 23c, Bryde's whale. 40c, Blue whale. 60c, Humpback whale. 75c, Killer whale.

1994, May 2
623 A106 23c multicolored .50 .50
624 A106 23c multicolored .50 .50
a. Pair, #623-624 1.00 1.00
625 A106 40c multicolored .75 .75
626 A106 40c multicolored .75 .75
a. Pair, #625-626 1.50 1.50
627 A106 60c multicolored 1.25 1.25
628 A106 60c multicolored 1.25 1.25
a. Pair, #627-628 2.50 2.50
629 A106 75c multicolored 1.50 1.50
630 A106 75c multicolored 1.50 1.50
a. Pair #629-630 3.00 3.00
Nos. 623-630 (8) 8.00 8.00

Value at UL on Nos. 623, 625, 627, 629; at UR on others.
Nos. 624a-630a have continuous designs.

Environmental Protection A107

Designs: 40c, Family on beach at sunset. 60c, Fish. 75c, Frigate birds.

1994, July 12
631 A107 40c multicolored .75 .75
632 A107 60c multicolored 1.00 1.00
633 A107 75c multicolored 1.50 1.50
Nos. 631-633 (3) 3.25 3.25

Independence, 15th anniv.

Butterflies — A108

Flowers — A109

Designs: 1c, Diaphania indica. 5c, Herpetogamma licarsisalis. 10c, Parotis suralis. 12c, Sufetula sunidesalis. 20c, Aedia sericea. 23c, Anomis vitiensis. 30c, Anticarsia irrorata. 35c, Spodoptera litura. 40c, Mocis frugalis. 45c, Agrius convolvuli. 50c, Cephonodes picus. 55c, Gnathothlibus erotus. 60c, Macroglossum hirundo. 75c, Badamia exclamationis. $1, Precis villida. $2, Danaus plexippus. $3, Hypolimnas bolina (male). $5, Hypolimnas bolina (female).

1994, Aug. 19
634 A108 1c multicolored .15 .15
635 A108 5c multicolored .15 .15
636 A108 10c multicolored .15 .15
637 A108 12c multicolored .20 .20
638 A108 20c multicolored .30 .30
639 A108 23c multicolored .35 .35
640 A108 30c multicolored .45 .45
641 A108 35c multicolored .55 .55
642 A108 40c multicolored .60 .60
643 A108 45c multicolored .65 .65
644 A108 50c multicolored .75 .75
645 A108 55c multicolored .80 .80
646 A108 60c multicolored .90 .90
647 A108 75c multicolored 1.10 1.10
648 A108 $1 multicolored 1.50 1.50
a. Souvenir sheet of 1 1.60 1.60
649 A108 $2 multicolored 3.00 3.00
650 A108 $3 multicolored 4.50 4.50
651 A108 $5 multicolored 7.50 7.50
Nos. 634-651 (18) 23.60 23.60

No. 648a issued 2/12/97 for Hong Kong '97.

1994, Oct. 31
652 A109 23c Nerium oleander .50 .50
653 A109 60c Catharanthus roseus 1.00 1.00
654 A109 75c Ipomea pes-caprae 1.25 1.25
655 A109 $1 Calophyllum mophyllum 1.75 1.75
Nos. 652-655 (4) 4.50 4.50

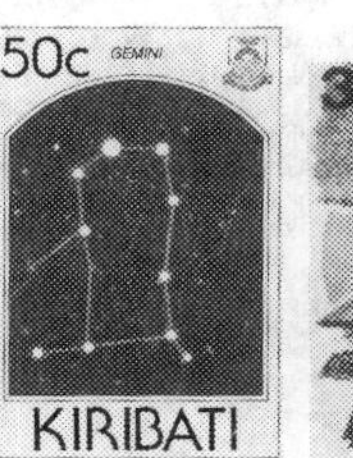

A110 A111

Constellations.

1995, Jan. 31
656 A110 50c Gemini .75 .75
657 A110 60c Cancer .90 .90
658 A110 75c Cassiopeia 1.10 1.10
659 A110 $1 Southern cross 1.50 1.50
Nos. 656-659 (4) 4.25 4.25

Perf. 14½
1995, Apr. 3 Litho. Wmk. 384

Scenes of Kiribati: No. 660: a, Architecture. b, Men, canoe, sailboat. c, Gun emplacement, Tarawa. d, Children, shells. e, Outdoor sports.

No. 661: a, Women traditionally attired. b, Windsurfing. c, Filleting fish. d, Snorkeling, scuba diving. e, Weaving.

660 A111 30c Strip of 5, #a.-e. 2.25 2.25
661 A111 40c Strip of 5, #a.-e. 3.00 3.00
f. Booklet pane, #660, #661 + 5 labels 6.75
Complete booklet, #661f 6.75

Visit South Pacific Year.

End of World War II, 50th Anniv.
Common Design Type

Designs: 23c, Grumman TBM-3E Avenger. 40c, Curtiss SOC. 3-1 seagull. 50c, Consolidated B-24J Liberator. 60c, Grumman Goose. 75c, Martin B-26 Marauder. $1, Northrop P-61B Black Widow. $2, Reverse of War Medal 1939-45.

Perf. 14x13½
1995, May 8 Wmk. 373
662 CD351 23c multicolored .35 .35
663 CD351 40c multicolored .60 .60
664 CD351 50c multicolored .75 .75
665 CD351 60c multicolored .90 .90
666 CD351 75c multicolored 1.10 1.10
667 CD351 $1 multicolored 1.50 1.50
Nos. 662-667 (6) 5.20 5.20

Souvenir Sheet
Perf. 14
668 CD352 $2 multicolored 3.00 3.00

For overprints see Nos. 691-697.

Souvenir Sheet of 4

Environmental Protection — A112

Marine life: a, Electus parrot, great frigate bird, coconut crab. b, Red-tailed tropic bird, common dolphin, pantropical spotted dolphin. c, Yellow & blue sea perch, green turtle, blue-barred orange parrot fish. d, Pennant coral fish, red-banded wrasse, violet squirrel fish.

Wmk. 373
1995, July 12 Litho. *Perf. 14*
669 A112 60c #a.-d. + 4 labels 3.50 3.50

For overprint see No. 672.

Souvenir Sheet

New Year 1995 (Year of the Boar) — A113

Design: $2, Sow, piglets. Illustration reduced.

1995, Sept. 1 Litho. *Perf. 13*
670 A113 $2 multicolored 3.00 3.00

Singapore '95.

Souvenir Sheet

Beijing '95 — A114

Design: $2, like #670, with sheet margin as shown in reduced illustration.

1995, Sept. 14
671 A114 $2 multicolored 3.00 3.00

No. 669 Overprinted

Wmk. 373
1995, Aug. 19 Litho. *Perf. 14*
672 A112 60c #a.-d. + 4 labels 3.50 3.50

Police Maritime Unit — A115

Patrol boat RKS Teanoai: No. 673, In harbor. No. 674, Under way.

Wmk. 373
1995, Nov. 30 Litho. *Perf. 13*
673 A115 75c multicolored 1.10 1.10
674 A115 75c multicolored 1.10 1.10
a. Pair, #673-674 2.25 2.25

Dolphins A116

Designs: 23c, Pantropical spotted. 60c, Spinner. 75c, Fraser's. $1, Rough-toothed.

Wmk. 384
1996, Jan. 15 Litho. *Perf. 14*
675 A116 23c multicolored .35 .35
676 A116 60c multicolored .90 .90
677 A116 75c multicolored 1.10 1.10
678 A116 $1 multicolored 1.50 1.50
Nos. 675-678 (4) 3.85 3.85

UNICEF, 50th Anniv. A117

Portion of UNICEF emblem and: a, Water faucet, clean water. b, Documents, chilren's rights. c, Hypodermic, health care. d, Open book, education.

Wmk. 373
1996, Apr. 22 Litho. *Perf. 13*
679 A117 30c Block of 4, #a.-d. 1.90 1.90

No. 679 is a continuous design.

Souvenir Sheet

CHINA '96, 9th Intl. Philatelic Exhibition — A118

Illustration reduced.

1996, Apr. 30 Wmk. 384 *Perf. 13½*
680 A118 50c multicolored .80 .80

New Year 1996, Year of the Rat.

Souvenir Sheet

No. 5609 Gilbert and Ellice Islands LMS Jubilee Class 4-6-0 Locomotive — A119

Wmk. 373
1996, June 8 Litho. *Perf. 12*
681 A119 $2 multicolored 3.25 3.25

CAPEX '96.

Sea Crabs A120

Wmk. 373
1996, Aug. 6 Litho. *Perf. 14*
682 A120 23c Rathbun red .35 .35
683 A120 60c Red & white painted .95 .95
684 A120 75c Red spotted 1.20 1.20
685 A120 $1 Red spotted white 1.60 1.60
Nos. 682-685 (4) 4.10 4.10

Souvenir Sheet

Taipei '96 — A121

Illustration reduced.

Perf. 14½
1996, Oct. 21 Litho. Wmk. 384
686 A121 $1.50 Outrigger canoe 2.40 2.40

Ships Type of 1989

23c, Whaling ship, "Potomac," 1843. 50c, Barkentine "Southern Cross IV," 1891. 60c, Bark "John Williams III," 1890. $1, HMS Dolphin, 1765.

Perf. 14½
1996, Dec. 2 Litho. Wmk. 384
687 A87 23c multicolored .35 .35
688 A87 50c multicolored .80 .80
689 A87 60c multicolored .95 .95
690 A87 $1 multicolored 1.60 1.60
Nos. 687-690 (4) 3.70 3.70

Nos. 662-668 Ovptd. with PACIFIC 97 Emblem

Perf. 14x13½
1997, May 29 Litho. Wmk. 373
691 CD351 23c multicolored .40 .40
692 CD351 40c multicolored .65 .65
693 CD351 50c multicolored .85 .85
694 CD351 60c multicolored 1.00 1.00
695 CD351 75c multicolored 1.25 1.25
696 CD351 $1 multicolored 1.70 1.70
Nos. 691-696 (6) 5.85 5.85

Souvenir Sheet
697 CD351 $2 multicolored 3.10 3.10

Queen Elizabeth II and Prince Philip, 50th Wedding Anniv. — A122

Designs: No. 698, Queen Elizabeth II. No. 699, Horse team going down river bank. No. 700, Queen in open carriage. No. 701, Prince Philip. No. 702, Prince, Queen. No. 703, Riding horse.
$2, Queen, Prince in open carriage, horiz.

Perf. 14½x14
1997, July 10 Litho. Wmk. 373
698 A122 50c multicolored .80 .80
699 A122 50c multicolored .80 .80
a. Pair, #698-699 1.60 1.60
700 A122 60c multicolored .95 .95
701 A122 60c multicolored .95 .95
a. Pair, #700-701 1.90 1.90
702 A122 75c multicolored 1.20 1.20
703 A122 75c multicolored 1.20 1.20
a. Pair, #702-703 2.40 2.40
Nos. 698-703 (6) 5.90 5.90

Souvenir Sheet
704 A122 $2 multicolored 3.10 3.10

Birds — A123

#705-706, Rock dove. #707-708, Pacific pigeon. #709-710, Micronesian pigeon.

Wmk. 373
1997, Dec. 1 Litho. *Perf. 14*
705 A123 50c Immature .70 .70
706 A123 50c Adult .70 .70
a. Pair, #705-706 1.40 1.40
707 A123 60c Adult .80 .80
708 A123 60c Immature .80 .80
a. Pair, #707-708 1.60 1.60
709 A123 75c Adult 1.00 1.00
710 A123 75c Immature 1.00 1.00
a. Pair, #709-710 2.00 2.00
Nos. 705-710 (6) 5.00 5.00

Nos. 705-706, 709-710 With Added Inscription

Wmk. 373
1997, Dec. 5 Litho. *Perf. 14*
711 A123 50c on #705 .70 .70
712 A123 50c on #706 .70 .70
a. Pair, #711-712 1.40 1.40
713 A123 75c on #709 1.00 1.00
714 A123 75c on #710 1.00 1.00
a. Pair, #713-714 2.00 2.00

Asia '97.

Spiny Lobster A124

Wmk. 373
1998, Feb. 2 Litho. *Perf. 14*
715 A124 25c shown .30 .30
716 A124 25c Crawling right .30 .30
717 A124 25c Crawling left .30 .30
718 A124 25c Looking upward .30 .30
Nos. 715-718 (4) 1.20 1.20

World Wildlife Fund.

POSTAGE DUE STAMPS

Natl. Arms — D1

1981, Aug. 27 Litho. *Perf. 14*
J1 D1 1c brt pink & black .15 .15
J2 D1 2c greenish blue & blk .15 .15
J3 D1 5c brt yel grn & black .15 .15
J4 D1 10c lt red brown & blk .15 .15
J5 D1 20c ultra & black .20 .20
J6 D1 30c yel bister & black .30 .30
J7 D1 40c brt pur & black .40 .40
J8 D1 50c green & black .55 .55
J9 D1 $1 red orange & blk 1.00 1.00
Nos. J1-J9 (9) 3.05 3.05

Imperfs exist from the liquidation of Format International. They are not errors

---

OFFICIAL STAMPS

Nos. 327a-340c Overprinted "O.K.G.S."

1981, May Litho. Unwmk. *Perf. 14*
O1 A52 1c multicolored .15 .15
O2 A52 3c multicolored .15 .15
O3 A52 5c multicolored .15 .15
O4 A52 7c multicolored .15 .15
O5 A52 10c multicolored .15 .15
O6 A52 12c multicolored .15 .15
O7 A52 15c multicolored .15 .15
O8 A52 20c multicolored .15 .15
O9 A52 25c multicolored .20 .20
O10 A52 30c multicolored .25 .25
O11 A52 35c multicolored .25 .25
O12 A52 50c multicolored .40 .40
O13 A52 $1 multicolored .75 .75
O14 A52 $2 multicolored 1.50 1.50
O15 A52 $5 multicolored 4.00 4.00
Nos. O1-O15 (15) 8.55 8.55

Nos. O1-O15 have thick overprint.

1981 Wmk. 373
O1a A52 1c multi 2.00 2.25
O5a A52 10c multi 15.00 15.00
O6a A52 12c multi 4.00 4.00
O7a A52 15c multi 15.00 15.00
O8a A52 20c multi 10.00 10.00
O10a A52 30c multi 6.00 7.00
O12a A52 50c multi 5.00 5.00
O13a A52 $1 multi 11.00 10.00
O14a A52 $2 multi 14.00 14.00
O15a A52 $5 multi 3.50 4.00
Nos. O1a-O15a (10) 85.50 86.25

Nos. 390, 393-394, 396, 398 Overprinted "O.K.G.S."

1983, June 28 Litho. *Perf. 14*
O16 A62 12c multicolored .20 .20
O17 A62 30c multicolored .45 .45
O18 A62 35c multicolored .50 .50
O19 A62 50c multicolored .75 .75
O20 A62 $2 multicolored 3.25 3.25
Nos. O16-O20 (5) 5.15 5.15

This overprint has shorter, thinner letters than the one used for Nos. O1-O15. It also exists on Nos. 327, 331-334, 336-340. These have been questioned.

KOREA

kə-'rē-ə

(Corea)

(Chosen, Tyosen, Tae Han)

LOCATION — Peninsula extending from Manchuria between the Yellow Sea and the Sea of Japan
GOVT. — Republic
AREA — 38,221 sq. mi.
POP. — 39,950,743 (1983)
CAPITAL — Seoul

Korea (or Corea) an independent monarchy for centuries under Chinese influence, came under Japanese influence in 1895. Chinese and Japanese stamps were used there as early as 1875. Administrative control was assumed by Japan in 1904 and annexation followed in 1910. Postage stamps of Japan were used in Korea from 1905 to early 1946.

At the end of World War II, American forces occupied South Korea and Russian forces occupied North Korea, with the 38th parallel of latitude as the dividing line. A republic was established in 1948 following an election in South Korea. North Korea issues its own stamps. See note following air post listings.

100 Mon = 1 Tempo
5 Poon = 1 Cheun
1000 Re = 100 Cheun = Weun
100 Weun = 1 Hwan (1953)
100 Chun = 1 Won (1962)

Catalogue values for unused stamps in this country are for Never Hinged items, beginning with Scott 283 in the regular postage section, Scott B5 in the semi-postal section, and Scott C23 in the airpost section.

Watermarks

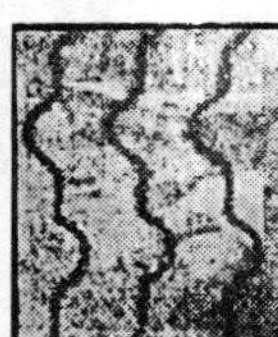
Wmk. 257- Curved Wavy Lines

Wmk. 312- Zigzag Lines

Wmk. 317- Communications Department Emblem

Stylized Yin Yang
A1 A2

Perf. 8½ to 11½

1884 **Typo.** **Unwmk.**

1	A1 5m rose	40.00	
2	A2 10m blue	9.00	

Reprints and counterfeits of Nos. 1-2 exist.

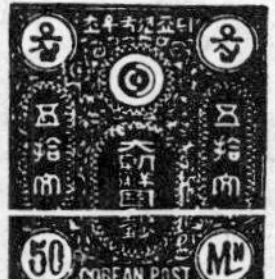

These stamps were never placed in use. Value, each $7.
Counterfeits exist.

Yin Yang — A6

Two types of 50p:
I - No period after "50."
II - Period after "50."

Perf. 11½, 12, 12½, 13 and Compound

1895 **Litho.**

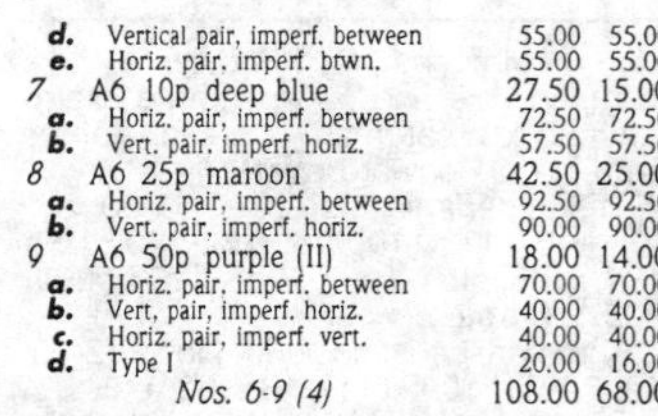

6	A6 5p green	20.00	14.00
a.	5p pale yellow green	27.50	17.00
b.	Vert. pair, imperf horiz.	50.00	50.00
c.	Horiz. pair, imperf. vert.	50.00	50.00
d.	Vertical pair, imperf. between	55.00	55.00
e.	Horiz. pair, imperf. btwn.	55.00	55.00
7	A6 10p deep blue	27.50	15.00
a.	Horiz. pair, imperf. between	72.50	72.50
b.	Vert. pair, imperf. horiz.	57.50	57.50
8	A6 25p maroon	42.50	25.00
a.	Horiz. pair, imperf. between	92.50	92.50
b.	Vert. pair, imperf. horiz.	90.00	90.00
9	A6 50p purple (II)	18.00	14.00
a.	Horiz. pair, imperf. between	70.00	70.00
b.	Vert, pair, imperf. horiz.	40.00	40.00
c.	Horiz. pair, imperf. vert.	40.00	40.00
d.	Type I	20.00	16.00
	Nos. 6-9 (4)	108.00	68.00

For overprints and surcharges see Nos. 10-17C, 35-38.
Counterfeits exist of Nos. 6-9 and all surcharges and overprints.

Overprinted "Tae Han" in Korean and Chinese Characters

1897

Red Overprint

10	A6 5p green	95.00	10.00
a.	5p pale yellow green	175.00	150.00
b.	Inverted overprint	150.00	150.00
c.	Without ovpt. at bottom	140.00	140.00
d.	Without overprint at top	140.00	140.00
f.	Double overprint at top	150.00	150.00
g.	Overprint at bottom in blk	175.00	175.00
h.	Pair, one without overprint	475.00	475.00
i.	Double overprint at top, inverted at bottom	550.00	
11	A6 10p deep blue	110.00	15.00
a.	Without ovpt. at bottom	150.00	150.00
b.	Without overprint at top	150.00	150.00
c.	Double overprint at top	165.00	165.00
d.	Bottom overprint inverted	150.00	150.00
e.	Top ovpt. dbl., one in blk	225.00	225.00
f.	Top overprint omitted, bottom overprint inverted	425.00	
12	A6 25p maroon	125.00	17.00
a.	Overprint at bottom invtd.	150.00	150.00
b.	Overprint at bottom in blk	225.00	225.00
c.	Bottom overprint omitted	150.00	150.00
e.	Top ovpt. dbl., one in blk	250.00	250.00
f.	Top and bottom overprints double, one of each in blk	275.00	275.00
g.	Pair, one without overprint	450.00	450.00
13	A6 50p purple	95.00	12.00
a.	Without ovpt. at bottom	125.00	125.00
b.	Without overprint at top	125.00	125.00
c.	Bottom overprint double	110.00	110.00
e.	Pair, one without overprint	300.00	300.00
	Nos. 10-13 (4)	425.00	54.00

1900

Black Overprint

13F	A6 5p green	325.00	
13G	A6 10p deep blue	325.00	
h.	Without ovpt. at bottom	375.00	
14	A6 25p maroon	325.00	
a.	Without ovpt. at bottom	350.00	
b.	Without overprint at top	350.00	
c.	Double overprint at bottom	350.00	
15	A6 50p purple	325.00	
a.	Without ovpt. at bottom	350.00	
	Nos. 13F-15 (4)	1,300.	

These stamps with black overprint, also No. 16A, are said not to have been officially authorized.

Nos. 6, 6a and 8 Surcharged in Red or Black

1900

15B	A6 1ch on 5p grn (R)	*2,500.*	*500.00*
c.	Yellow green		
16	A6 1ch on 25p mar	82.50	55.00

Same Surcharge in Red or Black on Nos. 10, 10a, 12, 12c and 14

16A	A6 1ch on 5p grn (R)	950.00	
b.	1ch on 5p pale yellow green	950.00	
17	A6 1ch on 25p (#12)	45.00	17.50
a.	Figure "1" omitted	80.00	
b.	On #12c	70.00	70.00
17C	A6 1ch on 25p (#14)	500.00	160.00

Counterfeit overprints and surcharges of Nos. 10-17C exist.

A8

A9

A10

A11

A12

A13

A14

A15

A16

A17

1900 **Typo.** ***Perf. 11***

18	A8	2re gray	9.50	3.50
19	A9	1ch yellow grn	10.50	4.00
21	A11	3ch orange red	12.50	4.50
a.		Vert. pair, imperf. horiz.	85.00	85.00
22	A12	4ch carmine	32.50	14.00
23	A13	5ch pink	15.00	8.00
24	A14	6ch dp blue	16.00	6.50
25	A15	10ch purple	32.50	10.00
26	A16	15ch gray vio	27.50	10.00
27	A17	20ch red brown	37.50	12.00
		Nos. 18-27 (9)	193.50	72.50

Nos. 22, 23, 25, 26 exist imperf.
Reprints of No. 24 were made in light blue, perf. 12x13, in 1905 for a souvenir booklet. See note after No. 54.

Perf. 10

18a	A8	2re	15.00	3.50
19a	A9	1ch	15.00	4.50
20	A10	2ch blue	35.00	18.00
a.		Horiz. pair, imperf. btwn.	*725.00*	
21b	A11	3ch	14.00	4.50
22a	A12	4ch	45.00	17.50
23a	A13	5ch	20.00	9.00
24a	A14	6ch	22.50	11.00
26a	A16	15ch	150.00	125.00
27a	A17	20ch	200.00	175.00
		Nos. 18a-27a (9)	516.50	368.00

A18

A19

A20

A21

1901 ***Perf. 11***

30	A18 2ch pale blue	12.00	8.00
a.	Perf. 10	50.00	45.00
31	A19 50ch ol grn & pink	275.00	95.00
32	A20 1wn rose, blk & bl	750.00	150.00
33	A21 2wn pur & yel grn	1,200.	225.00
	Nos. 30-33 (4)	2,237.	478.00

No. 33 exists imperf.
See Nos. 52-54.

Emperor's Crown — A22

1902, Oct. 18 ***Perf. 11½***

34	A22 3ch orange	40.00	17.50

40th year of the reign of Emperor Kojong. An imperf. single was part of the 1905 souvenir booklet. See note following No. 54.
Counterfeits exist.

Nos. 8 and 9 Handstamp Surcharged in Black

1ch 2ch 3ch

Perf. 11½, 12, 12½, 13 and Compound

1902

35	A6 1ch on 25p maroon	21.00	6.00
b.	Horiz. pair, imperf. btwn.	80.00	
c.	Imperf.	50.00	
d.	Vert. pair, imperf. horiz.	50.00	
e.	On No. 12	90.00	80.00
36	A6 2ch on 25p maroon	26.00	7.00
b.	Imperf.	45.00	
d.	On No. 12	90.00	80.00
e.	2ch on 50p purple	165.00	150.00
f.	As "e," character "cheun" unabbreviated (in two rows instead of one)	250.00	175.00
37	A6 3ch on 50p purple	26.00	7.00
b.	With character "cheun" unabbreviated (in two rows instead of one)	2,100.	800.00
d.	Horiz. pair, imperf. btwn.	60.00	
e.	Vert. pair, imperf. btwn.	60.00	
g.	On No. 13	50.00	50.00
38	A6 3ch on 25p maroon	60.00	50.00
	Nos. 35-38 (4)	133.00	70.00

There are several sizes of these surcharges. Being handstamped inverted and double surcharges exist.
Counterfeit surcharges exist.

WANTED KOREA
MINT, USED STAMPS, COVERS, CANCELLATIONS, REVENUES, COLLECTIONS, ACCUMULATIONS AND EVERYTHING.
SEND YOUR STAMPS FOR OUR CASH OFFER!
STEPHEN J. HASEGAWA
"Expert in Korea Philately. Communication in English or Korean language"
P.O. Box 40610 San Francisco, CA 94140-0610
Phone 415-648-0116 • FAX 415-821-9657 (24 Hours)
Member KSS.

KOREA
BUYING & SELLING

PAYING TOP PRICES FOR... COLLECTIONS & DEALER STOCKS.
Also Buying Korea Coins, Charms, Antiques and Banknotes!

NAMCHONG STAMPS & COINS
2777 N. Milwaukee Ave.
Chicago, IL 60647
TEL: 773-384-3766

FAX: 847-205-1008

KOREA
We offer the finest stock of Korean Stamps, Postal Histroy, Literature and Albums via net priced lists pegged to the competitive Korean market.

A purchase places you on the mailing list for 1 year. Send $1 ($2 Airmail) for comprehensive price list.

PUBLIC AUCTIONS
...stress Asian specialized material. Send $5 ($10 Airmail) for next comprehensive auction catalog.

ALWAYS BUYING:
CONTACT US NOW.
MICHAEL ROGERS, INC.
199 E. Welbourne Avenue
Winter Park, Florida 32789
Phone 407-644-2290
1-800-843-3751
FAX 407-645-4434

Falcon — A23

1903 *Perf. 13½x14*

No.	Type	Denomination	Unused	Used
39	A23	2re slate	22.50	4.00
40	A23	1ch violet brn	22.50	3.50
41	A23	2ch green	22.50	3.50
42	A23	3ch orange	37.50	3.50
43	A23	4ch rose	45.00	8.00
44	A23	5ch yellow brn	45.00	9.00
45	A23	6ch lilac	45.00	9.00
46	A23	10ch blue	45.00	9.00
47	A23	15ch red, *straw*	125.00	16.00
48	A23	20ch vio brn, *straw*	125.00	20.00
49	A23	50ch red, *grn*	175.00	65.00
50	A23	1wn vio, *lav*	300.00	95.00
51	A23	2wn vio, *org*	400.00	125.00
		Nos. 39-51 (13)	1,410.	370.50

Values are for copies with perfs touching the design.

Types of 1901

1903 *Perf. 12½*

Thin, Semi-Transparent Paper

No.	Type	Denomination	Unused	Used
52	A19	50ch pale ol grn & pale pink	*300.00*	*150.00*
53	A20	1wn rose, blk & bl	*600.00*	*200.00*
54	A21	2wn lt vio & lt grn	*700.00*	*200.00*
		Nos. 52-54 (3)	*1,600.*	550.00

No. 24, perf. 12x13, No. 34 imperf. and most examples of Nos. 52-54 unused are from souvenir booklets made up in 1905 when the Japanese withdrew all Korean stamps from circulation.

Nos. 1-54 Watermarked
In 1957 the Ministry of Communications issued 4000 presentation booklets containing Nos. 1-54 reproduced on watermark 312 paper.

Issued under US Military Rule

Stamps of Japan Nos. 331, 268, 342, 332, 339 and 337 Surcharged in Black

1946, Feb. 1 **Wmk. 257** *Perf. 13*

No.	Type	Denomination	Unused	Used
55	A86	5ch on 5s brn lake	4.50	10.00
56	A93	5ch on 14s rose lake & pale rose	.55	.90
a.		5ch on 40s dark violet (error)	110.00	
57	A154	10ch on 40s dk vio	.45	.65
58	A147	20ch on 6s lt ultra	.45	.65
a.		20ch on 27s rose brown (error)	80.00	
b.		Double surcharge	30.00	
59	A151	30ch on 27s rose brn	.45	.65
a.		30ch on 6s light ultra (error)	40.00	
b.		Double surcharge	25.00	
60	A151	5wn on 17s gray vio	2.50	6.00
		Nos. 55-60 (6)	8.90	18.85
		Set, never hinged	13.50	

Five essays for this provisional issue exist both with and without additional overprint of two Chinese characters ("specimen") in vermilion. The essays are: 20ch on Japan No. 269; 50ch on No. 272; 1wn on No. 336; 1wn on No. 273; 10wn on No. 265. Other denominations have been reported.

Korean Family and Flag — A24

Arms of Korea — A25

Perf. 10½

1946, May 1 **Litho.** **Wmk. 257**

No.	Type	Denomination	Unused	Used
61	A24	3ch orange yellow	.15	.30
62	A24	5ch green	.15	.20
63	A24	10ch carmine	.15	.20
64	A24	20ch dark blue	.25	.25
65	A25	50ch brown violet	.40	.50
66	A25	1wn lt brown	.55	.75
		Nos. 61-66 (6)	1.65	2.20
		Set, never hinged	3.25	

Liberation from Japan.

Imperfs., Part Perfs.
Imperforate and part-perforate examples of a great many Korean stamps from No. 61 onward exist.
The imperfs. include Nos. 61-90, 93-97, 116-117, 119-126, 132-173, 182-186, 195, 197-199, 202A, 203, 204-205, 217, etc.
The part-perfs. include Nos. 62-65, 69, 72-73, 109, 111-113, 132, etc.
Printers waste includes printed on both sides, etc.
As the field is so extensive, the editors believe that they belong more properly in a specialized catalogue.

Dove — A26

1946, Aug. 15 **Unwmk.**

No.	Type	Denomination	Unused	Used
67	A26	50ch deep violet	1.50	2.50
		Never hinged	2.25	

First anniversary of liberation.

Perforations often are rough on stamps issued between Aug. 1946 and the end of 1954.

Flags of US and Korea A27

1946, Sept. 9 *Perf. 11*

No.	Type	Denomination	Unused	Used
68	A27	10wn carmine	2.00	2.50
		Never hinged	3.00	

Resumption of postal communication with the US.

Astronomical Observatory, Kyongju — A28

Hibiscus with Rice — A29

Map of Korea — A30

Gold Crown of Silla Dynasty — A31

Admiral Li Sun-sin — A32

1946 *Rouletted 12*

No.	Type	Denomination	Unused	Used
69	A28	50ch dark blue	.25	.40
70	A29	1wn buff	.20	.40
71	A30	2wn indigo	.50	.50
72	A31	5wn magenta	2.00	3.00
73	A32	10wn emerald	3.00	2.25
		Nos. 69-73 (5)	5.95	6.55
		Set, never hinged	16.00	

Perf. 11

No.	Type	Denomination	Unused	Used
70a	A29	1wn	1.00	1.00
71a	A30	2wn	20.00	20.00
72a	A31	5wn	30.00	20.00
		Nos. 70a-72a (3)	51.00	41.00

Korean Phonetic Alphabet — A33

1946, Oct. 9 *Perf. 11*

No.	Type	Denomination	Unused	Used
74	A33	50ch deep blue	.60	1.25
		Never hinged	1.65	

500th anniv. of the introduction of the Korean phonetic alphabet (Hangul).

Li Jun — A34

Admiral Li Sun-sin — A35

Perf. 11½x11, 11½

1947, Aug. 1 **Litho.** **Wmk. 257**

No.	Type	Denomination	Unused	Used
75	A34	5wn lt blue green	2.00	3.50
76	A35	10wn light blue	2.00	3.50
		Set, never hinged	9.00	

Presentation Sheets
Starting in 1947 with No. 75, nearly 100 Korean stamps were printed in miniature or souvenir sheets and given to government officials and others. These sheets were released in quantities of 300 to 4,000. In 1957 the Ministry of Communications began to sell the souvenir sheets at post offices at face value to be used for postage. They are listed from No. 264a onward.

Letter-encircled Globe — A36

1947, Aug. 1 *Perf. 11½x11*

No.	Type	Denomination	Unused	Used
77	A36	10wn light blue	2.50	3.50
		Never hinged	5.00	

Resumption of international mail service between Korea and all countries of the world.

Granite Paper
Starting with No. 77, most Korean stamps through No. 751, except those on Laid Paper, are on Granite Paper. Granite Paper is noted above listing if the issue was printed on both ordinary and Granite Paper, such as Nos. 360a-374A.

Arch of Independence, Seoul — A37

Tortoise Ship, First Ironclad War Vessel — A38

1948, Apr.

No.	Type	Denomination	Unused	Used
78	A37	20wn rose	14.00	6.00
79	A38	50wn dull red brown	14.00	7.50
		Set, never hinged	55.00	

Republic

Flag and Ballot — A39

Woman and Man Casting Ballots — A40

Perf. 11x11½

1948, May 10 Litho. Wmk. 257

80 A39 2wn orange 2.50 .60
81 A39 5wn lilac rose 4.75 1.50
82 A39 10wn lt violet 12.00 4.00
83 A40 20wn carmine 18.00 8.00
84 A40 50wn blue 25.00 12.50
Nos. 80-84 (5) 62.25 26.60
Set, never hinged 125.00

South Korea election of May 10, 1948.

Korean Flag and Olive Branches A41

Olympic Torchbearer and Map of Korea — A42

1948, June 1 *Perf. 11x11½, 11½x11*

85 A41 5wn green 50.00 32.50
86 A42 10wn purple 25.00 8.00
Set, never hinged 140.00

Korea's participation in the 1948 Olympic Games.

National Assembly A43

1948, July 1 Wmk. 257 *Perf. 11½*

87 A43 4wn orange brown 8.00 6.00
Never hinged 15.00

Opening of the Assembly July 1, 1948.
Exists without period between "5" and "31."

Korean Family and Capitol — A44

Pres. Syngman Rhee — A46

Flag of Korea A45

1948, Aug. 1 Litho.

88 A44 4wn emerald 32.50 5.00
89 A45 10wn orange brown 10.00 5.00
Set, never hinged 80.00

Signing of the new constitution, July 17, 1948.

1948, Aug. 5

90 A46 5wn deep blue 80.00 6.00
Never hinged 160.00

Inauguration of Korea's first president, Syngman Rhee.

Dove — A47

Hibiscus — A48

Two types of 5wn:
I - "1948" 3mm wide; top inscription 9mm wide; periods in "8.15." barely visible.
II - "1948" 4mm wide; top inscription 9½mm; periods in "8.15." bold and strong.

1948 *Perf. 11, 11x11½*

91 A47 4wn blue 17.50 15.00
92 A48 5wn rose lilac (II) 13.00 12.50
a. Type I 80.00 60.00
Set, never hinged 60.00

Issued to commemorate the establishment of Korea's republican government.

Li Jun A49

Observatory, Kyongju A50

1948, Oct. 1 *Perf. 11½x11*

93 A49 4wn rose carmine .25 .20
94 A50 14wn deep blue .45 .30
a. 14wn light blue 75.00 30.00
Set, never hinged 1.10

For surcharges see Nos. 127, 174, 176.

Doves over UN Emblem — A51

Korean Citizen and Census Date — A52

1949, Feb. 12 Wmk. 257 *Perf. 11*

95 A51 10wn blue 10.00 12.50
Never hinged 20.00

Arrival of the UN Commission on Korea, Feb. 12, 1949.

1949, Apr. 25

96 A52 15wn purple 13.00 9.00
Never hinged 25.00

Census of May 1, 1949.

Korean Boy and Girl — A53

1949, May 5

97 A53 15wn purple 8.00 8.00
Never hinged 15.00

20th anniversary of Children's Day, May 5, 1949.

Postman — A54

Worker and Factory — A55

Rice Harvesting — A56

Japanese Cranes — A57

Diamond Mountains — A58

Ginseng Plant — A59

South Gate, Seoul — A60

Tabo Pagoda, Kyongju — A61

1949 Litho. *Perf. 11*

98 A54 1wn rose 1.50 1.50
99 A55 2wn dk blue gray .55 .30
100 A56 5wn yellow green 2.00 1.50
101 A57 10wn blue green .55 .50
102 A58 20wn orange brown .45 .35
103 A59 30wn blue green .85 .50
104 A60 50wn violet blue .65 .50
105 A61 100wn dull yellow grn .65 .50
Nos. 98-105 (8) 7.20 5.65
Set, never hinged 12.50

For surcharges see Nos. 129-131, 175, 177B-179, 181.

Phoenix and Yin Yang — A62

1949, Aug. 25

106 A62 15wn deep blue 9.00 7.00
Never hinged 16.00

1st anniv. of Korea's independence.

Express Train "Sam Chun Li" — A63

1949, Sept. 18 *Perf. 11½x12*

107 A63 15wn violet blue 27.50 17.00
Never hinged 55.00

50th anniversary of Korean railroads.

Korean Flag — A64

Perf. 11½x11

1949, Oct. 15 Wmk. 257

108 A64 15wn red org, yel & dk bl 6.75 8.50
Never hinged 12.00

75th anniv. of the UPU.

No. 108 exists unwatermarked. These are counterfeit.

Hibiscus A65

Magpies and Map of Korea A66

Stylized Bird and Globe — A67

Diamond Mountains A68

Admiral Li Sun-sin — A69

1949 Wmk. 257 Litho. *Perf. 11*

109 A65 15wn vermilion .20 .30
110 A66 65wn deep blue .20 .30
111 A67 200wn green .25 .30
112 A68 400wn brown .25 .40
113 A69 500wn deep blue .25 .30
Nos. 109-113 (5) 1.15 1.60
Set, never hinged 2.75

For surcharges see Nos. 128, 177, 180.

Canceled to Order

More than 100 Korean stamps and souvenir sheets were canceled to order, the cancellation incorporating the date "67.9.20." These include 81 stamps between Nos. 111 and 327, 18 airmail stamps between Nos. C6 and C26, and 5 souvenir sheets between Nos. 313 and 332, etc.

Also exists with later dates and on other stamps.

A70

A71

Ancient postal medal (Ma-Pae).

1950, Jan. 1

114 A70 15wn yellow green 6.25 5.50
115 A70 65wn red brown 5.00 4.50
Set, never hinged 25.00

50th anniv. of Korea's entrance into the UPU.

1950, Mar. 10 *Perf. 11½*

Revolutionists.

116 A71 15wn olive 8.00 4.50
117 A71 65wn light violet 5.75 4.00
Set, never hinged 27.50

41st anniversary of Korea's declaration of Independence.

Korean Emblem and National Assembly — A72

1950, May 30

118 A72 30wn bl, red, brn & grn 5.00 4.00
Never hinged 8.50

2nd natl. election of the Korean Republic.

Syngman Rhee A73

Korean Flag and White Mountains A74

Flags of UN and Korea, Map of Korea — A75

1950, Nov. 20 Wmk. 257 *Perf. 11*

119 A73 100wn blue .85 1.10
120 A74 100wn green 1.10 1.10
121 A75 200wn dark green 1.10 1.10
Nos. 119-121 (3) 3.05 3.30
Set, never hinged 6.00

Crane — A76

Tiger Mural — A77

Dove and Flag — A78

Postal Medal — A79

Mural from Ancient Tomb — A80

1951 Unwmk. *Perf. 11*
Ordinary Paper

122 A76 5wn orange brown .80 .75
123 A77 20wn purple .70 .75
124 A78 50wn green 1.75 1.00
125 A79 100wn deep blue 4.75 2.00
126 A80 1000wn green 12.00 2.50
Nos. 122-126 (5) 20.00 7.00
Set, never hinged 40.00

Rouletted 12

122a A76 5wn orange brown .45 .75
123a A77 20wn purple .70 1.50
124a A78 50wn green .85 .75
125a A79 100wn blue 1.10 2.00
Nos. 122a-125a (4) 3.10 5.00
Set, never hinged 6.50

No. 126 also exists perforated 12½. See Nos. 187-189.

No. 93 Surcharged with New Value and Wavy Lines in Blue

1951 Wmk. 257 *Perf. 11½x11*

127 A49 100wn on 4wn rose car .80 .60
a. Inverted surcharge 35.00

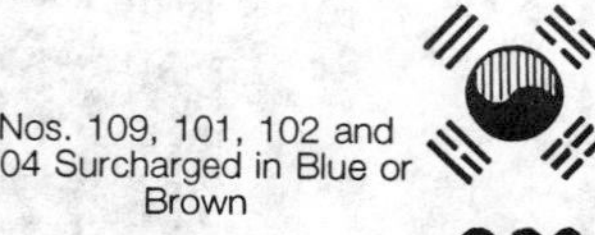
Nos. 109, 101, 102 and 104 Surcharged in Blue or Brown

Perf. 11

128 A65 200wn on 15wn 2.50 .75
a. Inverted surcharge 10.00 10.00
129 A57 300wn on 10wn (Br) 5.25 2.00
a. Inverted surcharge 17.50
130 A58 300wn on 20wn 3.50 1.50
a. Inverted surcharge 17.50
131 A60 300wn on 50wn (Br) 7.75 2.50
Nos. 127-131 (5) 19.80 7.35
Set, never hinged 35.00

Size of surcharge varies. Numeral upright on Nos. 129 and 131; numeral slanted on Nos. 175 and 179. See Nos. 174-181.

On No. 130, the zeros in "300" are octagonal; on No. 177B they are oval.

Flags of US and Korea and Statue of Liberty — A81

Design (blue stamps): Flag of same country as preceding green stamp, UN emblem and doves.

1951-52 Wmk. 257 *Perf. 11*
Flags in Natural Colors, Participating Country at Left

132 A81 500wn green 8.00 5.00
133 A81 500wn blue 8.00 5.00
134 A81 500wn grn (Australia) 6.50 5.00
135 A81 500wn blue 8.00 5.00
136 A81 500wn grn (Belgium) 6.50 4.50
137 A81 500wn blue 6.50 4.50
138 A81 500wn grn (Britain) 8.00 5.50
139 A81 500wn blue 8.00 5.50
140 A81 500wn grn (Canada) 8.00 5.50
141 A81 500wn blue 6.50 4.50
142 A81 500wn grn (Colombia) 6.50 4.50
143 A81 500wn blue 8.00 5.50
144 A81 500wn grn (Denmark) 12.50 17.00
145 A81 500wn blue 13.00 17.00
146 A81 500wn grn (Ethiopia) 6.50 4.50
147 A81 500wn blue 8.00 5.50
148 A81 500wn grn (France) 6.50 4.50
149 A81 500wn blue 8.00 5.50
150 A81 500wn grn (Greece) 8.00 5.50
151 A81 500wn blue 8.00 5.50
152 A81 500wn grn (India) 10.00 6.50
153 A81 500wn blue 10.00 6.50
154 A81 500wn grn (Italy) 10.00 6.50
a. Flag without crown ('52) 11.50
155 A81 500wn blue 10.00 6.50
a. Flag without crown ('52) 11.50
156 A81 500wn grn (Luxembourg) 10.00 6.50
157 A81 500wn blue 8.00 5.50
158 A81 500wn grn (Netherlands) 6.50 4.50
159 A81 500wn blue 6.50 4.50
160 A81 500wn grn (New Zealand) 8.00 5.50
161 A81 500wn blue 8.00 5.50
162 A81 500wn grn (Norway) 10.00 6.50
163 A81 500wn blue 10.00 6.50
164 A81 500wn grn (Philippines) 8.00 5.50
165 A81 500wn blue 8.00 5.50
166 A81 500wn grn (Sweden) 6.50 4.50
167 A81 500wn blue 8.00 5.50
168 A81 500wn grn (Thailand) 6.50 4.50
169 A81 500wn blue 8.00 5.50
170 A81 500wn grn (Turkey) 8.00 5.50
171 A81 500wn blue 8.00 5.50
172 A81 500wn grn (Union of So. Africa) 8.00 5.50
173 A81 500wn blue 8.00 5.50
Nos. 132-173 (42) 343.00 249.00
Set, never hinged 600.00

Twenty-two imperf. souvenir sheets of two, containing the green and the blue stamps for each participating country (including both types of Italy) were issued. Size: 140x90mm. Value, set $500.

Nos. 93-94, 101-105, 109-110 Surcharged Like Nos. 128-131 in Blue or Brown

1951 Wmk. 257 *Perf. 11½x11, 11*

174 A49 300wn on 4wn 1.50 .90
a. Inverted surcharge 70.00 50.00
175 A57 300wn on 10wn (Br) 1.00 .75
a. Inverted surcharge 50.00 40.00
176 A50 300wn on 14wn (Br) 1.75 1.25
a. 300wn on 14wn lt bl 1,400. 350.00
b. Inverted surcharge 50.00 50.00
177 A65 300wn on 15wn 1.50 .90
a. Inverted surcharge 40.00 40.00
177B A58 300wn on 20wn 4.00 3.50
178 A59 300wn on 30wn (Br) 1.50 .90
a. Inverted surcharge 42.50 40.00
179 A60 300wn on 50wn (Br) 1.50 .90
180 A66 300wn on 65wn (Br) 1.00 .75
a. Inverted monad 52.50 50.00
181 A61 300wn on 100wn 1.75 1.25
a. Inverted surcharge 50.00 40.00
Nos. 174-181 (9) 15.50 11.10
Set, never hinged 30.00

"300" slanted on Nos. 175, 177B and 179; "300" upright on Nos. 129 and 131. The surcharge exists double on several of these stamps.

No. 177B differs from No. 130 in detail noted after No. 131.

Syngman Rhee and "Happiness" A82

1952, Sept. 10 Litho. *Perf. 12½*

182 A82 1000wn dark green 1.25 1.00
Never hinged 3.00

Second inauguration of President Syngman Rhee, Aug. 15, 1952.

Sok Kul Am, Near Kyongju — A83

Bool Gook Temple, Kyongju — A84

Tombstone of Mu Yal Wang — A85

Choong Yul Sa Shrine, Tongyung — A86

1952 Wmk. 257 Typo. *Perf. 12½*

183 A83 200wn henna brown .45 .15
184 A84 300wn green .45 .15
185 A85 500wn carmine .65 .60
186 A86 2000wn deep blue .75 .15

Rough Perf. 10-11, 11½x11 and Compound
Litho.

186A A83 200wn henna brown .75 .50
186B A84 300wn green 1.25 .60
Nos. 183-186B (6) 4.30 2.15
Set, never hinged 6.25

Types of 1951
(Designs slightly smaller.)

1952-53 *Rough Perf. 10-11*

187 A77 20wn purple 2.25 .90
187A A78 50wn green 4.50 .30
187B A79 100wn deep blue 1.75 .40
187C A80 1000wn green 55.00 4.00
Nos. 187-187C (4) 63.50 5.60
Set, never hinged 110.00

(Designs slightly larger.)
Perf. 12½

187D A78 50wn green 1.00 .50
188 A79 100wn deep blue 1.00 .50
189 A80 1000wn green ('53) 3.25 .75
Nos. 187D-189 (3) 5.25 1.75
Set, never hinged 7.00

Type of 1952

1953

189A A85 500wn deep blue 11.00 50.00

All copies of No. 189A were affixed to postal cards before sale. Values are for copies removed from the cards.

See Nos. 191-192, 203B, 248.

Types of 1952 and

Planting Trees — A87

Perf. 12½
1953, Apr. 5 Wmk. 257 Litho.

190 A87 1h aqua .25 .28
191 A85 2h aqua .25 .32
192 A85 5h brt green .45 .32
193 A87 10h brt green .65 .18
194 A86 20h brown 1.40 .65
Nos. 190-194 (5) 3.00 1.75
Set, never hinged 4.00

See Nos. 203A, 247.

Map and YMCA Emblem — A88

1953, Oct. 25 *Perf. 13½*

195 A88 10h dk sl bl & red 1.25 1.25
Never hinged 2.50

50th anniv. of the Korean YMCA.

Tombstone of Mu Yal Wang — A88a

Sika Deer
A89 A90

1954, Apr. *Perf. 12½*

196 A88a 5h dark green .38 .15
197 A89 100h brown carmine 7.00 .50
198 A90 500h brown orange 19.00 1.25
199 A90 1000h bister brown 50.00 1.50
Nos. 196-199 (4) 76.38 3.40
Set, never hinged 175.00

See Nos. 203C, 203D, 238-239, 248A, 250-251, 259, 261-262, 269-270, 279, 281-282.

Dok Do (Dok Island) — A91

Design: 10h, Dok Do, lateral view.

1954, Sept. 15

200 A91 2h claret .20 .15
201 A91 5h blue .45 .20
202 A91 10h blue green .60 .25
Nos. 200-202 (3) 1.25 .60
Set, never hinged 2.00

Moth and Flag — A92

Pagoda Park, Seoul — A92a

1954, Apr. 16 Wmk. 257 *Perf. 12½*

202A A92 10h brown .80 .50
203 A92a 30h dark blue 1.00 .50
Set, never hinged 2.50

See Nos. 203E, 260, 280.

Types of 1952-54

1955-56 Unwmk. *Perf. 12½*
Laid Paper

203A A87 1h aqua ('56) .35 .20
203B A85 2h aqua ('56) .35 .20
203C A88a 5h brt green ('56) .35 .20
203D A89 100h brown carmine 4.00 .75
203E A92a 200h violet 3.25 1.00
Nos. 203A-203E (5) 8.30 2.35
Set, never hinged 16.00

On No. 203C the right hand character is redrawn as in illustration above No. 212D.

Nos. 203A and 203C are found on horizontally and vertically laid paper.

Erosion Control on Mountainside — A93

1954, Dec. 12 **Wmk. 257**

204 A93 10h dk grn & yel grn .35 .20
205 A93 19h dk grn & yel grn .60 .40
Set, never hinged 1.75

Issued to publicize the 1954 forestation campaign.

Presidents Rhee and Eisenhower Shaking Hands — A94

1954, Dec. 25 ***Perf. 13½***

206 A94 10h violet blue .40 .25
207 A94 19h brown .60 .40
208 A94 71h dull green 1.40 .75
Nos. 206-208 (3) 2.40 1.40
Set, never hinged 4.00

Adoption of the US-Korea mutual defense treaty.

"Reconstruction" — A95

Perf. 12½

1955, Feb. 10 **Wmk. 257** **Litho.**

209 A95 10h brown .80 .50
210 A95 15h violet .60 .50
211 A95 20h blue 500.00 7.50
Never hinged 1,000.
212 A95 50h plum 1.90 .40
Nos. 209-210,212 (3) 3.30
Nos. 209-212 (4) 8.90
Set, #209-210, 212, never hinged 8.00

Korea's industrial reconstruction.

1955, Oct. 19 **Unwmk.** ***Perf. 12½***
Laid Paper

212A A95 15h violet .70 .35
212B A95 20h blue .95 .60
212C A95 50h plum 1.40 .35
Nos. 212A-212C (3) 3.05 1.30
Set, never hinged 8.00

No. 212B is found on horizontally and vertically laid paper.

Same with Right Character at Top Redrawn

Original

Redrawn

1956, June 5 **Unwmk.** ***Perf. 12½***
Laid Paper

212D A95 10h brown 1.25 .35
212E A95 15h violet .80 .35
212F A95 20h blue .80 .30
a. Booklet pane of 6 22.50
Nos. 212D-212F (3) 2.85 1.00
Set, never hinged 7.00

Nos. 212D-212F are found on horizontally and vertically laid paper. See Nos. 248B, 256, 272, 276.

Rotary Emblem — A96

Syngman Rhee — A98

1955, Feb. 23 **Wmk. 257** ***Perf. 13½***

213 A96 20h violet .55 .35
214 A96 25h dull green .70 .50
215 A96 71h magenta .95 .85
Nos. 213-215 (3) 2.20 1.70
Set, never hinged 3.75

Rotary International, 50th anniversary.

1955, Mar. 26

217 A98 20h deep blue 2.00 1.00
Never hinged 4.00

80th birthday of Pres. Syngman Rhee, Apr. 26.

Flag and Arch of Independence — A99

1955, Aug. 15 **Litho.** ***Perf. 13½***

218 A99 40h Prus green .60 .40
219 A99 100h lake .90 .65
Set, never hinged 3.50

Tenth anniversary of independence.

UN Emblem in Circle of Clasped Hands — A100

Olympic Torch and Runners — A101

1955, Oct. 24

221 A100 20h bluish green .60 .40
222 A100 55h aqua .90 .65
Set, never hinged 3.00

United Nations, 10th anniversary.

1955, Oct. 23

223 A101 20h claret 1.00 .60
224 A101 55h dark green 1.50 1.00
Set, never hinged 3.50

36th National Athletic Meet.

Adm. Li Sun-sin, Navy Flag and Tortoise Ship — A102

Perf. 13x13½

1955, Nov. 11 **Unwmk.**
Laid Paper

225 A102 20h violet blue 1.00 1.75
Never hinged 1.90

Korean Navy, 10th anniversary.

Rhee Monument near Seoul — A103

Syngman Rhee — A104

1956 ***Perf. 13½x13***

226 A103 20h dull green .90 1.25
Never hinged 1.75

81st birthday of Pres. Syngman Rhee.

No. 226 is found on horizontally and vertically laid paper.

1956, Aug. 15 ***Perf. 13x13½***

227 A104 20h brown 21.00 1.10
228 A104 55h violet blue 9.00 1.50
Set, never hinged 80.00

Third inauguration of Pres. Syngman Rhee.

Olympic Rings and Torch — A105

1956, Nov. 1 **Litho.** ***Perf. 12½***
Laid Paper

229 A105 20h red orange .90 1.00
230 A105 55h brt green 1.25 1.75
Set, never hinged 4.00

16th Olympic Games in Melbourne, Nov. 22-Dec. 8, 1956.

Central Post Office, Seoul — A107

Stamp of 1884 — A108

Mail Delivered by Donkey A109

1956, Dec. 4 **Laid Paper** **Unwmk.**

232 A107 20h lt blue green 1.00 .60
233 A108 50h lt carmine 1.25 .90
234 A109 55h green 1.65 1.25
Nos. 232-234 (3) 3.90 2.75
Set, never hinged 9.00

Issued to commemorate Postal Day.

Types of 1954 Redrawn and

Hibiscus A110

King Sejong A111

Kyongju Observatory — A112

No Hwan Symbol; Redrawn Character

1956, Dec. 4 **Unwmk.** ***Perf. 12½***
Laid Paper

235 A110 10h lilac rose .90 .20
236 A111 20h lilac 1.50 .20
237 A112 50h violet 1.90 .20
238 A89 100h brown carmine 2.50 .50
239 A90 500h brown orange 17.50 .75
Nos. 235-239 (5) 24.30 1.85
Set, never hinged 50.00

On Nos. 238-239, the character after numeral has been omitted and the last character of the inscription has been redrawn as illustrated above No. 212D.

Nos. 235-236 are found on horizontally and vertically laid paper.

See Nos. 240-242, 253, 255, 258, 273, 275, 278, 291d, 291f, B3-B4.

Types of 1956

1957, Jan. 21 **Wmk. 312** ***Perf. 12½***

240 A110 10h lilac rose .35 .22
241 A111 20h red lilac .40 .40
242 A112 50h violet .80 .22
Nos. 240-242 (3) 1.55 .84
Set, never hinged 2.50

Telecommunication Symbols — A117

1957, Jan. 31 ***Perf. 13½***

243 A117 40h lt ultra .65 .50
244 A117 55h brt green .85 .75
Set, never hinged 2.25

5th anniv. of Korea's joining the ITU.

Boy Scout and Emblem A118

1957, Feb. 27 **Wmk. 312**

245 A118 40h pale purple .45 .40
246 A118 55h lt magenta 1.00 .75
Set, never hinged 2.25

50th anniversary of Boy Scout movement.

Types of 1953-56
Top Right Character Redrawn; Hwan Symbol Retained

1957 **Wmk. 312** ***Perf. 12½***

247 A87 1h aqua .35 .20
248 A85 2h aqua .25 .25
248A A88a 5h brt green .70 .25
248B A95 15h violet 1.25 .40
Nos. 247-248B (4) 2.55 1.10
Set, never hinged 4.00

Redrawn Types of 1954, 1956 and

Planting Trees — A119

South Gate, Seoul — A120

Tiger A121

Diamond Mountains A122

No Hwan Symbol; Redrawn Character

1957 **Wmk. 312** **Litho.** ***Perf. 12½***

249 A119 2h aqua .30 .20
250 A88a 4h aqua .30 .20
251 A88a 5h emerald .30 .20
252 A120 10h green .30 .20
253 A110 20h lilac rose .55 .20
254 A121 30h pale lilac .55 .25
255 A111 40h red lilac .85 .25
a. Booklet pane of 6 45.00
256 A95 50h lake 1.50 .30
257 A122 55h violet brn 3.00 1.50
258 A112 100h violet 2.50 .40
259 A89 200h brown car 6.75 .40
260 A92a 400h brt violet 10.50 1.25
261 A90 500h ocher 25.00 3.50
262 A90 1000h dk ol bis 35.00 8.00
Nos. 249-262 (14) 87.40 16.85
Set, never hinged 200.00

The "redrawn character" is illustrated above No. 212D.

See Nos. 268, 271, 274, 277, 291c, 291e.

Mercury and Flags of Korea and US — A123

1957, Nov. 7 Wmk. 312 *Perf. 13½*

263 A123 40h dp orange .45 .35
264 A123 205h emerald 1.40 .90
a. Souv. sheet of 2, #263-264, imperf. 750.00
Set, never hinged 2.25

Treaty of friendship, commerce and navigation between Korea and the US.

Star of Bethlehem and Pine Cone — A124

Designs: 25h, Christmas tree and tassel. 30h, Christmas tree, window and dog.

1957, Dec. 11 Litho. *Perf. 12½*

265 A124 15h org, brn & grn .95 .75
a. Souv. sheet of 1, imperf. 650.00
266 A124 25h lt grn, yel & red 1.10 1.00
a. Souv. sheet of 1, imperf. 650.00
267 A124 30h bl, lt grn & yel 1.50 1.25
a. Souv. sheet of 1, imperf. 650.00
Nos. 265-267 (3) 3.55 3.00
Set, never hinged 7.00

Issued for Christmas and the New Year.

Redrawn Types of 1954-57

Perf. 12½

1957-59 Litho. Wmk. 317

268 A119	2h	aqua	.30	.15
269 A88a	4h	aqua	.30	.15
270 A88a	5h	emerald ('58)	.40	.20
271 A120	10h	green	.55	.20
272 A95	15h	violet ('58)	.45	.20
273 A110	20h	lilac rose	.55	.20
274 A121	30h	pale lilac ('58)	.65	.20
275 A111	40h	red lilac	1.40	.25
276 A95	50h	lake ('58)	2.75	.20
277 A122	55h	vio brn ('59)	4.00	2.25
278 A112	100h	violet	4.00	.60
279 A89	200h	brn car ('59)	6.50	.75
280 A92a	400h	brt vio ('59)	16.00	4.50
281 A90	500h	ocher ('58)	22.50	2.50
282 A90	1000h	dk ol bis ('58)	35.00	3.00
		Nos. 268-282 (15)	95.35	15.35
		Set, never hinged	200.00	

Nos. 268-282 have no hwan symbol, and final character of inscription is the redrawn one illustrated above No. 212D.
See No. 291B.

Catalogue values for unused stamps in this section, from this point to the end of the section, are for Never Hinged items.

Winged Envelope — A125

1958, May 20 Wmk. 317

283 A125 40h dk blue & red .90 .60
a. Souv. sheet of 1, imperf. *1,500.*

Issued for the Second Postal Week.

Children Looking at Industrial Growth A126

Design: 40h, Hibiscus forming "10".

1958, Aug. 15 *Perf. 13½*

284 A126 20h gray .75 .30
285 A126 40h dk carmine 1.00 .45
a. Souv. sheet of 2, # 284-285, imperf. 325.00

10th anniversary of Republic of Korea.

UNESCO Building, Paris A127

1958, Nov. 3 Wmk. 317

286 A127 40h orange & green .60 .60
a. Souv. sheet of 1, imperf. 150.00

Opening of UNESCO. headquarters in Paris, Nov. 3.

Children Flying Kites — A128

Christmas Tree and Fortune Screen — A129

Children in Costume — A130

1958, Dec. 11 Litho. *Perf. 12½*

287 A128 15h yellow green 1.00 .60
a. Souv. sheet of 1, imperf. 67.50
288 A129 25h blue, red & yel 1.00 .60
a. Souv. sheet of 1. imperf. 67.50
289 A130 30h yellow, ultra & red 1.75 .85
a. Souv. sheet of 1, imperf. 67.50
Nos. 287-289 (3) 3.75 2.05
Nos. 287a-289a (3) 202.50

Issued for Christmas and the New Year.

Flag and Pagoda Park A131

1959, Mar. 1 *Perf. 13½*

290 A131 40h rose lilac & brn .60 .50
a. Souv. sheet of 1, imperf. 30.00

40th anniv. of Independence Movement Day.

Korean Marines Landing A132

1959, Apr. 15

291 A132 40h olive grn .65 .50
a. Souv. sheet of 1, imperf. 6.00

Korean Marine Corps, 10th anniversary.

Souvenir Sheet
Types of 1956-57
Wmk. 317

1959, May 20 Litho. *Imperf.*

291B Sheet of 4 4.00 7.50
c. A120 10h green .70 .50
d. A110 20h lilac rose .70 .50
e. A121 30h pale lilac .70 .50
f. A111 40h red lilac .70 .50

3rd Postal Week, May 20-26.

WHO Emblem and Family A133

1959, Aug. 17 Wmk. 317 *Perf. 13½*

292 A133 40h pink & rose vio .50 .35
a. Souv. sheet of 1, imperf. 5.50

10th anniv. of Korea's joining the WHO.

Diesel Train A134

1959, Sept. 18 Litho.

293 A134 40h brown & bister .60 .50
a. Souv. sheet of 1, imperf. 6.00

60th anniversary of Korean railroads.

Relay Race and Emblem A135

1959, Oct. 3

294 A135 40h lt bl & red brn .60 .60
a. Souv. sheet of 1, imperf. 7.50

40th National Athletic Meet.

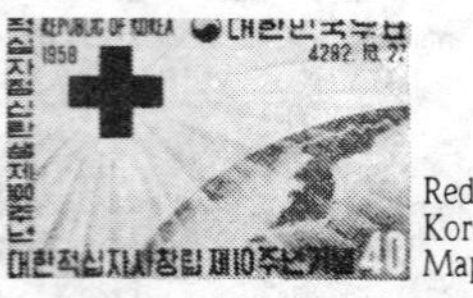

Red Cross and Korea Map — A136

Design: 55h, Red Cross superimposed on globe.

1959, Oct. 27 *Perf. 13½*

295 A136 40h red & bl grn .40 .20
296 A136 55h pale lilac & red .60 .30
a. Souv. sheet of 2, #295-296, imperf. 18.00

Centenary of the Red Cross idea.

Old Postal Flag and New Communications Flag — A137

1959, Dec. 4

297 A137 40h blue & red .60 .50
a. Souv. sheet of 1, imperf. 8.00

75th anniv. of the Korean postal system.

Mice and Chinese Happy New Year Character — A138

Designs: 25h, Children singing Christmas hymns. 30h, Red-crested crane.

1959, Dec. 15 *Perf. 12½*

298 A138 15h gray, vio bl & pink .80 .30
a. Souv. sheet of 1, imperf. 12.00
299 A138 25h blue, red & emer .95 .30
a. Souv. sheet of 1, imperf. 12.00
300 A138 30h lt lilac, blk & red 1.25 .30
a. Souv. sheet of 1, imperf. 12.00
Nos. 298-300 (3) 3.00 .90
Nos. 298a-300a (3) 36.00

Issued for Christmas and the New Year.

UPU Monument and Means of Transportation A139

Perf. 13½

1960, Jan. 1 Wmk. 317 Litho.

301 A139 40h grnsh bl & brn .50 .35
a. Souv. sheet of 1, imperf. 12.00

60th anniv. of Korean membership in the UPU.

Bee, Honeycomb and Clover — A140

Snail and Money Bag — A141

1960, Apr. 1 Wmk. 317 *Perf. 12½*

302 A140 10h emer, brn & org .25 .15
303 A141 20h pink, bl & brn .50 .25

Issued to encourage systematic saving by children. See No. 313, souvenir sheet.
See Nos. 377-380.

Uprooted Oak Emblem and Yin Yang A142

Dwight D. Eisenhower A143

1960, Apr. 7 Wmk. 312 *Perf. 13½*

304 A142 40h emer, car & ultra .60 .35
a. Souv. sheet of 1, imperf. 20.00

Issued to publicize World Refugee Year, July 1, 1959-June 30, 1960.

1960, June 19 Litho. Wmk. 317

305 A143 40h bl, red & bluish grn 1.40 .75
a. Souv. sheet of 1, imperf. 16.00

Pres. Eisenhower's visit to Korea, June 19.

Children in School and Ancient Home Teaching A144

1960, Aug. 3 Wmk. 317 *Perf. 13½*

306 A144 40h multicolored .50 .35
a. Souv. sheet of 1, imperf. 4.00

75th anniv. of the modern educational system.

Hibiscus and House of Councilors A145

1960, Aug. 8

307 A145 40h blue .50 .35
a. Souv. sheet of 1, imperf. 4.00

Inaugural session, House of Councilors.

Woman Holding Torch and Man with Flag — A146

1960, Aug. 15

308 A146 40h bis, lt bl & brn .50 .35
a. Souv. sheet of 1, imperf. 3.25

15th anniversary of liberation.

Weight Lifter — A147

40h, South Gate, Seoul, & Olympic emblem.

1960, Aug. 25 **Litho.**
309 A147 20h brn, lt bl & sal .45 .25
310 A147 40h brn, lt bl & dk bl .80 .40
a. Souv. sheet of 2, #309-310, imperf. 13.00

17th Olympic Games, Rome, Aug. 25-Sept. 11.

Swallow and Telegraph Pole — A148

1960, Sept. 28 *Perf. 13½*
311 A148 40h lt bl, lil & gray .50 .35
a. Souv. sheet of 1, imperf. 3.00

Establishment of telegraph service, 75th anniv.

Students and Sprout A149

1960, Oct. 1 **Wmk. 317**
312 A149 40h bl, sal pink & emer .50 .35
a. Souv. sheet of 1, imperf. 3.00

Rebirth of the Republic.

Souvenir Sheet
Savings Types of 1960

1960, Oct. 7 *Imperf.*
313 Sheet of two 1.75 1.75
a. A140 10h emerald, brown & orange .75 .75
b. A141 20h pink, blue & brown .75 .75

4th Postal Week, Oct. 7-13, and Intl. Letter Writing Week, Oct. 3-9.

Torch — A150

1960, Oct. 15 *Perf. 13½*
314 A150 40h dk bl, lt bl & yel .50 .35
a. Souv. sheet of 1, imperf. 2.75

Cultural Month (October).

UN Flag, Globe and Laurel — A151

UN Emblem and Grave Markers — A152

1960, Oct. 24 **Litho.**
315 A151 40h rose lil, bl & grn .50 .35
a. Souv. sheet of 1, imperf. 2.75

15th anniversary of United Nations.

1960, Nov. 1 **Wmk. 317**
316 A152 40h salmon & brn .50 .35
a. Souv. sheet of 1, imperf. 2.75

Establishment of the UN Memorial Cemetery, Tanggok, Pusan, Korea.

"Housing, Agriculture, Population" A153

1960, Nov. 15 *Perf. 13½*
317 A153 40h multicolored .50 .35
a. Souv. sheet of 1, imperf. 2.75

Issued to publicize the 1960 census.

Boy and Head of Ox — A154

Star of Bethlehem and Korean Sock — A155

Girl Giving New Year's Greeting — A156

1960, Dec. 15 **Litho.** *Perf. 12½*
318 A154 15h gray, brn & org yel .50 .30
a. Souv. sheet of 1, imperf. 5.00
319 A155 25h vio bl, red & grn .60 .30
a. Souv. sheet of 1, imperf. 5.00
320 A156 30h red, vio bl & yel .70 .40
a. Souv. sheet of 1, imperf. 5.00
Nos. 318-320 (3) 1.80 1.00
Nos. 318a-320a (3) 15.00

Issued for Christmas and the New Year.

UN Emblem, Windsock and Ancient Rain Gauge A157

1961, Mar. 23 *Perf. 13½*
321 A157 40h lt blue & ultra .50 .35
a. Souv. sheet of 1, imperf. 1.75

1st World Meteorological Day.

Children, Globe and UN Emblem A158

1961, Apr. 7 **Wmk. 317**
322 A158 40h salmon & brown .50 .35
a. Souv. sheet of 1, imperf. 1.75

10th World Health Day.

Students Demonstrating A159

1961, Apr. 19 **Litho.**
323 A159 40h red, grn & ultra .70 .40
a. Souv. sheet of 1, imperf. 4.50

1st anniv. of the Korean April revolution.

Workers — A160

1961, May 6
324 A160 40h brt green .50 .35
a. Souv. sheet of 1, imperf. 3.00

International Conference on Community Development, Seoul.

Girl Scout A161

1961, May 10
325 A161 40h brt green .70 .50
a. Souv. sheet of 1, imperf. 6.00

15th anniversary of Korea's Girl Scouts.

Soldier's Grave — A162

Soldier with Torch — A163

Perf. 13½

1961, June 6 **Wmk. 317** **Litho.**
326 A162 40h blk & ol gray .85 .35
a. Souv. sheet of 1, imperf. 3.00

6th National Mourning Day.

1961, June 16
327 A163 40h brown & yellow .85 .50
a. Souv. sheet of 1, imperf. 3.00

Military Revolution of May 16, 1961.

Map of Korea, Torch and Broken Chain — A164

1961, Aug. 15 **Wmk. 317** *Perf. 13½*
328 A164 40h dk bl, ver & aqua .85 .50
a. Souv. sheet of 1, imperf. 2.50

16th anniv. of liberation.

Flag and Servicemen A165

1961, Oct. 1 **Litho.**
329 A165 40h vio bl, red & brn .85 .50
a. Souv. sheet of 1, imperf. 2.50

Issued for Armed Forces Day.

Kyongbok Palace Art Museum — A166

1961, Nov. 1 **Wmk. 317** *Perf. 13½*
330 A166 40h beige & dk brn .60 .35
a. Souv. sheet of 1, imperf. 1.90

10th Natl. Exhibition of Fine Arts.

"UNESCO," Candle and Laurel A167

1961, Nov. 4
331 A167 40h lt grn & dk bl .60 .35
a. Souv. sheet of 1, imperf. 1.90

15th anniv. of UNESCO.

Mobile X-Ray Unit — A168

1961, Nov. 16
332 A168 40h rose beige & red brn .60 .35
a. Souv. sheet of 1, imperf. 1.90

Tuberculosis Prevention Week.

Ginseng A169

King Sejong and Hangul Alphabet A170

Tristram's Woodpecker A171

Rice Farmer A172

Ancient Drums — A173

1961-62 **Unwmk.** **Litho.** *Perf. 12½*
338 A169 20h rose brn ('62) 1.25 .25
339 A170 30h pale purple 1.65 .25
340 A171 40h dk blue & red 1.65 .25
341 A172 40h dk green ('62) 1.65 .25
342 A173 100h red brown 1.90 .60
Nos. 338-342 (5) 8.35 1.60

See #363-366, 368, 388-392, 517-519, B5-B7.

Globe with Map of Korea and ITU Emblem A175

1962, Jan. 31 Unwmk. *Perf. 13½*

348 A175 40h ver & dk blue .75 .35
 a. Souv. sheet of 1, imperf. 3.50

10th anniv. of Korea's joining the ITU.

Atomic Reactor and Atom Symbol A176

1962, Mar. 30 Litho. *Perf. 13½*

349 A176 40h lt bl, sl grn & ol gray .50 .35

Inauguration of the Triga Mark II atomic reactor.

Malaria Eradication Emblem and Mosquito A177

1962, Apr. 7 Unwmk.

350 A177 40h green & red org .60 .40
 a. Souv. sheet of 1, imperf. 1.50

WHO drive to eradicate malaria.

YWCA Emblem and Girl — A178

1962, Apr. 20 *Perf. 13½*

351 A178 40h pink & dk blue .65 .40

40th anniv. of the Korean Young Women's Christian Association.

South Gate and FPA Emblem A179

1962, May 12 Wmk. 317

352 A179 40h lt bl, dk vio & red .50 .35

Meeting of the Federation of Motion Picture Producers in Asia, May 12-16.

Men Pushing Cogwheel A180

Soldiers on Hang Kang Bridge — A181

Yin Yang and Factory A182

Perf. 13½

1962, May 16 Wmk. 317 Litho.

353 A180 30h brn & pale olive 1.90 .50
 a. Souv. sheet of 1, Korean text 4.50
 b. Souv. sheet of 1, English text 22.50

354 A181 40h brn, lt bl & citron 1.90 .50
 a. Souv. sheet of 1, Korean text 4.50
 b. Souv. sheet of 1, English text 22.50
355 A182 200h ultra, yel & red 3.75 .75
 a. Souv. sheet of 1, Korean text 11.00
 b. Souv. sheet of 1, English text 52.50
 Nos. 353-355 (3) 7.55 1.75

1st anniv. of the May 16th Revolution.
The souvenir sheets are imperf.
The sheets with English text also exist with "E" in "POSTAGE" omitted. The English-text sheets are not watermarked except those with "E" omitted. Value, each $20.

Tortoise Warship, 16th Century A183

Design: 4w, Tortoise ship, heading right.

1962, Aug. 14 Unwmk. *Perf. 13½*

356 A183 2w dk bl & pale bl 1.50 .75
357 A183 4w blk, bluish grn & lil 2.75 1.25

370th anniv. of Korea's victory in the naval battle with the Japanese off Hansan Island.

Flag, Scout Emblem and Tents — A184

Perf. 13½

1962, Oct. 5 Wmk. 312 Litho.

358 A184 4w brown, bl & red .90 .40
 a. Souv. sheet of 1, imperf., unwmkd. 2.00

Wmk. 317

359 A184 4w green, bl & red .90 .40
 a. Souv. sheet of 1, imperf., unwmkd. 2.00

40th anniv. of Korean Boy Scouts.

Types of 1961-62 and

Hanabusaya Asiatica — A185

Miruk Bosal — A186

Long-horned Beetle A186a

Symbols of Thrift and Development A186b

Meesun Blossoms and Fruit A186c

Library of Early Buddhist Scriptures A186d

Sika Deer — A186e

King Songdok Bell, 8th Cent. — A186f

Bodhisattva in Cavern Temple, Silla Dynasty — A187

Tile of Silla Dynasty — A187a

Designs: 20ch, Jin-Do dog. 1w, Folk dancers. 1.50w, Miruk Bosal. 2w, Ginseng. 3w, King Sejong. 4w, Rice farmer. 5w, Dragon waterpot. 10w, Ancient drums. 500w, Blue dragon fresco, Koguryo dynasty.

1962-66 Unwmk. Litho. *Perf. 12½*

Ordinary Paper

Size: 22x25mm, 25x22mm

360 A186 20ch gldn brown .65 .65
361 A185 40ch blue .90 .65
362 A186 50ch claret brn .95 .65
363 A169 1w brt blue ('63) 2.25 .65
364 A169 2w red brown 2.50 .65
365 A170 3w violet brown 3.25 .65
366 A172 4w green 3.50 .75
367 A186 5w grnsh blue 4.25 1.00
368 A173 10w red brown 32.50 1.50
369 A186c 20w lil rose ('63) 12.00 3.00
370 A186d 40w dl pur ('63) 52.50 5.00
 Nos. 360-370 (11) 115.25 15.15

1964-66

Granite Paper

360a A186 20ch orange brown .90 .40
361a A185 40ch blue .95 .40
362a A186 50ch claret brown 1.40 .40
362B A186a 60ch black ('66) .90 .40
363a A169 1w bright blue 1.90 .40
363B A186 1.50w dk sl grn ('66) .90 .40
364a A169 2w red brown 4.25 .40
365a A170 3w vio brown 15.00 .40
366a A172 4w green .55 .40
367a A186 5w grnsh blue 30.00 .40
367B A186b 7w lilac rose ('66) 2.50 .75
368a A173 10w red brown 5.00 .75
369a A186c 20w lilac rose 5.00 .75
370a A186d 40w vio brown 11.00 1.50
371 A186e 50w red brown 17.50 1.50
372 A186f 100w slate grn 62.50 1.50
373 A187 200w dk & lt grn ('65) 25.00 2.00
374 A187a 300w sl grn & buff ('65) 42.50 3.50
374A A187a 500w dk & lt bl ('65) 25.00 5.00
 Nos. 360a-374A (19) 252.75 21.25

The paper of Nos. 360a to 374A contains a few colored fibers; the paper of Nos. 385-396 contains many fibers.
Counterfeits exist of Nos. 369a, 370a and 371.
See Nos. 385-396, 516, 521-522, 582-584, 1076-1079, B8.

Map, Mackerel and Trawler A188

1962, Oct. 10 *Perf. 13½*

375 A188 4w dk bl & grnsh bl .55 .40

10th anniv. of the Pacific Fishery Council.

ICAO Emblem and Plane — A189

1962, Dec. 11 *Perf. 13½*

376 A189 4w blue & brown .65 .40
 a. Souv. sheet of 1, imperf. 2.50

10th anniv. of Korea's joining the ICAO.

Savings Types of 1960

1962-64 Unwmk. *Perf. 12½*

377 A140 1w emer, brn & org ('63) 2.25 .50
 a. Granite paper 30.00 .65
378 A141 2w pink, bl & brn 1.75 .75
 a. Granite paper 15.00 .75

Wmk. 317

379 A140 1w emer, brn & org ('64) 6.50 4.00
380 A141 2w pink, bl & brn ('64) 3.50 1.25
 Nos. 377-380 (4) 14.00 6.50

Wheat Emblem A190

Perf. 13½

1963, Mar. 21 Wmk. 317 Litho.

381 A190 4w emer, dk bl & ocher .45 .30
 a. Souv. sheet of 1, imperf. 1.50

FAO "Freedom from Hunger" campaign.

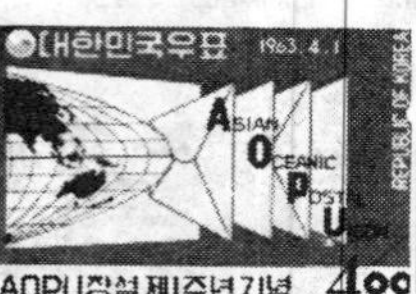

Globe and Letters A191

1963, Apr. 1

382 A191 4w rose lil, ol & dk bl .45 .30
 a. Souv. sheet of 1, imperf. 1.50

1st anniv. of the formation of the Asian-Oceanic Postal Union, AOPU.

Centenary Emblem and World Map — A192

1963, May 8 Litho.

383 A192 4w org, red & gray .75 .30
384 A192 4w lt bl, red & gray .75 .30
 a. Souv. sheet of 2, #383-384, imperf. 3.00

Cent. of the Intl. Red Cross.

Types of 1961-63

Designs as before.

1963-64 Wmk. 317 *Perf. 12½*

Granite Paper

Size: 22x25mm, 25x22mm

385 A186 20ch gldn brn ('64) .85 .25
386 A185 40ch blue .60 .25
387 A186 50ch cl brn ('64) .60 .25
388 A169 1w brt blue 2.25 .35
389 A169 2w red brown 3.50 .35
390 A170 3w vio brown 10.50 .35
391 A172 4w green 4.25 .60
392 A173 10w red brown 3.75 .60
393 A186c 20w lil rose ('64) 7.00 1.75
394 A186d 40w dull purple 20.00 1.50
395 A186e 50w brown 35.00 2.00
396 A186f 100w slate grn 50.00 4.00
 Nos. 385-396 (12) 138.30 12.25

Hibiscus and "15" A193

1963, Aug. 15 Wmk. 317 *Perf. 13½*

398 A193 4w vio bl, pale bl & red .75 .35

15th anniversary of the Republic.

Army Nurse and Corps Emblem A194

1963, Aug. 26 Litho.

399 A194 4w citron, grn & blk .65 .35

Army Nurses Corps, 15th anniversary.

First Five-Year Plan Issue

Transformer and Power Transmission Tower — A195

Irrigated Rice Fields — A196

#402, Cement factory. #403, Coal Miner. #404, Oil refinery. #405, Fishing industry (ships). #406, Cargo ship and cargo. #407, Fertilizer plant and grain. #408, Radar and telephone. #409, Transportation (plane, train, ship and map).

1962-66 Unwmk. *Perf. 12½*

400 A195 4w org & dk vio 1.75 .70
401 A196 4w lt bl & vio bl 1.75 .70

Wmk. 317

402 A195 4w dk bl & gray 1.75 .70
403 A196 4w buff & brn 1.75 .70
404 A195 4w yel & ultra 1.40 .55
405 A196 4w lt bl & blk 1.40 .55

Unwmk.

406 A195 4w pale pink & vio bl 1.25 .55
407 A196 4w bis brn & blk 1.25 .55
408 A195 7w yel bis & blk 1.65 .55
409 A196 7w vio bl & lt bl 1.65 .55
Nos. 400-409 (10) 15.60 6.10

Economic Development Five-Year Plan.

Issued: #400-401, 12/2/62; #402-403, 9/1/63; #404-405, 6/15/64; #406-407, 6/1/65; #408-409, 6/1/66.

Ramses Temple, Abu Simbel
A197 A198

Perf. 13½

1963, Oct. 1 Wmk. 317 Litho.

410 A197 3w gray & ol gray 1.50 .40
411 A198 4w gray & ol gray 2.00 .75
a. Souv. sheet of 2, #410-411, imperf. 3.25
b. Pair, #410-411 3.50 1.75

UNESCO world campaign to save historic monuments in Nubia.

Rugby and Torch Bearer A199

1963, Oct. 4 Wmk. 317 *Perf. 13½*

412 A199 4w pale bl, red brn & dk grn .75 .40

44th National Athletic Games.

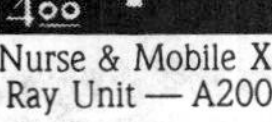

Nurse & Mobile X-Ray Unit — A200

Eleanor Roosevelt — A201

1963, Nov. 6 *Perf. 13½*

413 A200 4w org & bluish blk .60 .35

10h anniv. of the Korean Natl. Tuberculosis Association.

1963, Dec. 10 Litho. Wmk. 317

Design: 4w, Hands holding torch and globe.

414 A201 3w lt red brn & dk bl .40 .25
415 A201 4w dl org, ol & dk bl .60 .40
a. Souv. sheet of 2, 414-415, imperf. 1.75

Eleanor Roosevelt; 15th anniv. of the Universary Declaration of Human Rights.

Korean Flag and UN Headquarters A202

Tang-piri (Recorder) A203

1963, Dec. 12 Wmk. 317 *Perf. 13½*

416 A202 4w grnsh bl, ol & blk .60 .35
a. Souv. sheet of 1, imperf. 1.75

15th anniv. of Korea's recognition by the UN.

1963, Dec. 17 Unwmk.

Musical Instruments: No. 418, Pyen-kyeng (chimes). No. 419, Chang-ko (drums). No. 420, Tai-keum (large flute). No. 421, Taipyeng-so (Chinese oboe). No. 422, Na-bal (brass trumpet). No. 423, Hyang-pipa (Chinese short lute). No. 424, Wul-keum (banjo). No. 425, Kaya-ko (zither), horiz. No. 426, Wa-kong-hu (harp), horiz.

417 A203 4w pink, blk & car 1.75 .40
418 A203 4w bl, bl grn & blk 1.75 .40
419 A203 4w rose, vio bl & brn 1.75 .40
420 A203 4w tan, dk grn & brn 1.75 .40
421 A203 4w yel, vio bl & brn 1.75 .40
422 A203 4w gray, brn & vio 1.75 .40
423 A203 4w pink, vio bl & red brn 1.75 .40
424 A203 4w grnsh bl, blk & bl 1.75 .40
425 A203 4w rose, red brn & blk 1.75 .40
426 A203 4w lil, blk & bl 1.75 .40
Nos. 417-426 (10) 17.50 4.00

Pres. Park and Capitol A204

1963, Dec. 17 Wmk. 317

427 A204 4w black & brt grn 25.00 1.00

Inauguration of Pres. Park Chung Hee.

Symbols of Metric System A205

1964, Jan. 1 Litho.

428 A205 4w multicolored .50 .35
a. Imperf., pair 75.00

Introduction of the metric system.

UNESCO Emblem and Yin Yang — A206

1964, Jan. 30 Wmk. 317 *Perf. 13½*

429 A206 4w red, lt bl & ultra .55 .30

Korean Natl. Commission for UNESCO, 10th anniv.

Industrial Census A207

1964, Mar. 23 Wmk. 317 *Perf. 13½*

430 A207 4w gray, blk & red brn .60 .35

National Mining and Industrial Census.

YMCA Emblem and Head — A208

1964, Apr. 12 Litho.

431 A208 4w ap grn, dk bl & red .60 .35

50th anniv. of the Korean YMCA.

Unisphere, Ginseng and Cargo Ship — A209

Design: 100w, Korean pavilion and globe.

1964, Apr. 22 Wmk. 317 *Perf. 13½*

432 A209 40w buff, red brn & grn 6.00 .60
433 A209 100w bl red brn & ultra 9.25 1.75
a. Souv. sheet of 1, imperf. 16.00

New York World's Fair, 1964-65.

Secret Garden, Changdok Palace, Seoul — A210

Views: 2w, Whahong Gate, Suwon. 3w, Uisang Pavilion, Yangyang-gun. 4w, Maitreya Buddha, Bopju Temple at Mt. Songni. 5w, Paekma River and Rock of Falling Flowers. 6w, Anab Pond, Kyongju. 7w, Choksok Pavilion, Chinju. 8w, Kwanghan Pavilion. 9w, Whaom Temple, Mt. Chiri. 10w, Chonjeyon Falls, Soguipo.

1964, May 25 Wmk. 317 *Perf. 13½*

Light Blue Background

434 A210 1w green .65 .15
435 A210 2w gray .65 .15
436 A210 3w dk green 1.25 .25
437 A210 4w emerald 1.25 .25
438 A210 5w violet 1.65 .25
439 A210 6w vio blue 2.50 .30
a. Souv. sheet of 2 (5w, 6w) 3.75
440 A210 7w dk brown 2.50 .30
a. Souv. sheet of 2 (4w, 7w) 3.75
441 A210 8w brown 2.50 .35
a. Souv. sheet of 2 (3w, 8w) 3.75
442 A210 9w lt violet 4.50 .50
a. Souv. sheet of 2 (2w, 9w) 4.75
443 A210 10w slate grn 4.50 .60
a. Souv. sheet of 2 (1w, 10w) 4.75
Nos. 434-443 (10) 21.95 3.10
Nos. 439a-443a (5) 20.75

The five souvenir sheets are imperf.

Globe and Wheel A211

1964, July 1 Litho. *Perf. 13½*

444 A211 4w lt ol grn, dl brn & ocher .50 .35
a. Souv. sheet of 1, imperf. 1.50

Colombo Plan for co-operative economic development of south and southeast Asia.

Hands and World Health Organization Emblem A212

1964, Aug. 17 Wmk. 317 *Perf. 13½*

445 A212 4w brt yel grn, yel grn & blk .50 .35
a. Souv. sheet of 1, imperf. 1.50

15th anniv. of Korea's joining the UN.

Runner A213

1964, Sept. 3

446 A213 4w red lil, grn & pink .75 .35

45th Natl. Athletic Meet, Inchon, Sept. 3-8.

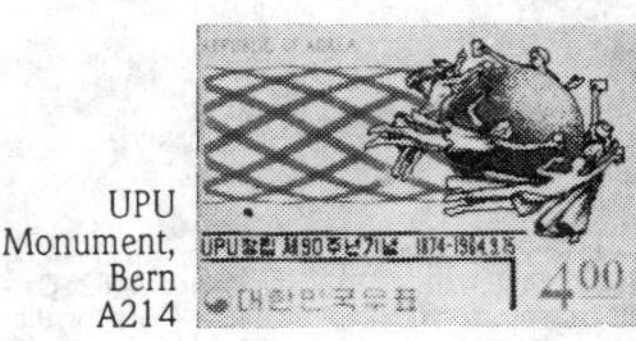

UPU Monument, Bern A214

1964, Sept. 15

447 A214 4w pink, red brn & bl .50 .40
a. Souv. sheet of 1, imperf. 1.50

1st Intl. Cong. for establishing the UPU, 90th anniv.

Crane Hook and Emblem — A215

1964, Sept. 29 Wmk. 317 *Perf. 13½*

448 A215 4w red brn & dull grn .45 .35

5th Convention of the Intl. Federation of Asian and Western Pacific Contractors' Assoc. (IFAWPCA), Seoul, Sept. 29-Oct. 7.

Marathon Runners A216

#453, "V," Olympic rings, laurel & track, vert.

1964, Oct. 10 Litho.

449 A216 4w shown 1.00 .25
450 A216 4w Equestrian 1.00 .25
451 A216 4w Gymnast 1.00 .25
452 A216 4w Rowing 1.00 .25
453 A216 4w multicolored 1.00 .25
Nos. 449-453 (5) 5.00 1.25

18th Olympic Games, Tokyo, Oct. 10-25.

Souvenir Sheets of 1, Imperf., Unwmk.

449a A216 4w 1.25
450a A216 4w 1.25
451a A216 4w 1.25
452a A216 4w 1.25
453a A216 4w 1.25
Nos. 449a-453a (5) 6.25

Korea stamps can be mounted in the annually supplemented Scott Korea album.

Stamp of 1885 — A217

Yong Sik Hong — A218

1964, Dec. 4 Unwmk. *Perf. 13½*

454 A217 3w lilac, vio & dl bl grn .65 .35
455 A218 4w gray, vio bl & blk .85 .50

80th anniv. of the Korean postal system. Yong Sik Hong (1855-84) was Korea's 1st general postmaster.

Pine Branch and Cones — A219

#457, Plum Blossoms. #458, Forsythia. #459, Azalea. #460, Lilac. #461, Sweetbrier. #462, Garden balsam. #463, Hibiscus. #464, Crape myrtle. #465, Chrysanthemum lucidum. #466, Paulownia coreana. #467, Bamboo.

1965 Litho. *Perf. 13½*

456 A219 4w pale grn, dp grn & brn .70 .20
457 A219 4w gray, blk, rose & yel .70 .20
458 A219 4w lt bl, yel & brn .70 .20
459 A219 4w brt grn, lil rose & sal .85 .20
460 A219 4w red lil & brt grn .70 .15
461 A219 4w yel grn, grn, car & brn .70 .20
462 A219 4w bl, grn & red .70 .20
463 A219 4w bluish gray, rose red & grn .70 .20
464 A219 4w multicolored .75 .15
465 A219 4w pale grn, dk brn, grn & car rose .85 .15
466 A219 4w buff, ol grn & brn .85 .15
467 A219 4w ultra & emer .75 .15
Nos. 456-467 (12) 8.95 2.15

Souvenir Sheets of 1, Imperf.

456a A219 4w 1.00
457a A219 4w 1.00
458a A219 4w 1.00
459a A219 4w 1.00
460a A219 4w 1.00
461a A219 4w 1.00
462a A219 4w 1.00
463a A219 4w 1.00
464a A219 4w 1.00
465a A219 4w 1.00
466a A219 4w 1.00
467a A219 4w 1.00
Nos. 456a-467a (12) 12.00

Dancing Women, PATA Emblem and Tabo Tower A220

1965, Mar. 26

468 A220 4w lt bl grn, dk brn & dk vio bl .50 .35
a. Souv. sheet of 1, imperf. 1.10

14th conf. of the Pacific Travel Association, Seoul, Mar. 26-Apr. 2.

Map of Viet Nam and Flag of Korean Assistance Group A221

1965, Apr. 20 *Perf. 13½*

469 A221 4w blk, lt yel grn & grnsh bl .50 .35
a. Souv. sheet of 1, imperf. 1.10

Issued to honor the Korean military assistance group in Viet Nam.

Symbols of 7-Year Plan — A222

1965, May 1 Litho.

470 A222 4w emer, dk grn & dk brn .45 .25

Issued to publicize the 7-year plan for increased food production.

Scales with Families and Homes A223

1965, May 8

471 A223 4w lt & dk grn & gray .45 .30
a. Souv. sheet of 1, imperf. 1.10

May as Month of Family Planning.

ITU Emblem, Old and New Communication Equipment — A224

1965, May 17

472 A224 4w lt bl, car & blk .45 .30
a. Souv. sheet of 1, imperf. 1.10

Cent. of the ITU.

UN Emblem and Flags of Australia, Belgium, Great Britain, Canada and Colombia A225

Gen. Douglas MacArthur and Flags of Korea, UN and US — A226

UN Emblem and Flags: No. 474, Denmark, Ethiopia, France, Greece and India. No. 475, Italy, Luxembourg, Netherlands, New Zealand and Norway. No. 476, Philippines, Sweden, Thailand, Turkey and South Africa.

1965, June 25

Flags in Original Colors

473 A225 4w gray & vio bl .60 .15
474 A225 4w grnsh bl & vio bl .60 .15
475 A225 4w grnsh bl & vio bl .60 .15
476 A225 4w grnsh bl & vio bl .60 .15
477 A226 10w lt bl, blk, vio bl & red 1.10 .45
Nos. 473-477 (5) 3.50 1.05

15th anniv. of the participation of UN Forces in the Korean war.

Souvenir Sheets of 1, Imperf.

473a A225 4w .85
474a A225 4w .85
475a A225 4w .85
476a A225 4w .85
477a A226 10w 1.75
Nos. 473a-477a (5) 5.15

Flag, Factories and "20" — A227

South Gate, Seoul, Fireworks and Yin Yang — A228

1965, Aug. 15 Litho.

478 A227 4w lt bl, vio bl & red .50 .25
479 A228 10w vio bl, lt bl & red 1.10 .45

20th anniv. of liberation from the Japanese.

Factory, Leaf and Ants — A229

1965, Sept. 20 *Perf. 13½*

480 A229 4w brt yel grn, brn & bis .45 .30

Issued to publicize the importance of saving.

Parabolic Antenna, Telephone Dial and Punched Tape — A230

Telegraph Operator, 1885 A231

1965, Sept. 28

481 A230 3w lt bl, blk & ol .40 .20
482 A231 10w cit, Prus bl & blk .75 .35

80th anniv. of telegraph service between Seoul and Inchon.

Korean Flag and Capitol, Seoul — A232

1965, Sept. 28

483 A232 3w org, sl grn & bl grn .65 .25

15th anniversary of recapture of Seoul.

Pole Vault A233

1965, Oct. 5

484 A233 3w black, lil & sal .55 .25

46th Natl. Athletic Meet, Kwangju, Oct. 5-10.

ICY Emblem A234

UN Flag and Headquarters, NY — A235

1965, Oct. 24 Litho.

485 A234 3w lt & dk grn & org brn .40 .25
a. Souv. sheet of 1, imperf. 1.10
486 A235 10w lt bl, vio bl & grn .70 .40
a. Souv. sheet of 1, imperf. 1.40

ICY, 1965, and 20th anniv. of the UN.

Child Posting Letter A236

Design: 10w, Airmail envelope, telephone.

1965, Dec. 4 *Perf. 13½*

487 A236 3w bl grn, blk, grn & red .60 .20
488 A236 10w ol, dk bl & red 1.10 .35

Tenth Communications Day.

Children with Sled — A237

Children and South Gate — A238

1965, Dec. 11 Litho. *Perf. 12½*

489 A237 3w pale grn, vio bl & red .40 .25
490 A238 4w lt bl, grn, vio bl & red .95 .60
a. Souv. sheet of 2, #489-490, imperf. 1.65

Issued for Christmas and the New Year.

Freedom House — A239

1966, Feb. 15 Unwmk. *Perf. 12½*

491 A239 7w brt grn, blk & cit 1.10 .30
492 A239 39w lil, blk & pale grn 2.50 .65
a. Souv. sheet of 2, #491-492, imperf. 4.75

Opening of "Freedom House" at Panmunjom.

Wildlife Issue

Mandarin Ducks — A240

Alaska Pollack — A241

Firefly — A242

Badger — A243

Birds: 5w, Japanese cranes. 7w, Ringnecked pheasants.

1966, Mar. 15 Litho. *Perf. 12½*

493 A240 3w multicolored .95 .25
494 A240 5w multicolored 1.40 .30
495 A240 7w multicolored 1.65 .35

1966, June 15

Fish: 5w, Manchurian trout. 7w, Yellow corvina.

496 A241 3w bl, dk brn & yel .85 .20
497 A241 5w grnsh bl, blk & mag 1.10 .25
498 A241 7w brt grnsh bl, blk & yel 1.50 .30

1966, Sept. 15

Insects: 5w, Grasshopper. 7w, Silk butterfly (sericinus telamon).

499 A242 3w multicolored .80 .20
500 A242 5w dp yellow & multi 1.10 .25
501 A242 7w lt blue & multi 1.65 .30

1966, Dec. 15

Animals: 5w, Asiatic black bear. 7w, Tiger.

502 A243 3w multicolored 1.10 .20
503 A243 5w multicolored 1.40 .25
504 A243 7w multicolored 1.50 .30
Nos. 493-504 (12) 15.00 3.15

Souvenir Sheets of 1, Imperf.

493a A240 3w 1.25
494a A240 5w 1.90
495a A240 7w 2.25
496a A241 3w 1.25
497a A241 5w 1.65
498a A241 7w 2.25
499a A242 3w 1.10
500a A242 5w 1.50
501a A242 7w 2.25
502a A243 3w 1.40
503a A243 5w 1.75
504a A243 7w 1.90
Nos. 493a-504a (12) 20.45

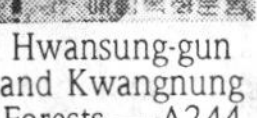
Hwansung-gun and Kwangnung Forests — A244

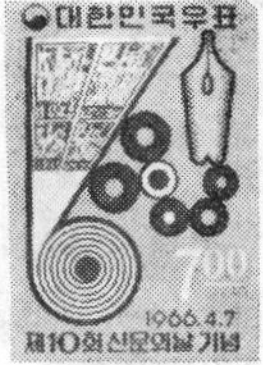
Symbolic Newspaper Printing and Pen — A245

1966, Apr. 5 Unwmk. *Perf. 12½*

505 A244 7w green & brown .45 .20

Forestation Movement.

1966, Apr. 7 Litho.

506 A245 7w lt bl, vio brn & yel .45 .20

Tenth Newspaper Day.

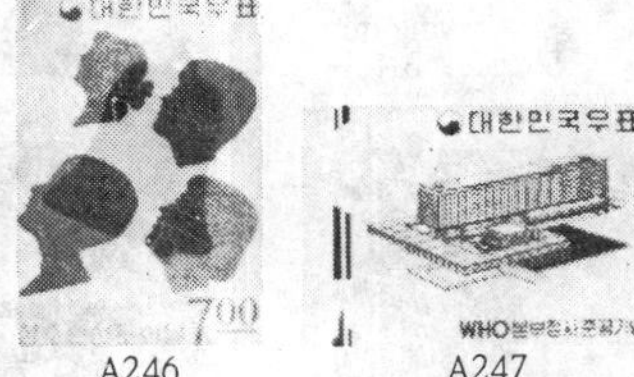
A246 A247

1966, May 1 Unwmk. *Perf. 12½*

507 A246 7w Children & bell .45 .20

Proper guidance of young people.

1966, May 3 Litho.

WHO headquarters, Geneva.

508 A247 7w lt bl, blk & yel .75 .15
a. Souv. sheet of 1, imperf. 1.50
509 A247 39w bluish gray, yel & red 2.25 .45

Inauguration of the WHO Headquarters, Geneva.

Girl Scout and Flag — A248

1966, May 10

510 A248 7w yel, emer & dk bl 1.00 .40

Girl Scouts of Korea, 20th anniversary.

Pres. Park and Flags of Korea, Malaysia, Thailand and Republic of China — A249

1966, May 10

511 A249 7w multicolored 1.00 .50

State visits of President Chung Hee Park.

Women's Ewha University, Seoul, and Student A250

1966, May 31

512 A250 7w lt bl, vio bl & dp org .60 .30

80th anniv. of modern education for women.

Types of 1961-66 Inscribed "Republic of Korea," and

Porcelain Incense Burner, 11th-12th Centuries A253

Celadon Vessel, 12th Century A254

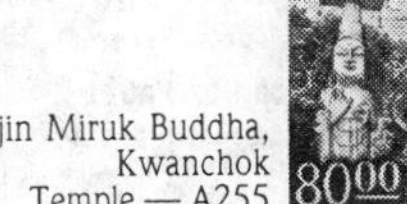
Unjin Miruk Buddha, Kwanchok Temple — A255

60ch, Long-horned beetle. 1w, Folk dancers. 2w, Ginseng. 3w, King Sejong. 5w, Dragon waterpot. 7w, Symbols of thrift & development.

Perf. 12½

1966, Aug. 20 Unwmk. Litho.

Size: 22x19mm, 19x22mm

Granite Paper

516 A186a 60ch gray green .40 .15
517 A169 1w green .50 .15
518 A169 2w blue green .50 .15
519 A170 3w dull red brn .50 .15
521 A186 5w gray green .55 .15
522 A186b 7w grnsh blue .95 .15

Size: 22x25mm

523 A253 13w vio blue 1.50 .15
524 A254 60w green 4.00 .30
525 A255 80w slate grn 7.25 .40
Nos. 516-525 (9) 16.15
Set value 1.40

Souvenir Sheet

Carrier Pigeons — A258

1966, July 13 Wmk. 317 *Imperf.*

Red Brown Surcharge

534 A258 7w on 40h emer & dk grn 1.25 .50

6th Intl. Letter Writing Week, June 13-19. No. 534 was not issued without surcharge.

Children and World Map Projection A259

1966, July 28 Unwmk. *Perf. 12½*

535 A259 7w lt & dk vio bl & gray .45 .20
a. Souv. sheet of 1, imperf. 1.50

15th annual assembly of WCOTP (World Conf. of Teaching Profession), Seoul, July 28-Aug. 9.

Factory, Money Bag and Honeycomb A260

1966, Sept. 1 Unwmk. *Perf. 12½*

536 A260 7w multicolored .45 .20

Issued to publicize systematic saving.

Map of Korea, and People — A261

1966, Sept. 1 Litho.

537 A261 7w multicolored .45 .20

Ninth national census.

CISM Emblem and Round-Table Conference A262

1966, Sept. 29 Unwmk. *Perf. 12½*

538 A262 7w multicolored .45 .20
a. Souv. sheet of 1, imperf. 1.50

21st General Assembly of the Intl. Military Sports Council (CISM), Seoul, Sept. 29-Oct. 9.

Flags of Korea and Viet Nam and Korean Soldiers — A263

1966, Oct. 1

539 A263 7w multicolored 1.10 .40

1st anniv. of Korean combat troops in Viet Nam.

Wrestlers A264

1966, Oct. 10

540 A264 7w red brn, buff & blk .70 .30

47th Natl. Athletic Meet, Seoul, Oct. 10-15.

Lions Emblem and Map of Southeast Asia — A265

1966, Oct. 15

541 A265 7w multicolored .50 .20
a. Souv. sheet of 1, imperf. 1.50

5th East and Southeast Asia Lions Convention, Seoul, Oct. 15-17.

Seoul University Emblem — A266

1966, Oct. 15 Litho.

542 A266 7w multicolored .45 .25

20th anniversary of Seoul University.

Anticommunist League Emblem A267

1966, Oct. 31 Unwmk. *Perf. 12½*

543 A267 7w multicolored .45 .25
a. Souv. sheet of 1, imperf. 1.10

12th Conf. of the Asian Anticommunist League, Seoul, Oct. 31-Nov. 7.

Presidents Park and Johnson, Flags of US and Korea — A268

1966, Oct. 31 Litho. *Perf. 12½*

544 A268 7w multicolored 2.00 .30
545 A268 83w multicolored 3.50 1.25
a. Souv. sheet of 2, #544-545, imperf. 6.00

Visit of Pres. Lyndon B. Johnson to Korea.

UNESCO Emblem and Symbols of Learning — A269

1966, Nov. 4

546 A269 7w multicolored .45 .30
a. Souvenir sheets 1.25

20th anniv. of UNESCO.

Good Luck Bag and "Joy" A270

Ram and "Completion" A271

Perf. 12½x13, 13x12½

1966, Dec. 10

547 A270 5w multicolored .35 .20
a. Souv. sheet of 1, imperf. 1.10
548 A271 7w multicolored .45 .30
a. Souv. sheet of 1, imperf. 1.40

Issued for Christmas and the New Year.

Syncom Satellite over Globe — A272

1967, Jan. 31 Litho. *Perf. 12½*

549 A272 7w dk blue & multi .55 .25
a. Souv. sheet of 1, imperf. 1.25

15th anniv. of Korea's membership in the ITU.

Presidents Park and Lübke — A273

Perf. 12½

1967, Mar. 2 Litho. Unwmk.

550 A273 7w multicolored 1.10 .50
a. Souv. sheet of 1, imperf. 3.00

Visit of Pres. Heinrich Lübke of Germany, Mar. 2-6.

Hand Holding Coin, Industrial and Private Buildings A274

1967, Mar. 3

551 A274 7w lt green & blk brn .45 .25

1st anniv. of the Natl. Taxation Office.

Folklore Series

Okwangdae Clown — A275

Perfect Peace Dance — A276

Girls on Seesaw A277

Korean Shuttlecock A278

5w, Sandi mask & dance, horiz. 7w, Hafoe mask.

1967, Mar. 15 Litho. *Perf. 12½*

552 A275 4w gray, blk & yel .75 .15
553 A275 5w multicolored 1.00 .20
554 A275 7w multicolored 1.50 .30

1967, June 15

Designs: 4w, Sword dance, horiz. 7w, Buddhist Monk dance.

555 A276 4w multicolored .75 .15
556 A276 5w multicolored 1.00 .20
557 A276 7w multicolored 1.50 .30

1967, Sept. 15

Designs: 4w, Girls on swing, horiz. 7w, Girls dancing in the moonlight.

558 A277 4w multicolored .75 .15
559 A277 5w multicolored 1.00 .20
560 A277 7w multicolored 1.50 .30

1967, Dec. 15

Designs: 5w, Girls celebrating full moon, horiz. 7w, Archery.

561 A278 4w multicolored .75 .15
562 A278 5w multicolored 1.00 .20
563 A278 7w multicolored 1.50 .30
Nos. 552-563 (12) 13.00 2.60

Souvenir Sheets of 1, Imperf.

552a	A275	4w	1.00
553a	A275	5w	1.25
554a	A275	7w	2.00
555a	A276	4w	1.00
556a	A276	5w	1.25
557a	A276	7w	2.00
558a	A277	4w	1.00
559a	A277	5w	1.25
560a	A277	7w	2.00
561a	A278	4w	1.00
562a	A278	5w	1.25
563a	A278	7w	2.00
	Nos. 552a-563a (12)		17.00

JCI Emblem and Kyunghoe Pavilion — A279

1967, Apr. 13 Litho. *Perf. 12½*

564 A279 7w dk brn, brt grn, bl & red .40 .30
a. Souv. sheet of 1, imperf. 1.50

Intl. Junior Chamber of Commerce Conf., Seoul, Apr. 13-16.

Emblem, Map of Far East — A280

1967, Apr. 24 Unwmk. *Perf. 12½*

565 A280 7w vio bl & multi .40 .25
a. Souv. sheet of 1, imperf. 1.50

Issued to publicize the 5th Asian Pacific Dental Congress, Seoul, Apr. 24-28.

EXPO '67 Korean Pavilion A281

1967, Apr. 28

566 A281 7w yel, blk & red 1.75 .50
567 A281 83w lt bl, blk & red 5.25 1.10
a. Souv. sheet of 2, #566-567, imperf. 6.00

EXPO '67, Intl. Exhibition, Montreal, Apr. 28-Oct. 27, 1967.

Worker, Soldier, Emblem and Buildings — A282

1967, May 1

568 A282 7w multicolored .45 .25

Veterans' Day, May 1.

Second Five-Year Plan Issue

Nut and Arrows A283

#570, Iron wheel and rail. #571, Express highway. #572, Cloverleaf intersection. #573, Rising income for fishermen and farmers (oysters, silk worm, mushrooms and bull's head). #574, Machine industry (cogwheels, automobile, wrench and motor). #575, Harbor. #576, Housing projects plans. #577, Atomic power plant. #578, Four Great River Valley development.

1967-71 Litho. *Perf. 12½*

569 A283 7w blk, red brn & dl org 1.00 .35
570 A283 7w dl org, yel & blk 1.00 .35
571 A283 7w grn, bl & ol 1.50 .30
572 A283 7w dk brn, yel & grn 1.50 .30

Perf. 13x12½

573 A283 7w brn, grn, yel & org .75 .25
574 A283 7w dk bl, lil rose & buff .75 .25
575 A283 10w dk bl, bl, yel & grn .75 .25
576 A283 10w lt bl, bl, grn & red .75 .25

Photo. *Perf. 13*

577 A283 10w blk, car & bl .75 .15
578 A283 10w blk, grn & brn .75 .15
Nos. 569-578 (10) 9.50 2.60

Second Economic Development Five-Year Plan.
Issued: #569-570, 6/1/67; #571-572, 12/5/68; #573-574, 12/5/69; #575-576, 12/5/70; #577-578, 12/5/71.

President Park and Phoenix — A284

1967, July 1 Unwmk. *Perf. 12½*

579 A284 7w multicolored 4.00 1.00
a. Souv. sheet of 1, imperf. 25.00

Inauguration of President Park Chung Hee for a 2nd term, July 1, 1967.

Korean Boy Scout, Emblem and Tents — A285

20w, Korean Boy Scout emblem, bridge & tents.

1967, Aug. 10 Litho. *Perf. 12½*

580 A285 7w multicolored .90 .25
a. Souv. sheet of 1, imperf. 1.50
581 A285 20w multicolored 1.90 .60
a. Souv. sheet of 1, imperf. 3.00

3rd Korean Boy Scout Jamboree, Hwarangdae, Seoul, Aug. 10-15.

Types of 1962-66 Redrawn (Inscribed "Republic of Korea")

Designs: 20w, Meesun blossoms and fruit. 40w, Library of early Buddhist scriptures. 50w, Deer.

1967, Aug. 25

Granite Paper

582 A186c 20w green & lt bl grn 7.50 .25
583 A186d 40w dk grn & lt ol 6.50 .35
584 A186e 50w dk brn & bister 6.00 .60
Nos. 582-584 (3) 20.00 1.20

The printing of redrawn designs of the regular issue of 1962-66 became necessary upon discovery of large quantities of counterfeits, made to defraud the post. The position of the denominations was changed and elaborate fine background tracings were added.

Freedom Center and Emblem — A286

Hand Breaking Chain — A287

Boxing — A288

1967, Sept. 25 Litho. *Perf. 12½*

586 A286 5w multicolored .35 .15
a. Souv. sheet of 1, imperf. .80
587 A287 7w multicolored .45 .25
a. Souv. sheet of 1, imperf. 2.00

1st Conf. of the World Anti-Communist League, WACL, Taipei, China, Sept. 25-29.

1967, Oct. 5

Design: 7w, Women's basketball.

588 A288 5w tan & multi .50 .35
589 A288 7w pale rose & multi 1.00 .50

48th Natl. Athletic Meet, Seoul, Oct. 5-10.

Students' Memorial, Kwangjoo — A289

Symbolic Water Cycle — A290

1967, Nov. 3 Litho. *Perf. 12½*

590 A289 7w lt green & multi .45 .25

Issued for Student Day commemorating 1929 students' uprising against Japan.

1967, Nov. 20

591 A290 7w multicolored .45 .25

Hydrological Decade (UNESCO), 1965-74.

Children Spinning Top — A291

Monkey and Oriental Zodiac — A292

1967, Dec. 10

592 A291 5w sal, org & vio bl .35 .20
a. Souv. sheet of 1, imperf. 1.00
593 A292 7w yel bis, brn & vio bl .65 .35
a. Souv. sheet of 1, imperf. 2.00

Issued for Christmas and New Year.

Parabolic Antenna and Electric Waves — A293

1967, Dec. 21

594 A293 7w lt bl, blk & yel .50 .25
a. Souv. sheet of 1, imperf. 1.25

Opening of the natl. microwave communications network, Dec. 21.

Carving from King Songdok Bell — A294

Earrings, 6th Cent. — A295

Flag — A296

Perf. 13x12½

1968, Feb. 1 Litho. Unwmk.
Granite Paper

595 A294 1w yellow & brown .35 .15
596 A295 5w dk green & yellow .45 .15
597 A296 7w dark blue & red .70 .20
Nos. 595-597 (3) 1.50 .50

WHO Emblem A297

EATA Emblem and Korean Buildings A298

1968, Apr. 7 Unwmk. *Perf. 12½*

598 A297 7w multicolored .45 .25
a. Souv. sheet of 1, imperf. 1.50

20th anniv. of the WHO.

1968, Apr. 9 Litho.

599 A298 7w multicolored .45 .25
a. Souv. sheet of 1, imperf. 1.50

2nd General Meeting of the East Asia Travel Association (EATA), Seoul, Apr. 9-13.

Door Knocker, Factories and Emblem — A299

1968, May 6 Unwmk. *Perf. 12½*

600 A299 7w multicolored .50 .30
a. Souv. sheet of 1, imperf. 1.50

2nd Conf. of the Confederation of Asian Chambers of Commerce and Industry, Seoul.

Pres. Park and Emperor Haile Selassie — A300

1968, May 18 Litho.

601 A300 7w multicolored 1.75 .50
a. Souv. sheet of 1, imperf. 3.00

Visit of Haile Selassie I, May 18-20.

Mailman's Pouch — A301

Mailman A302

1968, May 31 Unwmk. *Perf. 12½*

602 A301 5w multicolored .30 .15
603 A302 7w multicolored .45 .25

First Postman's Day, May 31, 1968.

Atom Diagram and Symbols of Development A303

1968, June 1 Litho.

604 A303 7w dk bl, citron & ver .45 .25

Issued to promote science and technology.

Kyung Hee University and Conference Emblem — A304

1968, June 18 Unwmk.

605 A304 7w bl, pink & blk .45 .35
a. Souv. sheet of 1, imperf. 3.50

2nd Conf. of the Intl. Association of University Presidents.

Liberated People — A305

1968, July 1 Litho. *Perf. 12½*

606 A305 7w multicolored .45 .25

Issued to publicize the movement to liberate people under communist rule.

Peacock and Industrial Plant — A306

1968, Aug. 15 Unwmk. *Perf. 12½*

607 A306 7w multicolored .45 .30

Republic of Korea, 20th anniversary.

Fair Entrance A307

1968, Sept. 9 Unwmk. *Perf. 12½*

608 A307 7w lilac & multi .50 .25

Issued to publicize the first Korean Trade Fair, Seoul, Sept. 9-Oct. 18.

Assembly Emblem and Pills — A308

Soldier, Insigne and Battle Scene — A309

1968, Sept. 16 Litho.

609 A308 7w multicolored .45 .25

3rd General Assembly of the Federation of Asian Pharmaceutical Associations, Seoul, Sept. 16-21.

1968, Oct. 1

#611, Sailor, insigne & ship's guns. #612, Servicemen & flags. #613, Aviator, insigne & planes. #614, Marine, insigne & landing group.

610 A309 7w green & org 2.50 .35
611 A309 7w lt & dk blue 2.50 .35
612 A309 7w dk blue & org 2.50 .35
613 A309 7w dk & lt blue 2.50 .35
614 A309 7w orange & grn 2.50 .35
a. Vert. strip of 5, #610-614 16.00 2.50

20th anniv. of the Korean armed forces.

Colombo Plan Emblem and Globe — A310

1968, Oct. 8 Litho. *Perf. 12½*

615 A310 7w dk brn, pale sal & grn .40 .25

19th meeting of the Consultative Committee of the Colombo Plan, Seoul, Oct. 8-28.

Bicycling (Type I) — A311

제19회 올림픽대회기념
대한민국우표

Type II (2nd line flush left)

#617, Bicycling, Type II. #618-619, Wrestling. #620-621, Boxing. #622-623, Olympic flame, "68" & symbols of various sports events.

1968, Oct. 12 Unwmk. *Perf. 12½*

616 A311 7w pink & multi (I) 1.50 .40
617 A311 7w pink & multi (II) 1.50 .40
a. Souv. sheet of 2, #616-617, imperf. 5.00
b. Pair, #616-617 14.00 4.50
618 A311 7w olive & multi (I) 1.50 .40
619 A311 7w olive & multi (II) 1.50 .40
a. Souv. sheet of 2, #618-619, imperf. 5.00
b. Pair, #618-619 14.00 4.50
620 A311 7w orange & multi (I) 1.50 .40
621 A311 7w orange & multi (II) 1.50 .40
a. Souv. sheet of 2, #620-621, imperf. 5.00
b. Pair, #620-621 14.00 4.50
622 A311 7w bluish grn & multi (I) 1.50 .40
623 A311 7w bluish grn & multi (II) 1.50 .40
a. Souv. sheet of 2, #622-623, imperf. 5.00
b. Pair, #622-623 14.00 4.50
Nos. 616-623 (8) 12.00 3.20

19th Olympic Games, Mexico City, Oct. 12-27.
The position of the "7" is reversed on Nos. 619, 621, 623 as are the designs of Nos. 619, 621.

"Search for Knowledge" and School Girls — A312

1968, Oct. 15

624 A312 7w multicolored .40 .25

60th anniv. of public secondary education for women.

Coin and Statistics A313

1968, Nov. 1

625 A313 7w multicolored .40 .25

National Wealth Survey.

Memorial to Students' Uprising — A314

1968, Nov. 23

626 A314 7w gray & multi .40 .25

Issued to commemorate the anti-communist students' uprising, Nov. 23, 1945.

Men With Banners Declaring Human Rights — A315

1968, Dec. 10

627 A315 7w multicolored .40 .30

Declaration of Human Rights, 20th anniv.

Christmas Decorations A316

Cock and Good Luck Characters A317

1968, Dec. 11

628 A316 5w salmon & multi 1.40 .60
a. Souv. sheet of 1, imperf. 1.75
629 A317 7w multicolored 1.40 .60
a. Souv. sheet of 1, imperf. 1.75

Issued for Christmas and the New Year.

UN Emblems and Korean House — A318

1968, Dec. 12

630 A318 7w lt blue & multi .40 .25

20th anniv. of the recognition of the Republic of Korea by the UN.

A319

A320

Design: Boy Scout Emblem.

1968, Sept. 30 Litho. *Perf. 12½*

631 A319 7w black & multi .50 .25

Regional Boy Scout conference.

1969, Mar. 1 Unwmk. *Perf. 12½*

Design: Torch, map and students Demonstrating against Japan, 1919.

632 A320 7w multicolored .45 .25

50th anniversary of Sam-il movement.

Hyun Choong Sa Shrine and Tortoise Ships — A321

1969, Apr. 28 Unwmk. *Perf. 12½*

633 A321 7w deep bl, grn & brn .50 .40

Completion of the Hyun Choong Sa Shrine at Onyang, dedicated to the memory of Adm. Li Sun-sin.

Pres. Park and Tuanku Nasiruddin of Malaysia A322

1969, Apr. 29 Litho.

634 A322 7w yellow & multi 1.50 .50
a. Souv. sheet of 1, imperf. *25.00*

Visit of Tuanku Ismail Nasiruddin, ruler of Malaysia, Apr. 29, 1969.

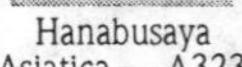

Hanabusaya Asiatica — A323

Flag of Korea — A324

Ancient Drums — A325

Red-crested Cranes — A326

Highway and Farm — A327

Pitcher (12-13th Centuries) — A328

Ceramic Duck (Water Jar) — A329

Library of Early Buddhist Scriptures — A330

Miruk Bosal — A333

1w, Old man's mask. #637, Stone lamp, 8th cent. #638, Chipmunk. #644, Tiger lily. #649, Bee. #651, Vase, Yi dynasty, 17th-18th centuries. #653, Gold crown, Silla Dynasty.

Zeros Omitted except 7w, No. 639

Perf. 13x12, 12x13 (Litho.); 13½x12½, 12½x13½ (Photo.)

Litho. (40ch, Nos. 641, 650); Photo.

1969-74 Unwmk.

Granite Paper (Lithographed); Ordinary Paper (Photogravure)

635 A323 40ch green .15 .15
636 A326 1w dk rose brn ('74) .15 .15
637 A328 5w brt plum .35 .15
638 A326 5w maroon ('74) .35 .15
639 A324 7w blue ("7.00") .65 .15
640 A324 7w blue ("7") .65 .15
641 A325 10w ultra 2.00 .15
642 A324 10w ultra ("10") ('70) 1.75 .15
643 A326 10w bl & dk bl ('73) 1.25 .15
644 A323 10w grn & multi ('73) 1.25 .15
645 A327 10w grn, red & gray ('73) 1.25 .15
647 A328 20w green 4.00 .20
648 A329 30w dull grn ('70) 4.50 .35
649 A326 30w yel & dk brn ('74) 4.00 .35
650 A330 40w vio bl & pink 8.50 .50
651 A328 40w ultra & lilac 8.50 .40
652 A333 100w dp claret & yel 57.50 1.75
653 A333 100w brn & yel ('74) 13.00 1.25
Nos. 635-653 (18) 109.80
Set value 5.25

See No. 1090. For surcharge see No. B18.

Red Cross, Faces and Doves — A336

1969, May 5 Litho. ***Perf. 12½***
654 A336 7w multicolored .40 .25
a. Souv. sheet of 1, imperf. 1.50

50th anniv. of the League of Red Cross Societies.

Savings Bank, Factories and Highway — A337

1969, May 20 Unwmk. ***Perf. 12½***
655 A337 7w yellow grn & multi .40 .20

Second Economy Drive.

Pres. Park, Pres. Thieu and Flags of Korea and Viet Nam — A338

1969, May 27 Litho.
656 A338 7w pink & multi 1.00 .40
a. Souv. sheet of 1, imperf. 2.50

Visit of Pres. Nguyen Van Thieu of Viet Nam, May 27.

"Reforestation and Parched Fields" — A339

Growing and Withering Plants — A340

1969, June 10
657 A339 7w multicolored .40 .20
658 A340 7w multicolored .40 .20

Issued to publicize the need for prevention of damages from floods and droughts.

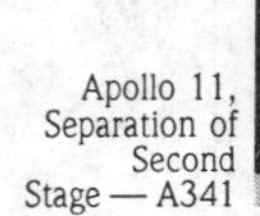

Apollo 11, Separation of Second Stage — A341

#660, Apollo 11, separation of 3rd Stage. #661, Orbits of command & landing modules around moon. #662, Astronauts gathering rock samples on moon. 40w, Spacecraft splashdown.

1969, Aug. 15 Unwmk. ***Perf. 12½***
659 A341 10w indigo, bl & red .35 .20
660 A341 10w indigo, bl & red .35 .20
661 A341 20w indigo, bl, red & lem .70 .30
662 A341 20w indigo, bl, red & lem .70 .30
663 A341 40w indigo, bl & red 1.40 .60
a. Souv. sheet of 5, #659-663, imperf. 6.00
b. Strip of 5, #659-663 5.00 2.00

Man's 1st landing on the moon, July 20, 1969. US astronauts Neil A. Armstrong and Col. Edwin E. Aldrin, Jr., with Lieut. Col. Michael Collins piloting Apollo 11.

Fable Issue

Girl and Stepmother — A342

The Sick Princess — A343

Mother Meeting Tiger — A344

Woodcutter Stealing Fairy's Clothes — A345

Heungbu and Wife Release Healed Swallow — A346

Kongji and Patji (Cinderella): 7w, Sparrows help Kongji separate rice. 10w, Ox helps Kongji to weed a field. 20w, Kongji in a sedan chair on the way to the palace.

1969, Sept. 1 Litho. ***Perf. 12½***
664 A342 5w apple grn & multi 1.00 .15
665 A342 7w yellow & multi 1.25 .15
666 A342 10w lt violet & multi 2.00 .20
667 A342 20w lt green & multi 3.25 .35

1969, Nov. 1 ***Perf. 13x12½***

"The Hare's Liver": 7w, Hare riding to the palace on back of turtle. 10w, Hare telling a lie to the King to save his life. 20w, Hare mocking the turtle.

668 A343 5w yellow & multi .75 .15
669 A343 7w lt vio & multi .75 .15
670 A343 10w lt grnsh bl & multi 1.25 .20
671 A343 20w lt yel grn & multi 2.25 .35

1970, Jan. 5

"The Sun and the Moon": 7w, Tiger disguised as mother at children's house. 10w, Tiger, and children on tree. 20w, Children safe on cloud, and tiger falling to his death.

672 A344 5w orange & multi .75 .15
673 A344 7w gray grn & multi .90 .15
674 A344 10w lt green & multi 1.25 .20
675 A344 20w gray & multi 2.25 .35

1970, Mar. 5

Designs: No. 677, Woodcutter with wife and children. No. 678, Wife taking children to heaven. No. 679, Husband joining family in heaven.

676 A345 10w dull bl grn & multi 1.25 .20
677 A345 10w buff & multi 1.25 .20
678 A345 10w lt grnsh bl & multi 1.25 .20
679 A345 10w pink & multi 1.25 .20

1970, May 5 ***Perf. 12½***

Designs: No. 681, Heungbu and wife finding gold treasure in gourd. No. 682, Nolbu and wife with large gourd. No. 683, Demon emerging from gourd punishing evil Nolbu and wife.

680 A346 10w lt grnsh bl & multi 1.75 .20
681 A346 10w orange & multi 1.75 .20
682 A346 10w apple grn & multi 1.75 .20
683 A346 10w tan & multi 1.75 .20
Nos. 664-683 (20) 29.65 4.15

Souvenir Sheets of 1, Imperf.

664a A342 5w .90
665a A342 7w 1.00
666a A342 10w 1.75
667a A342 20w 2.75
668a A343 5w 1.00
669a A343 7w 1.00
670a A343 10w 1.25
671a A343 20w 2.50
672a A344 5w 1.00
673a A344 7w 1.40
674a A344 10w 1.90
675a A344 20w 3.50
676a A345 10w 1.90
677a A345 10w 1.90
678a A345 10w 1.90
679a A345 10w 1.90
680a A346 10w 3.00
681a A346 10w 3.00
682a A346 10w 3.00
683a A346 10w 3.00
Nos. 664a-683a (20) 39.55

1869 Locomotive and Diesel Train — A347

Design: No. 685, Early locomotive.

Perf. 12½

1969, Sept. 18 Litho. Unwmk.
684 A347 7w yellow & multi .45 .20
685 A347 7w green & multi .45 .20

70th anniversary of Korean Railroads.

Formation of F-5A Planes — A348

Design: No. 687, F-4D Phantom.

1969, Oct. 1 Photo. ***Perf. 13½x13***
686 A348 10w blue, blk & car .65 .25

Litho. ***Perf. 13x12½***
687 A348 10w multicolored .65 .25

20th anniversary of Korean Air Force.

Cha-jun Game — A349

1969, Oct. 3
688 A349 7w ap grn, dk bl & blk .40 .25

10th National Festival of Traditional Skills.

Institute of Science and Technology A350

1969, Oct. 23
689 A350 7w bister, grn & choc .40 .25

Completion of the Korean Institute of Science and Technology, Hongnung, Seoul.

Pres. Park and Diori Hamani A351

1969, Oct. 27
690 A351 7w yellow grn & multi .80 .25
a. Souv. sheet of 1, imperf. 2.50

Visit of Diori Hamani, Pres. of Niger, Oct. 27.

Korean Wrestling A352

#692, Fencing. #693, Korean karate (taekwondo). #694, Volleyball, vert. #695, Soccer, vert.

Perf. 13x12½, 12½x13

1969, Oct. 28
691 A352 10w yellow grn & multi 1.00 .20
692 A352 10w blue & multi 1.00 .20
693 A352 10w green & multi 1.00 .20
694 A352 10w olive & multi 1.00 .20
695 A352 10w ultra & multi 1.00 .20
Nos. 691-695 (5) 5.00 1.00

50th Natl. Athletic Meet, Seoul, Oct. 28-Nov. 2.

Allegory of National Education Charter — A353

1969, Dec. 5 Litho. ***Perf. 12½x13***
696 A353 7w dull yel & multi .40 .25

1st anniv. of the proclamation of the Natl. Education Charter.

Toy Dogs and Lattice Pattern — A354

Candle, Lattice Door and Fence — A355

1969, Dec. 11 Photo. *Perf. 13½*

697 A354 5w green & multi	.35	.15
698 A355 7w blue & multi	.45	.25

Issued for New Year 1970.

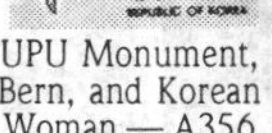

UPU Monument, Bern, and Korean Woman — A356

Education Year Emblem and Book — A357

1970, Jan. 1 Photo. *Perf. 13x13½*

699 A356 10w multicolored 6.00 .25

70th anniv. of Korea's admission to the UPU.

1970, Mar. 10 Litho. *Perf. 12½x13*

700 A357 10w pink & multi 2.25 .25

International Education Year 1970.

EXPO '70 Emblem, Seated Buddha, Korean Pavilion A358

1970, Mar. 15 *Perf. 13x12½*

701 A358 10w multicolored 1.50 .30

Issued to publicize EXPO '70 International Exhibition, Osaka, Japan, March 15-Sept. 13.

Korean Youths and 4-H Club Emblem — A359

1970, Mar. 28 *Perf. 12½x13*

702 A359 10w yellow & multi .40 .25

Issued to publicize the 15th Korean 4-H Club Central Contest, Suwon, March 28.

Money and Bank Emblem A360

1970, Apr. 9 Litho. *Perf. 13x12½*

703 A360 10w yellow & multi .40 .25

3rd annual Board of Governors' meeting of the Asian Development Bank, Seoul, Apr. 9-11.

Royal Palanquin A361

1899 Streetcar A362

Historic Means of Transportation: No. 706, Emperor Sunjong's Cadillac, 1903. No. 707, Nieuport biplane, 1922.

Perf. 13x13½, 13½x13

1970, May 20 Photo.

704 A361 10w citron & multi	1.25	.15
705 A362 10w yellow & multi	1.25	.15
706 A362 10w ocher & multi	1.25	.15
707 A362 10w aqua & multi	1.25	.15
Nos. 704-707 (4)	5.00	.60

UPU Headquarters A363

1970, May 30 *Perf. 13½x13*

708 A363 10w multicolored .40 .25

New UPU Headquarters in Bern, Switzerland.

Map, Radar and Satellite — A364

1970, June 2 *Perf. 13x13½*

709 A364 10w sky bl, vio bl & blk .70 .25

Issued to commemorate the completion of the Kum San Earth Station of the International Satellite Consortium (INTELSAT).

"PEN" and Manuscript Paper — A365

1970, June 28 Photo. *Perf. 13x13½*

710 A365 10w bl grn, bl & car .40 .25

37th Intl. P.E.N. Cong. (Poets, Playwrights, Editors, Essayists and Novelists), Seoul, June 28-July 4.

Seoul-Pusan Expressway — A366

1970, June 30

711 A366 10w multicolored .70 .30

Opening of Seoul-Pusan Expressway.

Postal Code Symbol and Number A367

Mail Sorting Machine A368

1970, July 1

712 A367 10w multicolored .40 .20

Issued to publicize the introduction of postal zone numbers, July 1, 1970.

1970, July 2

713 A368 10w lt violet & multi .40 .20
a. Souv. sheet, 2 each #712-713 *45.00*

Mechanization of Korean postal system.

Boy and Children's Hall — A369

1970, July 25

714 A369 10w pink & multi .40 .25

Paintings Issue

Jongyangsa Temple and Mt. Kumgang, by Chong Son (1676-1759) — A370

The Fierce Tiger, by Shim Sa-yung (1707-1769) A371

Paintings: No. 716, Mountains and Rivers, by Yi In-moon (1745-1821). No. 717, Mountains and Rivers in Moonlight, by Kim Doo-ryang (1696-1763).

Perf. 13x13½, 13½x13

1970, Aug. 31 Photo.

715 A370 10w blue & multi	1.00	.35
716 A370 10w buff & multi	1.00	.35
717 A371 10w multicolored	1.00	.35

1970, Oct. 30

Paintings: No. 719, Cats and Sparrows, by Pyun Sang-byuk (18th century). No. 720, Dog with puppies, by Yi Am (1499-?).

718 A371 30w multicolored	2.25	.65
719 A371 30w multicolored	2.25	.65
720 A371 30w multicolored	2.25	.65

Nos. 718-720 exist imperf.

1970, Dec. 30

Paintings: No. 721, Cliff and Boat, by Kim Hong-do (1745-?). No. 722, Cock, Hens and Chick, by Pyun Sang-byuk (early 18th century). No. 723, Woman Playing Flute, by Shin Yun-bok (late 18th century).

721 A371 10w yel brn, blk & red	.80	.40
722 A371 10w pale rose, blk & grn	.80	.40
723 A371 10w multicolored	.80	.40
Nos. 715-723 (9)	12.15	4.20

Souvenir Sheets of 2

715a A370 10w	2.00
716a A370 10w	2.00
717a A371 10w	2.00
718a A371 30w Imperf	12.00
719a A371 30w Imperf	12.00
720a A371 30w Imperf	12.00
721a A371 10w	2.75
722a A371 10w	2.75
723a A371 10w	2.75
Nos. 715a-723a (9)	50.25

Nos. 715a-717a have simulated perforations. Background color of stamps on No. 717a is yellow instead of greenish gray as on No. 717.

Nos. 718a-720a exist perf, twice the imperf values.

Nos. 721a-723a exist imperf.

P.T.T.I. Emblem and Map of Far East — A372

1970, Sept. 6 Litho. *Perf. 13x12½*

724 A372 10w lt yel grn, bl & dk bl .40 .25

Opening of the Councillors' Meeting of the Asian Chapter of the Postal, Telegraph and Telephone Intl. Org., Sept. 6-12.

Korean WAC and Emblem — A373

1970, Sept. 6 Photo. *Perf. 13x13½*

725 A373 10w blue & multi .50 .25

20th anniv. of the founding of the Korean Women's Army Corps.

Pres. Park, Korean Flag and Means of Transportation — A374

Pres. Park, Highways, Factories A375

1970 *Perf. 13x13½, 13½x13*

726 A374 10w vio bl, blk & car	1.50	.40
727 A375 10w dk bl, grnsh bl & blk	1.50	.40

Presidents Park and Hernandez, Flags of Korea, Salvador A376

1970, Sept. 28 Litho. *Perf. 13x12½*

728 A376 10w dk bl, red & blk 1.25 .35
a. Souv. sheet of 1, imperf. *18.00*

Visit of Gen. Fidel Sanchez Hernandez, President of El Salvador.

The first printing of 30,000 of No. 728a spelled "Salvadol." Second printing, also 30,000, corrected the error. Value is for first printing.

People and Houses — A377

1970, Oct. 1 Litho. *Perf. 13x12½*

729 A377 10w lilac & multi .40 .20

Natl. census of population & housing, Oct. 1.

Diver A378

1970, Oct. 6 Photo. *Perf. 12½x13½*

730 A378 10w shown 1.10 .20
a. Souv. sheet of 2, imperf. 3.50
731 A378 10w Field hockey 1.10 .20
a. Souv. sheet of 2, imperf. 3.50
732 A378 10w Baseball 1.10 .20
a. Souv. sheet of 2, imperf. 3.50
Nos. 730-732 (3) 3.30 .60
Nos. 730a-732a (3) 10.50

51st Natl. Athletic Games, Seoul, Oct. 6-11.

Police Emblem and Activities A379

1970, Oct. 21 Litho. *Perf. 12½*

733 A379 10w ultra & multi .50 .25

The 25th Policemen's Day.

Freedom Bell, UN Emblem over Globe — A380

1970, Oct. 24 Photo. *Perf. 13x13½*

734 A380 10w blue & multi .45 .25

25th anniversary of United Nations.

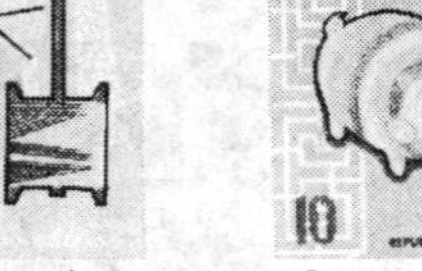

Kite and Holly — A380a

Boar — A381

1970, Dec. 1 Litho. *Perf. 13*

735 A380a 10w lt blue & multi .40 .20
a. Souvenir sheet of 3 3.50
736 A381 10w green & multi .40 .20
a. Souvenir sheet of 3 3.50

New Year 1971.

Pres. Park Quotation, Globe and Telecommunications Emblems — A382

1970, Dec. 4 Photo.

737 A382 10w multicolored .40 .25

For the 15th Communications Day.

Power Dam — A383

Coal Mining A384

Highway Intersection A385

#739, Crate wrapped in world map, & ships. #740, Irrigation project & farm, vert. #742, Cement factory, vert. #743, Fertilizer factory. #744, Increased national income (scales). #745, Increased savings (factories, bee & coins).

1971 *Perf. 13x13½, 13½x13*

738 A383 10w blue & multi .50 .15
739 A383 10w pale lil & multi .50 .15
740 A383 10w green & multi .50 .15
741 A384 10w bl grn, lt bl & blk .50 .15
742 A384 10w lt bl, vio & brt mag .50 .15
743 A384 10w vio, grn & bis .50 .15
744 A384 10w pink & multi .50 .15
745 A384 10w lt bl grn & multi .50 .15
746 A385 10w violet & multi .50 .15
Nos. 738-746 (9) 4.50 1.35

Economic Development.

Souvenir Sheets of 1, Imperf.

738a A383 10w 3.00
739a A383 10w 3.00
740a A383 10w 3.00

Souvenir Sheets of 2, Imperf.

741a A384 10w 3.00
742a A384 10w 3.00
743a A384 10w 3.00
744a A384 10w 3.00
745a A384 10w 3.00
746a A385 10w 3.00
Nos. 738a-746a (9) 27.00

Torch, Globe and Spider — A386

1971, Mar. 1 Litho. *Perf. 12½x13*

747 A386 10w gray & multi .45 .25

March, the month for anti-espionage and victory over communism.

Reservist, Reserve Forces Emblem — A387

1971, Apr. 3 Photo. *Perf. 13½x13*

748 A387 10w lt ultra & multi .45 .25

Home Reserve Forces Day, Apr. 3.

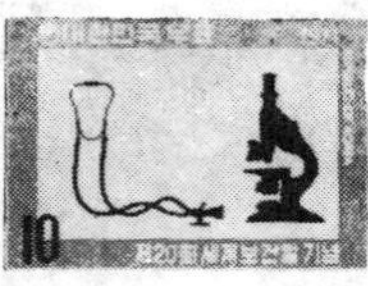

WHO Emblem, Stethoscope, Microscope A388

1971, Apr. 7

749 A388 10w lt bl, pur & yel .45 .25

20th World Health Day, Apr. 7.

Subway Tunnel and Train — A389

Soccer Player — A390

1971, Apr. 12 Litho. *Perf. 12½x13*

750 A389 10w multicolored .45 .25

Seoul subway construction start.

1971, May 2

751 A390 10w grn, dk brn & blk .50 .30

First Asian Soccer Games, Seoul, May 2-13.

Veterans Flag and Veterans — A391

Girl Scouts and Emblem — A392

1971, May 8 Photo. *Perf. 13x13½*

752 A391 10w ultra & multi .45 .25

20th Korean Veterans Day.

1971, May 10

753 A392 10w lilac & multi .45 .30

25th anniversary of the Korean Federation of Girl Scouts.

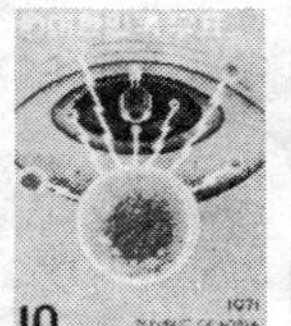

Torch and Development A393

"Telecommunication" A394

1971, May 16

754 A393 10w lt blue & multi .45 .25

10th anniversary of May 16th revolution.

1971, May 17

755 A394 10w blue & multi .45 .25

3rd World Telecommunications Day.

Security Council — A395

Korean Flag — A396

UN Organizations: No. 756, ILO. No. 757, FAO. No. 758, General Assembly (UN Headquarters). No. 759, UNESCO. No. 760, WHO. No. 761, World Bank. No. 762, Intl. Development Association (IDA). No. 763, Security Council. No. 764, Intl. Finance Corp. (IFC). No. 765, Intl. Monetary Fund. No. 766, ICAO. No. 767, Economic and Social Council. No. 768, Korean Flag. No. 769, Trusteeship Council. No. 770, UPU. No. 771, ITU. No. 772, World Meteorological Org. (WMO). No. 773, Intl. Court of Justice. No. 774, Intl. Maritime Consultative Org. No. 775, UNICEF. No. 776, Intl. Atomic Energy Agency. No. 777, UN Industrial Development Org. No. 778, UN Commission for the Unification and Rehabilitation of Korea. No. 779, UN Development Program. No. 780, UN Conf. on Trade and Development.

1971, May 30 *Perf. 13½x13*

756 A395 10w green, blk & pink 2.00 .25
757 A395 10w pink, blk & bl 2.00 .25
758 A395 10w bl, blk, grn & pink 2.00 .25
759 A395 10w pink, blk & bl 2.00 .25
760 A395 10w green, blk & pink 2.00 .25
761 A395 10w pink, blk & bl 2.00 .25
762 A395 10w blue, blk & pink 2.00 .25
763 A395 10w green, blk & pink 2.00 .25
764 A395 10w blue, blk & pink 2.00 .25
765 A395 10w pink, blk & bl 2.00 .25
766 A395 10w blue, blk & pink 2.00 .25
767 A395 10w green, blk & pink 2.00 .25
768 A396 10w blue, blk & pink 2.00 .25
769 A395 10w green, blk & pink 2.00 .25
770 A395 10w blue, blk & pink 2.00 .25
771 A395 10w pink, blk & bl 2.00 .25
772 A395 10w blue, blk & pink 2.00 .25
773 A395 10w green, blk & pink 2.00 .25
774 A395 10w blue, blk & pink 2.00 .25
775 A395 10w pink, blk & bl 2.00 .25
776 A395 10w green, blk & pink 2.00 .25
777 A395 10w pink, blk & bl 2.00 .25
778 A395 10w blue, blk & pink 2.00 .25
779 A395 10w pink, blk & bl 2.00 .25
780 A395 10w green, blk & pink 2.00 .25
Nos. 756-780 (25) 50.00 6.25

Sheet of 50 incorporates 2 each of #756-780.

Boat Ride, by Shin Yun-bok — A397

Man and Boy under Pine Tree — A398

Paintings by Shin Yun-bok: No. 782, Greeting travelers. No. 783, Sword dance. No. 784, Lady traveling with servants. No. 785, Man and woman on the road.

Perf. 13x13½, 13½x13

1971, June 20 Photo.

781 A397 10w multicolored 2.50 .20
782 A397 10w multicolored 2.50 .20
783 A397 10w multicolored 2.50 .20
784 A397 10w multicolored 2.50 .20
785 A397 10w multicolored 2.50 .20
786 A398 10w multicolored 2.50 .20
b. Vert. strip of 5, #781-785 10.00 3.00
Nos. 781-786 (6) 15.00 1.20

Souvenir Sheets of 2

781a A397 10w 4.25
782a A397 10w 4.25
783a A397 10w 4.25
784a A397 10w 4.25
785a A397 10w 4.25
786a A398 10w 4.25
Nos. 781a-786a (6) 25.50

Types A397-A398 with Inscription at Left

1971, July 20

Paintings: No. 787, Farmyard scene, by Kim Deuk-shin. No. 788, Family living in valley, by Lee Chae-kwan. No. 789, Man reading book under pine tree, by Lee Chae-kwan.

787 A397 10w pale grn & multi 1.40 .25
788 A398 10w pale grn & multi 1.40 .25
789 A398 10w lt yel grn & multi 1.40 .25
Nos. 787-789 (3) 4.20 .75

Souvenir Sheets of 2

787a A397 10w 3.25
788a A398 10w 3.25
789a A398 10w 3.25
Nos. 787a-789a (3) 9.75

Teacher and Students, by Kim Hong-do A399

Paintings by Kim Hong-do (Yi Dynasty): No. 791, Wrestlers. No. 792, Dancer and musicians. No. 793, Weavers. No. 794, At the Well.

1971, Aug. 20 ***Perf. 13½x13***

790	A399	10w blk, lt grn & rose	2.00	.25
791	A399	10w blk, lt grn & rose	2.00	.25
792	A399	10w blk, lt grn & rose	2.00	.25
793	A399	10w blk, lt grn & rose	2.00	.25
794	A399	10w blk, lt grn & rose	2.00	.25
b.		Horiz. strip of 5, #790-794	10.00	2.50

Souvenir Sheets of 2

790a	A399	10w	4.00
791a	A399	10w	4.00
792a	A399	10w	4.00
793a	A399	10w	4.00
794a	A399	10w	4.00
		Nos. 790a-794a (5)	20.00

Pres. Park, Highway and Phoenix — A400

1971, July 1 ***Perf. 13½x13***

795 A400 10w grn, blk & org 1.75 .50
a. Souvenir sheet of 2 *35.00*

Inauguration of President Park Chung Hee for a third term, July 1.

Campfire and Tents — A401

1971, Aug. 2 **Photo.** ***Perf. 13x13½***

796 A401 10w blue grn & multi .45 .25

13th Boy Scout World Jamboree, Asagiri Plain, Japan, Aug. 2-10.

Symbol of Conference A402

1971, Sept. 27 ***Perf. 13***

797 A402 10w multicolored .45 .25
a. Souvenir sheet of 2 *30.00*

Asian Labor Ministers' Conference, Seoul, Sept. 27-30.

Archers — A403

1971, Oct. 8 **Photo.** ***Perf. 13x13½***

798 A403 10w shown .75 .30
a. Souvenir sheet of 3 *15.00*
799 A403 10w Judo .75 .30
a. Souvenir sheet of 3 *15.00*

52nd National Athletic Meet.

Taeguk on Palette — A404

1971, Oct. 11 ***Perf. 13½x13***

800 A404 10w yellow & multi .40 .25

20th National Fine Arts Exhibition.

Physician, Globe and Emblem — A405

1971, Oct. 13

801 A405 10w multicolored .40 .25

7th Congress of the Confederation of Medical Associations in Asia and Oceania.

Symbols of Contest Events — A406

1971, Oct. 20 **Photo.** ***Perf. 13x13½***

802 A406 10w multicolored .40 .25
a. Souvenir sheet of 2 *20.00*

2nd National Skill Contest for High School Students.

Slide Caliper and KS Emblem — A407

1971, Nov. 11 ***Perf. 13x13½***

803 A407 10w multicolored .40 .25

10th anniversary of industrial standardization in Korea.

Rats — A408

Japanese Crane — A409

1971, Dec. 1

804 A408 10w multicolored .50 .20
a. Souvenir sheet of 3 *15.00*
805 A409 10w multicolored .50 .20
a. Souvenir sheet of 3 *15.00*

New Year 1972.

Emblem of Hangul Hakhoe and Hangul Letters — A410

1971, Dec. 3 **Photo.**

806 A410 10w dk blue & multi .40 .20

50th anniversary of Korean Language Research Society (Hangul Hakhoe).

Red Cross Headquarters and Map of Korea — A411

1971, Dec. 31 ***Perf. 13½x13***

807 A411 10w multicolored .50 .20
a. Souvenir sheet of 2 4.00

First South and North Korean Red Cross Conference, Panmunjom, Aug. 20, 1971.

Globe and Book — A412

1972, Jan. 5 ***Perf. 13x13½***

808 A412 10w multicolored .45 .30
a. Souvenir sheet of 2 5.00

International Book Year 1972.

Intelsat 4 Sending Signals to Korea — A413

1972, Jan. 31 ***Perf. 13½x13***

809 A413 10w dk blue & multi .45 .25

Korea's entry into ITU, 20th anniv.

Figure Skating, Sapporo '72 Emblem A414

Map of Korea with Forest Sites A415

Design: No. 811, Speed skating.

1972, Feb. 3 ***Perf. 13x13½***

810 A414 10w lt & dk bl & car .75 .15
811 A414 10w lt & dk bl & car .75 .15
a. Souvenir sheet of 2, #810-811 8.50

11th Winter Olympic Games, Sapporo, Japan, Feb. 3-13.

1972, Mar. 10 **Photo.** ***Perf. 13x13***

812 A415 10w buff, bl grn & red .40 .20

Publicity for forests planted to mark hope for reunification of Korea.

Junior Chamber of Commerce Emblem and Beetles — A416

1972, Mar. 19 ***Perf. 13½x13***

813 A416 10w pink & multi .40 .20

Junior Chamber of Commerce, 20th anniversary.

UN Emblem, Agriculture and Industry — A417

1972, Mar. 28 ***Perf. 13x13½***

814 A417 10w violet, grn & car .40 .20

Economic Commission for Asia and the Far East (ECAFE), 25th anniversary.

Flags — A418

1972, Apr. 1 ***Perf. 13½x13***

815 A418 10w blue & multi .40 .20

Asian-Oceanic Postal Union, 10th anniv.

Korean Flag — A419

YWCA Emblem, Butterflies — A420

1972, Apr. 1 **Photo.** ***Perf. 13x13½***

816 A419 10w yellow & multi .40 .25

Homeland Reserve Forces Day, Apr. 1.

1972, Apr. 20

817 A420 10w violet & multi .40 .20

50th anniv. of the YWCA of Korea.

Community Projects — A421

Korean Flag & Inscription — A422

1972, May 1 ***Perf. 13x13½***

818 A421 10w pink & multi .40 .20

Rural rehabilitation and construction movement.

1972, May 1

819 A422 10w green & multi .40 .20

Anti-espionage and victory over communism month.

Children with Balloons — A423

1972, May 5 ***Perf. 13½x13***

820 A423 10w yellow & multi .40 .20

Children's Day, May 5.

King Munyong's Gold Earrings — A424

Design: No. 822, Gold ornament from King's crown, vert.

Perf. 13½x13, 13x13½

1972, May 10

821 A424 10w green & multi .40 .20
822 A424 10w green & multi .40 .20

National treasures from tomb of King Munyong of Paekche, who reigned 501-523.

Kojo Island — A425

National parks: No. 823, Crater Lake.

1972, May 30 *Perf. 13½x13*

823 A425 10w blue grn & multi .40 .20
824 A425 10w green & multi .40 .20

Daisy, Environment Emblem — A426

1972, May 30 Litho. *Perf. 13x13½*

825 A426 10w green & multi .40 .20
a. Souvenir sheet of 2 3.00

UN Conference on Human Environment, Stockholm, June 5-16.

Gwanghwa Gate, Flags of Participants — A427

1972, June 14

826 A427 10w yellow & multi .40 .20

7th Meeting of Asian-Pacific Council (ASPAC).

Farm and Fish Hatchery — A428

Weight Lifting — A429

Third Five-Year Plan Issue

1972, July 1 Photo. *Perf. 13½x13*

827 A428 10w shown .50 .15
828 A428 10w Steel industry and products .50 .15
829 A428 10w Globe and cargo .50 .15
Nos. 827-829 (3) 1.50 .45

3rd Economic Development Five-Year Plan.

1972, Aug. 26 Photo. *Perf. 13x13½*

830 A429 20w shown .60 .15
831 A429 20w Judo .60 .15
a. Souvenir sheet of 2, #830-831 3.50
b. Pair, #830-831 1.25 .35
832 A429 20w Boxing .60 .15
833 A429 20w Wrestling .60 .15
a. Souvenir sheet of 2, #832-833 3.50
b. Pair, #832-833 1.25 .35
Nos. 830-833 (4) 2.40 .60

20th Olympic Games, Munich, Aug. 26-Sept. 11. Nos. 831b, 833b each printed checkerwise.

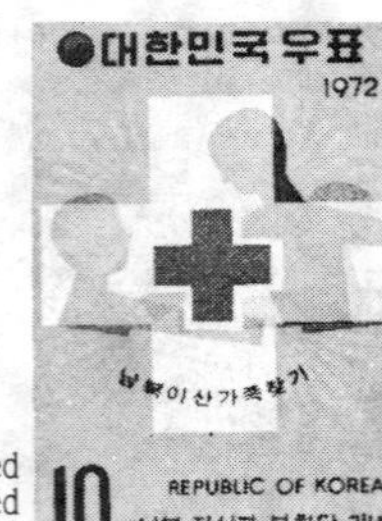

Families Reunited by Red Cross — A430

1972, Aug. 30 Photo. *Perf. 13½x13*

834 A430 10w lt blue & multi .50 .20
a. Souvenir sheet of 2 9.00

Plenary meeting of the South-North Red Cross Conference, Pyongyang, Aug. 30, 1972.

Bulkuk-sa Temple, Kyongju Park — A431

Bopju-sa Temple, Mt. Sokri Park — A432

1972, Sept. 20 Photo. *Perf. 13½x13*

835 A431 10w brown & multi .40 .20
836 A432 10w blue & multi .40 .20

National parks.

"5" and Conference Emblem — A433

1972, Sept. 25 *Perf. 13x13½*

837 A433 10w vio blue & multi .40 .15

Fifth Asian Judicial Conf., Seoul, Sept. 25-29.

Lions Emblem, Taeguk Fan — A434

1972, Sept. 28 *Perf. 13½x13*

838 A434 10w multicolored .40 .15

11th Orient and Southeast Asian Lions Convention, Seoul, Sept. 28-30.

Scout Taking Oath, Korean Flag and Scout Emblem — A435

1972, Oct. 5

839 A435 10w yellow & multi .40 .15

Boy Scouts of Korea, 50th anniversary.

Children and Ox — A436

Children in Balloon — A437

1972, Dec. 1 Photo. *Perf. 13x13½*

840 A436 10w green & multi .45 .15
a. Souvenir sheet of 2 2.25
841 A437 10w blue & multi .45 .15
a. Souvenir sheet of 2 2.25
Set value .25

New Year 1973.

Mt. Naejang Park and Temple — A438

Mt. Sorang and Madeungryong Pass — A439

Perf. 13x13½, 13½x13

1972, Dec. 10

842 A438 10w multicolored .40 .20
843 A439 10w multicolored .40 .20

National parks.

Pres. Park, Korean Flag and Modern Landscape — A440

1972, Dec. 27 *Perf. 13x13½*

844 A440 10w multicolored 1.25 .20
a. Souvenir sheet of 2 *25.00*

Inauguration of Park Chung Hee for a 4th term as president of Korea.

Tourism Issue

Kyongbok Palace (National Museum) A441

Mt. Sorak and Kejo-am Temple — A442

Palmi Island and Beach — A443

Sain-am Rock, Mt. Dokjol — A444

Shrine for Adm. Li Sun-sin — A445

Limestone Cavern, Kusan-ni A446

Namhae Bridge A447

Hongdo Island — A448

Mt. Mai — A449

Tangerine Orchard, Cheju Island — A450

1973, Feb. 20 Photo. *Perf. 13½x13*

845 A441 10w multicolored .35 .15
846 A442 10w multicolored .35 .15

1973, Apr. 20 *Perf. 13x13½*

847 A443 10w multicolored .35 .15
848 A444 10w multicolored .35 .15

1973, June 20

849 A445 10w multicolored .35 .15
850 A446 10w multicolored .35 .15

1973, Aug. 20 *Perf. 13½x13*

851 A447 10w multicolored .35 .15
852 A448 10w multicolored .35 .15

1973, Oct. 20

853 A449 10w multicolored .35 .15
854 A450 10w multicolored .35 .15
Nos. 845-854 (10) 3.50 1.50

Praying Family — A451

Flags of Korea and South Viet Nam, Victory Sign — A452

1973, Mar. 1 *Perf. 13x13½*

855 A451 10w yellow & multi .35 .15

Prayer for national unification.

1973, Mar. 1

856 A452 10w violet & multi .35 .15

Return of Korean Expeditionary Force from South Viet Nam.

Workers, Factory, Cogwheel A453

Satellite, WMO Emblem A454

1973, Mar. 10 **Unwmk.**

857 A453 10w blue & multi .35 .15

10th Labor Day.

1973, Mar. 23
858 A454 10w blue & multi .35 .15
a. Souvenir sheet of 2 2.75

Cent. of Intl. Meteorological Cooperation.

King's Ceremonial Robe — A455

Traditional Korean Costumes (Yi dynasty): No. 860, Queen's ceremonial dress. No. 861, King's robe. No. 862, Queen's robe. No. 863, Crown Prince. No. 864, Princess. No. 865, Courtier. No. 866, Royal bridal gown. No. 867, Official's wife. No. 868, Military official.

1973 Photo. *Perf. 13½x13*
859 A455 10w ocher & multi .75 .15
860 A455 10w salmon & multi .75 .15
861 A455 10w rose lilac & multi .75 .15
862 A455 10w apple grn & multi .75 .15
863 A455 10w lt blue & multi .75 .15
864 A455 10w lilac rose & multi .75 .15
865 A455 10w yellow & multi .75 .15
866 A455 10w lt blue & multi .75 .15
867 A455 10w ocher & multi .75 .15
868 A455 10w lil rose & multi .75 .15
Nos. 859-868 (10) 7.50
Set value 1.20

Issued: #859-860, 3/30; #861-862, 5/30; #863-864, 7/30; #865-866, 9/30; #867-868, 11/30.

Souvenir Sheets of 2

859a A455 10w (#1) 2.50
860a A455 10w (#2) 2.50
861a A455 10w (#3) 2.50
862a A455 10w (#4) 2.50
863a A455 10w (#5) 2.50
864a A455 10w (#6) 2.50
865a A455 10w (#7) 2.50
866a A455 10w (#8) 2.50
867a A455 10w (#9) 2.50
868a A455 10w (#10) 2.50
Nos. 859a-868a (10) 25.00

Parenthetical numbers after souvenir sheet listings appear in top marginal inscriptions.

Nurse Holding Lamp — A456

Homeland Reservists and Flag — A457

1973, Apr. 1 *Perf. 13½x13*
869 A456 10w rose & multi .35 .15

50th anniv. of Korean Nurses Association.

1973, Apr. 7 *Perf. 13x13½*
870 A457 10w yellow & multi .40 .15

Homeland Reserve Forces Day on 5th anniversary of their establishment.

Table Tennis Player, and Globe — A458

1973, May 23 *Perf. 13x13½*
871 A458 10w pink & multi .50 .15

Victory of Korean women's table tennis team, 32nd Intl. Table Tennis Championships, Sarajevo, Yugoslavia, Apr. 5-15.

World Vision Children's Choir — A459

1973, June 25 *Perf. 13x13½*
872 A459 10w multicolored .45 .15

20th anniversary of World Vision International, a Christian service organization.

Converter, Pohang Steel Works — A460

1973, July 3 *Perf. 13x13½*
873 A460 10w blue & multi .30 .15

Inauguration of Pohang iron and steel plant.

INTERPOL Emblem A461

1973, Sept. 3 *Perf. 13½x13*
874 A461 10w lt violet & multi .35 .15

50th anniversary of the International Criminal Police Organization (INTERPOL).

Children with Stamp Albums — A462

1973, Oct. 12 *Perf. 13½x13*
875 A462 10w dp green & multi .35 .15
a. Souvenir sheet of 2 3.00

Philatelic Week, Oct. 12-18.

Woman Hurdler — A463

1973, Oct. 12 *Perf. 12½x13½*
876 A463 10w shown .35 .15
877 A463 10w Tennis player .35 .15
Set value .25

54th Natl. Athletic Meet, Pusan, Oct. 12-17.

Soyang River Dam, Map Showing Location A464

1973, Oct. 15 *Perf. 13½x13*
878 A464 10w blue & multi .35 .15

Inauguration of Soyang River Dam and hydroelectric plant.

Fire from Match and Cigarette — A465

1973, Nov. 1 *Perf. 13x13½*
879 A465 10w multicolored .35 .15

10th Fire Prevention Day.

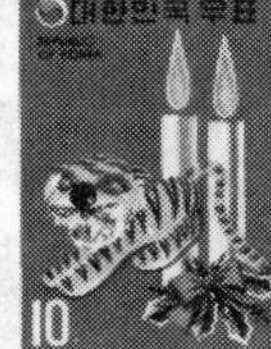

Tiger and Candles — A466

Toys — A467

1973, Dec. 1 Photo. *Perf. 13x13½*
880 A466 10w emerald & multi .40 .15
a. Souvenir sheet of 2 2.00
881 A467 10w blue & multi .40 .15
a. Souvenir sheet of 2 2.00
Set value .25

New Year 1974.

Human Rights Flame, and Head — A468

1973, Dec. 10 *Perf. 13½x13*
882 A468 10w orange & multi .25 .15

25th anniversary of Universal Declaration of Human Rights.

Musical Instruments Issue

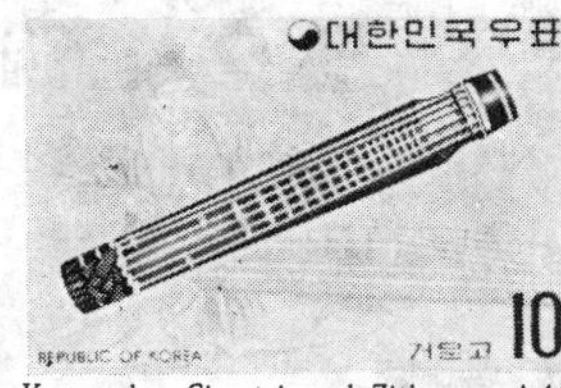

Komunko, Six-stringed Zither — A469

Design: 30w, Nagak, shell trumpet.

1974, Feb. 20 Photo. *Perf. 13x13½*
883 A469 10w lt bl, blk & brn .30 .15
884 A469 30w orange & multi .60 .20

1974, Apr. 20

Designs: 10w, Tchouk; wooden hammer in slanted box, used to start orchestra. 30w, Eu; crouching tiger, used to stop orchestra.

885 A469 10w brt blue & multi .30 .15
886 A469 30w lt green & multi .60 .20

1974, June 20

Designs: 10w, A-chaing, 7-stringed instrument. 30w, Kyobang-ko, drum.

887 A469 10w dull yel & multi .30 .15
888 A469 30w sal pink & multi .60 .20

1974, Aug. 20

Designs: 10w, So, 16-pipe ritual instrument. 30w, Kaikeum, 2-stringed fiddle.

889 A469 10w lt blue & multi .30 .15
890 A469 30w brt pink & multi .60 .20

1974, Oct. 20

Designs: 10w, Pak (clappers). 30w, Pyenchong (bell chimes).

891 A469 10w lt lilac & multi .30 .15
892 A469 30w lemon & multi .60 .20
Nos. 883-892 (10) 4.50 1.75

Souvenir Sheets of 2

883a A469 10w (#1) 2.00
884a A469 30w (#2) 2.50
885a A469 10w (#3) 1.40
886a A469 30w (#4) 2.50
887a A469 10w (#5) 1.40
888a A469 30w (#6) 2.50
889a A469 10w (#7) 1.40
890a A469 30w (#8) 2.50
891a A469 10w (#9) 1.40
892a A469 30w (#10) 2.50
Nos. 883a-892a (10) 20.10

Fruit Issue

Apricots — A470

1974, Mar. 30 Photo. *Perf. 13x13½*
893 A470 10w shown .30 .15
894 A470 30w Strawberries .60 .20

1974, May 30
895 A470 10w Peaches .30 .15
896 A470 30w Grapes .60 .20

1974, July 30
897 A470 10w Pears .30 .15
898 A470 30w Apples .60 .20

1974, Sept. 30
899 A470 10w Cherries .30 .15
900 A470 30w Persimmons .60 .20

1974, Nov. 30
901 A470 10w Tangerines .30 .15
902 A470 30w Chestnuts .60 .20
Nos. 893-902 (10) 4.50 1.75

Souvenir Sheets of 2

893a A470 10w (#1) 1.10
894a A470 30w (#2) 2.50
895a A470 10w (#3) 1.10
896a A470 30w (#4) 2.50
897a A470 10w (#5) 1.10
898a A470 30w (#6) 2.50
899a A470 10w (#7) 1.10
900a A470 30w (#8) 2.50
901a A470 10w (#9) 1.10
902a A470 30w (#10) 2.50
Nos. 893a-902a (10) 18.00

Reservist and Factory — A471

1974, Apr. 6 Photo. *Perf. 13½x13*
903 A471 10w yellow & multi .25 .15

Homeland Reserve Forces Day.

WPY Emblem and Scales — A472

1974, Apr. 10 *Perf. 13x13½*
904 A472 10w salmon & multi .25 .15
a. Souvenir sheet of 2 2.00

World Population Year 1974.

Train and Communications Emblem — A473

1974, Apr. 22 *Perf. 13½x13*
905 A473 10w multicolored .25 .15

19th Communications Day.

Emblem and Stylized Globe — A474

1974, May 6 Photo. *Perf. 13*

906 A474 10w red lilac & multi .25 .15

22nd Session of Intl. Chamber of Commerce (Eastern Division), Seoul, May 6-8.

New Dock at Inchon — A475

1974, May 10

907 A475 10w yellow & multi .25 .15

Dedication of dock, Inchon.

UNESCO Emblem, "20" and Yin Yang — A476

1974, June 14 Photo. *Perf. 13*

908 A476 10w org yel & multi .25 .15

20th anniversary of the Korean National Commission for UNESCO.

EXPLO '74 Emblems A477

Subway, Bus and Plane A478

Design: No. 910, EXPLO emblem rising from map of Korea.

1974, Aug. 13 Photo. *Perf. 13*

909 A477 10w orange & multi .25 .15
910 A477 10w blue & multi .25 .15
Set value .20

EXPLO '74, International Christian Congress, Yoido Islet, Seoul, Aug. 13-18.

1974, Aug. 15

911 A478 10w green & multi .25 .15

Inauguration of Seoul subway (first in Korea), Aug. 15, 1974.

Target Shooting — A479

1974, Oct. 8 Photo. *Perf. 13x13½*

912 A479 10w shown .35 .15
913 A479 30w Rowing .40 .15

55th National Athletic Meet.

UPU Emblem A480

1974, Oct. 9 *Perf. 13*

914 A480 10w yellow & multi .30 .15
a. Souvenir sheet of 2 2.00

Cent. of UPU. See No. C43.

International Landmarks — A481

1974, Oct. 11

915 A481 10w multicolored .25 .15

Intl. People to People Conf., Seoul, Oct. 11-14.

Korea Nos. 1-2 — A482

1974, Oct. 17

916 A482 10w lilac & multi .30 .15
a. Souvenir sheet of 2 2.50

Philatelic Week, Oct. 17-23 and 90th anniversary of first Korean postage stamps.

Taekwondo and Kukkiwon Center — A483

1974, Oct. 18

917 A483 10w yellow grn & multi .30 .15

First Asian Taekwondo (self-defense) Games, Seoul, Oct. 18-20.

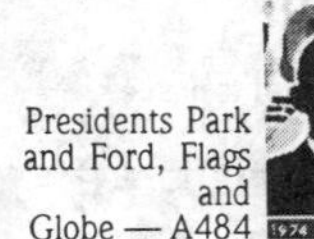

Presidents Park and Ford, Flags and Globe — A484

1974, Nov. 22 Photo. *Perf. 13*

918 A484 10y multicolored .60 .20
a. Souvenir sheet of 2 5.00

Visit of Pres. Gerald R. Ford to South Korea.

Yook Young Soo — A485

1974, Nov. 29

919 A485 10w green .50 .20
920 A485 10w orange .50 .20
921 A485 10w lilac .50 .20
922 A485 10w blue .50 .20
a. Souvenir sheet of 4, #919-922 20.00
b. Block of 4, #919-922 2.00 1.00

Yook Young Soo (1925-1974), wife of Pres. Park.

Rabbits — A486

Good-luck Purse — A487

1974, Dec. 1 Litho. *Perf. 12½x13*

923 A486 10w multicolored .30 .15
a. Souvenir sheet of 2 1.50
924 A487 10w multicolored .30 .15
a. Souvenir sheet of 2 1.50
Set value .25

New Year 1975.

Good-luck Key and Pigeon — A488

1975, Jan. 1 Photo. *Perf. 13*

925 A488 10w lt blue & multi .25 .15

Introduction of Natl. Welfare Insurance System.

UPU Emblem and "75" — A489

UPU Emblem and Paper Plane — A490

1975, Jan. 1

926 A489 10w yellow & multi .20 .15
927 A490 10w lt blue & multi .20 .15
Set value .20

75th anniv. of Korea's membership in UPU.

Dr. Schweitzer, Map of Africa, Hypodermic Needle — A491

1975, Jan. 14

928 A491 10w olive .35 .15
929 A491 10w brt rose .35 .15
930 A491 10w orange .35 .15
931 A491 10w brt green .35 .15
a. Block of 4, #928-931 1.50 .40

Dr. Albert Schweitzer (1875-1965), medical missionary, birth centenary.

Folk Dance Issue

Dancer — A492

Bupo Nori — A492a

#933, Dancer with fan. #934, Woman with butterfly sleeves. #935, Group of Women. #936, Pongsan mask dance. #937, Pusan mask dance. #938, Buddhist drum dance. #939, Bara (cymbals) dance. #940, Sogo dance.

1975, Feb. 20 Photo. *Perf. 13*

932 A492 10w emerald & multi .30 .15
933 A492 10w brt blue & multi .30 .15

1975, Apr. 20

934 A492 10w yel grn & multi .30 .15
935 A492 10w yellow & multi .30 .15

1975, June 20

936 A492 10w pink & multi .30 .15
937 A492 10w blue & multi .30 .15

1975, Aug. 20

938 A492 20w yellow & multi .30 .15
939 A492 20w salmon & multi .30 .15

1975, Oct. 20

940 A492 20w blue & multi .30 .15
941 A492a 20w yellow & multi .30 .15
Nos. 932-941 (10) 3.00
Set value 1.00

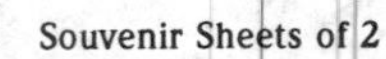

Souvenir Sheets of 2

932a A492 10w (#1) .75
933a A492 10w (#2) .75
934a A492 10w (#3) .75
935a A492 10w (#4) .75
936a A492 10w (#5) .75
937a A492 10w (#6) .75
938a A492 20w (#7) .75
939a A492 20w (#8) .75
940a A492 20w (#9) .75
941a A492 20w (#10) .75
Nos. 932a-941a (10) 7.50

Globe and Rotary Emblem — A493

1975, Feb. 23

942 A493 10w multicolored .30 .15

Rotary International, 70th anniversary.

Women and IWY Emblem A494

1975, Mar. 8

943 A494 10w multicolored .30 .15

International Women's Year 1975.

Flower Issue

Violets — A495

Anemones — A496

Clematis Patens — A496a

Broad-bell Flowers — A496b

Designs: No. 946, Rhododendron. No. 948, Thistle. No. 949, Iris. No. 951, Bush clover. No. 952, Camellia. No. 953, Gentian.

1975, Mar. 15

944 A495 10w orange & multi .30 .15
945 A496 10w yellow & multi .30 .15

1975, May 15

946 A495 10w dk green & multi .30 .15
947 A496a 10w yellow grn & multi .30 .15

1975, July 15

948 A495 10w emerald & multi .30 .15
949 A495 10w blue & multi .30 .15

1975, Sept. 15

950 A496b 20w yellow & multi .30 .15
951 A495 20w blue grn & multi .30 .15

1975, Nov. 15

952 A495 20w yellow & multi .30 .15
953 A496 20w salmon & multi .30 .15
Nos. 944-953 (10) 3.00
Set value 1.00

Forest and Water Resources — A497

Reduced illustration.

1975, Mar. 20

954 A497	Strip of 4		1.00	.30
a.	10w Saemaeul forest		.20	.15
b.	10w Dam and reservoir		.20	.15
c.	10w Green forest		.20	.15
d.	10w Timber industry		.20	.15

Natl. Tree Planting Month, Mar. 21-Apr. 20.

Map of Korea, HRF Emblem — A498

1975, Apr. 12 Photo. *Perf. 13*

955 A498 10w blue & multi .50 .20

Homeland Reserve Forces Day.

Lily — A499

Ceramic Jar — A500

Ceramic Vase A501

Adm. Li Sun-sin A502

1975, Oct. 10 Photo. *Perf. 13¹/₂x13*

963 A499	6w green & bl grn	.20	.15
964 A500	50w gray grn & brn	.50	.30
965 A501	60w brown & yellow	.60	.52
966 A502	100w carmine	.70	.40
	Nos. 963-966 (4)	2.00	1.37

Metric System Symbols — A507

1975, May 20 *Perf. 13*

975 A507 10w salmon & multi .25 .15

Centenary of International Meter Convention, Paris, 1875.

Praying Soldier, Incense Burner — A508

1975, June 6 Photo. *Perf. 13*

976 A508 10w multicolored .25 .15

20th Memorial Day.

Flags of Korea, UN and US — A509

1975, June 25 Photo. *Perf. 13*

977 A509	10w dk blue & multi	.25	.15
978 A509	10w dk blue & multi	.25	.15
979 A509	10w dk blue & multi	.25	.15
980 A509	10w dk blue & multi	.25	.15
a.	Strip of 4, #977-980	1.00	.40

25th anniv. of beginning of Korean War.

Designs (Flags of): No. 978, Ethiopia, France, Greece, Canada, South Africa. No. 979, Luxembourg, Australia, Great Britain, Colombia, Turkey. No. 980, Netherlands, Belgium, Philippines, New Zealand, Thailand.

Presidents Park and Bongo, Flags of Korea and Gabon — A510

1975, July 5

981 A510	10w blue & multi	.25	.15
a.	Souvenir sheet of 2	1.25	

Visit of Pres. Albert Bongo of Gabon, July 5-8.

Scout Emblem, Tents and Neckerchief — A511

1975, July 29 Photo. *Perf. 13*

982 A511	10w shown	.20	.15
983 A511	10w Pick and oath	.20	.15
984 A511	10w Tents	.20	.15
985 A511	10w Ax, rope and tree	.20	.15
986 A511	10w Campfire	.20	.15
a.	Strip of 5, #982-986	1.00	.45

Nordjamb 75, 14th Boy Scout Jamboree, Lillehammer, Norway, July 29-Aug. 7.

Flame and Broken Chain — A512

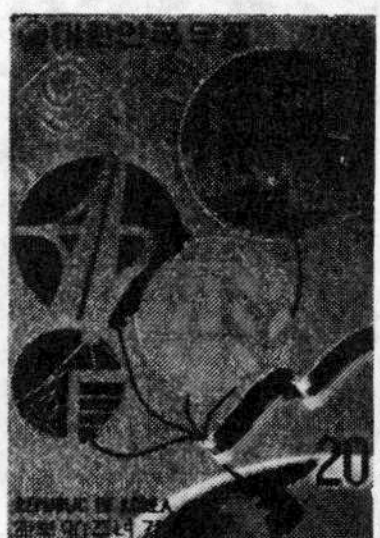

Balloons with Symbols of Development over Map — A513

1975, Aug. 15 *Perf. 13¹/₂x13*

987 A512	20w gold & multi	.25	.15
988 A513	20w silver & multi	.25	.15
	Set value		.20

30th anniversary of liberation.

Taekwondo — A514

1975, Aug. 26 *Perf. 13*

989 A514 20w multicolored .25 .15

2nd World Taekwondo Championships, Seoul, Aug. 25-Sept. 1.

National Assembly and Emblem — A515

1975, Sept. 1 Photo. *Perf. 13¹/₂x13*

990 A515 20w multicolored .25 .15

Completion of National Assembly Building.

Convention Emblem and Dump Truck — A516

1975, Sept. 7 Photo. *Perf. 13¹/₂x13*

991 A516 20w ultra & multi .25 .15

14th Convention of the Intl. Fed. of Asian and Western Pacific Contractors.

Cassegrainian Telescope and Morse Key — A517

1975, Sept. 28

992 A517 20w red lil, org & blk .25 .15

90th anniversary of Korean telecommunications system.

Stalactite Cave, Yeongweol A518

View of Mt. Sorak — A519

1975, Sept. 28

993 A518	20w multicolored	.25	.15
994 A519	20w multicolored	.25	.15
	Set value		.20

International Tourism Day.

Armed Forces Flag and Missiles — A519a

1975, Oct. 1 Photo. *Perf. 13*

994A A519a 20w multicolored .25 .15

Armed Forces Day.

Gymnastics A520

Handball A521

1975, Oct. 7 Photo. *Perf. 13*

995 A520	20w yellow & multi	.25	.15
996 A521	20w multicolored	.25	.15
	Set value		.20

56th Natl. Athletic Meet, Taegu, Oct. 7-12.

Stamp Collecting Kangaroo A522

Hands and UN Emblem A523

1975, Oct. 8

997 A522 20w multicolored .25 .15

Philatelic Week, Oct. 8-14.

1975, Oct. 24

998 A523 20w multicolored .25 .15

United Nations, 30th anniversary.

Red Cross and Activities A524

Emblem and Dove A525

1975, Oct. 30

999 A524 20w orange, red & brn .25 .15

Korean Red Cross, 70th anniversary.

1975, Nov. 30 Photo. *Perf. 13*

1000 A525 20w multicolored .25 .15

Asian Parliamentary Union, 10th anniv.

Children Playing — A526

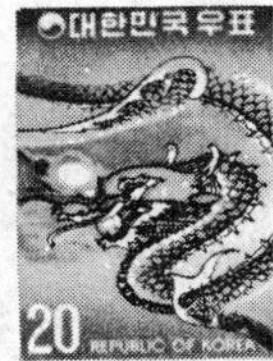

Dragon — A527

1975, Dec. 1

1001 A526	20w multicolored	.25	.15
a.	Souvenir sheet of 2	.85	
1002 A527	20w multicolored	.25	.15
a.	Souvenir sheet of 2	.85	
	Set value		.20

New Year 1976.

Inchong-Bukpyong Railroad — A528

1975, Dec. 5 Photo. *Perf. 13*

1003 A528 20w multicolored .25 .15

Opening of electric cross-country railroad.

Butterfly Issue

Dilipa Fenestra A529

Byasa Alcinous Klug — A529a

Graphium Sarpedon A529b

Fabriciana Nerippe A529c

Nymphalis Xanthomelas A529d

Butterflies: No. 1005, Luehdorfia puziloi. No. 1006, Papilio xuthus linne. No. 1007, Parnassius bremeri. No. 1008, Colias erate esper. No. 1010, Hestina assimilis.

1976, Jan. 20 Photo. *Perf. 13*

1004 A529 20w dp rose & multi .75 .15
1005 A529 20w dp blue & multi .75 .15

1976, Mar. 20

1006 A529 20w yellow & multi .75 .15
1007 A529 20w yel grn & multi .75 .15

1976, June 20

1008 A529 20w lt violet & multi .75 .15
1009 A529a 20w citron & multi .75 .15

1976, Aug. 20

1010 A529 20w tan & multi .75 .15
1011 A529b 20w lt gray & multi .75 .15

1976, Oct. 20

1012 A529c 20w lt green & multi .75 .15
1013 A529d 20w lilac & multi .75 .15
Nos. 1004-1013 (10) 7.50
Set value 1.00

Emblems of Science, Industry and KIST — A530

1976, Feb. 10 Photo. *Perf. 13*

1014 A530 20w multicolored .25 .15

Korean Institute of Science and Technology (KIST), 10th anniversary.

A531

A532

1976, Feb. 20 Photo. *Perf. 13x13½*

1015 A531 20w Siberian Bustard .50 .15
1016 A532 20w White-naped Crane .50 .15

A532a

A532b

1976, May 20

1017 A532a 20w Blue-winged pitta .50 .15
1018 A532b 20w Tristam's woodpecker .50 .15

A532c

A532d

1976, July 20

1019 A532c 20w Wood pigeon .50 .15
1020 A532d 20w Oyster catcher .50 .15

A532e

A532f

1976, Sept. 20

1021 A532e 20w Black-faced spoonbill .50 .15
1022 A532f 20w Black stork .50 .15

A532g

A532h

1976, Nov. 20

1023 A532g 20w Whooper swan .50 .15
1024 A532h 20w Black vulture .50 .15
Nos. 1015-1024 (10) 5.00
Set value 1.00

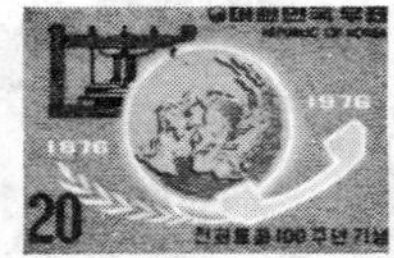

1876 and 1976 Telephones, Globe — A533

1976, Mar. 10

1025 A533 20w multicolored .25 .15

Centenary of first telephone call by Alexander Graham Bell, Mar. 10, 1876.

Homeland Reserves A534

1976, Apr. 3 Photo. *Perf. 13½x13*

1026 A534 20w multicolored .25 .15

8th Homeland Reserve Forces Day.

"People and Eye" — A535

1976, Apr. 7 *Perf. 13x13½*

1027 A535 20w multicolored .25 .15

World Health Day; "Foresight prevents blindness."

Pres. Park, Village Movement Flag — A536

Intellectual Pursuits — A537

1976, Apr. 22

1028 A536 20w shown .35 .15
1029 A537 20w shown .35 .15
1030 A537 20w Village improvement .35 .15
1031 A537 20w Agriculture .35 .15
1032 A537 20w Income from production .35 .15
a. Strip of 5, #1028-1032 1.75
Set value .50

6th anniv. of Pres. Park's New Village Movement for National Prosperity.

Mohenjo-Daro A538

1976, May 1 *Perf. 13½x13*

1033 A538 20w multicolored .25 .15

UNESCO campaign to save the Mohenjo-Daro excavations in Pakistan.

13-Star and 50-Star Flags A539

Girl Scouts, Campfire and Emblem A540

American Bicentennial (Bicentennial Emblem and): No. 1035, Statue of Liberty. No. 1036, Map of US and Mt. Rushmore monument. No. 1037, Liberty Bell. No. 1038, First astronaut on moon.

1976, May 8 *Perf. 13x13½*

1034 A539 100w blk, dp bl & red 1.75 .30
a. Souvenir sheet of 1 3.50
1035 A539 100w blk, dp bl & red 1.75 .30
1036 A539 100w blk, dp bl & red 1.75 .30
1037 A539 100w blk, dp bl & red 1.75 .30
1038 A539 100w blk, dp bl & red 1.75 .30
Nos. 1034-1038 (5) 8.75 1.50

1976, May 10

1039 A540 20w orange & multi .25 .15

Korean Federation of Girl Scouts, 30th anniv.

Stupas, Buddha of Borobudur A541

"Life Insurance" A542

1976, June 10

1040 A541 20w multicolored .25 .15

UNESCO campaign to save the Borobudur Temple, Java.

1976, July 1 Photo. *Perf. 13x13½*

1041 A542 20w multicolored .25 .15

National Life Insurance policies: "Over 100 billion-won," Apr. 30, 1976.

Volleyball — A543

1976, July 17

1042 A543 20w shown .25 .15
1043 A543 20w Boxing .25 .15
Set value .20

21st Olympic Games, Montreal, Canada, July 17-Aug. 1.

Children and Books — A544

1976, Aug. 10 *Perf. 13½x13*

1044 A544 20w brown & multi .25 .15

Books for children.

Civil Defense Corps, Flag and Members — A545

1976, Sept. 15 *Perf. 13x13½*

1045 A545 20w multicolored .25 .15

Civil Defense Corps, first anniversary.

Chamsungdan, Mani Mountain A546

Front Gate, Tongdosa Temple — A547

1976, Sept. 28 *Perf. 13½x13*

1046 A546 20w multicolored .25 .15
1047 A547 20w multicolored .25 .15
Set value .20

International Tourism Day.

Cadets and Academy
A548

1976, Oct. 1
1048 A548 20w multicolored .25 .15

Korean Military Academy, 30th anniversary.

Leaves and Stones, by Cheong Ju — A549

1976, Oct. 5 *Perf. 13x13½*
1049 A549 20w blk, gray & red .25 .15
a. Souvenir sheet of 2 1.25

Philatelic Week, Oct. 5-11.

Snake-headed Figure, Bas-relief — A550

Door-pull and Cranes — A551

1976, Dec. 1 Photo. *Perf. 13x13½*
1050 A550 20w multicolored .30 .15
a. Souvenir sheet of 2 .90
1051 A551 20w multicolored .30 .15
a. Souvenir sheet of 2 .90
Set value .20

New Year 1977.

Arrows, Cogwheels, Worker at Lathe — A552

No. 1053, Arrows, Cogwheels, ship in dock.

1977, Jan. 20 Photo. *Perf. 13½x13*
1052 A552 20w multicolored .25 .15
1053 A552 20w multicolored .25 .15
Set value .20

4th Economic Development Five-Year Plan.

Satellite Antenna and Microwaves — A553

1977, Jan. 31 *Perf. 13x13½*
1054 A553 20w multicolored .25 .15

Membership in ITU, 25th anniv.

Korean Broadcasting Center
A554

Parents and Two Children
A555

1977, Feb. 16 *Perf. 13½x13*
1055 A554 20w multicolored .25 .15

50th anniversary of broadcasting in Korea.

1977, Apr. 1 Photo. *Perf. 13½x13*
1056 A555 20w brt grn & orange .25 .15

Family planning.

Reservist on Duty
A556

Head with Symbols
A557

1977, Apr. 2 *Perf. 13x13½*
1057 A556 20w multicolored .25 .15

9th Homeland Reserve Forces Day.

1977, Apr. 21 Photo. *Perf. 13x13½*
1058 A557 20w dp lilac & multi .25 .15

10th anniversary of Science Day.

Book, Map, Syringe — A558

1977, Apr. 25
1059 A558 20w blue & multi .25 .15

35th International Meeting on Military Medicine.

Boy with Flowers and Dog — A559

Veteran's Emblem and Flag — A560

1977, May 5
1060 A559 20w multicolored .25 .15

Proclamation of Children's Charter, 20th anniversary.

1977, May 8
1061 A560 20w multicolored .25 .15

25th anniversary of Korean Veterans' Day.

Buddha, 8th Century, Sokkulam Grotto — A561

1977, May 25 Photo. *Perf. 13x13½*
1062 A561 20w sepia & olive .25 .15
a. Souvenir sheet of 2 1.25

"2600th" anniversary of birth of Buddha.

Ceramic Issues

Jar with Grape Design, 17th Century — A562

Celadon Vase, Bamboo Design, 12th Century — A563

Celadon Jar with Peonies
A564

Vase with Willow Reed Peony Pattern — A565

Celadon Manshaped Wine Jug — A566

Celadon Melon-shaped Vase — A567

Punch'ong Jar — A568

Celadon Cylindrical Vase — A569

1977, Mar. 15 Photo. *Perf. 13x13½*
1063 A562 20w vio brn & multi .30 .15
1064 A563 20w gray, grn & bis .30 .15

Perf. 13x13½, 13½x13

1977, June 15 **Photo.**
1065 A564 20w multicolored .30 .15
1066 A565 20w multicolored .30 .15

1977, July 15
1067 A566 20w multicolored .30 .15
1068 A567 20w multicolored .30 .15

1977, Aug. 15

Designs: No. 1069, White porcelain bowl with inlaid lotus vine design. No. 1070, Black Koryo ware vase with plum blossom vine.

1069 A564 20w multicolored .30 .15
1070 A565 20w multicolored .30 .15

1977, Nov. 15
1071 A568 20w multicolored .30 .15
1072 A569 20w multicolored .30 .15
Nos. 1063-1072 (10) 3.00
Set value 1.00

Types of 1962-66
Designs as Before

1976-77 Litho. *Perf. 12½*
Granite Paper
1076 A187 200w brown & lt grn
1077 A187a 300w sl grn & sal ('76)
1078 A187a 300w brown & salmon
1079 A187a 500w purple & lt grn

Magpie
A570

Nature Protection
A571

"Family Planning"
A572

Children on Swing
A573

Ceramic Horseman
A574

Muryangsu Hall, Busok Temple
A575

Pagoda, Pobjusa Temple
A576

Gold Crown, from Chonmachong Mound
A577

Monster Mask Tile, 6th or 7th Century
A578

Flying Angels from Bronze Bell from Sangwon-sa, 725 A.D.
A579

Perf. 12½x13½, 13½x12½

1977-79 **Photo.**
1088 A570 3w lt blue & blk .15 .15
1090 A326 10w emerald & blk .15 .15
1091 A571 20w multicolored .20 .15
1092 A572 20w emer & blk ('78) .20 .15
1093 A573 20w grn & org ('79) .20 .15
1097 A574 80w lt brn & sep .70 .40
1099 A575 200w salmon & brn 1.50 .50
1100 A576 300w brn purple 2.25 .60
1101 A577 500w multicolored 5.00 1.00

Perf. 13½x13
1102 A578 500w brown & purple 3.75 1.00

Perf. 13
1103 A579 1000w slate grn ('78) 7.50 2.00
Nos. 1088-1103 (11) 21.60 6.25

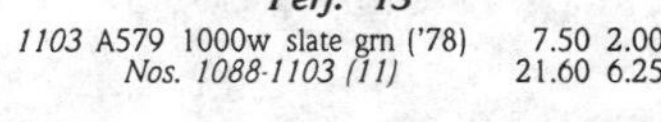

Ulleung Island — A580

Armed Forces — A581

Design: No. 1105, Haeundae Beach.

1977, Sept. 28 Photo. *Perf. 13*
1104 A580 20w multicolored .20 .15
1105 A580 20w multicolored .20 .15
Set value .20

World Tourism Day.

1977, Oct. 1 Photo. *Perf. 13*
1106 A581 20w green & multi .25 .15

Armed Forces Day.

Mt. Inwang after the Rain, by Chung Seon (1676-1759)
A582 A583

1977, Oct. 4

1107 A582 20w multicolored .25 .15
1108 A583 20w multicolored .25 .15
a. Souvenir sheet of 2 1.50
Set value .20

Philatelic Week, Oct. 4-10.

Rotary Emblem on Bronze Bell, Koryo Dynasty — A584

1977, Nov. 10 Photo. *Perf. 13*

1109 A584 20w multicolored .15 .15

Korean Rotary Club, 50th anniversary.

Korean Flag on Mt. Everest — A585

1977, Nov. 11

1110 A585 20w multicolored .30 .15

Korean Mt. Everest Expedition, reached peak, Sept. 15, 1977.

Children and Kites
A586

Horse-headed Figure, Bas-relief
A587

1977, Dec. 1 Photo. *Perf. 13*

1111 A586 20w multicolored .25 .15
a. Souvenir sheet of 2 .90
1112 A587 20w multicolored .25 .15
a. Souvenir sheet of 2 .90
Set value .20

New Year 1978.

Clay Pigeon Shooting
A588

Designs: No. 1114, Air pistol shooting. No. 1115, Air rifle shooting and target.

1977, Dec. 3

1113 A588 20w multicolored .20 .15
a. Souvenir sheet of 2 ('78) 1.00
1114 A588 20w multicolored .20 .15
a. Souvenir sheet of 2 ('78) 1.00
1115 A588 20w multicolored .20 .15
a. Souvenir sheet of 2 ('78) 1.00
Nos. 1113-1115 (3) .60
Set value .30
Nos. 1113a-1115a (3) 3.00

42nd World Shooting Championships, Seoul, 1978.

Boeing 727 over Globe, ICAO Emblem
A589

1977, Dec. 11

1116 A589 20w multicolored .25 .15

25th anniv. of Korea's membership in the ICAO.

Plane, Cargo, Freighter and Globe — A590

1977, Dec. 22 Photo. *Perf. 13*

1117 A590 20w multicolored .25 .15

Korean exports.

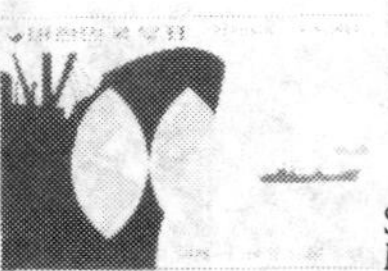

Ships and World Map — A591

1978, Mar. 13 Photo. *Perf. 13*

1118 A591 20w multicolored .25 .15

Maritime Day.

Stone Pagoda Issue

Four Lions Pagoda, Hwaom-sa — A592

Punhwang-sa Temple
A593

Kyongch'on sa Temple
A594

#1120, Seven-storied pagoda, T'appyongri.

1978, Mar. 20 Photo. *Perf. 13*

1119 A592 20w lt green & multi .35 .15
1120 A592 20w ocher & multi .35 .15

1978, May 20

Design: No. 1122, Miruk-sa Temple.

1121 A593 20w lt green & blk .35 .15
1122 A593 20w grn, brn & yel .35 .15

1978, June 20

Designs: #1123, Tabo Pagoda, Pulguk-sa. #1124, Three-storied pagoda, Pulguk-sa.

1123 A592 20w gray, lt grn & blk .35 .15
1124 A592 20w lilac & black .35 .15

1978, July 20 *Perf. 13½x12½*

Design: No. 1126, Octagonal Pagoda, Wolchong-sa Temple.

1125 A594 20w gray & brn .35 .15
1126 A594 20w lt green & blk .35 .15

1978, Nov. 20 *Perf. 13x13½*

Designs: No. 1127, 13-storied pagoda, Jeonghye-sa. No. 1128, Three-storied pagoda, Jinjeon-sa.

1127 A592 20w pale grn & multi .35 .15
1128 A592 20w lilac & multi .35 .15
Nos. 1119-1128 (10) 3.50
Set value 1.00

Ants and Coins — A595

Reservist with Flag — A596

1978, Apr. 1

1129 A595 20w multicolored .25 .15

Importance of saving.

1978, Apr. 1

1130 A596 20w multicolored .25 .15

10th Homeland Reserve Forces Day.

Seoul Cultural Center — A597

1978, Apr. 1

1131 A597 20w multicolored .25 .15

Opening of Seoul Cultural Center.

National Assembly in Plenary Session — A598

1978, May 31

1132 A598 20w multicolored .25 .15

30th anniversary of National Assembly.

Hands Holding Tools, Competition Emblem — A599

Bell of Joy and Crater Lake, Mt. Baegdu — A600

1978, Aug. 5 Photo. *Perf. 13*

1133 A599 20w multicolored .25 .15
a. Souvenir sheet of 2 1.25

24th World Youth Skill Olympics, Busan, Aug. 30-Sept. 15.

1978, Aug. 15

1134 A600 20w multicolored .25 .15

Founding of republic, 30th anniversary.

Nurse, Badge and Flowers
A601

Sobaeksan Observatory
A602

1978, Aug. 26

1135 A601 20w multicolored .25 .15

Army Nurse Corps, 30th anniversary.

1978, Sept. 13 Photo. *Perf. 13*

1136 A602 20w multicolored .25 .15

Opening of Sobaeksan Natl. Observatory.

Kyunghoeru Pavilion, Kyongbok Palace, Seoul — A603

Design: No. 1138, Baeg Do (island).

1978, Sept. 28

1137 A603 20w multicolored .25 .15
1138 A603 20w multicolored .25 .15
Set value .20

Tourist publicity.

Customs Flag and Officers
A604

1978, Sept. 28

1139 A604 20w multicolored .25 .15

Cent. of 1st Korean Custom House, Busan.

Armed Forces — A605

1978, Oct. 1 Photo. *Perf. 13*

1140 A605 20w multicolored .25 .15

Armed Forces, 30th anniversary.

Clay Figurines, Silla Dynasty
A606

Portrait of a Lady, by Shin Yoon-bok
A607

1978, Oct. 1

1141 A606 20w lt green & blk .25 .15

Culture Month, October 1978.

1978, Oct. 24

1142 A607 20w multicolored .25 .15
a. Souvenir sheet of 2 1.00

Philatelic Week, Oct. 24-29.

Young Men, YMCA Emblem — A608

1978, Oct. 28
1143 A608 20w multicolored .25 .15

75th anniv. of founding of Korean YMCA.

Hand Protecting Against Fire — A609

1978, Nov. 1 Photo. *Perf. 13*
1144 A609 20w multicolored .25 .15

Fire Prevention Day, Nov. 1.

Winter Landscape A610

Ram-headed Figure, Bas-relief A611

1978, Dec. 1 Photo. *Perf. 13x13½*
1145 A610 20w multicolored .25 .15
a. Souvenir sheet of 2 .75
1146 A611 20w multicolored .25 .15
a. Souvenir sheet of 2 .75
Set value .20

New Year 1979.

Hibiscus, Students, Globe — A612

President Park — A613

1978, Dec. 5
1147 A612 20w multicolored .25 .15

Proclamation of National Education Charter, 10th anniversary.

1978, Dec. 27
1148 A613 20w multicolored .40 .15
a. Souvenir sheet of 2 3.00

Inauguration of Park Chung Hee for fifth term as president.

Nature Conservation Issue

Golden Mandarinfish A614

Lace-bark Pines A615

Mandarin Ducks — A616

Neofinettia Orchid — A617

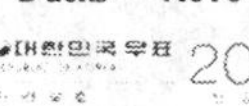

Goral — A618

Lilies of the Valley — A619

Rain Frog A620

Asian Polypody A621

Firefly — A622

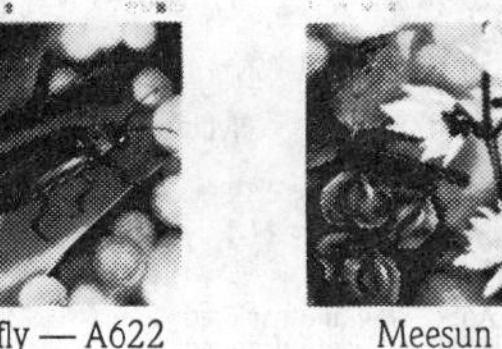

Meesun Tree — A623

1979, Feb. 20 Photo. *Perf. 13x13½*
1149 A614 20w multicolored .20 .15
1150 A615 20w multicolored .20 .15

1979, May 20
1151 A616 20w multicolored .20 .15
1152 A617 20w multicolored .20 .15

1979, June 20
1153 A618 20w multicolored .20 .15
1154 A619 20w multicolored .20 .15

1979, Nov. 25
1155 A620 20w multicolored .20 .15
1156 A621 20w multicolored .20 .15

1980, Jan. 20
1157 A622 30w multicolored .20 .15
1158 A623 30w multicolored .20 .15
Nos. 1149-1158 (10) 2.00
Set value .90

Samil Monument — A624

1979, Mar. 1 Photo. *Perf. 13x13½*
1159 A624 20w multicolored .25 .15

Samil independence movement, 60th anniv.

Worker and Bulldozer A625

1979, Mar. 10 *Perf. 13½x13*
1160 A625 20w multicolored .25 .15

Labor Day.

Hand Holding Tools, Gun and Grain — A626

Tabo Pagoda, Pulguk-sa Temple — A627

Women, Silk Screen — A628

1979, Apr. 1 *Perf. 13x13½*
1161 A626 20w multicolored .25 .15

Strengthening national security.

1979, Apr. 1

Art Treasures: No. 1163, Statue. No. 1164, Crown. No. 1165, Celadon Vase.

1162 A627 20w gray bl & multi .15 .15
1163 A627 20w bister & multi .15 .15
1164 A627 20w violet & multi .15 .15
1165 A627 20w brt grn & multi .15 .15
1166 A628 60w multicolored .35 .30
a. Souvenir sheet of 2 1.75
Set value .85 .70

5000 years of Korean art.
See Nos. 1175-1179, 1190.

Pulguk-sa Temple and PATA Emblem — A629

1979, Apr. 16 *Perf. 13½x13*
1167 A629 20w multicolored .20 .15

28th Pacific Area Travel Association (PATA) Conf., Seoul, Apr. 16-18, and Gyeongju, Apr. 20-21.

Presidents Park and Senghor A630

1979, Apr. 22 *Perf. 13½x13*
1168 A630 20w multicolored .25 .15
a. Souvenir sheet of 2 1.00

Visit of Pres. Leopold Sedar Senghor of Senegal.

Basketball — A631

1979, Apr. 29 *Perf. 13x13½*
1169 A631 20w multicolored .25 .15

8th World Women's Basketball Championship, Seoul, Apr. 29-May 13.

Children and IYC Emblem A632

1979, May 5 Photo. *Perf. 13½x13*
1170 A632 20w multicolored .25 .15
a. Souvenir sheet of 2 1.00

International Year of the Child.

Traffic Pollution — A633

1979, June 5 Photo. *Perf. 13x13½*
1171 A633 20w green & dk brn .15 .15

Pollution control.

Flags, Presidents Park and Carter — A634

1979, June 29 *Perf. 13½x13*
1172 A634 20w multicolored .25 .15
a. Souvenir sheet of 2 1.00

Visit of Pres. Jimmy Carter.

Korean Exhibition Center — A635

1979, July 3
1173 A635 20w multicolored .15 .15

Opening of Korean Exhibition Center.

Jet, Globe, Pagoda — A636

1979, Aug. 1 Photo. *Perf. 13½x13*
1174 A636 20w multicolored .15 .15

10th anniversary of Korean airlines.

Art Treasure Types

Designs: No. 1175, Porcelain jar, 17th century. No. 1176, Man on horseback, ceremonial pitcher, horiz. No. 1177, Sword Dance, by Shin Yun-bok. No. 1178, Golden Amitabha with halo, 8th century. No. 1179, Hahoe ritual mask.

1979 Photo. *Perf. 13x13½, 13½x13*
1175 A627 20w lilac & multi .15 .15
1176 A627 20w multicolored .15 .15
1177 A628 60w multicolored .50 .30
a. Souvenir sheet of 2 1.75
Nos. 1175-1177 (3) .80
Set value .50

Issued: #1177, Sept. 1; #1175-1176, Oct. 15.

1979, Nov. 15

1178 A627 20w dp green & multi .20 .15
1179 A627 20w multicolored .20 .15
Set value .20

Yongdu Rock — A637

1979, Sept. 28

1180 A637 20w shown .20 .15
1181 A637 20w Mt. Mai, vert. .20 .15
Set value .20

World Tourism Day.

People, Blood and Heart — A637a

1979, Oct. 1 *Perf. 13½x13*

1182 A637a 20w multicolored .15 .15

Blood Banks, 4th anniversary.

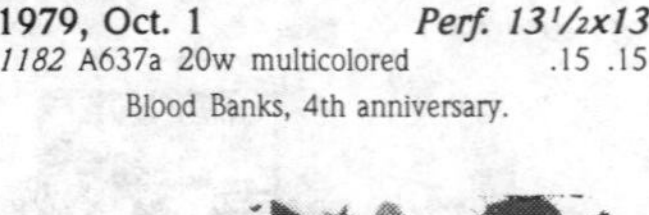

"My Life in the Year 2000" A638

1979, Oct. 30 *Perf. 13½x13*

1183 A638 20w multicolored .25 .15
a. Souvenir sheet of 2 1.00

Philatelic Week, Oct. 30-Nov. 4.

Monkey-headed Figure, Bas-relief A639

Children Playing Yut A640

1979, Dec. 1

1184 A639 20w multicolored .20 .15
a. Souvenir sheet of 2 .75
1185 A640 20w multicolored .20 .15
a. Souvenir sheet of 2 .75
Set value .20

New Year 1980.

Inauguration of Pres. Choi Kyu-hah — A641

1979, Dec. 21

1186 A641 20w multicolored .30 .15
a. Souvenir sheet of 2 1.50

President Park — A642

1980, Feb. 2 Photo. *Perf. 13x13½*

1187 A642 30w orange brn .20 .15
1188 A642 30w dull purple .20 .15
a. Souvenir sheet of 2 1.25
b. Pair, #1187-1188 .40 .30

President Park Chung Hee (1917-1979) memorial.

Art Treasure Type of 1979 and

Dragon-shaped Kettle — A643

Design: 60w, Landscape, by Kim Hong-do.

Perf. 13½x13, 13x13½

1980, Feb. 20 Photo.

1189 A643 30w multicolored .20 .15
1190 A628 60w multicolored .40 .30
a. Souvenir sheet of 2 1.75

Art Treasure Issue

Heavenly Horse, Saddle — A644

Dragon Head, Banner Staff — A645

Tiger, Granite Sculpture — A647

Mounted Nobleman Mural — A646

Human Face, Roof Tile — A648

Deva King Sculpture — A650

White Tiger Mural — A649

Earthenware Ducks A651 A652

Tiger, Folk Painting — A653

1980 Photo. *Perf. 13½x13, 13x13½*

1191 A644 30w multicolored .25 .15
1192 A645 30w multicolored .25 .15
1193 A646 30w multicolored .25 .15
1194 A647 30w multicolored .25 .15
1195 A648 30w multicolored .25 .15
1196 A649 30w multicolored .25 .15

Engr. *Perf. 12½x13*

1197 A650 30w black .25 .15
1198 A650 30w red .25 .15
Nos. 1191-1198 (8) 2.00
Set value .40

Issued: #1191-1192, 4/20; #1193-1194, 5/20; #1195-1196, 8/20; #1197-1198, 11/20.

1983 Litho. Engr. *Perf. 13*

1199 A651 1000w bis brn & red brn 5.00 .80
1200 A652 1000w bis brn & red brn 5.00 .80
a. Pair, #1199-1200 10.00 2.50
1201 A653 5000w multicolored 17.00 4.25
a. Souvenir sheet, perf. 13½x13 30.00
Nos. 1199-1201 (3) 27.00 5.85

Issued: #1199-1200, Nov. 25; #1201, Dec. 1.
No. 1201a for PHILAKOREA '84. No. 1201a exists imperf.

Lotus Blossoms and Ducks — A656

Tiger and Magpie — A657

Perf. 13x13½, 13½x13

1980, Mar. 10

1203 A656 30w multicolored .25 .15
1204 A657 60w multicolored .50 .30

Red Phoenix (in Form of Rooster) — A658

Moon Over Mt. Konryun — A659

No. 1207, Sun over Mt. Konryun. No. 1207a has continuous design.

1980, May 10 *Perf. 13x13½*

1205 A658 30w multicolored .35 .15
1206 A659 60w multicolored .70 .30
1207 A659 60w multicolored .70 .30
a. Souvenir sheet of 2, #1206-1207 1.75
b. Pair, #1206-1207 1.40 .60
Nos. 1205-1207 (3) 1.75 .75

Rabbits Pounding Grain in a Mortar — A660

Dragon in the Clouds — A661

1980, July 10 Photo. *Perf. 13x13½*

1208 A660 30w multicolored .25 .15
1209 A661 30w multicolored .25 .15
Set value .15

Pine Tree, Pavilion, Mountain A662

Flowers and Birds, Bridal Room Screen A663

1980, Aug. 9 Photo. *Perf. 13x13½*

1210 A662 30w multicolored .30 .15
1211 A663 30w multicolored .30 .15
Set value .15

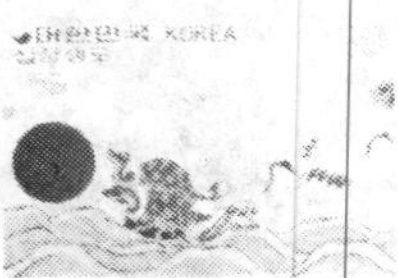

Tortoises and Cranes — A664

Designs: Symbols of longevity.

1980, Nov. 10 Photo. *Perf. 13½x13*

1212 Strip of 4 1.25 .20
a. A664 30w any single .30 .15

New Community Movement, 10th Anniv. — A668

Freighters at Sea — A669

1980, Apr. 22 *Perf. 13x13½*

1216 A668 30w multicolored .30 .15

1980, Mar. 13

1217 A669 30w multicolored .30 .15

Increase of Korea's shipping tonnage to 5 million tons.

Soccer — A670

1980, Aug. 23 *Perf. 13x13½*

1218 A670 30w multicolored .30 .15

10th President's Cup Soccer Tournament, Aug. 23-Sept. 5.

Mt. Sorak — A671

Paikryung Island — A672

Perf. 12½x13½

1980, Apr. 10 Photo.

1219 A671 15w multicolored .15 .15
1220 A672 90w multicolored .60 .15
Set value .15

Flag — A673

1980 *Perf. 13½x13*
1221 A673 30w multicolored .25 .15

Coil Stamp
Perf. Vert.
1221A A673 30w multicolored .25 .15

UN Intervention, 30th Anniv. — A674

Election of Miss World in Seoul — A675

1980, June 25 *Perf. 13x13½*
1222 A674 30w multicolored .25 .15

1980, July 8
1223 A675 30w multicolored .25 .15

Women's Army Corps, 30th Anniversary A676

1980, Sept. 6 *Perf. 13½x13*
1224 A676 30w multicolored .30 .15

Baegma River — A677

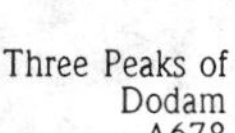
Three Peaks of Dodam A678

1980, Sept. 28
1225 A677 30w multicolored .25 .15
1226 A678 30w multicolored .25 .15
Set value .15

Inauguration of Pres. Chun Doo-hwan A679

1980, Sept. 1
1227 A679 30w multicolored .30 .15
a. Souvenir sheet of 2 1.00

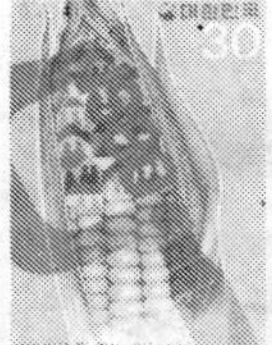
Ear of Corn — A680

Symbolic Tree — A681

1980, Oct. 20 *Perf. 13x13½*
1228 A680 30w multicolored .25 .15

12th population and housing census.

1980, Oct. 27
1229 A681 30w multicolored .25 .15

National Red Cross, 75th anniversary.

"Mail-Delivering Angels" A682

1980, Nov. 6 *Perf. 13½x13*
1230 A682 30w multicolored .25 .15
a. Souvenir sheet of 2 .75

Philatelic Week, Nov. 6-11.

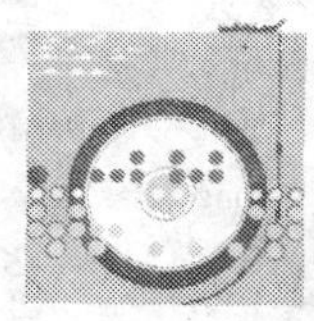
Korea-Japan Submarine Cable System Inauguration — A683

1980, Nov. 28 *Perf. 13x13½*
1231 A683 30w multicolored .25 .15

Rooster — A684

Cranes — A685

1980, Dec. 1
1232 A684 30w multicolored .35 .15
a. Souvenir sheet of 2 .75
1233 A685 30w multicolored .35 .15
a. Souvenir sheet of 2 .75
Set value .15

New Year 1981.

Second Inauguration of Pres. Chun Doo-hwan A686

1981, Mar. 3 Photo. *Perf. 13½x13*
1234 A686 30w multicolored .30 .15
a. Souvenir sheet of 2 1.00

Ship Issue

Oil Tanker — A687

Cargo Ship — A688

Oil Tanker — A689

Cargo Ship — A690

Tug Boat — A691

Stern Trawler — A692

Log Carrier — A693

Auto Carrier — A694

Chemical Carrier A695

Passenger Boat — A696

Perf. 13½x13, 13x13½

1981, Mar. 13
1235 A687 30w multicolored .25 .15
1236 A688 90w multicolored .75 .15

5th Maritime Day.

1981, May 10 Photo. *Perf. 13½x13*
1237 A689 30w multicolored .25 .15
1238 A690 90w multicolored .75 .15

1981, July 10 *Perf. 13½x13*
1239 A691 40w multicolored .30 .15
1240 A692 100w multicolored .80 .20

1981, Aug. 10
1241 A693 40w multicolored .40 .15
1242 A694 100w multicolored .95 .20

1981, Nov. 10 Engr. *Perf. 13x12½*
1243 A695 40w black .40 .15
1244 A696 100w dk blue .95 .20
Nos. 1235-1244 (10) 5.80
Set value 1.05

11th Natl. Assembly Opening Session — A697

1981, Apr. 17 Photo. *Perf. 13½x13*
1245 A697 30w gold & dk brn .25 .15

Hand Reading Braille, Helping Hands — A698

1981, Apr. 30 Photo. *Perf. 13x13½*
1246 A698 30w shown .20 .15
1247 A698 90w Man in wheelchair .55 .15
Set value .20

International Year of the Disabled.

Ribbon and Council Emblem A699

Clena River and Mountains A700

1981, June 5 Photo. *Perf. 13x13½*
1248 A699 40w multicolored .25 .15

Advisory Council on Peaceful Unification Policy (North and South Korea) anniv.

1981, June 5
1249 A700 30w shown .20 .15
1250 A700 90w Seagulls .55 .15
Set value .20

10th World Environment Day.

Pres. Chun and Pres. Suharto of Indonesia A701

Pres. Chun Visit to Asia: b, King of Malaysia. c, Korean, Singapore flags. d, King Bhumibol Adulyadej of Thailand. e, Pres. Marcos of Philippines.

1981, June 25 *Perf. 13½x13*
1251 Strip of 5 1.25 .25
a.-e. A701 40w, any single .25 .15
f. Souvenir sheet of 5, imperf. 1.25

Size: 49x33mm
Perf. 13x13½
1252 A701 40w multicolored .25 .15
a. Souvenir sheet of 2, imperf. 1.00
Set value .30

36th Anniv. of Liberation — A702

1981, Aug. 15 Photo. *Perf. 13x13½*
1253 A702 40w multicolored .30 .15

Tolharubang, "Stone Grandfather" A704

Rose of Sharon A705

Porcelain Jar, 17th Cent. — A706

Chomsongdae Observatory, 7th Cent. — A707

Mounted Warrior, Earthenware Jug, 5th Cent. A708

Family Planning A709

Walking Stick — A710

Ryu Kwan-soon (1904-20), Martyr — A711

"Tasan" Chung Yak-yong, Lee Dynasty Scholar — A712

Ahn Joong-guen (1879-1910), Martyr — A713

Ahn Chang-ho (1878-1938), Independence Fighter — A714

Koryo Celadon Incense Burner — A715

Kim Ku (1876-1949), Statesman — A716

Mountain Landscape Brick Bas-relief — A717

Mandarin Duck, Celadon Incense Burner — A718

Perf. 13½x12½ (Nos. 1256, 1257, 1266), 13, 13½x13, 13x13½

1981-89 Photo., Engr.

1255	A704	20w multi ('86)	.15	.15
1256	A705	40w multi	.25	.15
1257	A706	60w multi	.35	.15
1258	A707	70w multi	.45	.15
1259	A708	80w multi ('83)	.50	.15
1260	A709	80w multi ('86)	.25	.15
1261	A710	80w multi ('89)	.25	.15
1262	A711	100w lilac	.65	.15
1263	A712	100w gray blk ('86)	.30	.15
1264	A713	200w lt ol grn & ol	1.25	.25
1265	A714	300w dl lil ('83)	1.10	.25
1266	A715	400w multi	2.75	.50
1267	A715	400w pale grn & multi ('83)	2.50	.40
1268	A716	450w dk vio brn ('86)	1.25	.40
1269	A717	500w multi	3.00	.75
1270	A718	700w multi ('83)	4.25	.80
		Nos. 1255-1270 (16)	19.25	
		Set value		3.95

Inscription and denomination of No. 1266, colorless, No. 1267, dark brown.

See Nos. 1449, 1449C, 1594F.

Coil Stamp

Photo. ***Perf. 13 Horiz.***

1271 A707 70w multicolored .40 .15

Girl Flying Model Plane — A721

Air Force Chief of Staff Cup, 3rd Aeronautic Competition: Various model planes.

1981, Sept. 20 ***Perf. 13½x13***

1272 Strip of 5 1.50 .30
a. A721 10w multi .15 .15
b. A721 20w multi .15 .15
c. A721 40w multi .30 .15
d. A721 50w multi .35 .15
e. A721 80w multi .60 .15

WHO Emblem, Citizens — A722

World Tourism Day — A723

1981, Sept. 22 ***Perf. 13x13½***

1273 A722 40w multicolored .25 .15

WHO, 32nd Western Pacific Regional Committee Meeting, Seoul, Sept. 22-28.

1981, Sept. 28

1274 A723 40w Seoul Tower .25 .15
1275 A723 40w Ulreung Isld. .25 .15
Set value .15

Bicycle Racing — A724

1981, Oct. 10 ***Perf. 13½x13***

1276 A724 40w shown .25 .15
1277 A724 40w Swimming .25 .15
Set value .15

62nd Natl. Sports Festival, Seoul, Oct. 10-15.

Flags, Presidents Chun and Carazo — A725

1981, Oct. 12 ***Perf. 13½x13***

1278 A725 40w multicolored .25 .15

Visit of Pres. Rodrigo Carazo Odio of Costa Rica, Oct. 12-14.

World Food Day — A726

First Natl. Aviation Day — A727

1981, Oct. 16 ***Perf. 13x13½***

1279 A726 40w multicolored .25 .15

1981, Oct. 30 ***Perf. 13½x13***

1280 A727 40w multicolored .25 .15

1988 Olympic Games, Seoul — A728

9th Philatelic Week, Nov. 18-24 — A729

1981, Oct. 30 ***Perf. 13x13½***

1281 A728 40w multicolored .40 .15

1981, Nov. 18 ***Perf. 13½x13***

1282 A729 40w multicolored .25 .15
a. Souvenir sheet of 2 .90

Camellia and Dog — A730

Children Flying Kite — A731

1981, Dec. 1 ***Perf. 13x13½***

1283 A730 40w multicolored .25 .15
a. Souvenir sheet of 2 .65
1284 A731 40w multicolored .25 .15
a. Souvenir sheet of 2 .65
Set value .15

New Year 1982 (Year of the Dog).

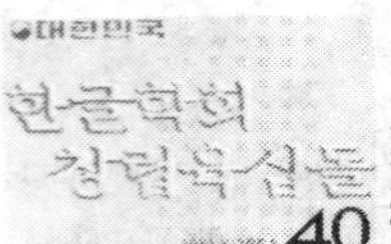
Hangul Hakhoe Language Society, 60th Anniv. — A732

1981, Dec. 3 ***Perf. 13½x13***

1285 A732 40w multicolored .25 .15

Telecommunications Authority Inauguration A733

Scouting Year A734

1982, Jan. 4 Photo. ***Perf. 13x13½***

1286 A733 60w multicolored .35 .15

1982, Feb. 22

1287 A734 60w multicolored .35 .15

60th Anniv. of YWCA in Korea — A735

Intl. Polar Year Centenary — A736

1982, Apr. 20 Photo. ***Perf. 13x13½***

1288 A735 60w multicolored .35 .15

1982, Apr. 21 ***Perf. 13½x13***

1289 A736 60w multicolored .35 .15

60th Children's Day — A737

1982, May 5 ***Perf. 13½x13***

1290 A737 60w multicolored .35 .15

Visit of Liberian Pres. Samuel K. Doe, May 9-13 A738

1982, May 9 Litho. ***Perf. 13x12½***

1291 A738 60w multicolored .35 .15
a. Souvenir sheet of 2, imperf. 1.00

Centenary of US-Korea Treaty of Amity — A739

1982, May 18 Photo. ***Perf. 13½x13***

1292 A739 60w Statue of Liberty, pagoda .35 .15
1293 A739 60w Emblem .35 .15
a. Souvenir sheet of 2 1.50
b. Pair, #1292-1293 .75 .25
Set value .15

Visit of Zaire Pres. Mobutu Sese Seko, June 7-10 — A740

1982, June 7 Litho. ***Perf. 13x12½***

1294 A740 60w multicolored .35 .15
a. Souvenir sheet of 2, imperf. 1.00

Historical Painting Issue

Gen. Kwon Yul's Victory at Haengju, by Oh Seung-woo — A747

Designs: No. 1295, Territorial Expansion by Kwanggaeto the Great, by Lee Chong-sang, 1975. No. 1296, Gen. Euljimunduck's Victory at Salsoo, by Park Kak-soon, 1975. No. 1297, Shilla's Repulse of Tang's Army, by Oh Seung-woo. No. 1298, Gen. Kang Kam-chan's Victory at Kyiju, by Lee Yong-hwan. No. 1299, Admiral Yi Sun-sin's Victory at Hansan, 1592, by Kim Hyung-ku. No. 1300, Gen. Kim Chwa-jin's Battle at Chungsanri, by Sohn Soo-kwang. No. 1302, Kim Chong-suh's Exploitation of Yukjin, 1434, by Kim Tae.

1982 Photo. ***Perf. 13x13½***

1295 A747 60w multicolored .60 .20
1296 A747 60w multicolored .60 .20
1297 A747 60w multicolored .60 .20
1298 A747 60w multicolored .60 .20
1299 A747 60w multicolored .60 .15
1300 A747 60w multicolored .60 .15
1301 A747 60w multicolored .60 .15
1302 A747 60w multicolored .60 .15
Nos. 1295-1302 (8) 4.80
Set value 1.20

Issued: #1295-1296, 6/15; #1297-1298, 7/15; #1299-1300, 10/15; #1301-1302, 12/15.

55th Intl. YMCA Convention, Seoul, July 20-23 — A749

Flags, Presidents Chun and Arap Moi — A750

1982, July 20

1303 A749 60w multicolored .35 .25

1982, Aug. 17 ***Perf. 13½x13***

Pres. Chun's Visit to Africa & Canada: #1304, Kenya (Pres. Daniel T. Arap Moi), Aug. 17-19. #1305, Nigeria (Pres. Alhaji Shehe Shagari), Aug. 19-22. #1306, Gabon (Pres. El Hadj Omar Bongo), Aug. 22-24. #1307, Senegal (Pres. Abdou Diouf), Aug. 24-26. #1308, Canada, Aug. 28-31.

1304 A750 60w multicolored .35 .25
1305 A750 60w multicolored .35 .25
1306 A750 60w multicolored .35 .25
1307 A750 60w multicolored .35 .25
1308 A750 60w multicolored .35 .25
Nos. 1304-1308 (5) 1.75 1.25

Souvenir Sheets of 2

1304a A750 60w 1.00
1305a A750 60w 1.00
1306a A750 60w 1.00
1307a A750 60w 1.00
1308a A750 60w 1.00
Nos. 1304a-1308a (5) 5.00

Natl. Flag Centenary A751

1982, Aug. 22

1309 A751 60w multicolored .35 .25
a. Souvenir sheet of 2 1.25

2nd Seoul Open Intl. Table Tennis Championship, Aug. 25-31 — A752

1982, Aug. 25

1310 A752 60w multicolored .35 .25

27th World Amateur Baseball Championship Series, Seoul, Sept. 4-18 — A753

1982, Sept. 4 **Engr.** ***Perf. 13***

1311 A753 60w red brn .35 .15

Seoul Intl. Trade Fair (SITRA '82), Sept. 24-Oct. 18 — A754

1982, Sept. 17 **Photo.** ***Perf. 13½x13***

1312 A754 60w multicolored .35 .15

Philatelic Week, Oct. 15-21 — A755

Design: Miners reading consolatory letters.

1982, Oct. 15

1313 A755 60w multicolored .35 .15
a. Souvenir sheet of 2 1.00

Visit of Indonesian Pres. Suharto, Oct. 16-19 A756

1982, Oct. 16 **Litho.** ***Perf. 13x12½***

1314 A756 60w multicolored .35 .15
a. Souvenir sheet of 2, imperf. 1.10

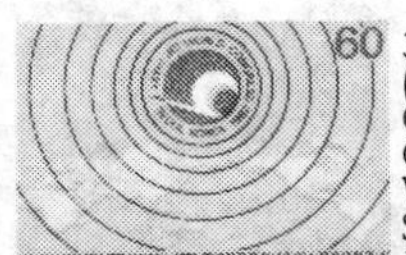

37th Jaycee (Intl. Junior Chamber of Commerce) World Congress, Seoul, Nov. 3-18 — A757

1982, Nov. 3 ***Perf. 13½x13***

1315 A757 60w multicolored .35 .15

2nd UN Conference on Peaceful Uses of Outer Space, Vienna, Aug. 9-21 — A758

1982, Nov. 20 ***Perf. 13x13½***

1316 A758 60w multicolored .35 .15

New Year 1983 (Year of the Boar) — A759

Flags of Korea and Turkey — A760

1982, Dec. 1

1317 A759 60w Magpies, money bag .35 .15
a. Souvenir sheet of 2 1.00
1318 A759 60w Boar, bas-relief .35 .15
a. Souvenir sheet of 2 1.00
Set value .15

1982, Dec. 20 ***Perf. 13***

1319 A760 60w multicolored .35 .15
a. Souvenir sheet of 2, imperf. 1.00

Visit of Pres. Kenan Evren of Turkey, Dec. 20-23.

Letter Writing Campaign A761

First Intl. Customs Day A762

1982, Dec. 31 **Photo.** ***Perf. 13x13½***

1320 A761 60w multicolored .35 .15

1983, Jan. 26 ***Perf. 13½x13***

1321 A762 60w multicolored .35 .15

Korean-made Vehicle Issue

Hyundai Pony-2 — A764

Daewoo Maepsy — A765

Super Titan Truck — A768

Flat-bed Truck — A770

1983 **Photo.** ***Perf. 13½x13***

1322 A764 60w Keohwa Jeep .45 .15
1323 A764 60w shown .45 .15
a. Pair, #1322-1323 .95 .30
1324 A765 60w shown .45 .15
1325 A764 60w Kia minibus .45 .15
a. Pair, #1324-1325 .95 .30
1326 A764 60w Highway bus .45 .15
1327 A768 60w shown .45 .15
1328 A764 70w Dump truck .55 .15
1329 A770 70w shown .55 .15
1330 A764 70w Cement mixer .55 .15
1331 A764 70w Oil truck .55 .15
Nos. 1322-1331 (10) 4.90
Set value .70

Issued: #1322-1323, Feb. 25; #1324-1325, Mar. 25; #1326-1327, May 25; #1328-1329, July 25; #1330-1331, Aug. 25.

Visit of Malaysian Seri Paduka Baginda, Mar. 22-26 — A773

1983, Mar. 22

1332 A773 60w multicolored .35 .15
a. Souvenir sheet of 2 1.25

Postal Service Issue

General Bureau of Postal Administration Building — A774

Mailman, 1884 — A776

Ancient Mail Carrier — A778

Nos. 1-2 — A780

Pre-modern Period Postal Symbol, Mailbox — A782

Designs: #1334, Seoul Central PO. #1336, Mailman on motorcycle, 1983. #1338, Modern mail transport. #1340, No. 1201. #1342, Current postal symbol, mailbox.

1983, Apr. 22 **Photo.** ***Perf. 13½x13***

1333 A774 60w multicolored .60 .15
1334 A774 60w multicolored .60 .15
1335 A776 70w multicolored .70 .15
1336 A776 70w multicolored .70 .15
1337 A778 70w multicolored .70 .15
1338 A778 70w multicolored .70 .15
1339 A780 70w multi ('84) .45 .15
1340 A780 70w multi ('84) .45 .15
1341 A782 70w multi ('84) .45 .15
1342 A782 70w multi ('84) .45 .15
Nos. 1333-1342 (10) 5.80
Set value .65

PHILAKOREA '84, Seoul, Oct. 22-31, 1984.
Issue dates: #1333-1334, Apr. 22; #1335-1336, June 10; #1337-1338, Aug. 10; #1339-1340, Feb. 10; #1341-1342, Mar. 10.

Teachers' Day — A784

1983, May 15 **Photo.** ***Perf. 13x13½***

1343 A784 60w Village schoolhouse, score .35 .15
a. Souvenir sheet of 2 1.50

World Communications Year — A785

1983, June 20

1344 A785 70w multicolored .40 .15
a. Souvenir sheet of 2 1.00

Communications Life Insurance Inauguration A786

1983, July 1 Photo. Perf. 13½x13
1345 A786 70w multicolored .40 .15

Science and Technology Symposium, Seoul, July 4-8 — A787

1983, July 4
1346 A787 70w multicolored .40 .15

Visit of Jordan's King Hussein, Sept. 10-13 A788

1983, Sept. 10 Litho. Perf. 13x12½
1347 A788 70w Pres. Hwan, King Hussein, flags .40 .15
a. Souvenir sheet of 2, imperf. 1.25

ASTA, 53rd World Travel Congress, Seoul — A789

1983, Sept. 25 Photo. Perf. 13
1348 A789 70w multicolored .40 .15

A790 A791

1983, Oct. 4 Photo. Perf. 13
1349 A790 70w multicolored .40 .15
a. Souvenir sheet of 2 1.00

70th Inter-Parliamentary Union Conference.

1983, Oct. 6 Photo. Perf. 13
1350 A791 70w Gymnastics .40 .15
1351 A791 70w Soccer .40 .15
Set value .15

64th National Sports Festival.

Pres. Chun and Pres. U San Yu of Burma — A791a

Pres. Chun's Curtailed Visit to Southwest Asia: No. 1351B, India. No. 1351C, Pres. Junius R. Jayawardene, Sri Lanka. No. 1351D, Australia, flag. No. 1351E, New Zealand, flag. Withdrawn after one day due to political assassination.

1983, Oct. 8 Photo. Perf. 13½x13
1351A A791a 70w multicolored 1.50
1351B A791a 70w multicolored 1.50
1351C A791a 70w multicolored 1.50
1351D A791a 70w multicolored 1.50
1351E A791a 70w multicolored 1.50
Nos. 1351A-1351E (5) 7.50

Souvenir Sheets of 2

1351f A791a 70w 2.25
1351g A791a 70w 2.25
1351h A791a 70w 2.25
1351i A791a 70w 2.25
1351j A791a 70w 2.25
Nos. 1351f-1351j (5) 11.25

Water Resource Development A792

Newspaper Publication Cent. A793

1983, Oct. 15 Litho. Perf. 13
1352 A792 70w multicolored .40 .15

1983, Oct. 31 Litho. Perf. 13
1353 A793 70w multicolored .30 .15

Natl. Tuberculosis Assoc., 30th Anniv. — A794

1983, Nov. 6 Photo. Perf. 13
1354 A794 70w multicolored .30 .15

Presidents Chun and Reagan, Natl. Flags — A795

1983, Nov. 12 Photo. Perf. 13
1355 A795 70w multicolored .30 .15
a. Souvenir sheet of 2 1.50

Visit of Pres. Ronald Reagan, Nov. 12-14.

11th Philatelic Week — A796

1983, Nov. 18 Photo. Perf. 13
1356 A796 70w multicolored .30 .15
a. Souvenir sheet of 2 2.25

New Year 1984
A797 A798

1983, Dec. 1 Photo. Perf. 13
1357 A797 70w Mouse, stone wall relief .25 .15
a. Souvenir sheet of 2 1.25
1358 A798 70w Cranes, pine tree .25 .15
a. Souvenir sheet of 2 1.25
Set value .15

Bicentenary of Catholic Church in Korea — A799

1984, Jan. 4 Photo. Perf. 13x13½
1359 A799 70w Cross .35 .15
a. Souvenir sheet of 2 3.00

Visit of Brunei's Sultan Bolkiah-Apr. 7-9 — A800

1984, Apr. 7 Litho. Perf. 13x12½
1360 A800 70w multicolored .25 .15
a. Souvenir sheet of 2, imperf. 1.10

Visit of Qatar's Sheik Khalifa, Apr. 20-22 A801

1984, Apr. 20
1361 A801 70w multicolored .25 .15
a. Souvenir sheet of 2, imperf. 1.00

Girl Mailing Letter — A802

Mailman in City — A803

1984, Apr. 22 Photo. Perf. 13½x13
1362 A802 70w multicolored .25 .15
a. Souvenir sheet of 2 1.00
1363 A803 70w multicolored .25 .15
a. Souvenir sheet of 2 1.00
Set value .15

Korean postal service.

Visit of Pope John Paul II, May 3-7 — A808

Engraved, Photogravure and Engraved
1984, May 3 Perf. 12½
1368 A808 70w dk brn .30 .15
1369 A808 70w multicolored .30 .15
a. Souvenir sheet of 2, #1368-1369, perf. 13½ 1.50
Set value .15

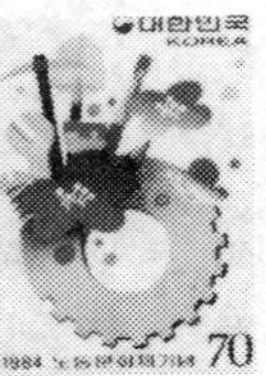
A809 A810

1984, May 11 Photo. Perf. 13x13½
1370 A809 70w Tools, brushes, flower .25 .15

Workers' Cultural Festival.

1984, May 21 Photo. Perf. 13x13½
1371 A810 70w Jet, ship, Asia map .25 .15

Customs Cooperation Council 63rd-64th Sessions, Seoul, May 21-25.

Visit of Sri Lanka's Pres. Jayewardene, May 27-30 — A811

1984, May 27 Perf. 13½x13
1372 A811 70w Asia map, flags, flowers .25 .15
a. Souvenir sheet of 2 1.10

Advertising Congress Emblem A812

'88 Olympic Expressway Opening A813

1984, June 18 Photo. Perf. 13x13½
1373 A812 70w ADASIA '84 emblem .25 .15

14th Asian Advertising Cong., Seoul, June 18-21.

1984, June 22
1374 A813 70w multicolored .25 .15

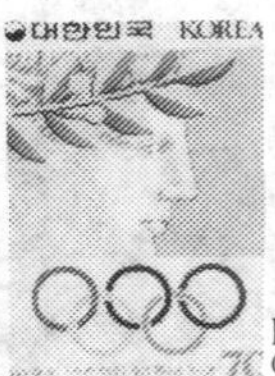
Intl. Olympic Committee, 90th Anniv. — A814

1984, June 23
1375 A814 70w multicolored .25 .15

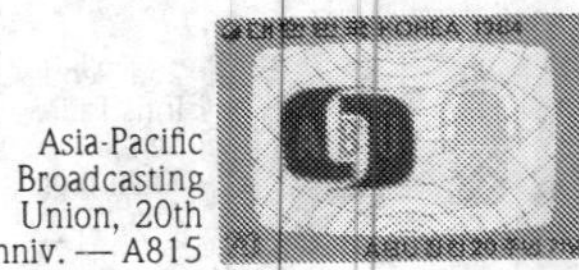
Asia-Pacific Broadcasting Union, 20th Anniv. — A815

1984, June 30 Perf. 13½x13
1376 A815 70w Emblem, microphone .25 .15

Visit of Senegal's Pres. Diouf, July 9-12 A816

1984, July 9 Litho. Perf. 13x12½
1377 A816 70w Flags of Korea & Senegal .25 .15
a. Souvenir sheet of 2, imperf. 1.10

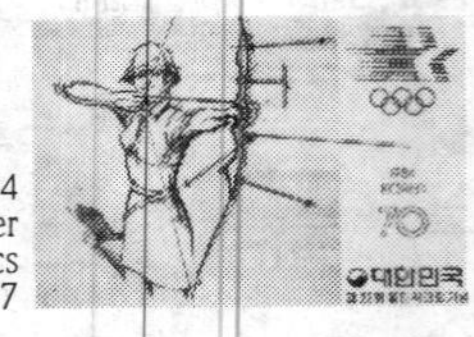
1984 Summer Olympics A817

Lithographed and Engraved
1984, July 28 Perf. 12½
1378 A817 70w Archery .20 .15
1379 A817 440w Fencing 1.25 .25
Set value .30

Korean Protestant Church Cent.
A818

Groom on Horseback
A819

Stained glass windows.

1984, Aug. 16 *Perf. 13*

1380 A818 70w Crucifixion .45 .15
1381 A818 70w Cross, dove .45 .15
a. Souvenir sheet of 2 4.00
b. Pair, #1380-1381 .90 .25

1984, Sept. 1 Photo. *Perf. 13x13½*

Wedding Procession: a, Lantern carrier. b, Groom. c, Musician. d, Bride in sedan chair (52x33mm).

1382 Strip of 4 1.40 .20
a.-d. A819 70w any single .25 .15
e. Souvenir sheet 1.50

No. 1382e contains No. 1382d.

Pres. Chun's Visit to Japan, Sept. 6-8 — A820

1984, Sept. 6 Litho. *Perf. 13x12½*

1383 A820 70w Chun, flag, Mt. Fuji .30 .15
a. Souvenir sheet of 2, imperf. 1.25

Visit of Gambia's Pres. Jawara, Sept. 12-17
A821

1984, Sept. 12

1384 A821 70w Flags of Korea & Gambia .25 .15
a. Souvenir sheet of 2, imperf. 1.25

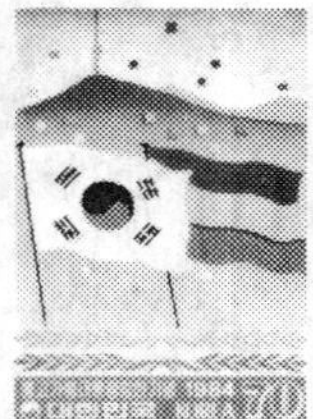

A822

A823

1984, Sept. 21 *Perf. 13*

1385 A822 70w Flags of Korea & Gabon .25 .15
a. Souvenir sheet of 2, imperf. 1.25

Visit of Gabon's Pres. Bongo, Sept. 21-23.

1984, Sept. 18 Photo. *Perf. 13x13½*

1386 A823 70w Products .25 .15

Seoul Intl. Trade Fair.

65th Natl. Sports Festival, Taegu, Oct. 11-16 — A824

1984, Oct. 11 Photo. *Perf. 13½x13*

1387 A824 70w Badminton .25 .15
1388 A824 70w Wrestling .25 .15
Set value .15

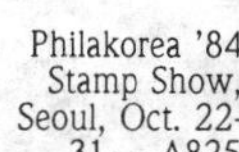

Philakorea '84 Stamp Show, Seoul, Oct. 22-31 — A825

Perf. 13½x13, 13x13½

1984, Oct. 22

1389 A825 70w South Gate, stamps .25 .15
a. Souvenir sheet of 4 1.50
1390 A825 70w Emblem under magnifier, vert. .25 .15
a. Souvenir sheet of 4 1.50
Set value .15

Visit of Maldives Pres. Maumoon Abdul Gayoom, Oct. 29-Nov. 1 — A826

1984, Oct. 29 Litho. *Perf. 13x12½*

1392 A826 70w multicolored .25 .15
a. Souvenir sheet of 2, imperf. 1.25

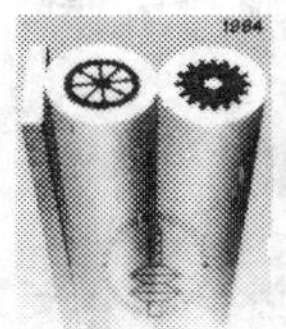

Chamber of Commerce and Industry Cent. — A827

Children Playing Jaegi-chagi — A828

1984, Oct. 31 Photo. *Perf. 13x13½*

1393 A827 70w "100" .25 .15

1984, Dec. 1 Photo. *Perf. 13x13½*

New Year 1985 (Year of the ox).

1394 A828 70w Ox, bas-relief .25 .15
a. Souvenir sheet of 2 .90
1395 A828 70w shown .25 .15
a. Souvenir sheet of 2 .90
Set value .15

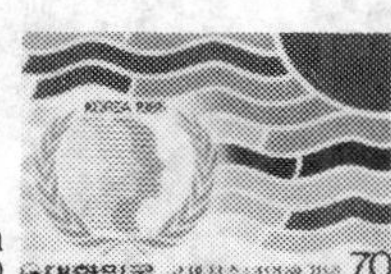

Intl. Youth Year — A829

1985, Jan. 25 Photo. *Perf. 13½x13*

1396 A829 70w IYY emblem .25 .15

Folkways — A830

1985, Feb. 19 Photo. *Perf. 13x13½*

1397 A830 70w Pounding rice .35 .15
1398 A830 70w Welcoming full moon .35 .15
Set value .15

1985, Aug. 20

1399 A830 70w Wrestling .20 .15
1400 A830 70w Janggi, Korean chess .20 .15
Set value .15

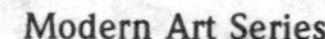

Modern Art Series

Rocky Mountain in the Early Spring, 1915, by Shimjoen, (Ahn Jung-shik)
A831

Still-life with a Doll, 1927, by Suhlcho, (Lee Chong-woo)
A832

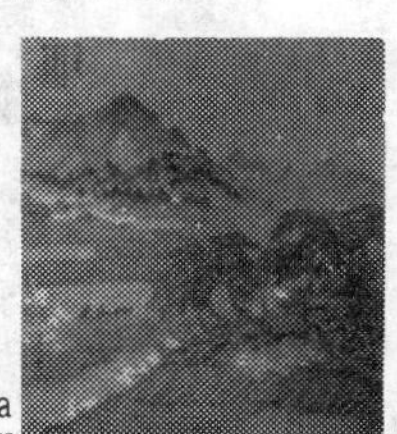

Spring Day on a Farm, 1961, by Eijai, (Huh Paik-ryun, 1903-1977)
A833

The Exorcist, 1941, by Chulma, (Kim Chung-hyun, 1901-1953) — A834

Chunhyang-do, by Kim Un-ho — A835

Flowers, by Lee Sang-bum — A836

Image of A Friend, by Ku Bon-wung
A837

Woman in a Ski Suit, by Son Ung-seng
A838

Valley of the Peach Blossoms, 1964, by Pyen Kwan-Sik (1899-1976)
A839

Rural Landscape, 1940, by Lee Yong-Wu (1904-1952)
A840

Male, 1932, by Lee Ma-Dong
A841

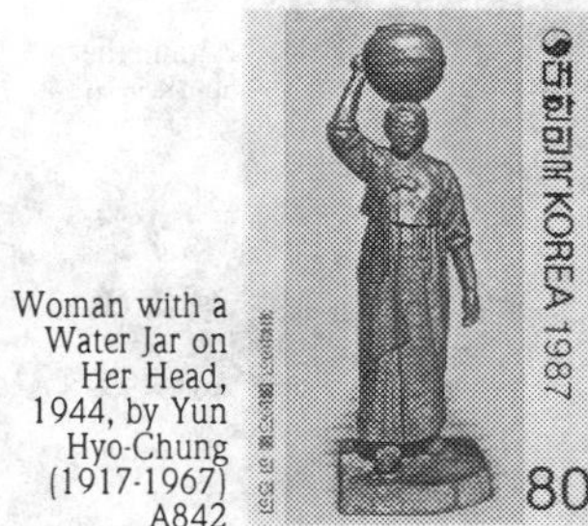

Woman with a Water Jar on Her Head, 1944, by Yun Hyo-Chung (1917-1967)
A842

Photo.; Litho. & Engr. (#1411-1412)

1985-87 *Perf. 13½x13, 13x13½*

1401 A831 70w multicolored .30 .15
1402 A832 70w multicolored .30 .15
1403 A833 70w multicolored .30 .15
1404 A834 70w multicolored .30 .15
1405 A835 80w multi ('86) .35 .15
1406 A836 80w multi ('86) .35 .15
1407 A837 80w multi ('86) .35 .15
1408 A838 80w multi ('86) .35 .15
1409 A839 80w multi ('87) *2.75* .15
1410 A840 80w multi ('87) *2.75* .15
1411 A841 80w multi ('87) *2.75* .15
1412 A842 80w multi ('87) *2.75* .15
Nos. 1401-1412 (12) *13.60*
Set value .85

Issued: #1401-1402, 4/10; #1403-1404, 7/5; #1405-1408, 12/1; #1409-1412, 6/12.

State Visit of Pres. Chun to the US — A843

Photo. & Engr.

1985, Apr. 24 *Perf. 13*

1413 A843 70w multicolored .30 .15
a. Souvenir sheet of 2 1.25

Coastal and Inland Fish Series

Gak-si- Bung-eo (silver carp) — A844

Dot-sac-chi (sword fish) — A845

Eoreumchi A846

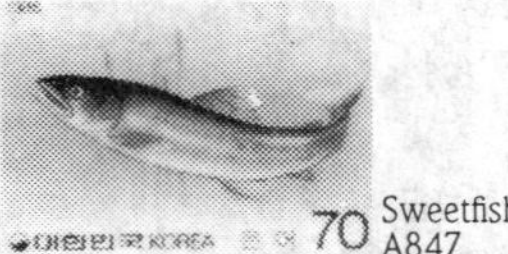

Sweetfish A847

Sardine — A848

Hammerhead Shark — A849

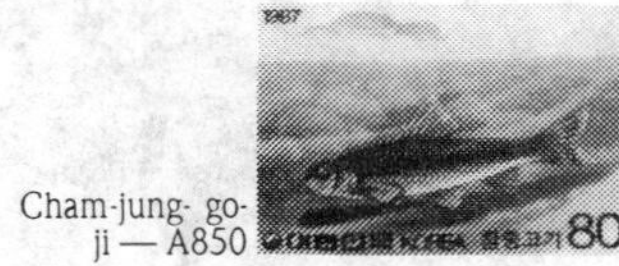

Cham-jung- go-ji — A850

Swi-ri — A851

Oar Fish — A852

Devil-ray A853

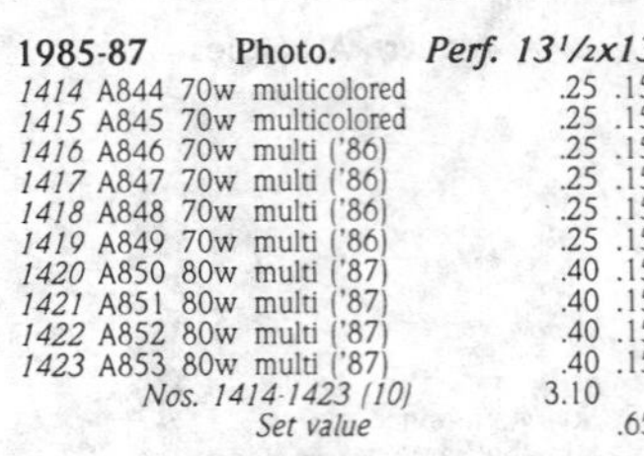

1985-87 Photo. *Perf. 13½x13*

1414 A844 70w multicolored .25 .15
1415 A845 70w multicolored .25 .15
1416 A846 70w multi ('86) .25 .15
1417 A847 70w multi ('86) .25 .15
1418 A848 70w multi ('86) .25 .15
1419 A849 70w multi ('86) .25 .15
1420 A850 80w multi ('87) .40 .15
1421 A851 80w multi ('87) .40 .15
1422 A852 80w multi ('87) .40 .15
1423 A853 80w multi ('87) .40 .15
Nos. 1414-1423 (10) 3.10
Set value .65

Issued: #1414-1415, 5/30; #1416-1423, 7/25.

Yonsei University and Medical School, Cent. A854

Photogravure and Engraved

1985, May 6 *Perf. 13*

1424 A854 70w Underwood Hall .20 .15

State Visit of Pres. Mohammad Zia-Ul-Haq of Pakistan, May 6-10 — A855

State Visit of Pres. Luis Alberto Monge of Costa Rica, May 19-23 — A856

1985, May 6 Photo. *Perf. 13x13½*

1425 A855 70w multicolored .20 .15
a. Souvenir sheet of 2 .40

1985, May 18 *Perf. 13½x13*

1426 A856 70w multicolored .20 .15
a. Souvenir sheet of 2 .40

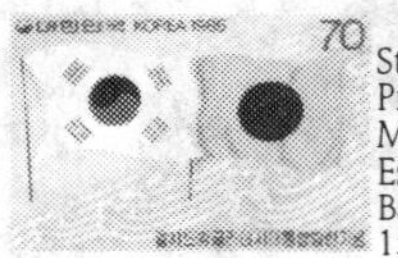

State Visit of Pres. Hussain Muhammad Eshrad of Bangladesh, June 15-19 — A857

1985, June 15

1427 A857 70w multicolored .20 .15
a. Souvenir sheet of 2, imperf. .40

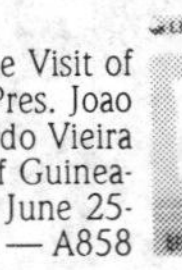

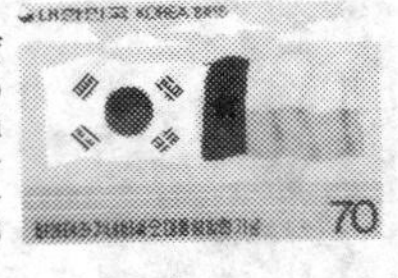

State Visit of Pres. Joao Bernardo Vieira of Guinea-Bissau, June 25-28 — A858

1985, June 25

1428 A858 70w multicolored .20 .15
a. Souvenir sheet of 2, imperf. .40

Liberation from Japanese Occupation Forces, 40th Anniv. A859

Design: Heavenly Lake, Mt. Paektu, natl. flower.

1985, Aug. 14 Litho. *Perf. 13x12½*

1429 A859 70w multicolored .20 .15

Folk Music Series

The Spring of My Home, Music by Hong Nan-pa and Lyrics by Lee Won-su — A860

A Leaf Boat, Music by Yun Yong-ha and Lyrics by Park Hong-Keun — A861

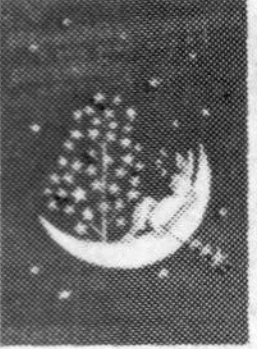

Half Moon, 1924, by Yun Keuk-Young A862

Let's Go and Pick the Moon, by Yun Seok-Jung and Park Tae Hyun A863

Korean Farm Music — A864

Barley Field, by Park Wha-mok and Yun Yong-ha — A865

Magnolia, by Cho Young-Shik and Kim Dong-jin — A866

Chusok, Harvest Moon Festival — A867

1985, Sept. 10 Photo. *Perf. 13x13½*

1430 A860 70w multicolored .20 .15
1431 A861 70w multicolored .20 .15
Set value .15

1986, June 25 Photo. *Perf. 13x13½*

1432 A862 70w multicolored .20 .15
1433 A863 70w multicolored .20 .15
Set value .15

1986, Aug. 26 Photo. *Perf. 13½x13*

Musicians with: a, Flag, hand gong. b, Drum flute. c, Drum, hand gong. d, Taborets, ribbons. e, Taboret, sun, woman, child. Has continuous design.

1434 Strip of 5 1.00 .35
a.-e. A864 70w, any single .20 .15

1987, Mar. 25 Photo. *Perf. 13x13½*

1435 A865 80w multicolored .25 .15
1436 A866 80w multicolored .25 .15
Set value .15

1987, Sept. 10 Photo. *Perf. 13x13½*

Harvest moon dance: No. 1437a, Eight dancers, harvest moon. No. 1437b, Four dancers, festival wheels, balloons. No. 1437c, Three dancers, children on see-saw. No. 1437d, Four dancers, women preparing meal.

1437 Strip of 4 1.25 .35
a.-d. A867 80w any single .30 .15

Folklore Series

Tano, Spring Harvest Festival — A868

Sick for Home, by Lee Eun-sang and Kim Kong-jin A869

Pioneer, by Yoon Hae-young and Cho Doo-nam A870

Mask Dance (Talchum) — A871

Designs: a, Woman on shore, riding a swing. b, Sweet flag coiffures. c, Boy picking flowers, girl on swing. d, Boys wrestling.
Illustration reduced.

1988, Aug. 25 Photo. *Perf. 13x13½*

1438 A868 Strip of 4 .90 .25
a.-d. 80w multicolored .20 .15

1988, Nov. 15

1439 A869 80w multicolored .25 .15
1440 A870 80w multicolored .25 .15
Set value .15

1989, Feb. 25

Designs: a, Two mask dancers with scarves. b, Dancers with fans. c, Dancers with scarf and laurel or fan. d, Three dancers, first as an animal and two more carrying fan and bells or torch.

1441 Strip of 4 1.00 .25
a.-d. A871 80w any single .24 .15

Korean Telecommunications, Cent. — A872

World Bank Conference, Seoul, Oct. 8-11 — A873

1985, Sept. 28 *Perf. 13½x13*

1442 A872 70w Satellite, emblem, dish receiver .20 .15

1985, Oct. 8 *Perf. 13x13½*

1443 A873 70w Emblem .20 .15

Intl. Bank for Reconstruction & Development, 40th Anniv.

UN, 40th Anniv. — A874

1985, Oct. 24 *Perf. 13½x13*

1444 A874 70w Emblem, doves .20 .15

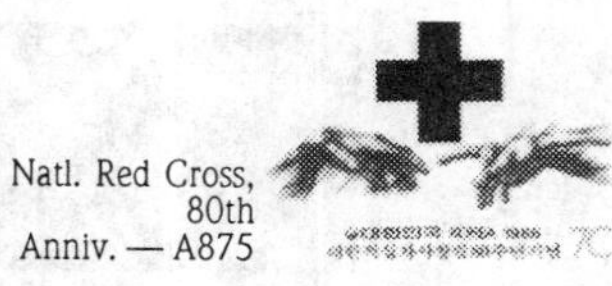

Natl. Red Cross, 80th Anniv. — A875

1985, Oct. 26

1445 A875 70w red, blk & bl .20 .15

Segment of Canceled Cover — A876

New Year 1986 — A877

1985, Nov. 18 Photo. ***Perf. 13½x13***

1446 A876 70w multicolored .20 .15

12th Philatelic Week, Nov. 18-23.

Lithographed and Engraved

1985, Dec. 2 ***Perf. 13x13½***

1447 A877 70w multicolored .20 .15

Mt. Fuji, Korean Airlines Jet — A878

1985, Dec. 18 **Photo.**

1448 A878 70w brt bl, blk & red .20 .15

Normalization of diplomatic relations between Korea and Japan, 20th anniv.

See No. C44.

Statesman Type of 1986 and Types of 1981-86

1986-87 Engr., Photo. (40w) ***Perf. 13***

1449 A716 550w indigo 2.00 .70

Coil Stamps

Perf. 13 Vert.

1449A A704 20w multicolored .15 .15

1449B A705 40w multicolored .20 .15

1449C A708 80w multicolored .48 .15

Nos. 1449A-1449C (3) .83

Set value .15

Issue dates: 550w, Dec. 10; others, 1987.

Intl. Peace Year — A879

State Visits of Pres. Chun — A880

1986, Jan. 15 Photo. ***Perf. 13x13½***

1450 A879 70w multicolored .20 .15

See No. C45

1986, Apr. 4 Litho. ***Perf. 12½x13***

Portrait, natl. flags and: No. 1452, Parliament, Brussels. No. 1453, Eiffel Tower, Paris. No. 1454, Cathedral, Cologne. No. 1455, Big Ben, London.

1452 A880 70w multicolored .15 .15

1453 A880 70w multicolored .15 .15

1454 A880 70w multicolored .15 .15

1455 A880 70w multicolored .15 .15

Nos. 1452-1455 (4) .60

Set value .20

Souvenir Sheets of 2

Perf. 13½

1452a A880 70w .35

1453a A880 70w .35

1454a A880 70w .35

1455a A880 70w .35

Nos. 1452a-1455a (4) 1.40

Science Series

Chomsongdae Observatory, Satellites — A881

Kwanchondae Observatory, Halley's Comet — A882

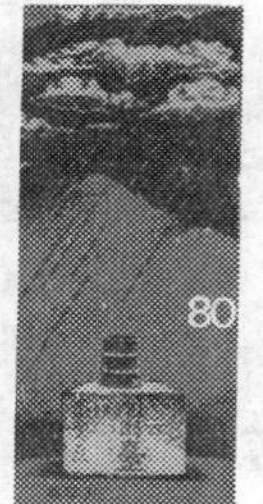

Weather

A883 A884

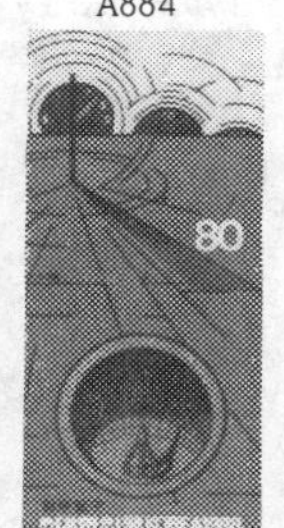

Clocks

A885 A886

Early Printing Methods

A887 A888

A889 A890

1986, Apr. 21 ***Perf. 13½x13***

1456 A881 70w multicolored .15 .15

1457 A882 70w multicolored .15 .15

a. Pair, #1456-1457 .30 .15

1987, Apr. 21 Photo. ***Perf. 13½***

Designs: No. 1458, Wind observatory stone foundation, Chosun Dynasty. No. 1459, Rain gauge, Sejong Period to Chosun Dynasty.

1458 A883 80w multicolored .30 .15

1459 A884 80w multicolored .30 .15

a. Pair, #1458-1459 .60 .20

1988, Apr. 21 Photo. ***Perf. 13½x13***

Designs: No. 1460, *Chagyokru,* water clock invented by Chang Yongshil and Kim Bin in 1434. No. 1461, *Angbuilgu,* sundial completed during King Sejong's reign (1418-1450).

1460 A885 80w multicolored .25 .15

1461 A886 80w multicolored .25 .15

a. Pair, #1460-1461 .50 .20

1989, Apr. 21

Designs: No. 1462, Sutra manuscript (detail) printed from wood type, Shila Dynasty, c.704-751. No. 1463, Character from a manuscript printed from metal type, Koryo, c.1237.

1462 A887 80w buff & sepia .25 .15

1463 A888 80w buff & sepia .25 .15

a. Pair, #1462-1463 .50 .20

1990, Apr. 21

Designs: No. 1464, 7th century gilt bronze Buddha. No. 1465, Bronze Age dagger, spear molds.

1464 A889 100w multicolored .45 .15

1465 A890 100w multicolored .45 .15

a. Pair, #1464-1465 .90 .30

Complete bklt., 2 each #1464-1465 1.80

Nos. 1456-1465 (10) 2.80

Pairs have continuous designs.

Souvenir Booklets

Booklets containing the stamps listed below have a stamp, pair or strip of stamps, tied to the booklet cover with a first day cancel.

1464-1465, 1523-1524, 1529-1532, 1535-1536, 1539-1540, 1553, 1559-1566, 1572-1576, 1583-1584, 1595-1608, 1613-1621, 1622-1623B, 1624, 1635-1650, 1655-1656, 1657-1668, 1669-1676, 1678-1690, 1693-1699, 1700-1702, 1713-1714, 1745-1748, 1751-1758, 1763-1764, 1767-1768, 1770-1773, 1776-1787, 1797, 1799-1802, 1803-1806, 1810-1811.

Assoc. of Natl. Olympic Committees, 5th General Assembly, Seoul, Apr. 21-25 — A891

1986, Apr. 21 ***Perf. 13x13½***

1466 A891 70w multicolored .15 .15

Souvenir Sheet

Butterflies A892

1986, May 22 Litho. ***Perf. 13½***

1467 Sheet of 6 6.00 2.00

a. A892 70w multicolored .20 .15

b. A892 370w multicolored 1.00 .35

c. A892 400w multicolored 1.10 .35

d. A892 440w multicolored 1.10 .40

e. A892 450w multicolored 1.25 .40

f. A892 470w multicolored 1.25 .45

AMERIPEX '86, Chicago, May 22-June 1. No. 1467 contains stamps of different sizes (370w, 42x41mm; 400w, 42x33mm; 440w, 39x45mm; 450w, 32x42mm; 470w, 33x44mm); margin continues the designs.

Women's Education, Cent. A893

1986, May 31 ***Perf. 13x12½***

1468 A893 70w multicolored .20 .15

State Visit of Pres. Andre Kolingba, Central Africa A894

1986, June 10 ***Perf. 13***

1469 A894 70w multicolored .20 .15

a. Souvenir sheet of 2, imperf. .40

Completion of Han River Development Project — A895

1986, Sept. 10 Litho. ***Perf. 13***

1470 Strip of 3 .60 .20

a. A895 30w Bridge .15 .15

b. A895 60w Buildings .20 .15

c. A895 80w Seoul Tower, buildings .30 .15

Printed in a continuous design.

Fireworks, Seoul Tower — A896

Games Emblem — A897

10th Asian Games, Seoul, Sept. 20-Oct. 5 — A898

Illustration A898 reduced.

1986, Sept. 20 Photo. ***Perf. 13x13½***

1471 A896 80w multicolored .25 .15

a. Souvenir sheet of 2 1.10

1472 A897 80w multicolored .25 .15

a. Souvenir sheet of 2 1.10

Set value .15

Souvenir Sheet

1986, Oct. 31

1473 A898 550w multicolored 1.60

Juan Antonio Samaranch, Korean IOC Delegation, 1981 — A899

1986, Sept. 30

1474 A899 80w multicolored .25 .15

Intl. Olympic Committee decision to hold 24th Olympic Games in Seoul, 5th anniv.

Philatelic Week — A900

1986, Nov. 18 Photo. ***Perf. 13½x13***
1475 A900 80w Boy fishing for stamp .25 .15

New Year 1987 (Year of the Hare) — A901

Birds — A902

1986, Dec. 1 Photo. ***Perf. 13x13½***
1476 A901 80w multicolored .25 .15

1986, Dec. 20 ***Perf. 13x14***
1477 A902 80w Waxwing .25 .15
1478 A902 80w Oriole .25 .15
1479 A902 80w Kingfisher .25 .15
1480 A902 80w Hoopoe .25 .15
1481 A902 80w Roller .25 .15
a. Strip of 5, #1477-1481 1.25 .40

Coil Stamps
Perf. 14 Horiz.

1481B A902 80w like No. 1479 .25 .15
1481C A902 80w like No. 1480 .25 .15
1481D A902 80w like No. 1481 .25 .15
1481E A902 80w like No. 1477 .25 .15
1481F A902 80w like No. 1478 .25 .15
g. Strip of 5, #1481B-1481F 1.25 .40

Wildlife Conservation A903

Endangered species: No. 1482, Panthera tigris altaica. No. 1483, Felis bengalensis. No. 1484, Vulpes vulpes. No. 1485, Sus scrofa.

1987, Feb. 25 Photo. ***Perf. 13½x13***
1482 A903 80w multicolored .25 .15
1483 A903 80w multicolored .25 .15
1484 A903 80w multicolored .25 .15
1485 A903 80w multicolored .25 .15
a. Strip of 4, #1482-1485 1.00 .35

Flowers — A904

1987, Mar. 20 Photo. ***Perf. 14x13***
1486 A904 550w Dicentra spectabilis 1.65 .55
1487 A904 550w Hanabusaya asiatica 1.65 .55
1488 A904 550w Erythronium japonicum 1.65 .55
1489 A904 550w Dianthus chinensis 1.65 .55
1490 A904 550w Chrysanthemum zawadskii coreanum 1.65 .55
a. Strip of 5, #1486-1490 8.25 2.75

Coil Stamps
Perf. 13 Vert.

1490B A904 550w like No. 1486 1.65 .55
1490C A904 550w like No. 1487 1.65 .55
1490D A904 550w like No. 1488 1.65 .55
1490E A904 550w like No. 1489 1.65 .55
1490F A904 550w like No. 1490 1.65 .55
g. Strip of 5, #1490B-1490F 8.25 2.75

State Visit of Pres. Ahmed Abdallah Abderemane of the Comoro Isls., Apr. 6-9 — A905

1987, Apr. 6 Litho. ***Perf. 13½x13***
1491 A905 80w multicolored .25 .15
a. Souvenir sheet of 2 .60

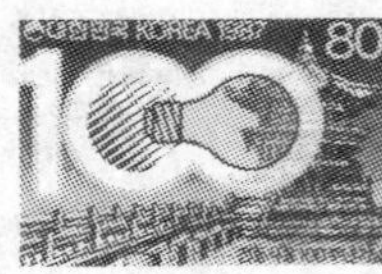

Electrification of Korea, Cent. — A906

1987, Apr. 10 **Photo.**
1492 A906 80w multicolored .30 .15

Int'l. Assoc. of Ports and Harbors, 15th General Session, Seoul — A907

1987, Apr. 25 Photo. ***Perf. 13½x13***
1493 A907 80w multicolored .30 .15

State Visit of Pres. U San Yu of Burma — A908

1987, June 8 Litho. ***Perf. 13½x13***
1494 A908 80w multicolored .30 .15
a. Souvenir sheet of 2 .60

Year of The Communications for Information Society — A909

1987, June 30 ***Perf. 13x13½***
1495 A909 80w Map, digital telephone .30 .15
1496 A909 80w Emblem .30 .15
Set value .15

Introduction of automatic switching telephone system.

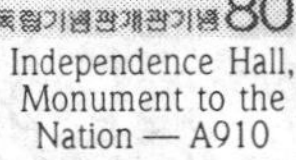

Independence Hall, Monument to the Nation — A910

Statue of Indomitable Koreans, Nat'l. Flag — A911

1987, Aug. 14 Photo. ***Perf. 13½x13***
1497 A910 80w multicolored .30 .15
a. Souvenir sheet of 2 .60
1498 A911 80w multicolored .30 .15
a. Souvenir sheet of 2 .60
Set value .15

Opening of Independence Hall, Aug. 15.

16th Pacific Science Congress, Seoul, Aug. 20-30 — A912

1987, Aug. 20 ***Perf. 13x13½***
1499 A912 80w multicolored .30 .15
a. Souvenir sheet of 2 .60

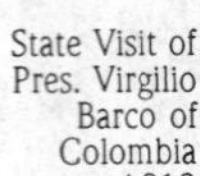

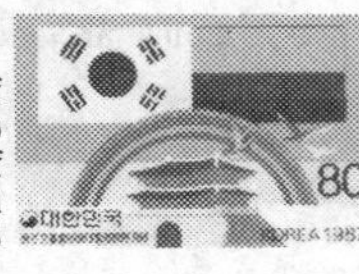

State Visit of Pres. Virgilio Barco of Colombia A913

1987, Sept. 8 Litho. ***Perf. 13½x13***
1500 A913 80w multicolored .30 .15
a. Souvenir sheet of 2 .60

Installation of 10-millionth Telephone A914

1987, Sept. 28 ***Perf. 13½x13***
1501 A914 80w multicolored .30 .15

A915

A916

Servicemen, flags of three military services.

1987, Sept. 30 Litho. ***Perf. 13***
1502 A915 80w multicolored .30 .15

Armed Forces Day, Armed Forces 39th Anniv.

1987, Nov. 18 Photo. ***Perf. 13½***
1503 A916 80w Boy playing the nalrali .30 .15

14th Philatelic Week, Nov. 18-24.

A917

A918

1987, Nov. 28 **Litho.**
1504 A917 80w multicolored .30 .15

Signing of the Antarctic Treaty by Korea, 1st anniv.

1987, Dec. 1 **Photo.**
1505 A918 80w multicolored .30 .15

New Year 1988 (Year of the Dragon).

Natl. Social Security Program — A919

1988, Jan. 4 Litho. ***Perf. 13½x13***
1506 A919 80w multicolored .25 .15

Completion of the Korean Antarctic Base — A919a

1988, Feb. Photo. ***Perf. 13x13½***
1506A A919a 80w multicolored .25 .15

Inauguration of Roh Tae-Woo, 13th President A920

1988, Feb. 24 Photo. ***Perf. 13½x13***
1507 A920 80w multicolored .25 .15
a. Souvenir sheet of 2 .55

World Wildlife Fund — A921

White-naped crane *(Grus vipio)* displaying various behaviors: a, Calling (1). b, Running (2). c, Spreading wings (3). d, Flying (4).

1988, Apr. 1 ***Perf. 13x13½***
1508 Strip of 4 1.10 .25
a.-d. A921 80w any single .25 .15

Intl. Red Cross & Red Crescent Organizations, 125th Annivs. — A922

Telepress Medium, 1st Anniv. — A923

1988, May 7 Photo. ***Perf. 13x13½***
1509 A922 80w multicolored .30 .15

1988, June 1 **Litho.**
1510 A923 80w multicolored .30 .15

Pierre de Coubertin, Olympic Flag — A924

Olympic Temple — A925

View of Seoul — A926

Folk Dancers — A927

Perf. 13½x13
1988, Sept. 16 **Litho. & Engr.**
1511 A924 80w multicolored .25 .15
1512 A925 80w multicolored .25 .15

Photo.
Perf. 13x13½

1513 A926 80w multicolored .25 .15
1514 A927 80w multicolored .25 .15
Nos. 1511-1514 (4) 1.00
Set value .25

1988 Summer Olympics, Seoul.

Souvenir Sheets of 2

1511a A924 80w .50
1512a A925 80w .50
1513a A926 80w .50
1514a A927 80w .50
Nos. 1511a-1514a (4) 2.00

Margin inscriptions on #1511a-1512a are photo.

OLYMPHILEX '88, Sept. 19-28, Seoul — A928

1988, Sept. 19 Photo. ***Perf. 13x13½***

1515 A928 80w multicolored .25 .15
a. Souvenir sheet of 2 .50

22nd Congress of the Intl. Iron and Steel Institute, Seoul — A929

1988, Oct. 8 ***Perf. 13½x13***

1516 A929 80w multicolored .25 .15

A930

A931

1988, Oct. 15 ***Perf. 13x13½***

1517 A930 80w shown .25 .15
1518 A930 80w Archer seated in wheelchair .25 .15
Set value .15

1988 Natl. Special Olympics (Paralympics), Seoul.

1988, Dec. 1 Photo. ***Perf. 13x13½***

1519 A931 80w multicolored .25 .15

New Year 1989 (Year of the Snake).

Souvenir Sheet

Successful Completion of the 1988 Summer Olympics, Seoul — A932

1988, Dec. 20 Litho. ***Perf. 13x12½***

1520 A932 550w Opening ceremony 1.75

Folklore Series

Arirang — A933

Doraji — A934

Pakyon Falls A935

Chonan-Samkori A936

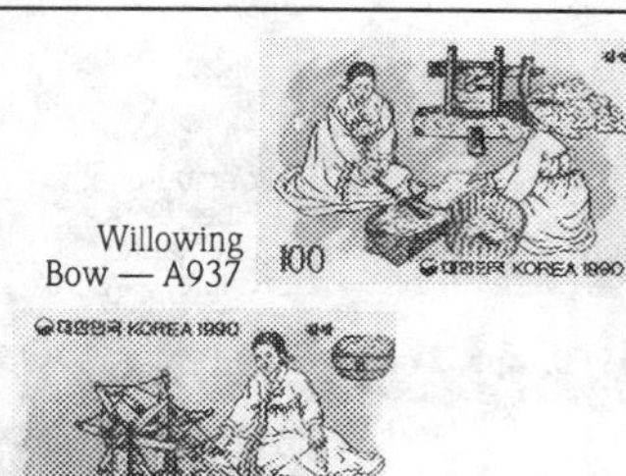

Willowing Bow — A937

Spinning Wheel — A938

Treating Threads A939

Weaving Fabric — A940

Orchard Avenue — A941

In Flower Garden — A942

A Swing — A943

Longing for Mt. Keumkang — A944

Natl. ballads.

1989, Mar. 27 Photo. ***Perf. 13x13½***

1521 A933 80w multicolored .25 .15
1522 A934 80w multicolored .25 .15

1990, Feb. 26 **Litho.**

1523 A935 80w multicolored .45 .15
Complete booklet, 4 #1523
1524 A936 80w multicolored .45 .15
Complete booklet, 4 #1524

Perf. 13½x13

1990, Sept. 25 **Litho. & Engr.**

1525 A937 100w multicolored .45 .15
1526 A938 100w multicolored .45 .15
1527 A939 100w multicolored .45 .15
1528 A940 100w multicolored .45 .15
a. Strip of 4, #1525-1528 1.80 .60

1991, Mar. 27 Litho. ***Perf. 13x13½***

1529 A941 100w multicolored .45 .15
Complete booklet, 4 #1529
1530 A942 100w multicolored .45 .15
Complete booklet, 4 #1530

1992, July 13 Litho. ***Perf. 13x13½***

1531 A943 100w multicolored .30 .15
Complete booklet, 4 #1531
1532 A944 100w multicolored .30 .15
Complete booklet, 4 #1532
Nos. 1521-1532 (12) 4.70
Set value 1.50

14th Asian-Pacific Dental Congress — A945

1989, Apr. 26 Photo. ***Perf. 13x13½***

1533 A945 80w multicolored .25 .15

Rotary Intl. Convention, Seoul, May 21-25 — A946

19th Cong. of the Intl. Council of Nurses, Seoul, May 28-June 2 — A947

1989, May 20 Photo. ***Perf. 13x13½***

1534 A946 80w multicolored .25 .15

1989, May 27

1535 A947 80w multicolored .25 .15
Complete booklet, 4 #1535

Information Industry Month — A948

World Environment Day — A949

1989, June 1

1536 A948 80w multicolored .25 .15
Complete booklet, 4 #1536

1989, June 5

1537 A949 80w multicolored .25 .15

Asia-Pacific Telecommunity, 10th Anniv. — A950

1989, July 1 Photo. ***Perf. 13x13½***

1538 A950 80w multicolored .25 .15

French Revolution, Bicent. — A951

1989, July 14 Litho. ***Perf. 13½x13***

1539 A951 80w multicolored .25 .15
Complete booklet, 4 #1539

Federation of Asian and Oceanian Biochemists 5th Congress A952

1989, Aug. 12 **Photo.**

1540 A952 80w multicolored .25 .15
Complete booklet, 4 #1540

Modern Art Series

A White Ox, by Lee Joong-Sub — A953

A Street Stall, by Park Lae-hyun A954

A Little Girl, by Lee Bong-Sang A955

An Autumn Scene, by Oh Ji-ho — A956

Litho. & Engr.; Photo. (#1542, 1544)
Perf. 13x13½, 13½x13

1989, Sept. 4

1541 A953 80w multicolored .25 .15
1542 A954 80w multicolored .25 .15
1543 A955 80w multicolored .25 .15
1544 A956 80w multicolored .25 .15
Nos. 1541-1544 (4) 1.00
Set value .25

Allegory: The Valiant Spirit of Koreans — A965

1989, Sept. 12 Litho. ***Perf. 13½x13***

1553 A965 80w multicolored .25 .15
Complete booklet, 4 #1553

1988 Seoul Olympics and the World Korean Sports Festival.

Personification of Justice and Ancient Codex — A966

1989, Sept. 18

1554 A966 80w multicolored .25 .15

Constitutional Court, 1st anniv.

Fish

A967

A968

A969

A970

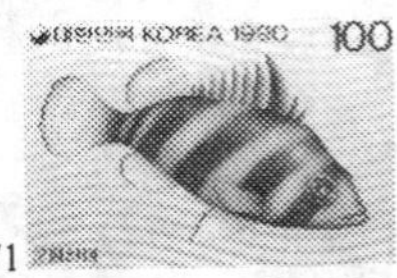
A971

A972

A973

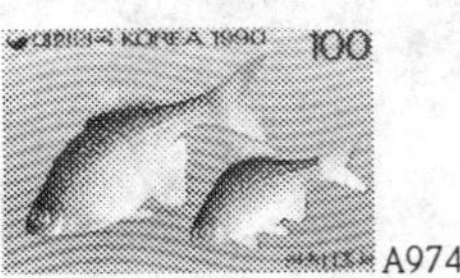
A974

A975

A976

A977

A978

1989, Sept. 30 Photo. ***Perf. $13^1/_2$x13***

1555 A967 80w Oplegnathus fasciatus .25 .15
1556 A968 80w Cobitis multifasciata .25 .15
1557 A969 80w Liobagrus mediadiposalis .25 .15
1558 A970 80w Monocentris japonicus .25 .15

1990, July 2

1559 A971 100w Hapalogenys mucronatus .45 .15
Complete booklet, 4 #1559
1560 A972 100w Fugu niphobles .45 .15
Complete booklet, 4 #1560
1561 A973 100w Oncorhynchus masou .45 .15
Complete booklet, 4 #1561
1562 A974 100w Rhodeus ocellatus .45 .15
Complete booklet, 4 #1562

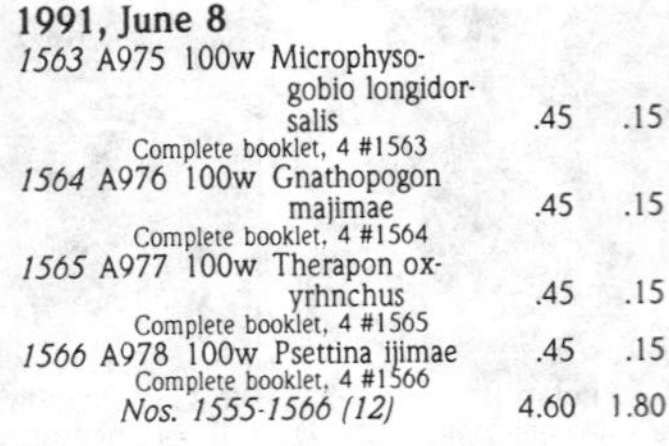

1991, June 8

1563 A975 100w Microphysogobio longidorsalis .45 .15
Complete booklet, 4 #1563
1564 A976 100w Gnathopogon majimae .45 .15
Complete booklet, 4 #1564
1565 A977 100w Therapon oxyrhnchus .45 .15
Complete booklet, 4 #1565
1566 A978 100w Psettina ijimae .45 .15
Complete booklet, 4 #1566
Nos. 1555-1566 (12) 4.60 1.80

Light of Peace Illuminating the World — A979

1989, Oct. 4

1567 A979 80w multicolored .25 .15

44th Intl. Eucharistic Cong., Seoul, Oct. 4-8.

29th World Congress of the Intl. Civil Airports Assoc., Seoul, Oct. 17-19 — A980

1989, Oct. 17

1568 A980 80w multicolored .25 .15

Philatelic Week — A981

Two Cranes — A982

Folk Festival Customs A983

1989, Nov. 18 Photo. ***Perf. 13x$13^1/_2$***

1569 A981 80w Lantern .25 .15
a. Souvenir sheet of 2 .60

1989, Dec. 1 ***Perf. 13x$13^1/_2$, $13^1/_2$x13***

1570 A982 80w multicolored .25 .15
a. Souvenir sheet of 2 .60
1571 A983 80w multicolored .25 .15
a. Souvenir sheet of 2 .60
Set value .15

New Year 1990.

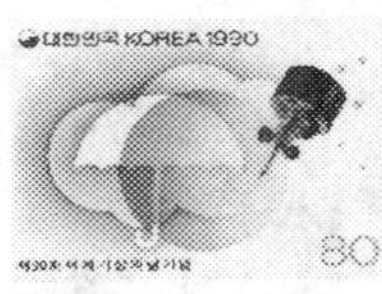
World Meteorological Day — A984

1990, Mar. 23 ***Perf. $13^1/_2$x13***

1572 A984 80w multicolored .45 .15
Complete booklet, 4 #1572

UNICEF in Korea, 40th Anniv. — A985

1990, Mar. 24 ***Perf. 13x$13^1/_2$***

1573 A985 80w multicolored .45 .15
Complete booklet, 4 #1573

Cheju-Kohung Fiber Optic Submarine Cable — A986

1990, Apr. 21 ***Perf. $13^1/_2$x13***

1574 A986 80w multicolored .45 .15
Complete booklet, 4 #1574

Saemaul Movement, 20th Anniv. — A987

1990, Apr. 21

1575 A987 100w multicolored .45 .15
Complete booklet, 4 #1575

Youth Month — A988

1990, May 1

1576 A988 100w multicolored .45 .15
Complete booklet, 4 #1576

Type of 1981 and

Korean Flag — A989

Korean Stork — A990

White Magnolia — A991

Korean White Pine — A991a

Cart-shaped Earthenware A992

Fire Safety A993

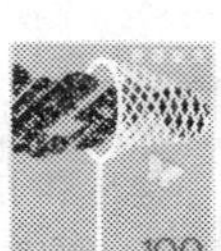
Environmental Protection — A994

Traffic Safety — A995

Waiting One's Turn — A996

Saving Energy — A997

Child Protection A997a

Purification of Language Movement A997b

Rose of Sharon — A997c

Give Life to Water — A997d

Ginger Jar — A998

Chong-IP'um-Song, Pine Tree Natl. Monument — A999

Drum, Drum Dance — A1001

Mask, Wrestlers — A1002

Hong Yung Sik — A1003

King Sejong, Korean Alphabet — A1004

Dragon Head, Banner Staff — A1005

Gilt-bronze Buddha Triad with Inscription of Keymi — A1006

Photo., Litho. (#1582), Litho. & Engr. (#1594)

1990-96 ***Perf. $13^1/_2$x13, 13x$13^1/_2$***

1577 A989 10w multicolored .15 .15
1578 A990 20w multicolored .15 .15
1579 A991 30w multicolored .15 .15
1580 A991a 40w multicolored .15 .15
1581 A992 50w multicolored .25 .15
1582 A993 80w multicolored .40 .15
1583 A994 100w multicolored .45 .15
Complete booklet, 10 #1583
1584 A995 100w multicolored .45 .15
Complete booklet, 10 #1584
1585 A996 100w multicolored .45 .15
1586 A997 100w multicolored .45 .15
1587 A997a 100w multicolored .30 .15
1588 A997b 100w multicolored .30 .15
1589 A997c 110w multicolored .30 .15
1590 A997d 110w multicolored .30 .15
1591 A998 150w multicolored .40 .20
a. Booklet pane, 20 #1591 8.25
Complete booklet, #1591a 8.25
1592 A999 160w multicolored .45 .25
1593 A1001 370w multicolored 1.00 .50
1594 A1002 440w multicolored 1.25 .60
1594A A1003 600w multicolored 2.50 .85
1594B A1004 710w multicolored 2.00 1.00
1594C A1005 800w multicolored 3.00 1.00
1594D A1006 900w multicolored 2.50 .85
Nos. 1577-1594D (22) 17.35 7.35

Issued: #1583, 6/5; 600w, 6/25; 150w, 7/2; 800w, 7/10; #1584, 7/25; 50w, 9/28; 80w, 11/1; #1585, 6/26/91; #1586, 11/1/91; #1587, 4/5/92; #1588, 11/2/92; 370w, 440w, 3/22/93; 10w, #1589, 3/30/93; 160w, 710w, 4/30/93; 20w, 30w, 40w, 5/24/93; #1590, 7/1/93; 900w, 9/20/93; #1591a, 3/20/96.

See Nos. 1715-1738, 1845, 1851-1852, 1860, 1862.

Coil Stamps

1990 Litho. ***Perf. 13 Horiz.***

1594E A992 50w multicolored .25 .15

Perf. 13 Vert.

1594F A706 60w multicolored .30 .15
1594G A994 100w multicolored .45 .15
1594H A997c 110w multicolored .55 .30
Nos. 1594E-1594H (4) 1.55 .75

Seoul Mail Center — A1007

1990, July 4 Litho. ***Perf. 13½x13***
1595 A1007 100w multicolored .45 .15
Complete booklet, 4 #1595

8th Korean Boy Scout Jamboree — A1008

1990, Aug. 8 ***Perf. 13x13½***
1596 A1008 100w multicolored .45 .15
Complete booklet, 4 #1596

Wild Flowers

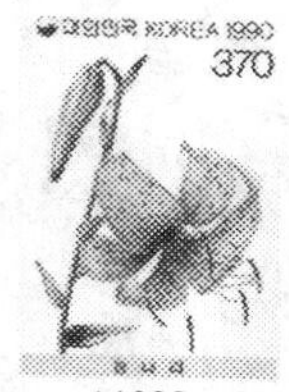

A1009

A1010

A1011 A1012

A1013

1990, Aug. 25 Photo.
1597 A1009 370w Lilium 1.65 .55
Complete booklet, 4 #1597
1598 A1010 400w Aster 1.75 .60
Complete booklet, 4 #1598
1599 A1011 440w Adonis 2.00 .65
Complete booklet, 4 #1599
1600 A1012 470w Scabiosa 2.25 .70
Complete booklet, 4 #1600

See Nos. 1759-1762, 1869-1872.

1991, July 26
1601 A1013 100w Aerides japonicum .35 .15
Complete booklet, 4 #1601
1602 A1013 100w Heloniopsis orientalis .35 .15
Complete booklet, 4 #1602
1603 A1013 370w Aquilegia buergeriana 1.10 .40
Complete booklet, 4 #1603
1604 A1013 440w Gentiana zollingeri 1.40 .50
Complete booklet, 4 #1604

1992, June 22 Photo. ***Perf. 13x13½***
1605 A1013 100w Lychnis wilfordii .30 .15
Complete booklet, 4 #1605
1606 A1013 100w Lycoris radiata .30 .15
Complete booklet, 4 #1606
1607 A1013 370w Commelina communis 1.00 .30
Complete booklet, 4 #1607
1608 A1013 440w Calanthe striata 1.25 .35
Complete booklet, 4 #1608
Nos. 1597-1608 (12) 13.70 4.65

See Nos. 1751-1758, 1907-1910.

A1021

A1022

1990, Sept. 29 Litho. ***Perf. 13x13½***
1609 A1021 100w .40 .15
Anglican Church of Korea, cent.

1990, Oct. 15
1610 A1022 100w blk, red & bl .40 .15
Opening of Seoul Tower, 10th anniv.

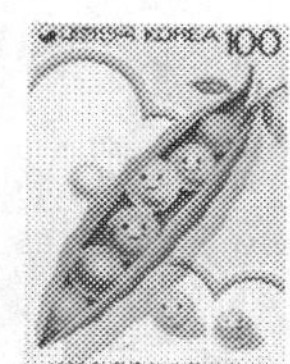

National Census — A1023

1990, Oct. 20 ***Perf. 13x13½***
1611 A1023 100w multicolored .40 .15

UN Development Program, 40th Anniv. — A1024

1990, Oct. 24
1612 A1024 100w multicolored .40 .15

Philatelic Week — A1025

Perf. 13x13½
1990, Nov. 16 Litho. & Engr.
1613 A1025 100w multicolored .40 .15
a. Souvenir sheet of 2 .85
Complete booklet, 4 #1613

New Year 1991 (Year of the Sheep) — A1026

Two Cranes — A1027

1990, Dec. 1 Litho. ***Perf. 13x13½***
1614 A1026 100w multicolored .40 .15
Complete booklet, 4 #1614
1615 A1027 100w multicolored .40 .15
Complete booklet, 4 #1615
a. Souv. sheet of 2, #1614-1615 .85

Taejon Expo '93

A1028

A1029

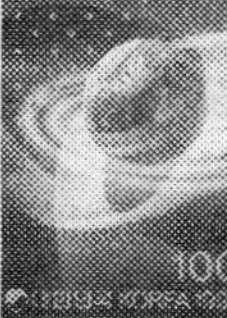

A1030

A1031

A1032

A1033

Government Pavilion A1034

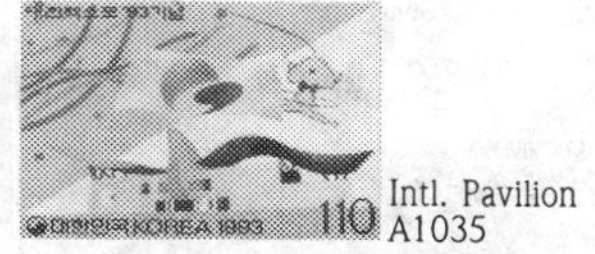

Intl. Pavilion A1035

Recycling Art Pavilion A1035a

Telcom Pavilion A1035b

1990, Dec. 12
1616 A1028 100w multicolored .40 .15
a. Souvenir sheet of 2 .85
Complete booklet, 4 #1616
1617 A1029 440w multicolored 1.90 .65
a. Souvenir sheet of 2 4.00
Complete booklet, 4 #1617

1991, Mar. 23
1618 A1030 100w multicolored .40 .15
a. Souvenir sheet of 2 .85
Complete booklet, 4 #1618
1619 A1031 100w multicolored .40 .15
a. Souvenir sheet of 2 .85
Complete booklet, 4 #1619

1992, Aug. 7 Photo. ***Perf. 13½x13***
1620 A1032 100w multicolored .30 .15
a. Souvenir sheet of 2 .60
Complete booklet, 4 #1620
1621 A1033 100w multicolored .30 .15
a. Souvenir sheet of 2 .60
Complete booklet, 4 #1621

1993, July 8
1622 A1034 110w multicolored .55 .15
a. Souvenir sheet of 2 1.10
Complete booklet, 4 #1622
1623 A1035 110w multicolored .55 .15
c. Souvenir sheet of 2 1.10
Complete booklet, 4 #1623
1623A A1035a 110w multicolored .55 .15
d. Souvenir sheet of 2 1.10
Complete booklet, 4 #1623A
1623B A1035b 110w multicolored .55 .15
e. Souvenir sheet of 2 1.10
Complete booklet, 4 #1623B
Nos. 1616-1623B (10) 5.90
Set value 1.15

Saemaul Minilibrary, 30th Anniv. A1036

1991, Jan. 2 Litho. ***Perf. 13½x13***
1624 A1036 100w multicolored .40 .15
Complete booklet, 4 #1624

Moth A1037

Beetle A1038

Butterfly A1039

Beetle A1040

Cicada — A1041

1991, Apr. 8 Photo. ***Perf. 13½x13***
1625 A1037 100w shown .40 .15
1626 A1038 100w shown .40 .15
1627 A1039 100w shown .40 .15
1628 A1040 100w shown .40 .15
1629 A1041 100w shown .40 .15
1630 A1040 100w Water beetle .40 .15
1631 A1040 100w Bee .40 .15
1632 A1040 100w Lady bug .40 .15
1633 A1037 100w Dragonfly .40 .15
1634 A1037 100w Grasshopper .40 .15
a. Strip of 10, #1625-1634 4.00 2.00

Printed in sheets of 100 with each row shifted one design.

Traditional Performing Arts Center, 40th Anniv. — A1042

1991, Apr. 10 ***Perf. 13x13½***
1635 A1042 100w multicolored .40 .15
Complete booklet, 4 #1635

Provisional Government, 72nd Anniv. A1043

1991, Apr. 13 ***Perf. 13½x13***
1636 A1043 100w multicolored .40 .15
Complete booklet, 4 #1636

Hire the Handicapped A1044

1991, Apr. 20
1637 A1044 100w multicolored .40 .15
Complete booklet, 4 #1637

Teachers' Day, 10th Anniv. A1045

1991, May 15 Litho. *Perf. 13½x13*

1638 A1045 100w multicolored .40 .15
Complete booklet, 4 #1638

A1046

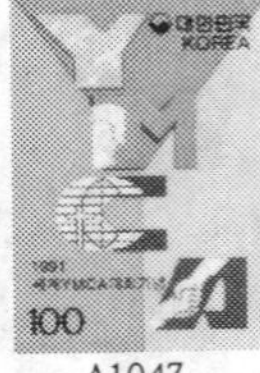

A1047

1991, Aug. 8 Litho. *Perf. 13x13½*

1639 A1046 100w multicolored .40 .15
a. Souvenir sheet of 2 1.10 .40
Complete booklet, 4 #1639

17th World Scouting Jamboree.

1991, Aug. 22 Litho. *Perf. 13x13½*

1640 A1047 100w multicolored .40 .15
Complete booklet, 4 #1640

YMCA World Assembly.

Natl. Desire for Reunification — A1048

1991, Sept. 11 Litho. *Perf. 13x13½*

1641 A1048 100w multicolored .40 .15
Complete booklet, 4 #1641

Admission to UN — A1049

1991, Sept. 18 *Perf. 13½x13*

1642 A1049 100w multicolored .40 .15
Complete booklet, 4 #1642

Musical Instruments

Deerskin Drum (Galgo) A1050

Mouth Organ (Saenghwang) A1051

Seated Drum — A1052

Small Gong — A1053

Designs: No. 1645, Brass chimes (Unra). No. 1646, Large gong (Jing). No. 1649, Dragon drum. No. 1650, Single bell chime.

1991-92 Photo. *Perf. 13x13½*
Background color

1643 A1050 100w gray .40 .15
Complete booklet, 4 #1643
1644 A1051 100w tan .40 .15
Complete booklet, 4 #1644
1645 A1050 100w lt violet .40 .15
Complete booklet, 4 #1645
1646 A1050 100w pale green .40 .15
Complete booklet, 4 #1646
1647 A1052 100w gray .40 .15
Complete booklet, 4 #1647
1648 A1053 100w tan .40 .15
Complete booklet, 4 #1648
1649 A1052 100w pale violet .40 .15
Complete booklet, 4 #1649
1650 A1053 100w pale green .40 .15
Complete booklet, 4 #1650
Nos. 1643-1650 (8) 3.20 1.20

Issued: #1643-1646, 9/26; others, 2/24/92.

Month of Culture A1056

Telecom '91 A1057

1991, Oct. 1 Litho. *Perf. 13x13½*

1655 A1056 100w multicolored .40 .15
Complete booklet, 4 #1655

1991, Oct. 7 Photo.

1656 A1057 100w multicolored .40 .15
Complete booklet, 4 #1656

Sixth World Telecommunication Exhibition & Forum, Geneva, Switzerland.

Beauty Series

A1058

A1059

Kottam Architectural Patterns
A1060 A1061

A1062

A1063

Norigae
A1064 A1065

A1066

A1067

Tapestries
A1068 A1069

1991, Oct. 18

1657 A1058 100w multicolored .40 .15
1658 A1059 100w multicolored .40 .15
1659 A1060 100w multicolored .40 .15
1660 A1061 100w multicolored .40 .15
a. Block or strip of 4, #1657-1660 1.65 .60
Complete booklet, 2 #1660a

1992, Sept. 21 Photo. & Engr.

1661 A1062 100w multicolored .30 .15
1662 A1063 100w multicolored .30 .15
1663 A1064 100w multicolored .30 .15
1664 A1065 100w multicolored .30 .15
a. Block or strip of 4, #1661-1664 1.25 .60
Complete booklet, 2 #1664a

1993, Oct. 11 Photo. *Perf. 13x13½*

1665 A1066 110w multicolored .30 .15
1666 A1067 110w multicolored .30 .15
1667 A1068 110w multicolored .30 .15
1668 A1069 110w multicolored .30 .15
a. Block or strip of 4, #1665-1668 1.25 .60
Complete booklet, 2 #1668a

Philatelic Week — A1070

1991, Nov. 16 Photo. *Perf. 13x13½*

1669 A1070 100w multicolored .40 .15
a. Souvenir sheet of 2 .85
Complete booklet, 4 #1669

New Year 1992, Year of the Monkey
A1071 A1072

1991, Dec. 2 Photo. & Engr.

1670 A1071 100w multicolored .40 .15
a. Souvenir sheet of 2 .85
Complete booklet, 4 #1670
1671 A1072 100w multicolored .40 .15
a. Souvenir sheet of 2 .85
Complete booklet, 4 #1671

Hibiscus Syriacus, Natl. Flower — A1073

1992, Mar. 9 Photo. *Perf. 13x13½*
Background color

1672 A1073 100w lt green .30 .15
1673 A1073 100w lt blue .30 .15

Im-Jin War, 400th Anniv. — A1074

1992, May 23 Photo. *Perf. 13½x13*

1674 A1074 100w multicolored .30 .15
Complete booklet, 4 #1674

Science Day, 25th Anniv. A1075

1992, Apr. 21 Photo. *Perf. 13½x13*

1675 A1075 100w multicolored .30 .15
Complete booklet, 4 #1675

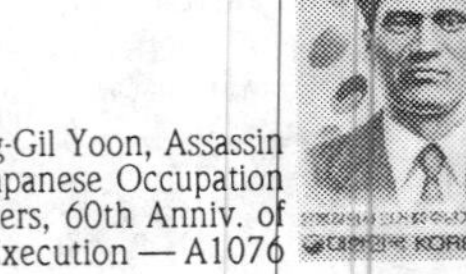

Pong-Gil Yoon, Assassin of Japanese Occupation Leaders, 60th Anniv. of Execution — A1076

Photo. & Engr.
1992, Apr. 29 *Perf. 13x13½*

1676 A1076 100w multicolored .28 .15
Complete booklet, 4 #1676

A1077

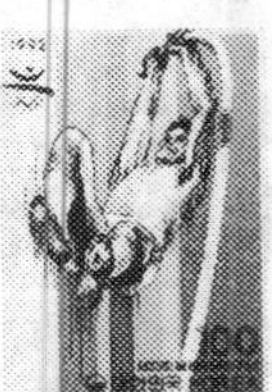

A1078

Perf. 13x13½
1992, May 25 Photo & Engr.

1678 A1077 100w multicolored .30 .15
Complete booklet, 4 #1678

60th Intl. Fertilizer Assoc. conf.

1992, July 25 Photo. *Perf. 13x13½*

1679 A1078 100w Pole vault .30 .15
Complete booklet, 4 #1679
1680 A1078 100w Rhythmic gymnastics .30 .15
Complete booklet, 4 #1680
Set value .15

1992 Summer Olympics, Barcelona.

21st Universal Postal Congress, Seoul, 1994 — A1079

Designs: No. 1681, Korean Exhibition Center, Namdae-mun Gate. No. 1682, Stone statue of Tolharubang, Songsan Ilchulbong Peak.

1992, Aug. 22 Photo. *Perf. 13½x13*

1681 A1079 100w red vio & multi .30 .15
a. Souvenir sheet of 2 .60
Complete booklet, 4 #1681
1682 A1079 100w brown & multi .30 .15
a. Souvenir sheet of 2 .60
Complete booklet, 4 #1682
Set value .15

A1086

A1087

Perf. 13x13½

1992, Oct. 10 Litho. & Engr.

1683 A1086 100w salmon & red brn .30 .15
Complete booklet, 4 #1683

Pong-Chang Yi (1900-1932), would-be assassin of Japanese Emperor Hirohito.

1992, Oct. 10 Litho.

Design: No. 1684, Hwang Young-Jo, 1992 Olympic marathon winner. No. 1685, Shon Kee-Chung, 1936 Olympic Marathon Winner.

1684 A1087 100w multicolored .30 .15
1685 A1087 100w grn & multi .30 .15
a. Pair, #1684-1685 .60
b. Souv. sheet of 2, #1684-1685 .60
Complete booklet, 2 #1685a
Set value .15

Discovery of America, 500th Anniv. — A1088

1992, Oct. 12 Photo.

1686 A1088 100w multicolored .30 .15
Complete booklet, 4 #1686

Philatelic Week — A1089

1992, Nov. 14 Photo. *Perf. 13½x13*

1687 A1089 100w multicolored .30 .15
a. Souvenir sheet of 2 .60
Complete booklet, 4 #1687

New Year 1993 (Year of the Rooster)
A1090 A1091

1992, Dec. 1 Photo. *Perf. 13x13½*

1688 A1090 100w multicolored .30 .15
a. Souvenir sheet of 2 .60
Complete booklet, 4 #1688
1689 A1091 100w multicolored .30 .15
a. Souvenir sheet of 2 .60
Complete booklet, 4 #1689
Set value .15

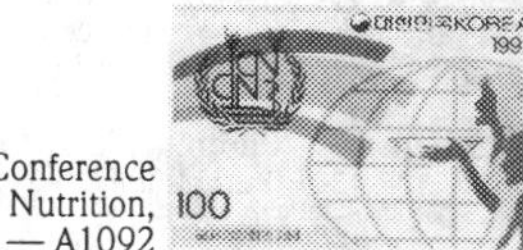

Intl. Conference on Nutrition, Rome — A1092

1992, Dec. 5 *Perf. 13½x13*

1690 A1092 100w multicolored .30 .15
Complete booklet, 4 #1690

Seoul Art Center, Grand Opening A1093

1993, Feb. 15 Photo. *Perf. 13½x13*

1691 A1093 110w multicolored .30 .15

Inauguration of Kim Young Sam, 14th President A1094

1993, Feb. 24

1692 A1094 110w multicolored .30 .15
a. Souvenir sheet of 2 .60

A1095 A1096

1993, May 27 Photo. *Perf. 13x13½*

1693 A1095 110w lilac & silver .30 .15
Complete booklet, 4 #1693

Student Inventions Exhibition.

1993, June 14 Photo. *Perf. 13x13½*

1694 A1096 110w multicolored .30 .15
Complete booklet, 4 #1694

UN Conference on Human Rights, Vienna.

A1098 A1099

Mushrooms

1993, July 26 Photo. *Perf. 13x13½*

1696 A1098 110w Ganoderma lucidum .30 .15
Complete booklet, 4 #1696
1697 A1098 110w Pleurotus ostreatus .30 .15
Complete booklet, 4 #1697
1698 A1098 110w Lentinula edodes .30 .15
Complete booklet, 4 #1698
1699 A1098 110w Tricholoma matsutake .30 .15
Complete booklet, 4 #1699
Nos. 1696-1699 (4) 1.20 .60

See Nos. 1770-1773, 1803-1806, 1883-1886, 1912-1915.

1993, Aug. 28 Photo. *Perf. 13x13½*

1700 A1099 110w multicolored .30 .15
Complete booklet, 4 #1700

19th World Congress of Intl. Society of Orthopedic Surgery and Trauma Study.

O-Dol-Odo-Gi A1100 Ong-He-Ya A1101

1993, Sept. 13

1701 A1100 110w multicolored .30 .15
Complete booklet, 4 #1701
1702 A1101 110w multicolored .30 .15
Complete booklet, 4 #1702

Visit Korea Year '94
A1112 A1113

1993, Sept. 27 Photo. *Perf. 13x13½*

1713 A1112 110w multicolored .30 .15
Complete booklet, 4 #1713
1714 A1113 110w multicolored .30 .15
Complete booklet, 4 #1714

Type of 1993 and

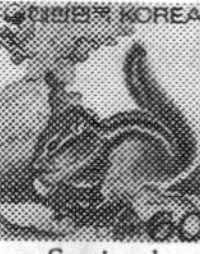

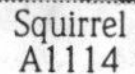

Squirrel A1114

Physalis Alkekengi A1115

Scops Owl A1116

Reduce Garbage A1117

Narcissus A1118

Little Tern A1119

Sea Turtle — A1120

Airplane — A1122

Passenger Airplane A1123

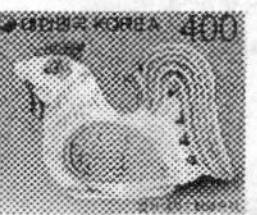

Porcelain Chicken Water Dropper A1124

Celedon Water Dropper A1125

Gilt Bronze Bongnae-san Incense Burner A1127

Celadon Pitcher A1128

Designs: 300w, Van. 540w, Train. 1190w, Passenger ship.

Perf. 13½x13, 13x13½ (210w, 1050w, #1728, 1732, 1734), 13½x12½ (60w, 90w), 12½x13½ (180w, 200w)

Photo., Litho. (#1726), Photo. & Engr. (#1734)

1993-95

1715 A1114 60w multicolored .15 .15
1716 A1115 70w multicolored .20 .15
1717 A1116 90w multicolored .25 .15
1718 A1117 110w multicolored .30 .15
1719 A997c 120w multicolored .30 .15
1720 A1118 130w multicolored .30 .15
a. Booklet pane of 20 6.50
Complete booklet, #1720a 6.50
1721 A1119 180w multicolored .50 .15
1722 A1120 200w multicolored .55 .30
1723 A1119 210w multicolored .55 .15
1724 A1123 300w multicolored .85 .40
1725 A1122 330w multicolored .90 .20
1726 A1123 390w multicolored 1.00 .50
1727 A1122 400w multicolored 1.00 .25
a. Booklet pane, 10 #1727 11.00
Complete booklet, #1727a 11.00
1728 A1124 400w multicolored 1.10 .30
1729 A1125 500w multicolored 1.25 .30
1730 A1123 540w multicolored 1.50 .75
1731 A1122 560w multicolored 1.50 .40
1732 A1127 700w multicolored 1.90 .95
1733 A1004 910w like #1594B 2.50 1.25
1734 A1128 930w blue & multi 2.25 1.10
1735 A1128 930w tan & multi 2.50 1.25
a. Booklet pane of 10 25.00
Complete booklet, #1735a 25.00
1736 A1128 1050w multicolored 2.75 .70
1737 A1123 1190w multicolored 3.00 1.50
1738 A1122 1300w multicolored 3.50 .85
Nos. 1715-1738 (24) 30.60 12.20

Issued: #1718, 11/1/93; 910w, 2/15/94; 90w, 4/22/94; 130w, 8/20/94; 80w, 9/12/94; 390w, #1734, 1190w, 10/1/94; 300w, 540w, 11/1/94; 60w, 200w, 12/19/94; #1720a, 2/28/95; 70w, 3/15/95; #1737, 3/11/95; #1735a, 3/20/95; 700w, 6/15/95; #1728, 8/28/95; #1727, 10/16/95; 1050w, 1300w, 10/5/95; 210w, 560w, 11/1/95; 500w, 11/6/95; 120w, 330w, 11/11/95; #1727a, 3/27/96.

Five versions of booklets with No. 1720a exist with blocks of different colors at the top of the booklet cover. The blocks of color match color bars printed in the selvage of the attached booklet pane.

See No. 1847.

Coil Stamp

1990 Litho. *Perf. 13 Vert.*

1739 A1118 130w multicolored .30 .15

Philatelic Week — A1144

21st UPU Congress, Seoul — A1145

1993, Nov. 13 Photo. *Perf. 13x13½*

1745 A1144 110w multicolored .30 .15
a. Souvenir sheet of 2 .65
Complete booklet, 4 #1745

Perf. 13x13½, 13½x13

1993, Nov. 18

1746 A1145 110w Dancer, muscians .30 .15
a. Souvenir sheet of 2 .65
Complete booklet, 4 #1746
1747 A1145 110w Weavers, horiz. .30 .15
a. Souvenir sheet of 2 .65
Complete booklet, 4 #1747

Trade Day, 30th Anniv. — A1146

1993, Nov. 30 *Perf. 13½x13*

1748 A1146 110w multicolored .30 .15
Complete booklet, 4 #1748

New Year 1994 (Year of the Dog) — A1147

1993, Dec. 1 *Perf. 13½x13, 13x13½*

1749 A1147 110w shown .30 .15
a. Souvenir sheet of 2 .65
1750 A1147 110w Stuffed toy dog, vert. .30 .15
a. Souvenir sheet of 2 .65

Flower Type of 1991

1993-95 Photo. *Perf. 13x13½*

1751 A1013 110w Weigela bortensis .30 .15
Complete booklet, 4 #1751
1752 A1013 110w Caltha palustris .30 .15
Complete booklet, 4 #1752
1753 A1013 110w Iris ruthenica .30 .15
Complete booklet, 4 #1753
1754 A1013 110w Aceriphyllum rosii .30 .15
Complete booklet, 4 #1754
1755 A1013 130w Leontopodium japonicum .35 .20
Complete booklet, 4 #1755
1756 A1013 130w Geranium eriostemon .35 .20
Complete booklet, 4 #1756
1757 A1013 130w Lycoris aurea .35 .20
Complete booklet, 4 #1757

1758 A1013 130w Gentiana jamesii .35 .20
Complete booklet, 4 #1758
1759 A1013 130w Halenia corniculata .40 .20
Complete booklet, 6 #1759 3.25
1760 A1013 130w Erthyronium japonicum .40 .20
Complete booklet, 6 #1760 3.25
1761 A1013 130w Iris odaesanensis .40 .20
Complete booklet, 6 #1761 3.25
1762 A1013 130w Leontice microrrhyncha .40 .20
Complete booklet, 6 #1762 3.25
Nos. 1755-1762 (8) 3.00 1.60

Issued: #1751-1754, 12/20/93; #1755-1758, 10/4/94; #1759-1762, 7/24/95.

Visit Korea Year
A1148 A1149

1994, Jan. 11 Photo. *Perf. 13x13½*
1763 A1148 110w Masked dancer .30 .15
Complete booklet, 4 #1763
1764 A1149 110w Piper, clouds .30 .15
Complete booklet, 4 #1764

21st UPU Congress, Seoul — A1150

1994, Jan. 24 *Perf. 13½x13*
1765 A1150 300w multicolored .85 .40
a. Souvenir sheet of 2 1.65
b. Booklet pane of 10 8.50
Complete booklet, #1765b 8.50

Samil Independence Movement, 75th Anniv. — A1151

1994, Feb. 28 Photo. *Perf. 13x13½*
1766 A1151 110w multicolored .30 .15

Wildlife Protection A1152

1994, Mar. 7 Photo. *Perf. 13½x13*
1767 A1152 110w Sasakia charonda .30 .15
a. Souvenir sheet of 2 .60
Complete booklet, 4 #1767
1768 A1152 110w Allomyrina dichotoma .30 .15
a. Souvenir sheet of 2 .60
Complete booklet, 4 #1768

Intl. Year of the Family A1153

1994, May 14 Photo. *Perf. 13*
1769 A1153 110w multicolored .30 .15

Mushroom Type of 1993

#1770, Oudemansiella platyphylla. #1771, Morchella esculenta. #1772, Cortinarius purpurascens. #1773, Gomphus floccosus.

1994, May 30 Photo. *Perf. 13x13½*
1770 A1098 110w multicolored .30 .15
a. Souvenir sheet of 2 .60
Complete booklet, 4 #1770
1771 A1098 110w multicolored .30 .15
a. Souvenir sheet of 2 .60
Complete booklet, 4 #1771
1772 A1098 110w multicolored .30 .15
a. Souvenir sheet of 2 .60
Complete booklet, 4 #1772
1773 A1098 110w multicolored .30 .15
a. Souvenir sheet of 2 .60
Complete booklet, 4 #1773
Nos. 1770-1773 (4) 1.20 .60
Nos. 1770a-1773a (4) 2.40

Opening of War Memorial Center — A1154

1994, June 10 Photo. *Perf. 13*
1774 A1154 110w multicolored .30 .15

PHILAKOREA '94, Seoul — A1155

1994, June 13 *Perf. 13*
1775 A1155 910w multicolored 2.50 1.25
a. Souvenir sheet of 1 2.50 1.25

Beauty Series

A1156 A1157

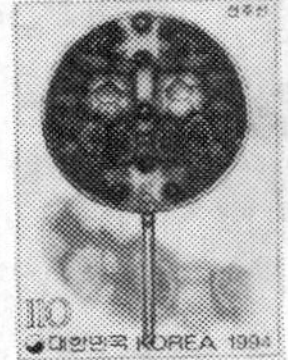

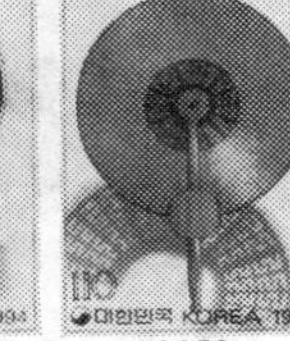

A1158 A1159
Fans

A1160 A1161
A1162 A1163
Gates

A1164 A1165
A1166 A1167
Pouches

1994, July 18 Photo. *Perf. 13x13½*
1776 A1156 110w Taeguk .30 .15
1777 A1157 110w Crane .30 .15
1778 A1158 110w Pearl .30 .15
1779 A1159 110w Wheel .30 .15
a. Strip of 4, #1776-1779 1.25 .60
Complete booklet, 2 #1779a

1995, May 22 Photo. *Perf. 13x13½*

#1780, Lofty Gate, traditional Yungban residence. #1781, Pomosa Temple. #1782, Osumun (Fish Water) Gate, Changdukkung Palace. #1783, Pullomun Gate, Changdukkung Palace.

1780 A1160 130w multicolored .40 .20
1781 A1161 130w multicolored .40 .20
1782 A1162 130w multicolored .40 .20
1783 A1163 130w multicolored .40 .20
a. Strip of 4, #1780-1783 1.60 .80
Complete booklet, 2 #1783a

1996, Nov. 1 Photo. *Perf. 13x13½*
1784 A1164 150w multicolored .40 .15
1785 A1165 150w multicolored .40 .15
1786 A1166 150w multicolored .40 .15
1787 A1167 150w multicolored .40 .15
a. Strip of 4, #1784-1787 1.60 .40
Complete booklet, 2 #1787a
Nos. 1776-1787 (12) 4.40

A1168

PHILAKOREA '94 — A1169

1994, Aug. 16 Photo. *Perf. 13*
1788 A1168 130w Winter scene .35 .15
a. Souvenir sheet of 2 .70
b. Booklet pane of 10 3.50
Complete booklet, #1788b 3.50
1789 A1168 130w Grape vines .35 .15
a. Souvenir sheet of 2 .70
b. Booklet pane of 10 3.50
Complete booklet, #1789b 3.50
1790 A1168 130w Cranes .35 .15
a. Souvenir sheet of 2 .70
b. Booklet pane of 10 3.50
Complete booklet, #1790b 3.50
Nos. 1788-1790 (3) 1.05
Set value .15

Souvenir Sheet

Litho. & Engr.

1791 Sheet of 7 8.25
a. A1169 130w Crane, mountains .35 .15
b. A1169 300w Two cranes, sun .80 .40
c. A1169 370w Two cranes in trees 1.00 .50
d. A1169 400w Two deer 1.10 .55
e. A1169 440w Turtle, rapids 1.25 .60
f. A1169 470w River 1.25 .60
g. A1169 930w Trees 2.50 1.25

A1170 A1171

21st UPU Congress, Seoul: No. 1792, Pens, glasses, stamps. No. 1793, Sword dance. No. 1794, Dove holding envelope. No. 1795, Hong Young-sik, Heinrich Von Stephan, horiz.

1994, Aug. 22 Photo. *Perf. 13*
1792 A1170 130w multicolored .35 .20
a. Souvenir sheet of 2 .70
b. Booklet pane of 10 3.50
Complete booklet, #1792b 3.50
1793 A1170 130w multicolored .35 .20
a. Souvenir sheet of 2 .70
b. Booklet pane of 10 3.50
Complete booklet, #1793b 3.50
1794 A1170 130w multicolored .35 .20
a. Souvenir sheet of 2 .70
b. Booklet pane of 10 3.50
Complete booklet, #1794b 3.50
1795 A1170 370w multicolored 1.00 .50
a. Souvenir sheet of 2 2.00
b. Souvenir sheet of 4, #1792-1795 6.25
c. Booklet pane of 10 10.00
Complete booklet, #1795b 10.00
Nos. 1792-1795 (4) 2.05 1.10

1994, Sept. 27
1796 A1171 130w multicolored .35 .20

Seoul, Capital of Korea, 600th anniv.

A1172 A1173

1994, Nov. 19 Photo. *Perf. 13x13½*
1797 A1172 130w multicolored .35 .20
a. Souvenir sheet of 2 .75
Complete booklet, 4 #1797 2.25

Philatelic Week. Complete booklet has one #1797 tied to cover with first day cancel.

1994, Nov. 29
1798 A1173 130w multicolored .35 .20

Seoul becomes Korea's capital, 600th anniv.

New Year 1995 (Year of the Boar) — A1174

1994, Dec. 1 *Perf. 13½x13*
1799 A1174 130w shown .35 .20
a. Souvenir sheet of 2 .75
Complete booklet, 4 #1799
1800 A1174 130w Family outing .35 .20
a. Souvenir sheet of 2 .75
Complete booklet, 4 #1800

Wildlife Protection A1175

1995, Jan. 23 Photo. *Perf. 13½x13*
1801 A1175 130w Rana plancyi .65 .30
a. Souv. sheet of 2, imperf. 1.25
Complete booklet, 4 #1801 2.50
1802 A1175 130w Bufo bufo .65 .30
a. Souv. sheet of 2, imperf. 1.25
Complete booklet, 4 #1802 2.50

Mushroom Type of 1993

Designs: No. 1803, Russula virescens. No. 1804, Lentinus lepideus. No. 1805, Coprinus comalus. No. 1806, Laetiporus sulphureus.

1995, Mar. 31 Photo. *Perf. 13x13½*
1803 A1098 130w multicolored .35 .20
a. Souvenir sheet of 2 .70
Complete booklet, 4 #1803 2.25
1804 A1098 130w multicolored .35 .20
a. Souvenir sheet of 2 .70
Complete booklet, 4 #1804 2.25
1805 A1098 130w multicolored .35 .20
a. Souvenir sheet of 2 .70
Complete booklet, 4 #1805 2.25
1806 A1098 130w multicolored .35 .20
a. Souvenir sheet of 2 .70
Complete booklet, 4 #1806 2.25
Nos. 1803-1806 (4) 1.40 .80

Completion of HANARO Research Reactor A1176

1995, Apr. 7 *Perf. 13½x13*

1807 A1176 130w multicolored .65 .35
Complete booklet, 4 #1807 2.25

Modern Judicial System, Cent. — A1177

1995, Apr. 25 Litho. *Perf. 13x13½*

1808 A1177 130w multicolored .40 .20

Modern Legal Education, Cent. — A1178

1995, Apr. 25 *Perf. 13½x13*

1809 A1178 130w multicolored .35 .20

Cartoons A1179

130w, "Dooly, the Little Dinosaur," baby, porpoise. 440w, "Kochuboo," riding in airplane.

1995, May 4

1810 A1179 130w multicolored .35 .20
a. Souvenir sheet of 1 .35
Complete booklet, 4 #1810 2.25
1811 A1179 440w multicolored 1.25 .65
a. Souvenir sheet of 1 1.25
Complete booklet, 4 #1811 7.50

78th Lions Clubs Intl. Convention A1180

1995, July 4 Photo. *Perf. 13½x13*

1812 A1180 130w multicolored .35 .20

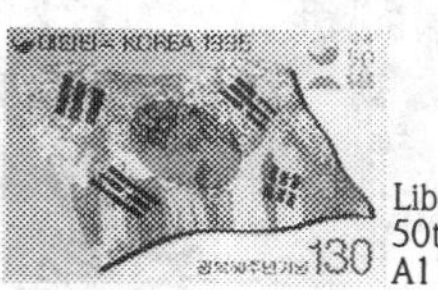

Liberation Day, 50th Anniv. A1181

Design: 440w, Mountain, yin/yang symbol.

1995, Aug. 14 Photo. *Perf. 13½x13*

1813 A1181 130w multicolored .35 .20
a. Booklet pane of 10 3.75
Complete booklet, #1813a 3.75
b. Souvenir sheet of 2 .75

Size: 97x19mm

Perf. 13x13½

1814 A1181 440w multicolored 1.25 .65
a. Souvenir sheet of 1 1.25

Opening of Bohyunsan Optical Astronomical Observatory — A1183

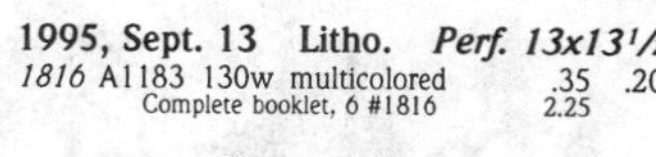

1995, Sept. 13 Litho. *Perf. 13x13½*

1816 A1183 130w multicolored .35 .20
Complete booklet, 6 #1816 2.25

Literature Series

Kuji-ga Song (The Turtle's Back Song) — A1184

Chongeop-sa Song — A1185

A1186

A1187

Record of Travel to Five Indian Kingdoms — A1188

A Poem to the Sui General Yu Zhong Wen — A1189

Perf. 13x13½13½x13

1995, Sept. 25 Photo.

1817 A1184 130w multicolored .35 .20
a. Souvenir sheet of 2 .70
Complete booklet, 6 #1817 2.25
1818 A1185 130w multicolored .35 .20
a. Souvenir sheet of 2 .70
Complete booklet, 6 #1818 2.25

1996, Sept. 16

1819 A1186 150w multicolored .40 .15
a. Souvenir sheet of 2 .80
Complete booklet, 10 #1819 4.75
1820 A1187 150w multicolored .40 .15
a. Souvenir sheet of 2 .80
Complete booklet, 10 #1820 4.75

1997, Dec. 12

1821 A1188 170w multicolored .25 .15
a. Sheet of 2 .50
1822 A1189 170w multicolored .25 .15
a. Sheet of 2 .50

FAO, 50th Anniv. — A1196

1995, Oct. 16 Litho. & Engr. *Perf. 13*

1829 A1196 150w dp vio & blk .45 .20
Complete booklet, 10 #1829 5.00

Korean Bible Society, Cent. — A1197

1995, Oct. 18 Litho.

1830 A1197 150w multicolored .45 .20
Complete booklet, 10 #1830 5.00

Population and Housing Census — A1198

1995, Oct. 20

1831 A1198 150w multicolored .45 .20
Complete booklet, 10 #1831 5.00

UN, 50th Anniv. A1199

1995, Oct. 24 Photo.

1832 A1199 150w multicolored .45 .20
Complete booklet, 10 #1832 7.00

Wilhelm Röntgen (1845-1923), Discovery of the X-Ray, Cent. — A1200

1995, Nov. 8 *Perf. 13½x13*

1833 A1200 150w multicolored .45 .20
Complete booklet, 10 #1833 5.00

Philatelic Week — A1201

1995, Nov. 18 Photo. *Perf. 13x13½*

1834 A1201 150w multicolored .45 .15
a. Souvenir sheet of 2 .90
Complete booklet, 10 #1834 5.00

New Year 1996 (Year of the Rat)
A1202 A1203

1995, Dec. 1 *Perf. 13x13½, 13½x13*

1835 A1202 150w multicolored .45 .15
a. Souvenir sheet of 2 .90
Complete booklet, 10 #1835 4.50
1836 A1203 150w multicolored .45 .15
a. Souvenir sheet of 2 .90
Complete booklet, 10 #1836 4.50

Normalization of Korea-Japan Relations, 30th Anniv. — A1204

1995, Dec. 18 Litho. *Perf. 13x13½*

1837 A1204 420w multicolored 1.25 .30
Complete booklet, 4 #1837 5.75

Types of 1993-97 and

Zosterops Japonica — A1208

Luffa Cylindrica — A1209

Numenius Madagascariensis A1210

Cambaroides Similis A1211

747 Airplane A1215

Soksu Stone Carving A1223

Perf. 13x13½, 13½x13

1996-97 Photo.

1841 A1208 80w multicolored .20 .15
1842 A1209 100w multicolored .25 .15

Perf. 13

1843 A1210 170w multicolored .30 .15

Perf. 13x13½, 13½x13

1844 A1211 170w multicolored .40 .20
1845 A997c 190w multicolored .45 .25

KOREA YEAR SETS
(Commemoratives, X-Mas & S/S)

YEAR	STAMP+S/S	PRICE
1973	38+14	$71.00
1974	43+28	93.00
1975	64+13	33.80
1976	48+4	36.00
1977	34+7	23.40
1978	31+58	20.00
1979	46+10	20.00
1980	30+6	15.60
1981	42+6	13.00
1982	35+14	20.00
1983	43+14	23.40
1984	35+20	139.00
1985	36+9	11.70
1986	42+17	94.90
1987	43+14	63.70
1988	30+11	35.00
1989	31+3	9.70
1990	32+5	19.50
1991	34+6	13.70
1992	32+8	13.00
1993	31+10	15.50
1994	*42+20	33.80
1995	*35+15	17.50
1996	38+14	15.50
1997	35+17	18.00

* Includes booklet pairs.
*Prices subject to change without notice.
Minmum order $50, postage $5 up to $100, $10 up to $300.00
KOREAN PHILATELIC CO., LTD.
C.P.O. BOX 323
SEOUL, 100-603 KOREA
Tel. 82 (1)754-2414
Fax. 82(1)752-9696

Perf. 13x14

1847 A1119 300w Alauda arvensis .85 .20

Perf. 13½x13, 13x13½

1849 A1215 340w green blue & multi .80 .40
1850 A1215 380w lt lilac & multi .90 .45
1851 A1001 420w like #1593 1.10 .25
1852 A1002 480w like #1594 1.25 .30
1857 A1223 1000w multicolored 2.50 .65
1858 A1215 1340w brt green & multi 3.10 1.60
1859 A1215 1380w pink & multi 3.20 1.60
Nos. 1841-1859 (13) 15.30 6.35

Coil Stamps

Perf. 13 Horiz., 13 Vert. (#1860, 1862)

1996-97 Photo.

1860 A998 150w like #1591 .45 .15
1861 A1211 170w like No. 1844 .25 .15
1862 A997c 190w like No. 1845 .30 .15

Issued: 300w, 1/22/96; 420w, 480w, 3/20/96; 1000w, 12/16/96; 100w, 3/5/97; 80w, 7/1/97; #1844-1845, 9/1/97; 340w, 380w, 1340w, 1380w, 9/12/97; #1861, 1862, 11/18/97; #1843, 12/15/97.

This is an expanding set. Numbers may change.

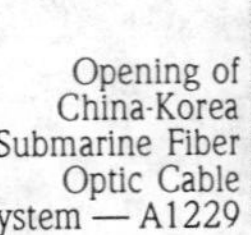
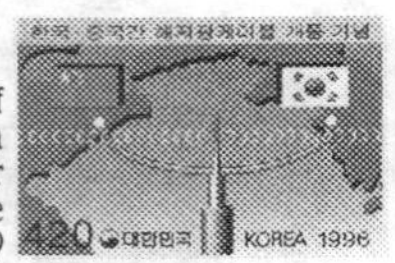

Opening of China-Korea Submarine Fiber Optic Cable System — A1229

1996, Feb. 8 Litho. *Perf. 13½x13*

1863 A1229 420w multicolored 1.25 .30
Complete booklet, 4 #1863 *5.75*

See People's Republic of China No. 2647.

Korea Institute of Science and Technology, 30th Anniv. — A1230

1996, Feb. 10 Photo. *Perf. 13½x13*

1864 A1230 150w multicolored .45 .15
Complete booklet, 10 #1864 *5.00*

Protection of Nature A1231

1996, Mar. 5 Photo. *Perf. 13½x13*

1865 A1231 150w Geoclemys reevesii .45 .15
a. Souvenir sheet of 2 .90
Complete booklet, 10 #1865 *5.00*
1866 A1231 150w Scincella laterale .45 .15
a. Souvenir sheet of 2 .90
Complete booklet, 10 #1866 *5.00*

Successful Launches of Mugunghwa Satellites A1232

1996, Mar. 18 Photo. *Perf. 13*

1867 A1232 150w multicolored .45 .15
Complete booklet, 10 #1867 *4.50*

Tongnip Shinmum, First Privately Published Newspaper, Cent. — A1233

Design: So Chae-p'il, lead article of first issue.

1996, Apr. 6 Litho. & Engr. *Perf. 13*

1868 A1233 150w multicolored .45 .15
Complete booklet, 10 #1868 *4.50*

Wildflower Type of 1992

Designs: No. 1869, Cypripedium macranthum. No. 1870, Trillium tschonoskii. No. 1871, Viola variegata. No. 1872, Hypericum ascyron.

1996, Apr. 22 Photo. *Perf. 13*

1869 A1013 150w multicolored .45 .15
Complete booklet, 10 #1869 *4.50*
1870 A1013 150w multicolored .45 .15
Complete booklet, 10 #1870 *4.50*
1871 A1013 150w multicolored .45 .15
Complete booklet, 10 #1871 *4.50*
1872 A1013 150w multicolored .45 .15
Complete booklet, 10 #1872 *4.50*
Nos. 1869-1872 (4) 1.80 .60

Korea Military Academy, 50th Anniv. — A1234

1996, May 1 Litho. *Perf. 13½x13*

1873 A1234 150w multicolored .45 .15
Complete booklet, 10 #1873 *5.00*

Cartoons A1235

1996, May 4 Photo.

1874 A1235 150w Gobau running .45 .15
a. Souvenir sheet of 1 .45
Complete booklet, 10 #1874 *5.00*
1875 A1235 150w Kkach'i in swordfight .45 .15
a. Souvenir sheet of 1 .45
Complete booklet, 10 #1875 *5.00*

Girl Scouts of Korea, 50th Anniv. — A1236

1996, May 10 Litho.

1876 A1236 150w multicolored .45 .15
Complete booklet, 10 #1876 *5.00*

35th IAA World Advertising Congress — A1237

1996, June 8 Litho. *Perf. 13*

1877 A1237 150w multicolored .45 .15
Complete booklet, 10 #1877 *5.00*

Campaign Against Illegal Drugs — A1238

1996, June 26 Photo. *Perf. 13½x13*

1878 A1238 150w multicolored .45 .15
Complete booklet, 10 #1878 *5.00*

Winter Universiade '97, Muju-Chonju A1239

1996, July 1 *Perf. 13½x13, 13x13½*

1879 A1239 150w shown .45 .15
Complete booklet, 10 #1879 *5.00*
1880 A1239 150w Emblem, vert. .45 .15
Complete booklet, 10 #1880 *5.00*

1996 Summer Olympic Games, Atlanta

A1240 A1241

1996, July 20 *Perf. 13x13½*

1881 A1240 150w multicolored .45 .15
Complete booklet, 10 #1881 *5.00*
1882 A1241 150w multicolored .45 .15
Complete booklet, 10 #1882 *5.00*

Mushroom Type of 1993

Designs: No. 1883, Paxillus atrotomentosus. No. 1884, Sarcodon imbricatum. No. 1885, Rhodophyllus crassipes. No. 1886, Amanita inaurata.

1996, Aug. 19 Photo. *Perf. 13x13½*

1883 A1098 150w multicolored .40 .15
a. Souvenir sheet of 2 .80
Complete booklet, 10 #1883 *5.00*
1884 A1098 150w multicolored .40 .15
a. Souvenir sheet of 2 .80
Complete booklet, 10 #1884 *5.00*
1885 A1098 150w multicolored .40 .15
a. Souvenir sheet o 2 .80
Complete booklet, 10 #1885 *5.00*
1886 A1098 150w multicolored .40 .15
a. Souvenir sheet of 2 .80
Complete booklet, 10 #1886 *5.00*
Nos. 1883-1886 (4) 1.60 .60

Souvenir Sheets

2002 World Cup Soccer Championships, Korea — A1242

#1887, Players, Korean flag. #1888, 2 players.

1996, Aug. 1 Photo. *Perf. 13½*

1887 A1242 400w Sheet of 4 4.25 2.00
1888 A1242 400w Sheet of 4 4.25 2.00

Korean Alphabet, 550th Anniv. — A1243

Perf. 13x13½

1996, Oct. 9 Litho. & Engr.

1889 A1243 150w multicolored .40 .15
a. Souvenir sheet of 2 .80
Complete booklet, 10 #1889 *4.75*

Suwon Castle, Bicent. — A1244

Photo. & Engr.

1996, Oct. 10 *Perf. 13½x13*

1890 A1244 400w multicolored 1.00 .25
Complete booklet, 10 #1890 *11.00*

Seoul Natl. University, 50th Anniv. — A1245

1996, Oct. 15 Photo. *Perf. 13½x13*

1891 A1245 150w multicolored .40 .15
Complete booklet, 10 #1891 *5.25*

Philatelic Week — A1246

Painting: Poppy and a Lizard, by Shin Saimdang.

1996, Nov. 18 Photo. *Perf. 13x13½*

1892 A1246 150w multicolored .40 .15
a. Souvenir sheet of 2 .80
Complete booklet, 10 #1892 *5.00*

A1247

New Year 1997 (Year of the Ox) — A1248

1996, Dec. 2 *Perf. 13*

1893 A1247 150w multicolored .40 .15
a. Souvenir sheet of 2 .80
Complete booklet, 10 #1893 *5.00*
1894 A1247 150w multicolored .40 .15
a. Souvenir sheet of 2 .80
Complete booklet, 10 #1894 *5.00*

Winter Universiade '97, Muju-Chonju — A1249

1997, Jan. 24 Photo. *Perf. 13*

1895 A1249 150w Skier .35 .15
Complete booklet, 10 #1895 *5.00*
1896 A1249 150w Ice skater .35 .15
Complete booklet, 10 #1896 *5.00*

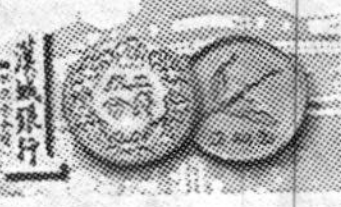

Modern Banking System in Korea, Cent. — A1250

1997, Feb. 19 Litho. *Perf. 13½x13*

1897 A1250 150w multicolored .40 .15
Complete booklet, 10 #1897 *5.25*

A1251 A1252

1997, Apr. 10 *Perf. 13x13½*

1898 A1251 150w multicolored .40 .15
Complete booklet, 10 #1898 *5.25*

97th Inter-Parliamentary Conference, 160th Inter-Parliamentary Council.

1997, Apr. 23 Litho.

1899 A1252 150w multicolored .40 .15
Complete booklet, 10 #1899 *5.25*

World Book & Copyright Day.

Cartoons
A1253

#1900, Mother holding child from "A Long, Long Journey in Search of Mommy." #1901, Girl in air holding medal from "Run, Run, Hannie."

1997, May 3 Photo. *Perf. 13½x13*

1900 A1253 150w multicolored .35 .15
  a. Souvenir sheet of 1 .35
  Complete booklet, 10 #1900 *4.50*
1901 A1253 150w multicolored .35 .15
  a. Souvenir sheet of 1 .35
  Complete booklet, 10 #1901 *4.50*

Nos. 1900a, 1901a are continuous designs.

2nd Pusan East Asian Games — A1254

1997, May 10 Litho. *Perf. 13x13½*

1902 A1254 150w multicolored .35 .15
  Complete booklet, 10 #1900 *4.50*

2002 World Cup Soccer, Korea/Japan
A1255 A1256

Designs: No. 1903, Jules Rimet, founder of World Cup. No. 1904, Painting of Ch'ukkuk match.

1997, May 31 Photo. *Perf. 13x13½*

1903 A1255 150w multicolored .35 .15
  a. Souvenir sheet of 2 .70
  Complete booklet, 10 #1903 *5.25*
1904 A1256 150w multicolored .35 .15
  a. Souvenir sheet of 3 1.00
  Complete booklet, 10 #1904 *5.25*

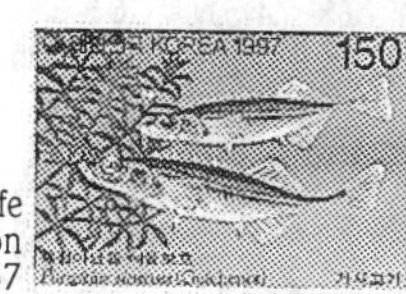

Wildlife Protection
A1257

Fish: No. 1905, Pungitius sinensis. No. 1906, Coreoperca kawamebari.

1997, June 5 *Perf. 13*

1905 A1257 150w multicolored .35 .15
  a. Souvenir sheet of 2 .70
  Complete booklet, 10 #1905 *5.25*
1906 A1257 150w multicolored .35 .15
  a. Souvenir sheet of 2 .70
  Complete booklet, 10 #1906 *5.25*

Wildflower Type of 1992

Designs: No. 1907, Belamcanda chinensis. No. 1908, Hylomecon ernale. No. 1909, Campanula takesimana. No. 1910, Magnolia sieboldii.

1997, June 19 Photo. *Perf. 13*

1907 A1013 150w multicolored .35 .15
  Complete booklet, 10 #1907 *4.25*
1908 A1013 150w multicolored .35 .15
  Complete booklet, 10 #1908 *4.25*
1909 A1013 150w multicolored .35 .15
  Complete booklet, 10 #1909 *4.25*
1910 A1013 150w multicolored .35 .15
  Complete booklet, 10 #1910 *4.25*
  Nos. 1907-1910 (4) 1.40 .60

1997 Kwangju Biennale — A1258

1997, July 1

1911 A1258 150w multicolored .35 .15
  Complete booklet, 10 #1911 *4.25*

Mushroom Type of 1993

Designs: No. 1912, Inocybe fastigiata. No. 1913, Panaeolus papilionaceus. No. 1914, Ramaria flava. No. 1915, Amanita muscaria.

1997, July 1 Photo. *Perf. 13x13½*

1912 A1098 150w multicolored .35 .15
  a. Souvenir sheet of 2 .70
1913 A1098 150w multicolored .35 .15
  a. Souvenir sheet of 2 .70
1914 A1098 150w multicolored .35 .15
  a. Souvenir sheet of 2 .70
1915 A1098 150w multicolored .35 .15
  a. Souvenir sheet of 2 .70
  Nos. 1912-1915 (4) 1.40 .60

85th World Dental Congress, Seoul — A1259

1997, Sept. 5 Photo. *Perf. 13½x13*

1916 A1259 170w multicolored .40 .15

Opening of Port of Mokpo, Cent. — A1260

Perf. 13½x13

1997, Oct. 1 Litho. & Engr.

1917 A1260 170w multicolored .40 .20

Soongsil Academy, Cent. — A1261

1997, Oct. 10 Photo. & Engr.

1918 A1261 170w multicolored .40 .20

Beauty Series

A1262 A1263

A1264 A1265

Wrapping Cloths

1997, Nov. 3 Photo. *Perf. 13x13½*

1919 A1262 170w multicolored .30 .15
1920 A1263 170w multicolored .30 .15
1921 A1264 170w multicolored .30 .15
1922 A1265 170w multicolored .30 .15
  a. Strip of 4, #1919-1922 1.20 .60

Philatelic Week — A1266

1997, Nov. 18

1923 A1266 170w multicolored .30 .15
  a. Souvenir sheet of 2 .60

New Year 1998 (Year of the Tiger)
A1267 A1268

1997, Dec. 1 Photo. *Perf. 13x13½*

1924 A1267 170w multicolored .30 .15
  a. Souvenir sheet of 2 .60
1925 A1268 170w multicolored .30 .15
  a. Souvenir sheet of 2 .60

Seated Buddha, Sokkuram Grotto — A1269

Pulguksa Temple — A1270

Perf. 13x13½

1997, Dec. 9 Litho. & Engr.

1926 Sheet of 14 10.00
  a. A1269 170w multicolored .25 .25
  b. A1270 380w multicolored .55 .55

Top part of No. 1926 contains one each #1926a-1926b and is separated from the bottom portion of the sheet by a row of perforations. The lower part of No. 1926 contains 9 #1926a and 3 #1926b.

Electric Power in Korea, Cent.
A1271

1998, Jan. 26 Photo. *Perf. 13½x13*

1927 A1271 170w multicolored .25 .15

SEMI-POSTAL STAMPS

Field Hospital
SP1

Nurses Supporting Patient — SP2

Perf. 13½x14, 14x13½

1953, Aug. 1 Litho. Wmk. 257

Crosses in Red

B1 SP1 10h + 5h bl grn 2.50 1.25
B2 SP2 10h + 5h blue 2.50 1.25
  Set, never hinged 8.00

The surtax was for the Red Cross. Nos. B1-B2 exist imperf.

Type of Regular Issue, 1956, with Added inscription at Upper Left

1957, Sept. 1 Wmk. 312 *Perf. 12½*

Granite Paper

B3 A111 40h + 10h lt bl grn .80 .60

Wmk. 317

B4 A111 40h + 10h lt bl grn .80 .60
  Set, never hinged 3.25

The surtax was for flood relief.

Catalogue values for unused stamps in this section, from this point to the end of the section, are for Never Hinged items.

Rice Farmer Type of Regular Issue, 1961-62

1963, July 10 Wmk. 317 *Perf. 12½*

B5 A172 4w + 1w dk bl 1.40 .45

The surtax was for flood victims in southern Korea.

1965, Oct. 1 Unwmk. *Perf. 12½*

B6 A172 4w + 2w indigo 1.40 .35

The surtax was for flood relief.

1965, Oct. 11

B7 A172 4w + 2w magenta .85 .30

The surtax was for a scholarship fund.

Type of Regular Issue 1964-66

1966, Nov. 10 Litho. *Perf. 12½*

Granite Paper

B8 A186b 7w + 2w car rose 1.40 .30

The surtax was to help the needy.

Soldier with Wife and Child
SP3

Reservist
SP4

1967, June 20 *Perf. 12½x13*

B9 SP3 7w + 3w rose lil & blk 1.65 .55

The surtax was for veterans of the war in Viet Nam and their families.

1968, Aug. 1 Litho. *Perf. 13x12½*

B10 SP4 7w + 3w grn & blk 3.25 1.90

Issued for the fund-raising drive to arm reservists.

The index in each volume of the Scott Catalogue contains many listings that help identify stamps.

Flag — SP5

"Pin of Love" — SP6

1968, Nov. 1 Litho. Unwmk.
B11 SP5 7w + 3w dk bl & red 13.00 3.00

The surtax was for disaster relief.

1969, Feb. 15
B12 SP5 7w + 3w lt grn, dk bl & red 3.00 .85

Surtax for military helicopter fund.

Flag Type of 1968 Redrawn
Zeros Omitted

1969, Nov. 1 Litho. *Perf. 13x12½*
B13 SP5 7w + 3w dk bl & red 3.00 .75

The surtax was for the searchlight fund.

Perf. 13½x12½

1972, Aug. 1 Photo.
B14 SP6 10w + 5w blue & car .90 .25

Disaster relief.

"Pin of Love" — SP7

Paddle and Ball — SP8

1973, July 1 Photo. *Perf. 12½x13½*
B15 SP7 10w + 5w multicolored .75 .25

Disaster relief.

Perf. 13½x12½

1973, Aug. 1 Photo.
B16 SP8 10w + 5w multicolored .70 .25

Surtax was for gymnasium to be built to commemorate the victory of the Korean women's table tennis team at the 32nd World Table Tennis Championships.

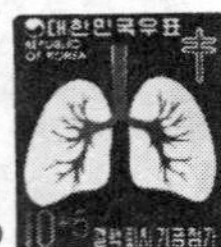
Lungs — SP9

1974, Nov. 1 *Perf. 13½x12½*
B17 SP9 10w + 5w green & red .65 .25

Surtax was for tuberculosis control.

No. 647 Surcharged 수해구제 + 10

Perf. 13½x12½

1977, July 25 Photo.
B18 A328 20w + 10w green 5.50 3.25

Surtax was for flood relief.

Seoul 1988 Olympic Games Series

'88 Seoul Games Emblem — SP10

Korean Tiger, Mascot — SP11

Track and Field — SP12

Equestrian — SP18

1985, Mar. 20 Photo. *Perf. 13x13½*
B19 SP10 70w + 30w blk & multi .35 .30
B20 SP11 70w + 30w blk & multi .35 .30
a. Souvenir sheet of 2, #B19-20 .75

1985, June 10
B21 SP12 70w + 30w shown .35 .30
B22 SP12 70w + 30w Rowing .35 .30
a. Souvenir sheet of 2, #B21-B22 .75

1985, Sept. 16
B23 SP12 70w + 30w Boxing .35 .30
B24 SP12 70w + 30w Women's basketball .35 .30
a. Souvenir sheet of 2, #B23-B24 .75

1985, Nov. 1
B25 SP12 70w + 30w Canoeing .35 .25
B26 SP12 70w + 30w Cycling .35 .25
a. Souvenir sheet of 2, #B25-B26 .75

Surtax for the 24th Summer Olympic Games, Sept. 17-Oct. 2, 1988.

1986, Mar. 25 Photo. *Perf. 13x13½*

Designs: No. B28, Fencing. No. B29, Soccer. No. B30, Gymnastic rings.

B27 SP18 70w + 30w multi .25 .20
B28 SP18 70w + 30w multi .25 .20
B29 SP18 70w + 30w multi .25 .20
B30 SP18 70w + 30w multi .25 .20

Souvenir Sheets

B31 Sheet of 4 5.25 1.25
a. SP18 370w + 100w like #B27 1.00 .30
B32 Sheet of 4 5.50 1.50
a. SP18 400w + 100w like #B28 1.10 .35
B33 Sheet of 4 6.00 1.50
a. SP18 440w + 100w like #B29 1.25 .40
B34 Sheet of 4 6.50 1.65
a. SP18 470w + 100w like #B30 1.25 .40

1986 Photo. *Perf. 13x13½*
B35 SP18 80w +50w Weight lifting .50 .30
B36 SP18 80w +50w Team handball .50 .30
B37 SP18 80w +50w Judo .50 .30
B38 SP18 80w +50w Field hockey .50 .30

Souvenir Sheets

B39 Sheet of 4 5.50
a. SP18 370w + 100w like #B35 1.25 1.00
B40 Sheet of 4 6.00
a. SP18 400w + 100w like #B36 1.40 1.10
B41 Sheet of 4 6.50
a. SP18 440w + 100w like #B37 1.50 1.25
B42 Sheet of 4 7.00
a. SP18 470w + 100w like #B38 1.65 1.25

Issue dates: Nos. B35-B36, B39-B40, Oct. 10; others, Nov. 1.

1987, May 25 Photo. *Perf. 13x13½*
B43 SP18 80w +50w Women's tennis .50 .35
B44 SP18 80w +50w Wrestling .50 .35
B45 SP18 80w +50w Dressage .50 .35
B46 SP18 80w +50w Diving .50 .35

1987, Oct. 10
B47 SP18 80w +50w Table Tennis .40 .30
B48 SP18 80w +50w Men's shooting .40 .30
B49 SP18 80w +50w Women's archery .40 .30
B50 SP18 80w +50w Women's volleyball .40 .30

1988, Mar. 5 Photo. *Perf. 13x13½*
B51 SP18 80w +20w Sailing .35 .25
B52 SP18 80w +20w Taekwondo .35 .25

1988, May 6 Photo. *Perf. 13½x13*
B53 SP18 80w +20w Torch relay, horiz. .35 .25

Litho. & Engr.

B54 SP18 80w +20w Olympic Stadium, horiz. .35 .25

See Greece No. 1627.

Souvenir Sheets of 2

B43a SP18 80w +50w 1.00
B44a SP18 80w +50w 1.00
B45a SP18 80w +50w 1.00
B46a SP18 80w +50w 1.00
B47a SP18 80w +50w .85
B48a SP18 80w +50w .85
B49a SP18 80w +50w .85
B50a SP18 80w +50w .85
B51a SP18 80w +20w .70
B52a SP18 80w +20w .70
B53a SP18 80w +20w .70
B54a SP18 80w +20w .70

AIR POST STAMPS

Four-motor Plane and Globe AP1

Perf. 11½x11

1947-50 Litho. Wmk. 257
C1 AP1 50wn carmine rose 2.25 1.75
a. Horiz. pair, imperf. btwn. 55.00

Perf. 11

C2 AP1 150wn blue ('49) .50 1.25
a. "KORFA" 14.00 10.00
C3 AP1 150wn green ('50) 3.25
Nos. C1-C3 (3) 6.00
Set, never hinged 9.50

Nos. C2-C3 are redrawn. Issued: 50wn, Oct. 1. For surcharge see No. C5.

Plane and Korea Map — AP2

Douglas C-47 and Ship — AP3

1950, Jan. 1
C4 AP2 60wn light blue 3.00 4.50
Never hinged 8.00

No. C2 Surcharged with New Value and Wavy Lines in Black

1951, Oct. 10
C5 AP1 500wn on 150wn bl 1.00 1.00
Never hinged 1.25
a. "KORFA" 15.00 12.50
b. Surcharge inverted 125.00

Perf. 13x12½

1952, Oct. 15 Litho. Wmk. 257
C6 AP3 1200wn red brown .25 .15
C7 AP3 1800wn lt blue .35 .15
C8 AP3 4200wn purple .60 .25
Nos. C6-C8 (3) 1.20 .55
Set, never hinged 1.75

Nos. C6-C8 exist imperf.

1953, Apr. 5
C9 AP3 12h dp blue .35 .30
C10 AP3 18h purple .50 .30
C11 AP3 42h Prus green 1.00 .40
Nos. C9-C11 (3) 1.85 1.00
Set, never hinged 2.50

Douglas DC-7 over East Gate, Seoul — AP4

1954, June 15 *Perf. 12½*
C12 AP4 25h brown .60 .15
C13 AP4 35h deep pink .95 .20
C14 AP4 38h dark green 1.40 .20
C15 AP4 58h ultra 1.50 .25
C16 AP4 71h deep blue 1.50 .35
Nos. C12-C16 (5) 5.95 1.15
Set, never hinged 8.00

Nos. C12-C16 exist imperf.

Type of 1954 Redrawn

1956, July 20 Unwmk.

Laid Paper

C17 AP4 70h brt bluish grn .80 .60
C18 AP4 110h brown 1.10 1.00
C19 AP4 205h magenta 1.75 1.00
Nos. C17-C19 (3) 3.65 2.60
Set, never hinged 8.00

Nos. C18-C19 are found on horizontally and vertically laid paper.

1957, July Wmk. 312 *Perf. 12½*

Granite Paper

C20 AP4 70h brt bluish grn 1.50 .50
C21 AP4 110h brown 2.25 .65
C22 AP4 205h magenta 3.75 1.00
Nos. C20-C22 (3) 7.50 2.15
Set, never hinged 8.50

On the redrawn stamps, Nos. C17-C22, the lines of the entire design are lighter, and the colorless character at right end of bottom row has been redrawn as in illustration above No. 212D.

Catalogue values for unused stamps in this section, from this point to the end of the section, are for Never Hinged items.

Girl on Palace Balcony — AP5

Designs: 100h, Suwon Castle. 200h, Songnyu Gate, Tuksu Palace. 400h, Kyunghoeru Pavilion.

Perf. 12½

1961, Dec. 1 Unwmk. Litho.
C23 AP5 50h lt blue & violet 5.00 .20
C24 AP5 100h pale grn & sepia 10.00 .25
C25 AP5 200h pale grn & brn 20.00 .50
C26 AP5 400h grn & pale bl 25.00 .85
Nos. C23-C26 (4) 60.00 1.80

Values in Won; Same Designs; Underlined Zeros Added

1962-63
C27 AP5 5w lt bl & vio ('63) 25.00 .15
C28 AP5 10w pale grn & sepia 42.50 .25
C29 AP5 20w pale grn & brn ('63) 85.00 .50
C30 AP5 40w grn & pale bl ('63) 45.00 .80
Nos. C27-C30 (4) 197.50 1.70

1964, May 10 Wmk. 317 *Perf. 12½*

Granite Paper

C32 AP5 10w pale grn & sepia 4.00 .25
C33 AP5 20w pale grn & brn 7.00 .50
C34 AP5 40w pale bl & grn 12.00 1.00
Nos. C32-C34 (3) 23.00 1.75

1964, Oct. Unwmk. *Perf. 12½*

Designs: 39w, Girl on palace balcony. 64w, Suwon Castle. 78w, Songnyu Gate, Tuksu Palace. 112w, Kyunghoeru Pavilion.

Granite Paper

C35 AP5 39w vio bl & gray olive 3.00 .25
C36 AP5 64w bl & grnsh gray 4.50 .35
C37 AP5 78w grnsh bl & ultra 5.50 .45
C38 AP5 112w blue & green 8.00 .65
Nos. C35-C38 (4) 21.00 1.70

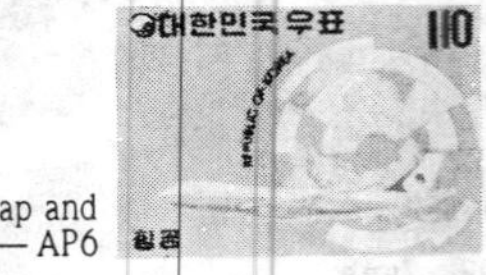
World Map and Plane — AP6

Designs: 135w, Plane over eastern hemisphere. 145w, Plane over world map. 180w, Plane over world map.

1973, Dec. 30 Photo. *Perf. 13x12½*
C39 AP6 110w pink & multi 6.50 .50
C40 AP6 135w yel grn & red 8.50 .60
C41 AP6 145w lt bl & rose 10.00 .65
C42 AP6 180w lilac & yellow 12.50 .75
Nos. C39-C42 (4) 37.50 2.50

UPU Type of 1974

1974, Oct. 9 Photo. *Perf. 13*
C43 A480 110w blue & multi 1.25 .50
a. Souvenir sheet of 2 2.50

Mt. Fuji, Korean Airlines Jet Type

1985, Dec. 18 Photo. *Perf. 13x13½*
C44 A878 370w brt bl, blk & red 1.75 .35

Int'l Year of Peace Type

1986, Jan. 15 Photo. *Perf. 13x13½*
C45 A879 400w multicolored 1.15 .35

Issued in sheets with two blocks of four.

KUWAIT

kú-'wāt

LOCATION — Northwestern coast of the Persian Gulf
GOVT. — Sheikdom
AREA — 7,000 sq. mi.
POP. — 1,910,856 (est. 1985)
CAPITAL — Kuwait

Kuwait was under British protection until June 19, 1961, when it became a fully independent state.

16 Annas = 1 Rupee
100 Naye Paise = 1 Rupee (1957)
1000 Fils = 1 Kuwaiti Dinar (1961)

Catalogue values for unused stamps in this country are for Never Hinged items, beginning with Scott 72 in the regular postage section, Scott C5 in the air post section, and Scott J1 in the postage due section.

There was a first or trial setting of the overprint with the word "Koweit." Twenty-four sets of regular and official stamps were printed with this spelling.

Catalogue values for Nos. 1-71 used, are for postally used examples. Stamps with telegraph cancellations are worth less.

Stamps of India, 1911-23, Overprinted

KUWAIT (a) KUWAIT (b)

1923-24 Wmk. 39 Perf. 14

No.	Type	Description	Unused	Used
1	A47(a)	1/2a green	.55	2.50
2	A48(a)	1a dk brown	.55	1.25
3	A58(a)	1 1/2a chocolate	.85	3.25
4	A49(a)	2a violet	.40	.80
5	A57(a)	2a6p ultra	.90	6.50
6	A51(a)	3a brown org	2.25	14.00
a.		Inverted overprint		
7	A51(a)	3a ultra ('24)	2.50	1.65
8	A52(a)	4a ol green	2.00	19.00
9	A53(a)	6a bister	2.50	10.50
10	A54(a)	8a red violet	4.00	21.00
11	A55(a)	12a claret	4.25	22.50
12	A56(b)	1r grn & red brown	12.00	16.00
13	A56(b)	2r brn & car rose	35.00	72.50
14	A56(b)	5r vio & ultra	75.00	165.00
15	A56(b)	10r car & green	165.00	350.00
		Nos. 1-15 (15)	307.75	706.45

Overprint "a" on India No. 102 is generally considered unofficial.
For overprints see Nos. O1-O13.

Stamps of India, 1926-35, Overprinted type "a"

1929-37 Wmk. 196

No.	Type	Description	Unused	Used
17	A47	1/2a green	.70	.25
18	A71	1/2a green ('34)	.95	.30
19	A48	1a dark brown	4.00	.40
20	A72	1a dk brown ('34)	1.75	1.00
21	A60	2a dk violet	.40	.30
22	A60	2a vermilion	24.00	37.50
23	A49	2a ver ('34)	15.00	5.25
a.		Small die	3.50	1.25
24	A51	3a ultramarine	3.25	1.00
25	A51	3a car rose ('34)	5.00	4.00
26	A61	4a olive green	24.00	30.00
27	A52	4a ol green ('34)	5.75	6.75
28	A53	6a bister ('37)	18.00	19.00
29	A54	8a red violet	8.00	7.25
30	A55	12a claret	18.00	22.50

Overprinted c KUWAIT

No.	Type	Description	Unused	Used
31	A56	1r green & brown	10.00	10.00
32	A56	2r buff & car rose	15.00	13.00
33	A56	5r dk vio & ultra ('37)	70.00	125.00
34	A56	10r car & grn ('34)	165.00	250.00
35	A56	15r ol grn & ultra ('37)	500.00	850.00
		Nos. 17-35 (19)	888.80	1,383.

For overprints see Nos. O15-O25.

Stamps of India, 1937, Overprinted type "a" (A80, A81) or "c" (A82)

1939 Wmk. 196 Perf. 13 1/2x14

No.	Type	Description	Unused	Used
45	A80	1/2a brown	.60	1.00
46	A80	1a carmine	.60	1.00
47	A81	2a scarlet	1.10	1.50
48	A81	3a yel green	1.65	1.75
49	A81	4a dark brown	2.50	10.00
50	A81	6a peacock blue	2.50	6.00
51	A81	8a blue violet	4.50	25.00
52	A81	12a car lake	5.25	25.00
53	A82	1r brown & slate	2.00	2.00
54	A82	2r dk brown & dk violet	11.00	8.00
55	A82	5r dp ultra & dk green	14.00	15.00
56	A82	10r rose car & dk violet	62.50	60.00
a.		Double overprint	350.00	350.00
57	A82	15r dk green & dk brown	77.50	125.00
		Nos. 45-57 (13)	185.70	281.25
		Set, never hinged	325.00	

Stamps of India 1940-43, Overprinted in Black KUWAIT

1945 Wmk. 196 Perf. 13 1/2x14

No.	Type	Description	Unused	Used
59	A83	3p slate	.50	.70
60	A83	1/2a rose violet	.20	.20
61	A83	9p lt green	.25	.30
62	A83	1a car rose	.25	.20
63	A84	1 1/2a dark purple	.45	.65
64	A84	2a scarlet	.45	.65
65	A84	3a violet	.70	.85
66	A84	3 1/2a ultramarine	1.00	1.40
67	A85	4a chocolate	.45	.40
68	A85	6a peacock blue	7.50	9.00
69	A85	8a blue violet	1.00	.90
70	A85	12a car lake	1.25	1.25
71	A81	14a rose violet	6.00	12.50
		Nos. 59-71 (13)	20.00	29.00
		Set, never hinged	55.00	

Catalogue values for unused stamps in this section, from this point to the end of the section, are for Never Hinged items.

British Postal Administration

See Oman (Muscat) for similar stamps with surcharge of new value only.

KUWAIT
1/2
ANNA

Great Britain Nos. 258 to 263, 243 and 248 Surcharged in Black

1948-49 Wmk. 251 Perf. 14 1/2x14

No.	Type	Description	Unused	Used
72	A101	1/2a on 1/2p grn	.25	.15
73	A101	1a on 1p ver	.25	.15
74	A101	1 1/2a on 1 1/2p lt red brown	.15	.15
75	A101	2a on 2p lt org	.15	.15
76	A101	2 1/2a on 2 1/2p ultra	.15	.15
77	A101	3a on 3p violet	.15	.15
a.		Pair, one without surcharge		
78	A102	6a on 6p rose lil	.25	.15
79	A103	1r on 1sh brown	.55	.40

Great Britain Nos. 249A, 250 and 251A Surcharged in Black

KUWAIT
2 RUPEES

Wmk. 259 Perf. 14

No.	Type	Description	Unused	Used
80	A104	2r on 2sh6p yel grn	1.90	3.00
81	A104	5r on 5sh dull red	6.00	3.75
81A	A105	10r on 10sh ultra	32.50	17.50
		Nos. 72-81A (11)	42.30	25.70

Issued: #72-81, Apr., 1948; 10r, July 4, 1949.
Bars of surcharge at bottom on No. 81A.

Silver Wedding Issue

Great Britain Nos. 267 and 268 Surcharged in Black

KUWAIT
2½
ANNAS

Perf. 14 1/2x14, 14x14 1/2

1948 Wmk. 251

No.	Type	Description	Unused	Used
82	A109	2 1/2a on 2 1/2p brt ultra	.15	.15
83	A110	15r on £1 deep chalky blue	32.50	45.00

Three bars obliterate the original denomination on No. 83.

Olympic Games Issue

Great Britain Nos. 271 to 274 Surcharged "KUWAIT" and New Value in Black

1948 Perf. 14 1/2x14

No.	Type	Description	Unused	Used
84	A113	2 1/2a on 2 1/2p brt ultra	.20	.20
85	A114	3a on 3p dp violet	.35	.35
86	A115	6a on 6p red violet	.60	.60
87	A116	1r on 1sh dk brown	1.00	1.00
		Nos. 84-87 (4)	2.15	2.15

A square of dots obliterates the original denomination on No. 87.

UPU Issue

Great Britain Nos. 276 to 279 Surcharged "KUWAIT", New Value and Square of Dots in Black

1949, Oct. 10 Photo.

No.	Type	Description	Unused	Used
89	A117	2 1/2a on 2 1/2p brt ultra	.25	.25
90	A118	3a on 3p brt vio	.50	.50
91	A119	6a on 6p red vio	.90	.90
92	A120	1r on 1sh brown	1.65	1.65
		Nos. 89-92 (4)	3.30	3.30

Great Britain Nos. 280-285 Surcharged Like Nos.72-79 in Black

1950-51 Wmk. 251 Perf. 14 1/2x14

No.	Type	Description	Unused	Used
93	A101	1/2a on 1/2p lt org	.50	1.00
94	A101	1a on 1p ultra	.50	.50
95	A101	1 1/2a on 1 1/2p green	.50	2.00
96	A101	2a on 2p lt red brown	.50	.50
97	A101	2 1/2a on 2 1/2p ver	.50	1.00
98	A102	4a on 4p ultra ('50)	.50	.40

KUWAIT
2 RUPEES

Great Britain Nos. 286-288 Surcharged in Black

Wmk. 259 Perf. 11x12

No.	Type	Description	Unused	Used
99	A121	2r on 2sh6p green	12.00	4.00
100	A121	5r on 5sh dl red	15.00	5.00
101	A122	10r on 10sh ultra	26.00	8.00
		Nos. 93-101 (9)	56.00	22.40

Longer bars, at lower right, on No. 101.
Issued: 4a, Oct. 2, 1950; others, May 3, 1951.

Stamps of Great Britain, 1952-54 Surcharged "KUWAIT" and New Value in Black or Dark Blue

1952-54 Wmk. 298 Perf. 14 1/2x14

No.	Type	Description	Unused	Used
102	A126	1/2a on 1/2p red org ('53)	.15	.15
103	A126	1a on 1p ultra ('53)	.15	.15
104	A126	1 1/2a on 1 1/2p green	.15	.15
105	A126	2a on 2p red brn ('53)	.15	.15
106	A127	2 1/2a on 2 1/2p scarlet	.15	.15
107	A127	3a on 3p dk pur (Dk Bl) ('54)	.15	.15
108	A128	4a on 4p ultra ('53)	.60	.15
109	A129	6a on 6p lilac rose ('54)	.90	.15
111	A132	12a on 1sh6p dk green ('53)	3.00	.75
112	A131	1r on 1sh6p dk blue ('53)	3.50	.65
		Nos. 102-112 (10)	8.90	
		Set value		2.00

Coronation Issue

Great Britain Nos. 313-316 Surcharged "KUWAIT" and New Value in Black

1953, June 3

No.	Type	Description	Unused	Used
113	A134	2 1/2a on 2 1/2p scarlet	1.00	.50
114	A135	4a on 4p brt ultra	1.25	.50
115	A136	12a on 1sh3p dk grn	3.50	1.25
116	A137	1r on 1sh6p dk blue	4.50	1.75
		Nos. 113-116 (4)	10.25	4.00

Squares of dots obliterate the original denominations on Nos. 115 and 116.

Great Britain Stamps of 1955-56 Surcharged "KUWAIT" and New Value in Black

1955 Wmk. 308 Engr. Perf. 11x12

No.	Type	Description	Unused	Used
117	A133	2r on 2sh6p dk brown	2.00	1.00
118	A133	5r on 5sh crimson	6.50	2.75
119	A133	10r on 10sh dp ultra	11.00	6.50
		Nos. 117-119 (3)	19.50	10.25

The surcharge on #117-119 exists in two types.

1956 Photo. Perf. 14 1/2x14

No.	Type	Description	Unused	Used
120	A126	1/2a on 1/2p red org	.45	.25
121	A126	1a on 1p ultra	.15	.15
122	A126	1 1/2a on 1 1/2p green	.15	.15
123	A126	2a on 2p red brown	.15	.15
124	A127	2 1/2a on 2 1/2p scar	.50	.15
125	A128	4a on 4p ultra	2.60	.65
126	A129	6a on 6p lil rose	.65	.20
127	A132	12a on 1sh3p dk grn	6.75	1.10
128	A131	1r on 1sh6p dk bl	1.65	.45
		Nos. 120-128 (9)	13.05	3.25

Great Britain Nos. 317-325, 328 and 332 Surcharged "KUWAIT" and New Value in Black

1957-58 Wmk. 308 Perf. 14 1/2x14

No.	Type	Description	Unused	Used
129	A129	1np on 5p lt brown	.15	.15
130	A126	3np on 1/2p red org	.15	.15
131	A126	6np on 1p ultra	.15	.15
132	A126	9np on 1 1/2p green	.15	.15
133	A126	12np on 2p red brn	.50	.30
134	A127	15np on 2 1/2p scar, type I	.60	.35
a.		Type II ('58)	30.00	30.00
135	A127	20np on 3p dk pur	.60	.25
136	A128	25np on 4p ultra	1.75	.60
137	A129	40np on 6p lilac rose	1.00	.55
138	A130	50np on 9p dp ol grn	4.50	1.50
139	A132	75np on 1sh3p dk grn	5.25	1.75
		Nos. 129-139 (11)	14.80	5.90

The arrangement of the surcharge varies on different values; there are three bars through value on No. 138.

Sheik Abdullah A1

Dhow A2

Oil Derrick A3

Designs: 50np, Pipe lines. 75np, Main square, Kuwait. 2r, Dhow, derrick and Sheik. 5r, Mosque and Sheik. 10r, Oil plant at Burgan and Sheik.

Perf. 12 1/2

1959, Feb. 1 Unwmk. Engr.

No.	Type	Description	Unused	Used
140	A1	5np green	.15	.15
141	A1	10np rose brown	.15	.15
142	A1	15np yellow brown	.40	.30
143	A1	20np gray violet	.25	.15
144	A1	25np vermilion	.25	.15
145	A1	40np rose claret	2.25	1.10
		Perf. 13 1/2x13		
146	A2	40np dark blue	.35	.30
147	A2	50np carmine	.35	.30
148	A2	75np olive green	.60	.45
		Perf. 14x13 1/2		
149	A3	1r claret	.70	.55
150	A3	2r red brn & dp bl	1.65	1.00
151	A3	5r green	4.00	2.25
152	A3	10r purple	13.00	6.50
		Nos. 140-152 (13)	24.10	13.35

No. 140-141 and 145 were issued in 1958 for local use. They became valid for international mail on Feb. 1, 1959, but No. 145 was withdrawn after two weeks.

Sheik Abdullah and Flag — A4

1960, Feb. 25 Engr. Perf. 14

No.	Type	Description	Unused	Used
153	A4	40np olive grn & red	.30	.15
154	A4	60np blue & red	.55	.30

10th anniv. of the accession of Sheik Sir Abdullah As-Salim As-Sabah.

Types of 1959, Redrawn

Designs: 20f, 3d, Mosque and Sheik. 25f, 100f, Vickers Viscount. 30f, 75f, Dhow, derrick and Sheik. 35f, 90f, Shuwaikh secondary school. 45f, 1d, Wara Hill, Burgan oil field.

1961 Perf. 12 1/2

No.	Type	Description	Unused	Used
155	A1	1f green	.15	.15
156	A1	2f rose brown	.15	.15
157	A1	4f yellow brown	.15	.15
158	A1	5f gray violet	.15	.15
159	A1	8f salmon pink	.15	.15
160	A1	15f rose claret	.15	.15
		Perf. 14x13 1/2, 13 1/2 (40f, 250f)		
161	A3	20f green	.15	.15
162	A3	25f blue	.15	.15
163	A3	30f red brn & dp bl	.25	.15
164	A3	35f ver & black	.50	.30
165	A2	40f dark blue	.25	.20
166	A3	45f violet brown	.25	.20
167	A3	75f green & sepia	.40	.20
168	A3	90f ultra & brown	.55	.30
169	A3	100f rose red	.55	.30
170	A2	250f olive grn	2.75	.70

171 A3 1d orange 8.50 3.75
172 A3 3d brick red 37.50 22.50
Nos. 155-172 (18) 52.70 29.80

Nos. 165 and 170 are 32x22mm.
Issued: 75f, 90f, 4/27; 35f, 5/8; others, 4/1.

Symbols of Telecommunications — A5

Perf. 11½

1962, Jan. 11 Unwmk. Photo.

Granite Paper

173 A5 8f blue & black .20 .15
174 A5 20f rose & black .50 .25

4th Arab Telecommunications Union Conference.

Mubarakiya School and Sheiks Abdullah and Mubarak — A6

1962, Apr. 15 Unwmk. ***Perf. 11½***

175 A6 8f gldn brn, blk, org & gold .20 .15
176 A6 20f lt blue, blk, org & gold .55 .30

50th anniversary of Mubarakiya School.

Arab League Building, Cairo, and Emblem — A7

1962, Apr. 23 ***Perf. 13½x13***

177 A7 20f purple .15 .15
178 A7 45f brown .55 .30

Arab Publicity Week, Mar. 22-28.

Flag of Kuwait — A8

Malaria Eradication Emblem — A9

1962, June 19 ***Perf. 11½***

Flag in Green, Black & Red

179 A8 8f black & tan .20 .15
180 A8 20f black & yellow .35 .30
181 A8 45f black & lt blue .55 .45
182 A8 90f black & lilac 1.50 .90
Nos. 179-182 (4) 2.60 1.80

Issued for National Day, June 19.

1962, Aug. 1 ***Perf. 13½x13***

183 A9 4f slate green & yel grn .15 .15
184 A9 25f green & gray .50 .30

WHO drive to eradicate malaria.
No. 184 has laurel leaves added and inscription rearranged.

Cogwheel, Oil Wells, Camels and Modern Building — A10

Perf. 11x13

1962, Dec. 8 Unwmk. Litho.

185 A10 8f multicolored .20 .15
186 A10 20f multicolored .24 .15
187 A10 45f multicolored .50 .24
188 A10 75f multicolored 1.00 .45
Nos. 185-188 (4) 1.94 .99

Bicentenary of the Sabah dynasty.

Mother and Child — A11

1963, Mar. 21 Photo. ***Perf. 14½x14***

189 A11 8f yel, red, blk & green .15 .15
190 A11 20f blue, red, blk & grn .30 .22
191 A11 45f lt ol, red, blk & grn .60 .42
192 A11 75f gray, red, blk & green .70 .70
Nos. 189-192 (4) 1.75 1.49

Issued for Mother's Day, Mar. 21, 1963.

Wheat Emblem, Date Palm, Cow and Sheep — A12

1963, Mar. 21 ***Perf. 14x14½***

193 A12 4f red brn, lt blue & grn .22 .15
194 A12 8f brown, yel & green .38 .15
195 A12 20f red brn, pale vio & green .55 .32
196 A12 45f red brn, rose & green 1.10 .65
Nos. 193-196 (4) 2.25 1.27

FAO "Freedom from Hunger" campaign.

Test Tube, Oil Drops and Ship — A13

1963, Apr. 15 Photo. ***Perf. 14½x14***

197 A13 4f brown, yel & blue .15 .15
198 A13 20f green, yel & blue .38 .24
199 A13 45f brt mag, yel & blue .70 .50
Nos. 197-199 (3) 1.23 .89

Issued for Education Day.

Sheik Abdullah, Flags and Map of Kuwait — A14

1963, June 19 ***Perf. 14x13***

Flags in Black, Bright Green & Red; Denominations in Black

200 A14 4f ultramarine .95 .60
201 A14 5f ocher 1.25 .75
202 A14 20f bright lilac 4.75 2.75
203 A14 50f olive 8.00 5.00
Nos. 200-203 (4) 14.95 9.10

Second anniversary of National Day.

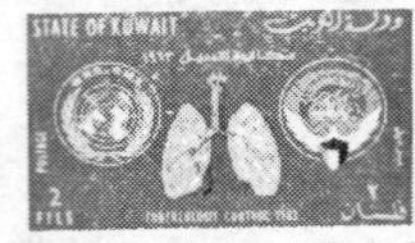

Lungs and Emblems of World Health Organization and Kuwait Tuberculosis Society — A15

1963, July 27 ***Perf. 13x13½***

Design in Yellow, Black, Emerald & Red

204 A15 2f ocher .15 .15
205 A15 4f dark green .24 .15
206 A15 8f lt violet blue .32 .15
207 A15 20f rose brown .55 .24
Nos. 204-207 (4) 1.26
Set value .52

Issued to publicize tuberculosis control.

Sheik Abdullah, Scroll and Scales of Justice — A16

1963, Oct. 29 Photo. ***Perf. 11x13***

Center in Gray

208 A16 4f dp red & red brn .15 .15
209 A16 8f dk green & red brn .15 .15
210 A16 20f vio brown & red brn .50 .25
211 A16 45f brown org & red brn .75 .40
212 A16 75f purple & red brown 1.25 .75
213 A16 90f ultra & red brown 1.50 .90
Nos. 208-213 (6) 4.30 2.60

Promulgation of the constitution.

Soccer — A17

Sports: 4f, Basketball. 5f, Swimming, horiz. 8f, Track. 15f, Javelin, horiz. 20f, Pole vault, horiz. 35f, Gymnast on rings, horiz. 45f, Gymnast on parallel bars.

1963, Nov. 8 Unwmk. ***Perf. 14½x14***

214 A17 1f multicolored .15 .15
215 A17 4f multicolored .15 .15
216 A17 5f multicolored .15 .15
217 A17 8f multicolored .25 .15
218 A17 15f multicolored .30 .15
219 A17 20f multicolored .50 .30
220 A17 35f multicolored 1.00 .40
221 A17 45f multicolored 2.00 .60
Nos. 214-221 (8) 4.50 2.05

Arab School Games of 1963.

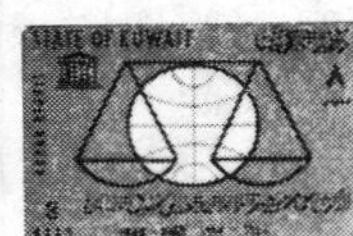

UNESCO Emblem, Scales and Globe — A18

1963, Dec. 10 Litho. ***Perf. 13x12½***

222 A18 8f violet, blk & pale grn .20 .15
223 A18 20f gray, black & yel .30 .15
224 A18 25f blue, black & tan .50 .18
Nos. 222-224 (3) 1.00
Set value .40

15th anniv. of the Universal Declaration of Human Rights.

Sheik Abdullah — A19

Perf. 12½x13

1964, Feb. 1 Unwmk. Photo.

Portrait in Natural Colors

225 A19 1f gray & silver .15 .15
a. Booklet pane of 6 ('66) 1.50
226 A19 2f brt blue & silver .15 .15
227 A19 4f ocher & silver .15 .15
a. Booklet pane of 6 ('66) 1.65
228 A19 5f fawn & silver .15 .15
229 A19 8f dk brown & sil .15 .15
230 A19 10f citron & sil .15 .15
a. Booklet pane of 6 ('66) 1.75
231 A19 15f brt green & sil .75 .75
a. Booklet pane of 6 ('66) 1.10
232 A19 20f blue gray & sil .35 .15
a. Booklet pane of 6 ('66) 2.25
233 A19 25f green & silver .45 .25
234 A19 30f gray grn & sil .50 .30
235 A19 40f brt vio & sil .70 .35
236 A19 45f violet & silver .75 .35
237 A19 50f olive & silver .90 .45
238 A19 70f red lilac & sil 1.50 .50
239 A19 75f rose red & sil 1.75 .60
240 A19 90f ultra & silver 2.00 .75
241 A19 100f pale lilac & sil 2.50 .80

Perf. 14x14½

Size: 25x30mm

242 A19 250f brown & sil 5.25 1.90
243 A19 1d brown vio & sil 21.00 8.00
Nos. 225-243 (19) 39.30 16.05

Ramses II Battling the Hittites (from Abu Simbel) — A20

Perf. 13x12½

1964, Mar. 8 Engr. & Litho.

244 A20 8f buff, ind & maroon .16 .15
245 A20 20f lt blue, indigo & vio .40 .30
246 A20 30f bluish grn, ind & vio .70 .48
Nos. 244-246 (3) 1.26 .93

UNESCO world campaign to save historic monuments in Nubia.

Mother and Child — A21

1964, Mar. 21 Litho. ***Perf. 14x13***

247 A21 8f green, gray & vio blk .16 .15
248 A21 20f green, red & vio blk .22 .15
249 A21 30f green, ol bis & vio blk .32 .20
250 A21 45f green, saph & vio blk .55 .40
Nos. 247-250 (4) 1.25 .90

Issued for Mother's Day, Mar. 21.

Nurse Giving TB Test, and Thorax — A22

Perf. 13x13½

1964, Apr. 7 Photo. Unwmk.

251 A22 8f brown & green .35 .22
252 A22 20f green & rose red 1.10 .40

Issued for World Health Day (fight against tuberculosis), Apr. 7, 1964.

Microscope and Dhow — A23

1964, Apr. 15 *Perf. 12½x13*

253 A23 8f multicolored .22 .15
254 A23 15f multicolored .24 .15
255 A23 20f multicolored .32 .15
256 A23 30f multicolored .50 .38
Nos. 253-256 (4) 1.28
Set value .70

Issued for Education Day.

Doves and State Seal — A24

1964, June 19 **Litho.** *Perf. 13½*

Seal in Blue, Brown, Black, Red & Green

257 A24 8f black & bister brn .30 .15
258 A24 20f black & green .45 .22
259 A24 30f black & gray .75 .38
260 A24 45f black & blue 1.00 .65
Nos. 257-260 (4) 2.50 1.40

Third anniversary of National Day.

Arab Postal Union Emblem — A25

1964, Nov. 21 **Photo.** *Perf. 11x11½*

261 A25 8f lt blue & brown .25 .15
262 A25 20f yellow & ultra .70 .30
263 A25 45f olive & brown 1.25 .65
Nos. 261-263 (3) 2.20 1.10

Permanent Office of the APU, 10th anniv.

Conference Emblem — A26

1965, Feb. 8 **Litho.** *Perf. 14*

264 A26 8f black, org brn & yel .45 .16
265 A26 20f multicolored .90 .25

First Arab Journalists' Conference.

Oil Derrick, Dhow, Sun and Doves A27

Mother and Children A28

1965, Feb. 25 *Perf. 13½*

266 A27 10f lt green & multi .20 .15
267 A27 15f pink & multi .35 .15
268 A27 20f gray & multi .65 .25
Nos. 266-268 (3) 1.20
Set value .48

Fourth anniversary of National Day.

1965, Mar. 21 **Unwmk.** *Perf. 13½*

269 A28 8f multicolored .22 .15
270 A28 15f multicolored .40 .15
271 A28 20f multicolored .50 .24
Nos. 269-271 (3) 1.12 .54

Mother's Day, Mar. 21.

Weather Balloon A29

1965, Mar. 23 **Photo.** *Perf. 11½x11*

272 A29 4f deep ultra & yellow .40 .15
273 A29 5f blue & dp orange .75 .15
274 A29 20f dk blue & emerald .95 .15
Nos. 272-274 (3) 2.10
Set value .38

Fifth World Meteorological Day.

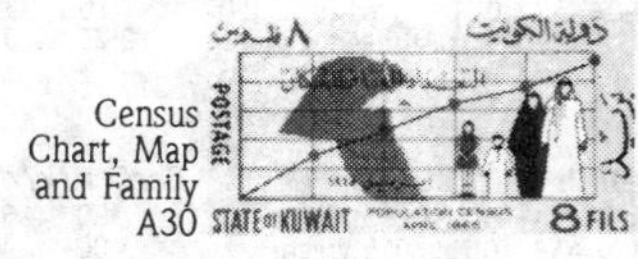

Census Chart, Map and Family A30

1965, Mar. 28 **Litho.** *Perf. 13½*

275 A30 8f multicolored .30 .15
276 A30 20f multicolored .90 .40
277 A30 50f multicolored 1.75 1.00
Nos. 275-277 (3) 2.95 1.55

Issued to publicize the 1965 census.

ICY Emblem A31

1965, Mar. 7 **Engr.**

278 A31 8f red & black .15 .15
279 A31 20f lt ultra & black .65 .40
280 A31 30f emerald & black 1.20 .65
Nos. 278-280 (3) 2.00 1.20

International Cooperation Year.

Dagger in Map of Palestine — A31a

Perf. 11x11½

1965, Apr. 9 **Photo.** **Unwmk.**

281 A31a 4f red & ultra .52 .32
282 A31a 45f red & emerald 1.50 .70

Deir Yassin massacre, Apr. 9, 1948. See Iraq Nos. 372-373.

Tower of Shuwaikh School and Atom Symbol — A32

1965, Apr. 15 **Litho.** *Perf. 14x13*

283 A32 4f multicolored .20 .15
284 A32 20f multicolored .45 .20
285 A32 45f multicolored .80 .40
Nos. 283-285 (3) 1.45 .75

Issued for Education Day.

ITU Emblem, Old and New Communication Equipment A33

1965, May 17 *Perf. 13½x14*

286 A33 8f dk blue, lt bl & red .60 .35
287 A33 20f green, lt grn & red 1.25 .60
288 A33 45f red, pink & blue 2.00 1.00
Nos. 286-288 (3) 3.85 1.95

ITU, centenary.

Library Aflame and Lamp A33a

1965, June 7 **Photo.** *Perf. 11*

289 A33a 8f black, green & red .65 .20
290 A33a 15f black, red & green 1.00 .20

Burning of Library of Algiers, June 2, 1962.

Falcon — A34

Book and Wreath Emblem — A35

1965, Dec. 1 **Engr.** *Perf. 13*

Center in Sepia

291 A34 8f red lilac 1.10 .20
292 A34 15f olive green .80 .22
293 A34 20f dark blue 1.35 .35
294 A34 25f orange 1.75 .50
295 A34 30f emerald 1.65 .55
296 A34 45f blue 2.75 .85
297 A34 50f claret 3.75 1.00
298 A34 90f carmine 6.75 2.00
Nos. 291-298 (8) 19.90 5.67

1966, Jan. 10 **Photo.** *Perf. 14x15*

299 A35 8f lt violet & multi .35 .15
300 A35 20f brown red & multi .60 .15
301 A35 30f blue & multi .65 .28
Nos. 299-301 (3) 1.60
Set value .50

Issued for Education Day.

Sheik Sabah as-Salim as-Sabah — A36

1966, Feb. 1 **Photo.** *Perf. 14x13*

302 A36 4f lt blue & multi .22 .15
303 A36 5f pale rose & multi .22 .15
304 A36 20f multicolored .70 .22
305 A36 30f lt violet & multi .75 .35
306 A36 40f salmon & multi 1.10 .50
307 A36 45f lt gray & multi 1.25 .60
308 A36 70f yellow & multi 1.90 .85
309 A36 90f pale green & multi 2.50 1.10
Nos. 302-309 (8) 8.64 3.92

Wheat and Fish — A37

1966, Feb. 15 *Perf. 11x11½*

310 A37 20f multicolored 1.40 .75
311 A37 45f multicolored 2.50 1.40

"Freedom from Hunger" campaign.

Eagle, Banner, Scales and Emblems A38

1966, Feb. 25 **Litho.** *Perf. 12½x13*

312 A38 20f tan & multi 1.10 .42
313 A38 25f lt green & multi 1.50 .45
314 A38 45f gray & multi 2.00 .85
Nos. 312-314 (3) 4.60 1.72

Fifth anniversary of National Day.

Wheel of Industry and Map of Arab Countries A39

1966, Mar. 1 *Perf. 14x13½*

315 A39 20f brt blue, brt grn & blk .48 .25
316 A39 50f lt red brn, brt grn & black 1.00 .65

Issued to publicize the conference on industrial development in Arab countries.

Mother and Children — A40

1966, Mar. 21 *Perf. 11½x11*

317 A40 20f pink & multi .70 .20
318 A40 45f multicolored 1.50 .40

Mother's Day, Mar. 21.

Medical Conference Emblem — A41

Composite View of a City — A42

1966, Apr. 1 **Photo.** *Perf. 14½x14*

319 A41 15f blue & red .60 .18
320 A41 30f red & blue 1.25 .60

Fifth Arab Medical Conference, Kuwait.

1966, Apr. 7 **Litho.** *Perf. 12½x13*

321 A42 8f multicolored .60 .18
322 A42 10f multicolored 1.50 .28

Issued for World Health Day, Apr. 7.

Inauguration of WHO Headquarters, Geneva A43

1966, May 3 **Litho.** *Perf. 11x11½*

323 A43 5f dull sal, ol grn & vio bl .90 .15
324 A43 10f lt grn, ol grn & vio blue 1.10 .20
Set value .15

Traffic Signal at Night A44

"Blood Transfusion" A45

1966, May 4

325 A44 10f green, red & black .85 .15
326 A44 20f green, red & black 1.25 .32

Issued for Traffic Day.

1966, May 5 *Perf. 13½*

327 A45 4f multicolored .60 .15
328 A45 8f multicolored .70 .15
Set value .22

Blood Bank Day, May 5.

Sheik Ahmad and Ship Carrying First Crude Oil Shipment
A46

1966, June 30 *Perf. 13½*

329	A46	20f multicolored	.85	.25
330	A46	45f multicolored	1.75	.35

20th anniv. of the first crude oil shipment, June 30, 1946.

Ministry of Guidance and Information — A47

1966, July 25 Photo. *Perf. 11½x11*

331	A47	4f rose & brown	.22	.15
332	A47	5f yel brown & brt green	.28	.15
333	A47	8f brt green & purple	.32	.15
334	A47	20f salmon & ultra	.38	.15
		Nos. 331-334 (4)	1.20	
		Set value		.40

Opening of Ministry of Guidance and Information Building.

Fishing Boat, Lobster, Fish, Crab and FAO Emblem
A48

1966, Oct. 10 Litho. *Perf. 13½*

335	A48	4f buff & multi	1.25	.15
336	A48	20f lt lilac & multi	1.65	.28
		Set value		.38

Fisheries' Conference of Near East Countries under the sponsorship of the FAO, Oct. 1966.

United Nations Flag — A49

UNESCO Emblem — A50

1966, Oct. 24 *Perf. 13x14*

337	A49	20f blue, dk blue & pink	1.40	.40
338	A49	45f blue, dk bl & pale grn	2.25	.75

Issued for United Nations Day.

1966, Nov. 4 Litho. *Perf. 12½x13*

339	A50	20f multicolored	1.75	.90
340	A50	45f multicolored	1.90	1.75

20th anniversary of UNESCO.

Kuwait University Emblem
A51

1966, Nov. 27 Photo. *Perf. 14½*

Emblem in Yellow, Bright Blue, Green and Gold

341	A51	8f lt ultra, vio & gold	.35	.18
342	A51	10f red, brown & gold	.80	.20
343	A51	20f lt yel grn, slate & gold	.95	.38
344	A51	45f buff, green & gold	1.75	1.00
		Nos. 341-344 (4)	3.85	1.76

Opening of Kuwait University.

Jabir al-Ahmad al-Jabir and Sheik Sabah
A52

1966, Dec. 11 *Perf. 14x13*

345	A52	8f yel green & multi	.65	.15
346	A52	20f yellow & multi	.85	.42
347	A52	45f pink & multi	1.65	1.00
		Nos. 345-347 (3)	3.15	1.57

Appointment of the heir apparent, Jabir al-Ahmad al-Jabir.

Scout Badge and Square Knot — A52a

1966, Dec. 21 Litho. *Perf. 14x13*

347A	A52a	4f lt ol green & fawn	.50	.15
347B	A52a	20f yel brn & blue grn	2.25	.40

Kuwait Boy Scouts, 30th anniversary.

"Symbols of Science and Peace" — A53

1967, Jan. 15 Litho. *Perf. 13x14*

348	A53	10f multicolored	.35	.16
349	A53	45f multicolored	1.10	.52

Issued for Education Day.

Fertilizer Plant — A54

1967, Feb. 19 Unwmk. *Perf. 13*

350	A54	8f lt blue & multi	.60	.18
351	A54	20f cream & multi	1.40	.42

Opening of Chemical Fertilizer Plant.

Sun, Dove and Olive Branch — A55

1967, Feb. 25 Litho. *Perf. 13*

352	A55	8f salmon & multi	.40	.16
353	A55	20f yellow & multi	1.10	.40

Sixth anniversary of National Day.

Map of Arab States and Municipal Building
A56

1967, Mar. 11 *Perf. 14½x13*

354	A56	20f gray & multi	1.50	.35
355	A56	30f lt brown & multi	2.50	.55

1st conf. of the Arab Cities Org., Kuwait.

Family — A57

Arab League Emblem — A58

1967, Mar. 21 Litho. *Perf. 13x13½*

356	A57	20f pale rose & multi	1.10	.35
357	A57	45f pale green & multi	2.75	.70

Issued for Family Day, Mar. 21.

1967, Mar. 27 *Perf. 13x14*

358	A58	8f gray & dk blue	.80	.15
359	A58	10f bister & green	1.00	.22

Issued for Arab Publicity Week.

Sabah Hospital and Physicians at Work — A59

1967, Apr. 7 *Perf. 14x13*

360	A59	8f dull rose & multi	1.25	.22
361	A59	20f gray & multi	1.50	.60

Issued for World Health Day.

Two Heads of Ramses II — A60

1967, Apr. 17 *Perf. 13½*

362	A60	15f citron, green & brn	.90	.30
363	A60	20f chalky blue, grn & pur	1.40	.35

Arab Week to Save the Nubian Monuments.

Traffic Policeman
A61

1967, May 4 Litho. *Perf. 14x13*

364	A61	8f lt green & multi	1.90	.35
365	A61	20f rose lilac & multi	2.00	.95

Issued for Traffic Day.

ITY Emblem — A62

1967, June 4 Photo. *Perf. 13*

366	A62	20f Prus blue, lt bl & blk	1.00	.60
367	A62	45f rose lilac, lt bl & blk	2.00	1.25

International Tourist Year.

Arab League Emblem and Hands Reaching for Knowledge — A63

Map of Palestine and UN Emblem — A64

1967, Sept. 8 Litho. *Perf. 13x14*

368	A63	8f blue & multi	1.10	.15
369	A63	20f dull rose & multi	1.40	.32

Issued to publicize the literacy campaign.

1967, Oct. 24 Litho. *Perf. 13*

370	A64	20f blue & pink	.70	.30
371	A64	45f orange & pink	1.65	.65

Issued for United Nations Day.

Factory and Cogwheels — A65

1967, Nov. 25 Photo. *Perf. 13*

372	A65	20f crimson & yellow	1.00	.30
373	A65	45f gray & yellow	2.25	.65

3rd Conf. of Arab Labor Ministers, Kuwait.

Flag and Open Book — A66

Map of Kuwait and Oil Derrick — A67

1968, Jan. 15 Litho. *Perf. 14*

374	A66	20f brt blue & multi	.90	.42
375	A66	45f yel orange & multi	1.90	.90

Issued for Education Day.

1968, Feb. 23 Litho. *Perf. 12*

376	A67	10f multicolored	1.00	.55
377	A67	20f multicolored	2.00	1.00

30th anniv. of the discovery of oil in the Greater Burgan Field.

Sheik Sabah and Sun — A68

1968, Feb. 25 Litho. *Perf. 14x15*

378	A68	8f red lilac & multi	.30	.20
379	A68	10f lt blue & multi	.40	.30
380	A68	15f violet & multi	.60	.40
381	A68	20f vermilion & multi	.70	.50
		Nos. 378-381 (4)	2.00	1.40

Seventh anniversary of National Day.

Open Book and Emblem — A69

1968, Mar. 2 *Perf. 14*

382 A69 8f yellow & multi .30 .15
383 A69 20f lilac rose & multi .40 .20
384 A69 45f orange & multi .80 .40
Nos. 382-384 (3) 1.50 .75

Issued for Teachers' Day.

Family Picnic — A70

1968, Mar. 21 *Perf. 13¹/₂x13*

385 A70 8f blue & multi .30 .15
386 A70 10f red & multi .30 .15
387 A70 15f lilac & multi .40 .15
388 A70 20f dk brown & multi .50 .15
Nos. 385-388 (4) 1.50
Set value .50

Issued for Family Day.

Sheik Sabah, Arms of WHO and Kuwait — A71

1968, Apr. 7 **Photo.** *Perf. 12*

389 A71 20f brt lilac & multi .80 .80
390 A71 45f multicolored 1.65 1.65

20th anniv. of WHO.

Dagger in Map of Palestine — A72

1968, Apr. 9 **Litho.** *Perf. 14*

391 A72 20f lt blue & vermilion .65 .30
392 A72 45f lilac & vermilion 1.40 .50

Deir Yassin massacre, 20th anniv.

Street Crossing A74

1968, May 4 **Photo.** *Perf. 14x14¹/₂*

395 A74 10f dk brown & multi 1.25 .90
396 A74 15f brt violet & multi 1.50 1.25
397 A74 20f green & multi 2.50 1.50
Nos. 395-397 (3) 5.25 3.65

Issued for Traffic Day.

Map of Palestine and Torch — A75

Perf. 13¹/₂x12¹/₂

1968, May 15 **Litho.**

398 A75 10f lt ultra & multi .25 .15
399 A75 20f yellow & multi 1.50 .30
400 A75 45f aqua & multi 3.25 .55
Nos. 398-400 (3) 5.00 1.00

Issued for Palestine Day.

Palestinian Refugees — A76

1968, June 5 **Litho.** *Perf. 13x13¹/₂*

401 A76 20f pink & multi .40 .15
402 A76 30f ultra & multi .55 .15
403 A76 45f green & multi .70 .20
404 A76 90f lilac & multi 1.25 .40
Nos. 401-404 (4) 2.90 .90

International Human Rights Year.

Museum of Kuwait — A77

Perf. 12¹/₂

1968, Aug. 25 **Unwmk.** **Engr.**

405 A77 1f dk brown & brt grn .15 .15
406 A77 2f dp claret & grn .15 .15
407 A77 5f black & orange .15 .15
408 A77 8f dk brown & grn .15 .15
409 A77 10f Prus blue & cl .15 .15
410 A77 20f org brown & blue .50 .15
411 A77 25f dk blue & orange .65 .20
412 A77 30f Prus blue & yel grn .75 .25
413 A77 45f plum & vio black 1.00 .30
414 A77 50f green & carmine 1.25 .40
Nos. 405-414 (10) 4.90
Set value 1.65

Man Reading Book, Arab League, UN and UNESCO Emblems A78

1968, Sept. 8 **Litho.** *Perf. 12¹/₂x13*

415 A78 15f blue gray & multi .60 .15
416 A78 20f pink & multi .80 .15
Set value .22

Issued for International Literacy Day.

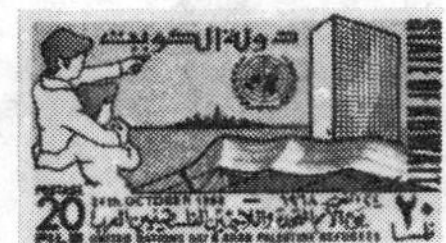

Map of Palestine on UN Building and Children with Tent — A79

1968, Oct. 25 **Litho.** *Perf. 13*

417 A79 20f multicolored .35 .15
418 A79 30f gray & multi .70 .20
419 A79 45f salmon pink & multi .85 .28
Nos. 417-419 (3) 1.90 .63

Issued for United Nations Day.

Kuwait Chamber of Commerce A80

1968, Nov. 6 **Litho.** *Perf. 13¹/₂x12¹/₂*

420 A80 10f dp orange & dk brn .20 .15
421 A80 15f rose claret & vio bl .42 .20
422 A80 20f brown org & dk green .60 .25
Nos. 420-422 (3) 1.22 .60

Opening of the Kuwait Chamber of Commerce Building.

Conference Emblem — A81

1968, Nov. 10 **Litho.** *Perf. 13*

Emblem in Ocher, Blue, Red and Black

423 A81 10f dk brown & blue .32 .15
424 A81 15f dk brown & orange .45 .20
425 A81 20f dk brown & vio blue .60 .25
426 A81 30f dk brown & org brn .95 .40
Nos. 423-426 (4) 2.32 1.00

14th Conference of the Arab Chambers of Commerce, Industry and Agriculture.

Shuaiba Refinery — A82

1968, Nov. 18 *Perf. 13¹/₂*

Emblem in Red, Black and Blue

427 A82 10f black & lt blue grn .50 .20
428 A82 20f black & gray 1.10 .40
429 A82 30f black & salmon 1.25 .65
430 A82 45f black & emerald 2.25 .85
Nos. 427-430 (4) 5.10 2.10

Opening of Shuaiba Refinery.

Koran, Scales and People A83

1968, Dec. 19 **Photo.** *Perf. 14x14¹/₂*

431 A83 5f multicolored .42 .22
432 A83 20f multicolored 1.00 .60
433 A83 30f multicolored 1.40 .85
434 A83 45f multicolored 2.00 1.25
Nos. 431-434 (4) 4.82 2.92

The 1400th anniversary of the Koran.

Boeing 707 A84

1969, Jan. 1 **Litho.** *Perf. 13¹/₂x14*

435 A84 10f brt yellow & multi .60 .20
436 A84 20f green & multi 1.10 .50
437 A84 25f multicolored 1.25 .60
438 A84 45f lilac & multi 2.00 1.10
Nos. 435-438 (4) 4.95 2.40

Introduction of Boeing 707 service by Kuwait Airways.

Globe, Retort and Triangle — A85

1969, Jan. 15 *Perf. 13*

439 A85 15f gray & multi .65 .32
440 A85 20f multicolored 1.00 .38

Issued for Education Day.

Kuwait Hilton Hotel — A86

1969, Feb. 15 **Litho.** *Perf. 14x12¹/₂*

441 A86 10f brt blue & multi .45 .15
442 A86 20f pink & multi 1.10 .15
Set value .25

Opening of the Kuwait Hilton Hotel.

Teachers' Society Emblem, Father and Children — A87

1969, Feb. 15 *Perf. 13*

443 A87 10f violet & multi .45 .20
444 A87 20f rose & multi 1.10 .45

Issued for Education week.

Wreath, Flags and Dove — A88

Emblem, Teacher and Students — A89

1969, Feb. 25 **Photo.** *Perf. 14¹/₂x14*

445 A88 15f lilac & multi .42 .25
446 A88 20f blue & multi .70 .30
447 A88 30f ocher & multi .90 .55
Nos. 445-447 (3) 2.02 1.10

Eighth anniversary of National Day.

1969, Mar. 8 **Litho.** *Perf. 13x12¹/₂*

448 A89 10f multicolored .32 .15
449 A89 20f deep red & multi .65 .20

Issued for Teachers' Day.

Family A90

1969, Mar. 21 *Perf. 13¹/₂*

450 A90 10f dark blue & multi .65 .15
451 A90 20f deep car & multi 1.10 .30

Issued for Family Day.

Avicenna, WHO Emblem, Patient and Microscope — A91

1969, Apr. 7 **Litho.** *Perf. 13¹/₂*

452 A91 15f red brown & multi .60 .15
453 A91 20f lt green & multi 1.40 .15
Set value .24

Issued for World Health Day, Apr. 7.

Motorized Traffic Police — A92

1969, May 4 Litho. *Perf. 12½x13*

454	A92	10f multicolored	.75	.25
455	A92	20f multicolored	3.25	.60

Issued for Traffic Day.

ILO Emblem — A93

1969, June 1 *Perf. 11½*

456	A93	10f red, black & gold	.35	.15
457	A93	20f lt blue grn, blk & gold	.80	.15
		Set value		.15

50th anniv. of the ILO.

S.S. Al Sabahiah A94

1969, June 10 Litho. *Perf. 13½*

458	A94	20f multicolored	1.00	.25
459	A94	45f multicolored	2.50	.80

4th anniversary of Kuwait Shipping Co.

UNESCO Emblem, Woman, Globe and Book — A95

1969, Sept. 8 Litho. *Perf. 13½*

460	A95	10f blue & multi	.20	.15
461	A95	20f rose red & multi	.42	.15
		Set value		.15

International Literacy Day, Sept. 8.

Sheik Sabah — A96

UN Emblem and Scroll — A97

1969-74 Litho. *Perf. 14*

462	A96	8f lt blue & multi	.15	.15
463	A96	10f pink & multi	.16	.16
464	A96	15f gray & multi	.30	.15
465	A96	20f yellow & multi	.38	.20
466	A96	25f violet & multi	.45	.30
467	A96	30f sal & multi	.58	.38
468	A96	45f tan & multi	.80	.50
469	A96	50f yel grn & multi	1.00	.58
470	A96	70f multicolored	1.25	.75
471	A96	75f ultra & multi	1.50	.80
472	A96	90f rose & multi	1.90	1.00
473	A96	250f lilac & multi	6.75	3.00
473A	A96	500f gray green & multi	13.00	9.50
473B	A96	1d lilac rose & multi	27.50	15.00
		Nos. 462-473B (14)	55.72	32.47

Nos. 473A-473B issued Jan. 12, 1974; others Oct. 5, 1969.

1969, Oct. 24 Litho. *Perf. 13*

474	A97	10f emer & multi	.20	.15
475	A97	20f bister & multi	.65	.18
476	A97	45f rose red & multi	1.25	.38
		Nos. 474-476 (3)	2.10	.71

Issued for United Nations Day.

Radar, Satellite Earth Station, Kuwait A98

Design: 45f, Globe and radar, vert.

1969, Dec. 15 Photo. *Perf. 14½*

477	A98	20f silver & multi	.65	.28
478	A98	45f silver & multi	1.65	.60

Inauguration of the Kuwait Earth Station for Satellite Communications.

Globe with Science Symbols, and Education Year Emblem A99

1970, Jan. 15 Photo. *Perf. 13½x13*

479	A99	20f brt lilac & multi	.80	.38
480	A99	45f blue & multi	1.25	.85

International Education Year.

Shoue A100

Old Kuwaiti Vessels: 10f, Sambook. 15f, Baghla. 20f, Batteel. 25f, Boom. 45f, Bakkara. 50f, Shipbuilding.

1970, Feb. 1 *Perf. 14½x14*

481	A100	8f multicolored	.45	.15
482	A100	10f multicolored	.65	.15
483	A100	15f multicolored	.75	.30
484	A100	20f multicolored	1.00	.24
485	A100	25f multicolored	1.50	.30
486	A100	45f multicolored	2.25	.70
487	A100	50f multicolored	3.25	.70
		Nos. 481-487 (7)	9.85	2.54

Refugee Father and Children A101

Kuwait Flag, Emblem and Sheik Sabah A102

1970 Photo. *Perf. 14x12½*

488	A101	20f red brown & multi	2.00	.65
489	A101	45f olive & multi	4.25	1.75

Issued for Universal Palestinian Refugees Week, Dec. 16-22, 1969.

1970, Feb. 25 *Perf. 13½x13*

490	A102	15f silver & multi	.55	.15
491	A102	20f gold & multi	.80	.20

Ninth anniversary of National Day.

Dome of the Rock, Jerusalem, and Boy Commando — A103

Designs: 20f, Dome and man commando. 45f, Dome and woman commando.

1970, Mar. 4 Litho. *Perf. 13*

492	A103	10f pale violet & multi	.95	.20
493	A103	20f lt blue & multi	1.90	.60
494	A103	45f multicolored	4.00	1.25
		Nos. 492-494 (3)	6.85	2.05

Honoring Palestinian commandos.

Parents and Children A104

1970, Mar. 21 *Perf. 14*

495	A104	20f multicolored	.50	.17
496	A104	30f pink & multi	.75	.32

Issued for Family Day.

Map of Arab League Countries, Flag and Emblem A104a

1970, Mar. 22 *Perf. 11½x11*

497	A104a	20f lt blue, grn & lt brn	.50	.25
498	A104a	45f salmon, grn & dk pur	1.40	.60

25th anniversary of the Arab League.

Census Graph and Kuwait Arms A105

1970, Apr. 1 Litho. *Perf. 13½x13*

499	A105	15f dull orange & multi	.28	.15
500	A105	20f yellow & multi	.35	.15
501	A105	30f pink & multi	.60	.28
		Nos. 499-501 (3)	1.23	.58

Issued to publicize the 1970 census.

"Fight Cancer," Kuwait Arms, WHO Emblem — A106

1970, Apr. 7 *Perf. 13½x13*

502	A106	20f blue, vio bl & rose lil	.42	.15
503	A106	30f dl yel, vio bl & lil rose	.55	.24

World Health Organization Day, Apr. 7, and to publicize the fight against cancer.

Traffic Signs — A107

1970, May 4 Photo. *Perf. 13½*

504	A107	20f multicolored	1.65	.65
505	A107	30f multicolored	2.75	1.00

Issued for Traffic Day.

Red Crescent A108

1970, May 8 Litho. *Perf. 12½x13½*

506	A108	10f yellow & multi	.65	.16
507	A108	15f emerald & multi	1.10	.25
508	A108	30f tan & multi	2.25	.70
		Nos. 506-508 (3)	4.00	1.11

Intl. Red Crescent and Red Cross Day.

Opening of UPU Headquarters, Bern — A109

1970, May 25 Photo. *Perf. 12x11½*

509	A109	20f multicolored	.85	.32
510	A109	30f multicolored	1.10	.50

Sheik Sabah — A110

1970, June 15 Photo. *Perf. 14*

511	A110	20f silver & multi	1.00	.20
512	A110	45f gold & multi	2.25	.50
a.		Miniature sheet of 2	5.00	1.75

Nos. 511-512 have circular perforation around vignette set within a white square of paper, perforated on 4 sides. #512a contains 2 imperf. stamps similar to #511-512.

UN Emblem, Symbols of Peace, Progress, Justice — A111

1970, July 1 Litho. *Perf. 13½x12½*

513	A111	20f lt green & multi	.52	.18
514	A111	45f multicolored	.95	.42

25th anniversary of the United Nations.

Tanker Loading Crude Oil from Sea Island A112

1970, Aug. 1 *Perf. 13½x13*

515	A112	20f multicolored	1.10	.35
516	A112	45f multicolored	2.75	.85

Issued to publicize the artificial "Sea Island" loading facilities in Kuwait.

"Writing," Kuwait and UN Emblems A113

1970, Sept. 8 Photo. *Perf. 13½*

517	A113	10f brt blue & multi	.85	.15
518	A113	15f brt green & multi	1.40	.15
		Set value		.17

International Literacy Day, Sept. 8.

National Guard and Emblem
A114

1970, Oct. 20 Photo. *Perf. 13x13½*

519 A114	10f gold & multi	.80	.15
520 A114	20f silver & multi	1.65	.26

First National Guard graduation.

Flag of Kuwait, Symbols of Development
A115

1971, Feb. 25 Litho. *Perf. 12*

521 A115	20f gray & multi	1.00	.40
522 A115	30f multicolored	1.40	.65

Tenth anniversary of National Day.

Charles H. Best, Frederick G. Banting
A116

1971, Apr. 7 Litho. *Perf. 14*

523 A116	20f multicolored	.55	.20
524 A116	45f multicolored	1.25	.55

World Health Day; discoverers of insulin.

Globe with Map of Palestine
A117

1971, May 3 Litho. *Perf. 12½x13*

525 A117	20f yel green & multi	1.50	1.10
526 A117	45f lilac & multi	3.00	2.25

International Palestine Week.

ITU Emblem and Waves
A118

1971, May 17 Photo. *Perf. 13x13½*

527 A118	20f silver, dk red & blk	1.25	.32
528 A118	45f gold, dk red & blk	2.50	.85

3rd World Telecommunications Day.

Men of 3 Races — A119

1971, June 5 Litho. *Perf. 11½x11*

529 A119	15f red brown & multi	.80	.30
530 A119	30f ultra & multi	1.25	.70

Intl. Year against Racial Discrimination.

Arab Postal Union Emblem
A120

1971, Aug. 30 *Perf. 13x12½*

531 A120	20f brown & multi	.65	.38
532 A120	45f blue & multi	1.40	.55

25th anniv. of the Conf. of Sofar, Lebanon, establishing the Arab Postal Union.

Symbols of Learning, UNESCO and Kuwait Emblems — A121

1971, Sept. 8 *Perf. 12*

533 A121	25f dull yellow & multi	.90	.25
534 A121	60f lt blue & multi	2.00	.90

International Literacy Day, Sept. 8.

Soccer
A122

Design: 30f, Soccer, different.

1971, Dec. 10 *Perf. 13*

535 A122	20f green & multi	1.25	.50
536 A122	30f ultra & multi	1.75	.70

Regional Sports Tournament, Kuwait, Dec.

UNICEF Emblem and Arms of Kuwait — A123

Perf. 11x11½

1971, Dec. 11 Litho. & Engr.

537 A123	25f gold & multi	.60	.28
538 A123	60f silver & multi	1.25	.70

25th anniv. of UNICEF.

Book Year Emblem
A124

1972, Jan. 2 Litho. *Perf. 14x13*

539 A124	20f black & buff	.80	.40
540 A124	45f black & lt blue grn	1.65	.90

International Book Year.

Kuwait Emblem with 11 Rays, Olive Branch
A125

1972, Feb. 25 Litho. *Perf. 13x13½*

541 A125	20f pink, gold & multi	1.25	.70
542 A125	45f lt blue, gold & multi	1.90	1.25

11th anniversary of National Day.

Telecommunications Center — A126

1972, Feb. 28 *Perf. 13½*

543 A126	20f lt blue & multi	1.50	.60
544 A126	45f multicolored	3.75	1.50

Opening of Kuwait Telecommunications Center.

"Your Heart is your Health" — A127

Nurse and Child — A128

1972, Apr. 7 Photo. *Perf. 14½x14*

545 A127	20f red & multi	1.65	.60
546 A127	45f red & multi	4.00	1.40

World Health Day.

1972, May 8 Litho. *Perf. 12½x13*

547 A128	8f vio blue, red & emer	1.10	.15
548 A128	40f pink & multi	3.50	1.00

Red Cross and Red Crescent Day.

Soccer, Olympic Emblems
A129

1972, Sept. 2 Litho. *Perf. 14½*

549 A129	2f shown	.15	.15
550 A129	4f Running	.15	.15
551 A129	5f Swimming	.15	.15
552 A129	8f Gymnastics	.15	.15
553 A129	10f Discus	.20	.16
554 A129	15f Equestrian	.75	.25
555 A129	20f Basketball	.85	.30
556 A129	25f Volleyball	1.10	.35
	Nos. 549-556 (8)	3.50	1.66

20th Olympic Games, Munich, Aug. 26-Sept. 11.

FAO Emblem, Vegetables, Fish and Ship — A130

1972, Sept. 9 Litho. *Perf. 14x13½*

557 A130	5f blue & multi	.40	.40
558 A130	10f emerald & multi	1.50	1.10
559 A130	20f orange & multi	3.00	2.00
	Nos. 557-559 (3)	4.90	3.50

11th FAO Regional Conference in the Near East, Kuwait, Sept.

National Bank Emblem
A131

1972, Nov. 15 Photo. *Perf. 13x14*

560 A131	10f green & multi	.45	.25
561 A131	35f dull red & multi	1.50	1.00

20th anniversary of Kuwait National Bank.

Capitals — A132

Relics of Failaka: 5f, View of excavations. 10f, Acanthus leaf capital. 15f, Excavations.

1972, Dec. 4 Litho. *Perf. 12*

562 A132	2f lilac rose & multi	.18	.15
563 A132	5f bister & multi	.18	.15
564 A132	10f lt blue & multi	.95	.22
565 A132	15f green & multi	1.40	.32
	Nos. 562-565 (4)	2.71	.84

Flower and Kuwait Emblem — A133

INTERPOL Emblem — A134

1973, Feb. 25 Litho. *Perf. 13½x13*

566 A133	10f lt olive & multi	.45	.25
567 A133	20f multicolored	.95	.65
568 A133	30f yellow & multi	1.40	.95
	Nos. 566-568 (3)	2.80	1.85

12th anniversary of National Day.

1973, June 3 Litho. *Perf. 12*

569 A134	10f emerald & multi	.75	.70
570 A134	15f red orange & multi	1.40	.95
571 A134	20f blue & multi	2.25	1.40
	Nos. 569-571 (3)	4.40	3.05

50th anniv. of Intl. Criminal Police Org. (INTERPOL).

I.C.M.S. Emblem and Flag of Kuwait — A135

Kuwait Airways Building — A136

1973, June 24 *Perf. 13*

572 A135	30f gray & multi	.95	.55
573 A135	40f brown & multi	1.50	.75

Intl. Council of Military Sports, 25th anniv.

1973, July 1 Litho. *Perf. 12½x14*

574 A136	10f lt green & multi	.50	.18
575 A136	15f lilac & multi	.70	.32
576 A136	20f lt ultra & multi	1.00	.40
	Nos. 574-576 (3)	2.20	.90

Opening of Kuwait Airways Corporation Building.

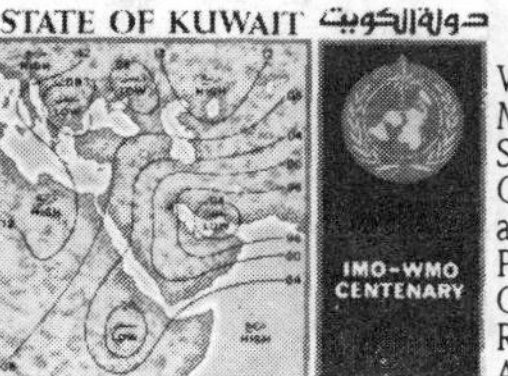
Weather Map of Suez Canal and Persian Gulf Region
A137

1973, Sept. 4 Photo. *Perf. 14*

No.	Type	Description	Unused	Used
577	A137	5f red & multi	.40	.16
578	A137	10f green & multi	.75	.16
579	A137	15f multicolored	1.25	.24
		Nos. 577-579 (3)	2.40	.56

Intl. meteorological cooperation, cent.

Sheiks Ahmad and Sabah — A138

1973, Nov. 12 Photo. *Perf. 14*

No.	Type	Description	Unused	Used
580	A138	10f lt green & multi	.50	.22
581	A138	20f yel orange & multi	1.00	.35
582	A138	70f lt blue & multi	3.50	1.40
		Nos. 580-582 (3)	5.00	1.97

Stamps overprinted "Kuwait," 50th anniv.

Mourning Dove, Eurasian Hoopoe, Rock Dove, Stone Curlew — A139

Designs: Birds and traps.

1973, Dec. 1 Litho. *Perf. 14*

Size (single stamp): 32x32mm

No.	Type	Description	Unused	Used
583	A139	Block of 4	2.75	1.40
a.		5f Mourning dove	.65	.30
b.		5f Eurasian hoopoe	.65	.30
c.		5f Rock dove	.65	.30
d.		5f Stone curlew	.65	.30
584	A139	Block of 4	3.50	1.75
a.		8f Great gray shrike	.80	.40
b.		8f Red-backed shrike	.80	.40
c.		8f Rufous-backed shrike	.80	.40
d.		8f Black-naped oriole	.80	.40
585	A139	Block of 4	4.25	2.50
a.		10f Willow warbler	1.00	.55
b.		10f Great reed warbler	1.00	.55
c.		10f Blackcap	1.00	.55
d.		10f Common (barn) swallow	1.00	.55
586	A139	Block of 4	7.00	4.25
a.		15f Common rock thrush	1.75	.90
b.		15f European redstart	1.75	.90
c.		15f Wheatear	1.75	.90
d.		15f Bluethroat	1.75	.90
587	A139	Block of 4	8.50	4.50
a.		20f Houbara bustard	2.00	1.00
b.		20f Pin-tailed sandgrouse	2.00	1.00
c.		20f Ypecaha wood rail	2.00	1.00
d.		20f Spotted crake	2.00	1.00

Size (single stamp): 35x35mm

No.	Type	Description	Unused	Used
588	A139	Block of 4	9.00	5.75
a.		25f American sparrow hawk	2.25	1.25
b.		25f Great black-backed gull	2.25	1.25
c.		25f Purple heron	2.25	1.25
d.		25f Wryneck	2.25	1.25
589	A139	Block of 4	13.00	7.00
a.		30f European bee-eater	4.00	1.65
b.		30f Goshawk	4.00	1.65
c.		30f Gray wagtail	4.00	1.65
d.		30f Pied wagtail	4.00	1.65
590	A139	Block of 4	18.00	10.00
a.		45f Crossbows	4.25	2.25
b.		45f Tent-shaped net	4.25	2.25
c.		45f Hand net	4.25	2.25
d.		45f Rooftop trap	4.25	2.25
		Nos. 583-590 (8)	66.00	37.15

Human Rights Flame — A141

1973, Dec. 10 Litho. *Perf. 12*

No.	Type	Description	Unused	Used
594	A141	10f red & multi	.60	.15
595	A141	40f lt green & multi	1.65	.52
596	A141	75f lilac & multi	2.25	.85
		Nos. 594-596 (3)	4.50	1.52

25th anniv. of the Universal Declaration of Human Rights.

Promoting Animal Resources — A142

Stylized Wheat and Kuwaiti Flag — A143

1974, Feb. 16 Litho. *Perf. 12½*

No.	Type	Description	Unused	Used
597	A142	30f violet blue & multi	.85	.30
598	A142	40f rose & multi	1.25	.42

4th Congress of the Arab Veterinary Union, Kuwait.

1974, Feb. 25 *Perf. 13½x13*

No.	Type	Description	Unused	Used
599	A143	20f lemon & multi	.28	.22
600	A143	30f bister brn & multi	1.00	.38
601	A143	70f silver & multi	1.90	.90
		Nos. 599-601 (3)	3.18	1.50

13th anniversary of National Day.

Conference Emblem and Sheik Sabah A144

1974, Mar. 8 *Perf. 12½*

No.	Type	Description	Unused	Used
602	A144	30f multicolored	1.90	.70
603	A144	40f yellow & multi	3.00	.90

12th Conf. of the Arab Medical Union and 1st Conf. of the Kuwait Medical Soc.

Tournament Emblem — A145

1974, Mar. 15

No.	Type	Description	Unused	Used
604	A145	25f multicolored	1.25	.50
605	A145	45f multicolored	2.25	.75

Third Soccer Tournament for the Arabian Gulf Trophy, Kuwait, Mar. 1974.

Scientific Research Institute — A146

1974, Apr. 3 Photo. *Perf. 12½*

No.	Type	Description	Unused	Used
606	A146	15f magenta & multi	1.00	.28
607	A146	20f green & multi	1.90	.32

Opening of Kuwait Scientific Research Institute.

Arab Postal Union, Kuwait and UPU Emblems A147

1974, May 1 *Perf. 13x14*

No.	Type	Description	Unused	Used
608	A147	20f gold & multi	.25	.18
609	A147	30f gold & multi	.40	.25
610	A147	60f gold & multi	.75	.52
		Nos. 608-610 (3)	1.40	.95

Centenary of Universal Postal Union.

Telephone Dial with Communications Symbols and Globe — A148

1974, May 17 *Perf. 14x13½*

No.	Type	Description	Unused	Used
611	A148	10f blue & multi	.40	.18
612	A148	30f multicolored	1.25	.58
613	A148	40f black & multi	1.65	.80
		Nos. 611-613 (3)	3.30	1.56

World Telecommunications Day, May 17.

Emblem of Unity Council and Flags of Member States — A149

1974, June 25 Litho. *Perf. 13½*

No.	Type	Description	Unused	Used
614	A149	20f red, black & green	.90	.40
615	A149	30f green, black & red	1.00	.55

17th anniversary of the signing of the Arab Economic Unity Agreement.

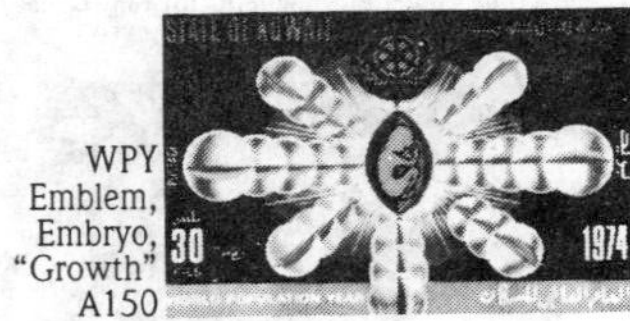

WPY Emblem, Embryo, "Growth" A150

1974, Aug. 19 Litho. *Perf. 14x14½*

No.	Type	Description	Unused	Used
616	A150	30f black & multi	1.25	.40
617	A150	70f violet blue & multi	2.00	.90

World Population Year.

Development Building and Emblem — A151

1974, Oct. 30 Litho. *Perf. 13x13½*

No.	Type	Description	Unused	Used
618	A151	10f pink & multi	.65	.15
619	A151	20f ultra & multi	1.10	.28

Kuwait Fund for Arab Economic Development.

Emblem of Shuaiba Industrial Area — A152

1974, Dec. 17 Litho. *Perf. 12½x12*

No.	Type	Description	Unused	Used
620	A152	10f lt blue & multi	.60	.20
621	A152	20f salmon & multi	1.50	.40
622	A152	30f lt green & multi	1.90	.80
		Nos. 620-622 (3)	4.00	1.40

Shuaiba Industrial Area, 10th anniversary.

Arms of Kuwait and "14" — A153

1975, Feb. 25 Litho. *Perf. 13x13½*

No.	Type	Description	Unused	Used
623	A153	20f multicolored	.50	.30
624	A153	70f yel green & multi	1.75	.85
625	A153	75f rose & multi	2.00	1.00
		Nos. 623-625 (3)	4.25	2.15

14th anniversary of National Day.

Male and Female Symbols — A154

1975, Apr. 14 Photo. *Perf. 11½x12*

No.	Type	Description	Unused	Used
626	A154	8f lt green & multi	.25	.15
627	A154	20f rose & multi	.35	.25
628	A154	30f blue & multi	.60	.42
629	A154	70f yellow & multi	1.65	.85
630	A154	100f black & multi	2.50	1.40
		Nos. 626-630 (5)	5.35	3.07

Kuwaiti census 1975.

IWY and Kuwaiti Women's Union Emblems A155

1975, June 10 Litho. *Perf. 14½*

No.	Type	Description	Unused	Used
631	A155	15f brown org & multi	.65	.25
632	A155	20f olive & multi	.85	.40
633	A155	30f violet & multi	1.25	.65
		Nos. 631-633 (3)	2.75	1.30

International Women's Year.

Classroom and UNESCO Emblem A156

1975, Sept. 8 Litho. *Perf. 12½x12*

No.	Type	Description	Unused	Used
634	A156	20f green & multi	.75	.24
635	A156	30f multicolored	1.25	.65

International Literacy Day.

Symbols of Measurements A157

UN Flag, Rifle and Olive Branch A158

1975, Oct. 14 Photo. *Perf. 14x13*

No.	Type	Description	Unused	Used
636	A157	10f green & multi	.40	.18
637	A157	20f purple & multi	.80	.40

World Standards Day.

1975, Oct. 24 Litho. *Perf. 12x12½*
638 A158 20f multicolored .70 .25
639 A158 45f orange & multi 1.50 .70

United Nations, 30th anniversary.

Sheik Sabah — A159

1975, Dec. 22 Litho. *Perf. 12½x12*
640 A159 8f yellow & multi .45 .22
641 A159 20f lilac & multi .75 .28
642 A159 30f buff & multi .95 .40
643 A159 50f salmon & multi 1.65 .70
644 A159 90f lt blue & multi 3.25 1.25
645 A159 100f multicolored 3.75 1.50
Nos. 640-645 (6) 10.80 4.35

"Progress" A160

1976, Feb. 25 Litho. *Perf. 12*
646 A160 10f multicolored .45 .15
647 A160 20f multicolored .95 .20

15th anniversary of National Day.

Medical Equipment, Emblem and Surgery — A161

Telephones, 1876 and 1976 — A162

1976, Mar. 1 Litho. *Perf. 14½*
648 A161 5f dull green & multi .15 .15
649 A161 10f blue & multi .95 .30
650 A161 30f gray & multi 2.75 .80
Nos. 648-650 (3) 3.85 1.25

Kuwait Medical Assoc., 2nd annual conference.

1976, Mar. 10 Litho. *Perf. 12*
651 A162 5f orange & black .25 .15
652 A162 15f lt blue & black .95 .20
Set value .25

Centenary of first telephone call by Alexander Graham Bell, Mar. 10, 1876.

Human Eye — A163

Photo. & Engr.

1976, Apr. 7 *Perf. 11½*
653 A163 10f multicolored .35 .15
654 A163 20f black & multi .65 .30
655 A163 30f multicolored 1.00 .45
Nos. 653-655 (3) 2.00 .90

World Health Day: "Foresight prevents blindness."

Red Crescent Emblem A164

1976, May 8 Litho. *Perf. 12x11½*
656 A164 20f brt green, blk & red .60 .35
657 A164 30f vio blue, blk & red 1.25 .45
658 A164 45f yellow, blk & red 1.40 .80
659 A164 75f lilac rose, blk & red 2.50 1.25
Nos. 656-659 (4) 5.75 2.85

Kuwait Red Crescent Society, 10th anniv.

Modern Suburb of Kuwait A165

1976, June 1 Photo. *Perf. 13x13½*
660 A165 10f light green & multi .50 .15
661 A165 20f salmon & multi .95 .25

Habitat, UN Conference on Human Settlements, Vancouver, Canada, May 31-June 11.

Basketball, Kuwait Olympic Emblem — A166

Various Races, Map of Sri Lanka — A167

Designs: 8f, Running. 10f, Judo. 15f, Fieldball. 20f, Gymnastics. 30f, Water polo. 45f, Soccer. 70f, Swimmers at start.

1976, July 17 Litho. *Perf. 14½*
662 A166 4f black & multi .15 .15
663 A166 8f red & multi .15 .15
664 A166 10f green & multi .20 .15
665 A166 15f lemon & multi .30 .16
666 A166 20f blue & multi .45 .20
667 A166 30f lilac & multi .65 .40
668 A166 45f multicolored .95 .55
669 A166 70f brown & multi 1.65 .85
Nos. 662-669 (8) 4.50 2.61

21st Olympic Games, Montreal, Canada, July 17-Aug. 1.

1976, Aug. 16 Photo. *Perf. 14*
670 A167 20f dk blue & multi .50 .15
671 A167 30f purple & multi .75 .45
672 A167 45f green & multi 1.25 .65
Nos. 670-672 (3) 2.50 1.25

5th Summit Conf. of Non-aligned Countries, Colombo, Sri Lanka, Aug. 9-19.

"UNESCO," Torch and Kuwait Arms A168

1976, Nov. 4 Litho. *Perf. 12x11½*
673 A168 20f yel green & multi .65 .15
674 A168 45f scarlet & multi 1.50 .70

30th anniversary of UNESCO.

Blindman's Buff — A169

Popular games. 5f, 15f, 30f, vertical.

Perf. 14½x14, 14x14½

1977, Jan. 10 Litho.
675 A169 5f Pot throwing .20 .20
676 A169 5f Kite flying .20 .20
677 A169 5f Balancing sticks .20 .20
678 A169 5f Spinning tops .20 .20
679 A169 10f shown .30 .20
680 A169 10f Rowing .30 .20
681 A169 10f Hoops .30 .20
682 A169 10f Ropes .30 .20
683 A169 15f Rope skipping .60 .35
684 A169 15f Marbles .60 .35
685 A169 15f Cart steering .60 .35
686 A169 15f Teetotum .60 .25
687 A169 20f Halma .80 .55
688 A169 20f Model boats .80 .55
689 A169 20f Pot and candle .80 .55
690 A169 20f Hide and seek .80 .55
691 A169 30f Throwing bones 1.10 .75
692 A169 30f Mystery gifts 1.10 .75
693 A169 30f Hopscotch 1.10 .75
694 A169 30f Catch as catch can 1.10 .75
695 A169 40f Bowls 1.75 1.00
696 A169 40f Sword fighting 1.75 1.00
697 A169 40f Mother and child 1.75 1.00
698 A169 40f Fivestones 1.75 1.00
699 A169 60f Hiding a cake 2.75 1.75
700 A169 60f Chess 2.75 1.75
701 A169 60f Dancing 2.75 1.75
702 A169 60f Treasure hunt 2.75 1.75
703 A169 70f Hobby-horses 3.00 1.90
704 A169 70f Hide and seek 3.00 1.90
705 A169 70f Catch 3.00 1.90
706 A169 70f Storytelling 3.00 1.90
Nos. 675-706 (32) 42.00 26.70

Stamps of same denomination printed se-tenant in blocks of 4, sheets of 100.

Diseased Knee — A170

1977, Feb. 15 *Perf. 13x13½*
707 A170 20f yellow & multi .50 .25
708 A170 30f multicolored .90 .45
709 A170 45f red & multi 1.25 .70
710 A170 75f black & multi 2.25 1.25
Nos. 707-710 (4) 4.90 2.65

World Rheumatism Year.

Sheik Sabah A171

1977, Feb. 25 Photo. *Perf. 13½x13*
711 A171 10f multicolored .20 .20
712 A171 15f multicolored .30 .22
713 A171 30f multicolored .50 .30
714 A171 80f multicolored 1.25 .80
Nos. 711-714 (4) 2.25 1.52

16th National Day.

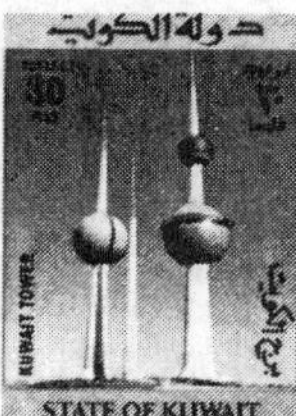

Kuwait Tower — A172

APU Emblem — A173

1977, Feb. 26 *Perf. 14x13½*
715 A172 30f multicolored .65 .25
716 A172 80f multicolored 1.65 .70

Inauguration of Kuwait Tower.

1977, Apr. 12 Litho. *Perf. 13½x14*
717 A173 5f yellow & multi .30 .15
718 A173 15f pink & multi .30 .15
719 A173 30f lt blue & multi .60 .30
720 A173 80f lilac & multi 1.50 .90
Nos. 717-720 (4) 2.70 1.50

Arab Postal Union, 25th anniversary.

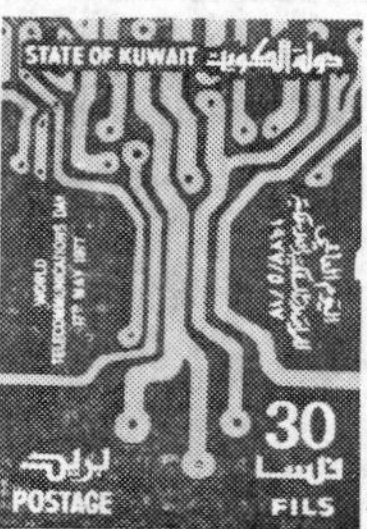

Electronic Tree — A174

1977, May 17 Litho. *Perf. 12x12½*
721 A174 30f brown & red .95 .40
722 A174 80f green & red 2.25 1.00

World Telecommunications Day.

Sheik Sabah — A175

Games Emblem — A176

1977, June 1 Photo. *Perf. 11½x12*
723 A175 15f blue & multi .40 .50
724 A175 25f yellow & multi .80 .50
725 A175 30f red & multi 1.00 .70
726 A175 80f violet & multi 3.25 1.75
727 A175 100f dp org & multi 3.50 2.00
728 A175 150f ultra & multi 5.50 3.25
729 A175 200f olive & multi 7.25 4.50
Nos. 723-729 (7) 21.70 13.20

1977, Oct. 1 Litho. *Perf. 12*
730 A176 30f multicolored .75 .75
731 A176 80f multicolored 1.90 1.50

4th Asian Basketball Youth Championship, Oct. 1-15.

Dome of the Rock, Bishop Capucci, Fatima Bernawi, Sheik Abu Tair A177

1977, Nov. 1 *Perf. 14*
732 A177 30f multicolored 1.90 1.00
733 A177 80f multicolored 4.00 2.25

Struggle for the liberation of Palestine.

Children and Houses A178

Children's Paintings: No. 735, Women musicians. No. 736, Boats. No. 737, Women preparing food, vert. No. 738, Women and children, vert. No. 739, Seated woman, vert.

1977, Nov. Photo. *Perf. 13½x13*
734 A178 15f lt green & multi .45 .30
735 A178 15f yellow & multi .45 .30
736 A178 30f brt yellow & multi .85 .60
737 A178 30f lt violet & multi .85 .60
738 A178 80f black & multi 2.00 1.65
739 A178 80f rose & multi 2.00 1.65
Nos. 734-739 (6) 6.60 5.10

Dentist Treating Patient — A179

1977, Dec. 3

740 A179 30f green & multi .85 .85
741 A179 80f violet & multi 2.50 1.65

10th Arab Dental Union Congress, Kuwait, Dec. 3-6.

Ships Unloading Water A180

Kuwait water resources. 30f, 80f, 100f, vert.

Perf. 14x13½, 13½x14

1978, Jan. 25 **Litho.**

742 Block of 4 .70 .40
 a. 5f shown .15 .15
 b. 5f Home delivery by camel .15 .15
 c. 5f Man with water bags .15 .15
 d. 5f Man with wheelbarrow .15 .15
743 Block of 4 1.10 .50
 a. 10f Well .25 .15
 b. 10f Trough .25 .15
 c. 10f Water hole .25 .15
 d. 10f Irrigation .25 .15
744 Block of 4 1.65 .70
 a. 15f Sheep drinking .40 .15
 b. 15f Laundresses .40 .15
 c. 15f Sheep and camels drinking .40 .15
 d. 15f Water stored in skins .40 .15
745 Block of 4 1.80 .90
 a. 20f Animals at well .45 .15
 b. 20f Water in home .45 .15
 c. 20f Water pot .45 .15
 d. 20f Communal fountain .45 .15
746 Block of 4 2.25 1.25
 a. 25f Distillation plant .55 .30
 b. 25f Motorized delivery .55 .30
 c. 25f Water trucks .55 .30
 d. 25f Water towers .55 .30
747 Block of 4 2.75 1.40
 a. 30f Shower bath .70 .30
 b. 30f Water tower .70 .30
 c. 30f Gathering rain water .70 .30
 d. 30f 2 water towers .70 .30
748 Block of 4 8.00 4.00
 a. 80f Donkey with water bags 2.00 .90
 b. 80f Woman with water can 2.00 .90
 c. 80f Woman with water skin 2.00 .90
 d. 80f Loading tank car 2.00 .90
749 Block of 4 10.00 4.75
 a. 100f Truck delivering water 2.50 1.10
 b. 100f Barnyard water supply 2.50 1.10
 c. 100f Children at water basin 2.50 1.10
 d. 100f Well in courtyard 2.50 1.10
 Nos. 742-749 (8) 28.25 13.90

Radar, Torch, Minarets A181

1978, Feb. 25 **Litho.** ***Perf. 14x14½***

750 A181 30f multicolored .50 .35
751 A181 80f multicolored 1.50 1.00

17th National Day.

Man with Smallpox, Target — A182

1978, Apr. 17 **Litho.** ***Perf. 12½***

752 A182 30f violet & multi .60 .42
753 A182 80f green & multi 1.75 1.10

Global eradication of smallpox.

Antenna and ITU Emblem A183

1978, May 17 ***Perf. 14***

754 A183 30f silver & multi .52 .38
755 A183 80f silver & multi 1.65 1.00

10th World Telecommunications Day.

Sheik Sabah — A184

1978, June 28 **Litho.** ***Perf. 13x14***

Portrait in Brown

Size: 21½x27mm

756 A184 15f green & gold .20 .20
757 A184 30f orange & gold .45 .45
758 A184 80f rose lilac & gold 1.10 1.10
759 A184 100f lt green & gold 1.25 1.25
760 A184 130f lt brown & gold 1.75 1.75
761 A184 180f violet & gold 2.75 2.75

Size: 23½x29mm

762 A184 1d red & gold 14.00 13.00
763 A184 4d blue & gold 60.00 60.00
 Nos. 756-763 (8) 81.50 80.50

Mt. Arafat, Pilgrims, Holy Kaaba A185

1978, Nov. 9 **Photo.** ***Perf. 11½***

764 A185 30f multicolored .75 .60
765 A185 80f multicolored 2.00 1.50

Pilgrimage to Mecca.

UN and Anti-Apartheid Emblems A186

1978, Nov. 27 **Litho.** ***Perf. 12***

766 A186 30f multicolored .50 .40
767 A186 80f multicolored 1.10 1.00
768 A186 180f multicolored 3.25 2.25
 Nos. 766-768 (3) 4.85 3.65

Anti-Apartheid Year.

Refugees, Human Rights Emblems A187

1978, Dec. 10 **Photo.** ***Perf. 13x13½***

769 A187 30f multicolored .60 .45
770 A187 80f multicolored 1.75 1.10
771 A187 100f multicolored 2.50 1.40
 Nos. 769-771 (3) 4.85 2.95

Declaration of Human Rights, 30th anniv.

Information Center A188

1978, Dec. 26 **Photo.** ***Perf. 13***

772 A188 5f multicolored .15 .15
773 A188 15f multicolored .22 .16
774 A188 30f multicolored .52 .35
775 A188 80f multicolored 1.25 .85
 Nos. 772-775 (4) 2.14 1.51

New Kuwait Information Center.

Kindergarten A189

1979, Jan. 24 **Photo.** ***Perf. 13½x14***

776 A189 30f multicolored .60 .48
777 A189 80f multicolored 1.50 1.25

International Year of the Child.

Flag and Peace Doves — A190

1979, Feb. 25 ***Perf. 14½x14***

778 A190 30f multicolored .60 .45
779 A190 80f multicolored 1.40 1.10

18th National Day.

Modern Agriculture in Kuwait A191

1979, Mar. 13 **Photo.** ***Perf. 14***

780 A191 30f multicolored .55 .42
781 A191 80f multicolored 1.40 1.10

4th Congress of Arab Agriculture Ministers of the Gulf and Arabian Peninsula.

World Map, Book, Symbols of Learning A192

1979, Mar. 22

782 A192 30f multicolored .55 .42
783 A192 80f multicolored 1.40 1.10

Cultural achievements of the Arabs.

Children with Balloons — A193

Children's Paintings: No. 785, Boys flying kites. No. 786, Girl and doves. No. 787, Children and houses, horiz. No. 788, Four children, horiz. No. 789, Children sitting in circle, horiz.

1979, Apr. 18 **Photo.** ***Perf. 14***

784 A193 30f yellow & multi .55 .45
785 A193 30f buff & multi .55 .45
786 A193 30f pale yel & multi .55 .45
787 A193 80f lt blue & multi 1.50 1.25
788 A193 80f yel green & multi 1.50 1.25
789 A193 80f lilac & multi 1.50 1.25
 Nos. 784-789 (6) 6.15 5.10

Cables, ITU Emblem, People A194

1979, May 17

790 A194 30f multicolored .50 .40
791 A194 80f multicolored 1.40 1.25

World Telecommunications Day.

Military Sports Council Emblem — A195

1979, June 1 **Photo.** ***Perf. 14***

792 A195 30f multicolored .50 .40
793 A195 80f multicolored 1.40 1.25

29th Intl. Military Soccer Championship.

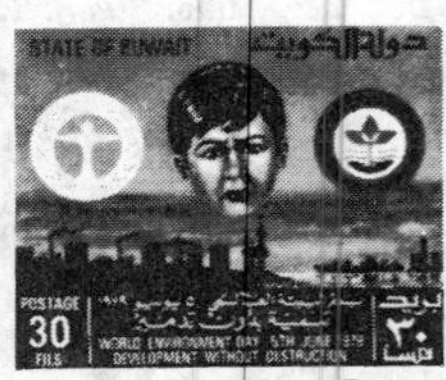

Child, Industrial Landscape, Environmental Emblems — A196

1979, June 5 ***Perf. 12x11½***

794 A196 30f multicolored .75 .60
795 A196 80f multicolored 2.00 1.65

World Environment Day, June 5.

Children Holding Globe, UNESCO Emblem — A197

1979, July 25 **Litho.** ***Perf. 11½x12***

796 A197 30f multicolored .50 .40
797 A197 80f multicolored 1.25 1.10
798 A197 130f multicolored 2.00 1.75
 Nos. 796-798 (3) 3.75 3.25

Intl. Bureau of Education, Geneva, 50th anniv.

Kuwait Kindergartens, 25th Anniversary A198

Children's Drawings: 80f, Children waving flags.

1979, Sept. 15 **Litho.** ***Perf. 12½***

799 A198 30f multicolored .60 .40
800 A198 80f multicolored 1.50 1.10

Pilgrims at Holy Ka'aba, Mecca Mosque A199

1979, Oct. 29 ***Perf. 14x14½***

801 A199 30f multicolored .60 .45
802 A199 80f multicolored 2.00 1.25

Hegira (Pilgrimage Year).

International Palestinian Solidarity Day — A200

1979, Nov. 29 Photo. *Perf. 11½x12*

803	A200	30f multicolored	1.90	.95
804	A200	80f multicolored	4.50	1.90

Kuwait Airways 25th Anniversary A201

1979, Dec. 24 Photo. *Perf. 13x13½*

805	A201	30f multicolored	.80	.60
806	A201	80f multicolored	2.25	1.75

19th National Day — A202

1980, Feb. 25 Litho. *Perf. 14x14½*

807	A202	30f multicolored	.55	.40
808	A202	80f multicolored	1.40	1.10

1980 Population Census A203

1980, Mar. 18 *Perf. 13½x14*

809	A203	30f multicolored	.50	.35
810	A203	80f multicolored	1.65	.85

World Health Day — A204

1980, Apr. 7

811	A204	30f multicolored	.85	.55
812	A204	80f multicolored	2.50	1.65

Kuwait Municipality, 50th Anniversary — A205

1980, May 1 Photo. *Perf. 14*

813	A205	15f multicolored	.28	.18
814	A205	30f multicolored	.60	.40
815	A205	80f multicolored	1.75	1.10
		Nos. 813-815 (3)	2.63	1.68

Citizens of Kuwait A206

Future Kuwait (Children's Drawings): 80f, Super highway.

1980, May 14 Litho. *Perf. 14x14½*

816	A206	30f multicolored	.70	.45
817	A206	80f multicolored	2.25	1.40

World Environment Day — A207

1980, June 5 Litho. *Perf. 12x11½*

818	A207	30f multicolored	.60	.30
819	A207	80f multicolored	1.90	.85

Swimming, Moscow '80 and Kuwait Olympic Committee Emblems — A208

1980, July 19 Litho. *Perf. 12x12½*

820	A208	15f Volleyball	.18	.15
821	A208	15f Tennis	.18	.15
822	A208	30f shown	.42	.32
823	A208	30f Weight lifting	.42	.32
824	A208	30f Basketball	.42	.32
825	A208	30f Judo	.42	.32
826	A208	80f Gymnast	1.40	.90
827	A208	80f Badminton	1.40	.90
828	A208	80f Fencing	1.40	.90
829	A208	80f Soccer	1.40	.90
		Nos. 820-829 (10)	7.64	5.18

22nd Summer Olympic Games, Moscow, July 19-Aug. 3. Stamps of same denomination se-tenant.

20th Anniversary of OPEC A209

1980, Sept. 16 Litho. *Perf. 14x14½*

830	A209	30f multicolored	.75	.50
831	A209	80f multicolored	2.25	.80

Hegira (Pilgrimage Year) A210

1980, Nov. 9 Photo. *Perf. 12x11½*

832	A210	15f multicolored	.32	.20
833	A210	30f multicolored	.70	.45
834	A210	80f multicolored	2.00	1.25
		Nos. 832-834 (3)	3.02	1.90

Dome of the Rock, Jerusalem A211

1980, Nov. 29 *Perf. 12x11½*

835	A211	30f multicolored	2.25	.60
836	A211	80f multicolored	4.50	1.65

International Palestinian Solidarity Day.

Avicenna (980-1037), Philosopher and Physician — A212

Conference Emblem — A213

1980, Dec. 7 *Perf. 12x12½*

837	A212	30f multicolored	1.25	.35
838	A212	80f multicolored	2.50	.95

1981, Jan. 12 Photo. *Perf. 13½x13*

839	A213	30f multicolored	.65	.45
840	A213	80f multicolored	2.00	1.25

First Islamic Medical Conference.

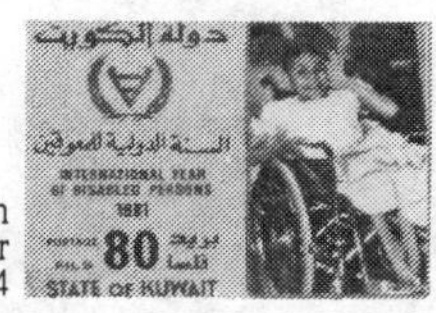

Girl in Wheelchair A214

International Year of the Disabled: 30f, Man in wheelchair playing billiards, vert.

Perf. 13½x13, 13x13½

1981, Jan. 26 **Photo.**

841	A214	30f multicolored	.65	.45
842	A214	80f multicolored	2.00	1.25

20th National Day — A215

1981, Feb. 25 Litho. *Perf. 13x13½*

843	A215	30f multicolored	.65	.45
844	A215	80f multicolored	2.00	1.25

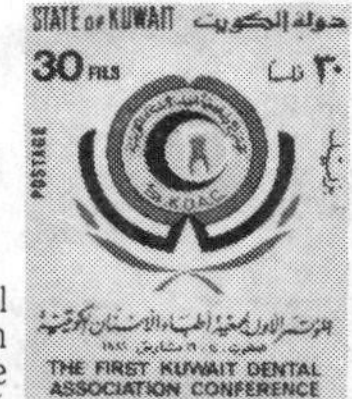

First Kuwait Dental Association Conference A216

1981, Mar. 14 *Perf. 11½x12*

845	A216	30f multicolored	1.25	.85
846	A216	80f multicolored	3.75	2.25

A217 A218

1981, May 8 Photo. *Perf. 14*

847	A217	30f multicolored	1.25	.80
848	A217	80f multicolored	3.75	2.25

Intl. Red Cross day.

1981, May 17 Litho. *Perf. 14½x14*

849	A218	30f multicolored	1.10	.75
850	A218	80f multicolored	3.25	2.00

13th World Telecommunications day.

World Environment Day — A219

1981, June 5 Photo. *Perf. 12*

851	A219	30f multicolored	1.10	.70
852	A219	80f multicolored	3.25	1.90

Sief Palace — A220

A221

1981, Sept. 16 Litho. *Perf. 12*

853	A220	5f multicolored	.15	.15
854	A220	10f multicolored	.15	.15
855	A220	15f multicolored	.15	.15
856	A220	25f multicolored	.22	.22
857	A220	30f multicolored	.28	.22
858	A220	40f multicolored	.32	.22
859	A220	60f multicolored	.50	.28
860	A220	80f multicolored	.65	.45
861	A220	100f multicolored	.85	.65
862	A220	115f multicolored	1.00	.80
863	A220	130f multicolored	1.10	1.00
864	A220	150f multicolored	1.40	1.00
865	A220	180f multicolored	1.65	1.10
866	A220	250f multicolored	2.25	1.25
867	A220	500f multicolored	4.50	1.65
868	A221	1d multicolored	8.25	2.25
869	A221	2d multicolored	17.00	3.25
870	A221	3d multicolored	25.00	10.00
871	A221	4d multicolored	32.50	12.50
		Nos. 853-871 (19)	97.92	37.29

Islamic Pilgrimage A222

1981, Oct. 7 Photo. *Perf. 13x13½*

872	A222	30f multicolored	.85	.70
873	A222	80f multicolored	3.00	1.75

World Food Day — A223

1981, Oct. 16 Litho. *Perf. 13*

874	A223	30f multicolored	.95	.65
875	A223	80f multicolored	3.00	1.75

A224 A225

1981, Dec. 30 Photo. *Perf. 14*

876	A224	30f multicolored	1.00	.65
877	A224	80f multicolored	3.00	1.75

20th anniv. of national television.

1982, Jan. 16 Photo. *Perf. 14*

878	A225	30f multicolored	.95	1.25
879	A225	80f multicolored	3.00	1.75

First Intl. Pharmacology of Human Blood Vessels Symposium, Jan. 16-18.

21st Natl. Day — A226

1982, Feb. 25 *Perf. 13½x13*
880 A226 30f multicolored .70 .45
881 A226 80f multicolored 2.00 1.25

Scouting Year — A227

1982, Mar. 22 Photo. *Perf. 12x11½*
882 A227 30f multicolored .90 .55
883 A227 80f multicolored 2.50 1.50

Arab Pharmacists' Day — A228

1982, Apr. 2 Litho. *Perf. 12x11½*
884 A228 30f lt green & multi 1.25 .90
885 A228 80f pink & multi 4.00 2.50

World Health Day — A229

Arab Postal Union, 30th Anniv. — A230

1982, Apr. 7 Litho. *Perf. 13½x13*
886 A229 30f multicolored 1.50 .95
887 A229 80f multicolored 4.50 2.50

1982, Apr. 12 Photo. *Perf. 13½x13*
888 A230 30f multicolored 1.25 .85
889 A230 80f multicolored 4.00 2.25

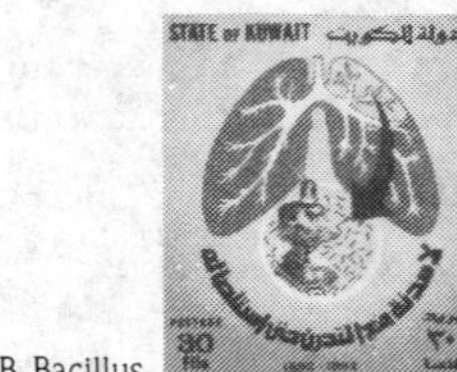

TB Bacillus Centenary — A231

1982, May 24 Litho. *Perf. 11½x12*
890 A231 30f multicolored 1.40 .90
891 A231 80f multicolored 4.25 2.50

1982 World Cup A232

1982, June 17 Photo. *Perf. 14*
892 A232 30f multicolored .95 .65
893 A232 80f multicolored 3.00 1.75

10th Anniv. of Science and Natural History Museum — A233

1982, July 14 *Perf. 14*
894 A233 30f multicolored 2.25 1.50
895 A233 80f multicolored 6.75 4.50

6th Anniv. of United Arab Shipping Co. — A234

Designs: Freighters.

1982, Sept. 1 *Perf. 13*
896 A234 30f multicolored 1.00 .40
897 A234 80f multicolored 2.25 1.10

Arab Day of the Palm Tree — A235

1982, Sept. 15 *Perf. 14*
898 A235 30f multicolored .75 .45
899 A235 80f multicolored 2.25 1.25

Islamic Pilgrimage A236

1982, Sept. 26 **Litho.**
900 A236 15f multicolored .45 .28
901 A236 30f multicolored 1.00 .65
902 A236 80f multicolored 2.75 1.75
Nos. 900-902 (3) 4.20 2.68

Desert Flowers & Plants — A237

1983, Jan. 25 Litho. *Perf. 12*
903 Strip of 10 1.10 .90
a.-j. A237 10f any single .15 .15
904 Strip of 10 1.40 1.10
a.-j. A237 15f any single .15 .15
905 Strip of 10 2.75 2.25
a.-j. A237 30f any single .25 .22
906 Strip of 10 3.25 2.75
a.-j A237 40f any single, horiz. .32 .25
907 Strip of 10 6.75 5.75
a.-j. A237 80f any single, horiz. .65 .55
Nos. 903-907 (5) 15.25 12.75

22nd Natl. Day — A238

1983, Feb. 25 Litho. *Perf. 12½*
908 A238 30f multicolored .80 .50
909 A238 80f multicolored 2.25 1.40

25th Anniv. of Intl. Maritime Org. A239

1983, Mar. 17 Photo. *Perf. 14*
910 A239 30f multicolored .50 .30
911 A239 80f multicolored 1.40 .85

Map of Middle East and Africa, Conference Emblem A240

1983, Mar. 19 *Perf. 13*
912 A240 15f multicolored .32 .22
913 A240 30f multicolored .75 .50
914 A240 80f multicolored 2.25 1.40
Nos. 912-914 (3) 3.32 2.12

3rd Intl. Conference on the Impact of Viral Diseases on the Development of the Middle East and Africa, Mar. 19-27.

World Health Day — A241

1983, Apr. 7 *Perf. 12x11½*
915 A241 15f multicolored .48 .30
916 A241 30f multicolored .95 .70
917 A241 80f multicolored 2.75 1.90
Nos. 915-917 (3) 4.18 2.90

World Communications Year — A242

1983, May 17 Photo. *Perf. 13x13½*
918 A242 15f multicolored .48 .30
919 A242 30f multicolored .95 .70
920 A242 80f multicolored 2.75 1.90
Nos. 918-920 (3) 4.18 2.90

World Environment Day — A243

1983, June 5 Litho. *Perf. 12½*
921 A243 15f multicolored .65 .30
922 A243 30f multicolored 1.25 .70
923 A243 80f multicolored 3.75 1.90
Nos. 921-923 (3) 5.65 2.90

Wall of Old Jerusalem A244

1983, July 25 Litho. *Perf. 12*
924 A244 15f multicolored .40 .25
925 A244 30f multicolored 1.00 .55
926 A244 80f multicolored 2.75 1.65
Nos. 924-926 (3) 4.15 2.45

World Heritage Year.

Islamic Pilgrimage A245

1983, Sept. 15 Photo. *Perf. 11½*
927 A245 15f multicolored .40 .25
928 A245 30f multicolored 1.00 .55
929 A245 80f multicolored 2.75 1.65
Nos. 927-929 (3) 4.15 2.45

Intl. Palestinian Solidarity Day — A246

1983, Nov. 29 Photo. *Perf. 14*
930 A246 15f multicolored .50 .25
931 A246 30f multicolored 1.25 .55
932 A246 80f multicolored 3.50 1.65
Nos. 930-932 (3) 5.25 2.45

21st Pan Arab Medical Congress, Jan. 30-Feb. 2 — A247

1984, Jan. 30 Litho. *Perf. 14½x14*
933 A247 15f purple & multi .50 .25
934 A247 30f blue grn & multi 1.25 .55
935 A247 80f pink & multi 3.25 1.65
Nos. 933-935 (3) 5.00 2.45

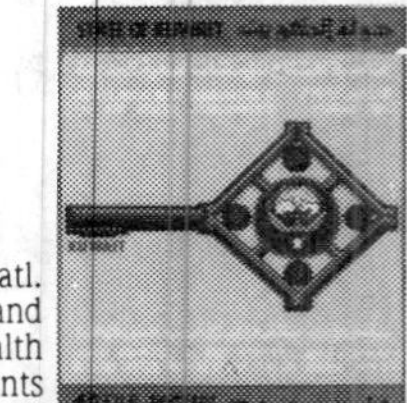

Key, Natl. Emblem, and Health Establishments Emblem — A248

1984, Feb. 20 Photo. *Perf. 13x13½*
936 A248 15f multicolored .45 .25
937 A248 30f multicolored 1.10 .55
938 A248 80f multicolored 3.00 1.65
Nos. 936-938 (3) 4.55 2.45

Inauguration of Amiri and Al-Razi Hospitals, Allergy Center and Medical Stores Center.

23rd National Day — A249

1984, Feb. 25 Litho. *Perf. 13½*
939 A249 15f multicolored .40 .25
940 A249 30f multicolored 1.00 .55
941 A249 80f multicolored 2.75 1.65
Nos. 939-941 (3) 4.15 2.45

2nd Kuwait Intl. Medical Science Conf., Mar. 4-8 — A250

1984, Mar. 4 Photo. *Perf. 12*
Granite Paper
942 A250 15f multicolored .40 .25
943 A250 30f multicolored 1.00 .55
944 A250 80f multicolored 2.75 1.65
Nos. 942-944 (3) 4.15 2.45

30th Anniv. of Kuwait Airways Corp. — A251

1984, Mar. 15 *Perf. 13½*

946 A251 30f multicolored .95 .90
947 A251 80f multicolored 2.50 1.65

Al-Arabi Magazine, 25th Anniv. — A252

1984, Mar. 20 *Perf. 14½x14*

948 A252 15f multicolored .35 .24
949 A252 30f multicolored .85 .52
950 A252 80f multicolored 2.25 1.50
Nos. 948-950 (3) 3.45 2.26

World Health Day — A253

1984, Apr. 7 *Perf. 12*

951 A253 15f multicolored .40 .25
952 A253 30f multicolored 1.00 .55
953 A253 80f multicolored 2.75 1.65
Nos. 951-953 (3) 4.15 2.45

Hanan Kuwaiti Orphan Village, Sudan — A254

1984, May 15 **Litho.** *Perf. 12*

954 A254 15f multicolored .40 .25
955 A254 30f multicolored 1.00 .55
956 A254 80f multicolored 2.75 1.65
Nos. 954-956 (3) 4.15 2.45

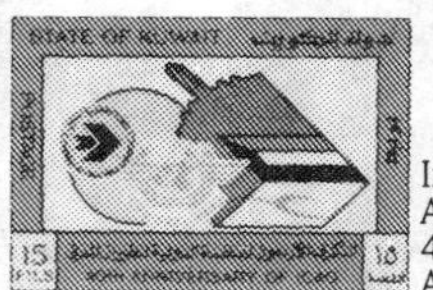

Intl. Civil Aviation Org., 40th Anniv. A255

1984, June 12

957 A255 15f multicolored .40 .25
958 A255 30f multicolored 1.00 .55
959 A255 80f multicolored 2.75 1.65
Nos. 957-959 (3) 4.15 2.45

Arab Youth Day — A256

1984, July 5 *Perf. 13½*

960 A256 30f multicolored 1.00 .55
961 A256 80f multicolored 2.75 1.65

1984 Summer Olympics A257

1984, July 28 *Perf. 15x14*

962 A257 30f Swimming .45 .35
963 A257 30f Hurdles .45 .35
a. Pair, #962-963 .85 .85
964 A257 80f Judo 1.10 .90
965 A257 80f Equestrian 1.10 .90
a. Pair, #964-965 2.25 2.25
Nos. 962-965 (4) 3.10 2.50

10th Anniv. of the Science Club A258

1984, Aug. 11 **Photo.** *Perf. 13½x13*

966 A258 15f multicolored .50 .25
967 A258 30f multicolored 1.25 .55
968 A258 80f multicolored 3.00 1.65
Nos. 966-968 (3) 4.75 2.45

Islamic Pilgrimage A259

1984, Sept. 4 **Photo.** *Perf. 12x11½*

969 A259 30f multicolored 1.25 .55
970 A259 80f multicolored 3.25 1.65

INTELSAT '84, 20th Anniv. A260

1984, Oct. 1 **Litho.** *Perf. 13½x14*

971 A260 30f multicolored 1.25 .55
972 A260 80f multicolored 3.00 1.65

G.C.C. Supreme Council, 5th Session A261

1984, Nov. 24 **Litho.** *Perf. 15x14*

973 A261 30f multicolored 1.00 .55
974 A261 80f multicolored 2.50 1.65

Map of Israel, Fists, Shattered Star of David — A262

1984, Nov. 29 **Photo.** *Perf. 12*

975 A262 30f multicolored 1.00 .55
976 A262 80f multicolored 2.50 1.65

Intl. Palestinian Solidarity Day.

Globe, Emblem — A263

1984, Dec. 24 *Perf. 12x11½*
Granite Paper

977 A263 30f multicolored 1.00 .25
978 A263 80f multicolored 2.75 1.10

Kuwait Oil Co., 50th anniv.

Intl. Youth Year — A264 24th Natl. Day — A265

1985, Jan. 15 *Perf. 13½*

979 A264 30f multicolored .55 .25
980 A264 80f multicolored 1.65 1.10

1985, Feb. 25 **Litho.** *Perf. 14x15*

981 A265 30f multicolored .80 .42
982 A265 80f multicolored 2.50 1.65

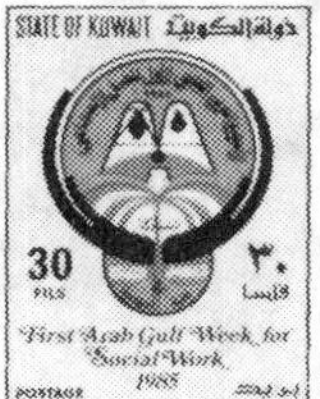

Intl. Program for the Development of Communications A266

1985, Mar. 4 **Photo.** *Perf. 11½*
Granite Paper

983 A266 30f multicolored 1.00 .55
984 A266 80f multicolored 2.50 1.65

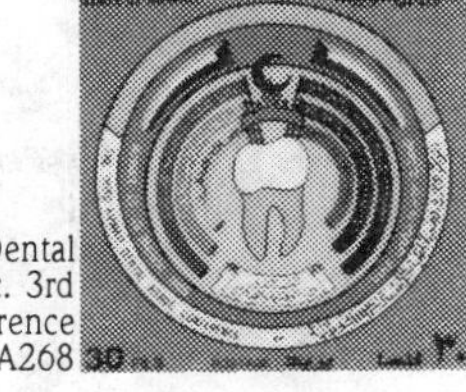

1st Arab Gulf Week for Social Work — A267

1985, Mar. 13 **Photo.** *Perf. 13½x13*

985 A267 30f multicolored 1.00 .55
986 A267 80f multicolored 2.50 1.65

Kuwait Dental Assoc. 3rd Conference A268

1985, Mar. 23 **Litho.** *Perf. 13½*

987 A268 30f multicolored 1.00 .55
988 A268 80f multicolored 2.50 1.65

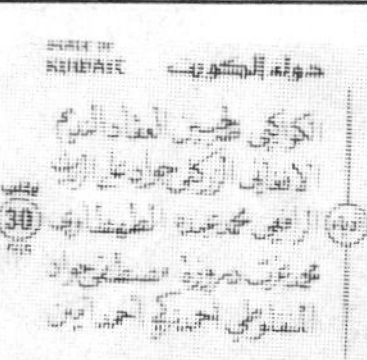

1985 Census — A269 World Health Day — A270

1985, Apr. 1 *Perf. 14x13½*

989 A269 30f multicolored 1.25 .55
990 A269 80f multicolored 2.75 1.65

1985, Apr. 7 **Photo.** *Perf. 13½x13*

991 A270 30f multicolored 1.25 .55
992 A270 80f multicolored 2.75 1.65

Names of Books, Authors and Poets in Arabic — A271

1985, May 20 *Perf. 12*
Granite Paper

993 Block of 4 2.75 1.75
a.-d. A271 30f any single .65 .42
994 Block of 4 7.25 5.00
a.-d. A271 80f any single 1.75 1.10

Central Library, 50th anniv.

World Environment Day — A272

1985, June 5 *Perf. 11½*

995 A272 30f multicolored 1.25 .55
996 A272 80f multicolored 2.75 1.65

Org. of Petroleum Exporting Countries, 25th Anniv. A273

1985, Sept. 1 *Perf. 13x13½*

997 A273 30f multicolored 1.25 .55
998 A273 80f multicolored 2.75 1.65

Inauguration of Civil Information System A274

1985, Oct. 1 **Photo.** *Perf. 12x11½*

999 A274 30f multicolored 1.25 .55
1000 A274 80f multicolored 2.75 1.65

Intl. Day of Solidarity with Palestinian People — A275

1985, Nov. 29 **Photo.** *Perf. 12*

1001 A275 15f multicolored 1.10 .45
1002 A275 30f multicolored 2.00 .90
1003 A275 80f multicolored 3.75 2.25
Nos. 1001-1003 (3) 6.85 3.60

25th Natl. Day — A276

1986, Feb. 25 **Litho.** *Perf. 15x14*

1004 A276 15f multicolored .32 .22
1005 A276 30f multicolored .95 .50
1006 A276 80f multicolored 2.25 1.25
Nos. 1004-1006 (3) 3.52 1.97

Natl. Red Crescent Soc., 20th Anniv. — A277

1986, Mar. 26 Photo. *Perf. 13½*

1007	A277	20f multicolored	.80	.65
1008	A277	25f multicolored	1.25	1.00
1009	A277	70f multicolored	3.75	2.75
		Nos. 1007-1009 (3)	5.80	4.40

World Health Day — A278

1986, Apr. 7 *Perf. 13½x13*

1010	A278	20f multicolored	.80	.65
1011	A278	25f multicolored	1.25	1.00
1012	A278	70f multicolored	3.75	2.75
		Nos. 1010-1012 (3)	5.80	4.40

Intl. Peace Year — A279

1986, June 5 Litho. *Perf. 13½*

1013	A279	20f multicolored	.60	.45
1014	A279	25f multicolored	1.10	.70
1015	A279	70f multicolored	3.00	2.00
		Nos. 1013-1015 (3)	4.70	3.15

United Arab Shipping Co., 10th Anniv. A280

1986, July 1 Photo. *Perf. 12x11½*

1016	A280	20f Al Mirqab	.80	.65
1017	A280	70f Al Mubarakiah	3.75	2.75

Gulf Bank, 25th Anniv. A281

1986, Oct. 1 Photo. *Perf. 12½*

1018	A281	20f multicolored	.70	.50
1019	A281	25f multicolored	1.25	.70
1020	A281	70f multicolored	3.50	2.25
		Nos. 1018-1020 (3)	5.45	3.45

Sadu Art — A282

Various tapestry weavings.

1986, Nov. 5 Photo. *Perf. 12x11½*
Granite Paper

1021	A282	20f multicolored	.50	.35
1022	A282	70f multicolored	2.00	1.40
1023	A282	200f multicolored	5.50	4.00
		Nos. 1021-1023 (3)	8.00	5.75

Intl. Day of Solidarity with the Palestinian People A283

1986, Nov. 29 *Perf. 14*

1024	A283	20f multicolored	1.10	.75
1025	A283	25f multicolored	1.50	1.00
1026	A283	70f multicolored	4.25	3.00
		Nos. 1024-1026 (3)	6.85	4.75

5th Islamic Summit Conference — A284

1987, Jan. 26 Litho. *Perf. 14½*

1027	A284	25f multicolored	.90	.45
1028	A284	50f multicolored	1.75	1.00
1029	A284	150f multicolored	5.00	3.00
		Nos. 1027-1029 (3)	7.65	4.45

26th Natl. Day A285

1987, Feb. 25 *Perf. 13½x14*

1030	A285	50f multicolored	1.50	1.00
1031	A285	150f multicolored	4.75	3.25

Natl. Health Sciences Center A286

1987, Mar. 15 Photo. *Perf. 12x11½*
Granite Paper

1032	A286	25f multicolored	.50	.35
1033	A286	150f multicolored	3.25	2.25

3rd Kuwait Intl. Medical Sciences Conference on Infectious Diseases in Developing Countries.

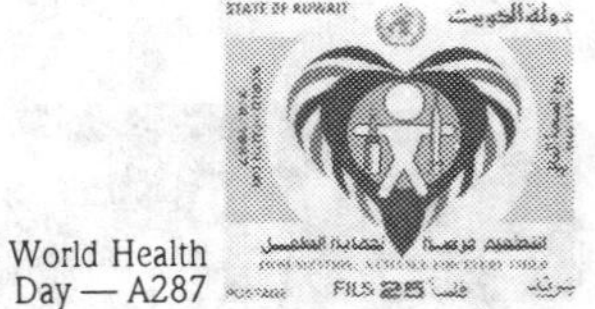
World Health Day — A287

1987, Apr. 7 Photo. *Perf. 13x13½*

1034	A287	25f multicolored	.65	.45
1035	A287	50f multicolored	1.40	.90
1036	A287	150f multicolored	4.25	2.50
		Nos. 1034-1036 (3)	6.30	3.85

Day of Ghods (Jerusalem) A288

1987, June 7 Photo. *Perf. 12x11½*

1037	A288	25f multicolored	.35	.22
1038	A288	50f multicolored	.80	.60
1039	A288	150f multicolored	2.75	1.75
		Nos. 1037-1039 (3)	3.90	2.57

Islamic Pilgrimage to Miqat Wadi Mihrim A289

1987, Aug. Photo. *Perf. 13½x14½*

1040	A289	25f multicolored	.50	.50
1041	A289	50f multicolored	1.00	.80
1042	A289	150f multicolored	3.25	2.00
		Nos. 1040-1042 (3)	4.75	3.30

Arab Telecommunications Day — A290

1987, Sept. 9 Litho. *Perf. 14x13½*

1043	A290	25f multicolored	.50	.30
1044	A290	50f multicolored	1.00	.80
1045	A290	150f multicolored	3.25	1.25
		Nos. 1043-1045 (3)	4.75	2.35

World Maritime Day A291

1987, Sept. 24 *Perf. 12x11½*
Granite Paper

1046	A291	25f multicolored	.50	.30
1047	A291	50f multicolored	1.00	.80
1048	A291	150f multicolored	3.25	2.00
		Nos. 1046-1048 (3)	4.75	3.10

Al Qurain Housing Project — A292

1987, Oct. 5 *Perf. 13x13½*

1049	A292	25f multicolored	.50	.30
1050	A292	50f multicolored	1.00	.80
1051	A292	150f multicolored	3.25	2.00
		Nos. 1049-1051 (3)	4.75	3.10

Port Authority, 10th Anniv. A293

1987, Nov. 16 Litho. *Perf. 14½*

1052	A293	25f multicolored	.40	.20
1053	A293	50f multicolored	.85	.50
1054	A293	150f multicolored	2.75	1.75
		Nos. 1052-1054 (3)	4.00	2.45

A294 A295

1987, Nov. 29 *Perf. 14x13½*

1055	A294	25f multicolored	.45	.30
1056	A294	50f multicolored	.90	.60
1057	A294	150f multicolored	2.50	2.00
		Nos. 1055-1057 (3)	3.85	2.90

Intl. Day of Solidarity with the Palestinian People

1988, Feb. 3 Photo. *Perf. 14*

1058	A295	25f multicolored	.45	.30
1059	A295	50f multicolored	.90	.50
1060	A295	150f multicolored	2.50	1.50
		Nos. 1058-1060 (3)	3.85	2.30

Women's Cultural and Social Soc., 25th anniv.

A296 A297

1988, Feb. 25

1061	A296	25f multicolored	.45	.30
1062	A296	50f multicolored	.90	.50
1063	A296	150f multicolored	2.50	1.50
		Nos. 1061-1063 (3)	3.85	2.30

National Day, 27th anniv.

1988, Apr. 7 Litho. *Perf. 14x15*

1064	A297	25f multicolored	.45	.20
1065	A297	50f multicolored	.90	.45
1066	A297	150f multicolored	2.50	1.40
		Nos. 1064-1066 (3)	3.85	2.05

World Health Day, WHO 40th anniv.

A298 A299

1988, Apr. 24 Photo. *Perf. 12*
Granite Paper

1067	A298	35f multicolored	.60	.35
1068	A298	50f multicolored	.90	.55
1069	A298	150f multicolored	2.75	1.75
		Nos. 1067-1069 (3)	4.25	2.65

Regional Marine Environment Day. Kuwait Regional Convention on the Marine Environment, 10th anniv. See Iraq Nos. 1333-1336.

1988, July 10 Photo. *Perf. 14*

1070	A299	25f multicolored	.45	.20
1071	A299	50f multicolored	.90	.55
1072	A299	150f multicolored	2.75	1.75
		Nos. 1070-1072 (3)	4.10	2.50

Kuwait Teachers Soc., 25th anniv.

Pilgrimage to Mecca A300

1988, Sept. 12 Litho. *Perf. 13½x14*
1073 A300 25f multicolored .45 .20
1074 A300 50f multicolored .90 .55
1075 A300 150f multicolored 2.75 1.75
Nos. 1073-1075 (3) 4.10 2.50

Palestinian "Children of Stone" Fighting Israelis — A301

1988, Sept. 15 Photo. *Perf. 13x13½*
1076 A301 50f multicolored 1.25 .70
1077 A301 150f multicolored 4.50 2.50

Palestinian Uprising. Dated 1987.

Arab Housing Day — A302

1988, Oct. 3
1078 A302 50f multicolored .85 .60
1079 A302 100f multicolored 1.75 1.10
1080 A302 150f multicolored 2.75 1.75
Nos. 1078-1080 (3) 5.35 3.45

Intl. Day for Solidarity with the Palestinian People — A303

1988, Nov. 29 Litho. *Perf. 14x13*
1081 A303 50f multicolored .85 .60
1082 A303 100f multicolored 1.75 1.10
1083 A303 150f multicolored 2.75 1.75
Nos. 1081-1083 (3) 5.35 3.45

A304

A305

1988, Dec. 5 *Perf. 13x14*
1084 A304 50f multicolored .75 .50
1085 A304 100f multicolored 1.65 1.00
1086 A304 150f multicolored 2.75 1.50
Nos. 1084-1086 (3) 5.15 3.00

Intl. Volunteers Day.

1989, Feb. 18 Litho. *Perf. 14x13½*
1087 A305 50f multicolored .45 .28
1088 A305 100f multicolored .90 .55
1089 A305 150f multicolored 1.75 .90
Nos. 1087-1089 (3) 3.10 1.73

18th Arab Engineering Conference.

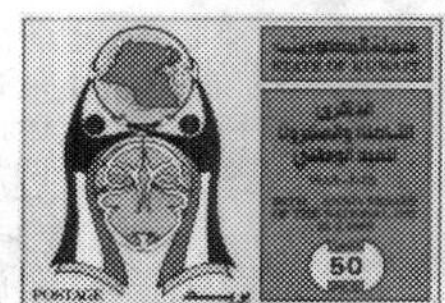

28th Natl. Day — A306

1989, Feb. 25 *Perf. 13x13½*
1090 A306 50f multicolored .45 .28
1091 A306 100f multicolored .90 .55
1092 A306 150f multicolored 1.75 .90
Nos. 1090-1092 (3) 3.10 1.73

5th Natl. Dental Assoc. Conference — A307

1989, Mar. 30 Litho. *Perf. 13½x13*
1093 A307 50f multicolored .50 .35
1094 A307 150f multicolored 1.50 1.00
1095 A307 250f multicolored 2.50 1.65
Nos. 1093-1095 (3) 4.50 3.00

World Health Day — A308

1989, Apr. 7 *Perf. 13x13½*
1096 A308 50f multicolored .50 .35
1097 A308 150f multicolored 1.50 1.00
1098 A308 250f multicolored 2.50 1.65
Nos. 1096-1098 (3) 4.50 3.00

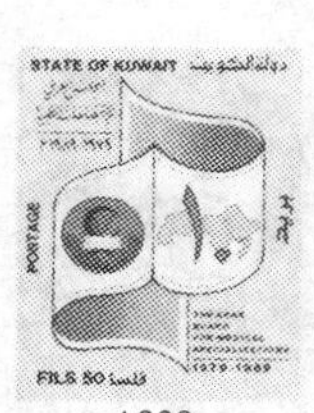

A309

A310

1989, May 10 *Perf. 13x14*
1099 A309 50f multicolored .50 .25
1100 A309 150f multicolored 1.50 .75
1101 A309 250f multicolored 2.50 1.25
Nos. 1099-1101 (3) 4.50 2.25

Arab Board for Medical Specializations, 10th anniv.

1989, June 10 Litho. *Perf. 14x15*
1102 A310 50f multicolored .60 .40
1103 A310 200f multicolored 2.25 1.50
1104 A310 250f multicolored 3.00 2.00
Nos. 1102-1104 (3) 5.85 3.90

Natl. Journalists Assoc., 25th anniv.

Al-Taneem Mosque A311

1989, July 9 Litho. *Perf. 13½x14½*
1105 A311 50f multicolored .52 .32
1106 A311 150f multicolored 1.65 .52
1107 A311 200f multicolored 2.00 1.40
Nos. 1105-1107 (3) 4.17 2.24

Pilgrimage to Mecca.

Arab Housing Day — A312

1989, Oct. 2 *Perf. 13½*
1108 A312 25f multicolored .28 .15
1109 A312 50f multicolored .60 .20
1110 A312 150f multicolored 1.90 .60
Nos. 1108-1110 (3) 2.78 .95

Annual Greenery Week Celebration — A313

Dhow — A314

1989, Oct. 15 *Perf. 13½x13*
1111 A313 25f multicolored .28 .15
1112 A313 50f multicolored .60 .20
1113 A313 150f multicolored 1.90 .60
Nos. 1111-1113 (3) 2.78 .95

Numbers in Black, Moon and Dhow in Gold

1989, Nov. 1 *Perf. 14x15*

Coil Stamps

1114 A314 50f brt apple grn *1.75 1.75*
1115 A314 100f brt blue *3.50 3.50*
1116 A314 200f vermilion *7.50 7.50*
Nos. 1114-1116 (3) *12.75 12.75*

Nos. 1114-1116 available only at two post office locations, where they were dispensed from machines. Printed in rolls of 3000 consecutively numbered stamps.

Gulf Investment Corp., 5th Anniv. — A315

1989, Nov. 4 *Perf. 15x14*
1117 A315 25f multicolored .40 .15
1118 A315 50f multicolored .75 .20
1119 A315 150f multicolored 2.25 .65
Nos. 1117-1119 (3) 3.40 1.00

Declaration of Palestinian State, 1st Anniv. — A316

Zakat House, Orphan Sponsorship Program — A317

1989, Nov. 15 Litho. *Perf. 14x15*
1120 A316 50f multicolored 1.00 .25
1121 A316 150f multicolored 3.00 .85
1122 A316 200f multicolored 4.00 1.10
Nos. 1120-1122 (3) 8.00 2.20

1989, Dec. 10 *Perf. 13½x13*
1123 A317 25f multicolored .35 .20
1124 A317 50f multicolored .75 .22
1125 A317 150f multicolored 2.25 .75
Nos. 1123-1125 (3) 3.35 1.17

Kuwait Police, 50th Anniv. — A318

1989, Dec. 30 Litho. *Perf. 15x14*
1126 A318 25f gray & multi .32 .15
1127 A318 50f lt ultra & multi .65 .20
1128 A318 150f lt violet & multi 2.00 .65
Nos. 1126-1128 (3) 2.97 1.00

National Day, 29th Anniv. — A319

1990, Feb. 25 *Perf. 14x13½*
1129 A319 25f multicolored .32 .15
1130 A319 50f multicolored .65 .20
1131 A319 150f multicolored 2.00 .65
Nos. 1129-1131 (3) 2.97 1.00

World Meteorological Day — A320

1990, Mar. 23 Litho. *Perf. 13½x14*
1132 A320 50f multicolored .80 .30
1133 A320 100f multicolored 1.75 .55
1134 A320 150f multicolored 2.50 .80
Nos. 1132-1134 (3) 5.05 1.65

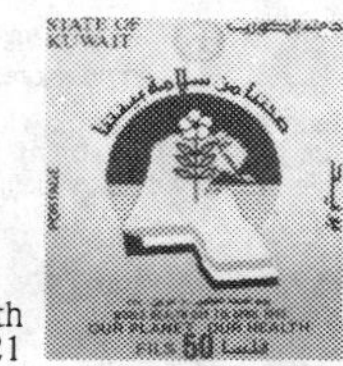

World Health Day — A321

1990, Apr. 7 *Perf. 14x15*
1135 A321 50f multicolored 1.00 .25
1136 A321 100f multicolored 2.00 .60
1137 A321 150f multicolored 2.75 1.00
Nos. 1135-1137 (3) 5.75 1.85

Warning

There are reports that a number of pre-war issues have gone back on sale at the post office. Nos. 1138-1140 have been specifically mentioned.

Hawk — A322

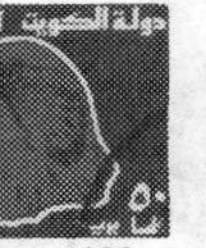
Liberation of Kuwait — A323

1990, July 7 Litho. *Perf. 14½*
1138 A322 50f blue & gold 3.25
1139 A322 100f maroon & gold 6.25
1140 A322 150f green & gold 9.25
Nos. 1138-1140 (3) 18.75

1991 Litho. *Perf. 14½*
1141 A323 25f multicolored .75
1142 A323 50f multicolored 1.50
1143 A323 150f multicolored 4.50
Nos. 1141-1143 (3) 6.75

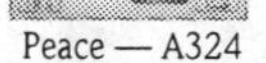
Peace — A324

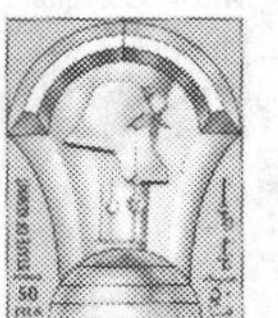
Reconstruction — A325

1991, May *Perf. 13½x14*
1144 A324 50f multicolored 1.20
1145 A324 100f multicolored 2.40
1146 A324 150f multicolored 3.60
Nos. 1144-1146 (3) 7.20

1991, May
1147 A325 50f multicolored 1.20
1148 A325 150f multicolored 3.60
1149 A325 200f multicolored 4.80
Nos. 1147-1149 (3) 9.60

Liberation of Kuwait — A326

Flags of forces joining international coalition for liberation of Kuwait: Sweden, USSR, US, Kuwait, Saudi Arabia, UN, Singapore, France, Italy, Egypt, Morocco, UK, Philippines, UAE, Syria, Poland, Australia, Japan, Hungary, Netherlands, Denmark, New Zealand, Czechoslovakia, Bahrain, Honduras, Turkey, Greece, Oman, Qatar, Belgium, Sierra Leone, Argentina, Norway, Canada, Germany, South Korea, Bangladesh, Bulgaria, Senegal, Spain, Niger, and Pakistan. No. 1151, all forces of coalition.

1991, July 25 **Litho.** *Perf. 14½*
1150 A326 50f Sheet of 42 *24.00*

Size: 87x134mm

Imperf

1151 A326 1d multicolored *15.00*

Individual stamps from No. 1150 are not given minor letters due to size of sheet. Each stamp can be identified by country name.

Invasion of Kuwait, 1st Anniv. — A327

1991, Aug. 2 *Perf. 14½*
1152 A327 50f Human terror *1.25*
1153 A327 100f Invasion of Kuwait *3.00*
1154 A327 150f Environmental terrorism, horiz. *4.50*

Size: 90x65mm

Imperf

1155 A327 250f Desert Storm *7.00*
Nos. 1152-1155 (4) *15.75*

12th Gulf Cooperation Council Summit A328

Design: 150f, Tree of flags.

1991, Dec. 23 **Litho.** *Perf. 14½*
1156 A328 25f multicolored .30
a. see footnote .30
1157 A328 150f multicolored 1.75
a. Sheet of 4, 2 each #1156-1157 6.25
b. Sheet of 4, 2 each #1156a, 1157 6.25

No. 1156a has tree with inscriptions (country names in Arabic) in colors of flags shown on No. 1157.

Intl. Literacy Year — A329

OPEC, 30th Anniv. (in 1990) — A330

1992, Feb. 12 **Litho.** *Perf. 13½x13*
1158 A329 50f dark blue & buff 1.00
1159 A329 100f dark blue & citron 2.00
1160 A329 150f dk blue & pale lil 3.00
Nos. 1158-1160 (3) 6.00

Dated 1990.

1992, Oct. 29 *Perf. 14½x13½*
1161 A330 25f red & multi .25
1162 A330 50f yellow & multi .50
1163 A330 150f green & multi 1.50
Nos. 1161-1163 (3) 2.25

31st Natl. Day A331

1992 *Perf. 14½*
1164 A331 50f Flag, doves .50
1165 A331 150f Flags 1.50
a. Miniature sheet 2 each #1164-1165 4.00

Liberation Day (No. 1165). Issue dates, 50f, Feb. 25; 150f, Feb. 26.

Don't Forget Our P.O.W.'s — A332

1991, Nov. 16
1166 A332 50f Flag, chains 1.00
1167 A332 150f Cell bars, chains 3.00
a. Min. sheet, 2 each #1166-1167 9.00

Dated 1991. Issued: 50f, Feb, 25. 150f, Feb. 26.

Camels A333

1991, Nov. 16 *Perf. 12½*
1168 A333 25f pink & multi .25
1169 A333 50f beige & multi .50
1170 A333 150f lt violet & multi 1.50
1171 A333 200f blue & multi 2.00
1172 A333 350f orange & multi 3.50
Nos. 1168-1172 (5) 7.75

Environmental Terrorism, by Jafar Islah — A334

Designs: No. 1174, Snake, flag, map. No. 1175, Skull, dead fish. No. 1176, Dying camel.

1992, June *Perf. 14½*
1173 A334 150f multicolored 2.25
1174 A334 150f multicolored 2.25
1175 A334 150f multicolored 2.25
1176 A334 150f multicolored 2.25
a. Block of 4, #1173-1176 9.00
b. Minature sheet of 4, #1173-1176 11.50

Earth Summit, Rio De Janeiro. No. 1176a printed in continuous design.

EXPO '92, Seville A335

Designs: No. 1177, Kuwaiti Pavilion, La Giralda Tower, Seville. No. 1178, Dhows. No. 1179, Dhow. No. 1180, Pavilion, dhow.

Flags of Spain or Kuwait and: No. 1181, Pavilion. No. 1182, La Giralda Tower. No. 1183, La Giralda Tower, dhow. No. 1184, Pavilion, dhow.

1992, June 19
1177 A335 50f multicolored .40
1178 A335 50f multicolored .40
1179 A335 50f multicolored .40
1180 A335 50f multicolored .40
a. Block of 4, #1177-1180 1.60
1181 A335 150f multicolored 1.20
1182 A335 150f multicolored 1.20
1183 A335 150f multicolored 1.20
1184 A335 150f multicolored 1.20
a. Block of 4, #1181-1184 4.80
b. Miniature sheet of 8, #1177-1184 6.40
Nos. 1177-1184 (8) 6.40

Nos. 1180a, 1184a have continuous designs.

Palace of Justice A336

1992, July 4 *Perf. 12½*
1185 A336 25f lilac & multi .20
1186 A336 50f lilac rose & multi .40
1187 A336 100f yel green & multi 1.20
1188 A336 150f yel orange & multi 1.25
1189 A336 250f blue green & multi 2.00
Nos. 1185-1189 (5) 5.05

1992 Summer Olympics, Barcelona — A337

Olympic flag, Fahed Al Ahmed Al Sabah, member of the Intl. Olympic committee and: 50f, Swimmer, soccer player. 100f, Runner, basketball player. 150f, Judo, equestrian.

1992, July 25 *Perf. 14½*
1190 A337 50f multicolored .90
1191 A337 100f multicolored 1.75
1192 A337 150f multicolored 2.75
Nos. 1190-1192 (3) 5.40

Invasion by Iraq, 2nd Anniv. — A338

Children's paintings: No. 1193, Tanks, people holding signs, two people being tortured. No. 1194, Truck, Iraqi soldiers looting. No. 1195, Iraqi soldiers killing civilians, tanks. No. 1196, Houses ablaze. No. 1197, Tanks, civilians, soldiers. No. 1198, Planes bombing in attack on fort. No. 1199, Tank, civilians holding flags, signs. No. 1200, Battlefield.

1992, Aug. 2 **Litho.** *Perf. 14x14½*
1193 A338 50f multicolored .40
1194 A338 50f multicolored .40
1195 A338 50f multicolored .40
1196 A338 50f multicolored .40
a. Block of 4, #1193-1196 1.60
1197 A338 150f multicolored 1.25
1198 A338 150f multicolored 1.25
1199 A338 150f multicolored 1.25
1200 A338 150f multicolored 1.25
a. Block of 4, #1197-1200 5.00
b. Min. sheet of 8, #1193-1200 7.00
Nos. 1193-1200 (8) 6.60

Extinguishing of Oil Well Fires, 1st Anniv. — A339

Various scenes showing oil well fire being extinguished.

1992 **Litho.** *Perf. 14½*
1201 A339 25f multi, vert. .18 .18
1202 A339 50f multi, vert. .38 .38
1203 A339 150f multi, vert. 1.10 1.10
1204 A339 250f multicolored 1.85 1.85
Nos. 1201-1204 (4) 3.51 3.51

Kuwait Tower — A340

A341

1993, Jan. 16 **Litho.** *Perf. 14x15*

Background Color

1205 A340 25f lilac .18 .18
1206 A340 100f blue .75 .75
1207 A340 150f salmon 1.10 1.10
Nos. 1205-1207 (3) 2.03 2.03

1993, Feb. 25 **Litho.** *Perf. 13½x14*
1208 A341 25f green & multi .18 .18
1209 A341 50f blue & multi .36 .36
1210 A341 150f pink & multi 1.10 1.10
Nos. 1208-1210 (3) 1.64 1.64

National Day, 32nd anniv.

Liberation Day, 2nd Anniv. — A342

1993, Feb. 26 *Perf. 15x14*
1211 A342 25f orange yel & multi .25 .25
1212 A342 50f green & multi .55 .55
1213 A342 150f red lilac & multi 1.65 1.65
Nos. 1211-1213 (3) 2.45 2.45

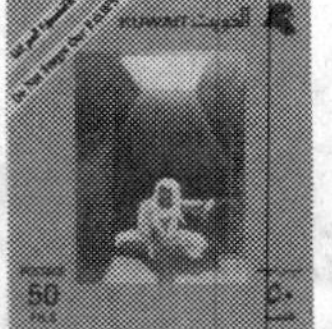

Remembering Prisoners of War — A343

Designs: 50f, Prisoner shackled in cell, vert. 150f, Shackled hand pointing to cell window, bird. 200f, Cell, prisoner's face, vert.

Perf. 13½x14, 14x13½

1993, May 15 **Litho.**

1214	A343	50f multicolored	.60	.60
1215	A343	150f multicolored	1.65	1.65
1216	A343	200f multicolored	2.25	2.25
		Nos. 1214-1216 (3)	4.50	4.50

A344

A345

1993, Apr. 20 **Litho.** ***Perf. 11½x12***

Granite Paper

1217	A344	25f gray & multi	.18	.18
1218	A344	50f green & multi	.38	.38
1219	A344	150f yellow & multi	1.15	1.15
1220	A344	350f blue & multi	2.65	2.65
		Nos. 1217-1220 (4)	4.36	4.36

18th Deaf Child Week.

1993, Aug. 2 **Litho.** ***Perf. 13½x14***

1221	A345	50f green & multi	.40	.40
1222	A345	150f orange & multi	1.25	1.25

Invasion by Iraq, 3rd anniv.

Kuwait Airforce, 40th Anniv. A346

1993, Dec. 9 **Litho.** ***Perf. 13x13½***

1223	A346	50f blue & multi	.38	.38
1224	A346	150f green & multi	1.10	1.10

Natl. Day, 33rd Anniv. — A347

Liberation Day, 3rd Anniv. — A348

1994, Feb. 25 **Litho.** ***Perf. 13½x14***

1225	A347	25f salmon & multi	.18	.18
1226	A347	50f yellow & multi	.38	.38
1227	A347	150f green & multi	1.10	1.10
		Nos. 1225-1227 (3)	1.66	1.66

1994, Feb. 26

1228	A348	25f yellow & multi	.18	.18
1229	A348	50f blue & multi	.38	.38
1230	A348	150f gray green & multi	1.10	1.10
		Nos. 1228-1230 (3)	1.66	1.66

Central Bank of Kuwait, 25th Anniv. — A349

1994, Apr. 20 **Litho.** ***Perf. 13½x13***

1231	A349	25f salmon & multi	.20	.20
1232	A349	50f green & multi	.40	.40
1233	A349	150f blue violet & multi	1.25	1.25
		Nos. 1231-1233 (3)	1.85	1.85

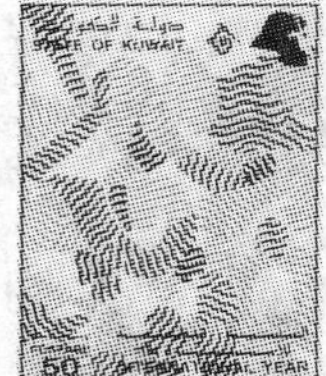

A350

A351

Intl. Year of the Family A352

1994, May 15 **Litho.** ***Perf. 13***

1234	A350	50f multicolored	.38	.38
1235	A351	150f multicolored	1.10	1.10
1236	A352	200f multicolored	1.50	1.50
		Nos. 1234-1236 (3)	2.98	2.98

A353

A354

1994, June 5 **Litho.** ***Perf. 14***

1237	A353	50f yellow & multi	.38	.38
1238	A353	100f blue & multi	.75	.75
1239	A353	150f green & multi	1.10	1.10
		Nos. 1237-1239 (3)	2.23	2.23

Industrial Bank of Kuwait, 20th anniv.

1994, June 15 **Litho.** ***Perf. 13***

1240	A354	50f Whirlpool	.38	.38
1241	A354	100f Shifting sands	.75	.75
1242	A354	150f Finger print	1.10	1.10
1243	A354	250f Clouds	1.90	1.90
a.		Miniature sheet of 4, #1240-1243	4.25	4.25
		Nos. 1240-1243 (4)	4.13	4.13

Martyr's Day.

A355

A356

1994, June 25 **Litho.** ***Perf. 14***

1244	A355	50f vio & multi	.38	.38
1245	A355	150f pink & multi	1.10	1.10
1246	A355	350f blue & multi	2.75	2.75
		Nos. 1244-1246 (3)	4.23	4.23

ILO, 75th anniv.

1994, Aug. 2 **Litho.** ***Perf. 12½x13½***

1247	A356	50f green blue & multi	.38	.38
1248	A356	150f blue & multi	1.10	1.10
1249	A356	350f lilac & multi	2.75	2.75
		Nos. 1247-1249 (3)	4.23	4.23

Invasion by Iraq, 4th anniv.

Port Authority — A357

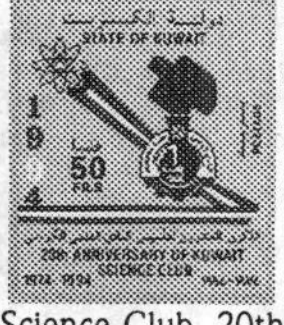

Science Club, 20th Anniv. — A358

1994, Aug. 31 **Litho.** ***Perf. 12½x14***

1250	A357	50f pink & multi	.38	.38
1251	A357	150f blue & multi	1.10	1.10
1252	A357	350f green & multi	2.75	2.75
		Nos. 1250-1252 (3)	4.23	4.23

1994, Sept. 11 ***Perf. 14***

1253	A358	50f blue & multi	.38	.38
1254	A358	100f green & multi	.75	.75
1255	A358	150f red & multi	1.10	1.10
		Nos. 1253-1255 (3)	2.23	2.23

A359

A360

Designs showing emblem and: 50f, Map of Arab countries, building. 100f, Windows, building. 150f, Doors below portico.

1994, Nov. 12 ***Perf. 11½***

1256	A359	50f multicolored	.38	.38
1257	A359	100f multicolored	.75	.75
1258	A359	150f multicolored	1.10	1.10
		Nos. 1256-1258 (3)	2.23	2.23

Arab Towns Organization, opening of headquarters.

1994, Dec. 7 ***Perf. 14½***

Designs: 100f, Emblems, sailing ship. 150f, Emblems, co-operation, co-ordination. 350f, Emblem, airplane in flight.

1259	A360	100f silver, gold & multi	.75	.75
1260	A360	150f silver, gold & multi	1.10	1.10
1261	A360	350f gold & multi	2.75	2.75
		Nos. 1259-1261 (3)	4.60	4.60

ICAO, 50th anniv.

A361

A362

1994, Dec. 20 ***Perf. 13x14***

1262	A361	50f lake & multi	.38	.38
1263	A361	100f green & multi	.75	.75
1264	A361	150f slate & multi	1.10	1.10
		Nos. 1262-1264 (3)	2.23	2.23

Kuwait Airways, 40th anniv.

1995, Feb. 6 **Litho.** ***Perf. 14***

1265	A362	50f yellow & multi	.38	.38
1266	A362	100f green & multi	.75	.75
1267	A362	150f brown & multi	1.10	1.10
		Nos. 1265-1267 (3)	2.23	2.23

1995 Census.

National Day, 34th Anniv. — A363

Liberation Day, 4th Anniv. — A364

1995, Feb. 25 ***Perf. 13***

1268	A363	25f blue & multi	.18	.18
1269	A363	50f yellow & multi	.38	.38
1270	A363	150f lilac & multi	1.10	1.10
		Nos. 1268-1270 (3)	1.66	1.66

1995, Feb. 26

1271	A364	25f blue & multi	.18	.18
1272	A364	50f green & multi	.38	.38
1273	A364	150f rose lilac & multi	1.10	1.10
		Nos. 1271-1273 (3)	1.66	1.66

Medical Research A365

1995, Mar. 20 ***Perf. 14***

1274	A365	50f Medical building	.38	.38
1275	A365	100f Classroom instruction	.75	.75
1276	A365	150f Map of Kuwait	1.10	1.10
		Nos. 1274-1276 (3)	2.23	2.23

Arab League, 50th Anniv. A366

Designs: 50f, Kuwaiti, league flags over emblems, map, vert. 100f, Flags over "50," emblem. 150f, Flags as clasping hands, vert.

1995, Mar. 22 ***Perf. 13***

1277	A366	50f multicolored	.38	.38
1278	A366	100f multicolored	.75	.75
1279	A366	150f multicolored	1.10	1.10
		Nos. 1277-1279 (3)	2.23	2.23

A367

A368

1995, Apr. 7 **Litho.** ***Perf. 13½x13***

1280	A367	50f blue & multi	.40	.40
1281	A367	150f pink & multi	1.10	1.10
1282	A367	200f yellow & multi	1.50	1.50
		Nos. 1280-1282 (3)	3.00	3.00

World Health Day.

1995, June 5 **Litho.** ***Perf. 14***

Designs: 50f, One gold ball. 100f, Gold "1," one gold ball. 150f, "1," both balls in gold.

1283	A368	50f shown	.35	.35
1284	A368	100f multicolored	.65	.65
1285	A368	150f multicolored	1.00	1.00
		Nos. 1283-1285 (3)	2.00	2.00

Volleyball, cent.

Invasion by Iraq, 5th Anniv. — A369

1995, Aug. 2 **Litho.** ***Perf. 13***

1286	A369	50f purple & multi	.40	.40
1287	A369	100f red & multi	.75	.75
1288	A369	150f green & multi	1.10	1.10
		Nos. 1286-1288 (3)	2.25	2.25

UN, 50th Anniv. A370

1995, Aug. 12 ***Perf. 13x13½***

1289	A370	25f multi	.20	.20
1290	A370	50f orange & multi	.40	.40
1291	A370	150f blue green & multi	1.10	1.10
		Nos. 1289-1291 (3)	1.70	1.70

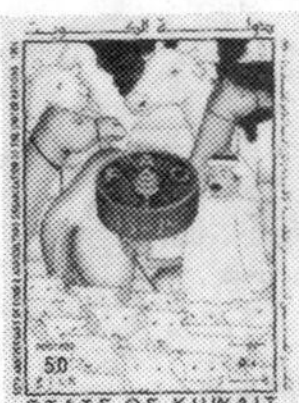

FAO, 50th Anniv. — A371

People in traditional dress with: 50f, Cattle, camels, sheep. 100f, Fish, boat. 150f, Poultry, fruits, vegetables.

1995, Sept. 21 *Perf. 13½x13*
1292 A371 50f multicolored .40 .40
1293 A371 100f multicolored .75 .75
1294 A371 150f multicolored 1.10 1.10
a. Min. sheet of 3, #1292-1294 2.25 2.25
Nos. 1292-1294 (3) 2.25 2.25

A372

World Standards Day — A373

1995, Oct. 14 *Perf. 13*
1295 A372 50f multicolored .40 .40
1296 A373 100f green & multi .75 .75
1297 A373 150f violet & multi 1.10 1.10
Nos. 1295-1297 (3) 2.25 2.25

Flowers — A374

Natl. Day, 35th Anniv. — A375

Designs: 5f, Onobrychis ptolemaica. 15f, Convolvulus oxyphyllus. 25f, Papaver rhoeas. 50f, Moltkiopsis ciliata. 150f, Senecio desfontainei.

1995, Nov. 15 **Litho.** *Perf. 14½*
1298 A374 5f multicolored .15 .15
1299 A374 15f multicolored .15 .15
1300 A374 25f multicolored .20 .20
1301 A374 50f multicolored .40 .40
1302 A374 150f multicolored 1.25 1.25
Nos. 1298-1302 (5) 2.15 2.15

1996, Feb. 25 *Perf. 14*
1303 A375 25f lil rose & multi .20 .20
1304 A375 50f blue green & multi .40 .40
1305 A375 150f salmon & multi 1.25 1.25
Nos. 1303-1305 (3) 1.85 1.85

Liberation Day, 5th Anniv. — A376

1996, Feb. 26
1306 A376 25f violet & multi .20 .20
1307 A376 50f brown & multi .40 .40
1308 A376 150f blue green & multi 1.25 1.25
Nos. 1306-1308 (3) 1.85 1.85

Arab City Day — A377

A378

1996, Mar. 1 *Perf. 13½*
1309 A377 50f yel grn & multi .40 .40
1310 A377 100f pink & multi .80 .80
1311 A377 150f blue green & multi 1.25 1.25
Nos. 1309-1311 (3) 2.45 2.45

1996, Jan. 27 *Perf. 14*
1312 A378 50f blue & multi .40 .40
1313 A378 100f gray & multi .80 .80
1314 A378 150f rose lilac & multi 1.25 1.25
Nos. 1312-1314 (3) 2.45 2.45

Scouting in Kuwait, 60th Anniv. — A379

Designs: 50f, On top of watchtower. 100f, Drawing water from well. 150f, Planting seedling.

1996, Jan. 14 *Perf. 13½*
1315 A379 50f yellow & multi .40 .40
1316 A379 100f lilac & multi .80 .80
1317 A379 150f blue green & multi 1.25 1.25
Nos. 1315-1317 (3) 2.45 2.45

Kuwait Money Show — A380

1996, Jan. 2 *Perf. 14*
1318 A380 25f gold & multi .20 .20
1319 A380 100f blue & multi .80 .80
1320 A380 150f dark gray & multi 1.25 1.25
Nos. 1318-1320 (3) 2.25 2.25

7th Kuwait Dental Assoc. Conference A381

UNESCO, 50th Anniv. A382

1996, Mar. 27 **Litho.** *Perf. 14x13½*
1321 A381 25f orange & multi .20 .20
1322 A381 50f violet & multi .40 .40
1323 A381 150f blue & multi 1.25 1.25
Nos. 1321-1323 (3) 1.85 1.85

1996, Apr. 10 *Perf. 13½x14*
1324 A382 25f violet & multi .20 .20
1325 A382 100f green & multi .80 .80
1326 A382 150f orange & multi 1.25 1.25
Nos. 1324-1326 (3) 2.25 2.25

1st Oil Exports, 50th Anniv. — A383

Rule of Al-Sabah Family, Cent. — A384

1996, June 30 **Litho.** *Perf. 13*
1327 A383 25f multicolored .25 .25
1328 A383 100f gray & multi 1.00 1.00
1329 A383 150f bister & multi 1.50 1.50
Nos. 1327-1329 (3) 2.75 2.75

1996, Aug. 12
1330 A384 25f shown .25 .25
1331 A384 50f Shiek, flags .50 .50
1332 A384 150f like #1329 1.50 1.50
Nos. 1330-1332 (3) 2.25 2.25

1996 Summer Olympic Games, Atlanta — A385

1996, Oct. 5 *Perf. 13½*
1333 A385 25f Shooting .25 .25
1334 A385 50f Running .50 .50
1335 A385 100f Weight lifting 1.00 1.00
1336 A385 150f Fencing 1.50 1.50
Nos. 1333-1336 (4) 3.25 3.25

A 750f souvenir sheet exists. Value $75.

Kuwait University, 30th Anniv. — A386

1st Children's Cultural Festival — A387

1996, Nov. 27 **Litho.** *Perf. 13½x14*
1337 A386 25f green & multi .20 .20
1338 A386 100f blue & multi .80 .80
1339 A386 150f yellow & multi 1.20 1.20
Nos. 1337-1339 (3) 2.20 2.20

1996, Nov. 20 *Perf. 14x13½*
1340 A387 25f brown gray & multi .20 .20
1341 A387 100f multicolored .80 .80
1342 A387 150f yellow grn & multi 1.20 1.20
Nos. 1340-1342 (3) 2.20 2.20

3rd Al-Qurain Cultrual Festival — A388

Liberation Tower — A389

1996, Nov. 20 *Perf. 14*
1343 A388 50f orange & multi .40 .40
1344 A388 100f blue & multi .80 .80
1345 A388 150f green & multi 1.20 1.20
Nos. 1343-1345 (3) 2.40 2.40

1996, Dec. 10 *Perf. 13x13½*
1346 A389 5f red & multi .15 .15
1347 A389 10f yel bis & multi .15 .15
1348 A389 15f brt rose & multi .15 .15
1349 A389 25f pale pink & multi .20 .20
a. Booklet pane of 4
Complete booklet, #1349a
1350 A389 50f violet & multi .40 .40
a. Booklet pane of 4
Complete booklet, #1350a
1351 A389 100f brt yel & multi .80 .80
1352 A389 150f blue & multi 1.15 1.15
a. Booklet pane of 4
Complete booklet, #1352a
1353 A389 200f pink & multi 1.55 1.55
1354 A389 250f dp blue & multi 1.90 1.90
1355 A389 350f blue & multi 2.70 2.70
Nos. 1346-1355 (10) 9.15 9.15
Set of 3 booklets, #1349a-1350a, 1352a 31.00

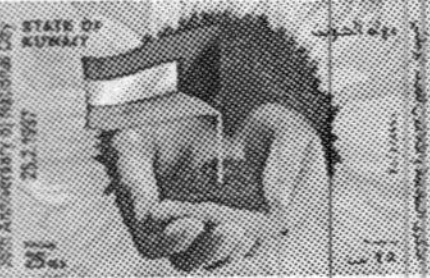

National Day, 36th Anniv. A390

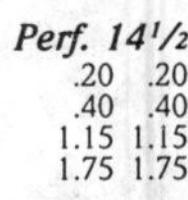

1997, Feb. 25 **Litho.** *Perf. 14½*
1356 A390 25f blue & multi .20 .20
1357 A390 50f lilac & multi .40 .40
1358 A390 150f orange & multi 1.15 1.15
Nos. 1356-1358 (3) 1.75 1.75

Liberation Day, 6th Anniv. A391

1997, Feb. 26 *Perf. 13x13½*
1359 A391 25f tan & multi .20 .20
1360 A391 50f lilac & multi .40 .40
1361 A391 150f blue & multi 1.15 1.15
Nos. 1359-1361 (3) 1.75 1.75

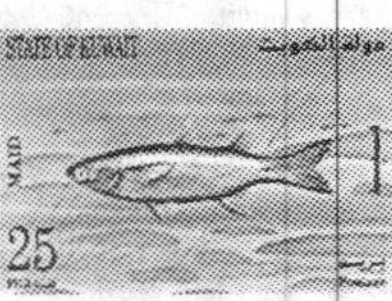

Marine Life — A392

No. 1368: Various views of a school of shrimp: a, b, c, d, 25f. e, f, g, h, 50f. i, j, k, l, 100f. m, n, o, p, 150f.

1997 *Perf. 14½*
1362 A392 25f Maid .20 .20
1363 A392 50f Sheim .40 .40
1364 A392 100f Hamoor .80 .80
1365 A392 150f Sobaity 1.20 1.20
1366 A392 200f Nagroor 1.60 1.60
1367 A392 350f Zobaidy 2.80 2.80
Nos. 1362-1367 (6) 7.00 7.00

Sheet of 16

1368 A392 Sheet of 16, #a.-p. 10.50 10.50

Montreal Protocol on Substances that Deplete Ozone Layer, 10th Anniv. — A393

1997 **Litho.** *Perf. 13½x13*
1369 A393 25f blue & multi .20 .20
1370 A393 50f violet & multi .35 .35
1371 A393 150f blue green & multi 1.10 1.10
Nos. 1369-1371 (3) 1.65 1.65

Industries Exhibition — A394

1997
1372 A394 25f brt pink & multi .20 .20
1373 A394 50f green & multi .40 .40
1374 A394 150f blue & multi 1.10 1.10
Nos. 1372-1374 (3) 1.70 1.70

22nd Kuwait Arabic Book Exhibition — A395

1997 Litho. *Perf. 13½x13*

Border Color

1375 A395 25f pink .20 .20
1376 A395 50f blue .35 .35
1377 A395 150f blue green 1.10 1.10
Nos. 1375-1377 (3) 1.65 1.65

Cultural History A396

a, 50f, Qibliya Girls School, 1937. b, 50f, Scissors cutting ribbon, Fine Arts Exhibition, 1959. c, 150f, Folk Theatre Group, 1956. d, 25f, 1st Book Fair, 1975. e, 25f, Kuwait Magazine, 1928. f, 50f, Mubarakiya School, 1912. g, 50f, Kuwait Natl. Museum, 1958. h, 150f, Academy of Music, 1972. i, 25f, A'lam Al-Fikr (periodical), 1970. j, 25f, Al'Bitha Magazine, 1946. k, 50f, Building complex, 1953 (Al-Arabi Magazine). l, 50f, Building, 1959. m, 150f, Al-Sharqiya Cinema, 1955. n, 25f, Al'Lam Al Ma'rifa (periodical), 1978. o, 25f, Dalil Almohtar Fi Alaam al-Bihar (boat), 1923. p, 50f, Alma'had Aldini (arabesques), 1947. q, 50f, Folklore Center, 1956. r, 150f, Theatrical Academy, 1967. s, 25f, Al-Arabi Magazine, 1958. t, 25f, Public Library (book), 1923. u, 50f, Al Ma'Arif Printing Press (Arabic writing), 1947. v, 50f, Literary Club, 1924. w, 150f, Bas Ya Bahar (1st Kuwaitii feature film), 1970. x, 25f, Al Thaqafa Al-Alamiya (periodical), 1981. y, 25f, The World Theatre (periodical), 1969.

1997

1378 A396 Sheet of 25, #a.-y. 11.00 11.00

Nos. 1378a-1378y each contain year date of event depicted.

Educational Science Museum, 25th Anniv. A397

Designs: 25f, Whale, quadrant, vert. 50f, Space exploration, whale, dinosaur. No. 1381, Astronaut, dinosaur, satellite dish, airplane, globe, skeleton encircling whale, vert.
No. 1382, Coelacanth.

1997 Litho. *Perf. 13½x13, 13x13½*

1379 A397 25f multicolored .20 .20
1380 A397 50f multicolored .40 .40
1381 A397 150f multicolored 1.10 1.10
Nos. 1379-1381 (3) 1.70 1.70

Souvenir Sheet

1382 A397 150f multicolored 7.25 7.25

No. 1382 is a continuous design and sold for 1d.

18th Summit of Gulf Cooperation Countries — A398

Designs: 25f, Flags of member countries, doves, vert. 50f, Map, birds with flag colors. 150f, Doves perched atop flags, vert.

1997 *Perf. 13½x14*

1383 A398 25f multicolored .20 .20
1384 A398 50f multicolored .40 .40
1385 A398 150f multicolored 1.10 1.10
Nos. 1383-1385 (3) 1.70 1.70

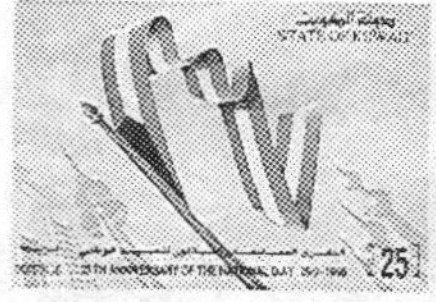

National Day, 37th Anniv. A399

1998, Feb. 25 Litho. *Perf. 13x13½*

1386 A399 25f yellow & multi .20 .20
1387 A399 50f pink & multi .35 .35
1388 A399 150f blue & multi 1.10 1.10
Nos. 1386-1388 (3) 1.65 1.65

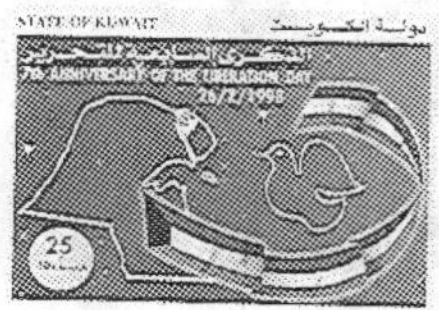

Liberation Day, 7th Anniv. A400

1998, Feb. 26

1389 A400 25f yellow & multi .20 .20
1390 A400 50f orange & multi .35 .35
1391 A400 150f green & multi 1.10 1.10
Nos. 1389-1391 (3) 1.65 1.65

AIR POST STAMPS

Air Post Stamps of India, 1929-30, Overprinted type "c"

1933-34 Wmk. 196 *Perf. 14*

C1 AP1 2a dull green 8.00 *11.00*
C2 AP1 3a deep blue 1.75 *2.25*
C3 AP1 4a gray olive 110.00 *150.00*
C4 AP1 6a bister ('34) 4.50 4.00
Nos. C1-C4 (4) 124.25 *167.25*

Counterfeits of Nos. C1-C4 exist.

> Catalogue values for unused stamps in this section, from this point to the end of the section, are for Never Hinged items.

Dakota and Comet Planes — AP1

Perf. 11x11½

1964, Nov. 29 Litho. Unwmk.

C5 AP1 20f multicolored .20 .30
C6 AP1 25f multicolored .75 .40
C7 AP1 30f multicolored 1.00 .40
C8 AP1 45f multicolored 1.25 .60
Nos. C5-C8 (4) 3.20 1.70

10th anniversary of Kuwait Airways.

POSTAGE DUE STAMPS

> Catalogue values for unused stamps in this section are for Never Hinged items.

D1

Perf. 14x15

1963, Oct. 19 Unwmk. Litho.

Inscriptions in Black

J1 D1 1f ocher .40 .15
J2 D1 2f lilac .45 .15
J3 D1 5f blue .60 .25
J4 D1 8f pale green .65 .30
J5 D1 10f yellow .70 .40
J6 D1 25f brick red 1.40 .65
Nos. J1-J6 (6) 4.20 1.90

D2

1965, Apr. 1 *Perf. 13*

J7 D2 4f rose & yellow .25 .20
J8 D2 15f dp rose & blue .50 .45
J9 D2 40f blue & brt yel grn 1.40 1.00
J10 D2 50f green & pink 1.90 1.25
J11 D2 100f dk blue & yel 3.50 2.50
Nos. J7-J11 (5) 7.55 5.40

OFFICIAL STAMPS

Stamps of India, 1911-23, Overprinted

KUWAIT   KUWAIT

SERVICE   SERVICE
Nos. O1-O9   Nos. O10-O14

1923-24 Wmk. 39 *Perf. 14*

O1 A47 ½a green .40 *5.00*
O2 A48 1a brown .50 *4.00*
O3 A58 1½a chocolate 1.25 *10.00*
O4 A49 2a violet 2.75 *12.50*
O5 A57 2a6p ultra 2.00 *17.50*
O6 A51 3a brown org 3.50 *27.50*
O7 A51 3a ultra ('24) 3.75 *22.50*
O8 A52 4a olive grn 2.00 *27.50*
O9 A54 8a red violet 4.25 *30.00*
O10 A56 1r grn & brn 10.00 *55.00*
O11 A56 2r brn & car rose 15.00 *90.00*
O12 A56 5r vio & ultra 62.50 *200.00*
O13 A56 10r car & grn 95.00 *225.00*
O14 A56 15r ol grn & ultra 160.00 *375.00*
Nos. O1-O14 (14) 362.90

Stamps of India, 1926-30, Overprinted

KUWAIT   KUWAIT

SERVICE   SERVICE
Nos. O15-O20   Nos. O21-O25

1929-33 Wmk. 196

O15 A48 1a dk brown 2.00 *7.50*
O16 A60 2a violet 50.00 *60.00*
O17 A51 3a blue 2.00 *8.00*
O18 A61 4a ol green 4.00 *5.00*
O19 A54 8a red violet 3.00 *7.00*
O20 A55 12a claret 18.00 *25.00*
O21 A56 1r green & brn 4.75 *15.00*
O22 A56 2r buff & car rose 7.00 *30.00*
O23 A56 5r dk vio & ultra 25.00 *100.00*
O24 A56 10r car & green 50.00 *140.00*
O25 A56 15r olive grn & ultra 125.00 *325.00*
Nos. O15-O25 (11) 290.75

KYRGYZSTAN

ˌkir–gi–ˈstan

(Kirghizia)

LOCATION — Bounded by Kazakhstan, Uzbekistan, Tadjikistan and China.
GOVT. — Independent republic, member of the Commonwealth of Independent States.
AREA — 76,642 sq. mi.
POP. — 4,300,000 (1989)
CAPITAL — Pishpek

With the breakup of the Soviet Union on Dec. 26, 1991, Kyrgyzstan and ten former Soviet republics established the Commonwealth of Independent States.

100 Kopecks = 1 Ruble
100 Tyiyn = 1 Som

> Catalogue values for all unused stamps in this country are for Never Hinged items.

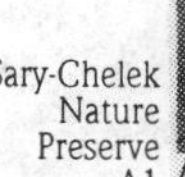

Sary-Chelek Nature Preserve A1

Unwmk.

1992, Feb. 4 Litho. *Perf. 12*

1 A1 15k multicolored .60

Hawk — A2

1992, Aug. 31 Litho. *Perf. 12½x12*

2 A2 50o multicolored .30

Man with Cattle, by G.A. Aytiev — A3

1992, Aug. 31

3 A3 1r multicolored .30

Handicrafts A4

1992, Dec. 1 Litho. *Perf. 12x11½*

4 A4 1.50r multicolored .20

Sites and Landmarks A5

Designs: 10k, Petroglyphs. 50k, 11th Cent. tower, vert. 1r + 25k, Mausoleum, vert. 2r + 50k, 12th Cent. mausoleum. 3r, Yurt. 5r + 50k, Equestrian statue, Pishpek. 9r, Commercial complex, Pishpek. 10r, Native jewelry.

1993, Mar. 21 Litho. *Perf. 12*

5 A5 10k multicolored .15
6 A5 50k multicolored .15
7 A5 1r +25k multi .15
8 A5 2r +50k multi .15
9 A5 3r multicolored .20
10 A5 5r +50k multi .35
11 A5 9r multi .75
Nos. 5-11 (7) 1.90

Souvenir Sheet

12 A5 10r multicolored 1.25

Independence and Admission to UN, 2nd Anniv. — A6

#15a, 120t, like #13. #15b, 130t, like #14.

Perf. 13x12½, 12½x13

1993, Aug. 31 Litho.

13 A6 50t Map .50
14 A6 60t UN emblem, flag, building, vert. .60

Souvenir Sheet

Imperf

15 A6 Sheet of 2, #a.-b. 5.00

Nos. 15a-15b have simulated perforations.

New Year 1994 (Year of the Dog) — A7

1994, Feb. 10 Litho. *Perf. 12x12½*

26 A7 60t multicolored .50

Musical Instrument — A8

1993, Dec. 30 Litho. *Perf. 13x12½*

27 A8 30t Komuz .45

Panthera Uncia — A9

1994, Mar. 21 Litho. *Perf. 12½x12*

29 A9 10t shown .20
30 A9 20t Lying down .45
31 A9 30t Seated .65
32 A9 40t Up close .90
Nos. 29-32 (4) 2.20

World Wildlife Fund.

Flowers — A10

Minerals — A11

Perf. 12x12½, 12½x12

1994, Aug. 31 Litho.

Color of Flower

33 A10 1t violet & white .15
34 A10 3t white & yellow, horiz. .15
a. Miniature sheet of 6 .30
35 A10 10t red & yellow .15
36 A10 16t white & yellow .25
37 A10 20t pink & yellow .30
38 A10 30t white & yellow .50
39 A10 40t yellow & brown .60
a. Miniature sheet of 6, #33, #35-39 1.75
b. Strip of 7, #33-39 2.00

Souvenir Sheet

40 A10 50t yellow & orange .75

1994, Dec. 1 Litho. *Perf. 13½x13*

41 A11 80t Florite-Cinnabar .15
42 A11 90t Calcite .15
43 A11 100t Getchellite .75
44 A11 110t Barite 1.00
45 A11 120t Orpiment 1.00
46 A11 140t Stibnite 1.25
Nos. 41-46 (6) 4.30

Souvenir Sheet

47 A11 200t Cinnabar 2.00
a. Miniature sheet of 6 6.00

No. 47a contains #42-46 and single from #47.

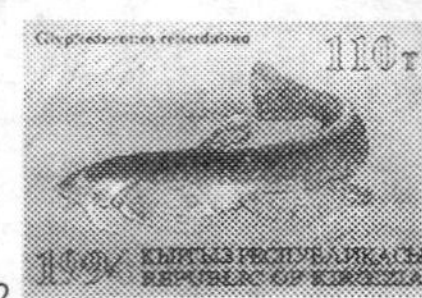

Fish — A12

Designs: 110t, Glyptosternum reticulatum. 120t, Leuciscus schmidti. 130t, Piptychus dybowskii. 140t, Nemachilus strauchi. 200t, Cyprinus carpio.

1994, Dec. 1 *Perf. 13x13½*

48 A12 110t multicolored .75
49 A12 120t multicolored .75
50 A12 130t multicolored .90
51 A12 140t multicolored 1.00
a. Miniature sheet, #48-51 5.00
Nos. 48-51 (4) 3.40

Souvenir Sheet

52 A12 200t multicolored 1.50

Wild Animals — A13

Perf. 12x12½, 12½x12

1995, Apr. 21 Litho.

#60a, 130t, Raptor, diff. b, 170t, Bighorn sheep.

53 A13 110t Bear .40
54 A13 120t Snow leopard, horiz. .45
55 A13 130t Raptor .50
56 A13 140t Woodchuck, horiz. .50
57 A13 150t Raptor, horiz. .55
58 A13 160t Vulture .60
59 A13 190t Fox, horiz. .70
Nos. 53-59 (7) 3.70

Souvenir Sheet

60 A13 Sheet of 2, #a.-b. 1.10

Nos. 53-60 exist imperf.

Natl. Costumes — A14

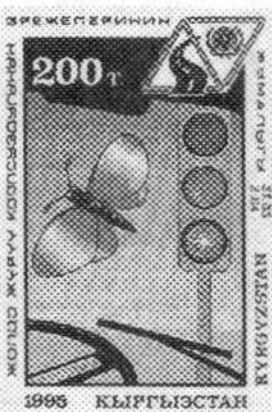

Traffic Safety — A15

1995, Mar. 24 *Perf. 12x12½*

61 A14 50t shown .20
62 A14 50t Man with mandolin .20
63 A14 100t Man with falcon .45
64 A14 100t Woman seated .45
Nos. 61-64 (4) 1.30

Nos. 61-64 exist imperf. Value, set *$4.*

1995, Mar. 24 *Perf. 12*

65 A15 200t multicolored .90

Souvenir Sheet

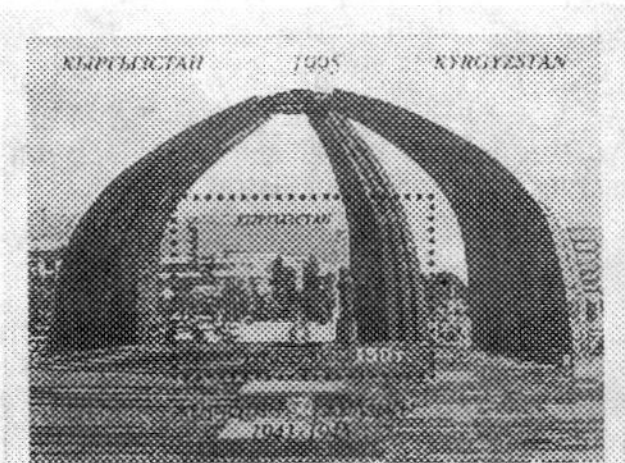

End of World War II, 50th Anniv. — A16

Illustration reduced.

1995, May 4 Litho. *Perf. 12x12½*

66 A16 150t multicolored 2.00

UPU Intl. Letter Week — A17

Natl. Arms — A18

1995, Oct. 3 Litho. *Perf. 12x12½*

67 A17 200t multicolored .55

1995, Oct. 13 *Perf. 12*

68 A18 20t purple .15
69 A18 50t blue .15
70 A18 100t brown .30
71 A18 500t green 1.65
Nos. 68-71 (4) 2.25

Horses A19

Various adult, juvenile horses.

Perf. 12½x12, 12x12½

1995, Oct. 16

Background Color

72 A19 10t olive brown .15
73 A19 50t light brown, vert. .15
74 A19 100t tan, vert. .25
75 A19 140t yellow brown, vert. .40
76 A19 150t lilac .45
77 A19 200t gray .50
78 A19 300t yellow green .70
Nos. 72-78 (7) 2.60

Souvenir Sheet

79 A19 600t Herd of horses, vert. 1.75

Raptors — A20

1995, Sept. 12 *Perf. 12x12½*

80 A20 10t Pandion haliaetus .15
81 A20 50t Aguila rapax .15
82 A20 100t Gups himalayensis .30
83 A20 140t Falco cherrug .40
84 A20 150t Circaetus gallicus .50
85 A20 200t Gupaetus barbatus .60
86 A20 300t Aguila chrysaetos .90
Nos. 80-86 (7) 3.00

Souvenir Sheet

87 A20 600t Halliaeetus albicilla 1.75

Souvenir Sheet

UN, 50th Anniv. A21

Designs: a, UN headquarters, NYC. b, Mountains, rainbow.

1995, Oct. 24 Litho. *Perf. 12½x12*

88 A21 100t Sheet of 2, #a.-b. .75

Natural Wonders of the World — A22

Designs: 10t, Nile River. 50t, Kilimanjaro. 100t, Sahara Desert. 140t, Amazon River, vert. 150t, Grand Canyon, vert. 200t, Victoria Falls, vert. 350t, Mount Everest. 400t, Niagara Falls.

Issyk-Kul Lake, Kyrgyzstan: No. 97, Raptor, row boat, sail boats. No. 98, Water bird, motor boat, row boat.

1995, Dec. 29 *Perf. 11½*

89 A22 10t multicolored .15
90 A22 50t multicolored .15
91 A22 100t multicolored .30
92 A22 140t multicolored .40
93 A22 150t multicolored .45
94 A22 200t multicolored .60
95 A22 350t multicolored .75
96 A22 400t multicolored 1.00
Nos. 89-96 (8) 3.80

Souvenir Sheets

97 A22 600t multicolored 1.75
98 A22 600t multicolored 1.75

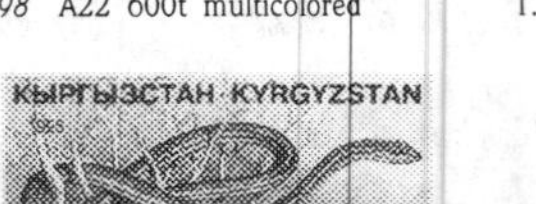

Reptiles A23

Designs: 20t, Psammophis lineolatum. No. 100, Natrix tessellata. No. 101, Eublepharis macularius. 100t, Agkistrodon halys. 150t, Eremias arguta. 200t, Elaphe dione. 250t, Asymblepharus. 500t, Lacerta agilis.

1996, Feb. 2 *Perf. 12½x12*

99 A23 20t multicolored .15
100 A23 50t multicolored .15
101 A23 50t multicolored .15
102 A23 100t multicolored .30
103 A23 150t multicolored .40
104 A23 200t multicolored .55
105 A23 250t multicolored .65
Nos. 99-105 (7) 2.35

Souvenir Sheet

106 A23 500t multicolored 1.50

Souvenir Sheet

Save the Aral Sea — A24

Designs: a, Felis caracal. b, Salmo trutta aralensis. c, Hyaena hyaena. d, Pseudoscaphirhynchus kaufmanni. e, Aspiolucius esocinus.

1996, Apr. 29 Litho. *Perf. 14*

107 A24 100t Sheet of 5, #a.-e. 3.00

See Kazakhstan No. 145. Tadjikistan No. 91, Turkmenistan No. 52, Uzbekistan No. 113.

Fauna — A27

a, Aquila chrysaetos. b, Capra falconeri. c, Ovis ammon. d, Gyps himalayensis. e, Equus hemionus. f, Canis lupus. g, Ursus arctor. h, Saiga tatarica.

1997, Aug. Litho. *Perf. 12x12½*

114 A27 600t Sheet of 8, #a.-h. 8.75

Kyrgyzstan stamps can be mounted in the annual Scott Commonwealth of Independent States supplement.

SEMI-POSTAL STAMPS

Natl. Epic Poem, Manas, Millennium — SP1

SP2

Designs: 10t+5t, Woman with bird in hand. 20t+10t, Bird on man's wrist. No. B3, Women watching as baby held up. No. B4, Woman with spear, leading horse. 40t+15t, Warrior looking at dead dragon. No. B6, Warrior on horse holding axe. No. B7, Man wearing tall hat on horseback. No. B8, Warrior with sword on horseback.

No. B9, Man in red cradling fallen warrior. No. B10, Man in black seated in desert, tornado.

1995, June 16 Litho. *Perf. 12*

B1 SP1 10t +5t blue & bister .15
B2 SP1 20t +10t blue & bister .25
B3 SP1 30t +10t blue & bister .35
B4 SP1 30t +10t blue & bister .35
B5 SP1 40t +15t blue & bister .50
B6 SP1 50t +15t blue & bister .65
B7 SP1 50t +15t blue & bister .65
B8 SP1 50t +15t blue & bister .65
a. Sheet of 8, #B1-B8 + label 3.25

Souvenir Sheets

B9 SP2 2s +50t multi 2.00
B10 SP2 2s +50t multi 2.00

1996 Summer Olympic Games, Atlanta SP3

Designs: 100t+20t, Equestrian events. 140t+30t, Boxing. 150t+30t, Archery. 300t+50t, Judo, hot air balloon, sailing, water skiing.

1996, July 10 Litho. *Perf. 12½x12*

B11 SP3 100t +20t multi .20
B12 SP3 140t +30t multi .30
B13 SP3 150t +30t multi .35
B14 SP3 300t +50t multi .65
Nos. B11-B14 (4) 1.50

LABUAN

lə–'bü–ən

LOCATION — An island in the East Indies, about six miles off the northwest coast of Borneo
GOVT. — A British possession, administered as a part of the North Borneo Colony
AREA — 35 sq. mi.
POP. — 8,963 (estimated)
CAPITAL — Victoria

The stamps of Labuan were replaced by those of Straits Settlements in 1906.

100 Cents = 1 Dollar

Watermark

Wmk. 46- C A over Crown

Queen Victoria — A1

On Nos. 1, 2, 3, 4 and 11 the watermark is 32mm high. It is always placed sideways and extends over two stamps.

1879, May Engr. Wmk. 46 *Perf. 14*

1 A1 2c green 600.00 575.00
2 A1 6c orange 140.00 125.00
3 A1 12c carmine 1,000. 400.00
4 A1 16c blue 45.00 *80.00*
Nos. 1-4 (4) 1,785. 1,180.

See Nos. 5-10, 16-24, 33-39, 42-48. For surcharges see Nos. 12-15, 25, 31, 40-41.

1880-82 Wmk. 1

5 A1 2c green 13.50 16.50
6 A1 6c orange 70.00 80.00
7 A1 8c carmine ('82) 60.00 75.00
8 A1 10c yel brown 65.00 75.00
9 A1 12c carmine 165.00 200.00
10 A1 16c blue ('81) 65.00 75.00
Nos. 5-10 (6) 438.50 521.50

A2

A3

A3a

A4

1880 Wmk. 46

11 A2 6c on 16c blue (with additional "6" across original value) (R) 1,250. 625.00

1880-83 Wmk. 1

12 A2 8c on 12c car ('80) 675.00 475.00
a. Original value not obliterated 1,000. 700.00
b. Additional surcharge "8" across original value 800.00 600.00
c. "8" inverted 750.00 500.00
13 A3 8c on 12c car ('81) 200.00 200.00
14 A3a 8c on 12c car ('81) 70.00 80.00
a. "Eighr" *7,500.*
b. Inverted surcharge 5,500.
c. Double surcharge 850.00 825.00
15 A4 $1 on 16c blue (R) ('83) *2,250.*

On No. 12 the original value is obliterated by a pen mark in either black or red.

1883-86 Wmk. 2

16 A1 2c green 10.00 15.00
a. Horiz. pair, imperf. btwn. 5,000.
17 A1 2c rose red ('85) 1.65 5.00
18 A1 8c carmine 135.00 75.00
19 A1 8c dk violet ('85) 13.50 7.00
20 A1 10c yellow brn 19.00 30.00
21 A1 10c black brn ('86) 6.75 20.00
22 A1 16c blue 67.50 *110.00*
23 A1 16c gray blue ('86) 67.50 110.00
24 A1 40c ocher 10.00 *47.50*
Nos. 16-24 (9) 330.90 419.50

Nos. 1-10, 16-24 are in sheets of 10. For surcharges see Nos. 26-30, 32.

A5

A6

A7

A8

1885 Wmk. 1

25 A5 2c on 16c blue 675.00 700.00

Wmk. 2

26 A5 2c on 8c car 125.00 225.00
a. Double surcharge
27 A6 2c on 16c blue 85.00 *135.00*
a. Double surcharge *2,000.*
28 A7 2c on 8c car 45.00 *75.00*

1891

Black or Red Surcharge

29 A8 6c on 8c violet 4.50 4.25
a. 6c on 8c dark violet 50.00 42.50
b. Double surcharge 225.00 —
c. As "a," "Cents" omitted 275.00 275.00
d. Inverted surcharge 45.00 50.00
e. Dbl. surch., one inverted 375.00 —
f. Dbl. surch., both inverted 375.00 —
g. "6" omitted 375.00
30 A8 6c on 8c dk vio (R) 475.00 225.00
a. Inverted surcharge 600.00 325.00

Wmk. 46

31 A8 6c on 16c blue 1,400. 1,400.
a. Inverted surcharge 3,750. 2,750.

Wmk. 2

32 A8 6c on 40c ocher 4,500. 2,750.
a. Inverted surcharge 3,000. 2,750.

From Jan. 1, 1890, to Jan. 1, 1906, Labuan was administered by the British North Borneo Co. During that period Nos. 33-39, 42-83, 53a, 63a, 64a, 65a, 66a, 68a, 85-86, 96-118, 103a, 107a, J1-J9, J3a and J6a were canceled to order by bars forming an oval. Values for these stamps used are for those with this form of cancellation. These stamps with dated town cancellation sell for 4 to 20 times as much as those with with bar cancellation. Nos. 63b, 64b, 65b, J6a, and possibly others, only exist c.t.o.

1892 Engr. Unwmk.

33 A1 2c rose 1.50 .30
34 A1 6c yellow green 4.00 .30
35 A1 8c violet 2.00 .30
36 A1 10c brown 4.00 .30
37 A1 12c deep ultra 3.00 .30
38 A1 16c gray 3.00 .30
39 A1 40c ocher 15.00 .30
Nos. 33-39 (7) 32.50 2.10

The 2c, 8c and 10c are in sheets of 30; others in sheets of 10.

Nos. 39 and 38 Surcharged **Two CENTS**

1893

40 A1 2c on 40c ocher 125.00 75.00
a. Inverted surcharge 200.00 *300.00*
41 A1 6c on 16c gray 200.00 125.00
a. Inverted surcharge 225.00 175.00
b. Surcharge sideways — —
c. "Six" omitted
d. "Cents" omitted

Surcharges on Nos. 40-41 each exist in 10 types. Counterfeits exist.

1894, Apr. Litho.

42 A1 2c bright rose 1.00 .15
43 A1 6c yellow green 5.00 .30
a. Horiz. pair, imperf. btwn. *2,750.*
44 A1 8c bright violet 4.75 .30
45 A1 10c brown 15.00 .30
46 A1 12c light ultra 14.00 .30
47 A1 16c gray 17.50 .30
48 A1 40c orange 27.50 .50
Nos. 42-48 (7) 84.75 2.15

Counterfeits exist.

Dyak Chieftain — A9

Malayan Sambar — A10

Sago Palm — A11

Argus Pheasant — A12

Arms of North Borneo — A13

Dhow — A14

Saltwater Crocodile — A15

Mt. Kinabalu — A16

Arms of North Borneo — A17

1894 Engr.

49 A9 1c lilac & black 1.25 .30
a. Vert. pair, imperf. between 400.00 250.00
50 A10 2c blue & black 2.75 .30
a. Imperf., pair 375.00
51 A11 3c bister & black 3.50 .30
52 A12 5c green & black 16.00 .30
53 A13 6c brown red & blk 2.50 .30
a. Imperf., pair 400.00 250.00
54 A14 8c red & black 8.00 .30
55 A15 12c orange & black 17.50 .30
56 A16 18c ol bister & blk 20.00 .30
57 A17 24c lilac & blue 13.00 .30
Nos. 49-57 (9) 84.50 2.70

For overprints see Nos. 66-71.

A18

A19

A20

A21

1895, June Litho.

58 A18 4c on $1 red 1.00 .35
59 A18 10c on $1 red 1.50 .35
60 A18 20c on $1 red 12.50 .35
61 A18 30c on $1 red 15.00 .35
62 A18 40c on $1 red 12.50 .35
Nos. 58-62 (5) 42.50 1.75

1896

63 A19 25c blue green 15.00 .80
a. Without overprint 11.00 2.00
b. As "a," imperf., pair 30.00
64 A20 50c claret 17.50 .80
a. Without overprint 10.00 2.00
b. As "a," imperf., pair 30.00
65 A21 $1 dark blue 35.00 .80
a. Without overprint 15.00 2.00
b. As "a," imperf., pair 30.00
Nos. 63-65 (3) 67.50 2.40

For surcharges and overprint see #93-95, 116-118, 120.

Nos. 49-54 Overprinted

1846
JUBILEE
1896

1896

No.		Description	Unused	Used
66	A9	1c lilac & black	14.00	.70
a.		Orange overprint	160.00	20.00
b.		Double overprint	190.00	190.00
c.		"JEBILEE"		250.00
67	A10	2c blue & black	20.00	.70
a.		Vert. pair, imperf. btwn.	350.00	
b.		"JEBILEE"	500.00	
68	A11	3c bister & black	22.50	.70
a.		Double overprint	200.00	125.00
b.		Triple overprint	800.00	
c.		"JEBILEE"		600.00
69	A12	5c green & black	35.00	.70
a.		Double overprint	225.00	225.00
70	A13	6c brown red & blk	17.50	.70
a.		Double overprint	275.00	275.00
71	A14	8c rose & black	25.00	.70
		Nos. 66-71 (6)	134.00	4.20

Cession of Labuan to Great Britain, 50th anniv.

Dyak Chieftain — A22

Malayan Sambar — A23

Sago Palm — A24

Argus Pheasant — A25

A26

Dhow — A27

Saltwater Crocodile — A28

Mt. Kinabalu "Postal Revenue" — A29

Coat of Arms — A30

1897-1900 **Engr.**

No.		Description	Unused	Used
72	A22	1c lilac & black	2.00	.20
72A	A22	1c red brn & black	5.00	.20
73	A23	2c blue & black	7.00	.20
74	A23	2c green & blk ('00)	3.50	.20
75	A24	3c bister & black	8.50	.20
76	A25	5c green & black	20.00	.30
77	A25	5c lt bl & blk ('00)	17.50	.40
78	A26	6c brown red & blk	5.00	.30
79	A27	8c red & black	18.00	.35
80	A28	12c red & black	25.00	.50
81	A29	18c ol bister & black	18.00	.50
82	A30	24c gray lilac & blue	11.00	.50
		Nos. 72-82 (12)	140.50	3.85

The 2c, 3c 6c and 18c exist in pairs, imperf. between.

For surcharges see Nos. 87-89, 110-112.

"Postage & Revenue" — A31

"Postage & Revenue" — A32

1897

No.		Description	Unused	Used
83	A31	18c bister & black	67.50	5.00
84	A32	24c brn lilac & blue	17.50	*40.00*

For surcharges see Nos. 92, 115.

"Postage & Revenue" — A33

"Postage & Revenue" — A34

1898

No.		Description	Unused	Used
85	A33	12c red & black	32.50	1.50
86	A34	18c bister & black	22.50	2.00

For surcharges see Nos. 90-91, 113-114.

Regular Issue Surcharged in Black

4
CENTS

1899

No.		Description	Unused	Used
87	A25	4c on 5c grn & blk	20.00	25.00
88	A26	4c on 6c brn red & blk	14.00	15.00
89	A27	4c on 8c red & blk	30.00	32.50
90	A33	4c on 12c red & blk	27.50	30.00
91	A34	4c on 18c bis & blk	16.00	16.00
a.		Double surcharge	250.00	*300.00*
92	A32	4c on 24c lil & bl	15.00	22.50
93	A19	4c on 25c blue grn	5.50	7.50
94	A20	4c on 50c claret	5.50	7.50
95	A21	4c on $1 dk blue	5.50	7.50
		Nos. 87-95 (9)	139.00	163.50

Orangutan A35

Sun Bear A36

Railroad Train — A37

Crown — A38

1899-1901

No.		Description	Unused	Used
96	A35	4c yel brown & blk	4.00	.20
a.		Vert. pair, imperf. btwn.	350.00	
97	A35	4c car & blk ('00)	7.50	.25
98	A36	10c gray vio & dk brn ('01)	32.50	.35
99	A37	16c org brn & grn (G) ('01)	50.00	.75
		Nos. 96-99 (4)	94.00	1.55

Perf. 12½ to 16 and Compound

1902-03 **Engr.**

No.		Description	Unused	Used
99A	A38	1c vio & black	2.75	.25
100	A38	2c green & blk	2.75	.25
100A	A38	3c sepia & blk	2.75	.25
101	A38	4c car & black	2.75	.25
102	A38	8c org & black	3.25	.25
103	A38	10c sl blue & brn	2.75	.25
a.		Vert. pair, imperf. between		400.00
104	A38	12c yel & black	3.25	.25
105	A38	16c org brn & grn	3.25	.25
106	A38	18c bis brn & blk	3.25	.25
107	A38	25c grnsh bl & grn	4.50	.25
a.		25c greenish blue & black		200.00
108	A38	50c gray lil & vio	9.50	.35
109	A38	$1 org & red brn	6.75	.40
		Nos. 99A-109 (12)	47.50	3.25

Part perforate examples exist of 12c (vert. strip of 3 imperf. between) and 16c (vert. pair, imperf. between).

Regular Issue of 1896-97 Surcharged in Black

4
cents

1904

No.		Description	Unused	Used
110	A25	4c on 5c green & blk	17.00	.90
111	A26	4c on 6c brown red & black	11.00	.90
112	A27	4c on 8c red & blk	15.00	.90
113	A33	4c on 12c red & blk	18.00	.90
114	A34	4c on 18c bis & blk	15.00	.90
115	A32	4c on 24c brn lil & bl	13.00	.90
116	A19	4c on 25c blue green	8.00	.90
117	A20	4c on 50c claret	8.00	.90
a.		Double surcharge	200.00	
118	A21	4c on $1 dark blue	8.00	.90
		Nos. 110-118 (9)	113.00	8.10

Stamps of North Borneo, 1893, and Labuan No. 65a Overprinted in Black:

LABUAN
a

LABUAN
b

c
LABUAN

1905

No.		Description	Unused	Used
119	A30(a)	25c slate blue	900.	425.
120	A21(c)	$1 blue		425.
121	A33(b)	$2 gray green	2,400.	950.
122	A34(c)	$5 red violet	3,750.	850.
123	A35(c)	$10 brown	—	*3,750.*

POSTAGE DUE STAMPS

Regular Issues Overprinted

POSTAGE DUE

1901 **Unwmk.** ***Perf. 14***

No.		Description	Unused	Used
J1	A23	2c green & black	9.00	.25
a.		Double overprint	140.00	
J2	A24	3c bister & black	14.00	.25
J3	A35	4c car & black	16.00	.25
a.		Double overprint		200.00
J4	A25	5c lt blue & black	20.00	.25
J5	A26	6c brown red & blk	22.50	.35
J6	A27	8c red & black	25.00	.25
a.		Center inverted, ovpt. reading down		*6,000.*
J7	A33	12c red & black	47.50	1.25
J8	A34	18c ol bister & blk	19.00	.35
J9	A32	24c brown lil & bl	35.00	.50
		Nos. J1-J9 (9)	208.00	3.70

See note after No. 32.

The stamps of Labuan were superseded by those of Straits Settlements in 1907.

LAGOS

'lā-ˌgäs

LOCATION — West Africa, bordering on the former Southern Nigeria Colony
GOVT. — British Crown Colony and Protectorate
AREA — 3,460 sq. mi. (approx.)
POP. — 1,500,000 (1901)
CAPITAL — Lagos

This territory was purchased by the British in 1861 and placed under the Governor of Sierra Leone. In 1874 it was detached and formed part of the Gold Coast Colony until 1886 when the Protectorate of Lagos was established. It was chartered to the Royal Niger Company until 1899 when all territories of this Company were surrendered to the Crown of Great Britain and formed into the Northern and Southern Nigeria Protectorates. In 1906 Lagos and Southern Nigeria were united to form the Colony and Protectorate of Southern Nigeria.

12 Pence = 1 Shilling

Queen Victoria — A1

1874-75 **Typo.** **Wmk. 1** ***Perf. 12½***

No.		Description	Unused	Used
1	A1	1p lilac	45.00	27.50
2	A1	2p blue	45.00	25.00
3	A1	3p red brown ('75)	85.00	37.50
a.		Value in chestnut	77.50	45.00
4	A1	4p rose	60.00	37.50
5	A1	6p blue green	65.00	10.00
a.		Value in yellow green	70.00	10.00
6	A1	1sh orange ('75)	225.00	55.00
a.		Value 15½mm instead of 16½mm long	325.00	140.00
		Nos. 1-6 (6)	525.00	192.50

1876 ***Perf. 14***

No.		Description	Unused	Used
7	A1	1p lilac	30.00	15.00
8	A1	2p blue	30.00	11.00
9	A1	3p red brown	85.00	17.50
10	A1	4p rose	150.00	10.00
11	A1	6p green	75.00	6.00
12	A1	1sh orange	475.00	65.00
		Nos. 7-12 (6)	845.00	124.50

The 4p exists with watermark sideways.

1882-1902 **Wmk. 2**

No.		Description	Unused	Used
13	A1	½p green ('86)	1.65	.40
14	A1	1p lilac	16.00	9.00
15	A1	1p car rose	1.65	.40
16	A1	2p blue	110.00	7.50
17	A1	2p gray	45.00	4.50
18	A1	2p lil & bl ('87)	1.90	1.25
19	A1	2½p ultra ('91)	1.90	1.65
a.		2½p blue	85.00	50.00
20	A1	3p orange brn	12.00	5.00
21	A1	3p lilac & brn orange ('91)	2.25	3.00
22	A1	4p rose	100.00	11.00
23	A1	4p violet	70.00	7.50
24	A1	4p lil & blk ('87)	2.25	1.65
25	A1	5p lil & grn ('94)	3.00	*10.00*
26	A1	6p olive green	5.50	*25.00*
27	A1	6p lilac & red violet ('87)	4.50	2.75
28	A1	6p lilac & car rose ('02)	4.50	*11.50*
29	A1	7½p lilac & car rose ('94)	22.50	*7.50*
30	A1	10p lil & yel ('94)	2.75	*12.50*
31	A1	1sh orange ('85)	5.50	*15.00*
32	A1	1sh green & blk ('87)	3.00	*16.50*
33	A1	2sh6p ol brn ('86)	375.00	300.00
34	A1	2sh6p green & car rose ('87)	20.00	*60.00*
35	A1	5sh blue ('86)	675.00	375.00
36	A1	5sh green & ultra ('87)	30.00	*110.00*
37	A1	10sh brn vio ('86)	1,500.	825.00
38	A1	10sh grn & brn ('87)	55.00	*150.00*

Excellent forgeries exist of Nos. 33, 35 and 37 on paper with genuine watermark.

No. 24 Surcharged in Black

HALF PENNY

1893

No.		Description	Unused	Used
39	A1	½p on 4p lilac & blk	3.25	2.25
a.		Double surcharge	60.00	60.00
b.		Triple surcharge	95.00	
c.		½p on 2p lilac & blue (#18)		12,000.

Four settings of surcharge.

King Edward VII — A3

1904, Jan. 22

No.		Description	Unused	Used
40	A3	½p grn & bl grn	2.25	*5.00*
41	A3	1p vio & blk, *red*	.75	.20
42	A3	2p violet & ultra	6.25	*9.25*
43	A3	2½p vio & ultra, *bl*	1.90	*2.75*
44	A3	3p vio & org brn	1.40	2.50
45	A3	6p vio & red vio	32.50	9.00
46	A3	1sh green & blk	30.00	27.50
47	A3	2sh6p grn & car rose	82.50	*175.00*
48	A3	5sh grn & ultra	150.00	*250.00*
49	A3	10sh green & brn	325.00	*775.00*
		Nos. 40-49 (10)	632.55	*1,256.*

1904-05 **Wmk. 3**

No.		Description	Unused	Used
50	A3	½p grn & bl grn	6.50	2.25
51	A3	1p vio & blk, *red*	1.00	.15
52	A3	2p violet & ultra	1.90	1.00
53	A3	2½p vio & ultra, *bl*	1.65	*15.00*
54	A3	3p vio & org brn	3.25	.85
55	A3	6p vio & red vio	4.00	1.25
56	A3	1sh green & blk	6.50	2.25
57	A3	2sh6p grn & car rose	10.00	*27.50*
58	A3	5sh grn & ultra	20.00	*75.00*
59	A3	10sh green & brn	45.00	*140.00*
		Nos. 50-59 (10)	99.80	*265.25*

The 2½p is on chalky paper, the other values are on both ordinary and chalky.

The stamps of Lagos were superseded by those of Southern Nigeria.

LAOS

'laùs

LOCATION — In northwestern Indo-China
GOVT. — Republic
AREA — 89,320 sq. mi.
POP. — 3,460,000 (est. 1977)
CAPITAL — Vientiane

Before 1949, Laos was part of the French colony of Indo-China and used its stamps until 1951. The kingdom was replaced by the Lao Peoples Democratic Republic Dec. 2, 1975.

100 Cents = 1 Piaster
100 Cents = 1 Kip (1955)

Imperforates

Most Laos stamps exist imperforate in issued and trial colors, and also in small presentation sheets in issued colors.

Catalogue values for all unused stamps in this country are for Never Hinged items.

Boat on Mekong River — A1

King Sisavang-Vong — A2

Laotian Woman — A3

Designs: 50c, 60c, 70c, Luang Prabang. 1pi, 2pi, 3pi, 5pi, 10pi, Temple at Vientiane.

1951-52 Unwmk. Engr. *Perf. 13*

1	A1	10c dk grn & emer	.15	.15
2	A1	20c dk car & car	.15	.15
3	A1	30c ind & dp ultra	1.10	.15
4	A3	30c ind & pur ('52)	.30	.15
5	A1	50c dark brown	.30	.15
6	A1	60c red & red org	.25	.15
7	A1	70c ultra & bl grn	.25	.15
8	A3	80c brt grn & dk bl green ('52)	.30	.15
9	A1	1pi dk pur & pur	.40	.25
10	A3	1.10pi dark plum & carmine ('52)	.60	.15
11	A2	1.50pi blk brn & vio brown	.65	.25
12	A3	1.90pi indigo & dp blue ('52)	.90	.50
13	A1	2pi dk grn & gray green	18.00	1.50
14	A1	3pi dk car & red	.70	.35
15	A3	3pi choc & black brown ('52)	1.50	.45
16	A1	5pi ind & dp ultra	1.00	.45
17	A1	10pi blk brn & vio brown	3.00	.75
		Nos. 1-17 (17)	29.55	5.85

A booklet containing 26 souvenir sheets was issued in 1952 on the anniversary of the first issue of Laos stamps. Each sheet contains a single stamp in the center (Nos. 1-17, C2-C4, J1-J6). Value $140.

See No. 223.

UPU Monument and King Sisavang-Vong — A4

1952, Dec. 7

18	A4	80c ind, blue & pur	.35	.30
19	A4	1pi dk car, car & org brown	.35	.30
20	A4	1.20pi dk pur, purple & ultra	.35	.30
21	A4	1.50pi dk grn, bl grn & dk brn	.35	.30
22	A4	1.90pi blk brn, vio brn & dk Prus grn	.35	.30
		Nos. 18-22,C5-C6 (7)	7.25	4.50

Laos' admission to the UPU, May 13, 1952.

Court of Love — A5

1953, July 14

23	A5	4.50pi indigo & bl grn	.75	.55
24	A5	6pi gray & dark brn	1.25	.55

Composite of Laotian Temples — A6

1954, Mar. 4

25	A6	2pi indigo & purple	25.00	13.00
26	A6	3pi blk brn & dk red	27.50	16.00
		Nos. 25-26,C13 (3)	127.50	104.00

Accession of King Sisavang-Vong, 50th anniv.

Buddha Statue and Monks — A7

1956, May 24 Engr. *Perf. 13*

27	A7	2k reddish brown	1.75	1.00
28	A7	3k black	2.00	1.00
29	A7	5k chocolate	3.00	1.40
		Nos. 27-29,C20-C21 (5)	38.75	27.40

2500th anniversary of birth of Buddha.

UN Emblem — A8

1956, Dec. 14 *Perf. 13½x13*

30	A8	1k black	.50	.35
31	A8	2k blue	.75	.55
32	A8	4k bright red	.90	.60
33	A8	6k purple	1.10	.75
		Nos. 30-33,C22-C23 (6)	11.00	10.00

Admission of Laos to the UN, 1st anniv.

Khouy Player — A9

Khene Player — A10

Musical Instrument: 8k, Ranat.

1957, Mar. 25 Unwmk. *Perf. 13*

34	A9	2k multicolored	1.65	1.25
35	A10	4k multicolored	1.65	1.50
36	A9	8k org, bl & red brn	1.65	1.50
		Nos. 34-36,C24-C26 (6)	11.70	9.30

See No. 224.

Harvesting Rice — A11

Drying Rice — A12

1957, July 22 Engr. *Perf. 13*

37	A11	3k shown	.80	.55
38	A12	5k shown	1.10	.65
39	A12	16k Winnowing rice	1.75	1.25
40	A11	26k Polishing rice	3.25	2.00
		Nos. 37-40 (4)	6.90	4.45

Elephants — A13

Various Elephants: 30c, 5k, 10k, 13k, vert.

1958, Mar. 17

41	A13	10c multi	.50	.15
42	A13	20c multi	.50	.15
43	A13	30c multi	.50	.15
44	A13	2k multi	.50	.25
45	A13	5k multi	1.75	1.00
46	A13	10k multi	1.90	1.25
47	A13	13k multi	3.25	1.65
		Nos. 41-47 (7)	8.90	4.60

For surcharge see No. B5.

Globe and Goddess — A14

UNESCO Building and Mother with Children — A15

Designs: 70c, UNESCO building, globe and mother with children. 1k, UNESCO building and Eiffel tower.

1958, Nov. 3 Engr. *Perf. 13*

48	A14	50c multicolored	.35	.30
49	A15	60c emer, vio & maroon	.35	.30
50	A15	70c ultra, rose red & brn	.35	.30
51	A14	1k ol bis, cl & grnsh bl	.35	.30
		Nos. 48-51 (4)	1.40	1.20

UNESCO Headquarters in Paris opening, Nov. 3.

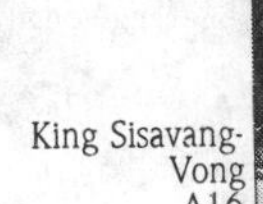

King Sisavang-Vong A16

1959, Sept. 16 Unwmk.

52	A16	4k rose claret	.35	.35
53	A16	6.50k orange red	.35	.35
54	A16	9k bright pink	.35	.35
55	A16	13k green	.35	.35
		Nos. 52-55 (4)	1.40	1.40

For surcharges see Nos. 112-113, B4.

Dancers A17

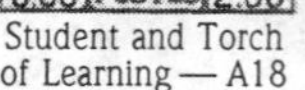

Student and Torch of Learning — A18

Portal of Wat Phou, Pakse — A19

Education and Fine Arts: 3k, Globe, key of knowledge and girl student. 5k, Dancers and temple.

1959, Oct. 1 Engr. *Perf. 13*

56	A17	1k vio blk, ol & bl	.35	.30
57	A18	2k maroon & black	.35	.30
58	A17	3k slate grn & vio	.35	.35
59	A18	5k rose vio, yel & brt grn	.60	.60
		Nos. 56-59 (4)	1.65	1.55

1959, Nov. 2 Unwmk. *Perf. 13*

Historic Monuments: 1.50k, That Inghang, Savannakhet, horiz. 2.50k, Phou Temple, Pakse, horiz. 7k, That Luang, Vientiane. 11k, That Luang, Vientiane, horiz. 12.50k, Phousi, Luang Prabang.

60	A19	50c sepia, grn & org	.20	.20
61	A19	1.50k multi	.20	.20
62	A19	2.50k pur, vio bl & ol	.35	.35
63	A19	7k vio, olive & claret	.35	.35
64	A19	11k brn, car & grn	.45	.45
65	A19	12.50k bl, vio & bister	.45	.45
		Nos. 60-65 (6)	2.00	2.00

Funeral Urn and Monks A20

King Sisavang-Vong A21

Designs: 6.50k, Urn under canopy. 9k, Catafalque on 7-headed dragon carriage.

1961, Apr. 29 Engr. *Perf. 13*

66	A20	4k black, bis & org	.70	.50
67	A20	6.50k black & bister	.70	.50
68	A20	9k black & bister	.70	.50
69	A21	25k black	1.90	1.25
		Nos. 66-69 (4)	4.00	2.75

King Sisavang-Vong's (1885-1959) funeral, Apr. 23-29, 1961.

King Savang Vatthana — A22

Boy and Malaria Eradication Emblem — A23

1962, Apr. 16 *Perf. 13*

Portrait in Brown and Carmine

70	A22	1k ultramarine	.25	.25
71	A22	2k lilac rose	.25	.25
72	A22	5k greenish blue	.30	.30
73	A22	10k olive	.70	.70
		Nos. 70-73 (4)	1.50	1.50

1962, July 19 Engr.

9k, Girl. 10k, Malaria eradication emblem.

74	A23	4k bluish grn, blk & buff	.15	.15
75	A23	9k lt bl, blk & lt brn	.40	.35
76	A23	10k ol, bis & rose red	.75	.60
		Nos. 74-76 (3)	1.30	1.10

WHO drive to eradicate malaria. A souvenir sheet exists.

Stamp Day A24

Royal Messenger — A25

Designs: 50c, Modern mail service (truck, train, plane). 1k, Ancient mail service (messenger on elephant).

1962, Nov. 15 Unwmk. *Perf. 13*

77	A24	50c multicolored	.35	.35
78	A24	70c multicolored	.35	.35
79	A25	1k dp claret, grn & blk	.40	.40
80	A25	1.50k multicolored	.40	.40
		Nos. 77-80 (4)	1.50	1.50

Souvenir sheets exist. One contains the 50c and 70c; the other, the 1k and 1.50k. The sheets exist both perf. and imperf.

Fishermen with Nets — A26

Threshing Rice — A27

Designs: 5k, Plowing and planting in rice paddy. 9k, Woman with infant harvesting rice.

1963, Mar. 21 *Perf. 13*

81	A26	1k grn, bister & pur	.30	.30
82	A27	4k bister, bl & grn	.30	.30
83	A26	5k grn, bis & indigo	.30	.30
84	A27	9k grn, vio bl & ocher	.60	.60
a.		Min. sheet of 4, #81-84, imperf.	2.50	2.25
		Nos. 81-84 (4)	1.50	1.50

FAO "Freedom from Hunger" campaign.

Queen Khamphouy Handing out Gifts — A28

1963, Oct. 10 Engr.

85	A28	4k brn, dp car & blue	.35	.35
86	A28	6k grn, red, yel & bl	.50	.50
87	A28	10k bl, dp car & dk brn	.55	.55
a.		Miniature sheet of 3, #85-87	2.00	1.75
		Nos. 85-87 (3)	1.40	1.40

Centenary of the International Red Cross.

Man Holding UN Emblem — A29

1963, Dec. 10 Unwmk. *Perf. 13*

88	A29	4k dk bl, dp org & vio brn	1.10	.60

15th anniv. of the Universal Declaration of Human Rights.

Temple of That Luang, Map of Nubia and Ramses II — A30

1964, Mar. 8 Engr.

89	A30	4k multicolored	.35	.35
90	A30	6k multicolored	.55	.55
91	A30	10k multicolored	.60	.60
a.		Miniature sheet of 3, #89-91	2.75	2.50
		Nos. 89-91 (3)	1.50	1.50

UNESCO world campaign to save historic monuments in Nubia. No. 91a sold for 25k.

Ceremonial Chalice — A31

Designs: 15k, Buddha. 20k, Soldier leading people through Mekong River Valley. 40k, Royal Palace, Luang Prabang.

1964, July 30 Unwmk. *Perf. 13*

92	A31	10k multicolored	.30	.20
93	A31	15k multicolored	.35	.30
94	A31	20k multicolored	.45	.35
95	A31	40k multicolored	.80	.65
a.		Miniature sheet of 4, #92-95	3.00	2.75
		Nos. 92-95 (4)	1.90	1.50

"Neutral and Constitutional Laos." When the stamps are arranged in a block of four with 40k and 15k in first row and 10k and 20k in second row, the map of Laos appears.

Prince Vet and Wife Mathie — A32

Lao Women — A33

Scenes from Buddhist Legend of Phra Vet Sandone: 32k, God of the Skies sending his son to earth. 45k, Phaune's daughter with beggar husband. 55k, Beggar cornered by guard and dogs.

1964, Nov. 17 Photo. *Perf. 13x12½*

96	A32	10k multicolored	.35	.35
97	A32	32k multicolored	.45	.45
98	A32	45k multicolored	.75	.75
99	A32	55k multicolored	.90	.90
a.		Miniature sheet of 4	4.25	3.75
		Nos. 96-99 (4)	2.45	2.45

#99a contains 4 imperf. stamps similar to #96-99.

1964, Dec. 15 Engr. *Perf. 13*

100	A33	25k blk, org brn & pale ol	.35	.30
		Nos. 100,C43-C45 (4)	1.50	1.45

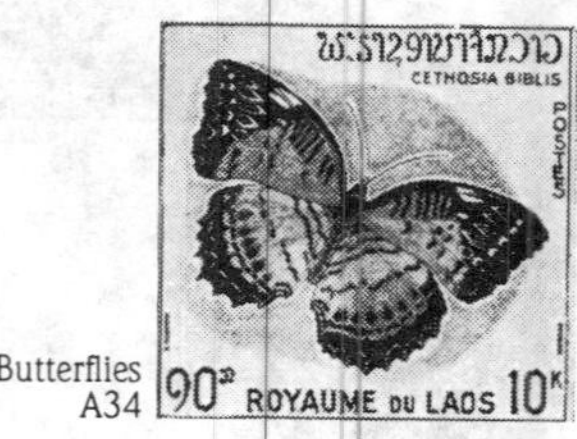

Butterflies A34

1965, Mar. 13 Unwmk. *Perf. 13*

Size: 36x36mm

101	A34	10k Cethosia biblis	1.65	.60
102	A34	25k Precis cebrene	1.90	.95

Size: 48x27mm

103	A34	40k Dysphania militaris	2.50	1.40
		Nos. 101-103,C46 (4)	7.95	4.05

Teacher and School, American Aid — A35

Designs: 25k, Woman at Wattay Airport, French aid, horiz. 45k, Woman bathing child and food basket, Japanese aid. 55k, Musicians broadcasting, British aid, horiz.

1965, Mar. 30 Engr. *Perf. 13*

104	A35	25k bl grn, brn & car rose	.15	.15
105	A35	45k ol grn & brn	.50	.50
106	A35	55k brt bl & bister	.60	.60
107	A35	75k multicolored	.75	.75
		Nos. 104-107 (4)	2.00	2.00

Issued to publicize foreign aid to Laos.

Hophabang Temple A36

1965, Apr. 23 Unwmk. *Perf. 13*

108	A36	10k multicolored	.30	.20

Telewriter, Map of Laos and Globe — A37

Designs: 30k, Communication by satellite and map of Laos. 50k, Globe, map of Laos and radio.

1965, June 15 Engr. *Perf. 13*

109 A37 5k vio bl, brn & red lil .15 .15
110 A37 30k bl, org brn & sl grn .50 .45
111 A37 50k crim, lt bl & bis .80 .70
a. Miniature sheet of 3, #109-111 3.25 3.00
Nos. 109-111 (3) 1.45 1.30

ITU, centenary.

Nos. 52-53 Surcharged in Dark Blue with New Value and Bars

1965, July 5 Unwmk. *Perf. 13*

112 A16 1k on 4k rose claret .20 .15
113 A16 5k on 6.50k org red .25 .15
Set value .20

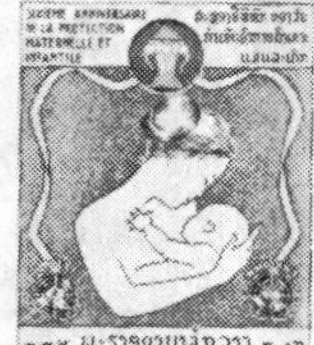

Mother and Child, UNICEF and WHO Emblems — A38

Map of Laos and UN Emblem — A39

1965, Sept. 1 Engr. *Perf. 13*

114 A38 35k lt ultra & dk red .75 .35
a. Miniature sheet 3.00 1.75

Mother and Child Protection movement, 6th anniv.

1965, Nov. 3 *Perf. 12½x13*

115 A39 5k emer, gray & vio bl .25 .25
116 A39 25k lil rose, gray & vio bl .40 .35
117 A39 40k bl, gray & vio bl .60 .60
Nos. 115-117 (3) 1.25 1.20

UN, 20th anniv. Although first day covers were canceled "Oct. 24," the actual day of issue is reported to have been Nov. 3.

Tikhy (Hockey) A40

Pastimes: 10k, Two bulls fighting. 25k, Canoe race. 50k, Rocket festival.

1965, Dec. 23 Engr. *Perf. 13*

118 A40 10k org, brn & gray .20 .15
119 A40 20k grn, ver & dk bl .30 .15
120 A40 25k brt blue & multi .30 .15
121 A40 50k orange & multi .70 .35
Nos. 118-121 (4) 1.50 .80

Slaty-headed Parakeet A41

Birds: 15k, White-crested laughing thrush. 20k, Osprey. 45k, Bengal roller.

1966, Feb. 10 Engr. *Perf. 13*

122 A41 5k car rose, ol & brn .65 .25
123 A41 15k bluish grn, brn & blk .85 .30
124 A41 20k dl bl, sep & bister 1.00 .45
125 A41 45k vio, Prus bl & sepia 2.00 1.25
Nos. 122-125 (4) 4.50 2.25

WHO Headquarters, Geneva A42

1966, May 3 Engr. *Perf. 13*

126 A42 10k bl grn & indigo .20 .15
127 A42 25k car & dk green .35 .25
128 A42 50k ultra & black .70 .70
a. Miniature sheet of 3, #126-128 6.00 5.25
Nos. 126-128 (3) 1.25 1.10

Inauguration of the WHO Headquarters, Geneva. No. 128a sold for 150k.

Ordination of Buddhist Monk — A43

Folklore: 25k, Women building ceremonial sand hills. 30k, Procession of the Wax Pagoda, vert. 40k, Wrist-tying ceremony (3 men, 3 women), vert.

1966, May 20 *Perf. 13*

129 A43 10k multicolored .20 .20
130 A43 25k multicolored .40 .35
131 A43 30k multicolored .45 .45
132 A43 40k multicolored .55 .55
Nos. 129-132 (4) 1.60 1.55

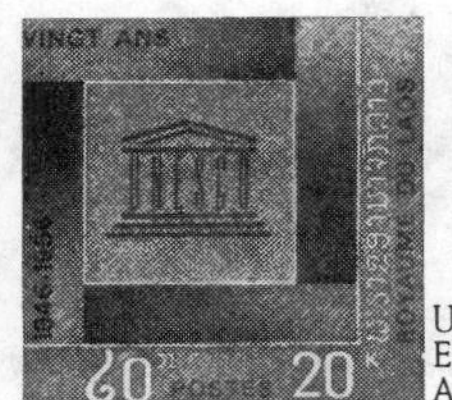

UNESCO Emblem A44

1966, July 7 Engr. *Perf. 13*

133 A44 20k ocher & gray .20 .15
134 A44 30k brt blue & gray .35 .30
135 A44 40k brt green & gray .45 .30
136 A44 60k crimson & gray .65 .35
a. Miniature sheet, #133-136 3.25 3.25
Nos. 133-136 (4) 1.65 1.10

UNESCO, 20th anniv. No. 136a sold for 250k.

Addressed Envelope Carrier Pigeon, Globe and Hand with Quill Pen — A45

1966, Sept. 7 Engr. *Perf. 13*

137 A45 5k red, brn & bl .20 .15
138 A45 20k bl grn, blk & lil .35 .15
139 A45 40k bl, red brn & dk ol bister .50 .20
140 A45 45k brt rose lil, bl grn & black .55 .25
a. Min. sheet of 4, #137-140 4.50 4.50
Nos. 137-140 (4) 1.60 .75

Intl. Letter Writing Week, Oct. 6-12. No. 140a sold for 250k.

Sculpture from Siprapouthbat Temple — A46

Sculptures: 20k, from Visoun Temple. 50k, from Xiengthong Temple. 70k, from Visoun Temple.

1967, Feb. 21 Engr. *Perf. 12½x13*

141 A46 5k olive grn & grn .15 .15
142 A46 20k brn ol & gray bl .25 .25
143 A46 50k dk brn & dp claret .45 .45
144 A46 70k dk brn & dk magenta .65 .65
Nos. 141-144 (4) 1.50 1.50

General Post Office — A47

1967, Apr. 6 Engr. *Perf. 13*

145 A47 25k brn, grn & vio brn .30 .15
146 A47 50k ind, brt blue & grn .50 .40
147 A47 70k dk red, grn & brn .70 .50
Nos. 145-147 (3) 1.50 1.05

Inauguration of the new Post and Telegraph Headquarters.

Snakehead A48

Fish: 35k, Giant catfish. 45k, Spiny eel. 60k, Knifefish.

1967, June 8 Engr. *Perf. 13x12½*

148 A48 20k dl bl, bis & blk .25 .15
149 A48 35k aqua, bis & gray .40 .20
150 A48 45k pale grn, bis & ol brn .65 .30
151 A48 60k sl grn, bis & blk .70 .35
Nos. 148-151 (4) 2.00 1.00

Drumstick Tree Flower — A49

Blossoms: 55k, Turmeric. 75k, Peacock flower. 80k, Pagoda tree.

1967, Aug. 10 Engr. *Perf. 12½x13*

152 A49 30k red lil, yel & grn .25 .15
153 A49 55k org, mag & lt grn .65 .30
154 A49 75k bl, red & lt grn .70 .30
155 A49 80k brt grn, mag & yel .90 .45
Nos. 152-155 (4) 2.50 1.20

Banded Krait — A50

Reptiles: 40k, Marsh crocodile. 100k, Malayan moccasin. 200k, Water monitor.

1967, Dec. 7 Engr. *Perf. 13*

156 A50 5k emer, ind & yel .65 .20
157 A50 40k sep, lt grn & yel .90 .35
158 A50 100k lt grn, brn & ocher 1.50 .90
159 A50 200k grn, blk & bister 2.25 2.00
Nos. 156-159 (4) 5.30 3.45

Human Rights Flame — A51

1968, Feb. 8 Engr. *Perf. 13*

160 A51 20k brt grn, red & grn .25 .15
161 A51 30k brn, red & grn .35 .25
162 A51 50k brt bl, red & grn .65 .45
a. Souv. sheet of 3, #160-162 1.75 1.75
Nos. 160-162 (3) 1.25 .85

Intl. Human Rights Year. #162a sold for 250k.

WHO Emblem — A52

1968, July 5 Engr. *Perf. 12½x13*

163 A52 15k rose vio, ver & ocher .15 .15
164 A52 30k brt bl, brt grn & ocher .20 .15
165 A52 70k ver, plum & ocher .50 .20
166 A52 110k brn, brt rose lil & ocher .80 .55
167 A52 250k brt grn, brt bl & ocher 2.25 1.00
a. Souv. sheet of 5, #163-167 5.00 4.00
Nos. 163-167 (5) 3.90 2.05

WHO, 20th anniv. No. 167a sold for 500k.

Parade and Memorial Arch — A53

Designs: 20k, Armored Corps with tanks. 60k, Three soldiers with Laotian flag.

1968, July 15 *Perf. 13*

168 A53 15k multicolored .15 .15
169 A53 20k multicolored .25 .15
170 A53 60k multicolored .50 .25
Nos. 168-170,C52-C53 (5) 3.75 2.40

Laotian Army. For souvenir sheet see No. C53a.

Chrysochroa Mnizechi — A54

Mangoes — A55

Insects: 50k, Aristobia approximator. 90k, Eutaenia corbetti.

1968, Aug. 28 Engr. *Perf. 13*

171 A54 30k vio bl, grn & yel .40 .25
172 A54 50k lil, blk & ocher .75 .40
173 A54 90k bis, blk & org 1.10 .65
Nos. 171-173,C54-C55 (5) 5.00 2.65

1968, Oct. 3 Engr. *Perf. 13*

Fruits: 50k, Tamarind. 180k, Jackfruit, horiz. 250k, Watermelon, horiz.

174 A55 20k ind, lt bl & emer .20 .15
175 A55 50k lt bl, emer & brn .35 .30
176 A55 180k sep, org & yel grn 1.00 .85
177 A55 250k sep, bis & emer 1.40 1.00
Nos. 174-177 (4) 2.95 2.30

New issue listings, plus the most interesting read in the hobby, characterize the "Scott Stamp Monthly." For more information, please call 1-800-572-6885.

Hurdling — A56

1968, Nov. 15 Engr. *Perf. 13*

178 A56	15k shown	.15	.15
179 A56	80k Tennis	.80	.35
180 A56	100k Soccer	.95	.50
181 A56	110k High jump	1.00	.55
	Nos. 178-181 (4)	2.90	1.55

19th Olympic Games, Mexico City, Oct. 12-27.

Wedding of Kathanam and Nang Sida — A57

Design: 200k, Thao Khathanam battling the serpent Ngou Xouang and the giant bird Phanga Houng. Design from panels of the central gate of Ongtu Temple, Vientiane. Design of 150k is from east gate.

1969, Feb. 28 Photo. *Perf. 12x13*

182 A57	150k blk, gold & red	1.40	.70
183 A57	200k blk, gold & red	2.00	1.00

Soukhib Ordered to Attack — A58

Scenes from Royal Ballet: 15k, Pharak pleading for Nang Sita. 20k, Thotsakan reviewing his troops. 30k, Nang Sita awaiting punishment. 40k, Pharam inspecting troops. 60k, Hanuman preparing to rescue Nang Sita.

1969 Photo. *Perf. 14*

184 A58	10k multicolored	.20	.15
185 A58	15k blue & multi	.25	.20
186 A58	20k lt bl & multi	.25	.25
187 A58	30k salmon & multi	.30	.25
188 A58	40k salmon & multi	.35	.30
189 A58	60k pink & multi	.60	.45
	Nos. 184-189,C56-C57 (8)	6.55	4.30

For surcharges see Nos. B12-B17, CB1-CB2.

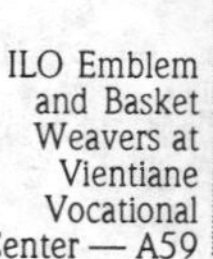

ILO Emblem and Basket Weavers at Vientiane Vocational Center — A59

1969, May 7 Engr. *Perf. 13*

190 A59	30k claret & violet	.30	.20
191 A59	60k slate grn & vio brn	.65	.40
	Nos. 190-191,C58 (3)	4.20	3.10

ILO, 50th anniv.

Chinese Pangolin — A60

1969, Nov. 6 Photo. *Perf. 13x12*

192 A60	15k multicolored	.20	.20
193 A60	30k multicolored	.40	.40
	Nos. 192-193,C59-C61 (5)	3.00	2.80

That Luang, Luang Prabang A61

King Sisavang-Vong A62

1969, Nov. 19 Engr. *Perf. 13*

194 A61	50k dk brn, bl & bister	.45	.20
195 A62	70k maroon & buff	.60	.30
a.	Pair, #194-195 + label	1.05	1.05

Death of King Sisavang-Vong, 10th anniv.

Carved Capital from Wat Xiengthong A63

1970, Jan. 10 Photo. *Perf. 12x13*

196 A63	70k multicolored	.65	.65
	Nos. 196,C65-C66 (3)	3.30	2.00

Kongphene (Midday) Drum — A64

Designs: 55k, Kongthong (bronze) drum.

1970, Mar. 30 Engr. *Perf. 13*

197 A64	30k bl gray, ol & org	.55	.20
198 A64	55k ocher, blk & yel grn	1.00	.55
	Nos. 197-198,C67 (3)	4.55	2.50

Lenin Explaining Electrification Plan, by L. Shmatko — A65

1970, Apr. 22 Litho. *Perf. 12½x12*

199 A65	30k blue & multi	.40	.30
200 A65	70k rose red & multi	1.10	.70

Lenin (1870-1924), Russian communist leader.

Silk Weaver and EXPO Emblem A66

1970, July 7 Engr. *Perf. 13*

201 A66	30k shown	.30	.25
202 A66	70k Woman winding thread	.75	.75
	Nos. 201-202,C69 (3)	2.30	2.25

Laotian silk industry; EXPO '70 Intl. Exposition, Osaka, Japan, Mar. 15-Sept. 13.

Wild Boar — A67

1970, Sept. 7 Engr. *Perf. 13*

203 A67	20k green & dp brn	.20	.20
204 A67	60k dp brn & ol bis	.65	.65
	Nos. 203-204,C70-C71 (4)	4.20	3.95

Buddha, UN Headquarters and Emblem — A68

1970, Oct. 24
Size: 22x36mm

205 A68	30k ultra, brn & rose red	.35	.20
206 A68	70k brt grn, sep & vio	.70	.40
	Nos. 205-206,C75 (3)	2.05	1.60

UN, 25th anniv.

Nakhanet, Symbol of Arts and Culture — A69

1971, Feb. 5

207 A69	70k shown	.60	.35
208 A69	85k Rahu swallowing the moon	.70	.45
	Nos. 207-208,C76 (3)	2.40	1.45

Silversmithing A70

1971, Apr. 12 Engr. *Perf. 13*
Size: 36x36mm

209 A70	30k shown	.25	.20
210 A70	50k Pottery	.40	.30

Size: 47x36mm

211 A70	70k Boat building	.60	.35
	Nos. 209-211 (3)	1.25	.85

Laotian and African Children, UN Emblem — A71

Design: 60k, Women musicians, elephants and UN emblem.

1971, May 1 Engr. *Perf. 13*

212 A71	30k lt grn, brn & blk	.30	.20
213 A71	60k yel, pur & dl red	.70	.45

Intl. year against racial discrimination.

Miss Rotary, Wat Ho Phrakeo — A72

Dendrobium Aggregatum — A73

Design: 30k, Monk on roof of That Luang and Rotary emblem, horiz.

1971, June 28 Engr. *Perf. 13*

214 A72	30k purple & ocher	.50	.20
215 A72	70k gray ol, dk bl & rose	1.00	.35

Rotary International, 50th anniversary.

Perf. 12½x13, 13x12½
1971, July 7 Photo.
Size: 26x36, 36x26mm

216 A73	30k shown	.45	.30
217 A73	50k Asocentrum ampullaceum, horiz.	.65	.40
218 A73	70k Trichoglottis fasciata, horiz.	.95	.50
	Nos. 216-218,C79 (4)	3.95	2.15

See Nos. 230-232, C89.

Palm Civet — A74

Animals: 40k, like 25k. 50k, Lesser Malay chevrotain. 85k, Sika deer.

1971, Sept. 16 Engr. *Perf. 13*

219 A74	25k pur, dk bl & blk	.20	.20
220 A74	40k grn, ol bis & blk	.25	.25
221 A74	50k brt grn & ocher	.30	.30
222 A74	85k sl grn, grn & brn orange	.45	.45
	Nos. 219-222,C83 (5)	2.95	2.10

Types of 1952-57 with Ornamental Panels and Inscriptions

Designs: 30k, Laotian woman. 40k, So player (like #C25). 50k, Rama (like #C19).

1971, Nov. 2

223 A3	30k brn vio & brn	.40	.40
a.	Souvenir sheet of 3	1.75	1.75
224 A10	40k sepia, blk & ver	.55	.55
225 AP7	50k ultra, blk & salmon	.80	.80
	Nos. 223-225,C84 (4)	3.15	3.15

20th anniv. of Laotian independent postal service. All stamps inscribed: "Vingtième Anniversaire de la Philatélie Lao," "Postes" and "1971." No. 223a contains No. 223 and 60k and 85k in design of 30k, sold for 250k.

Children Learning to Read — A75

1972, Jan. 30 Engr. *Perf. 13*

Size: 36x22mm

226 A75	30k shown	.25	.25
227 A75	70k Scribe writing on palm leaves	.50	.50
	Nos. 226-227,C87 (3)	1.50	1.50

Intl. Book Year.

Nam Ngum Hydroelectric Dam, Monument and ECAFE Emblem — A76

1972, Mar. 28 Engr. *Perf. 13*

228 A76	40k grn, ultra & lt brn	.25	.25
229 A76	80k grn, brn ol & dk bl	.40	.40
	Nos. 228-229,C88 (3)	1.45	1.45

25th anniv. of the Economic Commission for Asia and the Far East (ECAFE), which helped build the Nam Ngum Hydroelectric Dam.

Orchid Type of 1971

Orchids: 40k, Rynchostylis giganterum. 60k, Paphiopedilum exul. 80k, Cattleya, horiz.

1972, May 1 Photo. *Perf. 13*

Size: 26x36mm, 36x26mm

230 A73	40k lt bl & multi	.45	.20
231 A73	60k multicolored	.55	.30
232 A73	80k lt bl & multi	.85	.45
	Nos. 230-232,C89 (4)	3.35	1.75

Woman Carrying Water, UNICEF Emblem — A77

Children's drawings: 80k, Child learning bamboo-weaving, UNICEF emblem.

1972, July 20 Engr. *Perf. 13*

233 A77	50k blue & multi	.45	.45
234 A77	80k brown & multi	.65	.65
	Nos. 233-234,C90 (3)	2.10	2.10

25th anniv. (in 1971) of UNICEF.

Attopeu Costume, Religious Ceremony — A78

Lion from Wat That Luang and Lions Emblem — A79

Design: 90k, Phongsaly festival costume.

1973, Feb. 16 Engr. *Perf. 13*

235 A78	40k maroon & multi	.20	.20
236 A78	90k multicolored	.45	.45
	Nos. 235-236,C101-C102 (4)	2.00	2.00

1973, Mar. 30 Engr. *Perf. 13*

237 A79	40k vio bl, rose cl & lil	.40	.25
238 A79	80k pur, org brn & yel	.65	.40
	Nos. 237-238,C103 (3)	2.00	1.30

Lions International of Laos.

Dr. Hansen, Map of Laos, "Dok Hak" Flowers — A80

1973, June 28 Engr. *Perf. 13*

239 A80	40k multicolored	.30	.15
240 A80	80k multicolored	.70	.35

Centenary of the discovery by Dr. Armauer G. Hansen of the Hansen bacillus, the cause of leprosy.

Wat Vixun, Monk Blessing Girl Scouts — A81

1973, Sept. 1 Engr. *Perf. 13*

241 A81	70k ocher & brown	.30	.30
	Nos. 241,C106-C107 (3)	1.75	.90

25th anniv. of Laotian Scout Movement.

INTERPOL Headquarters A82

1973, Dec. 22 Engr. *Perf. 13x12½*

242 A82	40k greenish bl	.25	.25
243 A82	80k brown	.60	.60
	Nos. 242-243,C110 (3)	1.95	1.45

Intl. Criminal Police Org., 50th anniv.

Boy Mailing Letter — A83

Eranthemum Nervosum — A84

1974, Apr. 30 Engr. *Perf. 13*

244 A83	70k bl, lt grn & ocher	.25	.25
245 A83	80k lt grn, bl & ocher	.30	.30
	Nos. 244-245,C114-C115 (4)	4.15	3.15

UPU, cent.

1974, May 31

Size: 26x36mm, 36x26mm

246 A84	30k grn & vio	.20	.20
247 A84	50k Water lilies, horiz.	.30	.30
248 A84	80k Scheffler's kapokier, horiz.	.50	.50
	Nos. 246-248,C116 (4)	5.00	3.75

Mekong River Ferry — A85

Design: 90k, Samlo (passenger tricycle), vert.

1974, July 31 Engr. *Perf. 13*

249 A85	25k red brn & choc	.25	.25
250 A85	90k brown ol & lt ol	.75	.75
	Nos. 249-250,C117 (3)	3.00	2.50

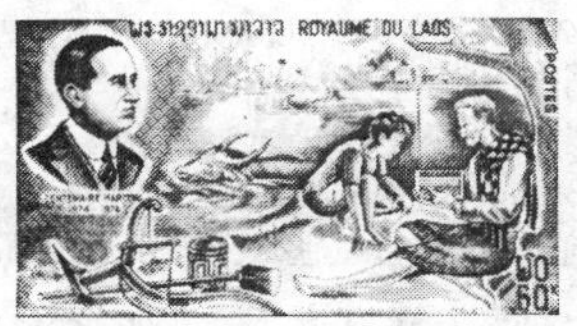

Marconi, Indigenous Transmission Methods, Transistor Radio — A86

1974, Aug. 28 Engr. *Perf. 13*

251 A86	60k multicolored	.35	.35
252 A86	90k multicolored	.55	.55
	Nos. 251-252,C118 (3)	2.30	2.00

Guglielmo Marconi (1874-1937), Italian electrical engineer and inventor.

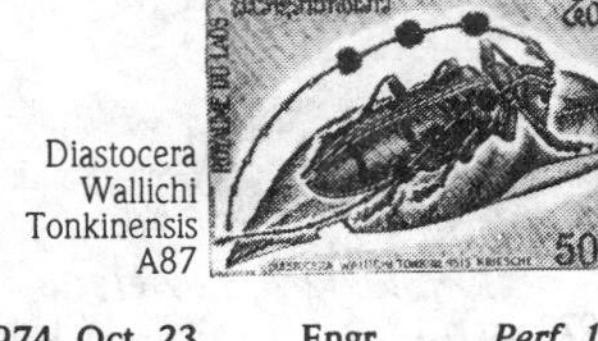

Diastocera Wallichi Tonkinensis A87

1974, Oct. 23 Engr. *Perf. 13*

253 A87	50k shown	.60	.60
254 A87	90k Macrochenus isabellunus	.85	.85
255 A87	100k Purpuricenus malaccensis	.95	.95
	Nos. 253-255,C119 (4)	4.05	3.35

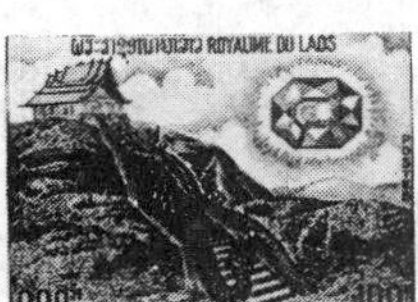

Temple, Houeisai, and Sapphire A88

1975, Feb. 12 Engr. *Perf. 13x12½*

256 A88	100k bl, brn & grn	.40	.40
257 A88	110k Sapphire panning at Attopeu	.60	.60

King Sisavang-Vong, Princes Souvanna Phouma and Souphanou-Vong — A89

1975, Feb. 21 Engr. *Perf. 13*

258 A89	80k olive & multi	.45	.30
259 A89	300k multicolored	1.00	.70
260 A89	420k multicolored	1.25	1.10
	Nos. 258-260 (3)	2.70	2.10

1st anniv. of Peace Treaty of Vientiane.

Fortuneteller Working on Forecast for New Year (Size of pair: 100x27mm) A90 A91

New Year Riding Rabbit, and Tiger (Old Year) — A92

1975, Apr. 14 Engr. *Perf. 13*

261 A90	40k bister & red brn	.30	.20
262 A91	200k bis, red brn & sl	1.10	.80
a.	Pair, #261-262	1.40	1.40
263 A92	350k blue & multi	2.00	1.65
	Nos. 261-263 (3)	3.40	2.65

New Year 1975, Year of the Rabbit.

UN Emblem, "Equality" — A93

Design: 200k, IWY emblem, man and woman.

1975, June 19 Engr.

264 A93	100k dl bl & vio bl	.40	.40
265 A93	200k multi	.85	.85
a.	Miniature sheet of 2, #264-265	1.65	1.65

International Women's Year.

UPU, Cent. — A93a

Designs: 15k, Runner, rocket reaching orbit, vert. 30k, Docked Soyuz capsules, chariot, vert. 40k, Biplane, Concorde. 1000k, Apollo spacecraft in orbit. 1500k, Apollo spacecraft, astronaut, vert. No. 266G, Mail truck, Concorde. No. 266H, Stagecoach. No. 266I, Zeppelin, locomotive.

Perf. 13x14, 14x13

1975, July 7 Litho.

266	A93a	10k multicolored
266A	A93a	15k multicolored
266B	A93a	30k multicolored
266C	A93a	40k multicolored
266D	A93a	1000k multicolored
266E	A93a	1500k multicolored

Litho. & Embossed

Perf. 13½

266G	A93a	3000k gold & multi

Souvenir Sheets

266H	A93a	2500k gold & multi
266I	A93a	3000k gold & multi

Nos. 266D-266E, 266G-266I are airmail.

Apollo-Soyuz Mission — A93b

Designs: 125k, Astronauts, Thomas Stafford, Vance D. Brand, Donald Slayton. 150k, Cosmonauts Alexei Leonov, Valery Koubasov. 200k, Apollo-Soyuz link-up. 300k, Handshake in space. 450k, Preparation for re-entry. 700k, Apollo splashdown.

1975, July 7 — Litho. — *Perf. 14x13*

No.	Type	Description		
267	A93b	125k multicolored		
267A	A93b	150k multicolored		
267B	A93b	200k multicolored		
267C	A93b	300k multicolored		
267D	A93b	450k multicolored		
267E	A93b	700k multicolored		

Nos. 267D-267E are airmail.

Scene from Vet Sandone Legend — A94

Designs: Scenes from Buddhist legend of Prince Vet Sandone.

1975, July 22 — Photo. — *Perf. 13*

No.	Type	Description		
268	A94	80k multicolored	.40	.25
268A	A94	110k multicolored	.50	.35
268B	A94	120k multicolored	.60	.45
268C	A94	130k multicolored	.75	.50
		Nos. 268-268C (4)	2.25	1.55

American Revolution, Bicent. — A94a

Presidents: 10k, Washington, J. Adams, Jefferson, Madison. 15k, Monroe, J.Q. Adams, Jackson, Van Buren. 40k, Harrison, Tyler, Polk, Taylor. 1000k, Truman, Eisenhower, Kennedy. 1500k, L. Johnson, Nixon, Ford.

1975, July 30 — Litho. — *Perf. 13½*

No.	Type	Description		
269	A94a	10k multicolored		
269A	A94a	15k multicolored		
269B	A94a	40k multicolored		
269C	A94a	1000k multicolored		
269D	A94a	1500k multicolored		

Nos. 269C-269D are airmail. Stamps of similar design in denominations of 50k, 100k, 125k, 150k, and 200k exist but were not available in Laotian post offices.

Buddha, Stupas of Borobudur — A95

Design: 200k, Borobudur sculptures and UNESCO emblem.

1975, Aug. 20 — Engr. — *Perf. 13*

No.	Type	Description		
270	A95	100k indigo & multi	.65	.35
271	A95	200k multicolored	1.25	.80
a.		Miniature sheet of 2, #270-271	3.75	3.00

UNESCO campaign to save Borobudur Temple, Java.

Coat of Arms of Republic — A96

Thathiang Pagoda, Vientiane — A97

1976, Dec. 2 — Litho. — *Perf. 14*

No.	Type	Description		
272	A96	1k blue & multi	.15	.15
273	A96	2k rose & multi	.15	.15
274	A96	5k brt grn & multi	.15	.15
275	A96	10k lilac & multi	.15	.15
276	A96	200k orange & multi	.80	.80
a.		Min. sheet of 5, #272-276	3.00	2.75
		Set value	1.00	1.00

1976, Dec. 18 — *Perf. 13½*

Designs: 2k, 80k, 100k, Phonsi Pagoda, Luang Prabang. 30k, 300k, like 1k.

No.	Type	Description		
277	A97	1k multicolored	.15	.15
278	A97	2k multicolored	.15	.15
279	A97	30k multicolored	.15	.15
280	A97	80k multicolored	.25	.25
281	A97	100k multicolored	.35	.35
282	A97	300k multicolored	1.00	1.00
		Nos. 277-282 (6)	2.05	2.05

Silversmith A98

Perf. 13x12½, 12½x13

1977, Apr. 1 — Litho.

No.	Type	Description		
283	A98	1k shown	.15	.15
284	A98	2k Weaver	.15	.15
285	A98	20k Potter	.25	.25
286	A98	50k Basket weaver, vert.	.50	.50
		Nos. 283-286 (4)	1.05	1.05

Miniature sheets of 2 exist, perf. and imperf.

Cosmonauts A.A. Gubarev, G.M. Grechko — A99

Government Palace, Vientiane, Kremlin, Moscow — A100

20k, 50k, Lenin speaking on Red Square.

Perf. 12x12½, 12½x12

1977, Oct. 25 — Litho.

No.	Type	Description		
287	A99	5k multicolored	.15	.15
288	A99	20k multicolored	.15	.15
289	A99	50k multicolored	.15	.15
290	A99	60k multicolored	.15	.15
291	A100	100k multicolored	.25	.25
a.		Souv. sheet of 3, #288, 290-291	1.75	1.00
292	A100	250k multicolored	.70	.70
a.		Souv. sheet of 3, #287, 289, 292	2.25	1.75
		Set value	1.30	1.30

60th anniv. of Russian October Revolution.

Natl. Arms — A101

A102

1978, May 26 — Litho. — *Perf. 12½*

No.	Type	Description		
293	A101	5k dull org & blk	.15	.15
294	A101	10k tan & black	.15	.15
295	A101	50k brt pink & blk	.35	.15
296	A101	100k yel grn & blk	.65	.25
297	A101	250k violet & blk	1.75	.65
		Nos. 293-297 (5)	3.05	
		Set value		1.10

Perf. 12½x12, 12x12½

1978, Sept. 15 — Litho.

Army Day: 20k, Soldiers with flag. 40k, Fighters and burning house, horiz. 300k, Anti-aircraft battery.

No.	Type	Description		
298	A102	20k multicolored	.15	.15
299	A102	40k multicolored	.15	.15
300	A102	300k multicolored	1.25	.70
		Nos. 298-300 (3)	1.55	
		Set value		.80

Marchers with Banner — A103

1978, Dec. 2 — Litho. — *Perf. 11½*

No.	Type	Description		
301	A103	20k shown	.15	.15
302	A103	50k Women with flag	.20	.15
303	A103	400k Dancer	1.65	.80
a.		Sheet of 3, #301-303, imperf.	2.25	
		Nos. 301-303 (3)	2.00	1.10

National Day. A second printing in slightly different colors and with rough perforation exists. Stamps in souvenir sheet are in reverse order.

Electronic Tree, Map of Laos, ITU Emblem — A104

Design: 250k, Electronic tree, map of Laos and broadcast tower.

1979, Jan. 18 — Litho. — *Perf. 12½*

No.	Type	Description		
304	A104	30k multicolored	.15	.15
305	A104	250k multicolored	.55	.55

World Telecommunications Day, 1978.

Woman Mailing Letter — A105

10k, 80k, Processing mail. 100k, like 5k.

1979, Jan. 18

No.	Type	Description		
306	A105	5k multicolored	.15	.15
307	A105	10k multicolored	.15	.15
308	A105	80k multicolored	.60	.20
309	A105	100k multicolored	.75	.25
		Nos. 306-309 (4)	1.65	
		Set value		.50

Asian-Oceanic Postal Union, 15th anniv.

Intl. Year of the Child A106

1979 — Litho. — *Perf. 11*

Without Gum

No.	Type	Description	
310	A106	20k Playing with ball, vert.	.15
311	A106	50k Studying	.18
312	A106	100k Playing musical instruments	.35
313	A106	200k Breast-feeding, vert.	.70
314	A106	200k Map, globe, vert.	.70
315	A106	500k Immunization, vert.	1.75
316	A106	600k Girl dancing, vert.	2.25
		Nos. 310-316 (7)	6.08

Issue dates: Nos. 310-311, 313, 315, Aug. 1. Others, Dec. 25. Imperf. sheets of 4 containing Nos. 310-311, 313, 315 issued Aug. 1; imperf. sheet of 3 containing Nos. 312, 314, 316 issued on Dec. 25.

Traditional Modes of Transportation — A107

1979, Oct. 9 — *Perf. 12½x13*

No.	Type	Description	
317	A107	5k Elephants, buffalo, pirogues	.15
318	A107	10k Buffalo, carts	.15
319	A107	70k like 10k	.35
320	A107	500k like 5k	2.50
		Nos. 317-320 (4)	3.15

5th Anniv. of the Republic A108

1980, May 30 — *Perf. 11*

No.	Type	Description	
321	A108	30c Agriculture, vert.	.15
322	A108	50c Education, health services	.15
323	A108	1k Three women, vert.	.60
324	A108	2k Hydroelectric energy	1.25
		Nos. 321-324 (4)	2.15

Imperf. souvenir sheet of 4 exists.

Lenin, 110th Birth Anniv. A109

1980, July 5 — *Perf. 12x12½, 12½x12*

No.	Type	Description	
325	A109	1k Lenin reading	.20
326	A109	2k Writing	.35
327	A109	3k Lenin, red flag, vert.	.60
328	A109	4k Orating, vert.	.80
		Nos. 325-328 (4)	1.95

Imperf. souvenir sheet of 4 exists.

5th Anniv. of the Republic — A110

1980, Dec. 2 *Perf. 11*

Without Gum

329 A110 50c Threshing rice .15
330 A110 1.60k Logging .25
331 A110 4.60k Veterinary medicine .60
332 A110 5.40k Rice paddy .70
Nos. 329-332 (4) 1.70

Imperf. souvenir sheet of 4 exists.

26th Communist Party (PCUS) Congress A111

1981, June 26 *Perf. 12x12½*

Without Gum

333 A111 60c shown .15
334 A111 4.60k Globe, broken chains .60
335 A111 5.40k Grain, cracked bomb .70
a. Souv. sheet of 3, #333-335, imperf. 4.00
Nos. 333-335 (3) 1.45

No. 335a sold for 15k.

Souvenir Sheet

PHILATOKYO '81 — A112

1981, Sept. 20 *Perf. 13*

Without Gum

336 A112 10k Pandas 2.25

1982 World Cup Soccer Championships, Spain — A113

Intl. Year of the Disabled — A114

1981, Oct. 15 *Perf. 12½*

Without Gum

337 A113 1k Heading ball .25
338 A113 2k Dribble .45
339 A113 3k Kick .65
340 A113 4k Goal, horiz. .85
341 A113 5k Dribble, diff. 1.10
342 A113 6k Kick, diff. 1.35
Nos. 337-342 (6) 4.65

1981 *Perf. 13*

Without Gum

343 A114 3k Office worker .70
344 A114 5k Teacher 1.10
345 A114 12k Weaver, fishing net 2.75
Nos. 343-345 (3) 4.55

Wildcats A115

1981 *Perf. 12½*

Without Gum

346 A115 10c Felis silvestris ornata .15
347 A115 20c Felis viverrinus .15
348 A115 30c Felis caracal .15
349 A115 40c Neofelis nebulosa .15
350 A115 50c Felis planiceps .15
351 A115 9k Felis chaus 2.50
Nos. 346-351 (6) 3.25

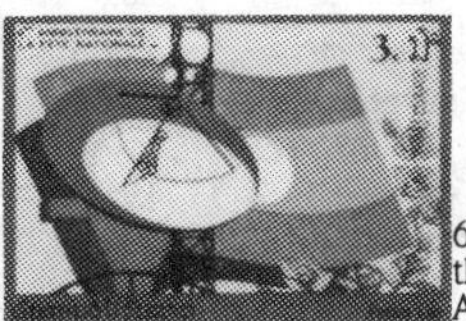
6th Anniv. of the Republic A116

1981, Dec. *Perf. 13*

Without Gum

352 A116 3k Satellite dish, flag .50
353 A116 4k Soldier, flag .65
354 A116 5k Map, flag, women, soldier .85
Nos. 352-354 (3) 2.00

Indian Elephants A117

1982, Jan. 23 *Perf. 12½x13*

Without Gum

355 A117 1k Head .25
356 A117 2k Carrying log in trunk .50
357 A117 3k Transporting people .75
358 A117 4k In trap 1.00
359 A117 5k Adult and young 1.25
360 A117 5.50k Herd 1.40
Nos. 355-360 (6) 5.15

Laotian Wrestling — A118

Various moves.

1982, Jan. 30 *Perf. 13*

Without Gum

361 A118 50c multicolored .15
362 A118 1.20k multi, diff. .25
363 A118 2k multi, diff. .45
364 A118 2.50k multi, diff. .55
365 A118 4k multi, diff. .85
366 A118 5k multi, diff. 1.10
Nos. 361-366 (6) 3.35

Water Lilies — A119

1982, Feb. 10 *Perf. 12½x13*

Without Gum

367 A119 30c Nymphaea zanzibariensis .15
368 A119 40c Nelumbo nucifera gaertn rose .15
369 A119 60c Nymphaea rosea .15
370 A119 3k Nymphaea nouchali .65
371 A119 4k Nymphaea white .85
372 A119 7k Nelumbo nucifera gaertn white 1.50
Nos. 367-372 (6) 3.45

Birds A120

1982, Mar. 9 *Perf. 13*

Without Gum

373 A120 50c Hirundo rustica, vert. .15
374 A120 1k Upupa epops, vert. .25
375 A120 2k Alcedo atthis, vert. .50
376 A120 3k Hypothymis azurea .75
377 A120 4k Motacilla cinerea 1.00
378 A120 10k Orthotomus sutorius 2.50
Nos. 373-378 (6) 5.15

A121

1982 World Cup Soccer Championships, Spain — A122

Various match scenes.

1982, Apr. 7

Without Gum

379 A121 1k multicolored .25
380 A121 2k multicolored .50
381 A121 3k multicolored .75
382 A121 4k multicolored 1.00
383 A121 5k multicolored 1.25
384 A121 6k multicolored 1.50
Nos. 379-384 (6) 5.25

Souvenir Sheet

385 A122 15k multicolored 5.75

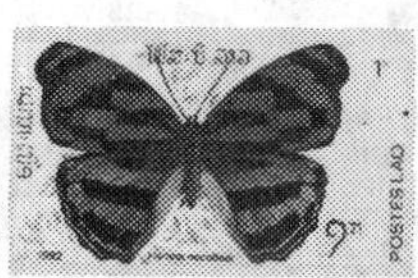
Butterflies A123

1982, May 5 *Perf. 12½x13*

Without Gum

386 A123 1k Herona marathus .25
387 A123 2k Neptis paraka .50
388 A123 3k Euripus halitherses .75
389 A123 4k Lebadea martha 1.00

Size: 42x26mm

Perf. 12½

390 A123 5k Iton semamora 1.25

Size: 54x36½mm

Perf. 13x12½

391 A123 6k Elymnias hypermnestra 1.50
Nos. 386-391 (6) 5.25

Souvenir Sheet

PHILEXFRANCE '82 — A124

1982, June 9 *Perf. 13*

Without Gum

392 A124 10k Temple, Vientiane 3.00

River Vessels A125

1982, June 24

Without Gum

393 A125 50c Raft .15
394 A125 60c River punt .20
395 A125 1k Houseboat .30
396 A125 2k Passenger steamer .55
397 A125 3k Ferry .85
398 A125 8k Self-propelled barge 2.00
Nos. 393-398 (6) 4.05

Pagodas A126

1982, Aug. 2

Without Gum

399 A126 50c Chanh .15
400 A126 60c Inpeng .20
401 A126 1k Dong Mieng .30
402 A126 2k Ho Tay .55
403 A126 3k Ho Pha Keo .85
404 A126 8k Sisaket 2.25
Nos. 399-404 (6) 4.30

Dogs A127

1982, Oct. 13

Without Gum

405 A127 50c Poodle .15
406 A127 60c Samoyed .20
407 A127 1k Boston terrier .30
408 A127 2k Cairn terrier .60
409 A127 3k Chihuahua .90
410 A127 8k Bulldog 2.50
Nos. 405-410 (6) 4.65

World Food Day — A128

1982, Oct. 16

Without Gum

411 A128 7k Watering seedlings 2.00
412 A128 8k Planting rice 2.25

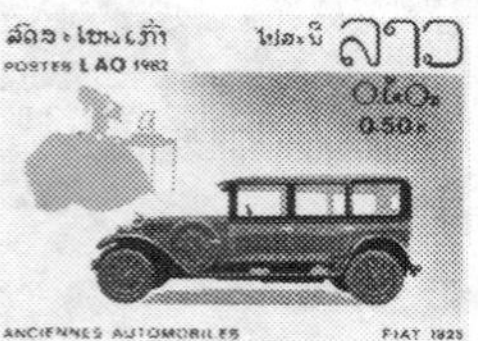
Classic Automobiles — A129

1982, Nov. 7

Without Gum

413 A129 50c 1925 Fiat .15
414 A129 60c 1925 Peugeot .20
415 A129 1k 1925 Berliet .30
416 A129 2k 1925 Ballot .60
417 A129 3k 1926 Renault .90
418 A129 8k 1925 Ford 2.50
Nos. 413-418 (6) 4.65

7th Anniv. of the Republic A130

1982, Dec. 2

Without Gum

419 A130 50c Souphanouvong, vert. .15
420 A130 1k Tractors, field, industry .25
421 A130 2k Cows, farm .50
422 A130 3k Truck, microwave dish .75
423 A130 4k Nurse, child, vert. 1.00
424 A130 5k Education 1.25
425 A130 6k Folk dancer, vert. 1.50
Nos. 419-425 (7) 5.40

Bulgarian Flag, Coat of Arms and George Dimitrov (1882-1949), Bulgarian Statesman — A131

1982, Dec. 15 *Perf. 12½*

Without Gum

426 A131 10k multicolored 2.75

Constitution of the USSR, 60th Anniv. — A132

1982, Dec. 30

Without Gum

427 A132 3k shown .90
428 A132 4k Maps 1.25

Souvenir Sheet

Perf. 13½x13

428A Sheet of 2 4.00
b. A132 5k like 3k 1.25
c. A132 10k like 4k 2.50

Nos. 428b-428c not inscribed in Laotian at top; buff and gold decorative margin contains the inscription.

1984 Summer Olympics, Los Angeles — A133

1983, Jan. 25 *Perf. 13*

Without Gum

429 A133 50c Hurdling .15
430 A133 1k Women's javelin .25
431 A133 2k Basketball .50
432 A133 3k Diving .75
433 A133 4k Gymnastics 1.00
434 A133 10k Weight lifting 2.50
Nos. 429-434 (6) 5.15

Souvenir Sheet

435 A133 15k Soccer 4.00

No. 435 contains one stamp 32x40mm.

Horses A134

Various breeds.

1983, Feb. 1

Without Gum

436 A134 50c multicolored .15
437 A134 1k multi, diff. .25
438 A134 2k multi, diff. .50
439 A134 3k multi, diff. .75
440 A134 4k multi, diff. 1.00
441 A134 10k multi, diff. 2.50
Nos. 436-441 (6) 5.15

A135

Raphael, 500th Birth Anniv. A136

Paintings (details) by Raphael: 50c, St. Catherine of Alexandra, Natl. Gallery, London. 1k, Adoration of the Kings (spectators), Vatican. 2k, Granduca Madonna, Pitti Gallery, Florence. 3k, St. George and the Dragon, The Louvre, Paris. 4k, Vision of Ezekiel, Pitti Gallery. No. 447, Adoration of the Kings (Holy Family), Vatican. No. 448, Coronation of the Virgin, Vatican.

1983, Mar. 9 *Perf. 12½x13*

Without Gum

442 A135 50c multicolored .15
443 A135 1k multicolored .30
444 A135 2k multicolored .55
445 A135 3k multicolored .85
446 A135 4k multicolored 1.10
447 A135 10k multicolored 2.75
Nos. 442-447 (6) 5.70

Souvenir Sheet

Perf. 13x13½

448 A136 10k multicolored 2.75

INTERCOSMOS Space Cooperation Program — A137

Cosmonaut and flags of USSR and participating nations.

1983, Apr. 12 *Perf. 12½*

449 A137 50c Czechoslovakia .15
450 A137 50c Poland .15
451 A137 1k East Germany .25
452 A137 1k Bulgaria .25
453 A137 2k Hungary .50
454 A137 3k Mongolia .80
455 A137 4k Romania 1.10
456 A137 6k Cuba 1.65
457 A137 10k France 2.50
Nos. 449-457 (9) 7.35

Souvenir Sheet

Perf. 13½x13

458 A137 10k Vietnam 3.00

No. 458 contains one stamp 32x40mm.

A138

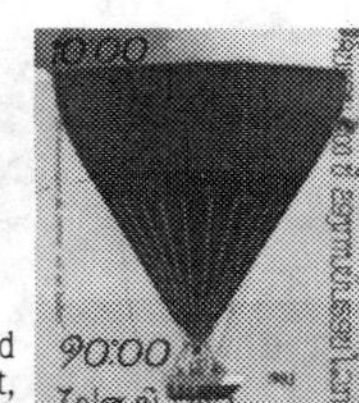
First Manned Balloon Flight, Bicent. — A139

Various balloons.

1983, May 4 *Perf. 12½x13*

459 A138 50c shown .15
460 A138 1k multi, diff. .25
461 A138 2k multi, diff. .50
462 A138 3k multi, diff. .75
463 A138 4k multi, diff. 1.00
464 A138 10k multi, diff. 2.50
Nos. 459-464 (6) 5.15

Souvenir Sheet

Perf. 13½x13

465 A139 10k shown 3.50

Souvenir Sheet

TEMBAL '83, Basel — A140

1983, May 21 *Perf. 13x13½*

Without Gum

466 A140 10k German Maybach 3.00

Flora A141

1983, June 10 *Perf. 13*

Without Gum

467 A141 1k Dendrobium sp. .25
468 A141 2k Aerides odoratum .50
469 A141 3k Dendrobium aggregatum .75
470 A141 4k Dendrobium 1.00
471 A141 5k Moschatum 1.25
472 A141 6k Dendrobium sp., diff. 1.50
Nos. 467-472 (6) 5.25

1984 Winter Olympics, Sarajevo A142

1983, July 2

Without Gum

473 A142 50c Downhill skiing .15
474 A142 1k Slalom .30
475 A142 2k Ice hockey .60
476 A142 3k Speed skating .90
477 A142 4k Ski jumping 1.25
478 A142 10k Luge 3.00
Nos. 473-478 (6) 6.20

Souvenir Sheet

Perf. 13x13½

479 A142 15k 2-Man bobsled 4.50

No. 479 contains one 40x32mm stamp.

Souvenir Sheet

BANGKOK '83 — A143

1983, Aug. 4 *Perf. 13½x13*

480 A143 10k Boats on river 2.50

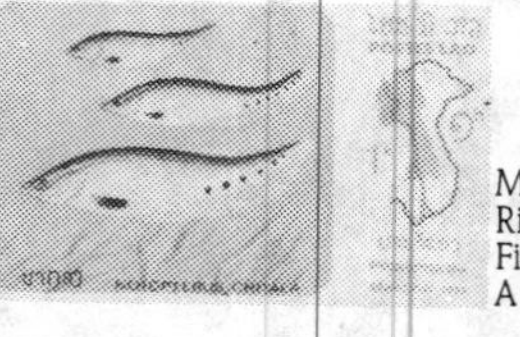
Mekong River Fish A144

1983, Sept. 5 *Perf. 12½*

Without Gum

481 A144 1k Notopterus chitala .25
482 A144 2k Cyprinus carpio .50
483 A144 3k Pangasius sp. .75
484 A144 4k Catlocarpio siamensis 1.00
485 A144 5k Morulius sp. 1.25
486 A144 6k Tilapia nilotica 1.50
Nos. 481-486 (6) 5.25

Explorers and Their Ships — A145

1983, Oct. 8 *Perf. 13x12½*

Without Gum

487 A145 1k Victoria, Magellan .25
488 A145 2k Grand Hermine, Cartier .50
489 A145 3k Santa Maria, Columbus .75
490 A145 4k Cabral and caravel 1.00
491 A145 5k Endeavor, Capt. Cook 1.25
492 A145 6k Pourquoi-Pas, Charcot 1.50
Nos. 487-492 (6) 5.25

No. 492 incorrectly inscribed "CABOT."

Domestic Cats — A146

1983, Nov. 9 *Perf. 12½x13*

Without Gum

493 A146 1k Tabby .25
494 A146 2k Long-haired Persian .50
495 A146 3k Siamese .75
496 A146 4k Burmese 1.00
497 A146 5k Persian 1.25
498 A146 6k Tortoiseshell 1.50
Nos. 493-498 (6) 5.25

Karl Marx (1818-1883) — A147

1983, Nov. 30 *Perf. 13*

Without Gum

499 A147 1k shown .25
500 A147 4k Marx, 3 flags, diff., vert. 1.00
501 A147 6k Marx, flag of Laos 1.50
Nos. 499-501 (3) 2.75

8th Anniv. of the Republic — A148

1983, Dec. 2 *Perf. 12½x13, 13x12½*

Without Gum

502 A148 1k Elephant dragging log, vert. .30
503 A148 4k Oxen, pig 1.10
504 A148 6k Produce, vert. 1.75
a. Souv. sheet of 6 with gutter between 5.50
Nos. 502-504 (3) 3.15

World Communications Year — A149

1983, Dec. 15 *Perf. 13*

505 A149 50c Teletype .15
506 A149 1k Telephone .25
507 A149 4k Television 1.00
508 A149 6k Satellite, dish receiver 1.50
Nos. 505-508 (4) 2.90

1984 Winter Olympics, Sarajevo A150

1984, Jan. 16

509 A150 50c Women's figure skating .15
510 A150 1k Speed skating .25
511 A150 2k Biathlon .50
512 A150 4k Luge 1.00
513 A150 5k Downhill skiing 1.25
514 A150 6k Ski jumping 1.50
515 A150 7k Slalom 1.75
Nos. 509-515 (7) 6.40

Souvenir Sheet

Perf. 13½x13

516 A150 10k Ice hockey 2.75

Nos. 509-511, 514-515 vert. No. 516 contains one stamp 32x40mm.

World Wildlife Fund A151

Panthera tigris.

1984, Feb. 1 *Perf. 13*

517 A151 25c Adult, vert. .15
518 A151 25c shown .15
519 A151 3k Nursing cubs .75
520 A151 4k Two cubs, vert. 1.00
Nos. 517-520 (4) 2.05

1984 Summer Olympics, Los Angeles — A152

Gold medals awarded during previous games, and athletes. 50c, Athens 1896, women's diving. 1k, Paris 1900, women's volleyball. 2k, St. Louis 1904, running. 4k, London 1908, basketball. 5k, Stockholm 1912, judo. 6k, Antwerp 1920, soccer. 7k, Paris 1924, gymnastics. 10k, Moscow 1980, wrestling.

1984, Mar 26

521 A152 50c multicolored .15
522 A152 1k multicolored .25
523 A152 2k multicolored .50
524 A152 4k multicolored 1.00
525 A152 5k multicolored 1.25
526 A152 6k multicolored 1.50
527 A152 7k multicolored 1.75
Nos. 521-527 (7) 6.40

Souvenir Sheet

Perf. 12½

528 A152 10k multicolored 3.00

No. 528 contains one stamp 32x40mm.

Musical Instruments — A153

1984, Mar. 27 *Perf. 13*

529 A153 1k Tuned drums .25
530 A153 2k Xylophone .55
531 A153 3k Pair of drums .80
532 A153 4k Hand drum 1.10
533 A153 5k Barrel drum 1.40
534 A153 6k Pipes, string instrument 1.65
Nos. 529-534 (6) 5.75

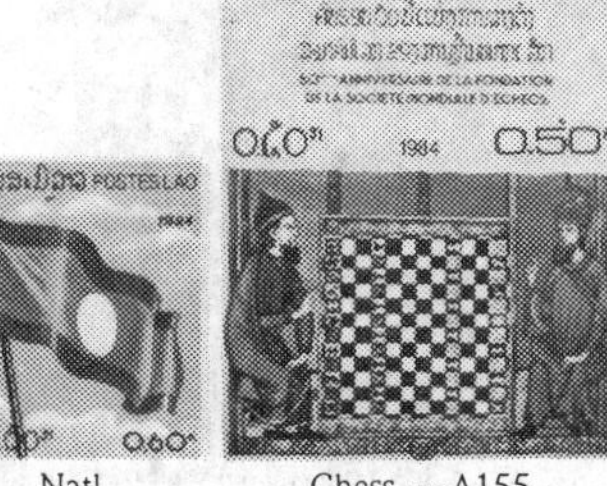

Natl. Day — A154

Chess — A155

1984, Mar. 30 *Perf. 12½*

535 A154 60c Natl. flag .15
536 A154 1k Natl. arms .20
537 A154 2k like 1k .40
Nos. 535-537 (3) .75

1984, Apr. 14 *Perf. 12½x13*

Illustrations of various medieval and Renaissance chess games.

538 A155 50c multi .15
539 A155 1k multi, diff. .30
540 A155 2k multi, red brn board, diff. .55
541 A155 2k multi, blk board, diff. .55
542 A155 3k multi, diff. .65
543 A155 4k multi, diff. 1.10
544 A155 8k multi, diff. 2.25
a. Souv. sheet of 6 with gutter between 5.50
Nos. 538-544 (7) 5.55

Souvenir Sheet

Perf. 13½x13

545 A155 10k Royal game, human chessmen 3.00

World Chess Federation, 60th anniv. No. 545 contains one stamp 32x40mm.

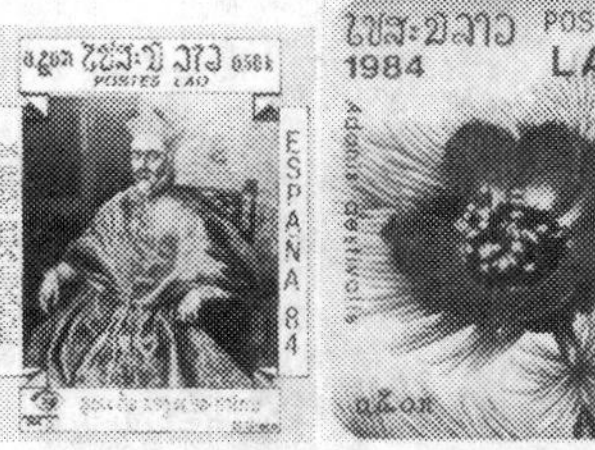

ESPANA '84, Madrid — A156

Woodland Flowers — A157

Paintings: 50c, Cardinal Nino de Guevara, by El Greco. 1k, Gaspar de Guzman, Duke of Olivares, on Horseback, by Velazquez. No. 548, The Annunciation, by Murillo. No. 549, Portrait of a Lady, by Francisco de Zurburan (1598-1664). 3k, The Family of Charles IV, by Goya. 4k, Two Harlequins, by Picasso. 8k, Abstract, by Miro. 10k, Burial of the Count of Orgaz, by El Greco.

1984, Apr. 27 *Perf. 12½*

546 A156 50c multicolored .15
547 A156 1k multicolored .25
548 A156 2k multicolored .50
549 A156 2k multicolored .50
550 A156 3k multicolored .75
551 A156 4k multicolored 1.00
552 A156 8k multicolored 2.00
Nos. 546-552 (7) 5.15

Souvenir Sheet

Perf. 13½x13

553 A156 10k multicolored 3.00

No. 553 contains one stamp 32x40mm.

1984, May 11 *Perf. 13*

554 A157 50c Adonis aestivalis .15
555 A157 1k Alpinia speciosa .25
556 A157 2k Aeschynanthus speciosus .50
557 A157 2k Cassia lechenaultiana .50
558 A157 3k Datura meteloides .75
559 A157 4k Quamoclit pennata 1.00
560 A157 8k Commelina benghalensis 2.00
Nos. 554-560 (7) 5.15

A158

19th UPU Congress, Hamburg — A159

Classic sport and race cars.

1984, June 19

561 A158 50c Nazzaro .15
562 A158 1k Daimler .25
563 A158 2k Delage .50
564 A158 2k Fiat S 57/14B .50
565 A158 3k Bugatti .75
566 A158 4k Itala 1.00
567 A158 8k Blitzen Benz 2.00
Nos. 561-567 (7) 5.15

Souvenir Sheet

Perf. 12½

568 A159 10k Winton Bullet 2.75

Paintings by Corregio (1494-1534) A160

Designs: 50c, Madonna and Child (Holy Family). 1k, Madonna and Child (spectators). No. 571, Madonna and Child (Holy Family, diff.). No. 572, Mystical Marriage of St. Catherine (Catherine, child, two women). 3k, The Four Saints. 4k, Noli Me Tangere. 8k, Christ Bids Farewell to the Virgin Mary. 10k, Madonna and Child, diff.

1984, June 26 *Perf. 13*

569 A160 50c multicolored .15
570 A160 1k multicolored .20
571 A160 2k multicolored .35
572 A160 2k multicolored .35
573 A160 3k multicolored .50
574 A160 4k multicolored .65
575 A160 8k multicolored 1.40
Nos. 569-575 (7) 3.60

Souvenir Sheet

Perf. 13½x13

576 A160 10k multicolored 4.00

No. 576 contains one stamp 32x40mm.

Space Exploration A161

1984, July 12 *Perf. 13*

577 A161 50c Luna 1 .15
578 A161 1k Luna 2 .25
579 A161 2k Luna 3 .45
580 A161 2k Sputnik 2, Kepler .45

581 A161 3k Lunokhod 2, Newton .65
582 A161 4k Luna 13, Jules Verne .90
583 A161 8k Space station, Copernicus 1.75
Nos. 577-583 (7) 4.60

Reptiles A162

1984, Aug. 20

584 A162 50c Malaclemys terrapin .15
585 A162 1k Bungarus fasciatus .25
586 A162 2k Python reticulatus .50
587 A162 2k Python molurus, vert. .50
588 A162 3k Gekko gecko .75
589 A162 4k Natrix subminiata 1.00
590 A162 8k Eublepharis macumiliaris 2.00
Nos. 584-590 (7) 5.15

Marsupials — A163

1984, Sept. 21

591 A163 50c Schoinobates volans .15
592 A163 1k Ornithorhynchus anatinus .25
593 A163 2k Sarcophilus harrisii .55
594 A163 2k Lasiorhinus latifrons .55
595 A163 3k Thylacinus cynocephalus .80
596 A163 4k Dasyurops maculatus 1.00
597 A163 8k Wallabia isabelinus 2.00
Nos. 591-597 (7) 5.30

Souvenir Sheet

Perf. **$12^1/_2$**

598 A163 10k Macropus rufus 3.00

AUSIPEX '84, Melbourne. No. 598 contains one stamp 32x40mm.

Stop Polio Campaign A164

1984, Sept. 29 ***Perf. 13***

599 A164 5k shown 1.25
600 A164 6k Vaccinating child 1.50

Art — A165

1984, Oct. 26

601 A165 50c Dragon (hand rail) .15
602 A165 1k Capital .30
603 A165 2k Oval panel .55
604 A165 2k Deity .55
605 A165 3k Leaves .80
606 A165 4k Floral pattern 1.00
607 A165 8k Lotus flower (round panel) 2.00
Nos. 601-607 (7) 5.35

Nos. 601-604 and 607 vert.

9th Anniv. of the Republic A166

1984, Dec. 17

608 A166 1k River boats .25
609 A166 2k Aircraft .50
610 A166 4k Bridge building 1.00
611 A166 10k Surveying, construction 2.50
Nos. 608-611 (4) 4.25

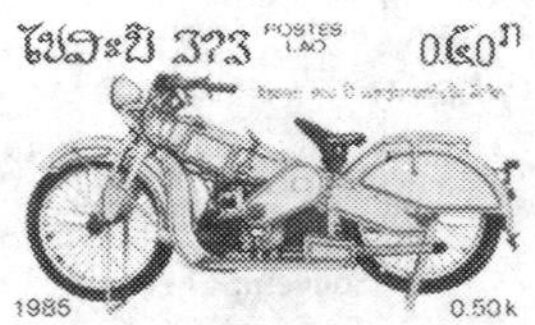

1986 World Cup Soccer Championships, Mexico — A167

Various match scenes and flag of Mexico.

1985, Jan. 18

612 A167 50c multicolored .15
613 A167 1k multi, diff. .25
614 A167 2k multi, diff. .50
615 A167 3k multi, diff. .75
616 A167 4k multi, diff. 1.00
617 A167 5k multi, diff. 1.25
618 A167 6k multi, diff. 1.50
Nos. 612-618 (7) 5.40

Souvenir Sheet

Perf. **$12^1/_2$**

619 A167 10k multi, diff. 2.75

No. 619 contains one stamp 32x40mm.

Motorcycle, Cent. — A168

1985, Feb. 25 ***Perf.*** **$12^1/_2$**

620 A168 50c shown .15
621 A168 1k 1920 Gnome Rhone .25
622 A168 2k 1928 F.N. M67C .50
623 A168 3k 1930 Indian Chief .75
624 A168 4k 1914 Rudge Multi 1.00
625 A168 5k 1953 Honda Benly J 1.25
626 A168 6k 1938 CZ 1.50
Nos. 620-626 (7) 5.40

Mushrooms A169

Lenin, 115th Birth Anniv. A170

1985, Apr. 8 ***Perf. 13***

627 A169 50c Amanita muscaria .15
628 A169 1k Boletus edulis .25
629 A169 2k Coprinus comatus .50
630 A169 2k Amanita rubescens .50
631 A169 3k Xerocomus subtomentosus .75
632 A169 4k Lepiota procera 1.00
633 A169 8k Paxillus involutus 2.00
Nos. 627-633 (7) 5.15

End of World War II, 40th Anniv. A169a

1k, Battle of Kursk. 2k, Red Army parade, Moscow. 4k, Battle of Stalingrad. 5k, Battle for Berlin. 6k, Victory parade through Brandenburg Gate.

1985, May **Litho.** ***Perf.*** **$12^1/_2$x12**

633A A169a 1k multicolored .30
633B A169a 2k multicolored .55
633C A169a 4k multicolored 1.10
633D A169a 5k multicolored 1.40
633E A169a 6k multicolored 1.65
Nos. 633A-633E (5) 5.00

1985, June 28 ***Perf.*** **$12^1/_2$**

634 A170 1k Reading Pravda, horiz. .30
635 A170 2k shown .60
636 A170 10k Addressing revolutionaries 2.00
Nos. 634-636 (3) 2.90

Orchids — A171 Fauna — A172

1985, July 5 ***Perf. 13***

637 A171 50c Cattleya percivaliana .15
638 A171 1k Odontoglossum luteopurpureum .25
639 A171 2k Cattleya lueddemanniana .50
640 A171 2k Maxillaria sanderiana .50
641 A171 3k Miltonia vexillaria .75
642 A171 4k Oncidium varicosum 1.00
643 A171 8k Cattleya dowiana aurea 2.00
Nos. 637-643 (7) 5.15

Souvenir Sheet

Perf. **$13^1/_2$x13**

644 A171 10k Catasetum fimbriatum 3.00

ARGENTINA '85, Buenos Aires. No. 644 contains one stamp 32x40mm.

1985, Aug. 15 ***Perf. 13***

645 A172 2k Macaca mulatta .45
646 A172 3k Bos sauveli .65
647 A172 4k Hystrix leucura, horiz. .90
648 A172 5k Selenarctos thibotanus, horiz. 1.10
649 A172 10k Manis pentadactyla 2.25
Nos. 645-649 (5) 5.35

Apollo-Soyuz Flight, 10th Anniv. — A173

1985, Sept. 6

650 A173 50c Apollo launch pad, vert. .15
651 A173 1k Soyuz launch pad, vert. .25
652 A173 2k Apollo approaching Soyuz .50
653 A173 2k Soyuz approaching Apollo .50
654 A173 3k Apollo, astronauts .75
655 A173 4k Soyuz, cosmonauts 1.00
656 A173 8k Docked spacecrafts 2.00
Nos. 650-656 (7) 5.15

Aircraft A174

1985, Oct. 25

657 A174 50c Fiat .15
658 A174 1k Cant z.501 .30
659 A174 2k MF-5 .60
660 A174 3k Macchi Castoldi .90
661 A174 4k Anzani 1.20
662 A174 5k Ambrosini 1.50
663 A174 6k Piaggio 1.75
Nos. 657-663 (7) 6.40

Souvenir Sheet

Perf. **$13x13^1/_2$**

664 A174 10k MF-4 6.50

ITALIA '85, Rome. No. 664 contains one stamp 40x32mm.

Miniature Sheet

Columbus's Fleet A175

1985, Oct. 25 ***Perf. 13***

665 Sheet of 5 + 4 labels 3.00
a. A175 1k Pinta .18
b. A175 2k Nina .35
c. A175 3k Santa Maria .55
d. A175 4k Columbus .75
e. A175 5k Map of 1st voyage .90

ITALIA '85.

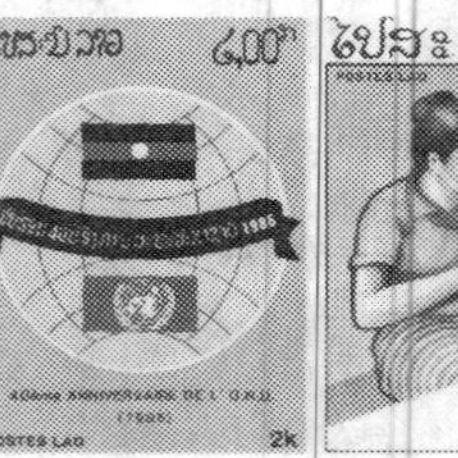

UN, 40th Anniv. — A176 Health — A177

1985, Oct.

666 A176 2k UN and natl. flag .65
667 A176 3k Coats of arms 1.00
668 A176 10k Map, globe 3.00
Nos. 666-668 (3) 4.65

1985, Nov. 15

669 A177 1k Mother feeding child .25
670 A177 3k Immunization, horiz. .75
671 A177 4k Hospital care, horiz. 1.00
672 A177 10k Breast-feeding 2.50
Nos. 669-672 (4) 4.50

10th Anniv. of the Republic A178

1985, Dec. 2

673 A178 3k shown .90
674 A178 10k multi, diff. 3.00

People's Revolutionary Party, 30th Anniv. — A179

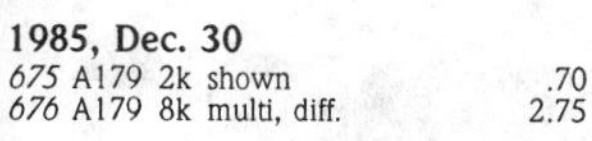

1985, Dec. 30

675 A179 2k shown .70
676 A179 8k multi, diff. 2.75

1986 World Cup Soccer Championships, Mexico — A180

Flowering Plants — A181

Various match scenes.

1986, Jan. 20

677 A180 50c multicolored .15
678 A180 1k multi, diff. .25
679 A180 2k multi, diff. .45
680 A180 3k multi, diff. .60
681 A180 4k multi, diff. .80
682 A180 5k multi, diff. 1.00
683 A180 6k multi, diff. 1.25
Nos. 677-683 (7) 4.50

Souvenir Sheet

Perf. 13x13½

684 A180 10k multi, diff. 2.30

No. 684 contains one stamp 40x32mm.

27th Congress of the Communist Party of the Soviet Union — A180a

1986, Jan. **Litho.** ***Perf. 12x12½***

684A A180a 4k Cosmonaut, spacecraft .85
684B A180a 20k Lenin 4.25

1986, Feb. 28 ***Perf. 13***

685 A181 50c Pelargonium grandiflorum .15
686 A181 1k Aquilegia vulgaris .25
687 A181 2k Fuchsia globosa .50
688 A181 3k Crocus aureus .70
689 A181 4k Althaea rosea .95
690 A181 5k Gladiolus purpureo 1.15
691 A181 6k Hyacinthus orientalis 1.40
Nos. 685-691 (7) 5.10

Butterflies A182

1986, Mar. 30

692 A182 50c Aporia hippia .15
693 A182 1k Euthalia irrubescens .25
694 A182 2k Japonica lutea .45
695 A182 3k Pratapa ctesia .65
696 A182 4k Kallina inachus .85
697 A182 5k Ixias pyrene 1.10
698 A182 6k Parantica sita 1.25
Nos. 692-698 (7) 4.70

A183

First Man in Space, 25th Anniv. — A184

Designs: 50c, Launch, Baikonur Space Center, vert. 1k, Molniya communications satellite, vert. 2k, Salyut space station. 3k, Yuri Gagarin, Sputnik 1 disengaging stage. 4k, Luna 3, the Moon, vert. 5k, Komarov on first space walk, vert. 6k, Luna 16 lifting off Moon, vert. 10k, Spacecrafts docking.

1986, Apr. 12

699 A183 50c multicolored .15
700 A183 1k multicolored .25
701 A183 2k multicolored .50
702 A183 3k multicolored .75
703 A183 4k multicolored 1.00
704 A183 5k multicolored 1.25
705 A183 6k multicolored 1.40
Nos. 699-705 (7) 5.30

Souvenir Sheet

Perf. 13x13½

706 A184 10k multicolored 3.00

Fauna A185

AMERIPEX '86, Chicago — A186

Perf. 12½x13, 13x12½

1986, May 22

707 A185 50c Giraffa camelopardalis .15
708 A185 1k Panthera leo .20
709 A185 2k Loxodonta africana africana .45
710 A185 3k Macropus rufus .65
711 A185 4k Gymnobelideus leadbeateri .85
712 A185 5k Phoenicopterus ruber 1.05
713 A185 6k Ailuropoda melanoleucus 1.25
Nos. 707-713 (7) 4.60

Souvenir Sheet

Perf. 13½x13

714 A186 10k Bison 3.00

Nos. 707-712 vert.

Pheasants — A187

1986, June 29 ***Perf. 12½x13***

715 A187 50c Argusianus argus .15
716 A187 1k Cennaeus nycthemerus .25
717 A187 2k Phasianus colchicus .50
718 A187 3k Chrysolophus amherstiae .70
719 A187 4k Symaticus reevesii .95
720 A187 5k Chrysolophus pictus 1.15
721 A187 6k Syrmaticus soemmerringii 1.40
Nos. 715-721 (7) 5.10

Snakes — A188

Perf. 12½x13, 13x12½

1986, July 21

722 A188 50c Elaphe guttata .15
723 A188 1k Thalerophis richardi .20
724 A188 1k Lampropeltis doliata annulata .20
725 A188 2k Diadophis amabilis .40
726 A188 4k Boiga dendrophila .80
727 A188 5k Python molurus 1.00
728 A188 8k Naja naja 1.60
Nos. 722-728 (7) 4.35

Nos. 722-723 and 728 vert.

Halley's Comet — A189

1986, Aug. 22 ***Perf. 12½x13***

729 A189 50c Acropolis, Athens .15
730 A189 1k Bayeux Tapestry .25
731 A189 2k Edmond Halley .50
732 A189 3k Vega space probe .70
733 A189 4k Galileo .95
734 A189 5k Comet 1.20
735 A189 6k Giotto probe 1.90
Nos. 729-735 (7) 5.65

Souvenir Sheet

Perf. 13x13½

736 A189 10k Comet, diff. 3.00

Nos. 730-731, 732-733 and 734-735 printed se-tenant in continuous designs. Size of Nos. 730, 732 and 735: 46x25mm. Size of Nos. 731, 733-734: 23x25mm. No. 736 contains one stamp 40x32mm.

Dogs — A190

Cacti — A191

1986, Aug. 28 ***Perf. 13***

737 A190 50c Keeshond .15
738 A190 1k Elkhound .20
739 A190 2k Bernese .45
740 A190 3k Pointing griffon .65
741 A190 4k Sheep dog (border collie) .85
742 A190 5k Irish water spaniel 1.05
743 A190 6k Briard 1.25
Nos. 737-743 (7) 4.60

Souvenir Sheet

Perf. 13x13½

744 A190 10k Brittany spaniels 2.00

STOCKHOLMIA '86. Nos. 738-743 horiz. No. 744 contains one 40x32mm stamp.

1986, Sept. 28 ***Perf. 13***

Designs: 50c, Mammillaria matudae. 1k, Mammillaria theresae. 2k, Ariocarpus trigonus. 3k, Notocactus crassigibbus. 4k, Astrophytum asterias hybridum. 5k, Melocactus manzanus. 6k, Astrophytum ornatum hybridum.

745 A191 50c multicolored .15
746 A191 1k multicolored .20
747 A191 2k multicolored .45
748 A191 3k multicolored .70
749 A191 4k multicolored .85
750 A191 5k multicolored 1.05
751 A191 6k multicolored 1.25
Nos. 745-751 (7) 4.65

Intl. Peace Year — A192

UNESCO Programs in Laos — A193

1986, Oct. 24

752 A192 3k Natl. arms, dove, globe .75
753 A192 5k Dove, shattered bomb 1.25
754 A192 10k Emblem held aloft 2.50
Nos. 752-754 (3) 4.50

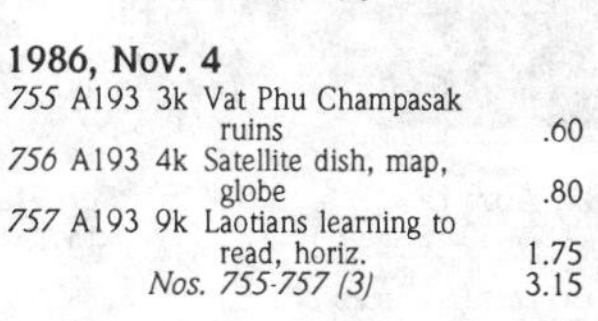

1986, Nov. 4

755 A193 3k Vat Phu Champasak ruins .60
756 A193 4k Satellite dish, map, globe .80
757 A193 9k Laotians learning to read, horiz. 1.75
Nos. 755-757 (3) 3.15

1988 Winter Olympics, Calgary A194

1987, Jan. 14

758 A194 50c Speed skating .15
759 A194 1k Biathlon .25
760 A194 2k Pairs figure skating .45
761 A194 3k Luge .65
762 A194 4k 4-Man bobsled .85
763 A194 5k Ice hockey 1.10
764 A194 6k Ski jumping 1.25
Nos. 758-764 (7) 4.70

Souvenir Sheet

Perf. 13½x13

765 A194 10k Slalom 2.50

Nos. 758-760 vert. No. 765 contains one stamp 32x40mm.

1988 Summer Olympics, Seoul — A195

1987, Feb. 2 ***Perf. 12½x13, 13x13½***

766 A195 50c Women's gymnastics .15
767 A195 1k Women's discus .25
768 A195 2k Running .45
769 A195 3k Equestrian .75
770 A195 4k Women's javelin .90
771 A195 5k High jump 1.10
772 A195 6k Wrestling 1.35
Nos. 766-772 (7) 4.95

Souvenir Sheet

Perf. 12½

773 A195 10k Runners leaving start 2.25

Nos. 766, 768, 770 and 772 vert. No. 773 contains one stamp 40x32mm.

Dogs — A196

1987, Mar. 5 *Perf. $12^1/_2$x13*

774	A196	50c	Great Dane	.15
775	A196	1k	Labrador retriever	.25
776	A196	2k	St. Bernard	.45
777	A196	3k	Schippercke	.75
778	A196	4k	Alsatian (German shepherd)	.90
779	A196	5k	Beagle	1.10
780	A196	6k	Spaniel	1.35
			Nos. 774-780 (7)	4.95

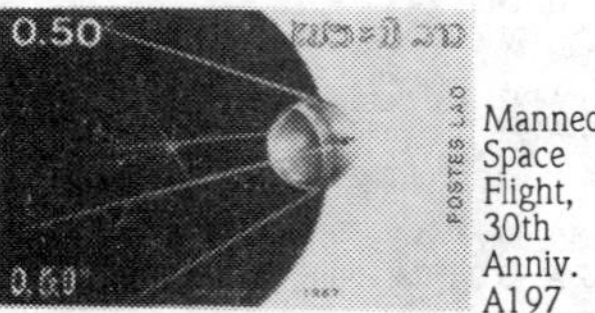

Manned Space Flight, 30th Anniv. A197

1987, Apr. 12 *Perf. 13*

781	A197	50c	Sputnik 1	.15
782	A197	1k	Sputnik 2	.20
783	A197	2k	Cosmos 87	.35
784	A197	3k	Cosmos	.55
785	A197	4k	Mars	.75
786	A197	5k	Luna 1	.90
787	A197	9k	Luna 3, vert.	1.65
			Nos. 781-787 (7)	4.55

Packet Ships and Stampless Packet Letters A198

Canada No. 282 A199

1987, May 12

788	A198	50c	"Montreal"	.15
789	A198	1k	"Paid Montreal"	.20
790	A198	2k	"Paid" and "Montreal Nov 24"	.40
791	A198	3k	"Williamsbvrg" and "Forwarded"	.60
792	A198	4k	"Montreal Fe 18 1844"	.80
793	A198	5k	"Paid" and "Montreal Jy 10 1848"	1.00
794	A198	6k	"Paid" and "Montreal Paid Ap 16 1861 Canada"	1.20
			Nos. 788-794 (7)	4.35

Souvenir Sheet

Perf. $12^1/_2$

795	A199	10k	multicolored	2.50

CAPEX '87.

Orchids — A200

1987, Aug. 10 **Litho.** *Perf. 13*

796	A200	3k	*Vanda teres*	.15
796A	A200	7k	*Laeliocattleya*	.20
796B	A200	10k	*Paphiopedilum hibrido*	.25
796C	A200	39k	*Sobralia*	.95
796D	A200	44k	*Paphiopedilum hibrido*, diff.	1.00
796E	A200	47k	*Paphiopedilum hibrido*, diff.	1.10
796F	A200	50k	*Cattleya trianaei*	1.15
			Nos. 796-796F (7)	4.80

Souvenir Sheet

Perf. $12^1/_2$

796G	A200	95k	*Vanda tricolor*	2.50

No. 796G contains one 32x40mm stamp.

Automobiles A201

1987, July 2 **Litho.** *Perf. $12^1/_2$*

797	A201	50c	Toyota 480	.15
798	A201	1k	Alfa 33	.25
799	A201	2k	Ford Fiesta	.75
800	A201	3k	Datsun	.68
801	A201	4k	Vauxhall Cavalier	.90
802	A201	5k	Renault 5	1.10
803	A201	6k	Rover-800	1.35
			Nos. 797-803 (7)	5.18

Miniature Sheet

Perf. 13

804	A201	10k	Talbot	2.25

HAFNIA '87, Denmark A202

Various Indian elephants.

1987, Sept. 2 *Perf. 13*

805	A202	50c	Adult, calf	.15
806	A202	1k	Two adults, calf	.25
807	A202	2k	Adult eating grass	.45
808	A202	3k	Adult, diff.	.75
809	A202	4k	Adult, calf drinking	.90
810	A202	5k	Adult, diff.	1.10
811	A202	6k	Adult, vert.	1.35
			Nos. 805-811 (7)	4.95

Souvenir Sheet

812	A202	10k	Herd, diff.	2.50

No. 812 contains one stamp 40x32mm.

Horses A203

Perf. 13x$12^1/_2$, $12^1/_2$x13

1987, June 3 **Litho.**

813	A203	50c	multicolored	.15
814	A203	1k	multi, diff.	.30
815	A203	2k	multi, diff.	.55
816	A203	3k	multi, diff.	.85
817	A203	4k	multi, diff.	1.15
818	A203	5k	multi, diff.	1.40
819	A203	6k	multi, diff.	1.70
			Nos. 813-819 (7)	6.10

Nos. 814-819 vert.

Fish A204

Designs: 3k, Botia macracantha. 7k, Oxymocanthus longirostris. 10k, Adioryx caudimaculatus. 39k, Synchiropus splendidus. 44k, Cephalopolis miniatus. 47k, Dendrochirus zebra. 50k, Pomacantus semicirculatus.

1987, Oct. 14 **Litho.** *Perf. 13x$12^1/_2$*

820	A204	3k	multicolored	.15
821	A204	7k	multicolored	.20
822	A204	10k	multicolored	.30
823	A204	39k	multicolored	.90
824	A204	44k	multicolored	1.00
825	A204	47k	multicolored	1.05
826	A204	50k	multicolored	1.15
			Nos. 820-826 (7)	4.75

World Food Day A205

1987, Oct. 16 *Perf. 13*

827	A205	1k	Tending crops	.15
828	A205	3k	Harvesting corn, vert.	.15
829	A205	5k	Harvesting wheat	.15
830	A205	63k	Youths, fish, vert.	1.45
831	A205	142k	Tending pigs, chickens	3.25
			Nos. 827-831 (5)	5.15

Cultivation of Rice in Mountainous Regions — A206

1987, Nov. 9 *Perf. 13*

832	A206	64k	Tilling soil	1.50
833	A206	100k	Rice paddy	2.30

October Revolution, Russia, 70th Anniv. — A207

Paintings: 1k, Wounded soldier on battlefield. 2k, Mother and child. 4k, Storming the Winter Palace. 8k, Lenin and revolutionaries. 10k, Rebuilding Red Square.

1987, Nov. *Perf. 12x$12^1/_2$*

834	A207	1k	multicolored	.25
835	A207	2k	multicolored	.45
836	A207	4k	multicolored	.80
837	A207	8k	multicolored	1.65
838	A207	10k	multicolored	2.25
			Nos. 834-838 (5)	5.40

Women Wearing Regional Costumes — A208

1987, Dec. 2

839	A208	7k	Mountain	.20
840	A208	38k	Urban	.95
841	A208	144k	Mountain, diff.	3.35
			Nos. 839-841 (3)	4.50

A209

1988 Winter Olympics, Calgary — A210

1988, Jan.10 *Perf. 13x$12^1/_2$*

842	A209	1k	Bobsled	.15
843	A209	4k	Biathlon	.15
844	A209	20k	Skiing	.50
845	A209	42k	Ice hockey	1.00
846	A209	63k	Speed skating	1.50
847	A209	70k	Slalom	1.65
			Nos. 842-847 (6)	4.95

Souvenir Sheet

Perf. 13

848	A210	95k	Slalom, diff.	2.50

No. 848 contains one stamp 40x32mm.

ESSEN '88 — A211

Locomotives: 6k, Nonpareil, vert. 15k, Rocket, vert. 20k, Royal George. 25k, Trevithick. 30k, Novelty. 100k, Tom Thumb. 95k, Locomotion.

1988 *Perf. $12^1/_2$x13, 13x$12^1/_2$*

849	A211	6k	multicolored	.15
850	A211	15k	multicolored	.35
851	A211	20k	multicolored	.50
852	A211	25k	multicolored	.60
853	A211	30k	multicolored	.70
854	A211	100k	multicolored	2.30
			Nos. 849-854 (6)	4.60

Souvenir Sheet

Perf. 13

855	A211	95k	multicolored	2.50

No. 855 contains one stamp 40x32mm.

Intl. Year of Shelter for the Homeless A212

1988 **Litho.** *Perf. 13*

856	A212	1k	Building frame of house	.15
857	A212	27k	Cutting lumber	.62
858	A212	46k	Completed house	1.15
859	A212	70k	Community	1.75
			Nos. 856-859 (4)	3.67

Dinosaurs — A213

Perf. 13x12½, 12½x13

1988, Mar. 3 **Litho.**

860 A213 3k Tyrannosaurus .15
861 A213 7k Ceratosaurus nasicornis .16
862 A213 39k Iguanodon bernissartensis .88
863 A213 44k Scolosaurus 1.00
864 A213 47k Phororhacus 1.10
865 A213 50k Trachodon 1.15
Nos. 860-865 (6) 4.44

Souvenir Sheet

Perf. 12½

866 A213 95k Pteranodon 2.50

JUVALUX '88. Nos. 861-864 vert.

Identifications on Nos. 860 and No. 865 are switched.

No. 866 contains one 40x32mm stamp.

WHO, 40th Anniv. A214

1988, Apr. 8 *Perf. 12½*

867 A214 5k Students, teacher .15
868 A214 27k Pest control .62
869 A214 164k Public water supply, vert. 3.75
Nos. 867-869 (3) 4.52

Flowers — A215 Birds — A216

1988 *Perf. 13x12½*

870 A215 8k *Plumieria rubra* .18
871 A215 9k *Althaea rosea* .22
872 A215 15k *Ixora coccinea* .40
873 A215 33k *Cassia fistula* .78
874 A215 64k *Dahlia coccinea* (pink) 1.50
875 A215 69k *Dahlia coccinea* (yellow) 1.65
Nos. 870-875 (6) 4.73

Souvenir Sheet

Perf. 13

876 A215 95k Plumieria, Althaea, Ixora 2.50

FINLANDIA '88. No. 876 contains one 32x40mm stamp.

1988 *Perf. 13*

877 A216 6k *Pelargopsis capensis* .15
878 A216 10k *Coturnix japonica* .24
879 A216 13k *Psittacula roseata* .32
880 A216 44k *Treron bicincta* 1.05
881 A216 63k *Pycnonotus melanicterus* 1.50
882 A216 64k *Ducula badia* 1.55
Nos. 877-882 (6) 4.81

1988 Summer Olympics, Seoul — A217

1988 *Perf. 12½x12*

883 A217 2k Javelin .15
884 A217 5k Long jump .15
885 A217 10k Horizontal bar .24
886 A217 12k Canoeing .30
887 A217 38k Balance beam .90
888 A217 46k Fencing 1.10
889 A217 100k Wrestling 2.35
Nos. 883-889 (7) 5.19

Souvenir Sheet

Perf. 13

889A A217 95k Horizontal bar, diff. 2.25

No. 889A contains one 40x32mm stamp.

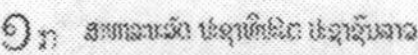

Decorative Stencils A218

1988 *Perf. 13*

890 A218 1k Scarf .15
891 A218 2k Pagoda entrance, vert. .15
892 A218 3k Pagoda wall, vert. .15
893 A218 25k Pagoda pillar .60
894 A218 163k Skirt 4.00
Nos. 890-894 (5) 5.05

Completion of the 5-Year Plan (1981-85) — A219

1988 **Litho.** *Perf. 13*

895 A219 20k Health care .45
896 A219 40k Literacy .88
897 A219 50k Irrigation 1.10
898 A219 100k Communication, transport 2.20
Nos. 895-898 (4) 4.63

Intl. Red Cross and Red Crescent Organizations, 125th Annivs. — A220

Designs: 4k, Dove, 3 stylized figures representing mankind, vert. 52k, Giving aid to the handicapped, vert. 144k, Child immunization.

1988

899 A220 4k multi .15
900 A220 52k multi 1.15
901 A220 144k multi 3.20
Nos. 899-901 (3) 4.50

Chess Champions — A220a

1988 **Litho.** *Perf. 13*

901A A220a 1k R. Segura .15
901B A220a 2k Adolph Anderssen .15
901C A220a 3k P. Morphy .15
901D A220a 6k W. Steinitz .15
901E A220a 7k E. Lasker .16
901F A220a 12k J.R. Capablanca .28
901G A220a 172k A. Alekhine 3.90
Nos. 901A-901G (7) 4.94

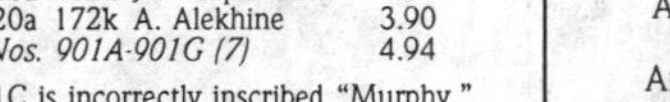

Nos. 901C is incorrectly inscribed "Murphy."

1990 World Cup Soccer Championships, Italy — A221

Various plays.

1989 *Perf. 13x12½*

902 A221 10k multi .22
903 A221 15k multi, diff. .35
904 A221 20k multi, diff. .45
905 A221 25k multi, diff. .58
906 A221 45k multi, diff. 1.00
907 A221 105k multi, diff. 2.40
Nos. 902-907 (6) 5.00

Souvenir Sheet

Perf. 13

907A A221 95k multi, diff. 2.25

No. 907A contains one 40x32mm stamp.

INDIA '89 A222

Cats.

1989, Jan. 7 *Perf. 12½*

908 A222 5k multi .15
909 A222 6k multi, diff. .15
910 A222 10k multi, diff. .22
911 A222 20k multi, diff. .45
912 A222 50k multi, diff. 1.15
913 A222 172k multi, diff. 3.90
Nos. 908-913 (6) 6.02

Souvenir Sheet

Perf. 13

914 A222 95k multi, diff. 2.25

No. 914 contains one 32x40mm stamp.

1992 Winter Olympics, Albertville A223

Various figure skaters.

1989, May 1 *Perf. 13*

915 A223 9k multi, vert. .20
916 A223 10k shown .22
917 A223 15k multi, diff., vert. .32
918 A223 24k multi, diff., vert. .55
919 A223 29k multi, diff., vert. .65
920 A223 114k multi, diff., vert. 2.55
Nos. 915-920 (6) 4.49

Souvenir Sheet

Perf. 12½

921 A223 95k Pairs figure skating 2.25

No. 921 contains one 32x40mm stamp.

People's Army, 40th Anniv. A224

1989, Jan. 20 *Perf. 13*

922 A224 1k shown .15
923 A224 2k Military school, vert. .15
924 A224 3k Health care .15
925 A224 250k Ready for combat 5.50
Nos. 922-925 (4) 5.95

1992 Summer Olympics, Barcelona — A225

Perf. 12x12½, 12½x12

1989, June 1 **Litho.**

926 A225 5k Pole vault, vert. .15
927 A225 15k Gymnastic rings, vert. .35
928 A225 20k Cycling .45
929 A225 25k Boxing .58
930 A225 70k Archery, vert. 1.60
931 A225 120k Swimming, vert. 2.70
Nos. 926-932 (7) 8.08

Souvenir Sheet

Perf. 13

932 A225 95k Baseball 2.25

No. 932 contains one 32x40mm stamp.

PHILEXFRANCE '89 — A226

Paintings by Picasso: 5k, *Beggars by the Edge of the Sea.* 7k, *Maternity.* 8k, *Portrait of Jaime S. Le Bock.* 9k, *Harlequins.* 105k, *Dog with Boy.* 114k, *Girl Balancing on Ball.*

1989, July 17 *Perf. 12½x13*

933 A226 5k multi .15
934 A226 7k multi .15
935 A226 8k multi .18
936 A226 9k multi .20
937 A226 105k multi 2.35
938 A226 114k multi 2.55
Nos. 933-938 (6) 5.58

Souvenir Sheet

Perf. 12½

939 A226 95k shown 2.25

No. 939 contains one 32x40mm stamp.

Cuban Revolution, 30th Anniv. — A227

1989, Apr. 20 **Litho.** *Perf. 13*

940 A227 45k shown 1.00
941 A227 50k Flags 1.15

Fight the Destruction of Forests — A228

1989, Mar. 30 Litho. *Perf. 13*

942 A228 4k Planting saplings .15
943 A228 10k Fight forest fires .22
944 A228 12k Do not chop down trees .28
945 A228 200k Map of woodland 4.50
Nos. 942-945 (4) 5.15

Nos. 944-945 are vert.

Jawaharlal Nehru (1889-1964), Indian Statesman — A229

1989, Nov. 9 Litho. *Perf. 12½*

946 A229 1k multicolored .15
947 A229 60k multi, horiz. 1.35
948 A229 200k multi, diff. 4.50
Nos. 946-948 (3) 6.00

Mani Ikara Zapota — A230

A231

1989, Sept. 18 *Perf. 12½x13*

949 A230 5k shown .15
950 A230 20k Psidium guajava .45
951 A230 20k Annona sguamosa .45
952 A230 30k Durio zibethinus .68
953 A230 50k Punica granatum 1.15
954 A230 172k Moridica charautia 4.00
Nos. 949-954 (6) 6.88

1989, Oct. 19 Litho. *Perf. 12½*

Historic Monuments: No. 955, That Sikhotabong, Khammouane. No. 956, That Dam, Vientiane. No. 957, That Ing Hang, Savannakhet. No. 958, Ho Vay Phra Thatluang, Vientiane.

955 A231 5k multicolored .15
956 A231 15k multicolored .35
957 A231 61k multicolored 1.40
958 A231 161k multicolored 3.70
Nos. 955-958 (4) 5.60

1992 Summer Olympics, Barcelona A232

1990, Mar. 5 Litho. *Perf. 12½x13*

959 A232 10k Basketball .24
960 A232 30k Hurdles .70
961 A232 45k High jump 1.03
962 A232 50k Cycling 1.15
963 A232 60k Javelin 1.40
964 A232 90k Tennis 2.00
Nos. 959-964 (6) 6.52

Souvenir Sheet

965 A232 95k Rhythmic gymnastics 2.20

1992 Winter Olympics, Albertville A233

1990, June 20 *Perf. 13*

966 A233 10k Speed skating .24
967 A233 25k Cross country skiing, vert. .60
968 A233 30k Slalom skiing .70
969 A233 35k Luge .80
970 A233 80k Ice dancing, vert. 1.85
971 A233 90k Biathlon 2.00
Nos. 966-971 (6) 6.19

Souvenir Sheet

972 A233 95k Hockey, vert. 2.20

New Zealand Birds A234

Designs: 10k, Prosthemadera novaeseelandie. 15k, Alauda arvensis. 20k, Haemotopus unicolor. 50k, Phalacrocorax carbo. 60k, Demigretta sacra. 100k Apteryx australis mantelli. 95k, Phalacrocorax corunculatus.

1990, Aug. 24 *Perf. 12½*

973 A234 10k multicolored .24
974 A234 15k multicolored .35
975 A234 20k multicolored .45
976 A234 50k multicolored 1.15
977 A234 60k multicolored 1.40
978 A234 100k multicolored 2.30
Nos. 973-978 (6) 5.89

Souvenir Sheet

979 A234 95k multicolored 2.20

World Stamp Expo, New Zealand '90. No. 979 contains one 32x40mm stamp.

That Luang Temple, 430th Anniv. A235

Perf. 13x12½, 12½x13

1990, July 25

980 A235 60k 1867 1.40
981 A235 70k 1930 1.60
982 A235 130k 1990, vert. 3.00
Nos. 980-982 (3) 6.00

Ho Chi Minh (1890-1969), Vietnamese Leader — A236

1990, May 11 *Perf. 13*

983 A236 40k Addressing people .90
984 A236 60k With Laotian President 1.40
985 A236 160k Waving, vert. 3.65
Nos. 983-985 (3) 5.95

UN Development Program, 40th Anniv. — A237

1990, Oct. 24 Litho. *Perf. 13*

986 A237 30k Surgeons .68
987 A237 45k Fishermen 1.00
988 A237 80k Flight controller, vert. 1.80
989 A237 90k Power plant 2.00
Nos. 986-989 (4) 5.48

15th Anniv. of the Republic A238

Designs: 15k, Placing flowers at monument. 20k, Celebratory parade. 80k, Visiting sick. 120k, Women marching with banner.

1990, Dec. 2 Litho. *Perf. 13*

990 A238 15k multicolored .35
991 A238 20k multicolored .45
992 A238 80k multicolored 1.80
993 A238 120k multicolored 2.75
Nos. 990-993 (4) 5.35

New Year's Day A239

1990, Nov. 20

994 A239 5k shown .15
995 A239 10k Parade .25
996 A239 50k Ceremony 1.15

Size: 40x29mm

997 A239 150k Ceremomy, diff. 3.35
Nos. 994-997 (4) 4.90

World Cup Soccer Championships, Italy — A240

Designs: Various soccer players in action.

1990 Litho. *Perf. 13*

998 A240 10k multicolored .25
999 A240 15k multicolored .35
1000 A240 20k multicolored .50
1001 A240 25k multicolored .60
1002 A240 45k multicolored 1.05
1003 A240 105k multicolored 2.50
Nos. 998-1003 (6) 5.25

Souvenir Sheet

Perf. 12½

1004 A240 95k multi, horiz. 2.25

No. 1004 contains one 39x31mm stamp.

Intl. Literacy Year — A241

1990, Feb. 27 Litho. *Perf. 12½*

1005 A241 10k shown .50
1006 A241 50k Woman with child, vert. 2.40
1007 A241 60k Monk teaching class 2.85
1008 A241 150k Two women, man reading 7.00
Nos. 1005-1008 (4) 12.75

Stamp World London '90 — A242

Stamps, modes of mail transport: 15k, Great Britain #1, stagecoach. 20k, US #1, train. 40k, France #3, balloons. 50k, Sardinia #1, post rider. 60k, Indo-China #3, elephant. 95k, Laos #272, jet. 100k, Spain #1, sailing ship.

1990, Apr. 26 Litho. *Perf. 13x12½*

1009 A242 15k multicolored .42
1010 A242 20k multicolroed .58
1011 A242 40k multicolored 1.15
1012 A242 50k multicolored 1.40
1013 A242 60k multicolored 1.70
1014 A242 100k multicolored 2.90
Nos. 1009-1014 (6) 8.15

Souvenir Sheet

Perf. 13

1015 A242 95k multicolored 2.85

No. 1015 contains one 40x32mm stamp.

Endangered Animals — A242a

1990, Sept. 15 Litho. *Perf. 12½*

1015A A242a 10k Brow-antlered deer .16
1015B A242a 20k Gaur .32
1015C A242a 40k Wild water buffalo .65
1015D A242a 45k Kouprey .72
1015E A242a 120k Javan rhinoceros 1.95
Nos. 1015A-1015E (5) 3.80

A243

1992 Olympics, Barcelona and Albertville A244

Perf. 12½x12, 12x12½, 13 (A244)

1991, Jan. 25

1016 A243 22k 2-man canoe .15
1017 A243 32k 1-man kayak .15
1018 A244 32k Bobsled, vert. .15
1019 A244 135k Cross country skiing .42
1020 A244 250k Ski jumping .78
1021 A244 275k Biathlon .85
1022 A243 285k Diving, vert. .90
1023 A243 330k Sailing, vert. 1.05
1024 A244 900k Speed skating 2.75
1025 A243 1000k Swimming 3.10
Nos. 1016-1025 (10) 10.30

Souvenir Sheets

Perf. 12½, 13½x13

1026 A243 700k 2-man kayak 2.20
1027 A244 700k Slalom skiing, vert. 2.20

No. 1026 contains one 40x32mm stamp. No. 1027 contains one 32x40mm stamp.

Tourism — A245

Designs: 155k, Rapids, Champassak. 220k, Vangvieng. 235k, Waterfalls, Saravane, vert. 1000k Plain of Jars, Xieng Khouang, vert.

1991 *Perf. 13x12½, 12½x13*

1028 A245 155k multicolored .50
1029 A245 220k multicolored .70
1030 A245 235k multicolored .75
1031 A245 1000k multicolored 3.10
Nos. 1028-1031 (4) 5.05

1994 World Cup Soccer Championships — A246

Designs: Various players in action.

1991 **Litho.** *Perf. 13*

1032 A246 32k multicolored .15
1033 A246 330k multicolored 1.00
1034 A246 340k multi, vert. 1.05
1035 A246 400k multicolored 1.25
1036 A246 500k multicolored 1.55
Nos. 1032-1036 (5) 5.00

Souvenir Sheet

Perf. 13½x13

1037 A246 700k multi, vert. 2.15

No. 1037 contains one 32x40mm stamp.

Espamer '91, Buenos Aires — A247

Espamer '91 Type

1991, June 30 **Litho.** *Perf. 12½x12*

1038 A247 25k Mallard 4-4-2 .15
1039 A247 32k Pacific 231 4-6-2 .15
1040 A247 285k American style 4-8-4 1.15
1041 A247 650k Canadian Pacific 4-6-2 2.65
1042 A247 750k Beyer-Garrant 4-8-2 2-8-4 3.00
Nos. 1038-1042 (5) 7.10

Souvenir Sheet

Perf. 12½

1043 A247 700k Inter-city diesel 2.60

Espamer '91, Buenos Aires. No. 1039 does not show denomination or country in Latin characters. Size of Nos. 1038, 1040-1042: 44x28mm.

Musical Celebrations — A248

Designs: 220k, Man playing mong, vert. 275k, Man, woman singing Siphandone, vert. 545k, Man, woman singing Khapngum. 690k, People dancing.

1991, July 10 **Litho.** *Perf. 13*

1044 A248 20k multicolored .15
1045 A248 220k multicolored .68
1046 A248 275k multicolored .85
1047 A248 545k multicolored 1.70
1048 A248 690k multicolored 2.15
Nos. 1044-1048 (5) 5.53

Butterflies — A248a

1991, Oct. 15 **Litho.** *Perf. 12½x12*

1048A A248a 55k Sasakia charonda .18
1048B A248a 90k Luendorfia puziloi .28
1048C A248a 255k Papilio bianor .80
1048D A248a 285k Papilio machaon .90
1048E A248a 900k Graphium doson 2.80
Nos. 1048A-1048E (5) 4.96

Souvenir Sheet

Perf. 13

1048F A248a 700k Cyrestis thyodamas 2.20

No. 1048F contains one 40x32mm stamp. Phila Nippon '91.

Arbor Day — A249

700k, 6 people planting trees. 800k, Nursery.

1991, June 1 *Perf. 12½*

1049 A249 250k multicolored .80
1050 A249 700k multicolored 2.20
1051 A249 800k multicolored 2.50
Nos. 1049-1051 (3) 5.50

1992 Winter Olympics, Albertville — A250

Perf. 12½x12, 12x12½

1992, Jan. 12 **Litho.**

1052 A250 200k Bobsled .65
1053 A250 220k Skiing .68
1054 A250 250k Skiing, horiz. .80
1055 A250 500k Luge 1.60
1056 A250 600k Figure skater 1.90
Nos. 1052-1056 (5) 5.63

Souvenir Sheet

Perf. 12½

1057 A250 700k Speed skater 2.20

No. 1057 contains one 32x40mm stamp.

1992 Summer Olympics, Barcelona — A251

1992, Feb. 21 **Litho.** *Perf. 12½*

1058 A251 32k Women's running .15
1059 A251 245k Baseball .78
1060 A251 275k Tennis .85
1061 A251 285k Basketball .90
1062 A251 900k Boxing, horiz. 2.85
Nos. 1058-1062 (5) 5.53

World Health Day A252

Designs: 200k, Spraying for mosquitoes. 255k, Campaign against smoking. 330k, Receiving blood donation. 1000k, Immunizing child, vert.

1992, Apr. 7

1063 A252 200k multicolored .62
1064 A252 255k multicolored .80
1065 A252 330k multicolored 1.05
1066 A252 1000k multicolored 3.10
Nos. 1063-1066 (4) 5.57

A253 A254

Flags, ball and players: 260k, Argentina, Italy. 305k, Germany, Great Britain. 310k, US, World Cup trophy (no players). 350k, Italy, Great Britain. 800k, Germany, Argentina.

1992, May 1 **Litho.** *Perf. 13*

1067 A253 260k multicolored .80
1068 A253 305k multicolored .90
1069 A253 310k multicolored .95
1070 A253 350k multicolored 1.10
1071 A253 800k multicolored 2.50
Nos. 1067-1071 (5) 6.25

Souvenir Sheet

Perf. 12½

1072 A253 700k Goalie 3.75

1994 World Cup Soccer Championships, US.

1992, Nov. 8 **Litho.** *Perf. 13*

Children playing.

1073 A254 220k Playing drum .95
1074 A254 285k Jumping rope, horiz. 1.20
1075 A254 330k Walking on stilts 1.40
1076 A254 400k Escape from line, horiz. 1.70
Nos. 1073-1076 (4) 5.25

Poisonous Snakes A255

Perf. 12½x13, 13x12½

1992, July 10 **Litho.**

1078 A255 280k Naja naja kaouthia 1.25
1079 A255 295k Naja naja atra 1.25
1080 A255 420k Trimeresurus wagleri 1.75
1081 A255 700k Ophiophagus hannah, vert. 3.00
Nos. 1078-1081 (4) 7.25

Restoration of Wat Phou — A256

Different views of Wat Phou.

Perf. 13x12½, 12½x13

1992, Aug. 22 **Litho.**

1082 A256 185k multicolored .55
1083 A256 220k multicolored .65
1084 A256 1200k multi, horiz. 3.65
Nos. 1082-1084 (3) 4.85

Genoa '92 A257

Sailing ships and maps by: 100k, Juan Martinez. 300k, Piri Reis, vert. 350k, Paolo del Pozo Toscanelli. 400k, Gabriel de Vallseca. 455k, Juan Martinez, diff. 700k, Juan de la Cosa.

Perf. 13x12½, 12½x13

1992, Sept. 12

1085 A257 100k multicolored .32
1086 A257 300k multicolored .95
1087 A257 350k multicolored 1.15
1088 A257 400k multicolored 1.30
1089 A257 455k multicolored 1.50
Nos. 1085-1089 (5) 5.22

Souvenir Sheet

Perf. 13

1090 A257 700k multicolored 2.25

Traditional Costumes of the Montagnards A258

Various costumes.

1992, Oct. 2 **Litho.** *Perf. 13*

1091 A258 25k multicolored .15
1092 A258 55k multicolored .18
1093 A258 400k multicolored 1.25
1094 A258 1200k multicolored 3.75
Nos. 1091-1094 (4) 5.33

A259 A260

UN, UNESCO emblems, stylized faces and: 330k, Drum. 1000k, Traditional flute.

1991, Nov. 1 **Litho.** *Perf. 13*

1095 A259 285k shown .90
1096 A259 330k multicolored 1.05
1097 A259 1000k multicolored 3.00
Nos. 1095-1097 (3) 4.95

Cultural Development Decade, 1988-1997.

1992, Dec. 22

Designs: Apes.

1098 A260 10k Black gibbon .15
1099 A260 100k Douc langur .32
1100 A260 250k Pileated gibbon .78
1101 A260 430k Francois langur 1.35
1102 A260 800k Pygmy loris 2.50
Nos. 1098-1102 (5) 5.10

Natl. Customs A261

Designs: 100k, Woman praying before Buddha, vert. 160k, Procession. 1500k, People giving food to monks.

1992, Dec. 2 *Perf. 12½*

1103 A261 100k multicolored .42
1104 A261 140k multicolored .60
1105 A261 160k multicolored .68
1106 A261 1500k multicolored 6.30
Nos. 1103-1106 (4) 8.00

First Subway System, 130th Anniv. A262

1993, Jan. 9 Litho. *Perf. 13*

1107	A262	15k	New York	.15
1108	A262	50k	Berlin	.20
1109	A262	100k	Paris	.42
1110	A262	200k	London	.85
1111	A262	900k	Moscow	3.70
			Nos. 1107-1111 (5)	5.32

Souvenir Sheet

Perf. 13x13½

1112 A262 700k Antique engine, vert. 3.00

No. 1112 contains one 32x40mm stamp.

Frogs A263

1993, Feb. 1 Litho. *Perf. 12½*

1113	A263	55k	Kaloula pulchra	.25
1114	A263	90k	Xenopus muelleri	.38
1115	A263	100k	Centrolenella vireovittata, vert.	.42
1116	A263	185k	Bufo marinus	.78
1117	A263	1200k	Hyla arborea, vert.	5.00
			Nos. 1113-1117 (5)	6.83

Animals — A264

1993, Mar. 13 Litho. *Perf. 13*

1118	A264	45k	Tupaia glis	.20
1119	A264	60k	Cynocephalus volans	.25
1120	A264	120k	Loris grasilis	.52
1121	A264	500k	Tarsium spectrum	2.15
1122	A264	600k	Symphalangus syndactylus	2.50
			Nos. 1118-1122 (5)	5.62

Native Houses A265

Various houses.

1993, July 12 Litho. *Perf. 13*

1123	A265	32k	multi, vert.	.15
1124	A265	200k	multicolored	.85
1125	A265	650k	multicolored	2.75
1126	A265	750k	multicolored	3.15
			Nos. 1123-1126 (4)	6.90

Campaign Against Illegal Drugs A266

Designs: 200k, Drugs, skull smoking cigarette. 430k, Burning confiscated drugs. 900k, Instructor showing danger of drugs to audience.

1993, June 26 *Perf. 12½*

1127	A266	200k	multicolored	.85
1128	A266	430k	multicolored	1.80
1129	A266	900k	multicolored	3.75
			Nos. 1127-1129 (3)	6.40

A267

A268

Shells: 20k, Chlamys senatorius nobilis. 30k, Epitonium prestiosum. 70k, Lambis rugosa. 500k, Conus aulicus. 1000k, Lambis millepeda.

1993, May 29 Litho. *Perf. 12x12½*

1130	A267	20k	multicolored	.15
1131	A267	30k	multicolored	.15
1132	A267	70k	multicolored	.30
1133	A267	500k	multicolored	2.00
1134	A267	1000k	multicolored	4.25
			Nos. 1130-1134 (5)	6.85

1993, Aug. 10 Litho. *Perf. 13*

Birds of prey.

1135	A268	10k	Aquila clanga	.15
1136	A268	100k	Athene brama	.42
1137	A268	330k	Circus melanoluecos	1.40
1138	A268	1000k	Circaetus gallicus	4.25
			Nos. 1135-1138 (4)	6.22

No. 1137 is horiz.

Environmental Protection — A269

Designs: 32k, Fighting forest fire. 40k, Animals around clean river. 260k, Rice paddies. 1100k, Water buffalo, people in water.

1993, Sept. 25 Litho. *Perf. 13*

1139	A269	32k	multicolored	.15
1140	A269	40k	multicolored	.16
1141	A269	260k	multicolored	1.10
1142	A269	1100k	multicolored	4.75
			Nos. 1139-1142 (4)	6.16

Bangkok '93 A270

Butterflies: 35k, Narathura atosia. 80k, Parides philoxenus. 150k, Euploea harrisi. 220k, Ixias pyrene. 500k, Elymnias hypermnestra. 700k, Stichopthalma louisa.

1993, Oct. 1 Litho. *Perf. 13*

1143	A270	35k	multicolored	.15
1144	A270	80k	multicolored	.35
1145	A270	150k	multicolored	.65
1146	A270	220k	multicolored	.95
1147	A270	500k	multicolored	2.25
			Nos. 1143-1147 (5)	4.35

Souvenir Sheet

1148 A270 700k multicolored 3.00

No. 1148 contains one 40x32mm stamp.

1994 World Cup Soccer Championships, US — A271

Various soccer players.

1993, Nov. 3 *Perf. 13*

1149	A271	10k	multicolored	.15
1150	A271	20k	multicolored	.15
1151	A271	285k	multicolored	1.25
1152	A271	400k	multicolored	1.75
1153	A271	800k	multicolored	3.50
			Nos. 1149-1153 (5)	6.80

Souvenir Sheet

Perf. 12½

1154 A271 700k multicolored 3.00

Nos. 1154 contains one 32x40mm stamp.

Prehistoric Birds — A272

1994, Jan. 20 Litho. *Perf. 13*

1155	A272	10k	Hesperornis	.15
1156	A272	20k	Dronte	.15
1157	A272	150k	Archaeopterix	.65
1158	A272	600k	Phororhachos	2.50
1159	A272	700k	Dinornis maximus	3.00
			Nos. 1155-1159 (5)	6.45

Souvenir Sheet

1160 A272 700k Teratornis, horiz. 3.00

Intl. Olympic Committee, Cent. — A273

Designs: 100k, Flag, flame, vert. 250k, Ancient Olympians. 1000k, Baron de Coubertin, Olympic runner, vert.

Perf. 12x12½, 12½x12

1994, Mar. 15 Litho.

1161	A273	100k	multicolored	.42
1162	A273	250k	multicolored	1.10
1163	A273	1000k	multicolored	4.25
			Nos. 1161-1163 (3)	5.77

1994 World Cup Soccer Championships, US — A274

Various soccer plays.

1994, June 15 Litho. *Perf. 12½*

1164	A274	40k	multicolored	.25
1165	A274	50k	multicolored	.30
1166	A274	60k	multicolored	.38
1167	A274	320k	multicolored	2.00
1168	A274	900k	multicolored	5.50
			Nos. 1164-1168 (5)	8.43

Souvenir Sheet

Perf. 13

1169 A274 700k multicolored 4.25

No. 1169 contains one 32x40mm stamp.

Pagodas A275

Various ornate gables.

1994, July 1 Litho. *Perf. 12½*

1170	A275	30k	multicolored	.18
1171	A275	150k	multicolored	.90
1172	A275	380k	multicolored	2.25
1173	A275	1100k	multicolored	6.75
			Nos. 1170-1173 (4)	10.08

Ursus Malayanus A276

1994, July 23

1174	A276	50k	shown	.45
1175	A276	90k	Adult	.80
1176	A276	200k	Cub, adult	1.90
1177	A276	220k	Adult standing	2.00
			Nos. 1174-1177 (4)	5.15

World Wildlife Fund.

Reptiles — A277

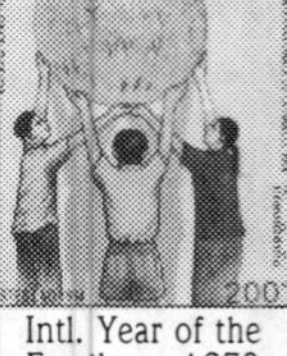

Intl. Year of the Family — A278

70k, Natrix natrix. 80k, Natrix tessellata. 90k, Salamandra salamandra. 600k, Triturus alpestris. 700k, Triturus cristatus. 800k, Lacerta viridis.

1994, Aug. 1 Litho. *Perf. 12½*

1178	A277	70k	multi, horiz.	.45
1179	A277	80k	multi, horiz.	.50
1180	A277	90k	multi, horiz.	.55
1181	A277	600k	multi, horiz.	3.75
1182	A277	800k	multicolored	5.00
			Nos. 1178-1182 (5)	10.25

Souvenir Sheet

1183 A277 700k multi, horiz. 4.50

No. 1183 contains one 40x32mm stamp.

1994, Sept. 24

Designs: 500k, Mother taking child to school, horiz. No. 1186, Mother walking with children. No. 1187, Family.

1184	A278	200k	multicolored	1.25
1185	A278	500k	multicolored	3.25
1186	A278	700k	multicolored	4.50
			Nos. 1184-1186 (3)	9.00

Souvenir Sheet

1187 A278 700k multicolored 4.50

No. 1187 contains one 32x40mm stamp.

Drums A279

Designs: 440k, Two people with hanging drum. 450k, Barrel shaped drum. 600k, Hanging drum.

Perf. 12½, 13x12½ (#1189)

1994, Oct. 20 Litho.

1188	A279	370k	multicolored	2.25
1189	A279	440k	multicolored	2.50
1190	A279	450k	multicolored	2.50
1191	A279	600k	multicolored	3.50
			Nos. 1188-1191 (4)	10.75

No. 1189 is 40x29mm.

Elephants A280

1994, Nov. 25

1192	A280	140k	shown	.80
1193	A280	400k	Beside railing	2.25
1194	A280	890k	Being ridden, vert.	5.00
			Nos. 1192-1194 (3)	8.05

Peace Bridge Between Laos and Thailand — A281

1994, Apr. 8 Litho. *Perf. 14x14½*

1195 A281 500k multicolored

World Tourism Organization, 20th Anniv. — A284

1995, Jan. 2 Litho. *Perf. 12½*

1203	A284	60k	Traditional music	.38
1204	A284	250k	Traditional dance	1.50
1205	A284	400k	Traditional food	2.50
1206	A284	650k	Waterfalls, vert.	4.00
			Nos. 1203-1206 (4)	8.38

Souvenir Sheet

Perf. 13

1207 A284 700k like #1206, vert. 4.50

No. 1207 contains one 32x44mm stamp.

Dinosaurs — A285

1995, Feb. 20 *Perf. 12½*

1208	A285	50k	Tracodont	.32
1209	A285	70k	Protoceratops	.45
1210	A285	300k	Brontosaurus	1.90
1211	A285	400k	Stegosaurus	2.50
1212	A285	600k	Tyranosaurus	3.75
			Nos. 1208-1212 (5)	8.92

Birds A286

1995, Mar. 10

1213	A286	50k	Acridotheres javanicus	.32
1214	A286	150k	Starnus burmannicus	.95
1215	A286	300k	Acridotheres tristis	1.90
1216	A286	700k	Gracula religiosa	4.50
			Nos. 1213-1216 (4)	7.67

Antique Containers A287

1995, May 1 Litho. *Perf. 12½*

1217	A287	70k	"Hanche" cup, vert.	.45
1218	A287	200k	Resin bowl	1.25
1219	A287	450k	Button design bowl	2.75
1220	A287	600k	Loving cup	3.75
			Nos. 1217-1220 (4)	8.20

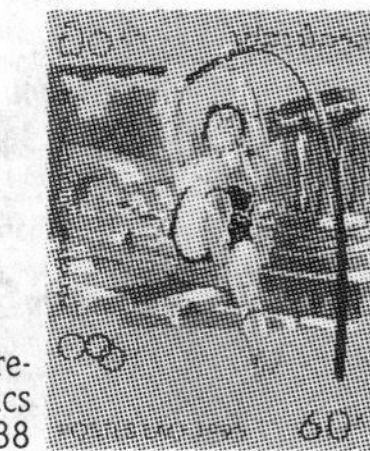

1996 Atlanta Pre-Olympics A288

1995, Apr. 5

1221	A288	60k	Pole vault	.38
1222	A288	80k	Javelin	.50
1223	A288	200k	Hammer throw	1.25
1224	A288	350k	Long jump	2.25
1225	A288	700k	High jump	4.50
			Nos. 1221-1225 (5)	8.88

Souvenir Sheet

1226 A288 700k Baseball 4.50

No. 1226 contains one 40x32mm stamp.

Rocket Festival A289

Designs: 80k, Launching rocket from scaffolding, vert. 160k, Carrying rocket in procession led by monk. 500k, Man carrying rocket on shoulder. 700k, People looking at rockets on tripods.

1995, June 1 Litho. *Perf. 13*

1227	A289	80k	multicolored	.45
1228	A289	160k	multicolored	.90
1229	A289	500k	multicolored	2.75
1230	A289	700k	multicolored	3.75
			Nos. 1227-1230 (4)	7.85

Domestic Cats A290

Designs: 40k, Red tabby longhair. 50k, Siamese seal point. 250k, Red tabby longhair. 400k, Tortoise-shell shorthair. 650k, Tortoise-shell shorthair, vert. 700k, Tortoise-shell shorthair.

1995, July 25 Litho. *Perf. 12½*

1231	A290	40k	multicolored	.25
1232	A290	50k	multicolored	.30
1233	A290	250k	multicolored	1.50
1234	A290	400k	multicolored	2.50
1235	A290	650k	multicolored	4.25
			Nos. 1231-1235 (5)	8.80

Souvenir Sheet

1236 A290 700k multicolored 4.50

No. 1236 contains one 40x32mm stamp.

Insect-Eating Plants — A291

Designs: 90k, Nepenthes villosa. 100k, Dionaea muscipula. 350k, Sarracenia flava. 450k, Sarracenia purpurea. 500k, Nepenthes ampullaria. 1000k, Nepenthes gracilis.

1995, Aug. 24

1237	A291	90k	multicolored	.25
1238	A291	100k	multicolored	.30
1239	A291	350k	multicolored	.95
1240	A291	450k	multicolored	1.25
1241	A291	500k	multicolored	1.40
			Nos. 1237-1241 (5)	4.15

Souvenir Sheet

1242 A291 1000k multicolored 8.50

No. 1242 contains one 40x32mm stamp.

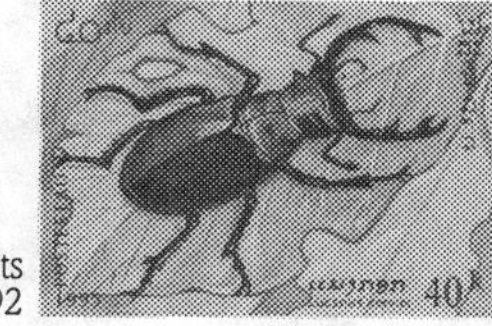

Insects A292

Designs: 40k, Lucanus cervus. 50k, Melolontha melolontha. 500k, Xylocopa violacea. 800k, Tettigonia viridissima.

1995, Sept. 20

1243	A292	40k	multicolored	.25
1244	A292	50k	multicolored	.30
1245	A292	500k	multicolored	3.00
1246	A292	800k	multicolored	5.00
			Nos. 1243-1246 (4)	8.55

FAO, 50th Anniv. A293

Designs: 80k, Cattle grazing. 300k, Farmer tilling rice paddy. 1000k, Planting, irrigating rice paddies, stocking pond with fish.

1995, Oct. 16 Litho. *Perf. 12½*

1247	A293	80k	multicolored	.40
1248	A293	300k	multicolored	1.50
1249	A293	1000k	multicolored	5.25
			Nos. 1247-1249 (3)	7.15

Traditional Culture A294

Designs: 50k, Man with musical instrument, two women. 280k, Dance. 380k, Playing game with bamboo poles. 420k, Woman, man with musical instruments.

1996, Jan. 10

1250	A294	50k	multicolored	.40
1251	A294	280k	multicolored	2.40
1252	A294	380k	multicolored	3.20
1253	A294	420k	multicolored	3.50
			Nos. 1250-1253 (4)	9.50

1996 Summer Olympics, Atlanta A295

1996, Feb. 20

1254	A295	30k	Cycling	.25
1255	A295	150k	Soccer	1.20
1256	A295	200k	Basketball, vert.	1.60
1257	A295	300k	Running, vert.	2.40
1258	A295	500k	Shooting	4.00
			Nos. 1254-1258 (5)	9.45

Souvenir Sheet

1259 A295 1000k Pole vault 7.20

No. 1259 contains one 38x30mm stamp.

Fauna — A296

Designs: 40k, Helarctos malayanus. 60k, Pelecanus philippensis. 200k, Panthera pardus. 250k, Papilio machaon. 700k, Python molurus.

1996, Feb. 26 Litho. *Perf. 13*

1260	A296	40k	multicolored	.30
1261	A296	60k	multicolored	.45
1262	A296	200k	multicolored	1.50
1263	A296	250k	multicolored	1.85
1264	A296	700k	multicolored	5.25
			Nos. 1260-1264 (5)	9.35

Intl. Women's Day A297

Designs: 20k, Weaving textile. 290k, Instructing calisthenics. 1000k, Feeding infant, vert.

1996, Mar. 8

1265	A297	20k	multicolored	.15
1266	A297	290k	multicolored	2.00
1267	A297	1000k	multicolored	6.75
			Nos. 1265-1267 (3)	8.90

A298

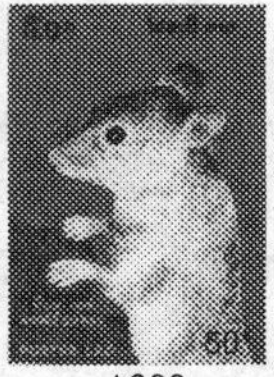

A299

Various soccer plays.

1996, May 3 Litho. *Perf. 13*

1268	A298	20k	multicolored	.15
1269	A298	50k	multicolored	.30
1270	A298	300k	multicolored	2.00
1271	A298	400k	multicolored	2.60
1272	A298	500k	multicolored	3.30
			Nos. 1268-1272 (5)	8.35

1998 World Soccer Cup Championships, France.

1996, Apr. 15 Litho. *Perf. 13½x13*

Various rats.

1274	A299	50k	purple & multi	.20
1275	A299	340k	blue & multi	1.20
1276	A299	350k	green & multi	1.25
1277	A299	370k	red & multi	1.30
			Nos. 1274-1277 (4)	3.95

New Year 1996 (Year of the Rat).

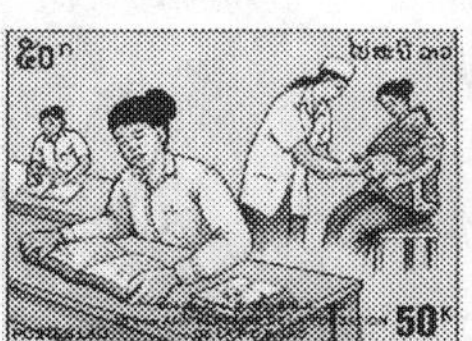

Laos Rural Development Program, 20th Anniv. — A300

50k, Instruction for giving medical care. 280k, Irrigation system. 600k, Bridge over waterway.

1995, Dec. 2 *Perf. 13*

1278	A300	50k	multicolored	.20
1279	A300	280k	multicolored	1.00
1280	A300	600k	multicolored	2.10
			Nos. 1278-1280 (3)	3.30

UN, 50th Anniv. A301

Designs: 290k, Men seated at round table. 310k, Men playing game, checkers. 440k, Boys in swing, playing ball.

1995, Oct. 24

1281	A301	290k	multicolored	1.00
1282	A301	310k	multicolored	1.10
1283	A301	440k	multicolored	1.50
			Nos. 1281-1283 (3)	3.60

Antique Aircraft A302

1996, July 5 Litho. *Perf. 13*

1284 A302 25k Morane .15
1285 A302 60k Sopwith Camel .35
1286 A302 150k De Haviland DH-4 .85
1287 A302 250k Albatros 1.40
1288 A302 800k Caudron 4.50
Nos. 1284-1288 (5) 7.25

Capex '96.

Carts A303

1996, Aug. 21

1289 A303 50k shown .30
1290 A303 100k Cart, diff. .55
1291 A303 440k Pulled by oxen 2.50
Nos. 1289-1291 (3) 3.35

Flowers — A304

Designs: 50k, Dendrobium secundum. 200k, Ascocentrum miniatum. 500k, Aerides multiflorum. 520k, Dendrobium aggregatum.

1996, Oct. 25 Litho. *Perf. 13*

1292 A304 50k multicolored .25
1293 A304 200k multicolored 1.00
1294 A304 500k multicolored 2.50
1295 A304 520k multicolored 2.60
Nos. 1292-1295 (4) 6.35

Draft Horses — A305

Various breeds.

1996, Nov. 5 Litho. *Perf. 13*

1296 A305 50k yellow & multi .20
1297 A305 80k green & multi .30
1298 A305 200k pink & multi .80
1299 A305 400k blue & multi 1.60
1300 A305 600k yellow & multi 2.40
Nos. 1296-1300 (5) 5.30

Souvenir Sheet

1301 A305 1000k pink & multi 3.90

No. 1301 contains one 32x40mm stamp.

UNICEF, 50th Anniv. A306

1996, Dec. 11 Litho.

1302 A306 200k Children in school .80
1303 A306 500k Child breastfeeding, vert. 2.00
1304 A306 600k Woman pumping water 2.40
Nos. 1302-1304 (3) 5.20

Greenpeace, 25th Anniv. — A306a

Turtles: 150k, Dermochelys coriacea on sand. 250k, Dermochelys coriacea in surf. 400k, Erethochelys imbricata. 450k, Chelonia agassizi.

1996, Dec. 27 Litho. *Perf. 13*

1304A A306a 150k multicolored .80
1304B A306a 250k multicolored 1.30
1304C A306a 400k multicolored 2.00
1304D A306a 450k multicolored 2.30
e. Souvenir sheet, #1304A-1304D 6.50
Nos. 1304A-1304D (4) 6.40

Steam Locomotives — A307

Designs: 100k, Kinnaird, 1846. 200k, Pioneer, 1836, portrait of George Stephenson. 300k, Portrait of Robert Stephenson, Long Boiler Express, 1848. 400k, Adler, 1835. 500k, Lord of the Isles, 1851-84. 600k, The Columbine, 1845.
2000k, Best friend of Charleston, 1830.

Perf. 12½x12, 12x13 (#1306-1309)

1997 Litho.

1305 A307 100k multicolored .40
1306 A307 200k multicolored .80
1307 A307 300k multicolored 1.25
1308 A307 400k multicolored 1.60
1309 A307 500k multicolored 2.00
1310 A307 600k multicolored 2.35
Nos. 1305-1310 (6) 8.40

Souvenir Sheet

Perf. 12½

1311 A307 2000k multicolored 7.75

Nos. 1306-1309 are 42x21mm.
No. 1311 contains one 40x32mm stamp.

Parrots — A308

Designs: 50k, Agapornis personata. 150k, Agapornis cana. 200k, Agapornis lilianae. 400k, Agapornis fischeri. 500k, Agapornis nigregenis. 800k, Agapornis roseicollis.
2000k, Agapornis taranta.

1997 *Perf. 12½*

1312 A308 50k multicolored .20
1313 A308 150k multicolored .60
1314 A308 200k multicolored .80
1315 A308 400k multicolored 1.60
1316 A308 500k multicolored 2.00
1317 A308 800k multicolored 3.15
Nos. 1312-1317 (6) 8.35

Souvenir Sheet

1318 A308 2000k multicolored 8.25

No. 1318 contains one 32x40mm stamp.

Cooking Utensils A309

50k, Cooking over open fire, vert. 340k, Traditional food containers. 370k, Traditional meal setting.

1997

1319 A309 50k multicolored .20
1320 A309 340k multicolored 1.35
1321 A309 370k multicolored 1.45
Nos. 1319-1321 (3) 3.00

Orchids — A310

Designs: 50k, Roeblingiana. 100k, Findlayanum. 150k, Crepidatum. 250k, Sarcanthus birmanicus. 400k, Cymbidium lowianum. 1000k, Dendrobium gratiosissimum.
2000k, Chamberlainianum.

1997 Litho. *Perf. 12½*

1322 A310 50k multicolored .20
1323 A310 100k multicolored .40
1324 A310 150k multicolored .60
1325 A310 250k multicolored 1.00
1326 A310 400k multicolored 1.60
1327 A310 1000k multicolored 4.00
Nos. 1322-1327 (6) 7.80

Souvenir Sheet

1328 A310 2000k multicolored 8.00

No. 1328 contains one 32x40mm stamp.

Elephants A311

Elephas maximus: 100k, Adult, vert. 250k, Adult holding log. 300k, Adult, calf.
Loxodonta africana: 350k, Adult. 450k, Adult in water. 550k, Adult, vert. 2000k, Head of adult.

1997 Litho. *Perf. 12½*

1329 A311 100k multicolored .40
1330 A311 250k multicolored 1.00
1331 A311 300k multicolored 1.15
1332 A311 350k multicolored 1.40
1333 A311 450k multicolored 1.75
1334 A311 550k multicolored 2.20
Nos. 1329-1334 (6) 7.90

Souvenir Sheet

1335 A311 2000k multicolored 7.75

No. 1335 contains one 32x40mm stamp.

Head Pieces and Masks A312

Various designs.

1997 Litho. *Perf. 12½*

1336 A312 50k multi, vert. .20
1337 A312 100k multi, vert .35
1338 A312 150k multi .55
1339 A312 200k multi, vert. .75
1340 A312 350k multi, vert. 1.30
Nos. 1336-1340 (5) 3.15

1998 World Cup Soccer Championships, France — A313

Various soccer plays.

1997 Litho. *Perf. 12½*

1341 A313 100k multicolored .35
1342 A313 200k multicolored .70
1343 A313 250k multicolored .85
1344 A313 300k multicolored 1.00
1345 A313 350k multicolored 1.20
1346 A313 700k multicolored 2.40
Nos. 1341-1346 (6) 6.50

Souvenir Sheet

1347 A313 2000k multicolored 6.75

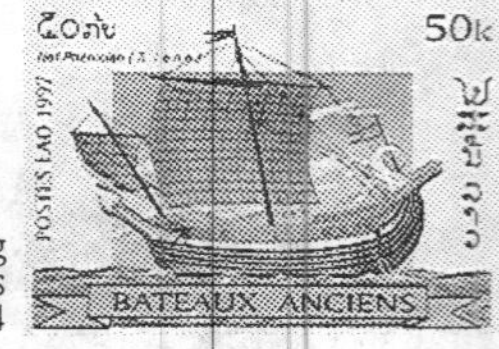

Sailing Ships A314

50k, Phoenician. 100k, 13th cent. ship. 150k, 15th cent. vessel. 200k, Portuguese caravel, 16th cent. 400k, Dutch, 17th cent. 900k, HMS Victory.
2000k, Grand Henry, 1514.

1997 *Perf. 13*

1348 A314 50k multicolored .20
1349 A314 100k multicolored .35
1350 A314 150k multicolored .55
1351 A314 200k multicolored .70
1352 A314 400k multicolored 1.40
1353 A314 900k multicolored 3.20
Nos. 1348-1353 (6) 6.40

Souvenir Sheet

1354 A314 2000k multicolored 6.75

No. 1354 contains one 40x28mm stamp.

SEMI-POSTAL STAMPS

Scott Specialty Series Album

LAOS - Includes spaces for regular postage, semi-postal, air post, air post semi-postal and postage dues.
Supplemented in July.

619LAS1	1951-1984	107 pgs	$59.95
619LAS2	1984-1993	74 pgs	$44.95
619S094	1994	5 pgs	$4.95
619S095	1995	6 pgs	$5.95
619S096	1996	6 pgs	$5.95

Available from your favorite stamp dealer or direct from Scott Publishing Co.

SCOTT

P.O. Box 828 Sidney OH 45365 Phone 1-800-572-6885

Laotian Children — SP1

Unwmk.

1953, July 14 Engr. *Perf. 13*

B1	SP1	1.50pi + 1pi multi	1.65	1.10
B2	SP1	3pi + 1.50pi multi	1.65	1.10
B3	SP1	3.90pi + 2.50pi multi	1.65	1.10
		Nos. B1-B3 (3)	4.95	3.30

The surtax was for the Red Cross.

Nos. 52 and 46 Surcharged: "1k ANNEE MONDIALE DU REFUGIE 1959-1960"

1960, Apr. 7

B4	A16	4k + 1k rose claret	.80	.80
B5	A13	10k + 1k multicolored	.80	.80

World Refugee Year, July 1, 1959-June 30, 1960. The surcharge was for aid to refugees.

Flooded Village — SP2

Designs: 40k+10k, Flooded market place and truck. 60k+15k, Flooded airport and plane.

1967, Jan. 18 Engr. *Perf. 13*

B6	SP2	20k + 5k multi	.25	.25
B7	SP2	40k + 10k multi	.40	.40
B8	SP2	60k + 15k multi	.65	.65
a.		Miniature sheet of 3	2.00	2.00
		Nos. B6-B8 (3)	1.30	1.30

The surtax was for victims of the Mekong Delta flood. No. B8a contains one each of Nos. B6-B8. Size: 148x99mm. Sold for 250k.

Women Working in Tobacco Field — SP3

1967, Oct. 5 Engr. *Perf. 13*

B9	SP3	20k + 5k multi	.30	.30
B10	SP3	50k + 10k multi	.50	.50
B11	SP3	60k + 15k multi	.65	.65
a.		Souv. sheet of 3, #B9-B11	2.25	2.25
		Nos. B9-B11 (3)	1.45	1.45

Laotian Red Cross, 10th anniv. No. B11a sold for 250k+30k.

Nos. 184-189 Surcharged: "Soutien aux Victimes / de la Guerre / + 5k"

1970, May 1 Photo. *Perf. 14*

B12	A58	10k + 5k multi	.30	.20
B13	A58	15k + 5k multi	.30	.20
B14	A58	20k + 5k multi	.40	.30
B15	A58	30k + 5k multi	.50	.30
B16	A58	40k + 5k multi	.70	.40
B17	A58	60k + 5k multi	.90	.50
		Nos. B12-B17,CB1-CB2 (8)	8.00	5.40

AIR POST STAMPS

Weaving — AP1

Design: 3.30pi, Wat Pra Keo.

Unwmk.

1952, Apr. 13 Engr. *Perf. 13*

C1	AP1	3.30pi dk pur & pur	.55	.25
C2	AP1	10pi ultra & bl grn	1.10	.70
C3	AP1	20pi deep cl & red	1.75	1.25
C4	AP1	30pi blk brn & dk brn violet	2.75	1.90
		Nos. C1-C4 (4)	6.15	4.10

See note following No. 17.

UPU Monument and King Sisavang-Vong — AP2

1952, Dec. 7

C5	AP2	25pi vio bl & indigo	2.75	1.50
C6	AP2	50pi dk brn & vio brn	2.75	1.50

Laos' admission to the UPU, May 13, 1952.

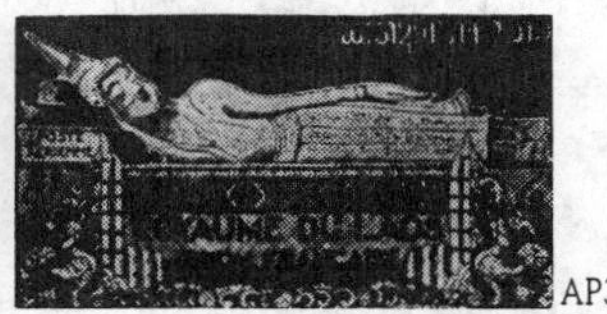
AP3

AP4

Designs: Various Buddha statues.

1953, Nov. 18

C7	AP3	4pi dark green	.45	.30
C8	AP4	6.50pi dk bl green	.40	.30
C9	AP4	9pi blue green	.60	.40
C10	AP3	11.50pi red, yel & dk vio brn	.65	.45
C11	AP4	40pi purple	1.25	.90
C12	AP4	100pi olive	3.75	2.75
		Nos. C7-C12 (6)	7.10	5.10

Great Oath of Laos ceremony.

Accession Type of Regular Issue

1954, Mar. 4 Unwmk.

C13	A6	50pi indigo & bl grn	75.00	75.00

Ravana — AP6

Sita and Rama — AP7

Scenes from the Ramayana: 4k, Hanuman, the white monkey. 5k, Ninh Laphath, the black monkey. 20k, Lucy with a friend of Ravana. 30k, Rama.

1955, Oct. 28 Engr. *Perf. 13*

C14	AP6	2k bl grn, emer & ind	.55	.40
C15	AP6	4k red brn, dk red brn & ver	.70	.55
C16	AP6	5k scar, sep & olive	1.25	.70
C17	AP7	10k blk, org & brn	2.00	1.25
C18	AP7	20k vio, dk grn & olive	2.75	1.75
C19	AP7	30k ultra, blk & salmon	3.75	2.75
		Nos. C14-C19 (6)	11.00	7.40

See No. 225.

Buddha Type of Regular Issue, 1956

1956, May 24

C20	A7	20k carmine rose	16.00	12.00
C21	A7	30k olive & olive bister	16.00	12.00

2500th anniversary of birth of Buddha.

UN Emblem AP8

1956, Dec. 14

C22	AP8	15k light blue	3.25	3.25
C23	AP8	30k deep claret	4.50	4.50

Admission of Laos to the UN, 1st anniv.

Types of Regular Issue, 1957

Musical Instruments: 12k, Khong vong. 14k, So. 20k, Kong.

1957, Mar. 25 Unwmk. *Perf. 13*

C24	A9	12k multicolored	2.00	1.40
C25	A10	14k multicolored	2.00	1.40
C26	A10	20k bl grn, yel grn & pur	2.75	2.25
		Nos. C24-C26 (3)	6.75	5.05

Monk Receiving Alms — AP9

Monks Meditating in Boat — AP10

Designs: 18k, Smiling Buddha. 24k, Ancient temple painting (horse and mythological figures.)

1957, Nov. 5

C27	AP9	10k dk pur, pale brn & dk grn	.50	.50
C28	AP10	15k dk vio brn, brn org & yel	.50	.50
C29	AP9	18k slate grn & ol	.75	.70
C30	AP10	24k claret, org yel & blk	1.25	1.00
		Nos. C27-C30 (4)	3.00	2.70

No. C28 measures 48x27mm. No. C30, 48x36mm. See No. C84.

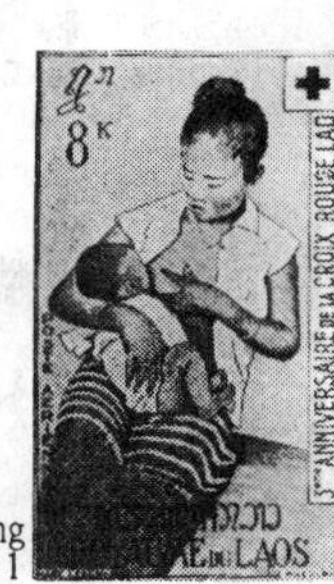

Mother Nursing Infant — AP11

1958, May 2

Cross in Red

C31	AP11	8k lil gray & dk gray	.95	.60
C32	AP11	12k red brn & brn	1.40	.80
C33	AP11	15k sl grn & bluish green	1.65	.95
C34	AP11	20k bister & vio	2.00	1.10
		Nos. C31-C34 (4)	6.00	3.45

3rd anniversary of Laotian Red Cross.

Plain of Stones, Xieng Khouang — AP12

Papheng Falls, Champassak — AP13

Natl. Tourism Industry: 15k, Buffalo cart. 19k, Buddhist monk and village.

1960, July 1 Engr. *Perf. 13*

C35	AP12	9.50k bl, ol & claret	.20	.20
C36	AP13	12k vio bl, red brn & gray	.25	.25
C37	AP13	15k yel grn, ol gray & cl	.25	.25
C38	AP12	19k multicolored	.35	.35
		Nos. C35-C38 (4)	1.05	1.05

Pou Gneu Nha Gneu Legend — AP14

Garuda — AP15

Hanuman, the White Monkey — AP16

Nang Teng One Legend AP17

1962, Feb. 19 Unwmk. *Perf. 13*
C39 AP14 11k grn, car & ocher .40 .40
C40 AP15 14k ultra & org .40 .40
C41 AP16 20k multicolored .60 .60
C42 AP17 25k multicolored .60 .60
Nos. C39-C42 (4) 2.00 2.00

Makha Bousa festival.

Yao Hunter — AP18

Phayre's Flying Squirrel — AP19

1964, Dec. 15 Engr. *Perf. 13*
C43 AP18 5k shown .15 .15
C44 AP18 10k Kha hunter .15 .15
C45 AP18 50k Meo woman .85 .85
a. Min. sheet of 4, #100, C43-C45 5.50 4.75
Nos. C43-C45 (3) 1.15 1.15

No. C45a exists imperf.

Butterfly Type of 1965

1965, Mar. 13
Size: 48x27mm
C46 A34 20k Atlas moth 1.90 1.10

1965, Oct. 7 Engr. *Perf. 13*

Designs: 25k, Leopard cat. 75k, Javan mongoose. 100k, Crestless porcupine. 200k, Binturong.

C47 AP19 25k dk brn, yel grn & ocher .40 .20
C48 AP19 55k brown & blue .65 .30
C49 AP19 75k brt grn & brn .85 .45
C50 AP19 100k ocher, brn & blk 1.00 .70
C51 AP19 200k red & black 2.00 1.50
Nos. C47-C51 (5) 4.90 3.15

Army Type of Regular Issue

Design: 200k, 300k, Parading service flags before National Assembly Hall.

1968, July 15 Engr. *Perf. 13*
C52 A53 200k multicolored 1.10 .75
C53 A53 300k multicolored 1.75 1.10
a. Souv. sheet of 5, #168-170, C52-C53 4.25 3.75

No. C53a sold for 600k.

Insect Type of Regular Issue

Insects: 120k, Dorysthenes walkeri, horiz. 160k, Megaloxantha bicolor, horiz.

1968, Aug. 28 Engr. *Perf. 13*
C54 A54 120k brn, org & blk 1.25 .60
C55 A54 160k rose car, Prus bl & yel 1.50 .75

Ballet Type of Regular Issue

Designs: 110k, Sudagnu battling Thotsakan. 300k, Pharam dancing with Thotsakan.

1969 Photo. *Perf. 14*
C56 A58 110k multicolored 1.10 .80
a. Souv. sheet of 4, #187-189, C56, imperf. 6.00 3.00
C57 A58 300k multicolored 3.50 1.90
a. Souv. sheet of 4, #184-186, C57, imperf. 14.00 7.00

No. C56a sold for 480k; No. C57a for 650k. For surcharges see Nos. CB1-CB2.

Timber Industry, Paksane AP20

1969, May 7 Engr. *Perf. 13*
C58 AP20 300k olive bister & blk 3.25 2.50

ILO, 50th anniversary.

Animal Type of Regular Issue

Animals: 70k, Asiatic black bear. 120k, White-handed gibbon, vert. 150k, Tiger.

1969, Nov. 6 Photo. *Perf. 12x13*
C59 A60 70k multicolored .45 .40
C60 A60 120k multicolored .85 .70
C61 A60 150k multicolored 1.10 1.10
Nos. C59-C61 (3) 2.40 2.20

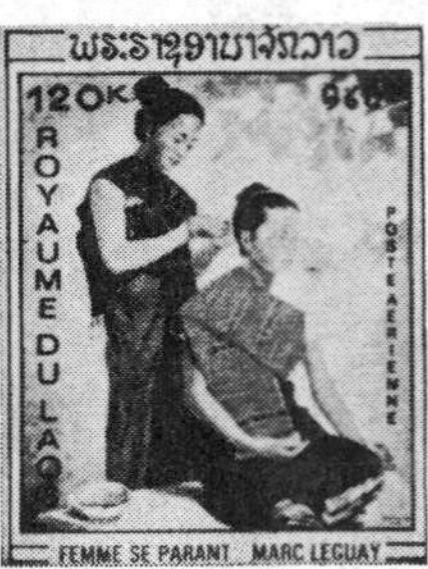

Hairdressing, by Marc Leguay AP21

Paintings: No. C63, Village Market, by Marc Leguay, horiz. No. C64, Tree on the Bank of the Mekong, by Marc Leguay, horiz.

1969-70 Photo. *Perf. 12x13, 13x12*
C62 AP21 120k multicolored .95 .40
C63 AP21 150k multicolored 2.00 .65
C64 AP21 150k multi ('70) 2.00 .65
Nos. C62-C64 (3) 4.95 1.70

See Nos. C72-C74.

Wat Xiengthong, Luang Prabang — AP22

1970, Jan. 10 *Perf. 12x13, 13x12*
C65 AP22 100k Library, Wat Sisaket, vert. 1.25 .55
C66 AP22 120k shown 1.40 .80

Drum Type of 1970

1970, Mar. 30 Engr. *Perf. 13*
C67 A64 125k Pong wooden drum, vert. 3.00 1.75

Franklin D. Roosevelt (1882-1945) AP23

1970, Apr. 12
C68 AP23 120k olive & slate 1.65 1.10

EXPO '70 Type of Regular Issue

Design: 125k, Woman boiling cocoons in kettle, and spinning silk thread.

1970, July 7 Engr. *Perf. 13*
C69 A66 125k ol & multi 1.25 1.25

See note after No. 202.

Animal Type of Regular Issue

1970, Sept. 7 Engr. *Perf. 13*
C70 A67 210k Leopard 1.10 1.10
C71 A67 500k Gaur 2.25 2.00

Painting Type of 1969-70

Paintings by Marc Leguay: 100k, Village Foot Path. 120k, Rice Field in Rainy Season, horiz. 150k, Village Elder.

Perf. 11½x13, 13x11½
1970, Dec. 21 Photo.
C72 AP21 100k multicolored 1.10 1.10
C73 AP21 120k multicolored 1.00 1.00
C74 AP21 150k multicolored 1.40 1.40
Nos. C72-C74 (3) 3.50 3.50

UN Type of Regular Issue

Design: 125k, Earth Goddess Nang Thorani wringing her hair; UN Headquarters and emblem.

1970, Oct. 24
Size: 26x36mm
C75 A68 125k brt bl, pink & dk grn 1.00 1.00

Hanuman and Nang Matsa — AP24

1971, Feb. 5
C76 AP24 125k multicolored 1.10 .65

Orchid Type of Regular Issue

Design: 125k, Brasilian cattleya.

1971, July Photo. *Perf. 13x12½*
Size: 48x27mm
C79 A73 125k Brasilian cattleya 1.90 .95

Laotian and French Women, That Luang Pagoda and Arms — AP25

1971, Aug. 6 Engr. *Perf. 13*
C80 AP25 30k brn & dl red .25 .15
C81 AP25 70k vio & lilac .50 .40
C82 AP25 100k sl grn & grn .70 .55
Nos. C80-C82 (3) 1.45 1.10

Kinship between the cities Keng Kok, Laos, and Saint Astier, France.

Animal Type of Regular Issue

1971, Sept. 16
C83 A74 300k Javan rhinoceros 1.75 .90

Type of 1957 with Ornamental Panel and Inscription

Design: Monk receiving alms (like No. C27).

1971, Nov. 2 Engr. *Perf. 13*
C84 AP9 125k dk pur, pale brn & dk grn 1.40 1.40

20th anniv. of Laotian independent postal service. No. C84 inscribed: "Vingtième Anniversaire de la Philatélie Lao," "Poste Aerienne" and "1971."

Sunset Over the Mekong, by Chamnane Prisayane — AP26

Design: 150k, "Quiet Morning" (village scene), by Chamnane Prisayane.

1971, Dec. 20 Photo. *Perf. 13x12*
C85 AP26 125k black & multi .80 .80
C86 AP26 150k black & multi .95 .95

Book Year Type of Regular Issue

Design: 125k, Father teaching children to read palm leaf book.

1972, Jan. 30 Engr. *Perf. 13*
Size: 48x27mm
C87 A75 125k bright purple .75 .75

Dam Type of Regular Issue

Design: 145k, Nam Ngum Hydroelectric Dam and ECAFE emblem.

1972, Mar. 28 Engr. *Perf. 13*
C88 A76 145k brown, bl & grn .80 .80

Orchid Type of Regular Issue 1971

1972, May 1 Photo. *Perf. 13x12½*
Size: 48x27mm
C89 A73 150k Vanda teres, horiz. 1.50 .80

UNICEF Type of Regular Issue

Design: 120k, Boy riding buffalo to water hole (child's drawing).

1972, July Engr. *Perf. 13*
C90 A77 120k multicolored 1.00 1.00

Nakharath, Daughter of the Dragon King — AP27

Wood carvings from Wat Sikhounvieng Dongmieng, Vientiane: 120k, Nang Kinnali, Goddess from Mt. Kailath. 150k, Norasing, Lion King from Himalayas.

1972, Sept. 15 Engr. *Perf. 13*
C91 AP27 100k blue green .55 .55
C92 AP27 120k violet .60 .60
C93 AP27 150k brn orange .85 .85
Nos. C91-C93 (3) 2.00 2.00

That Luang Religious Festival — AP28

1972, Nov. 18 Engr. *Perf. 13*
C94 AP28 110k Presentation of wax castles .90 .90
C95 AP28 125k Procession 1.10 1.10

Workers in Rice Field, by Leguay AP29

Paintings by Mark Leguay: No. C97, Women and water buffalo in rice field. Nos. C98, Rainy Season in Village (Water buffalo in water). No. C99, Rainy Season in Village (Water buffalo on land). 120k, Mother and Child.

1972, Dec. 23 Photo. *Perf. 13*
C96 AP29 50k multicolored .40 .40
C97 AP29 50k multicolored .40 .40
C98 AP29 70k multicolored .60 .60
C99 AP29 70k multicolored .60 .60
C100 AP29 120k yel & multi 1.00 1.00
Nos. C96-C100 (5) 3.00 3.00

Nos. C97, C99 have denomination and frame at right.

Costume Type of Regular Issue

Women's Costumes: 120k, Luang Prabang marriage costume. 150k, Vientiane evening costume.

1973, Feb. 16 Engr. *Perf. 13*
C101 A78 120k multicolored .60 .60
C102 A78 150k brown & multi .75 .75

Lions Club Emblems, King Sayasettha-Thirath — AP30

1973, Mar. 30 **Engr.** *Perf. 13*
C103 AP30 150k rose & multi .95 .65

Lions Club of Vientiane.

Rahu with Rockets and Sputnik — AP31

Space achievements: 150k, Laotian festival rocket and US lunar excursion module.

1973, May 11 **Engr.** *Perf. 13*
C104 AP31 80k ultra & multi .50 .25
C105 AP31 150k buff & ultra .75 .35

Dancing Around Campfire — AP32

Design: 125k, Boy Scouts helping during Vientiane Flood, 1966.

1973, Sept. 1 **Engr.** *Perf. 13*
C106 AP32 110k vio & orange .65 .30
C107 AP32 125k Prus grn & bis .80 .30

Laotian Scout Movement, 25th anniv.

Sun Chariot and WMO Emblem — AP33

Design: 90k, Nang Mékhala, the weather goddess, and WMO emblem, vert.

1973, Oct. 24 **Engr.** *Perf. 13*
C108 AP33 90k vio, red & ocher .60 .25
C109 AP33 150k ocher, red & brn ol .65 .40

Intl. meteorological cooperation, cent.

Woman in Poppy Field, INTERPOL Emblem — AP34

1973, Dec. 22 **Engr.** *Perf. 13*
C110 AP34 150k vio, yel grn & red 1.10 .60

Intl. Criminal Police Org., 50th anniv.

Phra Sratsvady, Wife of Phra Phrom AP35

Designs: 110k, Phra Indra on 3-headed elephant Erawan. 150k, Phra Phrom, the Creator, on phoenix. Designs show giant sculptures in park at Thadeua.

1974, Mar. 23 **Engr.** *Perf. 13*
C111 AP35 100k lilac, red & blk .50 .25
C112 AP35 110k car, vio & brn .60 .40
C113 AP35 150k ocher, vio & sepia .75 .45
Nos. C111-C113 (3) 1.85 1.10

UPU Emblem, Women Reading Letter — AP36

1974 **Engr.** *Perf. 13*
C114 AP36 200k lt brn & car 1.10 .85
C115 AP36 500k lilac & red 2.50 1.75
a. Souvenir sheet 5.00 5.00

Centenary of Universal Postal Union. Issue dates: 200k, Apr. 30; 500k, Oct. 9.

Flower Type of 1974

1974, May 31
Size: 36x36mm
C116 A84 500k Pitcher plant 4.00 2.75

Transportation Type of Regular Issue

1974, July 31 **Engr.** *Perf. 13*
C117 A85 250k Sampan 2.00 1.50

Marconi Type of 1974

Design: Old and new means of communications.

1974, Aug. 28 **Engr.** *Perf. 13*
C118 A86 200k vio bl & brn 1.40 1.10

Insect Type of 1974

1974, Oct. 23 **Engr.** *Perf. 13*
C119 A87 110k Sternocera multipunctata 1.65 .95

Boeing 747 AP37

1986, June 2 **Litho.** *Perf. 12½*
C120 AP37 20k shown 3.00
C121 AP37 50k IL86 7.00

AIR POST SEMI-POSTAL STAMPS

Nos. C56-C57 Surcharged: "Soutien aux Victimes / de la Guerre / + 5k"

1970, May 1 **Photo.** *Perf. 13*
CB1 A58 110k + 5k multi 1.65 1.25
CB2 A58 300k + 5k multi 3.25 2.25

The surtax was for war victims.

POSTAGE DUE STAMPS

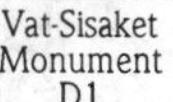
Vat-Sisaket Monument D1

Boat and Raft D2

Perf. 13½x13

1952-53 **Unwmk.** **Engr.**
J1 D1 10c dark brown .15 .15
J2 D1 20c purple .15 .15
J3 D1 50c carmine .15 .15
J4 D1 1pi dark green .15 .15
J5 D1 2pi deep ultra .15 .15
J6 D1 5pi rose violet .70 .70
J7 D2 10pi indigo ('53) .90 .90
Nos. J1-J7 (7) 2.35 2.35

Serpent — D3

1973, Oct. 31 **Photo.** *Perf. 13*
J8 D3 10k yellow & multi .25 .25
J9 D3 15k emerald & multi .25 .25
J10 D3 20k blue & multi .25 .25
J11 D3 50k scarlet & multi .35 .35
Nos. J8-J11 (4) 1.10 1.10

LATAKIA

ˌla–tə–ˈkē–ə

LOCATION — A division of Syria in Western Asia
GOVT. — French Mandate
AREA — 2,500 sq. mi.
POP. — 278,000 (approx. 1930)
CAPITAL — Latakia

This territory, included in the Syrian Mandate to France under the Versailles Treaty, was formerly known as Alaouites. The name Latakia was adopted in 1930. See Alaouites and Syria.

100 Centimes = 1 Piaster

Stamps of Syria Overprinted in Black or Red

LATTAQUIE or LATTAQUIE

Perf. 12x12½, 13½

1931-33 **Unwmk.**
1 A6 10c red violet .35 .35
2 A6 10c vio brn ('33) .35 .35
3 A7 20c dk blue (R) .35 .35
4 A7 20c brown org ('33) .35 .35
5 A8 25c gray grn (R) .35 .35
6 A8 25c dk bl gray (R) ('33) .35 .35
7 A9 50c violet .70 .70
8 A15 75c org red ('32) .70 .70
9 A10 1p green (R) .70 .70
10 A11 1.50p bis brn (R) 1.00 1.00
11 A11 1.50p dp grn ('33) 1.10 1.10
12 A12 2p dk vio (R) 1.10 1.10
13 A13 3p yel grn (R) 2.00 2.00
14 A14 4p orange 1.75 1.75
15 A15 4.50p rose car 1.75 1.75
16 A16 6p grnsh blk (R) 1.75 1.75
17 A17 7.50p dl blue (R) 1.90 1.90
18 A18 10p dp brown (R) 2.75 2.75
19 A19 15p dp green (R) 4.00 4.00
20 A20 25p violet brn 8.00 8.00
21 A21 50p dk brown (R) 7.00 7.00
22 A22 100p red orange 22.50 22.50
Nos. 1-22 (22) 60.80 60.80

AIR POST STAMPS

Air Post Stamps of Syria, 1931, Overprinted in Black or Red

LATTAQUIE

1931-33 **Unwmk.** *Perf. 13½*
C1 AP2 50c ocher .40 .40
a. Inverted overprint 350.00 350.00
C2 AP2 50c blk brn (R) ('33) .50 .50
C3 AP2 1p chestnut brn .80 .80
C4 AP2 2p Prus blue (R) 1.10 1.10
C5 AP2 3p blue grn (R) 1.65 1.65
C6 AP2 5p red violet 2.75 2.75
C7 AP2 10p slate grn (R) 4.00 4.00
C8 AP2 15p orange red 5.25 5.25
C9 AP2 25p orange brn 10.00 10.00
C10 AP2 50p black (R) 14.00 14.00
C11 AP2 100p magenta 14.00 14.00
Nos. C1-C11 (11) 54.45 54.45

POSTAGE DUE STAMPS

Postage Due Stamps of Syria, 1931, Overprinted like Regular Issue

1931 **Unwmk.** *Perf. 13½*
J1 D7 8p blk, *gray bl* (R) 11.00 11.00
J2 D8 15p blk, *dl rose* (R) 9.00 9.00

Stamps of Latakia were superseded in 1937 by those of Syria.

LATVIA

ˈlat–vē–ə

(Lettonia, Lettland)

LOCATION — Northern Europe, bordering on the Baltic Sea and the Gulf of Riga
GOVT. — Independent Republic
AREA — 25,395 sq. mi.
POP. — 1,994,506 (estimated 1939)
CAPITAL — Riga

Latvia was created a sovereign state following World War I and was admitted to the League of Nations in 1922. In 1940 it became a republic in the Union of Soviet Socialist Republics. Latvian independence was recognized by the Soviet Union on Sept. 6, 1991.

100 Kapeikas = 1 Rublis
100 Santims = 1 Lat (1923, 1993)
100 Kopecks = 1 Ruble (1991)

Catalogue values for unused stamps in this country are for Never Hinged items, beginning with Scott 1 in the regular postage section, Scott B1 in the semi-postal section, Scott C1 in the air post section, Scott CB1 in the air post semi-postal section, and Scott 2N45 in the Russian Occupation section.

Catalogue values for unused stamps in this section are for Never Hinged items.

Watermarks

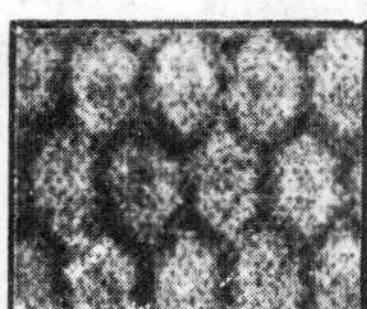
Wmk. 108- Honeycomb

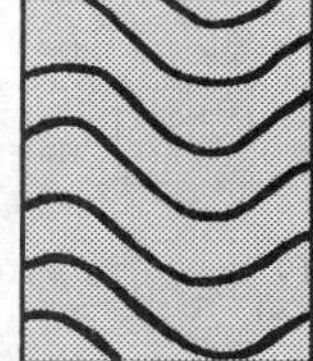
Wmk. 145- Wavy Lines

Wmk. 181- Wavy Lines

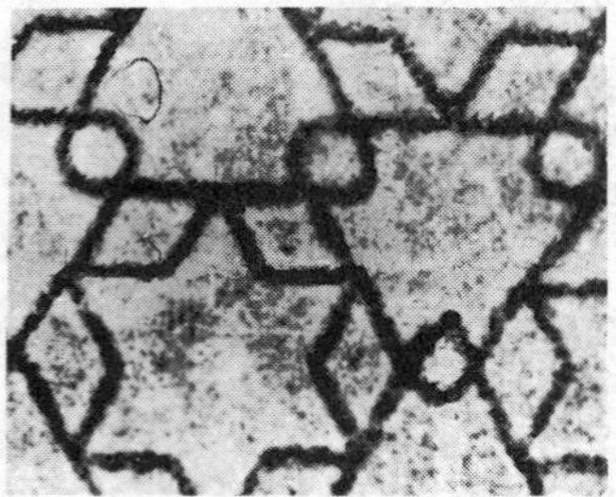
Wmk. 197- Star and Triangles

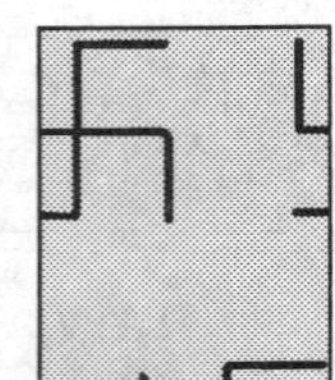
Wmk. 212- Multiple Swastikas

Wmk. 265- Multiple Waves

Arms — A1

Printed on the Backs of German Military Maps

Unwmk.

1918, Dec. 18 Litho. *Imperf.*

1 A1 5k carmine .90 .60

Perf. 11½

2 A1 5k carmine .90 .60

Stamps from outer rows of the sheets sometimes have no printing on the back.

Redrawn
Paper with Ruled Lines

1919 *Imperf.*

3 A1 5k carmine .65 .50
4 A1 10k dark blue .65 .50
5 A1 15k green .65 .50

Perf. 11½

6 A1 5k carmine 1.25 1.25
7 A1 10k dark blue 1.25 1.25
8 A1 15k deep green 2.00 1.50
Nos. 3-8 (6) 6.45 5.50

In the redrawn design the wheat heads are thicker, the ornament at lower left has five points instead of four, and there are minor changes in other parts of the design.

The sheets of this and subsequent issues were usually divided in half by a single line of perforation gauging 10. Thus stamps are found with this perforation on one side.

1919 Pelure Paper *Imperf.*

9 A1 3k lilac 4.50 3.75
10 A1 5k carmine .15 .15
11 A1 10k deep blue .15 .15
12 A1 15k dark green .15 .15
13 A1 20k orange .15 .15
13A A1 25k gray 30.00 25.00
14 A1 35k dark brown .18 .15
15 A1 50k purple .22 .18
16 A1 75k emerald 3.75 4.00
Nos. 9-16 (9) 39.25 33.68

Perf. 11½, 9½

17 A1 3k lilac 17.00 15.00
18 A1 5k carmine 1.00 .90
19 A1 10k deep blue 2.25 1.90
20 A1 15k dark green 2.25 1.90
21 A1 20k orange 2.00 1.90
22 A1 35k dark brown 2.75 2.50
23 A1 50k purple 4.25 3.75
24 A1 75k emerald 8.25 7.25
Nos. 17-24 (8) 39.75 35.10

Nos. 17-24 are said to be unofficially perforated varieties of Nos. 9-16.

1919 Wmk. 108 *Imperf.*

25 A1 3k lilac .18 .15
26 A1 5k carmine .18 .15
27 A1 10k deep blue .18 .15
28 A1 15k deep green .18 .15
29 A1 20k orange .20 .15
30 A1 25k gray .52 .40
31 A1 35k dark brown .52 .40
32 A1 50k purple .35 .30
33 A1 75k emerald .70 .50
Nos. 25-33 (9) 3.01 2.35

The variety "printed on both sides" exists for 3k, 10k, 15k, 20k and 35k.

See #57-58, 76-82. For surcharges and overprints see #86, 132-133, 2N1-2N8, 2N12-2N19.

Liberation of Riga — A2

Rising Sun — A4

1919 Wmk. 108

43 A2 5k carmine .38 .15
44 A2 15k deep green .38 .15
45 A2 35k brown .55 .25
Nos. 43-45 (3) 1.31 .55

Unwmk.
Pelure Paper

49 A2 5k carmine 15.00 15.00
50 A2 15k deep green 15.00 15.00
51 A2 35k brown 15.00 15.00
Nos. 49-51 (3) 45.00 45.00

For surcharge and overprints see Nos. 87, 2N9-2N11, 2N20-2N22.

1919 *Imperf.*

55 A4 10k gray blue .24 .18

Perf. 11½

56 A4 10k gray blue .65 .50

Type of 1918

1919 Laid Paper *Perf. 11½*

57 A1 3r slate & org 1.10 .80
58 A1 5r gray brn & org 1.10 .50

Independence Issue

Allegory of One Year of Independence — A5

1919, Nov. 18 Unwmk.

Wove Paper
Size: 33x45mm

59 A5 10k brown & rose .75 .60

Laid Paper

60 A5 10k brown & rose 1.10 .85

Size: 28x38mm

61 A5 10k brown & rose .32 .26
a. Imperf.
62 A5 35k indigo & grn .28 .22
a. Vert. pair, imperf. btwn. 25.00 20.00

Wmk. 197
Thick Wove Paper
Blue Design on Back

63 A5 1r green & red .75 .60
Nos. 59-63 (5) 3.20 2.53

There are two types of Nos. 59 and 60. In type I the trunk of the tree is not outlined. In type II it has a distinct white outline.

No. 63 was printed on the backs of unfinished 5r bank notes of the Workers and Soldiers Council, Riga.

For surcharges see Nos. 83-85, 88, 94.

Warrior Slaying Dragon — A6

1919-20 Unwmk. *Perf. 11½*
Wove Paper

64 A6 10k brown & car .25 .20
a. Horiz. pair, imperf. btwn. 30.00 25.00
65 A6 25k ind & yel grn .38 .30
a. Pair, imperf. btwn. 30.00 25.00
66 A6 35k black & bl ('20) .38 .30
a. Horiz. pair, imperf. btwn. 30.00 25.00
67 A6 1r dk grn & brn ('20) .75 .60
a. Horiz. pair, imperf. vert. 30.00 25.00
b. Horiz. pair, imperf. btwn. 30.00 25.00
Nos. 64-67 (4) 1.76 1.40

Issued in honor of the liberation of Kurzeme (Kurland). The paper sometimes shows impressed quadrille lines.

For surcharges see Nos. 91-93.

Latgale Relief Issue

Latvia Welcoming Home Latgale Province — A7

1920, Mar.
Brown and Green Design on Back

68 A7 50k dk green & rose .45 .38
a. Horiz. pair, imperf. vert. 30.00
69 A7 1r slate grn & brn .45 .38
a. Horiz. pair, imperf. vert. 30.00

No. 68-69 were printed on the backs of unfinished bank notes of the government of Colonel Bermondt-Avalov and on the so-called German "Ober-Ost" money.

For surcharges see Nos. 95-99.

First National Assembly Issue

Latvia Hears Call to Assemble — A8

1920

70 A8 50k rose .42 .20
a. Imperf., pair 7.25 6.00
71 A8 1r blue .42 .20
a. Vert. pair, imperf. btwn. 30.00 25.00
b. Imperf., pair 7.25 6.00
72 A8 3r dk brn & grn .75 .60
73 A8 5r slate & vio brn .90 .60
Nos. 70-73 (4) 2.49 1.60

For surcharges see Nos. 90, 134.

Type of 1918 Issue
Wove Paper

1920-21 Unwmk. *Perf. 11½*

76 A1 5k carmine .15 .15
78 A1 20k orange .18 .15
79 A1 40k lilac ('21) .22 .15
80 A1 50k violet .22 .15
81 A1 75k emerald .22 .15
82 A1 5r gray brn & org ('21) 1.75 .20
Nos. 76-82 (6) 2.74 .95

No. 63 Surcharged in Black, Brown or Blue

1920, Sept. 1

83 A5 10r on 1r grn & red (Bk) 1.90 1.10
84 A5 20r on 1r grn & red (Br) 5.50 3.50
85 A5 30r on 1r grn & red (Bl) 7.00 4.25
Nos. 83-85 (3) 14.40 8.85

Types of 1919 Surcharged

2
DIWI
RUBLI

1920-21 Wmk. 108 *Perf. 11½*

86 A1 2r on 10k dp blue 1.25 .85
87 A2 2r on 35k brown .65 .55

No. 62 Surcharged in Red

DIWI
RUBLI
2

Unwmk.

88 A5 2r on 35k ind & grn .70 .48

No. 70 Surcharged in Blue

DIVI
2 RUB. 2

1921

90 A8 2r on 50k rose .70 .48

Nos. 64-66 Surcharged in Red or Blue

WEENS
1
RUBLIS

1920-21

91 A6 1r on 35k blk & bl (R) .45 .28
92 A6 2r on 10k brn & rose (Bl) .45 .28
93 A6 2r on 25k ind & grn (R) .60 .20
a. Imperf.
Nos. 91-93 (3) 1.50 .76

On Nos. 92 and 93 the surcharge reads "DIVI 2 RUBLI."

No. 83 with Added Surcharge

Desmit
rubli.

1921 Wmk. 197

94 A5 10r on 10r on 1r 1.75 1.00

Latgale Relief Issue of 1920 Surcharged in Black or Blue

1921, May 31 Unwmk.

95 A7 10r on 50k grn & rose 1.50 .80
a. Imperf.
96 A7 20r on 50k grn & rose 6.00 3.00
97 A7 30r on 50k grn & rose 5.00 2.00
98 A7 50r on 50k grn & rose 10.00 4.75
99 A7 100r on 50k grn & rose (Bl) 20.00 11.00
Nos. 95-99 (5) 42.50 21.55

Excellent counterfeits exist.

Arms and Stars for Vidzeme, Kurzeme & Latgale — A10

Coat of Arms — A11

Type I, slanting cipher in value.
Type II, upright cipher in value.

Perf. 10, 11½ and Compound
Wmk. Similar to 181

1921-22 **Typo.**
101 A10 50k violet (II) .55 .15
102 A10 1r orange yel .55 .20
103 A10 2r deep green .55 .15
104 A10 3r brt green .30 .20
105 A10 5r rose .95 .15
106 A10 6r dp claret 1.90 .30
107 A10 9r orange 1.10 .25
108 A10 10r blue (I) 1.10 .15
109 A10 15r ultra 2.50 .85
a. Printed on both sides 37.50
110 A10 20r dull lilac (II) 11.00 2.25

1922, Aug. 21 **Perf. 11½**
111 A11 50r dk brn & pale brn (I) 25.00 2.00
112 A11 100r dk bl & pale bl (I) 30.00 3.00
Nos. 101-112 (12) 75.50 9.65

#101-131 sometimes show letters of a paper maker's watermark "PACTIEN LIGAT MILLS."
See Nos. 126-131, 152-154.

A12

2 SANTIMS
Type A, tail of "2" ends in an upstroke.
Type B, tail of "2" is nearly horizontal.

1923-25 **Perf. 10, 11, 11½**
113 A12 1s violet .75 .15
114 A12 2s org yel (A) .75 .15
115 A12 4s dark green 1.00 .15
a. Horiz. pair, imperf. btwn. 42.50 25.00
116 A12 5s lt green ('25) 2.00 .15
117 A12 6s grn, *yel* ('25) 4.00 .15
118 A12 10s rose red (I) 1.50 .15
a. Horiz. pair, imperf. btwn. 42.50 25.00
119 A12 12s claret .30 .15
120 A12 15s brn, *sal* 3.50 .15
a. Horiz. pair, imperf. btwn. 42.50 25.00
121 A12 20s dp blue (II) 2.50 .15
122 A12 25s ultra ('25) .30 .15
123 A12 30s pink (I) ('25) 4.50 .15
124 A12 40s lilac (I) 2.00 .15
125 A12 50s lil gray (II) 4.00 .20
126 A11 1 l dk brn & pale brn 12.50 .50
127 A11 2 l dk blue & blue 20.00 1.00
130 A11 5 l dp grn & pale grn 65.00 6.00
131 A11 10 l car rose & pale rose (I) 6.00 3.00
Nos. 113-131 (17) 130.60 12.50

Value in "Santims" (1s); "Santimi" (2s-6s) or "Santimu" (others).
See note after No. 110.
See Nos. 135-151, 155-157. For overprints and surcharges see Nos. 164-167, B21-B23.

15
SANTIMU
Nos. 79-80
Surcharged

1 Ls
No. 72
Surcharged

1927 **Unwmk.** **Perf. 11½**
132 A1 15s on 40k lilac .65 .65
133 A1 15s on 50k violet 1.00 1.00
134 A8 1 l on 3r brn & grn 5.75 5.50
Nos. 132-134 (3) 7.40 7.15

Types of 1923-25 Issue

1927-33 **Wmk. 212** **Perf. 10, 11½**
135 A12 1s dull violet .25 .15
136 A12 2s org yel (A) .25 .15
137 A12 2s org yel (B) ('33) .18 .15
138 A12 3s org red ('31) .25 .15
139 A12 4s dk green ('29) 2.75 1.25
140 A12 5s lt green ('31) .85 .15
141 A12 6s grn, *yel* .15 .15
142 A12 7s dk green ('31) .85 .22
143 A12 10s red (I) 2.25 .15
144 A12 10s grn, *yel* (I) ('32) 8.50 .15
145 A12 15s brn, *sal* 5.25 .15
146 A12 20s pink (I) 6.00 .15
147 A12 20s pink (II) 4.25 .15
148 A12 30s lt blue (I) 2.25 .15
149 A12 35s dk blue ('31) 1.75 .15
150 A12 40s dl lil (I) ('29) 2.25 .15
151 A12 50s gray (II) 3.25 .15
152 A11 1 l dk brn & pale brn 9.50 .28
153 A11 2 l dk bl & bl ('31) 22.50 1.10
154 A11 5 l grn & pale grn ('33) 175.00 20.00
Nos. 135-154 (20) 248.28 25.10

The paper of Nos. 141, 144 and 145 is colored on the surface only.

See note above No. 113 for types A and B, and note above No. 101 for types I and II.

Type of 1927-33 Issue
Paper Colored Through

1931-33 **Perf. 10**
155 A12 6s grn, *yel* .15 .15
156 A12 10s grn, *yel* (I) ('33) 21.00 .20
157 A12 15s brn, *salmon* 4.00 .15
Nos. 155-157 (3) 25.15 .50

View of Rezekne — A13

Designs (Views of Cities): 15s, Jelgava. 20s, Cesis (Wenden). 30s, Liepaja (Libau). 50s, Riga. 1 l, Riga Theater.

1928, Nov. 18 **Litho.** **Perf. 10, 11½**
158 A13 6s dp grn & vio .90 .30
159 A13 15s dk brn & ol grn .90 .30
160 A13 20s cerise & bl grn 1.50 .38
161 A13 30s ultra & vio brn 1.50 .50
162 A13 50s dk gray & plum 1.75 1.25
163 A13 1 l blk brn & brn 3.00 1.50
Nos. 158-163 (6) 9.55 4.23

10th anniv. of Latvian Independence.

Riga Exhibition Issue

Stamps of 1927-33 Overprinted

Latvijas ražojumu
Izstāde Rigā.
1932.g. 10.—18.IX.

1932, Aug. 30 **Perf. 10, 11**
164 A12 3s orange 2.50 .90
165 A12 10s green, *yel* 2.50 1.25
166 A12 20s pink (I) 2.50 .85
167 A12 35s dark blue 3.50 1.40
Nos. 164-167 (4) 11.00 4.40

Riga Castle — A19

Arms and Shield — A20

Allegory of Latvia — A21

Ministry of Foreign Affairs — A22

1934, Dec. 15 **Litho.** **Perf. 10½, 10**
174 A19 3s red orange .15 .15
175 A20 5s yellow grn 1.00 .15
176 A20 10s gray grn 4.00 .15
177 A21 20s deep rose 4.00 .15
178 A22 35s dark blue .25 .15
179 A19 40s brown .15 .15
Nos. 174-179 (6) 9.55
Set value .65

Atis Kronvalds — A23

A. Pumpurs — A24

Juris Maters — A25

Mikus Krogzemis (Auseklis) — A26

1936, Jan. 4 **Wmk. 212** **Perf. 11½**
180 A23 3s vermilion 3.50 2.75
181 A24 10s green 3.50 2.75
182 A25 20s rose pink 3.50 2.75
183 A26 35s dark blue 3.50 2.75
Nos. 180-183 (4) 14.00 11.00

President Karlis Ulmanis — A27

1937, Sept. 4 **Litho.** **Perf. 10, 11½**
184 A27 3s org red & brn org .85 .60
185 A27 5s yellow grn .85 .60
186 A27 10s dk sl grn .85 .60
187 A27 20s rose lake & brn lake 1.25 .60
188 A27 25s black vio 1.50 .75
189 A27 30s dark blue 1.50 .75
190 A27 35s indigo 2.50 2.00
191 A27 40s lt brown 1.90 2.00
192 A27 50s olive blk 2.50 2.00
Nos. 184-192 (9) 13.70 9.90

60th birthday of President Ulmanis.

Independence Monument, Rauna (Ronneburg) — A28

Independence Monument, Jelgava — A30

Monument Entrance to Cemetery at Riga — A29

War Memorial, Valka — A31

Independence Monument, Iecava — A32

Independence Monument, Riga — A33

Tomb of Col. Kalpaks — A34

Unwmk.
1937, July 12 **Litho.** **Perf. 10**
Thick Paper
193 A28 3s vermilion .65 .80
194 A29 5s yellow grn .65 .80
195 A30 10s deep grn .65 .80
196 A31 20s carmine 2.50 1.90
197 A32 30s lt blue 2.00 2.25

Perf. 11½
Engr. **Wmk. 212**
Thin Paper
198 A33 35s dark blue 2.00 2.25
199 A34 40s brown 3.00 2.75
Nos. 193-199 (7) 11.45 11.55

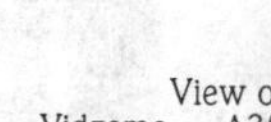

View of Vidzeme — A35

General J. Balodis — A37

President Karlis Ulmanis A38

Views: 5s, Latgale. 30s, Riga waterfront. 35s, Kurzeme. 40s, Zemgale.

1938, Nov. 17 **Perf. 10, 10½x10**
200 A35 3s brown org .25 .15
a. Booklet pane of 4 26.00
201 A35 5s yellow grn .45 .15
a. Booklet pane of 4 26.00
202 A37 10s dk green .60 .15
a. Booklet pane of 2 26.00
203 A38 20s red lilac .75 .15
a. Booklet pane of 2 20.00
204 A35 30s deep blue 1.75 .20
205 A35 35s indigo .95 .20
a. Booklet pane of 2 26.00
206 A35 40s rose violet 1.75 .25
Nos. 200-206 (7) 6.50
Set value 1.05

The 20th anniversary of the Republic.

School, Riga — A42

Independence Monument, Riga — A45

President Karlis Ulmanis — A49

Designs: 5s, Castle of Jelgava. 10s, Riga Castle. 30s, Symbol of Freedom. 35s, Community House Daugavpils. 40s, Powder Tower and War Museum, Riga.

1939, May 13 **Photo.** **Perf. 10**
207 A42 3s brown orange .85 .55
208 A42 5s deep green .85 .55
209 A42 10s dk slate grn 1.00 .55
210 A45 20s dk car rose 1.25 .70
211 A42 30s brt ultra 2.00 .55
212 A42 35s dark blue 1.65 1.40
213 A45 40s brown violet 2.00 1.10
214 A49 50s grnsh black 3.50 1.10
Nos. 207-214 (8) 13.10 6.50

5th anniv. of National Unity Day.

Harvesting Wheat — A50

Apple — A51

1939, Oct. 8
215 A50 10s slate green 1.00 .50
216 A51 20s rose lake 1.50 .65

8th Agricultural Exposition held near Riga.

Arms and Stars for Vidzeme, Kurzeme and Latgale — A52

1940

No.	Type	Description	Unused	Used
217	A52	1s dk vio brn	.15	.15
218	A52	2s ocher	.15	.15
219	A52	3s red orange	.15	.15
220	A52	5s dk olive brn	.15	.15
221	A52	7s dk green	.15	.15
222	A52	10s dk blue grn	.75	.15
224	A52	20s rose brown	.75	.15
225	A52	30s dp red brn	.90	.20
226	A52	35s brt ultra	.30	.55
228	A52	50s dk slate grn	.80	.40
229	A52	1 l olive green	1.75	1.10
		Nos. 217-229 (11)	6.00	
		Set value		2.50

Natl. Arms — A70

1991, Oct. 19 Litho. *Perf. 13x12½*

No.	Type	Description	Unused	Used
300	A70	5k multicolored	.20	.15
301	A70	10k multicolored	.35	.15
302	A70	15k multicolored	.55	.15
303	A70	20k multicolored	.75	.20
304	A70	40k multicolored	1.50	.40
305	A70	50k multicolored	1.75	.50

Size: 28x32mm

Perf. 13½x14

No.	Type	Description	Unused	Used
306	A70	100k silver & multi	3.50	1.00
307	A70	200k gold & multi	7.50	2.00
		Nos. 300-307 (8)	16.10	4.55

Most issues, Nos. 300-342, have one blocked value that was not freely available at Latvian post offices.

Russia Nos. 5984, 5985a Ovptd. "LATVIJA" and Surcharged in Red Lilac, Orange, Green, Violet

1991, Dec. 23 Photo. *Perf. 12x11½*

No.	Type	Description	Unused	Used
308	A2765	100k on 7k (RL)	.50	.15
a.		Vert. pair, one without ovpt.	9.00	
b.		Litho., perf. 12x12½	.60	.15

Perf. 12x12½

Litho.

No.	Type	Description	Unused	Used
309	A2765	300k on 2k (O)	1.65	.38
a.		Vert. pair, one without ovpt.	9.00	
310	A2765	500k on 2k (G)	2.50	.62
a.		Vert. pair, one without ovpt.	9.00	
311	A2765	1000k on 2k (V)	5.25	1.25
a.		Vert. pair, one without ovpt.	9.00	
		Nos. 308-311 (4)	9.90	2.40

On Nos. 308-311 the sixth row of the sheet was not surcharged.

Forgeries exist.

Liberty Monument, Riga — A71

1991, Dec. 28 *Perf. 12½x13*

No.	Type	Description	Unused	Used
312	A71	10k ol brn & multi	.15	.15
313	A71	15k violet & multi	.20	.15
314	A71	20k bl grn & multi	.25	.15
315	A71	30k ol grn & multi	.35	.15
316	A71	50k choc & multi	.60	.20
317	A71	100k dp blue & multi	1.00	.40
		Nos. 312-317 (6)	2.55	
		Set value		.90

Latvia stamps can be mounted in the annually supplemented Scott Baltic States album.

A72

A73

Monuments — A74

1992, Feb. 29 *Perf. 14*

No.	Type	Description	Unused	Used
318	A72	10k black	.20	.15
319	A73	20k violet black	.35	.15
320	A73	30k brown	.50	.15
321	A72	30k purple	.50	.15
322	A74	40k violet blue	.65	.16
323	A74	50k green	.75	.20
324	A73	50k olive green	.75	.20
325	A74	100k red brown	1.50	.40
326	A72	200k blue	2.50	.80
		Nos. 318-326 (9)	7.70	
		Set value		2.10

Russia Nos. 4599, 5984, 5985a Ovptd. "LATVIJA" and Surcharged in Red, Brown, Emerald and Violet

1992, Apr. 4 Photo. *Perf. 12x11½*

No.	Type	Description	Unused	Used
327	A2765	1r on 7k (R)	.25	.15

Perf. 12x12½

Litho.

No.	Type	Description	Unused	Used
328	A2765	3r on 2k (Br)	.65	.20
329	A2765	5r on 2k (E)	1.00	.30
330	A2765	10r on 2k (V)	2.00	.65
331	A2138	25r on 4k	5.00	1.50
		Nos. 327-331 (5)	8.90	2.80

Surcharged denominations expressed in rubles (large numerals) and kopecks (small zeros).

Birds of the Baltic Shores — A75

Perf. 12½x13

1992, Oct. 3 Litho. & Engr.

Booklet Stamps

No.	Type	Description	Unused	Used
332	A75	5r Pandion haliaetus	.45	.15
333	A75	5r Limosa limosa	.45	.15
334	A75	5r Mergus merganser	.45	.15
335	A75	5r Tadorna tadorna	.45	.15
a.		Booklet pane of 4, #332-335	2.50	

See Estonia Nos. 231-234a and Sweden Nos. 1975-1978a.

Christmas A76

Designs: 2r, 10r Angels with children around Christmas tree. 3r, Angels with musical instruments, Christmas tree. 15r, Nativity scene.

1992, Nov. 21 Litho. *Perf. 13½x13*

No.	Type	Description	Unused	Used
336	A76	2r silver & multi	.50	.15
337	A76	3r multicolored	.80	.20
338	A76	10r gold & multi	2.50	.60
339	A76	15r multicolored	4.00	1.00
		Nos. 336-339 (4)	7.80	1.95

Russia Nos. 4728, 5107, 5109 Surcharged in Brown or Blue

50

Perfs. & Printing Methods as Before

1993, Feb. 26

No.	Type	Description	Unused	Used
340	A2229	50r on 6k #4728 (Br)	.75	.35
341	A2435	100r on 6k #5109	1.50	.65
342	A2435	300r on 6k #5107	4.00	2.00
		Nos. 340-342 (3)	6.25	3.00

Traditional Costumes — A77

1993, Apr. 29 Litho. *Perf. 13x13½*

No.	Type	Description	Unused	Used
343	A77	5s Kuldiga	.15	.15
344	A77	10s Alsunga	.30	.15
345	A77	20s Lielvarde	.55	.30
346	A77	50s Rucava	1.50	.70
347	A77	100s Zemgale	3.00	1.50
348	A77	500s Ziemellatgale	14.00	7.00
a.		Miniature sheet of 6, #343-348	22.50	22.50
		Nos. 343-348 (6)	19.50	9.80

See Nos. 400, 415-416, 440-441.

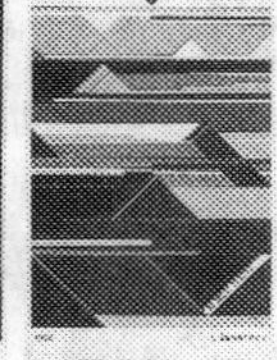

21st Natl. Song Festival
A78 A79

1993, July 3 Litho. *Perf. 12½x13*

No.	Type	Description	Unused	Used
349	A78	3s rose brn, gold & black	.15	.15
350	A78	5s purple, gold & black	.20	.15
351	A79	15s multicolored	.50	.25
		Nos. 349-351 (3)	.85	
		Set value		.38

A80

A81

1993, Aug. 28 Litho. *Perf. 14*

No.	Type	Description	Unused	Used
352	A80	15s Pope John Paul II	.75	.38

1993, Nov. 11 Litho. *Perf. 12½x13*

No.	Type	Description	Unused	Used
353	A81	5s silver, black & red	.18	.15
354	A81	15s gold, black & red	.55	.28

Independence, 75th anniv.

A82

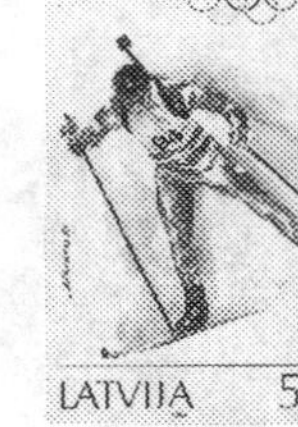

A83

1994, Apr. 2 Litho. *Perf. 14*

No.	Type	Description	Unused	Used
355	A82	15s multicolored	.55	.28

Evalds Valters, actor, 100th birthday.

1994, Apr. 20 Litho. *Perf. 12½x13*

No.	Type	Description	Unused	Used
356	A83	5s Biathlon	.18	.15
357	A83	10s 2-man bobsled	.35	.15
358	A83	15s Luge	.55	.25
359	A83	100s Men's figure skating	3.75	1.75
		Nos. 356-359 (4)	4.83	2.30

Souvenir Sheet

No.	Type	Description	Unused	Used
360	A83	200s like #357	7.25	3.75

1994 Winter Olympics, Lillehammer.

Ethnographical Open Air Museum — A84

1994, Apr. 30 Litho. *Perf. 13x12½*

No.	Type	Description	Unused	Used
361	A84	5s multicolored	.28	.15

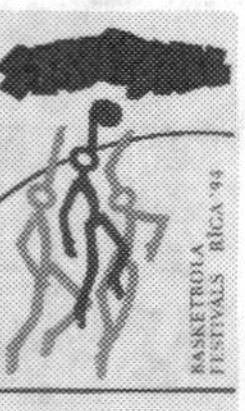

1994 Basketball Festival, Riga — A85

1994, June 4 Litho. *Perf. 12½x13*

No.	Type	Description	Unused	Used
362	A85	15s multicolored	.55	.28

Provincial Municipal Arms — A86

Perf. 13x12½, 14 (#373, 375)

1994-96

No.	Type	Description	Unused	Used
363	A86	1s Kurzeme	.15	.15
364	A86	2s Auce	.15	.15
365	A86	3s Zemgale	.15	.15
366	A86	5s Vidzeme	.18	.15
367	A86	8s Livani	.30	.15
368	A86	10s Latgale	.38	.18
369	A86	13s Preili	.45	.25
370	A86	16s Ainazi	.60	.30
371	A86	20s Grobina	.75	.38
372	A86	24s Tukums	.95	.48
373	A86	28s Madona	1.00	.50
374	A86	30s Riga	1.10	.55
375	A86	36s Priekule	1.30	.65
376	A86	50s Natl. arms	1.90	.95

Size: 29x24mm

Perf. 14

No.	Type	Description	Unused	Used
377	A86	100s Riga	3.75	1.90
377A	A86	200s Natl. arms	7.75	3.75
		Nos. 363-377A (16)	20.86	10.64

The 1s, 2s, 5s, 8s, 16s, 24s exist dated "1996;" 10s, "1997;" 1s, "1998."

Issued: 1s, 3s, 5s, 10s, 6/21/94; 30s, 50s, 100s, 200s, 12/21/94; 8s, 16s, 20s, 24s, 4/8/95; 2s, 13s, 4/12/96; 28s, 36s, 11/5/96.

See Nos. 450-451.

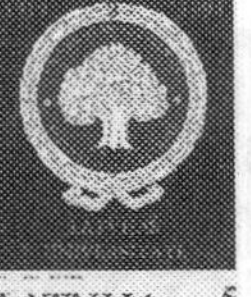

A87

A88

1994, Sept. 24 Litho. *Perf. 14*

No.	Type	Description	Unused	Used
378	A87	5s multicolored	.18	.15

University of Latvia, 75th anniv.

1994, Oct. 29 Litho. *Perf. 14x13½*

Items balanced on scales (Europa): 10s, Latvian coins. 50s, Locked chest, money card.

No.	Type	Description	Unused	Used
379	A88	10s multicolored	.38	.18
a.		Tete-beche pair	.80	.40
380	A88	50s multicolored	1.90	.95
a.		Tete-beche pair	4.00	2.00

Doormouse A89

1995, Nov. 19 Litho. *Perf. 13½x13*

381	A89	5s shown	.18	.15
382	A89	10s Among leaves	.38	.18
383	A89	10s Eating berries	.38	.18
384	A89	15s Berry, large mouse	.55	.28
		Nos. 381-384 (4)	*1.49*	*.79*

World Wildlife Fund.

A90

A91

Christmas: 3s, Angel. 8s, Angels playing flute & violin. 13c, Angels singing. 100s, Candles.

1995, Dec. 3 *Perf. 14*

385	A90	3s multicolored	.15	.15
386	A90	8s multicolored	.30	.15
387	A90	13s multicolored	.50	.25
388	A90	100s multicolored	3.75	1.90
		Nos. 385-388 (4)	*4.70*	*2.45*

Perf. 13x12½ on 3 Sides

1994, Dec. 17

Children's Fairy Tales, by Margarita Staraste: 5s, Elf with candle. No. 390, Small bear in snow. No. 391, Boy on sled.

Booklet Stamps

389	A91	5s multicolored	.20	.15
390	A91	10s multicolored	.40	.20
391	A91	10s multicolored	.40	.20
a.		Booklet pane, 2 each #389-391	2.00	
		Complete booklet, #391a + label	2.00	
		Nos. 389-391 (3)	*1.00*	*.55*

A92

A93

1995, Feb. 18 *Perf. 14*

392	A92	10s multicolored	.38	.15

European safe driving week.

1995, Mar. 4 Litho. *Perf. 14*

393	A93	15s silver, blue & red	.60	.30

UN, 50th anniv.

A94

A95

Via Baltica Highway Project: 8s, No. 395b, Castle, Bauska, Latvia. No. 395a, Beach Hotel, Parnu, Estonia. c, Kaunas, Lithuania.

1995, Apr. 20 Litho. *Perf. 14*

394	A94	8s multicolored	.30	.15

Souvenir Sheet

395	A94	18s Sheet of 3, #a.-c.	2.25	1.10

See Estonia #288-289, Lithuania #508-509.

1995, July 8 Litho. *Perf. 12½*

396	A95	8s Dendrocopos leucotos	.30	.15
397	A95	20s Crex crex	.75	.40
398	A95	24s Chlidonias leucopterus	.95	.50
		Nos. 396-398 (3)	*2.00*	*1.05*

European nature conservation year.

Julian Cardinal Vaivods, Birth Cent. — A96

1995, Aug. 18 Litho. *Perf. 14*

399	A96	8s multicolored	.30	.15

Traditional Costume Type of 1993

1995, Sept. 8 Litho. *Perf. 13x13½*

400	A77	8s Nica	.30	.15

Friendly Appeal, by Karlis Ulmanis, 60th Anniv. — A97

1995, Sept. 8 *Perf. 14*

402	A97	8s multicolored	.30	.15

Riga, 800th Anniv. — A98

1995, Sept. 23 *Perf. 13½*

403	A98	8s Natl. Opera	.30	.15
404	A98	16s Natl. Theatre	.60	.30

Size: 45x27mm

405	A98	24s Academy of Arts	.90	.45
406	A98	36s State Art Museum	1.40	.70
		Nos. 403-406 (4)	*3.20*	*1.60*

Peace and Freedom — A99

Heroes from national epic, Lacplesis, dates of independence: 16s, Spidola with sword and shield, 1918. 50s, Lacplesis with leaves and banner, 1991.

1995, Nov. 15 Litho. *Perf. 13½*

407	A99	16s multicolored	.60	.30
408	A99	50s multicolored	2.00	1.00

Europa.

Christmas A100

Designs: No. 409, Characters surrounding Christmas tree at night. No. 410, Santa gliding through sky holding candle. 15s, Characters outside snow-covered house. 24s, Santa standing between dog and cat.

1995, Dec. 2

409	A100	6s multicolored	.20	.15
410	A100	6s multicolored	.20	.15
411	A100	15s multicolored	.55	.25
412	A100	24s multicolored	.90	.45
		Nos. 409-412 (4)	*1.85*	*1.00*

Pauls Stradins (1896-1958), Physician — A101

1996, Jan. 17 Litho. *Perf. 14*

413	A101	8s multicolored	.30	.15

Zenta Maurina (1897-1978) A102

1996, May 10 Litho. *Perf. 13½x14*

414	A102	36s multicolored	1.25	.65

Europa.

Traditional Costume Type of 1993

1996, May 18 Litho. *Perf. 13x13½*

415	A77	8s Barta	.30	.15

Souvenir Sheet

416	A77	100s like No. 415	3.50	2.50

Souvenir Sheet

Children's Games — A103

1996, June 8 Litho. *Perf. 14x13½*

417	A103	48s Sheet of 1	1.90	.95

1996 Summer Olympic Games, Atlanta — A104

Perf. 14x13½, 13½x14

1996, June 19

418	A104	8s Cycling,vert.	.30	.15
419	A104	16s Basketball, vert	.65	.30
420	A104	24s Walking, vert.	.95	.50
421	A104	36s Canoeing	1.40	.70
		Nos. 418-421 (4)	*3.30*	*1.65*

Souvenir Sheet

422	A104	100s Javelin	3.50	1.75

Nature Museum, 150th Anniv. — A105

Butterflies: 8s, Papilio machaon. 24s, Catocala fraxini. 80s, Pericallia matronula.

1996, Aug. 30 *Perf. 13*

423	A105	8s multicolored	.25	.15
424	A105	24s multicolored	.60	.30
425	A105	80s multicolored	2.50	1.25
		Nos. 423-425 (3)	*3.35*	*1.70*

Car Production in Latvia — A106

Designs: 8s, 1912 Russo-Balt fire truck. 24s, 1899 Leutner-Russia. 36s, 1939 Ford-Vairogs.

1996, Oct. 25 Litho. *Perf. 13x12½*

426	A106	8s multicolored	.30	.15
427	A106	24s multicolored	.90	.45
428	A106	36s multicolored	1.40	.70
		Nos. 426-428 (3)	*2.60*	*1.30*

City of Riga, 800th Anniv. — A107

1996, Dec. 5 Litho. *Perf. 13½*

429	A107	8s Building front	.30	.15

Size: 30x26mm

430	A107	16s Stained glass window	.55	.30

Size: 37x26mm

431	A107	24s Buildings	.85	.40
432	A107	30s Art figures	1.00	.50
		Nos. 429-432 (4)	*2.70*	*1.35*

Christmas A108

Designs: 6s, Santa's elves, presents. 14s, Santa on skis, dog, children in animal costumes. 20s, Child in front of Christmas tree, santa in chair, pets.

1996, Dec. 7 *Perf. 14*

433	A108	6s multicolored	.20	.15
434	A108	14s multicolored	.50	.25
435	A108	20s multicolored	.70	.35
		Nos. 433-435 (3)	*1.40*	*.75*

See Nos. 458-460.

Birds — A109

Designs: 10s, Caprimulgus eurpaeus. 20s, Aquila clanga. 30s, Acrocephalus paludicola.

1997, Feb. 8 *Perf. 13x12½*

436	A109	10s multicolored	.35	.15
437	A109	20s multicolored	.65	.30
438	A109	30s multicolored	1.00	.50
		Nos. 436-438 (3)	*2.00*	*.95*

Turn of the Epochs — A110

Legend of Rozi Turaidas — A111

1997, Mar. 25 Litho. *Perf. 14*

439	A110	10s multicolored	.35	.15

Traditional Costume Type of 1993

1997, Apr. 3 *Perf. 13x13½*

440	A77	10s Rietumvidzeme	.35	.20

Souvenir Sheet

441	A77	100s like #440	3.50	1.75

Stamp Day.

1997, Apr. 26 Litho. *Perf. 12½x13*

442	A111	32s multicolored	1.10	.55

Europa.

Old Baltic Ships — A112

Designs: 10s, Linijkugis, 17th cent.
No. 444: a, Linijkugis, 17th cent., diff. b, Kurenas 16th cent. c, Maasilinn ship, 16th cent.

1997, May 10 *Perf. 14x14½*

443 A112 10s multicolored .35 .20

Souvenir Sheet

444 A112 20s Sheet of 3, #a.-c. 2.10 1.00

See Estonia No. 322, Lithuania Nos. 571-572.

Port of Ventspils, Cent. — A113

1997, May 21 Litho. *Perf. 13½x14*

445 A113 20s Hermes, Poseidon .70 .35

Children's Activities A114

Designs: 10s, Stamp collecting. 12s, Riding dirt bike, vert. 20s, Boy in hockey uniform, girl in skiwear, vert. 30s, Tennis, soccer, basketball.

1997, June 7 *Perf. 13½x13*

446	A114	10s multicolored	.30	.15
447	A114	12s multicolored	.40	.20
448	A114	20s multicolored	.65	.35
449	A114	30s multicolored	1.00	.50
		Nos. 446-449 (4)	2.35	1.20

Municipal Arms Type of 1994

1997, Sept. 6 Litho. *Perf. 13x12½*

450	A86	10s Valmiera	.35	.15
451	A86	20s Rezekne	.70	.35

No. 450 exists dated 1998.

Nature Preserves — A115

1997, Oct. 18 Litho. *Perf. 13x12½*

452	A115	10s Moricsala, 1912	.35	.15
453	A115	30s Slitere, 1921	1.00	.50

City of Riga, 800th Anniv. A116

Designs: 10s, Woman, house, 12th cent. 20s, Monument to Bishop Albert, seal of the bishop, rosary, writing tool, 13th-16th cent. 30s, Riga castle, weapons used during Middle Ages. 32s, Houses, arms of Riga, statue of St. John.

1997, Nov. 27 Litho. *Perf. 13x14*

454	A116	10s multicolored	.35	.15
455	A116	20s multicolored	.70	.35
456	A116	30s multicolored	1.00	.50

Size: 27x26mm

457	A116	32s multicolored	1.10	.55
		Nos. 454-457 (4)	3.15	1.55

Christmas Type of 1996

People dressed in masks, costumes for mummery: 8s, Santa, bear. 18s, Two goats. 28s, Horse.

1997, Nov. 29 *Perf. 14*

458	A108	8s multicolored	.30	.15
459	A108	18s multicolored	.60	.30
460	A108	28s multicolored	.95	.50
		Nos. 458-460 (3)	1.85	.95

1998 Winter Olympic Games, Nagano — A117

1998, Jan. 31 Litho. *Perf. 14x13½*

461 A117 20s multicolored .60 .30

SEMI-POSTAL STAMPS

Catalogue values for unused stamps in this section are for Never Hinged items.

"Mercy" Assisting Wounded Soldier — SP1

1920 Unwmk. Typo. *Perf. 11½*

Brown and Green Design on Back

B1	SP1	20(30)k dk brn & red	.50	.60
B2	SP1	40(55)k dk bl & red	.50	.60
B3	SP1	50(70)k dk grn & red	.50	.60
B4	SP1	1(1.30)r dl sl & red	.50	.75

Wmk. Star and Triangles (197)

Blue Design on Back

B5	SP1	20(30)k dk brn & red	.70	.75
B6	SP1	40(55)k dk bl & red	.70	.75
a.		Vert. pair, imperf. btwn.	30.00	
B7	SP1	50(70)k dk grn & red	.70	1.00
B8	SP1	1(1.30)r dk sl & red	.70	1.00

Wmk. Similar to 145

Pink Paper *Imperf.*

Brown, Green and Red Design on Back

B9	SP1	20(30)k dk brn & red	1.00	1.50
B10	SP1	40(55)k dk bl & red	1.00	1.50
B11	SP1	50(70)k dk grn & red	1.00	1.50
B12	SP1	1(1.30)r dk sl & red	1.00	1.50
		Nos. B1-B12 (12)	8.80	12.05

These semi-postal stamps were printed on the backs of unfinished bank notes of the Workers and Soldiers Council, Riga, and the Bermondt-Avalov Army.

Nos. B1-B8 Surcharged **RUB. 2 RUB.**

1921 Unwmk. *Perf. 11½*

Brown and Green Design on Back

B13	SP1	20k + 2r dk brn & red	1.40	1.65
B14	SP1	40k + 2r dk bl & red	1.40	1.65
B15	SP1	50k + 2r dk grn & red	1.40	1.65
B16	SP1	1r + 2r dk sl & red	1.40	1.65

Wmk. Star and Triangles (197)

Blue Design on Back

B17	SP1	20k + 2r dk brn & red	10.00	6.00
B18	SP1	40k + 2r dk bl & red	10.00	6.00
B19	SP1	50k + 2r dk grn & red	10.00	6.00
B20	SP1	1r + 2r dk sl & red	10.00	6.00
		Nos. B13-B20 (8)	45.60	30.60

Regular Issue of 1923-25 Surcharged in Blue

1923 Wmk. Similar to 181 *Perf. 10*

B21	A12	1s + 10s violet	.75	1.00
B22	A12	2s + 10s yellow	.75	1.00
B23	A12	4s + 10s dk green	.75	1.00
		Nos. B21-B23 (3)	2.25	3.00

The surtax benefited the Latvian War Invalids Society.

Lighthouse and Harbor, Liepaja (Libau) — SP2

Church at Liepaja — SP5

Coat of Arms of Liepaja — SP6

Designs: 15s (25s), City Hall, Liepaja. 25s (35s), Public Bathing Pavilion, Liepaja.

1925, May 29 *Perf. 11½*

B24	SP2	6s (12s) red brn & dp bl	1.75	.65
B25	SP2	15s (25s) dk bl & brn	.90	1.00
B26	SP2	25s (35s) vio & dk grn	1.50	1.00
B27	SP5	30s (40s) dk bl & lake	3.50	3.75
B28	SP6	50s (60s) dk grn & vio	5.00	6.00
		Nos. B24-B28 (5)	12.65	12.40

Tercentenary of Liepaja (Libau). The surtax benefited that city. Exist imperf.

President Janis Cakste — SP7

1928, Apr. 18 **Engr.**

B29	SP7	2s (12s) red orange	2.00	2.00
B30	SP7	6s (16s) deep green	2.00	2.00
B31	SP7	15s (25s) red brown	2.00	2.00
B32	SP7	25s (35s) deep blue	2.75	2.75
B33	SP7	30s (40s) claret	2.00	2.00
		Nos. B29-B33 (5)	10.75	10.75

The surtax helped erect a monument to Janis Cakste, 1st pres. of the Latvian Republic.

Venta River — SP8

Allegory, "Latvia" — SP9

View of Jelgava — SP10

National Theater, Riga — SP11

View of Cesis (Wenden) — SP12

Riga Bridge and Trenches — SP13

Perf. 11½, Imperf.

1928, Nov. 18 Wmk. 212 Litho.

B34	SP8	6s (16s) green	1.90	1.65
B35	SP9	10s (20s) scarlet	1.90	1.65
B36	SP10	15s (25s) maroon	2.00	1.90
B37	SP11	30s (40s) ultra	2.50	2.25
B38	SP12	50s (60s) dk gray	2.50	2.25
B39	SP13	1 l (1.10 l) chocolate	3.75	3.25
		Nos. B34-B39 (6)	14.55	12.95

The surtax was given to a committee for the erection of a Liberty Memorial.

Z. A. Meierovics — SP14

1929, Aug. 22 *Perf. 11½, Imperf.*

B46	SP14	2s (4s) orange	2.25	1.50
B47	SP14	6s (12s) deep green	2.25	2.50
B48	SP14	15s (25s) red brown	2.25	2.50
B49	SP14	25s (35s) deep blue	2.75	2.50
B50	SP14	30s (40s) ultra	2.75	2.50
		Nos. B46-B50 (5)	12.25	11.50

The surtax was used to erect a monument to Z. A. Meierovics, Latvian statesman.

Tuberculosis Cross — SP15

Allegory of Hope for the Sick — SP16

Gustavs Zemgals SP17

Riga Castle SP18

Daisies and Double-barred Cross — SP20

Tuberculosis Sanatorium, near Riga — SP22

Cakste, Kviesis and Zemgals SP23

Designs: No. B61, Janis Cakste, 1st pres. of Latvia. No. B63, Pres. Alberts Kviesis.

1930, Dec. 4 Typo. *Perf. 10, 11½*

No.	Type	Description	Unused	Used
B56	SP15	1s (2s) dk vio & red org	1.25	1.00
B57	SP15	2s (4s) org & red org	1.25	1.00
a.		Cliché of 1s (2s) in plate of 2s (4s)	600.00	600.00
B58	SP16	4s (8s) dk grn & red	1.65	1.25
B59	SP17	5s (10s) brt grn & dk brn	1.65	1.25
B60	SP18	6s (12s) ol grn & bis	1.65	1.65
B61	SP17	10s (20s) dp red & blk	2.00	1.50
B62	SP20	15s (30s) mar & dl grn	1.75	1.90
B63	SP17	20s (40s) rose lake & ind	2.50	1.90
B64	SP22	25s (50s) multi	4.00	3.00
B65	SP23	30s (60s) multi	4.75	4.50
		Nos. B56-B65 (10)	22.45	18.95

Surtax for the Latvian Anti-Tuberculosis Soc. For surcharges see Nos. B72-B81.

J. Rainis and New Buildings, Riga — SP24

Character from Play and Rainis SP25

Characters from Plays — SP26

Rainis and Lyre — SP27

Flames, Flag and Rainis SP28

1930, May 23 Wmk. 212 *Perf. 11½*

No.	Type	Description	Unused	Used
B66	SP24	1s (2s) dull violet	.80	.65
B67	SP25	2s (4s) yellow org	.80	.65
B68	SP26	4s (8s) deep green	.80	.65
B69	SP27	6s (12s) yel grn & red brn	.80	.65
B70	SP28	10s (20s) dark red	10.00	15.00
B71	SP27	15s (30s) red brn & yel grn	10.00	15.00
		Nos. B66-B71 (6)	23.20	32.60

Sold at double face value, surtax going to memorial fund for J. Rainis (Jan Plieksans, 1865-1929), writer and politician.

Exist imperf. Value twice that of perf. stamps.

Nos. B56 to B65 Surcharged in Black

9

1931, Aug. 19 *Perf. 10, 11½*

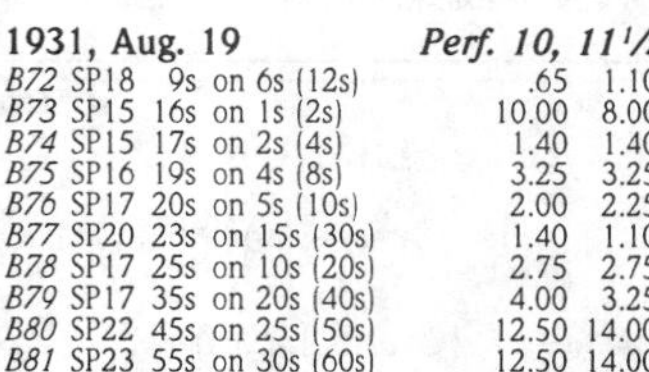

No.	Type	Description	Unused	Used
B72	SP18	9s on 6s (12s)	.65	1.10
B73	SP15	16s on 1s (2s)	10.00	8.00
B74	SP15	17s on 2s (4s)	1.40	1.40
B75	SP16	19s on 4s (8s)	3.25	3.25
B76	SP17	20s on 5s (10s)	2.00	2.25
B77	SP20	23s on 15s (30s)	1.40	1.10
B78	SP17	25s on 10s (20s)	2.75	2.75
B79	SP17	35s on 20s (40s)	4.00	3.25
B80	SP22	45s on 25s (50s)	12.50	14.00
B81	SP23	55s on 30s (60s)	12.50	14.00
		Nos. B72-B81 (10)	50.45	51.10

The surcharge replaces the original total price, including surtax.

Nos. B73-B81 have no bars in the surcharge. The surtax aided the Latvian Anti-Tuberculosis Society.

Lacplesis, the Deliverer SP29

Designs: 1s, Kriva telling stories under Holy Oak. 2s, Enslaved Latvians building Riga under knight's supervision. 4s, Death of Black Knight. 5s, Spirit of Lacplesis over freed Riga.

Inscribed: "AIZSARGI" (Army Reserve)

1932, Feb. 10 *Perf. 10½, Imperf.*

No.	Type	Description	Unused	Used
B82	SP29	1s (11s) vio brn & bluish	1.75	1.75
B83	SP29	2s (17s) ocher & ol grn	1.75	1.75
B84	SP29	3s (23s) red brn & org brn	1.75	2.00
B85	SP29	4s (34s) dk grn & grn	2.00	2.25
B86	SP29	5s (45s) green & emer	3.00	3.25
		Nos. B82-B86 (5)	10.25	11.00

Surtax aided the Militia Maintenance Fund.

Marching Troops — SP30

Infantry in Action — SP31

Nurse Binding Soldier's Wound — SP32

Army Soup Kitchen — SP33

Gen. J. Balodis — SP34

1932, May *Perf. 10½, Imperf.*

No.	Type	Description	Unused	Used
B87	SP30	6s (25s) ol brn & red vio	3.75	3.00
B88	SP31	7s (35s) dk bl grn & dk bl	3.75	3.00
B89	SP32	10s (45s) ol grn & blk brn	3.75	3.00
B90	SP33	12s (55s) lake & ol grn	4.00	3.75
B91	SP34	15s (75s) red org & brn vio	6.00	5.00
		Nos. B87-B91 (5)	21.25	17.75

The surtax aided the Latvian Home Guards.

Symbolical of Unified Latvia — SP35

Aid to the Sick — SP37

Symbolical of the Strength of the Latvian Union SP36

"Charity" SP38

Wmk. Multiple Swastikas (212)

1936, Dec. 28 Litho. *Perf. 11½*

No.	Type	Description	Unused	Used
B92	SP35	3s orange red	1.90	2.00
B93	SP36	10s green	1.90	2.00
B94	SP37	20s rose pink	1.90	2.00
B95	SP38	35s blue	1.90	2.00
		Nos. B92-B95 (4)	7.60	8.00

Souvenir Sheets

SP39

1938, May 12 Wmk. 212 *Perf. 11*

No.	Type	Description	Unused	Used
B96	SP39	Sheet of 2	7.00	15.00
a.		35s Justice Palace, Riga	2.00	2.50
b.		40s Power Station, Kegums	2.00	2.50

Sold for 2 l. The surtax of 1.25 l was for the National Reconstruction Fund.

Overprinted in Blue with Dates 1934 1939 and "15" over "V"

1939

No.	Type	Description	Unused	Used
B97	SP39	Sheet of 2	10.00	18.00

5th anniv. of Natl. Unity Day. Sold for 2 lats. Surtax for the Natl. Reconstruction Fund.

Natl. Olympic Committee SP50

1992, Feb. 8 Litho. *Perf. 13½x13*

Background Color

No.	Type	Description	Unused	Used
B150	SP50	50k +25k gray	1.50	1.50
B151	SP50	50k +25k buff	1.50	1.50
B152	SP50	100k +50k bister	3.00	3.00
		Nos. B150-B152 (3)	6.00	6.00

No. B150 inscribed "Berlin 18.09.91."

AIR POST STAMPS

Catalogue values for unused stamps in this section are for Never Hinged items.

Blériot XI — AP1

Wmk. Wavy Lines Similar to 181

1921, July 30 Litho. *Perf. 11½*

No.	Type	Description	Unused	Used
C1	AP1	10r emerald	2.25	1.25
a.		Imperf.	9.00	10.50
C2	AP1	20r dark blue	2.25	1.25
a.		Imperf.	9.00	10.50

1928, May 1

No.	Type	Description	Unused	Used
C3	AP1	10s deep green	1.75	1.10
C4	AP1	15s red	1.75	1.10
C5	AP1	25s ultra	2.25	3.50
a.		Pair, imperf. btwn.	30.00	
		Nos. C3-C5 (3)	5.75	5.70

Nos. C1-C5 sometimes show letters of a paper maker's watermark "PACTIEN LIGAT MILLS."

1931-32 Wmk. 212 *Perf. 11, 11½*

No.	Type	Description	Unused	Used
C6	AP1	10s deep green	1.40	.90
C7	AP1	15s red	2.25	1.40
C8	AP1	25s deep blue ('32)	2.75	1.65
		Nos. C6-C8 (3)	6.40	3.95

Type of 1921 Overprinted or Surcharged in Black

LATVIJA-AFRIKA
1933.

1933, May 26 Wmk. 212 *Imperf.*

No.	Type	Description	Unused	Used
C9	AP1	10s deep green	8.00	8.00
C10	AP1	15s red	8.00	8.00
C11	AP1	25s deep blue	15.00	16.00
C12	AP1	50s on 15s red	100.00	92.50
C13	AP1	100s on 25s dp blue	110.00	92.50
		Nos. C9-C13 (5)	241.00	217.00

Honoring and financing a flight from Riga to Bathurst, Gambia. The plane crashed at Neustettin, Germany.

Counterfeits exist of Nos. C1-C13.

AIR POST SEMI-POSTAL STAMPS

Catalogue values for unused stamps in this section are for Never Hinged items.

Durbes Castle, Rainis Birthplace — SPAP1

Perf. 11½

1930, May 26 Litho. Wmk. 212

No.	Type	Description	Unused	Used
CB1	SPAP1	10s (20s) red & ol grn	4.75	6.00
CB2	SPAP1	15s (30s) dk yel grn & cop red	4.75	6.00

Surtax for the Rainis Memorial Fund.

Imperf.

No.	Type	Description	Unused	Used
CB1a	SPAP1	10s (20s)	10.00	15.00
CB2a	SPAP1	15s (30s)	10.00	15.00

Nos. C6-C8 Surcharged in Magenta, Blue or Red

1931, Dec. 5

No.	Type	Description	Unused	Used
CB3	AP1	10s + 50s dp grn (M)	5.25	7.75
CB4	AP1	15s + 1 l red (Bl)	5.25	7.75
CB5	AP1	25s + 1.50 l dp bl	5.25	7.75
		Nos. CB3-CB5 (3)	15.75	23.25

Surtax for the Latvian Home Guards.

Imperf.

No.	Type	Description	Unused	Used
CB3a	AP1	10s + 50s	8.00	7.75
CB4a	AP1	15s + 1 l	8.00	7.75
CB5a	AP1	25s + 1.50 l	8.00	7.75
		Nos. CB3a-CB5a (3)	24.00	23.25

SPAP2

1932, June 17 *Perf. 10½*

No.	Type	Description	Unused	Used
CB6	SPAP2	10s (20s) dk sl grn & grn	12.50	15.00
CB7	SPAP2	15s (30s) brt red & buff	12.50	15.00
CB8	SPAP2	25s (50s) dp bl & gray	12.50	15.00
		Nos. CB6-CB8 (3)	37.50	45.00

Surtax for the Latvian Home Guards.

Imperf.

No.	Type	Description	Unused	Used
CB6a	SPAP2	10s (20s)	17.00	17.00
CB7a	SPAP2	15s (30s)	17.00	17.00
CB8a	SPAP2	25s (50s)	17.00	17.00
		Nos. CB6a-CB8a (3)	51.00	51.00

Icarus — SPAP3

Leonardo da Vinci — SPAP4

Charles Balloon — SPAP5

Wright Brothers Biplane SPAP6

Bleriot Monoplane SPAP7

1932, Dec. *Perf. 10, 11½*

CB9	SPAP3	5s (25s) ol bis & grn	10.50	8.50
CB10	SPAP4	10s (50s) ol brn & gray grn	10.50	8.50
CB11	SPAP5	15s (75s) red brn & gray grn	10.00	8.50
CB12	SPAP6	20s (1 l) gray grn & lil rose	8.25	7.50
CB13	SPAP7	25s (1.25 l) brn & bl	8.25	7.50
		Nos. CB9-CB13 (5)	47.50	40.50

Issued to honor pioneers of aviation. The surtax of four times the face value was for wounded Latvian aviators.

Imperf.

CB9a	SPAP3	5s (25s)	17.50	13.00
CB10a	SPAP4	10s (50s)	17.50	13.00
CB11a	SPAP5	15s (75s)	17.50	11.00
CB12a	SPAP6	20s (1 l)	12.50	11.00
CB13a	SPAP7	25s (1.25 l)	12.50	11.00
		Nos. CB9a-CB13a (5)	77.50	59.00

Icarus Falling SPAP8

Monument to Aviators SPAP9

Proposed Tombs for Aviators SPAP10 SPAP11

1933, Mar. 15 *Perf. 11½*

CB14	SPAP8	2s (52s) blk & ocher	9.25	15.00
CB15	SPAP9	3s (53s) blk & red org	9.25	15.00
CB16	SPAP10	10s (60s) blk & dk yel grn	9.25	12.00
CB17	SPAP11	20s (70s) blk & cer	9.25	15.00
		Nos. CB14-CB17 (4)	37.00	57.00

50s surtax for wounded Latvian aviators.

Imperf.

CB14a	SPAP8	2s (52s)	13.00	14.00
CB15a	SPAP9	3s (53s)	13.00	14.00
CB16a	SPAP10	10s (60s)	13.00	14.00
CB17a	SPAP11	20s (70s)	13.00	14.00
		Nos. CB14a-CB17a (4)	52.00	56.00

Monoplane Taking Off — SPAP12

Designs: 7s (57s), Biplane under fire at Riga. 35s (1.35 l), Map and planes.

1933, June 15 **Wmk. 212** *Perf. 11½*

CB18	SPAP12	3s (53s) org & sl bl	16.00	20.00
CB19	SPAP12	7s (57s) sl bl & dk brn	16.00	20.00
CB20	SPAP12	35s (1.35 l) dp ultra & ol blk	16.00	20.00
		Nos. CB18-CB20 (3)	48.00	60.00

Surtax for wounded Latvian aviators. Counterfeits exist.

Imperf.

CB18a	SPAP12	3s (53s)	21.00	24.00
CB19a	SPAP12	7s (57s)	21.00	24.00
CB20a	SPAP12	35s (1.35 l)	21.00	24.00
		Nos. CB18a-CB20a (3)	63.00	72.00

American Gee-Bee SPAP13

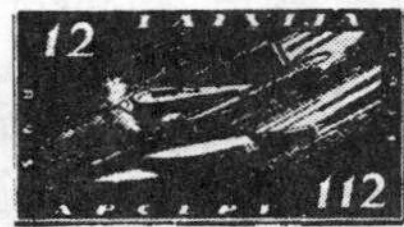

English Seaplane S6B — SPAP14

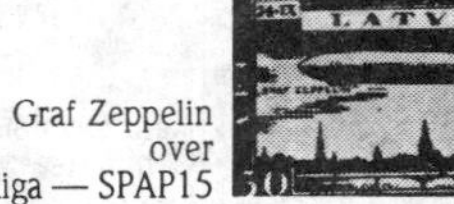

Graf Zeppelin over Riga — SPAP15

DO-X SPAP16

1933, Sept. 5 *Perf. 11½*

CB21	SPAP13	8s (68s) brn & gray blk	60.00	65.00
CB22	SPAP14	12s (1.12 l) brn car & ol grn	60.00	65.00
CB23	SPAP15	30s (1.30 l) bl & gray blk	60.00	65.00
CB24	SPAP16	40s (1.90 l) brn vio & ind	60.00	65.00
		Nos. CB21-CB24 (4)	240.00	260.00

Surtax for wounded Latvian aviators.

Imperf.

CB21a	SPAP13	8s (68s)	65.00	75.00
CB22a	SPAP14	12s (1.12 l)	65.00	75.00
CB23a	SPAP15	30s (1.30 l)	65.00	75.00
CB24a	SPAP16	40s (1.90 l)	65.00	75.00
		Nos. CB21a-CB24a (4)	260.00	300.00

OCCUPATION STAMPS

Issued under German Occupation

German Stamps of 1905-18 Handstamped

1919 **Wmk. 125** *Perf. 14, 14½*

Red Overprint

1N1	A22	2½pf gray	225.00	225.00
1N2	A16	5pf green	180.00	90.00
1N3	A22	15pf dk vio	275.00	90.00
1N4	A16	20pf blue vio	110.00	37.50
1N5	A16	25pf org & blk, *yel*	375.00	275.00
1N6	A16	50pf pur & blk, *buff*	375.00	275.00

Blue Overprint

1N7	A22	2½pf gray	225.00	225.00
1N8	A16	5pf green	110.00	57.50
1N9	A16	10pf carmine	92.50	27.50
1N10	A22	15pf dk vio	275.00	150.00
1N11	A16	20pf bl vio	110.00	27.50
1N12	A16	25pf org & blk, *yel*	375.00	275.00
1N13	A16	50pf pur & blk, *buff*	375.00	275.00

Inverted and double overprints exist, as well as counterfeit overprints.

Some experts believe that Nos. 1N1-1N7 were not officially issued. All used copies are canceled to order.

LATVIJA
1941.
1. VII

Russia Nos. 734, 616, 735, 617, 736 and 619A were overprinted in black or dark green with the three lines above in 1941. They were used in Latvia under the German occupation in July-September, 1941, and were replaced by German stamps in October, 1941.

Kurland

Four stamps of Germany were surcharged for use in Kurzeme in April, 1945, during World War II. Those are Germany Nos. 509, 511A and 516 (5pf, 10pf, 20pf with Hitler's head), surcharged "KURLAND" and "6", and No. MQ1 (red brown military parcel post stamp) surcharged "Kurland" and "12". After the Germans capitulated to the Russians May 8, 1945, in the territory of Latvia, these surcharged stamps were replaced by stamps of Russia.

ISSUED UNDER RUSSIAN OCCUPATION

The following stamps were issued at Mitau during the occupation of Kurland by the West Russian Army under Colonel Bermondt-Avalov.

Stamps of Latvia Handstamped

1919 **Wmk. 108** *Imperf.*

On Stamps of 1919

2N1	A1	3k lilac	12.50	17.50
2N2	A1	5k carmine	12.50	17.50
2N3	A1	10k dp blue	67.50	92.50
2N4	A1	20k orange	12.50	17.50
2N5	A1	25k gray	12.50	17.50
2N6	A1	35k dk brown	12.50	17.50
2N7	A1	50k purple	12.50	17.50
2N8	A1	75k emerald	15.00	22.50

On Riga Liberation Stamps

2N9	A2	5k carmine	7.50	12.50
2N10	A2	15k dp green	7.50	12.50
2N11	A2	35k brown	7.50	12.50

Stamps of Latvia Overprinted

On Stamps of 1919

2N12	A1	3k lilac	5.00	7.50
2N13	A1	5k carmine	5.00	7.50
2N14	A1	10k dp blue	60.00	92.50
2N15	A1	20k orange	10.00	15.00
2N16	A1	25k gray	17.50	32.50
2N17	A1	35k dk brown	12.50	17.50
2N18	A1	50k purple	12.50	17.50
2N19	A1	75k emerald	12.50	17.50

On Riga Liberation Stamps

2N20	A2	5k carmine	4.00	5.00
2N21	A2	15k dp green	4.00	5.00
2N22	A2	35k brown	4.00	5.00
a.		Inverted overprint	*115.00*	

The letters "Z. A." are the initials of "Zapadnaya Armiya"-i.e. Western Army.

Russian Stamps of 1909-17 Surcharged Like Illustration

Perf. 14, 14½x15

Unwmk.

On Stamps of 1909-12

2N23	A14	10k on 2k grn	4.00	5.00
a.		Inverted surcharge	*25.00*	
2N24	A15	30k on 4k car	3.50	4.50
2N25	A14	40k on 5k cl	3.50	4.50
2N26	A15	50k pn 10k dk bl	3.50	4.50
2N27	A11	70k on 15k red brn & bl	3.50	4.50
a.		Inverted surcharge	*50.00*	
2N28	A8	90k on 20k bl & car	3.50	4.50
2N29	A11	1r on 25k grn & vio	3.50	4.50
2N30	A11	1½r on 35k red brn & grn	22.50	37.50
2N31	A8	2r on 50k vio & grn	4.50	6.50
a.		Inverted surcharge	*30.00*	
2N32	A11	4r on 70k brn & org	12.50	15.00

Perf. 13½

2N33	A9	6r on 1r pale brn, brn & org	12.50	15.00

On Stamps of 1917

Imperf

2N34	A14	20k on 3k red	4.50	5.00
2N35	A14	40k on 5k claret	32.50	42.50
2N36	A12	10r on 3.50r mar & lt grn	32.50	42.55
a.		Inverted surcharge	*100.00*	
		Nos. 2N1-2N36 (36)	473.50	676.05

Eight typographed stamps of this design were prepared in 1919, but never placed in use. They exist both perforated and imperforate. Value, set, imperf. $1, perf. $2.

Reprints and counterfeits exist.

Catalogue values for unused stamps in this section, from this poit to the end of the section, are for Never Hinged items.

Arms of Soviet Latvia — OS1

1940 **Typo.** **Wmk. 265** *Perf. 10*

2N45	OS1	1s dk violet	.15	.15
2N46	OS1	2s orange yel	.15	.15
2N47	OS1	3s orange ver	.15	.15
2N48	OS1	5s dk olive grn	.15	.15
2N49	OS1	7s turq green	.15	.15
2N50	OS1	10s slate green	.45	.15
2N51	OS1	20s brown lake	.75	.15
2N52	OS1	30s light blue	.85	.25
2N53	OS1	35s brt ultra	.15	.15
2N54	OS1	40s chocolate	.60	.15
2N55	OS1	50s lt gray	.75	.15
2N56	OS1	1 l lt brown	1.50	.25
2N57	OS1	5 l brt green	15.00	6.00
		Nos. 2N45-2N57 (13)	20.80	8.00

Used values of #2N45-2N57 are for CTOs. Commercially use are worth three times as much.

LEBANON

'le–bə–nən

(Grand Liban)

LOCATION — Asia Minor, bordering on the Mediterranean Sea

GOVT. — Republic
AREA — 4,036 sq. mi.
POP. — 3,500,000 (est. 1984)
CAPITAL — Beirut

Formerly a part of the Syrian province of Turkey, Lebanon was occupied by French forces after World War I. It was mandated to France after it had been declared a separate state. Limited autonomy was granted in 1927 and full independence achieved in 1941. The French issued two sets of occupation stamps (with T.E.O. overprint) for Lebanon in late 1919. The use of these and later occupation issues (of 1920-24, with overprints "O.M.F." and "Syrie-Grand Liban") was extended to Syria, Cilicia, Alaouites and Alexandretta. By custom, these are all listed under Syria.

100 Centimes = 1 Piaster
100 Piasters = 1 Pound

Catalogue values for unused stamps in this country are for Never Hinged items, beginning with Scott 177 in the regular postage section, Scott B13 in the semi-postal section, Scott C97 in the airpost section, Scott CB5 in the airpost semi-postal section, Scott J37 in the postage due section, and Scott RA11 in the postal tax section.

Issued under French Mandate

Stamps of France 1900-21 Surcharged

GRAND LIBAN 50 CENTIEMES

1924 Unwmk. *Perf. 14x13½*

1 A16 10c on 2c vio brn .60 .35
a. Inverted surcharge 15.00 9.00
2 A22 25c on 5c orange .60 .15
3 A22 50c on 10c green .45 .15
4 A20 75c on 15c sl grn 1.10 .65
5 A22 1p on 20c red brn .65 .25
a. Double surcharge 15.00 9.00
b. Inverted surcharge 15.00 9.00
6 A22 1.25p on 25c blue 1.75 .80
7 A22 1.50p on 30c org .85 .50
8 A22 1.50p on 30c red .85 .50
9 A20 2.50p on 50c dl bl .85 .35
a. Inverted surcharge 15.00 9.00

Surcharged

GRAND LIBAN 2 PIASTRES

10 A18 2p on 40c red & pale bl 2.25 .80
a. Inverted surcharge 20.00 12.00
11 A18 3p on 60c violet & ultra 4.25 2.25
12 A18 5p on 1fr cl & ol green 4.25 2.25
13 A18 10p on 2fr org & pale bl 7.50 4.00
a. Inverted surcharge 30.00 18.00
14 A18 25p on 5fr dk bl & buff 12.50 6.50
a. Inverted surcharge 57.50 35.00
Nos. 1-14 (14) 38.45 19.50

Broken and missing letters and varieties of spacing are numerous in these surcharges.
For overprints see Nos. C1-C4.

Stamps of France, 1923, (Pasteur) Surcharged "GRAND LIBAN" and New Values

15 A23 50c on 10c green .60 .25
a. Inverted surcharge 17.50 11.00
16 A23 1.50p on 30c red .80 .45
17 A23 2.50p on 50c blue .60 .25
a. Inverted surcharge 17.50 11.00
Nos. 15-17 (3) 2.00 .95

Commemorative Stamps of France, 1924, (Olympic Games) Surcharged "GRAND LIBAN" and New Values

18 A24 50c on 10c gray grn & yel grn 15.00 15.00
a. Inverted surcharge 100.00
19 A25 1.25p on 25c rose & dk rose 15.00 15.00
a. Inverted surcharge 100.00
20 A26 1.50p on 30c brn red & blk 15.00 15.00
a. Inverted surcharge 100.00
21 A27 2.50p on 50c ultra & dk bl 15.00 15.00
a. Inverted surcharge 100.00
Nos. 18-21 (4) 60.00 60.00

Stamps of France, 1900-24, Surcharged

Gd Liban 0, P. 25 لبنان الكبير ١/٤ الغرش

c

1924-25

22 A16 10c on 2c vio brn .20 .15
23 A22 25c on 5c orange .45 .25
24 A22 50c on 10c green .65 .35
25 A20 75c on 15c gray grn .45 .25
26 A22 1p on 20c red brn .35 .20
27 A22 1.25p on 25c blue .75 .40
28 A22 1.50p on 30c red .65 .35
29 A22 1.50p on 30c orange 35.00 22.50
30 A22 2p on 35c vio ('25) .90 .45
31 A20 3p on 60c lt vio ('25) 1.00 .55
32 A20 4p on 85c ver 1.50 .90

Surcharged

Grand Liban 2 Piastres لبنان الكبير غرش ٢

33 A18 2p on 40c red & pale bl .35 .20
a. 2nd line of Arabic reads "2 Piastre" (singular) .90 .50
34 A18 2p on 45c green & blue ('25) 18.00 10.00
35 A18 3p on 60c violet & ultra 1.00 .55
36 A18 5p on 1fr cl & ol green 1.75 .90
37 A18 10p on 2fr org & pale bl 4.75 2.50
38 A18 25p on 5fr dk bl & buff 7.50 3.50
Nos. 22-38 (17) 75.25 44.00

Last line of surcharge on No. 33 has four characters, with a 9-like character between the third and fourth in illustration. Last line on No. 33a is as illustrated.
The surcharge may be found inverted on most of Nos. 22-38, and double on some values.
For overprints see Nos. C5-C8.

Stamps of France 1923-24 (Pasteur) Surcharged Type "c"

39 A23 50c on 10c green .45 .35
a. Inverted surcharge 12.50 12.50
b. Double surcharge 17.50 17.50
40 A23 75c on 15c green .55 .55
41 A23 1.50p on 30c red .65 .55
a. Inverted surcharge 16.00 16.00
42 A23 2p on 45c red 1.40 1.25
a. Inverted surcharge 13.00 12.00
43 A23 2.50p on 50c blue .55 .45
a. Inverted surcharge 13.00 13.00
b. Double surcharge 12.00 12.00
44 A23 4p on 75c blue 1.40 1.25
Nos. 39-44 (6) 5.00 4.40

France Nos. 198 to 201 (Olympics) Surcharged Type "c"

45 A24 50c on 10c 15.00 15.00
46 A25 1.25p on 25c 15.00 15.00
47 A26 1.50p on 30c 15.00 15.00
48 A27 2.50p on 50c 15.00 15.00
Nos. 45-48 (4) 60.00 60.00

France No. 219 (Ronsard) Surcharged Type "c"

49 A28 4p on 75c bl, *bluish* 1.25 1.10
a. Inverted surcharge 35.00 18.00

Cedar of Lebanon — A1

Crusader Castle, Tripoli — A3

View of Beirut — A2

Designs: 50c, Crusader Castle, Tripoli. 75c, Beit-ed-Din Palace. 1p, Temple of Jupiter, Baalbek. 1.25p, Mouktara Palace. 1.50p, Harbor of Tyre. 2p, View of Zahle. 2.50p, Ruins at Baalbek. 3p, Square at Deir-el-Kamar. 5p, Castle at Sidon. 25p, Square at Beirut.

1925 Litho. *Perf. 12½, 13½*

50 A1 10c dark violet .20 .15

Photo.

51 A2 25c olive black .55 .20
52 A2 50c yellow grn .20 .15
53 A2 75c brn orange .40 .15
54 A2 1p magenta .75 .30
55 A2 1.25p deep green 1.00 .50
56 A2 1.50p rose red .35 .15
57 A2 2p dark brown .60 .15
58 A2 2.50p peacock bl .75 .30
59 A2 3p orange brn 1.10 .40
60 A2 5p violet 1.10 .50
61 A3 10p violet brn 2.50 .80
62 A2 25p ultramarine 9.50 4.50
Nos. 50-62 (13) 19.00 8.25

For surcharges and overprints see Nos. 63-107, B1-B12, C9-C38, CB1-CB4.

Stamps of 1925 with Bars and Surcharged 3P.50 ٣غ ١/٢

1926

63 A2 3.50p on 75c brn org .55 .55
64 A2 4p on 25c ol blk 1.10 1.10
65 A2 6p on 2.50p pck bl .75 .75
66 A2 12p on 1.25p dp grn .70 .70
67 A2 20p on 1.25p dp grn 2.75 2.75

Stamps of 1925 with Bars and Surcharged 4P.50 ٤غ ١/٢

68 A2 4.50p on 75c brn org 1.10 1.10
69 A2 7.50p on 2.50p pck bl 1.10 1.10
70 A2 15p on 25p ultra 1.10 1.10
Nos. 63-70 (8) 9.15 9.15

No. 51 with Bars and Surcharged 4P. ٤غ

1927

71 A2 4p on 25c ol blk .90 .90

Issues of Republic under French Mandate

Stamps of 1925 Issue Overprinted in Black or Red République Libanaise

1927

72 A1 10c dark vio (R) .15 .15
a. Black overprint 20.00 11.00
73 A2 50c yellow grn .15 .15
74 A2 1p magenta .15 .15
75 A2 1.50p rose red .30 .30
76 A2 2p dark brown .55 .45
77 A2 3p orange brn .45 .20
78 A2 5p violet 1.00 .50
79 A3 10p violet brn 1.25 .55
80 A2 25p ultramarine 5.00 4.00
Nos. 72-80 (9) 9.00 6.45

On Nos. 72 and 79 the overprint is set in two lines. On all stamps the double bar obliterates GRAND LIBAN.

Same Overprint on Provisional Issues of 1926-27

15 PIASTERS ON 25 PIASTERS
TYPE I - "République Libanaise" at foot of stamp.
TYPE II - "République Libanaise" near top of stamp.

81 A2 4p on 25c ol blk .30 .20
82 A2 4.50p on 75c brn org .35 .20
83 A2 7.50p on 2.50p pck bl .45 .20
84 A2 15p on 25p ultra (I) 3.50 2.50
a. Type II 5.50 3.75
Nos. 81-84 (4) 4.60 3.10

Most of Nos. 72-84 are known with overprint double, inverted or on back as well as face.

Stamps of 1927 Overprinted in Black or Red الجمهورية اللبنانية

1928

86 A1 10c dark vio (R) .35 .35
a. French overprint omitted, on #50
87 A2 50c yel grn (Bk) 1.00 1.00
a. Arabic overprint inverted 18.00 18.00
88 A2 1p magenta (Bk) .45 .45
a. Inverted overprint 18.00 18.00
89 A2 1.50p rose red (Bk) 1.00 1.00
90 A2 2p dark brown (R) 1.40 1.40
90A A2 2p dk brn (Bk+R) 70.00 70.00
91 A2 3p org brown (Bk) .80 .80
92 A2 5p violet (Bk) 1.90 1.90
93 A2 5p violet (R) 1.50 1.50
a. French ovpt. below Arabic 14.00 14.00
94 A3 10p vio brn (Bk) 2.75 2.75
a. Double overprint
b. Double overprint inverted
c. Inverted overprint 70.00 70.00
95 A2 25p ultra (Bk+R) 5.75 5.75
95A A2 25p ultra (R) 6.25 6.25
Nos. 86-95A (12) 93.15 93.15

On all stamps the double bar with Arabic overprint obliterates Arabic inscription.

Same Overprint on Nos. 81-84

96 A2 4p on 25c (Bk+R) 1.00 1.00
97 A2 4.50p on 75c (Bk) 1.00 1.00
98 A2 7.50p on 2.50p (Bk+R) 2.00 2.00
99 A2 7.50p on 2.50p (R) 4.00 4.00
100 A2 15p on 25p (II) (Bk+R) 5.00 5.00
a. Arabic overprint inverted
101 A2 15p on 25p (I) (R) 7.00 7.00
Nos. 96-101 (6) 20.00 20.00

The new values are surcharged in black. The initials in ( ) refer to the colors of the overprints.

Stamps of 1925 Surcharged in Red or Black

1928-29 *Perf. 13½*

102 A2 50c on 75c brn org (Bk) ('29) .75 .40
103 A2 2p on 1.25p dp grn .75 .40
104 A2 4p on 25c ol blk .75 .40
a. Double surcharge 18.00 9.00
105 A2 7.50p on 2.50p pck bl 1.25 .60
a. Double surcharge 18.00 9.00
b. Inverted surcharge 18.00 9.00
106 A2 15p on 25p ultra 12.50 5.25
Nos. 102-106 (5) 16.00 7.05

On Nos. 103, 104 and 105 the surcharged numerals are 3¼mm high, and have thick strokes.

No. 86 Surcharged in Red 05 ٠٥

1928

107 A1 5c on 10c dk vio .60 .30

ARAZ STAMP CO.
LEBANON
WE MAINTAIN... COMPLETE SETS MINT & USED, IMPERFS, ERRORS, SOUVENIR SHEETS.
WE SELL & BUY... FRANCE FRENCH TERRITORIES FRENCH COLONIES LEBANON AND MIDDLE EAST
WANT LISTS WELCOME!
Contact us for your NEW ISSUES
ARAZ STAMP CO.
P.O. BOX 572807
Houston, TX 77257-2807
FAX (713) 558-1907
APS

Silkworm, Cocoon and Moth — A4

1930, Feb. 11 Typo. Perf. 11

108 A4 4p black brown 8.00 5.25
109 A4 4½p vermilion 8.00 5.25
110 A4 7½p dark blue 8.00 5.25
111 A4 10p dk violet 8.00 5.25
112 A4 15p dark green 8.00 5.25
113 A4 25p claret 8.00 5.25
Nos. 108-113 (6) 48.00 31.50

Sericultural Congress, Beirut. Presentation imperfs exist.

Pigeon Rocks, Ras Beirut — A5

View of Bickfaya — A8

Beit-ed-Din Palace — A10

Crusader Castle, Tripoli — A11

Ruins of Venus Temple, Baalbek A12

Ancient Bridge, Dog River — A13

Belfort Castle — A14

Afka Falls — A19

Designs: 20c, Cedars of Lebanon. 25c, Ruins of Bacchus Temple, Baalbek. 1p, Crusader Castle, Sidon Harbor. 5p, Arcade of Beit-ed-Din Palace. 6p, Tyre Harbor. 7.50p, Ruins of Sun Temple, Baalbek. 10p, View of Hasbeya. 25p, Government House, Beirut. 50p, View of Deir-el-Kamar. 75c, 100p, Ruins at Baalbek.

1930-35 Litho. Perf. 12½, 13½

114 A5 10c brown orange .15 .15
115 A5 20c yellow brn .20 .15
116 A5 25c deep blue .20 .15

Photo.

117 A8 50c orange brn .75 .30
118 A11 75c ol brn ('32) .20 .15
119 A8 1p deep green .50 .20
120 A8 1p brn vio ('35) .50 .20
121 A10 1.50p violet brn .85 .30
122 A10 1.50p dp grn ('32) 2.50 .25
123 A11 2p Prussian bl 1.50 .30
124 A12 3p black brown 1.00 .30
125 A13 4p orange brn 1.00 .15
126 A14 4.50p carmine 1.00 .40
127 A14 5p greenish blk .75 .20
128 A13 6p brn violet 2.75 .45
129 A10 7.50p deep blue 1.00 .25
130 A10 10p dk ol grn 3.50 .25
131 A19 15p blk violet 3.25 .40
132 A19 25p blue green 4.50 .55
133 A8 50p apple grn 17.50 2.50
134 A11 100p black 17.50 7.00
Nos. 114-134 (21) 61.10 14.60

See Nos. 135, 144, 152-155. For surcharges see Nos. 147-149, 161, 173-174.

Pigeon Rocks Type of 1930-35 Redrawn

1934 Litho. Perf. 12½x12

135 A5 10c dull orange 3.00 1.50

Lines in rocks and water more distinct. Printer's name "Hélio Vaugirard, Paris," in larger letters.

Cedar of Lebanon A23

President Emile Eddé A24

Dog River Panorama A25

1937-40 Typo. Perf. 14x13½

137 A23 10c rose car .15 .15
137A A23 20c aqua ('40) .15 .15
137B A23 25c pale rose lilac ('40) .15 .15
138 A23 50c magenta .20 .15
138A A23 75c brown ('40) .20 .15

Engr.
Perf. 13

139 A24 3p dk violet 1.50 .30
140 A24 4p black brown .25 .15
141 A24 4.50p carmine .35 .15
142 A25 10p brn carmine .85 .20
142A A25 12½p dp ultra ('40) .30 .15
143 A25 15p dk grn ('38) 1.50 .30
143A A25 20p chestnut ('40) .40 .20
143B A25 25p crimson ('40) .45 .25
143C A25 50p dk vio ('40) 2.50 .65
143D A25 100p sepia ('40) 1.50 .90
Nos. 137-143D (15) 10.45 4.00

Nos. 137A, 137B, 138A, 142A, 143A, 143B, 143C, and 143D exist imperforate.
For surcharges see Nos. 145-146A, 150-151, 160, 162, 175-176.

View of Bickfaya A26

Type A8 Redrawn

1937 Photo. Perf. 13½

144 A26 50c orange brown 6.00 3.50

Arabic inscriptions more condensed.

Stamps of 1930-37 Surcharged in Black or Red **2** ٢

1937-42 Perf. 13, 13½

145 A24 2p on 3p dk vio .50 .25
146 A24 2½p on 4p blk brn .50 .25
146A A24 2½p on 4p black brown (R) ('42) .50 .25
147 A10 6p on 7.50p dp bl (R) 1.75 .40

Stamps of 1930-35 and Type of 1937-40 Surcharged in Black or Red

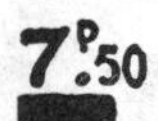

Perf. 13½, 13

148 A8 7.50p on 50p apple grn 1.00 .60
149 A11 7.50p on 100p black (R) 1.00 .60
150 A25 12.50p on 7.50p dk bl (R) 2.50 1.50

Type of 1937-40 Surcharged in Red with Bars and

12½ ١٢½

1939 Engr. Perf. 13

151 A25 12½p on 7.50p dk bl .75 .40
Nos. 145-151 (8) 8.50 4.25

Type of 1930-35 Redrawn
Imprint: "Beiteddine-Imp.-Catholique-Beyrouth-Liban."

1939 Litho. Perf. 11½

152 A10 1p dk slate grn .65 .15
153 A10 1.50p brn violet .65 .35
154 A10 7.50p carmine lake .65 .40

Bridge Type of 1930-35
Imprint: "Degorce" instead of "Hélio Vaugirard"

1940 Engr. Perf. 13

155 A13 5p grnsh blue .50 .15

Exists imperforate.

Independent Republic

Amir Beshir Shehab — A27

1942, Sept. 18 Litho. Perf. 11½

156 A27 50c emerald 1.25 1.25
157 A27 1.50p sepia 1.25 1.25
158 A27 6p rose pink 1.25 1.25
159 A27 15p dull blue 1.25 1.25
Nos. 156-159 (4) 5.00 5.00

1st anniv. of the Proclamation of Independence, Nov. 26, 1941.
Nos. 156-159 exist imperforate.

Nos. 140, 154 and 142A Surcharged in Blue, Green or Black

1943 Perf. 13, 11½

160 A24 2p on 4p (Bl) 2.50 2.00
161 A10 6p on 7.50p (G) .50 .20
162 A25 10p on 12½p (Bk) .50 .30
Nos. 160-162 (3) 3.50 2.50

The surcharge is arranged differently on each value.

Parliament Building A28

Government House, Beirut — A29

1943 Litho. Perf. 11½

163 A28 25p salmon rose 9.00 5.00
164 A29 50p bluish green 9.00 5.00
165 A28 150p light ultra 9.00 5.00
166 A29 200p dull vio brn 9.00 5.00
Nos. 163-166 (4) 36.00 20.00

2nd anniv. of Proclamation of Independence. Nos. 163-166 exist imperforate. See Nos. C82-C87. For overprints see Nos. 169-172.

Quarantine Station, Beirut — A30

1943, July 8 Photo.
Black Overprint

167 A30 10p cerise 2.75 2.00
168 A30 20p light blue 2.75 2.00
Nos. 167-168,C88-C90 (5) 11.55 8.50

Arab Medical Congress, Beirut.

Nos. 163 to 166 Overprinted in Blue, Violet, Red or Black

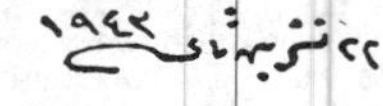

1944

169 A28 25p sal rose (Bl) 10.00 5.50
170 A29 50p bluish green (V) 10.00 5.50
171 A28 150p lt ultra (R) 10.00 5.50
172 A29 200p dull vio brn (Bk) 15.00 7.50
Nos. 169-172,C91-C96 (10) 115.00 94.00

Return to office of the president and his ministers, Nov. 22, 1943.

Type of 1930 and No. 142A Surcharged in Violet, Black or Carmine

2P. ٢ق

1945 Unwmk. Engr. Perf. 13

173 A13 2p on 5p dk bl grn (V) .50 .15
174 A13 3p on 5p dk bl grn (Bk) .50 .20
175 A25 6p on 12½p deep ultra (Bk) .60 .25
176 A25 7½p on 12½p deep ultra (C) 1.00 .65
Nos. 173-176 (4) 2.60 1.25

Trees at bottom on Nos. 175 and 176.

Catalogue values for unused stamps in this section, from this point to the end of the section, are for Never Hinged items.

Citadel of Jubayl (Byblos) A31

Crusader Castle, Tripoli — A32

1945 Litho. Perf. 11½

177 A31 15p violet brown 1.90 1.10
178 A31 20p deep green 1.90 1.10
179 A32 25p deep blue 1.90 1.10
180 A32 50p dp carmine 3.50 1.25
Nos. 177-180,C97-C100 (8) 53.70 10.45

See Nos. 229-233.

Soldiers and Flag of Lebanon A33

1946 Litho.
Stripes of Flag in Red Orange

181 A33 7.50p red & pale lil .40 .15
182 A33 10p lil & pale lilac .50 .15
183 A33 12.50p choc & yel grn .60 .15
184 A33 15p sepia & pink 1.25 .15
185 A33 20p ultra & pink 1.10 .15
186 A33 25p dk grn & yel green 1.90 .25
187 A33 50p dk bl & pale bl 3.00 .90
188 A33 100p gray blk & pale bl 5.00 2.25
Nos. 181-188 (8) 13.75 4.15

Type of 1946 Overprinted in Red

1946, May 8
Stripes of Flag in Red

189 A33 7.50p choc & pink .45 .15
190 A33 10p dk vio & pink .65 .15
191 A33 12.50p brn red & pale lilac .70 .35
192 A33 15p lt grn & yel green 1.40 .50

193 A33 20p sl grn & yel green 1.25 .55
194 A33 25p sl bl & pale bl 2.00 .75
195 A33 50p ultra & gray 3.50 .70
196 A33 100p blk & pale bl 5.50 1.75
Nos. 189-196 (8) 15.45 4.90

See Nos. C101-C106, note after No. C106.

Cedar of Lebanon A34

Night Herons over Mt. Sanin A35

1946-47 Unwmk. *Perf. 10½*
197 A34 50c red brn ('47) .50 .15
198 A34 1p purple ('47) .50 .15
199 A34 2.50p violet .90 .15
200 A34 5p red 1.50 .15
201 A34 6p gray ('47) 1.50 .15

Perf. 11½
202 A35 12.50p deep car 11.00 .15
Nos. 197-202,C107-C110 (10) 32.90 4.65

For surcharge see No. 246.

A36

Crusader Castle, Tripoli — A37

1947 Litho. *Perf. 14x13½*
203 A36 50c dark brown 1.10 .15
204 A36 2.50p bright green 2.00 .15
205 A36 5p car rose 2.25 .15

Perf. 11½
206 A37 12.50p rose pink 6.00 .15
207 A37 25p ultramarine 9.25 .20
208 A37 50p turq green 27.50 .35
209 A37 100p violet 37.50 2.25
Nos. 203-209 (7) 85.60 3.40

A38

Zebaide Aqueduct — A39

1948 *Perf. 14x13½*
210 A38 50c blue .25 .15
211 A38 1p yel brown .40 .15
212 A38 2.50p rose violet .90 .15
213 A38 3p emerald 1.50 .15
214 A38 5p crimson 1.90 .15

Perf. 11½
215 A39 7.50p rose red 7.25 .15
216 A39 10p dl violet 4.00 .15
217 A39 12.50p blue 11.00 .15
218 A39 25p blue vio 13.00 .25
219 A39 50p green 30.00 1.75
Nos. 210-219 (10) 70.20
Set value 2.45

See Nos. 227A-228A, 234-237. For surcharge see No. 245.

Europa A40

Avicenna A41

1948 Litho.
220 A40 10p dk red & org red 2.50 1.40
221 A40 12.50p pur & rose 3.25 1.90
222 A40 25p ol grn & pale green 4.00 1.50
223 A41 30p org brn & buff 5.75 1.50
224 A41 40p Prus grn & buff 7.25 1.50
Nos. 220-224 (5) 22.75 7.80

UNESCO. Nos. 220 to 224 exist imperforate (see note after No. C145).

Camel Post Rider — A42

1949, Aug. 16 Unwmk. *Perf. 11½*
225 A42 5p violet 1.10 .40
226 A42 7.50p red 1.65 .60
227 A42 12.50p blue 2.75 1.00
Nos. 225-227,C148-C149 (5) 12.50 5.25

UPU, 75th anniv. See note after No. C149.

Cedar Type of 1948 Redrawn and Jubayl Type of 1945

1949 Litho. *Perf. 14x13½*
227A A38 50c blue 1.00 .15
228 A38 1p red orange 1.40 .15
228A A38 2.50p rose lilac 10.50 .35

Perf. 11½
229 A31 7.50p rose red 2.50 .15
230 A31 10p violet brn 4.75 .15
231 A31 12.50p deep blue 11.00 .20
232 A31 25p violet 20.00 .40
233 A31 50p green 42.50 1.90
Nos. 227A-233 (8) 93.65 3.45

On No. 227A in left numeral tablet, top of "P" stands higher than flag of the 1¼mm high "5." On No. 210, tops of "P" and the 2mm "5" are on same line.

On No. 228, "1 P." is smaller than on No. 211, and has no line below "P."

On No. 228A, the "O" does not touch tablet frame; on No. 212, it does. No. 228A exists on gray paper.

Cedar Type of 1948 Redrawn and

Ancient Bridge across Dog River — A43

1950 Litho. *Perf. 14x13½*
234 A38 50c rose red .15 .15
235 A38 1p salmon .30 .15
236 A38 2.50p violet .60 .15
237 A38 5p claret 1.10 .15

Cedar slightly altered and mountains eliminated.

Perf. 11½
238 A43 7.50p rose red .65 .15
239 A43 10p rose vio 1.10 .15
240 A43 12.50p light blue 1.60 .15
241 A43 25p deep blue 3.75 .38
242 A43 50p emerald 8.75 1.65
Nos. 234-242 (9) 18.00
Set value 2.40

See Nos. 251-255, 310-312.

Flags and Building A44

Cedar A45

1950, Aug. 8 *Perf. 11½*
243 A44 7.50p gray .70 .20
244 A44 12.50p lilac rose .70 .20
Nos. 243-244,C150-C153 (6) 4.40 2.40

Conf. of Emigrants, 1950. See note after #C153.

Nos. 213 and 201 Surcharged with New Value and Bars in Carmine

1950 Unwmk. *Perf. 14x13½, 10½*
245 A38 1p on 3p emerald .20 .15
246 A34 2.50p on 6p gray .95 .15
Set value .15

1951 Litho. *Perf. 14x13½*
247 A45 50c rose red .30 .15
248 A45 1p light brown .75 .15
249 A45 2.50p slate gray 3.25 .15
250 A45 5p rose lake 3.25 .15

Bridge Type of 1950, Redrawn

Typo. *Perf. 11½*
251 A43 7.50p red 3.75 .15
252 A43 10p dl rose vio 6.00 .15
253 A43 12.50p blue 10.50 .20
254 A43 25p dull blue 13.00 .50
255 A43 50p green 30.00 3.50
Nos. 247-255 (9) 70.80 5.10

Nos. 238-242 are lithographed from a fine-screen halftone; "P" in the denomination has serifs. Nos. 251-255 are typographed and much coarser; "P" without serifs.

Cedar A46

Ruins at Baalbek A47

Design: 50p, 100p, Beaufort Castle.

1952 Litho. *Perf. 14x13½*
256 A46 50c emerald .40 .15
257 A46 1p orange brn .40 .15
258 A46 2.50p grnsh blue .65 .15
259 A46 5p car rose .95 .15

Perf. 11½
260 A47 7.50p red 1.40 .20
261 A47 10p brt violet 2.75 .25
262 A47 12.50p blue 2.75 .25
263 A47 25p violet bl 3.75 .45
264 A47 50p dk blue grn 10.00 .90
265 A47 100p chocolate 20.00 2.50
Nos. 256-265 (10) 43.05 5.15

Cedar of Lebanon A48

Postal Administration Building A49

1953 *Perf. 14x13½*
266 A48 50c blue .30 .15
267 A48 1p rose lake .30 .15
268 A48 2.50p lilac .45 .15
269 A48 5p emerald .80 .15

Perf. 11½
270 A49 7.50p car rose 1.25 .15
271 A49 10p dp yel grn 1.65 .25
272 A49 12.50p aquamarine 2.75 .30
273 A49 25p ultra 3.75 .40
274 A49 50p violet brn 6.50 1.00
Nos. 266-274 (9) 17.75 2.70

See No. 306.

A50

Gallery, Beit-ed-Din Palace — A51

1954 *Perf. 14x13½*
275 A50 50c blue .15 .15
276 A50 1p dp orange .20 .15
277 A50 2.50p purple .50 .15
278 A50 5p blue green 1.25 .15

Perf. 11½
279 A51 7.50p dp carmine 2.50 .20
280 A51 10p dl ol grn 3.00 .20
281 A51 12.50p blue 6.25 .25
282 A51 25p vio blue 7.75 .80
283 A51 50p aqua 11.00 1.40
284 A51 100p black brn 25.00 2.50
Nos. 275-284 (10) 57.60 5.95

Arab Postal Union Issue

Globe — A52

1955, Jan. 1 Litho. *Perf. 13½x13*
285 A52 12.50p blue green .50 .20
286 A52 25p violet .50 .25
Nos. 285-286,C197 (3) 1.50 .65

Founding of the APU, July 1, 1954.

Cedar A53

Jeita Cave A54

1955 *Perf. 14x13½*
287 A53 50c violet blue .15 .15
288 A53 1p vermilion .15 .15
289 A53 2.50p purple .15 .15
290 A53 5p emerald .30 .15

Perf. 11½
291 A54 7.50p deep orange .40 .15
292 A54 10p yellow grn .60 .15
293 A54 12.50p blue .65 .15
294 A54 25p dp vio blue 1.60 .15
295 A54 50p dk gray grn 2.25 .25
Nos. 287-295 (9) 6.25
Set value .70

See Nos. 308-309, 315-318, 341-343A. For overprint see No. 351.

Cedar of Lebanon A55

Globe and Columns A56

1955 Unwmk. *Perf. 13x13½*
296 A55 50c dark blue .15 .15
297 A55 1p deep orange .15 .15
298 A55 2.50p deep violet .15 .15
299 A55 5p green .15 .15
300 A56 7.50p yel org & cop red .25 .15
301 A56 10p emer & sal .35 .15
302 A56 12.50p ultra & bl grn .50 .15
303 A56 25p dp ultra & brt pink 1.00 .15
304 A56 50p dk grn & lt bl 1.40 .15
305 A56 100p dk brn & sal 2.00 .40
Nos. 296-305 (10) 6.10
Set value .90

For surcharge see No. 333.

Cedar Type of 1953 Redrawn

1956 Litho. *Perf. 13x13½*
306 A48 2.50p violet 4.50 1.40

No. 306 measures 17x20½mm. The "2p.50" is in Roman (upright) type face.

Cedar Type of 1955 Redrawn and Bridge Type of 1950, Second Redrawing

1957 Litho. *Perf. 13x13½*
308 A53 50c light ultra .20 .15
309 A53 2.50p claret .55 .20

Perf. 11½
310 A43 7.50p vermilion .80 .35
311 A43 10p brn orange 1.10 .40
312 A43 12.50p blue 1.50 .50
Nos. 308-312 (5) 4.15 1.60

On Nos. 308 and 309 numerals are slanted and clouds slightly changed.

Nos. 310-312 inscribed "Liban" instead of "Republique Libanaise," and different Arabic characters.

Runners — A57

1957, Sept. 12 **Litho.** ***Perf. 13***
313 A57 2.50p shown .45 .20
314 A57 12.50p Soccer players .75 .35
Nos. 313-314,C243-C244 (4) 3.40 2.05

Second Pan-Arab Games, Beirut.
A souvenir sheet of 4 contains Nos. 313-314, C243-C244.

Cedar Type of 1955 Redrawn and

Workers
A58

Ancient Potter
A59

1957 **Unwmk.** ***Perf. 13x13½***
315 A53 50c light blue .15 .15
316 A53 1p light brown .15 .15
317 A53 2.50p bright vio .35 .15
318 A53 5p light green .75 .15

Perf. 11½, 13½x13 (A59)
319 A58 7.50p crim rose .65 .15
320 A58 10p dull red brn .85 .15
321 A58 12.50p bright blue 1.25 .15
322 A59 25p dull blue .90 .15
323 A59 50p yellow grn 1.90 .15
324 A59 100p sepia 2.75 .60
Nos. 315-324 (10) 9.70
Set value 1.20

The word "piaster" is omitted on No. 315; on Nos. 316 and 318 there is a line below "P"; on No. 317 there is a period between "2" and "50."
Nos. 315-318 are 16mm wide and have three shading lines above tip of cedar. See No. 343A and footnote.
For surcharges see Nos. 334-335, 339.

Cedar of Lebanon
A60

Soldier and Flag
A61

1958 **Litho.** ***Perf. 13***
325 A60 50c blue .15 .15
326 A60 1p dull orange .15 .15
327 A60 2.50p violet .15 .15
328 A60 5p yellow grn .30 .15
329 A61 12.50p bright blue .60 .15
330 A61 25p dark blue .70 .15
331 A61 50p orange brn 1.00 .15
332 A61 100p black brn 2.00 .25
Nos. 325-332 (8) 5.05
Set value .75

For surcharges see Nos. 336-338.

مؤتمر المحامين العرب
من ١ الى ٥ ايلول ١٩٥٩

No. 304 Surcharged

30P. ٣٠ق
= =

1959, Sept. 1
333 A56 30p on 50p dk grn & lt bl .65 .25

Arab Lawyers Congress. See No. C265.

= =

No. 323 Surcharged مؤتمر المغتربين
صيف - ١٩٥٩

30P. ٣٠ق

1959 ***Perf. 13½x13***
334 A59 30p on 50p yel grn .50 .20
335 A59 40p on 50p yel grn .75 .35

Convention of the Assoc. of Arab Emigrants in the United States.

Nos. 329-330 and 323 Surcharged with New Value and Bars

1959 ***Perf. 13, 13½x13***
336 A61 7.50p on 12.50p brt bl .20 .15
337 A61 10p on 12.50p brt bl .25 .15
338 A61 15p on 25p dark blue .30 .15
339 A59 40p on 50p yel grn .80 .15
Nos. 336-339,C271 (5) 3.55
Set value .60

Arab League Center, Cairo — A62

1960 **Unwmk.** **Litho.** ***Perf. 13x13½***
340 A62 15p lt blue green .55 .15

Opening of the Arab League Center and the Arab Postal Museum in Cairo.
For overprint see No. 352.

Cedar Type of 1955, Second Redrawing

1960 **Litho.** ***Perf. 13x13½***
341 A53 50c light violet .15 .15
342 A53 1p rose claret .20 .15
343 A53 2.50p ultramarine .30 .15
343A A53 5p light green .35 .15
Nos. 341-343A (4) 1.00
Set value .20

Nos. 341-343A are 16½-17mm wide and have two shading lines above cedar. In other details they resemble the redrawn A53 type of 1957 (Nos. 315-318).

President Fuad Chehab
A63 A64

1960 **Photo.** ***Perf. 13½***
344 A63 50c deep green .15 .15
345 A63 2.50p olive .15 .15
346 A63 5p green .15 .15
347 A63 7.50p rose brown .25 .15
348 A63 15p bright blue .35 .15
349 A63 50p lilac .70 .15
350 A63 100p brown 1.25 .20
Nos. 344-350 (7) 3.00
Set value .55

Nos. 343A and 340 Overprinted in Red

1960, Nov. **Litho.** ***Perf. 13x13½***
351 A53 5p light green .15 .15
352 A62 15p lt blue green .50 .20
Set value .25

Arabian Oil Conference, Beirut.

1961, Feb. **Litho.** ***Perf. 13½x13***
353 A64 2.50p blue & light bl .15 .15
354 A64 7.50p dark vio & pink .15 .15
355 A64 10p red brn & yel .20 .15
Set value .40 .20

Cedar
A65

Post Office, Beirut
A66

1961 **Unwmk.** **Litho.** ***Perf. 13***
356 A65 2.50p green .85 .15

Redrawn
357 A65 2.50p orange 1.10 .25
358 A65 5p maroon .20 .15
359 A65 10p black .25 .15

Nos. 357-359 have no clouds.

Perf. 11½
361 A66 2.50p rose carmine .25 .15
362 A66 5p bright green .80 .15
363 A66 15p dark blue .50 .15
Nos. 356-363 (7) 3.95
Set value .65

Cedars — A67

Design: 10p, 15p, 50p, 100p, View of Zahle.

1961 **Litho.** ***Perf. 13***
365 A67 50c yellow green .15 .15
366 A67 1p brown .15 .15
367 A67 2.50p ultramarine .20 .15
368 A67 5p carmine .40 .15
369 A67 7.50p violet .60 .15
370 A67 10p dark brown .85 .15
371 A67 15p dark blue .95 .15
372 A67 50p dark green 1.50 .25
373 A67 100p black 1.75 .35
Nos. 365-373 (9) 6.55
Set value .90

See Nos. 381-384.

Unknown Soldier Monument — A68

1961, Dec. 30 **Unwmk.** ***Perf. 12***
374 A68 10p shown 1.25 .15
375 A68 15p Soldier & flag 1.65 .20

Anniv. of Lebanon's independence; evacuation of foreign troops, Dec. 31, 1946.
See Nos. C329-C330.

Bugler — A69

Scout Carrying Flag and Scout Emblem
A70

Designs: 2.50p, First aid. 6p, Lord Baden-Powell. 10p, Scouts building campfire.

1962, Mar. 1 **Litho.** ***Perf. 12***
376 A69 50c yel grn, blk & yel .15 .15
377 A70 1p multicolored .15 .15
378 A70 2.50p dk red, blk & grn .15 .15
379 A69 6p multicolored .15 .15
380 A70 10p dp bl, blk & yel .15 .15
Nos. 376-380,C331-C333 (8) 1.95
Set value .80

50th anniversary of Lebanese Boy Scouts.

Type of 1961 Redrawn

Designs as before.

1962 **Unwmk.** ***Perf. 13***
381 A67 50c yellow green .15 .15
382 A67 1p brown .15 .15
383 A67 2.50p ultramarine .25 .15
384 A67 15p dark blue 2.00 .20
Nos. 381-384,C341-C342 (6) 8.65
Set value .84

Temple of Nefertari, Abu Simbel — A71

Cherries — A72

1962, Aug. 1 **Unwmk.** ***Perf. 13***
390 A71 5p light ultra .55 .15
391 A71 15p brn lake & mar .80 .15

Campaign to save the historic monuments in Nubia. See Nos. C351-C352.

1962 **Litho.**

Designs: 50c, 2.50p, 7.50p, Cherries. 1p, 5p, Figs. 10p, 17.50p, 30p, Grapes. 50p, Oranges. 100p, Pomegranates.

Vignette Multicolored
392 A72 50c violet blue .15 .15
393 A72 1p gray blue .15 .15
394 A72 2.50p brown .15 .15
395 A72 5p bright blue .15 .15
396 A72 7.50p lilac rose .20 .15
397 A72 10p chocolate .25 .15
398 A72 17.50p slate .40 .15
399 A72 30p slate grn .75 .15
400 A72 50p green 1.10 .15
401 A72 100p brown blk 2.75 .50
Nos. 392-401,C359-C366 (18) 12.45
Set value 2.40

Elementary Schoolboy — A73

1962, Oct. 1 **Litho.** ***Perf. 12***
404 A73 30p multicolored .40 .18

Students' Day, Oct. 1. See No. C355.

Cedar of Lebanon
A74 A75

1963-64 **Unwmk.** ***Perf. 13x13½***
405 A74 50c green 4.25 .15
406 A75 50c gray grn ('64) .25 .15
407 A75 2.50p ultra ('64) .25 .15
408 A75 5p brt pink ('64) .40 .15
409 A75 7.50p orange ('64) .45 .15
410 A75 17.50p rose lil ('64) .85 .20
Nos. 405-410 (6) 6.45
Set value .65

Bicyclist — A76

Hyacinth — A77

1964, Feb. 11 **Litho.** ***Perf. 13***
415 A76 2.50p shown .15 .15
416 A76 5p Basketball .20 .15
417 A76 10p Track .20 .15
Nos. 415-417,C385-C387 (6) 1.90
Set value .55

4th Mediterranean Games, Naples, Sept. 21-29, 1963.

1964 Unwmk. ***Perf. 13x13½***
Size: 26x27mm

418 A77 50c shown .15 .15
419 A77 1p Hyacinth .15 .15
420 A77 2.50p Hyacinth .15 .15
421 A77 5p Cyclamen .15 .15
422 A77 7.50p Cyclamen .25 .15

Perf. 13
Size: 26x37mm

423 A77 10p Poinsettia .45 .15
424 A77 17.50p Anemone 1.10 .15
425 A77 30p Iris 1.50 .20
426 A77 50p Poppy 3.75 .45
Nos. 418-426 (9) 7.65
Set value 1.00

See Nos. C391-C397.

Temple of the Sun, Baalbek A78

1965, Jan. 11 Litho. ***Perf. 13x13½***

429 A78 2.50p blk & red org .20 .15
430 A78 7.50p black & blue .60 .15
Nos. 429-430,C420-C423 (6) 4.00 1.50

International Festival at Baalbek.

Swimmer A79

1965, Jan. 23 Engr. ***Perf. 13***

431 A79 2.50p shown .15 .15
432 A79 7.50p Fencer .40 .15
433 A79 10p Basketball, vert. .50 .20
Nos. 431-433,C424-C426 (6) 2.20
Set value .75

18th Olympic Games, Tokyo, Oct. 10-25, 1964.

Golden Oriole — A80

1965 Engr. ***Perf. 13***

434 A80 5p Bullfinch .50 .15
435 A80 10p European goldfinch 4.50 .15
436 A80 15p Hoopoe 2.00 .15
437 A80 17.50p Rock partridge 3.75 .15
438 A80 20p shown 4.50 .15
439 A80 32.50p European bee-eater 6.75 .15
Nos. 434-439 (6) 22.00
Set value .40

For surcharge see No. 459.

Cow and Calf — A81

1965 Photo. ***Perf. 11x12***

440 A81 50c shown .15 .15
441 A81 1p Rabbit .30 .15
442 A81 2.50p Ewe & lamb .35 .15
Nos. 440-442 (3) .80
Set value .35

Hippodrome, Beirut — A82

Designs: 1p, Pigeon Rocks. 2.50p, Tabarja. 5p, Ruins, Beit-Méry. 7.50p, Statue and ruins, Anjar.

1966 Unwmk. ***Perf. 12x11½***

443 A82 50c gold & multi .20 .15
444 A82 1p gold & multi .30 .15
445 A82 2.50p gold & multi .40 .15
446 A82 5p gold & multi .50 .15
447 A82 7.50p gold & multi .60 .15
Nos. 443-447 (5) 2.00
Set value .40

See #C486-C492. For surcharge see #460.

ITY Emblem and Cedars — A83

1967 Photo. ***Perf. 11x12***

448 A83 50c lem, blk & brt bl *1.25* .15
449 A83 1p sal, blk & brt bl *1.25* .15
450 A83 2.50p gray, blk & brt bl *1.25* .15
451 A83 5p lt rose lil, blk & brt bl *1.25* .15
452 A83 7.50p yel, blk & brt bl *1.25* .15
Nos. 448-452 (5) *6.25*
Set value .40

Intl. Tourist Year; used as a regular issue. See #C515-C522. For surcharge see #461.

Goat and Kid — A84

1968, Feb. Photo. ***Perf. 12x11½***

453 A84 50c shown *.85* .15
454 A84 1p Cattle *1.75* .15
455 A84 2.50p Sheep *2.50* .15
456 A84 5p Camels *3.25* .15
457 A84 10p Donkey *4.00* .15
458 A84 15p Horses *5.25* .15
Nos. 453-458 (6) *17.60*
Set value .30

See Nos. C534-C539.

No. 439 Surcharged

25P ق٢٥

1972, Apr. Engr. ***Perf. 13***

459 A80 25p on 32.50p multi *5.00* .15

Nos. 447 and 452 Surcharged with New Value and Bars

Perf. 12x11½, 11x12

1972, May Photo.

460 A82 5p on 7.50p multi *1.00* .15
461 A83 5p on 7.50p multi *1.00* .15
Set value .15

Cedar — A85

Army Badge — A86

1974 Litho. ***Perf. 11***

462 A85 50c orange & olive *25.00* .25

1980, Dec. 28 Litho. ***Perf. 11½***

463 A86 25p multicolored *1.10* .15

Army Day. See Nos. C792-C793.

Pres. Elias Sarkis — A87

World Communications Year — A89

World Food Day, Oct. 16, 1981 A88

1981, Sept. 23 Photo. ***Perf. 14x13½***

464 A87 125p multicolored 1.00 .50
465 A87 300p multicolored 1.00 1.00
466 A87 500p multicolored 2.75 1.50
Nos. 464-466 (3) 4.75 3.00

1982, Nov. 23 Photo. ***Perf. 12x11½***

467 A88 50p Stork carrying food packages .40 .25
468 A88 75p Wheat, globe .55 .40
469 A88 100p Produce .80 .50
Nos. 467-469 (3) 1.75 1.15

1983, Dec. 19 Photo. ***Perf. 14***

470 A89 300p multicolored 1.75

Illustrations from Khalil Gibran's The Prophet A90

1983, Dec. 19 ***Perf. 13½x14***

471 A90 200p The Soul Is Back .90
472 A90 300p The Family 1.40
473 A90 500p Self-portrait 2.25
474 A90 1000p The Prophet 5.00
a. Souvenir sheet, #471-474 12.50
Nos. 471-474 (4) 9.55

No. 474a sold for £25.

Scouting Year — A91

Cedar of Lebanon — A93

1983, Dec. 19 ***Perf. 14***

475 A91 200p Rowing 1.25
476 A91 300p Signaling 1.65
477 A91 500p Camp 3.00
Nos. 475-477 (3) 5.90

1984, Dec. Photo. ***Perf. 14½x13½***

481 A93 5p multicolored .60

Flowers — A94

Defense — A95

1984, Dec. Photo. ***Perf. 14½x13½***

482 A94 10p Iris of Sofar .25
483 A94 25p Periwinkle .55
484 A94 50p Flowering thorn .95
Nos. 482-484 (3) 1.75

1984, Dec. Photo. ***Perf. 14½x13½***

485 A95 75p Dove over city .35
486 A95 150p Soldier, cedar .75
487 A95 300p Olive wreath, cedar 1.40
Nos. 485-487 (3) 2.50

Temple Ruins — A96

1985 Photo. ***Perf. 13½x14½***

488 A96 100p Fakra .35
489 A96 200p Bziza .65
490 A96 500p Tyre 1.50
Nos. 488-490 (3) 2.50

Pres. Gemayel, Map of Lebanon, Dove, Text — A97

Pres. Gemayel, Military Academy Graduate — A98

1988, Feb. 1 Litho. ***Perf. 14***

491 A97 £50 multicolored 3.25

1988, Mar. 9

492 A98 £25 multicolored 2.75

Arab Scouts, 75th Anniv. — A99

1988, Mar. 9 ***Perf. 13½x14½***

493 A99 £20 multicolored 2.25

UN Child Survival Campaign — A100

1988, Mar. 9 ***Perf. 14½x13½***

494 A100 £15 multicolored 1.25

Prime Minister Rashid Karame (1921-1987), Satellite, Flags, Earth — A101

1988, Mar. 9 ***Perf. 13½x14½***

495 A101 £10 multicolored 1.00

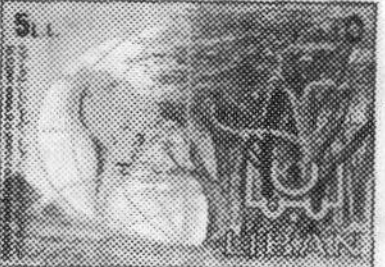

1st World Festival for Youths of Lebanese Descent in Uruguay A102

1988, Mar. 9

496 A102 £5 multicolored 1.00

Cedar — A103

1989 Photo. *Perf. 13x13½*

497 A103 £50 dk grn & vio .65
498 A103 £70 dk grn & brn .95
499 A103 £100 dk grn & brt yel 1.25
500 A103 £200 dk grn & bluish grn 2.75
501 A103 £500 dk grn & brt yel grn 6.75
Nos. 497-501 (5) 12.35

Independence, 50th Anniv. — A104

Designs: £200, Al Muntazah Restaurant, Zahle, 1883. £300, Sea Castle, Sidon, vert. £500, Presidential Palace, Baabda. £1000, Army graduation ceremony, vert. £3000, Beirut 2000, architectural plan. £5000, Pres. Elias Harawi, Lebanese flag, vert.

1993 Litho. *Perf. 14*

502 A104 £200 multicolored .25
503 A104 £300 multicolored .35
504 A104 £500 multicolored .60
505 A104 £1000 multicolored 1.25
506 A104 £3000 multicolored 3.50
507 A104 £5000 multicolored 6.00
Nos. 502-507 (6) 11.95

Size: 126x150mm

Imperf

508 A104 £10,000 multicolored 15.00

A105 A106

Environmental Protection: £100, Stop polluting atmosphere. £200, Stop fires. £500, Trees, building. £1000, Birds, trees in city. £2000, Mosaic of trees. £5000, Green tree in middle of polluted city.

1994, May 7 Litho. *Perf. 13*

509 A105 £100 multicolored .20
510 A105 £200 multicolored .40
511 A105 £500 multicolored 1.00
512 A105 £1000 multicolored 2.00
513 A105 £2000 multicolored 4.00
514 A105 £5000 multicolored 10.00
Nos. 509-514 (6) 17.60

1995 Litho. *Perf. 13½x13*

515 A106 £1500 Martyr's Day 3.75

Anniversaries and Events — A107 Anniversaries and Events of 1995 — A108

£500, UNICEF, 50th anniv., horiz. £1000, Intl. Year of the Family (1994), horiz. £2000, ILO, 75th anniv. (in 1994), horiz. £3000, Bar Association (Berytus Nutrix Legum), 75th anniv.

1996, Feb. 21 Litho. *Perf. 14*

516 A107 £500 multi, horiz. 1.10 .55
517 A107 £1000 multi, horiz. 2.25 1.10
518 A107 £2000 multi, horiz. 4.25 2.10
519 A107 £3000 multicolored 6.50 3.25

1996, Feb. 21 *Perf. 13½x13*

£100, Opening of Museum of Arab Postage Stamps. £500, FAO, 50th anniv. £1000, UN, 50th anniv. £2000, Arab League, 50th anniv. £3000, Former Pres. René Moawad (1925-89).

520 A108 £100 multicolored .25 .15
521 A108 £500 multicolored 1.10 .55
522 A108 £1000 multicolored 2.25 1.10
523 A108 £2000 multicolored 4.25 2.10
524 A108 £3000 multicolored 6.50 3.25

SEMI-POSTAL STAMPS

Regular Issue of 1925 Surcharged in Red or Black

Secours aux Réfugiés
اعانات للاجئين
Afft 0P.25 الاجرة ١/٤ غ

1926 Unwmk. *Perf. 14x13½*

B1 A2 25c + 25c ol blk 1.50 1.50
B2 A2 50c + 25c yellow green (B) 1.50 1.50
B3 A2 75c + 25c brown orange (B) 1.50 1.50
B4 A2 1p + 50c mag 1.50 1.50
B5 A2 1.25p + 50c dp grn 1.75 1.75
B6 A2 1.50p + 50c rose red (B) 1.75 1.75
a. Double surcharge 15.00 15.00
B7 A2 2p + 75c dk brn 1.50 1.50
B8 A2 2.50p + 75c pck bl 1.75 1.75
B9 A2 3p + 1p org brn 1.75 1.75
B10 A2 5p + 1p vio (B) 1.75 1.75
B11 A3 10p + 2p violet brown (B) 1.75 1.75
B12 A2 25p + 5p ultra 1.75 1.75
Nos. B1-B12 (12) 19.75 19.75

On No. B11 the surcharge is set in six lines to fit the shape of the stamp. All values of this series exist with inverted surcharge. Value each, $14.

See Nos. CB1-CB4.

Catalogue values for unused stamps in this section, from this point to the end of the section, are for Never Hinged items.

Boxing — SP1

1961, Jan. 12 Litho. *Perf. 13*

B13 SP1 2.50p + 2.50p shown .15 .15
B14 SP1 5p + 5p Wrestling .15 .15
B15 SP1 7.50p + 7.50p Shot put .20 .20
Nos. B13-B15,CB12-CB14 (6) 5.75 3.50

17th Olympic Games, Rome, Aug. 25-Sept. 11, 1960.

Nos. B13-B15 with Arabic and French Overprint in Black, Blue or Green and two Bars through Olympic Inscription: "CHAMPIONNAT D'EUROPE DE TIR, 2 JUIN 1962"

1962, June 2

B16 SP1 2.50p + 2.50p blue & brn (Bk) .20 .15
B17 SP1 5p + 5p org & brn (G) .40 .15
B18 SP1 7.50p + 7.50p vio & brn (Bl) .60 .40
Nos. B16-B18,CB15-CB17 (6) 5.65 3.25

European Marksmanship Championships held in Lebanon.

Red Cross — SP2

1988, June 8 Litho. *Perf. 14*

B19 SP2 £10 + £1 shown 1.25
B20 SP2 £20 + £2 Stylized profile 2.50
B21 SP2 £30 + £3 Globe, emblems, dove 3.50
Nos. B19-B21 (3) 7.25

AIR POST STAMPS

Nos. 10 to 13 with Additional Overprint

Poste par Avion

1924 Unwmk. *Perf. 14x13½*

C1 A18 2p on 40c 8.00 *8.00*
a. Double surcharge
C2 A18 3p on 60c 8.00 *8.00*
C3 A18 5p on 1fr 8.00 *8.00*
a. Dbl. surch. and ovpt.
C4 A18 10p on 2fr 8.00 *8.00*
a. Invtd. surch. and ovpt. 75.00
Nos. C1-C4 (4) 32.00 *32.00*

Nos. 33, 35-37 Overprinted

طيارة
Avion

C5 A18 2p on 40c 9.00 5.00
C6 A18 3p on 60c 9.00 5.00
C7 A18 5p on 1fr 9.00 5.00
a. Overprint reversed 30.00
C8 A18 10p on 2fr 9.00 5.00
a. Overprint reversed 30.00
b. Double surcharge 30.00
Nos. C5-C8 (4) 36.00 20.00

Nos. 57, 59-61 Overprinted in Green

A V I O N
طيارة

1925

C9 A2 2p dark brown 2.50 2.50
C10 A2 3p orange brown 2.50 2.50
C11 A2 5p violet 2.50 2.50
a. Inverted overprint
C12 A3 10p violet brown 2.50 2.50
Nos. C9-C12 (4) 10.00 10.00

Nos. 57, 59-61 Overprinted in Red

c

1926

C13 A2 2p dark brown 2.50 2.50
C14 A2 3p orange brown 2.50 2.50
C15 A2 5p violet 2.50 2.50
C16 A3 10p violet brown 2.50 2.50
Nos. C13-C16 (4) 10.00 10.00

Airplane poited down on No. C16.
Exist with inverted overprint. Value, each $15.

Issues of Republic under French Mandate

Nos. C13-C16 Overprinted

Republique Libanaise

d

1927

C17 A2 2p dark brown 3.25 3.25
C18 A2 3p orange brown 3.25 3.25
C19 A2 5p violet 3.25 3.25
C20 A3 10p violet brown 3.25 3.25
Nos. C17-C20 (4) 13.00 13.00

On No. C19 "Republique Libanaise" is above the bars. Overprint set in two lines on No. C20.

Nos. C17-C20 with Additional Overprint

الجمهورية اللبنانية

e

1928

Black Overprint

C21 A2 2p brown 9.00 4.00
a. Double overprint 25.00
b. Inverted overprint 25.00
C22 A2 3p orange brown 9.00 4.00
a. Double overprint 25.00
C23 A2 5p violet 9.00 4.00
a. Double overprint 15.00
C24 A3 10p violet brown 9.00 4.00
a. Double overprint 15.00
Nos. C21-C24 (4) 36.00 16.00

On Nos. C21-C24 the airplane is always in red.

Nos. 52, 54, 57, 59-62 Overprinted in Red or Black (No. C34)

f

1928

C25 A2 2p dark brown 2.50 .85
C26 A2 3p orange brown 2.50 .85
C27 A2 5p violet 2.50 .85
C28 A3 10p violet brown 3.00 .85

1929

C33 A2 50c yellow green .50 .40
a. Inverted overprint 20.00 15.00
C34 A2 1p magenta (Bk) .75 .50
a. Inverted overprint 20.00 15.00
C35 A2 25p ultra 175.00 100.00
a. Inverted overprint 350.00 250.00
Nos. C25-C34 (6) 11.75 4.30
Nos. C25-C35 (7) 186.75 104.30

On Nos. C25-C28 the airplane is always in red.

On No. C28 the overprinted orientation is horizontal. The bars covering the old country names are at the left.

The red overprint of a silhouetted plane and "Republique Libanaise," as on Nos. C25-C27, was also applied to Nos. C9-C12. These are believed to have been essays, and were not regularly issued.

No. 62 with Surcharge Added in Red

Two types of surcharge:

I - The "5" of "15 P." is italic. The "15" is 4mm high. Arabic characters for "Lebanese Republic" and for "15 P." are on same line in that order.

II - The "5" is in Roman type (upright) and smaller; "15" is 3½mm high. Arabic for "Lebanese Republic" is centered on line by itself, with Arabic for "15 P." below right end of line.

C36 A2 15p on 25p ultra (I) 200.00 175.00
a. Type II (#106) *600.00 600.00*

Nos. 102 Overprinted Type "c" in Blue

C37 A2 50c on 75c .50 .30
a. Airplane inverted 35.00
b. French and Arabic surch. invtd.
c. "P" omitted
d. Airplane double 35.00

No. 55 Surcharged in Red

1930

C38 A2 2p on 1.25p dp green 1.25 1.00
a. Inverted surcharge 17.50 15.00

Airplane over Racheya — AP2

Designs: 1p, Plane over Broumana. 2p, Baalbek. 3p, Hasroun. 5p, Byblos. 10p, Kadicha River. 15p, Beirut. 25p, Tripoli. 50p, Kabeljas. 100p, Zahle.

1930-31 Photo. *Perf. 13½*

C39 AP2 50c dk violet ('31) .15 .15
C40 AP2 1p yellow grn ('31) .25 .15
C41 AP2 2p dp orange ('31) .50 .40
C42 AP2 3p magenta ('31) .50 .40
C43 AP2 5p indigo .50 .40
C44 AP2 10p orange red 1.25 .65
C45 AP2 15p orange brn .75 .60
C46 AP2 25p gray vio ('31) 1.10 1.00
C47 AP2 50p dp claret 4.00 3.25
C48 AP2 100p olive brown 5.00 4.00
Nos. C39-C48 (10) 14.00 11.00

Nos. C39 to C48 exist imperforate.

Tourist Publicity Issue

Skiing in Lebanon AP12

Bay of Jounie AP13

1936, Oct. 12

C49 AP12	50c	slate grn	1.00	1.00
C50 AP13	1p	red orange	1.25	1.25
C51 AP12	2p	black violet	1.25	1.25
C52 AP13	3p	yellow grn	1.25	1.25
C53 AP12	5p	brown car	1.25	1.25
C54 AP13	10p	orange brn	1.25	1.25
C55 AP13	15p	dk carmine	17.50	17.50
C56 AP12	25p	green	50.00	50.00
		Nos. C49-C56 (8)	74.75	74.75

Nos. C49 to C56 exist imperforate.

Lebanese Pavilion at Exposition AP14

1937, July 1 *Perf. 13½*

C57 AP14	50c	olive black	.50	.50
C58 AP14	1p	yellow green	.50	.50
C59 AP14	2p	dk red orange	.50	.50
C60 AP14	3p	dk olive grn	.50	.50
C61 AP14	5p	deep green	.65	.65
C62 AP14	10p	carmine lake	3.50	3.50
C63 AP14	15p	rose lake	3.75	3.75
C64 AP14	25p	orange brn	6.50	6.50
		Nos. C57-C64 (8)	16.40	16.40

Paris International Exposition.

Arcade of Beit-ed-Din Palace AP15

Ruins of Baalbek AP16

1937-40 **Engr.** *Perf. 13*

C65 AP15	50c	ultra ('38)	.15	.15
C66 AP15	1p	henna brn ('40)	.20	.15
C67 AP15	2p	sepia ('40)	.20	.15
C68 AP15	3p	rose ('40)	.95	.35
C69 AP15	5p	lt green ('40)	.20	.15
C70 AP16	10p	dull violet	.20	.15
C71 AP16	15p	turq bl ('40)	.80	.50
C72 AP16	25p	violet ('40)	1.90	1.40
C73 AP16	50p	yellow grn ('40)	3.50	2.00
C74 AP16	100p	brown ('40)	1.90	1.00
		Nos. C65-C74 (10)	10.00	6.00

Nos. C65-C74 exist imperforate.

Medical College of Beirut AP17

1938, May 9 **Photo.** *Perf. 13*

C75 AP17	2p	green	.75	1.00
C76 AP17	3p	orange	.75	1.00
C77 AP17	5p	lilac gray	1.50	2.00
C78 AP17	10p	lake	3.00	5.00
		Nos. C75-C78 (4)	6.00	9.00

Medical Congress.

Maurice Noguès and View of Beirut AP18

1938, July 15 *Perf. 11*

C79 AP18	10p	brown carmine	3.00	1.50
a.		Souv. sheet of 4, perf. 13½	35.00	20.00
b.		Perf. 13½	7.50	4.00

10th anniversary of first Marseille-Beirut flight, by Maurice Noguès.

No. C79a has marginal inscriptions in French and Arabic. Exists imperf.; value $250.

Independent Republic

Plane Over Mt. Lebanon AP19

1942, Sept. 18 **Litho.** *Perf. 11½*

C80 AP19	10p	dk brown vio	1.50	2.00
C81 AP19	50p	dk gray grn	1.50	2.00

1st anniv. of the Proclamation of Independence, Nov. 26, 1941.

Nos. C80 and C81 exist imperforate.

Bechamoun AP20

Rachaya Citadel — AP21

Air View of Beirut — AP22

1943, May 1 *Perf. 11½*

C82 AP20	25p	yellow grn	1.25	1.00
C83 AP20	50p	orange	1.75	1.25
C84 AP21	100p	buff	1.75	1.10
C85 AP21	200p	blue vio	2.50	2.00
C86 AP22	300p	sage green	7.50	6.25
C87 AP22	500p	sepia	15.00	13.00
		Nos. C82-C87 (6)	29.75	24.60

2nd anniv. of the Proclamation of Independence. Nos. C82-C87 exist imperforate.

For overprints see Nos. C91-C96.

Bhannes Sanatorium AP23

1943, July 8 **Photo.**

Black Overprint

C88 AP23	20p	orange	1.65	1.25
C89 AP23	50p	steel blue	1.65	1.25
C90 AP23	100p	rose violet	2.75	2.00
		Nos. C88-C90 (3)	6.05	4.50

Arab Medical Congress, Beirut.

Nos. C82 to C87 Overprinted in Red, Blue or Violet

1944, Nov. 23

C91 AP20	25p	yel grn (R)	3.00	3.00
C92 AP20	50p	orange (Bl)	5.00	5.00
C93 AP21	100p	buff (V)	6.00	6.00
C94 AP21	200p	blue vio (R)	11.00	11.00
C95 AP22	300p	sage grn (R)	15.00	15.00
C96 AP22	500p	sepia (Bl)	30.00	30.00
		Nos. C91-C96 (6)	70.00	70.00

Return to office of the President and his ministers, Nov. 22, 1943.

Catalogue values for unused stamps in this section, from this point to the end of the section, are for Never Hinged items.

Falls of Litani — AP24

The Cedars — AP25

1945, July **Unwmk.** **Litho.**

C97 AP24	25p	gray brown	2.50	.60
C98 AP24	50p	rose violet	4.00	.80
C99 AP25	200p	violet	13.00	1.50
C100 AP25	300p	brown black	25.00	3.00
		Nos. C97-C100 (4)	44.50	5.90

Lebanese Soldiers at Bir Hacheim AP26

1946, May 8

C101 AP26	15p	bl blk, org & red org	.35	.25
C102 AP26	20p	red, lil & bl	.35	.30
C103 AP26	25p	brt bl, org & red	.40	.20
C104 AP26	50p	gray blk, bl & red	.60	.25
C105 AP26	100p	pur, pink & red	1.90	.60
C106 AP26	150p	brn, pink & red	2.25	1.90
		Nos. C101-C106 (6)	5.85	3.50

Victory of the Allied Nations in WWII, 1st anniv.

Three imperf. souvenir sheets of 14 exist. They contain one each of Nos. C101-C106 and 189-196 in changed colors. One has sepia inscriptions, and one on thin white card has blue inscriptions. Value $30 each. The third, with blue inscriptions, is on thick honeycombed chamois card. Value $110.

Night Herons Type

1946, Sept. 11

C107 A35	10p	orange	1.50	.40
C108 A35	25p	ultra	1.75	.20
C109 A35	50p	blue green	5.50	.65
C110 A35	100p	dk vio brn	8.25	2.50
		Nos. C107-C110 (4)	17.00	3.75

Symbols of Communications — AP28

1946, Nov. 22

C111 AP28	25p	deep blue	.75	.50
C112 AP28	50p	green	1.10	.60
C113 AP28	75p	orange red	2.25	1.25
C114 AP28	150p	brown black	3.50	2.00
		Nos. C111-C114 (4)	7.60	4.35

Arab Postal Congress, Sofar, 1946.

Stone Tablet, Dog River and Pres. Bechara el-Khoury AP29

1947, Feb. 11

C115 AP29	25p	ultra	1.10	.40
C116 AP29	50p	dull rose	1.75	.60
C117 AP29	75p	gray black	2.25	.65
C118 AP29	150p	blue green	4.50	1.40
		Nos. C115-C118 (4)	9.60	3.05

Evacuation of foreign troops from Lebanon, Dec. 31, 1946.

Bay of Jounie AP30

Government House, Beirut AP31

1947, Feb. 11

Grayish Paper

C119 AP30	5p	dp blue grn	.35	.15
C120 AP30	10p	rose vio	.55	.15
C121 AP30	15p	vermilion	1.25	.15
C122 AP30	20p	orange	1.40	.15
a.		20p red orange, white paper	1.50	.15
C123 AP30	25p	deep blue	1.75	.15
C124 AP30	50p	henna brn	3.25	.15
C125 AP30	100p	chocolate	7.75	.25
C126 AP31	150p	dk vio brn	14.00	.45
C127 AP31	200p	slate	20.00	2.00
C128 AP31	300p	black	32.50	5.00
		Nos. C119-C128 (10)	82.80	8.60

See Nos. C145A-C147B.

Post Horn and Letter — AP32

Phoenician Galley — AP33

1947, June 17 **Litho.**

C129 AP32	10p	brt ultra	.70	.35
C130 AP32	15p	rose car	.80	.35
C131 AP32	25p	bright blue	1.10	.60
C132 AP33	50p	dk slate grn	3.25	.65
C133 AP33	75p	purple	4.25	1.40
C134 AP33	100p	dark brown	5.75	1.90
		Nos. C129-C134 (6)	15.85	5.25

Lebanon's participation in the 12th UPU congress, Paris.

Lebanese Village AP34

1948, Sept. 1 *Perf. 11½*

C135 AP34	5p	dp orange	.25	.15
C136 AP34	10p	rose lilac	.60	.15
C137 AP34	15p	orange brn	1.40	.15
C138 AP34	20p	slate	2.00	.15
C139 AP34	25p	Prus blue	5.25	.55
C140 AP34	50p	gray black	8.50	.80
		Nos. C135-C140 (6)	18.00	1.95

Apollo AP35

Minerva AP36

1948, Nov. 23 **Unwmk.**

C141 AP35	7.50p	blue & lt blue	1.25	.80
C142 AP35	15p	black & gray	1.50	1.00
C143 AP35	20p	rose brn & rose	2.50	1.50
C144 AP36	35p	car rose & rose	4.50	2.00
C145 AP36	75p	bl grn & lt green	8.75	4.00
		Nos. C141-C145 (5)	18.50	9.30

UNESCO. Nos. C141-C145 exist imperforate, and combined with Nos. 220-224 in an imperforate souvenir sheet on thin buff cardboard, with black inscriptions in top margin in Arabic and at bottom in French. Value $175.

Bay Type of 1947 Redrawn

1949

White Paper

C145A AP30	10p	rose lilac	3.00	.40
C146 AP30	15p	dark green	3.75	.50
C147 AP30	20p	orange	8.25	3.50
C147A AP30	25p	dark blue	22.50	1.25
C147B AP30	50p	brick red	100.00	14.00
		Nos. C145A-C147B (5)	137.50	19.65

In the redrawn designs, Nos. C145A, C147 and C147B have zeros with broader centers than in the 1947 issue (Nos. C120, C122 and C124).

Helicopter Mail Delivery — AP37

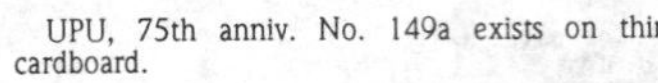

1949, Aug. 16 Unwmk. *Perf. 11½*

C148	AP37	25p	deep blue	2.75	1.50
C149	AP37	50p	green	4.25	1.75
a.			Souvenir sheet of 5, #225-227, C148-C149	22.50	11.00

UPU, 75th anniv. No. 149a exists on thin cardboard.

Homing Birds — AP38

Pres. Bechara el-Khoury AP39

1950, Aug. 8 Litho.

C150	AP38	5p	violet blue	.50	.35
C151	AP38	15p	rose vio	.75	.40
C152	AP39	25p	chocolate	.65	.50
C153	AP39	35p	gray green	1.10	.75
a.			Souvenir sheet of 6, #243-244, C150-C153, chamois paper	20.00	20.00
			Nos. C150-C153 (4)	3.00	2.00

Conference of Emigrants, 1950.

Crusader Castle, Sidon Harbor AP40

1950, Sept. 7

C154	AP40	10p	chocolate	.30	.15
C155	AP40	15p	dark green	.60	.15
C156	AP40	20p	crimson	1.65	.20
C157	AP40	25p	ultra	3.00	.50
C158	AP40	50p	gray black	4.50	1.40
			Nos. C154-C158 (5)	10.05	2.40

1951, June 9 Redrawn Typo.

C159	AP40	10p	grnsh black	.35	.15
C160	AP40	15p	black brown	.60	.15
C161	AP40	20p	vermilion	.60	.15
C162	AP40	25p	deep blue	.80	.15
C163	AP40	35p	lilac rose	2.25	1.00
C164	AP40	50p	indigo	3.50	1.00
			Nos. C159-C164 (6)	8.10	2.60

Nos. C154-C158 are lithographed from a fine-screen halftone; Nos. C159-C164 are typographed and much coarser, with larger plane and many other differences.

Khaldé International Airport, Beirut AP41

Design: 50p to 300p, Amphitheater, Byblos.

1952 Litho. *Perf. 11½*

C165	AP41	5p	crimson	.15	.15
C166	AP41	10p	dark gray	.15	.15
C167	AP41	15p	rose lilac	.25	.15
C168	AP41	20p	brown org	.40	.15
C169	AP41	25p	grnsh blue	.45	.20
C170	AP41	35p	violet bl	.60	.20
C171	AP41	50p	blue green	4.00	.25
C172	AP41	100p	deep blue	21.00	1.00
C173	AP41	200p	dk blue grn	11.00	1.50
C174	AP41	300p	black brn	17.00	3.25
			Nos. C165-C174 (10)	55.00	7.00

Lockheed Constellation — AP42

1953, Oct. 1

C175	AP42	5p	yellow green	.25	.15
C176	AP42	10p	deep plum	.50	.15
C177	AP42	15p	scarlet	.70	.15
C178	AP42	20p	aqua	.90	.15
C179	AP42	25p	blue	2.25	.15
C180	AP42	35p	orange brn	3.50	.15
C181	AP42	50p	violet blue	6.50	.25
C182	AP42	100p	black brown	11.00	2.00
			Nos. C175-C182 (8)	25.60	
			Set value		2.65

Ruins at Baalbek AP43

Irrigation Canal, Litani — AP44

1954, Mar.

C183	AP43	5p	yel green	.25	.15
C184	AP43	10p	dull purple	.45	.15
C185	AP43	15p	carmine	.60	.15
C186	AP43	20p	brown	.75	.15
C187	AP43	25p	dull blue	.90	.15
C188	AP43	35p	black brn	1.50	.15
C189	AP44	50p	dk olive grn	7.50	.25
C190	AP44	100p	deep carmine	15.00	.35
C191	AP44	200p	dark brown	22.50	.65
C192	AP44	300p	dk gray blue	40.00	1.50
			Nos. C183-C192 (10)	89.45	3.65

Khaldé International Airport, Beirut AP45

1954, Apr. 23 *Perf. 11½*

C193	AP45	10p	pink & rose red	.35	.20
C194	AP45	25p	dp bl & gray bl	.95	.35
C195	AP45	35p	dl brn & yel brn	1.25	.60
C196	AP45	65p	dp grn & grn	3.00	1.20
			Nos. C193-C196 (4)	5.55	2.35

Opening of Beirut's Intl. Airport. Exist imperf.

Arab Postal Union Type of Regular Issue, 1955

1955, Jan. 1 *Perf. 13½x13*

C197	A52	2.50p	yellow brn	.50	.20

Rotary Emblem AP47

1955, Feb. 23 *Perf. 11½*

C198	AP47	35p	dull green	.75	.40
C199	AP47	65p	dull blue	1.50	.55

Rotary International, 50th anniversary.

Skiing Among the Cedars — AP48

1955, Feb. 24 Litho.

C200	AP48	5p	blue green	.20	.15
C201	AP48	15p	crimson	.30	.15
C202	AP48	20p	lilac	.50	.15
C203	AP48	25p	blue	1.00	.15
C204	AP48	35p	olive brn	1.50	.20
C205	AP48	50p	chocolate	3.00	.30
C206	AP48	65p	deep blue	4.75	.75
			Nos. C200-C206 (7)	11.25	1.85

See #C233-C235. For surcharge see #C271.

Tourist — AP49

1955, Sept. 10 Unwmk. *Perf. 13*

C207	AP49	2.50p	brn vio & lt bl	.20	.15
C208	AP49	12.50p	ultra & lt bl	.45	.15
C209	AP49	25p	indigo & lt bl	1.10	.15
C210	AP49	35p	ol grn & lt bl	1.25	.20
a.			Sheet of 4, #C207-C210, imperf.	19.00	6.50
			Nos. C207-C210 (4)	3.00	
			Set value		.55

Tourist Year. No. C210a is printed on cardboard.

Oranges AP50

Designs: 25p, 35p, 50p, Grapes, vert. 65p, 100p, 200p, Apples.

1955, Oct. 15

C211	AP50	5p	yel grn & yel	.15	.15
C212	AP50	10p	dk grn & dp orange	.30	.15
C213	AP50	15p	yel grn & red orange	.35	.15
C214	AP50	20p	olive & yel org	.65	.15
C215	AP50	25p	blue & vio bl	.85	.15
C216	AP50	35p	green & cl	1.10	.15
C217	AP50	50p	blk brn & dl yellow	1.10	.15
C218	AP50	65p	green & lemon	2.75	.15
C219	AP50	100p	yel grn & dp orange	3.50	.40
C220	AP50	200p	green & car	5.75	2.00
			Nos. C211-C220 (10)	16.50	
			Set value		3.00

For surcharge see No. C265.

United Nations Emblem AP52

1956, Jan. 23 *Perf. 11½*

C221	AP52	35p	violet blue	3.50	1.50
C222	AP52	65p	green	4.00	1.75

UN, 10th anniv. (in 1955).

An imperf. souvenir sheet contains one each of Nos. C221 and C222. Value $40.

Temple of the Sun Colonnade, Masks and Lion's Head — AP53

Temple of Bacchus, Baalbek AP54

Design: 35p, 65p, Temple of the Sun colonnade, masks and violincello.

1956, Dec. 10 Litho. *Perf. 13*

C223	AP53	2.50p	dark brown	.55	.15
C224	AP53	10p	green	.80	.20
C225	AP54	12.50p	light blue	.80	.20
C226	AP54	25p	brt vio bl	1.25	.35
C227	AP53	35p	red lilac	2.50	.45
C228	AP53	65p	slate blue	3.50	.90
			Nos. C223-C228 (6)	9.40	2.25

International Festival at Baalbek.

Skiing Type of 1955 Redrawn and

Irrigation Canal, Litani — AP55

1957 Litho. *Perf. 11½*

C229	AP55	10p	brt violet	.20	.15
C230	AP55	15p	orange	.30	.15
C231	AP55	20p	yel green	.35	.15
C232	AP55	25p	slate blue	.50	.15
C233	AP48	35p	gray green	1.65	.15
C234	AP48	65p	dp claret	2.25	.20
C235	AP48	100p	brown	4.00	.50
			Nos. C229-C235 (7)	9.25	
			Set value		1.00

Different Arabic characters used for the country name; letters in "Liban" larger.

For surcharge see No. C271.

Pres. Camille Chamoun and King Saud — AP56

King Saud, Pres. Chamoun, King Hussein, Pres. Kouatly, King Faisal, Pres. Nasser — AP57

Pres. Chamoun and: No. C237, King Hussein. No. C238, Pres. Kouatly. No. C239, King Faisal. No. C240, Pres. Nasser. 25p, Map of Lebanon.

1957, July 15 Litho. *Perf. 13*

C236	AP56	15p	green	.45	.20
C237	AP56	15p	blue	.45	.20
C238	AP56	15p	red lilac	.45	.20
C239	AP56	15p	red orange	.45	.20
C240	AP56	15p	claret	.45	.20
C241	AP56	25p	blue	.45	.20
C242	AP57	100p	dl red brn	4.00	1.40
			Nos. C236-C242 (7)	6.70	2.60

Congr. of Arab Leaders, Beirut, 11/12-15/56.

Fencing AP58

50p, Pres. Chamoun and stadium with flags.

1957, Sept. 12 Unwmk. *Perf. 13*

C243	AP58	35p	claret	.95	.60
C244	AP58	50p	lt green	1.25	.90

2nd Pan-Arab Games, Beirut. See note on souvenir sheet below No. 314.

Symbols of Communications — AP59

Power Plant, Chamoun AP60

1957 *Perf. 13x13½, 11½ (AP60)*

C245	AP59	5p	brt green	.15	.15
C246	AP59	10p	yel orange	.25	.15
C247	AP59	15p	brown	.25	.15
C248	AP59	20p	maroon	.50	.15

C249 AP59	25p violet blue	.50	.15
C250 AP60	35p violet brn	.75	.15
C251 AP60	50p green	1.25	.20
C252 AP60	65p sepia	1.65	.20
C253 AP60	100p dark gray	2.25	.50
Nos. C245-C253 (9)		7.55	
Set value			1.40

Plane at Airport AP61

Cogwheel AP62

1958-59 Unwmk. Perf. 13

C254 AP61	5p green	.25	.15
C255 AP61	10p magenta	.30	.15
C256 AP61	15p dull violet	.50	.15
C257 AP61	20p orange ver	.75	.15
C258 AP61	25p dk vio bl	.90	.15
C259 AP62	35p grnsh gray	1.25	.15
C260 AP62	50p aquamarine	1.50	.15
C261 AP62	65p pale brown	3.00	.25
C262 AP62	100p brt ultra	3.50	.15
Nos. C254-C262 (9)		11.95	
Set value			1.00

Nos. C259 and C261 Surcharged in Black or Dark Blue

30P

1959 Unwmk. Litho. Perf. 13

C263 AP62	30p on 35p grnsh gray	.50	.20
C264 AP62	40p on 65p pale brn (Bl)	.75	.40

Arab Engineers Congress.

No. C217 Overprinted as Illustrated and Surcharged with New Value and Bars

1959, Sept. 1

C265 AP50	40p on 50p blk brn & dull yel	.70	.35

Arab Lawyers Congress.

Myron's Discobolus — AP63

Wreath and Hand Holding Torch AP64

1959, Oct. 11 Litho. Perf. 11½

C266 AP63	15p shown	.50	.15
C267 AP63	30p Weight lifter	.75	.30
C268 AP64	40p shown	1.40	.40
Nos. C266-C268 (3)		2.65	.85

3rd Mediterranean Games, Beirut.

A souvenir sheet on white cardboard contains one each of Nos. C266-C268, imperf. Sold for 100p. Value $25.

Soldiers and Flag — AP65

Hands Planting Tree — AP66

1959, Nov. 25 Perf. 13½x13

C269 AP65	40p sep, brick red & sl	1.00	.30
C270 AP65	60p sep, dk grn & brick red	1.50	.35

Lebanon's independence, 1941-1959.

No. C234 Surcharged with New Value and Bars

1959, Dec. 15 Perf. 11½

C271 AP48	40p on 65p dp claret	2.00	.25

1960, Jan. 18 Litho. Perf. 11½

C272 AP66	20p rose vio & grn	.65	.20
C273 AP66	40p dk brn & green	.85	.35

Friends of the Tree Society, 25th anniv.

Postal Administration Building — AP67

1960, Feb. Unwmk. Perf. 13

C274 AP67	20p green	.50	.15

President Fuad Chehab AP68

Uprooted Oak Emblem AP69

1960, Mar. 12 Photo. Perf. 13½

C275 AP68	5p green	.15	.15
C276 AP68	10p Prus blue	.15	.15
C277 AP68	15p orange brn	.20	.15
C278 AP68	20p brown	.25	.15
C279 AP68	30p olive	.35	.15
C280 AP68	40p dull red	.45	.15
C281 AP68	50p blue	.50	.15
C282 AP68	70p red lilac	.95	.15
C283 AP68	100p dark green	1.75	.35
Nos. C275-C283 (9)		4.75	
Set value			1.00

1960, Apr. 7 Litho. Perf. 13½x13

Size: 20½x36½mm

C284 AP69	25p yellow brn	.45	.20
C285 AP69	40p green	.65	.25
a.	Souv. sheet of 2, #C284-C285, imperf.	15.00	6.50

Size: 20x36mm

C284b AP69	25p yellow brown	.80	.40
C285b AP69	40p green	1.25	.60

World Refugee Year, July 1, 1959-June 30, 1960.

No. C285a sold for 150p.

Nos. C284b-C285b appear fuzzy and pale when compared to the bolder, clear-cut printing of Nos. C284-C285. Issue date: July 18.

Nos. C284b-C285b exist with carmine surcharges of "30P.+15P." (on C284b) and "20P.+10P." (on C285b), repeated in Arabic, with ornaments covering original denominations.

Martyrs' Monument — AP70

Martyrs of May 6th: 70p, Statues from Martyrs' monument, vert.

1960, May 6 Perf. 13x13½, 13½x13

C286 AP70	20p rose lilac & grn	.40	.15
C287 AP70	40p Prus grn & dk grn	.50	.25
C288 AP70	70p gray olive & blk	1.25	.50
Nos. C286-C288 (3)		2.15	.90

Pres. Chehab and King of Morocco AP71

1960, June 1 Perf. 13x13½

C289 AP71	30p choc & dk brn	.65	.30
C290 AP71	70p blk, dk brn & buff	1.25	.35

Visit of King Mohammed V of Morocco.

A souvenir sheet of 2 on white cardboard contains Nos. C289-C290, imperf.

Child Learning to Walk — AP72

Bird, Ribbon of Flags and Map of Beirut — AP73

1960, Aug. 16 Litho. Perf. 13½x13

C291 AP72	20p shown	.55	.15
C292 AP72	60p Mother & child	1.25	.42
Nos. C291-C292,CB10-CB11 (4)		4.25	1.22

Day of Mother and Child, Mar. 21-22.

Perf. 13½x13, 13x13½

1960, Sept. 20 Unwmk.

40p, Cedar & birds. 70p, Globes & cedar, horiz.

C293 AP73	20p multicolored	.25	.15
C294 AP73	40p vio, bl & grn	.50	.15
C295 AP73	70p multicolored	.75	.20
Nos. C293-C295 (3)		1.50	
Set value			.40

Union of Lebanese Emigrants in the World. A souvenir sheet of 3 contains Nos. C293-C295, imperf., printed on cardboard. Sold for 150p. Value $8.

Pres. Chehab and Map of — AP74

Casino, Maameltein Lebanon AP75

1961, Feb. Litho. Perf. 13½x13

C296 AP74	5p bl grn & yel grn	.15	.15
C297 AP74	10p brown & bister	.18	.15
C298 AP74	70p vio & rose lilac	1.00	.35

1961 Perf. 13x13½

C299 AP75	15p rose claret	.40	.20
C300 AP75	30p greenish blue	.60	.20
C301 AP75	40p brown	.70	.20
C302 AP75	200p bis brn & dl bl	4.00	1.25
Nos. C296-C302 (7)		7.03	
Set value			1.70

On Nos. C299-C301, the denomination, inscription and trees differ from type AP75.

UN Headquarters, New York — AP76

20p, UN Emblem & map of Lebanon. 30p, UN Emblem & symbolic building. 20p, 30p are vert.

1961, May 5 Perf. 13½x13, 13x13½

C306 AP76	20p lake & lt blue	.20	.15
C307 AP76	30p green & beige	.30	.15
C308 AP76	50p vio bl & grnsh bl	.45	.20
a.	Souvenir sheet of 3	4.00	4.00
Nos. C306-C308 (3)		.95	
Set value			.35

UN, 15th anniv. (in 1960).

No. C308a contains one each of Nos. C306-C308, imperf., against a light blue background showing UN emblem. Sold for 125p.

Pottery Workers AP77

1961, July 11 Litho. Perf. 13x13½

C309 AP77	30p shown	.75	.20
C310 AP77	70p Weaver	.30	.15

Issued for Labor Day, 1961.

Fireworks — AP78

Water Skiing — AP79

Design: 70p, Tourists on boat ride through cave.

1961, Aug. 8 Perf. 13½x13, 13x13½

C311 AP78	15p lt pur & dk bl	.90	.85
C312 AP79	40p blue & pink	1.40	1.10
C313 AP79	70p dull brn & pink	.45	.40
Nos. C311-C313 (3)		2.75	2.35

Issued to publicize tourist month.

Highway Circle at Dora, Beirut Suburb AP80

1961, Aug. Perf. 11½

C314 AP80	35p yellow green	.65	.30
C315 AP80	50p orange brown	.85	.45
C316 AP80	100p gray	.85	.55
Nos. C314-C316 (3)		2.35	1.30

Beach at Tyre — AP81

Afka Falls — AP82

1961, Sept. Litho. Perf. 13

C317 AP81	5p carmine rose	.20	.15
C318 AP81	10p brt violet	.45	.15
C319 AP81	15p bright blue	.65	.15
C320 AP81	20p orange	.80	.15
C321 AP81	30p brt green	1.00	.15
C322 AP82	40p dp claret	.50	.15
C323 AP82	50p ultramarine	.70	.20

C324 AP82 70p yellow green .95 .25
C325 AP82 100p dark brown 1.65 .40
Nos. C317-C325 (9) 6.90
Set value 1.25

See Nos. C341-C342.

Entrance to UNESCO Building AP83

"UNESCO" and Cedar — AP84

Design: 50p, UNESCO headquarters, Paris.

1961, Nov. 20 Unwmk. *Perf. 12*

C326 AP83 20p bl, buff & blk .25 .15
C327 AP84 30p lt grn, blk & mag .35 .15
C328 AP83 50p multicolored .75 .20
Nos. C326-C328 (3) 1.35
Set value .40

UNESCO, 15th anniv.

Emir Bechir and Fakhr-el-Din El Maani AP85

Design: 25p, Cedar emblem.

1961, Dec. 30 Litho.

C329 AP85 25p Cedar emblem .35 .15
C330 AP85 50p shown .65 .30

See note after No. 375.

Scout Types of Regular Issue, 1962

15p, Trefoil & cedar emblem. 20p, Hand making Scout sign. 25p, Lebanese Scout emblem.

1962, Mar. 1 Unwmk. *Perf. 12*

C331 A70 15p grn, blk & red .25 .15
C332 A69 20p lil, blk & yel .35 .15
C333 A70 25p multicolored .60 .25
Nos. C331-C333 (3) 1.20 .55

Arab League Building, Cairo — AP86

1962, Mar. 22 *Perf. 13*

C334 AP86 20p ultra & lt bl .30 .15
C335 AP86 30p red brn & pink .45 .15
C336 AP86 50p grn & grnsh bl .70 .30
Nos. C334-C336 (3) 1.45 .60

Arab League Week, Mar. 22-28. See Nos. C372-C375.

Blacksmith — AP87

Farm Tractor AP88

Perf. 13½x13, 13x13½

1962, May 1 Litho.

C337 AP87 5p green & lt blue .20 .15
C338 AP87 10p blue & pink .20 .15
C339 AP88 25p brt vio & pink .45 .15
C340 AP88 35p car rose & blue .65 .20
Nos. C337-C340 (4) 1.50
Set value .40

Issued for Labor Day.

Types of 1961 Redrawn with Large Numerals Similar to Redrawn Regular Issue of 1962

1962 *Perf. 13*

C341 AP81 5p carmine rose .60 .15
C342 AP82 40p deep claret 5.50 .35
Set value .40

Hand Reaching for Malaria Eradication Emblem — AP89

Bas-relief of Isis, Kalabsha Temple, Nubia — AP90

Design: 70p, Malaria eradication emblem.

1962, July 2 Litho. *Perf. 13½x13*

C349 AP89 30p tan & brown .45 .20
C350 AP89 70p bluish lil & vio .80 .40

WHO drive to eradicate malaria.

1962, Aug. 1 Unwmk. *Perf. 13*

C351 AP90 30p yellow green 1.65 .25
C352 AP90 50p slate 3.00 .60

Campaign to save historic monuments in Nubia.

Spade, Heart, Diamond, Club — AP91

College Student — AP92

1962, Sept.

C353 AP91 25p car rose, blk & red 1.75 .80
C354 AP91 40p multicolored 2.25 .80

European Bridge Championship Tournament.

1962, Oct. 1 *Perf. 12*

C355 AP92 45p multicolored .50 .20

Issued for Students' Day, Oct. 1.

Sword Severing Chain — AP93

Harvest — AP94

1962, Nov. 22 Litho. *Perf. 13*

C356 AP93 25p vio, lt bl & red .65 .25
C357 AP93 25p bl, lt bl & red .65 .25
C358 AP93 25p grn, lt bl & red .65 .25
Nos. C356-C358 (3) 1.95 .75

19th anniversary of independence.

Fruit Type of Regular Issue, 1962

5p, Apricots. 10p, 30p, Plums. 20p, 40p, Apples. 50p, Pears. 70p, Medlar. 100p, Lemons.

1962

Vignette Multicolored

C359 A72 5p orange brown .15 .15
C360 A72 10p black .25 .15
C361 A72 20p brown .45 .15
C362 A72 30p gray .55 .15
C363 A72 40p dark gray .65 .15
C364 A72 50p light brown .85 .20
C365 A72 70p gray olive 1.25 .30
C366 A72 100p blue 2.25 .45
Nos. C359-C366 (8) 6.40
Set value 1.40

1963, Mar. 21 Litho. *Perf. 13*

Design: 15p, 20p, UN Emblem and hand holding Wheat Emblem, horiz.

C367 AP94 2.50p ultra & yel .15 .15
C368 AP94 5p gray grn & yel .15 .15
C369 AP94 7.50p rose lil & yel .20 .15
C370 AP94 15p rose brn & pale grn .40 .15
C371 AP94 20p rose & pale grn .60 .15
Nos. C367-C371 (5) 1.50
Set value .45

FAO "Freedom from Hunger" campaign.

Redrawn Type of 1962, Dated "1963"

Design: Arab League Building, Cairo.

1963, Mar. Unwmk. *Perf. 12*

C372 AP86 5p violet & lt blue .15 .15
C373 AP86 10p green & lt blue .15 .15
C374 AP86 15p claret & lt blue .25 .15
C375 AP86 20p gray & lt blue .45 .25
Nos. C372-C375 (4) 1.00
Set value .55

Issued for Arab League Week.

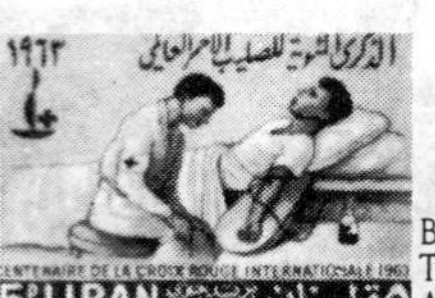
Blood Transfusion AP95

Design: 35p, 40p, Nurse and infant, vert.

1963, Oct. 5 Unwmk. *Perf. 13*

C376 AP95 5p green & red .15 .15
C377 AP95 20p grnsh bl & red .25 .15
C378 AP95 35p org, red & blk .45 .15
C379 AP95 40p purple & red .65 .20
Nos. C376-C379 (4) 1.50
Set value .45

Centenary of International Red Cross.

Lyre Player and Columns — AP96

Lebanon Flag, Rising Sun — AP97

1963, Nov. 7 Unwmk. *Perf. 13*

C380 AP96 35p lt bl, org & blk 1.00 .30

International Festival at Baalbek.

1964, Jan. 8 Litho.

C381 AP97 5p bluish grn, ver & yel .15 .15
C382 AP97 10p yel grn, ver & yel .25 .15
C383 AP97 25p ultra, ver & yel .50 .25
C384 AP97 40p gray, ver & yel .85 .40
Nos. C381-C384 (4) 1.75 .95

20th anniversary of Independence.

Sports Type of Regular Issue, 1964

1964, Feb. 11 Unwmk. *Perf. 13*

C385 A76 15p Tennis .30 .15
C386 A76 17.50p Swimming, horiz. .40 .15
C387 A76 30p Skiing, horiz. .65 .20
a. Souvenir sheet of 3 7.00 5.50
Nos. C385-C387 (3) 1.35
Set value .40

No. C387a contains three imperf. stamps similar to Nos. C385-C387 with simulated orange brown perforations and green marginal inscription. Sold for 100p.

Anemone — AP98

Flame and UN Emblem — AP100

Girls Jumping Rope — AP99

1964, June 9 Unwmk. *Perf. 13*

C391 AP98 5p Lily .25 .15
C392 AP98 10p Ranunculus .30 .15
C393 AP98 20p shown .50 .15
C394 AP98 40p Tuberose .75 .20
C395 AP98 45p Rhododendron .80 .20
C396 AP98 50p Jasmine .90 .20
C397 AP98 70p Yellow broom 1.40 .30
Nos. C391-C397 (7) 4.90 1.35

1964, Apr. 8

Children's Day: 20p, 40p, Boy on hobbyhorse, vert.

C398 AP99 5p emer, org & red .20 .15
C399 AP99 10p yel brn, org & red .25 .15
C400 AP99 20p dp ultra, lt bl & org .35 .20
C401 AP99 40p lil, lt bl & yel .65 .30
Nos. C398-C401 (4) 1.45
Set value .65

1964, May 15 Litho. Unwmk.

40p, Flame, UN emblem and broken chain.

C402 AP100 20p salmon, org & brn .25 .15
C403 AP100 40p lt bl, gray bl & org .50 .20
Set value .25

15th anniv. (in 1963) of the Universal Declaration of Human Rights.

Arab League Conference — AP101

1964, Apr. 20 *Perf. 13x13½*

C404 AP101 5p blk & pale sal .60 .20
C405 AP101 10p black 1.00 .35
C406 AP101 15p green 1.25 .50
C407 AP101 20p dk brn & pink 2.00 .65
Nos. C404-C407 (4) 4.85 1.70

Arab League meeting.

Child in Crib — AP102

Beit-ed-Din Palace and Children — AP103

1964, July 20 *Perf. 13½x13, 13½*

C408 AP102 2.50p multicolored .20 .15
C409 AP102 5p multicolored .20 .15
C410 AP102 15p multicolored .35 .15
C411 AP103 17.50p multicolored .40 .15
C412 AP103 20p multicolored .50 .15
C413 AP103 40p multicolored .60 .15
Nos. C408-C413 (6) 2.25
Set value .55

Ball of the Little White Beds, Beirut, for the benefit of children's hospital beds.

Clasped Hands and Map of Lebanon — AP104

1964, Oct. 16 **Litho.** *Perf. 13½x13*

C414 AP104 20p yel grn, yel & gray .40 .15
C415 AP104 40p slate, yel & gray .60 .35

Congress of the Intl. Lebanese Union.

Rocket Leaving Earth — AP105

Woman in Costume — AP107

Battle Scene — AP106

1964, Nov. 24 **Unwmk.** *Perf. 13½*

C416 AP105 5p multicolored .30 .15
C417 AP105 10p multicolored .30 .15
C418 AP106 40p sl blue & blk .90 .30
C419 AP106 70p dp claret & blk 1.50 .50
Nos. C416-C419 (4) 3.00 1.10

21st anniversary of independence.

1965, Jan. 11 **Litho.** *Perf. 13½*

Design: 10p, 15p, Man in costume.

C420 AP107 10p multicolored .35 .15
C421 AP107 15p multicolored .65 .20
C422 AP107 25p green & multi .95 .35
C423 AP107 40p brown & multi 1.25 .50
Nos. C420-C423 (4) 3.20 1.20

International Festival at Baalbek.

Equestrian AP108

1965, Jan. 23 **Engr.** *Perf. 13*

C424 AP108 15p shown .20 .15
C425 AP108 25p Target shooting, vert. .35 .15
C426 AP108 40p Gymnast on rings .60 .20
a. Souvenir sheet of 3, #C424-C426, imperf. 9.50 5.00
Nos. C424-C426 (3) 1.15
Set value .40

18th Olympic Games, Tokyo, Oct. 10-25, 1964. No. 426a sold for 100p.

Heliconius Cybria AP109

30p, Pericallia matronula. 40p, Red admiral. 45p, Satyrus semele. 70p, Machaon. 85p, Aurore. 100p, Morpho cypris. 200p, Erasmia sanguiflua. 300p, Papilio crassus. 500p, Charaxes ameliae.

1965 **Unwmk.** *Perf. 13*
Size: 36x22mm

C427 AP109 30p ver, yel & dk brown *.60* .15
C428 AP109 35p ol bis, dk bl & red *.75* .15
C429 AP109 40p sl grn, org & brown *.95* .15
C430 AP109 45p blk, Prus bl & yellow *1.25* .15
C431 AP109 70p multicolored *1.65* .25
C432 AP109 85p blk, grn & orange *2.25* .25
C433 AP109 100p dk pur & blue *3.25* .25
C434 AP109 200p dl pur, blk & blue *7.00* .45
C435 AP109 300p brn, sl grn & yellow *9.50* .80

Engr. and Litho.
Perf. 12
Size: 35x25mm

C436 AP109 500p lt ultra & blk *21.00* 2.00
Nos. C427-C436 (10) *48.20* 4.60

For surcharges see Nos. C654-C656.

Pope Paul VI and Pres. Chehab — AP110

1965, June 28 **Photo.** *Perf. 12*

C437 AP110 45p gold & brt vio 3.00 .80
a. Souv. sheet of 1, imperf. 40.00 25.00

Visit of Pope Paul VI to Lebanon. No. C437a sold for 50p.

Cedars of Friendship AP111

1965, Oct. 16 **Photo.** *Perf. 13x12½*

C438 AP111 40p multicolored .80 .15

Cocoon, Spindle and Silk — AP112

15p, 30p, 40p, 50p, Silk weaver at loom.

1965, Oct. 16 *Perf. 12½x13*
Design in Buff and Bright Green

C439 AP112 2.50p brown .15 .15
C440 AP112 5p dk olive grn .15 .15
C441 AP112 7.50p Prus blue .15 .15
C442 AP112 15p deep ultra .20 .15
C443 AP112 30p deep claret .35 .15
C444 AP112 40p brown .50 .20
C445 AP112 50p rose brown 1.00 .25
Nos. C439-C445 (7) 2.50
Set value .70

Parliament Building AP113

1965, Oct. 26 *Perf. 13x12½*

C446 AP113 35p red, buff & brn .40 .15
C447 AP113 40p emer, buff & brn .60 .15

Centenary of the Lebanese parliament.

UN Headquarters, NYC, UN Emblem and Lebanese Flags — AP114

1965, Nov. 10 **Engr.** *Perf. 12*

C448 AP114 2.50p dull blue .15 .15
C449 AP114 10p magenta .15 .15
C450 AP114 17.50p dull violet .20 .15
C451 AP114 30p green .30 .15
C452 AP114 40p brown .45 .20
Nos. C448-C452 (5) 1.25
Set value .45

UN, 20th anniv. A souvenir sheet contains one 40p imperf. stamp in bright rose lilac. Sold for 50p. Value $8.

Playing Card King, Laurel and Cedar AP115

Dagger in Map of Palestine AP116

1965, Nov. 15 **Photo.** *Perf. 12½x13*

C453 AP115 2.50p multicolored .15 .15
C454 AP115 15p multicolored .40 .15
C455 AP115 17.50p multicolored .45 .15
C456 AP115 40p multicolored .85 .20
Nos. C453-C456 (4) 1.85
Set value .40

Intl. Bridge Championships. A souvenir sheet contains two imperf. stamps similar to Nos. C454 and C456. Sold for 75p. Value $9.

1965, Dec. 13 *Perf. 12½x11*

C457 AP116 50p multicolored 3.00 .50

Deir Yassin massacre, Apr. 9, 1948.

ITU Emblem, Old and New Communication Equipment and Syncom Satellite — AP117

1966, Apr. 13 *Perf. 13x12½*

C458 AP117 2.50p multi .15 .15
C459 AP117 15p multi .25 .15
C460 AP117 17.50p multi .30 .15
C461 AP117 25p multi .60 .15
C462 AP117 40p multi .70 .20
Nos. C458-C462 (5) 2.00
Set value .55

ITU, centenary (in 1965).

Folk Dancers Before Temple of Bacchus — AP118

Designs: 7.50p, 15p, Dancers before Temple of Jupiter, vert. 30p, 40p, Orchestra before Temple of Bacchus.

1966, July 20 **Unwmk.** *Perf. 12*
Gold Frame

C463 AP118 2.50p brn vio, bl & orange .20 .15
C464 AP118 5p mag, bl & org .20 .15
C465 AP118 7.50p vio bl, bl & pink .20 .15
C466 AP118 15p pur, bl & pink .30 .15
C467 AP118 30p dk grn, org & blue .45 .15
C468 AP118 40p vio, org & bl .90 .20
Nos. C463-C468 (6) 2.25
Set value .55

11th International Festival at Baalbek.

Opening of WHO Headquarters, Geneva AP119

1966, Aug. 25 **Engr.** *Perf. 12*

C469 AP119 7.50p dp yel grn .15 .15
C470 AP119 17.50p car rose .35 .15
C471 AP119 25p blue .50 .15
Nos. C469-C471 (3) 1.00
Set value .25

Skier AP120

Designs: 5p, Children on toboggan. 17.50p, Cedar in snow. 25p, Ski lift.

1966, Sept. 15 **Photo.** *Perf. 12x11½*

C472 AP120 2.50p multi .25 .15
C473 AP120 5p multi .25 .15
C474 AP120 17.50p multi .45 .15
C475 AP120 25p multi .90 .15
Nos. C472-C475 (4) 1.85
Set value .35

International Festival of Cedars.

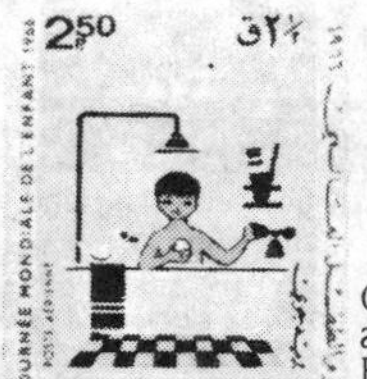

Sarcophagus of King Ahiram with Early Alphabet — AP121

15p, Phoenician ship. 20p, Map of the Mediterranean Sea showing Phoenician travel routes, and ship. 30p, Phoenician with alphabet tablet.

Litho. & Engr.

1966, Sept. 25 *Perf. 12*

C476 AP121 10p dl grn, blk & lt brn .15 .15
C477 AP121 15p rose lil, brn & ocher .25 .15
C478 AP121 20p tan, dk brn & bl .35 .15
C479 AP121 30p org, dk brn & yel .70 .20
Nos. C476-C479 (4) 1.45
Set value .45

Invention of alphabet by Phoenicians.

2.50 LIBAN
Child in Bathtub and UNICEF Emblem AP122

5p, Boy in rowboat. 7.50p, Girl skier. 12p, Girl feeding bird. 20p, Boy doing homework. 50p, Children of various races, horiz.

1966, Oct. 10 Photo. *Perf. 11½x12*

No.	Type	Value	Description	Unused	Used
C480	AP122	2.50p	multi	.15	.15
C481	AP122	5p	multi	.15	.15
C482	AP122	7.50p	multi	.25	.15
C483	AP122	15p	multi	.45	.15
C484	AP122	20p	multi	.65	.15
			Nos. C480-C484 (5)	1.65	
			Set value		.35

Miniature Sheet

Imperf

No.	Type	Value	Description	Unused	Used
C485	AP122	50p	dl yellow & multi	3.00	1.90

UNICEF; World Children's Day. No. C485 contains one horizontal stamp 43x33mm.

Scenic Type of Regular Issue, 1966

Designs: 10p, Waterfall, Djezzine. 15p, Castle of the Sea, Saida. 20p, Amphitheater, Jubayl (Byblos). 30p, Temple of the Sun, Baalbek. 50p, Beit-ed-Din Palace. 60p, Church of Christ the King, Nahr-el-Kalb. 75p, Abu Bakr Mosque, Tripoli.

1966, Oct. 12 *Perf. 12x11½*

No.	Type	Value	Description	Unused	Used
C486	A82	10p	gold & multi	.20	.15
C487	A82	15p	gold & multi	.30	.15
C488	A82	20p	gold & multi	.50	.15
C489	A82	30p	gold & multi	.65	.15
C490	A82	50p	gold & multi	1.40	.15
C491	A82	60p	gold & multi	1.75	.15
C492	A82	75p	gold & multi	2.50	.20
			Nos. C486-C492 (7)	7.30	
			Set value		.60

Symbolic Water Cycle — AP123

Daniel Bliss — AP124

15p, 20p, Different wave pattern without sun.

1966, Nov. 15 Photo. *Perf. 12½*

No.	Type	Value	Description	Unused	Used
C493	AP123	5p	red, bl & vio bl	.15	.15
C494	AP123	10p	org, bl & brn	.20	.15
C495	AP123	15p	org, emer & dk brn	.30	.15
C496	AP123	20p	org, emer & grnsh blue	.45	.15
			Nos. C493-C496 (4)	1.10	
			Set value		.30

Hydrological Decade (UNESCO), 1965-74.

1966, Dec. 3

Designs: 30p, Chapel, American University, Beirut. 50p, Daniel Bliss, D.D., and American University, horiz.

No.	Type	Value	Description	Unused	Used
C497	AP124	20p	grn, yel & brn	.35	.15
C498	AP124	30p	red brn, grn & blue	.40	.15
			Set value		.20

Souvenir Sheet

Imperf

No.	Type	Value	Description	Unused	Used
C499	AP124	50p	grn, brn & org brown	2.00	1.00

Cent. of American University, Beirut, founded by the Rev. Daniel Bliss (1823-1916). Nos. C497-C498 are printed each with alternating labels showing University emblem.

No. C499 contains one stamp 59x37mm.

Flags of Arab League Members, Hand Signing Scroll — AP125

1967, Aug. 2 Photo. *Perf. 12x11½*

No.	Type	Value	Description	Unused	Used
C500	AP125	5p	brown & multi	.15	.15
C501	AP125	10p	multicolored	.20	.15
C502	AP125	15p	black & multi	.30	.15
C503	AP125	20p	multicolored	.35	.15
			Nos. C500-C503 (4)	1.00	
			Set value		.40

Signing of Arab League Pact in 1945.

Veteran's War Memorial Building, San Francisco — AP126

10p, 20p, 30p, Scroll, flags of Lebanon & UN.

1967, Sept. 1 Photo. *Perf. 12x11½*

No.	Type	Value	Description	Unused	Used
C504	AP126	2.50p	blue & multi	.15	.15
C505	AP126	5p	multicolored	.15	.15
C506	AP126	7.50p	multicolored	.15	.15
C507	AP126	10p	blue & multi	.20	.15
C508	AP126	20p	multicolored	.30	.15
C509	AP126	30p	multicolored	.45	.15
			Nos. C504-C509 (6)	1.40	
			Set value		.40

22nd anniv. of the San Francisco Pact, the United Nations Charter.

Ruins at Baalbek — AP127

Intl. Tourist Year: 10p, Ruins at Anjar. 15p, Bridge over Ibrahim River and ruins. 20p, Boat on underground lake, Jaita cave. 50p, St. George's Bay, Beirut.

1967, Sept. 25 *Perf. 12½*

No.	Type	Value	Description	Unused	Used
C510	AP127	5p	multicolored	.25	.15
C511	AP127	10p	multicolored	.30	.15
C512	AP127	15p	violet & multi	.40	.15
C513	AP127	20p	brown & multi	.55	.15
			Nos. C510-C513 (4)	1.50	
			Set value		.25

Souvenir Sheet

Imperf

No.	Type	Value	Description	Unused	Used
C514	AP127	50p	multicolored	*25.00*	*20.00*

View of Tabarja AP128

Views: 15p, Pigeon Rock and shore, Beirut. 17.50p, Beit-ed-Din Palace. 20p, Ship at Sidon. 25p, Tripoli. 30p, Beach at Byblos. 35p, Ruins, Tyre. 40p, Temple of Bacchus, Baalbek.

1967, Oct. *Perf. 12x11½*

No.	Type	Value	Description	Unused	Used
C515	AP128	10p	multi	*.25*	.15
C516	AP128	15p	multi	*.85*	.15
C517	AP128	17.50p	multi	*1.25*	.15
C518	AP128	20p	multi	*1.25*	.15
C519	AP128	25p	multi	*1.25*	.15
C520	AP128	30p	multi	*1.90*	.15
C521	AP128	35p	multi	*2.00*	.15
C522	AP128	40p	multi	*3.00*	.15
			Nos. C515-C522 (8)	*11.75*	
			Set value		1.00

Intl. Tourist Year; used as a regular airmail issue.

India Day AP129

1967, Oct. 30 Engr. *Perf. 12*

No.	Type	Value	Description	Unused	Used
C523	AP129	2.50p	orange	.15	.15
C524	AP129	5p	magenta	.15	.15
C525	AP129	7.50p	brown	.20	.15
C526	AP129	10p	blue	.25	.15
C527	AP129	15p	green	.35	.15
			Set value	.75	.25

Globe and Arabic Inscription — AP130

Design: 10p, 20p, 30p, UN emblem.

1967, Nov. 25 Engr. *Perf. 12*

No.	Type	Value	Description	Unused	Used
C528	AP130	2.50p	rose	.15	.15
C529	AP130	5p	gray blue	.15	.15
C530	AP130	7.50p	green	.15	.15
C531	AP130	10p	brt carmine	.15	.15
C532	AP130	20p	violet blue	.30	.15
C533	AP130	30p	dark green	.40	.15
			Set value	1.10	.30

Lebanon's admission to the UN. A 100p rose red souvenir sheet in the globe design exists. Value $3.50.

Basking Shark AP131

Fish: 30p, Needlefish. 40p, Pollack. 50p, Cuckoo wrasse. 70p, Red mullet. 100p, Rainbow trout.

1968, Feb. Photo. *Perf. 12x11½*

No.	Type	Value	Description	Unused	Used
C534	AP131	20p	multi	.45	.15
C535	AP131	30p	multi	.45	.15
C536	AP131	40p	multi	.90	.15
C537	AP131	50p	multi	1.10	.15
C538	AP131	70p	multi	2.25	.15
C539	AP131	100p	multi	3.00	.15
			Nos. C534-C539 (6)	8.15	
			Set value		.45

Ski Jump AP132

Designs: 5p, 7.50p, 10p, Downhill skiers (various). 25p, Congress emblem (skis and cedar).

1968 *Perf. 12½x11½*

No.	Type	Value	Description	Unused	Used
C540	AP132	2.50p	multicolored	.15	.15
C541	AP132	5p	multicolored	.15	.15
C542	AP132	7.50p	multicolored	.15	.15
C543	AP132	10p	multicolored	.20	.15
C544	AP132	25p	multicolored	.45	.15
			Nos. C540-C544 (5)	1.10	
			Set value		.35

26th Intl. Ski Congress, Beirut. A 50p imperf. souvenir sheet exists in design of the 25p. Value $5.

Emir Fakhr al-Din II — AP133

2.50p, Emira Khaskiah. 10p, Citadel of Sidon, horiz. 15p, Citadel of Chekif & grazing sheep, horiz. 17.50p, Citadel of Beirut & harbor, horiz.

Perf. 11½x12, 12x11½

1968, Feb. 20 Litho.

No.	Type	Value	Description	Unused	Used
C546	AP133	2.50p	multicolored	.15	.15
C547	AP133	5p	multicolored	.15	.15
C548	AP133	10p	multicolored	.20	.15
C549	AP133	15p	multicolored	.45	.15
C550	AP133	17.50p	multicolored	.45	.15
			Nos. C546-C550 (5)	1.40	
			Set value		.35

In memory of the Emir Fakhr al-Din II. A 50p imperf. souvenir sheet exists showing the Battle of Anjar. Value $5.50.

Roman Bust — AP134

Ruins of Tyre: 5p, Colonnade, horiz. 7.50p, Arch, horiz. 10p, Banquet, bas-relief.

Litho. & Engr.

1968, Mar. 20 *Perf. 12*

No.	Type	Value	Description	Unused	Used
C552	AP134	2.50p	pink, brn & buff	.25	.15
C553	AP134	5p	yel, brn & lt bl	.30	.15
C554	AP134	7.50p	lt grnsh bl, brn & yel	.40	.15
C555	AP134	10p	sal, brn & lt bl	.50	.15
a.			Souvenir sheet	14.00	11.00
			Nos. C552-C555 (4)	1.45	
			Set value		.40

No. C555a contains one dark brown and light blue stamp, perf. 10½x11½. Sold for 50p. Exists imperf.

For surcharge see No. C657.

Emperor Justinian AP135

Design: 15p, 20p, Justinian and map of the Mediterranean, horiz.

Perf. 11½x12, 12x11½

1968, May 10 Photo.

No.	Type	Value	Description	Unused	Used
C556	AP135	5p	blue & multi	.15	.15
C557	AP135	10p	multicolored	.20	.15
C558	AP135	15p	red & multi	.25	.15
C559	AP135	20p	blue & multi	.35	.15
			Nos. C556-C559 (4)	.95	
			Set value		.28

Beirut, site of one of the greatest law schools in antiquity; Emperor Justinian (483-565), who compiled and preserved the Roman law.

Arab League Emblem — AP136

1968, June 6 Photo. *Perf. 12x11½*

No.	Type	Value	Description	Unused	Used
C560	AP136	5p	orange & multi	.15	.15
C561	AP136	10p	multicolored	.15	.15
C562	AP136	15p	pink & multi	.30	.15
C563	AP136	20p	multicolored	.45	.15
			Nos. C560-C563 (4)	1.05	
			Set value		.20

Issued for Arab League Week.

Cedar and Globe Emblem — AP137

1968, July 10

C564	AP137	2.50p sal pink, brn & green	.20	.15
C565	AP137	5p gray, brn & grn	.25	.15
C566	AP137	7.50p brt bl, brn & grn	.30	.15
C567	AP137	10p yel grn, brn & green	.45	.15
		Nos. C564-C567 (4)	1.20	
		Set value		.40

3rd Congress of Lebanese World Union.

Temple of Jupiter, Baalbek AP138

Designs: 10p, Fluted pilasters, cella of Bacchus Temple. 15p, Corniche, south peristyle of Jupiter Temple, horiz. 20p, Gate, Bacchus Temple. 25p, Ceiling detail, south peristyle of Bacchus Temple.

1968, Sept. 25 Photo. *Perf. 12½*

C568	AP138	5p gold & multi	.15	.15
C569	AP138	10p gold & multi	.15	.15
C570	AP138	15p gold & multi	.35	.15
C571	AP138	20p gold & multi	.50	.15
C572	AP138	25p gold & multi	.80	.20
		Nos. C568-C572 (5)	1.95	
		Set value		.50

13th Baalbek International Festival.

Broad Jump and Phoenician Statue — AP139

Designs: 10p, High jump and votive stele, Phoenician, 6th century B.C. 15p, Fencing and Olmec jade head, 500-400 B.C. 20p, Weight lifting and axe in shape of human head, Vera Cruz region. 25p, Aztec stone calendar and Phoenician ship.

1968, Oct. 19 Photo. *Perf. 12x11½*

C573	AP139	5p lt ultra, yel & gray	.15	.15
C574	AP139	10p mag, lt ultra & blk	.15	.15
C575	AP139	15p cit, ocher & brn	.20	.15
C576	AP139	20p dp org, brn & ocher	.40	.15
C577	AP139	25p light brown	.60	.20
		Nos. C573-C577 (5)	1.50	
		Set value		.45

19th Olympic Games, Mexico City, Oct. 12-27.

Human Rights Flame and Tractor — AP140

Human Rights Flame and: 15p, People. 25p, Boys of 3 races placing hands on globe.

1968, Dec. 10 Litho. *Perf. 11½*

C578	AP140	10p multicolored	.20	.15
C579	AP140	15p yellow & multi	.35	.15
C580	AP140	25p lilac & multi	.70	.15
		Nos. C578-C580 (3)	1.25	
		Set value		.20

International Human Rights Year.

Minshiya Stairs, Deir El-Kamar AP141

Views in Deir El-Kamar: 15p, The Seraglio Kiosk. 25p, Old paved city road.

1968, Dec. 26

C581	AP141	10p multicolored	.15	.15
C582	AP141	15p multicolored	.25	.15
C583	AP141	25p multicolored	.40	.15
		Nos. C581-C583 (3)	.80	
		Set value		.20

1st Municipal Council in Lebanon, established in Deir El-Kamar by Daoud Pasha, cent.

Nurse Treating Child, and UN Emblem — AP142

Designs: 10p, Grain, fish, grapes and jug. 15p, Mother and children. 20p, Reading girl and Phoenician alphabet. 25p, Playing children.

1969, Jan. 20 Litho. *Perf. 12*

C584	AP142	5p blk, lt bl & sepia	.15	.15
C585	AP142	10p blk, brt yel & grn	.15	.15
C586	AP142	15p blk, red lil & ver	.20	.15
C587	AP142	20p blk, citron & bl	.20	.15
C588	AP142	25p blk, pink & bis brn	.35	.15
		Set value	.85	.30

UNICEF, 22nd anniversary.

Silver Coin from Byblos, 5th Century B.C. — AP143

National Museum, Beirut: 5p, Gold dagger, Byblos, 18th cent. B.C. 7.50p, King Dining in the Land of the Dead, sarcophagus of Ahiram, 13-12th cent. B.C. 30p, Breastplate with cartouche of Amenemhat III (1849-1801 B.C.). 40p, Phoenician bird vase from Khalde, 8th cent. B.C.

Photogravure; Gold Impressed

1969, Feb. 20 *Perf. 12*

C589	AP143	2.50p grn, yel & lt bl	.25	.15
C590	AP143	5p vio, brn & yel	.30	.15
C591	AP143	7.50p dl yel, brn & pink	.45	.15
C592	AP143	30p blue & multi	.65	.15
C593	AP143	40p multicolored	.85	.20
		Nos. C589-C593 (5)	2.50	
		Set value		.45

Intl. Congress of Museum Councils; 20th anniv. of the Intl. Council of Museums.

Water Skier AP144

Designs: 5p, Water ballet. 7.50p, Parachutist, vert. 30p, Yachting, vert. 40p, Regatta.

1969, Mar. 3 Litho. *Perf. 11½*

C594	AP144	2.50p multicolored	.15	.15
C595	AP144	5p multicolored	.15	.15
C596	AP144	7.50p multicolored	.20	.15
C597	AP144	30p multicolored	.60	.20
C598	AP144	40p multicolored	.90	.25
		Nos. C594-C598 (5)	2.00	
		Set value		.60

Tomb of Unknown Soldier at Military School — AP145

2.50p, Frontier guard. 7.50p, Soldiers doing forestry work. 15p, Army engineers building road. 30p, Ambulance and helicopter. 40p, Ski patrol.

1969, Aug. 1 Litho. *Perf. 12x11½*

C599	AP145	2.50p multicolored	.15	.15
C600	AP145	5p multicolored	.15	.15
C601	AP145	7.50p multicolored	.15	.15
C602	AP145	15p multicolored	.15	.15
C603	AP145	30p multicolored	.35	.15
C604	AP145	40p multicolored	.45	.20
		Set value	1.25	.50

25th anniversary of independence.

Crosses and Circles — AP146

1971, Jan. 6 Photo. *Perf. 11½x12*

C605	AP146	15p shown	.25	.15
C606	AP146	85p Crosses, cedar	1.25	.45

Lebanese Red Cross, 25th anniversary.

Foil Fencing AP147

Designs: 10p, Flags of participating Arab countries. 15p, Flags of participating non-Arab countries. 40p, Sword fencing. 50p, Saber fencing.

1971, Jan. 15 Litho. *Perf. 12*

C607	AP147	10p yellow & multi	.15	.15
C608	AP147	15p yellow & multi	.15	.15
C609	AP147	35p yellow & multi	.30	.15
C610	AP147	40p yellow & multi	.40	.20
C611	AP147	50p yellow & multi	.45	.25
		Set value	1.25	.75

10th World Fencing Championships, held in Lebanon.

Agricultural Workers, Arab Painting, 12th Century AP148

1971, Feb. 1

C612	AP148	10p silver & multi	.70	.15
C613	AP148	40p gold & multi	1.25	.15
		Set value		.20

International Labor Organization.

UPU Building and Monument, Bern AP149

1971, Feb. 15 Litho. *Perf. 12*

C614	AP149	15p yel, blk & dp org	1.00	.15
C615	AP149	35p dp org, yel & blk	1.75	.35

Opening of new UPU Headquarters in Bern, Switzerland.

Ravens Burning Owls — AP150

Children's Day: 85p, Jackal and lion. Designs of the 15p and 85p are after 13th-14th century paintings, illustrations for the "Kalila wa Dumna."

1971, Mar. 1 Photo. *Perf. 11*

Size: 30x30mm

C616	AP150	15p gold & multi	.20	.15

Perf. 12x11½

Size: 38½x29mm

C617	AP150	85p gold & multi	1.10	.30
		Set value		.35

Map and Flag of Arab League AP151

1971, Mar. 20 *Perf. 12x11½*

C618	AP151	30p orange & multi	.40	.15
C619	AP151	70p yellow & multi	.85	.25

Arab League, 25th anniv.

Kahlil Gibran AP152

Famous Lebanese Men: No. C620, Symbolic design for Imam al Ouzai. No. C621, Bechara el Khoury. No. C622, Hassan Kamel al Sabbah.

1971, Apr. 10

C620	AP152	25p lt grn, gold & brn	.25	.15
C621	AP152	25p yel, gold & brn	.30	.15
C622	AP152	25p yel, gold & brn	.30	.15
C623	AP152	25p lt grn, gold & brn	.30	.15
		Nos. C620-C623 (4)	1.15	
		Set value		.35

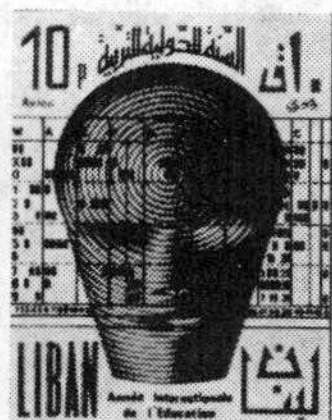

Education Year Emblem, Computer Card — AP153

1971, Apr. 30 Photo. *Perf. 11½x12*

C624	AP153	10p blk, vio & bl	.35	.15
C625	AP153	40p blk, org & yel	.70	.15
		Set value		.20

Intl. Education Year.

Jamhour Substation AP154

Designs: 10p, Maameltein Bridge. 15p, Hotel Management School. 20p, Litani Dam. 25p, Television set wiring. 35p, Temple of Bziza. 40p, Jounieh Port. 45p, Airport radar. 50p, Flower. 70p, New School of Sciences. 85p, Oranges. 100p, Arbanieh earth satellite station.

1971, May — Litho. — *Perf. 12*

C626	AP154	5p	multicolored	*.15*	.15
C627	AP154	10p	multicolored	*.20*	.15
C628	AP154	15p	multicolored	*.45*	.15
C629	AP154	20p	multicolored	*.85*	.15
C630	AP154	25p	multicolored	*1.25*	.15
C631	AP154	35p	multicolored	*1.65*	.15
C632	AP154	40p	multicolored	*1.65*	.15
C633	AP154	45p	multicolored	*1.75*	.15
C634	AP154	50p	multicolored	*2.75*	.15
C635	AP154	70p	multicolored	*4.00*	.15
C636	AP154	85p	multicolored	*5.50*	.20
C637	AP154	100p	multicolored	*7.00*	.40
	Nos. C626-C637 (12)			*27.20*	
	Set value				1.35

For overprints see Nos. C771, C775, C779.

Dahr-el-Bacheq Sanatorium AP155

1971, June 1

C638	AP155	50p	shown	.70	.15
C639	AP155	100p	multi, diff.	1.00	.35

Campaign against tuberculosis.

Solar Wheel (Festival Emblem) AP156

1971, July 1 — Photo. — *Perf. 11*

C640	AP156	15p	ultra & org	.20	.15
C641	AP156	85p	Corinthian capital	1.10	.30
	Set value				.35

16th Baalbek International Festival.

155mm Cannon AP157

Army Day: 25p, Mirage fighters flying over Baalbek ruins. 40p, Army Headquarters. 70p, Naval patrol boat.

1971, Aug. 1 — *Perf. 12x11½*

C642	AP157	15p	gold & multi	*3.25*	.15
C643	AP157	25p	gold & multi	*5.75*	.15
C644	AP157	40p	gold & multi	*7.75*	.15
C645	AP157	70p	gold & multi	*13.00*	.25
	Nos. C642-C645 (4)			*29.75*	
	Set value				.60

Wooden Console, Al Aqsa Mosque — AP158

1971, Aug. 21 — *Perf. 12*

C646	AP158	15p	dk brown & ocher	.75	.15
C647	AP158	35p	dk brown & ocher	1.25	.15
	Set value				.25

2nd anniversary of the burning of Al Aqsa Mosque in Jerusalem.

Lenin (1870-1924) AP159

1971, Oct. 1 — *Perf. 12x11½*

C648	AP159	30p	gold & multi	.60	.15
C649	AP159	70p	multicolored	1.40	.30

UN Emblem, World Map — AP160

1971, Oct. 24 — *Perf. 13x12½*

C650	AP160	15p	multicolored	.25	.15
C651	AP160	85p	multicolored	1.25	.25
	Set value				.30

UN, 25th anniv. (in 1970).

The Rape of Europa, Mosaic from Byblos AP161

1971, Nov 20 — Litho. — *Perf. 12*

C652	AP161	10p	slate & multi	*.50*	.15
C653	AP161	40p	gold & multi	*2.50*	.15
	Set value				.20

Publicity for World Lebanese Union (ULM).

Nos. C435-C436 Surcharged

Engr.; Engr. & Litho.

1972, May — *Perf. 13, 12*

C654	AP109	100p	on 300p multi	*6.00*	.40
C655	AP109	100p	on 500p multi	*6.00*	.40
C656	AP109	200p	on 300p multi	*9.00*	.80
	Nos. C654-C656 (3)			*21.00*	1.60

The numerals on No. C655 are taller (5mm) and bars spaced 1½mm apart.

No. C554 Surcharged

(Reduced)

1972, June — Litho. & Engr. — *Perf. 12*

C657	AP134	5p	on 7.50p multi	*3.00*	.15

Hibiscus AP162

Lebanese House AP163

1973 — Litho. — *Perf. 12*

C658	AP162	2.50p	shown	*.15*	.15
C659	AP162	5p	Roses	*.15*	.15
C660	AP162	15p	Tulips	*.35*	.15
C661	AP162	25p	Lilies	*1.00*	.15
C662	AP162	40p	Carnations	*1.10*	.15
C663	AP162	50p	Iris	*1.65*	.15
C664	AP162	70p	Apples	*1.25*	.15
C665	AP162	75p	Grapes	*1.40*	.15
C666	AP162	100p	Peaches	*1.90*	.35
C667	AP162	200p	Pears	*6.75*	.25
C668	AP162	300p	Cherries	*7.25*	.55
C669	AP162	500p	Oranges	*12.00*	.90
	Nos. C658-C669 (12)			*34.95*	
	Set value				2.70

For overprints see #C758-C759, C763, C766, C769, C772, C776, C778, C782, C785-C787.

1973 — *Perf. 14*

Designs: Old Lebanese houses.

C670	AP163	35p	yellow & multi	*2.50*	.15
C671	AP163	50p	lt blue & multi	*3.50*	.20
C672	AP163	85p	buff & multi	*5.75*	.30
C673	AP163	100p	multicolored	*7.75*	.40
	Nos. C670-C673 (4)			*19.50*	1.05

For overprints see #C768, C773, C780, C783.

Woman with Rose — AP164

Lebanese Costumes: 10p, Man. 20p, Man on horseback. 25p, Woman playing mandolin.

1973, Sept. 1 — Litho. — *Perf. 14*

C674	AP164	5p	yellow & multi	*1.25*	.15
C675	AP164	10p	yellow & multi	*3.75*	.15
C676	AP164	20p	yellow & multi	*5.75*	.15
C677	AP164	25p	yellow & multi	*8.25*	.15
	Nos. C674-C677 (4)			*19.00*	
	Set value				.25

For overprints see Nos. C760-C761, C764, C767.

Swimming, Temple at Baalbek — AP165

Designs: 10p, Running and portal. 15p, Woman athlete and castle. 20p, Women's volleyball and columns. 25p, Basketball and aqueduct. 50p, Women's table tennis and buildings. 75p, Handball and building. 100p, Soccer and cedar.

1973, Sept. 25 — Photo. — *Perf. 11½x12*

C678	AP165	5p	multicolored	.15	.15
C679	AP165	10p	multicolored	.20	.15
C680	AP165	15p	green & multi	.35	.15
C681	AP165	20p	multicolored	.35	.15
C682	AP165	25p	ultra & multi	.50	.15
C683	AP165	50p	org & multi	1.25	.30
C684	AP165	75p	vio & multi	1.50	.40
C685	AP165	100p	multicolored	2.75	.80
a.	Souvenir sheet			2.50	1.25
	Nos. C678-C685 (8)			7.05	2.25

5th Pan-Arabic Scholastic Games, Beirut. No. C685a contains one stamp with simulated perforations similar to No. C685; gold inscription and denomination.

View of Brasilia AP166

20p, Old Salvador (Bahia). 25p, Lebanese sailing ship enroute from the Old World to South America. 50p, Dom Pedro I & Emir Fakhr al-Din II.

1973, Nov. 15 — Litho. — *Perf. 12*

C686	AP166	5p	gold & multi	.40	.15
C687	AP166	20p	gold & multi	2.25	.35
C688	AP166	25p	gold & multi	2.25	.35
C689	AP166	50p	gold & multi	4.75	.65
	Nos. C686-C689 (4)			9.65	1.50

Sesquicentennial of Brazil's independence.

Inlay Worker AP167

1973, Dec. 1

C690	AP167	10p	shown	*.80*	.15
C691	AP167	20p	Weaver	*1.25*	.25
C692	AP167	35p	Glass blower	*2.00*	.35
C693	AP167	40p	Potter	*2.75*	.50
C694	AP167	50p	Metal worker	*3.00*	.50
C695	AP167	70p	Cutlery maker	*5.00*	.65
C696	AP167	85p	Lace maker	*7.00*	1.00
C697	AP167	100p	Handicraft Museum	*8.00*	1.40
	Nos. C690-C697 (8)			*29.80*	4.80

Lebanese handicrafts.

For overprints see Nos. C762, C765, C770, C774, C777, C781, C784.

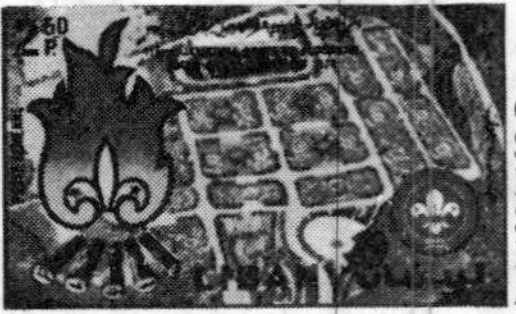

Camp Site, Log Fire and Scout Emblem AP168

Designs: 5p, Lebanese Scout emblem and map. 7½p, Lebanese Scout emblem and map of Middle East. 10p, Lord Baden-Powell, ruins of Baalbek. 15p, Girl Guide, camp and emblem. 20p, Lebanese Girl Guide and Scout emblems. 25p, Scouts around camp fire. 30p, Symbolic globe with Lebanese flag and Scout emblem. 35p, Flags of participating nations. 50p, Old man, and Scout chopping wood.

1974, Aug. 24 — Litho. — *Perf. 12*

C698	AP168	2.50p	multi	*.75*	.25
C699	AP168	5p	multi	*.75*	.25
C700	AP168	7.50p	multi	*1.40*	.25
C701	AP168	10p	multi	*1.40*	.25
C702	AP168	15p	multi	*1.75*	.55
a.	Vert. strip of 5, #C698-C702			*7.00*	
C703	AP168	20p	multi	*2.50*	.65
C704	AP168	25p	multi	*3.50*	.65
C705	AP168	30p	multi	*4.75*	.65
C706	AP168	35p	multi	*5.75*	.90
C707	AP168	50p	multi	*7.00*	1.40
a.	Vert. strip of 5, #C703-C707			*25.00*	
	Nos. C698-C707 (10)			*29.55*	5.80

11th Arab Boy Scout Jamboree, Smar-Jubeil, Aug. 1974. Nos. C702-C703 are for the 5th Girl Guide Jamboree, Deir-el-Kamar.

Mail Train and Postman Loading Mail, UPU Emblem — AP169

UPU Emblem and: 20p, Postal container hoisted onto ship. 25p, Postal Union Congress Building, Lausanne, and UPU Headquarters, Bern. 50p, Fork-lift truck loading mail on plane.

1974, Nov. 4 — Photo. — *Perf. 11½x12*

C708	AP169	5p	multicolored	*.45*	.15
C709	AP169	20p	multicolored	*2.00*	.25
C710	AP169	25p	multicolored	*3.00*	.25
C711	AP169	50p	ultra & multi	*6.25*	.70
	Nos. C708-C711 (4)			*11.70*	1.35

Centenary of Universal Postal Union.

Congress Building, Sofar — AP170

Arab Postal Union Emblem and: 20p, View of Sofar. 25p, APU Headquarters, Cairo. 50p, Ministry of Post, Beirut.

1974, Dec. 4 Litho. *Perf. 13x12½*

C712	AP170	5p	orange & multi	*.35*	.15
C713	AP170	20p	yellow & multi	*.60*	.20
C714	AP170	25p	blue & multi	*.90*	.25
C715	AP170	50p	multicolored	*4.25*	1.00
			Nos. C712-C715 (4)	*6.10*	1.60

Arab Postal Union, 25th anniversary.

Mountain Road, by Omar Onsi — AP171

Paintings by Lebanese artists: No. C717, Clouds, by Moustapha Farroukh. No. C718, Woman, by Gebran Kahlil Gebran. No. C719, Embrace, by Cesar Gemayel. No. C720, Self-portrait, by Habib Serour. No. C721, Portrait of a Man, by Daoud Corm.

1974, Dec. 6 Litho. *Perf. 13x12½*

C716	AP171	50p	lilac & multi	*2.00*	.50
C717	AP171	50p	blue & multi	*2.00*	.50
C718	AP171	50p	green & multi	*2.00*	.50
C719	AP171	50p	lt vio & multi	*2.00*	.50
C720	AP171	50p	brown & multi	*2.00*	.50
C721	AP171	50p	gray brn & multi	*2.00*	.50
			Nos. C716-C721 (6)	*12.00*	3.00

Hunter Spearing Lion — AP172

Excavations at Hermel: 10p, Statue of Astarte. 25p, Dogs hunting boar, tiled panel. 35p, Greco-Roman tomb.

1974, Dec. 13

C722	AP172	5p	blue & multi	*.40*	.15
C723	AP172	10p	lilac & multi	*.85*	.15
C724	AP172	25p	multicolored	*2.25*	.20
C725	AP172	35p	multicolored	*2.75*	.40
			Nos. C722-C725 (4)	*6.25*	
			Set value		.75

UNESCO Emblems and Globe AP173

1974, Dec. 16 *Perf. 12½x13*

C726	AP173	5p	violet & multi	.40	.15
C727	AP173	10p	bister & multi	.85	.15
C728	AP173	25p	blue & multi	2.00	.30
C729	AP173	35p	multicolored	2.50	.40
			Nos. C726-C729 (4)	5.75	1.00

International Book Year.

Symbolic Stamp under Magnifying Glass — AP174

Designs (Symbolic): 10p, Post horns. 15p, Stamp printing. 20p, Mounted stamp.

1974, Dec. 20 *Perf. 13x12½*

C730	AP174	5p	blue & multi	.20	.15
C731	AP174	10p	olive & multi	.40	.15
C732	AP174	15p	brown & multi	.80	.20
C733	AP174	20p	lilac & multi	1.00	.20
			Nos. C730-C733 (4)	2.40	
			Set value		.60

Georgina Rizk — AP175

5p, 25p, Georgina Rizk in Lebanese costume.

1974, Dec. 21

C734	AP175	5p	multicolored	.15	.15
C735	AP175	20p	violet & multi	.35	.15
C736	AP175	25p	yellow & multi	.50	.15
C737	AP175	50p	blue & multi	1.00	.20
a.			Souvenir sheet of 4	1.50	.80
			Nos. C734-C737 (4)	2.00	
			Set value		.40

Georgina Rizk, Miss Universe 1971. No. C737a contains 4 stamps similar to Nos. C734-C737 with simulated perforations.

UNICEF Emblem, Helicopter, Camel, Supplies AP176

UNICEF Emblem and: 25p, Child welfare clinic. 35p, Kindergarten class. 70p, Girls in chemistry laboratory.

1974, Dec. 28 Litho. *Perf. 12½x13*

C738	AP176	20p	multicolored	.15	.15
C739	AP176	25p	multicolored	.20	.15
C740	AP176	35p	blue & multi	.30	.15
C741	AP176	70p	blue & multi	.75	.15
a.			Souvenir sheet of 4	3.50	1.90
			Nos. C738-C741 (4)	1.40	
			Set value		.45

UNICEF, 25th anniv. No. C741a contains 4 stamps similar to Nos. C738-C741 with simulated perforations. Sold for 200p.

Discus and Olympic Rings — AP177

1974, Dec. 30 *Perf. 13x12½*

C742	AP177	5p	shown	.15	.15
C743	AP177	10p	Shot put	.30	.15
C744	AP177	15p	Weight lifting	.40	.15
C745	AP177	35p	Running	.85	.25
C746	AP177	50p	Wrestling	1.25	.25
C747	AP177	85p	Javelin	2.00	.35
a.			Souvenir sheet of 6	3.00	2.00
			Nos. C742-C747 (6)	4.95	
			Set value		.90

20th Olympic Games, Munich, Aug. 26-Sept. 11, 1972. No. C747a contains 6 stamps similar to Nos. C742-C747 with simulated perforations.

Clouds and Environment Emblem — AP178

1975

C748	AP178	5p	shown	.15	.15
C749	AP178	25p	Landscape	.35	.15
C750	AP178	30p	Flowers and tree	.35	.15
C751	AP178	40p	Waves	.55	.20
a.			Souvenir sheet of 4	2.00	1.40
			Nos. C748-C751 (4)	1.40	
			Set value		.40

UN Conf. on Human Environment, Stockholm, June 5-16, 1972. No. C751a contains four stamps similar to Nos. C748-C751 with simulated perforations. Sold for 150p.

Archaeology AP179

Symbols of: 25p, Science & medicine. 35p, Justice & commerce. 70p, Industry & commerce.

1975, Aug. Litho. *Perf. 12½x13*

C752	AP179	20p	multicolored	*.90*	.20
C753	AP179	25p	multicolored	*1.25*	.25
C754	AP179	35p	blue & multi	*1.75*	.40
C755	AP179	70p	buff & multi	*4.00*	.70
			Nos. C752-C755 (4)	*7.90*	1.55

Beirut, University City.

Stamps of 1971-73 Overprinted with Various Overall Patterns Including Cedars in Blue, Red, Orange, Lilac, Brown or Green

1978 Litho. *Perf. 12, 14*

C758	AP162	2.50p	(#C658;B)	.15	.15
C759	AP162	5p	(#C659;R)	.15	.15
C760	AP164	5p	(#C674;B)	.15	.15
C761	AP164	10p	(#C675;B)	.15	.15
C762	AP167	10p	(#C690;O)	.15	.15
C763	AP162	15p	(#C660;R)	.55	.15
C764	AP164	20p	(#C676;B)	.40	.15
C765	AP167	20p	(#C691;B)	.40	.15
C766	AP162	25p	(#C661;L)	.40	.15
C767	AP164	25p	(#C677;B)	.80	.15
C768	AP163	35p	(#C670;Br)	.95	.15
C769	AP162	40p	(#C662;L)	.95	.15
C770	AP167	40p	(#C693;G)	.95	.15
C771	AP154	45p	(#C633;L)	.95	.20
C772	AP162	50p	(#C663;L)	1.40	.20
C773	AP163	50p	(#C671;L)	1.40	.20
C774	AP167	50p	(#C694;Br)	1.40	.20
C775	AP154	70p	(#C635;L)	1.50	.30
C776	AP162	70p	(#C664;L)	1.50	.30
C777	AP167	70p	(#C695;B)	1.50	.30
C778	AP162	75p	(#C665;B)	2.50	.30
C779	AP154	85p	(#C636;R)	1.90	.35
C780	AP163	85p	(#C672;B)	1.90	.35
C781	AP167	85p	(#C696;G)	1.90	.35
C782	AP162	100p	(#C666;O)	2.75	.45
C783	AP163	100p	(#C673;B)	2.75	.45
C784	AP167	100p	(#C697;L)	2.75	.45
C785	AP162	200p	(#C667;O)	5.75	1.65
C786	AP162	300p	(#C668;O)	8.25	3.00
C787	AP162	500p	(#C669;O)	12.00	4.25
			Nos. C758-C787 (30)	58.25	15.25

Heart and Arrow — AP180

1978, Apr. 7 Litho. *Perf. 12*

C788	AP180	50p	blue, blk & red	.80	.65

World Health Day; drive against hypertension.

Poet Mikhail Naimy and Sannine Mountains — AP181

Designs: 50p, Naimy and view of Al Chakhroub Baskinta. 75p, Naimy portrait in sunburst, vert.

1978, May 17

C789	AP181	25p	gold & multi	*.85*	.25
C790	AP181	50p	gold & multi	*1.65*	.55
C791	AP181	75p	gold & multi	*2.50*	.80
			Nos. C789-C791 (3)	*5.00*	1.60

Mikhail Naimy Festival.

Army Day Type of 1980

Designs: 50p, Emir Fakhr al-Din statue, vert. 75p, Soldiers and flag.

1980, Dec. 28 Litho. *Perf. 11½*

C792	A86	50p	multicolored	*1.25*	.25
C793	A86	75p	multicolored	*1.65*	.40

28th UPU Congress, Rio de Janeiro, 1979 AP182

1981, Feb. 17 Photo. *Perf. 12x11½*

C794	AP182	25p	multicolored	.25	.15
C795	AP182	50p	multicolored	.65	.30
C796	AP182	75p	multicolored	1.10	.45
			Nos. C794-C796 (3)	2.00	.90

Intl. Year of the Child (1979) AP183

1981, Mar. 25 Litho. *Perf. 12x11½*

C797	AP183	100p	multicolored	1.25	.65

1974 Chess Championships — AP184

Various chess pieces. Nos. C799-C802 vert.

Perf. 12x11½, 11½x12

1980-81 Photo.

C798	AP184	50p	multicolored	1.10	.50
C799	AP184	75p	multicolored	1.25	.65
C800	AP184	100p	multicolored	1.65	1.00
C801	AP184	150p	multicolored	2.50	1.90
C802	AP184	200p	multicolored	3.50	2.50
			Nos. C798-C802 (5)	10.00	6.55

Makassed Islamic Institute Centenary (1978) AP185

1981 Photo. *Perf. 13½x14*

C803	AP185	50p	Children	.60	.15
C804	AP185	75p	Institute	1.00	.20
C805	AP185	100p	Makassed	1.25	.40
			Nos. C803-C805 (3)	2.85	.75

AIR POST SEMI-POSTAL STAMPS

#C13-C16 Surcharged Like #B1-B12

1926 *Perf. 13½*

No.	Type	Description	Unused	Used
CB1	A2	2pi + 1pi dark brown	3.00	2.25
CB2	A2	3pi + 2pi orabge brown	3.00	2.25
CB3	A2	5pi + 3pi violet	3.00	2.25
CB4	A3	10pi + 5pi violet brown	3.00	2.25
		Nos. CB1-CB4 (4)	12.00	9.00

These stamps were sold for their combined values, original and surcharged. The latter represented their postal franking value and the former was a contribution to the relief of refugees from the Djebel Druze War.

Catalogue values for unused stamps in this section, from this point to the end of the section, are for Never Hinged items.

Independent Republic

Natural Bridge, Faraya SPAP1

Bay of Jounie SPAP2

Perf. 11½

1947, June 27 Unwmk. Litho.

Cross in Carmine

No.	Type	Description	Unused	Used
CB5	SPAP1	12.50 + 25pi brt bl grn	6.25	3.00
CB6	SPAP1	25 + 50pi blue	7.25	3.50
CB7	SPAP2	50 + 100pi choc	9.00	4.00
CB8	SPAP2	75 + 150pi brt pur	18.00	8.00
CB9	SPAP2	100 + 200pi sl	27.50	11.00
		Nos. CB5-CB9 (5)	68.00	29.50

The surtax was for the Red Cross.

Mother & Child Type of Air Post Stamps, 1960

1960, Aug. 16 *Perf. 13½x13*

No.	Type	Description	Unused	Used
CB10	AP72	20p + 10p dk red & buff	.70	.15
CB11	AP72	60p + 15p bl & lt bl	1.75	.50

Olympic Games Type of Semi-Postal Issue, 1961

1961, Jan. 12 Unwmk. *Perf. 13*

No.	Type	Description	Unused	Used
CB12	SP1	15p + 15p Fencing	1.75	1.00
CB13	SP1	25p + 25p Bicycling	1.75	1.00
CB14	SP1	35p + 35p Swimming	1.75	1.00
		Nos. CB12-CB14 (3)	5.25	3.00

An imperf. souvenir sheet exists, containing one each of Nos. CB12-CB14. Value $22.50.

Nos. CB12-CB14 with Arabic and French Overprint in Green, Red or Maroon and two Bars through Olympic Inscription: "CHAMPIONNAT D'EUROPE DE TIR, 2 JUIN 1962"

1962, June 2

No.	Type	Description	Unused	Used
CB15	SP1	15p + 15p (G)	.80	.45
CB16	SP1	25p + 25p (M)	1.65	.90
CB17	SP1	35p + 35p (R)	2.00	1.20
		Nos. CB15-CB17 (3)	4.45	2.55

European Marksmanship Championships held in Lebanon.

POSTAGE DUE STAMPS

Postage Due Stamps of France, 1893-1920, Surcharged like Regular Issue

1924 Unwmk. *Perf. 14x13½*

No.	Type	Description	Unused	Used
J1	D2	50c on 10c choc	3.00	1.60
J2	D2	1p on 20c ol grn	3.00	1.60
J3	D2	2p on 30c red	3.00	1.60
J4	D2	3p on 50c vio brn	3.00	1.60
J5	D2	5p on 1fr red brn, *straw*	3.00	1.60
		Nos. J1-J5 (5)	15.00	8.00

Postage Due Stamps of France, 1893-1920, Surcharged

G^d Liban
2 Piastres
لبنان الكبير
غرش ٢

1924

No.	Type	Description	Unused	Used
J6	D2	50c on 10c choc	3.50	1.60
J7	D2	1p on 20c ol grn	3.50	1.60
J8	D2	2p on 30c red	3.50	1.60
J9	D2	3p on 50c vio brn	3.50	1.60
J10	D2	5p on 1fr red brn, *straw*	3.50	1.60
		Nos. J6-J10 (5)	17.50	8.00

Ancient Bridge across Dog River — D3

Designs: 1p, Village scene. 2p, Pigeon Rocks, near Beirut. 3p, Belfort Castle. 5p, Venus Temple at Baalbek.

1925 Photo. *Perf. 13½*

No.	Type	Description	Unused	Used
J11	D3	50c brown, *yellow*	.30	.15
J12	D3	1p violet, *rose*	.50	.25
J13	D3	2p black, *blue*	.80	.40
J14	D3	3p black, *red org*	1.50	.80
J15	D3	5p black, *bl grn*	2.75	1.40
		Nos. J11-J15 (5)	5.85	3.00

Nos. J11 to J15 Overprinted **République Libanaise**

1927

No.	Type	Description	Unused	Used
J16	D3	50c brown, *yellow*	.40	.20
J17	D3	1p violet, *rose*	.65	.30
J18	D3	2p black, *blue*	.90	.45
J19	D3	3p black, *red org*	2.50	1.40
J20	D3	5p black, *bl grn*	3.00	1.65
		Nos. J16-J20 (5)	7.45	4.00

Nos. J16 to J20 with Additional Overprint

الجمهورية اللبنانية

1928

No.	Type	Description	Unused	Used
J21	D3	50c brn, *yel* (Bk+R)	1.00	.50
J22	D3	1p vio, *rose* (Bk)	1.00	.50
J23	D3	2p blk, *bl* (Bk+R)	2.00	1.00
J24	D3	3p blk, *red org* (Bk)	4.00	2.00
J25	D3	5p blk, *bl grn* (Bk+R)	4.50	2.25
		Nos. J21-J25 (5)	12.50	6.25

No. J23 has not the short bars in the upper corners.

Postage Due Stamps of 1925 Overprinted in Red like Nos. J21-J25

1928

No.	Type	Description	Unused	Used
J26	D3	50c brn, *yel* (R)	.50	.20
J27	D3	2p blk, *bl* (R)	3.00	1.50
J28	D3	5p blk, *bl grn* (R)	9.00	4.00
		Nos. J26-J28 (3)	12.50	5.70

No. J28 has not the short bars in the upper corners.

D4

Bas-relief of a Ship — D5

D6

D7

D8

Bas-relief from Sarcophagus of King Ahiram — D9

D10

1930-40 Photo.; Engr. (No. J35)

No.	Type	Description	Unused	Used
J29	D4	50c black, *rose*	.30	.15
J30	D5	1p blk, *gray bl*	.60	.35
J31	D6	2p blk, *yellow*	.80	.50
J32	D7	3p blk, *bl grn*	.80	.50
J33	D8	5p blk, *orange*	3.75	2.25
J34	D9	8p blk, *lt rose*	2.50	1.50
J35	D8	10p dk green ('40)	4.00	2.00
J36	D10	15p black	3.25	1.40
		Nos. J29-J36 (8)	16.00	8.65

Nos. J29-J36 exist imperf.

Catalogue values for unused stamps in this section, from this point to the end of the section, are for Never Hinged items.

Independent Republic

National Museum, Beirut — D11

1945 Unwmk. Litho. *Perf. 11½*

No.	Type	Description	Unused	Used
J37	D11	2p brn black, *yel*	2.75	1.40
J38	D11	5p ultra, *rose*	4.00	1.60
J39	D11	25p blue, *bl green*	6.00	2.50
J40	D11	50p dark bl, *blue*	6.25	2.50

D12

1947

No.	Type	Description	Unused	Used
J41	D12	5p black, *green*	4.00	.50
J42	D12	25p blk, *yellow*	40.00	1.40
J43	D12	50p black, *blue*	20.00	2.00
		Nos. J41-J43 (3)	64.00	3.90

Hermel Monument D13

1948

No.	Type	Description	Unused	Used
J44	D13	2p blk, *yellow*	4.00	.35
J45	D13	3p black, *pink*	7.00	1.25
J46	D13	10p black, *blue*	18.00	2.25
		Nos. J44-J46 (3)	29.00	3.85

D14

1950

No.	Type	Description	Unused	Used
J47	D14	1p carmine rose	3.25	.15
J48	D14	5p violet blue	12.00	.35
J49	D14	10p gray green	25.00	.65
		Nos. J47-J49 (3)	40.25	1.15

D15

1952

No.	Type	Description	Unused	Used
J50	D15	1p dp rose lilac	.60	.15
J51	D15	2p bright violet	.60	.15
J52	D15	3p dk blue green	1.25	.15
J53	D15	5p blue	1.65	.15
J54	D15	10p chocolate	2.25	.20
J55	D15	25p black	18.00	.65
		Nos. J50-J55 (6)	24.35	
		Set value		1.20

D16

D17

1953

No.	Type	Description	Unused	Used
J56	D16	1p carmine rose	.15	.15
J57	D16	2p blue green	.15	.15
J58	D16	3p orange	.15	.15
J59	D16	5p lilac rose	.35	.15
J60	D16	10p brown	.70	.15
J61	D16	15p deep blue	1.25	.45
		Nos. J56-J61 (6)	2.75	
		Set value		.95

1955 Unwmk. *Perf. 13*

No.	Type	Description	Unused	Used
J62	D17	1p orange brown	.15	.15
J63	D17	2p yellow green	.15	.15
J64	D17	3p blue green	.15	.15
J65	D17	5p carmine lake	.20	.15
J66	D17	10p gray green	.30	.15
J67	D17	15p ultramarine	.40	.15
J68	D17	25p red lilac	.85	.25
		Nos. J62-J68 (7)	2.20	
		Set value		.60

Cedar of Lebanon — D18

Emir Fakhr al-Din II — D19

1966 Photo. *Perf. 11½*

No.	Type	Description	Unused	Used
J69	D18	1p bright green	.20	.15
J70	D18	5p rose lilac	.20	.15
J71	D18	15p ultramarine	.30	.15
		Nos. J69-J71 (3)	.70	
		Set value		.25

1968 Litho. *Perf. 11*

No.	Type	Description	Unused	Used
J72	D19	1p dk & lt gray	.35	.15
J73	D19	2p dk & lt blue grn	.35	.15
J74	D19	3p deep org & yel	.35	.15
J75	D19	5p brt rose lil & pink	.35	.15
J76	D19	10p olive & lemon	.35	.15
J77	D19	15p vio & pale violet	.40	.15
J78	D19	25p brt & lt blue	.70	.20
		Nos. J72-J78 (7)	2.85	
		Set value		.65

POSTAL TAX STAMPS

Fiscal Stamp Surcharged in Violet

R1

Wmk. A T 39 Multiple

1945 *Perf. 13½*

No.	Type	Description	Unused	Used
RA1	R1	5pi on 30c red brn	16.50	1.40

The tax was for the Lebanese Army.

No. RA1 Overprinted in Black طابع فلسطين

1948

RA2 R1 5pi on 30c red brn 16.50 1.40

Fiscal Stamps Surcharged in Various Colors

RA3 R1 5pi on 15pi dk vio bl (R) 14.00 1.60
a. Brown surcharge 18.00 2.25
RA4 R1 5pi on 25c dk blue green (R) 14.00 1.60
RA5 R1 5pi on 30c red brn (Bl) 16.00 1.60
RA6 R1 5pi on 60c lt ultra (Br) 22.50 1.60
RA7 R1 5pi on 3pi salmon rose (Ult) 14.00 1.60

Same With Additional Overprint طابع قضائي

RA8 R1 5pi on 10pi red *65.00* 5.00

Fiscal Stamp Surcharged Like Nos. RA3-RA7 with Top Arabic Characters Replaced by

ضريبة فلسطين

RA9 R1 5pi on 3pi rose (Bk+V) 16.50 1.40

Fiscal Stamp Surcharged in Black and Violet

RA10 R1 5pi on 3pi sal rose *190.00* 15.00

The tax was to aid the war in Palestine.

Catalogue values for unused stamps in this section, from this point to the end of the section, are for Never Hinged items.

Family among Ruins — R2

Building a House — R3

1956 Unwmk. Litho. *Perf. 13*

RA11 R2 2.50pi brown 1.75 .15

The tax was for earthquake victims. These stamps were obligatory on all inland mail and all mail going to Arab countries.

1957-58 *Perf. 13½x13*

RA12 R3 2.50p brown 1.10 .15
RA13 R3 2.50p dk blue grn ('58) .85 .15

Type of 1957 Redrawn

1959

RA14 R3 2.50p light brown 2.00 .15

On No. RA14 the denomination is on top and the Arabic lines are at the bottom of design.

Building a House

R4 R5

1961 Unwmk. *Perf. 13½x13*

RA15 R4 2.50p yellow brown 1.00 .15

1962 *Perf. 13½x14*

RA16 R5 2.50p blue green 3.75 .15

The tax was for the relief of earthquake victims.

LEEWARD ISLANDS

'lē–wərd 'ī–ləndz

LOCATION — A group of islands in the West Indies, southeast of Puerto Rico
GOVT. — British Colony
AREA — 423 sq. mi.
POP. — 108,847 (1946)
CAPITAL — St. John

While stamps inscribed "Leeward Islands" were in use, 1890-1956, the colony consisted of the presidencies (now colonies) of Antigua, Montserrat, St. Christopher (St. Kitts) with Nevis and Anguilla, the British Virgin Islands and Dominica (which became a separate colony in 1940).

Each presidency issued its own stamps, using them along with the Leeward Islands general issues. The Leeward Islands federation was abolished in 1956.

12 Pence = 1 Shilling
20 Shillings = 1 Pound
100 Cents = 1 Dollar

Catalogue values for unused stamps in this country are for Never Hinged items, beginning with Scott 116.

Queen Victoria — A1

1890 Typo. Wmk. 2 *Perf. 14*

1 A1 ½p lilac & green 2.25 .70
2 A1 1p lilac & car 1.50 .15
3 A1 2½p lilac & ultra 2.75 .30
4 A1 4p lilac & org 3.50 *7.00*
5 A1 6p lilac & brown 6.50 *8.00*
6 A1 7p lilac & slate 2.75 *10.00*
7 A1 1sh green & car 16.00 *30.00*
8 A1 5sh green & ultra 125.00 *225.00*
Nos. 1-8 (8) 160.25 *281.15*

Denomination of Nos. 7-8 are in color on plain tablet: "ONE SHILLING" or "FIVE SHILLINGS."
For overprints and surcharges see Nos. 9-19.

Jubilee Issue

Regular Issue of 1890 Handstamp Overprinted

1897, July 22

9 A1 ½p lilac & green 4.00 *8.00*
10 A1 1p lilac & car 4.00 *10.00*
11 A1 2½p lilac & ultra 4.00 10.00
12 A1 4p lilac & org 22.50 55.00
13 A1 6p lilac & brown 40.00 80.00
14 A1 7p lilac & slate 45.00 80.00
15 A1 1sh green & car 110.00 175.00
16 A1 5sh green & ultra 575.00 750.00
Nos. 9-16 (8) 804.50 1,168.

Double Overprints

9a A1 ½p *1,350.*
10a A1 1p *1,000.*
b. Triple overprint *3,500.*
11a A1 2½p *1,350.*
12a A1 4p *1,350.*
13a A1 6p *1,550.*
14a A1 7p *1,550.*
15a A1 1sh *1,950.*
16a A1 5sh *5,500.*

60th year of Queen Victoria's reign.
Excellent counterfeits of Nos. 9-16 exist.

Stamps of 1890 Surcharged in Black or Red:

One Penny
b

One Penny
c

1902, Aug.

17 A1(b) 1p on 4p lilac & org 1.00 3.75
a. Tall narrow "O" in "One" 27.50 60.00
18 A1(b) 1p on 6p lilac & brn 1.25 6.50
a. Tall narrow "O" in "One" 37.50 70.00
19 A1(c) 1p on 7p lilac & sl 1.25 3.00
Nos. 17-19 (3) 3.50 13.25

King Edward VII — A4

Numerals of ¼p, 2p, 3p and 2sh6p of type A4 are in color on plain tablet. The 1sh and 5sh denominations are expressed as "ONE SHILLING" and "FIVE SHILLINGS" on plain tablet.

1902

20 A4 ½p violet & green 2.25 .40
21 A4 1p vio & car rose 3.25 .15
22 A4 2p violet & bister 2.25 3.75
23 A4 2½p violet & ultra 2.25 1.25
24 A4 3p violet & black 2.00 *5.50*
25 A4 6p violet & brown 1.65 *6.50*
26 A4 1sh grn & car rose 2.50 *17.50*
27 A4 2sh6p green & blk 22.50 *50.00*
28 A4 5sh green & ultra 42.50 *60.00*
Nos. 20-28 (9) 81.15 *145.05*

1905-11 Wmk. 3

Chalky Paper

29 A4 ½p vio & grn ('06) 1.35 *1.65*
30 A4 1p vio & car rose 2.75 6.50
31 A4 2p vio & bis ('08) 3.50 *8.00*
32 A4 2½p vio & ultra 35.00 30.00
33 A4 3p violet & black 5.50 *27.50*
34 A4 3p violet, *yel* ('10) 2.25 4.50
35 A4 6p vio & brn ('08) 22.50 *45.00*
36 A4 6p violet & red violet ('11) 4.00 6.50
37 A4 1sh grn & car rose ('08) 32.50 *65.00*
38 A4 1sh blk, *grn* ('11) 5.00 *20.00*
39 A4 2sh6p blk & red, *blue* ('11) 30.00 *50.00*
40 A4 5sh grn & red, *yel* ('11) 35.00 *55.00*
Nos. 29-40 (12) 179.35 *319.65*

Nos. 29 and 33 are valued on ordinary paper. Values on chalky paper; No. 20, $4.50 unused or used; No. 33, $17.50 unused, $$40 used.

1907-11

Ordinary Paper

41 A4 ¼p brown ('09) 1.00 .75
42 A4 ½p green 1.25 .60
43 A4 1p red 3.25 .45
a. 1p rose carmine 17.50 1.35
44 A4 2p gray ('11) 1.25 *6.75*
45 A4 2½p ultramarine 2.25 2.25
Nos. 41-45 (5) 9.00 *10.80*

King George V
A5 A6

Dies I and II, type A5, described at back of volume.

The ½p, 1p, 2½p and 6p denominations of type A5 show the numeral on horizontally-lined tablet. The 1sh and 5sh denominations are expressed as "ONE SHILLING" and "FIVE SHILLINGS" on plain tablet.

Die I

1912

Ordinary Paper

46 A5 ¼p brown .50 .15
47 A5 ½p green .90 .40
48 A5 1p scarlet 1.25 .25
a. 1p carmine 1.00 .15
49 A5 2p gray 2.10 2.00
50 A5 2½p ultramarine 2.00 *5.00*
Nos. 46-50 (5) 6.75 *7.80*

1912-22

Chalky Paper

51 A5 3p violet, *yel* .50 *2.50*
52 A5 4p blk & red, *yel* (Die II) ('22) .75 *10.00*
53 A5 6p vio & red vio 1.25 *3.75*
54 A5 1sh blk, *bl grn*, ol back 1.25 *4.50*
a. 1sh black, *green* 3.50 3.00
55 A5 2sh vio & ultra, *bl* (Die II) ('22) 3.50 *22.50*
56 A5 2sh6p black & red, *blue* ('14) 8.75 17.50
57 A5 5sh green & red, *yellow* ('14) 7.50 *16.00*
Nos. 46-57 (12) 30.25 *84.55*

1914

Surface-colored Paper

58 A5 3p violet, *yel* 55.00 *50.00*
59 A5 1sh black, *green* 37.50 *37.50*
60 A5 5sh green & red, *yel* 47.50 *42.50*
Nos. 58-60 (3) 140.00 *130.00*

Die II

1921-32 Wmk. 4

Ordinary Paper

61 A5 ¼p dk brown ('22) .15 .15
a. ¼p dark brown (I) ('32) .15 .20
62 A5 ½p green .15 .15
a. ½p green (I) ('32) .75 *4.00*
63 A5 1p carmine .25 .15
a. 1p rose red (I) ('32) .80 .80
64 A5 1p dp violet ('22) .40 .15
65 A5 1½p rose red ('26) .85 .15
66 A5 1½p red brn ('29) .40 .15
a. 1½p red brown (I) ('32) 1.50 *2.50*
68 A5 2p gray ('22) .85 .50
69 A5 2½p orange ('23) 2.50 *24.00*
70 A5 2½p ultra ('27) .70 .25
a. Die I ('32) 3.00 3.00
71 A5 3p ultra ('23) 2.00 *13.00*

Chalky Paper

72 A5 3p violet, *yel* .55 *3.00*
73 A5 4p black & red, *yel* ('23) 1.00 *12.00*
74 A5 5p vio & olive grn ('22) .40 *3.50*
75 A5 6p vio & red vio ('23) 6.00 *20.00*
a. Die I ('32) 6.25 *10.00*
76 A5 1sh blk, *emerald* ('23) 2.00 6.00
a. 1sh black, *green* (I) ('32) 17.50 *22.50*
77 A5 2sh vio & ultra, *bl* ('22) 7.00 *32.50*
78 A5 2sh6p blk & red, *bl* ('23) 6.25 *18.00*
79 A5 3sh green & vio 8.00 *18.00*
80 A5 4sh black & scar 8.75 *27.50*
81 A5 5sh grn & red, *yel* 25.00 *40.00*
82 A6 10sh red & grn, *emer* ('28) 47.50 *60.00*

Wmk. 3

83 A6 £1 black & vio, *red* ('28) 225.00 *200.00*
Nos. 61-66,68-83 (22) 345.70 *479.15*

Common Design Types pictured following the introduction.

Silver Jubilee Issue

Common Design Type

Perf. 11x12

1935, May 6 Engr. Wmk. 4

96 CD301 1p car & dk blue .40 .40
97 CD301 1½p blk & ultra 1.00 1.00
98 CD301 2½p ultra & brn 1.75 1.75
99 CD301 1sh brn vio & ind 5.00 5.00
Nos. 96-99 (4) 8.15 8.15

Coronation Issue

Common Design Type

1937, May 12 *Perf. 13½x14*

100 CD302 1p carmine .15 .15
101 CD302 1½p brown .25 .25
102 CD302 2½p bright ultra .30 .30
Nos. 100-102 (3) .70 .70

Leeward Islands stamps can be mounted in the Scott British Leeward Islands album.

King George VI
A7 A8

1938-51 Typo. Perf. 14

103 A7 ¼p brown .15 .15
104 A7 ½p green .15 .15
105 A7 1p scarlet .15 .15
a. 1p carmine ('42) .40 .50
106 A7 1½p red brown .15 .15
107 A7 2p gray .15 .15
108 A7 2½p ultramarine .15 .15
109 A7 3p dl org ('42) .40 .50
a. 3p brown orange 3.50 .90
110 A7 6p vio & red vio .25 .25
111 A7 1sh blk, *emerald* 1.25 .60
112 A7 2sh vio & ultra, *bl* 1.65 1.10
113 A7 5sh grn & red, *yel* 5.50 6.50
114 A8 10sh red & grn, *emer* 22.50 17.50

Two dies were used for the 1p, differing in thickness of shading line at base of "1."

Wmk. 3 Perf. 13

115 A8 £1 blk & vio, *scar* ('51) 17.50 15.00
a. £1 black & brown purple, *red*, perf. 14 190.00 190.00
b. £1 black & purple, *carmine*, perf. 14 ('41) 27.50 20.00
c. £1 black & brown purple, *salmon*, perf. 14 ('43) 15.00 17.50
d. Wmkd. sideways (as #115, perf. 13) 2,000.
Nos. 103-115 (13) 49.95 42.35

Issued: £1, 12/13/51; others, 11/25/38.
See Nos. 120-125.

Catalogue values for unused stamps in this section, from this point to the end of the section, are for Never Hinged items.

Peace Issue
Common Design Type
Perf. 13½x14

1946, Nov. 1 Wmk. 4 Engr.

116 CD303 1½p brown .15 .15
117 CD303 3p deep orange .15 .15
Set value .25 .25

Silver Wedding Issue
Common Design Types

1949, Jan. 2 Photo. Perf. 14x14½

118 CD304 2½p bright ultra .15 .15

Perf. 11½x11
Engr.; Name Typographed

119 CD305 5sh green 5.75 5.75

George VI Type of 1938

1949, July 1 Typo. Perf. 13½x14

120 A7 ½p gray .15 .15
121 A7 1p green .15 .15
122 A7 1½p orange & black .15 .15
123 A7 2p crimson rose .25 .15
124 A7 2½p black & plum .25 .15
125 A7 3p ultramarine .25 .15
Nos. 120-125 (6) 1.20
Set value .65

UPU Issue
Common Design Types
Engr.; Name Typo. on 3p and 6p

1949, Oct. 10 Perf. 13½, 11x11½

126 CD306 2½p slate .40 .40
127 CD307 3p indigo .60 .60
128 CD308 6p red lilac 1.25 1.25
129 CD309 1sh blue green 1.50 1.50
Nos. 126-129 (4) 3.75 3.75

University Issue
Common Design Types
Perf. 14x14½

1951, Feb. 16 Engr. Wmk. 4

130 CD310 3c gray black & org .30 .30
131 CD311 12c lilac & rose car .95 .95

Coronation Issue
Common Design Type

1953, June 2 Perf. 13½x13

132 CD312 3c dk green & black .25 .25

Queen Elizabeth II
A9 A10

1954, Feb. 22 Typo. Perf. 14

133 A9 ½c brown .15 .15
134 A9 1c gray .15 .15
135 A9 2c green .15 .15
136 A9 3c orange & blk .15 .15
137 A9 4c rose red .15 .15
138 A9 5c blk & claret .20 .20
139 A9 6c orange .20 .20
140 A9 8c deep ultra .25 .25
141 A9 12c rose vio & mag .40 .40
142 A9 24c black & green .60 .60
143 A9 48c rose vio & ultra 1.25 1.25
144 A9 60c brown & green 1.65 1.65
145 A9 $1.20 yel grn & rose red 3.25 3.25

Perf. 13

146 A10 $2.40 red & blue grn 5.00 *8.00*
147 A10 $4.80 black & claret 9.50 *15.00*
Nos. 133-147 (15) 23.05 *31.55*

LESOTHO

lə-ˈsō-(ˌ)tō

LOCATION — An enclave within the Republic of South Africa
GOVT. — Independent state in British Commonwealth
AREA — 11,720 sq. mi.
POP. — 1,470,000 (est. 1984)
CAPITAL — Maseru

Basutoland, the British Crown Colony, became independent, October 4, 1966, taking the name Lesotho.

100 Cents = 1 Rand
100 Lisente (s) = 1 Maloti (1979)

Catalogue values for all unused stamps in this country are for Never Hinged items.

Watermark

Wmk. 362- Basotho Hat Multiple

Moshoeshoe I and II — A1

Perf. 12½x13

1966, Oct. 4 Photo. Unwmk.

1 A1 2½c red brn, blk & red .15 .15
2 A1 5c red brn, blk & brt bl .15 .15
3 A1 10c red brn, blk & brt green .25 .25
4 A1 20c red brn, blk & red lilac .45 .45
Nos. 1-4 (4) 1.00 1.00

Lesotho's independence, Oct. 4, 1966.

Basutoland Nos. 72-74, 76-82 Overprinted **LESOTHO**

Perf. 13½

1966, Nov. 1 Wmk. 4 Engr.

5 A7 ½c dk brown & gray .15 .15
6 A7 1c dp grn & gray blk .15 .15
7 A7 2c orange & dp blue .15 .15
8 A7 3½c dp blue & indigo .15 .15
9 A7 5c dk grn & org brn .16 .16
10 A7 10c rose vio & dk ol .32 .32
11 A7 12½c aqua & brown .40 .40
12 A7 25c lil rose & dp ultra .80 .80
13 A7 50c dp car & black 1.60 1.60

Perf. 11½

14 A8 1r dp claret & blk 4.40 4.40
a. "Lseotho" 100.00
Nos. 5-14 (10) 8.28 8.28

Same Overprint on Nos. 87-91 and Type of 1954

Wmk. 314 Perf. 13½

15 A7 1c green & gray blk .15 .15
16 A7 2½c car & ol green .15 .15
17 A7 5c dk grn & org brn .20 .20
18 A7 12½c aqua & brown .40 .40
19 A7 50c dp car & black 1.40 1.40

Perf. 11½

20 A8 1r dp claret & blk 2.75 2.75
a. "Lseotho" 50.00
Nos. 15-20 (6) 5.05 5.05

UNESCO Emblem, Microscope, Book, Violin and Retort — A2

Unwmk.

1966, Dec. 1 Litho. Perf. 14

21 A2 2½c green & ocher .15 .15
22 A2 5c olive & brt green .15 .15
23 A2 12½c ver & lt blue .40 .40
24 A2 25c dull blue & orange .65 .65
Nos. 21-24 (4) 1.35 1.35

20th anniv. of UNESCO.

King Moshoeshoe II and Corn — A3
King Moshoeshoe II — A4

Designs: 1c, Bull. 2c, Aloes. 2½c, Basotho hat. 3½c, Merino sheep. 5c, Basotho pony. 10c, Wheat. 12½c, Angora goat. 25c, Maletsunyane Falls. 50c, Diamonds. 1r, Coat of Arms.

Perf. 13½x14½

1967, Apr. 1 Photo. Unwmk.

25 A3 ½c violet & green .15 .15
26 A3 1c dk red & brown .15 .15
27 A3 2c green & yellow .15 .15
28 A3 2½c yel bister & blk .15 .15
29 A3 3½c yellow & black .15 .15
30 A3 5c brt blue & yel bis .18 .15
31 A3 10c gray & ocher .30 .20
32 A3 12½c orange & blk .35 .30
33 A3 25c ultra & blk .75 .75
34 A3 50c Prus green & blk 1.75 1.75
35 A3 1r gray & multi 2.75 2.75

Perf. 14½x13½

36 A4 2r mag, blk & gold 6.00 6.00
Nos. 25-36 (12) 12.83 12.65

See Nos. 47-59.

University Buildings and Graduates A4a

1967, Apr. 7 Perf. 14x14½

37 A4a 1c yel, sep & dp blue .15 .15
38 A4a 2½c blue, sep & dp bl .15 .15
39 A4a 12½c dl rose, sep & dp bl .25 .25
40 A4a 25c lt vio, sep & dp bl .45 .45
Set value .80 .80

1st conferment of degrees by the Univ. of Botswana, Lesotho and Swaziland at Roma, Lesotho.

Statue of Moshoeshoe I — A5

1st Anniv. of Independence: 12½c, Flag of Lesotho. 25c, Crocodile.

1967, Oct. 4 Photo. Perf. 14

41 A5 2½c apple green & black .15 .15
42 A5 12½c multicolored .35 .35
43 A5 25c tan, blk & dp green .65 .65
Nos. 41-43 (3) 1.15 1.15

Boy Scout and Lord Baden-Powell — A6

1967, Nov. 1 Unwmk. Perf. 14x14½

44 A6 15c lt ol grn, dk grn & brn .50 .50

60th anniversary of the Boy Scouts.

World Map and WHO Emblem A7

20th anniv. of WHO: 25c, Nurse and child, arms of Lesotho and WHO emblem.

1968, Apr. 8 Photo. Perf. 14x14½

45 A7 2½c dp bl, car rose & gold .15 .15
46 A7 25c gold, gray grn & redsh brown .45 .40
Set value .51 .45

Types of 1967

Design: 3c, Sorghum. Others as before.

Perf. 13½x14½

1968-69 Photo. Wmk. 362

47 A3 ½c violet & green .15 .15
48 A3 1c dk red & brown .15 .15
49 A3 2c green & yellow .15 .15
50 A3 2½c yel bister & blk .15 .15
51 A3 3c lt brn, dk brn & green .18 .18
52 A3 3½c yellow & black .18 .18
53 A3 5c brt bl & yel bis .22 .18
54 A3 10c gray & ocher .55 .45
55 A3 12½c org & blk ('69) .90 .75
56 A3 25c ultra & blk ('69) 1.60 1.25
57 A3 50c Prussian grn & black ('69) 3.50 2.75
58 A3 1r gray & multi 6.00 5.50

Perf. 14½x13½

59 A4 2r magenta, blk & gold ('69) 15.00 11.50
Nos. 47-59 (13) 28.73 23.34

Hunters, Rock Painting — A8

Rock Paintings: 3½c, Baboons. 5c, Javelin thrower, vert. 10c, Archers. 15c, Cranes, vert. 20c, Eland. 25c, Hunting scene.

Perf. 14½x14, 14x14½

1968, Nov. 1 Photo. Wmk. 362

60 A8 3c dk & lt green & brn .15 .15
61 A8 3½c dk brown & yel .15 .15
62 A8 5c sepia, yel & red brn .20 .20
63 A8 10c black, brt rose & org .45 .45
64 A8 15c olive brn & buff .75 .75
65 A8 20c black, yel & lt grn 1.00 1.00
66 A8 25c dk brown, yel & org 1.25 1.25
Nos. 60-66 (7) 3.95 3.95

Protection for Lesotho's rock paintings.

Queen Elizabeth II Hospital A9

Designs: 10c, Radio Lesotho. 12½c, Leabua Jonathan Airport. 25c, Royal Palace.

1969, Mar. 11 Litho. *Perf. 14x13½*

67 A9 2½c multicolored .15 .15
68 A9 10c multicolored .25 .25
69 A9 12½c multicolored .28 .28
70 A9 25c multicolored .65 .65
Nos. 67-70 (4) 1.33 1.33

Centenary of Maseru, capital of Lesotho.

Mosotho Horseman and Car A10

Designs: 12½c, Car on mountain pass. 15c, View from Sani Pass and signal flags. 20c, Map of Lesotho and Independence Trophy.

1969, Sept. 26 Photo. *Perf. 14½x14*

71 A10 2½c brown & multi .15 .15
72 A10 12½c multicolored .28 .28
73 A10 15c multicolored .35 .35
74 A10 20c yellow & multi .50 .50
Nos. 71-74 (4) 1.28 1.28

Roof of Africa Auto Rally, Sept. 19-20.

Plateosauravus and Footprints — A11

Prehistoric Reptile Footprints, Moyeni: 3c, Dinosaur. 5c, Gryponyx. 15c, Tritylodon. 25c, Massospondylus.

Perf. 14½x14

1970, Jan. 5 Wmk. 362

Size: 60x23mm

75 A11 3c brown, yel & black .15 .15

Perf. 15x14

Size: 40x23mm

76 A11 5c maroon, blk & pink .32 .32
77 A11 10c sepia, blk & yel .65 .65
78 A11 15c slate grn, blk & yel 1.10 1.10
79 A11 25c gray blue, blk & bl 1.50 1.50
Nos. 75-79 (5) 3.72 3.72

Moshoeshoe I — A12

Design: 25c, Moshoeshoe I with top hat.

Perf. 14x13½

1970, Mar. 11 Litho. Wmk. 362

80 A12 2½c brt grn & car rose .15 .15
81 A12 25c lt blue & org brn .65 .65

Cent. of the death of Moshoeshoe I, chief of the Bakoena clan of the Basothos.

UN Headquarters, New York — A13

Designs: 2½c, UN emblem. 12½c, UN emblem and people. 25c, UN emblem and peace dove.

1973, June 26 Litho. *Perf. 14½x14*

82 A13 2½c pink, red brn & bl .15 .15
83 A13 10c blue & multi .25 .20
84 A13 12½c olive, ver & lt blue .25 .22
85 A13 25c tan & multi .60 .50
Nos. 82-85 (4) 1.25 1.07

25th anniversary of the United Nations.

Basotho Hat Gift Shop, Maseru A14

Tourism: 5c, Trout fishing. 10c, Horseback riding. 12½c, Skiing, Maluti Mountains. 20c, Holiday Inn, Maseru.

1970, Oct. 27 *Perf. 14x14½*

86 A14 2½c multicolored .15 .15
87 A14 5c multicolored .20 .20
88 A14 10c multicolored .45 .45
89 A14 12½c multicolored .45 .45
90 A14 20c multicolored .65 .65
Nos. 86-90 (5) 1.90 1.90

Corn — A15

Designs: 1c, Bull. 2c, Aloes. 2½c, Basotho hat. 3c, Sorghum. 3½c, Merino sheep. 4c, National flag. 5c, Basotho pony. 10c, Wheat. 12½c, Angora goat. 25c, Maletsunyane Falls. 50c, Diamonds. 1r, Coat of Arms. 2r, Statue of King Moshoeshoe I in Maseru, vert.

1971 Litho. Wmk. 362 *Perf. 14*

91 A15 ½c lilac & green .15 .15
92 A15 1c brn red & brn .15 .15
93 A15 2c yel brn & yel .15 .15
94 A15 2½c dull yel & blk .15 .15
95 A15 3c bis, brn & grn .15 .15
96 A15 3½c yellow & black .15 .15
97 A15 4c ver & multi .15 .15
98 A15 5c blue & brown .15 .15
99 A15 10c gray & ocher .28 .28
100 A15 12½c orange & brn .32 .32
101 A15 25c ultra & black .70 .70
102 A15 50c lt bl grn & blk 1.75 1.75
103 A15 1r gray & multi 2.25 2.25
104 A15 2r ultra & brown 5.75 5.75
a. Unwmkd. ('80) 5.25 5.25
Nos. 91-104 (14) 12.25 12.25

Issue dates: 4c, Apr. 1; others, Jan. 4.
For overprints and surcharges see #132-135, 245, 312.

Lammergeier — A16

Birds: 5c, Bald ibis. 10c, Rufous rock jumper. 12½c, Blue korhaan (bustard). 15c, Painted snipe. 20c, Golden-breasted bunting. 25c, Ground woodpecker.

1971, Mar. 1 *Perf. 14*

105 A16 2½c multicolored .75 .25
106 A16 5c multicolored 1.25 .50
107 A16 10c multicolored 2.00 1.25
108 A16 12½c multicolored 3.00 1.50
109 A16 15c multicolored 3.50 2.00
110 A16 20c multicolored 4.75 2.50
111 A16 25c multicolored 5.25 3.50
Nos. 105-111 (7) 20.50 11.50

Lionel Collett Dam A17

Designs: 10c, Contour farming. 15c, Earth dams. 25c, Beaver dams.

1971, July 15 Litho. Wmk. 362

112 A17 4c multicolored .15 .15
113 A17 10c multicolored .32 .32
114 A17 15c multicolored .45 .45
115 A17 25c multicolored .75 .75
Nos. 112-115 (4) 1.67 1.67

Soil conservation and erosion control.

Diamond Mining A18

Designs: 10c, Potter. 15c, Woman weaver at loom. 20c, Construction worker and new buildings.

1971, Oct. 4

116 A18 4c olive & multi .15 .15
117 A18 10c ocher & multi .28 .28
118 A18 15c red & multi .45 .45
119 A18 20c dk brown & multi .60 .60
Nos. 116-119 (4) 1.48 1.48

Mail Cart, 19th Century A19

Designs: 10c, Postal bus. 15c, Cape of Good Hope No. 17, vert. 20c, Maseru Post Office.

1972, Jan. 3

120 A19 5c pink & black .15 .15
121 A19 10c lt blue & multi .35 .35
122 A19 15c gray, black & blue .50 .50
123 A19 20c yellow & multi .90 .90
Nos. 120-123 (4) 1.90 1.90

Centenary of mail service between Maseru and Aliwal North in Cape Colony.

Runner and Olympic Rings — A20

1972, Sept. 1

124 A20 4c shown .15 .15
125 A20 10c Shot put .25 .25
126 A20 15c Hurdles .35 .35
127 A20 25c Broad jump .75 .75
Nos. 124-127 (4) 1.50 1.50

20th Olympic Games, Munich, Aug. 26-Sept. 11.

Adoration of the Shepherds, by Matthias Stomer — A21

1972, Dec. 1 Litho. *Perf. 14*

128 A21 4c blue & multi .15 .15
129 A21 10c red & multi .35 .35
130 A21 25c emerald & multi .90 .90
Nos. 128-130 (3) 1.40 1.40

Christmas.

WHO Emblem A22

1973, Apr. 7 Litho. *Perf. 13½*

131 A22 20c blue & yellow .50 .50

WHO, 25th anniversary.

Nos. 94, 97-99 overprinted: "O.A.U. / 10th Anniversary / Freedom in Unity"

1973, May 25 Wmk. 362 *Perf. 14*

132 A15 2½c dull yellow & black .15 .15
133 A15 4c vermilion & multi .20 .20
134 A15 5c blue & brown .25 .25
135 A15 10c gray & ocher .50 .50
Nos. 132-135 (4) 1.10 1.10

Basotho Hat, WFP/FAO Emblem — A23

Designs: 15c, School lunch. 20c, Child drinking milk and cow. 25c, Map of mountain roads and farm workers.

1973, June 1 *Perf. 13½*

136 A23 4c ultra & multi .15 .15
137 A23 15c buff & multi .30 .30
138 A23 20c yellow & multi .40 .40
139 A23 25c violet & multi .60 .60
Nos. 136-139 (4) 1.45 1.45

World Food Program, 10th anniversary.

Christmas Butterfly A24

Designs: Butterflies of Lesotho.

1973, Sept. 3 *Perf. 14x14½*

140 A24 4c Mountain Beauty .30 .30
141 A24 5c shown .45 .45
142 A24 10c Painted lady .90 .90
143 A24 15c Yellow pansy 1.25 1.25
144 A24 20c Blue pansy 1.75 1.75
145 A24 25c African monarch 2.50 2.50
146 A24 30c Orange tip 3.50 3.50
Nos. 140-146 (7) 10.65 10.65

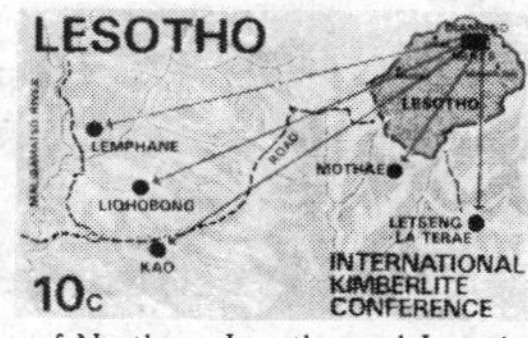

Map of Northern Lesotho and Location of Diamond Mines — A25

Designs: 15c, Kimberlite (diamond-bearing) rocks. 20c, Diagram of Kimberlite volcano, vert. 30c, Diamond prospector, vert.

Perf. 13½x14, 14x13½

1973, Oct. 1 Litho. Wmk. 362

147 A25 10c gray & multi .85 .50
148 A25 15c multicolored 1.25 .75
149 A25 20c multicolored 1.65 1.00
150 A25 30c multicolored 3.25 1.50
Nos. 147-150 (4) 7.00 3.75

International Kimberlite Conference.

Nurses' Training and Medical Care A26

Designs: 10c, Classroom, student with microscope. 20c, Farmers with tractor and bullock team and crop instruction. 25c, Potter and engineers with lathe. 30c, Boy scouts and young bricklayers.

1974, Feb. 18 Litho. *Perf. 13½x14*

151 A26 4c lt blue & multi .15 .15
152 A26 10c ocher & multi .20 .20
153 A26 20c multicolored .40 .40
154 A26 25c bister & multi .60 .60
155 A26 30c yellow & multi .75 .75
Nos. 151-155 (5) 2.10 2.10

Youth and development.

Open Book and Wreath — A27

Designs: 15c, Flags of Botswana, Lesotho and Swaziland; cap and diploma. 20c, Map of Africa and location of Botswana, Lesotho and Swaziland. 25c, King Moshoeshoe II, Chancellor of UBLS, capping graduate.

1974, Apr. 7 Litho. *Perf. 14*

156 A27	10c multicolored		.30	.30
157 A27	15c multicolored		.50	.50
158 A27	20c multicolored		.60	.60
159 A27	25c multicolored		.75	.75
	Nos. 156-159 (4)		2.15	2.15

10th anniversary of the University of Botswana, Lesotho and Swaziland.

Senqunyane River Bridge, Marakabei — A28

5c, Tsoelike River Bridge. 10c, Makhaleng River Bridge. 15c, Seaka Bridge, Orange/Senqu River. 20c, Masianokeng Bridge, Phuthiatsana River. 25c, Mahobong Bridge, Hlotse River.

1974, June 26 Wmk. 362 *Perf. 14*

160 A28	4c multicolored	.15	.15
161 A28	5c multicolored	.15	.15
162 A28	10c multicolored	.25	.25
163 A28	15c multicolored	.50	.40
164 A28	20c multicolored	.65	.50
165 A28	25c multicolored	.80	.60
	Nos. 160-165 (6)	2.50	2.05

Bridges and rivers of Lesotho.

UPU Emblem — A29

1974, Sept. 6 Litho. *Perf. 14x13*

166 A29	4c shown	.15	.15
167 A29	10c Map of Lesotho	.25	.25
168 A29	15c GPO, Maseru	.40	.40
169 A29	20c Rural mail delivery	.60	.60
	Nos. 166-169 (4)	1.40	1.40

Centenary of Universal Postal Union.

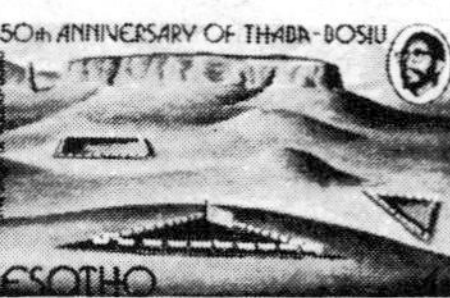

Siege of Thaba-Bosiu — A30

King Moshoeshoe I — A31

5c, King Moshoeshoe II laying wreath at grave of Moshoeshoe I. 20c, Makoanyane, warrior hero.

Perf. 12½x12, 12x12½

1974, Nov. 25

170 A30	4c multicolored	.15	.15
171 A30	5c multicolored	.18	.18
172 A31	10c multicolored	.35	.35
173 A31	20c multicolored	.85	.85
	Nos. 170-173 (4)	1.53	1.53

Sesquicentennial of Thaba-Bosiu becoming the capital of Basutoland and Lesotho.

Mamokhorong A32

Musical Instruments of the Basotho: 10c, Lesiba. 15c, Setolotolo. 20c, Meropa (drums).

Perf. 14x14½

1975, Jan. 25 Wmk. 362

174 A32	4c multicolored	.15	.15
175 A32	10c multicolored	.40	.40
176 A32	15c multicolored	.60	.60
177 A32	20c multicolored	.80	.80
a.	Souvenir sheet of 4, #174-177	2.50	2.50
	Nos. 174-177 (4)	1.95	1.95

View, Sehlabathebe National Park — A33

Designs: 5c, Natural arch. 15c, Mountain stream. 20c, Lake and mountains. 25c, Waterfall.

1975, Apr. 8 Litho. *Perf. 14*

178 A33	4c multicolored	.15	.15
179 A33	5c multicolored	.20	.20
180 A33	15c multicolored	.60	.60
181 A33	20c multicolored	.80	.80
182 A33	25c multicolored	1.00	1.00
	Nos. 178-182 (5)	2.75	2.75

Sehlabathebe National Park.

Moshoeshoe I (1824-1870) A34

Mofumahali Mantsebo Seeiso (1940-1960) A35

Leaders of Lesotho: 4c, Moshoeshoe II. 5c, Letsie I (1870-1891). 6c, Lerotholi (1891-1905). 10c, Letsie II (1905-1913). 15c, Griffith (1913-1939). 20c, Seeiso Griffith Lerotholi (1939-1940).

1975, Sept. 10 Litho. Wmk. 362

183 A34	3c dull blue & black	.15	.15
184 A34	4c lilac rose & black	.15	.15
185 A34	5c pink & black	.15	.15
186 A34	6c brown & black	.15	.15
187 A34	10c rose car & black	.25	.25
188 A34	15c orange & black	.35	.35
189 A34	20c olive & black	.45	.45
190 A35	25c lt blue & black	.60	.60
	Nos. 183-190 (8)	2.25	2.25

No. 190 issued for Intl. Women's Year.

Mokhibo, Women's Dance — A36

Traditional Dances: 10c, Ndlamo, men's dance. 15c, Raleseli, men and women. 20c, Mohobelo, men's dance.

1975, Dec. 17 *Perf. 14x14½*

191 A36	4c blue & multi	.15	.15
192 A36	10c black & multi	.35	.35
193 A36	15c black & multi	.50	.50
194 A36	20c blue & multi	.75	.75
a.	Souvenir sheet of 4, #191-194	3.00	3.00
	Nos. 191-194 (4)	1.75	1.75

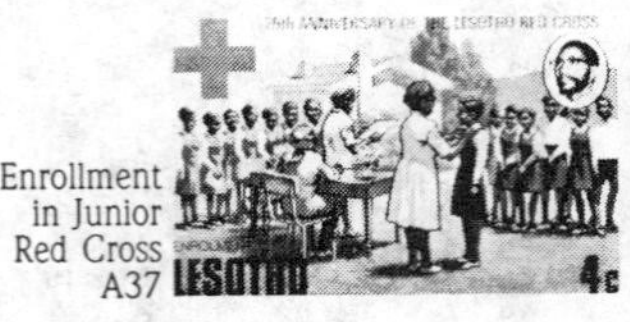

Enrollment in Junior Red Cross A37

Designs: 10c, First aid team and truck. 15c, Red Cross nurse on horseback in rural area. 25c, Supplies arriving by plane.

1976, Feb. 20 Litho. *Perf. 14*

195 A37	4c red & multi	.15	.15
196 A37	10c red & multi	.35	.35
197 A37	15c red & multi	.50	.50
198 A37	25c red & multi	.80	.80
	Nos. 195-198 (4)	1.80	1.80

Lesotho Red Cross, 25th anniversary.

Mosotho Horseman A38

King Moshoeshoe II — A39

Designs: 2c, Tapestry (weavers and citation). 4c, Map of Lesotho. 5c, Hand holding Lesotho brown diamond. 10c, Lesotho Bank. 15c, Flags of Lesotho and Organization of African Unity. 25c, Sehlabathebe National Park. 40c, Pottery. 50c, Prehistoric rock painting.

1976, June 2 *Perf. 14*

199 A38	2c multicolored	.15	.15
200 A38	3c multicolored	.15	.15
201 A38	4c multicolored	.15	.15
202 A38	5c multicolored	.15	.15
203 A38	10c multicolored	.30	.30
204 A38	15c multicolored	.45	.45
205 A38	25c multicolored	.75	.75
206 A38	40c multicolored	1.20	1.20
207 A38	50c multicolored	1.50	1.50
208 A39	1r multicolored	2.00	2.00
	Nos. 199-208 (10)	6.80	6.80

For surcharges see Nos. 302-311.

Soccer A40

Rising Sun of Independence A41

Olympic Rings and: 10c, Weight lifting. 15c, Boxing. 25c, Discus.

1976, Aug. 9 Litho. Wmk. 362

209 A40	4c citron & multi	.15	.15
210 A40	10c lilac & multi	.28	.25
211 A40	15c salmon & multi	.40	.35
212 A40	25c blue & multi	.80	.65
	Nos. 209-212 (4)	1.63	1.40

21st Olympic Games, Montreal, Canada, July 17-Aug. 1.

1976, Oct. 4 *Perf. 14*

Designs: 10c, Opening gates. 15c, Broken chain. 25c, Plane over Molimo Restaurant.

213 A41	4c yellow & multi	.15	.15
214 A41	10c pink & multi	.30	.30
215 A41	15c blue & multi	.45	.45
216 A41	25c dull blue & multi	.75	.75
	Nos. 213-216 (4)	1.65	1.65

Lesotho's independence, 10th anniversary.

Telephones, 1876 and 1976 A42

Designs: 10c, Woman using telephone, and 1895 telephone. 15c, Telephone operators and wall telephone. 25c, A.G. Bell and 1905 telephone.

Perf. 13x13½

1976, Dec. 6 Wmk. 362

217 A42	4c multicolored	.15	.15
218 A42	10c multicolored	.22	.22
219 A42	15c multicolored	.35	.35
220 A42	25c multicolored	.60	.60
	Nos. 217-220 (4)	1.32	1.32

Centenary of first telephone call by Alexander Graham Bell, Mar. 10, 1876.

Aloe Striatula — A43

Aloes and Succulents: 4c, Aloe aristata. 5c, Kniphofia caulescens. 10c, Euphorbia pulvinata. 15c, Aloe saponaria. 20c, Caralluma lutea. 25c, Aloe polyphylla.

1977, Feb. 14 Litho. *Perf. 14*

221 A43	3c multicolored	.18	.15
222 A43	4c multicolored	.22	.15
223 A43	5c multicolored	.25	.20
224 A43	10c multicolored	.50	.40
225 A43	15c multicolored	.90	.50
226 A43	20c multicolored	1.10	.75
227 A43	25c multicolored	1.25	1.00
	Nos. 221-227 (7)	4.40	3.15

Rock Rabbits — A44

Perf. 14x14½

1977, Apr. 25 Wmk. 362

228 A44	4c shown	.40	.15
229 A44	5c Porcupine	.50	.20
230 A44	10c Polecat	1.00	.40
231 A44	15c Klipspringers	1.60	.60
232 A44	25c Baboons	3.00	1.00
	Nos. 228-232 (5)	6.50	2.35

Man with Cane, Concentric Circles — A45

Man with Cane: 10c, Surrounded by flames of pain. 15c, Surrounded by chain. 25c, Man and globe.

1977, July 4 Litho. *Perf. 14*
233 A45 4c red & yellow .15 .15
234 A45 10c dk blue & lt blue .28 .15
235 A45 15c blue green & yellow .48 .35
236 A45 25c black & orange .80 .60
Nos. 233-236 (4) 1.71 1.25

World Rheumatism Year.

Small-mouthed Yellow-fish A46

Fresh-water Fish: 10c, Orange River mud fish. 15c, Rainbow trout. 25c, Oreodaimon quathlambae.

1977, Sept. 28 Wmk. 362 *Perf. 14*
237 A46 4c multicolored .15 .15
238 A46 10c multicolored .32 .25
239 A46 15c multicolored .48 .35
240 A46 25c multicolored .80 .60
Nos. 237-240 (4) 1.75 1.35

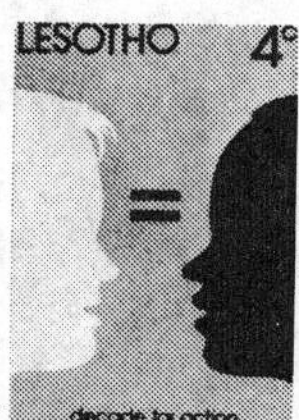

White and Black Equal — A47

Designs: 10c, Black and white jigsaw puzzle. 15c, White and black cogwheels. 25c, Black and white handshake.

1977, Dec. 12 Litho. *Perf. 14*
241 A47 4c lilac rose & black .15 .15
242 A47 10c brt blue & black .22 .22
243 A47 15c orange & black .35 .35
244 A47 25c lt green & black .60 .60
Nos. 241-244 (4) 1.32 1.32

Action to Combat Racism Decade.

No. 99 Surcharged **3**

1977, Dec. 7
245 A15 3c on 10c gray & ocher 1.60 1.40

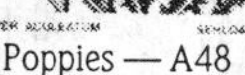

Poppies — A48

Edward Jenner Vaccinating Child — A49

Flowers of Lesotho: 3c, Diascia integerrima. 4c, Helichrysum trilineatum. 5c, Zaluzianskya maritima. 10c, Gladioli. 15c, Chironia krebsii. 25c, Wahlenbergia undulata. 40c, Brunsvigia radulosa.

1978, Feb. 13 Litho. Wmk. 362
246 A48 2c multicolored .15 .15
247 A48 3c multicolored .15 .15
248 A48 4c multicolored .15 .15
249 A48 5c multicolored .15 .15
250 A48 10c multicolored .25 .25
251 A48 15c multicolored .40 .40
252 A48 25c multicolored .65 .65
253 A48 40c multicolored 1.00 1.00
Nos. 246-253 (8) 2.90 2.90

1978, May 8 Litho. *Perf. 13½x13*

Global Eradication of Smallpox: 25c, Child's head and WHO emblem.

254 A49 5c multicolored .15 .15
255 A49 25c multicolored .75 .75

Tsoloane Falls — A50

Lesotho Waterfalls: 10c, Qiloane Falls. 15c, Tsoelikana Falls. 25c, Maletsunyane Falls.

1978, July 28 Litho. *Perf. 14*
256 A50 4c multicolored .15 .15
257 A50 10c multicolored .32 .32
258 A50 15c multicolored .50 .50
259 A50 25c multicolored .80 .80
Nos. 256-259 (4) 1.77 1.77

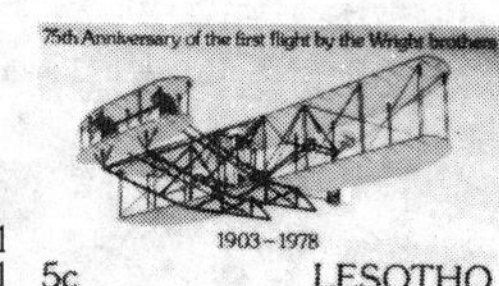

Flyer 1 A51 5c LESOTHO

Design: 25c, Orville and Wilbur Wright, Flyer 1.

1978, Oct. 9 Wmk. 362 *Perf. 14½*
260 A51 5c multicolored .15 .15
261 A51 25c multicolored .50 .50

75th anniversary of 1st powered flight.

Dragonflies A52

Lesotho 4c
Trees A53

Insects: 10c, Winged grasshopper. 15c, Wasps. 25c, Praying mantis.

1978, Dec. 18 Litho. *Perf. 14*
262 A52 4c multicolored .15 .15
263 A52 10c multicolored .30 .30
264 A52 15c multicolored .45 .45
265 A52 25c multicolored .75 .75
Nos. 262-265 (4) 1.65 1.65

1979, Mar. 26 Litho. *Perf. 14*
266 A53 4c Leucosidea Sericea .15 .15
267 A53 10c Wild olive .30 .30
268 A53 15c Blinkblaar .45 .45
269 A53 25c Cape holly .75 .75
Nos. 266-269 (4) 1.65 1.65

Reptiles A54

1979, June 4 Wmk. 362 *Perf. 14*
270 A54 4s Agama Lizard .15 .15
271 A54 10s Berg adder .30 .30
272 A54 15s Rock lizard .45 .45
273 A54 25s Spitting snake .75 .75
Nos. 270-273 (4) 1.65 1.65

A55

A56

1979, Oct. 22 Litho. *Perf. 14½*
274 A55 4s Basutoland No. 2 .15 .15
275 A55 15s Basutoland No. 72 .30 .30
276 A55 25s Penny Black .50 .50
Nos. 274-276 (3) .95 .95

Souvenir Sheet

277 A55 50s Lesotho No. 122 1.25 1.25

Sir Rowland Hill (1795-1879), originator of penny postage.

1979, Dec. 10 Wmk. 362 *Perf. 14½*

Children's Games, by Brueghel the Elder, and IYC emblem: 4s, Children Climbing Tree. 10s, Follow the leader. 15s, Three cup montie. 25s, Entire painting.

278 A56 4s multicolored .15 .15
279 A56 10s multicolored .22 .22
280 A56 15s multicolored .35 .35
Nos. 278-280 (3) .72 .72

Souvenir Sheet

281 A56 25s multicolored .60 .60

International Year of the Child.

Beer Strainer, Brooms and Mat A57

1980, Feb. 18 Litho. *Perf. 14½*
282 A57 4s shown .15 .15
283 A57 10s Winnowing basket .20 .20
284 A57 15s Basotho hat .30 .30
285 A57 25s Grain storage pots .50 .50
Nos. 282-285 (4) 1.15 1.15

Qalabane Ambush A58

Gun War Centenary: 4s, Praise poet, text. 5s, Basotho army commander Lerotholi. 15s, Snider and Martini-Henry rifles. 25s, Map of Basutoland showing battle sites.

1980, May 6 Litho. *Perf. 14*
286 A58 4s multicolored .15 .15
287 A58 5s multicolored .15 .15
288 A58 10s multicolored .25 .25
289 A58 15s multicolored .35 .35
290 A58 25s multicolored .60 .60
Nos. 286-290 (5) 1.50 1.50

St. Basil's, Moscow, Olympic Torch A59

1980, Sept. 20 Litho. *Perf. 14½*
291 A59 25s shown .55 .55
292 A59 25s Torch and flags .55 .55
293 A59 25s Soccer .55 .55
294 A59 25s Running .55 .55
295 A59 25s Misha and stadium .55 .55
a. Strip of 5, #291-295 2.75 2.75

Souvenir Sheet

296 A59 1.40m Classic and modern torch bearers 3.25 3.25

22nd Summer Olympic Games, Moscow, July 19-Aug. 3.

Beer Mug and Man Drinking A60

Prince Philip — A61

Wmk. 362

1980, Oct. 1 Litho. *Perf. 14*
297 A60 4s shown .15 .15
298 A60 10s Beer brewing pot .22 .22
299 A60 15s Water pot .35 .35
300 A60 25s Pots and jugs .60 .60
Nos. 297-300 (4) 1.32 1.32

Souvenir Sheet

Perf. 14x14½

301 Sheet of 4 3.50 2.25
a. A61 40s shown .70 .50
b. A61 40s Queen Elizabeth .70 .50
c. A61 40s Prince Charles .70 .50
d. A61 40s Princess Anne .70 .50

Traditional pottery; 250th birth anniversary of Josiah Wedgewood, potter.

Nos. 104, 199-208 Surcharged

Wmk. 362

1980, Oct. 20 Litho. *Perf. 14*
302 A38 2s on 2c multi .15 .15
303 A38 3s on 3c multi .15 .15
304 A38 5s on 5c multi .15 .15
a. 5s on 6s on 5c multi .15 .15
305 A38 6s on 4c multi .15 .15
306 A38 10s on 10c multi .18 .18
307 A38 25s on 25s multi .40 .40
308 A38 40s on 40c multi .65 .65
309 A38 50s on 50c multi .90 .90
310 A38 75s on 15c multi 2.25 2.25
311 A39 1m on 1r multi 2.75 2.75
312 A15 2m on 2r multi 5.00 5.00
Nos. 302-312 (11) 12.73 12.73

Souvenir Sheet

Queen Mother Elizabeth and Prince Charles — A62

Basutoland No. 36, Flags of Lesotho and Britain — A63

1980, Dec. 1 *Perf. 14½*
313 Sheet of 9 5.00 5.00
a. A62 5s shown .15 .15
b. A62 10s Portrait .20 .20
c. A63 1m shown 2.00 2.00

Queen Mother Elizabeth, 80th birthday. No. 313 contains 3 each Nos. 313a-313c.

St. Agnes' Anglican Church, Teyateyaneng — A63a

Nativity A64

1980, Dec. 8 *Perf. 14x14½*

314 A63a 4s Lesotho Evangelical Church, Morija .15 .15
315 A63a 15s shown .35 .35
316 A63a 25s Our Lady's Victory Cathedral, Maseru .60 .60
317 A63a 75s University Chapel, Roma 1.75 1.75
Nos. 314-317 (4) 2.85 2.85

Souvenir Sheet

318 A64 1.50m shown 3.25 2.00

Christmas.

Voyager Satellite and Saturn A65

1981, Mar. 15 **Litho.** *Perf. 14*

319 Strip of 5 2.75 2.75
a. A65 25s Voyager, planet .55 .55
b. A65 25s shown .55 .55
c. A65 25s Voyager, Saturn's rings .55 .55
d. A65 25s Columbia space shuttle .55 .55
e. A65 25s Columbia, diff. .55 .55

Souvenir Sheet

320 A65 1.40m Saturn 3.25 3.25

Voyager expedition to Saturn and flight of Columbia space shuttle.

Rock Pigeons A66

1981, Apr. 20 *Perf. 14½*

321 A66 1s Greater kestrel, vert. .15 .15
322 A66 2s shown .15 .15
323 A66 3s Crowned cranes, vert. .15 .15
324 A66 5s Bokmakierie, vert. .15 .15
325 A66 6s Cape robins, vert. .15 .15
326 A66 7s Yellow canary, vert. .18 .18
327 A66 10s Red-billed teal .25 .25
328 A66 25s Malachite kingfisher, vert. .60 .60
329 A66 40s Malachite sunbirds 1.00 1.00
330 A66 60s Orange-throated longclaw 1.50 1.50
331 A66 75s African hoopoe 1.75 1.75
332 A66 1m Red bishops 2.50 2.50
333 A66 2m Egyptian goose 4.75 4.75
334 A66 5m Lilac-breasted rollers 10.00 10.00
Nos. 321-334 (14) 23.28 23.28

For surcharges see Nos. 558A, 561-563, 598A, 599, 600B, 600C.

1981 **Litho.** *Perf. 13*

321a A66 1s
322a A66 2s
324a A66 5s
327a A66 10s

Perf. 14½

1982, June 14 **Litho.** **Wmk. 373**

321b A66 1s
322b A66 2s
323a A66 3s
324b A66 5s
325a A66 6s
326a A66 7s
327b A66 10s
328a A66 25s
329a A66 40s
330a A66 60s
331a A66 75s
332a A66 1m
333a A66 2m
334a A66 5m

Royal Wedding Issue

Common Design Type and

Royal Wedding — A66a

Illustration reduced.

1981, July 22 **Litho.** *Perf. 14*

335 CD331 25s Bouquet .40 .40
a. Booklet pane of 3 + label 1.25
336 CD331 50s Charles .75 .75
a. Booklet pane of 3 + label 2.50
337 CD331 75s Couple 1.10 1.10
b. Booklet pane of 3 + label 3.50
c. Bklt. pane of 3, #335-337 + label 2.75
Nos. 335-337 (3) 2.25 2.25

1981 **Litho.** *Perf. 14½*

337A A66a 1.50m Couple 3.00 3.00

Nos. 335-337A exist imperf.

Tree Planting A67

1981, Oct. 30 **Litho.** *Perf. 14½*

338 A67 6s Duke of Edinburgh .15 .15
339 A67 7s shown .15 .22
340 A67 25s Digging .50 .50
341 A67 40s Mountain climbing .80 .80
342 A67 75s Emblem 1.50 1.50
Nos. 338-342 (5) 3.10 3.17

Souvenir Sheet

343 A67 1.40m Duke of Edinburgh, diff. 2.75 2.75

Duke of Edinburgh's Awards, 25th anniv. #343 contains 1 45x29mm stamp, perf. 13½.

Santa Claus at Globe, by Norman Rockwell A68

The Mystic Nativity, by Botticelli — A69

Christmas: Saturday Evening Post covers by Norman Rockwell.

1981, Oct. 5 *Perf. 13½x14*

344 A68 6s multicolored .15 .15
345 A68 10s multicolored .20 .20
346 A68 15s multicolored .30 .30
347 A68 20s multicolored .40 .40
348 A68 25s multicolored .50 .50
349 A68 60s multicolored 1.25 1.25
Nos. 344-349 (6) 2.80 2.80

Souvenir Sheet

350 A69 1.25m multicolored 2.50 2.50

Chacma Baboons A70

Perf. 14x13½, 14½ (20s, 40s, 50s)

1982, Jan. 15 **Litho.**

351 A70 6s African wild cat .20 .20
352 A70 20s shown .80 .80
353 A70 25s Cape eland 1.00 1.00
354 A70 40s Porcupine 1.65 1.65
355 A70 50s Oribi 2.00 2.00
Nos. 351-355 (5) 5.65 5.65

Souvenir Sheet

Perf. 14

356 A70 1.50m Black-backed jackal 5.00 5.00

6s, 25s; 50x37mm. No. 356 contains one stamp 48x31mm.

Scouting Year — A71

1982, Mar. 5 **Litho.** *Perf. 14x13½*

357 A71 6s Bugle call .15 .15
358 A71 30s Hiking .60 .60
359 A71 40s Drawing .80 .80
360 A71 50s Holding flag 1.00 1.00
361 A71 75s Salute 1.50 1.50
a. Booklet pane of 10 + sheet 12.50
Nos. 357-361 (5) 4.05 4.05

Souvenir Sheet

362 A71 1.50m Baden-Powell 2.75 2.75

No. 361a contains 2 each Nos. 357-361 with gutter and No. 362.

#357-361 issued in sheets of 8 with gutter.

1982 World Cup Soccer A72

Championships, 1930-1978: a, Uruguay, 1930. b, Italy, 1934. c, France, 1938. d, Brazil, 1950. e, Switzerland, 1954. f, Sweden, 1958. g, Chile, 1962. h, England, 1966. i, Mexico, 1970. j, Germany, 1974. k, Argentina, 1978. l, World Cup.

1982, Apr. 14 *Perf. 14½*

363 Sheet of 12 3.25 3.25
a.-l. A72 15s any single .25 .25

Souvenir Sheet

364 A72 1.25m Stadium 2.50 2.50

Nos. 363b, 363c, 363f, 363g, 363j, 363k exist se-tenant in sheets of 72.

George Washington's Birth Bicentenary — A73

Designs: Paintings.

1982, June 7

365 A73 6s Portrait .15 .15
366 A73 7s With children .15 .15
367 A73 10s Indian Chief's Prophecy .20 .20
368 A73 25s With troops .50 .50
369 A73 40s Arriving at New York .80 .80
370 A73 1m Entry into New York 2.00 2.00
Nos. 365-370 (6) 3.80 3.80

Souvenir Sheet

371 A73 1.25m Crossing Delaware 2.50 2.50

Princess Diana Issue

Common Design Type

Wmk. 373

1982, July 1 **Litho.** *Perf. 14*

372 CD333 30s Arms .45 .45
373 CD333 50s Diana .75 .75
374 CD333 75s Wedding 1.10 1.10
375 CD333 1m Portrait 1.50 1.50
Nos. 372-375 (4) 3.80 3.80

Sesotho Bible Centenary — A74

Birth of Prince William of Wales, June 21 — A75

1982, Aug. 20 **Litho.** *Perf. 14½*

376 A74 6s Man reading bible .15 .15
377 A74 15s Angels, bible .25 .25

Size: 59½x40½mm

378 A74 1m Bible, Maseru Cathedral 1.75 1.75
Nos. 376-378 (3) 2.15 2.15

Issued in sheets of 9 (3 each Nos. 376-378).

1982, Sept. 30

379 A75 6s Congratulation .15 .15
380 A75 60s Diana, William 1.10 1.10

Issued in sheets of 6 (No. 379, 5 No. 380).

Christmas — A76

Designs: Scenes from Walt Disney's The Twelve Days of Christmas. Stamps of same denomination se-tenant.

1982, Dec. 1 **Litho.** *Perf. 11*

381 A76 2s multicolored .15 .15
382 A76 2s multicolored .15 .15
383 A76 3s multicolored .15 .15
384 A76 3s multicolored .15 .15
385 A76 4s multicolored .15 .15
386 A76 4s multicolored .15 .15
387 A76 75s multicolored 1.50 1.50
388 A76 75s multicolored 1.50 1.50
Nos. 381-388 (8) 3.90 3.90

Souvenir Sheet

Perf. 14x13½

389 A76 1.50m multicolored 3.25 3.25

Local Mushrooms — A77

1983, Jan. 11 *Perf. 14½*

390 A77 10s Lepista caffrorum .20 .20
391 A77 30s Broomexia congregate .60 .60
a. Booklet pane of 2, #390, 391 .85
392 A77 50s Afroboletus luteolus 1.00 1.00
393 A77 75s Lentinus tuberregium 1.50 1.50
a. Booklet pane of 4, #390-393 3.50
Nos. 390-393 (4) 3.30 3.30

Commonwealth Day — A78

1983, Mar. 14 **Litho.** *Perf. 14½*

394 A78 5s Ba-Leseli dance .15 .15
395 A78 30s Tapestry weaving .50 .50
396 A78 60s Elizabeth II 1.00 1.00
397 A78 75s Moshoeshoe II 1.10 1.10
Nos. 394-397 (4) 2.75 2.75

Trance Dancers A79

Hunters — A79a

Rock Paintings: 25s, Baboons, Sehonghong Thaba Tseka. 60s, Hunter attacking mountain reedbuck, Makhetha Berera. 75s, Eland, Leribe.

1983, May 20 Litho. Perf. 14½

398	A79	6s multicolored	.15	.15
399	A79	25s multicolored	.50	.50
400	A79	60s multicolored	1.25	1.25
401	A79	75s multicolored	1.50	1.50
		Nos. 398-401 (4)	3.40	3.40

Souvenir Sheet

402	Sheet of 5, #398-401, 402a	3.75	3.75
a.	A79a 10s multicolored	.20	.20

Manned Flight Bicentenary A80

1983, July 11 Litho. Perf. 14½

403	A80	7s Montgolfier, 1783	.15	.15
404	A80	30s Wright brothers	.40	.40
405	A80	60s 1st airmail plane	1.20	1.20
406	A80	1m Concorde	2.00	2.00
		Nos. 403-406 (4)	3.75	3.75

Souvenir Sheet

407	Sheet of 5	4.00	4.00
a.	A80 6s Dornier 228	.15	.15

#407 contains #403-406, 407a (60x60mm).

Sesquicentennial of French Missionaries' Arrival — A81

1983, Sept. 5 Litho. Perf. 13½x14

408	A81	6s Rev. Eugene Casalis, flags	.15	.15
409	A81	25s Morija, 1833	.50	.50
410	A81	40s Baptism of Libe	.80	.80
411	A81	75s Map of Basutoland, 1834	1.50	1.50
		Nos. 408-411 (4)	2.95	2.95

Christmas — A82

Scenes from Disney's Old Christmas, from Washington Irving's Sketch Book.

1983, Dec. Litho. Perf. 14

412	A82	1s shown	.15	.15
413	A82	2s Christmas eve, diff.	.15	.15
414	A82	3s Christmas day	.15	.15
415	A82	4s Christmas day, diff.	.15	.15
416	A82	5s Christmas dinner	.15	.15
417	A82	6s Christmas dinner, diff.	.15	.15
418	A82	75s Christmas games	1.50	1.50
419	A82	1m Christmas dancers	2.00	2.00
		Nos. 412-419 (8)	4.40	4.40

Souvenir Sheet

420	A82	1.75m Christmas eve	3.50	3.50

African Monarch A83

Butterflies.

1984, Jan. 20 Litho.

421	A83	1s shown	.15	.15
422	A83	2s Mountain Beauty	.15	.15
423	A83	3s Orange Tip	.15	.15
424	A83	4s Blue Pansy	.15	.15
425	A83	5s Yellow Pansy	.15	.15
426	A83	6s African Migrant	.15	.15
427	A83	7s African Leopard	.15	.15
428	A83	10s Suffused Acraea	.20	.20
429	A83	15s Painted Lady	.30	.30
430	A83	20s Lemon Traveller	.40	.40
431	A83	30s Foxy Charaxes	.60	.60
432	A83	50s Broad-Bordered Grass Yellow	1.00	1.00
433	A83	60s Meadow White	1.25	1.25
434	A83	75s Queen Purple Tip	1.50	1.50
435	A83	1m Diadem	2.00	2.00
436	A83	5m Christmas Butterfly	10.00	10.00
		Nos. 421-436 (16)	18.30	18.30

For surcharges see Nos. 559-560, 561A, 564-566, 600, 600A, 600D, 617A-617B.

Easter A84

Designs: Nos. 437a-437j, The Ten Commandments. 1.50m, Moses holding tablets.

1984, Mar. 30 Litho. Perf. 14

437	Sheet of 10 + 2 labels	3.50	3.50
a.-j.	A84 20s any single	.35	.35

Souvenir Sheet

438	A84	1.50m multicolored	2.50	2.50

No. 438 contains one stamp 45x29mm.

1984 Summer Olympics — A85

1984, May 5 Litho. Perf. 13½

439	A85	10s Torch bearer	.15	.15
440	A85	30s Equestrian	.45	.45
441	A85	50s Swimming	.75	.75
442	A85	75s Basketball	1.25	1.25
443	A85	1m Running	1.50	1.50
		Nos. 439-443 (5)	4.10	4.10

Souvenir Sheet

444	A85	1.50m Flags, flame, stadium	2.50	2.50

Prehistoric Footprints — A86

1984, July 2 Litho. Perf. 13½

445	A86	10s Sauropodomorph	.18	.18
446	A86	30s Lesothosaurus	.50	.50
447	A86	50s Carnivorous dinosaur	.90	.90
		Nos. 445-447 (3)	1.58	1.58

Mail Coach Bicentenary and Ausipex '84 — A87

6s, Wells Fargo, 1852. 7s, Basotho mail cart, 1900. 10s, Bath mail coach, 1784. 30s, Cobb coach, 1853. 50s, Exhibition buildings. 1.75m, Penny Black, Basutoland #O4, Western Australia #3.

1984, Sept. 5 Litho. Perf. 14

448	A87	6s multicolored	.15	.15
449	A87	7s multicolored	.15	.15
450	A87	10s multicolored	.18	.18
451	A87	30s multicolored	.55	.55

Size: 82x26mm

451A	A87	50s multicolored	.90	.90
		Nos. 448-451A (5)	1.93	1.93

Souvenir Sheet

452	A87	1.75m multicolored	3.00	3.00

No. 452 contains one stamp 82x26mm.

Trains A88

1984, Nov. 5 Litho. Perf. 13½

453	A88	6s Orient Express, 1900	.15	.15
454	A88	15s 05.001, Class 5, 1935	.20	.20
455	A88	30s Cardean, Caledonian, 1906	.40	.40
456	A88	60s Santa Fe, Super Chief, 1940	.75	.75
457	A88	1m Flying Scotsman, 1934	1.40	1.40
		Nos. 453-457 (5)	2.90	2.90

Souvenir Sheet

Perf. 14x13½

458	A88	2m The Blue Train, 1972	3.00	3.00

Indigenous Young Animals A89

1984, Dec. 20 Perf. 14½

459	A89	15s Cape Eland calf	.22	.22
460	A89	20s Chacma baboons	.26	.26
461	A89	30s Oribo calf	.38	.38
462	A89	75s Red rock hares	.95	.95

Size: 47x28mm

Perf. 13½

463	A89	1m Black-backed jackals	1.40	1.40
		Nos. 459-463 (5)	3.21	3.21

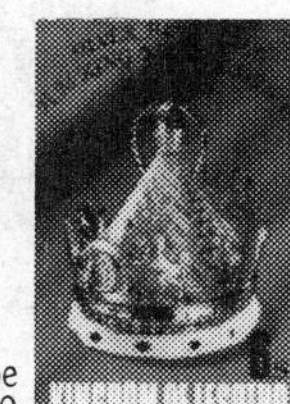
King Moshoeshoe II — A90

1985, Jan. 30 Litho. Perf. 15

464	A90	6s Royal crown, 1974	.15	.15
465	A90	30s Moshoeshoe II, 1966	.45	.45
466	A90	75s In Basotho dress	1.10	1.10
467	A90	1m In military uniform	1.50	1.50
		Nos. 464-467 (4)	3.20	3.20

25th anniversary of reign.

Miniature Sheet

Easter — A91

Stations of the Cross: a, Condemned to death. b, Bearing cross. c, Falls the first time. d, Meets his mother. e, Cyrenean helps carry cross. f, Veronica wipes His face. g, Second fall. h, Consoles women of Jerusalem. i, Third fall. j, Stripped. k, Nailed to cross. l, Dies on cross. m, Taken down from cross. n, Laid in sepulchre. No. 469, The Crucifixion, detail, by Mathias Grunewald (c. 1460-1528).

1985, Mar. 8 Perf. 11

468	Sheet of 14 + label	4.25	
a.-n.	A91 20s any single	.30	.30

Souvenir Sheet

Perf. 14

469	A91	2m multicolored	3.00	3.00

Queen Mother, 85th Birthday A92

Photographs: 10s, Queen Mother, Princess Elizabeth, 1931. 30s, 75th birthday portrait. 60s With Queen Elizabeth II and Princess Margaret, 80th birthday. No. 473, With Queen Elizabeth II, Princess Diana, Princes Henry and Charles, christening of Prince Henry. No. 474, like No. 473, with Prince William.

1985, May 30 Perf. 13½x14

470	A92	10s multicolored	.16	.16
471	A92	30s multicolored	.50	.50
472	A92	60s multicolored	1.25	1.25
473	A92	2m multicolored	3.00	3.00
		Nos. 470-473 (4)	4.91	4.91

Souvenir Sheet

474	A92	2m multicolored	3.00	3.00

No. 474 contains one stamp 38x51mm.

Automobile Centenary — A93

Luxury cars.

1985, June 10 Perf. 14

475	A93	6s BMW 732i	.15	.15
476	A93	10s Ford LTD Crown Victoria	.18	.18
477	A93	30s Mercedes-Benz 500SE	.55	.55
478	A93	90s Cadillac Eldorado Biarritz	1.50	1.50
479	A93	2m Rolls Royce Silver Spirit	3.50	3.50
		Nos. 475-479 (5)	5.88	5.88

Souvenir Sheet

480	A93	2m 1907 Rolls Royce Silver Ghost Tourer, vert.	3.75	3.75

No. 480 contains one stamp 38x51mm.

Audubon Birth Bicentenary A94

Illustrations of North American bird species by artist and naturalist John J. Audubon.

1985, Aug. 5 *Perf. 14½*
481 A94 5s Cliff swallow, vert. .15 .15
482 A94 6s Great crested grebe .15 .15
483 A94 10s Vesper sparrow .15 .15
484 A94 30s Greenshank .55 .55
485 A94 60s Stilt sandpiper 1.10 1.10
486 A94 2m Glossy ibis 3.75 3.75
Nos. 481-486 (6) 5.85 5.85

Nos. 481-486 printed in sheets of 5 with labels picturing various birds.

Intl. Youth Year, Girl Guides 75th Anniv. — A95

1985, Sept. 26 *Perf. 15*
487 A95 10s Mountain climbing .15 .15
488 A95 30s Medical research .45 .45
489 A95 75s Guides on parade 1.10 1.10
490 A95 2m Guide saluting 3.00 3.00
Nos. 487-490 (4) 4.70 4.70

Souvenir Sheet

491 A95 2m Lady Baden-Powell, World Chief Guide 3.00 3.00

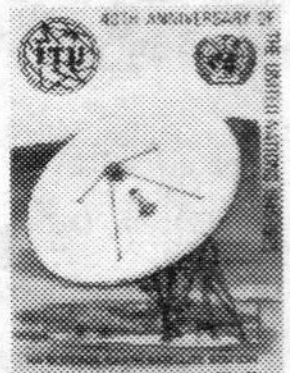

UN, 40th Anniv. A96

Wildflowers A97

Designs: 10s, UN No. 1, flag, horiz. 30s, Dish satellite, Ha Sofonia Earth Satellite Station, ITU emblem. 50s, Aircraft, Maseru Airport, ICAO emblem, horiz. 2m, Maimonides (1135-1204), medieval Jewish scholar, WHO emblem.

1985, Oct. 15 **Litho.** *Perf. 15*
492 A96 10s multicolored .15 .15
493 A96 30s multicolored .42 .42
494 A96 50s multicolored .80 .80
495 A96 2m multicolored 3.00 3.00
Nos. 492-495 (4) 4.37 4.37

1985, Nov. 11 *Perf. 11*
496 A97 6s Cosmos .15 .15
497 A97 10s Small agapanthus .20 .20
498 A97 30s Pink witchweed .75 .75
499 A97 60s Small iris 2.00 2.00
500 A97 90s Wild geranium 2.50 2.50
501 A97 1m Large spotted orchid 3.00 3.00
Nos. 496-501 (6) 8.60 8.60

Mark Twain, Author, Jacob and Wilhelm Grimm, Fabulists A98

Disney characters acting out Mark Twain quotes or portraying characters from The Wishing Table, by the Grimm Brothers.

1985, Dec. 2 *Perf. 11*
502 A98 6s multicolored .15 .15
503 A98 10s multicolored .15 .15
504 A98 50s multicolored .80 .80
505 A98 60s multicolored 1.00 1.00
506 A98 75s multicolored 1.25 1.25
507 A98 90s multicolored 1.40 1.40
508 A98 1m multicolored 1.65 1.65
509 A98 1.50m multicolored 2.75 2.75
Nos. 502-509 (8) 9.15 9.15

Souvenir Sheets
Perf. 14

510 A98 1.25m multicolored 2.00 2.00
511 A98 1.50m multicolored 2.75 2.75

Christmas. #505, 507 printed in sheets of 8.

World Wildlife Fund — A99
Flora and Fauna — A100

Lammergeier vulture.

1986, Jan. 20 *Perf. 15*
512 A99 7s Male .15 .15
513 A99 15s Male, female .22 .22
514 A99 50s Male in flight .75 .75
515 A99 1m Adult, young 1.50 1.50
Nos. 512-515 (4) 2.62 2.62

1986, Jan. 20
516 A100 9s Prickly pear .15 .15
517 A100 12s Stapelia .18 .18
518 A100 35s Pig's ears .52 .52
519 A100 2m Columnar cereus 3.25 3.25
Nos. 516-519 (4) 4.10 4.10

Souvenir Sheet

520 A100 2m Black eagle 3.25 3.25

1986 World Cup Soccer Championships, Mexico — A101

Various soccer plays.

1986, Mar. 17 *Perf. 14*
521 A101 35s multicolored .55 .55
522 A101 50s multicolored .75 .75
523 A101 1m multicolored 1.50 1.50
524 A101 2m multicolored 3.00 3.00
Nos. 521-524 (4) 5.80 5.80

Souvenir Sheet

525 A101 3m multicolored 5.00 5.00

A102

Halley's Comet A103

Designs: 9s, Hale Telescope, Mt. Palomar, Galileo. 15s, Venus 2 probe, 1985 sighting. 70s, 684 sighting illustration, Nuremberg Chronicles. 3m, 1066 sighting, Norman conquest of England. 4m, Comet over Lesotho.

1986, Apr. 5
526 A102 9s multicolored .15 .15
527 A102 15s multicolored .15 .15
528 A102 70s multicolored .70 .70
529 A102 3m multicolored 3.00 3.00
Nos. 526-529 (4) 4.00 4.00

Souvenir Sheet

530 A103 4m multicolored 4.00 4.00

Queen Elizabeth II, 60th Birthday
Common Design Type

Designs: 90s, In pantomime during youth. 1m, At Windsor Horse Show, 1971. 2m, At Royal Festival Hall, 1971. 4m, Age 8.

1986, Apr. 21
531 CD339 90s lt yel bis & black .90 .90
532 CD339 1m pale grn & multi 1.00 1.00
533 CD339 2m dull vio & multi 2.00 2.00
Nos. 531-533 (3) 3.90 3.90

Souvenir Sheet

534 CD339 4m tan & black 4.00 4.00

For overprints see Nos. 636-639.

Statue of Liberty, Cent. A104

Statue and famous emigrants: 15s, Bela Bartok (1881-1945), composer. 35s, Felix Adler (1857-1933), philosopher. 1m, Victor Herbert (1859-1924), composer. No. 538, David Niven (1910-1983), actor. No. 539, Statue, vert.

1986, May 1
535 A104 15s multicolored .15 .15
536 A104 35s multicolored .35 .35
537 A104 1m multicolored 1.00 1.00
538 A104 3m multicolored 3.00 3.00
Nos. 535-538 (4) 4.50 4.50

Souvenir Sheet

539 A104 3m multicolored 3.00 3.00

AMERIPEX '86 — A105

Walt Disney characters.

1986, May 22 *Perf. 11*
540 A105 15s Goofy, Mickey .15 .15
541 A105 35s Mickey, Pluto .40 .40
542 A105 1m Goofy 1.10 1.10
543 A105 2m Donald, Pete 2.25 2.25
Nos. 540-543 (4) 3.90 3.90

Souvenir Sheet
Perf. 14

544 A105 4m Goofy, Chip'n'Dale 4.50 4.50

Royal Wedding Issue, 1986
Common Design Type

Designs: 50s, Prince Andrew and Sarah Ferguson. 1m, Andrew. 3m, Andrew at helicopter controls. 4m, Couple, diff.

1986, July 23 *Perf. 14*
545 CD340 50s multicolored .50 .50
546 CD340 1m multicolored 1.00 1.00
547 CD340 3m multicolored 3.00 3.00
Nos. 545-547 (3) 4.50 4.50

Souvenir Sheet

548 CD340 4m multicolored 4.00 4.00

Natl. Independence, 20th Anniv. — A106

1986, Oct. 20 **Litho.** *Perf. 15*
549 A106 9s Basotho pony, rider .15 .15
550 A106 15s Mohair spinning .15 .15
551 A106 35s River crossing .35 .35
552 A106 3m Thaba Tseka P.O. 3.00 3.00
Nos. 549-552 (4) 3.65 3.65

Souvenir Sheet

553 A106 4m Moshoeshoe I 4.00 4.00

Christmas A107

Walt Disney characters.

1986, Nov. 4 **Litho.** *Perf. 11*
554 A107 15s Chip'n'Dale .15 .15
555 A107 35s Mickey, Minnie .35 .35
556 A107 1m Pluto 1.00 1.00
557 A107 2m Aunt Matilda 2.00 2.00
Nos. 554-557 (4) 3.50 3.50

Souvenir Sheet
Perf. 14

558 A107 5m Huey and Dewey 5.00 5.00

Butterfly and Bird Type of 1981-84 Surcharged

1986 **Litho.** *Perf. 14, 14½*
558A A66 9s on 10s #327b
b. 9s on 10s #327
559 A83 9s on 30s No. 431 .15 .15
a. 9s on 30s #431 (surcharge smaller & sans serif)
560 A83 9s on 60s No. 433 .15 .15
561 A66 15s on 1s No. 321 .15 .15
b. 15s on 1s #321a
c. 15s on 1s #321b
561A A83 15s on 1s No. 421 2.00 2.00
562 A66 15s on 2s No. 322 .15 .15
563 A66 15s on 60s No. 330 .15 .15
a. 15s on 60s #330a
564 A83 15s on 2s No. 422 .15 .15
565 A83 15s on 3s No. 423 .15 .15
566 A83 35s on 75s No. 434 .35 .35
a. 35s on 75s #434, small "s"

Issued: Nos. 559-560, July 1. Nos. 561-563, Aug. 22. Nos. 561A, 564-566, June 25.
See Nos. 617A-617B.

Roof of Africa Rally — A108

1988 Summer Olympics, Seoul — A109

1987, Apr. 28 **Litho.** *Perf. 14*
567 A108 9s White car .15 .15
568 A108 15s Motorcycle #26 .15 .15
569 A108 35s Motorcycle #25 .35 .35
570 A108 4m Red car 4.00 4.00
Nos. 567-570 (4) 4.65 4.65

1987, May 29 *Perf. 14*
571 A109 9s Tennis .15 .15
572 A109 15s Judo .15 .15
573 A109 20s Running .20 .20
574 A109 35s Boxing .35 .35
575 A109 1m Diving 1.00 1.00
576 A109 3m Bowling 3.00 3.00
Nos. 571-576 (6) 4.85 4.85

Souvenir Sheet

577 A109 2m Tennis, diff. 2.00 2.00
577A A109 4m Soccer 4.00 4.00

See Nos. 606-611.
No. 577A shows green at lower left diagonal half of the flag.

Inventors and Innovators A110

Designs: 5s, Sir Isaac Newton, reflecting telescope. 9s, Alexander Graham Bell, telephone. 75s, Robert H. Goddard, liquid fuel rocket. 4m, Chuck Yeager (b. 1923), test pilot. No. 582, Mariner 10 spacecraft.

1987, June 30 *Perf. 15*

578 A110 5s multicolored .15 .15
579 A110 9s multicolored .15 .15
580 A110 75s multicolored .75 .75
581 A110 4m multicolored 4.00 4.00
Nos. 578-581 (4) 5.05 5.05

Souvenir Sheet

582 A110 4m multicolored 4.00 4.00

Fauna and Flora A111

1987, Aug. 14

583 A111 5s Gray rhebuck .15 .15
584 A111 9s Cape clawless otter .15 .15
585 A111 15s Cape gray mongoose .15 .15
586 A111 20s Free state daisy .20 .20
587 A111 35s River bells .35 .35
588 A111 1m Turkey flower 1.00 1.00
589 A111 2m Sweet briar 2.00 2.00
590 A111 3m Mountain reedbuck 3.00 3.00
Nos. 583-590 (8) 7.00 7.00

Souvenir Sheet

591 A111 2m Pig-lily 2.00 2.00
592 A111 4m Cape wildebeest 4.00 4.00

Nos. 586-589 and 591 vert.

16th World Scout Jamboree, Australia, 1987-88 — A112

1987, Sept. 10 **Litho.** *Perf. 14*

593 A112 9s Orienteering .15 .15
594 A112 15s Playing soccer .15 .15
595 A112 35s Kangaroos .35 .35
596 A112 75s Salute, flag .75 .75
597 A112 4m Windsurfing 4.00 4.00
Nos. 593-597 (5) 5.40 5.40

Souvenir Sheet

598 A112 4m Map, flag of Australia 4.00 4.00

Nos. 324, 425, 424, 328 and 427 Surcharged **15s**

1987 **Litho.** *Perf. 14½, 14*

598A A66 9s on 5s No. 324 .15 .15
599 A66 15s on 5s No. 324 .15 .15
600 A83 15s on 5s No. 425 .15 .15
600A A83 20s on 4s No. 424 .20 .20
600B A66 35s on 25s No. 328 .35 .35
e. 35s on 25s #328, small "s"
f. 35s on 25s #328a
g. 35s on 25s #328a, small "s"
600C A66 35s on 75s #331
h. 35s on 75s #331, small "s"
600D A83 40s on 7s No. 427 .40 .40

Issue dates: Nos. 599-600, Nov. 16. No. 600B, Dec. 15. No. 598A, 600A and 600D, Dec. 30.

A113

A114

Religious paintings (details) by Raphael: 9s, Madonna and Child. 15s, Marriage of the Virgin. 35s, Coronation of the Virgin. 90s, Madonna of the Chair. 3m, Madonna and Child Enthroned with Five Saints.

1987, Dec. 21 *Perf. 14*

601 A113 9s multicolored .15 .15
602 A113 15s multicolored .18 .18
603 A113 35s multicolored .40 .40
604 A113 90s multicolored 1.05 1.05
Nos. 601-604 (4) 1.78 1.78

Souvenir Sheet

605 A114 3m multicolored 3.25 3.25

Christmas.

Summer Olympics Type of 1987

1987, Nov. 30 **Litho.** *Perf. 14*

606 A109 5s like 9s .15 .15
607 A109 10s like 15s .15 .15
608 A109 25s like 20s .25 .25
609 A109 40s like 35s .40 .40
610 A109 50s like 1m .50 .50
611 A109 3.50m like 3m 3.50 3.50
Nos. 606-611 (6) 4.95 4.95

Souvenir Sheet

612 A109 4m Soccer 4.00 4.00

No. 612 shows green at lower right diagonal half of the flag.

Discovery of America, 500th Anniv. (in 1992) A115

Columbus's fleet and marine life: 9s, Spotted trunkfish. 15s, Green sea turtle. 35s, Common dolphin. 5m, White-tailed tropicbird. 4m, Ship.

1987, Dec. 14 **Litho.** *Perf. 14*

613 A115 9s multicolored .15 .15
614 A115 15s multicolored .15 .15
615 A115 35s multicolored .35 .35
616 A115 5m multicolored 5.00 5.00
Nos. 613-616 (4) 5.65 5.65

Souvenir Sheet

617 A115 4m multicolored 4.00 4.00

No. 559 Surcharged

1988, Feb. 2 **Litho.** *Perf. 14*

617A A83 3s on 9s on 30s
617B A83 7s on 9s on 30s

Birds A116

1988, Apr. 5 **Litho.** *Perf. 15*

618 A116 2s Pied kingfisher .15 .15
619 A116 3s Three-banded plover .15 .15
620 A116 5s Spurwing goose .15 .15
621 A116 10s Clapper lark .15 .15
622 A116 12s Red-eyed bulbul .15 .15
623 A116 16s Cape weaver .16 .16
624 A116 20s Red-headed finch .20 .20
625 A116 30s Mountain chat .30 .30
626 A116 40s Stone chat .40 .40
627 A116 55s Pied barbet .55 .55
628 A116 60s Cape glossy starling .60 .60
629 A116 75s Cape sparrow .75 .75
630 A116 1m Cattle egret 1.00 1.00
631 A116 3m Giant kingfisher 3.00 3.00
632 A116 10m Crowned guinea fowl 10.00 10.00
Nos. 618-632 (15) 17.71 17.71

For surcharges see Nos. 755, 805-806.

1989, Sept. 18 *Perf. 14*

620a A116 5s multicolored .15 .15
622a A116 12s multicolored .15 .15
623a A116 16s multicolored .15 .15
624a A116 20s multicolored .16 .16
630a A116 1m multicolored .80 .80
631a A116 3m multicolored 2.40 2.40
632a A116 10m multicolored 8.00 8.00
Nos. 620a-632a (7) 11.81 11.81

Dated 1989.

1990 *Perf. 12½x12*

620b A116 5s multicolored .15 .15
622b A116 12s multicolored .15 .15
623b A116 16s multicolored .15 .15
624b A116 20s multicolored .16 .16
630b A116 1m multicolored .80 .80
631b A116 3m multicolored 2.40 2.40
632b A116 10m multicolored 8.00 8.00
Nos. 620b-632b (7) 11.81 11.81

Dated 1989.

1991 (?) *Perf. 11½x13*

620c A116 5s multicolored .15 .15
622c A116 12s multicolored .15 .15
623c A116 16s multicolored .15 .15
624c A116 20s multicolored .16 .16
630c A116 1m multicolored .80 .80
631c A116 3m multicolored 2.40 2.40
632c A116 10m multicolored 8.00 8.00
Nos. 620c-632c (7) 11.81 11.81

Dated 1989.

Nos. 531-534 Overprinted "40th WEDDING ANNIVERSARY / H.M. QUEEN ELIZABETH II / H.R.H. THE DUKE OF EDINBURGH" in Silver

1988, May 3 *Perf. 14*

636 CD339 90s lt yel bis & blk .90 .90
637 CD339 1m pale grn & multi 1.00 1.00
638 CD339 2m dull vio & multi 2.00 2.00
Nos. 636-638 (3) 3.90 3.90

Souvenir Sheet

639 CD339 4m tan & black 4.00 4.00

FINLANDIA '88, Helsinki, June 1-12 — A117

Disney animated characters and Helsinki sights.

1988, June 2 **Litho.** *Perf. 14x13½*

640 A117 1s Touring President's Palace .15 .15
641 A117 2s Sauna .15 .15
642 A117 3s Lake Country fishing .15 .15
643 A117 4s Finlandia Hall .15 .15
644 A117 5s Photographing Sibelius Monument .15 .15
645 A117 10s Pony trek, youth hostel .15 .15
646 A117 3m Olympic Stadium 2.25 2.25
647 A117 5m Santa Claus, Arctic Circle 3.50 3.50
Nos. 640-647 (8) 6.65 6.65

Souvenir Sheets

Perf. 14x13½, 13½x14

648 A117 4m Market Square 3.00 3.00
649 A117 4m Lapp encampment, vert. 3.00 3.00

Mickey Mouse, 60th anniv.

A118 A119

1988, Sept. 1 **Litho.** *Perf. 14*

650 A118 55s Pope giving communion .55 .55
651 A118 2m Leading procession 2.00 2.00
652 A118 3m Walking in garden 3.00 3.00
653 A118 4m Wearing scullcap 4.00 4.00
Nos. 650-653 (4) 9.55 9.55

Souvenir Sheet

654 A118 5m Pope, Archbishop Morapeli of Lesotho, horiz. 5.00 5.00

Visit of Pope John Paul II, Sept. 14-16.

1988, Oct. 13 **Litho.** *Perf. 14*

Small indigenous mammals.

655 A119 16s Rock hyrax .16 .16
656 A119 40s Honey badger .40 .40
657 A119 75s Genet .75 .75
658 A119 3m Yellow mongoose 3.00 3.00
Nos. 655-658 (4) 4.31 4.31

Souvenir Sheet

659 A119 4m Meerkat 4.00 4.00

Birth of Venus, 1480, by Botticelli A120

Paintings: 25s, View of Toledo, 1608, by El Greco. 40s, Maids of Honor, 1656, by Diego Velazquez. 50s, The Fifer, 1866, by Manet. 55s, The Starry Night, 1889, by Van Gogh. 75s, Prima Ballerina, 1876, by Degas. 2m, Bridge over Water Lilies, 1899, by Monet. 3m, Guernica, 1937, by Picasso. No. 668, The Presentation of the Virgin in the Temple, c. 1534, by Titian. No. 669, The Miracle of the Newborn Infant, 1511, by Titian.

1988, Oct. 17 **Litho.** *Perf. 13½x14*

660 A120 15s multicolored .15 .15
661 A120 25s multicolored .25 .25
662 A120 40s multicolored .40 .40
663 A120 50s multicolored .50 .50
664 A120 55s multicolored .55 .55
665 A120 75s multicolored .75 .75
666 A120 2m multicolored 2.00 2.00
667 A120 3m multicolored 3.00 3.00
Nos. 660-667 (8) 7.60 7.60

Souvenir Sheets

668 A120 4m multicolored 4.00 4.00
669 A120 4m multicolored 4.00 4.00

1988 Summer Olympics, Seoul — A121

Intl. Tennis Federation, 75th Anniv. — A122

1988, Nov. 11 **Litho.** *Perf. 14*

670 A121 12s Wrestling, horiz. .15 .15
671 A121 16s Equestrian .16 .16
672 A121 55s Shooting, horiz. .55 .55
673 A121 3.50m like 16s 3.50 3.50
Nos. 670-673 (4) 4.36 4.36

Souvenir Sheet

674 A121 4m Eternal flame 4.00 4.00

1988, Nov. 18

Tennis champions, views of cities or landmarks: 12s, Yannick Noah, Eiffel Tower, horiz. 20s, Rod Laver, Sydney Opera House and Harbor Bridge, horiz. 30s, Ivan Lendl, Prague, horiz. 65s, Jimmy Connors, Tokyo. 1m, Arthur Ashe, Barcelona. 1.55m, Althea Gibson, NYC. 2m, Chris Evert, Vienna. 2.40m, Boris Becker, London. 3m, Martina Navratilova, Golden Gate Bridge, horiz. 4m, Steffi Graf, Berlin, West Germany.

675 A122 12s multi .15 .15
676 A122 20s multi .20 .20
677 A122 30s multi .30 .30
678 A122 65s multi .65 .65
679 A122 1m multi 1.00 1.00
680 A122 1.55m multi 1.55 1.55
681 A122 2m multi 2.00 2.00

682 A122 2.40m multi 2.40 2.40
683 A122 3m multi 3.00 3.00
Nos. 675-683 (9) 11.25 11.25

Souvenir Sheet

684 A122 4m multi 4.00 4.00

No. 676 has "Sidney" instead of "Sydney." No. 679 has "Ash" instead of "Ashe".

Paintings by Titian — A123

Designs: 12s, The Averoldi Polyptych. 20s, Christ and the Adulteress (Christ). 35s, Christ and the Adulteress (adultress). 45s, Angel of the Annunciation. 65s, Saint Dominic. 1m, The Vendramin Family. 2m, Mary Magdalen. 3m, The Tribute Money. No. 693, Christ and the Woman Taken in Adultery. No. 694, The Mater Dolorosa.

1988, Dec. 1 *Perf. 14x13½*

685 A123 12s multicolored .15 .15
686 A123 20s multicolored .20 .20
687 A123 35s multicolored .35 .35
688 A123 45s multicolored .45 .45
689 A123 65s multicolored .65 .65
690 A123 1m multicolored 1.00 1.00
691 A123 2m multicolored 2.00 2.00
692 A123 3m multicolored 3.00 3.00
Nos. 685-692 (8) 7.80 7.80

Souvenir Sheets

693 A123 5m multicolored 5.00 5.00
694 A123 5m multicolored 5.00 5.00

Birth of Titian, 500th anniv. Nos. 685-693 inscribed "Christmas 1988."

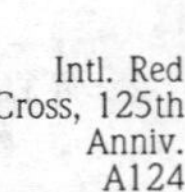

Intl. Red Cross, 125th Anniv. A124

Anniv. emblem, supply and ambulance planes: 12s, Pilatus PC-6 Turbo Porter. 20s, Cessna Caravan. 55s, De Havilland DHC-6 Otter. 3m, Douglas DC-3 in thunderstorm. 4m, Douglas DC-3, diff.

1989, Jan. 30 **Litho.** *Perf. 14*

695 A124 12s multicolored .15 .15
696 A124 20s multicolored .20 .20
697 A124 55s multicolored .55 .55
698 A124 3m multicolored 3.00 3.00
Nos. 695-698 (4) 3.90 3.90

Souvenir Sheet

699 A124 4m multi, vert. 4.00 4.00

Landscapes by Hiroshige — A125

Designs: 12s, Dawn Mist at Mishima. 16s, Night Snow at Kambara. 20s, Wayside Inn at Mariko Station. 35s, Shower at Shono. 55s, Snowfall on the Kisokaido Near Oi. 1m, Autumn Moon at Seba. 3.20m, Evening Moon at Ryogaku Bridge. 5m, Cherry Blossoms, Arashiyama. No. 708, Listening to the Singing Insects at Dokanyama. No. 709, Moonlight, Nagakubo.

1989, June 19 **Litho.** *Perf. 14x13½*

700 A125 12s multi .15 .15
701 A125 16s multi .15 .15
702 A125 20s multi .16 .16
703 A125 35s multi .28 .28
704 A125 55s multi .45 .45
705 A125 1m multi .80 .80
706 A125 3.20m multi 2.50 2.50
707 A125 5m multi 4.00 4.00
Nos. 700-707 (8) 8.49 8.49

Souvenir Sheets

708 A125 4m multi 3.60 3.60
709 A125 4m multi 3.60 3.60

Hirohito (1901-1989) and enthronement of Akihito as emperor of Japan.

PHILEXFRANCE '89, French Revolution Bicent. — A126

Disney characters wearing insurgent uniforms.

Perf. 13½x14, 14x13½

1989, July 10

710 A126 1s General .15 .15
711 A126 2s Infantry .15 .15
712 A126 3s Grenadier .15 .15
713 A126 4s Cavalry .15 .15
714 A126 5s Hussar .15 .15
715 A126 10s Marine .15 .15
716 A126 3m Natl. guard 2.40 2.40
717 A126 5m Admiral 4.00 4.00
Nos. 710-717 (8) 7.30 7.30

Souvenir Sheets

718 A126 4m Natl. guard, royal family, horiz. 3.60 3.60
719 A126 4m La Marseillaise 3.60 3.60

A127

A128

Maloti Mountains: a, Sotho thatched dwellings. b, Two trees, cliff edge. c, Waterfall. d, Tribesman.

1989, Sept. **Litho.** *Perf. 14*

720 Strip of 4 3.20 3.20
a.-d. A127 1m any single .80 .80

Souvenir Sheet

721 A127 4m Flora 4.00 4.00

1989, Sept. 8 **Litho.** *Perf. 14*

Mushrooms.

722 A128 12s *Paxillus involutus* .15 .15
723 A128 16s *Ganoderma applanatum* .15 .15
723A A128 55s *Suillus granulatus* .44 .44
724 A128 5m *Stereum hirsutum* 4.00 4.00
Nos. 722-724 (4) 4.74 4.74

Souvenir Sheet

725 A128 4m *Scleroderma flavidum* 3.20 3.20

Birds A129

1989, Oct. 23 **Litho.** *Perf. 14*

726 A129 12s Marsh sandpipers .15 .15
727 A129 65s Little stints .52 .52
728 A129 1m Ringed plovers .80 .80
729 A129 4m Curlew sandpipers 3.20 3.20
Nos. 726-729 (4) 4.67 4.67

Souvenir Sheet

730 A129 5m Ruff, vert. 4.00 4.00

1st Moon Landing, 20th Anniv. A130

Highlights of the Apollo 11 mission.

1989, Nov. 6 *Perf. 14*

731 A130 12s Liftoff .15 .15
732 A130 16s *Eagle* landing .15 .15
733 A130 40s Astronaut on ladder .32 .32
734 A130 55s Buzz Aldrin .45 .45
735 A130 1m Solar wind experiment .80 .80
736 A130 2m *Eagle* lifting off 1.60 1.60
737 A130 3m *Columbia* in orbit 2.40 2.40
738 A130 4m Splashdown 3.20 3.20
Nos. 731-738 (8) 9.07 9.07

Souvenir Sheet

739 A130 5m Astronaut, *Eagle* 4.00 4.00

Nos. 731, 733, 738-739 vert.

Postal Marking, England, 1680 A131

Cathedral Church of Sts. Peter and Paul, Washington, DC — A132

Designs (No. 740): b, Wax seal and feather, Germany, 1807. c, Crete #1. d, Perot postmaster's provisional, Bermuda, 1848. e, Pony Express handstamp, US, 1860. f, Finland #1. g, Fiji #1. h, Swedish newspaper handstamp, 1823. i, Bhor #1.

1989, Nov. 17 **Litho.** *Perf. 14*

740 Sheet of 9 3.80 3.80
a.-i. A131 75s any single .42 .42

Souvenir Sheet

741 A132 4m shown 3.00 3.00

World Stamp Expo '89.

Christmas — A133

Religious paintings by Velazquez: 12s, *The Immaculate Conception.* 20s, *St. Anthony Abbot and St. Paul the Hermit.* 35s, *St. Thomas the Apostle.* 55s, *Christ in the House of Martha and Mary.* 1m, *St. John Writing the Apocalypse on Patmos.* 3m, *The Virgin Presenting the Chasuble to St. Ildephonsus.* 4m, *The Adoration of the Magi.* 5m, *The Coronation of the Virgin.*

1989, Dec. 18

742 A133 12s multicolored .15 .15
743 A133 20s multicolored .16 .16
744 A133 35s multicolored .28 .28
745 A133 55s multicolored .45 .45
746 A133 1m multicolored .75 .75
747 A133 3m multicolored 2.25 2.25
748 A133 4m multicolored 3.00 3.00
Nos. 742-748 (7) 7.04 7.04

Souvenir Sheet

749 A133 5m multicolored 3.75 3.75

1990 World Cup Soccer Championships, Italy — A134

Various athletes, emblem and name of previous championship host nations.

1989, Dec. 27

750 A134 12s England, 1966 .15 .15
751 A134 16s Mexico, 1970 .15 .15
752 A134 55s West Germany, 1974 .45 .45
753 A134 5m Spain, 1982 3.75 3.75
Nos. 750-753 (4) 4.50 4.50

Souvenir Sheet

754 A134 4m Diego Maradona, Argentina 3.00 3.00

No. 622a Surcharged

1990 **Litho.** *Perf. 14*

755 A116 16s on 12s multi .15 .15

Orchids A135

1990, Mar. 12 **Litho.** *Perf. 14*

756 A135 12s *Satyrium princeps* .15 .15
757 A135 16s *Huttonaea pulchra* .15 .15
758 A135 55s *Herschelia graminifolia* .45 .45
759 A135 1m *Ansellia gigantea* .80 .80
760 A135 1.55m *Polystachya pubescens* 1.25 1.25
761 A135 2.40m *Penthea filicornis* 1.90 1.90
762 A135 3m *Disperis capensis* 2.40 2.40
763 A135 4m *Disa uniflora* 3.20 3.20
Nos. 756-763 (8) 10.30 10.30

Souvenir Sheet

764 A135 5m *Stenoglottis longifolia* 4.00 4.00

Expo '90.

Butterflies — A136

1990, Feb. 26 **Litho.** *Perf. 14*

765 A136 12s Pseudo ergolid .15 .15
766 A136 16s Painted lady .15 .15
767 A136 55s Ringed pansy .50 .50
768 A136 65s False acraea .58 .58
769 A136 1m Eyed pansy .90 .90
770 A136 2m Golden pansy 1.80 1.80
771 A136 3m African monarch 2.70 2.70
772 A136 4m African giant swallowtail 3.60 3.60
Nos. 765-772 (8) 10.38 10.38

Souvenir Sheet

773 A136 5m Citrus swallowtail 4.50 4.50

Queen Mother, 90th Birthday
A137 A138

1990, July 5 Litho. *Perf. 14*

774 A137 1.50m shown 1.20 1.20
775 A138 1.50m shown 1.20 1.20
776 A137 1.50m Young woman, diff. 1.20 1.20
Nos. 774-776 (3) 3.60 3.60

Souvenir Sheet

777 A138 5m Like No. 775 4.00 4.00

A139 A140

Designs: 12s, King Moshoeshoe II, Prince Mohato wearing blankets. 16s, Prince Mohato in Seana-Marena blanket. 1m, Pope John Paul II in Seana-Marena blanket. 3m, Basotho men on horses. 5m, Pope with blanket and hat.

1990, Aug. 17 Litho. *Perf. 14*

778 A139 12s multicolored .15 .15
779 A139 16s multicolored .15 .15
780 A139 1m multicolored .75 .75
781 A139 3m multicolored 2.30 2.30
Nos. 778-781 (4) 3.35 3.35

Souvenir Sheet

782 A139 5m multi, horiz. 4.00 4.00

1990, Aug. 24

Highland Water Project: 16s, Moving gravel. 20s, Fuel truck. 55s, Piers for bridge construction. 2m, Road construction. 5m, Drilling blasting holes.

783 A140 16s multicolored .15 .15
784 A140 20s multicolored .18 .18
785 A140 55s multicolored .48 .48
786 A140 2m multicolored 1.50 1.50
Nos. 783-786 (4) 2.31 2.31

Souvenir Sheet

787 A140 5m multicolored 4.00 4.00

A141

A142

1990, Sept. 26 Litho. *Perf. 14*

788 A141 12s Breastfeeding .15 .15
789 A141 55s Oral rehydration .48 .48
790 A141 1m Baby being weighed .75 .75
Nos. 788-790 (3) 1.38 1.38

UNICEF Save the Children campaign.

1990, Oct. 5

791 A142 16s Triple jump .15 .15
792 A142 55s 200-meter race .48 .48
793 A142 1m 5000-meter race .75 .75
794 A142 4m Equestrian show jumping 3.00 3.00
Nos. 791-794 (4) 4.38 4.38

Souvenir Sheet

795 A142 5m Lighting Olympic flame 3.75 3.75

1992 Summer Olympics, Barcelona.

Christmas A143

Different details from paintings by Rubens: 12s, 1m, 3m, Virgin and Child. 16s, 80s, 2m, 4m, Adoration of the Magi. 55s, Head of One of the Three Kings, diff. 5m, Assumption of the Virgin.

1990, Dec. 5 Litho. *Perf. 13½x14*

796 A143 12s multicolored .15 .15
797 A143 16s multicolored .15 .15
798 A143 55s multicolored .40 .40
799 A143 80s multicolored .60 .60
800 A143 1m multicolored .75 .75
801 A143 2m multicolored 1.50 1.50
802 A143 3m multicolored 2.25 2.25
803 A143 4m multicolored 3.00 3.00
Nos. 796-803 (8) 8.80 8.80

Souvenir Sheet

804 A143 5m multicolored 3.75 3.75

Nos. 625-626 Surcharged **16 s**

1991, Jan. 18 Litho. *Perf. 15*

805 A116 16s on 30s #625 .15 .15
806 A116 16s on 40s #626 .15 .15
Set value .24 .24

Phila Nippon '91 — A144

Walt Disney characters visit Japan: 20s, Mickey at Nagasaki Peace Park. 30s, Mickey at Kamakura Beach. 40s, Mickey, Donald entertain at Bunraku Puppet Theater. 50s, Mickey, Donald eat soba at noodle shop. 75s, Minnie, Mickey at tea house. 1m, Mickey, Bullet Train. 3m, Mickey, deer at Todaiji Temple. 4m, Mickey, Minnie before Imperial Palace. No. 815, Mickey skiing at Happo-One, Nagano. No. 816, Mickey, Minnie at Suizenji Park.

1991, June 10 Litho. *Perf. 14x13½*

807 A144 20s multicolored .16 .16
808 A144 30s multicolored .24 .24
809 A144 40s multicolored .32 .32
810 A144 50s multicolored .40 .40
811 A144 75s multicolored .60 .60
812 A144 1m multicolored .80 .80
813 A144 3m multicolored 2.40 2.40
814 A144 4m multicolored 3.20 3.20
Nos. 807-814 (8) 8.12 8.12

Souvenir Sheets

815 A144 6m multicolored 3.50 3.50
816 A144 6m multicolored 3.50 3.50

Entertainers in Films About Africa — A145

Designs: 12s, Stewart Granger, King Solomon's Mines. 16s, Johnny Weissmuller, Tarzan, the Ape Man. 30s, Clark Gable, Grace Kelly, Mogambo. 55s, Sigourney Weaver, Gorillas in the Mist. 70s, Humphrey Bogart, Katharine Hepburn, The African Queen. 1m, John Wayne, Hatari. 2m, Meryl Streep, Out of Africa. 4m, Eddie Murphy, Arsenio Hall, Coming to America. 5m, Elsa, Born Free.

1991, June 20 Litho. *Perf. 14*

817 A145 12s multicolored .15 .15
818 A145 16s multicolored .15 .15
819 A145 30s multicolored .24 .24
820 A145 55s multicolored .45 .45
821 A145 70s multicolored .55 .55
822 A145 1m multicolored .80 .80
823 A145 2m multicolored 1.60 1.60
824 A145 4m multicolored 3.20 3.20
Nos. 817-824 (8) 7.14 7.14

Souvenir Sheet

825 A145 5m multicolored 4.00 4.00

Butterflies A146

1991, Aug. 1 Litho. *Perf. 13½*

827 A146 2s Satyrus aello .15 .15
828 A146 3s Erebia medusa .15 .15
829 A146 5s Melanargia galathea .15 .15
830 A146 10s Erebia aethiops .15 .15
831 A146 20s Coenonympha pamphilus .16 .16
832 A146 25s Pyrameis atalanta .20 .20
833 A146 30s Charaxes jasius .24 .24
834 A146 40s Colias palaeno .32 .32
835 A146 50s Colias cliopatra .40 .40
836 A146 60s Colias philodice .48 .48
837 A146 70s Rhumni gonepterix .56 .56
838 A146 1m Colias caesonia .80 .80
839 A146 2m Pyrameis cardui 1.60 1.60
840 A146 3m Danaus chrysippus 2.40 2.40
840A A146 10m Apatura iris 8.00 8.00
Nos. 827-840A (15) 15.76 15.76

Exist dated 1992.
For surcharge see No. 1062.

SADCC, 10th Anniv. A147

Tourism: 12s, Wattled cranes. 16s, Butterfly, flowers in national parks. 25s, Tourist bus and Mukurub, the Finger of God. 3m, People in traditional dress.

1991, Oct. 10 Litho. *Perf. 14x13½*

841 A147 12s multicolored .15 .15
842 A147 16s multicolored .15 .15
843 A147 25s multicolored .20 .20
Nos. 841-843 (3) .50 .50

Souvenir Sheet

844 A147 3m multicolored 2.40 2.40

Say No to Drugs A148

1991, Oct. 10

845 A148 16s multicolored .15 .15

Charles de Gaulle, Birth Cent. — A149

DeGaulle: 40s, Wearing brigadier general's kepi. 50s, Facing left. 60s, Facing right. 4m, In later years.

1991, Dec. 6 Litho. *Perf. 14*

846 A149 20s black & brown .16 .16
847 A149 40s black & violet .32 .32
848 A149 50s black & olilve .40 .40
849 A149 60s black & dk blue .48 .48
850 A149 4m black & brn org 3.15 3.15
Nos. 846-850 (5) 4.51 4.51

Christmas A150

Engravings by Albrecht Durer: 20s, St. Anne with Mary and the Child Jesus. 30s, Mary on the Grass Bench. 50s, Mary with the Crown of Stars. 60s, Mary with Child beside a Tree. 70s, Mary with Child beside the Wall. 1m, Mary in a Halo on the Crescent Moon. 2m, Mary Breastfeeding Her Child. 4m, Mary with the Infant in Swaddling Clothes. No. 859, Holy Family with the Dragonfly. No. 860, The Birth of Christ.

1991, Dec. 13 Litho. *Perf. 12*

851 A150 20s rose & black .16 .16
852 A150 30s blue & black .24 .24
853 A150 50s green & black .40 .40
854 A150 60s red & black .48 .48
855 A150 70s yellow & black .55 .55
856 A150 1m yel org & black .80 .80
857 A150 2m violet & black 1.60 1.60
858 A150 4m dk blue & black 3.20 3.20
Nos. 851-858 (8) 7.43 7.43

Souvenir Sheets

Perf. 14½

859 A150 5m blue & black 4.00 4.00
860 A150 5m pink & black 4.00 4.00

Games A151

Walt Disney characters playing games: 20s, Mickey, Pluto playing pin the tail on the donkey. 30s, Mickey enjoying board game, Mancala. 40s, Mickey hoop rolling. 50s, Minnie with hula hoops. 70s, Mickey throwing Frisbee to Pluto. 1m, Donald trying to play Diabolo. 2m, Huey, Dewey and Louie playing marbles. 3m, Donald frustrated by Rubik's cube. No. 869, Donald and Mickey's nephews in tug-of-war. No. 870, Mickey, Donald stick fighting.

1991, Dec. 16 *Perf. 13½x14*

861 A151 20s multicolored .16 .16
862 A151 30s multicolored .24 .24
863 A151 40s multicolored .32 .32
864 A151 50s multicolored .40 .40
865 A151 70s multicolored .55 .55
866 A151 1m multicolored .80 .80
867 A151 2m multicolored 1.60 1.60
868 A151 3m multicolored 2.40 2.40
Nos. 861-868 (8) 6.47 6.47

Souvenir Sheets

869 A151 5m multicolored 4.00 4.00
870 A151 5m multicolored 4.00 4.00

Royal Family Birthday, Anniversary
Common Design Type

1991, Dec. 9 Litho. *Perf. 14*

871 CD347 50s multicolored .40 .40
872 CD347 70s multicolored .55 .55
873 CD347 1m multicolored .80 .80
874 CD347 3m multicolored 2.40 2.40
Nos. 871-874 (4) 4.15 4.15

Souvenir Sheet

875 CD347 4m Charles, Diana, sons 3.20 3.20

Charles and Diana, 10th wedding anniversary. Numbers have been reserved for additional values in this set.

Market value for a particular scarce stamp may remain relatively low if few collectors want it.

Queen Elizabeth II's Accession to the Throne, 40th Anniv.

Common Design Type

1992, Feb. 6 Litho. *Perf. 14*

881 CD348 20s multicolored .16 .16
882 CD348 30s multicolored .24 .24
883 CD348 1m multicolored .80 .80
884 CD348 4m multicolored 3.20 3.20
Nos. 881-884 (4) 4.40 4.40

Souvenir Sheet

885 CD348 5m multicolored 4.00 4.00

Birds — A152

Designs: a, Lanner falcon. b, Bataleur. c, Red-headed finch. d, Lesser-striped swallow. e, Alpine swift. f, Diederik cuckoo. g, Malachite sunbird. h, Crimson-breasted shrike. i, Pin-tailed whydah. j, Lilac-breasted roller. k, Black korhaan. l, Black-collared barbet. m, Secretary bird. n, Red-billed quelea. o, Red bishop. p, Ring-necked dove. q, Yellow canary. r, Orange-throated longclaw. s, Blue waxbill. t, Golden bishop.

1992, Feb. 10 *Perf. 14½*

886 A152 30s Sheet of 20, #a.-t. 4.80 4.80

World Columbian Stamp Expo '92, Chicago A153

Walt Disney characters depicting native Americans: 30s, Donald Duck making arrowheads. 40s, Goofy playing lacrosse. 1m, Mickey, Donald planting corn. 3m, Minnie Mouse mastering art of beading. No. 891, Mickey as "Blackhawk" hunting for moose.

1992, Apr. Litho. *Perf. 13½x14*

887 A153 30s multicolored .25 .25
888 A153 40s multicolored .32 .32
889 A153 1m multicolored .78 .78
890 A153 3m multicolored 2.35 2.35
Nos. 887-890 (4) 3.70 3.70

Souvenir Sheet

891 A153 5m multicolored 3.90 3.90

Granada '92 — A154

Walt Disney characters in Spanish costumes: 20s, Minnie Mouse as Lady of Rank, 1540-1660. 50s, Mickey as conqueror of Lepanto, 1571. 70s, Donald Duck from Galicia, 1880. 2m, Daisy Duck from Aragon, 1880. No. 901, Goofy as bullfighter.

1992, Apr. 13 Litho. *Perf. 13½x14*

897 A154 20s multicolored .15 .15
898 A154 50s multicolored .40 .40
899 A154 70s multicolored .55 .55
900 A154 2m multicolored 1.60 1.60
Nos. 897-900 (4) 2.70 2.70

Souvenir Sheet

901 A154 5m multicolored 3.90 3.90

Dinosaurs A155

1992, June 9 *Perf. 14*

907 A155 20s Stegosaurus .15 .15
908 A155 30s Ceratosaurus .25 .25
909 A155 40s Procompsognathus .32 .32
910 A155 50s Lesothosaurus .40 .40
911 A155 70s Plateosaurus .55 .55
912 A155 1m Gasosaurus .80 .80
913 A155 2m Massospondylus 1.60 1.60
914 A155 3m Archaeopteryx 2.40 2.40
Nos. 907-914 (8) 6.47 6.47

Souvenir Sheet

915 A155 5m Archaeopteryx, diff. 4.00 4.00
916 A155 5m Lesothosaurus, diff. 4.00 4.00

No. 915 printed in continuous design.

1992 Olympics, Barcelona and Albertville — A156

Designs: 20s, Discus. 30s, Long jump. 40s, Women's 4x100-meter relay. 70s, Women's 100-meter dash. 1m, Parallel bars. 2m, Two-man luge, horiz. 3m, Women's cross-country skiing, horiz. 4m, Biathlon. No. 925, Ice hockey, horiz. No. 926, Women's figure skating.

1992, Aug. 5 Litho. *Perf. 14*

917 A156 20s multicolored .15 .15
918 A156 30s multicolored .25 .25
919 A156 40s multicolored .32 .32
920 A156 70s multicolored .55 .55
921 A156 1m multicolored .78 .78
922 A156 2m multicolored 1.55 1.55
923 A156 3m multicolored 2.40 2.40
924 A156 4m multicolored 3.20 3.20
Nos. 917-924 (8) 9.20 9.20

Souvenir Sheet

925 A156 5m multicolored 4.00 4.00
926 A156 5m multicolored 4.00 4.00

Christmas A158

Details or entire paintings: 20s, Virgin and Child, by Sassetta. 30s, Coronation of the Virgin, by Master of Bonastre. 40s, Virgin and Child, by Master of Saints Cosmas and Damian. 70s, The Virgin of Great Panagia, by Russian School, 12th cent. 1m, Madonna and Child, by Vincenzo Foppa. 2m, Madonna and Child, by School of Lippo Memmi. 3m, Virgin and Child, by Barnaba da Modena. 4m, Virgin and Child, by Simone Dei Crocifissi. No. 935, Virgin & Child Enthroned & Surrounded by Angels, by Cimabue. No. 936, Virgin and Child with Saints (entire triptych), by Dei Crocifissi.

1992, Nov. 2 Litho. *Perf. 13½x14*

927 A158 20s multicolored .15 .15
928 A158 30s multicolored .24 .24
929 A158 40s multicolored .32 .32
930 A158 70s multicolored .55 .55
931 A158 1m multicolored .80 .80
932 A158 2m multicolored 1.60 1.60
933 A158 3m multicolored 2.40 2.40
934 A158 4m multicolored 3.20 3.20
Nos. 927-934 (8) 9.26 9.26

Souvenir Sheets

935 A158 5m multicolored 4.00 4.00
936 A158 5m multicolored 4.00 4.00

Souvenir Sheet

World Trade Center, New York City — A159

1992, Oct. 28 Litho. *Perf. 14*

937 A159 5m multicolored 4.00 4.00

Postage Stamp Mega Event '92, New York City.

Anniversaries and Events — A160

Designs: 20s, Baby harp seal. 30s, Giant panda. 40s, Graf Zeppelin, globe. 70s, Woman grinding corn. 4m, Zeppelin shot down over Cuffley, UK by Lt. Leefe Robinson flying BE 2c, WWI. No. 943, Valentina Tereshkova, first woman in space. No. 944, West African crowned cranes. No. 945, Dr. Ronald McNair.

1993, Jan. Litho. *Perf. 14*

938 A160 20s multicolored .20 .20
939 A160 30s multicolored .24 .24
940 A160 40s multicolored .32 .32
941 A160 70s multicolored .55 .55
942 A160 4m multicolored 3.20 3.20
943 A160 5m multicolored 4.00 4.00
Nos. 938-943 (6) 8.51 8.51

Souvenir Sheets

944 A160 5m multicolored 4.00 4.00
945 A160 5m multicolored 4.00 4.00

Earth Summit, Rio de Janeiro (#938-939, 944). Count Zeppelin, 75th death anniv. (#940, 942). Intl. Conference on Nutrition, Rome (#941). Intl. Space Year (#943, 945).

A number has been reserved for an additional value in this set.

Miniature Sheet of 8

Louvre Museum, Bicent. A161

Details or entire paintings, by Nicolas Poussin: No. 947a, Orpheus and Eurydice. b-c, Rape of the Sabine Women (left, right). d-e, The Death of Sapphira (left, right). f-g, Echo and Narcissus (left, right). h, Self-portrait.

No. 948, The Moneychanger and His Wife, by Quentin Metsys.

1993, Mar. 19 Litho. *Perf. 12*

947 A161 70s #a.-h. + label 4.50 4.50

Souvenir Sheet

Perf. 14½

948 A161 5m multicolored 4.00 4.00

No. 948 contains one 55x88mm stamp.

Flowers — A162

1993, June Litho. *Perf. 14*

949 A162 20s Healing plant .15 .15
950 A162 30s Calla lily .25 .25
951 A162 40s Bird of Paradise .32 .32
952 A162 70s Belladonna .58 .58
953 A162 1m African lily .80 .80
954 A162 2m Veldt lily 1.60 1.60
955 A162 4m Watsonia 3.25 3.25
956 A162 5m Gazania 4.00 4.00
Nos. 949-956 (8) 10.95 10.95

Souvenir Sheets

957 A162 7m Leadwort 5.75 5.75
958 A162 7m Desert rose 5.75 5.75

Miniature Sheet

Coronation of Queen Elizabeth II, 40th Anniv. — A163

Designs: a, 20s, Official coronation photograph. b, 40s, St. Edward's Crown, Scepter with the Cross. c, 1m, Queen Mother. d, 5m, Queen, family.

7m, Conversation Piece at Royal Lodge, Windsor, by Sir James Gunn, 1950.

1993, June 2 Litho. *Perf. 13½x14*

959 A163 Sheet, 2 each, #a.-d. 10.50 10.50

Souvenir Sheet

Perf. 14

960 A163 7m multicolored 5.50 5.50

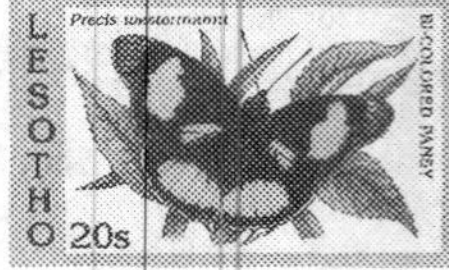

Butterflies A164

1993, June 30 Litho. *Perf. 14*

961 A164 20s Bi-colored pansy .16 .16
962 A164 40s Golden pansy .35 .35
963 A164 70s Yellow pansy .55 .55
964 A164 1m Pseudo ergolid .80 .80
965 A164 2m African giant swallowtail 1.65 1.65
966 A164 5m False acraea 4.00 4.00
Nos. 961-966 (6) 7.51 7.51

Souvenir Sheets

967 A164 7m Seasonal pansy 5.75 5.75
968 A164 7m Ringed pansy 5.75 5.75

African Trains A165

20s, East African Railways Vulcan 2-8-2, 1929. 30s, Zimbabwe Railways Class 15A, 1952. 40s, South African Railways Class 25 4-8-4, 1953. 70s, East African Railways A58 Class Garratt. 1m, South Africa Class 9E Electric. 2m, East African Railways Class 87, 1971. 3m, East African Railways Class 92, 1971. 5m, South Africa Class 26 2-D-2, 1982. #977, Algeria 231-132BT Class, 1937. #978, South African Railway Class 6E Bo-Bo, 1969.

1993, Sept. 24 Litho. *Perf. 14*

969 A165 20s multicolored .15 .15
970 A165 30s multicolored .25 .25
971 A165 40s multicolored .32 .32
972 A165 70s multicolored .58 .58
973 A165 1m multicolored .80 .80
974 A165 2m multicolored 1.65 1.65
975 A165 3m multicolored 2.50 2.50
976 A165 5m multicolored 4.00 4.00
Nos. 969-976 (8) 10.25 10.25

Souvenir Sheets

977 A165 7m multicolored 5.75 5.75
978 A165 7m multicolored 5.75 5.75

Taipei '93 — A166

Disney characters in Taiwan: 20s, Chung Cheng Park, Keelung. 30s, Chiao-Tienkung Temple Festival. 40s, Procession. 70s, Temple Festival. 1m, Queen's Head Rock Formation, Yehliu, vert. 1.20m, Natl. Concert Hall, Taiwan, vert. 2m, C.K.S. Memorial Hall, Taiwan, vert. 2.50m, Grand Hotel, Taipei.

#987, 6m, Natl. Palace Museum, Taipei. #988, 6m, Presidential Palace Museum, Taipei, vert.

1993 Litho. *Perf. 14x13½, 13½x14*

979-986 A166 Set of 10 6.00 6.00

Souvenir Sheets

987-988 A166 6m Set of 2 7.00 7.00

Domestic Cats — A167

Various cats: 20s, 30s, 70s, 5m.

No. 992A, Brown cat eating mouse, vert.

1993, Oct. 29 Litho. *Perf. 14*

989-992 A167 Set of 4 4.75 4.75

Souvenir Sheet

992A A167 5m multicolored 3.50 3.50

Traditional Houses A168

Designs: 20s, Khoaling, Khotla. 30s, Lelapa le seotloana morao ho, 1833. 70s, Thakaneng, Baroetsana. 4m, Mohlongoafatse pele ho, 1833.

No. 996A, Lelapa litema le mekhabiso.

1993, Sept. 24

993-996 A168 Set of 4 4.25 4.25

Souvenir Sheet

996A A168 4m multicolored 2.75 2.75

A169

A170

Players, country: 20s, Khomari, Lesotho. 30s, Mohale, Lesotho. 40s, Davor, Yugoslavia; Rincon, Colombia. 50s, Lekhotla, Lesotho. 70s, Khali, Lesotho. 1m, Milla, Cameroun. 1.20m, Platt, England. 2m, Rummenigge, Germany; Lerby, Denmark.

No. 1005, Stejskal & Hasek, Czechoslovakia; Baresi, Italy, horiz. No. 1006, Lindenberger, Czechoslovakia; Schillaci, Italy.

1993 Litho. *Perf. 13½x14*

997-1004 A169 Set of 8 5.00 5.00

Souvenir Sheets

Perf. 13

1005-1006 A169 6m Set of 2 10.00 10.00

1994 World Cup Soccer Championships, US.

1994, Apr. 2 Litho. *Perf. 14*

New Democratic Government: 20s, King Letsie III signs oath of office under new constitution. 30s, Parliament building. 50s, Dr. Ntsu Mokhehle sworn in as prime minister. 70s, Transfer of power from Major Gen. P. Ramaema to Dr. Mokhehle.

30s, 50s, 70s are horizontal.

1007 A170 20s multicolored	.15	.15
1008 A170 30s multicolored	.25	.25
1009 A170 50s multicolored	.40	.40
1010 A170 70s multicolored	.58	.58
Nos. 1007-1010 (4)	1.38	1.38

A171

PHILAKOREA '94 — A172

Frogs: 35c, Aquatic river. 50c, Bubbling kassina. $1, Guttural toad. $1.50, Common river.

No. 1015, Green frog statue. No. 1016, Black spotted frog, oriental white-eye bird, vert.

1994, Aug. 16 Litho. *Perf. 14*

1011-1014 A171 Set of 4 2.50 2.50

Souvenir Sheets

1015-1016 A172 5m each 3.50 3.50

ICAO, 50th Anniv. A173

35s, Airplane, passengers on ground. 50s, Airplane, control tower. 1m, Airplane banking, terminal, control tower. 1.50m, Airplane ascending.

1994 Litho. *Perf. 14*

1017 A173 35s multicolored	.20	.20
1018 A173 50s multicolored	.30	.30
1019 A173 1m multicolored	.60	.60
1020 A173 1.50m multicolored	.90	.90
Nos. 1017-1020 (4)	2.00	2.00

Medicinal Plants — A174

35s, Tagetes minuta. 50s, Plantago lanceolata. 1m, Amaranthus spinosus. 1.50m, Taraxacum officinale. 5m, Datura stramonium.

1995, May 22 Litho. *Perf. 14*

1021-1024 A174 Set of 4 2.00 2.00

Souvenir Sheet

1025 A174 5m multicolored 3.00 3.00

Pius XII Natl. University, 50th Anniv. — A175

Designs: 35s, Pius XII College, 1962. 50s, Univ. of Basutoland, Bechuanaland Protectorate & Swaziland, 1965. 70s, Univ. of Botswana, Lesotho & Swaziland, 1970. 1m, Univ. of Bostswana, Lesotho & Swaziland, 1975. 1.50m, Natl. Univ. of Lesotho, 1988. 2m, Natl. Univ. of Lesotho, procession of vice-chancellors at celebration.

1995, July 26 Litho. *Perf. 14*

1026-1031 A175 Set of 6 3.75 3.75

A176

A177

Designs: 35s, Qiloane Pinnacle, Thaba-Bosiu, horiz. 50s, Rock Formation, Ha Mohalenyane, horiz. 1m, Botsoela Falls, Malealea. 1.50m, Backpacking, Makhaleng River Gorge, horiz. 4m, Red hot porkers.

1995, Aug. 28 Litho. *Perf. 14*

1032-1035 A176 Set of 4 2.00 2.00

Souvenir Sheet

1036 A176 4m multicolored 2.50 2.50

No. 1036 contains one 38x58mm stamp.
World Tourism Organization, 20th anniv.

1995, Sept. 26

UN emblem and: 35s, Peace dove. 50s, Scales of justice. 1.50m, Handshake of reconciliation, horiz.

1037-1039 A177 Set of 3 1.40 1.40

UN, 50th anniv.

Christmas — A178

Roses: 35s, Sutter's Gold. 50s, Michele Meilland. 1m, J. Otto Thilow. 2m, Papa Meilland.

1995, Nov. 1 Litho. *Perf. 14*

1040-1043 A178 Set of 4 2.30 2.30

A179

A180

UNICEF, 50th Anniv.: 35s, Using iodized salt. 50s, Taking care of livestock, horiz. 70s, Children in classroom. horiz. 1.50m, Children learning traditional dance, singing, horiz.

1996, July 30 Litho. *Perf. 14*

1044-1047 A179 Set of 4 1.85 1.85

1996, Aug. 1

1996 Summer Olympic Games, Atlanta: 1m, US Basketball team, 1936, horiz. 1.50m, Olympic Stadium, Brandenburg Gate, Berlin, horiz. 2m, Jesse Owens, 1936. 3m, Motor boating, horiz.

Past Olympic medalists: No. 1052a, Glen Morris, long jump, decathlon, 1936. b, Said Aouita, 5000-meters, 1984. c, Arnie Robinson, long jump, 1976. d, Hans Woellke, shot put, 1936. e, Renate Stecher, 100-meters, 1972. f, Evelyn Ashford, 100-meters, 1984. g, Willie Davenport, 110-meter hurdles, 1968. h, Bob Beamon, long jump, 1968. i, Heidi Rosendhal, long jump, 1972.

No. 1053, Michael Gross, swimming, 1984. No. 1054, Kornelia Ender, swimming, 1976.

1048-1051 A180 Set of 4 4.50 4.50

1052 A180 1.50m Sheet of 9, #a.-i. 8.10 8.10

Souvenir Sheets

1053-1054 A180 8m each 4.80 4.80

Maps of Lesotho — A181

1911 Map: No. 1055: a, Lephaqlioa. b, Maqaleng. c, Molapo. d, Nkeu. e, No area specified. f, Rafanyane. g, No area specified (7800). h, Madibomatso River. i, Konyani. j, Semena River.

1978 Map: No. 1056a, No area specified. b, Lepaqoa. c, Mamoha (name). d, Ha Nkisi. e, Ha Rafanyan, Ha Thoora. f, Ha Mikia, Ha Ntseli. g, Ha Kosetabole, Ha Mpeli. h, Ha Selebeli, Ha Theko. i, Ha Rapooane, Ha Ramabotsa. j, Ha Ramani, Khohlontso (Kolberg).

Locations on 1994 Map: No. 1057a, Mafika-Lisiu Pass. b, Rampai's Pass, Ha Lesaoana. c, Ha Masaballa. d, Ha Nkisi, Ha Molotanyan. e, Ha Rafanyane, Kobong. f, Laitsoka Pass. g, Katse Reservoir. h, Seshote. i, Ha Rapoeea, Ha Kennan. j, Katse (i, name), Ha Mense.

1996

Sheets of 10

1055-1057 A181 35s #a.-j., each 2.75 2.75

Trains A182

No. 1058: a, ETR 450, Italy. b, TGV, France. c, XPT, Australia. d, Blue Train, South Africa. e, IC 255, Great Britain. f, Bullet Train, Japan.

No. 1059: a, WP Streamlined 4-6-2, India. b, Canadian Pacific 2471, Canada. c, The Caledonian 4-2-2, Scotland. d, William Mason 4-4-0, US. e, Trans-Siberian Express, Russia. f, Swiss Federal 4-6-0, Switzerland.

No. 1060, 52 Class, Germany. No. 1061, ICE, Germany.

1996, Sept. 1 Litho. *Perf. 14*

Sheets of 6

1058-1059 A182 1.50m #a.-f., each 5.40 5.40

Souvenir Sheets

1060-1061 A182 8m each 4.80 4.80

Nos. 1060-1061 each contain one 56x42mm stamp.

No. 833 Surcharged

20s **=**

1996 Litho. *Perf. 13½*

1062 A146 20s on 30s Charaxes jasius .15 .15

Christmas — A183

Women from Mother's Unions: 35s, Methodist Church. 50s, Roman Catholic Church. 1m, Lesotho Evangelical Church. 1.50m, Anglican Church.

1996, Dec. 10 Litho. *Perf. 14*

1063-1066 A183 Set of 4 1.70 1.70

Highlands Water Project — A184

35s, "Cooperation for Development." 50s, "Nature and Heritage." 1m, "An Engineering Feat." 1.50m, "LHDA 10th Anniv., 1986-1996."

1997 Litho. *Perf. 14*

1067-1070 A184 Set of 4 1.25 1.25

No. 1070 is 72x25mm.

1998 World Cup Soccer Championships, France — A185

Players: 1m, Schmeichel, Denmark. 1.50m, Bergkamp, Holland. 2m, Southgate, England. 2.50m, Asprilla, Colombia. 3m, Gascoigne, England. 4m, Giggs, Wales.

No. 1077: Various action scenes of Argentina vs. Holland, 1978.

No. 1078, Littbarski, W. Germany, horiz. No. 1079, Shearer, England.

1997, Oct. 31 Litho. *Perf. 13½*

1071-1076 A185 Set of 6 7.00 7.00
1077 A185 1.50m Sheet of 6, #a.-f. 4.50 4.50

Souvenir Sheets

1078-1079 A185 8m each 4.25 4.25

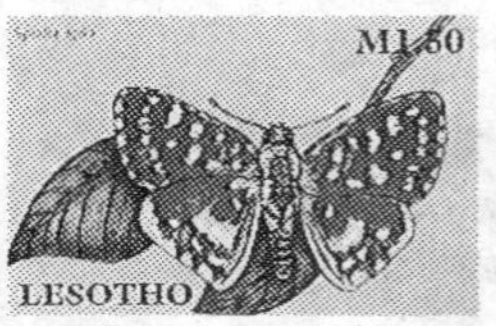

Butterflies — A186

a, Spialia spio. b, Cyclyrius pirithous. c, Acraea satis. d, Belenois aurota. e, Spindasis natalensis. f, Torynesis orangica. g, Lepidochrysops variabilis. h, Pinacopteryx eriphea. i, Anthene butleri.

No. 1081, Bematistes aganice. No. 1082, Papilio demodocus.

1997, Nov. 28 *Perf. 14*

1080 A186 1.50m Sheet of 9, #a.-i. 4.50 4.50

Souvenir Sheets

1081-1082 A186 8m each 4.25 4.25

Morija Museum and Archives, 40th Anniv. A187

Type A Perforations

Type A: On two longer sides, groups of three and eighteen holes separated by an oval hole equal in width to three holes.

Designs: 35s, Rock paintings, child, vert. 45s, Lower jaw of hippopotamus, hippo walking in water. 50s, Traditional attire, vert. 1m, Traditional musical instruments, vert. 1.50m, Award, Man with ceremonial garb, vert. 2m Boy riding bull.

1998, Jan. 30 Litho. *Perf. 14½*

1083-1088 A187 Set of 6 2.90 2.90

POSTAGE DUE STAMPS

Basutoland Nos. J9-J10 Overprinted: "LESOTHO"

Wmk. 314

1966, Nov. 1 Typo. *Perf. 14*

J1 D2 1c carmine .20 .25
 a. "Lseotho" *50.00*
J2 D2 5c dark purple .75 .60
 a. "Lseotho" *85.00*

D1

D2

Perf. 13½

1967, Apr. 1 Unwmk. Litho.

J3 D1 1c dark blue .15 .15
J4 D1 2c dull rose .24 .28
J5 D1 5c emerald .60 .70
 Nos. J3-J5 (3) .99 1.13

1976, Nov. 30 Wmk. 362

J7 D1 2c dull rose .15 .15
J8 D1 5c emerald .20 .20
 Set value .30 .30

1986 Litho. *Perf. 13x13½*

J9 D2 2s green .15 .15
J10 D2 5s blue .15 .15
J11 D2 25s purple .20 .20
 Set value .28 .28

This is an expanding set. Numbers will change if necessary.

LIBERIA

lī-'bir-ē-ə

LOCATION — West coast of Africa, between Ivory Coast and Sierra Leone
GOVT. — Republic
AREA — 43,000 sq. mi.
POP. — 1,900,000 (est. 1984)
CAPITAL — Monrovia

100 Cents = 1 Dollar

Catalogue values for unused stamps in this country are for Never Hinged items, beginning with Scott 330 in the regular postage section, Scott B19 in the semi-postal section, Scott C67 in the airpost section, and Scott CB4 in the airpost semi-postal section.

Values for unused stamps are for examples with original gum as defined in the catalogue introduction. Any exceptions will be noted. Very fine examples of Nos. 1-3, 13-21 and 157-159 will have perforations just clear of the design due to the narrow spacing of the stamps on the plates and/or imperfect perforating methods.

Watermarks

Wmk. 116- Crosses and Circles

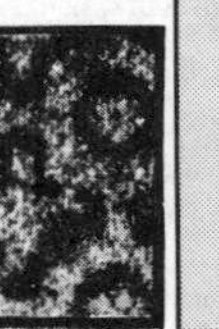

Wmk. 143

For watermarks 373 and 384 see British Watermark page.

"Liberia" — A1

1860 Unwmk. Litho. *Perf. 12*

Thick Paper

1 A1 6c red 125.00 125.00
 a. Imperf. 140.00
2 A1 12c deep blue 22.50 35.00
 a. Imperf. 90.00
3 A1 24c green 22.50 35.00
 a. Imperf. 90.00
 Nos. 1-3 (3) 170.00 195.00

Stamps set very close together. Copies of the 12c occasionally show traces of a frame line around the design.

Medium to Thin Paper
With a single-line frame around each stamp, about 1mm from the border

1864 *Perf. 11, 12*

7 A1 6c red 62.50 77.50
 a. Imperf. 100.00
8 A1 12c blue 72.50 87.50
 a. Imperf. 100.00
9 A1 24c lt green 82.50 95.00
 a. Imperf. 100.00
 Nos. 7-9 (3) 217.50 260.00

Stamps set about 5mm apart. Margins large and perforation usually outside the frame line.

Without Frame Line

1866-69

13 A1 6c lt red 20.00 30.00
14 A1 12c lt blue 20.00 30.00
15 A1 24c lt yellow grn 20.00 30.00
 Nos. 13-15 (3) 60.00 90.00

Stamps set 2-2½mm apart with small margins. Stamps are usually without frame line but those from one transfer show broken and irregular parts of a frame.

With Frame Line

1880 *Perf. 10½*

16 A1 1c ultra 5.00 7.50
17 A1 2c rose 5.00 4.75
 a. Imperf., pair 175.00
18 A1 6c violet 5.00 5.25
19 A1 12c yellow 5.00 4.75
20 A1 24c rose red 5.00 5.25
 Nos. 16-20 (5) 25.00 27.50

Unused values for Nos. 16-20 are for copies without gum.

For surcharges see Nos. 157-159.

Counterfeits

Counterfeits exist of Nos. 1-28, 32 and 64.

From Arms of Liberia — A2

1881

21 A2 3c black 5.00 5.00

Unused value is for copies without gum.

A3

A4

1882 *Perf. 11½, 12, 14*

22 A3 8c blue 37.50 7.00
23 A4 16c red 6.00 5.00

On No. 22 the openings in the figure "8" enclose a pattern of slanting lines. Compare with No. 32.

Canceled to Order

Beginning with the issue of 1885, values in the used column are for "canceled to order" stamps. Postally used copies sell for much more.

A5

A6

From Arms of Liberia — A7

A8

Perf. 10½, 11, 12, 11½x10½, 14, 14½

1885

24 A5 1c carmine 1.50 1.50
 a. 1c rose 1.50 1.50
25 A5 2c green 1.50 1.50
26 A5 3c violet 1.50 1.50
27 A5 4c brown 1.50 1.50
28 A5 6c olive gray 1.50 1.50
29 A6 8c bluish gray 3.75 3.75
 a. 8c lilac 5.00 5.00
30 A6 16c yellow 6.25 6.25
31 A7 32c deep blue 27.50 27.50
 Nos. 24-31 (8) 45.00 45.00

In the 1885 printing, the stamps are spaced 2mm apart and the paper is medium. In the 1892 printing, the stamps are 4½mm apart.

For surcharges see Nos. J1-J2.

Imperf., Pair

24b	A5	1c	3.00	
25a	A5	2c	4.25	
26a	A5	3c	5.00	
27a	A5	4c	5.00	
28a	A5	6c	4.25	4.25
29b	A6	8c	12.50	
30a	A6	16c	15.00	
31a	A7	32c	30.00	

Imperf. pairs with 2mm spacing sell for higher prices.

1889 *Perf. 12, 14*

32 A8 8c blue 4.25 4.25
 a. Imperf., pair 20.00

The openings in the figure "8" are filled with network. See No. 22.

A9

Elephant — A10

Oil Palm — A11

Pres. Hilary R. W. Johnson — A12

Vai Woman in Full Dress — A13

Coat of Arms — A14

Liberian Star — A15

Coat of Arms — A16

Hippopotamus A17

Liberian Star A18

President Johnson — A19

1892-96 Wmk. 143 Engr. *Perf. 15*

33 A9 1c vermilion .40 .30
a. 1c blue (error) 37.50
34 A9 2c blue .40 .30
a. 2c vermilion (error) 37.50
35 A10 4c green & blk 1.50 .75
a. Center inverted 92.50
36 A11 6c blue green .60 .40
37 A12 8c brown & blk .75 .75
a. Center inverted 400.00 400.00
b. Center sideways —
38 A12 10c chrome yel & indigo ('96) .75 .55
39 A13 12c rose red .75 .55
40 A13 15c slate ('96) .75 .55
41 A14 16c lilac 2.25 1.50
a. 16c deep greenish blue (error)
42 A14 20c vermilion ('96) 2.25 1.50
43 A15 24c ol grn, *yel* 1.25 .95
44 A15 25c yel grn ('96) 1.50 1.10
45 A16 30c steel bl ('96) 5.25 3.75
46 A16 32c grnsh blue 3.00 2.25
a. 32c lilac (error) *100.00*
47 A17 $1 ultra & blk 6.00 4.00
a. $1 blue & black 6.50 5.00
48 A18 $2 brown, *yel* 3.50 3.00
49 A19 $5 carmine & blk 6.25 5.25
a. Center inverted 300.00 300.00
Nos. 33-49 (17) 37.15 27.45

Many imperforates, part-perforated and misperforated varieties exist.

The 1c, 2c and 4c were issued in sheets of 60; 6c, sheet of 40; 8c, 10c, sheets of 30; 12c, 15c, 24c, 25c, sheets of 20; 16c, 20c, 30c, sheets of 15; $1, $2, $5, sheets of 10.

For overprints & surcharges see #50, 64B-64F, 66, 71-77, 79-81, 85-93, 95-100, 160, O1-O13, O15-O25, O37-O41, O44-O45.

No. 36 Surcharged:

5 5 5 5

Five Cents — a

Five Cents — b

1893

50 A11 (a) 5c on 6c blue grn 1.75 1.10
a. "5" with short flag 6.00 6.00
b. Both 5's with short flags 5.00 5.00
c. "i" dot omitted 19.00 19.00
d. Surcharge "b" 30.00 30.00

"Commerce," Globe and Krumen — A22

1894 Unwmk. Engr. *Imperf.*

52 A22 5c carmine & blk 3.00 2.50

Rouletted

53 A22 5c carmine & blk 5.00 3.50

For overprints see Nos. 69, O26-O27.

Oil Palm A23

Hippopotamus A24

Elephant — A25

Liberty — A26

1897-1905 Wmk. 143 *Perf. 14 to 16*

54 A23 1c lilac rose .80 .55
a. 1c violet .80 .55
55 A23 1c deep green ('00) 1.00 .75
56 A23 1c lt green ('05) 2.50 1.40
57 A24 2c bister & blk 2.00 1.40
58 A24 2c org red & blk ('00) 3.50 1.75
59 A24 2c rose & blk ('05) 2.00 1.40
60 A25 5c lake & black 2.00 1.40
a. 5c lilac rose & black 2.00 1.40
61 A25 5c gray bl & blk ('00) 4.00 4.00
62 A25 5c ultra & blk ('05) 3.00 2.25
a. Center inverted 625.00
63 A26 50c red brn & blk 2.75 3.00
Nos. 54-63 (10) 23.55 17.90

For overprints & surcharges see #65, 66A-68, 70, 78, 82-84, M1, O28-O36, O42, O92.

A27

Two types:
I - 13 pearls above "Republic Liberia."
II - 10 pearls.

1897 Unwmk. Litho. *Perf. 14*

64 A27 3c red & green (I) .25 .60
a. Type II *10.00* .15

No. 64a is considered a reprint, unissued. "Used" copies are CTO.

For surcharge see No. 128.

Official Stamps Handstamped in Black — ORDINARY

1901-02 Wmk. 143

On Nos. O7-O8, O10-O12

64B A14 16c lilac *400.00 400.00*
64C A15 24c ol grn, *yel* *375.00 375.00*
64D A17 $1 blue & blk *1,700. 1,700.*
64E A18 $2 brown, *yel*
64F A19 $5 carmine & blk

On Stamps with "O S" Printed

65 A23 1c green *35.00 40.00*
66 A9 2c blue *95.00 100.00*
66A A24 2c bister & blk — *150.00*
67 A24 2c org red & blk *35.00 40.00*
68 A25 5c gray bl & blk *27.50 35.00*
69 A22 5c vio & grn (No. O26) *275.00 300.00*
70 A25 5c lake & blk *225.00 225.00*
71 A12 10c yel & blue blk *35.00 60.00*
a. "O S" omitted
72 A13 15c slate *35.00 60.00*
73 A14 16c lilac *300.00 300.00*
74 A14 20c vermilion *40.00 50.00*
75 A15 24c ol grn,*yel* *40.00 50.00*
76 A15 25c yellow grn *40.00 50.00*
a. "O S" omitted
77 A16 30c steel blue *35.00 40.00*
78 A26 50c red brn & blk *47.50 52.50*
79 A17 $1 ultra & blk *275.00 275.00*
a. "O S" omitted
80 A18 $2 brn, *yel* *1,500. 1,500.*
81 A19 $5 car & blk *1,900. 1,900.*
a. "O S" omitted *2,750. 2,750.*

On Stamps with "O S" Handstamped

82 A23 1c deep green 62.50
83 A24 2c org red & blk 75.00
84 A25 5c lake & blk 125.00
85 A12 10c yel & bl blk 110.00
86 A14 20c vermilion 125.00
87 A15 24c ol grn, *yel* 125.00
88 A15 25c yel grn 150.00
89 A16 30c steel blue 300.00
90 A16 32c grnsh blue 175.00

Varieties of Nos. 65-90 include double and inverted overprints.

Nos. 47, O10, O23a Surcharged in Carmine — 75c.

1902

91 A17 75c on $1 #47 10.50 9.50
a. Thin "C" and comma 19.00 19.00
b. Inverted surcharge 62.50 62.50
c. As "a," inverted
92 A17 75c on $1 #O10 *2,250.*
a. Thin "C" and comma *3,000.*
93 A17 75c on $1 #O23a *2,400.*
a. Thin "C" and comma *3,000.*

Liberty — A29

1903 Unwmk. Engr. *Perf. 14*

94 A29 3c black .30 .15
a. Printed on both sides 45.00
b. Perf. 12 15.00 5.00

For overprint see No. O43.

Stamps of 1892 Surcharged in Blue

TEN Cents. — a

FIFTEEN Cents. — b

1903 Wmk. 143

95 A14 (a) 10c on 16c lilac 3.00 4.00
96 A15 (b) 15c on 24c ol grn, *yel* 4.50 5.50
97 A16 (b) 20c on 32c grnsh bl 6.25 7.75
Nos. 95-97 (3) 13.75 17.25

Nos. 50, O3 and 45 Surcharged in Black or Red

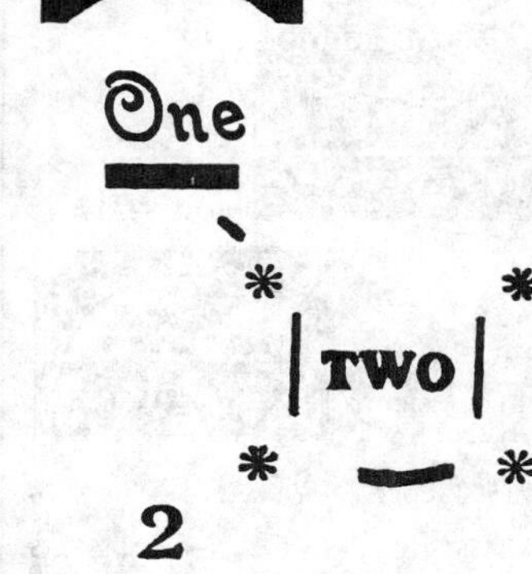

1904

98 A11 1c on 5c on 6c bl grn .60 .55
a. "5" with short flag 4.25 4.25
b. Both 5's with short flags 8.75 8.75
c. "i" dot omitted 10.00 10.00
d. Surcharge on #50d 12.50 12.50
e. Inverted surcharge 6.75 6.75
99 A10 2c on 4c grn & blk 1.50 2.75
a. Pair, one without surcharge 35.00
b. Double surcharge
c. Double surcharge, red and blk 62.50
d. Surcharged on back also 19.00
e. "Official" overprint missing 30.00
100 A16 2c on 30c stl bl (R) 8.75 14.00
Nos. 98-100 (3) 10.85 17.30

African Elephant — A33

Mercury — A34

Chimpanzee A35

Great Blue Touraco A36

Agama — A37

Egret — A38

Head of Liberty From Coin — A39

A40

Liberian Flag A41

Pygmy Hippopotamus A42

Liberty with Star of Liberia on Cap A43

Mandingos A44

Executive Mansion and Pres. Arthur Barclay — A45

1906 Unwmk. Engr. *Perf. 14*

101 A33 1c green & blk .75 .35
102 A34 2c carmine & blk .15 .15
103 A35 5c ultra & blk 1.65 .50
104 A36 10c red brn & blk 2.25 .50
105 A37 15c pur & dp grn 7.00 2.25
106 A38 20c orange & blk 5.00 1.65
107 A39 25c dull blue & gray .50 .15
108 A40 30c deep violet .55 .15
109 A41 50c dp green & blk .55 .15
110 A42 75c brown & blk 5.75 1.65
111 A43 $1 rose & gray 1.65 .20
112 A44 $2 dp green & blk 2.25 .25
113 A45 $5 red brown & blk 4.50 .35
Nos. 101-113 (13) 32.55 8.30

For surcharges see Nos. 114, 129, 130, 141, 145-149, 161, M2, M5, O72-O73, O82-O85, O96. For overprints see Nos. O46-O58.

Center Inverted

101a A33 1c 37.50 37.50
102a A34 2c 27.50 27.50
103a A35 5c 125.00 125.00
104a A36 10c 57.50 57.50
105a A37 15c 125.00 125.00
106b A38 20c 125.00 125.00
107a A39 25c 55.00 55.00
109b A41 50c 55.00 55.00
110b A42 75c 92.50 92.50
111a A43 $1 75.00 75.00
112a A44 $2 72.50 72.50

Imperf., Pairs

101b A33 1c 11.00
102b A34 2c 4.50
106a A38 20c 17.00
107b A39 25c 45.00 45.00
109a A41 50c 17.00
110a A42 75c 17.00
113a A45 $5 22.50

No. 104 Surcharged in Black

1909

114 A36 3c on 10c red brn & blk 4.50 4.50

Coffee Plantation — A46

Pres. Barclay — A47

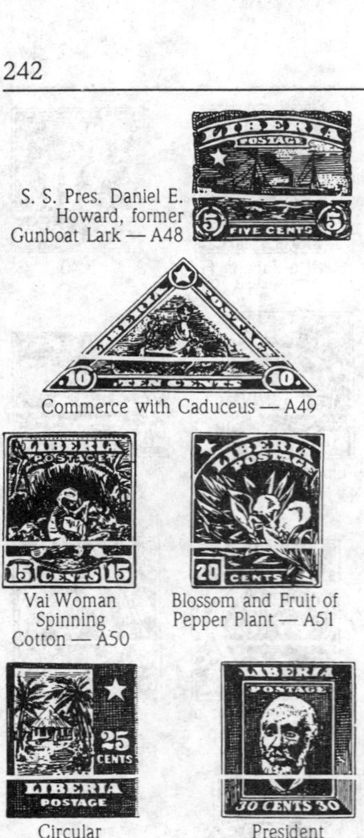

S. S. Pres. Daniel E. Howard, former Gunboat Lark — A48

Commerce with Caduceus — A49

Vai Woman Spinning Cotton — A50

Blossom and Fruit of Pepper Plant — A51

Circular House — A52

President Barclay — A53

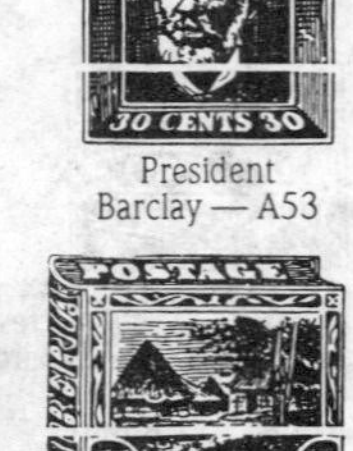

Men in Canoe — A54

Liberian Village — A55

1909-12 *Perf. 14*

No.	Type	Description	Unused	Used
115	A46	1c yel grn & blk	.35	.35
116	A47	2c lake & blk	.35	.35
117	A48	5c ultra & blk	.35	.35
118	A49	10c plum & blk, perf. 12½ ('12)	.35	.35
a.		Imperf., pair	11.00	
119	A50	15c indigo & blk	.70	.40
120	A51	20c rose & grn	2.25	.40
b.		Imperf.		
121	A52	25c dk brn & blk	.65	.40
a.		Imperf.		
122	A53	30c dark brown	2.25	.40
123	A54	50c green & blk	2.25	.40
124	A55	75c red brn & blk	2.25	.40
		Nos. 115-124 (10)	11.75	3.80

Rouletted

No.	Type	Description	Unused	Used
125	A49	10c plum & blk	.70	.45

For surcharges see Nos. 126-127E, 131-133, 136-140, 142-144, 151-156, 162, B1-B2, M3-M4, M6-M7, O70-O1, O74-O81, O86-O91, O97.

For overprints see Nos. O59-O69.

Center Inverted

No.	Type	Value	Unused	Used
116a	A47	2c	70.00	60.00
117a	A48	5c	62.50	55.00
119a	A50	15c	47.50	47.50
120a	A51	20c	70.00	55.00
121b	A52	25c	47.50	42.50
123a	A54	50c	75.00	62.50

Stamps and Types of 1909-12 Surcharged in Blue or Red

3 CENTS INLAND POSTAGE

1910-12 ***Rouletted***

No.	Type	Description	Unused	Used
126	A49	3c on 10c plum & blk (Bl)		.25
a.		"3" inverted		
126B	A49	3c on 10c blk & ultra (R)	22.50	5.00

#126B is roulette 7. It also exists in roulette 13.

Perf. 12½, 14, 12½x14

No.	Type	Description	Unused	Used
127	A49	3c on 10c plum & blk (Bl) ('12)	.40	.25
a.		Imperf., pair	22.50	
b.		Double surcharge, one invtd.	22.50	
c.		Double vertical surcharge		
127E	A49	3c on 10c blk & ultra (R) ('12)	17.00	.55
		Nos. 126-127E (4)	40.30	6.05

Nos. 64, 64a Surcharged in Dark Green

1913

No.	Type	Description	Unused	Used
128	A27	8c on 3c red & grn (I)	.30	.15
a.		Surcharge on No. 64a	3.00	.15
b.		Double surcharge	6.25	
c.		Imperf., pair	20.00	
d.		Inverted surcharge	25.00	

Stamps of Preceding Issues Surcharged

1914

On Issue of 1906

No.	Type	Description	Unused	Used
129	A39 (a)	2c on 25c dl bl & gray	7.50	2.25
130	A40 (b)	5c on 30c dp violet	7.50	2.25

On Issue of 1909

No.	Type	Description	Unused	Used
131	A52 (a)	2c on 25c brn & blk	7.50	2.25
132	A53 (b)	5c on 30c dk brown	7.50	2.25
133	A54 (a)	10c on 50c grn & blk	7.50	2.25
		Nos. 129-133 (5)	37.50	11.25

Liberian House — A57

Providence Island, Monrovia Harbor — A58

1915 Engr. Wmk. 116 *Perf. 14*

No.	Type	Description	Unused	Used
134	A57	2c red	.15	.15
135	A58	3c dull violet	.15	.15
		Set value		.20

For overprints see Nos. 196-197, O113-O114, O128-O129.

Nos. 109, 111-113, 119-124 Surcharged with New Values in Dark Blue, Black or Red:

1915-16 **Unwmk.**

No.	Type	Description	Unused	Used
136	A50 (c)	2c on 15c (R)	.90	.90
137	A52 (d)	2c on 25c (R)	8.00	8.00
138	A51 (e)	5c on 20c (Bk)	1.10	5.75
139	A53 (f)	5c on 30c (R)	4.50	4.50
a.		Double surcharge	14.00	14.00
140	A53 (g)	5c on 30c (R)	40.00	40.00
141	A41 (h)	10c on 50c (R)	8.00	8.00
a.		Double surch., one invtd.		
142	A54 (i)	10c on 50c (R)	14.00	14.00
a.		Double surcharge red & blk	35.00	35.00
b.		Blue surcharge	35.00	35.00
143	A54 (i)	10c on 50c (Bk)	15.00	15.00

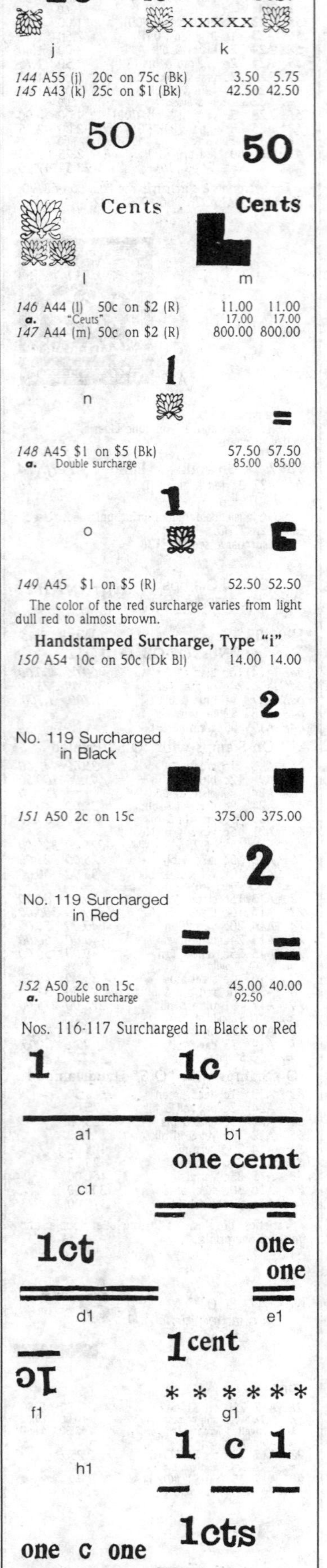

No.	Type	Description	Unused	Used
144	A55 (j)	20c on 75c (Bk)	3.50	5.75
145	A43 (k)	25c on $1 (Bk)	42.50	42.50
146	A44 (l)	50c on $2 (R)	11.00	11.00
a.		"Ceuts"	17.00	17.00
147	A44 (m)	50c on $2 (R)	800.00	800.00
148	A45	$1 on $5 (Bk)	57.50	57.50
a.		Double surcharge	85.00	85.00
149	A45	$1 on $5 (R)	52.50	52.50

The color of the red surcharge varies from light dull red to almost brown.

Handstamped Surcharge, Type "i"

No.	Type	Description	Unused	Used
150	A54	10c on 50c (Dk Bl)	14.00	14.00

No. 119 Surcharged in Black

No.	Type	Description	Unused	Used
151	A50	2c on 15c	375.00	375.00

No. 119 Surcharged in Red

No.	Type	Description	Unused	Used
152	A50	2c on 15c	45.00	40.00
a.		Double surcharge	92.50	

Nos. 116-117 Surcharged in Black or Red

No.	Type	Description	Unused	Used
153	A47	1c on 2c lake & blk	2.50	2.50
a.		Strip of 10 types	35.00	
154	A48	2c on 5c ultra & blk (R)	2.50	2.50
a.		Black surcharge	14.00	14.00
b.		Strip of 10 types (R)	35.00	
c.		Strip of 10 types (Bk)	165.00	

The 10 types of surcharge are repeated in illustrated sequence on 1c on 2c in each horiz. row and on 2c on 5c in each vert. row of sheets of 100 (10x10).

No. 116 and Type of 1909 Surcharged:

No.	Type	Description	Unused	Used
155	A47	1c on 2c lake & blk	150.00	150.00

No.	Type	Description	Unused	Used
156	A48	2c on 5c turq & blk	125.00	125.00

Nos. 18-20 Surcharged

1916

No.	Type	Description	Unused	Used
157	A1	3c on 6c violet	42.50	42.50
a.		Inverted surcharge	75.00	75.00
158	A1	5c on 12c yellow	3.00	3.00
a.		Inverted surcharge	12.50	12.50
b.		Surcharge sideways	12.50	
159	A1	10c on 24c rose red	2.75	3.00
a.		Inverted surcharge	15.00	15.00
b.		Surcharge sideways		
		Nos. 157-159 (3)	48.25	48.50

Unused values for Nos. 157-159 are for copies without gum.

Nos. 44 and 108 Surcharged

FOUR 1917 CENTS

p

1917 FIVE CENTS

r

1917 **Wmk. 143**

No.	Type	Description	Unused	Used
160	A15 (p)	4c on 25c yel grn	11.00	11.00
a.		"OUR"	25.00	25.00
b.		"FCUR"	25.00	25.00

Unwmk.

No.	Type	Description	Unused	Used
161	A40 (r)	5c on 30c dp vio	90.00	90.00

No. 118 Surcharged in Red

3 CENTS

1918

No.	Type	Description	Unused	Used
162	A49	3c on 10c plum & blk	2.25	2.25
a.		"3" inverted	9.25	9.25

Bongo Antelope — A59

Symbols of Liberia — A61

Two-spot Palm Civet — A60

A62

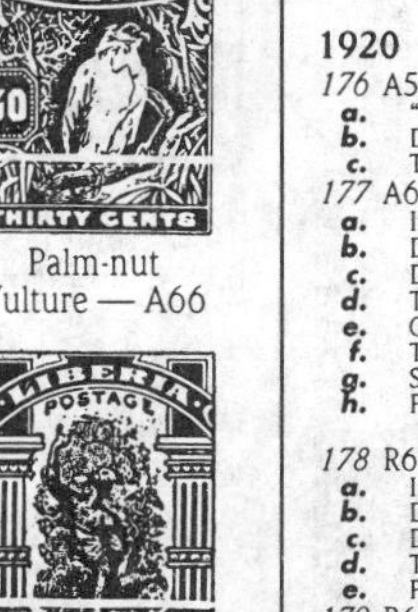

Palm-nut Vulture — A66

Oil Palm — A63

Mercury — A64

Traveler's Tree A65

"Mudskipper" or Bommi Fish — A67

Mandingos — A68

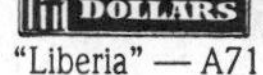

"Liberia" — A71

Coast Scene — A69

Liberia College — A70

1918 **Engr.** ***Perf. 12½, 14***

No.	Type	Description	Unused	Used
163	A59	1c dp grn & blk	.55	.15
164	A60	2c rose & blk	.70	.15
165	A61	5c gray bl & blk	.15	.15
166	A62	10c dark green	.20	.15
167	A63	15c blk & dk grn	2.50	.15
168	A64	20c claret & blk	.30	.15
169	A65	25c dk grn & grn	2.75	.15
170	A66	30c red vio & blk	10.00	.70
171	A67	50c ultra & blk	18.00	.90
172	A68	75c ol bis & blk	.75	.15
173	A69	$1 yel brn & bl	4.50	.15
174	A70	$2 lt vio & blk	5.50	.15
175	A71	$5 dark brown	5.75	.35
		Nos. 163-175 (13)	51.65	3.45

For surcharges see Nos. 176-177, 228-229, 248-270, B3-B15, O111-O112, O155-O157.
For overprints see Nos. O98-O110.

Nos. 163-164, F10-F14 Surcharged

1920 1920

THREE CENTS

5

1920
FOUR CENTS

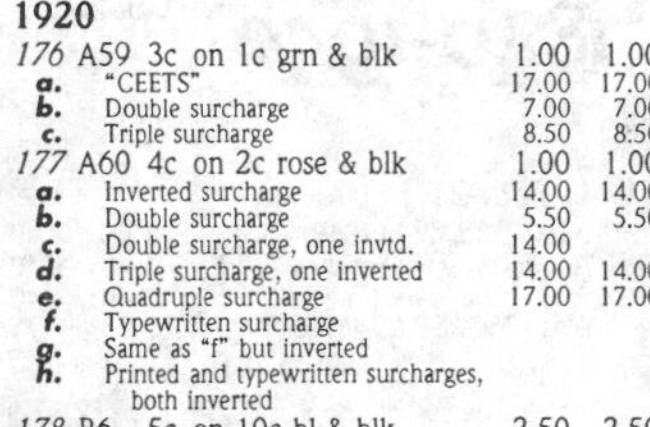

1920

No.	Type	Description	Unused	Used
176	A59	3c on 1c grn & blk	1.00	1.00
a.		"CEETS"	17.00	17.00
b.		Double surcharge	7.00	7.00
c.		Triple surcharge	8.50	8.50
177	A60	4c on 2c rose & blk	1.00	1.00
a.		Inverted surcharge	14.00	14.00
b.		Double surcharge	5.50	5.50
c.		Double surcharge, one invtd.	14.00	
d.		Triple surcharge, one inverted	14.00	14.00
e.		Quadruple surcharge	17.00	17.00
f.		Typewritten surcharge		
g.		Same as "f" but inverted		
h.		Printed and typewritten surcharges, both inverted		
178	R6	5c on 10c bl & blk	2.50	2.50
a.		Inverted surcharge	5.25	5.25
b.		Double surcharge	8.25	8.25
c.		Double surcharge, one invtd.	8.25	8.25
d.		Typewritten surcharge ("five")		72.50
e.		Printed and typewritten surcharges	72.50	
179	R6	5c on 10c org red & blk	2.50	2.50
a.		5c on 10c orange & black	4.00	2.75
b.		Inverted surcharge	8.25	
c.		Double surcharge	8.25	
d.		Double surcharge, one invtd.	10.50	9.50
e.		Typewritten surch. in violet	72.50	72.50
f.		Typewritten surch. in black		
g.		Printed and typewritten surcharges	72.50	
180	R6	5c on 10c grn & blk	2.50	2.50
a.		Double surcharge	8.25	8.25
b.		Double surcharge, one invtd.	12.50	12.50
c.		Inverted surcharge		12.50
d.		Quadruple surcharge	21.00	21.00
e.		Typewritten surcharge		72.50
f.		Printed and typewritten surcharges		
181	R6	5c on 10c vio & blk (Monrovia)	4.00	4.00
a.		Double surcharge, one invtd.	12.50	12.50
182	R6	5c on 10c mag & blk (Robertsport)	2.00	2.00
a.		Double surcharge	12.50	12.50
b.		Double surcharge, one invtd.	12.50	12.50
c.		Double surch., both invtd.	21.00	
		Nos. 176-182 (7)	15.50	15.50

Cape Mesurado A75

Pres. Daniel E. Howard — A76

Arms of Liberia — A77

Crocodile A78

Pepper Plant — A79

Leopard — A80

Village Scene — A81

Krumen in Dugout — A82

Rapids in St. Paul's River — A83

Bongo Antelope — A84

Hornbill — A85

Elephant — A86

1921 **Wmk. 116** ***Perf. 14***

No.	Type	Description	Unused	Used
183	A75	1c green	.15	.15
184	A76	5c dp bl & blk	.15	.15
185	A77	10c red & dl bl	.15	.15
186	A78	15c dl vio & grn	4.00	.30
187	A79	20c rose red & grn	1.75	.15
188	A80	25c org & blk	4.75	.30
189	A81	30c grn & dl vio	.25	.15
190	A82	50c org & ultra	.30	.15
191	A83	75c red & blk brn	.50	.15
a.		Center inverted		70.00
192	A84	$1 red & blk	20.00	1.10
193	A85	$2 yel & ultra	6.50	.45
194	A86	$5 car rose & vio	20.00	.60
		Nos. 183-194 (12)	58.50	
		Set value		3.15

For overprints see Nos. 195, 198-208, O115-O127, O130-O140.

Nos. 134-135, 183-194 Overprinted "1921"

No.	Type	Description	Unused	Used
195	A75	1c green	16.00	.30
196	A57	2c red	16.00	.30
197	A58	3c dull violet	22.50	.30
198	A76	5c dp bl & blk	3.50	.30
199	A77	10c red & dull bl	35.00	.30
200	A78	15c dull vio & grn	16.00	1.00
201	A79	20c rose red & grn, ovpt. invtd.	7.25	.75
202	A80	25c orange & blk	16.00	1.00
203	A81	30c grn & dull vio	2.50	.30
204	A82	50c orange & ultra	3.50	.30
205	A83	75c red & blk brn	4.75	.30
206	A84	$1 red & blk	45.00	1.50
207	A85	$2 yellow & ultra	16.00	1.50
208	A86	$5 car rose & vio	42.50	2.00
		Nos. 195-208 (14)	246.50	10.15

Overprint exists inverted in Nos. 195-208 and normal on No. 201.

First Settlers Landing at Cape Mesurado from U. S. S. Alligator A87

1923 **Litho.**

No.	Type	Description	Unused	Used
209	A87	1c lt blue & blk	14.00	.25
210	A87	2c claret & ol gray	20.00	.25
211	A87	5c ol grn & ind	20.00	.25
212	A87	10c bl grn & vio	.75	.25
213	A87	$1 rose & brn	2.50	.25
		Nos. 209-213 (5)	57.25	1.25

Centenary of founding of Liberia.

Memorial to J. J. Roberts, 1st Pres. — A88

Liberian Star — A90

Hall of Representatives, Monrovia A89

Pres. Charles Dunbar Burgess King A91 A92

Hippopotamus A93

Antelope — A94

West African Buffalo — A95

Grebos Making Dumboy — A96

Pineapple — A97

Carrying Ivory Tusk — A98

Rubber Planter's House — A99

Stockton Lagoon — A100

Grebo Houses A101

1923 *Perf. 13½x14½, 14½x13½*

White Paper

No.	Type	Description	Unused	Used
214	A88	1c yel grn & dp grn	4.00	.15
215	A89	2c claret & brn	4.00	.15
216	A90	3c lilac & blk	.30	.15
217	A91	5c bl vio & blk	60.00	.15
218	A92	10c slate & brn	.30	.15
219	A93	15c bister & bl	20.00	.30
220	A94	20c bl grn & vio	2.25	.30
221	A95	25c org red & brn	90.00	.35

White, Buff or Brownish Paper

No.	Type	Description	Unused	Used
222	A96	30c dk brn & vio	.55	.15
223	A97	50c dull vio & org	1.10	.15
224	A98	75c gray & bl	1.75	.35
225	A99	$1 dp red & dk vio	4.00	.55
a.		White paper	27.50	
226	A100	$2 orange & blue	4.50	.50
a.		Buff or brownish paper	5.25	.55
227	A101	$5 dp grn & brn	11.00	.50
a.		White paper	27.50	
		Nos. 214-227 (14)	203.75	
		Set value		3.75

Nos. 222-224 on buff or brownish paper sell for about 10% more.

For overprints see Nos. O141-O154.

No. 163 Surcharged **Two Cents**

1926 **Unwmk.** *Perf. 14*

No.	Type	Description	Unused	Used
228	A59	2c on 1c dp grn & blk	2.50	2.50
a.		Surcharge with ornamental design as on #O155	10.50	

No. 163 Surcharged in Red **Two Cents**

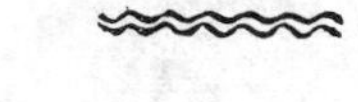

1927

No.	Type	Description	Unused	Used
229	A59	2c on 1c dp grn & blk	7.00	7.00
a.		"Ceuts"	10.00	
b.		"Vwo"	10.00	
c.		"Twc"	10.00	
d.		Double surcharge	20.00	
e.		Wavy lines omitted	12.50	

Palms — A102

Map of Africa — A103

President King — A104

1928 **Engr.** *Perf. 12*

No.	Type	Description	Unused	Used
230	A102	1c green	.55	.35
231	A102	2c dark violet	.35	.25
232	A102	3c bister brn	.35	.25
233	A103	5c ultra	.75	.40
234	A104	10c olive gray	1.00	.40
235	A103	15c dull violet	4.50	1.65
236	A103	$1 red brown	50.00	18.00
		Nos. 230-236 (7)	57.50	21.30

For surcharges & overprints see Nos. 288A, 289A, 290A-291, 292A, C1-C3, O158-O165.

Nos. 164-168, 170-175 Surcharged in Various Colors and Styles, "1936" and New Values

1936 *Perf. 12½, 14*

No.	Type	Description	Unused	Used
248	A60	1c on 2c (Bl)	.25	.25
249	A61	3c on 5c (Bl)	.15	.15
250	A62	4c on 10c (Br)	.15	.15
251	A63	6c on 15c (Bl)	.25	.25
252	A64	8c on 20c (V)	.15	.15
253	A66	12c on 30c (V)	.45	.45
254	A67	14c on 50c (Bl)	.50	.50
255	A68	16c on 75c (Br)	.25	.25
256	A69	18c on $1 (Bk)	.25	.25
a.		22c on $1 yellow brown & blue	3.75	
257	A70	22c on $2 (V)	.35	.35
258	A71	24c on $5 (Bk)	.45	.45
		Nos. 248-258 (11)	3.20	3.20

Official Stamps, Nos. O99-O110, Surcharged or Overprinted in various colors and styles with 6 pointed star and "1936"

1936

No.	Type	Description	Unused	Used
259	A60	1c on 2c (Bl)	.20	.20
260	A61	3c on 5c (Bl)	.15	.15
261	A62	4c on 10c (Bl)	.15	.15
262	A63	6c on 15c (Bl)	.20	.20
263	A64	8c on 20c (V)	.15	.15
264	A66	12c on 30c (V)	.35	.35
a.		"193" instead of "1936"	9.50	
265	A67	14c on 50c (Bl)	.45	.45
266	A68	16c on 75c (Bk)	.25	.25
267	A69	18c on $1 (Bk)	.25	.25
268	A70	22c on $2 (Bl)	.30	.30
269	A71	24c on $5 (Bk)	.35	.35
270	A65	25c (Bk)	.45	.45
		Nos. 259-270 (12)	3.25	3.25

Hornbill — A106

Designs: 2c, Bushbuck. 3c, West African dwarf buffalo. 4c, Pygmy hippopotamus. 5c, Lesser egret. 6c, Pres. E. J. Barclay.

Perf. Compound of 11½, 12, 12½, 14

1937, Apr. 10 **Engr.** **Unwmk.**

No.	Type	Description	Unused	Used
271	A106	1c green & blk	.55	.30
272	A106	2c carmine & blk	.55	.20
273	A106	3c violet & blk	.55	.30
274	A106	4c orange & blk	.85	.50
275	A106	5c blue & blk	.85	.35
276	A106	6c green & blk	.30	.15
		Nos. 271-276 (6)	3.65	1.80

Coast Line of Liberia, 1839 A107

Seal of Liberia, Map and Farming Scenes A108

Thomas Buchanan and Residence at Bassa Cove A109

1940, July 29 **Engr.** *Perf. 12*

No.	Type	Description	Unused	Used
277	A107	3c dark blue	.15	.15
278	A108	5c dull red brn	.15	.15
279	A109	10c dark green	.15	.15
		Set value	.30	.25

100th anniv. of the founding of the Commonwealth of Liberia.

For overprints & surcharges see Nos. 280-282, B16-B18, C14-C16, CB1-CB3, CE1, CF1, E1, F35.

Nos. 277-279 Overprinted in Red or Blue

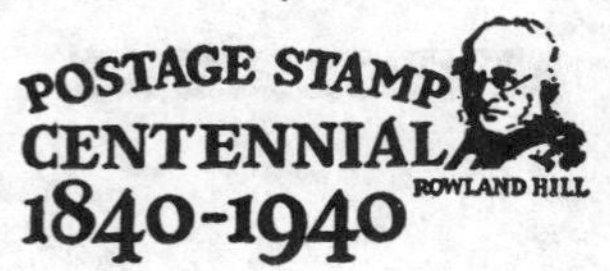

1941, Feb. 21

No.	Type	Description	Unused	Used
280	A107	3c dk blue (R)	1.40	1.40
281	A108	5c dull red brn (Bl)	1.40	1.40
282	A109	10c dark green (R)	1.40	1.40
		Nos. 280-282,C14-C16 (6)	7.95	7.95

Royal Antelope A110

Bay-thighed Diana Monkey A115

2c, Water chevrotain. 3c, White-shouldered duiker. 4c, Bushbuck. 5c, Zebra antelope.

1942 **Engr.**

No.	Type	Description	Unused	Used
283	A110	1c violet & fawn	.30	.15
284	A110	2c brt ultra & yel brn	.35	.20
285	A110	3c brt grn & yel brn	.50	.25
286	A110	4c blk & red org	.65	.50
287	A110	5c olive & fawn	.80	.50
288	A115	10c red & black	1.40	.65
		Nos. 283-288 (6)	4.00	2.25

Nos. 231, 233-234, 271-276 Surcharged with New Values and Bars or X's in Violet, Black, Red Brown or Blue

Perf. 12, 12x12½, 14

1944-46 **Unwmk.**

No.	Type	Description	Unused	Used
288A	A102	1c on 2c (Bk)	7.75	5.50
289	A106	1c on 4c (Bk)	42.50	40.00
289A	A104	1c on 10c (R Br)	10.50	8.00
290	A106	2c on 3c	52.50	42.50
290A	A103	2c on 5c (Bk)	2.25	2.25
290B	A103	2c on 5c (Bl)	17.50	7.75
291	A102	3c on 2c	25.00	
292	A106	4c on 5c	9.25	6.00
292A	A104	4c on 10c (Bk)	2.75	2.75
b.		Double surch., one inverted		
293	A106	5c on 1c (Bk)	70.00	42.50
294	A106	6c on 2c (Bk)	9.25	8.00
295	A106	10c on 6c	9.25	8.00

Surcharges on Nos. 289, 290, 293, 294 are found inverted. Values same as normal.

Pres. Franklin D. Roosevelt Reviewing Troops A116

1945, Nov. 26 **Engr.** *Perf. 12½*

Grayish Paper

No.	Type	Description	Unused	Used
296	A116	3c brt violet & blk	.15	.15
297	A116	5c dk blue & blk	.30	.30
		Nos. 296-297,C51 (3)	1.70	1.85

In memory of Pres. Franklin D. Roosevelt (1882-1945).

Monrovia Harbor A117

1947, Jan. 2

No.	Type	Description	Unused	Used
298	A117	5c deep blue	.15	.15

Opening of the Monrovia Harbor Project, Feb. 16, 1946. See No. C52.

Without Inscription at Top

1947, May 16

No.	Type	Description	Unused	Used
299	A117	5c violet	.15	.15

See No. C53.

1st US Postage Stamps and Arms of Liberia A118

1947, June 6

No.	Type	Description	Unused	Used
300	A118	5c carmine rose	.15	.15
		Set value, #300, C54-C56	.45	.45

Cent. of US postage stamps and the 87th anniv. of Liberian postal issues.

Matilda Newport Firing Cannon A119

1947, Dec. 1 **Engr. & Photo.**

Center in Gray Black

No.	Type	Description	Unused	Used
301	A119	1c brt blue green	.15	.15
302	A119	3c brt red violet	.20	.15
303	A119	5c brt ultra	.35	.15
304	A119	10c yellow	1.75	.45
		Nos. 301-304,C57 (5)	3.70	1.20

125th anniv. of Matilda Newport's defense of Monrovia, Dec. 1, 1822.

Liberian Star — A120

Cent. of Independence: 2c, Liberty. 3c, Liberian Arms. 5c, Map of Liberia.

1947, Dec. 22 **Engr.**

305 A120 1c dark green .15 .15
306 A120 2c brt red vio .15 .15
307 A120 3c brt purple .15 .15
308 A120 5c dark blue .15 .15
Set value, #305-308, C58-C60 1.15 .85

Centenary of independence.

Natives Approaching Village A124

Rubber Tapping and Planting A125

Landing of First Colonists A126

Jehudi Ashmun and Defenders A127

1949, Apr. 4 **Litho.** ***Perf. 11½***

309 A124 1c multicolored .30 .50
310 A125 2c multicolored .30 .50
311 A126 3c multicolored .30 .50
312 A127 5c multicolored .30 .50
Nos. 309-312,C63-C64 (6) 1.90 3.30

Nos. 309-312 exist perf. 12½ and sell at a much lower price. The status of the perf. 12½ set is indefinite.

Pres. Joseph J. Roberts A128

Liberian Presidents: 2c, Stephen Benson. 3c, Daniel B. Warner. 4c, James S. Payne. 5c, Executive mansion. 6c, Edward J. Roye. 7c, A. W. Gardner and A. F. Russell. 8c, Hilary R. W. Johnson. 9c, Joseph J. Cheeseman. 10c, William D. Coleman. 15c, Garretson W. Gibson. 20c, Arthur Barclay. 25c, Daniel E. Howard. 50c, Charles D. B. King. $1, Edwin J. Barclay.

1948-50 Unwmk. Engr. *Perf. 12½*

Caption and Portrait in Black

313 A128 1c green ('48) 1.40 *4.00*
314 A128 2c salmon pink .30 *.45*
315 A128 3c rose violet .30 *.45*
a. "1876-1878" added 10.00 *25.00*
316 A128 4c lt olive grn .65 .65
317 A128 5c ultra .35 *.65*
318 A128 6c red orange .65 *1.25*
319 A128 7c lt blue ('50) .80 *1.50*
320 A128 8c carmine .80 *1.75*
321 A128 9c red violet .90 *1.50*
322 A128 10c yellow ('50) .60 .40
323 A128 15c yellow orange .70 .50
324 A128 20c blue gray 1.00 1.00
325 A128 25c cerise 1.40 1.50
326 A128 50c aqua 2.75 1.00
327 A128 $1 rose lilac 4.50 1.00
Nos. 313-327,C65 (16) 17.70 *18.25*

Issued: 1c, 11/18; 7c, 10c, 1950; others, 7/21/49.

See Nos. 328, 371-378, C118.

Pres. Joseph J. Roberts A129

1950

328 A129 1c green & blk .20 .15

Hand Holding Book — A130

1950, Feb. 14

329 A130 5c deep blue .28 .15

National Literacy Campaign. See No. C66.

Catalogue values for unused stamps in this section, from this point to the end of the section, are for Never Hinged items.

UPU Monument A131

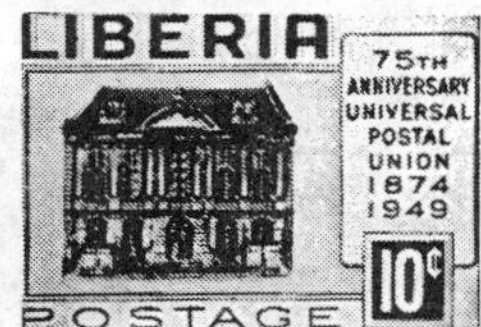

First UPU Building, Bern A132

1950, Apr. 21 **Engr.** **Unwmk.**

330 A131 5c green & blk .15 .15
331 A132 10c red vio & blk .18 .18
Nos. 330-331,C67 (3) 2.08 2.08

UPU, 75th anniv. (in 1949).
Exist imperf., same value.

Jehudi Ashmun and Seal of Liberia — A133

John Marshall, Ashmun and Map of Town of Marshall A134

Designs (Map or View and Two Portraits): 2c, Careysburg, Gov. Lott Carey (1780-1828), freed American slave, and Jehudi Ashmun (1794-1828), American missionary credited as founder of Liberia. 3c, Town of Harper, Robert Goodlow Harper (1765-1825), American statesman, and Ashmun. 5c, Upper Buchanan, Gov. Thomas Buchanan and Ashmun. 10c, Robertsport, Pres. Joseph J. Roberts and Ashmun.

1952, Apr. 10 ***Perf. 10½***

332 A133 1c deep green .15 .15
333 A133 2c scarlet & ind .15 .15
334 A133 3c purple & grn .15 .15
335 A134 4c brown & grn .15 .15
336 A133 5c ultra & org red .15 .15
337 A134 10c org red & dk bl .15 .15
Set value, #332-337, C68-C69 1.00 .95

Nos. 332-337 exist imperf. Value about two and one-half times that of the perf. set.

See No. C69a.

UN Headquarters Building — A135

Scroll and Flags A136

10c, Liberia arms, letters "UN" and emblem.

338 A135 1c ultra .15 .15
339 A136 4c car & ultra .15 .15
340 A136 10c red brn & yel .15 .15
a. Souvenir sheet of 3, #338-340 1.25 1.25
Set value, #328-340, C70 (4) .65 .55

Nos. 338-340 and 340a exist imperforate.

Pepper Bird — A137

Roller A138

1953, Nov. 18 ***Perf. 10½***

341 A137 1c shown .15 .15
342 A138 3c shown .15 .15
343 A137 4c Hornbill .15 .15
344 A137 5c Kingfisher .15 .15
345 A138 10c Jacana .24 .15
346 A138 12c Weaver .38 .15
Set value 1.00 .30

Exist imperf. Value, set unused $2.75.

Tennis A139

Callichilia Stenosepala A140

1955, Jan. 26 **Litho.** ***Perf. 12½***

347 A139 3c shown .15 .15
348 A139 5c Soccer .15 .15
349 A139 25c Boxing .16 .15
Set value, #347-349, C88-C90 .65 .65

1955, Sept. 28 **Unwmk.**

Various Native Flowers: 7c, Gomphia subcordata. 8c, Listrostachys caudata. 9c, Musaenda isertiana.

350 A140 6c yel grn, org & yel .15 .15
351 A140 7c emer, yel & car .15 .15
352 A140 8c yel grn, buff & bl .15 .15
353 A140 9c orange & green .15 .15
Set value, #350-353, C91-C92 .65 .65

Rubber Tapping — A141

1955, Dec. 5 ***Perf. 12½***

354 A141 5c emerald & yellow .15 .15
Nos. 354,C97-C98 (3) .60 .50

50th anniv. of Rotary Intl. No. 354 exists printed entirely in emerald.

Statue of Liberty — A142

Coliseum, New York City A143

Design: 6c, Globe inscribed FIPEX.

1956, Apr. 28 ***Perf. 12***

355 A142 3c brt grn & dk red brn .15 .15
356 A143 4c Prus grn & bis brn .15 .15
357 A143 6c gray & red lilac .15 .15
Set value, #355-357, C100-C102 .72 .40

Fifth International Philatelic Exhibition (FIPEX), NYC, Apr. 28-May 6, 1956.

Kangaroo and Emu A144

Discus Thrower — A145

Designs: 8c, Goddess of Victory and Olympic symbols. 10c, Classic chariot race.

1956, Nov. 15 **Litho.** **Unwmk.**

358 A144 4c lt ol grn & gldn brn .15 .15
359 A145 6c emerald & gray .15 .15
360 A144 8c lt ultra & redsh brn .15 .15
361 A144 10c rose red & blk .15 .15
Set value, #358-361, C104-C105 .70 .35

16th Olympic Games at Melbourne, Nov. 22-Dec. 8, 1956.

Idlewild Airport, New York A146

5c, Roberts Field, Liberia, plane & Pres. Tubman.

Lithographed and Engraved

1957, May 4 *Perf. 12*

362	A146	3c orange & dk blue	.15	.15
363	A146	5c red lilac & blk	.15	.15
		Set value, #362-363, C107-C110	1.00	.50

1st anniv. of direct air service between Roberts Field, Liberia, and Idlewild (Kennedy), NY.

Orphanage Playground A147

Orphanage and: 5c, Teacher and pupil. 6c, Singing boys and natl. anthem. 10c, Children and flag.

1957, Nov. 25 **Litho.** *Perf. 12*

364	A147	4c green & red	.15	.15
365	A147	5c bl grn & red brn	.15	.15
366	A147	6c brt vio & bis	.15	.15
367	A147	10c ultra & rose car	.15	.15
		Set value, #364-367, C111-C112	.62	.42

Founding of the Antoinette Tubman Child Welfare Foundation.

Windmill and Dutch Flag — A148

Designs: No. 369, German flag and Brandenburg Gate. No. 370, Swedish flag, palace and crowns.

Engraved and Lithographed

1958, Jan. 10 **Unwmk.** *Perf. 10½*

Flags in Original Colors

368	A148	5c reddish brn	.15	.15
369	A148	5c blue	.15	.15
370	A148	5c lilac rose	.15	.15
		Set value, #368-370, C114-C117	.58	.40

European tour of Pres. Tubman in 1956.

Presidential Types of 1948-50

Designs as before.

1958-60 **Engr.** *Perf. 12*

Caption and Portrait in Black

371	A129	1c salmon pink	.25	.20
372	A128	2c brt yellow	.25	.20
373	A128	10c blue gray	.30	.30
374	A128	15c brt bl & blk ('59)	.15	.15
375	A128	20c dark red	.35	.35
376	A128	25c blue	.35	.35
377	A128	50c red lil & blk ('59)	.40	.35
378	A128	$1 bister brn ('60)	3.00	.40
		Nos. 371-378,C118 (9)	5.45	2.60

Many shades of 1c.

Open Globe Projection A149

Designs: 5c, UN Emblem and building. 10c, UN Emblem. 12c, UN Emblem and initials of agencies.

1958, Dec. 10 **Litho.** *Perf. 12*

379	A149	3c gray, bl & blk	.15	.15
380	A149	5c blue & choc	.15	.15
381	A149	10c black & org	.16	.16
382	A149	12c black & car	.22	.22
		Set value	.52	.52

10th anniv. of the Universal Declaration of Human Rights. See No. C119.

People of Africa on the March — A150

Symbols of UNESCO — A151

1959, Apr. 15

383	A150	20c orange & brown	.24	.24

African Freedom Day, Apr. 15. See No. C120.

1959, May 11 **Unwmk.**

384	A151	25c dp plum & emer	.30	.35

Opening of UNESCO Headquarters in Paris, Nov. 3, 1958.

See Nos. C121, C121a.

Abraham Lincoln — A152

1959, Nov. 20 **Engr.** *Perf. 12*

385	A152	10c ultra & blk	.15	.15
386	A152	15c orange & blk	.18	.18
a.		Souv. sheet of 3, Nos. 385-386, C122, imperf.	.90	1.50
		Nos. 385-386,C122 (3)	.71	.71

150th anniv. of the birth of Abraham Lincoln.

Touré, Tubman and Nkrumah A153

1960, Jan. 27 **Litho.** **Unwmk.**

387	A153	25c crimson & blk	.30	.30

1959 "Big Three" conference of Pres. Sékou Touré of Guinea, Pres. William V. S. Tubman of Liberia and Prime Minister Kwame Nkrumah of Ghana at Saniquellie, Liberia. See No. C123.

World Refugee Year Emblem — A154

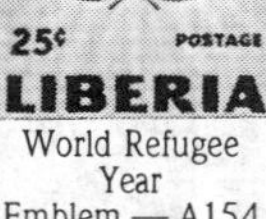

Map of Africa — A155

1960, Apr. 7 *Perf. 11½*

388	A154	25c emerald & blk	.30	.45

World Refuge Year, July 1, 1959-June 30, 1960. See No. C124, C124a.

1960, May 11 **Litho.** *Perf. 11½*

389	A155	25c green & black	.30	.30

10th anniv. of the Commission for Technical Cooperation in Africa South of the Sahara (C.C.T.A.). See No. C125.

Weight Lifter and Porter — A156

Liberian Stamps of 1860 — A157

Designs: 10c, Rower and canoeists, horiz. 15c, Walker and porter.

1960, Sept. 6 **Unwmk.**

390	A156	5c dk brn & emer	.15	.15
391	A156	10c brown & red lil	.15	.18
392	A156	15c brown & org	.25	.30
		Nos. 390-392,C126 (4)	1.05	1.01

17th Olympic Games, Rome, Aug. 25-Sept. 11.

1960, Dec. 1 **Litho.** *Perf. 11½*

393	A157	5c multicolored	.15	.15
394	A157	20c multicolored	.32	.32
		Nos. 393-394,C128 (3)	.79	.79

Liberian postage stamps, cent.

Laurel Wreath — A158

1961, May 19 **Unwmk.** *Perf. 11½*

395	A158	25c red & dk blue	.40	.40

Liberia's membership in the UN Security Council. Exists imperf. See Nos. C130-C131 and note after No. C131.

Anatomy Class — A159

1961, Sept. 8 *Perf. 11½*

396	A159	25c green & brown	.40	.40

15th anniv. of UNESCO. See #C132-C133.

Joseph J. Roberts Monument, Monrovia — A160

Design: 10c, Pres. Roberts and old and new presidential mansions, horiz.

1961, Oct. 25 **Litho.**

397	A160	5c orange & sepia	.15	.15
398	A160	10c ultra & sepia	.15	.15
		Nos. 397-398,C134 (3)	.60	.60

150th anniv. of the birth of Joseph J. Roberts, 1st pres. of Liberia.

Boy Scout — A161

Design: Insignia and Scouts camping.

1961, Dec. 4 **Unwmk.** *Perf. 11½*

399	A161	5c lilac & sepia	.15	.15
400	A161	10c ultra & bister	.25	.25
		Nos. 399-400,C135 (3)	1.15	1.15

Boy Scouts of Liberia. Exist imperf.

Dag Hammarskjold and UN Emblem A162

1962, Feb. 1 *Perf. 12*

401	A162	20c black & ultra	.30	.30

Dag Hammarskjold, Secretary General of the UN, 1953-61. See Nos. C137-C138.

Malaria Eradication Emblem — A163

1962, Apr. 7 **Litho.** *Perf. 12½*

402	A163	25c dk green & red	.35	.30

WHO drive to eradicate malaria. See Nos. C139-C140.

United Nations Emblem A164

1962, Oct. 22 *Perf. 12x12½*

403	A164	20c green & yel bis	.25	.25

Issued to mark the observance of United Nations Day, Oct. 24, as a national holiday.

See Nos. C144-C145.

Treasury Department Building, Monrovia A165

Buildings: 1c, 80c, Executive Mansion, Monrovia. 10c, Information Service. 15c, Capitol.

1962-64

403A	A165	1c vio bl & dp org ('64)	.15	.15
404	A165	5c lt blue & pur	.15	.15
405	A165	10c bister & brn	.15	.15
406	A165	15c salmon & dk bl	.18	.18
406A	A165	80c brn & yel ('64)	1.00	1.00
		Nos. 403A-406A,C146-C148 (9)	4.58	4.58

"FAO" Emblem and Food Bowl — A166

1963, Mar. 21 *Perf. 12½*

407	A166	5c aqua & dk car	.20	.20

FAO "Freedom from Hunger" campaign. See Nos. C149-C150.

Rocket in Space — A167

Design: 15c, Space capsule and globe.

1963, May 27 **Litho.** *Perf. 12½*

408	A167	10c dp vio bl & yel	.15	.15
409	A167	15c blue & red brn	.25	.25
		Nos. 408-409,C151 (3)	.80	.80

Achievements in space exploration for peaceful purposes.

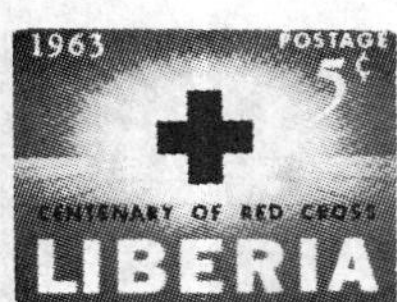

Red Cross — A168

Design: 10c, Centenary emblem and torch, vert.

1963, Aug. 26 Unwmk. *Perf. 11½*
410 A168 5c blue grn & red .15 .15
411 A168 10c gray & red .15 .15
Set value, #410-411, C153-C154 .80 .80

Intl. Red Cross, cent.

Palm Tree and Scroll — A169

Ski Jump — A170

1963, Oct. 28 *Perf. 12½*
412 A169 20c brown & green .30 .30

Conference of African heads of state for African Unity, Addis Ababa, May, 1963. See No. C156.

1963, Dec. 11 Unwmk. *Perf. 12½*
413 A170 5c rose red & dk vio bl .15 .15
Nos. 413,C157-C158 (3) .62 .62

9th Winter Olympic Games, Innsbruck, Austria, Jan. 29-Feb. 9, 1964.

John F. Kennedy A171

1964, Apr. 6 Litho.
414 A171 20c blk & brt blue .26 .26

John F. Kennedy (1917-63). See #C160-C161.

Syncom Satellite — A172

Satellites: 15c, Relay I, vert. 25c, Mariner II.

1964, June 22 Unwmk. *Perf. 12½*
415 A172 10c orange & emer .15 .15
416 A172 15c brt car rose & vio .20 .20
417 A172 25c blue, org & blk .40 .40
Nos. 415-417 (3) .75 .75

Progress in space communications and the peaceful uses of outer space. See No. C162.

Mt. Fuji — A173

Designs: 15c, Torii and Olympic flame. 25c, Cherry blossoms and stadium.

1964, Sept. 15 Litho.
418 A173 10c orange yel & emer .15 .15
419 A173 15c lt red & purple .20 .20
420 A173 25c ocher & red .55 .55
Nos. 418-420 (3) .90 .90

Issued for the 18th Olympic Games, Tokyo, Oct. 10-25, 1964. See No. C163.

Boy Scout Emblem and Scout Sign — A174

"Emancipation" by Thomas Ball — A175

10c, Bugle and Liberian Scout emblem, horiz.

1965, Mar. 8 Litho. *Perf. 12½*
421 A174 5c lt blue & brown .15 .15
422 A174 10c dk green & ocher .20 .20
Nos. 421-422,C164 (3) .80 .80

Liberian Boy Scouts.

1965, May 3 Unwmk. *Perf. 12½*

Designs: 20c, Abraham Lincoln and John F. Kennedy, horiz. 25c, Lincoln by Augustus St. Gaudens, Lincoln Park, Chicago.

423 A175 5c dk gray & brn org .15 .15
424 A175 20c emer & lt gray .28 .28
425 A175 25c maroon & blue .35 .35
Nos. 423-425 (3) .78 .78

Centenary of the death of Abraham Lincoln. See No. C166.

ICY Emblem A176

1965, June 21 Litho. *Perf. 12½*
426 A176 12c orange & brn .15 .15
427 A176 25c vio blue & brn .28 .28
428 A176 50c emerald & brn .60 .60
Nos. 426-428 (3) 1.03 1.03

Intl. Cooperation Year. See No. C167.

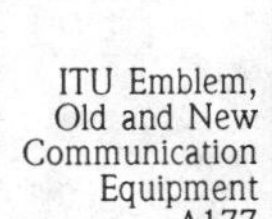

ITU Emblem, Old and New Communication Equipment A177

1965, Sept. 21 Unwmk. *Perf. 12½*
429 A177 25c brt grn & red brn .25 .25
430 A177 35c black & car rose .35 .35
Nos. 429-430,C168 (3) 1.10 1.05

Cent. of the ITU.

Pres. Tubman and Liberian Flag — A178

1965, Nov. 29 Litho.
431 A178 25c red, ultra & brn .40 .40

Pres. William V. S. Tubman's 70th birthday. See No. C169, C169a.

Churchill in Admiral's Uniform A179

Pres. Joseph J. Roberts A180

Designs: 15c, Churchill giving "V" sign, vert.

1966, Jan. 18 Litho. *Perf. 12½*
432 A179 15c orange & blk .18 .15
433 A179 20c black & brt grn .26 .15
Nos. 432-433,C170 (3) .74 .54

Issued in memory of Sir Winston Spencer Churchill (1874-1965), statesman and World War II leader.

1966-69 Litho. *Perf. 12½*

Presidents: 2c, Stephen Benson. 3c, Daniel Bashiel Warner. 4c, James S. Payne. 5c, Edward James Roye. 10c, William D. Coleman. 25c, Daniel Edward Howard. 50c, Charles Dunbar Burgess King. 80c, Hilary R. W. Johnson. $1, Edwin J. Barclay. $2, Joseph James Cheeseman ("Cheesman" on stamp).

434 A180 1c black & brick red .15 .15
435 A180 2c black & yellow .15 .15
436 A180 3c black & lilac .15 .15
437 A180 4c ap grn & blk ('67) .15 .15
438 A180 5c black & dull org .15 .15
439 A180 10c pale grn & blk ('67) .15 .15
440 A180 25c black & lt blue .30 .15
441 A180 50c blk & brt lil rose .65 .50
442 A180 80c dp rose & blk ('67) 1.00 .65
443 A180 $1 black & ocher 1.25 .15

Perf. 11½x11

443A A180 $2 blk & dp red lil ('69) 2.50 1.75
Nos. 434-443A,C182 (12) 7.20
Set value 3.60

Soccer Players and Globe — A181

Designs: 25c, World Championships Cup, ball and shoes, vert. 35c, Soccer player dribbling, vert.

1966, May 3 Litho. *Perf. 12½*
444 A181 10c brt green & dk brn .15 .15
445 A181 25c brt pink & brn .30 .20
446 A181 35c brown & orange .42 .26
Nos. 444-446 (3) .87 .61

World Cup Soccer Championships, Wembley, England, July 11-30. See No. C172.

Pres. Kennedy Taking Oath of Office — A182

20c, 1964 Kennedy stamps, Nos. 414, C160.

1966, Aug. 16 Litho. *Perf. 12½*
447 A182 15c red & blk .18 .15
448 A182 20c brt bl & red lil .22 .15
Nos. 447-448,C173-C174 (4) 1.03
Set value .50

3rd anniv. of Pres. Kennedy's death (Nov. 22).

Children on Seesaw and UNICEF Emblem — A183

Design: 80c, Boy playing doctor.

1966, Oct. 25 Unwmk. *Perf. 12½*
449 A183 5c brt blue & red .15 .15
450 A183 80c org brn & yel grn .75 .75

20th anniv. of UNICEF.

Giraffe — A184

Jamboree Badge — A185

Designs: 3c, Lion. 5c, Slender-nosed crocodile, horiz. 10c, Baby chimpanzees. 15c, Leopard, horiz. 20c, Black rhinoceros, horiz. 25c, Elephant.

1966, Dec. 20
451 A184 2c multicolored .15 .15
452 A184 3c multicolored .15 .15
453 A184 5c multicolored .15 .15
a. Black omitted ("5¢ LIBERIA" and imprint) *50.00*
454 A184 10c multicolored .15 .15
455 A184 15c multicolored .25 .15
456 A184 20c multicolored .35 .15
457 A184 25c multicolored .50 .20
Set value 1.30 .70

1967, Mar. 23 Litho. *Perf. 12½*

Designs: 25c, Boy Scout emblem and various sports, horiz. 40c, Scout at campfire and vision of moon landing, horiz.

458 A185 10c brt lil rose & grn .15 .15
459 A185 25c brt red & blue .35 .25
460 A185 40c brt grn & brn org .50 .40
Nos. 458-460 (3) 1.00 .80

12th Boy Scout World Jamboree, Farragut State Park, Idaho, Aug. 1-9. See No. C176.

A186

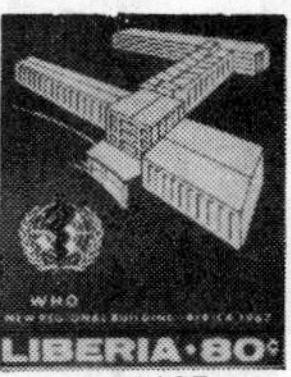

— A187

Pre-Hispanic Sculpture of Mexico: 25c, Aztec Calendar and Olympic rings. 40c, Mexican pottery, sombrero and guitar, horiz.

1967, June 20 Litho. *Perf. 12½*
461 A186 10c ocher & violet .15 .15
462 A186 25c lt bl, org & blk .35 .25
463 A186 40c yel grn & car .55 .40
Nos. 461-463 (3) 1.05 .80

Issued to publicize the 19th Olympic Games, Mexico City. See No. C177.

1967, Aug. 28 Litho. *Perf. 12½*

Designs: 5c, WHO Office for Africa, horiz. 80c, WHO Office for Africa.

464 A187 5c blue & yellow .15 .15
465 A187 80c brt grn & yel 1.00 1.00

Inauguration of the WHO Regional Office for Africa in Brazzaville, Congo.

Boy Playing African Rattle — A188

Africans Playing Native Instruments: 3c, Tom-tom and soko violin, horiz. 5c, Mang harp, horiz. 10c, Alimilim. 15c, Xylophone drums. 25c, Large tom-toms. 35c, Large harp.

1967, Oct. 16 Litho. *Perf. 14*
466 A188 2c violet & multi .15 .15
467 A188 3c blue & multi .15 .15
468 A188 5c lilac rose & multi .15 .15
469 A188 10c yel grn & multi .20 .15
470 A188 15c violet & multi .25 .15
471 A188 25c ocher & multi .55 .25
472 A188 35c dp rose & multi .90 .40
Nos. 466-472 (7) 2.35
Set value 1.00

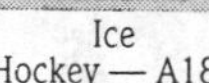
Ice Hockey — A189

Pres. William Tubman — A190

Designs: 25c, Ski jump. 40c, Bobsledding.

1967, Nov. 20 Litho. *Perf. 12½*

473 A189 10c emer & vio bl .15 .15
474 A189 25c grnsh bl & dp plum .25 .20
475 A189 40c ocher & org brn .45 .35
Nos. 473-475 (3) .85 .70

10th Winter Olympic Games, Grenoble, France, Feb. 6-18, 1968. See No. C178.

1967, Dec. 22 Litho. *Perf. 12½*

476 A190 25c ultra & brown .60 .30

Souvenir Sheet

Imperf

477 A190 50c ultra & brown 1.50 1.50

Inauguration of President Tubman, Jan. 1, 1968. No. 477 contains one stamp with simulated perforations and picture frame.

Human Rights Flame — A191

Martin Luther King, Jr. — A192

1968, Apr. 26 Litho. *Perf. 12½*

478 A191 3c ver & dp bl .15 .15
479 A191 80c brown & emer .75 .75

Intl. Human Rights Year. See No. C179.

1968, July 11 Unwmk. *Perf. 12½*

Designs: 15c, Mule-drawn hearse and Dr. King. 35c, Dr. King and Lincoln monument by Daniel Chester French, horiz.

480 A192 15c brt bl & brn .18 .15
481 A192 25c indigo & brn .26 .18
482 A192 35c olive & blk .40 .22
Nos. 480-482 (3) .84 .55

Rev. Dr. Martin Luther King, Jr. (1929-1968), American civil rights leader. See No. C180.

Javelin and Diana Statue, Mexico City — A193

Designs: 25c, Discus, pyramid and serpent god Quetzalcoatl. 35c, Woman diver and Xochicalco from ruins near Cuernavaca.

1968, Aug. 22 Litho. *Perf. 12½*

483 A193 15c dp vio & org brn .25 .15
484 A193 25c red & brt blue .45 .20
485 A193 35c brown & emer .65 .30
Nos. 483-485 (3) 1.35 .65

19th Olympic Games, Mexico City, Oct. 12-27. See No. C181.

Pres. Wm. V. S. Tubman — A194

Unification Monument, Voinjama-Lofa County — A195

1968, Dec. 30 Unwmk. *Perf. 12½*

486 A194 25c silver, blk & brn .85 .50

Souvenir Sheet

Imperf

487 A195 80c silver, ultra & red 2.00 1.50

25th anniv. of Pres. Tubman's administration.

"ILO" with Cogwheel and Wreath — A196

1969, Apr. 16 Litho. *Perf. 12½*

488 A196 25c lt blue & gold .40 .25

50th anniv. of the ILO. See No. C183.

Red Roofs, by Camille Pisarro — A197

Paintings: 3c, Prince Balthasar Carlos on Horseback, by Velazquez, vert. 10c, David and Goliath, by Caravaggio. 12c, Still Life, by Jean Baptiste Chardin. 15c, The Last Supper, by Leonardo da Vinci. 20c, Regatta at Argenteuil, by Claude Monet. 25c, Judgment of Solomon, by Giorgione. 35c, Sistine Madonna, by Raphael.

1969, June 26 Litho. *Perf. 11*

489 A197 3c gray & multi .20 .15
490 A197 5c gray & multi .20 .15
491 A197 10c lt blue & multi .20 .15
492 A197 12c gray & multi .30 .15
493 A197 15c gray & multi .30 .15
494 A197 20c gray & multi .50 .15
495 A197 25c gray & multi .60 .18
496 A197 35c gray & multi .80 .25
Nos. 489-496 (8) 3.10
Set value .90

See Nos. 502-509.

African Development Bank Emblem — A198

1969, Aug. 12 Litho. *Perf. 12½*

497 A198 25c blue & brown .35 .30
498 A198 80c yel grn & red 1.10 .60

5th anniversary of the African Development Bank.

Moon Landing and Liberia No. C174 — A199

15c, Memorial tablet left on moon, rocket, earth & moon, horiz. 35c, Take-off from moon.

1969, Oct. 15 Litho. *Perf. 12½*

499 A199 15c blue & bister .42 .15
500 A199 25c dk vio bl & org .65 .16
501 A199 35c gray & red .95 .22

Man's 1st landing on the moon, July 20, 1969. US astronauts Neil A. Armstrong and Col. Edwin E. Aldrin, Jr., with Lieut. Col. Michael Collins piloting Apollo 11. See No. C184.

Painting Type of 1969

1969, Nov. 18 Litho. *Perf. 11*

Paintings: 3c, The Gleaners, by Francois Millet. 5c, View of Toledo, by El Greco, vert. 10c, Heads of Negroes, by Rubens. 12c, The Last Supper, by El Greco. 15c, Dancing Peasants, by Brueghel. 20c, Hunters in the Snow, by Brueghel. 25c, Detail from Descent from the Cross, by Rogier van der Weyden, vert. 35c, The Ascension, by Murillo (inscribed "The Conception"), vert.

502 A197 3c lt blue & multi .20 .15
503 A197 5c lt blue & multi .20 .15
504 A197 10c lt blue & multi .20 .15
505 A197 12c gray & multi .25 .15
506 A197 15c gray & multi .35 .15
507 A197 20c lt blue & multi .45 .16
508 A197 25c gray & multi .60 .22
509 A197 35c lt blue & multi .80 .25
Nos. 502-509 (8) 3.05
Set value 1.00

Peace Dove, UN Emblem and Atom — A200

1970, Apr. 16 Litho. *Perf. 12½*

510 A200 5c green & silver .15 .15

25th anniv. of the UN. See No. C185.

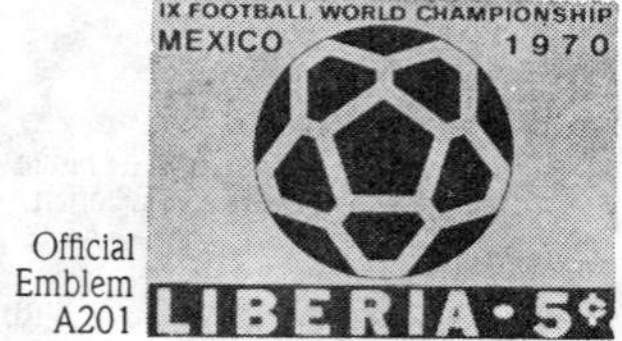

Official Emblem A201

Designs: 10c, Statue of rain god Tlaloc, vert. 25c, Jules Rimet cup and sculptured wall, vert. 35c, Sombrero and soccer ball. 55c, Two soccer players.

1970, June 10 Litho. *Perf. 12½*

511 A201 5c pale blue & brn .15 .15
512 A201 10c emerald & ocher .15 .15
513 A201 25c dp rose lil & gold .40 .20
514 A201 35c ver & ultra .60 .25
Nos. 511-514 (4) 1.30
Set value .55

Souvenir Sheet

Perf. 11½

515 A201 55c brt bl, yel & grn 1.75 1.00

9th World Soccer Championships for the Jules Rimet Cup, Mexico City, May 30-June 21, 1970.

EXPO '70 Emblem, Japanese Singer and Festival Plaza — A202

Designs (EXPO '70 Emblem and): 3c, Male Japanese singer, EXPO Hall and floating stage. 5c, Tower of the Sun and view of exhibition. 7c, Tanabata Festival. 8c, Awa Dance Festival. 25c, Sado-Okesa Dance Festival. 50c, Ricoh Pavilion with "eye," and Mt. Fuji, vert.

1970, July Litho. *Perf. 11*

516 A202 2c multicolored .15 .15
517 A202 3c multicolored .15 .15
518 A202 5c multicolored .25 .15
519 A202 7c multicolored .35 .15
520 A202 8c multicolored .45 .15
521 A202 25c multicolored 1.10 .24
Nos. 516-521 (6) 2.45
Set value .60

Souvenir Sheet

522 A202 50c multicolored 2.00 .65

Issued to publicize EXPO '70 International Exhibition, Osaka, Japan, Mar. 15-Sept. 13.

UPU Headquarters and Monument, Bern — A203

Design: 80c, Like 25c, vert.

1970, Aug. 25 *Perf. 12½*

523 A203 25c blue & multi .35 .28
524 A203 80c multicolored .80 .70

Inauguration of the new UPU Headquarters in Bern.

Napoleon as Consul, by Joseph Marie Vien, Sr. — A204

Paintings of Napoleon: 5c, Visit to a School, by unknown painter. 10c, Napoleon Bonaparte, by François Pascal Gerard. 12c, The French Campaign, by Ernest Meissonier. 20c, Napoleon Signing Abdication at Fontainebleau, by François Bouchot. 25c, Napoleon Meets Pope Pius VII, by Jean-Louis Demarne. 50c, Napoleon's Coronation, by Jacques Louis David.

1970, Oct. 20 Litho. *Perf. 11*

525 A204 3c blue & multi .20 .15
526 A204 5c blue & multi .20 .15
527 A204 10c blue & multi .35 .15
528 A204 12c blue & multi .50 .15
529 A204 20c blue & multi .75 .15
530 A204 25c blue & multi 1.40 .18
Nos. 525-530 (6) 3.40
Set value .62

Souvenir Sheet

Imperf

531 A204 50c blue & multi 2.00 .48

200th anniv. of the birth of Napoleon Bonaparte (1769-1821). No. 531 contains one stamp with simulated perforations.

Pres. Tubman A205

1970, Nov. 20 Litho. *Perf. 13½*

532 A205 25c multicolored .70 .35

Souvenir Sheet

Imperf

533 A205 50c multicolored 1.25 .70

Pres. Tubman's 75th birthday. No. 533 contains one imperf. stamp with simulated perforations.

Adoration of the Kings, by Rogier van der Weyden — A206

Paintings (Adoration of the Kings, by): 5c, Hans Memling. 10c, Stefan Lochner. 12c, Albrecht Altdorfer, vert. 20c, Hugo van der Goes, Adoration of the Shepherds. 25c, Hieronymus Bosch, vert. 50c, Andrea Mantegna (triptych).

Perf. 13½x14, 14x13½

1970, Dec. 21 Litho.

534 A206 3c multicolored .15 .15
535 A206 5c multicolored .15 .15
536 A206 10c multicolored .20 .15
537 A206 12c multicolored .25 .15
538 A206 20c multicolored .35 .15
539 A206 25c multicolored .50 .15
Nos. 534-539 (6) 1.60
Set value .50

Souvenir Sheet

Imperf

540 A206 50c multicolored 1.75 .50

Christmas 1970.
No. 540 contains one 60x40mm stamp.

Dogon Tribal Mask — A207

African Tribal Ceremonial Masks: 2c, Bapendé. 5c, Baoulé. 6c, Dédougou. 9c, Dan. 15c, Bamiléké. 20c, Bapendé mask and costume. 25c, Bamiléké mask and costume.

1971, Feb. 24 Litho. *Perf. 11*

541 A207 2c lt green & multi .15 .15
542 A207 3c pink & multi .15 .15
543 A207 5c lt blue & multi .15 .15
544 A207 6c lt green & multi .15 .15
545 A207 9c lt blue & multi .15 .15
546 A207 15c pink & multi .22 .15
547 A207 20c lt green & multi .50 .35
548 A207 25c pink & multi .26 .18
Set value 1.35 .90

Astronauts on Moon — A208

Designs: 5c, Astronaut and lunar transport vehicle. 10c, Astronaut with US flag on moon. 12c, Space capsule in Pacific Ocean. 20c, Astronaut leaving capsule. 25c, Astronauts Alan B. Shepard, Stuart A. Roosa and Edgar D. Mitchell.

1971, May 20 Litho. *Perf. 13½*

549 A208 3c vio blue & multi .20 .15
550 A208 5c vio blue & multi .20 .15
551 A208 10c vio blue & multi .30 .15
552 A208 12c vio blue & multi .40 .15
553 A208 20c vio blue & multi .55 .20
554 A208 25c vio blue & multi .70 .25
Nos. 549-554 (6) 2.35
Set value .70

Apollo 14 moon landing, Jan. 31-Feb. 9. See No. C186.

Map, Liberian Women and Pres. Tubman A209

3c, Pres. Tubman & women at ballot box, vert.

1971, May 27 *Perf. 12½*

555 A209 3c ultra & brn .15 .15
556 A209 80c green & brn 1.25 1.25

25th anniversary of women's suffrage.

Hall of Honor, Munich, and Olympic Flag — A210

Munich Views and Olympic Flag: 5c, General view. 10c, National Museum. 12c, Max Joseph's Square. 20c, Propylaeum on King's Square. 25c, Liesel-Karlstadt Fountain.

1971, June 28 Litho. *Perf. 11*

557 A210 3c multicolored .15 .15
558 A210 5c multicolored .15 .15
559 A210 10c multicolored .20 .15
560 A210 12c multicolored .25 .15
561 A210 20c multicolored .40 .20
562 A210 25c multicolored .60 .30
Nos. 557-562 (6) 1.75
Set value .80

Publicity for the 20th Summer Olympic Games, Munich, Germany, 1972. See No. C187.

Boy Scout, Emblem and US Flag — A211

Boy Scout, Natl. Flag & Boy Scout Emblem of: 5c, German Federal Republic. 10c, Australia. 12c, Great Britain. 20c, Japan. 25c, Liberia.

1971, Aug. 6 Litho. *Perf. 13½*

563 A211 3c multicolored .15 .15
564 A211 5c multicolored .15 .15
565 A211 10c multicolored .20 .15
566 A211 12c multicolored .25 .15
567 A211 20c multicolored .40 .15
568 A211 25c multicolored .50 .20
Nos. 563-568 (6) 1.65
Set value .55

13th Boy Scout World Jamboree, Asagiri Plain, Japan, Aug. 2-10. See No. C188.

Pres. Tubman (1895-1971) A212

1971, Aug. 23 *Perf. 12½*

569 A212 3c black, ultra & brn .15 .15
570 A212 25c blk, brt rose lil & brn .60 .60

Zebra and UNICEF Emblem — A213

Animals (UNICEF Emblem and Animals with their Young): 7c, Koala. 8c, Llama. 10c, Red fox. 20c, Monkey. 25c, Brown bear.

1971, Oct. 1 *Perf. 11*

571 A213 5c multicolored .20 .15
572 A213 7c multicolored .30 .15
573 A213 8c multicolored .30 .15
574 A213 10c multicolored .40 .15
575 A213 20c multicolored .80 .30
576 A213 25c multicolored 1.00 .40
Nos. 571-576 (6) 3.00
Set value 1.05

25th anniv. of UNICEF. See No. C189.

Sapporo 72 Emblem, Long-distance Skiing, Sika Deer — A214

3c, Sledding & black woodpecker. 5c, Ski Jump & brown bear. 10c, Bobsledding & murres. 15c, Figure skating & pikas. 25c, Downhill skiing & Japanese cranes.

1971, Nov. 4 *Perf. 13x13½*

577 A214 2c multicolored .15 .15
578 A214 3c multicolored .15 .15
579 A214 5c multicolored .15 .15
580 A214 10c multicolored .30 .15
581 A214 15c multicolored .40 .15
582 A214 25c multicolored 1.00 .20
Nos. 577-582 (6) 2.15
Set value .55

11th Winter Olympic Games, Sapporo, Japan, Feb. 3-13, 1972. See No. C190.

Dove Carrying Letter, APU Emblem A215

1971, Dec. 9 *Perf. 12½*

583 A215 25c ultra & dp org .40 .35
584 A215 80c gray & dp brn 1.25 1.00

10th anniversary of African Postal Union.

Pioneer Fathers' Monument, Monrovia — A216

Pres. William R. Tolbert, Jr. — A217

Designs: 3c, 25c, Sailing ship "Elizabeth," Providence Island, horiz. 35c, as 20c.

1972, Jan. 1

585 A216 3c blue & brt grn .15 .15
586 A216 20c orange & blue .60 .45
587 A216 25c orange & purple .65 .55
588 A216 35c lil rose & brt grn 1.10 .75
Nos. 585-588 (4) 2.50 1.90

Founding of Liberia, sesqui. See No. C191.

1972, Jan. 1

25c, Pres. Tolbert and map of Liberia, horiz.

589 A217 25c emerald & brown .40 .25
590 A217 80c blue & brown 1.40 .45

Inauguration of William R. Tolbert, Jr. as 19th president of Liberia.

Soccer and Swedish Flag — A218

Designs (Olympic Rings, "Motion" Symbol and): 5c, Swimmers at start and Italian flag. 10c, Equestrian and British flag. 12c, Bicycling and French flag. 20c, Long jump and American flag. 25c, Running and Liberian flag.

1972, May 19 Litho. *Perf. 11*

591 A218 3c lemon & multi .15 .15
592 A218 5c lt lilac & multi .15 .15
593 A218 10c multicolored .30 .15
594 A218 12c gray & multi .40 .15
595 A218 20c lt blue & multi .55 .24
596 A218 25c pink & multi .75 .30
Nos. 591-596 (6) 2.30
Set value .90

20th Olympic Games, Munich, Aug. 26-Sept. 10. See No. C192.

Y's Men's Club Emblem, Map — A219

Design: 90c, Y's Men's Club emblem and globe; inscribed "fifty and forward."

1972, June 12 *Perf. 13½*

597 A219 15c purple & gold .30 .20
598 A219 90c vio bl & emer 1.50 1.25

Intl. Y's Men's Club, 50th anniv.

Astronaut and Lunar Rover — A220

5c, Moon scene reflected in astronaut's helmet. 10c, Astronauts with cameras. 12c, Astronauts placing scientific equipment on moon. 20c, Apollo 16 badge. 25c, Astronauts riding lunar rover.

1972, June 26

599 A220	3c lt blue & multi	.20	.15
600 A220	5c red org & multi	.20	.15
601 A220	10c pink & multi	.30	.15
602 A220	12c yellow & multi	.50	.15
603 A220	20c lt vio & multi	.65	.15
604 A220	25c emerald & multi	.85	.20
	Nos. 599-604 (6)	2.70	
	Set value		.60

Apollo 16 US moon mission, Apr. 15-27, 1972. See No. C193.

Emperor Haile Selassie — A221

1972, July 21 *Perf. 14x14½*

605 A221	20c olive grn & yel	.45	.45
606 A221	25c maroon & yel	.55	.55
607 A221	35c brown & yel	.80	.80
	Nos. 605-607 (3)	1.80	1.80

80th birthday of Emperor Haile Selassie of Ethiopia.

Ajax, 1809, and Figurehead — A222

1972, Sept. 6 *Perf. 11*

608 A222	3c *shown*	.20	.15
609 A222	5c *Hogue, 1811*	.20	.15
610 A222	7c *Ariadne, 1816*	.30	.15
611 A222	15c *Royal Adelaide, 1828*	.55	.15
612 A222	20c *Rinaldo, 1860*	.70	.15
613 A222	25c *Nymphe, 1888*	.80	.25
	Nos. 608-613 (6)	2.75	
	Set value		.65

Famous sailing ships and their figureheads. See No. C194.

Pres. Tolbert Taking Oath, Richard A. Henries A223

1972, Oct. 23 **Litho.** *Perf. 13½*

614 A223	15c green & multi	.65	.55
615 A223	25c vio blue & multi	.90	.85

Pres. William R. Tolbert, Jr. sworn in as 19th President of Liberia, July 23, 1971. See No. C195.

Klaus Dibiasi, Italy, Diving — A224

8c, Valery Borzov, USSR, running. 10c, Hideaki Yanagida, Japan, wrestling. 12c, Mark Spitz, US, swimming. 15c, Kipchoge Keino, Kenya, 3000-meter steeplechase. 25c, Richard Meade, Great Britain, equestrian. 55c, Hans Winkler, Germany, grand prix jumping.

1973, Jan. 5 **Litho.** *Perf. 11*

616 A224	5c lt blue & multi	.15	.15
617 A224	8c violet & multi	.15	.15
618 A224	10c multicolored	.20	.15
619 A224	12c green & multi	.25	.15
620 A224	15c orange & multi	.35	.20
621 A224	25c pale salmon & multi	.50	.26
	Nos. 616-621 (6)	1.60	
	Set value		.90

Souvenir Sheet

622 A224	55c multicolored	1.25	.65

Gold medal winners in 20th Olympic Games.

Astronaut on Moon and Apollo 17 Badge — A225

Designs (Apollo 17 Badge and): 3c, Astronauts on earth in lunar rover. 10c, Astronauts collecting yellow lunar dust. 15c, Astronauts in lunar rover exploring moon crater. 20c, Capt. Eugene A. Cernan, Dr. Harrison H. Schmitt and Comdr. Ronald E. Evans on launching pad. 25c, Astronauts on moon with scientific equipment.

1973, Mar. 28 **Litho.** *Perf. 11*

623 A225	2c blue & multi	.20	.15
624 A225	3c blue & multi	.20	.15
625 A225	10c blue & multi	.20	.15
626 A225	15c blue & multi	.35	.16
627 A225	20c blue & multi	.50	.24
628 A225	25c blue & multi	.60	.32
	Nos. 623-628 (6)	2.05	
	Set value		.90

Apollo 17 US moon mission, Dec. 7-19, 1972. See No. C196.

Locomotive, England — A226

Designs: Locomotives, 1895-1905.

1973, May 4

629 A226	2c shown	.20	.15
630 A226	3c Netherlands	.20	.15
631 A226	10c France	.30	.15
632 A226	15c United States	.40	.15
633 A226	20c Japan	.60	.20
634 A226	25c Germany	.75	.26
	Nos. 629-634 (6)	2.45	
	Set value		.75

See No. C197.

OAU Emblem and Flags — A227

1973, May 24 **Litho.** *Perf. 13½*

635 A227	3c multicolored	.15	.15
636 A227	5c multicolored	.15	.15
637 A227	10c multicolored	.15	.15
638 A227	15c multicolored	.25	.20
639 A227	25c multicolored	.35	.25
640 A227	50c multicolored	.75	.50
	Nos. 635-640 (6)	1.80	
	Set value		1.20

10th anniv. of the Organization for African Unity.

WHO Emblem, Edward Jenner and Roses — A228

Designs (WHO Emblem and): 4c, Sigmund Freud and pansies. 10c, Jonas E. Salk and chrysanthemums. 15c, Louis Pasteur and scabiosa caucasia. 20c, Emil von Behring and rhododendron. 25c, Alexander Fleming and tree mallows.

1973, June 26 **Litho.** *Perf. 11*

641 A228	1c gray & multi	.15	.15
642 A228	4c orange & multi	.15	.15
643 A228	10c lt blue & multi	.15	.15
644 A228	15c rose & multi	.22	.15
645 A228	20c blue & multi	.30	.18
646 A228	25c yel grn & multi	.38	.24
	Set value	1.10	.65

25th anniv. of WHO. See No. C198.

Stanley Steamer, 1910 — A229

Designs: Classic automobiles.

1973, Sept. 11 **Litho.** *Perf. 11*

647 A229	2c shown	.15	.15
648 A229	3c Cadillac, 1903	.15	.15
649 A229	10c Clement-Bayard, 1904	.25	.15
650 A229	15c Rolls Royce, 1907	.35	.15
651 A229	20c Maxwell, 1905	.50	.20
652 A229	25c Chadwick, 1907	.60	.30
	Nos. 647-652 (6)	2.00	
	Set value		.80

See No. C199.

Copernicus, Armillary Sphere, Satellite Communication — A230

Portraits of Copernicus and: 4c, Eudoxus solar system. 10c, Aristotle, Ptolemy, Copernicus and satellites. 15c, Saturn and Apollo spacecraft. 20c, Orbiting astronomical observatory. 25c, Satellite tracking station.

1973, Dec. 14 **Litho.** *Perf. 13½*

653 A230	1c yellow & multi	.15	.15
654 A230	4c lt violet & multi	.15	.15
655 A230	10c lt blue & multi	.20	.15
656 A230	15c yel grn & multi	.30	.15
657 A230	20c bister & multi	.40	.18
658 A230	25c pink & multi	.50	.24
	Nos. 653-658 (6)	1.70	
	Set value		.65

Nicolaus Copernicus (1473-1543), Polish astronomer. See No. C200.

Radio Tower, Map of Africa — A231

Designs: 15c, 25c, Map of Liberia, Radio tower and man listening to broadcast. 17c, like 13c.

1974, Jan. 16 **Litho.** *Perf. 13½*

659 A231	13c multicolored	.35	.35
660 A231	15c yellow & multi	.35	.30
661 A231	17c lt gray & multi	.45	.35
662 A231	25c brt green & multi	.60	.40
	Nos. 659-662 (4)	1.75	1.40

20th anniv. of Radio ELWA, Monrovia.

Thomas Courts, 1817; Aureal, 1974; UPU Emblem — A232

Designs (UPU Emblem and): 3c, Jet, satellite, Post Office, Monrovia, ship. 10c, US and USSR telecommunication satellites. 15c, Mail runner and jet. 20c, Futuristic mail train and mail truck. 25c, American Pony Express rider.

1974, Mar. 4 **Litho.** *Perf. 13½*

663 A232	2c ocher & multi	.15	.15
664 A232	3c lt green & multi	.15	.15
665 A232	10c lt blue & multi	.20	.15
666 A232	15c pink & multi	.30	.15
667 A232	20c gray & multi	.40	.20
668 A232	25c lt lilac & multi	.50	.25
	Nos. 663-668 (6)	1.70	
	Set value		.75

Cent. of UPU. See No. C201.

Fox Terrier — A233

1974, Apr. 16 **Litho.** *Perf. 13½*

669 A233	5c shown	.20	.15
670 A233	10c Boxer	.20	.15
671 A233	16c Chihuahua	.40	.15
672 A233	19c Beagle	.45	.15
673 A233	25c Golden retriever	.50	.15
674 A233	50c Collie	1.10	.25
	Nos. 669-674 (6)	2.85	
	Set value		.65

See No. C202.

Soccer Game, West Germany and Chile — A234

Designs: Games between semi-finalists, and flags of competing nations.

1974, June 4 **Litho.** *Perf. 11*

675 A234	1c shown	.15	.15
676 A234	2c Australia and East Germany	.15	.15
677 A234	5c Brazil and Yugoslavia	.15	.15
678 A234	10c Zaire and Scotland	.15	.15
679 A234	12c Netherlands and Uruguay	.20	.15
680 A234	15c Sweden and Bulgaria	.25	.15
681 A234	20c Italy and Haiti	.35	.20
682 A234	25c Poland and Argentina	.40	.25
	Set value	1.50	.80

World Cup Soccer Championship, Munich, June 13-July 7. See No. C203.

Chrysiridia Madagascariensis — A235

Tropical Butterflies: 2c, Catagramma sorana. 5c, Erasmia pulchella. 17c, Morpho cypris. 25c, Agrias amydon. 40c, Vanessa cardui.

1974, Sept. 11 Litho. *Perf. 13½*

683 A235 1c gray & multi .15 .15
684 A235 2c gray & multi .15 .15
685 A235 5c gray & multi .20 .15
686 A235 17c gray & multi .60 .15
687 A235 25c gray & multi .80 .25
688 A235 40c gray & multi 1.50 .40
Nos. 683-688 (6) 3.40
Set value .85

See No. C204.

Pres. Tolbert and Medal A236

$1, Pres. Tolbert, medal & Liberian flag, vert.

1974, Dec. 10 Litho. *Perf. 13½*

689 A236 3c multicolored .15 .15
690 A236 $1 multicolored 1.65 1.25

Pres. William R. Tolbert, Jr., recipient of 1974 Family of Man Award.

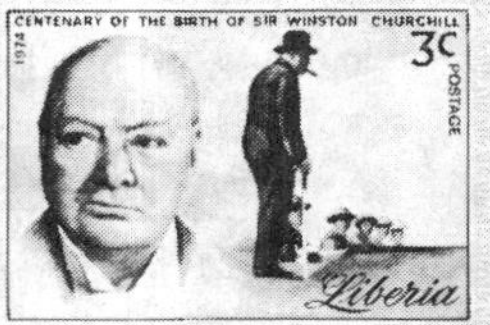

Winston Churchill, 1940 — A237

Designs (Churchill and): 10c, RAF planes in dog fight. 15c, In naval launch on way to Normandy. 17c, In staff car reviewing troops in desert. 20c, Aboard landing craft crossing Rhine. 25c, In conference with Pres. Roosevelt.

1975, Jan. 17 Litho. *Perf. 13½*

691 A237 3c multicolored .15 .15
692 A237 10c multicolored .15 .15
693 A237 15c multicolored .20 .15
694 A237 17c multicolored .25 .15
695 A237 20c multicolored .30 .15
696 A237 25c multicolored .50 .25
Nos. 691-696 (6) 1.55
Set value .70

Sir Winston Churchill (1874-1965), birth centenary. See No. C205.

Women's Year Emblem and Marie Curie A238

3c, Mahalia Jackson with microphone. 5c, Joan of Arc. 10c, Eleanor Roosevelt and children. 25c, Matilda Newport firing cannon. 50c, Valentina Tereshkova in space suit.

1975, Mar. 14 Litho. *Perf. 14½*

697 A238 2c citron & multi .15 .15
698 A238 3c dull orange & multi .15 .15
699 A238 5c lilac rose & multi .15 .15
700 A238 10c yellow & multi .20 .15
701 A238 25c yellow grn & multi .45 .15
702 A238 50c lilac & multi .85 .35
Nos. 697-702 (6) 1.95
Set value .65

Intl. Women's Year 1975. See No. C206.

Old State House, Boston, US No. 627 — A239

10c, George Washington, US #644. 15c, Town Hall & Court House, Philadelphia, US #798. 20c, Benjamin Franklin, US #835. 25c, Paul Revere's Ride, US #618. 50c, Santa Maria, US #231.

1975, Apr. 25 Litho. *Perf. 13½*

703 A239 5c multicolored .15 .15
704 A239 10c multicolored .25 .15
705 A239 15c multicolored .30 .15
706 A239 20c multicolored .45 .15
707 A239 25c multicolored .60 .15
708 A239 50c multicolored 1.25 .25
Nos. 703-708 (6) 3.00
Set value .70

American Revolution Bicentennial. See No. C207.

Dr. Schweitzer, Hospital and Baboon Mother — A240

Designs (Dr. Schweitzer and): 3c, Elephant, and tribesmen poling boat. 5c, Water buffalo, egret, man and woman paddling canoe. 6c, Antelope and dancer. 25c, Lioness, woman cooking outdoors. 50c, Zebra and colt, doctor's examination at clinic.

1975, June 26 Litho. *Perf. 13½*

709 A240 1c multicolored .15 .15
710 A240 3c multicolored .15 .15
711 A240 5c multicolored .15 .15
712 A240 6c multicolored .15 .15
713 A240 25c multicolored .75 .15
714 A240 50c multicolored 1.50 .40
Nos. 709-714 (6) 2.85
Set value .70

Dr. Albert Schweitzer (1875-1965), medical missionary, birth centenary. See No. C208.

American-Russian Handshake in Space — A241

Designs (Apollo-Soyuz Emblem and): 5c, Apollo. 10c, Soyuz. 20c, Flags and maps of US and USSR. 25c, A. A. Leonov, and V. N. Kubasov. 50c, D. K. Slayton, V. D. Brand, T. P. Stafford.

1975, Sept. 18 Litho. *Perf. 13½*

715 A241 5c multicolored .15 .15
716 A241 10c multicolored .15 .15
717 A241 15c multicolored .25 .15
718 A241 20c multicolored .35 .15
719 A241 25c multicolored .45 .15
720 A241 50c multicolored .90 .30
Nos. 715-720 (6) 2.25
Set value .65

Apollo Soyuz space test project (Russo-American cooperation), launching July 15; link-up, July 17. See No. C209.

Presidents Tolbert, Siaka Stevens; Treaty Signing; Liberia and Sierra Leone Maps — A242

1975, Oct. 3 Litho. *Perf. 13½*

721 A242 2c gray & multi .15 .15
722 A242 3c gray & multi .15 .15
723 A242 5c gray & multi .15 .15
724 A242 10c gray & multi .15 .15
725 A242 25c gray & multi .40 .25
726 A242 50c gray & multi .80 .50
Nos. 721-726 (6) 1.80
Set value 1.00

Mano River Union Agreement between Liberia and Sierra Leone, signed Oct. 3, 1973.

Figure Skating A243

Designs (Winter Olympic Games Emblem and): 4c, Ski jump. 10c, Slalom. 25c, Ice hockey. 35c, Speed skating. 50c, Two-man bobsled.

1976, Jan. 23 Litho. *Perf. 13½*

727 A243 1c lt blue & multi .15 .15
728 A243 4c lt blue & multi .15 .15
729 A243 10c lt blue & multi .15 .15
730 A243 25c lt blue & multi .45 .15
731 A243 35c lt blue & multi .65 .20
732 A243 50c lt blue & multi 1.00 .30
Nos. 727-732 (6) 2.55
Set value .72

12th Winter Olympic Games, Innsbruck, Austria, Feb. 4-15. See No. C210.

Pres. Tolbert Taking Oath of Office A244

25c, Pres. Tolbert at his desk, vert. $1, Seal & flag of Liberia, $400 commemorative gold coin.

1976, Apr. 5 Litho. *Perf. 13½*

733 A244 3c multicolored .15 .15
734 A244 25c multicolored .35 .35
735 A244 $1 multicolored 1.50 1.50
Nos. 733-735 (3) 2.00 2.00

Inauguration of President William R. Tolbert, Jr., Jan. 5, 1976.

Weight Lifting and Olympic Rings — A245

Designs (Olympic Rings and): 3c, Pole vault. 10c, Hammer and shot put. 25c, Yachting. 35c, Women's gymnastics. 50c, Hurdles.

1976, May 4 Litho. *Perf. 13½*

736 A245 2c gray & multi .15 .15
737 A245 3c orange & multi .15 .15
738 A245 10c lt violet & multi .15 .15
739 A245 25c lt green & multi .45 .15
740 A245 35c yellow & multi .60 .25
741 A245 50c pink & multi 1.00 .25
Nos. 736-741 (6) 2.50
Set value .80

21st Olympic Games, Montreal, Canada, July 17-Aug. 1. See No. C211.

A. G. Bell, Telephone and Receiver, 1876, UPU Emblem — A246

UPU Emblem and: 4c, Horsedrawn mail coach and ITU emblem. 5c, Intelsat IV satellite, radar and ITU emblem. 25c, A. G. Bell, ship laying underwater cable, 1976 telephone. 40c, A. G. Bell, futuristic train, telegraph and telephone wires. 50c, Wright brothers' plane, Zeppelin and Concorde.

1976, June 4 Litho. *Perf. 13½*

742 A246 1c green & multi .15 .15
743 A246 4c ocher & multi .15 .15
744 A246 5c orange & multi .15 .15
745 A246 25c green & multi .35 .15
746 A246 40c lilac & multi .55 .20
747 A246 50c blue & multi .75 .25
Nos. 742-747 (6) 2.10
Set value .65

Cent. of 1st telephone call by Alexander Graham Bell, Mar. 10, 1876. See No. C212.

Gold Nugget on Chain, Gold Panner A247

1976-81 Litho. *Perf. 14½*

749 A247 1c Mano River Bridge .15 .15
750 A247 3c shown .15 .15
751 A247 5c "V" ring .15 .15
752 A247 7c like 5c ('81) .20 .15
753 A247 10c Rubber tire, tree .25 .15
754 A247 15c Harvesting .40 .35
755 A247 17c like 55c ('81) .45 .35
756 A247 20c Hydroelectric plant .55 .45
757 A247 25c Mesurado shrimp .70 .15
758 A247 27c Woman tie-dying cloth .75 .55
759 A247 55c Lake Piso, barracuda 1.50 .40
760 A247 $1 Train hauling iron ore 2.75 2.00
Nos. 749-760 (12) 8.00 5.00

See Nos. 945-953.

Rhinoceros — A249

African Animals: 3c, Zebra antelope. 5c, Chimpanzee, vert. 15c, Pigmy hippopotamus. 25c, Leopard. $1, Gorilla, vert.

1976, Sept. 1 Litho. *Perf. 13½*

763 A249 2c orange & multi .15 .15
764 A249 3c gray & multi .15 .15
765 A249 5c blue & multi .15 .15
766 A249 15c brt blue & multi .25 .15
767 A249 25c ultra & multi .45 .25
768 A249 $1 multicolored 1.65 .75
Nos. 763-768 (6) 2.80
Set value 1.20

See No. C213.

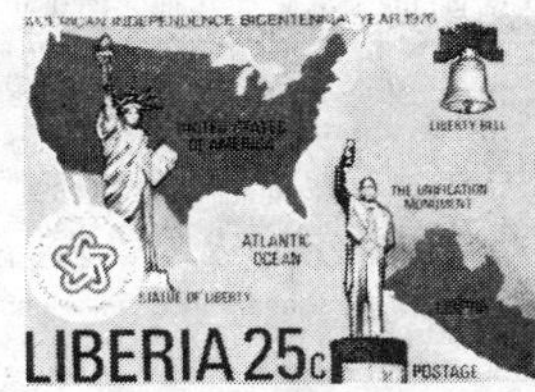

Maps of US and Liberia; Statue of Liberty, Unification Monument, Voinjama and Liberty Bell — A250

$1, George Washington, Gerald R. Ford, Joseph J. Roberts (1st Pres. of Liberia), William R. Tolbert, Jr., Bicentennial emblem, US & Liberian flags.

1976, Sept. 21 Litho. *Perf. 13½*

769 A250 25c multicolored .45 .25
770 A250 $1 multicolored 1.65 .60

American Bicentennial and visit of Pres. William R. Tolbert, Jr. to the US, Sept. 21-30. See No. C214.

Baluba Masks and Festival Emblem A251

Tribal Masks: 10c, Bateke. 15c, Basshilele. 20c, Igungun. 25c, Masai. 50c, Kifwebe.

1977, Jan. 20 Litho. *Perf. 13½*

No.	Type	Description	Unused	Used
771	A251	5c yellow & multi	.20	.15
772	A251	10c green & multi	.25	.15
773	A251	15c salmon & multi	.35	.15
774	A251	20c lt blue & multi	.40	.15
775	A251	25c violet & multi	.50	.18
776	A251	50c lemon & multi	.95	.28
		Nos. 771-776 (6)	2.65	
		Set value		.80

FESTAC '77, 2nd World Black and African Festival, Lagos, Nigeria, Jan. 15-Feb. 12. See No. C215.

Latham's Francolin — A252

Birds of Liberia: 10c, Narina trogon. 15c, Rufous-crowned roller. 20c, Brown-cheeked hornbill. 25c, Common bulbul. 50c, Fish eagle. 80c, Gold Coast touraco.

1977, Feb. 18 Litho. *Perf. 14*

No.	Type	Description	Unused	Used
777	A252	5c multicolored	.15	.15
778	A252	10c multicolored	.25	.15
779	A252	15c multicolored	.35	.15
780	A252	20c multicolored	.50	.15
781	A252	25c multicolored	.60	.20
782	A252	50c multicolored	1.50	.30
		Nos. 777-782 (6)	3.35	
		Set value		.85

Souvenir Sheet

No.	Type	Description	Unused	Used
783	A252	80c multicolored	2.25	1.50

Edmund Coffin, Military Dressage, US — A253

Designs: 15c, Alwin Schockemohle, single jump, Germany, vert. 20c, Christine Stuckelberger, Switzerland, single dressage. 25c, Prize of the Nations (team), France.

1977, Apr. 22 Litho. *Perf. 13½*

No.	Type	Description	Unused	Used
784	A253	5c ocher & multi	.15	.15
785	A253	15c ocher & multi	.30	.15
786	A253	20c ocher & multi	.35	.15
787	A253	25c ocher & multi	.45	.25
		Nos. 784-787,C216 (5)	2.25	1.20

Equestrian gold medal winners in Montreal Olympic Games. See No. C217.

Elizabeth II Wearing Crown — A254

Designs: 25c, Elizabeth II Prince Philip, Pres. and Mrs. Tubman. 80c, Elizabeth II, Prince Philip, royal coat of arms.

1977, May 23 Litho. *Perf. 13½*

No.	Type	Description	Unused	Used
788	A254	15c silver & multi	.30	.15
789	A254	25c silver & multi	.50	.15
790	A254	80c silver & multi	1.50	.45
		Nos. 788-790 (3)	2.30	.75

25th anniversary of the reign of Queen Elizabeth II. See No. C218.

Jesus Blessing Children A255

Christmas: 25c, The Good Shepherd. $1, Jesus and the Samaritan Woman. Designs after stained-glass windows, Providence Baptist Church, Monrovia.

1977, Nov. 3 Litho. *Perf. 13½*

No.	Type	Description	Unused	Used
791	A255	20c lt blue & multi	.40	.25
792	A255	25c lt blue & multi	.55	.30
793	A255	$1 lt blue & multi	1.75	.95
		Nos. 791-793 (3)	2.70	1.50

Dornier DOX, 1928 — A256

Progress of Aviation: 3c, Piggyback space shuttle, 1977. 5c, Eddie Rickenbacker and Douglas DC 3. 25c, Charles A. Lindbergh and Spirit of St. Louis. 35c, Louis Bleriot and Bleriot XI. 50c, Orville and Wilbur Wright and flying machine, 1903. 80c, Concorde landing at night at Dulles Airport, Washington, DC.

1978, Jan. 6 Litho. *Perf. 13½*

No.	Type	Description	Unused	Used
794	A256	2c multicolored	.15	.15
795	A256	3c multicolored	.15	.15
796	A256	5c multicolored	.15	.15
797	A256	25c multicolored	.45	.25
798	A256	35c multicolored	.65	.30
799	A256	50c multicolored	.95	.45
		Nos. 794-799 (6)	2.50	
		Set value		1.10

Souvenir Sheet

No.	Type	Description	Unused	Used
800	A256	80c multicolored	1.50	1.10

Baladeuse by Santos-Dumont, 1903 — A257

Airships: 3c, Baldwin's, 1908, and US flag. 5c, Tissandier brothers', 1883. 25c, Parseval PL VII, 1912. 40c, Nulli Secundus II, 1908. 50c, R34 rigid airship, 1919.

1978, Mar. 9 Litho. *Perf. 13½*

No.	Type	Description	Unused	Used
801	A257	2c multicolored	.15	.15
802	A257	3c multicolored	.15	.15
803	A257	5c multicolored	.15	.15
804	A257	25c multicolored	.35	.15
805	A257	40c multicolored	.55	.16
806	A257	50c multicolored	.75	.20
		Nos. 801-806 (6)	2.10	
		Set value		.55

75th anniv. of the Zeppelin. See No. C219.

Soccer, East Germany and Brazil — A258

Soccer Games: 2c, Poland and Argentina, vert. 10c, West Germany and Netherlands. 25c, Yugoslavia and Brazil. 35c, Poland and Italy, vert. 50c, Netherlands and Uruguay.

1978, May 16 Litho. *Perf. 13½*

No.	Type	Description	Unused	Used
807	A258	2c multicolored	.15	.15
808	A258	3c multicolored	.15	.15
809	A258	10c multicolored	.25	.15
810	A258	25c multicolored	.55	.30
811	A258	35c multicolored	.80	.40
812	A258	50c multicolored	1.10	.55
		Nos. 807-812 (6)	3.00	
		Set value		1.40

11th World Cup Soccer Championships, Argentina, June 1-25. See No. C220.

Coronation Chair — A259

Designs: 25c, Imperial state crown. $1, Buckingham Palace, horiz.

1978, June 12

No.	Type	Description	Unused	Used
813	A259	5c multicolored	.15	.15
814	A259	25c multicolored	.45	.15
815	A259	$1 multicolored	1.65	.65
		Nos. 813-815 (3)	2.25	
		Set value		.80

25th anniversary of coronation of Queen Elizabeth II. See No. C221.

Jinnah, Liberian and Pakistani Flags — A260

1978, June Litho. *Perf. 13*

No.	Type	Description	Unused	Used
816	A260	30c multicolored	*22.50*	5.00

Mohammed Ali Jinnah (1876-1948), first Governor General of Pakistan.

Carter and Tolbert Families — A261

Designs: 25c, Pres. Tolbert, Rosalynn Carter and Pres. Carter at microphone, Robertsfield Airport. $1, Jimmy Carter and William R. Tolbert, Jr. in motorcade from airport.

1978, Oct. 26 Litho. *Perf. 13½*

No.	Type	Description	Unused	Used
817	A261	5c multicolored	.15	.15
818	A261	25c multicolored	.50	.50
819	A261	$1 multicolored	2.00	2.00
		Nos. 817-819 (3)	2.65	2.65

Pres. Carter's visit to Liberia, Apr. 1978.

Soccer Game: Italy-France A262

Soccer Games: 1c, Brazil-Spain, horiz. 10c, Poland-West Germany, horiz. 27c, Peru-Scotland. 35c, Austria-West Germany. 50c, Argentina the victor.

1978, Dec. 8 Litho. *Perf. 13½*

No.	Type	Description	Unused	Used
820	A262	1c multicolored	.15	.15
821	A262	2c multicolored	.15	.15
822	A262	10c multicolored	.25	.15
823	A262	27c multicolored	.60	.40
824	A262	35c multicolored	.75	.50
825	A262	50c multicolored	1.10	.75
		Nos. 820-825 (6)	3.00	2.10

1978 World Cup Soccer winners. See No. C222.

Liberian Lumbermen — A263

Designs: 10c, Hauling timber by truck, vert. 25c, Felling trees with chain saw. 50c, Moving logs.

1978, Dec. 15 Litho. *Perf. 13½x14*

No.	Type	Description	Unused	Used
826	A263	5c multicolored	.15	.15
827	A263	10c multicolored	.25	.15
828	A263	25c multicolored	.55	.40
829	A263	50c multicolored	1.10	.80
		Nos. 826-829 (4)	2.05	1.50

8th World Forestry Congress, Djakarta, Indonesia.

"25" and Waves — A264

Design: $1, Radio tower and waves.

1979, Apr. 6 Litho. *Perf. 14x13½*

No.	Type	Description	Unused	Used
830	A264	35c multicolored	.75	.75
831	A264	$1 multicolored	2.00	2.00

25th anniversary of Radio ELWA.

Emblems of IYC, African Child's Decade and SOS Village — A265

Designs: 25c, $1, like 5c, with UNICEF emblem replacing SOS emblem. 35c, like 5c.

1979, Apr. 6 *Perf. 13½x14*

No.	Type	Description	Unused	Used
832	A265	5c multicolored	.15	.15
833	A265	25c multicolored	.45	.45
834	A265	35c multicolored	.75	.75
835	A265	$1 multicolored	1.75	1.75
		Nos. 832-835 (4)	3.10	3.10

IYC and Decade of the African Child.

Presidents Gardner and Tolbert, and Post Office, Monrovia — A266

Design: 35c, Anthony W. Gardner, William R. Tolbert, Jr. and UPU emblem.

1979, Apr. 2 Litho. *Perf. 13½x14*

No.	Type	Description	Unused	Used
836	A266	5c multicolored	.15	.15
837	A266	35c multicolored	.80	.80

Cent. of Liberia's joining UPU.

Unity Problem, Map of Africa, Torches — A267

Designs: 27c, Masks. 35c, Elephant, giraffe, lion, antelope, cheetah and map of Africa. 50c, Huts, pepper birds and map of Africa.

1979, July 6 Litho. *Perf. 14x13½*

838 A267	5c multicolored	.15	.15
839 A267	27c multicolored	.55	.55
840 A267	35c multicolored	.75	.75
841 A267	50c multicolored	1.10	1.10
	Nos. 838-841 (4)	2.55	2.55

Organization for African Unity, 16th anniversary, and OAU Summit Conference.

Liberia No. 666, Rowland Hill — A268

10c, Pony Express rider, 1860. 15c, British mail coach, 1800. 25c, Mail steamship John Penn, 1860. 27c, Stanier Pacific train, 1939. 50c, Concorde. $1, Curtiss Jenny, 1916.

1979, July 20

842 A268	3c multicolored	.15	.15
843 A268	10c multicolored	.16	.15
844 A268	15c multicolored	.28	.24
845 A268	25c multicolored	.45	.38
846 A268	27c multicolored	.50	.42
847 A268	50c multicolored	.90	.75
	Nos. 842-847 (6)	2.44	2.09

Souvenir Sheet

848 A268	$1 multicolored	1.75	1.25

Sir Rowland Hill (1795-1879), originator of penny postage.

Red Cross, Pres. Tolbert Donating Blood — A269

Design: 50c, Red Cross, Pres. Tolbert.

1979, Aug. 15 Litho. *Perf. 13½*

849 A269	30c multicolored	.60	.60
850 A269	50c multicolored	1.00	1.00

National Red Cross, 30th anniversary and blood donation campaign.

M.S. World Peace A270

Design: $1, M.S. World Peace, diff.

1979, Aug. 15

851 A270	5c multicolored	.15	.15
852 A270	$1 multicolored	1.90	1.90

2nd World Maritime Day, March 16; Liberia Maritime Program, 30th anniversary.

A Good Turn, by Norman Rockwell A271

Paintings: Scouting through the eyes of Norman Rockwell, 1925-1976. Each denomination in 10 different designs.

1979, Sept. 1 Litho. *Perf. 11*

853 A271	5c any single	.15	.15
854 A271	10c any single	.15	.15
855 A271	15c any single	.25	.20
856 A271	25c any single	.50	.30
857 A271	35c any single	.75	.50
a.	Set of 50	20.00	20.00

Mrs. Tolbert, Children, Children's Village Emblem — A272

40c, Mrs. Tolbert, children, emblem, vert.

1979, Nov. 14 Litho. *Perf. 14*

858 A272	25c multicolored	.50	.50
859 A272	40c multicolored	1.00	1.00

SOS Children's Village in Monrovia, Liberia.

Rotary International Headquarters, Evanston, Ill., Emblem — A273

Rotary Emblem and: 5c, Vocational services. 17c, Man in wheelchair, nurse, vert. 27c, Flags of several nations. 35c, People of various races holding hands around globe. 50c, Pres. Tolbert, map of Africa, vert. $1, "Gift of Life."

1979, Dec. 28 *Perf. 11*

860 A273	1c multicolored	.15	.15
861 A273	5c multicolored	.15	.15
862 A273	17c multicolored	.25	.25
863 A273	27c multicolored	.50	.50
864 A273	35c multicolored	.60	.60
865 A273	50c multicolored	1.00	1.00
	Nos. 860-865 (6)	2.65	2.65

Souvenir Sheet

866 A273	$1 multicolored	2.00	2.00

Rotary International, 75th anniversary.

Ski Jump, Lake Placid '80 Emblem — A274

Lake Placid '80 Emblem and: 5c, Figure skating. 17c, Bobsledding. 27c, Cross-country skiing. 35c, Women's speed skating. 50c, Ice hockey. $1, Slalom.

1980, Jan. 21

867 A274	1c multicolored	.15	.15
868 A274	5c multicolored	.15	.15
869 A274	17c multicolored	.35	.35
870 A274	27c multicolored	.70	.70
871 A274	35c multicolored	.70	.70
872 A274	50c multicolored	1.00	1.00
	Nos. 867-872 (6)	3.05	3.05

Souvenir Sheet

873 A274	$1 multicolored	2.00	2.00

13th Winter Olympic Games, Lake Placid, NY, Feb. 12-24.

Pres. Tolbert, Pres. Stevens, Maps of Liberia and Sierra Leone, Mano River — A275

1980, Mar. 6 Litho. *Perf. 14x13½*

874 A275	8c multicolored	.15	.15
875 A275	27c multicolored	.55	.55
876 A275	35c multicolored	.70	.70
877 A275	80c multicolored	1.60	1.60
	Nos. 874-877 (4)	3.00	3.00

Mano River Agreement, 5th anniversary; Mano River Postal Union, 1st anniversary.

Sgt. Doe and Soldiers, Clenched Hands Angel — A276

1981 Litho. *Perf. 14*

878 A276	1c Redemption horn, vert.	.15	.15
879 A276	6c like 1c	.15	.15
880 A276	10c shown	.15	.15
881 A276	14c Citizens, map, Flag	.20	.20
882 A276	23c like 10c	.30	.30
883 A276	31c like 14c	.45	.45
884 A276	41c like $2	.60	.60
885 A276	$2 Sgt. Samuel Doe, vert.	3.00	3.00
	Nos. 878-885 (8)	5.00	5.00

Establishment of new government under the People's Redemption Council, Apr. 12, 1980.

Soccer Players, World Cup, Flags of 1930 and 1934 Finalists — A277

Soccer Players, Cup, Flags of Finalists from: 5c, 1938, 1950. 20c, 1954, 1958. 27c, 1962, 1966. 40c, 1970, 1974. 55c. 1978. $1, Spanish team.

1981, Mar. 4 Litho. *Perf. 14*

886 A277	3c multicolored	.15	.15
887 A277	5c multicolored	.15	.15
888 A277	20c multicolored	.35	.35
889 A277	27c multicolored	.50	.50
890 A277	40c multicolored	.75	.75
891 A277	55c multicolored	1.00	1.00
	Nos. 886-891 (6)	2.90	2.90

Souvenir Sheet

892 A277	$1 multicolored	2.00	2.00

ESPANA '82 World Cup Soccer Championship.

Sgt. Samuel Doe and Citizens — A278

1981, Apr. 7 Litho. *Perf. 14*

893 A278	22c shown	.40	.40
894 A278	27c Doe, Liberian flag	.50	.50
895 A278	30c Clasped arms	.75	.75
896 A278	$1 Doe, soldiers, Justice	2.00	2.00
	Nos. 893-896 (4)	3.65	3.65

People's Redemption Council government, first anniversary.

Royal Wedding — A279

1981, Aug. 12 Litho. *Perf. 14x13½*

897 A279	31c Couple	.50	.50
898 A279	41c Initials, roses	.65	.65
899 A279	62c St. Paul's Cathedral	1.25	1.25
	Nos. 897-899 (3)	2.40	2.40

Souvenir Sheet

900 A279	$1 Couple	2.00	2.00

THE PRESIDENTS OF THE UNITED STATES OF AMERICA

John Adams, US President, 1797-1801 A280

LIBERIA 4c

Washington Crossing the Delaware A281

1981, July 4 *Perf. 11*

901 A280	4c shown	*.15*	*.15*
902 A280	5c William H. Harrison	*.15*	*.15*
903 A280	10c Martin Van Buren	*.16*	*.15*
904 A280	17c James Monroe	*.30*	*.24*
905 A280	20c John Q. Adams	*.35*	*.28*
906 A280	22c James Madison	*.40*	*.32*
907 A280	27c Thomas Jefferson	*.45*	*.38*
908 A280	30c Andrew Jackson	*.50*	*.40*
909 A280	40c John Tyler	*.70*	*.55*
910 A280	80c George Washington	*1.40*	*1.10*
	Nos. 901-910 (10)	*4.56*	*3.72*

Souvenir Sheet

911 A281	$1 multi	*2.00*	*2.00*

1981, Nov. 26 Litho. *Perf. 11*

912 A280	6c Rutherford B. Hayes	*.15*	*.15*
913 A280	12c Ulysses S. Grant	*.22*	*.18*
914 A280	14c Millard Fillmore	*.22*	*.18*
915 A280	15c Zachary Taylor	*.25*	*.20*
916 A280	20c Abraham Lincoln	*.35*	*.28*
917 A280	27c Andrew Johnson	*.45*	*.38*
918 A280	31c James Buchanan	*.50*	*.40*
919 A280	41c James A. Garfield	*.75*	*.60*
920 A280	50c James K. Polk	*.90*	*.70*
921 A280	55c Franklin Pierce	*1.00*	*.75*
	Nos. 912-921 (10)	*4.79*	*3.82*

Souvenir Sheet

922 A281	$1	Washington at Valley Forge	2.00	2.00

1982, Apr. 7 Litho. *Perf. 11*

923 A280	4c	William H. Taft	*.15*	*.15*
924 A280	5c	Calvin Coolidge	*.15*	*.15*
925 A280	6c	Benjamin Harrison	*.15*	*.15*
926 A280	10c	Warren G. Harding	*.16*	*.15*
927 A280	22c	Grover Cleveland	*.40*	*.32*
928 A280	27c	Chester Arthur	*.45*	*.38*
929 A280	31c	Woodrow Wilson	*.50*	*.40*
930 A280	41c	William McKinley	*.75*	*.60*
931 A280	80c	Theodore Roosevelt	*1.40*	*1.10*
		Nos. 923-931 (9)	*4.11*	*3.40*

Souvenir Sheet

932 A281	$1	Signing Constitution, horiz.	2.00	2.00

1982, July 15 Litho. *Perf. 11*

933 A280	4c	Jimmy Carter	*.15*	*.15*
934 A280	6c	Gerald Ford	*.15*	*.15*
935 A280	14c	Harry Truman	*.22*	*.18*
936 A280	17c	Franklin D. Roosevelt	*.30*	*.24*
937 A280	23c	Lyndon B. Johnson	*.40*	*.32*
938 A280	27c	Richard Nixon	*.45*	*.38*
939 A280	31c	John F. Kennedy	*.50*	*.40*
940 A280	35c	Ronald Reagan	*.60*	*.48*
941 A280	50c	Herbert Hoover	*.90*	*.70*
942 A280	55c	Dwight D. Eisenhower	*1.00*	*.75*
		Nos. 933-942 (10)	*4.67*	*3.75*

Souvenir Sheet

Perf. 14x13½

943 A281	$1	Battle of Yorktown	*2.00*	*2.00*

See No. 1113.

Type of 1976

1981-83 Litho. *Perf. 14½x13½*

Size: 34x20mm

945 A247	1c	like #749	.15	.15
946 A247	3c	like #750	.15	.15
947 A247	6c	like #753	.15	.15
948 A247	15c	like #754	.35	.35
949 A247	25c	like #757	.60	.60
950 A247	31c	like #756	.75	.75
951 A247	41c	like #758	1.00	1.00
952 A247	80c	like #759	2.00	2.00
953 A247	$1	like #760	3.00	3.00
		Nos. 945-953 (9)	8.15	8.15

Issued: #946-947, 949, 950, 11/27/81; #945, 953, 10/12/82; #948, 951, 12/10/82; #952, 11/3/83.

Intl. Year of the Disabled (1981) A282

Designs: Various disabled people.

1982, Mar. 24 Litho. *Perf. 14*

954 A282	23c	multi, vert.	.50	.50
955 A282	62c	multicolored	1.00	1.00

30th Anniv. of West African Examinations Council — A283

1982, Mar. 24

956 A283	6c	multicolored	.15	.15
957 A283	31c	multicolored	.60	.60

21st Birthday of Princess Diana — A284

31c, 41c, 62c, Diana portraits. $1, Wedding.

1982, July 1 *Perf. 14x13½*

958 A284	31c	multicolored	.50	.50
959 A284	41c	multicolored	.75	.75
960 A284	62c	multicolored	1.25	1.25
		Nos. 958-960 (3)	2.50	2.50

Souvenir Sheet

961 A284	$1	multicolored	2.00	2.00

Nos. 958-961 Overprinted in Silver: "ROYAL BABY / 21-6-82 / PRINCE WILLIAM"

1982, Aug. 30 Litho. *Perf. 14x13½*

962 A284	31c	multicolored	.50	.50
963 A284	41c	multicolored	.75	.75
964 A284	62c	multicolored	1.25	1.25
		Nos. 962-964 (3)	2.50	2.50

Souvenir Sheet

965 A284	$1	multicolored	2.00	2.00

Birth of Prince William of Wales, June 21.

3rd Natl. Redemption Day — A285

1983, Apr. 5 Litho. *Perf. 13½*

966 A285	3c	Fallah Varney	.15	.15
967 A285	6c	Samuel Doe	.15	.15
968 A285	10c	Jlatoh N. Podier, Jr.	.16	.16
969 A285	15c	Jeffry S. Gbatu	.25	.25
970 A285	31c	Thomas G. Quiwonkpa	.60	.60
971 A285	41c	Abraham D. Kollie	1.00	1.00
		Nos. 966-971 (6)	2.31	2.31

Souvenir Sheet

972 A285	$1	like 6c	2.00	2.00

Natl. Archives Opening — A286

Building views.

1983, Apr. 5

973 A286	6c	multicolored	*1.00*	*1.00*
974 A286	31c	multicolored	*1.50*	*1.50*

Christmas 1983 — A287

Raphael Paintings: 6c, Circumcision of Christ. 15c, Adoration of the Magi. 25c, Announcement to Mary. 31c, Madonna with Baldachin. 41c, Holy Family. 62c, Detail of Madonna with Child Surrounded by Five Saints. $1.25 Madonna of Foligno.

1983, Dec. 14 Litho. *Perf. 13½*

975 A287	6c	multicolored	.15	.15
976 A287	15c	multicolored	.40	.40
977 A287	25c	multicolored	.60	.60
978 A287	31c	multicolored	.75	.75
979 A287	41c	multicolored	1.00	1.00
980 A287	62c	multicolored	1.50	1.50
		Nos. 975-980 (6)	4.40	4.40

Souvenir Sheet

981 A287	$1.25	multicolored	3.00	3.00

Sheets of 1 showing entire painting exist.

Mano River Union, 10th Anniv. (1983) — A288

1984, Apr. 6 Litho. *Perf. 14x13½*

982 A288	6c	Training school graduates	.15	.15
983 A288	25c	Emblem	.50	.50
984 A288	31c	Maps, leaders	.65	.65
985 A288	41c	Guinea's accession	1.00	1.00
		Nos. 982-985 (4)	2.30	2.30

Souvenir Sheet

986 A288	75c	Guinea's accession, diff.	1.75	1.75

4th Natl. Redemption Day — A289

1984, Apr. 12 *Perf. 14½*

987 A289	3c	Hospital, New Kru Town	.15	.15
988 A289	10c	Ganta-Harper Highway construction	.15	.15
989 A289	20c	Constitution Assembly opening	.35	.35
990 A289	31c	Doe at highway construction	.75	.75
991 A289	41c	Draft Constitution presentation	1.00	1.00
		Nos. 987-991 (5)	2.40	2.40

Adoration of the Wise Men, by Rubens (1577-1640) A290

1984, June 1 Litho. *Perf. 13½*

992 A290	6c	shown	.15	.15
993 A290	15c	Crowning of Katharina	.25	.25
994 A290	25c	Mother and Child Adored by Wise Men	.50	.50
995 A290	31c	Madonna and Child with Halo	.75	.75
996 A290	41c	Adoration of the Shepherds	1.00	1.00
997 A290	62c	Madonna and Child with Saints	1.50	1.50
		Nos. 992-997 (6)	4.15	4.15

Souvenir Sheet

998 A290	$1.25	Madonna Adored by Saints	*3.00*	*3.00*

Sheets of 1 showing entire painting exist.

1984 Summer Olympics A291

1984, July 2 *Perf. 13½x14*

999 A291	3c	Jesse Owens, 1936	.15	.15
1000 A291	4c	Rafer Johnson, 1960	.15	.15
1001 A291	25c	Miruts Yifter, 1980	.55	.55
1002 A291	41c	Kipchoge Keino, 1968, 1972	.90	.90
1003 A291	62c	Muhammad Ali, 1960	1.25	1.25
		Nos. 999-1003 (5)	3.00	3.00

Souvenir Sheet

Perf. 14x13½

1004 A291	$1.25	Wilma Rudolph, 1960, horiz.	2.75	2.75

1984 Louisiana Expo A292

1984, July 24 *Perf. 14½*

1005 A292	6c	Water birds	.15	.15
1006 A292	31c	Ship, Buchanan Harbor	.60	.60
1007 A292	41c	Fish	.75	.75
1008 A292	62c	Train carrying iron ore	1.25	1.25
		Nos. 1005-1008 (4)	2.75	2.75

Pygmy Hippopotamus, World Wildlife Fund Emblem — A293

Various pygmy hippopotomi.

1984, Nov. 22 Litho. *Perf. 14½*

1009 A293	6c	multicolored	.40	.40
1010 A293	10c	multicolored	.85	.85
1011 A293	20c	multicolored	1.50	1.50
1012 A293	31c	multicolored	2.25	2.25
		Nos. 1009-1012 (4)	5.00	5.00

Indigent Children Home, Bensonville — A294

First Lady Mrs. Nancy Doe and various children.

1984, Dec. 14

1013 A294	6c	multicolored	.15	.15
1014 A294	31c	multicolored	.60	.60

Natl. Redemption Day, Apr. 12 — A295

1985, Apr. 5 Litho. *Perf. 14½*

1015 A295	6c	Army barracks, Monrovia	.15	.15
1016 A295	31c	Pan-African Plaza, Monrovia	.60	.60

Liberian Revolution, fifth anniv.

Audubon Birth Bicentenary — A296

Illustrations by artist/naturalist J. J. Audubon.

1985, Apr. 5

1017 A296	1c	Bohemian waxwing	.15	.15
1018 A296	3c	Bay-breasted warbler	.15	.15
1019 A296	6c	White-winged crossbill	.15	.15
1020 A296	31c	Red phalarope	.70	.70
1021 A296	41c	Eastern bluebird	1.00	1.00
1022 A296	62c	Northern cardinal	1.50	1.50
		Nos. 1017-1022 (6)	3.65	3.65

Venus and Mirror — A297

Paintings (details) by Rubens: 15c, Adam & Eve in Paradise. 25c, Andromeda. 31c, The Three Graces. 41c, Venus & Adonis. 62c, The Daughters of Leucippus. $1.25, The Judgement of Paris.

1985, Nov. 14 Litho. *Perf. 14*

1023	A297	6c multicolored	.15	.15
1024	A297	15c multicolored	.40	.40
1025	A297	25c multicolored	.60	.60
1026	A297	31c multicolored	.75	.75
1027	A297	41c multicolored	1.00	1.00
1028	A297	62c multicolored	1.75	1.75
		Nos. 1023-1028 (6)	4.65	4.65

Souvenir Sheet

1029	A297	$1.25 multicolored	2.50	2.50

Sheets of 1 showing entire painting exist.

1986 World Cup Soccer Championships, Mexico — A298

1985, Nov. 14

1030	A298	6c Germany-Morocco, 1970	.15	.15
1031	A298	15c Zaire-Brazil, 1974	.30	.30
1032	A298	25c Tunisia-Germany, 1978	.50	.50
1033	A298	31c Cameroun-Peru, 1982, vert.	.60	.60
1034	A298	41c Algeria-Germany, 1982	.75	.75
1035	A298	62c 1986 Senegal team	1.25	1.25
		Nos. 1030-1035 (6)	3.55	3.55

Souvenir Sheet

1036	A298	$1.25 Liberia-Nigeria	2.50	2.50

Queen Mother, 85th Birthday — A299

World Food Day — A300

1985, Dec. 12 Litho. *Perf. 14½*

1037	A299	31c Elizabeth in garter robes	.55	.55
1038	A299	41c At the races	.75	.75
1039	A299	62c In garden, waving	1.10	1.10
		Nos. 1037-1039 (3)	2.40	2.40

Souvenir Sheet

1040	A299	$1.25 Wearing diadem	2.50	2.50

1985, Dec. 12

1041	A300	25c multicolored	.50	.50
1042	A300	31c multicolored	.75	.75

AMERIPEX '86 — A301

Statue of Liberty, Cent. — A302

1986, June 10 Litho. *Perf. 14½*

1043	A301	25c The Alamo	.50	.50
1044	A301	31c Liberty Bell	.62	.62
1045	A301	80c #344, 802, C102	1.60	1.60
		Nos. 1043-1045 (3)	2.72	2.72

1986, June 10

1046	A302	20c Unveiling, 1886	.40	.40
1047	A302	31c Frederic A. Bartholdi	.62	.62
1048	A302	$1 Statue close-up	2.00	2.00
		Nos. 1046-1048 (3)	3.02	3.02

1988 Winter Olympics, Calgary — A303

1984 Gold medalists: 3c, Max Julen, Switzerland, men's giant slalom. 6c, Debbie Armstrong, US, women's giant slalom. 31c, Peter Angerer, West Germany, biathlon. 60c, Bill Johnson, US, men's downhill. 80c, East Germany, 4-man bobsled. $1.25, H. Stangassinger, F. Wembacher, West Germany, 2-man luge.

1987, Aug. 21 Litho. *Perf. 14*

1049	A303	3c multicolored	.15	.15
1050	A303	6c multicolored	.15	.15
1051	A303	31c multicolored	.62	.62
1052	A303	60c multicolored	1.20	1.20
1053	A303	80c multicolored	1.60	1.60
		Nos. 1049-1053 (5)	3.72	3.72

Souvenir Sheet

1054	A303	$1.25 multicolored	2.50	2.50

City of Berlin, 750th Anniv. — A304

6c, State (Royal) Theater in the Gendarmenmarkt, c. 1820, architect Schinkel. 31c, Kaiser Friedrich Museum, Museum Is. on River Spree. 60c, Charlottenburg Castle, 17th cent. 80c, Modern church bell tower & Kaiser Wilhelm Gedachteinskirche. $1.50, MIRAK rocket development, Spaceship Society Airfield, Reinickendorf, 1930.

1987, Sept. 4

1055	A304	6c multicolored	.15	.15
1056	A304	31c multicolored	.62	.62
1057	A304	60c multicolored	1.20	1.20
1058	A304	80c multicolored	1.60	1.60
		Nos. 1055-1058 (4)	3.57	3.57

Souvenir sheet

Perf. 11½

1059	A304	$1.50 buff & dk brown	3.00	3.00

No. 1059 contains one 25x61mm stamp.

Shakespearean Plays — A305

1987, Nov. 6 Litho. *Perf. 14*

1060	Sheet of 8	8.50	8.50
a.	A305 3c Othello	.15	.15
b.	A305 6c Romeo & Juliet	.15	.15
c.	A305 10c The Merry Wives of Windsor	.20	.20
d.	A305 15c Henry IV	.30	.30
e.	A305 31c Hamlet	.65	.65
f.	A305 60c Macbeth	1.25	1.25
g.	A305 80c King Lear	1.75	1.75
h.	A305 $2 Shakespeare and the Globe Theater, 1598	4.00	4.00

Amateur Radio Association, 25th Anniv. A306

1987, Nov. 23 Litho. *Perf. 14*

1061	A306	10c Emblem	.25	.25
1062	A306	10c Village	.25	.25
1063	A306	35c On-the-Air certificate	.85	.85
1064	A306	35c Globe, flags	.85	.85
		Nos. 1061-1064 (4)	2.20	2.20

Miniature Sheets

Statue of Liberty, Cent. (in 1986) A307

#1065: a, Torch, southern view of NYC. b, Overhead view of crown and scaffold. c, 4 workmen repairing crown. d, 5 workmen, crown. e, Statue's right foot.

#1066: a, Tall ship, statue. b, Bay Queen ferry. c, Statue on poster at a construction site, NYC. d, Tug boat, tall ship. e, Building frieze.

#1067: a, Statue flanked by fireworks. b, Lighting of the statue. c, Crown observatory illuminated. d, Statue surrounded by fireworks. e, Crown and torch observatories illuminated.

#1068: a, Liberty "Happy Birthday" poster at a construction site. b, Ships in NY Harbor. c, Woman renovating statue nose. d, Man & woman renovating nose. e, Man, nose. #1068a-1068e vert.

1987, Dec. 10 *Perf. 13½*

1065	Sheet of 5 + label	.60	
a.-e.	A307 6c any single	.15	.15
1066	Sheet of 5 + label	2.00	
a.-e.	A307 15c any single	.30	.30
1067	Sheet of 5 + label	4.00	
a.-e.	A307 31c any single	.62	.62
1068	Sheet of 5 + label	7.00	
a.-e.	A307 60c any single	1.20	1.20
	Nos. 1065-1068 (4)	13.60	.00

Nos. 1065-1068 contain label inscribed "CENTENARY OF THE STATUE OF LIBERTY" in two or five lines.

Second Republic, 2nd Anniv. — A308

Design: Natl. flag, coat of arms, hand grip, Pres. Doe and Vice Pres. Moniba.

1988, Jan. 6 *Perf. 14½*

1069	A308	10c multicolored	.30	.30
1070	A308	35c multicolored	1.00	1.00

UN Child Survival Campaign A309

Perf. 13x13½, 13½x13

1988, Jan. 15

1071	A309	3c Breast-feeding	.15	.15
1072	A309	6c Oral rehydration therapy, vert.	.15	.15
1073	A309	31c Immunization	.70	.70
1074	A309	$1 Growth monitoring, vert.	2.00	2.00
		Nos. 1071-1074 (4)	3.00	3.00

Inauguration of the Second Republic A310

Design: Pres. Doe greeting Chief Justice Emmanuel N. Gbalazeh.

1988, Jan. 15 *Perf. 13x13½*

1075	A310	6c multicolored	.15	.15

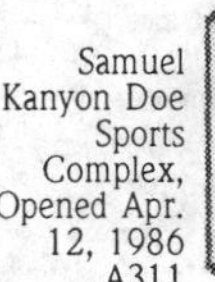

Samuel Kanyon Doe Sports Complex, Opened Apr. 12, 1986 A311

1988, Jan. 15

1076	A311	31c multicolored	.65	.65

Green (Agricultural) Revolution — A312

1988, Apr. 4 *Perf. 15*

1077	A312	10c multicolored	.25	.25
1078	A312	35c multicolored	.75	.75

US Peace Corps in Liberia, 25th Anniv. A313

1988, Apr. 4

1079	A313	10c multicolored	.25	.25
1080	A313	35c multicolored	.75	.75

Souvenir Sheet

1988 Summer Olympics, Seoul — A314

1988, Apr. 14 *Perf. 14*

1081	A314	$3 multicolored	7.00	7.00

Organization of African Unity, 25th Anniv. — A315

1988, May 25

1082 A315 10c multicolored .25 .25
1083 A315 35c multicolored .75 .75
1084 A315 $1 multicolored 2.50 2.50
Nos. 1082-1084 (3) 3.50 3.50

Rail Transport
A316

1988, July 30 Litho. *Perf. 14½*

1085 A316 10c GP10 at Nimba .30 .30
1086 A316 35c Triple-headed iron ore train .90 .90

Souvenir Sheets

Perf. 11

1087 A316 $2 King Edward II, 1930 *4.00 4.00*
1088 A316 $2 GWR 57 No. 3697, 1941 *4.00 4.00*
1089 A316 $2 GWR 0-4-2T No. 1408, 1932 *4.00 4.00*
1090 A316 $2 GWR No. 7034 Ince Castle, 1950 *4.00 4.00*

#1087-1090 contain one 64x44mm stamp each.

Nos. 1087-1090 with Added Text

1993, Aug. 3

Souvenir Sheets

1087a With added text in margin 4.00 4.00
1088a With added text in margin 4.00 4.00
1089a With added text in margin 4.00 4.00
1090a With added text in margin 4.00 4.00

Added text on Nos. 1087a-1090a reads: "25th ANNIVERSARY OF THE LAST STEAM TRAIN TO / RUN ON BRITISH RAIL 1968-1993."

1988 Summer Olympics, Seoul — A317

1988, Sept. 13 Litho.

1091 A317 10c Baseball .20 .20
1092 A317 35c Hurdles .70 .70
1093 A317 45c Fencing .90 .90
1094 A317 80c Synchronized swimming 1.60 1.60
1095 A317 $1 Yachting 2.00 2.00
Nos. 1091-1095 (5) 5.40 5.40

Souvenir Sheet

1096 A317 $1.50 Tennis 3.25 3.25

Intl. Tennis Federation, 75th anniv. ($1.50).

St. Joseph's Catholic Hospital, 25th Anniv. — A318

1988, Aug. 26 Litho. *Perf. 14½*

1097 A318 10c shown .20 .20
1098 A318 10c Hospital, 4 staff members .20 .20
1099 A318 35c St. John of God .70 .70
1100 A318 $1 Doctor, nurse, map 2.00 2.00
Nos. 1097-1100 (4) 3.10 3.10

Lloyds of London, 300th Anniv.

Common Design Type

CD341

Designs: 10c, Royal Exchange destroyed by fire, 1838, vert. 35c, Air Liberia BN2A aircraft. 45c, Supertanker *Chevron Antwerp*. $1, *Lakonia* on fire off Madeira, 1963, vert.

1988, Oct. 31 Litho. *Perf. 14*

1101 CD341 10c multicolored .25 .25
1102 CD341 35c multicolored .75 .75
1103 CD341 45c multicolored 1.00 1.00
1104 CD341 $1 multicolored 2.00 2.00
Nos. 1101-1104 (4) 4.00 4.00

Sasa Players
A319

Perf. 14x14½, 14½x14

1988, Sept. 30 Litho.

1105 A319 10c Monkey bridge, vert. .25 .25
1106 A319 35c shown .75 .75
1107 A319 45c Snake dancers, vert. 1.00 1.00
Nos. 1105-1107 (3) 2.00 2.00

Intl. Fund for Agricultural Development, 10th Anniv. — A320

1988, Oct. 7 Litho. *Perf. 14x14½*

1108 A320 10c Crops .25 .25
1109 A320 35c Spraying crops, livestock 1.00 1.00

3rd Anniv. of the 2nd Republic — A321

1989, Jan. 6 Litho. *Perf. 14*

1110 A321 10c Pres. Doe, officials .25 .25
1111 A321 35c like 10c .80 .80
1112 A321 50c Pres. Doe, doctor 1.25 1.25
Nos. 1110-1112 (3) 2.30 2.30

US Presidents Type of 1981-82

1989, Jan. 20 *Perf. 13½x14*

1113 A280 $1 George Bush 2.50 2.50

Rissho Kosei-Kai Buddhist Assoc., Tokyo, 50th Anniv. — A322

Natl. flags and: No. 1114, "Harmony" in Japanese. No. 1115, Organization headquarters, Tokyo. No. 1116, Nikkyo Niwano, founder. 50c, Statue of Buddha in the Great Sacred Hall.

1989, Feb. 28 Litho. *Perf. 14x14½*

1114 A322 10c multicolored .30 .30
1115 A322 10c multicolored .30 .30
1116 A322 10c multicolored .30 .30
1117 A322 50c multicolored 1.40 1.40
Nos. 1114-1117 (4) 2.30 2.30

Liberian-Japanese friendship.

Souvenir Sheet

Emperor Hirohito of Japan (1901-1989) — A323

Commemorative coins: a, Silver. b, Gold.

1989, Feb. 28 Unwmk. *Perf. 14½*

1118 A323 Sheet of 2 3.25 3.25
a.-b. 75c any single 1.65 1.65

For overprint see No. 1147.

Mano River Union, 15th Anniv.
A324

Natl. flag, crest and: 10c, Union Glass Factory, Gardnersville, Monrovia. 35c, Pres. Doe, Momoh of Sierra Leone and Conte of Guinea. 45c, Monrovia-Freetown Highway. 50c, Sierra Leone-Guinea land postal services. $1, Communique, 1988 summit.

Unwmk.

1989, May 8 Litho. *Perf. 14*

1119 A324 10c multicolored .20 .20
1120 A324 35c multicolored .70 .70
1121 A324 45c multicolored .90 .90
1122 A324 50c multicolored 1.00 1.00
1123 A324 $1 multicolored 2.00 2.00
Nos. 1119-1123 (5) 4.80 4.80

World Telecommunications Day — A325

1989, May 17 Litho. *Perf. 12½*

1124 A325 50c multicolored 1.00 1.00

Moon Landing, 20th Anniv.

Common Design Type

CD342

Apollo 11: 10c, Recovery ship USS *Okinawa*. 35c, Buzz Aldrin, Neil Armstrong and Michael Collins. 45c, Mission emblem. $1, Aldrin steps on the Moon. $2, Aldrin preparing to conduct experiments on the Moon's surface.

Perf. 14x13½, 14 (35c, 45c)

1989, July 20 Litho. Wmk. 384

Size of Nos. 1126-1127: 29x29mm

1125 CD342 10c multicolored .25 .25
1126 CD342 35c multicolored .75 .75
1127 CD342 45c multicolored 1.00 1.00
1128 CD342 $1 multicolored 2.25 2.25
Nos. 1125-1128 (4) 4.25 4.25

Souvenir Sheet

1129 CD342 $2 multicolored 4.25 4.25

Souvenir Sheet

The Women's March on Versailles — A326

1989, July 7 Wmk. 384 *Perf. 14*

1130 A326 $1.50 multicolored 3.25 3.25

French revolution, bicent., PHILEXFRANCE '89.

Souvenir Sheet

Renovation and Rededication of the Statue of Liberty, 1986 — A327

Photographs: a, Workman. b, French dignitary, US flag. c, Dignitaries at ceremony, statue.

Perf. 14x13½

1989, Oct. 2 Litho. Wmk. 373

1131 Sheet of 3 1.50 1.50
a.-c. A327 25c any single .50 .50

World Stamp Expo '89 and PHILEXFRANCE '89.

A328

A329

Souvenir Sheet

1989, Nov. 17 Unwmk. *Perf. 14½*

1132 A328 $2 black 4.50 4.50

World Stamp Expo '89, Washington, DC.

1989, Dec. 22 Unwmk. *Perf. 14*

1133 A329 45c Nehru, signature, flag .90 .90
1134 A329 50c Nehru, signature 1.00 1.00

Jawaharlal Nehru, 1st Prime Minister of independent India.

New Standard-A Earth Satellite Station
A330

1990, Jan. 5

1135 A330 10c shown .25 .25
1136 A330 35c multi, diff. .85 .85

US Educational & Cultural Foundation in Liberia, 25th Anniv. (in 1989)
A331

1990, Jan. 5
1137 A331 10c multicolored .25 .25
1138 A331 45c multicolored 1.00 1.00

Pan-African Postal Union, 10th Anniv. — A332

1990, Jan. 18 *Perf. 13x12½*
1139 A332 35c multicolored .75 .75

Flags of Liberian Counties — A333

Designs: a, Bomi. b, Bong. c, Grand Bassa. d, Grand Cape Mount. e, Grand Gedeh. f, Grand Kru. g, Lofa. h, Margibi. i, Maryland. j, Montserrado. k, Nimba. l, Rivercess. m, Sinoe.

Perf. 14x13½
1990, Mar. 2 Litho. Unwmk.
1140 Strip of 13 2.60 2.60
a.-m. A333 10c any single .20 .20
1141 Strip of 13 9.10 9.10
a.-m. A333 35c any single .70 .70
1142 Strip of 13 11.70 11.70
a.-m. A333 45c any single .90 .90
1143 Strip of 13 13.00 13.00
a.-m. A333 50c any single 1.00 1.00
1144 Strip of 13 26.00 26.00
a.-m. A333 $1 any single 2.00 2.00
Nos. 1140-1144 (5) 62.40 62.40

Queen Mother, 90th Birthday
Common Design Types

At Age 6
CD343

At Age 22
CD344

1991, Oct. 28 Wmk. 384 *Perf. 14x15*
1145 CD343 10c multicolored .20 .20
Perf. 14½
1146 CD344 $2 brn & blk 4.50 4.50

For overprints see Nos. 1162-1163.

Souvenir Sheet

No. 1118 Overprinted

日本国際切手展'91

Perf. 14½
1991, Nov. 16 Litho. Unwmk.
1147 A323 Sheet of 2 3.50 3.50
a.-b. 75c any single 1.75 1.75

National Unity — A334

35c, Hands clasp over map of Liberia. 45c, Liberian flag, hands, African map. 50c, All Liberia conference, March 1991, conferees, flag, map.

1991, Dec. 30 *Perf. 13½*
1148 A334 35c multicolored .70 .70
1149 A334 45c multicolored .90 .90
1150 A334 50c multicolored 1.00 1.00
Nos. 1148-1150 (3) 2.60 2.60

1992 Summer Olympics, Barcelona
A335

1992, Aug. 7 Litho. *Perf. 14*
1151 A335 45c Boxing .90 .90
1152 A335 50c Soccer 1.00 1.00
1153 A335 $1 Weight lifting 2.00 2.00
1154 A335 $2 Water polo 4.00 4.00
Nos. 1151-1154 (4) 7.90 7.90

Souvenir Sheet
1155 A335 $1.50 Running 3.00 3.00

Disarmament — A336

50c, Disarm today. $1, Join your parents & build Liberia. $2, Peace must prevail in Liberia.

1993, Feb. 10 Litho. *Perf. 13½x14*
1156 A336 50c multicolored 1.00 1.00
1157 A336 $1 multicolored 2.00 2.00
1158 A336 $2 multicolored 4.00 4.00
Nos. 1156-1158 (3) 7.00 7.00

See Nos. 1237-1239.

Miniature Sheets

Flora and Fauna — A337

Flora: No. 1159a, Papaya. b, Sausage tree. c, Angraecum eichlerianum. d, Arachnis flos-aeris. e, Screw pine. f, African tulip tree. g, Coffee tree. h, Bolusiella talbotii. i, Bulbophyllum lepidum. j, Oeceoclades maculata. k, Plectrelminthus caudatus. l, Diaphananthe rutila.

Fauna: No. 1160a, Diana monkey. b, Flying squirrel. c, Egyptian rousette. d, Serval. e, Potto. f, Chimpanzee. g, African horned chameleon. h, Royal python. i, Golden cat. j, Banded duiker. k, Pygmy hippopotamus. l, Water chevrotain.

Birds: No. 1161a, Grey heron. b, Bat hawk. c, Martial eagle. d, Little sparrow hawk. e, Hoopoe. f, Red bishop. g, Purple-throated sunbird. h, African fish eagle. i, African grey parrot. j, Black-crowned night heron. k, Swallow. l, Great white egret.

1993-94 Litho. *Perf. 14*
1159 A337 70c Sheet of 12, #a.-l. 17.50 17.50
1160 A337 90c Sheet of 12, #a.-l. 22.50 22.50
1161 A337 $1 Sheet of 12, #a.-l. 25.00 25.00
Nos. 1159-1161 (3) 65.00 65.00

Issued: 70c, 10/14; 90c, 11/18; $1, 1/14/94.

Nos. 1145-1146 Ovptd. with Hong Kong '94 Emblem

Perf. 14x15
1994, Feb. 18 Litho. Wmk. 384
1162 CD343 10c multicolored .20 .20
Perf. 14½
1163 CD344 $2 multicolored 4.00 4.00

Miniature Sheet of 8

Roberts Field, Monrovia, 50th Anniv.
A338

a, Vickers Supermarine Spitfire Mk IX. b, Boeing B-17G. c, Douglas A-20 Boston. d, North American B-25J Mitchell. e, Beech C-45 Expeditor. f, Douglas C-54. g, Piper L4 Cub. h, Martin PBM-3C.

1994, July 11 Litho. *Perf. 13½x13*
1164 A338 35c #a.-h. + label 5.75 5.75

Souvenir Sheets of 1

Locomotives — A339

Designs: No. 1165, Class A3 #60044 Melton, Class A4 #60017 Silver Fox. No. 1166, GWR 2-6-2 Prairie Tank #4561. No. 1167, GWR 2-6-2 Small Prairie. No. 1168, GWR Castle Class 4-6-0 No. Kinswear Castle. No. 1169, GWR 0-6-0 Pannier Tank. No. 1170, Bong Mining Company diesel hauling iron ore. Illustration reduced.

1994, Aug. 16 Litho. *Perf. 14*
1165-1170 A339 $1 each 2.00 2.00

See Nos. 1194-1199, 1205.

Liberian Natl. Red Cross, 75th Anniv. — A340

Designs: 70c, No. 1172, Globe. No. 1173, $2, Jean-Henri Dunant.

1994, Oct. 3 Litho. *Perf. 14½x14*
1171 A340 70c multicolored 1.40 1.40
1172 A340 $1 multicolored 2.00 2.00
1173 A340 $1 multicolored 2.00 2.00
1174 A340 $2 multicolored 4.00 4.00
Nos. 1171-1174 (4) 9.40 9.40

End of World War II, 50th Anniv.
Common Design Types

70c, Sunderland on U-boat patrol. 90c, US Army Engineer Task Force. $1, MV Abosso sunk off Liberia, 1942. #1178, MV Adda sunk off Liberia, 1941.

#1179, Obverse of US Victory Medal depicting Liberty.

1995, May 8 Litho. *Perf. 13½*
1175 CD351 70c multicolored 1.40 1.40
1176 CD351 90c multicolored 1.75 1.75
1177 CD351 $1 multicolored 2.00 2.00
1178 CD351 $2 multicolored 4.00 4.00
Nos. 1175-1178 (4) 9.15 9.15

Souvenir Sheet
Perf. 14
1179 CD352 $2 multicolored 4.00 4.00

Wild Animals — A341

1995, June 1 *Perf. 14*
1180 A341 70c Cheetah 1.40 1.40
1181 A341 70c Giraffe 1.40 1.40
1182 A341 90c Rhinoceros 1.75 1.75
1183 A341 $1 Elephant 2.00 2.00
1184 A341 $2 Lion 4.00 4.00
Nos. 1180-1184 (5) 10.55 10.55

Souvenir Sheet

1995 IAAF World Track & Field Championships, Gothenburg — A342

Designs: a, Merlene Ottey. b, Heike Drechsler. Illustration reduced.

1995, Aug. 4 Litho. *Perf. 14*
1185 A342 $1 Sheet of 2, #a.-b. 4.00 4.00

Miniature Sheet of 8

Orchids — A343

Designs: a, Ancistrochilus rothschildianus. b, Disa uniflora. c, Polystachya ottoniana. d, Aerangis brachycarpa. e, Plectrelminthus caudatus. f, Polystachya bella. g, Ansellia africana. h, Bulbophyllum cochleatum.

1995, Sept. 1 *Perf. 13*
1186 A343 70c #a.-h. + label 11.50 11.50

Singapore '95.

UN, 50th Anniv.
Common Design Type

Designs: 25c, UN Land Rovers. 50c, Delivering food supplies. $1, Ilyushin IL-76 freighter airlifting supplies. $2, MIL MI-8 helicopter.

1995, Oct. 24 Litho. *Perf. 14*
1187 CD353 25c multicolored .50 .50
1188 CD353 50c multicolored 1.00 1.00
1189 CD353 $1 multicolored 2.00 2.00
1190 CD353 $2 multicolored 4.00 4.00
Nos. 1187-1190 (4) 7.50 7.50

Economic Community of West African States, 20th Anniv.
A344

25c, Map, Liberian flag, soldiers, civilians. 50c, Soldier carrying child, vert. $1, Logo, vert.

Perf. 13½x13, 13½x13
1995, Nov. 10 Litho.
1191 A344 25c multicolored .50 .50
1192 A344 50c multicolored 1.00 1.00
1193 A344 $1 multicolored 2.00 2.00
Nos. 1191-1193 (3) 3.50 3.50

Train Type of 1994
Souvenir Sheets

Designs: No. 1194, 4-4-0 locomotive 11 "The Reno," galloping horses. No. 1195, Halwill station, Southern Region T9 class locomotive #30719. No. 1196, GWR 0-4-2T "1400" class locomotive #1408, cricket match. No. 1197, LMS Jubilee class 4-6-0, #45684 "Jutland," Kettering station. No. 1198, GWR 2-6-2 "Prairie" locomotive #4547, Lustleigh station. No. 1199, Wainwright "H" class 0-4-4T locomotive, winter countryside.

1996, Feb. 29 Litho. *Perf. 14x15*
1194-1199 A339 $1 each 2.00 2.00

Modern Olympic Games, Cent. — A345

1996, Apr. 22 **Litho.** ***Perf. 13***

1200	A345	20c	Runners	.40	.40
1201	A345	35c	Boxing	.70	.70
1202	A345	50c	Javelin	1.00	1.00
1203	A345	$1	Hurdles	2.00	2.00
			Nos. 1200-1203 (4)	4.10	4.10

Butterflies A346

Designs: a, Papilio zalmoxis. b, Papilio dardanus. c, Charaxes varanes. d, Acraea natalica. e, Euphaedra neophron. f, Craphium antheus. g, Salamis anacardii. h, Kallima cymodoce. i, Precis hierta.

1996, May 22 **Litho.** ***Perf. 13½***

1204 A346 70c Sheet of 9, #a.-i. 12.50 12.50

Train Type of 1994

Design: G4a Class Pacific locomotive, Canadian Pacific Railroad.

1996, June 8 **Litho.** ***Perf. 14x15***

1205 A339 $1 Sheet of 1 2.00 2.00

CAPEX '96.

Fish — A347

Designs: a, Atlantic Sailfish. b, Guinean flyingfish. c, Blue marlin. d, Little tunny (e). e, Common dolphinfish (f). f, Guachanche barracuda. g, Guinean parrotfish. h, Cadenat's chromis (g). i, Dusky grouper (h). j, Hoefler's butterflyfish (k). k, African hind (l). l, West African Angelfish.

1996, July 15 **Litho.** ***Perf. 14***

1206 A347 90c Sheet of 12, #a.-l. 21.50 21.50

The government of Liberia has been in chaos, and the country has been in a state of anarchy for some time. New issue stamps continue to be released into the philatelic market by agents. Stamps canceled-to-order and on first day covers probably exist.

Butterflies A348

No. 1207: a, Euphaedra judith. b, Euphaedra eleus. c, Acraea encedon. d, Euphaedra neophron. e, Liptena praestans. f, Neptis exalenca. g, Palla decius. h, Salamis cytora. i, Pseudacraea dolomena. j, Anaphaeis eriphia. k, Euphaedra themis. l, Hadrodontes varanes.

No. 1208: a, Papilio mnestheus. b, Papilio nobilis. c, Graphium antheus. d, Asterope benguelae. e, Graphium illyris. f, Emphaedra eupalus. g, Charaxes protoclea. h, Cymothoe beckeri. i, Euphaedra cyparissa. j, Coliades chalybe. k, Mimacraea neokoton. l, Charaxes ethalion.

$2, Charaxes pelias.

1996 **Litho.** ***Perf. 14***

1207 A348 20c Sheet of 12, #a.-l. 4.80
1208 A348 25c Sheet of 12, #a.-l. 6.00

Souvenir Sheet

1209 A348 $2 multicolored 4.00

Birds — A349

Marilyn Monroe (1926-62) — A350

Designs, horiz: 35c, African jacana. 50c, Pel's fishing owl. $1, Paradise whydah.

No. 1213: a, Turtle dove. b, Bee-eater. c, Golden oriole. d, Pied flycatcher. e, Sardinian warbler. f, Goliath heron. g, Rock thrush. h, Kestrel. i, Cattle egret. j, Woodchat shrike. k, Hoopoe. l, Great egret.

No. 1214, horiz: a, Red faced crimsonwing. b, Egyptian goose. c, African pitta. d, Paradise flycatcher. e, Garganey. f, Southern carmine bee-eater. g, Fulvous whistling duck. h, Village weaver. i, Martial eagle.

$2, Pintail duck, horiz.

1996

1210-1212 A349 Set of 3 3.75
1213 A349 25c Sheet of 12, #a.-l. 6.00
1214 A349 35c Sheet of 9, #a.-i. 6.30

Souvenir Sheet

1215 A349 $2 multicolored 4.00

1996

1216 A350 20c multicolored .40

No. 1216 was issued in sheets of 16.

UNICEF, 50th Anniv. A351

Designs: 35c, Education for all. 70c, Health care. $1, Children first.

1996, Sept. 16 ***Perf. 13½x13***

1217-1219 A351 35c Set of 3 4.10

1996 Summer Olympic Games, Atlanta A352

Designs: #1220, 20c, Cricket (discontinued sport), vert. #1221, 20c, Babe Didrikson, vert. #1222, 35c, Vitaly Scherpo, winner of 6 gold medals, 1992, vert. #1223, 35c, Betty Robinson, vert. #1224, 50c, Cuban baseball team, gold medal, 1992. #1225, 50c, Ancient Greek wall painting of boxers, vert. #1226, $1, Stadium, Barcelona, 1992. #1227, $1, Stadium, Amsterdam, 1928, vert.

Olympic events, vert: #1228a, Men's athletics. b, Men's gymnastics. c, Weight lifting. d, Women's volleyball. e, Women's diving. f, Women's gymnastics. g, Women's track. h, Women's tennis. i, Discus.

Boxing gold medalists, boxing, vert: #1229a, Tyrell Biggs, US. b, Isan Gura, Tanzania (no medal). c, Mark Breland, US. d, Teofilo Stevenson, Cuba. e, Ray Leonard, US. f, Michael Spinks, US. g, Joe Frazier, US. h, Floyd Patterson, US. i, George Foreman, US.

$2, Evelyn Ashford.

1996 **Litho.** ***Perf. 14***

1220-1227 A352 Set of 8 8.20

Sheets of 9

1228-1229 A352 35c #a.-i, each 6.30

Souvenir Sheet

1230 A352 $2 multicolored 4.00

Flowers and Flowering Trees — A353

a, Olive tree. b, Olive flower. c, Fig tree. d, Almond tree. e, Almug tree. f, Cedar. g, Pomegranate (b). h, Citron. i, Date palm (d, e, j). j, Date palm (fruit). k, Cedar of Lebanon. l, Rock rose. m, Narcissus. n, Oleander (i). o, Date palm (flower). p, Shittah tree. q, Hyacinth. r, Barley, flax (s). s, Grape vine. t, Lily of the field. u, Mandrake. v, Caper desire. w, Madonna lily. x, Aloe (s). y, Date palm tree.

1996

1231 A353 25c Sheet of 25, #a.-y. 12.50 12.50

History of Rock and Roll — A354

Designs: a, Wilson Pickett. b, Bill Haley. c, Otis Redding. d, Fats Domino. e, Buddy Holly. f, Chubby Checker. g, Marvin Gaye. h, Jimi Hendrix.

1996 ***Perf. 13½x14***

1232 A354 35c Sheet of 8, #a.-h. + label 5.50 5.50

A355

A356

Kingfishers: a, Striped. b, Grey-headed. c, Pied. d, Giant. e, Shining-blue.

1996, Oct. 7 **Litho.** ***Perf. 13½***

1233 A355 75c Strip of 5, #a.-e. 7.50

See No. 1236.

1996, Nov. 1 **Litho.** ***Perf. 14½x14***

1234 A356 $1 shown 2.00
1235 A356 $1 As older man 2.00

Mao Zedong, 20th death Anniv.

Kingfisher Type of 1996
Souvenir Sheet

1997, Feb. 3 **Litho.** ***Perf. 14***

1236 A355 $1 like #1233b 2.00

Hong Kong '97.
No. 1236 contains one 29x43mm stamp.

Disarmament Type of 1993
Inscribed "PEACE TODAY"

1997 **Litho.** **13½x14**

1237 A336 $1 like #1157 *1.90*
1238 A336 $2 like #1158 *3.75*
1239 A336 $3 like #1156 *5.75*
Nos. 1237-1239 (3) *11.40*

Nos. 1237-1239 are dated 1996.

Wildlife — A356

Designs: a, Olive baboon. b, Leopard. c, African tree pangolin. d, Vervet. e, Aardvark. f, Spotted hyena. g, Hunting dog. h, Thomson's gazelle. i, Warthog. j, African civet. k, Nile crocodile. l, African polecat.

1997, Apr. 2 **Litho.** ***Perf. 14***

1240 A356 50c Sheet of 12, #a.-l. 12.00

Deng Xiaoping (1904-97), British Transfer of Hong Kong — A358

Different portraits of Deng Xiaoping, "July 1, 1997," Hong Kong: 70c, In daylight, vert. $1, At night.

No. 1243: a, 50c. b, 70c. c, $1.20.

Illustration reduced.

1997 **Litho.** ***Perf. 14***

1241 A358 70c multicolored 1.40
1242 A358 $1 multicolored 2.00
1243 A358 Sheet of 3, #a.-c. 4.80

No. 1241 is 28x44mm, and was issued in sheets of 4. No. 1242 was issued in sheets of 3.

UNESCO, 50th Anniv. — A359

No. 1244, vert: a, Canals, Venice, Italy. b, Mosque of Badshahi, Gardens of Shalamar, Lahore, Pakistan. c, Palace of Orando, Spain. d, Grounds of Temple of Hera, Greece. e, Church and Monastery of Daphni, Greece. f, Fraser Island, Australia. g, Canadian Rocky Mountains Park, Canada. h, Church of Santo Domingo Puebla, Mexico.

No. 1245, vert: a, City of Ohrid and lake, Macedonia. b, Thracian Tomb of Sveshtari, Bulgaria. c, Monastery of Hossios Luckas, Greece. d, Church of Santa Cristina of Lena, Spain. e, Church of Santa Maria Della Salute, Venice, Italy. f, Center of Puebla, Mexico. g, Bagrati Cathedral, Georgia. h, Quebec City, Canada.

No. 1246: a, Ngorongoro Conservation Area, Tanzania. b, Garamba Natl. Park, Zaire. c, Canaima Natl. Park, Venezuela. d, Simien Natl. Park, Ethiopia. e, Mana Pools Natl. Park, Zimbabwe.

No. 1247, Palace of Diocletian, Split, Croatia. No., 1248, Monument of Nubia at Abu Simbel, Egypt. No. 1249, Quedlinberg, Germany.

Perf. 13½x14, 14x13½

1997, June 17 **Litho.**

Sheets of 8 + Label

1244-1245 A359 50c #a.-h., each 8.00

Sheet of 5 + Label

1246 A359 70c #a.-e. 7.00

Souvenir Sheets

1247-1249 A359 $2 each 4.00

Queen Elizabeth II, Prince Philip, 50th Wedding Anniv. A360

No. 1250: a, Queen holding umbrella. b, Royal arms. c, Prince in white uniform, Queen. d, Queen waving, Prince. e, Windsor Castle. f, Prince Philip.

No. 1251, Queen seated on sofa. No. 1252, Queen, Prince wearnig robes of Order of the Garter.

1997, June 17 ***Perf. 14***

1250 A360 50c Sheet of 6, #a.-f. 6.00 6.00

Souvenir Sheet

1251-1252 A360 $2 each 4.00 4.00

Grimm's Fairy Tales A361

Mother Goose — A362

Scenes from Rapunzel: a, Girl. b, Wicked person, raven. c, Prince. No. 1254, Prince rescuing girl.
No. 1255, Little Bo Peep, sheep.

1997, June 17 *Perf. 13½x14*

1253 A361 $1 Sheet of 3, #a.-c. 6.00

Souvenir Sheets

1254 A361 $2 multicolored 4.00

Perf. 14

1255 A362 $2 multicolored 4.00

A363

A364

1998 Winter Olympic Games, Nagano: 50c, Olympic Stadium, Lillehammer, 1994. 70c, Johann Koss, speed skating. $1, Katarina Witt, figure skating. $1.50, Sonia Henie, figure skating.

No. 1260: a, K. Seizinger, Alpine downhill skiing. b, J. Weissflog, 120-m ski jump. c, T. Kono, Nordic combined. d, G. Hackl, luge.

No. 1261: a, E. Bredesen, 90-m ski jump. b, L. Kjus, downhill skiing. c, B. Daehlie, cross-country skiing. d, P. Wiberg, combined Alpine skiing. e, S.L. Hattestad, freestyle skiing. f, G. Weder, D. Acklin, 2-man bobsled. g, Swedish hockey player. h, T. Alsgaard, cross-country skiing.

No. 1262, German biathlete, 1994. No. 1263, M. Wasmeier, giant slalom. No. 1264, J. Koss, speed skating, diff. No. 1265, V. Schneider, slalom.

1997, June 23 *Perf. 14*

1256-1259 A363 Set of 4 7.50
1260 A363 50c Strip or block of 4, #a.-d. 4.00
1261 A363 50c Sheet of 8, #a.-h. 8.00

Souvenir Sheets

1262-1265 A363 $2 each 4.00

No. 1260 was issued in sheets of 8 stamps.

1997, July 1 **Litho.** *Perf. 14*

Flowers: No. 1266: a, Sugar cane dahlia. b, Windsor tall phlox. c, Creative art daylily. d, Columbine. e, Infinite Grace bearded iris. f, Fairy lilies mini amaryllis.

No. 1267: a, White coneflower. b, Peggy Lee hybrid tea rose. c, Daffodil. d, Bowl of Beauty peony. e, Hardy lily. f, Windflower.

No. 1268, Lily-flowered tulip. No. 1269, Chrysanthemum Potomac.

Sheets of 6

1266-1267 A364 50c #a.-f., each 6.00 6.00

Souvenir Sheets

1268-1269 A364 $2 each 4.00 4.00

Flora and Fauna A365

No. 1270: a, Lovebirds. b, Genet. c, Leopard, crowned night heron. d, Gorilla. e, Giant wild boar. f, Elephant. g, Sterculia flower, skink. h, Ladybugs, bush baby. i, Cape primroses, ground hornbill.

No. 1271, Rufus-crowned roller. No. 1272, Gray heron.

1997, July 1

1270 A365 50c Sheet of 9, #a.-i. 9.00 9.00

Souvenir Sheets

1271-1272 A365 $2 each 4.00 4.00

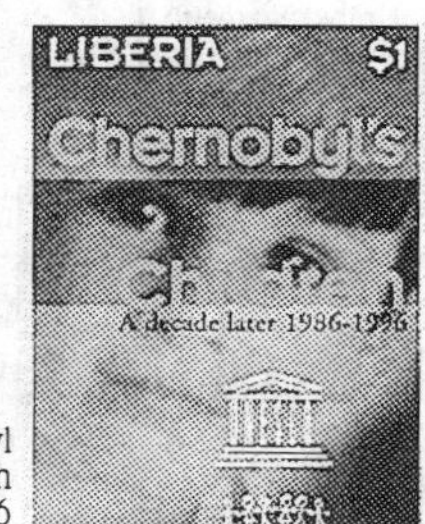

Chernobyl Disaster, 10th Anniv. — A366

1997, June 17 **Litho.** *Perf. 13½x14*

1273 A366 $1 UNESCO 2.00 2.00

Marcello Mastroianni (1923-96), Actor A367

Scenes from motion pictures: a, Casanova, 1970. b, Divorce Italian Style. c, 8½. d, La Dolce Vita.

1997, Sept. 3

1274 A367 75c Sheet of 4, #a.-d. 6.00 6.00

A368

A369

Contemporary Artists and Their Paintings: No. 1275: a, Andy Warhol (1927-87). b, "Multicolored Retrospective," by Warhol, 1979. c, "The Three Muscians," by Picasso, 1921. d, Pablo Picasso (1881-1973). e, Henri Matisse (1869-1954). f, "The Dance," by Matisse, 1910. g, "Lavender Mist," by Pollock, 1950. h, Jackson Pollock (1912-56).

No. 1276: a, Piet Mondrian (1872-1944). b, "Broadway Boogie Woogie," by Mondrian, 1942-43. c, "Persistence of Memory," by Dali, 1931. d, Salvador Dali (1904-89). e, Roy Lichtenstein (1923-97). f, "Artist's Studio: The Dance," by Lichtenstein, 1974. g, "Europe After the Rain," by Ernst, 1940-42. h, Max Ernst (1891-1976).

1997, Sept. 3 *Perf. 14*

Sheets of 8

1275-1276 A368 50c #a.-h., each 8.00 8.00

Nos. 1275b-1275c, 1275f-1275g, 1276b-1276c, 1276f-1276g are 53x38mm.

1997

Owls: a, Akun eagle. b, Shelley's eagle. c, African wood. d, Rufous fishing. e, Maned. f, Sandy scops.

1277 A369 50c Sheet of 6, #a.-f. 6.00 6.00

Birds — A370

Designs: 1c, Black bee-eater. 2c, Yellow-billed barbet. 3c, Carmine bee-eater. 4c, Malachite kingfisher. 5c, Emerald cuckoo. 10c, Blue-throated roller. 15c, Blue-headed bee-eater. 20c, Black-collared lovebird. 25c, Broad-billed roller. 50c, Blue-breasted kingfisher. 70c, Little bee-eater. 75c, Yellow spotted barbet. 90c, White-throated bee-eater. $1, Double-toothed barbet. $2, Blue-cheeked bee-eater. $3, Narina's trogon.

1997

1278 A370 1c multicolored .15 .15
1279 A370 2c multicolored .15 .15
1280 A370 3c multicolored .15 .15
1281 A370 4c multicolored .15 .15
1282 A370 5c multicolored .15 .15
1283 A370 10c multicolored .20 .20
1284 A370 15c multicolored .30 .30
1285 A370 20c multicolored .40 .40
1286 A370 25c multicolored .50 .50
1287 A370 50c multicolored 1.00 1.00
1288 A370 70c multicolored 1.40 1.40
1289 A370 75c multicolored 1.50 1.50
1290 A370 90c multicolored 1.80 1.80
1291 A370 $1 multicolored 2.00 2.00
1292 A370 $2 multicolored 4.00 4.00
1293 A370 $3 multicolored 6.00 6.00
Nos. 1278-1293 (16) 19.85 19.85

1998 World Cup Soccer — A371

Players, Country, vert: 50c, Salenko, Russia. 70c, Schillaci, Italy. $1, Lineker, England. $1.50, Pele, Brazil. $2, Fontaine, France. $2, Rahn, W. Germany.

No. 1300, vert: a, Ardiles, Argentina. b, Romario, Brazil. c, Rummenigge, Germany. d, Charlton, England. e, Villa, Argentina. f, Matthäus, Germany. g, Maradona, Argentina. h, Lineker, England.

No. 1301: a, Paulo Rossi, Italy. b, Ademir, Brazil. c, Grzegorz Lato, Poland. d, Gary Lineker, England. e, Gerd Muller, W. Germany. f, Johan Cruyff, Holland. g, Karl-Heinz Rummenigge, Germany. h, Mario Kempes, Argentina.

No. 1302, Beckenbauer, W. Germany, vert. No. 1303, Maier, W. Germany, vert.

Perf. 13½x14, 14x13½

1997, Oct. 1 **Litho.**

1294-1299 A371 Set of 6 6.50 6.50

Sheets of 8 + Label

1300-1301 A371 50c #a.-h., each 8.00 8.00

Souvenir Sheets

1302-1303 A371 $6 each 4.00 4.00

Marine Life A372

No. 1304: a, Flamingoes (beach, palm trees). b, Six flamingoes. c, Sailfish (d). d, Egret. e, Yellow-tail snapper. f, Manatee. g, Clown coris. h, White-collar butterflyfish. i, Royal angelfish. j, Titan triggerfish. k, Three-striped wrasse. l, Pacific blue-eye. m, Wobbegono. n, Jellyfish. o, Sea urchin, red sea triggerfish. p, Harlequin fish.

No. 1305, Seahorses, vert. No. 1306, Anemone fish.

1998, Mar. 9 **Litho.** *Perf. 14*

1304 A372 20c Sheet of 16, #a.-p. 6.50 6.50

Souvenir Sheets

Perf. 13½x14, 14x13½

1305-1306 A372 $2 each 4.00 4.00

No. 1305 contains one 38x51mm stamp, No. 1306 contains one 51x38mm stamp.

SEMI-POSTAL STAMPS

No. 127 Surcharged in Red

1915 **Unwmk.** *Perf. 14*

B1 A49 2c + 3c on 10c .85 2.75
  a. Double red surcharge
  b. Double blue surcharge
  c. Both surcharges double
  d. Pair, one without "2c"

Same Surcharge On Official Stamp of 1912

B2 A49 2c + 3c on 10c blk & ultra .85 2.75
  a. Double surcharge

Regular Issue of 1918 Surcharged in Black and Red

1918 *Perf. 12½, 14*

B3 A59 1c + 2c dp grn & blk .40 *2.00*
B4 A60 2c + 2c rose & blk .40 *2.00*
  a. Double surch., one inverted
  b. Invtd. surch., cross double
  c. Invtd. surch., cross omitted 17.00
B5 A61 5c + 2c gray bl & blk .15 *.50*
  a. Imperf., pair 9.25
B6 A62 10c + 2c dk green .15 *.50*
  a. Inverted surcharge 5.75 27.50
B7 A63 15c + 2c blk & dk grn .15 *.50*
B8 A64 20c + 2c claret & blk .30 *1.50*
B9 A65 25c + 2c dk grn & grn .55 *2.75*
B10 A66 30c + 2c red vio & blk .40 *2.00*
B11 A67 50c + 2c ultra & blk .55 *2.75*
B12 A68 75c + 2c ol bis & blk 1.10 *5.50*
B13 A69 $1 + 2c yel brn & bl 1.90 *9.50*
B14 A70 $2 + 2c lt vio & blk 2.25 *11.00*
B15 A71 $5 + 2c dk brown 9.50 *47.50*
Nos. B3-B15 (13) 17.80 *88.00*

Used values are for postally canceled stamps.

Nos. 277-279 Surcharged in Red or Blue

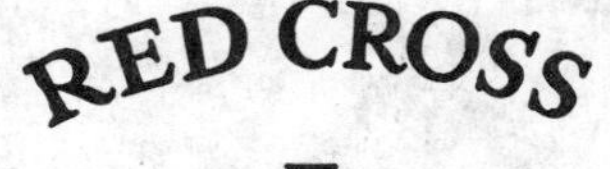

TWO CENTS

1941 **Unwmk.** *Perf. 12*

B16 A107 3c + 2c dk blue (R) 1.25 1.40
B17 A108 5c + 2c dull red brn 1.25 1.40
B18 A109 10c + 2c dk grn (R) 1.25 1.40
Nos. B16-B18 (3) 3.75 4.20

Catalogue values for unused stamps in this section, from this point to the end of the section, are for Never Hinged items.

Research SP1

Lithographed and Engraved

1954 **Unwmk.** *Perf. 12½*

B19 SP1 5c + 5c rose lilac & blk .15 .15
Nos. B19,CB4-CB6 (4) .68
Set value .35

The surtax was for the Liberian Government Hospital. No. B19 exists imperforate.

Remember the African Child — SP2

Designs: 25c + 10c, Village life. 70c + 20c, Mr. Sean feeding children. 75c + 15c, Fleeing conflict. 80c + 20c, Nuns teaching children. No. B24, Nuns killed in Oct. 1992, vert. No. B25, Sean Devereux (1964-93), vert.

Perf. 13½x14

1994, Jan. 6 Unwmk. Litho.

B20 SP2 25c +10c multi .70 .70
B21 SP2 70c +20c multi 1.75 1.75
B22 SP2 75c +15c multi 1.75 1.75
B23 SP2 80c +20c multi 2.00 2.00
Nos. B20-B23 (4) 6.20 6.20

Souvenir Sheets

B24 SP2 $1.50 +50c multi 4.00 4.00
B25 SP2 $1.50 +50c multi 4.00 4.00

Surtax for Sean Devereux Liberian Children's Fund.

Charities SP3

Designs: 25c+10c, No. B30, Natl. map in flag colors, blind man with cane. No. B27, Logo depicting children. No. B28, Blind man crossing street. No. B29, Dr. Herman Gmeiner, children.

1995 Litho. *Perf. 14*

B26 SP3 25c +10c multi .70 .70
B27 SP3 80c +20c multi 2.00 2.00
B28 SP3 80c +20c multi 2.00 2.00
B29 SP3 $1.50 +50c multi 4.00 4.00
B30 SP3 $1.50 +50c multi 4.00 4.00
Nos. B26-B30 (5) 12.70 12.70

Christian Assoc. of the Blind, 10th anniv. (#B26, B28, B30). SOS Children's Village (#B27, B29).
Issued: #B27, B29, 4/26; others, 4/28.

George Weah, Soccer Player — SP4

Designs: 50c+20c, In AC Milan strip. 75c+25c, In Liberia Natl. strip. 80c+20c, With 1989 Golden Ball Award. $1.50+50c, Two-time Golden Ball Winner.

1995, Oct. 6 Litho. *Perf. 13x13½*

B31 SP4 50c +20c multi 1.40 1.40
B32 SP4 75c +25c multi 2.00 2.00
B33 SP4 80c +20c multi 2.00 2.00
B34 SP4 $1.50 +50c multi 4.00 4.00
a. Souvenir sheet of 1, perf. 13 4.00 4.00
Nos. B31-B34 (4) 9.40 9.40

Issued: No. B34a, 6/24/96. Surcharge for Liberian charities supported by George Weah.

AIR POST STAMPS

Regular Issue of 1928 Surcharged in Black "AIR MAIL" and New Values

1936, Feb. 28 Unwmk. *Perf. 12*

C1 A102 6c on 2c violet 200.00 100.00
C2 A102 6c on 3c bis brn 200.00 100.00

Same Surcharge on Official Stamp of 1928

C3 A102 6c on 1c green 200.00 100.00
m. On No. 230 (error) *700.00*
Nos. C1-C3 (3) 600.00 300.00

Values are for stamps with disturbed gum.
Many counterfeits exist.

Waco Plane AP1

1936, Sept. 30 Engr. *Perf. 14*

C3A AP1 1c yellow grn & blk .15 .15
C3B AP1 2c carmine & blk .15 .15
C3C AP1 3c purple & blk .15 .15
C3D AP1 4c orange & blk .15 .15
C3E AP1 5c blue & blk .15 .15
C3F AP1 6c green & blk .15 .15
Nos. C3A-C3F (6) .90
Set value .40

Liberia's 1st air mail service of Feb. 28, 1936.
Nos. C3A-C3F exist in pairs imperf. between (value, $50 each) and in pairs imperf. (value $15 each).

Eagle in Flight — AP2

Sikorsky Amphibian — AP5

Trimotor Plane AP3

Egrets — AP4

Designs: 3c, 30c, Albatross.

1938, Sept. 12 Photo. *Perf. 12½*

C4 AP2 1c green .15 .15
C5 AP3 2c red orange .20 .15
C6 AP3 3c olive green .20 .15
C7 AP4 4c orange .25 .15
C8 AP4 5c brt blue grn .35 .15
C9 AP3 10c violet .35 .15
C10 AP5 20c magenta .50 .15
C11 AP3 30c gray black .70 .15
C12 AP2 50c brown 1.00 .15
C13 AP5 $1 blue 1.75 .15
Nos. C4-C13 (10) 5.45
Set value 1.10

For surcharges see Nos. C17-C36, C45-C46, C47-C48, C49-C50.

Nos. 280-282 Overprinted in Red or Dark Blue

AIR MAIL

1941, Feb. 25 *Perf. 12*

C14 A107 3c dark blue (R) 1.25 1.25
C15 A108 5c dull red brn (DB) 1.25 1.25
C16 A109 10c dark green (R) 1.25 1.25
Nos. C14-C16 (3) 3.75 3.75

Nos. C4-C13 Surcharged in Black

**First Flight
LIBERIA - U.S.
1941**

—— 50c

1941 *Perf. 12½*

C17 AP2 50c on 1c green *1,800.* 200.00
C18 AP3 50c on 2c red org 125.00 77.50
C19 AP3 50c on 3c ol grn 125.00 77.50
C20 AP4 50c on 4c orange 47.50 30.00
C21 AP4 50c on 5c brt bl grn 47.50 30.00
C22 AP3 50c on 10c violet 47.50 30.00
C23 AP5 50c on 20c magenta *1,500.* 50.00
C24 AP3 50c on 30c gray blk 40.00 22.50
C25 AP2 50c brown 40.00 22.50
C26 AP5 $1 blue 47.50 22.50

Nos. C17 to C26 with Additional Overprint of Two Bars, Obliterating "1941"

1942

C27 AP2 50c on 1c green 5.25 5.25
C28 AP3 50c on 2c red org 5.25 4.50
C29 AP3 50c on 3c ol grn 4.75 4.50
C30 AP4 50c on 4c orange 3.75 4.75
C31 AP4 50c on 5c brt bl grn 2.25 2.25
C32 AP3 50c on 10c violet 3.25 3.25
C33 AP5 50c on 20c magenta 3.25 3.25
C34 AP3 50c on 30c gray blk 3.75 3.75
C35 AP2 50c brown 3.75 3.75
C36 AP5 $1 blue 3.25 3.25
Nos. C27-C36 (10) 38.50 38.50

Plane and Air Route from United States to South America and Africa — AP6

Plane over House — AP7

1942-44 Engr. *Perf. 12*

C37 AP6 10c rose .15 .15
C38 AP7 12c brt ultra ('44) .15 .15
C39 AP7 24c turq grn ('44) .15 .15
C40 AP6 30c brt green .15 .15
C41 AP6 35c red lilac ('44) .15 .15
C42 AP6 50c violet .15 .15
C43 AP6 70c olive gray ('44) .30 .15
C44 AP6 $1.40 scarlet ('44) .70 .30
Nos. C37-C44 (8) 1.90
Set value 1.00

No. C3A-C3C, C5-C8, C12 Surcharged with New Values and Large Dot, Bar or Diagonal Line in Violet, Blue, Black or Violet and Black

1944-45 *Perf. 12½*

C45 AP3 10c on 2c (V+Bk) 25.00 19.00
C46 AP4 10c on 5c (V+Bk) ('45) 8.75 8.75
C46A AP1 30c on 1c (Bk) 95.00 50.00
C47 AP3 30c on 3c (V) 100.00 47.50
C48 AP4 30c on 4c (V+Bk) 8.75 8.75
C48A AP1 50c on 3c (Bk) 22.50 22.50
C48B AP1 70c on 2c (Bk) 42.50 42.50
C49 AP3 $1 on 3c (Bl) 16.00 16.00
C50 AP2 $1 on 50c (V) 25.00 19.00
Nos. C45-C50 (9) 343.50 234.00

These surcharges were handstamped with the possible exception of the large "10 CTS." of No. C46 and the "30 CTS." of No. C48. On No. C47, the new value was created by handstamping a small, violet, broken "O" beside the large "3" of the basic stamp.
Surcharges on Nos. C46A, C48A, C48B are found inverted. Values same as normal.

?Roosevelt Type of Regular Issue

1945, Nov. 26 Engr.

C51 A116 70c brn & blk, *grysh* 1.25 1.40

Copies on thick white paper appeared later on the stamp market at reduced prices.

Monrovia Harbor Type

1947, Jan. 2

C52 A117 24c brt bluish grn 1.00 1.25

Without Inscription at Top

1947, May 16

C53 A117 25c dark carmine .40 .45

1st US Postage Stamps Type

1947, June 6

C54 A118 12c green .15 .15
C55 A118 25c brt red violet .15 .15
C56 A118 50c brt blue .15 .15
a. Souv. sheet of 4, #300, C54-C56 37.50
Set value .35 .35

No. C56a exists imperf., same value.

Matilda Newport Firing Cannon AP11

1947, Dec. 1 Engr. & Photo.

C57 AP11 25c scar & gray blk 1.25 .30

See note after No. 304.

Monument to Joseph J. Roberts — AP12

Centenary Monument — AP14

Design: 25c, Flag of Liberia.

1947, Dec. 22 Engr.

C58 AP12 12c brick red .15 .15
C59 AP12 25c carmine .30 .15
C60 AP14 50c red brown .60 .45
Nos. C58-C60 (3) 1.05 .75

Centenary of independence.

L. I. A. Plane in Flight — AP15

1948, Aug. 17 *Perf. 11½*

C61 AP15 25c red 1.25 .75
C62 AP15 50c deep blue .65 .75

1st flight of Liberian Intl. Airways, Aug. 17, 1948.

Map and Citizens AP16

Farm Couple, Arms and Agricultural Products AP17

1949, Apr. 12 Litho. *Perf. 11½*

C63 AP16 25c multicolored .35 .65
C64 AP17 50c multicolored .35 .65

Nos. C63-C64 exist perf. 12½. Definite information concerning the status of the perf. 12½ set has not reached the editors. The set also exists imperf.

Type of Regular Issue of 1948-50
Design: William V. S. Tubman.

1949, July 21 Engr. *Perf. 12½*

C65 A128 25c blue & black .60 .65

See No. C118.

Sun and Open Book — AP18

UPU Monument — AP19

1950, Feb. 14 Engr. *Perf. 12½*

C66 AP18 25c rose carmine 1.00 .50
a. Souv. sheet of 2, #329, C66, imperf. 1.75 1.75

Campaign for National Literacy.

Catalogue values for unused stamps in this section, from this point to the end of the section, are for Never Hinged items.

1950, Apr. 21

C67 AP19 25c orange & vio 1.75 1.75
a. Souv. sheet of 3, #330-331, C67, imperf. 4.50 4.50

UPU, 75th anniv. (in 1949).
No. C67 exists imperf.

Map of Monrovia, James Monroe and Ashmun
AP20

50c, Jehudi Ashmun, President Tubman & map.

1952, Apr. 1 *Perf. 10½*

C68 AP20 25c lilac rose & blk .20 .20
C69 AP20 50c dk blue & car .40 .40
a. Souvenir sheet of 8 15.00

Nos. C68-C69 exist imperf. Value about two and one half times that of the perf. set.

Nos. C68-C69 exist with center inverted. Value $50 each.

No. C69a contains one each of Nos. 332 and C68, and types of Nos. 333-337 and C69 with centers in black; imperf.

The 25c exists in colors of the 50c and vice versa. Value, each $3.50.

Flags of Five Nations
AP21

1952, Dec. 10 *Perf. 12½*

C70 AP21 25c ultra & carmine .40 .32
a. Souvenir sheet 1.65 1.65

Nos. C70 and C70a exist imperforate.

Road Building
AP22

Designs: 25c, Ships in Monrovia harbor. 35c, Diesel locomotive. 50c, Free port, Monrovia. 70c, Roberts Field. $1, Wm. V. S. Tubman bridge.

1953, Aug. 3 Litho.

C71 AP22 12c orange brown .15 .15
C72 AP22 25c lilac rose .20 .15
C73 AP22 35c purple .28 .15
C74 AP22 50c orange .32 .18
C75 AP22 70c dull green .55 .20
C76 AP22 $1 blue .75 .30
Nos. C71-C76 (6) 2.25 1.13

See Nos. C82-C87.

Flags, Emblem and Children — AP23

1954, Sept. 27

Size: 51x39mm

C77 AP23 $5 bl, red, vio bl & blk 20.00 20.00

A reproduction of No. C77, size 63x49mm, was prepared for presentation purposes. Value $20.

Half the proceeds from the sale of No. C77 was given to the UNICEF.

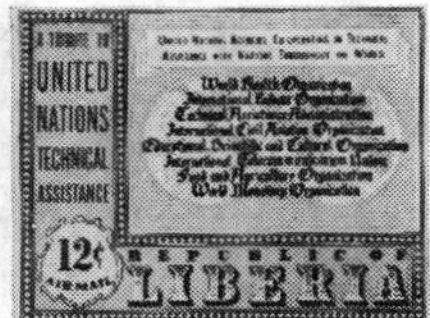

UN Technical Assistance Agencies
AP24

Designs: 15c, Printing instruction. 20c, Sawmill maintenance. 25c, Geography class.

1954, Oct. 25

C78 AP24 12c black & blue .15 .15
C79 AP24 15c dk brown & yel .15 .15
C80 AP24 20c black & yel grn .20 .15
C81 AP24 25c vio blue & red .25 .20
Nos. C78-C81 (4) .75
Set value .50

UN Technical Assistance program.

Type of 1953 Inscribed: "Commemorating Presidential Visit U. S. A.-1954"

Designs as before.

1954, Nov. 19

C82 AP22 12c vermilion .15 .15
C83 AP22 25c blue .20 .15
C84 AP22 35c carmine rose .28 .15
C85 AP22 50c rose violet .40 .15
C86 AP22 70c orange brown .55 .26
C87 AP22 $1 dull green .80 .32
Nos. C82-C87 (6) 2.38
Set value .98

Visit of Pres. William V.S. Tubman to the US. Exist imperforate.

Baseball
AP25

1955, Jan. 26 Litho. *Perf. 12½*

C88 AP25 10c shown .15 .15
C89 AP25 12c Swimming .15 .15
C90 AP25 25c Running .15 .15
a. Souvenir sheet 12.00 12.00
Set value .28 .28

#C90a contains 1 each of #349, C90 with colors transposed. Exists imperf.; same value.

Costus — AP26

Design: 25c, Barteria nigritiana.

1955, Sept. 28 Unwmk. *Perf. 12½*

C91 AP26 20c violet, grn & yel .15 .15
C92 AP26 25c green, red & yel .16 .16
Set value .25 .25

UN Emblem — AP27

UN Charter — AP28

Designs: 15c, General Assembly. 25c, Gabriel L. Dennis signing UN Charter for Liberia.

1955, Oct. 24 Unwmk. *Perf. 12*

C93 AP27 10c ultra & red .15 .15
C94 AP27 15c violet & blk .20 .15
C95 AP27 25c green & red brn .32 .15
C96 AP28 50c brick red & grn .70 .18
Nos. C93-C96 (4) 1.37
Set value .38

10th anniv. of the UN, Oct. 24, 1955.

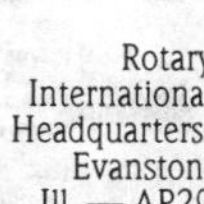

Rotary International Headquarters, Evanston, Ill. — AP29

Design: 15c, View of Monrovia.

1955, Dec. 5 Litho. *Perf. 12½*

C97 AP29 10c deep ultra & red .20 .15
C98 AP29 15c redsh brn, red & bis .30 .20

Souvenir Sheet

C99 AP29 50c deep ultra & red 1.00 1.00

No. C99 design as No. C97, but redrawn and with leaves omitted.

50th anniversary of Rotary International.

Nos. C97-C99 exist without Rotary emblem; No. C97 printed entirely in deep ultramarine; No. C98 with bister impression omitted.

FIPEX Type of Regular Issue

10c, New York Coliseum. 12c, Globe inscribed FIPEX. 15c, 50c, Statue of Liberty.

Design:

1956, Apr. 28 Unwmk. *Perf. 12*

C100 A143 10c rose red & ultra .15 .15
C101 A143 12c orange & purple .18 .15
C102 A142 15c aqua & red lilac .22 .15
Nos. C100-C102 (3) .55
Set value .21

Souvenir Sheet

C103 A142 50c lt green & brn 1.00 1.00

Olympic Park, Melbourne
AP32

20c, 40c, Map of Australia & Olympic torch.

1956, Nov. 15 Unwmk. *Perf. 12*

C104 AP32 12c emerald & vio .15 .15
C105 AP32 20c multicolored .18 .15
Set value .15

Souvenir Sheet

C106 AP32 40c multicolored 1.00 1.00

16th Olympic Games, Melbourne, 11/22-12/8.

Type of Regular Issue, 1957.

12c, 25c, Idlewild airport, NYC. 15c, 50c, Roberts Field, Liberia, plane & Pres. Tubman.

Lithographed and Engraved

1957, May 4 *Perf. 12*

C107 A146 12c brt grn & dk bl .15 .15
C108 A146 15c red brn & blk .15 .15
C109 A146 25c carmine & dk bl .24 .15
C110 A146 50c lt ultra & blk .45 .15
Nos. C107-C110 (4) .99
Set value .40

Type of Regular Issue, 1957

Orphanage and: 15c, Nurse inoculating boy. 35c, The Kamara triplets. 70c, Children and flag.

1957, Nov. 25 Litho. *Perf. 12*

C111 A147 15c lt blue & brn .15 .15
C112 A147 35c maroon & lt gray .22 .15
Set value .21

Souvenir Sheet

C113 A147 70c ultra & rose car .95 .85

Type of Regular Issue, 1958

10c, Italian flag & Colosseum. #C115, French flag & Arc de Triomphe. #C116, Swiss flag & chalet. #C117, Vatican flag & St. Peter's.

Engr. and Litho.

1958, Jan. 10 *Perf. 10½*

Flags in Original Colors

C114 A148 10c dark gray .15 .15
C115 A148 15c dp yellow grn .15 .15
C116 A148 15c ultra .15 .15
C117 A148 15c purple .15 .15
Set value .44 .25

Type of Regular Issue, 1948-50

Design: William V. S. Tubman.

1958 Engr. *Perf. 12*

C118 A128 25c lt green & blk .40 .30

Souvenir Sheet

Preamble to Declaration of Human Rights — AP33

1958, Dec. 10 Litho. *Perf. 12*

C119 AP33 20c blue & red 1.50 1.50

10th anniv. of the signing of the Universal Declaration of Human Rights.

Liberians Reading Proclamation — AP34

1959, Apr. 15 Unwmk.

C120 AP34 25c blue & brown .26 .26

African Freedom Day, Apr. 15.

UNESCO Building, Paris — AP35

1959, May 1

C121 AP35 25c ultra & red .30 .24
a. Souvenir sheet 1.00 1.00

Opening of UNESCO Headquarters in Paris, Nov. 3, 1958.

Lincoln Type of Regular Issue

1959, Nov. 20 Engr. *Perf. 12*

C122 A152 25c emerald & black .38 .38

For souvenir sheet see No. 386a.

Touré, Tubman and Nkrumah
AP36

1960, Jan. 27 Litho. Unwmk.

C123 AP36 25c beige, vio bl & blk .30 .30

See note after No. 387.

WRY Type of Regular Issue, 1960

1960, Apr. 7 *Perf. 11½*

C124 A154 25c ultra & black .42 .35
a. Souv. sheet of 2, #388, C124, imperf. 1.50 1.50

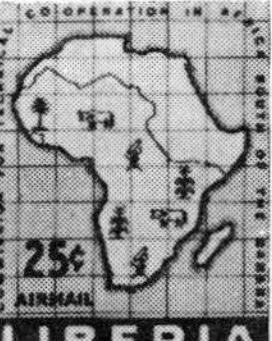

Map of Africa — AP37

1960, May 11 *Perf. 11½*

C125 AP37 25c ultra & brown .35 .35

See note after No. 389.

Olympic Games Type of 1960

Designs: 25c, Javelin thrower and hunter, horiz. 50c, Runner and stadium, horiz.

1960, Sept. 6 *Perf. 11½*
C126 A156 25c brown & brt ultra .50 .38

Souvenir Sheet
Imperf

C127 A156 50c lilac & brown 2.00 2.00

Stamp Centenary Type of 1960

1960, Dec. 1 Litho. *Perf. 11½*
C128 A157 25c multicolored .32 .32

Souvenir Sheet

C129 A157 50c multicolored 1.00 1.00

Globe, Dove and UN Emblem AP38

Design: 50c, Globe and dove.

1961, May 19 Unwmk. *Perf. 11½*
C130 AP38 25c indigo & red .25 .25

Souvenir Sheet

C131 AP38 50c red brn & emerald 1.25 1.25

Liberia's membership in the UN Security Council.
A second souvenir sheet contains one each of Nos. 395, C130 and the 50c from No. C131, imperf. Size: 133x83mm.
No. C130 exists imperf.

Science Class — AP39

Design: 50c, Science class, different design.

1961, Sept. 8 Litho.
C132 AP39 25c purple & brown .30 .20

Souvenir Sheet

C133 AP39 50c blue & brown 1.00 1.00

15th anniv. of UNESCO.

Joseph J. Roberts and Providence Island AP40

1961, Oct. 25 Litho. *Perf. 11½*
C134 AP40 25c emerald & sepia .30 .30
a. Souvenir sheet of 3 1.00 1.00

150th anniv. of the birth of Joseph J. Roberts, 1st pres. of Liberia.
No. C134a contains three imperf. stamps similar to Nos. 397-398 and C134, but printed in different colors; 5c, emerald & sepia. 10c, orange & sepia. 25c, ultramarine & sepia.

Scout Type of Regular Issue and

Boy Scout — AP41

1961, Dec. 4 Unwmk. *Perf. 11½*
C135 AP41 25c emerald & sepia .75 .75

Souvenir Sheet

Design: Like No. 399.

C136 A161 35c dull blue & sepia 1.50 1.50

Dag Hammarskjold Type of 1962

1962, Feb. 1 Unwmk. *Perf. 12*
C137 A162 25c black & red lilac .35 .35

Souvenir Sheet
Imperf

C138 A162 50c black & ultra 1.00 1.00

Malaria Eradication Emblem AP42

1962, Apr. 7 *Perf. 12½*
C139 AP42 25c purple & orange .35 .30

Souvenir Sheet
Imperf

C140 AP42 50c dark red & ultra 1.00 1.00

Pres. Tubman, Statue of Liberty, New York Skyline and Flags of US and Liberia — AP43

1962, Sept. 17 Litho. *Perf. 11½x12*
C141 AP43 12c multicolored .15 .15
C142 AP43 25c multicolored .35 .25
C143 AP43 50c multicolored .70 .50
Nos. C141-C143 (3) 1.20 .90

Pres. Tubman's visit to the US in 1961.

United Nations Emblem and Flags — AP44

Design: 50c, UN emblem.

1962, Oct. 22 *Perf. 12x12½*
C144 AP44 25c lt ultra & dk bl .30 .30

Souvenir Sheet
Imperf

C145 AP44 50c brt grnsh bl & blk .80 .80

Observance of UN Day, Oct. 24, as a national holiday.

Building Type of Regular Issue

12c, 70c, Capitol. 50c, Information Service. $1, Treasury Department Building, Monrovia.

1962-63 *Perf. 12x12½, 12 (70c)*
C146 A165 12c brt yel grn & mar .15 .15
C147 A165 50c orange & ultra .65 .65
C147A A165 70c brt pink & dk bl ('63) .90 .90
C148 A165 $1 salmon & blk ('63) 1.25 1.25
Nos. C146-C148 (4) 2.95 2.95

"FAO" Emblem and Globe — AP45

Design: 50c, "FAO" and UN Emblems.

1963, Mar. 21 Unwmk. *Perf. 12½*
C149 AP45 25c dk green & yel .35 .35

Souvenir Sheet
Perf. 12

C150 AP45 50c emerald & ultra 1.00 1.00

FAO "Freedom from Hunger" campaign.

Type of Regular Issue, 1963

Designs: 25c, Telstar satellite, vert. 50c, Telstar and rocket, vert.

1963, May 27 Litho. *Perf. 12½*
C151 A167 25c Prus blue & org .40 .40

Souvenir Sheet
Perf. 12

C152 A167 50c dp violet & yel 1.00 .55

Red Cross Type of Regular Issue

Design: 25c, Red Cross and globe. 50c, Centenary emblem and globe.

1963, Aug. 26 Unwmk. *Perf. 12*
C153 A168 25c purple & red .22 .22
C154 A168 50c deep ultra & red .42 .42

Map of Africa — AP46

1963, Oct. 28 *Perf. 12½*
C156 AP46 25c red orange & grn .25 .25

See note after No. 412.

Olympic Type of Regular Issue

Designs: 10c, Torch and mountains. 25c, Mountains, horiz. 50c, Torch, background like No. 413.

1963, Dec. 11 Litho. *Perf. 12½*
C157 A170 10c vio blue & red .15 .15
C158 A170 25c green & orange .32 .32

Souvenir Sheet
Perf. 12

C159 A170 50c gray & red 1.00 1.00

Kennedy Type of Regular Issue, 1964

Designs: 25c, John F. Kennedy, vert. 50c, John F. Kennedy (like No. 414).

1964, Apr. 6 Unwmk. *Perf. 12½*
C160 A171 25c blk & red lil .35 .30

Souvenir Sheet
Perf. 12

C161 A171 50c blk & red lil 1.00 .80

An imperf. miniature sheet containing one of No. C160 exists. No marginal inscription.

Satellite Type of Regular Issue
Souvenir Sheet

Design: Launching rocket separating from booster in space, vert.

1964, June 22 Litho.
C162 A172 50c vio bl & red 1.00 1.00

Olympic Type of Regular Issue
Souvenir Sheet

Design: 50c, Runner and Olympic rings.

1964, Sept. 15 Unwmk. *Perf. 12*
C163 A173 50c grnsh bl & red 1.00 .45

Scout Type of Regular Issue, 1965

Designs: 25c, Liberian flag and fleur-delis. 50c, Globe and Scout emblem.

1965, Mar. 8 Litho. *Perf. 12½*
C164 A174 25c crim & ultra .45 .45

Souvenir Sheet
Perf. 12

C165 A174 50c yel & lil .85 .85

Lincoln Type of Regular Issue
Souvenir Sheet

50c, Lincoln and John F. Kennedy, horiz.

1965, May 3 Unwmk. *Perf. 12*
C166 A175 50c dp plum & lt gray 1.00 1.00

ICY Type of Regular Issue, 1965
Souvenir Sheet

1965, June 21 Litho.
C167 A176 50c car rose & brn 1.00 1.00

ITU Type of Regular Issue, 1965

1965, Sept. 21 Unwmk. *Perf. 12½*
C168 A177 50c red org & vio bl .50 .45

Tubman Type of Regular Issue

Design: 25c, Pres. Tubman and coat of arms.

1965, Nov. 29 Litho. *Perf. 12½*
C169 A178 25c ultra, red & brn .40 .40
a. Souv. sheet of 2, #431, C169, imperf. 1.00 1.00

Churchill Type of Regular Issue

25c, "Angry Lion" portrait by Karsh & Parliament, London. 50c, "Williamsburg Award Dinner" portrait by Karsh & map of Europe.

1966, Jan. 18 Litho. *Perf. 12½*
C170 A179 25c blk & vio bl .30 .24

Souvenir Sheet
Perf. 12

C171 A179 50c blk & red lil 1.00 1.00

Soccer Type of Regular Issue
Souvenir Sheet

Design: 50c, Soccer match in stadium.

1966, May 3 Litho. *Perf. 11½*
C172 A181 50c ultra & red brn 1.00 1.00

Kennedy Type of Regular Issue

25c, UN General Assembly & Pres. Kennedy. 35c, Pres. Kennedy & rocket on launching pad, Cape Kennedy. 40c, Flame on grave at Arlington.

1966, Aug. 16 Litho. *Perf. 12½*
C173 A182 25c ultra, blk & ocher .28 .15
C174 A182 35c dk vio bl & pink .35 .20

Souvenir Sheet
Perf. 11½

C175 A182 40c dk vio bl & multi 1.25 1.25

Boy Scout Type of Regular Issue
Souvenir Sheet

50c, Scout at campfire & vision of moon landing.

1967, Mar. 23 Litho. *Perf. 12½*
C176 A185 50c brt red lil & scar 2.25 2.25

Olympic Type of Regular Issue
Souvenir Sheet

Design: 50c, Pre-Hispanic sculpture, serape and Olympic rings, horiz.

1967, June 20 Litho. *Perf. 12½*
C177 A186 50c vio & car 2.25 1.00

Winter Olympic Games Type of Regular Issue
Souvenir Sheet

Design: 50c, Woman skater.

1967, Nov. 20 Litho. *Perf. 11½*
C178 A189 50c ver & blk 1.25 .40

Human Rights Type of Regular Issue
Souvenir Sheet

1968, Apr. 26 Litho. *Perf. 11½*
C179 A191 80c bl & red 1.50 .55

M. L. King Type of Regular Issue
Souvenir Sheet

55c, Pres. Kennedy congratulating Dr. King.

1968, July 11 Litho. *Perf. 11½*
C180 A192 55c brn & blk 1.40 .40

Olympic Type of Regular Issue
Souvenir Sheet

Design: 50c, Steeplechase and ancient sculpture.

1968, Aug. 22 Litho. *Perf. 11½*
C181 A193 50c brt bl & org brn 1.25 .65

President Type of Regular Issue 1966-69

Design: 25c, Pres. William V. S. Tubman.

1969, Feb. 18 Litho. *Perf. 11½x11*
C182 A180 25c blk & emer .60 .30

ILO Type of Regular Issue

Design: 80c, "ILO" surrounded by cogwheel and wreath, vert.

1969, Apr. 16 Litho. *Perf. 12½*
C183 A196 80c emer & gold 1.25 .60

Apollo 11 Type of Regular Issue
Souvenir Sheet

65c, Astronauts Neil A. Armstrong, Col. Edwin E. Aldrin, Jr., & Lieut. Col. Michael Collins, horiz.

1969, Oct. 15 Litho. *Perf. 11½*
C184 A199 65c dk vio bl & brt red 1.40 .55

UN Type of 1970

Design: $1, UN emblem, olive branch and plane as symbols of peace and progress, vert.

1970, Apr. 16 Litho. *Perf. 12½*
C185 A200 $1 ultra & sil 1.40 .80

Apollo 14 Type of Regular Issue
Souvenir Sheet

Design: 50c, Moon, earth and star.

1971, May 20 Litho. *Imperf.*
C186 A208 50c multi 2.00 2.00

Souvenir Sheet

Olympic Yachting Village, Kiel, and Yachting — AP47

Illustration reduced.

1971, June 28 Litho. *Perf. 14½x14*

C187 AP47 Sheet of 2 1.25 1.25
a. 25c multi .50 .50
b. 30c multi .60 .60

Publicity for the 20th Summer Olympic Games, and the yachting races in Kiel, Germany, 1972.

Boy Scout Type of Regular Issue
Souvenir Sheet

Boy Scouts of various nations cooking, horiz.

1971, Aug. 6 Litho. *Perf. 15*

C188 A211 50c multi 1.50 1.50

UNICEF Type of Regular Issue
Souvenir Sheet

UNICEF emblem & Bengal tigress with cubs.

1971, Oct. 1 *Imperf.*

C189 A213 50c multi 1.75 1.75

Souvenir Sheet

Japanese Royal Family — AP48

1971, Nov. 4 *Perf. 15*

C190 AP48 50c multi 2.50 2.50

11th Winter Olympic Games, Sapporo, Japan, Feb. 3-13, 1972.

Sesquicentennial Type of Regular Issue
Souvenir Sheet

Design: 50c, Sailing ship "Elizabeth" between maps of America and Africa, horiz.

1972, Jan. 1 Litho. *Imperf.*

C191 A216 50c car & vio bl 1.50 1.50

Olympic Type of Regular Issue
Souvenir Sheet

Design: 55c, View of Olympic Stadium and symbol of "Motion."

1971, May 19 Litho. *Perf. 15*

C192 A218 55c multi 1.50 1.50

Apollo 16 Type of Regular Issue
Souvenir Sheet

Lt. Comdr. Thomas K. Mattingly, 2nd, Capt. John W. Young & Lt. Col. Charles M. Duke, Jr.

1972, June 26 Litho. *Perf. 15*

C193 A220 55c pink & multi 1.50 1.50

Ship Type of 1972
Souvenir Sheet

Design: Lord Nelson's flagship Victory, and her figurehead (1765).

1972, Sept. 6 Litho. *Perf. 15*

C194 A222 50c multi 1.75 1.75

Pres. Tolbert Type of 1972.
Souvenir Sheet

1972, Oct. 23 Litho. *Perf. 15*

C195 A223 55c multi 1.25 1.25

Apollo 17 Type of Regular Issue
Souvenir Sheet

Design: 55c, Apollo 17 badge, moon and earth.

1973, Mar. 28 Litho. *Perf. 11*

C196 A225 55c bl & multi 1.25 1.25

Locomotive Type of Regular Issue
Souvenir Sheet

Design: 55c, Swiss locomotive.

1973, May 4 Litho. *Perf. 11*

C197 A226 55c multi 1.75 1.75

WHO Type of Regular Issue 1973
Souvenir Sheet

Design: 55c, WHO emblem, Paul Ehrlich and poppy anemones.

1973, June 26 Litho. *Perf. 11*

C198 A228 55c lt vio & multi 1.40 1.40

Automobile Type of Regular Issue
Souvenir Sheet

Franklin 10 HP cross-engined 1904-05 models.

1973, Sept. 11 Litho. *Perf. 11*

C199 A229 55c multi 1.50 1.50

Copernicus Type of Regular Issue
Souvenir Sheet

Design: 55c, Copernicus and concept of orbiting station around Mars.

1973, Dec. 14 Litho. *Perf. 13½*

C200 A230 55c gray & multi 1.25 1.25

UPU Type of Regular Issue
Souvenir Sheet

55c, UPU emblem and English coach, 1784.

1974, Mar. 4 Litho. *Perf. 13½*

C201 A232 55c multi 1.25 1.25

Dog Type of Regular Issue
Souvenir Sheet

Design: Hungarian sheepdog (kuvasz).

1974, Apr. 16 Litho. *Perf. 13½*

C202 A233 75c multi 1.50 1.50

Soccer Type of Regular Issue
Souvenir Sheet

Design: 60c, World Soccer Championship Cup and Munich Stadium.

1974, June 4 Litho. *Perf. 11*

C203 A234 60c multi 1.50 1.50

Butterfly Type of Regular Issue
Souvenir Sheet

Tropical butterfly: 60c, Pierella nereis.

1974, Sept. 11 Litho. *Perf. 13½*

C204 A235 60c gray & multi *2.00 2.00*

Churchill Type of 1974
Souvenir Sheet

60c, Churchill at easel painting landscape.

1975, Jan. 17 Litho. *Perf. 13½*

C205 A237 60c multi 1.25 1.25

Women's Year Type of 1975
Souvenir Sheet

Design: 75c, Vijaya Lakshmi Pandit, Women's Year emblem and dais of UN General Assembly.

1975, Mar. 14 Litho. *Perf. 13*

C206 A238 75c gray & multi 1.75 1.75

American Bicentennial Type
Souvenir Sheet

Design: 75c, Mayflower and US No. 548.

1975, Apr. 25 Litho. *Perf. 13½*

C207 A239 75c multi 2.00 2.00

Dr. Schweitzer Type, 1975
Souvenir Sheet

Schweitzer as surgeon in Lambarene Hospital.

1975, June 26 Litho. *Perf. 13½*

C208 A240 60c multi 1.50 1.50

Apollo-Soyuz Type, 1975
Souvenir Sheet

Design: 75c, Apollo-Soyuz link-up and emblem.

1975, Sept. 18 Litho. *Perf. 13½*

C209 A241 75c multi 1.60 1.60

Winter Olympic Games Type, 1976
Souvenir Sheet

Downhill skiing & Olympic Games emblem.

1976, Jan. 23 Litho. *Perf. 13½*

C210 A243 75c multi 1.75 1.75

Olympic Games Type, 1976
Souvenir Sheet

Design: 75c, Dressage and jumping.

1976, May 4 Litho. *Perf. 13½*

C211 A245 75c multi 1.75 1.75

Bell Type
Souvenir Sheet

Design: 75c, A. G. Bell making telephone call, UPU and ITU emblems.

1976, June 4 Litho. *Perf. 13½*

C212 A246 75c ocher & multi 1.75 1.75

Animal Type of 1976
Souvenir Sheet

Design: 50c, Elephant, vert.

1976, Sept. 1 Litho. *Perf. 13½*

C213 A249 50c org & multi 2.75 2.75

Bicentennial Type of 1976
Souvenir Sheet

Design: 75c, Like No. 770.

1976, Sept. 21 Litho. *Perf. 13½*

C214 A250 75c multi 1.75 1.75

Mask Type of 1977
Souvenir Sheet

Design: 75c, Ibo mask and Festival emblem.

1977, Jan. 20 Litho. *Perf. 13½*

C215 A251 75c lil & multi 1.75 1.75

Equestrian Type of 1977

Designs: 55c, Military dressage (team), US. 80c, Winners receiving medals, vert.

1977, Apr. 22 Litho. *Perf. 13½*

C216 A253 55c ocher & multi 1.00 .50

Souvenir Sheet

C217 A253 80c ocher & multi 1.75 1.75

Elizabeth II Type of 1977
Souvenir Sheet

Design: 75c, Elizabeth II, laurel and crowns.

1977, May 23 Litho. *Perf. 13½*

C218 A254 75c sil & multi 1.75 1.25

Zeppelin Type of 1978
Souvenir Sheet

75c, Futuristic Goodyear aerospace airship.

1978, Mar. 9 Litho. *Perf. 13½*

C219 A257 75c multi 1.75 1.75

Soccer Type of 1978
Souvenir Sheet

Soccer game Netherlands & Uruguay, vert.

1978, May 16 Litho. *Perf. 13½*

C220 A258 75c multi 1.75

Coronation Type of 1978
Souvenir Sheet

Design: 75c, Coronation coach, horiz.

1978, June 12

C221 A259 75c multi 1.75

Soccer Winners' Type of 1978
Souvenir Sheet

Design: 75c, Argentine team, horiz.

1978, Dec. 8 Litho. *Perf. 13½*

C222 A262 75c multi 1.75

AIR POST SEMI-POSTAL STAMPS

Nos. C14-C16 Overprinted in Red or Blue Like Nos. B16-B18

1941 Unwmk. *Perf. 12*

CB1 A107 3c +2c dk bl (R) 1.25 1.25
CB2 A108 5c +2c dl red brn (Bl) 1.25 1.25
CB3 A109 10c +2c dk grn (R) 1.25 1.25
Nos. CB1-CB3 (3) 3.75 3.75

Catalogue values for unused stamps in this section, from this point to the end of the section, are for Never Hinged items.

Nurses Taking Oath SPAP1

Designs: 20c+5c, Liberian Government Hospital. 25c+5c, Medical examination.

1954, June 21 Litho. & Engr.

Size: 39½x28½mm

CB4 SPAP1 10c +5c car & blk .15 .15
CB5 SPAP1 20c +5c emer & blk .18 .15

Size: 45x34mm

CB6 SPAP1 25c +5c ultra, car & blk .20 .15
Nos. CB4-CB6 (3) .53
Set value .25

Surtax for the Liberian Government Hospital. Nos. CB4-CB6 exist imperf. No. CB6 exists with carmine omitted.

AIR POST SPECIAL DELIVERY STAMP

No. C15 Overprinted in Dark Blue Like No. E1

1941 Unwmk. *Perf. 12*

CE1 A108 10c on 5c dl red brn 1.65 1.10

AIR POST REGISTRATION STAMP

No. C15 Overprinted in Dark Blue Like No. F35

1941 Unwmk. *Perf. 12*

CF1 A108 10c on 5c dl red brn 1.65 1.10

SPECIAL DELIVERY STAMP

No. 278 Surcharged in Dark Blue

SPECIAL DELIVERY

10 CENTS 10

1941 Unwmk. *Perf. 12*

E1 A108 10c on 5c dl red brn 1.65 1.10

REGISTRATION STAMPS

R1

1893 Unwmk. Litho. *Perf. 14, 15*

Without Value Surcharged

F1 R1 (10c) blk (Buchanan) 250.00 250.00
F2 R1 (10c) blk (Greenville) *2,250. 2,250.*
F3 R1 (10c) blk (Harper) *2,250. 2,250.*
F4 R1 (10c) blk (Monrovia) 30.00 30.00
F5 R1 (10c) blk (Robertsport) 1,000. 1,000.

Types of 1893 Surcharged in Black

10 CENTS 10

10 CENTS 10

1894 *Perf. 14*
F6 R1 10c bl, *pink* (Buchanan) 5.00 5.25
F7 R1 10c grn, *buff* (Harper) 5.00 5.25
F8 R1 10c red, *yel* (Monrovia) 5.00 5.25
F9 R1 10c rose, *bl* (Robertsport) 5.00 5.25
Nos. F6-F9 (4) 20.00 21.00

Exist imperf or missing one 10. Value, each $10.

President Garretson W. Gibson — R6

1903 **Engr.** *Perf. 14*
F10 R6 10c bl & blk (Buchanan) 1.10 .15
a. Center inverted 100.00
F11 R6 10c org red & blk ("Grenville") 1.10
a. Center inverted 100.00
b. 10c orange & black 1.90 .15
F12 R6 10c grn & blk (Harper) 1.10 .15
a. Center inverted 100.00
F13 R6 10c vio & blk (Monrovia) 1.10 .15
a. Center inverted 100.00
b. 10c lilac & black 1.90
F14 R6 10c mag & blk (Robertsport) 1.10 .15
a. Center inverted 100.00
Nos. F10-F14 (5) 5.50
Nos. F10, F11b, F12-F14 .75

For surcharges see Nos. 178-182.

S.S. Quail on Patrol R7

1919 **Litho.** ***Serrate Roulette 12***
F15 R7 10c blk & bl (Buchanan) .50 1.00

Serrate Roulette 12, Perf. 14
F16 R7 10c ocher & blk ("Grenville") .50 1.00
F17 R7 10c grn & blk (Harper) .50 1.00
F18 R7 10c vio & bl (Monrovia) .50 1.00
F19 R7 10c rose & blk (Robertsport) .50 1.00
Nos. F15-F19 (5) 2.50 5.00

Gabon Viper R8

Wmk. Crosses and Circles (116)

1921 **Engr.** *Perf. 13x14*
F20 R8 10c cl & blk (Buchanan) 27.50 1.50
F21 R8 10c red & blk (Greenville) 17.50 1.50
F22 R8 10c ultra & blk (Harper) 22.50 1.50
F23 R8 10c org & blk (Monrovia) 17.50 1.50
a. Imperf., pair 150.00
F24 R8 10c grn & blk (Robertsport) 17.50 1.50
a. Imperf., pair 150.00
Nos. F20-F24 (5) 102.50 7.50

Preceding Issue Overprinted "1921"
F25 R8 10c (Buchanan) 20.00 3.00
F26 R8 10c (Greenville) 21.00 3.00
F27 R8 10c (Harper) 20.00 3.00
F28 R8 10c (Monrovia) 19.00 3.00
F29 R8 10c (Robertsport) 20.00 3.00
Nos. F25-F29 (5) 100.00 15.00

Nos. F25-F29 exist with "1921" inverted. Value same as normal.

Passengers Going Ashore from Ship — R9

Designs: No. F31, Transporting merchandise, shore to ship (Greenville). No. F32, Sailing ship (Harper). No. F33, Ocean liner (Monrovia). No. F34, Canoe in surf (Robertsport).

1924 **Litho.** *Perf. 14*
F30 R9 10c gray & carmine 3.50 .30
F31 R9 10c gray & blue grn 3.50 .30
F32 R9 10c gray & orange 3.50 .30
F33 R9 10c gray & blue 3.50 .30
F34 R9 10c gray & violet 3.50 .30
Nos. F30-F34 (5) 17.50 1.50

No. 278 Surcharged in Dark Blue

1941 **Unwmk.** *Perf. 12*
F35 A108 10c on 5c dull red brn 1.25 1.25

POSTAGE DUE STAMPS

Nos. 26, 28 Surcharged

POSTAGE DUE 3 CENTS.

1892 **Unwmk.** *Perf. 11*
J1 A5 3c on 3c violet 1.50 1.75
a. Imperf., pair 15.00
b. Inverted surcharge 45.00 45.00
c. As "a," inverted surcharge 110.00

Perf. 12
J2 A5 6c on 6c olive gray 7.50 9.00
a. Imperf., pair 22.50
b. Inverted surcharge 52.50 35.00

D2

Engr.; Figures of Value Typographed in Black

1893 **Wmk. 143** *Perf. 14, 15*
J3 D2 2c org, *yel* 1.25 .65
J4 D2 4c rose, *rose* 1.25 .65
J5 D2 6c brown, *buff* 1.25 .85
J6 D2 8c blue, *blue* 1.25 .85
J7 D2 10c grn, *lil rose* 1.50 1.00
J8 D2 20c vio, *gray* 1.50 1.00
a. Center inverted 110.00 110.00
J9 D2 40c ol brn, *grnsh* 3.00 2.00
Nos. J3-J9 (7) 11.00 7.00

All values of the above set exist imperforate.

MILITARY STAMPS

"LFF" are the initials of "Liberian Frontier Force." Nos. M1-M7 were issued for the use of troops sent to guard the frontier.

Issues of 1905, 1906 and 1909 Surcharged

L F F
1c

1916 **Wmk. 143**
M1 A23 1c on 1c lt grn 175.00 175.00
a. 2nd "F" inverted 250.00 250.00
b. "FLF" 250.00 250.00
c. Inverted surcharge 250.00 250.00

Unwmk.
M2 A33 1c on 1c grn & blk 500.00 500.00
a. 2nd "F" inverted 550.00 550.00
b. "FLF" 550.00 550.00
M3 A46 1c on 1c yel grn & blk 3.75 4.50
a. 2nd "F" inverted 7.50 7.50
b. "FLF" 7.50 7.50
M4 A47 1c on 2c lake & blk 3.75 4.50
a. 2nd "F" inverted 7.50 7.50
b. "FLF" 7.50 7.50

Surcharge exists sideways on Nos. M2, M5; double on Nos. M1-M4; inverted on Nos. M2-M4.

Nos. O46, O59-O60 Surcharged

L F F
1c

M5 A33 1c on 1c 400.00 400.00
a. 2nd "F" inverted 550.00 550.00
b. "FLF" 550.00 550.00
M6 A46 1c on 1c 3.75 4.50
a. 2nd "F" inverted 7.50 7.50
b. "FLF" 7.50 7.50
c. "LFF 1c" inverted 10.00 10.00
d. As "a" and "1c" inverted 14.00
e. "FLF 1c" inverted 14.00
M7 A47 1c on 2c 2.75 3.25
a. 2nd "F" inverted 5.75 5.75
b. "FLF" 5.75 5.75
c. Pair, one without "LFF 1c"

OFFICIAL STAMPS

Types of Regular Issues Overprinted "OFFICIAL" in Various Colors

Perf. 12½ to 15 and Compound

1892 **Wmk. 143**
O1 A9 1c vermilion .50 .50
O2 A9 2c blue .50 .50
O3 A10 4c grn & blk .50 .50
O4 A11 6c bl grn .50 .50
O5 A12 8c brn & blk .50 .50
O6 A13 12c rose red 1.25 1.25
O7 A14 16c red lilac 1.25 1.25
O8 A15 24c ol grn, *yel* 1.25 1.25
O9 A16 32c grnsh bl 1.25 1.25
O10 A17 $1 bl & blk 25.00 10.00
O11 A18 $2 brn, *yel* 10.50 7.25
O12 A19 $5 car & blk 15.00 6.50
Nos. O1-O12 (12) 58.00 31.25

1893
O13 A11 (a) 5c on 6c bl grn (No. 50) .95 .95
a. "5" with short flag 5.00 5.00
b. Both 5's with short flags 5.00 5.00
c. "i" dot omitted 19.00 19.00
d. Overprinted on #50d 45.00 45.00

1894

Overprinted "O S" in Various Colors
O15 A9 1c vermilion .35 .25
O16 A9 2c blue .50 .30
a. Imperf.
O17 A10 4c grn & blk .60 .40
O18 A12 8c brn & blk .60 .40
O19 A13 12c rose red .85 .45
O20 A14 16c red lilac .85 .45
O21 A15 24c ol grn, *yel* .85 .50
O22 A16 32c grnsh bl 1.25 .60
O23 A17 $1 bl & blk 15.00 15.00
a. $1 ultra & black 15.00 15.00
O24 A18 $2 brn, *yel* 15.00 15.00
O25 A19 $5 car & blk 92.50 62.50
Nos. O15-O25 (11) 128.35 95.85

Unwmk.

Imperf
O26 A22 5c vio & grn 3.00 1.90

Rouletted
O27 A22 5c vio & grn 3.00 1.90

Regular Issue of 1896-1905 Overprinted "O S" in Black or Red

1898-1905 **Wmk. 143** ***Perf. 14, 15***
O28 A23 1c lil rose .55 .55
O29 A23 1c dp grn ('00) .55 .55
O30 A23 1c lt grn (R) ('05) .55 .55
O31 A24 2c bis & blk 1.10 .30
a. Pair, one without overprint 62.50
O32 A24 2c org red & blk ('00) 1.75 .75
O33 A24 2c rose & blk ('05) 2.75 1.50
O34 A25 5c lake & blk 1.75 .75
O35 A25 5c gray bl & blk ('00) 2.25 .75
O36 A25 5c ultra & blk (R) ('05) 3.50 1.90
O37 A12 10c chr yel & ind 1.10 .95
O38 A13 15c slate 1.10 .95
O39 A14 20c vermilion 1.75 1.10
O40 A15 25c yel grn 1.10 .95
O41 A16 30c steel blue 2.75 1.50
O42 A26 50c red brn & blk 2.75 1.50
Nos. O28-O42 (15) 25.30 14.55

For surcharge see No. O92.

Official stamps overprinted "ORDINARY" or with a bar with an additional surcharge are listed as Nos. 64B-90, 92-93, 99.

Red Overprint — A29

1903 **Unwmk.** ***Perf. 14***
O43 A29 3c green .20 .15
a. Overprint omitted 5.00
b. Inverted overprint

Two overprint types: I - Thin, sharp, dark red. II - Thick, heavier, orange red. Same value.

On No. 50

O3

1904 **Black Surcharge** **Wmk. 143**
O44 A11 1c on 5c on 6c bl grn 1.25 1.50
a. "5" with short flag 4.25
b. Both "5s" with straight flag 8.00 8.00

Red Surcharge
O45 O3 2c on 30c steel blue 8.00 8.00
a. Double surcharge, red and black
b. Surcharge also on back

Types of Regular Issue Overprinted in Various Colors — a

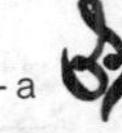

1906 **Unwmk.**
O46 A33 1c grn & blk (R) .45 .30
O47 A34 2c car & blk (Bl) .15 .15
a. Center and overprint inverted 16.00 11.00
b. Inverted overprint 4.50
O48 A35 5c ultra & blk (Bk) .45 .30
a. Inverted overprint 4.50 4.50
b. Center and overprint invtd. 27.50
O49 A36 10c dl vio & blk (R) .55 .40
a. Inverted overprint
b. Center and overprint invtd. 32.50
O50 A37 15c brn & blk (Bk) 2.25 .40
a. Inverted overprint 4.50
b. Overprint omitted
c. Center and overprint invtd. 40.00
O51 A38 20c dp grn & blk (R) .55 .40
a. Overprint omitted
O52 A39 25c plum & gray (Bl) .35 .15
a. With 2nd ovpt. in blue, invtd.
O53 A40 30c dk brn (Bk) .40 .15
O54 A41 50c org brn & dp grn (G) .55 .15
a. Inverted overprint 2.75
O55 A42 75c ultra & blk (Bk) 1.00 .70
a. Inverted overprint 9.50 5.75
b. Overprint omitted 22.50
O56 A43 $1 dp grn & gray (R) .65 .15
a. Inverted overprint
O57 A44 $2 plum & blk (Bl) 1.90 .15
a. Overprint omitted 22.50
O58 A45 $5 org & blk (Bk) 4.00 .15
a. Overprint omitted 11.00
b. Inverted overprint 6.25 4.00
Nos. O46-O58 (13) 13.25 3.55

Nos. O52, O54, O55, O56 and O58 are known with center inverted.

For surcharges see Nos. O72, O82-O85, O96.

1909-12
O59 A46 1c emer & blk (R) .25 .20
O60 A47 2c car rose & brn (Bl) .25 .20
a. Overprint omitted
O61 A48 5c turq & blk (Bk) .30 .20
a. Double overprint, one inverted 7.50
O62 A49 10c blk & ultra (R) ('12) .40 .20
O63 A50 15c cl & blk (Bl) .40 .30
O64 A51 20c bis & grn (Bk) .75 .35
O65 A52 25c ultra & grn (Bk) .75 .35
a. Double overprint 4.75 4.75
O66 A53 30c dk bl (R) .55 .20
O67 A54 50c brn & grn (Bk) .90 .25
a. Center inverted 27.50
b. Inverted overprint 4.00 2.75
O68 A55 75c pur & blk (R) 1.00 .20
Nos. O59-O68 (10) 5.55 2.45

Nos. O63, O64, O67 and O68 are known without overprint and with center inverted.

For surcharges see Nos. O74-O81, O86-O90, O97.

Rouletted
O69 A49 10c blk & ultra (R) .70 .70

Nos. 126B and 127E Overprinted type "a" ("OS") in Red

1910-12 ***Rouletted***
O70 A49 3c on 10c blk & ultra .60 1.00

Perf. 12½, 14, 12½x14

O71 A49 3c on 10c blk & ultra ('12) .60 .30
a. Pair, one without surch., the other with dbl. surch., one invtd.
b. Double surcharge, one inverted 3.75

Stamps of Preceding Issues Surcharged with New Values like Regular Issue and

c CENTS 20 OFFICIAL

1914

On Nos. O52 and 110

O72 A39 (a) 2c on 25c plum & gray 17.00 7.00
O73 A42 (c) 20c on 75c brn & blk 5.75 3.50

On Nos. O66 and O68

O74 A53 (b) 5c on 30c dk bl 5.75 3.50
O75 A55 (c) 20c on 75c pur & blk (R) 8.50 3.50
Nos. O72-O75 (4) 37.00 17.50

Official Stamps of 1906-09 Surcharged Like Regular Issues of Same Date

1915-16

O76 A50 (c) 2c on 15c (Bk) .75 .50
O77 A52 (d) 2c on 25c (Bk) 4.25 4.25
O78 A51 (e) 5c on 20c (Bk) .75 .50
O79 A53 (g) 5c on 30c (R) 7.00 7.00
O80 A54 (i) 10c on 50c (Bk) 4.50 2.75
O81 A55 (j) 20c on 75c (R) 2.25 2.25
O82 A43 (k) 25c on $1 (R) 16.00 16.00
a. "25" double 22.50
b. "OS" inverted 22.50
O83 A44 (l) 50c on $2 (Bk) 42.50 42.50
a. "Ceuts" 70.00 70.00
O84 A44 (m) 50c on $2 (Br) 18.00 18.00
O85 A45 (n) $1 on $5 (Bk) 17.00 17.00

Handstamped Surcharge

O86 A54 (i) 10c on 50c (Bk) 8.50 8.50

Nos. O60-O61 Surcharged like Nos. 153-154 in Black or Red

O87 A47 1c on 2c 2.25 2.25
Strip of 10 types 25.00
O88 A48 2c on 5c (R) 2.25 2.25
Strip of 10 types (R) 25.00
a. Black surcharge 8.50 8.50
Strip of 10 types (Bk) 125.00

See note following Nos. 153-154.

#O60-O61 Surcharged like #155-156

O90 A47 1c on 2c 125.00 125.00
O91 A48 2c on 5c 100.00 100.00

No. O42 Surcharged

O92 A26 10c on 50c (Bk) 11.00 11.00

No. O53 Surcharged like No. 161

1917

O96 A40 5c on 30c dk brn 17.00 17.00
a. "FIV" 27.50 27.50

The editors consider the 1915-17 issues unnecessary and speculative.

#O62 Surcharged in Red like #162

1918

O97 A49 3c on 10c blk & ultra 1.90 1.90

Types of Regular Issue of 1918 Overprinted Type "a" ("OS") in Black, Blue or Red

1918 Unwmk. *Perf. 12½, 14*

O98 A59 1c dp grn & red brn (Bk) .40 .20
O99 A60 2c red & blk (Bl) .40 .20
O100 A61 5c ultra & blk (R) .75 .15
O101 A62 10c ultra (R) .40 .15
O102 A63 15c choc & dk grn (Bl) 1.90 .40
O103 A64 20c gray lil & blk (R) .55 .15
O104 A65 25c choc & grn (Bk) 3.50 .45
O105 A66 30c brt vio & blk (R) 4.25 .45
O106 A67 50c mar & blk (Bl) 5.25 .45
a. Overprint omitted 11.00
O107 A68 75c car brn & blk (Bl) 2.00 .20
O108 A69 $1 ol bis & turq bl (Bk) 4.00 .20
O109 A70 $2 ol bis & blk (R) 6.25 .20
O110 A71 $5 yel grn (Bk) 8.00 .25
Nos. O98-O110 (13) 37.65 3.45

For surcharges see Nos. 259-269, O111-O112, O155-O157. For overprint see No. 270.

Official Stamps of 1918 Surcharged like Regular Issue

1920

O111 A59 3c on 1c grn & red brn .90 .55
a. "CEETS" 9.50
b. Double surcharge 2.75 2.75
c. Double surch., one invtd. 5.75 5.75
d. Triple surcharge 4.50 4.50
O112 A60 4c on 2c red & blk .55 .55
a. Inverted surcharge 4.50 4.50
b. Double surcharge 4.50 4.50
c. Double surch., one invtd. 7.00 7.00
d. Triple surcharge 7.00 7.00

Types of Regular Issues of 1915-21 Overprinted **OFFICIAL**

1921 Wmk. 116 *Perf. 14*

O113 A57 2c rose red 5.50 .15
O114 A58 3c brown 1.10 .15
O115 A79 20c brn & ultra 1.50 .25

Same, Overprinted "O S"

O116 A75 1c dp grn 1.10 .15
O117 A76 5c dp bl & brn 1.10 .15
O118 A77 10c red vio & blk .55 .15
O119 A78 15c blk & grn 3.25 .40
a. Double overprint
O120 A80 25c org & grn 4.25 .40
O121 A81 30c brn & red 1.10 .15
O122 A82 50c grn & blk 1.10 .15
a. Overprinted "S" only
O123 A83 75c bl & vio 2.25 .15
O124 A84 $1 bl & blk 15.00 .45
O125 A85 $2 grn & org 8.00 .65
O126 A86 $5 grn & bl 9.00 1.40
Nos. O113-O126 (14) 54.80
Set value 4.25

Preceding Issues Overprinted "1921"

1921

O127 A75 1c dp grn 4.75 .15
O128 A57 2c rose red 4.75 .15
O129 A58 3c brown 4.75 .15
O130 A76 5c dp bl & brn 2.75 .15
O131 A77 10c red vio & blk 4.75 .15
O132 A78 15c blk & grn 5.25 .15
O133 A79 20c brn & ultra 5.25 .25
O134 A80 25c org & grn 6.00 .50
O135 A81 30c brn & red 4.75 .15
O136 A82 50c grn & blk 5.50 .15
O137 A83 75c bl & vio 3.50 .15
O138 A84 $1 bl & blk 9.50 1.25
O139 A85 $2 org & grn 12.00 1.40
O140 A86 $5 grn & bl 9.50 2.00
Nos. O127-O140 (14) 83.00 6.75

Types of Regular Issue of 1923 Overprinted "O S"

1923 *Perf. 13½x14½, 14½x13½*

White Paper

O141 A88 1c bl grn & blk 5.75 .15
O142 A89 2c dl red & yel brn 5.75 .15
O143 A90 3c gray bl & blk 5.75 .15
O144 A91 5c org & dk grn 5.75 .15
O145 A92 10c ol bis & dk vio 5.75 .15
O146 A93 15c yel grn & bl .75 .25
O147 A94 20c vio & ind .75 .25
O148 A95 25c brn & red brn 22.50 .25

White, Buff or Brownish Paper

O149 A96 30c dp ultra & brn .75 .15
a. Overprint omitted
O150 A97 50c dl bis & red brn .75 .25
O151 A98 75c gray & grn .75 .15
O152 A99 $1 red org & grn 1.65 .45
a. Overprint omitted 11.00
O153 A100 $2 red lil & ver 2.25 .70
O154 A101 $5 bl & brn vio 4.00 .55
Nos. O141-O154 (14) 62.90 3.75

No. O98 Surcharged in Red Brown **Two Cents**

1926 Unwmk. *Perf. 14*

O155 A59 2c on 1c 2.25 2.25
a. "Gents" 7.25
b. Surcharged in black 5.75
c. As "b," "Gents" 9.50

No. O98 Surcharged in Black **Two Cents**

1926

O156 A59 2c on 1c .85 .85
a. Inverted surcharge
b. "Gents" 10.00

No. O98 Surcharged in Red **Two Cents**

1927

O157 A59 2c on 1c 22.50 22.50
a. "Ceuts" 40.00
b. "Vwo" 40.00
c. "Twc" 40.00

Regular Issue of 1928 Overprinted in Red or Black **OFFICIAL SERVICE**

1928 *Perf. 12*

O158 A102 1c grn (R) .80 .40
O159 A102 2c gray vio (R) 1.75 .70
O160 A102 3c bis brn (Bk) 1.75 1.50
O161 A103 5c ultra (R) .80 .40
O162 A104 10c ol gray (R) 2.50 1.25
O163 A103 15c dl vio (R) 1.75 .75
O164 A103 $1 red brn (Bk) 55.00 19.00
Nos. O158-O164 (7) 64.35 24.00

For surcharges see Nos. C3, O165.

No. O162 Surcharged with New Value and Bar in Black

1945 Unwmk. *Perf. 12*

O165 A104 4c on 10c (Bk) 6.50 6.50

LIBYA

'li-bē-ə

(Libia)

LOCATION — North Africa, bordering on the Mediterranean Sea
GOVT. — Republic
AREA — 679,358 sq. mi.
POP. — 3,500,000 (est. 1982)
CAPITAL — Tripoli

In 1939, the four northern provinces of Libya, a former Italian colony, were incorporated in the Italian national territory. Included in the territory is the former Turkish Vilayet of Tripoli, annexed in 1912. Libya became a kingdom on Dec. 24, 1951. The Libyan Arab Republic was established Sept. 1, 1969. "People's Socialist . . ." was added to its name in 1977. See Cyrenaica and Tripolitania.

100 Centesimi = 1 Lira
Military Authority Lira (1951)
Franc (1951)
1,000 Milliemes = 1 Pound (1952)
1,000 Dirhams = 1 Dinar (1972)

Watermarks

Wmk. 140- Crown

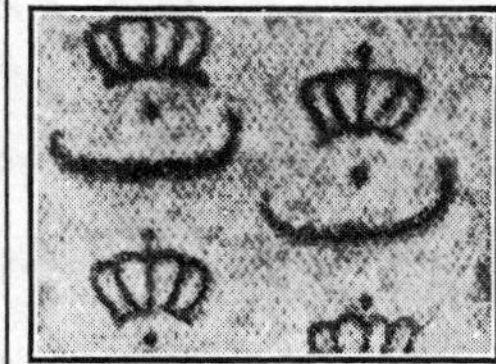

Wmk. 195- Multiple Crown and Arabic F

Wmk. 310- Multiple Crescent and Star

Catalogue values for unused stamps in this country are for Never Hinged items, beginning with Scott 102 in the regular postage section, Scott C51 in the airpost section, Scott E13 in the special delivery section, Scott J25 in the postage due section, Scott O1 in the official section, Scott N1 in the Fezzan-Ghadames section, Scott 2N1 in the Fezzan section, Scott 2NB1 in the Fezzan semi-postal section, Scott 2NC1 in the Fezzan airpost section, Scott 2NJ1 in the Fezzan postage due section, Scott 3N1 in the Ghadames section, and Scott 3NC1 in the Ghadames airpost section.

Used values in italics are for postaly used stamps. CTO's or stamps with fake cancels sell for about the same as unused, hinged stamps.

Stamps of Italy Overprinted in Black **Libia**

1912-22 Wmk. 140 *Perf. 14*

1 A42 1c brown ('15) .30 .50
a. Double overprint 150.00 150.00
2 A43 2c orange brn .30 .25
3 A48 5c green .30 .15
a. Double overprint 30.00 30.00
b. Imperf., pair 35.00 50.00
c. Inverted overprint *2,000.*
d. Pair, one without overprint 125.00 125.00
4 A48 10c claret .30 .15
a. Pair, one without overprint 175.00 175.00
b. Double overprint 45.00 45.00
5 A48 15c slate ('22) 3.00 *2.00*
6 A45 20c orange ('15) 1.00 .25
a. Double overprint 90.00 90.00
b. Pair, one without overprint 300.00
7 A50 20c brn org ('18) 1.00 *1.00*
8 A49 25c blue 1.00 .30
9 A49 40c brown 1.00 .62
10 A45 45c ol grn ('17) 13.00 *5.50*
a. Inverted overprint 150.00
11 A49 50c violet 2.50 .62
12 A49 60c brn car ('18) 5.25 *5.50*
13 A46 1 l brown & green ('15) 30.00 1.25
14 A46 5 l bl & rose ('15) 175.00 *80.00*
15 A51 10 l gray green & red ('15) 13.00 *18.00*
Nos. 1-15 (15) 246.95 *116.09*

For surcharges see Nos. 37-38.

Overprinted in Violet **LIBIA**

1912 Unwmk.

16 A58 15c slate 62.50 .80
a. Blue black overprint *1,800.* 3.75

No. 16 Surcharged **CENT 20**

1916, Mar. Unwmk.

19 A58 20c on 15c slate 13.00 2.00

Roman Legionary — A1

Diana of Ephesus — A2

Ancient Galley Leaving Tripoli — A3

"Victory" — A4

1921 Engr. Wmk. 140 *Perf. 14*

No.	Type	Description	Unused	Used
20	A1	1c blk & gray brn	.30	.70
21	A1	2c blk & red brn	.30	.70
22	A1	5c black & green	.30	.38
a.		5c black & red brown (error)	1,500.	
b.		Center inverted	40.00	21.00
c.		Imperf., pair	50.00	70.00
23	A2	10c blk & rose	.30	.25
a.		Center inverted	40.00	21.00
24	A2	15c blk brn & brn org	9.50	.50
a.		Center inverted	140.00	37.50
25	A2	25c dk bl & bl	.50	.20
a.		Center inverted	12.00	6.00
b.		Imperf., pair	100.00	150.00
26	A3	30c blk & blk brn	5.00	.50
a.		Center inverted	1,500.	500.00
27	A3	50c blk & ol grn	3.00	.15
a.		50c black & brown (error)	250.00	
b.		Center inverted		*825.00*
28	A3	55c black & vio	2.25	2.50
29	A4	1 l dk brn & brn	3.00	.16
30	A4	5 l blk & dk blue	11.00	3.75
31	A4	10 l dk bl & ol grn	60.00	25.00
		Nos. 20-31 (12)	95.45	34.79

Nos. 20-31 also exist perf. 14x13, with values somewhat higher.

See #47-61. For surcharges see #102-121.

Italy Nos. 136-139 Overprinted **LIBIA**

1921, Apr.

No.	Type	Description	Unused	Used
33	A64	5c olive green	.50	*1.50*
a.		Double overprint	190.00	90.00
34	A64	10c red	.50	*1.50*
a.		Double overprint	150.00	90.00
b.		Inverted overprint	125.00	90.00
35	A64	15c slate green	1.00	*2.50*
36	A64	25c ultramarine	1.00	*2.00*
		Nos. 33-36 (4)	3.00	*7.50*

3rd anniv. of the victory of the Piave.

Nos. 11, 8 Surcharged **C. 40**

1922, June 1

No.	Type	Description	Unused	Used
37	A49	40c on 50c violet	1.25	.70
38	A49	80c on 25c blue	2.00	*3.00*

Libyan Sibyl — A6

1924-31 Unwmk. *Perf. 14½x14*

No.	Type	Description	Unused	Used
39	A6	20c deep green	.50	.15
40	A6	40c brown	1.65	.35
41	A6	60c deep blue	.50	.15
42	A6	1.75 l orange ('31)	.40	.15
43	A6	2 l carmine	2.25	.60
44	A6	2.55 l violet ('31)	2.00	1.60
		Nos. 39-44 (6)	7.30	3.00

1926-29 *Perf. 11*

No.	Type	Description	Unused	Used
39a	A6	20c	13.00	.20
40a	A6	40c	11.00	1.25
41a	A6	60c	4.50	.15
43a	A6	2 l ('29)	24.00	2.00
		Nos. 39a-43a (4)	52.50	3.60

Type of 1921

1924-40 Unwmk. *Perf. 13½ to 14*

No.	Type	Description	Unused	Used
47	A1	1c blk & gray brown	.25	1.00
48	A1	2c blk & red brn	.38	1.00
49	A1	5c blk & green	.50	.38
50	A1	7½c blk & brown ('31)	.30	1.00
51	A2	10c blk & dl red	.15	.15
b.		Center inverted	25.00	
52	A2	15c blk brn & org	.80	.42
b.		Center inverted, perf. 11	550.00	
53	A2	25c dk bl & bl	3.00	.15
a.		Center inverted	25.00	37.50
54	A3	30c blk & blk brn	.22	.30
55	A3	50c blk & ol grn	.15	.15
b.		Center inverted	650.00	650.00
56	A3	55c black & vio	60.00	100.00
57	A4	75c violet & red ('31)	.15	.15
58	A4	1 l dk brn & brn	4.00	.15
59	A3	1.25 l indigo & ultra ('31)	.15	.15
60	A4	5 l blk & dark blue ('40)	11.00	10.00
		Nos. 47-60 (14)	81.05	115.00

Perf. 11

No.	Type	Description	Unused	Used
47a	A1	1c	110.00	
48a	A1	2c	110.00	
49a	A1	5c	20.00	2.50
51a	A2	10c	11.00	.50
52a	A2	15c	52.50	3.25
54a	A3	30c	32.50	.50
55a	A3	50c	375.00	.15
58a	A4	1 l	4.50	.20
60a	A4	5 l ('37)	*1,300.*	45.00
61	A4	10 l dk bl & olive grn ('37)	225.00	80.00

Italy #197 and 88 Overprinted Like #1-15

1929 Wmk. 140 *Perf. 14*

No.	Type	Description	Unused	Used
62	A86	7½c light brown	5.75	*13.50*
63	A46	1.25 l blue & ultra	26.00	5.00

Italy #193 Overprinted Like #33-36

1929 Unwmk. *Perf. 11*

No.	Type	Description	Unused	Used
64	A85	1.75 l deep brown	30.00	1.50

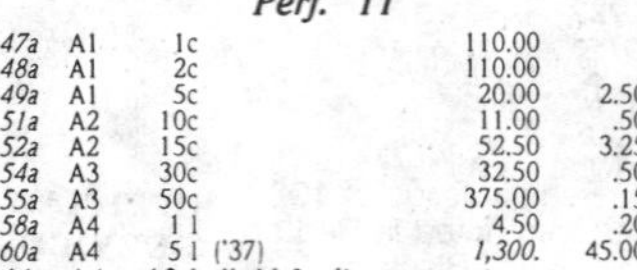

Water Carriers — A7

Man of Tripoli — A8

Designs: 25c, Minaret. 30c, 1.25 l, Tomb of Holy Man near Tagiura. 50c, Statue of Emperor Claudius at Leptis. 75c, Ruins of gardens.

1934, Feb. 17 Photo. *Perf. 14*

No.	Type	Description	Unused	Used
64A	A7	10c brown	2.00	*5.00*
64B	A8	20c carmine rose	2.00	*5.00*
64C	A8	25c green	2.00	*5.00*
64D	A7	30c dark brown	2.00	*5.00*
64E	A8	50c purple	2.00	*5.00*
64F	A7	75c rose	2.00	*5.00*
64G	A7	1.25 l blue	19.00	*32.50*
		Nos. 64A-64G (7)	31.00	*62.50*
		Nos. 64A-64G,C14-C18 (12)	237.50	*281.50*

8th Sample Fair, Tripoli.

Bedouin Woman — A15

Highway Memorial Arch — A16

1936, May 11 Wmk. 140 *Perf. 14*

No.	Type	Description	Unused	Used
65	A15	50c purple	1.00	*.75*
66	A15	1.25 l deep blue	1.75	*2.25*

10th Sample Fair, Tripoli.

1937, Mar. 15

No.	Type	Description	Unused	Used
67	A16	50c copper red	1.00	*2.50*
68	A16	1.25 l sapphire	1.00	*5.00*
		Nos. 67-68,C28-C29 (4)	4.50	*15.00*

Coastal road to the Egyptian frontier, opening.

Nos. 67-68 Overprinted in Black **XI FIERA DI TRIPOLI**

1937, Apr. 24

No.	Type	Description	Unused	Used
69	A16	50c copper red	5.25	*7.00*
70	A16	1.25 l sapphire	5.25	*7.00*
		Nos. 69-70,C30-C31 (4)	20.00	*28.00*

11th Sample Fair, Tripoli.

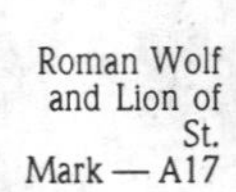

Roman Wolf and Lion of St. Mark — A17

View of Fair Buildings A18

1938, Mar. 12

No.	Type	Description	Unused	Used
71	A17	5c brown	.40	.38
72	A18	10c olive brown	.40	.38
73	A17	25c green	.50	.38
74	A18	50c purple	.50	.25
75	A17	75c rose red	1.00	*1.00*
76	A18	1.25 l dark blue	1.00	*1.10*
		Nos. 71-76,C32-C33 (8)	4.68	*6.01*

12th Sample Fair, Tripoli.

Augustus Caesar (Octavianus) A19

Goddess Abundantia A20

1938, Apr. 25

No.	Type	Description	Unused	Used
77	A19	5c olive brown	.40	.50
78	A20	10c brown red	.40	.50
79	A19	25c dk yel green	.50	.38
80	A20	50c dk violet	.50	.38
81	A19	75c orange red	1.00	*1.10*
82	A20	1.25 l dull blue	1.00	*1.10*
		Nos. 77-82,C34-C35 (8)	4.60	*5.96*

Birth bimillenary of Augustus Caesar (Octavianus), first Roman emperor.

Desert City — A21

View of Ghadames A22

1939, Apr. 12 Photo.

No.	Type	Description	Unused	Used
83	A21	5c olive brown	.40	.38
84	A22	20c red brown	.40	.38
85	A21	50c rose violet	.40	.38
86	A22	75c scarlet	.70	*.62*
87	A21	1.25 l gray blue	.75	*.70*
		Nos. 83-87,C36-C38 (8)	3.40	*4.41*

13th Sample Fair, Tripoli.

Modern City — A23

Oxen and Plow — A24

Mosque — A25

1940, June 3 Wmk. 140 *Perf. 14*

No.	Type	Description	Unused	Used
88	A23	5c brown	.40	.38
89	A24	10c red orange	.40	.38
90	A25	25c dull green	.50	*.70*
91	A23	50c dark violet	.50	*.70*
92	A24	75c crimson	1.00	*1.10*
93	A25	1.25 l ultramarine	1.00	*1.10*
94	A24	2 l + 75c rose lake	1.00	*1.50*
		Nos. 88-94,C39-C42 (11)	6.06	*11.56*

Triennial Overseas Exposition, Naples.

"Two Peoples, One War," Hitler and Mussolini A26

1941, May 16

No.	Type	Description	Unused	Used
95	A26	5c orange	.40	*2.50*
96	A26	10c brown	.40	*2.50*
97	A26	20c dull violet	.50	*2.50*
98	A26	25c green	.50	*2.50*
99	A26	50c purple	1.00	*2.50*
100	A26	75c scarlet	1.00	*5.00*
101	A26	1.25 l sapphire	1.00	*5.00*
		Nos. 95-101,C43 (8)	5.20	*32.50*

The Rome-Berlin Axis.

Catalogue values for unused stamps in this section, from this point to the end of the section, are for Never Hinged items.

United Kingdom of Libya

Stamps of Cyrenaica 1950 Surcharged in Black

2 MAL. LIBYA

For Use in Tripolitania

1951, Dec. 24 Unwmk. *Perf. 12½*

No.	Type	Description	Unused	Used
102	A2	1mal on 2m rose car	.15	.20
103	A2	2mal on 4m dk grn	.15	.20
104	A2	4mal on 8m red org	.15	.25
105	A2	5mal on 10m pur	.20	.38
106	A2	6mal on 12m red	.25	*.65*
a.		Inverted surcharge	25.00	25.00
107	A2	10mal on 20m dp bl	.35	*.60*
a.		Arabic "20" for "10"	20.00	20.00
108	A3	24mal on 50m choc & ultra	1.10	*2.50*
109	A3	48mal on 100m bl blk & car rose	4.25	*8.00*
110	A3	96mal on 200m vio & pur	9.00	*19.00*
111	A3	240mal on 500m dk grn & org	20.00	*42.50*
		Nos. 102-111 (10)	35.60	*74.28*

The surcharge is larger on Nos. 108 to 111.

Same Surcharge in Francs

For Use in Fezzan

No.	Type	Description	Unused	Used
112	A2	2fr on 2m rose car	.15	.22
113	A2	4fr on 4m dk grn	.15	.22
114	A2	8fr on 8m red org	.20	.28
115	A2	10fr on 10m pur	.20	.28
116	A2	12fr on 12m red	.70	1.10
117	A2	20fr on 20m dp bl	1.10	*1.60*
118	A3	48fr on 50m choc & ultra	11.00	*16.00*
119	A3	96fr on 100m bl blk & car rose	14.00	*21.00*
120	A3	192fr on 200m vio & pur	32.50	*50.00*
121	A3	480fr on 500m dk grn & org	25.00	*40.00*
		Nos. 112-121 (10)	85.00	*130.70*

The surcharge is larger on Nos. 118-121.

A second printing of Nos. 118-121 has an elongated first character in second line of Arabic surcharge.

Cyrenaica Nos. 65-77 Overprinted in Black

ليبيا

LIBYA

For Use in Cyrenaica

No.	Type	Description	Unused	Used
122	A2	1m dark brown	.15	.25
123	A2	2m rose carmine	.15	.25
124	A2	3m orange	.15	.38
125	A2	4m dark green	9.50	7.00
126	A2	5m gray	.40	*.70*
127	A2	8m red orange	.40	*.80*
128	A2	10m purple	.45	*.70*
129	A2	12m red	.45	*1.00*
130	A2	20m deep blue	.45	*.70*
131	A3	50m choc & ultra	4.00	*7.00*

132 A3 100m bl blk & car rose 7.00 *12.00*
133 A3 200m violet & pur 19.00 *30.00*
134 A3 500m dk grn & org 50.00 *90.00*
Nos. 122-134 (13) 92.10 *150.78*

Wider spacing between the two lines on Nos. 131-134.

King Idris
A27 A28

1952, Apr. 15 Engr. *Perf. 11½*

135 A27 2m yellow brown .15 .15
136 A27 4m gray .15 .15
137 A27 5m blue green 10.00 .16
138 A27 8m vermilion .16 .15
139 A27 10m purple 9.25 .15
140 A27 12m lilac rose .16 .15
141 A27 20m deep blue 9.25 .20
142 A27 25m chocolate 10.00 .25
143 A28 50m brown & blue .90 .35
144 A28 100m gray blk & car rose 1.40 .40
145 A28 200m dk blue & pur 2.75 2.25
146 A28 500m dk grn & brn orange 13.00 7.50
Nos. 135-146 (12) 57.17 11.86

For surcharge and overprints see #168, O1-O8.

Globe — A29

Perf. 13½x13

1955, Jan. 1 Photo. Wmk. 195

147 A29 5m yellow brown .40 .38
148 A29 10m green .80 .65
149 A29 30m violet 2.25 1.25
Nos. 147-149 (3) 3.45 2.28

Arab Postal Union founding, July 1, 1954.

Nos. 147-149 Overprinted

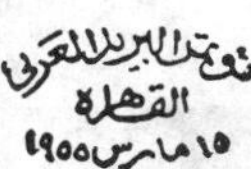

1955, Aug. 1

150 A29 5m yellow brn .22 .20
151 A29 10m green .32 .32
152 A29 30m violet 1.10 .65
Nos. 150-152 (3) 1.64 1.17

Arab Postal Congress, Cairo, Mar. 15.

Emblems of Tripolitania, Cyrenaica and Fezzan with Royal Crown — A30

1955 Engr. Wmk. 310 *Perf. 11½*

153 A30 2m lemon .65 .35
154 A30 3m slate blue .15 .15
155 A30 4m gray green .65 .60
156 A30 5m light blue grn .22 .15
157 A30 10m violet .40 .15
158 A30 18m crimson .15 .15
159 A30 20m orange .20 .15
160 A30 30m blue .45 .15
161 A30 35m brown .25 .15
162 A30 40m rose carmine .45 .15
163 A30 50m olive .42 .16

Size: 27½x32½mm

164 A30 100m dk green & pur .65 .25
165 A30 200m ultra & rose car 6.50 2.50
166 A30 500m grn & orange 8.00 6.00

Size: 26½x32mm

167 A30 £1 ocher, brn & grn, *yel* 14.00 7.00
Nos. 153-167 (15) 33.14 18.06

See Nos. 177-179, 192-206A.

No. 136 Surcharged 5 0

1955, Aug. 25 Unwmk.

168 A27 5m on 4m gray .80 .80

Tomb of El Senussi, Jagbub
A31

Perf. 13x13½

1956, Sept. 14 Photo. Wmk. 195

169 A31 5m green .15 .15
170 A31 10m bright violet .16 .15
171 A31 15m rose carmine .25 .25
172 A31 30m sapphire .70 .50
Nos. 169-172 (4) 1.26 1.05

Death centenary of the Imam Seyyid Mohammed Aly El Senussi (in 1859).

Map, Flags and UN Headquarters
A32

Globe and Postal Emblems
A33

1956, Dec. 14 Litho. *Perf. 13½x13*

173 A32 15m bl, ocher & ol bis .25 .15
174 A32 35m bl, ocher & vio brn .40 .28

Libya's admission to the UN, 1st anniv.

1957 Wmk. 195 *Perf. 13½x13*

175 A33 15m blue .90 .30
176 A33 500m yellow brown 4.50 3.50

Arab Postal Congress, Tripoli, Feb. 9.

Emblems Type of 1955

1957 Wmk. 310 Engr. *Perf. 11½*

177 A30 1m black, *yellow* .16 .15
178 A30 2m bister brown .16 .15
179 A30 4m brown carmine .16 .15
Nos. 177-179 (3) .48
Set value .24

UN Emblem and Broken Chain — A34

Unwmk.

1958, Dec. 10 Photo. *Perf. 14*

180 A34 10m bluish violet .15 .15
181 A34 15m green .20 .16
182 A34 30m ultramarine .50 .40
Nos. 180-182 (3) .85 .71

Universal Declaration of Human Rights, 10th anniv.

Date Palms and FAO Emblem
A35

1959, Dec. 5 Unwmk. *Perf. 14*

183 A35 10m pale vio & black .15 .15
184 A35 15m bluish grn & blk .20 .16
185 A35 45m light blue & blk .50 .45
Nos. 183-185 (3) .85 .76

1st Intl. Dates Conf., Tripoli, Dec. 5-11.

Arab League Center, Cairo, and Arms of Libya
A36

Perf. 13x13½

1960, Mar. 22 Wmk. 328

186 A36 10m dull grn & blk .28 .16

Opening of the Arab League Center and the Arab Postal Museum in Cairo.

Emblems of WRY and UN, Arms of Libya — A37

Palm Tree and Radio Mast — A38

1960, Apr. 7 Unwmk. *Perf. 14*

187 A37 10m violet & black .20 .16
188 A37 45m blue & black .70 .62

World Refugee Year, July 1, 1959-June 30, 1960.

1960, Aug. 4 Engr. *Perf. 13x13½*

189 A38 10m violet .15 .15
190 A38 15m blue green .20 .15
191 A38 45m dk carmine rose .65 .28
Nos. 189-191 (3) 1.00
Set value .45

3rd Arab Telecommunications Conf., Tripoli, Aug. 4.

Emblems Type of 1955

1960 Wmk. 310 Engr. *Perf. 11½*

Size: 18x21½mm

192 A30 1m black, *gray* .15 .15
193 A30 2m bis brn, *buff* .15 .15
194 A30 3m blue, *bluish* .15 .15
195 A30 4m brn car, *rose* .15 .15
196 A30 5m grn, *greenish* .15 .15
197 A30 10m vio, *pale vio* .15 .15
198 A30 15m brown, *buff* .15 .15
199 A30 20m orange, *buff* .15 .15
200 A30 30m red, *pink* .15 .15
201 A30 40m rose car, *rose* .15 .15
202 A30 45m blue, *bluish* .15 .16
203 A30 50m olive, *buff* .35 .16

Size: 27½x32½mm

204 A30 100m dk grn & pur, *gray* .50 .40
205 A30 200m bl & rose car, *bluish* 1.50 .60
206 A30 500m green & org, *greenish* 8.25 2.50

Size: 26½x32mm

206A A30 £1 ocher, brn & grn, *brn* 16.00 14.00
Nos. 192-206A (16) 28.25 19.32

Watchtower and Broken Chain — A39

1961, Aug. 9 Photo. Unwmk.

207 A39 5m lt yel grn & brn .35 .15
208 A39 15m light blue & brn .50 .16

Issued for Army Day, Aug. 9, 1961.

Map of Zelten Oil Field and Tanker at Marsa Brega — A40

1961, Oct. 25 *Perf. 11½*

209 A40 15m ol grn & buff .15 .15
210 A40 50m red brn & pale vio .50 .30
211 A40 100m ultra & blue 1.00 .65
Nos. 209-211 (3) 1.65 1.10

Opening of first oil pipe line in Libya.

Hands Breaking Chain, Tractor and Cows — A41

Designs: 50m, Modern highways and buildings. 100m, Machinery.

1961, Dec. 24 *Perf. 11½*

Granite Paper

212 A41 15m pale grn, grn & brown .15 .15
213 A41 50m buff & brown .50 .30
214 A41 100m sal, vio & brn 1.00 .65
Nos. 212-214 (3) 1.65 1.10

10th anniversary of independence.

Camel Riders — A42

15m, Well. 50m, Oil installations in desert.

1962, Feb. 20 Photo. *Perf. 12*

215 A42 10m choc & org brn .15 .15
216 A42 15m plum & yel grn .40 .32
217 A42 50m emer & ultra 1.10 .80
a. Souv. sheet of 3, #215-217, imperf. 20.00 13.00
Nos. 215-217 (3) 1.65 1.27

Intl. Fair, Tripoli, Feb. 20-Mar. 20.
Nos. 215-217 exist imperf. Value about twice that of perf.

Malaria Eradication Emblem and Palm — A43

Ahmed Rafik El Mehdawi (1989-1961), Poet — A44

1962, Apr. 7 Unwmk. *Perf. 11½*

218 A43 15m multicolored .35 .16
219 A43 50m grn, yel & brn .45 .45

WHO drive to eradicate malaria.
Exist imperf. Value about three times that of perf.
Two imperf. souvenir sheets exist, one containing the 15m, the other the 50m. Sold for 20m and 70m respectively. Value for both, $6.

1962, July 6 Engr. *Perf. 13x14*

220 A44 15m green .15 .15
221 A44 20m brown .28 .22

El Mehdawi, 1st death anniv.

15-Cent Minimum Value
The minimum value for a single stamp is 15 cents. This value reflects the costs of handling inexpensive stamps.

Clasped Hands and Scout Emblem — A45

Drop of Oil with New City, Desert, Oil Wells and Map of Coast Line — A46

Designs: 10m, 30m, Boy Scouts. 15m, 50m, Scout emblem and tents.

1962, July 13 Photo. *Perf. 12*

222	A45	5m yel, blk & red	.15	.15
223	A45	10m bl, blk & yel	.22	.15
224	A45	15m multicolored	.28	.20
		Nos. 222-224 (3)	.65	
		Set value		.40

Souvenir Sheet

Imperf

225		Sheet of 3	3.75	3.50
a.		A45 20m yellow, black & red	.65	.65
b.		A45 30m blue, black & yellow	.65	.65
c.		A45 50m blue gray, yel, blk & grn	.65	.65

Third Libyan Scout meeting (Philia).
Nos. 222-224 exist imperf. Value for set, $1.50.

1962, Nov. 25 *Perf. 11x11½*

226	A46	15m grn & vio blk	.15	.15
227	A46	50m brn org & ol	.45	.35

Opening of the Essider Terminal Sidrah pipeline system.

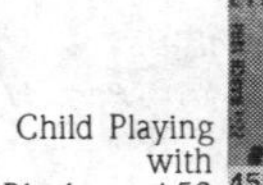
Centenary Emblem — A47

Litho. & Photo.

1963, Jan. 1 *Perf. 11½*

228	A47	10m rose, blk, red & bl	.15	.15
229	A47	15m citron, blk, red & bl	.20	.15
230	A47	20m gray, blk, red & bl	.45	.35
		Nos. 228-230 (3)	.80	
		Set value		.55

Centenary of the International Red Cross.

Rainbow and Arches over Map of Africa and Libya — A48

1963, Feb. 28 Litho. *Perf. 13½*

231	A48	15m multicolored	.20	.15
232	A48	30m multicolored	.38	.35
233	A48	50m multicolored	.55	.50
		Nos. 231-233 (3)	1.13	1.00

Tripoli Intl. Fair "Gateway of Africa," Feb. 28-Mar. 28. Every other horizontal row inverted in sheet of 50 (25 tête bêche pairs).

Date Palm and Well — A49

Designs: 15m, Camel and flock of sheep. 45m, Sower and tractor.

1963, Mar. 21 Photo. *Perf. 11½*

234	A49	10m green, lt bl & bis	.15	.15
235	A49	15m pur, lt grn & bis	.15	.15
236	A49	45m dk bl, sal & sep	.55	.28
		Nos. 234-236 (3)	.85	
		Set value		.48

FAO "Freedom from Hunger" campaign.

Man with Whip and Slave Reaching for UN Emblem — A50

1963, Dec. 10 Unwmk. *Perf. 11½*

237	A50	5m red brown & bl	.15	.15
238	A50	15m deep claret & bl	.15	.15
239	A50	50m green & blue	.38	.25
		Nos. 237-239 (3)	.68	
		Set value		.40

Universal Declaration of Human Rights, 15th anniv.

Exhibition Hall and Finger Pointing to Libya — A51

1964, Feb. 28 Photo. *Perf. 11½*

240	A51	10m red brn, gray grn & brn	.15	.15
241	A51	15m pur, gray grn & brn	.28	.20
242	A51	30m dk bl, gray grn & brn	.75	.38
		Nos. 240-242 (3)	1.18	.73

3rd Intl. Fair, Tripoli, Feb. 28-Mar. 20.

Child Playing with Blocks — A52

Design: 15m, Child in bird's nest.

1964, Mar. 22 *Perf. 11½*

243	A52	5m multicolored	.15	.15
244	A52	15m multicolored	.15	.15
245	A52	45m multicolored	.42	.28
a.		Souvenir sheet of 3, #243-245, imperf.	2.00	2.00
		Nos. 243-245 (3)	.72	
		Set value		.48

Children's Day. Exist imperf. Value about 1½ times that of perf.
No. 245a sold for 100m.

Lungs and Stethoscope — A53

1964, Apr. 7 Photo. *Perf. 13½x14*

246	A53	20m deep purple	.50	.25

Campaign against tuberculosis.

Map of Libya — A54

1964, Apr. 27 Unwmk. *Perf. 11½*

247	A54	5m emerald & org	.15	.15
248	A54	50m blue & yellow	.38	.28
		Set value		.32

First anniversary of Libyan union.

Moth Emerging from Cocoon, Veiled and Modern Women — A55

Hand Giving Scout Sign, Scout and Libyan Flags — A56

1964, June 15 Litho. & Engraved

249	A55	10m vio bl & lt grn	.15	.15
250	A55	20m vio blue & yel	.15	.15
251	A55	35m vio bl & pink	.30	.28
a.		Souv. sheet of 3, #249-251	2.00	2.00
		Nos. 249-251 (3)	.60	
		Set value		.40

To honor Libyan women in a new epoch. No. 251a sold for 100m.

1964, July 24 Photo. *Perf. 12x11½*

Design: 20m, Libyan Scout emblem and hands.

252	A56	10m lt bl & multi	.65	.25
253	A56	20m multicolored	1.10	.40
a.		Souvenir sheet of 2, #252-253, imperf.	2.75	2.75

Opening of new Boy Scout headquarters; installation of Crown Prince Hassan al-Rida el Senussi as Chief Scout. No. 253a sold for 50m.
Nos. 252-253 exist imperf. Value about 1½ times that of perf.

Bayonet, Wreath and Map A57

Ahmed Bahloul el-Sharef A58

1964, Aug. 9 Litho. *Perf. 14x13½*

254	A57	10m yel grn & brn	.15	.15
255	A57	20m org & blk	.25	.15
		Set value	.32	.16

Founding of the Senussi Army.

1964, Aug. 11 Engr. *Perf. 11½*

256	A58	15m lilac	.15	.15
257	A58	20m greenish blue	.35	.16
		Set value		.20

Poet Ahmed Bahloul el-Sharef, died 1953.

Soccer A59

1964, Oct. 1 Litho. *Perf. 14*

Black Inscriptions and Gold Olympic Rings

258	A59	5m shown	.35	.35
259	A59	10m Bicycling	.35	.35
260	A59	20m Boxing	.35	.35
261	A59	30m Sprinter	.35	.35
262	A59	35m Woman diver	.35	.35
263	A59	50m Hurdling	.35	.35
a.		Block of 6, #258-263	2.25	2.25

18th Olympic Games, Tokyo, Oct. 10-25. No. 263a printed in sheet of 48. The two blocks in each double row are inverted in relation to the two blocks in the next row, providing various tete beche and se-tenant arrangements.
#258-263 exist imperf. Value for set, $7.50.
Perf. and imperf. souvenir sheets exist containing six 15m stamps in the designs and colors of Nos. 258-263. Sheets sold for 100m. Value for both, $13.50.

Arab Postal Union Emblem — A59a

1964, Dec. 1 Photo. *Perf. 11x11½*

264	A59a	10m yellow & blue	.15	.15
265	A59a	15m pale vio & org brn	.16	.15
266	A59a	30m lt yel grn & brn	.55	.40
		Nos. 264-266 (3)	.86	
		Set value		.56

Permanent Office of the APU, 10th anniv.

International Cooperation Year Emblem A60

1965, Jan. 1 Litho. *Perf. 14½x14*

267	A60	5m vio bl & gold	.15	.15
268	A60	15m rose car & gold	.50	.50

Imperfs. exist. Value about twice that of perfs.
See Nos. C51-C51a.

European Bee Eater — A61

Birds: 5m, Long-legged buzzard, vert. 15m, Chestnut-bellied sandgrouse. 20m, Houbara bustard. 30m, Spotted sandgrouse. 40m, Libyan Barbary partridge.

1965, Feb. 10 Photo. *Perf. 11½*

Granite Paper

Birds in Natural Colors

269	A61	5m gray & black	.15	.15
270	A61	10m lt bl & org brn	.16	.15
271	A61	15m lt green & blk	.35	.15
272	A61	20m pale lil & blk	.42	.16
273	A61	30m tan & dark brn	.55	.22
274	A61	40m dull yel & blk	.65	.40
		Nos. 269-274 (6)	2.28	1.23

Map of Africa with Libya A62

1965, Feb. 28 Photo. *Perf. 11½*

Granite Paper

275	A62	50m multicolored	.35	.20

4th Intl. Tripoli Fair, Feb. 28-Mar. 20.

Compass Rose, Rockets, Satellites and Stars — A63

1965, Mar. 23 Litho.

276	A63	10m multicolored	.15	.15
277	A63	15m multicolored	.15	.15
278	A63	50m multicolored	.40	.28
		Set value	.56	.30

Fifth World Meteorological Day.

ITU Emblem, Old and New Communication Equipment — A64

1965, May 17 **Unwmk.**

279	A64	10m	sepia	.15	.15
280	A64	20m	red lilac	.15	.15
281	A64	50m	lilac rose	.28	.20
			Set value	.48	.32

ITU, centenary.

Library Aflame and Lamp — A65

1965, June **Litho.** ***Perf. 11½***

282	A65	15m	multicolored	.15	.15
283	A65	50m	multicolored	.40	.20
			Set value		.28

Burning of the Library of Algiers, June 7, 1962.

Rose — A66

Jet Plane and Globe — A67

1965, Aug. **Litho.** ***Perf. 14***

284	A66	1m	shown	.16	.15
285	A66	2m	Iris	.16	.15
286	A66	3m	Opuntia	.35	.15
287	A66	4m	Sunflower	.50	.22
			Nos. 284-287 (4)	1.17	
			Set value		.52

1965, Oct. **Photo.** ***Perf. 11½***

288	A67	5m	multicolored	.15	.15
289	A67	10m	multicolored	.15	.15
290	A67	15m	multicolored	.28	.15
			Set value	.45	.25

Issued to publicize Libyan Airlines.

Forum, Cyrene — A68

Mausoleum at Germa — A69

Designs: 100m, Arch of Trajan. 200m, Temple of Apollo, Cyrene. 500m, Antonine Temple of Jupiter, Sabratha, horiz. £1, Theater, Sabratha.

Perf. 12x11½, 11½x12

1965, Dec. 24 **Engr.** **Wmk. 310**

291	A68	50m	vio blue & ol	.32	.15
292	A68	100m	Prus bl & dp org	.65	.22
293	A68	200m	pur & Prus bl	1.60	.32
294	A68	500m	car rose & grn	2.50	1.40
295	A68	£1	grn & dp org	7.50	2.75
			Nos. 291-295 (5)	12.57	4.84

Nos. 293-295 with "Kingdom of Libia" in both Arabic and English blocked out with a blue felt-tipped pen were issued June 21, 1970, by the Republic.

Perf. 11½

1966, Feb. 10 **Unwmk.** **Litho.**

296	A69	70m	pur & salmon	.35	.25

"POLIGRAFICA & CARTEVALORI-NAPLES" and Libyan Coat of Arms printed on back in yellow green. See No. E13.

Booklet pane containing 4 No. 296 and 4 No. E13 exists.

Globe in Space, Satellites — A70

1966, Feb. 28 ***Perf. 12***

297	A70	15m	multicolored	.15	.15
298	A70	45m	multicolored	.20	.20
299	A70	55m	multicolored	.62	.35
			Nos. 297-299 (3)	.97	
			Set value		.60

5th Intl. Fair at Tripoli, Feb. 28-Mar. 20.

Arab League Center, Cairo, and Emblem — A71

Litho. & Photo.

1966, Mar. 22 ***Perf. 11***

300	A71	20m	car, emer & blk	.15	.15
301	A71	55m	brt bl, ver & blk	.30	.25

Issued to publicize the Arab League.

Souvenir Sheet

WHO Headquarters, Geneva, and Emblem — A72

1966, May 3 **Litho.** ***Imperf.***

302	A72	50m	multicolored	1.90	1.90

Inauguration of the WHO headquarters. See Nos. C55-C57.

Tuareg and Camel — A73

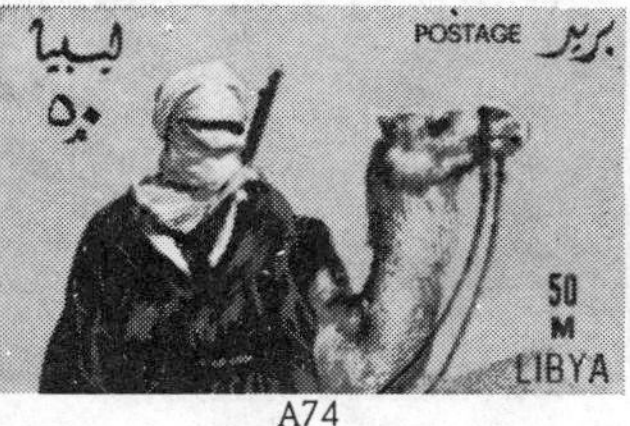

A74

Three Tuareg Riders — A75

Design: 20m, like 10m, facing left.

1966, June 20 **Unwmk.** ***Perf. 10***

303	A73	10m	bright red	.25	.20
304	A73	20m	ultramarine	.55	.40
305	A74	50m	multicolored	.90	.80
a.			Strip of 3, Nos. 303-305	1.90	1.90

Imperf

306	A75	100m	multicolored	2.50	2.00

Gazelle — A76

Emblem — A77

Perf. 13x11, 11x13

1966, Aug. 12 **Litho.**

307	A76	5m	lt grn, blk & red	.16	.15
308	A77	25m	multicolored	.35	.20
309	A77	65m	multicolored	.65	.35
			Nos. 307-309 (3)	1.16	.70

1st Arab Girl Scout Camp (5m); 7th Arab Boy Scout Camp, Good Daim, Libya, Aug. 12 (25m, 60m).

UNESCO Emblem — A78

1967, Jan. **Litho.** ***Perf. 10x10½***

310	A78	15m	multicolored	.15	.15
311	A78	25m	multicolored	.20	.16
			Set value		.24

UNESCO, 20th anniv. (in 1966).

Castle of Columns, Tolemaide A79

Fair Emblem A80

Design: 55m, Sebha Fort, horiz.

Perf. 13x13½, 13½x13

1966, Dec. 24 **Engr.**

312	A79	25m	lil, red brn & blk	.16	.15
313	A79	55m	blk, lil & red brn	.35	.28

1967, Feb. 28 **Photo.** ***Perf. 11½***

314	A80	15m	multicolored	.16	.15
315	A80	55m	multicolored	.35	.20
			Set value		.25

6th Intl. Fair, Tripoli, Feb. 28-Mar. 20.

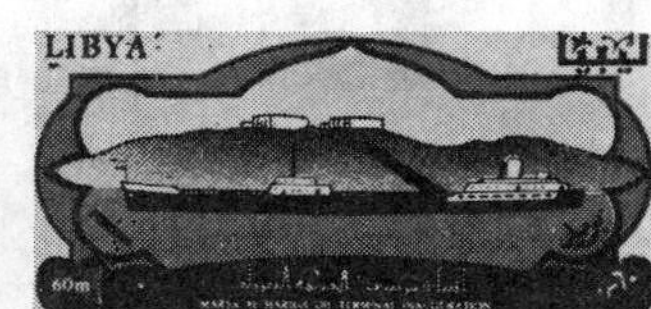

Oil Tanker, Marsa Al Hariga Terminal — A81

1967, Feb. 14 **Litho.** ***Perf. 10***

316	A81	60m	multicolored	.40	.22

Opening of Marsa Al Hariga oil terminal.

Tourist Year Emblem — A82

1967, May 1 **Litho.** ***Perf. 10½x10***

317	A82	5m	gray, blk & brt bl	.15	.15
318	A82	10m	lt bl, blk & brt bl	.15	.15
319	A82	45m	pink, blk & brt bl	.28	.16
			Set value	.40	.25

International Tourist Year.

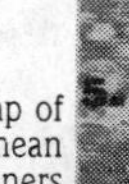
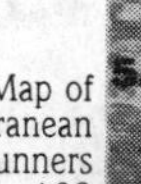

Map of Mediterranean and Runners A83

1967, Sept. 8 **Litho.** ***Perf. 10½***

320	A83	5m	shown	.15	.15
321	A83	10m	Javelin	.15	.15
322	A83	15m	Bicyling	.15	.15
323	A83	45m	Soccer	.20	.16
324	A83	75m	Boxing	.50	.25
			Set value	.90	.55

5th Mediterranean Games, Tunis, Sept. 8-17.

A84

A85

Arab League emblem and hands reaching for knowledge.

1967, Oct. 1 **Litho.** ***Perf. 12½x13***

325	A84	5m	orange & dk pur	.15	.15
326	A84	10m	brt grn & dk pur	.15	.15
327	A84	15m	lilac & dk pur	.15	.15
328	A84	25m	blue & dk pur	.28	.15
			Set value	.45	.22

Literacy campaign.

1968, Jan. 15 **Litho.** ***Perf. 13½x14***

Human rights flame.

329	A85	15m	grn & vermilion	.16	.15
330	A85	60m	org & vio bl	.28	.25
			Set value		.30

International Human Rights Year.

Map, Derrick, Plane and Camel Riders — A86

1968, Feb. 28 **Photo.** ***Perf. 11½***

331	A86	55m	car rose, brn & yel	.45	.35

7th Intl. Fair, Tripoli, Feb. 28-Mar. 20.

Arab League Emblem A87

1968, Mar. 22 **Engr.** ***Perf. 13½***

332	A87	10m	blue gray & car	.15	.15
333	A87	45m	fawn & green	.38	.25

Issued for Arab League Week.

Children, Statuary Group — A88

Children's Day: 55m, Mother and children.

1968, Mar. 21 Litho. *Perf. 11*

334 A88 25m gray, blk & mag .16 .15
335 A88 55m gray & multi .28 .20
Set value .28

Hands Reaching for WHO Emblem — A89

Perf. 13½x14½

1968, Apr. 7 Photo.

336 A89 25m rose cl, dk bl & gray bl .20 .15
337 A89 55m bl, blk & gray .45 .20
Set value .28

WHO, 20th anniversary.

From Oil Field to Tanker — A90

1968, Apr. 23 Litho. *Perf. 11*

338 A90 10m multicolored .16 .15
339 A90 60m multicolored .45 .25

Opening of the Zueitina oil terminal.

Teacher and Crowd A91

1968, Sept. 8 Litho. *Perf. 13½*

340 A91 5m bright pink .15 .15
341 A91 10m orange .15 .15
342 A91 15m blue .15 .15
343 A91 20m emerald .25 .16
Set value .42 .32

Literacy campaign.

Arab Labor Emblem A92

1968, Nov. 3 Photo. *Perf. 14x13½*

344 A92 10m multicolored .15 .15
345 A92 15m multicolored .25 .15
Set value .20

4th session of the Arab Labor Ministers' Conf., Tripoli, Nov. 3-10.

Wadi el Kuf Bridge and Road Sign — A93

1968, Dec. 25 Litho. *Perf. 11x11½*

346 A93 25m ultra & multi .16 .15
347 A93 60m emer & multi .35 .20

Opening of the Wadi el Kuf Bridge.

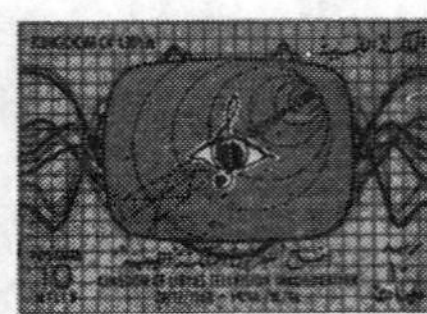
Television Screen and Chart — A94

1968, Dec. 25 Photo. *Perf. 14x13½*

348 A94 10m yellow & multi .15 .15
349 A94 30m lilac & multi .25 .16
Set value .20

Inauguration of television service, Dec. 24.

Melons — A95

1969, Jan. Photo. *Perf. 11½*

Granite Paper

350 A95 5m shown .15 .15
351 A95 10m Peanuts .15 .15
352 A95 15m Lemons .15 .15
353 A95 20m Oranges .30 .15
354 A95 25m Peaches .38 .15
355 A95 35m Pears .50 .30
Set value 1.40 .70

Nos. 350-355 with "Kingdom of Libya" in both English and Arabic blocked out with a blue felt-tipped pen were issued in December, 1971, by the Republic.

Tripoli Fair Emblem — A96

1969, Apr. 8

Granite Paper

356 A96 25m silver & multi .15 .15
357 A96 35m bronze & multi .15 .15
358 A96 40m gold & multi .28 .16
Set value .48 .32

8th Intl. Fair, Tripoli, Mar. 6-26.

Weather Balloon and Observer A97

1969, Mar. 21 Photo. *Perf. 14x13*

359 A97 60m gray & multi .40 .35

World Meteorological Day, Mar. 23.

Cogwheel and Workers A98

1969, Mar. 29 Litho. *Perf. 13½*

360 A98 15m blue & multi .15 .15
361 A98 55m salmon & multi .35 .20
Set value .28

10th anniversary of Social Insurance.

ILO Emblem — A99

1969, June 1 Photo. *Perf. 14*

362 A99 10m bl grn, blk & lt ol .15 .15
363 A99 60m car rose, blk & lt ol .38 .20
Set value .28

ILO, 50th anniversary.

African Tourist Year Emblem A100

1969, July *Perf. 11½*

Emblem in Emerald, Light Blue & Red

364 A100 15m emer & silver .20 .15
365 A100 30m blk & gold .40 .20
Set value .28

Issued to publicize African Tourist Year.

Libyan Arab Republic

Soldiers, Tanks and Planes — A101

Radar, Flags and Carrier Pigeon — A102

1969, Dec. 7 Photo. *Perf. 12x12½*

366 A101 5m org & multi .15 .15
367 A101 10m ultra & multi .15 .15
368 A101 15m multicolored .20 .15
369 A101 25m multicolored .30 .15
370 A101 45m brt bl & multi .45 .25
371 A101 60m multicolored .80 .40
Nos. 366-371 (6) 2.05
Set value 1.00

Establishment of the Libyan Arab Republic, Sept. 1, 1969. See Nos. 379-384.

1970, Mar. 1 Photo. *Perf. 11½*

Granite Paper

372 A102 15m multicolored .22 .15
373 A102 20m multicolored .38 .18
374 A102 25m multicolored .45 .22
375 A102 40m multicolored .60 .38
Nos. 372-375 (4) 1.65 .93

Map of Arab League Countries, Flag and Emblem A102a

1970, Mar. 22

376 A102a 10m lt bl, brn & grn .15 .15
377 A102a 15m org, brn & grn .15 .15
378 A102a 20m ol, brn & grn .22 .20
Nos. 376-378 (3) .52
Set value .42 .35

25th anniversary of the Arab League.

Type A101 Redrawn — A103

1970, May 2 Photo. *Perf. 12x12½*

379 A103 5m org & multi .15 .15
380 A103 10m ultra & multi .15 .15
381 A103 15m multicolored .16 .15
382 A103 25m multicolored .25 .15
383 A103 45m brt bl & multi .50 .20
384 A103 60m multicolored .60 .25
Nos. 379-384 (6) 1.81
Set value .70

On Nos. 379-384 the numerals are in black, the bottom inscription is in 2 lines and several other changes.

Inauguration of UPU Headquarters, Bern — A104

1970, May 20 Photo. *Perf. 11½x11*

385 A104 10m multicolored .15 .15
386 A104 25m multicolored .20 .15
387 A104 60m multicolored .45 .22
Nos. 385-387 (3) .80
Set value .38

Arms of Libyan Arab Republic A105

Flags, Soldiers and Tank A106

1970, June 20 Photo. *Perf. 11*

388 A105 15m black & brt rose .15 .15
389 A105 25m vio bl, yel & brt rose .22 .15
390 A105 45m emer, yel & brt rose .55 .20
Nos. 388-390 (3) .92
Set value .35

Evacuation of US military base in Libya.

1970, Sept. 1 Photo. *Perf. 11x11½*

391 A106 20m multicolored .45 .16
392 A106 25m multicolored .55 .22
393 A106 30m blue & multi .90 .45
Nos. 391-393 (3) 1.90 .83

Libyan Arab Republic, 1st anniv.

UN Emblem, Dove and Scales — A107

1970, Oct. 24 Photo. *Perf. 11x11½*

394 A107 5m org & multi .38 .15
395 A107 10m olive & multi .45 .22
396 A107 60m multicolored .90 .40
Nos. 394-396 (3) 1.73 .77

25th anniversary of the United Nations.

Map and Flags of UAR, Libya, Sudan A107a

1970, Dec. 27 Photo. *Perf. 11½*

397 A107a 15m lt grn, car & blk 1.50 .60

Signing of the Charter of Tripoli affirming the unity of UAR, Libya and the Sudan, Dec. 27, 1970.

UN Emblem, Dove and Globe — A108

1971, Jan. 10 Litho. *Perf. 12x11½*

398 A108 15m multicolored .38 .15
399 A108 20m multicolored .45 .16
400 A108 60m lt vio & multi .90 .30
Nos. 398-400 (3) 1.73 .61

UN declaration on granting of independence to colonial countries and peoples, 10th anniv.

Education Year Emblem — A109

Al Fatah Fighter — A110

1971, Jan. 16

401 A109 5m red, blk & ocher .16 .15
402 A109 10m red, blk & emer .30 .15
403 A109 20m red, blk & vio bl .60 .15
Nos. 401-403 (3) 1.06
Set value .28

International Education Year.

1971, Mar. 14 Photo. *Perf. 11*

404 A110 5m ol & multi .50 .15
405 A110 10m yel & multi .80 .15
406 A110 100m multicolored 1.90 .20
Nos. 404-406 (3) 3.20 .50

Fight for the liberation of Palestine.

Tripoli Fair Emblem A111

10th Anniv. of OPEC A112

1971, Mar. 18 Litho. *Perf. 14*

407 A111 15m multicolored .20 .15
408 A111 30m org & multi .30 .15
Set value .22

9th International Fair at Tripoli.

1971, May 29 Litho. *Perf. 12*

409 A112 10m yellow & brown .15 .15
410 A112 70m pink & vio bl .55 .25
Set value .30

Globe and Waves A113

1971, June 10 *Perf. 14½x13½*

411 A113 25m brt grn, blk & vio bl .20 .15
412 A113 35m gray & multi .22 .15
Set value .24

3rd World Telecommunications Day, May 17, 1971.

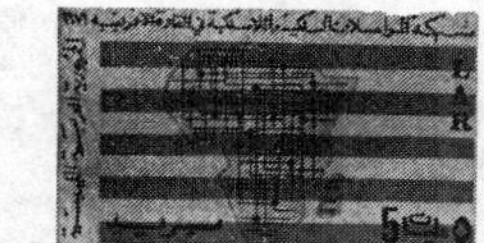

Map of Africa and Telecommunications Network — A114

1971, June 10

413 A114 5m yel, blk & grn .15 .15
414 A114 15m dl bl, blk & grn .40 .22
Set value .28

Pan-African telecommunications system.

Torchbearer and Banner — A115

Ramadan Suehli — A116

1971, June 15 Photo. *Perf. 11½x12*

415 A115 5m yel & multi .20 .15
416 A115 10m org & multi .35 .15
417 A115 15m multicolored .50 .15
Nos. 415-417 (3) 1.05
Set value .16

Evacuation of US military base, 1st anniv.

1971, Aug. 24 *Perf. 14x14½*

418 A116 15m multicolored .15 .15
419 A116 55m bl & multi .22 .15
Set value .20

Ramadan Suehli (1879-1920), freedom fighter.
See #422-423, 426-427, 439-440, 479-480.

Date Palm — A117

Gamal Abdel Nasser (1918-1970), President of Egypt — A118

1971, Sept. 1

420 A117 5m multicolored .20 .15
421 A117 15m multicolored .40 .15
Set value .16

Sept. 1, 1969 Revolution, 2nd anniv.

Portrait Type of 1971

Portrait: Omar el Mukhtar (1858-1931), leader of the Martyrs.

1971, Sept. 16 *Perf. 14x14½*

422 A116 5m lt grn & multi .15 .15
423 A116 100m multicolored .70 .25
Set value .30

1971, Sept. 28 Photo. *Perf. 11x11½*

424 A118 5m lil, grn & blk .15 .15
425 A118 15m grn, lil & blk .22 .15
Set value .22

Portrait Type of 1971

Ibrahim Usta Omar (1908-50), patriotic poet.

1971, Oct. 8 Litho. *Perf. 14x14½*

426 A116 25m vio bl & multi .20 .15
427 A116 30m multicolored .25 .15

Racial Equality Emblem A119

Arab Postal Union Emblem A120

1971, Oct. 24 *Perf. 13½x14½*

428 A119 25m multicolored .22 .15
429 A119 35m multicolored .30 .15
Set value .22

Intl. Year Against Racial Discrimination.

1971, Nov. 6 Litho. *Perf. 14½*
Emblem in Black, Yellow and Blue

430 A120 5m red .15 .15
431 A120 10m violet .15 .15
432 A120 15m bright rose lilac .20 .15
Set value .36 .20

Conference of Sofar, Lebanon, establishing Arab Postal Union, 25th anniv.

Postal Union Emblem and Letter A121

25m, 55m, APU emblem, letter and dove.

1971, Dec. Photo. *Perf. 11½x11*

433 A121 10m org brn, bl & blk .15 .15
434 A121 15m org, lt bl & blk .15 .15
435 A121 25m lt grn, org & blk .22 .15
436 A121 55m lt brn, yel & blk .42 .22
Nos. 433-436 (4) .94
Set value .40

10th anniversary of African Postal Union.
Issued: 25m, 55m, Dec. 2; 10m, 15m, Dec. 12.

Despite the change from milliemes to dirhams in 1972, both currencies appear on stamps until August.

Book Year Emblem A122

Coat of Arms A123

1972, Jan. 1 Litho. *Perf. 12½x13*

437 A122 15m ultra, brn, gold & blk .20 .15
438 A122 20m gold, brn, ultra & blk .22 .15

International Book Year.

Portrait Type of 1971

Ahmed Gnaba (1898-1968), poet of unity.

1972, Jan. 12 *Perf. 14x14½*

439 A116 20m red & multi .20 .15
440 A116 35m olive & multi .22 .15
Set value .20

1972, Feb. 10 Photo. *Perf. 14½*
Size: 19x23mm

441 A123 5m gray & multi .15 .15
442 A123 10m lt ol & multi .16 .15
443 A123 15d lilac & multi .15 .15
445 A123 25m lt bl & multi .15 .15
446 A123 30m rose & multi .22 .15
447 A123 35m lt ol & multi .35 .15
448 A123 40m dl yel & multi .25 .15
449 A123 45m lt grn & multi .30 .15
451 A123 55m multicolored .35 .20
452 A123 60m bister & multi .50 .20
453 A123 65d multicolored .40 .22
454 A123 70d lt vio & multi .55 .22
455 A123 80d ocher & multi .70 .25
456 A123 90m bl & multi 1.10 .35

Size: 27x32mm
Perf. 14x14½

457 A123 100d multicolored 1.50 .38
458 A123 200d multicolored 2.25 .45
459 A123 500d multicolored 4.50 2.50
460 A123 £1 multicolored 9.00 5.00
Nos. 441-460 (18) 22.58 10.97

During the transition from millimemes and pounds to dirhams and dinars, stamps were issued in both cuurencies.

A124

20m

50m

Coil Stamps

1972, July 27 Photo. *Perf. 14½x14*

461 A124 5m sl bl, ocher & black .70 .15
462 A124 20m bl, lil & blk 2.75 .30
463 A124 50m bl, ol & blk 6.00 1.10
Nos. 461-463 (3) 9.45 1.55

See Nos. 496-498, 575-577.

Tombs at Ghirza — A125

Fair Emblem — A126

Designs: 10m, Kufic inscription, Agedabia, horiz. 15m, Marcus Aurelius Arch, Tripoli. 25m, Exchange of weapons, mural from Wan Amil Cave. 55m, Garamanthian (Berber) chariot, petroglyph, Wadi Zigza. 70m, Nymph Cyrene strangling a lion, bas-relief, Cyrene.

1972, Feb. 15 Litho. *Perf. 14*

464 A125 5m lilac & multi .15 .15
465 A125 10m multicolored .15 .15
466 A125 15m dp org & multi .16 .15
467 A125 25m emer & multi .25 .15
468 A125 55m scar & multi .70 .22
469 A125 70m ultra & multi 1.00 .38
Nos. 464-469 (6) 2.41
Set value .92

1972, Mar. 1

470 A126 25d gray & multi .22 .15
471 A126 35d multicolored .30 .18
472 A126 50d multicolored .55 .25
473 A126 70d multicolored .70 .38
Nos. 470-473 (4) 1.77 .96

10th International Fair at Tripoli.

Dissected Arm, and Heart — A127

"Arab Unity" — A128

1972, Apr. 7 *Perf. 14½*

474 A127 15d multicolored .80 .30
475 A127 25d multicolored 1.50 .60

"Your heart is your health," World Health Day.

Perf. 13½x13

1972, Apr. 17 Litho. & Engr.

476 A128 15d bl, yel & blk .15 .15
477 A128 20d lt grn, yel & blk .20 .15
478 A128 25d lt ver, yel & blk .55 .20
Nos. 476-478 (3) .90
Set value .40

Fed. of Arab Republics Foundation, 1st anniv.

Portrait Type of 1971

Suleiman el Baruni (1870-1940), patriotic writer.

1972, May 1 Litho. *Perf. 14x14½*

479 A116 10m yellow & multi .70 .22
480 A116 70m dp org & multi 1.10 .60

Environment Emblem A129

Olympic Emblems A130

1972, Aug. 15 Litho. *Perf. 14½*

481 A129 15m red & multi .38 .15
482 A129 55m green & multi .80 .22

UN Conference on Human Environment, Stockholm, June 5-16.

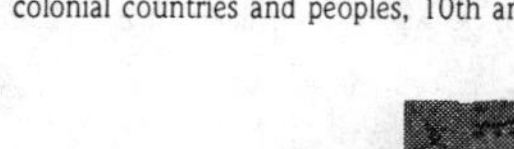

1972, Aug. 26
483 A130 25d brt bl & multi .70 .30
484 A130 35d red & multi 1.10 .60

20th Olympic Games, Munich, Aug. 26-Sept. 11.

Emblem and Broken Chain A131

Dome of the Rock, Jerusalem A132

1972, Oct. 1 Litho. *Perf. 14x13½*
485 A131 15d blue & multi .15 .15
486 A131 25d yellow & multi .30 .15
Set value .18

Libyan Arab Republic, 3rd anniv.

1972 *Perf. 12½x13*
487 A132 10d multicolored .35 .15
488 A132 25d multicolored .50 .15
Set value .16

Nicolaus Copernicus (1473-1543), Polish Astronomer A133

Blind Person, Books, Loom and Basket A135

Eagle and Fair Buildings A134

Design: 25d, Copernicus in Observatory, by Jan Matejko, horiz.

Perf. 14½x13½, 13½x14½
1973, Feb. 26
489 A133 15d yellow & multi .18 .15
490 A133 25d blue & multi .22 .15
Set value .22

1973, Mar. 1 *Perf. 13½x14½*
491 A134 5d dull red & multi .20 .15
492 A134 10d blue grn & multi .22 .15
493 A134 15d vio blue & multi .45 .15
Nos. 491-493 (3) .87
Set value .28

11th International Fair at Tripoli.

1973, Apr. 18 Photo. *Perf. 12x11½*
494 A135 20d gray & multi 2.25 .45
495 A135 25d dull yel & multi 4.50 1.40

Role of the blind in society.

Coil Stamps
Numeral Type of 1972 Denominations in Dirhams

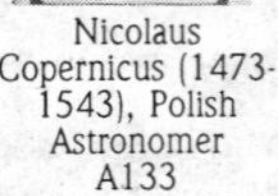

5d *20d* *50d*

1973, Apr. 26 Photo. *Perf. 14½x14*
496 A124 5d sl bl, ocher & blk .50 .15
497 A124 20d blue, lilac & blk .65 .16
498 A124 50d blue, olive & blk 1.50 .22
Nos. 496-498 (3) 2.65
Set value .42

Map of Africa — A136

1973, May 25 Photo. *Perf. 11x11½*
499 A136 15d yel, green & brown .22 .15
500 A136 25d lt yel grn, grn & blk .38 .15
Set value .22

"Freedom in Unity" (Org. for African Unity).

INTERPOL Emblem and General Secretariat, Paris — A138

Perf. 13½x14½
1973, June 30 Litho.
501 A138 10d lilac & multi .15 .15
502 A138 15d ocher & multi .22 .15
503 A138 25d lt grn & multi .38 .15
Nos. 501-503 (3) .75
Set value .24

50th anniv. of Intl. Criminal Police Org.

Map of Libya, Houses, People, Factories, Tractor A139

1973, July 15 Photo. *Perf. 11½*
504 A139 10d rose red, black & ultra .90 .25
505 A139 25d ultra, blk & grn 1.50 .50
506 A139 35d grn, blk & org 2.50 .75
Nos. 504-506 (3) 4.90 1.50

General census.

UN Emblem — A140

1973, Aug. 1 *Perf. 12½x11*
507 A140 5d ver, blk & bl .15 .15
508 A140 10d yel grn, blk & bl .22 .15
Set value .15

Intl. meteorological cooperation, cent.

Soccer — A141

1973, Aug. 10 Photo. *Perf. 11½*
509 A141 5d yel grn & dk brn .42 .16
510 A141 25d orange & dk brn .80 .15

2nd Palestinian Cup Soccer Tournament.

Torch and Grain — A142

Writing Hand, Lamp and Globe — A143

1973, Sept. 1 Litho. *Perf. 14*
511 A142 15d brown & multi .18 .15
512 A142 25d emer & multi .45 .15
Set value .16

4th anniv. of Sept. 1 Revolution.

1973, Sept. 8
513 A143 25d multicolored .30 .15

Literacy campaign.

Gate of First City Hall A144

Militia, Flag and Factories A145

1973, Sept. 18 *Perf. 13*
514 A144 10d shown .20 .15
515 A144 25d Khondok fountain .22 .15
516 A144 35d Clock tower .38 .15
Nos. 514-516 (3) .80
Set value .24

Centenary of Tripoli as a municipality.

1973, Oct. 7 Photo. *Perf. 11½x11*
517 A145 15d yel, blk & red .20 .15
518 A145 25d green & multi .22 .15
Set value .16

Libyan Militia.

Revolutionary Proclamation by Khadafy — A146

Design: 70d, as 25d, with English inscription.

1973, Oct. 15 Litho. *Perf. 12½*
519 A146 25d orange & multi .20 .15
520 A146 70d green & multi .45 .22
Set value .28

Proclamation of People's Revolution by Pres. Muammar Khadafy.

FAO Emblem, Camel Pulling Plow A147

1973, Nov. 1 Photo. *Perf. 11*
521 A147 10d ocher & multi .15 .15
522 A147 25d dk brn & multi .20 .15
523 A147 35d black & multi .22 .15
Nos. 521-523 (3) .57
Set value .22

World Food Org., 10th anniv.

Human Rights Flame — A148

1973, Dec. 20 Photo. *Perf. 11x11½*
524 A148 25d pur, car & dk bl .20 .15
525 A148 70d lt grn, car & dk bl .45 .22
Set value .28

Universal Declaration of Human Rights, 25th anniv.

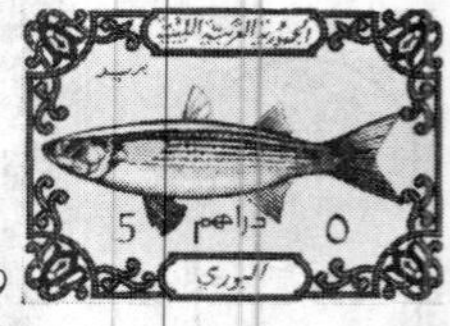
Fish — A149

Designs: Various fish from Libyan waters.

1973, Dec. 31 Photo. *Perf. 14x13½*
526 A149 5d light blue & multi .15 .15
527 A149 10d light blue & multi .20 .15
528 A149 15d light blue & multi .25 .15
529 A149 20d light blue & multi .42 .15
530 A149 25d light blue & multi .70 .16
Nos. 526-530 (5) 1.72
Set value .45

1975, Jan. 5
526a A149 5d greenish blue & multi .15 .15
527a A149 10d greenish blue & multi .15 .15
528a A149 15d greenish blue & multi .16 .15
529a A149 20d greenish blue & multi .35 .15
530a A149 25d greenish blue & multi .38 .15
Nos. 526a-530a (5) 1.19
Set value .30

Scout, Sun and Scout Signs — A150

Fair Emblem, Flags of Participants — A151

1974, Feb. 1 Litho. *Perf. 11½*
531 A150 5d blue & multi .28 .15
532 A150 20d light lilac & multi .70 .18
533 A150 25d light green & multi 1.50 .30
Nos. 531-533 (3) 2.48 .63

Libyan Boy Scouts.

1974, Mar. 1 Litho. *Perf. 12x11½*
534 A151 10d lt ultra & multi .22 .15
535 A151 25d tan & multi .38 .15
536 A151 35d lt green & multi .50 .15
Nos. 534-536 (3) 1.10
Set value .25

12th Tripoli International Fair.

Protected Family, WHO Emblem — A152

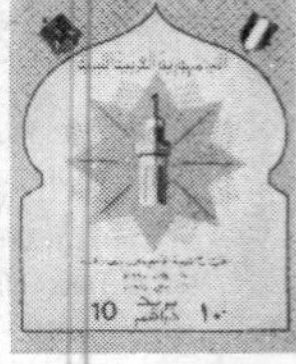
Minaret and Star — A153

1974, Apr. 7 Litho. *Perf. 12½*
537 A152 5d lt green & multi .15 .15
538 A152 25d red & multi .22 .15
Set value .20

World Health Day.

1974, Apr. 16 *Perf. 11½x11*

539 A153 10d pink & multi .16 .15
540 A153 25d yellow & multi .30 .15
541 A153 35d orange & multi .60 .22
Nos. 539-541 (3) 1.06
Set value .38

City University of Bengazi, inauguration.

UPU Emblem and Star — A154

Traffic Signs — A156

Perf. 13½x14½

1974, May 22 **Litho.**

542 A154 25d multicolored 2.25 .38
543 A154 70d multicolored 5.00 .80

Centenary of Universal Postal Union.

1974, June 8 **Photo.** *Perf. 11*

547 A156 5d gold & multi .15 .15
548 A156 10d gold & multi .15 .15
549 A156 25d gold & multi .20 .15
Nos. 547-549 (3) .50
Set value .24

Automobile and Touring Club of Libya.

Tank, Oil Refinery, Book — A157

Symbolic "5" — A158

1974, Sept. 1 **Litho.** *Perf. 14*

550 A157 5d red & multi .15 .15
551 A157 20d violet & multi .15 .15
552 A157 25d vio bl & multi .15 .15
553 A157 35d green & multi .15 .15
Set value .34 .22

Souvenir Sheet

Perf. 13

554 A158 55d yel & maroon 2.00 1.75

Revolution of Sept. 1, 5th anniv. English inscription on No. 553.

WPY Emblem and Crowd — A159

Libyan Woman — A160

1974, Oct. 19 *Perf. 14*

555 A159 25d multicolored .20 .15
556 A159 35d lt brn & multi .22 .15
Set value .22

World Population Year.

1975, Mar. 1 **Litho.** *Perf. 13x12½*

Libyan Costumes: 10d, 15d, Women. 20d, Old man. 25d, Man riding camel. 50d, Man on horseback.

557 A160 5d org yel & multi .15 .15
558 A160 10d org yel & multi .15 .15
559 A160 15d org yel & multi .15 .15
560 A160 20d org yel & multi .15 .15
561 A160 25d org yel & multi .20 .15
562 A160 50d org yel & multi .42 .20
Set value .95 .45

Congress Emblem — A161

1975, Mar. 4 **Litho.** *Perf. 12x12½*

563 A161 10d brown & multi .15 .15
564 A161 25d vio & multi .15 .15
565 A161 35d gray & multi .22 .15
Set value .38 .25

Arab Labor Congress.

Teacher Pointing to Blackboard A162

1975, Mar. 10 *Perf. 11½*

566 A162 10d gold & multi .15 .15
567 A162 25d gold & multi .15 .15
Set value .22 .15

Teacher's Day.

Bodies, Globe, Proclamation A163

Woman and Man in Library A164

1975, Apr. 7 **Litho.** *Perf. 12½*

568 A163 20d lilac & multi .15 .15
569 A163 25d emer & multi .18 .15
Set value .15

World Health Day.

1975, May 25 **Litho.** *Perf. 12½*

570 A164 10d bl grn & multi .15 .15
571 A164 25d olive & multi .15 .15
572 A164 35d lt vio & multi .20 .15
Nos. 570-572 (3) .50
Set value .22

Libyan Arab Book Exhibition.

Festival Emblem — A165

Games Emblem and Arms — A166

1975, July 5 **Litho.** *Perf. 13x12½*

573 A165 20d lt bl & multi .15 .15
574 A165 25d orange & multi .20 .15
Set value .15

2nd Arab Youth Festival.

Coil Stamps

Redrawn Type of 1973 Without "LAR"

1975, Aug. 15 **Photo.** *Perf. 14½x14*

575 A124 5d blue, org & blk .25 .15
576 A124 20d blue, yel & blk .50 .15
577 A124 50d blue, grn & blk .65 .15
Nos. 575-577 (3) 1.40
Set value .22

1975, Aug. 23 *Perf. 13x12½*

578 A166 10d salmon & multi .15 .15
579 A166 25d lilac & multi .15 .15
580 A166 50d yellow & multi .30 .16
Nos. 578-580 (3) .60
Set value .28

7th Mediterranean Games, Algiers, 8/23-9/6.

Peace Dove, Symbols of Agriculture and Industry — A167

Khadafy's Head Over Desert — A168

Design: 70d, Peace dove, diff.

1975, Sept. **Litho.** *Perf. 13x12½*

581 A167 25d multicolored .20 .15
582 A167 70d multicolored .45 .15

Souvenir Sheet

Imperf

Litho. & Embossed

583 A168 100d multicolored 1.90 1.90

6th anniversary of Sept. 1 revolution. No. 583 contains one stamp with simulated perforations.

Khalil Basha Mosque — A169

Al Kharruba Mosque — A170

Mosques: 10d, Sidi Abdulla El Shaab. 15d, Sidi Ali El Fergani. 25d, Katikhtha. 30d, Murad Agha. 35d, Maulai Mohammed.

1975, Dec. 13 **Litho.** *Perf. 12½*

584 A169 5d gray & multi .15 .15
585 A169 10d purple & multi .15 .15
586 A169 15d green & multi .16 .15
587 A170 20d ocher & multi .20 .15
588 A170 25d multicolored .22 .15
589 A170 30d multicolored .25 .15
590 A170 35d lilac & multi .35 .15
Nos. 584-590 (7) 1.48
Set value .40

Mohammed's 1405th birthday.

Arms of Libya and People — A171

Islamic- Christian Dialogue Emblem — A172

1976, Jan. 15 **Photo.** *Perf. 13*

591 A171 35d blue & multi .20 .15
592 A171 40d multicolored .22 .15
Set value .18

General National (People's) Congress.

1976, Feb. 5 **Litho.** *Perf. 13x12½*

593 A172 40d gold & multi .20 .15
594 A172 115d gold & multi .55 .15
Set value .20

Seminar of Islamic-Christian Dialogue, Tripoli, Feb. 1-5.

Woman Blowing Horn — A173

National Costumes: 20d, Lancer. 30d, Drummer. 40d, Bagpiper. 100d, Woman carrying jug on head.

1976, Mar. 1 **Litho.** *Perf. 13x12½*

595 A173 10d multicolored .15 .15
596 A173 20d multicolored .15 .15
597 A173 30d pink & multi .20 .15
598 A173 40d multicolored .22 .15
599 A173 100d yel & multi .70 .28
Nos. 595-599 (5) 1.42
Set value .64

14th Tripoli International Fair.

Telephones, 1876 and 1976, ITU and UPU Emblems A174

Design: 70d, Alexander Graham Bell, telephone, satellites, radar, ITU and UPU emblems.

1976, Mar. 10 **Photo.** *Perf. 13*

600 A174 40d multicolored .60 .15
a. Souvenir sheet of 4 5.00 5.00
601 A174 70d multicolored 1.20 .20
a. Souvenir sheet of 4 6.50 6.50

Centenary of first telephone call by Alexander Graham Bell, Mar. 10, 1876.

Mother and Child — A175

Hands, Eye and Head — A176

1976, Mar. 21 *Perf. 12*

602 A175 85d gray & multi .40 .25
603 A175 110d pink & multi .60 .30

International Children's Day.

1976, Apr. 7 **Photo.** *Perf. 13½x13*

604 A176 30d multicolored .15 .15
605 A176 35d multicolored .16 .15
606 A176 40d multicolored .20 .15
Nos. 604-606 (3) .51
Set value .30

"Foresight prevents blindness;" World Health Day.

Little Bittern A177

Birds of Libya: 10d, Great gray shrike. 15d, Songbird. 20d, European bee-eater, vert. 25d, Hoopoe.

Perf. 13x13½, 13½x13

1976, May 1 **Litho.**

607 A177 5d orange & multi *.22* .15
608 A177 10d ultra & multi *.42* .16
609 A177 15d rose & multi *.80* .22
610 A177 20d yellow & multi *1.20* .30
611 A177 25d blue & multi *1.50* .45
Nos. 607-611 (5) *4.14* 1.28

Al Barambekh — A178

Bicycling — A179

Designs: 15d, Whale, horiz. 30d, Lizard (alwaral), horiz. 40d, Mastodon skull, horiz. 70d, Hawk. 115d, Wild mountain sheep.

1976, June 20 Litho. *Perf. 12½*

612 A178 10d multicolored .15 .15
613 A178 15d multicolored .22 .15
614 A178 30d multicolored .32 .15
615 A178 40d multicolored .38 .18
616 A178 70d multicolored .75 .32
617 A178 115d multicolored 1.40 .55
Nos. 612-617 (6) 3.22
Set value 1.25

Museum of Natural History.

1976, July 17 Litho. *Perf. 12x11½*

Granite Paper

618 A179 15d shown .15 .15
619 A179 25d Boxing .15 .15
620 A179 70d Soccer .35 .20
Nos. 618-620 (3) .65
Set value .32

Souvenir Sheet

621 A179 150d Symbolic of various sports *9.00 9.00*

21st Olympic Games, Montreal, Canada, July 17-Aug. 1.

Tree Growing from Globe — A180

Symbols of Agriculture and Industry — A181

Drummer and Pipeline — A182

1976, Aug. 9 *Perf. 13*

622 A180 115d multicolored .45 .30

5th Conference of Non-Aligned Countries, Colombo, Sri Lanka, Aug. 9-19.

Beginning with No. 622 numerous issues are printed with multiple coats of arms in pale green on back of stamps.

1976, Sept. 1 *Perf. 14½x14*

623 A181 30d yel & multi .15 .15
624 A181 40d multicolored .15 .15
625 A181 100d multicolored .40 .25
Nos. 623-625 (3) .70
Set value .42

Souvenir Sheet

Perf. 13

626 A182 200d multicolored 1.90 1.90

Sept. 1 Revolution, 7th anniv.

Sports, Torch and Emblems A183

Chess Board, Rook, Knight, Emblem A184

145d, Symbolic wrestlers and various emblems.

1976, Oct. 6 Litho. *Perf. 13*

627 A183 15d multicolored .15 .15
628 A183 30d multicolored .22 .15
629 A183 100d multicolored .60 .25
Nos. 627-629 (3) .97
Set value .38

Souvenir Sheet

630 A183 145d multi, horiz. 1.50 1.50

5th Arab Games, Damascus, Syria.

1976, Oct. 24 Photo. *Perf. 11½*

631 A184 15d pink & multi .55 .15
632 A184 30d buff & multi 1.10 .20
633 A184 100d multicolored 1.40 .30
Nos. 631-633 (3) 3.05 .65

The "Against" (protest) Chess Olympiad, Tripoli, Oct. 24-Nov. 15.

A185

Designs: Various local flowers.

1976, Nov. 1 Photo. *Perf. 11½*

Granite Paper

634 A185 15d lilac & multi .15 .15
635 A185 20d multicolored .15 .15
636 A185 35d yellow & multi .20 .15
637 A185 40d salmon & multi .25 .15
638 A185 70d multicolored .60 .22
Nos. 634-638 (5) 1.35
Set value .58

International Archives Council Emblem and Document — A186

1976, Nov. 10 Litho. *Perf. 13x13½*

639 A186 15d brown, org & buff .15 .15
640 A186 35d brn, brt grn & buff .15 .15
641 A186 70d brown, blue & buff .30 .20
Nos. 639-641 (3) .60
Set value .32

Arab Regional Branch of International Council on Archives, Baghdad.

Holy Ka'aba and Pilgrims A187

Numeral A188

1976, Dec. 12 Litho. *Perf. 14*

642 A187 15d multicolored .15 .15
643 A187 30d multicolored .15 .15
644 A187 70d multicolored .25 .20
645 A187 100d multicolored .40 .25
Set value .82 .58

Pilgrimage to Mecca.

Coil Stamps

1977, Jan. 15 Photo. *Perf. 14½x14*

646 A188 5d multicolored .15 .15
647 A188 20d multicolored .15 .15
648 A188 50d multicolored .22 .15
Set value .36 .25

Covered Basket — A189

Designs: 20d, Leather bag. 30d, Vase. 40d, Embroidered slippers. 50d, Ornate saddle. 100d, Horse with saddle and harness.

1977, Mar. 1 Litho. *Perf. 12½x12*

649 A189 10d multicolored .15 .15
650 A189 20d multicolored .15 .15
651 A189 30d multicolored .16 .15
652 A189 40d multicolored .20 .15
653 A189 50d multicolored .25 .15
Set value .75 .45

Souvenir Sheet

Imperf

654 A189 100d multicolored .60 .60

15th Tripoli International Fair. No. 654 contains one stamp 49x53mm with simulated perforations.

Girl and Flowers, UNICEF Emblem A190

Children's drawings, UNICEF Emblem and: 30d, Clothing store. 40d, Farm yard.

1977, Mar. 28 Litho. *Perf. 13x13½*

655 A190 10d multicolored .15 .15
656 A190 30d multicolored .16 .15
657 A190 40d multicolored .20 .15
Set value .40 .28

Children's Day.

Gun, Fighters, UN Headquarters A191

1977, Mar. 13 *Perf. 13½*

658 A191 15d multicolored *.50* .15
659 A191 25d multicolored *.65* .15
660 A191 70d multicolored *1.40* .22
Nos. 658-660 (3) *2.55*
Set value .35

Battle of Al-Karamah, 9th anniversary.

Child, Raindrop, WHO Emblem — A192

Arab Postal Union, 25th Anniv. — A193

1977, Apr. 7 Litho. *Perf. 13x12½*

661 A192 15d multicolored .15 .15
662 A192 30d multicolored .25 .15
Set value .15

World Health Day.

1977, Apr. 12 *Perf. 13½*

663 A193 15d multicolored .15 .15
664 A193 30d multicolored .25 .15
665 A193 40d multicolored .40 .16
Nos. 663-665 (3) .80
Set value .28

Maps of Africa and Libya A194

1977, May 8 Litho. *Perf. 14x13½*

666 A194 40d multicolored .50 .20
667 A194 70d multicolored .65 .30

African Labor Day.

Map of Libya and Heart — A195

1977, May 10 *Perf. 14½x14*

668 A195 5d multicolored .15 .15
669 A195 10d multicolored .22 .15
670 A195 30d multicolored .42 .15
Nos. 668-670 (3) .79
Set value .24

Libyan Red Crescent Society.

Electronic Tree, ITU Emblem, Satellite and Radar A196

Electronic Tree, ITU Emblem and: 115d, Communications satellite, Montreal Olympics emblem, boxer on TV screen. 200d, Spacecraft over earth. 300d, Solar system.

1977, May 17 Litho. *Perf. 13½x13*

671 A196 60d multicolored .30 .20
672 A196 115d multicolored .62 .38
673 A196 200d multicolored 1.20 .62
Nos. 671-673 (3) 2.12 1.20

Souvenir Sheet

674 A196 300d multicolored *3.00 3.00*

9th World Telecommunications Day. No. 674 contains one stamp 52x35mm.

Plane over Tripoli, Messenger A197

UPU Emblem and: 25d, Concorde, messenger on horseback. 150d, Loading transport plane and messenger riding camel. 300d, Graf Zeppelin LZ127 over Tripoli.

1977, May 17 Litho. *Perf. 13½*

675 A197	20d multicolored	.15	.15
676 A197	25d multicolored	.15	.15
677 A197	150d multicolored	.90	.45
	Nos. 675-677 (3)	1.20	
	Set value		.58

Souvenir Sheet

678 A197 300d multicolored *3.00 3.00*

UPU centenary (in 1974). No. 678 contains one stamp 52x35mm.

Mosque — A198

Various Mosques. 50d, 100d, vertical.

1977, June 1 Photo. *Perf. 14*

679 A198	40d multicolored	.20	.15
680 A198	50d multicolored	.25	.15
681 A198	70d multicolored	.35	.20
682 A198	90d multicolored	.45	.30
683 A198	100d multicolored	.55	.38
684 A198	115d multicolored	.62	.40
	Nos. 679-684 (6)	2.42	1.58

Palestinian Archbishop Hilarion Capucci, Jailed by Israel in 1974, Map of Palestine — A199

1977, Aug. 18 Litho. *Perf. 13½*

687 A199	30d multicolored	.35	.15
688 A199	40d multicolored	.50	.15
689 A199	115d multicolored	.70	.38
	Nos. 687-689 (3)	1.55	
	Set value		.58

Raised Hands, Pylons, Wheel, Buildings — A200

Star and Ornament — A201

1977, Sept. 1 Litho. *Perf. 13½x12½*

690 A200	15d multicolored	.16	.15
691 A200	30d multicolored	.35	.15
692 A200	85d multicolored	.50	.22
	Nos. 690-692 (3)	1.01	
	Set value		.35

Souvenir Sheet

Perf. 12½

693 A201 100d gold & multi .70 .70

8th anniversary of Sept. 1 Revolution.

Team Handball A202

1977, Oct. 8 *Perf. 13½*

694 A202	5d Swimmers, vert.	.15	.15
695 A202	10d shown	.15	.15
696 A202	15d Soccer, vert.	.15	.15
697 A202	25d Table tennis	.22	.20
698 A202	40d Basketball, vert.	.38	.22
	Set value	.85	.60

7th Arab School Games.

Steeplechase — A203

Show Emblem and: 10d, Bedouin on horseback. 15d, Show emblem (Horse and "7"), vert. 45d, Steeplechase. 100d, Hurdles. 115d, Bedouins on horseback.

1977, Oct. 10 *Perf. 14½*

699 A203	5d multicolored	.15	.15
700 A203	10d multicolored	.15	.15
701 A203	15d multicolored	.15	.15
702 A203	45d multicolored	.30	.15
703 A203	115d multicolored	.70	.40
	Set value	1.25	.70

Souvenir Sheet

704 A203 100d multicolored .70 .70

7th Intl. Turf Championships, Tripoli, Oct. 1977.

Dome of the Rock, Jerusalem — A204

1977, Oct. 14 *Perf. 14½x14*

705 A204	5d multicolored	.38	.15
706 A204	10d multicolored	.50	.15
	Set value		.15

Palestinian fighters and their families.

"The Green Book" — A205

35d, Hands with broken chain holding hook over citadel. 40d, Hands above chaos. 115d, Dove and Green Book rising from Africa, world map.

1977 Litho. *Perf. 14*

707 A205	Strip of 3	1.65	1.65
a.	35d multicolored	.35	.35
b.	40d multicolored	.50	.50
c.	115d multicolored	.65	.65

The Greek Book, by Khadafy outlines Libyan democracy. Green descriptive inscription on back beneath gum, in English on 35d, French on 40d, Arabic on 115d.

Emblems A206

1977 *Perf. 12½x13*

708 A206	5d multicolored	.15	.15
709 A206	15d multicolored	.15	.15
710 A206	30d multicolored	.16	.15
	Set value	.28	.20

Standardization Day.

Crocodile and Young A207

Rock Carvings, Wadi Mathendous, c. 8000 B.C.: 15d, Elephant hunt. 20d, Giraffe, vert. 30d, Antelope. 40d, Trumpeting elephant.

1978, Jan. 1 *Perf. 12½x13, 13x12½*

711 A207	10d multicolored	.15	.15
712 A207	15d multicolored	.15	.15
713 A207	20d multicolored	.15	.15
714 A207	30d multicolored	.20	.15
715 A207	40d multicolored	.22	.20
	Set value	.70	.50

Silver Pendant — A208

Emblem, Compass and Lightning — A209

Silver Jewelry: 10d, Ornamental plate. 20d, Necklace with pendants. 25d, Crescent-shaped brooch. 115d, Armband.

1978, Mar. 1 Litho. *Perf. 13x12½*

716 A208	5d multicolored	.15	.15
717 A208	10d multicolored	.15	.15
718 A208	20d multicolored	.15	.15
719 A208	25d multicolored	.15	.15
720 A208	115d multicolored	.60	.38
	Set value	.90	.55

Tripoli International Fair.

1978, Mar. 10 *Perf. 13½*

721 A209	30d multicolored	.20	.15
722 A209	115d multicolored	.70	.38

Arab Cultural Education Organization.

Bride and Attendants A210

Children's drawings and UNESCO emblem.

1978, Mar. 21

723 A210	40d Dancing	.20	.15
724 A210	40d Children with posters	.20	.15
725 A210	40d Shopping street	.20	.15
726 A210	40d Playground	.20	.15
727 A210	40d shown	.20	.15
a.	Strip of 5, #723-727	1.00	.75

Children's Day.

Clenched Fist, Made of Bricks A211

1978, Mar. 22

728 A211	30d multicolored	.65	.15
729 A211	115d multicolored	1.20	.38

Determination of Arab people.

Blood Pressure Gauge, WHO Emblem — A212

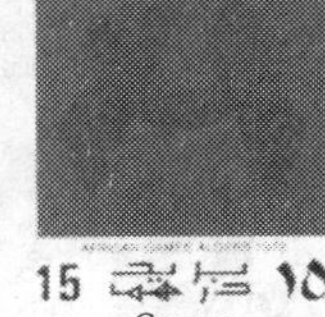

Games Emblem — A214

Antenna and ITU Emblem A213

1978, Apr. 7 *Perf. 13x12½*

730 A212	30d multicolored	.16	.15
731 A212	115d multicolored	.55	.38

World Health Day, drive against hypertension.

1978, May 17 Photo. *Perf. 13½*

732 A213	30d silver & multi	.16	.15
733 A213	115d gold & multi	.55	.38

10th World Telecommunications Day.

1978, July 13 Litho. *Perf. 12½*

734 A214	15d multicolored	.15	.15
735 A214	30d multicolored	.15	.15
736 A214	115d multicolored	.60	.38
	Nos. 734-736 (3)	.90	
	Set value		.50

3rd African Games, Algiers, 1978.

Inauguration of Tripoli International Airport — A215

1978, Aug. 10 Litho. *Perf. 13½*

737 A215	40d shown	*.50*	.15
738 A215	115d Terminal	*1.50*	.38

View of Ankara — A216

Soldiers, Jet, Ship — A217

1978, Aug. 17

739 A216	30d multicolored	*.42*	.15
740 A216	35d multicolored	*.45*	.15
741 A216	115d multicolored	*1.50*	.38
	Nos. 739-741 (3)	*2.37*	
	Set value		.55

Turkish-Libyan friendship.

1978, Sept. 1 *Perf. 14½*

Designs: 35d, Tower, Green Book, oil derrick. 100d, View of Tripoli with mosque and modern buildings. 115d, View of Tripoli within cogwheel.

742 A217	30d multicolored	*.42*	.15
743 A217	35d org & multi	*.45*	.15
744 A217	115d blue & multi	*1.50*	.38
	Nos. 742-744 (3)	*2.37*	
	Set value		.55

Souvenir Sheet

745 A217 100d multicolored *2.50* .50

9th anniversary of Sept. 1 Revolution. No. 745 contains one stamp 50x41mm.

Quarry and Symposium Emblem — A218

Designs: 40d, Oasis lake. 115d, Crater.

1978, Sept. 16 *Perf. 13½*

746 A218	30d multicolored	*.20*	.15
747 A218	40d multicolored	*.38*	.15
748 A218	115d multicolored	*.60*	.38
	Nos. 746-748 (3)	*1.18*	
	Set value		.56

2nd Symposium on Libyan Geology.

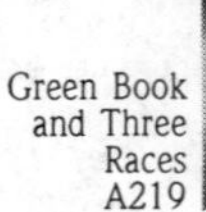

Green Book and Three Races
A219

1978, Oct. 18 *Perf. 12½*

749 A219 30d multicolored .15 .15
750 A219 40d multicolored .20 .15
751 A219 115d multicolored .45 .38
Nos. 749-751 (3) .80
Set value .56

International Anti-Apartheid Year.

Pilgrims, Minarets, Holy Kaaba
A220

1978, Nov. 9 Photo. *Perf. 12*

752 A220 5d multicolored .15 .15
753 A220 10d multicolored .15 .15
754 A220 15d multicolored .15 .15
755 A220 20d multicolored .15 .15
Set value .30 .22

Pilgrimage to Mecca.

Handclasp over Globe — A221

Fists, Guns, Map of Israel — A222

1978, Nov. 10 Litho. *Perf. 13½*

756 A221 30d multicolored *.42* .15
757 A221 40d multicolored *.50* .15
758 A221 115d multicolored *1.50* .38
Nos. 756-758 (3) *2.42*
Set value .56

Technical Cooperation Among Developing Countries Conference, Buenos Aires, Argentina, Sept. 1978.

1978, Dec. 5 Litho. *Perf. 13½*

Designs: 40d, 115d, Map of Arab countries and Israel, eagle and crowd, horiz. 145d, like 30d.

759 A222 30d multicolored .22 .15
760 A222 40d multicolored .40 .15
761 A222 115d multicolored .70 .38
762 A222 145d multicolored 1.40 .40
Nos. 759-762 (4) 2.72 1.08

Anti-Israel Summit Conf., Baghdad, Dec. 2-8.

Scales, Globe and Human Rights Flame — A223

Libyan Fort and Horse Racing — A224

1978, Dec. 10

763 A223 15d multicolored *.20* .15
764 A223 30d multicolored *.30* .15
765 A223 115d multicolored *.60* .38
Nos. 763-765 (3) *1.10* .68

Universal Declaration of Human Rights, 30th anniv.

1978, Dec. 11

766 A224 20d multicolored *.38* .15
767 A224 40d multicolored *.50* .15
768 A224 115d multicolored *1.50* .38
Nos. 766-768 (3) *2.38*
Set value .55

Libyan Study Center.

Lilienthal's Glider, 1896 — A225

Mounted Stag's Head — A226

Designs: 25d, Spirit of St. Louis, 1927. 30d, Adm. Byrd's Polar flight, 1929. 50d, Graf Zeppelin, 1934, hydroplane and storks. 115d, Wilbur and Orville Wright and Flyer A. No. 774, Icarus falling. No. 775, Eagle and Boeing 727.

1978, Dec. 26 Litho. *Perf. 14*

769 A225 20d multicolored .15 .15
770 A225 25d multicolored .15 .15
771 A225 30d multicolored .16 .15
772 A225 50d multicolored .20 .15
773 A225 115d multicolored .50 .38
Nos. 769-773 (5) 1.16
Set value .72

Souvenir Sheets

774 A225 100d multicolored .55 .55
775 A225 100d multicolored .55 .55

75th anniversary of 1st powered flight. Nos. 769-773 issued also in sheets of 4.

Coil Stamps

1979, Jan. 15 Photo. *Perf. 14½x14*

776 A226 5d multicolored *.35* .15
777 A226 20d multicolored *.50* .15
778 A226 50d multicolored *.65* .15
Nos. 776-778 (3) *1.50*
Set value .22

Carpobrotus Acinaciformis
A227

Flora of Libya: 15d, Caralluma europaea. 20d, Arum cirenaicum. 35d, Lavatera arborea. 40d, Capparis spinosa. 50d, Ranunculus asiaticus.

1979, May 15 Litho. *Perf. 14*

779 A227 10d multicolored .15 .15
780 A227 15d multicolored .15 .15
781 A227 20d multicolored .15 .15
782 A227 35d multicolored .28 .18
783 A227 40d multicolored .28 .18
784 A227 50d multicolored .35 .22
Set value 1.12 .75

People, Torch, Olive Branches — A228

1979 Litho. *Perf. 13x12½*

Size: 18x23mm

785 A228 5d multi *.15* .15
786 A228 10d multi *.15* .15
787 A228 15d multi *.15* .15
788 A228 30d multi *.30* .15
789 A228 50d multi *.38* .15
790 A228 60d multi *.42* .15
791 A228 70d multi *.48* .15
792 A228 100d multi *.75* .18
793 A228 115d multi *1.10* .20

Perf. 13½

Size: 26½x32mm

794 A228 200d multi *1.20* .35
795 A228 500d multi *2.25* .70
796 A228 1000d multi *5.00* 1.75
Nos. 785-796 (12) *12.33*
Set value 3.60

See Nos. 1053-1055.

Tortoise
A229

Animals: 10d, Antelope. 15d, Hedgehog. 20d, Porcupine. 30d, Arabian camel. 35d, African wild-cat. 45d, Gazelle. 115d, Cheetah. 10d, 30d, 35d, 45d, vert.

1979, Feb. 1 Litho. *Perf. 14½*

797 A229 5d multicolored .15 .15
798 A229 10d multicolored .15 .15
799 A229 15d multicolored .15 .15
800 A229 20d multicolored .15 .15
801 A229 30d multicolored .15 .15
802 A229 35d multicolored .20 .15
803 A229 45d multicolored .25 .20
804 A229 115d multicolored .55 .35
Set value 1.40 .90

Rug and Tripoli Fair Emblem — A230

Tripoli Fair emblem and various rugs.

1979, Mar. 1 Litho. *Perf. 11*

805 A230 10d multicolored .15 .15
806 A230 15d multicolored .15 .15
807 A230 30d multicolored .15 .15
808 A230 45d multicolored .15 .15
809 A230 115d multicolored .50 .38
Set value .90 .60

17th Tripoli Fair.

Shepherd, Sheep and Dog
A231

Children's drawings and IYC emblem.

1979, Mar. 20 *Perf. 13½*

810 A231 20d Families and planes .50 .15
811 A231 20d shown .50 .15
812 A231 20d Beach umbrellas .50 .15
813 A231 20d Boat in storm .50 .15
814 A231 20d Traffic policeman .50 .15
a. Strip of 5, #810-814 2.50 1.25

Intl. Year of the Child.

Book, World Map, Arab Achievements
A232

1979, Mar. 22 *Perf. 13*

815 A232 45d multicolored .20 .15
816 A232 70d multicolored .30 .20

WMO Emblem, Weather Map and Tower — A233

1979, Mar. 23

817 A233 15d multicolored .15 .15
818 A233 30d multicolored .15 .15
819 A233 50d multicolored .20 .15
Set value .38 .25

World Meteorological Day.

Medical Services, WHO Emblem
A234

1979, Apr. 7

820 A234 40d multicolored .18 .15

Farmer Plowing and Sheep — A235

1979, Sept. 1 Litho. *Perf. 14½*

821 Block of 4 .30 .20
a. A235 15d shown .15 .15
b. A235 15d Men holding Green Book .15 .15
c. A235 15d Oil field .15 .15
d. A235 15d Oil refinery .15 .15
822 Block of 4 .60 .38
a. A235 30d Dish antenna .15 .15
b. A235 30d Hospital .15 .15
c. A235 30d Doctor examining patient .15 .15
d. A235 30d Surgery .15 .15
823 Block of 4 .75 .42
a. A235 40d Street, Tripoli .18 .15
b. A235 40d Steel mill .18 .15
c. A235 40d Tanks .18 .15
d. A235 40d Tuareg horsemen .18 .15
824 Block of 4 1.50 .80
a. A235 70d Revolutionaries, Green Book .35 .20
b. A235 70d Crowd, map of Libya .35 .20
c. A235 70d Mullah .35 .20
d. A235 70d Student .35 .20
Nos. 821-824 (4) 3.15 1.80

Souvenir Sheets

Imperf

825 A235 50d Revolution symbols, Green Book .80 .65
826 A235 50d Monument .80 .65

Sept. 1st revolution, 10th anniversary.

Volleyball — A236

1979, Sept. 10

827 A236 45d shown .25 .15
828 A236 115d Soccer .60 .30

Universiade '79 World University Games, Mexico City, Sept.

Mediterranean Games, Split, Yugoslavia — A237

1979, Sept. 15 Litho. *Perf. 12x11½*

829 A237	15d multicolored	.16	.15
830 A237	30d multicolored	.35	.15
831 A237	70d multicolored	.65	.22
	Nos. 829-831 (3)	1.16	
	Set value		.36

Exhibition Emblem — A238

1979, Sept. 25 Photo. *Perf. 11½x11*

832 A238	45d multicolored	.28	.15
833 A238	115d multicolored	.75	.30

TELECOM '79, 3rd World Telecommunications Exhibition, Geneva, Sept. 20-26.

Seminar Emblem, Green Book, Crowd — A239

1979, Oct. 1

834 A239	10d shown	.15	.15

Size: 67x43½mm

835 A239	35d Meeting hall	.28	.15

Size: 32x43½mm

836 A239	100d Col. Khadafy	.65	.30
a.	Miniature sheet, imperf.	.90	.60
	Nos. 834-836 (3)	1.08	
	Set value		.46

Intl. Seminar of the Green Book, Benghazi, Oct. 1-3. Nos. 834-836 se-tenant in continuous design. No. 836a contains an imperf. design similar to type A239.

Evacuation of Foreign Forces — A240

1979, Oct. 7

837 A240	30d shown	.26	.15
838 A240	40d Tuareg horsemen	.38	.15
	Set value		.22

Souvenir Sheet

Imperf

839 A240	100d Vignettes	.40	.40

Cyclist, Championship Emblem — A241

1979, Nov. 21

840 A241	15d shown	.15	.15
841 A241	30d Cyclists, emblem, diff.	.25	.15
	Set value		.15

Junior Cycling Championships, Tripoli, Nov. 21-23. Issued in sheetlets of 4.

Hurdles, Olympic Rings, Moscow '80 Emblem — A242

1979, Nov. 21

842 A242	45d Equestrian	.18	.15
843 A242	60d Javelin	.28	.15
844 A242	115d shown	.60	.20
845 A242	160d Soccer	.75	.28
	Nos. 842-845 (4)	1.81	.78

Souvenir Sheets

846 A242	150d like #844	1.25	.65
847 A242	150d like #845	2.50	.65

Pre-Olympics (Moscow '80 Olympic Games). Nos. 842-845 issued in sheetlets of 4 and sheets of 20 (4x5) with silver Moscow '80 Emblem covering background of every 20 stamps.

Intl. Day of Cooperation with Palestinian People — A242a

1979, Nov. 29 Photo. *Perf. 12*

847A A242a	30d multicolored	.20	.15
847B A242a	115d multicolored	.70	.40

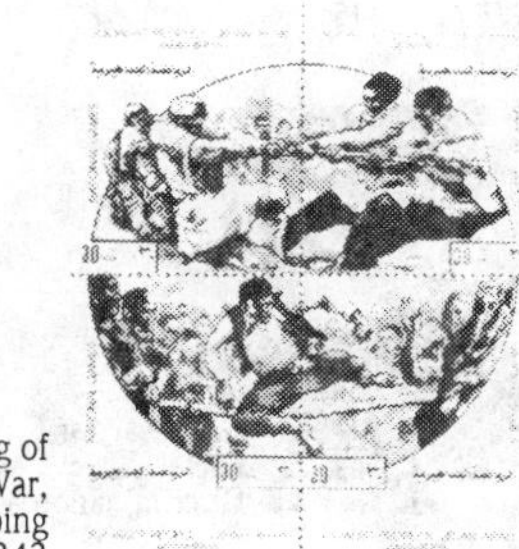

Tug of War, Jumping A243

National Games: No. 848, Polo, leap frog. No. 849, Racing, ball game, No. 850, Wrestling, log rolling. No. 852, Horsemen.

1980, Feb. 15

848 A243	Block of 4	.40	.40
a.-d.	10d, single stamp	.15	.15
849 A243	Block of 4	.50	.40
a.-d.	15d, single stamp	.15	.15
850 A243	Block of 4	.70	.40
a.-d.	20d, single stamp	.16	.15
851 A243	Block of 4	1.00	.65
a.-d.	30d, single stamp	.25	.16
852 A243	Block of 4	1.65	1.00
a.-d.	45d, single stamp	.40	.25
	Nos. 848-852 (5)	4.25	2.85

Battle of Gardabia, 1915 — A244

1980 Litho. *Perf. 14½*

853 A244	20d shown	.24	.15
854 A244	20d Shoghab, 1913	.24	.15
855 A244	20d Fundugh Al-Shibani, 1922	.24	.15
856 A244	20d Ghira	.24	.15
857 A244	35d Gardabia, diff.	.45	.15
858 A244	35d Shoghab, diff.	.45	.15
859 A244	35d Fundugh Al-Shibani, diff.	.45	.15
860 A244	35d Ghira, diff.	.45	.15
	Nos. 853-860 (8)	2.76	
	Set value		.88

Issue dates: Gardabia, Apr. 28. Shoghab, May 25. Fundugh Al-Shibani, June 1. Ghira, Aug. 15. Stamps of same battle se-tenant in continuous design.

See Nos. 893-900, 921-944, 980-1003, 1059-1082.

Girl Guides Examining Plant — A245

1980, Aug. 22 *Perf. 13½*

861 A245	15d shown	.15	.15
862 A245	30d Guides cooking	.30	.15
863 A245	50d Scouts at campfire	.48	.30
864 A245	115d Scouts reading map	1.25	.60
	Nos. 861-864 (4)	2.18	1.20

Souvenir Sheets

865 A245	100d like #861	1.00	.50
866 A245	100d like #863	1.00	.50

8th Pan Arab Girl Guide and 14th Pan Arab Scout Jamborees, Aug.

Men Holding OPEC Emblem — A246

1980, Sept. 15 *Perf. 14½*

867 A246	45d Emblem, globe	.50	.15
868 A246	115d shown	1.10	.60

20th anniversary of OPEC.

Martyrdom of Omar Muktar, 1931 — A247

1980, Sept. 16

869 A247	20d multicolored	.15	.15
870 A247	35d multicolored	.45	.15
	Set value		.20

Souvenir Sheet

870A A247	100d multicolored	1.90	1.90

UNESCO Emblem and Avicenna — A248

1980, Sept. 20

871 A248	45d Scientific symbols	.70	.15
872 A248	115d shown	1.65	.60

School Scientific Exhibition, Sept. 20-24 and birth millenium of Arab physician Avicenna (115d).

18th Tripoli Fair — A249

Various musical instruments. 15d vert.

1980 Litho. *Perf. 13½*

873 A249	5d multicolored	.15	.15
874 A249	10d multicolored	.15	.15
875 A249	15d multicolored	.18	.15
876 A249	20d multicolored	.25	.15
877 A249	25d multicolored	.32	.18
	Nos. 873-877 (5)	1.05	
	Set value		.25

Souvenir Sheet

878 A249	100d Musicians	1.25	1.25

World Olive Oil Year A250

1980, Jan. 15 Litho. *Perf. 13½*

879 A250	15d multicolored	.15	.15
880 A250	30d multicolored	.28	.15
881 A250	45d multicolored	.45	.22
	Nos. 879-881 (3)	.88	.52
	Set value		.42

Intl. Year of the Child (1979) A251

Children's drawings: a, Riding horses. b, water sports. c, Fish. d, Gift sale. e, Preparing feast.

1980, Mar. 21

882	Strip of 5	1.25	.60
a.-e.	A251 20d any single	.24	.15

The Hegira, 1500th Anniv. A252

1980, Apr. 1

883 A252	50d multicolored	.48	.24
884 A252	115d multicolored	1.10	.55

Operating Room, Hospital — A253

1980, Apr. 7 Litho. *Perf. 13½*

885 A253	20d multicolored	.30	.15
886 A253	50d multicolored	.70	.38

World Health Day.

Sheik Zarruq Festival, Misurata, June 16-20
A254

Arabian Towns Organization
A255

1980, June 16

887 A254 40d multicolored .52 .24
888 A254 115d multicolored 1.25 .65

Souvenir Sheet

889 A254 100d multicolored 1.25 1.25

1980, July 1 *Perf. 11½x12*

890 A255 15d Ghadames .15 .15
891 A255 30d Derna .38 .15
892 A255 50d Tripoli .60 .30
Nos. 890-892 (3) 1.13 .60

Battles Type of 1980

1980 *Perf. 13½*

893 A244 20d Yefren, 1915 .25 .15
894 A244 20d El Hani, 1911 .25 .15
895 A244 20d Sebha, 1914 .25 .15
896 A244 20d Sirt, 1912 .25 .15
897 A244 35d Yefren, diff. .45 .30
898 A244 35d El Hani, diff. .45 .30
899 A244 35d Sebha, diff. .45 .30
900 A244 35d Sirt, diff. .45 .30
Nos. 893-900 (8) 2.80 1.80

Issue dates: Yefren, July 16. El Hani, Oct. 23. Sebha, Nov. 27. Sirt, Dec. 31. Stamps of same battle printed se-tenant in a continuous design.

Sept. 1 Revolution, 11th Anniv.
A256

Achievements of the Revolution.

1980, Sept. 1

901 A256 5d Oil industry .15 .15
902 A256 10d Youth festival .15 .15
903 A256 15d Agriculture .15 .15
904 A256 25d Transportation .30 .15
905 A256 40d Education .50 .24
906 A256 115d Housing 1.40 .65
Nos. 901-906 (6) 2.65
Set value 1.25

Souvenir Sheet

907 A256 100d Montage of achievements 1.25 1.25

No. 907 contains one stamp 30x50mm.

World Tourism Conference
A257

1980, Sept. 10

908 A257 45d multicolored .50 .30
909 A257 115d multicolored 1.40 .65

Intl. Year of the Disabled — A258

1981, Jan. 1 *Perf. 15*

910 A258 20d multicolored .24 .15
911 A258 45d multicolored .55 .30
912 A258 115d multicolored 1.25 .65
Nos. 910-912 (3) 2.04 1.10

Redrawn

1981, Nov. 21 Litho. *Perf. 15*

913 A258 45d multicolored .55 .30
914 A258 115d multicolored 1.25 .65

UPA Disabled Persons Campaign. Design redrawn to include Arab League Emblem.

Mosaics
A259

1981, Jan. 15 *Perf. 13½*

915 A259 10d Horse .15 .15
916 A259 20d Sailing ship .20 .15
917 A259 30d Peacocks .30 .15
918 A259 40d Panther .45 .15
919 A259 50d Musician .55 .25
920 A259 115d Fish 1.25 .60
Nos. 915-920 (6) 2.90 1.45

Battles Type of 1980

Perf. 13½, 14½ (#926, 932, 938, 944)

1981

921 A244 20d Dernah, 1912 .50 .16
922 A244 20d Bir Tagreft, 1928 .50 .16
923 A244 20d Tawargha, 1923 .50 .16
924 A244 20d Zuara, 1912 .50 .16
925 A244 20d Funduk El-Jamel Misurata, 1915 .50 .16
926 A244 20d Sidi El-Khemri, 1915 .35 .16
927 A244 20d El-Khoms, 1913 .50 .16
928 A244 20d Roghdalin, 1912 .50 .16
929 A244 20d Rughbat El-Naga, 1925 .50 .16
930 A244 20d Tobruk, 1911 .50 .16
931 A244 20d Bir Ikshadia, 1924 .35 .16
932 A244 20d Ain Zara, 1924 .50 .16
933 A244 35d Dernah, diff. .80 .30
934 A244 35d Bir Tagreft, diff. .80 .30
935 A244 35d Tawargha, diff. .80 .30
936 A244 35d Zuara, diff. .80 .30
937 A244 35d Funduk El-Jamel Misurata, diff. .80 .30
938 A244 35d Sidi El-Khemri, diff. .80 .30
939 A244 35d El-Khoms, diff. .80 .30
940 A244 35d Roghdalin, diff. .80 .30
941 A244 35d Rughbat El-Naga, diff. .80 .30
942 A244 35d Tobruk, diff. .80 .30
943 A244 35d Bir Ikshadia, diff. .80 .30
944 A244 35d Ain Zara, diff. .80 .30
Nos. 921-944 (24) 15.30 5.52

Issue dates: Dernah, Jan. 17. Bir Tagreft, Feb. 25. Tawargha, Mar. 20. Zuara, Apr. 13. Funduk El-Jamel Misurata, May 26. Sidi El-Khemri, June 4. El-Khoms, July 27. Roghdalin, Aug. 15. Rughbat El-Naga, Sept. 16. Tobruk, Oct. 27. Bir Ikshadia, Nov. 19. Ain Zara, Dec. 4. Stamps of the same battle printed se-tenant in a continuous design.

Tripoli Intl. Fair — A260

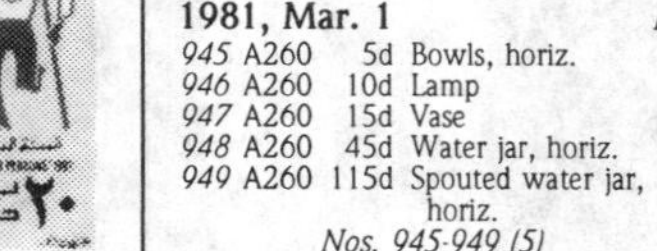

No. 707b, Crowd — A261

Ceramicware.

1981, Mar. 1 *Perf. 13½*

945 A260 5d Bowls, horiz. .15 .15
946 A260 10d Lamp .15 .15
947 A260 15d Vase .20 .15
948 A260 45d Water jar, horiz. .65 .25
949 A260 115d Spouted water jar, horiz. 1.50 .85
Nos. 945-949 (5) 2.65 1.55

1981, Mar. 2 *Perf. 15*

950 A261 50d multicolored .50 .15
951 A261 115d multicolored 1.10 .55

People's Authority Declaration, The Green Book.

Children's Day, IYC — A262

Children's illustrations: a, Desert camp. b, Women doing chores. c, Village scene. d, Airplane over playground. e, Minaret, camel, man.

1981, Mar. 21 Litho. *Perf. 13½*

952 Strip of 5 1.25 .60
a.-e. A262 20d any single .24 .15

Bank of Libya, 25th Anniv. — A263

1981, Apr. 1 Litho. *Perf. 13½*

953 A263 45d multicolored .48 .20
954 A263 115d multicolored 1.25 .60

Souvenir Sheet

955 A263 50d multicolored 1.10 1.10

World Health Day — A264

1981, Apr. 7 *Perf. 14*

956 A264 45d multicolored .60 .25
957 A264 115d multicolored 1.50 .75

Intl. Year for Combating Racial Discrimination — A265

1981, July 1 *Perf. 15*

958 A265 45d multicolored .55 .15
959 A265 50d multicolored .65 .15

September 1 Revolution, 12th Anniv. — A266

Designs: #960a-960b, Helicopter and jets. #960c-960d, Paratroopers. #961a-961b, Tanks. #961c-961d, Frogman parade. #962a-962b, Twelve-barrel rocket launchers. #962c-962d, Trucks with rockets. #963a-963b, Sailor parade. #963c-963d, Jeep and trucks with twelve-barrel rocket launchers. #964a-964b, Wheeled tanks and jeeps. #964c-964d, Tank parade.

1981, Sept. 1 *Perf. 14½*

960 Block of 4 .20 .20
a.-d. A266 5d, any single .15 .15
961 Block of 4 .22 .20
a.-d. A266 10d, any single .15 .15
962 Block of 4 .32 .20
a.-d. A266 15d, any single .15 .15
963 Block of 4 .42 .22
a.-d. A266 20d, any single .15 .15
964 Block of 4 .55 .25
a.-d. A266 25d, any single .15 .15
Nos. 961-964 (4) 1.51 .87

Souvenir Sheet

Perf. 11

965 A266 50d Naval troop marching *1.25* .35

Horizontal pairs within 960-964 printed in continuous designs. Nos. 960-962 vert.

No. 965 contains one stamp 63x38mm.

Miniature Sheet

Butterflies — A267

1981, Oct. 1 *Perf. 14½*

966 Sheet of 16 *5.50*
a.-d. A267 5d, any single *.15* .15
e.-h. A267 10d, any single *.20* .15
i.-l. A267 15d, any single *.30* .15
m.-p. A267 25d, any single *.45* .15

Nos. 966a-966p printed se-tenant in a continuous design, stamps of same denomination in blocks of 4. Sheetlets exist containing blocks of 4 for each denomination.

World Food Day — A268

1981, Oct. 16 *Perf. 15*

967 A268 45d multicolored .45 .15
968 A268 200d multicolored 2.25 1.10

Fruit — A269

1981, Nov. 17 *Perf. 13½*

969 A269 5d Grapes .15 .15
970 A269 10d Dates .15 .15
971 A269 15d Lemons .22 .15
972 A269 20d Oranges .30 .15
973 A269 35d Cactus fruit .45 .15
974 A269 55d Pomegranates .60 .15
Nos. 969-974 (6) 1.87
Set value .50

Miniature Sheet

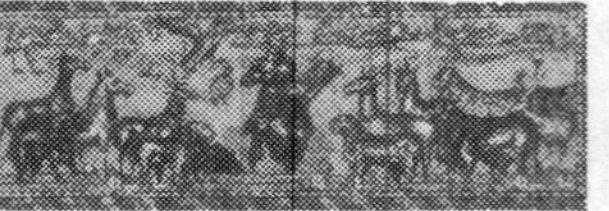

Orpheus Playing Music to the Animals — A270

Mosaics: d, Fish. e, Fishermen. f, Fish in basket. g, Farm yard. h, Birds eating fruit. i, Milking a goat. Illustration reduced.

1982, Jan. 1 *Perf. 13½*

975 Sheet of 9 5.00
a.-i. A270 45d any single .50 .22

Nos. 975a-975c, shown in illustration, printed in continuous design.

3rd Intl. Koran Reading Contest — A271

Designs: 10d, Stone tablets, Holy Ka'aba, Mecca. 35d, Open Koran, creation of the world. 115d, Scholar, students.

1982, Jan. 7

976 A271 10d multicolored .15 .15
977 A271 35d multicolored .40 .18
978 A271 115d multicolored 1.25 .55
Nos. 976-978 (3) 1.80 .88

Souvenir Sheet

979 A271 100d like 115d 1.25 1.25

Battles Type of 1980

Perf. 13½, 14½ (#985-988, 997-1000)

1982

980 A244 20d Hun Gioffra, 1915 .50 .24
981 A244 20d Gedabia, 1914 .50 .24
982 A244 20d El-Asaba, 1913 .50 .24
983 A244 20d El-Habela, 1917 .50 .24
984 A244 20d Suk El-Ahad, 1915 .50 .24
985 A244 20d El-Tangi, 1913 .50 .24
986 A244 20d Sokna, 1913 .50 .24
987 A244 20d Wadi Smalus, 1925 .50 .24
988 A244 20d Sidi Abuagela, 1917 .50 .24
989 A244 20d Sidi Surur, 1914 .50 .24
990 A244 20d Kuefia, 1911 .50 .24
991 A244 20d Abunjeim, 1940 .50 .24
992 A244 35d Hun Gioffra, diff. .90 .45
993 A244 35d Gedabia, diff. .90 .45
994 A244 35d El-Asaba, diff. .90 .45
995 A244 35d El-Habela, diff. .90 .45
996 A244 35d Suk El-Ahad, diff. .90 .45
997 A244 35d El-Tangi, diff. .90 .45
998 A244 35d Sokna, diff. .90 .45
999 A244 35d Wadi Smalus, diff. .90 .45
1000 A244 35d Sidi Abuagela, diff. .90 .45
1001 A244 35d Sidi Surur, diff. .90 .45
1002 A244 35d Kuefia, diff. .90 .45
1003 A244 35d Abunjeim, diff. .90 .45
Nos. 980-1003 (24) 16.80 8.28

Issued: #980, 992, Jan. 26; #981, 993, Mar. 8; #982, 994, Mar. 23; #983, 995, Apr. 24; #984, 996, May 15; #985, 997, June 19; #986, 998, July 23; #987, 999, Aug. 11; #988, 1000, Sept. 4; #989, 1001, Oct. 14; #990, 1002, Nov. 28; #991, 1003, Dec. 13. Stamps of same battle printed se-tenant in a continuous design.

Tripoli Intl. Fair — A272

1982, Mar. 1 ***Perf. 13x12½***

1004 A272 5d Grinding stone .15 .15
1005 A272 10d Ox-drawn plow .18 .15
1006 A272 25d Pitching hay .30 .15
1007 A272 35d Tapestry weaving .42 .15
1008 A272 45d Traditional cooking .45 .22
1009 A272 100d Grain harvest 1.10 .55
Nos. 1004-1009 (6) 2.60
Set value 1.20

People's Authority Declaration, The Green Book — A273

1982, Mar. 2 ***Perf. 13½***

1010 Strip of 3 7.50 3.50
a. A273 100d Harvester combine 1.10 .48
b. A273 200d Khadafy, scholar, rifles 2.50 1.10
c. A273 300d Govt. building, citizens 3.75 1.50

Scouting Movement, 75th Anniv. A274

13th African Soccer Cup Championships A275

1982, Mar. 2

1011 Strip of 4 10.00 5.00
a. A274 100d Cub scout, blimp 1.00 .50
b. A274 200d Scouts, dog 2.00 1.00
c. A274 300d Scholar, scout 3.00 1.40
d. A274 400d Boy scout, rocket 4.00 2.00

Souvenir Sheets

1012 A274 500d Green Book 5.00 5.00
1013 A274 500d Khadafy, scouts 5.00 5.00

Nos. 1012-1013 each contain one stamp 39x42mm.

1982, Mar. 5

1014 A275 100d multi 1.00 .50
1015 A275 200d multi 2.00 1.00

1982 World Cup Soccer Championships, Spain — A276

World Cup trophy and various soccer plays.

1982, Mar. 15 ***Perf. 14½***

1016 A276 45d multi .45 .22
1017 A276 100d multi 1.00 .50
1018 A276 200d multi 2.00 1.00
1019 A276 300d multi 3.00 1.65
Nos. 1016-1019 (4) 6.45 3.37

Souvenir Sheets

1020 A276 500d like 45d 5.00 5.00
1021 A276 500d like 100d 5.00 5.00

Nos. 1016-1019 issued in sheets of 8 overprinted in silver with soccer ball in motion. Sheetlets of 4 in each denomination exist without overprint.

Nos. 1020-1021 have Arabic text in green on reverse.

Palestinian Children's Day — A277

Designs: a, Two children. b, Girl with bowl. c, Girl with kaffiyeh. d, Girl hiding. e, Boy.

1982, Mar. 7 ***Perf. 13½***

1022 Strip of 5 2.00 .85
a.-e. A277 20d, any single .35 .16

Birds — A278

Arab Postal Union, 30th — A280

Teaching Hospitals Anniv. A279

Miniature Sheet

1982, Apr. 1 ***Perf. 14½***

1023 Sheet of 16 9.00
a.-d. A278 15d, any single .15 .15
e.-h. A278 25d, any single .35 .15
i.-l. A278 45d, any single .60 .22
m.-p. A278 95d, any single .95 .45

No. 1023a-1023p printed se-tenant in a continuous design; stamps of same denomination in blocks of 4.

1982, Apr. 7 ***Perf. 13x12½***

1024 A279 95d multi .90 .45
1025 A279 100d multi 1.00 .50
1026 A279 205d multi 2.00 1.00
Nos. 1024-1026 (3) 3.90 1.95

1982, Apr. 12 ***Perf. 13½***

1027 A280 100d multi 1.00 .50
1028 A280 200d multi 2.00 1.00

1982 World Chess Championships — A281

Board positions and chessmen: a, Chinese piece. b, African piece. c, Modern piece. d, European piece.

1982, May 1

1029 Block of 4 4.00 1.75
a.-d. A281 100d, any single 1.00 .40

Souvenir Sheet

1030 A281 500d Overhead view of chessboard 5.00 5.00

No. 1030 contains one stamp 39x42mm.

World Telecommunications Day — A282

1982, May 17

1031 A282 100d multi 1.00 .50
1032 A282 200d multi 2.00 1.00

Map of Libya, Green Book — A283

1982, June 11

1033 A283 200d multi 2.00 .75

Souvenir Sheet

1034 A283 300d multi 3.75 3.75

Post Day, FIP 51st anniv.

Organization of African Unity, 19th Summit — A284

1982, Aug. 5 ***Perf. 14***

1035 A284 50d OAU flag, Arab family .50 .25
1036 A284 100d Map of Africa, emblem 1.00 .50

Size: 69x40mm

1037 A284 200d Khadafy, Green Book 2.00 1.00
Nos. 1035-1037 (3) 3.50 1.75

Souvenir Sheet

Perf. 13x13½

1038 A284 300d Fist, map 3.75 3.75

No. 1038 contains one stamp 29x42mm.

September 1 Revolution, 13th Anniv. — A285

Khadafy in uniforms and various armed forces' exercises.

1982, Sept. 1 ***Perf. 11½***

1039 A285 15d multi *.24* .15
1040 A285 20d multi *.30* .15
1041 A285 30d multi *.32* .15
1042 A285 45d multi *.50* .16
1043 A285 70d multi *.65* .24
1044 A285 100d multi *.90* .38
Nos. 1039-1044 (6) *2.91* 1.23

Souvenir Sheet

Imperf

1045 A285 200d multi *2.50 2.50*

Libyan Red Crescent, 25th Anniv. — A286

Intl. Day of Cooperation with Palestinian People — A287

1982, Oct. 5 ***Perf. 13½***

1046 A286 100d Palm tree 1.00 .50
1047 A286 200d "25," crescents 2.00 1.00

1982, Nov. 29

1048 A287 100d gray grn & blk 1.25 .48
1049 A287 200d brt bl, gray grn & blk 2.75 .90

Al-Fateh University Symposium on Khadafy's Green Book — A288

1982, Dec. 1 ***Perf. 12***

1050 A288 100d Khadafy in uniform *1.00* .25
1051 A288 200d Khadafy, map, Green Book *2.00* .50

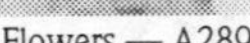
Flowers — A289

Customs Cooperation Council, 30th Anniv. — A290

Miniature Sheet

Designs: a, Philadelphus. b, Hypericum. c, Antinhinum. d, Lily. e, Capparis. f, Tropaeolum. g, Rose. h, Chrysanthemum. i, Nigella damascena. j, Gaillardia lanceolata. k, Dahlia. l, Dianthus carophyllus. m, Notobasis syriaca. n, Nerium oleander. o, Iris histriodes. p, Scolymus hispanicus.

1983, Jan. 1 *Perf. 14½*
1052 Sheet of 16 5.00
a.-p. A289 25d, any single .30 .20

Torch Type of 1979

1983, Jan. 2 *Perf. 13½*
Size: 26½x32mm
1053 A228 250d multi 3.50 1.10
1054 A228 1500d multi 15.00 6.50
1055 A228 2500d multi 27.50 10.00
Nos. 1053-1055 (3) 46.00 17.60

1983, Jan. 15 *Perf. 14½x14*
1056 A290 25d Arab riding horse .25 .15
1057 A290 50d Riding camel .50 .25
1058 A290 100d Drawing sword 1.00 .50
Nos. 1056-1058 (3) 1.75 .90

Battles Type of 1980

1983 *Perf. 13½*
1059 A244 50d Ghaser Ahmed, 1922 1.25 .70
1060 A244 50d Same, right 1.25 .70
1061 A244 50d Sidi Abuarghub, 1923 1.25 .70
1062 A244 50d Same, right 1.25 .70
1063 A244 50d Ghar Yunes, 1913 1.25 .70
1064 A244 50d Same, right 1.25 .70
1065 A244 50d Bir Otman, 1926 1.25 .70
1066 A244 50d Same, right 1.25 .70
1067 A244 50d Sidi Sajeh, 1922 1.25 .70
1068 A244 50d Same, right 1.25 .70
1069 A244 50d Ras El-Hamam, 1915 1.25 .70
1070 A244 50d Same, right 1.25 .70
1071 A244 50d Zawiet Ishghefa, 1913 1.25 .70
1072 A244 50d Same, right 1.25 .70
1073 A244 50d Wadi Essania, 1930 1.25 .70
1074 A244 50d Same, right 1.25 .70
1075 A244 50d El-Meshiashta, 1917 1.25 .70
1076 A244 50d Same, right 1.25 .70
1077 A244 50d Gharara, 1925 1.25 .70
1078 A244 50d Same, right 1.25 .70
1079 A244 50d Abughelan, 1922 1.25 .70
1080 A244 50d Same, right 1.25 .70
1081 A244 50d Mahruka, 1913 1.25 .70
1082 A244 50d Same, right 1.25 .70
Nos. 1059-1082 (24) 30.00 16.80

Issue dates: #1059-1060, Jan. 26. #1061-1062, Feb. 2. #1063-1064, Mar. 26. #1065-1066, Apr. 9. #1067-1068, May 2. #1069-1070, June 24. #1071-1072, July 13. #1073-1074, Aug. 8. #1075-1076, Sept. 9. #1077-1078, Oct. 22. #1079-1080, Nov. 17. #1081-1082, Dec. 24.

Miniature Sheet

Farm Animals — A291

Designs: a, Camel. b, Cow. c, Horse. d, Bull. e, Goat. f, Dog. g, Sheep. h, Ram. i, Goose. j, Turkey hen. k, Rabbit. l, Pigeon. m, Turkey. n, Rooster. o, Hen. p, Duck.

1983, Feb. 15 *Perf. 14½*
1083 Sheet of 16 5.00
a.-p. A291 25d any single .30 .20

Tripoli Intl. Fair — A292

Libyans playing traditional instruments.

1983, Mar. 5 *Perf. 14½x14, 14x14½*
1084 A292 40d multi, vert. .40 .15
1085 A292 45d multicolored .45 .18
1086 A292 50d multi, vert. .50 .22
1087 A292 55d multicolored .55 .25
1088 A292 75d multi, vert. .75 .40
1089 A292 100d multi, vert. 1.00 .50
Nos. 1084-1089 (6) 3.65 1.70

Intl. Maritime Organization, 25th Anniv. — A293

Early sailing ships.

1983, Mar. 17 *Perf. 14½*
1090 A293 100d Phoenician 1.10 .60
1091 A293 100d Viking 1.10 .60
1092 A293 100d Greek 1.10 .60
1093 A293 100d Roman 1.10 .60
1094 A293 100d Libyan 1.10 .60
1095 A293 100d Pharoah's ship 1.10 .60
Nos. 1090-1095 (6) 6.60 3.60

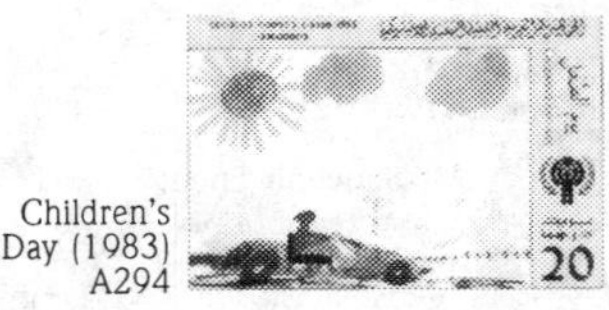
Children's Day (1983) A294

Children's illustrations: a, Car. b, Tractor towing trailer. c, Children, dove. d, Boy Scouts. e, Dinosaur.

1983, Mar. 21 *Perf. 14x14½*
1096 Strip of 5 *3.00* .35
a.-e. A294 20d, any single *.55* .15

1st Intl. Symposium on Khadafy's Green Book — A295

1983, Apr. 1 *Perf. 13½*
1097 A295 50d Khadafy, Green Book, map .42 .15
1098 A295 70d Lecture hall, emblem .60 .20
1099 A295 80d Khadafy, Green Book, emblem .90 .25
Nos. 1097-1099 (3) 1.92 .60

Souvenir Sheet
Perf. 12½
1100 A295 100d Khadafy, Green Books *3.00* 1.25

No. 1100 contains one stamp 57x48mm.

World Health Day A296

1983, Apr. 7 *Perf. 12½*
1101 A296 25d Healthy children, vert. *.25* .15
1102 A296 50d Man in wheelchair, vert. *.52* .16
1103 A296 100d Girl in hospital bed *.85* .32
Nos. 1101-1103 (3) *1.62* .63

Pan-African Economic Committee, 25th Anniv. — A297

1983, Apr. 20 *Perf. 13½*
1104 A297 50d multi .48 .15
1105 A297 100d multi .90 .45
1106 A297 250d multi 2.75 1.25
Nos. 1104-1106 (3) 4.13 1.85

Miniature Sheet

Fish A298

Designs: a, Labrus bimaculatus. b, Trigloporus lastoviza. c, Thalassoma pavo. d, Apogon imberbis. e, Scomber scombrus. f, Spondyliosoma cantharus. g, Trachinus draco. h, Blennius pavo. i, Scorpaena notata. j, Serranus scriba. k, Lophius piscatorius. l, Uranoscopus scaber. m, Auxis thazard. n, Zeus faber. o, Dactylopterus volitans. p, Umbrina cirrosa.

1983, May 15 *Perf. 14½*
1107 Sheet of 16 5.00
a.-p. A298 25d any single .30 .20

Still-life by Gauguin (1848-1903) — A299

Paintings: No. 1108b, Abstract, unattributed. c, The Conquest of Tunis by Charles V, by Rubens. d, Arab Musicians in a Carriage, unattributed.

No. 1109a, Khadafy Glorified on Horseback, unattributed, vert. b, Triumph of David over the Syrians, by Raphael, vert. c, Laborers, unattributed, vert. d, Flower Vase, by van Gogh, vert.

1983, June 1 *Perf. 11*
1108 Strip of 4 2.00 .90
a.-d. A299 50d, any single .50 .20
1109 Strip of 4 2.00 .90
a.-d. A299 50d, any single .50 .20

Souvenir Sheet

Ali Siala — A300

Scientists: No. 1110b, Ali El-Najar.

1983, June 1
1110 Sheet of 2 *2.50* 1.50
a.-b. A300 100d, any single *1.10* .65

1984 Summer Olympic Games, Los Angeles — A301

1983, June 15 *Perf. 13½*
1111 A301 10d Basketball .15 .15
1112 A301 15d High jump .15 .15
1113 A301 25d Running .20 .15
1114 A301 50d Gymnastics .40 .20
1115 A301 100d Wind surfing .90 .40
1116 A301 200d Shot put 1.90 .90
Nos. 1111-1116 (6) 3.70 1.95

Souvenir Sheets
1117 A301 100d Equestrian *1.00 1.00*
1118 A301 100d Soccer *1.00 1.00*

#1111-1116 also exist in miniature sheets of 4.

World Communications Year — A302

1983, July 1 *Perf. 13*
1119 A302 10d multicolored .15 .15
1120 A302 50d multicolored .40 .20
1121 A302 100d multicolored .90 .40
Nos. 1119-1121 (3) 1.45 .75

The Green Book, by Khadafy A303

Ideologies: 10d, The House is to be served by its residents. 15d, Power, wealth and arms are in the hands of the people. 20d, Masters in their own castles, vert. 35d, No democracy without popular congress. 100d, The authority of the people, vert. 140d, The Green Book is the guide of humanity for final release.

1983, Aug. 1 *Perf. 13½*
1122 A303 10d multi .15 .15
1123 A303 15d multi .20 .15
1124 A303 20d multi .25 .15
1125 A303 35d multi .38 .15
1126 A303 100d multi .90 .40
1127 A303 140d multi 1.40 .75
Nos. 1122-1127 (6) 3.28 1.75

Souvenir Sheet
Litho. & Embossed
1128 A303 200d Khadafy in uniform 1.65 1.65

No. 1128 contains one gold embossed stamp 36x51mm.

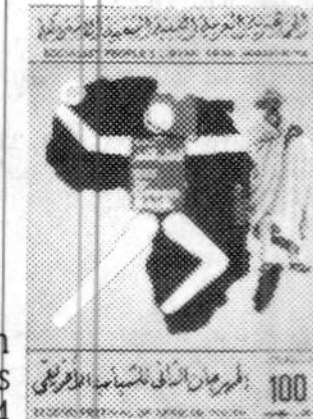
2nd African Youth Sports Festival — A304

Designs: a, Team Handball. b, Basketball. c, Javelin. d, Running. e, Soccer.

1983, Aug. 22 **Litho.**
1129 Strip of 5 5.00 2.75
a.-e. A304 100d, any single 1.00 .50

September 1 Revolution, 14th Anniv. — A305

Women in the Armed Forces.

1983, Sept. 1 *Perf. $11^1/_2$*

1130 A305 65d multi .55 .30
1131 A305 75d multi .75 .40
1132 A305 90d multi .85 .42
1133 A305 100d multi .90 .45
1134 A305 150d multi 1.40 .75
1135 A305 250d multi 2.75 1.25
Nos. 1130-1135 (6) 7.20 3.57

Souvenir Sheet

Perf. 11

1136 A305 200d multi 2.00 2.00

No. 1136 contains one stamp 63x38mm.

2nd Islamic Scout Jamboree — A306

1983, Sept. 2 *Perf. $12^1/_2$*

1137 A306 50d Saluting .60 .18
1138 A306 100d Camping .90 .35

Souvenir Sheet

1139 Sheet of 2 1.25 .90
a. A306 100d like 50d .60 .40

No. 1139 contains Nos. 1138 and 1139a.

Traffic Day A307

Saadun (1893-1923) A308

1983, Oct. 1 *Perf. $14^1/_2$x14*

1140 A307 30d Youth traffic monitors .30 .15
1141 A307 70d Traffic officer .65 .30
1142 A307 200d Motorcycle police 1.90 .90
Nos. 1140-1142 (3) 2.85 1.35

1983, Oct. 11 *Perf. $13^1/_2$*

1143 A308 100d multicolored 1.00 .50

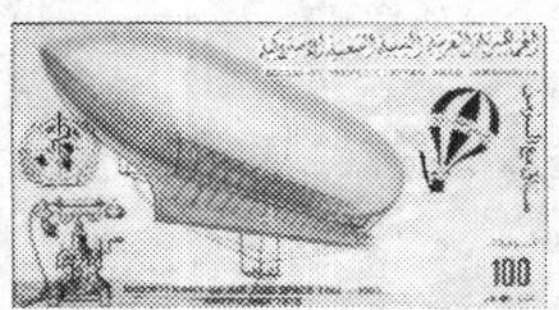

1st Manned Flight, Bicent. — A309

Early aircraft and historic flights: a, Americana, 1910. b, Nulli Secundus, 1907. c, J. B. Meusnier, 1785. d, Blanchard and Jeffries, 1785, vert. e, Pilatre de Rozier, 1784, vert. f, Montgolfiere, Oct. 19, 1783, vert.

1983, Nov. 1

1144 Strip of 6 7.50 3.50
a.-f. A309 100d. any single 1.25 .55

Intl. Day of Cooperation with Palestinian People — A310

1983, Nov. 29 *Perf. $14^1/_2$x14*

1145 A310 30d pale vio & lt bl grn .30 .15
1146 A310 70d lil & lt yel grn .90 .30
1147 A310 200d lt ultra & grn 2.75 .90
Nos. 1145-1147 (3) 3.95 1.35

Miniature Sheet

Roman Mosaic — A311

Designs: Nos. 1148a-1148c, Gladiators. Nos. 1148d-1148f, Musicians, Nos. 1148g-1148i, Hunters. Illustration reduced.

1983, Dec. 1 *Perf. 12*

1148 Sheet of 9 5.50
a.-i. A311 50d, any single .60 .25

#1148a-1148c, 1148d-1148f and 1148g-1148i se-tenant in a continuous design.

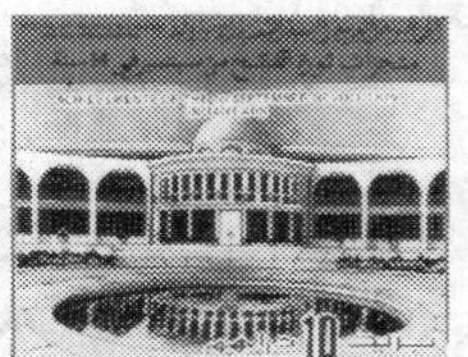

Achievements of the Sept. 1 Revolution — A312

1983, Dec. 15 *Perf. $13^1/_2$*

1149 A312 10d Mosque .15 .15
1150 A312 15d Agriculture .15 .15
1151 A312 20d Industry .22 .15
1152 A312 35d Office building .35 .15
1153 A312 100d Health care .90 .40
1154 A312 140d Airport 1.25 .65
Nos. 1149-1154 (6) 3.02 1.65

Souvenir Sheet

Litho. & Embossed

1155 A312 200d Khadafy 2.50 2.50

No. 1155 contains one gold embossed stamp 36x51mm.

Khadafy, Irrigation Project Survey Map — A313

1983, Dec. 15

1156 A313 150d multicolored 1.50 .75

A314

A315

Famous men: No. 1157a, Mahmud Burkis. No. 1157b, Ahmed El-Bakbak. No. 1157c, Mohamed El-Misurati. No. 1157d, Mahmud Ben Musa. No. 1157e, Abdulhamid Ben Ashiur. No. 1158a, Hosni Fauzi El-Amir. No. 1158b, Ali Haidar El-Saati. No. 1159, Mahmud Mustafa Dreza. No. 1160, Mehdi El-Sherif. No. 1161a, Ali El-Gariani. No. 1161b, Muktar Shakshuki. No. 1161c, Abdurrahman El-Busayri. No. 1161d, Ibbrahim Bakir. No. 1161e, Mahmud El-Janzuri. No. 1162a, Ahmed El-Feghi Hasan. No. 1162b, Bashir El Jawab.

1984 **Litho.** *Perf. $13^1/_2$*

1157 Strip of 5 5.00 2.75
a.-e. A314 100d any single 1.00 .55
1158 Pair 2.25 1.00
a.-b. A314 100d any single 1.10 .50
1159 A314 100d multi 1.10 .50
1160 A315 100d multi 1.10 .50
1161 Strip of 5 10.00 5.00
a.-e. A314 200d any single 2.00 1.00
1162 Pair 4.00 2.25
a.-b. A315 200d any single 2.00 1.10
Nos. 1157-1162 (6) 23.45 12.00

Issued: #1158, 1161-1162, 1/1; others, 2/20.

Miniature Sheet

Water Sports — A316

Designs: a, Two windsurfers. b, Two-man craft. c, Two-man craft, birds. d, Wind sailing, skis. e, Water skier facing front. f, Fisherman in boat. g, Power boating. h, Water skier facing right. i, Fisherman in surf. j, Kayaking. k, Surfing. l, Water skier wearing life jacket. m, Scuba diver sketching underwater. n, Diver. o, Snorkel diver removing fish from harpoon. p, Scuba diver surfacing.

1984, Jan. 10 *Perf. $14^1/_2$*

1164 Sheet of 16 5.00 2.50
a.-p. A316 25d any single .30 .15

African Children's Day — A317

Designs: a, Khadafy, girl scouts. b, Khadafy, children. c, Map, Khadafy, children (size: 63x44mm).

1984, Jan. 15 **Litho.** *Perf. $14^1/_2$*

1165 Strip of 3 1.90 .50
a.-b. A317 50d. any single .42 .15
c. A317 100d multi .80 .20

Women's Emancipation A318

70d, Women, diff., vert. 100d, Soldiers, Khadafy.

1984, Jan. 20 *Perf. 12*

1166 A318 55d multicolored .55 .25
1167 A318 70d multicolored .75 .38
1168 A318 100d multicolored 1.00 .45
Nos. 1166-1168 (3) 2.30 1.08

Irrigation — A319

#1169: a, Desert, water. b, Produce, sheep grazing. c, Khadafy, irrigation of desert (size: 63x44mm). #1170-1171, Khadafy, map.

1984, Feb. 1 *Perf. $14^1/_2$*

1169 Strip of 3 2.00 1.00
a.-b. A319 50d any single .45 .22
c. A319 100d multicolored 1.00 .50

Size: 72x36mm

Perf. $13^1/_2$

1170 A319 100d multicolored 1.00 .50

Souvenir Sheet

1171 A319 300d multicolored *3.75 3.75*

World Heritage — A320

Architectural ruins. No. 1174 vert.

1984, Feb. 10 *Perf. 12*

1172 A320 50d Theater, Sabratha .48 .15
1173 A320 60d Temple, Cyrene .60 .30
1174 A320 70d Monument, Sabratha .75 .35
1175 A320 100d Arena, Leptis Magna 1.00 .45
1176 A320 150d Temple, Cyrene, diff. 1.50 .75
1177 A320 200d Basilica, Leptis Magna 2.25 1.10
Nos. 1172-1177 (6) 6.58 3.10

Silver Dirhams Minted A.D. 671-757 — A321

Designs: a, Hegira 115. b, Hegira 93. c, Hegira 121. d, Hegira 49. e, Hegira 135.

Litho. & Embossed

1984, Feb. 15 *Perf. $13^1/_2$*

1178 Strip of 5 10.00 5.00
a.-e. A321 200d, any single 2.00 1.00

Tripoli Intl. Fair A322

Tea served in various settings.

1984, Mar. 5 **Litho.** *Perf. $12^1/_2$*

1179 A322 25d multicolored .20 .15
1180 A322 35d multicolored .35 .15
1181 A322 45d multicolored .45 .16
1182 A322 55d multicolored .55 .20
1183 A322 75d multicolored .75 .35
1184 A322 100d multicolored 1.00 .45
Nos. 1179-1184 (6) 3.30 1.46

Musicians — A323

Designs: a, Muktar Shiaker Murabet. b, El-Aref El-Jamal. c, Ali Shiaalia. d, Bashir Fehmi.

1984, Mar. 15 *Perf. $14^1/_2$*

1185 Strip of 4 + label 4.00 2.00
a.-d. A323 100d, any single .95 .45

No. 1185 has center label picturing musical instruments.

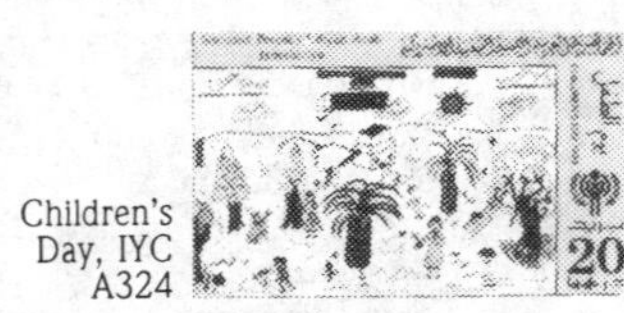

Children's Day, IYC A324

Children's drawings: a, Recreation. b, Rainy day. c, Military strength. d, Playground. e, Porch swing, children, motorcycle.

1984, Mar. 21 *Perf. 14*

1186	Strip of 5	2.00	.90
a.-e.	A324 20d. any single	.40	.18

Arab League Constitution, 39th Anniv. — A325

1984, Mar. 22 *Perf. 13½*

1187	A325 30d multicolored	.32	.15
1188	A325 40d multicolored	.40	.20
1189	A325 50d multicolored	.50	.25
	Nos. 1187-1189 (3)	1.22	.60

Miniature Sheet

Automobiles, Locomotives — A326

1984, Apr. 1

1190	Sheet of 16	20.00	9.00
a.-h.	A326 100d. Car, any single	1.25	.55
i.-p.	A326 100d. Locomotive, any single	1.25	.55

No. 1190 pictures outline of two camels in gold. Size: 214x135mm.

World Health Day A327

1984, Apr. 7 *Perf. 14½*

1191	A327 20d Stop Polio	.20	.15
1192	A327 30d No. 910	.32	.15
1193	A327 40d Arabic text	.40	.20
	Nos. 1191-1193 (3)	.92	.50

Crafts — A328

Designs: a, Shoemaker. b, Saddler. c, Women, wool. d, Spinner. e, Weaver. f, Tapestry weavers.

1984, May 1 *Perf. 12½*

1194	Strip of 6	9.00	4.50
a.-f.	A328 150d. any single	1.50	.75

Postal and Telecommunications Union Congress — A329

Designs: a, Telephones, mail. b, Computer operators. c, Emblem.

1984, May 15 *Perf. 14½*

1195	Strip of 3	2.00	1.00
a.-b.	A329 50d. any single	.50	.25
c.	A329 100d multicolored	1.00	.50

Armed Crowd — A330

Map, Fire, Military — A331

Designs: No. 1197b, Soldiers. No. 1197c, Khadafy. No. 1198, Khadafy giving speech.

1984, May 17 *Perf. 12, 14½ (#1197)*

1196	A330 50d multi	.55	.25
1197	Strip of 3	2.25	1.25
a.-b.	A331 50d. any single	.55	.28
c.	A331 100d multi	1.10	.55
1198	A330 100d multi	1.25	.55
	Nos. 1196-1198 (3)	4.05	2.05

Abrogation of the May 17 Treaty. Size of No. 1197c: 63x45mm.

Youth War Casualties A332

1984, June 4 *Perf. 10*

1199	A332 70d Damaged flag	.75	.35
1200	A332 100d Children imprisoned	1.00	.45

Miniature Sheet

Green Book Quotations A333

Designs: a, The Party System Aborts Democracy. b, Khadafy. c, Partners Not Wage-Workers. d, No Representation in Lieu of the People . . . e, Green Book. f, Committees Everywhere. g, Forming Parties Splits Societies. h, Party building, text on track. i, No Democracy without Popular Congresses.

1984, June 20 *Perf. 14*

1201	Sheet of 9	9.00	4.50
a.-i.	A333 100d. any single	1.00	.45

See No. 1270.

Folk Costumes — A334

Background colors: a, Green. b, Beige. c, Violet. d, Pale greenish blue. e, Salmon rose. f, Blue.

1984, July 1 *Perf. 14½x14*

1202	Strip of 6	6.00	3.00
a.-f.	A334 100d. any single	1.00	.50

Miniature Sheet

Natl. Soccer Championships — A335

Stadium, star, world cup and various action scenes.

1984, July 15 *Perf. 13½*

1203	Sheet of 16	11.00	5.00
a.-p.	A335 70d. any single	.65	.30

1984 Los Angeles Olympics — A336

World Food Day — A337

1984, July 28

1204	A336 100d Soccer	1.00	.45
1205	A336 100d Basketball	1.00	.45
1206	A336 100d Swimming	1.00	.45
1207	A336 100d Sprinting	1.00	.45
1208	A336 100d Windsurfing	1.00	.45
1209	A336 100d Discus	1.00	.45
	Nos. 1204-1209 (6)	6.00	2.70

Souvenir Sheets

1210	A336 250d Equestrian	1.90	.90
1211	A336 250d Arab equestrian	1.90	.90

1984, Aug. 1 *Perf. 12*

1212	A337 100d Forest scenes	1.00	.45
1213	A337 200d Men riding camels, oasis	2.00	1.00

Miniature Sheet

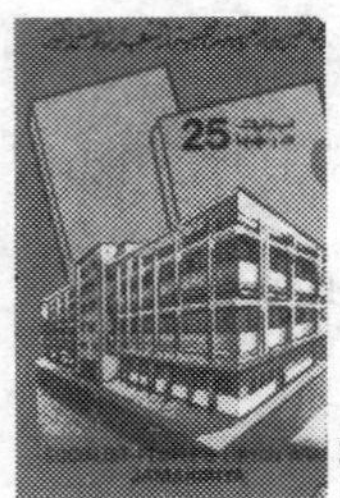

Sept. 1 Revolution, 15th Anniv. — A338

Designs: a, Green books, building at right angle. b, Green book, building, minaret. c, Minaret, party building and grounds. d, Revolution leader. e, Eight-story building. f, Construction, dome. g, Highway, bridge. h, Green book, building at left angle. i, Shepherd, sheep. j, Harvester. k, Tractors. l, Industry. m, Khadafy. n, Irrigation pipe, man drinking. o, Silos, factory. p, Shipping.

1984, Sept. 15 *Perf. 14½*

1214	Sheet of 16	5.00	5.00
a.-p.	A338 25d any single	.30	.20

A339

Evacuation Day A340

Designs: No. 1215b, Warrior facing left. No. 1215c, Khadafy leading battle (size: 63x45mm). No. 1216, Female rider. No. 1217, Battle scene. No. 1218, Italian whipping Libyan.

1984, Oct. 7

1215	Strip of 3	2.00	1.00
a.-b.	A339 50d. any single	.50	.22
c.	A339 100d multi	1.00	.45

Perf. 11½

1216	A340 100d multicolored	1.00	.45
1217	A340 100d multicolored	1.00	.45
1218	A340 100d multicolored	1.00	.45
	Nos. 1215-1218 (4)	5.00	2.35

Miniature Sheet

Equestrians A341

Various jumping, racing and dressage exercises printed in a continuous design.

1984, Oct. 15 *Perf. 13½*

1219	Sheet of 16	5.00	5.00
a.-p.	A341 25d any single	.30	.20

PHILAKOREA '84.

Agricultural Traditions — A342

Designs: a, Farmer. b, Well, man, ox. c, Basket weaver. d, Shepherd, ram. e, Tanning hide. f, Coconut picker.

1984, Nov. 1 *Perf. 13½*

1220	Strip of 6	6.00	3.00
a.-f.	A342 100d. any single	1.00	.50

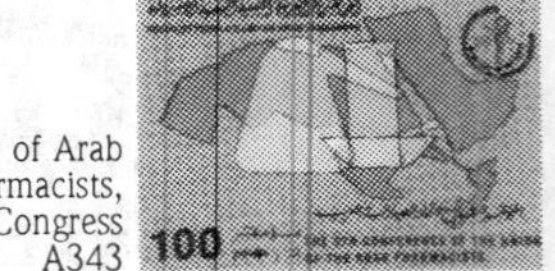

Union of Arab Pharmacists, 9th Congress A343

1984, Nov. 6 *Perf. 12*

1221	A343 100d multicolored	1.00	.45
1222	A343 200d multicolored	2.00	1.00

Arab-African Union — A344

1984, Nov. 15 *Perf. 12*

1223	A344 100d Map, banner, crowd	1.00	.45
1224	A344 100d Men, flags	1.00	.45

Nos. 1046, 1147 A345

1984, Nov. 29 ***Perf. 12½***

1225	A345	100d pink & multi	1.25	.60
1226	A345	150d brt yel grn & multi	1.75	.90

Intl. Day of Cooperation with the Palestinian People.

Miniature Sheet

Intl. Civil Aviation Organization, 40th Anniv. — A346

Aircraft: a, Boeing 747 SP, 1975. b, Concorde, 1969. c, Lockheed L1011-500 Tristar, 1978. d, Airbus A310, 1982. e, Tupolev TU-134A, 1962. f, Shorts 360, 1981. g, Boeing 727, 1963. h, Caravelle 10, 1965. i, Fokker F27, 1955. j, Lockheed 749A Constellation, 1946. k, Martin 130, 1955. l, Douglas DC-3, 1936. m, Junkers JU-52, 1932. n, Lindbergh's Spirit of St. Louis, 1927 Ryan. o, De Havilland Moth, 1925. p, Wright Flyer, 1903.

1984, Dec. 7 ***Perf. 13½***

1227	Sheet of 16	14.00	7.50
a.-p.	A346 70d any single	.85	.45

African Development Bank, 20th Anniv. — A347

UN Child Survival Campaign — A348

"20" in different configurations and: 70d, Map, symbols of industry, education and agriculture. 100d, Symbols of research and development.

1984, Dec. 15

1228	A347	50d multicolored	.50	.25
1229	A347	70d multicolored	.75	.40
1230	A347	100d multicolored	1.10	.50
		Nos. 1228-1230 (3)	2.35	1.15

1985, Jan. 1 ***Perf. 12***

1231	A348	70d Mother, child	.70	.30
1232	A348	70d Children	.70	.30
1233	A348	70d Boys at military school	.70	.30
1234	A348	70d Khadafy, children	.70	.30
		Nos. 1231-1234 (4)	2.80	1.20

Irrigation — A349

Drop of Water, Map A350

1985, Jan. 15 ***Perf. 14½x14***

1235	A349	100d shown	1.00	.45
1236	A349	100d Flowers	1.00	.45
1237	A349	100d Map, water	1.00	.45
		Nos. 1235-1237 (3)	3.00	1.35

Souvenir Sheet

Perf. 14x14½

1238	A350	200d shown	2.50	2.50

Musicians — A351

#1239a, Kamel El-Ghadi. #1239b, Lute. #1240a, Ahmed El-Khogia. #1240b, Violin. #1241a, Mustafa El-Fallah. #1241b, Zither. #1242a, Mohamed Hamdi. #1242b, Mask.

1985, Feb. 1 ***Perf. 14½***

1239	Pair	3.00	1.50
a.-b.	A351 100d, any single	1.50	.75
1240	Pair	3.00	1.50
a.-b.	A351 100d, any single	1.50	.75
1241	Pair	3.00	1.50
a.-b.	A351 100d, any single	1.50	.75
1242	Pair	3.00	1.50
a.-b.	A351 100d, any single	1.50	.75
	Nos. 1239-1242 (4)	12.00	6.00

Nos. 1239-1242 printed in sheets of 20, four strips of 5 consisting of two pairs each musician flanking center stamps picturing instruments.

Gold Dinars Minted A.D. 699-727 — A352

#1243a, Hegira 105. #1243b, Hegira 91. #1243c, Hegira 77. #1244, Dinar from Zuela.

Litho. and Embossed

1985, Feb. 15 ***Perf. 13½***

1243	Strip of 3	6.00	3.00
a.-c.	A352 200d, any single	2.00	1.00

Souvenir Sheet

1244	A352	300d multi	3.75	1.75

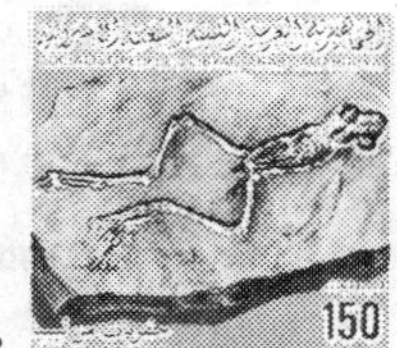

Fossils — A353

1985, Mar. 1 **Litho.** ***Perf. 13½***

1245	A353	150d Frog	1.40	.65
1246	A353	150d Fish	1.40	.65
1247	A353	150d Mammal	1.40	.65
		Nos. 1245-1247 (3)	4.20	1.95

People's Authority Declaration — A354

Khadafy wearing: a, Folk costume. b, Academic robe. c, Khaki uniform. d, Black uniform. e, White uniform.

1985, Mar. 2 **Litho.** ***Perf. 14½***

1248	Strip of 5	6.50	3.25
a.-e.	A354 100d, any single	1.25	.65

Tripoli Intl. Fair — A355

Musicians playing: a, Cymbals. b, Double flute, bongo. c, Wind instrument, drum. d, Drum. e, Tambourine.

1985, Mar. 5 ***Perf. 14***

1249	Strip of 5	5.00	2.50
a.-e.	A355 100d, any single	1.00	.50

Children's Day, IYC — A356

Children's drawings, various soccer plays: a, Goalie and player. b, Four players. c, Players as letters of the alphabet. d, Goalie save. e, Player heading the ball.

1985, Mar. 21 ***Perf. 12***

1250	Strip of 5	2.00	.75
a.-e.	A356 20d, any single	.40	.15

Intl. Program for Development of Telecommunications A357

World Health Day A358

1985, Apr. 1

1251	A357	30d multicolored	.35	.16
1252	A357	70d multicolored	.75	.35
1253	A357	100d multicolored	1.10	.50
		Nos. 1251-1253 (3)	2.20	1.01

1985, Apr. 7

1254	A358	40d Invalid, nurses	.38	.18
1255	A358	60d Nurse, surgery	.60	.30
1256	A358	100d Nurse, child	1.10	.50
		Nos. 1254-1256 (3)	2.08	.98

Miniature Sheet

Sea Shells — A359

Designs: a, Mytilidae. b, Muricidae (white). c, Cardiidae. d, Corallophilidae. e, Muricidae. f, Muricacea. g, Turridae. h, Argonautidae. i, Tonnidae. j, Aporrhaidae. k, Trochidae. l, Cancellariidae. m, Epitoniidae. n, Turbnidae. o, Mitridae. p, Pectinidae.

1985, Apr. 20

1257	Sheet of 16	5.00	2.75
a.-p.	A359 25d, any single	.30	.15

Tripoli Intl. Book Fair — A360

Intl. Youth Year — A361

1985, Apr. 28 ***Perf. 13½***

1258	A360	100d multi	1.00	.50
1259	A360	200d multi	2.00	1.00

1985, May 1

Games: No. 1260a, Jump rope. No. 1260b, Board game. No. 1260c, Hopscotch. No. 1260d, Stickgame. No. 1260e, Tops. No. 1261a, Soccer. No. 1261b, Basketball.

1260	Strip of 5	1.90	.90
a.-e.	A361 20d, any single	.55	.18

Souvenir Sheet

1261	Sheet of 2	2.50	1.10
a.-b.	A361 100d, any single	1.25	.50

No. 1261 contains 2 stamps 30x42mm.

Miniature Sheet

Mosque Minarets and Towers — A362

Mosques: a, Abdussalam Lasmar. b, Zaoviat Kadria. c, Zaoviat Amura. d, Gurgi. e, Mizran. f, Salem. g, Ghat. h, Ahmed Karamanli. i, Atya. j, El Kettani. k, Benghazi. l, Derna. m, El Derug. n, Ben Moussa. o, Ghadames. p, Abdulwahab.

1985, May 15 ***Perf. 12***

1262	Sheet of 16	11.00	5.00
a.-p.	A362 50d, any single	.60	.30

A363

A364

1985, June 1 Litho. *Perf. 13½*

1263 A363 100d Hamida El-Anezi 1.00 .40
1264 A363 100d Jamila Zemerli 1.00 .40

Teachers' Day.

1985 June 12

Battle of the Philadelphia: a, Ship sinking. b, Militia. c, Hand-to-hand combat.

1265 Strip of 3 2.00 1.00
a.-b. A364 50d. any single .50 .25
c. A364 100d multicolored 1.00 .50

Size of No. 1265c: 60x48mm. Continuous design with No. 1265c in middle.

A365

Khadafy's Islamic Pilgrimage A366

"The Holy Koran is the Law of Society" and Khadafy: a, Writing. b, Kneeling. c, With Holy Kaaba. d, Looking in window. e, Praying at pilgrimage ceremony.

1985, June 16

1266 Strip of 5 10.00 4.50
a.-e. A365 200d. any single 2.00 .90

Souvenir Sheet

1267 A366 300d multicolored 5.50 5.50

Miniature Sheet

Mushrooms A367

Designs: a, Leucopaxillus lepistoides. b, Amanita caesarea. c, Coriolus hirsutus. d, Cortinarius subfulgens. e, Dermocybe pratensis. f, Macrolepiota excoriata. g, Amanita curtipes. h, Trametes ljubarskyi. i, Pholiota aurivella. j, Boletus edulis. k, Geastrum sessile. l, Russula sanguinea. m, Cortinarius herculeus. n, Pholiota lenta. o, Amanita rubenscens. p, Scleroderma polyrhizum.

1985, July 15

1268 Sheet of 16 10.00 4.50
a.-p. A367 50d. any single .60 .25

Women's Folk Costumes — A368

Designs: a, Woman in violet. b, In white. c, In brown and blue. d, In blue. e, In red.

1985, Aug. 1 *Perf. 14½x14*

1269 Strip of 5 5.00 2.25
a.-e. A368 100d. any single 1.00 .45

Green Book Quotations Type of 1984
Miniature Sheet

Designs: a, In Need Freedom Is Latent. b, Khadafy reading. c, To Make A Party You Split Society. d, Public Sport Is for All the Masses. e, Green Books, doves. f, Wage-Workers Are a Type of Slave . . . g, People Are Only Harmonious with Their Own Arts and Heritages. h, Khadafy orating. i, Democracy Means Popular Rule Not Popular Expression.

1985, Aug. 15 *Perf. 14*

1270 Sheet of 9 9.00 4.50
a.-i. A333 100d, any single 1.00 .50

A369

September 1 Revolution, 16th Anniv. — A370

Designs: a, Food. b, Oil pipeline, refinery. c, Capital, olive branch. d, Mosque, modern buildings. e, Flag, mountains. f, Telecommunications apparatus.

1985, Sept. 1 *Perf. 12½*

1271 Strip of 6 6.00 3.00
a.-f. A369 100d, any single 1.00 .50
1272 A370 200d multi 2.50 1.25

Mosque Entrances — A371

Designs: a, Zauiet Amoura, Janzour. b, Shiaieb El-ain, Tripoli. c, Zauiet Abdussalam El-asmar, Zliten. d, Karamanli, Tripoli. e, Gurgi, Tripoli.

1985, Sept. 15 *Perf. 14*

1273 Strip of 5 5.00 2.25
a.-e. A371 100d. any single 1.00 .45

Miniature Sheet

Basketball — A372

Various players in action.

1985, Oct. 1 Litho. *Perf. 13x12½*

1274 Sheet of 16 5.00 2.50
a. A372 25d any single .30 .15

Evacuation A373

Designs: a, Man on crutches, web, tree. b, Man caught in web held by disembodied hands. c, Three men basking in light.

1985, Oct. 7 *Perf. 15*

1275 Strip of 3 3.00 1.50
a.-c. A373 100d any single 1.00 .50

Stamp Day — A374

Italia 85: a, Man sitting at desk, Type A228, Earth. b, Magnifying glass, open stock book, Type A228. c, Stamps escaping envelope.

1985, Oct. 25 *Perf. 12*

1276 Strip of 3 1.50 .75
a.-c. A374 50d. any single .50 .25

1986 World Cup Soccer Championships A375

1985, Nov. 1 *Perf. 13½*

1277	A375	100d	Block, heading the ball	1.00	.50
1278	A375	100d	Kick, goalie catching ball	1.00	.50
1279	A375	100d	Goalie, block, dribble	1.00	.50
1280	A375	100d	Goalie, dribble, sliding block	1.00	.50
1281	A375	100d	Goalie catching the ball	1.00	.50
1282	A375	100d	Block	1.00	.50
			Nos. 1277-1282 (6)	6.00	3.00

Souvenir Sheet

1283 A375 200d Four players 2.50 1.25

Intl. Day of Cooperation with the Palestinian People — A376

1985, Nov. 29 Litho. *Perf. 12½*

1284 A376 100d multi 1.25 .60
1285 A376 150d multi 1.90 .90

A set of 12 stamps picturing Khadafy was to be issued Jan. 1, 1986. Supposedly these were on sale for two hours.

Importation Prohibited
Importation of the stamps of Libya was prohibited as of Jan. 7, 1986.

General Post and Telecommunications Co. — A378

1986, Jan. 15 *Perf. 12*

1298 A378 100d yel & multi
1299 A378 150d yel grn & multi

Peoples Authority Declaration — A379

Designs: b, Hand holding globe and paper. c, Dove, Khadafy's Green Book (size: 53x37mm).

1986, Mar. 2 *Perf. 12½x13*

1300 Strip of 3
a.-b. A379 50d. any single
c. A379 100d multicolored

Musical Instruments A380

Designs: a, Flute. b, Drums. c, Horn. d, Cymbals. e, Hand drum.

1986, Mar. 5

1301 Strip of 5
a.-e. A380 100d any single

Tripoli International Fair.

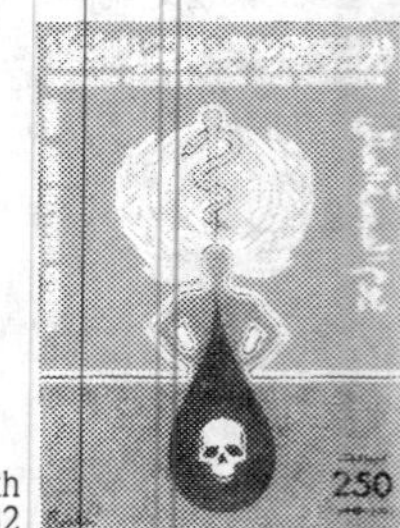

Intl. Children's Day — A381

Designs: a, Boy Scout fishing. b, Riding camel. c, Chasing butterflies. d, Beating drum. e, Soccer game.

1986, Mar. 21 *Perf. 13½*

1302 Strip of 5
a.-e. A381 50d any single

World Health Day — A382

1986, Apr. 7

1303 A382 250d sil & multi
1304 A382 250d gold & multi

Government Programs — A383

Designs: a, Medical examinations. b, Education. c, Farming (size: 63x42mm).

1986, May 1 *Perf. 14½*

1305 Strip of 3
a.-b. A383 50d any single
c. A383 100d multicolored

Miniature Sheet

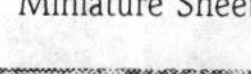

World Cup Soccer Championships, Mexico — A384

Designs: No. 1306a, 2 players. No. 1306b, 3 players in red and white shirts, one in green. No. 1306c, 2 players, referee. No. 1306d, Shot at goal. No. 1306e, 2 players with striped shirts. No. 1306f, 2 players with blue shirts, one with red. No. 1307, 7 players. No. 1308, 1st Libyan team, 1931.

1986, May 31 *Perf. 13½*

1306 Sheet of 6
a.-f. A384 50d any single

Souvenir Sheets

1307 A384 200d multicolored
1308 A384 200d multicolored

Nos. 1307-1308 each contain one 52x37mm stamp.

Miniature Sheet

Vegetables — A385

Designs: a, Peas. b, Zucchini. c, Beans. d, Eggplant. e, Corn. f, Tomato. g, Red pepper. h, Cucumbers. i, Garlic. j, Cabbage. k, Cauliflower. l, Celery. m, Onions. n, Carrots. o, Potato. p, Radishes.

1986, June 1 *Perf. 13x12½*

1309 Sheet of 16
a.-p. A385 50d any single

No. 1309 has a continuous design.

Miniature Sheet

Khadafy and Irrigation Project A386

Khadafy and: a, Engineer reviewing plans, drill rig. b, Map. c, Well. d, Drought conditions. e, Water pipe. f, Pipes, pulleys, equipment. g, Lowering water pipe. h, Construction workers, trailer. i, Hands holding water. j, Opening water valve. k, Laying pipeline. l, Trucks hauling pipes. m, Khadafy holding green book, city. n, Giving vegetables to people. o, Boy drinking, man cultivating field. p, Men in prayer, irrigation. (Khadafy not shown on Nos. 1310h, 1310i, 1310k, 1310 l, 1310o.)

1986, July 1 *Perf. 13½*

1310 Sheet of 16
a.-p. A386 100d any single

A387

A388

American Attack on Libya, Apr. 15 — A389

Designs: Nos. 1311a-1311p, Various scenes in Tripoli during and after air raid. No. 1312a, F14 aircraft. No. 1312b, Aircraft carrier, people. No. 1312c, Sinking of USS *Philadelphia,* 1801.
Illustration A389 is reduced.

1986, July 13

1311 A387 Sheet of 16, #a.-p.
1312 Strip of 3
a.-b. A388 50d multicolored
c. A388 100d multicolored
1313 A389 100d multicolored

No. 1312 has a continuous design. Size of No. 1312b: 60x38mm.

Khadafy's Peace Methods A390

Khadafy: b, Reading Green Book. c, With old woman. d, Praying with children. e, Visiting sick. f, Driving tractor.

1986, July 13

1314 Sheet of 6
a.-f. A390 100d any single

Miniature Sheet

Green Book Quotations A391

Designs: a, The House Must be Served by its Own Tenant. b, Khadafy. c, The Child is Raised by His Mother. d, Democracy is the Supervision of the People by the People. e, Green Books. f, Representation is a Falsification of Democracy. g, The Recognition of Profit is an Acknowledgement of Exploitation. h, Flowers. i, Knowledge is a Natural Right of Every Human Being...

1986, Aug. 1 *Perf. 14*

1315 Sheet of 9
a.-i. A391 100d any single

Sept. 1st Revolution, 17th Anniv. — A392

a, Public health. b, Agriculture. c, Sunflowers by Vincent Van Gogh. d, Defense. e. Oil industry.

1986, Sept. 1

1316 Strip of 5
a.-e. A392 200d any single

A393

Arab-African Union, 1st Anniv. A394

1986, Sept. 15 *Perf. 12*

1317 A393 250d Libyan, Arab horsemen
1318 A394 250d Women in native dress

Evacuation Day — A395

Designs: a, Mounted warrior. b, Two horsemen, infantry. c, Cavalry charge.

1986, Oct. 7 *Perf. 13½*

1319 Strip of 3
a. A395 50d multicolored
b. A395 100d multicolored
c. A395 150d multicolored

Intl. Peace Year A396

1986, Oct. 24 *Perf. 14½*

1320 A396 200d bl & multi
1321 A396 200d grn & multi

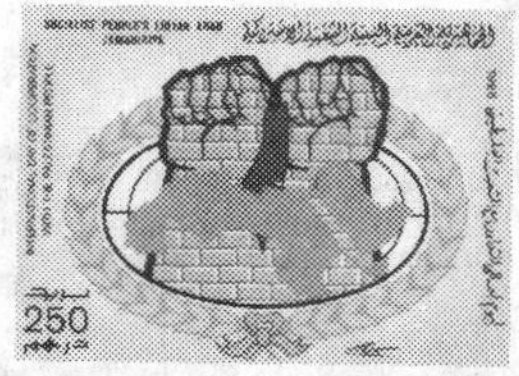

Solidarity with the Palestinians — A397

1986, Nov. 29 *Perf. 12½*

1322 A397 250d pink & multi
1323 A397 250d blue & multi

Music and Dance — A398

Designs: a, Man beating drum. b, Masked dancer. c, Woman dancing with jugs on her head. d, Man playing bagpipe. e, Man beating hand drum.

1986, Dec. 1 *Perf. 12*

1324 Strip of 5
a.-e. A398 70d any single

Gazella Leptoceros A399

1987, Mar. 2 *Perf. 13½*

1325 A399 100d Two adults
1326 A399 100d Fawn nursing
1327 A399 100d Adult sleeping
1328 A399 100d Adult drinking

World Wildlife Fund.

A400

A401

Crowd of People and: a, Oilfields. b, Buildings. c, Khadafy, buildings, globe.

1987, Mar. 2 *Perf. 13½*

1329 Strip of 3
a.-b. A400 500d multicolored
c. A400 1000d multicolored

People's Authority declaration.
No. 1329 has a continuous design. Size of No. 1329c: 42x37mm.

1987, Sept. 1 *Perf. 13½*

Sept. 1st Revolution, 18th Anniv.: a, Shepherd, sheep. b, Khadafy. c, Mosque. d, Irrigation pipeline. e, Combine in field. f, Khadafy at microphones. g, Harvesting grain. h, Irrigation. i, Soldier. j, Militiaman. k, Fountain. l, Skyscrapers. m, House, women. n, Children. o, Assembly hall. p, Two girls.

Miniature Sheet

1330 Sheet of 16
a.-p. A401 150d any single

No. 1330 has a continuous design.

Libyan Freedom Fighters — A402

No. 1331: a, Omer Abed Anabi Al Mansuri. b, Ahmed Ali Al Emrayd. c, Khalifa Said Ben Asker. d, Mohamed Ben Farhat Azawi. e, Mohamed Souf Al Lafi Al Marmori.

1988, Feb. 15

1331 Strip of 5
a. A402 100d multicolored
b. A402 200d multicolored
c. A402 300d multicolored
d. A402 400d multicolored
e. A402 500d multicolored

Freedom Festival Day — A403

1988, June 1

1332 A403 100d yel & multi
1333 A403 150d grn & multi
1334 A403 250d brn org & multi

Miniature Sheet

American Attack on Libya, 2nd Anniv. — A404

Khadafy: a, With woman and children. b, Playing chess. c, Fleeing from bombing with children. d, Praying in desert. e, Praying with children. f, Visiting wounded child. g, With infants and children, horiz. h, Delivering speech, horiz. i, With family, horiz.

#1336, In desert, vert. #1337, Making speech.

1988, July 13

1335 Sheet of 9
a.-i. A404 150d any single

Souvenir Sheets

Litho. & Embossed

1336 A404 500d gold & multi
1337 A404 500d gold & multi

No. 1335 exists imperf.

September 1st Revolution, 19th Anniv. A405

1988, Sept. 19 **Litho.**

1338 A405 100d brt bl & multi
1339 A405 250d gray & multi
1340 A405 300d cit & multi
1341 A405 500d bl grn & multi

1988 Summer Olympics, Seoul — A406

1988, Sept. 17

1342 A406 150d Tennis
1343 A406 150d Equestrian
1344 A406 150d Relay race
1345 A406 150d Soccer
1346 A406 150d Distance race
1347 A406 150d Cycling

Souvenir Sheet

1348 A406 750d Soccer, diff.

#1348 contains one 30x42mm stamp. Exists imperf. #1342-1347 exist in miniature sheets of 1.

Miniature Sheet

1988 Summer Olympics, Seoul — A407

1988, Sept 17

1350 Sheet of 3
a. A407 100d Bedouin rider
b. A407 200d shown
c. A407 200d Show jumping, diff.

Olymphilex '88, Seoul.

A408 A409

Design: Libyan Palm Tree.

1988, Nov. 1

1351 A408 500d Fruit
1352 A408 1000d Palm tree

1988

1353 Strip of 3
a. A409 100d shown
b. A409 200d Boy with rocks
c. A409 300d Flag, map

Palestinian uprising. #1353b, size: 45x39mm.

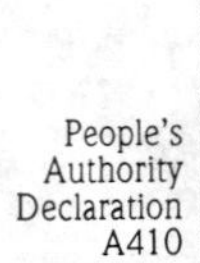

People's Authority Declaration A410

1989

1354 A410 260d dk grn & multi
1355 A410 500d gold & multi

Miniature Sheet

September 1 Revolution, 20th Anniv. — A411

Designs: a, Crowd, Green Books, emblem. b, Soldiers, Khadafy, irrigation pipeline. c, Military equipment, Khadafy, communication and transportation. d, Mounted warriors. e, Battle scenes.

1989 ***Perf. 13½***

1356 Sheet of 5
a.-e. A411 150d any single
f. Bklt. pane of 5, perf. 13½ horiz.

Souvenir Sheet

1357 A411 250d Khadafy

No. 1357 contains one 36x51mm stamp. Stamps from No. 1356f have gold border at right.

Libyans Deported to Italy — A412

Designs: No. 1359, Libyans in boats. No. 1360, Khadafy, crescent moon. No. 1361, Khadafy at left, in desert. No. 1362, Khadafy at right, soldiers. No. 1363, Khadafy in center, Libyans.

1989

1358 A412 100d shown
1359 A412 100d multicolored
1360 A412 100d multicolored
1361 A412 100d multicolored
1362 A412 100d multicolored

Souvenir Sheet

1363 A412 150d multicolored

No. 1363 contains one 72x38mm stamp.

A413 A414

1989 ***Perf. 12***

1364 A413 150d multicolored
1365 A413 200d multicolored

Demolition of Libyan-Tunisian border fortifications.

1989 ***Perf. 12x11½***

1366 A414 100d shown
1367 A414 300d Man, flag, crowd
1368 A414 500d Emblem

Solidarity with the Palestinians.

Ibn Annafis, Physician A415

1989 ***Perf. 12***

1369 A415 100d multicolored
1370 A415 150d multicolored

A416 A417

1990, Oct. 18 **Litho.** ***Perf. 14***

Granite Paper

1371 A416 100d multicolored
1372 A416 300d multicolored

Intl. Literacy Year.

1990, Oct. 18

Granite Paper

1373 A417 100d multicolored
1374 A417 400d multicolored

Organization of Petroleum Exporting Countries (OPEC), 30th anniv.

A418 A419

1990, June 28 ***Perf. 11½x12***

1375 A418 100d brt org & multi
1376 A418 400d grn & multi

Evacuation of US military base, 20th anniv.

1990, Apr. 24

1377 A419 300d bl & multi
1378 A419 500d vio & multi

People's authority declaration.

A420 A421

Plowing Season in Libya: 2000d, Man on tractor plowing field.

1990, Dec. 4 ***Perf. 14***

Granite Paper

1379 A420 500d multicolored
1380 A420 2000d multicolored

1990, Nov. 5 ***Perf. 14***

Granite Paper

1381 A421 100d grn & multi
1382 A421 400d vio & multi
1383 A421 500d bl & multi

Souvenir Sheet

Perf. 11½

1384 A421 500d Trophy, map, horiz.

World Cup Soccer Championships, Italy. No. 1384 contains one 38x33mm stamp.

Sept. 1st Revolution, 21st Anniv. — A422

1990, Sept. 3 ***Perf. 14***

Granite Paper

1385 A422 100d multicolored
1386 A422 400d multicolored
1387 A422 1000d multicolored

Imperf

Size: 120x90mm

1388 A422 200d multi, diff.

Maghreb Arab Union, 2nd Anniv. — A423

1991, Mar. 10 **Litho.** ***Perf. 13½***

1389 A423 100d multicolored
1390 A423 300d gold & multi

People's Authority Declaration — A424

1991, Mar. 10

1391 A424 300d multicolored
1392 A424 400d silver & multi

Children's Day — A425

World Health Day — A426

1991, Mar. 22

1393 A425 100d Butterflies, girl
1394 A425 400d Bird, boy

1991, Apr. 7

1395 A426 100d blue & multi
1396 A426 200d green & multi

Scenes from Libya A427

1991, June 20

1397 A427 100d Wadi el Hayat, vert.
1398 A427 250d Mourzuk
1399 A427 500d Ghadames

Irrigation Project A428

a, Laborers, heavy equipment. b, Khadafy, heavy equipment. c, Livestock, fruit & vegetables.

1991, Aug. 28 *Perf. 12*

1400 A428 50d Strip of 3, #a.-c.

No. 1400 has a continuous design. Size of No. 1400b: 60x36mm.

Sept. 1st Revolution, 22nd Anniv. A429

1991, Sept. 1 *Perf. 13½*

1401 A429 300d Chains, roses & "22"
1402 A429 400d Chains, "22"
a. Souv. sheet of 2, #1401-1402

Telecom '91 — A430

1991, Oct. 7 **Litho.** *Perf. 13½*

1403 A430 100d Emblems, vert.
1404 A430 500d Buildings, satillite dish

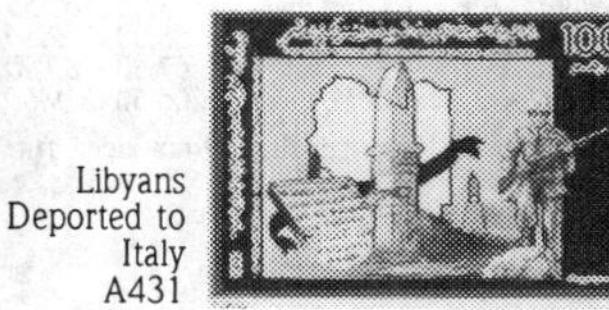

Libyans Deported to Italy A431

1991, Oct. 26 **Litho.** *Perf. 13½*

1405 A431 100d Monument, soldier
1406 A431 400d Ship, refugees, soldiers
a. Souv. sheet of 2, #1405-1406

Arab Unity — A432

1991, Nov. 15 *Perf. 12*

1407 A432 50d tan & multi
1408 A432 100d blue & multi

Miniature Sheet

Trucks, Automobiles and Motorcycles A433

Designs: a-d, Various trucks. e-h, Various off-road race cars. i-p, Various motorcycles.

1991, Dec. 28 *Perf. 14*

1409 A433 50d Sheet of 16, #a.-p.

Eagle — A434

Col. Khadafy — A434a

1992 *Perf. 11½*

Granite Paper (#1412-1419)

Background Colors

1412 A434 100d yellow
1413 A434 150d blue gray
1414 A434 200d bright blue
1415 A434 250d orange
1416 A434 300d purple
1418 A434 400d bright pink
1419 A434 450d bright green

Perf. 13½

1420 A434a 500d yellow green
1421 A434a 1000d rose
1422 A434a 2000d blue
1423 A434a 5000d violet
1424 A434a 6000d yellow brown

Issued: #1412-1416, 1418-1419, 1/1/92; #1420-1424, 9/1/92.

This is an expanding set. Numbers may change.

People's Authority Declaration — A435

1992, Mar. **Litho.** *Perf. 12*

1425 A435 100d yellow & multi
1426 A435 150d blue & multi

African Tourism Year (in 1991) A436

1992, Apr. 5 *Perf. 14½*

Granite Paper

1427 A436 50d purple & multi
1428 A436 100d pink & multi

1992 Summer Olympics, Barcelona — A437

1992, June 15 *Perf. 12*

1429 A437 50d Tennis
1430 A437 50d Long jump
1431 A437 50d Discus

Size: 106x82mm

Imperf

1432 A437 100d Olympic torch, rings

Revolutionary Achievements — A438

Designs: 100d, Palm trees. 150d, Steel mill. 250d, Cargo ship. 300d, Libyan Airlines. 400d, Natl. Assembly, Green Books. 500d, Irrigation pipeline, Khadafy.

1992, June 30 *Perf. 14*

Granite Paper

1433 A438 100d multicolored
1434 A438 150d multicolored
1435 A438 250d multicolored
1436 A438 300d multicolored
1437 A438 400d multicolored
1438 A438 500d multicolored

Tripoli Intl. Fair A439

1992, Mar. *Perf. 12*

1439 A439 50d Horse & buggy
1440 A439 100d Horse & sulky

Mahgreb Arab Union Philatelic Exhibition — A440

1992, Feb. 17 *Perf. 14½*

1441 A440 75d blue green & multi
1442 A440 80d blue & multi

Miniature Sheet

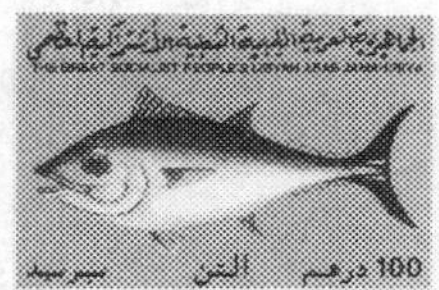

Fish — A441

Designs: a, Fish with spots near eye. b, Thin fish. d, Brown fish, currents. e, Fish, plants at LR. f, Fish, plants at LL.

1992, Apr. 15 *Perf. 14*

1443 A441 100d Sheet of 6, #a.-f.

Miniature Sheet

Horsemanship — A442

Designs: a, Woman rider with gun. b, Man on white horse. c, Mongol rider. d, Roman officer. e, Cossack rider. f, Arab rider. 250d, Two Arab riders.

1992, Apr. 25 *Perf. 13½x14*

1444 A442 100d Sheet of 6, #a.-f.

Souvenir Sheet

1445 A442 250d multicolored

Khadafy — A443

Designs: No. 1450a, like No. 1446. b, like No. 1447. c, like No. 1448. d, like No. 1449.

1992, Jan. 1 *Perf. 14x13½*

1446 A443 100d blue green & multi
1447 A443 100d gray & multi
1448 A443 100d rose lake & multi
1449 A443 100d yellow & multi

Souvenir Sheet

1450 A443 150d Sheet of 4, #a.-d.

Evacuation of Foreign Forces — A444

Costumes — A445

1992, Oct. 7 **Litho.** *Perf. 14*

1451 A444 75d Horse, broken chain
1452 A444 80d Flag, broken chain

1992, Dec. 15 **Litho.** *Perf. 12*

Women wearing various traditional costumes. Denomination color: a, green. b, black. c, violet blue. d, sky blue. e, yellow brown.

1453 A445 50d Strip of 5, #a.-e.

Sept. 1st Revolution, 23rd Anniv. — A446

1992, Sept. 1

1454 A446 50d Torch, "23"
1455 A446 100d Flag, "23"

Souvenir Sheet

1456 A446 250d Eagle, "23"

No. 1456 contains one 50x40mm stamp.

Libyans Deported to Italy — A447

1992, Oct. 26

1457 A447 100d tan & multi
1458 A447 250d blue & multi

Oasis — A448

Designs: 100d, Gazelle drinking. 200d, Camels, palm trees, vert. 300d, Palm trees, camel and rider.

1992, Oct. 1 ***Perf. 14***

1459 A448 100d multicolored
1460 A448 200d multicolored
1461 A448 300d multicolored

SEMI-POSTAL STAMPS

Many issues of Italy and Italian Colonies include one or more semipostal denominations. To avoid splitting sets, these issues are generally listed as regular postage, semipostals or airmails, etc.

Semi-Postal Stamps of Italy Overprinted **LIBIA**

1915-16 **Wmk. 140** ***Perf. 14***

B1	SP1 10c + 5c rose		1.90	*2.25*
B2	SP2 15c + 5c slate		4.25	*6.00*
B3	SP2 20c + 5c org ('16)		2.50	*3.25*
	Nos. B1-B3 (3)		8.65	*11.50*

No. B2 with Additional Surcharge **20**

1916, Mar.

B4 SP2 20c on 15c + 5c slate 4.25 *6.00*

View of Port, Tripoli — SP1

Designs: B5, B6, View of port, Tripoli. B7, B8, Arch of Marcus Aurelius. B9, B10, View of Tripoli.

1927, Feb. 15 **Litho.**

B5	SP1 20c + 5c brn vio & black	2.25	1.90
B6	SP1 25c + 5c bl grn & black	2.25	1.90
B7	SP1 40c + 10c blk brn & black	2.25	1.90
B8	SP1 60c + 10c org brn & black	2.25	1.90
B9	SP1 75c + 20c red & black	2.25	1.90
B10	SP1 1.25 l + 20c bl & blk	15.00	7.00
	Nos. B5-B10 (6)	26.25	16.50

First Sample Fair, Tripoli. Surtax aided fair. See Nos. EB1-EB2.

View of Tripoli — SP2

Knights of Malta Castle SP3

Designs: 50c+20c, Date palm. 1.25 l+20c, Camel riders. 2.55 l+50c, View of Tripoli. 5 l+1 l, Traction well.

1928, Feb. 20 **Wmk. 140** ***Perf. 14***

B11	SP2 30c + 20c mar & blk	1.00	*2.50*
B12	SP2 50c + 20c bl grn & blk	1.00	*2.50*
B13	SP2 1.25 l + 20c red & blk	1.00	*2.50*
B14	SP3 1.75 l + 20c bl & blk	1.00	*2.50*
B15	SP3 2.55 l + 50c brn & blk	2.75	*4.00*
B16	SP3 5 l + 1 l pur & blk	6.25	*6.00*
	Nos. B11-B16 (6)	13.00	*20.00*

2nd Sample Fair, Tripoli, 1928. The surtax was for the aid of the Fair.

Olive Tree — SP4

Herding SP5

Designs: 50c+20c, Dorcas gazelle. 1.25 l+20c, Peach blossoms. 2.55 l+50c, Camel caravan. 5 l+1 l, Oasis with date palms.

1929, Apr. 7

B17	SP4 30c + 20c mar & blk	5.00	*7.00*
B18	SP4 50c + 20c bl grn & blk	5.00	*7.00*
B19	SP4 1.25 l + 20c scar & blk	5.00	*7.00*
B20	SP5 1.75 l + 20c bl & blk	5.00	*7.00*
B21	SP5 2.55 l + 50c yel brn & blk	5.00	*7.00*
B22	SP5 5 l + 1 l pur & blk	110.00	*100.00*
	Nos. B17-B22 (6)	135.00	*135.00*

3rd Sample Fair, Tripoli, 1929. The surtax was for the aid of the Fair.

Harvesting Bananas — SP6

Water Carriers — SP7

Designs: 50c, Tobacco plant. 1.25 l, Venus of Cyrene. 2.55 l+45c, Black bucks. 5 l+1 l, Motor and camel transportation. 10 l+2 l, Rome pavilion.

1930, Feb. 20 **Photo.**

B23	SP6 30c dark brown	1.40	*2.50*
B24	SP6 50c violet	1.40	*2.50*
B25	SP6 1.25 l deep blue	1.40	*2.50*
B26	SP7 1.75 l + 20c scar	1.40	*4.00*
B27	SP7 2.55 l + 45c dp grn	7.25	*7.00*
B28	SP7 5 l + 1 l dp org	5.50	*7.00*
B29	SP7 10 l + 2 l dk vio	9.00	*15.00*
	Nos. B23-B29 (7)	27.35	*40.50*

4th Sample Fair at Tripoli, 1930. The surtax was for the aid of the Fair.

Statue of Ephebus — SP8

Exhibition Pavilion SP9

Designs: 25c, Arab musician. 50c, View of Zeughet. 1.25 l, Snake charmer. 1.75 l+25c, Windmill. 2.75 l+45c, "Zaptie." 5 l+1 l, Mounted Arab.

1931, Mar. 8

B30	SP8 10c black brown	3.00	*3.00*
B31	SP8 25c green	3.00	*3.00*
B32	SP8 50c purple	3.00	*3.00*
B33	SP8 1.25 l blue	3.00	*3.00*
B34	SP8 1.75 l + 25c car rose	4.00	*5.00*
B35	SP8 2.75 l + 45c org	4.00	*5.00*
B36	SP8 5 l + 1 l dl vio	10.00	*9.00*
B37	SP9 10 l + 2 l brn	26.00	*37.50*
	Nos. B30-B37 (8)	56.00	*68.50*
	Nos. B30-B37,C3,EB3 (10)	60.00	*80.50*

Fifth Sample Fair, Tripoli. Surtax aided fair.

Papaya Tree — SP10

Dorcas Gazelle — SP12

Ar Tower, Mogadiscio SP11

Designs: 10c, 50c, Papaya tree. 20c, 30c, Euphorbia abyssinica. 25c, Fig cactus. 75c, Mausoleum, Ghirza. 1.75 l+25c, Lioness. 5 l+1 l, Bedouin with camel.

1932, Mar. 8

B38	SP10 10c olive brn	4.00	*5.00*
B39	SP10 20c brown red	4.00	*5.00*
B40	SP10 25c green	4.00	*5.00*
B41	SP10 30c olive blk	4.00	*5.00*
B42	SP10 50c dk violet	4.00	*5.00*
B43	SP10 75c carmine	5.75	*7.00*
B44	SP11 1.25 l dk blue	5.75	*7.00*
B45	SP11 1.75 l + 25c ol brn	15.00	*22.50*
B46	SP11 5 l + 1 l dp bl	16.00	*22.50*
B47	SP12 10 l + 2 l brn violet	67.50	*65.00*
	Nos. B38-B47 (10)	130.00	*149.00*
	Nos. B38-B47,C4-C7 (14)	228.00	*273.00*

Sixth Sample Fair, Tripoli. Surtax aided fair.

Ostrich SP13

Arab Musician SP14

Designs: 25c, Incense plant. 30c, Arab musician. 50c, Arch of Marcus Aurelius. 1.25 l, African eagle. 5 l+1 l, Leopard. 10 l+2.50 l, Tripoli skyline and fasces.

1933, Mar. 2 **Photo.** **Wmk. 140**

B48	SP13 10c dp violet	18.00	7.00
B49	SP13 25c dp green	8.50	*5.00*
B50	SP14 30c orange brn	8.50	*7.00*
B51	SP13 50c purple	5.75	*5.00*
B52	SP13 1.25 l dk blue	30.00	*32.50*
B53	SP14 5 l + 1 l ol brn	35.00	*55.00*
B54	SP13 10 l + 2.50 l car	35.00	*62.50*
	Nos. B48-B54 (7)	140.75	*174.00*
	Nos. B48-B54,C8-C13 (13)	211.75	*255.00*

Seventh Sample Fair, Tripoli. Surtax aided fair.

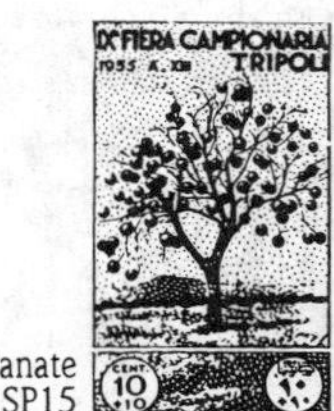

Pomegranate Tree — SP15

Designs: 50c+10c, 2 l+50c, Musician. 75c+15c, 1.25 l+25c, Tribesman.

1935, Feb. 16

B55	SP15 10c + 10c brown	.65	*2.25*
B56	SP15 20c + 10c rose red	.65	*2.25*
B57	SP15 50c + 10c purple	.65	*2.25*
B58	SP15 75c + 15c car	.65	*2.25*
B59	SP15 1.25 l + 25c dl blue	.65	*2.25*
B60	SP15 2 l + 50c ol grn	.65	*2.25*
	Nos. B55-B60 (6)	3.90	*13.50*
	Nos. B55-B60,C19-C24 (12)	14.90	*38.50*

Ninth Sample Fair, Tripoli. Surtax aided fair.

AIR POST STAMPS

Italy Nos. C3 and C5 Overprinted **Libia**

1928-29 **Wmk. 140** ***Perf. 14***

C1	AP2 50c rose red	4.75	1.50
C2	AP2 80c brn vio & brn ('29)	9.25	*11.00*

Airplane AP1

1931, Mar. 8 **Photo.** **Wmk. 140**

C3 AP1 50c blue 1.75 *5.00*

See note after No. B37.

Seaplane over Bedouin Camp — AP2

Designs: 50c, 1 l, Seaplane over Bedouin camp. 2 l+1 l, 5 l+2 l, Seaplane over Tripoli.

1932, Mar. 1 ***Perf. 14***

C4	AP2 50c dark blue	6.50	*7.00*
C5	AP2 1 l org brown	6.50	*7.00*
C6	AP2 2 l + 1 l dk gray	20.00	*30.00*
C7	AP2 5 l + 2 l car	65.00	*80.00*
	Nos. C4-C7 (4)	98.00	*124.00*

See note after No. B47.

Seaplane Arriving at Tripoli — AP3

Designs: 50c, 2 l+50c, Seaplane arriving at Tripoli. 75c, 10 l+2.50 l, Plane over Tagiura. 1 l, 4 l+1 l, Seaplane leaving Tripoli.

1933, Mar. 1

C8	AP3 50c dp green	6.00	*7.00*
C9	AP3 75c carmine	6.00	*7.00*
C10	AP3 1 l dk blue	6.00	*7.00*
C11	AP3 2 l + 50c pur	14.00	*10.00*
C12	AP3 5 l + 1 l org brn	15.00	*25.00*
C13	AP3 10 l + 2.50 l gray blk	24.00	*25.00*
	Nos. C8-C13 (6)	71.00	*81.00*

See note after No. B54.

Seaplane over Tripoli Harbor AP4

Airplane and Camel — AP5

Designs: 50c, 5 l+1 l, Seaplane over Tripoli harbor. 75c, 10 l+2 l, Plane and minaret.

1934, Feb. 17 **Photo.** **Wmk. 140**

C14	AP4 50c slate bl	4.50	*7.00*
C15	AP4 75c red org	4.50	*7.00*
C16	AP4 5 l + 1 l dp grn	65.00	*62.50*
C17	AP4 10 l + 2 l dl vio	65.00	*62.50*
C18	AP5 25 l + 3 l org brn	67.50	*80.00*
	Nos. C14-C18 (5)	206.50	*219.00*

Eighth Sample Fair, Tripoli. Surtax aided fair. See Nos. CE1-CE2.

Plane and Ancient Tower — AP6

Camel Train — AP7

Designs: 25c+10c, 3 l+1.50 l, Plane and ancient tower. 50c+10c, 2 l+30c, Camel train. 1 l+25c, 10 l+5 l, Arab watching plane.

1935, Apr. 12

C19 AP6	25c + 10c green	.90	*2.50*
C20 AP7	50c + 10c slate bl	.90	*2.50*
C21 AP7	1 l + 25c blue	.90	*2.50*
C22 AP7	2 l + 30c rose red	.90	*2.50*
C23 AP6	3 l + 1.50 l brn	.90	*2.50*
C24 AP7	10 l + 5 l dl vio	6.50	*12.50*
	Nos. C19-C24 (6)	11.00	*25.00*

See note after No. B60.

Cyrenaica No. C6 Overprinted **LIBIA** in Black

1936, Oct.

C25 AP2 50c purple .38 .15

Same on Tripolitania Nos. C8 and C12

1937

C26 AP1	50c rose carmine	.20	.15
C27 AP2	1 l deep blue	.55	.35
	Set value		.40

See Nos. C45-C50.

Ruins of Odeon Theater, Sabrata AP8

1937, Mar. 15 **Photo.**

C28 AP8	50c dark violet	1.25	*3.25*
C29 AP8	1 l vio black	1.25	*4.25*

Opening of a coastal road to the Egyptian frontier.

Nos. C28-C29 Overprinted "XI FIERA DI TRIPOLI"

1937, Mar. 15

C30 AP8	50c dark violet	4.75	*7.00*
C31 AP8	1 l violet blk	4.75	*7.00*

11th Sample Fair, Tripoli.

View of Tripoli AP9

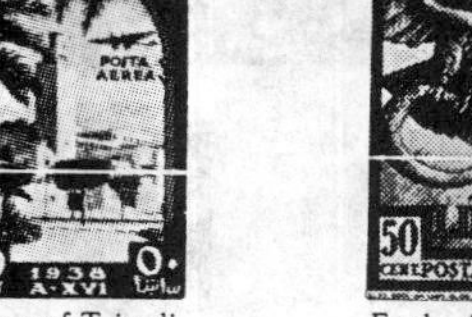

Eagle Attacking Serpent AP10

1938, Mar. 12 *Perf. 14*

C32 AP9	50c dk olive grn	.38	*.62*
C33 AP9	1 l slate blue	.50	*1.90*

12th Sample Fair, Tripoli.

1938, Apr. 25 **Wmk. 140**

C34 AP10	50c olive brown	.30	*.60*
C35 AP10	1 l brn violet	.50	*1.40*

Birth bimillenary Augustus Caesar (Octavianus), first Roman emperor.

Arab and Camel AP11

Design: 50c, Fair entrance.

1939, Apr. 12 **Photo.**

C36 AP11	25c green	.20	*.65*
C37 AP11	50c olive brown	.25	*.65*
C38 AP11	1 l rose violet	.30	*.65*
	Nos. C36-C38 (3)	.75	*1.95*

13th Sample Fair, Tripoli.

Plane Over Modern City — AP12

Design: 1 l, 5 l+2.50 l, Plane over oasis.

1940, June 3

C39 AP12	50c brn blk	.25	*1.25*
C40 AP12	1 l brn vio	.25	*1.25*
C41 AP12	2 l + 75c indigo	.38	*1.60*
C42 AP12	5 l + 2.50 l copper brn	.38	*1.60*
	Nos. C39-C42 (4)	1.26	*5.70*

Triennial Overseas Exposition, Naples.

Hitler, Mussolini and Inscription "Two Peoples, One War" AP13

1941, Apr. 24

C43 AP13 50c slate green .40 *10.00*

Rome-Berlin Axis.

Cyrenaica No. C9 Overprinted in Black Like No. C25

1941

C44 AP3 1 l black 3.00 *10.00*

Same Overprint on Tripolitania Nos. C9-C11, C13-C15

C45 AP1	60c red orange	.42
C46 AP1	75c deep blue	.42
C47 AP1	80c dull violet	.42
C48 AP2	1.20 l dark brown	.42
C49 AP2	1.50 l orange red	.42
C50 AP2	5 l green	.42
	Nos. C44-C50 (7)	5.52

Catalogue values for unused stamps in this section, from this point to the end of the section, are for Never Hinged items.

United Kingdom of Libya

ICY Type of Regular Issue

Perf. 14½x14

1965, Jan. 1 **Litho.** **Unwmk.**

C51 A60	50m dp lil & gold	.80	.80
a.	Souvenir sheet	2.00	2.00

No. C51a exists imperf.; same value.

Hands Holding Facade of Abu Simbel AP14

1966, Jan. 1 **Photo.** *Perf. 11½*

Granite Paper

C52 AP14	10m bis & dk brn	.15	.15
a.	Souvenir sheet of 4	.75	.75
C53 AP14	15m gray grn & dk grn	.15	.15
a.	Souvenir sheet of 4	.75	.75
C54 AP14	40m dl sal & dk brn	.28	.28
a.	Souvenir sheet of 4	1.50	.90
	Set value	.46	.42

UNESCO world campaign to save historic monuments in Nubia.

Inauguration of WHO Headquarters, Geneva AP15

Perf. 10x10½

1966, May 3 **Litho.** **Unwmk.**

C55 AP15	20m blk, yel & bl	.15	.15
C56 AP15	50m blk, yel grn & red	.20	.16
C57 AP15	65m blk, sal & brn red	.35	.25
	Nos. C55-C57 (3)	.70	.56

Flag and Globe — AP16

1966, Oct. 1 **Photo.** *Perf. 11½*

Granite Paper

C58 AP16	25m multicolored	.15	.15
C59 AP16	60m multicolored	.28	.20
C60 AP16	85m gray & multi	.40	.35
	Nos. C58-C60 (3)	.83	.70

Inauguration of Kingdom of Libya Airlines, 1st anniv.

AIR POST SPECIAL DELIVERY STAMPS

APSD1

Wmk. 140

1934, Feb. 17 **Photo.** *Perf. 14*

CE1 APSD1	2.25 l olive blk	20.00	*30.00*
CE2 APSD1	4.50 l + 1 l gray blk	20.00	*30.00*

8th Sample Fair at Tripoli. The surtax was for the aid of the Fair.

SPECIAL DELIVERY STAMPS

Special Delivery Stamps of Italy Overprinted **Libia**

1915, Nov. **Wmk. 140** *Perf. 14*

E1 SD1	25c rose red	9.00	3.00
E2 SD2	30c blue & rose	5.50	*7.00*

For surcharges see Nos. E7-E8.

"Italia" SD3

1921-23 **Engr.** *Perf. 13½*

E3 SD3	30c blue & rose	2.25	*1.50*
E4 SD3	50c rose red & brn	3.00	*2.00*
E5 SD3	60c dk red & brn ('23)	5.50	*4.00*
E6 SD3	2 l dk bl & red ('23)	8.00	*8.00*
	Nos. E3-E6 (4)	18.75	*15.50*

30c, 2 l inscribed "EXPRES."

For surcharges see Nos. E9-E12.

Nos. E1-E2 Surcharged

Cent. 60 1,60 LIRE 1,60

1922, June 1

E7 SD1	60c on 25c rose red	6.00	*4.00*
E8 SD2	1.60 l on 30c bl & rose	9.00	*8.00*

Nos. E5-E6 Surcharged in Blue or Red:

70 ٧٠

No. E9

2,50 ٢,٥٠

Nos. E10, E12

LIRE 1,25

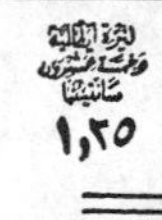

١,٢٥

No. E11

1926-36

E9 SD3	70c on 60c	4.50	*4.00*
E10 SD3	2.50 l on 2 l (R)	8.00	*8.00*

Perf. 11

E11 SD3	1.25 l on 60c	3.00	.50
a.	Perf. 14 ('36)	12.00	1.60
b.	Black surcharge	30,000.	1,900.
E12 SD3	2.50 l on 2 l (R)	57.50	*100.00*
	Nos. E9-E12 (4)	73.00	*112.50*

Issued: #E9-E10, July 1926; #E11-E12, 1927.

Catalogue values for unused stamps in this section, from this point to the end of the section, are for Never Hinged items.

United Kingdom of Libya

Zuela Saracen Castle — SD4

Perf. 11½

1966, Feb. 10 **Unwmk.** **Litho.**

E13 SD4 90m car rose & lt grn .65 .50

Coat of Arms of Libya and "POLIGRAFICA & CARTEVALORI - NAPLES" printed on back in yellow green.

SEMI-POSTAL SPECIAL DELIVERY STAMPS

Camel Caravan SPSD1

Wmk. 140

1927, Feb. 15 **Litho.** *Perf. 14*

EB1 SPSD1	1.25 l + 30c pur & blk	7.50	6.25
EB2 SPSD1	2.50 l + 1 l yel & blk	7.50	6.25

See note after No. B10.

No. EB2 is inscribed "EXPRES."

War Memorial SPSD2

1931, Mar. 8 **Photo.**

EB3 SPSD2 1.25 l + 20c car rose 2.25 *7.00*

See note after No. B37.

AUTHORIZED DELIVERY STAMPS

Italy No. EY1 Overprinted in Black **LIBIA**

1929, May 11 **Wmk. 140** *Perf. 14*

EY1 AD1	10c dull blue	12.00	8.00
a.	Perf. 11	50.00	40.00

Italy No. EY2 Overprinted in Black **LIBIA**

1941, May *Perf. 14*

EY2 AD2 10c dark brown 5.00 3.25

A variety of No. EY2, with larger "LIBIA" and yellow gum, was prepared in 1942, but not issued. Value 35 cents.

AD1

1942 Litho. Wmk. 140

EY3 AD1 10c sepia .35

No. EY3 was not issued.

POSTAGE DUE STAMPS

Italian Postage Due Stamps, 1870-1903 Overprinted in Black **Libia**

1915, Nov. Wmk. 140 *Perf. 14*

J1	D3 5c buff & magenta	1.10	*1.25*
J2	D3 10c buff & magenta	1.40	*1.25*
J3	D3 20c buff & magenta	1.65	*2.50*
a.	Double overprint	50.00	50.00
b.	Inverted overprint	50.00	50.00
J4	D3 30c buff & magenta	1.65	*2.50*
J5	D3 40c buff & magenta	1.65	*2.50*
a.	"40" in black	*1,500.*	
J6	D3 50c buff & magenta	1.65	*2.50*
J7	D3 60c buff & magenta	3.25	*3.75*
J8	D3 1 l blue & magenta	1.65	.60
a.	Double overprint	*2,000.*	*1,500.*
J9	D3 2 l blue & magenta	21.00	*12.50*
J10	D3 5 l blue & magenta	32.50	*16.00*
	Nos. J1-J10 (10)	67.50	*45.35*

1926

J11 D3 60c buff & brown 18.00 *37.50*

Postage Due Stamps of Italy, 1934, Overprinted in Black **LIBIA**

1934

J12	D6 5c brown	.30	*.60*
J13	D6 10c blue	.30	*.60*
J14	D6 20c rose red	.75	.50
J15	D6 25c green	.85	.50
J16	D6 30c red orange	.75	*.80*
J17	D6 40c black brn	.85	*1.25*
J18	D6 50c violet	.95	.25
J19	D6 60c black	1.50	*3.00*
J20	D7 1 l red orange	.95	.25
J21	D7 2 l green	18.00	3.75
J22	D7 5 l violet	42.50	9.00
J23	D7 10 l blue	9.25	*9.00*
J24	D7 20 l carmine	9.25	*11.00*
	Nos. J12-J24 (13)	86.20	*40.50*

In 1942 a set of 11 "Segnatasse" stamps, picturing a camel and rider and inscribed "LIBIA," was prepared but not issued. Value, $4.

Catalogue values for unused stamps in this section, from this point to the end of the section, are for Never Hinged items.

United Kingdom of Libya

Postage Due Stamps of Cyrenaica, 1950 Surcharged in Black

-- ليبيا --
٢ ليرة ع.
2 MAL. LIBYA

For Use in Tripolitania

1951 Unwmk. *Perf. 12½*

J25	D1 1mal on 2m dk brown	4.00	5.00
J26	D1 2mal on 4m dp grn	1.50	*5.00*
J27	D1 4mal on 8m scar	4.50	*10.00*
J28	D1 10mal on 20m org yel	10.00	*20.00*
a.	Arabic "20" for "10"	*200.00*	
J29	D1 20mal on 40m dp bl	14.00	*25.00*
	Nos. J25-J29 (5)	34.00	*65.00*

ليبيا

Cyrenaica Nos. J1-J7 Overprinted in Black

LIBYA

For Use in Cyrenaica

Overprint 13mm High

1952 Unwmk. *Perf. 12½*

J30	D1 2m dark brown	2.00	*3.75*
J31	D1 4m deep green	2.00	*3.75*
J32	D1 8m scarlet	2.00	*3.75*
J33	D1 10m vermilion	4.50	*7.00*
J34	D1 20m orange yel	6.00	*10.00*
J35	D1 40m deep blue	11.00	*20.00*
J36	D1 100m dk gray	15.00	*25.00*
	Nos. J30-J36 (7)	42.50	*73.25*

D1

Castle at Tripoli — D2

1952 Litho. *Perf. 11½*

J37	D1 2m chocolate	.15	.15
J38	D1 5m blue green	.60	.30
J39	D1 10m carmine	1.10	.65
J40	D1 50m violet blue	3.50	1.90
	Nos. J37-J40 (4)	5.35	3.00

1964, Feb. 1 Photo. *Perf. 14*

J41	D2 2m red brown	.16	.20
J42	D2 6m Prus green	.16	.20
J43	D2 10m rose red	.16	.20
J44	D2 50m brt blue	.50	.60
	Nos. J41-J44 (4)	.98	1.20

Men in Boat, Birds, Mosaic — D3

Ancient Mosaics: 10d, Head of Medusa. 20d, Peacock. 50d, Fish.

1976, Nov. 15 Litho. *Perf. 14*

J45	D3 5d bister & multi	.15	.15
J46	D3 10d orange & multi	.16	.15
J47	D3 20d blue & multi	.35	.15
J48	D3 50d emerald & multi	.65	.15
	Nos. J45-J48 (4)	1.31	
	Set value		.26

Nos. J45-J48 have multiple coat of arms printed on back in pale green beneath gum.

OFFICIAL STAMPS

Catalogue values for unused stamps in this section are for Never Hinged items.

United Kingdom of Libya

رسمي

Nos. 135-142 Overprinted in Black

Official

1952 Unwmk. *Perf. 11½*

O1	A27 2m yel brn	1.10	1.10
O2	A27 4m gray	.25	.38
O3	A27 5m bl grn	2.50	3.75
O4	A27 8m vermilion	1.00	1.10
O5	A27 10m purple	2.25	2.25
O6	A27 12m lil rose	4.75	3.75
O7	A27 20m dp bl	5.75	7.50
O8	A27 25m chocolate	7.50	11.00
	Nos. O1-O8 (8)	25.10	30.83

PARCEL POST STAMPS

These stamps were used by affixing them to the way bill so that one half remained on it following the parcel, the other half staying on the receipt given the sender. Most used halves are right halves. Complete stamps were obtainable canceled, probably to order. Both unused and used values are for complete stamps.

Italian Parcel Post Stamps, 1914-22, Overprinted **LIBIA**

1915-24 Wmk. 140 *Perf. 13½*

Q1	PP2 5c brown	.45	*2.00*
a.	Double overprint	50.00	
Q2	PP2 10c deep blue	.45	*2.00*
Q3	PP2 20c blk ('18)	.90	*2.00*
Q4	PP2 25c red	1.10	*2.00*
Q5	PP2 50c orange	1.25	*2.50*
Q6	PP2 1 l violet	1.10	*2.00*
Q7	PP2 2 l green	2.25	*3.00*
Q8	PP2 3 l bister	2.75	*3.00*
Q9	PP2 4 l slate	3.50	*3.00*
Q10	PP2 10 l rose lil ('24)	30.00	*30.00*
Q11	PP2 12 l red brn ('24)	67.50	*65.00*
Q12	PP2 15 l ol grn ('24)	70.00	*65.00*
Q13	PP2 20 l brn vio ('24)	75.00	*65.00*
	Nos. Q1-Q13 (13)	256.25	*246.50*

Same Overprint on Parcel Post Stamps of Italy, 1927-36

1927-38

Q14	PP3 10c dp bl ('36)	.75	*3.00*
Q15	PP3 25c red ('36)	.75	*3.00*
Q16	PP3 30c ultra ('29)	.15	*1.00*
Q17	PP3 50c orange	87.50	150.00
a.	Overprint 8½x2mm ('31)	100.00	*200.00*
Q18	PP3 60c red ('29)	.15	*1.00*
Q19	PP3 1 l lilac ('36)	18.00	*30.00*
Q20	PP3 2 l grn ('38)	18.00	*30.00*
Q21	PP3 3 l bister	.35	*1.50*
Q22	PP3 4 l gray	.35	*1.50*
Q23	PP3 10 l rose lil ('36)	140.00	125.00
Q24	PP3 20 l brn vio ('36)	140.00	*150.00*
	Nos. Q14-Q24 (11)	406.00	*496.00*

The overprint measures 10x1½mm on No. Q17.

Same Overprint on Italy No. Q24

1939

Q25 PP3 5c brown *5,000.*

The overprint was applied to the 5c in error. Few copies exist.

OCCUPATION STAMPS

Catalogue values for unused stamps in this section are for Never Hinged items.

Issued under French Occupation

Stamps of Italy and Libya were overprinted in 1943: "FEZZAN Occupation Française" and "R. F. FEZZAN" for use in this region when General Leclerc's forces 1st occupied it.

Fezzan-Ghadames

Sebha Fort — OS1

Mosque and Fort Turc Murzuch OS2

Map of Fezzan-Ghadames, Soldier and Camel — OS3

1946 Unwmk. Engr. *Perf. 13*

1N1	OS1 10c black	.15	.15
1N2	OS1 50c rose	.15	.15
1N3	OS1 1fr brown	.15	.15
1N4	OS1 1.50fr green	.15	.15
1N5	OS1 2fr ultramarine	.15	.15
1N6	OS2 2.50fr violet	.20	.18
1N7	OS2 3fr rose carmine	.30	.30
1N8	OS2 5fr chocolate	.35	.38
1N9	OS2 6fr dark green	.22	.25
1N10	OS2 10fr blue	.35	.38
1N11	OS3 15fr violet	.35	.38
1N12	OS3 20fr red	.50	.65
1N13	OS3 25fr sepia	.50	.65
1N14	OS3 40fr dark green	.70	.80
1N15	OS3 50fr deep blue	.70	.80
	Nos. N1-N15 (15)	4.92	5.52

FEZZAN

Catalogue values for unused stamps in this section are for Never Hinged items.

Monument, Djerma Oasis — OS1

Tombs of the Beni-Khettab OS2

Well at Gorda — OS3

Col. Colonna d'Ornano and Fort at Murzuch OS4

Philippe F. M. de Hautecloque (Gen. Jacques Leclerc) OS5

1949 Unwmk. Engr. *Perf. 13*

2N1	OS1 1fr black	.20	.20
2N2	OS1 2fr lil pink	.20	.20
2N3	OS2 4fr red brn	.70	.70
2N4	OS2 5fr emerald	.70	.70
2N5	OS3 8fr blue	.42	.42
2N6	OS3 10fr brown	1.40	1.40
2N7	OS3 12fr dk grn	2.50	2.50
2N8	OS4 15fr sal red	3.50	3.50
2N9	OS4 20fr brn blk	1.10	1.10
2N10	OS5 25fr dk bl	1.60	1.60
2N11	OS5 50fr cop red	2.25	2.25
	Nos. 2N1-2N11 (11)	14.57	14.57

Camel Raising — OS6

Agriculture OS7

Well Drilling — OS8

Ahmed Bey — OS9

1951

2N12	OS6 30c brown	.40	.40
2N13	OS6 1fr dp bl	.40	.40
2N14	OS6 2fr rose car	.40	.40
2N15	OS7 4fr red	.40	.40
2N16	OS7 5fr green	.42	.42
2N17	OS7 8fr dp bl	.42	.42
2N18	OS8 10fr sepia	1.60	1.60
2N19	OS8 12fr dp grn	1.75	1.75
2N20	OS8 15fr brt red	2.00	2.00
2N21	OS9 20fr blk brn & vio brn	2.00	2.00
2N22	OS9 25fr dk bl & bl	2.50	2.50
2N23	OS9 50fr ind & brn org	2.50	2.50
	Nos. 2N12-2N23 (12)	14.79	14.79

OCCUPATION SEMI-POSTAL STAMPS

Catalogue values for unused stamps in this section are for Never Hinged items.

"The Unhappy Ones"
OSP1 OSP2

1950	Unwmk.	Engr.	*Perf. 13*	
2NB1	OSP1	15fr + 5fr red brn	1.00	1.00
2NB2	OSP2	25fr + 5fr blue	1.00	1.00

The surtax was for charitable works.

OCCUPATION AIR POST STAMPS

Catalogue values for unused stamps in this section are for Never Hinged items.

Airport in Fezzan OAP1

Plane over Fezzan — OAP2

1948	Unwmk.	Engr.	*Perf. 13*	
2NC1	OAP1	100fr red	2.50	2.50
2NC2	OAP2	200fr indigo	4.00	4.00

Oasis — OAP3

Murzuch OAP4

1951				
2NC3	OAP3	100fr dark blue	4.00	4.50
2NC4	OAP4	200fr vermilion	5.00	5.50

OCCUPATION POSTAGE DUE STAMPS

Catalogue values for unused stamps in this section are for Never Hinged items.

Oasis of Brak — D1

1950	Unwmk.	Engr.	*Perf. 13*	
2NJ1	D1	1fr brown black	.30	.30
2NJ2	D1	2fr deep green	.40	.40
2NJ3	D1	3fr red brown	.50	.50
2NJ4	D1	5fr purple	.60	.60
2NJ5	D1	10fr red	1.10	1.10
2NJ6	D1	20fr deep blue	1.75	1.75
		Nos. 2NJ1-2NJ6 (6)	4.65	4.65

GHADAMES

Catalogue values for unused stamps in this section are for Never Hinged items.

Cross of Agadem — OS1

1949	Unwmk.	Engr.	*Perf. 13*	
3N1	OS1	4fr sep & red brn	.75	.75
3N2	OS1	5fr pck bl & dk grn	.75	.75
3N3	OS1	8fr sep & org brn	1.90	1.90
3N4	OS1	10fr blk & dk ultra	1.90	1.90
3N5	OS1	12fr vio & red vio	5.50	5.50
3N6	OS1	15fr brn & red brn	3.00	3.00
3N7	OS1	20fr sep & emer	4.25	4.25
3N8	OS1	25fr sepia & blue	4.25	4.25
		Nos. 3N1-3N8 (8)	22.30	22.30

OCCUPATION AIR POST STAMPS

Catalogue values for unused stamps in this section are for Never Hinged items.

Cross of Agadem — OAP1

1949	Unwmk.	Engr.	*Perf. 13*	
3NC1	OAP1	50fr pur & rose	5.50	5.50
3NC2	OAP1	100fr sep & pur brn	7.00	7.00

LIECHTENSTEIN

'lik-tən-ˌshtin

LOCATION — Central Europe southeast of Lake Constance, between Austria and Switzerland
GOVT. — Principality
AREA — 61.8 sq. mi.
POP. — 29,386 (est. 1991)
CAPITAL — Vaduz

The Principality of Liechtenstein is a sovereign state consisting of the two counties of Schellenberg and Vaduz. Since 1921 the post office has been administered by Switzerland.

100 Heller = 1 Krone
100 Rappen = 1 Franc (1921)

Catalogue values for unused stamps in this country are for Never Hinged items, beginning with Scott 368 in the regular postage section, Scott B22 in the semi-postal section, and Scott O47 in the offical section.

Watermarks

Greek Cross — Wmk. 183

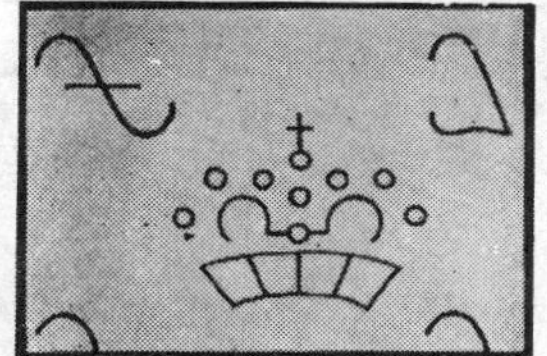

Crown and Initials — Wmk. 296

Austrian Administration of the Post Office

Prince Johann II — A1

1912	Unwmk.	Typo.	*Perf. 12½x13*	
		Thick Chalky Paper		
1	A1	5h yellow green	12.00	4.50
2	A1	10h rose	37.50	4.50
3	A1	25h dark blue	45.00	22.50
		Nos. 1-3 (3)	94.50	31.50

1915				
		Thin Unsurfaced Paper		
1a	A1	5h yellow green	5.50	6.75
2a	A1	10h rose	42.50	13.00
3a	A1	25h dark blue	450.00	90.00
b.		25h ultramarine	275.00	200.00

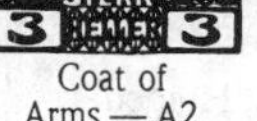

Coat of Arms — A2

Prince Johann II — A3

1917-18				
4	A2	3h violet	.75	.60
5	A2	5h yellow green	.75	.60
6	A3	10h claret	.75	.60
7	A3	15h dull red	.75	.60
8	A3	20h dark green	.75	.60
9	A3	25h deep blue	.75	.60
		Nos. 4-9 (6)	4.50	3.60

Exist imperf.
For surcharges see Nos. 11-16.

Prince Johann II — A4

1918				
		Dates in Upper Corners		
10	A4	20h dark green	.50	.65

Accession of Prince Johann II, 60th anniv.
Exists imperf.

National Administration of the Post Office

Stamps of 1917-18 Overprinted or Surcharged

a

b

c

1920				
11	A2(a)	5h yellow green	1.40	4.00
a.		Inverted overprint	70.00	
b.		Double overprint	22.50	*45.00*
12	A3(a)	10h claret	1.40	4.00
a.		Inverted overprint	70.00	
b.		Double overprint	22.50	*45.00*
c.		Overprint type "c"	15.00	70.00
13	A3(a)	25h deep blue	1.40	4.00
a.		Inverted overprint	70.00	
14	A2(b)	40h on 3h violet	1.40	4.00
a.		Inverted surcharge	70.00	
15	A3(c)	1k on 15h dull red	1.40	4.00
a.		Inverted surcharge	70.00	
b.		Overprint type "a"	62.50	*150.00*
16	A3(c)	2½k on 20h dk grn	1.40	4.00
a.		Inverted surcharge	70.00	
		Nos. 11-16 (6)	8.40	24.00

Coat of Arms A5

Chapel of St. Mamertus A6

Coat of Arms with Supporters — A15

Designs: 40h, Gutenberg Castle. 50h, Courtyard, Vaduz Castle. 60h, Red Tower, Vaduz. 80h, Old Roman Tower, Schaan. 1k, Castle at Vaduz. 2k, View of Bendern. 5k, Prince Johann I. 7½k, Prince Johann II.

1920		Engr.	*Imperf.*	
18	A5	5h olive bister	.15	.15
19	A5	10h deep orange	.15	.15
20	A5	15h dark blue	.15	.15
21	A5	20h deep brown	.15	.15
22	A5	25h dark green	.15	.15
23	A5	30h gray black	.15	.15
24	A5	40h dark red	.15	.15
25	A6	1k blue	.15	.15
		Perf. 12½		
32	A5	5h olive bister	.15	.20
33	A5	10h deep orange	.15	.20
34	A5	15h deep blue	.15	.20
35	A5	20h red brown	.15	.20
36	A6	25h olive green	.15	.20
37	A5	30h dark gray	.15	.20
38	A6	40h claret	.15	.20
39	A6	50h yellow green	.15	.20
40	A6	60h red brown	.15	.20
41	A6	80h rose	.15	.20
42	A6	1k dull violet	.15	.20
43	A6	2k light blue	.20	.35
44	A6	5k black	.30	.35
45	A6	7½k slate	.30	.35
46	A15	10k ocher	.30	.35
		Nos. 18-46 (23)	3.95	4.80

Used values for Nos. 18-46 are for canceled to order stamps.

Many denominations of Nos. 32-46 are found imperforate, imperforate vertically and imperforate horizontally.

For surcharges see Nos. 51-52.

Efficient supply at fair market prices.
Careful and prompt settlement of want lists.
Free price list on request.
Just let me know your requirements.

WANT LIST SERVICE
LIECHTENSTEIN
SWITZERLAND
GERMANY - CEPT
AUSTRIA - FRANCE
TOPICALS

Buying rare issues, high value lots and collections.

Hans P. Walser
P.O. Box 754/SC
8630 Ruti/Switzerland
Phone/Fax 01141-55-240 44 31
APS

Madonna and Child — A16

1920, Oct. 5

47	A16	50h olive green	.20	.65
48	A16	80h brown red	.20	.65
49	A16	2k dark blue	.20	.65
		Nos. 47-49 (3)	.60	1.95

80th birthday of Prince Johann II.

Imperf., Pairs

47a	A16	50h	4.25
48a	A16	80h	4.25
49a	A16	2k	4.25

Swiss Administration of the Post Office

No. 19 Surcharged

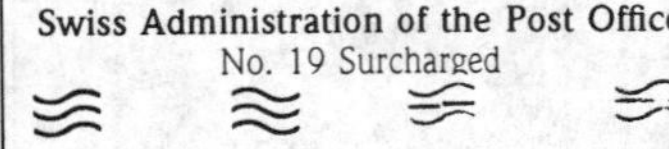

2 Rp. 2 Rp.

No. 51 No. 52

1921 Unwmk. Engr. ***Imperf.***

51	A5	2rp on 10h dp org	.30	*13.00*
a.		Double surcharge	30.00	*65.00*
b.		Inverted surcharge	30.00	*80.00*
c.		Double surch., one inverted	30.00	*65.00*
52	A5	2rp on 10h dp org	.30	*13.00*
a.		Double surcharge	57.50	*150.00*
b.		Inverted surcharge	57.50	*150.00*
c.		Double surch., one inverted	57.50	*150.00*

Comprehensive Stock!
Top Quality Material!

LIECHTENSTEIN

Complete NH Collection
1958-1997..... $920.00
(All sets & S/S included)

FREE PRICE LIST

Complete Liechtenstein Sets and Singles 1912 to date, NH, Hinged and Used, Perf varieties, NH Year sets 1958 to date, all Back of the Book and Maximum Cards. Also available: Collections, Covers, Proofs and Specialized Material.

WE BUY

Don't sell your Liechtenstein until you talk to our knowledgeable buyer! We buy Liechtenstein and all Worldwide stamps. Large collections and Dealer's stock especially desired including quantities of later mint material. Forerunners, all covers urgently needed.

1-800-9-4-STAMP (1-800-947-8267)

DISCOVER AMERICAN EXPRESS

Henry Gitner Philatelists, Inc.

Philately - The Quiet Excitement!

P.O. Box 3077-S, Middletown, NY 10940
Tel: 914-343-5151 Fax: 914-343-0068
Email: hgitner@hgitner.com http://www.hgitner.co
Toll Free: 1-800-947-8267

Arms with Supporters A19

Chapel of St. Mamertus A20

View of Vaduz — A21

Designs: 25rp, Castle at Vaduz. 30rp, View of Bendern. 35rp, Prince Johann II. 40rp, Old Roman Tower at Schaan. 50rp, Gutenberg Castle. 80rp, Red Tower at Vaduz.

Perf. 12½, 9½ (2rp, 10rp, 15rp)

1921

Surface Tinted Paper (#54-61)

54	A19	2rp	lemon	.60	*6.75*
55	A19	2½rp	black	.75	*8.00*
a.			Perf. 9½	.75	*40.00*
56	A19	3rp	orange	.75	*7.25*
a.			Perf. 9½	90.00	*3,000.*
57	A19	5rp	olive green	6.00	7.00
a.			Perf. 9½	32.50	*6.50*
58	A19	7½rp	dark blue	4.00	*20.00*
a.			Perf. 9½	150.00	*825.00*
59	A19	10rp	yellow green	40.00	3.00
a.			Perf. 12½	30.00	4.00
60	A19	13rp	brown	7.00	*37.50*
a.			Perf. 9½	67.50	*2,000.*
61	A19	15rp	dark violet	9.00	1.50
a.			Perf. 12½	12.00	12.00
62	A20	20rp	dull vio & blk	40.00	1.40
63	A20	25rp	rose red & blk	1.75	2.00
64	A20	30rp	dp grn & blk	40.00	1.00
65	A20	35rp	brn & blk, *straw*	1.65	1.65
66	A20	40rp	dk blue & blk	2.00	1.40
67	A20	50rp	dk green & blk	3.00	1.50
68	A20	80rp	gray & blk	12.00	*35.00*
69	A21	1fr	dp claret & blk	21.00	20.00
			Nos. 54-69 (16)	189.50	*154.95*

Nos. 54-69 exist imperforate; Nos. 54-61, partly perforated. See Nos. 73, 81. For surcharges see Nos. 70-71.

Nos. 58, 60a Surcharged in Red **10**

1924 ***Perf. 12½, 9½***

70	A19	5rp on 7½rp	.70	1.50
a.		Perf. 9½	5.50	5.00
71	A19	10rp on 13rp	.45	1.10
a.		Perf. 12½	10.50	25.00

Type of 1921

1924 Wmk. 183 ***Perf. 11½***

Granite Paper

73	A19	10rp green	14.00	.75

Peasant A28

Government Palace and Church at Vaduz A30

Design: 10rp, 20rp, Courtyard, Vaduz Castle.

1924-28 Typo. ***Perf. 11½***

74	A28	2½rp ol grn & red vio ('28)	2.00	*4.00*
75	A28	5rp brown & blue	2.50	.65
76	A28	7½rp bl grn & brn ('28)	1.50	*4.00*
77	A28	15rp red brn & bl grn ('28)	5.00	*21.00*

Engr.

78	A28	10rp yellow grn	9.00	.65
79	A28	20rp deep red	18.00	.65
80	A30	1½fr blue	60.00	65.00
		Nos. 74-80 (7)	98.00	95.95

Bendern Type of 1921

1925

81	A20	30rp blue & blk	16.00	1.00

Prince Johann II — A31

Prince Johann II as Boy and Man — A32

1928, Nov. 12 Typo. Wmk. 183

82	A31	10rp lt brn & ol grn	1.50	3.00
83	A31	20rp org red & ol grn	3.75	5.75
84	A31	30rp sl bl & ol grn	19.00	18.00
85	A31	60rp red vio & ol grn	50.00	*62.50*

Engr.

Unwmk.

86	A32	1.20fr ultra	45.00	*100.00*
87	A32	1.50fr black brown	65.00	*145.00*
88	A32	2fr deep carmine	65.00	*145.00*
89	A32	5fr dark green	65.00	*200.00*
		Nos. 82-89 (8)	314.25	*679.25*

70th year of the reign of Prince Johann II.

Prince Francis I, as a Child — A33

Prince Francis I as a Man — A34

Princess Elsa — A35

Prince Francis and Princess Elsa — A36

1929, Dec. 2 Photo.

90	A33	10rp olive green	.75	*2.00*
91	A34	20rp carmine	.75	*3.25*
92	A35	30rp ultra	2.50	*13.00*
93	A36	70rp brown	16.00	*72.50*
		Nos. 90-93 (4)	20.00	*90.75*

Accession of Prince Francis I, Feb. 11, 1929.

Grape Girl — A37

Chamois Hunter — A38

Mountain Cattle — A39

Courtyard, Vaduz Castle — A40

Mt. Naafkopf — A41

Chapel at Steg — A42

Rofenberg Chapel — A43

Chapel of St. Mamertus — A44

Alpine Hotel, Malbun — A45

Gutenberg Castle — A46

Schellenberg Monastery — A47

Castle at Vaduz — A48

Mountain Cottage — A49

Prince Francis and Princess Elsa — A50

1930 *Perf. 10½, 11½, 11½x10½*

No.	Type	Denomination / Color	Unused	Used
94	A37	3rp brown lake	.30	.65
95	A38	5rp deep green	.60	.45
96	A39	10rp dark violet	.75	.35
a.		Perf. 11½x10½	7.25	19.00
97	A40	20rp dp rose red	11.00	.50
98	A41	25rp black	3.75	21.00
a.		Perf. 11½	92.50	165.00
99	A42	30rp dp ultra	2.50	.90
a.		Perf. 11½x10½	1,200.	1,200.
100	A43	35rp dark green	3.50	9.25
a.		Perf. 11½	4,250.	4,250.
101	A44	40rp lt brown	3.50	3.25
102	A45	50rp black brn	42.50	11.50
a.		Perf. 11½	160.00	105.00
103	A46	60rp olive blk	42.50	12.50
104	A47	90rp violet brn	42.50	80.00
105	A48	1.20fr olive brn	42.50	125.00
a.		Perf. 11½x10½	2,400.	3,250.
106	A49	1.50fr black violet	25.00	40.00
107	A50	2fr gray grn & red brn	32.50	65.00
a.		Perf. 11½x10½	2,500.	3,000.
		Nos. 94-107 (14)	253.40	370.35

For overprints see Nos. O1-O8.

Mt. Naafkopf A51

Gutenberg Castle A52

Vaduz Castle — A53

1933, Jan. 23 *Perf. 14½*

No.	Type	Denomination / Color	Unused	Used
108	A51	25rp red orange	150.00	40.00
109	A52	90rp dark green	8.50	50.00
110	A53	1.20fr red brown	75.00	200.00
		Nos. 108-110 (3)	233.50	290.00

For overprints see Nos. O9-O10.

Prince Francis I

A54 A55

1933, Aug. 28 *Perf. 11*

No.	Type	Denomination / Color	Unused	Used
111	A54	10rp purple	16.00	27.50
112	A54	20rp brown carmine	16.00	27.50
113	A54	30rp dark blue	16.00	27.50
		Nos. 111-113 (3)	48.00	82.50

80th birthday of Prince Francis I.

1933, Dec. 15 **Engr.** *Perf. 12½*

No.	Type	Denomination / Color	Unused	Used
114	A55	3fr violet blue	90.00	160.00
		Never hinged	160.00	

See No. 152.

Agricultural Exhibition Issue
Souvenir Sheet

Arms of Liechtenstein — A56

1934, Sept. 29 *Perf. 12*

Granite Paper

No.	Type	Denomination / Color	Unused	Used
115	A56	5fr brown	1,250.	2,000.
		Never hinged	1,900.	

See No. 131.

Coat of Arms — A57

"Three Sisters" (Landmark) — A58

Church of Schaan — A59

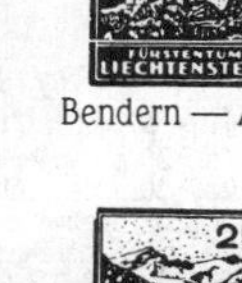

Bendern — A60

Rathaus, Vaduz — A61

Samina Valley — A62

Samina Valley in Winter — A63

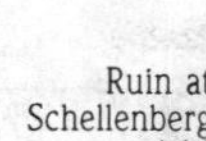

Ruin at Schellenberg A64

Government Palace — A65

Vaduz Castle — A66

Gutenberg Castle — A68

Alpine Hut — A69

Princess Elsa — A70

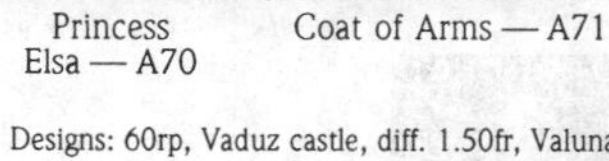

Coat of Arms — A71

Designs: 60rp, Vaduz castle, diff. 1.50fr, Valuna.

Perf. 11½, 11x11½, 12½

1934-35 **Photo.**

No.	Type	Denomination / Color	Unused	Used
116	A57	3rp copper red	.20	.50
117	A58	5rp emerald	2.75	.45
118	A59	10rp deep violet	.85	.35
119	A60	15rp red org ('35)	.40	1.00
120	A61	20rp red ('35)	.70	.45
121	A62	25rp brown ('35)	22.50	27.50
122	A63	30rp dk blue ('35)	3.75	1.25
123	A64	35rp gray grn ('35)	.75	4.00
124	A65	40rp brown ('35)	.85	2.50
125	A66	50rp lt brown	22.50	18.00
126	A66	60rp claret	1.25	4.50
127	A68	90rp deep green	6.00	18.00
128	A69	1.20fr deep blue	1.65	15.00
129	A69	1.50fr brown car ('35)	2.50	22.50
		Nos. 116-129 (14)	66.65	116.00
		Set, never hinged	150.00	

Engr.

No.	Type	Denomination / Color	Unused	Used
130	A70	2fr henna brn ('35)	57.50	135.00
		Never hinged	100.00	
131	A71	5fr dk violet ('35)	375.00	725.00
		Never hinged	550.00	

No. 131 has the same design as the 5fr in the souvenir sheet, No. 115. See #226, B14. For overprints see Nos. O11-O20.

Bridge at Malbun A72

Labor: 20rp, Constructing Road to Triesenberg. 30rp, Binnen Canal. 50rp, Bridge near Planken.

1937, June 30 **Photo.**

No.	Type	Denomination / Color	Unused	Used
132	A72	10rp brt violet	.95	.65
133	A72	20rp red	.95	.65
134	A72	30rp brt blue	.95	1.00
135	A72	50rp yellow brown	.95	1.65
		Nos. 132-135 (4)	3.80	3.95
		Set, never hinged	9.00	

Ruin at Schalun — A76

Peasant in Rhine Valley — A77

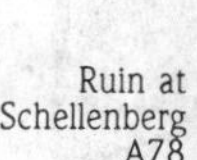

Ruin at Schellenberg A78

Knight and Gutenberg Castle — A79

Baron von Brandis and Vaduz Castle — A80

Designs: 5rp, Chapel at Masescha. 10rp, Knight and Vaduz Castle. 15rp, Upper Valüna Valley. 20rp, Wooden Bridge over Rhine, Bendern. 25rp, Chapel at Steg. 90rp, "The Three Sisters". 1fr, Frontier stone. 1.20fr, Gutenberg Castle and Harpist. 1.50fr, Alpine View of Lawena and Schwartzhorn.

1937-38

No.	Type	Denomination / Color	Unused	Used
136	A76	3rp yellow brown	.15	.35

Pale Buff Shading

No.	Type	Denomination / Color	Unused	Used
137	A76	5rp emerald	.15	.25
138	A76	10rp violet	.15	.15
139	A76	15rp dk slate grn	.30	.45
140	A76	20rp brown orange	.30	.25
141	A76	25rp chestnut	.55	2.00
142	A77	30rp blue & gray	3.25	.65
144	A78	40rp dark green	2.75	1.50
145	A79	50rp dark brown	1.00	2.00
146	A80	60rp dp claret ('38)	2.25	2.00
147	A80	90rp gray vio ('38)	10.00	10.50
148	A80	1fr red brown	1.75	8.75
149	A80	1.20fr dp brown ('38)	7.75	17.50
150	A80	1.50fr slate bl ('38)	7.00	17.50
		Nos. 136-150 (14)	37.35	63.85
		Set, never hinged	70.00	

For overprints see Nos. O21-O29.

Souvenir Sheet

Josef Rheinberger A91

1938, July 30 **Engr.** *Perf. 12*

No.	Type	Denomination / Color	Unused	Used
151		Sheet of 4	19.00	19.00
		Never hinged	45.00	
a.	A91	50rp slate gray	2.50	3.25
		Never hinged	5.50	

Third Philatelic Exhibition of Liechtenstein. Sheet size: 99¾x135mm.

See No. 153.

Francis Type of 1933

Thick Wove Paper

1938, Aug. 15 *Perf. 12½*

No.	Type	Denomination / Color	Unused	Used
152	A55	3fr black, *buff*	10.00	60.00
		Never hinged	17.00	

Issued in memory of Prince Francis I, who died July 25, 1938. Sheets of 20.

Josef Gabriel Rheinberger (1839-1901), German Composer and Organist — A92

1939, Mar. 31

153 A92 50rp slate green .70 *3.50*
Never hinged 1.10

Issued in sheets of 20. See No. 151.

Scene of Homage, 1718 — A93

1939, May 29

154 A93 20rp green lake .80 1.25
155 A93 30rp slate blue .80 1.25
156 A93 50rp gray green .80 1.25
Nos. 154-156 (3) 2.40 3.75
Set, never hinged 5.50

Honoring Prince Franz Joseph II. Sheets of 20.

Cantonal Coats of Arms — A94

Prince Franz Joseph II — A96

Design: 3fr, Arms of Principality.

1939

157 A94 2fr dk green, *buff* 5.75 *27.50*
158 A94 3fr indigo, *buff* 5.00 *30.00*
159 A96 5fr brown, *buff* 12.00 *32.50*
a. Sheet of 4 85.00 *130.00*
Never hinged 120.00
Nos. 157-159 (3) 22.75 *90.00*
Set, never hinged 50.00

2fr, 3fr issued in sheets of 12; 5fr in sheets of 4.

Prince Johann as a Child — A100

Memorial Tablet — A101

Prince Johann II — A102

Designs: 30rp, Prince Johann and Tower at Vaduz. 50rp, Prince Johann and Gutenberg Castle. 1fr, Prince Johann in 1920 and Vaduz Castle.

1940 Photo. *Perf. 11½.*

160 A100 20rp henna brown .50 *1.95*
161 A100 30rp indigo .70 *2.50*
162 A100 50rp dk slate grn 1.40 *5.75*
163 A100 1fr brown vio 7.25 *45.00*
164 A101 1.50fr violet blk 6.75 *45.00*
165 A102 3fr brown 3.40 *13.00*
Nos. 160-165 (6) 20.00 *113.20*
Set, never hinged 37.50

Birth centenary of Prince Johann II.

Nos. 160-164 issued in sheets of 25; No. 165 in sheets of 12. pIssue dates: 3fr, Oct. 5; others Aug. 10.

Gathering Corn A103

Wine Press A104

Sharpening Scythe A105

Milkmaid and Cow — A106

Native Costume A107

1941, Apr. 7

166 A103 10rp dull red brown .20 .40
167 A104 20rp lake .35 .85
168 A105 30rp royal blue .45 *1.50*
169 A106 50rp myrtle green 1.90 *10.00*
170 A107 90rp deep claret 1.90 *13.00*
Nos. 166-170 (5) 4.80 *25.75*
Set, never hinged 12.50

Madonna and Child — A108

1941, July 7 Engr.

171 A108 10fr brown carmine 47.50 100.00
Never hinged 85.00

Issued in sheets of 4.

Johann Adam Andreas — A109

Designs: 30rp, Wenzel. 100rp, Anton Florian. 150rp, Joseph Adam.

1941, Dec. 18 Photo.

172 A109 20rp brown car .40 .55
173 A109 30rp royal blue .45 *1.40*
174 A109 100rp violet blk 1.50 *10.50*
175 A109 150rp slate green 1.50 *10.50*
Nos. 172-175 (4) 3.85 *22.95*
Set, never hinged 9.50

Saint Lucius A113

Designs: 30rp, Reconstruction of Vaduz Castle. 50rp, Signing the Treaty of May 3, 1342. 1fr, Battle of Gutenberg. 2fr, Scene of Homage, 1718.

1942, Apr. 22 Engr. *Perf. 11½*

176 A113 20rp brn org, *buff* 1.00 .55
177 A113 30rp steel bl, *buff* .80 1.65
178 A113 50rp dk ol grn, *buff* 2.00 *5.75*
179 A113 1fr dull brn, *buff* 2.00 *12.00*
180 A113 2fr vio blk, *buff* 1.75 *13.00*
Nos. 176-180 (5) 7.55 *32.95*
Set, never hinged 19.00

600th anniversary of the separation of Liechtenstein from the House of Monfort.

Johann Karl — A118

30rp, Franz Joseph I. 1fr, Alois I. 1.50fr, Johann I.

1942, Oct. 5 Photo.

181 A118 20rp rose .30 .70
182 A118 30rp brt blue .45 *1.40*
183 A118 1fr rose lilac 1.25 *10.50*
184 A118 1.50fr deep brown 1.40 *10.50*
Nos. 181-184 (4) 3.40 *23.10*
Set, never hinged 8.00

Prince Franz Joseph II — A122

Countess Georgina von Wilczek — A123

Prince and Princess A124

1943, Mar. 5

185 A122 10rp dp rose violet .45 .70
186 A123 20rp henna brown .45 .70
187 A124 30rp slate blue .45 .70
Nos. 185-187 (3) 1.35 2.10
Set, never hinged 2.50

Marriage of Prince Franz Joseph II and Countess Georgina von Wilczek.

Prince Johann II — A126

Princes: 20rp, Alois II. 100rp, Franz Joseph I. 150rp, Franz Joseph II.

Perf. 11½

1943, July 5 Unwmk. Photo.

188 A126 20rp copper brown .20 *.45*
189 A126 30rp deep ultra .40 *.90*
190 A126 100rp olive gray 1.10 *6.25*
191 A126 150rp slate green 1.10 *6.25*
Nos. 188-191 (4) 2.80 *13.85*
Set, never hinged 6.00

Sheets of 20.

Terrain before Reclaiming A129

Designs: 30rp, Draining the Canal. 50rp, Plowing Reclaimed Land. 2fr, Harvesting Crops.

1943, Sept. 6

192 A129 10rp violet black .15 *.45*
193 A129 30rp deep blue .35 *2.50*
194 A129 50rp slate green .75 *6.75*
195 A129 2fr olive brown 1.75 *10.00*
Nos. 192-195 (4) 3.00 *19.70*
Set, never hinged 6.00

Vaduz A133

Gutenberg A134

1943, Dec. 27

196 A133 10rp dark gray .50 .35
197 A134 20rp chestnut brown .60 *.90*
Set, never hinged 2.25

Planken — A135

Bendern — A136

Designs: 10rp, Triesen. 15rp, Ruggell. 20rp, Vaduz. 25rp, Triesenberg. 30rp, Schaan. 40rp, Balzers. 50rp, Mauren. 60rp, Schellenberg. 90rp, Eschen. 1fr, Vaduz Castle. 120rp, Valuna Valley. 150rp, Lawena.

1944-45

198 A135 3rp dk brn & buff .15 .20
199 A136 5rp sl grn & buff .15 .15
200 A136 10rp gray & buff .25 .15
201 A136 15rp bl gray & buff .35 *.75*
202 A136 20rp org red & buff .30 .20
203 A136 25rp dk rose vio & buff .35 *.80*
204 A136 30rp blue & buff .35 .45
205 A136 40rp brown & buff .55 .95
206 A136 50rp bluish blk & pale gray .65 1.10
207 A136 60rp green & buff 3.50 2.75
208 A136 90rp ol grn & buff 3.50 3.75
209 A136 1fr dp cl & buff 1.75 *3.50*
210 A136 120rp red brown 1.90 *3.75*
211 A136 150rp royal blue 1.90 *4.50*
Nos. 198-211 (14) 15.65 *23.00*
Set, never hinged 37.50

Issue years: 10rp, 15rp, 40rp-1fr, 1945; others, 1944. See No. 239. For surcharge and overprints see No. 236, O30-O36.

Crown and Rose — A149

1945, Apr. 9

212 A149 20rp multicolored .85 *.55*
213 A149 30rp multicolored .85 *1.40*
214 A149 1fr multicolored 1.00 *4.50*
Nos. 212-214 (3) 2.70 *6.45*
Set, never hinged 4.25

Birth of Prince Johann Adam Pius, Feb. 14, 1945. Sheets of 20.

Prince Franz Joseph II — A150

Arms of Liechtenstein and Vaduz Castle — A152

Design: 3fr, Princess Georgina.

1944-45 Photo.

215 A150 2fr brown, *buff* 5.50 *4.50*
216 A150 3fr dark green 3.50 *4.25*

Engr.

217 A152 5fr bl gray, *cr* ('45) 11.00 *11.00*
Nos. 215-217 (3) 20.00 *19.75*
Set, never hinged 37.50

Nos. 215-217 were issued in sheets of 8. See Nos. 222, 259-260.

Saint Lucius — A153

1946, Mar. 14 Unwmk. *Perf. 11½*

218 A153 10fr gray blk, *cr* 22.50 *24.00*
Never hinged 35.00
Sheet of 4 165.00 *115.00*
Never hinged 190.00

Issued in sheets measuring 105x130mm.

Red Deer — A154

Varying Hare — A155

Capercaillie — A156

1946, Dec. 10 Photo.

219 A154 20rp henna brown 1.25 1.25
220 A155 30rp grnsh blue 1.65 1.50
221 A156 150rp olive brown 2.75 *9.50*
Nos. 219-221 (3) 5.65 *12.25*
Set, never hinged 10.50

Arms Type of 1945

1947, Mar. 20 Engr.

222 A152 5fr henna brn, *cream* 12.00 *27.50*
Never hinged 25.00

Issued in sheets of 8.

Chamois — A157

Alpine Marmot — A158

Golden Eagle — A159

1947, Oct. 15 Photo. Unwmk.

223 A157 20rp henna brown 1.65 2.75
224 A158 30rp grnsh blue 2.00 3.50
225 A159 150rp dark brown 3.00 *11.00*
Nos. 223-225 (3) 6.65 *17.25*
Set, never hinged 14.00

Elsa Type of 1935

1947, Dec. 10 Engr. *Perf. 14½*

226 A70 2fr black, *yelsh* 2.25 *10.00*
Never hinged 3.50

Issued in memory of Princess Elsa, who died Sept. 28, 1947. Sheets of 20.

Portrait of Ginevra dei Benci by Leonardo da Vinci — A160

Designs: 20rp, Girl, Rubens. 30rp, Self-portrait, Rembrandt. 40rp, Canon, Massys. 50rp, Madonna, Memling. 60rp, French Painter, 1456, Fouquet. 80rp, Lute Player, Gentileschi. 90rp, Man, Strigel. 120rp, Man, Raphael.

1949, Mar. 15 Photo. *Perf. 11½*

227 A160 10rp dark green .65 .50
228 A160 20rp henna brown .85 .50
229 A160 30rp sepia 1.65 2.00
230 A160 40rp blue 4.25 .70
231 A160 50rp violet 3.75 5.50
232 A160 60rp grnsh gray 6.50 6.25
233 A160 80rp brown orange 1.75 5.50
234 A160 90rp olive bister 6.50 5.50
235 A160 120rp claret 1.75 4.75
Nos. 227-235 (9) 27.65 31.20
Set, never hinged 45.00

Issued in sheets of 12.
See No. 238.

No. 198 Surcharged with New Value and Bars in Dark Brown

1949, Apr. 14

236 A135 5rp on 3rp dk brn & buff .25 .30
Never hinged .50

Map, Post Horn and Crown A161

1949, May 23

237 A161 40rp blue & indigo 2.00 4.75
Never hinged 3.25

75th anniversary of the UPU.
For surcharge see No. 246.

Portrait Type of 1949
Souvenir Sheet
Unwmk.

1949, Aug. 6 Photo. *Imperf.*

238 Sheet of 3 60.00 *110.00*
a. A160 10rp dull green 10.50 14.00
b. A160 20rp lilac rose 10.50 14.00
c. A160 40rp blue 10.50 14.00
Never hinged 120.00

5th Philatelic Exhibition.
Sheet size: 121½x69½mm. Sold for 3fr.

Scenic Type of 1944

1949, Dec. 1 *Perf. 11½*

239 A136 5rp dk brown & buff 15.00 .45
Never hinged 26.00

Rossauer Castle, Vienna — A163

Church at Bendern A164

Prince Johann Adam Andreas — A165

1949, Nov. 15 Engr. *Perf. 14½*

240 A163 20rp dark violet .80 1.65
241 A164 40rp blue 4.25 8.00
242 A165 150rp brown red 5.75 8.50
Nos. 240-242 (3) 10.80 18.15
Set, never hinged 18.00

250th anniv. of the purchase of the former dukedom of Schellenberg. Sheets of 20.
For surcharge see No. 265.

Roe Deer — A166

Black Grouse — A167

Badger — A168

1950, Mar. 7 Photo. *Perf. 11½*

243 A166 20rp red brown 3.75 1.75
244 A167 30rp Prus green 5.75 4.25
245 A168 80rp dark brown 21.00 42.50
Nos. 243-245 (3) 30.50 48.50
Set, never hinged 62.50

Issued in sheets of 20.

No. 237 Surcharged with New Value and Bars Obliterating Commemorative Inscriptions

1950, Nov. 7

246 A161 1fr on 40rp bl & ind 14.00 *40.00*
Never hinged 25.00

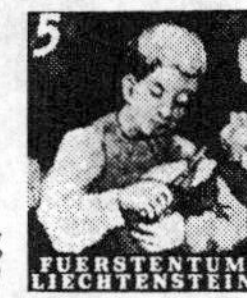

Boy Cutting Bread — A169

Designs: 10rp, Laborer. 15rp, Cutting hay. 20rp, Harvesting corn. 25rp, Load of hay. 30rp, Wine grower. 40rp, Farmer and scythe. 50rp, Cattle raising. 60rp, Plowing. 80rp, Woman with potatoes. 90rp, Potato cultivation. 1fr, Tractor with potatoes.

Perf. 11½

1951, May 3 Unwmk. Photo.

247 A169 5rp claret .30 .15
248 A169 10rp green .40 .15
249 A169 15rp yellow brown 2.75 4.50
250 A169 20rp olive brown .90 .30
251 A169 25rp rose brown 2.75 4.50
252 A169 30rp grnsh gray 1.75 .70
253 A169 40rp deep blue 5.25 5.50
254 A169 50rp violet brown 4.25 2.70
255 A169 60rp brown 4.00 2.75
256 A169 80rp henna brown 5.50 9.00
257 A169 90rp olive green 9.00 4.25
258 A169 1fr indigo 32.50 6.00
Nos. 247-258 (12) 69.35 40.50
Set, never hinged 130.00

Types of 1944, Redrawn
Perf. 12½x12

1951, Nov. 20 Engr. Wmk. 296

259 A150 2fr dark blue 7.75 *35.00*
a. Perf. 14½ 575.00 165.00
260 A150 3fr dk red brown 100.00 80.00
a. Perf. 14½ 90.00 *225.00*
Set, never hinged 160.00
Set, perf. 14½, never hinged 1,100.

Issued in sheets of 20.

Portrait, Savolodo A170

Madonna, Botticelli A171

Design: 40rp St. John, Del Sarto.

Perf. 11½

1952, May 27 Unwmk. Photo.

261 A170 20rp violet brown 21.00 3.75
262 A171 30rp brown olive 13.00 6.50
263 A170 40rp violet blue 8.00 5.25
Nos. 261-263 (3) 42.00 15.50
Set, never hinged 75.00

Issued in sheets of 12.

Vaduz Castle — A172

Perf. 14½

1952, Sept. 25 Wmk. 296 Engr.

264 A172 5fr deep green 125.00 165.00
Never hinged 190.00

Issued in sheets of 9.

No. 241 Surcharged with New Value and Wavy Lines in Red

1952, Sept. 25 Unwmk.

265 A164 1.20fr on 40rp blue 15.00 *45.00*
Never hinged 27.50

Portrait of a Young Man A173

St. Nicholas by Zeitblom A174

Designs: 30rp, St. Christopher by Cranach. 40rp, Leonhard, Duke of Hag, by Kulmbach.

Perf. 11½

1953, Feb. 5 Unwmk. Photo.

266 A173 10rp dk olive green .45 1.00
267 A174 20rp olive brown 7.75 1.90
268 A174 30rp violet brown 17.00 7.50
269 A173 40rp slate blue 17.00 *45.00*
Nos. 266-269 (4) 42.20 *55.40*
Set, never hinged 75.00

Issued in sheets of 12.

Lord Baden-Powell A175

1953, Aug. 4 Engr. *Perf. 13x13½*

270 A175 10rp deep green 1.00 1.25
271 A175 20rp dark brown 7.00 2.75
272 A175 25rp red 7.00 16.00
273 A175 40rp deep blue 6.75 7.50
Nos. 270-273 (4) 21.75 27.50
Set, never hinged 40.00

Intl. Scout Conf. Sheets of 20.

Alemannic Disc, 600 A. D. — A176

Prehistoric Settlement of Borscht — A177

Design: 1.20fr, Rössen jug.

1953, Nov. 26 *Perf. 11½*

274 A176 10rp orange brown 4.75 *12.00*
275 A177 20rp deep gray green 4.75 *9.00*
276 A176 1.20fr dark blue gray 25.00 *30.00*
Nos. 274-276 (3) 34.50 *51.00*
Set, never hinged 65.00

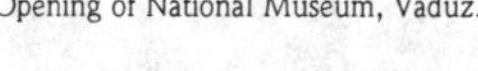
Opening of National Museum, Vaduz.

Soccer Players — A178

Designs: 20rp, Player kicking ball. 25rp, Goalkeeper. 40rp, Two opposing players.

1954, May 18 **Photo.**

277 A178 10rp dull rose & brn 1.65 .65
278 A178 20rp olive green 2.50 .65
279 A178 25rp orange brown 9.25 20.00
280 A178 40rp lilac gray 6.25 5.00
Nos. 277-280 (4) 19.65 26.30
Set, never hinged 37.50

See #289-292, 297-300, 308-311, 320-323.

Nos. B19-B21 Surcharged with New Value and Bars in Color of Stamp

1954, Sept. 28 **Unwmk.** *Perf. 11½*

281 SP15 35rp on 10rp+10rp 1.10 3.25
282 SP16 60rp on 20rp+10rp 11.50 10.00
283 SP15 65rp on 40rp+10rp 3.50 6.50
Nos. 281-283 (3) 16.10 19.75
Set, never hinged 27.50

Madonna in Wood, 14th Century — A179

1954, Dec. 16 **Engr.**

284 A179 20rp henna brown 1.50 2.75
285 A179 40rp gray 8.50 19.00
286 A179 1fr dark brown 8.50 19.00
Nos. 284-286 (3) 18.50 40.75
Set, never hinged 37.50

Prince Franz Joseph II — A180

Princess Georgina — A181

1955, Apr. 5 *Perf. 14½*

Cream Paper

287 A180 2fr dark brown 47.50 35.00
288 A181 3fr dark green 47.50 35.00
Set, never hinged 165.00

Issued in sheets of 9.

Sports Type of 1954

Designs: 10rp, Slalom. 20rp, Mountain climbing. 25rp, Skiing. 40rp, Resting on summit.

1955, June 14 **Photo.** *Perf. 11½*

289 A178 10rp aqua & brn vio 1.00 .85
290 A178 20rp green & ol bis 2.50 .85
291 A178 25rp lt ultra & sep 9.00 14.00
292 A178 40rp olive & pink 6.50 3.50
Nos. 289-292 (4) 19.00 19.20
Set, never hinged 35.00

Prince Johann Adam — A183

Eagle, Crown and Oak Leaves — A184

Portraits: 20rp, Prince Philipp. 40rp, Prince Nikolaus. 60rp, Princess Nora.

1955, Dec. 14

Granite Paper

Cross in Red

293 A183 10rp dull violet .50 .40
294 A183 20rp slate green 2.75 1.40
295 A183 40rp olive brown 4.00 7.00
296 A183 60rp rose brown 2.75 5.25
Nos. 293-296 (4) 10.00 14.05
Set, never hinged 20.00

Liechtenstein Red Cross, 10th anniversary.

Sports Type of 1954

Designs: 10rp, Javelin thrower. 20rp, Hurdling. 40rp, Pole vaulting. 1fr, Sprinters.

Perf. 11½

1956, June 21 **Unwmk.** **Photo.**

Granite Paper

297 A178 10rp lt red brn & ol grn .65 .30
298 A178 20rp lt ol grn & pur 1.65 .55
299 A178 40rp blue & vio brn 2.50 3.25
300 A178 1fr org ver & ol brn 7.00 7.75
Nos. 297-300 (4) 11.80 11.85
Set, never hinged 22.50

1956, Aug. 21

Granite Paper

301 A184 10rp dk brown & gold 1.10 1.00
302 A184 120rp slate blk & gold 5.75 3.50
Set, never hinged 14.00

150th anniversary of independence.

Prince Franz Joseph II — A185

Prince Johann Adam — A186

1956, Aug. 21

303 A185 10rp dark green .90 .40
304 A185 15rp bright ultra 2.00 2.75
305 A185 25rp purple 2.25 2.75
306 A185 60rp dark brown 4.00 2.75
Nos. 303-306 (4) 9.15 8.65
Set, never hinged 15.00

50th birthday of Prince Franz Joseph II.

1956, Aug. 21

Granite Paper

307 A186 20rp olive green 1.65 .48
Never hinged 2.75

Issued to publicize the 6th Philatelic Exhibition, Vaduz, Aug. 25-Sept. 2. Sheets of 9.

Sports Type of 1954

Designs: 10rp, Somersault on bar. 15rp, Jumping over vaulting horse. 25rp, Exercise on rings. 1.50fr, Somersault on parallel bars.

1957, May 14 **Photo.** *Perf. 11½*

308 A178 10rp pale rose & ol grn .75 .52
309 A178 15rp pale grn & dl pur 2.50 4.50
310 A178 25rp ol bis & Prus grn 2.50 6.50
311 A178 1.50fr lemon & sepia 7.00 14.00
Nos. 308-311 (4) 12.75 25.52
Set, never hinged 25.00

Pine A187

Lord Baden-Powell A188

Designs: 20rp, Wild roses. 1fr, Birches.

1957, Sept. 10 *Perf. 11½*

Granite Paper

312 A187 10rp dark violet 2.25 2.50
313 A187 20rp brown carmine 2.25 .80
314 A187 1fr green 3.50 5.50
Nos. 312-314 (3) 8.00 8.80
Set, never hinged 15.00

See Nos. 326-328, 332-334, 353-355.

1957, Sept. 10 **Unwmk.**

Design: 10rp, Symbolical torchlight parade.

315 A188 10rp blue black .85 1.40
316 A188 20rp dark brown .85 1.40
a. Sheet of 12, 6 each #315-316 12.00 18.00
Never hinged 20.00
Set, never hinged 3.00

Cent. of the birth of Lord Baden-Powell and the 60th anniv. of the Boy Scout movement.

Chapel of St. Mamertus — A189

40rp, Madonna and saints. 1.50fr, Pieta.

1957, Dec. 16 *Perf. 11½*

317 A189 10rp dark brown .35 .35
318 A189 40rp dark blue 1.10 5.50
319 A189 1.50fr brown lake 6.50 9.50
Nos. 317-319 (3) 7.95 15.35
Set, never hinged 15.00

Issued in sheets of 20. Sheet inscribed: "Furstentum Liechtenstein" and "Weihnacht 1957" (Christmas 1957).

Sports Type of 1954

Designs: 15rp, Girl swimmer. 30rp, Fencers. 40rp, Tennis. 90rp, Bicyclists.

1958, Mar. 18 **Photo.**

Granite Paper

320 A178 15rp lt blue & pur .65 1.00
321 A178 30rp pale rose lil & ol gray 3.25 6.00
322 A178 40rp sal pink & sl bl 3.25 6.00
323 A178 90rp lt ol grn & vio brn 1.65 4.00
Nos. 320-323 (4) 8.80 17.00
Set, never hinged 12.50

Relief Map of Liechtenstein A190

1958, Mar. 18

324 A190 25rp bister, vio & red .35 .75
325 A190 40rp blue, vio & red .35 .75
Set, never hinged 1.50

World's Fair, Brussels, Apr. 17-Oct. 19. Sheets of 25. For surcharges see Nos. B22-B23.

Tree-Bush Design of 1957

Designs: 20rp, Maples at Lawena. 50rp, Holly at Schellenberg. 90rp, Yew at Maurerberg.

1958, Aug. 12 *Perf. 11½*

Granite Paper

326 A187 20rp chocolate 1.75 .75
327 A187 50rp olive green 7.00 4.50
328 A187 90rp violet blue 1.75 2.75
Nos. 326-328 (3) 10.50 8.00
Set, never hinged 19.00

Sts. Moritz and Agatha A191

"The Good Shepherd" A192

Christmas: 35rp, St. Peter. 80rp, Chapel of St. Peter, Mals-Balzers.

1958, Dec. 4 **Photo.** **Unwmk.**

Granite Paper

329 A191 20rp dk slate green 1.90 2.50
330 A191 35rp dk blue violet 1.90 2.50
331 A191 80rp dark brown 1.90 2.50
Nos. 329-331 (3) 5.70 7.50
Set, never hinged 9.50

Issued in sheets of 20.

Tree-Bush Type of 1957

Designs: 20rp, Larch in Lawena. 50rp, Holly on Alpila. 90rp, Linden in Schaan.

1959, Apr. 15 *Perf. 11½*

332 A187 20rp dark violet 2.50 2.00
333 A187 50rp henna brown 2.50 2.00
334 A187 90rp dark green 2.50 2.00
Nos. 332-334 (3) 7.50 6.00
Set, never hinged 14.00

1959, Apr. 15 **Unwmk.**

335 A192 30rp rose violet & gold .50 .85
Never hinged .85

Issued in memory of Pope Pius XII.

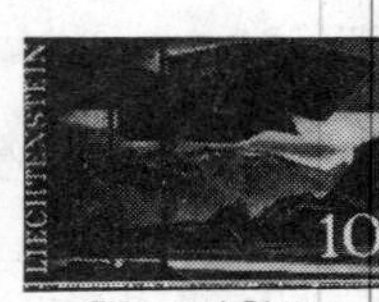

Flags and Rhine Valley — A193

Man Carrying Hay — A194

Apple Harvest — A195

Designs: 5rp, Church at Bendern and sheaves. 20rp, Rhine embankment. 30rp, Gutenberg Castle. 40rp, View from Schellenberg. 50rp, Vaduz Castle. 60rp, Naafkopf, Falknis Range. 75rp, Woman gathering sheaves. 90rp, Woman in vineyard. 1fr, Woman in kitchen. 1.30fr, Return from the field. 1.50fr, Family saying grace.

1959-64

Granite Paper

336 A193 5rp gray olive ('61) .15 .15
337 A193 10rp dull violet .15 .15
338 A193 20rp lilac rose .15 .15
339 A193 30rp dark red .15 .15
340 A193 40rp olive grn ('61) 1.10 .55
341 A193 50rp deep blue .30 .35
342 A193 60rp brt grnsh bl .45 .55
343 A194 75rp deep ocher ('60) 1.10 1.00
344 A194 80rp olive grn ('61) .90 .90
345 A194 90rp red lilac ('61) .90 .90
346 A194 1fr chestnut ('61) .90 .90
347 A195 1.20fr orange ver ('60) 1.40 1.10
348 A195 1.30fr brt green ('64) 1.10 .90
349 A195 1.50fr brt blue ('60) 1.40 1.40
Nos. 336-349 (14) 10.15 9.15
Set, never hinged 12.50

Belfry, Bendern Church — A196

Christmas: 60rp, Sculpture, bell, St. Theodul's church. 1fr, Sculpture, tower of St. Lucius' church.

1959, Dec. 2 **Unwmk.** *Perf. 11½*

350 A196 5rp dk slate green .55 .25
351 A196 60rp olive 3.50 4.25
352 A196 1fr deep claret 2.75 2.50
Nos. 350-352 (3) 6.80 7.00
Set, never hinged 11.00

Issued in sheets of 20.

Tree-Bush Type of 1957

Designs: 20rp, Beech tree on Gafadura. 30rp, Juniper on Alpila. 50rp, Pine on Sass.

1960, Sept. 19

353 A187 20rp brown 4.50 6.00
354 A187 30rp deep plum 4.50 6.00
355 A187 50rp Prus green 15.00 6.00
Nos. 353-355 (3) 24.00 18.00
Set, never hinged 40.00

Europa Issue, 1960

Honeycomb A197

1960, Sept. 19 *Perf. 14*

356 A197 50rp multicolored 70.00 70.00
Never hinged 110.00

Issued to promote the idea of a united Europe. Sheets of 20.

Princess Gina
A198

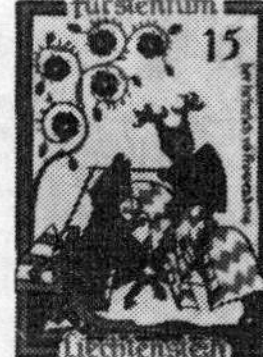
Heinrich von Frauenberg
A199

Portraits: 1.70fr, Prince Johann Adam Pius. 3fr, Prince Franz Joseph II.

1960-64 Engr. *Perf. 14*

356A	A198	1.70fr violet ('64)	1.00	1.50
b.		Imperf., pair	*1,750.*	*1,750.*
357	A198	2fr dark blue	2.25	2.00
a.		Imperf., pair	*1,750.*	*1,750.*
358	A198	3fr deep brown	2.25	2.00
		Nos. 356A-358 (3)	5.50	5.50
		Set, never hinged	7.00	

Issued in sheets of 16.

1961-62 Photo. *Perf. 11½*

Minnesingers: 20rp, King Konradin. 25rp, Ulrich von Liechtenstein. 30rp, Kraft von Toggenburg. 35rp, Ulrich von Gutenberg. 40rp, Heinrich von Veldig. 1fr, Konrad von Alstetten. 1.50fr, Walther von der Vogelweide. 2fr, Tannhäuser. (Designs from 14th century Manesse manuscript.)

359	A199	15rp multicolored	.60	.75
360	A199	20rp multicolored ('62)	.30	.30
361	A199	25rp multicolored	1.25	1.65
362	A199	30rp multicolored ('62)	.40	.40
363	A199	35rp multicolored	1.50	2.00
364	A199	40rp multicolored ('62)	.65	.65
365	A199	1fr multicolored	2.50	2.00
366	A199	1.50fr multicolored	9.25	15.00
367	A199	2fr multicolored ('62)	1.65	1.65
		Nos. 359-367 (9)	18.10	24.40
		Set, never hinged	22.50	

Issued in sheets of 20. See #381-384, 471.

Catalogue values for unused stamps in this section, from this point to the end of the section, are for Never Hinged items.

Europa Issue, 1961

Cogwheels
A200

1961, Oct. 3 Unwmk. *Perf. 13½*

368 A200 50rp multicolored .25 .25

Printed in sheets of 20.

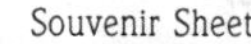
Souvenir Sheet

Prince Johann II — A201

Portraits: 10rp, Francis I. 25rp, Franz Joseph II.

1962, Aug. 2 Photo. *Perf. 11½*

369		Sheet of 3	7.00	5.00
a.	A201	5rp gray green	1.40	1.25
b.	A201	10rp deep rose	1.40	1.25
c.	A201	25rp blue	1.40	1.25

50th anniv. of Liechtenstein's postage stamps and in connection with the Anniv. Stamp Exhib., Vaduz, Aug. 4-12. No. 369 sold for 3fr.

Hands — A202

1962, Aug. 2

370 A202 50rp indigo & red .60 .60

Europa. Issued in sheets of 20.

Malaria Eradication Emblem — A203

Pietà — A204

1962, Aug. 2 Engr.

371 A203 50rp turquoise blue .35 .35

WHO drive to eradicate malaria. Sheets of 20.

1962, Dec. 6 Photo.

Designs: 50rp, Angel with harp, fresco. 1.20fr, View of Mauren.

372	A204	30rp magenta	.60	.60
373	A204	50rp deep orange	.85	.85
374	A204	1.20fr deep blue	1.10	1.10
		Nos. 372-374 (3)	2.55	2.55

Issued in sheets of 20.

Prince Franz Joseph II
A205

1963, Apr. 3 Engr. *Perf. 13½x14*

375 A205 5fr dull green 4.00 3.00

Accession of Prince Franz Joseph II, 25th anniv. Sheets of 8. Exists imperf. Value $1,500.

Angel of the Annunciation
A206

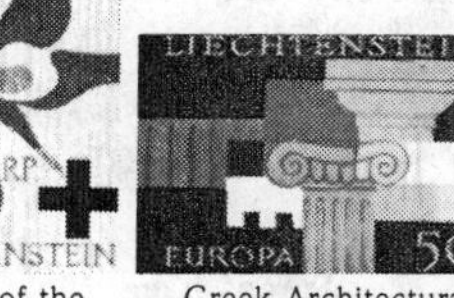
Greek Architectural Elements
A207

Perf. 11½

1963, Aug. 26 Unwmk. Photo.

376	A206	20rp shown	.30	.30
377	A206	80rp Three Kings	.70	.70
378	A206	1fr Family	.70	.70
		Nos. 376-378 (3)	1.70	1.70

Centenary of the International Red Cross.

Europa Issue, 1963

1963, Aug. 26

379 A207 50rp multicolored 1.50 1.50

Bread and Milk — A208

1963, Aug. 26

380 A208 50rp dk red pur & brn .40 .40

FAO "Freedom from Hunger" campaign.

Minnesinger Type of 1961-62

Minnesingers: 25rp, Heinrich von Sax. 30rp, Kristan von Hamle. 75rp, Werner von Teufen. 1.70fr, Hartmann von Aue.

Perf. 11½

1963, Dec. 5 Unwmk. Photo.

381	A199	25rp multicolored	.30	.30
382	A199	30rp multicolored	.30	.30
383	A199	75rp multicolored	.75	.75
384	A199	1.70fr multicolored	1.25	1.25
		Nos. 381-384 (4)	2.60	2.60

Issued in sheets of 20.

Olympic Rings, Flags of Austria and Japan — A209

1964, Apr. 15 *Perf. 11½*

385 A209 50rp Prus bl, red & blk .40 .40

Olympic Games 1964. Sheets of 20.

Arms of Counts of Werdenberg-Vaduz
A210

Coats of Arms: 30rp, Barons of Brandis. 80rp, Counts of Sulz. 1.50fr, Counts of Hohenems.

1964, Sept. 1 Photo.

386	A210	20rp multicolored	.15	.15
387	A210	30rp multicolored	.20	.20
388	A210	80rp multicolored	.45	.45
389	A210	1.50fr multicolored	.70	.70
		Nos. 386-389 (4)	1.50	1.50

See Nos. 396-399.

Europa Issue, 1964

Roman Castle, Schaan — A211

1964, Sept. 1 *Perf. 13x14*

390 A211 50rp multicolored 3.00 .95

Masescha Chapel — A212

Peter Kaiser — A213

40rp, Mary Magdalene, altarpiece. 1.30fr, Madonna with Sts. Sebastian & Roch, altarpiece.

1964, Dec. 9 Photo. *Perf. 11½*

391	A212	10rp violet black	.15	.15
392	A212	40rp dark blue	.40	.40
393	A212	1.30fr deep claret	1.00	1.00
		Nos. 391-393 (3)	1.55	1.55

Issued in sheets of 20.

1964, Dec. 9 Engr.

394 A213 1fr dk grn, *buff* .55 .55

Kaiser (1793-1864), historian. Sheets of 20.

Madonna, Wood Sculpture, 18th Century — A214

Perf. 11½

1965, Apr. 22 Unwmk. Engr.

395 A214 10fr orange red 7.00 6.00

Issued in sheets of 4.

Arms Type of 1965

Lords of: 20rp, Schellenberg. 30rp, Gutenberg. 80rp, Frauenberg. 1fr, Ramschwag.

Perf. 11½

1965, Aug. 31 Unwmk. Photo.

396	A210	20rp multicolored	.15	.15
397	A210	30rp multicolored	.15	.15
398	A210	80rp multicolored	.50	.50
399	A210	1fr multicolored	.55	.55
		Nos. 396-399 (4)	1.35	1.35

Alemannic Ornament
A215

Europa: The design is from a belt buckle, about 600 A.D., found in a man's tomb near Eschen.

1965, Aug. 31

400 A215 50rp vio bl, gray & brn .60 .45

The Annunciation by Ferdinand Nigg — A216

Princess Gina and Prince Franz Josef Wenzel — A217

Paintings by Nigg: 30rp, The Three Kings. 1.20fr, Jesus in the Temple, horiz.

1965, Dec. 7 Photo. *Perf. 11½*

401	A216	10rp yel grn & dk grn	.15	.15
402	A216	30rp orange & red brn	.25	.25
403	A216	1.20fr ultra & grnsh bl	.50	.50
		Nos. 401-403 (3)	.90	.90

Ferdinand Nigg (1865-1949), painter.

1965, Dec. 7

404 A217 75rp gray, buff & gold .40 .40

Communication Symbols — A218

1965, Dec. 7

405 A218 25rp multicolored .20 .20

Centenary of the ITU.

Soil Conservation, Tree — A219

Designs: 20rp, Clean air, bird. 30rp, Unpolluted water, fish. 1.50fr, Nature preservation, sun.

1966, Apr. 26 Photo. *Perf. 11½*

406	A219	10rp brt yellow & grn	.15	.15
407	A219	20rp blue & dk blue	.15	.15
408	A219	30rp brt green & ultra	.20	.20
409	A219	1.50fr yellow & red	.60	.60
		Nos. 406-409 (4)	1.10	1.10

Issued to publicize nature conservation.

Prince Franz Joseph II
A220

Arms of Barons of Richenstein
A221

1966, Apr. 26

410 A220 1fr gray, gold, buff & dk brn .50 .50

60th birthday of Prince Franz Joseph II.

1966, Sept. 6 Photo. *Perf. 11½*

Coats of Arms: 30rp, Vaistli knights. 60rp, Lords of Trisun. 1.20fr, von Schiel.

Light Gray Background

411 A221 20rp multicolored .15 .15
412 A221 30rp multicolored .15 .15
413 A221 60rp multicolored .20 .20
414 A221 1.20fr multicolored .45 .45
Nos. 411-414 (4) .95 .95

Common Design Types pictured following the introduction.

Europa Issue, 1966
Common Design Type

1966, Sept. 6 Photo. *Perf. 14x13*
Size: 25x32mm

415 CD9 50rp ultra, dp org & lt grn .40 .40

Vaduz Parish Church — A222

St. Florin — A223

Designs: 30rp, Madonna. 1.70fr, God the Father.

1966, Dec. 6 Photo. *Perf. 11½*

416 A222 5rp orange red & cit .15 .15
417 A223 20rp lemon & magenta .15 .15
418 A223 30rp dull rose & dp bl .20 .20
419 A223 1.70fr gray & red brown .65 .65
Nos. 416-419 (4) 1.15 1.15

Restoration of the Vaduz Parish Church.

Europa Issue, 1967
Common Design Type

1967, Apr. 20 Photo. *Perf. 11½*

420 CD10 50rp multicolored .40 .40

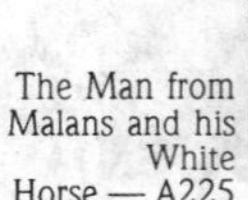

The Man from Malans and his White Horse — A225

Fairy Tales of Liechtenstein: 30rp, The Treasure of Gutenberg. 1.20fr, The Giant of Guflina slaying the Dragon.

1967, Apr. 20

421 A225 20rp multicolored .15 .15
422 A225 30rp multicolored .20 .15
423 A225 1.20fr green & multi .70 .65
Nos. 421-423 (3) 1.05 .95

See Nos. 443-445, 458-460.

Souvenir Sheet

Prince Hans Adam and Countess Kinsky — A226

1967, June 26 Engr. *Perf. 14x13½*

424 A226 Sheet of 2 2.00 2.00
a. 1.50fr slate blue (Prince) 1.00 1.00
b. 1.50fr red brown (Countess) 1.00 1.00

Wedding of Prince Hans Adam of Liechtenstein and Marie Aglae Countess Kinsky of Wichnitz and Tettau, July 30, 1967.

EFTA Emblem — A227

1967, Sept. 28 Photo. *Perf. 11½*

425 A227 50rp multicolored .45 .45

European Free Trade Association. See note after Norway No. 501.

A228

A229

Christian Symbols: 20rp, Alpha and Omega. 30rp, Trophaeum (The Victorious Cross). 70rp, Chrismon.

1967, Sept. 28

426 A228 20rp rose cl, blk, & gold .20 .15
427 A228 30rp multicolored .20 .15
428 A228 70rp dp ultra, blk & gold .55 .45
Nos. 426-428 (3) .95 .75

1967, Sept. 28 Engr. & Litho.

429 A229 1fr rose claret & pale grn .75 .55

Johann Baptist Büchel (1853-1927), priest, educator, historian and poet. Printed on fluorescent paper.

Peter and Paul, Patron Saints of Mauren — A230

Patron Saints: 5rp, St. Joseph, Planken. 10rp, St. Laurentius, Schaan. 30rp, St. Nicholas, Balzers. 40rp, St. Sebastian, Nendeln. 50rp, St. George, Schellenberg Chapel. 60rp, St. Martin, Eschen. 70rp, St. Fridolin, Ruggell. 80rp, St. Gallus, Triesen. 1fr, St. Theodul, Triesenberg. 1.20fr, St. Ann, Vaduz Castle. 1.50fr, St. Mary, Bendern-Gamprin. 2fr, St. Lucius, patron saint of the Principality.

1967-71 Photo. *Perf. 11½*

430 A230 5rp multi ('68) .15 .15
431 A230 10rp multi ('68) .15 .15
432 A230 20rp blue & multi .15 .15
433 A230 30rp dark red & multi .25 .15
433A A230 40rp multi ('71) .45 .35
434 A230 50rp multi ('68) .40 .30
435 A230 60rp multi ('68) .45 .35
436 A230 70rp multi .50 .40
437 A230 80rp multi ('68) .55 .50
438 A230 1fr multi ('68) .75 .55
439 A230 1.20fr violet bl & multi .80 .90
440 A230 1.50fr multi ('68) 1.10 .95
441 A230 2fr multi ('68) 1.25 1.25
Nos. 430-441 (13) 6.95 6.15

Issued: 20rp, 30rp, 70rp, 1.20fr, 12/7/67; 5rp, 1.50fr, 8/29/68; 40rp, 6/11/71; 2fr, 12/5/68; others 4/25/68.

Europa Issue, 1968
Common Design Type

1968, Apr. 25
Size: 32½x23mm

442 CD11 50rp crimson, gold & ultra .45 .45

Fairy Tale Type of 1967

30rp, The Treasure of St. Mamerten. 50rp, The Goblin from the Bergerwald. 80rp, The Three Sisters. (Denominations at right.)

1968, Aug. 29

443 A225 30rp Prus blue, yel & red .20 .15
444 A225 50rp green, yel & bl .35 .30
445 A225 80rp brt bl, yel & lt bl .55 .55
Nos. 443-445 (3) 1.10 1.00

Arms of Liechtenstein and Wilczek — A231

1968, Aug. 29

446 A231 75rp multicolored .65 .65

Silver wedding anniversary of Prince Franz Joseph II and Princess Gina.

Sir Rowland Hill — A232

Coat of Arms — A233

Portraits: 30rp, Count Philippe de Ferrari. 80rp, Carl Lindenberg. 1fr, Maurice Burrus. 1.20fr, Théodore Champion.

1968-69 Engr. *Perf. 14x13½*

447 A232 20rp green .15 .15
448 A232 30rp red brown .25 .20
449 A232 80rp dark brown .55 .45
450 A232 1fr black .70 .65
451 A232 1.20fr dark blue .90 .70
Nos. 447-451 (5) 2.55 2.15

Issued to honor "Pioneers of Philately."
Issued: 80rp, 1.20fr, 8/28/69; others, 12/5/68.
See Nos. 509-511.

1969, Apr. 24 Engr. *Perf. 14x13½*

452 A233 3.50fr dark brown 2.50 1.65

Sheets of 16.

Europa Issue, 1969
Common Design Type

1969, Apr. 24 Photo. *Perf. 14*
Size: 33x23mm

453 CD12 50rp brn red, yel & grn .60 .60

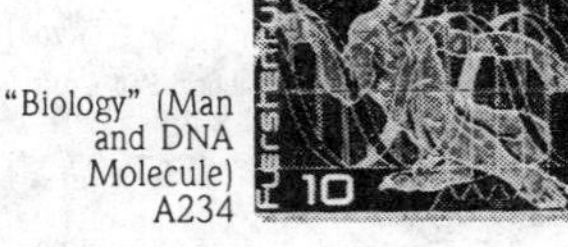

"Biology" (Man and DNA Molecule) A234

30rp, "Physics" (man and magnetic field). 50rp, "Astronomy" (man and planets). 80rp, "Art" (artist and Prince Franz Joseph II and Princess Gina).

1969, Aug. 28 Photo. *Perf. 11½*

454 A234 10rp grn, dk bl & dp cl .15 .15
455 A234 30rp brown & multi .25 .15
456 A234 50rp ultra & green .45 .30
457 A234 80rp brn, dk brn & yel .70 .50
Nos. 454-457 (4) 1.55 1.10

250th anniv. of the Duchy of Liechtenstein.

Fairy Tale Type of 1967

20rp, The Cheated Devil. 50rp, The Fiery Red Goat. 60rp, The Grafenberg Treasure (toad). (Denominations at right.)

1969, Dec. 4 Photo. *Perf. 11½*

458 A225 20rp multicolored .15 .15
459 A225 50rp yellow & multi .40 .35
460 A225 60rp red & multi .55 .45
Nos. 458-460 (3) 1.10 .95

"T" and Arms of Austria-Hungary, Liechtenstein and Switzerland A235

1969, Dec. 4 *Perf. 13½*

461 A235 30rp gold & multi .30 .25

Cent. of the Liechtenstein telegraph system.

Arms of St. Lucius Monastery, Chur — A236

Prince Wenzel — A237

Arms of Ecclesiastic Patrons: 50rp, Pfäfers Abbey (dove). 1.50fr, Chur Bishopric (stag).

1969, Dec. 4 *Perf. 11½*

462 A236 30rp multicolored .25 .20
463 A236 50rp multicolored .40 .35
464 A236 1.50fr multicolored 1.00 1.00
Nos. 462-464 (3) 1.65 1.55

See Nos. 475-477, 486-488.

1970, Apr. 30 Photo. *Perf. 11½*

465 A237 1fr sepia & multi .80 .80

25th anniv. of the Liechtenstein Red Cross.

Orange Lily — A238

Native Flowers: 30rp, Bumblebee orchid. 50rp, Glacier crowfoot. 1.20fr, Buck bean.

1970, Apr. 30

466 A238 20rp multicolored .20 .15
467 A238 30rp green & multi .25 .25
468 A238 50rp olive & multi .55 .55
469 A238 1.20fr multicolored 1.10 1.10
Nos. 466-469 (4) 2.10 2.05

Issued to publicize the European Conservation Year 1970. See Nos. 481-484, 500-503.

Europa Issue, 1970
Common Design Type

1970, Apr. 30 Litho. *Perf. 14*
Size: 31½x20½mm

470 CD13 50rp emerald, dk bl & yel .50 .50

Minnesinger Type of 1961-62
Souvenir Sheet

Minnesingers: 30rp, Wolfram von Eschenbach. 50rp, Reinmar der Fiedler. 80rp, Hartmann von Starkenberg. 1.20fr, Friedrich von Hausen.

1970, Aug. 27 Photo. *Perf. 11½*

471 Sheet of 4 2.25 2.25
a. A199 30rp multicolored .15 .15
b. A199 50rp multicolored .30 .30
c. A199 80rp multicolored .50 .50
d. A199 1.20fr multicolored .65 .65

Wolfram von Eschenbach (1170-1220), German minnesinger (poet). Sold for 3fr.

Prince Franz Joseph II — A239

Mother & Child, Sculpture by Rudolf Schädler — A240

Portrait: 2.50fr, Princess Gina.

1970-71 Engr. *Perf. 14x13½*

472 A239 2.50fr violet blue 1.90 1.10
473 A239 3fr black 2.00 1.25

Issued: 2.50fr, 6/11/71; 3fr, 12/3/70. Sheets of 16.

1970, Dec. 3 Photo. *Perf. 11½*

474 A240 30rp dark red & multi .30 .30

Christmas.

Ecclesiastic Arms Type of 1969

Arms of Ecclesiastic Patrons: 20rp, Abbey of St. John in Thur Valley (Lamb of God). 30rp, Ladies' Abbey, Schänis (crown). 75rp, Abbey of St. Gallen (bear rampant).

1970, Dec. 3

475 A236 20rp lt blue & multi .20 .20
476 A236 30rp gray, red & gold .25 .25
477 A236 75rp multicolored .60 .60
Nos. 475-477 (3) 1.05 1.05

Bronze Boar, La Tène Period — A241

Designs: 30rp, Peacock, Roman, 2nd century. 75rp, Decorated copper bowl, 13th century.

1971, Mar. 11 Photo. *Perf. 11½*

478 A241 25rp dp ultra & bluish blk .25 .25
479 A241 30rp dk brown & green .25 .25
480 A241 75rp green, yel & brn .60 .60
Nos. 478-480 (3) 1.10 1.10

Opening of the National Museum, Vaduz.

Flower Type of 1970

Flowers: 10rp, Cyclamen. 20rp, Moonwort. 50rp, Superb pink. 1.50fr, Alpine columbine.

1971, Mar. 11

481 A238 10rp multicolored .15 .15
482 A238 20rp multicolored .15 .15
483 A238 50rp multicolored .45 .45
484 A238 1.50fr multicolored 1.25 1.10
Nos. 481-484 (4) 2.00 1.85

Europa Issue, 1971

Common Design Type

1971, June 11 Photo. *Perf. 13½*

Size: 31x21mm

485 CD14 50rp grnsh bl, yel & blk .55 .55

Ecclesiastic Arms Type of 1969

Arms of Ecclesiastic Patrons: 30rp, Knights of St. John, Feldkirch (Latin and moline crosses). 50rp, Weingarten Abbey (grapes). 1.20fr, Ottobeuren Abbey (eagle and cross).

1971, Sept. 2 Photo. *Perf. 11½*

486 A236 30rp bister & multi .25 .25
487 A236 50rp multicolored .35 .35
488 A236 1.20fr gray & multi .90 .90
Nos. 486-488 (3) 1.50 1.50

Princely Crown — A242

Design: 70rp, Page from constitution.

1971, Sept. 2

489 A242 70rp grn, gold, blk & cop .55 .55
490 A242 80rp dk bl, gold, red & plum .65 .65

50th anniversary of the constitution.

Madonna, by Andrea della Robbia — A243

Long-distance Skiing — A244

1971, Dec. 9

491 A243 30rp multicolored .30 .25

Christmas 1971.

1971, Dec. 9

Olympic Rings and: 40rp, Ice hockey. 65rp, Downhill skiing, women's. 1.50fr, Figure skating, women's.

492 A244 15rp lemon & dk brn .15 .15
493 A244 40rp multicolored .35 .30
494 A244 65rp multicolored .55 .55
495 A244 1.50fr multicolored 1.25 1.10
Nos. 492-495 (4) 2.30 2.10

11th Winter Olympic Games, Sapporo, Japan, Feb. 3-13, 1972.

1972, Mar. 16 Photo. *Perf. 11*

10rp, Gymnast. 20rp, High jump. 40rp, Running, women's. 60rp, Discus. All horiz.

496 A244 10rp claret, brn & gray .15 .15
497 A244 20rp olive, brn & yel .20 .20
498 A244 40rp red, brn & gray .30 .30
499 A244 60rp brn, dk brn & bl .65 .50
Nos. 496-499 (4) 1.30 1.15

20th Olympic Games, Munich, Aug. 26-Sept. 10.

Flower Type of 1970

Flowers: 20rp, Anemone. 30rp, Turk's cap. 60rp, Alpine centaury. 1.20fr, Reed mace.

1972, Mar. 16

500 A238 20rp dk blue & multi .20 .15
501 A238 30rp olive & multi .25 .20
502 A238 60rp multicolored .55 .55
503 A238 1.20fr multicolored 1.00 1.00
Nos. 500-503 (4) 2.00 1.90

Europa Issue, 1972

Common Design Type

1972, Mar. 16

504 CD15 40rp dk ol, bl grn & rose red .50 .50

Souvenir Sheet

Bendern and Vaduz Castle — A246

1972, June 8 Engr. *Perf. 13½*

505 A246 Sheet of 2 2.75 2.75
a. 1fr violet blue .90 .90
b. 2fr carmine 1.75 1.75

8th Liechtenstein Philatelic Exhibition, LIBA 1972, Vaduz, Aug. 18-27.

Faun, by Rudolf Schädler A247

Madonna with Angels, by Ferdinand Nigg A248

1972, Sept. 7 Photo. *Perf. 11½*

506 A247 20rp shown .15 .15
507 A247 30rp Dancer .20 .20
508 A247 1.10fr Owl .85 .80
Nos. 506-508 (3) 1.20 1.15

Sculptures made of roots and branches by Rudolf Schädler.

Portrait Type of 1968-69

Portraits: 30rp, Emilio Diena. 40rp, André de Cock. 1.30fr, Theodore E. Steinway.

1972, Sept. 7 Engr. *Perf. 14x13½*

509 A232 30rp Prus green .20 .15
510 A232 40rp dk violet brn .30 .25
511 A232 1.30fr violet blue 1.00 .90
Nos. 509-511 (3) 1.50 1.30

Pioneers of Philately.

1972, Dec. 7 Photo. *Perf. 11½*

512 A248 30rp black & multi .30 .25

Christmas 1972.

Lawena Springs — A249

Nautilus Cup — A250

Landscapes: 5rp, Silum. 15rp, Ruggell Marsh. 25rp, Steg, Kirchlispitz. 30rp, Fields, Schellenberg. 40rp, Rennhof, Mauren. 50rp, Tidrüfe Vaduz. 60rp, Eschner Riet. 70rp, Mittagspitz. 80rp, Three Sisters, Schaan Forest. 1fr, St. Peter's and Tower House, Mäls. 1.30fr, Road, Frommenhaus. 1.50fr, Ox Head Mountain. 1.80fr, Hehlawangspitz. 2fr, Saminaschlucht.

1972-73 Engr. & Litho. *Perf. 11½*

513 A249 5rp brown, yel & mag .15 .15
514 A249 10rp slate grn & cit .15 .15
515 A249 15rp red brn & citron .15 .15
516 A249 25rp dk vio & pale grn .25 .15
517 A249 30rp purple & buff .25 .20
518 A249 40rp vio & pale salmon .30 .25
519 A249 50rp vio bl & rose .40 .35
520 A249 60rp green & yellow .50 .45
521 A249 70rp dk & lt blue .60 .50
522 A249 80rp Prus grn & cit .65 .55
523 A249 1fr red brn & lt grn .85 .65
524 A249 1.30fr ultra & lt grn 1.10 1.00
525 A249 1.50fr brn & lt blue 1.25 1.00
526 A249 1.80fr brown & buff 1.50 1.25
527 A249 2fr sepia & pale grn 1.65 1.40
Nos. 513-527 (15) 9.75 8.20

Issued: 10rp, 15rp, 80rp, 1fr, 1.50fr, 12/7; 30rp, 1.30fr, 1.80fr, 3/8/73; 50rp, 60rp, 70rp, 6/7/73; 5rp, 25rp, 40rp, 2fr, 12/6/73.

Europa Issue, 1973

Common Design Type

1973, Mar. 8 Photo. *Perf. 11½*

Size: 33x23mm

528 CD16 30rp purple & multi .30 .30
529 CD16 40rp blue & multi .45 .45

1973, June 7 Photo. *Perf. 11½*

70rp, Ivory tankard. 1.10fr, Silver goblet.

530 A250 30rp gray & multi .20 .20
531 A250 70rp multicolored .50 .50
532 A250 1.10fr dk blue & multi .90 .90
Nos. 530-532 (3) 1.60 1.60

Drinking vessels from the Princely Treasury.

Arms of Liechtenstein and Municipalities A251

Engraved & Photogravure

1973, Sept. 6 *Perf. 14x13½*

533 A251 5fr black & multi 4.00 3.00

Coenonympha Oedippus A252

Designs: 15rp, Alpine newt. 25rp, European viper (adder). 40rp, Common curlew. 60rp, Edible frog. 70rp, Dappled butterfly. 80rp, Grass snake. 1.10fr, Three-toed woodpecker.

1973-74 Photo. *Perf. 11½*

534 A252 15rp multicolored .15 .15
535 A252 25rp multicolored .30 .25
536 A252 30rp orange & multi .25 .25
537 A252 40rp brown & multi .35 .35
538 A252 60rp multicolored .60 .60
539 A252 70rp multicolored .65 .60
540 A252 80rp multicolored .70 .70
541 A252 1.10fr multicolored 1.00 1.00
Nos. 534-541 (8) 4.00 3.90

Issue dates: 30rp, 40rp, 60rp, 80rp, Dec. 6. Others, June 6, 1974.

Virgin and Child, by Bartolomeo di Tommaso — A253

The Vociferant Horseman, by Andrea Riccio — A254

Engraved & Lithographed

1973, Dec. 6 *Perf. 13½*

542 A253 30rp gold & multi .40 .30

Christmas 1973.

1974, Mar. 21 Photo. *Perf. 11½*

Europa: 40rp, Kneeling Venus, by Antonio Susini.

543 A254 30rp tan & multi .40 .35
544 A254 40rp ultra & multi .55 .50

Chinese Vase, 19th Century A255

Soccer A256

Designs: Chinese vases from Princely Treasury.

1974, Mar. 21

545 A255 30rp shown .30 .25
546 A255 50rp from 1740 .45 .40
547 A255 60rp from 1830 .55 .55
548 A255 1fr circa 1700 .95 .95
Nos. 545-548 (4) 2.25 2.15

1974, Mar. 21

549 A256 80rp lemon & multi .80 .75

World Soccer Championships, Munich June 13-July 7.

Post Horn and UPU Emblem A257

1974, June 6 *Perf. 13½*

550 A257 40rp gold, green & blk .35 .30
551 A257 60rp gold, red & blk .55 .40

Centenary of Universal Postal Union.

Bishop F. A. Marxer — A258

Photogravure and Engraved

1974, June 6 *Perf. 14x13½*

552 A258 1fr multicolored .85 .85

Bicentenary of the death of Bishop Franz Anton Marxer (1703-1775).

Prince Constantin A259

Prince Hans Adam — A260

Princess Gina and Prince Franz Joseph II — A261

80rp, Prince Maximilian. 1.20fr, Prince Alois.

1974-75 Photo. *Perf. 11½*

553 A259 70rp dk green & gold .70 .55
554 A259 80rp dp claret & gold .75 .65
555 A259 1.20fr bluish blk & gold 1.10 1.00

Engr.

Perf. 14x13½

556 A260 1.70fr slate green 1.40 1.25

Photogravure and Engraved

Perf. 13½x14

557 A261 10fr gold & choc 8.00 8.00
Nos. 553-557 (5) 11.95 11.45

No. 557 printed in sheets of 4.
Issue dates: 1.70fr, Dec. 5, 1974; 10fr, Sept. 5, 1974; others, Mar. 13, 1975.

St. Florian — A262

Designs: 50rp, St. Wendelin. 60rp, Virgin Mary with Sts. Anna and Joachim. 70rp, Nativity.

1974, Dec. 5 Photo. *Perf. 12*

560 A262 30rp multicolored .30 .25
561 A262 50rp multicolored .40 .35
562 A262 60rp multicolored .50 .50
563 A262 70rp multicolored .65 .65
Nos. 560-563 (4) 1.85 1.75

Designs are from 19th century devotional glass paintings. Christmas 1974.

"Cold Sun," by Martin Frommelt A263

Europa: 60rp, "Village," by Louis Jaeger.

1975, Mar. 13 *Perf. 11½*

564 A263 30rp multicolored .25 .25
565 A263 60rp multicolored .55 .55

Red Cross Activities — A264

Imperial Crown — A266

Coronation Robe — A265

1975, June 5 Photo. *Perf. 11½*

566 A264 60rp dk blue & multi .55 .55

30th anniv. of the Liechtenstein Red Cross.

1975 Engr. & Photo. *Perf. 14*

567 A266 30rp Imperial cross .45 .40
568 A266 60rp Imperial sword .70 .70
569 A266 1fr Orb 1.40 1.25
570 A265 1.30fr shown 18.00 17.50
571 A266 2fr shown 3.50 2.75
Nos. 567-571 (5) 24.05 22.60

Treasures of the Holy Roman Empire from the Treasury of the Hofburg in Vienna, Austria.
Issue dates: 1.30fr, Sept. 4; others, June 5.
See Nos. 617-620.

St. Mamerten, Triesen — A267

Designs: 50rp, Red House, Vaduz, 14th century. 70rp, Prebendary House, Eschen, 14th century. 1fr, Gutenberg Castle.

1975, Sept. 4 Photo. *Perf. 11½*

572 A267 40rp multicolored .40 .35
573 A267 50rp multicolored .45 .35
574 A267 70rp plum & multi .85 .85
575 A267 1fr dk blue & multi 1.10 1.10
Nos. 572-575 (4) 2.80 2.65

European Architectural Heritage Year 1975.

Speed Skating — A268

Designs (Olympic Rings and): 25rp, Ice hockey. 70rp, Downhill skiing. 1.20fr, Slalom.

1975, Dec. 4 Photo. *Perf. 11½*

576 A268 20rp multicolored .20 .15
577 A268 25rp multicolored .25 .20
578 A268 70rp multicolored .60 .50
579 A268 1.20fr yellow & multi 1.10 .95
Nos. 576-579 (4) 2.15 1.80

12th Winter Olympic Games, Innsbruck, Austria, Feb. 4-15, 1976.

Daniel in the Lions' Den A269

River Crayfish A270

Designs: 60rp, Virgin and Child. 90rp, St. Peter. All designs are after Romanesque sculptured capitals in Chur Cathedral, c. 1208.

Photogravure and Engraved

1975, Dec. 4 *Perf. 14*

580 A269 30rp gold & purple .25 .25
581 A269 60rp gold & green .40 .40
582 A269 90rp gold & claret .75 .75
Nos. 580-582 (3) 1.40 1.40

Christmas and Holy Year 1975.

1976, Mar. 11 Photo. *Perf. 11½*

World Wildlife Fund: 40rp, European pond turtle. 70rp, Old-world otter. 80rp, Lapwing.

583 A270 25rp multicolored .35 .35
584 A270 40rp multicolored .50 .50
585 A270 70rp multicolored .85 .85
586 A270 80rp multicolored 1.25 1.25
Nos. 583-586 (4) 2.95 2.95

Mouflon — A271

Europa: 80rp, Pheasant family. Ceramics by Prince Hans von Liechtenstein.

1976, Mar. 11

587 A271 40rp multicolored .50 .40
588 A271 80rp violet & multi 1.00 .85

Roman Fibula, 3rd Century — A272

1976, Mar. 11

589 A272 90rp vio bl, grn & gold 1.00 .80

Historical Association of Liechtenstein, 75th anniversary.

Souvenir Sheet

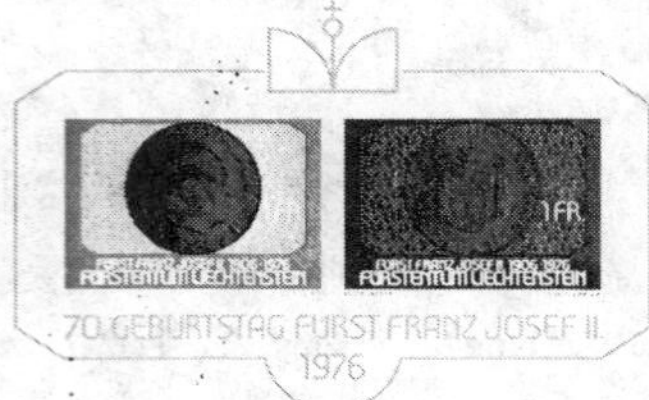

Franz Josef II 50fr-Memorial Coin — A273

1976, June 10 Photo. *Imperf.*

590 A273 Sheet of 2 1.75 1.75
a. 1fr blue & multi .85 .85
b. 1fr red & multi .85 .85

70th birthday of Prince Franz Joseph II of Liechtenstein.

Judo and Olympic Rings — A274

Rubens' Sons, Albrecht and Nikolas — A275

Designs (Olympic Rings and): 50rp, volleyball. 80rp, Relay race. 1.10fr, Long jump, women's.

1976, June 10 *Perf. 11½*

591 A274 35rp multicolored .25 .25
592 A274 50rp multicolored .45 .45
593 A274 80rp multicolored .65 .65
594 A274 1.10fr multicolored .90 .90
Nos. 591-594 (4) 2.25 2.25

21st Olympic Games, Montreal, Canada, July 17-Aug. 1.

1976, Sept. 9 Engr. *Perf. 13½x14*

Rubens Paintings: 50rp, Singing Angels. 1fr, The Daughters of Cecrops, horiz. (from Collection of Prince of Liechtenstein).

Size: 24x38mm

595 A275 50rp gold & multi 1.40 1.40
596 A275 70rp gold & multi 2.00 2.00

Size: 48x38mm

597 A275 1fr gold & multi 5.50 5.50
Nos. 595-597 (3) 8.90 8.90

400th anniversary of the birth of Peter Paul Rubens (1577-1640), Flemish painter. Sheets of 8 (2x4).

Zodiac Signs — A276

1976-78 Photo. *Perf. 11½*

598 A276 20rp Pisces .20 .20
599 A276 40rp Aries .35 .35
600 A276 40rp Cancer ('77) .40 .35
601 A276 40rp Scorpio ('78) .45 .45
602 A276 50rp Sagittarius ('78) .50 .45
603 A276 70rp Leo ('77) .65 .65
604 A276 80rp Taurus .75 .70
605 A276 80rp Virgo ('77) .75 .75
606 A276 80rp Capricorn ('78) .75 .70
607 A276 90rp Gemini 1.00 .75
608 A276 1.10fr Libra ('77) 1.10 1.10
609 A276 1.50fr Aquarius 1.25 1.25
Nos. 598-609 (12) 8.15 7.70

Flight into Egypt A277

Ortlieb von Brandis, Sarcophagus A278

Monastic Wax Works: 20rp, Holy Infant of Prague, horiz. 80rp, Holy Family and Trinity. 1.50fr, Holy Family, horiz.

1976, Dec. 9 Photo. *Perf. 11½*

610 A277 20rp multicolored .20 .20
611 A277 50rp multicolored .40 .40
612 A277 80rp multicolored .55 .55
613 A277 1.50fr multicolored 1.25 1.25
Nos. 610-613 (4) 2.40 2.40

Christmas 1976.

Photogravure and Engraved

1976, Dec. 9 *Perf. 13½x14*

614 A278 1.10fr gold & dk brown .90 .70

Ortlieb von Brandis, Bishop of Chur (1458-1491).

Map of Liechtenstein, by J. J. Heber, 1721 — A279

Europa: 80rp, View of Vaduz, by Ferdinand Bachmann, 1815.

1977, Mar. 10 Photo. *Perf. 12½*

615 A279 40rp multicolored .45 .45
616 A279 80rp multicolored .90 .90

Treasure Type of 1975

40rp, Holy Lance and Particle of the Cross. 50rp, Imperial Evangel of St. Matthew. 80rp, St. Stephen's Purse. 90rp, Tabard of Imperial Herald.

Engraved and Photogravure

1977, June 8 *Perf. 14*

617 A266 40rp gold & multi .40 .30
618 A266 50rp gold & multi .50 .45
619 A266 80rp gold & multi .70 .65
620 A266 90rp gold & multi 1.00 .90
Nos. 617-620 (4) 2.60 2.30

Treasures of the Holy Roman Empire from the Treasury of the Hofburg in Vienna.

Emperor Constantius II Coin — A280

Coins: 70rp, Lindau bracteate, c. 1300. 80rp, Ortlieb von Brandis, 1458-1491.

1977, June 8 Photo. *Perf. 11½*

Granite Paper

621	A280	35rp	gold & multi	.35	.30
622	A280	70rp	silver & multi	.60	.55
623	A280	80rp	silver & multi	.80	.65
			Nos. 621-623 (3)	1.75	1.50

Frauenthal Castle — A281

Castles: 50rp, Gross Ullersdorf. 80rp, Liechtenstein Castle near Mödling, Austria. 90rp, Liechtenstein Palace, Vienna.

Engraved and Photogravure

1977, Sept. 8 *Perf. 13½x14*

624	A281	20rp	slate grn & gold	.20	.20
625	A281	50rp	magenta & gold	.50	.50
626	A281	80rp	dk violet & gold	.80	.80
627	A281	90rp	dk blue & gold	.90	.90
			Nos. 624-627 (4)	2.40	2.40

Children — A282

Traditional Costumes: 70rp, Two girls. 1fr, Woman in festival dress.

1977, Sept. 8 Photo. *Perf. 11½*

Granite Paper

628	A282	40rp	multicolored	.50	.42
629	A282	70rp	multicolored	.75	.70
630	A282	1fr	multicolored	1.25	1.10
			Nos. 628-630 (3)	2.50	2.22

Princess Tatjana A283

1977, Dec. 7 Photo. *Perf. 11½*

631	A283	1.10fr	brown & gold	.90	.85

Angel — A284

Liechtenstein Palace, Vienna — A285

Sculptures by Erasmus Kern: 50rp, St. Rochus. 80rp, Virgin and Child. 1.50fr, God the Father.

1977, Dec. 7

632	A284	20rp	multicolored	.15	.15
633	A284	50rp	multicolored	.45	.45
634	A284	80rp	multicolored	.75	.75
635	A284	1.50fr	multicolored	1.50	1.50
			Nos. 632-635 (4)	2.85	2.85

Christmas 1977.

Photogravure and Engraved

1978, Mar. 2 *Perf. 14*

Europa: 80rp, Feldsberg Castle.

636	A285	40rp	gold & slate blue	.40	.40
637	A285	80rp	gold & claret	.80	.80

Residential Tower, Balzers-Mäls — A286

Designs: 10rp, Farmhouse, Triesen. 20rp, Houses, Upper Village, Triesen. 35rp, Barns, Balzers. 40rp, Monastery, Bendern. 70rp, Parish house. 80rp, Farmhouse, Schellenberg. 90rp, Parish house, Balzers. 1fr, Rheinberger House, Music School, Vaduz. 1.10fr, Street, Mitteldorf, Vaduz. 1.50fr, Town Hall, Triesenberg. 2fr, National Museum and Administrator's Residence, Vaduz.

1978 Photo. *Perf. 11½*

638	A286	10rp	multicolored	.15	.15
639	A286	20rp	multicolored	.15	.15
640	A286	35rp	multicolored	.30	.30
641	A286	40rp	multicolored	.30	.30
642	A286	50rp	multicolored	.40	.40
643	A286	70rp	multicolored	.55	.55
644	A286	80rp	multicolored	.60	.60
645	A286	90rp	multicolored	.70	.70
646	A286	1fr	multicolored	.75	.75
647	A286	1.10fr	multicolored	.90	.90
648	A286	1.50fr	multicolored	1.10	1.10
649	A286	2fr	multicolored	1.50	1.50
			Nos. 638-649 (12)	7.40	7.40

Vaduz Castle — A287

Vaduz Castle: 50rp, Courtyard. 70rp, Staircase. 80rp, Triptych from High Altar, Castle Chapel.

Engraved and Photogravure

1978, June 1 *Perf. 13½x14*

650	A287	40rp	gold & multi	.45	.45
651	A287	50rp	gold & multi	.60	.60
652	A287	70rp	gold & multi	.85	.85
653	A287	80rp	gold & multi	1.10	1.10
			Nos. 650-653 (4)	3.00	3.00

40th anniversary of reign of Prince Franz Joseph II. Sheet of 8.

Prince Karl I, Coin, 1614 A288

Adoration of the Shepherds A289

Designs: 50rp, Prince Johann Adam, medal, 1694. 80rp, Prince Josef Wenzel, medal, 1773.

1978, Sept. 7 Photo. *Perf. 11½*

654	A288	40rp	multicolored	.35	.35
655	A288	50rp	multicolored	.50	.50
656	A288	80rp	multicolored	.95	.95
			Nos. 654-656 (3)	1.80	1.80

1978, Dec. 7 Photo. *Perf. 11½*

Stained-glass Windows, Triesenberg: 50rp, Holy Family. 80rp, Adoration of the Kings.

657	A289	20rp	multicolored	.20	.20
658	A289	50rp	multicolored	.50	.50
659	A289	80rp	multicolored	.80	.80
			Nos. 657-659 (3)	1.50	1.50

Christmas 1978.

Piebald, by Hamilton and Faistenberger A290

Golden Carriage of Prince Joseph Wenzel, by Martin von Meytens — A291

Design: 80rp, Black stallion, by Johann Georg von Hamilton.

Photo. & Engr.

1978, Dec. 7 *Perf. 13½x14*

660	A290	70rp	multicolored	.60	.60
661	A290	80rp	multicolored	.70	.70

Perf. 12

662	A291	1.10fr	multicolored	.95	.95
			Nos. 660-662 (3)	2.25	2.25

Sheets of 8.

Mail Plane over Schaan — A292

Europa: 80rp, Zeppelin over Vaduz Castle.

1979, Mar. 8 Photo. *Perf. 11½*

663	A292	40rp	multicolored	.70	.70
664	A292	80rp	multicolored	.80	.80

First airmail service, St. Gallen to Schaan, Aug. 31, 1930, and first Zeppelin flight to Liechtenstein, June 10, 1931.

Child Drinking — A293

90rp, Child eating. 1.10fr, Child reading.

1979, Mar. 8

665	A293	80rp	silver & multi	.75	.70
666	A293	90rp	silver & multi	.85	.85
667	A293	1.10fr	silver & multi	.95	.95
			Nos. 665-667 (3)	2.55	2.50

International Year of the Child.

Ordered Wave Fields A294

Sun over Continents A296

Council of Europe A295

1979, June 7 Litho. *Perf. 11½*

668	A294	50rp	multicolored	.35	.35

Photo.

669	A295	80rp	multicolored	.75	.75
670	A296	100rp	multicolored	.75	.75
			Nos. 668-670 (3)	1.85	1.85

Intl. Radio Consultative Committee (CCIR) of the Intl. Telecommunications Union, 50th anniv. (50rp); Entry into Council of Europe (80rp); aid to developing countries (100rp).

Heraldic Panel of Carl Ludwig von Sulz — A297

Heraldic Panels of: 70rp, Barbara von Sulz, née zu Staufen. 1.10fr, Ulrich von Ramschwag and Barbara von Hallwil.

Photogravure and Engraved

1979, June 1 *Perf. 13½*

671	A297	40rp	multicolored	.30	.30
672	A297	70rp	multicolored	.50	.50
673	A297	1.10fr	multicolored	.95	.95
			Nos. 671-673 (3)	1.75	1.75

Sts. Lucius and Florin, Fresco in Waltensburg-Vuorz Church — A298

Photogravure and Engraved

1979, Sept. 6 *Perf. 13½*

674	A298	20fr	multicolored	15.00	15.00

Patron saints of Liechtenstein. Printed in sheets of 4.

Annunciation, Embroidery — A299

Christmas (Ferdnand Nigg Embroideries): 50rp, Christmas. 80rp, Blessed Are the Peacemakers.

1979, Dec. 6 Engr. *Perf. 13½*

675 A299 20rp multicolored	.20	.20
676 A299 50rp multicolored	.45	.45
677 A299 80rp multicolored	.70	.70
Nos. 675-677 (3)	1.35	1.35

Cross-Country Skiing — A300

Olympic Rings and: 70rp, Oxhead Mountain. 1.50fr, Ski lift.

1979, Dec. 6 Photo. *Perf. 12*

678 A300 40rp multicolored	.30	.25
679 A300 70rp multicolored	.55	.50
680 A300 1.50fr multicolored	1.25	1.10
Nos. 678-680 (3)	2.10	1.85

13th Winter Olympic Games, Lake Placid, NY, Feb. 12-24, 1980.

Arms of Bailiff Andreas Buchel, 1690 — A301

Designs: Various arms.

1980, Mar. 10 Photo. *Perf. 11½*
Granite Paper

681 A301 40rp shown	.30	.30
682 A301 70rp Georg Marxer, 1745	.50	.50
683 A301 80rp Luzius Frick, 1503	.60	.60
684 A301 1.10fr Adam Oehri, 1634	.95	.95
Nos. 681-684 (4)	2.35	2.35

See Nos. 704-707, 729-732.

Princess Maria Leopoldine Esterhazy, by Antonio Canova — A302

Europa: 80rp, Maria Theresa, Duchess of Savoy, by Martin van Meytens.

1980, Mar. 10

685 A302 40rp multicolored	.80	.80
686 A302 80rp multicolored	.80	.80

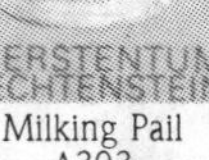

Milking Pail A303 — Liechtenstein A304

Old Alpine Farm Tools: 50rp, Wooden heart, ceremonial cattle decoration. 80rp, Butter churn.

1980, Sept. 8

687 A303 20rp multicolored	.20	.20
688 A303 50rp multicolored	.45	.45
689 A303 80rp multicolored	.75	.75
Nos. 687-689 (3)	1.40	1.40

1980, Sept 8

690 A304 80rp multicolored	.75	.75

Postal Museum, 50th anniversary.

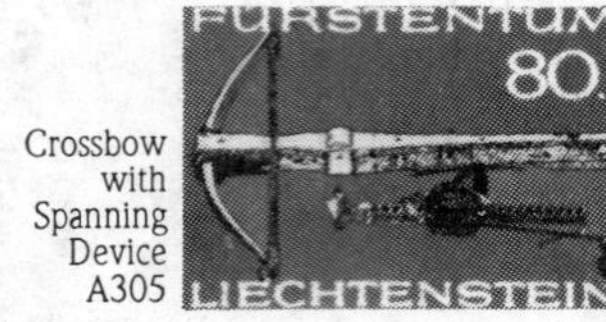

Crossbow with Spanning Device A305

1980, Sept. 8 Engr. *Perf. 13½x14*

691 A305 80rp shown	.70	.70
692 A305 90rp Spear, knife	.75	.75
693 A305 1.10fr Rifle, powderhorn	1.00	1.00
Nos. 691-693 (3)	2.45	2.45

Triesenberg Family In Traditional Costumes A306

1980, Sept. 8 Photo. *Perf. 12*
Granite Paper

694 A306 40rp shown	.35	.35
695 A306 70rp Folk dancers, Schellenberg	.55	.55
696 A306 80rp Brass band, Mauren	.65	.65
Nos. 694-696 (3)	1.55	1.55

Green Beeches, Matrula Forest — A307

Glad Tidings — A308

Photogravure and Engraved
1980, Dec. 9 *Perf. 14*

697 A307 40rp shown	.35	.35
698 A307 50rp White firs, Valorsch Valley	.45	.45
699 A307 80rp Beech forest, Schaan	.65	.65
700 A307 1.50fr Forest, Oberplanken	1.25	1.25
Nos. 697-700 (4)	2.70	2.70

1980, Dec. 9 Photo. *Perf. 11½*
Granite Paper

701 A308 20rp shown	.15	.15
702 A308 50rp Creche	.45	.45
703 A308 80rp Epiphany	.70	.70
Nos. 701-703 (3)	1.30	1.30

Christmas 1980.

Bailiff Arms Type of 1980

1981, Mar. 9 Photo. *Perf. 11½*
Granite Paper

704 A301 40rp Anton Meier, 1748	.30	.30
705 A301 70rp Kaspar Kindle, 1534	.50	.50
706 A301 80rp Hans Adam Negele, 1600	.60	.60
707 A301 1.10fr Peter Matt, 1693	.90	.90
Nos. 704-707 (4)	2.30	2.30

Fireworks at Vaduz Castle — A309

Europa: 80rp, National Day procession.

1981, Mar. 9 *Perf. 12½*
Granite Paper

708 A309 40rp multicolored	.45	.45
709 A309 80rp multicolored	.90	.90

Souvenir Sheet

Prince Alois, Princess Elisabeth and Prince Franz Joseph II — A310

1981, June 9 Photo. *Perf. 13*
Granite Paper

710 Sheet of 3	2.50	2.50
a. A310 70rp shown	.50	.50
b. A310 80rp Princes Alois and Franz Joseph II	.55	.55
c. A310 150rp Prince Franz Joseph II	1.00	1.00

75th birthday of Prince Franz Joseph II.

Scout Emblems A311

Man in Wheelchair A312

1981, June 9

711 A311 20rp multicolored	.15	.15

50th anniversary of Boy Scouts and Girl Guides.

1981, June 9

712 A312 40rp multicolored	.25	.25

International Year of the Disabled.

St. Theodul, 1600th Birth Anniv. — A313

Mosses and Lichens — A314

1981, June 9

713 A313 80rp multicolored	.55	.55

Photogravure and Engraved
1981, Sept. 7 *Perf. 13½*

714 A314 40rp Xanthoria parietina	.30	.30
715 A314 50rp Parmelia physodes	.35	.35
716 A314 70rp Sphagnum palustre	.50	.50
717 A314 80rp Amblystegium	.60	.60
Nos. 714-717 (4)	1.75	1.75

Gutenberg Castle — A315

1981, Sept. 7

718 A315 20rp shown	.15	.15
719 A315 40rp Castle yard	.30	.30
720 A315 50rp Parlor	.35	.35
721 A315 1.10fr Great Hall	.85	.85
Nos. 718-721 (4)	1.65	1.65

St. Charles Borromeo (1538-1584) — A316

St. Nicholas — A317

Famous Visitors to Liechtenstein (Paintings): 70rp, Goethe (1749-1832), by Angelica Kauffmann. 80rp, Alexander Dumas (1824-1895). 1fr, Hermann Hesse (1877-1962), by Cuno Amiet.

Lithographed and Engraved
1981, Dec. 7 *Perf. 14*

722 A316 40rp multicolored	.35	.35
723 A316 70rp multicolored	.60	.60
724 A316 80rp multicolored	.70	.70
725 A316 1fr multicolored	.80	.80
Nos. 722-725 (4)	2.45	2.45

See Nos. 747-750.

1981, Dec. 7 Photo. *Perf. 11½*
Granite Paper

726 A317 20rp shown	.15	.15
727 A317 50rp Adoration of the Kings	.45	.45
728 A317 80rp Holy Family	.70	.70
Nos. 726-728 (3)	1.30	1.30

Christmas 1981.

Bailiff Arms Type of 1980

1982, Mar. 8 Photo.
Granite Paper

729 A301 40rp Johann Kaiser, 1664	.35	.35
730 A301 70rp Joseph Anton Kaufmann, 1748	.55	.55
731 A301 80rp Christoph Walser, 1690	.70	.70
732 A301 1.10fr Stephan Banzer, 1658	1.00	1.00
Nos. 729-732 (4)	2.60	2.60

Europa 1982 — A318

1982, Mar. 8
Granite Paper

733 A318 40rp Peasants' Uprising, 1525	.35	.35
734 A318 80rp Imperial Direct Rule, 1396	.70	.70

Hereditary Prince Hans Adam — A319

1982, June 7 Granite Paper

735 A319 1fr shown	.75	.75
736 A319 1fr Princess Marie Aglae	.75	.75

LIBA '82, 10th Liechtenstein Philatelic Exhibition, Vaduz, July 31-Aug. 8.

1982 World Cup — A320

Designs: Sports arenas.

1982, June 7 Granite Paper

737 A320 15rp Triesenberg	.15	.15
738 A320 25rp Mauren	.20	.20
739 A320 1.80fr Balzers	1.25	1.25
Nos. 737-739 (3)	1.60	1.60

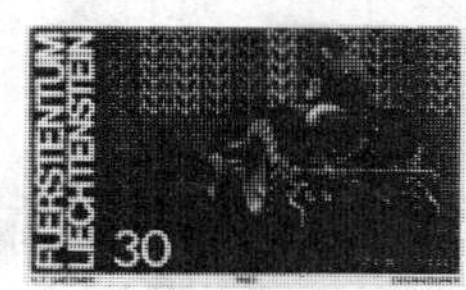

Farming A321

1982, Sept. 20 Photo. *Perf. 11½*

Granite Paper

740 A321 30rp shown .25 .25

741 A321 50rp Horticulture .40 .40

742 A321 70rp Forestry .50 .50

743 A321 150rp Dairy farming 1.10 1.10

Nos. 740-743 (4) 2.25 2.25

View of Neu-Schellenberg, 1861, by Moriz Menzinger (1832-1914) — A322

Photogravure and Engraved

1982, Sept. 20 *Perf. 13½x14*

744 A322 40rp shown .30 .30

745 A322 50rp Vaduz, 1860 .35 .35

746 A322 100rp Bendern, 1868 .85 .85

Nos. 744-746 (3) 1.50 1.50

Visitor Type of 1981

Paintings: 40rp, Emperor Maximilian I (1459-1519), by Bernhard Strigel. 70rp, Georg Jenatsch (1596-1639). 80rp, Angelika Kaufmann (1741-1807), self portrait. 1fr, Fidelis von Sigmaringen (1577-1622).

1982, Dec. 6 *Perf. 14*

747 A316 40rp multicolored .30 .30

748 A316 70rp multicolored .50 .50

749 A316 80rp multicolored .60 .60

750 A316 1fr multicolored .75 .75

Nos. 747-750 (4) 2.15 2.15

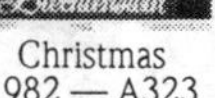

Christmas 1982 — A323 Europa 1983 — A324

Designs: Chur Cathedral sculptures.

1982, Dec. 6 Photo. *Perf. 11½*

Granite Paper

751 A323 20rp Angel playing lute .15 .15

752 A323 50rp Virgin and Child .40 .40

753 A323 80rp Angel playing organ .65 .65

Nos. 751-753 (3) 1.20 1.20

1983, Mar. 7 Photo.

Designs: 40rp, Notker Balbulus of St. Gall (840-912), Benedictine monk, poet and liturgical composer. 80rp, St. Hildegard of Bingen (1098-1179).

754 A324 40rp multicolored .35 .35

755 A324 80rp multicolored .60 .60

A325 A326

Shrovetide and Lenten customs: 40rp, Last Thursday before Lent. 70rp, Begging for eggs on Shrove Tuesday. 180fr, Bonfire, first Sunday in Lent.

Photogravure and Engraved

1983, Mar. 7 *Perf. 14*

756 A325 40rp multicolored .35 .35

757 A325 70rp multicolored .60 .60

758 A325 1.80fr multicolored 1.50 1.50

Nos. 756-758 (3) 2.45 2.45

See Nos. 844-846, 915-917.

1983, June 6 Photo. *Perf. 12*

Designs: Landscapes by Anton Ender (b. 1898).

759 A326 40rp Schaan, on the Zollstrasse .35 .35

760 A326 50rp Balzers with Gutenberg Castle .40 .40

761 A326 2fr Stag by the Reservoir 1.75 1.75

Nos. 759-761 (3) 2.50 2.50

Protection of Shores and Coasts — A327

1983, June 6

762 A327 20rp shown .25 .25

763 A327 40rp Manned flight bicentenary .35 .35

764 A327 50rp World communications year .45 .45

765 A327 80rp Humanitarian aid .70 .70

Nos. 762-765 (4) 1.75 1.75

Pope John Paul II A328

1983, Sept. 5 Photo.

766 A328 80rp multicolored 1.00 1.00

Princess Gina — A329

1983, Sept. 5 *Perf. 12x11½*

767 A329 2.50fr shown 2.25 2.25

768 A329 3fr Prince Franz Joseph II 2.75 2.75

Christmas 1983 — A330

1983, Dec. 5 Photo. *Perf. 12*

Granite Paper

769 A330 20rp Seeking shelter .15 .15

770 A330 50rp Child Jesus .40 .40

771 A330 80rp The Three Magi .70 .70

Nos. 769-771 (3) 1.25 1.25

1984 Winter Olympics, Sarajevo — A331

Snowflakes.

1983, Dec. 5 Photo. *Perf. 11½x12*

Granite Paper

772 A331 40rp multicolored .40 .40

773 A331 80rp multicolored .80 .80

774 A331 1.80fr multicolored 1.65 1.65

Nos. 772-774 (3) 2.85 2.85

Famous Visitors to Liechtenstein A332

Paintings: 40rp, Count Alexander Wassiljewitsch Suworow-Rimnikski (1730-1800), Austro-Russian Army general. 70rp, Karl Rudolf Count von Buol-Schauenstein (1760-1833). 80rp, Carl Zuckmayer (1896-1977), playwright. 1fr, Curt Goetz (1888-1960), actor and playwright.

Photogravure and Engraved

1984, Mar. 12 *Perf. 14*

775 A332 40rp multicolored .40 .40

776 A332 70rp multicolored .70 .70

777 A332 80rp multicolored .80 .80

778 A332 1fr multicolored 1.00 1.00

Nos. 775-778 (4) 2.90 2.90

A333 A334

1984, Mar. 12 Photo. *Perf. 12*

Granite Paper

779 A333 50rp multicolored .45 .45

780 A333 80rp multicolored .70 .70

Europa (1959-1984).

Photogravure and Engraved

1984, June 12 *Perf. 14*

The Destruction of Trisona Fairy Tale Illustrations: Root Carvings by Beni Gassner.

781 A334 35rp Warning messenger .35 .35

782 A334 50rp Buried town .50 .50

783 A334 80rp Spared family .80 .80

Nos. 781-783 (3) 1.65 1.65

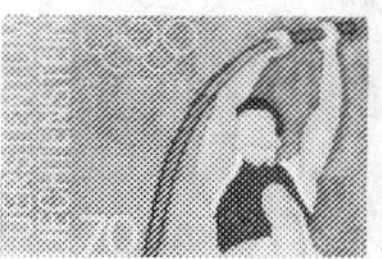

1984 Summer Olympics A335

1984, June 12 Photo. *Perf. 11½*

Granite Paper

784 A335 70rp Pole vault .65 .65

785 A335 80rp Discus .75 .75

786 A335 1fr Shot put 1.00 1.00

Nos. 784-786 (3) 2.40 2.40

Industries and Occupations A336

1984, Sept. 10 Photo. *Perf. 11½*

787 A336 5rp Banking & trading .15 .15

788 A336 10rp Construction, plumbing .15 .15

789 A336 20rp Production, factory worker .25 .25

790 A336 35rp Contracting, draftswoman .35 .35

791 A336 45rp Manufacturing, sales rep .45 .45

792 A336 50rp Catering .50 .50

793 A336 60rp Carpentry .60 .60

794 A336 70rp Public health .70 .70

795 A336 80rp Industrial research .80 .80

796 A336 1fr Masonry 1.00 1.00

797 A336 1.20fr Industrial management 1.25 1.25

798 A336 1.50fr Posta & communications 1.50 1.50

Nos. 787-798 (12) 7.70 7.70

Princess Marie Aglae — A337 Christmas 1984 — A338

Photogravure and Engraved

1984, Dec. 10 *Perf. 14x13½*

799 A337 1.70fr shown 1.50 1.50

800 A337 2fr Prince Hans Adam 1.90 1.90

1984, Dec. 10 Photo. *Perf. 11*

801 A338 35rp Annunciation .35 .35

802 A338 50rp Holy Family .55 .55

803 A338 80rp Three Kings .80 .75

Nos. 801-803 (3) 1.70 1.65

Europa 1985 — A339

1985, Mar. 11 Photo. *Perf. 11½*

804 A339 50rp Three Muses .50 .50

805 A339 80rp Pan and Muses .75 .75

Orders and Monestaries A340

Photogravure and Engraved

1985, Mar. 11 *Perf. 13½x14*

806 A340 50rp St. Elisabeth .55 .55

807 A340 1fr Schellenberg Convent 1.10 1.10

808 A340 1.70fr Gutenberg Mission 1.90 1.90

Nos. 806-808 (3) 3.55 3.55

Cardinal Virtues — A341

1985, June 10 Photo. *Perf. 11½x12*

809 A341 35rp Justice .35 .35

810 A341 50rp Temperance .50 .50

811 A341 70rp Prudence .70 .70

812 A341 1fr Fortitude 1.00 1.00

Nos. 809-812 (4) 2.55 2.55

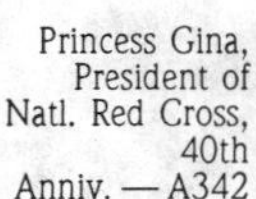

Princess Gina, President of Natl. Red Cross, 40th Anniv. — A342

Portrait and: 20rp, Helping refugees, 1945. 50rp, Rescue service. 1.20fr, Child refugees, 1979.

1985, June 10 *Perf. 12x11½*

813 A342 20rp multicolored .20 .20

814 A342 50rp multicolored .55 .55

815 A342 1.20fr multicolored 1.40 1.40

Nos. 813-815 (3) 2.15 2.15

Souvenir Sheet

State Visit of Pope John Paul II — A343

Designs: 50rp, Papal coat of arms. 80rp, Chapel of St. Maria zum Trost, Dux, Schaan. 1.70fr, Our Lady of Liechtenstein, St. Mary the Comforter.

1985, Feb. 2 *Perf. 11½*

816 Sheet of 3 4.25 4.25
a. A343 50rp multi 1.40 1.40
b. A343 80rp multi 1.40 1.40
c. A343 1.70fr multi 1.40 1.40

Paintings from the Princely Collections
A344

Christmas 1985
A345

50rp, Portrait of a Canon, by Quintin Massys (1466-1530). 1fr, Portrait of Clara Serena Rubens, by Peter Paul Rubens (1577-1640). 1.20fr, Portrait of the Duke of Urbino, by Raphael (1483-1520).

Photogravure and Engraved

1985, Sept. 2 *Perf. 14*

817 A344 50rp multicolored .50 .50
818 A344 1fr multicolored 1.10 1.10
819 A344 1.20fr multicolored 1.40 1.40
Nos. 817-819 (3) 3.00 3.00

1985, Dec. 9 Photo. *Perf. 11½x12*

820 A345 35rp Frankincense .35 .35
821 A345 50rp Gold .50 .50
822 A345 80rp Myrrh .85 .85
Nos. 820-822 (3) 1.70 1.70

Kirchplatz Theater, 15th Anniv. — A346

Photogravure and Engraved

1985, Dec. 9 *Perf. 14*

823 A346 50rp Tragedy .40 .40
824 A346 80rp Commedia dell'arte .55 .55
825 A346 1.50rp Opera buffa 1.75 1.75
Nos. 823-825 (3) 2.70 2.70

Weapons from the Prince's Armory
A347

Designs: 35rp, Halberd, bodyguard of Prince Charles I. 50rp, German morion, 16th cent. 80rp, Halberd, bodyguard of Prince Carl Eusebius.

1985, Dec. 9 *Perf. 13½x14½*

826 A347 35rp multicolored .35 .35
827 A347 50rp multicolored .50 .50
828 A347 80rp multicolored .85 .85
Nos. 826-828 (3) 1.70 1.70

A348

A349

1986, Mar. 10 Photo. *Perf. 12*

829 A348 50rp Swallows .50 .50
830 A348 90rp Robin 1.00 1.00

Europa 1986.

1986-89 Photo. *Perf. 11½x12*

Views of Vaduz Castle.

Granite Paper

832 A349 20rp Outer courtyard .15 .15
833 A349 25rp View from the south ('89) .35 .35
835 A349 50rp Castle, mountains .40 .40
838 A349 90rp Inner gate ('87) 1.10 1.10
840 A349 1.10fr Back view .90 .90
841 A349 1.40fr Inner courtyard ('87) 1.75 1.75
Nos. 832-841 (6) 4.65 4.65

This is an expanding set. Numbers will change if necessary.

Fasting Sacrifice — A350

A352

1986, Mar. 10 Photo. *Perf. 12*

843 A350 1.40fr multicolored 1.40 1.40

Type of 1983

Photogravure and Engraved

1986, June 9 *Perf. 13½*

844 A325 35rp shown .40 .40
845 A325 50rp Wedding .60 .60
846 A325 70rp Rogation Day procession .80 .80
Nos. 844-846 (3) 1.80 1.80

1986, June 9 Photo. *Perf. 11½*

Karl Freiherr Haus von Hausen (1823-89), founder.

847 A352 50rp multicolored .55 .55

Natl. Savings Bank, Vaduz, 125th anniv.

A353

Hunting — A354

Photogravure and Engraved

1986, June 9 *Perf. 13½*

848 A353 3.50fr multicolored 4.50 4.50

Prince Franz Joseph II, 80th birthday.

1986, Sept. 9 *Perf. 13x13½*

849 A354 35rp Roebuck, Ruggeller Riet .40 .40
850 A354 50rp Chamois in winter, Rappenstein .60 .60
851 A354 1.70fr Rutting stag, Lawena 2.00 2.00
Nos. 849-851 (3) 3.00 3.00

Crops — A355

1986, Sept. 9 Photo. *Perf. 12x11½*

852 A355 50rp White cabbage, beets .65 .65
853 A355 80rp Red cabbage 1.10 1.10
854 A355 90rp Potatoes, onions, garlic 1.25 1.25
Nos. 852-854 (3) 3.00 3.00

Christmas
A356

Trees
A357

Archangels.

1986, Dec. 9 *Perf. 11½*

855 A356 35rp Michael .45 .40
856 A356 50rp Gabriel .65 .65
857 A356 90rp Raphael 1.25 1.25
Nos. 855-857 (3) 2.35 2.30

1986, Dec. 9

858 A357 25rp Silver fir .30 .30
859 A357 90rp Spruce 1.10 1.10
860 A357 1.40fr Oak 1.65 1.65
Nos. 858-860 (3) 3.05 3.05

Europa 1987 — A358

Nicholas Among the Thorns — A359

Modern architecture: 50rp, Primary school, 1980, Gamprin. 90rp, Parish church, c. 1960, Schellenburg.

1987, Mar. 9 Photo. *Perf. 11½x12*

Granite Paper

861 A358 50rp multicolored .65 .65
862 A358 90rp multicolored 1.25 1.25

1987, Mar. 9 *Perf. 11½*

Granite Paper

863 A359 1.10fr multicolored 1.50 1.50

Nicholas von der Flue (1417-1487), canonized in 1947.

Hereditary Prince Alois — A360

Fish — A361

Photo. & Engr.

1987, June 9 *Perf. 14*

864 A360 2fr multicolored 2.50 2.50

No. 864 printed in sheets of 8.

1987, June 9 Photo. *Perf. 11½*

865 A361 50rp Cottus gobio .60 .60
866 A361 90rp Salmo trutta fario 1.10 1.10
867 A361 1.10fr Thymallus thymallus 1.40 1.40
Nos. 865-867 (3) 3.10 3.10

A362

A363

Liechtenstein City Palace, Vienna.

1987, Sept. 7 Photo. *Perf. 11½*

Granite Paper

868 A362 35rp Arch .45 .45
869 A362 50rp Entrance .60 .60
870 A362 90rp Staircase 1.10 1.10
Nos. 868-870 (3) 2.15 2.15

1987, Sept. 7 *Perf. 11½*

871 A363 1.40fr House of Liechtenstein coat of arms 1.90 1.90

Purchase of County of Vaduz, 275th anniv.

Diet, 125th Anniv. A364

1987, Sept. 7 *Perf. 11½*

872 A364 1.70fr Constitution of 1862 2.25 2.25

Christmas — A365

The Evangelists, illuminated codices from the Golden Book, c. 1100, Abbey of Pfafers, purportedly made under the direction of monks from Reichenau Is.

1987, Dec. 7 Photo. & Engr. *Perf. 14*

873 A365 35rp St. Matthew .30 .30
874 A365 50rp St. Mark .40 .40
875 A365 60rp St. Luke .50 .50
876 A365 90rp St. John .75 .75
Nos. 873-876 (4) 1.95 1.95

1988 Winter Olympics, Calgary — A366

Humorous drawings by illustrator Paul Flora of Austria: 25rp, The Toil of the Cross-country Skier. 90rp, Courageous Pioneer of Skiing. 1.10fr, As Grandfather Used to Ride on a Bobsled.

1987, Dec. 7 *Perf. 14x13½*

877 A366 25rp multicolored .30 .30
878 A366 90rp multicolored 1.10 1.10
879 A366 1.10fr multicolored 1.40 1.40
Nos. 877-879 (3) 2.80 2.80

See Nos. 888-891.

Europa 1988 — A367

Modern communication & transportation.

1988, Mar. 7 Photo. *Perf. 11½x12*

Granite Paper

880 A367 50rp Satellite dish .65 .65
881 A367 90rp High-speed monorail 1.10 1.10

European Campaign to Protect Undeveloped and Developing Lands
A368

1988, Mar. 7 *Perf. 12*

Granite Paper

882 A368 80rp Forest preservation 1.00 1.00
883 A368 90rp Layout for village development 1.10 1.10
884 A368 1.70rp Traffic planning 2.00 2.00
Nos. 882-884 (3) 4.10 4.10

Balancing nature conservation with natl. development.

Souvenir Sheet

Succession to the Throne — A369

Portraits: a, Crown Prince Hans Adam. b, Prince Alois, successor to the crown prince. c, Prince Franz Josef II, ruler.

Perf. 14½x13½

1988, June 6 — Photo. & Engr.

No.	Type	Description	Unused	Used
885	A369	Sheet of 3	4.00	4.00
a.		50rp black, gold & bright blue	.65	.65
b.		50rp black, gold & sage green	.65	.65
c.		2fr black, gold & deep rose	2.50	2.50

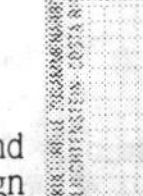

North and South Campaign A370

Perf. 12x11½

1988, June 6 — Photo. — Granite Paper

No.	Type	Description	Unused	Used
886	A370	50rp Public radio	.65	.65
887	A370	1.40fr Adult education	1.75	1.75

Cultural cooperation with Costa Rica. See Costa Rica Nos. 401-402.

Olympics Type of 1988

Humorous drawings by illustrator Paul Flora of Austria: 50rp, Cycling. 80rp, Gymnastics. 90rp, Running. 1.40fr, Equestrian.

Photo. & Engr.

1988, Sept. 5 *Perf. 14x13½*

No.	Type	Description	Unused	Used
888	A366	50rp multicolored	.65	.65
889	A366	80rp multicolored	1.00	1.00
890	A366	90rp multicolored	1.10	1.10
891	A366	1.40fr multicolored	1.75	1.75
		Nos. 888-891 (4)	4.50	4.50

Roadside Shrines — A371

Christmas — A372

Perf. 11½x12

1988, Sept. 5 — Photo. — Granite Paper

No.	Type	Description	Unused	Used
892	A371	25rp Kaltweh Chapel, Balzers	.35	.35
893	A371	35rp Oberdorf, Vaduz, c. 1870	.45	.45
894	A371	50rp Bangstrasse, Ruggell	.65	.65
		Nos. 892-894 (3)	1.45	1.45

1988, Dec. 5 — Photo. *Perf. 11½x12*

Granite Paper

No.	Type	Description	Unused	Used
895	A372	35rp Joseph, Mary	.40	.40
896	A372	50rp Christ child	.55	.55
897	A372	90rp Adoration of the Magi	1.00	1.00
		Nos. 895-897 (3)	1.95	1.95

The Letter — A373

Europa 1989 — A374

Details of Portrait of Marie-Therese de Lamballe (The Letter), by Anton Hickel (1745-1798): 90rp, Handkerchief and writing materials in open desk. 2fr, Entire painting.

Photo. & Engr.

1988, Dec. 5 *Perf. 13x13½*

No.	Type	Description	Unused	Used
898	A373	50rp shown	.65	.65
899	A373	90rp multicolored	1.10	1.10
900	A373	2fr multicolored	2.50	2.50
		Nos. 898-900 (3)	4.25	4.25

1989, Mar. 6 — Photo. *Perf. 11½x12*

Traditional children's games.

Granite Paper

No.	Type	Description	Unused	Used
901	A374	50rp Cat and Mouse	.55	.55
902	A374	90rp Stockleverband	1.00	1.00

Josef Gabriel Rheinberger (1839-1901), Composer, and Score — A375

Photo. & Engr.

1989, Mar. 6 *Perf. 14x13½*

No.	Type	Description	Unused	Used
903	A375	2.90fr multicolored	3.50	3.50

Fish — A376

1989, June 5 — Photo. *Perf. 12x11½*

Granite Paper

No.	Type	Description	Unused	Used
904	A376	50rp *Esox lucius*	.65	.65
905	A376	1.10fr *Salmo trutta lacustris*	1.40	1.40
906	A376	1.40fr *Noemacheilus barbatulus*	1.75	1.75
		Nos. 904-906 (3)	3.80	3.80

World Wildlife Fund — A377

1989, June 5 *Perf. 12*

Granite Paper

No.	Type	Description	Unused	Used
907	A377	25rp *Charadrius dubuis*	.30	.30
908	A377	35rp *Hyla arborea*	.45	.45
909	A377	50rp *Libelloides coccajus*	.65	.65
910	A377	90rp *Putorius putorius*	1.10	1.10
		Nos. 907-910 (4)	2.50	2.50

Mountains — A378

1989, Sept. 4 — Photo. *Perf. 11½*

Granite Paper

No.	Type	Description	Unused	Used
911	A378	50rp Falknis	.60	.60
912	A378	75rp Plassteikopf	.90	.90
913	A378	80rp Naafkopf	.95	.95
914	A378	1.50fr Garsellitum	1.75	1.75
		Nos. 911-914 (4)	4.20	4.20

See Nos. 930-939.

Folklore Type of 1983

Autumn activities: 35rp, Alpine herdsman and flock return from pasture. 50rp, Shucking corn. 80rp, Cattle market.

1989, Sept. 4 — Photo. & Engr. *Perf. 14*

No.	Type	Description	Unused	Used
915	A325	35rp multicolored	.40	.40
916	A325	50rp multicolored	.60	.60
917	A325	80rp multicolored	.95	.95
		Nos. 915-917 (3)	1.95	1.95

Christmas — A379

Details of the triptych *Adoration of the Magi*, by Hugo van der Goes (50rp) and student (35rp, 90rp), late 15th cent.: 35rp, Melchior and Balthazar. 50rp, Caspar and holy family. 90rp, Donor with St. Stephen.

1989, Dec. 4 *Perf. 13½*

Size of 35rp and 90rp: 23x41mm

No.	Type	Description	Unused	Used
918	A379	35rp multicolored	.45	.45
919	A379	50rp shown	.60	.60
920	A379	90rp multicolored	1.10	1.10
		Nos. 918-920 (3)	2.15	2.15

Minerals A380

1989, Dec. 4 *Perf. 13½x13*

No.	Type	Description	Unused	Used
921	A380	50rp Scepter quartz	.55	.55
922	A380	1.10fr Pyrite ball	1.25	1.25
923	A380	1.50fr Calcite	1.65	1.65
		Nos. 921-923 (3)	3.45	3.45

Europa 1990 — A381

Postage Stamps, 150th Anniv. — A382

Post offices.

Perf. 11½x12

1990, Mar. 5 — Photo. — Granite Paper

No.	Type	Description	Unused	Used
924	A381	50rp shown	.60	.60
925	A381	90rp Modern p.o.	1.10	1.10

1990, Mar. 5 *Perf. 11½*

Granite Paper

No.	Type	Description	Unused	Used
926	A382	1.50fr Penny Black	1.65	1.65

1990 World Cup Soccer Championships, Italy — A383

1990, Mar. 5 — Granite Paper *Perf. 12*

No.	Type	Description	Unused	Used
927	A383	2fr multicolored	2.50	2.50

Princess Gina A384

1990, June 5 — Litho. *Perf. 11½*

Granite Paper

No.	Type	Description	Unused	Used
928	A384	2fr shown	2.75	2.75
929	A384	3fr Prince Franz Joseph II	4.00	4.00

1st anniv of death.

Mountains Type of 1989

1990-93

Granite Paper

No.	Type	Description	Unused	Used
930	A378	5rp Augstenberg	.15	.15
931	A378	10rp Hahnenspiel	.15	.15
933	A378	35rp Nospitz	.50	.50
933A	A378	40rp Ochsenkopf	.50	.50
934	A378	45rp Drei Schwestern	.60	.60
935	A378	60rp Kuhgrat	.90	.90
936	A378	70rp Galinakopf	.95	.95
938	A378	1fr Schonberg	1.25	1.25
939	A378	1.20fr Bleikaturm	1.75	1.75
940	A378	1.60fr Schwarzhorn	2.00	2.00
941	A378	2fr Scheienkopf	2.50	2.50
		Nos. 930-941 (11)	11.25	11.25

Issued: 5, 45, 70rp, 1fr, 6/5; 10, 35, 60rp, 1.20fr, 9/3; 40rp, 6/3/91; 1.60fr, 3/2/92; 2fr, 3/1/93.

This is an expanding set. Numbers will change if neccessary.

A385 A386

Paintings by Benjamin Steck (1902-1981).

1990, June 5 — Photo. & Engr. *Perf. 14*

No.	Type	Description	Unused	Used
942	A385	50rp shown	.65	.65
943	A385	80rp Fruit, dish	1.00	1.00
944	A385	1.50fr Basket, fruit, stein	2.00	2.00
		Nos. 942-944 (3)	3.65	3.65

Photo. & Engr.

1990, Sept. 3 *Perf. 13x13½*

Game birds.

No.	Type	Description	Unused	Used
945	A386	25rp Pheasant	.35	.35
946	A386	50rp Blackcock	.65	.65
947	A386	2fr Mallard duck	2.75	2.75
		Nos. 945-947 (3)	3.75	3.75

European Postal Communications, 500th Anniv. — A387

1990, Dec. 3 *Perf. 13½x14*

No.	Type	Description	Unused	Used
948	A387	90rp multicolored	1.25	1.25

A388 A389

Christmas (Lenten Cloth of Bendern): 35rp, The Annunciation. 50rp, Birth of Christ. 90rp, Adoration of the Magi.

1990, Dec. 3 — Photo. *Perf. 12*

Granite Paper

No.	Type	Description	Unused	Used
949	A388	35rp multicolored	.50	.50
950	A388	50rp multicolored	.70	.70
951	A388	90rp multicolored	1.25	1.25
		Nos. 949-951 (3)	2.45	2.45

1990, Dec. 3 — Photo. & Engr. *Perf. 14*

Holiday Customs: 35rp, St. Nicholas Visiting Children on Feast of St. Nicholas. 50rp, Waking "sleepyheads" on New Year's Day. 1.50fr, Good wishes on New Year's Day.

No.	Type	Description	Unused	Used
952	A389	35rp multicolored	.45	.45
953	A389	50rp multicolored	.65	.65
954	A389	1.50fr multicolored	2.00	2.00
		Nos. 952-954 (3)	3.10	3.10

Liechtenstein stamps can be mounted in the annually supplemented Scott Liechtenstein album.

Europa — A390

Designs: 50rp, Telecommunications satellite, Olympus I. 90rp, Weather satellite, Meteosat.

1991, Mar. 4 Photo. *Perf. 11½*

Granite Paper

955 A390 50rp multicolored .65 .65
956 A390 90rp multicolored 1.25 1.25

St. Ignatius of Loyola (1491-1556), Founder of Jesuit Order — A391

Designs: 90rp, Wolfgang Amadeus Mozart (1756-1791), composer.

1991, Mar. 4 *Perf. 11½*

Granite Paper

957 A391 80rp multicolored 1.10 1.10
958 A391 90rp multicolored 1.25 1.25

A392 A393

1991, Mar. 4 *Perf. 11½*

Granite Paper

959 A392 2.50fr multicolored 3.50 3.50

UN membership, 1990.

1991, June 3 Photo. *Perf. 11½*

Paintings: 50rp, Maloja, by Giovanni Giacometti. 80rp, Rheintal, by Ferdinand Gehr. 90rp, Bergell, by Augusto Giacometti. 1.10fr, Hoher Kasten, by Hedwig Scherrer.

Granite Paper

960 A393 50rp multicolored .60 .60
961 A393 80rp multicolored .95 .95
962 A393 90rp multicolored 1.00 1.00
963 A393 1.10fr multicolored 1.40 1.40
Nos. 960-963 (4) 3.95 3.95

Swiss Confederation, 700th anniv.

Military Uniforms A394

Designs: 50rp, Non-commissioned officer, private. 70rp, Uniform tunic, trunk. 1fr, Sharpshooters, officer and private.

Photo. & Engr.

1991, June 3 *Perf. 13½x14*

964 A394 50rp multicolored .60 .60
965 A394 70rp multicolored .85 .85
966 A394 1fr multicolored .95 .95
Nos. 964-966 (3) 2.40 2.40

Last action of Liechtenstein's military, 1866 (70rp).

Princess Marie — A395

Photo. & Engr.

1991, Sept. 2 *Perf. 13x13½*

967 A395 3fr shown 3.75 3.75
968 A395 3.40fr Prince Hans Adam II 4.25 4.25

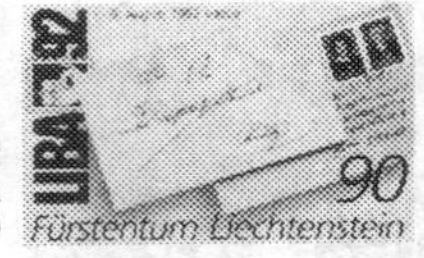

LIBA 92, Natl. Philatelic Exhibition A396

1991, Sept. 2 Photo. *Perf. 11½*

Granite Paper

969 A396 90rp multicolored 1.10 1.10

A397 A398

Christmas (Altar of St. Mamertus Chapel, Triesen): 50rp, Mary. 80rp, Madonna and Child. 90rp, Angel Gabriel.

Photo. & Engr.

1991, Dec. 2 *Perf. 13½x14*

970 A397 50rp multicolored .70 .70
971 A397 80rp multicolored 1.10 1.10
972 A397 90rp multicolored 1.25 1.25
Nos. 970-972 (3) 3.05 3.05

1991, Dec. 2 Photo. *Perf. 11½x12*

1992 Winter Olympics, Albertville: 70rp, Cross-country skiers, doping check. 80rp, Hockey players, good sportsmanship. 1.60rp, Downhill skier, safety precautions.

Granite Paper

973 A398 70rp multicolored .95 .95
974 A398 80rp multicolored 1.10 1.10
975 A398 1.60fr multicolored 2.25 2.25
Nos. 973-975 (3) 4.30 4.30

1992, Mar. 2 Photo. *Perf. 11½*

1992 Summer Olympics, Barcelona: 50rp, Women's relay, drugs, broken medal. 70rp, Cycling, safety precautions. 2.50fr, Judo, good sportsmanship.

Granite Paper

976 A398 50rp multicolored .65 .65
977 A398 70rp multicolored .90 .90
978 A398 2.50fr multicolored 3.25 3.25
Nos. 976-978 (3) 4.80 4.80

Discovery of America, 500th Anniv. A400

1992, Mar. 2

Granite Paper

979 A400 80rp shown 1.00 1.00
980 A400 90rp New York skyline 1.25 1.25

Europa.

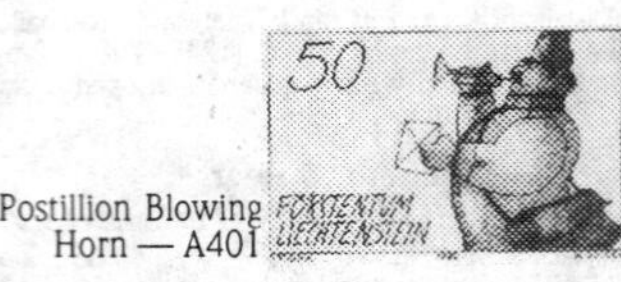

Postillion Blowing Horn — A401

Clown in Envelope — A402

Designs: No. 982, Postillion delivering valentine. No. 984, Wedding violinist.

Photo. & Engr.

1992, June 1 *Perf. 14x13½*

981 A401 50rp multicolored .65 .65
982 A401 50rp multicolored .65 .65

Photo.

Perf. 12½

Granite Paper

983 A402 50rp multicolored .65 .65
984 A402 50rp multicolored .65 .65
Nos. 981-984 (4) 2.60 2.60

Souvenir Sheet

Prince Hans-Adam and Princess Marie, 25th Wedding Anniv. — A403

Designs: a, 2fr, Coat of Arms of Liechtenstein-Kinsky Alliance. b, 2.50fr, Prince Hans-Adam and Princess Marie.

1992, June 1 *Perf. 11½*

Granite Paper

985 A403 Sheet of 2, #a.-b. 5.75 5.75

Ferns — A404

40rp, Blechnum spicant. 50rp, Asplenium trichomanes. 70rp, Phyllitis scolopendrium. 2.50fr, Asplenium ruta-muraria.

1992, Sept. 7 Photo. & Engr. *Perf. 14*

986 A404 40rp multicolored .65 .65
987 A404 50rp multicolored .75 .75
988 A404 70rp multicolored 1.10 1.10
989 A404 2.50fr multicolored 4.00 4.00
Nos. 986-989 (4) 6.50 6.50

Creation of Vaduz County, 650th Anniv. — A405

1992, Sept. 7 *Perf. 13½x14*

990 A405 1.60fr multicolored 2.50 2.50

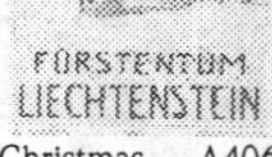

Christmas — A406 Hereditary Prince Alois — A407

Scenes in Triesen: 50rp, Chapel, St. Mamertus. 90rp, Nativity scene, St. Gallus Church. 1.60rp, St. Mary's Chapel.

1992, Dec. 7 Photo. *Perf. 11½*

Granite Paper

991 A406 50rp multicolored .60 .60
992 A406 90rp multicolored 1.10 1.10
993 A406 1.60fr multicolored 2.00 2.00
Nos. 991-993 (3) 3.70 3.70

Photo. & Engr.

1992, Dec. 7 *Perf. 13x13½*

994 A407 2.50fr multicolored 3.50 3.50

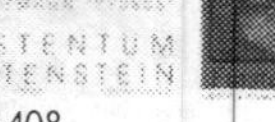

A408 A409

Europa (Contemporary paintings): 80rp, 910805, by Bruno Kaufmann. 1fr, The Little Blue, by Evi Kliemand.

1993, Mar. 1 Photo. *Perf. 11½x12*

Granite Paper

995 A408 80rp multicolored 1.00 1.00
996 A408 1fr multicolored 1.25 1.25

1993, Mar. 1 *Perf. 11½*

Paintings by Hans Gantner (1853-1914): 50rp, Chalets in Steg and Naafkopf. 60rp, Sass Mountain with Hunting Lodge. 1.80fr, Red House in Vaduz.

Granite Paper

997 A409 50rp multicolored .65 .65
998 A409 60rp multicolored .75 .75
999 A409 1.80fr multicolored 2.25 2.25
Nos. 997-999 (3) 3.65 3.65

Tibetan Art — A410

60rp, Detail from Thangka painting, Tale of the Ferryman. 80rp, Religious dance mask. 1fr, Detail from Thangka painting, The Tale of the Fish.

1993, June 7 Photo. *Perf. 11½*

Granite Paper

1000 A410 60rp multicolored .75 .75
1001 A410 80rp multicolored 1.00 1.00
1002 A410 1fr multicolored 1.25 1.25
Nos. 1000-1002 (3) 3.00 3.00

A411 A412

1993, June 7 *Perf. 11½x12*

Granite Paper

1003 A411 1.80fr Tree of life 2.25 2.25

Church Missionary Work.

Photo. & Engr.

1993, June 7 *Perf. 14x13½*

Contemporary painting: Black Hatter, by Friedensreich Hundertwasser.

1004 A412 2.80fr multicolored 3.50 3.50

Souvenir Sheet

Marriage of Hereditary Prince Alois and Duchess Sophie of Bavaria, July 3 — A413

1993, June 7 Photo. *Perf. 11½*
Granite Paper

1005	A413	4fr multicolored	5.25	5.25

Wild Animals — A414

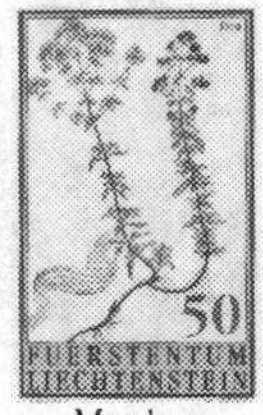

Meadow Plants — A415

Photo. & Engr.
1993, Sept. 6 *Perf. 13x13½*

1006	A414	60rp Badger	.80	.80
1007	A414	80rp Marten	1.00	1.00
1008	A414	1fr Fox	1.25	1.25
		Nos. 1006-1008 (3)	3.05	3.05

See Nos. 1056-1059.

1993, Sept. 6

1009	A415	50rp Origanum vulgare	.65	.65
1010	A415	60rp Salvia pratensis	.80	.80
1011	A415	1fr Seseli annuum	1.25	1.25
1012	A415	2.50fr Prunella grandiflora	3.25	3.25
		Nos. 1009-1012 (4)	5.95	5.95

Christmas — A416

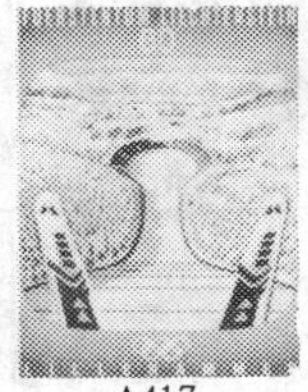

A417

Calligraphic Christmas texts by: 60rp, Rainer Maria Rilke. 80rp, Th. Friedrich. 1fr, Rudolph Alexander Schroder.

1993, Dec. 6 Photo. *Perf. 11½x12*
Granite Paper

1013	A416	60rp multicolored	.80	.80
1014	A416	80rp multicolored	1.00	1.00
1015	A416	1fr multicolored	1.25	1.25
		Nos. 1013-1015 (3)	3.05	3.05

1993, Dec. 6
Granite Paper

1016	A417	60rp Ski jump	.80	.80
1017	A417	80rp Slalom skiing	1.00	1.00
1018	A417	2.40fr Bobsled	3.00	3.00
		Nos. 1016-1018 (3)	4.80	4.80

1994 Winter Olympics, Lillehammer.

Anniversaries and Events — A418

A419

A420

1994, Mar. 7 Photo. *Perf. 11½*
Granite Paper

1019	A418	60rp multicolored	.75	.75
1020	A419	1.80fr multicolored	2.25	2.25
1021	A420	2.80fr multicolored	3.50	3.50
		Nos. 1019-1021 (3)	6.50	6.50

Principality of Liechtenstein, 275th anniv. (#1019). Intl. Olympic Committee, cent. (#1020). 1994 World Cup Soccer Championships, US (#1021).

Alexander von Humboldt (1769-1859) — A421

Europa: 80rp, Vultur gryphus. 1fr, Rhexia cardinalis.

Photo. & Engr.
1994, Mar. 7 *Perf. 13x13½*

1022	A421	80rp multicolored	1.00	1.00
1023	A421	1fr multicolored	1.25	1.25

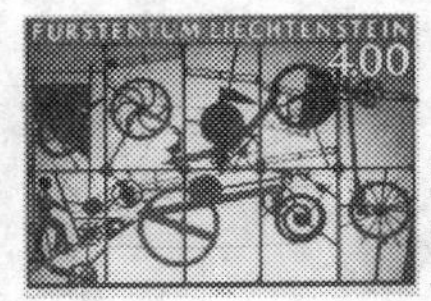

Mobile, by Jean Tinguely (1925-91) A422

Photo. & Engr.
1994, June 6 *Perf. 13½x14*

1024	A422	4fr multicolored	5.50	5.50

Letter Writing — A423

1994, June 6 Photo. *Perf. 12½*
Granite Paper

1025	A423	60rp Elephant	.80	.80
1026	A423	60rp Cherub	.80	.80
1027	A423	60rp Pig	.80	.80
1028	A423	60rp Dog	.80	.80
		Nos. 1025-1028 (4)	3.20	3.20

Life Cycle of Grape Vine — A424

Designs: No. 1029, Spring, vine beginning to flower. No. 1030, Summer, green grapes on vine. No. 1031, Autumn, ripe grapes ready for harvest. No. 1032, Winter, bare vine in snow.

1994, Sept 5 Photo. *Perf. 11½*
Granite Paper

1029	A424	60rp multicolored	.80	.80
1030	A424	60rp multicolored	.80	.80
1031	A424	60rp multicolored	.80	.80
1032	A424	60rp multicolored	.80	.80
a		Block of 4, #1029-1032	3.25	3.25

No. 1032a is continuous design.

Minerals A425

Perf. 13½x12½
1994, Sept. 5 Photo. & Engr.

1033	A425	60rp Strontianite	.80	.80
1034	A425	80rp Faden quartz	1.10	1.10
1035	A425	3.50fr Ferrous dolomite	4.75	4.75
		Nos. 1033-1035 (3)	6.65	6.65

A426

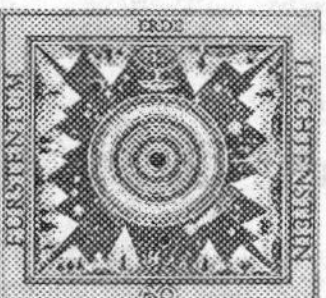

A427

Christmas contemporary art, by Anne Frommelt: 60rp, The True Light. 80rp, Peace on Earth. 1fr, See the House of God.

1994, Dec. 5 Photo. *Perf. 11½*
Granite Paper

1036	A426	60rp multicolored	.90	.90
1037	A426	80rp multicolored	1.25	1.25
1038	A426	1fr multicolored	1.50	1.50
		Nos. 1036-1038 (3)	3.65	3.65

1994, Dec. 5 Photo. & Engr. *Perf. 14*

The Four Elements, by Ernst Steiner.

1039	A427	60rp Earth	.90	.90
1040	A427	80rp Water	1.25	1.25
1041	A427	1fr Fire	1.50	1.50
1042	A427	2.50fr Air	4.00	4.00
		Nos. 1039-1042 (4)	7.65	7.65

Peace and Freedom A428

Europa: 80rp, 1fr, Excerpts from speeches of Prince Franz Josef II.

1995, Mar. 6 Photo. *Perf. 11½*
Granite Paper

1043	A428	80rp multicolored	1.25	1.25
1044	A428	1fr multicolored	1.65	1.65

A429

Anniversaries and Events
A430 A431

Design: 60rp, Princess Marie, Bosnian children.

1995, Mar. 6
Granite Paper

1045	A429	60rp multicolored	.95	.95
1046	A430	1.80fr multicolored	3.00	3.00
1047	A431	3.50fr multicolored	5.50	5.50
		Nos. 1045-1047 (3)	9.45	9.45

Liechtenstein Red Cross, 50th anniv. (#1045). UN, 50th anniv. (#1046). The Alps, European Landscape of the Year 1995-96 (#1047).

Falknis Group, by Anton Frommelt (1895-1975) — A432

Paintings: 80rp, Three Oaks. 4.10fr, Rhine below Triesen.

1995, June 6 Photo. *Perf. 12*
Granite Paper

1048	A432	60rp multicolored	1.00	1.00
1049	A432	80rp multicolored	1.40	1.40
1050	A432	4.10fr multicolored	7.25	7.25
		Nos. 1048-1050 (3)	9.65	9.65

Letter Writing — A433

Designs: No. 1051, Girl, boy building heart with bricks. No. 1052, Boy, girl bandaging sunflower. No. 1053, Girl, boy & rainbow. No. 1054, Boy in hot air balloon delivering letter to girl.

1995, June 6 *Perf. 12½*
Granite Paper

1051	A433	60rp multicolored	1.00	1.00
1052	A433	60rp multicolored	1.00	1.00
1053	A433	60rp multicolored	1.00	1.00
1054	A433	60rp multicolored	1.00	1.00
a.		Vert. strip of 4, #1051-1054 + label	4.00	4.00

Liechtenstein-Switzerland Postal Relationship — A434

Litho. & Engr.
1995, Sept. 5 *Perf. 13½*

1055	A434	60rp multicolored	1.00	1.00

See Switzerland No. 960.

No. 1055 and Switzerland No. 960 are identical. This issue was valid for postage in both countries.

Plant Type of 1993
Photo. & Engr.
1995, Sept. 5 *Perf. 13x13½*

1056	A414	60rp Arnica montana	1.00	1.00
1057	A414	80rp Urtica dioica	1.40	1.40
1058	A414	1.80fr Valeriana officinalis	3.00	3.00
1059	A414	3.50fr Ranunculus ficaria	6.00	6.00
		Nos. 1056-1059 (4)	11.40	11.40

A435 A436

Paintings by Lorenzo Monaco: 60rp, Angel kneeling, facing right. 80rp, Madonna and Child, two angels at her feet. 1fr, Angel kneeling, facing left.

Perf. 14½x13½
1995, Dec. 4 Photo. & Engr.

1060	A435	60rp multicolored	1.00	1.00
1061	A435	80rp multicolored	1.40	1.40
1062	A435	1fr multicolored	1.75	1.75
		Nos. 1060-1062 (3)	4.15	4.15

Christmas.

1995, Dec. 4

Painting: 4fr, Lady with Lap Dog, by Paul Wunderlich.

1063	A436	4fr multicolored	6.75	6.75

Bronze Age in Europe — A437

1996, Mar. 4 Photo. Perf. 11½

Granite Paper

1064 A437 90rp Crucible, pin 1.50 1.50

Countess Nora Kinsky (1888-1923), Nurse, Mother of Princess Gina — A438

Profile and: 90rp, Mar. 7, 1917 diary entry. 1.10fr, Feb. 28, 1917 diary entry.

1996, Mar. 4

Granite Paper

1065 A438 90rp multicolored 1.50 1.50
1066 A438 1.10fr multicolored 1.75 1.75

Paintings of Village Views, by Marianne Siegl, Based on Sketches by Otto Zeiller — A439

10rp, Eschen. 20rp, Farmhouse, St. Joseph's Chapel, Planken. 1.30fr, Upper Village, Triesen. 1.70fr, St. Theresa's Church, Schaanwald. 5fr, Vaduz Castle.

1996-97 Photo. Perf. 12

Granite Paper

1068 A439 10rp multicolored .15 .15
1069 A439 20rp multicolored .30 .30
1073 A439 1.30fr multicolored 1.75 1.75
1074 A439 1.70fr multicolored 2.25 2.25
1077 A439 5fr multicolored 8.25 8.25
Nos. 1068-1077 (5) 12.70 12.70

Issued: 10rp, 5fr, 3/4/96; 20rp, 1.30fr, 1.70fr, 3/3/97.

This is an expanding set. Numbers may change.

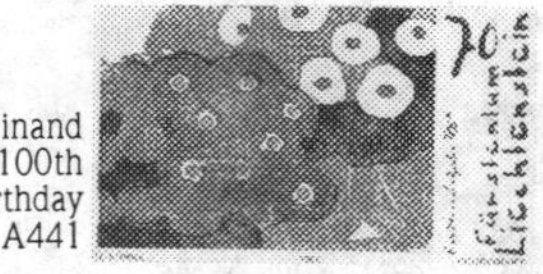

Modern Olympic Games, Cent. — A440

1996, June 3 Photo. Perf. 11½

Granite Paper

1079 A440 70rp Gymnastics 1.10 1.10
1080 A440 90rp Hurdles 1.50 1.50
1081 A440 1.10fr Cycling 1.75 1.75
Nos. 1079-1081 (3) 4.35 4.35

Ferdinand Gehr, 100th Birthday A441

Various paintings of flowers.

1996, June 3

Granite Paper

1083 A441 70rp multicolored 1.10 1.10
1084 A441 90rp multicolored 1.50 1.50
1085 A441 1.10fr multicolored 1.75 1.75

Size: 33x23mm

1086 A441 1.80fr multicolored 3.00 3.00
Nos. 1083-1086 (4) 7.35 7.35

Austria, Millennium A442

Photo. & Engr.

1996, Sept. 2 Perf. 13½

1087 A442 90rp multicolored 1.50 1.50

New Constitution, 75th Anniv. — A443

Litho., Engr. & Embossed

1996, Sept. 2 Perf. 14

1088 A443 10fr Natl. arms 16.50 16.50

A444

A445

Paintings by Russian Artist, Eugen Zotow (1881-1953): 70rp, "Country Estate in Poltava." 1.10fr, "Three Bathers in a Park in Berlin." 1.40fr, "View of Vaduz."

1996, Dec. 2 Photo. & Engr. Perf. 14

1089 A444 70rp multicolored 1.10 1.10
1090 A444 1.10fr multicolored 1.75 1.75
1091 A444 1.40fr multicolored 2.25 2.25
Nos. 1089-1091 (3) 5.10 5.10

1996, Dec. 2

Christmas: Illuminated manuscripts, symbols of the Evangelists.

1092 A445 70rp Matthew 1.10 1.10
1093 A445 90rp Mark 1.40 1.40
1094 A445 1.10fr Luke 1.75 1.75
1095 A445 1.80fr John 3.00 3.00
Nos. 1092-1095 (4) 7.25 7.25

A446

A447

Photo. & Engr.

1997, Mar. 3 Perf. 13½

1096 A446 70rp multicolored .95 .95

Franz Schubert (1797-1828), composer.

1997, Mar. 3 Photo. Perf. 12

Europa, Liechtenstein Myths: 90rp, Wild Gnomes. 1.10fr, Foal of Planken.

Granite Paper

1097 A447 90rp multicolored 1.25 1.25
1098 A447 1.10fr multicolored 1.50 1.50

St. Lucius, Virgin Mary Holding Infant Jesus, St. Florin, by Gabriel Dreher A448

Photo. & Engr.

1997, June 2 Perf. 13½x13

1099 A448 20fr multicolored 30.00 30.00

A449 A450

Painting, "Jeune Fille en Fleur," by Enrico Baj.

1997, Aug. 22 Photo. Perf. 11½

Granite Paper

1100 A449 70rp multicolored .95 .95

Photo. & Engr.

1997, Aug. 22 Perf. 14

Mushrooms: 70rp, Phaeolepiota aurea. 90rp, Helvella silvicola. 1.10fr, Aleuria aurantia.

1101 A450 70rp multicolored .95 .95
1102 A450 90rp multicolored 1.20 1.20
1103 A450 1.10fr multicolored 1.50 1.50
Nos. 1101-1103 (3) 3.65 3.65

Railway in Liechtenstein, 125th Anniv. A451

Train stations: 70rp, Schaanwald. 90rp, Nendeln. 1.80fr, Schaan-Vaduz.

1997, Aug. 22 Photo. Perf. 11½

Granite Paper

1104 A451 70rp multicolored .95 .95
1105 A451 90rp multicolored 1.20 1.20
1106 A451 1.80fr multicolored 2.40 2.40
Nos. 1104-1106 (3) 4.55 4.55

Christmas Tree Decorations A452

1997, Dec. 1 Photo. & Engr. Perf. 14

1107 A452 70rp shown 1.00 1.00
1108 A452 90rp Bell 1.25 1.25
1109 A452 1.10fr Oval with pointed ends 1.50 1.50
Nos. 1107-1109 (3) 3.75 3.75

A453

A454

Skiing, 1998 Winter Olympic Games, Nagano.

1997, Dec. 1 *Perf. 12½*

Granite Paper

1110 A453 70rp Cross-country 1.00 1.00
1111 A453 90rp Slalom 1.25 1.25
1112 A453 1.80fr Downhill 2.50 2.50
Nos. 1110-1112 (3) 4.75 4.75

1998, Mar. 2 Photo. *Perf. 12*

Contemporary Art, Paintings by Heinz Mack: No. 1113, Verano (Der Sommer). No. 1114, Hommage An Liechtenstein. No. 1115, Zwischen Tag Und Traum. No. 1116, Salute Chirico!.

Granite Paper

1113 A454 70rp multicolored .95 .95
1114 A454 70rp multicolored .95 .95
1115 A454 70rp multicolored .95 .95
1116 A454 70rp multicolored .95 .95
a. Block or strip of 4, #1113-1116 3.80 3.80

Festivals A455

Europa: 90rp, National holiday. 1.10fr, Festival of the Musical Societies.

1998, Mar. 2

Granite Paper

1117 A455 90rp multicolored 1.25 1.25
1118 A455 1.10fr multicolored 1.50 1.50

Customs Treaty with Switzerland, 75th Anniv. — A456

1998, Mar. 2

Granite Paper

1119 A456 1.70fr multicolored 2.25 2.25

1998 World Cup Soccer Championships, France — A457

1998, Mar. 2

Granite Paper

1120 A457 1.80fr multicolored 2.50 2.50

SEMI-POSTAL STAMPS

Prince Johann II — SP1

Coat of Arms — SP2

Perf. 11½

1925, Oct. 5 Engr. Wmk. 183

B1 SP1 10rp yellow green 27.50 12.50
B2 SP1 20rp deep red 20.00 12.50
B3 SP1 30rp deep blue 6.00 4.50
Nos. B1-B3 (3) 53.50 29.50
Set, never hinged 150.00

85th birthday of the Prince Regent. Sold at a premium of 5rp each, the excess being devoted to charities.

1927, Oct. 5 Typo.

B4 SP2 10rp multicolored 6.75 *13.00*
B5 SP2 20rp multicolored 6.75 *13.00*
B6 SP2 30rp multicolored 6.75 *13.00*
Nos. B4-B6 (3) 20.25 *39.00*
Set, never hinged 50.00

87th birthday of Prince Johann II.

These stamps were sold at premiums of 5, 10 and 20rp respectively. The money thus obtained was devoted to charity.

Railroad Bridge Demolished by Flood — SP3

Designs: 10rp+10rp, Inundated Village of Ruggel. 20rp+10rp, Austrian soldiers rescuing refugees. 30rp+10rp, Swiss soldiers salvaging personal effects.

1928, Feb. 6 Litho. Unwmk.

B7 SP3 5rp + 5rp brn vio & brn 11.00 20.00
B8 SP3 10rp + 10rp bl grn & brn 14.00 20.00
B9 SP3 20rp + 10rp dl red & brn 14.00 20.00
B10 SP3 30rp + 10rp dp bl & brn 11.00 20.00
Nos. B7-B10 (4) 50.00 80.00
Set, never hinged 175.00

The surtax on these stamps was used to aid the sufferers from the Rhine floods.

Coat of Arms — SP7

Princess Elsa — SP8

Design: 30rp, Prince Francis I.

1932, Dec. 21 Photo.

B11 SP7 10rp (+ 5rp) olive grn 20.00 *24.00*
B12 SP8 20rp (+ 5rp) rose red 20.00 *24.00*
B13 SP8 30rp (+ 10rp) ultra 20.00 *24.00*
Nos. B11-B13 (3) 60.00 *72.00*
Set, never hinged 140.00

The surtax was for the Child Welfare Fund.

Postal Museum Issue
Souvenir Sheet

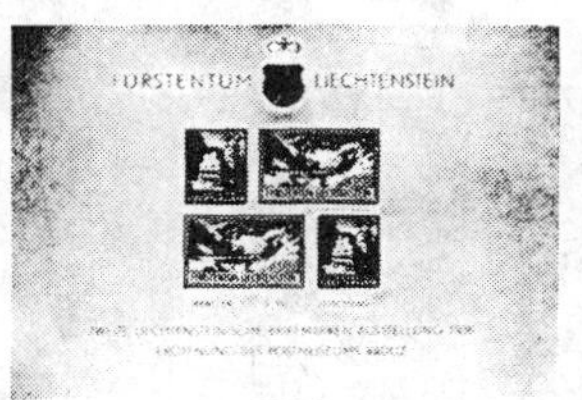
SP10

1936, Oct. 24 Litho. *Imperf.*

B14 SP10 Sheet of 4 15.00 *37.50*
Never hinged 40.00

Sheet contains 2 each, #120, 122. Sold for 2fr.

"Protect the Child" — SP11

Designs: No. B16, "Take Care of the Sick." No. B17, "Help the Aged."

Perf. 11½

1945, Nov. 27 Photo. Unwmk.

B15 SP11 10rp + 10rp multi .55 *1.75*
B16 SP11 20rp + 20rp multi .65 *2.00*
B17 SP11 1fr + 1.40fr multi 4.75 *16.00*
Nos. B15-B17 (3) 5.95 *19.75*
Set, never hinged 10.50

Souvenir Sheet

Post Coach SP14

1946, Aug. 10

B18 SP14 Sheet of 2 21.00 *30.00*
Never hinged 35.00
a. 10rp dark violet brown & buff 8.50 *13.00*
Never hinged 15.00

25th anniv. of the Swiss-Liechtenstein Postal Agreement. Sheet, size: 82x60½mm, sold for 3fr.

Canal by Albert Cuyp — SP15

Willem van Huythuysen by Frans Hals — SP16

40rp+10rp, Landscape by Jacob van Ruysdael.

1951, July 24 *Perf. 11½*

B19 SP15 10rp + 10rp olive grn 5.25 7.00
B20 SP16 20rp + 10rp dk vio brn 5.25 14.00
B21 SP15 40rp + 10rp blue 5.25 7.00
Nos. B19-B21 (3) 15.75 28.00
Set, never hinged 27.50

Issued in sheets of 12. For surcharges see Nos. 281-283.

Catalogue values for unused stamps in this section, from this point to the end of the section, are for Never Hinged items.

Nos. 324-325 Surcharged with New Value and Uprooted Oak Emblem

1960, Apr. 7

B22 A190 30rp + 10rp on 40rp .90 .90
B23 A190 50rp + 10rp on 25rp 1.50 1.50

World Refugee Year, July 1, 1959-June 30, 1960. The surtax was for aid to refugees.

Growth Symbol — SP17

1967, Dec. 7 Photo. *Perf. 11½*

B24 SP17 50rp + 20rp multi .85 .60

Surtax was for development assistance.

AIR POST STAMPS

Airplane over Snow-capped Mountain Peaks — AP1

Airplane above Vaduz Castle — AP2

Airplane over Rhine Valley — AP3

Perf. 10½, 10½x11½

1930, Aug. 12 Photo. Unwmk.

Gray Wavy Lines in Background

C1 AP1 15rp dark brown 6.00 6.25
C2 AP1 20rp slate 12.50 11.00
C3 AP2 25rp olive brown 9.00 9.50
C4 AP2 35rp slate blue 12.50 9.50
C5 AP3 45rp olive green 22.50 37.50
C6 AP3 1fr lake 42.50 27.50
Nos. C1-C6 (6) 105.00 101.25
Set, never hinged 375.00

For surcharge see No. C14.

Zeppelin over Naafkopf, Falknis Range — AP4

Design: 2fr, Zeppelin over Valüna Valley.

1931, June 1 *Perf. 11½*

C7 AP4 1fr olive black 52.50 100.00
C8 AP4 2fr blue black 110.00 275.00
Set, never hinged 375.00

Golden Eagle — AP6

15rp, Golden Eagle in flight, diff. 20rp, Golden Eagle in flight, diff. 30rp, Osprey. 50rp, Eagle.

1934-35

C9 AP6 10rp brt violet ('35) 4.50 13.00
C10 AP6 15rp red orange ('35) 12.00 30.00
C11 AP6 20rp red ('35) 14.00 30.00
C12 AP6 30rp brt blue ('35) 14.00 30.00
C13 AP6 50rp emerald 8.00 21.00
Nos. C9-C13 (5) 52.50 124.00
Set, never hinged 150.00

No. C6 Surcharged with New Value

1935, June 24 *Perf. 10½x11½*

C14 AP3 60rp on 1fr lake 25.00 35.00
Never hinged 87.50

Airship "Hindenburg" AP11

Design: 2fr, Airship "Graf Zeppelin."

1936, May 1 *Perf. 11½*

C15 AP11 1fr rose carmine 32.50 67.50
C16 AP11 2fr violet 27.50 62.50
Set, never hinged 140.00

AP13

AP20

10rp, Barn swallows. 15rp, Black-headed Gulls. 20rp, Gulls. 30rp, Eagle. 50rp, Northern Goshawk. 1fr, Lammergeier. 2fr, Lammergeier.

1939, Apr. 3 Photo.

C17 AP13 10rp violet .30 .20
C18 AP13 15rp red orange .80 1.65
C19 AP13 20rp dark red 1.00 .45
C20 AP13 30rp dull blue 1.00 .80
C21 AP13 50rp brt green 2.75 1.65
C22 AP13 1fr rose car 2.75 *12.00*
C23 AP13 2fr violet 2.00 *12.00*
Nos. C17-C23 (7) 10.60 *28.75*
Set, never hinged 20.00

1948

Designs: 10rp, Leonardo da Vinci. 15rp, Joseph Montgolfier. 20rp, Jacob Degen. 25rp, Wilhelm Kress. 40rp, E. G. Robertson. 50rp, W. S. Henson. 1fr, Otto Lilienthal. 2fr, S. A. Andrée. 5fr, Wilbur Wright. 10fr, Icarus.

C24 AP20 10rp dark green 1.25 .50
C25 AP20 15rp dark violet 1.00 1.00
C26 AP20 20rp brown 1.00 .50
a. 20rp reddish brown 42.50 2.00
Never hinged 100.00
C27 AP20 25rp dark red 1.25 2.50
C28 AP20 40rp violet blue 1.75 1.25
C29 AP20 50rp Prus blue 2.50 2.25
C30 AP20 1fr chocolate 2.50 2.50
C31 AP20 2fr rose lake 3.50 3.50
C32 AP20 5fr olive green 3.50 8.00
C33 AP20 10fr slate black 22.50 13.00
Nos. C24-C33 (10) 40.75 35.00
Set, never hinged 65.00

Issued in sheets of 9.
Exist imperf. Value, set $6,500.

Helicopter, Bell 47-J — AP21

Planes: 40rp, Boeing 707 jet. 50rp, Convair 600 jet. 75rp, Douglas DC-8.

1960, Apr. 7 Unwmk. *Perf. 11½*

C34 AP21 30rp red orange 1.10 1.75
C35 AP21 40rp blue black 2.25 1.75
C36 AP21 50rp deep claret 4.25 3.75
C37 AP21 75rp olive green 2.25 1.75
Nos. C34-C37 (4) 9.85 9.00
Set, never hinged 16.00

30th anniv. of Liechtenstein's air post stamps.

POSTAGE DUE STAMPS

National Administration of the Post Office

D1

1920 Unwmk. Engr. *Perf. 12½*

J1 D1 5h rose red .15 .20
J2 D1 10h rose red .15 .20
J3 D1 15h rose red .15 .20
J4 D1 20h rose red .15 .20
J5 D1 25h rose red .15 .20
J6 D1 30h rose red .15 .20
J7 D1 40h rose red .15 .20
J8 D1 50h rose red .15 .20
J9 D1 80h rose red .15 .20
J10 D1 1k dull blue .15 .20
J11 D1 2k dull blue .15 .30
J12 D1 5k dull blue .15 .30
Set value 1.00
Set, never hinged 2.50
Nos. J1-J12 (12) 1.80 2.60

Nos. J1-J12 exist imperf. and part perf.

Swiss Administration of the Post Office

D2

Post Horn — D3

1928 Litho. Wmk. 183 *Perf. 11½*
Granite Paper

J13 D2 5rp purple & orange .80 1.75
J14 D2 10rp purple & orange .90 1.75
J15 D2 15rp purple & orange 2.25 *8.50*
J16 D2 20rp purple & orange 1.40 2.50
J17 D2 25rp purple & orange 2.25 *7.00*
J18 D2 30rp purple & orange 5.25 *8.75*
J19 D2 40rp purple & orange 5.50 *9.75*
J20 D2 50rp purple & orange 5.50 *12.00*
Nos. J13-J20 (8) 23.85 *52.00*
Set, never hinged 70.00

Engraved; Value Typographed in Dark Red

1940 Unwmk. *Perf. 11½*

J21 D3 5rp gray blue 1.50 *5.50*
J22 D3 10rp gray blue .65 .90
J23 D3 15rp gray blue .60 *3.50*
J24 D3 20rp gray blue .60 1.25
J25 D3 25rp gray blue 1.25 *3.25*
J26 D3 30rp gray blue 2.50 4.50
J27 D3 40rp gray blue 2.50 4.00
J28 D3 50rp gray blue 2.50 5.00
Nos. J21-J28 (8) 12.10 *27.90*
Set, never hinged 35.00

OFFICIAL STAMPS

Regular Issue of 1930 Overprinted in Various Colors with Crown and:

REGIERUNGS DIENSTSACHE

Perf. 10½, 11½, 11½x10½

1932 Unwmk.

O1 A38 5rp dark green (Bk) 5.50 9.00
O2 A39 10rp dark vio (R) 37.50 7.50
a. Perf. 11½x10½ *650.00 1,050.*
O3 A40 20rp dp rose red (Bl) 50.00 7.50
a. Perf. 10½ 175.00 40.00
O4 A42 30rp ultra (R) 7.75 9.00
a. Perf. 10½ 22.50 13.00
O5 A43 35rp dp green (Bk) 5.50 14.00
a. Perf. 11½ *3,500. 5,500.*
O6 A45 50rp black brn (Bl) 37.50 11.00
a. Perf. 11½ 130.00 130.00
O7 A46 60rp olive blk (R) 5.50 30.00
O8 A48 1.20fr olive brn (G) 77.50 265.00
Nos. O1-O8 (8) 226.75 353.00

Nos. 108, 110 Overprinted in Black

1933 *Perf. 14½*

O9 A51 25rp red orange 37.50 40.00
O10 A53 1.20fr red brown 60.00 *175.00*

Same Overprint in Various Colors on Regular Issue of 1934-35

1934-36 *Perf. 11½*

O11 A58 5rp emerald (R) .45 1.25
O12 A59 10rp dp violet (Bk) .20 1.10
O13 A60 15rp red orange (V) .20 .40
O14 A61 20rp red (Bk) .35 1.10
O15 A62 25rp brown (R) 27.50 *80.00*
O16 A62 25rp brown (Bk) 1.50 *8.75*
O17 A63 30rp dark blue (R) 1.90 3.50
O18 A66 50rp lt brown (V) .90 2.00
O19 A68 90rp dp green (Bk) 5.00 *24.00*
O20 A70 1.50fr brown car (Bl) 35.00 *110.00*
Nos. O11-O20 (10) 73.00 *232.10*

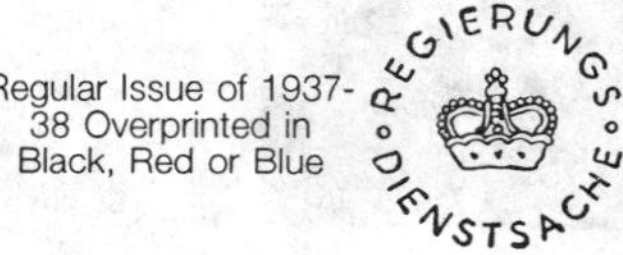
Regular Issue of 1937-38 Overprinted in Black, Red or Blue

1937-41

O21 A76 5rp emerald (Bk) .15 .15
O22 A76 10rp vio & buff (R) .15 .25
O23 A76 20rp brown org (Bl) .95 1.00
O24 A76 20rp brn org (Bk) ('41) .95 1.00
O25 A76 25rp chestnut (Bk) .50 1.25
O26 A77 30rp blue & gray (Bk) .75 .50
O27 A79 50rp dk brn & buff (R) .45 1.00
O28 A80 1fr red brown (Bk) .85 *4.25*
O29 A80 1.50fr slate bl (Bk) ('38) 2.75 *7.25*
Nos. O21-O29 (9) 7.50 *16.65*
Set, never hinged 15.00

Stamps of 1944-45 Overprinted in Black

DIENSTMARKE

1947

O30 A136 5rp slate grn & buff .55 .75
O31 A136 10rp gray & buff .75 .75
O32 A136 20rp org red & buff .75 .75
O33 A136 30rp blue & buff 1.50 1.40
O34 A136 50rp bluish blk & pale gray 1.50 *3.00*
O35 A136 1fr dp cl & buff 3.75 *9.00*
O36 A136 150rp royal blue 4.75 *9.00*
Nos. O30-O36 (7) 13.55 *24.65*
Set, never hinged 30.00

Crown — O1

Government Building, Vaduz — O2

Engr.; Value Typo.
1950-68 Unwmk. *Perf. 11½*
Buff Granite Paper
Narrow Gothic Numerals

O37 O1 5rp red vio & gray .15 .15
O38 O1 10rp ol grn & mag .15 .15
O39 O1 20rp org brn & bl .15 .20
O40 O1 30rp dk red brn & org red .15 .30
O41 O1 40rp blue & hn brn .20 .45
O42 O1 55rp dk gray grn & red 1.00 1.50
a. White paper ('68) 30.00 *125.00*
O43 O1 60rp slate & mag 1.00 1.50
a. White paper ('68) 4.75 *32.50*
O44 O1 80rp red org & gray .50 .75
O45 O1 90rp choc & blue .60 1.10
O46 O1 1.20fr grnsh bl & org .70 1.40
Nos. O37-O46 (10) 4.60 7.50
Set, never hinged 6.00
Set, #O42a, O43a, never hinged 65.00

Catalogue values for unused stamps in this section, from this point to the end of the section, are for Never Hinged items.

1968-69 *Perf. 11½*
White Granite Paper
Broad Numerals, Varying Thickness

O47 O1 5rp olive brn & org .15 .15
O48 O1 10rp violet & car .15 .15
O49 O1 20rp ver & emer .15 .15
O50 O1 30rp green & red .20 .20
O51 O1 50rp ultra & red .25 .25
O52 O1 60rp orange & ultra .30 .30
O53 O1 70rp maroon & emer .35 .35
O54 O1 80rp bl grn & car .40 .40
O55 O1 95rp slate & red ('69) .65 .65
O56 O1 1fr rose cl & grn .50 .50
O57 O1 1.20fr lt red brn & grn .60 .60
O58 O1 2fr brn & org ('69) 1.10 1.10
Nos. O47-O58 (12) 4.80 4.80

1976-89 Engr., Value Typo. *Perf. 14*

O59 O2 10rp yel brn & vio .15 .15
O60 O2 20rp car lake & bl .15 .15
O61 O2 35rp blue & red .15 .20
O62 O2 40rp dull pur & grn .20 .25
O63 O2 50rp slate & mag .25 .35
O64 O2 70rp vio brn & bl grn .30 .40
O65 O2 80rp green & mag .40 .50
O66 O2 90rp vio & bl grn .45 .60
O67 O2 1fr olive & mag .50 .70
O68 O2 1.10fr brown & ultra .60 .75
O69 O2 1.50fr dull grn & red .85 1.10
O70 O2 2fr orange & blue 1.00 1.25
O75 O2 5fr rose vio & brn org 6.00 6.00
Nos. O59-O75 (13) 11.00 12.40

Issued: 5fr, Sept. 4, 1989; others, Dec. 9, 1976.
This is an expanding set. Numbers will change if necessary.

LITHUANIA

ˌli-thə-ˈwā-nē-ə

(Lietuva)

LOCATION — Northern Europe bordering on the Baltic Sea
GOVT. — Independent republic
AREA — 22,959 sq. mi.
POP. — 2,879,070 (1940)
CAPITAL — Vilnius

Lithuania was under Russian rule when it declared its independence in 1918. The League of Nations recognized it in 1922. In 1940 it became a republic in the Union of Soviet Socialist Republics.

Lithuania declared its independence on March 11, 1990. Lithuanian independence was recognized by the Soviet Union on Sept. 6, 1991.

100 Skatiku = 1 Auksinas
100 Centai = 1 Litas (1922, 1993)
100 Kopecks = 1 Ruble (1991)

Catalogue values for unused stamps in this country are for Never Hinged items, beginning with Scott 30, Scott B43 in the semi-postal section, Scott C1 in the air post section, Scott CB1 in the air post semi-postal section and Scott 2N9 in the Russian occupation section.

Nos. 1-26 were printed in sheets of 20 (5x4) which were imperf. at the outer sides, so that only 6 stamps in each sheet were fully perforated. Values are for the stamps partly imperf. The stamps fully perforated sell for at least double these values. There was also a printing of Nos. 19-26 in a sheet of 160, composed of blocks of 20 of each stamp. Pairs or blocks with different values se-tenant sell for considerably more than the values for the stamps singly.

Nos. 1-26 are without gum.

Watermarks

Wmk. 109- Webbing

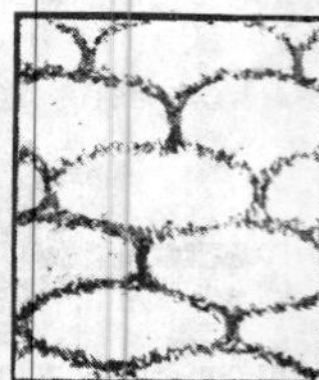
Wmk. 144- Network

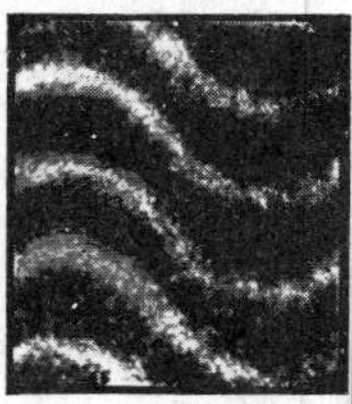
Wmk. 145- Wavy Lines

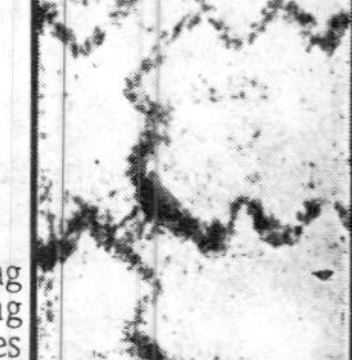
Wmk. 146- Zigzag Lines Forming Rectangles

Wmk. 147- Parquetry

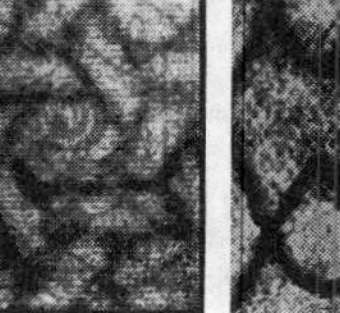
Wmk. 198- Intersecting Diamonds

Wmk. 209- Multiple Ovals

Wmk. 238-Multiple Letters

A1 A2

Perf. 11½

1918, Dec. 27 Unwmk. Typeset

First Vilnius Printing

Thin Figures

No.	Type	Description	Unused	Used
1	A1	10sk black	75.00	75.00
2	A1	15sk black	75.00	75.00

1918, Dec. 31

Second Vilnius Printing

Thick Figures

No.	Type	Description	Unused	Used
3	A1	10sk black	40.00	27.50
4	A1	15sk black	40.00	25.00
5	A1	20sk black	5.00	4.00
6	A1	30sk black	5.00	4.00
7	A1	40sk black	5.00	4.00
8	A1	50sk black	5.00	4.00
		Nos. 3-8 (6)	100.00	68.50

First Kaunas Issue

1919, Jan. 29

No.	Type	Description	Unused	Used
9	A2	10sk black	6.00	3.50
10	A2	15sk black	6.00	3.50
a.		"5" for "15"	50.00	50.00
11	A2	20sk black	6.00	3.50
12	A2	30sk black	6.00	3.50
		Nos. 9-12 (4)	24.00	14.00

A3 A4

Second Kaunas Issue

1919, Feb. 18

No.	Type	Description	Unused	Used
13	A3	10sk black	2.50	1.25
14	A3	15sk black	2.50	1.25
15	A3	20sk black	2.50	1.25
a.		"astas" for "pastas"	60.00	55.00
16	A3	30sk black	2.50	1.25
17	A3	40sk black	2.50	1.50
18	A3	50sk black	2.50	1.50
19	A3	60sk black	2.50	1.50
		Nos. 13-19 (7)	17.50	9.50

Third Kaunas Issue

1919, Mar. 1

No.	Type	Description	Unused	Used
20	A4	10sk black	1.50	1.25
21	A4	15sk black	1.50	1.25
22	A4	20sk black	1.50	1.25
23	A4	30sk black	1.50	1.25
24	A4	40sk black	1.50	1.25
25	A4	50sk black	1.50	1.25
26	A4	60sk black	1.50	1.50
		Nos. 20-26 (7)	10.50	9.00

Catalogue values for unused stamps in this section, from this point to the end of the section, are for Never Hinged items.

The White Knight "Vytis"
A5 A6

A7

A8

Perf. 10½ to 14 & Compound

1919 Litho. Wmk. 144

Gray Granite Paper

No.	Type	Description	Unused	Used
30	A5	10sk deep rose	.28	.22
a.		Wmk. vert.	14.00	6.75
31	A5	15sk violet	.28	.20
a.		Wmk. vert.	14.00	6.75
32	A5	20sk dark blue	.28	.20
33	A5	30sk deep orange	.28	.20
a.		Wmk. vert.	14.00	6.75
34	A5	40sk dark brown	.28	.20
35	A6	50sk blue green	.48	.28
36	A6	75sk org & dp rose	.48	.20
37	A7	1auk gray & rose	.48	.28
38	A7	3auk bis brn & rose	.48	.30
39	A7	5auk blue grn & rose	.48	.38
		Nos. 30-39 (10)	3.80	2.46

Nos. 30a, 31a and 33a are from the first printing with watermark vertical showing points to left; various perforations.

Nos. 30-39 exist imperf. Value in pairs, $50.

Issued: #30a, 31a, 33a, 2/17/19; #30-36, 3/20/19.

1919 Wmk. 145 Thick White Paper

No.	Type	Description	Unused	Used
40	A5	10sk dull rose	.16	.15
41	A5	15sk violet	.16	.15
42	A5	20sk dark blue	.16	.15
43	A5	30sk orange	.16	.15
44	A5	40sk red brown	.16	.15
45	A6	50sk green	.16	.15
46	A6	75sk yel & dp rose	.16	.15
47	A7	1auk gray & rose	.32	.20
48	A7	3auk yellow brn & rose, perf. 12½	.32	.20
49	A7	5auk bl grn & rose	.45	.28
		Nos. 40-49 (10)	2.21	1.73

Nos. 40-49 exist imperf. Value in pairs, $42.50.

Perf. 10½ to 14 & Compound

1919, May 8

Thin White Paper

No.	Type	Description	Unused	Used
50	A5	10sk red	.15	.15
51	A5	15sk lilac	.15	.15
52	A5	20sk dull blue	.15	.15
53	A5	30sk buff	.15	.15
54	A5	40sk gray brn	.15	.15
55	A6	50sk lt green	.15	.15
56	A6	60sk violet & red	.15	.15
57	A6	75sk bister & red	.15	.15
58	A8	1auk gray & red	.15	.15
59	A8	3auk lt brown & red	.18	.15
60	A8	5auk blue grn & red	.24	.15
		Set value	1.40	.95

Nos. 50-60 exist imperf. Value, pairs $70.

See Nos. 93-96. For surcharges see Nos. 114-115, 120-139, 149-150.

"Lithuania" Receiving Benediction
A9

The Spirit of Lithuania Rises
A10

"Lithuania" with Chains Broken — A11

White Knight — A12

1920, Feb. 16 Wmk. 146 *Perf. 11½*

No.	Type	Description	Unused	Used
70	A9	10sk dp rose	2.00	1.25
71	A9	15sk lt violet	2.00	1.25
72	A9	20sk gray blue	2.00	1.25
73	A10	30sk yellow brn	2.00	1.25
74	A11	40sk brown & grn	2.00	1.25
75	A10	50sk deep rose	2.00	1.25
76	A10	60sk lt violet	2.00	1.25
77	A11	80sk purple & red	2.00	1.25
78	A11	1auk green & red	2.00	1.25
79	A12	3auk brown & red	2.00	1.25

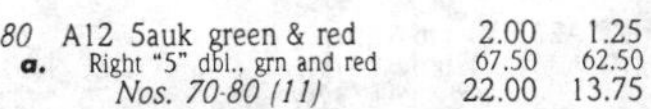

No.	Type	Description	Unused	Used
80	A12	5auk green & red	2.00	1.25
a.		Right "5" dbl., grn and red	67.50	62.50
		Nos. 70-80 (11)	22.00	13.75

Anniv. of natl. independence. The stamps were on sale only 3 days in Kaunas. The stamps were available in other cities after that. Only a limited number of stamps was sold at post offices but 40,000 sets were delivered to the bank of Kaunas.

All values exist imperforate.

White Knight
A13

Grand Duke Vytautas
A14

Grand Duke Gediminas
A15

Sacred Oak and Altar
A16

1920, Aug. 25

No.	Type	Description	Unused	Used
81	A13	10sk rose	.55	.40
a.		Imperf., pair	15.00	
82	A13	15sk dark violet	.55	.40
83	A14	20sk grn & lt grn	.55	.40
84	A13	30sk brown	.55	.40
a.		Pair, #82, 84	15.00	
85	A15	40sk gray grn & vio	.55	.40
86	A14	50sk brn & brn org	1.25	1.00
87	A14	60sk red & org	1.40	1.00
88	A15	80sk blk, db & red	1.40	1.00
89	A16	1auk orange & blk	1.40	1.00
90	A16	3auk green & blk	1.40	1.00
91	A16	5auk gray vio & blk	1.40	1.00
		Nos. 81-91 (11)	11.00	8.00

Opening of Lithuanian National Assembly. On sale for three days.

1920

No.	Type	Description	Unused	Used
92	A14	20sk green & lilac	60.00	
92A	A15	40sk gray grn, buff & vio	60.00	
92B	A14	50sk brown & gray lil	60.00	
92C	A14	60sk red & green	60.00	
92D	A15	80sk black, grn & red	60.00	
		Nos. 92-92D (5)	300.00	

Nos. 92 to 92D were trial printings. By order of the Ministry of Posts, 2,000 copies of each were placed on sale at post offices.

Type of 1919 Issue

1920 Unwmk. *Perf. 11½*

No.	Type	Description	Unused	Used
93	A5	15sk lilac	4.25	1.50
94	A5	20sk deep blue	3.50	1.50

Wmk. 109

No.	Type	Description	Unused	Used
95	A5	20sk deep blue	2.00	.75
96	A5	40sk gray brown	2.75	1.00
		Nos. 93-96 (4)	12.50	4.75

Watermark horizontal on Nos. 95-96.
No. 96 exists perf. 10½x11½.

Imperf., Pairs

No.	Type	Description	Unused	Used
93a	A5	15sk	6.00	2.00
94a	A5	20sk	6.00	2.00
95a	A5	20sk	6.25	2.50
96a	A5	40sk	6.25	3.75

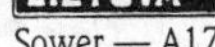

Sower — A17

Peasant Sharpening Scythe — A18

Prince Kestutis
A19

Black Horseman
A20

Perf. 11, 11½ and Compound

1921-22

No.	Type	Description	Unused	Used
97	A17	10sk brt rose	.20	.55
98	A17	15sk violet	.20	.70
99	A17	20sk ultra	.15	.15
100	A18	30sk brown	.50	1.10
101	A19	40sk red	.18	.15
102	A18	50sk olive	.15	.15
103	A18	60sk grn & vio	.32	1.65
104	A19	80sk brn org & car	.24	.15
105	A19	1auk brown & grn	.18	.15
106	A19	2auk gray bl & red	.20	.15
107	A20	3auk yel brn & dk bl	.40	.42
108	A17	4auk yel & dk bl ('22)	.32	.15
109	A20	5auk gray blk & rose	.50	1.00
110	A17	8auk grn & blk ('22)	.50	.15
111	A20	10auk rose & vio	1.00	.55
112	A20	25auk bis brn & grn	1.25	.85
113	A20	100auk dl red & gray blk	6.00	6.50
		Nos. 97-113 (17)	12.29	14.52

Imperf., Pairs

No.	Type	Description	Unused
97a	A17	10sk	17.00
98a	A17	15sk	13.00
99a	A17	20sk	17.00
100a	A18	30sk	24.00
102a	A18	50sk	1.65
103a	A18	60sk	17.00
104a	A19	80sk	17.00
105a	A19	1auk	17.00
106a	A19	2auk	17.00
107a	A20	3auk	17.00
109a	A20	5auk	20.00
110a	A17	8auk	13.00

For surcharges see Nos. 140-148, 151-160.

No. 57 Surcharged

Perf. 12½x11½

1922, May Wmk. 145

No.	Type	Description	Unused	Used
114	A6	4auk on 75sk bis & red	.90	.15
a.		Inverted surcharge	25.00	25.00

Same with Bars over Original Value

No.	Type	Description	Unused	Used
115	A6	4auk on 75sk bis & red	1.75	.38
a.		Double surcharge	25.00	25.00

Povilas Luksis — A20a

Justinas Staugaitis, Antanas Smetona, Stasys Silingas
A20b

Portraits: 40s, Lt. Juozapavicius. 50s, Dr. Basanavicius. 60s, Mrs. Petkeviciute. 1auk, Prof. Voldemaras. 2auk, Pranas Dovidaitis. 3auk, Dr. Slezevicius. 4auk, Dr. Galvanauskas. 5auk, Kazys Grinius. 6auk, Dr. Stulginskis. 8auk, Pres. Smetona.

1922 Litho. Unwmk.

No.	Type	Description	Unused	Used
116	A20a	20s blk & car rose	.50	.42
116A	A20a	40s bl grn & vio	.50	.42
116B	A20a	50s plum & grnsh bl	.50	.42
117	A20a	60s pur & org	.50	.42
117A	A20a	1auk car & lt bl	.50	.42
117B	A20a	2auk dp bl & yel brn	.50	.42
c.		Center inverted	70.00	70.00
118	A20a	3auk mar & ultra	.50	.42
118A	A20a	4auk dk grn & red vio	.50	.42
118B	A20a	5auk blk brn & dp rose	.50	.42
119	A20a	6auk dk bl & grnsh bl	.50	.42
a.		Cliché of 8auk in sheet of 6auk	30.00	25.00
119B	A20a	8auk ultra & bis	.65	.55
119C	A20b	10auk dk vio & bl grn	1.25	1.10
		Nos. 116-119C (12)	6.90	5.85

League of Nations' recognition of Lithuania. Sold only on Oct. 1, 1922.

Forty sheets of the 6auk each included eight copies of the 8auk.

Stamps of 1919-22 Surcharged in Black, Carmine or Green

1 CENT **10 CENTU**

On Nos. 37-39

1922 Wmk. 144 ***Perf. 11½x12***

Gray Granite Paper

120 A7 3c on 1auk 100.00 72.50
121 A7 3c on 3auk 82.50 60.00
122 A7 3c on 5auk 40.00 27.50
Nos. 120-122 (3) 222.50 160.00

White Paper

Wmk. 145

Perf. 14, 11½, 12½x11½

123 A5 1c on 10sk red .60 .70
124 A5 1c on 15sk lilac .60 .70
125 A5 1c on 20sk dull bl .60 .70
126 A5 1c on 30sk orange 95.00 80.00
127 A5 1c on 30sk buff .30 .22
128 A5 1c on 40sk gray brn .60 .70
129 A6 2c on 50sk green .60 .70
130 A6 2c on 60sk vio & red .16 .15
131 A6 2c on 75sk bis & red .42 .70
132 A8 3c on 1auk gray & red .42 .25
133 A8 3c on 3auk brn & red .22 .18
134 A8 3c on 5auk bl grn & red .22 .18
Nos. 123-125,127-134 (11) 4.74 5.18

On Stamps of 1920

1922 Unwmk. ***Perf. 11***

136 A5 1c on 20sk dp bl (C) .80 .75

Wmk. Webbing (109)

Perf. 11, 11½

138 A5 1c on 20sk dp bl (C) .80 .65
139 A5 1c on 40sk gray brn (C) 2.00 1.25

On Stamps of 1921-22

140 A18 1c on 50sk ol (C) .16 .15
a. Imperf., pair 30.00
b. Inverted surcharge 25.00
c. Double surch., one invtd.
141 A17 3c on 10sk 2.00 1.25
142 A17 3c on 15sk .25 .15
143 A17 3c on 20sk .30 .25
144 A18 3c on 30sk 1.50 1.00
145 A19 3c on 40sk .24 .15
a. Imperf., pair
146 A18 5c on 50sk .16 .15
147 A18 5c on 60sk .75 .65
148 A19 5c on 80sk .25 .15
a. Imperf., pair 25.00 15.00

Wmk. Wavy Lines (145)

Perf. 12½x11½

149 A6 5c on 4auk on 75sk (No. 114) (G) .65 .65
150 A6 5c on 4auk on 75sk (No. 115) (G) 2.00 1.50

Wmk. Webbing (109)

Perf. 11, 11½

151 A19 10c on 1auk .50 .15
a. Inverted surcharge 32.50
152 A19 10c on 2auk .24 .15
a. Inverted surcharge 25.00
b. Imperf., pair 25.00
153 A17 15c on 4auk .24 .15
a. Inverted surcharge 25.00
154 A20 25c on 3auk 3.75 2.50
155 A20 25c on 5auk 3.25 1.50
156 A20 25c on 10auk 2.50 1.00
a. Imperf., pair 25.00
157 A17 30c on 8auk (C) .50 .24
a. Inverted surcharge 25.00 15.00
158 A20 50c on 25auk 3.00 1.75
160 A20 1 l on 100auk 4.25 2.00
Nos. 136-160 (23) 30.09 18.14

A21

Ruin — A22

Seminary Church, Kaunas — A23

1923 Litho. Wmk. 109 ***Perf. 11***

165 A21 10c violet 4.25 .15
166 A21 15c scarlet 1.75 .15
167 A21 20c olive brown 1.75 .15
168 A21 25c deep blue 1.75 .15
169 A22 50c yellow green 1.75 .15
170 A22 60c red 1.75 .15
171 A23 1 l orange & grn 10.50 .15
172 A23 3 l red & gray 6.75 .25
173 A23 5 l brown & blue 12.50 1.00
Nos. 165-173 (9) 42.75
Set value 1.85

See Nos. 189-209, 281-282. For surcharges see Nos. B1-B42.

Memel Coat of Arms — A24

Lithuanian Coat of Arms — A25

Biruta Chapel — A26

Kaunas, War Memorial — A27

Trakai Ruins — A28

Memel Lighthouse A29

Memel Harbor — A30

Perf. 11, 11½, 12

1923, Aug. Unwmk.

176 A24 1c rose, grn & blk 1.75 1.65
177 A25 2c dull vio & blk 1.75 1.65
178 A26 3c yellow & blk 1.75 1.65
179 A24 5c bl, buff & blk 2.00 1.90
180 A27 10c orange & blk 2.00 1.90
181 A27 15c green & blk 2.25 2.50
182 A28 25c brt vio & blk 2.25 2.50
183 A25 30c red vio & blk 2.75 2.75
184 A29 60c ol grn & blk 2.75 2.75
185 A30 1 l brn & blk 2.75 2.75
186 A26 2 l red & black 3.50 3.50
187 A28 3 l blue & black 5.25 5.00
188 A29 5 l ultra & black 6.75 6.75
Nos. 176-188 (13) 37.50 37.25

This series was issued ostensibly to commemorate the incorporation of Memel with Lithuania.

Type of 1923 Issue

1923 Unwmk. ***Perf. 11***

189 A21 5c pale green 2.50 .15
190 A21 10c violet 3.75 .15
a. Imperf., pair 32.50
191 A21 15c scarlet 4.25 .15
a. Imperf., pair 32.50
193 A21 25c blue 7.00 .15
Nos. 189-193 (4) 17.50
Set value .20

1923 Wmk. 147

196 A21 2c pale brown 1.25 .25
197 A21 3c olive bister 1.40 .18
198 A21 5c pale green 1.40 .15
199 A21 10c violet 3.25 .15
202 A21 25c deep blue 7.00 .15
a. Imperf., pair 32.50
204 A21 36c orange brown 10.50 .50
Nos. 196-204 (6) 24.80 1.38

Perf. 11½, 14½, 11½x14½

1923-25 Wmk. 198

207 A21 25c deep blue 250.00 180.00
208 A22 50c deep green ('25) 3.25 .15
209 A22 60c carmine ('25) 4.00 .15

Double-barred Cross — A31

Dr. Jonas Basanavicius — A32

1927, Jan. ***Perf. 11½, 14½***

210 A31 2c orange 1.10 .15
211 A31 3c deep brown 1.10 .15
212 A31 5c green 2.00 .15
a. Imperf., pair 20.00
213 A31 10c violet 3.25 .15
214 A31 15c red 2.75 .15
a. Imperf., pair 20.00
215 A31 25c blue 2.75 .15
Nos. 210-215 (6) 12.95
Set value .48

1927-29 Wmk. 147 ***Perf. 14½***

216 A31 5c green 22.50 10.00
217 A31 30c blue ('29) 15.00 2.50

See Nos. 233-240, 278-280.

Perf. 11½, 14½x11½

1927 Unwmk.

219 A32 15c claret & blk .90 .38
220 A32 25c dull blue & blk .90 .38
221 A32 50c dk green & blk 1.65 .75
222 A32 60c dk violet & blk 2.25 1.00
Nos. 219-222 (4) 5.70 2.51

Dr. Jonas Basanavicius (1851-1927), patriot and folklorist.

National Arms — A33

1927, Dec. 23 Wmk. 109 ***Perf. 14½***

223 A33 1 l blue grn & gray 2.25 .15
224 A33 3 l vio & pale grn 3.50 .45
225 A33 5 l brown & gray 6.25 .80
Nos. 223-225 (3) 12.00 1.40

Pres. Antanas Smetona — A34

Decade of Independence — A35

Dawn of Peace — A36

1928, Feb. Wmk. 109

226 A34 5c org brn & grn .52 .28
227 A34 10c violet & blk .70 .28
228 A34 15c orange & brn .70 .28
229 A34 25c blue & indigo .70 .28
230 A35 50c ultra & dl vio .70 .28
231 A35 60c carmine & blk 1.10 .55
232 A36 1 l blk brn & drab 1.10 .70
Nos. 226-232 (7) 5.52 2.65

10th anniv. of Lithuanian independence.

Type of 1926 Issue

1929-31

233 A31 2c orange ('31) 1.75 .15
234 A31 5c green 1.75 .15
235 A31 10c violet ('31) 8.50 .15
237 A31 15c red 2.50 .15
a. Tête bêche pair 14.00 10.00
239 A31 30c dark blue 4.25 .15

Unwmk.

240 A31 15c red 8.75 .15
Nos. 233-240 (6) 27.50
Set value .52

Grand Duke Vytautas A37

Grand Duke, Mounted A38

1930, Feb. 16 ***Perf. 14***

242 A37 2c yel brn & dk brn .32 .15
243 A37 3c dk brn & vio .32 .15
244 A37 5c yel grn & dp org .32 .15
245 A37 10c vio & emer .32 .15
246 A37 15c dp rose & vio .32 .15
247 A37 30c dk bl & brn vio .50 .15
248 A37 36c brn vio & ol blk .50 .15
249 A37 50c dull grn & ultra .50 .15
250 A37 60c dk blue & rose .50 .15
251 A38 1 l bl grn, db & red brn 1.25 .20
252 A38 3 l dk brn, sal & dk vio 1.65 1.00
253 A38 5 l ol brn, gray & red 3.25 1.00
254 A38 10 l multicolored 19.00 9.00
255 A38 25 l multicolored 37.50 20.00
Nos. 242-255 (14) 66.25 32.55

5th cent. of the death of the Grand Duke Vytautas.

Kaunas, Railroad Station — A39

Cathedral at Vilnius — A39a

Designs: 15c, 25c, Landscape on the Neman River. 50c, Main Post Office, Kaunas.

Perf. 14, Imperf.

1932, July 21 Wmk. 238

256 A39 10c dk red brn & ocher .30 .25
257 A39 15c dk brown & ol .45 .40
258 A39 25c dk blue & ol .60 .55
259 A39 50c gray blk & ol 1.00 1.10
260 A39a 1 l dk blue & ol 2.25 2.75
261 A39a 3 l red brn & gray grn 5.00 5.00

Wmk. 198

262 A39 5c vio bl & ocher .30 .25
263 A39a 60c grnsh blk & lil 2.25 2.00
Nos. 256-263 (8) 12.15 12.30

Issued for the benefit of Lithuanian orphans.

In September, 1935, a red overprint was applied to No. 259: "ORO PASTAS / LITUANICA II / 1935 / NEW YORK-KAUNAS." Value, $250.

Vytautas Fleeing from Prison, 1382 A40

Designs: 15c, 25c, Conversion of Ladislas II Jagello and Vytautas (1386). 50c, 60c, Battle at Tannenberg (1410). 1 l, 3 l, Meeting of the Nobles (1429).

1932 Wmk. 209 ***Perf. 14, Imperf.***

264 A40 5c red & rose lake .30 .30
265 A40 10c ol bis & org brn .30 .30
266 A40 15c rose lil & ol grn .40 .35
267 A40 25c dk vio brn & ocher 1.00 1.25
268 A40 50c dp grn & bis brn 1.50 1.50
269 A40 60c ol grn & brn car 1.75 1.75
270 A40 1 l ultra & ol grn 2.00 2.10
271 A40 3 l dk brn & dk grn 3.00 3.25
Nos. 264-271 (8) 10.25 10.80

15th anniversary of independence.

A. Visteliauskas
A41

Mother and Child
A42

Designs: 15c, 25c, Petras Vileisis. 50c, 60c, Dr. John Sliupas. 1 l, 3 l, Jonas Basanavicius.

1933 *Perf. 14, Imperf.*

272	A41	5c yel grn & car	.18	.15
273	A41	10c ultra & car	.18	.15
274	A41	15c orange & red	.22	.22
275	A41	25c dk bl & blk brn	.35	.35
276	A41	50c ol gray & dk bl	.90	1.10
277	A41	60c org brn & chnt	1.75	2.00
277A	A41	1 l red & vio brn	2.25	2.25
277B	A41	3 l turq grn & vio brn	3.75	4.50
		Nos. 272-277B (8)	9.58	10.72

50th anniv. of the 1st newspaper, "Ausra," in lithuanian language.

1933, Sept. *Perf. 14, Imperf.*

Designs: 15c, 25c, Boy reading. 50c, 60c, Boy playing with blocks. 1 l, 3 l, Woman and boy at the Spinning Wheel.

277C	A42	5c dp yel grn & org brn	.15	.15
277D	A42	10c rose brn & ultra	.15	.15
277E	A42	15c ol grn & plum	.25	.25
277F	A42	25c org & gray blk	.35	.35
277G	A42	50c ol grn & car	.90	1.10
277H	A42	60c blk & yel org	1.75	2.00
277I	A42	1 l dk brn & ultra	2.00	2.25
277K	A42	3 l rose lil & ol grn	3.50	*4.75*
		Nos. 277C-277K (8)	9.05	*11.00*

Issued for the benefit of Lithuanian orphans.

Types of 1923-26 Issues

1933-34 **Wmk. 238** *Perf. 14*

278	A31	2c orange	14.00	1.65
279	A31	10c dark violet	12.00	1.65
280	A31	15c red	19.00	.80
281	A22	50c green	9.50	1.65
282	A22	60c red	12.00	.80
		Nos. 278-282 (5)	66.50	6.55

Pres. Antanas Smetona, 60th Birthday — A43

1934 **Unwmk.** **Engr.** *Perf. 11½*

283	A43	15c red	5.00	.15
284	A43	30c green	7.00	.15
285	A43	60c blue	10.00	.20
		Nos. 283-285 (3)	22.00	
		Set value		.36

A44

A47

Arms — A45

Knight — A48

Girl with Wheat — A46

Wmk. 198; Wmk. 209 (35c, 10 l)

1934-35 **Litho.** *Perf. 14*

286	A44	2c rose & dull org	.80	.15
287	A44	5c bl grn & grn	.80	.15
288	A45	10c chocolate	1.75	.15
289	A46	25c dk brn & emer	3.00	.15
290	A45	35c carmine	3.00	.15
291	A46	50c dk blue & blue	3.75	.15
292	A47	1 l sl & mar	20.00	.15
293	A47	3 l grn & gray grn	.25	.15
294	A48	5 l maroon & gray bl	.35	.45
295	A48	10 l choc & yel	2.00	1.50
		Nos. 286-295 (10)	35.70	
		Set value		2.05

No. 290 exists imperf. Value, pair $35.
For overprint see No. 2N9.

1936-37 **Wmk. 238** *Perf. 14*
Size: 17½x23mm

296	A44	2c orange ('37)	.22	.15
297	A44	5c green	.32	.15
		Set value		.18

Pres. Smetona — A49

Arms — A50

1936-37 **Unwmk.**

298	A49	15c carmine	6.00	.15
299	A49	30c green ('37)	8.00	.15
300	A49	60c ultra ('37)	8.00	.15
		Nos. 298-300 (3)	22.00	
		Set value		.30

1937-39 **Wmk. 238** *Perf. 14*
Paper with Gray Network

301	A50	10c green	1.25	.15
302	A50	25c magenta	.18	.15
303	A50	35c red	.60	.15
304	A50	50c brown	.15	.15
305	A50	1 l dp vio bl ('39)	.15	.15
		Nos. 301-305 (5)	2.33	
		Set value		.45

No. 304 exists in two types:
I - "50" is fat and broad, with "0" leaning to right.
II - "50" is thinner and narrower, with "0" straight.
For overprint see No. 2N10.

Jonas Basanavicius Reading Act of Independence A51

President Antanas Smetona — A52

Perf. 13x13½
1939, Jan. 15 **Engr.** **Unwmk.**

306	A51	15c dark red	.42	.30
307	A52	30c deep green	.42	.30
308	A51	35c red lilac	.95	.45
309	A52	60c dark blue	.95	.45
a.		Souvenir sheet of 2, #308-309	6.50	11.00
b.		As "a," imperf.	20.00	19.00
		Nos. 306-309 (4)	2.74	1.50

20th anniv. of Independence.
Nos. 309a, 309b sold for 2 l.

Same Overprinted in Blue

1939

310	A51	15c dark red	.60	.80
311	A52	30c deep green	.75	.80
312	A51	35c red lilac	.90	.90
313	A52	60c dark blue	1.25	.90
		Nos. 310-313 (4)	3.50	3.40

Recovery of Vilnius.

View of Vilnius — A53

Gediminas — A54

Trakai Ruins — A55

Unwmk.
1940, May 6 **Photo.** *Perf. 14*

314	A53	15c brn & pale brn	.40	.20
315	A54	30c dk grn & lt grn	.52	.20
316	A55	60c dk bl & lt bl	1.10	.40
a.		Souv. sheet of 3, #314-316, imperf.	5.00	7.00
		Nos. 314-316 (3)	2.02	.80

Return of Vilnius to Lithuania, Oct. 10, 1939. Exist imperf.
No. 316a has simulated perforations in gold. Sold for 2 l.

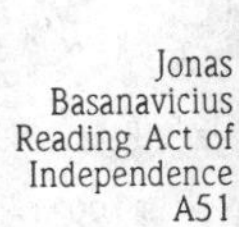

White Knight — A56

Angel — A57

Woman Releasing Dove — A58

Mother and Children — A59

Liberty Bell — A60

Mythical Animal — A61

1940

317	A56	5c brown carmine	.15	.15
318	A57	10c green	.15	.15
319	A58	15c dull orange	.15	.15
320	A59	25c light brown	.15	.15
321	A60	30c Prussian green	.15	.15
322	A61	35c red orange	.16	.25
		Set value	.50	
		Nos. 317-322 (6)		1.00

Nos. 317-322 exist imperf.
For overprints see Nos. 2N11-2N16.

Grand Duke Gediminas, 650th Death Anniv. — A75

1991, Sept. 28 **Litho.** *Perf. 13x13½*

400	A75	30k Castle	1.00	.50
401	A75	50k Grand Duke	1.50	.75
402	A75	70k Early view of Vilnius	2.00	1.00
		Nos. 400-402 (3)	4.50	2.25

Ciconia Nigra — A76

Design: 50k, Grus grus.

1991, Nov. 21 **Litho.** *Perf. 14*

403	A76	30k +15k multi	1.75	.90
404	A76	50k multicolored	2.00	1.00

A77

1991, Dec. 20 **Photo.** *Perf. 14*
Background Colors

411	A77	40k black	.40	.20
412	A77	50k purple	.50	.25
415	A77	100k dark green	.75	.40
418	A77	500k blue	4.00	2.00
		Nos. 411-418 (4)	5.65	2.85

Additional values of type A77 dated 1990 or 1991 were issued prior to Soviet recognition of Lithuanian independence.
For surcharges see Nos. 450-452.
This is an expanding set, numbers may change.

A78

A79

1992, Mar. 15 **Litho.** *Perf. 13x13½*

421	A78	100k multicolored	.60	.30

Lithuanian admission to UN.

1992, Mar. 22

Emblems.

422	A79	50k +25k Olympic Committee	.75	.40
423	A79	130k Albertville	1.00	.50
424	A79	280k Barcelona	2.25	1.10
		Nos. 422-424 (3)	4.00	2.00

Lithuanian Olympic participation. Surtax for Lithuanian Olympic Committee.

A80

A81

1992, July 11 *Perf. 12½x13*

425	A80	200k Cypripedium	1.50	.75
426	A80	300k Eringium maritimum	2.50	1.25

Perf. 12½x13
1992, Oct. 3 **Litho. & Engr.**

Birds of the Baltic Shores: No. 427, Pandion haliaetus. No. 428, Limosa limosa. No. 429, Mergus merganser. No. 430, Tadorna tadorna.

Booklet Stamps

427 A81 B (15r) grn & grnsh blk .75 .40
428 A81 B (15r) grn & red brn .75 .40
429 A81 B (15r) grn, red brn & brn .75 .40
430 A81 B (15r) grn & red brn .75 .40
a. Booklet pane of 4, #427-430 3.00

See Estonia Nos. 231-234a, Latvia Nos. 332-335a and Sweden Nos. 1975-1978a.

Coats of Arms — A82

19th Cent. Costumes — A83

1992, Oct. 11 Litho. *Perf. 14*

431 A82 2r Kedainiai .25 .15
432 A82 3r Vilnius .40 .20
433 A82 10r National 1.35 .65
Nos. 431-433 (3) 2.00 1.00

See Nos. 454-456, 497-499, 521-522, 554-556, 586-588.

1992, Oct. 18 *Perf. 13x13½*

Couples in different traditional costumes of the Suwalki region.

434 A83 2r multicolored .20 .15
435 A83 5r multicolored .45 .25
436 A83 7r multicolored .65 .35
Nos. 434-436 (3) 1.30 .75

See Nos. 465-467, 493-495, 511-513, 539-541.

Churches — A84

300k, Zapishkis Church, 16th cent. 1000k, Saints Peter & Paul Church, Vilnius, 17th cent. 1500k, Christ Church of the Resurrection, Kaunas, 1934.

1993, Jan. 15 Litho. *Perf. 12*

437 A84 300k bister & blk .25 .15
438 A84 1000k blue green & blk 1.00 .50
439 A84 1500k gray & blk 1.25 .65
Nos. 437-439 (3) 2.50 1.30

See Nos. 502-504

Independence — A85

Designs: A, Jonas Basanavicius (1851-1927), journalist and politician. B, Jonas Vileisis (1872-1942), lawyer and politician.

1993, Feb. 16

440 A85 (A) red & multi .20 .15
441 A85 (B) green & multi 1.10 .55

No. 440 sold for 3r and No. 441 sold for 15r on day of issue.

See Nos. 479-480, 506-507, 536-537, 563-564, 592-593.

Grand Duke Vytautas, 600th Birth Anniv.
A86 A87

Designs: 500k, Royal Seal. 1000k, 5000k, Portrait. 1500k, Vytautas in Battle of Grunwald, by Jan Matejko.

1993, Feb. 27

442 A86 500k bister, red & black .35 .20
443 A87 1000k citron, black & red .65 .35
444 A87 1500k lemon, black & red 1.00 .50
Nos. 442-444 (3) 2.00 1.05

Souvenir Sheet

445 A87 5000k citron, black & red 4.00 2.00

Famous Lithuanians A88

Designs: 1000k, Simonas Daukantas (1793-1864), educator and historian. 2000k, Vydunas (1868-1953), preserver of Lithuanian traditional culture. 4500k, Vincas Mykolaitis Putinas (1893-1967), philosopher and psychologist.

1993, Mar. 13

446 A88 1000k multicolored .25 .15
447 A88 2000k multicolored .55 .30
448 A88 4500k multicolored 1.25 .65
Nos. 446-448 (3) 2.05 1.10

See Nos. 475-477, 514-516, 533-535, 560-562.

No. 411 and Type A77 Surcharged

** **
100

1993 Photo, Litho. (#451) *Perf. 14*

450 A77 100k on 30k magenta .15 .15
451 A77 100k on 30k magenta, imperf, without gum .15 .15
452 A77 300k on 40k #411 .15 .15
Nos. 450-452 (3) .45 .45

Issued: 300k, 1/19; #450, 1/26; #451, 3/10.
Nos. 450-451 without surcharge was issued prior to Soviet recognition of Lithuanian Independence.

Coat of Arms Type of 1992

1993, July 3 Litho. *Perf. 11*

454 A82 5c Skuodas .15 .15
455 A82 30c Telsiai .60 .30
456 A82 50c Klaipeda .85 .45
Nos. 454-456 (3) 1.60 .90

Each value exist in tete-beche pairs.

World Lithuanian Unity Day — A89

Designs: 5c, The Spring, by M. K. Ciurlionis. 80c, Capts. Steponas Darius and Stasys Girenas.

1993, July 17 *Perf. 13*

457 A89 5c multicolored .15 .15
458 A89 80c multicolored 1.50 .75

Deaths of Darius and Girenas, 60th anniv. (#458).

Natl. Arms — A90

1993, July 21 Litho. *Perf. 13x12½*

459 A90 (A) bister & multi .15 .15
460 A90 (B) green & multi .80 .40

No. 459 sold for 5c and No. 460 for 80c on day of issue.
Dated 1992.

Visit of Pope John Paul II — A91

1993, Sept. 3 Litho. *Perf. 13½x13*

461 A91 60c Kryziu Kalnas .55 .30
462 A91 60c Siauliai .55 .30
463 A91 80c Vilnius .70 .35
464 A91 80c Kaunas .70 .35
Nos. 461-464 (4) 2.50 1.30

Natl. Costumes Type of 1992

Couples in different traditional costumes of the Dzukai.

1993, Oct. 30 Litho. *Perf. 12*
Size: 23x36mm

465 A83 60c multicolored .40 .20
466 A83 80c multicolored .50 .25
467 A83 1 l multicolored .60 .30
Nos. 465-467 (3) 1.50 .75

Lithuanian Postal System, 75th Anniv. A92

Post offices: No. 468, Klaipeda. No. 469, Kaunas. 80c, Vilnius. 1 l, No. 1.

1993, Nov. 16

468 A92 60c multicolored .35 .20
469 A92 60c multicolored .35 .20
470 A92 80c multicolored .50 .25
471 A92 1 l multicolored .60 .30
Nos. 468-471 (4) 1.80 .95

Europa — A93

Endangered Species — A94

80c, Senas Meistras, by A. Gudaitis, 1939.

1993, Dec. 24 Litho. *Perf. 12*

472 A93 80c multicolored .60 .30

Exists in tete-beche pairs.

1993, Dec. 30 Litho. *Perf. 12*

473 A94 80c Emys orbicularis .60 .30
474 A94 1 l Bufo calamita .75 .40

See Nos. 500-501, 519-520.

Famous Lithuanians Type of 1993

Designs: 60c, Kristijonas Donelaitis (1714-80), poet. 80c, Vincas Kudirka (1858-99), physician, writer. 1 l, Maironis (1862-1932), poet.

1994, Mar. 26 Litho. *Perf. 12*

475 A88 60c multicolored .35 .20
476 A88 80c multicolored .45 .25
477 A88 1 l multicolored .65 .35
Nos. 475-477 (3) 1.45 .80

1994 Winter Olympics, Lillehammer — A95

1994, Feb. 11

478 A95 1.10 l multicolored .75 .40

Independence Type of 1993

Designs: No. 479, Pres. Antanas Smetona (1874-1944). No. 480, Aleksandras Stulginskis.

1994, Feb. 16

479 A85 1 l red brown & multi .55 .30
480 A85 1 l brown & multi .55 .30

A96

Natl. Arms — A96a

Perf. 12, 13½ (40c), 13½x13 (50c)
1994-97 Litho.

481 A96 5c dark brown .15 .15
482 A96 10c deep violet .15 .15
483 A96 20c dark green .20 .15
484 A96 40c deep rose magenta .20 .15
485 A96 50c green blue .30 .15
486 A96a 1 l gray & multi .50 .25
a. Souvenir sheet of 4 2.00 2.00
487 A96a 2 l buff & multi 1.00 .50
488 A96a 3 l green & multi 1.50 .75
Nos. 481-488 (8) 4.00 2.25

Independence, 5th anniv. (#486a).
Issued: 5c, 10c, 4/9/94; 20c, 11/19/94; 2 l, 3 l, 7/23/94; 1 l, 3/11/95; 40c, 5/4/96; 50c, 4/5/97.
This is an expanding set. Numbers may change.

Europa — A97

1994, May 7 Litho. *Perf. 12*

491 A97 80c Artillery rockets, 17th cent. .50 .25

Souvenir Sheet

100th Postage Stamp — A98

Illustration reduced.

1994, May 21 Litho. *Perf. 12*

492 A98 10 l multicolored 7.00 7.00

No. 492 sold for 12 l.

Natl. Costumes Type of 1992

Couples in different traditional costumes of Samogitia.

1994, June 25 Litho. *Perf. 12*

493 A83 5c multicolored .15 .15
494 A83 80c multicolored .40 .20
495 A83 1 l multicolored .50 .25
Nos. 493-495 (3) 1.05 .60

Lithuanian World Song Festival — A99

1994, July 6

496 A99 10c multicolored .15 .15

Coat of Arms Type of 1992

1994, Sept. 10 Litho. *Perf. 12*

497 A82 10c Punia .15 .15
498 A82 60c Alytus .35 .20
499 A82 80c Perloja .50 .25
Nos. 497-499 (3) 1.00 .60

Endangered Species Type of 1993

Mammals.

1994, Oct. 22 Litho. *Perf. 12*

500 A94 20c Nyctalus noctula .25 .15
501 A94 20c Glis glis .25 .15
Set value .15

Church Type of 1993

1994, Nov. 12

502 A84 10c Kaunus, 16th cent. .15 .15
503 A84 60c Kedainiu, 17th cent. .40 .20
504 A84 80c Vilnius, 18th cent. .55 .30
Nos. 502-504 (3) 1.10 .65

Christmas A101

1994, Dec. 3 Litho. *Perf. 12*

505 A101 20c multicolored .18 .15

Independence Type of 1993

#506, Pranas Dovydaitis. #507, Steponas Kairys.

1995, Feb. 16 Litho. *Perf. 12*

506 A85 20c multicolored .25 .15
507 A85 20c multicolored .25 .15
Set value .15

Via Baltica Highway Project — A102

No. 509: a, Parnu. b, Bauska. c, Like #508.

1995, Apr. 20 Litho. *Perf. 14*

508 A102 20c multicolored .15 .15

Souvenir Sheet

509 A102 1 l Sheet of 3, #a.-c. 1.50 1.50

See Estonia Nos. 288-289, Latvia Nos. 394-395.

Sculpture, Mother's School — A103

1995, Apr. 29 Litho. *Perf. 12*

510 A103 1 l multicolored .50 .25

Europa.

Natl. Costumes Type of 1992

Couples in traditional costumes of Aukstaiciai.

1995, May 20 Litho. *Perf. 12*

511 A83 20c multicolored .15 .15
512 A83 70c multicolored .35 .20
513 A83 1 l multicolored .50 .25
Set value .50

Europa.

Famous People Type of 1993

Writers: 30c, Motiejus Valancius (1801-75). 40c, Zemaite (1845-1921). 70c, Kipras Petrauskas (1885-1968).

1995, May 27 Litho. *Perf. 12*

514 A88 30c multicolored .15 .15
515 A88 40c multicolored .20 .15
516 A88 70c multicolored .30 .15
Nos. 514-516 (3) .65
Set value .35

A104 A105

1995, June 14 Litho. *Perf. 12*

517 A104 20c multicolored .15 .15

Day of mourning & hope.

1995, July 30 Litho. *Perf. 12*

518 A105 30c multicolored .35 .20

5th World Sports Games.

Endangered Species Type of 1993

Moths, butterflies.

1995, Aug. 26 Litho. *Perf. 12*

519 A94 30c Arctia villica .25 .15
520 A94 30c Baptria tibiale .25 .15

Coat of Arms Type of 1992

Arms of villages in Suvalkija: 40c, Virbalis. 1 l, Kudirkos Naumiestis, horiz.

1995, Sept. 16 Litho. *Perf. 12*

521 A82 40c multicolored .20 .15
522 A82 1 l multicolored .50 .25

Valerie Mesalina, by Pranciskus Smuglevicius A106

1995, Oct. 6 Litho. *Perf. 12½*

523 A106 40c multicolored .30 .15

Castles — A107

1995, Nov. 18 *Perf. 11½x12*

524 A107 40c Vilnius .20 .15
525 A107 70c Trakai .35 .20
526 A107 1 l Birzai .55 .30
Nos. 524-526 (3) 1.10 .65

Christmas — A108

Designs: 40c, People celebrating Christmas in outdoor snow scene. 1 l, People with lanterns walking toward church.

1995, Dec. 2 Litho. *Perf. 13*

527 A108 40c multicolored .20 .15
528 A108 1 l multicolored .50 .25

Bison Bonasus — A109

1996, Jan. 20 *Perf. 13x13½*

529 A109 30c shown .15 .15
530 A109 40c Two adults .20 .15
531 A109 70c Adult, calf .35 .15
532 A109 1 l Two adults, calf .50 .25
a. Miniature sheet, 2 each #529-532 2.50 1.25
Nos. 529-532 (4) 1.20 .70

World Wildlife Fund.

Famous Lithuanians Type of 1993

Designs: 40c, Kazys Grinius (1866-1950). No. 534, Antanas Zmudzinavicius (1876-1966). No. 535, Balys Sruoga (1896-1947).

1996, Feb. 2 Litho. *Perf. 13x13½*

533 A88 40c multicolored .20 .15
534 A88 1 l multicolored .50 .25
535 A88 1 l multicolored .50 .25
Nos. 533-535 (3) 1.20 .65

Independence Type of 1993

#536, Vladas Mironas. #537, Jurgis Saulys.

1996, Feb. 16 Litho. *Perf. 13½x13*

536 A85 40c gray, blk & buff .20 .15
537 A85 40c olive, blk & buff .20 .15

Barbora Radvilaite (1520-51) — A110

1996, Apr. 27 Litho. *Perf. 13½x13*

538 A110 1 l multicolored .60 .30

Europa.

19th Cent. Costumes Type of 1992

Couples in different traditional costumes of the Klaipeda region: #540, Man in blue coat. #541, Man wearing wooden shoes.

1996, May 25 Litho. *Perf. 13½*

539 A83 40c multicolored .25 .15
540 A83 1 l multicolored .60 .30
541 A83 1 l multicolored .60 .30
Nos. 539-541 (3) 1.45 .75

A116 A117

1996, June 14 Litho. *Perf. 13½*

547 A116 40c Christ .30 .15
548 A116 40c Angel .30 .15

Day of Mourning and Hope.

1996, July 19 *Perf. 13½x13*

Designs: No. 549, Greek discus thrower. No. 550, Basketball players.

549 A117 1 l multicolored 1.00 .50
550 A117 1 l multicolored 1.00 .50

1996 Summer Olympic Games, Atlanta.

Paintings, by M.K. Ciurlionis — A118

No. 551, Kapines, 1909. No. 552, Auka, 1909. No. 553: a, Andante, 1908. b, Allegro, 1908.

1996, Sept. 21 Litho. *Perf. 13½x13*

551 A118 40c multicolored .30 .15
552 A118 40c multicolored .30 .15

Souvenir Sheet

Perf. 12½x11½

553 A118 3 l Sheet of 2, #a.-b. 4.00 2.00

No. 553 contains 26x53mm stamps.

Coat of Arms Type of 1992

1996, Oct. 19 Litho. *Perf. 13½x13*

554 A82 50c Seduva .40 .20
555 A82 90c Panevezys .60 .30
556 A82 1.20 l Zarasai .90 .45
Nos. 554-556 (3) 1.90 .95

Souvenir Sheet

Lithuanian Basketball Team, Bronze Medalists, 1996 Summer Olympic Games, Atlanta — A119

1996, Nov. 16 *Perf. 12½*

557 A119 4.20 l multicolored 2.00 1.00

Christmas — A120

1996, Nov. 30 *Perf. 13½x13*

558 A120 50c Angels .25 .15
559 A120 1.20 l Santa on horse .60 .30

Famous Lithuanians Type of 1993

Designs: 50c, Ieva Simonaityte (1897-1978). 90c, Jonas Sliupas (1861-1944). 1.20 l, Vladas Jurgutis (1885-1966).

1997, Jan. 23 Litho. *Perf. 13x13½*

560 A88 50c brown & greem .30 .15
561 A88 90c gray & yellow .55 .30
562 A88 1.20 l blue green & orange .75 .40
Nos. 560-562 (3) 1.60 .85

Independence Type of 1993

#563, Mykolas Birziska. #564, Kazimieras Saulys.

1997, Feb. 16 Litho. *Perf. 13½x13*

563 A85 50c multicolored .30 .15
564 A85 50c multicolored .30 .15

First Lithuanian Book, 450th Anniv. — A121

1997, Feb. 15 Litho. *Perf. 13½x13*

565 A121 50c gray & red .30 .15

Souvenir Sheet

566 A121 4.80 l like #565 2.40 1.20

No. 566 contains one 29x38mm stamp.

Lithuania stamps can be mounted in the annually supplemented Scott Baltic States album.

Souvenir Sheet

Flag on Mountain Top — A122

1997, Feb. 25 *Perf. 11½x12½*
567 A122 4.80 l multicolored 2.40 1.20

Expeditions to highest peaks on each continent.

Stories and Legends A123

Children's drawings: No. 568, Girl, horse. No. 569, King, moon, stars, bird, vert.

1997, Apr. 12 **Litho.** *Perf. 13*
568 A123 1.20 l multicolored .60 .30
569 A123 1.20 l multicolored .60 .30

Europa.

A124 A125

1997, May 9 **Litho.** *Perf. 13*
570 A124 50c multicolored .25 .15

First Lithuanian School, 600th Anniv.

1997, May 10 *Perf. 14x14½*

Old Ships of the Baltic Sea: 50c, Kurenas, 16th cent.
No. 572: a, Kurenas, 16th cent., diff. b, Maasilinn ship, 16th cent. c, Linijkugis, 17th cent.

571 A125 50c multicolored .30 .15
572 A125 1.20 l Sheet of 3, #a.-c. 1.80 .90

See Estonia No. 322, Latvia Nos. 443-444.

Palanga Botanical Park, Cent. — A126

1997, June 1 **Litho.** *Perf. 13½x13*
573 A126 50c multicolored .25 .15

No. 573 printed in tete-beche pairs.
Numbers 574-577 are unassigned.

2nd Baltic Sea Games — A127

1997, June 25 **Litho.** *Perf. 13½*
578 A127 90c multicolored .45 .25

Museum Art A128

Designs: 90c, Animal face carved on ritual staff. 1.20 l, Coins, 15th cent.

1997, July 12 *Perf. 13½x13*
579 A128 90c multicolored .45 .25
580 A128 1.20 l multicolored .60 .30

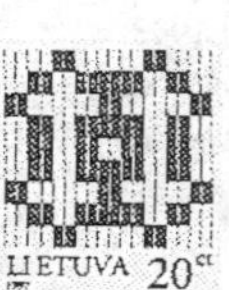

A129

A130

Double-Barred Crosses.

1997, Aug. 2 **Litho.** *Perf. 13½*
581 A129 20c olive .15 .15
582 A129 50c brown .25 .15

No. 582 exists dated 1998.

1997, Sept. 20 **Litho.** *Perf. 13½x13*

Mushrooms: No. 583, Morchella elata. No. 584, Boletus aereus.

583 A130 1.20 l multicolored .60 .30
584 A130 1.20 l multicolored .60 .30

Nos. 583-584 were each printed in tete-beche pairs.

Letters of Grand Duke Gediminas A131

1997, Oct. 4 *Perf. 14*
585 A131 50c multicolored .25 .15

Coat of Arms Type of 1992

1997, Oct. 18 **Litho.** *Perf. 13½x13*
586 A82 50c Neringa .25 .15
587 A82 90c Vilkaviskis .45 .25
588 A82 1.20 l Pasvalys .60 .30
Nos. 586-588 (3) 1.30 .70

Christmas and New Year — A132

1997, Nov. 22 **Litho.** *Perf. 13*
589 A132 50c shown .25 .15
590 A132 1.20 l Snow on trees .60 .30

1998 Winter Olympic Games, Nagano — A133

1998, Jan. 17 **Litho.** *Perf. 14*
591 A133 1.20 l multicolored .60 .30

Independence Type of 1993 and

Declaration of Independence — A134

Designs: 50c, Alfonsas Petrulis. 90c, Jokubas Sernas. Illustration reduced.

Perf. 13½x12½

1998, Feb. 16 **Litho.**
592 A85 50c olive and black .25 .15
593 A85 90c brown and black .45 .25

Souvenir Sheet

Perf. 12½x11½

594 A134 6.60 l multicolored 3.25 1.65

Independence, 80th anniv.

Souvenir Sheet

National Anthem, Cent. — A135

Illustration reduced.

1998, Feb. 16 *Perf. 12½*
595 A135 5.20 l multicolored 2.60 1.30

SEMI-POSTAL STAMPS

Regular Issue of 1923-24 Surcharged in Blue, Violet or Black:

On A21

On A22

On A23

1924, Feb. **Wmk. 147** *Perf. 11*
B1 A21 2c + 2c pale brn (Bl) .55 .55
B2 A21 3c + 3c ol bis (Bl) .55 .55
B3 A21 5c + 5c pale grn (V) .55 .55
B4 A21 10c + 10c vio (Bk) 1.40 1.40
B5 A21 36c + 34c org brn (V) 4.75 4.75

Wmk. Webbing (109)

B6 A21 10c + 10c vio (Bk) 6.00 6.00
B7 A21 15c + 15c scar (V) 1.40 1.40
B8 A21 20c + 20c ol brn (Bl) 1.90 1.90
B9 A21 25c + 25c bl (Bk) 15.00 15.00
B10 A22 50c + 50c yel grn (V) 4.75 4.75
B11 A22 60c + 60c red (V) 6.00 6.00
B12 A23 1 l + 1 l org & grn (V) 6.00 6.00
B13 A23 3 l + 2 l red & gray (V) 7.75 7.75
B14 A23 5 l + 3 l brn & bl (V) 13.00 13.00

Unwmk.

B15 A21 25c + 25c dp bl (Bk) 3.75 3.75
Nos. B1-B15 (15) 73.35 73.35

For War Invalids

Semi-Postal Stamps of 1924 Surcharged

Surcharged in Gold or Copper

1926, Dec. 3 **Wmk. 147**
B16 A21 1 + 1c on #B1 .42 .42
a. Inverted surcharge 10.00
B17 A21 2 + 2c on #B2 (C) .55 .55
B19 A21 2 + 2c on #B3 .55 .55
a. Double surch., one inverted 10.00
B20 A21 5 + 5c on #B4 1.10 1.10
B21 A21 14 + 14c on #B5 3.50 3.50

Wmk. Webbing (109)

B22 A21 5 + 5c on #B6 10.00 10.00
B23 A21 5 + 5c on #B7 1.10 1.10
B24 A21 10 + 10c on #B8 1.10 1.10
B25 A21 10 + 10c on #B9 55.00 55.00

Unwmk.

B26 A21 10 + 10c on #B15 2.75 2.75

Surcharged in Copper or Silver:

On A22 On A23

Wmk. Webbing (109)

B27 A22 20 + 20c on #B10 2.75 2.75
B28 A22 25 + 25c on #B11 4.25 4.25
B29 A23 30 + 30c on #B12 (S) 5.50 5.50
Nos. B16-B29 (13) 88.57 88.57

For War Orphans

Surcharged in Gold

1926, Dec. 3 **Wmk. 147**
B30 A21 1 + 1c on #B1 .55 .55
B31 A21 2 + 2c on #B2 .55 .55
a. Inverted surcharge 6.00
B32 A21 2 + 2c on #B3 .55 .55
a. Inverted surcharge
B33 A21 5 + 5c on #B4 1.10 1.10
B34 A21 19 + 19c on #B5 2.75 2.75

Wmk. Webbing (109)

B35 A21 5 + 5c on #B6 9.50 9.50
B36 A21 10 + 10c on #B7 1.10 1.10
B37 A21 15 + 15c on #B8 1.10 1.10
B38 A21 15 + 15c on #B9 55.00 55.00

Unwmk.

B39 A21 15 + 15c on #B15 2.75 2.75

Surcharged in Gold:

On A22

On A23

Wmk. 109

B40 A22 25c on #B10 3.25 3.25
B41 A22 30c on #B11 5.50 5.50
B42 A23 50c on #B12 5.50 5.50
Nos. B30-B42 (13) 89.20 89.20

Catalogue values for unused stamps in this section, from this point to the end of the section, are for Never Hinged items.

Archery — SP1

Natl. Olympiad, July 15-20: 15c+5c, Javelin throwing. 30c+10c, Diving. 60c+15c, Running.

Unwmk.

1938, July 13 **Photo.** *Perf. 14*
B43 SP1 5c + 5c grn & dk grn 1.50 1.00
B44 SP1 15c + 5c org & red org 3.00 1.75
B45 SP1 30c + 10c bl & dk bl 5.00 3.00
B46 SP1 60c + 15c tan & brn 10.00 5.00
Nos. B43-B46 (4) 19.50 10.75

Same Overprinted in Red, Blue or Black:

Nos. B47, B50

Nos. B48-B49

1938, July 13

B47 SP1 5c + 5c (R)	10.00	6.00
B48 SP1 15c + 5c (Bl)	10.00	6.00
B49 SP1 30c + 10c (R)	12.50	7.50
B50 SP1 60c + 15c (Bk)	17.50	10.00
Nos. B47-B50 (4)	50.00	29.50

National Scout Jamboree, July 12-14.

Basketball Players
SP6 SP7

Flags of Competing Nations and Basketball — SP8

1939 Photo. *Perf. 14*

B52 SP6 15c + 10c copper brn & brn	2.50	2.25
B53 SP7 30c + 15c myrtle grn & grn	4.00	2.25
B54 SP8 60c + 40c blue vio & gray vio	6.50	5.50
Nos. B52-B54 (3)	13.00	10.00

3rd European Basketball Championships held at Kaunas. The surtax was used for athletic equipment. Nos. B52-B54 exist imperf. Value, each pair, $175.

AIR POST STAMPS

Catalogue values for unused stamps in this section are for Never Hinged items.

Winged Posthorn — AP1

Airplane over Neman River — AP2

Air Squadron — AP3

Plane over Gediminas Castle — AP4

1921 Litho. Wmk. 109 *Perf. 11½*

C1 AP1 20sk ultra	1.00	.75
C2 AP1 40sk red orange	.85	.75
C3 AP1 60sk green	.85	.75
a. Imperf., pair	25.00	
C4 AP1 80sk lt rose	.85	.75
a. Horiz. pair, imperf. vert.	30.00	22.50
C5 AP2 1auk green & red	1.00	.50
a. Imperf., pair	15.00	12.50
C6 AP3 2auk brown & blue	1.10	.75
C7 AP4 5auk slate & yel	1.75	1.25
Nos. C1-C7 (7)	7.40	5.50

For surcharges see Nos. C21-C26, C29.

Allegory of Flight — AP5

1921, Nov. 6

C8 AP5 20sk org & gray bl	.85	1.10
C9 AP5 40sk dl bl & lake	.85	1.10
C10 AP5 60sk vio bl & ol grn	.85	1.10
C11 AP5 80sk ocher & dp grn	.85	1.10
a. Vert. pair, imperf. btwn.	20.00	15.00
C12 AP5 1auk bl grn & bl	.85	1.10
C13 AP5 2auk gray & brn org	1.10	1.10
C14 AP5 5auk dl lil & Prus bl	1.10	1.10
Nos. C8-C14 (7)	6.45	7.70

Opening of airmail service.

Plane over Kaunas — AP6

Black Overprint

1922, July 16 *Perf. 11, 11½*

C15 AP6 1auk ol brn & red	1.00	1.10
a. Imperf., pair	50.00	
C16 AP6 3auk violet & grn	1.00	1.10
C17 AP6 5auk dp blue & yel	1.75	1.40
Nos. C15-C17 (3)	3.75	3.60

Nos. C15-C17, without overprint, were to be for the founding of the Air Post service but they were not put in use at that time. Subsequently the word "ZENKLAS" (stamp) was overprinted over "ISTEIGIMAS" (founding) and the date "1921, VI, 25" was obliterated by short vertical lines.

For surcharge see No. C31.

Plane over Gediminas Castle — AP7

1922, July 22

C18 AP7 2auk blue & rose	1.00	.85
C19 AP7 4auk brown & rose	1.00	.85
C20 AP7 10auk black & gray bl	1.75	1.40
Nos. C18-C20 (3)	3.75	3.10

For surcharges see Nos. C27-C28, C30.

Nos. C1-C7, C17-C20 Surcharged like Regular Issues in Black or Carmine

1922

C21 AP1 10c on 20sk	1.25	1.25
C22 AP1 10c on 40sk	1.25	1.25
C23 AP1 10c on 60sk	.95	.90
a. Inverted surcharge	22.50	
C24 AP1 10c on 80sk	1.25	1.25
C25 AP2 20c on 1auk	3.25	3.00
C26 AP3 20c on 2auk	5.25	4.50
a. Without "CENT"	165.00	125.00
C27 AP7 25c on 2auk	.95	.50
a. Inverted surcharge	22.50	17.50
C28 AP7 30c on 4auk (C)	.95	.65
a. Double surcharge	26.00	20.00
C29 AP4 50c on 5auk	1.25	.75
C30 AP7 50c on 10auk	.85	.65
a. Inverted surcharge	26.00	20.00
C31 AP6 1 l on 5auk	10.00	8.75
a. Double surcharge	35.00	
Nos. C21-C31 (11)	27.20	23.45

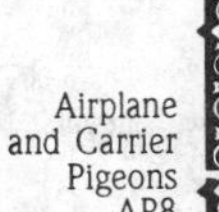

Airplane and Carrier Pigeons AP8

"Flight" AP9

1924, Jan. 28 Wmk. 147 *Perf. 11*

C32 AP8 20c yellow	1.40	.50
C33 AP8 40c emerald	1.40	.50
a. Horiz. or vert. pair, imperf. between	40.00	
C34 AP8 60c rose	1.65	.50
a. Imperf., pair	75.00	
C35 AP9 1 l dk brown	2.00	.50
Nos. C32-C35 (4)	6.45	2.00

Most copies, if not all, of the "unwatermarked" varieties show faint traces of watermark, according to experts.

For surcharges see Nos. CB1-CB4.

Swallow — AP10

1926, June 17 Wmk. 198 *Perf. 14½*

C37 AP10 20c carmine rose	1.10	.70
a. Horiz. or vert. pair, imperf. between	30.00	
C38 AP10 40c violet & red org	1.10	.70
a. Horiz. or vert. pair, imperf. between	30.00	
C39 AP10 60c blue & black	1.35	.70
a. Horiz. or vert. pair, imperf. between	30.00	
c. Center inverted	225.00	150.00
Nos. C37-C39 (3)	3.55	2.10

Juozas Tubelis — AP11

Vytautas and Airplane over Kaunas — AP12

Vytautas and Antanas Smetona — AP13

1930, Feb. 16 Wmk. 109 *Perf. 14*

C40 AP11 5c blk, bis & brn	.52	.28
C41 AP11 10c dk bl, db & blk	.52	.28
C42 AP11 15c mar, gray & bl	.52	.28
C43 AP12 20c dk brn, org & dl red	.52	.35
C44 AP12 40c dk bl, lt bl & vio	.85	.42
C45 AP13 60c bl grn, lil & blk	1.10	.55
C46 AP13 1 l dl red, lil & blk	1.40	.70
Nos. C40-C46 (7)	5.43	2.86

5th cent. of the death of the Grand Duke Vytautas.

Map of Lithuania, Klaipeda and Vilnius — AP14

15c, 20c, Airplane over Neman. 40c, 60c, City Hall, Kaunas. 1 l, 2 l, Church of Vytautas, Kaunas.

Wmk. Multiple Letters (238)

1932, July 21 *Perf. 14, Imperf.*

C47 AP14 5c ver & ol grn	.40	.60
C48 AP14 10c dk red brn & ocher	.40	.60
C49 AP14 15c dk bl & org yel	.40	.60
C50 AP14 20c sl blk & org	.60	.75
C51 AP14 60c ultra & ocher	2.25	3.00
C52 AP14 2 l dk bl & yel	3.25	4.00

Wmk. 198

C53 AP14 40c vio brn & yel	1.75	2.75
C54 AP14 1 l vio brn & grn	2.75	3.50
Nos. C47-C54 (8)	11.80	15.80

Issued for the benefit of Lithuanian orphans.

Mindaugas in the Battle of Shauyai, 1236 — AP15

15c, 20c, Coronation of Mindaugas (1253). 40c, Grand Duke Gediminas and his followers. 60c, Founding of Vilnius by Gediminas (1332). 1 l, Gediminas capturing the Russian Fortifications. 2 l, Grand Duke Algirdas before Moscow (1368).

Perf. 14, Imperf.

1932, Nov. 28 Wmk. 209

C55 AP15 5c grn & red lil	.60	.75
C56 AP15 10c emer & rose	.60	.75
C57 AP15 15c rose vio & bis brn	.60	.75
C58 AP15 20c rose red & blk brn	.60	.50
C59 AP15 40c choc & dk gray	1.10	1.10
C60 AP15 60c org & gray blk	1.50	1.75
C61 AP15 1 l rose vio & grn	2.00	2.00
C62 AP15 2 l dp bl & brn	3.00	3.00
Nos. C55-C62 (8)	10.00	10.60

Anniv. of independence.

Nos. C58-C62 exist with overprint "DARIUS-GIRENAS / NEW YORK-1933- KAUNAS" below small plane. The overprint was applied in New York with the approval of the Lithuanian consul general. Lithuanian postal authorities seem not to have been involved in the creation or release of these overprints.

Trakai Castle, Home of the Grand Duke Kestutis — AP16

Designs: 15c, 20c, Meeting of Kestutís and the Hermit Birute. 40c, 60c, Hermit Birute. 1 l, 2 l, Kestutis and his Brother Algirdas.

1933, May 6 *Perf. 14, Imperf.*

C63 AP16 5c ol gray & dp bl	.35	.40
C64 AP16 10c gray vio & org brn	.35	.40
C65 AP16 15c dp blue & lilac	.35	.40
C66 AP16 20c org brn & lilac	.70	.80
C67 AP16 40c lt ultra & lilac	1.00	*1.50*
C68 AP16 60c brown & lt ultra	1.75	*2.00*
C69 AP16 1 l ol gray & dp bl	2.25	*2.75*
C70 AP16 2 l vio gray & yel grn	3.25	*3.75*
Nos. C63-C70 (8)	10.00	*12.00*

Reopening of air service to Berlin-Kaunas-Moscow, and 550th anniv. of the death of Kestutis.

Joseph Maironis — AP17

Joseph Tumas-Vaizgantas — AP17a

Designs: 40c, 60c, Vincas Kudirka. 1 l, 2 l, Julia A. Zemaite.

1933, Sept. 15 *Perf. 14, Imperf.*

C71 AP17 5c crim & dp bl	.55	.55
C72 AP17 10c bl vio & grn	.55	.55
C73 AP17a 15c dk grn & choc	.55	.55
C74 AP17a 20c brn car & ultra	.65	.60
C75 AP17 40c red brn & ol grn	1.00	1.10
C76 AP17 60c dk bl & choc	1.50	1.50
C77 AP17 1 l citron & indigo	1.75	1.75
C78 AP17 2 l dp grn & red brn	2.50	2.50
Nos. C71-C78 (8)	9.05	9.10

Issued for the benefit of Lithuanian orphans.

Capts. Steponas Darius and Stas. Girenas AP18

Ill-Fated Plane "Lituanica" AP19

The Dark Angel of Death — AP20

"Lituanica" over Globe — AP21

"Lituanica" and White Knight — AP22

Perf. 11½

1934, May 18 Unwmk. Engr.

C79	AP18	20c scarlet & blk	.15	.15
C80	AP19	40c dp rose & bl	.15	.15
C81	AP18	60c dk vio & blk	.15	.15
C82	AP20	1 l black & rose	.35	.15
C83	AP21	3 l gray grn & org	.90	.45
C84	AP22	5 l dk brn & bl	1.75	1.10
		Nos. C79-C84 (6)	3.45	
		Set value		1.75

Death of Capts. Steponas Darius and Stasys Girenas on their New York-Kaunas flight of 1933.

No. C80 exists with diagonal overprint: "F. VAITKUS / nugalejo Atlanta / 21-22-IX-1935." Value $300.

Felix Waitkus and Map of Transatlantic Flight — AP23

Wmk. 238

1936, Mar. 24 Litho. *Perf. 14*

C85	AP23	15c brown lake	1.00	.65
C86	AP23	30c dark green	1.25	.65
C87	AP23	60c blue	1.75	1.25
		Nos. C85-C87 (3)	4.00	2.55

Transatlantic Flight of the Lituanica II, Sept. 21-22, 1935.

AIR POST SEMI-POSTAL STAMPS

> Catalogue values for unused stamps in this section are for Never Hinged items.

Nos. C32-C35 Surcharged like Nos. B1-B9 (No. CB1), Nos. B10-B11 (Nos. CB2-CB3), and Nos. B12-B14 (No. CB4) in Red, Violet or Black

1924 Wmk. 147 *Perf. 11*

CB1	AP8	20c + 20c yellow (R)	6.75	6.75
CB2	AP8	40c + 40c emerald (V)	6.75	6.75
CB3	AP8	60c + 60c rose (V)	6.75	6.75
CB4	AP9	1 l + 1 l dk brown	6.75	6.75
		Nos. CB1-CB4 (4)	27.00	27.00

Surtax for the Red Cross. See note following No. C35.

SOUTH LITHUANIA

GRODNO DISTRICT

Russian Stamps of 1909-12 Surcharged in Black or Red — Lietuva Літва. 50 skatikų грашэй.

1919 Unwmk. *Perf. 14, 14½x15*

L1	A14	50sk on 3k red	75.00	45.00
a.		Double surcharge		
L2	A14	50sk on 5k claret	50.00	45.00
a.		Imperf., pair	300.00	300.00
L3	A15	50sk on 10k dk bl (R)	50.00	45.00
L4	A11	50sk on 15k red brn & bl	50.00	45.00
a.		Imperf., pair	350.00	350.00
L5	A11	50sk on 25k grn & gray vio (R)	50.00	45.00
L6	A11	50sk on 35k red brn & grn	50.00	45.00
L7	A8	50sk on 50k vio & grn	50.00	45.00
L8	A11	50sk on 70k brn & org	50.00	45.00
		Nos. L1-L8 (8)	425.00	360.00

Excellent counterfeits are plentiful.

This surcharge exists on Russia No. 119, the imperf. 1k orange of 1917. Value, unused $90, used $60.

OCCUPATION STAMPS

ISSUED UNDER GERMAN OCCUPATION

German Stamps Overprinted in Black — Postgebiet Ob. Ost

On Stamps of 1905-17

1916-17 Wmk. 125 *Perf. 14, 14½*

1N1	A22	2½pf gray	.15	.15
1N2	A16	3pf brown	.15	.15
1N3	A16	5pf green	.20	.15
1N4	A22	7½pf orange	.15	.15
1N5	A16	10pf carmine	.20	.20
1N6	A22	15pf yel brn	4.00	4.00
1N7	A22	15pf dk vio ('17)	.20	.20
1N8	A16	20pf ultra	.55	.55
1N9	A16	25pf org & blk, *yel*	.20	.35
1N10	A16	40pf lake & blk	.75	1.00
1N11	A16	50pf vio & blk, *buff*	.75	.65
1N12	A17	1m car rose	12.50	7.00
		Nos. 1N1-1N12 (12)	19.80	14.55
		Set, never hinged	40.00	

These stamps were used in the former Russian provinces of Suvalki, Vilnius, Kaunas, Kurland.

ISSUED UNDER RUSSIAN OCCUPATION

> Catalogue values for unused stamps in this section are for Never Hinged items.

Lithuanian Stamps of 1937-40 Overprinted in Red or Blue — LTSR 1940 VII 21

1940 Wmk. 238 *Perf. 14*

2N9	A44	2c orange (Bl)	.30	.40
2N10	A50	50c brown (Bl)	.55	.50

Unwmk.

2N11	A56	5c brown car (Bl)	.30	.40
2N12	A57	10c green (R)	2.00	1.75
2N13	A58	15c dull orange (Bl)	.30	.40
2N14	A59	25c lt brown (R)	.30	.40
2N15	A60	30c Prus green (R)	.55	.50
2N16	A61	35c red orange (Bl)	.85	1.00
		Nos. 2N9-2N16 (8)	5.15	5.35

Values for used stamps are for CTOs. Postally used examples are considerably more.

The Lithuanian Soviet Socialist Republic was proclaimed July 21, 1940.

LOURENCO MARQUES

lə-ˈren(t)-(ˌ)sō-ˌmär-ˈkes

LOCATION — In the southern part of Mozambique in Southeast Africa

GOVT. — Part of Portuguese East Africa Colony

AREA — 28,800 sq. mi. (approx.)

POP. — 474,000 (approx.)

CAPITAL — Lourenço Marques

Stamps of Mozambique replaced those of Lourenço Marques in 1920.

1000 Reis = 1 Milreis

100 Centavos = 1 Escudo (1913)

King Carlos — A1

Perf. 11½, 12½, 13½

1895 Typo. Unwmk.

1	A1	5r yellow	.75	.25
2	A1	10r redsh violet	.75	.35
3	A1	15r chocolate	1.00	.50
4	A1	20r lavender	1.00	.50
5	A1	25r blue green	1.00	.30
a.		Perf. 11½	3.00	.85
6	A1	50r light blue	2.00	.60
a.		Perf. 13½	10.00	3.75
b.		Perf. 11½		
7	A1	75r rose	1.50	1.25
8	A1	80r yellow grn	4.50	2.75
9	A1	100r brn, *yel*	3.00	1.00
a.		Perf. 12½	5.00	3.25
10	A1	150r car, *rose*	5.00	3.00
11	A1	200r dk bl, *bl*	6.00	3.00
12	A1	300r dk bl, *sal*	7.50	4.00
		Nos. 1-12 (12)	34.00	17.50

For surcharges and overprints see Nos. 29, 58-69, 132-137, 140-143, 156-157, 160.

Saint Anthony of Padua Issue

Regular Issues of Mozambique, 1886 and 1894, Overprinted in Black — L. MARQUES — CENTENARIO DE S. ANTONIO — MDCCCXCV

1895 Without Gum *Perf. 12½*

On 1886 Issue

13	A2	5r black	15.00	8.00
14	A2	10r green	25.00	8.00
15	A2	20r rose	35.00	8.75
16	A2	25r lilac	40.00	14.00
17	A2	40r chocolate	19.00	11.00
18	A2	50r bl, perf. 13½	30.00	8.75
a.		Perf. 12½	50.00	27.50
19	A2	100r yellow brn	60.00	27.50
20	A2	200r gray vio	40.00	22.50
21	A2	300r orange	50.00	30.00

On 1894 Issue

Perf. 11½

22	A3	5r yellow	35.00	25.00
23	A3	10r redsh vio	40.00	15.00
24	A3	50r light blue	40.00	20.00
a.		Perf. 12½	40.00	35.00
25	A3	75r rose, perf. 12½	50.00	30.00
26	A3	80r yellow grn	75.00	40.00
27	A3	100r brown, *buff*	350.00	100.00
28	A3	150r car, *rose*, perf. 12½	30.00	18.00
		Nos. 13-28 (16)	934.00	386.50

No. 12 Surcharged in Black — 50 réis

1897, Jan. 2

29	A1	50r on 300r	175.00	75.00

Most copies of No. 29 were issued without gum.

King Carlos — A2

1898-1903 *Perf. 11½*

Name, Value in Black except 500r

30	A2	2½r gray	.20	.20
31	A2	5r orange	.20	.20
32	A2	10r lt green	.20	.20
33	A2	15r brown	1.00	.85
34	A2	15r gray green ('03)	.55	.35
a.		Imperf.		
35	A2	20r gray violet	.55	.20
a.		Imperf.		
36	A2	25r sea green	.70	.30
a.		Perf. 13½	30.00	6.75
b.		25r light green (error)	32.50	32.50
c.		Perf. 12½	40.00	50.00
37	A2	25r car ('03)	.30	.20
a.		Imperf.		
38	A2	50r blue	2.00	.40
39	A2	50r brown ('03)	.80	.70
40	A2	65r dull bl ('03)	12.00	8.00
41	A2	75r rose	1.75	1.40
42	A2	75r lilac ('03)	1.10	.95
a.		Imperf.		
43	A2	80r violet	2.50	1.25
44	A2	100r dk blue, *blue*	1.75	.65
a.		Perf. 13½	14.00	4.75
45	A2	115r org brn, *pink* ('03)	7.00	5.00
46	A2	130r brn, *straw* ('03)	7.00	5.00
47	A2	150r brn, *straw*	2.00	1.40
48	A2	200r red lil, *pnksh*	2.75	1.25
49	A2	300r dk bl, *rose*	3.00	1.25
50	A2	400r dl bl, *straw* ('03)	7.00	5.00
51	A2	500r blk & red, *bl* ('01)	6.00	3.00
52	A2	700r vio, *yelsh* ('01)	9.00	6.00
		Nos. 30-52 (23)	69.35	43.75

For surcharges and overprints see Nos. 57, 71-74, 76-91, 138, 144-155.

Coat of Arms — A3

Surcharged On Upper and Lower Halves of Stamp

1899 *Imperf.*

53	A3	5r on 10r grn & brn	20.00	6.00
54	A3	25r on 10r grn & brn	20.00	6.00
55	A3	50r on 30r grn & brn	30.00	11.00
a.		Inverted surcharge		
56	A3	50r on 800r grn & brn	40.00	15.00
		Nos. 53-56 (4)	110.00	38.00

The lower half of No. 55 can be distinguished from that of No. 56 by the background of the label containing the word "REIS." The former is plain, while the latter is formed of white intersecting curved horizontal lines over vertical shading of violet brown.

Values are for undivided stamps. Halves sell for ¼ as much.

Most copies of Nos. 53-56 were issued without gum. Values are for copies without gum.

No. 41 Surcharged in Black — 50 Réis

1899 *Perf. 11½*

57	A2	50r on 75r rose	5.00	2.50

Most copies of No. 57 were issued without gum. Values are for copies without gum.

Surcharged in Black — 65 RÉIS

On Issue of 1895

1902 *Perf. 11½, 12½*

58	A1	65r on 5r yellow	4.00	2.50
59	A1	65r on 15r choc	4.00	2.50
60	A1	65r on 20r lav	5.00	2.50
a.		Perf. 12½	25.00	15.00
61	A1	115r on 10r red vio	5.00	3.00
62	A1	115r on 200r bl, *bl*	5.00	3.00
63	A1	115r on 300r bl, *sal*	5.00	3.00
64	A1	130r on 25r grn, perf. 12½	2.00	2.00
a.		Perf. 11½	30.00	22.50
65	A1	130r on 80r yel grn	3.00	3.00
66	A1	130r on 150r car, *rose*	4.00	3.00
67	A1	400r on 50r lt bl	8.00	6.00
68	A1	400r on 75r rose	8.00	6.00
69	A1	400r on 100r brn, *buff*	7.00	6.00

On Newspaper Stamp of 1893

70	N1	65r on 2½ brn	4.00	2.00
		Nos. 58-70 (13)	64.00	44.50

Surcharge exists inverted on Nos. 61, 70.

Nos. 64, 67 and 68 have been reprinted on thin white paper with shiny white gum and clean-cut perforation 13½. Value $2 each.

For overprints see Nos. 132-137, 140-143, 156-157, 160.

Issue of 1898-1903 Overprinted in Black

PROVISORIO

1903 *Perf. 11½*

No.	Type	Description	Unused	Used
71	A2	15r brown	2.00	.85
72	A2	25r sea green	1.50	.85
73	A2	50r blue	2.50	.85
74	A2	75r rose	3.00	1.40
a.		Inverted overprint	50.00	50.00
		Nos. 71-74 (4)	9.00	3.95

Surcharged in Black

50 RÉIS

1905

No.	Type	Description	Unused	Used
76	A2	50r on 65r dull blue	1.75	1.50

Regular Issues Overprinted in Carmine or Green

1911

No.	Type	Description	Unused	Used
77	A2	2½r gray	.20	.20
78	A2	5r orange	.20	.20
a.		Double overprint	10.00	10.00
b.		Inverted overprint	10.00	10.00
79	A2	10r lt grn	.30	.25
80	A2	15r gray grn	.30	.25
a.		Inverted overprint	10.00	10.00
81	A2	20r dl vio	.60	.40
82	A2	25r car (G)	.30	.25
83	A2	50r brown	.60	.40
84	A2	75r lilac	.60	.40
85	A2	100r dk bl, *bl*	.80	.40
86	A2	115r org brn, *pink*	5.50	2.00
87	A2	130r brn, *straw*	.80	.60
88	A2	200r red lil, *pnksh*	.75	.50
89	A2	400r dl bl, *straw*	1.00	.80
90	A2	500r blk & red, *bl*	1.25	.85
91	A2	700r vio, *yelsh*	1.50	1.00
		Nos. 77-91 (15)	14.70	8.50

Vasco da Gama Issue of Various Portuguese Colonies Common Design Types Surcharged

REPUBLICA
LOURENCO MARQUES
¼ C.

1913 *Perf. 12½-16*

On Stamps of Macao

No.	Type	Description	Unused	Used
92	CD20	¼c on ½a bl grn	2.25	2.25
93	CD21	½c on 1a red	2.25	2.25
94	CD22	1c on 2a red vio	2.25	2.25
95	CD23	2½c on 4a yel grn	2.25	2.25
96	CD24	5c on 8a dk bl	2.25	2.25
97	CD25	7½c on 12a vio brn	4.25	4.25
98	CD26	10c on 16a bis brn	3.50	3.50
a.		Inverted surcharge		
99	CD27	15c on 24a bister	3.75	3.75
		Nos. 92-99 (8)	22.75	22.75

On Stamps of Portuguese Africa

No.	Type	Description	Unused	Used
100	CD20	¼c on 2½r bl grn	1.40	1.40
101	CD21	½c on 5r red	1.40	1.40
102	CD22	1c on 10r red vio	1.40	1.40
103	CD23	2½c on 25r yel grn	1.40	1.40
104	CD24	5c on 50r dk bl	1.40	1.40
105	CD25	7½c on 75r vio brn	3.50	3.50
106	CD26	10c on 100r bis brn	2.50	2.50
107	CD27	15c on 150r bis	2.50	2.50
		Nos. 100-107 (8)	15.50	15.50

On Stamps of Timor

No.	Type	Description	Unused	Used
108	CD20	¼c on ½a bl grn	1.75	1.75
109	CD21	½c on 1a red	1.75	1.75
110	CD22	1c on 2a red vio	1.75	1.75
111	CD23	2½c on 4a yel grn	1.75	1.75
112	CD24	5c on 8a dk bl	1.75	1.75
113	CD25	7½c on 12a vio brn	3.50	3.50
114	CD26	10c on 16a bis brn	2.75	2.75
115	CD27	15c on 24a bister	2.75	2.75
		Nos. 108-115 (8)	17.75	17.75
		Nos. 92-115 (24)	56.00	56.00

Ceres — A4

1914 **Typo.** *Perf. 15x14*

Name and Value in Black

No.	Type	Description	Unused	Used
116	A4	¼c olive brn	.15	.15
117	A4	½c black	.15	.15
a.		Value omitted		
118	A4	1c blue grn	.15	.15
119	A4	1½c lilac brn	.15	.15
a.		Imperf.		
120	A4	2c carmine	.15	.15
121	A4	2½c lt vio	.15	.15
122	A4	5c dp blue	.15	.15
123	A4	7½c yellow brn	.15	.15
124	A4	8c slate	.15	.15
125	A4	10c orange brn	1.50	.85
126	A4	15c plum	1.00	.35
127	A4	20c yellow grn	2.50	.50
128	A4	30c brown, *green*	3.50	1.00
129	A4	40c brown, *pink*	7.50	4.00
130	A4	50c orange, *sal*	5.00	3.00
131	A4	1e green, *blue*	7.00	3.00
		Nos. 116-131 (16)	29.35	14.05

Values of Nos. 116-124 are for stamps on ordinary paper. Those on chalky paper sell for 8 to 12 times as much. Nos. 127-131 issued only on chalky paper.

For surcharges see Nos. 139, 159, 161-162, B1-B12.

In 1921 Nos. 117 and 119 were surcharged 10c and 30c respectively, for use in Mozambique as Nos. 230 and 231. These same values, surcharged 5c and 10c respectively, with the addition of the word "PORTEADO," were used in Mozambique as postage dues, Nos. J44 and J45.

Provisional Issue of 1902 Overprinted Locally in Carmine

1914 *Perf. 11½, 12½*

No.	Type	Description	Unused	Used
132	A1	115r on 10r red vio	.70	.45
a.		"Republica" inverted		
133	A1	115r on 200r bl, *bl*	.70	.45
134	A1	115r on 300r bl, *sal*	.85	.45
a.		Double overprint	40.00	40.00
135	A1	130r on 25r grn	1.10	.70
a.		Perf. 12½	3.25	1.65
136	A1	130r on 80r yel grn	.85	.35
137	A1	130r on 150r car, *rose*	.85	.35
		Nos. 132-137 (6)	5.05	2.75

No. 135a was issued without gum.

Nos. 78 and 117 Perforated Diagonally and Surcharged in Carmine

¼

1915 *Perf. 11½*

No.	Type	Description	Unused	Used
138	A2	¼c on half of 5r org, pair	5.00	5.00
a.		Pair without dividing perfs.	20.00	20.00

Perf. 15x14

No.	Type	Description	Unused	Used
139	A4	¼c on half of ½c blk, pair	9.00	9.00

The added perforation on Nos. 138-139 runs from lower left to upper right corners, dividing the stamp in two. Values are for pairs, both halves of the stamp.

Provisional Issue of 1902 Overprinted in Carmine

1915 *Perf. 11½, 12½*

No.	Type	Description	Unused	Used
140	A1	115r on 10r red vio	.55	.40
141	A1	115r on 200r bl, *bl*	.55	.40
142	A1	115r on 300r bl, *sal*	.55	.40
143	A1	130r on 150r car, *rose*	.55	.40
		Nos. 140-143 (4)	2.20	1.60

Nos. 34 and 80 Surcharged

Dois
centavos

1915

On Issue of 1903

No.	Type	Description	Unused	Used
144	A2	2c on 15r gray grn	.75	.70

On Issue of 1911

No.	Type	Description	Unused	Used
145	A2	2c on 15r gray grn	.75	.70
a.		New value inverted	22.50	

Regular Issues of 1898-1903 Overprinted Locally in Carmine

REPUBLICA

1916

No.	Type	Description	Unused	Used
146	A2	15r gray grn	1.50	1.00
147	A2	50r brown	2.50	2.00
a.		Inverted overprint		
148	A2	75r lilac	3.00	2.00
149	A2	100r blue, *bl*	2.00	1.00
150	A2	115r org brn, *pink*	2.00	1.00
151	A2	130r brown, *straw*	9.00	5.00
152	A2	200r red lil, *pnksh*	5.00	2.00
153	A2	400r dull bl, *straw*	12.00	4.00
154	A2	500r blk & red, *bl*	6.00	3.00
155	A2	700r vio, *yelsh*	10.00	5.00
		Nos. 146-155 (10)	53.00	26.00

Same Overprint on Nos. 67-68

1917

No.	Type	Description	Unused	Used
156	A1	400r on 50r lt blue	1.25	.65
a.		Perf. 13½	11.50	9.00
157	A1	400r on 75r rose	2.50	1.00

No. 69 exists with this overprint. It was not officially issued.

Type of 1914 Surcharged in Red

Quatro
centavos

1920 *Perf. 15x14*

No.	Type	Description	Unused	Used
159	A4	4c on 2½c violet	1.00	.30

Stamps of 1914 Surcharged in Green or Black

Um quarto de centavo
a

1 Centavo
b

1921

No.	Type	Description	Unused	Used
160	A1(a)	¼c on 115r on 10r red vio (G)	.80	.80
161	A4(b)	1c on 2½c vio (Bk)	.60	.40
a.		Inverted surcharge	40.00	
162	A4(b)	1½c on 2½c vio (Bk)	.80	.60
		Nos. 160-162 (3)	2.20	1.80

Nos. 159-162 were postally valid throughout Mozambique.

SEMI-POSTAL STAMPS

Regular Issue of 1914 Overprinted or Surcharged:

$20 + 9-3-18 (a) · 1$ + 9-3-18 (b) · + 9-3-18 (c)

1918 *Perf. 15x14½*

No.	Type	Description	Unused	Used
B1	A4(a)	¼c olive brn	2.00	3.00
B2	A4(a)	½c black	2.00	4.00
B3	A4(a)	1c bl grn	2.00	4.00
B4	A4(a)	2½c violet	4.00	4.00
B5	A4(a)	5c blue	4.00	6.00
B6	A4(a)	10c org brn	5.00	7.00
B7	A4(b)	20c on 1½c lil brn	5.00	8.00
B8	A4(a)	30c brn, *grn*	5.00	9.00
B9	A4(b)	40c on 2c car	5.00	10.00
B10	A4(b)	50c on 7½c bis	8.00	12.00
B11	A4(b)	70c on 8c slate	10.00	15.00
B12	A4(c)	$1 on 15c mag	10.00	15.00
		Nos. B1-B12 (12)	62.00	97.00

Nos. B1-B12 were used in place of ordinary postage stamps on Mar. 9, 1918.

NEWSPAPER STAMPS

Numeral of Value — N1

Perf. 11½

1893, July 28 **Typo.** **Unwmk.**

No.	Type	Description	Unused	Used
P1	N1	2½r brown	.25	.65
a.		Perf. 12½	20.00	17.50

For surcharge see No. 70.

Saint Anthony of Padua Issue

Mozambique No. P6 Overprinted

L. MARQUES
CENTENARIO
DE
S. ANTONIO
MDCCCXCV

1895, July 1 *Perf. 11½, 13½*

No.	Type	Description	Unused	Used
P2	N3	2½r brown	20.00	17.50
a.		Inverted overprint	30.00	30.00

LUXEMBOURG

'lək-səm-ˌbərg

LOCATION — Western Europe between southern Belgium, Germany and France
GOVT. — Grand Duchy
AREA — 998 sq. mi.
POP. — 365,800 (est. 1984)
CAPITAL — Luxembourg

12½ Centimes = 1 Silbergroschen
100 Centimes = 1 Franc

Catalogue values for unused stamps in this country are for Never Hinged items, beginning with Scott 357 in the regular postage section, Scott B216 in the semi-postal section.

Watermarks

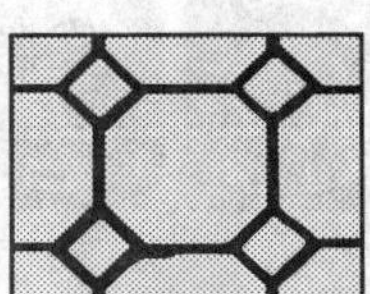

Wmk. 110- Octagons

Wmk. 149- W

Wmk. 213 - Double Wavy Lines

Wmk. 216- Multiple Airplanes

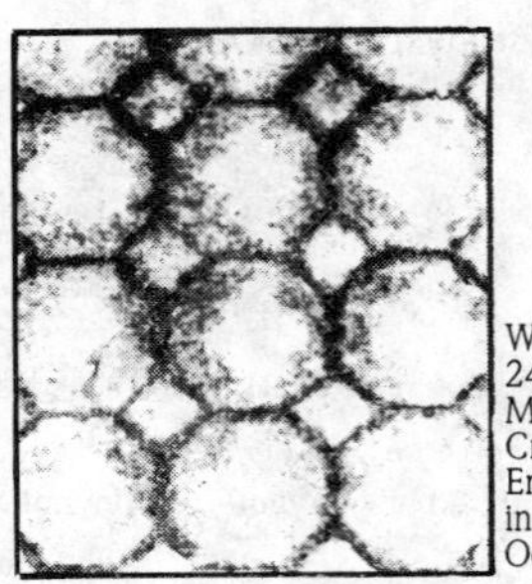

Wmk. 246- Multiple Cross Enclosed in Octagons

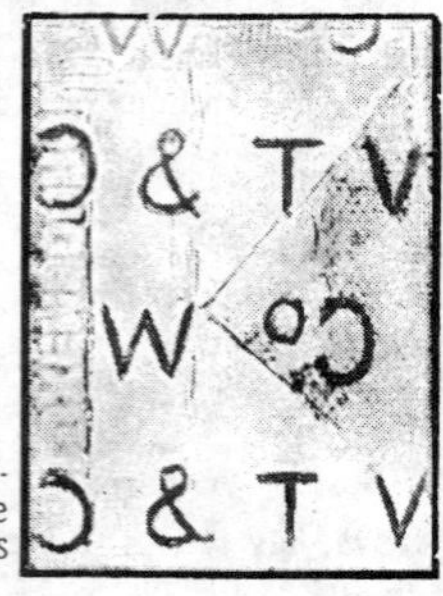

Wmk. 247- Multiple Letters

Grand Duke William III — A1

Luxembourg Print

Wmk. 149

1852, Sept. 15 Engr. *Imperf.*

1 A1 10c gray black *1,600.* 40.00
a. 10c black *2,250.* 80.00
2 A1 1sg brick red 1,100. 60.00
a. 1sg brown red 1,100. 67.50
b. 1sg orange red 1,200. 67.50
c. 1sg copper red 1,100. 60.00
3 A1 1sg rose 1,000. 62.50
Nos. 1-3 (3) 162.50

Reprints of both values exist on watermarked paper. Some of the reprints show traces of lines cancelling the plates, but others can be distinguished only by an expert.

See Nos. 278-279, 1603.

Coat of Arms
A2 A3

No. 26

Un Franc.

No. 39

Frankfort Print

1859-63 Typo. Unwmk.

4 A2 1c buff ('63) 110.00 *300.00*
5 A2 2c black ('60) 80.00 *400.00*
6 A2 4c yellow ('60) 140.00 140.00
a. 4c orange 165.00 140.00
7 A3 10c blue 150.00 12.50
8 A3 12½c rose 225.00 125.00
9 A3 25c brown 275.00 200.00
10 A3 30c rose lilac 250.00 160.00
11 A3 37½c green 250.00 140.00
12 A3 40c red orange 675.00 140.00

Counterfeits of Nos. 1-12 exist.

See Nos. 13-25, 27-38, 40-47. For surcharges and overprints see Nos. 26, 39, O1-O51.

1865-71 *Rouletted*

13 A2 1c red brown 140.00 200.00
14 A2 2c black ('67) 12.00 8.50
15 A2 4c yellow ('67) 550.00 150.00
16 A2 4c green ('71) 30.00 16.00
Nos. 13-16 (4) 732.00 374.50

1865-74 *Rouletted in Color*

17 A2 1c red brown ('72) 15.00 5.00
18 A2 1c orange ('69) 24.00 4.50
a. 1c brown orange ('67) 100.00 27.50
19 A3 10c lilac 87.50 1.25
a. 10c rose lilac 95.00 1.25
b. 10c gray lilac 95.00 1.25
20 A3 12½c carmine 150.00 4.50
a. 12½c rose 250.00 6.00
21 A3 20c gray brown ('72) 90.00 3.25
a. 20c yellow brown ('69) 95.00 5.00
22 A3 25c blue ('72) 650.00 10.00
22A A3 25c ultra ('65) 650.00 10.00
23 A3 30c lilac rose 650.00 55.00
24 A3 37½c bister ('66) 600.00 200.00
25 A3 40c pale orange ('74) 30.00 65.00
a. 40c orange red ('66) 800.00 50.00
26 A4 1fr on 37½c bis ('73) 750.00 55.00
a. Surcharge inverted *3,250.*

Luxembourg Print

1874 Typo. *Imperf.*

27 A2 4c green 80.00 80.00

1875-79 *Perf. 13*

Narrow Margins

29 A2 1c red brown ('78) 30.00 3.00
30 A2 2c black 110.00 20.00
31 A2 4c green 1.50 *5.00*
32 A2 5c yellow ('76) 150.00 10.00
a. 5c orange yellow 500.00 100.00
b. Imperf. 475.00 400.00
33 A3 10c gray lilac 400.00 1.00
b. 10c lilac 1,300. 24.00
c. Imperf. 1,500. *2,200.*
34 A3 12½c lilac rose ('76) 500.00 16.00
35 A3 12½c car rose ('77) 325.00 16.00
36 A3 25c blue ('77) 700.00 11.00
37 A3 30c dull rose ('78) 650.00 400.00
38 A3 40c orange ('79) 1.00 *8.00*
39 A5 1fr on 37½c bis ('79) 8.00 *15.00*
a. "Pranc" *5,000.* *6,250.*
b. Without surcharge 400.00
c. As "b," imperf. 400.00

In the Luxembourg print the perforation is close to the border of the stamp. Excellent forgeries of No. 39a are plentiful, as well as faked cancellations on Nos. 31, 38 and 39.

Nos. 32b and 33c are said to be essays; Nos. 39b and 39c printer's waste.

Haarlem Print

Perf. 11½x12, 12½x12, 13½

1880-81

Wide Margins

40 A2 1c yellow brn ('81) 8.50 6.00
41 A2 2c black 6.00 1.40
42 A2 5c yellow ('81) 175.00 75.00
43 A3 10c gray lilac 150.00 .65
44 A3 12½c rose ('81) 175.00 160.00
45 A3 20c gray brown ('81) 40.00 11.00
46 A3 25c blue 250.00 3.50
47 A3 30c dull rose ('81) 3.00 13.00

Stamps on gray yellowish paper were not regularly issued.

Gray Yellowish Paper

Perf. 12½

42a A2 5c 5.00
43a A3 10c 1.50
44a A3 12½c 7.50
46a A3 25c 3.00

"Industry" and "Commerce"
A6

Grand Duke Adolphe
A7

Perf. 11½x12, 12½x12, 12½, 13½

1882, Dec. 1 Typo.

48 A6 1c gray lilac .20 .25
49 A6 2c olive gray .20 .20
a. 2c olive brown .25 .40
50 A6 4c olive bister .40 .60
51 A6 5c lt green .60 .20
52 A6 10c rose 4.75 .20
53 A6 12½c slate 3.00 6.00
54 A6 20c orange 4.50 1.40
55 A6 25c ultra 165.00 1.00
56 A6 30c gray green 25.00 13.00
57 A6 50c bister brown 1.10 2.00
58 A6 1fr pale violet 1.10 6.00
59 A6 5fr brown orange 30.00 70.00
Nos. 48-59 (12) 235.85 100.85

For overprints see Nos. O52-O64.

Perf. 11, 11½, 11½x11 and 12½

1891-93 Engr.

60 A7 10c carmine .15 .20
a. Sheet of 25 60.00
61 A7 12½c slate grn ('93) .35 .30
62 A7 20c orange ('93) 6.50 .40
a. 20c brown (error) *130.00* 200.00
63 A7 25c blue .40 .25
a. Sheet of 25 *725.00*
64 A7 30c olive grn ('93) 1.25 .85
65 A7 37½c green ('93) 2.50 2.00
66 A7 50c brown ('93) 4.50 2.00
67 A7 1fr dp violet ('93) 11.00 4.00
68 A7 2½fr black ('93) 1.00 *16.00*
69 A7 5fr lake ('93) 30.00 50.00
Nos. 60-69 (10) 57.65 76.00

No. 62a was never on sale at any post office, but exists postally used.

Perf. 11½ stamps are from the sheets of 25.

For overprints see Nos. O65-O74.

Grand Duke Adolphe — A8

1895, May 4 Typo. *Perf. 12½*

70 A8 1c pearl gray 3.00 .20
71 A8 2c gray brown .25 .20
72 A8 4c olive bister .25 .45
73 A8 5c green 3.00 .20
74 A8 10c carmine 9.00 .20
Nos. 70-74 (5) 15.50 1.25

For overprints see Nos. O75-O79.

Coat of Arms — A9

Grand Duke William IV — A10

1906-26 Typo. *Perf. 12½*

75 A9 1c gray ('07) .15 .15
76 A9 2c olive brn ('07) .15 .15
77 A9 4c bister ('07) .15 .15
78 A9 5c green ('07) .15 .15
79 A9 5c lilac ('26) .15 .15
80 A9 6c violet ('07) .15 .32
81 A9 7½c orange ('19) .15 .65

Engr.

Perf. 11, 11½x11

82 A10 10c scarlet 1.40 .15
a. Souvenir sheet of 10 375.00 *725.00*
83 A10 12½c slate grn ('07) 1.65 .15
84 A10 15c orange brn ('07) 1.65 .50
85 A10 20c orange ('07) 2.00 .40
86 A10 25c ultra ('07) 42.50 .20
87 A10 30c olive grn ('08) .90 .40
88 A10 37½c green ('07) .90 .40
a. Perf. 12½ 25.00 4.50
89 A10 50c brown ('07) 2.75 .60
90 A10 87½c dk blue ('08) 1.65 5.75
91 A10 1fr violet ('08) 3.25 1.25
92 A10 2½fr vermilion ('08) 60.00 65.00
93 A10 5fr claret ('08) 8.00 24.00
Nos. 75-93 (19) 127.70 100.52

No. 82a for accession of Grand Duke William IV to the throne.

For surcharges and overprints see Nos. 94-96, 112-117, O80-O98.

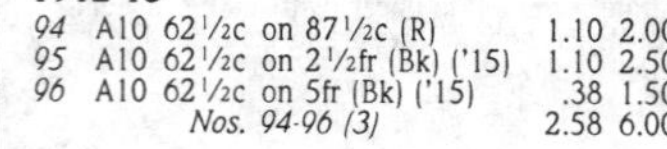

1912-15

94 A10 62½c on 87½c (R) 1.10 2.00
95 A10 62½c on 2½fr (Bk) ('15) 1.10 2.50
96 A10 62½c on 5fr (Bk) ('15) .38 1.50
Nos. 94-96 (3) 2.58 6.00

Grand Duchess Marie Adelaide
A11

Grand Duchess Charlotte
A12

1914-17 Engr. *Perf. 11½, 11½x11*

97 A11 10c lake .15 .15
98 A11 12½c dull green .15 .15
99 A11 15c sepia .15 .20
100 A11 17½c dp brown ('17) .15 .25
101 A11 25c ultra .15 .15
102 A11 30c bister .15 .25
103 A11 35c dark blue .15 .20
104 A11 37½c black brn .15 .20
105 A11 40c orange .15 .20
106 A11 50c dark gray .20 .33
107 A11 62½c blue green .35 1.40
108 A11 87½c orange ('17) .35 1.65
109 A11 1fr orange brown 2.00 .60
110 A11 2½fr red 1.00 1.65
111 A11 5fr dark violet 5.25 13.00
Nos. 97-111 (15) 10.50 20.38

For surcharges and overprints see Nos. 118-124, B7-B10, O99-O113.

Stamps of 1906-19 Surcharged with New Value and Bars in Black or Red

1916-24

112 A9 2½c on 5c ('18) .15 .15
113 A9 3c on 2c ('21) .15 .18
114 A9 5c on 1c ('23) .15 .18
115 A9 5c on 4c ('23) .15 .28
116 A9 5c on 7½c ('24) .15 .18
117 A9 6c on 2c (R) ('22) .15 .20
118 A11 7½c on 10c ('18) .15 .15
119 A11 17½c on 30c .15 .38
120 A11 20c on 17½c ('21) .15 .20
121 A11 25c on 37½c ('23) .15 .18
a. Double surcharge 75.00
122 A11 75c on 62½c (R) ('22) .15 .20
123 A11 80c on 87½c ('22) .15 .20
124 A11 87½c on 1fr .60 1.50
Nos. 112-124 (13) 2.40 3.98

1921, Jan. 6 Engr. *Perf. 11½*

125 A12 15c rose .15 .15
a. Sheet of 5, perf 11 125.00 125.00
b. Sheet of 25, perf. 11½, 11x11½, 12x11½ 4.50 14.00

Birth of Prince Jean, first son of Grand Duchess Charlotte, Jan. 5 (No. 125a). No. 125 was printed in sheets of 100.

See Nos. 131-150. For surcharges and overprints see Nos. 154-158, O114-O131, O136.

Vianden Castle — A13

Foundries at Esch — A14

Adolphe Bridge — A15

1921-34 *Perf. 11, 11x11½, 11½*

126 A13 1fr carmine .15 .30
127 A13 1fr dk blue ('26) .18 .28

Perf. 11½x11; 11½ (#129)

128 A14 2fr indigo .15 .50
129 A14 2fr dk brown ('26) 1.25 .90
130 A15 5fr dk violet 7.50 4.50
a. Perf. 12½ ('34) 16.00 9.50
Nos. 126-130 (5) 9.23 6.48

For overprints see Nos. O132-O135, O137-138, O140.

Charlotte Type of 1921

1921-26 *Perf. 11½*

131 A12 2c brown .15 .15
132 A12 3c olive green .15 .15
a. Sheet of 25 8.50 17.50
133 A12 6c violet .15 .15
a. Sheet of 25 8.50 17.50
134 A12 10c yellow grn .18 .15
135 A12 10c olive brn ('24) .15 .15
136 A12 15c brown olive .18 .15
137 A12 15c pale green ('24) .15 .15
138 A12 15c dp orange ('26) .15 .15
139 A12 20c dp orange .18 .15
a. Sheet of 25 50.00 80.00
140 A12 20c yellow grn ('26) .15 .15
141 A12 25c dk green .18 .15
142 A12 30c carmine rose .18 .15
143 A12 40c brown orange .20 .15
144 A12 50c deep blue .38 .23
145 A12 50c red ('24) .25 .35
146 A12 75c red .25 .38
a. Sheet of 25 350.00
147 A12 75c deep blue ('24) .20 .15
148 A12 80c black .38 .30
a. Sheet of 25 350.00
Nos. 131-148 (18) 3.61 3.36

For surcharges and overprints see Nos. 154-158, O114-O131, O136.

Philatelic Exhibition Issue

1922, Aug. 27 *Imperf.*

Laid Paper

149 A12 25c dark green 1.65 2.75
150 A12 30c carmine rose 1.65 2.75

Nos. 149 and 150 were sold exclusively at the Luxembourg Phil. Exhib., Aug. 1922.

Souvenir Sheet

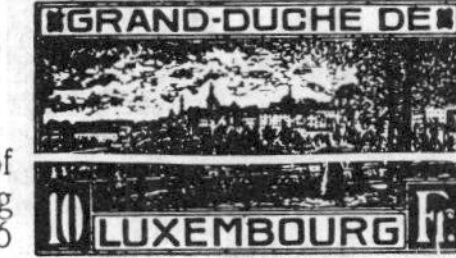

View of Luxembourg A16

1923, Jan. 3 *Perf. 11*

151 A16 10fr dp grn, sheet 1,000. *1,500.*

Birth of Princess Elisabeth.

1923, Mar. *Perf. 11½*

152 A16 10fr black 5.00 *14.00*
a. Perf. 12½ ('34) 4.00 *8.50*

For overprint see No. O141.

The Wolfsschlucht near Echternach — A17

1923-34 *Perf. 11½*

153 A17 3fr dk blue & blue 1.00 1.00
a. Perf. 12½ ('34) .80 .60

For overprint see No. O139.

Stamps of 1921-26 Surcharged with New Values and Bars

1925-28

154 A12 5c on 10c yel grn .20 .20
155 A12 15c on 20c yel grn ('28) .15 .20
a. Bars omitted
156 A12 35c on 40c brn org ('27) .15 .20
157 A12 60c on 75c dp bl ('27) .15 .20
158 A12 60c on 80c blk ('28) .35 .32
Nos. 154-158 (5) 1.00 1.12

Grand Duchess Charlotte — A18

1926-35 **Engr.** *Perf. 12*

159 A18 5c dk violet .15 .15
160 A18 10c olive grn .15 .15
161 A18 15c black ('30) .15 .25
162 A18 20c orange .15 .18
163 A18 25c yellow grn .15 .18
164 A18 25c vio brn ('27) .15 .20
165 A18 30c yel grn ('27) .20 .38
166 A18 30c gray vio ('30) .16 .30
167 A18 35c gray vio ('28) 1.00 .22
168 A18 35c yel grn ('30) .15 .15
169 A18 40c olive gray .15 .18
170 A18 50c red brown .15 .15
171 A18 60c blue grn ('28) 1.00 .15
172 A18 65c black brn .15 .50
173 A18 70c blue vio ('35) .15 .15
174 A18 75c rose .15 .25
175 A18 75c bis brn ('27) .15 .15
176 A18 80c bister brn .18 .50
177 A18 90c rose ('27) .45 .75
178 A18 1fr black .35 .50
179 A18 1fr rose ('30) .16 .40
180 A18 1¼fr dk blue .15 .35
181 A18 1¼fr yellow ('30) 4.75 1.00
182 A18 1¼fr blue grn ('31) .28 .18
183 A18 1¼fr rose car ('34) 20.00 1.40
184 A18 1½fr dp blue ('27) .80 1.00
185 A18 1¾fr dk blue ('30) .32 .38
Nos. 159-185 (27) 31.75 10.15

For surcharges and overprints see Nos. 186-193, N17-N29, O142-O178.

Stamps of 1926-35, Surcharged with New Values and Bars

1928-39

186 A18 10(c) on 30c yel grn ('29) .20 .20
187 A18 15c on 25c yel grn .30 .32
187A A18 30c on 60c bl grn ('39) .15 .32
188 A18 60c on 65c blk brn .30 .32
189 A18 60c on 75c rose .30 .28
190 A18 60c on 80c bis brn .35 .40
191 A18 70(c) on 75c bis brn ('35) 8.00 .20
192 A18 75(c) on 90c rose ('29) 1.00 .20
193 A18 1¾(fr) on 1½fr dp bl ('29) 2.00 1.40
Nos. 186-193 (9) 12.60 3.64

The surcharge on No. 187A has no bars.

View of Clervaux A19

1928-34 *Perf. 12½*

194 A19 2fr black ('34) 1.00 .50
Never hinged 3.50
a. Perf. 11½ ('28) 1.25 .50
Never hinged 6.50

See No. B66. For overprint see No. O179.

Coat of Arms — A20

1930, Dec. 20 **Typo.** *Perf. 12½*

195 A20 5c claret .35 .25
196 A20 10c olive green .55 .15
Set value .32
Set, never hinged 2.75

View of the Lower City of Luxembourg A21

Gate of "Three Towers" A22

1931, June 20 **Engr.**

197 A21 20fr deep green 3.00 7.25
Never hinged 4.75

For overprint see No. O180.

1934, Aug. 30 *Perf. 14x13½*

198 A22 5fr blue green 1.25 2.75
Never hinged 2.75

For surcharge and overprint see Nos. N31, O181.

Castle From Our Valley A23

1935, Nov. 15 *Perf. 12½x12*

199 A23 10fr green 2.00 4.75
Never hinged 4.00

For surcharge and overprint see Nos. N32, O182.

Municipal Palace — A24

1936, Aug. 26 **Photo.** *Perf. 11½*

Granite Paper

200 A24 10c brown .15 .20
201 A24 35c green .15 .40
202 A24 70c red orange .18 *.60*
203 A24 1fr carmine rose 1.00 *4.00*
204 A24 1.25fr violet 1.75 *7.25*
205 A24 1.75fr brt ultra 1.00 *4.00*
Nos. 200-205 (6) 4.23 *16.45*
Set, never hinged 12.00

11th Cong. of Intl. Federation of Philately.

Arms of Luxembourg A25

William I A26

Designs: 70c, William II. 75c, William III. 1fr, Prince Henry. 1.25fr, Grand Duke Adolphe. 1.75fr, William IV. 3fr, Regent Marie Anne. 5fr, Grand Duchess Marie Adelaide. 10fr, Grand Duchess Charlotte.

1939, May 27 **Engr.** *Perf. 12½x12*

206 A25 35c brt green .25 .20
207 A26 50c orange .25 .25
208 A26 70c slate green .15 .15
209 A26 75c sepia .55 *1.00*
210 A26 1fr red 1.40 *2.75*
211 A26 1.25fr brown violet .15 .20
212 A26 1.75fr dark blue .15 .20
213 A26 3fr lt brown .25 .40
214 A26 5fr gray black .40 *.80*
215 A26 10fr copper red .65 *2.25*
Nos. 206-215 (10) 4.20 *8.20*
Set, never hinged 7.00

Centenary of Independence.

Allegory of Medicinal Baths — A35

1939, Sept. 18 **Photo.** *Perf. 11½*

216 A35 2fr brown rose .40 1.10
Never hinged .80

Elevation of Mondorf-les-Bains to town status.
For surcharge see No. N30.

Souvenir Sheet

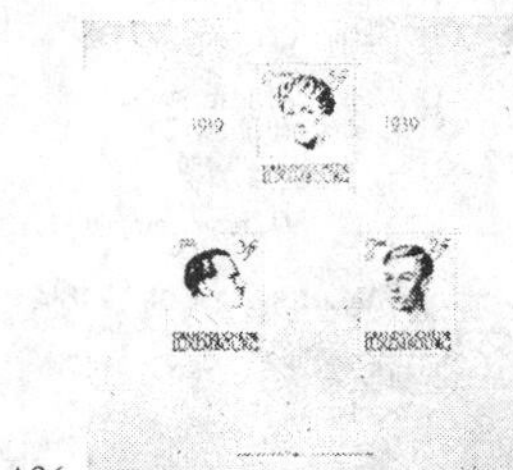

A36

1939, Dec. 20 **Engr.** *Perf. 14x13*

217 A36 Sheet of 3 27.50 *65.00*
Sheet, never hinged 55.00
a. 2fr vermilion, *buff* 7.50 *12.50*
b. 3fr dark green, *buff* 7.50 *12.50*
c. 5fr blue, *buff* 7.50 *12.50*

20th anniv. of the reign of Grand Duchess Charlotte (Jan. 15, 1919) and her marriage to Prince Felix (Nov. 6, 1919).
See Nos. B98-B103.

Grand Duchess Charlotte A37

Lion from Duchy Arms A38

1944-46 **Unwmk.** *Perf. 12*

218 A37 5c brown red .15 .15
219 A37 10c black .15 .15
219A A37 20c orange ('46) .15 .15
220 A37 25c sepia .15 .15
220A A37 30c carmine ('46) .15 .15
221 A37 35c green .15 .15
221A A37 40c dk blue ('46) .15 .15
222 A37 50c dk violet .15 .15
222A A37 60c orange ('46) 1.00 .15
223 A37 70c rose pink .15 .15
223A A37 70c dp green ('46) .30 .55
223B A37 75c sepia ('46) .20 .18
224 A37 1fr olive .15 .15
225 A37 1¼fr red orange .15 .15
226 A37 1½fr red orange ('46) .15 .15
227 A37 1¾fr blue .15 .25
228 A37 2fr rose car ('46) 1.50 .25
229 A37 2½fr dp violet ('46) 2.25 *4.00*
230 A37 3fr dp yel grn ('46) .30 .45
231 A37 3½fr brt blue ('46) .45 *.70*
232 A37 5fr dk blue grn .15 .18
233 A37 10fr carmine .20 .55
234 A37 20fr deep blue .30 *4.50*
Nos. 218-234 (23) 8.60 *13.56*
Set, never hinged 14.00

1945 **Engr.** *Perf. 14x13*

235 A38 20c black .15 .15
236 A38 30c brt green .15 .15
237 A38 60c deep violet .15 .15
238 A38 75c brown red .15 .15
239 A38 1.20fr red .15 .15
240 A38 1.50fr rose lilac .15 .15
241 A38 2.50fr lt blue .15 .15
Set value .70 .85
Set, never hinged 1.00

Patton's Grave, US Military Cemetery, Hamm A39

Gen. Patton, Broken Chain and Advancing Tanks — A40

1947, Oct. 24 **Photo.** *Perf. 11½*

242 A39 1.50fr dk carmine .15 *.20*
243 A40 3.50fr dull blue .65 *3.00*
244 A39 5fr dk slate grn .65 *2.00*
245 A40 10fr chocolate 3.00 *12.00*
Nos. 242-245 (4) 4.45 *17.20*
Set, never hinged 7.50

George S. Patton, Jr. (1885-1945), American general.

Oesling Mountain Forts A41

Luxembourg A44

Moselle River — A42

Steel Mills — A43

Perf. 11½x11, 11x11½

1948, Aug. 5 Engr. Unwmk.

246 A41 7fr dark brown 5.00 .60
247 A42 10fr dark green .35 .20
248 A43 15fr carmine .35 .60
249 A44 20fr dark blue .50 .20
Nos. 246-249 (4) 6.20 1.60
Set, never hinged 13.00

Grand Duchess Charlotte — A45

1948-49 *Perf. 11½*

250 A45 15c olive brn ('49) .15 .15
251 A45 25c slate .15 .15
252 A45 60c brown ('49) .25 .15
253 A45 80c green ('49) .25 .15
254 A45 1fr red lilac .65 .15
255 A45 1.50fr grnsh bl .65 .15
256 A45 1.60fr slate gray ('49) .65 .80
257 A45 2fr dk vio brn .65 .15
258 A45 4fr violet blue 1.25 .28
259 A45 6fr brt red vio ('49) 2.00 .28
260 A45 8fr dull green ('49) 2.00 .60
Nos. 250-260 (11) 8.65
Set, never hinged 16.00
Set value 2.50

See Nos. 265-271, 292, 337-340, B151.

Self-Inking Canceller A46

1949, Oct. 6 Photo.

261 A46 80c blk, Prus grn & pale grn .20 .55
262 A46 2.50fr dk brn, brn red & sal rose 1.00 2.75
263 A46 4fr blk, bl & pale bl 2.75 7.25
264 A46 8fr dk brn, brn & buff 8.75 25.00
Nos. 261-264 (4) 12.70 35.55
Set, never hinged 25.00

UPU, 75th anniv.

Charlotte Type of 1948-49

1951, Mar. 15 Engr. Unwmk.

265 A45 5c red orange .15 .15
266 A45 10c ultra .15 .15
267 A45 40c crimson .15 .20
268 A45 1.25fr dk brown .65 .28
269 A45 2.50fr red .65 .15
270 A45 3fr blue 2.50 .28
271 A45 3.50fr rose lake 1.75 .40
Nos. 265-271 (7) 6.00 1.61
Set, never hinged 11.00

Agriculture and Industry A47

Globe and Scales — A48

1fr, 3fr, People of Europe & Charter of Freedom.

1951, Oct. 25 Photo. *Perf. 11½*

272 A47 80c deep green 6.00 5.00
273 A47 1fr purple 3.00 .42
274 A48 2fr black brown 15.00 .42
275 A47 2.50fr dk carmine 19.00 13.00
276 A47 3fr orange brn 35.00 21.00
277 A48 4fr blue 42.50 30.00
Nos. 272-277 (6) 120.50 69.84
Set, never hinged 190.00

Issued to promote a united Europe.

Grand Duke William III — A49

Perf. 13½x13

1952, May 24 Engr. Unwmk.

Dates, Ornaments in Olive Green

278 A49 2fr black 20.00 50.00
Never hinged 30.00
279 A49 4fr red brown 20.00 50.00
Never hinged 30.00

Printed in sheets containing two panes of eight stamps each, alternating the two denominations. Centenary of Luxembourg's postage stamps. Price per set, 26fr, which included admission to the CENTILUX exhibition.

See Nos. C16-C20.

Hurdle Race — A50

Designs: 2fr, Football. 2.50fr, Boxing. 3fr, Water polo. 4fr, Bicycle racing. 8fr, Fencing.

1952, Aug. 20 Photo. *Perf. 11½*

Designs in Black

280 A50 1fr pale green .20 .30
281 A50 2fr brown buff .60 .30
282 A50 2.50fr salmon pink 1.40 1.00
283 A50 3fr buff 1.70 1.65
284 A50 4fr lt blue 8.50 8.25
285 A50 8fr lilac 5.00 5.50
Nos. 280-285 (6) 17.40 17.00
Set, never hinged 35.00

15th Olympic Games, Helsinki; World Bicycling Championships of 1952.

Wedding of Princess Josephine-Charlotte of Belgium and Hereditary Grand Duke Jean — A51

1953, Apr. 1

286 A51 80c dull violet .22 .20
287 A51 1.20fr lt brown .22 .20
288 A51 2fr green .50 .20
289 A51 3fr red lilac .80 .60
290 A51 4fr brt blue 3.00 1.10
291 A51 9fr brown red 3.00 1.10
Nos. 286-291 (6) 7.74 3.40
Set, never hinged 12.00

Charlotte Type of 1948-49

1953, May 18 Engr.

292 A45 1.20fr gray .45 .28
Never hinged 1.00

Radio Luxembourg A52

Victor Hugo's Home, Vianden A53

1953, May 18 *Perf. 11½x11*

293 A52 3fr purple 2.50 1.40
294 A53 4fr Prussian blue 1.65 1.40
Set, never hinged 8.00

150th birth anniv. of Victor Hugo (No. 294).

St. Willibrord Basilica Restored — A54

Pierre d'Aspelt — A55

Design: 2.50fr, Interior view.

1953, Sept. 18 *Perf. 13x13½*

295 A54 2fr red 1.50 .40
296 A54 2.50fr dk gray grn 2.50 6.50
Set, never hinged 8.00

Consecration of St. Willibrord Basilica at Echternach.

1953, Sept.

297 A55 4fr black 4.75 5.00
Never hinged 7.00

Pierre d'Aspelt (1250-1320), chancellor of the Holy Roman Empire and Archbishop of Mainz.

Fencing Swords, Mask and Glove — A56

Winged "L" Over Map — A57

1954, May 6 *Perf. 13½x13*

298 A56 2fr red brn & blk brn, *gray* 4.50 .50
Never hinged 6.50

World Fencing Championship Matches, Luxembourg, June 10-22.

1954, May 6 Photo. *Perf. 11½*

299 A57 4fr dp bl, yel & red 6.00 3.50
Never hinged 13.00

6th Intl. Fair, Luxembourg, July 10-25.

Flowers — A58

Artisan, Wheel and Tools — A59

1955, Apr. 1

300 A58 80c Tulips .15 .15
301 A58 2fr Daffodils .15 .15
302 A58 3fr Hyacinths 1.40 3.00
303 A58 4fr Parrot tulips 1.65 3.50
Nos. 300-303 (4) 3.35 6.80
Set, never hinged 6.25

Flower festival at Mondorf-les-Bains.

See Nos. 351-353.

1955, Sept. 1 Engr. *Perf. 13*

304 A59 2fr dk gray & blk brn .60 .32
Never hinged 1.00

Natl. Handicraft Exposition at Luxembourg Limpertsburg, Sept. 3-12.

Dudelange Television Station A60

1955, Sept. 1 Unwmk.

305 A60 2.50fr dk brn & redsh brn .60 .32
Never hinged 1.00

Installation of the Tele-Luxembourg station at Dudelange.

United Nations Emblem and Children Playing A61

UN, 10th anniv.: 80c, "Charter". 4fr, "Justice" (Sword and Scales). 9fr, "Assistance" (Workers).

1955, Oct. 24 *Perf. 11x11½*

306 A61 80c black & dk bl .22 .42
307 A61 2fr red & brown 1.75 .15
308 A61 4fr dk blue & red 1.40 3.75
309 A61 9fr dk brn & sl grn .55 1.40
Nos. 306-309 (4) 3.92 5.72
Set, never hinged 7.75

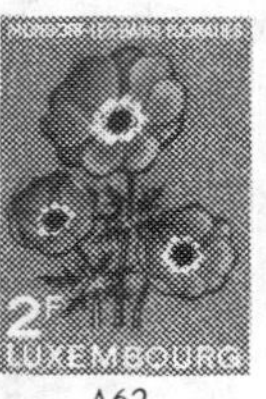

A62

A63

2fr, Anemones. 2.50fr, 4fr, Roses. 3fr, Crocuses.

1956 Photo. *Perf. 11½*

Flowers in Natural Colors

310 A62 2fr gray violet .25 .18
311 A62 2.50fr brt blue 2.25 4.50
312 A62 3fr red brown .95 1.50
313 A62 4fr purple 1.10 1.50
Nos. 310-313 (4) 4.55 7.68
Set, never hinged 8.50

Flower Festival at Mondorf-les-Bains (Nos. 310, 312). Nos. 311 and 313 are inscribed: "Luxembourg-Ville des Roses."

Issued: #310, 312, Apr. 27; #311, 313, May 30.

1956, May 30

Steel beam and city emblem.

314 A63 2fr brt grnsh bl, red & blk .75 .40
Never hinged 1.65

50th anniversary of Esch-sur-Alzette.

Bessemer Converter and Blast Furnaces A64

Steel Beam and Model of City of Luxembourg A65

"Rebuilding Europe" A66

Design: 4fr, 6-link chain, miner's lamp.

Perf. 11x11½, 11½x11

1956, Aug. 10 Engr.

315 A64 2fr dull red 9.50 2.25
316 A65 3fr dark blue 9.50 19.00
317 A64 4fr green 1.90 3.25
Nos. 315-317 (3) 20.90 24.50
Set, never hinged 37.50

4th anniv. of the establishment in Luxembourg of the headquarters of the European Coal and Steel Community.

1956, Sept. 15 *Perf. 13*
318 A66 2fr brown & black 75.00 .28
319 A66 3fr brick red & car 24.00 37.50
320 A66 4fr brt bl & dp bl 2.75 4.00
Nos. 318-320 (3) 101.75 41.78
Set, never hinged 225.00

Cooperation among the six countries comprising the Coal and Steel Community.

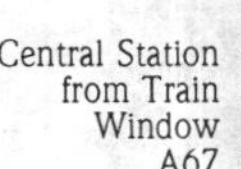

Central Station from Train Window A67

1956, Sept. 29 *Perf. 13x12½*
321 A67 2fr black & sepia .75 .45
Never hinged 2.00

Electrification of Luxembourg railways.

Ignace de la Fontaine — A68

Design: 7fr, Grand Duchess Charlotte.

1956, Nov. 7 *Perf. 11½*
322 A68 2fr gray brown 1.00 .30
323 A68 7fr dull purple 2.00 .65
Set, never hinged 4.75

Centenary of the Council of State.

Lord Baden-Powell and Luxembourg Scout Emblems — A69

Designs: 2.50fr, Lord Baden-Powell and Luxembourg Girl Scout emblems.

1957, June 17 *Perf. 11½x11*
324 A69 2fr ol grn & red brn .52 .28
325 A69 2.50fr dk vio & claret 2.50 *4.25*
Set, never hinged 4.00

Birth centenary of Robert Baden-Powell and 50th anniv. of the founding of the Scout movement.

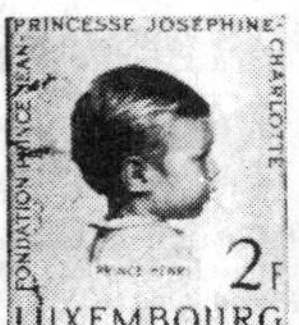

Prince Henry — A70

Children's Clinic — A71

Design: 4fr, Princess Marie-Astrid.

1957, June 17 **Photo.** *Perf. 11½*
326 A70 2fr brown .45 .16
327 A71 3fr bluish grn 1.75 *3.50*
328 A70 4fr ultra 2.00 *3.75*
Nos. 326-328 (3) 4.20 *7.41*
Set, never hinged 5.75

Children's Clinic of the Prince Jean-Princess Josephine-Charlotte Foundation.

"United Europe" — A72

Fair Building and Flags — A73

1957, Sept. 16 **Engr.** *Perf. 12½x12*
329 A72 2fr reddish brn .60 .32
330 A72 3fr red 9.75 *18.00*
331 A72 4fr rose lilac 9.75 11.00
Nos. 329-331 (3) 20.10 *29.32*
Set, never hinged 55.00

A united Europe for peace and prosperity.

1958, Apr. 16 *Perf. 12x11½*
332 A73 2fr ultra & multi .15 .18
Never hinged .25

10th International Luxembourg Fair.

Luxembourg Pavilion, Brussels — A74

1958, Apr. 16 **Unwmk.**
333 A74 2.50fr car & ultra .15 .25
Never hinged .20

International Exposition at Brussels.

St. Willibrord — A75

1fr, Sts. Willibrord & Irmina from "Liber Aureus." 5fr, St. Willibrord, young man & wine cask.

1958, May 23 **Engr.** *Perf. 13x13½*
334 A75 1fr red .15 .32
335 A75 2.50fr olive brn .18 .28
336 A75 5fr blue .48 *1.00*
Nos. 334-336 (3) .81 *1.60*
Set, never hinged 1.50

1300th birth anniv. of St. Willibrord, apostle of the Low Countries and founder of Echternach Abbey.

Charlotte Type of 1948-49

1958 **Unwmk.** *Perf. 11½*
337 A45 20c dull claret .15 .15
338 A45 30c olive .15 .15
339 A45 50c dp org .18 .15
340 A45 5fr violet 4.75 .55
Nos. 337-340 (4) 5.23
Set, never hinged 9.00
Set value .78

Europa Issue, 1958

Common Design Type

1958, Sept. 13 **Litho.** *Perf. 12½x13*
Size: 21x34mm
341 CD1 2.50fr car & bl .15 .15
342 CD1 3.50fr green & org .15 .22
343 CD1 5fr blue & red .35 .55
Nos. 341-343 (3) .65 .92
Set, never hinged .95

Wiltz Open-Air Theater A76

Vintage, Moselle A77

1958, Sept. 13 **Engr.** *Perf. 11x11½*
344 A76 2.50fr slate & sepia .20 .15
345 A77 2.50fr lt grn & sepia .20 .15
Set value .24
Set, never hinged .75

No. 345 issued to publicize 2,000 years of grape growing in Luxembourg region.

Grand Duchess Charlotte A78

NATO Emblem A79

1959, Jan. 15 **Photo.** *Perf. 11½*
346 A78 1.50fr pale grn & dk grn .15 .25
347 A78 2.50fr pink & dk brn .15 .15
348 A78 5fr lt bl & dk bl .25 *.90*
Nos. 346-348 (3) .55 *1.30*
Set, never hinged 1.00

40th anniv. of the accession to the throne of the Grand Duchess Charlotte.

1959, Apr. 3 *Perf. 12½x12*
349 A79 2.50fr brt ol & bl .15 .15
350 A79 8.50fr red brn & bl .25 .45
Set, never hinged .55

NATO, 10th anniversary.

Flower Type of 1955, Inscribed "1959"

1fr, Iris. 2.50fr, Peonies. 3fr, Hydrangea.

1959, Apr. 3 *Perf. 11½*
Flowers in Natural Colors
351 A58 1fr dk bl grn .20 .40
352 A58 2.50fr deep blue .25 .50
353 A58 3fr deep red lilac .25 .50
Nos. 351-353 (3) .70 1.40
Set, never hinged 1.00

Flower festival, Mondorf-les-Bains.

Europa Issue, 1959

Common Design Type

Perf. 12½x13½

1959, Sept. 19 **Litho.**
Size: 22x33mm
354 CD2 2.50fr olive .16 .40
355 CD2 5fr dk blue .35 .80
Set, never hinged 1.00

Locomotive of 1859 and Hymn — A80

1959, Sept. 19 **Engr.** *Perf. 13½*
356 A80 2.50fr red & ultra .45 .18
Never hinged 1.25

Centenary of Luxembourg's railroads.

Catalogue values for unused stamps in this section, from this point to the end of the section, are for Never Hinged items.

Man and Child Knocking at Door — A81

Holy Family, Flight into Egypt — A82

Perf. 11½x11, 11x11½

1960, Apr. 7 **Unwmk.**
357 A81 2.50fr org & slate .15 .15
358 A82 5fr pur & slate .30 .30

World Refugee Year, July 1, 1959-June 30, 1960.

Steel Worker Drawing CECA Initials and Map of Member Countries A83

1960, May 9 *Perf. 11x11½*
359 A83 2.50fr dk car rose .60 .20

10th anniv. of the Schumann Plan for a European Steel and Coal Community.

European School and Children A84

1960, May 9
360 A84 5fr bl & gray blk .90 .90

Establishment of the first European school in Luxembourg.

Heraldic Lion and Tools — A85

1960, June 14 **Photo.** *Perf. 11½*
361 A85 2.50fr gray, red, bl & blk 1.40 .32

Natl. Exhibition of Craftsmanship, Luxembourg-Limpertsberg, July 9-18.

Grand Duchess Charlotte — A86

1960-64 **Engr.** **Unwmk.**
362 A86 10c claret ('61) .15 .15
363 A86 20c rose red ('61) .20 .15
363A A86 25c org ('64) .15 .15
364 A86 30c gray olive .20 .15
365 A86 50c dull grn .60 .15
366 A86 1fr vio blue .75 .15
367 A86 1.50fr rose lilac .75 .20
368 A86 2fr blue ('61) .80 .15
369 A86 2.50fr rose vio 1.40 .20
370 A86 3fr vio brn ('61) 1.60 .15
371 A86 3.50fr aqua ('64) 2.25 1.90
372 A86 5fr lt red brn 2.25 .25
373 A86 6fr slate ('64) 2.75 .20
Nos. 362-373 (13) 13.85 3.95

The 50c, 1fr and 3fr were issued in sheets and in coils. Every fifth coil stamp has control number on back.

Europa Issue, 1960

Common Design Type

1960, Sept. 19 *Perf. 11x11½*
Size: 37x27mm
374 CD3 2.50fr indigo & emer .25 .20
375 CD3 5fr maroon & blk .40 .35

Great Spotted Woodpecker A87

Clervaux and Abbey of St. Maurice and St. Maur A88

Designs: 1.50fr, Cat, horiz. 3fr, Filly, horiz. 8.50fr, Dachshund.

1961, May 15 Photo. *Perf. 11½*

376 A87	1fr multicolored	.15	.15
377 A87	1.50fr multicolored	.15	.15
378 A87	3fr gray, buff & red brn	.40	.40
379 A87	8.50fr lt grn, blk & ocher	.80	.60
	Nos. 376-379 (4)	1.50	1.30

Issued to publicize animal protection.

1961, June 8 Engr. *Perf. 11½x11*

380 A88 2.50fr green .25 .15

General Patton Monument, Ettelbruck A89

1961, June 8 *Perf. 11x11½*

381 A89 2.50fr dark blue & gray .25 .15

The monument commemorates the American victory of the 3rd Army under Gen. George S. Patton, Jr., Battle of the Ardennes Bulge, 1944-45.

Europa Issue, 1961

Common Design Type

1961, Sept. 18 *Perf. 13x12½*

Size: 29½x27mm

382 CD4	2.50fr red	.15	.15
383 CD4	5fr blue	.20	.16
	Set value	.25	.24

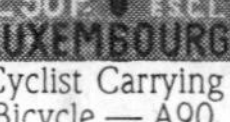

Cyclist Carrying Bicycle — A90

St. Laurent's Church, Diekirch — A91

Design: 5fr, Emblem of 1962 championship.

1962, Jan. 22 Photo. *Perf. 11½*

384 A90	2.50fr lt ultra, crim & blk	.25	.17
385 A90	5fr multicolored	.45	.40

Intl. Cross-country Bicycle Race, Esch-sur-Alzette, Feb. 18.

Europa Issue, 1962

Common Design Type

1962, Sept. 17 Unwmk. *Perf. 11½*

Size: 32½x23mm

386 CD5	2.50fr ol bis, yel grn & brn blk	.15	.15
387 CD5	5fr rose lil, lt grn & brn blk	.30	.25

1962, Sept. 17 Engr. *Perf. 11½x11*

388 A91 2.50fr brown & blk .30 .18

Bock Rock Castle, 10th Century — A92

Gate of Three Towers, 11th Century — A93

Designs (each stamp represents a different century): No. 391, Benedictine Abbey, Munster. No. 392, Great Seal of Luxembourg, 1237. No. 393, Rham Towers. No. 394, Black Virgin, Grund. No. 395, Grand Ducal Palace. No. 396, The Citadel of the Holy Ghost. No. 397, Castle Bridge. No. 398, Town Hall. No. 399, Municipal theater, bridge and European Community Center.

Perf. 14x13 (A92), 11½ (A93)

Engr. (A92), Photo. (A93)

1963, Apr. 13

389 A92	1fr slate blue	.45	.42
390 A93	1fr multicolored	.15	.15
391 A92	1.50fr dl red brn	.45	.42
392 A93	1.50fr multicolored	.15	.15
393 A92	2.50fr gray grn	.45	.42
394 A93	2.50fr multicolored	.20	.18
395 A92	3fr brown	.45	.42
396 A93	3fr multicolored	.15	.15
397 A92	5fr brt violet	.60	.60
398 A93	5fr multicolored	.60	.60
399 A92	11fr multicolored	.90	.90
	Nos. 389-399 (11)	4.55	4.41

Millennium of the city of Luxembourg; MELUSINA Intl. Phil. Exhib., Luxembourg, Apr. 13-21. Set sold only at exhibition. Value of 62fr included entrance ticket. Nos. 390, 392, 394 and 396 however were sold without restriction.

Blackboard Showing European School Buildings — A94

1963, Apr. 13 Photo. *Perf. 11½*

400 A94 2.50fr gray, grn & mag .20 .20

10th anniv. of the European Schools in Luxembourg, Brussels, Varese, Mol and Karlsruhe.

Colpach Castle and Centenary Emblem A95

1963, May 8 Engr. *Perf. 13*

401 A95 2.50fr hn brn, gray & red .20 .20

Centenary of the Intl. Red Cross. Colpach Castle, home of Emile Mayrisch, was donated to the Luxembourg League of the Red Cross for a rest home.

Twelve Stars of Council of Europe — A96

Brown Trout Taking Bait — A97

1963, June 25 *Perf. 13x14*

402 A96 2.50fr dp ultra, *gold* .20 .20

10th anniv. of the European Convention of Human Rights.

Europa Issue, 1963

Common Design Type

1963, Sept. 16 Photo. *Perf. 11½*

Size: 32½x23mm

403 CD6	3fr bl grn, lt grn & org	.25	.15
404 CD6	6fr red brn, org red & org	.30	.30

1963, Sept. 16 Engr. *Perf. 13*

405 A97 3fr indigo .25 .15

World Fly-Fishing Championship, Wormeldange, Sept. 22.

Map of Luxembourg, Telephone Dial and Stars — A98

Power House — A99

1963, Sept. 16 Photo. *Perf. 11½*

406 A98 3fr ultra, brt grn & blk .25 .15

Completion of telephone automation.

1964, Apr. 17 Engr. *Perf. 13*

3fr, Upper reservoir, horiz. 6fr, Lohmuhle dam.

407 A99	2fr red brn & sl	.15	.15
408 A99	3fr red, sl grn & lt bl	.20	.15
409 A99	6fr choc, grn & bl	.25	.22
	Nos. 407-409 (3)	.60	.52

Inauguration of the Vianden hydroelectric station.

Barge Entering Lock at Grevenmacher Dam — A100

1964, May 26 Unwmk.

410 A100 3fr indigo & brt bl .35 .18

Opening of Moselle River canal system.

Europa Issue, 1964

Common Design Type

1964, Sept. 14 Photo. *Perf. 11½*

Size: 22x38mm

411 CD7	3fr org brn, yel & dk bl	.20	.20
412 CD7	6fr yel grn, yel & dk brn	.35	.32

New Atheneum Educational Center and Students — A101

1964, Sept. 14 Unwmk.

413 A101 3fr dk bl grn & blk .20 .15

Benelux Issue

King Baudouin, Queen Juliana and Grand Duchess Charlotte — A101a

1964, Oct. 12

Size: 45x26mm

414 A101a 3fr dull bl, yel & brn .25 .20

20th anniv. of the customs union of Belgium, Netherlands and Luxembourg.

Grand Duke Jean and Grand Duchess Josephine Charlotte — A102

1964, Nov. 11 Photo. *Perf. 11½*

415 A102	3fr indigo	.35	.16
416 A102	6fr dk brown	.35	.28

Grand Duke Jean's accession to throne.

Rotary Emblem and Cogwheels A103

Grand Duke Jean A104

1965, Apr. 5 Photo. *Perf. 11½*

417 A103 3fr gold, car, gray & ultra .40 .20

Rotary International, 60th anniversary.

1965-71 Engr. Unwmk.

418 A104	25c olive bister ('66)	.15	.15
419 A104	50c rose red	.24	.15
420 A104	1fr ultra	.24	.15
421 A104	1.50fr dk vio brn ('66)	.15	.15
422 A104	2fr magenta ('66)	.18	.15
423 A104	2.50fr orange ('71)	.35	.15
424 A104	3fr gray	.48	.15
425 A104	3.50fr brn org ('66)	.35	.20
426 A104	4fr vio brn ('71)	.30	.15
427 A104	5fr green ('71)	.35	.15
428 A104	6fr purple	.95	.15
429 A104	8fr bl grn ('71)	.80	.15
	Nos. 418-429 (12)	4.54	
	Set value		1.05

The 50c, 1fr, 2fr, 3fr and 6fr were issued in sheets and in coils. Every fifth coil stamp has control number on back.

See Nos. 570-576.

ITU Emblem, Old and New Communication Equipment — A105

1965, May 17 Litho. *Perf. 13½*

431 A105 3fr dk pur, claret & blk .22 .20

ITU, centenary.

Europa Issue, 1965

Common Design Type

Perf. 13x12½

1965, Sept. 27 Photo. Unwmk.

Size: 30x23½mm

432 CD8	3fr grn, maroon & blk	.25	.18
433 CD8	6fr tan, dk bl & grn	.40	.40

Inauguration of WHO Headquarters, Geneva A106

1966, Mar. 7 Engr. *Perf. 11x11½*

434 A106 3fr green .20 .15

Torch and Banner — A107

Key and Arms of City of Luxembourg, and Arms of Prince of Chimay — A108

1966, Mar. 7 Photo. *Perf. 11½*

435 A107 3fr gray & brt red .20 .15

50th anniversary of the Workers' Federation in Luxembourg.

1966, Apr. 28 Engr. *Perf. 13x14*

Designs: 2fr, Interior of Cathedral of Luxembourg, painting by Juan Martin. 3fr, Our Lady of Luxembourg, engraving by Richard Collin. 6fr, Column and spandrel with sculptured angels from Cathedral.

436 A108	1.50fr green	.15	.15
437 A108	2fr dull red	.15	.15
438 A108	3fr dk blue	.15	.15
439 A108	6fr red brown	.25	.25
	Set value	.55	.55

300th anniv. of the Votum Solemne (Solemn Promise) which made the Virgin Mary Patron Saint of the City of Luxembourg.

Europa Issue, 1966

Common Design Type

Perf. 13½x12½

1966, Sept. 26 Litho.

Size: 25x37mm

440 CD9	3fr gray & vio bl	.20	.15
441 CD9	6fr olive & dk grn	.30	.30

Diesel Locomotive A109

Design: 3fr, Electric locomotive.

1966, Sept. 26 Photo. *Perf. 11½*

442 A109 1.50fr multicolored .20 .20
443 A109 3fr multicolored .25 .20

5th Intl. Philatelic Exhibition of Luxembourg Railroad Men, Sept. 30-Oct. 3.

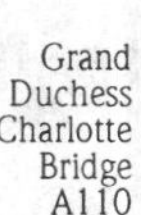

Grand Duchess Charlotte Bridge A110

1966, Sept. 26 Engr. *Perf. 13*

444 A110 3fr dk car rose .20 .15

Tower Building, Kirchberg, Seat of European Community — A111

Design: 13fr, Design for Robert Schuman monument, Luxembourg.

1966, Sept. 26

445 A111 1.50fr dk green .16 .16
446 A111 13fr deep blue .55 .25

"Luxembourg, Center of Europe."

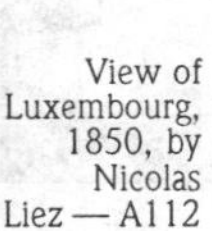

View of Luxembourg, 1850, by Nicolas Liez — A112

Map of Luxembourg Fortress, 1850, by Theodore de Cederstolpe — A113

1967, Mar. 6 Engr. *Perf. 13*

447 A112 3fr bl, vio brn & grn .20 .15
448 A113 6fr blue, brn & red .25 .20

Centenary of the Treaty of London, which guaranteed the country's neutrality after the dismantling of the Fortress of Luxembourg.

Europa Issue, 1967

Common Design Type

1967, May 2 Photo. *Perf. 11½*

Size: 33x22mm

449 CD10 3fr cl brn, gray & buff .30 .20
450 CD10 6fr dk brn, vio gray & lt bl .35 .35

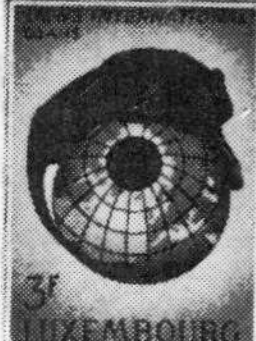

Lion, Globe and Lions Emblem — A115

NATO Emblem and European Community Administration Building — A116

1967, May 2 Photo. *Perf. 11½*

451 A115 3fr multicolored .18 .15

Lions International, 50th anniversary.

> **Canceled to Order**
> Luxembourg's Office des Timbres, Direction des Postes, was offering, at least as early as 1967, to sell commemorative issues canceled to order.

1967, June 13 Litho. *Perf. 13x12½*

452 A116 3fr lt grn & dk grn .25 .15
453 A116 6fr dp rose & dk car .40 .40

NATO Council meeting, Luxembourg, June 13-14.

Youth Hostel, Ettelbruck A117

Home Gardener A118

1967, Sept. 14 Photo. *Perf. 11½*

454 A117 1.50fr multicolored .20 .15

Luxembourg youth hostels.

1967, Sept. 14

455 A118 1.50fr brt grn & org .18 .15

16th Congress of the Intl. Assoc. of Home Gardeners.

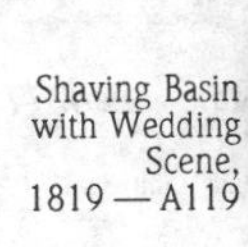

Shaving Basin with Wedding Scene, 1819 — A119

Design: 3fr, Ornamental vase, 1820, vert.

1967, Sept. 14

456 A119 1.50fr ol grn & multi .15 .15
457 A119 3fr ultra & lt gray .25 .20

Faience industry in Luxembourg, 200th anniv.

Wormeldingen on Mosel River — A120

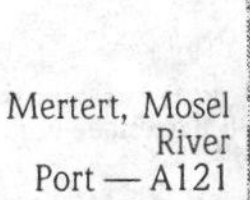

Mertert, Mosel River Port — A121

1967, Sept. 14 Engr. *Perf. 13*

458 A120 3fr dp bl, claret & ol .25 .15
459 A121 3fr violet bl & slate .25 .15

Swimming — A122

Sport: 1.50fr, Soccer. 2fr, Bicycling. 3fr, Running. 6fr, Walking. 13fr, Fencing.

1968, Feb. 22 Photo. *Perf. 11½*

460 A122 50c bl & grnsh bl .15 .15
461 A122 1.50fr brt grn & emer .15 .15
462 A122 2fr yel grn & lt yel grn .15 .15
463 A122 3fr dp org & dl org .15 .15
464 A122 6fr grnsh bl & pale grn .30 .20
465 A122 13fr rose cl & rose .50 .50
Nos. 460-465 (6) 1.40 1.30

Issued to publicize the 19th Olympic Games, Mexico City, Oct. 12-27.

Europa Issue, 1968

Common Design Type

1968, Apr. 29 Photo. *Perf. 11½*

Size: 32½x23mm

466 CD11 3fr ap grn, blk & org brn .20 .15
467 CD11 6fr brn org, blk & ap grn .40 .30

Kind Spring Pavilion — A123

1968, Apr. 29 Photo. *Perf. 11½*

468 A123 3fr multicolored .20 .15

Issued to publicize Mondorf-les-Bains.

Fair Emblem A124

1968, Apr. 29

469 A124 3fr dp vio, dl bl gold & red .20 .15

20th Intl. Fair, Luxembourg City, May 23-June 2.

Children's Village of Mersch A125

Orphan and Foster Mother — A126

1968, Sept. 18 Engr. *Perf. 13*

470 A125 3fr slate grn & dk red brn .15 .15
471 A126 6fr slate bl, blk & brn .28 .20

Mersch children's village. (Modeled after Austrian SOS villages for homeless children.)

Red Cross and Symbolic Blood Transfusion — A127

1968, Sept. 18 Photo. *Perf. 11½*

472 A127 3fr lt blue & car .20 .15

Voluntary Red Cross blood donors.

Luxair Plane over Luxembourg A128

1968, Sept. 18 Engr. *Perf. 13*

473 A128 50fr olive, bl & dk bl 1.65 .70

Issued for tourist publicity.

Souvenir Sheet

"Youth and Leisure" — A129

Designs, a, 3fr, Doll. b, 6fr, Ballplayers. c, 13fr, Book, compass rose and ball.

1969, Apr. 3 Photo. *Perf. 11½*

Granite Paper

474 A129 Sheet of 3 4.00 3.25
a.-c. any single 1.25 1.00

1st Intl. Youth Phil. Exhib., JUVENTUS 1969, Luxembourg, Apr. 3-8.

No. 474 was on sale only at the exhibition. Sold only with entrance ticket for 40fr.

Europa Issue, 1969

Common Design Type

1969, May 19 Photo. *Perf. 11½*

Size: 32½x23mm

475 CD12 3fr gray, brn & org .25 .15
476 CD12 6fr vio gray, blk & yel .40 .35

Boy on Hobbyhorse, by Joseph Kutter (1894-1941) A130

Design: 6fr, View of Luxembourg, by Kutter.

1969, May 19 Engr. *Perf. 12x13*

477 A130 3fr multicolored .25 .15
a. Green omitted *150.00 150.00*
478 A130 6fr multicolored .35 .35

ILO, 50th Anniv. — A131

Photo.; Gold Impressed (Emblem)

1969, May 19 *Perf. 14x14½*

479 A131 3fr brt grn, vio & gold .20 .15

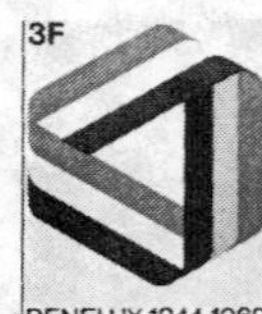

Mobius Strip in Benelux Colors — A131a

1969, Sept. 8 Litho. *Perf. 12½x13½*

480 A131a 3fr multicolored .28 .20

25th anniv. of the signing of the customs union of Belgium, Netherlands and Luxembourg.

NATO, 20th Anniv. — A132

Grain and Mersch Agricultural Center — A133

1969, Sept. 8 *Perf. 13½x12½*

481 A132 3fr org brn & dk brn .32 .20

1969, Sept. 8 Photo. *Perf. 11½*

482 A133 3fr bl grn, gray & blk .20 .15

Issued to publicize agricultural progress.

St. Willibrord's Basilica and Abbey, Echternach A134

Design: #484, Castle and open-air theater, Wiltz.

1969, Sept. 8 Engr. *Perf. 13*

483 A134 3fr dark blue & indigo .22 .15
484 A134 3fr slate green & indigo .22 .15
Set value .24

Pasqueflower — A135

Design: 6fr, Hedgehog and 3 young.

1970, Mar. 9 Photo. *Perf. 11½*

485 A135 3fr multicolored .24 .20
486 A135 6fr green & multi .45 .40

European Conservation Year.

Goldcrest A136

1970, Mar. 9 Engr. *Perf. 13*

487 A136 1.50fr org, grn & blk brn .20 .15

Luxembourg Society for the protection and study of birds, 50th anniv.

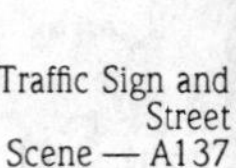

Traffic Sign and Street Scene — A137

1970, May 4 Photo. *Perf. 11½*

488 A137 3fr rose mag, red & blk .22 .15

The importance of traffic safety.

Europa Issue, 1970

Common Design Type

1970, May 4

Size: 32½x23mm

489 CD13 3fr brown & multi .24 .15
490 CD13 6fr green & multi .48 .40

Empress Kunigunde and Emperor Henry II, Window, Luxembourg Cathedral — A138

1970, Sept. 14 Photo. *Perf. 12*

491 A138 3fr multicolored .20 .20

Centenary of the Diocese of Luxembourg.

Census Symbol — A139

1970, Sept. 14 *Perf. 11½*

492 A139 3fr dk grn, grnsh bl & red .20 .15

Census of Dec. 31, 1970.

Lion, Luxembourg City Hall — A140

1970, Sept. 14

493 A140 3fr bister, lt bl & dk brn .18 .15

50th anniversary of the City of Luxembourg through the union of 5 municipalities.

UN Emblem A141

Perf. 12½x13½

1970, Sept. 14 Litho.

494 A141 1.50fr bl & vio bl .18 .15

25th anniversary of the United Nations.

Monks in Abbey Workshop A142

Olympic Rings, Arms of Luxembourg A143

Miniatures Painted at Echternach, about 1040: 3fr, Laborers going to the vineyard (Matthew 20:1-6). 6fr, Laborers toiling in vineyard. 13fr, Workers searching for graves of the saints.

1971, Mar. 15 Photo. *Perf. 12*

495 A142 1.50fr gold & multi .15 .15
496 A142 3fr gold & multi .15 .15
497 A142 6fr gold & multi .25 .20
498 A142 13fr gold & multi .52 .45
Nos. 495-498 (4) 1.07
Set value .82

1971, May 3 Photo. *Perf. 12½*

499 A143 3fr ultra & multi .25 .15

Intl. Olympic Committee, 71st session.

Europa Issue, 1971

Common Design Type

1971, May 3 *Perf. 12½x13*

Size: 34x25mm

500 CD14 3fr ver, brn & blk .32 .15
501 CD14 6fr brt grn, brn & blk .45 .35

A145

1971, May 3 Litho. *Perf. 13x13½*

502 A145 3fr org, dk brn & yel .20 .20

Christian Workers Union, 50th anniv.

Artificial Lake, Upper Sure — A146

Designs: No. 504, Water treatment plant, Esch-sur-Sure. 15fr, ARBED Steel Corporation Headquarters, Luxembourg.

1971, Sept. 13 Engr. *Perf. 13*

503 A146 3fr ol, grnsh bl & indigo .18 .15
504 A146 3fr brn, sl grn & grnsh bl .24 .15
505 A146 15fr indigo & blk brn .70 .40
Nos. 503-505 (3) 1.12
Set value .60

School Girl with Coin — A147

1971, Sept. 13 Photo. *Perf. 11½*

506 A147 3fr violet & multi .22 .15

School children's savings campaign.

Coins of Luxembourg and Belgium A148

Bronze Mask A149

1972, Mar. 6

507 A148 1.50fr lt grn, sil & blk .18 .15

Economic Union of Luxembourg and Belgium, 50th anniversary.

1972, Mar. 6

Archaeological Objects, 4th to 1st centuries, B.C.: 1fr, Bronze bowl, horiz. 8fr, Limestone head. 15fr, Glass jug in shape of head.

508 A149 1fr lemon & multi .15 .15
509 A149 3fr multicolored .15 .15
510 A149 8fr multicolored .60 .60
511 A149 15fr multicolored .80 .80
Nos. 508-511 (4) 1.70 1.70

Europa Issue 1972

Common Design Type

1972, May 2 Photo. *Perf. 11½*

Size: 22x33mm

512 CD15 3fr rose vio & multi .25 .15
513 CD15 8fr gray blue & multi .80 .80

Archer — A150

1972, May 2

514 A150 3fr crimson, blk & olive .38 .22

3rd European Archery Championships.

Robert Schuman Medal — A151

The Fox Wearing Tails — A152

1972, May 2 Engr. *Perf. 13*

515 A151 3fr gray & slate green .50 .18

Establishment in Luxembourg of the European Coal and Steel Community, 20th anniv.

1972, Sept. 11 Photo. *Perf. 11½*

516 A152 3fr scarlet & multi .35 .20

Centenary of the publication of "Renert," satirical poem by Michel Rodange.

National Monument A153

Court of Justice of European Communities, Kirchberg A154

1972, Sept. 11 Engr. *Perf. 13*

517 A153 3fr sl grn, olive & vio .22 .15
518 A154 3fr brn, bl & slate grn .28 .22

Epona on Horseback — A155

Archaeological Objects: 4fr, Panther killing swan, horiz. 8fr, Celtic gold stater inscribed Pottina. 15fr, Bronze boar, horiz.

1973, Mar. 14 Photo. *Perf. 11½*

519 A155 1fr salmon & multi .15 .15
520 A155 4fr beige & multi .20 .15
521 A155 8fr multicolored .65 .65
522 A155 15fr multicolored .65 .65
Nos. 519-522 (4) 1.65 1.60

Europa Issue 1973

Common Design Type

1973, Apr. 30 Photo. *Perf. 11½*

Size: 32x22mm

523 CD16 4fr org, dk vio & lt bl .38 .15
524 CD16 8fr ol, vio blk & yel 1.10 .75

Bee on Honeycomb A156

Nurse Holding Child A157

1973, Apr. 30 Photo. *Perf. 11½*

525 A156 4fr ocher & multi	.35	.15

Publicizing importance of beekeeping.

1973, Apr. 30

526 A157 4fr multicolored	.28	.20

Publicizing importance of day nurseries.

Laurel Branch — A158

1973, Sept. 10 Photo. *Perf. 11½*

527 A158 3fr violet bl & multi	.22	.18

50th anniv. of Luxembourg Board of Labor.

Jerome de Busleyden A159

National Strike Memorial, Wiltz A160

1973, Sept. 10 Engr. *Perf. 13*

528 A159 4fr black, brn & pur	.28	.20

Council of Mechelen, 500th anniv.

1973, Sept. 10

529 A160 4fr ol bis, sl & sl grn	.22	.20

In memory of the Luxembourg resistance heroes who died during the great strike of 1942.

Capital, Byzantine Hall, Vianden — A161

St. Gregory the Great — A161a

Designs: No. 534, Sts. Cecilia and Valerian crowned by angel, Hollenfels Church. No. 535, Interior, Septfontaines Church. 8fr, Madonna and Child, St. Irmina's Chapel, Rosport. 12fr, St. Augustine Sculptures by Jean-Georges Scholtus from pulpit in Feulen parish church, c. 1734.

1973-77 *Perf. 13x12½, 14 (6fr, 12fr)*

533 A161 4fr green & rose vio	.25	.15
534 A161 4fr red brn, grn & lil	.40	.20
535 A161 4fr gray, brn & dk vio	.40	.20
536 A161a 6fr maroon	.32	.28
537 A161 8fr sepia & vio bl	.70	.60
538 A161a 12fr slate blue	.75	.65
Nos. 533-538 (6)	2.82	2.08

Architecture of Luxembourg: Romanesque, Gothic, Baroque.
Issue dates: No. 533, 8fr, Sept. 10, 1973; Nos. 534-535, Sept. 9, 1974; 6fr, 12fr, Sept. 16, 1977.

Princess Marie Astrid — A162

Torch — A163

1974, Mar. 14 Photo. *Perf. 11½*

540 A162 4fr blue & multi	.65	.18

Princess Marie-Astrid, president of the Luxembourg Red Cross Youth Section.

1974, Mar. 14

541 A163 4fr ultra & multi	.20	.15

50th anniversary of Luxembourg Mutual Insurance Federation.

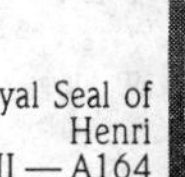

Royal Seal of Henri VII — A164

Seals from 13th-14th Centuries: 3fr, Equestrian, seal of Jean, King of Bohemia. 4fr, Seal of Town of Diekirch. 19fr, Virgin and Child, seal of Convent of Marienthal.

1974, Mar. 14

542 A164 1fr purple & multi	.15	.15
543 A164 3fr green & multi	.32	.25
544 A164 4fr multicolored	.45	.15
545 A164 19fr multicolored	1.50	1.25

Hind, by Auguste Trémont A165

Winston Churchill, by Oscar Nemon A166

Europa: 8fr, "Growth," abstract sculpture, by Lucien Wercollier.

1974, Apr. 29 Photo. *Perf. 11½*

546 A165 4fr ocher & multi	.38	.24
547 A165 8fr brt blue & multi	1.25	1.00

1974, Apr. 29

548 A166 4fr lilac & multi	.28	.15

Sir Winston Churchill (1874-1965), statesman.

Fairground, Aerial View — A167

Theis, the Blind — A168

1974, Apr. 29

549 A167 4fr silver & multi	.28	.15

Publicity for New International Fairground, Luxembourg-Kirchberg.

1974, Apr. 29

550 A168 3fr multicolored	.32	.20

Mathias Schou, Theis the Blind (1747-1824), wandering minstrel.

UPU Emblem and "100" — A169

1974, Sept. 9 Photo. *Perf. 11½*

551 A169 4fr multicolored	.32	.32
552 A169 8fr multicolored	.80	.80

Centenary of Universal Postal Union.

"BENELUX" A170

1974, Sept. 9

553 A170 4fr bl grn, dk grn & lt bl	.80	.20

30th anniversary of the signing of the customs union of Belgium, Netherlands and Luxembourg.

View of Differdange A171

1974, Sept. 9 Engr. *Perf. 13*

554 A171 4fr rose claret	.22	.15

Bourglinster A172

Designs: 1fr, Fish Market, Old Luxembourg, vert. 4fr, Market Square, Echternach. 19fr, St. Michael's Square, Mersch, vert.

Perf. 14x13½, 13½x14

1975, Mar. 10 Engr.

555 A172 1fr olive green	.75	.20
556 A172 3fr deep brown	1.40	.40
557 A172 4fr dark purple	1.50	.60
558 A172 19fr copper red	1.25	1.00
Nos. 555-558 (4)	4.90	2.20

European Architectural Heritage Year.

Joseph Kutter, Self-portrait A173

Moselle Bridge, Remich, by Nico Klopp A174

Paintings: 8fr, Still Life, by Joseph Kutter. 20fr, The Dam, by Dominique Lang.

1975, Apr. 28 Photo. *Perf. 11½*

559 A173 1fr multicolored	.28	.18
560 A174 4fr multicolored	.45	.25
561 A174 8fr multicolored	2.20	.75
562 A173 20fr multicolored	1.65	.85
Nos. 559-562 (4)	4.58	2.03

Cultural series. #560-561 are Europa Issue.

Robert Schuman, Gaetano Martino, Paul-Henri Spaak Medals — A175

1975, Apr. 28

563 A175 4fr yel grn, gold & brn	1.10	.25

25th anniversary of Robert Schuman's declaration establishing European Coal and Steel Community.

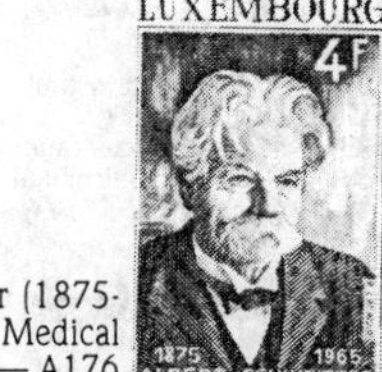

Albert Schweitzer (1875-1965), Medical Missionary — A176

1975, Apr. 28 Engr. *Perf. 13*

564 A176 4fr bright blue	.90	.20

Civil Defense Emblem A177

Figure Skating A178

1975, Sept. 8 Photo. *Perf. 11½*

565 A177 4fr multicolored	.65	.25

Civil Defense Org. for protection and rescue.

1975, Sept. 8 Engr. *Perf. 13*

4fr, Water skiing, horiz. 15fr, Mountain climbing.

566 A178 3fr green, bl & lilac	.25	.15
567 A178 4fr dk brn, grn & lt brn	.40	.30
568 A178 15fr brown, indigo & grn	1.25	.70
Nos. 566-568 (3)	1.90	1.15

Grand Duke Type of 1965-71

1975-91 Engr. *Perf. 11½*

Granite Paper (14fr, 22fr)

570 A104 7fr orange	.35	.20
571 A104 9fr yellow green	.55	.35
572 A104 10fr black	.45	.15
573 A104 12fr brick red	.50	.45
573A A104 14fr dark blue	.85	.85
574 A104 16fr green	.70	.60
574A A104 18fr brown olive	.65	.58
575 A104 20fr blue	.90	.40
576 A104 22fr orange brown	1.35	1.35
Nos. 570-576 (9)	6.30	4.93

Issue dates: 10fr, Jan. 9; 9fr, 12fr, 20fr, Dec. 23; 16fr, Feb. 25, 1982; 7fr, July 1, 1983; 18fr, Mar. 3, 1986; 14fr, Jan. 2, 1990. 22fr, Sept. 23, 1991.
This is an expanding set. Numbers will change if necessary.

Grand Duchess Charlotte — A179

Design: No. 580, Prince Henri.

1976, Mar. 8 Litho. *Perf. 14x13½*

579 A179 6fr green & multi	.40	.22
580 A179 6fr dull blue & multi	.90	.25

80th birthday of Grand Duchess Charlotte and 21st birthday of Prince Henri, heir to the throne.

Gold Brooch — A180

5fr, Footless beaker, horiz. 6fr, Decorated vessel, horiz. 12fr, Gold coin. All designs show excavated items of Franco-Merovingian period.

Perf. 13½x12½, 12½x13½

1976, Mar. 8

581	A180	2fr blue & multi	.15	.15
582	A180	5fr black & multi	.30	.28
583	A180	6fr lilac & multi	.45	.28
584	A180	12fr multicolored	1.00	1.10
		Nos. 581-584 (4)	1.90	1.81

Soup Tureen — A181

Europa: 12fr, Deep bowl. Tureen and bowl after pottery from Nospelt, 19th century.

1976, May 3 Photo. *Perf. 11½*

585	A181	6fr lt violet & multi	.55	.15
586	A181	12fr yel grn & multi	1.50	1.00

Independence Hall, Philadelphia A182

Boomerang A183

1976, May 3

587	A182	6fr lt blue & multi	.35	.25

American Bicentennial.

1976, May 3

588	A183	6fr brt rose lil & gold	.35	.20

21st Olympic Games, Montreal, Canada, July 17-Aug. 1.

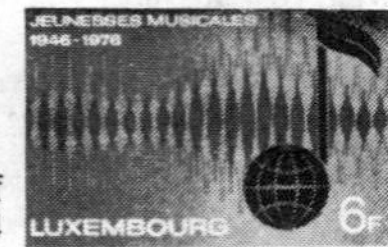

"Vibrations of Sound" — A184

1976, May 3

589	A184	6fr red & multi	.35	.20

Jeunesses Musicales (Young Music Friends), association to foster interest in music and art.

Alexander Graham Bell — A185

Virgin and Child with St. Anne — A186

1976, Sept. 9 Engr. *Perf. 13*

590	A185	6fr slate green	.35	.25

Centenary of first telephone call by Alexander Graham Bell, Mar. 10, 1876.

1976, Sept. 9 Photo. *Perf. 11½*

Renaissance sculptures: 12fr, Grave of Bernard de Velbruck, Lord of Beaufort.

591	A186	6fr gold & multi	.35	.20
592	A186	12fr gold, gray & blk	.70	.70

Johann Wolfgang von Goethe A187

Old Luxembourg A188

Portraits: 5fr, J. M. William Turner. 6fr, Victor Hugo. 12fr, Franz Liszt.

1977, Mar. 14 Engr. *Perf. 13*

593	A187	2fr lake	.15	.15
594	A187	5fr purple	.30	.24
595	A187	6fr slate green	.35	.28
596	A187	12fr violet blue	.70	.65
		Nos. 593-596 (4)	1.50	1.32

Famous visitors to Luxembourg.

1977, May 3 Photo. *Perf. 11½*

Europa: 12fr, Adolphe Bridge and European Investment Bank headquarters.

597	A188	6fr multicolored	.45	.15
598	A188	12fr multicolored	1.25	.65

Esch-sur-Sure A189

Marguerite de Busbach A190

Design: 6fr, View of Ehnen.

1977, May 3 Engr. *Perf. 13*

599	A189	5fr Prus blue	.40	.25
600	A189	6fr deep brown	.35	.25

1977, May 3 Photo. *Perf. 11½*

Design: #602, Louis Braille, by Lucienne Filippi.

601	A190	6fr multicolored	.35	.20
602	A190	6fr multicolored	.35	.20

Notre Dame Congregation, founded by Marguerite de Busbach, 350th anniversary; Louis Braille (1809-1852), inventor of the Braille system of writing for the blind.

Souvenir Sheet

Luxembourg Nos. 1-2 — A191

Engr. & Photo.

1977, Sept. 15 *Perf. 13½*

603	A191	40fr gray & red brown	5.25	5.25

125th anniv. of Luxembourg's stamps.

Head of Medusa, Roman Mosaic, Diekirch, 3rd Century A.D. — A192

1977, Sept. 15 Photo. *Perf. 11½*

604	A192	6fr multicolored	.50	.32

Orpheus and Eurydice, by C. W. Gluck A193

1977, Sept. 15 *Perf. 11½x12*

605	A193	6fr multicolored	.60	.25

Intl. Wiltz Festival, 25th anniv.

Europa Tamed, by R. Zilli, and Map of Europe A194

1977, Dec. 5 Photo. *Perf. 11½*

606	A194	6fr multicolored	.60	.30

20th anniversary of the Treaties of Rome, setting up the European Economic Community and the European Atomic Energy Commission.

Souvenir Sheet

Grand Duke and Grand Duchess of Luxembourg — A195

Photogravure and Engraved

1978, Apr. 3 *Perf. 13½x14*

607	A195	Sheet of 2	2.00	2.00
a.		6fr dark blue & multi	.90	.90
b.		12fr dark red & multi	.90	.90

Silver wedding anniversary of Grand Duke Jean and Grand Duchess Josephine Charlotte.

Souvenir Sheet

Youth Fountain, Streamer and Dancers — A196

1978, Apr. 3 Photo. *Perf. 11½*

608	A196	Sheet of 3	4.25	4.25
a.		5fr ultra & multi	1.40	1.40
b.		6fr orange & multi	1.40	1.40
c.		20fr yellow green & multi	1.40	1.40

Juphilux 78, 5th International Young Philatelists' Exhibition, Luxembourg, Apr. 6-10.

Charles IV, Statue, Charles Bridge, Prague A197

Emile Mayrish, by Theo Van Rysselberghe A198

Europa: 12fr, Pierre d'Aspelt, tomb, Mainz Cathedral.

1978, May 18 Engr. *Perf. 13½*

609	A197	6fr dark violet blue	.30	.20
610	A197	12fr dull rose lilac	.85	.70

Charles IV (1316-78), Count of Luxembourg, Holy Roman Emperor. Pierre d'Aspelt (c. 1250-1320), Archbishop of Mainz and Prince-Elector.

1978, May 18 *Perf. 11½*

611	A198	6fr multicolored	.85	.30

Emile Mayrish (1862-1928), president of International Steel Cartel and promoter of United Europe.

Our Lady of Luxembourg A199

Trumpeters and Old Luxembourg A200

1978, May 18 Photo. *Perf. 11½*

612	A199	6fr multicolored	.25	.25
613	A200	6fr multicolored	.25	.25

Our Lady of Luxembourg, patroness, 300th anniv.; 135th anniv. of Grand Ducal Military Band.

Starving Child, Helping Hand, Millet — A201

League Emblem, Lungs, Open Window — A202

Open Prison Door — A203

1978, Sept. 11 Photo. *Perf. 11½*

614	A201	2fr multicolored	.15	.15
615	A202	5fr multicolored	.25	.25
616	A203	6fr multicolored	.40	.30
		Nos. 614-616 (3)	.80	.70

"Terre des Hommes," an association to help underprivileged children; Luxembourg Anti-Tuberculosis League, 70th anniv.; Amnesty Intl. and 30th anniv. of Universal Declaration of Human Rights.

Squared Stone Emerging from Rock, City of Luxembourg
A204

1978, Sept. 11 Engr. *Perf. 13½x13*

617 A204 6fr violet blue		.45	.25

Masonic Grand Lodge of Luxembourg, 175th anniversary.

Julius Caesar on Denarius, c. 44 B.C.
A205

St. Michael's Church, Mondorf-les-Bains
A206

Roman Coins, Found in Luxembourg: 6fr, Empress Faustina I on Sestertius, 141 A.D. 9fr, Empress Helena on Follis, c. 324-330. 26fr, Emperor Valens on Solidus, c. 367-375.

1979, Mar. 5 Photo. *Perf. 11½*

618 A205 5fr multicolored		.22	.22
619 A205 6fr multicolored		.22	.22
620 A205 9fr multicolored		.65	.55
621 A205 26fr multicolored		1.25	1.00
	Nos. 618-621 (4)	2.34	1.99

1979, Mar. 5 Engr. *Perf. 13*

Design: 6fr, Luxembourg Central Station.

622 A206 5fr multicolored		.30	.20
623 A206 6fr rose claret		.60	.30

Troisvièrges Stagecoach
A207

Europa: 12fr, Early wall telephone, vert.

1979, Apr. 30 Photo. *Perf. 11½*

624 A207 6fr multicolored		1.10	.40
625 A207 12fr multicolored		2.50	.90

Michel Pintz Facing Jury — A208

1979, Apr. 30 Engr. *Perf. 13*

626 A208 2fr rose lilac		.30	.15

180th anniversary of peasant uprising against French occupation.

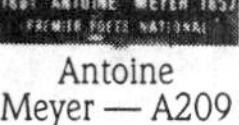

Antoine Meyer — A209

Abundance Crowning Work and Thrift, by Auguste Vinet — A210

Design: 6fr, Sidney Gilchrist Thomas.

1979, Apr. 30

627 A209 5fr carmine		.32	.20
628 A209 6fr light blue		.32	.25
629 A210 9fr black		.50	.35
	Nos. 627-629 (3)	1.14	.80

Antoine Meyer (1801-1857), mathematician and first national poet; centenary of acquisition of Thomas process for production of high-quality steel; 50th anniversary of Luxembourg Stock Exchange.

European Parliament
A211

1979, June 7 Photo. *Perf. 11½*

630 A211 6fr multi		5.00	.90

European Parliament, first direct elections, June 7-10.

Angel with Chalice, by Barthelemy Namur — A212

Rococo Art: 12fr, Angel with anchor, by Namur, from High Altar, St. Michael's Church, Luxembourg.

Engraved and Photogravure

1979, Sept. 10 *Perf. 13½*

631 A212 6fr multi		.35	.25
632 A212 12fr multi		.65	.50

Road Safety for Children
A213

1979, Sept. 10 Photo. *Perf. 11½*

633 A213 2fr multi		.18	.15

International Year of the Child.

Radio Tele-Luxembourg Emblem — A214

1979, Sept. 10

634 A214 6fr ultra, blue & red		.45	.25

50 years of broadcasting in Luxembourg.

John the Blind, Silver Coin, 1331 — A215

Ettelbruck Town Hall — A216

14th Century Coins: 2fr, Sts. Gervase and Protais, silver grosso. 6fr, Easter lamb, gold coin. 20fr, Crown and arms, silver grosso.

1980, Mar. 5 Photo. *Perf. 11½*

635 A215 2fr multi		.15	.15
636 A215 5fr multi		.25	.25
637 A215 6fr multi		.35	.35
638 A215 20fr multi		1.20	1.20
	Nos. 635-638 (4)	1.95	1.95

See Nos. 651-654.

1980, Mar. 5 Engr. *Perf. 13*

Design: No. 640, State Archives Building, horiz.

639 A216 6fr brn & dk red		.35	.25
640 A216 6fr multi		.35	.25

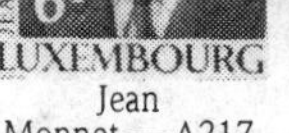

Jean Monnet — A217

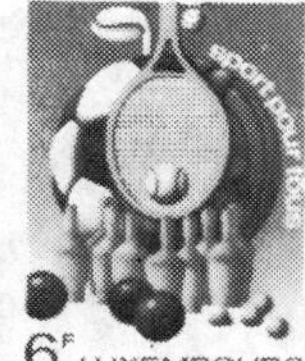

Sports for All — A218

Europa: 12fr, St. Benedict of Nursia.

1980, Apr. 28 *Perf. 13½*

641 A217 6fr dark blue		.52	.25
642 A217 12fr olive green		1.00	.60

1980, Apr. 28 Photo. *Perf. 11½*

Granite Paper

643 A218 6fr multi		.95	.22

Worker Pouring Molten Iron — A219

Mercury by Jean Mich — A220

Design: 6fr, Man, hand, gears, horiz.

1980, Apr. 28

644 A219 2fr multi		.15	.15
645 A219 6fr multi		.42	.22
	Set value		.30

9th World Congress on Prevention of Occupational Accidents & Diseases, Amsterdam, May 6-9.

1980, Sept. 10 Engr. *Perf. 14*

Art Nouveau Sculpture by Jean Mich.

646 A220 8fr shown		.48	.40
647 A220 12fr Ceres		.70	.55

Introduction of Postal Code — A221

1980, Sept. 10 Photo. *Perf. 11½*

648 A221 4fr multi		.42	.15

Police Car and Officers
A222

1980, Sept. 10

649 A222 8fr multi		.48	.32

State control of police force, 50th anniv.

Grand Duke Jean — A223

Arms of Grand Duke Jean — A224

Photo. & Engr.

1981, Jan. 5 *Perf. 13½*

650	Sheet of 3	2.50	2.50
a.	A223 8fr multi	.65	.65
b.	A224 12fr multi	.75	.75
c.	A223 30fr multi	1.00	1.00

Grand Duke Jean, 60th birthday.

Coin Type of 1980

Silver Coins: 4fr, Philip IV patagon, 1635. 6fr, Empress Maria Theresa 12 sol, 1775. 8fr, Emperor Joseph II 12 sol, 1789. 30fr, Emperor Francois II 72 sol, 1795.

1981, Mar. 5 Photo. *Perf. 11½*

651 A215 4fr multi		.18	.16
652 A215 6fr multi		.25	.20
653 A215 8fr multi		.32	.32
654 A215 30fr multi		1.25	1.10
	Nos. 651-654 (4)	2.00	1.78

National Library
A225

1981, Mar. 5 Engr. *Perf. 13*

655 A225 8fr shown		.35	.20
656 A225 8fr European Hemicycle, Kirchberg		.35	.20

Hammelsmarsch (Sheep Procession) — A226

Europa: 12fr, Bird-shaped whistle, Eimaischen market.

1981, May 4 Photo. *Perf. 13½*

657 A226 8fr multi		.38	.30
658 A226 12fr multi		.60	.50

Knight on Chessboard
A227

Savings Account Book, State Bank
A228

First Bank Note, 1856 — A229

1981, May 4 *Perf. 11½*

Granite Paper

659 A227 4fr multi		.25	.22
660 A228 8fr multi		.35	.35
661 A229 8fr multi		.35	.35

Luxembourg Chess Federation, 50th anniv.; State Savings Bank, 125th anniv.; Intl. Bank of Luxembourg, 125th anniv. of issuing rights.

Wedding of Prince Henri and Maria Teresa Mestre, Feb. 14
A230

Photo. & Engr.

1981, June 22 *Perf. 13½*

662 A230 8fr multi .50 .40

Sheets of 12.

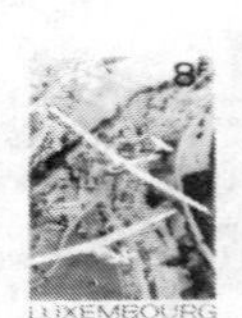

Single-seater Gliders A231

Energy Conservation A232

1981, Sept. 28 Photo. *Perf. 11½*

Granite Paper

663 A231 8fr shown .30 .30
664 A231 16fr Propeller planes, horiz. .60 .60
665 A231 35fr Jet, Luxembourg Airport, horiz. 1.50 1.40
Nos. 663-665 (3) 2.40 2.30

1981, Sept. 28

Granite Paper

666 A232 8fr multi .35 .35

Apple Trees in Blossom, by Frantz Seimetz (1858-1914)
A233

World War II Resistance
A234

Landscape Paintings: 6fr, Summer Landscape, by Pierre Blanc (1872-1946). 8fr, The Larger Hallerbach, by Guido Oppenheim (1862-1942). 16fr, Winter Evening, by Eugene Mousset (1877-1941).

1982, Feb. 25 Engr. *Perf. 11½*

667 A233 4fr multi .18 .18
668 A233 6fr multi .28 .28
669 A233 8fr multi .40 .40
670 A233 16fr multi .80 .80
Nos. 667-670 (4) 1.66 1.66

1982, Feb. 25

Design: Cross of Hinzert (Natl. Monument of the Resistance and Deportation) and Political Prisoner, by Lucien Wercollier.

671 A234 8fr multi .38 .35

Europa 1982
A235

St. Theresa of Avila (1515-1582)
A236

1982, May 4 Photo.

Granite Paper

672 A235 8fr Treaty of London, 1867 .50 .35
673 A235 16fr Treaty of Paris, 1951 .90 .65

1982, May 4

Design: 8fr, Raoul Follereau (1903-1977), "Apostle of the Lepers."

Granite Paper

674 A236 4fr multi .20 .18
675 A236 8fr multi .40 .38

State Museums — A237

1982, May 4 Photo. & Engr.

676 A237 8fr shown .45 .35
677 A237 8fr Synagogue of Luxembourg .45 .35

Bourscheid Castle — A238

Intl. Youth Hostel Federation, 50th Anniv. — A239

Designs: Restored castles.

1982, Sept. 9 Engr. *Perf. 11½*

Granite Paper

678 A238 6fr shown .32 .25
679 A238 8fr Vianden, horiz. .45 .35

1982, Sept. 9 Photo.

680 A239 4fr shown .30 .15
681 A239 8fr Scouting year, vert. .60 .35

Civilian and Military Deportation Monument — A240

1982, Sept. 9

682 A240 8fr multi .50 .35

Mercury, Sculpture by Auguste Tremond
A241

NATO Emblem, Flags
A242

1983, Mar. 7 Photo. *Perf. 11½*

Granite Paper

683 A241 4fr multi .20 .15

FOREX '83, 25th Intl. Assoc. of Foreign Exchange Dealers' Congress, June 2-5.

1983, Mar. 7

Granite Paper

684 A242 6fr multi .25 .25

25th anniv. of NAMSA (NATO Maintenance and Supply Agency).

Echternach Cross of Justice, 1236 — A243

Globe, CCC Emblem — A244

1983, Mar. 7

Granite Paper

685 A243 8fr multi .45 .35

30th Cong. of Intl. Union of Barristers, July 3-9.

1983, Mar. 7

Granite Paper

686 A244 8fr multi .45 .35

30th anniv. of Council of Customs Cooperation.

Natl. Federation of Fire Brigades Centenary
A245

1983, Mar. 7

Granite Paper

687 A245 8fr Fire engine, 1983 .45 .35
688 A245 16fr Hand pump, 1740 .85 .65

Europa 1983 — A246

The Good Samaritan, Codex Aureus Escorialensis Miniatures, 11th Cent., Echternach.

1983, May 3 Photo.

689 A246 8fr Highway robbers .52 .35
690 A246 16fr Good Samaritan 1.00 .65

Giant Bible, 11th Cent. — A247

World Communications Year — A248

Illuminated Letters.

1983, May 3 Photo. & Engr. *Perf. 14*

691 A247 8fr "h," Book of Baruch .45 .35
692 A247 35fr "B," letter of St. Jerome 2.00 1.50

1983, May 3 Photo. *Perf. 11½*

693 A248 8fr Post code .42 .35
694 A248 8fr Satellite relay, horiz. .42 .35

Town Hall, Dudelange
A249

Designs: 7fr, St. Lawrence Church, Diekirch, vert.

1983, Sept. 7 Photo. & Engr.

695 A249 7fr multi .38 .25
696 A249 10fr multi .55 .35

Basketball Fed., 50th Anniv.
A250

European Working Dog Championship
A251

Tourism — A252

1983, Sept. 7 Photo.

Granite Paper

697 A250 7fr multi .38 .25
698 A251 10fr Alsatian sheepdog .55 .35
699 A252 10fr View of Luxembourg .55 .35
Nos. 697-699 (3) 1.48 .95

Environment Protection
A253

1984, Mar. 6 Photo. *Perf. 11½*

Granite Paper

700 A253 7fr Pedestrian zoning .35 .16
701 A253 10fr Water purification .50 .24

2nd European Parliament Election — A254

1984, Mar. 6

Granite Paper

702 A254 10fr Hands holding emblem .60 .40

A255

A256

1984, Mar. 6 Engr. *Perf. 12½x13*

703 A255 10fr No. 1 .50 .35
704 A255 10fr Union meeting .50 .35
705 A255 10fr Mail bag .50 .35
706 A255 10fr Train .50 .35
Nos. 703-706 (4) 2.00 1.40

Philatelic Federation (1934); Civil Service Trade Union (1909); Postal Workers' Union (1909); Railroad (1859).

1984, May 7 Photo. *Perf. 11½x12*

707 A256 10fr The Race, by Jean Jacoby (1891-1936) .55 .35

1984 Summer Olympics.

Europa (1959-84)
A257

1984, May 7 *Perf. 11½*

Granite Paper

708 A257 10fr green .75 .30
709 A257 16fr orange 1.00 .60

Young Turk Caressing His Horse, by Delacroix A258

Paintings: 4fr, The Smoker, by David Teniers the Younger (1610-90). 10fr, Epiphany, by Han Steen (1626-79). 50fr, The Lacemaker, by Pieter van Slingelandt (1640-91). 4fr, 50fr vert.

1984, May 7 Photo. & Engr. *Perf. 14*

710 A258 4fr multi .25 .22
711 A258 7fr multi .40 .24
712 A258 10fr multi .60 .35
713 A258 50fr multi 2.75 2.00
Nos. 710-713 (4) 4.00 2.81

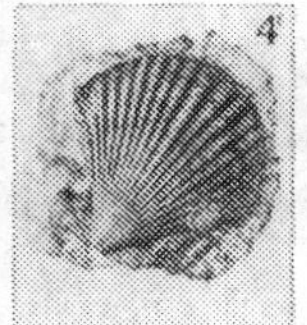
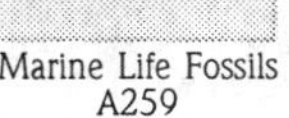

Marine Life Fossils A259

Restored Castles A260

1984, Sept. 10 Photo. *Perf. 11½*

714 A259 4fr Pecten sp. .22 .15
715 A259 7fr Gryphaea arcuata .38 .25
716 A259 10fr Coeloceras raqyinianum .55 .35
717 A259 16fr Daildius .90 .60
Nos. 714-717 (4) 2.05 1.35

1984, Sept. 10 **Engr.**

718 A260 7fr Hollenfels .38 .25
719 A260 10fr Larochette .55 .40

A261

A262

1984, Sept. 10 *Perf. 12x12½*

720 A261 10fr Soldier, US flag .75 .35

40th Anniv. of D Day (June 6).

1985, Mar. 4 Photo. *Perf. 11½*

Portrait medals in the state museum: 4fr, Jean Bertels (1544-1607), Historian, Abbott of Echternach. 7fr, Emperor Charles V (1500-1558). 10fr, King Philip II of Spain (1527-1598). 30fr, Prince Maurice of Orange-Nassau, Count of Vianden (1567-1625).

Granite Paper

721 A262 4fr multi .24 .22
722 A262 7fr multi .40 .22
723 A262 10fr multi .60 .32
724 A262 30fr multi 1.75 .90
Nos. 721-724 (4) 2.99 1.66

See Nos. 739-742.

Anniversaries A263

Designs: No. 725, Benz Velo, First automobile in Luxembourg, 1895. No. 726, Push-button telephone, sound waves. No. 727, Fencers.

1985, Mar. 4 *Perf. 12x11½*

Granite Paper

725 A263 10fr multi .65 .40
726 A263 10fr multi .65 .40
727 A263 10fr multi .65 .40
Nos. 725-727 (3) 1.95 1.20

Centenary of the first automobile; Luxembourg Telephone Service, cent.; Luxembourg Fencing Federation, 50th anniv.

Visit of Pope John Paul II — A264

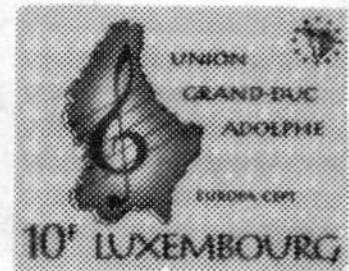

Europa 1985 — A265

1985, Mar. 4 *Perf. 11½x12*

Granite Paper

728 A264 10fr Papal arms .75 .40

1985, May 8 *Perf. 11½*

Designs: 10fr, Grand-Duke Adolphe Music Federation. 16fr, Luxembourg Music School.

729 A265 10fr multi .80 .40
730 A265 16fr multi 1.25 .60

Souvenir Sheet

End of World War II, 40th Anniv. — A266

Designs: a, Luxembourg resistance fighters, Wounded Fighters medal. b, Luxembourg War Cross. c, Badge of the Union of Luxembourg Resistance Movements. d, Liberation of the concentration camps.

1985, May 8 *Perf. 11½x12*

Granite Paper

731 Sheet of 4 2.75 2.75
a.-d. A266 10fr, any single .60 .38

Endangered Wildlife — A267

1985, Sept. 23 Photo. *Perf. 12x11½*

732 A267 4fr Athene nocturna .20 .15
733 A267 7fr Felis silvestris .38 .22
734 A267 10fr Vanessa atalantica, vert. .55 .35
735 A267 50fr Hyla arborea, vert. 2.75 1.65
Nos. 732-735 (4) 3.88 2.37

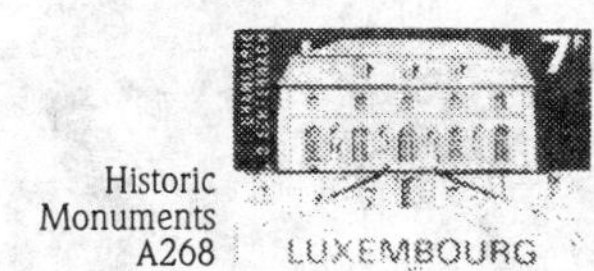

Historic Monuments A268

1985, Sept. 23 Engr. *Perf. 11½*

736 A268 7fr Echternach Orangery, 1750 .45 .22
737 A268 10fr Mohr de Waldt House, 17th cent. .65 .45

Natl. Art Collection — A269

Photo. & Engr.

1985, Sept. 23 *Perf. 14*

738 A269 10fr 18th cent. book cover, Natl. Library .40 .22

Portrait Medals Type of 1985

1986, Mar. 3 Photo. *Perf. 11½*

Granite Paper

739 A262 10fr Count of Monterey, 1675 .65 .40
740 A262 12fr Louis XIV, 1684 .70 .45
741 A262 18fr Pierre de Weyms, c. 1700 1.10 .70
742 A262 20fr Duke of Marlborough, 1706 1.25 .80
Nos. 739-742 (4) 3.70 2.35

Federation of Luxembourg Beekeepers' Associations, Cent. — A270

Mondorf State Spa, Cent. — A271

Natl. Table Tennis Federation, 50th Anniv. — A272

1986, Mar. 3 *Perf. 11½*

743 A270 12fr Bee collecting pollen .75 .50
744 A271 12fr Mosaic .75 .50
745 A272 12fr Boy playing table tennis .75 .50
Nos. 743-745 (3) 2.25 1.50

Europa 1986 A273

Fortifications A274

1986, May 5 Photo. *Perf. 12*

Granite Paper

751 A273 12fr Polluted forest, city .75 .50
752 A273 20fr Man, pollution sources 1.25 .80

1986, May 5

Granite Paper

753 A274 15fr Ft. Thungen, horiz. .90 .60
754 A274 18fr Invalid's Gate 1.10 .72
755 A274 50fr Malakoff Tower 3.00 2.00
Nos. 753-755 (3) 5.00 3.32

Robert Schuman (1886-1963), European Cooperation Promulgator — A275

1986, June 26 *Perf. 12 on 3 Sides*

Granite Paper

756 A275 2fr pink & blk .15 .15
a. Bklt. pane of 4 .32
757 A275 10fr lt bl & blk .65 .40
a. Bklt. pane of 4 2.75
b. Bklt. pane of 2, #756-757 + 2 labels 1.40

Nos. 756-757 issued in booklets only.

European Road Safety Year — A276

Countess Ermesinde (1186-1247), Ruler of Luxembourg — A278

Bas-relief, Town Hall, Esch-Sur-Alzette — A277

1986, Sept. 15 Photo. *Perf. 11½*

758 A276 10fr multi .55 .40

Photogravure & Engraved

1986, Sept. 15 *Perf. 14x13½*

Design: No. 760, Stairs to the Chapel of the Cross, Grevenmacher.

759 A277 12fr shown .75 .50
760 A277 12fr multi .75 .50

1986, Sept. 15 *Perf. 13½x14*

Designs: No. 761, Presentation of the letter of freedom to Echternach inhabitants, 1236, engraving (detail) by P.H. Witkamp, c. 1873. 30fr, Charter seal, Marienthal Convent, 1238.

761 A278 12fr multi .70 .50
762 A278 30fr multi 1.65 1.20

A279

A280

A281

1987, Mar. 9 Photo. *Perf. 11½*

763 A279 6fr Eliomys quercinus .30 .24
764 A279 10fr Calopteryx splendens, vert. .52 .40
765 A279 12fr Cinclus cinclus, vert. .60 .48
766 A279 25fr Salamandra salamandra terrestris 1.40 1.00
Nos. 763-766 (4) 2.82 2.12

Wildlife conservation.

1987, Mar. 9

767 A280 12fr multi .62 .48

Natl. Home Amateur Radio Operators Network, 50th anniv.

1987, Mar. 9

768 A281 12fr multi .62 .48

Luxembourg Intl. Fair, 50th anniv.

Luxembourg stamps can be mounted in the annually supplemented Scott Luxembourg album.

Europa 1987 — A282

Designs: 12fr, Aquatic Sports Center. 20fr, European Communities Court of Justice and abstract sculpture by Henry Moore (1898-1986).

1987, May 4 Photo. *Perf. 11½*

769 A282 12fr multi 1.00 .50
770 A282 20fr multi 1.65 .80

St. Michael's Church Millenary A283

Designs: 12fr, Consecration of the church by Archbishop Egbert of Trier, 987, stained glass window by Gustav Zanter. 20fr, Baroque organ-chest, 17th century.

Photogravure & Engraved

1987, May 4 *Perf. 14*

771 A283 12fr multi .75 .48
772 A283 20fr multi 1.25 .80

15th Century Paintings by Giovanni Ambrogio Bevilacqua — A284

Polyptych panels in the State Museum: 10fr, St. Bernard of Sienna and St. John the Baptist. 18fr, St. Jerome and St. Francis of Assisi.

1987, May 4 *Perf. 11½*

773 A284 10fr multi .55 .40
774 A284 18fr multi 1.00 .72

Rural Architecture A285

Photo. & Engr.

1987, Sept. 14 *Perf. 13½*

775 A285 10fr Hennesbau Bark Mill, 1826, Niederfeulen .50 .40
776 A285 12fr Health Center, 18th cent., Mersch .60 .48
777 A285 100fr Post Office, 18th cent., Bertrange 5.00 4.00
Nos. 775-777 (3) 6.10 4.88

Chamber of Deputies (Parliament) 139th Anniv. — A286

Designs: 6fr, Charles Metz (1799-1853), first President. 12fr, Parliament, 1860, designed by Antoine Hartmann (1817-1891).

1987, Sept. 14 Engr. *Perf. 14*

778 A286 6fr violet brn .24 .24
779 A286 12fr blue black .48 .48

Flowers by Botanical Illustrator Pierre-Joseph Redoute (1759-1840) A287

1988, Feb. 8 Photo. *Perf. 11½x12*

780 A287 6fr Orange lily, water lily .40 .40
781 A287 10fr Primula, double narcissus .65 .65
782 A287 12fr Tulip .80 .80
783 A287 50fr Iris, gorteria 3.25 3.25
Nos. 780-783 (4) 5.10 5.10

European Conf. of Ministers of Transport A288

Eurocontrol, 25th Anniv. A289

1988, Feb. 8 *Perf. 12*

784 A288 12fr multi .72 .72
785 A289 20fr multi 1.20 1.20

Souvenir Sheet

Family of Prince Henri — A290

1988, Mar. 29 Photo. *Perf. 12*

786 A290 Sheet of 3 4.75 4.75
a. 12fr Maria Theresa .68 .68
b. 18fr Guillaume, Felix and Louis 1.00 1.00
c. 50fr Prince Henri 2.75 2.75

JUVALUX '88, 9th intl. youth philatelic exhibition, Mar. 29-Apr. 4.

Europa 1988 — A291

Communication.

1988, June 6 Photo. *Perf. 11½*

787 A291 12fr Automatic mail handling .90 .90
788 A291 20fr Electronic mail 1.50 1.50

Tourism — A292

Designs: 10fr, Wiltz town hall and Cross of Justice Monument, c. 1502. 12fr, Castle, Differdange, 16th cent., vert.

Photo. & Engr.

1988, June 6 *Perf. 13½*

789 A292 10fr multi .60 .60
790 A292 12fr multi .72 .72

See Nos. 824-825, 841-842.

League of Luxembourg Student Sports Associations (LASEL), 50th Anniv. A293

1988, June 6 Photo. *Perf. 11½*

791 A293 12fr multi .72 .72

Doorways — A294

Architectural drawings by Joseph Wegener (1895-1980) and his students, 1949-1951: 12fr, Septfontaines Castle main entrance, 1785. 25fr, National Library regency north-wing entrance, c. 1720. 50fr, Holy Trinity Church baroque entrance, c. 1740.

Litho. & Engr.

1988, Sept. 12 *Perf. 14*

792 A294 12fr black & buff .65 .65
793 A294 25fr blk & citron 1.30 1.30
794 A294 50fr blk & yel bister 2.60 2.60
Nos. 792-794 (3) 4.55 4.55

Jean Monnet (1888-1979), French Economist — A295

1988, Sept. 12 Engr.

795 A295 12fr multi .65 .65

European Investment Bank, 30th Anniv. A296

1988, Sept. 12 Litho. & Engr.

796 A296 12fr yel grn & blk .65 .65

A297 A298

1988, Sept. 12 Photo. *Perf. 11½*

797 A297 12fr multi .65 .65

1988 Summer Olympics, Seoul.

1989, Mar. 6 Photo. *Perf. 11½x12*

Design: 12fr, Portrait and excerpt from his speech to the Chamber of Deputies, 1896.

798 A298 12fr multi .62 .62

C.M. Spoo (1837-1914), advocate of Luxembourgish as the natl. language.

Book Workers' Fed., 125th Anniv. — A299

Natl. Red Cross, 75th Anniv. — A300

1989, Mar. 6

799 A299 18fr multi .95 .95

1989, Mar. 6

800 A300 20fr Henri Dunant 1.05 1.05

Independence of the Grand Duchy, 150th Anniv. — A301

Design: 12fr, Lion, bronze sculpture by Auguste Tremont (1892-1980) guarding the grand ducal family vault, Cathedral of Luxembourg.

Photo. & Engr.

1989, Mar. 6 *Perf. 14*

801 A301 12fr multi .62 .62

Astra Telecommunications Satellite — A302

1989, Mar. 6 Photo. *Perf. 11½*

802 A302 12fr multi .62 .62

Europa 1989 — A303

Tour de France — A304

Paintings (children at play): 12fr, *Three Children in a Park*, 19th cent., anonymous. 20fr, *Child with Drum*, 17th cent., anonymous.

1989, May 8 Photo. *Perf. 11½x12*

803 A303 12fr multi .62 .62
804 A303 20fr multi 1.05 1.05

1989, May 8 *Perf. 11½*

805 A304 9fr multi .48 .48

Start of the bicycle race in Luxembourg City.

A305

A306

1989, May 8 *Perf. 11½x12*
806 A305 12fr multi .62 .62

Interparliamentary Union, cent.

1989, May 8
807 A306 12fr multi .62 .62

European Parliament 3rd elections.

Council of Europe, 40th Anniv. A307

1989, May 8 *Perf. 12x11½*
808 A307 12fr multi .62 .62

Reign of Grand Duke Jean, 25th Anniv. A308

Charles IV (1316-1378) A309

1989, Sept. 18 Photo. *Perf. 12x11½*

Booklet Stamps

810 A308 3fr black & orange .15 .15
a. Bklt. pane of 4 .56
811 A308 9fr black & blue green .42 .42
a. Bklt. pane of 4 1.70
b. Bklt. pane, 1 each #810, 811 + 2 labels .56
Booklet, 1 each #810a, 811a, 811b 2.85

Photo. & Engr.

1989, Sept. 18 *Perf. 13½x14*

Stained-glass windows by Joseph Oberberger in the Grand Ducal Loggia, Cathedral of Luxembourg: 20fr, John the Blind (1296-1346). 25fr, Wenceslas II (1361-1419).

821 A309 12fr shown .58 .58
822 A309 20fr multi .95 .95
823 A309 25fr multi 1.20 1.20
Nos. 821-823 (3) 2.73 2.73

Independence of the Grand Duchy, 150th anniv.

Tourism Type of 1988

Designs: 12fr, Clervaux Castle interior courtyard, circa 12th cent. 18fr, Bronzed wild boar of Titelberg, 1st cent., vert.

Litho. & Engr.

1989, Sept. 18 *Perf. 13½*
824 A292 12fr multi .58 .58
825 A292 18fr multi .88 .88

Views of the Former Fortress of Luxembourg, 1814-1815, Engravings by Christoph Wilhelm Selig (1791-1837) — A310

1990, Mar. 5 Photo. *Perf. 12x11½*
826 A310 9fr shown .52 .52
827 A310 12fr multi, diff. .70 .70
828 A310 20fr multi, diff. 1.15 1.15
829 A310 25fr multi, diff. 1.40 1.40
Nos. 826-829 (4) 3.77 3.77

Congress of Vienna, 1815, during which the Duchy of Luxembourg was elevated to the Grand Duchy of Luxembourg.

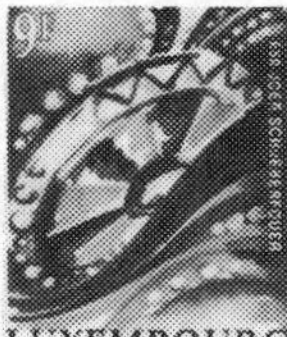

Schueberfouer Carnival, 650th Anniv. — A311

1990, Mar. 15 *Perf. 11½x12*
830 A311 9fr Carnival ride .52 .52

Batty Weber (1860-1940), Writer — A312

ITU, 125th Anniv. — A313

1990, Mar. 15
831 A312 12fr multi .70 .70

1990, Mar. 15
832 A313 18fr multicolored 1.05 1.05

Europa — A314

Post offices: 12fr, Luxembourg City. 20fr, Esch-Sur-Alzette, vert.

Litho. & Engr.

1990, May 28 *Perf. 13½*
833 A314 12fr buff & blk .72 .72
834 A314 20fr lt bl & blk 1.20 1.20

Paul Eyschen (1841-1915) — A315

Prime Ministers: 12fr, Emmanuel Servais (1811-1890).

Photo. & Engr.

1990, May 28 *Perf. 14x13½*
835 A315 9fr multicolored .55 .55
836 A315 12fr multicolored .72 .72

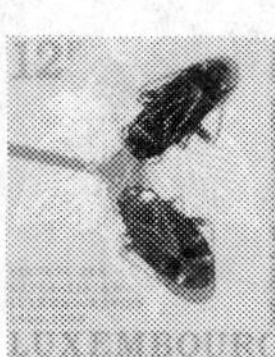

A316

A317

1990, May 28 Photo. *Perf. 11½*
837 A316 12fr Psallus Pseudoplatani .72 .72

Luxembourg Naturalists' Society, cent.

Litho. & Engr.

1990, Sept. 24 *Perf. 14*

Fountains: 12fr, Sheep's march by Will Lofy. 25fr, Fountain of Doves. 50fr, "Maus Ketty" by Lofy.

838 A317 12fr multicolored .72 .72
839 A317 25fr multicolored 1.50 1.50
840 A317 50fr multicolored 3.00 3.00
Nos. 838-840 (3) 5.22 5.22

Tourism Type of 1988

1990, Sept. 24 *Perf. 13½*
841 A292 12fr Mondercange .72 .72
842 A292 12fr Schifflange .72 .72

Souvenir Sheet

Nassau-Weilbourg Dynasty, Cent. — A318

Designs: a, Grand Duke Adolphe. b, Grand Duchess Marie-Adelaide. c, Grand Ducal House arms. d, Grand Duchess Charlotte. e, Grand Duke Guillaume. f, Grand Duke Jean.
Illustration reduced.

Photo. & Engr.

1990, Nov. 26 *Perf. 14x13½*
843 A318 Sheet of 6 6.00 6.00
a.-b. 12fr multicolored .72 .72
c.-d. 18fr multicolored 1.10 1.10
e.-f. 20fr multicolored 1.20 1.20

View From the Trier Road by Sosthene Weis (1872-1941) — A319

Paintings: 18fr, Vauban Street and the Viaduct. 25fr, St. Ulric Street.

Perf. 12x11½, 11½x12

1991, Mar. 4 **Photo.**
844 A319 14fr multicolored .85 .85
845 A319 18fr multicolored 1.10 1.10
846 A319 25fr multi, vert. 1.50 1.50
Nos. 844-846 (3) 3.45 3.45

Fungi — A320

1991, Mar. 4 *Perf. 11½*
847 A320 14fr Geastrum varians .85 .85
848 A320 14fr Agaricus (Gymnopus) thiebautii .85 .85
849 A320 18fr Agaricus (lepiota) lepidocephalus 1.10 1.10
850 A320 25fr Morchella favosa 1.50 1.50
Nos. 847-850 (4) 4.30 4.30

Europa — A321

1991, May 13 Photo. *Perf. 12x11½*
851 A321 14fr Astra 1A, 1B satellites .85 .85
852 A321 18fr Betzdorf ground station 1.10 1.10

Natl. Miners' Monument, Kayl — A322

Art by Emile Kirscht — A323

Designs: No. 854, Magistrates' Court, Redange-Sur-Attert, horiz.

Perf. 11½x12, 12x11½

1991, May 23
853 A322 14fr multicolored .85 .85
854 A322 14fr multicolored .85 .85

1991, May 23 *Perf. 11½*

#856, Edmund de la Fontaine (1823-91), poet.

855 A323 14fr multicolored .85 .85
856 A323 14fr multicolored .85 .85

Labor Unions, 75th anniv. (No. 855).

Post and Telecommunications Museum — A324

Perf. 11½ on 3 sides

1991, Sept. 23 **Photo.**

Booklet Stamps

857 A324 4fr Old telephone .25 .25
a. Bklt. pane of 1 + 3 labels .25
858 A324 14fr Old postbox .85 .85
a. Bklt. pane of 4 3.40

A325

A326

1991, Sept. 23 *Perf. 11½*
859 A325 14fr Stamp of Type A24 .85 .85

Stamp Day, 50th anniv.

Photo. & Engr.

1991, Sept. 23 *Perf. 14*

Designs: Gargoyles.

860 A326 14fr Young girl's head .85 .85
861 A326 25fr Woman's head 1.50 1.50
862 A326 50fr Man's head 3.00 3.00
Nos. 860-862 (3) 5.35 5.35

See Nos. 874-876.

Jean-Pierre Pescatore Foundation, Cent. — A327

Buildings: No. 864, High Technology Institute. No. 865, New Fair and Congress Centre.

1992, Mar. 16 Photo. *Perf. 11½*

863 A327 14fr lil rose & multi .85 .85
864 A327 14fr grn & multi .85 .85
865 A327 14fr brt bl & multi .85 .85
Nos. 863-865 (3) 2.55 2.55

Bettembourg Castle — A328

1992, Mar. 16

866 A328 18fr shown 1.05 1.05
867 A328 25fr Walferdange station 1.50 1.50

Europa A329

Emigrants to US: 14fr, Nicholas Gonner (1835-1892), newspaper editor. 22fr, N. E. Becker (1842-1920), journalist.

Perf. 13½x14½

1992, May 18 Photo. & Engr.

868 A329 14fr multicolored .85 .85
869 A329 22fr multicolored 1.35 1.35

Lions Clubs Intl., 75th Anniv. — A330

General Strike, 50th Anniv. — A331

1992, May 18 Photo. *Perf. 11½*

870 A330 14fr multicolored .85 .85
871 A331 18fr sepia & lake 1.10 1.10

1992 Summer Olympics, Barcelona A332

1992, May 18 *Perf. 12x11½*

872 A332 14fr multicolored .85 .85

Expo '92, Seville — A333

1992, May 18 *Perf. 11½*

873 A333 14fr Luxembourg pavilion .85 .85

Gargoyle Type of 1991

1992, Oct. 5 Photo. & Engr. *Perf. 14*

874 A326 14fr Ram's head .85 .85
875 A326 22fr Lion's head 1.30 1.30
876 A326 50fr Satyr's head 3.00 3.00
Nos. 874-876 (3) 5.15 5.15

Stained Glass Windows, by Auguste Tremont — A334

1992, Oct. 5 Photo. *Perf. 11½x12*

877 A334 14fr Post horn, letters .85 .85
878 A334 22fr Post rider 1.30 1.30
879 A334 50fr Insulators 3.00 3.00
Nos. 877-879 (3) 5.15 5.15

Luxembourg Post and Telecommunications, 150th anniv.

Single European Market A335

1992, Oct. 5 *Perf. 11½x12*

880 A335 14fr multicolored .85 .85

Fountain of the Children with Grapes, Schwebsingen A336

Design: No. 882, Old Ironworks Cultural Center, Steinfort.

1993, Mar. 8 Photo. *Perf. 12x11½*

881 A336 14fr multicolored .85 .85
882 A336 14fr multicolored .85 .85

Grand Duke Jean — A337

Perf. 13½x13

1993-95 Litho. & Engr.

Background Color

883 A337 1fr yellow brown .15 .15
883A A337 2fr olive gray .15 .15
884 A337 5fr yellow green .30 .30
885 A337 7fr brick red .42 .42
886 A337 10fr blue .70 .70
887 A337 14fr pink .85 .85
888 A337 15fr green .90 .90
889 A337 16fr orange 1.10 1.10
890 A337 18fr orange 1.10 1.10
891 A337 20fr red 1.25 1.25
892 A337 22fr dark green 1.30 1.30
893 A337 25fr gray blue 1.50 1.50
894 A337 100fr brown 6.00 6.00
Nos. 883-894 (13) 15.72 15.72

Issued: 5fr, 7fr, 14fr, 18fr, 22fr, 25fr, 3/8/93; 1fr, 15fr, 20fr, 100fr, 3/7/94; 2fr, 10fr, 16fr, 1/30/95.

See No. 957.

New Technologies in Surgery — A338

1993, May 10 Photo. *Perf. 11½*

895 A338 14fr multicolored .85 .85

Contemporary Paintings — A339

Europa: 14fr, Rezlop, by Fernand Roda. 22fr, So Close, by Sonja Roef.

1993, May 10

896 A339 14fr multicolored .85 .85
897 A339 22fr multicolored 1.35 1.35

A340 A341

Designs: 14fr, Burgundy Residence. 20fr, Simons House. 50fr, Cassal House.

Photo. & Engr.

1993, May 10 *Perf. 14*

898 A340 14fr multicolored .85 .85
899 A340 20fr multicolored 1.20 1.20
900 A340 50fr multicolored 3.00 3.00
Nos. 898-900 (3) 5.05 5.05

1993, Sept. 20 Photo. *Perf. 11½*

901 A341 14fr multicolored .85 .85

Environmental protection.

A342 A343

1993, Sept. 20

902 A342 14fr multicolored .85 .85
903 A343 14fr multicolored .85 .85

Jean Schortgen (1880-1918), 1st worker elected to Parliament (#902); Artistic Circle of Luxembourg, cent.

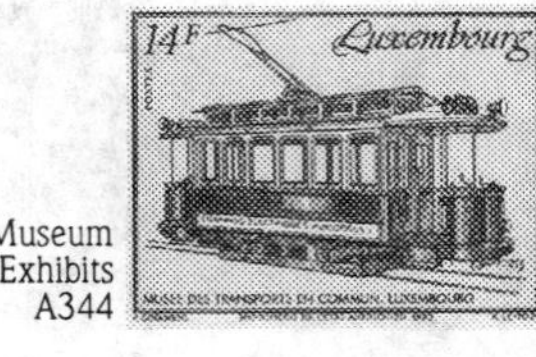

Museum Exhibits A344

14fr, Electric tram, Tram & Bus Museum, City of Luxembourg. 22fr, Iron ore tipper wagon, Natl. Mining Museum, Rumelange. 60fr, Horse-drawn carriage, Wiltz Museum of Ancient Crafts.

Photo. & Engr.

1993, Sept. 20 *Perf. 14*

904 A344 14fr multicolored .85 .85
905 A344 22fr multicolored 1.40 1.40
906 A344 60fr multicolored 3.75 3.75
Nos. 904-906 (3) 6.00 6.00

See Nos. 933-935.

Snow-Covered Landscape, by Joseph Kutter (1894-1941) — A345

Design: No. 908, The Moselle, by Nico Klopp (1894-1930).

1994, Mar. 7 Photo. *Perf. 11½x12*

907 A345 14fr multicolored .85 .85
908 A345 14fr multicolored .85 .85

4th General Elections to European Parliament A346

1994, May 16 Photo. *Perf. 11½*

909 A346 14fr multicolored .85 .85

European Inventions, Discoveries A347

1994, May 16

910 A347 14fr Armillary sphere .85 .85
911 A347 22fr Sail boats, map 1.40 1.40

Europa.

21st Intl. Congress of Genealogy & Heraldry — A348

14th World Congress of Intl. Police Assoc. — A349

Intl. Year of the Family — A350

1994, May 16 *Perf. 11½*

912 A348 14fr multicolored .85 .85
913 A349 18fr multicolored 1.10 1.10
914 A350 25fr multicolored 1.50 1.50
Nos. 912-914 (3) 3.45 3.45

Europe A351

1994, Sept. 19 *Perf. 11½*

915 A351 14fr Dove, stars .85 .85
916 A351 14fr Circle of stars .85 .85
917 A351 14fr Bronze Age bowl .85 .85
Nos. 915-917 (3) 2.55 2.55

Western European Union, 40th anniv. (#915). Office for Official Publications of European Communities, 25th anniv. (#916). European Bronze Age Research Campaign (#917).

Liberation, 50th Anniv. A352

1994, Sept. 19 Photo. ***Perf. 12x11½***
918 A352 14fr multicolored .80 .80

Former Refuges in Luxembourg A353

Designs: 15fr, Munster Abbey. 25fr, Holy Spirit Convent. 60fr, St. Maximine Abbey of Trier.

Photo. & Engr.

1994, Sept. 19 ***Perf. 14***
919 A353 15fr multicolored .90 .90
920 A353 25fr multicolored 1.50 1.50
921 A353 60fr multicolored 3.75 3.75
Nos. 919-921 (3) 6.15 6.15

A354

City of Luxembourg, 1995 European City of Culture — A355

Paintings by Hundertwasser
A356 A357

Panoramic view of city showing buildings and: No. 923a, Steeples, trees. b, Gateway through fortress wall. c, Angles in fortress wall. d, Roof of church.

Designs: No. 924, The King of the Antipodes. No. 925, The House with the Arcades and the Yellow Tower. No. 926, Small Path.

Perf. 12x11½, 11½x12

1995, Mar. 6 **Photo.**
922 A354 16fr multicolored 1.10 1.10
923 Strip of 4 4.50 4.50
a.-d. A355 16fr any single 1.10 1.10

Photo. & Engr.

Perf. 14
924 A356 16fr gold, silver & multi 1.10 1.10
925 A357 16fr black & multi 1.10 1.10
926 A357 16fr yellow & multi 1.10 1.10
Nos. 922-926 (5) 8.90 8.90

No. 923 is a continuous design.

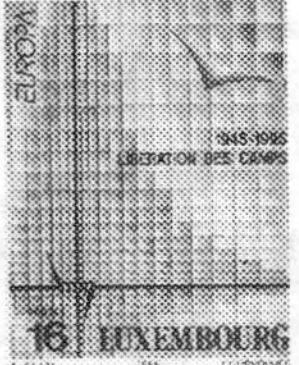

Liberation of the Concentration Camps, 50th Anniv. — A358

Europa: 25fr, Barbed wire, cracked plaster.

1995, May 15 Photo. ***Perf. 11½x12***
927 A358 16fr multicolored 1.10 1.10
928 A358 25fr multicolored 1.75 1.75

European Nature Conservation Year — A359

1995, May 15 Litho. ***Perf. 13½***
929 A359 16fr multicolored 1.10 1.10

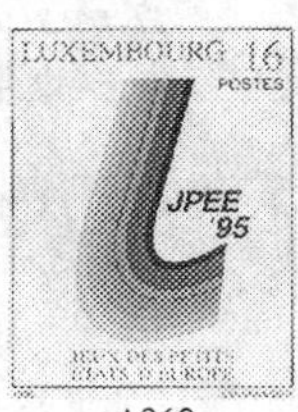

A360 A362

European Geodynamics and Seismology Center — A361

1995, May 15 Photo. ***Perf. 11½x12***
930 A360 16fr multicolored 1.10 1.10

Small States of Europe Games, Luxembourg.

1995, May 15 ***Perf. 11½***
931 A361 32fr multicolored 2.25 2.25

1995, May 15 ***Perf. 11½x12***
932 A362 80fr multicolored 5.75 5.75

UN, 50th anniv.

Museum Exhibits Type of 1993

Designs, vert: 16fr, Churn, Country Art Museum, Vianden. 32fr, Wine press, Wine Museum, Ehnen. 80fr, Sculpture of a Potter, by Leon Nosbusch, Pottery Museum, Nospelt.

Photo. & Engr.

1995, Sept. 18 ***Perf. 14***
933 A344 16fr multicolored 1.10 1.10
934 A344 32fr multicolored 2.25 2.25
935 A344 80fr multicolored 5.50 5.50
Nos. 933-935 (3) 8.85 8.85

Luxembourg-Reykjavik, Iceland Air Route, 40th Anniv. — A363

1995, Sept. 18 Litho. ***Perf. 13***
936 A363 16fr multicolored 1.10 1.10

See Iceland # 807.

Tourism A364

1995, Sept. 18 Photo. ***Perf. 11½***
937 A364 16fr Erpeldange 1.10 1.10
938 A364 16fr Schengen 1.10 1.10

Portrait of Emile Mayrisch (1862-1928), by Théo Van Rysselberghe (1862-1926) A365

1996, Mar. 4 Photo. ***Perf. 11½***
939 A365 (A) multicolored 1.10 1.10

On day of issue No. 939 was valued at 16fr. See Belgium No. 1602.

National Railway, 50th Anniv. — A366

Passenger train: a, Cab facing left. b, Hooked together. c, Cab facing right.

1996, Mar. 4 Photo. ***Perf. 11½***
940 Strip of 3 3.30 3.30
a.-c. A366 16fr Any single 1.10 1.10

No. 940 is a continuous design.

Grand Duchess Charlotte (1896-1985) — A367

Design: Statue, Luxembourg City.

1996, Mar. 4

Booklet Stamp
941 A367 16fr multicolored 1.10 1.10
a. Booklet pane of 8 8.80
Complete booklet, #941a 8.80

Mihály Munkácsy (1844-1900), Hungarian Painter — 368

Designs: No. 942, Portrait of Munkácsy, by Edouard Charlemont, 1884. No. 943, Portrait of Marie Munchen, by Munkácsy, 1885, vert.

1996, May 20 Photo. ***Perf. 11½***
942 A368 16fr multicolored 1.00 1.00
943 A368 16fr multicolored 1.00 1.00

Famous Women — A369

Europa: 16fr, Marie de Bourgogne (1457-82), duchess of Luxembourg. 25fr, Empress Maria-Theresa of Austria (1717-80), duchess of Luxembourg.

Photo. & Engr.

1996, May 20 ***Perf. 14x13½***
944 A369 16fr multicolored 1.00 1.00
945 A369 25fr multicolored 1.60 1.60

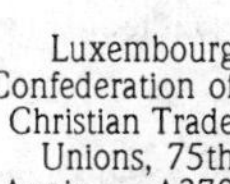

Luxembourg Confederation of Christian Trade Unions, 75th Anniv. — A370

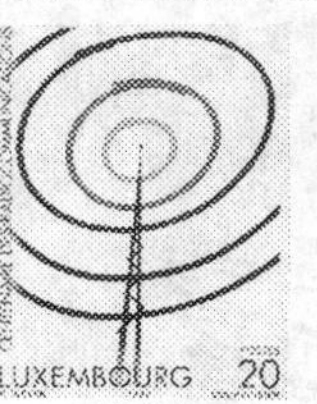
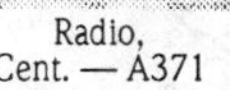

Radio, Cent. — A371

Modern Olympic Games, Cent. — A372

Motion Pictures, Cent. — A373

Perf. 12x11½, 11½x12

1996, May 20 **Photo.**
946 A370 16fr multicolored 1.00 1.00
947 A371 20fr multicolored 1.30 1.30
948 A372 25fr multicolored 1.60 1.60
949 A373 32fr multicolored 2.00 2.00
Nos. 946-949 (4) 5.90 5.90

Registration and Property Administration, Bicent. — A374

1996, Sept. 23 Photo. ***Perf. 11½***
950 A374 16fr multicolored 1.00 1.00

Let Us Live Together A375

#951, Four children. #952, "L'Abbraccio," bronze statue by M.J. Kerschen, vert.

1996, Sept. 23
951 A375 16fr multicolored 1.00 1.00
952 A375 16fr multicolored 1.00 1.00

Mustelidae A376

Litho. & Engr.

1996, Sept. 23 ***Perf. 13½***
953 A376 16fr Meles meles 1.00 1.00
954 A376 20fr Mustela putorius 1.25 1.25
955 A376 80fr Lutra lutra 5.00 5.00
Nos. 953-955 (3) 7.25 7.25

John the Blind (1296-1346), King of Bohemia, Count of Luxembourg — A377

Litho. & Engr.

1996, Dec. 9 ***Perf. 13½***
956 A377 32fr multicolored 1.80 1.80

Grand Duke Jean Type of 1993

Perf. 13½x13

1997, Jan. 2 **Litho. & Engr.**

957 A337 8fr green & black .40 .40

Treaties of Rome, 40th Anniv. A378

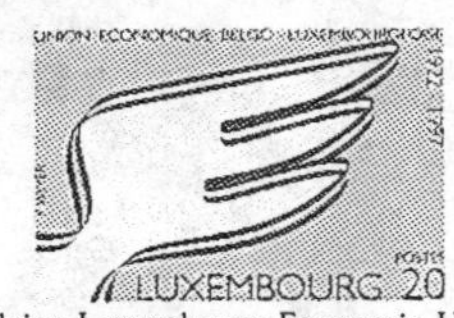

Belgian-Luxembourg Economic Union, 75th Anniv. — A379

1997, Mar. 3 **Photo.** *Perf. 11½*

958 A378 16fr multicolored .85 .85
959 A379 20fr multicolored 1.00 1.00

Tourism A380

Designs: No. 960, Servais House, Mersch. No. 961, Baroque Church, Koerich, vert.

1997, Mar. 3

960 A380 16fr multicolored .85 .85
961 A380 16fr multicolored .85 .85

CAMPO RODAN
RUE DU LOMBARD 9
1000 BRUSSELS, BELGIUM
PHONE: 011-32-2-514-5292
FAX: 011-32-2-514-5415

Specialists in...
BELGIUM
and former territories:
CONGO - ZAIRE
KATANGA
SOUTH KASAI
RUANDA
URUNDI
RWANDA
BURUNDI
LUXEMBOURG
EUROPE

Charge it! We accept:

11th World Congress of Rose Societies — A381

Roses: 16fr, Grand Duchess Charlotte. 20fr, Beautiful Sultana. 80fr, In Memory of Jean Soupert.

1997, Mar. 3 *Perf. 11½*

962 A381 16fr multicolored .85 .85

Size: 33x25mm

963 A381 20fr multicolored 1.00 1.00
964 A381 80fr multicolored 4.25 4.25

Stories and Legends — A382

Europa: 16fr, Melusina of Luxembourg. 25fr, Hunter of Hollenfels.

1997, May 12

965 A382 16fr multicolored .85 .85
966 A382 25fr multicolored 1.30 1.30

A383

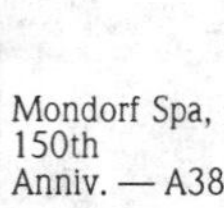

A384

Mondorf Spa, 150th Anniv. — A385

1997, May 12

967 A383 16fr multicolored .85 .85
968 A384 16fr multicolored .85 .85
969 A385 20fr multicolored 1.00 1.00
Nos. 967-969 (3) 2.70 2.70

Grand-Ducal Gendarmerie, bicent. (#967). Union of Small Domestic Animals Farming Societies, 75th anniv. (#968).

JUVALUX 98 — A386

1997, May 12

970 A386 16fr Emblem .85 .85
971 A386 80fr Postal history 4.25 4.25

Saar-Lorraine-Luxembourg Summit — A387

1997, Oct. 16 **Photo.** *Perf. 11½*

972 A387 16fr multicolored .90 .90

See Germany No. 1982 and France No. 2613.

Mills — A388

Clocks — A389

Litho. & Engr.

1997, Oct. 16 *Perf. 13½*

973 A388 16fr Kalborn Mill, horiz. .90 .90
974 A388 50fr Ramelli Mill 2.75 2.75

Photo. & Engr.

1997, Oct. 16 *Perf. 13x13½*

Designs: 16fr, Oak wall clock, 1816. 32fr, Astronomic clock with walnut case, mid 19th cent. 80fr, Pear tree wood wall clock, 1815.

975 A389 16fr multicolored .90 .90
976 A389 32fr multicolored 1.80 1.80
977 A389 80fr multicolored 4.50 4.50
Nos. 975-977 (3) 7.20 7.20

Henry V, the Blonde (1247-81), Count of Luxembourg A390

1997, Dec. 8 **Photo.** *Perf. 11½*

978 A390 32fr multicolored 1.75 1.75

Tourism A391

#979, Hesperange. #980, Rodange Church, vert.

1998, Mar. 23 **Photo.** *Perf. 11½*

979 A391 16fr multicolored .85 .85
980 A391 16fr multicolored .85 .85

Freshwater Fish — A392

Designs: 16fr, Salmo trutta. 25fr, Cottus gobio. 50fr, Alburnoides bipunctatus.

Perf. 13½x13

1998, Mar. 23 **Litho. & Engr.**

981 A392 16fr multicolored .85 .85
982 A392 25fr multicolored 1.25 1.25
983 A392 50fr multicolored 2.50 2.50
Nos. 981-983 (3) 4.60 4.60

NGL (Independent Luxembourg Trade Union), 50th Anniv. — A393

Broom Festival, Wiltz, 50th Anniv. — A394

Jean Antoine Zinnen (1827-98), Composer — A395

Abolition of Censorship, 150th Anniv. — A396

1998, Mar. 23 **Photo.** *Perf. 11½*

984 A393 16fr multicolored .85 .85
985 A394 16fr multicolored .85 .85
986 A395 20fr multicolored 1.10 1.10
987 A396 50fr multicolored 2.50 2.50
Nos. 984-987 (4) 5.30 5.30

SEMI-POSTAL STAMPS

Clervaux Monastery SP1

Designs: 15c+10c, View of Pfaffenthal. 25c+10c, View of Luxembourg.

Engr.; Surcharge Typo. in Red

1921, Aug. 2 **Unwmk.** *Perf. 11½*

B1 SP1 10c + 5c green .15 *.90*
B2 SP1 15c + 10c org red .15 *1.10*
B3 SP1 25c + 10c dp grn .15 *.90*
Nos. B1-B3 (3) .45 *2.90*
Set, never hinged 1.00

The amount received from the surtax on these stamps was added to a fund for the erection of a monument to the soldiers from Luxembourg who died in World War I.

Nos. B1-B3 with Additional Surcharge in Red or Black

+ 25

× 27 mai 1923 ×

1923, May 27

B4 SP1 25c on #B1 (R) 1.00 *5.75*
B5 SP1 25c on #B2 1.25 *7.25*
B6 SP1 25c on #B3 1.00 *5.75*
Nos. B4-B6 (3) 3.25 *18.75*
Set, never hinged 7.00

Unveiling of the monument to the soldiers who died in World War I.

Regular Issue of 1914-15 Surcharged in Black or Red

CARITAS

+10c

1924, Apr. 17 *Perf. 11½x11*

B7 A11 12½c + 7½c grn .15 .18
B8 A11 35c + 10c dk bl (R) .15 .18
B9 A11 2½fr + 1fr red .60 *4.50*
B10 A11 5fr + 2fr dk vio .35 *2.50*
Nos. B7-B10 (4) 1.25 *7.36*
Set, never hinged 2.75

Nurse and Patient SP4

Prince Jean SP5

1925, Dec. 21 Litho. *Perf. 13*

B11	SP4	5c (+ 5c) dl vio	.15	.20
B12	SP4	30c (+ 5c) org	.15	.28
B13	SP4	50c (+ 5c) red brn	.24	*.80*
B14	SP4	1fr (+ 10c) dp bl	.35	*2.00*
		Nos. B11-B14 (4)	.89	*3.28*
		Set, never hinged	1.65	

1926, Dec. 15 Photo. *Perf. 12½x12*

B15	SP5	5c (+ 5c) vio & blk	.15	.15
B16	SP5	40c (+ 10) grn & blk	.15	.20
B17	SP5	50c (+ 15c) lem & blk	.15	.20
B18	SP5	75c (+ 20c) lt red & blk	.25	*1.50*
B19	SP5	1.50fr (+ 30c) gray bl & blk	.30	*2.50*
		Nos. B15-B19 (5)	1.00	*4.55*
		Set, never hinged	1.65	

Grand Duchess Charlotte and Prince Felix — SP6

1927, Sept. 4 Engr. *Perf. 11½*

B20	SP6	25c dp vio	.70	*4.50*
B21	SP6	50c green	1.10	*7.50*
B22	SP6	75c rose lake	.70	*4.50*
B23	SP6	1fr gray blk	.70	*4.50*
B24	SP6	1½fr dp bl	.70	*4.50*
		Nos. B20-B24 (5)	3.90	*25.50*
		Set, never hinged	15.00	

Introduction of postage stamps in Luxembourg, 75th anniv. These stamps were sold exclusively at the Luxembourg Philatelic Exhibition, September 4-8, 1927, at a premium of 3 francs per set, which was donated to the exhibition funds.

Princess Elisabeth SP7

Princess Marie Adelaide SP8

1927, Dec. 1 Photo. *Perf. 12½*

B25	SP7	10c (+ 5c) turq bl & blk	.15	*.28*
B26	SP7	50c (+ 10c) dk brn & blk	.15	*.45*
B27	SP7	75c (+ 20c) org & blk	.15	*.75*
B28	SP7	1fr (+ 30c) brn lake & blk	.24	*3.00*
B29	SP7	1½fr (+ 50c) ultra & blk	.18	*3.00*
		Set value	.66	
		Set, never hinged	1.65	
		Nos. B25-B29 (5)		*7.48*

The surtax was for Child Welfare societies.

1928, Dec. 12 *Perf. 12½x12*

B30	SP8	10c (+ 5c) ol grn & brn vio	.15	*.80*
B31	SP8	60c (+ 10c) brn & ol grn	.25	*1.65*
B32	SP8	75c (+ 15c) vio rose & bl grn	.40	*3.00*
B33	SP8	1fr (+ 25c) dk grn & brn	.80	*4.75*
B34	SP8	1½fr (+ 50c) cit & bl	.80	*4.75*
		Nos. B30-B34 (5)	2.40	*14.95*
		Set, never hinged	8.00	

Princess Marie Gabrielle SP9

Prince Charles SP10

1929, Dec. 14 *Perf. 13*

B35	SP9	10c (+ 10c) mar & dp grn	.15	*.90*
B36	SP9	35c (+ 15c) dk grn & red brn	.60	*4.25*
B37	SP9	75c (+ 30c) ver & blk	.60	*4.25*
B38	SP9	1¼fr (+ 50c) mag & bl grn	1.10	*7.75*
B39	SP9	1¾fr (+ 75c) Prus bl & sl	1.10	*7.75*
		Nos. B35-B39 (5)	3.55	*24.90*
		Set, never hinged	16.00	

The surtax was for Child Welfare societies.

1930, Dec. 10 *Perf. 12½*

B40	SP10	10c (+ 5c) bl grn & ol brn	.15	.35
B41	SP10	75c (+ 10c) vio brn & bl grn	.60	*2.25*
B42	SP10	1fr (+ 25c) car rose & vio	1.75	*6.75*
B43	SP10	1¼fr (+ 75c) ol bis & dk brn	2.50	*9.00*
B44	SP10	1¾fr (+ 1.50fr) ultra & red brn	4.00	*12.00*
		Nos. B40-B44 (5)	9.00	*30.35*
		Set, never hinged	45.00	

The surtax was for Child Welfare societies.

Princess Alix SP11

Countess Ermesinde SP12

1931, Dec. 10

B45	SP11	10c (+ 5c) brn org & gray	.25	.38
B46	SP11	75c (+ 10c) claret & bl grn	2.00	*8.25*
B47	SP11	1fr (+ 25c) dp grn & gray	4.00	*16.00*
B48	SP11	1¼fr (+ 75c) dk vio & bl grn	4.00	*12.50*
B49	SP11	1¾fr (+ 1.50fr) bl & gray	7.75	*32.50*
		Nos. B45-B49 (5)	18.00	*69.63*
		Set, never hinged	100.00	

The surtax was for Child Welfare societies.

1932, Dec. 8

B50	SP12	10c (+ 5c) ol bis	.30	.48
B51	SP12	75c (+ 10c) dp vio	1.25	*5.75*
B52	SP12	1fr (+ 25c) scar	5.00	*22.50*
B53	SP12	1¼fr (+ 75c) red brn	6.00	*24.00*
B54	SP12	1¾fr (+ 1.50fr) dp bl	6.00	*24.00*
		Nos. B50-B54 (5)	18.55	*76.73*
		Set, never hinged	85.00	

The surtax was for Child Welfare societies.

Count Henry VII — SP13

John the Blind — SP14

1933, Dec. 12

B55	SP13	10c (+ 5c) yel brn	.35	.35
B56	SP13	75c (+ 10c) dp vio	2.00	*7.25*
B57	SP13	1fr (+ 25c) car rose	7.50	*22.50*
B58	SP13	1¼fr (+ 75c) org brn	9.50	*32.50*
B59	SP13	1¾fr (+ 1.50fr) brt bl	9.50	*32.50*
		Nos. B55-B59 (5)	28.85	*95.10*
		Set, never hinged	100.00	

1934, Dec. 5

B60	SP14	10c (+ 5c) dk vio	.18	.28
B61	SP14	35c (+ 10c) dp grn	1.00	*4.75*
B62	SP14	75c (+ 15c) rose lake	1.00	*4.75*
B63	SP14	1fr (+ 25c) dp rose	7.50	*30.00*
B64	SP14	1¼fr (+ 75c) org	9.50	*32.50*
B65	SP14	1¾fr (+ 1.50fr) brt bl	9.50	*32.50*
		Nos. B60-B65 (6)	28.68	*104.78*
		Set, never hinged	120.00	

Teacher SP15

Sculptor and Painter — SP16

Journalist SP17

Engineer SP18

Scientist SP19

Lawyer SP20

University SP21

Surgeon SP22

1935, May 1 Unwmk. *Perf. 12½*

B65A	SP15	5c violet	.15	*.24*
B65B	SP16	10c brown red	.18	*.28*
B65C	SP17	15c olive	.20	*.45*
B65D	SP18	20c orange	.35	*.90*
B65E	SP19	35c yellow grn	.45	*1.25*
B65F	SP20	50c gray blk	.50	*1.25*
B65G	SP21	70c dk green	.75	*1.75*
B65H	SP22	1fr car red	1.00	*2.50*
B65J	SP19	1.25fr turq	4.00	*10.00*
B65K	SP18	1.75fr blue	5.00	*20.00*
B65L	SP16	2fr lt brown	20.00	*50.00*
B65M	SP17	3fr dk brown	24.00	*57.50*
B65N	SP20	5fr lt blue	40.00	*95.00*
B65P	SP15	10fr red vio	110.00	*250.00*
B65Q	SP22	20fr dk green	150.00	*300.00*
		Nos. B65A-B65Q (15)	356.58	*791.12*
		Set, never hinged	850.00	

Sold at double face, surtax going to intl. fund to aid professional people.

Philatelic Exhibition Issue

Type of Regular Issue of 1928

Wmk. 246

1935, Aug. 15 Engr. *Imperf.*

B66	A19	2fr (+ 50c) blk	4.00	*12.00*
		Never hinged	12.00	

Philatelic exhibition held at Esch-sur-Alzette.

Charles I — SP23

Perf. 11½

1935, Dec. 2 Photo. Unwmk.

B67	SP23	10c (+ 5c) vio	.15	.16
B68	SP23	35c (+ 10c) grn	.18	*.70*
B69	SP23	70c (+ 20c) dk brn	.42	*1.40*
B70	SP23	1fr (+ 25c) rose lake	8.00	*22.50*
B71	SP23	1.25fr (+ 75c) org brn	8.00	*22.50*
B72	SP23	1.75fr (+ 1.50fr) bl	8.00	*22.50*
		Nos. B67-B72 (6)	24.75	*69.76*
		Set, never hinged	90.00	

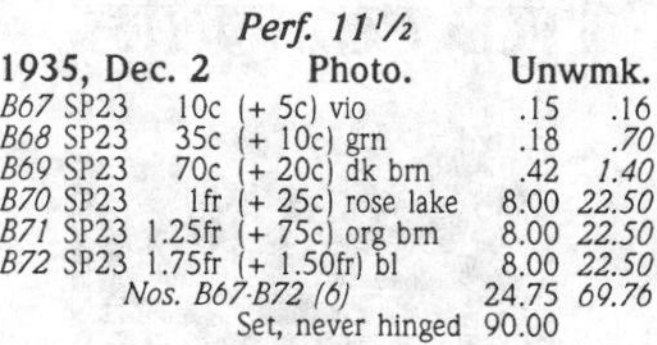

Wenceslas I, Duke of Luxembourg — SP24

1936, Dec. 1 *Perf. 11½x13*

B73	SP24	10c + 5(c) blk brn	.15	.20
B74	SP24	35c + 10(c) bl grn	.15	*.40*
B75	SP24	70c + 20(c) blk	.25	*.80*
B76	SP24	1fr + 25(c) rose car	1.00	*4.00*
B77	SP24	1.25fr + 75(c) vio	2.00	*8.75*
B78	SP24	1.75fr + 1.50(fr) saph	1.55	*6.00*
		Nos. B73-B78 (6)	5.10	*20.15*
		Set, never hinged	27.50	

Wenceslas II — SP25

1937, Dec. 1 *Perf. 11½x12½*

B79	SP25	10c + 5c car & blk	.15	.18
B80	SP25	35c + 10c red vio & grn	.15	.20
B81	SP25	70c + 20c ultra & red brn	.25	.40
B82	SP25	1fr + 25c dk grn & scar	1.50	*3.25*
B83	SP25	1.25fr + 75c dk brn & vio	1.75	*3.75*
B84	SP25	1.75fr + 1.50fr blk & ultra	1.90	*4.50*
		Nos. B79-B84 (6)	5.70	*12.28*
		Set, never hinged	14.00	

Souvenir Sheet

SP26

Wmk. 110

1937, July 25 Engr. *Perf. 13*

B85	SP26	Sheet of 2	2.25	*7.00*
		Never hinged	7.00	
a.		2fr red brown, single stamp	.85	*2.75*

National Philatelic Exposition at Dudelange on July 25-26.

Sold for 5fr per sheet, of which 1fr was for the aid of the exposition.

Portrait of St. Willibrord — SP28

St. Willibrord, after a Miniature — SP29

Abbey at Echternach — SP30

Designs: No, B87, The Rathaus at Echternach. No. B88, Pavilion in Abbey Park, Echternach. No. B91, Dancing Procession in Honor of St. Willibrord.

Perf. 14x13, 13x14

1938, June 5 Engr. Unwmk.

B86 SP28	35c + 10c dk bl grn		.15	*.40*
B87 SP28	70c + 10c ol gray		.40	*.42*
B88 SP28	1.25fr + 25c brn car		.85	*1.25*
B89 SP29	1.75fr + 50c sl bl		1.40	1.75
B90 SP30	3fr + 2fr vio brn		4.75	5.25
B91 SP30	5fr + 5fr dk vio		4.75	5.25
	Nos. B86-B91 (6)		12.30	14.32
	Set, never hinged		55.00	

12th centenary of the death of St. Willibrord. The surtax was used for the restoration of the ancient Abbey at Echternach.

Grand Duke Sigismond — SP32

Prince Jean — SP33

1938, Dec. 1 Photo. *Perf. 11½*

B92 SP32	10c + 5c lil & blk	.15	.15
B93 SP32	35c + 10c grn & blk	.15	.15
B94 SP32	70c + 20c buff & blk	.25	*.42*
B95 SP32	1fr + 25c red org & blk	2.25	*4.00*
B96 SP32	1.25fr + 75c gray bl & blk	2.25	*4.00*
B97 SP32	1.75fr + 1.50fr bl & blk	2.50	*5.75*
	Nos. B92-B97 (6)	7.55	*14.47*
	Set, never hinged	25.00	

1939, Dec. 1 Litho. *Perf. 14x13*

Designs: Nos. B99, B102, Prince Felix. Nos. B100, B103, Grand Duchess Charlotte.

B98 SP33	10c + 5c red brn, *buff*	.15	.20
B99 SP33	35c + 10c sl grn, *buff*	.15	.45
B100 SP33	70c + 20c blk, *buff*	.18	*.90*
B101 SP33	1fr + 25c red org, *buff*	1.75	*8.00*
B102 SP33	1.25fr + 75c vio brn, *buff*	2.25	*8.75*
B103 SP33	1.75fr + 1.50fr lt bl, *buff*	5.00	*20.00*
	Nos. B98-B103 (6)	9.48	*38.30*
	Set, never hinged	40.00	

See No. 217 (souvenir sheet).

Allegory of Medicinal Baths — SP36

1940, Mar. 1 Photo. *Perf. 11½*

B104 SP36	2fr + 50c gray, blk & slate grn	1.00	*6.00*
	Never hinged	2.50	

Stamps of 1944, type A37, surcharged "+50C," "+5F" or "+15F" in black, were sold only in canceled condition, affixed to numbered folders. The surtax was for the benefit of Luxembourg evacuees. Value for folder, $15.

Homage to France SP37

Thanks to: No. B118, Russia. No. B119, Britannia. No. B120, America.

1945, Mar. 1 Engr. *Perf. 13*

B117 SP37	60c + 1.40fr dp grn	.15	.15
B118 SP37	1.20fr + 1.80fr red	.15	.15
B119 SP37	2.50fr + 3.50fr dp bl	.15	.20
B120 SP37	4.20fr + 4.80fr dp vio	.15	.20
	Set value	.38	.60
	Set, never hinged	.70	

Issued to honor the Allied Nations. Exist imperf. Value, set $60.

Statue Carried in Procession SP41

Statue of Our Lady "Patrona Civitatis" SP42

"Our Lady of Luxembourg" SP43

Cathedral Façade SP44

Altar with Statue of Madonna — SP45

1945, June 4

B121 SP41	60c + 40c grn	.15	.25
B122 SP42	1.20fr + 80c red	.15	.25
B123 SP43	2.50fr + 2.50fr dp bl	.15	*1.10*
B124 SP44	5.50fr + 6.50fr dk vio	.60	*9.25*
B125 SP45	20fr + 20fr choc	.60	*9.25*
	Nos. B121-B125 (5)	1.65	*20.10*
	Set, never hinged	3.50	

Exist imperf. Value, set $52.50.

Souvenir Sheet

"Our Lady of Luxembourg" — SP46

1945, Sept. 30 Engr. *Imperf.*

B126 SP46	50fr + 50fr blk	1.10	*50.00*
	Never hinged	1.90	

Young Fighters SP47

Refugee Mother and Children SP48

Political Prisoner SP49

Executed Civilian SP50

1945, Dec. 20 Photo. *Perf. 11½*

B127 SP47	20c + 30c sl grn & buff	.15	*.80*
B128 SP48	1.50fr + 1fr brn red & buff	.15	*.80*
B129 SP49	3.50fr + 3.50fr bl, dp bl & buff	.18	*5.75*
B130 SP50	5fr + 10fr brn, dk brn & buff	.16	*5.75*
	Set value	.48	
	Set, never hinged	1.25	
	Nos. B127-B130 (4)	.64	

Souvenir Sheet

1946, Jan. 30 Unwmk. *Perf. 11½*

B131	Sheet of 4	8.00	*225.00*
	Never hinged	15.00	
a.	SP47 2.50fr + 2.50fr sl grn & buff	2.00	*45.00*
b.	SP48 3.50fr + 6.50fr brown red & buff	2.00	*45.00*
c.	SP49 5fr + 15fr bl, dp bl & buff	2.00	*45.00*
d.	SP50 20fr + 20fr brown, dark brown & buff	2.00	*45.00*

Tribute to Luxembourg's heroes and martyrs. The surtax was for the National Welfare Fund.

Souvenir Sheet

61215

Old Rolling Mill, Dudelange — SP52

1946, July 28 Engr. & Typo.

B132 SP52	50fr brn & dk bl, *buff*	5.00	*15.00*
	Never hinged	12.00	

National Postage Stamp Exhibition, Dudelange, July 28-29, 1946. The sheets sold for 55fr.

Jean l'Aveugle — SP53

1946, Dec. 5 Photo.

B133 SP53	60c + 40c dk grn	.15	*.40*
B134 SP53	1.50fr + 50c brn red	.15	*.55*
B135 SP53	3.50fr + 3.50fr dp bl	.55	*4.50*
B136 SP53	5fr + 10fr sepia	.28	*3.75*
	Nos. B133-B136 (4)	1.13	*9.20*
	Set, never hinged	2.25	

600th anniv. of the death of Jean l'Aveugle (John the Blind), Count of Luxembourg.

Ruins of St. Willibrord Basilica — SP54

Twelfth Century Miniature of St. Willibrord SP59

Designs: #B138, Statue of Abbot Jean Bertels. #B139, Emblem of Echternach Abbey. #B140, Ruins of the Basilica's Interior. #B141, St. Irmine and Pepin of Hersta Holding Model of the Abbey.

Perf. 13x14, 14x13

1947, May 25 Engr.

B137 SP54	20c + 10c blk	.20	.25
B138 SP54	60c + 10c dk grn	.35	.45
B139 SP54	75c + 25c dk car	.50	.70
B140 SP54	1.50fr + 50c dk brn	.65	.70
B141 SP54	3.50fr + 2.50fr dk bl	1.25	*3.00*
B142 SP59	25fr + 25fr dk pur	14.00	*22.50*
	Nos. B137-B142 (6)	16.95	*27.60*
	Set, never hinged	45.00	

The surtax was to aid in restoring the Basilica of Saint Willibrord at Echternach.

Michel Lentz SP60

Edmond de La Fontaine (Dicks) SP61

1947, Dec. 4 Photo. *Perf. 11½*

B143 SP60	60c + 40c sep & buff	.25	.80
B144 SP60	1.50fr + 50c dp plum & buff	.25	.80
B145 SP60	3.50fr + 3.50fr dp bl & gray	2.25	*7.25*
B146 SP60	10fr + 5fr dk grn & gray	2.25	*7.25*
	Nos. B143-B146 (4)	5.00	*16.10*
	Set, never hinged	15.00	

1948, Nov. 18

B147 SP61	60c + 40c brn & pale bis	.20	.55
B148 SP61	1.50fr + 50c brn car & buff	.30	.60
B149 SP61	3.50fr + 3.50fr dp bl & gray	3.75	*9.25*
B150 SP61	10fr + 5fr dk grn & gray	3.75	*9.25*
	Nos. B147-B150 (4)	8.00	*19.65*
	Set, never hinged	17.00	

125th anniversary of the birth of Edmond de La Fontaine, poet and composer.

Type of Regular Issue of 1948

Souvenir Sheet

1949, Jan. 8 Unwmk. *Perf. 11½*

B151	Sheet of 3	55.00	70.00
	Never hinged	82.50	
a.	A45 8fr + 3fr blue gray	15.00	24.00
b.	A45 12fr + 5fr green	15.00	24.00
c.	A45 15fr + 7fr brown	15.00	24.00

30th anniversary of Grand Duchess Charlotte's ascension to the throne. Border and dates "1919-1949" in gray.

Michel Rodange — SP62

1949, Dec. 5

B152 SP62 60c + 40c ol grn & gray .22 .45
B153 SP62 2fr + 1fr dk vio & rose 2.00 *5.50*
B154 SP62 4fr + 2fr sl blk & gray 2.50 *6.75*
B155 SP62 10fr + 5fr brn & buff 3.25 *8.50*
Nos. B152-B155 (4) 7.97 *21.20*
Set, never hinged 20.00

Wards of the Nation
SP63 SP64

1950, June 24 Engr. *Perf. 12½x12*

B156 SP63 60c + 15c dk sl bl .30 .40
B157 SP64 1fr + 20c dk car rose .70 .90
B158 SP63 2fr + 30c red brn .70 .90
B159 SP64 4fr + 75c dk bl 6.00 *12.00*
B160 SP63 8fr + 3fr blk 20.00 *40.00*
B161 SP64 10fr + 5fr lil rose 20.00 *40.00*
Nos. B156-B161 (6) 47.70 *94.20*
Set, never hinged 82.50

The surtax was for child welfare.

Jean A. Zinnen
SP65

Laurent Menager
SP66

1950, Dec. 5 Photo. *Perf. 11½*

B162 SP65 60c + 10c ind & gray .18 .40
B163 SP65 2fr + 15c cer & buff .24 .55
B164 SP65 4fr + 15c vio bl & bl gray 1.25 *5.00*
B165 SP65 8fr + 5fr dk brn & buff 8.00 *15.00*
Nos. B162-B165 (4) 9.67 *20.95*
Set, never hinged 25.00

1951, Dec. 5

Gray Background

B166 SP66 60c + 10c sepia .15 .35
B167 SP66 2fr + 15c dl ol grn .24 .55
B168 SP66 4fr + 15c blue 1.00 *3.00*
B169 SP66 8fr + 5fr vio brn 8.50 *24.00*
Nos. B166-B169 (4) 9.89 *27.90*
Set, never hinged 25.00

50th anniversary of the death of Laurent Menager, composer.

J. B. Fresez — SP67

Candlemas Singing — SP68

1952, Dec. 3

B170 SP67 60c + 15c dk bl grn & pale bl .15 .35
B171 SP67 2fr + 25c chnt brn & buff .20 .55
B172 SP67 4fr + 25c dk vio bl & gray 1.10 *3.50*
B173 SP67 8fr + 4.75fr dp plum & lil gray 8.25 *24.00*
Nos. B170-B173 (4) 9.70 *28.40*
Set, never hinged 30.00

1953, Dec. 3

Designs: 80c+20c, 4fr+50c, Procession with ratchets. 1.20fr+30c, 7fr+3.35fr, Breaking Easter eggs.

B174 SP68 25c + 15c red org & dp car .15 .18
B175 SP68 80c + 20c vio brn & bl gray .15 .18
B176 SP68 1.20fr + 30c bl grn & ol grn .25 .70
B177 SP68 2fr + 25c brn car & brn .15 .35
B178 SP68 4fr + 50c grnsh bl & vio bl 1.90 *4.25*
B179 SP68 7fr + 3.35fr vio & pur 4.75 *12.00*
Nos. B174-B179 (6) 7.35 *17.66*
Set, never hinged 19.00

The surtax was for the National Welfare Fund of Grand Duchess Charlotte.

Clay Censer and Whistle — SP69

Toys for St. Nicholas Day — SP70

Designs: 80c+20c, 4fr+50c, Sheep and bass drum. 1.20fr+30c, 7fr+3.45fr, Merry-go-round horses. 2fr+25c, As No. B180.

1954, Dec. 3

B180 SP69 25c + 5c car lake & cop brn .15 .15
B181 SP69 80c + 20c dk gray .15 .15
B182 SP69 1.20fr + 30c dk bl grn & cr .25 .65
B183 SP69 2fr + 25c brn & ocher .15 .30
B184 SP69 4fr + 50c brt bl 1.40 *3.25*
B185 SP69 7fr + 3.45fr pur 4.00 *12.00*
Nos. B180-B185 (6) 6.10 *16.50*
Set, never hinged 30.00

1955, Dec. 5 Unwmk. *Perf. 11½*

Designs: 80c+20c, 4fr+50c, Christ child and lamb (Christmas). 1.20fr+30c, 7fr+3.45fr, Star, crown and cake (Epiphany).

B186 SP70 25c + 5c sal & dk car .15 .15
B187 SP70 80c + 20c gray & gray blk .15 .15
B188 SP70 1.20fr + 30c ol grn & sl grn .30 .60
B189 SP70 2fr + 25c buff & dk brn .20 .20
B190 SP70 4fr + 50c lt bl & brt bl 1.25 *2.75*
B191 SP70 7fr + 3.45fr rose vio & claret 5.00 *12.00*
Nos. B186-B191 (6) 7.05 *15.85*
Set, never hinged 21.00

Arms of Echternach — SP71

Arms: 80c+20c, 4fr+50c, Esch-sur-Alzette. 1.20fr+30c, 7fr+3.45fr, Grevenmacher.

1956, Dec. 5 Photo.

Arms in Original Colors

B192 SP71 25c + 5c blk & sal pink .15 .25
B193 SP71 80c + 20c ultra & yel .15 .25
B194 SP71 1.20fr + 30c ultra & gray .20 .40
B195 SP71 2fr + 25c blk & buff .15 .25
B196 SP71 4fr + 50c ultra & lt bl 1.10 *3.25*
B197 SP71 7fr + 3.45fr ultra & pale vio 3.00 *8.75*
Nos. B192-B197 (6) 4.75 *13.15*
Set, never hinged 13.00

1957, Dec. 4 Unwmk. *Perf. 11½*

25c+5c, 2fr+25c, Luxembourg. 80c+20c, 4fr+50c, Mersch. 1.20fr+30c, 7fr+3.45fr, Vianden.

Arms in Original Colors

B198 SP71 25c + 5c ultra & org .15 .22
B199 SP71 80c + 20c blk & lem .15 .22
B200 SP71 1.20fr + 30c ultra & lt bl grn .22 .32
B201 SP71 2fr + 25c ultra & pale brn .15 .22
B202 SP71 4fr + 50c blk & pale vio bl .45 .70
B203 SP71 7fr + 3.45fr ultra & rose lil 3.00 4.50
Nos. B198-B203 (6) 4.12 6.18
Set, never hinged 9.00

1958, Dec. 3 *Perf. 11½*

30c+10c, 2.50fr+50c, Capellen. 1fr+25c, 5fr+50c, Diekirch. 1.50fr+25c, 8.50fr+4.60fr, Redange.

Arms in Original Colors

B204 SP71 30c + 10c blk & pink .15 .15
B205 SP71 1fr + 25c ultra & buff .15 .15
B206 SP71 1.50fr + 25c ultra & pale grn .15 .24
B207 SP71 2.50fr + 50c blk & gray .15 .15
B208 SP71 5fr + 50c ultra .40 .60
B209 SP71 8.50fr + 4.60fr ultra & lil 2.25 *4.75*
Nos. B204-B209 (6) 3.25 *6.04*
Set, never hinged 7.50

1959, Dec. 2

30c+10c, 2.50fr+50c, Clervaux. 1fr+25c, 5fr+50c, Remich. 1.50fr+25c, 8.50fr+4.60fr, Wiltz.

Arms in Original Colors

B210 SP71 30c + 10c ultra & pink .15 .15
B211 SP71 1fr + 25c ultra & pale lem .15 .15
B212 SP71 1.50fr + 25c blk & pale grn .15 .20
B213 SP71 2.50fr + 50c ultra & pale fawn .15 .15
B214 SP71 5fr + 50c ultra & lt bl .40 .75
B215 SP71 8.50fr + 4.60fr blk & pale vio 1.90 *3.75*
Nos. B210-B215 (6) 2.90 *5.15*
Set, never hinged 8.00

Catalogue values for unused stamps in this section, from this point to the end of the section, are for Never Hinged items.

Princess Marie-Astrid
SP72

Prince Jean
SP73

1fr+25c, 5fr+50c, Princess in party dress. 1.50fr+25c, 8.50fr+4.60fr, Princess with book.

1960, Dec. 5 Photo. *Perf. 11½*

B216 SP72 30c + 10c brn & lt bl .15 .15
B217 SP72 1fr + 25c brn & pink .15 .15
B218 SP72 1.50fr + 25c brn & lt bl .25 .25
B219 SP72 2.50fr + 50c brn & yel .20 .20
B220 SP72 5fr + 50c brn & pale lil 1.65 1.65
B221 SP72 8.50fr + 4.60fr brn & pale ol 6.00 6.00
Nos. B216-B221 (6) 8.40 8.40

Type of 1960

Prince Henri: 30c+10c, 2.50fr+50c, Infant in long dress. 1fr+25c, 5fr+50c, Informal portrait. 1.50fr+25c, 8.50fr+ 4.60fr, In dress suit.

1961, Dec. 4 Unwmk. *Perf. 11½*

B222 SP72 30c + 10c brn & brt pink .15 .15
B223 SP72 1fr + 25c brn & lt vio .15 .15
B224 SP72 1.50fr + 25c brn & sal .15 .15
B225 SP72 2.50fr + 50c brn & pale grn .35 .35
B226 SP72 5fr + 50c brn & cit .90 .90
B227 SP72 8.50fr + 4.60fr brn & gray 5.00 5.00
Nos. B222-B227 (6) 6.70 6.70

1962, Dec. 3 Photo. *Perf. 11½*

Designs: Different portraits of the twins Prince Jean and Princess Margaretha. Nos. B228 and B233 are horizontal.

Inscriptions and Portraits in Dark Brown

B228 SP73 30c + 10c org yel .15 .15
B229 SP73 1fr + 25c lt bl .15 .15
B230 SP73 1.50fr + 25c pale ol .25 .25
B231 SP73 2.50fr + 50c rose .25 .25
B232 SP73 5fr + 50c lt yel grn .45 .45
B233 SP73 8.50fr + 4.60fr lil gray 3.00 3.00
Nos. B228-B233 (6) 4.25 4.25

St. Roch, Patron of Bakers — SP74

Three Towers — SP75

Patron Saints: 1fr+25c, St. Anne, tailors. 2fr+25c, St. Eloi, smiths. 3fr+50c, St. Michael, shopkeepers. 6fr+50c, St. Bartholomew, butchers. St. Theobald, seven crafts.

1963, Dec. 2 Unwmk. *Perf. 11½*

Multicolored Design

B234 SP74 50c + 10c pale lil .15 .15
B235 SP74 1fr + 25c tan .15 .15
B236 SP74 2fr + 25c lt grnsh bl .15 .15
B237 SP74 3fr + 50c lt bl .20 .25
B238 SP74 6fr + 50c buff .95 .80
B239 SP74 10fr + 5.90fr pale yel grn 1.10 .95
Nos. B234-B239 (6) 2.70 2.45

1964, Dec. 7 Photo. *Perf. 11½*

Children's paintings: 1fr+25c, 6fr+50c, Grand Duke Adolphe Bridge, horiz. 2fr+25c, 10fr+5.90fr, The Lower City.

B240 SP75 50c + 10c multi .15 .15
B241 SP75 1fr + 25c multi .15 .15
B242 SP75 2fr + 25c multi .20 .30
a. Value omitted 300.00
B243 SP75 3fr + 50c multi .20 .30
B244 SP75 6fr + 50c multi 1.00 1.50
B245 SP75 10fr + 5.90fr multi 1.10 1.50
Nos. B240-B245 (6) 2.80 3.90

The Roman Lady of Titelberg — SP76

Fairy Tales of Luxembourg: 1fr+25c, Schäppchen, the Huntsman. 2fr+25c, The Witch of Koerich. 3fr+50c, The Gnomes of Schoenfels. 6fr+50c, Tollchen, Watchman of Hesperange. 10fr+5.90fr, The Old Spinster of Heispelt.

1965, Dec. 6 Photo. *Perf. 11½*

B246 SP76 50c + 10c multi .15 .15
B247 SP76 1fr + 25c multi .15 .15
B248 SP76 2fr + 25c multi .15 .15
B249 SP76 3fr + 50c multi .15 .20
B250 SP76 6fr + 50c multi .50 .90
B251 SP76 10fr + 5.90fr multi .85 1.40
Nos. B246-B251 (6) 1.95 2.95

Fairy Tale Type of 1965

Fairy Tales of Luxembourg: 50c+10c, The Veiled Matron of Wormeldange. 1.50fr+25c, Jekel, Warden of the Wark. 2fr+25c, The Black Man of Vianden. 3fr+50c, The Gracious Fairy of Rosport. 6fr+1fr, The Friendly Shepherd of Donkolz. 13fr+6.90fr, The Little Sisters of Trois-Vièrges.

1966, Dec. 6 Photo. *Perf. 11½*

B252 SP76 50c + 10c multi .15 .15
B253 SP76 1.50fr + 25c multi .15 .15
B254 SP76 2fr + 25c multi .15 .15
B255 SP76 3fr + 50c multi .15 .30
B256 SP76 6fr + 1fr multi .30 .60
B257 SP76 13fr + 6.90fr multi .85 1.90
Nos. B252-B257 (6) 1.75 3.25

Prince Guillaume
SP77

Castle of Berg
SP78

Portraits: 1.50fr+25c, Princess Margaretha. 2fr+25c, Prince Jean. 3fr+50c, Prince Henri as Boy Scout. 6fr+1fr, Princess Marie-Astrid.

1967, Dec. 6 Photo. *Perf. 11½*

B258 SP77 50c + 10c yel & brn .15 .15
B259 SP77 1.50fr + 25c gray bl & brn .15 .15
B260 SP77 2fr + 25c pale rose & brn .15 .15
B261 SP77 3fr + 50c lt ol & brn .35 .60

B262 SP77 6fr + 1fr lt vio & brn .45 .60
B263 SP78 13fr + 6.90fr multi .60 1.40
Nos. B258-B263 (6) 1.85 3.05

Medico-professional Institute at Cap — SP79

Deaf-mute Child Imitating Bird — SP80

Handicapped Children: 2fr+25c, Blind child holding candle. 3fr+50c, Nurse supporting physically handicapped child. 6fr+1fr, Cerebral palsy victim. 13fr+6.90fr, Mentally disturbed child.

1968, Dec. 5 Photo. *Perf. 11½*

Designs and Inscriptions in Dark Brown

B264 SP79 50c + 10c lt bl .15 .15
B265 SP80 1.50fr + 25c lt grn .15 .15
B266 SP80 2fr + 25c yel .15 .15
B267 SP80 3fr + 50c bl .20 .30
B268 SP80 6fr + 1fr buff .50 1.10
B269 SP80 13fr + 6.90fr pink .75 1.50
Nos. B264-B269 (6) 1.90 3.35

Vianden Castle SP81

Children of Bethlehem SP82

Luxembourg Castles: 1.50fr+25c, Lucilinburhuc. 2fr+25c, Bourglinster. 3fr+50c, Hollenfels. 6fr+1fr, Ansembourg. 13fr+6.90fr, Beaufort.

1969, Dec. 8 Photo. *Perf. 11½*

B270 SP81 50c + 10c multi .15 .15
B271 SP81 1.50fr + 25c multi .15 .15
B272 SP81 2fr + 25c multi .15 .15
B273 SP81 3fr + 50c multi .15 .30
B274 SP81 6fr + 1fr multi .60 1.00
B275 SP81 13fr + 6.90fr multi .85 1.50
Nos. B270-B275 (6) 2.05 3.25

1970, Dec. 7 Photo. *Perf. 11½*

Luxembourg Castles: 50c+10c, Clervaux. 1.50fr+25c, Septfontaines. 2fr+25c, Bourscheid. 3fr+50c, Esch-sur-Sure. 6fr+1fr, Larochette. 13fr+6.90fr, Brandenbourg.

B276 SP81 50c + 10c multi .15 .15
B277 SP81 1.50fr + 25c multi .15 .15
B278 SP81 2fr + 25c multi .15 .15
B279 SP81 3fr + 50c multi .15 .30
B280 SP81 6fr + 1fr multi .60 1.00
B281 SP81 13fr + 6.90fr multi .85 1.75
Nos. B276-B281 (6) 2.05 3.50

The surtax on Nos. B180-B281 was for charitable purposes.

1971, Dec. 6 Photo. *Perf. 11½*

Wooden Statues from Crèche of Beaufort Church: 1.50fr+25c, Shepherds. 3fr+50c, Nativity. 8fr+1fr, Herdsmen. 18fr+6.50fr, King offering gift.

Sculptures in Shades of Brown

B282 SP82 1fr + 25c lilac .15 .15
B283 SP82 1.50fr + 25c olive .15 .15
B284 SP82 3fr + 50c gray .20 .35
B285 SP82 8fr + 1fr lt ultra 1.10 1.50
B286 SP82 18fr + 6.50fr grn 1.90 4.00
Nos. B282-B286 (5) 3.50 6.15

The surtax was for various charitable organizations.

Angel — SP83

Sts. Anne and Joachim — SP84

Stained Glass Windows, Luxembourg Cathedral: 1.50fr+25c, St. Joseph. 3fr+50c, Virgin and Child. 8fr+1fr, People of Bethlehem. 18fr+6.50fr, Angel facing left.

1972, Dec. 4

B287 SP83 1fr + 25c multi .15 .15
B288 SP83 1.50fr + 25c multi .15 .15
B289 SP83 3fr + 50c multi .15 .15
B290 SP83 8fr + 1fr multi .95 1.00
B291 SP83 18fr + 6.50fr multi 2.25 3.75
Nos. B287-B291 (5) 3.65 5.20

Surtax was for charitable purposes.

1973, Dec. 5 Photo. *Perf. 11½*

Sculptures: 3fr+25c, Mary meeting Elizabeth. 4fr+50c, Virgin and Child and a King. 8fr+1fr, Shepherds. 15fr+7fr, St. Joseph holding candle. Designs from 16th century reredos, Hermitage of Hachiville.

B292 SP84 1fr + 25c multi .15 .15
B293 SP84 3fr + 25c multi .15 .20
B294 SP84 4fr + 50c multi .25 .70
B295 SP84 8fr + 1fr multi 1.10 2.00
B296 SP84 15fr + 7fr multi 1.90 3.75
Nos. B292-B296 (5) 3.55 6.80

Annunciation SP85

Crucifixion SP86

Designs: 3fr+25c, Visitation. 4fr+50c, Nativity. 8fr+1fr, Adoration of the King. 15fr+7fr, Presentation at the Temple. Designs of Nos. B297-B301 are from miniatures in the "Codex Aureus Epternacensis" (Gospel from Echternach Abbey). The Crucifixion is from the carved ivory cover of the Codex, by the Master of Echternach, c. 983-991.

1974, Dec. 5 Photo. *Perf. 11½*

B297 SP85 1fr + 25c multi .15 .15
B298 SP85 3fr + 25c multi .15 .18
B299 SP85 4fr + 50c multi .20 .35
B300 SP85 8fr + 1fr multi 1.10 1.75
B301 SP85 15fr + 7fr multi 1.75 2.75
Nos. B297-B301 (5) 3.35 5.18

Souvenir Sheet

Photogravure & Engraved

Perf. 13½

B302 SP86 20fr + 10fr multi 3.50 5.00

50th anniversary of Caritas issues. No. B302 contains one 34x42mm stamp.

Fly Orchid — SP87

Lilies of the Valley — SP88

Flowers: 3fr+25c, Pyramidal orchid. 4fr+50c, Marsh hellebore. 8fr+1fr, Pasqueflower. 15fr+7fr, Bee orchid.

1975, Dec. 4 Photo. *Perf. 11½*

B303 SP87 1fr + 25c multi .15 .15
B304 SP87 3fr + 25c multi .20 .25
B305 SP87 4fr + 50c multi .25 .35
B306 SP87 8fr + 1fr multi 1.00 1.40
B307 SP87 15fr + 7fr multi 2.25 3.00
Nos. B303-B307 (5) 3.85 5.15

The surtax on Nos. B303-B317 was for various charitable organizations.

1976, Dec. 6

Flowers: 2fr+25c, Gentian. 5fr+25c, Narcissus. 6fr+50c, Red hellebore. 12fr+1fr, Late spider orchid. 20fr+8fr, Two-leafed squill.

B308 SP87 2fr + 25c multi .15 .15
B309 SP87 5fr + 25c multi .25 .30
B310 SP87 6fr + 50c multi .30 .60
B311 SP87 12fr + 1fr multi .65 1.10
B312 SP87 20fr + 8fr multi 2.00 2.75
Nos. B308-B312 (5) 3.35 4.90

1977, Dec. 5 Photo. *Perf. 11½*

Flowers: 5fr+25c, Columbine. 6fr+50c, Mezereon. 12fr+1fr, Early spider orchid. 20fr+8fr, Spotted orchid.

B313 SP88 2fr + 25c multi .15 .15
B314 SP88 5fr + 25c multi .15 .20
B315 SP88 6fr + 50c multi .25 .40
B316 SP88 12fr + 1fr multi .95 1.75
B317 SP88 20fr + 8fr multi 1.90 2.75
Nos. B313-B317 (5) 3.40 5.25

St. Matthew — SP89

Spring — SP90

Behind-glass Paintings, 19th Century: 5fr+25c, St. Mark. 6fr+50c, Nativity. 12fr+1fr, St. Luke. 20fr+8fr, St. John.

1978, Dec. 5 Photo. *Perf. 11½*

B318 SP89 2fr + 25c multi .15 .15
B319 SP89 5fr + 25c multi .25 .32
B320 SP89 6fr + 50c multi .25 .35
B321 SP89 12fr + 1fr multi .65 .90
B322 SP89 20fr + 8fr multi 1.90 2.50
Nos. B318-B322 (5) 3.20 4.22

Surtax was for charitable organizations.

1979, Dec. 5 Photo. *Perf. 12*

Behind-glass Paintings, 19th Century: 5fr+25c, Summer. 6fr+50c, Charity. 12fr+1fr, Autumn. 20fr+8fr, Winter.

B323 SP90 2fr + 25c multi .15 .15
B324 SP90 5fr + 25c multi .25 .25
B325 SP90 6fr + 50c multi .30 .30
B326 SP90 12fr + 1fr multi .85 .85
B327 SP90 20fr + 8fr multi 1.75 1.75
Nos. B323-B327 (5) 3.30 3.30

St. Martin — SP91

Behind-glass Paintings, 19th Century: 6fr+50c, St. Nicholas. 8fr+1fr, Madonna and Child. 30fr+1fr, St. George the Martyr.

1980, Dec. 5 Photo. *Perf. 11½*

B328 SP91 4fr + 50c multi .20 .20
B329 SP91 6fr + 50c multi .25 .25
B330 SP91 8fr + 1fr multi .45 .45
B331 SP91 30fr + 10fr multi 1.75 1.75
Nos. B328-B331 (4) 2.65 2.65

Surtax was for charitable organizations.

Arms of Petange SP92

Nativity, by Otto van Veen (1556-1629) SP93

1981, Dec. 4 Photo.

Granite Paper

B332 SP92 4fr + 50c shown .25 .30
B333 SP92 6fr + 50c Larochette .30 .35
B334 SP93 8fr + 1fr shown .50 .60
B335 SP92 16fr + 2fr Stadtbredimus .90 1.10
B336 SP92 35fr + 12fr Weiswampach 2.25 2.75
Nos. B332-B336 (5) 4.20 5.10

Surtax was for charitable organizations.

1982, Dec. 6 Photo. *Perf. 11½*

Design: 8fr+1fr, Adoration of the Shepherds, stained-glass window, by Gust Zanter, Hoscheid Parish Church.

Granite Paper

B337 SP92 4fr + 50c Bettembourg .25 .25
B338 SP92 6fr + 50c Frisange .35 .35
B339 SP93 8fr + 1fr multi .45 .45
B340 SP92 16fr + 2fr Mamer .90 .90
B341 SP92 35fr + 12fr Heinerscheid 2.25 2.25
Nos. B337-B341 (5) 4.20 4.20

Surtax was for charitable organizations.

1983, Dec. 5 Photo.

B342 SP92 4fr + 1fr Winseler .20 .20
B343 SP92 7fr + 1fr Beckerich .40 .40
B344 SP93 10fr + 1fr Nativity .50 .50
B345 SP92 16fr + 2fr Feulen .85 .85
B346 SP92 40fr + 13fr Mertert 3.00 3.00
Nos. B342-B346 (5) 4.95 4.95

Surtax was for charitable organizations.

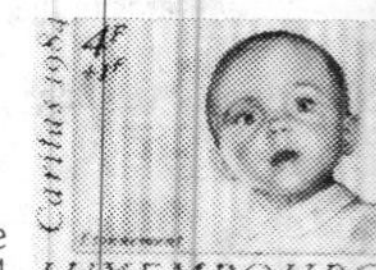
Inquisitive Child — SP94

Children Exhibiting Various Moods.

1984, Dec. 5 Photo.

B347 SP94 4fr + 1fr shown .20 .20
B348 SP94 7fr + 1fr Daydreaming .45 .45
B349 SP94 10fr + 1fr Nativity .55 .55
B350 SP94 16fr + 2fr Sulking .95 .95
B351 SP94 40fr + 13fr Admiring 3.25 3.25
Nos. B347-B351 (5) 5.40 5.40

Surtax was for charitable organizations.

1985, Dec. 5 Photo.

B352 SP94 4fr + 1fr Girl drawing .20 .20
B353 SP94 7fr + 1fr Two boys .30 .30
B354 SP94 10fr + 1fr Adoration of the Magi .40 .40
B355 SP94 16fr + 2fr Fairy tale characters 1.00 1.00
B356 SP94 40fr + 13fr Embarrassed girl 2.75 2.75
Nos. B352-B356 (5) 4.65 4.65

Surtax was for charitable organizations.

SP95

SP96

Book of Hours, France, c. 1550, Natl. Library — SP97

Christmas: illuminated text.

1986, Dec. 8 Photo. *Perf. 11½*

B357 SP95 6fr + 1fr Annunciation .45 .45
B358 SP95 10fr + 1fr Angel appears to the Shepherds .55 .55
B359 SP95 12fr + 2fr Nativity .70 .70
B360 SP95 18fr + 2fr Adoration of the Magi 1.00 1.00
B361 SP95 20fr + 8fr Flight into Egypt 1.40 1.40
Nos. B357-B361 (5) 4.10 4.10

1987, Dec. 1 *Perf. 12*

B362 SP96 6fr + 1fr Annunciation .40 .40
B363 SP96 10fr + 1fr Visitation .65 .65
B364 SP96 12fr + 2fr Adoration of the Magi .85 .85
B365 SP96 18fr + 2fr Presentation in the Temple 1.15 1.15
B366 SP96 20fr + 8fr Flight into Egypt 1.60 1.60
Nos. B362-B366 (5) 4.65 4.65

1988, Dec. 5 *Perf. 11½*

B367 SP97 9fr +1fr Annunciation to the Shepherds .55 .55
B368 SP97 12fr +2fr Adoration of the Magi .75 .75

B369 SP97 18fr +2fr Virgin and Child 1.10 1.10
B370 SP97 20fr +8fr Pentecost 1.50 1.50
Nos. B367-B370 (4) 3.90 3.90

Surtax for charitable organizations.

Christmas SP98

Chapels: No. B371, St. Lambert and St. Blase, Fennange, vert. No. B372, St. Quirinus, Luxembourg. No. B373, St. Anthony the Hermit, Reisdorf, vert. No. B374, The Hermitage, Hachiville.

1989, Dec. 11 Photo. *Perf. 12x11½*

B371 SP98 9fr +1fr multi .50 .50
B372 SP98 12fr +2fr multi .70 .70
B373 SP98 18fr +3fr multi 1.10 1.10
B374 SP98 25fr +8fr multi 1.65 1.65
Nos. B371-B374 (4) 3.95 3.95

Surtax for social work.

1990, Nov. 26 Photo. *Perf. 11½*

Chapels: No. B375, Congregation of the Blessed Virgin Mary, Vianden, vert. No. B376, Our Lady, Echternach. No. B377, Our Lady, Consoler of the Afflicted, Grentzingen. B378, St. Pirmin, Kaundorf, vert.

B375 SP98 9fr +1fr multi .60 .60
B376 SP98 12fr +2fr multi .85 .85
B377 SP98 18fr +3fr multi 1.25 1.25
B378 SP98 25fr +8fr multi 2.00 2.00
Nos. B375-B378 (4) 4.70 4.70

Surtax for charitable organizations.

Chapels: No. B379, St. Donatus, Arsdorf, vert. No. B380, Our Lady of Sorrows, Brandenbourg. No. B381, Our Lady, Luxembourg. No. B382, The Hermitage, Wolwelange, vert.

1991, Dec. 9 Photo. *Perf. 11½*

B379 SP98 14fr +2fr multi .95 .95
B380 SP98 14fr +2fr multi .95 .95
B381 SP98 18fr +3fr multi 1.25 1.25
B382 SP98 22fr +7fr multi 1.75 1.75
Nos. B379-B382 (4) 4.90 4.90

Surtax used for philanthropic work.

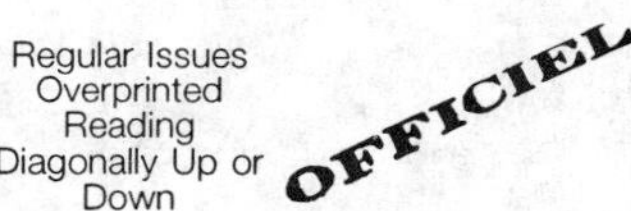

Endangered Birds — SP99

Designs: No. B383, Hazel grouse. No. B384, Golden oriole, vert. 18fr+3fr, Black stork. 22fr+7fr, Red kite, vert.

1992, Dec. 7 Photo. *Perf. 11½*

B383 SP99 14fr +2fr multi 1.00 1.00
B384 SP99 14fr +2fr multi 1.00 1.00
B385 SP99 18fr +3fr multi 1.25 1.25
B386 SP99 22fr +7fr multi 1.75 1.75
Nos. B383-B386 (4) 5.00 5.00

Surtax for Luxembourg charitable organizations.

1993, Dec. 6 Photo. *Perf. 11½*

Designs: No. B387, Snipe. No. B388, Kingfisher, vert. 18fr+3fr, Little ringed plover. 22fr+7fr, Sand martin, vert.

B387 SP99 14fr +2fr multi .90 .90
B388 SP99 14fr +2fr multi .90 .90
B389 SP99 18fr +3fr multi 1.25 1.25
B390 SP99 22fr +7fr multi 1.65 1.65
Nos. B387-B390 (4) 4.70 4.70

Surtax for Luxembourg charitable organizations.

1994, Sept. 19 Photo. *Perf. 11½*

Designs: No. B391, Partridge. No. B392, Stonechat, vert. 18fr+3fr, Blue-headed wagtail. 22fr+7fr, Great grey shrike, vert.

B391 SP99 14fr +2fr multi 1.00 1.00
B392 SP99 14fr +2fr multi 1.00 1.00
B393 SP99 18fr +3fr multi 1.25 1.25
B394 SP99 22fr +7fr multi 1.90 1.90
Nos. B383-B394 (12) 14.85 14.85

Christmas SP100 — Trees SP101

Design: 16fr + 2fr, Stained glass window, parish church of Alzingen.

1995, Dec. 4 Photo. *Perf. 11½*

B395 SP100 16fr +2fr multi 1.25 1.25

Surtax for Luxembourg charitable organizations.

1995, Dec. 4

Designs: No. B396, Tilia platyphyllos. No. B397, Aesculus hippocastanum, horiz. 20fr+3fr, Quercus pedunculata, horiz. 32fr+7fr, Betula pendula.

B396 SP101 16fr +2fr multi 1.25 1.25
B397 SP101 16fr +2fr multi 1.25 1.25
B398 SP101 20fr +3fr multi 1.50 1.50
B399 SP101 32fr +7fr multi 2.75 2.75
Nos. B396-B399 (4) 6.75 6.75

Surtax for Luxembourg charitable organizations.
See Nos. B400-B403, B405-B408.

1996, Dec. 9

Designs: No. B400, Fraxinus excelsior. No. B401, Salix SSP, horiz. 20fr+3fr, Sorbus domestica, horiz. 32fr+7fr, Fagus silvatica.

B400 SP101 16fr +2fr multi 1.00 1.00
B401 SP101 16fr +2fr multi 1.00 1.00
B402 SP101 20fr +3fr multi 1.30 1.30
B403 SP101 32fr +7fr multi 2.20 2.20
Nos. B400-B403 (4) 5.50 5.50

Surtax for Luxembourg charitable organizations.

Christmas SP102

1996, Dec. 9

B404 SP102 16fr +2fr multi 1.00 1.00

Surtax for Luxembourg charitable organizations.

Tree Type of 1995

Designs: No. B405, Ulmus glabra. No. B406, Acer platanoides. 20fr+3fr, Prunus avium. 32fr+7fr, Juglans regia, horiz.

1997, Dec. 8 Photo. *Perf. 11½*

B405 SP101 16fr +2fr multi 1.00 1.00
B406 SP101 16fr +2fr multi 1.00 1.00
B407 SP101 20fr +3fr multi 1.25 1.25
B408 SP101 32fr +7fr multi 2.25 2.25
Nos. B405-B408 (4) 5.50 5.50

Christmas SP103

1997, Dec. 8

B409 SP103 16fr +2fr multi 1.00 1.00

AIR POST STAMPS

Airplane over Luxembourg AP1

1931-33 Unwmk. Engr. *Perf. 12½*

C1 AP1 50c green ('33) .50 *1.10*
C2 AP1 75c dark brown .35 .80
C3 AP1 1fr red .35 .80
C4 AP1 1¼fr dark violet .35 .80
C5 AP1 1¾fr dark blue .35 .80
C6 AP1 3fr gray black ('33) .50 *1.65*
Nos. C1-C6 (6) 2.40 *5.95*
Set, never hinged 6.00

Air View of Mosel River AP2

Wing and View of Luxembourg AP3

Vianden Castle — AP4

1946, June 7 Photo. *Perf. 11½*

C7 AP2 1fr dk ol grn & gray .15 .15
C8 AP3 2fr chnt brn & buff .15 .15
C9 AP4 3fr sepia & brown .15 .15
C10 AP2 4fr dp vio & gray vio .15 .25
C11 AP3 5fr dp mag & buff .15 .25
C12 AP4 6fr dk brown & gray .15 .35
C13 AP2 10fr henna brn & buff .90 .35
C14 AP3 20fr dk blue & cream .90 1.50
C15 AP4 50fr dk green & gray 1.75 1.50
Nos. C7-C15 (9) 4.45 4.65
Set, never hinged 9.00

1852 and 1952 AP5

1952, May 24

Stamps in Gray and Dark Violet Brown

C16 AP5 80c olive grn .35 .50
C17 AP5 2.50fr brt car .75 1.25
C18 AP5 4fr brt blue 1.50 2.75
C19 AP5 8fr brown red 27.50 *50.00*
C20 AP5 10fr dull brown 20.00 *42.50*
Nos. C16-C20 (5) 50.10 *97.00*
Set, never hinged 90.00

Centenary of Luxembourg's postage stamps. Nos. C16-C18 were available at face, but complete sets sold for 45.30fr, which included admission to the CENTILUX exhibition.

POSTAGE DUE STAMPS

Coat of Arms — D1

1907 Unwmk. Typo. *Perf. 12½*

J1 D1 5c green & black .15 .15
J2 D1 10c green & black 2.50 .18
J3 D1 12½c green & black .60 .70
J4 D1 20c green & black .60 .45
J5 D1 25c green & black 24.00 1.40
J6 D1 50c green & black .60 1.40
J7 D1 1fr green & black .30 *1.10*
Nos. J1-J7 (7) 28.75 5.38

See Nos. J10-J22.

Nos. J3, J5 Surcharged

1920

J8 D1 15c on 12½c 2.75 2.25
J9 D1 30c on 25c 2.75 3.00

Arms Type of 1907

1921-35

J10 D1 5c green & red .30 .30
J11 D1 10c green & red .30 .30
J12 D1 20c green & red .45 .30
J13 D1 25c green & red .45 .30
J14 D1 30c green & red .50 .55
J15 D1 35c green & red ('35) 1.10 .30
J16 D1 50c green & red .50 .55
J17 D1 60c green & red ('28) .85 .30
J18 D1 70c green & red ('35) 1.10 .30
J19 D1 75c green & red ('30) .85 .25
J20 D1 1fr green & red .65 .70
J21 D1 2fr green & red ('30) 1.50 2.00
J22 D1 3fr green & red ('30) 3.50 5.50
Nos. J10-J22 (13) 12.05 11.65
Set, never hinged 25.00

D2

D3

1946-48 Photo. *Perf. 11½*

J23 D2 5c bright green .15 .25
J24 D2 10c bright green .15 .25
J25 D2 20c bright green .15 .25
J26 D2 30c bright green .15 .25
J27 D2 50c bright green .15 .25
J28 D2 70c bright green .15 .50
J29 D2 75c brt green ('48) .65 .25
J30 D3 1fr carmine .15 .25
J31 D3 1.50fr carmine .15 .25
J32 D3 2fr carmine .15 .25
J33 D3 3fr carmine .18 .25
J34 D3 5fr carmine .50 .40
J35 D3 10fr carmine .85 1.00
J36 D3 20fr carmine 2.50 5.00
Nos. J23-J36 (14) 6.03 9.40
Set, never hinged 12.00

OFFICIAL STAMPS

Forged overprints on Nos. O1-O64 abound.

Regular Issues Overprinted Reading Diagonally Up or Down

OFFICIEL

Frankfort Print

Rouletted in Color except 2c

1875 Unwmk.

O1 A2 1c red brown 15.00 30.00
O2 A2 2c black 15.00 30.00
O3 A3 10c lilac 1,200. 900.00
O4 A3 12½c rose 350.00 450.00
O5 A3 20c gray brn 25.00 30.00
O6 A3 25c blue 150.00 100.00
O7 A3 25c ultra 1,000. 800.00
O8 A3 30c lilac rose 26.00 *60.00*
O9 A3 40c pale org 135.00 160.00
a. 40c org red, thick paper 140.00 150.00
c. As "a," thin paper 1,000. 825.00
O10 A4 1fr on 37½c bis 95.00 15.00

Double overprints exist on Nos. O1-O6, O8-O10.
Overprints reading diagonally down sell for more.

Inverted Overprint

O1a A2 1c 110.00 160.00
O2a A2 2c 110.00 175.00
O3a A3 10c 1,600. 1,600.
O4a A3 12½c 500.00 550.00
O5a A3 20c 25.00 32.50
O6a A3 25c 725.00 725.00
O7a A3 25c 1,600. 1,350.
O8a A3 30c 360.00 450.00
O9b A3 40c pale orange 175.00 225.00
O10a A4 1fr on 37½c 140.00 35.00

Luxembourg Print

1875-76 *Perf. 13*

O11 A2 1c red brown 10.00 20.00
O12 A2 2c black 12.50 20.00
O13 A2 4c green 90.00 175.00
O14 A2 5c yellow 50.00 90.00
a. 5c orange yellow 55.00 90.00
O15 A3 10c gray lilac 75.00 90.00
O16 A3 12½c rose 65.00 37.50
O17 A3 12½c lilac rose 140.00 125.00
O18 A3 25c blue 6.75 *35.00*
O19 A5 1fr on 37½c bis 37.50 60.00
Nos. O11-O19 (9) 486.75 652.50

Double overprints exist on Nos. O11-O15.

Inverted Overprint

O11a A2 1c 40.00 *85.00*
O12a A2 2c 135.00 175.00
O13a A2 4c 150.00 200.00
O14b A2 5c 450.00 600.00
O15a A3 10c 140.00 175.00
O16a A3 12½c 350.00 475.00
O17a A3 12½c 350.00 475.00

O18a	A3	25c	110.00	150.00
O19a	A5	1fr on 37½c	175.00	250.00
		Nos. O11a-O19a (9)	1,900.	2,585.

Haarlem Print

1880 ***Perf. 11½x12, 12½x12, 13½***

O22	A3	25c blue	3.00	4.00

Overprinted OFFICIEL

Frankfort Print

1878 ***Rouletted in Color***

O23	A2	1c red brown	80.00	95.00
O25	A3	20c gray brn	125.00	125.00
O26	A3	30c lilac rose	525.00	500.00
O27	A3	40c orange	225.00	300.00
O28	A4	1fr on 37½c bis	400.00	90.00
		Nos. O23-O28 (5)	1,355.	1,110.

Inverted Overprint

O23a	A2	1c	275.00	350.00
O25a	A3	20c	275.00	350.00
O26a	A3	30c	800.00	650.00
O27a	A3	40c	800.00	800.00
O28a	A4	1fr on 37½c	625.00	135.00

Luxembourg Print

1878-80 ***Perf. 13***

O29	A2	1c red brown	575.00	675.00
O30	A2	2c black	150.00	200.00
O31	A2	4c green	165.00	165.00
O32	A2	5c yellow	350.00	350.00
O33	A3	10c gray lilac	350.00	375.00
O34	A3	12½c rose	65.00	75.00
O35	A3	25c blue	475.00	575.00
		Nos. O29-O35 (7)	2,130.	2,415.

Inverted Overprint

O29a	A2	1c	90.00	140.00
O30a	A2	2c	13.00	20.00
O31a	A2	4c	100.00	125.00
O32a	A2	5c		
O33a	A3	10c	75.00	85.00
O34a	A3	12½c	425.00	500.00
O35a	A3	25c	650.00	750.00

Overprinted **S. P.**

Frankfort Print

1881 ***Rouletted in Color***

O39	A3	40c orange	30.00	57.50
a.		Inverted overprint	185.00	250.00

"S.P." are initials of "Service Public."

Luxembourg Print
Perf. 13

O40	A2	1c red brown	125.00	150.00
O41	A2	4c green	190.00	185.00
a.		Inverted overprint	225.00	
O42	A2	5c yellow	475.00	450.00
O43	A5	1fr on 37½c bis	24.00	35.00
		Nos. O40-O43 (4)	814.00	820.00

Haarlem Print
Perf. 11½x12, 12½x12, 13½

O44	A2	1c yellow brn	6.75	8.00
O45	A2	2c black	8.00	8.00
O46	A2	5c yellow	110.00	140.00
a.		Inverted overprint	200.00	
O47	A3	10c gray lilac	110.00	140.00
O48	A3	12½c rose	200.00	225.00
O49	A3	20c gray brown	60.00	85.00
O50	A3	25c blue	65.00	85.00
O51	A3	30c dull rose	67.50	90.00
		Nos. O44-O51 (8)	627.25	781.00

Stamps of the 1881 issue with overprint of type "d" were never issued.

Overprinted
S. P.
d

Perf. 11½x12, 12½x12, 12½, 13½
1882

O52	A6	1c gray lilac	.40	.45
a.		"S" omitted		
O53	A6	2c ol gray	.40	.45
O54	A6	4c ol bister	.60	.60
O55	A6	5c lt green	1.00	.75
O56	A6	10c rose	20.00	18.00
O57	A6	12½c slate	3.50	2.75
O58	A6	20c orange	3.50	2.75
O59	A6	25c ultra	25.00	25.00
O60	A6	30c gray grn	7.50	9.00
O61	A6	50c bis brown	1.25	2.00
O62	A6	1fr pale vio	1.25	2.00
O63	A6	5fr brown org	19.00	22.50
		Nos. O52-O63 (12)	83.40	86.25

Nos. O52-O63 exist without one or both periods, also with varying space between "S" and "P." Nine denominations exist with double overprint, six with inverted overprint.

Overprinted **S. P.**

1883 ***Perf. 13½***

O64	A6	5fr brown org	*1,600.*	*1,200.*

Overprinted **S. P.**

Perf. 11, 11½, 11½x11, 12½
1891-93

O65	A7	10c carmine	.32	.30
a.		Sheet of 25	60.00	
O66	A7	12½c slate grn	8.00	5.50
O67	A7	20c orange	12.00	6.50
O68	A7	25c blue	.40	.35
a.		Sheet of 25	75.00	
O69	A7	30c olive grn	9.00	7.50
O70	A7	37½c green	9.00	9.00
O71	A7	50c brown	11.00	9.00
O72	A7	1fr dp vio	11.00	10.00
O73	A7	2½fr black	35.00	62.50
O74	A7	5fr lake	25.00	37.50
		Nos. O65-O74 (10)	120.72	148.15

1895 ***Perf. 12½***

O75	A8	1c pearl gray	1.50	1.75
O76	A8	2c gray brn	1.50	1.75
O77	A8	4c olive bis	1.50	1.75
O78	A8	5c green	3.50	4.00
O79	A8	10c carmine	42.50	32.50
		Nos. O75-O79 (5)	50.50	41.75

Nos. O66-O79 exist without overprint and perforated "OFFICIEL" through the stamp. Value for set, $25.

Nos. O65a and O68a were issued to commemorate the coronation of Duke Adolphe.

Regular Issue of 1906-26 Overprinted *Officiel*

1908-26 ***Perf. 11x11½, 12½***

O80	A9	1c gray	.15	.18
a.		Inverted overprint	110.00	
O81	A9	2c olive brn	.15	.16
O82	A9	4c bister	.15	.16
a.		Double overprint	125.00	
O83	A9	5c green	.15	.16
O84	A9	5c lilac ('26)	.15	.20
O85	A9	6c violet	.15	.16
O86	A9	7½c org ('19)	.15	.16
O87	A10	10c scarlet	.24	.32
O88	A10	12½c slate grn	.24	.32
O89	A10	15c orange brn	.35	.42
O90	A10	20c orange	.35	.60
O91	A10	25c ultra	.35	.32
O92	A10	30c olive grn	3.50	3.75
O93	A10	37½c green	.60	.60
O94	A10	50c brown	1.00	1.10
O95	A10	87½c dk blue	2.50	2.50
O96	A10	1fr violet	3.50	3.25
O97	A10	2½fr vermilion	42.50	42.50
O98	A10	5fr claret	42.50	42.50
		Nos. O80-O98 (19)	98.68	99.36

On Regular Issue of 1914-17

1915-17

O99	A11	10c lake	.30	.40
O100	A11	12½c dull grn	.30	.40
O101	A11	15c olive blk	.30	.40
O102	A11	17½c dp brn ('17)	.30	.40
O103	A11	25c ultra	.30	.40
O104	A11	30c bister	.85	1.25
O105	A11	35c dk blue	.30	.40
O106	A11	37½c blk brn	.30	.40
O107	A11	40c orange	.40	.80
O108	A11	50c dk gray	.40	.80
O109	A11	62½c blue grn	.40	.80
O110	A11	87½c org ('17)	.40	.80
O111	A11	1fr orange brn	.40	.80
O112	A11	2½fr red	.40	.80
O113	A11	5fr dk violet	.40	.80
		Nos. O99-O113 (15)	5.75	9.65

On Regular Issues of 1921-26 in Black

1922-26 ***Perf. 11½, 11½x11, 12½***

O114	A12	2c brown	.15	.15
O115	A12	3c olive grn	.15	.15
O116	A12	6c violet	.15	.15
O117	A12	10c yellow grn	.15	.30
O118	A12	10c ol grn ('24)	.15	.30
O119	A12	15c brown ol	.15	.30
O120	A12	15c pale grn ('24)	.15	.30
O121	A12	15c dp org ('26)	.15	.25
O122	A12	20c dp orange	.15	.30
O123	A12	20c yel grn ('26)	.15	.25
O124	A12	25c dk green	.15	.30
O125	A12	30c car rose	.15	.30
O126	A12	40c brown org	.15	.30
O127	A12	50c dp blue	.20	.40
O128	A12	50c red ('24)	.15	.30
O129	A12	75c red	.20	.40
O130	A12	75c dp bl ('24)	.20	.40
O131	A12	80c black	4.25	10.00
O132	A13	1fr carmine	.35	.80
O133	A14	2fr indigo	2.75	6.00
O134	A14	2fr dk brn ('26)	1.65	4.50
O135	A15	5fr dk vio	16.00	37.50
		Nos. O114-O135 (22)	27.70	63.65

On Regular Issues of 1921-26 in Red
Perf. 11, 11½, 11½x11, 12½

1922-34

O136	A12	80c blk, perf. 11½	.15	.32
O137	A13	1fr dk bl, perf. 11½ ('26)	.22	.50
O138	A14	2fr ind, perf. 11½x11	.40	1.10
O139	A17	3fr dk bl & bl, perf. 11	2.50	2.50
a.		Perf. 11½	.80	1.25
b.		Perf. 12½	1.50	2.00
O140	A15	5fr dk vio, perf. 11½x11	3.50	6.75
a.		Perf. 12½ ('34)	25.00	25.00
O141	A16	10fr blk, perf. 11½	9.25	19.00
a.		Perf. 12½	25.00	25.00
		Nos. O136-O141 (6)	16.02	30.17

On Regular Issue of 1926-35

1926-27 ***Perf. 12***

O142	A18	5c dk violet	.15	.22
O143	A18	10c olive grn	.15	.22
O144	A18	20c orange	.15	.22
O145	A18	25c yellow grn	.15	.22
O146	A18	25c blk brn ('27)	.30	.48
O147	A18	30c yel grn ('27)	.60	1.00
O148	A18	40c olive gray	.15	.22
O149	A18	50c red brown	.15	.22
O150	A18	65c black brn	.15	.22
O151	A18	75c rose	.15	.22
O152	A18	75c bis brn ('27)	.38	.65
O153	A18	80c bister brn	.18	.32
O154	A18	90c rose ('27)	.30	.48
O155	A18	1fr black	.18	.32
O156	A18	1¼fr dk blue	.15	.22
O157	A18	1½fr dp blue ('27)	.48	.80
		Nos. O142-O157 (16)	3.77	6.03

Type of Regular Issue, 1926-35, Overprinted *Officiel*

1928-35 **Wmk. 213**

O158	A18	5c dk violet	.15	.20
O159	A18	10c olive grn	.15	.20
O160	A18	15c black ('30)	.20	.60
O161	A18	20c orange	.40	.60
O162	A18	25c violet brn	.40	.60
O163	A18	30c yellow grn	.42	.65
O164	A18	30c gray vio ('30)	.20	.60
O165	A18	35c yel grn ('30)	.20	.60
O166	A18	35c gray vio	.45	.65
O167	A18	40c olive gray	.45	.65
O168	A18	50c red brown	.40	.60
O169	A18	60c blue grn	.40	.60
O170	A18	70c blue vio ('35)	3.25	6.50
O171	A18	75c bister brn	.40	.60
O172	A18	90c rose	.45	.65
O173	A18	1fr black	.45	.65
O174	A18	1fr rose ('30)	.20	.60
O175	A18	1¼fr yel ('30)	1.65	4.00
O176	A18	1¼fr bl grn ('31)	1.65	4.00
O177	A18	1½fr deep blue	.45	.65
O178	A18	1¾fr dk blue ('30)	.20	.60
		Nos. O158-O178 (21)	12.52	24.80

Type of Regular Issues of 1928-31 Overprinted Like Nos. O80-O98

1928-31 **Wmk. 216** ***Perf. 11½***

O179	A19	2fr black	.45	.95

Wmk. 110 ***Perf. 12½***

O180	A21	20fr dp green ('31)	2.00	4.50

No. 198 Overprinted Like Nos. O80-O98

1934 **Unwmk.** ***Perf. 14x13½***

O181	A22	5fr blue green	2.00	3.00

Type of Regular Issue of 1935 Overprinted Like Nos. O158-O178 in Red

1935 **Wmk. 247** ***Perf. 12½x12***

O182	A23	10fr green	1.50	3.50

OCCUPATION STAMPS

Issued under German Occupation

Stamps of Germany, 1933-36, Overprinted in Black

Luxemburg

1940 **Wmk. 237** ***Perf. 14***

N1	A64	3pf olive bis	.25	*.50*
N2	A64	4pf dull blue	.25	*.55*
N3	A64	5pf bright green	.25	*.50*
N4	A64	6pf dark green	.25	*.50*
N5	A64	8pf vermilion	.25	*.50*
N6	A64	10pf chocolate	.25	*.50*
N7	A64	12pf deep carmine	.25	*.50*
N8	A64	15pf maroon	.25	*.70*
a.		Inverted overprint	*450.00*	*1,300.*
N9	A64	20pf bright blue	.25	*1.25*
N10	A64	25pf ultra	.35	*1.75*
N11	A64	30pf olive green	.35	*1.75*
N12	A64	40pf red violet	.50	*1.90*
N13	A64	50pf dk green & blk	.50	*2.00*
N14	A64	60pf claret & blk	.50	*2.75*
N15	A64	80pf dk blue & blk	1.00	*3.75*
N16	A64	100pf orange & blk	1.25	*5.75*
		Nos. N1-N16 (16)	6.70	*25.15*
		Set, never hinged	16.00	

Nos. 159-162, 164, 168-171, 173, 175, 179, 182, 216, 198-199 Surcharged in Black

—60 Rpf
b

80 Rpf

4 Rpf
a

c

100 Rpf
d

Perf. 12, 14x13½, 12½x12, 11½

1940 **Unwmk.**

N17	A18(a)	3rpf on 15c	.15	*.35*
N18	A18(a)	4rpf on 20c	.15	*.40*
N19	A18(a)	5rpf on 35c	.15	*.40*
N20	A18(a)	6rpf on 10c	.15	*.40*
N21	A18(a)	8rpf on 25c	.15	*.40*
N22	A18(a)	10rpf on 40c	.15	*.40*
N23	A18(a)	12rpf on 60c	.15	*.40*
N24	A18(a)	15rpf on 1fr rose	.15	*.40*
N25	A18(a)	20rpf on 50c	.15	*.75*
N26	A18(a)	25rpf on 5c	.15	*1.25*
N27	A18(a)	30rpf on 70c	.15	*.60*
N28	A18(a)	40rpf on 75c	.15	*1.00*
N29	A18(a)	50rpf on 1¼fr	.15	*.60*
N30	A35(b)	60rpf on 2fr	1.40	*12.50*
N31	A22(c)	80rpf on 5fr	.40	*2.25*
N32	A23(d)	100rpf on 10fr	.50	*3.00*
		Set value	3.00	
		Set, never hinged	7.00	
		Nos. N17-N32 (16)		*25.10*

OCCUPATION SEMI-POSTAL STAMPS

Semi-Postal Stamps of Germany, 1940 Overprinted in Black **Luxemburg**

1941 **Unwmk.** ***Perf. 14***

NB1	SP153	3pf + 2pf dk brn	.20	*.85*
NB2	SP153	4pf + 3pf bluish blk	.20	*.85*
NB3	SP153	5pf + 3pf yel grn	.20	*.85*
NB4	SP153	6pf + 4pf dk grn	.20	*.85*
NB5	SP153	8pf + 4pf dp org	.20	*.85*
NB6	SP153	12pf + 6pf carmine	.20	*.85*
NB7	SP153	15pf + 10pf dk vio brn	.28	*1.90*
NB8	SP153	25pf + 15pf dp ultra	.85	*3.75*
NB9	SP153	40pf + 35pf red lil	1.50	*6.25*
		Nos. NB1-NB9 (9)	3.83	*17.00*
		Set, never hinged	7.50	

MACAO

mə-'kaú

LOCATION — Off the Chinese coast at the mouth of the Canton River
GOVT. — Portuguese Overseas Territory
AREA — 6 sq. mi.
POP. — 261,680 (1981)
CAPITAL — Macao

The territory includes the two small adjacent islands of Coloane and Taipa.

1000 Reis = 1 Milreis
78 Avos = 1 Rupee (1894)
100 Avos = 1 Pataca (1913)

Catalogue values for unused stamps in this country are for Never Hinged items, beginning with Scott 339 in the regular postage section, Scott C16 in the air post section, Scott J50 in the semi-postal section, and Scott RA11 in the postal tax section.

Watermark

Wmk. 232- Maltese Cross

CORREIO MACAU 5 REIS — Portuguese Crown — A1

Perf. 12½, 13½

1884-85 Typo. Unwmk.

1 A1 5r black 12.00 6.50
2 A1 10r orange 22.50 9.00
3 A1 10r green ('85) 27.50 8.00
a. Perf. 13½ 75.00 60.00
4 A1 20r bister 30.00 17.00
5 A1 20r rose ('85) 40.00 14.00
6 A1 25r rose 20.00 5.00
7 A1 25r violet ('85) 27.50 10.00
a. Perf. 13½ 125.00 60.00
8 A1 40r blue 80.00 25.00
a. Perf. 12½ 125.00 45.00
9 A1 40r yellow ('85) 37.50 20.00
a. Perf. 13½ 125.00 60.00
10 A1 50r green 225.00 75.00
a. Perf. 12½ 400.00 150.00
11 A1 50r blue ('85) 52.50 25.00
a. Perf. 13½ 200.00 70.00
12 A1 80r gray ('85) 52.50 30.00
13 A1 100r red lilac 35.00 15.00
a. 100r lilac 35.00 15.00
14 A1 200r orange 65.00 20.00
a. Perf. 12½ 110.00 40.00
15 A1 300r chocolate 95.00 25.00
a. Perf. 13½ 225.00 100.00
Nos. 1-15 (15) 822.00 304.50

The reprints of the 1885 issue are printed on smooth, white chalky paper, ungummed and on thin white paper with shiny white gum and clean-cut perforation 13½.

For surcharges see Nos. 16-28, 108-109.

No. 13a Surcharged in Black

1884

16 A1 80r on 100r lilac 80.00 30.00
a. Inverted surcharge *165.00 60.00*
b. Without accent on "e" of "reis" 125.00 55.00
c. Perf. 13½ 110.00 30.00
d. As "b," perf. 13½ 70.00 32.50

Nos. 16-16d were issued without gum.

Nos. 6 and 10 Surcharged in Black, Blue or Red:

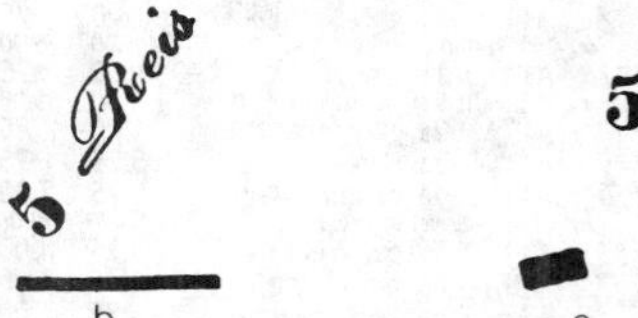

1885

Without Gum

17 A1(b) 5r on 25r rose, perf. 12½ (Bk) 15.00 6.50
a. With accent on "e" of "Reis" 25.00 12.00
b. Double surcharge 200.00 150.00
c. Inverted surcharge 175.00 110.00
d. Perf. 13½ 125.00 100.00
18 A1(b) 10r on 25r rose (Bl) 32.50 12.00
a. Accent on "e" of "Reis"
b. Pair, one without surcharge —
19 A1(b) 10r on 50r grn, perf. 13½ (Bl) 125.00 55.00
a. Perf. 12½ 250.00 80.00
20 A1(b) 20r on 50r green (Bk) 32.50 10.00
a. Double surcharge 150.00
b. Accent on "e" of "Reis"
21 A1(b) 40r on 50r grn, perf. 12½ (R) 125.00 50.00
a. Perf. 13½ 165.00 50.00
Nos. 17-21 (5) 330.00 133.50

1885

Without Gum

22 A1(c) 5r on 25r rose (Bk) 32.50 11.00
a. Original value not obliterated
23 A1(c) 10r on 50r green (Bk) 32.50 11.00
a. Inverted surcharge
b. Perf. 12½ 32.50 11.00

Nos. 12, 13a and 14 Surcharged in Black

5
Reis

1887

Without Gum

24 A1 5r on 80r gray 20.00 6.00
a. "R" of "Reis" 4mm high 80.00 50.00
b. Perf. 12½ 95.00 45.00
25 A1 5r on 100r lilac 80.00 25.00
a. Perf. 12½ 60.00 27.50
26 A1 10r on 80r gray 40.00 13.00
a. "R" 4mm high 90.00 47.50
27 A1 10r on 200r orange 90.00 35.00
a. "R" 4mm high, "e" without accent 125.00 50.00
b. Perf. 13½ 90.00 35.00
28 A1 20r on 80r gray 65.00 22.50
a. "R" 4mm high 110.00 47.50
b. Perf. 12½ 50.00
c. "R" 4mm high, "e" without accent 100.00 47.50
Nos. 24-28 (5) 295.00 101.50

The surcharges with larger "R" (4mm) have accent on "e." Smaller "R" is 3mm high.

Nos. 24-28 were issued without gum. Occasionally Nos. 24, 26 and 28 may be found with original gum. Values the same.

Coat of Arms — A6

Red Surcharge

1887, Oct. 20 *Perf. 12½*

Without Gum

32 A6 5r green & buff 12.00 5.50
a. With labels, 5r on 10r 65.00 65.00
b. With labels, 5r on 20r 75.00 65.00
c. With labels, 5r on 60r 65.00 65.00
33 A6 10r green & buff 12.00 8.00
a. With labels, 10r on 10r 80.00 75.00
b. With labels, 10r on 60r 90.00 75.00
34 A6 40r green & buff 12.00 *12.00*
a. With labels, 40r on 20r 125.00 *110.00*
Nos. 32-34 (3) 36.00 25.50

The 10r also exists with 20r labels, and 40r with 10r labels.

King Luiz — A7

King Carlos — A9

Typographed and Embossed

1888, Jan. *Perf. 12½, 13½*

Chalk-surfaced Paper

35 A7 5r black 14.00 4.00
36 A7 10r green 14.00 6.00
a. Perf. 13½ 50.00 25.00
37 A7 20r carmine 22.50 6.00
38 A7 25r violet 24.00 6.00
39 A7 40r chocolate 24.00 6.00
a. Perf. 13½ 40.00 15.00
40 A7 50r blue 40.00 10.00
41 A7 80r gray 65.00 15.00
a. Imperf., pair —
42 A7 100r brown 30.00 10.00
43 A7 200r gray lilac 60.00 16.00
44 A7 300r orange 47.50 15.00
Nos. 35-44 (10) 341.00 94.00

Nos. 37-44 were issued without gum.

For surcharges and overprints see Nos. 45, 58-66B, 110-118, 164-170, 239.

No. 43 Surcharged in Red

30 30

1892

Without Gum

45 A7 30r on 200r gray lilac 30.00 20.00
a. Inverted surcharge 125.00 75.00

1894, Nov. 15 Typo. *Perf. 11½*

46 A9 5r yellow 7.25 2.50
47 A9 10r redsh violet 7.25 2.50
48 A9 15r chocolate 11.00 3.50
49 A9 20r lavender 12.50 4.00
50 A9 25r green 30.00 8.00
51 A9 50r lt blue 32.50 8.00
a. Perf. 13½ 275.00 200.00
52 A9 75r carmine 60.00 20.00
53 A9 80r yellow green 32.50 15.00
54 A9 100r brown, *buff* 35.00 15.00
55 A9 150r carmine, *rose* 40.00 15.00
56 A9 200r dk blue, *blue* 55.00 20.00
57 A9 300r dk blue, *sal* 72.50 25.00
Nos. 46-57 (12) 395.50 138.50

Nos. 49-57d were issued without gum, No. 49 with or without gum.

For surcharges and overprints see Nos. 119-130, 171-181, 183-186, 240, 251, 257-258.

Stamps of 1888 Surcharged in Red, Green or Black

1 avo

仙 壹

1894 Without Gum *Perf. 12½*

58 A7 1a on 5r black (R) 11.00 3.00
a. Short "1" 9.50 3.00
b. Inverted surcharge 35.00 27.50
c. Double surcharge *150.00*
d. Surch. on back instead of face 35.00 35.00
59 A7 3a on 20r carmine (G) 19.00 4.00
a. Inverted surcharge
60 A7 4a on 25r violet (Bk) 19.00 5.50
a. Inverted surcharge 60.00 50.00
61 A7 6a on 40r choc (Bk) 19.00 5.50
a. Perf. 13½ 25.00 12.00
62 A7 8a on 50r blue (R) 55.00 12.00
a. Double surch., one inverted
b. Inverted surcharge 125.00 60.00
c. Perf. 13½ 60.00 27.50
63 A7 13a on 80r gray (Bk) 22.50 6.25
a. Double surcharge
64 A7 16a on 100r brown (Bk) 45.00 8.00
a. Inverted surcharge
b. Perf. 13½ 115.00 110.00
65 A7 31a on 200r gray lil (Bk) 72.50 11.00
a. Inverted surcharge 150.00 75.00
b. Perf. 13½ 75.00 12.00
66 A7 47a on 300r orange (G) 72.50 11.00
a. Double surcharge
Nos. 58-66 (9) 335.50 66.25

The style of type used for the word "PROVISORIO" on Nos. 58 to 66 differs for each value.

A 2a on 10r green was unofficially surcharged and denounced by the authorities.

On No. 45

66B A7 5a on 30r on 200r 150.00 50.00

WE BUY & SELL
MACAU
AND
WE SELL
WORLDWIDE
STAMPS
CALL, FAX OR WRITE TO INDICATE YOUR OFFERS AND NEEDS
WANT LISTS FILLED!
CHUCK Q. MOO
P.O. BOX 11370
TORRANCE, CA 90510
TEL 310-530-3768
FAX 310-539-7738

We're Buying!
MACAU
Don't Sell!
Until you've checked our highest buy prices! Collections, Accumulations, dealer's stocks of Macau including booklets, covers, S/S urgently needed.
Also buying China, Hong Kong, Japan and all other Asia.
Ship for immediate cash offer!
Asia hotline: 1-888-613-6182
Or call: 1-800-9-4-STAMP
(1-800-947-8267)
Want lists invited for all Macau and Asia!

Henry Gitner Philatelists, Inc.
P.O. Box 3077-S
Middletown, NY 10940
Toll Free: 1-800-947-8267
Fax: 914-343-0068
Email: hgitner@hgitner.com
http://www.hgitner.com
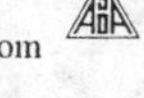
Philately - The Quiet Excitement!

Vasco da Gama Issue
Common Design Types

1898, Apr. 1 Engr. *Perf. 12½ to 16*

No.	Type	Description	Unused	Used
67	CD20	½a blue green	7.50	2.25
68	CD21	1a red	7.50	2.25
69	CD22	2a red violet	7.50	2.25
70	CD23	4a yellow green	7.50	2.25
71	CD24	8a dark blue	14.00	3.00
72	CD25	12a violet brown	22.50	4.50
73	CD26	16a bister brown	19.00	3.00
74	CD27	24a bister	22.50	7.50
		Nos. 67-74 (8)	108.00	27.00

For overprints and surcharges see Nos. 187-194.

King Carlos — A11

1898-1903 Typo. *Perf. 11½*
Name and Value in Black except #103

No.	Type	Description	Unused	Used
75	A11	½a gray	4.50	.80
a.		Perf. 12½	15.00	3.50
76	A11	1a orange	4.50	.80
a.		Perf. 12½	15.00	3.50
77	A11	2a yellow green	5.75	1.50
78	A11	2a gray green ('03)	6.25	1.50
79	A11	2½a red brown	7.50	1.65
80	A11	3a gray violet	7.50	2.00
81	A11	3a slate ('03)	6.25	1.65
82	A11	4a sea green	9.00	2.25
83	A11	4a carmine ('03)	6.25	1.50
84	A11	5a gray brn ('00)	14.00	2.50
85	A11	5a pale yel brn ('03)	9.00	2.25
86	A11	6a red brown ('03)	10.00	2.00
87	A11	8a blue	12.50	2.25
88	A11	8a gray brn ('03)	15.00	4.00
89	A11	10a slate blue ('00)	15.00	2.25
90	A11	12a rose	15.00	4.50
91	A11	12a red lilac ('03)	62.50	15.00
92	A11	13a violet	18.00	4.50
93	A11	13a gray lilac ('03)	22.50	4.50
94	A11	15a pale ol grn ('00)	90.00	10.00
95	A11	16a dk blue, *bl*	17.00	4.50
96	A11	18a org brn, *pink* ('03)	32.50	10.00
97	A11	20a brn, *yelsh* ('00)	90.00	4.75
98	A11	24a brown, *buff*	27.50	6.00
99	A11	31a red lilac	27.50	9.00
100	A11	31a red lil, *pink* ('03)	32.50	10.50
101	A11	47a dk blue, *rose*	50.00	11.00
102	A11	47a dull bl, *straw* ('03)	60.00	13.00
103	A11	78a blk & red, *bl* ('00)	77.50	12.50
		Nos. 75-103 (29)	755.50	148.65

Issued without gum: Nos. 76a, 77, 79-80, 82, 84, 89, 94, 97 and 103.

For surcharges and overprints see Nos. 104-107, 132-136, 141, 147-157D, 159-161, 182, 195-209, 253-255, 258A.

Nos. 92, 95, 98-99 Surcharged in Black — 5 ≡ PROVISORIO

1900

No.	Type	Description	Unused	Used
104	A11	5a on 13a violet	14.00	2.75
105	A11	10a on 16a dk bl, *bl*	16.00	4.00
106	A11	15a on 24a brn, *buff*	16.00	4.00
107	A11	20a on 31a red lilac	18.00	6.50

Nos. 106-107 were issued without gum.

Regular Issues Surcharged

AVOS

On Stamps of 1884-85

1902 *Perf. 11½*
Black Surcharge

No.	Type	Description	Unused	Used
108	A1	6a on 10r orange	24.00	5.50
a.		Double surcharge	110.00	75.00
109	A1	6a on 10r green	16.00	5.00

On Stamps of 1888

Red Surcharge
Perf. 12½, 13½

No.	Type	Description	Unused	Used
110	A7	6a on 5r black	8.00	2.00
a.		Inverted surcharge	90.00	60.00

Black Surcharge

No.	Type	Description	Unused	Used
111	A7	6a on 10r green	6.50	2.25
112	A7	6a on 40r choc	6.50	2.25
a.		Double surcharge	100.00	50.00
b.		Perf. 13½	22.50	6.50
113	A7	18a on 20r rose	13.00	4.50
a.		Double surcharge	125.00	70.00
114	A7	18a on 25r violet	140.00	50.00
115	A7	18a on 80r gray	150.00	60.00
a.		Double surcharge	175.00	175.00
116	A7	18a on 100r brown	22.50	8.00
a.		Perf. 13½	70.00	35.00
117	A7	18a on 200r gray lil	80.00	60.00
a.		Perf. 12½	150.00	60.00
118	A7	18a on 300r orange	22.50	10.00
a.		Perf. 13½	45.00	25.00

Issued without gum: Nos. 110-118.

Nos. 109 to 118 inclusive, except No. 111, have been reprinted. The reprints have white gum and clean-cut perforation 13½ and the colors are usually paler than those of the originals.

On Stamps of 1894

1902-10 *Perf. 11½, 13½*

No.	Type	Description	Unused	Used
119	A9	6a on 5r yellow	6.00	2.25
a.		Inverted surcharge	60.00	50.00
120	A9	6a on 10r red vio	20.00	5.00
121	A9	6a on 15r choc	20.00	5.00
122	A9	6a on 25r green	6.00	2.25
123	A9	6a on 80r yel grn	6.00	2.25
124	A9	6a on 100r brn, *buff*	12.00	3.00
a.		Perf. 11½	20.00	8.00
125	A9	6a on 200r bl, *bl*	8.00	2.25
a.		Vert. half used as 3a on cover ('10)		
126	A9	18a on 20r lavender	16.00	4.00
127	A9	18a on 50r lt blue	20.00	4.00
a.		Perf. 13½	60.00	14.00
128	A9	18a on 75r carmine	16.00	4.00
129	A9	18a on 150r car, *rose*	16.00	4.00
130	A9	18a on 300r bl, *salmon*	20.00	4.00

On Newspaper Stamp of 1893
Perf. 12½

No.	Type	Description	Unused	Used
131	N3	18a on 2½r brown	8.00	3.25
a.		Perf. 13½	21.00	7.00
b.		Perf. 11½	35.00	14.00
		Nos. 108-131 (24)	663.00	254.75

Issued without gum: Nos. 122-130, 131b.

Stamps of 1898-1900 Overprinted in Black — PROVISORIO

1902 *Perf. 11½*

No.	Type	Description	Unused	Used
132	A11	2a yellow green	16.00	4.00
133	A11	4a sea green	16.00	4.00
134	A11	8a blue	16.00	4.00
135	A11	10a slate blue	20.00	5.00
136	A11	12a rose	52.50	7.00
		Nos. 132-136 (5)	120.50	24.00

Issued without gum: Nos. 133, 135.

Reprints of No. 133 have shiny white gum and clean-cut perforation 13½. Value $1.

No. 91 Surcharged — 10 AVOS

1905

No.	Type	Description	Unused	Used
141	A11	10a on 12a red lilac	20.00	12.00

Nos. J1-J3 Overprinted

1910, Oct. *Perf. 11½x12*

No.	Type	Description	Unused	Used
144	D1	½a gray green	15.00	6.00
a.		Inverted overprint	30.00	30.00
145	D1	1a yellow green	15.00	7.00
a.		Inverted overprint	30.00	30.00
146	D1	2a slate	20.00	7.00
a.		Inverted overprint	30.00	30.00
		Nos. 144-146 (3)	50.00	20.00

Stamps of 1898-1903 Overprinted in Carmine or Green

Lisbon Overprint

1911, Apr. 2 *Perf. 11½*

No.	Type	Description	Unused	Used
147	A11	½a gray	1.90	.75
a.		Inverted overprint	5.00	5.00
147B	A11	1a orange	1.90	.75
c.		Inverted overprint	5.00	5.00
148	A11	2a gray green	1.90	.75
149	A11	3a slate	5.75	.75
150	A11	4a carmine (G)	5.75	2.00
a.		4a pale yel brn (error)	*50.00*	*50.00*
151	A11	5a pale yel brn	5.75	4.00
152	A11	6a red brown	5.75	4.00
153	A11	8a gray brown	5.75	4.00
154	A11	10a slate blue	5.75	4.00
155	A11	13a gray lilac	9.25	5.00
156	A11	16a dk blue, *bl*	9.25	5.00
157	A11	18a org brn, *pink*	15.00	6.00
157A	A11	20a brown, *straw*	15.00	6.00
157B	A11	31a red lil, *pink*	27.50	8.00
157C	A11	47a dull bl, *straw*	45.00	10.00
157D	A11	78a blk & red, *bl*	75.00	12.00
		Nos. 147-157D (16)	236.20	73.00

Issued without gum: Nos. 153-157D.

Coat of Arms — A14

1911 *Perf. 11½x12*
Red Surcharge

No.	Type	Description	Unused	Used
158	A14	1a on 5r brn & buff	24.00	12.50
a.		"1" omitted	50.00	50.00
b.		Inverted surcharge	35.00	25.00

Stamps of 1900-03 Surcharged

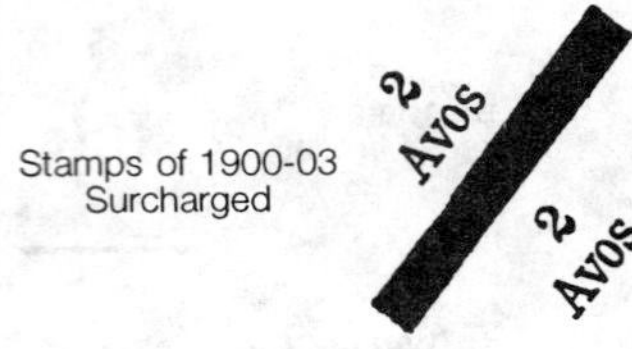

Diagonal Halves

1911 Without Gum *Perf. 11½*
Black Surcharge

No.	Type	Description	Unused	Used
159	A11	2a on half of 4a car	32.50	32.50
a.		"2" omitted	80.00	80.00
b.		Inverted surcharge	65.00	65.00
d.		Entire stamp	65.00	65.00
159C	A11	5a on half of 10a sl bl (#89)	*2,600.*	—
e.		Entire stamp		

Red Surcharge

No.	Type	Description	Unused	Used
160	A11	5a on half of 10a sl bl (#89)	*475.00*	*475.00*
a.		Inverted surcharge	*475.00*	*475.00*
b.		Entire stamp	—	—
161	A11	5a on half of 10a sl bl (#135)	80.00	80.00
a.		Inverted surcharge	165.00	165.00
b.		Entire stamp	165.00	165.00

A15

1911 *Perf. 12x11½*
Laid or Wove Paper

No.	Type	Description	Unused	Used
162	A15	1a black	475.00	—
a.		"Corrieo"	1,900.	—
163	A15	2a black	575.00	—
a.		"Corrieo"	1,900.	—

The vast majority of used stamps were not canceled.

Surcharged Stamps of 1902 Overprinted in Red or Green — REPUBLICA

Local Overprint

1913 Without Gum *Perf. 11½*

No.	Type	Description	Unused	Used
164	A1	6a on 10r green (R)	30.00	12.00

Perf. 12½, 13½

No.	Type	Description	Unused	Used
165	A7	6a on 5r black (G)	12.00	3.50
166	A7	6a on 10r green (R)	24.00	8.00
167	A7	6a on 40r choc (R)	8.00	3.00
a.		Perf. 13½	40.00	20.00
168	A7	18a on 20r car (G)	16.00	6.00
169	A7	18a on 100r brown (R)	100.00	40.00
a.		Perf. 13½	80.00	50.00
170	A7	18a on 300r org (R)	25.00	9.00
a.		Perf. 13½	40.00	10.00
		Nos. 164-170 (7)	215.00	81.50

"Republica" overprint exists inverted on Nos. 164-170.

"Republica" overprint exists double on No. 164.

1913 Without Gum *Perf. 11½, 13½*

No.	Type	Description	Unused	Used
171	A9	6a on 10r red vio (G)	9.00	3.00
172	A9	6a on 10r red vio (R)	80.00	26.00
173	A9	6a on 15r choc (R)	9.00	4.00
174	A9	6a on 25r green (R)	10.00	4.00
175	A9	6a on 80r yel grn (R)	9.00	4.00
176	A9	6a on 100r brn, *buff* (R)	18.00	7.00
a.		Perf. 11½	20.00	8.00
177	A9	18a on 20r lav (R)	12.00	4.00
178	A9	18a on 50r lt bl (R)	12.00	4.00
a.		Perf. 13½	13.00	5.00
179	A9	18a on 75r car (G)	12.00	4.50
180	A9	18a on 150r car, *rose* (G)	13.00	5.00
181	A9	18a on 300r dk bl, *buff* (R)	20.00	10.00

On No. 141

No.	Type	Description	Unused	Used
182	A11	10a on 12a red lil (R)	8.00	3.50
		Nos. 171-182 (12)	212.00	79.00

"Republica" overprint exists inverted on Nos. 171-181.

Stamps of Preceding Issue Surcharged — 2 ≡

1913 Without Gum *Perf. 11½*

No.	Type	Description	Unused	Used
183	A9	2a on 18a on 20r (R)	8.00	4.00
184	A9	2a on 18a on 50r (R)	8.00	4.00
a.		Perf. 13½	9.00	4.25
185	A9	2a on 18a on 75r (G)	8.00	4.00
186	A9	2a on 18a on 150r (G)	8.00	4.00
		Nos. 183-186 (4)	32.00	16.00

"Republica" overprint exists inverted on Nos. 183-186. Value, each $10.

The 2a surcharge exists inverted or double on Nos. 183-186. Value, each $25.

Vasco da Gama Issue Overprinted or Surcharged:

REPUBLICA (j) — REPUBLICA 10 A. (k)

No.	Type	Description	Unused	Used
187	CD20 (j)	½a blue green	4.50	2.00
188	CD21 (j)	1a red	5.00	2.00
189	CD22 (j)	2a red violet	5.00	2.00
a.		Double ovpt., one inverted	100.00	
190	CD23 (j)	4a yellow grn	4.50	2.00
191	CD24 (j)	8a dk blue	8.00	2.00
192	CD25 (k)	10a on 12a vio brn	14.00	5.00
193	CD26 (j)	16a bister brn	10.00	4.00
194	CD27 (j)	24a bister	16.00	5.00
		Nos. 187-194 (8)	67.00	24.00

Stamps of 1898-1903 Overprinted in Red or Green — REPUBLICA

1913 Without Gum *Perf. 11½*

No.	Type	Description	Unused	Used
195	A11	4a carmine (G)	190.00	100.00
196	A11	5a yellow brn	21.00	20.00
a.		Inverted overprint	*40.00*	*40.00*
197	A11	6a red brown	60.00	40.00
198	A11	8a gray brown	475.00	300.00
199	A11	13a violet	60.00	32.50
a.		Inverted overprint	75.00	
200	A11	13a gray lilac	30.00	20.00
201	A11	16a blue, *bl*	35.00	20.00
202	A11	18a org brn, *pink*	35.00	20.00
203	A11	20a brown, *yelsh*	35.00	20.00
204	A11	31a red lil, *pink*	52.50	30.00
205	A11	47a dull bl, *straw*	77.50	40.00
		Nos. 195-205 (11)	1,071.	642.50

Stamps of 1911-13 Surcharged — ½ Avo

On Stamps of 1911 With Lisbon "Republica"

1913
206 A11 ½a on 5a yel brn (R) 8.00 3.00
a. "½ Avo" inverted 70.00 70.00
207 A11 4a on 8a gray brn (R) 16.00 4.00
a. "4 Avos" inverted 80.00 70.00

On Stamps of 1913 With Local "Republica"
208 A11 1a on 13a violet (R) 70.00 30.00
209 A11 1a on 13a gray lil (R) 8.00 3.00
Nos. 206-209 (4) 102.00 40.00
Issued without gum: Nos. 207-209.

"Ceres" — A16

1913-24 *Perf. 12x11½, 15x14*
Name and Value in Black
210 A16 ½a olive brown 1.75 .15
a. Inscriptions inverted 50.00
211 A16 1a black 1.75 .15
a. Inscriptions inverted 50.00
b. Inscriptions double 50.00
212 A16 1½a yel grn ('24) 1.75 .15
213 A16 2a blue green 1.75 .15
a. Inscriptions inverted 40.00
214 A16 3a orange ('23) 10.00 3.00
215 A16 4a carmine 6.75 1.00
216 A16 4a lemon ('24) 14.00 2.25
217 A16 5a lilac brown 7.75 3.00
218 A16 6a lt violet 7.75 3.00
219 A16 6a gray ('23) 47.50 7.50
220 A16 8a lilac brown 7.75 3.00
221 A16 10a deep blue 7.75 3.00
222 A16 10a pale blue ('23) 27.50
223 A16 12a yellow brn 11.00 3.00
224 A16 14a lilac ('24) 42.50 12.00
225 A16 16a slate 20.00 5.00
226 A16 20a orange brn 20.00 5.00
227 A16 24a slate grn ('23) 25.00 7.00
228 A16 32a orange brn ('24) 25.00 8.00
229 A16 40a plum 21.00 5.00
230 A16 56a dull rose ('24) 50.00 15.00
231 A16 58a brown, *grn* 35.00 12.00
232 A16 72a brown ('23) 67.50 20.00
233 A16 76a brown, *pink* 50.00 14.00
234 A16 1p orange, *sal* 67.50 20.00
235 A16 1p orange ('24) 200.00 30.00
236 A16 3p green, *bl* 200.00 50.00
237 A16 3p pale turq ('24) 425.00 60.00
238 A16 5p car rose ('24) 350.00 75.00
Nos. 210-238 (29) 1,753.
Nos. 210-221,223-238 (28) 367.35
For surcharges see Nos. 256, 259-267.

Preceding Issues and No. P4 Overprinted in Carmine

On Stamps of 1902
Perf. 11½, 12, 12½, 13½, 11½x12
1915
239 A7 6a on 10r green 8.00 2.00
240 A9 6a on 5r yellow 8.00 2.00
241 A9 6a on 10r red vio 8.00 2.00
242 A9 6a on 15r choc 7.00 1.50
243 A9 6a on 25r green 6.50 1.50
244 A9 6a on 80r yel grn 6.50 1.50
245 A9 6a on 100r brn, *buff* 12.00 3.00
246 A9 6a on 200r bl, *bl* 6.00 2.00
247 A9 18a on 20r lav 12.00 4.00
248 A9 18a on 50r lt bl 25.00 4.00
249 A9 18a on 75r car 22.50 4.00
250 A9 18a on 150r car, *rose* 25.00 4.00
251 A9 18a on 300r bl, *sal* 22.50 4.00
252 N3 18a on 2½r brn 18.00 2.00

With Additional Overprint PROVISORIO

253 A11 8a blue 8.00 3.00
254 A11 10a slate blue 8.00 3.00
a. "Provisorio" double 60.00

On Stamp of 1905
255 A11 10a on 12a red lilac 8.00 3.00
Nos. 239-255 (17) 211.00 46.50
Issued without gum: Nos. 243-251 and 255.

No. 217 Surcharged ½ AVO

1919-20
Without Gum
256 A16 ½a on 5a lilac brn 75.00 25.00

Nos. 243 and 244 Surcharged 2

257 A9 2a on 6a on 25r green 190.00 75.00
258 A9 2a on 6a on 80r yel grn 75.00 30.00

No. 152 Surcharged 2 avos

258A A11 2a on 6a red brown 85.00 60.00
Nos. 256-258A (4) 425.00 190.00
Issued without gum: Nos. 256-258A.

Stamps of 1913-24 Surcharged 7 avos

1931-33
259 A16 1a on 24a slate grn 10.00 3.00
260 A16 2a on 32a org brn 10.00 3.00
261 A16 4a on 12a bis brn 10.00 3.00
262 A16 5a on 6a lt gray 40.00 18.00
263 A16 5a on 6a lt vio 20.00 10.00
264 A16 7a on 8a lil brn ('31) 16.00 4.00
265 A16 12a on 14a lil ('31) 16.00 4.00
266 A16 15a on 16a dk gray 16.00 4.00
267 A16 20a on 56a dl rose 26.00 10.00
Nos. 259-267 (9) 164.00 59.00

"Portugal" and Vasco da Gama's Flagship "San Gabriel" — A17

Perf. 11½
1934, Feb. 1 **Typo.** **Wmk. 232**
268 A17 ½a bister .45 .40
269 A17 1a olive brown .45 .15
270 A17 2a blue green 1.10 .50
271 A17 3a violet 1.40 .50
272 A17 4a black 1.75 .50
273 A17 5a gray 1.75 .80
274 A17 6a brown 1.75 .80
275 A17 7a brt rose 3.25 1.00
276 A17 8a brt blue 3.25 1.00
277 A17 10a red orange 7.25 2.00
278 A17 12a dark blue 7.25 2.00
279 A17 14a olive green 7.25 2.00
280 A17 15a maroon 7.25 2.00
281 A17 20a orange 7.25 2.00
282 A17 30a apple green 14.00 3.00
283 A17 40a violet 14.00 3.00
284 A17 50a olive bister 21.00 4.00
285 A17 1p lt blue 110.00 15.00
286 A17 2p brown org 140.00 30.00
287 A17 3p emerald 225.00 40.00
288 A17 5p dark violet 350.00 50.00
Nos. 268-288 (21) 925.40 160.65
See Nos. 316-323. For overprints and surcharges see Nos. 306-315, C1-C6, J43-J49.

Common Design Types
Perf. 13½x13
1938, Aug. 1 **Engr.** **Unwmk.**
Name and Value in Black
289 CD34 1a gray green 1.10 .50
290 CD34 2a orange brown 1.40 .75
291 CD34 3a dk vio brn 1.40 .75
292 CD34 4a brt green 1.40 .75
293 CD35 5a dk carmine 1.40 .75
294 CD35 6a slate 1.40 .75
295 CD35 8a rose violet 2.25 3.00
296 CD36 10a brt red vio 2.75 3.00
297 CD36 12a red 3.50 3.50
298 CD36 15a orange 3.50 3.50
299 CD37 20a blue 18.00 4.00
300 CD37 40a gray black 18.00 5.00
301 CD37 50a brown 18.00 5.00
302 CD38 1p brown car 55.00 10.00
303 CD38 2p olive green 110.00 15.00
304 CD38 3p blue violet 140.00 30.00
305 CD38 5p red brown 275.00 50.00
Nos. 289-305 (17) 654.10 136.25
For surcharge see No. 315A.

Stamps of 1934 Surcharged in Black:

5 avos (a) 5 avos (b)

1941 **Wmk. 232** *Perf. 11½x12*
306 A17(a) 1a on 6a brown 6.75 2.00
307 A17(b) 2a on 6a brown 2.75 1.00
308 A17(b) 3a on 6a brown 2.75 1.00
309 A17(a) 5a on 7a brt rose 275.00 50.00
310 A17(b) 5a on 7a brt rose 2.75 1.00
311 A17(a) 5a on 8a brt blue 9.50 4.00
312 A17(b) 5a on 8a brt blue 2.75 1.00
313 A17(b) 8a on 30a apple grn 5.75 2.50
314 A17(b) 8a on 40a violet 5.75 2.50
315 A17(b) 8a on 50a olive bis 5.75 2.50
Nos. 306-315 (10) 319.50 67.50

No. 294 Surcharged in Black: 3 avos

1941 **Unwmk.** *Perf. 13½x13*
315A CD35 3a on 6a slate 47.50 20.00
Counterfeits exist.

"Portugal" Type of 1934
1942 **Litho.** *Rough Perf. 12*
Thin Paper Without Gum
316 A17 1a olive brown 2.00 .75
317 A17 2a blue green 2.00 .75
318 A17 3a vio, perf. 11 24.00 3.00
a. Perf. 12 30.00 3.25
319 A17 6a brown 30.00 3.00
a. Perf. 10 60.00 7.00
b. Perf. 11 50.00 6.00
320 A17 10a red orange 16.00 2.00
321 A17 20a orange 16.00 2.00
a. Perf. 11 50.00 5.00
322 A17 30a apple green 30.00 3.25
323 A17 40a violet 40.00 4.00
Nos. 316-323 (8) 160.00 18.75

Macao Dwelling — A18
Gate of Cerco — A19

Designs: 2a, Mountain fort. 3a, View of Macao. 8a, Praia Grande Bay. 10a, Leal Senado Square. 20a, Sao Jeronimo Hill. 30a, Marginal Ave. 50a, Relief of Goddess Ma. 2p, Pagoda of Barra. 3p, Post Office. 5p, Solidao Walk.

1948, Dec. 20 **Litho.** *Perf. 10½*
324 A18 1a dk brn & org 2.00 .50
325 A19 2a rose brn & rose 1.50 .50
326 A18 3a brn vio & lil 3.50 .50
327 A18 8a rose car & rose 2.00 .50
328 A18 10a lilac rose & rose 3.50 .75
329 A18 20a dk blue & gray 4.25 .85
330 A18 30a black & gray 8.50 1.00
331 A18 50a brn & pale bis 12.50 1.25
332 A19 1p emer & pale grn 100.00 10.00
333 A19 2p scarlet & rose 85.00 10.00
334 A19 3p dl grn & gray grn 125.00 15.00
335 A18 5p vio bl & gray 250.00 22.50
Nos. 324-335 (12) 597.75 63.35
See Nos. 341-347A.

Lady of Fatima Issue
Common Design Type
1949, Feb. 1 **Unwmk.** *Perf. 14½*
336 CD40 8a scarlet 26.00 3.00

Symbols of the UPU — A20

Dragon — A21

1949, Dec. 24 **Litho.** **Unwmk.**
337 A20 32a claret & rose 45.00 10.00
75th anniv. of the formation of the UPU.

Catalogue values for unused stamps in this section, from this point to the end of the section, are for Never Hinged items.

Holy Year Issue
Common Design Types
1950, July 26 *Perf. 13x13½*
339 CD41 32a dk slate gray 35.00 4.00
340 CD42 50a carmine 35.00 4.00

Scenic Types of 1948
Designs as before.

1950-51 *Perf. 14*
341 A18 1a violet & rose 5.50 .50
342 A19 2a ol bis & yel 5.50 .50
343 A18 3a org red & buff 7.25 .50
344 A18 8a slate & gray 7.25 .50
345 A18 10a red brn & org 16.00 .75
346 A18 30a vio bl & bl 21.00 1.00
347 A18 50a ol grn & yel grn 37.50 1.00
347A A19 1p dk org brn & org brn 110.00 2.00
Nos. 341-347A (8) 210.00 6.75
A 1p ultra & vio, perf. 11, was not sold in Macao. Value $60.
#341-347 issued in 1951, the 1p in 1950.

1951 *Perf. 11½x12*
348 A21 1a org yel, *lemon* 5.25 .85
349 A21 2a dk grn, *blue* 5.25 .85
350 A21 10a vio brn, *blue* 5.25 .85
351 A21 10a brt pink, *blue* 5.25 .85
Nos. 348-351 (4) 21.00 3.40
For overprints see Nos. J50-J52.

Holy Year Extension Issue
Common Design Type
1951, Dec. 3 **Litho.** *Perf. 14*
352 CD43 60a magenta & pink 80.00 5.00

Fernao Mendes Pinto — A22

Portraits: 2a and 10a, St. Francis Xavier. 3a and 50a, Jorge Alvares. 6a and 30a, Luis de Camoens.

1951, Aug. 27 *Perf. 11½*
353 A22 1a steel bl & gray bl 2.25 .25
354 A22 2a dk brown & ol grn 2.75 .25
355 A22 3a deep grn & grn 2.25 .25
356 A22 6a purple 11.00 .40
357 A22 10a red brn & org 22.50 .50
358 A22 20a brown car 37.50 1.00
359 A22 30a dk brn & ol grn 37.50 1.00
360 A22 50a red & orange 80.00 2.00
Nos. 353-360 (8) 195.75 5.65

Sampan — A23

Junk — A24

Design: 5p, Junk.

1951, Nov. 1 **Unwmk.**
361 A23 1p vio bl & bl 52.50 1.40
362 A24 3p black & vio 125.00 4.00
363 A23 5p henna brown 375.00 12.00
Nos. 361-363 (3) 552.50 17.40

Medical Congress Issue
Common Design Type
Design: Sao Rafael Hospital.
1952, June 16 **Unwmk.** *Perf. 13½*
364 CD44 6a black & purple 9.50 .60

Statue of St. Francis Xavier — A25

Statue of Virgin Mary — A26

St. Francis Xavier Issue
16a, Arm of St. Francis. 40a, Tomb of St. Francis.

1952, Nov. 28 Litho. *Perf. 14*

365 A25 3a blk, *grnsh gray* 6.25 .45
366 A25 16a choc, *buff* 24.00 1.00
367 A25 40a blk, *blue* 45.00 3.00
Nos. 365-367 (3) 75.25 4.45

400th anniv. of the death of St. Francis Xavier.

1953, Apr. 28 Unwmk. *Perf. 13½*

368 A26 8a choc & dull ol 8.00 .50
369 A26 10a blue blk & buff 27.50 1.00
370 A26 50a slate grn & ol grn 45.00 3.00
Nos. 368-370 (3) 80.50 4.50

Exhibition of Sacred Missionary Art, held at Lisbon in 1951.

Stamp of Portugal and Arms of Colonies — A27

1954, Mar. 9 Photo. *Perf. 13*

371 A27 10a multicolored 7.00 1.00

Cent. of Portugal's first postage stamps.

Firecracker Flower — A28

Map of Colony — A29

Flowers: 3a, Forget-me-not. 5a, Dragon claw. 10a, Nunflower. 16a, Narcissus. 30a, Peach flower. 39a, Lotus flower. 1p, Chrysanthemum. 3p, Cherry blossoms. 5p, Tangerine blossoms.

1953, Sept. 22 *Perf. 11½*

Flowers in Natural Colors

372 A28 1a dark red .35 .15
373 A28 3a dark green .35 .15
374 A28 5a dark brown .55 .15
375 A28 10a dp grnsh blue 1.25 .15
376 A28 16a yellow brown 2.00 .15
377 A28 30a dk olive grn 2.00 .15
378 A28 39a violet blue 2.50 .15
379 A28 1p deep plum 10.50 1.10
380 A28 3p dark gray 17.50 2.00
381 A28 5p deep carmine 22.50 4.00
Nos. 372-381 (10) 59.50 8.15

Sao Paulo Issue

Common Design Type

1954, Aug. 4 Litho. *Perf. 13½*

382 CD46 39a orange, cream & blk 10.00 .50

Sao Paulo founding, 400th anniversary.

Perf. 12½x13½

1956, May 10 Photo.

Inscriptions and design in brown, red, green, ultra & yellow (buff on 10a, 40a, 90a)

383 A29 1a gray .90 .15
384 A29 3a pale gray 1.10 .15
385 A29 5a pale pink 1.40 .15
386 A29 10a buff 3.00 .15
387 A29 30a lt blue 6.75 .15
388 A29 40a pale green 14.00 .50
389 A29 90a pale gray 22.50 .75
390 A29 1.50p pink 35.00 1.00
Nos. 383-390 (8) 84.65 3.00

Macao stamps can be mounted in the annually supplemented Scott Portugal album.

Exhibition Emblems and View — A30

Armillary Sphere — A31

1958, Nov. 8 Litho. *Perf. 14½*

391 A30 70a multicolored 5.00 .50

World's Fair, Brussels, Apr. 17-Oct. 19.

Tropical Medicine Congress Issue

Common Design Type

Design: Cinnamomum camphora.

1958, Nov. 15 *Perf. 13½*

392 CD47 20a multicolored 9.00 2.00

1960, June 25 Litho. *Perf. 13½*

393 A31 2p multicolored 18.00 1.25

500th anniversary of the death of Prince Henry the Navigator.

Sports Issue

Common Design Type

Sports: 10a, Field hockey. 16a, Wrestling. 20a, Table tennis. 50a, Motorcycling. 1.20p, Relay race. 2.50p, Badminton.

1962, Feb. 9 *Perf. 13½*

Multicolored Design

394 CD48 10a blue & yel grn 2.25 .20
395 CD48 16a brt pink 8.75 .50
396 CD48 20a orange 4.50 .75
397 CD48 50a rose 4.50 .75
398 CD48 1.20p blue & beige 15.00 1.50
399 CD48 2.50p gray & brown 35.00 3.00
Nos. 394-399 (6) 70.00 6.70

Anti-Malaria Issue

Common Design Type

Design: Anopheles hyrcanus sinensis.

1962, Apr. 7 Litho. *Perf. 13½*

400 CD49 40a multicolored 10.00 1.00

Bank Building — A32

1964, May 16 Unwmk. *Perf. 13½*

401 A32 20a multicolored 24.00 1.90

Centenary of the National Overseas Bank of Portugal.

ITU Issue

Common Design Type

1965, May 17 Litho. *Perf. 14½*

402 CD52 10a pale grn & multi *11.00* 1.10

National Revolution Issue

Common Design Type

Design: 10a, Infante D. Henrique School and Count de S. Januario Hospital.

1966, May 28 Litho. *Perf. 11½*

403 CD53 10a multicolored 7.00 .50

Drummer, 1548 — A32a

Designs: 15a, Soldier with sword, 1548. 20a, Harquebusier, 1649. 40a, Infantry officer, 1783. 50a, Infantry soldier, 1783. 60a, Colonial infantry soldier (Indian), 1902. 1p, Colonial infantry soldier (Chinese), 1903. 3p, Colonial infantry soldier (Chinese) 1904.

1966, Aug. 8 Litho. *Perf. 13*

404 A32a 10a multicolored 3.00 .50
405 A32a 15a multicolored 3.50 .50
406 A32a 20a multicolored 3.50 .50
407 A32a 40a multicolored 5.50 .60
408 A32a 50a multicolored 5.50 .60
409 A32a 60a multicolored 15.00 .90
410 A32a 1p multicolored 21.00 .90
411 A32a 3p multicolored 35.00 2.50
Nos. 404-411 (8) 92.00 7.00

Navy Club Issue, 1967

Common Design Type

Designs: 10a, Capt. Oliveira E. Carmo and armed launch Vega. 20a, Capt. Silva Junior and frigate Dom Fernando.

1967, Jan. 31 Litho. *Perf. 13*

412 CD54 10a multicolored 6.00 1.00
413 CD54 20a multicolored 16.00 2.00

Arms of Pope Paul VI and Golden Rose — A33

Cabral Monument, Lisbon — A34

1967, May 13 *Perf. 12½x13*

414 A33 50a multicolored 5.00 .50

50th anniversary of the apparition of the Virgin Mary to three shepherd children at Fatima.

Cabral Issue

Design: 70a, Cabral monument, Belmonte.

1968, Apr. 22 Litho. *Perf. 14*

415 A34 20a multicolored 5.00 1.00
416 A34 70a multicolored 15.00 1.25

500th anniversary of the birth of Pedro Alvares Cabral, navigator who took possession of Brazil for Portugal.

Admiral Coutinho Issue

Common Design Type

Design: 20a, Adm. Coutinho with sextant, vert.

1969, Feb. 17 Litho. *Perf. 14*

417 CD55 20a multicolored 5.00 .60

Church of Our Lady of the Relics, Vidigueira — A35

Bishop D. Belchior Carneiro — A36

Vasco da Gama Issue

1969, Aug. 29 Litho. *Perf. 14*

418 A35 1p multicolored 20.00 .70

Vasco da Gama (1469-1524), navigator.

Administration Reform Issue

Common Design Type

1969, Sept. 25 Litho. *Perf. 14*

419 CD56 90a multicolored 5.00 .70

1969, Oct. 16 Litho. *Perf. 13*

420 A36 50a multicolored 5.00 .75

4th centenary of the founding of the Santa Casa da Misericordia in Macao.

King Manuel I Issue

Portal of Mother Church, Golega — A37

1969, Dec. 1 Litho. *Perf. 14*

421 A37 30a multicolored 5.00 .60

500th anniversary of the birth of King Manuel I.

Marshal Carmona Issue

Common Design Type

5a, Antonio Oscar Carmona in general's uniform.

1970, Nov. 15 Litho. *Perf. 14*

422 CD57 5a multicolored 4.00 .75

Dragon Mask — A38

1971, Sept. 30 *Perf. 13½*

423 A38 5a lt blue & multi 1.00 .15
424 A38 10a Lion mask 2.75 .50

Lusiads Issue

Portuguese Delegation at Chinese Court — A39

1972, May 25 Litho. *Perf. 13*

425 A39 20a citron & multi 17.00 .65

4th centenary of publication of The Lusiads by Luiz Camoens.

Olympic Games Issue

Common Design Type

Design: Hockey and Olympic emblem.

1972, June 20 *Perf. 14x13½*

426 CD59 50a multicolored 8.00 1.40

Lisbon-Rio de Janeiro Flight Issue

Common Design Type

Design: "Santa Cruz" landing in Rio de Janeiro.

1972, Sept. 20 Litho. *Perf. 13½*

427 CD60 5p multicolored 24.00 5.75

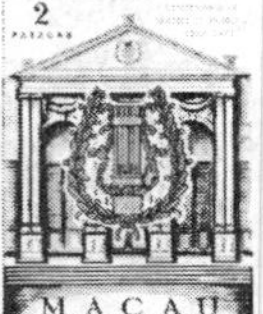

Pedro V Theater and Lyre — A42

1972, Dec. 25 Litho. *Perf. 13½*

428 A42 2p multicolored 20.00 2.50

Centenary of Pedro V Theater, Macao.

WMO Centenary Issue

Common Design Type

1973, Dec. 15 Litho. *Perf. 13*

429 CD61 20a blue grn & multi 3.00 .75

Viscount St. Januario — A44

Design: 60a, Hospital, 1874 and 1974.

1974, Jan. 25 Litho. *Perf. 13½*
430 A44 15a multicolored 2.75 .20
431 A44 60a multicolored 5.25 .45

Viscount St. Januario Hospital, Macao, cent.
For surcharge see No. 457.

George Chinnery, Self-portrait — A45

1974, Sept. 23 Litho. *Perf. 14*
432 A45 30a multicolored 4.00 .45

George Chinnery (1774-1852), English painter who lived in Macao.

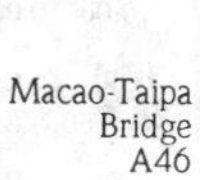

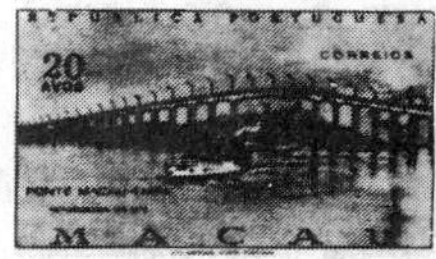

Macao-Taipa Bridge A46

Design: 2.20p, Different view of bridge.

1974, Oct. 7 Litho. *Perf. 14x13½*
433 A46 20a multicolored 4.75 .25
434 A46 2.20p multicolored 24.00 1.50

Inauguration of the Macao-Taipa Bridge.

Man Raising Banner A47

1975, Apr. 25 *Perf. 12*
435 A47 10a ocher & multi 6.00 .75
436 A47 1p multicolored 30.00 1.65

Revolution of Apr. 25, 1974, 1st anniv.

Pou Chai Pagoda — A48

Design: 20p, Tin Hau Pagoda.

1976, Jan. 30 Litho. *Perf. 13½x13*
437 A48 10p multicolored *21.00* 5.50
438 A48 20p multicolored *45.00* 7.75

A 1p stamp for the 400th anniv. of the Macao Diocese was prepared but not issued. Some copies were sold in Lisbon.

"The Law" — A50

1978 Litho. *Perf. 13½*
440 A50 5a blk, dk & lt blue *7.00* .35
441 A50 2p blk, org brn & buff *100.00* 2.75
442 A50 5p blk, ol & yel grn *175.00* 4.75
Nos. 440-442 (3) *282.00* 7.85

Legislative Assembly, Aug. 9, 1976.

Nos. 376, 378, 382, 434 Surcharged

1979, Nov.
443 A28 10a on 16a *10.00* 1.25
444 A28 30a on 39a (#378) *10.00* 1.25
445 CD46 30a on 39a (#382) *70.00* 7.00
446 A46 2p on 2.20p *30.00* 1.75
Nos. 443-446 (4) *120.00* 11.25

Luis de Camoens (1524-80), Poet — A51

Buddha, Macao Cathedral — A52

1981, June Litho. *Perf. 13½*
447 A51 10a multicolored *.60* .15
448 A51 30a multicolored *1.40* .15
449 A51 1p multicolored *3.00* .50
450 A51 3p multicolored *11.00* 1.00
Nos. 447-450 (4) *16.00* 1.80

1981, Sept.
451 A52 15a multicolored .50 .15
452 A52 40a multicolored 1.00 .15
453 A52 50a multicolored 1.50 .15
454 A52 60a multicolored 2.25 .15
455 A52 1p multicolored 3.25 .50
456 A52 2.20p multicolored 7.50 .95
Nos. 451-456 (6) 16.00 2.05

Transcultural Psychiatry Symposium.

No. 431 Surcharged

1981 Litho. *Perf. 13½*
457 A44 30a on 60a multi 1.00 .50

Health Services Building — A53

Designs: Public Buildings and Monuments.

1982, June 10 Litho. *Perf. 12x12½*
458 A53 30a shown .25 .15
459 A53 40a Guia Lighthouse .35 .15
460 A53 1p Portas do Cerco .90 .25
461 A53 2p Luis de Camoes Museum 1.75 .50
462 A53 10p School Welfare Service Building 9.00 2.50
Nos. 458-462 (5) 12.25 3.55

See Nos. 472-476, 489-493.

Autumn Festivals A54

Designs: Painted paper lanterns.

1982, Oct. 1 *Perf. 12x11½*
463 A54 40a multicolored 1.25 .15
464 A54 1p multicolored 3.00 .50
465 A54 2p multicolored 6.50 1.00
466 A54 5p multicolored 17.00 2.00
Nos. 463-466 (4) 27.75 3.65

Geographical Position — A55

1982, Dec. 1 Litho. *Perf. 13*
467 A55 50a Aerial view 1.90 .15
468 A55 3p Map 12.00 1.00

World Communications Year — A56

1983, Feb. 16 *Perf. 13½*
469 A56 60a Telephone operators 1.00 .15
470 A56 3p Mailman, mailbox 5.00 .95
471 A56 6p Globe, satellites 10.00 2.00
Nos. 469-471 (3) 16.00 3.10

Architecture Type of 1982

1983, May 12 Litho. *Perf. 13*
472 A53 10a Social Welfare Institute .25 .15
473 A53 80a St. Joseph's Seminary 1.25 .40
474 A53 1.50p St. Dominic's Church 3.25 .80
475 A53 2.50p St. Paul's Church ruins 5.25 1.40
476 A53 7.50p Senate House 16.00 4.25
Nos. 472-476 (5) 26.00 7.00

Medicinal Plants — A57

1983, July 14 Litho. *Perf. 13½x14*
477 A57 20a Asclepias curassavica 1.10 .50
478 A57 40a Acanthus ilicifolius 1.65 1.00
479 A57 60a Melastoma sanguineum 2.75 1.00
480 A57 70a Nelumbo nucifera 3.50 1.00
481 A57 1.50p Bombax malabaricum 8.25 3.00
482 A57 2.50p Hibiscus mutabilis 11.00 3.00
a. Souvenir sheet of 6, #477-482 *275.00*
Nos. 477-482 (6) 28.25 9.50

No. 482a sold for 6.50p.

16th Century Discoveries
A58 A59

1983, Nov. 15 Litho. *Perf. 13½x14*
483 A58 4p multicolored *10.00* 1.50
484 A59 4p multicolored *10.00* 1.50
a. Pair, #483-484 *20.00* 3.00

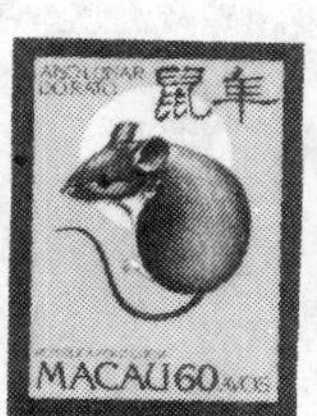

A60

A61

1984, Jan. 25 Litho. *Perf. 13½*
485 A60 60a multicolored *9.00* .25
a. Booklet pane of 5 *55.00*

New Year 1984 (Year of the Rat).
See Nos. 504, 522, 540, 560, 583, 611, 639, 662, 684, 718, 757, 804.

1984, Mar. 1 Litho. *Perf. 12½*

Design of First Stamp Issue, 1884.

486 A61 40a orange & blk .40 .15
487 A61 3p gray & blk 3.00 .50
488 A61 5p sepia & blk 4.50 .75
a. Souvenir sheet of 3, #486-488 *70.00*
Nos. 486-488 (3) 7.90 1.40

Centenary of Macao postage stamps.

Architecture Type of 1982

1984, May 18 Litho. *Perf. 13½*
489 A53 20a Holy House of Mercy .25 .15
490 A53 60a St. Lawrence Church .25 .15
491 A53 90a King Peter V Theater .40 .15
492 A53 3p Palace of St. Sancha 1.40 .25
493 A53 15p Moorish barracks 6.50 1.25
Nos. 489-493 (5) 8.80 1.95

Birds, Ausipex '84 Emblem A62

1984, Sept. 21 Litho. *Perf. 13*
494 A62 30a Kingfishers .70 .35
495 A62 40a European jay 1.25 .35
496 A62 50a White eyes 1.65 .35
497 A62 70a Hoopoe 1.75 .35
498 A62 2.50p Peking nightingale 7.25 .70
499 A62 6p Wild duck 13.00 1.25
Nos. 494-499 (6) 25.60 3.35

Philakorea '84 Emblem, Fishing Boats — A63

1984, Oct. 22 Litho.
500 A63 20a Hok lou t'eng .75 .25
501 A63 60a Tai t'ong 2.25 .25
502 A63 2p Tai mei chai 8.00 .65
503 A63 5p Ch'at pong t'o 17.00 1.65
Nos. 500-503 (4) 28.00 2.80

New Year Type of 1984

1985, Feb. 13 Litho. *Perf. 13½*
504 A60 1p Buffalo 4.50 .25
a. Booklet pane of 5 *30.00*

Intl. Youth Year — A65

1985, Apr. 19 Litho. *Perf. 13½*
505 A65 2.50p shown .90 .60
506 A65 3p Clasped hands 1.10 .75

Visit of President Eanes of Portugal A66

1985, May 27 Litho.
507 A66 1.50p multicolored 1.50 .50

Luis de Camoens Museum, 25th Anniv. — A67

Silk paintings by Chen Chi Yun.

1985, June 27 **Litho.**

508 A67 2.50p Two travelers, hermit 3.75 .85
509 A67 2.50p Traveling merchant 3.75 .85
510 A67 2.50p Conversation in a garden 3.75 .85
511 A67 2.50p Veranda of a house 3.75 .85
a. Strip of 4, #508-511 37.50 7.00

Butterflies, World Tourism Assoc. Emblem — A68

1985, Sept. 27 **Litho.**

512 A68 30a Euploea midamus .50 .15
513 A68 50a Hebomoia glaucippe .85 .15
514 A68 70a Lethe confusa 1.10 .30
515 A68 2p Heliophorus epicles 2.75 .70
516 A68 4p Euthalia phemius seitzi 8.00 2.00
517 A68 7.50p Troides helena 12.50 3.00
a. Sheet of 6, #512-517 300.00
Nos. 512-517 (6) 25.70 6.30

World Tourism Day.

Cargo Boats — A69

Designs: 50a, Tou. 70a, Veng Seng Lei motor junk. 1p, Tong Heng Long No. 2 motor junk. 6p, Fong Vong San cargo ship.

1985, Oct. 25 ***Perf. 14***

518 A69 50a multicolored .90 .15
519 A69 70a multicolored 1.25 .50
520 A69 1p multicolored 2.50 .45
521 A69 6p multicolored 12.00 2.50
Nos. 518-521 (4) 16.65 3.60

New Year Type of 1984

1986, Feb. 3 ***Perf. 13½***

522 A60 1.50p Tiger 3.50 1.65
a. Booklet pane of 5 24.00

City of Macau, 400th Anniv. — A71

1986, Apr. 10 **Litho.** ***Perf. 13½***

523 A71 2.20p multicolored 1.50 .55

Musical Instruments — A72

1986, May 22

524 A72 20a Suo-na .90 .25
525 A72 50a Sheng 1.90 .25
526 A72 60a Er-hu 2.25 .25
527 A72 70a Ruan 3.25 .50
528 A72 5p Cheng 13.00 3.00
529 A72 8p Pi-pa 19.00 5.00
a. Souvenir sheet of 6, #524-529 250.00
Nos. 524-529 (6) 40.30 9.25

AMERIPEX '86.

Ferries — A73

1986, Aug. 28 **Litho.** ***Perf. 13***

530 A73 10a Hydrofoil .25 .15
531 A73 40a Hovermarine .50 .15
532 A73 3p Jetfoil 5.75 1.40
533 A73 7.5p High-speed ferry 14.00 3.25
Nos. 530-533 (4) 20.50 4.95

Fortresses A74

1986, Oct. 3 **Litho.** ***Perf. 12½***

534 A74 2p Taipa 16.00 3.00
535 A74 2p Sao Paulo do Monte 16.00 3.00
536 A74 2p Our Lady of Guia 16.00 3.00
537 A74 2p Sao Francisco 16.00 3.00
a. Strip of 4, #534-537 65.00 12.00

Macao Security Forces, 10th anniv. No. 537a has continuous design.

Dr. Sun Yat-sen
A75 A76

1986, Nov. 12 **Litho.** ***Perf. 12½***

538 A75 70a multicolored 8.00 2.50

Souvenir Sheet

539 A76 1.30p shown 75.00 35.00

New Year Type of 1984

1987, Jan. 21 ***Perf. 13½***

540 A60 1.50p Hare 4.00 1.00
a. Booklet pane of 5 25.00

Shek Wan Ceramic Figures in the Luis de Camoens Museum — A78

1987, Apr. 10 **Litho.** ***Perf. 13½***

541 A78 2.20p Medicine man 12.00 3.75
542 A78 2.20p Choi San, god of good fortune 12.00 3.75
543 A78 2.20p Yi, sun god 12.00 3.75
544 A78 2.20p Chung Kuei, conqueror of demons 12.00 3.75

Printed se-tenant in blocks of four.

Dragon Boat Festival A79

1987, May 29 **Litho.** ***Perf. 13½***

545 A79 50a Dragon boat race 1.00 .15
546 A79 5p Figurehead 4.00 1.40

Decorated Fans — A80 Casino Gambling — A81

1987, July 29 **Litho.** ***Perf. 12½***

547 A80 30a multicolored 2.50 .55
548 A80 70a multi, diff. 5.50 .80
549 A80 1p multi, diff. 7.00 1.00
550 A80 6p multi, diff. 50.00 6.50
a. Souvenir sheet of 4, #547-550 600.00
Nos. 547-550 (4) 65.00 8.85

1987, Sept. 30 ***Perf. 13½***

551 A81 20a Fan-tan 1.25 .30
552 A81 40a Cussec 1.50 .40
553 A81 4p Baccarat 15.00 3.00
554 A81 7p Roulette 26.00 5.00
Nos. 551-554 (4) 43.75 8.70

Traditional Transportation — A82

1987, Nov. 18 **Litho.** ***Perf. 13½***

555 A82 10a Market wagon .30 .15
556 A82 70a Sedan chair .50 .25
557 A82 90a Rickshaw .70 .35
558 A82 10p Tricycle rickshaw 6.50 3.25
Nos. 555-558 (4) 8.00 4.00

Souvenir Sheet

559 A82 7.50p Sedan chair, diff. 77.50

New Year Type of 1984

1988, Feb. 10 **Litho.** ***Perf. 13½***

560 A60 2.50p Dragon 6.00 2.00
a. Booklet pane of 5 45.00

Wildlife Protection A84

1988, Apr. 14 **Litho.** ***Perf. 12½x12***

561 A84 3p Erinacens europaeus 7.00 4.50
562 A84 3p Meles meles 7.00 4.50
563 A84 3p Lutra lutra 7.00 4.50
564 A84 3p Manis pentadactyla 7.00 4.50
a. Strip of 4, #561-564 30.00 18.00

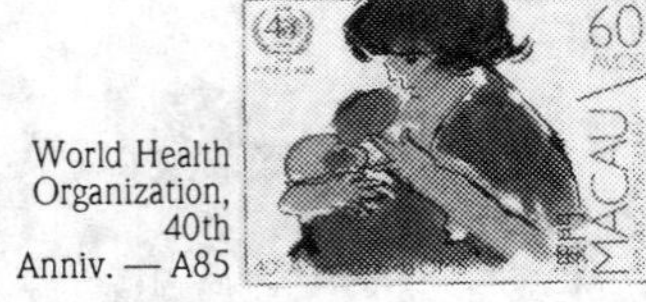

World Health Organization, 40th Anniv. — A85

1988, June 1 **Litho.** ***Perf. 13½***

565 A85 60a Breast-feeding 1.40 .25
566 A85 80a Immunization 1.75 .45
567 A85 2.40p Blood donation 4.75 1.50
Nos. 565-567 (3) 7.90 2.20

Modes of Transportation — A86

1988, July 15 **Litho.**

568 A86 20a Bicycles .30 .30
569 A86 50a Vespa, Lambretta .50 .40
570 A86 3.30p 1907 Rover 20hp 3.00 2.75
571 A86 5p 1912 Renault delivery truck 4.25 3.50
Nos. 568-571 (4) 8.05 6.95

Souvenir Sheet

572 A86 7.50p 1930s Sedan 85.00

1988 Summer Olympics, Seoul — A87

1988, Sept. 19 **Litho.**

573 A87 40a Hurdles .65 .15
574 A87 60a Basketball 1.00 .20
575 A87 1p Soccer 1.75 .45
576 A87 8p Table tennis 12.00 3.50
Nos. 573-576 (4) 15.40 4.30

Sheet

577 Sheet of 5, #573-576, 577a 90.00
a. A87 5p Tae kwon do 8.75

World Post Day — A88 35th Macao Grand Prix — A89

1988, Oct. 10 **Litho.** ***Perf. 14***

578 A88 13.40p Electronic mail 3.25 3.25
579 A88 40p Express mail 10.00 10.00

1988, Nov. 24 **Litho.** ***Perf. 12½***

580 A89 80a Sedan .80 .35
581 A89 2.80p Motorcycle 3.50 1.25
582 A89 7p Formula 3 8.00 2.75
a. Souvenir sheet of 3, #580-582 100.00
Nos. 580-582 (3) 12.30 4.35

New Year Type of 1984

1989, Jan. 20 **Litho.** ***Perf. 13½***

583 A60 3p Snake 2.00 1.00
a. Booklet pane of 5 24.00

Occupations — A91

1989, Mar. 1 **Litho.** ***Perf. 12x12½***

584 A91 50a Water carrier .50 .15
585 A91 1p Tan-kya woman .80 .40
586 A91 4p Tin-tin (junk) man 3.50 1.40
587 A91 5p Tofu peddler 3.75 1.75
Nos. 584-587 (4) 8.55 3.70

See Nos. 612-615, 640-643.

Watercolors by George Smirnoff in the Luis de Camoens Museum A92

1989, Apr. 10 **Litho.** ***Perf. 12½x12***

588 A92 2p multi (4-1) 2.00 .80
589 A92 2p multi (4-2) 2.00 .80
590 A92 2p multi (4-3) 2.00 .80
591 A92 2p multi (4-4) 2.00 .80
a. Strip of 4, #588-591 8.00 3.25

Snakes
A93

1989, July 7 **Litho.**
592 A93 2.50p *Naja naja* 2.50 1.00
593 A93 2.50p *Bungarus fasciatus* 2.50 1.00
594 A93 2.50p *Trimeresurus albolabris* 2.50 1.00
595 A93 2.50p *Elaphe radiata* 2.50 1.00
a. Strip of 4, #592-595 10.00 4.00

Traditional Games — A94

1989, July 31 **Litho.** ***Perf. 13½***
596 A94 10a Talu .15 .15
597 A94 60a Triol .30 .15
598 A94 3.30p Chiquia 1.50 .85
599 A94 5p Xadrez Chines 2.25 1.40
Nos. 596-599 (4) 4.20 2.55

Seaplanes — A95

1989, Oct. 9 **Litho.**
600 A95 50a Over church .30 .15
601 A95 70a American over lighthouse .40 .20
602 A95 2.80p shown 1.75 .70
603 A95 4p Over junk 2.50 1.00
Nos. 600-603 (4) 4.95 2.05

Souvenir Sheet

604 A95 7.50p Over harbor 40.00

No. 604 contains one 40x30mm stamp.

World Stamp Expo '89, Washington, DC — A96

1989, Nov. 17 **Litho.** ***Perf. 12½***
605 A96 40a Malaca .15 .15
606 A96 70a Thailand .30 .20
607 A96 90a India .35 .25
608 A96 2.50p Japan .90 .65
609 A96 7.50p China 2.75 1.90
Nos. 605-609 (5) 4.45 3.15

Souvenir Sheet

610 Sheet of 6, #605-609, 610a 37.50
a. A96 3p Macao 1.10

Influence of the Portuguese in the Far East.

New Year Type of 1984

1990, Jan. 19 **Litho.** ***Perf. 13½***
611 A60 4p Horse 2.50 2.00
a. Booklet pane of 5 15.00

Occupations Type of 1989

1990, Mar. 1 **Litho.** ***Perf. 12x12½***
612 A91 30a Long chau singer .20 .15
613 A91 70a Cobbler .50 .25
614 A91 1.50p Scribe .70 .50
615 A91 7.50p Net fisherman 3.50 2.00
Nos. 612-615 (4) 4.90 2.90

Souvenir Sheet

Penny Black, 150th Anniv. — A99

1990, May 3 **Litho.** ***Perf. 12***
616 A99 10p multicolored 30.00 15.00

Stamp World London 90.

Lutianus Malabaricus
A100

1990, June 8 ***Perf. 12x12½***
617 A100 2.40p shown 2.00 2.00
618 A100 2.40p Epinephelus megachir 2.00 2.00
619 A100 2.40p Macropodus opercularis 2.00 2.00
620 A100 2.40p Ophiocephalus maculatus 2.00 2.00
a. Strip of 4, #617-620 8.00 8.00

Decorative Porcelain
A101

1990, Aug. 24 **Litho.** ***Perf. 12½***
621 A101 3p shown 2.75 2.75
622 A101 3p Furniture 2.75 2.75
623 A101 3p Toys 2.75 2.75
624 A101 3p Artificial flowers 2.75 2.75
a. Souvenir sheet of 4, #621-624 50.00 25.00
b. Block or strip of 4, #621-624 11.00 11.00

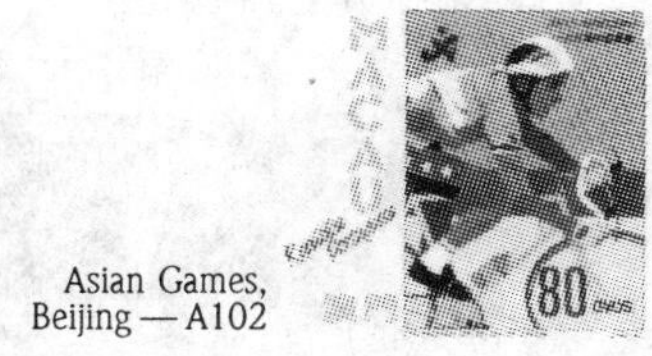

Asian Games, Beijing — A102

1990, Sept. 22 **Litho.** ***Perf. 13½***
625 A102 80a Cycling .35 .20
626 A102 1p Swimming .50 .25
627 A102 3p Judo 1.50 1.00
628 A102 4.20p Shooting 2.00 1.40
Nos. 625-628 (4) 4.35 2.85

Souvenir Sheet

629 Sheet of 5, #625-628, 629a 70.00 35.00
a. A102 6p Martial arts 2.50 2.50

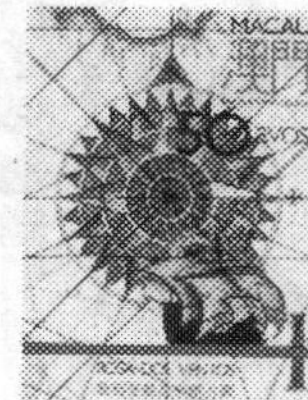

Compass Roses from Portuguese Charts — A103

Charts by 16th century cartographers: Lazaro Luis, Diogo Homem, Fernao Vaz Dourado, and Luiz Teixeira.

1990, Oct. 9 **Litho.** ***Perf. 13½***
630 A103 50a shown .50 .25
631 A103 1p multi, diff. 1.00 .50
632 A103 3.50p multi, diff. 2.75 1.50
633 A103 6.50p multi, diff. 5.00 2.50
Nos. 630-633 (4) 9.25 4.75

Souvenir Sheet

634 A103 5p multi, diff. 65.00 45.00

Games with Animals
A104

1990, Nov. 15 **Litho.** ***Perf. 14***
635 A104 20a Cricket fight .15 .15
636 A104 80a Bird fight .25 .20
637 A104 1p Greyhound race .35 .25
638 A104 10p Horse race 3.50 2.50
Nos. 635-638 (4) 4.25 3.10

New Year Type of 1984

1991, Feb. 8 **Litho.** ***Perf. 13½***
639 A60 4.50p Sheep 3.50 2.00
b. Booklet pane of 5 19.00

Occupations Type of 1987

1991, Mar. 1 ***Perf. 14***
640 A91 80a Knife grinder .45 .30
641 A91 1.70p Flour puppet vender .95 .75
642 A91 3.50p Street barber 2.00 1.50
643 A91 4.20p Fortune teller 2.50 1.75
Nos. 640-643 (4) 5.90 4.30

Shells
A106

1991, Apr. 18 **Litho.** ***Perf. 14***
644 A106 3p Murex pecten 3.00 3.00
645 A106 3p Harpa harpa 3.00 3.00
646 A106 3p Chicoreus rosarius 3.00 3.00
647 A106 3p Tonna zonata 3.00 3.00
a. Strip of 4, #644-647 12.00 12.00

Chinese Opera — A107

Various performers in costume.

1991, June 5 **Litho.** ***Perf. 13½***
648 A107 60a multicolored .50 .25
649 A107 80a multicolored .80 .40
650 A107 1p multicolored 1.00 .50
651 A107 10p multicolored 11.00 5.00
Nos. 648-651 (4) 13.30 6.15

Flowers
A108

Designs: 1.70p, Delonix regia. 3p, Ipomoea cairica. 3.50p, Jasminum mesnyi. 4.20p, Bauhinia variegata.

1991, Oct. 9 **Litho.** ***Perf. 13½***
652 A108 1.70p multicolored .80 .70
653 A108 3p multicolored 1.25 1.00
654 A108 3.50p multicolored 1.65 1.25
655 A108 4.20p multicolored 2.25 1.75
a. Souvenir sheet of 4, #652-655 50.00 25.00
Nos. 652-655 (4) 5.95 4.70

Cultural Exchange — A109

Namban screen: No. 656, Unloading boat.

1991, Nov. 16 **Litho.** ***Perf. 12***
656 A109 4.20p multicolored 1.25 1.10
657 A109 4.20p shown 1.25 1.10
a. Souvenir sheet of 2, #656-657 15.00 7.50

Holiday Greetings
A110

1991, Nov. 29 **Litho.** ***Perf. 14½***
658 A110 1.70p Lunar New Year .80 .65
659 A110 3p Santa Claus, Christmas 1.50 1.00
660 A110 3.50p Old man 1.40 1.10
661 A110 4.20p Girl at New Year party 1.65 1.40
Nos. 658-661 (4) 5.35 4.15

New Year Type of 1984

1992, Jan. 28 **Litho.** ***Perf. 13½***
662 A60 4.50p Monkey 3.00 2.50
a. Booklet pane of 5 22.50

Paintings of Doors and Windows
A111

1992, Mar. 1 ***Perf. 14***
663 A111 1.70p multicolored .60 .60
664 A111 3p multi, diff. .90 .90
665 A111 3.50p multi, diff. 1.00 1.00
666 A111 4.20p multi, diff. 1.25 1.25
Nos. 663-666 (4) 3.75 3.75

Mythological Chinese Gods
A112

1992, Apr. 3 **Litho.** ***Perf. 14***
667 A112 3.50p T'it Kuai Lei (4-1) 10.00 5.00
668 A112 3.50p Chong Lei Kun (4-2) 10.00 5.00
669 A112 3.50p Cheong Kuo Lou (4-3) 10.00 5.00

670 A112 3.50p Loi Tong Pan (4-4) 10.00 5.00
a. Block or strip of 4, #667-670 *40.00 20.00*

See Nos. 689-692.

Lion Dance Costume A113

Designs: 2.70p, Lion, diff. 6p, Dragon.

1992, May 18
671 A113 1p multicolored .50 .40
672 A113 2.70p multicolored 1.25 1.00
673 A113 6p multicolored 2.25 2.00
Nos. 671-673 (3) 4.00 3.40

World Columbian Stamp Expo '92, Chicago.

1992 Summer Olympics, Barcelona — A114

1992, July 1 Litho. *Perf. 13*
674 A114 80a High jump .50 .40
675 A114 4.20p Badminton 1.90 1.50
676 A114 4.70p Roller hockey 2.50 1.65
677 A114 5p Yachting 2.75 1.75
a. Souvenir sheet of 4, #674-677 *26.00 13.00*
Nos. 674-677 (4) 7.65 5.30

Temples A115

1992, Oct. 9 *Perf. 14*
678 A115 1p Na Cha .45 .40
679 A115 1.50p Kun Iam .65 .60
680 A115 1.70p Hong Kon .65 .60
681 A115 6.50p A Ma 2.50 2.25
Nos. 678-681 (4) 4.25 3.85

See Nos. 685-688.

Portuguese-Chinese Friendship — A116

1992, Nov. 1 Litho. *Perf. 14*
682 A116 10p multicolored 4.00 3.50
a. Souv. sheet, perf. 13½ *20.00 10.00*

Tung Sin Tong Charity Organization, Cent. — A117

1992, Nov. 27 *Perf. 12x11½*
683 A117 1p multicolored .75 .75

New Year Type of 1984

1993, Jan. 18 Litho. *Perf. 13½*
684 A60 5p Rooster 2.75 2.00
a. Booklet pane of 5 16.00

Temple Type of 1992

1993, Mar. 1 Litho. *Perf. 14*
685 A115 50a T'am Kong .15 .15
686 A115 2p T'in Hau .65 .60
687 A115 3.50p Lin Fong 1.10 1.00
688 A115 8p Pau Kong 2.25 2.25
Nos. 685-688 (4) 4.15 4.00

Mythological Chinese Gods Type of 1992

Designs: No. 689, Lam Ch'oi Wo seated on crane in flight. No. 690, Ho Sin Ku, seated on peach flower.No. 691, Hon Seong Chi throwing peonies from basket. No. 692, Ch'ou Kuok K'ao seated on gold plate.

1993, Apr. 1 Litho. *Perf. 14*
689 A112 3.50p multicolored (4-1) *4.00 2.25*
690 A112 3.50p multicolored (4-2) *4.00 2.25*
691 A112 3.50p multicolored (4-3) *4.00 2.25*
692 A112 3.50p multicolored (4-4) *4.00 2.25*
a. Block of 4, #689-692 *16.00 9.00*

Chinese Wedding — A118

#693, Three children celebrating. #694, Bride. #695, Groom. #696, Woman with parasol, person being carried. 8p, Bride & groom.

1993, May 19 *Perf. 14*
693 A118 3p multicolored *2.00 1.50*
694 A118 3p multicolored *2.00 1.50*
695 A118 3p multicolored *2.00 1.50*
696 A118 3p multicolored *2.00 1.50*
a. Strip of 4, #693-696 *8.00 6.00*

Souvenir Sheet

Perf. 14½x14
697 A118 8p multicolored *20.00 10.00*

No. 697 contains one 50x40mm stamp.

World Environment Day — A119 Birds — A120

1993, June 5 Litho. *Perf. 14*
698 A119 1p multicolored .60 .60

1993, June 27
699 A120 3p Falco peregrinus 1.25 1.00
700 A120 3p Aquila obrysaetos 1.25 1.00
701 A120 3p Asio otus 1.25 1.00
702 A120 3p Tyto alba 1.25 1.00
a. Block or strip of 4, #699-702 5.00 4.00
b. Souvenir sheet of 4, #699-702 *16.00 8.00*

Union of Portuguese Speaking Capitals A121

1993, July 30 Litho. *Perf. 13½*
703 A121 1.50p multicolored .60 .60

Portuguese Arrival in Japan, 450th Anniv. A122

Designs: 50a, Japanese using musket. 3p, Catholic priests 3.50p, Exchanging items of trade.

1993, Sept. 22 Litho. *Perf. 12x11½*
704 A122 50a multicolored .20 .20
705 A122 3p multicolored 1.00 1.00
706 A122 3.50p multicolored 1.25 1.25
Nos. 704-706 (3) 2.45 2.45

See Portugal Nos. 1964-1966.

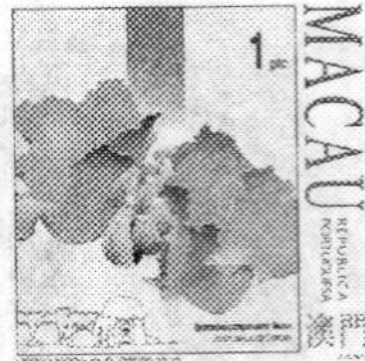

Flowers — A123

Designs: 1p, Spathodea campanulata. 2p, Tithonia diversifolia. 3p, Rhodomyrtus tomentosa. 8p, Passiflora foetida.

1993, Oct. 9 *Perf. 14½*
707 A123 1p multicolored .40 .40
708 A123 2p multicolored .65 .65
709 A123 3p multicolored .90 .90
710 A123 8p multicolored 2.50 2.50
a. Souvenir sheet of 4, #707-710 *20.00 10.00*
Nos. 707-710 (4) 4.45 4.45

Portuguese Ships — A124

1993, Nov. 5 Litho. *Perf. 14*
711 A124 1p Caravel .50 .40
712 A124 2p Round caravel .80 .65
713 A124 3.50p Nau 1.40 1.10
714 A124 4.50p Galleon 1.90 1.50
a. Souvenir sheet of 4, #711-714 *18.00 9.00*
Nos. 711-714 (4) 4.60 3.65

Macao Grand Prix, 40th Anniv. A125

1993, Nov. 16 Litho. *Perf. 13½*
715 A125 1.50p Stock car .50 .50
716 A125 2p Motorcycle .65 .65
717 A125 4.50p Formula 1 race car 1.50 1.50
Nos. 715-717 (3) 2.65 2.65

New Year Type of 1984

1994, Feb. 3 Litho. *Perf. 13½*
718 A60 5p Dog 2.50 1.50
a. Booklet pane of 5 14.00

New Year 1994 (Year of the Dog).

Prince Henry the Navigator (1394-1460) — A126

Illustration reduced.

1994, Mar. 4 Litho. *Perf. 12*
719 A126 3p multicolored 1.25 .80

See Portugal No. 1987.

Scenes of Macao, by George Chinnery (1774-1852) — A127

Designs: No. 720, Hut, natives. No. 721, S. Tiago Fortress. No. 722, Overview of Praia Grande. No. 723, S. Francisco Church.

1994, Mar. 21 *Perf. 14*
720 A127 3.50p multi (4-1) 1.00 .95
721 A127 3.50p multi (4-2) 1.00 .95
722 A127 3.50p multi (4-3) 1.00 .95
723 A127 3.50p multi (4-4) 1.00 .95
a. Strip or block of 4, #720-723 4.00 3.75
b. Souvenir sheet of 4, #720-723 *15.00 7.50*

Spring Festival of New Lunar Year — A128

Designs: 1p, Girl, woman shopping. 2p, Celebration. 3.50p, Couple preparing food at table. 4.50p, Old man making decorations.

1994, Apr. 6
724 A128 1p multicolored .25 .25
725 A128 2p multicolored .55 .55
726 A128 3.50p multicolored .95 .95
727 A128 4.50p multicolored 1.25 1.25
Nos. 724-727 (4) 3.00 3.00

Mythological Chinese Gods — A129

Statuettes: No. 728, Happiness. No. 729. Prosperity. No. 730, Longevity.

1994, May 9 Litho. *Perf. 12*
728 A129 3p multi (3-1) *2.50 1.25*
729 A129 3p multi (3-2) *2.50 1.25*
730 A129 3p multi (3-3) *2.50 1.25*
a. Strip of 3, #728-730 *7.50 3.75*
b. Souvenir sheet of 3, #728-730 *12.50 7.00*

A130

A131

1994 World Cup Soccer Championships, US: Various soccer players.

1994, June 1
731 A130 2p multicolored .55 .55
732 A130 3p multicolored .80 .80
733 A130 3.50p multicolored .95 .95
734 A130 4.50p multicolored 1.25 1.25
a. Souvenir sheet of 4, #731-734 *17.00 8.50*
Nos. 731-734 (4) 3.55 3.55

1994, June 27 Litho. *Perf. 12*

Traditional Chinese shops.

735 A131 1p Rice shop .25 .25
736 A131 1.50p Medicinal drink shop .40 .40
737 A131 2p Salt fish shop .55 .55
738 A131 3.50p Pharmacy .95 .95
Nos. 735-738 (4) 2.15 2.15

Navigation Instruments — A132

1994, Sept. 13 Litho. *Perf. 12*

739 A132 3p Astrolabe 1.10 .80
740 A132 3.50p Quadrant 1.25 .95
741 A132 4.50p Sextant 1.65 1.25
Nos. 739-741 (3) 4.00 3.00

12th Asian Games, Hiroshima 1994 — A133

1994, Sept. 30 Litho. *Perf. 12*

742 A133 1p Fencing .50 .30
743 A133 2p Gymnastics 1.10 .55
744 A133 3p Water polo 1.50 .80
745 A133 3.50p Pole vault 1.90 .95
Nos. 742-745 (4) 5.00 2.60

Bridges A134

1994, Oct. 8

746 A134 1p Nobre de Carvalho .35 .30
747 A134 8p Friendship 2.25 2.00

Fortune Symbols — A135

Designs: 3p, Child, carp, water lily. 3.50p, Basket of peaches, child, bats. 4.50p, Flower, child playing mouth organ.

1994, Nov. 7 Litho. *Perf. 12*

748 A135 3p multicolored 1.50 1.00
749 A135 3.50p multicolored 1.65 1.25
750 A135 4.50p multicolored 2.25 1.50
Nos. 748-750 (3) 5.40 3.75

Religious Art — A136

Designs: 50a, Stained glass, angel's head. 1p, Stained glass, Holy Ghost. 1.50p, Silver sacrarium. 2p, Silver salver. 3p, Ivory sculpture, Escape to Egypt. 3.50p, Gold & silver chalice.

1994, Nov. 30

751 A136 50a multicolored .20 .15
752 A136 1p multicolored .40 .25
753 A136 1.50p multicolored .65 .40
754 A136 2p multicolored .90 .55
755 A136 3p multicolored 1.25 .80
756 A136 3.50p multicolored 1.50 .95
Nos. 751-756 (6) 4.90 3.10

New Year Type of 1984

1995, Jan. 23 Litho. *Perf. 13½*

757 A60 5.50p Boar 1.50 1.50

Tourism A138

Scenes of Macao, by Lio Man Cheong: 50a, Walkway beside pond. 1p, Lighthouse. 1.50p, Temple. 2p, Buildings along coast. 2.50p, Columns, temple. 3p, Ruins on hill overlooking city. 3.50p, Bridge. 4p, Trees in park.

1995, Mar. 1 Litho. *Perf. 12*

758 A138 50a multicolored .25 .15
759 A138 1p multicolored .50 .30
760 A138 1.50p multicolored .65 .40
761 A138 2p multicolored .90 .55
762 A138 2.50p multicolored 1.10 .65
763 A138 3p multicolored 1.25 .80
764 A138 3.50p multicolored 1.50 .95
765 A138 4p multicolored 1.75 1.10
Nos. 758-765 (8) 7.90 4.90

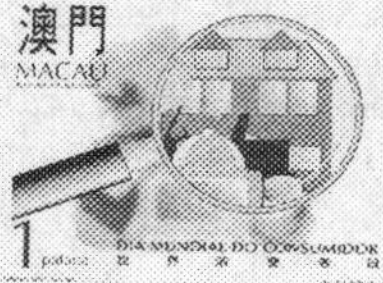

World Day of the Consumer A139

1995, Mar. 15

766 A139 1p multicolored .30 .30

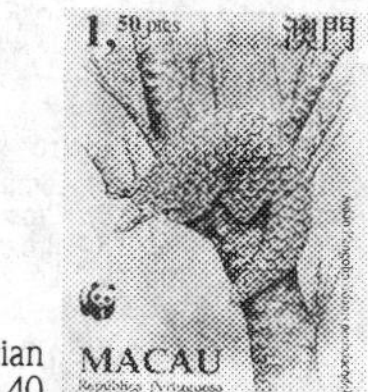

Asian Pangolin — A140

1995, Apr. 10

767 A140 1.50p Facing left (4-1) *2.50* .40
768 A140 1.50p Hanging by tail (4-2) *2.50* .40
769 A140 1.50p On tree limb (4-3) *2.50* .40
770 A140 1.50p On tree stump (4-4) *2.50* .40
a. Strip or block of 4, #767-770 *10.00* 1.60

World wildlife Fund.
Issued in sheets of 16 stamps.

Legend of Buddhist Goddess Kun Iam — A141

#772, Seated atop dragon, holding flower. #773, Meditating. #774, Holding infant.
8p, Goddess with many faces, hands.

1995, May 5 Litho. *Perf. 12*

771 A141 3p multicolored 1.50 .80
772 A141 3p multicolored 1.50 .80
773 A141 3p multicolored 1.50 .80
774 A141 3p multicolored 1.50 .80
a. Strip or block of 4, #771-774 6.00 3.25

Souvenir Sheet

775 A141 8p multicolored *24.00 12.00*

Senado Square — A142

Designs: No. 776, Street, bell tower. No. 777, Street, plaza, shops. No. 778, Fountain, plaza. No. 779, Plaza, buildings.
8p, Bell tower, building, horiz.

1995, June 24 Litho. *Perf. 12*

776 A142 2p multicolored 1.00 .65
777 A142 2p multicolored 1.00 .65
778 A142 2p multicolored 1.00 .65
779 A142 2p multicolored 1.00 .65
a. Strip of 4, #776-779 4.00 2.75

Souvenir Sheet

780 A142 8p multicolored 14.00 7.00

Temple Type of 1992

1995, July 17 Litho. *Perf. 12*

781 A115 50a Kuan Tai .15 .15
782 A115 1p Pak Tai .25 .25
783 A115 1.50p Lin K'ai .40 .40
784 A115 3p Sek Kam Tong .80 .80
785 A115 3.50p Fok Tak .95 .95
Nos. 781-785 (5) 2.55 2.55

Singapore '95 — A143

Birds: No. 786, Gurrulax canorus. No. 787, Serinus canarius. No. 788, Zosterops japonica. No. 789, Leiothrix lutea. 10p, Copsychus saularis.

1995, Sept. 1 Litho. *Perf. 12*

786 A143 2.50p multicolored .75 .65
787 A143 2.50p multicolored .75 .65
788 A143 2.50p multicolored .75 .65
789 A143 2.50p multicolored .75 .65
a. Strip of 4, #786-789 3.00 2.60

Souvenir Sheet

790 A143 10p multicolored *14.00 6.00*

Intl. Music Festival — A144

1995, Oct. 9 Litho. *Perf. 12*

791 A144 1p Pipa (6-1) .45 .25
792 A144 1p Erhu (6-2) .45 .25
793 A144 1p Gongo (6-3) .45 .25
794 A144 1p Sheng (6-4) .45 .25
795 A144 1p Xiao (6-5) .45 .25
796 A144 1p Tambor (6-6) .45 .25
a. Block of 6, #791-796 2.75 1.50

Souvenir Sheet

797 A144 8p Musicians, horiz. *14.00 6.00*

UN, 50th Anniv. A145

1995, Oct. 24 Litho. *Perf. 12*

798 A145 4.50p multicolored 1.75 1.25

Macao Intl. Airport A146

Designs: 1p, Airplane above terminal. 1.50p, Boeing 747 on ground, terminal. 2p, Hangars, 747 with boarding ramp at door. 3p, Airplane, control tower. 8p, Boeing 747 over runway.

1995, Dec. 8 Litho. *Perf. 12*

799 A146 1p multicolored .25 .25
800 A146 1.50p multicolored .40 .40
801 A146 2p multicolored .50 .50
802 A146 3p multicolored .75 .75
Nos. 799-802 (4) 1.90 1.90

Souvenir Sheet

Perf. 12½

803 A146 8p multicolored *15.00 7.50*

No. 803 contains one 51x38mm stamp.

New Year Type of 1984
Miniature Sheet of 12

Designs: a, like #485. b, like #504. c, like #522. d, like #540. e, like #560. f, like #583. g, like #611. h, like #639. i, like #662. j, like #684. k, like #718. l, like #757.

1996 Litho. *Perf. 13½*

804 A60 1.50p #a.-l. + label *17.50 8.75*

New Year 1996 (Year of the Rat) — A147

1996, Feb. 12 Litho. *Perf. 12*

805 A147 5p multicolored 2.00 1.25

Souvenir Sheet

806 A147 10p like No. 805 *27.50* 14.00

Traditional Chinese Bird Cages — A148

Various styles.

1996, Mar. 1 Litho. *Perf. 12*

807 A148 1p red & multi (4-1) .25 .25
808 A148 1.50p green & multi (4-2) .40 .40
809 A148 3p red violet & multi (4-3) .75 .75
810 A148 4.50p blue & multi (4-4) 1.10 1.10
Nos. 807-810 (4) 2.50 2.50

Souvenir Sheet

811 A148 10p purple & multi *12.00* 2.50

Paintings, by Herculano Estorninho A149

Scenes of Macao: 50a, Boats. 1.50p, Street, buildings at night, vert. 3p, Fronts of buildings during day, vert. 5p, Townhouse complex.
10p, Entrance to building, vert.

1996, Apr. 1

812 A149 50a multi (4-1) .15 .15
813 A149 1.50p multi (4-2) .40 .40
814 A149 3p multi (4-3) .75 .75
815 A149 5p multi (4-4) 1.25 1.25
Nos. 812-815 (4) 2.55 2.55

Souvenir Sheet

816 A149 10p multi *10.00* 2.50

Myths and Legends — A150

Designs: No. 817, Man holding staff. No. 818, Man riding tiger. No. 819, Man on top of fireplace.

1996, Apr. 30 Litho. *Perf. 12*

817 A150 3.50p Tou Tei (3-1) .95 .95
818 A150 3.50p Choi San (3-2) .95 .95
819 A150 3.50p Chou Kuan (3-3) .95 .95
a. Strip of 3, #817-819 3.00 3.00
b. Souvenir sheet of 3, #817-819 *12.00* 3.00

Traditional Chinese Tea Houses A151

Designs: No. 820, Two men seated at table. No. 821, Cook holding steaming tray of food, woman, baby. No. 822, Woman holding up papers. No. 823, Waiter pouring tea, man seated.
8p, Food, serving bowl.

1996, May 17 *Perf. 12*

820 A151 2p multi (4-1) .55 .55
821 A151 2p multi (4-2) .55 .55
822 A151 2p multi (4-3) .55 .55
823 A151 2p multi (4-4) .55 .55
a. Block of 4, #820-823 2.25 2.25

Souvenir Sheet

824 A151 8p multi *12.00* 2.25

No. 823a is a continuous design. China '96 (#824).

Greetings Stamps A152

Designs: 50a, Get well. 1.50p, Congratulations on new baby. 3p, Happy birthday. 4p, Marriage congratulations.

1996, June 14 **Litho.** *Perf. 12*

825 A152 50a multi (4-1) .15 .15
826 A152 1.50p multi (4-2) .40 .40
827 A152 3p multi (4-3) .75 .75
828 A152 4p multi (4-4) 1.00 1.00
Nos. 825-828 (4) 2.30 2.30

1996 Summer Olympic Games, Atlanta A153

1996, July 19

829 A153 2p Swimming (4-1) .50 .50
830 A153 3p Soccer (4-2) .80 .80
831 A153 3.50p Gymnastics (4-3) .90 .90
832 A153 4.50p Sailboarding (4-4) 1.10 1.10
Nos. 829-832 (4) 3.30 3.30

Souvenir Sheet

833 A153 10p Boxing *12.00* 2.50

MACAU

For information write to:

MACAU POST OFFICE
PHILATELIC DIVISION
MACAU(ASIA)

FAX: (853)921663/3969104

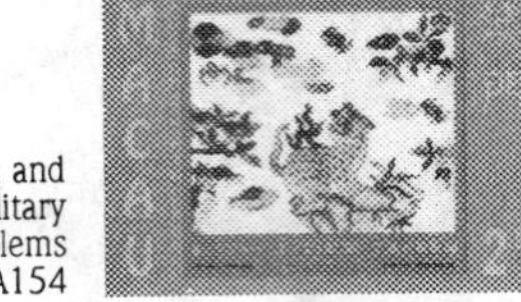

Civil and Military Emblems A154

#834, Bird looking left. #835, Dragon. #836, Bird looking right. #837, Leopard.

1996, Sept. 18

834 A154 2.50p blue & multi (4-1) .65 .65
835 A154 2.50p green & multi (4-2) .65 .65
836 A154 2.50p green & multi (4-3) .65 .65
837 A154 2.50p purple & multi (4-4) .65 .65
a. Block of 4, #834-837 2.60 2.60

Fishing with Nets — A155

Boats, fish in sea: No. 838, Six small nets extended from mast of boat. No. 839, Modern trawler. No. 840, Junk trawling. No. 841, Sailboat with nets extended from both sides.

1996, Oct. 9 **Litho.** *Perf. 12*

838 A155 3p multi (4-1) 1.25 1.25
839 A155 3p multi (4-2) 1.25 1.25
840 A155 3p multi (4-3) 1.25 1.25
841 A155 3p multi (4-4) 1.25 1.25
a. Strip of 4, #838-841 5.00 5.00

Legislative Assembly, 20th Anniv. — A156

Illustration reduced.

1996, Oct. 15 **Litho.** *Perf. 12x12½*

842 A156 2.80p multicolored .75 .75

Souvenir Sheet

843 A156 8p like No. 842 *11.00* 6.00

Paper Kites A157

1996, Oct. 21 **Litho.** *Perf. 12*

844 A157 3.50p Dragonfly (4-1) 1.25 1.25
845 A157 3.50p Butterfly (4-2) 1.25 1.25
846 A157 3.50p Owl in flight (4-3) 1.25 1.25
847 A157 3.50p Standing owl (4-4) 1.25 1.25
a. Block of 4, #844-847 5.25 5.25

Souvenir Sheet

Perf. 12½

848 A157 8p Dragon *15.00* 7.50

No. 848 contains one 51x38mm stamp.

Traditional Chinese Toys — A158

1996, Nov. 13 **Litho.** *Perf. 12*

849 A158 50a shown .15 .15
850 A158 1p Fish .25 .25
851 A158 3p Doll .80 .80
852 A158 4.50p Dragon 1.25 1.25
Nos. 849-852 (4) 2.45 2.45

New Year 1997 (Year of the Ox) — A159

1997, Jan. 23 **Litho.** *Perf. 12*

853 A159 5.50p multicolored *3.00* *3.00*

Souvenir Sheet

854 A159 10p multicolored *14.00* *14.00*

No. 854 is a continuous design.

Lucky Numbers A160

1996 **Litho.** *Perf. 12*

855 A160 2p "2," Simplicity .75 .75
856 A160 2.80p "8," Prosperity 1.00 1.00
857 A160 3p "3," Progress 1.15 1.15
858 A160 3.90p "9," Longevity 1.50 1.50
Nos. 855-858 (4) 4.40 4.40

Souvenir Sheet

859 A160 9p Man outside house *12.00* *12.00*

Hong Kong '97 (#859).

Paintings of Macao, by Kwok Se — A161

Designs: 2p, Junks. 3p, Fortress on side of mountain. 3.50p, Retreat house. 4.50p, Cerco Gate. 8p, Rooftop of building, horiz.

1997, Mar. 1 **Litho.** *Perf. 12*

860 A161 2p multicolored .70 .70
861 A161 3p multicolored 1.00 1.00
862 A161 3.50p multicolored 1.20 1.20
863 A161 4.50p multicolored 1.50 1.50
Nos. 860-863 (4) 4.40 4.40

Souvenir Sheet

864 A161 8p multicolored 10.50 10.50

A162 A163

Boat People: 1p, Old woman seated. 1.50p, Woman wearing hat. 2.50p, Woman carrying baby. 5.50p, Man, boy.

1997, Mar. 26 **Litho.** *Perf. 12*

865 A162 1p multicolored .85 .85
866 A162 1.50p multicolored 1.30 1.30
867 A162 2.50p multicolored 2.15 2.15
868 A162 5.50p multicolored 4.70 4.70
a. Block of 4, #865-868 9.00 9.00

1997, Apr. 29 **Litho.** *Perf. 12*

Temple A-Ma: No. 869, Steps leading to entrance. No. 870, People strolling past temple, one with umbrella. No. 871, People outside pagoda, pedicab. No. 872, Towers from temple, one emiting smoke.

869 A163 3.50p multicolored .95 .95
870 A163 3.50p multicolored .95 .95
871 A163 3.50p multicolored .95 .95
872 A163 3.50p multicolored .95 .95
a. Strip of 4, #869-872 3.75 3.75

Souvenir Sheet

873 A163 8p Boat *8.25* *8.25*

Drunken Dragon Festival — A164

Stylized designs: 2p, Two men, one holding dragon. 3p, Man holding up dragon. 5p, Two men, one holding horn.
9p, Dragon, man, horiz.

1997, May 14

874 A164 2p multicolored .55 .55
875 A164 3p multicolored .80 .80
876 A164 5p multicolored 1.30 1.30
a. Strip of 3, #874-876 2.65 2.65

Souvenir Sheet

877 A164 9p multicolored *9.75* *9.75*

Father Luís Fróis, 400th Death Anniv. A165

Designs: No. 879, Father Fróis, cathedral, vert.

1997, June 9 **Litho.** *Perf. 12*

878 A165 2.50p multi (2-1) .65 .65
879 A165 2.50p multi (2-2) .65 .65

Legends and Myths — A166

Gods of Protection: #880, Wat Lot. #881, San Su. #882, Chon Keng. #883, Wat Chi Kong.
10p, Chon Keng and Wat Chi Kong.

1997, June 18 **Litho.** *Perf. 12*

880 A166 2.50p multicolored 1.00 1.00
881 A166 2.50p multicolored 1.00 1.00
882 A166 2.50p multicolored 1.00 1.00
883 A166 2.50p multicolored 1.00 1.00
a. Block of 4, #880-883 4.00 4.00

Souvenir Sheet

884 A166 10p multicolored 7.25 7.25

No. 884 contains one 40x40mm stamp.

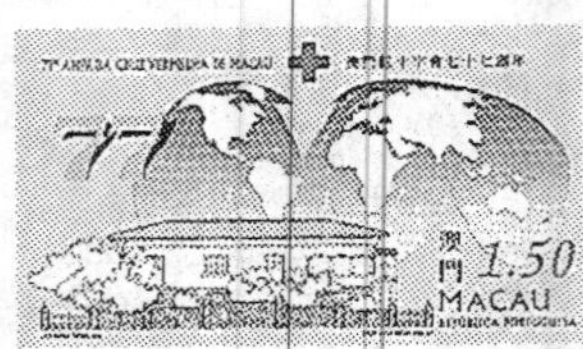

Macao Red Cross, 77th Anniv. — A167

1997, July 12 *Perf. 12½*

885 A167 1.50p multicolored .40 .40

No. 885 is printed se-tenant with label.

Verandas A168

Various architectural styles.
8p, Close up of veranda, vert.

1997, July 30 **Litho.** *Perf. 12*

886 A168 50a multi (6-1) .15 .15
887 A168 1p multi (6-2) .25 .25
888 A168 1.50p multi (6-3) .40 .40

889 A168 2p multi (6-4) .50 .50
890 A168 2.50p multi (6-5) .65 .65
891 A168 3p multi (6-6) .75 .75
a. Block of 6, #886-891 2.70 2.70

Souvenir Sheet

892 A168 8p multicolored 2.10 2.10

Traditional Chinese Fans A169 — Fong Soi (Chinese Geomancy) A170

1997, Sept. 24 Litho. *Perf. 12*

893 A169 50a Planta (4-1) .15 .15
894 A169 1p Papel (4-2) .25 .25
895 A169 3.50p Seda (4-3) .95 .95
896 A169 4p Pluma (4-4) 1.10 1.10
a. Block of 4, #893-896 2.40 2.40

Souvenir Sheet

897 A169 9p Sandalo 7.00 7.00

1997, Oct. 9 Litho. *Perf. 12*

Chinese principles of Yin and Yang related to the five elements of the ancient Zodiac.

898 A170 50a green & multi .15 .15
899 A170 1p orange & multi .25 .25
900 A170 1.50p brown & multi .40 .40
901 A170 2p yellow & multi .55 .55
902 A170 2.50p blue & multi .65 .65
a. Strip of 5, #898-902 2.00 2.00

Souvenir Sheet

903 A170 10p green & multi 2.60 2.60

Martial Arts — A171

1997, Nov. 19

904 A171 1.50p Kung Fu .40 .40
905 A171 3.50p Judo .95 .95
906 A171 4p Karate 1.10 1.10
a. Strip of 3, #904-906 2.40 2.40

New Year 1998 (Year of the Tiger) — A172

1998, Jan. 18 Litho. *Perf. 12*

907 A172 5.50p multicolored 1.50 1.50

Souvenir Sheet

908 A172 10p multicolored 2.75 2.75

No. 908 is a continuous design.

AIR POST STAMPS

Stamps of 1934 Overprinted or Surcharged in Black

a b

1936 Wmk. 232 *Perf. 11½*

C1 A17 (a) 2a blue green 2.50 .75
C2 A17 (a) 3a violet 4.25 .75
C3 A17 (b) 5a on 6a brown 4.25 .75
C4 A17 (a) 7a brt rose 4.25 .75
C5 A17 (a) 8a brt blue 7.00 1.00
C6 A17 (a) 15a maroon 27.50 4.00
Nos. C1-C6 (6) 49.75 8.00

Common Design Type
Name and Value in Black
Perf. 13½x13

1938, Aug. 1 Engr. Unwmk.

C7 CD39 1a scarlet .80 .50
C8 CD39 2a purple 1.00 .50
C9 CD39 3a orange 1.50 .90
C10 CD39 5a ultra 3.00 1.25
C11 CD39 10a lilac brn 5.00 1.25
C12 CD39 20a dk green 10.00 3.00
C13 CD39 50a red brown 16.00 4.00
C14 CD39 70a rose car 20.00 5.00
C15 CD39 1p magenta 40.00 18.00
Nos. C7-C15 (9) 97.30 34.40

No. C13 exists with overprint "Exposicao Internacional de Nova York, 1939-1940" and Trylon and Perisphere.

Catalogue values for unused stamps in this section, from this point to the end of the section, are for never hinged items.

Plane over Bay of Grand Beach — AP1

1960, Dec. 11 Litho. *Perf. 14*

C16 AP1 50a shown 2.25 .20
C17 AP1 76a Penha Chapel 6.00 .30
C18 AP1 3p Macao 10.00 1.25
C19 AP1 5p Bairro de Mong Ha 16.00 1.75
C20 AP1 10p Penha and Bay 27.50 2.50
Nos. C16-C20 (5) 61.75 6.00

No. C17 Surcharged

1979, Aug. 3 Litho. *Perf. 14*

C21 AP1 70a on 76a multi 8.00 1.50

POSTAGE DUE STAMPS

Numeral of Value — D1

Perf. 11½x12

1904, July Typo. Unwmk.

Name and Value in Black

J1 D1 ½a gray green 1.50 1.25
a. Name & value inverted 42.50 22.50
J2 D1 1a yellow grn 1.90 1.25
J3 D1 2a slate 1.90 1.25
J4 D1 4a pale brown 1.90 1.25
J5 D1 5a red orange 3.50 2.00
J6 D1 8a gray brown 3.75 2.00
J7 D1 12a red brown 5.00 2.00
J8 D1 20a dull blue 8.25 4.50
J9 D1 40a carmine 10.50 6.00
J10 D1 50a orange 19.00 12.00
J11 D1 1p gray violet 37.50 25.00
Nos. J1-J11 (11) 94.70 58.50

Issued without gum: Nos. J7-J11. Issued with or without gum: No. J4. Others issued with gum.
For overprints see Nos. 144-146, J12-J32.

Issue of 1904 Overprinted in Carmine or Green

REPUBLICA

1911

J12 D1 ½a gray green .30 .15
J13 D1 1a yellow green .30 .15
J14 D1 2a slate .30 .15
J15 D1 4a pale brown .40 .20
J16 D1 5a orange .40 .20
J17 D1 8a gray brown .50 .20
J18 D1 12a red brown 1.25 .40
J19 D1 20a dull blue 2.50 .85
J20 D1 40a carmine (G) 8.50 1.25
J21 D1 50a orange 15.00 2.50
J22 D1 1p gray violet 30.00 3.50
Nos. J12-J22 (11) 59.45 9.55

Issued without gum: Nos. J19-J22.

Issue of 1904 Overprinted in Red or Green

REPUBLICA

1914

J22A D1 ½a gray green 1,500. 600.00
J23 D1 1a yellow green 3.00 .35
J24 D1 2a slate 3.00 .35
J25 D1 4a pale brown 3.00 .35
J26 D1 5a orange 3.50 .35
J27 D1 8a gray brown 3.50 .35
J28 D1 12a red brown 3.50 .35
J29 D1 20a dull blue 12.50 2.00
J30 D1 40a car (G) 35.00 4.00
a. Double ovpt., red and green 100.00 22.50
J31 D1 50a orange 35.00 4.00
J32 D1 1p gray violet 70.00 8.00
Nos. J23-J32 (10) 172.00 20.10

Issued without gum: Nos. J28, J30-J32.

IMPERIO COLONIAL PORTUGUES MACAU 1 avo PORTEADO D2

Name and Value in Black

1947 Typo. *Perf. 11½x12*

J33 D2 1a red violet 2.25 1.00
J34 D2 2a purple 2.25 1.00
J35 D2 4a dark blue 2.25 1.00
J36 D2 5a chocolate 2.25 1.00
J37 D2 8a red violet 2.25 1.00
J38 D2 12a orange brown 7.50 1.00
J39 D2 20a yellow green 4.25 3.00
J40 D2 40a brt carmine 7.50 3.50
J41 D2 50a orange yellow 19.00 7.75
J42 D2 1p blue 19.00 4.00
Nos. J33-J42 (10) 68.50 24.25

Stamps of 1934 Surcharged "PORTEADO" and New Values in Carmine

1949, May 1 Wmk. 232

J43 A17 1a on 4a black 3.75 .85
J44 A17 2a on 6a brown 3.75 .85
J45 A17 4a on 8a brt blue 4.25 .85
J46 A17 5a on 10a red org 4.75 .85
J47 A17 8a on 12a dk blue 4.75 1.40
J48 A17 12a on 30a apple grn 6.50 1.50
J49 A17 20a on 40a violet 6.50 1.50
Nos. J43-J49 (7) 34.25 7.80

Catalogue values for unused stamps in this section, from this point to the end of the section, are for Never Hinged items.

Nos. 348, 349 and 351 Overprinted or Surcharged in Black or Carmine

PORTEADO

1951, June 6 Unwmk.

J50 A21 1a org yel, *lem* 1.00 .20
J51 A21 2a dk grn, *bl* (C) 1.00 .20
J52 A21 7a on 10a brt pink, *bl* 1.00 .20
Nos. J50-J52 (3) 3.00 .60

Common Design Type

1952 Photo. & Typo. *Perf. 14*

Numeral in Red; Frame Multicolored

J53 CD45 1a violet blue .25 .15
J54 CD45 3a chocolate .25 .15
J55 CD45 5a indigo .25 .15
J56 CD45 10a dark red 1.00 .40
J57 CD45 30a indigo 1.25 .50
J58 CD45 1p chocolate 4.00 1.50
Nos. J53-J58 (6) 7.00 2.85

WAR TAX STAMPS

Victory WT1

1919, Aug. 11 Unwmk. *Perf. 15x14*

Overprinted in Black or Carmine

MR1 WT1 2a green 2.25 1.00
MR2 WT1 11a green (C) 3.50 1.40

Nos. MR1-MR2 were also for use in Timor.
A 9a value was issued for revenue use.

NEWSPAPER STAMPS

JORNAES

JORNAES

2½ 2½

Nos. P1-P2 No. P3

Typographed and Embossed

1892-93 Unwmk. *Perf. 12½, 13½*

Black Surcharge

Without Gum

P1 A7 2½r on 40r choc 4.00 2.50
a. Inverted surcharge 40.00 30.00
P2 A7 2½r on 80r gray 4.00 2.50
a. Inverted surcharge 40.00 35.00
b. Double surcharge
c. Perf. 13½ 40.00 35.00
P3 A7 2½r on 10r grn ('93) 4.00 2.50
a. Double surcharge
Nos. P1-P3 (3) 12.00 7.50

N3

N4

Perf. 11½, 12½, 13½

1893-94 Typo.

P4 N3 2½r brown 3.25 2.00
P5 N4 ½a on 2½r brn (Bk) ('94) 3.25 2.25
a. Double surcharge

For surcharges see Nos. 131, 252.

POSTAL TAX STAMPS

Pombal Commemorative Issue

Common Design Types

Perf. 12½

1925, Nov. 3 Engr. Unwmk.

RA1 CD28 2a red org & blk 1.40 .70
RA2 CD29 2a red org & blk 1.40 .70
RA3 CD30 2a red org & blk 1.40 .70
Nos. RA1-RA3 (3) 4.20 2.10

Symbolical of Charity
PT1 PT2

1930, Dec. 25 Litho. *Perf. 11*

RA4 PT1 5a dk brown, *yel* 7.00 5.00

1945-47 *Perf. 11½, 12, 10*

RA5 PT2 5a blk brn, *yel* 10.50 7.50
RA6 PT2 5a bl, *bluish* ('47) 30.00 6.75
RA7 PT2 10a grn, *citron* 10.00 3.75
RA8 PT2 15a org, *buff* 1.50 3.75
RA9 PT2 20a rose red, *sal* 60.00 6.75
RA10 PT2 50a red vio, *pnksh* 3.00 3.00
Nos. RA5-RA10 (6) 115.00 31.50

Catalogue values for unused stamps in this section, from this point to the end of the section, are for Never Hinged items.

1953-56 *Perf. 10½x11½*

RA11 PT2 10a bl, *pale grn* ('56) .65 .20
RA12 PT2 20a chocolate, *yel* 9.50 2.50
RA13 PT2 50a car, *pale rose* 8.75 2.75
Nos. RA11-RA13 (3) 18.90 5.45

1958 *Perf. 12x11½*

RA14 PT2 1a gray grn, *grnsh* .15 .15
RA15 PT2 2a rose lilac, *grysh* .15 .15
Set value .20

Type of 1945-47 Redrawn
Imprint: "Lito. Imp. Nac.-Macau"

1961-66 *Perf. 11*

RA16	PT2 1a gray grn, *grnsh*	.15	.15
RA17	PT2 2a rose lil, *grysh*	.15	.15
RA18	PT2 10a bl, *pale grn* ('62)	.25	.20
RA19	PT2 20a brn, *yel* ('66)	.35	.20
	Nos. RA16-RA19 (4)	.90	
	Set value		.55

Nos. RA16-RA19 have accent added to "E" in "Assistencia."

Nos. RA4-RA19 were issued without gum.

Type of 1945-47 Redrawn and Surcharged

贰 毫
20 avos

1979 **Litho.** *Perf. 11x11½*

RA20 PT2 20a on 1p yel grn, *cream*

No. RA20 has no accent above "E," no imprint and was not issued without surcharge.

POSTAL TAX DUE STAMPS

Pombal Commemorative Issue
Common Design Types

1925 **Unwmk.** *Perf. 12½*

RAJ1	CD28 4a red orange & blk	1.25	.70
RAJ2	CD29 4a red orange & blk	1.25	.70
RAJ3	CD30 4a red orange & blk	1.25	.70
	Nos. RAJ1-RAJ3 (3)	3.75	2.10

MACEDONIA

ˌma-sə-ˈdō-nē-ə

LOCATION — Central Balkans, bordered by on the north by Serbia, to the east by Bulgaria, on the south by Greece and by Albania on the west.
GOVT. — Republic
AREA — 9,928 sq. mi.
POP. — 2,038,847 (1991 est.)
CAPITAL — Skopje

Formerly a constituent republic in the Socialist Federal Republic of Yugoslavia. Declared independence on Nov. 21, 1991.

100 Deni (de) = 1 Denar (d)

Catalogue values for all unused stamps in this country are for Never Hinged items.

A provisional issue of 8 Bulgarian stamps surcharged for use in Macedonia in 1944 exists. The set is considered speculative.

Bas Relief — A1

1992-93 **Litho.** *Perf. 13½x13*

1 A1 30d multicolored .65 .65

Perf. 10

2 A1 40d multicolored .18 .18

Issued: 30d, 9/8/92. 40d, 3/15/93.
For surcharges see Nos. 21, 42.

Christmas — A2

Frescoes: 100d, Nativity Scene, 16th cent. 500d, Virgin and Child, 1422.

1992, Dec. 10 **Litho.** *Perf. 13x13½*

3	A2 100d multicolored	.42	.42
4	A2 500d multicolored	2.25	2.25

Natl. Flag — A3

1993, Mar. 15 *Perf. 13½x13*

5	A3 10d multicolored	.15	.15
6	A3 40d multicolored	.15	.15
7	A3 50d multicolored	.18	.18
	Set value	.35	.35

For surcharges see Nos. 23, 40-41.

Fish — A4

Designs: 50d, 1000d, Rutilus macedonicus. 100d, 2000d, Salmothymus achridanus.

1993, Mar. 15 *Perf. 10*

8	A4 50d multicolored	.16	.16
9	A4 100d multicolored	.32	.32
10	A4 1000d multicolored	3.25	3.25
11	A4 2000d multicolored	6.50	6.50
	Nos. 8-11 (4)	10.23	10.23

Easter — A5

1993, Apr. 16

12 A5 300d multicolored .52 .52

Trans-Balkan Telecommunications Network — A6

1993, May 6

13 A6 500d multicolored 1.25 1.25

Admission to the UN, Apr. 8, 1993 — A7

1993, July 28

14 A7 10d multicolored 1.75 1.75

A8 A9

1993, Aug. 2

15 A8 10d multicolored 1.75 1.75

Souvenir Sheet
Imperf

16 A8 30d multicolored 6.00 6.00

Ilinden Uprising, 90th anniv.

1993, Nov. 4

17 A9 4d multicolored .38 .38

Size: 85x67mm
Imperf

18 A9 40d multicolored 3.75 3.75

Macedonian Revolutionary Organization, cent.

Christmas — A10

1993, Dec. 31 *Perf. 10*

19	A10 2d Nativity Scene	.20	.20
20	A10 20d Adoration of the Magi	2.00	2.00

Nos. 1, 5, RA1 Surcharged 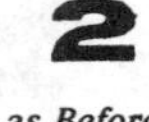

1994, Apr. 2 *Perfs., Etc. as Before*

21	A1 2d on 30d multi	.16	.16
22	PT1 8d on 2.50d multi	.65	.65
23	A3 15d on 10d multi	1.25	1.25
	Nos. 21-23 (3)	2.06	2.06

Size and location of surcharge varies.

Easter A11 Revolutionaries A12

1994, Apr. 29 **Litho.** *Perf. 10*

24 A11 2d multicolored .18 .18

1994, May 23

Designs: 8d, Kosta Racin (1908-43), writer. 15d, Grigor Prlicev (1830-93), writer. 20d, Nikola Vapzarov (1909-42), poet. 50d, Goce Delchev (1872-1903), politician.

25	A12 8d multicolored	.55	.55
26	A12 15d multicolored	1.00	1.00
27	A12 20d multicolored	1.40	1.40
28	A12 50d multicolored	3.50	3.50
	Nos. 25-28 (4)	6.45	6.45

Intl. Year of the Family — A13

1994, June 21

29 A13 2d multicolored .22 .22

Liberation Day, 50th Anniv. — A14 Swimming Marathon, Ohrid Lake — A15

Designs: 5d, St. Prohor Pcinski Monastery, up close. 50d, View of entire grounds.

1994, Aug. 2 **Litho.** *Perf. 10*

30 A14 5d multicolored .32 .32

Size: 108x73mm
Imperf

31 A14 50d multicolored 3.25 3.25

1994, Aug. 22

32 A15 8d multicolored 1.00 1.00

Stamp Day — A16

1994, Sept. 12

33 A16 2d multicolored .25 .25

Nova Makedonija, Mlad Boretz, & Makedonka Newspapers, 50th Anniv. — A17

1994, Sept. 13 **Litho.** *Perf. 10*

34 A17 2d multicolored .25 .25

St. Kliment of Ohrid Library, 50th Anniv. A18

Manuscripts: 2d, 15th cent. 10d, 13th cent., vert.

1994, Sept. 29 **Litho.** *Perf. 10*

35	A18 2d multicolored	.25	.25
36	A18 10d multicolored	1.25	1.25

Macedonian Radio, 50th Anniv. — A19

1994, Dec. 26 **Litho.** *Perf. 10*

37 A19 2d multicolored .25 .25

Wildlife Conservation A20

1994, Dec. 26 **Litho.** ***Perf. 10***
38 A20 5d Pinus peluse *.45 .45*
39 A20 10d Lynx lynx martinoi *.85 .85*

Nos. 2, 6 Surcharged in Black or Gold

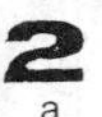
a

2
b

Perfs., Etc. as Before

1995, Mar. 13 **Litho.**
40 A3(a) 2d on 40d #6 *.30 .30*
41 A3(b) 2d on 40d #6 *.30 .30*
42 A1(a) 5d on 40d #2 (G) *.80 .80*
Nos. 40-42 (3) *1.40 1.40*

Easter A21

1995, Apr. 23 **Litho.** ***Perf. 10***
43 A21 4d multicolored *.45 .45*

End of World War II, 50th Anniv. A22

1995, May 9 **Litho.** ***Perf. 10***
44 A22 2d multicolored *.30 .30*

Macedonian Red Cross, 50th Anniv. — A23

1995, May 20 **Litho.** ***Perf. 10***
45 A23 2d multicolored *.30 .30*

Wilhelm Röntgen (1845-1923), Discovery of the X-Ray, Cent. — A24

1995, May 20
46 A24 2d multicolored *.30 .30*

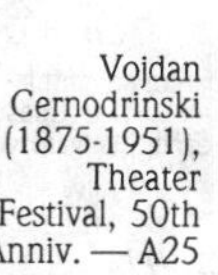

Vojdan Cernodrinski (1875-1951), Theater Festival, 50th Anniv. — A25

1995, June 8
47 A25 10d multicolored *1.50 1.50*

Death of Prince Marko Kraljevic, 600th Anniv. A26

1995, June 22
48 A26 20d multicolored *3.00 3.00*

Gorgi Puleski (1818-95), Writer — A27

1995, July 8
49 A27 2d multicolored *.30 .30*

Writer's Festival, Struga — A28

1995, Aug. 23 **Litho.** ***Perf. 10***
50 A28 2d multicolored *.30 .30*

A29

A30

1995, Oct. 4
51 A29 15d Mosque of Tetovo *2.20 2.20*

1995, Oct. 4 **Litho.** ***Perf. 10***

Architecture.

52 A30 2d Malesevija *.20 .20*
53 A30 20d Krakornica *1.85 1.85*

Motion Pictures, Cent. A31

Film strip of early movie and: No. 54, Auguste and Louis Lumiére. No. 55, Milton and Janaki Manaki, Macedonian cinematographers.

1995, Oct. 6 ***Perf. 10 on 3 Sides***
54 A31 10d multicolored *.85 .85*
55 A31 10d multicolored *.85 .85*
a. Pair, #54-55 *1.70 1.70*

UN, 50th Anniv. — A32

1995, Oct. 24
56 A32 20d Blocks, globe in nest *1.50 1.50*
57 A32 50d Blocks, sun *4.00 4.00*

Christmas A33

1995, Dec. 13
58 A33 15d multicolored *1.30 1.30*

Birds — A34

15d, Pelecanus crispus. 40d, Gypaetus barbatus.

1995, Dec. 14
59 A34 15d multicolored *1.20 1.20*
60 A34 40d multicolored *3.20 3.20*

Reform of Macedonian Language, 50th Anniv. — A35

1995, Dec. 18
61 A35 5d multicolored *.45 .45*

St. Bogorodica Church, Ohrid, 700th Anniv. A36

Designs: 8d, Detail of fresco, St. Kliment of Ohrid (840-916), exterior view of church. 50d, Portion of fresco inside church, #62.

1995, Dec. 19
62 A36 8d multicolored *.65 .65*

Size: 80x61mm

Imperf

62A A36 50d multicolored *6.75 6.75*

Macedonia's Admission to UPU, 1st Anniv. — A37

1995, Dec. 27
62B A37 10d Post office, Skopje *.85 .85*

Admission to Council of Europe (CE) and Organization for Security and Cooperation in Europe (OSCE) — A37a

1995, Dec. 27
62C A37a 20d multicolored *1.65 1.65*

Modern Olympic Games, Cent., 1996 Summer Olympic Games, Atlanta A38

1996, May 20 **Litho.** ***Perf. 10***
63 A38 2d Kayak race *.20 .20*
64 A38 8d Basketball, vert. *.80 .80*
65 A38 15d Swimming *1.50 1.50*
66 A38 20d Wrestling *2.00 2.00*
67 A38 40d Boxing, vert. *4.00 4.00*
68 A38 50d Running, vert *5.00 5.00*
Nos. 63-68 (6) *13.50 13.50*

Intl. Decade to Fight Illegal Drugs — A39

1996, July 11 **Litho.** ***Perf. 10***
69 A39 20d multicolored *1.65 1.65*

Children's Paintings — A40

1996, July 15
70 A40 2d Boy *.15 .15*
71 A40 8d Girl *.65 .65*

Peak of Czar Samuel of Bulgaria's Power, 1000th Anniv. A41

1996, July 19
72 A41 40d multicolored *3.25 3.25*

G. Petrov (1865-1921), Revolutionary A42

1996, Aug. 2
73 A42 20d multicolored *1.65 1.65*

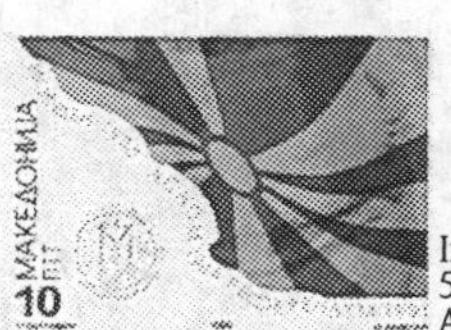
Independence, 5th Anniv. — A43

1996, Sept. 8
74 A43 10d multicolored *.80 .80*

Vera Ciriviri-Trena (1920-44), Freedom Fighter — A44

Mother Teresa (1910-97) — A45

1996, Nov. 22 **Litho.** ***Perf. 13x13½***
75 A44 20d multicolored *5.50 5.50*
76 A45 40d multicolored *11.25 11.25*

Europa.

Christmas — A46 Terra Cotta Tiles — A47

Designs: No. 77, Tree, children caroling in snow. No. 78, Candle, nuts, apples.

1996, Dec. 14 Litho. *Perf. 10*
77 A46 10d multicolored .85 .85
78 A46 10d multicolored .85 .85
a. Pair, #77-78 1.70 1.70

1996, Dec. 19

#79a, 80a, 4d, Daniel in lions den. #79b, 80b, 8d, Sts. Christopher & George. #79c, 80c, 20d, Joshua, Caleb. #79d, 80d, 50d, Unicorn.

Blocks of 4, #a.-d.
79 A47 bl grn & multi 7.00 7.00
80 A47 yel grn & multi 7.00 7.00

Traditional Architecture — A48

1996
81 A48 2d House, Nistrovo .20 .20
82 A48 8d House, Brodets .70 .70
83 A48 10d House, Niviste .85 .85
Nos. 81-83 (3) 1.75 1.75

Issued: 8d, 12/20; 2d, 10d, 12/25.

Butterflies A49

4d, Pseudochazara cingovskii. 40d, Colias balcanica.

1996, Dec. 21
84 A49 4d multicolored .35 .35
85 A49 40d multicolored 3.40 3.40

UNICEF, 50th Anniv. — A50

1996, Dec. 31 *Perf. 14½*
86 A50 20d shown 1.75 1.75
87 A50 40d UNESCO, 50th anniv. 3.50 3.50

Alpine Skiing Championships, 50th Anniv. — A51

1997, Feb. 7 *Perf. 10*
88 A51 20d multicolored 1.75 1.75

Alexander Graham Bell (1847-1922) A52

1997, Mar. 12
89 A52 40d multicolored 3.50 3.50

Ancient Roman Mosaics, Heraklia and Stobi — A53

1997, Mar. 26 *Perf. 10*
90 A53 2d Wild dog .20 .20
91 A53 8d Bull .70 .70
92 A53 20d Lion 1.75 1.75
93 A53 40d Leopard with prey 3.50 3.50
Nos. 90-93 (4) 6.15 6.15

Size: 79x56mm

Imperf
94 A53 50d Deer, peacocks 4.25 4.25

No. 94 has simulated perforations within the design.

Cyrilic Alphabet, 1100th Anniv. — A54

Cyrillic inscriptions and: No. 95, Gold embossed plate. No. 96, St. Cyril (827-69), St. Methodius (825-84), promulgators of Cyrillic alphabet.

1997, May 2 *Perf. 10*
95 A54 10d multicolored .85 .85
96 A54 10d multicolored .85 .85
a. Pair, #95-96 1.70 1.70

A55 A56

Europa (Stories and Legends): 20d, Man kneeling down, another seated in background. 40d, Man, tree, bird dressed as man.

1997, June 6 *Perf. 15x14*
97 A55 20d multicolored 1.70 1.70
98 A55 40d multicolored 3.40 3.40

1997, June 5 *Perf. 10*
99 A56 15d multicolored 1.30 1.30

5th Natl. Ecology Day.

St. Naum — A57

1997, July 3 *Perf. 10*
100 A57 15d multicolored 1.30 1.30

Mushrooms A58

2d, Cantharellus cibarius. 15d, Boletus aereus. 27d, Amanita caesarea. 50d, Morchella conica.

1997, Nov. 7 Litho. *Perf. 10*
101 A58 2d multicolored .45 .45
102 A58 15d multicolored 1.25 1.25
103 A58 27d multicolored 2.25 2.25
104 A58 50d multicolored 4.25 4.25
Nos. 101-104 (4) 8.20 8.20

Week of the Child — A59 Minerals — A60

1997, Oct. 11
105 A59 27d multicolored 2.30 2.30

1997, Oct. 10
106 A60 27d Stibnite 2.25 2.25
107 A60 40d Lorandite 3.50 3.50

POSTAL TAX STAMPS

Men Blowing Horns — PT1

1991, Dec. 30 Litho. *Perf. 13½*
RA1 PT1 2.50d multicolored .30 .30

No. RA1 was required on mail Dec. 31, 1991-Sept. 8, 1992. For surcharge see No. 22.

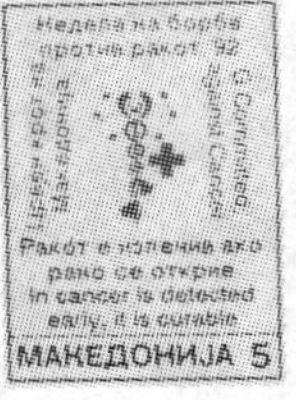

Anti-Cancer Week — PT2

Designs: Nos. RA2, RA6, Emblems, inscriptions. Nos. RA3, RA7, Magnetic resonance imaging scanner. Nos. RA4, RA8, Overhead scanner, examination table. No. RA5, RA9c, Mammography imager. No. RA9, Ultra sound computer.

1992, Mar. 1 Litho. *Perf. 10*
RA2 PT2 5d multicolored .32 .32
RA3 PT2 5d multicolored .32 .32
RA4 PT2 5d multicolored .32 .32
RA5 PT2 5d multicolored .32 .32
a. Block of 4, #RA2-RA5 1.25 1.25
RA6 PT2 5d multicolored .32 .32
RA7 PT2 5d multicolored .32 .32
RA8 PT2 5d multicolored .32 .32
RA9 PT2 5d multicolored .32 .32
a. Block of 4, #RA6-RA9 1.25 1.25
b. Souv. sheet of 3, #RA7-RA9, RA9c 1.25 1.25
c. PT2 5d multicolored .32 .32
Nos. RA2-RA9 (8) 2.56 2.56

Inscription at right reads up on No. RA2 and down on No. RA6. Designs on Nos. RA7-RA8, RA9c are without red cross symbol. Souvenir folders with perf. and imperf. sheets of RA9b sold for 40d. Obligatory on mail Mar. 1-8.
See Nos. RA28-RA31.

Red Cross Week — PT3

Designs: RA10, Slogans. No. RA11, Airplanes dropping supplies. No. RA12, Aiding traffic accident victim. No. RA13, Evacuating casualties from building.

1992, May 8 *Perf. 10*
RA10 PT3 10d multicolored .16 .16
RA11 PT3 10d multicolored .16 .16
RA12 PT3 10d multicolored .16 .16
RA13 PT3 10d multicolored .16 .16
a. Block of 4, #RA10-RA13 .64 .64

Nos. RA10-RA13 exist with silver-colored borders in perf. and imperf. miniature sheets that sold for 80d. Obligatory on mail May 8-15.

PT4 PT5

Solidarity Week: No. RA14, Skopje earthquake. No. RA15, Woman holding girl. No. RA16, Mother carrying infant. No. RA17, Mother, children, airplane.
130d, Woman, child, airport control tower.

1992, June 1 *Perf. 10*
RA14 PT4 20d multicolored .16 .16
RA15 PT4 20d multicolored .16 .16
RA16 PT4 20d multicolored .16 .16
RA17 PT4 20d multicolored .16 .16
a. Block of 4 .64 .64

Size: 74x97mm

Imperf
RA18 PT4 130d multicolored 2.00 2.00

No. RA18 also exists with perf. vignette. Obligatory on mail June 1-7.
See No. RA55.

1992, Sept. 14 *Perf. 10*

Anti-Tuberculosis Week: No. RA20, Nurse, infant. No. RA21, Nurse giving oxygen to patient. No. RA22, Infant in bed.
200d, Child being treated by nurse.

RA19 PT5 20d multicolored .28 .28
RA20 PT5 20d multicolored .28 .28
RA21 PT5 20d multicolored .28 .28
RA22 PT5 20d multicolored .28 .28
a. Block of 4, #RA19-RA22 1.12 1.12

Size: 74x97mm

Imperf
RA23 PT5 200d vermilion & multi 2.75 2.75

No. RA23 exists with magenta inscriptions, and also with perf. vignette and either magenta or vermilion inscriptions. Obligatory on mail Sept. 14-21.

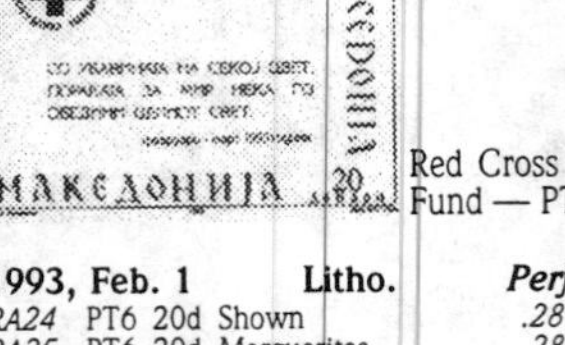

Red Cross Fund — PT6

1993, Feb. 1 Litho. *Perf. 10*
RA24 PT6 20d Shown .28 .28
RA25 PT6 20d Marguerites .28 .28
RA26 PT6 20d Carnations .28 .28
RA27 PT6 20d Mixed bouquet .28 .28
a. Block of 4, #RA24-RA27 1.12 1.12

Nos. RA24-RA27 exist in perf. or imperf. miniature sheets with either gold or silver backgrounds and inscriptions, that sold for 500d each. Obligatory on mail Feb. 1-28.

Cancer Therapy Type of 1992

Designs: No. RA28, Nuclear medicine caduceus, inscriptions. No. RA29, Radiographic equipment. No. RA30, Radiology machine. No. RA31, Scanner.

1993, Mar. 1 Litho. *Perf. 10*
RA28 PT2 20d multicolored .45 .45
RA29 PT2 20d multicolored .45 .45
RA30 PT2 20d multicolored .45 .45
RA31 PT2 20d multicolored .45 .45
a. Block of 4, #RA28-RA31 1.80 1.80

#RA28-RA31 exist in perf. & imperf. miniature sheets with gold background or inscription, that sold for 500d each. Obligatory on mail Mar. 1-8.

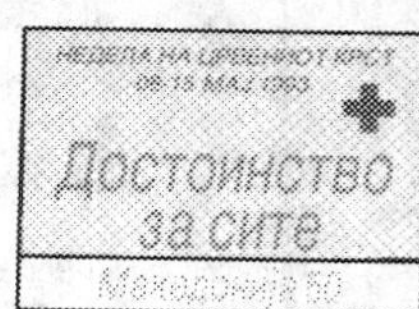

Red Cross Week — PT7

1993, May 8 Litho. *Perf. 10*

RA32 PT7 50d Inscriptions .38 .38

RA33 PT7 50d Man holding baby .38 .38

RA34 PT7 50d Patient in wheelchair .38 .38

RA35 PT7 50d Carrying stretcher .38 .38

a. Block of 4, #RA32-RA35 1.52 1.52

Perf. & imperf. miniature sheets of Nos. RA32-RA35 exist with yellow inscription tablets that sold for 700d each. Obligatory on mail May 8-15.

1993, June 1 *Perf. 10*

RA36 PT7 50de Skopje earthquake .38 .38

RA37 PT7 50de Unloading boxes .38 .38

RA38 PT7 50de Labeling boxes .38 .38

RA39 PT7 50de Boxes, fork lift .38 .38

a. Block of 4, #RA36-RA39 1.52 1.52

Perf. & imperf. miniature sheets of Nos. RA36-RA39 exist with gold inscription tablets that sold for 7d each. Obligatory on mail June 1-7.

1993, Sept. 14 *Perf. 10*

Designs: Nos. RA40, Inscriptions. Nos. RA41, Children in meadow. Nos. RA42, Bee on flower. No. RA43, Goat behind rock.

RA40 PT7 50de black, gray & red .28 .28

RA41 PT7 50de green & multi .28 .28

RA42 PT7 50de green & multi .28 .28

RA43 PT7 50de green & multi .28 .28

a. Block of 4, #RA40-RA43 1.25 1.25

Nos. RA41-RA43 exist in perf. & imperf. miniature sheets that sold for 15d each. Nos. RA40-RA43 exist with yellow omitted. Obligatory on mail Sept. 14-21.

See Nos. RA52-RA54.

Anti-Cancer Week — PT8

1994, Mar. 1 *Perf. 10*

RA44 PT8 1d Inscription, emblem .28 .28

RA45 PT8 1d Lily .28 .28

RA46 PT8 1d Mushroom .28 .28

RA47 PT8 1d Swans .28 .28

a. Block of 4, #RA44-RA47 1.12 1.12

Nos. RA44-RA47 without silver color exist in perf. & imperf. miniature sheets and sold for 20d. Obligatory on mail Mar. 1-8.

Red Cross Type of 1993 and

PT9

1994, May 8 Litho. *Perf. 10*

RA51 PT9 1d shown .15 .15

RA52 PT7 1d like #RA41 .15 .15

RA53 PT7 1d like #RA39 .15 .15

RA54 PT7 1d like #RA33 .15 .15

a. Block of 4, #RA51-RA54 .25 .25

Nos. RA51-RA54 exist without denomination in perf. & imperf. miniature sheets and sold for 30d each. Obligatory on mail May 8-15, 1994.

Skopje Earthquake Type of 1993

1994, June 1

RA55 PT4 1d like #RA14 .15 .15

Obligatory on mail June 1-7, 1994.

01 - 08.12.1994
НЕДЕЛА НА БОРБА
ПРОТИВ СИДАТА
СИТЕ ЗАЕДНО
ПРОТИВ СИДАТА
МАКЕДОНИЈА 2

Red Cross Fund — PT10

1994, Dec. 1 Litho. *Perf. 10*

RA56 PT10 2d shown .15 .15

RA57 PT10 2d Globe .15 .15

RA58 PT10 2d AIDS awareness .15 .15

RA59 PT10 2d Condoms .15 .15

a. Block of 4, No. RA56-RA59 .35 .35

Size: 80x95mm

Imperf

RA60 PT10 40d like RA57 3.25 3.25

Country name and value omitted from vignette on No. RA60, which also exists with perf. vignette. Obligatory on mail Dec. 1-8.

НЕДЕЛА НА ЦРВЕН КРСТ 8-15 МАЈ 1995
ДОСТОИНСТВО ЗА СИТЕ ПОЧИТ КОН ЖЕНИТЕ
1.00 МАКЕДОНИЈА

Anti-Cancer Week — PT11 | Red Cross Fund — PT12

1995, Mar. 1

RA61 PT11 1d shown .15 .15

RA62 PT11 1d White lilies .15 .15

RA63 PT11 1d Red lilies .15 .15

RA64 PT11 1d Red roses .15 .15

a. Block of 4, Nos. RA61-RA64 .45 .45

Size: 97x74mm

Imperf

RA65 PT11 30d like #RA61, RA64 3.25 3.25

Blue inscriptions, country name, and value omitted from vignette on No. RA65, which also exists with perf. vignette. Obligatory on mail Mar. 1-8.

1995, May 8

Designs: No. RA66, Red Cross emblem. No. RA67, Red Cross volunteers holding clipboards. No. RA68, Young volunteers wearing white shirts. No. RA69, RA70, Red Cross, Red Crescent symbols, globe.

RA66 PT12 1d multicolored .15 .15

RA67 PT12 1d multicolored .15 .15

RA68 PT12 1d multicolored .15 .15

RA69 PT12 1d blue & multi .15 .15

a. Strip of 4, Nos. RA70-RA73 .40 .40

Size: 68x85mm

Imperf

RA70 PT12 30d multicolored 3.00 3.00

No. RA70 also exists with perf. vignette. Obligatory on mail May 8-15.

Solidarity Week — PT13

1995, June 1

RA71 PT13 1d shown .20 .20

Size: 85x70

Imperf

RA72 PT13 30d like No. RA75 6.00 6.00

No. RA72 also exists with perf. vignette. Obligatory on mail June 1-7.

Robert Koch (1843-1910), Bacteriologist PT14

1995, Sept. 14 Litho. *Perf. 10*

RA73 PT14 1d shown .20 .20

Size: 90x73mm

Imperf

RA74 PT14 30d like No. RA73 6.00 6.00

No. RA74 exists with perf. vignette. Obligatory on mail Sept. 14-21.

PT15

PT16

1995, Oct. 2 Litho. *Die Cut*

Self-Adhesive

RA75 PT15 2d blue violet & red 1.35 1.35

Children's Week. Obligatory on mail Oct. 2-8.

1995, Nov. 1 Litho. *Perf. 10*

RA76 PT16 1d multicolored .20 .20

Size: 90x72mm

Imperf

RA77 PT16 30d like #RA76 3.00 3.00

Red Cross, AIDS awareness.
No. RA77 also exists with perf. vignette.
Obligatory on mail Nov. 1-7.

Red Cross — PT17

1996, Mar. 1 Litho. *Perf. 10*

RA78 PT17 1d multicolored .20 .20

Size: 98x76mm

Imperf

RA79 PT17 30d like #RA78 3.00 3.00

No. RA79 also exists with perf. vignette. Obligatory on mail Mar. 1-8.

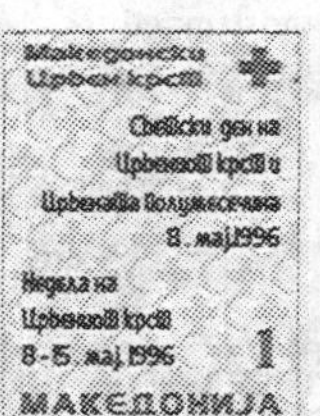

МАКЕДОНИЈА 1

Red Cross Week

PT18 PT19

Fundamental principles of Red Cross, Red Crescent Societies, inscriptions in: No. RA81, Macedonian. No. RA82, English. No. RA83, French. RA84, Spanish.

1996, May 8 Litho. *Perf. 10*

RA80 PT18 1d multicolored .15 .15

RA81 PT19 1d multicolored .15 .15

RA82 PT19 1d multicolored .15 .15

RA83 PT19 1d multicolored .15 .15

RA84 PT19 1d multicolored .15 .15

a. Strip of 5, #RA80-RA84 .45 .45

Obligatory on mail May 8-15.

Red Cross, Solidarity Week — PT20

1996, June 1 Litho. *Perf. 10*

RA86 PT20 1d multicolored .15 .15

Obligatory on mail June 1-7, 1996.

Red Cross, Fight Tuberculosis Week — PT21

1996, Sept. 14 Litho. *Perf. 10*

RA87 PT21 1d multicolored .15 .15

Size: 80x90mm

Imperf

RA88 PT21 30d like #RA87 3.00 3.00

No. RA88 also exists with perf. vignette. Obligatory on mail Sept. 14-21.

Red Cross, AIDS Awareness PT22

1996, Dec. 6

RA89 PT22 1d multicolored .15 .15

Size: 90x73mm

Imperf

RA90 PT22 30d like #RA89 3.00 3.00

No. RA90 also exists with perf. vignette. Obligatory on mail Dec. 1-7.

Red Cross, Cancer Week — PT23 | Red Cross — PT24

1997, Apr. 1

RA91 PT23 1d multicolored .15 .15

Obligatory on mail Apr. 1-8.

1997, May 8

RA92 PT24 1d multicolored .15 .15

Obligatory on mail May 8-15.

Children's Day PT25 | Red Cross, Anti-Tuberculosis PT26

1997, June 1

RA93 PT25 1d multicolored .15 .15

Obligatory on mail June 1-8.

1997, Sept. 14

RA94 PT26 1d multicolored .15 .15

Obligatory on mail, Sept. 14-21.

MADAGASCAR

ˌmad–ə–ˈgas–kər

British Consular Mail

Postage stamps issued by the British Consulate in Madagascar were in use for a short period until the British relinquished all claims to this territory in favor of France in return for which France recognized Great Britain's claims in Zanzibar.

See Malagasy for stamps inscribed "Madagascar."

12 Pence = 1 Shilling

> British Consular Mail stamps of Madagascar were gummed only in one corner. Unused values are for stamps without gum. Examples having the original corner gum will command higher prices. Most used examples of these stamps have small faults and values are for stamps in this condition. Used stamps without faults are scarce and are worth more. Used stamps are valued with the commonly used crayon or pen cancellations.

"B C M" and Arms — A1

Handstamped "British Vice-Consulate"

1884 Unwmk. Typo. *Rouletted*

Black Seal Handstamped

1 A1 1p violet 425. 350.
  b. Seal omitted 3,400. 3,400.
2 A1 2p violet 300. 250.
3 A1 3p violet 300. *250.*
4 A1 4p violet 1 oz. 2,600. 2,600.
  a. "1 oz." corrected to "4 oz." in mss. 750. 625.
  b. Seal omitted *3,400.* 3,400.
5 A1 6p violet 450. 425.
6 A1 1sh violet 400. 400.
7 A1 1sh6p violet 400. 400.
8 A1 2sh violet 600. 600.
9 A1 1p on 1sh vio
10 A1 4½ on 1sh vio
11 A1 6p red 550. 475.

1886

Violet Seal Handstamped

12 A1 4p violet 1,250. —
13 A1 6p violet 1,750. —

Handstamped "British Consular Mail" as on A3

Black Seal Handstamped

14 A1 4p violet 1,750. 1,750.

Violet Seal Handstamped

15 A1 4p violet 3,250. —

The 1, 2, 3 and 4 pence are inscribed "POSTAL PACKET," the other values of the series are inscribed "LETTER."

> *Madagascar stamps can be mounted in the Scott British Africa album.*

"British Vice-Consulate" — A2

Three types of A2 and A3:
I - "POSTAGE" 29½mm. Periods after "POSTAGE" and value.
II - "POSTAGE" 29½mm. No periods.
III - "POSTAGE" 24½mm. Period after value.

1886

Violet Seal Handstamped

16 A2 1p rose, I 300. 250.
  a. Type II 950. —
17 A2 1½p rose, I 800. 800.
  a. Type II 1,450. —
18 A2 2p rose, I 325. 300.
19 A2 3p rose, I 400. 325.
  a. Type II 1,100. —
20 A2 4p rose, III 450. —
21 A2 4½p rose, I 450. 300.
  a. Type II 1,350. —
22 A2 6p rose, II 1,250. —
23 A2 8p rose, I 1,100. 1,000.
  a. Type III 550. —
24 A2 9p rose 1,000. 1,000.
24A A2 1sh rose, III —
24B A2 1sh6p rose, III 2,900. —
25 A2 2sh rose, III 1,750. —

Black Seal Handstamped

Type I

26 A2 1p rose 110. *125.*
27 A2 1½p rose 1,100. 975.
28 A2 2p rose 150. 160.
29 A2 3p rose 1,050. 900.
30 A2 4½p rose 900. 475.
31 A2 8p rose 1,750. 1,750.
32 A2 9p rose 2,750. 2,750.
32A A2 2sh rose, III — —

"British Consular Mail" A3

1886

Violet Seal Handstamped

33 A3 1p rose, II 100. —
34 A3 1½p rose, II 110. —
35 A3 2p rose, II 150. —
36 A3 3p rose, II 140. —
37 A3 4p rose, III 300. —
38 A3 4½p rose, II 140. —
39 A3 6p rose, II 300. —
40 A3 8p rose, III 500. —
  a. Type I 1,300. 1,300.
41 A3 9p rose, I 275. —
42 A3 1sh rose, III 1,200. —
43 A3 1sh6p rose, III 1,300. —
44 A3 2sh rose, III 1,600. —

Black Seal Handstamped

45 A3 1p rose, I 75. 60.
  a. Type II 80. 100.
46 A3 1½p rose, I 75. 60.
  a. Type II 75. 80.
47 A3 2p rose, I 90. 80.
  a. Type II 75. 80.
48 A3 3p rose, I 90. *110.*
  a. Type II 80. 85.
49 A3 4p rose, III 200. 175.
50 A3 4½p rose, I 90. *110.*
  a. Type II 80. 85.
51 A3 6p rose, II 80. 85.
52 A3 8p rose, I 110. 110.
  a. Type III 600. 575.
53 A3 9p rose, I 110. *145.*
54 A3 1sh rose, III 450. —
55 A3 1sh6p rose, III 475. —
56 A3 2sh rose, III 600. —

Seal Omitted

45b A3 1p rose, II 1,600.
46b A3 1½p rose, II 1,600.
48b A3 3p rose, II 2,100.
49a A3 4p rose, III 1,900.
50b A3 4½p rose, II 2,150.
51a A3 6p rose, II 2,400.
52b A3 8p rose, III 1,950.
53a A3 9p rose, I 2,400.
54a A3 1sh rose, III 1,950.
55a A3 1sh6p rose, III 2,750.
56a A3 2sh rose, III 2,750.

Some students of these issues doubt that the 1886 "seal omitted" varieties were regularly issued.

Red Seal Handstamped

57 A3 3p rose, I *6,750.*
58 A3 4½p rose, I *4,250.*

MADEIRA

mə–ˈdir–ə

LOCATION — A group of islands in the Atlantic Ocean northwest of Africa
GOVT. — Part of the Republic of Portugal
AREA — 314 sq. mi.
POP. — 150,574 (1900)
CAPITAL — Funchal

These islands are considered an integral part of Portugal and since 1898 postage stamps of Portugal have been in use. See Portugal for issues also inscribed Madeira, starting in 1980.

1000 Reis = 1 Milreis
100 Centavos = 1 Escudo (1925)

> It is recommended that the rare overprinted 1868-81 stamps be purchased accompanied by certificates of authenticity from competent experts.

King Luiz
A1 A2

Stamps of Portugal Overprinted

1868, Jan. 1 Unwmk. *Imperf.*

Black Overprint

2 A1 20r bister 200.00 150.00
  a. Inverted overprint —
  b. Rouletted —
3 A1 50r green 200.00 150.00
4 A1 80r orange 225.00 150.00
  a. Double overprint —
5 A1 100r lilac 225.00 150.00
  Nos. 2-5 (4) 850.00 600.00

The 5r black does not exist as a genuinely imperforate original.

Reprints of 1885 are on stout white paper, ungummed. (Also, 5r, 10r and 25r values were overprinted.) Reprints of 1905 are on ordinary white paper with shiny gum and have a wide "D" and "R." Value, $12 each.

Lozenge Perf.

2c A1 20r —
3a A1 50r —
4b A1 80r —
5a A1 100r —

Overprinted in Red or Black

1868-70 *Perf. 12½*

6 A1 5r black (R) 55.00 37.50
8 A1 10r yellow 90.00 80.00
9 A1 20r bister 140.00 110.00
10 A1 25r rose 57.50 12.00
  a. Inverted overprint —
11 A1 50r green 175.00 140.00
  a. Inverted overprint —
12 A1 80r orange 175.00 140.00
13 A1 100r lilac 175.00 140.00
  a. Inverted overprint —
14 A1 120r blue 115.00 80.00
15 A1 240r violet ('70) 500.00 400.00
  Nos. 6-15 (9) 1,482. 1,139.

Two types of 5r differ in the position of the "5" at upper right.

The reprints are on stout white paper, ungummed, with rough perforation 13½, and on thin white paper with shiny white gum and clean-cut perforation 13½. The overprint has the wide "D" and "R" and the first reprints included the 5r with both black and red overprint. Value $10 each.

Overprinted in Red or Black

1871-80 *Perf. 12½, 13½*

16 A2 5r black (R) 8.50 6.00
  a. Inverted overprint —
  b. Double overprint 55.00 55.00
  c. Perf. 14 90.00 55.00
18 A2 10r yellow 30.00 22.50
19 A2 10r bl grn ('79) 135.00 115.00
  a. Perf. 13½ 165.00 135.00
20 A2 10r yel grn ('80) 65.00 52.50
21 A2 15r brn ('75) 19.00 11.50
22 A2 20r bister 30.00 22.50
23 A2 25r rose 11.00 4.50
  a. Inverted overprint 32.50 32.50
  b. Double overprint 32.50 32.50
24 A2 50r green ('72) 62.50 30.00
  a. Double overprint —
  b. Inverted overprint 155.00 155.00
25 A2 50r blue ('80) 120.00 55.00
26 A2 80r orange ('72) 77.50 67.50
27 A2 100r pale lil ('73) 82.50 40.00
  a. Perf. 14 200.00 85.00
  b. Perf. 13½ 110.00 57.50
28 A2 120r blue 115.00 80.00
29 A2 150r blue ('76) 165.00 145.00
  a. Perf. 13½ 180.00 150.00
30 A2 150r yel ('79) 275.00 235.00
31 A2 240r vio ('74) 700.00 500.00
32 A2 300r vio ('76) 75.00 67.50
  Nos. 16-32 (16) 1,971. 1,454.

There are two types of the overprint, the second one having a broad "D."

The reprints have the same characteristics as those of the 1868-70 issues.

King Luiz
A4 A5

1880-81

33 A4 5r black 25.00 21.00
34 A5 25r pearl gray 27.50 21.00
  a. Inverted overprint 52.50 52.50
35 A4 25r lilac 30.00 11.00
  a. 25r purple brown 30.00 11.00
  b. 25r gray 27.50 10.00
  Nos. 33-35 (3) 82.50 53.00

No. 35 is overprinted on Portugal type A18.

Nos. 33, 34 and 35 have been reprinted on stout white paper, ungummed, and the last three on thin white paper with shiny white gum. The perforations are as previously described.

Common Design Types pictured following the introduction.

Vasco da Gama Issue

Common Design Types

1898, Apr. 1 Engr. *Perf. 14-15*

37 CD20 2½r blue grn 2.40 1.25
38 CD21 5r red 2.40 1.25
39 CD22 10r red violet 3.00 1.50
40 CD23 25r yel green 2.75 1.25
41 CD24 50r dk blue 8.50 3.25
42 CD25 75r vio brown 10.00 7.00
43 CD26 100r bister brn 10.00 7.00
44 CD27 150r bister 15.00 11.50
  Nos. 37-44 (8) 54.05 34.00

Nos. 37-44 with "REPUBLICA" overprint and surcharges are listed as Portugal Nos. 199-206.

Ceres — A6

1928, May 1 Engr. *Perf. 13½*

Value Typographed in Black

45 A6 3c deep violet .30 *.60*
46 A6 4c orange .30 *.60*
47 A6 5c light blue .30 *.60*
48 A6 6c brown .30 *.60*
49 A6 10c red .30 *.60*
50 A6 15c yel green .30 *.60*
51 A6 16c red brown .35 *.60*
52 A6 25c violet rose .40 *.60*
53 A6 32c blue grn .40 *.60*
54 A6 40c yel brown 1.25 *1.75*
55 A6 50c slate 1.25 *1.75*
56 A6 64c Prus blue 1.50 *3.00*
57 A6 80c dk brown 1.50 *3.00*

No.	Type	Description	Unused	Used
58	A6	96c carmine rose	1.50	3.00
59	A6	1e black	1.50	3.00
a.		Value omitted		
60	A6	1.20e light rose	1.50	3.00
61	A6	1.60e ultra	1.50	3.00
62	A6	2.40e yellow	2.25	3.50
63	A6	3.36e dull green	3.50	5.75
64	A6	4.50e brown red	4.50	9.00
65	A6	7e dark blue	5.75	17.50
		Nos. 45-65 (21)	30.45	62.65

It was obligatory to use these stamps in place of those in regular use on May 1, June 5, July 1 and Dec. 31, 1928, Jan. 1 and 31, May 1 and June 5, 1929. The amount obtained from this sale was donated to a fund for building a museum.

NEWSPAPER STAMP

Numeral of Value — N1

Newspaper Stamp of Portugal Overprinted in Black

Perf. 12½, 13½

1876, July 1 **Unwmk.**

No.	Type	Description	Unused	Used
P1	N1	2½r olive	8.50	4.25
a.		Inverted overprint	30.00	

The reprints have the same papers, gum, perforations and overprint as the reprints of the regular issues.

POSTAL TAX STAMPS

Pombal Commemorative Issue

Common Design Types

1925 **Unwmk.** **Engr.** ***Perf. 12½***

No.	Type	Description	Unused	Used
RA1	CD28	15c gray & black	.60	.65
RA2	CD29	15c gray & black	.60	.65
RA3	CD30	15c gray & black	.60	.65
		Nos. RA1-RA3 (3)	1.80	1.95

POSTAL TAX DUE STAMPS

Pombal Commemorative Issue

Common Design Types

1925 **Unwmk.** ***Perf. 12½***

No.	Type	Description	Unused	Used
RAJ1	CD28	30c gray & black	.85	3.50
RAJ2	CD29	30c gray & black	.85	3.50
RAJ3	CD30	30c gray & black	.85	3.50
		Nos. RAJ1-RAJ3 (3)	2.55	10.50

MALAGASY

ˌmal–lə–ˈgə–sē

Madagascar (French)

LOCATION — Large island off the coast of southeastern Africa
GOVT. — Republic
AREA — 226,658 sq. mi.
POP. — 9,735,000 (est. 1984)
CAPITAL — Antananarivo

Madagascar became a French protectorate in 1885 and a French colony in 1896 following several years of dispute among France, Great Britain, and the native government. The colony administered the former protectorates of Anjouan, Grand Comoro, Mayotte, Diego-Suarez, Nossi-Be and Sainte-Marie de Madagascar. Previous issues of postage stamps are found under these individual headings. The Malagasy Republic succeeded the colony in 1958 and became the Democratic Republic of Malagasy in 1975.

For British Consular Mail stamps of 1884-1886, see Madagascar.

100 Centimes = 1 Franc
100 Centimes = 1 Ariary (1976)

Catalogue values for unused stamps in this country are for Never Hinged items, beginning with Scott 241 in the regular postage section, Scott B15 in the semi-postal section, Scott C37 in the airpost section, and Scott J31 in the postage due section.

French Offices in Madagascar

The general issues of French Colonies were used in these offices in addition to the stamps listed here.

Stamps of French Colonies Surcharged in Black:

25 05 5
a b c

1889 **Unwmk.** ***Perf. 14x13½***

Overprint Type "a"

No.	Type	Description	Unused	Used
1	A9	05c on 10c blk, *lav*	550.	165.
a.		Inverted surcharge	1,250.	900.
2	A9	05c on 25c blk, *rose*	550.	165.
a.		Inverted surcharge	1,250.	900.
b.		25c on 10c lav (error)	6,500.	5,750.
3	A9	25c on 40c red, *straw*	500.	135.
a.		Inverted surcharge	1,100.	800.

1891

Overprint Type "b"

No.	Type	Description	Unused	Used
4	A9	05c on 40c red, *straw*	130.00	72.50
5	A9	15c on 25c blk, *rose*	130.00	72.50
a.		Surcharge vertical	155.00	100.00

Overprint Type "c"

No.	Type	Description	Unused	Used
6	A9	5c on 10c blk, *lav*	190.00	100.00
a.		Double surcharge	650.00	
7	A9	5c on 25c blk, *rose*	190.00	100.00

See Senegal Nos. 4, 8 for similar surcharge on 20c, 30c.

Forgeries of Nos. 1-7 exist.

A4

1891 **Type-set** ***Imperf.***

Without Gum

No.	Type	Description	Unused	Used
8	A4	5c blk, *green*	150.00	30.00
9	A4	10c blk, *lt bl*	90.00	30.00
10	A4	15c ultra, *pale bl*	90.00	30.00
11	A4	25c brn, *buff*	20.00	12.50
12	A4	1fr blk, *yellow*	1,000.	250.00
13	A4	5fr vio & blk, *lil*	2,000.	1,100.

Ten varieties of each. Nos. 12-13 have been extensively forged.

Stamps of France 1876-90, Overprinted in Red or Black

POSTE
FRANÇAISE
Madagascar

1895 ***Perf. 14x13½***

No.	Type	Description	Unused	Used
14	A15	5c grn, *grnsh* (R)	12.50	7.50
15	A15	10c blk, *lav* (R)	40.00	22.50
16	A15	15c bl (R)	57.50	14.00
17	A15	25c blk, *rose* (R)	75.00	17.50
18	A15	40c red, *straw* (Bk)	62.50	25.00
19	A15	50c rose, *rose* (Bk)	75.00	35.00
20	A15	75c dp vio, *org* (R)	75.00	35.00
21	A15	1fr brnz grn, *straw* (Bk)	100.00	47.50
22	A15	5fr vio, *lav* (Bk)	130.00	65.00
		Nos. 14-22 (9)	627.50	269.00

Majunga Issue

Stamps of France, 1876-86, Surcharged with New Value

1895

Manuscript Surcharge in Red

No.	Type	Description	Unused	Used
22A	A15	0,15c on 25c blk, *rose*	5,500.	
22B	A15	0,15c on 1fr brnz grn, *straw*	4,250.	

Handstamped in Black

No.	Type	Description	Unused	Used
22C	A15	15c on 25c blk, *rose*	4,500.	
22D	A15	15c on 1fr brnz grn, *straw*	4,250.	

On most of #22C and all of #22D the manuscript surcharge of #22A-22B was washed off. Three types of "15" were used for No. 22C.

Stamps of France, 1876-84, Surcharged with New Value

1896

No.	Type	Description	Unused	Used
23	A15	5c on 1c blk, *bl*	4,500.	1,700.
24	A15	15c on 2c brn, *buff*	1,850.	825.
25	A15	25c on 3c gray, *grysh*	2,000.	900.
26	A15	25c on 4c cl, *lav*	5,000.	1,500.
27	A15	25c on 40c red, *straw*	1,050.	625.

The oval of the 5c and 15c surcharges is smaller than that of the 25c, and it does not extend beyond the edges of the stamp as the 25c surcharge does.

Excellent counterfeits of the surcharges on Nos. 22A to 27 exist.

Issues of the Colony

Navigation and Commerce — A7

1896-1906 **Typo.** ***Perf. 14x13½***

Colony Name in Blue or Carmine

No.	Type	Description	Unused	Used
28	A7	1c blk, *lil bl*	.80	.70
29	A7	2c brn, *buff*	.80	.70
a.		Name in blue black	3.50	3.50
30	A7	4c claret, *lav*	1.20	.75
31	A7	5c grn, *grnsh*	4.75	1.20
32	A7	5c yel grn ('01)	.80	.60
33	A7	10c blk, *lav*	5.25	1.00
34	A7	10c red ('00)	2.00	.60
35	A7	15c blue, quadrille paper	7.50	.80
36	A7	15c gray ('00)	1.20	1.00
37	A7	20c red, *grn*	4.50	.90
38	A7	25c blk, *rose*	6.75	3.50
39	A7	25c blue ('00)	17.50	15.00
40	A7	30c brn, *bis*	6.25	2.25
41	A7	35c blk, *yel* ('06)	32.50	5.25
42	A7	40c red, *straw*	6.25	3.25
43	A7	50c car, *rose*	9.00	1.20
44	A7	50c brn, *az* ('00)	22.50	20.00
45	A7	75c dp vio, *org*	2.75	1.25
46	A7	1fr brnz grn, *straw*	8.00	2.25
a.		Name in blue ('99)	17.50	10.00
47	A7	5fr red lil, *lav* ('99)	32.50	20.00
		Nos. 28-47 (20)	172.80	82.20

Perf. 13½x14 stamps are counterfeits.

For surcharges see Nos. 48-55, 58-60, 115-118, 127-128.

Surcharged in Black **05**

1902

No.	Type	Description	Unused	Used
48	A7	05c on 50c car, *rose*	4.00	4.00
a.		Inverted surcharge	67.50	67.50
49	A7	10c on 5fr red lil, *lav*	16.00	16.00
a.		Inverted surcharge	80.00	—
50	A7	15c on 1fr ol grn, *straw*	6.75	6.75
a.		Inverted surcharge	80.00	—
b.		Double surcharge	250.00	—
		Nos. 48-50 (3)	26.75	26.75

Surcharged in Black **0,01**

No.	Type	Description	Unused	Used
51	A7	0,01 on 2c brn, *buff*	6.25	6.25
a.		Inverted surcharge	50.00	50.00
b.		"00,1" instead of "0,01"	65.00	65.00
c.		As "b" inverted		
d.		Comma omitted	145.00	150.00
e.		Name in blue black	7.50	7.50
52	A7	0,05 on 30c brn, *bis*	8.00	8.00
a.		Inverted surcharge	50.00	50.00
b.		"00,5" instead of "0,05"	65.00	65.00
c.		As "b" inverted	210.00	210.00
d.		Comma omitted	145.00	150.00
53	A7	0,10 on 50c car, *rose*	8.00	8.00
a.		Inverted surcharge	50.00	50.00
b.		Comma omitted	145.00	150.00
54	A7	0,15 on 75c vio, *org*	6.25	6.25
a.		Inverted surcharge	60.00	60.00
b.		Comma omitted	160.00	160.00
55	A7	0,15 on 1fr ol grn, *straw*	11.50	11.50
a.		Inverted surcharge	75.00	75.00
b.		Comma omitted	175.00	175.00

Surcharged On Stamps of Diego-Suarez

No.	Type	Description	Unused	Used
56	A11	0,05 on 30c brn, *bis*	115.00	115.00
a.		"00,5" instead of "0,05"	650.00	650.00
b.		Inverted surcharge	850.00	850.00
57	A11	0,10 on 50c car, *rose*	4,750.	4,500.
		Nos. 51-55 (5)	40.00	40.00

Counterfeits of Nos. 56-57 exist with surcharge both normal and inverted.

Surcharged in Black **0,01**

No.	Type	Description	Unused	Used
58	A7	0,01 on 2c brn, *buff*	5.75	5.75
a.		Inverted surcharge	47.50	47.50
b.		Comma omitted	145.00	150.00
59	A7	0,05 on 30c brn, *bis*	6.75	6.75
a.		Inverted surcharge	47.50	47.50
b.		Comma omitted	145.00	150.00
60	A7	0,10 on 50c car, *rose*	5.75	5.75
a.		Inverted surcharge	47.50	47.50
b.		Comma omitted	145.00	150.00
		Nos. 58-60 (3)	18.25	18.25

Surcharged On Stamps of Diego-Suarez

No.	Type	Description	Unused	Used
61	A11	0,05 on 30c brn, *bis*	115.00	115.00
a.		Inverted surcharge	850.00	850.00
62	A11	0,10 on 50c car, *rose*	4,750.	4,500.

BISECTS

During alleged stamp shortages at several Madagascar towns in 1904, it is claimed that bisects were used. After being affixed to letters, these bisects were handstamped "Affranchissement - exceptionnel - (faute de timbres)" and other inscriptions of similar import. The stamps bisected were 10c, 20c, 30c and 50c denominations of Madagascar type A7 and Diego-Suarez type A11. The editors believe these provisionals were unnecessary and speculative.

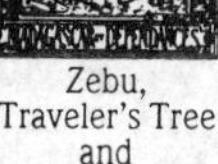

Zebu, Traveler's Tree and Lemur — A8

Transportation by Sedan Chair — A9

1903 **Engr.** ***Perf. 11½***

No.	Type	Description	Unused	Used
63	A8	1c dk violet	.70	.65
a.		On bluish paper	5.00	4.00
64	A8	2c olive brn	.70	.65
65	A8	4c brown	.70	.65
66	A8	5c yellow grn	5.00	.65
67	A8	10c red	6.00	.65
68	A8	15c carmine	9.00	.70
a.		On bluish paper	150.00	
69	A8	20c orange	3.50	1.10
70	A8	25c dull blue	22.50	3.25
71	A8	30c pale red	25.00	7.50
72	A8	40c gray vio	20.00	3.50
73	A8	50c brown org	35.00	15.00
74	A8	75c orange yel	40.00	15.00
75	A8	1fr dp green	40.00	22.50
76	A8	2fr slate	50.00	25.00
77	A8	5fr gray black	60.00	50.00
		Nos. 63-77 (15)	318.10	146.80

Nos. 63-77 exist imperf. Value of set, $500.

For surcharges see Nos. 119-124, 129.

1908-28 **Typo.** ***Perf. 13½x14***

No.	Type	Description	Unused	Used
79	A9	1c violet & ol	.15	.15
80	A9	2c red & ol	.15	.15
81	A9	4c ol brn & brn	.15	.15
82	A9	5c bl grn & ol	.15	.15
83	A9	5c blk & rose ('22)	.15	.15
84	A9	10c rose & brown	.15	.15
85	A9	10c bl grn & ol grn ('22)	.15	.15
86	A9	10c org brn & vio ('25)	.15	.15
87	A9	15c dl vio & rose ('16)	.15	.15
88	A9	15c dl grn & lt grn ('27)	.15	.15
89	A9	15c dk bl & rose red ('28)	.75	.60
90	A9	20c org & brn	.15	.15
91	A9	25c blue & blk	1.25	.25
92	A9	25c vio & blk ('22)	.15	.15
93	A9	30c brown & blk	1.50	.75
94	A9	30c rose red & brn ('22)	.15	.15
95	A9	30c grn & red vio ('25)	.15	.15
96	A9	30c dp grn & yel grn ('27)	.70	.60
97	A9	35c red & black	.70	.30
98	A9	40c vio brn & blk	.70	.25
99	A9	45c bl grn & blk	.50	.30
100	A9	45c red & ver ('25)	.15	.15
101	A9	45c gray lil & mag ('27)	.70	.45

102 A9	50c violet & blk	.50	.25
103 A9	50c blue & blk ('22)	.15	.15
104 A9	50c blk & org ('25)	.35	.15
105 A9	60c vio, *pnksh* ('25)	.35	.30
106 A9	65c black & bl ('25)	.60	.50
107 A9	75c rose red & blk	.50	.15
108 A9	85c grn & ver ('25)	.85	.70
109 A9	1fr brown & ol	.45	.15
110 A9	1fr dull blue ('25)	.60	.50
111 A9	1fr rose & grn ('28)	4.50	3.25
112 A9	1.10fr bis & bl grn ('28)	.85	.70
113 A9	2fr blue & olive	2.50	.65
114 A9	5fr vio & vio brn	8.00	4.00
	Nos. 79-114 (36)	29.25	17.20

75c violet on pinkish stamps of type A9 are No. 138 without surcharge.
For surcharges and overprints see Nos. 125-126, 130-146, 178-179, B1, 212-214.

Preceding Issues Surcharged in Black or Carmine

05 **10**

1912, Nov. *Perf. 14x13½*

115 A7	5c on 15c gray (C)	.35	.35
116 A7	5c on 20c red, *grn*	.45	.45
a.	Inverted surcharge	125.00	125.00
117 A7	5c on 30c brn, *bis* (C)	.50	.50
118 A7	10c on 75c vio, *org*	5.00	5.00
a.	Double surcharge	165.00	165.00
119 A8	5c on 2c ol brn (C)	.35	.35
120 A8	5c on 20c org	.40	.40
121 A8	5c on 30c pale red	.75	.75
122 A8	10c on 40c gray vio (C)	.80	.80
123 A8	10c on 50c brn org	2.00	2.00
124 A8	10c on 75c org yel	4.00	4.00
a.	Inverted surcharge	140.00	140.00
	Nos. 115-124 (10)	14.60	14.60

Two spacings between the surcharged numerals are found on Nos. 115 to 118.
Stamps of Anjouan, Grand Comoro Island, Mayotte and Mohéli with similar surcharges were also available for use in Madagascar and the entire Comoro archipelago.

Preceding Issues Surcharged in Red or Black

0,30 g **1 FR.** h

1921

On Nos. 98 & 107

125 A9 (g)	30c on 40c (R)	1.00	1.00
126 A9 (g)	60c on 75c	1.40	1.40

On Nos. 45 & 47

127 A7 (g)	60c on 75c (R)	3.25	3.25
a.	Inverted surcharge	175.00	175.00
128 A7 (h)	1fr on 5fr	.48	.48

On No. 77

129 A8 (h)	1fr on 5fr (R)	45.00	45.00
	Nos. 125-129 (5)	51.13	51.13

Stamps and Type of 1908-16 Surcharged in Black or Red

0,25

I cent.

130 A9	1c on 15c dl vio & rose	.50	.50
131 A9	25c on 35c red & blk	3.00	3.00
132 A9	25c on 35c red & blk (R)	10.00	10.00
133 A9	25c on 40c brn & blk	2.75	2.75
134 A9	25c on 45c grn & blk	2.00	2.00
	Nos. 130-134 (5)	18.25	18.25
	Nos. 125-134 (10)	69.38	69.38

Stamps and Type of 1908-28 Surcharged with New Value and Bars

1922-27

135 A9	25c on 15c dl vio & rose	.20	.15
a.	Double surcharge	55.00	
136 A9	25c on 2fr bl & ol	.25	.15
137 A9	25c on 5fr vio & vio brn	.45	.15
138 A9	60c on 75c vio, *pnksh*	.35	.25
139 A9	65c on 75c rose red & blk	.50	.25
140 A9	85c on 45c bl grn & blk	.50	.25
141 A9	90c on 75c dl red & rose red	.45	.20
142 A9	1.25fr on 1fr lt bl (R)	.25	.15
143 A9	1.50fr on 1fr dp bl & dl bl	.25	.15
144 A9	3fr on 5fr grn & vio	.60	.50
145 A9	10fr on 5fr org & rose lil	4.00	3.00
146 A9	20fr on 5fr rose & sl bl	5.50	5.00
	Nos. 135-146 (12)	13.30	10.20

Years of issue: #138, 1922; #136, 137, 1924; #135, 139-140, 1925; #142, 1926; #141, 142-146, 1927.
See Nos. 178-179.

Sakalava Chief — A10

Hova Woman — A12

Hova with Oxen — A11

Bétsiléo Woman A13

Perf. 13½x14, 14x13½

1930-44 **Typo.**

147 A11	1c dk bl & bl grn ('33)	.15	.15
148 A10	2c brn red & dk brn	.15	.15
149 A10	4c dk brn & vio	.15	.15
150 A11	5c lt grn & red	.15	.15
151 A12	10c ver & dp grn	.15	.15
152 A13	15c dp red	.15	.15
153 A11	20c yel brn & dk bl	.15	.15
154 A12	25c vio & dk brn	.15	.15
155 A13	30c Prus blue	.30	.15
156 A10	40c grn & red	.40	.30
157 A13	45c dull violet	.70	.40
158 A11	65c ol grn & vio	.70	.30
159 A13	75c dk brown	.55	.30
160 A11	90c brn red & dk red	.75	.45
161 A12	1fr yel brn & dk bl	1.00	.60
162 A12	1fr dk red & car rose ('38)	.50	.30
163 A12	1.25fr dp bl & dk brn ('33)	.75	.45
164 A10	1.50fr dk & dp bl	4.00	.85
165 A10	1.50fr brn & dk red ('38)	.20	.15
165A A10	1.50fr dk red & brn ('44)	.20	.16
166 A10	1.75fr dk brn & dk red ('33)	2.25	.65
167 A10	5fr vio & dk brn	1.00	.30
168 A10	20fr yel brn & dk bl	1.50	.90
	Nos. 147-168 (23)	16.00	
	Set value		6.60

For surcharges and overprints see #211, 215, 217-218, 222-223, 228-229, 233, 235, 239, 257 and note after #B10.

Common Design Types pictured following the introduction.

Colonial Exposition Issue
Common Design Types

1931 **Engr.** *Perf. 12½*

Name of Country in Black

169 CD70	40c deep green	.60	.40
170 CD71	50c violet	1.00	.50
171 CD72	90c red orange	.75	.60
172 CD73	1.50fr dull blue	1.25	.75
	Nos. 169-172 (4)	3.60	2.25

General Joseph Simon Galliéni — A14

1931 **Engr.** *Perf. 14*

Size: 21½x34½mm

173 A14	1c ultra	.35	.15
174 A14	50c orange brn	.60	.15
175 A14	2fr deep red	3.50	2.75
176 A14	3fr emerald	3.00	1.50
177 A14	10fr dp orange	1.75	1.50
	Nos. 173-177 (5)	9.20	6.05

See Nos. 180-190. For overprints and surcharges see Nos. 216, 219, 221, 224, 232, 258.

25c

Nos. 113 and 109 Surcharged

1932 *Perf. 13½x14*

178 A9	25c on 2fr bl & ol	.50	.30
179 A9	50c on 1fr brn & ol	.50	.30

No. 178 has numerals in thick block letters.
No. 136 has thin shaded numerals.

Galliéni Type of 1931

1936-40 **Photo.** *Perf. 13½, 13x13½*

Size: 21x34mm

180 A14	3c sapphire ('40)	.15	.15
181 A14	45c brt green ('40)	.15	.15
182 A14	50c yellow brown	.15	.15
183 A14	60c brt red lil ('40)	.15	.15
184 A14	70c brt rose ('40)	.20	.20
185 A14	90c copper brn ('39)	.15	.15
186 A14	1.40fr org yel ('40)	.35	.22
187 A14	1.60fr purple ('40)	.35	.28
188 A14	2fr dk carmine	.15	.15
189 A14	3fr green	2.00	1.00
190 A14	3fr olive blk ('39)	.60	.32
	Nos. 180-190 (11)	4.40	
	Set value		2.50

For overprint see note after #B10.

Paris International Exposition Issue
Common Design Types

1937, Apr. 15 **Engr.** *Perf. 13*

191 CD74	20c dp violet	.60	.60
192 CD75	30c dk green	.60	.60
193 CD76	40c car rose	.60	.60
194 CD77	50c dk brn & blk	.50	.50
195 CD78	90c red	.75	.75
196 CD79	1.50fr ultra	.75	.75
	Nos. 191-196 (6)	3.80	3.80

Colonial Arts Exhibition Issue
Common Design Type
Souvenir Sheet

1937 *Imperf.*

197 CD74	3fr orange red	3.25	3.25

Jean Laborde A15

1938-40 *Perf. 13*

198 A15	35c green	.35	.20
199 A15	55c dp purple	.35	.20
200 A15	65c orange red	.35	.20
201 A15	80c violet brn	.35	.20
202 A15	1fr rose car	.35	.20
203 A15	1.25fr rose car ('39)	.15	.15
204 A15	1.75fr dk ultra	.65	.20
205 A15	2.15fr yel brn	1.20	.80
206 A15	2.25fr dk ultra ('39)	.30	.15
207 A15	2.50fr blk brn ('40)	.20	.20
208 A15	10fr dk green ('40)	.60	.35
	Nos. 198-208 (11)	4.85	2.85

Nos. 198-202, 204, 205 commemorate the 60th anniv. of the death of Jean Laborde, explorer.
For overprints and surcharges see Nos. 220, 225-227, 230-231, 234, 236-237.

New York World's Fair Issue
Common Design Type

1939, May 10 **Engr.** *Perf. 12½x12*

209 CD82	1.25fr car lake	.65	.65
210 CD82	2.25fr ultra	.65	.65

For surcharge see No. 240.

Porters Carrying Man in Chair, and Marshal Petain — A15a

1941 **Engr.** *Perf. 12x12½*

210A A15a	1fr bister brn	.35	
210B A15a	2.50fr blue	.35	

Nos. 210A-210B were issued by the Vichy government and were not placed on sale in the colony.
For overprints see note after #B10.

Type of 1930-44 Surcharged in Black with New Value

1942 *Perf. 14x13½*

211 A11	50c on 65c dk brn & mag	.65	.15

V2

Stamps of the design shown above and types A10, A11, A12 and A14, without "RF," were issued in 1942-44 by the Vichy government, but were not placed on sale in the colony.

Nos. 143, 145-146 with Additional Overprint in Red or Black **FRANCE LIBRE**

1942 **Unwmk.** *Perf. 14x13½*

212 A9	1.50fr on 1fr (R)	.55	.55
213 A9	10fr on 5fr (Bk)	3.50	3.50
214 A9	20fr on 5fr (R)	5.00	5.00

Stamps of 1930-40 Overprinted Like Nos. 212-214 in Black or Red or:

FRANCE LIBRE

215 A10	2c brn red & dk brn	.55	.55
216 A14	3c sapphire (R)	90.00	90.00
217 A13	15c deep red	4.50	4.50
218 A11	65c dk brn & mag	.45	.45
219 A14	70c brt rose	.40	.40
220 A15	80c violet brn	1.10	1.10
221 A14	1.40fr orange yel	.40	.40
222 A10	1.50fr dk bl & dp bl (R)	.65	.65
223 A10	1.50fr brn & dk red	.65	.65
224 A14	1.60fr purple	.45	.45
225 A15	2.25fr dk ultra (R)	.35	.35
226 A15	2.50fr black brn (R)	1.60	1.60
227 A15	10fr dk green	2.25	2.25
228 A10	20fr yel brn & dk bl (R)	700.00	700.00

Stamps of 1930-40 Surcharged in Black or Red

FRANCE LIBRE 0,10 ×

229 A11	5c on 1c dk bl & bl grn	.28	.28
230 A15	10c on 55c dp pur	.65	.65
231 A15	30c on 65c org red	.40	.40
232 A14	50c on 90c cop brn	.20	.20
233 A12	1fr on 1.25fr dp bl & dk brn	1.00	1.00
234 A15	1fr on 1.25fr rose car	4.00	4.00
235 A10	1.50fr on 1.75fr dk brn & dk red	.35	.35
236 A15	1.50fr on 1.75fr ultra (R)	.35	.35
237 A15	2fr on 2.15fr yel brn	.80	.80

No. 211 with additional Overprint Like Nos. 217-218 in Black

239 A11	50c on 65c dk brn & mag	.28	.28

New York World's Fair Stamp Overprinted Like #217-218 in Red
Perf. 12½x12

240 CD82 2.25fr ultra .28 .28
Nos. 212-227,229-240 (27) 120.99 120.99

Catalogue values for unused stamps in this section, from this point to the end of the section, are for Never Hinged items.

Traveler's Tree — A16

1943 Unwmk. Photo. *Perf. 14x14½*

241 A16 5c ol gray .15 .15
242 A16 10c pale rose vio .15 .15
243 A16 25c emerald .15 .15
244 A16 30c dp orange .15 .15
245 A16 40c slate bl .15 .15
246 A16 80c dk red brn .15 .15
247 A16 1fr dull blue .15 .15
248 A16 1.50fr crim rose .30 .30
249 A16 2fr dull yel .15 .15
250 A16 2.50fr brt ultra .15 .15
251 A16 4fr aqua & red .25 .20
252 A16 5fr green & blk .40 .20
253 A16 10fr sal pink & dk bl .55 .40
254 A16 20fr dl vio & brn .75 .60
Nos. 241-254 (14) 3.60
Set value 2.30

For surcharges see Nos. 255-256, 261-268.

Nos. 241 and 242 Surcharged with New Values and Bars in Red or Blue

1944

255 A16 1.50fr on 5c (R) .40 .40
256 A16 1.50fr on 10c (Bl) .60 .60

Nos. 229 and 224 Surcharged with New Values and Bars in Red or Black
Perf. 14x13½, 14

257 A11 50c on 5c on 1c (R) .30 .30
258 A14 1.50fr on 1.60fr (Bk) .40 .40
Nos. 255-258 (4) 1.70 1.70

Eboue Issue
Common Design Type

1945 Engr. *Perf. 13*

259 CD91 2fr black .45 .35
260 CD91 25fr Prus green .75 .65

Nos. 241, 243 and 250 Surcharged with New Values and Bars in Carmine or Black

1945 *Perf. 14x14½*

261 A16 50c on 5c ol gray (C) .40 .20
262 A16 60c on 5c ol gray (C) .70 .35
263 A16 70c on 5c ol gray (C) .25 .15
264 A16 1.20fr on 5c ol gray (C) .50 .25
265 A16 2.40fr on 25c emer .40 .20
266 A16 3fr on 25c emer .25 .15
267 A16 4.50fr on 25c emer .75 .40
268 A16 15fr on 2.50fr brt ultra (C) .55 .30
Nos. 261-268 (8) 3.80 2.00

Southern Dancer — A17

Gen. J. S. Galliéni — A20

Herd of Zebus — A18

Sakalava Man and Woman A19

Betsimisaraka Mother and Child — A21

General Jacques C. R. A. Duchesne A22

Marshal Joseph J. C. Joffre A23

Perf. 13x13½, 13½x13

1946 Photo. Unwmk.

269 A17 10c green .15 .15
270 A17 30c orange .15 .15
271 A17 40c brown ol .15 .15
272 A17 50c violet brn .15 .15
273 A18 60c dp ultra .15 .15
274 A18 80c blue grn .15 .15
275 A19 1fr brown .15 .15
276 A19 1.20fr green .15 .15
276A A20 1.50fr dk red .15 .15
277 A20 2fr slate blk .15 .15
278 A20 3fr dp claret .15 .15
278A A21 3.60fr dk car rose .65 .50
279 A21 4fr dp ultra .15 .15
280 A21 5fr red orange .35 .15
281 A22 6fr dk grnsh bl .15 .15
282 A22 10fr red brn .35 .15
283 A23 15fr violet brn .65 .15
284 A23 20fr dk vio bl .70 .38
285 A23 25fr brown 1.00 .45
Nos. 269-285 (19) 5.65
Set value 2.00

Military Medal Issue
Common Design Type

Engraved and Typographed

1952, Dec. 1 Unwmk. *Perf. 13*

286 CD101 15fr multicolored 1.00 .75

Creation of the French Military Medal, cent.

Tropical Flowers — A24

Long-tailed Ground Roller — A25

1954 Engr.

287 A24 7.50fr ind & gray grn .80 .15
288 A25 8fr brown carmine .60 .20
289 A25 15fr dk grn & dp ultra 1.60 .15
Nos. 287-289 (3) 3.00
Set value .35

Colonel Lyautey and Royal Palace, Tananarive A26

1954-55

290 A26 10fr vio bl, ind & bl ('55) .65 .15
291 A26 40fr dk sl bl & red brn 1.10 .15
Set value .20

FIDES Issue
Common Design Type

Designs: 3fr, Tractor and modern settlement. 5fr, Gallieni school. 10fr, Pangalanes Canal. 15fr, Irrigation project.

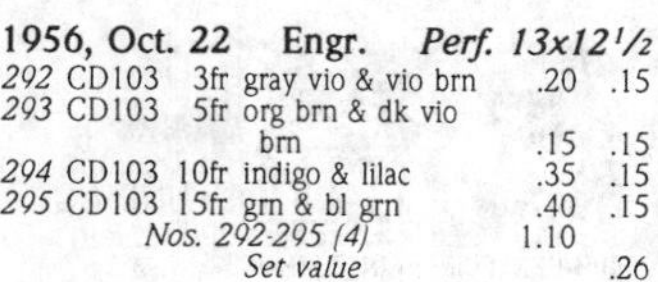

1956, Oct. 22 Engr. *Perf. 13x12½*

292 CD103 3fr gray vio & vio brn .20 .15
293 CD103 5fr org brn & dk vio brn .15 .15
294 CD103 10fr indigo & lilac .35 .15
295 CD103 15fr grn & bl grn .40 .15
Nos. 292-295 (4) 1.10
Set value .26

Coffee — A26a

1956, Oct. 22 *Perf. 13*

296 A26a 20r red brn & dk brn .75 .15

Manioc — A27

Vanilla — A28

Design: 4fr, Cloves.

1957, Mar. 12 Unwmk. *Perf. 13*

297 A27 2fr bl, grn & sepia .25 .15
298 A28 4fr dp grn & red .45 .15
299 A28 12fr dk vio, dl grn & sepia .80 .25
Nos. 297-299 (3) 1.50
Set value .36

Malagasy Republic
Human Rights Issue
Common Design Type

1958, Dec. 10 Engr. *Perf. 13*

300 CD105 10fr brn & dk bl .22 .15

Universal Declaration of Human Rights, 10th anniversary.
"CF" stands for "Communauté française."

Imperforates
Most Malagasy stamps from 1958 onward exist imperforate in issued and trial colors, and also in small presentation sheets in issued colors.

Flower Issue
Common Design Type
Perf. 12½x12, 12x12½

1959, Jan. 31 Photo.

301 CD104 6fr Datura, horiz. .15 .15
302 CD104 25fr Poinsettia .22 .15
Set value .28 .15

Flag and Assembly Building A29

Flag and Map — A30

French and Malagasy Flags and Map — A31

1959, Feb. 28 Engr. *Perf. 13*

303 A29 20fr brn vio, car & emer .22 .15
304 A30 25fr gray, red & emer .30 .16

Proclamation of the Malagasy Republic.

1959, Feb. 28

305 A31 60fr multi .60 .30

Issued to honor the French Community.

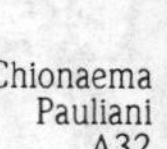

Chionaema Pauliani A32

Ylang-ylang — A33

Designs: 30c, 40c, 50c, 3fr, Various butterflies. 5fr, Sisal. 8fr, Pepper. 10fr, Rice. 15fr, Cotton.

1960 Unwmk. *Perf. 13*

306 A32 30c multicolored .15 .15
307 A32 40c emer, sep & red brn .15 .15
308 A32 50c vio brn, blk & stl bl .15 .15
309 A32 1fr ind, red & dl pur .15 .15
310 A32 3fr ol, vio blk & org .15 .15
311 A32 5fr red, brn & emer .15 .15
312 A33 6fr dk grn & brt yel .15 .15
313 A32 8fr crim rose, emer & blk .15 .15
314 A33 10fr dk grn, yel grn & lt brn .15 .15
315 A32 15fr brown & grn .18 .15
Set value .75 .60

Family Planting Trees — A34

1960, Feb. 1 Engr. *Perf. 13*

316 A34 20fr red brn, buff & grn .22 .15

Issued for the "Week of the Tree," Feb. 1-7.

C.C.T.A. Issue
Common Design Type

1960, Feb. 22

317 CD106 25fr lt bl grn & plum .40 .30

Pres. Philibert Tsiranana and Map — A36

1960, Mar. 25 Unwmk. *Perf. 13*

318 A36 20fr green & brn .20 .15

Athletes of Two Races — A37

Pres. Philibert Tsiranana — A38

1960 Engr. *Perf. 13*

319 A37 25fr choc, org brn & ultra .35 .22

First Games of the French Community, Apr. 13-18, at Tananarive.

1960, July 29 Unwmk. *Perf. 13*

320 A38 20fr red, blk & brt grn .20 .15

Issued to honor Pres. Tsiranana, "Father of Independence." For surcharge see No. B18.

Gray Lemur — A39

Designs: 4fr, Ruffed lemur, horiz. 12fr, Mongoose lemur.

1961, Dec. 9 *Perf. 13*

321 A39 2fr brn & grnsh bl .15 .15
322 A39 4fr brn, grn & blk .15 .15
323 A39 12fr grn & red brn .20 .15
Nos. 321-323,C67-C69 (6) 4.45 2.25

Pres. Tsiranana Bridge, Sofia River — A40

1962, Jan. 4 Unwmk. *Perf. 13*

324 A40 25fr bright blue .22 .15

First Train Built at Tananarive A41

1962, Feb. 1

325 A41 20fr dk grn .20 .15

UN and Malagasy Flags over Government Building, Tananarive — A42

1962, Mar. 14 *Perf. 13*

326 A42 25fr multicolored .22 .16
327 A42 85fr multicolored .80 .55

Malagasy Republic's admission to the UN. For surcharge see No. 409.

Ranomafana Village — A43

Designs: 30fr, Tritriva crater lake. 50fr, Foulpointe shore. 60fr, Fort Dauphin.

1962, May 7 Engr. *Perf. 13*

328 A43 10fr sl grn, grnsh bl & cl .15 .15
329 A43 30fr sl grn, cl & grnsh bl .22 .15
330 A43 50fr ultra, cl & sl grn .40 .25
331 A43 60fr cl, ultra & sl grn .50 .35
Nos. 328-331,C70 (5) 1.97 1.30

African and Malgache Union Issue

Common Design Type

1962, Sept. 8 Photo. *Perf. 12½x12*

332 CD110 30fr grn, bluish grn, red & gold .42 .35

First anniversary of the African and Malgache Union.

Arms of Republic and UNESCO Emblem A44

1962, Sept. 3 **Unwmk.**

333 A44 20fr rose, emer & blk .25 .20

First Conference on Higher Education in Africa, Tananarive, Sept. 3-12.

Power Station — A45

Designs: 8fr, Atomic reactor and atom symbol, horiz. 10fr, Oil derrick. 15fr, Tanker, horiz.

Perf. 12x12½, 12½x12

1962, Oct. 18 **Litho.**

334 A45 5fr blue, yel & red .15 .15
335 A45 8fr blue, red & yel .15 .15
336 A45 10fr multicolored .15 .15
337 A45 15fr bl, red brn & blk .15 .15
Set value .38 .26

Industrialization of Madagascar.

Factory and Globe — A46

1963, Jan. 7 Typo. *Perf. 14x13½*

338 A46 25fr dp org & blk .22 .15

International Fair at Tamatave.

Hertzian Cable, Tananarive-Fianarantsoa — A47

1963, Mar. 7 Photo. *Perf. 12½x12*

339 A47 20fr multi .20 .15

Madagascar Blue Pigeon — A48

Gastrorchis Humblotii — A49

Birds: 2fr, Blue coua. 3fr, Red fody. 6fr, Madagascar pigmy kingfisher.

Orchids: 10fr, Eulophiella roempleriana. 12fr, Angraecum sesquipedale.

1963 Unwmk. *Perf. 13*

340 A48 1fr multi .20 .20
341 A48 2fr multi .20 .20
342 A48 3fr multi .20 .20
343 A48 6fr multi .20 .20
344 A49 8fr multi .16 .15
345 A49 10fr multi .25 .22
346 A49 12fr multi .25 .22
Nos. 340-346,C72-C74 (10) 4.81 2.86

Arms of Fianarantsoa — A50

Arms of: 1.50fr, Antsirabe. 5fr, Antalaha. 10fr, Tulear. 15fr, Majunga. 25fr, Tananarive. 50fr, Diégo-Suarez.

Imprint: "R. Louis del. So. Ge. Im."

1963-65 Litho. *Perf. 13*

Size: 23½x35½mm

347 A50 1.50fr multi ('64) .15 .15
348 A50 5fr multi ('65) .15 .15
349 A50 10fr multi ('64) .15 .15
350 A50 15fr multi ('64) .15 .15
351 A50 20fr multi .20 .15
352 A50 25fr multi .22 .15
353 A50 50fr multi ('65) .40 .30
Set value 1.10 .70

See Nos. 388-390, 434-439. For surcharge see No. 503.

Map and Centenary Emblem — A51

Globe and Hands Holding Torch — A52

1963, Sept. 2 *Perf. 12x12½*

354 A51 30fr multi .55 .50

Centenary of the International Red Cross.

1963, Dec. 10 Engr. *Perf. 12½*

355 A52 60fr ol, ocher & car .50 .35

Universal Declaration of Human Rights, 15th anniv.

Scouts and Campfire A53

1964, June 6 Engr. *Perf. 13*

356 A53 20fr dk red, org & car .22 .15

40th anniv. of the Boy Scouts of Madagascar.

Europafrica Issue, 1964

Dove and Globe — A54

1964, July 20 **Engr.**

357 A54 45fr ol grn, brn red & blk .40 .25

First anniversary of economic agreement between the European Economic Community and the African and Malgache Union.

Carved Statue of Woman — A55

University Emblem — A56

Malagasy Art: 30fr, Statue of sitting man.

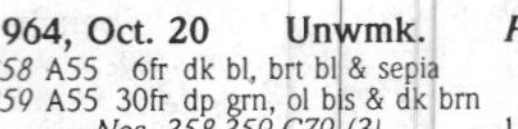

1964, Oct. 20 Unwmk. *Perf. 13*

358 A55 6fr dk bl, brt bl & sepia .15 .15
359 A55 30fr dp grn, ol bis & dk brn .30 .20
Nos. 358-359,C79 (3) 1.35 .97

Cooperation Issue

Common Design Type

1964, Nov. 7 Engr. *Perf. 13*

360 CD119 25fr blk, dk brn & org brn .25 .16

1964, Dec. 5 Litho. *Perf. 13x12½*

361 A56 65fr red, blk & grn .50 .35

Founding of the University of Madagascar, Tananarive. The inscription reads: "Foolish is he who does not do better than his father."

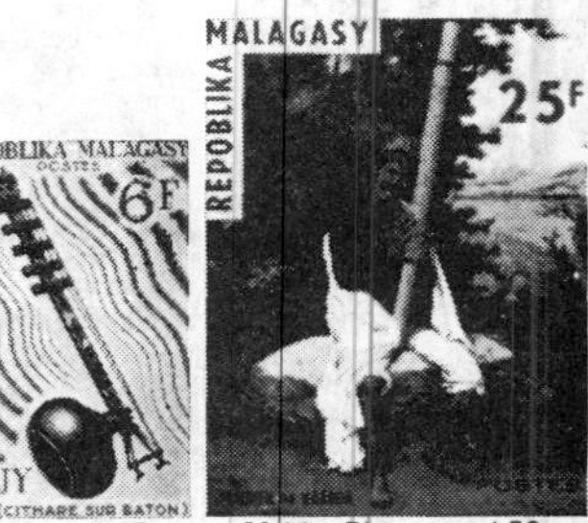

Jejy — A57 Valiha Player — A58

Musical instruments: 3fr, Kabosa (lute). 8fr, Hazolahy (sacred drum).

1965 Engr. *Perf. 13*

Size: 22x36mm

362 A57 3fr mag, vio bl & dk brn .15 .15
363 A57 6fr emer, rose lil & dk brn .15 .15
364 A57 8fr brn, grn & blk .15 .15

Photo. *Perf. 12½x13*

365 A58 25fr multi .25 .16
Nos. 362-365,C80 (5) 2.60
Set value 1.35

PTT Receiving Station, Foulpointe A59

1965, May 8 Engr. *Perf. 13*

366 A59 20fr red org, dk grn & ocher .16 .15

Issued for Stamp Day, 1965.

ITU Emblem, Old and New Telecommunication Equipment — A60

1965, May 17

367 A60 50fr ultra, red & grn .65 .40

ITU, centenary.

Jean Joseph Rabearivelo A61

Pres. Philibert Tsiranana A62

1965, June 22 Photo. *Perf. 13x12½*

368 A61 40fr dk brn & org .38 .22

Issued to honor the poet Jean Joseph Rabearivelo, pen name of Joseph Casimir, (1901-37).

1965, Oct. 18 *Perf. 13x12½*

369 A62 20fr multi .15 .15
a. Souv. sheet of 4 .55 .55

370 A62 25fr multi .15 .15
a. Souv. sheet of 4 .65 .65
Set value .18

55th birthday of President Philibert Tsiranana.

Mail Coach — A63

History of the Post: 3fr, Early automobile. 4fr, Litter. 10fr, Mail runner, vert. 12fr, Mail boat. 25fr, Oxcart. 30fr, Old railroad mail car. 65fr, Hydrofoil.

1965-66 Engr. *Perf. 13*

371 A63 3fr vio, dp bis & sky bl ('66) .15 .15
372 A63 4fr ultra, grn & dk brn ('66) .15 .15
373 A63 10fr multi .15 .15
374 A63 12fr multi .15 .15
375 A63 20fr bis, grn & red brn .25 .15
376 A63 25fr sl grn, dk brn & org .30 .15
377 A63 30fr pck bl, red & sep ('66) .35 .20
378 A63 65fr vio, brn & Prus bl ('66) .55 .35
Nos. 371-378 (8) 2.05 1.45

Leper's Crippled Hands — A64

1966, Jan. 30

379 A64 20fr dk grn, dk brn & red .25 .20

Issued for the 13th World Leprosy Day.

Couple Planting Trees — A65

1966, Feb. 21

380 A65 20fr dk brn, pur & bl grn .20 .15

Reforestation as a national duty.

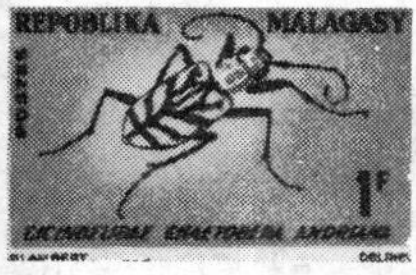

Tiger Beetle — A66

Insects: 6fr, Mantis. 12fr, Long-horned beetle. 45fr, Weevil.

1966 Photo. *Perf. 12½x12*
Insects in Natural Colors

381 A66 1fr brick red .15 .15
382 A66 6fr rose claret .15 .15
383 A66 12fr Prus blue .15 .15
384 A66 45fr lt yel grn .38 .20
Set value .60 .40

Stamp of 1903 — A67

1966, May 8 Engr. *Perf. 13*

385 A67 25fr red & sepia .25 .20

Issued for Stamp Day 1966.

Betsileo Dancers A68

1966, June 13 Photo. *Perf. 12½x13*
Size: 36x23mm

386 A68 5fr multi .15 .15

See No. C83.

Symbolic Tree and Emblems — A69

1966, June 26

387 A69 25fr multi .22 .15

Conference of the Organisation Commune Africaine et Malgache (OCAM), Tananarive.

No. 387 dated "JUIN 1966," original date "Janvier 1966" obliterated with bar. Exists without overprint "JUIN 1966" and bar. Value $45.

Arms Type of 1963-65
Imprint: "S. Gauthier So. Ge. Im."

20fr, Mananjary. 30fr, Nossi-Bé. 90fr, Antsohihy.

1966-68 Litho. *Perf. 13*
Size: 23½x35½mm

388 A50 20fr multi ('67) .15 .15
389 A50 30fr multi .20 .15
390 A50 90fr multi ('68) .55 .35
Nos. 388-390 (3) .90
Set value .50

For surcharge see No. 503.

Singers and Map of Madagascar — A70

1966, Oct. 14 Engr. *Perf. 13*

392 A70 20fr red brn, grn & dk car rose .15 .15

Issued in honor of the National Anthem.

UNESCO Emblem A71

1966, Nov. 4

393 A71 30fr red, yel & slate .25 .20

UNESCO, 20th anniv.

Lions Emblem — A72

1967, Jan. 14 Photo. *Perf. 13x12½*

394 A72 30fr multi .25 .16

50th anniversary of Lions International.

Rice Harvest A73

1967, Jan. 27 *Perf. 12½x13*

395 A73 20fr multi .16 .15

FAO International Rice Year.

Adventist Temple, Tanambao-Tamatave — A74

Designs: 5fr, Catholic Cathedral, Tananarive, vert. 10fr, Mosque, Tamatave.

1967, Feb. 20 Engr. *Perf. 13*

396 A74 3fr lt ultra, grn & bis .15 .15
397 A74 5fr brt rose lil, grn & vio .15 .15
398 A74 10fr dp bl, brn & grn .15 .15
Set value .20 .15

Norbert Raharisoa at Piano — A75

1967, Mar. 23 Photo. *Perf. 12½x12*

399 A75 40fr cit & multi .35 .15

Norbert Raharisoa (1914-1963), composer.

Jean Raoult Flying Blériot Plane, 1911 — A76

45fr, Barnard-Bougault and hydroplane, 1926.

1967, Apr. 28 Engr. *Perf. 13*
Size: 35½x22mm

400 A76 5fr gray bl, brn & grn .15 .15
401 A76 45fr brn, stl bl & blk .40 .22
Nos. 400-401,C84 (3) 4.55 1.77

History of aviation in Madagascar.

Ministry of Equipment and Communications — A77

1967, May 8 Engr. *Perf. 13*

402 A77 20fr ocher, ultra & grn .16 .15

Issued for Stamp Day, 1967.

Lutheran Church, Tananarive, Madagascar Map — A78

Map of Madagascar and Emblems — A79

1967, Sept. 24 Photo. *Perf. 12x12½*

403 A78 20fr multi .16 .15

Lutheran Church in Madagascar, cent.

1967, Oct. 16 Engr. *Perf. 13*

404 A79 90fr red brn, bl & dk red .65 .40

Hydrological Decade (UNESCO), 1965-74.

Dance of the Bilo Sakalavas — A80

Design: 30fr, Atandroy dancers.

1967, Nov. 25 Photo. *Perf. 13x12½*
Size: 22x36mm

405 A80 2fr lt grn & multi .15 .15
406 A80 30fr multi .25 .15
Nos. 405-406,C86-C87 (4) 2.65 1.38

Woman's Face, Scales and UN Emblem A81

1967, Dec. 16 *Perf. 12½x13*

407 A81 50fr emer, dk bl & brn .38 .25

UN Commission on the Status of Women.

Human Rights Flame — A82

1968, Mar. 16 Litho. *Perf. 13x12½*

408 A82 50fr blk, ver & grn .38 .22

International Human Rights Year.

No. 327 Surcharged with New Value and 3 Bars

1968, June 4 Engr. *Perf. 13*

409 A42 20fr on 85fr multi .16 .15

"Industry" A83

Designs: 20fr, "Agriculture" (mother and child carrying fruit and grain, and cattle), vert. 40fr, "Communications and Investments," (train, highway, factory and buildings).

1968, July 15

410 A83 10fr rose car, grn & dk pur .15 .15
411 A83 20fr dp car, grn & blk .16 .15
412 A83 40fr brn, vio & sl bl .35 .16
Nos. 410-412 (3) .66
Set value .32

Completion of Five-year Plan, 1964-68.

Church, Translated Bible, Cross and Map of Madagascar A84

1968, Aug. 18 Photo. *Perf. 12½x12*

413 A84 20fr multi .16 .15

Sesquicentennial of Christianity in Madagascar.

Isotry-Fitiavana Protestant Church — A85

Designs: 12fr, Catholic Cathedral, Fianarantsoa. 50fr, Aga Khan Mosque, Tananarive.

1968, Sept. 10 Engr. *Perf. 13*

414 A85 4fr red brn, brt grn & dk brn .15 .15
415 A85 12fr plum, bl & hn brn .15 .15
416 A85 50fr brt grn, bl & indigo .35 .20
Set value .52 .32

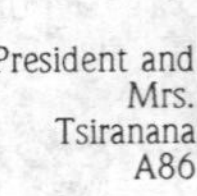

President and Mrs. Tsiranana A86

1968, Oct. 14 Photo. *Perf. 12½x12*

417 A86 20fr car, org & blk .15 .15
418 A86 30fr car, grnsh bl & blk .20 .15
a. Souv. sheet of 4, 2 each #417-418 1.10 1.10
Set value .17

10th anniv. of the Republic.

Madagascar Map and Cornucopia with Coins — A87

Striving Mankind — A88

1968, Nov. 3 Photo. *Perf. 12x12½*

419 A87 20fr multi .16 .15

50th anniversary of the Malagasy Savings Bank.

1968, Dec. 3 Photo. *Perf. 12½x12*

Design: 15fr, Mother, child and physician, horiz.

420 A88 15fr ultra, yel & crim .15 .15
421 A88 45fr vio bl & multi .35 .22
Set value .30

Completion of Five-Year Plan, 1964-68.

Queen Adelaide Receiving Malagasy Delegation, London, 1836 — A89

1969, Mar. 29 Photo. *Perf. 12x12½*

422 A89 250fr multi 2.25 1.40

Malagasy delegation London visit, 1836-1837.

Cogwheels, Wrench and ILO Emblem A90

1969, Apr. 11 *Perf. 12½x12*

423 A90 20fr grn & multi .16 .15

ILO, 50th anniv.

Telecommunications and Postal Building, Tananarive — A91

1969, May 8 Engr. *Perf. 13*

424 A91 30fr bl, brt grn & car lake .22 .15

Issued for Stamp Day 1969.

Steering Wheel, Map, Automobiles — A92

1969, June 1 Photo. *Perf. 12*

425 A92 65fr multi .50 .25

Automobile Club of Madagascar, 20th anniv.

Pres. Philibert Tsiranana — A93

Banana Plants — A94

1969, June 26 Photo. *Perf. 12x12½*

426 A93 20fr multi .15 .15

10th anniversary of the inauguration of Pres. Philibert Tsiranana.

1969, July 7 Engr. *Perf. 13*

427 A94 5fr shown .15 .15
428 A94 15fr Lichi tree .15 .15
Set value .18 .15

Runners A95

1969, Sept. 9 Engr. *Perf. 13*

429 A95 15fr yel grn, brn & red .16 .15

Issued to commemorate the 19th Olympic Games, Mexico City, Oct. 12-27, 1968.

Malagasy House, Highlands — A96

Carnelian — A97

Designs (Malagasy Houses): No. 430, Betsileo house, Highlands. No. 431, Tsimihety house, West Coast, horiz. 60fr, Malagasy house, Highlands.

1969-70 Engr. *Perf. 13*

430 A96 20fr bl, ol & ver .15 .15
431 A96 20fr sl, brt grn & red .15 .15
432 A96 40fr blk, bl & dk red .30 .15
433 A96 60fr vio bl, dp grn & brn .45 .20
Nos. 430-433 (4) 1.05
Set value .48

Issuesd: 40fr, 60fr, 11/25/69; others, 11/25/70.

Arms Type of 1963-65

Arms: 1fr, Maintirano. 10fr, Ambalavao. No. 436, Morondava. No. 437, Ambatondrazaka. No. 438, Fenerive-Est. 80fr, Tamatave.

1970-72 Photo. *Perf. 13*

434 A50 1fr multi ('72) .15 .15
435 A50 10fr multi ('72) .15 .15
436 A50 25fr multi ('71) .22 .15
437 A50 25fr multi ('71) .22 .15
438 A50 25fr multi ('72) .20 .15
439 A50 80fr pink & multi .55 .30
Nos. 434-439 (6) 1.49
Set value .80

The 10fr and 80fr are dated "1970." No. 437 is dated "1971." Nos. 434, 438 are dated "1972."

Sizes: #434, 438, 22x37mm; others, 25½x36mm.

Imprints: "S. Gauthier" on Nos. 434, 438; "S. Gauthier Delrieu" on others.

Perf. 12x12½ (5, 20fr), 13 (12, 15fr)
1970-71 Photo.

Semi-precious Stones: 12fr, Yellow calcite. 15fr, Quartz. 20fr, Ammonite.

440 A97 5fr brn, dl rose & yel .15 .15
441 A97 12fr multi ('71) .15 .15
442 A97 15fr multi ('71) .16 .15
443 A97 20fr grn & multi .20 .15
Nos. 440-443 (4) .66
Set value .42

UPU Headquarters Issue
Common Design Type

1970, May 20 Engr. *Perf. 13*

444 CD133 20fr lil rose, brn & ultra .20 .15

UN Emblem and Symbols of Justice — A98

1970, June 26 Engr. *Perf. 13*

445 A98 50fr blk, ultra & org .38 .20

25th anniversary of the United Nations.

Fruits of Madagascar — A99

1970, Aug. 18 Photo. *Perf. 13*

446 A99 20fr multi .15 .15

Volute Delessertiana A100

Shells: 10fr, Murex tribulus. 20fr, Spondylus.

1970, Sept. 9 Photo. *Perf. 13*

447 A100 5fr Prus bl & multi .15 .15
448 A100 10fr vio & multi .15 .15
449 A100 20fr multi .20 .15
Set value .36 .18

Aye-aye — A101

1970, Oct. 7 Photo. *Perf. 12½*

450 A101 20fr multi .35 .25

Intl. Conference for Nature Conservation, Tananarive, Oct. 7-10.

Pres. Tsiranana — A102

1970, Dec. 30 Photo. *Perf. 12½*

451 A102 30fr grn & lt brn .20 .15

60th birthday of Pres. Philibert Tsiranana.

Tropical Soap Factory, Tananarive A103

Designs: 15fr, Comina chromium smelting plant, Andriamena. 50fr, Textile mill, Majunga.

1971, Apr. 14 Photo. *Perf. 12½x12*

452 A103 5fr multi .15 .15

Engr. *Perf. 13*

453 A103 15fr vio bl, blk & ocher .15 .15

Photo. *Perf. 13*

454 A103 50fr multi .38 .20
Set value .55 .32

Economic development.

Globe, Agriculture, Industry, Science A104

1971, Apr. 22 Photo. *Perf. 12½x12*

455 A104 5fr multi .15 .15

Extraordinary meeting of the Council of the C.E.E.-E.A.M.A. (Communauté Economique Européen-Etats Africains et Malgache Associés).

Mobile Rural Post Office — A105

1971, May 8 *Perf. 13*

456 A105 25fr multi .20 .15

Stamp Day.

Gen. Charles de Gaulle — A106

Madagascar Hilton, Tananarive — A107

1971, June 26 Engr. *Perf. 13*

457 A106 30fr ultra, blk & rose .40 .20

In memory of Charles de Gaulle (1890-1970), President of France.

For surcharge see No. B24.

1971, July 23 **Photo.**

Design: 25fr, Hotel Palm Beach, Nossi-Bé.

458 A107 25fr multi .20 .15

Engr.

459 A107 65fr vio bl, brn & lt grn .45 .25

Trees and Post Horn — A108

1971, Aug. 6 **Photo.** ***Perf. 12½x12***

460 A108 3fr red, yel & grn .15 .15

Forest preservation campaign.

House, South West Madagascar A109

Design: 10fr, House from Southern Madagascar.

1971, Nov. 25 ***Perf. 13x12½***

461 A109 5fr lt bl & multi .15 .15
462 A109 10fr lt bl & multi .15 .15
Set value .15 .15

Children Playing, and Cattle A110

1971, Dec. 11 **Litho.** ***Perf. 13***

463 A110 50fr grn & multi .40 .22

UNICEF, 25th anniv.

Cable-laying Railroad Car, PTT Emblem A111

1972, Apr. 8 **Engr.** ***Perf. 13***

464 A111 45fr slate grn, red & choc .35 .22

Coaxial cable connection between Tananarive and Tamatave.

Philibert Tsiranana Radar Station — A112

1972, Apr. 8 **Photo.** ***Perf. 13½***

465 A112 85fr bl & multi .65 .38

A113

A114

Voters and Pres. Tsiranana.

1972, May 1 ***Perf. 12½x13***

466 A113 25fr yel & multi .40 .35

Presidential election, Jan. 30, 1972.

1972, May 30 **Photo.** ***Perf. 12x12½***

467 A114 10fr Mail delivery .15 .15

Stamp Day 1972.

Emblem and Stamps of Madagascar — A115

Design: Stamps shown are #352, 410, 429, 449.

1972, June 26 ***Perf. 13***

468 A115 25fr org & multi .15 .15
469 A115 40fr org & multi .25 .16
470 A115 100fr org & multi .65 .35
a. Souv470. sheet of 3, #468-470 1.40 1.40
Nos. 468-(1) .15 .15

2nd Malgache Philatelic Exhibition, Tananarive, June 26-July 9.

Andapa-Sambava Road and Monument — A116

1972, July 6 ***Perf. 12½x12***

471 A116 50fr multi .30 .20

Opening of the Andapa-Sambava road.

Diesel Locomotive A117

1972, July 6 **Engr.** ***Perf. 13***

472 A117 100fr multicolored .65 .40

Razafindrahety College, A118

1972, Aug. 6

473 A118 10fr choc, bl & red brn .15 .15

Razafindrahety College, Tananarive, sesqui.

Volleyball A119

1972, Aug. 6 **Typo.** ***Perf. 12½x13***

474 A119 12fr orange, blk & brn .15 .15

African volleyball championship.

Oil Refinery, Tamatave A120

1972, Sept. 18 **Engr.** ***Perf. 13***

475 A120 2fr bl, bister & slate grn .15 .15

Ravoahangy Andrianavalona Hospital — A121

1972, Oct. 14 **Photo.** ***Perf. 13x12½***

476 A121 6fr multi .15 .15

Plowing A122

1972, Nov. 15 **Photo.** ***Perf. 13½x14***

477 A122 25fr gold & multi .15 .15

Betsimisaraka Costume A123

Design: 15fr, Merina costume.

1972, Dec. 30 **Photo.** ***Perf. 13x12½***

478 A123 10fr blue & multi .15 .15
479 A123 15fr brown & multi .15 .15
Set value .16 .15

Farmer and Produce — A124

1973, Feb. 6 **Photo.** ***Perf. 13***

480 A124 25fr lt blue & multi .16 .15

10th anniversary of the Malagasy Committee of "Freedom from Hunger Campaign."

For surcharge see No. 499.

Volva Volva — A125

Shells: 10fr, 50fr, Lambis chiragra. 15fr, 40fr, Harpa major. 25fr, Like 3fr.

1973, Apr. 5 **Litho.** ***Perf. 13***

481 A125 3fr olive & multi .15 .15
482 A125 10fr blue grn & multi .15 .15
483 A125 15fr brt blue & multi .15 .15
484 A125 25fr lt blue & multi .16 .15
485 A125 40fr multicolored .25 .16
486 A125 50fr red lilac & multi .40 .22
Nos. 481-486 (6) 1.26 .98

Tsimandoa Mail Carrier — A126

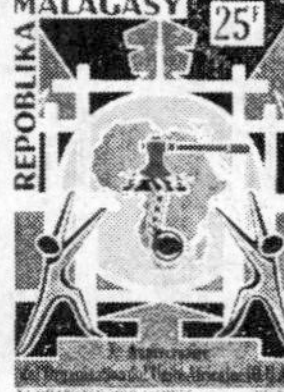

Builders and Map of Africa — A127

1973, May 13 **Engr.** ***Perf. 13***

487 A126 50fr ind, ocher & sl grn .35 .16

Stamp Day 1973.

1973, May 25 **Photo.** ***Perf. 13***

488 A127 25fr multicolored .15 .15

Organization for African Unity, 10th anniversary.

Campani Chameleon A128

Various Chameleons: 5fr, 40fr, Male nasutus. 10fr, 85fr, Female nasutus. 60fr, Like 1fr.

1973, June 15 **Photo.** ***Perf. 13x12½***

489 A128 1fr dp carmine & multi .15 .15
490 A128 5fr brown & multi .15 .15
491 A128 10fr green & multi .15 .15
492 A128 40fr red lilac & multi .25 .15
493 A128 60fr dk blue & multi .42 .22
494 A128 85fr brown & multi .65 .35
Set value 1.50 .85

Lady's Slipper — A129

Orchids: 25fr, 40fr, Pitcher plant.

1973, Aug. 6 **Photo.** ***Perf. 12½***

495 A129 10fr multicolored .15 .15
496 A129 25fr rose & multi .16 .15
497 A129 40fr lt blue & multi .22 .15
498 A129 100fr multicolored .52 .40
Nos. 495-498 (4) 1.05
Set value .70

No. 480 Surcharged with New Value, 2 Bars, and Overprinted in Ultramarine: "SECHERESSE / SOLIDARITE AFRICAINE"

1973, Aug. 16 ***Perf. 13***

499 A124 100fr on 25fr multi .52 .35

African solidarity in drought emergency.

African Postal Union Issue

Common Design Type

1973, Sept. 12 **Engr.** ***Perf. 13***

500 CD137 100fr vio, red & slate grn .55 .35

Greater Dwarf Lemur A131

Design: 25fr, Weasel lemur, vert.

1973, Oct. 9 **Engr.** ***Perf. 13***

501 A131 5fr brt green & multi .15 .15
502 A131 25fr ocher & multi .15 .15
Nos. 501-502,C117-C118 (4) 2.40 1.65

Lemurs of Madagascar.

25 Fmg

No. 389 Surcharged

1974, Feb. 9 Litho. *Perf. 13*

503 A50 25fr on 30fr multi .15 .15

Scouts Helping to Raise Cattle — A132

Mother with Children and Clinic — A133

Design: 15fr, Scouts building house; African Scout emblem.

1974, Feb. 14 Engr. *Perf. 13*

504 A132 4fr blue, slate & emer .15 .15
505 A132 15fr chocolate & multi .15 .15
Nos. 504-505,C122-C123 (4) 2.45 1.22

Malagasy Boy Scouts.

1974, May 24 Photo. *Perf. 13*

506 A133 25fr multicolored .15 .15

World Population Year.

Rainibetsimisaraka A134

1974, July 26 Photo. *Perf. 13*

507 A134 25fr multicolored .15 .15

In memory of Rainibetsimisaraka, independence leader.

Marble Blocks A135

Design: 25fr, Marble quarry.

1974, Sept. 27 Photo. *Perf. 13*

508 A135 4fr multicolored .15 .15
509 A135 25fr multicolored .15 .15
Set value .18 .15

Malagasy marble.

Europafrica Issue, 1974

Links, White and Black Faces, Map of Europe and Africa — A136

1974, Oct. 17 Engr. *Perf. 13*

510 A136 150fr dk brown & org .80 .35

Grain and Hand — A137

1974, Oct. 29

511 A137 80fr light blue & ocher .42 .25

World Committee against Hunger.

Tuléar Dog — A138

Design: 100fr, Hunting dog.

1974, Nov. 26 Photo. *Perf. 13x13½*

512 A138 50fr multicolored .25 .20
513 A138 100fr multicolored .55 .42

Malagasy Citizens — A139

1974, Dec. 9 *Perf. 13½x13*

514 A139 5fr blue grn & multi .15 .15
515 A139 10fr multicolored .15 .15
516 A139 20fr yellow grn & multi .15 .15
517 A139 60fr orange & multi .35 .20
Set value .56 .36

Introduction of "Fokonolona" community organization.

Symbols of Development A140

1974, Dec. 16 Photo. *Perf. 13x13½*

518 A140 25fr ultra & multi .16 .15
519 A140 35fr blue grn & multi .20 .15
Set value .24

National Council for Development.

Woman, Rose, Dove and Emblem — A141

1975, Jan. 21 Engr. *Perf. 13*

520 A141 100fr brown, emer & org .55 .22

International Women's Year 1975.

Col. Richard Ratsimandrava A142

1975, Apr. 25 Photo. *Perf. 13*

521 A142 15fr brown & salmon .15 .15
522 A142 25fr black, bl & brn .15 .15
523 A142 100fr black, lt grn & brn .52 .25
Set value .75 .36

Ratsimandrava (1933-1975), head of state.

Sofia Bridge A143

1975, May 29 Litho. *Perf. 12½*

524 A143 45fr multicolored .22 .15

Count de Grasse and "Randolph" — A144

Design: 50fr, Marquis de Lafayette, "Lexington" and HMS "Edward."

1975, June 30 Litho. *Perf. 11*

525 A144 40fr multicolored .30 .15
526 A144 50fr multicolored .38 .16
Nos. 525-526,C137-C139 (5) 4.38 1.91

American Bicentennial.
For overprints see Nos. 564-565, C164-C167.

Euphorbia Viguieri A145

Tropical Plants: 25fr, Hibiscus. 30fr, Plumieria rubra acutitolia. 40fr, Pachypodium rosulatum.

1975, Aug. 4 Photo. *Perf. 12½*

527 A145 15fr lemon & multi .15 .15
528 A145 25fr black & multi .15 .15
529 A145 30fr orange & multi .16 .15
530 A145 40fr dk red & multi .22 .20
Nos. 527-530,C141 (5) 1.13 1.00

Brown, White, Yellow and Black Hands Holding Globe — A146

1975, Aug. 26 Litho. *Perf. 12*

531 A146 50fr multicolored .25 .16

Namibia Day (independence for South-West Africa.)

Woodpecker — A147

1975, Sept. 16 Litho. *Perf. 14x13½*

532 A147 25fr shown .20 .15
533 A147 40fr Rabbit .25 .15
534 A147 50fr Frog .35 .20
535 A147 75fr Tortoise .45 .25
Nos. 532-535,C145 (5) 2.05 1.20

International Exposition, Okinawa.

Lily Waterfall A148

Design: 40fr, Lily Waterfall, different view.

1975, Sept. 17 Litho. *Perf. 12½*

536 A148 25fr multicolored .15 .15
537 A148 40fr multicolored .22 .15
Set value .20

4-man Bob Sled A149

Designs: 100fr, Ski jump. 140fr, Speed skating.

1975, Nov. 19 Litho. *Perf. 14*

538 A149 75fr multicolored .45 .20
539 A149 100fr multicolored .60 .22
540 A149 140fr multicolored .90 .30
Nos. 538-540,C149-C150 (5) 4.70 1.92

12th Winter Olympic games, Innsbruck, 1976.
For overprints see Nos. 561-563, C161-C163.

Pirogue A150

Designs: 45fr, Boutre (Arabian coastal vessel).

1975, Nov. 20 Photo. *Perf. 12½*

541 A150 8fr multicolored .15 .15
542 A150 45fr ultra & multi .22 .15
Set value .36 .18

Canadian Canoe and Kayak — A151

Design: 50fr, Sprint and Hurdles.

1976, Jan. 21 Litho. *Perf. 14x13½*

543 A151 40fr multicolored .25 .15
544 A151 50fr multicolored .35 .16
Nos. 543-544,C153-C155 (5) 4.35 2.01

21st Summer Olympic games, Montreal.
For overprints see Nos. 571-572, C168-C171.

Count Zeppelin and LZ-127 over Fujiyama, Japan — A152

Designs (Count Zeppelin and LZ-127 over): 50fr, Rio. 75fr, NYC. 100fr, Sphinx.

1976, Mar. 3 *Perf. 11*

545	A152	40fr multicolored	.28	.15
546	A152	50fr multicolored	.38	.15
547	A152	75fr multicolored	.55	.20
548	A152	100fr multicolored	.60	.25
		Nos. 545-548,C158-C159 (6)	4.81	2.25

75th anniversary of the Zeppelin.

Worker, Globe, Eye Chart and Eye — A153

1976, Apr. 7 **Photo.** *Perf. 12½*

549	A153	100fr multicolored	.55	.35

World Health Day: "Foresight prevents blindness."

Aragonite A154

Designs: 50fr, Petrified wood. 150fr, Celestite.

1976, May 7 **Photo.** *Perf. 12½*

550	A154	25fr blue & multi	.15	.15
551	A154	50fr blue grn & multi	.25	.15
552	A154	150fr orange & multi	.80	.42
		Nos. 550-552 (3)	1.20	.72

Alexander Graham Bell and First Telephone — A155

50fr, Telephone lines, 1911. 100fr, Central office, 1895. 200fr, Cable ship, 1925. 300fr, Radio telephone. 500fr, Telstar satellite and globe.

1976, May 13 **Litho.** *Perf. 14*

553	A155	25fr multicolored	.16	.15
554	A155	50fr multicolored	.35	.15
555	A155	100fr multicolored	.62	.30
556	A155	200fr multicolored	1.20	.55
557	A155	300fr multicolored	1.90	.75
		Nos. 553-557 (5)	4.23	1.90

Souvenir Sheet

558	A155	500fr multicolored	3.25	1.40

Cent. of 1st telephone call by Alexander Graham Bell, Mar. 10, 1876.

Children with Books A156

Design: 25fr, Children with books, vert.

1976, May 25 **Litho.**

559	A156	10fr multicolored	.15	.15
560	A156	25fr multicolored	.15	.15
		Set value	.18	.15

Books for children.

Nos. 538-540 Overprinted

a. VAINQUEUR ALLEMAGNE FEDERALE
b. VAINQUEUR KARL SCHNABL AUTRICHE
c. VAINQUEUR SHEILA YOUNG ETATS-UNIS

1976, June 17

561	A149 (a)	75fr multi	.40	.20
562	A149 (b)	100fr multi	.55	.30
563	A149 (c)	140fr multi	.70	.42
		Nos. 561-563,C161-C162 (5)	3.50	1.87

12th Winter Olympic games winners.

Nos. 525-526 Overprinted "4 Juillet / 1776-1976"

1976, July 4

564	A144	40fr multicolored	.30	.15
565	A144	50fr multicolored	.35	.16
		Nos. 564-565,C164-C166 (5)	4.45	1.91

American Bicentennial.

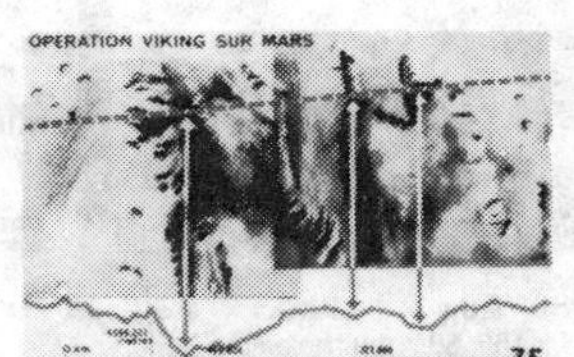

Graph of Projected Landing Spots on Mars — A157

Viking project to Mars: 100fr, Viking probe in flight. 200fr, Viking probe on Mars. 300fr, Viking probe over projected landing spot. 500fr, Viking probe approaching Mars.

1976, July 17 **Litho.** *Perf. 14*

566	A157	75fr multicolored	.35	.20
567	A157	100fr multicolored	.50	.20
568	A157	200fr multicolored	1.00	.40
569	A157	300fr multicolored	1.50	.60
		Nos. 566-569 (4)	3.35	1.40

Souvenir Sheet

570	A157	500fr multicolored	2.50	1.00

Nos. 543-544 Overprinted

a. A. ROGOV / V. DIBA
b. H. CRAWFORD / J. SCHALLER

1977, Jan.

571	A151 (a)	40fr multi	.30	.15
572	A151 (b)	50fr multi	.38	.16
		Nos. 571-572,C168-C170 (5)	4.25	1.91

21st Summer Olympic games winners.

Rainandriamampandry — A158

Portrait: No. 574, Rabezavana.

1976-77 **Litho.** *Perf. 12x12½*

573	A158	25fr multicolored	.15	.15
574	A158	25fr multicolored	.15	.15
		Set value		.20

Rainandriamampandry was Malagasy Foreign Minister who signed treaties in 1896.

Issued: #73, Oct. 15; #74, Mar. 29, 1977.

Doves, Indian Ocean on Globe — A159

Design: 12a, Globe with Africa and Indian Ocean, doves, vert.

Perf. 12½x12, 12x12½

1976, Nov. 18

575	A159	60fr multicolored	.35	.20
576	A159	160fr multicolored	.90	.50

"Indian Ocean - Zone of Peace."

Coat of Arms — A160

1976, Dec. 30 **Litho.** *Perf. 12*

577	A160	25fr multicolored	.15	.15

Democratic Republic of Malagasy, 1st anniv.

Lt. Albert Randriamaromanana — A161

Portrait: #578, Avana Ramanantoanina.

1977, Mar. 29

578	A161	25fr multicolored	.15	.15
579	A161	25fr multicolored	.15	.15
		Set value		.20

National Mausoleum — A162

1977, Mar. 29 *Perf. 12½x12*

580	A162	100fr multicolored	.50	.35

Family — A163

1977, Apr. 7 *Perf. 12x12½*

581	A163	5fr yellow & multi	.15	.15

World Health Day: Immunization protects the children.

Tananarive Medical School — A164

1977, June 30 **Litho.** *Perf. 12½x12*

582	A164	250fr multicolored	1.40	.65

80th anniversary of Tananarive Medical School.

Mail Bus A165

1977, Aug. 18 **Litho.** *Perf. 12½x12*

583	A165	35fr multicolored	.20	.15

Rural mail delivery.

Telegraph Operator — A166

1977, Sept. 13 **Litho.** *Perf. 12½x12*

584	A166	15fr multicolored	.15	.15

Telegraph service Tananarive-Tamatave, 90th anniv.

Malagasy Art — A167

1977, Sept. 29 *Perf. 12x12½*

585	A167	10fr multicolored	.15	.15

Malagasy Academy, 75th anniversary.

Lenin and Russian Flag — A168

1977, Nov. 7 **Litho.** *Perf. 12½x12*

586	A168	25fr multicolored	.15	.15

60th anniversary of Russian October Revolution.

Raoul Follereau, Map of Malagasy A169

1978, Jan. 28 **Litho.** *Perf. 12x12½*

587	A169	5fr multicolored	.15	.15

25th anniversary of Leprosy Day.

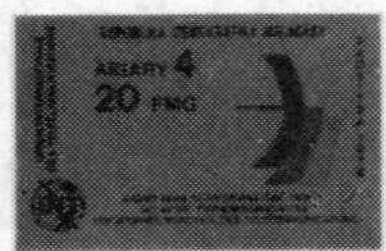

Antenna, ITU Emblem A170

1978, May 17 Litho. *Perf. 12x12½*

588 A170 20fr multicolored .40 .15

10th World Telecommunications Day.

Black and White Men Breaking Chains of Africa — A171

1978, June 22 Photo. *Perf. 12½x12*

589 A171 60fr multicolored .40 .16

Anti-Apartheid Year.

Boy and Girl, Arch: Pen, Gun and Hoe — A172

Farm Workers, Factory, Tractor — A173

1978, July 28 Litho. *Perf. 12½x12*

590 A172 125fr multicolored .80 .35

Youth, the pillar of revolution.

1978, Aug. 24

591 A173 25fr multicolored .16 .15

Socialist cooperation.

Women — A174

Children Bringing Gifts — A175

1979, Mar. 8 Litho. *Perf. 12½x12*

592 A174 40fr multicolored .25 .15

Women, supporters of the revolution.

1979, June 1 Litho. *Perf. 12x12½*

593 A175 10fr multicolored .15 .15

International Year of the Child.

Lemur Macaco A176

Fauna: 25fr, Lemur catta, vert. 1000fr, Foussa.

Perf. 12½x12, 12x12½

1979, July 6 Litho.

594	A176	25fr multi	.16	.15
595	A176	125fr multi	.80	.35
596	A176	1000fr multi	6.50	2.50
		Nos. 594-596,C172-C173 (5)	8.23	3.37

Jean Verdi Salomon A177

1979, July 25 *Perf. 12x12½*

597 A177 25fr multicolored .16 .15

Jean Verdi Salomon (1913-1978), poet.

Talapetraka (Medicinal Plant) A178

1979, Sept. 27 Litho. *Perf. 12½*

598 A178 25fr multicolored .16 .15

Map of Magagascar, Dish Antenna — A179

1979, Oct. 12

599 A179 25fr multicolored .16 .15

Stamp Day 1979 A180

1979, Nov. 9

600 A180 500fr multicolored 3.50 1.40

Jet, Map of Africa A181

1979, Dec. 12 *Perf. 12½*

601 A181 50fr multicolored .35 .15

ASECNA (Air Safety Board), 20th anniversary.

Lenin Addressing Workers in the Winter Palace — A182

1980, Apr. 22 Litho. *Perf. 12x12½*

602 A182 25fr multicolored .16 .15

Lenin's 110th birth anniversary.

Bus and Road in Madagascar Colors — A183

Flag and Map under Sun — A184

1980, June 15 Litho. *Perf. 12x12½*

603 A183 30fr multicolored .20 .15

Socialist Revolution, 5th anniversary.

1980, June 26 *Perf. 12½x12*

604 A184 75fr multicolored .50 .22

Independence, 20th anniversary.

Armed Forces Day A185

1980, Aug. Litho. *Perf. 12½x12*

605 A185 50fr multicolored .35 .15

Dr. Joseph Raseta (1886-1979) A186

1980, Oct. 15 Litho. *Perf. 12x12½*

606 A186 30fr multicolored .20 .15

Anatirova Temple Centenary — A187

1980, Nov. 27 Litho. *Perf. 12½x12*

607 A187 30fr multicolored .20 .15

Hurdles, Olympic Torch, Moscow '80 Emblem — A188

1980, Dec. 29

608	A188	30fr shown	.20	.15
609	A188	75fr Boxing	.50	.22
		Nos. 608-609,C175-C176 (4)	5.80	2.57

22nd Summer Olympic Games, Moscow, July 19-Aug. 3.

Democratic Republic of Madagascar, 5th Anniversary A189

1980, Dec. 30 *Perf. 12x12½*

610 A189 30fr multicolored .20 .15

Downhill Skiing — A190

1981, Jan. 26 Litho. *Perf. 12½x12*

611 A190 175fr multicolored 1.20 .50

13th Winter Olympic Games, Lake Placid, Feb. 12-24, 1980.

Angraecum Leonis — A191

1981, Mar. 23 Litho. *Perf. 11½*

612	A191	5fr shown	.15	.15
613	A191	80fr Angraecum ramosum	.55	.22
614	A191	170fr Angraecum sesquipedale	1.10	.45
		Nos. 612-614 (3)	1.80	.82

A192 A193

1981, June 12 Litho. *Perf. 12*

615	A192	25fr Student at desk	.16	.15
616	A192	80fr Carpenter	.55	.22
		Set value		.28

Intl. Year of the Disabled.

1981, July 10 Litho. *Perf. 12½x12*

617	A193	15fr multi	.15	.15
618	A193	45fr multi	.30	.15
		Set value		.15

13th World Telecommunications Day.

Neil Armstrong on Moon (Apollo 11) — A194

Space Anniversaries.

1981, July 23 *Perf. 11½*

619 A194 30fr Valentina Tereshkova .20 .15
620 A194 80fr shown .55 .22
621 A194 90fr Yuri Gagarin .60 .25
Nos. 619-621 (3) 1.35 .62

Brother Raphael Louis Rafiringa (1854-1919) A195

1981, Aug. 10 **Litho.** *Perf. 12*

622 A195 30fr multi .20 .15

World Literacy Day — A196

1981, Sept. 8

623 A196 30fr multi .20 .15

World Food Day — A197

1981, Oct. 16 **Litho.** *Perf. 12x12½*

624 A197 200fr multi 1.40 .55

See No. 635.

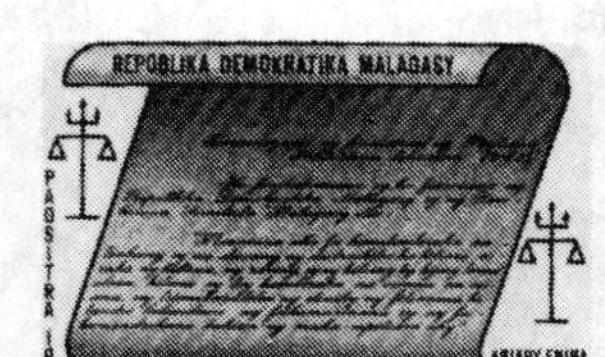

Oaths of Magistracy Renewal — A198

1981, Oct. 30 *Perf. 12½x12*

625 A198 30fr blk & lil rose .20 .15

Dove, by Pablo Picasso (1881-1973) — A199

1981, Nov. 18 **Photo.** *Perf. 11½x12*

626 A199 80fr multi .55 .20

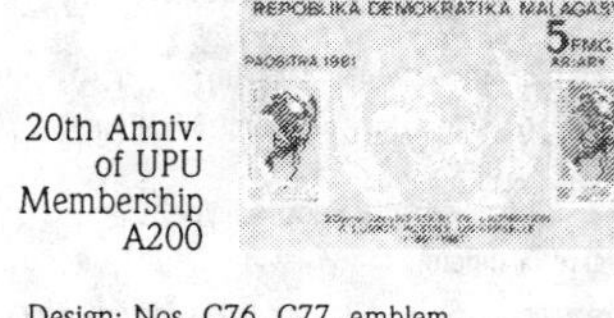

20th Anniv. of UPU Membership A200

Design: Nos. C76, C77, emblem.

1981, Nov. 19 **Litho.** *Perf. 12*

627 A200 5fr multi .15 .15
628 A200 30fr multi .20 .15
Set value .25 .15

TB Bacillus Centenary A201

1982, June 21 **Litho.** *Perf. 12*

629 A201 30fr multi .20 .15

Jeannette Mpihira (1903-1981), Actress and Singer — A202

Haliaeetus Vociferoides — A203

1982, June 24 *Perf. 12½*

630 A202 30fr multi .20 .15

1982, July

631 A203 25fr Vanga curvirostris, horiz. .16 .15
632 A203 30fr Leptostomus discolor, horiz. .20 .15
633 A203 200fr shown 1.40 .55
Nos. 631-633 (3) 1.76
Set value .70

Pierre Louis Boiteau (1911-1980), Educator A204

1982, Sept. 13

634 A204 30fr multi .20 .15

World Food Day Type of 1981

1982, Oct. 16 *Perf. 12x12½*

635 A197 80fr multi .55 .22

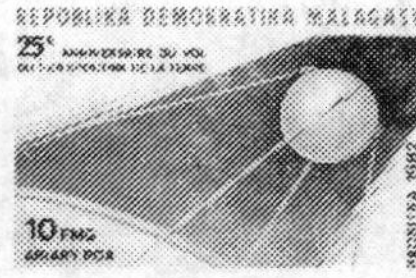

25th Anniv. of Launching of Sputnik I — A205

1982, Oct. 4 **Litho.** *Perf. 12*

636 A205 10fr Sputnik I .15 .15
637 A205 80fr Yuri Gagarin, Vostok I .55 .22
638 A205 100fr Soyuz-Salyut .65 .25
Nos. 636-638 (3) 1.35
Set value .50

1982 World Cup — A206

Designs: Various soccer players.

1982, Oct. 14 *Perf. 12x12½*

639 A206 30fr multi .15 .15
640 A206 40fr multi .20 .15
641 A206 80fr multi .40 .18
Nos. 639-641 (3) .75
Set value .32

Souvenir Sheet

Perf. 11½x12½

642 A206 450fr multi 2.25 .90

Scene at a Bar, by Edouard Manet (1832-1883) — A207

1982, Nov. 25 *Perf. 12½x12*

643 A207 5fr shown .15 .15
644 A207 30fr Lady in a White Dress .20 .15
645 A207 170fr Portrait of Mallarme 1.10 .50
Nos. 643-645 (3) 1.45
Set value .62

Souvenir Sheet

Perf. 11½x12½

646 A207 400fr The Fifer, vert. 2.50 1.00

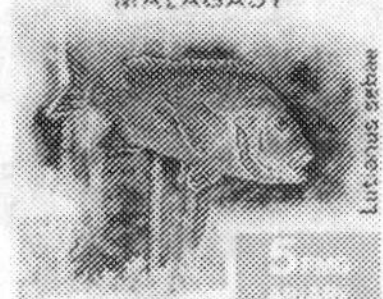

Local Fish — A208

1982, Dec. 14 *Perf. 11½*

647 A208 5fr Lutianus sebae .15 .15
648 A208 20fr Istiophorus platypterus .15 .15
649 A208 30fr Pterois volitans .20 .15
650 A208 50fr Thunnus albacares .35 .15
651 A208 200fr Epinephelus fasciatus 1.40 .50
Nos. 647-651 (5) 2.25
Set value .80

Souvenir Sheet

Perf. 12½x12

652 A208 450fr Latimeria chalumnae 3.00 1.20

No. 652 contains one stamp 38x26mm.

Fort Mahavelona Ruins — A209

1982, Dec. 22 *Perf. 12½x12*

653 A209 10fr shown .15 .15
654 A209 30fr Ramena Beach .20 .15
655 A209 400fr Flowering jacaranda trees 2.50 1.00
Nos. 653-655 (3) 2.85 1.30

60th Anniv. of USSR — A210

1982, Dec. 29

656 A210 10fr Tractors .15 .15
657 A210 15fr Pylon .15 .15
658 A210 30fr Kremlin, Lenin .20 .15
659 A210 150fr Arms 1.00 .40
Nos. 656-659 (4) 1.50
Set value .55

World Communications Year — A211

Design: 80fr, Stylized figures holding wheel.

1983, May 17 **Litho.** *Perf. 12*

660 A211 30fr multi .20 .15
661 A211 80fr multi .55 .20

United African Organization, 20th Anniv. — A212

1983, May 25 **Litho.** *Perf. 12*

662 A212 30fr multi .20 .15

Henri Douzon, Lawyer and Patriot — A213

1983, June 27 **Litho.** *Perf. 12*

663 A213 30fr multi .20 .15

Souvenir Sheet

Manned Flight Bicentenary A214

1983, July 20 **Litho.** *Perf. 12*

664 A214 500fr Montgolfiere balloon 1.60 .80

Souvenir Sheet

Raphael, 500th Birth Anniv. A215

1983, Aug. 10 **Litho.** ***Perf. 12***
665 A215 500fr The Madonna Connestable 1.60 .80

Lemur — A216

Various lemurs. Nos. 668-669, 671 vert.

Perf. 12½x12, 12x12½
1983, Dec. 6 **Litho.**
666 A216 30fr Daubentonia madagascariensis .15 .15
667 A216 30fr Microcebus murinus .15 .15
668 A216 30fr Lemur variegatus .15 .15
669 A216 30fr Propithecus verreauxi .15 .15
670 A216 200fr Indri indri .65 .35
Set value 1.00 .50

Souvenir Sheet

671 A216 500fr Perodicticus potto 1.60 .80

1984 Winter Olympics A217

1984, Jan. 20 **Litho.** ***Perf. 11½***
672 A217 20fr Ski jumping .15 .15
673 A217 30fr Speed skating .15 .15
674 A217 30fr Downhill skiing .15 .15
675 A217 30fr Hockey .15 .15
676 A217 200fr Figure skating .50 .25
Set value .78 .40

Souvenir Sheet

677 A217 500fr Cross-country skiing 1.25 .65

No. 677 contains one stamp 48x32mm.

Vintage Cars — A218

1984, Jan. 27 ***Perf. 12½x12***
678 A218 15fr Renault, 1907 .15 .15
679 A218 30fr Benz, 1896 .15 .15
680 A218 30fr Baker, 1901 .15 .15
681 A218 30fr Blake, 1901 .15 .15
682 A218 200fr FIAL, 1908 .65 .35
Set value 1.00 .50

Souvenir Sheet

Perf. 12½x11½

683 A218 450fr Russo-Baltique, 1909 1.50 .80

Pastor Ravelojaona (1879-1956), Encyclopedist A219

1984, Feb. 14 ***Perf. 12x12½***
684 A219 30fr multi .15 .15

See No. 704.

Madonna and Child, by Correggio (1489-1534) A220

Various Correggio paintings.

1984, May 5 **Litho.** ***Perf. 12x12½***
685 A220 5fr multi .15 .15
686 A220 20fr multi .15 .15
687 A220 30fr multi .15 .15
688 A220 80fr multi .25 .15
689 A220 200fr multi .65 .35
Set value 1.10 .60

Souvenir Sheet

690 A220 400fr multi 1.40 .65

A221

A222

1984, July 27
691 A221 5fr Paris landmarks .15 .15
692 A221 20fr Wilhelm Steinitz .15 .15
693 A221 30fr Champion, cup .15 .15
694 A221 30fr Vera Menchik .15 .15
695 A221 215fr Champion, cup, diff. .70 .38
Set value 1.00 .55

Souvenir Sheet

696 A221 400fr Children playing chess 1.40 .65

World Chess Federation, 60th anniv.

1984, Aug. 10
697 A222 100fr Soccer .35 .16

1984 Summer Olympics.

Butterflies A223

1984, Aug. 30 **Litho.** ***Perf. 11½***
698 A223 15fr Eudaphaenura splendens .15 .15
699 A223 50fr Othreis boseae .15 .15
700 A223 50fr Pharmacophagus antenor .15 .15
701 A223 50fr Acraea hova .15 .15
702 A223 200fr Epicausis smithii .55 .25
Nos. 698-702 (5) 1.15
Set value .50

Miniature Sheet

Perf. 11½x12½

703 A223 400fr Papilio delandii 1.10 .55

No. 703 contains one stamp 37x52mm.

Famous People Type

Jean Ralaimongo (1884-1944).

1984, Oct. 4 ***Perf. 12x12½***
704 A219 50fr Portrait .15 .15

Children's Rights A225

1984, Nov. 20 **Litho.** ***Perf. 12½x12***
705 A225 50fr Youths in school bag .15 .15

Malagasy Orchids — A226

Cotton Seminar, UN Trade and Development Conference — A227

1984, Nov. 20 **Litho.** ***Perf. 12***
706 A226 20fr Disa incarnata .15 .15
707 A226 235fr Eulophiella roempleriana .62 .32
Nos. 706-707,C180-C182 (5) 1.22
Set value .56

Miniature Sheet

Perf. 12x12½

708 A226 400fr Gastrorchis tuberculosa 1.10 .55

No. 708 contains one stamp 30x42mm.

1984, Dec. 15 **Litho.** ***Perf. 13x12½***
709 A227 100fr UN emblem, cotton bolls .25 .15

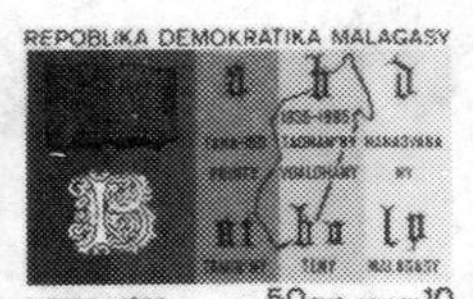

Malagasy Language Bible, 150th Anniv. A228

1985, Feb. 11 **Litho.** ***Perf. 12½x12***
710 A228 50fr multi .16 .15

1985 Agricultural Census — A229

1985, Feb. 21 **Litho.** ***Perf. 12x12½***
711 A229 50fr Census taker, farmer .15 .15

Allied Defeat of Nazi Germany, 40th Anniv. — A230

20fr, Russian flag-raising, Berlin, 1945. 50fr, Normandy-Niemen squadron shooting down German fighter planes. #714, Soviet Victory Parade, Red Square, Moscow. #715, Victorious French troops marching through Arc de Triomphe, vert.

1985 ***Perf. 12½x12, 12x12½***
712 A230 20fr multi .15 .15
713 A230 50fr multi .15 .15
714 A230 100fr multi .30 .15
715 A230 100fr multi .30 .15
Nos. 712-715 (4) .90
Set value .42

Issue dates: #712-714, May 9; #715, Oct.

Cats and Dogs — A231

Perf. 12x12½, 12½x12
1985, Apr. 25
716 A231 20fr Siamese .15 .15
717 A231 20fr Bichon .15 .15
718 A231 50fr Abyssinian, vert. .15 .15
719 A231 100fr Cocker spaniel, vert. .30 .15
720 A231 235fr Poodle .65 .35
Nos. 716-720 (5) 1.40
Set value .65

Souvenir Sheet

721 A231 400fr Kitten 1.20 1.20

No. 721 contains one stamp 42x30mm, perf. 12½x12.

Gymnastic Event, Natl. Stadium, Atananarivo A232

1985, July 9 ***Perf. 12½x12***
722 A232 50fr multi .15 .15

Natl. Socialist Revolution, 10th anniv.

Commemorative Medal, Memorial Stele — A233

1985, July 9
723 A233 50fr multi .15 .15

Independence, 25th anniv.

Intl. Youth Year — A234

Natl. Red Cross, 70th Anniv. — A235

1985, Sept. 18 ***Perf. 12***
724 A234 100fr Emblem, map .30 .15

1985, Oct. 3 ***Perf. 12x12½***
725 A235 50fr multi .15 .15

Indira Gandhi — A236

22nd World Youth and Student's Festival, Moscow — A237

1985, Oct. 31 *Perf. 13½*
726 A236 100fr multi .30 .15

1985, Nov. *Perf. 12*
727 A237 50fr multi .15 .15

Rouen Cathedral at Night, by Monet — A238

UN, 40th Aniv. — A239

Impressionist paintings: No. 729, View of Sea at Sainte-Marie, by van Gogh, horiz. 45fr, Young Women in Black, by Renoir. 50fr, The Red Vineyard at Arles, by van Gogh, horiz. 100fr, Boulevard des Capucines in Paris, by Monet, horiz. 400fr, In the Garden, by Renoir.

1985, Oct. 25 **Litho.** *Perf. 12*
728 A238 20fr multi .15 .15
729 A238 20fr multi .15 .15
730 A238 45fr multi .15 .15
731 A238 50fr multi .15 .15
732 A238 100fr multi .30 .15
Set value .65 .38

Souvenir Sheet
Perf. 12x12½
733 A238 400fr multi 1.20 1.20

No. 733 contains one 30x42mm stamp.

1985, Oct. 31 *Perf. 12*
734 A239 100fr multi .30 .15

Orchids A240

1985, Nov. 8
735 A240 20fr Aeranthes grandiflora .15 .15
736 A240 45fr Angraecum magdalanae .15 .15
737 A240 50fr Aerangis stylosa .15 .15
738 A240 100fr Angraecum eburneum longicalcar .30 .15
739 A240 100fr Angraecum sesquipedale .30 .15
Nos. 735-739 (5) 1.05
Set value .50

Souvenir Sheet
Perf. 12x12½
740 A240 400fr Angraecum aburneum superbum 1.20 1.20

Nos. 735, 737-740 vert. No. 740 contains one 30x42mm stamp.

INTERCOSMOS — A241

Cosmonauts, natl. flags, rockets, satellites and probes.

1985, Nov. *Perf. 12x12½*
741 A241 20fr USSR, Czechoslovakia .15 .15
742 A241 20fr Soyuz-Apollo emblem .15 .15
743 A241 50fr USSR, India .15 .15
744 A241 100fr USSR, Cuba .30 .15
745 A241 200fr USSR, France .60 .30
Nos. 741-745 (5) 1.35 .90

Souvenir Sheet
746 A241 400fr Halley's Comet, probe 1.20 1.20

No. 746 contains one stamp 42x30mm.

Independence, 10th Anniv. — A242

1985, Dec. 30 **Litho.** *Perf. 12½x12*
747 A242 50fr Industrial symbols .16 .15

Natl. Insurance and Securities Co. (ARO), 10th Anniv. — A243

1986, Jan. 20 *Perf. 12x12½*
748 A243 50fr dk brn, yel org & gray brn .16 .15

Paintings in the Tretyakov Gallery, Moscow — A244

Designs: 20fr, Still-life with Flowers and Fruit, 1839, by I. Chroutzky. No. 750, Portrait of Alexander Pushkin, 1827, by O. Kiprenski, vert. No. 751, Portrait of an Unknown Woman, 1883, by I. Kramskoi. No. 752, The Crows Have Returned, 1872, by A. Sakrassov, vert. 100fr, March, 1895, by I. Levitan. 450fr, Portrait of Pavel Tretyakov, 1883, by I. Repin, vert.

Perf. 12½x12, 12x12½
1986, Apr. 26 **Litho.**
749 A244 20fr multi .15 .15
750 A244 50fr multi .16 .15
751 A244 50fr multi .16 .15
752 A244 50fr multi .16 .15
753 A244 100fr multi .35 .16
Nos. 749-753 (5) .98
Set value .45

Souvenir Sheet
754 A244 450fr multi 1.50 .70

1986 World Cup Soccer Championships, Mexico — A245

1986, May 31 *Perf. 13½*
755 A245 150fr multi .50 .25

Paintings in Russian Museums — A246

#756, David and Urie, by Rembrandt, vert. #757, Danae, by Rembrandt. #758, Portrait of the Nurse of the Infant Isabella, by Rubens, vert. #759, The Alliance of Earth and Water, by Rubens, vert. #760, Portrait of an Old Man in Red, by Rembrandt. #761, The Holy Family, by Raphael.

Perf. 12x12½, 12½x12
1986, Mar. 24 **Litho.**
756 A246 20fr multi .15 .15
757 A246 50fr multi .16 .15
758 A246 50fr multi .16 .15
759 A246 50fr multi .16 .15
760 A246 50fr multi .16 .15
Nos. 756-760 (5) .79
Set value .35

Souvenir Sheet
Perf. 11½x12½
761 A246 450fr multi 1.50 .70

UN Child Survival Campaign — A247

A248

Wildcats A249

1986, June 1 **Litho.** *Perf. 12x12½*
762 A247 60fr multi .20 .15

1986, July 17
763 A248 10fr Sable .15 .15
764 A248 10fr Chaus .15 .15
765 A248 60fr Serval .20 .15
766 A248 60fr Caracal .20 .15
767 A248 60fr Bengal .20 .15
Set value .70 .38

Souvenir Sheet
Perf. 12½x12
768 A249 450fr Golden 1.40 .65

Intl. Peace Year A249a

1986, Sept. 12 *Perf. 12*
769 A249a 60fr shown .20 .15
770 A249a 150fr Hemispheres, emblem, vert. .42 .22

World Post Day — A250

1986, Oct. 9 **Litho.** *Perf. 13x12½*
771 A250 60fr multi .20 .15
772 A250 150fr multi .42 .22

No. 772 is airmail.

A251

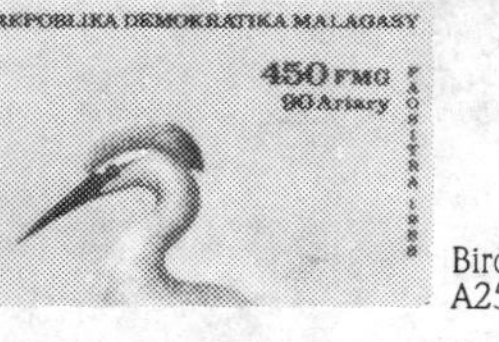

Birds A252

Perf. 12x12½, 12½x12
1986, Dec. 23 **Litho.**
773 A251 60fr Xenopirostris daimi, vert. .20 .15
774 A251 60fr Falculea palliata .20 .15
775 A251 60fr Coua gigas .20 .15
776 A251 60fr Coua cristata .20 .15
777 A251 60fr Cianolanius madagascariensis, vert. .20 .15
Nos. 773-777 (5) 1.00
Set value .50

Souvenir Sheet
778 A252 450fr Bubulcus ibis ibis 1.50 .70

A253

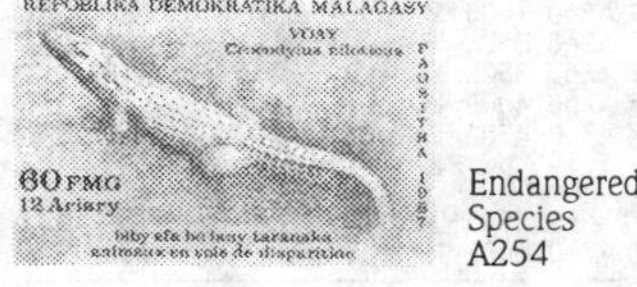

Endangered Species A254

Perf. 12x12½, 12½x12
1987, Mar. 13 **Litho.**
779 A253 60fr Lophotibis cristata, vert. .20 .15
780 A253 60fr Coracopsis nigra .20 .15
781 A254 60fr Crocodylus niloticus .20 .15
782 A254 60fr Geochelone yniphora .20 .15
Nos. 779-782 (4) .80
Set value .40

Souvenir Sheet
783 A253 450fr Centropus toulou, vert. 1.50 .70

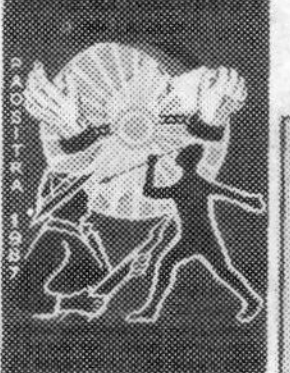

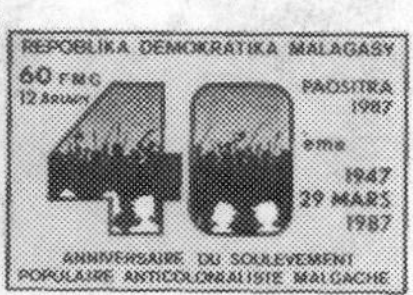

Anti-Colonial Revolt, 40th Anniv.
A255 A256

1987, Mar. 29 *Perf. 12*
784 A255 60fr multi .20 .15
785 A256 60fr multi .20 .15
Set value .20

1st Games of Indian Ocean Towns — A257

1987, Apr. 15 *Perf. 13½*

786 A257 60fr multi .22 .15
787 A257 150fr multi .60 .30

Le Sarimanok A258

1987, Apr. 15

788 A258 60fr Port side .22 .15
789 A258 150fr Starboard side .60 .30

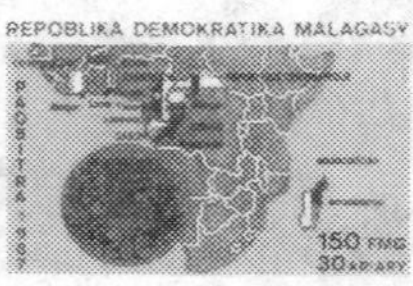

African and Madagascar Coffee Organization, 25th Anniv. A259

1987, Apr. 24 **Litho.** *Perf. 12*

790 A259 60fr Coffee plant .22 .15
791 A259 150fr Map .60 .30

Halley's Comet — A260

Space probes.

1987, May 13 *Perf. 13½*

792 A260 60fr Giotto, ESA .20 .15
793 A260 150fr Vega 1, Russia .50 .25
794 A260 250fr Vega 2, Russia .85 .40
795 A260 350fr Planet-A1, Japan 1.10 .60
796 A260 400fr Planet-A2, Japan 1.40 .65
797 A260 450fr ICE, US 1.50 .70
Nos. 792-797 (6) 5.55 2.75

Souvenir Sheet

798 A260 600fr Halley, Giotto 2.00 1.00

Litho. & Embossed 'Gold Foil' Stamps
These stamps generally are of a different design format than the rest of the issue. Since there is a commemorative inscription tying them to the issue a separate illustration is not being shown.

1988 Calgary Winter Olympics — A261

Jean-Joseph Rabearivelo (d. 1937), Poet — A263

Men's Downhill A262

1987, May 13

799 A261 60fr Biathlon .20 .15
800 A261 150fr shown .50 .25
801 A261 250fr Luge .85 .40
802 A261 350fr Speed skating 1.10 .60
803 A261 400fr Hockey 1.40 .65
804 A261 450fr Pairs figure skating 1.50 .70
Nos. 799-804 (6) 5.55 2.75

Litho. & Embossed

804A A261 1500fr Speed skating

Souvenir Sheets

Litho.

805 A262 600fr shown 2.00 1.00

Litho. & Embossed

805A A262 1500fr Slalom skiing

No. 804A exists in souvenir sheet of 1.

1987, June 22 *Perf. 13½*

806 A263 60fr multi .20 .15

1992 Summer Olympics, Barcelona — A264

Athletes, emblem and art or architecture: 60fr, Equestrian, and the Harlequin, by Picasso. 150fr, Weight lifting, church. 250fr, Hurdles, Canaletas Fountain. 350fr, High jump, amusement park. 400fr, Men's gymnastics, abbey. 450fr, Rhythmic gymnastics, Arc de Triomphe. 600fr, Equestrian, Columbus monument.

1987, Oct. 7 **Litho.** *Perf. 13½*

807 A264 60fr multi .20 .15
808 A264 150fr multi .50 .25
809 A264 250fr multi .85 .42
810 A264 350fr multi 1.10 .60
811 A264 400fr multi 1.40 .65
812 A264 450fr multi 1.50 .70
Nos. 807-812 (6) 5.55 2.77

Souvenir Sheet

813 A264 600fr multi 2.00 1.00

Nos. 811-813 are airmail.

A265

Discovery of America, 500th Anniv. (in 1992) A266

Anniv. emblem and: 60fr, Bartolomeu Dias (c. 1450-1500), Portuguese navigator, departure from De Palos, 1492. 150fr, Henry the Navigator (1394-1460), prince of Portugal, Samana Cay. 250fr, A. De Marchena landing, 1492. 350fr, Paolo Toscanelli dal Pozzo (1397-1482), Italian physician and cosmographer, La Navidad Fort. 400fr, Queen Isabella I, Barcelona, 1493. 450fr, Christopher Columbus, the Nina. 600fr, Landing in New World, 1492.

1987, Sept. 24 **Litho.** *Perf. 13½*

814 A265 60fr multi .28 .15
815 A265 150fr multi .70 .35
816 A265 250fr multi 1.10 .55
817 A265 350fr multi 1.65 .85
818 A265 400fr multi 1.90 1.00
819 A265 450fr multi 2.25 1.10
Nos. 814-819 (6) 7.88 4.00

Souvenir Sheet

820 A266 600fr multi 3.00 1.50

A267

A268

1987, July 27 *Perf. 12½x12*

821 A267 60fr multi .22 .15

Natl. telecommunications research laboratory.

1987, Aug. 14

822 A268 60fr lt blue, blk & brt ultra .22 .15

Rafaravavy Rasalama (d. 1837), Christian martyr.

Antananarivo-Tamatave Telegraph Link, Cent. — A269

1987, Sept. 15 *Perf. 12x12½*

823 A269 60fr multi .22 .15

Pasteur Institute, Paris, Cent. — A270

1987, Oct. 26 *Perf. 13½*

824 A270 250fr multi 1.00 .45

City of Berlin, 750th Anniv. — A271

Design: Anniv. emblem, television tower and the Interhotel in East Berlin.

1987, Oct. 18 **Litho.** *Perf. 12½x12*

825 A271 150fr multi .22 .15

Schools Festival A272

1987, Oct. 23 *Perf. 12x12½*

826 A272 60fr multi .15 .15

Paintings in the Pushkin Museum, Moscow — A273

Designs: 10fr, After the Shipwreck (1847), by Eugene Delacroix (1798-1863). No. 828, Still-life with Swan (c. 1620), by Frans Snyders (1579-1647). No. 829, Jupiter and Callisto (1744), by Francois Boucher (1703-1770), vert. No. 830, Chalet in the Mountains (1874), by Jean Desire Gustav Courbet (1819-1877). 150fr, At the Market (1564), by Joachim Bueckelaer. 1000fr, Minerva (1560), by Paolo Veronese (1528-1588), vert.

Perf. 12½x12, 12x12½

1987, Nov. 10

827 A273 10fr multi .15 .15
828 A273 60fr multi .15 .15
829 A273 60fr multi .15 .15
830 A273 60fr multi .15 .15
831 A273 150fr multi .22 .15
Set value .55 .35

Souvenir Sheet

832 A273 1000fr multi 1.50 1.50

Pan-African Telecommunications Union, 10th Anniv. — A274

1987, Dec. 28 *Perf. 13x12½*

833 A274 250fr multi 1.00 .45

Intl. Year of Shelter for the Homeless A275

1988, Feb. 15 **Litho.** *Perf. 12*

834 A275 80fr shown .16 .15
835 A275 250fr Family in shelter, rain, vert. .52 .25

Fauna A276

1988, Apr. 18 **Litho.** *Perf. 13½*

836 A276 60fr Hapalemur simus .15 .15
837 A276 150fr Propithecus diadema diadema .32 .16
838 A276 250fr Indri indri .55 .28
839 A276 350fr Varecia variegata variegata .75 .38
840 A276 550fr Madagascar young heron 1.20 .60
841 A276 1500fr Nossi-Be chameleon 3.15 1.60
Nos. 836-841 (6) 6.12 3.17

Souvenir Sheet

842 A276 1500fr Uratelornis (bird) 3.25 3.25

Conservation and service organization emblems: World Wildlife Fund (60fr, 150fr, 250fr and 350fr); Rotary Intl. (550fr and No. 842); and Scouting trefoil (No. 841).
Nos. 840-841 exist in souvenir sheet of 2.
For overprints see Nos. 1134, 1154.

October Revolution, Russia, 70th Anniv. — A277

1988, Mar. 7 **Litho.** *Perf. 12x12½*

843 A277 60fr Lenin .15 .15
844 A277 60fr Revolutionaries .15 .15
845 A277 150fr Lenin, revolutionaries .32 .16
Nos. 843-845 (3) .62
Set value .32

1988 Winter Olympics, Calgary — A278

1988, May 11 *Perf. 11½*

846	A278	20fr	Pairs figure skating	.15	.15
847	A278	60fr	Slalom	.15	.15
848	A278	60fr	Speed skating	.15	.15
849	A278	100fr	Cross-country skiing	.22	.15
850	A278	250fr	Ice hockey	.55	.28
			Nos. 846-850 (5)	1.22	
			Set value		.58

Souvenir Sheet

851 A278 800fr Ski jumping 1.75 1.75

Discovery of Radium by Pierre and Marie Curie, 90th Anniv. A279

1988, July 14 **Litho.** *Perf. 12*

852 A279 150fr blk & rose lil .35 .18

OAU, 25th Anniv. A280

1988, May 25 **Litho.** *Perf. 13*

853 A280 80fr multi .20 .15

Natl. Telecommunications and Posts Institute, 20th Anniv. — A281

1988, June 22 *Perf. 13½*

854 A281 80fr multi .20 .15

Saint-Michel College, Cent. — A282

1988, July 9

855 A282 250fr multi .55 .28

Alma-Ata Declaration, 10th Anniv. — A283

WHO, 40th Anniv. — A284

1988, Aug. 11 **Litho.** *Perf. 12*

856 A283 60fr multi .15 .15

1988, Aug. 11

857 A284 150fr multi .32 .16

Tsimbazaza Botanical and Zoological Park, 150th Anniv. — A285

Perf. 12x12½, 12½x12

1988, Aug. 22

858	A285	20fr	Lemur habitat	.15	.15
859	A285	80fr	Lemur and young	.20	.15
860	A285	250fr	shown	.55	.28
			Nos. 858-860 (3)	.90	
			Set value		.42

Souvenir Sheet

861 A285 1000fr Lemur and mate 2.25 2.25

Size of No. 859: 25x37mm.

Boy Scouts Studying Birds and Butterflies — A286

Designs: 80fr, Upupa epops maginata, Coua caerulea and scout photographing bird. 250fr, Chrysiridia croesus and comparing butterfly to a sketch. 270fr, Nelicurvius nelicourvi, Foudia omissa and constructing bird feeder. 350fr, Papilio dardanus and studying butterflies with magnifying glass. 550fr, Coua critata and tagging bird. No. 867, Argema mittrei and writing observations. No. 868, Merops superciliosus and recording bird calls. No. 868A, Euchloron megaera. No. 868B, Rhynchee.

1988, Sept. 29

862	A286	80fr	multi	.20	.15
863	A286	250fr	multi	.55	.28
864	A286	270fr	multi	.60	.30
865	A286	350fr	multi	.78	.40
866	A286	550fr	multi	1.20	.60
867	A286	1500fr	multi	3.25	1.65
			Nos. 862-867 (6)	6.58	3.38

Souvenir Sheet

868 A286 1500fr multi 3.25 3.25

Litho. & Embossed

Perf. 13½

868A A286 5000fr gold & multi

Souvenir Sheet

868B A286 5000fr gold & multi

No. 868 contains one stamp 36x51mm.

Nos. 868A-868B dated 1989. Nos. 868A-868B exist imperf.

Composers and Entertainers A287

Designs: 80fr, German-made clavier and Carl Philipp Emanuel Bach (1714-1788), organist and composer. 250fr, Piano and Franz Peter Schubert (1797-1828), Austrian composer. 270fr, Scene from opera Carmen, 1875, and Georges Bizet (1838-1875), French composer. 350fr, Scene from opera Pelleas et Melisande, 1902, and Claude Debussy (1862-1918), French composer. 550fr, George Gershwin (1898-1937), American composer. No. 874, Elvis Presley (1935-1977), American entertainer. No. 875, Rimsky-Korsakov (1844-1908), Russian composer, and Le Coq d'Or from the opera of the same name.

Perf. 12x12½, 12½x12

1988, Oct. 28

869	A287	80fr	multi	.20	.15
870	A287	250fr	multi	.55	.28
871	A287	270fr	multi	.60	.30
872	A287	350fr	multi	.78	.40
873	A287	550fr	multi	1.20	.60
874	A287	1500fr	multi	3.25	1.65
			Nos. 869-874 (6)	6.58	3.38

Souvenir Sheet

875 A287 1500fr multi 3.25 3.25

For overprints see Nos. 1135-1136.

Intl. Fund for Agricultural Development (IFAD), 10th Anniv. A288

1988, Sept. 4 **Litho.** *Perf. 12*

876 A288 250fr multi .48 .25

School Feast — A289

1988, Nov. 22

877 A289 80fr multi .16 .15

A290

Ships — A291

Paintings: 20fr, The Squadron of the Sea, Black Feodossia, by Ivan Aivazovski, vert. No. 879, Seascape with Sailing Ships, by Simon de Vlieger, vert. No. 880, The Ship Lesnoie, by N. Semenov, vert. 100fr, The Merchantman, Orel, by N. Golitsine. 250fr, Naval Exercises, by Adam Silo, vert. 550fr, On the River, by Abraham Beerstraten.

1988, Dec. 5 *Perf. 12x12½, 12½x12*

878	A290	20fr	multi	.15	.15
879	A290	80fr	multi	.16	.15
880	A290	80fr	multi	.16	.15
881	A290	100fr	shown	.20	.15
882	A290	250fr	multi	.48	.25
			Nos. 878-882 (5)	1.15	
			Set value		.55

Souvenir Sheet

Perf. 11½x12½

883 A291 550fr shown 1.05 1.05

World Wildlife Fund — A292

Insect species in danger of extinction: 20fr, Tragocephala crassicornis. 80fr, Polybothris symptuosa-gema. 250fr, Euchroea auripigmenta. 350fr, Stellognata maculata.

1988, Dec. 13 *Perf. 12*

884	A292	20fr	multi	.15	.15
885	A292	80fr	multi	.16	.15
886	A292	250fr	multi	.48	.25
887	A292	350fr	multi	.68	.35
			Nos. 884-887 (4)	1.47	
			Set value		.72

Intl. Red Cross and Red Crescent Organizations, 125th Annivs. A293

1988, Dec. 27 **Litho.** *Perf. 12*

888	A293	80fr	Globe, stretcher-bearers, vert.	.16	.15
889	A293	250fr	Emblems, Dunant	.48	.24
			Set value		.32

UN Declaration of Human Rights, 40th Anniv. (in 1988) — A294

1989, Jan. 10

890	A294	80fr	shown	.16	.15
891	A294	250fr	Hands, "4" and "0"	.48	.24
			Set value		.32

Dated 1988.

Transportation — A295

Designs: 80fr, 1909 Mercedes-Benz Blitzen Benz. 250fr, Micheline ZM 517 Tsikirity, Tananarive-Moramanga line. 270fr, Bugatti Coupe Binder 41. 350fr, Electric locomotive 1020-DES OBB, Germany. 1500fr, Souleze Autorail 701 DU CFN, Madagascar. No. 897, 1913 Opel race car. No. 898, Bugatti Presidential Autorail locomotive and Bugatti Type 57 Atalante automobile.

1989, Jan. 24 *Perf. 13½*

892	A295	80fr	multi	.16	.15
893	A295	250fr	multi	.48	.24
894	A295	270fr	multi	.52	.25
895	A295	350fr	multi	.70	.35

896	A295	1500fr	multi	2.85	1.45
897	A295	2500fr	multi	4.75	2.40
			Nos. 892-897 (6)	9.46	4.84

Souvenir Sheet

898	A295	2500fr	multi	4.75	4.75

Nos. 893-

Dinosaurs — A296

1989, Feb. 1 Litho. *Perf. 12½x12*

899	A296	20fr	Tyrannosaurus	.15	.15
900	A296	80fr	Stegosaurus	.16	.15
901	A296	250fr	Arsinoitherium	.48	.24
902	A296	450fr	Triceratops	.90	.45
			Nos. 899-902 (4)	1.69	
			Set value		.80

Souvenir Sheet

Perf. 11½x12½

903	A296	600fr	Sauralophus, vert.	1.20	1.20

Women as the Subject of Paintings — A297

Designs: 20fr, *Tahitian Pastorales*, by Gauguin. No 905, *Portrait of a Young Woman*, by Titian, vert. No. 906, *Portrait of a Little Girl*, by Jean-Baptiste Greuze (1725-1805), vert. 100fr, *Woman in Black*, by Renoir, vert. 250fr, *Lacemaker*, by Vassili Tropinine, vert. 550fr, *The Annunciation*, by Cima Da Conegliano (c. 1459-1517), vert.

Perf. 12½x12, 12x12½

1989, Feb. 10

904	A297	20fr	multi	.15	.15
905	A297	80fr	multi	.16	.15
906	A297	80fr	multi	.16	.15
907	A297	100fr	multi	.20	.15
908	A297	250fr	multi	.48	.24
			Nos. 904-908 (5)	1.15	
			Set value		.55

Souvenir Sheet

Perf. 11½x12½

909	A297	550fr	multi	1.05	1.05

Orchids A298

1989, Feb. 28 Litho. *Perf. 12*

910	A298	5fr	*Sobennikoffia robusta*, vert.	.15	.15
911	A298	10fr	*Grammangis fallax*	.15	.15
912	A298	80fr	*Cymbidiella humblotii*, vert.	.15	.15
913	A298	80fr	*Angraecum sororium*, vert.	.15	.15
914	A298	250fr	*Oenia oncidiiflora*, vert.	.38	.18
			Set value	.70	.40

Souvenir Sheet

915	A298	1000fr	*Aerangis curnowiana*	1.40	1.40

Jawaharlal Nehru (1889-1964), 1st Prime Minister of Independent India — A299

1989, Mar. 7 Litho. *Perf. 13*

916	A299	250fr	multi	.48	.24

Ornamental Mineral Industry A300

1989, Apr. 12 Litho. *Perf. 13½*

917	A300	80fr	Rose quartz	.16	.15
918	A300	250fr	Petrified wood	.48	.24
			Set value		.32

Views of Antananarivo A301

Designs: 5fr, Mahamasina Sports Complex, Ampefiloha Quarter. 20fr, Andravoahangy and Anjanahary Quarters. No. 921, Zoma Market and Faravohitra Quarter. No. 922, Andohan'Analakely Quarter and March 29th monument. 250fr, Independence Avenue and Jean Ralaimongo monument. 550fr, Queen's Palace and Andohalo School on Lake Anosy.

1989, Mar. 31 Litho. *Perf. 13½*

919	A301	5fr	multi	.15	.15
920	A301	20fr	multi	.15	.15
921	A301	80fr	multi	.48	.24
922	A301	80fr	multi	.48	.24
923	A301	250fr	multi	1.50	.75
924	A301	550fr	multi	3.25	1.65
			Nos. 919-924 (6)	6.01	3.18

Visit of Pope John Paul II — A302

1989, Apr. 28 *Perf. 12x12½*

925	A302	80fr	shown	.48	.24
926	A302	250fr	Pope, map	1.50	.75

French Revolution, Bicent. A303

1989, July 7 Litho. *Perf. 12½*

927	A303	250fr	Storming of the Bastille	.48	.24

Phobos Space Program for the Exploration of Mars A304

1989, Aug. 29 Litho. *Perf. 12½x12*

928	A304	20fr	Mars 1	.15	.15
929	A304	80fr	Mars 3	.15	.15
930	A304	80fr	Sond 2	.15	.15
931	A304	250fr	Mariner 9	.32	.16
932	A304	270fr	Viking 2	.35	.18
			Set value	.90	.45

Souvenir Sheet

933	A304	550fr	Phobos	.70	.70

PHILEXFRANCE '89 and French Revolution, Bicent. — A305

Exhibition emblems, key people and scenes from the revolution: 250fr, Honore-Gabriel Riqueti (1749-1791), Count of Mirabeau, at the meeting of Estates-General, June 23, 1789. 350fr, Camille Desmoulins (1760-1794), call to arms, July 12, 1789. 1000fr, Lafayette (1757-1834), women's march on Versailles, Oct. 5, 1789. 1500fr, King tried by the National Convention, Dec. 26, 1792. 2500fr, Charlotte Corday (1768-1793), assassination of Marat, July 13, 1793. 3000fr, Bertrand Barere de Vieuzac, Robespierre, Jean-Marie Collot D'Herbois, Lazare Nicolas Carnot, George Jacques Danton, Georges Auguste Couthon, Pierre-Louis Prieur, Antoine Saint-Just and Marc Guillaume Vadiez, Committee of Public Safety, July, 1793. No. 939A, Family saying farewell to Louis XVI. No. 939B, Danton and the Club of the Cordeliers. (Illustration reduced).

1989, July 14 Litho. *Perf. 13½*

934	A305	250fr	multicolored	.32	.16
935	A305	350fr	multicolored	.45	.22
936	A305	1000fr	multicolored	1.30	.65
937	A305	1500fr	multicolored	1.95	.98
938	A305	2500fr	multicolored	3.25	1.65
			Nos. 934-938 (5)	7.27	3.66

Souvenir Sheet

939	A305	3000fr	multicolored	4.00	4.00

Litho. & Embossed

939A	A305	5000fr	gold & multi

Souvenir Sheet

939B	A305	5000fr	gold & multi

Nos. 939A-939B exist imperf.
For overprints see #1161-1165, 1166A-1166B.

French Revolution, Bicent. — A306

Paintings and sculpture: 5fr, *Liberty Guiding the People*, by Eugene Delacroix. 80fr, "La Marseillaise" from *Departure of the Volunteers in 1792*, high relief on the Arc de Triomphe, 1833-35, by Francois Rude. 250fr, *The Tennis Court Oath*, by David.

1989, Oct. 25 *Perf. 12½x12*

940	A306	5fr	multicolored	.15	.15
941	A306	80fr	multicolored	.15	.15
942	A306	250fr	multicolored	.32	.16
			Set value	.46	.20

No. 942 is airmail.

Rene Cassin (1887-1976), Nobel Peace Prize Winner and Institute Founder — A307

1989, Nov. 21 *Perf. 12*

943	A307	250fr	multicolored	.35	.18

Intl. Law Institute of the French-Speaking Nations, 25th anniv.

Hapalemur aureus A308

1989, Dec. 5 Litho. *Perf. 12*

944	A308	250fr	multicolored	.38	.20

A309 A309a

Various athletes, cup and: 350fr, Cavour Monument, Turin. 1000fr, Christopher Columbus Monument, Genoa, 1903. 1500fr, Michelangelo's *David*. 2500fr, *Abduction of Prosperina*, by Bernini, Rome. 3000fr, Statue of Leonardo da Vinci, 1903. 5000fr, Castel Nuovo, Naples.

1989, Dec. 12 Litho. *Perf. 13½*

945	A309	350fr	multicolored	.45	.22
946	A309	1000fr	multicolored	1.30	.65
947	A309	1500fr	multicolored	2.00	1.00
948	A309	2500fr	multicolored	3.25	1.65
			Nos. 945-948 (4)	7.00	3.52

Souvenir Sheet

949	A309	3000fr	multicolored	4.00	2.00

Litho. & Embossed

949A	A309a	5000fr	gold & multi

1990 World Cup Soccer Championships, Italy.
For overprints see Nos. 1137-1140.

A310

1989, Oct. 7 Litho. *Perf. 13½*

950	A310	80fr	Long jump	.15	.15
951	A310	250fr	Pole vault	.35	.18
952	A310	550fr	Hurdles	.78	.40
953	A310	1500fr	Cycling	2.15	1.10
954	A310	2000fr	Baseball	2.85	1.45
955	A310	2500fr	Tennis	3.50	1.75
			Nos. 950-955 (6)	9.78	5.03

Souvenir Sheet

956	A310	3000fr	Soccer	4.25	2.15

1992 Summer Olympics, Barcelona.

Scenic Views and Artifacts A311

1990, May 29
Size: 47x33mm (#958, 960)

957 A311 70fr Queen Isalo Rock .15 .15
958 A311 70fr Sakalava pipe .15 .15
959 A311 150fr Sakalava combs .22 .15
960 A311 150fr Lonjy Is., Diego Suarez Bay .22 .15
Set value .64 .32

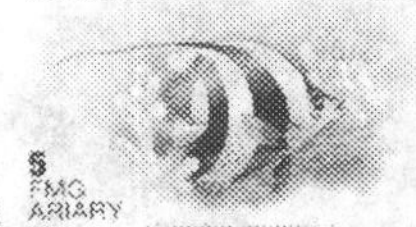
Fish — A312

1990, Apr. 26 Litho. *Perf. 12*

961 A312 5fr Heniochus acuminatus .15 .15
962 A312 20fr Simenhelys dofleinl .15 .15
963 A312 80fr Phinobatos perceli .15 .15
964 A312 250fr Epinephelus fasciatus .40 .20
965 A312 320fr Sphurna zygaena .50 .25
Set value 1.10 .60

Souvenir Sheet

966 A312 550fr Latimeria chalumnae .90 .90

Nos. 962-963 vert. Nos. 961-966 inscribed 1989.

Moon Landing, 20th Anniv. — A314

Designs: 80fr, Voyager 2, Neptune. 250fr, Hydro 2000 flying boat. 550fr, NOAA satellite. 1500fr, Magellan probe, Venus. 2000fr, Concorde. 2500fr, Armstrong, Aldrin, Collins, lunar module. 3000fr, Apollo 11 astronauts, first step on moon.

1990, June 19 Litho. *Perf. 13½*

967 A314 80fr multicolored .15 .15
968 A314 250fr multicolored .35 .18
969 A314 550fr multicolored .82 .40
970 A314 1500fr multicolored 2.25 1.10
971 A314 2000fr multicolored 3.00 1.50
972 A314 2500fr multicolored 3.75 1.90
Nos. 967-972 (6) 10.32 5.23

Souvenir Sheet

973 A314 3000fr multicolored 4.50 2.25

For ocerprint see No. 1304.

A315 A316

1990, July 17

974 A315 350fr Bobsled .52 .25
975 A315 1000fr Speed skating 1.50 .75
976 A315 1500fr Nordic skiing 2.25 1.10
977 A315 2500fr Super giant slalom 3.75 1.90
Nos. 974-977 (4) 8.02 4.00

Souvenir Sheet

978 A315 3000fr Giant slalom 4.50 2.25

Litho. & Embossed

978A A315 5000fr Pairs figure skating

Souvenir Sheet

978B A315 5000fr Ice hockey

1992 Winter Olympics, Albertville. Nos. 978A-978B exist imperf.
For overprints see Nos. 1141-1145.

1990, June 19 Litho. *Perf. 12*

979 A316 250fr blk, ultra & bl .40 .20

Intl. Maritime Organization, 30th anniv.

African Development Bank, 25th Anniv. — A317

1990, June 19

980 A317 80fr multicolored .15 .15

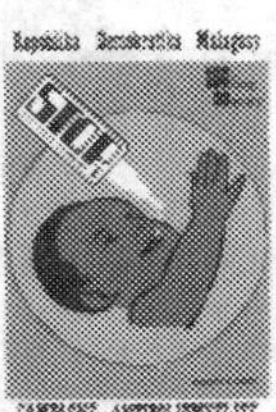
A318

A319

1990, June 28

981 A318 150fr multicolored .22 .15

Campaign against polio.

1990, Aug. 22

982 A319 100fr multicolored .16 .15

Independence, 30th anniv.

A320

A322

1990, Aug. 24 *Perf. 12½x12*

983 A320 100fr yellow & multi .16 .15
984 A320 350fr lil rose & multi .52 .25
Set value .32

3rd Indian Ocean Games.

1990, Oct. 19 Litho. *Perf. 12*

986 A322 350fr multicolored .60 .30

Ho Chi Minh (1890-1969), Vietnamese leader.

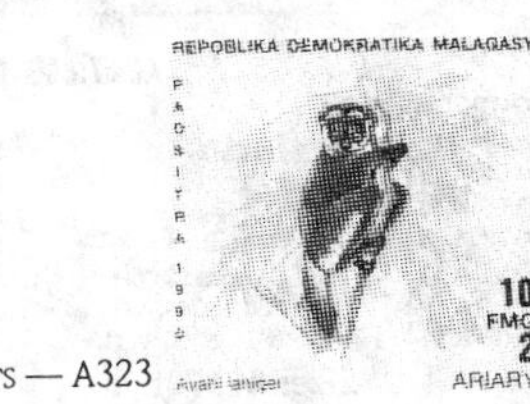
Lemurs — A323

1990, Nov. 23 Litho. *Perf. 11½*

987 A323 10fr Avahi laniger .15 .15
988 A323 20fr Lemur fulvus sanfordi .15 .15
989 A323 20fr Lemur fulvus albifrons .15 .15
990 A323 100fr Lemur fulvus collaris .18 .15
991 A323 100fr Lepulemur ruficaudatus .18 .15
Set value .46 .23

Souvenir Sheet

992 A323 350fr Lemur fulvus fulvus .60 .30

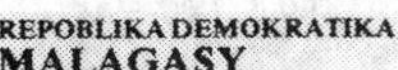
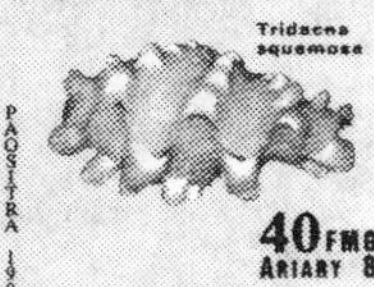
Shells A324

1990, Dec. 21 *Perf. 12½*

993 A324 40fr Tridacna squamosa .15 .15
994 A324 50fr Terebra demidiata, Terebra subulata .15 .15
Set value .18 .15

Anniversaries and Events — A325

100fr, Charles de Gaulle, liberation of Paris, 1944. 350fr, Galileo probe orbiting Jupiter. 800fr, Apollo 11 crew & Columbia command module, 1st Moon landing, 1969. 900fr, De Gaulle, 1942. 1250fr, Concorde jet, TGV high-speed train. 2500fr, De Gaulle as head of provisional government, 1944. 3000fr, Apollo 11 crew, Eagle lunar module. #1001A, De Gaulle with Roosevelt & Churchill. #1001B, Charles de Gaulle.

1990, Dec. 28 Litho. *Perf. 13½*

995 A325 100fr multi .18 .15
996 A325 350fr multi .60 .30
997 A325 800fr multi 1.40 .70
998 A325 900fr multi 1.60 .80
999 A325 1250fr multi 2.20 1.10
1000 A325 2500fr multi 4.40 2.20
Nos. 995-1000 (6) 10.38 5.25

Souvenir Sheet

1001 A325 3000fr multi 5.30 2.65

Litho. & Embossed

1001A A325 5000fr gold & multi

Souvenir Sheet

1001B A325 5000fr gold & multi

#995-1000, 1001A exist in souvenir sheets of 1.

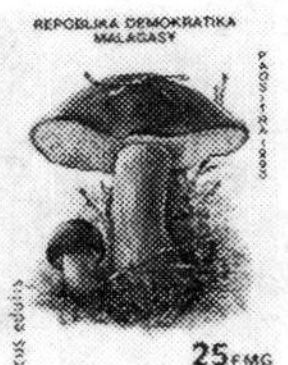
Mushrooms — A325b

Designs: 25fr, Boletus edulis. 100fr, Suillus luteus. 350fr, Amanita muscaria. 450fr, Boletus calopus. 680fr, Boletus erythropus. 800fr, Leccinum scabrum. 900fr, Leccinum testaceoscabrum.

1990, Dec. 28 Litho. *Perf. 12*

1001C A325b 25fr multicolored .15 .15
1001D A325b 100fr multicolored .15 .15
1001E A325b 350fr multicolored .45 .22
1001F A325b 450fr multicolored .58 .30
1001G A325b 680fr multicolored .90 .45
1001H A325b 800fr multicolored 1.05 .52
1001I A325b 900fr multicolored 1.20 .60
Nos. 1001C-1001I (7) 4.48 2.39

A number has been reserved for a souvenir sheet with this set.

Intl. Literacy Year — A326

1990, Dec. 30 *Perf. 12*

1002 A326 20fr Book, guiding hands, vert. .15 .15
1003 A326 100fr shown .18 .15
Set value .22 .15

Dogs — A326a

1991, Mar. 20 Litho. *Perf. 12*

1003A A326a 30fr Greyhound .15 .15
1003B A326a 50fr Japanese spaniel .15 .15
1003C A326a 140fr Toy terrier .18 .15
1003D A326a 350fr Chow .45 .22
1003E A326a 500fr Miniature pinscher .65 .32
1003F A326a 800fr Afghan 1.05 .52
1003G A326a 1140fr Papillon 1.50 .75
Nos. 1003A-1003G (7) 4.13 2.26

Imperf
Size: 70x90mm

1003H A326a 1500fr Shih tzu 2.00 1.00

Nos. 1003D-1003H are airmail.

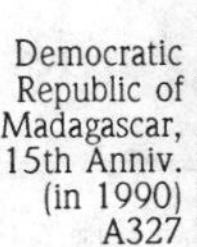

Democratic Republic of Madagascar, 15th Anniv. (in 1990) A327

1991, Apr. 8 Litho. *Perf. 12*

1004 A327 100fr multicolored .18 .15

Dated 1990.

Trees — A328

1991, June 20 Litho. *Perf. 13½*

1005 A328 140fr Adansonia fony .22 .15
1006 A328 500fr Didierea madagascariensis .75 .40

Scouts, Insects and Mushrooms A329

Insects: 140fr, Helictopleurus splendidicollis. 640fr, Cocles contemplator. 1140fr, Euchroea oberthurii.
Mushrooms: 500fr, Russula radicans. 1025fr, Russula singeri. 3500fr, Lactariopsis pandani.
4500fr, Euchroea spinnasuta fairmaire and Russula aureotacta.

1991, Aug. 2 Litho. *Perf. 13½*

1007 A329 140fr multicolored .18 .15
1008 A329 500fr multicolored .65 .32
1009 A329 640fr multicolored .82 .40
1010 A329 1025fr multicolored 1.30 .65
1011 A329 1140fr multicolored 1.45 .72
1012 A329 3500fr multicolored 4.50 2.25
Nos. 1007-1012 (6) 8.90 4.49

Souvenir Sheet

1013 A329 4500fr multicolored 5.85 5.85

Nos. 1007-1012 exist in souvenir sheets of 1.
For overprints see Nos. 1149-1156.

Discovery of America, 500th Anniv. A330

Designs: 15fr, Ship, 9th cent.. 65fr, Clipper ship, 1878. 140fr, Golden Hind. 500fr, Galley, 18th cent. 640fr, Galleon Ostrust, 1721, vert. 800fr, Caravel Amsterdam, 1539, vert. 1025fr, Santa Maria, 1492. 1500fr, Map.

1991, Sept. 10 Litho. *Perf. 12*

1014 A330 15fr multicolored .15 .15
1015 A330 65fr multicolored .15 .15
1016 A330 140fr multicolored .18 .15
1017 A330 500fr multicolored .65 .32
1018 A330 640fr multicolored .85 .42
1019 A330 800fr multicolored 1.05 .52
1020 A330 1025fr multicolored 1.35 .65
Nos. 1014-1020 (7) 4.38 2.36

Size: 90x70mm

1021 A330 1500fr multicolored 2.00 1.00

No. 1021 contains one 40x27mm perf. 12 label in center of stamp picturing ships and Columbus.

Domesticated Animals — A331

Designs: 140fr, Dog. 500fr, Arabian horse. 640fr, House cats. 1025fr, Himalayan cats. 1140fr, Draft horse. 5000fr, German shepherd. 10,000fr, Horse, cat & dog.

1991, Sept. 27 Litho. *Perf. 13½*

1022 A331 140fr multicolored .18 .15
1023 A331 500fr multicolored .65 .32
1024 A331 640fr multicolored .82 .40
1025 A331 1025fr multicolored 1.30 .65
1026 A331 1140fr multicolored 1.45 .72
1027 A331 5000fr multicolored 6.50 3.25
Nos. 1022-1027 (6) 10.90 5.49

Souvenir Sheet

1028 A331 10,000fr multicolored 13.00 6.50

Nos. 1022-1028 exist imperf. and in souvenir sheets of 1.

Birds A332

Designs: 40fr, Hirundo rustica. 55fr, Circus melanoluecos, vert. 60fr, Cuculas canorus, vert. 140fr, Threskiornis aethiopicus. 210fr, Porphyrio poliocephalus. 500fr, Coracias garrulus. 2000fr, Oriolus oriolus. 1500fr, Upupa epops.

Perf. 12½x12, 12x12½

1991, Dec. 10 Litho.

1029 A332 40fr multicolored .15 .15
1030 A332 55fr multicolored .15 .15
1031 A332 60fr multicolored .15 .15
1032 A332 140fr multicolored .18 .15
1033 A332 210fr multicolored .28 .15
1034 A332 500fr multicolored .65 .32
1035 A332 2000fr multicolored 2.50 1.25

Size: 70x90mm

Imperf

1036 A332 1500fr multicolored 2.00 1.00
Nos. 1029-1036 (8) 6.06 3.32

1992 Winter Olympics, Albertville — A333

1991, Dec. 30 Litho. *Perf. 12x12½*

1037 A333 5fr Cross-country skiing .15 .15
1038 A333 15fr Biathlon .15 .15
1039 A333 60fr Ice hockey .15 .15
1040 A333 140fr Downhill skiing .18 .15
1041 A333 640fr Figure skating .85 .42
1042 A333 1000fr Ski jumping 1.30 .65
1043 A333 1140fr Speed skating 1.50 .75
Nos. 1037-1043 (7) 4.28 2.42

Imperf

Size: 90x70mm

1044 A333 1500fr Three hockey players 2.00 1.00

Paul Minault College, 90th Anniv. — A333a

1991 Litho. *Perf. 13½*

1044A A333a 140fr multicolored .60 .30

Space Program A334

Designs: 140fr, Astronaunts repairing space telescope. 500fr, Soho solar observation probe. 640fr, Topex-Poseidon, observing oceans. 1025fr, Hipparcos probe, Galaxy 3C75. 1140fr, Voyager II surveying Neptune. 5000fr, Adeos, ETS VI, earth observation and communications satellites. 7500fr, Crew of Apollo 11.

1992, Apr. 22 *Perf. 13½*

1045 A334 140fr multi .18 .15
1046 A334 500fr multi .65 .32
1047 A334 640fr multi .82 .40
1048 A334 1025fr multi 1.30 .65
1049 A334 1140fr multi 1.45 .72
1050 A334 5000fr multi 6.50 3.20
a. Souvenir sheet of 6, #1045-1050 19.00 19.00
Nos. 1045-1050 (6) 10.90 5.44

Souvenir Sheet

1051 A334 7500fr multi 9.75 9.75

#1045-1050 exist in souvenir sheets of one.

Entertainers A335

1992, Apr. 29

1052 A335 100fr Ryuichi Sakamoto .15 .15
1053 A335 350fr John Lennon .45 .22
1054 A335 800fr Bruce Lee 1.05 .52
1055 A335 900fr Sammy Davis, Jr. 1.18 .58
1056 A335 1250fr John Wayne 1.65 .80
1057 A335 2500fr James Dean 3.25 1.65
Nos. 1052-1057 (6) 7.73 3.92

Souvenir Sheet

1058 A335 3000fr Clark Gable & Vivien Leigh 3.90 1.95

#1021-1026 exist in souvenir sheets of one.

Fight Against AIDS — A336

1990 Sports Festival — A338

Reforestation A337

1992, July 29 Litho. *Perf. 12*

1059 A336 140fr lil rose & black .24 .15

Dated 1991.

1992, July 29 Litho. *Perf. 12*

1060 A337 140fr black & green .24 .15

Dated 1991.

1992, Aug. 20

1061 A338 140fr multicolored .24 .15

Dated 1991.

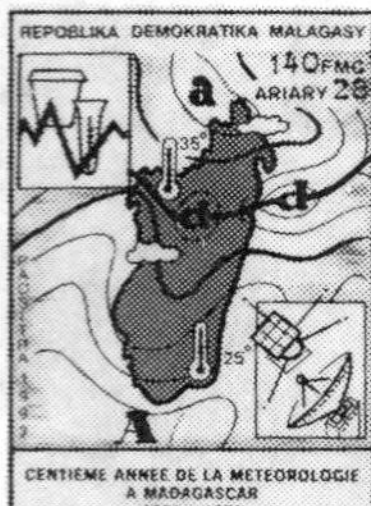

Meteorology in Madgascar, Cent. — A339

1992, Nov. 10 Litho. *Perf. 12x12½*

1062 A339 140fr multicolored .22 .15

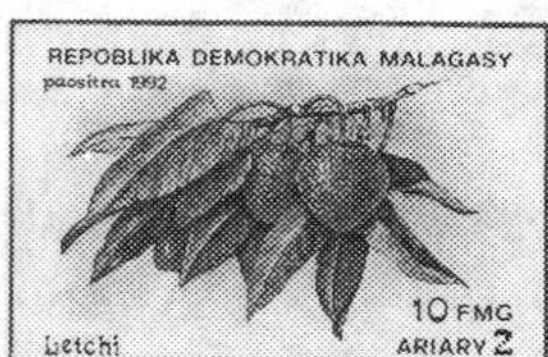

Fruit A341

Perf. 12½x12, 12x12½

1992, May 27 Litho.

1064 A341 10fr Litchis .15 .15
1065 A341 50fr Oranges .15 .15
1066 A341 60fr Apples .15 .15
1067 A341 140fr Peaches .18 .15
1068 A341 555fr Bananas, vert. .75 .38
1069 A341 800fr Avocados, vert. 1.00 .50
1070 A341 1400fr Mangoes, vert. 1.75 .90

Size: 89x70mm

Imperf

1071 A341 1600fr Mixed fruit 2.00 1.00
Nos. 1064-1071 (8) 6.13 3.38

1992 Summer Olympics, Barcelona A342

1992, June 30 *Perf. 11½*

1072 A342 65fr Women's gymnastics .15 .15
1073 A342 70fr High jump .15 .15
1074 A342 120fr Archery .15 .15
1075 A342 140fr Cycling .18 .15
1076 A342 675fr Weight lifting .90 .45
1077 A342 720fr Boxing .95 .48
1078 A342 1200fr Canoeing 1.50 .75

Imperf

Size: 90x70mm

1078A A342 1600fr Volleyball 2.75 1.40
Nos. 1072-1078A (8) 6.73 3.68

Litho. & Embossed

Perf. 13½

1079 A343 5000fr Judo

Butterflies — A344

Designs: 15fr, Eusemia bisma. 35fr, Argema mittrei, vert. 65fr, Alcidis aurora. 140fr, Agarista agricola. 600fr, Trogonoptera croesus. 850fr, Trogonodtera priamus. 1300fr, Pereute leucodrosime. 1500fr, Chrysirridia madagaskariensis.

Perf. 12½x12, 12x12½

1992, June 24 Litho.

1080 A344 15fr multicolored .15 .15
1081 A344 35fr multicolored .15 .15
1082 A344 65fr multicolored .15 .15
1083 A344 140fr multicolored .18 .15
1084 A344 600fr multicolored .75 .38
1085 A344 850fr multicolored 1.10 .55
1086 A344 1300fr multicolored 1.65 .82

Imperf

Size: 70x90mm

1087 A344 1500fr multicolored 1.90 .95
Nos. 1080-1087 (8) 6.03 3.30

Anniversaries and Events — A345

Designs: 500fr, Jean-Henri Dunant, delivery of Red Cross supplies. 640fr, Charles de Gaulle, battle of Bir Hacheim. 1025fr, Brandenburg Gate, people on Berlin wall. 1500fr, Village health clinic, Rotary, Lions emblems. 3000fr, Konrad Adenauer. 3500fr, Dirigible LZ4, hanger on Lake Constance, Ferdinand von Zeppelin. 7500fr, Wolfgang Amadeus Mozart at piano, palace, cathedral in Salzburg.

1992, Dec. 8 Litho. *Perf. 13½*

1088 A345 500fr multicolored .70 .35
1089 A345 640fr multicolored .90 .45
1090 A345 1025fr multicolored 1.50 .75
1091 A345 1500fr multicolored 2.00 1.00
1092 A345 3000fr multicolored 4.25 2.00
1093 A345 3500fr multicolored 5.00 2.50
Nos. 1088-1093 (6) 14.35 7.05

Souvenir Sheet

1094 A345 7500fr multicolored 10.00 5.00

Intl. Red Cross (#1088). Battle of Bir Hacheim, 50th anniv. (#1089). Brandenburg Gate, bicent. and destruction of Berlin Wall, 3rd anniv. (#1090). Konrad Adenauer, 25th death anniv. (#1092). Ferdinand von Zeppelin, 75th death anniv. (#1093). Mozart, death bicent. (in 1991), (#1094).

For overprint see No. 1146.

1994 World Cup Soccer Championships, US — A346

Soccer players, Georgia landmarks: 140fr, Ficklin Home, Macon. 640fr, Herndon Home, Atlanta. 1025fr, Cultural Center, Augusta. 5000fr, Old Governor's Mansion, Milledgeville.

7500fr, Player, stars, stripes.

1992, Dec. 15 Litho. *Perf. 13½*

1095	A346	140fr multicolored		.20	.15
1096	A346	640fr multicolored		.90	.45
1097	A346	1025fr multicolored		1.45	.75
1098	A346	5000fr multicolored		7.00	3.50
		Nos. 1095-1098 (4)		9.55	4.85

Souvenir Sheet

1099	A346	7500fr multicolored	10.25	5.15

Miniature Sheet

Inventors and Inventions A347

No. 1100: a, Gutenberg (1394?-1468), printing press. b, Newton (1642-1727), telescope. c, John Dalton (1766-1844), atomic theory. d, Louis-Jacques-Mande Daguerre (1789-1851), photographic equipment. e, Faraday (1791-1867), electric motor. f, Orville (1871-1948), Wilbur Wright (1867-1912), motor-powered airplane. g, Bell (1847-1922), telephone. h, Edison (1847-1931), phonograph. i, Benz (1844-1929), motor-driven vehicle. j, Charles Parsons (1854-1931), steam turbine. k, Diesel (1858-1913), Diesel engine. l, Marconi, radio. m, Auguste-Marie-Louis Lumiere (1862-1954), Louis-Jean Lumiere (1864-1948), motion pictures. n, Oberth (1894-1989), rocketry. o, John W. Mauchly (1907-1980), John P. Eckert, electronic computer. p, Arthur Shawlow, laser.

1993, Apr. 27

1100	A347	500fr Sheet of 16, #a.-p.	11.00	5.50

Dated 1990.

Transportation — A348

Race cars: No. 1101a, 20fr, 1956 Bugatti. b, 20fr, 1968 Ferrari. c, 140fr, 1962 Lotus MK25. d, 140fr, 1970 Matra. e, 1250fr, 1963 Porsche. f, 1250fr, 1980 Ligier JS11. g, 3000fr, 1967 Honda. h, 3000fr, 1992 B192 Benetton.

Locomotives: No. 1102a, 20fr, C62, Japan, 1948. b, 20fr, SZD, USSR, 1975. c, 140fr, MU A1A-A1A, Norway, 1954. d, 140fr, Series 26 2-D-2, Africa, 1982. e, 1250fr, Amtrak Metroliner, US, 1967. f, 1250fr, VIA, Canada, 1982. g, 3000fr, Diesel, Union Pacific RR, US, 1969. h, 3000fr, Atlantic, TGV, France, 1990.

1993, Mar. 23

1101	A348	Block of 8, #a.-h.	12.00	6.00
1102	A348	Block of 8, #a.-h.	12.00	6.00

Dated 1990.

Wildlife A349

Birds: No. 1103a, 45fr, Coua verreauxi. b, 45fr, Asio helvola hova. c, 60fr, Coua cristata. d, 60fr, Euryceros prevostii. e, 140fr, Coua gigas. f, 140fr, Foudia madagascariensis. g, 3000fr, Falculea palliata. h, 3000fr, Eutriorchis astur.

Butterflies: No. 1104a, 45fr, Chrysiridia madagascariensis. b, 45fr, Hypolimnas misippus. c, 60fr, Charaxes antamboulou. d, 60fr, Papilio antenor. e, 140fr, Hypolimnas dexithea. f, 140fr, Charaxes andranodorus. g, 3000fr, Euxanthe madagascariensis. h, 3000fr, Papilio grosesmithi.

1993, May 27

1103	A349	Block of 8, #a.-h.	8.75	4.35
1104	A349	Block of 8, #a.-h.	8.75	4.35

Dated 1991.

Intl. Conference on Nutrition, Rome A350

1992, Nov. 3

1105	A350	500fr multicolored	.65	.35

Automobiles A351

1993, Jan. 28 Litho. *Perf. 12*

1106	A351	20fr BMW	.15	.15
1107	A351	40fr Toyota	.15	.15
1108	A351	60fr Cadillac	.15	.15
1109	A351	65fr Volvo	.15	.15
1110	A351	140fr Mercedes Benz	.25	.15
1111	A351	640fr Ford	1.10	.55
1112	A351	3000fr Honda	5.50	2.75

Size: 90x70mm

Imperf

1113	A351	2000fr Renault	3.50	1.75
		Nos. 1106-1113 (8)	10.95	5.80

Birds — A352

50fr, Anodorhynchus hiacinthinus. 60fr, Nymphicus hollandicus. 140fr, Melopsittacus undulatus. 500fr, Aratinga jandya. 675fr, Melopsittacus undulatus, diff. 800fr, Cyanoramphus novaezelandiae. 1750fr, Nestor notabilis. 2000fr, Ara militaris.

1993, Feb. 24

1114	A352	50fr multicolored	.15	.15
1115	A352	60fr multicolored	.15	.15
1116	A352	140fr multicolored	.25	.15
1117	A352	500fr multicolored	.90	.45
1118	A352	675fr multicolored	1.25	.65
1119	A352	800fr multicolored	1.40	.70
1120	A352	1750fr multicolored	3.00	1.50

Size: 71x91mm

Imperf

1121	A352	2000fr multicolored	3.50	1.75
		Nos. 1114-1121 (8)	10.60	5.50

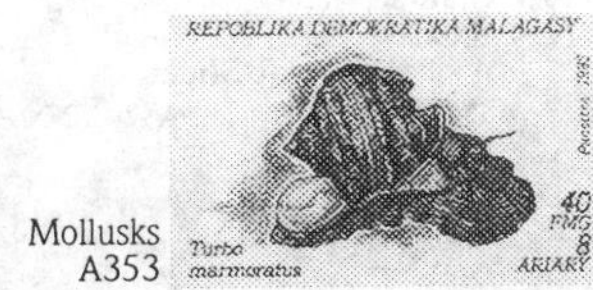

Mollusks A353

1993, Feb. 3

1122	A353	40fr Turbo marmoratus	.15	.15
1123	A353	60fr Mitra mitra	.15	.15
1124	A353	65fr Argonauta argo	.15	.15
1125	A353	140fr Conus textile	.25	.15
1126	A353	500fr Aplysia depilans	.90	.45
1127	A353	675fr Harpa amouretta	1.25	.65
1128	A353	2500fr Cypraea tigris	4.50	2.25

Size: 70x90mm

Imperf

1129	A353	2000fr Architectonica maxima	3.50	1.75
		Nos. 1122-1129 (8)	10.85	5.70

Boat, Barges, Pangalanes Canal A354

1993, Jan. 29 Litho. *Perf. 12*

1130	A354	140fr multicolored	.24	.15

Miniature Sheet

Ships A355

Designs: a, 5fr, Egyptian ship. b, 5fr, Mediterranean galley. c, 5fr, Great Western, England, 1837. d, 5fr, Mississippi River sidewheeler, US, 1850. e, 15fr, Bireme, Phoenicia. f, 15fr, Viking long ship. g, 15fr, Clermont, US, 1806. h, 15fr, Pourquoi-pas, France, 1936. i, 140fr, Santa Maria, Spain, 1492. j, 140fr, HMS Victory, England, 1765. k, 140fr, Fast motor yacht, Monaco. l, 140fr, Bremen, Germany, 1950. m, 10,000fr, Sovereign of the Seas, England, 1637. n, 10,000fr, Cutty Sark, England, 1869. o, 10,000fr, Savannah, US, 1959. p, 10,000fr, Condor, Australia.

1993, Apr. 6 Litho. *Perf. 13½*

1131	A355	Sheet of 16, #a.-p.	50.00	25.00

Miniature Sheet

Nobel Prize Winners in Physics, Chemistry and Medicine A356

Designs: a, Albert Einstein, Niels Bohr. b, Wolfgang Pauli, Max Born. c, Joseph Thomson, Johannes Stark. d, Otto Hahn, Hideki Yukawa. e, Owen Richardson, William Shockley. f, Albert Michelson, Charles Townes. g, Wilhelm Wien, Lev Landau. h, Karl Braun, Sir Edward Appleton. i, Percy Bridgman, Nikolai Semenov. j, Sir William Ramsay, Glenn Seaborg. k, Otto Wallach, Hermann Staudinger. l, Richard Synge, Alex Theorell. m, Thomas Morgan, Hermann Muller. n, Allvar Gullstrand, Willem Einthoven. o, Sir Charles Sherrington, Otto Loewi. p, Jules Bordet, Sir Alexander Fleming.

1993, Mar. 11

1132	A356	500fr Sheet of 16, #a.-p.	11.00	5.50

Alex misspelled on No. 1132l.

Miniature Sheet

Lemurs — A357

Designs: a, 60fr, Hapalemur simus. b, 150fr, Propithecus diadema. c, 250fr Indri indri. d, 350fr, Varecia variegata.

1992, Oct. 9 Litho. *Perf. 13½*

1133	A357	Sheet of 4, #a.-d.	4.00	2.00

World Post Day.

No. 840 Ovptd. in Silver

75eme ANNIVERSAIRE LION

1993, Sept. 28 Litho. *Perf. 13½*

1134	A276	550fr multicolored	*3.75*	*1.90*

No. 874 Ovptd. in Silver with Guitar and "THE ELVIS'S GUITAR / 15th ANNIVERSARY OF HIS DEATH / 1977-1992" in English or French

1993, Sept. 28

1135	A287	1500fr English ovpt.	2.25	1.10
1136	A287	1500fr French ovpt.	2.25	1.10
a.		Pair, #1135-1136	4.50	2.25

Nos. 945-948 Ovptd. in Gold

VAINQUEUR ALLEMAGNE

1993, Sept. 28

1137	A309	350fr multicolored	.55	.28
1138	A309	1000fr multicolored	1.50	.75
1139	A309	1500fr multicolored	2.25	1.25
1140	A309	2500fr multicolored	3.75	1.90
		Nos. 1137-1140 (4)	8.05	4.18

Nos. 974-978 Ovptd. in Gold

MEDAILLE D'OR

BOB A QUATRE (AUT)
INGO APPELT
HARALD WINKLER
GERHARD HAIDACHER
THOMAS SCHROLL

1993, Sept. 28

1141	A315	350fr multicolored	.55	.28
1142	A315	1000fr multicolored	1.50	.75
1143	A315	1500fr multicolored	2.25	1.10
1144	A315	2500fr multicolored	3.75	1.90
		Nos. 1141-1144 (4)	8.05	4.03

Souvenir Sheet

1145	A315	3000fr multicolored	4.75	2.50

No. 1088 Ovptd. in Red

130e ANNIVERSAIRE
DE LA CREATION DE LA CROIX-ROUGE
1863-1993

1993, Sept. 28

1146	A345	500fr multicolored	*3.50*	*1.75*

Miniature Sheet

Commercial Airlines — A358

Designs: a, 10fr, Lufthansa, Germany. b, 10fr, Air France. c, 10fr, Air Canada. d. 10fr, ANA, Japan. e, 60fr, British Airways. f, 60fr, DO-X, Germany. g, 60fr, Shinmeiwa, Japan. h, 60fr, Royal Jordanian. i, 640fr, Alitalia, Italy. j, 640fr, Hydro 2000, France-Europe. k, 640fr, Boeing 314 Clipper, US. l, 640fr, Air Madagascar. m, 5000fr, Emirates Airlines, United Arab Emirates n, 5000fr, Scandinavian Airways. o, 5000fr, KLM, Netherlands. p, 5000fr, Air Caledonia.

1993, Nov. 22 Litho. *Perf. 13½*

1147	A358	Sheet of 16, #a.-p.	30.00	15.00

Dated 1990.

Miniature Sheet

Painters — A359

Designs: a, 50fr, Da Vinci. b, 50fr, Titian. c, 50fr, Rembrandt. d, 50fr, J.M.W. Turner (1775-1851). e, 640fr, Michelangelo. f, 640fr, Rubens. g, 640fr, Goya. h, 640fr, Delacroix (1798-1863). i, 1000fr, Monet. j, 1000fr, Gauguin. k, 1000fr, Toulouse Lautrec (1864-1901). l, 1000fr, Dali (1904-89). m,

2500fr, Renoir. n, 2500fr, Van Gogh. o, 2500fr, Picasso. p, 2500fr, Andy Warhol.

1993, May 10

1148 A359 Sheet of 16, #a.-p. 22.50 11.50

The local currency on Nos. 1148m-1148p is obliterated by a black overprint.

Nos. 1007-1013 Ovptd. in Gold

50ème ANNIVERSAIRE
DE LA MORT DE
BADEN POWEL

No. 841 Ovptd. in Metallic Green

50ème ANNIVERSAIRE
DE LA MORT DE
BADEN POWEL

1993, Sept. 28	**Litho.**	***Perf. 13½***		
1149 A329	140fr multicolored		.18	.15
1150 A329	500fr multicolored		.65	.32
1151 A329	640fr multicolored		.85	.40
1152 A329	1025fr multicolored		1.25	.60
1153 A329	1140fr multicolored		1.50	.75
1154 A276	1500fr multicolored		2.00	1.00
1155 A329	3500fr multicolored		4.50	2.25
	Nos. 1149-1155 (7)		10.93	5.47

Souvenir Sheet

1156 A329 4500fr multicolored 6.00 3.00

Fauna A360

Dogs: No. 1157a, 40fr, Golden retriever. b, 140fr, Fox terrier. c, 40fr, Coton de tulear. d, 140fr, Langhaar.

Cats: No. 1158a, 40fr, Birman. b, 140fr, Egyptian. c, 40fr, European creme. d, 140fr, Rex du Devon.

Reptiles: No. 1159a, 1000fr, Phelsuma madagascariensis. b, 2000fr, Cameleon de parson. c, 1000fr, Laticauda laticaudate. d, 2000fr, Testudo radiata.

Beetles: No. 1160a, 1000fr, Euchroea spininasuta. b, 2000fr, Orthophagus minnulus klug. c, 1000fr, Helictopleurus radicollis. d, 2000fr, Euchroea coelestis.

1993, Dec. 7	**Litho.**	***Perf. 13½***	
1157 A360	Block of 4, #a.-d.	.50	.25
1158 A360	Block of 4, #a.-d.	.50	.25
1159 A360	Block of 4, #a.-d.	8.00	4.00
1160 A360	Block of 4, #a.-d.	8.00	4.00
e.	Sheet of 16, #1157-1160	17.00	8.50

Dated 1991.

Nos. 934-938 Ovptd. in Metallic Blue, Nos. 939A-939B Ovptd. in Metallic Red Lilac

BICENTENAIRE
DE L'AN I
DE LA REPUBLIQUE
FRANCAISE

1993, Sept. 28			
1161 A305	250fr multicolored	.35	.18
1162 A305	350fr multicolored	.52	.25
1163 A305	1000fr multicolored	1.50	.75
1164 A305	1500fr multicolored	2.25	1.10
1165 A305	2500fr multicolored	3.75	1.90
	Nos. 1161-1165 (5)	8.37	4.18

Litho. & Embossed

Perf. 13½

1166A A305a 5000fr gold & multi

Souvenir Sheet

1166B A305a 5000fr gold & multi

A number has been reserved for an additional value in this set.

Marine Life — A361

Shells: No. 1167a, 15fr, Chicoreus torrefactus. b, 15fr, Fasciolaria filamentosa. c, 30fr, Stellaria solaris. d, 30fr, Harpa ventricosa lamarck.

Crustaceans: No. 1168a, 1250fr, Panulirus (#1167c). b, 1250fr, Stenopus hispidus (#1167d). c, 1500fr, Pagure. d, 1500fr, Bernard l'hermite (#1168b).

Fish: No. 1169a, 15fr, Pigopytes diacanthus. b, 15fr, Coelacanth latimeria chalumnae. c, 30fr, Ostracion cyanurus. d, 30fr, Coris gaimardi. e, 1250fr, Balistapus undulatus. f, 1250fr, Forcipiger longirostris. g, 1500fr, Adioryx diadema. h, 1500fr, Pterois lunulata.

1993, Nov. 26		***Perf. 13½***	
1167 A361	Block of 4, #a.-d.	.15	.15
1168 A361	Block of 4, #a.-d.	7.25	3.50
1169 A361	Block of 8, #a.-h.	7.25	3.50
i.	Sheet of 16, #1167-1169	15.00	7.50

Dated "1991."

Flora — A362

Orchids: No. 1170a, 45fr, Oceonia oncidiflora. b, 60fr, Cymbidella rhodochica. c, 140fr, Vanilla planifolia. d, 3000fr, Phaius humblotii.

Fruits: No. 1171a, 45fr, Artocarpus altilis. b, 60fr, Eugenia malaceensis. c, 140fr, Jambosa domestica. d, 3000fr, Papaya.

Mushrooms: No. 1172a, 45fr, Russula annulata. b, 60fr, Lactarius claricolor. c, 140fr, Russula tuberculosa. d, 3000fr, Russula fistulosa.

Vegetables: No. 1173a, 45fr, Sweet potatoes. b, 60fr, Yams. c, 140fr, Avocados. d, 3000fr, Mangoes.

1993, Dec. 15	**Litho.**	***Perf. 13***	
1170 A362	Strip of 4, #a.-d.	4.25	2.25
1171 A362	Strip of 4, #a.-d.	4.25	2.25
1172 A362	Strip of 4, #a.-d.	4.25	2.25
1173 A362	Strip of 4, #a.-d.	4.25	2.25
e.	Sheet of 16, #1170-1173	17.00	9.00

1994 Winter Olympics, Lillehammer A362a

Designs: 140fr, Biathlon. 1250fr, Ice hockey. 2000fr, Figure skating. 2500fr, Slalom skiing.

5000fr, Downhill skiing. #1173K, Ski jumping. #1173L, Speed skating.

1994, Jan. 19	**Litho.**	***Perf. 13***	
1173F-1173I	A362a Set of 4	*18.50*	*9.25*

Souvenir Sheet

1173J A362a 5000fr multi *7.25 3.50*

Litho. & Embossed

1173K A362a 10,000fr gold & multi

Souvenir Sheet

1173L A362a 10,000fr gold & multi

No. 1173K exists in a souvenir sheet of 1.
For overprints see # 1288A-1288E.

1996 Summer Olympics, Atlanta — A362b

Scene in Atlanta, event: 640fr, 1892 Windsor Hotel Americus, dressage. 1000fr, Covington Courthouse, women's shot put. 1500fr, Carolton Community Activities Center, table tennis. 3000fr, Newman Historic Commercial Court Square, soccer.

7500fr, Relay race runner. No. 1173R, Pole vault, vert. No. 1173S, Hurdles, vert.

1994, Jan. 19

1173M-1173P A362b Set of 4 *19.50 9.60*

Souvenir Sheet

1173Q A362b 7500fr multi *27.00 13.50*

Litho. & Embossed

1173R A362b 5000fr gold & multi

Souvenir Sheet

1173S A362b 5000fr gold & multi

Prehistoric Animals A363

Designs: 35fr, Dinornis maximus, vert. 40fr, Ceratosaurus, vert. 140fr, Mosasavrus, vert. 525fr, Protoceratops. 640fr, Styvacosaurus. 755fr, Smilodon. 1800fr, Uintatherium.

2000fr, Tusks of mammuthus, trees, vert.

1995, Feb. 23	**Litho.**	***Perf. 12***	
1174-1180 A363	Set of 7	4.25	2.25

Souvenir Sheet

1181 A363 2000fr multicolored 2.00 1.00

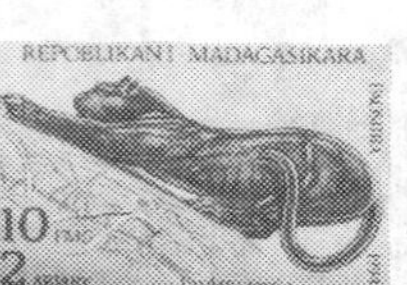

Wild Animals A364

Designs: 10fr, Panthera pardus. 30fr, Martes. 60fr, Vulpes vulpes. 120fr, Canis lupus. No. 1186, Fennecus zerda. No. 1187, Panthera leo. 3500fr, Uncia uncia.

2000fr, Panthera onca.

1995, Mar. 21

1182-1188 A364 Set of 7 4.25 2.25

Souvenir Sheet

1189 A364 2000fr multicolored 2.00 1.00

D-Day Landings, Normandy, 50th Anniv. — A365

Designs: No. 1190a, 3000fr, American troops, flamethrower. b, 1500fr, Coming ashore. c, 3000fr, Explosion, German commander pointing.

Liberation of Paris, 50th anniv.: No. 1191a, 3000fr, Notre Dame, resistance fighters, crowd. b, 1500fr, Arch de Triomphe, woman cheering. c, 3000fr, Eiffel Tower, parade, French troops.

1994		***Perf. 13½***	
1190 A365	Strip of 3, #a.-c.	6.75	3.50
1191 A365	Strip of 3, #a.-c.	6.75	3.50

Nos. 1190b, 1191b are 30x47mm. Nos. 1190-1191 are continuous design.

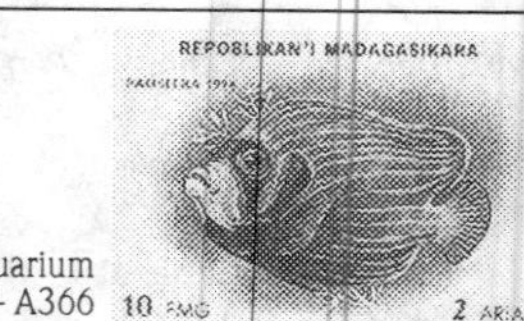

Aquarium Fish — A366

Designs: 10fr, Pomacanthus imperator. 30fr, Betta splendens. 45fr, Trichogaster leeri. 95fr, Labrus bimaculatus. No. 1196, 140fr, Synodontis nigreventris. No. 1197, 140fr, Cichlasoma biocellatum. 3500fr, Fudulus heteroclitus.

2000fr, Carassius auratus, vert.

1994, June 28	**Litho.**	***Perf. 12½x12***	
1192-1198 A366	Set of 7	4.00	2.00

Souvenir Sheet

Perf. 12x12½

1199 A366 2000fr multicolored 2.00 1.00

Modern Locomotives A367

Designs: 5fr, Superviem Odoriko. 15fr, Morrison Knudsen Corporation. 140fr, ER-200. 265fr, General Motors. 300fr, New Jersey Transit. 575fr, Siemens Inter-City Express. 2500fr, Sweden's Fast Train.

2000fr, Alstham T60.

1993, Nov. 10		***Perf. 12***	
1200-1206 A367	Set of 7	4.00	2.00

Souvenir Sheet

1207 A367 2000fr multicolored 2.00 1.00

Cathedrals — A368 Insects — A369

Cathedral, location: 10fr, Antwerp, Belgium. 100fr, Cologne, Germany. 120fr, Antsirabe, Masdagascar. 140fr, Kremlin, Moscow. 525fr, Notre Dame, Paris. 605fr, Toledo, Spain. 2500fr, St. Stephens, Vienna.

2000fr, Westminster Abbey, London.

1995, Feb. 14		***Perf. 12x12½***	
1208-1214 A368	Set of 7	4.00	2.00

Souvenir Sheet

1215 A368 2000fr multicolored 2.00 1.00

1994, Feb. 2 ***Perf. 12***

Designs: 20fr, Necrophorus tomentosus. 60fr, Dynastes tityus. 140fr, Megaloxantha bicolor. 605fr, Calosoma sycophanta. 720fr, Chrysochroa mirabilis. 1000fr, Crioceris asparaqi. 1500fr, Cetonia aurata.

2000fr, Goliathus goliathus.

1216-1222 A369 Set of 7 4.00 2.00

Size: 85x58mm

Imperf

1223 A369 2000fr multicolored 2.00 1.00

Miniature Sheet

PHILAKOREA '94 — A370

Celebrities: a, 100fr, John Lennon, Ella Fitzgerald. b, 140fr, Marilyn Monroe, Elvis Presley. c, 550fr, US Pres. Bill Clinton, Louis Armstrong.

1995, Feb. 23 ***Perf. 12***

1224 A370 Sheet of 2 each, #a.-c. + 3 labels 6.00 3.00

Ancient Art & Architecture — A371

Designs: No. 1225, 350fr, Statue of Augustus, vert. No. 1226, 350fr, Statue, Land Surveyor, vert. No. 1227, 350fr, Painting, "Child of Thera," vert. No. 1228, 350fr, Sarcophagous, Cerveteri and Wife, vert. No. 1229, 350fr, Statue, Athena of Fidia, vert. No. 1230, 405fr, Colosseum, Rome. No. 1231, 405fr, Mask of Agamemnon, vert. No. 1232, 405fr, Forum of Caesar. No. 1233, 405fr, She-Wolf suckling Romulus & Remus. No. 1234, 405fr, Parthenon, Athens. No. 1235, 525fr, Carthaginian mask, vert. No. 1236, 525fr, Bust of Emperor Tiberius, vert. No. 1237, 525fr, Statue of Alexandar the Great, vert. No. 1238, 525fr, Detail, Taormina Theater, vert. No. 1239, 525fr, Denarius of Caesar. No. 1240, 605fr, Forum, Pompeii, vert. No. 1241, 605fr, Bronze statue, Riace, vert. No. 1242, 605fr, Venus de Milo, vert. No. 1243, 605fr, Bronze statue, Archer, vert. No. 1244, 605fr, Pont Du Gard Aqueduct, Nimes.

1994 **Litho.** ***Perf. 13½***
1225-1244 A371 Set of 20 6.50 3.25

Elvis Presley (1935-77) A371a

Litho. & Embossed

1994, June 8 ***Perf. 13½***
1244A A371a 10,000fr gold & multi

Exists in sheets of 4.

Motion Pictures, Cent. — A372

The Stuff of Heroes, by Philip Kaufman: a, 140fr, Astronaut. b, 140fr, Astronaut up close, walking. c, 5000fr, Spacecraft, astronaut.

1994
1245 A372 Strip of 3, #a.-c. 3.75 1.90

No. 1245 is a continuous design and exists in souvenir sheet of 1 with scenes from the film "Blade Runner."
No. 1245c is 60x47mm.

Intl. Olympic Committee, Cent. — A373

Designs: a, 2500fr, Flag. b, 2500fr, Olympic flame. c, 3500fr, Pierre de Coubertin.

1994
1246 A373 Strip of 3, #a.-c. 5.75 2.75

No. 1246 is a continuous design and exists in souvenir sheet of 1. No. 1246c is 60x47mm.

ILO, 75th Anniv. — A374

1994 **Litho.** ***Perf. 13½***
1247 A374 140fr multicolored .22 .15

Modern Ships — A375

Ships: 45fr, Russian car ferry. 50fr, Australian cargo. 100fr, Japanese cruise. 140fr, US cruise. 300fr, English hovercraft. 350fr, Danish cargo. 3000fr, Korean container ship.
2000fr, Finnish car ferry, vert.

1994 **Litho.** ***Perf. 12***
1248-1254 A375 Set of 7 4.00 2.00

Souvenir Sheet

1255 A375 2000fr multicolored 2.00 2.00

A377

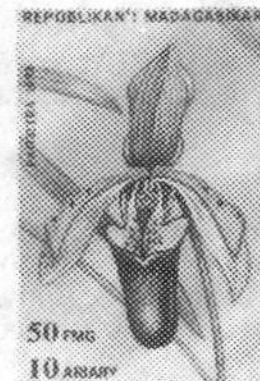
A378

Sports: 5fr, Hurdles. 140fr, Boxing. 525fr, Gymnastics. 550fr, Weight lifting. 640fr, Swimming. 720fr, Equestrian. 1500fr, Soccer.
2000fr, Race walking, horiz.

1995, Apr. 4 **Litho.** ***Perf. 12***
1264-1270 A377 Set of 7 4.00 4.00

Souvenir Sheet

1271 A377 2000fr multicolored 1.90 1.90

1993, Nov. 10 **Litho.** ***Perf. 12***

Orchids: 50fr, Paphiopedilum siamense. 65fr, Cypripedium calceolus. 70fr, Ophrys oestrifera. 140fr, Cephalanthera rubra. 300fr, Cypripedium macranthon. 640fr, Calanthe vestita. 2500fr, Cypripedium guttatum. 2000fr, Oncidium tigrinum.

1272-1278 A378 Set of 7 3.75 3.75

Size: 90x70mm

Imperf

1279 A378 2000fr multicolored 2.00 2.00

Sharks A379

10fr, Galeocerdo cuvieri. 45fr, Pristiophorus japonicus. 140fr, Rincodon typus. 270fr, Sphyrna zygaena. 600fr, Carcharhinus longimanus. 1200fr, Stegostoma tigrinum. 1500fr, Scapanorhynchus owstoni. 2000fr, Galeoshinas zyopterus.

1993, Sept. 22 ***Perf. 12***
1280-1286 A379 Set of 7 3.75 3.75

Size: 70x90mm

Imperf

1287 A379 2000fr multicolored 2.00 2.00

Archaea Workmani — A380

1994 ***Perf. 15***
1288 A380 500fr multicolored .75 .75

Nos. 1173F-1173J Ovptd. With Names of Winners in Silver or Gold

1994 **Litho.** ***Perf. 13***
1288A-1288D A362a Set of 4 *18.50 9.25*

Souvenir Sheet

1288E A362a 5000fr multicolored *7.25 3.50*

Overprinted in silver: 140fr, "M. BEDARD / CANADA." 1250fr, "MEDAILLE D'OR / SUEDE." 2000fr, "O. BAYUL / UKRAINE." 2500fr, "M. WASMEIER / ALLEMAGNE." 5000fr,
Overprinted in gold: 5000fr, "D. COMPAGNONI / ITALIE."

Marilyn Monroe (1926-62), Elvis Presley (1935-77) — A381

Scenes from films: No. 1289, 100fr, Gentlemen Prefer Blondes. No. 1290, 100fr, Clambake, Roustabout, Viva Las Vegas. 550fr, Some Like it Hot. 1250fr, Girls, Girls, Girls, King Creole. 5000fr, Niagara. 10,000fr, Double Trouble, Kid Gallahad, Speedway.
Illustration reduced.

1995 **Litho.** ***Perf. 13½***
1289-1294 A381 Set of 6 12.50 12.50

Nos. 1289-1294 exist in souvenir sheets of 1.

Motion Pictures, Cent. — A382

Actor, film: No. 1295, 140fr, James Dean, Rebel Without a Cause. No. 1296, 140fr, Burt Lancaster, Vera Cruz. 5000fr, Elvis Presley, Speedway. 10,000fr, Marilyn Monroe, How to Marry a Millionaire.

1995 **Litho.** ***Perf. 13½***
1295-1298 A382 Set of 4 11.00 11.00
a. Miniature sheet of 4, #1295-1298 *17.50 17.50*

Nos. 1295-1298 exist in souvenir sheets of 1.

Locusts A383

Designs: No. 1299, Assylidae, natural enemy of the locust. No. 1300, Locust eating corn, vert. No. 1301, Gathering locusts for consumption.

1995, Sept. 26 **Litho.** ***Perf. 13½***
1299 A383 140fr multicolored .15 .15
1300 A383 140fr multicolored .15 .15
1301 A383 140fr multicolored .15 .15
Set value .35 .35

Malagasyan Bible, 160th Anniv. — A384

World Post Day — A385

1995, June 21 **Litho.** ***Perf. 15***
1302 A384 140fr multicolored .15 .15

1995, Oct. 9 ***Perf. 13½***
1303 A385 500fr multicolored .60 .60

No. 971 Ovptd. in Silver

20ème ANNIVERSAIRE
DU 1er VOL COMMERCIAL
DU CONCORDE

1976 1996

1996 **Litho.** ***Perf. 13½***
1304 A314 2000fr on No. 971 *3.60 1.80*

No. 1304 exists in souvenir sheet of 1.

Death of Charles de Gaulle, 25th Anniv. A386

Designs: a, 100fr, World War I battle. b, 100fr, As President of France. c, 100fr, Brazzaville, 1940. d, 500fr, Pierre Brossolette, Churchill, De Gaulle. e, 500fr, Young woman. f, 500fr, Yak 9T, Gen. Leclerc. g, 1500fr, Liberation of Paris. h, 1500fr, De Gaulle as younger man. i, 1500fr, Jean Moulin, Free French barricade in Paris. j, 7500fr, Writing Tourbillon de L'Histoire, Colombey Les Deux Eglises. k, 7500fr, Giving speech as older diplomat. l, 7500fr, Doves, French flag, older De Gaulle standing on hilltop.

1996 **Litho.** ***Perf. 13½***
1305 A386 Sheet of 12, #a.-l. 21.50 10.75

See designs A390, A391.

Famous People A387

Designs: 1500fr, Wilhelm Steinitz (1836-1900), American chess master. 1750fr, Emmanuel Lasker (1868-1941), German chess master. 2000fr, Enzo Ferrari (1898-1988), automobile designer. 2500fr, Thomas Stafford, American astronaut, A.A. Leonov, Russian cosmonaut. 3000fr, Jerry Garcia (d. 1995), musician. 3500fr, Ayrton Senna (1960-94), race car driver. 5000fr, Paul-Emile Victor (1907-95), polar explorer. 7500fr, Paul Harris (1868-1947), founder of Rotary Intl.

1996
1306-1313 A387 Set of 8 20.00 10.00

Nos. 1306-1313 exist in souvenir sheets of 1.

UN and UNICEF, 50th Anniv. — A388

Designs: No. 1314, 140fr, Hand holding shaft of grain, UN emblem. No. 1315, 140fr, UN building, flags, map, woman feeding child. No. 1316, 140fr, Child holding plate of food, child holding UNICEF emblem. 7500fr, Two children, UNICEF emblem.

1996, Aug. 30

1314-1317 A388 Set of 4 5.25 2.60

Nos. 1314-1317 exist in souvenir sheets of 1.

Jade A389

a, People on mountain. b, Carving of insect, leaves. c, Chops on a chain. d, Insect in stone.

1996 Litho. *Perf. 13½*

1318 A389 175fr Sheet of 4, #a.-d. 2.60 1.30

A390

#1319: Bruce Lee (1940-73), various portraits.
#1320: John Lennon (1940-80), various portraits.
#1321: Locomotives: a, Train going left. b, Train going right. c, ICE Train, Germany. d, Eurostar.
#1322: Louis Pasteur (1822-95), various portraits.
#1323: Francois Mitterrand (1916-96), various portraits.
#1324: Intl. Space Station: a, Shuttle Atlantis, MIR Space Station. b, MIR. c, Intl. Space Station. d, Shuttle, Alpha section of station.

1996 Litho. *Perf. 13½*

1319	A390	500fr	Sheet of 4, #a.-d.	2.25	1.10
1320	A391	1500fr	Sheet of 4, #a.-d.	3.70	1.90
1321	A392	1500fr	Sheet of 4, #a.-d.	3.70	1.85
1322	A393	1750fr	Sheet of 4, #a.-d.	4.25	2.10
1323	A394	2000fr	Sheet of 4, #a.-d.	5.00	2.50
1324	A395	2500fr	Sheet of 4, #a.-d.	6.25	3.00

Post Day A396

Various local post offices: a, 500fr. b, 1000fr. c, 3500fr. d, 5000fr.

1996 Litho. *Perf. 13½*

1325 A396 Sheet of 4, #a.-d. 6.25 3.00

Sports Cars A397

Designs: a, Mercedes W196 driven by Juan Manuel Fangio. b, Porsche 911 Carrera. c, Porsche 917-30. d, Mercedes 600 SEC.

1996

1326 A397 3000fr Sheet of 4, #a.-d. 7.50 3.75

UN, 50th Anniv. — A398

1995, Oct. 24 Litho. *Perf. 11½*

1328 A398 500fr Lemur, tortoise

Three additional stamps exist in this set. The editors would like to examine them.

1998 Winter Olympics, Nagano — A399

Designs: 160fr, Ice hockey. 350fr, Pairs figure skating. 5000fr, Biathlon. 7500fr, Free-style skiing. 12,500fr, Speed skating.

1997 Litho. *Perf. 13½*

1331-1334 A399 Set of 4 6.75 3.40

Souvenir Sheet

1335 A399 12,500fr multicolored 6.50 3.25

No. 1335 contains one 42x60mm stamp.

1998 World Cup Soccer Championships, France — A400

Various soccer plays: 300fr, 1350fr, 3000fr, 10,000fr.

1997

1336-1339 A400 Set of 4 7.75 3.90

Souvenir Sheet

1340 A400 12,500fr Player, ball 6.50 3.25

No. 1340 contains one 42x60mm stamp.

Greenpeace, 25th Anniv. A401

Views of Rainbow Warrior I: 1500fr, At anchor. 3000fr, Under sail. 3500fr, Going left, small raft. 5000fr, Going forward at full speed.
12,500fr, Under sail, vert.

1996, Jan. 10 Litho. *Perf. 13½*

1341-1344 A401 Set of 4 5.40 2.70

Souvenir Sheet

1345 A401 12,500fr multicolored 5.40 2.70

Dinosaurs — A402

No. 1346: a, Herrerasaurus, archaeopteryx. b, Segnosaurus, dimorphodon. c, Sauropelta, proavis.
No. 1347: a, Eudimorphodon, eustreptospondylus. b, Triceratops, rhamphorychus. c, Pteranodon, segnosaurus.
12,500fr, Tenontosaurus, deinonychus, vert.

1998, Feb. 25

Sheets of 3

1346 A402 1350fr #a.-c. 2.25 1.10
1347 A402 5000fr #a.-c. 8.00 4.00

Souvenir Sheet

1348 A402 12,500fr multicolored 6.60 3.30

Dated 1997.

Meteorites and Minerals — A403

Meteorites: No. 1349: a, Iron, found in Chile. b, Iron, found in Alvord, Iowa. c, Silicate in lunar meteorite, found in Antarctica.
Minerals: No. 1350: a, Agate, dioptase. b, Malachite, granite. c, Chrysolite, wolfenite.
12,500fr, Mars meterorite, found in Antarctia.

1998, Feb. 25

Sheets of 3

1349 A403 3000fr #a.-c. 5.00 2.50
1350 A403 7500fr #a.-c. 12.00 6.00

Souvenir Sheet

1351 A403 12,500fr multicolored 6.60 3.30

Dated 1997.

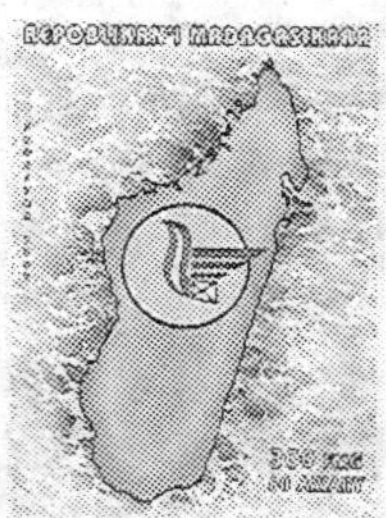

World Post Day — A404

1997 Litho. *Perf. 13½*

1352 A404 300fr multicolored 5.50 2.75

Diana, Princess of Wales (1961-97) A405

Portraits of Diana: No. 1354: a, Wearing jeweled necklace. b, With Pope John Paul II. c, Wearing beaded jacket. d, With Nelson Mandela. e, With man from India. f, With Emperor Akihito. g, Holding infant. h, Receiving flowers from child. i, Visiting sick child.
No. 1355, With Mother Teresa (in margin). No. 1356, With Princess Grace (in margin). No. 1357, With land mine victim.

1998, Feb. 18 Litho. *Perf. 13½*

1354 A405 1750fr Sheet of 9, #a.-i. 8.50 4.25

Souvenir Sheets

1355-1357 A405 12,500fr each 6.75 6.75

Nos. 1355-1357 each contain one 42x60mm stamp.
Numbers have been reserved for additional values in this set.

SEMI-POSTAL STAMPS

No. 84 Surcharged in Red **+5c**

1915, Feb. Unwmk. *Perf. 13½x14*

B1 A9 10c + 5c rose & brn .75 .75

Curie Issue
Common Design Type

1938, Oct. 24 *Perf. 13*

B2 CD80 1.75fr + 50c brt ultra 6.50 6.50

French Revolution Issue
Common Design Type
Name and Value Typographed in Black

1939, July 5 Photo.

B3	CD83	45c + 25c grn		5.50	5.50
B4	CD83	70c + 30c brn		5.50	5.50
B5	CD83	90c + 35c red org		5.50	5.50
B6	CD83	1.25fr + 1fr rose pink		5.50	5.50
B7	CD83	2.25fr + 2fr blue		5.50	5.50
		Nos. B3-B7 (5)		27.50	27.50

Common Design Type and

Malgache Sharpshooter — SP1

Tank Corpsman SP2

1941 Photo. *Perf. 13½*

B8	SP1	1fr + 1fr red	.80
B9	CD86	1.50fr + 3fr maroon	.80
B10	SP2	2.50fr + 1fr blue	1.00
		Nos. B8-B10 (3)	2.60

Nos. B8-B10 were issued by the Vichy government, and were not placed on sale in the colony.
Nos. 162 and 190 surcharged "SECOURS +50c NATIONAL," and Nos. 210A-210B surcharged "OEUVRES COLONIALES" and surtax (including change of denomination of the 2.50fr to 50c) were issued in 1942-44 by the Vichy government, and not placed on sale in the colony.

Catalogue values for unused stamps in this section, from this point to the end of the section, are for Never Hinged items.

Red Cross Issue
Common Design Type

1944 Unwmk. *Perf. 14½x14*

B15 CD90 5fr + 20fr dk grn .40 .40

The surtax was for the French Red Cross and national relief.

Gen. J. S. Galliéni and Malagasy Plowing — SP3

1946, Nov. Engr. *Perf. 13*
B16 SP3 10fr + 5fr dk vio brn .30 .30

50th anniv. of Madagascar's as a French Colony.

Tropical Medicine Issue
Common Design Type

1950, May 15
B17 CD100 10fr + 2fr dk Prus grn & brn vio 2.75 2.75

The surtax was for charitable work.

Malagasy Republic
No. 320 Surcharged in Ultramarine with New Value and: "FETES DE L'INDEPENDANCE"

1960, July 29 Engr. *Perf. 13*
B18 A38 20fr + 10fr red, blk & brt grn .40 .35

Anti-Malaria Issue
Common Design Type

1962, Apr. 7 *Perf. 12½x12*
B19 CD108 25fr + 5fr yel grn .50 .50

Post Office, Tamatave — SP4

1962, May 8 Engr. *Perf. 13*
B20 SP4 25fr + 5fr sl grn, bl & lt red brn .25 .25

Issued for Stamp Day, 1962.

Freedom from Hunger Issue
Common Design Type

1963, Mar. 21 *Perf. 13*
B21 CD112 25fr + 5fr red org, plum & brn .45 .45

FAO "Freedom from Hunger" campaign.

Type of 1962
20fr+5fr, Central Parcel P. O., Tananarive.

1963, May 8 Engr.
B22 SP4 20fr + 5fr bl grn & red brn .30 .30

Issued for Stamp Day, 1963.

Postal Savings and Checking Accounts Building, Tananarive — SP5

1964, May 8 Unwmk. *Perf. 13*
B23 SP5 25fr + 5fr bl, bis & dk grn .40 .40

Issued for Stamp Day, 1964.

No. 457 Surcharged in Violet Blue

+ 20^{F}
MEMORIAL

1972, June 26 Engr. *Perf. 13*
B24 A106 30fr + 20fr multi .40 .40

Charles de Gaulle memorial.

SP6 SP7

1989, June 15 Litho.
B25 SP6 80fr +20fr Torch bearer .20 .15

Village games.

1990, Aug. 7 Litho. *Perf. 12*
B26 SP7 100fr+20fr on 80fr+20fr .20 .15
B27 SP7 350fr+20fr on 250fr+20fr .60 .30

3rd Indian Ocean Games. Nos. B26-B27 were not issued without surcharge.

AIR POST STAMPS

Airplane and Map of Madagascar — AP1

Perf. 13x13½

1935-41 Photo. Unwmk.
C1 AP1 50c yel grn & red .50 .35
C2 AP1 90c yel grn & red ('41) .30
C3 AP1 1.25fr claret & red .35 .32
C4 AP1 1.50fr brt bl & red .35 .32
C5 AP1 1.60fr brt bl & red ('41) .15 .15
C6 AP1 1.75fr org & red 5.00 3.25
C7 AP1 2fr Prus bl & red .50 .32
C8 AP1 3fr dp org & red ('41) .15 .15
C9 AP1 3.65fr ol blk & red ('38) .35 .32
C10 AP1 3.90fr pck grn & red ('41) .15 .15
C11 AP1 4fr rose & red 27.50 2.00
C12 AP1 4.50fr blk & red 17.50 1.25
C13 AP1 5.50fr ol blk & red ('41) .25 .15
C14 AP1 6fr rose lil & red ('41) .25 .18
C15 AP1 6.90fr dl vio & red ('41) .15 .15
C16 AP1 8fr rose lil & red .60 .52
C17 AP1 8.50fr grn & red .70 .70
C18 AP1 9fr ol grn & red ('41) .35 .35
C19 AP1 12fr vio brn & red .60 .40
C20 AP1 12.50fr dl vio & red 1.25 .65
C21 AP1 15fr org yel & red ('41) .65 .45
C22 AP1 16fr ol grn & red 1.00 .85
C23 AP1 20fr dk brn & red 1.50 .85
C24 AP1 50fr brt ultra & red ('38) 2.50 2.00
Nos. C1,C3-C24 (23) 62.30 15.83

According to some authorities the 90c was not placed on sale in Madagascar.

V5

Stamps of type AP1, without "RF" monogram, and stamp of design shown above were issued in 1942 to 1944 by the Vichy Government, but were not placed on sale in the colony.

Air Post Stamps of 1935-38 Overprinted in Black

FRANCE LIBRE

1942 *Perf. 13x13½*
C27 AP1 1.50fr brt bl & red 3.25 3.25
C28 AP1 1.75fr org & red 50.00 50.00
C29 AP1 8fr rose lil & red .75 .75
C30 AP1 12fr vio brn & red 1.10 1.10
C31 AP1 12.50fr dl vio & red .80 .80
C32 AP1 16fr ol grn & red 3.25 3.25
C33 AP1 50fr brt ultra & red 2.50 2.50

FRANCE LIBRE

Nos. C3, C9, C17 Surcharged in Black

1,00 ×

C34 AP1 1fr on 1.25fr 2.75 2.75
C35 AP1 3fr on 3.65fr .65 .65
C36 AP1 8fr on 8.50fr .65 .65
Nos. C27-C36 (10) 65.70 65.70

Catalogue values for unused stamps in this section, from this point to the end of the section, are for Never Hinged items.

Common Design Type

1943 Photo. *Perf. 14½x14*
C37 CD87 1fr dk orange .15 .15
C38 CD87 1.50fr brt red .15 .15
C39 CD87 5fr brown red .15 .15
C40 CD87 10fr black .30 .20
C41 CD87 25fr ultra .50 .25
C42 CD87 50fr dk green .75 .40
C43 CD87 100fr plum 1.25 .50
Nos. C37-C43 (7) 3.25
Set value 1.50

Victory Issue
Common Design Type

Perf. 12½

1946, May 8 Unwmk. Engr.
C44 CD92 8fr brown red .40 .25

European victory of the Allied Nations in World War II.

Chad to Rhine Issue
Common Design Types

1946, June 6
C45 CD93 5fr brt blue 1.00 .60
C46 CD94 10fr dk car rose 1.00 .60
C47 CD95 15fr gray grn 1.00 .60
C48 CD96 20fr brown olive 1.25 .75
C49 CD97 25fr dk violet 1.25 .75
C50 CD98 50fr brown org 1.25 .75
Nos. C45-C50 (6) 6.75 4.05

Tamatave — AP2

Allegory of Air Mail — AP3

Plane over Map of Madagascar — AP4

Perf. 13½x12½, 12½x13½

1946 Photo. Unwmk.
C51 AP2 50fr bl vio & car .85 .50
C52 AP3 100fr brn & car 2.00 .75
C53 AP4 200fr bl grn & brn 4.25 2.00
Nos. C51-C53 (3) 7.10 3.25

No. C52 Overprinted in Carmine

TERRE ADÉLIE
DUMONT D'URVILLE
1840

1948, Oct. 26 *Perf. 12½x13½*
C54 AP3 100fr brn & car 30.00 32.50

Issued to publicize the French claim to Antarctic Adelie Land, discovered by Jules S. C. Dumont d'Urville in 1840.

UPU Issue
Common Design Type

1949, July 4 Engr. *Perf. 13*
C55 CD99 25fr multi 3.00 2.00

Scene Near Bemananga — AP5

1952, June 30 Unwmk. *Perf. 13*
C56 AP5 500fr brn, blk brn & dk grn 22.50 12.50

Liberation Issue
Common Design Type

1954, June 6
C57 CD102 15fr vio & vio brn 2.00 .65

Pachypodes — AP6

Designs: 100fr, Antsirabé viaduct, grey-headed gull. 200fr, Ring-tailed lemurs.

1954, Sept. 20
C58 AP6 50fr dk bl grn & dk grn 3.00 .15
C59 AP6 100fr dp ultra, blk & choc 5.00 .85
C60 AP6 200fr dk grn & sep 12.00 2.00
Nos. C58-C60 (3) 20.00 3.00

Malagasy Republic

Sugar Cane Harvest — AP7

Charaxes Antamboulou — AP8

Designs: 40fr, Tobacco field. 100fr, Chrysiridia Madagascariensis. 200fr, Argema mittrel, vert. 500fr, Mandrare bridge.

1960 Unwmk. Engr. *Perf. 13*
C61 AP7 30fr grn, vio brn & pale brn .42 .15
C62 AP7 40fr Prus grn & ol gray .65 .20
C63 AP8 50fr multi .70 .16
C64 AP8 100fr sl grn, emer & org 1.50 .22
C65 AP8 200fr pur & yel 2.25 .60
C66 AP7 500fr Prus grn, bis & ultra 5.50 1.50
Nos. C61-C66 (6) 11.02 2.83

Diademed Sifakas — AP9

Lemurs: 85fr, Indri. 250fr, Verreaux's sifaka.

1961, Dec. 9 Unwmk. *Perf. 13*

C67 AP9 65fr slate grn & red brn .65 .25
C68 AP9 85fr olive, blk & brn .80 .35
C69 AP9 250fr Prus grn, blk & mar 2.50 1.20
Nos. C67-C69 (3) 3.95 1.80

For surcharge see No. C90.

Plane over Nossi-Bé — AP10

1962, May 7 Engr. *Perf. 13*

C70 AP10 100fr red brn, bl & dk grn .70 .40
a. Souv. sheet of 5, #328-331, C70 1.50 1.50

1st Malagasy Philatelic Exhibition, Tananarive, May 5-13.

Turbojet Airliner, Emblem — AP11

1963, Apr. 18 Unwmk. *Perf. 13*

C71 AP11 500fr dk bl, red & grn 3.50 1.25

Madagascar commercial aviation.

Helmet Bird — AP12

Birds: 100fr, Pitta-like ground roller. 200fr, Crested wood ibis.

1963, Aug. 12 Photo. *Perf. 13x12½*

C72 AP12 40fr multi .35 .25
C73 AP12 100fr multi 1.00 .42
C74 AP12 200fr multi 2.00 .80
Nos. C72-C74 (3) 3.35 1.47

African Postal Union Issue
Common Design Type

1963, Sept. 8 *Perf. 12½*

C75 CD114 85fr grn, ocher & red 1.00 .70

Map of Madagascar, Jet Plane and UPU Emblem — AP13

1963, Nov. 2 Engr. *Perf. 13*

C76 AP13 45fr dk car, grnsh bl & ultra .40 .20
C77 AP13 85fr dk car, vio & bl .70 .40

Malagasy Republic's admission to the UPU, Nov. 2, 1961.

Meteorological Center, Tananarive and Tiros Satellite — AP14

1964, Mar. 23 Unwmk.

C78 AP14 90fr org brn, ultra & grn 1.20 .50

UN 4th World Meteorological Day, Mar. 23.

Zebu, Wood Sculpture — AP15

1964, Oct. 20 Engr. *Perf. 13*

C79 AP15 100fr lil rose, dk vio & brn .90 .62

Musical Instrument Type of Regular Issue

200fr, Lokanga bara (stringed instrument).

1965, Feb. 16 Unwmk. *Perf. 13*
Size: 26x47mm

C80 A57 200fr grn, org & choc 1.90 1.00

Nurse Weighing Infant, and ICY Emblem — AP16

Design: 100fr, Small boy and girl, child care scenes and ICY emblem.

1965, Sept. 20 Engr. *Perf. 13*

C81 AP16 50fr multi .42 .25
C82 AP16 100fr multi .80 .50

International Cooperation Year.

Dance Type of Regular Issue

250fr, Dance of a young girl, Sakalava, vert.

1966, June 13 Photo. *Perf. 13*
Size: 27x49mm

C83 A68 250fr multi 2.00 .80

Aviation Type of Regular Issue

Design: 500fr, Dagnaux-Dufert and his Bréguet biplane, 1927.

1967, Apr. 28 Engr. *Perf. 13*
Size: 48x27mm

C84 A76 500fr Prus bl, blk & brn 4.00 1.40

No. C84 for the 40th anniv. of the 1st Majunga-Tananarive flight.

African Postal Union Issue, 1967
Common Design Type

1967, Sept. 9 Engr. *Perf. 13*

C85 CD124 100fr ol bis, red brn & brt pink .80 .35

Dancer Type of Regular Issue

Designs: 100fr, Tourbillon dance, horiz. 200fr, Male dancer from the South.

1967-68 Photo. *Perf. 11½*
Size: 38x23mm

C86 A80 100fr multi ('68) .65 .38

Perf. 13
Size: 27x48mm

C87 A80 200fr multi 1.60 .70

Issue dates: 100fr, Nov. 25; 200fr, Nov. 25.

WHO Emblem, Bull's Head Totem and Palm Fan — AP17

1968, Apr. 7 Photo. *Perf. 12½x13*

C88 AP17 200fr bl, yel brn & red 1.50 .80

WHO, 20th anniv.; Intl. Congress of Medical Science, Apr. 2-12.

Tananarive-Ivato International Airport — AP18

1968, May 8 Engr. *Perf. 13*

C89 AP18 500fr lt red brn, dl bl & dl grn 3.75 2.00

Issued for Stamp Day.

No. C68 Surcharged in Vermilion with New Value and 2 Bars

1968, June 24 Engr. *Perf. 13*

C90 AP9 20fr on 85fr multi .16 .15

PHILEXAFRIQUE Issue

Lady Sealing Letter, by Jean Baptiste Santerre AP19

1968, Dec. 30 Photo. *Perf. 12½x12*

C91 AP19 100fr lilac & multi 1.10 .60

Issued to publicize PHILEXAFRIQUE Philatelic Exhibition in Abidjan, Feb. 14-23. Printed with alternating lilac label.

2nd PHILEXAFRIQUE Issue
Common Design Type

Design: 50fr, Madagascar No. 274, map of Madagascar and Malagasy emblem.

1969, Feb. 14 Engr. *Perf. 13*

C92 CD128 50fr gray, brn red & sl grn .60 .35

Sunset over Madagascar Highlands, by Henri Ratovo — AP20

Painting: 100fr, On the Seashore of the East Coast of Madagascar, by Alfred Razafinjohany.

1969, Nov. 5 Photo. *Perf. 12x12½*

C93 AP20 100fr brn & multi .80 .50
C94 AP20 150fr multi 1.20 .80

Lunar Landing Module and Man on the Moon — AP21

1970, July 20 Engr. *Perf. 13*

C95 AP21 75fr ultra, dk gray & sl grn .45 .38

1st anniv. of man's 1st landing on the moon.

Boeing 737 — AP22

1970, Dec. 18 Engr. *Perf. 13*

C96 AP22 200fr bl, red brn & grn 1.20 .65

Jean Ralaimongo (1884-1944) — AP23

Portraits: 40fr, René Rakotobe (1918-71). 65fr, Albert Sylla (1909-67). 100fr, Joseph Ravoahangy Andrianavalona (1893-1970).

1971-72 Photo. *Perf. 12½; 13 (40fr)*

C97 AP23 25fr red brn, org & blk .16 .15
C98 AP23 40fr dp cl, ocher & blk .22 .16
C99 AP23 65fr grn, lt grn & blk .35 .25
C100 AP23 100fr vio bl, lt bl & blk .60 .35
Nos. C97-C100 (4) 1.33 .91

Famous Malagasy men.

Issued: #C98, July 25, 1972; others, Oct. 14, 1971.

African Postal Union Issue, 1971

"Mpisikidy" by G. Rakotovao and UAMPT Building, Brazzaville, Congo — AP24

1971, Nov. 13 Photo. *Perf. 13x13½*

C105 AP24 100fr bl & multi .65 .42

10th anniv. of African and Malagasy Posts and Telecommunications Union (UAMPT).

Running, Olympic Village AP25

Design: 200fr, Judo, Olympic Stadium.

1972, Sept. 11 Photo. *Perf. 13½*

C106 AP25 100fr multi	.65	.35
C107 AP25 200fr multi	1.10	.55

20th Olympic Games, Munich, Aug. 26-Sept. 11.

Mohair Goat AP26

1972, Nov. 15

C108 AP26 250fr multi	1.90	1.00

Adoration of the Kings, by Andrea Mantegna — AP27

Christmas: 85fr, Virgin and Child, Florentine School, 15th century, vert.

1972, Dec. 15 Photo. *Perf. 13*

C109 AP27 85fr gold & multi	.50	.25
C110 AP27 150fr gold & multi	.90	.42

Landing Module, Astronauts and Lunar Rover — AP28

1973, Jan. 25 Engr. *Perf. 13*

C111 AP28 300fr dp cl, gray & brn	1.50	1.25

Apollo 17 moon mission, Dec. 7-19, 1972.

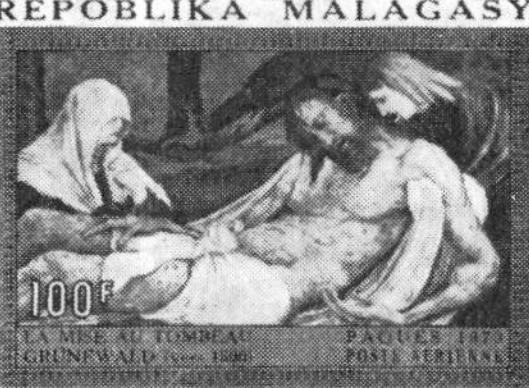

The Burial of Christ, by Grunewald — AP29

Easter: 200fr, Resurrection, by Mattias Grunewald, horiz. Both paintings from panels of Issenheim altar.

1973, Mar. 22 Photo. *Perf. 13*

C112 AP29 100fr gold & multi	.45	.25
C113 AP29 200fr gold & multi	1.00	.50

Early Excursion Car — AP30

Design: 150fr, Early steam locomotive.

1973, July 25 Photo. *Perf. 13x12½*

C114 AP30 100fr multi	.45	.25
C115 AP30 150fr multi	.70	.40

WMO Emblem, Radar, Map of Madagascar, Hurricane — AP31

Pres. John F. Kennedy, US Flag — AP32

1973, Sept. 3 Engr. *Perf. 13*

C116 AP31 100fr blk, ultra & org	.60	.30

Cent. of intl. meteorological cooperation.

Lemur Type of Regular Issue

Designs: 150fr, Lepilemur mustelinus, vert. 200fr, Cheirogaleus major.

1973, Oct. 9 Engr. *Perf. 13*

C117 A131 150fr multi	.90	.55
C118 A131 200fr multi	1.20	.80

1973, Nov. 22 Photo. *Perf. 13*

C119 AP32 300fr multi	1.60	1.00

10th anniv. of the death of John F. Kennedy.

Soccer — AP33

1973, Dec. 20 Engr. *Perf. 13*

C120 AP33 500fr lil rose, dk brn & org brn	3.00	2.00

World Soccer Cup, Munich, 1974.
For overprint see No. C130.

Copernicus, Skylab and Heliocentric System — AP34

1974, Jan. 22

C121 AP34 250fr multi	1.20	.45

500th anniversary of the birth of Nicolaus Copernicus (1473-1543), Polish astronomer.

Scout Type of Regular Issue

Designs (African Scout Emblem and): 100fr, Scouts bringing sick people to Red Cross tent, horiz. 300fr, Scouts fishing and fish, horiz.

1974, Feb. 14 Engr. *Perf. 13*

C122 A132 100fr multi	.55	.22
C123 A132 300fr multi	1.60	.70

Camellia, Hummingbird, Table Tennis Player — AP35

100fr, Girl player, flower and bird design.

1974, Mar. 19 Engr. *Perf. 13*

C124 AP35 50fr bl & multi	.25	.15
C125 AP35 100fr multi	.55	.25

Table Tennis Tournament, Peking.

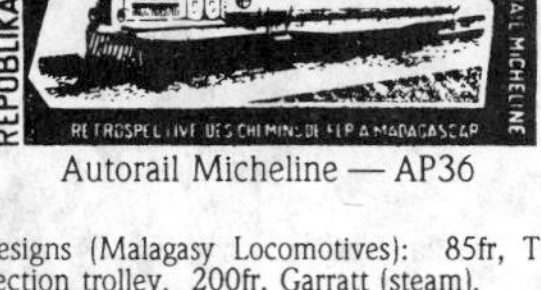

Autorail Micheline — AP36

Designs (Malagasy Locomotives): 85fr, Track inspection trolley. 200fr, Garratt (steam).

1974, June 7 Engr. *Perf. 13*

C126 AP36 50fr multi	.25	.16
C127 AP36 85fr multi	.42	.22
C128 AP36 200fr multi	1.10	.80
Nos. C126-C128 (3)	1.77	1.18

Letters and UPU Emblem — AP37

1974, July 9 Engr. *Perf. 13*

C129 AP37 250fr multi	1.40	.65

Centenary of Universal Postal Union.
For overprint see No. C133.

No. C120 Overprinted: "R.F.A. 2 / HOLLANDE 1"

1974, Aug. 20 Engr. *Perf. 13*

C130 AP33 500fr multi	2.50	1.50

World Cup Soccer Championship, 1974, victory of German Federal Republic.

Link-up in Space, Globe, Emblem — AP38

250fr, Link-up, globe and emblem, diff.

1974, Sept. 12

C131 AP38 150fr org, bl & slate grn	.80	.65
C132 AP38 250fr bl, brn & slate grn	1.40	.90

Russo-American space cooperation.
For overprints see Nos. C142-C143.

No. C129 Overprinted **100 ANS DE COLLABORATION INTERNATIONALE**

1974, Oct. 9 Engr. *Perf. 13*

C133 AP37 250fr multi	1.40	.65

100 years of international collaboration.

Adoration of the Kings, by J. L. David — AP39

Christmas: 300fr, Virgin of the Cherries and Child, by Quentin Massys.

1974, Dec. 20 Photo. *Perf. 13*

C134 AP39 200fr gold & multi	.90	.40
C135 AP39 300fr gold & multi	1.40	.60

UN Emblem and Globe — AP40

1975, June 24 Litho. *Perf. 12½*

C136 AP40 300fr grn, bl & blk	1.60	.80

United Nations Charter, 30th anniversary.

American Bicentennial Type, 1975

Designs: 100fr, Count d'Estaing and "Languedoc." 200fr, John Paul Jones, "Bonhomme Richard" and "Serapis." 300fr, Benjamin Franklin, "Millern" and "Montgomery." 500fr, George Washington and "Hanna."

1975, June 30 Litho. *Perf. 11*

C137 A144 100fr multi	.60	.25
C138 A144 200fr multi	1.20	.55
C139 A144 300fr multi	1.90	.80
Nos. C137-C139 (3)	3.70	1.60

Souvenir Sheet

C140 A144 500fr multi	3.25	1.50

For overprints see Nos. C164-C167.

Flower Type of 1975

Design: 85fr, Turraea sericea.

1975, Aug. 4 Photo. *Perf. 12½*

C141 A145 85fr dp grn, yel & org	.45	.35

Nos. C131-C132 Overprinted **JONCTION 17 JUILLET 1975**

1975, Aug. 5 Engr. *Perf. 13*

C142 AP38 150fr multi	.80	.40
C143 AP38 250fr multi	1.40	.65

Apollo Soyuz link-up in space, July 17, 1975.

Bas-relief and Stupas — AP41

1975, Aug. 10 Engr. *Perf. 13*

C144 AP41 50fr bl, car & bister	.25	.16

UNESCO campaign to save Borobudur Temple, Java.

Exposition Type, 1975

1975, Sept. 16 Litho. *Perf. 14x13½*

C145 A147 125fr Deer	.80	.45

Souvenir Sheet

C146 A147 300fr Jay	2.00	1.00

Hurdling and Olympic Rings — AP42

200fr, Weight lifting and Olympic rings, vert.

1975, Oct. 9 Litho. *Perf. 12½*

C147 AP42 75fr multi	.40	.20
C148 AP42 200fr multi	1.10	.55

Pre-Olympic Year 1975.

12th Winter Olympics Type, 1975

Designs: 200fr, Cross-country skiing. 245fr, Down-hill skiing. 450fr, Figure skating, pairs.

1975, Nov. 19 *Perf. 14*

C149 A149 200fr multi	1.25	.55
C150 A149 245fr multi	1.50	.65

Souvenir Sheet

C151 A149 450fr multi	3.00	1.50

For overprints see Nos. C161-C163.

Landing Module, Apollo 14 Emblem — AP43

1976, Jan. 18 Engr. *Perf. 13*

C152 AP43 150fr red, grn & indigo .80 .40

Apollo 14 moon landing, 5th anniversary.
For overprint see No. C157.

21st Summer Olympics Type, 1976

Designs: 100fr, Shot-put and long jump. 200fr, Gymnastics, horse and balance bar. 300fr, Diving, 3-meter and platform. 500fr, Swimming, free-style and breast stroke.

1976, Jan. 21 Litho. *Perf. 13½*

C153 A151 100fr multi	.60	.28
C154 A151 200fr multi	1.25	.62
C155 A151 300fr multi	1.90	.80
Nos. C153-C155 (3)	3.75	1.70

Souvenir Sheet

C156 A151 500fr multi 3.25 1.50

For overprints see Nos. C168-C171.

No. C152 Overprinted: "5e Anniversaire / de la mission / APOLLO XIV"

1976, Feb. 5 Engr. *Perf. 13*

C157 AP43 150fr red, grn & indigo .80 .40

Apollo 14 moon landing, 5th anniversary.

Zeppelin Type of 1976

Designs (Count Zeppelin and LZ-127 over): 200fr, Brandenburg Gate, Berlin 300fr, Parliament, London. 450fr, St. Peter's Cathedral, Rome.

1976, Mar. 3 Litho. *Perf. 11*

C158 A152 200fr multi	1.40	.60
C159 A152 300fr multi	1.60	.90

Souvenir Sheet

C160 A152 450fr multi 3.00 1.40

Nos. C149-C151 Overprinted

a. VAINQUEUR IVAR FORMO NORVEGE
b. VAINQUEUR ROSI MITTERMAIER ALLEMAGNE DE L'OUEST
c. VAINQUEUR IRINA RODNINA ALEXANDER ZAITSEV URSS

1976, June 17

C161 A149 (a) 200fr multi	.85	.45
C162 A149 (b) 245fr multi	1.00	.50

Souvenir Sheet

C163 A149 (c) 450fr multi 1.75 1.20

12th Winter Olympic games winners.

Nos. C137-C140 Overprinted "4 Juillet / 1776-1976"

1976, July 4

C164 A144 100fr multi	.65	.25
C165 A144 200fr multi	1.25	.55
C166 A144 300fr multi	1.90	.80
Nos. C164-C166 (3)	3.80	1.60

Souvenir Sheet

C167 A144 500fr multi 3.25 1.60

American Bicentennial.

Nos. C153-C156 Overprinted

a. U. BEYER / A. ROBINSON
b. N. ANDRIANOV / N. COMANECI
c. K. DIBIASI / E. VAYTSEKHOVSKAIA,
d. J. MONTGOMERY / H. ANKE

1977, Jan.

C168 A151 (a) 100fr multi	.62	.25
C169 A151 (b) 200fr multi	1.20	.55
C170 A151 (c) 300fr multi	1.75	.80
Nos. C168-C170 (3)	3.57	1.60

Souvenir Sheet

C171 A151 (d) 500fr multi 3.25 1.60

21st Summer Olympic Games winners.

Fauna Type of 1979

1979, July 6

C172 A176 20fr Tortoises	.15	.15
C173 A176 95fr Macaco lemurs	.62	.22
Set value		.36

International Palestinian Solidarity Day — AP44

1979, Nov. 29 Litho. *Perf. 12x12½*

C174 AP44 60fr multi .40 .16

Olympic Type of 1980

1980, Dec. 29 Litho. *Perf. 12½x12*

C175 A188 250fr Judo	1.60	.70
C176 A188 500fr Swimming	3.50	1.50

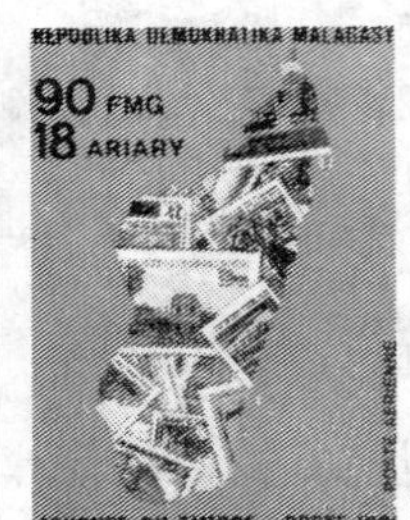

Stamp Day — AP45

1981, Dec. 17 Litho. *Perf. 12x12½*

C177 AP45 90fr multi .60 .22

20th Anniv. of Pan-African Women's Org. — AP46

1982, Aug. 6 Litho. *Perf. 12*

C178 AP46 80fr dk brn & lt brn .55 .22

Hydroelectric Plant, Andekaleka — AP47

1982, Sept. 13 *Perf. 12½x12*

C179 AP47 80fr multi .55 .22

Orchid Type of 1984

1984, Nov. 20 Litho. *Perf. 12*

C180 A226 50fr Eulophiella elisabethae, horiz.	.15	.15
C181 A226 50fr Grammangis ellisii, horiz.	.15	.15
C182 A226 50fr Grammangis spectabilis	.15	.15
Nos. C180-C182 (3)	.45	
Set value		.20

Solar Princess, by Sadiou Diouf AP48

1984, Dec. 22 Litho. *Perf. 12*

C183 AP48 100fr multi .30 .15

Intl. Civil Aviation Org., 40th anniv.

Halley's Comet AP49

1986, Apr. 5 Litho. *Perf. 12½x13*

C184 AP49 150fr multi .50 .25

Admission of Madagascar into the UPU, 25th Anniv. — AP50

1986, Dec. 23 Litho. *Perf. 11½*

C185 AP50 150fr multi .50 .25

Air Madagascar, 25th Anniv. AP51

1987, June 17 Litho. *Perf. 12x12½*

C186 AP51 60fr Piper Aztec	.22	.15
C187 AP51 60fr Twin Otter	.22	.15
C188 AP51 150fr Boeing 747	.60	.28
Nos. C186-C188 (3)	1.04	
Set value		.48

Socialist Revolution, 15th Anniv. — AP52

1990, June 16 Litho. *Perf. 13½*

C189 AP52 100fr Map	.16	.15
C190 AP52 350fr Architecture	.58	.30
Set value		.38

Madagascan Bible Society, 25th Anniv. AP53

1990, Sept. 17 *Perf. 12½*

C191 AP53 25fr lt bl & multi	.15	.15
C192 AP53 100fr bl, blk & grn, vert.	.16	.15
Set value	.20	.15

Stamp Day — AP54

1990, Oct. 9 Litho. *Perf. 13x12½*

C193 AP54 350fr multicolored .60 .30

AP55

AP56

1992, June 5 Litho. *Perf. 12½*

C194 AP55 140fr multicolored .25 .15

World Environment Day.

1992, Oct. 9 Litho. *Perf. 13½*

C195 AP56 500fr multicolored .68 .35

World Post Day.

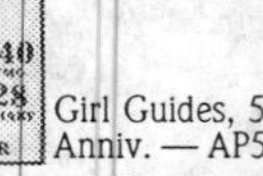

Girl Guides, 50th Anniv. — AP57

1993 Litho. *Perf. 11½*

C196 AP57 140fr multicolored .22 .15

AP58

AP59

1993, Nov. 20 Litho. *Perf. 12*

C197 AP58 500fr multicolored .60 .30

African Industrialization Day.

1994 Litho. *Perf. 11½x11, 11x11½*

C198 AP59 140fr shown	.20	.15
C199 AP59 500fr Logo, vert.	.70	.35

Zone A conference.

Madagascar Hilton, 25th Anniv. AP60

1995, Oct. 8 Litho. *Perf. 13½*

C200 AP60 500fr black, blue & bister .60 .60

15-Cent Minimum Value

The minimum catalogue value is 15 cents. Separating se-tenant pieces into individual stamps does not increase the value of the stamps since demand for the separated stamps may be small.

AIR POST SEMI-POSTAL STAMPS

French Revolution Issue
Common Design Type
Unwmk.

1939, July 5 Photo. *Perf. 13*
Name and Value in Orange

CB1	CD83	4.50fr + 4fr brn blk	8.00	8.00

V6

V7

V8

Stamps of the designs shown above, and type of Cameroun V10 inscribed "Madagascar", were issued in 1942 by the Vichy Government, but were not placed on sale in the colony.

POSTAGE DUE STAMPS

D1

Governor's Palace — D2

Postage Due Stamps of French Colonies Overprinted in Red or Blue

1896 Unwmk. *Imperf.*

J1	D1 5c blue (R)		5.00	5.00
J2	D1 10c brown (R)		5.00	5.00
J3	D1 20c yellow (Bl)		5.00	6.00
J4	D1 30c rose red (Bl)		5.00	6.00
J5	D1 40c lilac (R)		55.00	35.00
J6	D1 50c gray vio (Bl)		7.50	8.00
J7	D1 1fr dk grn (R)		60.00	50.00
	Nos. J1-J7 (7)		142.50	115.00

1908-24 Typo. *Perf. 13¹/₂x14*

J8	D2 2c vio brn	.15	.15
J9	D2 4c violet	.15	.15
J10	D2 5c green	.15	.15
J11	D2 10c deep rose	.15	.15
J12	D2 20c olive green	.15	.15
J13	D2 40c brn, *straw*	.15	.15
J14	D2 50c brn, *bl*	.15	.15
J15	D2 60c orange ('24)	.35	.35
J16	D2 1fr dark blue	.45	.45
	Set value	1.25	1.25

Type of 1908 Issue Surcharged **60c**

1924-27

J17	D2 60c on 1fr org	1.50	1.50

Surcharged **2f**

J18	D2 2fr on 1fr lil rose ('27)	.75	.75
J19	D2 3fr on 1fr ultra ('27)	.75	.75

Postage Due Stamps of 1908-27 Overprinted or Surcharged in Black

FRANCE LIBRE

1943 *Perf. 13¹/₂x14*

J20	D2 10c dp rose	.60	.60
J21	D2 20c olive grn	.60	.60
J22	D2 30c on 5c green	.60	.60
J23	D2 40c brn, *straw*	.60	.60
J24	D2 50c brn, *blue*	.60	.60
J25	D2 60c orange	.60	.60
J26	D2 1fr dark blue	.60	.60
J27	D2 1fr on 2c vio brn	2.25	2.25
J28	D2 2fr on 1fr lil rose	.60	.60
J29	D2 2fr on 4c vio	.90	.90
J30	D2 3fr on 1fr ultra	.60	.60
	Nos. J20-J30 (11)	8.55	8.55

Catalogue values for unused stamps in this section, from this point to the end of the section, are for Never Hinged items.

D3

Independence Monument — D4

1947 Photo. *Perf. 13*

J31	D3 10c dk violet	.15	.15
J32	D3 30c brown	.15	.15
J33	D3 50c dk bl grn	.15	.15
J34	D3 1fr dp orange	.15	.15
J35	D3 2fr red violet	.15	.15
J36	D3 3fr red brown	.15	.15
J37	D3 4fr blue	.75	.25
J38	D3 5fr henna brown	1.00	.30
J39	D3 10fr slate green	1.25	.45
J40	D3 20fr vio blue	2.25	.80
	Nos. J31-J40 (10)	6.15	
	Set value		2.30

Malagasy Republic
Engraved; Denomination Typographed

1962, May 7 Unwmk. *Perf. 13*

J41	D4 1fr brt green	.15	.15
J42	D4 2fr copper brn	.15	.15
J43	D4 3fr brt violet	.15	.15
J44	D4 4fr slate	.15	.15
J45	D4 5fr red	.15	.15
J46	D4 10fr yellow grn	.15	.15
J47	D4 20fr dull claret	.20	.15
J48	D4 40fr blue	.45	.38
J49	D4 50fr rose red	.70	.65
J50	D4 100fr black	1.40	1.20
	Set value	3.00	2.65

MALAWI

mə-'lä-wē

LOCATION — Southeast Africa
GOVT. — Republic in British Commonwealth
AREA — 36,100 sq. mi.
POP. — 5,530,000 (est. 1977)
CAPITAL — Lilongwe

The British Protectorate of Nyasaland became the independent state of Malawi on July 6, 1964, and a republic on July 6, 1966.

12 Pence = 1 Shilling
20 Shillings = 1 Pound
100 Tambalas = 1 Kwacha (1970)

Catalogue values for all unused stamps in this country are for Never Hinged items.

Watermark

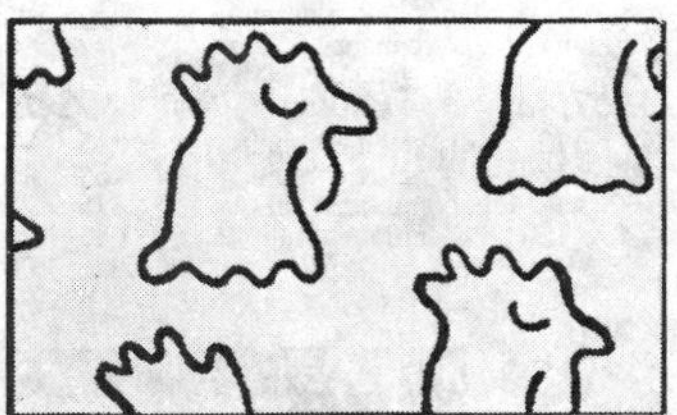
Wmk. 357- Multiple Cockerel

Dr. H. Kamuzu Banda and Independence Monument — A1

Prime Minister Banda and: 6p, Sun rising from lake. 1sh3p, National flag. 2sh6p, Coat of Arms.

Perf. 14¹/₂
1964, July 6 Unwmk. Photo.

1	A1	3p dk gray & lt ol green	.15	.15
2	A1	6p car rose, red, gold & bl	.15	.15
3	A1	1sh3p dull vio, blk, red & grn	.18	.18
4	A1	2sh6p multicolored	.40	.40
		Set value	.70	.70

Malawi's independence, July 6, 1964.

Mother and Child — A2

Designs: 1p, Chambo fish. 2p, Zebu bull. 3p, Peanuts. 4p, Fishermen in boat. 6p, Harvesting tea. 9p, Tung nut, flower and leaves. 1sh, Lumber and tropical pine branch. 1sh3p, Tobacco drying and Turkish tobacco plant. 2sh6p, Cotton industry. 5sh, Monkey Bay, Lake Nyasa. 10sh, Afzelia tree (pod mahogany). £1, Nyala antelope, vert.

1964, July 6
Size: 23x19mm

5	A2	¹/₂p lilac	.15	.15
6	A2	1p green & black	.15	.15
7	A2	2p red brown	.15	.15
8	A2	3p pale brn, brn red & grn	.15	.15
9	A2	4p org yel & indigo	.15	.15

Size: 41¹/₂x25, 25x41¹/₂mm

10	A2	6p bl, vio bl & brt yel grn	.25	.15
11	A2	9p grn, yel & brn	.30	.25
12	A2	1sh yel, brn & dk green	.35	.25
13	A2	1sh3p red brn & olive	.40	.30
14	A2	2sh6p blue & brown	.50	.50
15	A2	5sh "Monkey Bay-Lake Nyasa"	2.00	1.50
16	A2	10sh org brn, grn & gray	2.25	2.00
17	A2	£1 yel & dk brn	5.00	3.50
		Nos. 5-17 (13)	11.80	9.20

See #26, 41-51. For surcharges see #27-28.

Star of Bethlehem over World — A3

1964, Dec. 1 Photo. *Perf. 14¹/₂*

18	A3	3p brt green & gold	.15	.15
19	A3	6p lilac rose & gold	.15	.15
20	A3	1sh3p lilac & gold	.25	.25
21	A3	2sh6p ultra & gold	.50	.50
a.		Souvenir sheet of 4	1.50	1.50
		Nos. 18-21 (4)	1.05	1.05

Christmas. No. 21a contains Nos. 18-21 with simulated perforations.

Sixpence, Shilling, Florin and Half-Crown Coins — A4

1965, Mar. 1 Unwmk. *Perf. 13x13¹/₂*
Coins in Silver and Black

22	A4	3p green	.15	.15
23	A4	9p rose	.15	.15
a.		Silver omitted		
24	A4	1sh6p rose violet	.25	.25
25	A4	3sh dark blue	.50	.50
a.		Souvenir sheet of 4	1.50	1.40
		Nos. 22-25 (4)	1.05	1.05

First coinage of Malawi. No. 25a contains Nos. 22-25 with simulated perforations. Sold for 6sh.

Type of 1964 Redrawn

1965, June 1 Photo. *Perf. 14¹/₂*

26	A2	5sh "Monkey Bay-Lake Malawi"	1.25	1.00

Nos. 13-14 Surcharged with New Value and Two Bars

1965, June 14

27	A2	1sh6p on 1sh3p	.20	.20
28	A2	3sh on 2sh6p	.35	.35

John Chilembwe, Rebels and Church at Mbwombwe — A5

1965, Aug. 20 Photo. *Perf. 14¹/₂*

29	A5	3p yel grn & purple	.15	.15
30	A5	9p red org & olive	.15	.15
31	A5	1sh6p dk blue & red brn	.20	.20
32	A5	3sh dull bl & green	.40	.40
a.		Souvenir sheet of 4, #29-32	6.25	5.25
		Nos. 29-32 (4)	.90	.90

50th anniversary of the revolution of Jan. 23, 1915, led by John Chilembwe (1871-1915), missionary.

Microscope and Open Book — A6

1965, Oct. 6 *Perf. 14*

33	A6	3p emer & slate	.15	.15
34	A6	9p brt rose & slate	.15	.15
35	A6	1sh6p purple & slate	.20	.20
36	A6	3sh ultra & slate	.35	.35
a.		Souvenir sheet of 4, #33-36	4.25	4.25
		Set value	.70	.70

Opening of the University of Malawi in temporary quarters in Chichiri secondary school, Blantyre. The University will be located in Zomba.

African Danaine A7

Designs: Various butterflies.

Perf. 13x13¹/₂
1966, Feb. 15 Unwmk.

37	A7	4p multicolored	.30	.20
38	A7	9p multicolored	.75	.60
39	A7	1sh6p lil, blk & blue	1.50	1.25
40	A7	3sh blue, dk brn & bis	3.50	2.50
a.		Souvenir sheet of 4, #37-40	16.00	12.50
		Nos. 37-40 (4)	6.05	4.55

See No. 51.

Type of 1964

Designs: 1sh6p, Curing tobacco and Burley tobacco plant. £2, Cyrestis camillus sublineatus (butterfly). Other designs as in 1964.

Perf. 14½

1966-67 Photo. Wmk. 357

Size: 23x19mm

41 A2 ½p lilac .15 .15
42 A2 1p green & black .15 .15
43 A2 2p red brown ('67) .15 .15
44 A2 3p multi ('67) .18 .15

Size: 41½x25mm

45 A2 6p blue, vio bl & brt yel grn ('67) .45 .15
46 A2 9p grn, yel & brn ('67) .52 .25
47 A2 1sh yel, brn & dk green .58 .28
48 A2 1sh6p choc & emer .95 .58
49 A2 5sh multi ('67) 6.50 2.25
50 A2 10sh org brn, grn & gray ('67) 10.50 5.25
51 A2 £2 dl vio, yel & blk 29.00 22.00
Nos. 41-51 (11) 49.13 31.36

British Central Africa Stamp 1891 — A8

President Kamuzu Banda — A9

1966, May 4 *Perf. 14½*

54 A8 4p yel grn & sl blue .15 .15
55 A8 9p dull rose & sl blue .15 .15
56 A8 1sh6p lil & slate blue .25 .25
57 A8 3sh blue & slate blue .50 .50
a. Souvenir sheet of 4, #54-57 4.50 3.00
Nos. 54-57 (4) 1.05 1.05

Postal service, 75th anniv.

Perf. 14x14½

1966, July 6 Wmk. 357

58 A9 4p green, sil & brn .15 .15
59 A9 9p magenta, sil & brn .15 .15
60 A9 1sh6p violet, sil & brn .20 .20
61 A9 3sh blue, sil & brn .40 .40
a. Souvenir sheet of 4, #58-61 2.50 1.75
Nos. 58-61 (4) .90 .90

Republic Day, July 6, 1966; 2nd anniv. of Independence.

Star over Bethlehem A10

1966, Oct. 12 Photo. *Perf. 14½x14*

63 A10 4p deep green & gold .15 .15
64 A10 9p plum & gold .20 .20
65 A10 1sh6p orange & gold .25 .25
66 A10 3sh deep blue & gold .50 .50
Nos. 63-66 (4) 1.10 1.10

Christmas.

Ilala I, 1875 A11

Steamers on Lake Malawi: 9p, Dove, 1892. 1sh6p, Chauncey Maples, 1901. 3sh, Guendolen, 1899.

1967, Jan. 4 *Perf. 14½x14*

67 A11 4p emer, black & yel .15 .15
a. Yellow omitted —
68 A11 9p car rose, blk & yellow .30 .25
69 A11 1sh6p lt vio, blk & red .60 .50
70 A11 3sh ultra, black & red 1.50 1.00
Nos. 67-70 (4) 2.55 1.90

Pseudotropheus Auratus — A12

Fish of Lake Malawi: 9p, Labeotropheus trewavasae. 1sh6p, Pseudotropheus zebra. 3sh, Pseudotropheus tropheops.

1967, May 3 Photo. *Perf. 12½x12*

71 A12 4p green & multi .15 .15
72 A12 9p ocher & multi .35 .15
73 A12 1sh6p multicolored .75 .25
74 A12 3sh ultra & multi 1.50 1.25
Nos. 71-74 (4) 2.75 1.80

Rising Sun and Cogwheel A13

Perf. 13½x13

1967, July 5 Litho. Unwmk.

75 A13 4p black & brt grn .15 .15
76 A13 9p black & car rose .15 .15
77 A13 1sh6p black & brt pur .20 .20
78 A13 3sh black & brt ultra .30 .30
a. Souvenir sheet of 4, #75-78 1.25 1.25
Nos. 75-78 (4) .80 .80

Malawi industrial development.

Nativity — A14

Perf. 14x14½

1967, Oct. 12 Photo. Wmk. 357

79 A14 4p vio blue & green .15 .15
80 A14 9p vio blue & red .15 .15
81 A14 1sh6p vio blue & yel .20 .20
82 A14 3sh bright blue .30 .30
a. Souvenir sheet of 4, #79-82, perf. 14x13½ 1.75 1.75
Nos. 79-82 (4) .80 .80

Christmas.

Calotropis Procera A15

Wild Flowers: 9p, Borreria dibrachiata. 1sh6p, Hibiscus rhodanthus. 3sh, Bidens pinnatipartita.

1968, Apr. 24 Litho. *Perf. 13½x13*

83 A15 4p green & multi .15 .15
84 A15 9p pale green & multi .20 .20
85 A15 1sh6p lt green & multi .35 .35
86 A15 3sh brt blue & multi .65 .65
a. Souvenir sheet of 4, #83-86 2.50 2.50
Nos. 83-86 (4) 1.35 1.35

Thistle No. 1, 1902 A16

Locomotives: 9p, G-class steam engine, 1954. 1sh6p, "Zambesi" diesel locomotive No. 202, 1963. 3sh, Diesel rail car No. 1, 1955.

1968, July 24 Photo. *Perf. 14x14½*

87 A16 4p gray grn & multi .20 .20
88 A16 9p red & multi .50 .50
89 A16 1sh6p cream & multi 1.00 1.00
90 A16 3sh lt ultra & multi 2.00 2.00
a. Souv. sheet of 4, #87-90, perf. 14 5.00 5.00
Nos. 87-90 (4) 3.70 3.70

Nativity, by Piero della Francesca A17

Paintings: 9p, Adoration of the Shepherds, by Murillo. 1sh6p, Adoration of the Shepherds, by Guido Reni. 3sh, Nativity with God the Father and the Holy Ghost, by Giovanni Batista Pittoni.

1968, Nov. 6 Photo. Wmk. 357

91 A17 4p black & multi .15 .15
92 A17 9p multicolored .15 .15
93 A17 1sh6p multicolored .25 .25
94 A17 3sh blue & multi .35 .35
a. Souvenir sheet of 4, #91-94, perf. 14x13½ 1.00 1.00
Nos. 91-94 (4) .90 .90

Christmas.

Scarlet-chested Sunbird A18

Nyasa Lovebird A19

Birds: 2p, Violet-backed starling. 3p, White-browed robin-chat. 4p, Red-billed firefinch. 9p, Yellow bishop. 1sh, Southern carmine bee-eater. 1sh6p, Grayheaded bush shrike. 2sh, Paradise whydah. 3sh, African paradise flycatcher. 5sh, Bateleur. 10sh, Saddlebill. £1, Purple heron. £2, Livingstone's lorie.

1968, Nov. 13 *Perf. 14½*

Size: 23x19, 19x23mm

95 A18 1p multicolored .15 .15
96 A18 2p multicolored .20 .15
97 A18 3p multicolored .25 .15
98 A18 4p multicolored .40 .15
99 A19 6p multicolored .60 .25
100 A19 9p multicolored .75 .30

Perf. 14

Size: 42x25, 25x42mm

101 A18 1sh multicolored .90 .50
102 A18 1sh6p multicolored 1.75 .80
103 A18 2sh multicolored 2.75 1.25
104 A19 3sh multicolored 4.00 2.25
105 A19 5sh multicolored 5.00 3.50
106 A19 10sh multicolored 8.50 6.00
107 A19 £1 multicolored 17.50 12.00
109 A18 £2 multicolored 27.50 25.00
Nos. 95-109 (14) 70.25 52.45

No. 104 was surcharged "30t Special United Kingdom Delivery Service" in 5 lines and issued Feb. 8, 1971, during the British postal strike. The 30t was to pay a private postal service.

See Nos. 136-137. For overprint see No. 131.

ILO Emblem A20

Photo., Gold Impressed (Emblem)

Perf. 14x14½

1969, Feb. 5 Wmk. 357

110 A20 4p deep green .15 .15
111 A20 9p dk rose brown .15 .15
112 A20 1sh6p dark gray .20 .20
113 A20 3sh dark blue .30 .30
a. Souvenir sheet of 4, #110-113 3.00 3.00
Nos. 110-113 (4) .80 .80

ILO, 50th anniversary.

White Fringed Ground Orchid A21

Malawi Orchids: 9p, Red ground orchid. 1sh6p, Leopard tree orchid. 3sh, Blue ground orchid.

1969, July 9 Litho. *Perf. 13½*

114 A21 4p gray & multi .20 .15
115 A21 9p gray & multi .25 .25
116 A21 1sh6p gray & multi .50 .50
117 A21 3sh gray & multi 1.00 1.00
a. Souvenir sheet of 4, #114-117 1.75 1.75
Nos. 114-117 (4) 1.95 1.90

African Development Bank Emblem — A22

1969, Sept. 10 *Perf. 14*

118 A22 4p multicolored .15 .15
119 A22 9p multicolored .15 .15
120 A22 1sh6p multicolored .20 .20
121 A22 3sh multicolored .30 .30
a. Souvenir sheet of 4, #118-121 1.00 1.00
Nos. 118-121 (4) .80 .80

African Development Bank, 5th anniv.

"Peace on Earth" — A23

1969, Nov. 5 Photo. *Perf. 14x14½*

122 A23 2p citron & blk .15 .15
123 A23 4p Prus blue & blk .15 .15
124 A23 9p scarlet & blk .15 .15
125 A23 1sh6p purple & blk .20 .20
126 A23 3sh ultra & blk .30 .30
a. Souvenir sheet of 5, #122-126 1.25 1.25
Nos. 122-126 (5) .95 .95

Christmas.

Elegant Grasshopper A24

Runner A25

Insects: 9p, Bean blister beetle. 1sh6p, Pumpkin ladybird. 3sh, Praying mantis.

1970, Feb. 4 Litho. *Perf. 14x14½*

127 A24 4p multicolored .15 .15
128 A24 9p multicolored .20 .20
129 A24 1sh6p multicolored .35 .35
130 A24 3sh multicolored .65 .65
a. Souvenir sheet of 4, #127-130 2.25 2.25
Nos. 127-130 (4) 1.35 1.35

No. 102 Overprinted:
"Rand Easter Show / 1970"

1970, Mar. 18 Photo. *Perf. 14*

131 A18 1sh6p multicolored .50 .50

75th Anniversary Rand Easter Show, Johannesburg, South Africa, Mar. 24-Apr. 6.

1970, June 3 Litho. *Perf. 13*

132 A25 4p green & dk blue .15 .15
133 A25 9p rose & dk bl .15 .15
134 A25 1sh6p dull yel & dk bl .20 .20
135 A25 3sh blue & dk blue .30 .30
a. Souvenir sheet of 4, #132-135 1.00 1.00
Nos. 132-135 (4) .80 .80

9th Commonwealth Games, Edinburgh, Scotland, July 16-25.

Dual Currency Issue

Bird Type of 1968 with Denominations in Tambalas

Designs: 10t/1sh, Southern carmine bee-eater. 20t/2sh, Paradise whydah.

1970, Sept. 2 Photo. *Perf. 14½*

Size: 42x25mm

136 A18 10t/1sh multicolored .75 .40
137 A18 20t/2sh multicolored 1.25 1.25

Aegocera Trimenii A26

Moths of Malawi: 9p, Epiphora bauhiniae. 1sh6p, Parasa karschi. 3sh, Teracotona euprepia.

Perf. 11x11½

1970, Sept. 30 Wmk. 357

138 A26 4p multicolored .15 .15
139 A26 9p multicolored .35 .30
140 A26 1sh6p lt vio & multi .70 .65
141 A26 3sh multicolored 1.50 1.25
a. Souvenir sheet of 4, #138-141 5.00 5.00
Nos. 138-141 (4) 2.70 2.35

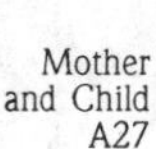
Mother and Child A27

1970, Nov. 4 Litho. *Perf. 14½*

142 A27 2p black & yel .15 .15
143 A27 4p black & emer .15 .15
144 A27 9p black & dp org .20 .20
145 A27 1sh6p black & red lil .25 .25
146 A27 3sh black & ultra .30 .30
a. Souv. sheet of 5, #142-146 + label 1.25 1.25
Nos. 142-146 (5) 1.05 1.05

Christmas.

Decimal Currency

Greater Kudu — A28 Eland — A29

Antelopes: 2t, Nyala. 3t, Reedbuck. 5t, Puku. 8t, Impala. 15t, Klipspringer. 20t, Livingstone's suni. 30t, Roan antelope. 50t, Waterbuck. 1k, Bushbuck. 2k, Red duiker. 4k, Gray bush duiker.

Perf. 13½x14 (A28), 14x14½ (A29)

1971, Feb. 15 Litho. Wmk. 357

148 A28 1t dull vio & multi .15 .15
a. Perf. 14½x14, coil .15 .15
b. Perf. 14 ('74) .20 .15
149 A28 2t dp yel & multi .15 .15
150 A28 3t ap grn & multi .15 .15
a. Perf. 14 ('74) .30 .30
151 A28 5t multicolored .20 .15
a. Perf. 14 ('74) .40 .30
152 A28 8t org red & multi .30 .20
153 A29 10t green & multi .35 .30
154 A29 15t brt pur & multi .60 .35
155 A29 20t bl gray & multi .75 .40
156 A29 30t dull blue & multi 1.25 .60
157 A29 50t multicolored 2.00 .75
158 A29 1k multicolored 3.00 1.25
159 A29 2k gray & multi 6.00 3.00
160 A29 4k multicolored 20.00 15.00
Nos. 148-160 (13) 34.90 22.45

Decimal Coins A30

1971, Feb. 15 *Perf. 14½*

161 A30 3t multicolored .15 .15
162 A30 8t dull red & multi .15 .15
163 A30 15t purple & multi .30 .30
164 A30 30t brt blue & multi .50 .50
a. Souvenir sheet of 4, #161-164 1.75 1.75
Nos. 161-164 (4) 1.10 1.10

Introduction of decimal currency and coinage.

Christ on the Cross, by Dürer — A31

Design: Nos. 166, 168, 170, 172, The Resurrection, by Albrecht Dürer.

1971, Apr. 7 Litho. *Perf. 14x13½*

165 A31 3t emerald & black .15 .15
166 A31 3t emerald & black .15 .15
a. Pair, #165-166 .15 .15
167 A31 8t orange & black .15 .15
168 A31 8t orange & black .15 .15
a. Pair, #167-168 .20 .20
169 A31 15t red lilac & black .20 .20
170 A31 15t red lilac & black .20 .20
a. Pair, #169-170 .40 .40
171 A31 30t blue & black .30 .30
a. Souv. sheet of 4, #165, 167, 169, 171 1.75 1.75
172 A31 30t blue & black .30 .30
a. Souv. sheet of 4, #166, 168, 170, 172 1.75 1.75
b. Pair, #171-172 .60 .60
Nos. 165-172 (8) 1.60 1.60

Easter. Printed checkerwise in sheets of 25.

Holarrhena Febrifuga — A32 Drum Major — A33

Flowering Shrubs and Trees: 8t, Brachystegia spiciformis. 15t, Securidaca longepedunculata. 30t, Pterocarpus rotundifolius.

1971, July 14 Litho. Wmk. 357

173 A32 3t gray & multi .15 .15
174 A32 8t gray & multi .15 .15
175 A32 15t gray & multi .30 .30
176 A32 30t gray & multi .60 .60
a. Souvenir sheet of 4, #173-176 2.00 2.00
Nos. 173-176 (4) 1.20 1.20

1971, Oct. 5 *Perf. 14x14½*

177 A33 30t lt blue & multi .90 .90

50th anniversary of Malawi Police Force.

Madonna and Child, by William Dyce — A34

Paintings of Holy Family by: 8t, Martin Schongauer. 15t, Raphael. 30t, Bronzino.

1971, Nov. 10 *Perf. 14½*

178 A34 3t green & multi .15 .15
179 A34 8t carmine & multi .15 .15
180 A34 15t dp claret & multi .35 .35
181 A34 30t dull blue & multi .60 .60
a. Souvenir sheet of 4, #178-181 2.00 2.00
Nos. 178-181 (4) 1.25 1.25

Christmas.

Vickers Viscount — A35

Airplanes: 8t, Hawker Siddeley 748. 15t, Britten Norman Islander. 30t, B.A.C. One Eleven.

1972, Feb. 9 Litho. *Perf. 13½x14*

182 A35 3t brt grn, blk & red .15 .15
183 A35 8t red org & black .25 .25
184 A35 15t dp rose lil, red & black .75 .75
185 A35 30t vio blue & multi 1.50 1.50
a. Souvenir sheet of 4, #182-185 7.50 7.50
Nos. 182-185 (4) 2.65 2.65

Publicity for Air Malawi.

Figures, Chencherere Hill — A36

Rock Paintings: 8t, Lizard and cat, Chencherere Hill. 15t, Symbols, Diwa Hill. 30t, Sun behind rain, Mikolongwe Hill.

1972, May 10 *Perf. 13½*

186 A36 3t black & yel grn .20 .15
187 A36 8t black & dp car .30 .20
188 A36 15t black, vio & car .60 .40
189 A36 30t black, blue & yel 1.25 .90
a. Souv. sheet of 4, #186-189, perf. 15 4.00 4.00
Nos. 186-189 (4) 2.35 1.65

Athlete and Olympic Rings — A37

1972, Aug. 9 *Perf. 14x14½*

190 A37 3t gray, black & green .15 .15
191 A37 8t gray, black & scar .15 .15
192 A37 15t gray, black & lilac .25 .25
193 A37 30t gray, black & blue .50 .50
a. Souvenir sheet of 4, #190-193 1.75 1.75
Nos. 190-193 (4) 1.05 1.05

20th Olympic Games, Munich, Aug. 26-Sept. 10.

Malawi Coat of Arms — A38

1972, Oct. 20 Litho. *Perf. 13½x14*

194 A38 15t blue & multi .50 .50

18th Commonwealth Parliamentary Conference, Malawi, Oct. 1972.

Adoration of the Kings, by Orcagna — A39

Paintings of the Florentine School: 8t, Madonna and Child Enthroned, anonymous. 15t, Madonna and Child with Sts. Bonaventura and Louis of Toulouse, by Carlo Crivelli. 30t, Madonna and Child with St. Anne, by Jean de Bruges.

Perf. 14½x14

1972, Nov. 8 Wmk. 357

195 A39 3t lt olive & multi .15 .15
196 A39 8t carmine & multi .15 .15
197 A39 15t purple & multi .25 .25
198 A39 30t blue & multi .60 .60
a. Souvenir sheet of 4, #195-198 1.50 1.50
Nos. 195-198 (4) 1.15 1.15

Christmas.

Charaxes Bohemani — A40

1973 *Perf. 13½x14*

199 A40 3t shown .20 .16
200 A40 8t Uranothauma crawshayi .60 .50
201 A40 15t Charaxes acuminatus 1.25 1.00
202 A40 30t "Euphaedra zaddachi" 3.25 2.00
a. Souvenir sheet of 4, #199-202 9.00 7.00
203 A40 30t Amauris ansorgei 2.75 2.00
Nos. 199-203 (5) 8.05 5.66

Issued: #199-202, Feb. 7; #203, Apr. 5.

Dr. Livingstone and Map of West Africa — A41

Livingstone Choosing Site for Mission — A42

1973 Litho. *Perf. 13½x14*

204 A41 3t apple grn & multi .15 .15
205 A41 8t red orange & multi .15 .15
206 A41 15t multicolored .30 .30
207 A41 30t blue & multi .60 .60
a. Souvenir sheet of 4, #204-207 1.50 1.50
208 A42 50t black & multi .75 .75
a. Souvenir sheet of 1 1.00 1.00
Nos. 204-208 (5) 1.95 1.95

Dr. David Livingstone (1813-73), medical missionary and explorer.

Issued: #204-207, 207a, 5/1; #208, 208a, 12/12.

Thumb Dulcitone (Kalimba) A43

African Musical Instruments: 8t, Hand zither (bangwe; vert.). 15t, Hand drum (ng'oma; vert.). 30t, One-stringed fiddle (kaligo).

1973, Aug. 8 Wmk. 357 *Perf. 14*

209 A43 3t brt green & multi .15 .15
210 A43 8t red & multi .20 .20
211 A43 15t violet & multi .30 .30
212 A43 30t blue & multi .60 .60
a. Souvenir sheet of 4, #209-212 2.75 2.75
Nos. 209-212 (4) 1.25 1.25

The Three Kings A44

1973, Nov. 8 *Perf. 13½x14*
213 A44 3t blue & multi .15 .15
214 A44 8t ver & multi .15 .15
215 A44 15t multicolored .20 .20
216 A44 30t orange & multi .40 .40
a. Souvenir sheet of 4, #213-216 1.25 1.25
Nos. 213-216 (4) .90 .90

Christmas.

Largemouth Black Bass — A45

Designs: Game fish.

1974, Feb. 20 Litho. *Perf. 14x14½*
217 A45 3t shown .15 .15
218 A45 8t Rainbow trout .25 .25
219 A45 15t Lake salmon .65 .65
220 A45 30t Triggerfish 1.25 1.25
a. Souvenir sheet of 4, #217-220 2.50 2.50
Nos. 217-220 (4) 2.30 2.30

30th anniv. of Angling Society of Malawi.

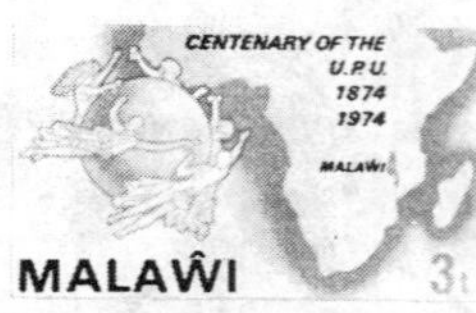

UPU Emblem, Map of Africa with Malawi — A46

1974, Apr. 24 *Perf. 13½*
221 A46 3t green & bister .15 .15
222 A46 8t ver & bister .15 .15
223 A46 15t lilac & bister .25 .25
224 A46 30t gray & bister .60 .60
a. Souvenir sheet of 4, #221-224 1.50 1.50
Nos. 221-224 (4) 1.15 1.15

Centenary of Universal Postal Union.

Capital Hill, Lilongwe and Pres. Kamuzu Banda — A47

1974, July 3 Litho. *Perf. 14*
225 A47 3t emerald & multi .15 .15
226 A47 8t red & multi .15 .15
227 A47 15t lilac & multi .15 .15
228 A47 30t vio blue & multi .30 .30
a. Souvenir sheet of 4, #225-228 1.00 1.00
Nos. 225-228 (4) .75 .75

10th anniversary of independence.

Madonna of the Meadow, by Giovanni Bellini — A48

Paintings: 8t, Holy Family, by Jacob Jordaens. 15t, Nativity, by Peter F. de Grebber. 30t, Adoration of the Shepherds, by Lorenzo di Credi.

1974, Dec. 4 Litho. *Perf. 13½x14*
229 A48 3t dk green & multi .15 .15
230 A48 8t multicolored .15 .15
231 A48 15t purple & multi .20 .20
232 A48 30t dk blue & multi .40 .40
a. Souvenir sheet of 4, #229-232 1.00 1.00
Nos. 229-232 (4) .90 .90

Christmas.

African Snipe — A49

Double-banded Sandgrouse — A50

Malawi Coat of Arms — A51

Birds: 3t, Blue quail. 5t, Red-necked francolin. 8t, Harlequin quail. 10t, Spurwing goose. 15t, Denham's bustard. 20t, Knob-billed duck. 30t, Helmeted guinea fowl. 50t, Pigmy goose. 1k, Garganey. 2k, White-faced tree duck. 4k, Green pigeon.

Wmk. 357
1975, Feb. 19 Litho. *Perf. 14*
Size: 17x21, 21x17mm
233 A49 1t multicolored .20 .25
234 A50 2t multicolored .35 .25
235 A50 3t multicolored 1.25 1.00
236 A49 5t multicolored 3.50 1.25
237 A50 8t multicolored 4.00 1.00

Perf. 14½
Size: 25x41, 41x25mm
238 A49 10t multicolored 7.50 .50
239 A49 15t multicolored 3.00 3.00
240 A49 20t multicolored 1.00 1.00
241 A49 30t multicolored 1.25 .75
242 A50 50t multicolored 2.00 1.25
243 A50 1k multicolored 3.50 3.25
244 A49 2k multicolored 12.50 7.00
245 A50 4k multicolored 14.00 11.00
Nos. 233-245 (13) 54.05 31.50

See #270-279. For overprints see #263, 294.

Coil Stamps

1975-85 *Perf. 14½x14*
246 A51 1t dark violet blue .35 .15
247 A51 5t red ('85) .75 .25

"Mpasa" A52

Designs: Lake Malawi ships.

1975, Mar. 12 Wmk. 357 *Perf. 13½*
251 A52 3t shown .15 .15
252 A52 8t "Ilala II" .30 .30
253 A52 15t "Chauncy Maples" .60 .60
254 A52 30t "Nkwazi" 1.25 1.25
a. Souvenir sheet of 4, #251-254, perf. 14½ 2.75 2.75
Nos. 251-254 (4) 2.30 2.30

Habenaria Splendens — A53

Bush Baby — A54

Orchids of Malawi: 10t, Eulophia cucullata. 20t, Disa welwitschii. 40t, Angraecum conchiferum.

1975, June 6 Litho. *Perf. 14½*
255 A53 3t lt green & multi .15 .15
256 A53 10t red orange & multi .40 .40
257 A53 20t dull vio & multi .75 .75
258 A53 40t multicolored 1.50 1.50
a. Souvenir sheet of 4, #255-258 7.00 7.00
Nos. 255-258 (4) 2.80 2.80

1975, Sept. 3 Litho. *Perf. 14*
259 A54 3t shown .15 .15
260 A54 10t Leopard .40 .40
261 A54 20t Roan antelope .90 .90
262 A54 40t Burchell's zebra 1.75 1.75
a. Souvenir sheet of 4, #259-262 4.25 4.25
Nos. 259-262 (4) 3.20 3.20

Animals of Malawi.

No. 242 Overprinted: "10th ACP / Ministerial / Conference / 1975"

1975, Dec. 9 Litho. *Perf. 14½*
263 A50 50t multicolored 1.25 1.25

10th African, Caribbean and Pacific Ministerial Conference.

Adoration of the Kings, French A55

Christmas: 10t, Nativity, 16th century, Spanish. 20t, Nativity, by Pierre Raymond, 16th century. 40t, Angel Appearing to the Shepherds, 14th century, English.

1975, Dec. 12 *Perf. 13x13½*
264 A55 3t multicolored .15 .15
265 A55 10t multicolored .15 .15
266 A55 20t purple & multi .25 .25
267 A55 40t blue & multi .50 .50
a. Souv. sheet of 4, #264-267, perf. 14 1.75 1.75
Nos. 264-267 (4) 1.05 1.05

Bird Types of 1975

1975 Litho. Unwmk. *Perf. 14*
Size: 21x17mm
270 A50 3t multicolored 3.00 1.25

Perf. 14½
Size: 25x41mm
273 A49 10t multicolored 2.00 1.25
274 A49 15t multicolored 2.00 1.75
279 A49 2k multicolored 7.00 7.50
Nos. 270-279 (4) 14.00 11.75

For overprint see No. 293.

Alexander Graham Bell — A56

President Kamuzu Banda — A57

Perf. 14x14½
1976, Mar. 24 Litho. Wmk. 357
281 A56 3t green & black .15 .15
282 A56 10t dp lilac rose & blk .20 .20
283 A56 20t brt purple & blk .30 .30
284 A56 40t brt blue & blk .60 .60
a. Souvenir sheet of 4, #281-284 1.50 1.50
Nos. 281-284 (4) 1.25 1.25

Centenary of first telephone call by Alexander Graham Bell, Mar. 10, 1876.

1976, July 1 Photo. *Perf. 13*
285 A57 3t brt green & multi .15 .15
286 A57 10t multicolored .15 .15
287 A57 20t violet & multi .30 .30
288 A57 40t dull blue & multi .50 .50
a. Souvenir sheet of 4, #285-288 1.50 1.50
Nos. 285-288 (4) 1.10 1.10

10th anniversary of the Republic.

Bagnall Diesel No. 100 A58

Diesel Locomotives: 10t, Shire class No. 503. 20t, Nippon Sharyo No. 301. 40t, Hunslet No. 110.

1976, Oct. 1 Litho. *Perf. 14½*
289 A58 3t emerald & multi .20 .15
290 A58 10t red & multi .65 .30
291 A58 20t lilac & multi 1.25 .60
292 A58 40t blue & multi 2.50 1.25
a. Souvenir sheet of 4, #289-292 5.00 4.00
Nos. 289-292 (4) 4.60 2.30

Malawi Railways.

Nos. 274 and 241 Overprinted: **Blantyre Mission Centenary 1876-1976**

1976, Oct. 22 Litho. Unwmk.
293 A49 15t multicolored .65 .50

Wmk. 357
294 A49 30t multicolored 1.25 1.25

Blantyre Mission centenary.

Christ Child on Straw Bed — A59

Ebony Ancestor Figures — A60

1976, Dec. 6 Wmk. 357 *Perf. 14*
295 A59 3t green & multi .15 .15
296 A59 10t magenta & multi .15 .15
297 A59 20t purple & multi .25 .25
298 A59 40t dk blue & multi .50 .50
a. Souvenir sheet of 4, #295-298 1.50 1.50
Nos. 295-298 (4) 1.05 1.05

Christmas.

1977, Apr. 1 Litho. Wmk. 357

Handicrafts: 10t, Ebony elephant, horiz. 20t, Ebony rhinoceros, horiz. 40t, Wooden antelope.

299 A60 4t yellow & multi .15 .15
300 A60 10t black & multi .20 .20
301 A60 20t ocher & multi .25 .25
302 A60 40t ver & multi .50 .50
a. Souvenir sheet of 4, #299-302 1.75 1.75
Nos. 299-302 (4) 1.10 1.10

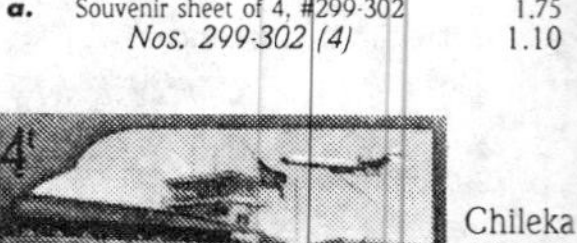

Chileka Airport, Blantyre, and VC10 A61

Transportation in Malawi: 10t, Leyland bus on Blantyre-Lilongwe Road. 20t, Ilala II on Lake Malawi. 40t, Freight train of Blantyre-Nacala line on overpass.

1977, July 12 Litho. *Perf. 14½*
303 A61 4t multicolored .15 .15
304 A61 10t multicolored .30 .30
305 A61 20t multicolored .60 .60
306 A61 40t multicolored 1.50 1.50
a. Souvenir sheet of 4, #303-306 3.25 3.25
Nos. 303-306 (4) 2.55 2.55

Pseudotropheus Johanni — A62

Lake Malawi Fish: 10t, Pseudotropheus livingstoni. 20t, Pseudotropheus zebra. 40t, Genyochromis mento.

Wmk. 357, Unwmkd.
1977, Oct. 4 Litho. *Perf. 13½x14*
307 A62 4t multicolored .15 .15
308 A62 10t multicolored .25 .25
309 A62 20t multicolored 1.25 .50
310 A62 40t multicolored 1.00 1.00
a. Souvenir sheet of 4, #307-310 3.00 3.00
Nos. 307-310 (4) 2.65 1.90

Virgin and Child, by Bergognone A63

Entry into Jerusalem, by Giotto A64

Virgin and Child: 10t, with God the Father and Angels, by Ambrogio Bergognone. 20t, detail from Bottigella altarpiece, by Vincenzo Foppa. 40t, with the fountain, by Jan Van Eyck.

Perf. 14x13½

1977, Nov. 21 Unwmk.

311 A63 4t multicolored .15 .15
312 A63 10t red & multi .15 .15
313 A63 20t lilac & multi .25 .25
314 A63 40t vio blue & multi .60 .60
a. Souvenir sheet of 4, #311-314 2.00 2.00
Nos. 311-314 (4) 1.15 1.15

Christmas.

1978, Mar. 1 Litho. *Perf. 12x12½*

Giotto Paintings: 10t, Crucifixion. 20t, Descent from the Cross. 40t, Jesus Appearing to Mary.

315 A64 4t multicolored .15 .15
316 A64 10t multicolored .15 .15
317 A64 20t multicolored .25 .25
318 A64 40t multicolored .60 .60
a. Souvenir sheet of 4, #315-318 2.00 1.75
Nos. 315-318 (4) 1.15 1.15

Easter.

Lions, Wildlife Fund Emblem A65

Animals and Wildlife Fund Emblem: 4t, Nyala, vert. 20t, Burchell's zebras. 40t, Reedbuck, vert.

1978, June 1 Unwmk. *Perf. 13x13½*

319 A65 4t multicolored 1.00 .25
320 A65 10t multicolored 2.50 .50
321 A65 20t multicolored 6.00 1.00
322 A65 40t multicolored 12.50 5.00
a. Souvenir sheet of 4, #319-322, perf. 13½ 27.50 20.00
Nos. 319-322 (4) 22.00 6.75

Malamulo Seventh Day Adventist Church — A66

Virgin and Child and: 10t, Likoma Cathedral. 20t, St. Michael's and All Angel's, Blantyre. 40t, Zomba Catholic Cathedral.

1978, Nov. 15 Wmk. 357 *Perf. 14*

323 A66 4t multicolored .15 .15
324 A66 10t multicolored .20 .20
325 A66 20t multicolored .30 .30
326 A66 40t multicolored .50 .50
a. Souvenir sheet of 4, #323-326 1.00 1.00
Nos. 323-326 (4) 1.15 1.15

Christmas.

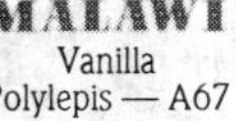

Vanilla Polylepis — A67

MALAWI

Brachystegia Spiciformis — A68

Orchids of Malawi: 2t, Cirrhopetalum umbellatum. 5t, Calanthe natalensis. 7t, Ansellia gigantea. 8t, Tridactyle bicaudata. 10t, Acampe pachyglossa. 15t, Eulophia quartiniana. 20t, Cyrtorchis arcuata. 30t, Eulophia tricristata. 50t, Disa hamatopetala. 75t, Cynorchis glandulosa. 1k, Aerangis kotschyana. 1.50k, Polystachya dendrobiiflora. 2k, Disa ornithantha. 4k, Cytorchis praetermissa.

1979, Jan. 2 Litho. *Perf. 13½*

327 A67 1t multicolored .15 .15
328 A67 2t multicolored .15 .15
329 A67 5t multicolored .15 .15
330 A67 7t multicolored .15 .15
331 A67 8t multicolored .15 .15
332 A67 10t multicolored .20 .15
333 A67 15t multicolored .30 .25
334 A67 20t multicolored .35 .35
335 A67 30t multicolored .50 .50
336 A67 50t multicolored 1.00 .90
337 A67 75t multicolored 1.50 1.40
338 A67 1k multicolored 1.75 1.75
339 A67 1.50k multicolored 2.50 2.50
340 A67 2k multicolored 3.25 3.25
341 A67 4k multicolored 7.50 7.50
Nos. 327-341 (15) 19.60 19.30

1979, Jan. 21 *Perf. 14x13½*

Trees: 10t, Widdringtonia nodiflora. 20t, Sandalwood. 40t, African mahogany.

342 A68 5t multicolored .15 .15
343 A68 10t multicolored .25 .25
344 A68 20t multicolored .45 .45
345 A68 40t multicolored .90 .90
a. Souvenir sheet of 4, #342-345 1.75 1.75
Nos. 342-345 (4) 1.75 1.75

National Tree Planting Day.

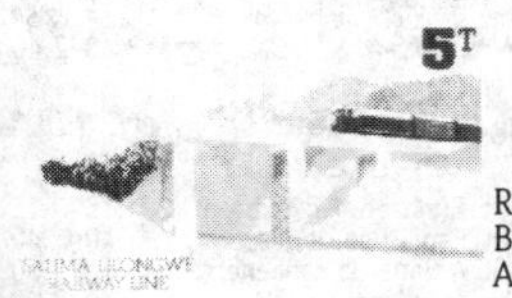

Railroad Bridge A69

Designs: 10t, Station and train. 20t, 40t, Train passing through man-made pass, diff.

1979, Feb. 17 Litho. *Perf. 14½*

346 A69 5t multicolored .15 .15
347 A69 10t multicolored .25 .25
348 A69 20t multicolored .60 .60
349 A69 40t multicolored 1.25 1.25
a. Souvenir sheet of 4, #346-349 4.00 4.00
Nos. 346-349 (4) 2.25 2.25

Inauguration of Salima-Lilongwe Railroad.

Malawi Boy and IYC Emblem — A70

Designs: Malawi children and IYC emblem.

1979, July 10 Wmk. 357 *Perf. 14*

350 A70 5t multicolored .15 .15
351 A70 10t multicolored .15 .15
352 A70 20t multicolored .30 .30
353 A70 40t multicolored .60 .60
Nos. 350-353 (4) 1.20 1.20

International Year of the Child.

Malawi No. 1 A71

Stamps of Malawi: 10t, #2. 20t, #3. 40t, #4.

1979, Sept. 17 Litho. *Perf. 13½x14*

354 A71 5t multicolored .15 .15
355 A71 10t multicolored .15 .15
356 A71 20t multicolored .25 .25
357 A71 40t multicolored .40 .40
a. Souvenir sheet of 4, #354-357 1.00 1.00
Nos. 354-357 (4) .95 .95

Sir Rowland Hill (1795-1879), originator of penny postage.

Christmas — A72

Designs: Landscapes.

1979, Nov. 15 Litho. *Perf. 13½x14*

358 A72 5t multicolored .15 .15
359 A72 10t multicolored .15 .15
360 A72 20t multicolored .25 .25
361 A72 40t multicolored .50 .50
Nos. 358-361 (4) 1.05 1.05

MALAŴI 5t

LIMBE CLUB

1905 1980

75th ANNIVERSARY OF ROTARY

Limbe Rotary Club Emblem — A73

Malawi Rotary Club Emblems: 10t, Blantyre. 20t, Lilongwe. 40t, Rotary International.

1980, Feb. 23 Litho. *Perf. 13½*

362 A73 5t multicolored .15 .15
363 A73 10t multicolored .15 .15
364 A73 20t multicolored .25 .25
365 A73 40t multicolored .50 .50
a. Souvenir sheet of 4, #362-365 1.50 1.50
Nos. 362-365 (4) 1.05 1.05

Rotary International, 75th anniversary.

Mangochi District Post Office, 1976, London 1980 Emblem A74

London 1980 Emblem and: 10t, New Blantyre sorting office, 1979. 20t, Mail transfer hut, Walala. 1k, Nyasaland Post Office, Chiromo, 1891.

1980, May 6 Wmk. 357 *Perf. 14½*

366 A74 5t blue green & blk .15 .15
367 A74 10t red & black .15 .15
368 A74 20t dp violet & black .25 .25
369 A74 1k dk blue & black .75 .75
a. Souvenir sheet of 4, #366-369 2.00 2.00
Nos. 366-369 (4) 1.30 1.30

London 1980 International Stamp Exhibition, May 6-14.

Agate Nodule — A75

1980, Aug. 20 Litho. *Perf. 13½*

370 A75 5t shown .25 .25
371 A75 10t Sunstone .50 .50
372 A75 20t Smoky Quartz 1.00 1.00
373 A75 1k Kyanite crystal 5.00 5.00
Nos. 370-373 (4) 6.75 6.75

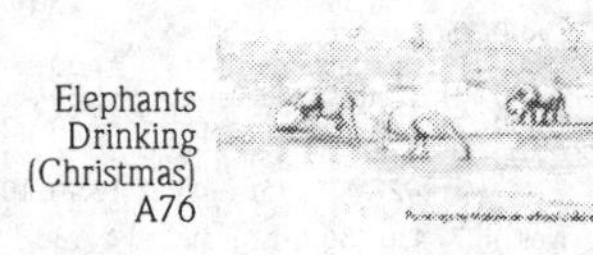

Elephants Drinking (Christmas) A76

1980, Nov. 10 Litho. *Perf. 13*

374 A76 5t shown .15 .15
375 A76 10t Flowers .15 .15
376 A76 20t Train .35 .35
377 A76 1k Bird 1.75 1.75
Nos. 374-377 (4) 2.40 2.40

Livingstone's Suni — A77

1981, Feb. 4 Litho. *Perf. 14½*

378 A77 7t shown .15 .15
379 A77 10t Blue duikers .20 .20
380 A77 20t African buffalo .40 .40
381 A77 1k Lichtenstein's hartebeests 2.00 2.00
Nos. 378-381 (4) 2.75 2.75

Standard A Earth Station A78

1981, Apr. 24 Litho. *Perf. 14½*

382 A78 7t shown .15 .15
383 A78 10t Blantyre International Gateway Exchange .16 .16
384 A78 20t Standard B Earth Station .35 .35
385 A78 1k Satellite and earth 1.75 1.75
a. Souvenir sheet of 4, #382-385 2.50 2.50
Nos. 382-385 (4) 2.41 2.41

International communications.

World Food Day A79

1981, Sept. 11 Litho. *Perf. 14*

386 A79 7t Corn .15 .15
387 A79 10t Rice .15 .15
388 A79 20t Finger millet .25 .25
389 A79 1k Wheat 1.50 1.50
Nos. 386-389 (4) 2.05 2.05

Holy Family, by Lippi A80

Christmas: 7t, Adoration of the Shepherds, by Murillo, vert. 20t, Adoration of the Shepherds, by Louis Le Nain. 1k, Virgin and Child, St. John the Baptist and Angel, by Paolo Morando, vert.

Perf. 13½x13, 13x13½

1981, Nov. 26 Litho.

390 A80 7t multicolored .15 .15
391 A80 10t multicolored .15 .15
392 A80 20t multicolored .25 .25
393 A80 1k multicolored 1.50 1.50
Nos. 390-393 (4) 2.05 2.05

Wildlife in Natl. Parks A81

1982, Mar. 15 Litho. *Perf. 14½x14*

394 A81 7t Impalas .15 .15
395 A81 10t Lions .15 .15
396 A81 20t Kudus .50 .50
397 A81 1k Flamingos 2.00 2.00
Nos. 394-397 (4) 2.80 2.80

Kamuzu Academy A82

Designs: Academy views.

1982, July 1 Litho. *Perf. 14½*

398 A82 7t multicolored .15 .15
399 A82 20t multicolored .25 .25
400 A82 30t multicolored .35 .35
401 A82 1k multicolored 1.25 1.25
Nos. 398-401 (4) 2.00 2.00

1982 World Cup — A83

1982, Sept. *Perf. 14x14½*

402 A83 7t Players .35 .35
403 A83 20t World Cup 1.00 1.00
404 A83 30t Stadium 1.25 1.25
Nos. 402-404 (3) 2.60 2.60

Souvenir Sheet

405 A83 1k Emblem on field 2.00 2.00

Remembrance Day — A84

Designs: War Memorials.

1982, Nov. 5 *Perf. 14½*

406 A84 7t Blantyre .15 .15
407 A84 20t Zomba .20 .20
408 A84 30t Chichiri, badges .30 .30
409 A84 1k Lilongwe 1.00 1.00
Nos. 406-409 (4) 1.65 1.65

A85

1983, Mar. 14 Wmk. 357 *Perf. 14*

410 A85 7t Kwacha Intl. Conf. Ctr. .15 .15
411 A85 20t Tea picking, Mulanje .20 .20
412 A85 30t Map .35 .35
413 A85 1k Pres. Banda, flag 1.25 1.25
Nos. 410-413 (4) 1.95 1.95

Commonwealth Day.

The Miraculous Draught of Fishes, by Raphael (1483-1517) — A86

Designs: 7t, 20t, 30t, Details. 1k, Entire painting. 7t, 20t vert.

1983, Apr. 4 Litho. Wmk. 357

414 A86 7t multicolored .25 .25
415 A86 20t multicolored .75 .75
416 A86 30t multicolored 1.00 1.00
Nos. 414-416 (3) 2.00 2.00

Souvenir Sheet

417 A86 1k multicolored 2.00 2.00

Fish Eagles — A87

Designs: a, Lakeside sentinel. b, Gull-like, far-carrying call. c, Diving on its fish prey. d, Prey captured. e, Feeding on its catch. Nos. 418a-418e in continuous design.

1983, July 11 Wmk. 357 *Perf. 14½*

418 Strip of 5 5.00 5.00
a.-e. A87 30t multicolored .75 .75

Manned Flight Bicentenary A88

Kamuzu Intl. Airport.

1983, Aug. 31 Litho. *Perf. 14*

419 A88 7t multicolored .15 .15
420 A88 20t multi, diff. .35 .35
421 A88 30t multi, diff. .50 .50
422 A88 1k multi, diff. 1.75 1.75
a. Souvenir sheet of 4, #419-422 3.00 3.00
Nos. 419-422 (4) 2.75 2.75

Christmas — A89

Local flowers.

1983, Nov. 1 Wmk. 357 *Perf. 14*

423 A89 7t Clerodendium myricoides .25 .25
424 A89 20t Gloriosa superba .75 .75
425 A89 30t Gladiolus laxiflorus 1.00 1.00
426 A89 1k Aframomum angustifolium 3.50 3.50
Nos. 423-426 (4) 5.50 5.50

Aquarium Species, Lake Malawi — A90

Perf. 14½x14

1984, Feb. 2 Wmk. 373

427 A90 1t Melanochromis auratus .15 .15
428 A90 2t Haplochromis compressiceps .15 .15
429 A90 5t Labeotropheus fuelleborni .15 .15
430 A90 7t Pseudotropheus lombardoi .15 .15
431 A90 8t Gold pseudotropheus zebra .15 .15
432 A90 10t Trematocranus jacobfreibergi .15 .15
433 A90 15t Melanochromis crabro .20 .20
434 A90 20t Marbled pseadotropheus .25 .20
435 A90 30t Labidochromis caeruleus .35 .30
436 A90 40t Haplochromis venustus .45 .40
437 A90 50t Aulonacara of Thumbi .75 .50
438 A90 75t Melanochromis vermivorus 1.00 .75
439 A90 1k Pseudotropheus zebra 1.50 1.00
440 A90 2k Trematocranus spp. 3.00 2.00
441 A90 4k Aulonacara of Mbenje 5.50 4.00
Nos. 427-441 (15) 13.90 10.25

Nos. 427, 430-436 exist inscribed "1986."

Nyika Red Hare A91

1984, Feb. 2 Wmk. 357 *Perf. 14*

442 A91 7t shown .15 .15
443 A91 20t Sun squirrel .38 .38
444 A91 30t Hedgehog .55 .55
445 A91 1k Genet 1.75 1.75
Nos. 442-445 (4) 2.83 2.83

1984 Summer Olympics A92

Local Butterflies A93

1984, June 1 Litho. *Perf. 14*

446 A92 7t Running .15 .15
447 A92 20t Boxing .30 .30
448 A92 30t Bicycling .45 .45
449 A92 1k Long jump 1.50 1.50
a. Souvenir sheet of 4, #446-449 2.50 2.50
Nos. 446-449 (4) 2.40 2.40

1984, Aug. 1 Photo. *Perf. 11½*

Granite Paper

450 A93 7t Euphaedra neophron .15 .15
451 A93 20t Papilio dardanus .40 .40
452 A93 30t Antanartia schaeneia .60 .60
453 A93 1k Spindasis 2.00 2.00
Nos. 450-453 (4) 3.15 3.15

Christmas — A94

Virgin and Child Paintings.

Perf. 14½

1984, Oct. 15 Litho. Wmk. 357

454 A94 7t Duccio .15 .15
455 A94 20t Raphael .40 .40
456 A94 30t Lippi .60 .60
457 A94 1k Wilton diptych 2.00 2.00
Nos. 454-457 (4) 3.15 3.15

Fungi A94a

1985, Jan. 23 *Perf. 14½x14*

458 A94a 7t Leucopaxillus gracillimus .25 .25
459 A94a 20t Limacella guttata 1.25 1.25
460 A94a 30t Termitomyces eurhizles 1.75 1.75
461 A94a 1k Xerulina asprata 6.00 6.00
Nos. 458-461 (4) 9.25 9.25

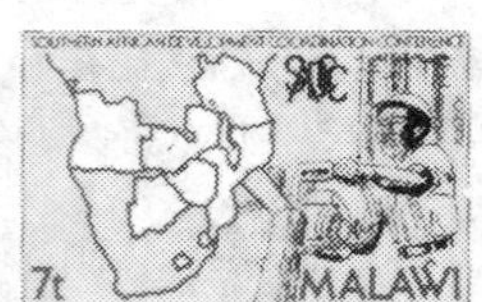

Southern African Development Coordination Conference — A95

1985, Apr. 1 Litho. *Perf. 14*

462 A95 7t Forestry .15 .15
463 A95 15t Communications .18 .18
464 A95 20t Transportation .24 .24
465 A95 1k Fishing 1.20 1.20
Nos. 462-465 (4) 1.77 1.77

Ships on Lake Malawi A96

1985, June 3 *Perf. 13½x13*

466 A96 7t Ufulu .15 .15
467 A96 15t Chauncy Maples .28 .28
468 A96 20t Mtendere .35 .35
469 A96 1k Ilala 1.90 1.90
a. Souvenir sheet of 4, #466-469, perf. 13x12 2.75 2.75
Nos. 466-469 (4) 2.68 2.68

Audubon Birth Bicent. — A97

1985, Aug. 1 Litho. *Perf. 14*

470 A97 7t Stierling's woodpecker .20 .20
471 A97 15t Lesser seed-cracker .42 .42
472 A97 20t Gunning's akalat .55 .55
473 A97 1k Boehm's bee-eater 2.75 2.75
a. Souvenir sheet of 4, #470-473 4.50 4.50
Nos. 470-473 (4) 3.92 3.92

Christmas — A98

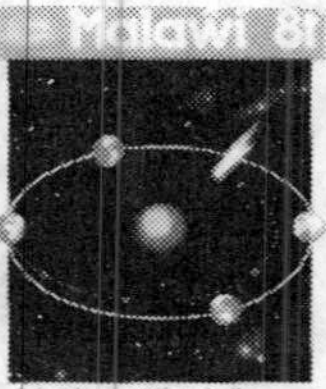

Halley's Comet — A99

Paintings: 7t, The Virgin of Humility, by Jaime Serra. 15t, Adoration of the Magi, by Stefano da Zevio. 20t, Madonna and Child, by Gerard van Honthorst. 1k, Virgin of Zbraslav, by a Master of Vissi Brod.

Perf. 11½x12

1985, Oct. 14 Unwmk.

474 A98 7t multicolored .15 .15
475 A98 15t multicolored .30 .30
476 A98 20t multicolored .35 .35
477 A98 1k multicolored 2.00 2.00
Nos. 474-477 (4) 2.80 2.80

1986, Feb. 10 Wmk. 357 *Perf. 14½*

478 A99 8t Earth, comet and Giotto trajectories .15 .15
479 A99 15t Comet over Earth .18 .18
480 A99 20t Over Malawi .24 .24
481 A99 1k Giotto probe 1.20 1.20
Nos. 478-481 (4) 1.77 1.77

1986 World Cup Soccer Championships, Mexico — A100

Various soccer plays.

Perf. 12x11½

1986, May 26 Unwmk.

Granite Paper

482 A100 8t multicolored .15 .15
483 A100 15t multicolored .28 .28
484 A100 20t multicolored .35 .35
485 A100 1k multicolored 1.75 1.75
a. Souvenir sheet of 4, #482-485 2.75 2.75
Nos. 482-485 (4) 2.53 2.53

Natl. Independence, 20th Anniv. A101

Christmas A102

1986, June 30 Litho. *Perf. 14*

486 A101 8t Pres. Banda .15 .15
487 A101 15t Natl. flag .18 .18
488 A101 20t Natl. crest .24 .24
489 A101 1k Natl. airline 1.20 1.20
Nos. 486-489 (4) 1.77 1.77

1986, Dec. 15 Litho. *Perf. 11½*

Paintings: 8t, Virgin and Child, by Botticelli (1445-1510). 15t, Adoration of the Shepherds, by Guido Reni (1575-1642). 20t, Madonna of the Veil, by Carlo Dolci (1616-86). 1k, Adoration of the Magi, by Jean Bourdichon.

490 A102 8t multicolored .15 .15
491 A102 15t multicolored .20 .20
492 A102 20t multicolored .25 .25
493 A102 1k multicolored 1.25 1.25
Nos. 490-493 (4) 1.85 1.85

World Wildlife Fund — A103

Bugeranus carunculatus.

1987, Jan. 30 Wmk. 357 *Perf. 14½*

494 A103 8t Wattled crane .20 .20
495 A103 15t Two cranes .40 .40
496 A103 20t Nesting .55 .55
497 A103 75t Crane in water 2.00 2.00
Nos. 494-497 (4) 3.15 3.15

1988, Oct. Wmk. 373

494a A103 8t .15 .15
495a A103 15t .15 .15
496a A103 20t .15 .15
497a A103 75t .58 .58
Nos. 494a-497a (4) 1.03 1.03

British Steam Locomotives A104

1987, May 25 Litho. *Perf. 14x13½*

498 A104 10t Shamrock No. 2, 1902 .15 .15
499 A104 25t D Class No. 8, 1914 .35 .35
500 A104 30t Thistle No. 1, 1902 .45 .45
501 A104 1k Kitson No. 6, 1903 1.40 1.40
Nos. 498-501 (4) 2.35 2.35

Hippopotamus A105

1987, Aug. 24 Photo. *Perf. 12½*
Granite Paper

502 A105 10t Feeding .18 .18
503 A105 25t Swimming, roaring .28 .28
504 A105 30t Mother and young swimming .35 .35
505 A105 1k At rest, egret 1.25 1.25
a. Souvenir sheet of 4, #502-505 2.00 2.00
Nos. 502-505 (4) 2.06 2.06

Wild Flowers — A106

Locally Carved and Staunton Chessmen — A107

Unwmk.

1987, Oct. 19 Litho. *Perf. 14*

506 A106 10t Stathmostelma spectabile .15 .15
507 A106 25t Pentanisia schweinfurthii .30 .30
508 A106 30t Chironia krebsii .38 .38
509 A106 1k Ochna macrocalyx 1.25 1.25
Nos. 506-509 (4) 2.08 2.08

1988, Feb. 8 Wmk. 384 *Perf. 14½*

510 A107 15t Knights .15 .15
511 A107 35t Bishops .35 .35
512 A107 50t Rooks .50 .50
513 A107 2k Queens 2.00 2.00
Nos. 510-513 (4) 3.00 3.00

1988 Summer Olympics, Seoul — A108

Birds — A109

1988, June 13 Unwmk. *Perf. 14*

514 A108 15t High jump .15 .15
515 A108 35t Javelin .35 .35
516 A108 50t Women's tennis .48 .48
517 A108 2k Shot put 1.90 1.90
a. Souvenir sheet of 4, #514-517 2.90 2.90
Nos. 514-517 (4) 2.88 2.88

1988 Photo. *Perf. 14x14½*
Granite Paper (1t-4k)

518 A109 1t Eastern forest scrub-warbler .15 .15
519 A109 2t Yellow-throated warbler .15 .15
520 A109 5t Moustached green tinkerbird .15 .15
521 A109 7t Waller's chestnut-wing starling .15 .15
522 A109 8t Oriole finch .15 .15
523 A109 10t Starred robin .15 .15
524 A109 15t Bar-tailed trogon .15 .15
525 A109 20t Green twinspot .15 .15
526 A109 30t Gray cuckoo shrike .20 .20
527 A109 40t Black-fronted bush shrike .28 .28
528 A109 50t White-tailed crested flycatcher .35 .35
529 A109 75t Green barbet .52 .52
530 A109 1k Cinnamon dove .70 .70
531 A109 2k Silvery-cheeked hornbill 1.40 1.40
532 A109 4k Crowned eagle 2.75 2.75
533 A109 10k Red-and-blue sunbird 7.00 7.00
Nos. 518-533 (16) 14.40 14.40

Issue dates: 10k, Oct. 3, others, July 25.

1994 *Perf. 11½x12*

533A A109 10k Starred robin

Lloyds of London, 300th Anniv.
Common Design Type

Designs: 15t, Royal Exchange, 1844. 35t, Opening of the Nkula Falls hydroelectric power station, horiz. 50t, Air Malawi passenger jet, horiz. 2k, Cruise ship Queen Elizabeth (Seawise University) on fire, Hong Kong, 1972.

Wmk. 373

1988, Oct. 24 Litho. *Perf. 14*

534 CD341 15t multicolored .15 .15
535 CD341 35t multicolored .28 .28
536 CD341 50t multicolored .38 .38
537 CD341 2k multicolored 1.50 1.50
Nos. 534-537 (4) 2.31 2.31

Christmas — A110

Paintings: 15t, Madonna in the Church, by Jan Van Eyck (d. 1441). 35t, Virgin, Infant Jesus and St. Anne, by Leonardo da Vinci. 50t, Virgin and Angels, by Cimabue (c. 1240-1302). 2k, Virgin and Child, by Alesso Baldovinetti (c. 1425-1499).

1988, Nov. 28 Unwmk. *Perf. 14*

538 A110 15t multicolored .15 .15
539 A110 35t multicolored .25 .25
540 A110 50t multicolored .38 .38
541 A110 2k multicolored 1.50 1.50
Nos. 538-541 (4) 2.28 2.28

Angling Soc. of Malawi, 50th Anniv. A111

1989, Apr. 11

542 A111 15t Tsungwa .15 .15
543 A111 35t Mpasa .25 .25
544 A111 50t Yellow fish .38 .38
545 A111 2k Tiger fish 1.50 1.50
Nos. 542-545 (4) 2.28 2.28

Natl. Independence, 25th Anniv. — A112

1989, June 26

546 A112 15t Independence Arch .15 .15
547 A112 35t Grain silos .25 .25
548 A112 50t Capital Hill .35 .35
549 A112 2k Reserve Bank Headquarters 1.45 1.45
Nos. 546-549 (4) 2.20 2.20

African Development Bank, 25th Anniv. — A113

1989, Oct. 30

550 A113 15t Blantyre Digital Telex Exchange .15 .15
551 A113 40t Dzalanyama steer .30 .30
552 A113 50t Mikolongwe heifer .38 .38
553 A113 2k Zebu bull 1.50 1.50
Nos. 550-553 (4) 2.33 2.33

Cooperation with the UN, 25th Anniv. — A114

1989, Dec. 1 *Perf. 14*

554 A114 15t shown .15 .15
555 A114 40t House, diff. .30 .30
556 A114 50t Thatched dwelling, house .38 .38
557 A114 2k Tea Plantation 1.50 1.50
Nos. 554-557 (4) 2.33 2.33

Rural Housing Program.

Christmas A115

Designs: 15t, St. Michael and All Angels Church. 40t, Limbe Cathedral. 50t, Nkhoma CCAP Church. 2k, Likoma Is. Cathedral.

1989, Dec. 15

558 A115 15t multicolored .15 .15
559 A115 40t multicolored .30 .30
560 A115 50t multicolored .38 .38
561 A115 2k multicolored 1.50 1.50
Nos. 558-561 (4) 2.33 2.33

Classic Cars A116

Perf. 14x13½

1990, Apr. 2 Litho. Unwmk.

562 A116 15t Ford Sedan, 1915 .18 .18
563 A116 40t Two-seater Ford, 1915 .38 .38
564 A116 50t Ford, 1915 .50 .50
565 A116 2k Chevrolet Luxury Bus, 1930 1.90 1.90
a. Souvenir sheet of 4, #562-565, perf. 13x12 3.00 3.00
Nos. 562-565 (4) 2.96 2.96

World Cup Soccer Championships, Italy — A117

1990, June 14 Litho. *Perf. 14*

566 A117 15t shown .15 .15
567 A117 40t Two players .28 .28
568 A117 50t Shot on goal .35 .35
569 A117 2k World Cup Trophy 1.40 1.40
a. Souvenir sheet of 4, #566-569 2.25 2.25
Nos. 566-569 (4) 2.18 2.18

SADCC, 10th Anniv. A118

1990, Aug. 24 Litho. *Perf. 14*

570 A118 15t Map .15 .15
571 A118 40t Chambo .28 .28
572 A118 50t Cedar trees .35 .35
573 A118 2k Nyala 1.40 1.40
a. Souvenir sheet of 4, #570-573 2.25 2.25
Nos. 570-573 (4) 2.18 2.18

Christmas — A119

Orchids — A120

Paintings by Raphael: 15t, Virgin and Child. 40t, The Transfiguration, detail. 50t, St. Catherine of Alexandrie. 2k, The Transfiguration.

1990, Dec. *Perf. 13½x14*

574 A119 15t multicolored .15 .15
575 A119 40t multicolored .28 .28
576 A119 50t multicolored .35 .35
577 A119 2k multicolored 1.40 1.40
a. Souvenir sheet of 4, #574-577, perf. 12x13 2.25 2.25
Nos. 574-577 (4) 2.18 2.18

1990, Dec.

578 A120 15t Aerangis kotschyana .20 .20
579 A120 40t Angraecum eburneum .35 .35
580 A120 50t Aerangis luteo alba .50 .50
581 A120 2k Cyrtorchis arcuata 1.90 1.90
a. Souvenir sheet of 4, #578-581, perf. 12x13 3.00 3.00
Nos. 578-581 (4) 2.95 2.95

Wild Animals A121

1991, Apr. 23 Litho. *Perf. 14x13½*

582 A121 20t Buffalo .15 .15
583 A121 60t Cheetah .45 .45
584 A121 75t Greater kudu .55 .55
585 A121 2k Black rhinoceros 1.50 1.50
a. Souvenir sheet of 4, #582-585, perf. 13x12 2.65 2.65
Nos. 582-585 (4) 2.65 2.65

Malawi Postal Services, Cent. A122

Designs: 20t, Chiromo Post Office, 1891. 60t, Mail exchange hut, Walala. 75t, Mangochi Post Office. 2k, Standard A Earth station, 1981.

1991, July 2 *Perf. 14x13½*

586 A122	20t multicolored		.15	.15
587 A122	60t multicolored		.45	.45
588 A122	75t multicolored		.55	.55
589 A122	2k multicolored		1.50	1.50
a.	Souvenir sheet of 4, #586-589, perf. 13x12		2.65	2.65
	Nos. 586-589 (4)		2.65	2.65

Insects — A123

Christmas — A124

1991, Sept. 21 *Perf. 13½x14*

590 A123	20t Red locust	.15	.15
591 A123	60t Weevil	.45	.45
592 A123	75t Cotton stainer bug	.55	.55
593 A123	2k Pollen beetle	1.50	1.50
	Nos. 590-593 (4)	2.65	2.65

1991, Nov. 26 Litho. *Perf. 13½x14*

594 A124	20t Christ Child in manger	.15	.15
595 A124	60t Adoration of the Magi	.45	.45
596 A124	75t Nativity	.55	.55
597 A124	2k Virgin and Child	1.50	1.50
	Nos. 594-597 (4)	2.65	2.65

Birds A125

Designs: a, Red bishop. b, Lesser striped swallow. c, Long-crested eagle. d, Lilac-breasted roller. e, African paradise flycatcher. f, White-fronted bee-eater. g, White-winged black tern. h, Brown-backed fire-finch. i, White-browed robin-chat. j, African fish eagle. k, Malachite kingfisher. l, Cabani's masked weaver. m, African barn owl. n, Yellow-bellied sunbird. o, Lesser flamingo. p, Crowned crane. q, African pitta. r, African darter. s, White-faced tree duck. t, African pied wagtail.

1992, Apr. 7 Litho. *Perf. 14*

598 A125	75t Sheet of 20, #a.-t.	11.00	11.00

A number has been reserved for an additional value in this set.

1992 Summer Olympics, Barcelona A126

1992, July 28 Litho. *Perf. 13½*

600 A126	20t Long jump	.15	.15
601 A126	60t High jump	.45	.45
602 A126	75t Javelin	.55	.55
603 A126	2k Running	1.50	1.50
a.	Souvenir sheet of 4, #600-603	2.65	2.65
	Nos. 600-603 (4)	2.65	2.65

Christmas — A127

Details from paintings: 20t, Angel from The Annunciation, by Philippe de Champaigne. 75t, Virgin and Child, by Bernardino Luini. 95t, Virgin and Child, by Sassoferrato. 2k, Mary from The Annunciation, by Champaigne.

1992, Nov. 9 Litho. *Perf. 14*

604 A127	20t multicolored	.15	.15
605 A127	75t multicolored	.38	.38
606 A127	95t multicolored	.48	.48
607 A127	2k multicolored	1.05	1.05
	Nos. 604-607 (4)	2.06	2.06

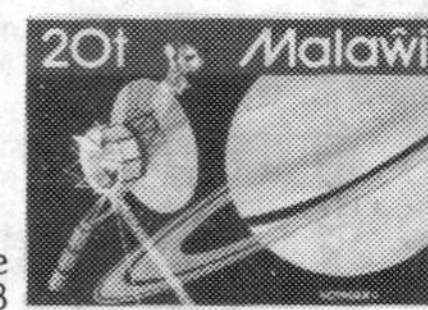

Intl. Space Year — A128

Designs: 20t, Voyager II, Saturn. 75t, Center of a galaxy. 95t, Kanjedza II ground station. 2k, Communication satellite.

1992, Dec. 7 Litho. *Perf. 13½*

608 A128	20t multicolored	.15	.15
609 A128	75t multicolored	.38	.38
610 A128	95t multicolored	.48	.48
611 A128	2k multicolored	1.00	1.00
	Nos. 608-611 (4)	2.01	2.01

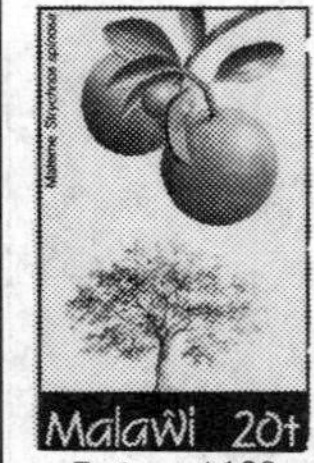

Fruit — A129

Butterflies — A130

1993, Mar. 21 Litho. *Perf. 13½x14*

612 A129	20t Strychnos spinosa	.15	.15
613 A129	75t Adansonia digitata	.35	.35
614 A129	95t Ximenia caffra	.42	.42
615 A129	2k Uapaca kirkiana	.90	.90
	Nos. 612-615 (4)	1.82	1.82

1993, June 28 Litho. *Perf. 13*

616 A130	20t Apaturopsis cleocharis	.15	.15
617 A130	75t Euryphura achlys	.35	.35
618 A130	95t Cooksonia aliciae	.42	.42
619 A130	2k Charaxes protoclea azota	.90	.90
	Nos. 616-619 (4)	1.82	1.82

A131

Dinosaurs A132

Designs: No. 623a, Tyrannosaurus Rex. b, Dilophosaurus. c, Brachiosaurus. d, Gallimimus. e, Triceratops. f, Velociraptor.

1993, Dec. 30 Litho. *Perf. 13*

620 A131	20t Kentrosaurus	.15	.15
621 A131	75t Stegosaurus	.35	.35
622 A131	95t Sauropod	.42	.42
	Nos. 620-622 (3)	.92	.92

Miniature Sheet

623 A132	2k Sheet of 6, #a.-f.	5.50	5.50

Christmas — A133

1993, Nov. 30 Photo. *Perf. 11½*

Granite Paper

624 A133	20t Holy family	.15	.15
625 A133	75t Shepherds	.35	.35
626 A133	95t Wise men	.42	.42
627 A133	2k Adoration of the magi	.90	.90
	Nos. 624-627 (4)	1.82	1.82

Fish of Lake Malawi A134

Designs: 20t, Pseudotropheus socolofi. 75t, Melanochromis auratus. 95t, Pseudotropheus lombardoi. 1k, Labeotropheus trewavasae. 2k, Pseudotropheus zebra. 4k, Pseudotropheus elongatus.

1994, Mar. 21 Litho. *Perf. 14x15*

628 A134	20t multicolored	.15	.15
629 A134	75t multicolored	.35	.35
630 A134	95t multicolored	.42	.42
631 A134	1k multicolored	.45	.45
632 A134	2k multicolored	.90	.90
633 A134	4k multicolored	1.75	1.75
	Nos. 628-633 (6)	4.02	4.02

Ships of Lake Malawi A135

1994, Oct. 19 Litho. *Perf. 13x13½*

634 A135	20t Ilala	.15	.15
635 A135	75t MV Ufulu	.15	.15
636 A135	95t The Pioneer	.16	.16
637 A135	2k Dove	.35	.35
	Set value	.68	.68

Souvenir Sheet

638 A135	5k Monteith	.90	.90

Christmas — A136

Details or entire paintings: 20t, Virgin and Child, by Durer, vert. 75t, Magi Present Gifts to Infant Jesus, Franco-Flemish Book of Hours, vert. 95t, The Nativity, by Fra Filippo Lippi. 2k, Nativity with Magi, by Rogier van der Weyden.

1994, Nov. 30 Litho. *Perf. 14½*

639 A136	20t multicolored	.15	.15
640 A136	75t multicolored	.15	.15
641 A136	95t multicolored	.16	.16
642 A136	2k multicolored	.35	.35
	Set value	.68	.68

Pres. Bakili Muluzi — A137

1995, Apr. 10 Litho. *Perf. 11½x12*

643 A137	40t red & multi	.15	.15
644 A137	1.40k green & multi	.20	.20
645 A137	1.80k blue & multi	.20	.20
646 A137	2k brn org & multi	.25	.25
	Nos. 643-646 (4)	.80	.80

Establishment of COMESA (Common Market for Eastern & Southern African States).

Christmas A138

1995, Nov. 13 Litho. *Perf. 11½*

Granite Paper

647 A138	40t Pre-schoolers	.15	.15
648 A138	1.40k Dispensing medicine	.20	.20
649 A138	1.80k Water supply	.25	.25
650 A138	2k Voluntary return	.30	.30
	Nos. 647-650 (4)	.90	.90

Butterflies A139

1996, Dec. 5 Photo. *Perf. 11½*

Granite Paper

651 A139	60t Precis tugela	.15	.15
652 A139	3k Papilo pelodorus	.40	.40
653 A139	4k Acrea acrita	.55	.55
654 A139	10k Malantis leda	1.30	1.30
	Nos. 651-654 (4)	2.40	2.40

Christmas — A140

Designs: 10t, Instructor, children raising hands. 20t, Children enacting nativity scene. 30t, Children standing with hands clasped. 60t, Mother and child.

1996, Dec. 12

Granite Paper

655 A140	10t multicolored	.15	.15
656 A140	20t multicolored	.15	.15
657 A140	30t multicolored	.15	.15
658 A140	60t multicolored	.15	.15
	Set value	.20	.20

UN, 50th Anniv. A141

40t, Telecommunications & training. 1.40k, Clean water is essential for health. 1.80k, Protecting the environment, Mt. Mulanje. 2k, Food security.

1995, Oct. 30 Litho. *Perf. 11½*

659 A141	40t multicolored	.15	.15
660 A141	1.40k multicolored	.20	.20
661 A141	1.80k multicolored	.25	.25
662 A141	2k multicolored	.25	.25
a.	Souvenir sheet, #659-662	.75	.75
	Nos. 659-662 (4)	.85	.85

Paul Harris (1868-1947), Founder of Rotary, Intl. — A142

Rotary, Intl. emblem and: 60t, Map of Malawi. 3k, Eagle. 4.40k, Leopard.

1997 Litho. *Perf. 11½*

663 A142 60t multicolored .15 .15
664 A142 3k multicolored .35 .35
665 A142 4.40k multicolored .50 .50
666 A142 5k shown .55 .55
Nos. 663-666 (4) 1.55 1.55

POSTAGE DUE STAMPS

D1

Perf. 11½

1967, Sept. 1 Litho. Wmk. 357

J1 D1 1p deep lilac rose .15 *1.50*
J2 D1 2p sepia .15 *1.50*
J3 D1 4p lilac .30 *1.50*
J4 D1 6p dark blue .40 *1.50*
J5 D1 8p emerald .60 *1.50*
J6 D1 1sh black .75 *1.75*
Nos. J1-J6 (6) 2.35 *9.25*

Values in Decimal Currency

1971, Feb. 15
Size: 18x23mm

J7 D1 2t sepia .20 *1.50*
J8 D1 4t lilac .35 *1.50*
J9 D1 6t dark blue .60 *1.50*
J10 D1 8t green .75 *1.50*
J11 D1 10t black 1.00 *1.50*
Nos. J7-J11 (5) 2.90 *7.50*

Type of 1971 Redrawn

1975 Wmk. 357 *Perf. 14*
Size: 17x21mm

J12 D1 2t brown 1.50 *2.50*

No. J12 has accent mark over "W."

1977-78 Litho. Unwmk. *Perf. 14*
Size: 18x21mm

J13 D1 2t sepia 4.00 4.00
J14 D1 4t rose lilac 4.00 4.00
J15 D1 8t brt green ('78) 2.00 *4.00*
J16 D1 10t black 4.00 *4.50*
Nos. J13-J16 (4) 14.00 *16.50*

1982 Wmk. 357, Sideways

J13a D1 2t .50 *1.00*
J14a D1 4t .50 *1.00*
J16a D1 10t .50 *1.00*
Nos. J13a-J16a (3) 1.50 *3.00*

1989 Litho. Unwmk. *Perf. 15x14*
Size: 18x20½mm

J13b D1 2t
J14b D1 4t
J15a D1 6t
J16b D1 10t

MALAYA

mə-'lā-ə

Federated Malay States

LOCATION — Malay peninsula
GOVT. — British Protectorate
AREA — 27,585 sq. mi.
CAPITAL — Kuala Lumpur

The Federated Malay States consisted of the sultanates of Negri Sembilan, Pahang, Perak and Selangor.

Stamps of the Federated Malay States replaced those of the individual states and were used until 1935, when individual issues were resumed.

100 Cents = 1 Dollar

Catalogue values for unused stamps in this country are for Never Hinged items, beginning with Scott 80 in the regular postage section, Scott J20 in the postage due section, Scott 128 in Johore, Scott 55 in Kedah, Scott 44 in Kelantan, Scott 1 in Malacca, Scott 36 in Negri Sembilan, Scott 44 in Pahang, Scott 1 in Penang, Scott 99 in Perak, Scott 1 in Perlis, Scott 74 in Selangor, and Scott 47 in Trengganu.

Watermarks

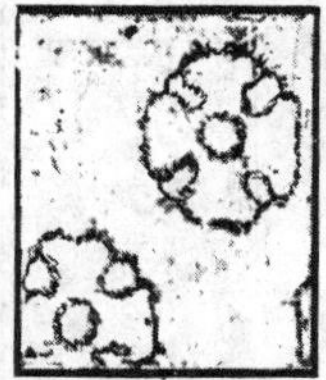
Wmk. 47 - Multiple Rosettes

Wmk. 71- Rosette

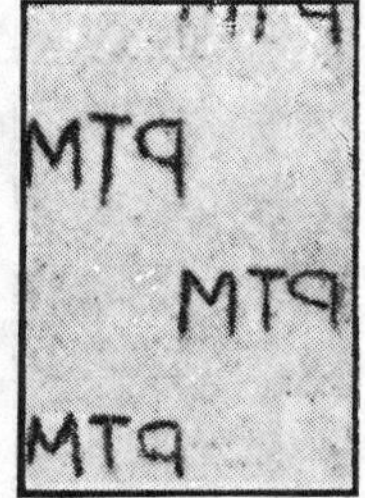

Wmk. 338- PTM Multiple

(PTM stands for Persekutuan Tanah Melayu, or Federation of Malaya.)

Stamps of Straits Settlements overprinted "BMA MALAYA" are listed in Straits Settlements.

Stamps and Type of Negri Sembilan Overprinted in Black

FEDERATED
MALAY STATES

1900 Wmk. 2 *Perf. 14*

1 A2 1c lilac & green 1.75 *2.75*
2 A2 2c lilac & brown 22.50 *45.00*
3 A2 3c lilac & black 2.25 *3.50*
4 A2 5c lilac & olive 60.00 *110.00*
5 A2 10c lilac & org 3.00 *12.50*
6 A2 20c green & olive 50.00 *70.00*
7 A2 25c grn & car rose 150.00 *200.00*
8 A2 50c green & black 60.00 *85.00*
Nos. 1-8 (8) 349.50 *528.75*

Overprinted on Perak Nos. 51, 53, 57-58, 60-61

1900

9 A9 5c lilac & olive 10.00 *45.00*
10 A9 10c lilac & org 55.00 *55.00*

Wmk. 1

11 A10 $1 green & lt grn 100.00 *125.00*
12 A10 $2 green & car rose 85.00 *120.00*
13 A10 $5 green & ultra 175.00 *300.00*
13A A10 $25 green & org *5,000.*
Revenue cancel 200.00
Nos. 9-13 (5) 425.00 *645.00*

No. 10 with bar omitted is an essay.

Elephants and Howdah — A3

Tiger — A4

Stamps of type A4 are watermarked sideways.

1900 Typo.

14 A3 $1 green & lt green 65.00 65.00
15 A3 $2 grn & car rose 75.00 75.00
16 A3 $5 green & ultra 125.00 130.00
17 A3 $25 grn & orange 1,300. 675.00
Nos. 14-17 (4) 1,565. 945.00

High values with revenue cancellations are plentiful and inexpensive.

1901 Wmk. 2

18 A4 1c blue grn & blk 1.00 .30
19 A4 3c brown & gray 2.50 .20
20 A4 4c rose & black 4.00 .40
21 A4 5c scar & grn, *yel* 2.00 1.50
22 A4 8c ultra & blk 25.00 3.00
23 A4 10c violet & blk 35.00 3.75
24 A4 20c black & gray vio 22.50 6.00
25 A4 50c brn org & black 57.50 25.00
Nos. 18-25 (8) 149.50 40.15

1904-10 Wmk. 3

26 A4 1c green & black 17.50 .60
27 A4 3c brown & gray 17.50 .30
28 A4 4c rose & black 4.00 .25
29 A4 5c scar & grn, *yel* 4.50 1.25
30 A4 8c ultra & black ('05) 6.25 3.00
31 A4 10c violet & black 12.50 .35
32 A4 20c blk & gray vio ('05) 3.00 .35
33 A4 50c brn org & blk ('05) 25.00 4.00

The 1c and 4c are on ordinary paper, the other values on both ordinary and chalky papers.

Chalky Paper

34 A3 $1 green & lt green ('07) 40.00 25.00
35 A3 $2 green & car rose ('06) 60.00 85.00
36 A3 $5 grn & ultra ('06) 85.00 *90.00*
37 A3 $25 grn & org ('10) 1,000. 475.00
Nos. 26-36 (11) 275.25 *210.10*

High values with revenue cancellations are plentiful and inexpensive.

1906-22 Ordinary Paper

Two dies for Nos. 38 and 44:
I - Thick line under "Malay."
II - Thin line under "Malay."

38 A4 1c dull grn, die II 1.90 .20
b. Die I 6.50 .40
39 A4 1c brown ('19) 2.00 1.10
40 A4 2c green ('19) .75 .30
41 A4 3c brown 4.50 .15
42 A4 3c carmine ('09) 2.25 .15
43 A4 3c dp gray ('19) 1.10 .15
44 A4 4c scar, die II 1.10 .30
b. Die I ('19) 1.75 2.00
45 A4 6c orange ('19) 1.90 1.25
46 A4 8c ultra ('09) 12.00 .80
47 A4 10c ultra ('19) 6.00 .80
48 A4 35c red, *yellow* 6.00 11.00
Nos. 38-48 (11) 39.50 16.20

1922-32 Wmk. 4

Ordinary Paper

49 A4 1c brown ('22) 1.75 1.75
50 A4 1c black ('23) .45 .15
51 A4 2c dk brown ('25) 3.75 1.75
52 A4 2c green ('26) .60 .15
53 A4 3c dp gray ('23) 2.75 4.25
54 A4 3c green ('24) 2.25 1.75
55 A4 3c brown ('27) .60 .30
56 A4 4c scar (II) ('23) 2.25 .40
57 A4 4c orange ('26) .50 .15
c. Unwatermarked 200.00 95.00
58 A4 5c vio, *yel* ('22) .75 .15
59 A4 5c dk brown ('32) 1.50 .15
60 A4 6c orange ('22) .50 .35
61 A4 6c scarlet ('26) .75 .15
62 A4 10c ultra ('23) 1.25 *5.00*
63 A4 10c ultra & blk ('23) 1.75 .50
64 A4 10c vio, *yel* ('31) 5.75 .35
65 A4 12c ultra ('22) 1.25 .15
66 A4 20c blk & vio ('23) 4.50 .25

Chalky Paper

67 A4 25c red vio & ol vio ('29) 2.25 .75
68 A4 30c yel & dl vio ('29) 3.00 1.50
69 A4 35c red, *yel* ('28) 5.75 *12.50*
70 A4 35c dk vio & car ('31) 12.00 10.50
71 A4 50c org & blk ('24) 12.00 3.75
72 A4 50c blk, *bl grn* ('31) 4.00 1.25
73 A3 $1 gray grn & yel grn ('26) 12.00 *27.50*
a. $1 green & blue green 17.50 *50.00*
74 A3 $2 grn & car ('26) 12.00 *50.00*
75 A3 $5 grn & ultra ('25) 60.00 *90.00*
76 A3 $25 grn & org ('28) 700.00 350.00
Nos. 49-75 (27) 155.90 *215.45*

#64 is on chalky paper; #66 exists on both ordinary and chalky paper; #69 is on ordinary paper.

1931-34

77 A4 $1 red & blk, *blue* 11.00 2.50
78 A4 $2 car & green, *yel* ('34) 27.50 26.00
79 A4 $5 car & green, *emer* ('34) 125.00 *125.00*
Nos. 77-79 (3) 163.50 *153.50*

FEDERATION OF MALAYA

GOVT. — Sovereign state in British Commonwealth of Nations
AREA — 50,700 sq. mi.
POP. — 7,139,000 (est. 1961)
CAPITAL — Kuala Lumpur

The Federation comprised the nine states of Johore, Pahang, Negri Sembilan, Selangor, Perak, Kedah, Perlis, Kelantan and Trengganu and the settlements of Penang and Malacca.

Malaya joined the Federation of Malaysia in 1963.

100 Sen (Cents) = 1 Dollar (1957)

Catalogue values for unused stamps in this section are for Never Hinged items.

The Peace Issue of 1946 8c stamp inscribed "MALAYAN UNION" was not issued.

Rubber Tapping A5

Map of Federation A6

Designs: 12c, Federation coat of arms. 25c, Tin dredge and flag.

Perf. 13x12½, 12½
Engr., Litho.

1957, May 5 Wmk. 314

80 A5 6c blue, red & yel .15 .15
a. Yellow omitted 40.00
81 A5 12c car & multi .15 .15
82 A5 25c multicolored .25 .15
83 A6 30c dp claret & red org .40 .15
Nos. 80-83 (4) .95
Set value .20

Chief Minister Tunku Abdul Rahman and People of Various Races — A7

Perf. 12½

1957, Aug. 31 Wmk. 4 Engr.

84 A7 10c brown .15 .15

Independence Day, Aug. 31.

United Nations Emblem — A8

Design: 30c, UN emblem, vert.

Perf. 13½, 12½

1958, Mar. 5 Wmk. 314

85 A8 12c rose red .35 .25
86 A8 30c plum .45 .30

Conf. of the Economic Commission for Asia and the Far East (ECAFE), Kuala Lumpur, Mar. 5-15.

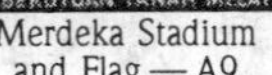

Merdeka Stadium and Flag — A9

Tuanku Abdul Rahman, Paramount Ruler of Malaya — A10

Perf. 13½x14½, 14½x13½

1958, Aug. 31 Photo. Wmk. 314

87 A9 10c multicolored .15 .15
88 A10 30c multicolored .45 .30
Set value .35

1st anniv. of the Independence of the Federation of Malaya.

Torch of Freedom and Broken Chain A11 A12

Perf. 12½x13, 13x12½

1958, Dec. 10 Litho. Wmk. 314

89 A11 10c multicolored .15 .15

Photo.

90 A12 30c green .50 .35
Set value .45

10th anniv. of the signing of the Universal Declaration of Human Rights.

Mace and People — A13 WRY Emblem — A14

Perf. 12½x13½

1959, Sept. 12 Photo. Unwmk.

91 A13 4c rose red .15 .15
92 A13 10c violet .15 .15
93 A13 25c yellow green .40 .30
Nos. 91-93 (3) .70
Set value .50

1st Federal Parliament of Malaya, inauguration.

Perf. 13½, 13

1960, Apr. 7 Engr. Wmk. 314

Design: 30c, Similar to 12c, vert.

94 A14 12c lilac .25 .25
95 A14 30c dark green .30 .20

World Refugee Year, July 1, 1959-June 30, 1960.

Rubber Tree Seedling on Map of Malaya — A15 Tuanku Syed Putra — A16

Perf. 13x13½

1960, Sept. 19 Litho. Unwmk.

96 A15 6s red brown, grn & blk .15 .15
97 A15 30s ultra, yel grn & blk .55 .40
Set value .45

15th meeting of the Intl. Rubber Study Group and the Natural Rubber Research Conference, Kuala Lumpur, Sept. 26-Oct. 1.

Perf. 13½x14½

1961, Jan. 4 Photo. Wmk. 314

98 A16 10s blue & black .15 .15

Installation of Tuanku Syed Putra of Perlis as Paramount Ruler (Yang di-Pertuan Agong.)

Colombo Plan Emblem — A17 Malaria Eradication Emblem — A18

1961, Oct. 30 Unwmk. *Perf. 13½*

99 A17 12s rose pink & black .30 .20
100 A17 25s brt yellow & black .40 .30
101 A17 30s brt blue & black .55 .20
Nos. 99-101 (3) 1.25 .70

13th meeting of the Consultative Committee for Technical Co-operation in South and South East Asia, Kuala Lumpur, Oct. 30-Nov. 18.

Wmk. PTM Multiple (338)

1962, Apr. 7 *Perf. 14x14½*

102 A18 25s orange brown .30 .15
103 A18 30s dull violet .30 .20
104 A18 50s ultramarine .55 .35
Nos. 102-104 (3) 1.15 .70

WHO drive to eradicate malaria.

Palmyra Leaf — A19

1962, July 21 Photo. *Perf. 13½*

105 A19 10s violet & gldn brown .15 .15
106 A19 20s bluish grn & gldn brn .25 .15
107 A19 50s car rose & gldn brown .50 .35
Nos. 105-107 (3) .90
Set value .50

National Language Month. Watermark inverted on alternating stamps.

Children and their Future Shadows — A20

1962, Oct. 1 Wmk. 338 *Perf. 13½*

108 A20 10s bright rose lilac .15 .15
109 A20 25s ocher .40 .30
110 A20 30s bright green .50 .30
Nos. 108-110 (3) 1.05
Set value .60

Free primary education introduced Jan. 1962.

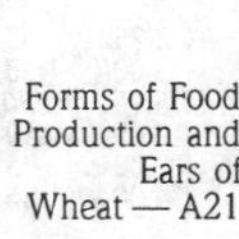

Forms of Food Production and Ears of Wheat — A21

1963, Mar. 21 Unwmk. *Perf. 11½*

Granite Paper

111 A21 25s lt ol grn & lilac rose .90 .25
112 A21 30s dk car & lilac rose 1.25 .20
113 A21 50s ultra & lilac rose 1.50 .35
Nos. 111-113 (3) 3.65 .80

FAO "Freedom from Hunger" campaign.

Cameron Highlands Dam and Pylon — A22

1963, June 26 Wmk. 338 *Perf. 14*

114 A22 20s purple & brt green .45 .30
115 A22 30s ultra & brt green .65 .45

Opening of the Cameron Highlands hydroelectric plant.

Check listings for individual states for additional stamps inscribed "Malaya."

POSTAGE DUE STAMPS

D1

D2

Perf. 14½x14

1924-26 Typo. Wmk. 4

J1 D1 1c violet 2.25 2.25
J2 D1 2c black 1.40 1.75
J3 D1 4c green ('26) 5.50 *9.50*
J4 D1 8c red 5.00 *11.00*
J5 D1 10c orange 5.50 *11.00*
J6 D1 12c ultramarine 8.50 *18.00*
Nos. J1-J6 (6) 28.15 *53.50*

1936-38 *Perf. 14½x14*

J7 D2 1c dk violet ('38) 2.50 .50
J8 D2 4c yellow green 4.25 1.00
J9 D2 8c scarlet 3.00 *4.25*
J10 D2 10c yel orange 3.00 .45
J11 D2 12c blue violet 4.00 *5.00*
J12 D2 50c black ('38) 13.00 *12.50*
Nos. J7-J12 (6) 29.75 *23.70*

#J7-J12 were also used in Straits Settlements.

For overprints see #NJ1-NJ20, Malacca #NJ1-NJ6.

1945-49

J13 D2 1c reddish violet 2.50 1.50
J14 D2 3c yel green 7.25 10.00
J15 D2 5c org scarlet 10.00 *12.00*
J16 D2 8c yel org ('49) 20.00 10.00
J17 D2 9c yel orange 45.00 35.00
J18 D2 15c blue vio 80.00 35.00
J19 D2 20c dk blue ('48) 10.00 12.00
Nos. J13-J19 (7) 174.75 115.50

For surcharge see No. J34.

> **Catalogue values for unused stamps in this section, from this point to the end of the section, are for Never Hinged items.**

1951-62 Wmk. 4 *Perf. 14*

J20 D2 1c dull violet ('52) .30 .35
J21 D2 2c dk gray ('53) .35 .50
J22 D2 3c green ('52) 12.50 10.00
J23 D2 4c dk brown ('53) .40 2.50
J24 D2 5c vermilion 27.50 10.00
J25 D2 8c yel orange 2.00 2.50
J26 D2 12c magenta ('54) 1.00 2.50
J27 D2 20c deep blue 5.00 6.00
Nos. J20-J27 (8) 49.05 34.35

Nos. J13-J27 were used throughout the Federation and in Singapore, later in Malaysia.

1957-62 *Perf. 12½*

J21a D2 2c ('60) .30 *7.50*
J23a D2 4c ('60) .65 *7.00*
J26a D2 12c ('62) 1.50 *12.50*
J27a D2 20c 5.00 *25.00*
Nos. J21a-J27a (4) 7.45 *52.00*

1965 Wmk. 314 *Perf. 12*

J28 D2 1c plum .20 *2.00*
J29 D2 2c bluish black .25 *5.00*
J30 D2 4c brown .30 *7.50*
J31 D2 8c yel orange 4.50 *10.00*
J32 D2 12c magenta 2.50 *20.00*
J33 D2 20c dark blue 3.50 *27.50*
Nos. J28-J33 (6) 11.25 *72.00*

Nos. J28-J33 were used in Malaysia.

1964, Apr. 14 *Perf. 12½*

J28a D2 1c .20 *2.00*
J29a D2 2c .30 *7.50*
J30a D2 4c .65 *7.00*
J32a D2 12c 1.50 *12.50*
J33a D2 20c 5.00 *25.00*
Nos. J28a-J33a (5) 7.65 *54.00*

No. J16 Surcharged **10 cents**

1965, Jan. Wmk. 4

J34 D2 10c on 8c yel orange .50 *1.00*

OCCUPATION STAMPS

Issued Under Japanese Occupation

Malayan Fruit and Fronds OS1

Tin Dredging OS2

Monument to Japanese War Dead OS3

Malayan Plowman OS4

1943 Unwmk. Litho. *Perf. 12½*

N30 OS1 2c emerald .25 .25
a. Rouletted 1.25 1.25
b. Imperf., pair 3.75 3.75
N31 OS2 4c rose red .25 .25
a. Rouletted 1.25 1.25
b. Imperf., pair 3.50 3.50
N32 OS3 8c dull blue .25 .25
Nos. N30-N32 (3) .75 .75

1943, Sept. 1

N33 OS4 8c violet 8.50 3.50
N34 OS4 15c carmine red 8.50 3.50

Publicity for Postal Savings which had reached a $10,000,000 total in Malaya.

Rubber Tapping — OS5

Seaside Houses — OS6

Japanese Shrine, Singapore — OS7

Sago Palms — OS8

Johore Bahru and Strait of Johore — OS9

Malay Mosque, Kuala Lumpur — OS10

1943, Oct. 1

N35 OS5 1c gray green .50 .40
N36 OS5 3c olive gray .50 .40
N37 OS6 10c red brown .50 .40
N38 OS7 15c violet .65 .65
N39 OS8 30c olive green .65 .65
N40 OS9 50c blue 1.25 1.25
N41 OS10 70c dull blue 15.00 16.00
Nos. N35-N41 (7) 19.05 19.75

Rice Planting and Map of Malaysia — OS11

1944, Feb. 15

N42 OS11 8c carmine 7.50 3.50
N43 OS11 15c violet 4.50 3.50

Issued on the anniversary of the fall of Singapore to commemorate the "Birth of New Malaya".

OCCUPATION POSTAGE DUE STAMPS

Stamps and Type of Postage Due Stamps of 1936-38 Handstamped in Black, Red or Brown

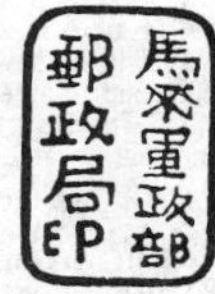

1942 Wmk. 4 Perf. 14½x14

NJ1 D2 1c violet 12.50 15.00
NJ2 D2 3c yellow green 25.00 17.50
NJ3 D2 4c yellow green 20.00 20.00
NJ4 D2 8c red 30.00 35.00
NJ5 D2 10c yellow orange 22.50 25.00
NJ6 D2 12c blue violet 22.50 25.00
NJ7 D2 50c black 50.00 50.00
Nos. NJ1-NJ7 (7) 182.50 187.50

Overprinted in Black **DAI NIPPON 2602 MALAYA**

1942

NJ8 D2 1c violet 2.50 2.50
NJ9 D2 3c yel green 3.50 3.75
NJ10 D2 4c yel green 6.00 6.50
NJ11 D2 8c red 7.50 12.00
NJ12 D2 10c yel orange 3.25 4.00
NJ13 D2 12c blue violet 3.25 4.00
Nos. NJ8-NJ13 (6) 26.00 32.75

The 9c and 15c with this overprint were not regularly issued.

Postage Due Stamps of 1936-45 Overprinted

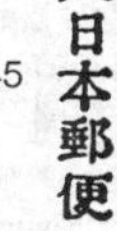

1943

NJ14 D2 1c reddish vio 1.00 1.75
NJ15 D2 3c yel green 1.00 1.75
NJ15A D2 4c yel green 50.00 45.00
NJ16 D2 5c scarlet 1.00 2.50
NJ17 D2 9c yel orange 1.50 1.75
NJ18 D2 10c yel orange 1.50 1.75
NJ19 D2 12c blue violet 1.50 1.75
NJ20 D2 15c blue violet 1.50 1.75
Nos. NJ14-NJ20 (8) 59.00 58.00

#NJ15A is said to have been extensively forged.

ISSUED UNDER THAI OCCUPATION

For use in Kedah, Kelantan, Perlis and Trengganu

War Memorial — OS1

Perf. 12½

1943, Dec. Unwmk. Litho.

2N1 OS1 1c pale yellow 10.00 10.00
2N2 OS1 2c buff 6.00 6.00
2N3 OS1 3c pale green 7.50 10.00
a. Imperf., pair 175.00
2N4 OS1 4c dull lilac 7.50 15.00
2N5 OS1 8c rose 7.50 10.00
2N6 OS1 15c lt blue 20.00 35.00
Nos. 2N1-2N6 (6) 58.50 86.00

These stamps, in cent denominations, were for use only in the four Malayan states ceded to Thailand by the Japanese. The states reverted to British rule in September, 1945.

JOHORE

jə-'hōr

LOCATION — At the extreme south of the Malay Peninsula.
AREA — 7,330 sq. mi.
POP. — 1,009,649 (1960)
CAPITAL — Johore Bahru

Stamps of the Straits Settlements Overprinted in Black

Overprinted

1876 Wmk. 1 Perf. 14

1 A2 2c brown 7,500. 3,000.

Overprinted **JOHORE.**

Overprint 13 to 14mm Wide

1884-86 Wmk. 2

1A A2 2c rose 85.00 90.00

Without Period

Overprint 16 to 17x2mm

2 A2 2c rose 450.00 200.00
a. Double overprint 1,200.

Overprinted **JOHORE**

Overprint 11x2½mm

3 A2 2c rose 45.00 60.00

Overprinted **JOHORE**

Overprint 17½x2¾mm

4 A2 2c rose 1,500. 1,000.

Overprinted **JOHOR**

Overprint 12½ to 15x2¾mm

5 A2 2c rose 6.00 9.00

Overprinted **JOHOR**

Overprint 9x2½mm

6 A2 2c brown
7 A2 2c rose 30.00 30.00
a. Double overprint 750.00

Overprinted **JOHOR**

Overprint 9x3mm

8 A2 2c rose 25.00 24.00

Overprinted **JOHOR**

Overprint 14 to 15x3mm

9 A2 2c rose 4.25 4.25

Tall "J" 3½mm high

10 A2 2c rose 110.00 125.00

Overprinted **JOHOR**

Overprint 15 to 15½x3mm

11 A2 2c rose 60.00 35.00

Overprinted **JOHOR**

1891

Overprint 12½ to 13x2½mm

12 A2 2c rose 9.00 7.50

Overprint 12x2¾mm

13 A2 2c rose 5,250.

Surcharged in Black:

JOHOR Two CENTS — a
JOHOR Two CENTS — b
JOHOR Two CENTS — c
JOHOR Two CENTS — d

1891

14 A3(a) 2c on 24c green 30.00 45.00
15 A3(b) 2c on 24c green 80.00 80.00
16 A3(c) 2c on 24c green 20.00 32.50
a. "CENST" 475.00 300.00
17 A3(d) 2c on 24c green 70.00 70.00
Nos. 14-17 (4) 200.00 227.50

Sultan Abubakar — A5

1892-94 Typo. Unwmk.

18 A5 1c lilac & vio ('94) .25 .50
19 A5 2c lilac & yellow .25 1.25
20 A5 3c lilac & car rose ('94) .45 .55
21 A5 4c lilac & black 2.50 7.25
22 A5 5c lilac & green 6.00 17.50
23 A5 6c lilac & blue 7.00 18.00
24 A5 $1 green & car rose 45.00 87.50
Nos. 18-24 (7) 61.45 132.55

For surcharges and overprints see #26-36.

Stamps of 1892-94 Surcharged in Black **3 cents.**

1894

26 A5 3c on 4c lilac & blk .95 .50
a. No period after "Cents" 35.00 35.00
27 A5 3c on 5c lilac & grn .95 1.50
a. No period after "Cents" 42.50 55.00
28 A5 3c on 6c lilac & bl 1.25 1.75
a. No period after "Cents" 60.00 65.00
29 A5 3c on $1 green & car 8.75 37.50
a. No period after "Cents" 150.00 300.00
Nos. 26-29 (4) 11.90 41.25

Coronation Issue

Stamps of 1892-94 Overprinted "KEMAHKOTAAN"

1896

30 A5 1c lilac & violet .45 .80
31 A5 2c lilac & yellow .40 .90
32 A5 3c lilac & car rose 1.10 .90
33 A5 4c lilac & black .90 2.00
34 A5 5c lilac & green 5.00 6.50
35 A5 6c lilac & blue 3.25 5.50
36 A5 $1 green & car rose 35.00 65.00
Nos. 30-36 (7) 46.10 81.60

Overprinted "KETAHKOTAAN"

30a A5 1c 2.75 3.50
31a A5 2c 3.00 3.50
32a A5 3c 4.00 6.00
33a A5 4c 2.50 6.00
34a A5 5c 3.25 6.75
35a A5 6c 3.50 5.50
36a A5 $1 27.50 70.00
Nos. 30a-36a (7) 46.50 101.25

Coronation of Sultan Ibrahim.

Sultan Ibrahim — A7

1896-99 Typo. Wmk. 71

37 A7 1c green .60 .40
38 A7 2c green & blue .35 .30
39 A7 3c green & vio 1.10 .70
40 A7 4c green & car rose .40 .45
41 A7 4c yel & red ('99) .65 .45
42 A7 5c green & brn .65 1.25
43 A7 6c green & yel .70 1.75
44 A7 10c green & black 6.75 35.00
45 A7 25c green & vio 7.25 27.50
46 A7 50c grn & car rose 14.00 35.00
47 A7 $1 lilac & green 20.00 50.00
48 A7 $2 lilac & car rose 20.00 50.00
49 A7 $3 lilac & blue 25.00 72.50
50 A7 $4 lilac & brn 27.50 60.00
51 A7 $5 lilac & orange 60.00 82.50
Nos. 37-51 (15) 184.95 417.80

On Nos. 44-46 the numerals are on white tablets. Numerals of Nos. 48-51 are on tablets of solid color.

Stamps of 1896-1926 with revenue cancellations sell for a fraction of those used postally.

For surcharges see Nos. 52-58.

Nos. 40-41 Surcharged in Black **3 cents.**

1903

52 A7 3c on 4c yel & red .75 .75
a. Without bars 2.50 4.25
53 A7 10c on 4c grn & car rose 2.25 3.00
a. Without bars 22.50 35.00

Bars on Nos. 52-53 were handruled with pen and ink.

Surcharged **50 Cents.**

54 A7 50c on $3 lilac & blue 22.50 55.00

Surcharged **One Dollar**

55 A7 $1 on $2 lilac & car rose 47.50 80.00
a. Inverted "e" in "one" 1,250.

Surcharged **10 CENTS**

1904

56 A7 10c on 4c yel & red 22.50 32.50
a. Double surcharge 7,500.
57 A7 10c on 4c grn & car rose 8.00 30.00
58 A7 50c on $5 lil & org 50.00 90.00
Nos. 56-58 (3) 80.50 152.50

Sultan Ibrahim — A8

The 10c, 21c, 25c, 50c, and $10 to $500 denominations of type A8 show the numerals on white tablets. The numerals of the 8c, 30c, 40c, and $2 to $5 demonimations are shown on tablets of solid colors.

1904-08 Typo. Wmk. 71

59 A8 1c violet & green .50 .20
60 A8 2c violet & brn org 1.00 1.50
61 A8 3c violet & black 1.00 .25
62 A8 4c violet & red 6.00 1.00
63 A8 5c violet & ol grn .70 2.00
64 A8 8c violet & blue 2.00 4.00
65 A8 10c violet & black 25.00 7.00
66 A8 25c violet & green 2.50 15.00
67 A8 50c violet & red 25.00 11.00
68 A8 $1 green & vio 12.00 45.00
69 A8 $2 green & car 17.00 40.00
70 A8 $3 green & blue 21.00 55.00
71 A8 $4 green & brn 22.50 75.00
72 A8 $5 green & org 30.00 65.00
73 A8 $10 green & blk 42.50 100.00
74 A8 $50 green & blue 140.00 200.00
75 A8 $100 green & scar 275.00 400.00
Revenue cancel 30.00
Nos. 59-73 (15) 208.70 421.95

The 1c, 2c and 10c also exist on chalky paper.

Nos. 74 and 75 were theoretically available for postage but were mostly used for revenue purposes.

For surcharge see No. 86.

1910-18 Wmk. 47

Chalky Paper

76 A8 1c violet & green .25 .15
77 A8 2c violet & orange 3.50 .50
78 A8 3c violet & black 2.50 .50
79 A8 4c violet & red 2.00 .60
80 A8 5c violet & ol grn 1.75 .50
81 A8 8c violet & blue 3.25 3.50
82 A8 10c violet & black 18.00 2.00
83 A8 25c violet & green 3.50 17.00
84 A8 50c violet & red 45.00 60.00
85 A8 $1 green & vio 50.00 55.00
Nos. 76-85 (10) 129.75 139.75

#78-79, 82 exist with horizontal watermark.

No. 64 Surcharged **3 CENTS.**

1912 Wmk. 71

86 A8 3c on 8c vio & blue 2.00 4.00
a. "T" of "CENTS" omitted 400.00

1918-19 Typo. Wmk. 3
Chalky Paper

87 A8 2c violet & orange .60 1.25
88 A8 2c violet & grn ('19) .40 .55
89 A8 4c violet & red .45 .15
90 A8 5c vio & olive grn ('19) 1.25 1.75
91 A8 10c violet & blue 1.25 1.25
92 A8 21c violet & orange 2.25 3.50
93 A8 25c vio & grn ('19) 6.50 12.00
94 A8 50c vio & red ('19) 15.00 25.00
95 A8 $1 grn & red vio 8.75 35.00
96 A8 $2 green & scar 18.00 35.00
97 A8 $3 green & blue 22.50 60.00
98 A8 $4 green & brn 35.00 75.00
99 A8 $5 green & org 45.00 85.00
100 A8 $10 green & blk 100.00 *150.00*
Nos. 87-100 (14) 256.95 *485.45*

1921-40 Wmk. 4

101 A8 1c violet & black .15 .15
102 A8 2c violet & brn .55 1.10
103 A8 2c green & dk grn ('28) .15 .15
104 A8 3c green ('25) 1.40 2.75
105 A8 3c dull vio & brn ('28) .90 1.00
106 A8 4c vio & red 1.40 .15
107 A8 5c vio & ol grn .30 .15
108 A8 6c vio & red brown .25 .15
109 A8 10c vio & blue 15.00 24.00
110 A8 10c vio & yel ('22) .30 .15
111 A8 12c vio & blue 1.00 1.25
111A A8 12c ultra ('40) 27.50 5.00
112 A8 21c dull vio & org ('28) 2.25 2.25
113 A8 25c vio & green 1.25 .75
114 A8 30c dull vio & org ('36) 2.25 2.00
115 A8 40c dull vio & brn ('36) 2.25 *3.25*
116 A8 50c violet & red 2.25 1.00
117 A8 $1 grn & red violet 2.25 .70
118 A8 $2 grn & red 5.00 3.50
119 A8 $3 grn & blue 35.00 45.00
120 A8 $4 grn & brn ('26) 60.00 90.00
121 A8 $5 grn & org 40.00 *45.00*
122 A8 $10 grn & blk 125.00 *150.00*
123 A8 $50 grn & ultra 500.00
124 A8 $100 grn & red 1,200.
125 A8 $500 ultra & org brn ('26) *17,000.*
Revenue cancel 140.00
Nos. 101-122 (23) 326.40 *379.45*

Nos. 123, 124 and 125 were available for postage but were probably used only fiscally.

A9

A10

1935, May 15 Engr. *Perf. 12½*
126 A9 8c Sultan Ibrahim, Sultana 1.75 .55

1940, Feb. *Perf. 13½*
127 A10 8c Sultan Ibrahim 7.00 .25

Catalogue values for unused stamps in this section, from this point to the end of the section, are for Never Hinged items.

Silver Wedding Issue
Common Design Types
Inscribed: "Malaya Johore"
Perf. 14x14½

1948, Dec. 1 Wmk. 4 Photo.
128 CD304 10c purple .20 .20

Perf. 11½x11
Engr.; Name Typo.
129 CD305 $5 green 24.00 24.00

Common Design Types
Pictured following the introduction.

Sultan Ibrahim — A11

1949-55 Wmk. 4 Typo. *Perf. 18*
130 A11 1c black .30 .15
131 A11 2c orange .30 .15
132 A11 3c green .85 .35
133 A11 4c chocolate .30 .15
134 A11 5c rose vio ('52) .40 .15
135 A11 6c gray .50 .20
a. Wmk. 4a (error) 425.00
136 A11 8c rose red 1.65 .90
137 A11 8c green ('52) .85 1.00
138 A11 10c plum .50 .15
a. Imperf., pair 850.00
139 A11 12c rose red ('52) 1.00 1.75
140 A11 15c ultra 1.65 .45
141 A11 20c dk grn & blk 1.65 .60
142 A11 20c ultra ('52) 1.10 .25
143 A11 25c org & rose lil 1.25 .20
144 A11 30c plum & rose red ('55) 3.25 1.50
145 A11 35c dk vio & rose red ('52) 2.50 1.40
146 A11 40c dk vio & rose red 3.00 4.50
147 A11 50c ultra & blk 2.25 .25
148 A11 $1 vio brn & ultra 4.50 1.25
149 A11 $2 rose red & emer 16.00 4.00
150 A11 $5 choc & emer 32.50 8.50
Nos. 130-150 (21) 76.30 27.85

UPU Issue
Common Design Types
Inscribed: "Malaya-Johore"
Engr.; Name Typo. on 15c, 25c

1949, Oct. 10 *Perf. 13½, 11x11½*
151 CD306 10c rose violet .35 .20
152 CD307 15c indigo .55 .80
153 CD308 25c orange .70 1.10
154 CD309 50c slate 1.40 1.75
Nos. 151-154 (4) 3.00 3.85

Coronation Issue
Common Design Type

1953, June 2 Engr. *Perf. 13½x13*
155 CD312 10c magenta & black .25 .15

Sultan Ibrahim — A12

1955, Nov. 1 Wmk. 4 *Perf. 14*
156 A12 10c carmine lake .25 .15

Sultan Ibrahim's Diamond Jubilee.

Sultan Ismail and Johore State Crest Seal — A13

Perf. 11½
1960, Feb. 10 Unwmk. Photo.
Granite Paper
157 A13 10c multicolored .25 .15

Coronation of Sultan Ismail.

Types of Kedah 1957 with Portrait of Sultan Ismail

1960 Wmk. 314 Engr. *Perf. 13*
158 A8 1c black .15 .15
159 A8 2c red orange .15 .15
160 A8 4c dark brown .15 .15
161 A8 5c dk car rose .15 .15
162 A8 8c dark green 1.00 .30
163 A7 10c violet brown .25 .15
164 A7 20c blue .35 .15
165 A7 50c ultra & black .85 .15
166 A8 $1 plum & ultra 1.75 .55
167 A8 $2 red & green 3.50 2.00
168 A8 $5 ol, grn & brn 13.50 *8.50*
Nos. 158-168 (11) 21.80 *12.40*

Starting in 1965, issues of Johore are listed with Malaysia.

POSTAGE DUE STAMPS

D1

Perf. 12½
1938, Jan. 1 Typo. Wmk. 4
J1 D1 1c rose red 6.75 *25.00*
J2 D1 4c green 24.00 *32.50*
J3 D1 8c dull yellow 27.50 *110.00*
J4 D1 10c bister brown 27.50 *40.00*
J5 D1 12c rose violet 35.00 *100.00*
Nos. J1-J5 (5) 120.75 *307.50*

OCCUPATION POSTAGE DUE STAMPS

Issued under Japanese Occupation

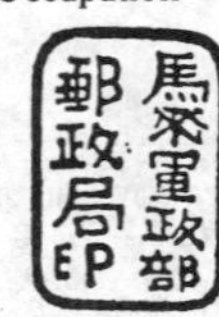
Johore Nos. J1-J5 Overprinted in Black, Brown or Red

1942 Wmk. 4 *Perf. 12½*
NJ1 D1 1c rose red 42.50 70.00
NJ2 D1 4c green 55.00 70.00
NJ3 D1 8c dull yellow 65.00 80.00
NJ4 D1 10c bister brown 15.00 45.00
NJ5 D1 12c rose violet 25.00 45.00
Nos. NJ1-NJ5 (5) 202.50 310.00

Johore Nos. J1-J5 Overprinted in Black 大日本郵便

1943
NJ6 D1 1c rose red 2.00 *10.00*
NJ7 D1 4c green 2.00 *10.00*
NJ8 D1 8c dull yellow 7.00 *12.50*
NJ9 D1 10c bister brown 5.00 *15.00*
NJ10 D1 12c rose violet 5.00 *20.00*
Nos. NJ6-NJ10 (5) 21.00 *67.50*

Nos. NJ6-NJ10 exist with second character sideways.

KEDAH

'ke-də

LOCATION — On the west coast of the Malay Peninsula.
AREA — 3,660 sq. mi.
POP. — 752,706 (1960)
CAPITAL — Alor Star

Sheaf of Rice — A1

Native Plowing — A2

Council Chamber — A3

1912-21 Engr. Wmk. 3 *Perf. 14*
1 A1 1c green & black .25 .25
2 A1 1c brown ('19) .35 .40
3 A1 2c green ('19) .50 .25
4 A1 3c car & black 2.00 .25
5 A1 3c dk violet ('19) .50 .45
6 A1 4c slate & car 7.50 .25
7 A1 4c scarlet ('19) 1.50 .20
8 A1 5c org brown & grn 1.75 *2.50*
9 A1 8c ultra & blk 1.25 *2.00*
10 A2 10c black brn & bl 1.50 .75
11 A2 20c yel grn & blk 2.50 *3.50*
12 A2 21c red vio & vio ('19) 5.00 *30.00*
13 A2 25c red vio & bl ('21) 1.65 *17.50*
14 A2 30c car & black 1.65 *8.00*
15 A2 40c lilac & blk 2.75 *10.00*
16 A2 50c dull bl & brn 7.50 *10.00*
17 A3 $1 scar & blk, *yel* 11.00 *15.00*
18 A3 $2 dk brn & dk grn 12.50 *50.00*
19 A3 $3 dk bl & blk, *bl* 45.00 *100.00*
20 A3 $5 car & black 50.00 *90.00*
Nos. 1-20 (20) 156.65 *341.30*

There are two types of No. 7, one printed from separate plates for frame and center, the other printed from a single plate.
Overprints are listed after No. 45.

Stamps of 1912 Surcharged **FIFTY CENTS**

1919
21 A3 50c on $2 dk brn & dk grn 45.00 *55.00*
a. "C" of ovpt. inserted by hand 900.00 725.00
22 A3 $1 on $3 dk bl & blk, *blue* 25.00 *75.00*

1921-36 Wmk. 4

Two types of 1c:
I - The 1's have rounded corners, small top serif. Small letters "c."
II - The 1's have square-cut corners, large top serif. Large letters "c."

Two types of 2c:
I - The 2's have oval drops. Letters "c" are fairly thick and rounded.
II - The 2's have round drops. Letters "c" thin and slightly larger.

23 A1 1c brown .35 .15
24 A1 1c blk (I) ('22) .25 .15
a. 1c black (II) ('39) 25.00 4.00
25 A1 2c green (I) .45 .15
a. 2c green (II) ('40) 55.00 8.00
26 A1 3c dk violet .70 .60
27 A1 3c green ('22) 1.25 .70
28 A1 4c carmine 4.25 .15
29 A1 4c dull vio ('26) .75 .15
30 A1 5c yellow ('22) 1.25 .15
31 A1 6c scarlet ('26) .60 .55
32 A1 8c gray ('36) 7.75 .15
33 A2 10c blk brn & bl 1.50 .65
34 A2 12c dk ultra & blk ('26) 1.90 *3.50*
35 A2 20c green & blk 2.25 1.75
36 A2 21c red vio & vio 1.75 *11.00*
37 A2 25c red vio & bl 1.90 *3.50*
38 A2 30c red & blk ('22) 2.50 *2.50*
39 A2 35c claret ('26) 4.25 *21.00*
40 A2 40c red vio & blk 2.50 *17.50*
41 A2 50c dp blue & brn 1.90 4.00
42 A3 $1 scar & blk, *yel* ('22) 5.50 6.50
43 A3 $2 brn & green 11.00 *65.00*
44 A3 $3 dk bl & blk, *bl* 32.50 *47.50*
45 A3 $5 car & black 40.00 *87.50*
Nos. 23-45 (23) 127.05 *274.80*

For overprints see Nos. N1-N6.

Stamps of 1912-21 Overprinted in Black: "MALAYA-BORNEO EXHIBITION." in Three Lines

1922 Wmk. 3
3a A1 2c green 5.75 *17.00*
12a A2 21c red vio & vio 20.00 *67.50*
13a A2 25c red vio & blue 20.00 *82.50*
b. Inverted overprint 750.00
16a A2 50c dull blue & brn 22.50 *85.00*

Wmk. 4
23a A1 1c brown 2.00 *14.00*
26a A1 3c dark violet 3.00 *25.00*
28a A1 4c carmine 3.00 *25.00*
33a A2 10c blk brn & blue 5.75 *35.00*
Nos. 3a-33a (8) 82.00 *351.00*

Industrial fair at Singapore, Mar. 31-Apr. 15, 1922.
On Nos. 12a, 13a and 16a, "BORNEO" exists both 14mm and 15mm wide.

Sultan of Kedah, Sir Abdul Hamid Halim Shah — A4

1937, July Wmk. 4 *Perf. 12½*
46 A4 10c sepia & ultra 2.00 .35
47 A4 12c gray vio & blk 17.00 *9.00*
48 A4 25c brn vio & ultra 5.50 *3.25*
49 A4 30c dp car & yel grn 6.25 *7.00*
50 A4 40c brn vio & blk 2.00 *10.00*
51 A4 50c dp blue & sepia 3.00 *3.25*
52 A4 $1 dk green & blk 2.25 *7.50*
53 A4 $2 dk brn & yel grn 75.00 60.00
54 A4 $5 dp car & black 25.00 *62.50*
Nos. 46-54 (9) 138.00 *162.85*

For overprints see Nos. N7-N15.

Catalogue values for unused stamps in this section, from this point to the end of the section, are for Never Hinged items.

Silver Wedding Issue
Common Design Types
Inscribed: "Malaya Kedah"

1948, Dec. 1 Photo. *Perf. 14x14½*
55 CD304 10c purple .20 .20

Perf. 11½x11
Engraved; Name Typographed
56 CD305 $5 rose car 25.00 25.00

UPU Issue
Common Design Types
Inscribed: "Malaya-Kedah"

Engr.; Name Typo. on 15c, 25c
1949, Oct. 10 *Perf. 13½, 11x11½*
57 CD306 10c rose violet .20 .20
58 CD307 15c indigo .40 .40
59 CD308 25c orange .70 .70
60 CD309 50c slate 1.50 1.50
Nos. 57-60 (4) 2.80 2.80

Sheaf of Rice — A5 Sultan Tungku Badlishah — A6

1950-55 Wmk. 4 Typo. *Perf. 18*
61 A5 1c black .15 .15
62 A5 2c orange .15 .15
63 A5 3c green .35 .35
64 A5 4c chocolate .15 *.20*
65 A5 5c rose vio ('52) .15 .15
66 A5 6c gray .20 .15
67 A5 8c rose red .55 *1.25*
68 A5 8c green ('52) .35 *1.25*
69 A5 10c plum .15 .15
70 A5 12c rose red ('52) .30 *2.50*
71 A5 15c ultramarine 1.10 *.85*
72 A5 20c dk green & blk 1.10 *2.50*
73 A5 20c ultra ('52) .50 .25
74 A6 25c org & rose lilac .60 .45
75 A6 30c plum & rose red ('55) 2.50 *.85*
76 A6 35c dk vio & rose red ('52) .75 *1.65*
77 A6 40c dk vio & rose red 1.50 *5.50*
78 A6 50c ultra & black .80 .20
79 A6 $1 yel brown & ultra 5.50 1.65
80 A6 $2 rose red & emer 20.00 *21.00*
81 A6 $5 choc & emerald 26.00 *27.50*
Nos. 61-81 (21) 62.85 *68.70*

Coronation Issue
Common Design Type

1953, June 2 Engr. *Perf. 13½x13*
82 CD312 10c magenta & black .30 .15

Fishing Craft — A7 Weaving and Sultan — A8

Portrait of Sultan Tungku Badlishah and: 1c, Copra. 2c, Pineapples. 4c, Rice field. 5c, Mosque. 8c, East Coast Railway. 10c, Tiger. 50c, Aborigines with blowpipes. $1, Government offices. $2, Bersilat.

Perf. 13x12½, 12½x13
1957 Engr. Wmk. 314
83 A8 1c black .15 .15
84 A8 2c red orange .15 .15
85 A8 4c dark brown .15 .15
86 A8 5c dk car rose .15 .15
87 A8 8c dark green 1.40 2.00
88 A7 10c chocolate .20 .15
89 A7 20c blue .75 .20

Perf. 12½, 13½ ($1)
90 A7 50c ultra & black 1.10 .50
91 A8 $1 plum & ultra 2.25 .80
92 A8 $2 red & green 14.00 3.75
Revenue cancel .15
93 A8 $5 ol grn & brown 25.00 5.75
Revenue cancel .30
Nos. 83-93 (11) 45.30 13.75

See Nos. 95-105.

Sultan Abdul Halim — A9

Perf. 14x14½
1959, Feb. 20 Photo. Wmk. 314
94 A9 10c ultra, red & yellow .20 .15

Installation of the Sultan of Kedah, Abdul Halim.

Types of 1957

Designs as before with portrait of Sultan Abdul Halim.

Perf. 13x12½, 12½x13, 12½, 13½
1959-62 Engr. Wmk. 314
95 A8 1c black .15 .15
96 A8 2c red orange .15 .15
97 A8 4c dark brown .15 .15
98 A8 5c dk car rose .15 .15
99 A8 8c dark green .15 .15
100 A7 10c chocolate .55 .15
101 A7 20c blue .50 .15
102 A7 50c ultra & blk, perf. 12½x13 ('60) .90 .15
a. Perf. 12½ .80 .28
103 A8 $1 plum & ultra 2.75 .60
104 A8 $2 red & green 6.75 2.25
105 A8 $5 ol grn & brn, perf. 13x12½ ('62) 15.00 3.75
a. Perf. 12½ 10.00 3.75
Nos. 95-105 (11) 27.20 7.80

Starting in 1965, issues of Kedah are listed with Malaysia.

OCCUPATION STAMPS

Issued Under Japanese Occupation

Stamps of Kedah 1922-36, Overprinted in Red or Black

DAI NIPPON
2602

1942, May 13 Wmk. 4 *Perf. 14*
N1 A1 1c black (R) 1.75 2.00
N2 A1 2c green (R) 30.00 40.00
N3 A1 4c dull violet (R) 2.50 3.00
N4 A1 5c yellow (R) 2.25 3.00
a. Black overprint 250.00 300.00
N5 A1 6c scarlet (Bk) 1.75 3.50
N6 A1 8c gray (R) 2.75 2.75

Nos. 46 to 54 Overprinted in Red

DAI NIPPON
2602

Perf. 12½
N7 A4 10c sepia & ultra 5.00 5.50
N8 A4 12c gray vio & blk 13.00 15.00
N9 A4 25c brn vio & ultra 6.50 8.00
a. Black overprint 100.00 100.00
N10 A4 30c dp car & yel grn 60.00 65.00
N11 A4 40c brn vio & blk 25.00 30.00
N12 A4 50c dp blue & sep 25.00 25.00
N13 A4 $1 dk grn & blk 125.00 125.00
a. Inverted overprint 250.00 250.00
N14 A4 $2 dk brn & yel green 200.00 140.00
N15 A4 $5 dp car & blk 85.00 90.00
a. Black overprint 210.00 225.00
Nos. N1-N15 (15) 585.50 557.75

KELANTAN

kə–'lan–,tan

LOCATION — On the eastern coast of the Malay Peninsula.
AREA — 5,750 sq. mi.
POP. — 545,620 (1960)
CAPITAL — Kota Bharu

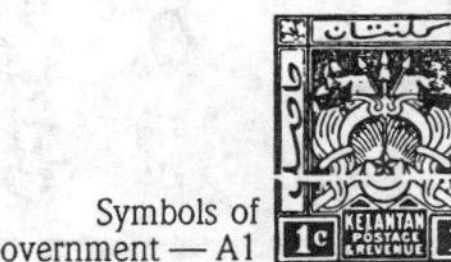
Symbols of Government — A1

1911-15 Typo. Wmk. 3 *Perf. 14*
Ordinary Paper
1 A1 1c gray green 1.00 .25
a. 1c green .15 .15
2 A1 3c rose red .25 .15
3 A1 4c black & red .30 .15
4 A1 5c grn & red, *yel* .90 .15
5 A1 8c ultramarine 3.25 1.10
6 A1 10c black & violet 4.00 .30

Chalky Paper
7 A1 30c violet & red 6.00 .45
8 A1 50c black & org 3.75 2.75
9 A1 $1 green & emer 42.50 45.00
10 A1 $1 grn & brn ('15) 25.00 3.00
11 A1 $2 grn & car rose 1.50 *4.00*
12 A1 $5 green & ultra 11.50 *9.00*
13 A1 $25 green & org 45.00 *72.50*
Nos. 1-13 (13) 144.95 *138.80*

For overprints see listings after No. 26. For surcharges see Nos. N20-N22.

1921-28 Wmk. 4
Ordinary Paper
14 A1 1c green 4.00 .55
15 A1 1c black ('23) .45 .45
16 A1 2c brown 4.00 *3.50*
17 A1 2c green ('26) .90 .35
18 A1 3c brown ('27) 2.50 1.40
19 A1 4c black & red .75 .15
20 A1 5c grn & red, *yel* .65 .15
21 A1 6c claret 2.25 *1.75*
22 A1 6c rose red ('28) 3.75 5.00
23 A1 10c black & violet 1.75 .15

Chalky Paper
24 A1 30c dull vio & red ('26) 3.75 *5.00*
25 A1 50c black & orange 4.50 *35.00*
26 A1 $1 green & brown 25.00 *55.00*
Nos. 14-26 (13) 54.25 *108.45*

Stamps of 1911-21 Overprinted in Black: "MALAYA BORNEO EXHIBITION" in Three Lines

1922 Wmk. 3
3a A1 4c black & red 2.75 *25.00*
4a A1 5c green & red, *yel* 4.25 *27.50*
7a A1 30c violet & red 5.50 *50.00*
8a A1 50c black & orange 7.00 *55.00*
10a A1 $1 green & brown 22.50 *75.00*
11a A1 $2 green & car rose 55.00 *140.00*
12a A1 $5 green & ultra 140.00 *325.00*

Wmk. 4
14a A1 1c green 2.00 *25.00*
23a A1 10c black & violet 4.75 *45.00*
Nos. 3a-23a (9) 243.75

Industrial fair at Singapore. Mar. 31-Apr. 15, 1922.

Sultan Ismail
A2 A2a

1928-33 Engr. *Perf. 12*
Size: 21½x30mm
27 A2 $1 ultramarine 14.00 *35.00*

Perf. 14
28 A2 $1 blue ('33) 50.00 *47.50*

1937-40 *Perf. 12*
Size: 22½x34½mm
29 A2a 1c yel & ol green .15 .40
30 A2a 2c deep green .95 .15
31 A2a 4c brick red 1.90 .50
32 A2a 5c red brown 1.90 .15
33 A2a 6c car lake 4.75 3.50
34 A2a 8c gray green 1.90 .15
35 A2a 10c dark violet 9.00 2.50
36 A2a 12c deep blue 1.25 *3.75*
37 A2a 25c vio & red org 1.90 *3.25*
38 A2a 30c scar & dk vio 17.00 *15.00*
39 A2a 40c blue grn & org 3.50 *20.00*
40 A2a 50c org & ol grn 21.00 *4.50*
41 A2a $1 dp grn & dk violet 20.00 *11.00*
42 A2a $2 red & red brn ('40) 165.00 *165.00*
43 A2a $5 rose lake & org ('40) 275.00 *400.00*
Nos. 29-43 (15) 525.20 *629.85*

For overprints see Nos. N1-N19.

Catalogue values for unused stamps in this section, from this point to the end of the section, are for Never Hinged items.

Silver Wedding Issue
Common Design Types
Inscribed: "Malaya Kelantan"

Perf. 14x14½
1948, Dec. 1 Wmk. 4 Photo.
44 CD304 10c purple .20 .20

Perf. 11½x11
Engraved; Name Typographed
45 CD305 $5 rose car 24.00 *25.00*

Common Design Types pictured following the introduction.

UPU Issue
Common Design Types
Inscribed: "Malaya-Kelantan"

Engr.; Name Typo. on 15c, 25c
1949, Oct. 10 *Perf. 13½, 11x11½*
46 CD306 10c rose violet .30 .30
47 CD307 15c indigo .60 .60
48 CD308 25c orange .85 .85
49 CD309 50c slate 1.50 1.50
Nos. 46-49 (4) 3.25 3.25

Sultan Ibrahim — A3

Wmk. 4
1951, July 11 Typo. *Perf. 18*
50 A3 1c black .15 .25
51 A3 2c orange .45 .25
52 A3 3c green 2.75 1.00
53 A3 4c chocolate .15 .15
54 A3 6c gray .20 .15
55 A3 8c rose red .65 *2.50*
56 A3 10c plum .20 .15
57 A3 15c ultramarine 2.50 .50
58 A3 20c dk green & blk .40 3.50
59 A3 25c orange & plum .50 .50
60 A3 40c vio brn & rose red 3.75 7.50
61 A3 50c dp ultra & blk .90 .30
62 A3 $1 vio brown & ultra 5.50 3.00
63 A3 $2 rose red & emer 20.00 17.00
64 A3 $5 choc & emer 45.00 35.00

1952-55
65 A3 5c rose violet .40 .30
66 A3 8c green .65 *1.50*
67 A3 12c rose red .65 *2.00*
68 A3 20c ultramarine .70 *.20*
69 A3 30c plum & rose red ('55) 1.10 1.50
70 A3 35c dk vio & rose red .80 *1.25*
Nos. 50-70 (21) 87.40 78.50

Compare with Pahang A8, Perak A16, Selangor A15, Trengganu A5.

Coronation Issue
Common Design Type

1953, June 2 Engr. *Perf. 13½x13*
71 CD312 10c magenta & black .25 .20

Fishing Craft — A4 Government Offices and Sultan — A5

Portrait of Sultan Ibrahim and: 1c, Copra. 2c, Pineapples. 4c, Rice field. 5c, Mosque. 8c, East Coast Railway. 10c, Tiger. 50c, Aborigines with blowpipes. $2, Bersilat. $5, Weaving.

Perf. 13x12½, 12½x13, 13½ ($1)
1957-63 Engr. Wmk. 314
72 A5 1c black .15 .30
73 A5 2c red orange .60 .40
74 A5 4c dark brown .15 .15
75 A5 5c dk car rose .15 .15
76 A5 8c dark green .70 2.25
77 A4 10c chocolate .50 .15
78 A4 20c blue .40 .30
79 A4 50c ultra & blk ('60) 1.75 .30
a. Perf 12½ .70 .65
80 A5 $1 plum & ultra 3.50 1.50
81 A5 $2 red & grn ('63) 7.50 *16.00*
a. Perf. 12½ 7.00 *7.00*
82 A5 $5 ol grn & brn ('63) 17.50 *17.50*
a. Perf. 12½ 16.00 *25.00*
Nos. 72-82 (11) 32.90 *39.00*

Sultan Yahya Petra — A6

1961, July 17 Photo. *Perf. 14½x14*
83 A6 10s multicolored .30 .20

Installation of Sultan Yahya Petra.

Types of 1957 with Portrait of Sultan Yahya Petra

Designs as before.

Perf. 13x12½, 12½x13
1961-62 Engr. Wmk. 338
84 A5 1c black .25 .15
85 A5 2c red orange .25 .15
86 A5 4c dark brown .25 .15
87 A5 5c dk car rose .25 .15
88 A5 8c dark green 2.00 .70
89 A4 10c violet brown ('61) .25 .15
90 A4 20c blue .85 .25
Nos. 84-90 (7) 4.10
Set value 1.20

Starting in 1965, issues of Kelantan are listed with Malaysia.

OCCUPATION STAMPS

Issued Under Japanese Occupation

Kelantan No. 35 Handstamped in Black

1942 Wmk. 4 *Perf. 12*
N1 A2a 10c dark violet 300.00 375.00

Some authorities believe No. N1 was not regularly issued.

Kelantan Nos. 29-40 Surcharged in Black or Red and Handstamped with Oval Seal "a" in Red

1 Cents

Sunakawa — a

Handa — b

1942
N2 1c on 50c org & ol green 150.00 150.00
a. With "b" seal 47.50 47.50
N3 2c on 40c bl grn & orange 250.00 250.00
a. With "b" seal 40.00 47.50
N4 5c on 12c dp bl (R) 150.00 150.00
N5 8c on 5c red brn (R) 170.00 125.00
a. With "b" seal (R) 120.00 140.00
N6 10c on 6c car lake 70.00 110.00
a. With "b" seal 70.00 110.00
N7 12c on 8c gray green (R) 45.00 100.00
N8 30c on 4c brick red 800.00 900.00
N9 40c on 2c dp grn (R) 45.00 75.00
N10 50c on 1c yel & ol green 850.00 800.00

Kelantan Nos. 29-40, 19-20, 22 Surcharged in Black or Red and Handstamped with Oval Seal "a" in Red

2 CENTS **$1.00**

N10A 1c on 50c org & ol green 95.00 80.00
N11 2c on 40c bl grn & orange 95.00 90.00
N11A 4c on 30c scar & dark vio 850.00 900.00
N12 5c on 12c dp bl (R) 150.00 150.00
N13 6c on 25c vio & red org 150.00 150.00
N14 8c on 5c red brown (R) 85.00 65.00
N15 10c on 6c car lake 85.00 90.00
N16 12c on 8c gray grn (R) 165.00 175.00
a. With "b" seal (R) 55.00 75.00
N17 25c on 10c dk vio 875.00 *925.00*
N17A 30c on 4c brick red 1,200. *1,300.*
N18 40c on 2c dp grn (R) 45.00 75.00
N19 50c on 1c yel & ol green *850.00* 800.00

Perf. 14
N20 $1 on 4c blk & red (R) 47.50 65.00
N21 $2 on 5c grn & red, *yel* 47.50 65.00
N22 $5 on 6c rose red 47.50 65.00

Examples of Nos. N2-N22 without handstamped seal are from the remainder stocks sent to Singapore after Kelantan was ceded to Thailand. Some authorities believe stamps without seals were used before June 1942.

ISSUED UNDER THAI OCCUPATION

OS1

1943, Nov. 15 *Perf. 11*
2N1 OS1 1c violet & black *125.00 150.00*
2N2 OS1 2c violet & black *140.00 150.00*
2N3 OS1 4c violet & black *140.00 175.00*
2N4 OS1 8c violet & black *125.00 150.00*
2N5 OS1 10c violet & black *175.00 200.00*
Nos. 2N1-2N5 (5) *705.00 825.00*

Stamps with centers in red are revenues.

MALACCA

mə-'la-kə

Melaka

LOCATION — On the west coast of the Malay peninsula.
AREA — 640 sq. mi.
POP. — 318,110 (1960)
CAPITAL — Malacca

Catalogue values for unused stamps in this section are for Never Hinged items.

Silver Wedding Issue
Common Design Types
Inscribed: "Malaya Malacca"

Perf. 14x14½
1948, Dec. 1 Wmk. 4 Photo.
1 CD304 10c purple .25 .25

Engraved; Name Typographed
Perf. 11½x11
2 CD305 $5 lt brown 25.00 25.00

Type of Straits Settlements, 1937-41, Inscribed "Malacca"

Wmk. 4
1949, Mar. 1 Typo. *Perf. 18*
3 A29 1c black .15 .60
4 A29 2c orange .45 .35
5 A29 3c green .30 *1.25*
6 A29 4c chocolate .20 .20
7 A29 6c gray .40 .25
8 A29 8c rose red .30 *3.50*
9 A29 10c plum .15 .15
10 A29 15c ultramarine .30 .50
11 A29 20c dk green & blk .30 *3.50*
12 A29 25c org & rose lil .30 .75
13 A29 40c dk vio & rose red 1.25 *8.00*
14 A29 50c ultra & black .55 .15
15 A29 $1 vio brn & ultra 5.25 *11.00*
16 A29 $2 rose red & emer 18.00 *16.00*
17 A29 $5 choc & emer 42.50 *35.00*
Nos. 3-17 (15) 70.40 *81.20*

See Nos. 22-26.

UPU Issue
Common Design Types
Inscribed: "Malaya-Malacca"

Engr.; Name Typo. on 15c, 25c
Perf. 13½, 11x11½
1949, Oct. 10 Wmk. 4
18 CD306 10c rose violet .25 .40
19 CD307 15c indigo .55 *1.50*
20 CD308 25c orange .75 *3.00*
21 CD309 50c slate 1.25 *3.75*
Nos. 18-21 (4) 2.80 *8.65*

Type of Straits Settlements, 1937-41, Inscribed "Malacca"

1952, Sept. 1 Wmk. 4 *Perf. 18*
22 A29 5c rose violet .45 *1.00*
23 A29 8c green .90 *3.00*
24 A29 12c rose red .95 *3.00*
25 A29 20c ultramarine 1.25 1.75
26 A29 35c dk vio & rose red 1.00 *2.00*
Nos. 22-26 (5) 4.55 *10.75*

Coronation Issue
Common Design Type

1953, June 2 Engr. *Perf. 13½x13*
27 CD312 10c magenta & black .45 .15

Queen Elizabeth II — A1

1954-55 Wmk. 4 Typo. *Perf. 18*
29 A1 1c black .15 .15
30 A1 2c orange .20 .15
31 A1 4c chocolate .25 .15
32 A1 5c rose violet .15 .15
33 A1 6c gray .15 .15
34 A1 8c green .20 .30
35 A1 10c plum .25 .15
36 A1 12c rose red .15 .25
37 A1 20c ultramarine .15 .45
38 A1 25c orange & plum .15 .20
39 A1 30c plum & rose red ('55) .15 .40
40 A1 35c vio brn & rose red .15 .55
41 A1 50c ultra & black .20 .45
42 A1 $1 vio brn & ultra 2.00 1.10
43 A1 $2 rose red & grn 15.00 3.50
44 A1 $5 choc & emerald 15.00 8.50
Nos. 29-44 (16) 34.30 16.60

Types of Kedah with Portrait of Queen Elizabeth II

Perf. 13x12½, 12½x13
1957 Engr. Wmk. 314
45 A8 1c black .15 .15
46 A8 2c red orange .15 .15
47 A8 4c dark brown .15 .15
48 A8 5c dark car rose .15 .15
49 A8 8c dark green .60 .25
50 A7 10c chocolate .45 .15
51 A7 20c blue .65 .15

Perf. 12½, 13½ ($1)
52 A7 50c ultra & black 1.00 .20
53 A8 $1 plum & ultra 1.90 1.00
54 A8 $2 red & green 6.25 3.00
55 A8 $5 olive grn & brn 13.00 6.00
Nos. 45-55 (11) 24.45 11.35

Types of Kedah, 1957, With Melaka Tree and Mouse Deer Replacing Portrait of Queen Elizabeth II

Perf. 13x12½, 12½x13, 13½ ($1)
1960, Mar. 15 Engr. Wmk. 314
56 A8 1c black .15 .15
57 A8 2c red orange .15 .15
58 A8 4c dark brown .15 .15
59 A8 5c dark car rose .15 .15
60 A8 8c dark green .45 .20
61 A7 10c violet brown .20 .15
62 A7 20c blue .40 .15
63 A7 50c ultra & black .90 .20
64 A8 $1 plum & ultra 1.50 .65
65 A8 $2 red & green 3.50 1.50
66 A8 $5 ol grn & brn 9.00 2.75
Nos. 56-66 (11) 16.55 6.20

Starting in 1965, issues of Malacca (Melaka) are listed with Malaysia.

OCCUPATION STAMPS

Issued Under Japanese Occupation
Stamps of Straits Settlements, 1937-41 Handstamped in Carmine

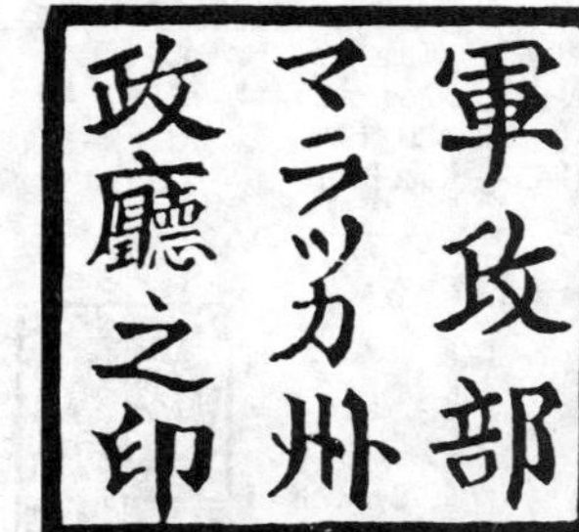

The handstamp covers four stamps. Values are for single stamps. Blocks of four showing complete handstamp sell for six times the price of singles.

1942 Wmk. 4 *Perf. 14*
N1 A29 1c black 100.00 60.00
N2 A29 2c brown orange 90.00 60.00
N3 A29 3c green 100.00 60.00
N4 A29 5c brown 90.00 100.00
N5 A29 8c gray 125.00 150.00
N6 A29 10c dull violet 100.00 70.00
N7 A29 12c ultramarine 80.00 85.00
N8 A29 15c ultramarine 60.00 65.00
N9 A29 30c org & vio *1,900. 1,900.*
N10 A29 40c dk vio & rose red 800.00 600.00
N11 A29 50c blk, *emerald* 950.00 700.00
N12 A29 $1 red & blk, *bl* 1,000. 900.00
N13 A29 $2 rose red & gray grn *1,500. 1,250.*
N14 A29 $5 grn & red, *grn* *1,750. 2,100.*

Some authorities believe Nos. N9, N13, and N14 were not regularly issued.

OCCUPATION POSTAGE DUE STAMPS

Malaya Postage Due Stamps and Type of 1936-38, Handstamped Like Nos. N1-N14 in Carmine

1942 Wmk. 4 *Perf. 14½x14*
NJ1 D2 1c violet *200.00 140.00*
NJ2 D2 4c yel green *200.00 200.00*
NJ3 D2 8c red *1,250. 1,250.*
NJ4 D2 10c yel orange *200.00 200.00*
NJ5 D2 12c blue violet *500.00 300.00*
NJ6 D2 50c black *1,250. 900.00*
Nos. NJ1-NJ6 (6) *3,600. 2,990.*

Pricing note above No. N1 also applies to Nos. NJ1-NJ6.

NEGRI SEMBILAN

'ne-grē səm-'bē-lən

LOCATION — South of Selangor on the west coast of the Malay Peninsula, bordering on Pahang on the east and Johore on the south.
AREA — 2,580 sq. mi.
POP. — 401,742 (1960)
CAPITAL — Seremban

Stamps of the Straits Settlements Overprinted in Black

Negri Sembilan

1891 Wmk. 2 *Perf. 14*
Overprint 14½ to 15mm Wide
1 A2 2c rose 2.50 4.25

Tiger — A1

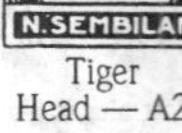

Tiger Head — A2

1891-94 Typo.
2 A1 1c green ('93) 2.50 1.10
3 A1 2c rose 3.50 4.50
4 A1 5c blue ('94) 22.50 *27.50*
Nos. 2-4 (3) 28.50 *33.10*

For surcharges see Nos. 17-18.

1895-99
5 A2 1c lilac & green 4.50 2.00
6 A2 2c lilac & brown 24.00 *80.00*
7 A2 3c lilac & car rose 4.00 .65
8 A2 5c lilac & olive 5.00 5.00
9 A2 8c lilac & blue 22.50 12.00
10 A2 10c lilac & orange 25.00 11.00
11 A2 15c green & vio 27.50 55.00
12 A2 20c grn & ol ('99) 32.50 *32.50*
13 A2 25c grn & car rose 60.00 *75.00*
14 A2 50c green & black 47.50 55.00
Nos. 5-14 (10) 252.50 *328.15*

For surcharges see Nos. 15-16, 19-20.

Stamps of 1891-99 Surcharged

Four cents.

1899 Green Surcharge
15 A2 4c on 8c lil & blue 2.25 3.50
a. Double surcharge 1,250. 1,250.
b. Pair, one without surcharge — 2,000.

c. Double surcharge, 1 green, 1 red 750.00 750.00

Black Surcharge

16 A2 4c on 8c lil & blue 800.00 *850.00*

Same Surcharge and Bar in Black

17 A1 4c on 1c green 1.25 *12.00*
18 A1 4c on 5c blue 1.25 *11.00*
19 A2 4c on 3c lil & car rose 2.75 *12.00*
a. Double surcharge 900.00 800.00
b. Pair, one without surcharge 2,250. *2,250.*
d. Bar double 600.00

Bar at bottom on #17-18, at top on #19.

No. 11 Surcharged in Black **One cent.**

1900

20 A2 1c on 15c grn & vio 80.00 *140.00*
a. Inverted period 275.00 *450.00*

Arms of Negri Sembilan
A4 A5

1935-41 Typo. Wmk. 4

21 A4 1c black ('36) .75 .15
22 A4 2c dp green ('36) .50 .15
22A A4 2c brown org ('41) .15 *27.50*
22B A4 3c green ('41) .15 *4.00*
23 A4 4c brown orange .50 .15
24 A4 5c chocolate .50 .15
25 A4 6c rose red 2.75 .90
25A A4 6c gray ('41) 1.90 *50.00*
26 A4 8c gray 1.25 .25
27 A4 10c dull vio ('36) 1.25 .20
28 A4 12c ultra ('36) 1.50 .45
28A A4 15c ultra ('41) 2.00 *35.00*
29 A4 25c rose red & dull vio ('36) 1.50 1.50
30 A4 30c org & dull vio ('36) 2.00 2.75
31 A4 40c dull vio & car .90 *3.50*
32 A4 50c blk, *emer* ('36) 3.75 .90
33 A4 $1 red & blk, *bl* ('36) 1.50 2.00
34 A4 $2 rose red & grn ('36) 20.00 26.00
35 A4 $5 brn red & grn, *emer* ('36) 15.00 *35.00*
Nos. 21-35 (19) 57.85 *190.55*

For overprints see Nos. N1-N31.

Catalogue values for unused stamps in this section, from this point to the end of the section, are for Never Hinged items.

Silver Wedding Issue
Common Design Types
Inscribed: "Malaya Negri Sembilan"

1948, Dec. 1 Photo. *Perf. 14x14½*

36 CD304 10c purple .20 .20

Perf. 11½x11

Engraved; Name Typographed

37 CD305 $5 green 22.50 25.00

1949-55 Wmk. 4 Typo. *Perf. 18*

38 A5 1c black .15 .15
39 A5 2c orange .15 .15
40 A5 3c green .35 .30
41 A5 4c chocolate .15 .15
42 A5 5c rose violet .20 .15
43 A5 6c gray .30 .15
44 A5 8c rose red .55 .60
45 A5 8c green 2.00 2.00
46 A5 10c plum .30 .15
47 A5 12c rose red 2.00 2.00
48 A5 15c ultramarine 1.50 .40
49 A5 20c dk green & blk .80 .85
50 A5 20c ultramarine 1.00 .30
51 A5 25c org & rose lilac .45 .25
52 A5 30c plum & rose red ('55) 2.50 1.50
53 A5 35c dk vio & rose red 1.00 2.00
54 A5 40c dk vio & rose red 1.10 *4.00*
55 A5 50c ultra & black 1.10 .40
56 A5 $1 vio brn & ultra 2.50 1.00
57 A5 $2 rose red & emer 10.00 8.00
58 A5 $5 choc & emerald 45.00 30.00
Nos. 38-58 (21) 73.10 54.50

UPU Issue
Common Design Types
Inscribed: "Malaya-Negri Sembilan"

Engr.; Name Typo. on 15c, 25c

1949, Oct. 10 *Perf. 13½, 11x11½*

59 CD306 10c rose violet .20 .20
60 CD307 15c indigo .40 .40
61 CD308 25c orange .75 .75
62 CD309 50c slate 1.50 2.25
Nos. 59-62 (4) 2.85 3.60

Coronation Issue
Common Design Type

1953, June 2 Engr. *Perf. 13½x13*

63 CD312 10c magenta & black .35 .15

Types of Kedah with Arms of Negri Sembilan

Perf. 13x12½, 12½x13, 13½ ($1)

1957-63 Engr. Wmk. 314

64 A8 1c black .15 .15
65 A8 2c red orange .15 .15
66 A8 4c dark brown .15 .15
67 A8 5c dk car rose .15 .15
68 A8 8c dark green .25 1.00
69 A7 10c chocolate .40 .15
70 A7 20c blue .25 .15
71 A7 50c ultra & blk ('60) .65 .20
a. Perf. 12½ .65 .20
72 A8 $1 plum & ultra 1.50 .50
73 A8 $2 red & grn ('63) 4.00 6.00
a. Perf. 12½ 3.50 4.25
74 A8 $5 ol grn & brn ('62) 10.00 10.00
a. Perf. 12½ 8.25 5.75
Nos. 64-74 (11) 17.65 18.60

Negri Sembilan State Crest and Tuanku Munawir — A6

1961, Apr. 17 Unwmk. *Perf. 14x13*

75 A6 10s blue & multi .20 .15

Installation of Tuanku Munawir as ruler (Yang di-Pertuan Besar) of Negri Sembilan.

Starting in 1965, issues of Negri (Negeri) Sembilan are listed with Malaysia.

OCCUPATION STAMPS

Issued under Japanese Occupation

Stamps and Type of Negri Sembilan, 1935-41, Handstamped in Red, Black, Brown or Violet

1942 Wmk. 4 *Perf. 14*

N1 A4 1c black 18.00 12.00
N2 A4 2c brown org 12.00 13.00
N3 A4 3c green 16.00 16.00
N4 A4 5c chocolate 21.00 20.00
N5 A4 6c rose red 450.00 450.00
N6 A4 6c gray 110.00 110.00
N7 A4 8c gray 65.00 65.00
N8 A4 8c rose red 40.00 35.00
N9 A4 10c dark violet 80.00 80.00
N10 A4 12c ultramarine 650.00 650.00
N11 A4 15c ultramarine 15.00 8.00
N12 A4 25c rose red & dk vio 25.00 30.00
N13 A4 30c org & dk vio 125.00 140.00
N14 A4 40c dk vio & car 550.00 550.00
N15 A4 $1 red & blk, *bl* 100.00 100.00
N16 A4 $5 brn red & grn, *emerald* 325.00 350.00

The 8c rose red is not known to have been issued without overprint.

Some authorities believe Nos. N5 and N7 were not regularly issued.

Stamps of Negri Sembilan, 1935-41, Overprinted in Black

DAI NIPPON
2602
MALAYA

N17 A4 1c black 1.00 1.00
a. Inverted overprint 12.50 20.00
b. Dbl. ovpt., one invtd. 35.00 *50.00*
N18 A4 2c brown orange 1.25 1.00
N19 A4 3c green 1.00 .75
N20 A4 5c chocolate .65 .65
N21 A4 6c gray 1.50 1.50
a. Inverted overprint *750.00*
N22 A4 8c rose red 2.00 2.00
N23 A4 10c dk violet 4.00 4.00
N24 A4 15c ultramarine 6.00 3.50
N25 A4 25c rose red & dk vio 1.50 *5.00*
N26 A4 30c org & dk vio 3.00 *3.75*
N27 A4 $1 red & blk, *bl* 100.00 125.00
Nos. N17-N27 (11) 121.90 148.15

The 8c rose red is not known to have been issued without overprint.

Negri Sembilan, Nos. 21, 24 and 29, Overprinted or Surcharged in Black:

大日本郵便 (a) — 大日本郵便 2 cts. (b) — 大日本郵便 6 cts. (c)

1943

N28 A4 1c black .50 .50
a. Inverted overprint 12.50 17.50
N29 A4 2c on 5c choc .40 .50
N30 A4 6c on 5c choc .50 .65
a. "6 cts." inverted 250.00 *300.00*
N31 A4 25c rose red & dk violet 1.50 2.00
Nos. N28-N31 (4) 2.90 3.65

The Japanese characters read: "Japanese Postal Service."

PAHANG

pə-'haŋ

LOCATION — On the east coast of the Malay Peninsula.
AREA — 13,820 sq. mi.
POP. — 338,210 (1960)
CAPITAL — Kuala Lipis

Stamps of the Straits Settlements Overprinted in Black

Overprinted **PAHANG**

Overprint 16x2¾mm

1889 Wmk. 2 *Perf. 14*

1 A2 2c rose 70.00 40.00
2 A3 8c orange 1,600. 1,250.
3 A7 10c slate 250.00 250.00

Overprinted **PAHANG**

Overprint 12½x2mm

4 A2 2c rose 3.00 6.50

Overprinted **PAHANG**

1890 Overprint 15x2½mm

5 A2 2c rose — 850.00

Overprinted **PAHANG**

Overprint 16x2¾mm

6 A2 2c rose 60.00 14.00

Surcharged in Black:

PAHANG *Two* CENTS (a) — **PAHANG Two CENTS** (b) — **PAHANG *Two* CENTS** (c) — **PAHANG Two CENTS** (d)

1891

7 A3 (a) 2c on 24c green 300.00 400.00
8 A3 (b) 2c on 24c green 85.00 110.00
9 A3 (c) 2c on 24c green 80.00 80.00
10 A3 (d) 2c on 24c green 300.00 400.00
Nos. 7-10 (4) 765.00 990.00

A5

A6

1892-95 Typo.

11 A5 1c green 4.75 4.50
12 A5 2c rose 2.25 1.65
13 A5 5c blue 6.50 *20.00*
Nos. 11-13 (3) 13.50 *26.15*

For surcharges see Nos. 21-22.

1895-99

14 A6 3c lilac & car rose 3.00 1.75
14A A6 4c lil & car rose ('99) 10.00 6.25
15 A6 5c lilac & olive 18.00 *12.00*
Nos. 14-15 (3) 31.00 *20.00*

For surcharge see No. 28.

Stamps of Perak, 1895-99, Overprinted **Pahang.**

1898-99

16 A9 10c lilac & orange 15.00 *22.50*
17 A9 25c green & car rose 60.00 *85.00*
18 A9 50c green & black 140.00 *175.00*
18A A9 50c lilac & black 140.00 125.00

Overprinted **Pahang.**

Wmk. 1

19 A10 $1 green & lt grn 165.00 175.00
20 A10 $5 green & ultra 525.00 650.00
Nos. 16-20 (6) 1,045. 1,232.

No. 13 Cut in Half and Surcharged With New Value and Initials in ms.

1897 Wmk. 2

Red Surcharge

21 A5 2c on half of 5c blue *850.* *300.*
a. Black surcharge *5,000.* *2,000.*
22 A5 3c on half of 5c blue *850.* *300.*
a. Black surcharge *5,000.* *2,000.*

Perak No. 52 Surcharged **Pahang Four cents**

1899

25 A9 4c on 8c lilac & blue 3.00 *5.00*
b. Inverted surcharge 1,600. 850.00

Same Surcharge on pieces of White Paper

1898 Without Gum *Imperf.*

26 4c black 1,400.
27 5c black 900.00

Pahang No. 15 Surcharged **Four cents.**

1899 *Perf. 14*

28 A6 4c on 5c lilac & olive 8.50 *35.00*

Sultan Abu Bakar
A7 A8

1935-41 Typo. Wmk. 4 *Perf. 14*

29 A7 1c black ('36) .15 .15
30 A7 2c dp green ('36) .90 .15
30A A7 3c green ('41) .20 *3.25*
31 A7 4c brown orange .50 .15
32 A7 5c chocolate .60 .15
33 A7 6c rose red ('36) 2.25 *6.00*
34 A7 8c gray 1.50 .15
34A A7 8c rose red ('41) .50 *16.00*
35 A7 10c dk violet ('36) .50 .15
36 A7 12c ultra ('36) 2.00 1.90
36A A7 15c ultra ('41) 1.25 *20.00*
37 A7 25c rose red & pale vio ('36) 1.50 .65
38 A7 30c org & dk vio ('36) .90 1.00
39 A7 40c dk vio & car 1.25 1.
40 A7 50c black, *emer* ('36) 5.00
41 A7 $1 red & blk, *blue* ('36) 2.7
42 A7 $2 rose red & green ('36)

43 A7 $5 brn red & grn, *emer* ('36) 8.75 *45.00*
Nos. 29-43 (18) 54.50 *146.35*

The 3c was printed on both ordinary and chalky paper; the 15c only on ordinary paper; other values only on chalky paper.

A 2c brown orange and 6c gray, type A7, exist, but are not known to have been regularly issued.

For overprints see Nos. N1-N21.

Catalogue values for unused stamps in this section, from this point to the end of the section, are for Never Hinged items.

Silver Wedding Issue
Common Design Types
Inscribed: "Malaya Pahang"

Perf. 14x14½

1948, Dec. 1 Photo. Wmk. 4
44 CD304 10c purple .20 .20

Perf. 11½x11

Engraved; Name Typopgraphed
45 CD305 $5 green 24.00 35.00

UPU Issue
Common Design Types
Inscribed: "Malaya-Pahang"

Engr.; Name Typo. on 15c, 25c

1949, Oct. 10 *Perf. 13½, 11x11½*
46 CD306 10c rose violet .20 .20
47 CD307 15c indigo .30 .30
48 CD308 25c orange .80 .80
49 CD309 50c slate 1.40 1.40
Nos. 46-49 (4) 2.70 2.70

1950, June 1 Wmk. 4 Typo. *Perf. 18*
50 A8 1c black .15 .15
51 A8 2c orange .15 .15
52 A8 3c green .20 .30
53 A8 4c chocolate .15 .15
54 A8 6c gray .15 .15
55 A8 8c rose red .20 *1.50*
56 A8 10c plum .15 .15
57 A8 15c ultramarine .25 .15
58 A8 20c dk green & blk .25 *1.65*
59 A8 25c org & rose lilac .25 .15
60 A8 40c dk vio & rose red .80 *5.50*
61 A8 50c dp ultra & black .65 .15
62 A8 $1 vio brn & ultra 2.25 1.50
63 A8 $2 rose red & emer 12.00 15.00
64 A8 $5 choc & emer 50.00 *32.50*

1952-55
65 A8 5c rose violet .20 .15
66 A8 8c green .75 .65
67 A8 12c rose red .75 1.00
68 A8 20c ultramarine .65 .15
69 A8 30c plum & rose red ('55) 1.10 .30
70 A8 35c dk vio & rose red .55 .25
Nos. 50-70 (21) 71.60 *61.65*

Coronation Issue
Common Design Type

1953, June 2 Engr. *Perf. 13½x13*
71 CD312 10c magenta & black .25 .15

Types of Kedah with Portrait of Sultan Abu Bakar

Perf. 13x12½, 12½x13, 13½ ($1)

1957-62 Engr. Wmk. 314
72 A8 1c black .15 .15
73 A8 2c red orange .15 .15
74 A8 4c dark brown .15 .15
75 A8 5c dark car rose .15 .15
76 A8 8c dark green .25 .20
77 A7 10c chocolate .20 .15
78 A7 20c blue .40 .15
79 A7 50c ultra & blk ('60) .65 .25
a. Perf. 12½ .65 .25
80 A8 $1 plum & ultra 1.50 .65
81 A8 $2 red & green ('62) 3.50 2.00
a. Perf. 12½ 3.50 2.00
82 A8 $5 ol grn & brn ('60) 8.75 5.00
a. Perf. 12½ 8.75 5.00
Nos. 72-82 (11) 15.85 9.00

Starting in 1965, issues of Pahang are listed with Malaysia.

OCCUPATION STAMPS

...er Japanese Occupation

...ng, 1935-
... in Black,
... Violet

1942 Wmk. 4 *Perf. 14*
N1 A7 1c black 25.00 30.00
N1A A7 3c green 90.00 100.00
N2 A7 5c chocolate 11.00 7.00
N3 A7 8c rose red 19.00 8.00
N3A A7 8c gray 175.00 175.00
N4 A7 10c dk violet 45.00 45.00
N5 A7 12c ultramarine 900.00 900.00
N6 A7 15c ultramarine 65.00 65.00
N7 A7 25c rose red & pale vio 16.00 27.50
N8 A7 30c org & dk vio 12.50 24.00
N9 A7 40c dk vio & car 13.00 25.00
N10 A7 50c blk, *emerald* 225.00 250.00
N11 A7 $1 red & blk, *bl* 75.00 90.00
N12 A7 $5 brown red & grn, *emer* 575.00 625.00

Some authorities claim the 2c green, 4c brown orange, 6c rose red and $2 rose red and green were not regularly issued with this overprint.

Stamps of Pahang, 1935-41, Overprinted in Black

DAI NIPPON
2602
MALAYA

N13 A7 1c black 1.50 .80
N14 A7 5c chocolate 1.50 1.50
N15 A7 8c rose red 26.00 2.75
N16 A7 10c violet brown 15.00 6.75
N17 A7 12c ultramarine 1.50 2.25
N18 A7 25c rose red & pale vio 5.50 *7.75*
N19 A7 30c org & dk vio 2.00 *4.00*
Nos. N13-N19 (7) 53.00 *25.80*

Pahang No. 32 Overprinted and Surcharged in Black

大日本郵便 6 cts. e
大日本郵便 6 cts. f

1943
N20 A7(e) 6c on 5c chocolate 1.00 1.00
N21 A7(f) 6c on 5c chocolate 1.50 1.10

The Japanese characters read: "Japanese Postal Service."

PENANG

pə–naŋ

LOCATION — An island off the west coast of the Malay Peninsula, plus a coastal strip called Province Wellesley.
AREA — 400 sq. mi.
POP. — 616,254 (1960)
CAPITAL — Georgetown

Catalogue values for unused stamps in this section are for Never Hinged items.

Silver Wedding Issue
Common Design Types
Inscribed: "Malaya Penang"

Perf. 14x14½

1948, Dec. 1 Wmk. 4 Photo.
1 CD304 10c purple .20 .20

Perf. 11½x11

Engraved; Name Typographed
2 CD305 $5 lt brown 27.50 24.00

Type of Straits Settlements, 1937-41, Inscribed "Penang"

1949-52 *Perf. 18*
3 A29 1c black .15 .15
4 A29 2c orange .15 .15
5 A29 3c green .15 .25
6 A29 4c chocolate .15 .15
7 A29 5c rose vio ('52) .35 1.00
8 A29 6c gray .15 .15
9 A29 8c rose red .25 *2.50*
10 A29 8c green ('52) .70 .90
11 A29 10c plum .15 .15
12 A29 12c rose red ('52) .75 .60
13 A29 15c ultramarine .20 *2.00*
14 A29 20c dk grn & blk .20 1.00
15 A29 20c ultra ('52) .50 .35
16 A29 25c org & rose lilac .70 .15
17 A29 35c dk vio & rose red ('52) .55 .80
18 A29 40c dk vio & rose red .70 *6.00*
19 A29 50c ultra & black .90 .15
20 A29 $1 vio brn & ultra 10.00 .85
21 A29 $2 rose red & emer 11.00 .90
22 A29 $5 choc & emerald 42.50 1.25
Nos. 3-22 (20) 70.20 *19.45*

UPU Issue
Common Design Types
Inscribed: "Malaya-Penang"

Engr.; Name Typo. on 15c, 25c

1949, Oct. 10 *Perf. 13½, 11x11½*
23 CD306 10c rose violet .20 .15
24 CD307 15c indigo .40 .45
25 CD308 25c orange .70 .70
26 CD309 50c slate 1.40 1.40
Nos. 23-26 (4) 2.70 2.70

Coronation Issue
Common Design Type

1953, June 2 Engr. *Perf. 13½x13*
27 CD312 10c magenta & black .40 .15

Type of Malacca, 1954

1954-55 Wmk. 4 Typo. *Perf. 18*
29 A1 1c black .15 .25
30 A1 2c orange .40 .25
31 A1 4c chocolate .65 .15
32 A1 5c rose violet 2.00 1.50
33 A1 6c gray .20 .15
34 A1 8c green .20 *1.50*
35 A1 10c plum .20 .15
36 A1 12c rose red .30 2.00
37 A1 20c ultramarine .50 .15
38 A1 25c orange & plum .40 .15
39 A1 30c plum & rose red ('55) 1.00 .50
40 A1 35c vio brn & rose red .85 .50
41 A1 50c ultra & black .85 .35
42 A1 $1 vio brn & ultra 2.25 .35
43 A1 $2 rose red & grn 4.25 1.40
44 A1 $5 choc & emerald 19.00 3.25
Nos. 29-44 (16) 33.20 12.60

Types of Kedah with Portrait of Queen Elizabeth II

Perf. 13x12½, 12½x13

1957 Engr. Wmk. 314
45 A8 1c black .15 .20
46 A8 2c red orange .15 .25
47 A8 4c dark brown .15 .15
48 A8 5c dk car rose .15 .15
49 A8 8c dark green .80 1.00
50 A7 10c chocolate .25 .15
51 A7 20c blue .55 .15

Perf. 12½, 13½ ($1)
52 A7 50c ultra & black .95 .20
53 A8 $1 plum & ultra 1.40 .25
54 A8 $2 red & green 6.00 5.00
55 A8 $5 ol green & brown 12.00 6.00
Nos. 45-55 (11) 22.55 13.50

Types of Kedah, 1957 with Penang State Crest and Areca-nut Palm Replacing Portrait of Elizabeth II

Perf. 13x12½, 12½x13, 13½ ($1)

1960, Mar. 15 Engr. Wmk. 314
56 A8 1c black .15 .15
57 A8 2c red orange .15 .15
58 A8 4c dark brown .15 .15
59 A8 5c dk car rose .15 .15
60 A8 8c dark green .60 .40
61 A7 10c violet brown .15 .15
62 A7 20c blue .20 .15
63 A7 50c ultra & black .50 .15
64 A8 $1 plum & ultra 1.00 .30
65 A8 $2 red & green 2.50 .70
Revenue cancel .20
66 A8 $5 ol green & brown 7.00 1.25
Nos. 56-66 (11) 12.55
Set value 3.00

Starting in 1965, issues of Penang (Pulau Pinang) are listed with Malaysia.

OCCUPATION STAMPS

Issued under Japanese Occupation

Stamps of Straits Settlements, 1937-41, Overprinted in Red or Black

DAI NIPPON
2602
PENANG

1942 Wmk. 4 *Perf. 14*
N1 A29 1c black (R) 1.25 1.25
N2 A29 2c brown orange 6.50 3.25
N3 A29 3c green (R) 1.25 1.25
N4 A29 5c brown (R) 1.25 1.25
N5 A29 8c gray (R) 3.25 1.25
N6 A29 10c dull vio (R) 2.00 2.00
N7 A29 12c ultra (R) 2.75 *5.00*
N8 A29 15c ultra (R) 2.00 2.00
N9 A29 40c dk vio & rose red 3.25 *5.25*
N10 A29 50c black, *emer* (R) 5.25 *12.50*
N11 A29 $1 red & blk, *bl* 14.00 *17.50*
N12 A29 $2 rose red & gray grn 35.00 *50.00*
N13 A29 $5 grn & red, *grn* 475.00 450.00
Nos. N1-N13 (13) 552.75 552.50

Stamps of Straits Settlements Handstamped in Red

Okugawa Seal

1942 Wmk. 4 *Perf. 14*
N14 A29 1c black 14.00 12.50
N15 A29 2c brown orange 22.50 20.00
N16 A29 3c green 20.00 22.50
N17 A29 5c brown 35.00 25.00
N18 A29 8c gray 25.00 25.00
N19 A29 10c dull violet 40.00 40.00
N20 A29 12c ultramarine 35.00 25.00
N21 A29 15c ultramarine 25.00 30.00
N22 A29 40c dk vio & rose red 125.00 90.00
N23 A29 50c blk, *emerald* 125.00 140.00
N24 A29 $1 red & blk, *bl* 150.00 175.00
N25 A29 $2 rose red & gray grn 325.00 350.00
N26 A29 $5 grn & red, *grn* 900.00 950.00
Nos. N14-N26 (13) 1,841. 1,905.

Handstamped in Red

Uchibori Seal

N14a A29 1c 80.00 70.00
N15a A29 2c 85.00 70.00
N16a A29 3c 60.00 70.00
N17a A29 5c 600.00 600.00
N18a A29 8c 45.00 50.00
N19a A29 10c 45.00 55.00
N20a A29 12c 45.00 55.00
N21a A29 15c 45.00 55.00
Nos. N14a-N21a (8) 1,005. 1,025.

PERAK

ˈper–ə–ˌak

LOCATION — On the west coast of the Malay Peninsula.
AREA — 7,980 sq. mi.
POP. — 1,327,120 (1960)
CAPITAL — Taiping

Straits Settlements No. 10 Handstamped in Black

1878 Wmk. 1 *Perf. 14*
1 A2 2c brown 1,400. 1,000.

Overprinted **PERAK**

Overprint 17x3½mm Wide

1880
2 A2 2c brown 22.50 42.50

Overprinted **PERAK**

Overprint 10 to 14½mm Wide
3 A2 2c brown 70.00 75.00

Same Overprint on Straits Settlements Nos. 40, 41a

1883 Wmk. 2
4 A2 2c brown 17.00 25.00
5 A2 2c rose 11.00 22.50

Overprinted **PERAK**

Overprint 14 to 15½mm Wide
6 A2 2c rose 1.00 .90
a. Inverted overprint 250.00 375.00
b. Double overprint 575.00

Overprinted **PERAK**

Overprint 12¾ to 14mm Wide

1886-90
7 A2 2c rose 1.25 5.00
a. "FERAK" corrected by pen 165.00 200.00

Overprinted **PERAK**

Overprint 10x1 ¾mm

8 A2 2c rose 10.00 25.00

Overprinted **PERAK**

Overprint 13x2 ¾mm

10 A2 2c rose 3.25 12.00
a. Double overprint 1,150.

Overprinted **PERAK**

Overprint 10 ¾x2 ½mm

11 A2 2c rose 60.00 80.00

Straits Settlements Nos. 42, 41a Surcharged in Black or Blue

2 CENTS PERAK — q

ONE CENT PERAK. — r

ONE CENT PERAK — s

PERAK ONE CENT. — t

12 A2(q) 2c on 4c rose 500.00 250.00
13 A2(t) 1c on 2c rose 125.00 87.50
a. Without period after "PERAK" ('90) — 160.00
14 A2(r) 1c on 2c rose 35.00 50.00
a. Without period after "PERAK" 350.00 350.00
15 A2(s) 1c on 2c rose (Bl) 22.50 30.00
15A A2(s) 1c on 2c rose (Bk) 1,250. 925.00

In type "r" PERAK is 11 ½ to 14mm wide.

Surcharged in Black **1 CENT PERAK**

16 A2 1c on 2c rose 65.00 65.00
a. Double surcharge *1,500.*

Surcharged **1 CENT PERAK**

17 A2 1c on 2c rose

Some authorities question the status of No. 17.

Surcharged **1 CENT PERAK**

18 A2 1c on 2c rose 900.00 900.00
b. Double surcharge, one inverted
c. "PREAK"

Surcharged **1 CENT PERAK**

18A A2 1c on 2c rose 325.00 325.00

Surcharged ***One CENT PERAK***

19 A2 1c on 2c rose .75 4.50
a. Double surcharge, one inverted
b. Inverted surcharge
c. "One" inverted *2,000.*
d. Double surcharge *900.00*

Straits Settlements No. 41a Surcharged

One CENT PERAK — u
One CENT PERAK — v
One CENT PERAK — w
One CENT PERAK — x
One CENT PERAK — y
One CENT PERAK — z

One CENT PERAK — h

1889-90

20 A2(u) 1c on 2c rose .50 1.75
a. Italic Roman "K" in "PERAK" 125.00 150.00
b. Double surcharge
21 A2(v) 1c on 2c rose 350.00 400.00
23 A2(w) 1c on 2c rose 7.50 18.00
a. "PREAK" 250.00 350.00
24 A2(x) 1c on 2c rose 80.00 87.50
25 A2(y) 1c on 2c rose 4.25 5.00
26 A2(z) 1c on 2c rose 3.00 8.75
27 A2(h) 1c on 2c rose 11.00 21.00

Straits Settlements Nos. 41a, 48, 54 Surcharged in Black:

PERAK One CENT — a
PERAK Two CENTS — b
PERAK One CENT — c
PERAK One CENT — d
PERAK One CENT — e
PERAK One CENT — f
PERAK One CENT — g

1891 Wmk. 2

28 A2(a) 1c on 2c rose .70 2.75
a. Bar omitted 125.00
29 A2(a) 1c on 6c violet 35.00 25.00
30 A3(b) 2c on 24c green 8.00 8.00
31 A2(c) 1c on 2c rose 4.25 12.00
a. Bar omitted *600.00*
32 A2(d) 1c on 2c rose .80 3.50
a. Bar omitted 150.00
33 A2(d) 1c on 6c violet 60.00 60.00
34 A3(d) 2c on 24c green 30.00 25.00
35 A2(e) 1c on 2c rose 5.00 11.00
a. Bar omitted *600.00*
36 A2(e) 1c on 6c violet 110.00 125.00
37 A3(e) 2c on 24c green 75.00 50.00
38 A2(f) 1c on 6c violet 110.00 110.00
39 A3(f) 2c on 24c green 75.00 60.00
40 A2(g) 1c on 6c violet 100.00 110.00
41 A3(g) 2c on 24c green 75.00 60.00
Nos. 28-41 (14) 688.75 662.25

A7

1892-95 Typo. *Perf. 14*

42 A7 1c green 2.00 .45
43 A7 2c rose 1.40 .45
44 A7 2c orange ('95) .55 *3.25*
45 A7 5c blue 3.25 3.00
Nos. 42-45 (4) 7.20 *7.15*

For overprint see No. O10.

Type of 1892 Surcharged in Black **3 CENTS**

1895

46 A7 3c on 5c rose .50 *2.25*

A9 A10

1895-99 Wmk. 2 *Perf. 14*

47 A9 1c lilac & green .85 .35
48 A9 2c lilac & brown .65 .35
49 A9 3c lilac & car rose 1.90 .25
50 A9 4c lil & car rose ('99) 6.50 *4.25*
51 A9 5c lilac & olive 2.25 .50
52 A9 8c lilac & blue 27.50 .50
53 A9 10c lilac & orange 7.50 .40
54 A9 25c grn & car rose ('96) 90.00 10.00
55 A9 50c lilac & black 27.50 27.50
56 A9 50c grn & blk ('99) 100.00 100.00

Wmk. 1

57 A10 $1 green & lt grn 75.00 75.00
58 A10 $2 grn & car rose ('96) 110.00 110.00
59 A10 $3 green & ol ('96) 140.00 140.00
60 A10 $5 green & ultra 300.00 275.00
61 A10 $25 grn & org ('96) 4,000. 1,250.
Nos. 47-57 (11) 339.65 219.10

For surcharges and overprint see #62-68, O11, Malaya 9-13A.

Stamps of 1895-99 Surcharged in Black:

One Cent. — i

ONE CENT. — k

Three Cent. — m

1900 Wmk. 2

62 A9(i) 1c on 2c lilac & brown .45 1.40
63 A9(k) 1c on 4c lilac & car rose .50 4.00
a. Double surcharge 675.00
64 A9(i) 1c on 5c lilac & ol .65 5.00
65 A9(i) 3c on 8c lilac & blue 2.00 2.00
a. No period after "Cent" 80.00 *100.00*
b. Double surcharge 300.00 300.00
66 A9(i) 3c on 50c green & black 1.25 3.50
a. No period after "Cent" 70.00 *110.00*

Wmk. 1

67 A10(m) 3c on $1 grn & lt green 50.00 *110.00*
a. Double surcharge 1,150.
68 A10(m) 3c on $2 grn & car rose 25.00 *72.50*
Nos. 62-68 (7) 79.85 *198.40*

Sultan Iskandar
A14 A15

1935-37 Typo. Wmk. 4

Chalky Paper

69 A14 1c black ('36) .15 .15
70 A14 2c dp green ('36) .15 .15
71 A14 4c brown orange .25 .15
72 A14 5c chocolate .15 .15
73 A14 6c rose red ('37) 3.00 1.75
74 A14 8c gray 2.00 .30
75 A14 10c dk vio ('36) .55 .15
76 A14 12c ultra ('36) 2.50 .85
77 A14 25c rose red & pale vio ('36) 1.25 .95
78 A14 30c org & dark vio ('36) 1.25 1.50
79 A14 40c dk vio & car 4.00 3.25
80 A14 50c blk, *emerald* ('36) 2.50 1.40
81 A14 $1 red & blk, *bl* ('36) 2.00 1.50
82 A14 $2 rose red & green ('36) 16.00 8.50
83 A14 $5 brn red & grn, *emer* ('36) 32.50 20.00
Nos. 69-83 (15) 68.25 40.75

1938-41

84 A15 1c black ('39) 1.75 .15
85 A15 2c dp green ('39) 1.25 .15
85A A15 2c brn org ('41) .45 *1.25*
85B A15 3c green ('41) .75 .30
86 A15 4c brn org ('39) 12.50 .15
87 A15 5c choc ('39) 1.25 .15
88 A15 6c rose red ('39) 12.50 .15
89 A15 8c gray 12.50 .15
89A A15 8c rose red ('41) .50 *4.00*
90 A15 10c dk violet 12.50 .15
91 A15 12c ultramarine 12.50 1.90
91A A15 15c ultra ('41) 1.10 *11.00*
92 A15 25c rose red & pale vio ('39) 45.00 2.50
93 A15 30c org & dk vio 6.50 1.65
94 A15 40c dk vio & rose red 30.00 1.65
95 A15 50c blk, *emerald* 15.00 .40
96 A15 $1 red & blk, *bl* ('40) 70.00 13.00
97 A15 $2 rose red & grn ('40) 70.00 50.00
98 A15 $5 red, *emer* ('40) 125.00 *200.00*
Nos. 84-98 (19) 431.05 *288.70*

For overprints see Nos. N1-N40.

> Catalogue values for unused stamps in this section, from this point to the end of the section, are for Never Hinged items.

Silver Wedding Issue
Common Design Types
Inscribed: "Malaya Perak"

1948, Dec. 1 Photo. *Perf. 14x14½*

99 CD304 10c purple .15 .15

Perf. 11½x11
Engraved; Name Typographed

100 CD305 $5 green 24.00 24.00

UPU Issue
Common Design Types
Inscribed: "Malaya-Perak"
Engr.; Name Typo. on 15c, 25c
Perf. 13½, 11x11½

1949, Oct. 10 Wmk. 4

101 CD306 10c rose violet .20 .20
102 CD307 15c indigo .45 .40
103 CD308 25c orange .65 .80
104 CD309 50c slate 1.50 1.75
Nos. 101-104 (4) 2.80 3.15

Sultan Yussuf Izuddin Shah — A16

1950, Aug. 17 Typo. *Perf. 18*

105 A16 1c black .15 .15
106 A16 2c orange .15 .15
107 A16 3c green 1.25 .50
108 A16 4c chocolate .15 .15
109 A16 6c gray .15 .15
110 A16 8c rose red .25 .40
111 A16 10c plum .15 .15
112 A16 15c ultramarine .25 .25
113 A16 20c dk grn & blk .25 .45
114 A16 25c org & plum .25 .15
115 A16 40c vio brn & rose red 1.25 2.50
116 A16 50c dp ultra & blk .45 .15
117 A16 $1 vio brn & ultra 6.00 .40
118 A16 $2 rose red & emer 11.00 2.50
119 A16 $5 choc & emerald 32.50 10.00

1952-55

120 A16 5c rose violet .30 .15
121 A16 8c green .90 .50
122 A16 12c rose red .90 1.25
123 A16 20c ultramarine .65 .15
124 A16 30c plum & rose red ('55) 1.10 .20
125 A16 35c dk vio & rose red .60 .25
Nos. 105-125 (21) 58.65 20.55

Coronation Issue
Common Design Type

1953 Engr. *Perf. 13½x13*

126 CD312 10c magenta & black .25 .15

Types of Kedah with Portrait of Sultan Yussuf Izuddin Shah

Perf. 13x12½, 12½x13, 13½ ($1)

1957-61 Engr. Wmk. 314

127 A8 1c black .15 .15
128 A8 2c red orange .15 .15
129 A8 4c dark brown .15 .15
130 A8 5c dk car rose .15 .15
131 A8 8c dark green 1.00 .25
132 A7 10c chocolate .15 .15
133 A7 20c blue .25 .15
134 A7 50c ultra & blk ('60) .60 .20
a. Perf. 12½ .60 .20
135 A8 $1 plum & ultra 1.25 .25
136 A8 $2 red & grn ('61) 3.00 .65
a. Perf. 12½ 3.00 .90
137 A8 $5 ol grn & brn ('60) 10.00 2.00
a. Perf. 12½ 10.00 2.75
Nos. 127-137 (11) 16.85 4.25

Starting with 1963, issues of Perak are listed with Malaysia.

OFFICIAL STAMPS

Stamps and Types of Straits Settlements Overprinted in Black

1890 Wmk. 1 *Perf. 14*

O1 A3 12c blue 125.00 150.00
O2 A3 24c green 425.00 *450.00*

Wmk. 2

O3 A2 2c rose 1.75 2.75
a. No period after "S" 40.00 40.00
b. Double overprint 1,100. 1,100.
O4 A2 4c brown 6.50 15.00
a. No period after "S" 72.50 *100.00*
O5 A2 6c violet 16.00 32.50
O6 A3 8c orange 21.00 55.00
O7 A7 10c slate 55.00 60.00
O8 A3 12c vio brown 150.00 175.00
O9 A3 24c green 90.00 *125.00*

P.G.S. stands for Perak Government Service.

Perak No. 45 Overprinted **Service.**

1894

O10 A7 5c blue 35.00 .75
a. Inverted overprint 550.00 400.00

Same Overprint on No. 51

1897

O11 A9 5c lilac & olive 1.25 .30
a. Double overprint 325.00 350.00

OCCUPATION STAMPS

Issued under Japanese Occupation

Stamps of Perak, 1938-41, Handstamped in Black, Red, Brown or Violet

1942 Wmk. 4 *Perf. 14*

N1 A15 1c black 35.00 25.00
N2 A15 2c brn orange 25.00 16.00
N3 A15 3c green 25.00 27.50
N4 A15 5c chocolate 8.50 8.00
N5 A15 8c gray 40.00 27.50
N6 A15 8c rose red 18.00 25.00
N7 A15 10c dk violet 17.00 20.00
N8 A15 12c ultramarine 110.00 110.00
N9 A15 15c ultramarine 22.50 25.00
N10 A15 25c rose red & pale vio 20.00 22.00
N11 A15 30c org & dk vio 25.00 30.00
N12 A15 40c dk vio & rose red 125.00 140.00
N13 A15 50c blk, *emerald* 42.50 *45.00*
N14 A15 $1 red & blk, *bl* 200.00 225.00
N15 A15 $2 rose red & grn *1,100.* *1,100.*
N16 A15 $5 red, *emerald* 550.00 550.00

Some authorities claim No. N6 was not regularly issued. This overprint also exists on No. 85

Stamps of Perak, 1938-41, Overprinted in Black

DAI NIPPON
2602
MALAYA

N16A A15 1c black 30.00 30.00
N17 A15 2c brown orange 1.25 1.25
a. Inverted overprint 20.00 21.00
N18 A15 3c green .95 1.00
a. Inverted overprint 20.00 22.50
N18B A15 5c chocolate 30.00
N19 A15 8c rose red .95 .50
a. Inverted overprint 7.50 7.50
b. Dbl. ovpt., one invtd. 175.00 200.00
c. Pair, one without ovpt. 350.00 350.00
N20 A15 10c dk violet 6.25 7.00
N21 A15 15c ultramarine 4.50 5.00
N21A A15 30c org & dk vio 25.00 25.00
N22 A15 50c blk, *emerald* 3.00 4.50
N23 A15 $1 red & blk, *bl* 250.00 *275.00*
N24 A15 $5 red, *emerald* 45.00 50.00
a. Inverted overprint 250.00 *300.00*

Some authorities claim Nos. N16A, N18B and N21A were not regularly issued.

Overprinted on Perak No. 87 and Surcharged in Black "2 Cents"

N25 A15 2c on 5c chocolate 1.50 1.00

Perak Nos. 84 and 89A Over[illegible]d in Black **DAI NIPPON YUBIN**

[illegible]k 2.50 3.00
[illegible]rint 25.00 30.00
[illegible]ed 2.50 1.50
[illegible]nt 15.00 17.50

[illegible] Perak No. 87 and [illegible] Black "2 Cents"

[illegible]colate 3.75 3.75
[illegible] 25.00 35.00
[illegible]tted 37.50 42.50

Stamps of Perak, 1938-41, Overprinted or Surcharged in Black:

大日本郵便 — n
大日本郵便 **2 Cents** — No. N31
大日本郵便 **2 cts.** — No. N32

1943

N29 A15 1c black .50 .50
N30 A15 2c brn orange 26.00 26.00
N31 A15 2c on 5c choc .75 .75
a. "2 Cents" inverted 25.00 30.00
b. Entire surcharge inverted 25.00 30.00
N32 A15 2c on 5c choc 1.00 1.00
a. Vertical characters invtd. 25.00 30.00
b. Entire surcharge inverted 25.00 30.00
N33 A15 3c green 27.50 27.50
N34 A15 5c chocolate .75 .75
a. Inverted overprint 37.50 45.00
N35 A15 8c gray 25.00 25.00
N36 A15 8c rose red .75 .75
a. Inverted overprint 25.00 30.00
N37 A15 10c dk violet .90 .90
N38 A15 30c org & dk vio 2.00 3.00
N39 A15 50c blk, *emerald* 4.00 7.00
N40 A15 $5 red, *emerald* 55.00 62.50
Nos. N29-N40 (12) 144.15 155.65

No. N34 was also used in the Shan States of Burma. The Japanese characters read: "Japanese Postal Service."

Some authorities claim Nos. N30, N33 and N35 were not regularly issued.

PERLIS

'per-ləs

LOCATION — On the west coast of the Malay peninsula, adjoining Siam and Kedah.
AREA — 310 sq. mi.
POP. — 97,645 (1960)
CAPITAL — Kangar

Catalogue values for unused stamps in this section are for Never Hinged items.

Silver Wedding Issue
Common Design Types
Inscribed: "Malaya Perlis"
Perf. 14x14½

1948, Dec. 1 Photo. Wmk. 4

1 CD304 10c purple .20 .20

Engraved; Name Typographed
Perf. 11½x11

2 CD305 $5 lt brown 25.00 27.50

UPU Issue
Common Design Types
Inscribed: "Malaya-Perlis"

Engr.; Name Typo. on 15c, 25c
1949, Oct. 10 *Perf. 13½, 11x11½*

3 CD306 10c rose violet .25 .25
4 CD307 15c indigo .50 .50
5 CD308 25c orange .85 .85
6 CD309 50c slate 1.90 1.90
Nos. 3-6 (4) 3.50 3.50

Raja Syed Putra — A1

Wmk. 4

1951, Mar. 26 Typo. *Perf. 18*

7 A1 1c black .15 *.15*
8 A1 2c orange .15 *.15*
9 A1 3c green 1.00 *2.00*
10 A1 4c chocolate .25 .25
11 A1 6c gray .25 .30
12 A1 8c rose red .75 2.00
13 A1 10c plum .40 .15
14 A1 15c ultramarine 1.25 3.00
15 A1 20c dk green & blk 2.50 3.50
16 A1 25c org & rose lilac 1.00 .85
17 A1 40c dk vio & rose red 2.50 *4.00*
18 A1 50c ultra & black 1.90 1.15
19 A1 $1 vio brn & ultra 6.25 4.25
20 A1 $2 rose red & emer 8.50 *15.00*
21 A1 $5 choc & emerald 40.00 *47.50*

1952-55

22 A1 5c rose violet .20 .30
23 A1 8c green .50 *2.00*
24 A1 12c rose red .50 *2.50*
25 A1 20c ultramarine .70 .75
26 A1 30c plum & rose red ('55) 4.00 *5.00*
27 A1 35c dk vio & rose red 1.25 *3.00*
Nos. 7-27 (21) 74.00 *97.80*

Coronation Issue
Common Design Type

1953, June 2 Engr. *Perf. 13½x13*

28 CD312 10c magenta & black .35 .35

Types of Kedah with Portrait of Raja Syed Putra

Perf. 13x12½, 12½x13, 12½ ($2, $5), 13½ ($1)

1957-62 Engr. Wmk. 314

29 A8 1c black .15 .15
30 A8 2c red orange .15 *.15*
31 A8 4c dark brown .15 .15
32 A8 5c dk car rose .15 .15
33 A8 8c dark green 1.00 .35
34 A7 10c chocolate .15 .15
35 A7 20c blue .15 .15
36 A7 50c ultra & blk ('62) .60 .50
a. Perf. 12½ .50 .40
37 A8 $1 plum & ultra 1.25 *1.50*
38 A8 $2 red & green 3.00 *2.50*
39 A8 $5 ol green & brown 10.00 *5.50*
Nos. 29-39 (11) 16.75 *11.25*

Starting in 1965, issues of Perlis are listed with Malaysia.

SELANGOR

sə-'laŋ-ər

LOCATION — South of Perak on the west coast of the Malay Peninsula.
AREA — 3,160 sq. mi.
POP. — 1,012,891 (1960)
CAPITAL — Kuala Lumpur

Stamps of the Straits Settlements Overprinted

Handstamped in Black or Red

1878 Wmk. 1 *Perf. 14*

1 A2 2c brown (Bk)
2 A2 2c brown (R)

The authenticity of Nos. 1-2 and the 2c brown, watermarked Crown and CA, is questioned.

Overprinted in Black **S.**

1882 Wmk. 2

3 A2 2c brown 1,400.
4 A2 2c rose

Overprinted **SELANGOR**

Overprint 16 to 16¾mm Wide

1881 Wmk. 1

5 A2 2c brown 40.00 50.00
a. Double overprint

Overprint 16 to 17mm Wide

1882-83 Wmk. 2

6 A2 2c brown 75.00 65.00
7 A2 2c rose 75.00 65.00

Overprinted **SELANGOR**

Overprint 14¼x3mm

8 A2 2c rose 4.00 4.50
a. Double overprint

Overprinted **SELANGOR**

Overprint 14½ to 15½mm Wide

1886-89

9 A2 2c rose 15.00 15.00

Overprinted **SELANGOR**

Overprint 16½x1¾mm

9A A2 2c rose 35.00 32.50

Overprinted **SELANGOR**

Overprint 15½ to 17mm Wide
With Period

10 A2 2c rose 22.50 22.50

Without Period

11 A2 2c rose 4.00 2.00

Same Overprint, but Vertically

12 A2 2c rose 12.50 12.50

Overprinted **SELANGOR**

12A A2 2c rose 32.50 2.25

Overprinted ***Selangor***

Overprint 17mm Wide

13 A2 2c rose 675.00 *725.00*

Overprinted ***SELANGOR***

14 A2 2c rose 250.00 150.00

Overprinted Vertically **SELANGOR**

1889

15 A2 2c rose 82.50 16.00

Overprinted Vertically ***SELANGOR***

Overprint 19 to 20¾mm Wide

16 A2 2c rose 60.00 30.00

Similar Overprint, but Diagonally

17 A2 2c rose 1,100.

Overprinted Vertically **SELANGOR**

18 A2 2c rose 35.00 5.25

Same Overprint Horizontally

18A A2 2c rose 3,250.

Surcharged in Black:

SELANGOR ***Two*** **CENTS** — a
SELANGOR ***Two*** **CENTS** — b
SELANGOR Two CENTS — c
SELANGOR Two CENTS — d
SELANGOR Two CENTS — e

1891

19 A3 (a) 2c on 24c green 12.50 13.00
20 A3 (b) 2c on 24c green 80.00
21 A3 (c) 2c on 24c green 80.00
22 A3 (d) 2c on 24c green 50.00
23 A3 (e) 2c on 24c green 85.00
Nos. 19-23 (5) 307.50

A6

1891-95 Typo. Wmk. 2

24 A6 1c green .55 .20
25 A6 2c rose 2.75 .35
26 A6 2c orange ('95) 1.25 .35
27 A6 5c blue 12.50 2.50
Nos. 24-27 (4) 17.05 3.40

Type of 1891 Surcharged **3 CENTS**

1894

28 A6 3c on 5c rose 1.25 .40

A8

A9

1895-99 Wmk. 2 Perf. 14

29 A8 3c lilac & car rose 2.00 .15
30 A8 5c lilac & olive .45 .25
31 A8 8c lilac & blue 32.50 5.00
32 A8 10c lilac & orange 6.50 .50
33 A8 25c grn & car rose 40.00 17.50
34 A8 50c lilac & black 27.50 12.50
35 A8 50c green & black 125.00 37.50

Wmk. 1

36 A9 $1 green & lt grn 42.50 55.00
37 A9 $2 grn & car rose 90.00 90.00
38 A9 $3 green & olive 200.00 125.00
39 A9 $5 green & ultra 125.00 125.00
40 A9 $10 grn & brn vio 325.00 250.00
41 A9 $25 green & org 1,400.

High values with revenue cancellations are plentiful and inexpensive.

Surcharged in Black:

One cent. Three cents.

1900 Wmk. 2

42 A8 1c on 5c lilac & olive 50.00 *75.00*
43 A8 1c on 50c grn & blk 1.00 1.25
a. Double surcharge 1,200.
44 A8 3c on 50c grn & blk 6.50 *9.50*
Nos. 42-44 (3) 57.50 *85.75*

Mosque at Klang
A12

Sultan Sulaiman
A13

1935-41 Typo. Wmk. 4 Perf. 14

45 A12 1c black ('36) .25 .15
46 A12 2c dp green ('36) .50 .15
46A A12 2c org brn ('41) 2.00 1.00
46B A12 3c green ('41) .65 *1.25*
47 A12 4c orange brown .25 .15
48 A12 5c chocolate .50 .15
49 A12 6c rose red 4.00 .15
50 A12 8c gray .45 .15
51 A12 10c dk violet ('36) .45 .15
52 A12 12c ultra ('36) 1.25 .15
52A A12 15c ultra ('41) 6.50 *20.00*
53 A12 25c rose red & pale vio ('36) 1.25 *.55*
54 A12 30c org & dk vio ('36) 1.10 *.80*
55 A12 40c dk vio & car 1.50 1.00
56 A12 50c blk, *emer* ('36) 1.25 .45
57 A13 $1 red & black, *blue* ('36) 4.25 .65
58 A13 $2 rose red & green ('36) 16.00 4.25
59 A13 $5 brn red & grn, *emer* ('36) 42.50 *26.00*
Nos. 45-59 (18) 84.65 *57.15*

Nos. 46A-46B were printed on both ordinary and chalky paper; 15c only on ordinary paper; other values only on chalky paper.
An 8c rose red was prepared but not issued.
For overprints see #N1-N15, N18A-N24, N26-N39.

Sultan Hisam-ud-Din Alam Shah
A14 A15

1941

72 A14 $1 red & blk, *blue* 6.50 3.25
73 A14 $2 car & green 40.00 *20.00*

A $5 stamp of type A14, issued during the Japanese occupation with different overprints (Nos. N18, N25A, N42), also exists without overprint. The unoverprinted stamp was not issued before or after the occupation.

For overprints see #N16-N17, N24A, N25, N40-N41.

Catalogue values for unused stamps in this section, from this point to the end of the section, are for Never Hinged items.

Silver Wedding Issue
Common Design Types
Inscribed: "Malaya Selangor"

Perf. 14x14½

1948, Dec. 1 Photo. Wmk. 4

74 CD304 10c purple .20 .20

Perf. 11½x11

Engraved; Name Typographed

75 CD305 $5 green 25.00 24.00

UPU Issue
Common Design Types
Inscribed: "Malaya-Selangor"

Engr.; Name Typo. on Nos. 77 & 78

1949, Oct. 10 Perf. 13½, 11x11½

76 CD306 10c rose violet .30 .30
77 CD307 15c indigo .40 .40
78 CD308 25c orange .65 .65
79 CD309 50c slate 1.40 1.40
Nos. 76-79 (4) 2.75 2.75

1949, Sept. 12 Typo. Perf. 18

80 A15 1c black .15 .15
81 A15 2c orange .15 .15
82 A15 3c green .30 .70
83 A15 4c chocolate .20 .15
84 A15 6c gray .25 .15
85 A15 8c rose red .30 .70
86 A15 10c plum .20 .15
87 A15 15c ultramarine .80 .15
88 A15 20c dk grn & black 1.40 .40
89 A15 25c orange & rose lil .75 .15
90 A15 40c dk vio & rose red 1.75 3.00
91 A15 50c ultra & black .50 .15
92 A15 $1 vio brn & ultra 2.00 .20
93 A15 $2 rose red & emer 6.00 .75
94 A15 $5 choc & emerald 42.50 1.50

1952-55

95 A15 5c rose violet .20 .15
96 A15 8c green .25 .15
97 A15 12c rose red .50 .30
98 A15 20c ultramarine 1.00 .15
99 A15 30c plum & rose red ('55) 1.40 .30
100 A15 35c dk vio & rose red .80 .40
Nos. 80-100 (21) 61.40 9.90

Coronation Issue
Common Design Type

1953, June 2 Engr. Perf. 13½x13

101 CD312 10c magenta & black .25 .15

Sultan Hisam-ud-Din Alam Shah
A16 A17

Designs as in Kelantan, 1957.

Perf. 13x12½, 12½x13, 13½ ($1)

1957-60 Engr. Wmk. 314

102 A17 1c black .15 .15
103 A17 2c red orange .15 .15
104 A17 4c dark brown .15 .15
105 A17 5c dark car rose .15 .15
106 A17 8c dark green 1.00 .25
107 A16 10c chocolate .15 .15
108 A16 20c blue .20 .15
109 A16 50c ultra & blk ('60) .55 .15
a. Perf. 12½ .55 .20
110 A17 $1 plum & ultra 1.10 .30
111 A17 $2 red & grn ('60) 3.00 1.00
a. Perf. 12½ 3.00 1.25
112 A17 $5 ol grn & brn ('60) 6.25 2.00
a. Perf. 12½ 8.00 2.75
Nos. 102-112 (11) 12.85
Set value 4.00

See Nos. 114-120.

Sultan Salahuddin Abdul Aziz Shah — A18

1961, June 28 Photo. Perf. 14½x14

113 A18 10s multicolored .30 .15

Sultan Salahuddin Abdul Aziz Shah, installation.

Types of 1957 with Portrait of Sultan Salahuddin Abdul Aziz Shah

Designs as before.

Perf. 13x12½, 12½x13

1961-62 Engr. Wmk. 338

114 A17 1c black .15 .15
115 A17 2c red orange .15 .15
116 A17 4c dark brown .15 .15
117 A17 5c dark car rose .15 .15
118 A17 8c dark green .80 .80
119 A16 10c vio brown ('61) .60 .15
120 A16 20c blue .90 .25
Set value 1.50 .94

Starting in 1965, issues of Selangor are listed with Malaysia.

OCCUPATION STAMPS

Issued under Japanese Occupation

Stamps of Selangor 1935-41 Handstamped Vertically or Horizontally in Black, Red, Brown or Violet

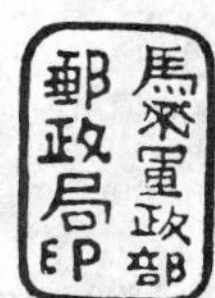

1942, Apr. 3 Wmk. 4 Perf. 14

N1 A12 1c black 11.00 16.00
N2 A12 2c deep green 450.00 450.00
N3 A12 2c orange brown 40.00 40.00
N4 A12 3c green 25.00 12.50
N5 A12 5c chocolate 7.50 7.50
N6 A12 6c rose red 150.00 150.00
N7 A12 8c gray 20.00 20.00
N8 A12 10c dark violet 17.00 20.00
N9 A12 12c ultramarine 35.00 35.00
N10 A12 15c ultramarine 12.50 15.00
N11 A12 25c rose red & pale vio 60.00 70.00
N12 A12 30c org & dk vio 11.00 22.50
N13 A12 40c dk vio & car 75.00 100.00
N14 A12 50c blk, *emerald* 30.00 35.00
N15 A13 $5 brn red & grn, *emer* 200.00 200.00

Some authorities believe No. N15 was not issued regularly.

Handstamped Vertically on Stamps and Type of Selangor 1941 in Black or Red

N16 A14 $1 red & blk, *bl* 45.00 60.00
N17 A14 $2 car & green 60.00 85.00
N18 A14 $5 brn red & grn, *emer* 80.00 80.00

Stamps and Type of Selangor, 1935-41, Overprinted in Black

DAI NIPPON
2602
MALAYA

1942, May

N18A A12 1c black 80.00 80.00
N19 A12 3c green .75 .75
N19A A12 5c chocolate 80.00 80.00
N20 A12 10c dark violet 25.00 25.00
N21 A12 12c ultramarine 2.00 3.75
N22 A12 15c ultramarine 4.00 3.00
N23 A12 30c org & dk vio 25.00 25.00
N24 A12 40c dk vio & car 3.00 3.00
N24A A14 $1 red & blk, *bl* 25.00 25.00
N25 A14 $2 car & green 17.50 22.50
N25A A14 $5 red & grn, *emer* 40.00 40.00
Nos. N18A-N25A (11) 302.25 308.00

Overprint is horizontal on $1, $2, $5.
On Nos. N18A and N19 the overprint is known reading up, instead of down.
Some authorities claim Nos. N18A, N19A, N20, N23, N24A and N25A were not regularly issued.

Selangor No. 46B Overprinted in Black

DAI NIPPON
YUBIN

1942, Dec.

N26 A12 3c green 300.00 300.00

Stamps and Type of Selangor, 1935-41, Overprinted or Surcharged in Black or Red:

大日本郵便 (i)
大日本郵便 (k)
大日本郵便
6 cts. (l)
大日本郵便
6 cts. (m)

1943

N27 A12(i) 1c black 1.00 1.00
N28 A12(k) 1c black (R) .65 .65
N29 A12(l) 2c on 5c choc (R) .65 .65
N30 A12(i) 3c green .75 .75
N31 A12(l) 3c on 5c choc .50 .75
N32 A12(k) 5c choc (R) .50 .75
N33 A12(l) 6c on 5c choc .25 *.65*
N34 A12(m) 6c on 5c choc .25 *.75*
N35 A12(i) 12c ultra 1.00 1.25
N36 A12(i) 15c ultra 5.00 7.50
N37 A12(k) 15c ultra 10.00 10.00
N38 A12(m) $1 on 10c dk vio .35 *1.00*
N39 A12(m) $1.50 on 30c org & dk vio .35 *1.00*
N40 A14(i) $1 red & blk, *blue* 5.00 6.25
N41 A14(i) $2 car & grn 17.50 17.50
N42 A14(i) $5 brn red & grn, *emer* 37.50 40.00
Nos. N27-N42 (16) 81.25 90.45

The "i" overprint is vertical on Nos. N40-N42 and is also found reading in the opposite direction on Nos. N30, N35 and N36.
The overprint reads: "Japanese Postal Service."

Singapore is listed following Sierra Leone.

SUNGEI UJONG

'sùŋə ü–jùŋ

Formerly a nonfederated native state on the Malay Peninsula, which in 1895 was consolidated with the Federated State of Negri Sembilan.

Stamps of the Straits Settlements Overprinted in Black

Overprinted

1878 Wmk. 1 Perf. 14

2 A2 2c brown 2,500. 2,250.

Overprinted SUNGEI UJONG

4 A2 2c brown 90.00
5 A2 4c rose *800.00*

No. 5 is no longer recognized by some experts.

Overprinted S.U.

1882-83 Wmk. 2

6 A2 2c brown 125. 125.
7 A2 4c rose 1,600. 1,800.

This overprint on the 2c brown, wmk. 1, is probably a trial printing.

Overprinted SU

11 A2 2c brown 125.00 175.00

Overprinted **SUNGEI UJONG**

1881-84

14 A2 2c brown 165.00 150.00
15 A2 2c rose 80.00 90.00
a. "Ujong" printed sideways
b. "Sungei" printed twice
16 A2 4c brown 72.50 72.50
17 A3 8c orange 825.00 550.00
18 A7 10c slate 500.00 400.00

Overprinted **SUNGEI UJONG.**

19 A2 2c brown 30.00 70.00

Overprinted ***SUNGEI UJONG***

1885-90

Without Period

20 A2 2c rose 16.00 17.00

With Period

21 A2 2c rose 45.00 50.00
a. "UNJOG" 2,100. 2,100.

Overprinted ***Sungei Ujong***

22 A2 2c rose 35.00 37.50
a. Double overprint 400.00 400.00

Overprinted **SUNGEI UJONG**

23 A2 2c rose 35.00 37.50

Overprinted **SUNGEI UJONG**

24 A2 2c rose 9.00 25.00
a. Double overprint

Overprinted **SUNGEI UJONG**

25 A2 2c rose 27.50 30.00

Overprinted **SUNGEI UJONG**

26 A2 2c rose 45.00 47.50
c. Double overprint

Overprinted **SUNGEI UJONG**

Overprint 14-16x3mm

26A A2 2c rose 4.50 6.00

Overprinted **SUNGEI UJONG**

26B A2 2c rose 25.00 12.50

Stamp of 1883-91 Surcharged:

SUNGEI UJONG *Two* CENTS — a

SUNGEI UJONG Two CENTS — b

SUNGEI UJONG Two CENTS — c

SUNGEI UJONG *Two* CENTS — d

1891

27 A3 (a) 2c on 24c green 85.00 110.00
28 A3 (b) 2c on 24c green 325.00 350.00
29 A3 (c) 2c on 24c green 110.00 120.00
30 A3 (d) 2c on 24c green 225.00 275.00
Nos. 27-30 (4) 745.00 855.00

On Nos. 27-28, SUNGEI is 14½mm, UJONG 12¾x2½mm.

A3

A4

1891-94 **Typo.** ***Perf. 14***

31 A3 2c rose 22.50 27.50
32 A3 2c orange ('94) 1.75 4.50
33 A3 5c blue ('93) 4.00 5.50
Nos. 31-33 (3) 28.25 37.50

Type of 1891 Surcharged in Black **1 CENT**

1894

34 A3 1c on 5c green 1.50 1.50
35 A3 3c on 5c rose 2.75 2.50

1895

36 A4 3c lilac & car rose 4.00 3.00

Stamps of Sungei Ujong were superseded by those of Negri Sembilan in 1895.

TRENGGANU

tre-'gä-(,)nü

LOCATION — On the eastern coast of the Malay Peninsula.
AREA — 5,050 sq. mi.
POP. — 302,171 (1960)
CAPITAL — Kuala Trengganu

Sultan Zenalabidin
A1 A2

1910-19 **Typo.** **Wmk. 3** ***Perf. 14***

Ordinary Paper

1 A1 1c gray green .45 .75
2 A1 2c red vio & brn ('15) .35 .65
3 A1 3c rose red 1.75 1.50
4 A1 4c brn orange 3.00 *4.50*
5 A1 4c grn & org brn ('15) 1.75 *4.25*
6 A1 4c scarlet ('19) .55 *1.50*
7 A1 5c gray 1.10 *2.50*
8 A1 5c choc & gray ('15) 2.00 2.25
9 A1 8c ultramarine 1.10 5.00
10 A1 10c red & grn, *yel* ('15) .90 2.25

Chalky Paper

11 A1 10c violet, *yel* 2.75 2.00
12 A1 20c red vio & vio 2.25 *3.00*
13 A1 25c dl vio & grn ('15) 4.50 *17.50*
14 A1 30c blk & dl vio ('15) 5.75 *30.00*
15 A1 50c blk & sep, *grn* 4.00 *5.00*
16 A1 $1 red & blk, *blue* 12.50 *17.00*
17 A1 $3 red & grn, *grn* ('15) 85.00 *150.00*
18 A2 $5 lil & blue grn 90.00 *275.00*
19 A2 $25 green & car 675.00
Revenue Cancel 200.00
Nos. 1-18 (18) 219.70 *524.65*

On No. 19 the numerals and Arabic inscriptions at top, left and right are in color on a colorless background.

Overprints are listed after No. 41. For surcharges see Nos. B1-B4.

Sultan Badaru'l-alam
A3 A4

1921-38 **Wmk. 4** ***Perf. 14***

Chalky Paper

20 A3 1c black ('25) 1.10 .60
21 A3 2c deep green 1.10 .65
22 A3 3c dp grn ('25) 1.40 .60
23 A3 3c lt brn ('38) 15.00 *7.25*
24 A3 4c rose red 1.10 .25
25 A3 5c choc & gray 1.75 2.75
26 A3 5c vio, *yel* ('25) 1.50 .50
27 A3 6c orange ('24) 2.25 .25
28 A3 8c gray ('38) 15.00 2.75
29 A3 10c ultramarine 1.75 .40
30 A3 12c ultra ('25) 3.75 *2.75*
31 A3 20c org & dl vio 1.75 *1.25*
32 A3 25c dk vio & grn 2.00 *1.90*
33 A3 30c blk & dl vio 3.00 1.25
34 A3 35c red, *yel* ('25) 4.00 *6.75*
35 A3 50c car & green 4.50 1.25
36 A3 $1 ultra & vio, *bl* ('29) 8.00 3.00
37 A3 $3 red & green, *emer* ('25) 45.00 *75.00*
38 A4 $5 red & grn, *yel* ('38) 225.00 *600.00*
39 A4 $25 blue & lil 500.00 *700.00*
40 A4 $50 org & green 1,100. *1,600.*
41 A4 $100 red & green 3,500.
Nos. 20-37 (18) 113.95 *109.15*

On Nos. 39 to 41 the numerals and Arabic inscriptions at top, left and right are in color on a colorless background.

A 2c orange, 6c gray, 8c rose red and 15c ultramarine, type A3, exist, but are not known to have been regularly issued.

For surcharges and overprints see Nos. 45-46, N1-N60.

Stamps of 1910-21 Overprinted in Black: "MALAYA BORNEO EXHIBITION" in THREE LINES

1922, Mar. **Wmk. 3**

8a A1 5c chocolate & gray 2.50 *20.00*
10a A1 10c red & green, *yel* 2.50 *20.00*
12a A1 20c red vio & violet 2.25 *25.00*
13a A1 25c dull vio & green 2.25 *25.00*
14a A1 30c black & dull vio 2.25 *25.00*
15a A1 50c blk & sepia, *grn* 2.25 *25.00*
16a A1 $1 red & blk, *blue* 10.00 *50.00*
17a A1 $3 red & grn, *green* 110.00 *300.00*
18a A2 $5 lil & blue green 200.00 *400.00*

Wmk. 4

21a A3 2c deep green 1.50 *24.00*
24a A3 4c rose red 4.00 *24.00*
Nos. 8a-24a (11) 339.50 *938.00*

Industrial fair at Singapore, Mar. 31-Apr. 15.

1921 **Wmk. 3**

Chalky Paper

42 A3 $1 ultra & vio, *bl* 12.00 *17.00*
43 A3 $3 red & grn, *emer* 70.00 *70.00*
44 A4 $5 red & green, *yel* 70.00 *65.00*
Nos. 42-44 (3) 152.00 *152.00*

Types of 1921-25 Surcharged in Black **8 CENTS**

1941, May 1 **Wmk. 4** ***Perf. 13½x14***

45 A3 2c on 5c magenta, *yel* 5.00 *4.00*
46 A3 8c on 10c lt ultra 8.00 *4.00*

For overprints see #N30-N33, N46-N47, N59-N60.

Catalogue values for unused stamps in this section, from this point to the end of the section, are for Never Hinged items.

Silver Wedding Issue
Common Design Types
Inscribed: "Malaya Trengganu"

1948, Dec. 1 **Photo.** ***Perf. 14x14½***

47 CD304 10c purple .20 .20

Engraved; Name Typographed
Perf. 11½x11

48 CD305 $5 rose car 24.00 30.00

UPU Issue
Common Design Types
Inscribed: "Malaya-Trengganu"
Engr.; Name Typo. on 15c, 25c
Perf. 13½, 11x11½

1949, Oct. 10 **Wmk. 4**

49 CD306 10c rose violet .35 .35
50 CD307 15c indigo .45 1.25
51 CD308 25c orange .75 2.00
52 CD309 50c slate 1.25 2.00
Nos. 49-52 (4) 2.80 5.60

Sultan Ismail Nasiruddin Shah — A5

1949, Dec. 27 **Typo.** ***Perf. 18***

53 A5 1c black .25 .15
54 A5 2c orange .25 .15
55 A5 3c green .60 .45
56 A5 4c chocolate .30 .15
57 A5 6c gray .60 .35
58 A5 8c rose red .85 .60
59 A5 10c plum .35 .15
60 A5 15c ultramarine .90 .50
61 A5 20c dk grn & black 1.25 1.50
62 A5 25c org & rose lilac 1.10 1.00
63 A5 40c dk vio & rose red 2.25 8.00
64 A5 50c dp ultra & black 1.40 .80
65 A5 $1 vio brn & ultra 2.75 3.00
66 A5 $2 rose red & emer 15.00 7.50
67 A5 $5 choc & emerald 40.00 20.00

1952-55

68 A5 5c rose violet .25 .15
69 A5 8c green .85 1.00
70 A5 12c rose red .85 *2.00*
71 A5 20c ultramarine .85 .45
72 A5 30c plum & rose red ('55) 1.65 2.00
73 A5 35c dk vio & rose red 1.90 2.00
Nos. 53-73 (21) 74.20 51.90

Coronation Issue
Common Design Type

1953, June 2 **Engr.** ***Perf. 13½x13***

74 CD312 10c magenta & blk .35 .20

Types of Kedah with Portrait of Sultan Ismail

Perf. 13x12½, 12½x13, 13½ ($1), 12½ ($2)

1957-63 **Engr.** **Wmk. 314**

75 A8 1c black .15 .15
76 A8 2c red orange .50 .20
77 A8 4c dark brown .15 .15
78 A8 5c dark car rose .15 .15
79 A8 8c dark green 3.50 .20
80 A7 10c chocolate .25 .15
81 A7 20c blue .40 .25
82 A7 50c blue & blk .25 .60
a. Perf. 12½ .25 .60
83 A8 $1 plum & ultra 3.75 2.50
84 A8 $2 red & green 7.25 3.00
85 A8 $5 ol grn & brn, perf. 12½ 11.00 6.25
a. Perf. 13x12½ 12.00 8.00
Nos. 75-85 (11) 27.35 13.60

Issued: 20c, #85, 6/26/57; 2c, 50c, $1, 7/25/57; 10c, 8/4/57; 1c, 4c, 5c, 8c, $2, 8/21/57; #82a, 5/17/60; #85a, 8/13/63.

Starting in 1965, issues of Trengganu are listed with Malaysia.

SEMI-POSTAL STAMPS

Nos. 3, 4 and 9 Surcharged **RED CROSS 2c.**

1917, Oct. **Wmk. 3** ***Perf. 14***

B1 A1 3c + 2c rose red .35 *2.25*
a. "CSOSS" 40.00 *65.00*
b. Comma after "2c" 2.50 *6.50*
c. Pair, one without surcharge 1,750. 1,750.
B2 A1 4c + 2c brn org .55 *3.25*
a. "CSOSS" 165.00 *165.00*
b. Comma after "2c" 10.00 *26.00*
B3 A1 8c + 2c ultra .90 *6.50*
a. "CSOSS" 110.00 *125.00*
b. Comma after "2c" 8.25 *32.50*
Nos. B1-B3 (3) 1.80 *12.00*

Same Surcharge on No. 5

1918

B4 A1 4c + 2c grn & org brn 1.25 *6.50*
a. Pair, one without surcharge 1,400.

POSTAGE DUE STAMPS

D1

Wmk. 4

1937, Aug. 10 **Typo.** ***Perf. 14***

J1 D1 1c rose red 8.50 *40.00*
J2 D1 4c green 8.50 *40.00*
J3 D1 8c lemon 50.00 *200.00*
J4 D1 10c light brown 75.00 *75.00*
Nos. J1-J4 (4) 142.00 *355.00*

For overprints see Nos. NJ1-NJ4.

OCCUPATION STAMPS

Issued under Japanese Occupation

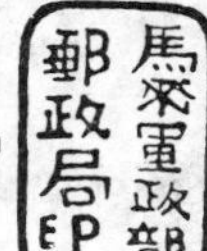

Stamps of Trengganu, 1921-38, Handstamped in Black or Brown

1942 Wmk. 4 *Perf. 14*

N1 A3 1c black 85.00 80.00
N2 A3 2c deep green 140.00 200.00
N3 A3 3c lt brown 100.00 80.00
N4 A3 4c rose red 200.00 140.00
N5 A3 5c violet, *yel* 13.00 14.00
N6 A3 6c orange 10.00 15.00
N7 A3 8c gray 13.00 18.00
N8 A3 10c ultramarine 10.00 20.00
N9 A3 12c ultramarine 11.00 18.00
N10 A3 20c org & dl vio 11.00 17.00
N11 A3 25c dk vio & grn 10.00 20.00
N12 A3 30c blk & dl vio 10.00 18.00
N13 A3 35c red, *yel* 17.00 20.00
N14 A3 50c car & grn 85.00 70.00
N15 A3 $1 ultra & vio, *blue* 1,200. 1,300.
N16 A3 $3 red & grn, *emerald* 90.00 100.00
N17 A4 $5 red & grn, *yellow* 175.00 175.00
N17A A4 $25 blue & lil 1,100.
N17B A4 $50 org & grn *6,500.*
N17C A4 $100 red & grn 700.00

Handstamped in Red

N18 A3 1c black 200.00 160.00
N19 A3 2c dp green 100.00 125.00
N20 A3 5c violet, *yel* 25.00 15.00
N21 A3 6c orange 15.00 15.00
N22 A3 8c gray 200.00 175.00
N23 A3 10c ultramarine 200.00 200.00
N24 A3 12c ultramarine 40.00 40.00
N25 A3 20c org & dl vio 25.00 25.00
N26 A3 25c dk vio & grn 30.00 30.00
N27 A3 30c blk & dl vio 25.00 25.00
N28 A3 35c red, *yellow* 25.00 15.00
N29 A3 $3 red & grn, *emerald* 75.00 30.00
N29A A3 $25 blue & lil 500.00 500.00

Handstamped on Nos. 45 and 46 in Black or Red

N30 A3 2c on 5c (Bk) 100.00 100.00
N31 A3 2c on 5c (R) 75.00 75.00
N32 A3 8c on 10c (Bk) 18.00 25.00
N33 A3 8c on 10c (R) 35.00 40.00

Stamps of Trengganu, 1921-38, Overprinted in Black

DAI NIPPON
2602
MALAYA

1942

N34 A3 1c black 11.00 12.50
N35 A3 2c deep green 75.00 *100.00*
N36 A3 3c light brown 12.00 21.00
N37 A3 4c rose red 11.00 15.00
N38 A3 5c violet, *yel* 7.50 15.00
N39 A3 6c orange 7.50 12.50
N40 A3 8c gray 50.00 15.00
N41 A3 12c ultramarine 7.50 10.00
N42 A3 20c org & dl vio 10.00 18.00
N43 A3 25c dk vio & grn 10.00 12.50
N44 A3 30c blk & dl vio 10.00 15.00
N45 A3 $3 red & grn, *emer* 75.00 100.00

Overprinted on Nos. 45 and 46 in Black

N46 A3 2c on 5c mag, *yel* 10.00 12.50
N47 A3 8c on 10c lt ultra 8.50 15.00
Nos. N34-N47 (14) 305.00 *374.00*

Stamps of Trengganu, 1921-38, Overprinted in Black

大日本郵便

1943

N48 A3 1c black 10.00 14.00
N49 A3 2c deep green 10.00 20.00
N50 A3 5c violet, *yel* 8.50 20.00
N51 A3 6c orange 11.00 20.00
N52 A3 8c gray 70.00 50.00
N53 A3 10c ultramarine 75.00 125.00
N54 A3 12c ultramarine 14.00 *25.00*
N55 A3 20c org & dl vio 15.00 *25.00*
N56 A3 25c dl vio & grn 14.00 *25.00*
N57 A3 30c blk & dl vio 15.00 *25.00*
N58 A3 35c red, *yellow* 15.00 *30.00*

Overprinted on Nos. 45 and 46 in Black

N59 A3 2c on 5c mag, *yel* 8.00 *25.00*
N60 A3 8c on 10c lt ultra 20.00 *25.00*
Nos. N48-N60 (13) 285.50 *429.00*

The Japanese characters read: "Japanese Postal Service."

OCCUPATION POSTAGE DUE STAMPS

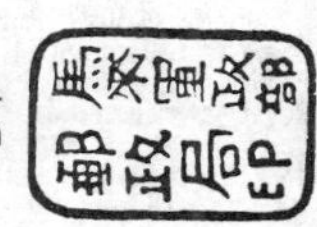

Trengganu Nos. J1-J4 Handstamped in Black or Brown

1942 Wmk. 4 *Perf. 14*

NJ1 D1 1c rose red 50.00 *70.00*
NJ2 D1 4c green 90.00 *90.00*
NJ3 D1 8c lemon 18.00 *50.00*
NJ4 D1 10c light brown 18.00 *50.00*
Nos. NJ1-NJ4 (4) 176.00 *260.00*

The handstamp reads: "Seal of Post Office of Malayan Military Department."

MALAYSIA

mə-'lā-zh(ē-)ə

LOCATION — Malay peninsula and northwestern Borneo
GOVT. — Federation within the British Commonwealth
AREA — 128,328 sq. mi.
POP. — 15,070,000 (est. 1984)
CAPITAL — Kuala Lumpur

The Federation of Malaysia was formed Sept. 16, 1963, by a merger of the former Federation of Malaya, Singapore, Sarawak, and North Borneo (renamed Sabah), totaling 14 states. Singapore withdrew in 1965.

Sabah and Sarawak, having different rates than mainland Malaysia, continued to issue their own stamps after joining the federation. The system of individual state issues was extended to Perak in Oct. 1963, and to the 10 other members in Nov. 1965.

100 Cents (Sen) = 1 Dollar (Ringgit)

Catalogue values for all unused stamps in this country are for Never Hinged items.

Watermarks

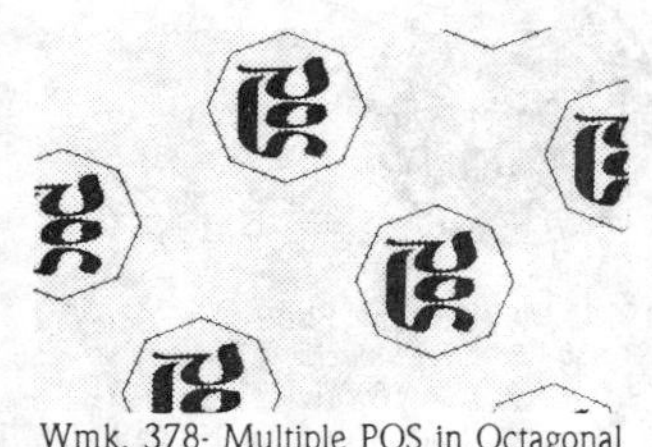

Wmk. 378- Multiple POS in Octagonal Frame

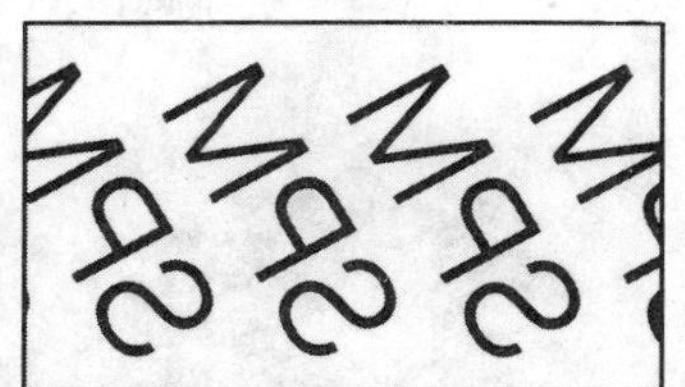

Wmk. 388- Multiple "SPM"

Map of Malaysia and 14-point Star — A1

Wmk. PTM Multiple (338)

1963, Sept. 16 Photo. *Perf. 14*

1 A1 10s violet & yellow .35 .15
a. Yellow omitted 100.00
2 A1 12s green & yellow 1.00 .30
3 A1 50s dk red brown & yel 1.40 .30
Nos. 1-3 (3) 2.75 .75

Formation of the Federation of Malaysia.

Orchids — A2

1963, Oct. 3 Unwmk. *Perf. 13x14*

4 A2 6s red & multi .60 .15
5 A2 25s black & multi 3.00 .40

4th World Orchid Conf., Singapore, Oct. 8-11.

Parliament and Commonwealth Parliamentary Association Emblem — A4

1963, Nov. 4 *Perf. 13½*

7 A4 20s dk car rose & gold .40 .15
8 A4 30s dk green & gold .80 .25

9th Commonwealth Parliamentary Assoc. Conf.

Globe, Torch, Snake and Hands — A5

1964, Oct. 10 Photo. *Perf. 14x13*

9 A5 25s Prus green, red & black .15 .15
10 A5 30s lt violet, red & blk .20 .15
11 A5 50s dull yellow, red & blk .40 .20
Nos. 9-11 (3) .75
Set value .40

Eleanor Roosevelt, 1884-1962.

ITU Emblem and Radar Tower — A6

1965, May 17 Photo. *Perf. 11½*
Granite Paper

12 A6 2c violet, blk & org .15 .15
13 A6 25c brown, blk & org .75 .20
14 A6 50c emerald, blk & brn 1.75 .30
Nos. 12-14 (3) 2.65
Set value .55

Cent. of the ITU.

National Mosque, Kuala Lumpur — A7

1965, Aug. 27 Wmk. 338 *Perf. 14½*

15 A7 6c dark car rose .15 .15
16 A7 15c dark red brown .25 .15
17 A7 20c Prussian green .40 .15
Nos. 15-17 (3) .80
Set value .30

Natl. Mosque at Kuala Lumpur, opening.

Control Tower and Airport — A8

Crested Wood Partridge — A9

1965, Aug. 30 *Perf. 14½x14*

18 A8 15c blue, blk & grn .25 .15
a. Green omitted 18.00
19 A8 30c brt pink, blk & grn .60 .15
Set value .20

Intl. Airport at Kuala Lumpur, opening.

1965, Sept. 9 Photo. *Perf. 14½*

Birds: 30c, Fairy bluebird. 50c, Blacknaped oriole. 75c, Rhinoceros hornbill. $1, Zebra dove. $2, Argus pheasant. $5, Indian paradise flycatcher. $10, Banded pitta.

20 A9 25c orange & multi .50 .15
21 A9 30c tan & multi .65 .15
a. Blue omitted 87.50
22 A9 50c rose & multi 1.00 .15
a. Rose omitted 42.50
23 A9 75c yel green & multi 2.00 .15
24 A9 $1 ultra & multi 3.00 .15
25 A9 $2 maroon & multi 8.50 .45
26 A9 $5 dk green & multi 21.00 1.25
27 A9 $10 brt red & multi 42.50 4.25
Nos. 20-27 (8) 79.15 6.70

Soccer and Sepak Raga (Ball Game) — A10

National Monument, Kuala Lumpur — A11

1965, Dec. 14 Unwmk. *Perf. 13*

28 A10 25c shown .20 .15
29 A10 30c Runner .45 .25
30 A10 50c Diver .80 .55
Nos. 28-30 (3) 1.45 .95

3rd South East Asia Peninsular Games, Kuala Lumpur, Dec. 14-21.

1966, Feb. 8 Wmk. 338 *Perf. 13½*

31 A11 10c yellow & multi .15 .15
a. Blue omitted 52.50
32 A11 20c ultra & multi .65 .35
Set value .40

The National Monument by US sculptor Felix W. de Weldon commemorates the struggle of the people of Malaysia for peace and for freedom from communism.

Tuanku Ismail Nasiruddin A12

Penang Free School A13

1966, Apr. 11 Unwmk. *Perf. 13½*

33 A12 15c yellow & black .15 .15
34 A12 50c blue & black .45 .40
Set value .50

Installation of Tuanku Ismail Nasiruddin of Trengganu as Paramount Ruler (Yang di-Pertuan Agong).

Perf. 13x12½

1966, Oct. 21 Photo. Wmk. 338

Design: 50c, like 20c with Malayan inscription and school crest added.

35 A13 20c multicolored .35 .15
36 A13 50c multicolored .85 .40

Penang Free School, 150th anniversary.

Mechanized Plowing and Palms — A14

Designs: No. 38, Rural health nurse, mother and child, dispensary. No. 39, Communication: train, plane, ship, cars and radio tower. No. 40, School children. No. 41, Dam and rice fields.

1966, Dec. 1 Unwmk. *Perf. 13*

37 A14 15c bister brn & multi .45 .15
38 A14 15c blue & multi .45 .15
39 A14 15c crimson & multi .45 .15
40 A14 15c ol green & multi .45 .15
41 A14 15c yellow & multi .45 .15
Nos. 37-41 (5) 2.25 .75

Malaysia's First Development Plan.

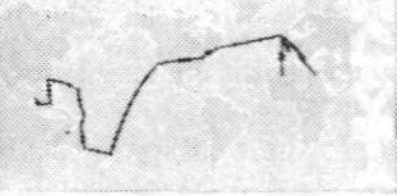

Maps Showing International and South East Asia Telephone Links — A15

1967, Mar. 30 Photo. *Perf. 13*

42 A15 30c multicolored .75 .25
43 A15 75c multicolored 3.50 .90

Completion of the Hong Kong-Malaysia link of the South East Asia Commonwealth Cable, SEACOM.

Hibiscus and Rulers of Independent Malaysia — A16

1967, Aug. 31 Wmk. 338 *Perf. 14*

44 A16 15c yellow & multi .15 .15
45 A16 50c blue & multi .65 .35
Set value .45

10th anniversary of independence.

Arms of Sarawak and Council Mace — A17

1967, Sept. 8 Photo.

46 A17 15c yel green & multi .15 .15
47 A17 50c multicolored .55 .35
Set value .40

Representative Council of Sarawak, cent.

Straits Settlements No. 13 and Malaysia No. 20 A18

30c, Straits Settlements #15, Malaysia #21. 50c, Straits Settlements #17, Malaysia #22.

1967, Dec. 2 Unwmk. *Perf. 11½*

48 A18 25c brt blue & multi 1.40 .35
49 A18 30c dull green & multi 1.50 .35
50 A18 50c yellow & multi 3.00 .75
Nos. 48-50 (3) 5.90 1.45

Cent. of the Malaysian (Straits Settlements) postage stamps.

Tapped Rubber Tree and Molecular Unit — A20

Tapped Rubber Tree and: 30c, Rubber packed for shipment. 50c, Rubber tires for Vickers VC 10 plane.

Wmk. 338

1968, Aug. 29 Litho. *Perf. 12*

53 A20 25c brick red, blk & org .25 .15
54 A20 30c yellow, black & org .40 .20
55 A20 50c ultra, black & org .65 .50
Nos. 53-55 (3) 1.30 .85

Natural Rubber Conference, Kuala Lumpur.

Olympic Rings, Mexican Hat and Cloth — A21

Tunku Abdul Rahman Putra Al-Haj — A22

75c, Olympic rings & Malaysian batik cloth.

1968, Oct. 12 Wmk. 338 *Perf. 12*

56 A21 30c rose red & multi .20 .15
57 A21 75c ocher & multi .60 .45

19th Olympic Games, Mexico City, Oct. 12-27.

Perf. 13½

1969, Feb. 8 Photo. Unwmk.

Designs: Various portraits of Prime Minister Tunku Abdul Rahman Putra Al-Haj with woven pandanus patterns as background. 50c is horiz.

58 A22 15c gold & multi .15 .15
59 A22 20c gold & multi .20 .15
60 A22 50c gold & multi .45 .35
Nos. 58-60 (3) .80 .65

Issued for Solidarity Week, 1969.

Malaysian Girl Holding Sheaves of Rice — A23

1969, Dec. 8 Wmk. 338 *Perf. 13½*

61 A23 15c silver & multi .25 .15
62 A23 75c gold & multi 1.10 .80

International Rice Year.

Kuantan Radar Station A24

Intelsat III Orbiting Earth A25

Perf. 14x13

1970, Apr. 6 Photo. Unwmk.

63 A24 15c multicolored .70 .15
64 A25 30c multicolored 1.40 .55
65 A25 30c gold & multi 1.25 .30
Nos. 63-65 (3) 3.35 1.00

Satellite Communications Earth Station at Kuantan, Pahang, Malaysia.

No. 63 was printed tete beche (50 pairs) in sheet of 100 (10x10).

Blue-branded King Crow — A26

ILO Emblem — A27

Butterflies: 30c, Saturn. 50c, Common Nawab. 75c, Great Mormon. $1, Orange albatross. $2, Raja Brooke's birdwing. $5, Centaur oakblue. $10, Royal Assyrian.

1970, Aug. 31 Litho. *Perf. 13x13½*

66 A26 25c multicolored .45 .15
67 A26 30c multicolored .60 .15
68 A26 50c multicolored .80 .15
69 A26 75c multicolored 1.25 .15
70 A26 $1 multicolored 1.65 .15
71 A26 $2 multicolored 3.50 .50
72 A26 $5 multicolored 7.75 1.40
73 A26 $10 multicolored 17.00 4.00
Nos. 66-73 (8) 33.00 6.65

1970, Sept. 7 *Perf. 14½x13½*

74 A27 30c gray & blue .20 .15
75 A27 75c rose & blue .60 .40

50th anniv. of the ILO.

UN Emblem and Doves — A28

Sultan Abdul Halim — A29

Designs: 25c, Doves in elliptical arrangement. 30c, Doves arranged diagonally.

1970, Oct. 24 Litho. *Perf. 13x12½*

76 A28 25c lt brown, blk & yel .45 .20
77 A28 30c lt blue, yel & black .50 .25
78 A28 50c lt ol green & black .85 .50
Nos. 76-78 (3) 1.80 .95

25th anniversary of the United Nations.

Perf. 14½x14

1971, Feb. 20 Photo. Unwmk.

79 A29 10c yellow, blk & gold .15 .15
80 A29 15c purple, blk & gold .30 .15
81 A29 50c blue, blk & gold 1.00 .80
Nos. 79-81 (3) 1.45 1.10

Installation of Sultan Abdul Halim of Kedah as Paramount Ruler.

Bank Building and Crescent — A30

1971, May 15 Photo. *Perf. 14*

82 A30 25c silver & black .90 .50
83 A30 50c gold & brown 1.75 1.25

Opening of Main office of the Negara Malaysia Bank. Nos. 82-83 have circular perforations around vignette set within a white square of paper, perf. on 4 sides.

Malaysian Parliament — A31

Malaysian Parliament, Kuala Lumpur — A32

1971, Sept. 13 Litho. *Perf. 13½*

84 A31 25c multicolored 1.40 .25

Perf. 12½x13

85 A32 75c multicolored 3.25 .95

17th Commonwealth Parliamentary Conference, Kuala Lumpur.

Malaysian Festival — A33

1971, Sept. 18 *Perf. 14½*

86 A33 Strip of 3 5.50 5.50
a. 30c Dancing couple 1.65 .75
b. 30c Dragon 1.65 .75
c. 30c Flags and stage horse 1.65 .75

Visit ASEAN (Association of South East Asian Nations) Year.

Elephant and Tiger — A34

Children's Drawings: No. 88, Cat and kittens. No. 89, Sun, flower and chick. No. 90, Monkey, elephant and lion in jungle. No. 91, Butterfly and flowers.

1971, Oct. 2 *Perf. 12½*

Size: 35x28mm

87 A34 15c pale yellow & multi 2.00 .30
88 A34 15c pale yellow & multi 2.00 .30

Size: 21x28mm

89 A34 15c pale yellow & multi 2.00 .30

Size: 35x28mm

90 A34 15c pale yellow & multi 2.00 .30
91 A34 15c pale yellow & multi 2.00 .30
a. Strip of 5, #87-91 10.50 2.50

25th anniv. of UNICEF.

Track and Field — A35

30c, Sepak Raga (a ball game). 50c, Hockey.

1971, Dec. 11 *Perf. 14½*

92 A35 25c orange & multi .60 .45
93 A35 30c violet & multi .75 .60
94 A35 50c green & multi 1.50 1.10
Nos. 92-94 (3) 2.85 2.15

6th South East Asia Peninsular Games. Kuala Lumpur, Dec. 11-18.

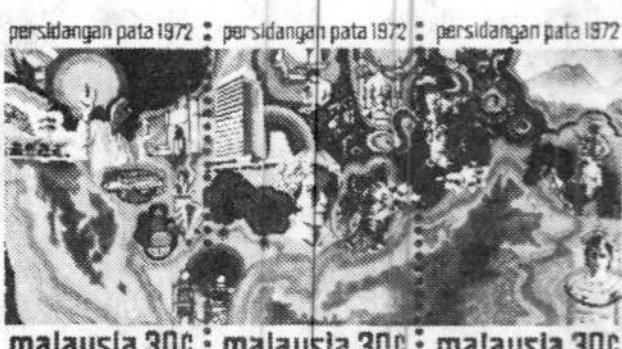

South East Asian Tourist Attractions — A36

Designs include stylized map.

1972, Jan. 31 Litho. *Perf. 14½*

95 A36 Strip of 3 7.00 7.00
a. 30c Flag at left 2.25 1.00
b. 30c High rise building 2.25 1.00
c. 30c Horse & rider 2.25 1.00

Pacific Area Tourist Assoc. Conference.

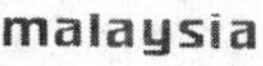

Secretariat Building — A37

50c, Kuala Lumpur Secretariat Building by night.

1972, Feb. 1 *Perf. 14½x14*

96 A37 25c lt blue & multi 1.10 .40
97 A37 50c black & multi 2.25 .80

Achievement of city status by Kuala Lumpur.

Social Security Emblem A38

WHO Emblem A39

1973, July 2 Litho. *Perf. 14½x13½*

98 A38 10c orange & multi .15 .15
99 A38 15c yellow & multi .30 .15
100 A38 50c gray & multi 1.00 .75
Nos. 98-100 (3) 1.45 1.05

Introduction of Social Security System.

1973, Aug. 1 *Perf. 13x12½, 12½x13*

Design: 30c, WHO emblem, horiz.

101 A39 30c yellow & multi .60 .35
102 A39 75c blue & multi 1.90 1.10

25th anniv. of World Health Org.

Flag of Malaysia, Fireworks, Hibiscus — A40

1973, Aug. 31 Litho. *Perf. 14½*

103 A40 10c olive & multi .30 .15
104 A40 15c brown & multi .40 .20
105 A40 50c gray & multi 1.90 1.00
Nos. 103-105 (3) 2.60 1.35

10th anniversary of independence.

INTERPOL and Malaysian Police Emblems A41

Design: 75c, "50" with INTERPOL and Malaysian police emblems.

1973, Sept. 15 *Perf. 12½*

106 A41 25c brown org & multi .85 .40
107 A41 75c deep violet & multi 2.50 1.50

50th anniv. of the Intl. Criminal Police Organization (INTERPOL).

MAS Emblem and Plane — A42

1973, Oct. 1 Litho. *Perf. 14½*

108 A42 15c green & multi .25 .15
109 A42 30c blue & multi .55 .40
110 A42 50c brown & multi 1.00 .80
Nos. 108-110 (3) 1.80 1.35

Inauguration of Malaysian Airline System.

View of Kuala Lumpur — A43

1974, Feb. 1 Litho. *Perf. 12½x13*

111 A43 25c multicolored .65 .50
112 A43 50c multicolored 1.40 1.25

Establishment of Kuala Lumpur as a Federal Territory.

Development Bank Emblem and Projects — A44

1974, Apr. 25 Litho. *Perf. 13½*

113 A44 30c gray & multi .50 .40
114 A44 75c bister & multi 1.25 1.25

7th annual meeting of the Board of Governors of the Asian Development Bank.

Map of Malaysia and Scout Emblem — A45

Scout Saluting, Malaysian and Scout Flags — A46

Design: 50c, Malaysian Scout emblem.

Perf. 14x13½, 13x13½ (15c)

1974, Aug. 1 Litho.

115 A45 10c multicolored .25 .15
116 A46 15c multicolored .55 .20
117 A45 50c multicolored 2.75 .95
Nos. 115-117 (3) 3.55 1.30

Malaysian Boy Scout Jamboree.

Power Installations, NEB Emblem — A47

National Electricity Board Building A48

Perf. 14x14½, 13½x14½

1974, Sept. 1 Litho.

118 A47 30c multicolored .50 .40
119 A48 75c multicolored 1.25 1.25

National Electricity Board, 25th anniversary.

"100," UPU and P.O. Emblems A49

1974, Oct. 9 Litho. *Perf. 14½x13½*

120 A49 25c olive, red & yel .25 .20
121 A49 30c blue, red & yel .30 .25
122 A49 75c ocher, red & yel .80 .80
Nos. 120-122 (3) 1.35 1.25

Centenary of Universal Postal Union.

Gravel Pump Tin Mine — A50

Designs: 20c, Open cast mine. 50c, Silver tin ingot and tin dredge.

1974, Oct. 31 Litho. *Perf. 14*

123 A50 15c silver & multi .80 .20
124 A50 20c silver & multi 1.25 .30
125 A50 50c silver & multi 4.75 .85
Nos. 123-125 (3) 6.80 1.35

4th World Tin Conference, Kuala Lumpur.

Hockey, Cup and Emblem A51

1975, Mar. 1 Litho. *Perf. 14*

126 A51 30c yellow & multi 1.00 .40
127 A51 75c blue & multi 3.25 1.25

Third World Cup Hockey Tournament, Kuala Lumpur, Mar. 1-15.

Trade Union Emblem and Workers — A52

1975, May 1 Litho. *Perf. 14x14½*

128 A52 20c orange & multi .25 .25
129 A52 25c lt green & multi .35 .30
130 A52 30c ultra & multi .40 .40
Nos. 128-130 (3) 1.00 .95

Malaysian Trade Union Cong., 25th anniv.

National Women's Organization Emblem and Heads — A53

1975, Aug. 25 Litho. *Perf. 14*

131 A53 10c emerald & multi .25 .15
132 A53 15c lilac rose & multi .45 .15
133 A53 50c blue & multi 1.65 .75
Nos. 131-133 (3) 2.35 1.05

International Women's Year.

Ubudiah Mosque, Perak — A54

b, Zahir Mosque, Kedah. c, National Mosque, Kuala Lumpur. d, Sultan Abu Bakar Mosque, Johore. e, Kuching State Mosque, Sarawak.

1975, Sept. 22 Litho. *Perf. 14½x14*

134 Strip of 5 8.00 8.00
a.-e. A54 15c single stamp 1.50 .60

Koran reading competition 1975, Malaysia.

Rubber Plantation and Emblem A55

Designs: 30c, "50" in form of latex cup and tire with emblem. 75c, Six test tubes showing various aspects of natural rubber.

1975, Oct. 22 Litho. *Perf. 14x14½*

135 A55 10c gold & multi .40 .15
136 A55 30c gold & multi 1.00 .45
137 A55 75c gold & multi 2.75 1.10
Nos. 135-137 (3) 4.15 1.70

Rubber Research Institute of Malaysia, 50th anniversary.

Butterflies A55a

Coil Stamps

1976, Feb. 6 *Perf. 14*

137A A55a 10c Hebomoia glaucippe aturia .95 .45
137B A55a 15c Precis orithya wallacei 1.00 .50

Scrub Typhus — A56

Sultan Jahya Petra — A57

Designs: 25c, Malaria (microscope, blood cells, slides). $1, Beri-beri (grain and men).

1976, Feb. 6 Litho. *Perf. 14*

138 A56 20c red orange & multi .30 .20
139 A56 25c ultra & multi .35 .25
140 A56 $1 yellow & multi 2.00 1.00
Nos. 138-140 (3) 2.65 1.45

Institute for Medical Research, Kuala Lumpur, 75th anniversary.

Perf. 14½x13½

1976, Feb. 28 Photo.

141 A57 10c yel, black & bis .35 .15
142 A57 15c lilac, black & bis .50 .20
143 A57 50c blue, black & bis 2.75 .95
Nos. 141-143 (3) 3.60 1.30

Installation of Sultan Jahya Petra of Kelantan as Paramount Ruler (Yang di-Pertuan Agong).

Council and Administrative Buildings A58

1976, Aug. 17 Litho. *Perf. 12½*

144 A58 15c orange & black .35 .20
145 A58 20c brt red lilac & black .50 .25
146 A58 50c blue & black 1.25 .80
Nos. 144-146 (3) 2.10 1.25

Opening of the State Council Complex and Administrative Building, Sarawak.

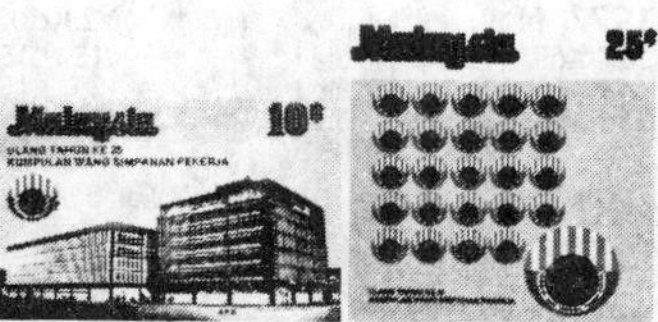

Provident Fund Building — A59

Provident Fund Emblems — A60

Design: 50c, Provident Fund Building at night.

Perf. 13½x14½, 14½ (A60)

1976, Oct. 18 **Litho.**

147	A59	10c blue & multi	.15	.15
148	A60	25c gray & multi	.30	.25
149	A59	50c violet & multi	.75	.60
		Nos. 147-149 (3)	1.20	1.00

Employees' Provident Fund, 25th anniv.

Rehabilitation of the Blind — A61

Design: 75c, Blind man casting large shadow.

1976, Nov. 20 *Perf. 13½x14½*

150	A61	10c multicolored	.20	.15
151	A61	75c multicolored	1.50	1.25

25th anniv. of the Malaysian Assoc. for the Blind.

Abdul Razak and Crowd — A62

Designs: b, Abdul Razak in cap and gown at lectern. c, Abdul Razak pointing to new roads and bridges on map. d, New constitution. e, Abdul Razak addressing Association of Southeast Asian Countries.

1977, Jan. 14 **Photo.** *Perf. 14x14½*

152		Strip of 5	7.00	7.00
a.-e.	A62	15c single stamp	1.00	.75

Prime Minister Tun Haji Abdul Razak bi Dato Hussein (1922-1976).

FELDA Housing Development A63

Design: 30c, View of oil palm settlement area and FELDA emblem.

1977, July 7 **Litho.** *Perf. 13½x14½*

153	A63	15c multicolored	.30	.15
154	A63	30c multicolored	.70	.35

Federal Land Development Authority (FELDA), 21st anniversary.

"10" — A64

ASEAN, 10th anniv.: 75c, Flags of ASEAN members: Malaysia, Philippines, Singapore, Thailand and Indonesia.

1977, Aug. 8 **Litho.** *Perf. 13½x14½*

155	A64	10c multicolored	.15	.15
156	A64	75c multicolored	1.10	.80

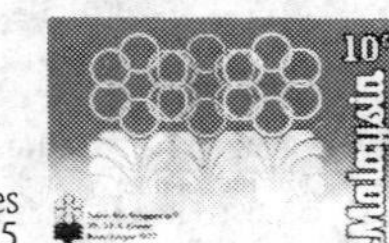

SEA Games Emblems — A65

Designs: 20c, Ball, symbolic of 9 participating nations. 75c, Running.

Perf. 13½x14½

1977, Nov. 19 **Litho.**

157	A65	10c multicolored	.15	.15
158	A65	20c multicolored	.20	.15
159	A65	75c multicolored	1.00	.55
		Nos. 157-159 (3)	1.35	.85

9th South East Asia Games, Kuala Lumpur.

Bank Emblem A66

1978, Mar. 15 **Litho.** *Perf. 14*

160	A66	30c multicolored	.25	.20
161	A66	75c multicolored	.75	.50

2nd annual meeting of Islamic Development Bank Governors, Kuala Lumpur, Mar. 1978.

Government Building — A67

Designs: Views of Shah Alam.

1978, Dec. 7 **Litho.** *Perf. 13½x14½*

162	A67	10c multicolored	.15	.15
163	A67	30c multicolored	.25	.20
164	A67	75c multicolored	.65	.55
		Nos. 162-164 (3)	1.05	.90

Inauguration of Shah Alam as state capital of Selangor.

Mobile Post Office in Village — A68

Designs: 25c, General Post Office, Kuala Lumpur. 50c, Motorcyclist, rural mail delivery.

1978, July 10 *Perf. 13*

165	A68	10c multicolored	.25	.15
166	A68	25c multicolored	.60	.40
167	A68	50c multicolored	1.25	.85
		Nos. 165-167 (3)	2.10	1.40

4th Conf. of Commonwealth Postal Administrators.

Jamboree Emblem — A69 15c

Bees and Honeycomb A70

1978, July 26 **Litho.** *Perf. 13½*

168	A69	15c multicolored	.45	.20
169	A70	$1 multicolored	3.25	1.25

4th Boy Scout Jamboree, Sarawak.

Globe, Crest and WHO Emblem — A71

1978, Sept. 30 *Perf. 13½x14½*

170	A71	15c blue, red & black	.15	.15
171	A71	30c green, red & black	.30	.30
172	A71	50c pink, red & black	.50	.50
		Nos. 170-172 (3)	.95	.95

Global eradication of smallpox.

Dome of the Rock — A72

1978, Aug. 21 **Litho.** *Perf. 12½*

173	A72	15c red & multi	.55	.25
174	A72	30c blue & multi	1.25	.55

For Palestinian fighters and their families.

Tiger — A73

Designs: 40c, Cobego. 50c, Chevrotain. 75c, Pangolin. $1, Leatherback turtle. $2, Tapir. $5, Gaur. $10, Orangutan, vert.

Perf. 15x14½, 14½x15

1979, Jan. 4 **Litho.** **Wmk. 378**

175	A73	30c multicolored	.40	.25
176	A73	40c multicolored	.45	.30
177	A73	50c multicolored	.60	.40
178	A73	75c multicolored	.90	.60
179	A73	$1 multicolored	1.25	.85
180	A73	$2 multicolored	2.50	1.65
181	A73	$5 multicolored	6.00	4.00
182	A73	$10 multicolored	12.50	8.00
		Nos. 175-182 (8)	24.60	16.05

1983-87

Unwmk.

175a	A73	30c ('84)	.75	.75
176a	A73	40c ('84)	1.00	1.00
177a	A73	50c ('84)	1.25	1.25
178a	A73	75c ('87)	1.75	1.75
179a	A73	$1	2.50	2.50
180a	A73	$2	4.75	4.75
181a	A73	$5 ('85)	12.00	12.00
182a	A73	$10 ('86)	25.00	25.00
		Nos. 175a-182a (8)	49.00	49.00

Central Bank of Malaysia — A74

Year of the Child Emblem — A75

10c, Central Bank of Malaysia & emblem.

Perf. 13½

1979, Jan. 26 **Litho.** **Unwmk.**

183	A74	10c multicolored, horiz.	.15	.15
184	A74	75c multicolored	.70	.70

Central Bank of Malaysia, 30th anniv.

1979, Feb. 24 *Perf. 14*

Intl. Year of the Child: 15c, Children of the world, globe and ICY emblem. $1, Children at play, ICY emblem.

185	A75	10c multicolored	.15	.15
186	A75	15c multicolored	.25	.15
187	A75	$1 multicolored	2.25	1.10
		Nos. 185-187 (3)	2.65	1.40

Symbolic Rubber Plant — A76

Designs: 10c, Symbolic palm. 75c, Symbolic rubber products.

1979, Apr. 30 **Litho.** *Perf. 13*

188	A76	10c brt green & gold	.15	.15
189	A76	20c multicolored	.20	.20
190	A76	75c brt green & gold	.65	.65
		Nos. 188-190 (3)	1.00	1.00

Centenary of rubber production (in 1977).

Rafflesia Hasseltii — A77

Flowers: 2c, Pterocarpus indicus. 5c, Lagerstroemia speciosa. 10c, Durio zibethinus. 15c, Hibiscus. 20c, Rhododendron scortechinii. 25c, Phaeomeria speciosa.

Perf. 15x14½

1979, Apr. 30 **Wmk. 378**

191	A77	1c multicolored	.15	.15
192	A77	2c multicolored	.15	.15
193	A77	5c multicolored	.15	.15
a.		Unwmkd. ('84)		
194	A77	10c multicolored	.15	.15
a.		White flowers, unwmkd. ('84)	.15	.15
195	A77	15c multicolored	.15	.15
a.		15c yellow & multi. unwmkd. ('83)	.15	.15
196	A77	20c multicolored	.25	.15
a.		20c greenish & multi. unwmkd. ('83)	.25	.15
197	A77	25c multicolored	.30	.15
a.		Unwmkd. ('85)	5.00	
		Set value	1.15	.45

Temengor Hydroelectric Dam — A78

Designs: 25c, 50c, Dam and river, diff.

Perf. 13½x14½

1979, Sept. 19 **Litho.**

198	A78	15c multicolored	.20	.15
199	A78	25c multicolored	.35	.15
200	A78	50c multicolored	.65	.25
		Nos. 198-200 (3)	1.20	
		Set value		.45

"TELECOM 79" — A79

Telecom Emblem and: 15c, Telephone receiver and globes. 50c, Modes of communication.

1979, Sept. 20 *Perf. 13½*

Size: 34x25mm

201	A79	10c multicolored	.15	.15
202	A79	15c multicolored	.20	.15

Perf. 14

Size: 29x28mm

203	A79	50c multicolored	.65	.30
		Nos. 201-203 (3)	1.00	
		Set value		.40

3rd World Telecommunications Exhibition, Geneva, Sept. 20-26.

Haji Ahmad Shah — A80

1980, July 10 **Litho.** *Perf. 14½*

204	A80	10c multicolored	.15	.15
205	A80	15c multicolored	.15	.15
206	A80	50c multicolored	.60	.25
		Nos. 204-206 (3)	.90	
		Set value		.40

Installation of Sultan Haji Ahmad Shah of Pahang as Paramount Ruler (Yang di-Pertuan Agong).

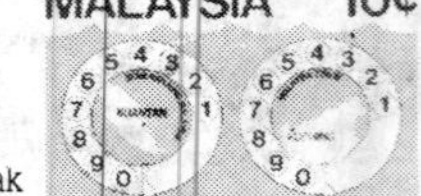

Pahang-Sarawak Cable — A81

Designs: 15c, Dial with views of Kuantan and Kuching. 50c, Telephone and maps.

1980, Aug. 31 **Litho.** *Perf. 13½*

207	A81	10c shown	.15	.15
208	A81	15c multicolored	.20	.15
209	A81	50c multicolored	.60	.20
		Nos. 207-209 (3)	.95	
		Set value		.30

National University of Malaysia, 10th Anniversary A82

15c, Jalan Pantai Baru campus. 75c, Great Hall & Tun Haji Abdul Razak (1st chancellor).

1980, Sept. 2 Litho. *Perf. 13½*

210 A82 10c shown	.15	.15
211 A82 15c multicolored	.20	.15
212 A82 75c multicolored	1.00	.35
Nos. 210-212 (3)	1.35	
Set value		.45

Hegira (Pilgrimage Year) — A83

1980, Nov. 9

213 A83 15c multicolored	.20	.15
214 A83 50c multicolored	.60	.35
Set value		.40

A84

Emblem — A85

1981, Feb. 14 Litho. *Perf. 13½*

215 A84 10c Child learning to walk	.30	.15
216 A84 15c Seamstress	.50	.15
217 A84 75c Athlete	2.75	.40
Nos. 215-217 (3)	3.55	
Set value		.50

International Year of the Disabled.

1981, Mar. 21 Litho. *Perf. 14½*

218 A85 10c multicolored	.20	.15
219 A85 15c multicolored	.30	.15
220 A85 50c multicolored	1.10	.30
Nos. 218-220 (3)	1.60	
Set value		.40

Installation of Sultan Mahmud of Trengganu.

Industrial Training Seminar — A86

Designs: Various workers.

1981, May 2 Litho. *Perf. 13½*

221 A86 10c multicolored	.15	.15
222 A86 15c multicolored	.15	.15
223 A86 30c multicolored	.35	.15
224 A86 75c multicolored	.85	.25
Nos. 221-224 (4)	1.50	
Set value		.45

Sources of Energy — A87

1981, June 17 Litho. *Perf. 13½*

225 A87 10c "25"	.20	.15
226 A87 15c shown	.35	.15
227 A87 75c Non-renewable energy	1.75	.40
Nos. 225-227 (3)	2.30	
Set value		.55

World Energy Conference, 25th anniv.

Centenary of Sabah — A88

1981, Aug. 31 Litho. *Perf. 12*

228 A88 15c Views, 1881 and 1981	.60	.15
229 A88 80c Traditional and modern farming	3.50	.40
Set value		.45

Rain Tree — A89

1981, Dec. 16 Litho. *Perf. 14*

230 A89 15c shown	.45	.15
231 A89 50c Simber tree, vert.	1.65	.25
232 A89 80c Borneo camphor-wood, vert.	3.25	.50
Nos. 230-232 (3)	5.35	.90

Scouting Year and Jamboree, Apr. 9-16 A90

1982, Apr. 10 Litho. *Perf. 13½x13*

233 A90 15c Jamboree emblem	.30	.15
234 A90 50c Flag, emblem	1.10	.25
235 A90 80c Emblems, knot	1.65	.35
Nos. 233-235 (3)	3.05	.75

15th Anniv. of Assoc. of South East Asian Nations (ASEAN) A91

1982, Aug. 8 Litho. *Perf. 14*

236 A91 15c Meeting Center	.15	.15
237 A91 $1 Flags	1.25	.55

Dome of the Rock, Jerusalem A92

1982, Aug. 21 *Perf. 13½*

238 A92 15c multicolored	.70	.15
239 A92 $1 multicolored	5.00	.55

For the freedom of Palestine.

25th Anniv. of Independence A93

1982, Aug. 31 Litho. *Perf. 14*

240 A93 10c Kuala Lumpur	.15	.15
241 A93 15c Independence celebration	.20	.15
242 A93 50c Parade	.75	.25
243 A93 80c Independence ceremony	1.00	.35
a. Souvenir sheet of 4, #240-243	8.75	2.50
Nos. 240-243 (4)	2.10	
Set value		.70

Traditional Games — A94

1982, Oct. 30 *Perf. 13½*

244 A94 10c Shadow play	.30	.15
245 A94 15c Cross top	.55	.15
246 A94 75c Kite flying	2.75	.40
Nos. 244-246 (3)	3.60	
Set value		.50

Handicrafts — A95

1982, Nov. 26 Litho. *Perf. 13x13½*

247 A95 10c Sabah hats	.20	.15
248 A95 15c Gold-threaded cloth	.25	.15
249 A95 75c Sarawak pottery	1.40	.35
Nos. 247-249 (3)	1.85	
Set value		.45

Commonwealth Day — A96

1983, Mar. 14 Litho. *Perf. 14*

250 A96 15c Flag	.15	.15
251 A96 20c Seri Paduka Baginda	.20	.15
252 A96 40c Oil palm refinery	.35	.15
253 A96 $1 Globe	.90	.40
Nos. 250-253 (4)	1.60	
Set value		.65

First Shipment of Natural Gas, Bintulu, Sarawak A97

1983, Jan. 22 Litho. *Perf. 12*

254 A97 15c Bintulu Port Authority emblem	.80	.15
a. Perf. 13½	7.00	
255 A97 20c Freighter Tenaga Satu	.95	.15

Perf. 13½

256 A97 $1 Gas plant	5.25	.45
Nos. 254-256 (3)	7.00	
Set value		.55

Freshwater Fish — A98

1983, June 15 *Perf. 12x12½*

257 Pair	2.25	.40
a. A98 20c Tilapia nilotica	1.10	.25
b. A98 20c Cyprinus carpio	1.10	.25
258 Pair	4.75	1.10
a. A98 40c Puntius gonionotus	2.25	.40
b. A98 40c Ctenopharyngodon idellus	2.25	.40
c. As #258, perf. 13½x14	5.00	3.00

Opening of East-West Highway — A99

1983, July 1 *Perf. 14x13½*

259 A99 15c Lower Sungei Pergau Bridge	.65	.15
260 A99 20c Sungei Perak Reservoir Bridge	.90	.15
261 A99 $1 Map	5.00	.45
Nos. 259-261 (3)	6.55	
Set value		.55

Armed Forces, 50th Anniv. A100

Designs: 15c, Royal Malaysian Aircraft. 20c, Navy vessel firing missile. 40c, Battle at Pasir Panjang. 80c, Trooping of the Royal colors.

1983, Sept. 16 Litho. *Perf. 13½*

262 A100 15c multicolored	.60	.15
263 A100 20c multicolored	1.10	.15
264 A100 40c multicolored	1.90	.20
265 A100 80c multicolored	4.25	.40
a. Souvenir sheet of 4, #262-265	9.25	2.50
Nos. 262-265 (4)	7.85	
Set value		.75

Helmeted Hornbill — A101

Various hornbills.

1983, Oct. 26 Litho. *Perf. 13½*

266 A101 15c shown	.35	.20
267 A101 20c Wrinkled	.65	.20
268 A101 50c White crested	1.65	.45
269 A101 $1 Rhinoceros hornbill	3.25	1.10
Nos. 266-269 (4)	5.90	1.95

25th Anniv. of Begara Bank A102

Branch offices.

1984, Jan. 26 Litho. *Perf. 13½x14*

270 A102 20c Ipoh	.40	.15
271 A102 $1 Alor Setar	2.50	.40
Set value		.50

10th Anniv. of Federal Territory A103

Views of Kuala Lumpur. 20c, 40c vert.

Perf. 14x13½, 13½x14

1984, Feb. 1 Litho.

272 A103 20c multicolored	.65	.15
273 A103 40c multicolored	1.40	.20
274 A103 80c multicolored	3.00	.40
Nos. 272-274 (3)	5.05	.75

Labuan Federal Territory A104

Traditional Weapons A105

1984, Apr. 16 Litho. *Perf. 13½x14*

275 A104 20c Development symbols, map, arms	.75	.15
276 A104 $1 Flag, map	4.00	.40
Set value		.50

1984, May 30 *Perf. 13x14*

277 A105 40c Keris Semenanjung	1.50	.20
278 A105 40c Keris Pekakak	1.50	.20
279 A105 40c Keris Jawa	1.50	.20
280 A105 40c Tumbuk Lada	1.50	.20
a. Block of 4, #277-280	6.00	.80

Asia-Pacific Broadcasting Union, 20th Anniv. — A106

1984, June 23 *Perf. 14x14½*

281 A106 20c Map, waves	.65	.15
282 A106 $1 "20"	3.25	.40
Set value		.50

Kuala Lumpur Post Office Opening A107

1984, Oct. 29 *Perf. 12x11½*

No.	Type	Value	Description	Unused	Used
283	A107	15c	Facsimile transmission	.40	.15
284	A107	20c	Building	.60	.15
285	A107	$1	Mail bag conveyor	3.00	.50
			Nos. 283-285 (3)	4.00	
			Set value		.65

Installation of Sultan of Johore as 8th Paramount Ruler of Malaysia — A108

Sultan Mahmood, Arms — A109

1984, Nov. 15 **Litho.** *Perf. 12*

No.	Type	Value	Description	Unused	Used
286	A108	15c	multicolored	.45	.15
287	A108	20c	multicolored	.50	.15
288	A109	40c	multicolored	1.10	.15
289	A109	80c	multicolored	2.25	.35
			Nos. 286-289 (4)	4.30	
			Set value		.65

A110 A111

Malaysian hibiscus.

1984, Dec. 12 **Litho.** *Perf. 13½*

No.	Type	Value	Description	Unused	Used
290	A110	10c	White hibiscus	.35	.15
291	A110	20c	Red hibiscus	.80	.15
292	A110	40c	Pink hibiscus	1.65	.15
293	A110	$1	Orange hibiscus	4.75	.40
			Nos. 290-293 (4)	7.55	
			Set value		.65

Perf. 13½x14, 14x13½

1985, Mar. 30 **Litho.**

No.	Type	Value	Description	Unused	Used
294	A111	20c	Badge, vert.	.65	.15
295	A111	$1	Parliament, Kuala Lumpur	2.75	.40
			Set value		.45

Parliament, 25th anniv.

Protected Wildlife A112

1985, Apr. 25 *Perf. 14*

No.	Type	Value	Description	Unused	Used
296	A112	10c	Prionodon linsang	.40	.15
297	A112	40c	Nycticebus coucang, vert.	1.75	.15
298	A112	$1	Petaurista elegans, vert.	4.75	.40
			Nos. 296-298 (3)	6.90	
			Set value		.60

Intl. Youth Year — A113

1985, May 15 *Perf. 13*

No.	Type	Value	Description	Unused	Used
299	A113	20c	Youth solidarity	.75	.15
300	A113	$1	Participation in natl. development	3.75	.40

Malaya Railways Centenary A114

Locomotives.

1985, June 1 *Perf. 13*

No.	Type	Value	Description	Unused	Used
301	A114	15c	Steam engine, 1885	.75	.15
302	A114	20c	Diesel-electric, 1957	1.00	.15
303	A114	$1	Diesel, 1963	5.25	.40
			Nos. 301-303 (3)	7.00	
			Set value		.55

Souvenir Sheet

Perf. 14x13

No.	Type	Value	Description	Unused	Used
304	A114	80c	Train leaving Kuala Lumpur Station, 1938	7.00	2.00

No. 304 contains one stamp 48x32mm.

Proton Saga — A115

1985, July 9 *Perf. 14*

No.	Type	Value	Description	Unused	Used
305	A115	20c	multicolored	.55	.15
306	A115	40c	multicolored	1.25	.15
307	A115	$1	multicolored	3.00	.40
			Nos. 305-307 (3)	4.80	.70

Inauguration of natl. automotive industry.

Sultan Salahuddin Abdul Aziz, Selangor Coat of Arms — A116

1985, Sept. 5 *Perf. 13*

No.	Type	Value	Description	Unused	Used
308	A116	15c	multicolored	.20	.15
309	A116	20c	multicolored	.25	.15
310	A116	$1	multicolored	1.10	.40
			Nos. 308-310 (3)	1.55	
			Set value		.55

25th anniv. of coronation.

Penang Bridge Opening A117

1985, Sept. 15 **Litho.** *Perf. 13½x13*

No.	Type	Value	Description	Unused	Used
311	A117	20c	shown	.80	.15
312	A117	40c	Bridge, map	1.65	.20

Size: 44x28mm

Perf. 12½

No.	Type	Value	Description	Unused	Used
313	A117	$1	Map	4.00	.40
			Nos. 311-313 (3)	6.45	
			Set value		.65

Natl. Oil Industry A118

1985, Nov. 4 *Perf. 12½*

No.	Type	Value	Description	Unused	Used
314	A118	15c	Offshore rig, vert.	.60	.15
315	A118	20c	1st refinery	.90	.15
316	A118	$1	Map of oil and gas fields	4.75	.45
			Nos. 314-316 (3)	6.25	
			Set value		.60

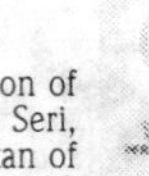

Coronation of Paduka Seri, Sultan of Perak — A119

1985, Dec. 9 *Perf. 14*

No.	Type	Value	Description	Unused	Used
317	A119	15c	lt blue & multi	.35	.15
318	A119	20c	lilac & multi	.50	.15
319	A119	$1	gold & multi	2.50	.40
			Nos. 317-319 (3)	3.35	
			Set value		.55

Birds A120

1986, Mar. 11 **Litho.** *Perf. 13½*

No.	Type	Value	Description	Unused	Used
320	A120	20c	Lophura ignita, vert.	2.00	.25
321	A120	20c	Pavo malacense, vert.	2.00	.25
a.			Pair, #320-321	4.00	.50
322	A120	40c	Lophura bulweri	4.00	.40
a.			Perf. 12	1.25	
323	A120	40c	Argusianus argus	4.00	.40
a.			Pair, #322-323	8.00	.80
b.			Perf. 12	1.25	
c.			Pair, #322a, 323b	2.50	

PATA '86, Pacific Area Travel Assoc. Conference, Persidangan — A121

No. 324: a, Two women dancing. b, Woman in red. c, Man and woman.

No. 325: a, Woman in gold. b, Woman holding fan. c, Woman in violet.

1986, Apr. 14 **Litho.** *Perf. 15x14½*

No.	Type	Value	Description	Unused	Used
324			Strip of 3	2.25	.75
a.-c.	A121	20c	any single	.75	.15
325			Strip of 3	4.50	1.50
a.-c.	A121	40c	any single	1.50	.15

Malaysia Games — A122

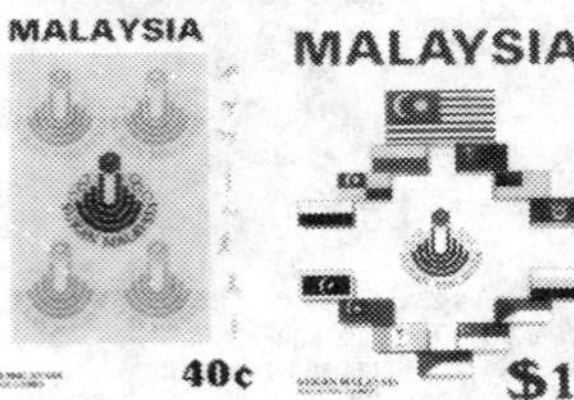

Games Emblem — A123 Flags — A124

1986, Apr. 14 **Litho.** *Perf. 12*

No.	Type	Value	Description	Unused	Used
326	A122	20c	multicolored	1.40	.15
327	A123	40c	multicolored	2.75	.15
328	A124	$1	multicolored	7.50	.40
			Nos. 326-328 (3)	11.65	
			Set value		.60

Nephelium Lappaceum A125 Averrhoa Carambola A126

1986, June 5

No.	Type	Value	Description	Unused	Used
329	A125	40c	shown	.25	.15
330	A125	50c	Ananas comosus	.30	.15
331	A125	80c	Durio zibethinus	.50	.25
332	A125	$1	Garcinia mangostana	.65	.30

Perf. 13½

No.	Type	Value	Description	Unused	Used
333	A126	$2	shown	1.40	.65
334	A126	$5	Musa sapientum	3.25	1.50
335	A126	$10	Mangifera odorata	6.50	3.00
336	A126	$20	Carica papaya	13.00	6.00
			Nos. 329-336 (8)	25.85	12.00

Natl. Assoc. for the Prevention of Drug Abuse, 10th Anniv. A127

1986, June 26 *Perf. 13*

No.	Type	Value	Description	Unused	Used
337	A127	20c	Skull	.65	.15
338	A127	40c	Dove	1.40	.15
339	A127	$1	Addict, vert.	3.75	.40
			Nos. 337-339 (3)	5.80	.70

Malaysian Airlines Kuala Lumpur-Los Angeles Inaugural Flight — A128

1986, July 31 *Perf. 14x13½*

No.	Type	Value	Description	Unused	Used
340	A128	20c	Flight routes map	.65	.15
341	A128	40c	MAS emblem, new route	1.40	.15
342	A128	$1	Emblem, stops	3.75	.40
			Nos. 340-342 (3)	5.80	.70

Industrial Productivity — A129

1986, Nov. 3 **Litho.** *Perf. 14*

No.	Type	Value	Description	Unused	Used
343	A129	20c	Construction, vert.	.95	.15
344	A129	40c	Industry	2.00	.15
345	A129	$1	Automobile factory	5.25	.40
			Nos. 343-345 (3)	8.20	.70

Historic Buildings A130

15c, Istana Lama Seri Menanti, Negri Sembilan. 20c, Istana Kenangan, Perak. 40c, Bangunan Stadthuys, Malacca. $1, Istana Kuching, Sarawak.

1986, Dec. 20 *Perf. 13*

No.	Type	Value	Description	Unused	Used
346	A130	15c	multicolored	.35	.15
347	A130	20c	multicolored	.45	.15
348	A130	40c	multicolored	.90	.15
349	A130	$1	multicolored	2.25	.40
			Nos. 346-349 (4)	3.95	
			Set value		.70

See design A146.

Folk Music Instruments — A131

1987, Mar. 7 **Litho.** *Perf. 12*

No.	Type	Value	Description	Unused	Used
350	A131	15c	Sompotan	.40	.15
351	A131	20c	Sapih	.55	.15
352	A131	50c	Serunai, vert.	1.40	.20
353	A131	80c	Rebab, vert.	2.25	.30
			Nos. 350-353 (4)	4.60	
			Set value		.65

Intl. Year of Shelter for the Homeless A132

1987, Apr. 6 Litho. *Perf. 12*

354 A132 20c Model village .40 .15
355 A132 $1 Symbols of family, shelter 2.00 .45

UN Anti-Drug Campaign and Congress, Vienna — A133

1987, June 8 Litho. *Perf. 13½x13*

356 A133 20c Health boy, family, rainbow 1.00 .15
357 A133 20c Holding drugs 1.00 .15
a. Pair, #356-357 2.00 .75
358 A133 40c Child warding off drugs 2.00 .15
359 A133 40c Drugs, damaged body in capsule 2.00 .15
a. Pair, #358-358 4.25 1.25
Nos. 356-359 (4) 6.00
Set value .45

Nos. 357a, 359a have continuous designs.

Kenyir Hydroelectric Power Station Inauguration — A134

1987, July 13 *Perf. 12*

360 A134 20c Power facility, dam .80 .15
361 A134 $1 Side view 4.25 .45

33rd Commonwealth Parliamentary Conference — A135

1987, Sept. 1 Litho. *Perf. 12*

362 A135 20c Maces, parliament .40 .15
363 A135 $1 Parliament, maces, diff. 2.00 .45

Transportation and Communications Decade in Asia and the Pacific (1985-94) — A136

Designs: 15c, Satellites, Earth, satellite dish. 20c, Car, diesel train, Kuala Lumpur Station. 40c, MISC container ship. $1, Malaysia Airlines jet, Kuala Lumpur Airport.

1987, Oct. 26 *Perf. 13½x13*

364 A136 15c multicolored .50 .15
365 A136 20c multicolored .65 .15
366 A136 40c multicolored 1.40 .20
367 A136 $1 multicolored 3.25 .45
Nos. 364-367 (4) 5.80
Set value .75

Protected Wildcats A137

1987, Nov. 14

368 A137 15c Felis temminckii .80 .15
369 A137 20c Felis planiceps 1.00 .15
370 A137 40c Felis marmorata 2.25 .20
371 A137 $1 Neofelis nebulosa 5.75 .45
Nos. 368-371 (4) 9.80
Set value .75

ASEAN, 20th Anniv. A138

1987, Dec. 14 Litho. *Perf. 13*

372 A138 20c "20," flags .30 .15
373 A138 $1 Flags, Earth 1.75 .45

Opening of Sultan Salahuddin Abdul Aziz Shah Mosque, Selangor A139

Dome, minarets and: 15c, Arches. 20c, Sultan Abdul Aziz Shah, Selangor crest. $1, Interior, vert.

1988, Mar. 11 Litho. *Perf. 12*

374 A139 15c multicolored .25 .15
375 A139 20c multicolored .35 .15
376 A139 $1 multicolored 1.75 .40
Nos. 374-376 (3) 2.35
Set value .55

Opening of Sultan Ismail Power Station, Trengganu A140

1988, Apr. 4 *Perf. 13*

377 A140 20c shown .35 .15
378 A140 $1 Station, diff. 1.75 .40

Wildlife Protection — A141

Birds.

1988, June 30 Litho. *Perf. 13*

379 A141 20c Hypothymis azurea 1.00 .15
380 A141 20c Dicaeum cruentatum 1.00 .15
a. Pair, #379-380 2.00 .50
381 A141 50c Aethopyga siparaja 2.50 .20
382 A141 50c Cymbirhynchus macrorhynchos 2.50 .20
a. Pair, #381-382 5.00 1.00
Nos. 379-382 (4) 7.00
Set value .60

Independence of Sabah and Sarawak, 25th Anniv.
A142 A143

1988, Aug. 31 Litho. *Perf. 13x13½*

383 A142 20c Sabah .40 .15
384 A142 20c Sarawak .40 .15
a. Pair, #383-384 .80 .20
385 A143 $1 State and natl. symbols 1.75 .40
Nos. 383-385 (3) 2.55
Set value .60

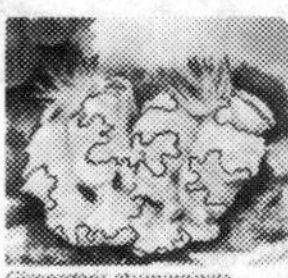

A144

Marine Life — A145

Nudibranchs: No. 386: a, Glossodoris atromarginata. b, Phyllidia ocellata. c, Chromodoris annae. d, Flabellina macassarana. e, Fryeria ruppelli.

1988, Dec. 17 Litho. *Perf. 12*

386 Strip of 5 4.00 1.25
a.-e. A144 20c any single .80 .25

Souvenir Sheet

Perf. 14

387 A145 $1 Pomacanthus annularis 3.00 1.00

No. 387 contains one stamp 50x40mm.

Historic Buildings, Malacca A146

#388, Perisytiharan Kemerdekaan Memorial. #389, Istana Kesultanan. $1, Porta da Santiago.

Perf. 13½x13, 13x13½

1989, Apr. 15 Litho.

388 A146 20c multicolored .35 .15
389 A146 20c multicolored .35 .15
390 A146 $1 multicolored, vert. 1.90 .40
Nos. 388-390 (3) 2.60
Set value .55

See design A130.

Crustaceans A147

Wmk. 388

1989, June 29 Litho. *Perf. 12*

391 A147 20c *Tetralia nigrolineata* .55 .15
392 A147 20c *Neopetrolisthes maculatus* .55 .15
a. Pair, #391-392 1.10 .40
393 A147 40c *Periclimenes holthuisi* 1.10 .15
394 A147 40c *Synalpheus neomeris* 1.10 .15
a. Pair, #393-394 2.25 .80
Nos. 391-394 (4) 3.30
Set value .50

7th Natl. Scout Jamboree A148

1989, July 26 *Perf. 13x13½*

395 A148 10c Map, badges .30 .15
396 A148 20c Scout salute, natl. flag .60 .15
397 A148 80c Camping out 2.50 .35
Nos. 395-397 (3) 3.40
Set value .45

Nos. 395-396 vert.

15th SEA Games, Kuala Lumpur — A149

Installation of Sultan Azlan as Supreme Ruler — A150

Designs: 10c, Cycling, horiz. 20c, Track events, horiz. 50c, Swimming. $1, Torch-bearer, stadium and flags.

Perf. 13½x13, 13x13½

1989, Aug. 20 Litho. Wmk. 388

398 A149 10c multicolored .15 .15
399 A149 20c multicolored .35 .15
400 A149 50c multicolored .80 .20
401 A149 $1 multicolored 1.65 .40
Nos. 398-401 (4) 2.95
Set value .75

1989, Sept. 18 *Perf. 13x13½*

402 A150 20c multicolored .30 .15
403 A150 40c multicolored .60 .15
404 A150 $1 multicolored 1.40 .40
Nos. 402-404 (3) 2.30 .70

Commonwealth Heads of Government Meeting A151

Perf. 13½x13, 13x13½

1989, Oct. 18

405 A151 20c Conference center .30 .15
406 A151 50c Folk dancers, vert. .75 .20
407 A151 $1 Map, flag 1.40 .40
Nos. 405-407 (3) 2.45 .75

Malaysia Airlines Inaugural Non-stop Flight to London, Dec. 2 A152

#408, Passenger jet, Malaysian clock tower, Big Ben. #409, Passenger jet, Malaysian skyscraper, Westminster Palace. $1, Map, passenger jet.

1989, Dec. 2 Wmk. 388 *Perf. 13*

408 A152 20c shown .50 .15
409 A152 20c multicolored .50 .15
a. Pair, #408-409 1.00 .15
410 A152 $1 multicolored 2.50 .40
Nos. 408-410 (3) 3.50
Set value .55

National Park, 50th Anniv. — A153

1989, Dec. 28 *Perf. 13x13½*

411 A153 20c Map, sloth .50 .15
412 A153 $1 Crested arguses 2.50 .40

Visit Malaysia.

Visit Malaysia Year — A154

1990, Jan. 11 *Perf. 12*

413 A154 20c Map .30 .15
414 A154 50c Drummers .75 .20
415 A154 $1 Yachts, scuba divers 1.40 .40
Nos. 413-415 (3) 2.45 .75

Wildflowers — A155

1990, Mar. 12

416 A155	15c	*Dillenia suffruticosa*	.20 .15
417 A155	20c	*Mimosa pudica*	.30 .15
418 A155	50c	*Ipomoea carnea*	.70 .20
419 A155	$1	*Nymphaea pubescens*	1.40 .40
		Nos. 416-419 (4)	2.60
		Set value	.75

Kuala Lumpur A156

Wmk. 388

1990, May 14 Litho. *Perf. 12*

420 A156	20c	Flag, rainbow, vert.	.25 .15
421 A156	40c	shown	.50 .15
422 A156	$1	Cityscape	1.25 .40
		Nos. 420-422 (3)	2.00 .70

South-South Consultation and Cooperation Conference — A157

1990, June 1 *Perf. 13*

423 A157	20c	shown	.40 .15
424 A157	80c	Emblem	1.90 .30

Alor Setar, 250th Anniv. — A158

1990, June 2 *Perf. 12*

425 A158	20c	shown	.30 .15
426 A158	40c	Musicians, vert.	.65 .15
427 A158	$1	Government bldg., vert.	1.40 .40
		Nos. 425-427 (3)	2.35 .70

Intl. Literacy Year — A159

1990, Sept. 8

428 A159	20c	Letters, sign language	.20 .15
429 A159	40c	People reading	.45 .15
430 A159	$1	Globe, pen nib, vert.	1.00 .40
		Nos. 428-430 (3)	1.65 .70

Turtles A160

1990, Nov. 17

431 A160	15c	Dermochelys coriacea	.25 .15
432 A160	20c	Chelonia mydas	.30 .15
433 A160	40c	Eretmochelys imbricata	.90 .15
434 A160	$1	Lepidochelys olivacea	2.25 .40
		Nos. 431-434 (4)	3.70
		Set value	.70

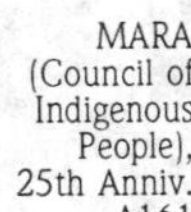

MARA (Council of Indigenous People), 25th Anniv. A161

1991, Apr. 25

435 A161	20c	Construction	.20 .15
436 A161	40c	Education	.45 .15
437 A161	$1	Banking & industry	1.10 .40
		Nos. 435-437 (3)	1.75 .70

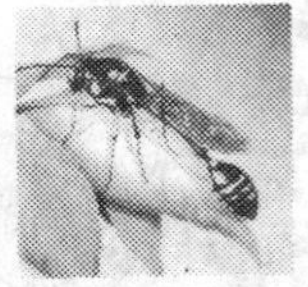

Wasps — A162

Designs: 15c, Eustenogaster calyptodoma. 20c, Vespa affinis indonensis. 50c, Sceliphorn javanum. $1, Ampulex compressa.

1991, July 29

438 A162	15c	multicolored	.20 .15
439 A162	20c	multicolored	.30 .15
440 A162	50c	multicolored	.70 .20
441 A162	$1	multicolored	1.40 .40
a.		Souvenir sheet of 4, #438-441, perf. 14½x14	3.25
		Nos. 438-441 (4)	2.60
		Set value	.70

Prime Ministers — A163

#442, Tunku Abdul Rahman Putra Al-Haj (1903-90). #443, Tun Hussein Onn (1922-90). #444, Tun Abdul Razak Hussein (1922-76).

1991, Aug. 30

442 A163	$1	multicolored	1.00 .40
443 A163	$1	multicolored	1.00 .40
444 A163	$1	multicolored	1.00 .40
		Nos. 442-444 (3)	3.00 1.20

Historic Buildings A164

Designs: 15c, Istana Maziah, Trengganu. 20c, Istana Besar, Johore. 40c, Istana Bandar, Kuala Langat, Selangor. $1, Istana Jahar, Kelantan.

1991, Nov. 7

445 A164	15c	multicolored	.20 .15
446 A164	20c	multicolored	.25 .15
447 A164	40c	multicolored	.55 .15
448 A164	$1	multicolored	1.40 .40
		Nos. 445-448 (4)	2.40
		Set value	.70

Sarawak Museum, Cent. — A165

Museum buildings, fabric pattern and: 30c, Brass lamp. $1, Vase.

1991, Dec. 21

449 A165	30c	multicolored	.35 .15
450 A165	$1	multicolored	1.40 .40

Malaysian Postal Service — A166

Designs: No. 451a, Postman on bicycle. b, Postman on motorcycle. c, Mail truck. d, Mail truck, diff., oil tank. e, Globe, airplane.

1992, Jan. 1

451 A166	30c	Strip of 5, #a.-e.	2.75 .60

Malaysian Tropical Forests — A167

Designs: 20c, Hill Dipterocarp Forest, Dyera costulata. 50c, Mangrove Swamp Forest, Rhizophora apiculata. $1, Lowland Dipterocarp Forest, Neobalanocarpus heimii.

1992, Mar. 23

452 A167	20c	multicolored	.20 .15
453 A167	50c	multicolored	.55 .20
454 A167	$1	multicolored	1.00 .40
		Nos. 452-454 (3)	1.75 .75

Installation of Yang di-Pertuan Besar of Negri Sembilan, Silver Jubilee — A168

1992, Apr. 18

455 A168	30c	Portrait, arms	.35 .15
456 A168	$1	Building	1.40 .40

1992 Thomas Cup Champions in Badminton — A169

1992, July 25 *Perf. 12*

457 A169	$1	Cup, flag	.90 .40
458 A169	$1	Players	.90 .40

Souvenir Sheet

459 A169	$2	multicolored	2.50 .75

No. 459 contains one 75x28mm stamp.

ASEAN, 25th Anniv. A170

1992, Aug. 8

460 A170	30c	shown	.40 .15
461 A170	50c	Flora	.80 .20
462 A170	$1	Architecture	1.50 .40
		Nos. 460-462 (3)	2.70 .75

Postage Stamps in Malaysia, 125th Anny. — A171

Designs: No. 463, Straits Settlements #1, Malaya #84. No. 464, Straits Settlements #2, Malaysia #2. No. 465, Straits Settlements #11, Malaysia #421. No. 466, Straits Settlements #14, Malaysia #467. No. 467, Flag, simulated stamp.

1992, Sept. 1

463 A171	30c	multicolored	.55 .15
464 A171	30c	multicolored	.55 .15
a.		Pair #463-464	1.10 .20
465 A171	50c	multicolored	1.10 .20
466 A171	50c	multicolored	1.10 .20
a.		Pair #465-466	2.25 .40
		Nos. 463-466 (4)	3.30
		Set value	.60

Souvenir Sheet

467 A171	$2	multicolored	3.25 .75

Kuala Lumpur '92.

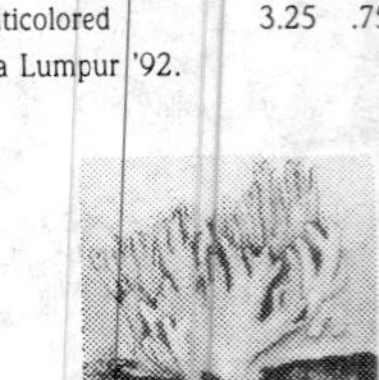

A173

Coral A174

No. 471: a, Acropora. b, Dendronephthya. c, Dendrophyllia. d, Sinularia. e, Melithaea.
No. 472, Subergorgia.

1992, Dec. 21

471 A173	30c	Strip of 5, #a.-e.	3.75 .60

Souvenir Sheet

472 A174	$2	multicolored	3.75 .80

16th Asian-Pacific Dental Congress A175

Children from various countries: No. 473, Four girls. No. 474, Four girls, one holding koala.
Dentists, flags of: No. 475, Japan, Malaysia, South Korea. No. 476, New Zealand, Thailand, People's Republic of China, Indonesia.

1993, Apr. 24

473 A175	30c	multicolored	.50 .15
474 A175	30c	multicolored	.50 .15
a.		Pair, #473-474	1.00 .25
475 A175	50c	multicolored	.75 .20
476 A175	$1	multicolored	1.50 .40
a.		Pair, #475-476	2.25 .60
		Nos. 473-476 (4)	3.25 .90

A176 A177

1993, June 24

477 A176	30c	Fairway, vert.	.60 .15
478 A176	50c	Old, new club houses, vert.	.95 .20
479 A176	$1	Sand trap	1.90 .40
		Nos. 477-479 (3)	3.45 .75

Royal Selangor Golf Club, cent.

1993, Aug. 2

Wildflowers.

480 A177	20c	Alpinia rafflesiana	.25 .15
481 A177	30c	Achasma megalocheilos	.40 .15
482 A177	50c	Zingiber spectabile	.65 .20
483 A177	$1	Costus speciosus	1.25 .40
		Nos. 480-483 (4)	2.55 .90

14th Commonwealth Forestry Conference A178

1993, Sept. 13

No.	Type	Description	Unused	Used
484	A178	30c Globe, forest	.50	.15
485	A178	50c Hand holding trees	.80	.20
486	A178	$1 Trees under dome, vert.	1.50	.40
		Nos. 484-486 (3)	2.80	.75

Nos. 484-486 with Bangkok '93 Emblem Added

Wmk. 388

1993, Oct. 1 Litho. *Perf. 12*

No.	Type	Description	Unused	Used
486A	A178	30c multicolored	*1.10*	*.55*
486B	A178	50c multicolored	*1.90*	*.90*
486C	A178	$1 multicolored	*3.75*	*1.90*
		Nos. 486A-486C (3)	*6.75*	*3.35*

Kingfishers — A179

1993, Oct. 23

No.	Type	Description	Unused	Used
487	A179	30c Halcyon smyrnensis	.60	.15
488	A179	30c Alcedo meninting	.60	.15
a.		Pair, #487-488	1.25	.30
489	A179	50c Halcyon concreta	1.00	.20
490	A179	50c Ceyx erithacus	1.00	.20
a.		Pair, #489-490	2.00	.40
		Nos. 487-490 (4)	3.20	.70

Langkawi Intl. Maritime and Aerospace Exhibition (LIMA '93) — A180

1993, Dec. 7

No.	Type	Description	Unused	Used
491	A180	30c SME MD3-160 airplane	.35	.15
492	A180	50c Eagle X-TS airplane	.70	.20
493	A180	$1 Patrol boat KD Kasturi	1.25	.40
		Nos. 491-493 (3)	2.30	.75

Souvenir Sheet

No.	Type	Description	Unused	Used
494	A180	$2 Map of Malaysia	2.50	.75

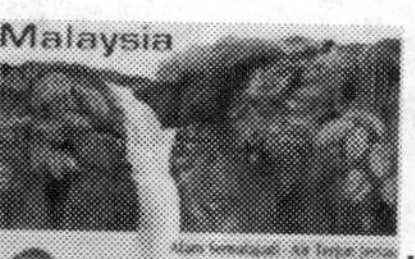

Visit Malaysia Year — A181

1994, Jan. 1

No.	Type	Description	Unused	Used
495	A181	20c Jeriau Waterfalls	.20	.15
496	A181	30c Flowers	.30	.15
497	A181	50c Marine life	.55	.20
498	A181	$1 Wildlife	1.00	.40
		Nos. 495-498 (4)	2.05	.90

See Nos. 527A-527D.

Kuala Lumpur Natl. Planetarium A182

Designs: 30c, Exterior. 50c, Interior displays. $1, Theater auditorium.

1994, Feb. 7

No.	Type	Description	Unused	Used
499	A182	30c multicolored	.35	.15
500	A182	50c multicolored	.75	.20
501	A182	$1 multicolored	1.40	.40
		Nos. 499-501 (3)	2.50	.75

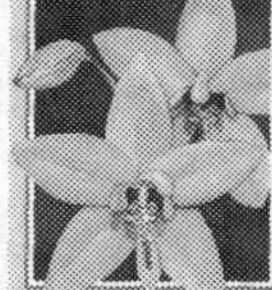

Orchids — A183

Designs: 20c, Spathoglottis aurea. 30c, Paphiopedilum barbatum. 50c, Bulbophyllum lobbii. $1, Aerides odorata. $2, Grammatophyllum speciosum.

1994, Feb. 17

No.	Type	Description	Unused	Used
502	A183	20c multicolored	.25	.15
503	A183	30c multicolored	.35	.15
504	A183	50c multicolored	.55	.20
505	A183	$1 multicolored	1.10	.40
		Nos. 502-505 (4)	2.25	.90

Souvenir Sheet

No.	Type	Description	Unused	Used
506	A183	$2 multicolored	2.25	1.65

Hong Kong '94 (#506).

A184

A185

1994, June 17

No.	Type	Description	Unused	Used
507	A184	20c Decorative bowl	.25	.15
508	A184	30c Celestial sphere	.35	.15
509	A184	50c Dinar coins	.55	.20
510	A184	$1 Decorative tile	1.10	.40
		Nos. 507-510 (4)	2.25	.90

World Islamic Civilization Festival '94. See Nos. 528-531.

1994, July 26

No.	Type	Description	Unused	Used
511	A185	30c shown	.35	.15
512	A185	50c Meat processing	.55	.20
513	A185	$1 Cattle, laboratory	1.10	.40
		Nos. 511-513 (3)	2.00	.75

Veterinary Services, cent.

Electrification, Cent. — A186

1994, Sept. 3

No.	Type	Description	Unused	Used
514	A186	30c Laying cable	.30	.15
515	A186	30c Lighted city	.30	.15
a.		Pair, #514-515	.65	.25
516	A186	$1 Futuristic city	1.00	.40
		Nos. 514-516 (3)	1.60	.70

North-South Expressway A187

1994, Sept. 8

No.	Type	Description	Unused	Used
517	A187	30c shown	.30	.15
518	A187	50c Interchange	.45	.20
519	A187	$1 Bridge	.95	.40
		Nos. 517-519 (3)	1.70	.75

A188

A189

1994, Sept. 22

No.	Type	Description	Unused	Used
520	A188	30c pink & multi	.30	.15
521	A188	50c yellow & multi	.45	.20
522	A188	$1 green & multi	.95	.40
		Nos. 520-522 (3)	1.70	.75

Installation of 10th Yang Di-Pertuan Agong (Head of State).

Wmk. 388

1994, Oct. 29 Litho. *Perf. 12*

No.	Type	Description	Unused	Used
523	A189	$1 shown	1.00	.40
524	A189	$1 Mascot	1.00	.40
a.		Pair, #523-524 + label	2.00	.80

1998 Commonwealth Games, Kuala Lumpur.

Official Opening of Natl. Library Building A190

1994, Dec. 16

No.	Type	Description	Unused	Used
525	A190	30c Library building	.30	.15
526	A190	50c Computer terminal	.45	.20
527	A190	$1 Manuscript	.95	.40
		Nos. 525-527 (3)	1.70	.75

Nos. 495-498 with Added Inscription

Wmk. 388

1994, Nov. 8 Litho. *Perf. 12*

No.	Type	Description	Unused	Used
527A	A181	20c multicolored	*.40*	*.20*
527B	A181	30c multicolored	*.60*	*.30*
527C	A181	50c multicolored	*1.00*	*.50*
527D	A181	$1 multicolored	*2.00*	*1.00*
		Nos. 527A-527D (4)	*4.00*	*2.00*

Nos. 507-510 with Added Inscription

1994 Litho. Wmk. 388 *Perf. 12*

No.	Type	Description	Unused	Used
528	A184	20c multicolored	.20	.15
529	A184	30c multicolored	.30	.15
530	A184	50c multicolored	.45	.20
531	A184	$1 multicolored	.95	.40
		Nos. 528-531 (4)	1.90	.90

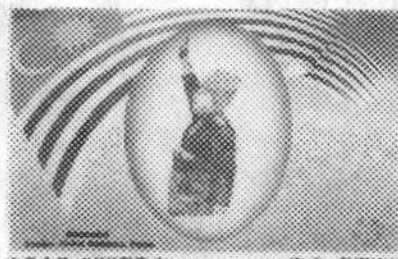

Memorial to Tunku Abdul Rahman Putra Al-Haj (1903-1990), Former Prime Minister A191

1994, Nov. 10 Unwmk. *Perf. 14½*

No.	Type	Description	Unused	Used
532	A191	30c shown	.30	.15
533	A191	$1 Building complex	1.00	.40

Fungi — A192

1995, Jan. 18 *Perf. 14½x14*

No.	Type	Description	Unused	Used
534	A192	20c Bracket fungus	.25	.15
535	A192	30c Cup fungus	.40	.15
536	A192	50c Veil fungus	.60	.20
537	A192	$1 Coral fungus	1.25	.40
		Nos. 534-537 (4)	2.50	.90

Neofelis Nebulosa A193

1995, Apr. 18 Wmk. 373 *Perf. 13½*

No.	Type	Description	Unused	Used
538	A193	20c shown	.20	.15
539	A193	30c With young	.30	.15
540	A193	50c With mouth open	.50	.20
541	A193	$1 Lying on rock	1.00	.40
a.		Strip of 4, #538-541	2.00	.80

Nos. 538-541 were issued in sheets of 16 stamps. World Wildlife Fund.

Marine Life — A194

1995, Apr. 10 Wmk. 388 *Perf. 12*

No.	Type	Description	Unused	Used
542	A194	20c Feather stars	.25	.15
543	A194	20c Sea fans	.25	.15
a.		Pair, #542-543	.50	.15
544	A194	30c Soft coral	.40	.15
545	A194	30c Cup coral	.40	.15
a.		Pair, #544-545	.85	.25
		Nos. 542-545 (4)	1.30	.60

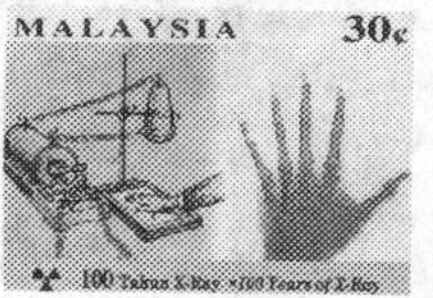

X-Ray, Cent. A195

Designs: No. 546, Early machine x-raying hand. No. 547, CAT scan machine. No. $1, Chest x-ray.

1995, May 29

No.	Type	Description	Unused	Used
546	A195	30c multicolored	.30	.15
547	A195	30c multicolored	.30	.15
a.		Pair, #546-547	.65	.20
548	A195	$1 multicolored	1.25	.40
		Nos. 546-548 (3)	1.85	.70

1998 Commonwealth Games, Kuala Lumpur — A196

Various sporting events: No. 549, Badminton, cricket, shooting, tennis, weight lifting, hurdles, field hockey. No. 550, Cycling, lawn bowling, boxing, basketball, rugby, gymnastics.

Wmk. 388

1995, Sept. 10 Litho. *Perf. 14*

No.	Type	Description	Unused	Used
549	A196	$1 multicolored	1.10	.40
550	A196	$1 multicolored	1.10	.40
a.		Pair, #549-550 + label	2.25	.80

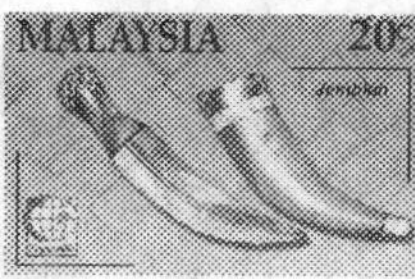

Traditional Weapons A197

1995, Sept. 1 Litho. *Perf. 14*

No.	Type	Description	Unused	Used
551	A197	20c Jemblah	.20	.15
552	A197	30c Keris panjang	.35	.25
553	A197	50c Kerambit	.55	.40
554	A197	$1 Keris sundang	1.10	.80
		Nos. 551-554 (4)	2.20	1.60

Souvenir Sheet

No.	Type	Description	Unused	Used
555	A197	$2 Lading terus	2.25	1.65

Singapore '95.

UN, 50th Anniv. A198

1995, Oct. 24 *Perf. 13½*

No.	Type	Description	Unused	Used
556	A198	30c shown	.30	.15
557	A198	$1 UN emblem	1.00	.40

Intl. Assoc. of Travel Agents (IATA), 50th Anniv. — A199

Jet, globe and: No. 558, Historic buildings. No. 559, Sydney Opera House, Great Wall of China. No. 560, Eiffel Tower, Tower Bridge. No. 561, Hollywood Walk of Fame, Latin American pyramid.

1995, Oct. 30 *Perf. 14*

558 A199 30c multicolored .25 .15
559 A199 30c multicolored .25 .15
a. Pair, #558-559 .50 .25
560 A199 50c multicolored .40 .20
561 A199 50c multicolored .40 .20
a. Pair, #560-561 .80 .40

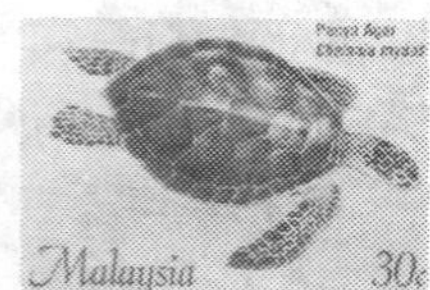

Turtles A200

Perf. 14x14½

1995, Sept. 26 Litho. Wmk. 388

Booklet Stamps

562 A200 30c Chelonia mydas .25 .15
563 A200 30c Dermochelys coriacea .25 .15
a. Booklet pane, 5 each #562-563 2.50
Complete booklet, #563a 2.50

Proton Cars, 10th Anniv. — A201

#564, 1985 Saga 1.5. #565, 1992 Iswara 1.5 aeroback. #566, 1992, Iswara 1.5 sedan. #567, 1993 Wira 1.6 sedan. #568, 1993 Wira 1.6 aeroback. #569, 1994 Rally. #570, 1994 Satria 1.6. #571, 1995 Perdana 2.0. #572, 1995 Wira 1.6 aeroback. #573, 1995 Wira 1.8 sedan.

1995, Dec. Litho. *Perf. 14*

Booklet Stamps

564 A201 30c multicolored .25 .15
565 A201 30c multicolored .25 .15
566 A201 30c multicolored .25 .15
567 A201 30c multicolored .25 .15
568 A201 30c multicolored .25 .15
569 A201 30c multicolored .25 .15
570 A201 30c multicolored .25 .15
571 A201 30c multicolored .25 .15
572 A201 30c multicolored .25 .15
573 A201 30c multicolored .25 .15
a. Booklet pane, Nos. 564-573 2.50
Complete booklet, No. 573a 2.50

A202

A203

Malaysia East Asia Satellite: 30c, Ariane 4 being launched. 50c, Satellite in Earth orbit over East Asia. $1, Satellite Control Center, Langkawai.
$5, Satellite entering orbit, horiz.

1996, Jan. 13 *Perf. 13½*

574 A202 30c multicolored .25 .15
575 A202 50c multicolored .40 .20
576 A202 $1 multicolored .80 .40
Nos. 574-576 (3) 1.45 .75

Souvenir Sheet

Perf. 14

577 A202 $5 multicolored 4.00 4.00

No. 577 contains a holographic image. Soaking in water may affect the hologram.

Perf. 13½

1996, Apr. 16 Litho. Wmk. 388

Pitcher Plants: No. 578, Nepenthes sanguinea. No. 579, Nepenthes macfarlanei. No. 580, Nepenthes rajah. No. 581, Nepenthes lowii.

578 A203 30c multicolored .25 .15
579 A203 30c multicolored .25 .15
a. Pair, Nos. 578-579 .50 .25
580 A203 50c multicolored .45 .20
581 A203 50c multicolored .45 .20
a. Pair, Nos. 580-581 .90 .45
Nos. 578-581 (4) 1.40 .70

Birds of Prey A204

Designs: 20c, Haliastur indus. 30c, Spilornis cheela. 50c, Haliaeetus leucogaster. $1, Spizaetus cirrhatus.
$2, Spizaetus alboniger, vert.

Wmk. 388

1996, May 18 Litho. *Perf. 14*

582 A204 20c multicolored .20 .15
583 A204 30c multicolored .20 .15
584 A204 50c multicolored .45 .25
585 A204 $1 multicolored .85 .40
Nos. 582-585 (4) 1.70 .95

Souvenir Sheet

586 A204 $2 multicolored 1.75 1.75

CHINA '96 (#586).

Intl. Day Against Drug Abuse and Illicit Drug Trafficking A205

Designs: No. 587, Family, drugs burning. No. 588, Various sporting activities, marajuana plants. $1, Family, rainbow.

Wmk. 388

1996, June 26 Litho. *Perf. 14*

587 A205 30c multicolored .20 .15
588 A205 30c multicolored .20 .15
a. Pair, #587-588 .40 .20
589 A205 $1 multicolored .85 .40
Nos. 587-589 (3) 1.25 .70

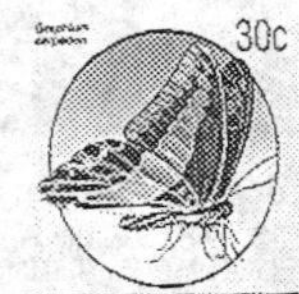

Butterflies — A206

#590, Graphium sarpedon. #591, Melanocyma faunula. #592, Delias hyparete. #593, Trogonoptera brookiana. #594, Terinos terpander.

1996, Sept. 27 Litho. *Perf. 14½x14*

Booklet Stamps

590 A206 30c multicolored .30 .15
591 A206 30c multicolored .30 .15
592 A206 30c multicolored .30 .15
593 A206 30c multicolored .30 .15
594 A206 30c multicolored .30 .15
a. Pane of 10, 2 each #590-594 3.00

Kuala Lumpur Tower A207

Designs: 30c, Artist's impression. 50c, Tower head diagram. $1, Tower head, city at night.
$2, Kuala Lumpur Tower, vert.

Perf. 13½

1996, Oct. 1 Litho. Unwmk.

595 A207 30c multicolored .25 .15
596 A207 50c multicolored .45 .25
597 A207 $1 multicolored .85 .40
Nos. 595-598 (4) 3.30 2.55

Souvenir Sheet

598 A207 $2 multicolored 1.75 1.75
a. With added inscription in sheet margin 1.75 1.75

No. 598a inscribed with TAIPEI '96 emblem, issued 10/16/96.

14th Conference of Confederation of Asian and Pacific Accountants A208

1996, Oct. 7 *Perf. 13½x14*

599 A208 30c CAPA logo .25 .15
600 A208 $1 Globe .85 .40

MALAYSIA 30¢

Natl. Science Center A209

30c, Model of molecular structure. 50c, Model of atom, Science Center. $1, Natl. Science Center.

Unwmk.

1996, Nov. 29 Litho. *Perf. 14*

601 A209 30c multicolored .25 .15
602 A209 50c multicolored .40 .20
603 A209 $1 multicolored .80 .40
Nos. 601-603 (3) 1.45 .75

Souvenir Sheet

Stamp Week — A210

Wildlife: a, 20c, Nycticebus coucang. b, 30c, Callosciurus prevostii. c, 50c, Attacus atlas. d, $1, Hylobates lar. e, $1, Buceros rhinoceros. f, $2, Hemigalus derbyanus.

1996, Dec. 2

604 A210 Sheet of 6, #a.-f. 4.00 4.00

No. 604d is 30x60mm. Nos. 605e-605f are 60x30mm.

Birds — A211

Designs: 20c, Muscicapella hodgsoni. 30c, Leiothrix argentauris. 50c, Dicaeum celibicum. $1, Aethopyga mystacalis.

1996 Litho. Unwmk. *Perf. 13½x14*

605 A211 20c multicolored .20 .15
606 A211 30c multicolored .25 .15
607 A211 50c multicolored .40 .20
608 A211 $1 multicolored .80 .40
Nos. 605-608 (4) 1.65 .90

16th Commonwealth Games, Kuala Lumpur '98 — A212

1996 *Perf. 12*

609 A212 30c Running .25 .15
610 A212 30c Hurdles .25 .15
a. Pair, #609-610 .50 .25
611 A212 50c High jump .40 .20
612 A212 50c Javelin .40 .20
a. Pair, #611-612 .80 .40
Nos. 609-612 (4) 1.30 .70

Intl. Cricket Cup Champions — A213

1997, Mar. 24 Litho. *Perf. 14*

613 A213 30c shown .25 .15
614 A213 50c Batsman .40 .20
615 A213 $1 Wicket keeper .80 .40
Nos. 613-615 (3) 1.45 .75

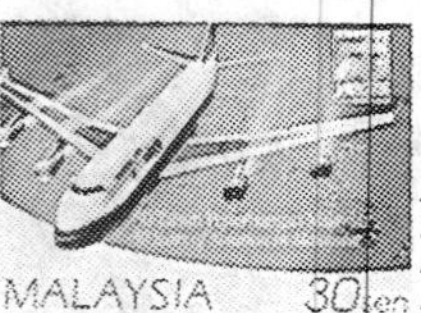

Aviation in Malaysia, 50th Anniv. A214

Designs: 30c, Jet, world map. 50c, Jet approaching Kuala Lumpur. $1, Airplane tailfins of four Malaysian airlines.

1997, Apr. 2 Wmk. 388

616 A214 30c multicolored .25 .15
617 A214 50c multicolored .45 .25
618 A214 $1 multicolored .85 .40
Nos. 616-618 (3) 1.55 .80

MALAYSIA 30sen

A215

A216

Light Rail Transit System: No. 620, Two trains, one on bridge, Kuala Lumpur skyline.

Perf. 14x14½

1997, Mar. 1 Litho. Unwmk.

Booklet Stamps

619 A215 30c shown .25 .15
620 A215 30c multicolored .25 .15
a. Booklet pane, 5 each #619-620 2.50
Complete booklet, #620a 2.50

1997, May 7 *Perf. 14½x14*

Highland Flowers: No. 621, Schima wallichi. No. 622, Aeschynanthus longicalyx. No. 623. Aeschynanthus speciosa. No. 624, Phyllagathis tuberculata. No. 625, Didymocarpus quinquevulnerus.

Booklet Stamps

621 A216 30c multicolored .25 .15
622 A216 30c multicolored .25 .15
623 A216 30c multicolored .25 .15
624 A216 30c multicolored .25 .15
625 A216 30c multicolored .25 .15
a. Booklet pane, 2 each #621-625 2.50
Complete booklet, #625a 2.50
Nos. 621-625 (5) 1.25 .75

Ruler's Council, Cent. A217

Unwmk.

1997, July 31 Litho. *Perf. 14*

626 A217 30c Photo, 1897 .25 .15
627 A217 50c Emblem, arms .40 .20
628 A217 $1 Emblem .80 .40
Nos. 626-628 (3) 1.45 .75

ASEAN, 30th Anniv. A218

1997, Aug. 8 Wmk. 388 *Perf. 13½*
629 A218 30c shown .25 .15
630 A218 50c "30," emblem .40 .20
631 A218 $1 Emblem, color bars .80 .40
Nos. 629-631 (3) 1.45 .75

A219

A220

Coral: 20c, Tubastrea. 30c, Melithaea. 50c, Aulostomus chinensis. $1, Symphillia.

1997, Aug. 23 Unwmk. *Perf. 14½*
632 A219 20c multicolored .20 .15
633 A219 30c multicolored .25 .15
634 A219 50c multicolored .40 .20
635 A219 $1 multicolored .80 .40
Nos. 632-635 (4) 1.65 .90

1997 *Perf. 13x13½*
Booklet Stamps
636 A220 30c Career women .25 .15
637 A220 30c Family .25 .15
a. Booklet pane, 5 each #636-637 2.50
Complete booklet, #637a 2.50

20th Intl. Conf. of Pan-Pacific and Southeast Asia Women's Assoc., Kuala Lumpur.

9th World Youth Soccer Championships A221

30c, Mascot. 50c, Soccer ball, players, flag. $1, Map of Malaysia, silhouettes of players, soccer ball.

1997 Unwmk. *Perf. 13½x13*
638 A221 30c multicolored .25 .15
639 A221 50c multicolored .40 .20

Perf. 13x12½
640 A221 $1 multicolored .80 .40
Nos. 638-640 (3) 1.45 .75

Souvenir Sheet

Chelonia Mydas — A222

Illustration reduced.

1997, Aug. 23 Litho. *Perf. 14½*
641 A222 $2 multicolored 1.20 1.20

Year of the Coral Reef.

7th Summit Level of the Group of 15 — A223

$1, Emblem, natl. flags of member nations.

Unwmk.
1997, Nov. 3 Litho. *Perf. 12*
642 A223 30c shown .20 .15
643 A223 $1 multicolored .60 .30

Stamp Week A224

Protected wildlife: a, 20c, Tomistoma schlegelli. b, 30c, Tarsius bancanus, vert. c, 50c, Cervus unicolor, vert. d, $2, Rollulus rouloul. e, $2, Scleropages formosus.

1997, Dec. 1 *Perf. 14½*
644 A224 Sheet of 5, #a.-e. 3.00 3.00

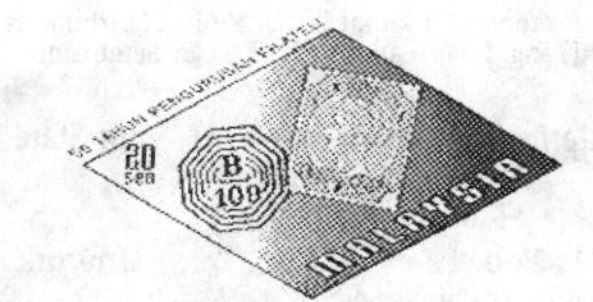

Philately in Malaysia, 50th Anniv. — A225

Malpex '97: a, 20c, Straits Settlements #7. b, 30c, #605-608. c, 50c, #604. d, $1, Early cover from Straits Settlements.

1997 *Perf. 12½*
645 A225 Sheet of 4, #a.-d. 1.60 1.60

Rare Fruit — A226

1998, Jan. 10 *Perf. 13½*
646 A226 20c Bouea macrophylla .15 .15
647 A226 30c Sandoricum koetjape .20 .15
648 A226 50c Nephelium ramboutan-ake .30 .15
649 A226 $1 Garcinia atroviridis .60 .30
Nos. 646-649 (4) 1.25 .75

Kuala Lumpur '98 Games A227

1998, Feb. 23 *Perf. 12*
650 A227 30c Field hockey .20 .15
651 A227 30c Women's netball .20 .15
a. Pair, #650-651 + label .40 .20
652 A227 50c Cricket .30 .15
653 A227 50c Rugby .30 .15
a. Pair, #652-653 + label .60 .30
Nos. 650-653 (4) 1.00 .60

POSTAGE DUE STAMPS

Until 1966 Malaysia used postage due stamps of the Malayan Postal Union. See listings under Malaya.

D1

D2

Wmk. 338 Upright
1966, Aug. 15 Litho. *Perf. 14½x14*
J1 D1 1c pink .15 .15
J2 D1 2c slate .15 .15
J3 D1 4c lt yellow green .15 .15
J4 D1 8c bright green .50 .20
J5 D1 10c ultramarine .50 .20
J6 D1 12c purple .25 .15
J7 D1 20c brown 1.25 .45
J8 D1 50c olive bister 3.25 1.25
Nos. J1-J8 (8) 6.20 2.70

Wmk. 338 Sideways
J4a D1 8c bright green 1.00 .50
J5a D1 10c ultramarine 1.50 .75
J7a D1 20c brown 2.00 1.00
J8a D1 50c olive bister 5.00 2.50
Nos. J4a-J8a (4) 9.50 4.75

1981-84 Litho. Unwmk. *Perf. 15x14*
J9 D1 2c slate .35 .15
J10 D1 8c bright green .35 .15
J11 D1 10c blue .35 .15
J11A D1 12c maroon ('84) 14.00 8.00
J12 D1 20c brown .45 .15
J13 D1 50c olive bister 1.10 .30
Nos. J9-J13 (6) 16.60 8.90

1988, Sept. 15 Litho. *Perf. 12*
J14 D2 5c brt rose & lil rose .15 .15
J15 D2 10c black & gray .15 .15
J16 D2 20c deep org & yel org .15 .15
J17 D2 50c blue grn & lt bl grn .40 .40
J18 D2 $1 brt blue & lt ultra .80 .80
Nos. J14-J18 (5) 1.65 1.65

JOHORE

Vanda Hookeriana and Sultan Ismail — A14

Orchids: 2c, Arundina graminifolia. 5c, Paphiopedilum niveum. 6c, Spathoglottis plicata. 10c, Arachnis flosaeris. 15c, Rhyncostylis retusa. 20c, Phalaenopsis violacea.

Perf. 14½
1965, Nov. 15 Photo. Wmk. 338
Flowers in Natural Colors
169 A14 1c blk & lt grnsh bl .15 .15
a. Black omitted 50.00
b. Watermark sideways ('70) .15 .15
170 A14 2c black, red & gray .30 .15
171 A14 5c black & Prus bl .60 .15
a. Yellow omitted 24.00
172 A14 6c black & lt lil .65 .15
173 A14 10c black & lt ultra .95 .15
a. Watermark sideways ('70) 1.25 .55
174 A14 15c blk, lil rose & grn 1.40 .30
175 A14 20c black & brown 2.00 .50
Nos. 169-175 (7) 6.05
Set value 1.00

Malayan Jezebel and Sultan Ismail — A15

Butterflies: 2c, Black-veined tiger. 5c, Clipper. 6c, Lime butterfly. 10c, Great orange tip. 15c, Blue pansy. 20c, Wanderer.

Perf. 13½x13
1971, Feb. 1 Litho. Unwmk.
176 A15 1c multicolored .15 .15
177 A15 2c multicolored .25 .15
178 A15 5c multicolored .50 .15
179 A15 6c multicolored .65 .15
180 A15 10c multicolored 1.00 .25
181 A15 15c multicolored 1.65 .35
182 A15 20c multicolored 2.25 .60
Nos. 176-182 (7) 6.45
Set value .88

1977 Photo.
176a A15 1c 1.90 .20
177a A15 2c 1.90 .20
178a A15 5c 1.90 .20
180a A15 10c 3.00 .30
181a A15 15c 6.25 .45
182a A15 20c 7.50 .55
Nos. 176a-182a (6) 22.45 1.90

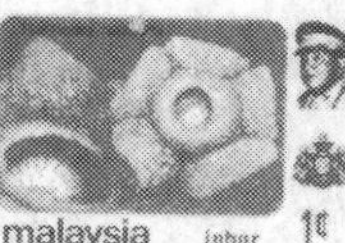

Rafflesia Hasseltii and Sultan Ismail — A16

Flowers: 2c, Pterocarpus indicus. 5c, Lagerstroemia speciosa. 10c, Durio zibethinus. 15c, Hibiscus. 20c, Rhododendron scortechinii. 25c, Phaeomeria speciosa.

Perf. 14½
1979, Apr. 30 Litho. Wmk. 378
183 A16 1c multicolored .15 .15
184 A16 2c multicolored .15 .15
185 A16 5c multicolored .15 .15
186 A16 10c multicolored .15 .15
187 A16 15c multicolored .25 .15
188 A16 20c multicolored .30 .15
189 A16 25c multicolored .40 .15
Nos. 183-189 (7) 1.55
Set value .45

1984
"Johor" in round type
185a A16 5c .15 .15
186a A16 10c .15 .15
187a A16 15c .25 .15
188a A16 20c .30 .15
Nos. 185a-188a (4) .85 .60

Agriculture, State Arms and Sultan Mahmood Iskandar Al-Haj, Regent — A19

Wmk. 388
1986, Oct. 25 Litho. *Perf. 12*
190 A19 1c Coffea liberica .15 .15
191 A19 2c Cocos nucifera .15 .15
192 A19 5c Theobroma cacao .15 .15
193 A19 10c Piper nigrum .15 .15
194 A19 15c Hevea brasiliensis .15 .15
195 A19 20c Elaeis guineensis .20 .15
196 A19 30c Oryza sativa .35 .15
Set value 1.00 .45

KEDAH

Orchid Type of Johore, 1965, with Portrait of Sultan Abdul Halim

Perf. 14½
1965, Nov. 15 Photo. Wmk. 338
Flowers in Natural Colors
106 A14 1c blk & lt grnsh bl .20 .15
a. Black omitted 50.00
b. Watermark sideways ('70) 1.50 1.50
107 A14 2c black, red & gray .30 .15
108 A14 5c black & Prus bl .50 .15
109 A14 6c black & lt lil .60 .15
110 A14 10c black & lt ultra .95 .15
a. Watermark sideways ('70) 6.50 5.00
111 A14 15c blk, lil rose & grn 1.25 .20
112 A14 20c black & brown 1.75 .30
Nos. 106-112 (7) 5.55
Set value .75

Butterfly Type of Johore, 1971, with Portrait of Sultan Abdul Halim

Perf. 13½x13
1971, Feb. 1 Litho. Unwmk.
113 A15 1c multicolored .20 .15
114 A15 2c multicolored .35 .15
115 A15 5c multicolored .55 .15
116 A15 6c multicolored .70 .15
117 A15 10c multicolored .95 .15
118 A15 15c multicolored 1.75 .20
119 A15 20c multicolored 2.00 .20
Nos. 113-119 (7) 6.50
Set value .70

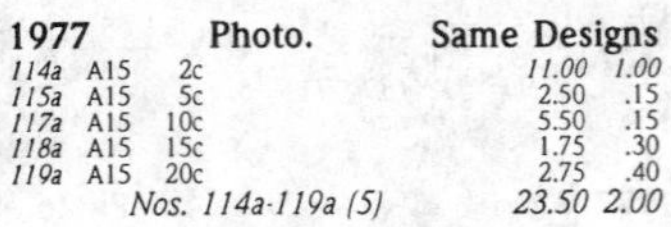

1977 Photo. Same Designs
114a A15 2c 11.00 1.00
115a A15 5c 2.50 .15
117a A15 10c 5.50 .15
118a A15 15c 1.75 .30
119a A15 20c 2.75 .40
Nos. 114a-119a (5) 23.50 2.00

Flower Type of Johore, 1979, with Portrait of Sultan Abdul Halim

Perf. 14½

1979, Apr. 30 Litho. Wmk. 378
120 A16 1c multicolored .15 .15
121 A16 2c multicolored .15 .15
122 A16 5c multicolored .15 .15
123 A16 10c multicolored .15 .15
a. Unwmkd. ('85)
124 A16 15c multicolored .25 .15
a. Unwmkd. ('84) 3.25
125 A16 20c multicolored .40 .15
a. Pale yellow flowers ('84) .40 .15
126 A16 25c multicolored .45 .15
Set value 1.45 .60

25th Anniv. of Installation of Sultan Abdul Halim — A10

1983, July 15 Litho. *Perf. 13½*
127 A10 20c Portrait, vert. .75 .15
128 A10 40c View from Mt. Gunung Jerai 1.75 .25
129 A10 50c Rice fields, Mt. Gunung Jerai 1.90 .30
Nos. 127-129 (3) 4.40 .70

Agriculture and State Arms Type of Johore with Sultan Abdul Halim

Wmk. 388

1986, Oct. 25 Litho. *Perf. 12*
130 A19 1c multicolored .15 .15
131 A19 2c multicolored .15 .15
132 A19 5c multicolored .15 .15
133 A19 10c multicolored .15 .15
134 A19 15c multicolored .15 .15
135 A19 20c multicolored .20 .15
136 A19 30c multicolored .35 .15
Set value 1.00 .45

KELANTAN

Orchid Type of Johore, 1965, with Portrait of Sultan Yahya Petra

Perf. 14½

1965, Nov. 15 Photo. Wmk. 338

Flowers in Natural Colors

91 A14 1c blk & lt grnsh bl .15 .15
a. Watermark sideways ('70) .50 .35
92 A14 2c black, red & gray .15 .15
93 A14 5c black & Prus bl .50 .15
94 A14 6c black & lt lil .65 .15
95 A14 10c black & lt ultra .95 .20
a. Watermark sideways ('70) 2.25 1.10
96 A14 15c blk, lil rose & grn 1.40 .35
97 A14 20c black & brown 2.00 .60
Nos. 91-97 (7) 5.80 1.75

Butterfly Type of Johore, 1971, with Portrait of Sultan Yahya Petra

Perf. 13½x13

1971, Feb. 1 Litho. Unwmk.
98 A15 1c multicolored .15 .15
99 A15 2c multicolored .20 .15
100 A15 5c multicolored .60 .15
101 A15 6c multicolored .65 .15
102 A15 10c multicolored 1.00 .18
103 A15 15c multicolored 1.90 .30
104 A15 20c multicolored 2.25 .40
Nos. 98-104 (7) 6.75
Set value 1.20

1977 Photo.
98a A15 1c 1.25 .30
100a A15 5c 1.25 .30
102a A15 10c 2.50 .45
103a A15 15c 6.00 1.00
Nos. 98a-103a (4) 11.00 2.05

Flower Type of Johore, 1979, with Portrait of Sultan Yahya Petra

Perf. 14½

1979, Apr. 30 Litho. Wmk. 378
105 A16 1c multicolored .15 .15
106 A16 2c multicolored .15 .15
107 A16 5c multicolored .15 .15
a. Unwmkd. ('86) 1.10
108 A16 10c multicolored .15 .15
a. White flowers ('84) .15 .15
109 A16 15c multicolored .30 .15
110 A16 20c multicolored .35 .15
a. Pale yellow flowers ('84) .35 .15
111 A16 25c multicolored .45 .15
Set value 1.45 .55

Sultan Tengku Ismail Petra, Installation — A7

1980, Mar. 30 Litho. *Perf. 14½*
112 A7 10c multicolored .20 .15
113 A7 15c multicolored .30 .15
114 A7 50c multicolored .95 .25
Nos. 112-114 (3) 1.45
Set value .35

Agriculture and State Arms Type of Johore with Sultan Ismail Petra

Wmk. 388

1986, Oct. 25 Litho. *Perf. 12*
115 A19 1c multicolored .15 .15
116 A19 2c multicolored .15 .15
117 A19 5c multicolored .15 .15
118 A19 10c multicolored .15 .15
119 A19 15c multicolored .15 .15
120 A19 20c multicolored .20 .15
121 A19 30c multicolored .35 .15
Set value 1.00 .45

MALACCA

(Melaka)

Orchid Type of Johore, 1965, with State Crest

Perf. 14½

1965, Nov. 15 Photo. Wmk. 338

Flowers in Natural Colors

67 A14 1c blk & lt grnsh blue .15 .15
a. Watermark sideways ('70) .40 .40
68 A14 2c blk, red & gray .25 .15
69 A14 5c black & Prus bl .55 .15
70 A14 6c black & lt lilac .75 .15
71 A14 10c black & lt ultra 1.10 .15
a. Watermark sideways ('70) 2.00 1.50
72 A14 15c blk, lil rose & grn 1.40 .45
73 A14 20c black & brown 2.50 .80
Nos. 67-73 (7) 6.70
Set value 1.05

Butterfly Type of Johore, 1971, with State Crest

Perf. 13½x13

1971, Feb. 1 Litho. Unwmk.
74 A15 1c multicolored .30 .15
75 A15 2c multicolored .30 .15
76 A15 5c multicolored .50 .15
77 A15 6c multicolored .65 .15
78 A15 10c multicolored 1.00 .35
79 A15 15c multicolored 1.90 .60
80 A15 20c multicolored 2.25 .70
Nos. 74-80 (7) 6.90
Set value 1.15

1977 Photo.
74a A15 1c 1.25 .35
76a A15 5c .95 .25
78a A15 10c 1.65 .50
79a A15 15c 3.25 .85
80a A15 20c 4.00 1.10
Nos. 74a-80a (5) 11.10 3.05

Flower Type of Johore, 1979, with State Crest

Perf. 14½

1979, Apr. 30 Litho. Wmk. 378
81 A16 1c multicolored .15 .15
82 A16 2c multicolored .15 .15
83 A16 5c multicolored .15 .15
84 A16 10c multicolored .15 .15
85 A16 15c multicolored .30 .15
86 A16 20c multicolored .35 .15
87 A16 25c multicolored .45 .15
Set value 1.45 .55

1983-86 Unwmk.
84a A16 10c ('85) 2.25
85a A16 15c ('86) 3.25
86a A16 20c 4.25
Nos. 84a-86a (3) 9.75

Agriculture and State Arms Type of Johore

Wmk. 388

1986, Oct. 25 Litho. *Perf. 12*
88 A19 1c multicolored .15 .15
89 A19 2c multicolored .15 .15
90 A19 5c multicolored .15 .15
91 A19 10c multicolored .15 .15
92 A19 15c multicolored .15 .15
93 A19 20c multicolored .20 .15
94 A19 30c multicolored .35 .15
Set value 1.00 .45

NEGRI SEMBILAN

(Negeri Sembilan)

Orchid Type of Johore, 1965, with State Crest

Perf. 14½

1965, Nov. 15 Photo. Wmk. 338

Flowers in Natural Colors

76 A14 1c blk & lt grnsh blue .25 .15
a. Watermark sideways ('70) 2.50 1.00
77 A14 2c black, red & gray .25 .15
78 A14 5c black & Prus blue .50 .15
79 A14 6c black & lt lilac .75 .15
80 A14 10c black & lt ultra 1.00 .15
81 A14 15c blk, lil rose & grn 1.40 .15
82 A14 20c black & brown 2.00 .30
Nos. 76-82 (7) 6.15
Set value .75

Tuanku Ja'afar and Crest of Negri Sembilan — A7

1968, Apr. 8 Photo. *Perf. 13½*
83 A7 15c brt blue & multi .20 .15
84 A7 50c yellow & multi .60 .50

Installation of Tuanku Ja'afar ibni Al-Marhum as ruler (Yang di-Pertuan Besar) of Negri Sembilan.

Butterfly Type of Johore, 1971, with State Crest

Perf. 13½x13

1971, Feb. 1 Litho. Unwmk.
85 A15 1c multicolored .30 .15
86 A15 2c multicolored .30 .15
87 A15 5c multicolored .55 .15
88 A15 6c multicolored .70 .15
89 A15 10c multicolored 1.10 .15
90 A15 15c multicolored 1.75 .20
91 A15 20c multicolored 2.25 .25
Nos. 85-91 (7) 6.95
Set value .85

1977 Photo.
86a A15 2c 2.75 .20
87a A15 5c 2.75 .20
89a A15 10c 5.50 .45
90a A15 15c 10.00 .75
91a A15 20c 13.00 1.10
Nos. 86a-91a (5) 34.00 2.70

Flower Type of Johore, 1979, with State Crest

Perf. 14½

1979, Apr. 30 Litho. Wmk. 378
92 A16 1c multicolored .15 .15
93 A16 2c multicolored .15 .15
94 A16 5c multicolored .15 .15
a. Unwmkd. ('85) 1.10
95 A16 10c multicolored .15 .15
a. White flowers ('84) .15 .15
96 A16 15c multicolored .30 .15
a. Unwmkd. ('84) 3.25
97 A16 20c multicolored .35 .15
a. Pale yellow flowers ('84) .35 .15
98 A16 25c multicolored .45 .15
Set value 1.45 .55

Agriculture and State Arms Type of Johore

Wmk. 388

1986, Oct. 25 Litho. *Perf. 12*
99 A19 1c multicolored .15 .15
100 A19 2c multicolored .15 .15
101 A19 5c multicolored .15 .15
102 A19 10c multicolored .15 .15
103 A19 15c multicolored .15 .15
104 A19 20c multicolored .35 .15
105 A19 30c multicolored .20 .15
Set value 1.00 .45

PAHANG

Orchid Type of Johore, 1965, with Portrait of Sultan Abu Bakar

Perf. 14½

1965, Nov. 15 Photo. Wmk. 338

Flowers in Natural Colors

83 A14 1c blk & lt grnsh bl .15 .15
a. Watermark sideways ('70) .15 .15
84 A14 2c black, red & gray .20 .15
a. Unwmkd. ('85)
85 A14 5c black & Prus bl .45 .15
86 A14 6c black & lt lil .70 .15
87 A14 10c black & lt ultra 1.10 .15
a. Watermark sideways ('70) 1.75 1.00
88 A14 15c blk, lil rose & grn 1.50 .15
89 A14 20c black & brown 2.00 .25
Nos. 83-89 (7) 6.10
Set value .75

Butterfly Type of Johore, 1971, Portrait of Sultan Abu Bakar

Perf. 13½x13

1971, Feb. 1 Litho. Unwmk.
90 A15 1c multicolored .15 .15
91 A15 2c multicolored .15 .15
92 A15 5c multicolored .15 .15
93 A15 6c multicolored .75 .15
94 A15 10c multicolored 1.25 .15
95 A15 15c multicolored 1.90 .20
96 A15 20c multicolored 2.25 .25
Nos. 90-96 (7) 6.60
Set value .75

In 1973 booklet panes of 4 of the 5c, 10c, 15c were made from sheets.

Sultan Haji Ahmad Shah — A9

1975, May 8 Litho. *Perf. 14x14½*
97 A9 10c lilac, gold & black .25 .15
98 A9 15c yellow, green & black .60 .20
99 A9 50c ultra, dk blue & black 1.90 .65
Nos. 97-99 (3) 2.75 1.00

Installation of Sultan Haji Ahmad Shah as ruler of Pahang.

A18

1977-78
100 A18 2c multi ('78) 15.00 15.00
101 A18 5c multicolored .20 .20
102 A18 10c multi ('78) .35 .35
103 A18 15c multi ('78) .70 .70
104 A18 20c multi ('78) 1.25 1.25
Nos. 100-104 (5) 17.50 17.50

Flower Type of Johore, 1979, with Portrait of Sultan Haji Ahmad Shah

Perf. 14½

1979, Apr. 30 Litho. Wmk. 378
105 A16 1c multicolored .15 .15
106 A16 2c multicolored .15 .15
107 A16 5c multicolored .15 .15
a. 5c brt rose pink & yel flowers ('84) .15 .15
108 A16 10c multicolored .15 .15
a. Unwmkd. ('85) 2.25
109 A16 15c multicolored .30 .15
110 A16 20c multicolored .35 .15
a. Unwmkd. ('84) .40 .15
111 A16 25c multicolored .45 .15
Set value 1.45 .55

Agriculture and State Arms Type of Johore with Sultan Haji Ahmad Shah

Wmk. 388

1986, Oct. 25 Litho. *Perf. 12*
112 A19 1c multicolored .15 .15
113 A19 2c multicolored .15 .15
114 A19 5c multicolored .15 .15
115 A19 10c multicolored .15 .15
116 A19 15c multicolored .15 .15
117 A19 20c multicolored .20 .15
118 A19 30c multicolored .35 .15
Set value 1.00 .45

PENANG
(Pulau Pinang)

Orchid Type of Johore, 1965, with State Crest

Perf. 14½

1965, Nov. 15 Photo. Wmk. 338

Orchids in Natural Colors

67 A14 1c black & lt grnsh bl .25 .15
a. Watermark sideways ('70) .90 .90
68 A14 2c black, red & gray .30 .15
69 A14 5c black & Prus blue .60 .15
a. Prussian blue omitted
b. Yellow omitted
70 A14 6c black & lt lilac .65 .15
71 A14 10c black & lt ultra 1.10 .15
a. Watermark sideways ('70) 3.75 3.00
72 A14 15c black, lil rose & grn 1.40 .15
73 A14 20c black & brown 2.00 .20
Nos. 67-73 (7) 6.30
Set value .55

Butterfly Type of Johore, 1971, with State Crest

Perf. 13½x13

1971, Feb. 1 Litho. Unwmk.

74 A15 1c multicolored .30 .15
75 A15 2c multicolored .35 .15
76 A15 5c multicolored .60 .15
77 A15 6c multicolored .70 .15
78 A15 10c multicolored 1.00 .15
79 A15 15c multicolored 1.90 .20
80 A15 20c multicolored 2.25 .25
Nos. 74-80 (7) 7.10
Set value .75

1977 Photo.

74a A15 1c 19.00 1.25
76a A15 5c 1.65 .15
78a A15 10c 2.25 .15
79a A15 15c 6.50 .40
80a A15 20c 8.00 .50
Nos. 74a-80a (5) 37.40 2.45

Flower Type of Johore, 1979, with State Crest

Perf. 14½

1979, Apr. 30 Litho. Wmk. 378

81 A16 1c multicolored .15 .15
82 A16 2c multicolored .15 .15
83 A16 5c multicolored .15 .15
84 A16 10c multicolored .15 .15
85 A16 15c multicolored .30 .15
86 A16 20c multicolored .35 .15
87 A16 25c multicolored .45 .15
Set value 1.45 .55

1984-85 Unwmk.

83a A16 5c .40 .15
84a A16 10c ('85)
85a A16 15c 3.25
86a A16 20c .40 .15

The State arms are larger on Nos. 83a-86a.

Agriculture and State Arms Type of Johore

Wmk. 388

1986, Oct. 25 Litho. *Perf. 12*

88 A19 1c multicolored .15 .15
89 A19 2c multicolored .15 .15
90 A19 5c multicolored .15 .15
91 A19 10c multicolored .15 .15
92 A19 15c multicolored .15 .15
93 A19 20c multicolored .20 .15
94 A19 30c multicolored .35 .15
Set value 1.00 .45

PERAK

Sultan Idris Shah — A17

Wmk. 338

1963, Oct. 26 Photo. *Perf. 14*

138 A17 10c yel, blk, blue & brn .30 .15

Installation of Idris Shah as Sultan of Perak.

Orchid Type of Johore, 1965, with Portrait of Sultan Idris Shah

1965, Nov. 15 Wmk. 338 *Perf. 14½*

Flowers in Natural Colors

139 A14 1c blk & lt grnsh bl .25 .15
a. Watermark sideways ('70) .50 .50
140 A14 2c black, red & gray .25 .15
141 A14 5c black & Prus blue .50 .15
a. Yellow omitted 20.00
142 A14 6c black & lt lilac .65 .15
143 A14 10c black & lt ultra 1.00 .15
a. Watermark sideways ('70) 2.00 1.90
144 A14 15c blk, lil rose & grn 1.25 .15
a. Lilac rose omitted 80.00
145 A14 20c black & brown 1.90 .25
Nos. 139-145 (7) 5.80
Set value .65

Butterfly Type of Johore, 1971, with Portrait of Sultan Idris Shah

Perf. 13½x13

1971, Feb. 1 Litho. Unwmk.

146 A15 1c multicolored .15 .15
147 A15 2c multicolored .25 .15
148 A15 5c multicolored .60 .15
149 A15 6c multicolored .70 .15
150 A15 10c multicolored 1.10 .15
151 A15 15c multicolored 1.90 .25
152 A15 20c multicolored 2.25 .25
Nos. 146-152 (7) 6.95
Set value .90

In 1973 booklet panes of 4 of the 5c, 10c, 15c were made from sheets.

1977 Photo.

146a A15 1c .80 .15
148b A15 5c 1.25 .20
150b A15 10c 1.40 .25
151b A15 15c 3.25 .50
152a A15 20c 4.25 .60
Nos. 146a-152a (5) 10.95 1.70

Flower Type of Johore, 1979, with Portrait of Sultan Idris Shah

Perf. 14½

1979, Apr. 30 Litho. Wmk. 378

153 A16 1c multicolored .15 .15
154 A16 2c multicolored .15 .15
155 A16 5c multicolored .15 .15
a. Brt rose pink & yel flowers ('84) .15 .15
156 A16 10c multicolored .15 .15
a. White flowers ('84) .15 .15
157 A16 15c multicolored .30 .15
a. Unwmkd. ('85) 3.25
158 A16 20c multicolored .35 .15
a. Unwmkd. ('84) .45 .15
159 A16 25c multicolored .45 .15
Set value 1.45 .55

Agriculture and State Arms Type of Johore with Tun Azlan Shah, Raja

Wmk. 388

1986, Oct. 25 Litho. *Perf. 12*

160 A19 1c multicolored .15 .15
161 A19 2c multicolored .15 .15
162 A19 5c multicolored .15 .15
163 A19 10c multicolored .15 .15
164 A19 15c multicolored .15 .15
165 A19 20c multicolored .20 .15
166 A19 30c multicolored .35 .15
Set value 1.00 .45

PERLIS

Orchid Type of Johore, 1965, with Portrait of Regent Yang Teramat Mulia

Perf. 14½

1965, Nov. 15 Photo. Wmk. 338

Flowers in Natural Colors

40 A14 1c black & lt grnsh bl .30 .15
41 A14 2c black, red & gray .35 .15
42 A14 5c black & Prus blue .50 .15
43 A14 6c black & lt lilac .55 .15
44 A14 10c black & ultra .85 .25
45 A14 15c blk, lil rose & grn 1.50 .50
46 A14 20c black & brown 2.50 .80
Nos. 40-46 (7) 6.55 2.15

Butterfly Type of Johore, 1971, with Portrait of Sultan Syed Putra

Perf. 13½x13

1971, Feb. 1 Litho. Unwmk.

47 A15 1c multicolored .15 .15
48 A15 2c multicolored .25 .15
49 A15 5c multicolored .50 .15
50 A15 6c multicolored .65 .20
51 A15 10c multicolored 1.65 .25
52 A15 15c multicolored 1.65 .40
53 A15 20c multicolored 2.00 .55
Nos. 47-53 (7) 6.85 1.85

In 1973 booklet panes of 4 of the 5c, 10c, 15c were made from sheets.

1977 Photo.

51b A15 10c *20.00 20.00*
52b A15 15c *4.00 3.00*
53a A15 20c *17.00 17.00*
Nos. 51b-53a (3) *41.00 40.00*

Sultan Syed Putra — A2

1971, Mar. 28 Litho. *Perf. 13½x13*

54 A2 10c silver, yel & black .15 .15
55 A2 15c silver, blue & blk .25 .25
56 A2 50c silver, lt vio & blk .85 .85
Nos. 54-56 (3) 1.25 1.25

25th anniversary of the installation of Syed Putra as Raja of Perlis. Sold throughout Malaysia on Mar. 28, then only in Perlis.

Flower Type of Johore, 1979, with Portrait of Sultan Syed Putra

Perf. 14½

1979, Apr. 30 Litho. Wmk. 378

57 A16 1c multicolored .15 .15
58 A16 2c multicolored .15 .15
59 A16 5c multicolored .15 .15
60 A16 10c multicolored .15 .15
61 A16 15c multicolored .30 .15
62 A16 20c multicolored .35 .15
a. Unwmk. ('85) 4.25
63 A16 25c multicolored .45 .15
Set value 1.45 .55

Agriculture and State Arms Type of Johore with Tuanku Syed Putra, Raja

Wmk. 388

1986, Oct. 25 Litho. *Perf. 12*

64 A19 1c multicolored .15 .15
65 A19 2c multicolored .15 .15
66 A19 5c multicolored .15 .15
67 A19 10c multicolored .15 .15
68 A19 15c multicolored .15 .15
69 A19 20c multicolored .20 .15
70 A19 30c multicolored .35 .15
Set value 1.00 .45

Reign of Tuanku Syed Putra Jamalullail, Raja of Perlis, 50th Anniv. — A3

30c, Industry and produce. $1, Palace.

Wmk. 388

1995, Dec. 4 Litho. *Perf. 14*

71 A3 30c green & multi .25 .25
72 A3 $1 blue & multi .80 .80

SABAH

North Borneo Nos. 280-295 Overprinted:

SABAH On 1c-75c **SABAH** On $1-$10

Perf. 13x12½, 12½x13

1964, July 1 Engr. Wmk. 314

1 A92 1c lt red brn & grn .15 .15
2 A92 4c orange & olive .15 .15
3 A92 5c violet & sepia .15 .15
4 A92 6c bluish grn & sl .15 .15
5 A92 10c rose red & lt grn .15 .15
6 A92 12c dull green & brn .15 .15
7 A92 20c ultra & blue grn .20 .15
8 A92 25c rose red & gray .50 .25
9 A92 30c gray ol & sepia .60 .35
10 A92 35c redsh brn & stl bl .75 .40
11 A92 50c brn org & blue grn 1.00 .50
12 A92 75c red vio & sl blue 1.50 .70
13 A93 $1 yel green & brn 2.25 1.00
14 A93 $2 slate & brown 4.50 2.75
15 A93 $5 brown vio & grn 12.00 6.50
16 A93 $10 blue & carmine 24.00 13.00
Nos. 1-16 (16) 48.20 26.50

Orchid Type of Johore, 1965, with State Crest

Perf. 14½

1965, Nov. 15 Wmk. 338 Photo.

Flowers in Natural Colors

17 A14 1c black & lt grnsh bl .25 .15
18 A14 2c black, red & gray .25 .15
19 A14 5c black & Prus bl .40 .15
20 A14 6c black & lt lilac .60 .15
21 A14 10c black & lt ultra 1.00 .20
a. Watermark sideways ('70) 1.40 .50
22 A14 15c black, lil rose & grn 1.65 .20
23 A14 20c black & brown 2.50 .45
Nos. 17-23 (7) 6.65
Set value 1.10

Butterfly Type of Johore, 1971, with State Crest

Perf. 13½x13

1971, Feb. 1 Litho. Unwmk.

24 A15 1c multicolored .15 .15
25 A15 2c multicolored .30 .15
26 A15 5c multicolored .40 .15
27 A15 6c multicolored .55 .15
28 A15 10c multicolored 1.10 .15
29 A15 15c multicolored 1.40 .20
30 A15 20c multicolored 2.50 .25
Nos. 24-30 (7) 6.40
Set value .75

In 1973 booklet panes of 4 of the 5c, 10c, 15c were made from sheets.

1977 Photo.

24a A15 1c 1.75 .15
25a A15 2c 1.75 .15
26b A15 5c 10.00 .15
28b A15 10c 2.50 .15
29b A15 15c 2.50 .30
Nos. 24a-29b (5) 18.50 .90

Flower Type of Johore, 1979, with State Crest

Perf. 14½

1979, Apr. 30 Wmk. 378 Litho.

32 A16 1c multicolored .15 .15
33 A16 2c multicolored .15 .15
34 A16 5c multicolored .15 .15
35 A16 10c multicolored .15 .15
36 A16 15c multicolored .30 .15
37 A16 20c multicolored .35 .15
38 A16 25c multicolored .45 .15
Set value 1.45 .45

1983-85 Unwmk.

35a A16 10c ('85) 7.50
36a A16 15c 6.00
37a A16 20c

Agriculture and State Arms Type of Johore

Wmk. 388

1986, Oct. 25 Litho. *Perf. 12*

39 A19 1c multicolored .15 .15
40 A19 2c multicolored .15 .15
41 A19 5c multicolored .15 .15
42 A19 10c multicolored .15 .15
43 A19 15c multicolored .15 .15
44 A19 20c multicolored .20 .15
45 A19 30c multicolored .35 .15
Set value 1.00 .45

Sarawak

Stamps of types A14, A16 and A19 issued for Sarawak are listed in the "S" section.

SELANGOR

Orchid Type of Johore, 1965, with Portrait of Sultan Salahuddin Abdul Aziz Shah

Perf. 14½

1965, Nov. 15 Photo. Wmk. 338

Flowers in Natural Colors

121 A14 1c blk & lt grnsh bl .15 .15
a. Watermark sideways ('70) 1.00 .15
122 A14 2c black, red & gray .30 .15
a. Rose carmine omitted
123 A14 5c black & Prus blue .50 .15
124 A14 6c black & lt lilac .65 .15
125 A14 10c black & lt ultra 1.00 .15
a. Watermark sideways ('70) 3.50 .40
126 A14 15c blk, lil rose & grn 1.25 .15
127 A14 20c black & brown 2.25 .25
a. Watermark sideways ('70) 6.00 .60
Nos. 121-127 (7) 6.10
Set value .55

Butterfly Type of Johore, 1971, with Portrait of Sultan Salahuddin

Perf. 13½x13

1971, Feb. 1 Litho. Unwmk.

128 A15 1c multicolored .20 .15
129 A15 2c multicolored .30 .15
130 A15 5c multicolored .50 .15
131 A15 6c multicolored .75 .15
132 A15 10c multicolored 1.10 .15
133 A15 15c multicolored 1.75 .15
134 A15 20c multicolored 2.25 .20
Nos. 128-134 (7) 6.85
Set value .70

In 1973 booklet panes of 4 of the 5c, 10c, 15c were made from sheets.

1977 **Photo.**

128a A15 1c .85 .15
130b A15 5c 1.25 .20
132b A15 10c 1.50 .22
133b A15 15c 3.25 .50
134a A15 20c 4.00 .65
Nos. 128a-134a (5) 10.85 1.72

Flower Type of Johore, 1979, with Portrait of Sultan Salahuddin Abdul Aziz Shah

Perf. 14½

1979, Apr. 30 Litho. Wmk. 378

135 A16 1c multicolored .15 .15
136 A16 2c multicolored .15 .15
137 A16 5c multicolored .15 .15
a. brt rose pink & yel flowers ('84) .15 .15
138 A16 10c multicolored .15 .15
a. Unwmkd. ('85) 2.25
139 A16 15c multicolored .25 .15
a. Unwmkd. ('84) 3.25
140 A16 20c multicolored .35 .15
a. pale yellow flowers ('84) .35 .15
141 A16 25c multicolored .50 .15
Set value 1.45 .60

Agriculture and State Arms Type of Johore with Sultan Salahuddin Abdul Aziz Shah

Wmk. 388

1986, Oct. 25 Litho. *Perf. 12*

142 A19 1c multicolored .15 .15
143 A19 2c multicolored .15 .15
144 A19 5c multicolored .15 .15
145 A19 10c multicolored .15 .15
146 A19 15c multicolored .15 .15
147 A19 20c multicolored .20 .15
148 A19 30c multicolored .35 .15
Set value 1.00 .45

TRENGGANU

Orchid Type of Johore, 1965, with Portrait of Sultan Ismail

Perf. 14½

1965, Nov. 15 Photo. Wmk. 338

Flowers in Natural Colors

86 A14 1c black & lt grnsh bl .15 .15
87 A14 2c black, red & gray .35 .15
88 A14 5c black & Prus blue .55 .15
89 A14 6c black & lt lilac .70 .15
90 A14 10c black & lt ultra .95 .15
91 A14 15c blk, lil rose & grn 1.40 .20
92 A14 20c black & brown 2.00 .30
Nos. 86-92 (7) 6.10
Set value .75

Tuanku Ismail Nasiruddin — A6

Perf. 14½x13½

1970, Dec. 16 Photo. Unwmk.

93 A6 10c multicolored .20 .20
94 A6 15c brt yellow multi .35 .35
95 A6 50c dp plum & multi 1.10 1.10
Nos. 93-95 (3) 1.65 1.65

Installation of Tuanku Ismail Nasiruddin Shah as Sultan of Trengganu, 25th anniv.

Butterfly Type of Johore, 1971, with Portrait of Sultan Ismail Nasiruddin

Perf. 13½x13

1971, Feb. 1 Litho. Unwmk.

96 A15 1c multicolored .15 .15
97 A15 2c multicolored .25 .15
98 A15 5c multicolored .50 .15
99 A15 6c multicolored .75 .20
100 A15 10c multicolored 1.00 .25
101 A15 15c multicolored 1.90 .35
102 A15 20c multicolored 2.25 .40
Nos. 96-102 (7) 6.80 1.65

In 1973 booklet panes of 4 of the 5c, 10c, 15c were made from sheets.

1977 **Photo.**

98b A15 5c 10.00 10.00
100b A15 10c 2.50 2.50
101b A15 15c 2.50 2.50
Nos. 98b-101b (3) 15.00 15.00

Flower Type of Johore, 1979, with Portrait of Sultan Ismail Nasiruddin

Perf. 14½

1979, Apr. 30 Litho. Wmk. 378

103 A16 1c multicolored .15 .15
104 A16 2c multicolored .15 .15
105 A16 5c multicolored .15 .15
106 A16 10c multicolored .15 .15
107 A16 15c multicolored .30 .15
108 A16 20c multicolored .35 .15
109 A16 25c multicolored .45 .15
Set value 1.45 .55

1983-86 **Unwmk.**

106a A16 10c ('86) 13.00 .15
107a A16 15c ('85) 2.00
108a A16 20c 4.00
109a A16 25c Pale salmon flowers .75 .15
Nos. 106a-109a (4) 19.75

The portrait and State arms are smaller.

Agriculture and State Arms Type of Johore with Sultan Mahmud Al Marhum

Wmk. 388

1986, Oct. 25 Litho. *Perf. 12*

110 A19 1c multicolored .15 .15
111 A19 2c multicolored .15 .15
112 A19 5c multicolored .15 .15
113 A19 10c multicolored .15 .15
114 A19 15c multicolored .15 .15
115 A19 20c multicolored .20 .15
116 A19 30c multicolored .30 .15
Set value .90 .45

WILAYAH PERSEKUTUAN

Agriculture and State Arms Type of Johore

Wmk. 388

1986, Oct. 25 Litho. *Perf. 12*

1 A19 1c multicolored .15 .15
2 A19 2c multicolored .15 .15
3 A19 5c multicolored .15 .15
4 A19 10c multicolored .15 .15
5 A19 15c multicolored .15 .15
6 A19 20c multicolored .25 .15
7 A19 30c multicolored .40 .15
Set value 1.20 .45

MALDIVE ISLANDS

'mȯl-,dīv 'ī-lənds

LOCATION — A group of 2,000 islands in the Indian Ocean about 400 miles southwest of Ceylon.
GOVT. — Republic
AREA — 115 sq. mi.
POP. — 168,000 (est. 1983)
CAPITAL — Male

Maldive Islands was a British Protectorate, first as a dependency of Ceylon, then from 1948 as an independent sultanate, except for a year (1953) as a republic. The islands became completely independent on July 26, 1965, and became a republic again on November 11, 1968.

100 Cents = 1 Rupee
100 Larees = 1 Rafiyaa (1951)

Catalogue values for unused stamps in this country are for Never Hinged items, beginning with Scott 20.

Watermarks

Wmk. 47- Multiple Rosette

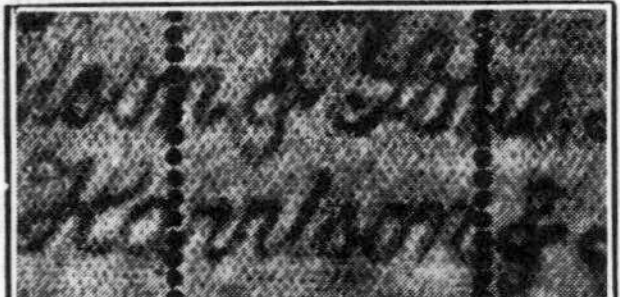

Wmk. 233- "Harrison & Sons, London" in Script

Stamps of Ceylon, 1904-05, Overprinted **MALDIVES**

1906, Sept. 9 Wmk. 3 *Perf. 14*

1 A36 2c orange brown 11.00 15.00
2 A37 3c green 12.50 17.50
3 A37 4c yellow & blue 30.00 42.50
4 A38 5c dull lilac 5.00 6.00
5 A40 15c ultramarine 52.50 75.00
6 A40 25c bister 62.50 85.00
Nos. 1-6 (6) 173.50 241.00

Minaret of Juma Mosque, near Male — A1

1909 Engr. Wmk. 47

7 A1 2c orange brown 1.50 .75
8 A1 3c green .50 .60
9 A1 5c red violet .50 .30
10 A1 10c carmine 1.50 .75
Nos. 7-10 (4) 4.00 2.40

Type of 1909 Issue Redrawn

Perf. 14½x14

1933 Photo. Wmk. 233

11 A1 2c gray 1.50 1.50
12 A1 3c yellow brown 1.00 1.10
13 A1 5c brown lake 5.00 7.50
14 A1 6c brown red 3.25 3.75
15 A1 10c green .80 1.00
16 A1 15c gray black 3.75 4.00
17 A1 25c red brown 3.75 4.00
18 A1 50c red violet 3.75 4.00
19 A1 1r blue black 5.00 3.75
Nos. 11-19 (9) 27.80 30.60

On the 6c, 15c, 25c and 50c, the right hand panel carries only the word "CENTS."

Nos. 11-19 exist with watermark vert. or horiz. The 5c with vert. watermark sells for twice the price of the horiz. watermark.

Catalogue values for unused stamps in this section, from this point to the end of the section, are for Never Hinged items.

Palm Tree and Seascape — A2

Maldive Fish — A3

Unwmk.

1950, Dec. 24 Engr. *Perf. 13*

20 A2 2 l olive green .90 .90
21 A2 3 l deep blue 3.75 2.25
22 A2 5 l dp blue green 3.75 2.50
23 A2 6 l red brown .60 .60
24 A2 10 l red .60 .60
25 A2 15 l orange .70 .70
26 A2 25 l rose violet .75 .75
27 A2 50 l violet blue 1.50 1.50
28 A2 1r dark brown 6.75 6.75
Nos. 20-28 (9) 19.30 16.55

1952

29 A3 3 l shown .30 .30
30 A3 5 l Urns .20 .20

Harbor of Male — A4

Fort and Governor's Palace — A5

Perf. 13½ (A4), 11½x11 (A5)

1956 Engr. Unwmk.

31 A4 2 l lilac .15 .15
32 A4 3 l gray green .15 .15
33 A4 5 l reddish brown .15 .15
34 A4 6 l blue violet .15 .15
35 A4 10 l light green .15 .15
36 A4 15 l brown .15 .15
37 A4 25 l rose red .15 .15
38 A4 50 l orange .20 .20
39 A5 1r light green .40 .40
40 A5 5r ultramarine 1.50 1.50
41 A5 10r magenta 2.50 2.50
Set value 5.00 5.00

Bicyclists and Olympic Emblem — A6

Design: 25 l, 50 l, 1r, Basketball, vert.

Perf. 11½x11, 11x11½

1960, Aug. 20 Engr.

42 A6 2 l rose violet & green .15 .15
43 A6 3 l grnsh gray & plum .15 .15
44 A6 5 l vio brn & dk blue .15 .15
45 A6 10 l brt green & brn .15 .15
46 A6 15 l brown & blue .15 .15
47 A6 25 l rose red & olive .20 .20
48 A6 50 l orange & dk vio .30 .30
49 A6 1r brt green & plum .50 .50
Set value 1.30 1.30

17th Olympic Games, Rome, Aug. 25-Sept. 11.

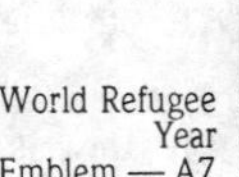

World Refugee Year Emblem — A7

1960, Oct. 15 *Perf. 11½x11*

50 A7 2 l orange, vio & grn .15 .15
51 A7 3 l green, brn & red .15 .15
52 A7 5 l sepia, grn & red .15 .15
53 A7 10 l dull pur, grn & red .15 .15
54 A7 15 l gray grn, pur & red .15 .15
55 A7 25 l redsh brn, ultra & olive .15 .15
56 A7 50 l rose, olive & blue .20 .20
57 A7 1r gray, car rose & vio .35 .35
Set value 1.00 1.00

WRY, July 1, 1959-June 30, 1960.

Tomb of Sultan — A8

Designs: 3 l, Custom house. 5 l, Cowry shells. 6 l, Old royal palace. 10 l, Road to Minaret, Juma Mosque, Male. 15 l, Council house. 25 l, Government secretariat. 50 l, Prime minister's office. 1r, Tomb and sailboats. 5r, Tomb by the sea. 10r, Port.

1960, Oct. 15 *Perf. 11½x11*

Various Frames

58 A8 2 l lilac .15 .15
59 A8 3 l green .15 .15
60 A8 5 l brown orange .15 .15
61 A8 6 l bright blue .15 .15
62 A8 10 l carmine rose .15 .15
63 A8 15 l sepia .15 .15
64 A8 25 l dull violet .15 .15
65 A8 50 l slate .20 .20
66 A8 1r orange .35 .35
67 A8 5r dark blue 1.60 1.60
68 A8 10r dull green 3.50 3.50
Nos. 58-68 (11) 6.70 6.70

Stamps in 25r, 50r and 100r denominations were also issued, but primarily for revenue purposes.

Coconuts — A9

Map of Male Showing Population Distribution A10

Perf. 14x14½, 14½x14

1961, Apr. 20 Photo. Unwmk.

Coconuts in Ocher

69 A9 2 l green .15 .15
70 A9 3 l ultramarine .15 .15
71 A9 5 l lilac rose .15 .15
72 A9 10 l red orange .15 .15
73 A9 15 l black .15 .15

74 A10 25 l multicolored .15 .15
75 A10 50 l multicolored .25 .25
76 A10 1r multicolored .45 .45
Set value 1.10 1.10

Pigeon and 5c Stamp of 1906 — A11

Designs: 10 l, 15 l, 20 l, Post horn and 3c stamp of 1906. 25 l, 50 l, 1r, Laurel branch and 2c stamp of 1906.

1961, Sept. 9 *Perf. 14½x14*

77 A11 2 l violet blue & mar .15 .15
78 A11 3 l violet blue & mar .15 .15
79 A11 5 l violet blue & mar .15 .15
80 A11 6 l violet blue & mar .15 .15
81 A11 10 l maroon & green .15 .15
82 A11 15 l maroon & green .15 .15
83 A11 20 l maroon & green .15 .15
84 A11 25 l green, mar & blk .15 .15
85 A11 50 l green, mar & blk .20 .20
86 A11 1r green, mar & blk .35 .35
a. Souvenir sheet of 4 1.80 1.80
Set value 1.00 1.00

55th anniv. of the 1st postage stamps of the Maldive Islands.

No. 86a contains 4 No. 86, with simulated performations.

Malaria Eradication Emblem — A12

1962, Apr. 7 **Engr.** *Perf. 13½x13*

87 A12 2 l orange brown .15 .15
88 A12 3 l green .15 .15
89 A12 5 l blue .15 .15
90 A12 10 l vermilion .15 .15
91 A12 15 l black .15 .15
92 A12 25 l dark blue .15 .15
93 A12 50 l green .25 .25
94 A12 1r purple .45 .45
Set value 1.15 1.15

WHO drive to eradicate malaria.

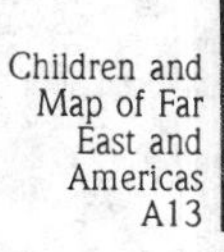

Children and Map of Far East and Americas A13

UNICEF, 15th Anniv.: 25 l, 50 l, 1r, 5r, Children and Map of Africa, Europe and Asia.

Perf. 14½x14

1962, Sept. 9 **Photo.** **Unwmk.**

Children in Multicolor

95 A13 2 l sepia .15 .15
96 A13 6 l violet .15 .15
97 A13 10 l dark green .15 .15
98 A13 15 l ultramarine .15 .15
99 A13 25 l blue .15 .15
100 A13 50 l bright green .15 .15
101 A13 1r rose claret .20 .20
102 A13 5r emerald .90 .90
Set value 1.50 1.50

Sultan Mohamed Farid Didi — A14

1962, Nov. 29 *Perf. 14x14½*

Portrait in Orange Brown and Sepia

103 A14 3 l bluish green .15 .15
104 A14 5 l slate .15 .15
105 A14 10 l blue .15 .15
106 A14 20 l olive .15 .15
107 A14 50 l dk carmine rose .20 .20
108 A14 1r dark purple .40 .40
Set value .80 .80

9th anniv. of the enthronement of Sultan Mohamed Farid Didi.

Regal Angelfish, Sultan's Crest and Skin Diver — A15

Tropical Fish: 10 l, 25 l, Moorish idol. 50 l, Diadem squirrelfish. 1r, Surgeonfish. 5r, Orange butterflyfish.

1963, Feb. 2 *Perf. 13½*

109 A15 2 l multicolored .15 .15
110 A15 3 l multicolored .15 .15
111 A15 5 l multicolored .15 .15
112 A15 10 l multicolored .15 .15
113 A15 25 l multicolored .28 .28
114 A15 50 l multicolored .55 .55
115 A15 1r multicolored 1.10 1.10
116 A15 5r multicolored 5.75 5.75
Nos. 109-116 (8) 8.28 8.28

Fish in Net — A16

Design: 5 l, 10 l, 50 l, Wheat emblem and hand holding rice, vert.

1963, Mar. 21 **Photo.** *Perf. 12*

117 A16 2 l green & lt brown .15 .15
118 A16 5 l dull rose & lt brn .15 .15
119 A16 7 l grnsh blue & lt brn .15 .15
120 A16 10 l blue & lt brown .15 .15
121 A16 25 l brn red & lt brn .50 .50
122 A16 50 l violet & lt brown 1.00 1.00
123 A16 1r rose cl & lt brn 2.00 2.00
Nos. 117-123 (7) 4.10 4.10

FAO "Freedom from Hunger" campaign.

Centenary Emblem A17

1963, Oct. **Unwmk.** *Perf. 14x14½*

124 A17 2 l dull purple & red .15 .15
125 A17 15 l slate green & red .15 .15
126 A17 50 l brown & red .25 .25
127 A17 1r dk blue & red .50 .50
128 A17 4r dk ol grn & red 1.75 1.75
Nos. 124-128 (5) 2.80 2.80

Centenary of the International Red Cross.

Scout Emblem and Knot — A18

1963, Dec. 7 **Unwmk.** *Perf. 13½*

129 A18 2 l purple & dp green .15 .15
130 A18 3 l brown & dp green .15 .15
131 A18 25 l dk blue & dp green .15 .15
132 A18 1r dp car & dp grn .40 .40
Set value .60 .60

11th Boy Scout Jamboree, Marathon, Aug. 1963. Printed in sheets of 12 (3x4) with ornamental borders and inscriptions.

Mosque at Male — A19

Perf. 11½

1964, Aug. 10 **Engr.** **Wmk. 314**

133 A19 2 l rose violet .15 .15
134 A19 3 l green .15 .15
135 A19 10 l carmine rose .15 .15
136 A19 40 l black brown .16 .16
137 A19 60 l blue .24 .24
138 A19 85 l orange brown .35 .35
Set value .85 .85

Conversion of the Maldive Islanders to Mohammedanism in 1733 (1153 by Islamic calendar).

Shot Put and Maldive Arms — A20

Design: 15 l, 25 l, 50 l, 1r, Runner and Maldive arms.

Perf. 14x13½

1964, Oct. 6 **Litho.** **Wmk. 314**

139 A20 2 l grnsh bl & dull vio .15 .15
140 A20 3 l red brn & maroon .15 .15
141 A20 5 l dk green & gray .15 .15
142 A20 10 l plum & indigo .15 .15
143 A20 15 l bis brn & dk brn .15 .15
144 A20 25 l dk bl & bluish blk .16 .16
145 A20 50 l olive & black .32 .32
146 A20 1r gray & dk purple .60 .60
a. Souvenir sheet of 3 2.00 2.00
Set value 1.40 1.40

18th Olympic Games, Tokyo, Oct. 10-25. #146a contains 3 imperf. stamps similar to #144-146.

General Electric Observation Communication Satellite — A21

Perf. 14½

1965, July 1 **Photo.** **Unwmk.**

147 A21 5 l dark blue .15 .15
148 A21 10 l brown .18 .18
149 A21 25 l green .45 .45
150 A21 1r magenta 1.75 1.75
Nos. 147-150 (4) 2.53 2.53

Quiet Sun Year, 1964-65. Printed in sheets of 9 (3x3) with ornamental borders and inscriptions.

Queen Nefertari Holding Sistrum and Papyrus — A22

Designs: 3 l, 10 l, 25 l, 1r, Ramses II.

1965, Sept. 1 **Litho.** **Wmk. 314**

151 A22 2 l dull bl grn & mar .15 .15
152 A22 3 l lake & green .15 .15
153 A22 5 l green & lake .15 .15
154 A22 10 l dk blue & ocher .15 .15
155 A22 15 l redsh brn & ind .15 .15
156 A22 25 l dull lil & indigo .15 .15
157 A22 50 l green & brown .30 .30
158 A22 1r brown & green .60 .60
Set value 1.35 1.35

UNESCO world campaign to save historic monuments in Nubia.

John F. Kennedy and Doves — A23

Design: 1r, 2r, President Kennedy and hands holding olive branches.

Unwmk.

1965, Oct. 1 **Photo.** *Perf. 12*

159 A23 2 l slate & brt pink .15 .15
160 A23 5 l brown & brt pink .15 .15
161 A23 25 l blue blk & brt pink .15 .15
162 A23 1r red lil, yel & grn .28 .28
163 A23 2r sl green, yel & grn .55 .55
a. Souvenir sheet of 4 3.75 3.75
Set value 1.00 1.00

#163a contains 4 imperf. stamps similar to #163.

UN Flag — A24

1965, Nov. 24 **Photo.** *Perf. 12*

Flag in Aquamarine

164 A24 3 l red brown .15 .15
165 A24 10 l violet .15 .15
166 A24 1r dark olive brown .50 .50
Set value .60 .60

20th anniversary of the United Nations.

ICY Emblem A25

1965, Dec. 20 **Photo.** *Perf. 12*

167 A25 5 l bister & dk brn .15 .15
168 A25 15 l dull vio & dk brn .15 .15
169 A25 50 l olive & dk brn .22 .22
170 A25 1r orange & dk brn .45 .45
171 A25 2r blue & dk brn .90 .90
a. Souvenir sheet of 3 2.25 2.25
Nos. 167-171 (5) 1.87 1.87

Intl. Cooperation Year. No. 171a contains three imperf. stamps with simulated perforation similar to Nos. 169-171.

Sea Shells — A26

A27

Coat of Arms and: 2 l, 10 l, 30 l, No. 181, Conus alicus and cymatium maldiviensis (shells). 5 l, 10r, Conus litteratus and distorsia reticulata (shells). 7 l, No. 182, 2r, India-rubber vine flowers. 15 l, 50 l, 5r, Crab plover and gull. 3 l, 20 l, 1.50r, Reinwardtia trigynia.

1966, June 1 **Unwmk.** *Perf. 12*

172 A26 2 l multicolored .15 .15
173 A27 3 l multicolored .15 .15
174 A26 5 l multicolored .15 .15
175 A27 7 l multicolored .15 .15

176 A26 10 l multicolored .15 .15
177 A26 15 l multicolored .15 .15
178 A27 20 l multicolored .16 .16
179 A26 30 l multicolored .22 .22
180 A26 50 l multicolored .40 .40
181 A26 1r multicolored .80 .80
182 A27 1r multicolored .80 .80
183 A27 1.50r multicolored 1.20 1.20
184 A27 2r multicolored 1.60 1.60
185 A26 5r multicolored 4.00 4.00
186 A26 10r multicolored 8.00 8.00
Nos. 172-186 (15) 18.08 18.08

Flag A28

1966, July 26 ***Perf. 14x14½***

187 A28 10 l grnsh blue, red & grn .15 .15
188 A28 1r ocher, brn, red & grn .50 .50
Set value .55 .55

1st anniv. of full independence from Great Britain.

Luna 9 on Moon — A29

Designs: 25 l, 1r, 5r, Gemini 6 and 7, rendezvous in space. 2r, Gemini spaceship as seen from second Gemini spaceship.

1966, Nov. 1 Litho. ***Perf. 15x14***

189 A29 10 l gray bl, lt brn & ultramarine .15 .15
190 A29 25 l car rose & green .15 .15
191 A29 50 l green & dp org .20 .20
192 A29 1r org brn & grnsh bl .45 .45
193 A29 2r violet & green .90 .90
194 A29 5r Prus blue & pink 2.25 2.25
a. Souvenir sheet of 3 4.25 4.25
Nos. 189-194 (6) 4.10 4.10

Rendezvous in space of Gemini 6 and 7 (US), Dec. 4, 1965, and the soft landing on Moon by Luna 9 (USSR), Feb. 3, 1966. No. 194a contains 3 imperf. stamps similar to Nos. 192-194 with simulated perforations.

UNESCO Emblem, Owl and Book — A30

20th anniv. of UNESCO: 3 l, 1r, Microscope, globe and communication waves. 5 l, 5r, Palette, violin and mask.

1966, Nov. 15 Litho. ***Perf. 15x14***

195 A30 2 l green & multi .15 .15
196 A30 3 l lt violet & multi .15 .15
197 A30 5 l orange & multi .15 .15
198 A30 50 l rose & multi .30 .30
199 A30 1r citron & multi .60 .60
200 A30 5r multicolored 3.00 3.00
Nos. 195-200 (6) 4.35 4.35

Winston Churchill and Coffin on Gun Carriage — A31

Designs: 10 l, 25 l, 1r, Churchill and catafalque.

1967, Jan. 1 ***Perf. 14½x13½***

201 A31 2 l ol grn, red & dk blue .15 .15
202 A31 10 l Prus grn, red & dk blue .15 .15
203 A31 15 l grn, red & dk bl .15 .15
204 A31 25 l vio, red & dk bl .25 .25
205 A31 1r brn, red & dk bl 1.00 1.00
206 A31 2.50r brn lake, red & dk blue 2.50 2.50
Nos. 201-206 (6) 4.20 4.20

Sir Winston Spencer Churchill (1874-1965), statesman and World War II leader.

Soccer and Jules Rimet Cup A32

Designs: 3 l, 5 l, 25 l, 50 l, 1r, Various scenes from soccer and Jules Rimet Cup. 2r, British flag, Games' emblem and Big Ben Tower, London.

Perf. 14x13½

1967, Mar. 22 Photo. Unwmk.

207 A32 2 l yer & multi .15 .15
208 A32 3 l olive & multi .15 .15
209 A32 5 l brt purple & multi .15 .15
210 A32 25 l brt green & multi .18 .18
211 A32 50 l orange & multi .40 .40
212 A32 1r brt blue & multi .75 .75
213 A32 2r brown & multi 1.50 1.50
a. Souvenir sheet of 3 2.50 2.50
Nos. 207-213 (7) 3.28 3.28

England's victory in the World Soccer Cup Championship. No. 213a contains 3 imperf. stamps similar to Nos. 211-213.

Clown Butterflyfish — A33

Tropical Fish: 3 l, 1r, Four-saddled puffer. 5 l, Indo-Pacific blue trunkfish. 6 l, Striped triggerfish. 50 l, 2r, Blue angelfish.

1967, May 1 Photo. ***Perf. 14***

214 A33 2 l brt violet & multi .15 .15
215 A33 3 l emerald & multi .15 .15
216 A33 5 l org brn & multi .15 .15
217 A33 6 l brt blue & multi .15 .15
218 A33 50 l olive & multi .25 .25
219 A33 1r rose red & multi .50 .50
220 A33 2r orange & multi 1.00 1.00
Set value 1.90 1.90

Plane at Hulule Airport — A34

Designs: 5 l, 15 l, 50 l, 10r, Plane over administration building, Hulule Airport.

1967, July 26 ***Perf. 14x13½***

221 A34 2 l citron & lil .15 .15
222 A34 5 l violet & green .15 .15
223 A34 10 l lt green & lilac .15 .15
224 A34 15 l yel bister & grn .15 .15
225 A34 30 l sky blue & vio bl .15 .15
226 A34 50 l brt pink & brn .20 .20
227 A34 5r org & vio blue 1.75 1.75
228 A34 10r lt ultra & dp brn 3.50 3.50
Nos. 221-228 (8) 6.20 6.20

For overprints see Nos. 235-242.

Man and Music Pavilion and EXPO '67 Emblem — A35

Designs: 5 l, 50 l, 2r, Man and his Community Pavilion and EXPO '67 emblem.

Perf. 14x13½

1967, Oct. 1 Photo. Unwmk.

EXPO '67 Emblem in Gold

229 A35 2 l ol gray, ol & brt rose .15 .15
230 A35 5 l ultra, grnsh blue & brn .15 .15
231 A35 10 l brn red, lt grn & red org .15 .15
232 A35 50 l brn, grnsh blue & org .20 .20
233 A35 1r vio, grn & rose lil .40 .40
234 A35 2r dk grn, emer & red brn .80 .80
a. Souvenir sheet of 2 1.50 1.50
Set value 1.50 1.50

EXPO '67 Intl. Exhibition, Montreal, Apr. 28-Oct. 27. No. 234a contains 2 imperf. stamps similar to Nos. 233-234 with simulated perforations.

Nos. 221-228 Overprinted in Gold: "International Tourist Year 1967"

1967, Dec. 1 Photo. ***Perf. 14x13½***

235 A34 2 l citron & lilac .15 .15
236 A34 5 l violet & green .15 .15
237 A34 10 l lt green & lilac .15 .15
238 A34 15 l yel bister & grn .15 .15
239 A34 30 l sky blue & vio bl .15 .15
240 A34 50 l brt pink & brn .20 .20
241 A34 5r org & vio blue 1.75 1.75
242 A34 10r lt ultra & dp brn 3.50 3.50
Nos. 235-242 (8) 6.20 6.20

The overprint is in 3 lines on the 2 l, 10 l, 30 l, 5r; one line on the 5 l, 15 l, 50 l, 10r.

Lord Baden-Powell, Wolf Cubs, Campfire and Flag Signals — A36

Boy Scouts: 3 l, 1r, Lord Baden-Powell, Boy Scout saluting and drummer.

1968, Jan. 1 Litho. ***Perf. 14x14½***

243 A36 2 l yel, brown & green .15 .15
244 A36 3 l lt bl, ultra & rose car .15 .15
245 A36 25 l dp org, red brn & vio blue .22 .22
246 A36 1r yel grn, grn & red brn .90 .90
Nos. 243-246 (4) 1.42 1.42

Sheets of 12 (4x3) with decorative border.
For overprints see Nos. 278-281.

French Satellites D-1 and A-1 — A37

3 l, 25 l, Luna 10, USSR. 7 l, 1r, Orbiter & Mariner, US. 10 l, 2r, Edward White, Virgil Grissom & Roger Chaffee, US. 5r, Astronaut V. M. Komarov, USSR.

1968, Jan. 27 Photo. ***Perf. 14***

247 A37 2 l dp ultra & brt pink .15 .15
248 A37 3 l dk ol bis & vio .15 .15
249 A37 7 l rose car & ol .15 .15
250 A37 10 l blk, gray & dk bl .15 .15
251 A37 25 l purple & brt grn .15 .15
252 A37 50 l brown org & blue .20 .20
253 A37 1r dk sl grn & vio brn .40 .40
254 A37 2r blk, bl & dk brn .80 .80
a. Souvenir sheet of 2 1.75 1.75
255 A37 5r blk, tan & lil rose 2.00 2.00
Nos. 247-255 (9) 4.15 4.15

International achievements in space and to honor American and Russian astronauts, who gave their lives during space explorations in 1967. No. 254a contains 2 imperf. stamps similar to Nos. 253-254.

Shot Put — A38

Design: 6 l, 15 l, 2.50r, Discus.

1968, Feb. Litho. ***Perf. 14½***

256 A38 2 l emerald & multi .15 .15
257 A38 6 l dull yel & multi .15 .15
258 A38 10 l multicolored .15 .15
259 A38 15 l orange & multi .15 .15
260 A38 1r blue & multi .80 .80
261 A38 2.50r rose & multi 2.00 2.00
Nos. 256-261 (6) 3.40 3.40

19th Olympic Games, Mexico City, Oct. 12-27.

On the Adria, by Charles P. Bonington — A39

Seascapes: 1r, Ulysses Deriding Polyphemus (detail), by Joseph M. W. Turner. 2r, Sailboat at Argenteuil, by Claude Monet. 5r, Fishing Boats at Saintes-Maries, by Vincent Van Gogh.

1968, Apr. 1 Photo. ***Perf. 14***

262 A39 50 l ultra & multi .25 .25
263 A39 1r dk green & multi .55 .55
264 A39 2r multicolored 1.10 1.10
265 A39 5r multicolored 2.75 2.75
Nos. 262-265 (4) 4.65 4.65

Montgolfier Balloon, 1783, and Zeppelin LZ-130, 1928 — A40

History of Aviation: 3 l, 1r, Douglas DC-3, 1933, and Boeing 707, 1958. 5 l, 50 l, Lilienthal's glider, 1892, and Wright brothers' plane, 1905. 7 l, 2r, British-French Concorde and Supersonic Boeing 733, 1968.

1968, June 1 Photo. ***Perf. 14x13***

266 A40 2 l yel grn, ultra & bis brn .15 .15
267 A40 3 l org brn, greenish bl & lil .15 .15
268 A40 5 l grnsh bl, sl grn & lilac .15 .15
269 A40 7 l org, cl & ultra .15 .15
270 A40 10 l rose lil, bl & brn .15 .15
271 A40 50 l ol, sl grn & mag .25 .25
272 A40 1r ver, blue & emer .50 .50
273 A40 2r ultra, ol & brn vio 1.50 1.00
Set value 2.50 2.00

Issued in sheets of 12.

WHO Headquarters, Geneva — A41

1968, July 15 Litho. ***Perf. 14½x13***

274 A41 10 l grnsh bl, bl grn & vio .15 .15
275 A41 25 l org, ocher & green .15 .15
276 A41 1r emer, brt grn & brown .50 .50
277 A41 2r rose lil, dp rose lil & dk blue 1.00 1.00
Nos. 274-277 (4) 1.80 1.80

20th anniv. of WHO.

Nos. 243-246 Overprinted: "International / Boy Scout Jamboree, / Farragut Park, Idaho, / U.S.A. / August 1-9, 1967"

1968, Aug. 1 ***Perf. 14x14½***

278 A36 2 l multicolored .15 .15
279 A36 3 l multicolored .15 .15
280 A36 25 l multicolored .25 .25
281 A36 1r multicolored 1.00 1.00
Nos. 278-281 (4) 1.55 1.55

1st anniv. of the Intl. Boy Scout Jamboree in Farragut State Park, ID.

Marine Snail Shells — A42

2 l, 50 l, Common curlew & redshank. 1r, Angel wings (clam shell) & marine snail shell.

1968, Sept. 24 **Photo.** ***Perf. 14x13***

282	A42	2 l ultra & multi	.15	.15
283	A42	10 l brown & multi	.15	.15
284	A42	25 l multicolored	.20	.15
285	A42	50 l multicolored	.40	.30
286	A42	1r multicolored	.75	.60
287	A42	2r multicolored	1.50	1.20
		Nos. 282-287 (6)	3.15	2.55

Discus A43

50 l, Runner. 1r, Bicycling. 2r, Basketball.

1968, Oct. 12 ***Perf. 14***

288	A43	10 l ultra & multi	.15	.15
289	A43	50 l multicolored	.40	.40
290	A43	1r plum & multi	.80	.80
291	A43	2r violet & multi	1.60	1.60
		Nos. 288-291 (4)	2.95	2.95

19th Olympic Games, Mexico City, Oct. 12-27.
For overprints see Nos. 302-303.

Republic

Dhow A44

Republic Day: 1r, Coat of arms, map and flag of Maldive Islands.

Perf. 14x14½

1968, Nov. 11 **Unwmk.**

292	A44	10 l yel grn, ultra & dk brn	.15	.15
293	A44	1r ultra, red & emerald	1.10	.75

The Thinker, by Auguste Rodin — A45

Rodin Sculptures and UNESCO Emblem: 10 l, Hands. 1.50r, Sister and Brother. 2.50r, The Prodigal Son.

1969, Apr. 10 **Photo.** ***Perf. 13½***

294	A45	6 l emerald & multi	.15	.15
295	A45	10 l multicolored	.15	.15
296	A45	1.50r brt blue & multi	.50	.50
297	A45	2.50r multicolored	.85	.85
a.		Souvenir sheet of 2	2.50	2.50
		Set value	1.40	1.40

Intl. Human Rights Year and honoring UNESCO.
No. 297a contains 2 imperf. stamps similar to Nos. 296-297.

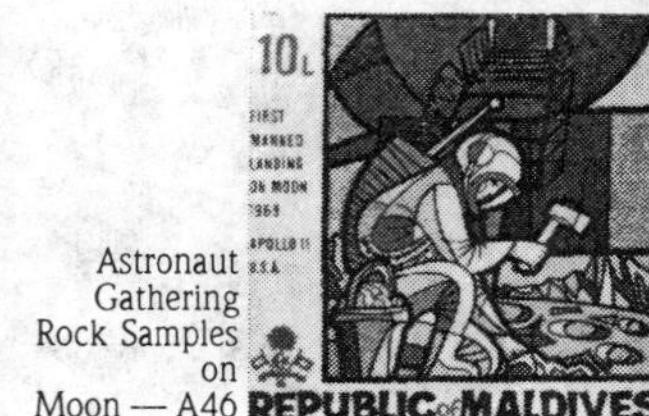

Astronaut Gathering Rock Samples on Moon — A46

Designs: 6 l, Lunar landing module. 1.50r, Astronaut on steps of module. 2.50r, Astronaut with television camera.

1969, Sept. 25 **Litho.** ***Perf. 14***

298	A46	6 l multicolored	.15	.15
299	A46	10 l multicolored	.15	.15
300	A46	1.50r multicolored	1.00	1.00
301	A46	2.50r multicolored	1.60	1.60
a.		Souvenir sheet of 4	2.25	2.25
		Nos. 298-301 (4)	2.90	2.90

Man's 1st moon landing. See note after US #C76.
Exist imperf.
No. 301a contains stamps similar to Nos. 298-301, with designs transposed on 10 l and 2.50r. Simulated perfs.
For overprints see Nos. 343-345.

Nos. 289-290 Overprinted: "REPUBLIC OF MALDIVES" and Commemorative Inscriptions

Designs: 50 l, overprinted "Gold Medal Winner / Mohamed Gammoudi / 5000m. run / Tunisia". 1r, overprinted "Gold Medal Winner / P. Trentin—Cycling / France."

1969, Dec. 10 **Photo.** ***Perf. 14***

302	A43	50 l multicolored	.30	.30
303	A43	1r multicolored	.60	.60

Columbia Daumon Victoria, 1899 — A47

Automobiles (pre-1908): 5 l, 50 l, Duryea Phaeton, 1902. 7 l, 1r, Packard S.24, 1906. 10 l, 2r, Autocar Runabout, 1907. 25 l, like 2 l.

1970, Feb. 1 **Litho.** ***Perf. 12***

304	A47	2 l multicolored	.15	.15
305	A47	5 l brt pink & multi	.15	.15
306	A47	7 l ultra & multi	.15	.15
307	A47	10 l ver & multi	.15	.15
308	A47	25 l ocher & multi	.15	.15
309	A47	50 l olive & multi	.30	.25
310	A47	1r orange & multi	.62	.50
311	A47	2r multicolored	1.25	1.00
a.		Souvenir sheet of 2, #310-311, perf. 11½	2.50	2.00
		Set value	2.50	2.00

Exist imperf.

Orange Butterflyfish — A48

Fish: 5 l, Spotted triggerfish. 25 l, Spotfin turkeyfish. 50 l, Forceps fish. 1r, Imperial angelfish. 2r, Regal angelfish.

1970, Mar. 1 **Litho.** ***Perf. 10½***

312	A48	2 l blue & multi	.15	.15
313	A48	5 l orange & multi	.15	.15
314	A48	25 l emerald & multi	.15	.15
315	A48	50 l brt pink & multi	.30	.25
316	A48	1r lt vio bl & multi	.62	.50
317	A48	2r olive & multi	1.25	1.00
		Nos. 312-317 (6)	2.62	2.20

UN Headquarters, New York and UN Emblem — A49

25th anniv. of the UN: 10 l, Surgeons, nurse and WHO emblem. 25 l, Student, performer, musician and UNESCO emblem. 50 l, Children reading and playing, and UNICEF emblem. 1r, Lamb, cock, fish, grain and FAO emblem. 2r, Miner and ILO emblem.

1970, June 26 **Litho.** ***Perf. 13½***

318	A49	2 l multicolored	.15	.15
319	A49	10 l multicolored	.15	.15
320	A49	25 l multicolored	.15	.15
321	A49	50 l multicolored	.25	.25
322	A49	1r multicolored	.55	.55
323	A49	2r multicolored	1.10	1.10
		Nos. 318-323 (6)	2.35	2.35

IMCO Emblem, Buoy and Ship — A50

EXPO Emblem and Australian Pavilion — A51

Design: 1r, Lighthouse and ship.

1970, July 26 **Litho.** ***Perf. 13½***

324	A50	50 l multicolored	.25	.20
325	A50	1r multicolored	.50	.40

10th anniv. of the Intergovernmental Maritime Consultative Organization (IMCO).

1970, Aug. 1 ***Perf. 13½x14***

EXPO Emblem and: 3 l, West German pavilion. 10 l, US pavilion. 25 l, British pavilion. 50 l, Russian pavilion. 1r, Japanese pavilion.

326	A51	2 l green & multi	.15	.15
327	A51	3 l violet & multi	.15	.15
328	A51	10 l brown & multi	.15	.15
329	A51	25 l multicolored	.15	.15
330	A51	50 l claret & multi	.30	.30
331	A51	1r ultra & multi	.60	.60
		Set value	1.20	1.20

EXPO '70 International Exhibition, Osaka, Japan, Mar. 15-Sept. 13, 1970.

Guitar Player, by Watteau — A52

Paintings: 7 l, Guitar Player in Spanish Costume, by Edouard Manet. 50 l, Guitar-playing Clown, by Antoine Watteau. 1r, Mandolin Player and Singers, by Lorenzo Costa (inscribed Ercole Roberti). 2.50r, Guitar Player and Lady, by Watteau. 5r, Mandolin Player, by Frans Hals.

1970, Aug. 1 **Litho.** ***Perf. 14***

332	A52	3 l gray & multi	.15	.15
333	A52	7 l yellow & multi	.15	.15
334	A52	50 l multicolored	.20	.20
335	A52	1r multicolored	.40	.40
336	A52	2.50r multicolored	1.00	1.00
337	A52	5r multicolored	2.00	2.00
a.		Souvenir sheet of 2	4.25	4.25
		Nos. 332-337 (6)	3.90	3.90

No. 337a contains 2 stamps similar to Nos. 336-337 but rouletted 13 and printed se-tenant.

Education Year Emblem and Adult Education — A53

Education Year Emblem and: 10 l, Teacher training. 25 l, Geography class. 50 l, Classroom. 1r, Instruction by television.

1970, Sept. 7 **Litho.** ***Perf. 14***

338	A53	5 l multicolored	.15	.15
339	A53	10 l multicolored	.15	.15
340	A53	25 l multicolored	.15	.15
341	A53	50 l multicolored	.35	.35
342	A53	1r multicolored	.85	.85
		Set value	1.40	1.40

Issued for International Education Year.

Nos. 299-301 Overprinted in Silver: "Philympia / London 1970"

1970, Sept. 18

343	A46	10 l multicolored	.15	.15
344	A46	1.50r multicolored	.75	.75
345	A46	2.50r multicolored	1.25	1.25
		Nos. 343-345 (3)	2.15	2.15

Issued to commemorate Philympia 1970, London Philatelic Exhibition, Sept. 18-26.
This overprint was also applied to No. 301a. Value $2.25.

Soccer Play, Rimet Cup — A54

Boy Holding UNICEF Flag — A55

Designs: Various Soccer Scenes, and Rimet Cup.

1970 **Litho.** ***Perf. 13½***

346	A54	3 l emerald & multi	.15	.15
347	A54	6 l rose lilac & multi	.15	.15
348	A54	7 l dp orange & multi	.15	.15
349	A54	25 l blue & multi	.15	.15
350	A54	1r olive & multi	.60	.60
		Set value	.90	.90

Jules Rimet 9th World Soccer Championships, Mexico City, May 30-June 21.

1971, Apr. 1 **Litho.** ***Perf. 12***

UNICEF, 25th. Anniv.: 10 l, 2r, Girl holding balloon with UNICEF emblem.

351	A55	5 l pink & multi	.15	.15
352	A55	10 l lt blue & multi	.15	.15
353	A55	1r yellow & multi	.50	.50
354	A55	2r pale lilac & multi	1.00	1.00
		Nos. 351-354 (4)	1.80	1.80

Astronauts Swigert, Lovell and Haise — A56

Flowers Symbolizing Races and World — A57

Safe return of Apollo 13: 20 l, Spacecraft and landing module. 1r, Capsule and boat in Pacific Ocean.

1971, Apr. 27 *Perf. 14*

355	A56	5 l dull purple & multi	.15	.15
356	A56	20 l multicolored	.20	.20
357	A56	1r brt blue & multi	1.00	1.00
		Nos. 355-357 (3)	1.35	1.35

1971, May 3

358	A57	10 l multicolored	.15	.15
359	A57	25 l gray & multi	.15	.15
		Set value	.21	.21

Intl. year against racial discrimination.

Mother and Child, by Auguste Renoir — A58

Mother and Child Paintings by: 7 l, Rembrandt. 10 l, Titian. 20 l, Degas. 25 l, Berthe Morisot. 1r, Rubens. 3r, Renoir.

1971, Sept. Litho. *Perf. 12*

360	A58	5 l multicolored	.15	.15
361	A58	7 l multicolored	.15	.15
362	A58	10 l multicolored	.15	.15
363	A58	20 l multicolored	.15	.15
364	A58	25 l multicolored	.15	.15
365	A58	1r multicolored	.50	.50
366	A58	3r multicolored	1.50	1.50
		Set value	2.40	2.40

Capt. Alan B. Shepard, Jr. — A59

Designs: 10 l, Maj. Stuart A. Roosa. 1.50r, Com. Edgar D. Mitchell. 5r, Apollo 14 shoulder patch.

1971, Nov. 11 Photo. *Perf. 12½*

367	A59	6 l dp green & multi	.15	.15
368	A59	10 l claret & multi	.15	.15
369	A59	1.50r ultra & multi	.90	.90
370	A59	5r multicolored	3.00	3.00
		Nos. 367-370 (4)	4.20	4.20

Apollo 14 US moon landing mission, 1/31-2/9.

Ballerina, by Degas — A60

Paintings: 10 l, Dancing Couple, by Auguste Renoir. 2r, Spanish Dancer, by Edouard Manet. 5r, Ballerinas, by Degas. 10r, Moulin Rouge, by Henri Toulouse-Lautrec.

1971, Nov. 19 Litho. *Perf. 14*

371	A60	5 l plum & multi	.15	.15
372	A60	10 l green & multi	.15	.15
373	A60	2r org brown & multi	1.10	1.10
374	A60	5r dk blue & multi	2.75	2.75
375	A60	10r multicolored	5.50	5.50
		Nos. 371-375 (5)	9.65	9.65

Nos. 371-375 Overprinted Vertically: "ROYAL VISIT 1972"

1972, Mar. 13 Litho. *Perf. 14*

376	A60	5 l plum & multi	.15	.15
377	A60	10 l green & multi	.15	.15
378	A60	2r org brown & multi	1.10	1.10
379	A60	5r dk blue & multi	2.75	2.75
380	A60	10r multicolored	5.50	5.50
		Nos. 376-380 (5)	9.65	9.65

Visit of Elizabeth II and Prince Philip.

Book Year Emblem — A61

1972, May 1 *Perf. 13x13½*

381	A61	25 l orange & multi	.15	.15
382	A61	5r multicolored	2.75	2.75

International Book Year.

National Costume of Scotland A62

National Costumes: 15 l, Netherlands. 25 l, Norway. 50 l, Hungary. 1r, Austria. 2r, Spain.

1972, May 15 *Perf. 12*

383	A62	10 l gray & multi	.15	.15
384	A62	15 l lt brown & multi	.15	.15
385	A62	25 l multicolored	.15	.15
386	A62	50 l lt brown & multi	.25	.25
387	A62	1r gray & multi	.50	.50
388	A62	2r lt olive & multi	1.00	1.00
		Nos. 383-388 (6)	2.20	2.20

Stegosaurus — A63

Designs: Prehistoric reptiles.

1972, May 31 *Perf. 14*

389	A63	2 l shown	.15	.15
390	A63	7 l Edaphosaurus	.15	.15
391	A63	25 l Diplodocus	.15	.15
392	A63	50 l Triceratops	.30	.30
393	A63	2r Pteranodon	1.20	1.20
394	A63	5r Tyrannosaurus	3.00	3.00
		Nos. 389-394 (6)	4.95	4.95

A souvenir sheet has five stamps similar to Nos. 389-394 with simulated perforations. It was not regularly issued.

Sapporo '72 Emblem, Cross Country Skiing — A64

1972, June Litho. *Perf. 14*

395	A64	3 l shown	.15	.15
396	A64	6 l Bobsledding	.15	.15
397	A64	15 l Speed skating	.15	.15
398	A64	50 l Ski jump	.30	.30
399	A64	1r Figure skating	.60	.60
400	A64	2.50r Ice hockey	1.50	1.50
		Nos. 395-400 (6)	2.85	2.85

11th Winter Olympic Games, Sapporo, Japan, Feb. 3-13.

Boy Scout Saluting — A65

Olympic Emblems, Bicycling — A66

Scout: 15 l, with signal flags. 50 l, Bugler. 1r, Drummer.

1972, Aug. 1

401	A65	10 l Prus green & multi	.15	.15
402	A65	15 l dk red & multi	.15	.15
403	A65	50 l dp green & multi	.38	.30
404	A65	1r purple & multi	.80	.62
		Nos. 401-404 (4)	1.48	1.22

13th International Boy Scout Jamboree, Asagiri Plain, Japan, Aug. 2-11, 1971.

1972, Oct. Litho. *Perf. 14½x14*

405	A66	5 l shown	.15	.15
406	A66	10 l Running	.15	.15
407	A66	25 l Wrestling	.15	.15
408	A66	50 l Hurdles, women's	.25	.25
409	A66	2r Boxing	1.00	1.00
410	A66	5r Volleyball	2.50	2.50
		Nos. 405-410 (6)	4.20	4.20

Souvenir Sheet

Perf. 15

411	Sheet of 2	4.00	4.00
a.	A66 3r like 50 l	1.50	1.50
b.	A66 4r like 10 l	1.90	1.90

20th Olympic Games, Munich, Aug. 26-Sept. 11.
For overprints see Nos. 417-419.

Globe, Environment Emblem — A67

1972, Nov. 15 Litho. *Perf. 14½*

412	A67	2 l violet & multi	.15	.15
413	A67	3 l brown & multi	.15	.15
414	A67	15 l blue & multi	.15	.15
415	A67	50 l red & multi	.30	.30
416	A67	2.50r green & multi	1.50	1.50
		Nos. 412-416 (5)	2.25	2.25

UN Conference on Human Environment, Stockholm, June 5-16.

Nos. 409-411 Overprinted in Violet Blue:
a. LEMECHEV / MIDDLE-WEIGHT /GOLD MEDALLIST
b. JAPAN / GOLD MEDAL / WINNER
c. EHRHARDT / 100 METER / HURDLES / GOLD MEDALLIST
d. SHORTER / MARATHON / GOLD MEDALLIST

1973, Feb. Litho. *Perf. 14½x14*

417	A66(a)	2r multicolored	1.00	1.00
418	A66(b)	5r multicolored	2.50	2.50

Souvenir Sheet

419	Sheet of 2	4.00	4.00
a.	A66(c) 3r multicolored	1.50	1.50
b.	A66(d) 4r multicolored	1.90	1.90

Gold medal winners in 20th Olympic Games: Viatschesiav Lemechev, USSR, middleweight boxing; Japanese team, volleyball. Annelie Ehrhardt, Germany, 100m. hurdles; Frank Shorter, US, marathon.

Flowers, by Vincent Van Gogh — A68

Paintings of Flowers by: 2 l, 3 l, 1r, 3r, 5r, Auguste Renoir (each different). 50 l, 5 l, Ambrosius Bosschaert.

1973, Feb. *Perf. 13½*

420	A68	1 l blue & multi	.15	.15
421	A68	2 l tan & multi	.15	.15
422	A68	3 l lilac & multi	.15	.15
423	A68	50 l ultra & multi	.25	.25
424	A68	1r emerald & multi	.50	.50
425	A68	5r magenta & multi	2.50	2.50
		Nos. 420-425 (6)	3.70	3.70

Souvenir Sheet

Perf. 15

426	Sheet of 2	3.25	3.25
a.	A68 2r black & multi	1.25	1.25
b.	A68 3r black & multi	1.75	1.75

Scouts Treating Injured Lamb A69

Designs: 2 l, 1r, Lifesaving. 3 l, 5r, Agricultural training. 4 l, 2r, Carpentry. 5 l, Leapfrog.

1973, Aug. Litho. *Perf. 14½*

427	A69	1 l black & multi	.15	.15
428	A69	2 l black & multi	.15	.15
429	A69	3 l black & multi	.15	.15
430	A69	4 l black & multi	.15	.15
431	A69	5 l black & multi	.15	.15
432	A69	1r black & multi	.50	.50
433	A69	2r black & multi	1.00	1.00
434	A69	3r black & multi	1.50	1.50
		Set value	3.25	3.25

Souvenir Sheet

435	A69	5r black & multi	3.50	3.50

24th Boy Scout World Conference (1st in Africa), Nairobi, Kenya, July 16-21.
For overprints see Nos. 571-574.

Herschel's Marlin A70

Fish and Ships: 2 l, 4r, Skipjack tuna. 3 l, Bluefin tuna. 5 l, 2.50r, Dolphinfish. 60 l, 75 l, Red snapper. 1.50r, Yellow crescent tail. 3r, Plectropoma maculatum. 5r, Like 1 l. 10r, Spanish mackerel.

1973, Aug. *Perf. 14½*

Size: 38½x24mm

436	A70	1 l lt green & multi	.15	.15
437	A70	2 l dull org & multi	.15	.15
438	A70	3 l brt red & multi	.15	.15
439	A70	5 l multicolored	.15	.15

Size: 28x22mm

440	A70	60 l yellow & multi	.38	.38
441	A70	75 l purple & multi	.45	.45

Size: 38½x24mm

442	A70	1.50r violet & multi	.90	.90
443	A70	2.50r blue & multi	1.50	1.50
444	A70	3r multicolored	1.90	1.90
445	A70	10r orange & multi	6.25	6.25
		Nos. 436-445 (10)	11.98	11.98

Souvenir Sheet

Perf. 15

446	Sheet of 2	5.25	5.25
a.	A70 4r carmine & multi	2.00	2.00
b.	A70 5r bright green & multi	3.00	3.00

Nos. 436-445 exist imperf.

Goldenfronted Leafbird — A71

Designs: 2 l, 3r, Fruit bat. 3 l, 50 l, Indian starred tortoise. 4 l, 5r, Kallima inachus (butterfly).

1973, Oct. Litho. *Perf. 14½*

447	A71	1 l	brt pink & multi	.15	.15
448	A71	2 l	brt blue & multi	.15	.15
449	A71	3 l	ver & multi	.15	.15
450	A71	4 l	citron & multi	.15	.15
451	A71	50 l	emerald & multi	.30	.30
452	A71	2r	lt violet & multi	1.20	1.20
453	A71	3r	multicolored	1.75	1.75
			Nos. 447-453 (7)	3.85	3.85

Souvenir Sheet

454	A71	5r	yellow & multi	3.25	3.25

Lantana Camara — A72

Native Flowers: 2 l, Nerium oleander. 3 l, 2r, Rosa polyantha. 4 l, Hibiscus manihot. 5 l, Bougainvillea glabra. 10 l, 3r, Plumera alba. 50 l, Poinsettia pulcherrima. 5r, Ononis natrix.

1973, Dec. 19 Litho. *Perf. 14*

455	A72	1 l	ultra & multi	.15	.15
456	A72	2 l	dp orange & multi	.15	.15
457	A72	3 l	emerald & multi	.15	.15
458	A72	4 l	blue grn & multi	.15	.15
459	A72	5 l	lemon & multi	.15	.15
460	A72	10 l	lilac & multi	.15	.15
461	A72	50 l	yel grn & multi	.20	.20
462	A72	5r	red & multi	2.25	2.25
			Set value	2.70	2.70

Souvenir Sheet

463			Sheet of 2	3.25	3.25
a.	A72 2r lilac & multi			1.10	1.10
b.	A72 3r blue & multi			1.90	1.90

Tiros Weather Satellite A73

Designs: 2 l, 10r, Nimbus satellite. 3 l, 3r, Nomad weather ("weater") station. 4 l, A.P.T. instant weather picture (radar). 5 l, Richard's electrical wind speed recorder. 2r, like 1 l.

1974, Jan. 10 *Perf. 14½*

464	A73	1 l	olive & multi	.15	.15
465	A73	2 l	multicolored	.15	.15
466	A73	3 l	brt blue & multi	.15	.15
467	A73	4 l	ocher & multi	.15	.15
468	A73	5 l	ocher & multi	.15	.15
469	A73	2r	ultra & multi	1.00	1.00
470	A73	3r	orange & multi	1.50	1.50
			Set value	2.70	2.70

Souvenir Sheet

471	A73	10r	lilac & multi	5.50	5.50

World Meteorological Cooperation, cent.

Apollo Spacecraft, John F. Kennedy A74

Designs: 2 l, 3r, Mercury spacecraft and John Glenn. 3 l, Vostok 1 and Yuri Gagarin. 4 l, Vostok 6 and Valentina Tereshkova. 5 l, Soyuz 11 and Salyut spacecrafts. 2r, Skylab. 10r, Like 1 l.

1974, Feb. 1 Litho. *Perf. 14½*

472	A74	1 l	multicolored	.15	.15
473	A74	2 l	multicolored	.15	.15
474	A74	3 l	multicolored	.15	.15
475	A74	4 l	multicolored	.15	.15
476	A74	5 l	multicolored	.15	.15
477	A74	2r	multicolored	1.25	1.25
478	A74	3r	multicolored	1.90	1.90
			Set value	3.35	3.35

Souvenir Sheet

479	A74	10r	multicolored	6.25	6.25

Space explorations of US and USSR.

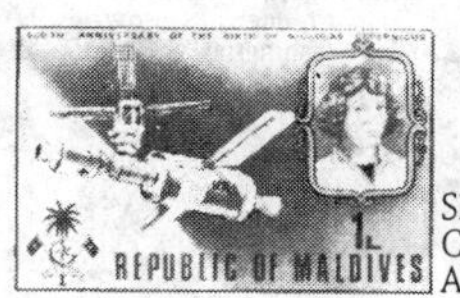

Skylab and Copernicus A75

Copernicus, Various Portraits and: 2 l, 1.50r, Futuristic orbiting station. 3 l, 5r, Futuristic flight station. 4 l, Mariner 2 on flight to Venus. 5 l, Mariner 4 on flight to Mars. 25 l, like 1 l. 10r, Copernicus Orbiting Observatory.

1974, Apr. 10 Litho. *Perf. 14½*

480	A75	1 l	multicolored	.15	.15
481	A75	2 l	multicolored	.15	.15
482	A75	3 l	multicolored	.15	.15
483	A75	4 l	multicolored	.15	.15
484	A75	5 l	multicolored	.15	.15
485	A75	25 l	multicolored	.15	.15
486	A75	1.50r	multicolored	.70	.70
487	A75	5r	multicolored	2.40	2.40
			Set value	3.40	3.40

Souvenir Sheet

488	A75	10r	multicolored	6.25	6.25

500th anniversary of the birth of Nicolaus Copernicus (1473-1543), Polish astronomer.

"Motherhood," by Picasso — A76

Picasso Paintings: 2 l, Harlequin and his Companion. 3 l, Pierrot Sitting. 20 l, 2r, Three Musicians. 75 l, L'Aficionada. 3r, 5r, Still life.

1974, May *Perf. 14*

489	A76	1 l	multicolored	.15	.15
490	A76	2 l	multicolored	.15	.15
491	A76	3 l	multicolored	.15	.15
492	A76	20 l	multicolored	.15	.15
493	A76	75 l	multicolored	.45	.45
494	A76	5r	multicolored	3.00	3.00
			Nos. 489-494 (6)	4.05	4.05

Souvenir Sheet

495			Sheet of 2	4.00	4.00
a.	A76 2r multicolored			1.10	1.10
b.	A76 3r multicolored			1.75	1.75

Pablo Picasso (1881-1973), painter.

UPU Emblem, Old and New Trains A77

UPU Emblem and: 2 l, 2.50r, Old and new ships. 3 l, Zeppelin and jet. 1.50r, Mail coach and truck. 4r, 5r, Like 1 l.

1974, May Litho. *Perf. 14½, 13½*

496	A77	1 l	lt green & multi	.15	.15
497	A77	2 l	yellow & multi	.15	.15
498	A77	3 l	rose & multi	.15	.15
499	A77	1.50r	yel green & multi	1.00	.75
500	A77	2.50r	blue & multi	1.40	1.25
501	A77	5r	ocher & multi	2.75	2.25
			Nos. 496-501 (6)	5.60	4.70

Souvenir Sheet

502	A77	4r	ver & multi	*9.50*	

UPU cent. No. 502 exists imperf.

Nos. 496-501 were printed in sheets of 50, perf. 14½, and also in sheets of 5 plus label, perf. 13½. The label shows UPU emblem, post horn, globe and carrier pigeon.

Capricorn A78

Designs: Zodiac signs and constellations.

1974, July 3

503	A78	1 l	shown	.15	.15
504	A78	2 l	Aquarius	.15	.15
505	A78	3 l	Pisces	.15	.15
506	A78	4 l	Aries	.15	.15
507	A78	5 l	Taurus	.15	.15
508	A78	6 l	Gemini	.15	.15
509	A78	7 l	Cancer	.15	.15
510	A78	10 l	Leo	.15	.15
511	A78	15 l	Virgo	.15	.15
512	A78	20 l	Libra	.15	.15
513	A78	25 l	Scorpio	.15	.15
514	A78	5r	Sagittarius	2.75	1.40
			Set value	3.50	1.80

Souvenir Sheet

515	A78	10r	Sun	5.50	5.50

Stamp size of 10r: 50x37mm.

Soccer and Games' Emblem — A79

Various soccer scenes & games' emblem.

1974, July 31 Litho. *Perf. 14½*

516	A79	1 l	brown & multi	.15	.15
517	A79	2 l	green & multi	.15	.15
518	A79	3 l	ultra & multi	.15	.15
519	A79	4 l	red & multi	.15	.15
520	A79	75 l	lt blue & multi	.35	.35
521	A79	4r	olive & multi	2.00	2.00
522	A79	5r	lilac & multi	2.50	2.50
			Nos. 516-522 (7)	5.45	5.45

Souvenir Sheet

523	A79	10r	rose & multi	5.50	5.50

World Cup Soccer Championship, Munich, June 13-July 7.

Churchill and WWII Plane A80

Churchill: 2 l, As pilot. 3 l, First Lord of the Admiralty and battleship. 4 l, Aircraft carrier. 5 l, RAF fighters. 60 l, Anti-aircraft unit. 75 l, Tank. 5r, Seaplane.

Design: 10r, Like 4 l.

1974, Nov. 30 Litho. *Perf. 14½*

524	A80	1 l	multicolored	.15	.15
525	A80	2 l	multicolored	.15	.15
526	A80	3 l	multicolored	.15	.15
527	A80	4 l	multicolored	.15	.15
528	A80	5 l	multicolored	.15	.15
529	A80	60 l	multicolored	.30	.30
530	A80	75 l	multicolored	.35	.35
531	A80	5r	multicolored	2.50	2.50
			Set value	3.35	3.35

Souvenir Sheet

532	A80	10r	multicolored	5.00	5.00

Sir Winston Churchill (1874-1965).

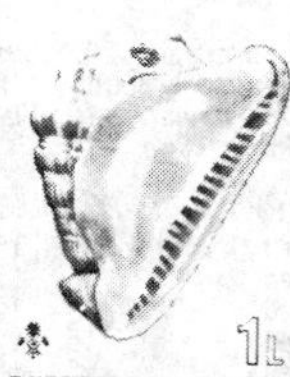

Cassis Nana A81

Cypraea Diliculum A82

1975, Jan. 25 *Perf. 14½, 14 (A82)*

533	A81	1 l	shown	.15	.15
534	A81	2 l	Murex triremus	.15	.15
535	A81	3 l	Harpa major	.15	.15
536	A81	4 l	Lambis chiragra	.15	.15
537	A81	5 l	Conus pennaceus	.15	.15
538	A82	60 l	shown	.30	.30
539	A82	75 l	Clanculus pharaonis	.40	.40
540	A81	5r	Chicoreus ramosus	3.00	3.00
			Nos. 533-540 (8)	4.45	4.45

Souvenir Sheet

Perf. 13½

541			Sheet of 2	2.75	2.75
a.	A81 2r like 3 l			.80	.80
b.	A81 3r like 2 l			1.20	1.20

Sea shells, including cowries.

Republic of Maldives Throne — A83

Eid-Miskith Mosque A84

Designs: 10 l, Ornamental candlesticks (dullisa). 25 l, Tree-shaped lamp. 60 l, Royal umbrellas. 3r, Tomb of Al-Hafiz Abu-al Barakath al-Barubari.

1975, Feb. 22 Litho. *Perf. 14*

542	A83	1 l	multicolored	.15	.15
543	A83	10 l	multicolored	.15	.15
544	A83	25 l	multicolored	.15	.15
545	A83	60 l	multicolored	.30	.30
546	A84	75 l	multicolored	.40	.40
547	A84	3r	multicolored	1.60	1.60
			Nos. 542-547 (6)	2.75	2.75

Historic relics and monuments.

Republic of Maldives Tropical Fruit — A85

1975, Mar. Litho. *Perf. 14½*

548	A85	2 l	Guava	.15	.15
549	A85	4 l	Maldive mulberry	.15	.15
550	A85	5 l	Mountain apples	.15	.15
551	A85	10 l	Bananas	.15	.15
552	A85	20 l	Mangoes	.15	.15
553	A85	50 l	Papaya	.28	.28
554	A85	1r	Pomegranates	.52	.52
555	A85	5r	Coconut	2.75	2.75
			Nos. 548-555 (8)	4.30	4.30

Souvenir Sheet

Perf. 13½

556			Sheet of 2	3.50	3.50
a.	A85 2r like 10 l			1.25	1.25
b.	A85 3r like 2 l			1.75	1.75

Phyllangia — A86

Designs: Corals, sea urchins and starfish.

1975, June 6 Litho. *Perf. 14½*

557	A86	1 l	shown	.15	.15
558	A86	2 l	Madrepora oculata	.15	.15
559	A86	3 l	Acropora gravida	.15	.15
560	A86	4 l	Stylotella	.15	.15
561	A86	5 l	Acropora cervicornis	.15	.15
562	A86	60 l	Strongylocentrotus pupuratus	.30	.30
563	A86	75 l	Pisaster ochraceus	.40	.40
564	A86	5r	Marthasterias glacialis	2.50	2.50

		Set value	3.40	3.40

Souvenir Sheet

Imperf

565	A86	4r shown	3.25	3.25

"10," Clock Tower and Customs House A87

"10" and: 5 l, Government offices. 7 l, North Eastern waterfront, Male. 15 l, Mosque and Minaret. 10r, Sultan Park and Museum.

1975, July 26 Litho. *Perf. 14½*

566	A87	4 l salmon & multi	.15	.15
567	A87	5 l lt blue & multi	.15	.15
568	A87	7 l bister & multi	.15	.15
569	A87	15 l lilac & multi	.15	.15
570	A87	10r lt green & multi	6.00	6.00
		Nos. 566-570 (5)	6.60	6.60

10th anniversary of independence.

Nos. 432-435 Overprinted: "14th Boy Scout Jamboree / July 29-Aug. 7, 1975"

1975, July 26 Litho. *Perf. 14½*

571	A69	1r multicolored	.50	.50
572	A69	2r multicolored	1.20	1.20
573	A69	3r multicolored	1.80	1.80
		Nos. 571-573 (3)	3.50	3.50

Souvenir Sheet

574	A69	5r multicolored	3.00	3.00

Nordjamb 75, 14th World Boy Scout Jamboree, Lillehammer, Norway, July 29-Aug. 7.

Madura-Prau Bedang A88

Sailing ships, except 5r: 2 l, Ganges patile. 3 l, Indian palla, vert. 4 l, "Odhi," vert. 5 l, Maldivian schooner. 25 l, Cutty Sark. 1r, 10r, Maldivian baggala, vert. 5r, Freighter Maldive Courage.

1975, July 26 *Perf. 14½*

575	A88	1 l multicolored	.15	.15
576	A88	2 l multicolored	.15	.15
577	A88	3 l multicolored	.15	.15
578	A88	4 l multicolored	.15	.15
579	A88	5 l multicolored	.15	.15
580	A88	25 l multicolored	.15	.15
581	A88	1r multicolored	.60	.60
582	A88	5r multicolored	3.00	3.00
		Nos. 575-582 (8)	4.50	4.50

Souvenir Sheet

Perf. 13½

583	A88	10r multicolored	6.00	6.00

Brahmaea Wallichii A89

Designs: Butterflies.

1975, Sept. 7 Litho. *Perf. 14½*

584	A89	1 l shown	.15	.15
585	A89	2 l Teinopalpus imperialis	.15	.15
586	A89	3 l Cethosia biblis	.15	.15
587	A89	4 l Hestia jasonia	.15	.15
588	A89	5 l Apatura	.15	.15
589	A89	25 l Kallima horsfieldi	.16	.15
590	A89	1.50r Hebomoia leucippe	1.25	.70
591	A89	5r Papilio memnon	3.00	2.50
		Nos. 584-591 (8)	5.16	4.10

Souvenir Sheet

Perf. 13½

592	A89	10r like 25 l	6.25	6.25

Dying Slave by Michelangelo A90

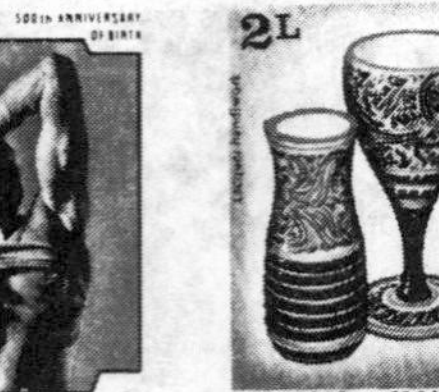

Cup and Vase A91

Works by Michelangelo: 2 l, 4 l, 1r, 5r, paintings from Sistine Chapel. 3 l, Apollo. 5 l, Bacchus. 2r, 10r, David.

1975, Oct. 9 Litho. *Perf. 14½*

593	A90	1 l blue & multi	.15	.15
594	A90	2 l multicolored	.15	.15
595	A90	3 l red & multi	.15	.15
596	A90	4 l multicolored	.15	.15
597	A90	5 l emerald & multi	.15	.15
598	A90	1r multicolored	.60	.60
599	A90	2r red & multi	1.25	1.25
600	A90	5r multicolored	3.25	3.25
		Nos. 593-600 (8)	5.85	5.85

Souvenir Sheet

Perf. 13½

601	A90	10r multicolored	6.00	6.00

Michelangelo Buonarotti (1475-1564), Italian sculptor, painter and architect.

1975, Dec. Litho. *Perf. 14*

Designs: 4 l, Boxes. 50 l, Vase with lid. 75 l, Bowls with covers. 1r, Worker finishing vases.

602	A91	2 l ultra & multi	.15	.15
603	A91	4 l rose & multi	.15	.15
604	A91	50 l multicolored	.30	.30
605	A91	75 l blue & multi	.45	.45
606	A91	1r multicolored	.55	.55
		Set value	1.40	1.40

Maldivian lacquer ware.

Map of Islands and Atolls A92

Designs: 5 l, Yacht at anchor. 7 l, Sailboats. 15 l, Deep-sea divers and corals. 3r, Hulule Airport. 10r, Cruising yachts.

1975, Dec. 25 Litho. *Perf. 14*

607	A92	4 l multicolored	.15	.15
608	A92	5 l multicolored	.15	.15
609	A92	7 l multicolored	.15	.15
610	A92	15 l multicolored	.15	.15
611	A92	3r multicolored	1.75	1.75
612	A92	10r multicolored	5.50	5.50
		Nos. 607-612 (6)	7.85	7.85

Tourist publicity.

Cross-country Skiing — A93

Gen. Burgoyne, by Joshua Reynolds — A94

Winter Olympic Games' Emblem and: 2 l, Speed skating. 3 l, Figure skating, pair. 4 l, Bobsled. 5 l, Ski jump. 25 l, Figure skating, woman. 1.15r, Slalom. 4r, Ice hockey. 10r, Skiing.

1976, Jan. 10 Litho. *Perf. 14½*

613	A93	1 l multicolored	.15	.15
614	A93	2 l multicolored	.15	.15
615	A93	3 l multicolored	.15	.15
616	A93	4 l multicolored	.15	.15
617	A93	5 l multicolored	.15	.15
618	A93	25 l multicolored	.15	.15
619	A93	1.15r multicolored	.65	.65
620	A93	4r multicolored	2.25	2.25
		Set value	3.20	3.20

Souvenir Sheet

Perf. 13½

621	A93	10r multicolored	6.25	6.25

12th Winter Olympic Games, Innsbruck, Austria, Feb. 4-15.

1976, Feb. 15 *Perf. 14½*

Paintings: 2 l, John Hancock, by John S. Copley. 3 l, Death of Gen. Montgomery, by John Trumbull, horiz. 4 l, Paul Revere, by Copley. 5 l, Battle of Bunker Hill, by Trumbull, horiz. 2r, Crossing of the Delaware, by Thomas Sully, horiz. 3r, Samuel Adams, by Copley. 5r, Surrender of Cornwallis, by Trumbull, horiz. 10r, Washington at Dorchester Heights, by Gilbert Stuart.

622	A94	1 l multicolored	.15	.15
623	A94	2 l multicolored	.15	.15
624	A94	3 l multicolored	.15	.15
625	A94	4 l multicolored	.15	.15
626	A94	5 l multicolored	.15	.15
627	A94	2r multicolored	1.25	1.25
628	A94	3r multicolored	1.75	1.75
629	A94	5r multicolored	3.00	3.00
		Nos. 622-629 (8)	6.75	6.75

Souvenir Sheet

Perf. 13½

630	A94	10r multicolored	6.25	6.25

American Bicentennial.

For overprints see Nos. 639-642.

Thomas Alva Edison A95

Designs: 2 l, Alexander Graham Bell and his telephone. 3 l, Telephones of 1919, 1937 and 1972. 10 l, Cable tunnel. 20 l, Equalizer circuit assembly. 1r, Ships laying underwater cable. 4r, Telephones of 1876, 1890 and 1879 Edison telephone. 10r, Intelsat IV-A over earth station.

1976, Mar. 10 Litho. *Perf. 14½*

631	A95	1 l multicolored	.15	.15
632	A95	2 l multicolored	.15	.15
633	A95	3 l multicolored	.15	.15
634	A95	10 l multicolored	.15	.15
635	A95	20 l multicolored	.15	.15
636	A95	1r multicolored	.60	.60
637	A95	10r multicolored	6.00	6.00
		Nos. 631-637 (7)	7.35	7.35

Souvenir Sheet

Perf. 13½

638	A95	4r multicolored	2.50	2.50

Centenary of first telephone call by Alexander Graham Bell, Mar. 10, 1876.

Nos. 627-630 Overprinted in Silver or Black: MAY 29TH-JUNE 6TH "INTERPHIL" 1976

1976, May 29 Litho. *Perf. 14½*

639	A94	2r multicolored (S)	1.20	1.20
640	A94	3r multicolored (S)	1.80	1.80
641	A94	5r multicolored (B)	3.00	3.00
		Nos. 639-641 (3)	6.00	6.00

Souvenir Sheet

Perf. 13½

642	A94	10r multicolored (S)	6.25	6.25

Interphil 76 Intl. Philatelic Exhibition, Philadelphia, Pa., May 29-June 6. Overprint on 3r and 10r vertical. Same overprint in one horizontal silver line in margin of No. 642.

Wrestling — A96

Bonavist Beans — A97

Olympic Rings and: 2 l, Shot put. 3 l, Hurdles. 4 l, Hockey. 5 l, Women running. 6 l, Javelin. 1.50r, Discus. 5r, Team handball. 10r, Hammer throw.

1976, June 1 *Perf. 14½*

643	A96	1 l multicolored	.15	.15
644	A96	2 l multicolored	.15	.15
645	A96	3 l salmon & multi	.15	.15
646	A96	4 l multicolored	.15	.15
647	A96	5 l pink & multi	.15	.15
648	A96	6 l multicolored	.15	.15
649	A96	1.50r bister & multi	.90	.90
650	A96	5r lilac & multi	3.00	3.00
		Nos. 643-650 (8)	4.80	4.80

Souvenir Sheet

Perf. 13½

651	A96	10r lemon & multi	6.25	6.25

21st Olympic Games, Montreal, Canada, July 17-Aug. 1.

1976-77 Litho. *Perf. 14*

Designs: 4 l, 20 l, Beans. 10 l, Eggplant. 50 l, Cucumber. 75 l, 2r, Snake gourd. 1r, Balsam pear.

652	A97	2 l green & multi	.15	.15
653	A97	4 l lt blue & multi	.15	.15
654	A97	10 l ocher & multi	.15	.15
655	A97	20 l blue & multi ('77)	.15	.15
656	A97	50 l multicolored	.25	.25
657	A97	75 l bister & multi	.32	.32
658	A97	1r lilac & multi	.45	.45
659	A97	2r bis & multi ('77)	.90	.90
		Set value	2.15	2.15

1976 stamps issued July 26.

Viking I and Mars A98

Design: 20r, Landing craft on Mars.

1976, Dec. 2 Litho. *Perf. 14*

660	A98	5r multicolored	3.00	3.00

Souvenir Sheet

661	A98	20r multicolored	12.00	12.00

Viking I US Mars Mission.

Coronation Ceremony — A99

Designs: 2 l, Elizabeth II and Prince Philip. 3 l, Queen, Prince Philip, Princes Edward and Andrew. 1.15r, Queen in procession. 3r, State coach. 4r, Queen, Prince Philip, Princess Anne and Prince Charles. 10r, Queen and Prince Charles.

1977, Feb. 6 *Perf. 14x13½, 12*

662	A99	1 l multicolored	.15	.15
663	A99	2 l multicolored	.15	.15
664	A99	3 l multicolored	.15	.15
665	A99	1.15r multicolored	.80	.80
666	A99	3r multicolored	1.40	1.40
667	A99	4r multicolored	2.00	2.00
		Nos. 662-667 (6)	4.65	4.65

Souvenir Sheet

668	A99	10r multicolored	5.00	5.00

25th anniv. of the reign of Elizabeth II.

Nos. 662-667 were printed in sheets of 40 (4x10), perf. 14x13½, and sheets of 5 plus label, perf. 12, in changed colors.

Beethoven in Bonn, 1785 A100

Designs: 2 l, Moonlight Sonata and portrait, 1801. 3 l, Goethe and Beethoven, Teplitz, 1811. 4 l, Beethoven, 1815, and his string instruments. 5 l, Beethoven House, Heiligenstadt, 1817. 25 l, Composer's hands, gold medal. 2r, Missa Solemnis, portrait, 1823. 4r, Piano, room where Beethoven died, death mask. 5r, Portrait, 1825, hearing aids.

1977, Mar. 26 Litho. *Perf. 14*

669	A100	1 l multicolored	.15	.15
670	A100	2 l multicolored	.15	.15
671	A100	3 l multicolored	.15	.15
672	A100	4 l multicolored	.15	.15
673	A100	5 l multicolored	.15	.15

674 A100 25 l multicolored .15 .15
675 A100 2r multicolored 1.10 1.10
676 A100 5r multicolored 2.75 2.75
Set value 4.10 4.10

Souvenir Sheet

677 A100 4r multicolored 2.10 2.10

Ludwig van Beethoven (1770-1827), composer, 150th death anniversary.

Electronic Tree and ITU Emblem A101

Designs: 90 l, Central Telegraph Office, Maldives. 5r, Intelsat IV over map. 10r, Parabolic antenna, satellite communications earth station.

1977, May 17 Litho. *Perf. 14*

678 A101 10 l multicolored .15 .15
679 A101 90 l multicolored .45 .45
680 A101 10r multicolored 5.50 5.50
Nos. 678-680 (3) 6.10 6.10

Souvenir Sheet

681 A101 5r multicolored 2.50 2.50

Inauguration of Satellite Earth Station and for World Telecommunications Day.

Portrait by Gainsborough A102

Lesser Frigate Birds A103

Paintings: 2 l, 5 l, 10r, Rubens. 3 l, 95 l, 5r, Titian. 4 l, 1r, Gainsborough.

1977, May 20

682 A102 1 l multicolored .15 .15
683 A102 2 l multicolored .15 .15
684 A102 3 l multicolored .15 .15
685 A102 4 l multicolored .15 .15
686 A102 5 l multicolored .15 .15
687 A102 95 l multicolored .45 .45
688 A102 1r multicolored .50 .50
689 A102 10r multicolored 5.00 5.00
Nos. 682-689 (8) 6.70 6.70

Souvenir Sheet

690 A102 5r multicolored 2.50 2.50

Birth annivs. of Thomas Gainsborough; Peter Paul Rubens; Titian.

1977, July 26 Litho. *Perf. 14½*

Birds: 2 l, Crab plovers. 3 l, Long-tailed tropic bird. 4 l, Wedge-tailed shearwater. 5 l, Gray heron. 20 l, White tern. 95 l, Cattle egret. 1.25r, Blacknaped terns. 5r, Pheasant coucals. 10r, Striated herons.

691 A103 1 l multicolored .15 .15
692 A103 2 l multicolored .15 .15
693 A103 3 l multicolored .15 .15
694 A103 4 l multicolored .15 .15
695 A103 5 l multicolored .15 .15
696 A103 20 l multicolored .15 .15
697 A103 95 l multicolored .62 .50
698 A103 1.25r multicolored .90 .62
699 A103 5r multicolored 3.75 2.50
Nos. 691-699 (9) 6.17 4.52

Souvenir Sheet

700 A103 10r multicolored 5.00 5.00

Charles A. Lindbergh — A104

Designs: 2 l, Lindbergh and Spirit of St. Louis. 3 l, Mohawk plane, horiz. 4 l, Lebaudy I airship, 1902, horiz. 5 l, Count Ferdinand von Zeppelin, and Zeppelin in Pernambuco. 1r, Los Angeles, U. S. Navy airship, 1924, horiz. 3r, Henry Ford and Lindbergh, 1942. 5r, Spirit of St. Louis, Statue of Liberty and Eiffel Tower, horiz. 7.50r, German naval airship over battleship, horiz. 10r, Vickers airship, 1917.

Perf. 13x13½, 13½x13

1977, Oct. 31 Litho.

701 A104 1 l multicolored .15 .15
702 A104 2 l multicolored .15 .15
703 A104 3 l multicolored .15 .15
704 A104 4 l multicolored .15 .15
705 A104 5 l multicolored .15 .15
706 A104 1r multicolored .48 .48
707 A104 3r multicolored 1.50 1.50
708 A104 10r multicolored 4.75 4.75
Nos. 701-708 (8) 7.48 7.48

Souvenir Sheet

709 Sheet of 2 6.75 6.75
a. A104 5r multicolored 2.50 2.50
b. A104 7.50r multicolored 3.75 3.75

Charles A. Lindbergh's solo transatlantic flight from New York to Paris, 50th anniv., and 75th anniv. of first navigable airship.

Boat Building A105

Maldivian Occupations: 15 l, High sea fishing. 20 l, Cadjan weaving. 90 l, Mat weaving. 2r, Lacemaking, vert.

1977, Dec. 12

710 A105 6 l multicolored .15 .15
711 A105 15 l multicolored .15 .15
712 A105 20 l multicolored .15 .15
713 A105 90 l multicolored .45 .45
714 A105 2r multicolored 1.00 1.00
Set value 1.65 1.65

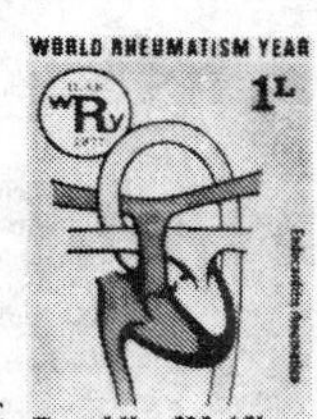

Rheumatic Heart — A106

X-Ray Pictures: 50 l, Shoulder. 2r, Hand. 3r, Knee.

1978, Feb. 9 *Perf. 14*

715 A106 1 l multicolored .15 .15
716 A106 50 l multicolored .30 .30
717 A106 2r multicolored 1.25 1.25
718 A106 3r multicolored 1.75 1.75
Nos. 715-718 (4) 3.45 3.45

World Rheumatism Year.

Otto Lilienthal's Glider, 1890 A107

Designs: 2 l, Chanute's glider, 1896. 3 l, Wright brothers testing glider, 1900. 4 l, A. V. Roe's plane with paper-covered wings, 1908. 5 l, Wilbur Wright showing his plane to King Alfonso of Spain, 1909. 10 l, Roe's second biplane. 20 l, Alexander Graham Bell and Wright brothers in Washington D.C., 1910. 95 l, Clifton Hadley's triplane, 1910. 5r, British B.E.2 planes, Upavon Field, 1914. 10r, Wilbur Wright flying first motorized plane, 1903.

1978, Feb. 27 Litho. *Perf. 13x13½*

719 A107 1 l multicolored .15 .15
720 A107 2 l multicolored .15 .15
721 A107 3 l multicolored .15 .15
722 A107 4 l multicolored .15 .15
723 A107 5 l multicolored .15 .15
724 A107 10 l multicolored .15 .15
725 A107 20 l multicolored .15 .15
726 A107 95 l multicolored .45 .45
727 A107 5r multicolored 2.50 2.50
Set value 3.25 3.25

Souvenir Sheet

Perf. 14

728 A107 10r multicolored 4.50 4.50

75th anniversary of first motorized airplane.

Edward Jenner, Vaccination Discoverer — A108

TV with Maldives Broadcasting Symbol — A109

Designs: 15 l, Foundling Hospital, London, where children were first inoculated, 1743, horiz. 50 l, Newgate Prison, London, where first experiments were carried out, 1721.

1978, Mar. 15 *Perf. 14*

729 A108 15 l multicolored .15 .15
730 A108 50 l multicolored .20 .20
731 A108 2r multicolored .80 .80
Nos. 729-731 (3) 1.15 1.15

World eradication of smallpox.

1978, Mar. 29

Designs: 25 l, Circuit pattern. 1.50r, Station control panel, horiz.

732 A109 15 l multicolored .15 .15
733 A109 25 l multicolored .16 .16
734 A109 1.50r multicolored 1.00 1.00
Nos. 732-734 (3) 1.31 1.31

Inauguration of Maldive Islands television.

Sailing Ship — A110

The Ampulla — A111

Ships: 1 l, Phoenician. 2 l, Two-master. 5 l, Freighter Maldive Trader. 1r, Trading schooner. 1.25r, 4r, Sailing boat. 3r, Barque Bangala. (1 l, 2 l, 5 l, 1.25r, 4r, horiz.)

1978, Apr. 27 Litho. *Perf. 14½*

735 A110 1 l multicolored .15 .15
736 A110 2 l multicolored .15 .15
737 A110 3 l multicolored .15 .15
738 A110 5 l multicolored .15 .15
739 A110 1r multicolored .40 .40
740 A110 1.25r multicolored .50 .50
741 A110 3r multicolored 1.20 1.20
742 A110 4r multicolored 1.60 1.60
a. Souvenir sheet of 2 2.20 2.20
Nos. 735-742 (8) 4.30 4.30

No. 742a contains No. 742 and a 1r stamp in the design of No. 736.

1978, May 15 *Perf. 14*

Designs: 2 l, Scepter with dove. 3 l, Orb with cross. 1.15r, St. Edward's crown. 2r, Scepter with cross. 5r, Queen Elizabeth II. 10r, Anointing spoon.

743 A111 1 l multicolored .15 .15
744 A111 2 l multicolored .15 .15
745 A111 3 l multicolored .15 .15
746 A111 1.15r multicolored .55 .55
747 A111 2r multicolored 1.00 1.00
748 A111 5r multicolored 2.50 2.50
Nos. 743-748 (6) 4.50 4.50

Souvenir Sheet

749 A111 10r multicolored 4.75 4.75

Coronation of Elizabeth II, 25th anniv.

#743-748 were printed in sheets of 40 and in sheets of 3 + label, in changed colors. Labels show coronation regalia.

Capt. James Cook — A112 1L

Designs: 2 l, Kamehameha I statue, Honolulu. 3 l, "Endeavour" and boat. 25 l, Capt. Cook and route of his 3rd voyage. 75 l, "Discovery" and "Resolution," map of Hawaiian Islands, horiz. 1.50r, Capt. Cook's first meeting with Hawaiians, horiz. 5r, "Endeavour." 10r, Capt. Cook's death, horiz.

1978, July 15 Litho. *Perf. 14½*

750 A112 1 l multicolored .15 .15
751 A112 2 l multicolored .15 .15
752 A112 3 l multicolored .15 .15
753 A112 25 l multicolored .15 .15
754 A112 75 l multicolored .35 .35
755 A112 1.50r multicolored .75 .75
756 A112 10r multicolored 4.75 4.75
Nos. 750-756 (7) 6.45 6.45

Souvenir Sheet

757 A112 5r multicolored 2.25 2.25

Schizophrys Aspera — A113

Maldivian Crabs and Lobster: 2 l, Atergatis floridus. 3 l, Percnon planissimum. 90 l, Portunus granulatus. 1r, Carpilius maculatus. No. 763, Huenia proteus. No. 765, Panulirus longipes, vert. 25r, Etisus laevimanus.

1978, Aug. 30 Litho. *Perf. 14*

758 A113 1 l multicolored .15 .15
759 A113 2 l multicolored .15 .15
760 A113 3 l multicolored .15 .15
761 A113 90 l multicolored .48 .48
762 A113 1r multicolored .55 .55
763 A113 2r multicolored 1.10 1.10
764 A113 25r multicolored 12.50 12.50
Nos. 758-764 (7) 15.08 15.08

Souvenir Sheet

765 A113 2r multicolored 1.00 1.00

Four Apostles, by Dürer — A114

Paintings by Albrecht Dürer (1471-1528): 20 l, Self-portrait, age 27. 55 l, Virgin and Child with Pear. 1r, Rhinoceros, horiz. 1.80r, Hare. 3r, The Great Piece of Turf. 10r, Columbine.

1978, Oct. 28 Litho. *Perf. 14*

766 A114 10 l multicolored .15 .15
767 A114 20 l multicolored .15 .15
768 A114 55 l multicolored .30 .30
769 A114 1r multicolored .52 .52
770 A114 1.80r multicolored 1.00 1.00
771 A114 3r multicolored 1.60 1.60
Nos. 766-771 (6) 3.72 3.72

Souvenir Sheet

772 A114 10r multicolored 4.75 4.75

Palms and Fishing Boat A115

Designs: 5 l, Montessori School. 10 l, TV tower and ITU emblem, vert. 25 l, Island with beach. 50 l, Boeing 737 over island. 95 l, Walk along the beach. 1.25r, Fishing boat at dawn. 2r, Presidential residence. 3r, Fishermen preparing nets. 5r, Afeefuddin Mosque.

1978, Nov. 11 Litho. *Perf. 14½*

773 A115	1 l multicolored	.15	.15
774 A115	5 l multicolored	.15	.15
775 A115	10 l multicolored	.15	.15
776 A115	25 l multicolored	.15	.15
777 A115	50 l multicolored	.25	.25
778 A115	95 l multicolored	.45	.45
779 A115	1.25r multicolored	.62	.62
780 A115	2r multicolored	1.00	1.00
781 A115	5r multicolored	2.50	2.50
	Nos. 773-781 (9)	5.42	5.42

Souvenir Sheet

782 A115 3r multicolored 1.75 1.75

10th anniversary of Republic.

Human Rights Emblem A116

1978, Dec. 10 *Perf. 14*

783 A116	30 l multicolored	.15	.15
784 A116	90 l multicolored	.45	.45
785 A116	1.80r multicolored	.90	.90
	Nos. 783-785 (3)	1.50	1.50

Universal Declaration of Human Rights, 30th anniversary.

Rare Spotted Cowrie — A117

Bellman Delivering Mail — A118

Sea Shells: 2 l, Imperial cone. 3 l, Green turban. 10 l, Giant spider conch. 1r, Leucodon cowrie. 1.80r, Fig cone. 3r, Glory of the sea. 5r, Top vase.

1979, Jan. Litho. *Perf. 14*

786 A117	1 l multicolored	.15	.15
787 A117	2 l multicolored	.15	.15
788 A117	3 l multicolored	.15	.15
789 A117	10 l multicolored	.15	.15
790 A117	1r multicolored	.48	.48
791 A117	1.80r multicolored	.90	.90
792 A117	3r multicolored	1.40	1.40
	Nos. 786-792 (7)	3.38	3.38

Souvenir Sheet

793 A117 5r multicolored 3.00 3.00

1979, Feb. 28 Litho. *Perf. 14*

Designs: 2 l, Royal mail coach, 1840, horiz. 3 l, First London letter box, 1855. 1.55r, Great Britain No. 1 and post horn. 5r, Maldive Islands No. 5 and carrier pigeon. 10r, Rowland Hill.

794 A118	1 l multicolored	.15	.15
795 A118	2 l multicolored	.15	.15
796 A118	3 l multicolored	.15	.15
797 A118	1.55r multicolored	.65	.60
798 A118	5r multicolored	2.00	2.00
	Nos. 794-798 (5)	3.10	3.05

Souvenir Sheet

799 A118 10r multicolored 4.75 4.75

Sir Rowland Hill (1795-1879), originator of penny postage.

For overprints see Nos. 853-855.

Girl with Teddy Bear — A119

IYC Emblem, Boy and: 1.25r, Model boat. 2r, Rocket launcher. 3r, Blimp. 5r, Train.

1979, May 10 Litho. *Perf. 14*

800 A119	5 l multicolored	.15	.15
801 A119	1.25r multicolored	.62	.62
802 A119	2r multicolored	1.00	1.00
803 A119	3r multicolored	1.50	1.50
	Nos. 800-803 (4)	3.27	3.27

Souvenir Sheet

804 A119 5r multicolored 2.50 2.50

International Year of the Child.

White Feathers, by Matisse A120

Paintings by Henri Matisse (1869-1954): 25 l, Joy of Life. 30 l, Eggplants. 1.50r, Harmony in Red. 4r, Water Pitcher. 5r, Still-life.

1979, Aug. 20 Litho. *Perf. 14*

805 A120	20 l multicolored	.15	.15
806 A120	25 l multicolored	.15	.15
807 A120	30 l multicolored	.15	.15
808 A120	1.50r multicolored	.75	.75
809 A120	5r multicolored	2.50	2.50
	Nos. 805-809 (5)	3.70	3.70

Souvenir Sheet

810 A120 4r multicolored 2.25 2.25

Sari and Mosque — A121

Gloriosa Superba — A122

National Costumes: 75 l, Sashed apron dress. Male Harbor. 90 l, Serape with necklace, radar station. 95 l, Flowered dress, mosque and minaret.

1979, Aug. 22 Litho. *Perf. 14*

811 A121	50 l multicolored	.25	.25
812 A121	75 l multicolored	.38	.38
813 A121	90 l multicolored	.45	.45
814 A121	95 l multicolored	.48	.48
	Nos. 811-814 (4)	1.56	1.56

1979, Oct. 29 Litho. *Perf. 14*

815 A122	1 l shown	.15	.15
816 A122	3 l Hibiscus	.15	.15
817 A122	50 l Barringtonia asiatica	.25	.25
818 A122	1r Abutilon indicum	.50	.50
819 A122	5r Guettarda speciosa	2.50	2.50
	Nos. 815-819 (5)	3.55	3.55

Souvenir Sheet

820 A122 4r Pandanus odoratissimus 2.00 2.00

Maldive wildflowers.

Handicraft Exhibition A123

1979, Nov. 11

821 A123	5 l shown	.15	.15
822 A123	10 l Jar and cup	.15	.15
823 A123	1.30r Tortoise-shell jewelry	.65	.65
824 A123	2r Wooden boxes	1.00	1.00
	Nos. 821-824 (4)	1.95	1.95

Souvenir Sheet

825 A123 5r Bracelets, necklace 2.25 2.25

Postal Scenes A123a

1 l, Goofy delivering package. 2 l, Mickey at mailbox. 3 l, Goofy buried in letters. 4 l, Minnie Mouse, Pluto. 5 l, Mickey Mouse on skates. 10 l, Donald Duck at mailbox. 15 l, Chip and Dale carrying letter. 1.50r, Donald Duck on unicycle. 4r, Pluto at mailbox. 5r, Donald Duck wheeling crate.

1979, Dec. Litho. *Perf. 11*

826 A123a	1 l multicolored	.15	.15
827 A123a	2 l multicolored	.15	.15
828 A123a	3 l multicolored	.15	.15
829 A123a	4 l multicolored	.15	.15
830 A123a	5 l multicolored	.15	.15
831 A123a	10 l multicolored	.15	.15
832 A123a	15 l multicolored	.15	.15
833 A123a	1.50r multicolored	.90	.90
834 A123a	5r multicolored	3.00	3.00
	Set value	4.25	4.25

Souvenir Sheet

Imperf

835 A123a 4r multicolored 14.00 14.00

Post Ramadan Dancing A124

Designs: 15 l, Festival of Eeduu. 95 l, Sultan's ceremonial band. 2r, Music festival.

1980, Jan. 19 Litho. *Perf. 14*

836 A124	5 l multicolored	.15	.15
837 A124	15 l multicolored	.15	.15
838 A124	95 l multicolored	.48	.48
839 A124	2r multicolored	1.00	1.00
	Nos. 836-839 (4)	1.78	1.78

Souvenir Sheet

840 A124 5r multicolored 3.00 3.00

National Day.

Leatherback Turtle — A125

1980, Feb. 17 Litho. *Perf. 14*

841 A125	1 l shown	.15	.15
842 A125	2 l Flatback turtle	.15	.15
843 A125	5 l Hawksbill turtle	.15	.15
844 A125	10 l Loggerhead turtle	.15	.15
845 A125	75 l Olive ridley	.40	.40
846 A125	10r Atlantic ridley	5.00	5.00
	Nos. 841-846 (6)	6.00	6.00

Souvenir Sheet

847 A125 4r Green turtle 2.00 2.00

Paul Harris in Rotary Emblem — A126

1980, Mar. Litho. *Perf. 14*

848 A126	75 l shown	.38	.38
849 A126	90 l Family	.45	.45
850 A126	1r Grain	.50	.50
851 A126	10r Caduceus	5.00	5.00
	Nos. 848-851 (4)	6.33	6.33

Souvenir Sheet

852 A126 5r Anniversary emblem 2.50 2.50

Rotary International, 75th anniversary.

Nos. 797-799 Overprinted "LONDON 1980"

1980, May 6 Litho. *Perf. 14*

853 A118	1.55r multicolored	.78	.78
854 A118	5r multicolored	2.50	2.50

Souvenir Sheet

855 A118 10r multicolored 5.00 5.00

London 1980 International Stamp Exhibition, May 6-14. Sheet margin overprinted "Earls Court—London 6-14 May 1980."

Swimming, Moscow '80 Emblem A127

1980, June 4 Litho. *Perf. 14*

856 A127	10 l shown	.15	.15
857 A127	50 l Sprinting	.25	.25
858 A127	3r Shot put	1.50	1.50
859 A127	4r High jump	2.00	2.00
	Nos. 856-859 (4)	3.90	3.90

Souvenir Sheet

860 A127 5r Weight lifting 2.50 2.50

22nd Summer Olympic Games, Moscow, July 19-Aug. 3.

White-tailed Tropic Bird A128

1980, July 10 Litho. *Perf. 14*

861 A128	75 l shown	.38	.38
862 A128	95 l Sooty tern	.48	.48
863 A128	1r Brown noddy	.50	.50
864 A128	1.55r Eurasian curlew	.78	.78
865 A128	2r Wilson's petrel	1.00	1.00
866 A128	4r Caspian tern	2.00	2.00
	Nos. 861-866 (6)	5.14	5.14

Souvenir Sheet

867 A128 5r Red-footed & brown boobies 2.50 2.50

Seal of Sultan Ibrahim II (1720-1750) A129

Sultans' Seals: 2 l, Mohamed Imadudeen II (1704-1720). 5 l, Mohamed Bin Haji Ali (1692-1701). 1r, Kuda Mohamed Rasgefaanu (1687-1691). 2r, Ibrahim Iskander I (1648-1687). 3r, Ibrahim Iskander, second seal.

1980, July 26

868 A129	1 l violet brn & blk	.15	.15
869 A129	2 l violet brn & blk	.15	.15
870 A129	5 l violet brn & blk	.15	.15
871 A129	1r violet brn & blk	.50	.50
872 A129	2r violet brn & blk	1.00	1.00
	Set value	1.60	1.60

Souvenir Sheet

873 A129 3r violet brn & blk 1.50 1.50

Queen Mother Elizabeth, 80th Birthday A130

1980, Sept. 29 *Perf. 14*

874 A130 4r multicolored 2.00 2.00

Souvenir Sheet
Perf. 12

875 A130 5r multicolored 2.50 2.50

Munnaaru Tower A131

1980, Nov. 9 Litho. *Perf. 15*

876 A131 5 l shown .15 .15
877 A131 10 l Hukuru Miskiiy Mosque .15 .15
878 A131 30 l Medhuziyaaraiy Shrine .15 .15
879 A131 55 l Koran verses on wooden tablets .28 .28
880 A131 90 l Mother teaching son .45 .45
Set value .95 .95

Souvenir Sheet

881 A131 2r Map and arms of Maldives 1.00 1.00

Hegira (Pilgrimage Year).

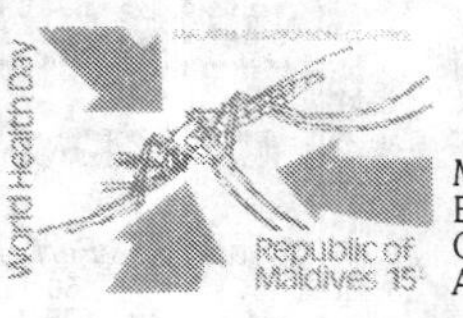

Malaria Eradication Control A132

1980, Nov. 30 *Perf. 14*

882 A132 15 l shown .15 .15
883 A132 25 l Balanced diet .15 .15
884 A132 1.50r Oral hygiene .75 .75
885 A132 5r Clinic visit 2.50 2.50
Nos. 882-885 (4) 3.55 3.55

Souvenir Sheet

886 A132 4r like #885 2.00 2.00

World Health Day. No. 886 shows design of No. 885 in changed colors.

The Cheshire Cat — A133

Designs: Scenes from Walt Disney's Alice in Wonderland. 5r, vert.

1980, Dec. 22 *Perf. 11*

887 A133 1 l multicolored .15 .15
888 A133 2 l multicolored .15 .15
889 A133 3 l multicolored .15 .15
890 A133 4 l multicolored .15 .15
891 A133 5 l multicolored .15 .15
892 A133 10 l multicolored .15 .15
893 A133 15 l multicolored .15 .15
894 A133 2.50r multicolored 1.25 1.25
895 A133 4r multicolored 2.00 2.00
Set value 3.60 3.60

Souvenir Sheet

896 A133 5r multicolored 3.50 3.50

Ridley Turtle A134

1980, Dec. 29 Litho. *Perf. 14*

897 A134 90 l shown .45 .45
898 A134 1.25r Angel flake fish .62 .62
899 A134 2r Spiny lobster 1.00 1.00
Nos. 897-899 (3) 2.07 2.07

Souvenir Sheet

900 A134 4r Fish 2.00 2.00

Tomb of Ghaazee Muhammad Thakurufaan — A135

National Day (Furniture and Palace of Muhammad Thakurufaan): 20 l, Hanging lamp, 16th century, vert. 30 l, Chair, vert. 95 l, Utheem Palace. 10r, Couch, vert.

1981, Jan. 7 *Perf. 15*

901 A135 10 l multicolored .15 .15
902 A135 20 l multicolored .15 .15
903 A135 30 l multicolored .15 .15
904 A135 95 l multicolored .48 .48
905 A135 10r multicolored 5.00 5.00
Nos. 901-905 (5) 5.93 5.93

Royal Wedding Issue
Common Design Type

1981, June 22 Litho. *Perf. 14*

906 CD331 1r Couple .25 .25
907 CD331 2r Buckingham Palace .50 .50
908 CD331 5r Charles 1.25 1.25
Nos. 906-908 (3) 2.00 2.00

Souvenir Sheet

909 CD331 10r Royal state coach 2.50 2.50

Nos. 906-908 also printed in sheets of 5 plus label, perf. 12, in changed colors.

Majlis Chamber, 1932 A136

50th Anniv. of Citizens' Majlis (Grievance Rights); 1r, Sultan Muhammed Shamsuddin III (instituted system, 1932), vert. 4r, Constitution, 1932.

1981, June 27 *Perf. 15*

910 A136 95 l multicolored .35 .35
911 A136 1r multicolored .40 .40

Souvenir Sheet

912 A136 4r multicolored 2.00 2.00

Self-portrait with Palette, by Picasso (1881-1973) — A137

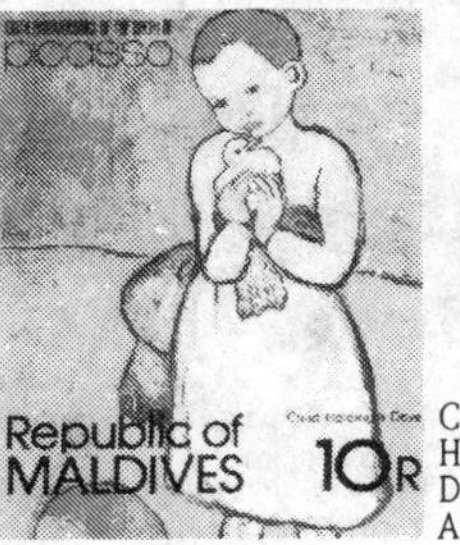

Child Holding a Dove A138

1981, Aug. 26 Litho. *Perf. 14*

913 A137 5 l shown .15 .15
914 A137 10 l Woman in Blue .15 .15
915 A137 25 l Boy with a Pipe .15 .15
916 A137 30 l Card Player .15 .15
917 A137 90 l Sailor .22 .22
918 A137 3r Self-portrait .75 .75
919 A137 5r Harlequin 1.25 1.25

Imperf

920 A138 10r shown 4.75 4.75
Nos. 913-920 (8) 7.57 7.57

No. 5 on Airmail Cover — A139

1981, Sept. 9 Litho. *Perf. 14*

921 A139 25 l multicolored .15 .15
922 A139 75 l multicolored .30 .30
923 A139 5r multicolored 2.00 2.00
Nos. 921-923 (3) 2.45 2.45

Postal service, 75th anniv.

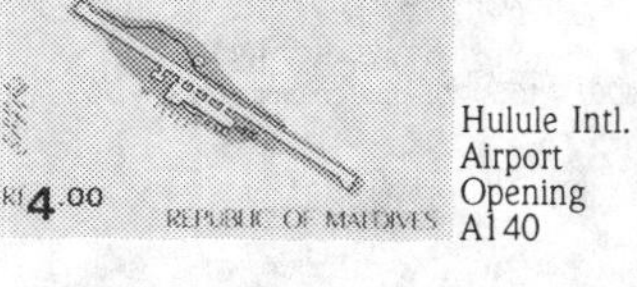

Hulule Intl. Airport Opening A140

1981, Nov. 11

924 A140 5 l Jet taking off .15 .15
925 A140 20 l Passengers leaving jet .15 .15
926 A140 1.80r Refueling .80 .80
927 A140 4r shown 1.75 1.75
Nos. 924-927 (4) 2.85 2.85

Souvenir Sheet

928 A140 5r Terminal 2.00 2.00

Intl. Year of the Disabled — A141

Decade for Women — A142

1981, Nov. 18 Litho. *Perf. 14½*

929 A141 2 l Homer .15 .15
930 A141 5 l Cervantes .15 .15
931 A141 1r Beethoven .50 .50
932 A141 5r Van Gogh 2.50 2.50
Nos. 929-932 (4) 3.30 3.30

Souvenir Sheet

933 A141 4r Helen Keller, Anne Sullivan 2.00 2.00

1981, Nov. 25 *Perf. 14*

934 A142 20 l Preparing fish .15 .15
935 A142 90 l 16th cent. woman .45 .45
936 A142 1r Tending yam crop .50 .50
937 A142 2r Making coir rope 1.00 1.00
Nos. 934-937 (4) 2.10 2.10

Fishermen's Day — A143

1981, Dec. 10

938 A143 5 l Collecting bait .15 .15
939 A143 15 l Fishing boats .15 .15
940 A143 90 l Fisherman holding catch .45 .45
941 A143 1.30r Sorting fish .70 .70
Nos. 938-941 (4) 1.45 1.45

Souvenir Sheet

942 A143 3r Loading fish for export 1.50 1.50

World Food Day — A144

1981, Dec. 30 Litho. *Perf. 14*

943 A144 10 l Breadfruit .15 .15
944 A144 25 l Hen, chicks .15 .15
945 A144 30 l Corn .15 .15
946 A144 75 l Skipjack tuna .38 .38
947 A144 1r Pumpkins .50 .50
948 A144 2r Coconuts 1.00 1.00
Nos. 943-948 (6) 2.33 2.33

Souvenir Sheet

949 A144 5r Eggplants 2.25 2.25

50th Anniv. of Walt Disney's Pluto (1980) A145

1982, Mar. 29 Litho. *Perf. 13½x14*

950 A145 4r Scene from Chain Gang, 1930 2.50 2.50

Souvenir Sheet

951 A145 6r The Pointer, 1939 4.00 4.00

Princess Diana Issue
Common Design Type

1982, July 15 Litho. *Perf. 14½x14*

952 CD332 95 l Balmoral .50 .50
953 CD332 3r Honeymoon 1.50 1.50
954 CD332 5r Diana 2.50 2.50
Nos. 952-954 (3) 4.50 4.50

Souvenir Sheet

955 CD332 8r Diana, diff. 3.50 3.50

#952-954 also issued in sheetlets of 5 plus label.

For overprints and surcharges see Nos. 966-969, 1050, 1052, 1054, 1056.

Scouting Year A146

1982, Aug. 9 Litho. *Perf. 14*

956 A146 1.30r Saluting .65 .65
957 A146 1.80r Fire building .90 .90
958 A146 4r Lifesaving 2.00 2.00
959 A146 5r Map reading 2.50 2.50
Nos. 956-959 (4) 6.05 6.05

Souvenir Sheet

960 A146 10r Flag, emblem 4.75 4.75

1982 World Cup — A147

TB Bacillus Cent. — A148

Various soccer players.

1982, Oct. 4 Litho. *Perf. 14*

961 A147 90 l multicolored .45 .45
962 A147 1.50r multicolored .75 .75
963 A147 3r multicolored 1.50 1.50
964 A147 5r multicolored 2.50 2.50
Nos. 961-964 (4) 5.20 5.20

Souvenir Sheet

965 A147 10r multicolored 5.00 5.00

Nos. 952-955 Overprinted: "ROYAL BABY/21.6.82"

1982, Oct. 18 *Perf. 14½x14*

966 CD332 95 l multicolored .50 .50
967 CD332 3r multicolored 1.50 1.50
968 CD332 5r multicolored 2.50 2.50
Nos. 966-968 (3) 4.50 4.50

Souvenir Sheet

969 CD332 8r multicolored 4.00 4.00

Birth of Prince William of Wales, June 21. #966-968 also issued in sheetlets of 5 + label.

For surcharges see #1051, 1053, 1055, 1057.

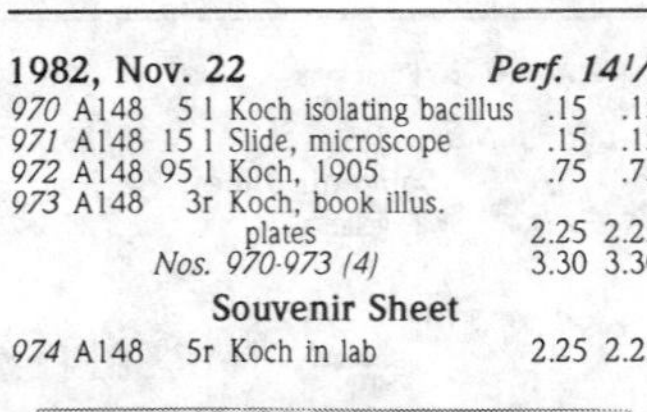

1982, Nov. 22 *Perf. 14½*

970 A148 5 l Koch isolating bacillus .15 .15
971 A148 15 l Slide, microscope .15 .15
972 A148 95 l Koch, 1905 .75 .75
973 A148 3r Koch, book illus. plates 2.25 2.25
Nos. 970-973 (4) 3.30 3.30

Souvenir Sheet

974 A148 5r Koch in lab 2.25 2.25

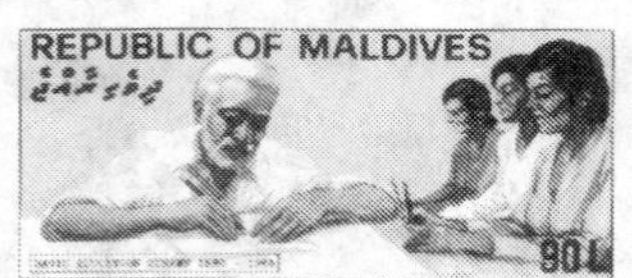

Natl. Education — A149

Designs: 90 l, Basic education scheme, 1980-85. 95 l, Formal primary education. 1.30r, Teacher training. 2.50r, Educational materials production. 6r, Thanna typewrite.

1982, Nov. 15

975 A149 90 l multicolored .35 .35
976 A149 95 l multicolored .38 .38
977 A149 1.30r multicolored .55 .55
978 A149 2.50r multicolored .90 .90
Nos. 975-978 (4) 2.18 2.18

Souvenir Sheet

979 A149 6r multicolored 2.75 2.75

Manned Flight Bicentenary A150

1983, July 28 **Litho.** *Perf. 14*

980 A150 90 l Blohm & Voss Ha-139 .45 .45
981 A150 1.45r Macchi Castoldi MC-72 .72 .72
982 A150 4r Boeing F4B-3 2.00 2.00
983 A150 5r Le France 2.50 2.50
Nos. 980-983 (4) 5.67 5.67

Souvenir Sheet

984 A150 10r Nadar's Le Geant 4.75 4.75

For overprints see Nos. 1020-1022.

Roughtooth Dolphin A151

1983, Sept. 6 **Litho.** *Perf. 14*

985 A151 30 l shown .15 .15
986 A151 40 l Indopacific humpback dolphin .20 .20
987 A151 4r Finless porpoise 2.00 2.00
988 A151 6r Pygmy sperm whale 3.00 3.00
Nos. 985-988 (4) 5.35 5.35

Souvenir Sheet

989 A151 5r Striped dolphins 2.50 2.50

Classic Cars A152

1983, Aug. 15 **Litho.** *Perf. 14½x15*

990 A152 5 l Curved Dash Oldsmobile, 1902 .15 .15
991 A152 30 l Aston Martin Tourer, 1932 .15 .15
992 A152 40 l Lamborghini Miura, 1966 .20 .20
993 A152 1r Mercedes-Benz 300sl, 1954 .50 .50
994 A152 1.45r Stutz Bearcat, 1913 .72 .72
995 A152 5r Lotus Elite, 1958 2.50 2.50
Nos. 990-995 (6) 4.22 4.22

Souvenir Sheet

996 A152 10r Grand Prix Sunbeam, 1924 4.75 4.75

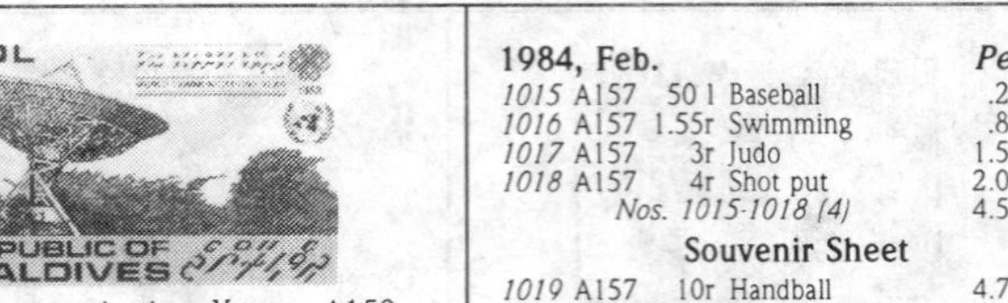

World Communications Year — A153

Designs: 50 l, Dish antenna. 1r, Mail transport. 2r, Ship-to-shore communications. 10r, Land-air communications. 20r, Telephone calls.

1983, Oct. 9 *Perf. 14*

997 A153 50 l multicolored .25 .25
998 A153 1r multicolored .50 .50
999 A153 2r multicolored 1.00 1.00
1000 A153 10r multicolored 5.00 5.00
Nos. 997-1000 (4) 6.75 6.75

Souvenir Sheet

1001 A153 20r multicolored 9.50 9.50

Raphael, 500th Birth Anniv. A154

1983, Oct. 25 **Litho.** *Perf. 13½x14*

1002 A154 90 l La Donna Gravida .45 .45
1003 A154 3r Jean of Aragon 1.50 1.50
1004 A154 4r The Woman with the Unicorn 2.00 2.00
1005 A154 6r La Muta 3.00 3.00
Nos. 1002-1005 (4) 6.95 6.95

Souvenir Sheet

1006 A154 10r The Knights Dream 4.75 4.75

Intl. Palestinian Solidarity Day — A155

Various refugees, mosque.

1983, Nov. 29 **Litho.** *Perf. 14*

1007 A155 4r multicolored 2.00 2.00
1008 A155 5r multicolored 2.50 2.50
1009 A155 6r multicolored 3.00 3.00
Nos. 1007-1009 (3) 7.50 7.50

Natl. Development Programs — A156

1983, Dec. 10 **Litho.** *Perf. 13½x14*

1010 A156 7 l Education .15 .15
1011 A156 10 l Health care .15 .15
1012 A156 5r Food production 2.50 2.50
1013 A156 6r Fishing industry 3.00 3.00
Nos. 1010-1013 (4) 5.80 5.80

Souvenir Sheet

1014 A156 10r Inter-atoll transportation 4.75 4.75

A157

Tourism — A158

1984, Feb. *Perf. 14*

1015 A157 50 l Baseball .25 .25
1016 A157 1.55r Swimming .80 .80
1017 A157 3r Judo 1.50 1.50
1018 A157 4r Shot put 2.00 2.00
Nos. 1015-1018 (4) 4.55 4.55

Souvenir Sheet

1019 A157 10r Handball 4.75 4.75

23rd Olympic Games, Los Angeles, 7/28-8/12.
For overprints see Nos. 1090-1094.

Nos. 982-984 Overprinted: "19th UPU/CONGRESS HAMBURG"

1984 **Litho.** *Perf. 14*

1020 A150 4r multicolored 2.00 2.00
1021 A150 5r multicolored 2.50 2.50

Souvenir Sheet

1022 A150 10r multicolored 4.75 4.75

1984, Sept. 21 **Litho.** *Perf. 14½*

1023 A158 7 l Island resorts .15 .15
1024 A158 15 l Cruising .15 .15
1025 A158 20 l Snorkelling .15 .15
1026 A158 2r Wind surfing .55 .55
1027 A158 4r Scuba diving 1.10 1.10
1028 A158 6r Night fishing 1.75 1.75
1029 A158 8r Big game fishing 2.25 2.25
1030 A158 10r Nature (turtle) 2.75 2.75
Nos. 1023-1030 (8) 8.85 8.85

50th Anniv. of Donald Duck A160

Scenes from various cartoons and movies.

1984, Nov. **Litho.** *Perf. 14*

1040 A160 3 l multi .15 .15
1041 A160 4 l multi .15 .15
1042 A160 5 l multi .15 .15
1043 A160 10 l multi .15 .15
1044 A160 15 l multi .15 .15
1045 A160 25 l multi .15 .15
1045A A160 5r multi, perf. 12x12½ 1.75 1.75
1046 A160 8r multi 2.75 2.75
1047 A160 10r multi 3.50 3.50
Nos. 1040-1047 (9) 8.90 8.90

Souvenir Sheets

1048 A160 15r multi 5.00 5.00
1049 A160 15r multi 5.00 5.00

Nos. 952-955, 966-969 Surcharged

1984, July **Litho.** *Perf. 14½x14*

1050 CD332 1.45r on 95 l #952 *2.50* 2.00
1051 CD332 1.45r on 95 l #966 *2.50* 2.00
1052 CD332 1.45r on 3r #953 *2.50* 2.00
1053 CD332 1.45r on 3r #967 *2.50* 2.00
1054 CD332 1.45r on 5r #954 *2.50* 2.00
1055 CD332 1.45r on 5r #968 *2.50* 2.00
Nos. 1050-1055 (6) *15.00* 12.00

Souvenir Sheet

1056 CD332 1.45r on 8r #955 *10.00* 8.00
1057 CD332 1.45r on 8r #969 *10.00* 8.00

Namibia Day A161

1984, Aug. 26 *Perf. 15*

1058 A161 6r Breaking chain 1.75 1.75
1059 A161 8r Family, rising sun 2.25 2.25

Souvenir Sheet

1060 A161 10r Map, sun 2.75 2.75

Ausipex '84 — A162

1984, Sept. 21

1061 A162 5r Frangipani 2.00 2.00
1062 A162 10r Cooktown orchid 4.00 4.00

Souvenir Sheet

1063 A162 15r Sun orchids 6.00 6.00

150th Birth Anniv. of Edgar Degas — A163

1984, Oct. **Litho.** *Perf. 14*

1064 A163 75 l Portrait of Edmond Iduranty .20 .20
1065 A163 2r Portrait of James Tissot .55 .55
1066 A163 5r Portrait of Achille Degas 1.40 1.40
1067 A163 10r Lady with Chrysanthemums 2.75 2.75
Nos. 1064-1067 (4) 4.90 4.90

Souvenir Sheet

1068 A163 15r Self-Portrait 4.00 4.00

Opening of Islamic Center A164

1984, Nov. 11 **Litho.** *Perf. 15*

1069 A164 2r Mosque .50 .50
1070 A164 5r Mosque, minaret, vert. 1.25 1.25

40th Anniv., International Civil Aviation Organization A165

1984, Nov. 19 **Litho.** *Perf. 14*

1071 A165 7 l Boeing 737 .15 .15
1072 A165 4r Lockheed L-1011 1.10 1.10
1073 A165 6r McDonnell Douglas DC-10 1.75 1.75
1074 A165 8r Lockheed L-1011 2.25 2.25
Nos. 1071-1074 (4) 5.25 5.25

Souvenir Sheet

1075 A165 15r Shorts SC7 Skyvan 4.00 4.00

450th Anniv. of the Death of Correggio — A166

1984, Dec. 10 **Litho.** *Perf. 14*

1076 A166 5r Detail from The Day 1.40 1.40
1077 A166 10r Detail from The Night 2.75 2.75

Souvenir Sheet

1078 A166 15r Portrait of a Man 4.00 4.00

John J. Audubon A167

Illustrations from Audubon's Birds of America.

1985, Mar. 9 **Litho.** *Perf. 14*

1079 A167 3r Flesh-footed shearwater, vert. .90 .90
1080 A167 3.50r Little grebe 1.00 1.00
1081 A167 4r Great cormorant, vert. 1.10 1.10
1082 A167 4.50r White-faced storm petrel 1.25 1.25
Nos. 1079-1082 (4) 4.25 4.25

Souvenir Sheet

1083 A167 15r Red-necked phalarope 4.00 4.00

See Nos. 1195-1204.

Natl. Security Services — A168

1985, June 6 Litho. *Perf. 14*

1084 A168 15 l Drill .15 .15
1085 A168 20 l Combat training .15 .15
1086 A168 1r Fire fighting .30 .30
1087 A168 2r Coast guard .60 .60
1088 A168 10r Parade, vert. 3.00 3.00
Nos. 1084-1088 (5) 4.20 4.20

Souvenir Sheet

1089 A168 10r Badge, cannon 3.00 3.00

Nos. 1015-1019 Ovptd. with Country or "Gold Medalist," Winner and Nation in 3 Lines

1985, July 17

1090 A157 50 l Japan .15 .15
1091 A157 1.55r Theresa Andrews .45 .45
1092 A157 3r Frank Wieneke .90 .90
1093 A157 4r Claudia Loch 1.25 1.25
Nos. 1090-1093 (4) 2.75 2.75

Souvenir Sheet

1094 A157 10r US 3.00 3.00

Queen Mother, 85th Birthday — A169 Johann Sebastian Bach, Composer — A170

1985-86 *Perf. 14, 12 (1r, 4r, 10r)*

1095 A169 1r Wearing tiara .22 .22
1096 A169 3r like 1r .70 .70
1097 A169 4r At Middlesex Hospital, horiz. .90 .90
1098 A169 5r like 4r 1.10 1.10
1099 A169 7r Wearing fur stole 1.50 1.50
1100 A169 10r like 7r 2.25 2.25
Nos. 1095-1100 (6) 6.67 6.67

Souvenir Sheet

1101 A169 15r With Prince of Wales 4.25 4.25

Issued: 1r, 4r, 10r, 1/4/86; 3r, 5r, 7r, 15r, 8/20/85. #1095, 1097, 1100 printed in sheets of 5 + label.

1985, Sept. 3 *Perf. 14*

Portrait, Invention No. 1 in C Major and: 15 l, Lira da Braccio. 2r, Tenor oboe. 4r, Serpent. 10r, Table organ.

1102 A170 15 l multi .15 .15
1103 A170 2r multi .60 .60
1104 A170 4r multi 1.25 1.25
1105 A170 10r multi 3.00 3.00
Nos. 1102-1105 (4) 5.00 5.00

Souvenir Sheet

1106 A170 15r Portrait 4.25 4.25

Ships A171

1985, Sept. 23

1107 A171 3 l Masodi .15 .15
1108 A171 5 l Naalu Baththeli .15 .15
1109 A171 10 l Addu Odi .15 .15
1110 A171 2.60r Masdhoni, 2nd generation .78 .78
1111 A171 2.70r Masdhoni .80 .80
1112 A171 3r Baththeli Dhoni .90 .90
1113 A171 5r Inter 1 1.50 1.50
1114 A171 10r Yacht Dhoni 3.00 3.00
Nos. 1107-1114 (8) 7.43 7.43

World Tourism Org., 10th Anniv. A172

1985, Oct. 2

1115 A172 6r Wind surfing 1.75 1.75
1116 A172 8r Scuba diving 2.50 2.50

Souvenir Sheet

1117 A172 15r Kuda Hithi Resort 4.25 4.25

Maldives Admission to UN, 20th Anniv. A173

1985, Oct. 24

1118 A173 20 l shown .15 .15
1119 A173 15r Flags, UN building 4.25 4.25

UN 40th Anniv., Intl. Peace Year A174

1985, Oct. 24 Litho. *Perf. 14*

1120 A174 15 l UN Building .15 .15
1121 A174 2r IPY emblem .60 .60
1122 A174 4r Security Council 1.20 1.20
1123 A174 10r Lion, lamb 3.00 3.00
Nos. 1120-1123 (4) 4.95 4.95

Souvenir Sheet

1124 A174 15r UN Building, diff. 4.50 4.50

Nos. 1120-1121, 1123-1124, vert.

Intl. Youth Year — A175

1985, Nov. 20 *Perf. 15*

1125 A175 90 l Culture .28 .28
1126 A175 6r Games 1.75 1.75
1127 A175 10r Community service, vert. 3.00 3.00
Nos. 1125-1127 (3) 5.03 5.03

Souvenir Sheet

1128 A175 15r Youth camp, vert. 4.25 4.25

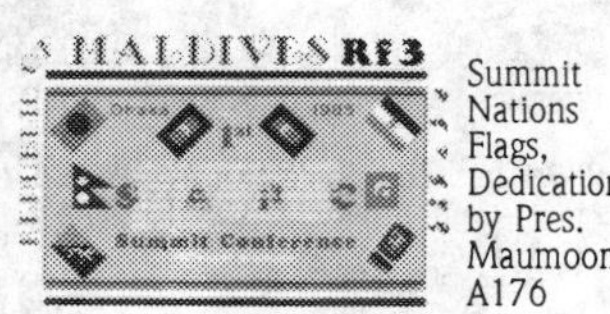

Summit Nations Flags, Dedication by Pres. Maumoon A176

1985, Dec. 8 *Perf. 14*

1129 A176 3r multicolored .90 .90

South Asian Regional Cooperation, SARC, 1st Summit, Dec. 7-8, 1985.

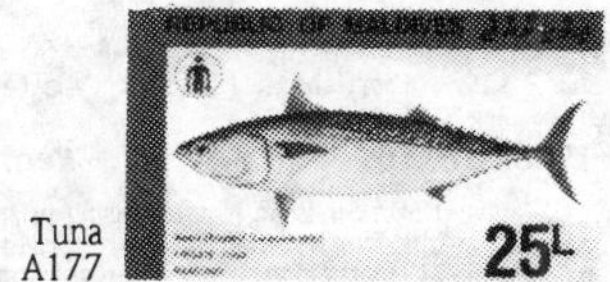

Tuna A177

1985, Dec. 10

1130 A177 25 l Frigate .15 .15
1131 A177 75 l Little tuna .22 .22
1132 A177 3r Dogtooth .90 .90
1133 A177 5r Yellowfin 1.50 1.50
Nos. 1130-1133 (4) 2.77 2.77

Souvenir Sheet

1134 A177 15r Skipjack 4.25 4.25

Fisherman's Day.

Mark Twain, American Novelist A178

Disney characters and Twain quotes.

1985, Dec. 21

1135 A178 2 l multicolored .15 .15
1136 A178 3 l multicolored .15 .15
1137 A178 4 l multicolored .15 .15
1138 A178 20 l multicolored .15 .15
1139 A178 4r multicolored 1.25 1.25
1140 A178 13r multicolored 4.00 4.00
Nos. 1135-1140 (6) 5.85 5.85

Souvenir Sheet

1141 A178 15r multicolored 4.50 4.50

Intl. Youth Year. 4r issued in sheet of 8.

The Brothers Grimm — A179

Disney characters in Doctor Knowall.

1985, Dec. 21

1142 A179 1 l multicolored .15 .15
1143 A179 5 l multicolored .15 .15
1144 A179 10 l multicolored .15 .15
1145 A179 15 l multicolored .15 .15
1146 A179 3r multicolored .90 .90
1147 A179 14r multicolored 4.25 4.25
Nos. 1142-1147 (6) 5.75 5.75

Souvenir Sheet

1148 A179 15r multicolored 4.50 4.50

3r issued in sheets of 8.

World Disarmament Day — A180

1986, Feb. 10 *Perf. 14½x14*

1149 A180 1.50r shown .45 .45
1150 A180 10r Dove 3.00 3.00

Halley's Comet A181

Designs: 20 l, NASA space telescope. 1.50r, Giotto space probe. 2r, Plant-A probe, Japan. 4r, Edmond Halley, Stonehenge. 5r, Vega probe, USSR. 15r, Comet over Male.

1986, Apr. 29

1151 A181 20 l multicolored .15 .15
1152 A181 1.50r multicolored .45 .45
1153 A181 2r multicolored .60 .60
1154 A181 4r multicolored 1.20 1.20
1155 A181 5r multicolored 1.50 1.50
Nos. 1151-1155 (5) 3.90 3.90

Souvenir Sheet

1156 A181 15r multicolored 4.50 4.50

See Nos. 1210-1215.

Statue of Liberty, Cent. A182

Detail of statue and: 50 l, Walter Gropius (1883-1969), architect. 70 l, John Lennon (1940-1980), musician. 1r, George Balanchine (1904-1983), choreographer. 10r, Franz Werfel (1890-1945), writer. 15r, Close-up of statue, vert.

1986, May 5

1157 A182 50 l multicolored .15 .15
1158 A182 70 l multicolored .20 .20
1159 A182 1r multicolored .30 .30
1160 A182 10r multicolored 3.00 3.00
Nos. 1157-1160 (4) 3.65 3.65

Souvenir Sheet

1161 A182 15r multicolored 4.50 4.50

AMERIPEX '86 — A183

US stamps and Disney portrayals of American legends: 3 l, No. 1317, Johnny Appleseed. 4 l, No. 1122, Paul Bunyan. 5 l, No. 1381, Casey at the Bat. 10 l, No. 1548, Tales of Sleepy Hollow. 15 l, No. 922, John Henry. 20 l, No. 1061, Windwagon Smith. 13r, No. 1409, Mike Fink. 14r, No. 993, Casey Jones. No. 1170, Remember the Alamo, No. 1330. No. 1171, Pocahontas, Nos. 328-330.

1986, May 22 *Perf. 11*

1162 A183 3 l multicolored .15 .15
1163 A183 4 l multicolored .15 .15
1164 A183 5 l multicolored .15 .15
1165 A183 10 l multicolored .15 .15
1166 A183 15 l multicolored .15 .15
1167 A183 20 l multicolored .15 .15
1168 A183 13r multicolored 3.75 3.75
1169 A183 14r multicolored 4.00 4.00
Nos. 1162-1169 (8) 8.65 8.65

Souvenir Sheets

Perf. 14

1170 A183 15r multicolored 4.50 4.50
1171 A183 15r multicolored 4.50 4.50

Queen Elizabeth II, 60th Birthday

Common Design Type

1986, May 29 *Perf. 14*

1172 CD339 1r Girl Guides' rally, 1938 .30 .30
1173 CD339 2r Canada visit, 1985 .60 .60
1174 CD339 12r At Sandringham, 1970 3.60 3.60
Nos. 1172-1174 (3) 4.50 4.50

Souvenir Sheet

1175 CD339 15r Royal Lodge, 1940 4.50 4.50

For overprints see Nos. 1288-1291.

1986 World Cup Soccer Championships, Mexico — A184

Various soccer plays.

1986, June 18 Litho. *Perf. 14*

1176 A184 15 l multicolored .15 .15
1177 A184 2r multicolored .60 .60
1178 A184 4r multicolored 1.20 1.20
1179 A184 10r multicolored 3.00 3.00
Nos. 1176-1179 (4) 4.95 4.95

Souvenir Sheet

1180 A184 15r multicolored 4.50 4.50

For overprints see Nos. 1205-1209.

Royal Wedding Issue, 1986
Common Design Type

Designs: 10 l, Prince Andrew and Sarah Ferguson. 2r, Andrew. 12r, Andrew on ship's deck in uniform. 15r, Couple, diff.

1986, July 23

1181 CD340 10 l multi .15 .15
1182 CD340 2r multi .60 .60
1183 CD340 12r multi 3.60 3.60
Nos. 1181-1183 (3) 4.35 4.35

Souvenir Sheet

1184 CD340 15r multi 4.50 4.50

Marine Life — A185

1986, Sept. 22 Litho. *Perf. 15*

1185 A185 50 l Sea fan, moorish idol .15 .15
1186 A185 90 l Regal angelfish .28 .28
1187 A185 1r Anemone fish .30 .30
1188 A185 2r Stinging coral, tiger cowrie .60 .60
1189 A185 3r Emperor angelfish, staghorn coral .90 .90
1190 A185 4r Black-naped tern 1.20 1.20
1191 A185 5r Fiddler crab, staghorn coral 1.50 1.50
1192 A185 10r Hawksbill turtle 3.00 3.00
Nos. 1185-1192 (8) 7.93 7.93

Souvenir Sheets

1193 A185 15r Trumpet fish 4.50 4.50
1194 A185 15r Long-nosed butterflyfish 4.50 4.50

Nos. 1185-1187, 1189 and 1193 show the World Wildlife Fund emblem.

Audubon Type of 1985

1986, Oct. 9 Litho. *Perf. 14*

1195 A167 3 l Little blue heron .15 .15
1196 A167 4 l White-tailed kite, vert. .15 .15
1197 A167 5 l Greater shearwater .15 .15
1198 A167 10 l Magnificent frigatebird, vert. .15 .15
1199 A167 15 l Eared grebe, vert. .15 .15
1200 A167 20 l Common merganser, vert. .15 .15
1201 A167 13r Great-footed hawk 4.00 4.00
1202 A167 14r Greater prairie chicken 4.25 4.25
Nos. 1195-1202 (8) 9.15 9.15

Souvenir Sheets

1203 A167 15r White-fronted goose 4.50 4.50
1204 A167 15r Northern fulmar, vert. 4.50 4.50

Nos. 1197, 1199-1201 printed se-tenant with labels picturing a horned puffin, gray kingbird, downy woodpecker and water pipit, respectively.

Nos. 1176-1180 Ovptd. "WINNERS / Argentina 3 / W. Germany 2" in Gold

1986, Oct. 25

1205 A184 15 l multicolored .15 .15
1206 A184 2r multicolored .60 .60
1207 A184 4r multicolored 1.20 1.20
1208 A184 10r multicolored 3.00 3.00
Nos. 1205-1208 (4) 4.95 4.95

Souvenir Sheet

1209 A184 15r multicolored 4.50 4.50

Nos. 1151-1156 Printed with Halley's Comet Symbol in Silver

1986, Oct. 30

1210 A181 20 l multicolored .15 .15
1211 A181 1.50r multicolored .45 .45
1212 A181 2r multicolored .60 .60
1213 A181 4r multicolored 1.20 1.20
1214 A181 5r multicolored 1.50 1.50
Nos. 1210-1214 (5) 3.90 3.90

Souvenir Sheet

1215 A181 15r multicolored 4.50 4.50

UNESCO, 40th Anniv. — A186

1986, Nov. 4 *Perf. 15*

1216 A186 1r Aviation .30 .30
1217 A186 2r Boat-building .60 .60
1218 A186 3r Education .90 .90
1219 A186 5r Research 1.50 1.50
Nos. 1216-1219 (4) 3.30 3.30

Souvenir Sheet

1220 A186 15r Ocean exploration 4.50 4.50

Mushrooms A187

1986, Dec. 31 Litho. *Perf. 15*

1221 A187 15 l Hypholoma fasciculare .15 .15
1222 A187 50 l Kuehneromyces mutabilis .15 .15
1223 A187 1r Amanita muscaria .30 .30
1224 A187 2r Agaricus campestris .60 .60
1225 A187 3r Amanita pantherina .90 .90
1226 A187 4r Coprinus comatus 1.20 1.20
1227 A187 5r Pholiota spectabilis 1.50 1.50
1228 A187 10r Pluteus cervinus 3.00 3.00
Nos. 1221-1228 (8) 7.80 7.80

Souvenir Sheets

1229 A187 15r Armillaria mellea 4.50 4.50
1230 A187 15r Stropharia aeruginosa 4.50 4.50

Nos. 1222-1223, 1225-1226 vert.

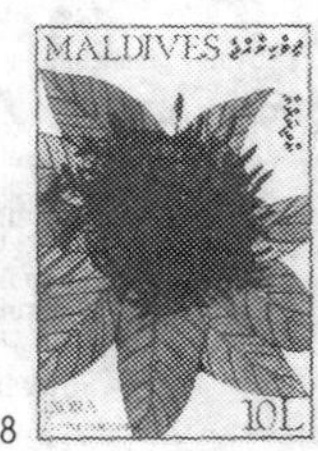

Flowers — A188

1987, Jan. 29 Litho. *Perf. 15*

1231 A188 10 l Ixora .15 .15
1232 A188 20 l Frangipani .15 .15
1233 A188 50 l Crinum .15 .15
1235 A188 2r Pink rose .60 .60
1236 A188 4r Flamboyant 1.20 1.20
1238 A188 10r Ground orchid 3.00 3.00
Nos. 1231-1238 (6) 5.25 5.25

Souvenir Sheet

1239 A188 15r Gardenia 4.50 4.50
1240 A188 15r Oleander 4.50 4.50

Girl Guides, 75th Anniv. (in 1985) A189

1987, Apr. 4 Litho. *Perf. 15*

1241 A189 15 l Nature study .15 .15
1242 A189 2r Guides, rabbits .60 .60
1243 A189 4r Bird-watching 1.20 1.20
1244 A189 12r Lady Baden-Powell, flag 3.50 3.50
Nos. 1241-1244 (4) 5.45 5.45

Souvenir Sheet

1245 A189 15r Sailing 4.50 4.50

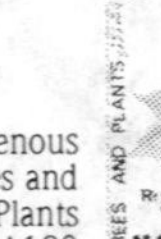

Indigenous Trees and Plants A190

1987, Apr. 22 Litho. *Perf. 14*

1246 A190 50 l Thespesia populnea, vert. .15 .15
1247 A190 1r Cocos nucifera, vert. .30 .30
1248 A190 2r Calophyllum mophyllum, vert. .60 .60
1249 A190 3r Xanthosoma indica .90 .90
1250 A190 5r Ipomoea batatas 1.50 1.50
1251 A190 7r Artocarpus altilis, vert. 2.00 2.00
Nos. 1246-1251 (6) 5.45 5.45

Souvenir Sheet

1252 A190 15r Cocos nucifera, diff., vert. 4.50 4.50

A191

America's Cup A192

1987, May 4 Litho. *Perf. 15*

1253 A191 15 l Intrepid, 1970 .15 .15
1254 A191 1r France II, 1974 .30 .30
1255 A191 2r Gretel, 1962 .60 .60
1256 A191 12r Volunteer, 1887 3.50 3.50
Nos. 1253-1256 (4) 4.55 4.55

Souvenir Sheet

1257 A192 15r Defender Vs. Valkyrie III, 1895 4.50 4.50

Butterflies — A193

Scientists — A194

1987, Dec. 16 Litho. *Perf. 15*

1258 A193 15 l Precis octavia .15 .15
1259 A193 20 l Pachliopta hector .15 .15
1260 A193 50 l Teinopalpus imperialis .15 .15
1261 A193 1r Kallima horsfieldi .30 .30
1262 A193 2r Cethosia biblis .60 .60
1263 A193 4r Hestia jasonia 1.20 1.20
1264 A193 7r Papilio memnon 2.10 2.10
1265 A193 10r Meneris tulbaghia 3.00 3.00
Nos. 1258-1265 (8) 7.65 7.65

Souvenir Sheets

1266 A193 15r Acraea violae acraeinae 4.50 4.50
1267 A193 15r Hebomoia leucippe 4.50 4.50

1988, Jan. 10 *Perf. 14*

Designs: 1.50r, Sir Isaac Newton using prism to demonstrate his Theory of Light, horiz. 3r, Euclid (c. 300 B.C.), mathematician. 4r, Gregor Johann Mendel (1822-1884), botanist; father of genetics. 5r, Galileo, 1st man to observe 4 moons of Jupiter, horiz. 15r, Apollo spacecraft orbiting the moon.

1268 A194 1.50r multicolored .45 .45
1269 A194 3r multicolored .90 .90
1270 A194 4r multicolored 1.15 1.15
1271 A194 5r multicolored 1.50 1.50
Nos. 1268-1271 (4) 4.00 4.00

Souvenir Sheet

1272 A194 15r multicolored 4.50 4.50

Disney Characters, Space Exploration — A195

1988, Feb. 15

1273 A195 3 l Weather satellite .15 .15
1274 A195 4 l Navigation satellite .15 .15
1275 A195 5 l Communication satellite .15 .15
1276 A195 10 l Moon rover .15 .15
1277 A195 20 l Space shuttle .15 .15
1278 A195 13r Space docking 3.50 3.50
1279 A195 14r Voyager 2 3.75 3.75
Nos. 1273-1279 (7) 8.00 8.00

Souvenir Sheets

1280 A195 15r 1st Man on Moon 4.00 4.00
1281 A195 15r Space station colony 4.00 4.00

Nos. 1276-1278 and 1281 vert.

WHO, 40th Anniv. A196

1988, Apr. 7 Litho. *Perf. 14*

1282 A196 2r Immunization .58 .58
1283 A196 4r Clean water 1.15 1.15

For overprints see Nos. 1307-1308.

World Environment Day — A197

1988, May 9 *Perf. 15*

1284 A197 15 l Save water .15 .15
1285 A197 75 l Protect the reef .22 .22
1286 A197 2r Conserve nature .58 .58
Nos. 1284-1286 (3) .95 .95

Souvenir Sheet

1287 A197 15r Banyan tree, vert. 4.25 4.25

Nos. 1172-1175 Ovptd. "40th WEDDING ANNIVERSARY/ H.M. QUEEN ELIZABETH II/ H.R.H. THE DUKE OF EDINBURGH" in Gold

1988, July 7 Litho. *Perf. 14*

1288 CD339 1r multicolored .30 .30
1289 CD339 2r multicolored .58 .58
1290 CD339 12r multicolored 3.40 3.40
Nos. 1288-1290 (3) 4.28 4.28

Souvenir Sheet

1291 CD339 15r multicolored 4.25 4.25

Transportation and Communication Decade for Asia and the Pacific — A198

Globe and: 2r, Postal communications. 3r, Earth satellite telecommunications technology. 5r, Space telecommunications technology. 10r, Automobile, aircraft and ship.

1988, May 31 Litho. *Perf. 14*

1292 A198 2r multicolored .58 .58
1293 A198 3r multicolored .85 .85
1294 A198 5r multicolored 1.45 1.45
1295 A198 10r multicolored 2.85 2.85
Nos. 1292-1295 (4) 5.73 5.73

1988 Summer Olympics, Seoul — A199

Intl. Year of Shelter for the Homeless — A200

1988, July 16

1296 A199 15 l Discus .15 .15
1297 A199 2r 100-Meter sprint .58 .58
1298 A199 4r Gymnastics, horiz. 1.15 1.15
1299 A199 12r Steeplechase, horiz. 3.45 3.45
Nos. 1296-1299 (4) 5.33 5.33

Souvenir Sheet

1300 A199 20r Tennis, horiz. 5.25 5.25

For overprints see Nos. 1311-1315.

1988, July 20

1301 A200 50 l Medical clinic .15 .15
1302 A200 3r Prefab housing .90 .90

Souvenir Sheet

1303 A200 15r Construction site 4.25 4.25

Intl. Fund for Agricultural Development (IFAD), 10th Anniv. — A201

1988, July 30

1304 A201 7r Breadfruit 2.00 2.00
1305 A201 10r Mango, vert. 2.75 2.75

Souvenir Sheet

1306 A201 15r Coconut palm, yellowtail tuna 4.25 4.25

Nos. 1282-1283 Ovptd. 

1988, Dec. 1 Litho. *Perf. 14*

1307 A196 2r multicolored .58 .58
1308 A196 4r multicolored 1.15 1.15

Intl. Day for the Fight Against Aids.

John F. Kennedy (1917-1963), 35th US President — A202

Space achievements: a, Apollo launch. b, 1st Man on the Moon. c, Earth and astronaut driving moon rover. d, Space module and Kennedy. 15r, Kennedy addressing the nation.

1989, Feb. 19

1309 Strip of 4 5.80 5.80
a.-d. A202 5r any single 1.45 1.45

Souvenir Sheet

1310 A202 15r multicolored 4.25 4.25

Nos. 1296-1300 Overprinted for Olympic Winners

1989, Apr. 29 Litho. *Perf. 14*

1311 A199 15 l "J. SCHULT / DDR" .15 .15
1312 A199 2r "C. LEWIS / USA" .58 .58
1313 A199 4r "MEN'S ALL AROUND / V. ARTEMOV USSR" 1.15 1.15
1314 A199 12r "TEAM SHOW JUMPING / W. GERMANY" 3.45 3.45
Nos. 1311-1314 (4) 5.33 5.33

Souvenir Sheet

1315 A199 20r multi 5.25 5.25

No. 1315 has marginal ovpt. "OLYMPIC WINNERS / MEN'S SINGLES / GOLD M. MECIR / CZECH. / SILVER T. MAYOTTE / USA / BRONZE B. GILBERT / USA."

Paintings by Titian (b. 1489) A203

Designs: 15 l, Portrait of Benedetto Varchi, c. 1540. 1r, Portrait of a Young Man in a Fur, 1515. 2r, King Francis I of France, 1538. 5r, Portrait of Pietro Aretino, 1545. 15r, The Bravo, c. 1520. 20r, The Concert, 1512. No. 1322, An Allegory of Prudence, c. 1565. No. 1323, Portrait of Francesco Maria Della Rovere.

1989, May 15 Litho. *Perf. 13½x14*

1316 A203 15 l multicolored .15 .15
1317 A203 1r multicolored .25 .25
1318 A203 2r multicolored .50 .50
1319 A203 5r multicolored 1.25 1.25
1320 A203 15r multicolored 3.75 3.75
1321 A203 20r multicolored 5.00 5.00
Nos. 1316-1321 (6) 10.90 10.90

Souvenir Sheets

1322 A203 20r multicolored 5.00 5.00
1323 A203 20r multicolored 5.00 5.00

"Thirty-six Views of Mt. Fuji" — A204

Prints by Hokusai (1760-1849): 15 l, Fuji from Hodogaya. 50 l, Fuji from Lake Kawaguchi. 1r, Fuji from Owari. 2r, Fuji from Tsukudajima in Edo. 4r, Fuji from a Teahouse at Yoshida. 6r, Fuji from Tagonoura. 10r, Fuji from Mishima-goe. 12r, Fuji from the Sumida River in Edo. No. 1332, Fuji from Fukagawa in Edo. No. 1333, Fuji from Inume Pass.

1989 *Perf. 14*

1324 A204 15 l multicolored .15 .15
1325 A204 50 l multicolored .15 .15
1326 A204 1r multicolored .25 .25
1327 A204 2r multicolored .50 .50
1328 A204 4r multicolored 1.00 1.00
1329 A204 6r multicolored 1.50 1.50
1330 A204 10r multicolored 2.50 2.50
1331 A204 12r multicolored 3.00 3.00
Nos. 1324-1331 (8) 9.05 9.05

Souvenir Sheets

1332 A204 20r multicolored 5.00 5.00
1333 A204 20r multicolored 5.00 5.00

Hirohito (1901-1989) and enthronement of Akihito as emperor of Japan.
Issue dates: #1332, Oct. 16, others, Sept. 2.

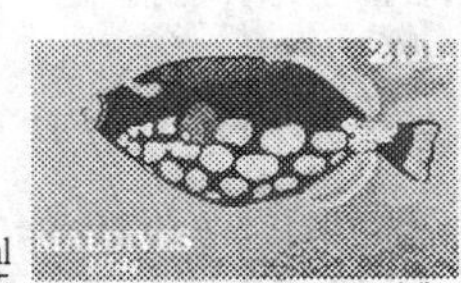

Tropical Fish — A205

1989, Oct. 16 Litho. *Perf. 14*

1334 A205 20 l Clown triggerfish .15 .15
1335 A205 50 l Blue surgeonfish .15 .15
1336 A205 1r Bluestripe snapper .25 .25
1337 A205 2r Oriental sweetlips .50 .50
1338 A205 3r Wrasse .75 .75
1339 A205 8r Treadfin butterflyfish 2.00 2.00
1340 A205 10r Bicolor parrotfish 2.50 2.50
1341 A205 12r Saber squirrelfish 3.00 3.00
Nos. 1334-1341 (8) 9.30 9.30

Souvenir Sheet

1342 A205 15r Butterfly perch 3.75 3.75
1343 A205 15r Semicircle angelfish 3.75 3.75

Nos. 1293-1294 Ovptd. "ASIA-PACIFIC / TELECOMMUNITY / 10 YEARS" in Silver

1989, July 5 Litho. *Perf. 14*

1344 A198 3r multicolored .75 .75
1345 A198 5r multicolored 1.25 1.25

World Stamp Expo '89 Emblem, Disney Characters and Japanese Automobiles — A206

Designs: 15 l, 1907 Takuri Type 3. 50 l, 1917 Mitsubishi Model A. 1r, 1935 Datsun Roadstar. 2r, 1940 Mazda. 4r, 1959 Nissan Bluebird 310. 6r, 1958 Subaru 360. 10r, 1966 Honda 5800. 12r, 1966 Daihatsu Fellow. No. 1354, 1981 Isuzu Trooper II. No. 1355, 1985 Toyota Supra.

1989, Nov. 17 Litho. *Perf. 14x13½*

1346 A206 15 l multicolored .15 .15
1347 A206 50 l multicolored .15 .15
1348 A206 1r multicolored .22 .22
1349 A206 2r multicolored .45 .45
1350 A206 4r multicolored .90 .90
1351 A206 6r multicolored 1.35 1.35
1352 A206 10r multicolored 2.25 2.25
1353 A206 12r multicolored 2.75 2.75
Nos. 1346-1353 (8) 8.22 8.22

Souvenir Sheets

1354 A206 20r multicolored 4.50 4.50
1355 A206 20r multicolored 4.50 4.50

Souvenir Sheet

The Marine Corps War Memorial, Arlington, VA — A207

1989, Nov. 17 Litho. *Perf. 14*

1356 A207 8r multicolored 2.00 2.00

World Stamp Expo '89.

1st Moon Landing, 20th Anniv. A208

1989, Nov. 24 *Perf. 14*

1357 A208 1r *Eagle* lunar module .25 .25
1358 A208 2r Aldrin taking soil samples .50 .50
1359 A208 6r Solar wind experiment 1.50 1.50
1360 A208 10r Nixon, astronauts 2.50 2.50
Nos. 1357-1360 (4) 4.75 4.75

Souvenir Sheet

1361 A208 18r Armstrong descending ladder 4.50 4.50

Railway Pioneers — A209

Designs: 10 l, Sir William Cornelius Van Horne (1843-1915), chairman of Canadian Pacific Railway, map and locomotive, 1894. 25 l, Matthew Murray, built rack locomotives for Middleton Colliery. 50 l, Louis Favre (1826-1879), built the St. Gotthard (spiral) Tunnel, 1881. 2r, George Stephenson (1781-1848), locomotive, 1825. 6r, Richard Trevithick (1771-1833), builder of 1st rail locomotive, 1804. 8r, George Nagelmackers, Orient Express dining car, 1869. 10r, William Jessop, Surrey horse-drawn cart on rails, 1770. 12r, Isambard Kingdom Brunel (1806-1859), chief engineer of Great Western Railway, introduced broad gauge, 1830's. No. 1370, George Pullman (1831-1897), *Pioneer* passenger car. No. 1371, Rudolf Diesel (1858-1913), inventor of the diesel engine, 1892, and diesel train.

1989, Dec. 26 Litho. *Perf. 14*

1362 A209 10 l multicolored .15 .15
1363 A209 25 l multicolored .15 .15
1364 A209 50 l multicolored .15 .15
1365 A209 2r multicolored .48 .48
1366 A209 6r multicolored 1.45 1.45
1367 A209 8r multicolored 1.90 1.90
1368 A209 10r multicolored 2.40 2.40
1369 A209 12r multicolored 2.85 2.85
Nos. 1362-1369 (8) 9.53 9.53

Souvenir Sheets

1370 A209 18r multicolored 4.50 4.50
1371 A209 18r multicolored 4.50 4.50

Anniversaries and Events (in 1989) — A210

Designs: 20 l, Flag of India, Jawaharlal Nehru, Mahatma Gandhi. 50 l, Syringe, opium poppies, vert. 1r, William Shakespeare, birthplace, Stratford-on-Avon. 2r, Flag of France, storming of the Bastille, Paris, 1789, vert. 3r, Concorde jet, flags of France, Britain. 8r, George Washington, Mount Vernon estate, Virginia. 10r, Capt. William Bligh, the *Bounty*. 12r, Ships in port. No. 1380, 1st Televised baseball game, 1939, vert. No. 1381, Franz von Taxis (1458-1517), vert.

1990, Feb. 15 Litho. *Perf. 14*

1372 A210 20 l multicolored .15 .15
1373 A210 50 l multicolored .15 .15
1374 A210 1r multicolored .25 .25
1375 A210 2r multicolored .50 .50
1376 A210 3r multicolored .75 .75
1377 A210 8r multicolored 2.00 2.00
1378 A210 10r multicolored 2.50 2.50
1379 A210 12r multicolored 3.00 3.00
Nos. 1372-1379 (8) 9.30 9.30

Souvenir Sheets

1380 A210 18r multicolored 4.50 4.50
1381 A210 18r multicolored 4.50 4.50

Birth cent. of Nehru (20 l); SAARC Year for Combatting Drug Abuse (50 l); 425th birth anniv. of Shakespeare (1r); French Revolution, bicent. (2r); first test flight of the Concorde supersonic jet, 20th anniv. (3r); American presidency, bicent. (8r); Mutiny on the *Bounty*, bicent. (10r); Hamburg, 800th anniv. (12r); 1st televised baseball game, 50th anniv. (No. 1380); and European postal communications, 500th anniv. (No. 1381).

Johann von Taxis was the first postmaster of Thurn & Taxis in 1489, not Franz, who is credited on No. 1381.

Natl. Independence, 25th Anniv. — A211

Designs: 20 l, Bodu Thakurufaanu Memorial Center, Utheemu. 25 l, Islamic Center, Male. 50 l, Natl. flag, UN, Islamic Conf., Commonwealth and SAARC emblems. 2r, Muleeaage, Male. 5r, Natl.

Security Service, Maldives. 10r, Natl. crest, emblem of the Citizens' Majlis (parliament).

1990, Jan. 1 **Litho.** ***Perf. 14***
1382 A211 20 l multicolored .15 .15
1383 A211 25 l multicolored .15 .15
1384 A211 50 l multicolored .15 .15
1385 A211 2r multicolored .50 .50
1386 A211 5r multicolored 1.25 1.25
Nos. 1382-1386 (5) 2.20 2.20

Souvenir Sheet

1387 A211 10r multicolored 2.50 2.50

French Revolution, Bicent. (in 1989) — A212

Paintings: 15 l, *Louis XVI in Coronation Robes*, by Duplessis. 50 l, *Monsieur Lavoisier and His Wife*, by David. 1r, *Madame Pastoret*, by David. 2r, *Oath of Lafayette at the Festival of Federation*, artist unknown. 4r, *Madame Trudaine*, by David. 6r, *Chenard Celebrating the Liberation of Savoy*, by Boilly. 10r, *An Officer Swears Allegiance to the Constitution*, artist unknown. 12r, *Self-portrait*, by David. No. 1396, *The Tennis Court Oath, June 20, 1789*, by David, horiz. No. 1397, *Jean-Jacques Rousseau and the Symbols of the Revolution*, by Jeaurat.

1990, Jan. 11 **Litho.** ***Perf. 14***
1388 A212 15 l multicolored .15 .15
1389 A212 50 l multicolored .15 .15
1390 A212 1r multicolored .24 .24
1391 A212 2r multicolored .48 .48
1392 A212 4r multicolored .95 .95
1393 A212 6r multicolored 1.45 1.45
1394 A212 10r multicolored 2.40 2.40
1395 A212 12r multicolored 2.85 2.85
Nos. 1388-1395 (8) 8.67 8.67

Souvenir Sheets

1396 A212 20r multicolored 4.75 4.75
1397 A212 20r multicolored 4.75 4.75

Stamp World London '90 — A213

Walt Disney characters demonstrating sports popular in Britain.

1990 **Litho.** ***Perf. 14x13½***
1398 A213 15 l Rugby .15 .15
1399 A213 50 l Curling .15 .15
1400 A213 1r Polo .24 .24
1401 A213 2r Soccer .48 .48
1402 A213 4r Cricket .95 .95
1403 A213 6r Horse racing, Ascot 1.45 1.45
1404 A213 10r Tennis 2.40 2.40
1405 A213 12r Lawn bowling 2.85 2.85
Nos. 1398-1405 (8) 8.67 8.67

Souvenir Sheets

1406 A213 20r Fox hunting 4.75 4.75
1407 A213 20r Golf, St. Andrews, Scotland 4.75 4.75

Penny Black, 150th Anniv. A214

1990, May 3 **Litho.** ***Perf. 15x14***
1408 A214 8r Silhouettes 2.00 2.00
1409 A214 12r Silhouettes, diff. 3.00 3.00

Souvenir Sheet

1410 A214 18r Penny Black 4.50 4.50

Queen Mother 90th Birthday
A215 A216

1990, July 8 ***Perf. 14***
1411 A215 6r shown 1.50 1.50
1412 A216 6r shown 1.50 1.50
1413 A215 6r As Lady Bowes-Lyon, diff. 1.50 1.50
Nos. 1411-1413 (3) 4.50 4.50

Souvenir Sheet

1414 A216 18r On Wedding Day, diff. 4.50 4.50

Nos. 1411-1413 printed in sheets of 9.

A217

A218

A219

Islamic Heritage Year A220

1990, July 22 **Litho.** ***Perf. 14***
1415 A217 1r blue & black .25 .25
1416 A218 1r blue & black .25 .25
1417 A218 1r Building, diff. .25 .25
1418 A219 2r blue & black .50 .50
1419 A220 2r blue & black .50 .50
1420 A219 2r Building, diff. .50 .50
a. Block of 6, #1415-1420 2.25 2.25

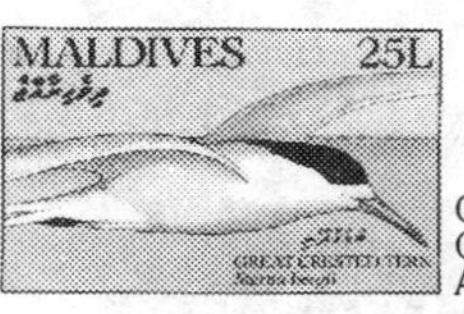

Great Crested Tern A221

1990, Aug. 9 **Litho.** ***Perf. 14***
1421 A221 25 l shown .15 .15
1422 A221 50 l Koel .15 .15
1423 A221 1r White tern .25 .25
1424 A221 3.50r Cinnamon bittern .88 .88
1425 A221 6r Sooty tern 1.50 1.50
1426 A221 8r Audubon's shearwater 2.00 2.00
1427 A221 12r Brown noddy 3.00 3.00
1428 A221 15r Lesser frigatebird 3.75 3.75
Nos. 1421-1428 (8) 11.68 11.68

Souvenir Sheets

1429 A221 18r White-tailed tropicbird 4.50 4.50
1430 A221 18r Grey heron 4.50 4.50

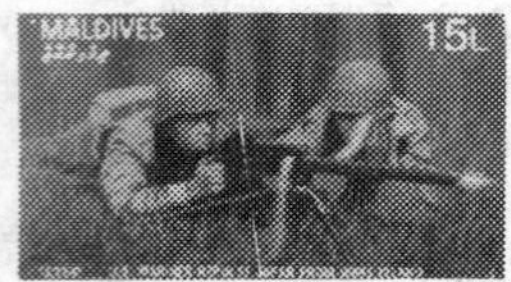

World War II Milestones — A222

Designs: 15 l, US Marines repulse Japanese invasion of Wake Island, Dec. 11, 1941. 25 l, Gen. Stilwell begins offensive in Burma, Mar. 4, 1944. 50 l, US begins offensive in Normandy, July 3, 1944. 1r, US forces secure Saipan, July 9, 1944. 2.50r, D-Day, June 6, 1944. 3.50r, Allied forces land in Norway, Apr. 14, 1940. 4r, Adm. Mountbatten named Chief of Combined Operations, Mar. 18, 1942. 6r, Gen. MacArthur accepts Japanese surrender, Sept. 2, 1945. 10r, Potsdam Conference, July 16, 1945. 12r, Allied invade Sicily, July 10, 1943. 18r, Atlantic convoys.

1990, Aug. 9 **Litho.** ***Perf. 14***
1431 A222 15 l multicolored .15 .15
1432 A222 25 l multicolored .15 .15
1433 A222 50 l multicolored .15 .15
1434 A222 1r multicolored .25 .25
1435 A222 2.50r multicolored .62 .62
1436 A222 3.50r multicolored .88 .88
1437 A222 4r multicolored 1.00 1.00
1438 A222 6r multicolored 1.50 1.50
1439 A222 10r multicolored 2.50 2.50
1440 A222 12r multicolored 3.00 3.00
Nos. 1431-1440 (10) 10.20 10.20

Souvenir Sheet

1441 A222 18r multicolored 4.50 4.50

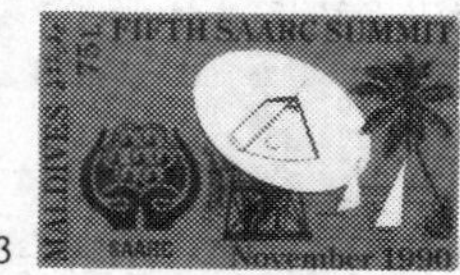

A223

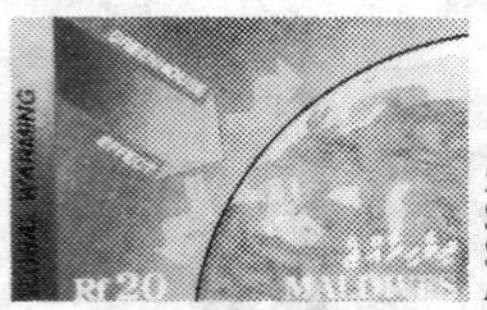

5th SAARC Summit A224

1990, Nov. 21 **Litho.** ***Perf. 14***
1442 A223 75 l Satellite communications .18 .18
1443 A223 3.50r Flags .88 .88

Souvenir Sheet

1444 A224 20r Map 5.00 5.00

Flowers — A225 Bonsai — A226

1990, Dec. 9 **Litho.** ***Perf. 14***
1445 A225 20 l Spathoglottis plicata .15 .15
1446 A225 75 l Hippeastrum puniceum .18 .18
1447 A225 2r Tecoma stans .50 .50
1448 A225 3.50r Catharanthus roseus .88 .88
1449 A225 10r Ixora coccinea 2.50 2.50
1450 A225 12r Clitoria ternatea 3.00 3.00
1451 A225 15r Caesalpinia pulcherrima 3.75 3.75
Nos. 1445-1451 (7) 10.96 10.96

Souvenir Sheets

1452 A225 20r Rosa sp. 5.00 5.00
1453 A225 20r Plumeria obtusa 5.00 5.00
1454 A225 20r Jasminum grandiflorum 5.00 5.00
1455 A225 20r Hibiscus tiliaceous 5.00 5.00

Expo '90, Intl. Garden and Greenery Exposition, Osaka, Japan.
2r, 3.50r, 10r, 12r are horiz.

1990-91
1456 A226 20 l Winged Euonymus .15 .15
1457 A226 50 l Japanese black pine .15 .15
1458 A226 1r Japanese five needle pine .25 .25
1459 A226 3.50r Flowering quince .88 .88
1460 A226 5r Chinese elm 1.25 1.25
1461 A226 8r Japanese persimmon 2.00 2.00
1462 A226 10r Japanese wisteria 2.50 2.50
1463 A226 12r Satsuki azalea 3.00 3.00
Nos. 1456-1463 (8) 10.18 10.18

Souvenir Sheets

1464 A226 20r Sargent juniper 5.00 5.00
1465 A226 20r Trident maple 5.00 5.00

Expo '90, Intl. Garden and Greenery Exposition, Osaka, Japan.

Issued: 50 l, 1r, 8r, 10r, #1464, 12/9/90; 20 l, 3.50r, 5r, 12r, #1465, 1/29/91.

Aesop's Fables — A227

Walt Disney characters: 15 l, Tortoise and the Hare. 50 l, Town Mouse and Country Mouse. 1r, Fox and the Crow. 3.50r, Travellers and the Bear. 4r, Fox and the Lion. 6r, Mice and the Cat. 10r, Fox and the Goat. 12r, Dog in the Manger. No. 1474, Miller, his Son and the Ass, vert. No. 1475, Miser's Gold, vert.

1990, Dec. 11 **Litho.** ***Perf. 14***
1466 A227 15 l multicolored .15 .15
1467 A227 50 l multicolored .15 .15
1468 A227 1r multicolored .25 .25
1469 A227 3.50r multicolored .88 .88
1470 A227 4r multicolored 1.00 1.00
1471 A227 6r multicolored 1.50 1.50
1472 A227 10r multicolored 2.50 2.50
1473 A227 12r multicolored 3.00 3.00
Nos. 1466-1473 (8) 9.43 9.43

Souvenir Sheets

1474 A227 20r multicolored 5.00 5.00
1475 A227 20r multicolored 5.00 5.00

Intl. Literacy Year.

A228 A229

Steam Locomotives: 20 l, "31" Class, East African Railways. 50 l, Mikado, Sudan Railways. 1r, Beyer-Garratt GM Class, South African Railways. 3r, "7th" Class, Rhodesia Railways. 5r, Central Pacific 229. 8r, Reading 415. 10r, Porter Narrow-guage. 12r, Great Northern 515. No. 1484, American Standard 315. No. 1485, East African Railways 5950.

1990, Dec. 15
1476 A228 20 l multicolored .15 .15
1477 A228 50 l multicolored .15 .15
1478 A228 1r multicolored .25 .25
1479 A228 3r multicolored .75 .75
1480 A228 5r multicolored 1.25 1.25
1481 A228 8r multicolored 2.00 2.00
1482 A228 10r multicolored 2.50 2.50
1483 A228 12r multicolored 3.00 3.00
Nos. 1476-1483 (8) 10.05 10.05

Souvenir Sheets

1484 A228 20r multicolored 5.00 5.00
1485 A228 20r multicolored 5.00 5.00

1990, Dec. 27

Various players from participating countries.

1486 A229 1r Holland .25 .25
1487 A229 2.50r England .62 .62
1488 A229 5r Brazil 1.25 1.25
1489 A229 10r Russia 2.50 2.50
Nos. 1486-1489 (4) 4.62 4.62

Souvenir Sheets

1490 A229 18r Austria 4.50 4.50
1491 A229 18r South Korea 4.50 4.50
1492 A229 20r Italy (dk blue shirt) 5.00 5.00
1493 A229 20r Argentina (blue & white shirt) 5.00 5.00

World Cup Soccer Championships, Italy.

Peter Paul Rubens (1577-1640), Painter — A230

Entire works or details from paintings by Rubens: 20 l, Summer. 50 l, Landscape with Rainbow. 1r, Wreckage of Aeneas. 2.50r, Chateau de Steen. 3.50r, Landscape with Herd of Cows. 7r, Ruins of Palantine. 10r, Landscape with Peasants and Cows. 12r, Wagon Fording a Stream. No. 1502, Landscape with a Sunset. No. 1503, Peasants with Cattle by a Stream in a Woody Landscape. No. 1504, Shepherd with his Flock in a Wooded Landscape. No. 1505, Stuck Wagon.

1991, Feb. 7 Litho. *Perf. 14x13½*

1494 A230 20 l multicolored .15 .15
1495 A230 50 l multicolored .15 .15
1496 A230 1r multicolored .25 .25
1497 A230 2.50r multicolored .62 .62
1498 A230 3.50r multicolored .88 .88
1499 A230 7r multicolored 1.75 1.75
1500 A230 10r multicolored 2.50 2.50
1501 A230 12r multicolored 3.00 3.00
Nos. 1494-1501 (8) 9.30 9.30

Souvenir Sheets

1502-1505 A230 20r each 5.00 5.00

First Marathon Run, 490 B.C. — A231

Events and anniversaries (in 1990): 1r, Anthony Fokker (1890-1939), aircraft builder. 3.50r, Launch of first commercial satellite, 25th anniv. 7r, East, West German foreign ministers sign re-unification documents, Oct. 3, 1990, horiz. 8r, Magna Carta, 775th anniv. 10r, Dwight D. Eisenhower. 12r, Winston Churchill. 15r, Pres. Reagan destroying Berlin Wall, horiz. No. 1514, Brandenburg Gate, horiz. No. 1515, Battle of Britain, 50th anniv., horiz.

1991, Mar. 11 *Perf. 14*

1506 A231 50 l multicolored .15 .15
1507 A231 1r multicolored .25 .25
1508 A231 3.50r multicolored .88 .88
1509 A231 7r multicolored 1.75 1.75
1510 A231 8r multicolored 2.00 2.00
1511 A231 10r multicolored 2.50 2.50
1512 A231 12r multicolored 3.00 3.00
1513 A231 15r multicolored 3.75 3.75
Nos. 1506-1513 (8) 14.28 14.28

Souvenir Sheets

1514 A231 20r multicolored 5.00 5.00
1515 A231 20r multicolored 5.00 5.00

Global Warming A232

1991, Apr. 10

1516 A232 3.50r Dhoni .88 .88
1517 A232 7r Freighter 1.75 1.75

Year of the Girl Child — A233

1991, Apr. 14

1518 A233 7r multicolored 1.75 1.75

Year of the Child A234

Children's drawings: 3.50r, Beach scene. 5r, City scene. 10r, Visualizing fruit. 25r, Scuba diver.

1991, May 10

1519 A234 3.50r multicolored .88 .88
1520 A234 5r multicolored 1.25 1.25
1521 A234 10r multicolored 2.50 2.50
1522 A234 25r multicolored 6.25 6.25
Nos. 1519-1522 (4) 10.88 10.88

Paintings by Vincent Van Gogh — A235

Designs: 15 l, Japanese Vase with Roses and Anemones, vert. 20 l, Still Life: Red Poppies and Daisies, vert. 2r, Vincent's Bedroom in Arles. 3.50r, The Mulberry Tree. 7r, Blossoming Chestnut Branches. 10r, Morning: Peasant Couple Going to Work. 12r, Still Life: Pink Roses. 15r, Child with Orange, vert. No. 1531, Courtyard of the Hospital at Arles. No. 1532, Houses in Auvers, vert.

1991, June 6 Litho. *Perf. 13½*

1523 A235 15 l multicolored .15 .15
1524 A235 20 l multicolored .15 .15
1525 A235 2r multicolored .50 .50
1526 A235 3.50r multicolored .88 .88
1527 A235 7r multicolored 1.75 1.75
1528 A235 10r multicolored 2.50 2.50
1529 A235 12r multicolored 3.00 3.00
1530 A235 15r multicolored 3.75 3.75
Nos. 1523-1530 (8) 12.68 12.68

Sizes: 100x75mm, 75x100mm

Imperf

1531 A235 25r multicolored 6.25 6.25
1532 A235 25r multicolored 6.25 6.25

Royal Family Birthday, Anniversary

Common Design Type

1991, July 4 Litho. *Perf. 14*

1533 CD347 1r multi .25 .25
1534 CD347 2r multi .50 .50
1535 CD347 3.50r multi .88 .88
1536 CD347 5r multi 1.25 1.25
1537 CD347 7r multi 1.75 1.75
1538 CD347 8r multi 2.00 2.00
1539 CD347 12r multi 3.00 3.00
1540 CD347 15r multi 3.75 3.75
Nos. 1533-1540 (8) 13.38 13.38

Souvenir Sheets

1541 CD347 25r Elizabeth, Philip 6.25 6.25
1542 CD347 25r Charles, Diana, sons 6.25 6.25

1r, 3.50r, 7r, 15r, No. 1542, Charles and Diana, 10th wedding anniversary. Others, Queen Elizabeth II, 65th birthday.

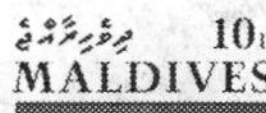

Hummel Figurines — A236

Designs: 10 l, No. 1552a, Child painting. 25 l, No. 1552b, Boy reading at table. 50 l, No. 1552c, Boy with back pack. 2r, No. 1551a, School Girl. 3.50r, No. 1551b, The Bookworm (boy sitting and reading). 8r, No. 1551c, Little Brother's Lesson. 10r, No. 1551d, School Girls. 25r, No. 1552d, Three school boys.

1991, July 25 Litho. *Perf. 14*

1543 A236 10 l multicolored .15 .15
1544 A236 25 l multicolored .15 .15
1545 A236 50 l multicolored .15 .15
1546 A236 2r multicolored .50 .50
1547 A236 3.50r multicolored .88 .88
1548 A236 8r multicolored 2.00 2.00
1549 A236 10r multicolored 2.50 2.50
1550 A236 25r multicolored 6.25 6.25
Nos. 1543-1550 (8) 12.58 12.58

Souvenir Sheets

1551 A236 5r Sheet of 4, #a.-d. 5.00 5.00
1552 A236 8r Sheet of 4, #a.-d. 8.00 8.00

Japanese Steam Locomotives — A237

1991, Aug. 25 Litho. *Perf. 14*

1553 A237 15 l C 57, vert. .15 .15
1554 A237 25 l Series 6250 .15 .15
1555 A237 1r D 51, vert. .25 .25
1556 A237 3.50r Series 8620 .88 .88
1557 A237 5r Class 10 1.25 1.25
1558 A237 7r C 61, vert. 1.75 1.75
1559 A237 10r Series 9600 2.50 2.50
1560 A237 12r D 52 3.00 3.00
Nos. 1553-1560 (8) 9.93 9.93

Souvenir Sheets

1561 A237 20r Class 1080 5.00 5.00
1562 A237 20r C 56 5.00 5.00

Phila Nippon '91.

Butterflies A238

1991, Dec. 2 Litho. *Perf. 14*

1563 A238 10 l Blue salamis .15 .15
1564 A238 25 l Mountain beauty .15 .15
1565 A238 50 l Lucerne blue .15 .15
1566 A238 2r Monarch .50 .50
1567 A238 3.50r Common rose .88 .88
1568 A238 5r Black witch 1.25 1.25
1569 A238 8r Oriental swallowtail 2.00 2.00
1570 A238 10r Gaudy commodore 2.50 2.50
Nos. 1563-1570 (8) 7.58 7.58

Souvenir Sheets

1571 A238 20r Pearl crescent 5.00 5.00
1572 A238 20r Friar 5.00 5.00

No. 1570 inscribed "guady."

Japanese Space Program A239

Designs: 15 l, H-11 Launch Vehicle. 20 l, H-II Orbiting plane. 2r, Geosynchronous satellite 5. 3.50r, Marine observation satellite-1. 7r, Communications satellite 3. 10r, Broadcasting satellite-2. 12r, H-1 Launch Vehicle, vert. 15r, Space flier unit, space shuttle. No. 1581, Katsura tracking and data acquisition station. No. 1582, M-3S II Launch vehicle, vert.

1991, Dec. 11

1573 A239 15 l multicolored .15 .15
1574 A239 20 l multicolored .15 .15
1575 A239 2r multicolored .50 .50
1576 A239 3.50r multicolored .88 .88
1577 A239 7r multicolored 1.75 1.75
1578 A239 10r multicolored 2.50 2.50
1579 A239 12r multicolored 3.00 3.00
1580 A239 15r multicolored 3.75 3.75
Nos. 1573-1580 (8) 12.68 12.68

Souvenir Sheets

1581 A239 20r multicolored 5.00 5.00
1582 A239 20r multicolored 5.00 5.00

Miniature Sheet

World War II Leaders of the Pacific Theater A240

Designs: a, Franklin D. Roosevelt. b, Douglas MacArthur. c, Chester Nimitz. d, Jonathan Wainwright. e, Ernest King. f, Claire Chennault. g, William Halsey. h, Marc Mitscher. i, James Doolittle. j, Raymond Spruance.

1991, Dec. 30 Litho. *Perf. 14½x15*

1583 A240 3.50r Sheet of 10, #a.-j. 8.80 8.80

Grand Prix Race Cars A241

Designs: 20 l, Williams FW-07. 50 l, Brabham BT50 BMW Turbo. 1r, Williams FW-11 Honda. 3.50r, Ferrari 312 T3. 5r, Lotus Honda 99T. 7r, Benetton Ford B188. 10r, Tyrrell P34 Six-wheeler. 21r, Renault RE-30B Turbo. No. 1592, Ferrari F189. No. 1593, Brabham BT50 BMW Turbo, diff.

1991, Dec. 28 Litho. *Perf. 14*

1584 A241 20 l multicolored .15 .15
1585 A241 50 l multicolored .15 .15
1586 A241 1r multicolored .25 .25
1587 A241 3.50r multicolored .88 .88
1588 A241 5r multicolored 1.25 1.25
1589 A241 7r multicolored 1.75 1.75
1590 A241 10r multicolored 2.50 2.50
1591 A241 21r multicolored 5.25 5.25
Nos. 1584-1591 (8) 12.18 12.18

Souvenir Sheets

1592 A241 25r multicolored 6.25 6.25
1593 A241 25r multicolored 6.25 6.25

Miniature Sheet

Enzo Ferrari (1898-1988) — A242

Race cars: a, 1957 Testa Rossa. b, 1966 275GTB. c, 1951 "Aspirarta." d, Testarossa. f, 1958 Dino 246. g, 1952 Type 375. h, Mansell's Formula One. i, 1975 312T.

1991, Dec. 28

1594 A242 5r Sheet of 9, #a.-i. 11.25 11.25

17th World Scout Jamboree A243

Designs: 10r, Scouts diving on reef. 11r, Hand making scout sign, emblem, vert. 18r, Lord Robert Baden-Powell, vert. 20r, Czechoslovakian scout (local) stamp, vert.

1991, Dec. 30

1595 A243 10r multicolored 2.00 2.00
1596 A243 11r multicolored 2.20 2.20

Souvenir Sheets

1597 A243 18r multicolored 4.50 4.50
1598 A243 20r multicolored 5.00 5.00

Wolfgang Amadeus Mozart, Death Bicent. A244

Portrait of Mozart and: 50 l, Schwarzenberg Palace. 1r, Spa at Baden. 2r, Royal Palace, Berlin. 5r, Viennese Masonic seal. 7r, St. Marx. No. 1604, Josepsplatz, Vienna.

1991, Dec. 30

1599 A244 50 l multicolored .15 .15
1600 A244 1r multicolored .25 .25
1601 A244 2r multicolored .50 .50
1602 A244 5r multicolored 1.25 1.25
1603 A244 7r multicolored 1.75 1.75
1604 A244 20r multicolored 5.00 5.00
Nos. 1599-1604 (6) 8.90 8.90

Souvenir Sheet

1605 A244 20r Bust of Mozart, vert. 5.00 5.00

Brandenburg Gate, Bicent. — A245

Designs: 20 l, Flag. 1.75 l, Man embracing child, Berlin wall. 4r, Soldiers behind barricade, demonstrator. 15r, World War I Iron Cross. No. 1610, Helmet. No. 1611, 1939 helmet. No. 1612, Studded helmet.

1991, Dec. 30

1606 A245 20 l multicolored .15 .15
1607 A245 1.75r multicolored .45 .45
1608 A245 4r multicolored 1.00 1.00
1609 A245 15r multicolored 3.75 3.75
Nos. 1606-1609 (4) 5.35 5.35

Souvenir Sheets

1610 A245 18r multicolored 4.50 4.50
1611 A245 18r multicolored 4.50 4.50
1612 A245 18r multicolored 4.50 4.50

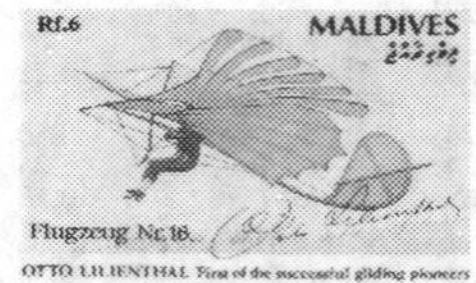

Anniversaries and Events — A246

Designs: No. 1613, Otto Lilienthal, glider No. 16. No. 1614, "D-Day," Normandy 1944, Charles de Gaulle. 7r, Front of locomotive, vert. 8r, Kurt Schwitters, artist and Landesmuseum. 9r, Map, man in Swiss costume. 10r, Charles de Gaulle in Madagascar, 1958. 12r, Steam locomotive. 15r, Portrait of Charles de Gaulle, vert. 20r, Locomotive and coal car.

1991, Dec. 30 Litho. *Perf. 14*

1613 A246 6r multicolored 1.50 1.50
1614 A246 6r multicolored 1.50 1.50
1615 A246 7r multicolored 1.75 1.75
1616 A246 8r multicolored 2.00 2.00
1617 A246 9r multicolored 2.25 2.25
1618 A246 10r multicolored 2.50 2.50
1619 A246 12r multicolored 3.00 3.00
Nos. 1613-1619 (7) 14.50 14.50

Souvenir Sheets

1620 A246 15r multicolored 3.75 3.75
1621 A246 20r multicolored 5.00 5.00

First glider flight, cent. (#1613). Charles de Gaulle, birth cent. in 1990 (#1614, #1618, & #1620). Trans-Siberian Railway, cent. (#1615, #1619 & #1621). Hanover, 750th anniv. (#1616). Swiss Confederation, 700th anniv. (#1617).

No. 1621 contains one 58x43mm stamp.

Birds — A247

Perf. 14¹/₂, 13 (6.50r+50 l, 30r, 40r)

1992-94

1624 A247 10 l Numenius phaeopus .15 .15
1625 A247 25 l Egretta alba .15 .15
1626 A247 50 l Ardea cinerea .15 .15
1627 A247 2r Phalacro- corax aristotelis .50 .50
1628 A247 3.50r Sterna dougallii .90 .90
1629 A247 5r Tringa nebularia 1.25 1.25
1630 A247 6.50r +50 l Neophron percnopterus 1.40 1.40
1631 A247 8r Upupa epops 2.00 2.00
1632 A247 10r Elanus caeruleus 2.50 2.50
1633 A247 25r Eudocimus ruber 6.25 6.25
1634 A247 30r Falco peregrinus 6.00 6.00
1635 A247 40r Milvus migrans 8.00 8.00
1636 A247 50r Pluvialis squatarola 10.00 10.00
Nos. 1624-1636 (13) 39.25 39.25

Issued: 10 l, 25 l, 50 l, 2r, 3.50r, 5r, 8r, 10r, 25r, 2/17/92; 6.50r+50 l, 30r, 11/93; 40r, 1994(?).

Queen Elizabeth II's Accession to the Throne, 40th Anniv.

Common Design Type

1992, Feb. 6 *Perf. 14*

1637 CD348 1r multicolored .25 .25
1638 CD348 3.50r multicolored .90 .90
1639 CD348 7r multicolored 1.75 1.75
1640 CD348 10r multicolored 2.50 2.50
Nos. 1637-1640 (4) 5.40 5.40

Souvenir Sheets

1641 CD348 18r Queen, palm trees 4.50 4.50
1642 CD348 18r Queen, boat 4.50 4.50

This set differs from the common design in that the Queen's portrait and local view are separated by a curved line rather than with a cypher outline.

MALDIVES 50l

Disney Characters on World Tour — A248

Goofy - Time On His Hands

Designs: 25 l, Mickey on Flying Carpet Airways. 50 l, Goofy at Big Ben, London. 1r, Mickey in Holland. 2r, Pluto eating pasta, Italy. 3r, Mickey, Donald do sombero stomp in Mexico. 3.50r, Mickey, Goofy, and Donald form Miki Tiki, Polynesia. 5r, Goofy's Alpine antics, Austria. 7r, Mickey Maus, Germany. 10r, Donald as Samurai Duck. 12r, Mickey in Russia. 15r, Mickey's Oom-pah Band in Germany. 25r, Mickey, globe. No. 1651, Donald in Ireland chasing leprechaun with pot of gold at end of rainbow, horiz. No. 1655A, Pluto, kangaroo with joey, Australia.

1992, Feb. 4 *Perf. 13x13¹/₂*

1643 A248 25 l multi .15 .15
1644 A248 50 l multi .15 .15
1645 A248 1r multi .25 .25
1646 A248 2r multi .50 .50
1647 A248 3r multi .75 .75
1648 A248 3.50r multi .70 .70
1649 A248 5r multi 1.00 1.00
1650 A248 7r multi 1.40 1.40
1651 A248 10r multi 2.00 2.00
1652 A248 12r multi 2.50 2.50
1653 A248 15r multi 3.75 3.75
Nos. 1643-1653 (11) 13.15 13.15

Souvenir Sheets

1654 A248 25r multi 6.25 6.25
1655 A248 25r multi 5.00 5.00
1655A A248 25r multi 5.00 5.00

While the rest of the set has the same issue date as Nos. 1644-1645, 1647, 1653-1654, their dollar value was lower when they were released.

Fish A249

1992, Mar. 23 Litho. *Perf. 14*

1656 A249 7 l Blue surgeonfish .15 .15
1657 A249 20 l Bigeye .15 .15
1658 A249 50 l Yellowfin tuna .15 .15
1659 A249 1r Two-spot red snapper .20 .20
1660 A249 3.50r Sabre squirrelfish .70 .70
1661 A249 5r Picasso triggerfish 1.00 1.00
1662 A249 8r Bennet's butterfly fish 1.60 1.60
1663 A249 10r Parrotfish 2.00 2.00
1664 A249 12r Grouper 2.50 2.50
1665 A249 15r Skipjack tuna 3.00 3.00
Nos. 1656-1665 (10) 11.45 11.45

Souvenir Sheets

1666 A249 20r Clownfish 4.00 4.00
1667 A249 20r Sweetlips 4.00 4.00
1667A A249 20r Threadfin butterflyfish 4.00 4.00
1667B A249 20r Clown triggerfish 4.00 4.00

World Columbian Stamp Expo '92, Chicago A250

Walt Disney characters in Chicago: 1r, Mickey as Indian with Jean Baptiste Pointe du Sable, founder of Chicago. 3.50r, Donald at old Chicago post office, 1831. 7r, Donald in old Fort Dearborn. 15r, Goofy, mastodon at Museum of Science and Industry. 25r, Minnie and Mickey at Ferris wheel midway, Columbian Exposition, 1893, horiz.

1992, Apr. 15 *Perf. 13¹/₂x14*

1668 A250 1r multicolored .20 .20
1669 A250 3.50r multicolored .70 .70
1670 A250 7r multicolored 1.40 1.40
1671 A250 15r multicolored 3.00 3.00
Nos. 1668-1671 (4) 5.30 5.30

Souvenir Sheet

Perf. 14x13¹/₂

1672 A250 25r multicolored 5.00 5.00

No. 1671 identifies Field Museum as Museum of Science and Industry.

Granada '92 — A251

Disney characters in old Alhambra, Granada: 2r, Minnie in Court of Lions. 5r, Goofy bathing in Lions Fountain. 8r, Mickey walking near Gate of Justice. 12r, Donald Duck serenading Daisy in Vermilion Towers. No. 1682, Goofy and Mickey outside Towers of the Alhambra.

1992, Apr. 15 *Perf. 13¹/₂x14*

1678 A251 2r multicolored .40 .40
1679 A251 5r multicolored 1.00 1.00
1680 A251 8r multicolored 1.60 1.60
1681 A251 12r multicolored 2.50 2.50
Nos. 1678-1681 (4) 5.50 5.50

Souvenir Sheet

1682 A251 25r multicolored 5.00 5.00

A252

Flowers of the World — A253

1992, Apr. 26 Litho. *Perf. 14¹/₂*

1688 A252 25 l United States .15 .15
1689 A252 50 l Australia .15 .15
1690 A252 2r England .40 .40
1691 A252 3.50r Brazil .70 .70
1692 A252 5r Holland 1.00 1.00
1693 A252 8r France 1.60 1.60
1694 A252 10r Japan 2.00 2.00
1695 A252 15r Africa 3.00 3.00
Nos. 1688-1695 (8) 9.00 9.00

Souvenir Sheets

Perf. 14

1696 A253 25r org, yel & red vio flowers 5.00 5.00
1696A A253 25r Red, pink & yellow flowers 5.00 5.00

No. 1696 contains one 57x43mm stamp. No. 1696A contains one 57x34mm stamp.

Natl. Security Service, Cent. A254

1992, Apr. 21 *Perf. 14*

1697 A254 3.50r Coast Guard .70 .70
1698 A254 5r Infantry 1.00 1.00
1699 A254 10r Aakoatey 2.00 2.00
1700 A254 15r Fire department 3.00 3.00
Nos. 1697-1700 (4) 6.70 6.70

Souvenir Sheet

1701 A254 20r Sultan in procession 4.00 4.00

A255

MALDIVES

A256

Mushrooms: 10 l, Laetiporus sulphureus. 25 l, Coprinus atramentarius. 50 l, Gandoderma lucidum. 3.50r, Russula aurata. 5r, Polyporus umbellatus. 8r, Suillus grevillei. 10r, Clavaria zollingeri. No. 1709, Boletus edulis. No. 1710, Trametes cinnabarina. No. 1711, Marasmius oreades.

1992, May 14 Litho. *Perf. 14*

1702 A255 10 l multicolored .15 .15
1703 A255 25 l multicolored .15 .15
1704 A255 50 l multicolored .15 .15
1705 A255 3.50r multicolored .70 .70
1706 A255 5r multicolored 1.00 1.00
1707 A255 8r multicolored 1.60 1.60
1708 A255 10r multicolored 2.00 2.00
1709 A255 25r multicolored 5.00 5.00
Nos. 1702-1709 (8) 10.75 10.75

Souvenir Sheets

1710 A255 25r multicolored 5.00 5.00
1711 A255 25r multicolored 5.00 5.00

1992, June 1

1712 A256 10 l Hurdles .15 .15
1713 A256 1r Boxing .20 .20
1714 A256 3.50r Women's running .70 .70
1715 A256 5r Discus 1.00 1.00
1716 A256 7r Basketball 1.40 1.40
1717 A256 10r Running 2.00 2.00
1718 A256 12r Rhythmic gymnastics 2.50 2.50
1719 A256 20r Fencing 4.00 4.00
Nos. 1712-1719 (8) 11.95 11.95

Souvenir Sheets

1720 A256 25r Torch 5.00 5.00
1721 A256 25r Olympic rings, flags 5.00 5.00

1992 Summer Olympics, Barcelona.

A256a

Dinosaurs — A257

1992 Winter Olympics, Albertville: 5r, Two-man bobsled. 8r, Free-style ski jump. 10r, Women's cross-country skiing. No. 1725, Women's slalom skiing, horiz. No. 1726, Men's figure skating.

1992, June 1 **Litho.** ***Perf. 14***

1722 A256a 5r multicolored 1.00 1.00
1723 A256a 8r multicolored 1.60 1.60
1724 A256a 10r multicolored 2.00 2.00
Nos. 1722-1724 (3) 4.60 4.60

Souvenir Sheets

1725 A256a 25r multicolored 5.00 5.00
1726 A256a 25r multicolored 5.00 5.00

1992, Sept. 15 **Litho.** ***Perf. 14***

1727 A257 5 l Deinonychus .15 .15
1728 A257 10 l Styracosaurus .15 .15
1729 A257 25 l Mamenchisaurus .15 .15
1730 A257 50 l Stenonychosaurus .15 .15
1731 A257 1r Parasaurolophus .20 .20
1732 A257 1.25r Scelidosaurus .25 .25
1733 A257 1.75r Tyrannosaurus .35 .35
1734 A257 2r Stegosaurus .40 .40
1735 A257 3.50r Iguanodon .70 .70
1736 A257 4r Anatosaurus .80 .80
1737 A257 5r Monoclonius 1.00 1.00
1738 A257 7r Tenontosaurus 1.40 1.40
1739 A257 8r Brachiosaurus 1.60 1.60
1740 A257 10r Euoplocephalus 2.00 2.00
1741 A257 25r Triceratops 5.00 5.00
1742 A257 50r Apatosaurus 10.00 10.00
Nos. 1727-1742 (16) 24.30 24.30

Souvenir Sheets

1743 A257 25r Iguanodon, allosaurus 5.00 5.00
1744 A257 25r Hadrosaur 5.00 5.00
1745 A257 25r Tyrannosaurus, triceratops 5.00 5.00
1746 A257 25r Brachiosaurus, iguanodons 5.00 5.00

Genoa '92.

1992 Summer Olympics, Barcelona A258

1992, June 1 **Litho.** ***Perf. 14***

1747 A258 10 l Pole vault, vert. .15 .15
1748 A258 25 l Pommel horse .15 .15
1749 A258 50 l Shot put, vert. .15 .15
1750 A258 1r Horizontal bar .20 .20
1751 A258 2r Triple jump .40 .40
1752 A258 3.50r Table tennis, vert. .70 .70
1753 A258 7r Wrestling 1.40 1.40
1754 A258 9r Baseball, vert. 1.80 1.80
1755 A258 12r Swimming 2.40 2.40
Nos. 1747-1755 (9) 7.35 7.35

Souvenir Sheet

1756 A258 25r Decathlon (high jump) 5.00 5.00

Souvenir Sheets

Mysteries of the Universe — A259

#1757, Loch Ness monster. #1758, Explosion of the Hindenburg. #1759, Crystal skulls. #1760, Black holes. #1761, UFO over Washington State. #1762, UFO near Columbus, Ohio. #1763, Explosion at Chernobyl, 1986. #1764, Crop circles of Great Britain. #1765, Ghosts of English castles and mansions. #1766, Drawings of Plain of Nasca, Peru, vert. #1767, Stonehenge, England, vert. #1768, Bust of Plato, the disappearance of Atlantis. #1769, Footprint of Yeti (abominable snowman), vert. #1770, Pyramids of Giza. #1771, Bermuda Triangle. #1772, The Mary Celeste, vert.

1992, Oct. 28

1757-1772 A259 25r each 5.00 5.00

1994 World Cup Soccer Championships, US — A260

Players of 1990 German team: 10 l, Jurgen Klinsmann. 25 l, Pierre Littbarski. 50 l, Lothar Matthaus. 1r, Rudi Voller. 2r, Thomas Hassler. 3.50r, Thomas Berthold. 4r, Jurgen Kohler. 5r, Berti Vogts, trainer. 6r, Bodo Illgner. 7r, Klaus Augenthaler. 8r, Franz Beckenbauer, coach. 10r, Andreas Brehme. 12r, Guido Buchwald.

No. 1786, Team members, horiz. No. 1787, Unidentified player in action, horiz.

1992, Aug. 10 **Litho.** ***Perf. 14***

1773 A260 10 l multicolored .15 .15
1774 A260 25 l multicolored .15 .15
1775 A260 50 l multicolored .15 .15
1776 A260 1r multicolored .20 .20
1777 A260 2r multicolored .40 .40
1778 A260 3.50r multicolored .70 .70
1779 A260 4r multicolored .80 .80
1780 A260 5r multicolored 1.00 1.00
1781 A260 6r multicolored 1.20 1.20
1782 A260 7r multicolored 1.40 1.40
1783 A260 8r multicolored 1.60 1.60
1784 A260 10r multicolored 2.00 2.00
1785 A260 12r multicolored 2.40 2.40
Nos. 1773-1785 (13) 12.15 12.15

Souvenir Sheets

1786 A260 35r multicolored 7.00 7.00
1787 A260 35r multicolored 7.00 7.00

Souvenir Sheet

New York Public Library — A261

1992, Oct. 28 **Litho.** ***Perf. 14***

1788 A261 20r multicolored 4.00 4.00

Postage Stamp Mega Event '92, New York City.

Walt Disney's Goofy, 60th Anniv. — A262

Scenes from Disney cartoon films: 10 l, Father's Weekend, 1953. 50 l, Symphony Hour, 1942. 75 l, Frank Duck Brings 'Em Back Alive, 1946. 1r, Crazy with the Heat, 1947. 2r, The Big Wash, 1948. 3.50r, How to Ride a Horse, 1950. 5r, Two Gun Goofy, 1952. 8r, Saludos Amigos, 1943, vert. 10r, How to Be a Detective, 1952. 12r, For Whom the Bulls Toil, 1953. 15r, Double Dribble, 1946, vert.

No. 1801, Mickey and the Beanstalk, 1947. No. 1802, Double Dribble, 1946, vert., diff. No. 1803, The Goofy Success Story, 1955.

Perf. 14x13 1/2, 13 1/2x14

1992, Dec. 7 **Litho.**

1789 A262 10 l multicolored .15 .15
1791 A262 50 l multicolored .15 .15
1792 A262 75 l multicolored .15 .15
1793 A262 1r multicolored .20 .20
1794 A262 2r multicolored .40 .40
1795 A262 3.50r multicolored .70 .70
1796 A262 5r multicolored 1.00 1.00
1797 A262 8r multicolored 1.60 1.60
1798 A262 10r multicolored 2.00 2.00
1799 A262 12r multicolored 2.40 2.40
1800 A262 15r multicolored 3.00 3.00
Nos. 1789-1800 (11) 11.75 11.75

Souvenir Sheets

1801 A262 20r multicolored 4.00 4.00
1802 A262 20r multicolored 4.00 4.00
1803 A262 20r multicolored 4.00 4.00

A number has been reserved for an additional value in this set.

A263

Anniversaries and Events — A264

Designs: 1r, Zeppelin on bombing raid over London during World War I. No. 1805, German, French flags, Konrad Adenauer, Charles de Gaulle. No. 1806, Radio telescope. No. 1807, Columbus studying globe. No. 1808, Indian rhinoceros. 7r, WHO, ICN, and FAO emblems. 8r, Green sea turtle. No. 1822, Scarlet macaw. No. 1811, Lion's Intl. emblem and Melvin Jones, founder. No. 1812, Yacht America, first America's Cup winner, 1851. 12r, Columbus claiming San Salvador for Spain. No. 1814, Voyager 1 approaching Saturn. No. 1815, NATO flag, airplanes, Adenauer. 20r, Graf Zeppelin over New York City. No. 1817, Landsat satellite. No. 1818, Count Zeppelin. No. 1819, Santa Maria. No. 1820, Konrad Adenauer. No. 1821, Zubin Mehta, music director, NY Philharmonic, vert. No. 1823, Friedrich Schmiedl (b. 1902), rocket mail pioneer.

1992-93 **Litho.** ***Perf. 14***

1804 A263 1r multicolored .20 .20
1805 A263 3.50r multicolored .70 .70
1806 A263 3.50r multicolored .70 .70
1807 A263 6r multicolored 1.20 1.20
1808 A263 6r multicolored 1.20 1.20
1809 A263 7r multicolored 1.40 1.40
1810 A263 8r multicolored 1.60 1.60
1811 A263 10r multicolored 2.00 2.00
1812 A263 10r multicolored 2.00 2.00
1813 A263 12r multicolored 2.40 2.40
1814 A263 15r multicolored 3.00 3.00
1815 A263 15r multicolored 3.00 3.00
1816 A263 20r multicolored 4.00 4.00
Nos. 1804-1816 (13) 23.40 23.40

Souvenir Sheets

1817 A263 20r multicolored 4.00 4.00
1818 A263 20r multicolored 4.00 4.00
1819 A263 20r multicolored 4.00 4.00
1820 A263 20r multicolored 4.00 4.00
1821 A264 20r multicolored 4.00 4.00
1822 A263 20r multicolored 4.00 4.00
1823 A263 25r multicolored 5.00 5.00
Nos. 1817-1823 (7) 29.00 29.00

Count Zeppelin, 75th anniv. of death (#1804, 1816, 1818). Konrad Adenauer, 25th anniv. of death (#1805, 1815, 1820). Intl. Space Year (#1806, 1814, 1817). Columbus' discovery of America, 500th anniversary (#1807, 1813, 1819). Earth Summit, Rio de Janeiro (#1808, 1810, 1822). Intl. Conference on Nutrition, Rome (#1809). Lions Intl., 75th anniversary (#1811). America's Cup yacht race (#1812). New York Philharmonic, 150th anniv. (#1821).

No. 1823 contains one 27x35mm stamp.

Issue dates: Nos. 1805, 1808, 1810, 1815, 1820, 1822, Jan. 1993. Others, Nov. 1992.

Miniature Sheet

Western Films A265

Actors and film: No. 1824a, Jimmy Stewart and Marlene Dietrich, Destry Rides Again, 1939. b, Gary Cooper, The Westerner, 1940. c, Henry Fonda, My Darling Clementine, 1940. d, Alan Ladd, Shane, 1953. e, Kirk Douglas and Burt Lancaster, Gunfight at the O.K. Coral, 1957. f, Steve McQueen, The Magnificent Seven, 1960. g, Robert Redford and Paul Newman, Butch Cassidy & The Sundance Kid, 1969. h, Jack Nicholson and Randy Quaid, The Missouri Breaks, 1976.

No. 1825, Clint Eastwood, Pale Rider. No. 1826, John Wayne, The Searchers, 1956.

1992 **Litho.** ***Perf. 13 1/2x14***

1824 A265 5r Sheet of 8, #a.-h. 8.00 8.00

Souvenir Sheets

1825 A265 20r multicolored 4.00 4.00
1826 A265 20r multicolored 4.00 4.00

Issued: #1824-1825, 1992; #1825, Jan. 1993.

Miniature Sheet

Opening of Euro Disney Resort, Paris — A266

Disney characters in paintings by French impressionists: No. 1827a, Minnie on theater balcony. b, Goofy playing cards. c, Mickey and Minnie walking by outdoor cafe. d, Mickey fishing. e, Goofy dancing to music of harp player. f, Mickey and Minnie in boat. g, Minnie on dance floor. h, Mickey strolling through country. i, Minnie standing behind Polynesian woman.

1992, Dec. ***Perf. 14x13 1/2***

1827 A266 5r Sheet of 9, #a.-i. 6.30 6.30

Souvenir Sheets

1828 A266 20r Goofy 4.00 4.00
1829 A266 20r Minnie 4.00 4.00
1830 A266 20r Mickey 4.00 4.00

Perf. 13 1/2x14

1831 A266 20r Doinald Duck, vert. 4.00 4.00

SAARC Year of the Environment — A267

Designs: 25 l, Waterfall, drought area. 50 l, Clean, polluted beaches. 5r, Clean, polluted ocean. 10r, Clean island with vegetation, island polluted with trees dying.

1992, Dec. **Litho.** ***Perf. 14***

1832	A267	25 l multicolored	.15	.15
1833	A267	50 l multicolored	.15	.15
1834	A267	5r multicolored	1.00	1.00
1835	A267	10r multicolored	2.00	2.00
		Nos. 1832-1835 (4)	3.30	3.30

Elvis Presley (1935-1977) — A268

a, Portrait. b, With guitar. c, With microphone.

1993

1836	A268	3.50r Strip of 3, #a.-c.	2.10	2.10

South Asia Tourism Year A269

Designs: 7 l, Presidential Palace. 50 l, Fish. 3.50r, Beach Cafe (Bodufinolhu). 10r, Fun Island (Bodufinolhu).

1993, Apr. **Litho.** ***Perf. 14***

1837	A269	7 l multicolored	.15	.15
1838	A269	50 l multicolored	.15	.15
1839	A269	3.50r multicolored	.70	.70
1840	A269	10r multicolored	2.00	2.00
		Nos. 1837-1840 (4)	3.00	3.00

Miniature Sheets

Louvre Museum, Bicent. A270

Details or entire paintings, by Jacques-Louis David: No. 1841a, Madame Seriziat. b, Pierre Seriziat. c, Madame de Verninac. d, Madame Recamier. e, Self-portrait. f, General Bonaparte. g-h, The Lictors Returning to Brutus the Bodies of his Sons (left, right).

No. 1842a, Self-portrait. b, The Woman in Blue. c, The Jeweled Woman. d, Young Girl in her Dressing Room. e, Haydee. f, Chartres Cathedral. g, The Belfry at Douai. h, The Bridge at Mantes.

Paintings by Jean-Honore Fragonard (1732-1806): No. 1843a, The Study. b, Denis Diderot. c, Marie-Madeleine Guimard. d, The Inspiration. e, Tivoli Cascades. f, The Music Lesson. g, The Bolt. h, Blindman's Buff.

No. 1844, The Gardens of the Villa D'Este, Tivoli, by Jean-Baptiste-Camille Corot, horiz.

No. 1845, Young Tiger Playing with its Mother, by Delacroix.

1993, Jan. 7 **Litho.** ***Perf. 12***

1841	A270	8r Sheet of 8, #a.-h. + label	13.00	13.00
1842	A270	8r Sheet of 8, #a.-h. + label	13.00	13.00
1843	A270	8r Sheet of 8, #a.-h. + label	13.00	13.00

Souvenir Sheets

Perf. 14½

1844	A270	20r multicolored	4.00	4.00
1845	A270	20r multicolored	4.00	4.00

Nos. 1844-1845 contains one 88x55mm stamp.

Miniature Sheet

Coronation of Queen Elizabeth II, 40th Anniv. — A271

Designs: a, 3.50r, Official coronation photograph. b, 5r, St. Edward's crown. c, 10r, Dignataries viewing ceremony. d, 10r, Queen, Prince Philip examining banknote.

1993, June 2 ***Perf. 13½x14***

1846	A271	Sheet, 2 each #a.-d.	13.50	13.50

A number has been reserved for an additional value in this set.

Shells — A272

Endangered Animals — A273

1993, July 15 **Litho.** ***Perf. 14***

1848	A272	7 l Precious wentletrap	.15	.15
1849	A272	15 l Purple sea snail	.15	.15
1850	A272	50 l Arabian cowrie	.15	.15
1850A	A272	3.50r Major harp	.70	.70
1850B	A272	4r Royal paper bubble	.80	.80
1851	A272	5r Sieve cowrie	1.00	1.00
1852	A272	6r Episcopal miter	1.20	1.20
1852A	A272	7r Camp pitar-venus	1.40	1.40
1853	A272	8r Eyed auger	1.60	1.60
1854	A272	10r Onyx cowrie	2.00	2.00
1854A	A272	12r Map cowrie	2.40	2.40
1855	A272	20r Caltrop murex	4.00	4.00
		Nos. 1848-1855 (12)	15.55	15.55

Souvenir Sheets

1856	A272	25r Scorpion spider conch	5.00	5.00
1857	A272	25r Black striped triton	5.00	5.00
1857A	A272	25r Bull's-mouth helmet	5.00	5.00

1993, July 20 **Litho.** ***Perf. 14***

1857B	A273	7 l Sifaka lemur	.15	.15
1858	A273	10 l Snow leopard	.15	.15
1859	A273	15 l Numbat	.15	.15
1859A	A273	25 l Gorilla	.15	.15
1860	A273	2r Koalas	.40	.40
1860A	A273	3.50r Cheetah	.70	.70
1861	A273	5r Yellow-footed rock wallaby	1.00	1.00
1862	A273	7r Orangutan	1.40	1.40
1863	A273	8r Black lemur	1.60	1.60
1864	A273	10r Black rhinoceros	2.00	2.00
1865	A273	15r Humpback whale	3.00	3.00
1865A	A273	20r Mauritius parakeet	4.00	4.00
		Nos. 1857B-1865A (12)	14.70	14.70

Souvenir Sheets

1866	A273	25r Asian elephant	5.00	5.00
1867	A273	25r Tiger	5.00	5.00
1867A	A273	25r Giant panda	5.00	5.00

Miniature Sheets

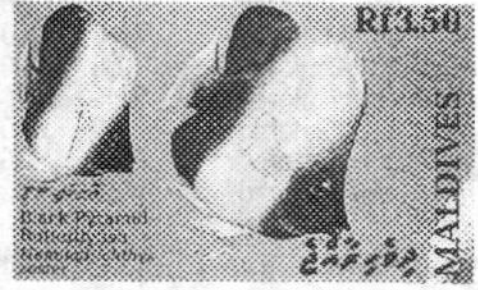

Fish A274

Designs: No. 1868b, Black pyramid butterflyfish. c, Bird wrasse. d, Checkerboard wrasse. e, Blue face angelfish. f, Bannerfish. g, Threadfin butterflyfish. h, Picasso triggerfish. i, Pennantfish. j, Grouper. k, Black back butterflyfish. l, Redfin triggerfish. m, Redfin butterflyfish.

No. 1868n, Yellow goatfish. o, Emperor angelfish. p, Madagascar butterflyfish. q, Empress angelfish. r, Longnose butterfly. s, Racoon butterflyfish. t, Harlequin filefish. u, Wedgetailed triggerfish. v, Clark's anemonefish. w, Clown triggerfish. x, Zebra lionfish. y, Maldive clownfish.

No. 1869, Goldbelly anemone, vert. No. 1869A, Klein's butterflyfish, vert.

1993, June 30 ***Perf. 14x13½***

Sheets of 12

1868	A274	3.50r #b.-m.	8.40	8.40
1868A	A274	3.50r #n.-y.	8.50	8.50

Souvenir Sheets

Perf. 12x13

1869	A274	25r multicolored	5.00	5.00
1869A	A274	25r multicolored	5.00	5.00

Miniature Sheets

Birds — A275

No. 1870: a, Pallid harrier. b, Cattle egret. c, Koel (b). d, Tree pipit. e, Short-ear owl. f, European kestrel. g, Yellow wagtail. h, Common heron. i, Black bittern. j, Common snipe. k, Little egret. l, Little stint.

No. 1871a, Gull-billed tern. b, Long-tailed tropicbird (a). c, Frigate bird. d, Wilson's petrel. e, White tern. f, Brown booby. g, Marsh harrier. h, Common noddy. i, Little heron. j, Turnstone. k, Curlew. l, Crab plover.

No. 1872, Caspian tern, horiz. No. 1873, Audubon's shearwater, horiz.

1993, July 5 ***Perf. 13½x14***

1870	A275	3.50r Sheet of 12, #a.-l.	8.40	8.40
1871	A275	3.50r Sheet of 12, #a.-l.	8.50	8.50

Souvenir Sheet

Perf. 13x12

1872	A275	25r multicolored	5.00	5.00
1873	A275	25r multicolored	5.00	5.00

No. 1871 is horiz.

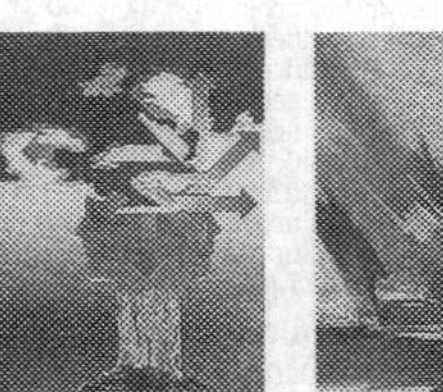

Year of Productivity A276 A277

1993, July 25 ***Perf. 14***

1874	A276	7r multicolored	1.40	1.40
1875	A277	10r multicolored	2.00	2.00

A278

A279

Picasso (1881-1973): 3.50r, Still Life with Pitcher and Apples, 1919. 5r, Bowls and Jug, 1908. 10r, Bowls of Fruit and Loaves, 1908. 20r, Green Still Life, 1914, horiz.

1993, Oct. 11 **Litho.** ***Perf. 14***

1876	A278	3.50r multicolored	.70	.70
1877	A278	5r multicolored	1.00	1.00
1878	A278	10r multicolored	2.00	2.00
		Nos. 1876-1878 (3)	3.70	3.70

Souvenir Sheet

1879	A278	20r multicolored	4.00	4.00

1993, Oct. 11

Copernicus (1473-1543): 3.50r, Early astronomical instrument. 15r, Astronaut wearing Manned Maneuvering Unit. 20r, Copernicus.

1880	A279	3.50r multicolored	.70	.70
1881	A279	15r multicolored	3.00	3.00

Souvenir Sheet

1882	A279	20r multicolored	4.00	4.00

A280

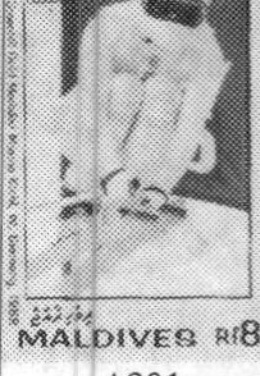

A281

Royal Wedding of Crown Prince Naruhito, Princess Masako: 3.50r, Princess Masako. 10r, Crown Prince Naruhito. 25r, Princess Masako, horiz.

1993, Oct. 11

1883	A280	3.50r multicolored	.70	.70
1884	A280	10r multicolored	2.00	2.00

Souvenir Sheet

1885	A280	25r multicolored	5.00	5.00

1993, Oct. 11

1994 Winter Olympics, Lillehammer, Norway: 8r, Marina Kiehl, gold medalist, women's downhill, 1988. 15r, Vegard Ulvang, gold medalist, cross-country skiing, 1992. 25r, Soviet ice hockey goalie, 1980.

1886	A281	8r multicolored	1.65	1.65
1887	A281	15r multicolored	3.00	3.00

Souvenir Sheet

1888	A281	25r multicolored	5.00	5.00

Polska '93 — A282

Fine arts: 3.50r, Zolte Roze, by Menasze Seidenbeurel, 1932. 5r, Cracow Historical Museum. 18r, Apples and Curtain, by Waclaw Borowski. 25r, Seascape, by Roman Sielski, 1931, horiz.

1993, Oct. 11 **Litho.** ***Perf. 14***

1889	A282	3.50r multicolored	.70	.70
1890	A282	5r multicolored	1.00	1.00
1891	A282	8r multicolored	1.65	1.65
		Nos. 1889-1891 (3)	3.35	3.35

Souvenir Sheet

1892	A282	25r multicolored	5.00	5.00

Butterflies A283

1993, Oct. 25

1893	A283	7 l Commander	.15	.15
1894	A283	20 l Blue tiger	.15	.15
1895	A283	25 l Centaur oakblue	.15	.15
1896	A283	50 l Common banded peacock	.15	.15
1897	A283	5r Glad-eye bushbrown	1.00	1.00
1898	A283	6.50r + 50 l Common tree nymph	1.40	1.40
1899	A283	7r Lemon emigrant	1.40	1.40
1900	A283	10r Blue pansy	2.00	2.00
1901	A283	12r Painted lady	2.50	2.50

1902 A283 15r Blue mormon 3.00 3.00
1903 A283 18r Tamil yeoman 3.50 3.50
1904 A283 20r Crimson rose 4.00 4.00
Nos. 1893-1904 (12) 19.40 19.40

Souvenir Sheets

1905 A283 25r Common imperial 5.00 5.00
1906 A283 25r Great orange tip 5.00 5.00
1907 A283 25r Black prince 5.00 5.00

Nos. 1905-1907 are vert.

Aviation Anniversaries — A284

Designs: 3.50r, Zeppelin on bombing raid caught in British search lights, vert. 5r, Homing pigeon. 10r, Dr. Hugo Eckener, vert. 15r, Airmail service medal, Jim Edgerton's Jenny, mail truck. 20r, USS Macon approaching mooring mast, vert.
#1913, Blanchard's balloon, 1793, vert. #1914, Santos-Dumont's flight around Eiffel Tower, 1901, vert.

1993, Nov. 22 Litho. *Perf. 14*
1908-1912 A284 Set of 5 11.00 11.00

Souvenir Sheets

1913-1914 A284 25r each 5.00 5.00

Dr. Hugo Eckener, 125th birth anniv. (3.50r, 10r, 20r, No. 1913).

Miniature Sheets

First Ford Engine, First Benz Four-Wheeled Car, Cent. — A285

#1915: a, 1915 Model T (b, d-e). b, Henry Ford (e). c, Drawing of 1st Ford engine (b, e-f). d, 1993 Ford Probe GT (e). e, 1947 Ford Sportsman, front (f). f, As "f," rear (e). g, 1915 Ford advertisement (j). h, 1955 Ford Thunderbird (g, i). i, Ford emblem (f, h). j, 1958 Edsel Citation. k, 1941 Ford half-ton pickup. l, Model T.
#1916: a, 1937 Daimler-Benz Straight 8 (b). b, Karl Benz (e). c, Mercedes-Benz advertisement (f). d, 1929 Mercedes 38-250SS (e). e, 1893 Benz Viktoria (f, h). f, Mercedes star emblem (i). g, WWI Mercedes engine. h, 1957 Mercedes-Benz 300SL Gullwing (g). i, 1993 Mercedes Benz SL coupe/roadster (h). j, 1906 Benz 4-cylinder car (k). k, Early Benz advertisement. l, Benz Viktoria, 1893.

1993, Nov. 22
1915 A285 3.50r Sheet of 12, #a.-l. 8.50 8.50
1916 A285 3.50r Sheet of 12, #a.-l. 8.50 8.50

Souvenir Sheets

1917 A285 25r 1933 Ford Model Y 5.00 5.00
1918 A285 25r 1955 Mercedes 300S 5.00 5.00

Peter and the Wolf — A286

Characters and scenes from Disney animated film: 7 l, 15 l, 20 l, 25 l, 50 l, 1r.
Nos. 1925a-1925i: Part 1.
Nos. 1926a-1926i: Part 2.

1993, Dec. 20
1919-1924 A286 Set of 6 .32 .32

Miniature Sheet

1925 A286 3.50r Sheet of 9, #a.-i. 6.25 6.25
1926 A286 3.50r Sheet of 9, #a.-i. 6.25 6.25

Souvenir Sheets

1927 A286 25r Sonia 5.00 5.00
1928 A286 25r Ivan 5.00 5.00

Fine Art — A287

Paintings by Rembrandt: 50 l, Girl with a Broom. No. 1931, 3.50r, Young Girl at half-open Door. 5r, The Prophetess Hannah (Rembrandt's Mother). 7r, Woman with a Pink Flower. 12r, Lucretia. No. 1939, 15r, Lady with an Ostich Feather Fan.
Paintings by Matisse: 2r, Girl with Tulips (Jeanne Vaderin). No. 1932, 3.50r. Portrait of Greta Moll. 6.50r, The Idol. 9r, Mme. Matisse in Japanese Robe. 10r, Portrait of MMe Matisse (The Green Line). No. 1940, 15r, The Woman with the Hat.
No. 1941, Married Couple with 3 Children (A Family Group), by Rembrandt, horiz. No. 1942, The Painter's Family, by Matisse. No. 1942A: The Music Makers, by Rembrandt.

1994, Jan. 11 Litho. *Perf. 13*
1929-1940 A287 Set of 12 17.50 17.50

Souvenir Sheets

1941-1942A A287 25r each 7.50 7.50

No. 1942A issued Feb. 2.

1994 World Cup Soccer US — A288

Players, country: 7 l, Windischmann, US; Giannini, Italy. 20 l, Carnevale, Gascoigne. 25 l, Platt & teammates, England. 3.50r, Koeman, Holland; Klinsmann, Germany. 5r, Quinn, Ireland; Maldini, Italy. 7r, Lineker, England. 15r, Hassam, Egypt; Moran, Ireland. 18r, Canniggia, Argentina.
No. 1951, Conejo, Costa Rica; Mozer, Brazil, horiz. No. 1952, Armstrong & Barboa, US; Orgis, Austria.

1994, Jan. 11 *Perf. 14*
1943-1950 A288 Set of 8 10.00 10.00

Souvenir Sheets

1951-1952 A288 25r each 5.00 5.00

A289

Hong Kong '94 — A290

Stamps, Moon-Lantern Festival, Hong Kong: No. 1953, Hong Kong #416, girls, lanterns. No. 1954, Lanterns, #660.
Cloisonne Enamel, Qing Dynasty: No. 1955a, Vase. b, Flower holder. c, Elephant with vase on back. d, Pot (Tibetan-style lama's milk-tea pot. e, Fo-dog. f, Pot with swing handle.

1994, Feb. 18 Litho. *Perf. 14*
1953 A289 4r multicolored .80 .80
1954 A289 4r multicolored .80 .80
a. Pair, #1953-1954 1.65 1.65

Miniature Sheet

1955 A290 2r Sheet of 6, #a.-f. 2.50 2.50

Nos. 1953-1954 issued in sheets of 5 pairs. No. 1954a is a continuous design.
New Year 1994 (Year of the Dog) (#1955e).

Miniature Sheets of 6 or 8

Sierra Club, Cent. A290a

Various animals: Nos. 1956a-1956b, Prairie dog. c.-e, Woodland caribou. f, Galapagos penguin.
No. 1957, vert: a, Humpback whale. b.-c, Ocelot. d, Snow monkey. e, Prairie dog. f, Golden lion tamarin.
No. 1958: a.-b, Golden lion tamarin. c.-d, Humpback whale. e, Bengal tiger. f, Ocelot. g.-h, Snow monkey.
No. 1959, vert: a.-b, Galapagos penguin. c.-d, Bengal tiger. e.-g, Philippine tarsier. h, Sierra Club centennial emblem.

1994, May 20 Litho. *Perf. 14*
1956-1957 A290a 6.50r #a.-f, each 7.25 7.25
1958-1959 A290a 6.50r #a.-h, each 9.50 9.50

Dome of the Rock, Jerusalem — A291

1994, June 10 *Perf. 13½*
1960 A291 8r multicolored 1.50 1.50

A292

Designs: 25 l, Elasmosaurus. 50 l, Dilophosaurus. 1r, Avimimus. 5r, Chasmosaurus. 8r, Edmontonia. 10r, Anatosaurus. 15r, Velociraptor. 20r, Spinosaurus.
No. 1969: a, Dimorphodon. b, Megalosaurus. c, Kuehneosaurus. d, Dryosaurus. e, Kentrosaurus. f, Baraposaurus (c). g, Tenontosaurus. h, Elaphrosaurus (i). i, Maiasaura. j, Huayangosaurus. k, Rutiodon. l, Pianitzkysaurus.
No. 1970: a, Quetzalcoatlus. b, Daspletosaurus. c, Pleurocoelus. d, Baryonyx. e, Pentaceratops. f, Kritosaurus. g, Microvenator (h). h, Nodosaurus. i, Montanaceratops. j, Dromiceiomimus. k, Dryptosaurus. l, Parkosaurus.
#1971, Gallimimus. #1972, Plateosaurus, vert.

1994, June 20 *Perf. 14*
1961-1968 A292 Set of 8 11.00 11.00

Miniature Sheets of 12

1969-1970 A292 3r #a.-l, each 6.50 6.50

Souvenir Sheets

1971-1972 A292 25r each 4.50 4.50

Nos. 1969-1970 are continuous design.

Locomotives A293

Domestic Cats A294

Designs: 25 l, 2-6-6-0 Mallet, Indonesia, horiz. 50 l, C62, Japan, horiz. 1r, D51, Japan. 5r, 4-6-0 Steam, India. 8r, Class 485 electric, Japan, horiz. 10r, Class WP Pacific, India. 15r, "People" class RM 4-6-2, China. 20r, C57, Japan, horiz.
No. 1981: a, W Class 0-6-2, India. b, C53 Class, Indonesia. c, C-10, Japan. d, Hanomag 4-8-0, India. e, Hakari bullet train, Japan. f, C-55, Japan.
No. 1982, 4-4-0, Indonesia. No. 1983, Series 8620, Japan.

1994, July 4
1973-1980 A293 Set of 8 11.00 11.00

Miniature Sheet of 6

1981 A293 6.50r +50 l, #a.-f. 7.50 7.50

Souvenir Sheets

1982-1983 A293 25r each 4.50 4.50

1994, July 11

Designs: 7 l, Japanese bobtail, horiz. 20 l, Siamese. 25 l, Persian longhair, horiz. 50 l, Somali. 3.50r, Oriental shorthair, horiz. 5r, Burmese, horiz. 7r, Bombay, horiz. 10r, Turkish van. 12r, Javanese. 15r, Singapura, horiz. 18r, Turkish angora. 20r, Egyptian mau.
#1996, Birman. #1997, Korat. #1998, Abyssinian.

1984-1995 A294 Set of 12 17.00 17.00

Souvenir Sheets

1996-1998 A294 25r each 4.50 4.50

Miniature Sheets of 6

1994 World Cup Soccer Championships, US — A295

No. 1999a, 10 l, Franco Baresi, Italy, Stuart McCall, Scotland. b, 25 l, McCarthy, Great Britain, Lineker, Ireland. c, 50 l, J. Helt, Denmark, R. Gordillo, Spain. d, 5r, Martin Vasquez, Spain, Enzo Scifo, Belgium. e, 10r, Emblem. f, 12f, Tomas Brolin, Sweden, Gordon Durie, Scotland.
No. 2000a, Bebeto, Brazil. b, Lothar Matthaus, Great Britain. c, Diego Maradona, Argentina. d, Stephane Chapuasti, Switzerland. e, George Hagi, Romania. f, Carlos Valderama, Colombia.
No. 2001, Hossam Hassan, 2nd Egyptian player.

1994, Aug. 4 Litho. *Perf. 14*
1999 A295 #a.-f. 5.00 5.00
2000 A295 6.50r #a.-f, vert. 7.00 7.00

Souvenir Sheet

2001 A295 10r multicolored 1.75 1.75

D-Day, 50th Anniv. A296

Designs: 2r, Amphibious DUKW approaches Utah Beach. 4r, Landing craft tank, Sword Beach. 18r, Landing craft infantry damaged at Omaha Beach.
No. 2006, Canadian commandos, Juno Beach.

1994, Aug. 8
2003-2005 A296 Set of 3 4.50 4.50

Souvenir Sheet

2006 A296 25r multicolored 4.50 4.50

Intl. Olympic Committee, Cent.
A297 A298

Designs: 7r, Linford Christie, Great Britain, track 1988. 12r, Koji Gushiken, Japan, gymnastics, 1984.
25r, George Hackl, Germany, single luge, 1994.

1994, Aug. 8
2007 A297 7r multicolored 1.25 1.25

2008 A297 12r multicolored 2.25 2.25

Souvenir Sheet

2009 A298 25r multicolored 4.50 4.50

A299

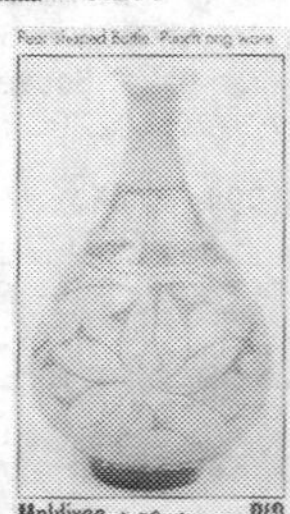

PHILAKOREA '94 — A300

Designs: 50 l, Suwan Folk Village duck pond. 3.50r, Youngduson Park. 20r, Ploughing, Hahoe Village, Andong region.

Ceramics, Choson & Koryo Dynasties: No. 2013a, Pear-shaped bottle. b, Vase. c, Vase with repaired lip. d, Labed vase, stoneware. e, Vase, celadon-glazed. f, Vase, unglazed stone. g, Ritual water sprinkler. h, Celadon-glazed vase.

25r, Hunting (detail from eight-panel screen, Choson Dynasty), vert.

1994, Aug. 8 ***Perf. 14, 13½ (#2013)***

2010-2012 A299 Set of 3 4.25 4.25

Miniature Sheet of 8

2013 A300 3r #a.-h. 4.25 4.25

Souvenir Sheet

2014 A299 25r multicolored 4.50 4.50

Miniature Sheets of 6

First Manned Moon Landing, 25th Anniv. A301

No. 2015: a, Apollo 11 crew. b, Apollo 11 patch, signatures of crew. c, "Buzz" Aldrin, lunar module, Eagle. d, Apollo 12 crew. e, Apollo 12 patch, signatures of crew. f, Alan Bean transporting ALSEP.

No. 2016: a, Apollo 16 crew. b, Apollo 16 patch, signatures of crew. c, John Young gives a "Navy salute." d, Apollo 17 crew. e, Apollo 17 patch, signatures of crew. f, Night launch of Apollo 17.

25r, Launch at Baikonur.

1994, Aug. 8 ***Perf. 14***

2015-2016 A301 5r #a.-f, each 5.50 5.50

Souvenir Sheet

2017 A301 25r multicolored 4.50 4.50

UN Development Plan — A302

1r, Woman, baby, undernourished man, city on island. 8r, Island native, case worker, island, ship.

1994 **Litho.** ***Perf. 14***

2018 A302 1r multicolored .18 .18

2019 A302 8r multicolored 1.40 1.40

Miniature Sheet of 12

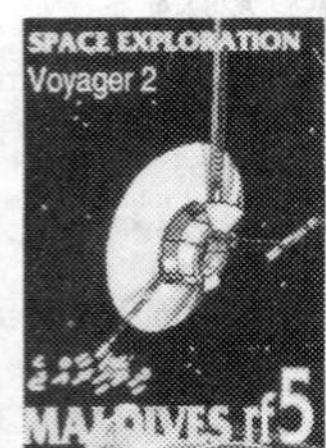

Space Exploration A304

Designs: No. 2020a, Voyager 2. b, Sputnik. c, Apollo-Soyuz. d, Apollo 10 descent. e, Apollo 11 mission insignia. f, Hubble space telescope. g, Buzz Aldrin. h, RCA lunar cam. i, Lunar rover. j, Jim Irwin. k, Apollo 12 lunar module. l, Lunar soil extraction.

No. 2021, David Scott in open hatch of Apollo 9 command module. No. 2022, Alan Shepard, Jr. waving salute from moon, Apollo 14, horiz.

1994, Aug. 8 **Litho.** ***Perf. 14***

2020 A304 5r #a.-l. 11.00 11.00

Souvenir Sheets

2021-2022 A304 25r each 4.50 4.50

Aminiya School, 50th Anniv. A305

15 l, Discipline. 50 l, Arts. 1r, Emblem, hand holding book, vert. 8r, Girls carrying books, vert. 10r, Sports. 11r, Girls cheering, vert. 13r, Science.

1994, Nov. 28

2023-2029 A305 Set of 7 7.75 7.75

ICAO, 50th Anniv. A306

Designs: 50 l, Boeing 747. 1r, De Havilland Comet 4. 2r, Male Intl. Airport, Maldives. 3r, Lockheed 1649 Super Star. 8r, European Airbus. 10r, Dornier Do228. 25r, Concorde.

1994, Dec. 31

2030-2035 A306 Set of 6 4.50 4.50

Souvenir Sheet

2036 A306 25r multicolored 4.50 4.50

Miniature Sheets of 9

Water Birds A307

Designs: No. 2037a, Northern pintail (b, d). b, Comb duck (c). c, Ruddy duck. d, Garganey (a, e, g, h). e, Lesser whistling duck (b, c, f). f, Green winged teal. g, Fulvous whistling duck. h, Northern shoveler (e). i, Cotton pygmy goose (h).

No. 2038, vert.: a, Pochard (b). b, Mallard (c, e, f). c, Wigeon. d, Northern shoveler (e, g). e, Northern pintail (h). f, Garganey (e, i). g, Tufted duck. h, Ferruginous duck (i). i, Red-crested pochard.

No. 2039, Cotton pygmy goose, vert. No. 2040, Garganey, diff.

1995, Feb. 27 **Litho.** ***Perf. 14***

2037 A307 5r #a.-i. 8.25 8.25

2038 A307 6.50r + 50 l #a.-i. 11.50 11.50

Souvenir Sheets

2039-2040 A307 25r each 4.50 4.50

Monuments of the World A308

Designs: 7 l, Taj Mahal. 10 l, Washington Monument. 15 l, Mt. Rushmore Memorial. 25 l, Arc de Triomphe, vert. 50 l, Sphinx, vert. 5r, El Castillo Monument of the Toltec, Chichen Itza, Yucatan, Mexico. 8r, Toltec monument, Tula, Mexico, vert. 12r, Victory Column, Berlin, vert.

No. 2049, Moai statues, Easter Island. No. 2050, Stonehenge.

1995, Feb. 28

2041-2048 A308 Set of 8 4.75 4.75

Souvenir Sheets

2049-2050 A308 25r each 4.50 4.50

No. 2049 contains one 43x57mm stamp, No. 2050 one 85x28mm stamp.

Donald Duck, 50th Birthday (in 1994) — A309

Scenes from "Donald and the Wheel:" 3 l, Racing chariot. 4 l, Standing on log. 5 l, Operating steam locomotive. 10 l, Looking at cave drawing, vert. 20 l, Sitting in "junked" car, vert. 25 l, Listening to phonograph. 5r, Climbing on mammoth. 20r, Pushing old car.

Disney Duck family orchestra, vert: No. 2059a, Donald Duck, saxophone. b, Moby Duck, violin. c, Feathry Duck, banjo. d, Daisy Duck, harp. e, Gladstone Gander, clarinet. f, Dewey, Louie, Huey, oboe. g, Gus Goose, flute. h, Ludwig von Drake, trombone.

Donald Duck family portraits, vert: No. 2060a, Daisy. b, Donald. c, Grandma. d, Gus Goose. e, Gyro Gearloose, f, Huey, Dewey, Louie. g, Ludwig von Drake. h, Scrooge McDuck.

No. 2061, Dixieland band, vert. No. 2062, Donald conducting symphony orchestra. No. 2063, Donald being photographed, vert. No. 2064, Huey, Dewey, Louie in family portrait.

Perf. 13½x13, 13x13½

1995, Mar. 22 **Litho.**

2051-2058 A309 Set of 8 4.75 4.75

Miniature Sheets of 8

2059-2060 A309 5r #a.-h., each 7.25 7.25

Souvenir Sheets

2061-2064 A309 25r each 4.50 4.50

EID Greetings — A310

1r, Mosque. 1r, Rose. 8r, Hibiscus. 10r, Orchids.

1995, May 1 **Litho.** ***Perf. 14***

2065-2068 A310 Set of 4 3.75 3.75

Whales, Dolphins, & Porpoises A311

Nos. 2069-2072: 1r, Killer whale. 2r, Bottlenose dolphin. 8r, Humpback whale. 10r, Common dolphin.

No. 2073: a, Hourglass dolphin. b, Bottlenose dolphin. c, Dusky dolphin. d, Spectacled porpoise. e, Fraser's dolphin. f, Camerson's dolphin. g, Spinner dolphin. h, Dalls dolphin. i, Spotted dolphin. j, Indus river dolphin. k, Hector's dolphin. l, Amazon river dolphin.

No. 2074: a, Right whale (d). b, Killer whale (a). c, Humpback whale (f). d, Beluga. e, Narwhale. f, Blue whale (e, g). g, Bowhead whale (h, k). h, Fin whale (d, e, g). i, Pilot whale. j, Grey whale. k, Sperm whale (l). l, Goosebeaked whale.

No. 2075, Hourglass dolphin. No. 2076, Sperm whale.

1995, May 16

2069-2072 A311 Set of 4 3.75 3.75

Miniature Sheets of 12

2073-2074 A311 3r #a.-l., each 6.50 6.50

Souvenir Sheets

2075-2076 A311 25r each 4.50 4.50

Singapore '95.

UN, 50th Anniv. A311a

Designs: 30 l, Emblem, security of small states. 8r, Women in development. 11r, Peace keeping, peace making operations. 13r, Disarmament.

1995, July 6 **Litho.** ***Perf. 14***

2076A-2076D A311a Set of 3 5.75 5.75

UN, 50th Anniv. — A312

No. 2077: a, 6.50r+50 l, Child, dove flying left. b, 8r, Earth from space. c, 10r, Child, Dove flying right.

25r, UN emblem, dove.

1995, July 6 **Litho.** ***Perf. 14***

2077 A312 Strip of 3, #a.-c. 4.50 4.50

Souvenir Sheet

2078 A312 25r multicolored 4.50 4.50

No. 2077 is a continuous design.

FAO, 50th Anniv. — A312a A313

1995 **Litho.** ***Perf. 14***

2078A A312a 7r Food for all 1.25 1.25

2078B A312a 8r Dolphin-friendly fishing 1.40 1.40

1995, July 6

No. 2079: a, 6.50r+50 l, Child eating. b, 8r, FAO emblem. c, 10r, Mother, child.

25r, Food emblem, child, horiz.

2079 A313 Strip of 3, #a.-c. 4.50 4.50

Souvenir Sheet

2080 A313 25r multicolored 4.50 4.50

1995 Boy Scout Jamboree, Holland A314

No. 2081: a, 10r, Natl. flag, scouts, tents. b, 12r, Scout cooking. c, 15r, Scouts sitting before tents.

25r, Scout playing flute, camp at night, vert.

1995, July 6

2081 A314 Strip of 3, #a.-c. 6.75 6.75

Souvenir Sheet

2082 A314 25r multicolored 4.50 4.50

No. 2081 is a continuous design.

Queen Mother, 95th Birthday A315

No. 2083: a, Drawing. b, Blue print dress, pearls. c, Formal portrait. d, Blue outfit.
25r, Pale violet hat, violet & blue dress.

1995, July 6 *Perf. 13½x14*
2083 A315 5r Block or strip of 4, #a.-d. 1.75 1.75

Souvenir Sheet

2084 A315 25r multicolored 4.50 4.50

No. 2083 was issued in sheets of 2.

Natl. Library, 50th Anniv. A316

Designs: 2r, Boys seated at library table. 8r, Two people standing, two at table.
10r, Library entrance.

1995, July 12 *Perf. 14*
2085 A316 2r multicolored .35 .35
2086 A316 8r multicolored 1.40 1.40

Size: 100x70mm
Imperf

2087 A316 10r multicolored 1.75 1.75

Miniature Sheets of 6 or 8

End of World War II, 50th Anniv. A317

No. 2088: a, 203mm Red Army howitzer. b, Ruins of Hitler's residence, Berchtesgaden. c, Operation Manna, Allies drop food to starving Dutch. d, Soviet IL-1 fighter. e, Inmates, British troops burn last hut at Belsen. f, Last V1 Buzz Bomb launched against London. g, US 3rd Armored Division passes through ruins of Cologne. h, Gutted Reichstag, May 7, 1946.
No. 2089: a, Grumman F6F-3 Hellcat. b, F4-U1 attacking with rockets. c, Douglas Dauntless. d, Guadalcanal, Aug. 7, 1942. e, US Marines in Alligator landing craft. f, US Infantry landing craft.
No. 2090, Allied soldiers with smiling faces. No. 2091, Corsair fighters.

1995, July 6 Litho. *Perf. 14*
2088 A317 5r #a.-h. + label 7.25 7.25
2089 A317 6.50r +50 l #a.-f. + label 7.50 7.50

Souvenir Sheets

2090-2091 A317 25r each 4.50 4.50

Turtles A318

Hawksbill turtle: No. 2092a, Crawling. b, Two in water. c, One crawling out of water. d, Swimming.
No. 2093: a, Spur-thighed tortoise. b, Aldabra turtle. c, Loggerhead turtle. d, Olive ridley. e, Leatherback turtle. f, Green turtle. g, Atlantic ridley. h, Hawsbill turtle.
25r, Chelonia mydas.

1995, Aug. 22
2092 A318 10r Strip of 4, #a.-d. 7.25 7.25

Miniature Sheet of 8

2093 A318 3r #a.-h. 4.25 4.25

Souvenir Sheet

2094 A318 25r multicolored 4.50 4.50

World Wildlife Fund (#2092). No. 2092 was printed in sheets of 12 stamps.

Miniature Sheets

Singapore '95 A319

Mushrooms, butterflies: No. 2095a, Russula aurata, papilio demodocus. b, Kallimoides rumia, lepista saeva. c, Lapista nuda, hypolimnas salmacis. d, Precis octavia, boletus subtomentosus.
No. 2096: a, 5r, Gyroporus castaneus, hypolimnas salmacis. b, 8r, Papilio dardanus, Gomphidius glutinosus. c, 10r, Russula olivacea, precis octavia. d, 12r, Prepona praeneste, boletus edulis.
No. 2097, Hypolimnas salmacis, boletus rhodoxanthus, vert. No. 2098, Amanita musearia, kallimoides rumia, vert.

1995, Oct. 18 Litho. *Perf. 14*
2095 A319 2r Sheet of 4, #a.-d. 1.40 1.40
2096 A319 Sheet of 4, #a.-d. 6.25 6.25

Souvenir Sheets

2097-2098 A319 25r each 5.00 5.00

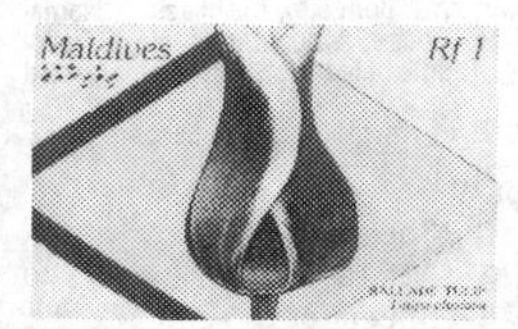

Flowers A320

Designs: 1r, Ballade tulip. 3r, White mallow. 5r, Regale trumpet lily. 7r, Lilactime dahlia. 8r, Blue ideal iris. 10r, Red crown imperial.
No. 2105, a, Dendrobium waipahu beauty. b, Brassocattleya Jean Murray "Allan Christenson." c, Cymbidium Fort George "Lewes." d, Paphiopedilum malipoense. e, Cycnoches chlorochilon. f, Rhyncholaelia digbgana. g, Lycaste deppei. h, Masdevallia constricta. i, Paphiopedilum Clair de Lune "Edgard Van Belle."
No. 2106, Psychopsis krameriana. No. 2107, Cockleshell orchid.

1995, Dec. 4 Litho. *Perf. 14*
2099-2104 A320 Set of 6 6.25 6.25

Miniature Sheet

2105 A320 5r Sheet of 9, #a.-i. 8.25 8.25

Souvenir Sheets

2106-2107 A320 25r each 4.50 4.50

Miniature Sheet

Elvis Presley (1935-77) A321

Various portraits.

1995, Dec. 8 *Perf. 13½x14*
2108 A321 5r Sheet of 9, #a.-i. 8.00 8.00

Souvenir Sheet
Perf. 14x13½

2109 A321 25r multi, horiz. 4.50 4.50

Miniature Sheets

John Lennon (1940-80), Entertainer — A322

No. 2110, Various portraits.
No. 2111: a, 10r, As young man. b, 8r, Younger man with glasses. c, 3r, With beard. d, 2r, Older picture without beard.
No. 2112, Standing at microphone.

1995, Dec. 8
2110 A322 5r Sheet of 6, #a.-f. 5.50 5.50
2111 A322 Sheet of 4, #a.-d. 4.25 4.25

Souvenir Sheet

2112 A322 25r multicolored 4.50 4.50

Miniature Sheets of 9

Nobel Prize Fund Established, Cent. — A323

Recipients: No. 2113a, Bernardo A. Houssay, medicine, 1947. b, Paul H. Müller, medicine, 1948. c, Walter R. Hess, medicine, 1949. d, Sir MacFarlane Burnet, medicine, 1960. e, Baruch S. Blumberg, medicine, 1976. f, Daniel Nathans, medicine, 1978. g, Glenn T. Seaborg, chemistry, 1951. h, Ilya Prigogine, chemistry, 1977. i, Kenichi Fukui, chemistry, 1981.
No. 2114: a, Johannes Van Der Waals, physics, 1910. b, Charles Édouard Guillaume, physics, 1920. c, Sir James Chadwick, physics, 1935. d, Willem Einthoven, medicine, 1924. e, Henrik Dam, medicine, 1943. f, Sir Alexander Fleming, medicine, 1945. g, Hermann J. Muller, medicine, 1946. h, Rodney R. Porter, medicine, 1972. i, Werner Arber, medicine, 1978.
No. 2115: a, Dag Hammarskjold, peace, 1961. b, Alva R. Myrdal, peace, 1982. c, Archbishop Desmond M. Tutu, peace, 1984. d, Rudolf C. Eucken, literature, 1908. e, Aleksandr Solzhenitsyn, literature, 1970. f, Gabriel Garcia Márquez, literature, 1982. g, Chen N. Yang, physics, 1957. h, Karl A. Müller, physics, 1987. i, Melvin Schwartz, physics, 1988.
No. 2116: a, Niels Bohr, physics, 1922. b, Ben R. Mottelson, physics, 1975. c, Patrick White, literature, 1973. d, Elias Canetti, literature, 1981. e, Theodor Kocher, medicine, 1909. f, August Krogh, medicine, 1920. g, William P. Murphy, medicine, 1934. h, John H. Northrop, chemistry, 1946. i, Luis F. Leloir, chemistry, 1970.
No. 2117: a, Carl Spitteler, literatue, 1919. b, Henri Bergson, literature, 1927. c, Johannes V. Jensen, literature, 1944. d, Antoine-Henri Becquerel, physics, 1903. e, Sir William H. Bragg, physics, 1915. f, Sir William L. Bragg, physics, 1915. g, Fredrik Bajer, peace, 1908. h, Léon Bourgeois, peace, 1920. i, Karl Branting, peace, 1921.
No. 2118: a, Robert A. Millikan, physics, 1923. b, Louis V. de Broglie, physics, 1929. c, Ernest Walton, physics, 1951. d, Richard Willstätter, chemistry, 1915. e, Lars Onsager, chemistry, 1968. f, Gerhard Herzberg, chemistry, 1971. g, William B. Yeats, literature, 1923. h, George B. Shaw, literature, 1925. i, Eugene O'Neill, literature, 1936.
No. 2119, Eisaku Sato, peace, 1974. No. 2120, Robert Koch, medicine, 1905. No. 2121, Otto Wallach, chemistry, 1910. No. 2122, Konrad Bloch, medicine, 1964. No. 2123, Samuel Beckett, literature, 1969. No. 2124, Hideki Yukawa, physics, 1949.

1995, Dec. 28 Litho. *Perf. 14*
2113-2118 A323 5r #a.-i., each 8.00 8.00

Souvenir Sheets

2119-2124 A323 25r each 4.50 4.50

1996 Summer Olympics, Atlanta A324

Designs: 1r, Rhythmic gymnastics, Tokyo, 1964. 3r, Archery, Moscow, 1980. 5r, Diving, Stockholm, 1912. 7r, High jump, London, 1948. 10r, Track and field, Berlin, 1936. 12r, Hurdles, Amsterdam 1928.
No. 2131: a, Montreal 1976. b, Decathlon. c, Olympic pin, Moscow, 1980. d, Fencing. e, Olympic medal. f, Equestrian. g, Sydney, 2000. h, Track and field. i, Seoul, 1988.
No. 2132, Olympic torch, vert. No. 2133, Olympic flame, vert.

1996, Jan. 25 Litho. *Perf. 14*
2125-2130 A324 Set of 6 7.00 7.00

Miniature Sheet

2131 A324 5r Sheet of 9, #a.-i. 8.25 8.25

Souvenir Sheets

2132-2133 A324 25r each 4.50 4.50

Sheets of 8

Paintings from Metropolitan Museum of Art — A325

No. 2134: a, Self-portrait, by Degas. b, Andromache & Astyanax, by Prud'hon. c, René Grenier, by Toulouse-Lautrec. d, The Banks of the Biéve Near Bicétre, by Rousseau. e, The Repast of the Lion, by Rousseau. f, Portrait Yves Gobillard-Morisot, by Degas. g, Sunflowers, by Van Gogh. h, The Singer in Green, by Degas.
No. 2135: a, Still Life, by Fantin-Latour. b, Portrait of a Lady in Gray, by Degas. c, Apples & Grapes, by Monet. d, The Englishman, by Toulouse-Lautrec. e, Cypresses, by Van Gogh. f, Flowers in Chinese Vase, by Redon. g, The Gardener, by Seurat. h, Large Sunflowers I, by Nolde.
By Manet: No. 2136: a, The Spanish Singer. b, Young Man in Costume of Majo. c, Mademoisselle Victorine. d, Boating. e, Peonies. f, Woman with a Parrot. g, George Moore. h, The Monet Family in Their Garden.
No. 2137: a, Goldfish, by Matisse. b, Spanish Woman: Harmony in Blue, by Matisse. c, Nasturtiums & the "Dance" II, by Matisse. d, The House Behind Trees, by Braque. e, Mäda Primavesi, by Klimt. f, Head of a Woman, by Picasso. g, Woman in White, by Picasso. h, Harlequin, by Picasso.
No. 2138, Northeaster, by Homer. No. 2139, The Fortune Teller, by Georges de la Tour. No. 2140, Santi (Sanzio), Ritratto di Andrea Navagero E Agostino Beazzano, by Raphael. No. 2141, Portrait of a Woman, by Rubens.

1996, Apr. 22 Litho. *Perf. 13½x14*
2134-2137 A325 4r #a.-h. + label, each 5.75 5.75

Souvenir Sheets
Perf. 14

2138-2141 A325 25r each 4.50 4.50

Nos. 2138-2141 each contain one 85x57mm stamp.
Nos. 2140-2141 are not in the Metropolitan Museum.

Sheets of 5 or 6

Disney Characters Visit China — A326

No. 2142: a, Mickey at the Great Wall. b, Pluto's encounter in the Temple Garden. c, Minnie saves the pandas. d, Mickey sails with the junks. e, Goofy at the grottoes. f, Donald, Daisy at the marble boat.

No. 2143: a, Mickey leads terra cotta statues. b, Goofy's masks. c, Traditional fishing with Donald, Goofy. d, Mickey, Minnie in dragon boat. e, Donald at Peking Opera. f, Mickey, Minnie, in Chinese Garden.

No. 2144, vert: a, Mickey, Minnie snowballing at ice pagoda. b, Donald, Mickey fly Chinese kites. c, Goofy plays anyiwu. d, Mickey, Goofy, origami. e, Donald, Mickey in dragon dance.

5r, Mickey viewing Guilin. 7r, Mickey, Minnie at Moon Festival. 8r, Donald enjoying traditional Chinese food.

Perf. 14x13½, 13½x14

1996, May 10

2142-2143 A326 2r #a.-f., each 2.25 2.25
2144 A326 3r #a.-e. + label, each 2.75 2.75

Souvenir Sheets

2145 A326 5r multicolored .90 .90
2146 A326 7r multicolored 1.25 1.25
2147 A326 8r multicolored 1.40 1.40

CHINA '96, 9th Asian Intl. Philatelic Exhibition.

1996 Summer Olympic Games, Atlanta A327

Gold medalists: 1r, Stella Walsh, 100-meters, 1932. 3r, Emil Zatopek, 10,000-meters, 1952, vert. 10r, Olga Fikotova, discus throw, 1956. 12r, Joan Benoit, women's marathon, 1984.

No. 2152: a, Ethel Catherwood, high jump, 1928. b, Mildred "Babe" Didrikson, javelin, 1932. c, Francina (Fanny) Blankers-Koen, hurdles, 1948. d, Tamara Press, shot put, 1960. e, Lia Manoliu, discus, 1968. f, Rosa Mota, women's marathon, 1988.

Gold medalists in weight lifting, vert: No. 2153a, Yanko Rusev, lightweight, 1980. b, Peter Baczako, middle heavyweight, 1980. c, Leonid Taranenko, heavyweight, 1980. d, Aleksandr Kurlovich, heavyweight, 1988. e, Assen Zlateu, middleweight, 1980. f, Zeng Guoqiang, flyweight, 1984. g, Yurik Vardanyan, heavyweight, 1980. h, Sultan Rakhmanov, super heavyweight, 1980. i, Vassily Alexeev, super heavyweight, 1972.

No. 2154, Irena Szewinska, gold medal winner, 400-meters, 1976. No. 2155, Naim Suleymanoglu, gold medal winner, weight lifting, 1988, vert.

1996, May 27 Litho. *Perf. 14*

2148-2151 A327 Set of 4 4.70 4.70

Miniature Sheets

2152 A327 5r Sheet of 6, #a.-f. 5.40 5.40
2153 A327 5r Sheet of 9, #a.-i. 8.10 8.10

Souvenir Sheets

2154-2155 A327 25r each 4.50 4.50

Olymphilex '96 (#2155).

Queen Elizabeth II, 70th Birthday A329

Designs: a, Portrait. b, As younger woman wearing hat, pearls. c, Younger picture seated at desk. 25r, On balcony with Queen Mother.

1996, June 21 Litho. *Perf. 13½x14*

2164 A329 8r Strip of 3, #a.-c. 5.25 5.25

Souvenir Sheet

2165 A329 25r multicolored 4.50 4.50

No. 2164 was issued in sheets of 9 stamps.

UNICEF, 50th Anniv. — A330

Designs: 5r (#2166), 7r (#2167), 7r (#2167A, girl, blue margin), 10r (#2168), Girls of different races.

25r, Baby girl.

1996, July 10 *Perf. 14*

2166-2168 A330 Set of 3 4.00 4.00

Souvenir Sheet

2169 A330 25r multicolored 4.50 4.50

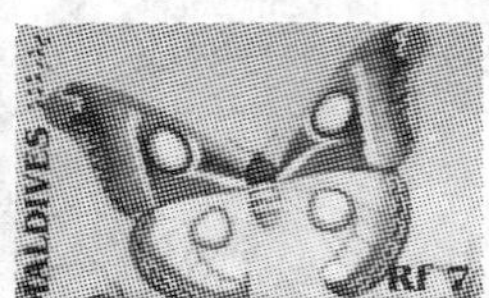

Butterflies — A331

No. 2170, vert: a, Cymothoe cocccinata. b, Morpho rhetenor. c, Callicore lidwina (b, d). d, Heliconius erato.

No. 2171: a, Epiphora albida. b, Satyrus dryas. c, Satyrus lena. d, Papilio tynderaeus. e, Urota Suraka. f, Satyrus nercis.

No. 2172, vert: a, Spicebush swallowtail. b, Giant swallowtail. c, Lime swallowtail caterpillar (b). d, Painted beauty (c). e, Monarch caterpillar. f, Monarch (e, g). g, Monarch caterpillar & pupa. h, Harris' checkerspot.

No. 2173, Heliconius cydno, vert. No. 2174, Zebra, vert.

1996, July 10

2170 A331 7r Strip of 4, #a.-d. 5.00 5.00
2171 A331 7r Sheet of 6, #a.-f. 7.50 7.50
2172 A331 7r Sheet of 8, #a.-h. 10.00 10.00

Souvenir Sheets

2173-2174 A331 25r each 4.50 4.50

No. 2170 was issued in sheets of 8 stamps.

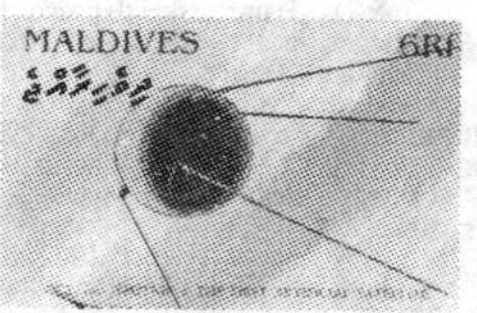

Space Exploration — A332

Designs: No. 2175a, Sputnik I, 1957. b, Apollo 11 Command Module returns to earth, 1969. c, Skylab, 1973. d, Edward White, 1st US astronaut to walk in space, 1965. e, Mariner 9, 1st artificial satellite of Mars, 1971. f, Apollo and Soviet Soyuz dock together, 1975.

25r, Apollo 8 being launched, 1968, vert.

1996, July 10 *Perf. 14*

2175 A332 6r Sheet of 6, #a.-f. 6.50 6.50

Souvenir Sheet

2176 A332 25r multicolored 4.50 4.50

Trains A333

No. 2177: a, Electric container train, Germany. b, John Blenkinsop's rack locomotive. c, DB Diesel electric, West Germany. d, Timothy Hackworth's "Royal George," 1827. e, Robert Stephenson (1803-59). f, Trevithick's "New Castle" locomotive. g, Deltic locomotives, British Rail. h, Stockton No. 5, 1826. i, Passenger shuttle, English Channel Tunnel.

No. 2178: a, Southern Pacific's "Daylight," San Francisco, US, 1952. b, Timothy Hackworth's "Sans Pareil." c, Chicago & North Western, US. d, Richard Trevithick's "Pen-Y-Darran" locomotive. e, Isambard Kingdom Brunel (1806-59). f, Great Western engine of 1838. g, Passenger train, Canada. h, Mohawk & Hudson Railroad "Experiment," 1832. i, "The ICE," Germany.

No. 2179: a, F4 OPH Diesel locomotives, US. b, Stephenson's "Experiment." c, Indian Pacific Intercontinental, Australia. d, George Stephenson's engine, 1815. e, George Stephenson (1781-1848). f, Stephenson's "Rocket," 1829. g, British Rail 125 HST. h, First rail passenger coach, "Experiment," 1825. i, TOFAC, US.

No. 2180, Tom Thumb, 1830. No. 2181, The DeWitt Clinton, 1831. No. 2182, The General, 1855.

1996, Sept. 2 Litho. *Perf. 14*

Sheets of 9

2177-2179 A333 3r #a.-i, each 4.90 4.90

Souvenir Sheets

2180-2182 A333 25r each 4.50 4.50

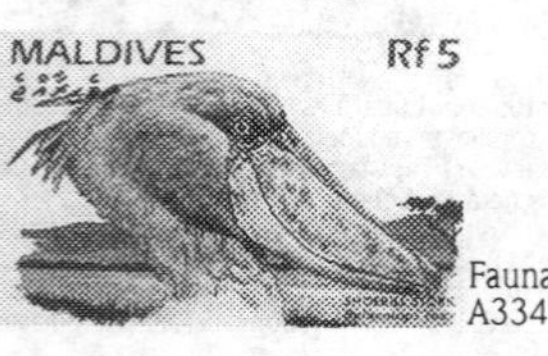

Fauna A334

Endangered animals: No. 2183a, Shoebill stork. , Red-billed hornbill. c, Hippopotamus. d, Gorilla. e, Lion. f, Gray-crowned crane.

No. 2184: a, Giant panda. b, Indian elephant. c, Arrow poison frog. d, Mandrill. e, Snow leopard. f, California condor.

Wildlife, vert: No. 2185a, Yellow baboon. b, Zebra duiker. c, Yellow-backed duiker. d, Pygmy hippopotamus. e, Large-spotted genet. f, African spoonbill. g, White-faced whistling duck. h, Helmeted gunieafowl.

No. 2186, vert,: a, Bongo. b, Bushback. c, Namaqua dove. d, Hoopoe. e, African fish eagle. f, Egyptian goose. g, Saddle-billed stork. h, Blue-breasted kingfisher.

No. 2187, Tiger, vert. No. 2188, Leopard.

1996, Sept. 9

Sheets of 6

2183-2184 A334 5r #a.-f., each 5.40 5.40

Sheets of 8

2185-2186 A334 5r #a.-h., each 7.25 7.25

Souvenir Sheets

2187-2188 A334 25r each 4.50 4.50

Motion Pictures, Cent. — A335

Progressive scenes from "Pluto and the Flypaper:": Nos. 2189a-2189h, Scenes 1-8. No. 2191a-2191i, Scenes 9-17.

Progressive scenes from "Mickey Mouse in The Little Whirlwind:" Nos. 2190a-2190h, Scenes 1-8. Nos. 2192a-2192i, Scenes 9-17.

No. 2193, Scene from "Pluto and the Flypaper." No. 2194, Scene from "Mickey Mouse in The Little Whirlwind."

1996, Dec. 2 Litho. *Perf. 13½x14*

Sheets of 8 + Label

2189-2190 A335 4r #a.-h., each 5.75 5.75

Sheets of 9

2191-2192 A335 4r #a.-i., each 6.50 6.50

Souvenir Sheets

2193-2194 A335 25r each 4.50 4.50

Fauna A336

Designs: a, Saguinus oedipus. b, Bison bonasus. c, Panthera tigris. d, Tetrao urogallus. e, Ailuropoda melanoleuca. f, Trogonoptera brookiana. g, Castor canadensis. h, Leiopelma hamiltoni. i, Trichechus manatus latirostris.

25r, Pan troglodytes.

1996 Litho. *Perf. 14*

2195 A336 7r Sheet of 9, #a.-i. 11.30 11.30

Souvenir Sheet

2196 A336 25r multicolored 4.50 4.50

Hong Kong '97 — A337

Chinese motifs inside letters: No. 2197a, "H." b, "O." c, "N." d, "G" (birds). e, "K." f, "O," diff. g, "N." h, "G" (junk).

25r, "Hong Kong."

1997, Feb. 12 Litho. *Perf. 14*

2197 A337 5r Sheet of 8, #a.-h. 7.20 7.20

Souvenir Sheet

2198 A337 25r multicolored 4.50 4.50

No. 2198 contains one 77x39mm stamp.

Birds — A338

a, Gymnogyps californianus. b, Larus audouinii. c, Fratercula artica. d, Pharomachrus mocinno. e, Amazona vittata. f, Paradisaea minor. g, Nipponia nippon. h, Falco punctatus. i, Strigops habroptilus.

25r, Campephilus principalis.

1997, Feb. 12

2199 A338 5r Sheet of 9, #a.-i. 8.00 8.00

Souvenir Sheet

2200 A338 25r multicolored 4.50 4.50

Eagles

A339 A340

Designs: 1r, Crowned solitary eagle. 2r, African hawk eagle, horiz. 3r, Lesser spotted eagle. 5r, Stellar's sea eagle. 8r, Spanish imperial eagle, horiz. 10r, Harpy eagle. 12r, Crested serpent eagle, horiz.

Bald eagles: No. 2208: a, Wings upward in flight. b, Looking backward on limb. c, Up close, head left. d, Up close, head right. e, On limb. f, In flight.

No. 2209, American bald eagle, horiz. No. 2210, Bald eagle.

1997, Mar. 20 Litho. *Perf. 14*

2201-2207 A339 Set of 7 7.50 7.50
2208 A340 5r Sheet of 6, #a.-f. 5.50 5.50

Souvenir Sheets

2209 A339 25r multicolored 4.50 4.50
2210 A340 25r multicolored 4.50 4.50

Automobiles — A340

No. 2211: a, 1911 Blitzer Benz, Germany. b, 1917 Datsun, Japan. c, 1929 Auburn 8-120, US. d, 1996 Mercedes-Benz C280, Germany. e, Suzuki UR-1, Japan. f, Chrysler Atlantic, US.

No. 2212: a, 1961 Mercedes-Benz 190SL, Germany. b, 1916 Kwaishinha DAT, Japan. c, 20/25 Rolls-Royce Roadster, England. d, 1997 Mercedes-Benz SLK, Germany. e, 1996 Toyota Camry, Japan. f, 1959 Jaguar MK2, England.

No. 2213, 1939 VW built by Dr. Porsche. No. 2214, Mazda RX-01.

1997, Mar. 27

Sheets of 6

2211-2212 A341 5r #a.-f., each 5.50 5.50

Souvenir Sheets

2213-2214 A341 25r each 4.50 4.50

1998 Winter Olympics, Nagano — A342

Medalists: 2r, Ye Qiabo, 1992 speed skating. 3r, Leonhard Stock, 1980 downhill. 8r, Bjorn Daehlie, 1992 cross-country skiing. 12r, Wolfgang Hoppe, 1984 bobsledding.

No. 2219: a, Herma Von Szabo-Planck, 1924 figure skating. b, Katarina Witt, 1988 figure skating. c, Natalia Bestemianova, Andrei Bukin, 1988 ice dancing. d, Jayne Torvill, Christopher Dean, 1984 ice dancing.

No. 2220, Sonja Henie, 1924 figure skating. No. 2221, Andree Joly, Pierre Brunet, 1932 figure skating.

1997, Mar. 13 Litho. *Perf. 14*

2215-2218 A342 Set of 4 4.50 4.50
2219 A342 5r Block of 4, #a.-d. 3.60 3.60

Souvenir Sheets

2220-2221 A342 25r each 4.50 4.50

No. 2219 was issued in sheets of 8 stamps.

Ships A343

Designs: 1r, SS Patris II, 1926, Greece. 2r, MV Infanta Beatriz, 1928, Spain. 8r, SS Stavangerjord, 1918, Norway. 12r, MV Baloeran, 1929, Holland.

No. 2226: a, SS Vasilefs Constantinos, 1914, Greece. b, SS Cunene, 1911, Portugal. c, MV Selandia, 1912, Denmark. d, SS President Harding, 1921, US. e, MV Ulster Monarch, 1929, Great Britain. f, SS Matsonia, 1913, US. g, SS France, 1911, France. h, SS Campania, 1893, Great Britain. i, SS Klipfontein, 1922, Holland.

No. 2227: a, MV Eridan, 1929, France. b, SS Mount Clinton, 1921, US. c, SS Infanta Isabel, 1912, Spain. d, SS Suwa Maru, 1914, Japan. e, SS Yorkshire, 1920, Great Britain. f, MV Highland Chieftan, 1929, Great Britain. g, MV Sardinia, 1920, Norway. h, SS San Guglielmo, 1911, Italy. i, SS Avila, 1927, Great Britain.

No. 2228, SS Mauritania, 1907, Great Britain. No. 2229, SS United States, 1952, US. No. 2230, SS Queen Mary, 1930, Great Britain. No. 2231, Royal Yacht Brittania sailing into Hong Kong harbor.

1997, Apr. 1

2222-2225 A343 Set of 4 4.15 4.15

Sheets of 9

2226-2227 A343 3r #a.-i., each 4.90 4.90

Souvenir Sheets

2228-2231 A343 25r each 4.50 4.50

No. 2231 contains one 57x42mm stamp.

UNESCO, 50th Anniv. — A344

1r, Prayer wheels, Lhasa, vert. 2r, Roman ruins, Temple of Diana, Portugal. 3r, Cathedral of Santa Maria Hildesheim, Germany. 7r, Monument of Nubia at Abu Simbel, Egypt, vert. 8r, Entrance to Port of Mandraki, Rhodes, Greece. 10r, Nature Reserve of Scandola, France. 12r, Temple on the Lake, China.

No. 2232, vert: a, Virunga Natl. Park, Zaire. b, Valley of Mai Nature Reserve, Seychelles. c, Kandy, Sri Lanka. d, Taj Mahal, India. e, Istanbul, Turkey. f, Sana'a, Yemen. g, Blenheim Palace, Oxfordshire, England. h, Grand Canyon Natl. Park, US.

No. 2233, vert: a, Gondar, Ethiopia. b, Bwindi Natl. Park, Uganda. c, Bemaraha Nature Reserve, Madagascar. d, Buddhist ruins of Takht-i-Bahi, Pakistan. e, Anuradhapura, Sri Lanka. f, Cairo, Egypt. g, Ruins at Petra, Jordan. h, Natl. Park of Ujung Kulon, Indonesia.

Sites in China, vert: No. 2234: a-f, Mount Taishan. g-h, Terracotta warriors.

Sites in Japan: No. 2235: a-e, Horyu-Ji.

No. 2236: a, Monastery of Agios Stefanos Meteora, Greece. b, Taj Mahal, India. c, Cistercian Abbey of Fontenay, France. d, Yakushima, Japan. e, Cloisters of the Convent, San Gonzalo, Portugal.

No. 2237: a, Olympic Natl. Park, US. b, Nahanni Waterfalls, Canada. c, Los Glaciares Natl. Park, Argentina. d, Bonfin Salvador Church, Brazil. e, Convent of the Companions of Jesus, Morelia, Mexico.

No. 2238, Temple, Chengde, China. No. 2239, Serengeti Natl. Park, Tanzania. No. 2240, Anuradhapura, Sri Lanka. No. 2241, Monument to Fatehpur Sikri, India.

1997, Apr. 7

2231A-2231G A344 Set of 7 5.75 5.75

Sheets of 8 + Label

2232-2234 A344 5r #a.-h., each 7.25 7.25

Sheets of 5 + Label

2235-2237 A344 8r #a.-e., each 7.25 7.25

Souvenir Sheets

2238-2241 A344 25r each 4.50 4.50

Queen Elizabeth II, Prince Philip, 50th Wedding Anniv. A345

No. 2242: a, Queen. b, Royal Arms. c, Queen, Prince seated on thrones. d, Queen, Prince holding baby. e, Buckingham Palace. f, Prince.

25r, Queen wearing crown.

1997, June 12 Litho. *Perf. 14*

2242 A345 5r Sheet of 6, #a.-f. 5.50 5.50

Souvenir Sheet

2243 A345 25r multicolored 4.50 4.50

Paintings by Hiroshige (1797-1858) A346

No. 2244: a, Dawn at Kanda Myojin Shrine. b, Kiyomizu Hall & Shinobazu Pond at Ueno. c, Ueno Yamashita. d, Moon Pine, Ueno. e, Flower Pavilion, Dango Slope, Sendagi. f, Shitaya Hirokoji.

No. 2245, Seido and Kanda River from Shohei Bridge. No. 2246, Hilltop View, Yushima Tenjin Shrine.

1997, June 12 *Perf. 13½x14*

2244 A346 8r Sheet of 6, #a.-f. 6.75 6.75

Souvenir Sheets

2245-2246 A346 25r each 4.50 4.50

Heinrich von Stephan (1831-97) A347

a, Early mail messenger, India. b, Von Stephan, UPU emblem. c, Autogiro, Washington DC.

1997, June 12 *Perf. 14*

2247 A347 2r Sheet of 3, #a.-c. 3.75 3.75

PACIFIC 97.

A number has been reserved for a souvenir sheet with this set.

South Asian Assoc. for Regional Cooperation (SAARC) Summit A348

1997 Litho. *Perf. 13*

2249 A348 3r shown .55 .55
2250 A348 5r Flags, "SAARC" .90 .90

A349 A350

Birds: 30 l, Anous stolidus. 1r, Spectacled owl. 2r, Buffy fish owl. 3r, Peregrine falcon. 5r, Golden eagle. 8r, Bateleur. No. 2257, 10r, Crested caracara. No. 2258, 10r, Childonias hybrida. 15r, Sula sula.

No. 2260: a, Rueppell's parrot. b, Blue-headed parrot. c, St. Vincent parrot. d, Gray parrot. e, Masked lovebird. f, Sun parakeet.

No. 2261, Secretary bird. No. 2262, Bald eagle.

1997 *Perf. 14*

2251-2259 A349 Set of 9 9.75 9.75
2260 A349 7r Sheet of 6, #a.-f. 7.50 7.50

Souvenir Sheets

2261-2262 A349 25r each 4.50 4.50

1997, June 24 Litho. *Perf. 14½x14*

Flowers: 1r, Canarina eminii. 2r, Delphinium macrocentron. 3r, Leucadendron discolor. 5r, Nymphaea caerulea. 7r, Rosa multiflora. 8r, Bulbophyllum barbigerum. 12r, Hibiscus vitifolius.

No. 2270, horiz: a, Acacia seyal. b, Gloriosa superba. c, Gnidia subcordata. d, Platycelphium voense. e, Aspilia mossambicensis. f, Adenium obesum.

No. 2271, Aerangis rhodosticta, horiz. No. 2272, Dichrostachys cinerea, horiz.

2263-2269 A350 Set of 6 6.25 6.25

Perf. 14x14½

2270 A350 8r Sheet of 6, #a.-f. 8.75 8.75

Souvenir Sheets

2271-2272 A350 25r each 4.50 4.50

No. 2267 is 16x20mm.

A351

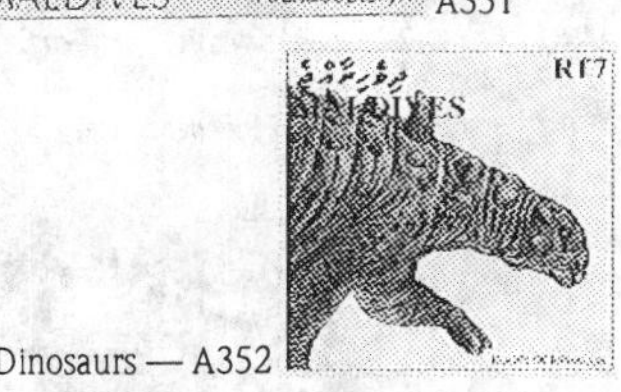

Dinosaurs — A352

Designs: 5r, Archaeopteryx. 8r, Mosasaurus. 12r, Deinonychus. 15r, Triceratops.

No. 2277: a, Diplodocus (b, c, d, e, f). b. Tyrannosaurus rex (c, e, f). c, Pteranodon. d, Montanaceratops. e, Dromaeosaurus (d). f, Oviraptor (e).

No. 2278: a, Euoplocephalus. b, Compsognathus. c, Herrerasaurus. d, Styracosaurus. e, Baryonyx. f, Lesothosaurus.

No. 2279: a, Triceratops. b, Pachycephalosaurus. c, Iguanodon. d, Tyrannosaurus. e, Corythosaurus. f, Stegosaurus.

No. 2280: a, Troodon (d). b, Brachosaurus (c). c, Saltasaurus (a, b, d, e, f). d, Oviraptor. e, Parasaurolophus (f). f, Psittacosaurus.

No. 2281, Tyrannosaurus rex. No. 2282, Archaeopteryx.

1997, Nov. 20 Litho. *Perf. 14*

2273-2276 A351 Set of 4 7.25 7.25

Sheets of 6

2277 A351 7r #a.-f. 7.50 7.50
2278-2280 A352 7r #a.-f., each 7.50 7.50

Souvenir Sheets

2281 A351 25r multicolored 4.50 4.50
2282 A352 25r multicolored 4.50 4.50

1998 World Cup Soccer Championships, France — A353

Past winners: 1r, Brazil, 1994. 2r, West Germany, 1954. 3r, Argentina, 1986. 7r, Argentina, 1978. 8r, England, 1966. 10r, Brazil, 1970.

Various scenes from 1966 finals, England v. West Germany: Nos. 2289a-2289h.

Italian tournament winners: No. 2290: a, Raulo Rossi, Italy, 1982. b, Zoff & Gentile, Italy, 1982. c, Angelo Schiavio, Italy. d, 1934 team. e, 1934 team entering stadium. f, 1982 team. g, San Paolo Stadium, Italy. h, 1938 team.

Brazilian teams, players: No. 2291: a, 1958 team pictue. b, Luis Bellini, 1958. c, 1962 team. d, Carlos Alberto, 1970. e, Mauro, 1962. f, 1970 team. g, Dunga, 1994. h, 1994 team.

No. 2292, Klinsmann, Germany. No. 2293, Ronaldo, Brazil, vert. No. 2294, Schmeichel, Denmark, vert.

Perf. 14x13½, 13½x14

1997, Dec. 10 Litho.

2283-2288 A353 Set of 6 5.60 5.60

Sheets of 8 + Label

2289-2291 A353 3r #a.-h., each 4.25 4.25

Souvenir Sheets

2292-2294 A353 25r each 4.50 4.50

Diana, Princess of Wales (1961-97) — A354

Various portraits, color of sheet margin: No. 2295, Pale pink. No. 2296, Pale yellow. No. 2297, Pale blue.

No. 2298, Diana on ski lift. No. 2299, In polka dot dress. No. 2300, Wearing lei.

1998, Feb. 9 Litho. *Perf. 13½*

Sheets of 6

2295-2297 A354 7r #a.-f., each 7.50 7.50

Souvenir Sheets

2298-2300 A354 25r each 4.50 4.50

John F. Kennedy (1917-63) A355

Various portraits.

1998 Litho. *Perf. 13½x14*

2301 A355 5r Sheet of 9, #a.-i. 8.00 8.00

Nelson Mandela, Pres. of South Africa — A356

1998 *Perf. 14*
2302 A356 4r multicolored 1.25 1.25

Classic Airplanes A357

No. 2303: a, Yakovlev Yak 18. b, Beechcraft Bonanza. c, Piper Cub. d, Tupolev Tu-95. e, Lockheed C-130 Hercules. f, Piper PA-28 Cherokee. g, Mikoyan-Gurevich MiG-21. h, Pilatus PC-6 Turbo Porter. i, Antonov An-2.
25r, KC-135E.

1998
2303 A357 5r Sheet of 9, #a.-i. 8.00 8.00

Souvenir Sheet
2304 A357 25r multicolored 4.50 4.50

No. 2304 contains one 85x28mm stamp.

MALI

'mä-lē

(Federation of Mali)

LOCATION — West Africa
GOVT. — Republic within French Community
AREA — 531,000 sq. mi.
POP. — 5,862,000 (est.)
CAPITAL — Dakar and Bamako

The Federation of Mali, founded Jan. 17, 1959, consisted of the Republic of Senegal and the French Sudan. It broke up in June, 1960. See Senegal.

100 Centimes = 1 Franc

Catalogue values for all unused stamps in this country are for Never Hinged items.

Flag and Map of Mali A1

Unwmk.
1959, Nov. 7 Engr. *Perf. 13*
1 A1 25fr grn, car & dp claret .35 .35

Founding of the Federation of Mali.

Imperforates
Most Mali stamps exist imperforate in issued and trial colors, and also in small presentation sheets in issued colors.

Parrotfish A2

Fish: 10fr, Triggerfish. 15fr, Psetta. 20fr, Blepharis crinitus. 25fr, Butterflyfish. 30fr, Surgeonfish. 85fr, Dentex.

1960, Mar. 5
Fish in Natural Colors

2	A2	5fr olive	.18	.15
3	A2	10fr brt grnsh blue	.20	.15
4	A2	15fr dark blue	.25	.16
5	A2	20fr gray green	.38	.20
6	A2	25fr slate green	.42	.25
7	A2	30fr dark blue	.60	.40
8	A2	85fr dark green	1.40	1.00
		Nos. 2-8 (7)	3.43	2.31

For overprints see Nos. 10-12.

Common Design Types pictured following the introduction.

C.C.T.A. Issue
Common Design Type

1960, May 21 *Perf. 13*
9 CD106 25fr lt violet & magenta .70 .55

MALI

Republic of

GOVT. — Republic
AREA — 463,500 sq. mi.
POP. — 5,990,000 (est. 1977)
CAPITAL — Bamako

The Republic of Mali, formerly the French Sudan, proclaimed its independence on June 20, 1960, when the Federation of Mali ceased to exist.

Nos. 5, 6 and 8 Overprinted "REPUBLIQUE DU MALI" and Bar

Unwmk.
1961, Jan. 15 Engr. *Perf. 13*
Fish in Natural Colors

10	A2	20fr gray green	.32	.25
11	A2	25fr slate green	.40	.25
12	A2	85fr dark green	.90	.55
		Nos. 10-12 (3)	1.62	1.05

Pres. Mamadou Konate — A3

Design: 25fr, Pres. Modibo Keita.

1961, Mar. 18

13	A3	20fr green & baclk	.15	.15
14	A3	25fr maroon & black	.18	.15
		Set value		.15

For miniature sheet see No. C11a.

Reading Class, Bullock Team and Factory — A4

1961, Sept. 22 Unwmk. *Perf. 13*
15 A4 25fr multi .35 .20

First anniversary of Independence.

Shepherd and Sheep — A5

Designs: 1fr, 10fr, 40fr, Cattle. 2fr, 15fr, 50fr, Mali Arts Museum. 3fr, 20fr, 60fr, Plowing. 4fr, 25fr, 85fr, Harvester.

Unwmk.
1961, Dec. 24 Engr. *Perf. 13*

16	A5	50c car rose, blk & dk grn	.15	.15
17	A5	1fr grn, bl & bister	.15	.15
18	A5	2fr ultra, grn & org red	.15	.15
19	A5	3fr bl, grn & brn	.15	.15
20	A5	4fr bl grn, indigo & bis	.15	.15
21	A5	5fr bl, olive & maroon	.15	.15
22	A5	10fr ol blk, bl & sepia	.15	.15
23	A5	15fr ultra, grn & bis brn	.15	.15
24	A5	20fr bl, grn & org red	.16	.15
25	A5	25fr dk bl & yel grn	.20	.15
26	A5	30fr vio, grn & dk brn	.24	.16
27	A5	40fr sl grn, bl & org red	.32	.15
28	A5	50fr ultra, grn & rose car	.30	.15
29	A5	60fr blue, green & brown	.40	.16
30	A5	85fr bl, bis & dk red brn	.60	.20
		Set value	2.65	1.20

King Mohammed V of Morocco and Map of Africa — A6

1962, Jan. 4 Photo. *Perf. 12*

31	A6	25fr multicolored	.20	.15
32	A6	50fr multicolored	.38	.15
		Set value		.24

1st anniv. of the conference of African heads of state at Casablanca.

Patrice Lumumba A7

1962, Feb. 12 Unwmk. *Perf. 12*
33 A7 25fr choc & brn org .16 .15
34 A7 100fr choc & emerald .65 .38

Issued in memory of Patrice Lumumba, Premier of the Congo (Democratic) Republic.

Pegasus and UPU Monument, Bern — A8

1962, Apr. 21 *Perf. 12½x12*
35 A8 85fr red brn, yel & brt grn .65 .50

1st anniv. of Mali's admission to the UPU.

Map of Africa and Post Horn — A8a

1962, Apr. 23 *Perf. 13½x13*
36 A8a 25fr dk red brn & dp grn .18 .15
37 A8a 85fr dp green & org .60 .35

Establishment of African Postal Union.

Sansanding Dam — A9

Cotton Plant — A10

1962, Oct. 27 Photo. *Perf. 12*
38 A9 25fr dk gray, ultra & grn .18 .15
39 A10 45fr multicolored .42 .20

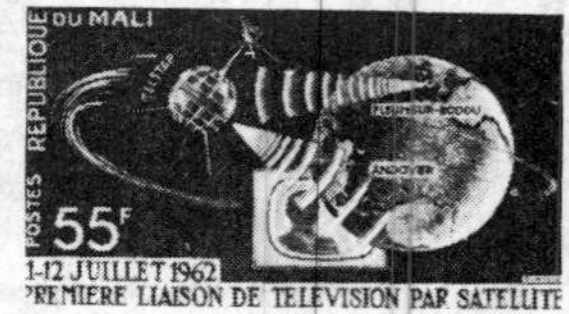
Telstar, Earth and Television Set — A10a

1962, Nov. 24 Engr. *Perf. 13*
40 A10a 45fr dk car, vio & brn .50 .40
41 A10a 55fr green, vio & ol .70 .50

1st television connection of the US and Europe through the Telstar satellite, July 11-12.

Bull, Chemical Equipment, Chicks — A11

1963, Feb. 23 Unwmk. *Perf. 13*
42 A11 25fr red brn & grnsh bl .22 .15

Sotuba Zootechnical Institute. See No. C15.

Tractor A12

1963, Mar. 21 Engr.
43 A12 25fr vio bl, dk brn & blk .18 .15
44 A12 45fr bl grn, red brn & grn .40 .25

FAO "Freedom from Hunger" campaign.

High Altitude Balloon and WMO Emblem — A13

Winners, 800-meter Race — A14

1963, June 12 Photo. *Perf. 12½*
Green Emblem; Yellow and Black Balloon

45	A13	25fr ultra	.20	.15
46	A13	45fr carmine rose	.38	.25
47	A13	60fr red brown	.50	.40
		Nos. 45-47 (3)	1.08	.80

Studies of the atmosphere.

1963, Aug. 10 Unwmk. *Perf. 12*

Designs: 20fr, Acrobatic dancers, horiz. 85fr, Soccer, horiz.

48	A14	5fr multicolored	.15	.15
49	A14	10fr multicolored	.15	.15
50	A14	20fr multicolored	.18	.15
51	A14	85fr multicolored	.60	.35
		Set value	.92	.62

Issued to publicize Youth Week.

Centenary Emblem — A15

Kaempferia Aethiopica — A16

1963, Sept. 1 *Perf. $13^1/_2$x13*
Emblem in Gray, Yellow and Red

52 A15 5fr lt ol grn & blk .15 .15
53 A15 10fr yellow & blk .15 .15
54 A15 85fr red & blk .60 .40
Nos. 52-54 (3) .90
Set value .58

Centenary of the International Red Cross.

1963, Dec. 23 **Unwmk.** *Perf. 13*

Tropical plants: 70fr, Bombax costatum. 100fr, Adenium Honghel.

55 A16 30fr multicolored .22 .15
56 A16 70fr multicolored .55 .22
57 A16 100fr multicolored .70 .25
Nos. 55-57 (3) 1.47 .62

Plane Spraying, Locust and Village — A17

Designs (each inscribed "O.I.C.M.A."): 5fr, Head of locust and map of Africa, vert. 10fr, Locust in flight over map of Mali, vert.

1964, June 15 **Engr.** *Perf. 13*

58 A17 5fr org brn, dl cl & grn .15 .15
59 A17 10fr org brn, ol & bl grn .15 .15
60 A17 20fr bis, org brn & yel grn .20 .15
Nos. 58-60 (3) .50
Set value .26

Anti-locust campaign.

Soccer Player and Tokyo Stadium — A18

Designs (stadium in background): 10fr, Boxer, vert. 15fr, Runner, vert. 85fr, Hurdler.

1964, June 27 **Unwmk.**

61 A18 5fr red, brt grn & dk pur .15 .15
62 A18 10fr blk, dl bl & org brn .15 .15
63 A18 15fr violet & dk red .16 .15
64 A18 85fr vio, dk brn & sl grn .65 .45
a. Min. sheet of 4, #61-64 1.40 1.40
Nos. 61-64 (4) 1.11
Set value .70

18th Olympic Games, Tokyo, Oct. 10-25.

IQSY Emblem and Eclipse of Sun — A19

1964, July 27 **Engr.** *Perf. 13*

65 A19 45fr multicolored .45 .20

International Quiet Sun Year, 1964-65.

Map of Viet Nam A20

Defassa Waterbuck A21

1964, Nov. 2 **Photo.** *Perf. 12x$12^1/_2$*

66 A20 30fr multicolored .22 .15

Issued to publicize the solidarity of the workers of Mali and those of South Viet Nam.

1965, Apr. 5 **Engr.**

Designs: 5fr, Cape buffalo, horiz. 10fr, Scimitar-horned oryx. 30fr, Leopard, horiz. 90fr, Giraffe.

67 A21 1fr choc, brt bl & grn .15 .15
68 A21 5fr grn, ocher & choc .15 .15
69 A21 10fr grn, brt pink & bis brn .15 .15
70 A21 30fr dk red, grn & choc .22 .15
71 A21 90fr bis brn, sl & yel grn .60 .42
Set value 1.00 .72

Abraham Lincoln — A22

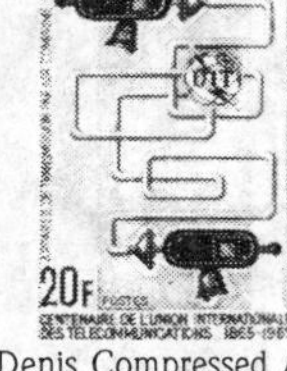

Denis Compressed Air Transmitter — A23

1965, Apr. 15 **Photo.** *Perf. 13x$12^1/_2$*

72 A22 45fr black & multi .40 .30
73 A22 55fr dp green & multi .45 .40

Centenary of the death of Lincoln.

1965, May 17 **Engr.** *Perf. 13*

Designs: 30fr, Hughes telegraph system, horiz. 50fr, Lescurre heliograph.

74 A23 20fr orange, blk & bl .18 .15
75 A23 30fr org, ocher & sl grn .22 .16
76 A23 50fr org, dk brn & sl grn .38 .25
Nos. 74-76 (3) .78 .56

Centenary of the ITU.

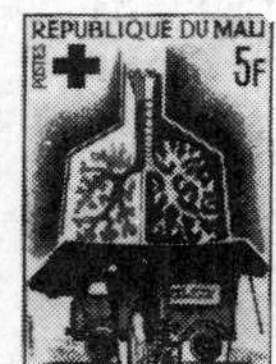

Mobile X-ray Unit and Lungs — A24

Designs: 10fr, Mother and infants. 25fr, Examination of patient at Marchoux Institute and slide. 45fr, Biology laboratory.

1965, July 5 **Unwmk.** *Perf. 13*

77 A24 5fr lake, red & vio .15 .15
78 A24 10fr brn ol, red & sl grn .15 .15
79 A24 25fr dk brn, red & grn .18 .15
80 A24 45fr dk brn, red & sl grn .35 .22
Set value .68 .48

Issued to publicize the Health Service.

Swimmer A25

1965, July 19 **Engr.**

81 A25 5fr shown .15 .15
82 A25 15fr Judo .16 .15
Set value .24 .16

1st African Games, Brazzaville, July 18-25.

Globe, Vase, Quill, Trumpet A26

Designs: 55fr, Mask, palette and microphones. 90fr, Dancers, mask and printed cloth.

1966, Apr. 4 **Engr.** *Perf. 13*

83 A26 30fr black, red & ocher .22 .15
84 A26 55fr car rose, emer & blk .38 .25
85 A26 90fr ultra, org & dk brn .60 .38
Nos. 83-85 (3) 1.20 .78

International Negro Arts Festival, Dakar, Senegal, Apr. 1-24.

WHO Headquarters, Geneva A27

1966, May 3 **Photo.** *Perf. $12^1/_2$x13*

86 A27 30fr org yel, bl & ol grn .22 .15
87 A27 45fr org yel, bl & dl red .30 .20

Inauguration of the WHO Headquarters.

Fishermen with Nets — A28

River Fishing: 4fr, 60fr, Group fishing with large net. 20fr, 85fr, Commercial fishing boats.

1966, May 30 **Engr.** *Perf. 13*

88 A28 3fr ultra & brn .15 .15
89 A28 4fr Prus bl & org brn .15 .15
90 A28 20fr dk brn, ultra & grn .15 .15
91 A28 25fr dk brn, bl & brt grn .18 .15
92 A28 60fr mag, brn & brt grn .38 .16
93 A28 85fr dk pur, dl bl & grn .50 .25
Set value 1.30 .65

Initiation of Pioneers A29

Design: 25fr, Dance and Pioneer emblem.

1966, July 25 **Engr.** *Perf. 13*

94 A29 5fr multicolored .15 .15
95 A29 25fr multicolored .18 .15
Set value .22 .15

Issued to honor the pioneers of Mali.

Inoculation of Zebu — A30

1967, Jan. 16 **Photo.** *Perf. $12^1/_2$x13*

96 A30 10fr dp grn, yel grn & brn .15 .15
97 A30 30fr Prus bl, bl & brn .20 .15
Set value .26 .20

Campaign against cattle plague.

View of Timbuktu and Tourist Year Emblem A31

1967, May 15 **Engr.** *Perf. 13*

98 A31 25fr Prus bl, red lil & org .18 .15

International Tourist Year, 1967.

Ugada Grandicollis A32

Insects: 5fr, Chelorrhina polyphemus, vert. 50fr, Phymateus cinctus.

1967, Aug. 14 **Engr.** *Perf. 13*

99 A32 5fr brt bl, sl grn & brn .15 .15
100 A32 15fr sl grn, dk brn & red .16 .15
101 A32 50fr sl grn, dk brn & dp org .35 .20
Nos. 99-101 (3) .66
Set value .32

Teacher and Adult Class — A33

1967, Sept. 8 **Photo.** *Perf. $12^1/_2$x13*

102 A33 50fr black, grn & car .35 .15

International Literacy Day, Sept. 8.

Europafrica Issue

Birds, New Buildings and Map — A34

1967, Sept. 18 *Perf. $12^1/_2$x12*

103 A34 45fr multicolored .38 .16

Lions Emblem and Crocodile — A35

1967, Oct. 16 **Photo.** *Perf. 13x$12^1/_2$*

104 A35 90fr yellow & multi .45 .25

50th anniversary of Lions International.

Water Cycle and UNESCO Emblem A36

1967, Nov. 15 **Photo.** *Perf. 13*

105 A36 25fr multicolored .16 .15

Hydrological Decade (UNESCO), 1965-74.

WHO Emblem A37

1968, Apr. 8 **Engr.** *Perf. 13*

106 A37 90fr sl grn, dk car rose & bl .38 .15

20th anniv. of the World Health Organization.

Linked Hearts and People — A38

1968, Apr. 28 **Engr.** *Perf. 13*

107 A38 50fr sl grn, red & vio bl .22 .18

International Day of Sister Communities.

Books, Student, Chart, and Map of Africa — A39

1968, Aug. 12 **Engr.** *Perf. 13*
108 A39 100fr carmine, ol & blk .40 .20

10th anniv. of the Intl. Assoc. for the Development of Libraries and Archives in Africa.

Draisienne, 1809 — A40

Designs: 5fr, De Dion-Bouton automobile, 1894, horiz. 10fr, Michaux bicycle, 1861. 45fr, Panhard & Levassor automobile, 1914, horiz.

1968, Aug. 12
109 A40 2fr grn, olive & magenta .15 .15
110 A40 5fr lemon, indigo & red .15 .15
111 A40 10fr brt grn, indigo & brn .15 .15
112 A40 45fr ocher, gray grn & blk .18 .15
Nos. 109-112,C60-C61 (6) 1.30
Set value .70

Tourist Emblem with Map of Africa and Dove — A41

1969, May 12 **Photo.** *Perf. 12½x13*
113 A41 50fr lt ultra, grn & red .18 .15

Year of African Tourism.

ILO Emblem and "OIT" — A42

1969, May 12 **Engr.** *Perf. 13*
114 A42 50fr vio, slate grn & brt bl .22 .15
115 A42 60fr slate, red & ol brn .25 .15
Set value .20

Intl. Labor Organization, 50th anniv.

Panhard, 1897, and Citroen 24, 1969 — A43

30fr, Citroen, 1923, and Citroen DS 21, 1969.

1969, May 30 **Engr.** *Perf. 13*
116 A43 25fr blk, maroon & lemon .15 .15
117 A43 30fr blk, brt grn & dk grn .16 .15
Nos. 116-117,C71-C72 (4) .96
Set value .55

Play Blocks A44

Toys: 10fr, Mule on wheels. 15fr, Ducks. 20fr, Racing car and track.

1969 **Photo.** *Perf. 12½x13*
118 A44 5fr red, gray & yel .15 .15
119 A44 10fr red, yel & olive .15 .15
120 A44 15fr red, salmon & yel grn .15 .15
121 A44 20fr red, indigo & org .15 .15
Set value .38 .22

Intl. Toy Fair in Nuremberg, Germany.

Ram — A45

1969, Aug. 18 **Engr.** *Perf. 13*
122 A45 1fr shown .15 .15
123 A45 2fr Goat .15 .15
124 A45 10fr Donkey .15 .15
125 A45 35fr Horse .22 .16
126 A45 90fr Dromedaries .55 .35
Set value .90 .68

Development Bank Issue
Common Design Type

1969, Sept. 10
127 CD130 50fr brt lil, grn & ocher .20 .15
128 CD130 90fr ol brn, grn & ocher .38 .15

Boy Being Vaccinated A46

1969, Nov. 10 **Engr.** *Perf. 13*
129 A46 50fr brn, indigo & brt grn .22 .15

Campaign against smallbox and measles.

ASECNA Issue
Common Design Type

1969, Dec. 12 **Engr.** *Perf. 13*
130 CD132 100fr dark slate green .40 .20

African and Japanese Women A47

150fr, Flags and maps of Mali and Japan.

1970, Apr. 13 **Engr.** *Perf. 13*
131 A47 100fr brown, bl & ocher .42 .16
132 A47 150fr dk red, yel grn & org .60 .20

Issued to publicize EXPO '70 International Exhibition, Osaka, Japan, Mar. 15-Sept. 13.

Satellite Telecommunications, Map of Africa and ITU Emblem — A48

1970, May 17 **Engr.** *Perf. 13*
133 A48 90fr car rose & brn .40 .20

World Telecommunications Day.

UPU Headquarters Issue
Common Design Type

1970, May 20 **Engr.** *Perf. 13*
134 CD133 50fr dk red, bl grn & ol .20 .15
135 CD133 60fr red lil, ultra & red brn .25 .16

Post Office, Bamako A49

Public Buildings: 40fr, Chamber of Commerce, Bamako. 60fr, Public Works Ministry, Bamako. 80fr, City Hall, Segou.

1970, Nov. 23 **Engr.** *Perf. 13*
136 A49 30fr brn, brt grn & olive .15 .15
137 A49 40fr brn, sl grn & dp cl .15 .15
138 A49 60fr brn red, sl grn & gray .20 .15
139 A49 80fr brn, brt grn & emer .25 .16
Nos. 136-139 (4) .75
Set value .45

Gallet 030T, 1882 — A50

Old Steam Locomotives: 40fr, Felou 030T, 1882. 50fr, Bechevel 230T, 1882. 80fr, Type 231, 1930. 100fr, Type 141, 1930.

1970, Dec. 14 **Engr.** *Perf. 13*
140 A50 20fr brt grn, dk car & blk .15 .15
141 A50 40fr blk, dk grn & ocher .18 .15
142 A50 50fr bis brn, bl grn & blk .20 .15
143 A50 80fr car rose, blk & bl grn .25 .20
144 A50 100fr ocher, bl grn & blk .40 .22
Nos. 140-144 (5) 1.18 .87

Scout Sounding Retreat — A51

Bambara Mask, San — A52

Boy Scouts: 5fr, Crossing river, horiz. 100fr, Canoeing, horiz.

Perf. 13x12½, 12½x13

1970, Dec. 28 **Litho.**
145 A51 5fr multicolored .15 .15
146 A51 30fr multicolored .15 .15
147 A51 100fr multicolored .38 .18
Set value .56 .30

1971, Jan. 25 **Photo.** *Perf. 12x12½*

Designs: 25fr, Dogon mask, Bandiagara. 50fr, Kanaga ideogram. 80fr, Bambara ideogram.

148 A52 20fr orange & multi .15 .15
149 A52 25fr brt green & multi .15 .15
150 A52 50fr dk purple & multi .20 .15
151 A52 80fr blue & multi .30 .15
Set value .68 .36

Boy, Medical and Scientific Symbols A53

1971, Mar. 22 **Engr.** *Perf. 13*
152 A53 100fr dp car, ocher & grn .42 .22

B.C.G. inoculation (Bacillus-Calmette-Guerin) against tuberculosis, 50th anniv.

Boy Scouts, Mt. Fuji, Japanese Print — A54

1971, Apr. 19
153 A54 80fr lt ultra, dp plum & brt grn .22 .15

13th Boy Scout World Jamboree, Asagiri Plain, Japan, Aug. 2-10.

UNICEF Emblem, Hands and Rose — A55

60fr, UNICEF emblem, women & children, vert.

1971, May 24 **Engr.** *Perf. 13*
154 A55 50fr brn org, car & dk brn .16 .15
155 A55 60fr vio bl, grn & red brn .18 .15
Set value .22

25th anniv. of UNICEF.

Mali Farmer — A56

Map of Africa with Communications Network — A57

Costumes of Mali: 10fr, Mali farm woman. 15fr, Tuareg. 60fr, Embroidered robe, Grand Boubou. 80fr, Ceremonial robe, woman.

1971, June 14 **Photo.** *Perf. 13*
156 A56 5fr gray & multi .15 .15
157 A56 10fr vio bl & multi .15 .15
158 A56 15fr yellow & multi .15 .15
159 A56 60fr gray & multi .18 .15
160 A56 80fr tan & multi .22 .16
Set value .60 .40

1971, Aug. 16 **Photo.** *Perf. 13*
161 A57 50fr bl, vio bl & org .20 .15

Pan-African telecommunications system.

Hibiscus A58

Flowers: 50fr, Poinsettia. 60fr, Adenium obesum. 80fr, Dogbane. 100fr, Satanocrater berhautii.

1971, Oct. 4 **Litho.** *Perf. 14x13½*
162 A58 20fr multicolored .15 .15
163 A58 50fr multicolored .16 .15
164 A58 60fr multicolored .22 .15
165 A58 80fr multicolored .25 .15
166 A58 100fr multicolored .35 .15
Nos. 162-166 (5) 1.13
Set value .42

For surcharge see No. 204.

Mother, Child and Bird (Sculpture) A59

1971, Dec. 27 **Engr.** *Perf. 13x12½*
167 A59 70fr mag, sepia & bl grn .22 .15

Natl. Institute of Social Security, 15th anniv.

ITU Emblem A60

1972, May 17 **Photo.** *Perf. 13x13½*
168 A60 70fr blue, maroon & blk .22 .15

4th World Telecommunications Day.

Clay Funerary Statuette — A61

Mali Art: 40fr, Female torso, wood. 50fr, Masked figure, painted stone. 100fr, Animals and men, wrought iron.

1972, May 29 *Perf. 12½x13*

169 A61	30fr	org red & multi	.15	.15
170 A61	40fr	yellow & multi	.15	.15
171 A61	50fr	red & multi	.16	.15
172 A61	100fr	lt green & multi	.30	.15
		Set value		.42

Morse and Telegraph A62

1972, June 5 **Engr.** *Perf. 13*

173 A62 80fr red, emer & choc .22 .15

Centenary of the death of Samuel F. B. Morse (1791-1872), inventor of the telegraph.

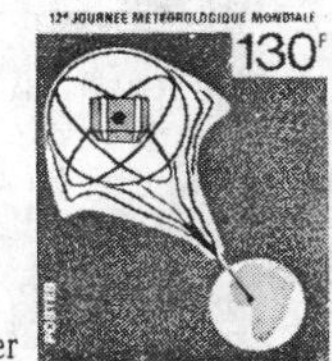

Weather Balloon over Africa — A63

1972, July 10 **Photo.** *Perf. 12½x13*

174 A63 130fr multicolored .40 .22

12th World Meteorology Day.

Sarakolé Dance, Kayes — A64

People, Book, Pencil — A65

Designs: Folk dances.

1972, Aug. 21 **Photo.** *Perf. 13*

175 A64	10fr	shown	.15	.15
176 A64	20fr	LaGomba, Bamako	.15	.15
177 A64	50fr	Hunters' dance, Bougouni	.15	.15
178 A64	70fr	Koré Duga, Ségou	.18	.15
179 A64	80fr	Kanaga, Sanga	.20	.15
180 A64	120fr	Targui, Timbuktu	.25	.16
		Set value	.90	.65

1972, Sept. 8 **Typo.** *Perf. 12½x13*

181 A65 80fr black & yel grn .20 .15

World Literacy Day, Sept. 8.

"Edison Classique," Mali Instruments — A66

1972, Sept. 18 **Engr.** *Perf. 13*

182 A66 100fr multicolored .30 .15

First Anthology of Music of Mali.

Aries A67

Signs of the Zodiac: No. 184, Taurus. No. 185, Gemini. No. 186, Cancer. No. 187, Leo. No. 188, Virgo. No. 189, Libra. No. 190, Scorpio. No. 191, Sagittarius. No. 192, Capricorn. No. 193, Aquarius. No. 194, Pisces.

1972, Oct. 23 **Engr.** *Perf. 11*

183 A67	15fr	lilac & bis brn	.15	.15
184 A67	15fr	bister brn & blk	.15	.15
185 A67	35fr	maroon & indigo	.15	.15
186 A67	35fr	emerald & mar	.15	.15
187 A67	40fr	blue & red brn	.15	.15
188 A67	40fr	dk pur & red brn	.15	.15
189 A67	45fr	dk blue & mar	.16	.15
190 A67	45fr	maroon & brt grn	.16	.15
191 A67	65fr	dk violet & ind	.20	.15
192 A67	65fr	dk vio & gray ol	.20	.15
193 A67	90fr	brt pink & ind	.22	.16
194 A67	90fr	brt pink & grn	.22	.16
		Set value	1.75	1.20

Arrival of First Locomotive in Bamako, 1906 — A68

Designs (Locomotives): 30fr, Thies-Bamako, 1920. 60fr, Thies-Bamako, 1927. 120fr, Two Alsthom BB, 1947.

1972, Dec. 11 **Engr.** *Perf. 13*

195 A68	10fr	ind, brn & sl grn	.15	.15
196 A68	30fr	sl grn, ind & brn	.15	.15
197 A68	60fr	sl grn, ind & brn	.20	.15
198 A68	120fr	sl grn & choc	.35	.20
		Set value	.72	.45

2nd African Games, Lagos, Nigeria, Jan. 7-18 — A69

1973, Jan. 15 **Photo.** *Perf. 12½*

199 A69	70fr	High jump	.22	.15
200 A69	270fr	Discus	.80	.40
201 A69	280fr	Soccer	.85	.40
		Nos. 199-201 (3)	1.87	.95

INTERPOL Emblem and Headquarters A70

1973, Feb. 28 **Photo.** *Perf. 13*

202 A70 80fr multi .22 .15

50th anniversary of International Criminal Police Organization (INTERPOL).

Blind Man and Disabled Boy — A71

Cora — A72

1973, Apr. 24 **Engr.** *Perf. 12½x13*

203 A71 70fr dk car, brick red & blk .22 .15

Help for the handicapped.

No. 166 Surcharged with New Value, 2 Bars, and Overprinted: "SECHERESSE / SOLIDARITE AFRICAINE"

1973, Aug. 16 **Litho.** *Perf. 13½*

204 A58 200fr on 100fr multi .55 .35

African solidarity in drought emergency.

Perf. 12½x13, 13x12½

1973, Dec. 10 **Engr.**

Musical Instruments: 10fr, Balafon, horiz. 15fr, Djembe. 20fr, Guitar. 25fr, N'Djarka. 30fr, M'Bolon. 35fr, Dozo N'Goni. 40fr, N'Tamani.

205 A72	5fr	mar, dk grn & brn	.15	.15
206 A72	10fr	bl & choc	.15	.15
207 A72	15fr	brn, dk red & yel	.15	.15
208 A72	20fr	mar & brn ol	.15	.15
209 A72	25fr	org, yel & blk	.15	.15
210 A72	30fr	vio bl & blk	.15	.15
211 A72	35fr	dk red & brn	.15	.15
212 A72	40fr	dk red & choc	.15	.15
		Set value	.65	.45

Farmer with Newspaper, Corn — A73

Soccer, Goalkeeper, Symbolic Globe and Net — A74

1974, Mar. 11 **Engr.** *Perf. 12½x13*

213 A73 70fr multi .20 .15

2nd anniversary of "Kibaru," rural newspaper.

1974, May 6 **Engr.** *Perf. 13*

Design: 280fr, Games' emblem, soccer and ball.

214 A74	270fr	multi	.80	.42
215 A74	280fr	multi	.85	.42

World Cup Soccer Championships, Munich, June 13-July 7.
For surcharges see Nos. 219-220.

Old and New Ships, UPU Emblem — A75

Artisans of Mali — A76

Designs: 90fr, Old and new planes, UPU emblem. 270fr, Old and new trains, UPU emblem.

1974, June 2 **Engr.** *Perf. 12½x13*

216 A75	80fr	brn & multir	.22	.16
217 A75	90fr	ultra & multi	.30	.20
218 A75	270fr	lt grn & multi	.80	.42
		Nos. 216-218 (3)	1.32	.78

Centenary of Universal Postal Union.
For surcharges see Nos. 229-230.

Nos. 214-215 Surcharged and Overprinted in Black or Red: "R.F.A. 2 / HOLLANDE 1"

1974, Aug. 28 **Engr.** *Perf. 13*

219 A74	300fr	on 270fr multi	.90	.45
220 A74	330fr	on 280fr multi (R)	.90	.45

World Cup Soccer Championship, 1974, victory of German Federal Republic.

1974, Sept. 16 **Photo.** *Perf. 12½x13*

221 A76	50fr	Weaver	.15	.15
222 A76	60fr	Potter	.16	.15
223 A76	70fr	Smiths	.20	.15
224 A76	80fr	Sculptor	.22	.15
		Nos. 221-224 (4)	.73	
		Set value		.44

Niger River near Gao — A77

Landscapes: 20fr, The Hand of Fatma (rock formation), vert. 40fr, Gouina Waterfall. 70fr, Dogon houses, vert.

Perf. 13x12½, 12½x13

1974, Sept. 23

225 A77	10fr	multi	.15	.15
226 A77	20fr	multi	.15	.15
227 A77	40fr	multi	.15	.15
228 A77	70fr	multi	.20	.15
		Set value	.40	.40

Nos. 216 and 218 Surcharged and Overprinted in Black or Red: "9 OCTOBRE 1974"

1974, Oct. 9 **Engr.** *Perf. 13*

229 A75	250fr	on 80fr multi	.90	.45
230 A75	300fr	on 270fr multi (R)	.90	.45

UPU Day.

Mao Tse-tung, Flags, Great Wall — A78

1974, Oct. 21 **Engr.** *Perf. 13*

231 A78 100fr multi .25 .16

People's Republic of China, 25th anniversary.

Artisans and Lions Emblem — A79

100fr, View of Samanko and Lions emblem.

1975, Feb. 3 **Photo.** *Perf. 13*

232 A79	90fr	red & multi	.25	.16
233 A79	100fr	blue & multi	.30	.20

5th anniversary of lepers' rehabilitation village, Samanko, sponsored by Lions International.
For surcharges see Nos. 303-304.

Tetrodon Fahaka A80

Designs: Fish.

1975, May 12 **Engr.** *Perf. 13*

234 A80	60fr	*shown*	.16	.15
235 A80	70fr	*Malopterurus electricus*	.20	.15
236 A80	80fr	*Citharinus latus*	.20	.15
237 A80	90fr	*Hydrocyon forskali*	.22	.15
238 A80	110fr	*Lates niloticus*	.25	.15
		Nos. 234-238 (5)	1.03	
		Set value		.62

See Nos. 256-260.

Woman and IWY Emblem — A81

1975, June 9 **Engr.** *Perf. 13*

239 A81 150fr red & grn .40 .20

International Women's Year 1975.

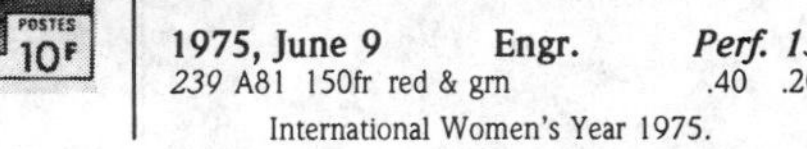

Morris "Oxford," 1913 — A82

Automobiles: 130fr, Franklin "E," 1907. 190fr, Daimler, 1900. 230fr, Panhard & Levassor, 1895.

1975, June 16

240 A82	90fr blk, ol & lil	.22	.15
241 A82	130fr vio bl, gray & red	.35	.20
242 A82	190fr bl, grn & ind	.50	.30
243 A82	230fr red, ultra & brn ol	.60	.38
	Nos. 240-243 (4)	1.67	1.03

Carthaginian Tristater, 500 B.C. — A83

Ancient Coins: 170fr, Decadrachma, Syracuse, 413 B.C. 190fr, Acanthe tetradrachma, 400 B.C. 260fr, Didrachma, Eritrea, 480-445 B.C.

1975, Oct. 13 Engr. *Perf. 13*

244 A83	130fr bl, cl & blk	.35	.18
245 A83	170fr emer, brn & blk	.42	.22
246 A83	190fr grn, red & blk	.50	.30
247 A83	260fr dp bl, org & blk	.65	.42
	Nos. 244-247 (4)	1.92	1.12

UN Emblem and "ONU" — A84

1975, Nov. 10 Engr. *Perf. 13*

248 A84	200fr emer & brt bl	.55	.35

30th anniversary of UN.

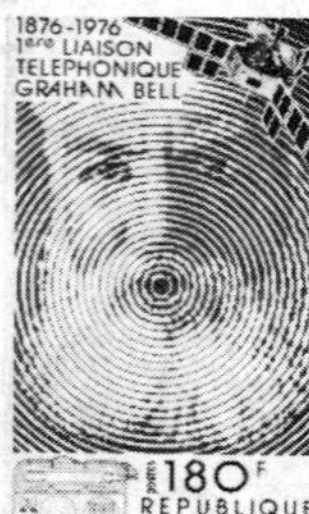

A. G. Bell, Waves, Satellite, Telephone — A85

1976, Mar. 8 Litho. *Perf. 12x12½*

249 A85	180fr brn, ultra & ocher	.50	.25

Centenary of first telephone call by Alexander Graham Bell, Mar. 10, 1876.

Chameleon A86

1976, Mar. 31 Litho. *Perf. 12½*

250 A86	20fr shown	.15	.15
251 A86	30fr Lizard	.15	.15
252 A86	40fr Tortoise	.15	.15
253 A86	90fr Python	.22	.15
254 A86	120fr Crocodile	.35	.20
	Set value	.80	.45

Konrad Adenauer and Cologne Cathedral — A87

1976, Apr. 26 Engr. *Perf. 13*

255 A87	180fr mag & dk brn	.45	.25

Konrad Adenauer (1876-1967), German Chancellor, birth centenary.

Fish Type of 1975

1976, June 28 Engr. *Perf. 13*

256 A80	100fr *Heterotis niloticus*	.25	.16
257 A80	120fr *Synodontis budgetti*	.35	.18
258 A80	130fr *Heterobranchus bidorsalis*	.38	.18
259 A80	150fr *Tilapia monodi*	.40	.20
260 A80	220fr *Alestes macrolepidotus*	.55	.35
	Nos. 256-260 (5)	1.93	1.07

Page from Children's Book — A88

"Le Roi de l'Air" — A89

1976, July 19

261 A88	130fr red & multi	.35	.20

Books for children.

1976, July 26 Litho. *Perf. 12½x13*

262 A89	120fr multi	.30	.16

First lottery, sponsored by L'Essor newspaper.

"Do not overload scaffold" — A90

1976, Aug. 16 Litho. *Perf. 13*

263 A90	120fr multi	.30	.16

National Insurance Institute, 20th anniv.

Letters, UPU and UN Emblems — A91

1976, Oct. 4 Engr. *Perf. 13*

264 A91	120fr lil, org & grn	.30	.16

UN Postal Administration, 25th anniv.

Moto-Guzzi 254, Italy — A92

Motorcycles: 120fr, BMW 900, Germany. 130fr, Honda-Egli, Japan. 140fr, Motobecane LT-3, France.

1976, Oct. 18 Engr. *Perf. 13*

265 A92	90fr multi	.22	.15
266 A92	120fr multi	.32	.20
267 A92	130fr multi	.35	.20
268 A92	140fr multi	.38	.22
	Nos. 265-268 (4)	1.27	.77

Fishing Boat, Masgat — A93

Designs: 180fr, Coaster, Cochin China. 190fr, Fireboat, Dunkirk, 1878. 200fr, Nile river boat.

1976, Dec. 6 Engr. *Perf. 13*

269 A93	160fr multi	.42	.18
270 A93	180fr multi	.45	.22
271 A93	190fr multi	.50	.25
272 A93	200fr multi	.55	.25
	Nos. 269-272 (4)	1.92	.90

Indigo Finch — A94

Birds: 25fr, Yellow-breasted barbet. 30fr, Vitelline masked weaver. 40fr, Bee-eater. 50fr, Senegal parrot.

1977, Apr. 18 Photo. *Perf. 13*

273 A94	15fr multi	.15	.15
274 A94	25fr multi	.15	.15
275 A94	30fr multi	.15	.15
276 A94	40fr multi	.16	.15
277 A94	50fr multi	.20	.15
	Set value	.62	.40

See Nos. 298-302.

Braille Statue, Script and Reading Hands — A95

1977, Apr. 25 Engr. *Perf. 13*

278 A95	200fr multi	.55	.30

Louis Braille (1809-1852), inventor of the reading and writing system for the blind.

Electronic Tree, ITU Emblem — A96

1977, May 17 Photo.

279 A96	120fr dk brn & org	.32	.18

World Telecommunications Day.

Dragonfly A97

Insects: 10fr, Praying mantis. 20fr, Tropical wasp. 35fr, Cockchafer. 60fr, Flying stag beetle.

1977, June 15 Photo. *Perf. 13x12½*

280 A97	5fr multi	.15	.15
281 A97	10fr multi	.15	.15
282 A97	20fr multi	.15	.15
283 A97	35fr multi	.15	.15
284 A97	60fr multi	.22	.16
	Set value	.52	.40

Knight and Rook — A98

Chess Pieces: 130fr, Bishop and pawn, vert. 300fr, Queen and King.

1977, June 27 Engr. *Perf. 13*

285 A98	120fr multi	.50	.25
286 A98	130fr multi	.50	.25
287 A98	300fr multi	1.20	.65
	Nos. 285-287 (3)	2.20	1.15

Europafrica Issue

Symbolic Ship, White and Brown Persons — A99

1977, July 18 Litho. *Perf. 13*

288 A99	400fr multi	1.10	.65

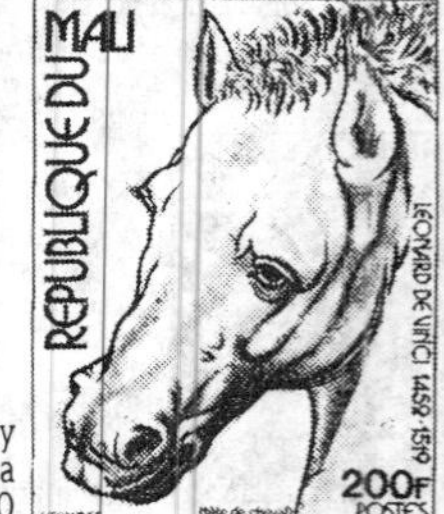

Horse, by Leonardo da Vinci — A100

Drawings by Leonardo da Vinci: 300fr, Head of Young Woman. 500fr, Self-portrait.

1977, Sept. 5 Engr. *Perf. 13*

289 A100	200fr dk brn & blk	.55	.35
290 A100	300fr dk brn & ol	.80	.42
291 A100	500fr dk brn & red	1.40	.62
	Nos. 289-291 (3)	2.75	1.39

Hotel de l'Amitié, Bamako — A101

1977, Oct. 15 Litho. *Perf. 13x12½*
292 A101 120fr multi .35 .18

Opening of the Hotel de l'Amitié, Oct. 15.

Dome of the Rock Jerusalem — A102

1977, Oct. 17 *Perf. 12½*
293 A102 120fr multi .35 .18
294 A102 180fr multi .45 .25

Palestinian fighters and their families.

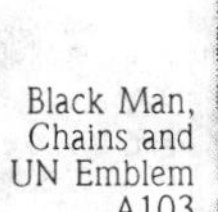

Black Man, Chains and UN Emblem A103

130fr, Statue of Liberty, people & UN emblem. 180fr, Black children & horse behind fence.

1978, Mar. 13 Engr. *Perf. 13*
295 A103 120fr multi .35 .18
296 A103 130fr multi .35 .18
297 A103 180fr multi .45 .25
Nos. 295-297 (3) 1.15 .61

International Year against Apartheid.

Bird Type of 1977

Birds: 20fr, Granatine bengala. 30fr, Lagonosticta vinacea. 50fr, Lagonosticta. 70fr, Turtle dove. 80fr, Buffalo weaver.

1978, Apr. 10 Litho. *Perf. 13*
298 A94 20fr multi .15 .15
299 A94 30fr multi .15 .15
300 A94 50fr multi .15 .15
301 A94 70fr multi .18 .15
302 A94 80fr multi .20 .15
Set value .65 .40

Nos. 232-233 Surcharged with New Value, Bar and: "XXe ANNIVERSAIRE DU LIONS CLUB DE BAMAKO 1958-1978"

1978, May 8 Photo.
303 A79 120fr on 90fr multi .32 .16
304 A79 130fr on 100fr multi .35 .18

20th anniversary of Bamako Lions Club.

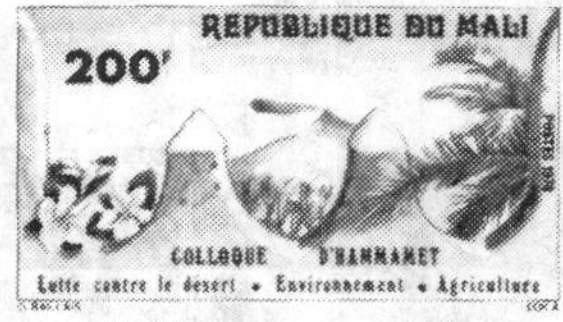

Wall and Desert — A105

1978, May 18 Litho. *Perf. 13*
306 A105 200fr multi .55 .25

Hammamet Conference for reclamation of the desert.

Mahatma Gandhi and Roses — A106

1978, May 29 Engr.
307 A106 140fr blk, brn & red .38 .18

Mohandas K. Gandhi (1869-1948), Hindu spiritual leader, 30th death anniversary.

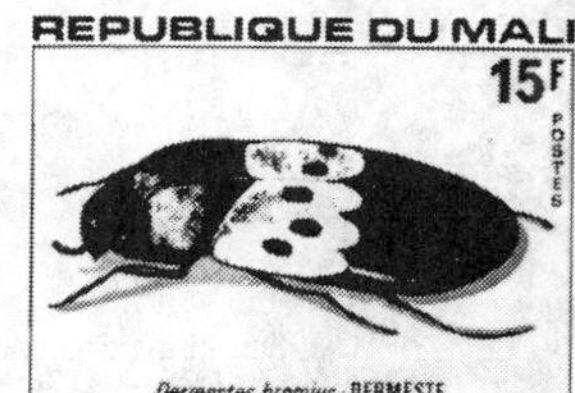

Dermestes — A107

Insects: 25fr, Ground beetle. 90fr, Cricket. 120fr, Ladybird. 140fr, Goliath beetle.

1978, June 12 Photo. *Perf. 13*
308 A107 15fr multi .15 .15
309 A107 25fr multi .15 .15
310 A107 90fr multi .22 .15
311 A107 120fr multi .35 .18
312 A107 140fr multi .38 .20
Set value 1.05 .60

Bridge — A108

Design: 100fr, Dominoes, vert.

1978, June 26 Engr.
313 A108 100fr multi .25 .15
314 A108 130fr multi .35 .18

Aristotle — A109

1978, Oct. 16 Engr. *Perf. 13*
315 A109 200fr multi .55 .25

Aristotle (384-322 B.C.), Greek philosopher.

Human Rights and UN Emblems — A110

1978, Dec. 11 Engr. *Perf. 13*
316 A110 180fr red, bl & brn .48 .22

Universal Declaration of Human Rights, 30th anniversary.

Manatee — A111

Endangered Wildlife: 120fr, Chimpanzee. 130fr, Damaliscus antelope. 180fr, Oryx. 200fr, Derby's eland.

1979, Apr. 23 Litho. *Perf. 12½*
317 A111 100fr multi .25 .15
318 A111 120fr multi .32 .16
319 A111 130fr multi .35 .18
320 A111 180fr multi .48 .25
321 A111 200fr multi .55 .30
Nos. 317-321 (5) 1.95 1.04

Boy Praying and IYC Emblem — A112

IYC emblem and: 200fr, Girl and Boy Scout holding bird. 300fr, IYC emblem, boys with calf.

1979, May 7 Engr. *Perf. 13*
322 A112 120fr multi .32 .20
323 A112 200fr multi .55 .30
324 A112 300fr multi .80 .40
Nos. 322-324 (3) 1.67 .90

International Year of the Child.

Judo and Notre Dame, Paris — A113

1979, May 14 Engr. *Perf. 13*
325 A113 200fr multi .55 .30

World Judo Championship, Paris.

Telecommunications A114

Wood Carving A115

1979, May 17 Litho.
326 A114 120fr multi .32 .16

11th Telecommunications Day.

1979, May 18 *Perf. 13x12½*

Sculptures from National Museum: 120fr, Ancestral figures. 130fr, Animal heads, and kneeling woman.

327 A115 90fr multi .25 .16
328 A115 120fr multi .32 .16
329 A115 130fr multi .35 .18
Nos. 327-329 (3) .92 .50

International Museums Day.

Rowland Hill and Mali No. 15 — A116

130fr, Zeppelin & Saxony #1. 180fr, Concorde & France #3. 200fr, Stagecoach & US #2. 300fr, UPU emblem & Penny Black.

1979, May 21 Engr. *Perf. 13*
330 A116 120fr multi .32 .16
331 A116 130fr multi .35 .18
332 A116 180fr multi .50 .25
333 A116 200fr multi .55 .30
334 A116 300fr multi .80 .45
Nos. 330-334 (5) 2.52 1.34

Sir Rowland Hill (1795-1879), originator of penny postage.

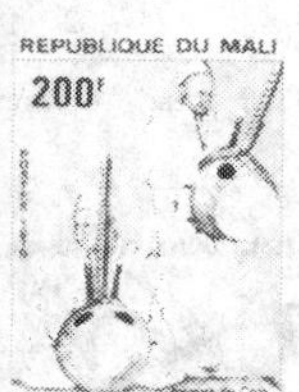

Cora Players — A117

1979, June 4 Litho. *Perf. 13*
335 A117 200fr multi .55 .30

Adenium Obesum and Sankore Mosque — A118

Design: 300fr, Satellite, mounted messenger, globe and letter, vert.

1979, June 8 Photo.
336 A118 120fr multi .32 .16

Engr.
337 A118 300fr multi .80 .45

Philexafrique II, Libreville, Gabon, June 8-17. Nos. 336, 337 printed in sheets of 10 and 5 labels showing exhibition emblem.

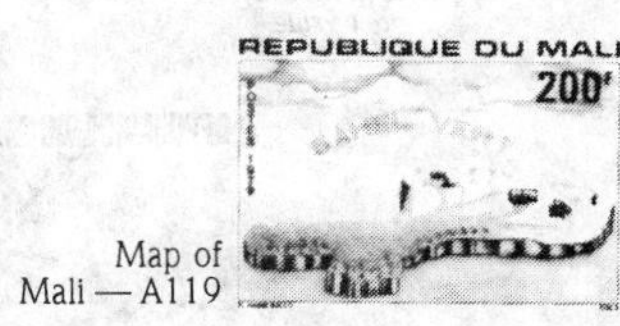

Map of Mali — A119

Design: 300fr, Men planting trees.

1979, June 18 Litho. *Perf. 13x12½*
338 A119 200fr multi .55 .30
339 A119 300fr multi .80 .45

Operation Green Sahel.

Lemons — A120

Sigmund Freud — A121

1979, June 25 *Perf. 12½x13*

340 A120 10fr shown .15 .15
341 A120 60fr Pineapple .16 .15
342 A120 100fr Papayas .25 .15
343 A120 120fr Soursops .32 .16
344 A120 130fr Mangoes .35 .18
Nos. 340-344 (5) 1.23
Set value .60

1979, Sept. 17 **Engr.** *Perf. 13*

345 A121 300fr vio bl & sepia .80 .45

Sigmund Freud (1856-1939), founder of psychoanalysis.

Timbuktu, Man and Camel
A122

Design: 130fr, Caillié, Map of Sahara.

1979, Sept. 27 *Perf. 13x12½*

346 A122 120fr multi .32 .16
347 A122 130fr multi .35 .18

René Caillié (1799-1838), French explorer, 180th birth anniversary.

Eurema Brigitta
A123

1979, Oct. 15 **Litho.** *Perf. 13*

348 A123 100fr *shown* .25 .15
349 A123 120fr *Papilio pylades* .32 .16
350 A123 130fr *Melanitis leda satyridae* .35 .18
351 A123 180fr *Gonimbrasia belina occidentalis* .48 .25
352 A123 200fr *Bunaea alcinoe* .55 .30
Nos. 348-352 (5) 1.95 1.04

Greyhound
A124

Designs: Dogs.

1979, Nov. 12 **Litho.** *Perf. 12½*

353 A124 20fr multi .15 .15
354 A124 50fr multi .15 .15
355 A124 70fr multi .18 .15
356 A124 80fr multi .20 .15
357 A124 90fr multi .25 .15
Nos. 353-357 (5) .93
Set value .35

Wild Donkey — A125

1980, Feb. 4 **Litho.** *Perf. 13x13½*

358 A125 90fr shown .25 .15
359 A125 120fr Addax .32 .15
360 A125 130fr Cheetahs .35 .15
361 A125 140fr Mouflon .35 .15
362 A125 180fr Buffalo .50 .20
Nos. 358-362 (5) 1.77 .80

Photovoltaic Cell Pumping Station, Koni — A126

Solar Energy Utilization: 100fr, Sun shields, Dire. 120fr, Solar stove, Bamako. 130fr, Heliodynamic solar energy generating station, Dire.

1980, Mar. 10 **Litho.** *Perf. 13*

363 A126 90fr multi .25 .15
364 A126 100fr multi .25 .15
365 A126 120fr multi .32 .15
366 A126 130fr multi .35 .15
Nos. 363-366 (4) 1.17
Set value .45

For surcharge see No. 511.

Horse Breeding, Mopti — A127

1980, Mar. 17

367 A127 100fr shown .25 .15
368 A127 120fr Nioro .32 .15
369 A127 130fr Koro .35 .15
370 A127 180fr Coastal zone .50 .20
371 A127 200fr Banamba .55 .22
Nos. 367-371 (5) 1.97 .87

Alexander Fleming (Discoverer of Penicillin)
A128

1980, May 5 **Engr.** *Perf. 13*

372 A128 200fr multi .55 .20

Avicenna and Medical Instruments
A129

Design: 180fr, Avicenna as teacher (12th century manuscript illustration)

1980, May 12 *Perf. 13x12½*

373 A129 120fr multi .32 .15
374 A129 180fr multi .50 .20

Avicenna (980-1037), Arab physician and philosopher, 1000th birth anniversary.

Pilgrim at Mecca — A130

Guavas — A131

1980, May 26 **Litho.** *Perf. 13*

375 A130 120fr shown .32 .15
376 A130 130fr Praying hands, stars, Mecca .35 .15
377 A130 180fr Pilgrims, camels, horiz. .50 .20
Nos. 375-377 (3) 1.17 .50

Hegira, 1500th Anniversary.

1980, June 9

378 A131 90fr shown .22 .15
379 A131 120fr Cashews .32 .15
380 A131 130fr Oranges .35 .15
381 A131 140fr Bananas .38 .15
382 A131 180fr Grapefruit .50 .20
Nos. 378-382 (5) 1.77 .80

League of Nations, 60th Anniversary
A132

1980, June 23 **Engr.** *Perf. 13*

383 A132 200fr multi .55 .20

Festival Emblem, Mask, Xylophone
A133

1980, July 5 **Litho.** *Perf. 12½*

384 A133 120fr multi .32 .15

6th Biennial Arts and Cultural Festival, Bamako, July 5-15.

Sun Rising over Map of Africa — A134

1980, July 7 **Engr.** *Perf. 13*

385 A134 300fr multi .80 .38

Afro-Asian Bandung Conference, 25th anniversary.

Market Place, Conference Emblem
A135

1980, Sept. 15 **Litho.** *Perf. 13*

386 A135 120fr View of Mali, vert. .32 .15
387 A135 180fr shown .50 .20

World Tourism Conf., Manila, Sept. 27.

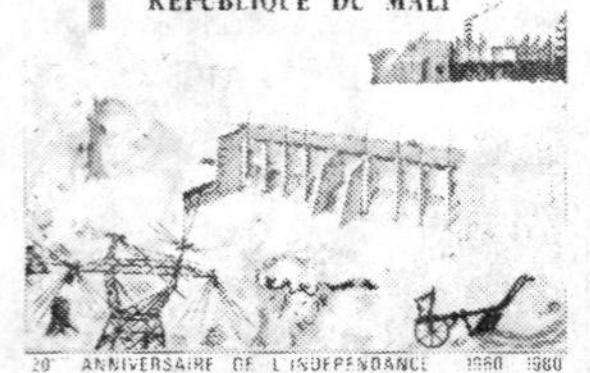

Hydro-electric Dam and Power Station — A136

20th Anniversary of Independence: 120fr, Pres. Traore, flag of Mali, National Assembly building. 130fr, Independence monument, Bamako, Political Party badge, vert.

1980, Sept. 15 *Perf. 13x12½*

388 A136 100fr multi .25 .15
389 A136 120fr multi .32 .15
390 A136 130fr multi .35 .15
Nos. 388-390 (3) .92
Set value .35

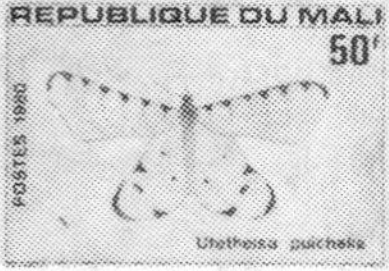

Utetheisa Pulchella
A137

1980, Oct. 6 *Perf. 13½*

391 A137 50fr *shown* .15 .15
392 A137 60fr *Mylothis chloris pieridae* .16 .15
393 A137 70fr *Hypolimnas misippus* .18 .15
394 A137 80fr *Papilio demodocus* .20 .15
Nos. 391-394,C402 (5) 1.89
Set value .75

Fight Against Cigarette Smoking — A138

1980, Oct. 13 **Litho.** *Perf. 12½x12*

395 A138 200fr multi .55 .20

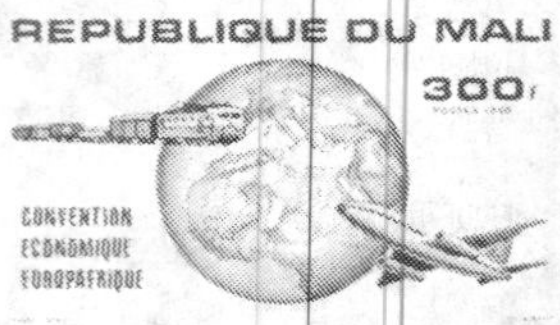

European-African Economic Convention — A139

1980, Oct. 20 *Perf. 12½*

396 A139 300fr multi .80 .38

Agricultural Map of West Africa
A140

West African Economic Council, 5th anniversary (Economic Maps): 120fr, Transportation. 130fr, Industry. 140fr, Communications.

1980, Nov. 5 *Perf. 13½x13*

397 A140 100fr multi .25 .15
398 A140 120fr multi .32 .15
399 A140 130fr multi .35 .15
400 A140 140fr multi .38 .16
Nos. 397-400 (4) 1.30
Set value .52

African Postal Union, 5th Anniv. — A141

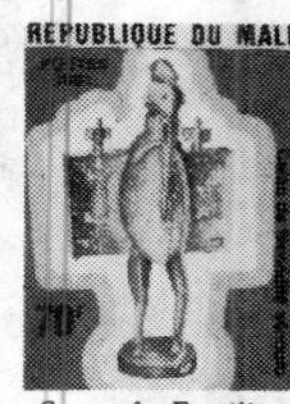

Senuofo Fertility Statue — A142

1980, Dec. 24 **Photo.** *Perf. 13½*

401 A141 130fr multi .35 .15

1981, Jan. 12 **Litho.** *Perf. 13*

Designs: Fertility statues.

402 A142 60fr Nomo dogon .16 .15
403 A142 70fr shown .18 .15
404 A142 90fr Bamanan .25 .15
405 A142 100fr Spirit .25 .15
406 A142 120fr Dogon .32 .15
Nos. 402-406 (5) 1.16
Set value .46

Mambi Sidibe — A143

Hegira (Pilgrimage Year) — A144

Designs: Philosophers.

1981, Feb. 16 *Perf. 12½x13*

407 A143 120fr shown .32 .15
408 A143 130fr Amadou Hampate .35 .15

1981, Feb. 23 *Perf. 13*
409 A144 120fr multi .32 .15
410 A144 180fr multi .50 .20

Maure Zebu A145

Designs: Cattle breeds.

1981, Mar. 9 *Perf. 12½*
411 A145 20fr Kaarta zebu .15 .15
412 A145 30fr Peul du Macina zebu .15 .15
413 A145 40fr Maure zebu .15 .15
414 A145 80fr Touareg zebu .20 .15
415 A145 100fr N'Dama cow .25 .15
Set value .65 .35

See Nos. 433-437.

Hibiscus Double Rose — A146

Designs: Flowers.

1981, Mar. 16
416 A146 50fr Crinum de Moore .15 .15
417 A146 100fr Double Rose Hibiscus .25 .15
418 A146 120fr Pervenche .32 .15
419 A146 130fr Frangipani .35 .15
420 A146 180fr Orgueil de Chine .50 .20
Nos. 416-420 (5) 1.57
Set value .60

See Nos. 442-446.

Wrench Operated by Artificial Hand — A147

Perf. 13x12½, 12x13
1981, May 4 **Engr.**
421 A147 100fr Heads, vert. .25 .15
422 A147 120fr shown .32 .15
Set value .22

Intl. Year of the Disabled.

13th World Telecommunications Day — A148

1981, May 17 **Litho.** *Perf. 13x12½*
423 A148 130fr multi .35 .15

Pierre Curie, Lab Equipment A149

1981, May 25 **Engr.**
424 A149 180fr multi .50 .20

Curie (1859-1906), discoverer of radium.

Scouts at Water Hole — A150

1981, June 8 **Litho.** *Perf. 13*
425 A150 110fr shown .30 .15
426 A150 160fr Sending signals .42 .20
427 A150 300fr Salute, vert. .80 .35
Nos. 425-427 (3) 1.52 .70

Souvenir Sheet

428 A150 500fr Lord Baden-Powell 1.40 .65

4th African Scouting Conf., Abidjan, June.

Nos. 425-428 Overprinted in Red in 2 or 3 Lines: "DAKAR 8 AOUT 1981/28e CONFERENCE MONDIALE DU SCOUTISME"

1981, June 29
429 A150 110fr multi .30 .15
430 A150 160fr multi .42 .20
431 A150 300fr multi .80 .35
Nos. 429-431 (3) 1.52 .70

Souvenir Sheet

432 A150 500fr multi 1.40 .65

28th World Scouting Conf., Dakar, Aug. 8.

Cattle Type of 1981

Various goats.

1981, Sept. 14 **Litho.** *Perf. 13x13½*
433 A145 10fr Maure .15 .15
434 A145 25fr Peul .15 .15
435 A145 140fr Sahel .40 .16
436 A145 180fr Tuareg .50 .20
437 A145 200fr Djallonke .55 .20
Nos. 433-437 (5) 1.75
Set value .65

World UPU Day — A151

1981, Oct. 9 **Engr.** *Perf. 13*
438 A151 400fr multi 1.10 .42

World Food Day — A152

1981, Oct. 16
439 A152 200fr multi .55 .20

Europafrica Economic Convention — A153

1981, Nov. 23 **Engr.** *Perf. 13*
440 A153 700fr multi 1.90 1.20

60th Anniv. of Tuberculosis Inoculation A154

1981, Dec. 7 *Perf. 13x12½*
441 A154 200fr multi .55 .20

Flower Type of 1981

1982, Jan. 18 **Litho.** *Perf. 13*
442 A146 170fr White water lilies .45 .20
443 A146 180fr Red kapok bush .50 .20
444 A146 200fr Purple mimosa .55 .22
445 A146 220fr Pobego lilies .60 .22
446 A146 270fr Satan's chalices .70 .30
Nos. 442-446 (5) 2.80 1.14

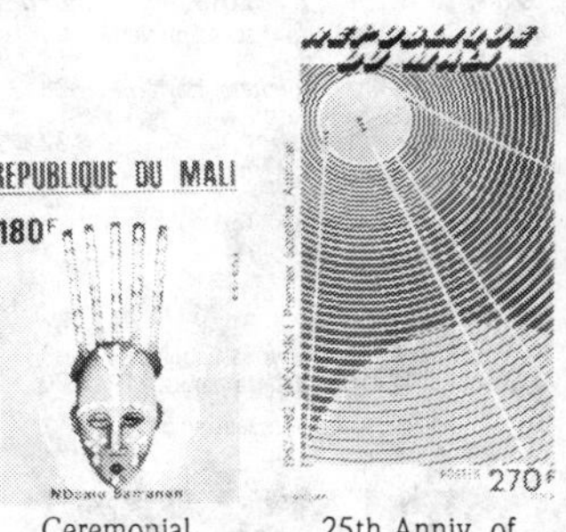
Ceremonial Mask — A155

25th Anniv. of Sputnik I Flight — A156

Designs: Various masks.

1982, Feb. 22 **Litho.** *Perf. 12½*
447 A155 5fr multi .15 .15
448 A155 35fr multi .15 .15
449 A155 180fr multi .50 .20
450 A155 200fr multi .55 .22
451 A155 250fr multi .65 .25
Nos. 447-451 (5) 2.00
Set value .75

1982, Mar. 29 **Litho.** *Perf. 13*
452 A156 270fr multi .70 .28

Fight Against Polio — A157

1982, May 3
453 A157 180fr multi .50 .20

Lions Intl. and Day of the Blind — A158

1982, May 10 **Engr.**
454 A158 260fr multi .65 .25

"Good Friends" Hairstyle — A159

Designs: Various hairstyles.

1982, May 24 **Litho.**
455 A159 140fr multi .40 .16
456 A159 150fr multi .42 .18
457 A159 160fr multi .45 .20
458 A159 180fr multi .50 .20
459 A159 270fr multi .70 .30
Nos. 455-459 (5) 2.47 1.04

Zebu A160

Designs: Various breeds of zebu.

1982, July 5 *Perf. 12½*
460 A160 10fr multi .15 .15
461 A160 60fr multi .16 .15
462 A160 110fr multi .30 .15
463 A160 180fr multi .50 .20
464 A160 200fr multi .55 .22
Nos. 460-464 (5) 1.66
Set value .62

Wind Surfing (New Olympic Class) — A161

Pres. John F. Kennedy — A162

Designs: Various wind surfers.

1982, Nov. 22 **Litho.** *Perf. 12½x13*
465 A161 200fr multi .55 .20
466 A161 270fr multi .70 .30
467 A161 300fr multi .90 .38
Nos. 465-467 (3) 2.15 .88

1983, Apr. 4 **Engr.** *Perf. 13*
468 A162 800fr shown 2.25 .90
469 A162 800fr Martin Luther King 2.50 .90

Oua Traditional Hairstyle — A163

1983, Apr. 25 **Litho.**
470 A163 180fr shown .50 .20
471 A163 200fr Nation .60 .22
472 A163 270fr Rond point .70 .28
473 A163 300fr Naamu-Naamu .80 .35
474 A163 500fr Bamba-Bamba 1.40 .55
Nos. 470-474 (5) 4.00 1.60

World Communications Year — A164

1983, May 17 **Litho.** *Perf. 13*
475 A164 180fr multi .50 .20

Bicent. of Lavoisier's Water Analysis — A165

Musicians — A166

1983, May 27 Engr. *Perf. 13*
476 A165 300fr multi .90 .38

1983, June 13 Litho. *Perf. 13x13½*
477 A166 200fr Banzoumana Sissoko .60 .22
478 A166 300fr Batourou Sekou Kouyate .90 .38

Nicephore Niepce, Photography Pioneer, (1765-1833) A167

1983, July 4 Engr. *Perf. 13*
479 A167 400fr Portrait, early camera 1.20 .45

2nd Pan African Youth Festival — A168

Palestinian Solidarity — A169

14th World UPU Day — A170

1983, Aug. 22 Litho. *Perf. 12½*
480 A168 240fr multi .70 .30
481 A169 270fr multi .80 .32

1983, Oct. 10 Engr. *Perf. 12½*
482 A170 240fr multi .70 .30

For surcharge see No. 500.

Sahel Goat — A171

1984, Jan. 30 Litho. *Perf. 13*
483 A171 20fr shown .15 .15
484 A171 30fr Billy goat .15 .15
485 A171 50fr Billy goat, diff. .15 .15
486 A171 240fr Kaarta goat .70 .18
487 A171 350fr Southern goats 1.10 .32
Nos. 483-487 (5) 2.25
Set value .68

For surcharges see Nos. 497-499, 501-502.

Rural Development A172

Fragrant Trees A173

1984, June 1 Litho. *Perf. 13*
488 A172 5fr Crop disease prevention .15 .15
489 A172 90fr Carpenters, horiz. .28 .15
490 A172 100fr Tapestry weaving, horiz. .32 .16
491 A172 135fr Metal workers, horiz. .42 .20
Nos. 488-491 (4) 1.17
Set value .55

1984, June 1
492 A173 515fr Borassus flabelifer 1.60 .80
493 A173 1225fr Vitelaria paradoxa 4.00 1.90

For surcharge see No. 583.

UN Infant Survival Campaign — A174

1984, June 12 Engr.
494 A174 120fr Child, hearts .40 .20
495 A174 135fr Children .42 .20

1984 UPU Congress — A175

1984, June 18
496 A175 135fr Anchor, UPU emblem, view of Hamburg .42 .20

Nos. 482-487 Overprinted and Surcharged

1984
497 A171 10fr on 20fr #483 .15 .15
498 A171 15fr on 30fr #484 .15 .15
499 A171 25fr on 50fr #485 .15 .15
500 A170 120fr on 240fr #482 .35 .16
501 A171 120fr on 240fr #486 .35 .16
502 A171 175fr on 350fr #487 .45 .22
Set value 1.35 .65

West African Economic Community, CEAO, 10th Anniv. A176

1984, Oct. 22 Litho. *Perf. 13½*
503 A176 350fr multi 1.00 .35

For surcharge see No. 588.

Prehistoric Animals A177

1984, Nov. 5 Litho. *Perf. 12½*
504 A177 10fr Dimetrodon .15 .15
505 A177 25fr Iguanodon, vert. .15 .15
506 A177 30fr Archaeopteryx, vert. .15 .15
507 A177 120fr Like 10fr .35 .15
508 A177 175fr Like 25fr .50 .15
509 A177 350fr Like 30fr 1.00 .30
510 A177 470fr Triceratops 1.40 .40
Nos. 504-510 (7) 3.70
Set value 1.00

For surcharges see Nos. 579, 593.

No. 366 Overprinted "Aide au Sahel 84" and Surcharged

1984 Litho. *Perf. 13*
511 A126 470fr on 130fr 1.40 .40

Issued to publicize drought relief efforts.

Mali Horses A178

1985, Jan. 21 Litho. *Perf. 13½*
512 A178 90fr Modern horse .25 .15
513 A178 135fr Horse from Beledougou .38 .15
514 A178 190fr Horse from Nara .50 .16
515 A178 530fr Horse from Trait 1.50 .45
Nos. 512-515 (4) 2.63 .91

For surcharges see Nos. 586, 591.

Fungi — A179

1985, Jan. 28 Litho. *Perf. 12½*
516 A179 120fr Clitocybe nebularis .35 .15
517 A179 200fr Lepiota cortinarius .55 .18
518 A179 485fr Agavicus semotus 1.40 .42
519 A179 525fr Lepiota procera 1.50 .45
Nos. 516-519 (4) 3.80 1.20

For surcharges see Nos. 589-590.

Health — A180

Designs: 120fr, 32nd World Leprosy Day, Emile Marchoux (1862-1943), Marchoux Institute, 150th anniv. 135fr, Lions Intl., Samanko Convalescence Village, 15th anniv. 470fr, Anti-polio campaign, research facility, victim.

1985, Feb. 18 Litho. *Perf. 13*
520 A180 120fr multi .35 .15
521 A180 135fr multi .38 .15
522 A180 470fr multi 1.40 .40
Nos. 520-522 (3) 2.13 .70

For surcharges see Nos. 580, 584. No. 522 is airmail.

Cultural and Technical Cooperation Agency, 15th Anniv. — A181

1985, Mar. 20
523 A181 540fr brn & brt bl grn 1.50 .45

Intl. Youth Year — A182

Youth activities.

1985, May 13 *Perf. 12½x13*
524 A182 120fr Natl. Pioneers Movement emblem .35 .15
525 A182 190fr Agricultural production .50 .16
526 A182 500fr Sports 1.40 .42
Nos. 524-526 (3) 2.25 .73

For surcharge see No. 587.

PHILEXAFRICA '85, Lome, Togo — A183

1985, June 24 *Perf. 13*
527 A183 250fr Education, telecommunications .65 .20
528 A183 250fr Road, dam, computers .65 .20

Nos. 527-528 show the UPU emblem and are printed se-tenant with center label picturing map of Africa or UAPT emblem. See Nos. C517-C518.

Cats — A184

1986, Feb. 15 Litho. *Perf. 13½*
529 A184 150fr Gray .60 .20
530 A184 200fr White .70 .25
531 A184 300fr Tabby 1.25 .40
Nos. 529-531 (3) 2.55 .85

For surcharge see No. 582.

Fight Against Apartheid — A185

1986, Feb. 24 *Perf. 13*
532 A185 100fr shown .38 .15
533 A185 120fr Map, broken chain .42 .15

Telecommunications and Agriculture — A186

1986, May 17 Litho. *Perf. 13*
534 A186 200fr multi .75 .25

1986 World Cup Soccer Championships, Mexico — A187

Various soccer plays.

1986, May 24 Litho. *Perf. 12½*
535 A187 160fr multi .60 .20
536 A187 225fr multi .80 .25

Souvenir Sheet

537 A187 500fr multi 2.00 .60

For overprints surcharges see #539-541, 585.

James Watt (1736-1819), Inventor, and Steam Engine — A188

1986, May 26 *Perf. 12½x12*
538 A188 110fr multi .40 .15

For surcharge see No. 581.

Nos. 535-537 Ovptd. "ARGENTINE 3 / R.F.A. 2" in Red

1986, July 30 Litho. *Perf. 12½*
539 A187 160fr multi .60 .20
540 A187 225fr multi .80 .28

Souvenir Sheet

541 A187 500fr multi 2.00 .60

World Wildlife Fund — A189

Derby's Eland, Taurotragus derbianus.

1986, Aug. 11 Litho. *Perf. 13*
542 A189 5fr Adult head .15 .15
543 A189 20fr Adult in brush .15 .15
544 A189 25fr Adult walking .15 .15
545 A189 200fr Calf suckling .75 .25
Set value .98 .40

Henry Ford (1863-1947), Auto Manufacturer, Inventor of Mass Production — A190

1987, Feb. 16 Litho. *Perf. 13*
546 A190 150fr Model A, 1903 .60 .20
547 A190 200fr Model T, 1923 .70 .25
548 A190 225fr Thunderbird, 1968 .80 .28
549 A190 300fr Lincoln Continental, 1963 1.10 .38
Nos. 546-549 (4) 3.20 1.11

Bees — A191

1987, May 11 Litho. *Perf. 13½*
550 A191 100fr Apis florea, Asia .38 .20
551 A191 150fr Apis dorsata, Asia .55 .25
552 A191 175fr Apis adansonii, Africa .65 .35
553 A191 200fr Apis mellifica, worldwide .70 .38
Nos. 550-553 (4) 2.28 1.18

Lions Club Activities — A192

1988, Jan. 13 Litho. *Perf. 12½*
554 A192 200fr multi 1.00 .50

World Health Organization, 40th Anniv. — A193

1988, Feb. 22 Litho. *Perf. 12½x12*
555 A193 150fr multi .70 .38

For surcharge see No. 557.

John F. Kennedy (1917-1963), 35th US President — A194

1988, June 6 Litho. *Perf. 13*
556 A194 640fr multi 4.25 2.15

For surcharge see No. 592.

No. 555 Surcharged in Dark Red

MISSION MALI
HOPITAL de MOPTI 300F

1988, June 13 *Perf. 12½x12*
557 A193 300fr on 150fr multi 2.00 1.00

Mali Mission Hospital in Mopti and World Medicine organization.

Organization of African Unity, 25th Anniv. — A194a

1988, June 27 Litho. *Perf. 12½*
558 A194a 400fr multi 2.65 1.35

Universal Immunization Campaign A195

1989, May 2 Litho. *Perf. 13½*
559 A195 20fr shown .15 .15
560 A195 30fr Inoculating woman .18 .15
561 A195 50fr Emblem, needles, diff. .30 .15
562 A195 175fr Inoculating boy 1.05 .52
Nos. 559-562 (4) 1.68
Set value .82

Intl. Law Institute of the French-Speaking Nations — A196

1989, May 15 *Perf. 12½*
563 A196 150fr multi .90 .45
564 A196 200fr multi 1.20 .60

World Post Day — A197

1989, Oct. 9 Litho. *Perf. 13*
565 A197 625fr multicolored 4.00 2.00

For surcharge see No. 594.

Visit of Pope John Paul II — A198

1990, Jan. 28 Litho. *Perf. 13x12½*
566 A198 200fr multicolored 1.45 .72

Multinational Postal School, 20th Anniv. — A199

1990, May 31 Litho. *Perf. 12½*
567 A199 150fr multicolored 1.10 .55

Independence, 30th Anniv. — A200

1990, Sept. 20 Litho. *Perf. 13x12½*
568 A200 400fr multicolored 3.00 1.50

Intl. Literacy Year — A201

1990, Sept. 24 Litho. *Perf. 13½*
569 A201 150fr grn & multi 1.30 .65
570 A201 200fr org & multi 1.75 .90

A202 A203

Lions Intl. Water Project, 6th anniv.: No. 572, Rotary Club fight against polio, 30th anniv.

1991, Feb. 25 Litho. *Perf. 13x12½*
571 A202 200fr multicolored 1.75 .90
572 A202 200fr multicolored 1.75 .90

1991, Apr. 29 Litho. *Perf. 12½*

Designs: Tribal dances of Mali.

573 A203 50fr Takamba .45 .22
574 A203 100fr Mandiani .90 .45
575 A203 150fr Kono 1.40 .70
576 A203 200fr Songho 1.75 .90
Nos. 573-576 (4) 4.50 2.27

A204 A205

1991, Dec. 2 Litho. *Perf. 12½*
577 A204 200fr multicolored 1.75 .90

Central Fund for Economic Cooperation, 50th anniv.

1992, Mar. 26 Litho. *Perf. 12½*
578 A205 150fr multicolored 1.20 .60

National Women's Movement.

Various Stamps of 1984-89 Surcharged in Black or Black and Silver

25F

1992, June Litho. *Perfs. as Before*
579 A177 25fr on 470fr #510 .20 .15
580 A180 25fr on 470fr #522 .20 .15
581 A188 30fr on 110fr #538 .24 .15
582 A184 50fr on 300fr #531 .40 .20
583 A173 50fr on 1225fr #493 .40 .20
584 A180 150fr on 135fr #521 (Bk & S) 1.20 .60
585 A187 150fr on 160fr #535 1.20 .60
586 A178 150fr on 190fr #514 1.20 .60
587 A182 150fr on 190fr #525 1.20 .60
588 A176 150fr on 350fr #503 1.20 .60
589 A179 150fr on 485fr #518 1.20 .60
590 A179 150fr on 525fr #519 1.20 .60
591 A178 150fr on 530fr #515 1.20 .60
592 A194 200fr on 640fr #556 1.60 .80
593 A177 240fr on 350fr #509 1.95 1.00
594 A197 240fr on 625fr #565 1.95 1.00
Nos. 579-594 (16) 16.54 8.45

No. 580 is airmail. Size and location of surcharge varies. No. 585 also overprinted "Euro '92."

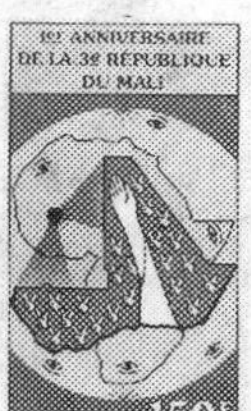

New Constitution, 1st Anniv. — A205a

1993, Jan. 12 Litho. *Perf. 11½x12*
594A A205a 150fr pink & multi
594B A205a 225fr green & multi
Set value 42.50

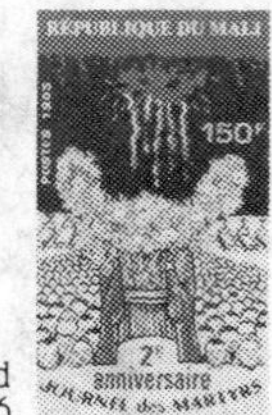

Martyr's Day, 2nd Anniv. — A206

1993, Mar. 26 Litho. *Perf. 11½*
595 A206 150fr blue & multi 1.10 .55
596 A206 160fr yellow & multi 1.25 .60

Rotary Intl. and World Health Organization (WHO) A206a

Designs: 150fr, Polio victims, Rotary emblem. 200fr, WHO emblem, pregnant woman receiving vaccination.

1993, Apr. 16 Litho. *Perf. 14*
596A A206a 150fr multicolored
596B A206a 200fr multicolored
Set value 42.50

Lions Club in Mali, 35th Anniv. A207

1993, Dec. 20 Litho. *Perf. 14½*
597 A207 200fr blue & multi .75 .38
598 A207 225fr red & multi .85 .42

Monument, Liberty Place — A207a

1993, Dec. 20 Photo. *Perf. 12*
598A A207a 20fr multicolored
598D A207a 100fr multicolored
598F A207a 150fr multicolored
598G A207a 200fr multicolored
598H A207a 225fr multicolored
598I A207a 240fr multicolored

This is a set of 10. The editors would like to examine the other four stamps.

1994 Winter Olympics, Lillehammer A208

1994, Feb. 12 Litho. *Perf. 13*
599 A208 150fr Pairs figure skating .55 .28
600 A208 200fr Giant slalom .75 .38
601 A208 225fr Ski jumping .85 .42
602 A208 750fr Speed skating 2.75 1.40
Nos. 599-602 (4) 4.90 2.48

Souvenir Sheet

603 A208 2000fr Downhill skiing 7.50 3.75

No. 603 contains one 36x36mm stamp.
For overprints see Nos. 671-676.

1994 World Cup Soccer Championships, US — A209

Designs: 200fr, Juan Schiaffino, Uruguay. 240fr, Diego Maradona, Argentina. 260fr, Paolo Rossi, Italy. 1000fr, Franz Beckenbauer, Germany. 2000fr, Just Fontaine, France.

1994, Mar. 15 Litho. *Perf. 13*
604 A209 200fr multicolored .75 .38
605 A209 240fr multicolored .90 .45
606 A209 260fr multicolored 1.00 .50
607 A209 1000fr multicolored 3.75 1.90
Nos. 604-607 (4) 6.40 3.23

Souvenir Sheet

608 A209 2000fr multicolored 7.50 3.75

For overprints see Nos. 677-681.

Miniature Sheet

Dinosaurs A210

a, 5fr, Scaphonyx. b, 10fr, Cynognathus. c, 15fr, Lesothosaurus. d, 20fr, Scutellosaurus. e, 25fr, Ceratosaurus. f, 30fr, Dilophosaurus. g, 40fr, Dryosaurus. h, 50fr, Heterodontosaurus. i, 60fr, Anatosaurus. j, 70fr, Saurornithoides. k, 80fr, Avimimus. l, 90fr, Saltasaurus. m, 300fr, Dromaeosaurus. n, 400fr, Tsintaosaurus. o, 600fr, Velociraptor. p, 700fr, Ouranosaurus.
2000fr, Daspletosaurus, iguanodon.

1994, Mar. 28
609 A210 Sheet of 16, #a.-p. 9.50 4.75

Souvenir Sheet

610 A210 2000fr multicolored 7.50 3.75

Insects A211

Designs: 40fr, Sternuera castanea, vert. 50fr, Eudicella gralli. 100fr, Homoderus mellyi, vert. 200fr, Kraussaria angulifera.

1994, Mar. 30 Litho. *Perf. 13*
611 A211 40fr multicolored .16 .15
612 A211 50fr multicolored .20 .15
613 A211 100fr multicolored .40 .20
614 A211 200fr multicolored .80 .40
Nos. 611-614 (4) 1.56 .90

Vaccination Campaign Against Measles A212

1994, Apr. 7 Litho. *Perf. 13½*
615 A212 150fr black & green .70 .35
616 A212 200fr black & blue .90 .45

Birds A213

1994, Apr. 25
617 A213 25fr Pigeons .15 .15
618 A213 30fr Turkeys .15 .15
619 A213 150fr Crowned cranes, vert. .60 .30
620 A213 200fr Chickens, vert. .80 .40
Nos. 617-620 (4) 1.70 1.00

Intl. Year of the Family — A213a

1994, May 2
620A A213a 220fr multicolored .95 .48

Jazz Musicians A214

1994 Litho. *Perf. 13*
621 A214 200fr Ella Fitzgerald .80 .40
622 A214 225fr Lionel Hampton .90 .45
623 A214 240fr Sarah Vaughan .95 .48
624 A214 300fr Count Basie 1.25 .62
625 A214 400fr Duke Ellington 1.50 .75
626 A214 600fr Miles Davis 2.50 1.25
Nos. 621-626 (6) 7.90 3.95

Souvenir Sheet

627 A214 1500fr Louis Armstrong 6.00 6.00

No. 627 contains one 45x45mm stamp.

Ancient Art — A215

15fr, Venus of Brassempoury, vert. 25fr, Petroglyphs, Tanum, vert. 45fr, Prehistoric cave drawings, vert. 50fr, Cave paintings, Lascaux. 55fr, Tomb of Amonherkhopeshef, vert. 65fr, Goddess Anubis and the pharaoh. 75fr, Sphinx. 85fr, Bust of Nefertiti, vert. 95fr, Statue of Shibum, vert. 100fr, Standard of Ur. 130fr, Mesopotamian bull's head harp, vert. 135fr, Mesopotamian scroll. 140fr, Assyrian dignitary, vert. 180fr, Enameled horse, Babylon. 190fr, Assyrian carving of hunters, vert. 200fr, Mona Lisa of Nimrud, vert. 225fr, Carthaginian coin. 250fr, Phoenician sphinx, vert. 275fr, Persian archer, vert. 280fr, Ceramic and glass mask, vert.

1994, Aug. 24 Litho. *Perf. 13½*
628-647 A215 Set of 20 10.50 5.25

D-Day Landings, Normandy, 50th Anniv. — A216

Villiers-Bocage, June 12: No. 648a, Explosion, men being killed. b, Tank firing. c, Tank, men with weapons.
Beaumont-Sur-Sarthe, June 6: No. 649a, Explosion, airplanes. b, British airplanes, tanks. c, German tanks, soldier firing machine gun.
Utah Beach, June 6: No. 650a, Explosion, bow of landing craft. b, Stern of landing craft, soldiers. c, Landing craft filled with troops.
Aerial battle: No. 651a, British planes dropping bombs. b, British, German planes. c, British, German planes, explosion.
Sainte-Mere-Eglise, June 5: No. 652a, German troops firing on paratroopers. b, Church tower. c, Paratroopers, German troops.

1994, June 6
648 A216 200fr Strip of 3, #a.-c. 2.50 1.25
649 A216 300fr Strip of 3, #a.-c. 3.50 1.75
650 A216 300fr Strip of 3, #a.-c. 3.50 1.75
651 A216 400fr Strip of 3, #a.-c. 4.75 2.50
652 A216 400fr Strip of 3, #a.-c. 4.75 2.50
Nos. 648-652 (5) 19.00 9.75

Nos. 648-652 are each continuous designs. Nos. 648b, 649b, 650b, 651b, 652b are each 30x47mm.

Orchids, Vegetables, & Mushrooms A217

Orchids: 25fr, Disa kewensis. 50fr, Angraecum eburneum. 100fr, Ansellia africana.
Vegetables: 140fr, Sorghum. 150fr, Onions. 190fr, Corn.
Mushrooms: 200fr, Lepiota (clitocybe) nebularis. 225fr, Macrolepiota (lepiota) procera. 500fr, Lepiota aspera.

1994
653 A217 25fr multicolored .15 .15
654 A217 50fr multicolored .20 .15
655 A217 100fr multicolored .42 .20
a. Souvenir sheet of 3, #653-655 *12.00 6.00*
656 A217 140fr multicolored .55 .28
657 A217 150fr multicolored .60 .30
658 A217 190fr multicolored .75 .40
a. Souvenir sheet of 3, #656-658 *12.00 6.00*
659 A217 200fr multicolored .85 .42
660 A217 225fr multicolored .95 .45
661 A217 500fr multicolored 2.00 1.00
a. Souvenir sheet of 3, #659-661 *12.00 6.00*
Nos. 653-661 (9) 6.47 3.35

Moths, Butterflies & Insects — A218

Designs: 20fr, Polyptychus roseus. 30fr, Elymniopsis bammakoo. 40fr, Deilephila nerii. 150fr, Utetheisa pulchella. 180fr, Charaxes jasius. 200fr, Mylothris chloris.
Insects: 225fr, Goliath beetle. 240fr, Locust. 350fr, Praying mantis.

1994
662 A218 20fr multicolored .15 .15
663 A218 30fr multicolored .15 .15
664 A218 40fr multicolored .16 .15
665 A218 150fr multicolored .60 .30
666 A218 180fr multicolored .75 .35

667 A218 200fr multicolored .80 .40
a. Souvenir sheet of 6, #662-667 *22.50 11.00*
668 A218 225fr multicolored .90 .45
669 A218 240fr multicolored 1.00 .50
670 A218 350fr multicolored 1.40 .70
a. Souvenir sheet of 3, #668-670 *12.00 6.00*
Nos. 662-670 (9) 5.91 3.15

Nos. 599-603 Ovptd. in Silver or Gold with Name of Olympic Medalist, Country

Overprints in silver: No. 671a, "Y. GORDEYEVA / S. GRINKOV / RUSSIE." No. 671b, "O. GRISHCHUK / Y. PLATOV / RUSSIE." No. 672a, "D. COMPAGNONI / ITALIE." No. 672b, "M. WASMEIER / ALLEMAGNE." No. 673a, "E. BREDESEN /NORVEGE." No. 673b, "J. WEISSFLOG / ALLEMAGNE." No. 674a, "B. BLAIR, U.S.A." No. 674b, "J.O. KOSS / NORVEGE."

Overprint in gold: No. 675, "L. KJUS / NORVEGE." No. 676, "P. WIBERG / SUEDE."

1994 Litho. *Perf. 13*
671 A208 150fr Pair, #a.-b. 1.25 .60
672 A208 200fr Pair, #a.-b. 1.65 .85
673 A208 225fr Pair, #a.-b. 1.90 .95
674 A208 750fr Pair, #a.-b. 6.25 3.00
Nos. 671-674 (4) 11.05 5.40

Souvenir Sheet

675 A208 2000fr multicolored 7.50 3.75
676 A208 2000fr multicolored 7.50 3.75

Nos. 604-608 Ovptd. in Metallic Red

1 . BRESIL
2 . ITALIE
3 . SUEDE

1994 Litho. *Perf. 13*
677 A209 200fr multicolored .80 .40
678 A209 240fr multicolored 1.00 .50
679 A209 260fr multicolored 1.10 .55
680 A209 1000fr multicolored 4.00 2.00
Nos. 677-680 (4) 6.90 3.45

Souvenir Sheet

681 A209 2000fr multicolored 8.00 4.00

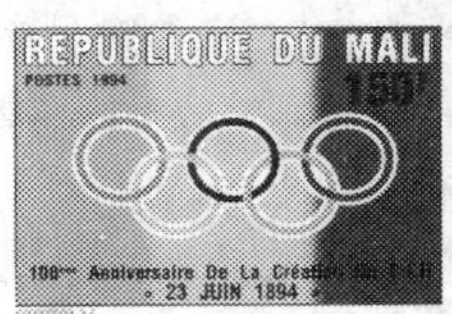

Intl. Olympic Committee, Cent. A218a

1994, June 23 Litho. *Perf. 13½*
681A A218a 150fr multicolored .65 .32
681B A218a 200fr multicolored .80 .40

Exist in imperf souvenir sheets of 1.

Intl. Olympic Committee, Cent. — A219

Pierre de Coubertin and: 225fr, Woman carrying flame, vert. 240fr, Olympic rings, vert. 300fr, Torch bearer. 500fr, Gold medal of Olympic rings.
600fr, Flame, statue of flag bearer.

1994, June 23 *Perf. 13½*
682 A219 225fr multicolored .90 .45
683 A219 240fr multicolored 1.00 .50
684 A219 300fr multicolored 1.25 .60
685 A219 500fr multicolored 2.00 1.00
Nos. 682-685 (4) 5.15 2.55

Souvenir Sheet

686 A219 600fr multicolored 2.50 1.25

Anniversaries & Events — A220

Designs: 150fr, Erst Julius Opik, Galileo probe, impact of comet on Jupiter. 200fr, Clyde Tombaugh, probe moving toward Pluto. 500fr, Intl. Red Cross, Henri Dunant. 650fr, Crew of Apollo 11, 1st manned moon landing. 700fr, Lions Intl., Rotary Intl. 800fr, Gary Kasparov chess champion.

1994, Apr. 10 Litho. *Perf. 13½*
687 A220 150fr multicolored .65 .32
688 A220 200fr multicolored .90 .45
689 A220 500fr multicolored 2.25 1.10
690 A220 650fr multicolored 2.75 1.40
691 A220 700fr multicolored 3.00 1.50
692 A220 800fr multicolored 3.50 1.75
Nos. 687-692 (6) 13.05 6.52

Nos. 687-692 exist in souvenir sheets of 1.

Motion Picture, Cent. — A221

Movie star, movie: 100fr, Kirk Douglas, Spartacus. 150fr, Elizabeth Taylor, Cleopatra. 200fr, Clint Eastwood, Sierra Torrid. 225fr, Marilyn Monroe, The River of No Return. 500fr, Arnold Schwartzenegger, Conan the Barbarian. 1000fr, Elvis Presley, Loving You. 1500fr, Charlton Heston, The Ten Commandments.

1994, May 23 Litho. *Perf. 13½*
693-698 A221 Set of 6 8.75 4.25

Souvenir Sheet

699 A221 1500fr multicolored 6.00 3.00

No. 695 is airmail.

Fight Against AIDS A222

Designs: 150fr, Woman, man holding condoms. 225fr, Nurse with AIDS patient, researcher looking into microscope.

1994, June 30
700 A222 150fr multicolored .60 .30
701 A222 225fr multicolored .90 .45

Tourism A223

Designs: 150fr, Traditional buildings, statue, vert. 200fr, Sphinx, pyramids, ruins.

1994, Dec. 5
702 A223 150fr multicolored .60 .30
703 A223 200fr multicolored .80 .40

1996 Summer Olympics, Atlanta — A224

Designs: 25fr, Reiner Klimke, dressage. 50fr, Kristin Otto, swimming. 100fr, Hans-Gunther Winkler, equestrian. 150fr, Birgit Fischer-Schmidt, kayak. 200fr, Nicole Uphoff, dressage, vert. 225fr, Renate Stecher, track, vert. 230fr, Michael Gross, swimming. 240fr, Karin Janz, gymnastics. 550fr, Anja Fichtel, fencing, vert. 700fr, Heide Rosendahl-Ecker, track, vert.

1995, Mar. 27
704-713 A224 Set of 10 10.00 5.00

Dated 1994.

Rotary Intl., 90th Anniv. — A225

1995, Oct. 18 Litho. *Perf. 14*
714 A225 1000fr Paul Harris, logo 4.00 2.00

Souvenir Sheet

715 A225 1500fr 1905, 1995 Logos 6.00 3.00

Miniature Sheets

Birds, Butterflies — A226

No. 716: a, Campephilos imperialis. b, Momotus momota. c, Ramphastos sulfuratus. d, Halcyon malimbica. e, Trochilus polytmus. f, Cardinalis cardinalis. g, Pharomachrus mocinno. h, Aratinga solstitialis. i, Amazona arausiaca. j, Eudocimus ruber. k, Carduelis cucullatus. l, Anodorhynchus hyacinthinus. m, Passerina leclancherii. n, Pipra mentalis. o, Rupicola rupicola. p, Sicalis flaveola.

No. 717: a, Carito niger. b, Chloroceryle amazona. c, Tersina virdis. d, Momotus momota. e, Campephilus menaloleucos. f, Leistes militaris. g, Sarcoramphus papa. h, Pilherodius pileatus. i, Tityra cayana. j, Tangara chilinsis. k, Amazona ochrocephala. l, Saltator maximus. m, Paroaria dominicana. n, Egretta tricolor. o, Piaya melano gaster. p, Thamnophilus doliatus.

No. 718: a, Paradise whydah (g). b, Red-necked francolin. c, Whale-headed stork (i). d, Ruff (j). e, Marabou stork (k). f, White pelican. g, Western curlew. h, Scarlet ibis. i, Great crested crebe. j, White spoonbill. k, African jacana. l, African pygmy goose.

No. 719: a, Ruby-throated hummingbird. b, Grape shoemaker, blue morpho butterflies. c, Northern hobby. d, Cuvier toucan (g). e, Black-necked red cotinga (h). f, Green-winged macaws (i). g, Flamingo (j). h, Malachite kingfisher. i, Bushy-crested hornbill (l). j, Purple swamphen (k). k, Striped body (j, l). l, Painted lady butterfly.

No. 720, Topaza pella. No. 721, Sporophila lineola.

1995, Oct. 20 Litho. *Perf. 14*
716 A226 50fr Sheet of 16, #a.-p. 3.25 1.65
717 A226 100fr Sheet of 16, #a.-p. 6.50 3.25
718 A226 150fr Sheet of 12, #a.-l. 7.25 3.75
719 A226 200fr Sheet of 12, #a.-l. 9.75 4.75
Nos. 716-719 (4) 26.75 13.40

Souvenir Sheets

720-721 A226 1000fr each 4.00 2.00

John Lennon (1940-80) A227

1995 Litho. *Perf. 14*
722 A227 150fr multicolored .60 .30

No. 722 was issued in sheets of 16.

Miniature Sheets

Motion Pictures, Cent. A228

Western actors: No. 723:a, George Barnes. b, William S. Hart. c, Tom Mix. d, Wallace Beery. e, Gary Cooper. f, John Wayne.

Actresses and their directors: No. 724: a, Marlene Dietrich, Josef Von Sternberg. b, Jean Harlow, George Cukor. c, Mary Astor, John Houston. d, Ingrid Bergman, Alfred Hitchcock. e, Claudette Colbert, Cecil B. De Mille. f, Marilyn Monroe, Billy Wilder.

Musicals and their stars: No. 725: a, Singin' in the Rain, Gene Kelly. b, The Bandwagon, Anne Miller, Ray Bolger. c, Cabaret, Liza Minnelli, Joel Gray. d, The Sound of Music, Julie Andrews. e, Top Hat, Ginger Rogers, Fred Astaire. f, Saturday Night Fever, John Travolta.

No. 726, Robert Redford as the Sundance Kid. No. 727, Liv Ullman, actress, Ingmar Bergman, director. No. 728, Judy Garland in the Wizard of Oz.

1995, Dec. 8 Litho. *Perf. 13½x14*
723 A228 150fr Sheet of 6, #a.-f. 3.50 1.75
724 A228 200fr Sheet of 6, #a.-f. 4.75 2.50
725 A228 240fr Sheet of 6, #a.-f. 5.75 3.00
Nos. 723-725 (3) 14.00 7.25

Souvenir Sheets

726-728 A228 1000fr each 4.00 2.00

Nos. 723-728 have various styles of lettering.

Miniature Sheet

Stars of Rock and Roll — A229

No. 729: a, Connie Francis. b, The Ronettes. c, Janis Joplin. d, Debbie Harry of Blondie. e, Cyndi Lauper. f, Carly Simon.

No. 730, Bette Midler.

1995, Dec. 8
729 A229 225fr Sheet of 6, #a.-f. 5.50 2.25

Souvenir Sheet

730 A229 1000fr multicolored 4.00 2.00

Traditional Cooking Utensils — A230

Designs: 5fr, Canaris, vert. 50fr, Mortier, calebasse, vert. 150fr, Fourneau. 200fr, Vans, vert. 500fr, Vans.

1995, Nov. 20 Litho. *Perf. 14*

731-734 A230 Set of 4 1.65 .85

Souvenir Sheet

735 A230 500fr multicolored 2.00 1.00

18th World Scout Jamboree, Holland — A231

Scout examining butterfly or mushroom: 150fr, Saturnia pyri. 225fr, Gonepteryx rhamni. 240fr, Myrina silenus. 500fr, Clitocybe nebularis. 650fr, Agaricus semotus. 725fr, Lepiota procera.
1500fr, Morpho cypris.

1995 Litho. *Perf. 13½*

736-741 A231 Set of 6 11.50 5.75

Souvenir Sheet

742 A231 1500fr multicolored 9.25 4.60

Nos. 736-741 exist in souvenir sheets of 1.

UN, 50th Anniv. A232

Designs: 20fr, 170fr, UN emblem, scales of justice, doves, vert. 225fr, 240fr, Doves, UN emblem, four men of different races.

1995 Litho. *Perf. 13*

743 A232 20fr light blue & multi .15 .15
744 A232 170fr light green & multi .75 .40
745 A232 225fr light purple & multi 1.00 .50
746 A232 240fr light orange & multi 1.10 .55
Nos. 743-746 (4) 3.00 1.60

Ayrton Senna (1960-94), F-1 Race Car Driver — A233

1000fr, Jerry Garcia (1942-95), entertainer.

1995 *Perf. 13½*

747 A233 500fr multicolored 2.25 1.10
748 A233 1000fr multicolored 4.50 2.25

Nos. 747-748 exist in souvenir sheets of one.

1945-49 Greenland Expeditions of Paul Emile Victor — A234

1995

749 A234 150fr Charles de Gaulle .70 .35
750 A234 200fr De Gaulle, liberation of Paris .90 .45
751 A234 240fr Enzo Ferrari 1.15 .55
752 A234 650fr multicolored 3.00 1.50
753 A234 725fr Paul Harris 3.25 1.65
754 A234 740fr Michael Schumacher 3.40 1.70
Nos. 749-754 (6) 12.40 6.20

Nos. 749-754 exist in souvenir sheets of 1.

A235 A236

Designs: 150fr, Second election party emblems, horiz. 200fr, Pres. Alpha Oumar Konare. 225fr, First election party emblems, horiz. 240fr, Natl. flag, map, party representations.

1995 Litho. *Perf. 13½*

755 A235 150fr multicolored .70 .35
756 A235 200fr multicolored .90 .45
757 A235 225fr multicolored 1.00 .50
758 A235 240fr multicolored 1.10 .55
Nos. 755-758 (4) 3.70 1.85

Second Presidential elections.

1995

Economic Community of West African States (ECOWAS): 150fr, Regional integration, horiz. 200fr, Cooperation. 220fr, Prospect of creating one currency, horiz. 225fr, Peace and security, horiz.

759 A236 150fr multicolored .70 .35
760 A236 200fr multicolored .90 .45
761 A236 220fr multicolored 1.00 .50
762 A236 225fr multicolored 1.00 .50
Nos. 759-762 (4) 3.60 1.80

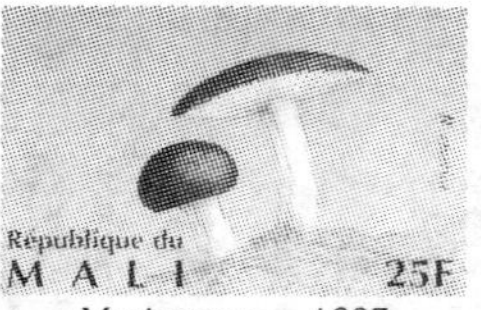

Mushrooms — A237

Genus Russula: No. 763: a, Emetica. b, Laurocerasi. c, Rosacea. d, Occidentalis. e, Fragilis. f, Mariae. g, Eeruginea. h, Compacta.
Genus Boletus: No. 764: a, Felleus. b, Elagans. c, Castaneus. d, Edulis. e, Aereus. f, Granulatus. g, Cavipes. h, Badius.
Genus Lactarius: No. 765: a, Deliciosus. b, Luculentus. c, Pseudomucidus. d, Scrobiculatus. e, Deceptivus. f, Indigo. g, Peckii. h, Lignyotus.
Genus Amanita: No. 766a, Caesarea. b, Muscaria. c, Solitaria. d, Verna. e, Malleata. f. Phalloides. g, Citrina. h, Pantherina.
No. 767, Coprinus atramentarius. No. 768, Panaeolus subbalteatus.

1996, Mar. 15 Litho. *Perf. 14*

763 A237 25fr Sheet of 8, #a.-h. .90 .45
764 A237 150fr Sheet of 8, #a.-h. 5.40 2.70
765 A237 200fr Sheet of 8, #a.-h. 7.20 3.60
766 A237 225fr Sheet of 8, #a.-h. 8.10 4.00

Souvenir Sheets

767-768 A237 1000fr each 4.50 2.25

Sites in Beijing — A238

No. 769: a, Bridge, Gateway to Hall of Supreme Harmony. b, Temple of Heaven. c, Great Wall. d, Hall of Supreme Harmony. e, Courtyard, Gate of Heavenly Purity, f, Younghe Gong Temple. g, Lang Ru Ting, Bridge of Seventeen Arches. h, Meridian Gate (Wu Men). i, Corner Tower.
No. 770, Pagoda, vert. No. 771, Li Peng.

1996, May 13

769 A238 100fr Sheet of 9, #a.-i. 4.00 2.00

Souvenir Sheets

770-771 A238 500fr each 2.25 1.10

No. 771 contains one 47x72mm stamp.

CHINA '96 (Nos. 769, 771).

Trains A239

Historic: No. 772: a, "Novelty," 1829. b, Premiere class Liverpool & Manchester Line, 1830. c, William Norris, 1843. d, Trevithick, 1808. e, Robert Stephenson "Rocket," 1829. f, "Puffing Billy," William Hedley, 1813.
No. 773: a, Subway Train, London. b, San Francisco cable car. c, Japanese monorail. d, Pantograph car, Stockholm. e, Double-decker tram, Hong Kong. f, Sacre-Coeur Cog Train, Montmartre, France.
No. 774: a, Docklands Light Railway, London. b, British Railway's high-speed diesel train. c, Japanese Bullet Train. d, Germany Inter-City Electric high speed train. e, French TGV high-speed electric train. f, German "Wuppertal" monorail.
Trains of China: No. 775: a, RM Class Pacific. b, Manchurian steam engine. c, SY Class 2-8-2, Tangshan. d, SL Class 4-6-2 Pacific. e, Chengtu-Kunming steam. f, Lanchow passenger train.
No. 776, Rheingold Express, 1925. No. 777, Matterhorn cable car, vert. No. 778, Superchief, best long-distance diesel, US. No. 779, Shanghai-Nanking Railway.

1996, July 29

772 A239 180fr Sheet of 6, #a.-f. 4.90 2.40
773 A239 250fr Sheet of 6, #a.-f. 6.75 3.40
774 A239 310fr Sheet of 6, #a.-f. 8.40 4.20
775 A239 320fr Sheet of 6, #a.-f. 8.60 4.30

Souvenir Sheets

776-779 A239 500fr each 2.25 1.10

Nos. 776-779 each contain one 57x43mm stamp.

Express Mail Service, 10th Anniv. A240

Designs: 30fr, Man with package, vert. 40fr, Bird holding package, letter, vert. 90fr, World map, woman with letter holding telephone receiver. 320fr, 320fr, Mail van, hands holding letters, map.

1996, Sept. 1 Litho. *Perf. 14*

780 A240 30fr multicolored .15 .15
781 A240 40fr multicolored .30 .15
782 A240 90fr multicolored .40 .20
783 A240 320fr multicolored 1.40 .70
Nos. 780-783 (4) 2.25 1.20

Queen Elizabeth II, 70th Birthday A241

Designs: a, Portrait. b, Wearing blue & red hat. c, Portrait as young woman.
1000fr, Portrait as young girl.

1996, Sept. 9 *Perf. 13½x14*

784 A241 370fr Strip of 3, #a.-c. 4.50 2.25

Souvenir Sheet

785 A241 1000fr multicolored 4.00 2.00

No. 784 was issued in sheets of 9 stamps.

Nanking Bridge — A242

1996 Litho. *Perf. 13½*

786 A242 270fr multicolored 1.25 .60

Mosques A243

1996

787 A243 250fr Djenne 1.40 1.40
788 A243 310fr Sankore 1.75 1.75

Pandas, Dogs, and Cats A244

Panda, vert: No. 789: a, Climbing on branch. b, On bare limb. c. Closer view. d, Lying in branch with leaves.
Dogs, cats: No. 790: a, Azawakh. b, Basenji. c, Javanais. d, Abyssin.

1996

789 A244 150fr Sheet of 4, #a.-d. 2.75 1.35
790 A244 310fr Sheet of 4, #a.-d. 5.50 2.75

Nos. 789a-789d are 39x42mm.

Marilyn Monroe (1926-62) A245

Various portraits.

1996

791 A245 320fr Sheet of 9, #a.-i. 13.00 6.50

Souvenir Sheet

792 A245 2000fr multicolored 9.00 4.50

No. 792 contains one 42x60mm stamp.

Entertainers A246

Designs: No. 793: a, Frank Sinatra. b, Johnny Mathis. c, Dean Martin. d, Bing Crosby. e, Sammy

Davis, Jr. f, Elvis Presley. g, Paul Anka. h, Tony Bennett. i, Nat "King" Cole.
No. 794, Various portraits of John Lennon.

1996

793 A246 250fr Sheet of 9, #a.-i. 10.00 5.00
794 A246 310fr Sheet of 9, #a.-i. 12.50 6.25

US Space Shuttle, Challenger — A247

Designs: a, Halley's Comet, Andromeda Galaxy. b, Mars. c, Challenger, Saturn. d, Moon, Jupiter.
1000fr, Shuttle Challenger.

1996, Oct. 14 *Perf. 14*

795 A247 320fr Sheet of 4, #a.-d. 5.75 2.90

Souvenir Sheet

796 A247 1000fr multicolored 4.50 2.25

No. 796 contains one 85x29mm stamp.

Mickey's ABC's — A248

Disney characters in various scenes with: No. 797: a, "MICKEY." b, "A." c, "B." d, "C." e, "D." f, "E." g, "F." h, "G." i, "H."
No. 798: a, "I." b, "J." c, "K." d, "L." e, "M." f, "N." g, "O." h, "P." i, "Q."
No. 799: a, "R." b, "S." c, "T." d, "U." e, "V." f, "W." g, "X." h, "Y." i, "Z."
No. 800, Mouse child holding "DE MICKEY" sign, horiz. No. 801, Mouse children with various letters.

1996, Oct. 15 Litho. *Perf. 13½x14*

797 A248 50fr Sheet of 9, #a.-i. 1.80 .90
798 A248 100fr Sheet of 9, #a.-i. 3.60 1.80
799 A248 200fr Sheet of 9, #a.-i. 7.20 3.60

Souvenir Sheets

800-801 A248 1000fr each 4.70 2.35

Sites in Beijing A249

Designs: No. 802, Hall of Supreme Harmony. No. 803, Great Wall. No. 804, Hall of Prayers for Good Harvests, Temple of Heaven.

1996 *Perf. 13½*

802 A249 180fr multicolored .80 .40
803 A249 180fr multicolored .80 .40
804 A249 180fr multicolored .80 .40
Nos. 802-804 (3) 2.40 1.20

Cotton Production A250

Designs: 20fr, Cotton plant, vert. 25fr, People working in cotton fields. 50fr, Holding plant, vert. 310fr, Dumping cotton into cart.

1996 *Perf. 13½*

805 A250 20fr multicolored .15 .15
806 A250 25fr multicolored .15 .15
807 A250 50fr multicolored .25 .15
808 A250 310fr multicolored 1.40 .70
Nos. 805-808 (4) 1.95 1.15

Birds and Snakes A251

a, Crowned eagle in flight. b, Tufted eagle. c, Python. d, Gabon viper.
Songbirds: No. 810: a, Choucador splendide. b, Astrid ondulé. c, Martin chasseur. d, Coucou didric.
Butterflies: No. 811a, Salamis parhassus. b, Charaxes bohemani. c, Coeliades forestan. d, Mimacrea marshalli.

1996

809 A251 180fr Sheet of 4, #a.-d. 3.25 1.60
810 A251 250fr Sheet of 4, #a.-d. 4.50 2.25
811 A251 320fr Sheet of 4, #a.-d. 5.75 2.90

Third World — A252

Design: 250fr, Hot air balloon in flight.

1996

812 A252 180fr shown .80 .40
813 A252 250fr multicolored 1.10 .55

A253 A254

1996

814 A253 180fr green & multi .80 .40
815 A253 250fr bister & multi 1.10 .55

Death of Abdoul Karim Camara (Cabral), 16th anniv.

1997, Jan. 10 Litho. *Perf. 14*

Dogs: No. 816, Airdale terrier. No. 817, Briard. No. 818, Schnauzer. No. 819, Chow chow.
Cats: No. 820, Turkish van. No. 821, Sphynx. No. 822, Korat. No. 823, American curl.
Dogs, horiz.: No. 824: a, Basset hound. b, Dachshund. c, Brittany spaniel. d, Saint Bernard. e, Bernese mountain. f, Irish setter. g, Gordon setter. h, Poodle. i, Pointer.
Cats, horiz: No. 825: a, Scottish fold. b, Javanese. c, Norwegian forest. d, American shorthair. e, Turkish angora. f, British shorthair. g, Egyptian mau. h, Maine coon. i, Burmese.
No. 826, Newfoundland. No. 827, Flame point Himalayan Persian.

816-819 A254 100fr Set of 4 1.60 .80
820-823 A254 150fr Set of 4 2.40 1.20
824 A254 150fr Sheet of 9, #a.-i. 5.40 2.70
825 A254 180fr Sheet of 9, #a.-i. 6.50 3.25

Souvenir Sheets

826-827 A254 1000fr each 4.00 2.00

Environmental Protection A255

Fauna: No. 828: a, Dolphin. b, Ok, Rhea. d, Black rhinocrhinoceros. e, Malayan tapir. f, Galapagos tortoise. g, Walrus. h, Gray wolf. i, Giraffe.
1000fr, Koala.

1997, Feb. 3

828 A255 250fr Sheet of 9, #a.-i. 9.00 4.50

Souvenir Sheet

829 A255 1000fr multicolored 4.00 2.00

Ships A256

Warships: No. 830: a, Bellerophon, England, 1867. b, Chen Yuan, China 1882. c, Hiei, Japan, 1877. d, Kaiser, Austria, 1862. e, King Wilhelm, Germany, 1869. f, Re D'Italia, Italy, 1864.
Paddle steamers: No. 831: a, Arctic, US, 1849. b, Washington, France, 1847. c, Esploratore, Italy, 1863. d, Fuad, Turkey, 1864. e, Hope, Confederate States of America, 1864. f, Britannia, England, 1840.
No. 832, Arabia, England, 1851. No. 833, Northumberland, England, 1867.

1996, Dec. 20 Litho. *Perf. 14*

830 A256 250fr Sheet of 6, #a.-f. 6.00 3.00
831 A256 320fr Sheet of 6, #a.-f. 7.70 3.80

Souvenir Sheets

832-833 A256 1000fr each 4.00 2.00

Wildlife A257

Designs: a, Hippotragus niger. b, Damaliscus hunter. c, G. demidovii. d, Chimpanzee.

1996 Litho. *Perf. 13½*

834 A257 250fr Sheet of 4, #a.-d. 4.25 2.25

UNESCO, 50th anniv.

Red Cross A258

Dogs: a, Rottweiler. b, Newfoundland. c, German shepherd. d, Bobtail (English sheepdog).

1996

835 A258 250fr Sheet of 4, #a.-d. 4.25 2.15

African Education Year — A259

Designs: 100fr, Student with book, map, vert. 150fr, Classroom. 180fr, Families watching video program on farming techniques. 250fr, African people being educated, map, vert.

1996, Apr. 4 *Perf. 14*

836 A259 100fr multicolored .45 .45
837 A259 150fr multicolored .65 .65
838 A259 180fr multicolored .80 .80
839 A259 250fr multicolored 1.10 1.10
Nos. 836-839 (4) 3.00 3.00

Nos. 836-839 were not available until March 1997.

Folk Dances — A260

1996 *Perf. 13½*

840 A260 150fr Dounouba .65 .65
841 A260 170fr Gomba .75 .75
842 A260 225fr Sandia 1.00 1.00
843 A260 230fr Sabar 1.10 1.10
Nos. 840-843 (4) 3.50 3.50

Service Organizations — A261

No. 844: a, Man carrying bags. b, Man drinking water. c, Child holding bowl of food. d, Mother feeding infant.
No. 845: a, Girl with food. b, Man holding rice bowl. c, Woman holding bowl of food. d, Child opening box of food.

1996

844 A261 500fr Sheet of 4, #a.-d. 8.50 4.25
845 A261 650fr Sheet of 4, #a.-d. 11.50 5.75

79th Lions Intl. Convention (#844). 91st Rotary Intl. Convention (#845).

City of Canton, 2210th Anniv. A262

Designs: a, Statue of goats. b, Seal. c, Boat. d, Fruits, tea pot. e, Buildings. f, Dragon.

1996

846 A262 50fr Sheet of 6, #a.-f. 1.40 .70

FAO, 50th Anniv. A264

Space satellite, fauna: a, MOP.2, grasshopper. b, Meteosat P.2, lion. c, Envisat, dolphins. d, Radar satellite, whale.

1996 Litho. *Perf. 13½*

847 A264 310fr Sheet of 4, #a.-d. 5.00 2.50

Artifacts from Natl. Museum — A265

1996

848 A265 5fr Kara .15 .15
849 A265 10fr Hambe .15 .15
850 A265 180fr Pinge .80 .40
851 A265 250fr Merenkun 1.10 .55
Nos. 848-851 (4) 2.20 1.25

Nos. 848-851 exist in souvenir sheets of 1.

1998 Winter Olympics, Nagano A266

Designs: 250fr, Speed skating. 310fr, Slalom skiing. 750fr, Figure skating. 900fr, Hockey. 2000fr, Downhill skiing.

1996

852 A266 250fr multicolored 1.00 .50
853 A266 310fr multicolored 1.25 .65
854 A266 750fr multicolored 3.00 1.50
855 A266 900fr multicolored 3.75 1.80
Nos. 852-855 (4) 9.00 4.45

Souvenir Sheet

856 A266 2000fr multicolored 8.20 4.10

Fauna, Mushrooms A267

a, Ploceus ocularis. b, Hemiolaus coecolus. c, Hebeloma radicosum. d, Sparassus dufouri simon.

1996

857 A267 750fr Sheet of 4, #a.-d. 13.00 6.60

New Year 1997 (Year of the Ox) — A268

1997

858 A268 500fr shown 2.00 1.00

Size: 53x35mm

859 A268 500fr Black porcelain ox 2.00 1.00

Nos. 858-859 exist in souvenir sheets of 1.

Butterflies — A269

#860, Black-lined eggar. #861, Common opae. #862, Veined tiger. #863, The basker.

No. 864: a, Natal barred blue. b, Common grass blue. c, Fire grid. d, Mocker swallowtail. e, Azure hairstreak. f, Mother-of-pearl butterfly. g, Boisduval's false asraea. h, Pirate butterfly. i, African moon moth.

No. 865, vert.: a, Striped policeman. b, Mountain sandman. c, Brown-veined white. d, Bowker's widow. e, Foxy charaxes. f, Pirate. g, African clouded yellow. h, Garden inspector.

No. 866, Plain tiger. No. 867, Beautiful tiger. No. 868, African clouded yellow, vert. No. 869, Zebra white, vert.

1997, Jan. 27 *Perf. 14*

860-863 A269 180fr Set of 4 3.00 1.50
864 A269 150fr Sheet of 9, #a.-i. 5.50 2.75
865 A259 210fr Sheet of 8, #a.-h. 6.75 3.35

Souvenir Sheets

866-869 A269 1000fr each 4.00 2.00

Disney Characters A270

Greetings stamps: 25fr, Goofy, Bon Voyage. 50fr, Mickey, Happy New Year. 100fr, Goofy, Happy Birthday. 150fr, Donald writing. 180fr, Minnie writing. 250fr, Mickey, Minnie, anniversary. 310fr, Mickey, Minnie going on vacation. 320fr, Mickey, Minnie kissing.

No. 878, Daisy Duck, horiz. No. 879, Huey, Dewey, Louie throwing school books in air, horiz.

1997, Mar. 1 *Perf. 13½x14*

870-877 A270 Set of 8 5.50 2.75

Souvenir Sheets

878-879 A270 1500fr each 6.00 3.00

Bridges — A271

1997 **Litho.** *Perf. 14*

880 A271 100fr Mahina .40 .20
881 A271 150fr Selingue Dam .60 .30
882 A271 180fr King Fahd .75 .35
883 A271 250fr Martyrs 1.00 .50
Nos. 880-883 (4) 2.75 1.35

Dated 1996.

1998 World Cup Soccer Championships, France — A272

Various action scenes.

1997 *Perf. 13½*

884 A272 180fr multicolored .75 .35
885 A272 250fr multicolored 1.00 .50
886 A272 320fr multicolored 1.30 .65
887 A272 1060fr multicolored 4.25 2.10
Nos. 884-887 (4) 7.30 3.60

Souvenir Sheet

888 A272 2000fr multicolored 8.25 4.00

Dated 1996. No. 888 contains one 36x42mm stamp.

Formula I Race Car Drivers — A273

Designs: a, Michael Schumacher. b, Damon Hill. c, Jacques Villeneuve. d, Gerhard Berger.

1996 **Litho.** *Perf. 13½*

889 A273 650fr Sheet of 4, #a.-d. 10.00 5.00

John F. Kennedy (1917-63) A274

Various portraits.

1997

890 A274 390fr Sheet of 9, #a.-i. 13.50 6.75

John Lennon (1940-80) A275

Various portraits.

1997

891 A275 250fr Sheet of 9, #a.-i. 8.75 4.40

Deng Xiaoping (1904-97), Chinese Leader A276

Designs: a, As young man. b, Without hat. c, With hat. d, As middle-aged man.

250fr, Being kissed by child.

1997 *Perf. 13½*

892 A276 250fr Sheet of 4, #a.-d. 3.75 1.90

Souvenir Sheet

Perf. 13x13½

893 A276 250fr multicolored 1.00 .50

No. 893 contains 69x50mm stamp.

Elvis Presley, 20th Death Anniv. A277

No. 894, Various portraits. No. 895, Portrait, Elvis on motorcycle.

1997 **Litho.** *Perf. 13½*

894 A277 310fr Sheet of 9, #a.-i. 10.75 5.25

Souvenir Sheet

895 A277 2000fr multicolored 7.75 3.75

No. 895 contains one 42x51mm stamp.

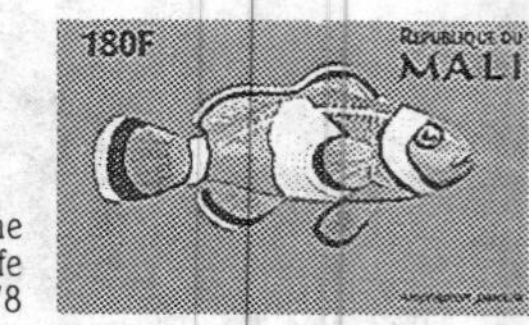

Marine Life A278

No. 896: a, Chaetodon auriga. b, Balistoides conspicillum. c, Forcipiger longirostris. d, Chelmon rostratus. e, Plectorhinchus diagrammus. f, Stegastes leucostictus. g, Chaetodon kleinii. h, Synchiropus splendidus. i, Platax orbicularis.

No. 897: a, Amphiprion percula. b, Holacanthus ciliaris. c, Chaetodon reticulatus. d, Pomacanthus imperator. e, Heniochus acuminatus. f, Lienardella fasciata. g, Zanclus cornutus. h, Scarus guacamaia. i, Lutjanus sebae.

No. 898: a, Tursiops truncatus. b, Phaethon lepturus. c, Istiophorus platypterus. d, Sphyma zygaena. e, Reinhardtius hippoglossoides. f, Manta birostris. g, Thunnus albacares. h, Himantolophus groenlandicus. i, Tridacana gigas.

No. 899: a, Cypselurus heterurus. b, Sailboat. c, Delphinus delphis. d, Carcharodon carcharias. e, Orcinus orca (b, f). f, Salmo salar. g, Conger conger. h, Pomatomus saltatrix. i, Sphyraena barracuda.

No. 900, Balaenoptera musculus. No. 901, Megaptera novaeangliae, vert.

1997, Mar. 2 **Litho.** *Perf. 14*

896 A278 150fr Sheet of 9, #a.-i. 4.50 4.50
897 A278 180fr Sheet of 9, #a.-i 5.50 5.50
898 A278 250fr Sheet of 9, #a.-i. 7.75 7.75
899 A278 310fr Sheet of 9, #a.-i. 9.50 9.50

Souvenir Sheets

900-901 A278 1000fr each 3.50 3.50

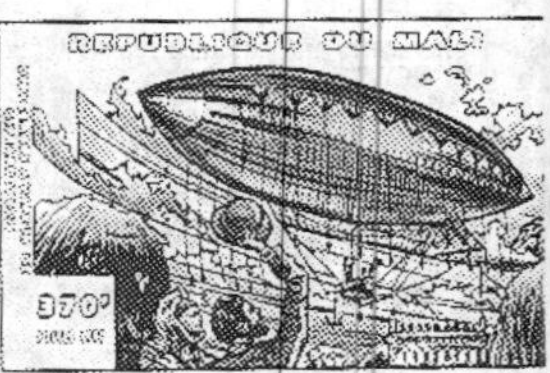

Transportation — A279

Cyclists: No. 902: a, Rudolph Lewis, 1912. b, Jacques Anquetil, 4-time Tour de France winner. c, Miguel Indurain, hour record holder.

Sailing ships: No. 903: a, Lightning, by Donald McKay, 1856. b, Olivier de Kersauson, winner of Jules Verne trophy. c. Lockheed Sea Shadow, US.

Motorcycles, cyclists: No. 904: a, Coventry Eagle-Jap 998cm3. b, Michael Doohan, Honda 500 NSRV4. c, Harley-Davidson, Heritage Softail classic FLSTC.

Airships: No. 905: a, "Gifford," steam-powered dirigible, 1852. b, Count Ferdinand von Zeppelin, Zeppelin NT LZ N07. c, Nobile N1, "Norge," 1926.

Trains: No. 906: a, Locomotive G 4/5 2-8-0, Switzerland. b, W.V. Siemens, ICE train, Germany. c, Maglev HSST-5, Japan.

Race cars: No. 907: a, 1949 Ferrari Type 166/MM. b, Michael Schumacher, F1 310B Ferrari. c, Ferrari F50.

Sled dogs: No. 908: a, Eskimo. b, Alaskan malamute. c, Siberian husky.

Aircraft: No. 909: a, Wright Brothers' first flight at Kitty Hawk. b, Andre Turcat, Concorde. c, X34 space vehicle.

1997 **Litho.** *Perf. 13½*

902 A279 180fr Strip of 3, #a.-c. 2.10 1.00
903 A279 250fr Strip of 3, #a.-c. 3.00 1.50
904 A279 320fr Strip of 3, #a.-c. 3.75 2.00
905 A279 370fr Strip of 3, #a.-c. 4.25 2.25
906 A279 460fr Strip of 3, #a.-c. 5.50 2.75
907 A279 490fr Strip of 3, #a.-c. 5.75 3.00
908 A279 530fr Strip of 3, #a.-c. 6.50 3.25
909 A279 750fr Strip of 3, #a.-c. 8.75 4.50

Movie Stars — A281

Designs: a, John Wayne. b, Frank Sinatra. c, Rita Hayworth. d, Sammy Davis, Jr. e, Marilyn Monroe. f, Eddie Murphy. g, Elizabeth Taylor. h, James Dean. i, Robert Mitchum.

1997

910 A281 320fr Sheet of 9, #a.-i. 11.25 5.50

A282

A283

Diana, Princess of Wales (1961-97) A284

Designs: No. 911, Various close-up portraits. No. 912, Pictures of various times in Diana's life.

No. 913, In pink dress with Pres. Clinton (in margin). No. 914, Wearing strapless evening dress. No. 915, Wearing hat and veil. No. 916, In blue dress with Nelson Mandela (in margin).

1997 Litho. *Perf. 13½*

911 A282 250fr Sheet of 9, #a.-i. 8.75 4.50
912 A283 370fr Sheet of 9, #a.-i. 13.00 6.50

Souvenir Sheets

913-916 A284 1500fr each 5.75 2.90

Mars Pathfinder A285

Dr. Cheick M. Diarra: a, blue & multi background. b, green & multi background. c, Part of Mars in background. d, violet black & multi background.

1997

917 A285 180fr Sheet of 4, #a.-d. 2.75 1.30

Crested Porcupine A286

World Wildlife Fund: a, Two adults. b, One adult crawling right. c, Mother with young. d, Adult with quills raised.

1998

918 A286 250fr Block of 4, #a.-d. 3.75 1.90

SEMI-POSTAL STAMPS

Anti-Malaria Issue

Common Design Type

Perf. 12½x12

1962, Apr. 7 Engr. Unwmk.

B1 CD108 25fr + 5fr pale vio bl .50 .50

Algerian Family — SP1

1962, Dec. 24 Photo. *Perf. 12x12½*

B2 SP1 25fr + 5fr multi .22 .22

Issued for the national campaign to show the solidarity of the peoples of Mali and Algeria.

AIR POST STAMPS

Federation

Composite View of St. Louis, Senegal — AP1

Unwmk.

1959, Dec. 11 Engr. *Perf. 13*

C1 AP1 85fr multi 1.00 .80

Founding of St. Louis, Senegal, tercentenary, and opening of the 6th meeting of the executive council of the French Community.

AP2

AP3

Birds: 100fr, Amethyst starling. 200fr, Bateleur eagle, horiz. 500fr, Barbary shrike.

Perf. 12½x13, 13x12½

1960, Feb. 13 Photo.

C2 AP2 100fr multi 1.00 .55
C3 AP2 200fr multi 1.65 1.00
C4 AP2 500fr multi 6.50 4.50
Nos. C2-C4 (3) 9.15 6.05

Republic

Nos. C2-C4 Overprinted or Surcharged "REPUBLIQUE DU MALI" and Bars

1960, Dec. 18

C5 AP2 100fr multi 1.40 .90
C6 AP2 200fr multi 2.25 1.50
C7 AP2 300fr on 500fr multi 3.50 3.00
C8 AP2 500fr multi 6.25 4.75
Nos. C5-C8 (4) 13.40 10.15

1961, Mar. 18 Engr. *Perf. 13*

Designs: 200fr, Mamadou Konate. 300fr, Pres. Modibo Keita.

C9 AP3 200fr claret & gray brn 1.60 .65
C10 AP3 300fr grn & blk 2.25 .90

Flag, Map, UN Emblem — AP4

1961, Mar. 18

C11 AP4 100fr multi .75 .60
a. Min. sheet of 3, #13, 14, C11 1.40 1.40

Proclamation of independence and admission to UN.

Sankore Mosque, Timbuktu — AP5

200fr, View of Timbuktu. 500fr, Bamako & arms.

1961, Apr. 15 Unwmk. *Perf. 13*

C12 AP5 100fr Prus bl, red brn & gray .65 .20
C13 AP5 200fr grn, brn & red 1.25 .65
C14 AP5 500fr red brn, Prus bl & dk grn 3.50 1.25
Nos. C12-C14 (3) 5.40 2.10

Inauguration of Timbuktu airport and Air Mali.

Bull, Chemical Equipment and Chicks — AP6

1963, Feb. 23 Engr.

C15 AP6 200fr bis, mar & grnsh bl 1.50 .70

Sotuba Zootechnical Institute.

Air Ambulance — AP7

Designs: 55fr, National Line plane loading. 100fr, Intl. Line Vickers Viscount in flight.

1963, Nov. 2 Unwmk. *Perf. 13*

C16 AP7 25fr dk bl, emer & red brn .22 .15
C17 AP7 55fr bis, bl & red brn .50 .25
C18 AP7 100fr dk bl, red brn & yel grn .80 .42
Nos. C16-C18 (3) 1.52 .82

Issued to publicize Air Mali.

Crowned Crane and Giant Tortoise — AP8

1963, Nov. 23 Unwmk. *Perf. 13*

C19 AP8 25fr sepia, org & ver .40 .25
C20 AP8 200fr multi 1.90 1.25

Animal protection.

UN Emblem, Flag, Doves — AP9

1963, Dec. 10 Engr.

C21 AP9 50fr lt grn, yel & red .40 .20

15th anniversary of the Universal Declaration of Human Rights.

Cleopatra and Ptolemy at Kôm Ombo — AP10

1964, Mar. 9 Unwmk. *Perf. 12*

C22 AP10 25fr dp claret & bister .35 .15
C23 AP10 55fr dp claret & lt ol grn .60 .30

UNESCO world campaign to save historic monuments in Nubia.

Pres. John F. Kennedy — AP11

1964, Oct. 26 Photo. *Perf. 12½*

C24 AP11 100fr sl, red brn & blk .65 .65
a. Souv. sheet of 4 3.00 3.00

Touracos — AP12

200fr, Abyssinian ground hornbills, vert. 300fr, Egyptian vultures, vert. 500fr, Goliath herons.

1965, Feb. 15 Engr. *Perf. 13*
C25 AP12 100fr grn, dk bl & red .65 .38
C26 AP12 200fr blk, red & brt bl 1.10 .55
C27 AP12 300fr blk, sl grn & yel 1.65 1.00
C28 AP12 500fr sl grn, dk brn & claret 3.50 1.50
Nos. C25-C28 (4) 6.90 3.43

UN Headquarters, New York, and ICY Emblem — AP13

1965, Mar. 15 Unwmk. *Perf. 13*
C29 AP13 55fr bis, dk bl & vio brn .45 .30

International Cooperation Year.

Pope John XXIII — AP14

Perf. 12½x13
1965, Sept. 14 Photo. Unwmk.
C30 AP14 100fr multi .90 .60

Winston Churchill — AP15

1965, Oct. 11 Engr. *Perf. 13*
C31 AP15 100fr brn & indigo .90 .60

Dr. Albert Schweitzer and Sick Child — AP16

1965, Dec. 20 Photo. *Perf. 12½*
C32 AP16 100fr multi 1.00 .60
a. Souv. sheet of 4 4.00 3.25

Major Edward H. White and Gemini 4 — AP17

#C34, Lt. Col. Alexei A. Leonov. 300fr, Gordon Cooper, Charles Conrad, Alexei Leonov & Pavel Belyayev, Parthenon, Athens, & vase, vert.

1966, Jan. 10
C33 AP17 100fr vio, yel, lt bl & blk .90 .40
C34 AP17 100fr bl, red, yel & blk .90 .40
C35 AP17 300fr multi 2.75 1.75
Nos. C33-C35 (3) 4.55 2.55

Achievements in space research and 16th Intl. Astronautical Congress, Athens, Sept. 12-18, 1965.

Papal Arms and UN Emblem — AP18

1966, July 11 Engr. *Perf. 13*
C36 AP18 200fr brt bl, grnsh bl & grn 1.60 .55

Visit of Pope Paul VI to the UN, NYC, Oct. 4, 1965.

People and UNESCO Emblem — AP19

1966, Sept. 5 Engr. *Perf. 13*
C37 AP19 100fr dk car rose, sl grn & ultra .70 .42

20th anniv. of UNESCO.

Soccer Players, Ball, Globe, and Jules Rimet Cup — AP20

1966, Oct. 31 Photo. *Perf. 13*
C38 AP20 100fr multi .70 .42

8th International Soccer Championship Games, Wembley, England, July 11-30.

Crab and Mt. Fuji — AP21

UNICEF Emblem and Children — AP22

1966, Nov. 30 Photo. *Perf. 13*
C39 AP21 100fr multi .70 .35

9th Intl. Anticancer Cong., Tokyo, Oct. 23-29.

1966, Dec. 10 Engr.
C40 AP22 45fr dp bl, bis brn & red lil .38 .16

20th anniv. of UNICEF.

Land Cruisers in Hoggar Mountain Pass — AP23

1967, Mar. 20 Engr. *Perf. 13*
C41 AP23 200fr multi 1.25 .65

"Black Cruise 1924," which crossed Africa from Beni-Abbes, Algeria to the Indian Ocean and on to Tananarive, Madagascar, Oct. 28, 1924-June 26, 1925.

Diamant Rocket and Francesco de Lana's 1650 Flying Boat — AP24

Designs: 100fr, A-1 satellite and rocket launching adapted from Jules Verne. 200fr, D-1 satellite and Leonardo da Vinci's bird-borne flying machine.

1967, Apr. 17 Engr. *Perf. 13*
C42 AP24 50fr brt bl, pur & grn .60 .35
C43 AP24 100fr dk Prus bl, dk car & lil 1.40 .65
C44 AP24 200fr sl bl, ol & pur 2.25 1.00
Nos. C42-C44 (3) 4.25 2.00

Honoring French achievements in space.

Amelia Earhart and Map of Mali — AP25

1967, May 29 Photo. *Perf. 13*
C45 AP25 500fr bl & multi 2.75 1.25

Amelia Earhart's stop at Gao, West Africa, 30th anniv7.

Paul as Harlequin, by Picasso AP26

Picasso Paintings: 50fr, Bird Cage. 250fr, Flutes of Pan.

1967, June 16 *Perf. 12½*
C46 AP26 50fr multi .30 .16
C47 AP26 100fr multi .60 .32
C48 AP26 250fr multi 1.40 .75
Nos. C46-C48 (3) 2.30 1.23

See No. C82.

Jamboree Emblem, Scout Knots and Badges — AP27

Design: 100fr, Scout with portable radio transmitter, tents and Jamboree badge.

1967, July 10 Engr. *Perf. 13*
C49 AP27 70fr dk car, emer & bl grn .42 .22
C50 AP27 100fr dk car lake, sl grn & blk .65 .30
a. Strip of 2, #C49-C50 + label 1.40 1.20

12th Boy Scout World Jamboree, Farragut State Park, Idaho, Aug. 1-9.

Head of Horse, by Toulouse-Lautrec — AP28

300fr, Cob-drawn gig, by Toulouse-Lautrec, vert.

Perf. 12x12½, 12½x12
1967, Dec. 11 Photo.
C51 AP28 100fr multi .60 .40
C52 AP28 300fr multi 1.75 .75

See Nos. C66-C67.

Grenoble — AP29

Design: 150fr, Bobsled course on Huez Alp.

1968, Jan. 8 Engr. *Perf. 13*
C53 AP29 50fr bl, yel brn & grn .25 .15
C54 AP29 150fr brn, vio bl & stl bl .65 .30

10th Winter Olympic Games, Grenoble, France, Feb. 6-18.

Roses and Anemones, by Van Gogh — AP30

Paintings: 150fr, Peonies in Vase, by Edouard Manet (36x49mm). 300fr, Bouquet, by Delarcroix (41x42mm). 500fr, Daisies in Vase, by Jean François Millet (49x37mm).

Perf. 13, 12½x12, 12x12½

1968, June 24 **Photo.**

C55 AP30 50fr multi .25 .15
C56 AP30 150fr grn & multi .65 .30
C57 AP30 300fr grn & multi 1.20 .65
C58 AP30 500fr car & multi 2.25 .90
Nos. C55-C58 (4) 4.35 2.00

Martin Luther King, Jr. — AP31 Long Jumper and Satellite — AP32

1968, July 22 *Perf. 12½*

C59 AP31 100fr rose lil, sal pink & blk .38 .16

Bicycle Type of Regular Issue

Designs: 50fr, Bicyclette, 1918. 100fr, Mercedes Benz, 1927, horiz.

1968, Aug. 12 **Engr.** *Perf. 13*

C60 A40 50fr gray, dk grn & brick red .22 .20
C61 A40 100fr lemon, indigo & car .45 .22

1968, Nov. 25 **Photo.** *Perf. 12½*

100fr, Soccer goalkeeper and satellite, horiz.

C62 AP32 100fr multi .42 .25
C63 AP32 150fr multi .65 .35

19th Olympic Games, Mexico City, Oct. 12-27.

PHILEXAFRIQUE Issue

Editorial Department, by François Marius Granet AP33

1968, Dec. 23 **Photo.** *Perf. 12½x12*

C64 AP33 200fr multi .90 .65

Issued to publicize PHILEXAFRIQUE Philatelic Exhibition in Abidjan, Feb. 14-23. Printed with alternating light green label.

See Nos. C85-C87, C110-C112, C205-C207, C216-C217.

2nd PHILEXAFRIQUE Issue

Common Design Type

Design: 100fr, French Sudan #64, sculpture.

1969, Feb. 14 **Engr.** *Perf. 13*

C65 CD128 100fr pur & multi .50 .50

Painting Type of 1967

Paintings: 150fr, Napoleon as First Consul, by Antoine Jean Gros, vert. 250fr, Bivouac at Austerlitz, by Louis François Lejeune.

Perf. 12½x12, 12x12½

1969, Feb. 25 **Photo.**

C66 AP28 150fr multi 1.20 .70
C67 AP28 250fr multi 1.60 1.20

Napoleon Bonaparte (1769-1821).

Concorde — AP34

Designs: 50fr, Montgolfier's balloon. 150fr, Ferber 5, experimental biplane.

1969, Mar. 10 **Photo.** *Perf. 13*

C68 AP34 50fr multi .25 .15
C69 AP34 150fr multi .65 .25
C70 AP34 300fr multi 1.40 .70
a. Strip of 3, #C68-C70 2.50 2.00

1st flight of the prototype Concorde plane at Toulouse, France, Mar. 1, 1969.

For overprints see Nos. C78-C80.

Auto Type of Regular Issue

Designs: 55fr, Renault, 1898, Renault 16, 1969. 90fr, Peugeot, 1893, Peugeot 404, 1969.

1969, May 30 **Engr.** *Perf. 13*

C71 A43 55fr rose car, blk & brt pink .25 .20
C72 A43 90fr blk, dp car & indigo .40 .20

Ronald Clarke, Australia, 10,000-meter Run, 1965 — AP35

World Records: 90fr, Yanis Lusis, USSR, Javelin, 1968. 120fr, Yoshinobu Miyake, Japan, weight lifting, 1967. 140fr, Randy Matson, US, shot put, 1968. 150fr, Kipchoge Keino, Kenya, 3,000-meter run, 1965.

1969, June 23 **Engr.** *Perf. 13*

C73 AP35 60fr bl & ol brn .18 .15
C74 AP35 90fr car rose & red brn .28 .16
C75 AP35 120fr emer & gray ol .35 .16
C76 AP35 140fr gray & brn .45 .20
C77 AP35 150fr red org & blk .50 .25
Nos. C73-C77 (5) 1.76 .92

Issued to honor sports world records.

Nos. C68-C70 Overprinted in Red with Lunar Landing Module and: "L'HOMME SUR LA LUNE / JUILLET 1969 / APOLLO 11"

1969, July 25 **Photo.** *Perf. 13*

C78 AP34 50fr multi .42 .30
C79 AP34 150fr multi 1.10 .80
C80 AP34 300fr multi 2.25 1.60
a. Strip of 3, #C78-C80 4.00 3.50

Man's 1st landing on moon, July 20, 1969. US astronauts Neil A. Armstrong and Col. Edwin E. Aldrin, Jr., with Lieut. Col. Michael Collins piloting Apollo 11.

Apollo 8, Moon and Earth AP35a

Embossed on Gold Foil

1969, July 24 ***Die-cut perf 10½***

C81 AP35a 2000fr gold 9.00 9.00

US Apollo 8 mission, the 1st men in orbit around the moon, Dec. 21-27, 1968.

Painting Type of 1967

Design: 500fr, Mona Lisa, by Leonardo da Vinci.

1969, Oct. 20 **Photo.** *Perf. 12½*

C82 AP26 500fr multi 2.25 1.65

Mahatma Gandhi — AP36

1969, Nov. 24 **Engr.** *Perf. 13*

C83 AP36 150fr brt bl, ol brn & red brn .65 .35

Map of West Africa, Post Horns and Lightning Bolts — AP37

1970, Feb. 23 **Photo.** *Perf. 12½*

C84 AP37 100fr multi .42 .25

11th anniversary of the West African Postal Union (CAPTEAO).

Painting Type of 1968

Paintings: 100fr, Madonna and Child, from Rogier van der Weyden school. 150fr, Nativity, by the master of Flemalle. 250fr, Madonna and Child with St. John, from the Dutch School.

1970, Mar. 2

C85 AP33 100fr multi .38 .22
C86 AP33 150fr multi .55 .35
C87 AP33 250fr multi .90 .55
Nos. C85-C87 (3) 1.83 1.12

Roosevelt — AP38 Lenin — AP39

1970, Mar. 30 **Photo.** *Perf. 12½*

C88 AP38 500fr red, lt ultra & blk 2.75 1.35

Pres. Franklin D. Roosevelt (1882-1945).

1970, Apr. 22

C89 AP39 300fr pink, grn & blk 1.25 .55

Jules Verne and Firing of Moon Rockets — AP40

150fr, Jules Verne, rockets, landing modules & moon. 300fr, Jules Verne & splashdown.

1970, May 4

C90 AP40 50fr multi .35 .16
C91 AP40 150fr multi 1.20 .42
C92 AP40 300fr multi 2.00 .80
Nos. C90-C92 (3) 3.55 1.38

Nos. C90-C92 Overprinted in Red or Blue: "APOLLO XIII / EPOPEE SPATIALE / 11-17 AVRIL 1970"

1970, June **Photo.** *Perf. 12½*

C93 AP40 50fr multi (Bl) .40 .25
C94 AP40 150fr multi (R) 1.00 .42
C95 AP40 300fr multi (Bl) 2.25 1.40
Nos. C93-C95 (3) 3.65 2.07

Flight and safe return of Apollo 13, Apr. 11-13, 1970.

Intelsat III — AP41

Telecommunications Through Space: 200fr, Molniya I satellite. 300fr, Radar. 500fr, "Project Symphony" (various satellites).

1970, July 13 **Engr.** *Perf. 13*

C96 AP41 100fr gray, brt bl & org .65 .35
C97 AP41 200fr bl, gray & red lil 1.40 .60
C98 AP41 300fr org, dk brn & gray 1.90 .80
C99 AP41 500fr dk brn, sl & grnsh bl 3.00 1.40
Nos. C96-C99 (4) 6.95 3.15

For surcharges see Nos. C108-C109.

Auguste and Louis Lumière, Jean Harlow and Marilyn Monroe AP42

1970, July 27 **Photo.** *Perf. 12½x12*

C100 AP42 250fr multi .90 .55

Issued to honor Auguste Lumière (1862-1954), and his brother Louis Jean Lumière (1864-1948), inventors of the Lumière process of color photography and of a motion picture camera.

Soccer — AP43

1970, Sept. 7 **Engr.** *Perf. 13*

C101 AP43 80fr bl, dp car & brn ol .35 .16
C102 AP43 200fr dp car, bl grn & ol brn .70 .42

9th World Soccer Championships for the Jules Rimet Cup, Mexico City, May 30-June 21, 1970.

*Find what you're looking for in the **"Scott Stamp Monthly."** New issue and topical listings, as well as fascinating features, are found in each issue.*
Please call 1-800-572-6885 for more information.

Rotary Emblem, Map of Mali and Ceremonial Antelope Heads — AP44

Men Holding UN Emblem, and Doves — AP45

1970, Sept. 21 Photo. *Perf. 12½*

C103 AP44 200fr multi .70 .42

Issued to honor Rotary International.

1970, Oct. 5 Engr. *Perf. 13*

C104 AP45 100fr dk pur, red brn & dk bl .38 .22

25th anniversary of the United Nations.

Koran Page, Baghdad, 11th Century AP46

Moslem Art: 200fr, Tree, and lion killing deer, mosaic, Jordan, c. 730, horiz. 250fr, Scribe, miniature, Baghdad, 1287.

1970, Oct. 26 Photo. *Perf. 12½x12*

C105 AP46 50fr multi	.22	.15
C106 AP46 200fr multi	.60	.30
C107 AP46 250fr multi	.70	.38
Nos. C105-C107 (3)	1.52	.83

Nos. C97-C98 Surcharged and Overprinted: "LUNA 16 / PREMIERS PRELEVEMENTS AUTOMATIQUES / SUR LA LUNE / SEPTEMBRE 1970"

1970, Nov. 9 Engr. *Perf. 13*

C108 AP41 150fr on 200fr multi	1.10	.55
C109 AP41 250fr on 300fr multi	2.00	.85

Unmanned moon probe of the Russian space ship Luna 16, Sept. 12-24.

Painting Type of 1968

100fr, Nativity, Antwerp School, c. 1530. 250fr, St. John the Baptist, by Hans Memling. 300fr, Adoration of the Kings, Flemish School, 17th cent.

1970, Dec. 1 Photo. *Perf. 12½x12*

C110 AP33 100fr brown & multi	.32	.16
C111 AP33 250fr brown & multi	.65	.32
C112 AP33 300fr brown & multi	.90	.40
Nos. C110-C112 (3)	1.87	.88

Christmas 1970.

Gamal Abdel Nasser — AP47

Embossed on Gold Foil

1970, Nov. 25 *Perf. 12½*

C113 AP47 1000fr gold 5.00 5.00

In memory of Gamal Abdel Nasser (1918-1970), President of Egypt.

Charles de Gaulle AP48

Embossed on Gold Foil

1971, Feb. 8 *Die-cut Perf. 10*

C114 AP48 2000fr gold, red & dp ultra 12.00 12.00

In memory of Gen. Charles de Gaulle (1890-1970), President of France.

Alfred Nobel — AP49

Tennis, Davis Cup — AP50

1971, Feb. 22 Engr. *Perf. 13*

C115 AP49 300fr multi .90 .60

Alfred Nobel (1833-1896), inventor of dynamite, sponsor of Nobel Prize.

1971, Mar. 8

Designs: 150fr, Derby at Epsom, horiz. 200fr, Racing yacht, America's Cup.

C116 AP50 100fr bl, lil & slate	.25	.15
C117 AP50 150fr brn, brt grn & ol	.38	.16
C118 AP50 200fr brt bl, ol & brn	.65	.22
Nos. C116-C118 (3)	1.28	.53

The Arabian Nights — AP51

Designs: 180fr, Ali Baba and the 40 Thieves. 200fr, Aladdin's Lamp.

1971, Apr. 5 Photo. *Perf. 13*

C119 AP51 120fr gold & multi	.35	.22
C120 AP51 180fr gold & multi	.42	.25
C121 AP51 200fr gold & multi	.65	.38
Nos. C119-C121 (3)	1.42	.85

Olympic Rings and Sports — AP52

1971, June 28 Photo. *Perf. 12½*

C122 AP52 80fr ultra, yel grn & brt mag .22 .15

Pre-Olympic Year.

Mariner 4 — AP53

Design: 300fr, Venera 5 in space.

1971, Sept. 13 Engr. *Perf. 13*

C123 AP53 200fr multi	.55	.30
C124 AP53 300fr multi	.80	.42

Space explorations of US Mariner 4 (200fr); and USSR Venera 5 (300fr).

Santa Maria, 1492 — AP54

Famous Ships: 150fr, Mayflower, 1620. 200fr, Potemkin, 1905. 250fr, Normandie, 1935.

1971, Sept. 27

C125 AP54 100fr brn, bluish grn & pur	.22	.15
C126 AP54 150fr sl grn, brn & pur	.38	.20
C127 AP54 200fr car, bl & dk ol	.60	.35
C128 AP54 250fr blk, bl & red	.70	.42
Nos. C125-C128 (4)	1.90	1.12

Symbols of Justice and Maps — AP55

1971, Oct. 18

C129 AP55 160fr mar, ocher & dk brn .50 .22

25th anniversary of the International Court of Justice in The Hague, Netherlands.

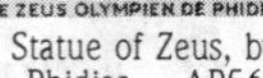

Statue of Zeus, by Phidias — AP56

Nat "King" Cole — AP57

The Seven Wonders of the Ancient World: 80fr, Cheops Pyramid and Sphinx. 100fr, Temple of Artemis, Ephesus, horiz. 130fr, Lighthouse at Alexandria. 150fr, Hanging Gardens of Babylon, horiz. 270fr, Mausoleum of Halicarnassus. 280fr, Colossus of Rhodes.

1971, Dec. 13

C130 AP56 70fr ind, dk red & pink	.22	.15
C131 AP56 80fr brn, bl & blk	.22	.15
C132 AP56 100fr org, ind & pur	.30	.16
C133 AP56 130fr rose lil, blk & grnsh bl	.40	.16
C134 AP56 150fr brn, brt grn & bl	.42	.16
C135 AP56 270fr sl, brn & plum	.80	.20
C136 AP56 280fr sl lil & ol	.80	.20
Nos. C130-C136 (7)	3.16	1.18

1971, Dec. 6 Photo. *Perf. 13x12½*

Famous American Black Musicians: 150fr, Erroll Garner. 270fr, Louis Armstrong.

C137 AP57 130fr blk, brn & yel	.40	.16
C138 AP57 150fr blk, bl & yel	.42	.18
C139 AP57 270fr blk, rose car & yel	.80	.35
Nos. C137-C139 (3)	1.62	.69

Slalom and Japanese Child — AP58

200fr, Ice hockey & character from Noh play.

1972, Jan. 10 Engr. *Perf. 13*

C140 AP58 150fr multicolored	.42	.20
C141 AP58 200fr multicolored	.60	.35
a. Souv. sheet of 2, #C140-C141	1.40	1.40

11th Winter Olympic Games, Sapporo, Japan, Feb. 3-13.

Santa Maria della Salute, by Ippolito Caffi — AP59

Paintings of Venice, by Ippolito Caffi: 270fr, Rialto Bridge. 280fr, St. Mark's Square, vert.

1972, Feb. 21 Photo. *Perf. 13*

C142 AP59 130fr gold & multi	.45	.22
C143 AP59 270fr gold & multi	.80	.42
C144 AP59 280fr gold & multi	.90	.55
Nos. C142-C144 (3)	2.15	1.19

UNESCO campaign to save Venice.

Hands of 4 Races Holding Scout Flag — AP60

1972, Mar. 27 Engr. *Perf. 13*

C145 AP60 200fr dk red, ocher & ol gray .55 .28

World Boy Scout Seminar, Cotonou, Dahomey, March, 1972.

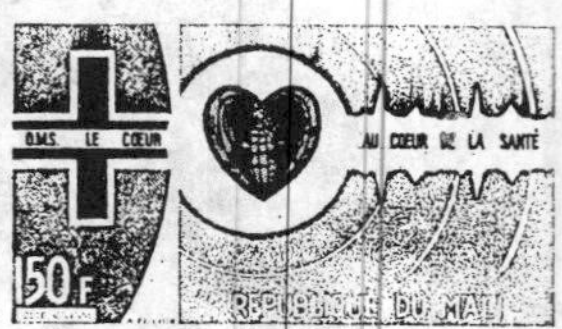

"Your Heart is your Health" — AP61

1972, Apr. 7 Engr. *Perf. 13*

C146 AP61 150fr brt bl & red .42 .25

World Health Day.

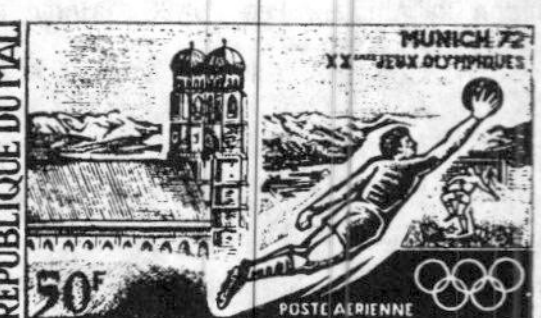

Soccer Player and Frauenkirche, Munich — AP62

Designs (Sport and Munich Landmarks): 150fr, Judo and TV Tower, vert. 200fr, Steeplechase and Propylaeum, vert. 300fr, Runner and Church of the Theatines.

1972, Apr. 17

C147 AP62 50fr ocher, dk bl & grn .20 .15
C148 AP62 150fr dk bl, ocher & grn .45 .20
C149 AP62 200fr grn, dk bl & ocher .60 .28
C150 AP62 300fr dk bl, grn & ocher .90 .40
a. Min. sheet of 4, #C147-C150 3.00 3.00
Nos. C147-C150 (4) 2.15 1.03

20th Olympic Games, Munich, Aug. 26-Sept. 10.
For overprints see Nos. C165-C166, C168.

Apollo 15, Lunar Rover, Landing Module — AP63

Design: 250fr, Cugnot's steam wagon and Montgolfier's Balloon.

1972, Apr. 27

C151 AP63 150fr multicolored .55 .25
C152 AP63 250fr multicolored .80 .38

Development of transportation.

Cinderella AP64

Fairy Tales: 80fr, Puss in Boots. 150fr, Sleeping Beauty.

1972, June 19 Engr. *Perf. 13x12½*

C153 AP64 70fr multicolored .25 .15
C154 AP64 80fr multicolored .35 .18
C155 AP64 150fr multicolored .55 .25
Nos. C153-C155 (3) 1.15 .58

Charles Perrault (1628-1703), French writer.

Astronauts and Lunar Rover on Moon — AP65

1972, July 24 Engr. *Perf. 13*

C156 AP65 500fr multicolored 1.60 .75

US Apollo 16 moon mission, Apr. 15-27.

Book Year Emblem — AP66

1972, Aug. 7 Litho. *Perf. 12½*

C157 AP66 80fr bl, gold & grn .25 .16

International Book Year 1972.

Bamako Rotary Emblem with Crocodiles — AP67

1972, Oct. 9 Engr. *Perf. 13*

C158 AP67 170fr dk brn, red & ultra .55 .20

10th anniv. of the Bamako Rotary Club.

Hurdler, Olympic Rings, Melbourne Cathedral, Kangaroo — AP68

Designs (Olympic Rings and): 70fr, Boxing, Helsinki Railroad Station, arms of Finland, vert. 140fr, Running, Colosseum, Roman wolf. 150fr, Weight lifting, Tokyo stadium, phoenix, vert. 170fr, Swimming, University Library, Mexico City; Aztec sculpture. 210fr, Javelin, Munich Stadium, Arms of Munich. Stamps inscribed with name of gold medal winner of event shown.

1972, Nov. 13 Engr. *Perf. 13*

C159 AP68 70fr red, ocher & ind .20 .15
C160 AP68 90fr red brn, bl & sl .25 .16
C161 AP68 140fr brn, brt grn & ol gray .40 .16
C162 AP68 150fr dk car, emer & gray ol .42 .18
C163 AP68 170fr red lil, brn & Prus bl .45 .20
C164 AP68 210fr ultra, emer & brick red .65 .35
Nos. C159-C164 (6) 2.37 1.20

Retrospective of Olympic Games 1952-1972.
For overprint see No. C167.

Nos. C148-C150 and C164 Overprinted:

a. JUDO / RUSKA / 2 MEDAILLES D'OR
b. STEEPLE / KEINO / MEDAILLE D'OR
c. MEDAILLE D'OR / 90m. 48
d. 100m.-200m. / BORZOV / 2 MEDAILLES D'OR

1972, Nov. 27 Engr. *Perf. 13*

C165 AP62 150fr multi (a) .42 .22
C166 AP62 200fr multi (b) .55 .25
C167 AP68 210fr multi (c) .60 .30
C168 AP62 300fr multi (d) .90 .42
Nos. C165-C168 (4) 2.47 1.19

Gold medal winners in 20th Olympic Games: Wim Ruska, Netherlands, heavy-weight judo (#C165); Kipchoge Keino, Kenya, 3000m. steeplechase (#C166); Klaus Wolfermann, Germany, javelin (#C167); Valery Borzov, USSR, 100m., 200m. race (#C168).

Emperor Haile Selassie — AP69

1972, Dec. 26 Photo. *Perf. 12½*

C169 AP69 70fr grn & multi .22 .15

80th birthday of Emperor Haile Selassie of Ethiopia.

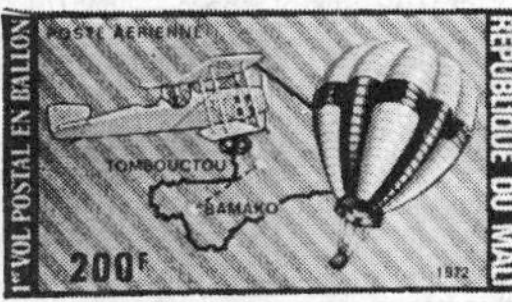

Plane, Balloon, Route Timbuktu to Bamako — AP70

300fr, Balloon, jet & route Timbuktu to Bamako.

1972, Dec. 29 *Perf. 13½*

C170 AP70 200fr multi .65 .30
C171 AP70 300fr bl & multi .90 .42

First postal balloon flight in Mali.

Bishop of 14th Century European Chess Set — AP71

Design: 200fr, Knight (elephant), from 18th century Indian set.

1973, Feb. 19 Engr. *Perf. 13*

C172 AP71 100fr dk car, bl & ind .40 .20
C173 AP71 200fr blk, red & brn .65 .30

World Chess Championship, Reykjavik, Iceland, July-Sept., 1972.

Postal Union Emblem, Letter and Dove — AP72

1973, Mar. 9 Photo. *Perf. 11½x11*

C174 AP72 70fr bl, blk & org .22 .16

10th anniv. (in 1971) of African Postal Union. This stamp was to be issued Dec. 8, 1971. It was offered by the agency on Mar. 9, 1973. Copies were sold in Mali as early as July or August, 1972.

No. C20, Collector's Hand and Philatelic Background — AP73

1973, Mar. 12 Engr. *Perf. 13*

C175 AP73 70fr multi .30 .16

Stamp Day, 1973.

Astronauts and Lunar Rover on Moon — AP74

1973, Mar. 26

C176 AP74 250fr bl, ind & bis .70 .42

Souvenir Sheet

C177 AP74 350fr choc, vio bl & ultra 1.10 1.10

Apollo 17 US moon mission, Dec. 7-19, 1972.

Nicolaus Copernicus — AP75

1973, Apr. 9 Engr. *Perf. 13*

C178 AP75 300fr brt bl & mag 1.00 .50

500th anniversary of the birth of Nicolaus Copernicus (1473-1543), Polish astronomer.

Dr. Armauer G. Hansen and Leprosy Bacillus — AP76

1973, May 7 Engr. *Perf. 13*

C179 AP76 200fr blk, yel grn & red .65 .40

Centenary of the discovery of the Hansen bacillus, the cause of leprosy.

Bentley and Alfa Romeo, 1930 — AP77

Designs: 100fr, Jaguar and Talbot, 1953. 200fr, Matra and Porsche, 1972.

1973, May 21 Engr. *Perf. 13*

C180 AP77 50fr bl, org & grn .16 .15
C181 AP77 100fr grn, ultra & car .35 .15
C182 AP77 200fr ind, grn & car .65 .25
Nos. C180-C182 (3) 1.16
Set value .46

50th anniversary of the 24-hour automobile race at Le Mans, France.

Camp Fire, Fleur-de-Lis AP78

Designs (Fleur-de-Lis and): 70fr, Scouts saluting flag, vert. 80fr, Scouts with flags. 130fr, Lord Baden-Powell, vert. 270fr, Round dance and map of Africa.

1973, June 4

C183 AP78 50fr dk red, ultra & choc .16 .15
C184 AP78 70fr sl grn, dk brn & red .22 .15
C185 AP78 80fr mag, sl grn & ol .25 .15
C186 AP78 130fr brn, ultra & sl grn .45 .20
C187 AP78 270fr mag, gray & vio bl .90 .45
Nos. C183-C187 (5) 1.98 1.10

Mali Boy and Girl Scouts and International Scouts Congress.
For surcharges see Nos. C222-C223.

Swimming, US and "Africa" Flags — AP79

80fr, Discus and javelin, vert. 330fr, Runners.

1973, July 30 Engr. *Perf. 13*

C188 AP79 70fr red, sl grn & bl .22 .15
C189 AP79 80fr vio bl, dk ol & red .30 .16
C190 AP79 330fr red & vio bl 1.00 .42
Nos. C188-C190 (3) 1.52 .73

First African-United States sports meet.

The Scott Catalogue value is a retail value; that is, what you could expect to pay for the stamp in a grade of Very Fine. The value listed reflects recent actual dealer selling prices.

Head and City Hall, Brussels — AP80

Perseus, by Benvenuto Cellini — AP81

1973, Sept. 17 Engr. *Perf. 13*

C191 AP80 70fr brt ultra, ol & vio .22 .15

Africa Weeks, Brussels, Sept. 15-30, 1973.

1973, Sept. 24

Famous Sculptures: 150fr, Pietá, by Michelangelo. 250fr, Victory of Samothrace, Greek 1st century B.C.

C192 AP81 100fr dk car & sl grn .35 .20
C193 AP81 150fr dk car & dp cl .45 .25
C194 AP81 250fr dk car & dk ol .80 .42
Nos. C192-C194 (3) 1.60 .87

Stephenson's Rocket and Buddicom Engine — AP82

Locomotives: 150fr, Union Pacific, 1890, and Santa Fe, 1940. 200fr, Mistral and Tokaido, 1970.

1973, Oct. 8 Engr. *Perf. 13*

C195 AP82 100fr brn, bl & blk .30 .15
C196 AP82 150fr red, brt ultra & dk car .45 .20
C197 AP82 200fr ocher, bl & ind .65 .30
Nos. C195-C197 (3) 1.40 .65

Apollo XI on Moon — AP83

75fr, Landing capsule, Apollo XIII. 100fr, Astronauts & equipment on moon, Apollo XIV. 280fr, Rover, landing module % astronauts on moon, Apollo XV. 300fr, Lift-off from moon, Apollo XVII.

1973, Oct. 25

C198 AP83 50fr vio, org & sl grn .16 .15
C199 AP83 75fr slate, red & bl .22 .15
C200 AP83 100fr slate, bl & ol brn .35 .16
C201 AP83 280fr vio bl, red & sl grn .80 .38
C202 AP83 300fr slate, red & sl grn 1.00 .45
Nos. C198-C202 (5) 2.53 1.29

Apollo US moon missions.
For surcharges see Nos. C224-C225.

Pablo Picasso — AP84

John F. Kennedy — AP85

1973, Nov. 7 Litho. *Perf. 12½*

C203 AP84 500fr multi 1.60 .80

Pablo Picasso (1881-1973), painter.

1973, Nov. 12

C204 AP85 500fr gold, brt rose lil & blk 1.60 .80

Painting Type of 1968

100fr, Annunciation, by Vittore Carpaccio, horiz. 200fr, Virgin of St. Simon, by Federigo Baroccio. 250fr, Flight into Egypt, by Andrea Solario.

Perf. 13x12½, 12½x12, 12½x13

1973, Nov. 30 Litho.

C205 AP33 100fr blk & multi .30 .20
C206 AP33 200fr blk & multi .65 .30
C207 AP33 250fr blk & multi .80 .40
Nos. C205-C207 (3) 1.75 .90

Christmas 1973.

Soccer Player and Ball — AP86

250fr, Goalkeeper & ball. 500fr, Frauenkirche, Munich, Arms of Munich & soccer ball, horiz.

1973, Dec. 3 Engr. *Perf. 13*

C208 AP86 150fr emer, ol brn & red .50 .25
C209 AP86 250fr emer, vio bl & ol brn .80 .38

Souvenir Sheet

C210 AP86 500fr bl & multi 1.60 1.60

World Soccer Cup, Munich.

Musicians, Mosaic from Pompeii — AP87

Designs (Mosaics from Pompeii): 250fr, Alexander the Great in battle, vert. 350fr, Bacchants, vert.

1974, Jan. 21 Engr. *Perf. 13*

C211 AP87 150fr sl bl, ol & rose .45 .25
C212 AP87 250fr mag, ol & ocher .80 .42
C213 AP87 350fr ol, dp brn & ocher 1.25 .60
Nos. C211-C213 (3) 2.50 1.27

Winston Churchill — AP88

1974, Mar. 18 Engr. *Perf. 13*

C214 AP88 500fr black 1.25 .85

Chess Game AP89

1974, Mar. 25 Engr. *Perf. 13*

C215 AP89 250fr multi .90 .42

21st Chess Olympic Games, Nice 1974.

Painting Type of 1968

Paintings: 400fr, Crucifixion, Alsatian School, c. 1380, vert. 500fr, Burial of Christ, by Titian.

Perf. 12½x13, 13x12½

1974, Apr. 12 Photo.

C216 AP33 400fr multi .90 .50
C217 AP33 500fr multi 1.10 .55

Easter 1974.

Lenin AP90

1974, Apr. 22 Engr. *Perf. 13*

C218 AP90 150fr vio bl & lake .40 .20

50th anniversary of the death of Lenin.

Women's Steeplechase — AP91

1974, May 20 Engr. *Perf. 13*

C219 AP91 130fr bl, lil & brn .40 .22

World Horsewomen's Championship, La Baule, France, June 30-July 7.

Skylab Docking in Space — AP92

Design: 250fr, Skylab over globe with Africa.

1974, July 1 Engr. *Perf. 13*

C220 AP92 200fr bl, sl & org .55 .30
C221 AP92 250fr lil, sl & org .65 .38

Skylab's flight over Africa, 1974.

Nos. C184-C185 Surcharged in Violet Blue with New Value, Two Bars and:

a. 11e JAMBOREE ARABE / AOUT 1974 LIBAN
b. CONGRES PANARABE LIBAN / AOUT 1974

1974, July 8 Engr. *Perf. 13*

C222 AP78 130fr on 70fr (a) .40 .25
C223 AP78 170fr on 80fr (b) .55 .40

11th Pan-Arab Jamboree and Pan-Arab Congress, Batrun, Lebanon, Aug. 1974.

Nos. C200-C201 Surcharged in Red with New Value, Two Bars and:

c. 1er DEBARQUEMENT / SUR LA LUNE / 20-VII-69
d. 1er PAS SUR LA / LUNE 21-VII-69

1974, July 15

C224 AP83 130fr on 100fr (c) .38 .25
C225 AP83 300fr on 280fr (d) .80 .42

First manned moon landing, July 20, 1969, and first step on moon, July 21, 1969.

1906 and 1939 Locomotives — AP93

Locomotives: 120fr, Baldwin, 1870, and Pacific, 1920. 210fr, Al., 1925, and Buddicom, 1847. 330fr, Hudson, 1938, and La Gironde, 1839.

1974, Oct. 7 Engr. *Perf. 13*

C226 AP93 90fr dk car & multi .25 .16
C227 AP93 120fr ocher & multi .35 .20
C228 AP93 210fr org & multi .55 .30
C229 AP93 330fr grn & multi .90 .42
Nos. C226-C229 (4) 2.05 1.08

Skier, Winter Sports and Olympic Rings — AP94

1974, Oct. 7

C230 AP94 300fr multi .80 .42

Holy Family, by Hans Memling AP95

310fr, Virgin & Child, Bourgogne School. 400fr, Adoration of the Kings, by Martin Schongauer.

1974, Nov. 4 Photo. *Perf. 12½*

C231 AP95 290fr multi .80 .38
C232 AP95 310fr multi .80 .42
C233 AP95 400fr multi 1.10 .55
Nos. C231-C233 (3) 2.70 1.35

Christmas 1974.
See Nos. C238-C240, C267-C269.

Raoul Follereau — AP96

1974, Nov. 18 Engr. *Perf. 13*

C234 AP96 200fr brt bl .55 .35

Raoul Follereau (1903-1977), apostle to the lepers and educator of the blind. See No. C468.

Europafrica Issue

Train, Jet, Cogwheel, Grain, Maps of Africa and Europe — AP97

1974, Dec. 27 **Engr.** ***Perf. 13***

C235 AP97 100fr brn, grn & indigo .25 .16
C236 AP97 110fr ocher, vio bl & pur .30 .20

Painting Type of 1974

Designs: 200fr, Christ at Emmaus, by Phillipe de Champaigne, horiz. 300fr, Christ at Emmaus, by Paolo Veronese, horiz. 500fr, Christ in Majesty, Limoges, 13th century.

Perf. 13x12½, 12½x13

1975, Mar. 24 **Litho.**

C238 AP95 200fr multi .55 .35
C239 AP95 300fr multi .80 .42
C240 AP95 500fr multi 1.40 .70
Nos. C238-C240 (3) 2.75 1.47

Easter 1975.

"Voyage to the Center of the Earth" — AP99

Jules Verne's Stories: 170fr, "From Earth to Moon" and Verne's portrait. 190fr, "20,000 Leagues under the Sea." 220fr, "A Floating City."

1975, Apr. 7 **Engr.** ***Perf. 13***

C241 AP99 100fr multi .25 .18
C242 AP99 170fr multi .45 .25
C243 AP99 190fr multi .55 .30
C244 AP99 220fr multi .60 .38
Nos. C241-C244 (4) 1.85 1.11

Dawn, by Michelangelo AP100

Design: 500fr, Moses, by Michelangelo.

1975, Apr. 28 **Photo.** ***Perf. 13***

C245 AP100 400fr multi 1.10 .65
C246 AP100 500fr multi 1.40 .80

Michelangelo Buonarroti (1475-1564), Italian sculptor, painter and architect.

Astronaut on Moon — AP101

Designs: 300fr, Constellations Virgo and Capricorn. 370fr, Statue of Liberty, Kremlin, Soyuz and Apollo spacecraft.

1975, May 19 **Engr.** ***Perf. 13***

C247 AP101 290fr multi 1.20 .50
C248 AP101 300fr multi 1.20 .65
C249 AP101 370fr multi 1.50 .80
Nos. C247-C249 (3) 3.90 1.95

Soviet-American space cooperation.
For overprints see Nos. C264-C266.

Boy Scout, Globe, Nordjamb 75 Emblem AP103

150fr, Boy Scout giving Scout sign. 290fr, Scouts around campfire.

1975, June 23 **Engr.** ***Perf. 13***

C251 AP103 100fr claret, brn & bl .25 .16
C252 AP103 150fr red, brn & grn .40 .20
C253 AP103 290fr bl, grn & claret .80 .42
Nos. C251-C253 (3) 1.45 .78

Nordjamb 75, 14th Boy Scout Jamboree, Lillehammer, Norway, July 29-Aug. 7.

Battle Scene and Marquis de Lafayette — AP104

300fr, Battle scene & George Washington. 370fr, Battle of Chesapeake Bay & Count de Grasse.

1975, July 7 **Engr.** ***Perf. 13***

C254 AP104 290fr lt bl & indigo .80 .42
C255 AP104 300fr lt bl & indigo .80 .42
C256 AP104 370fr lt bl & indigo .90 .55
a. Strip of 3, #C254-C256 2.50 1.90

Bicentenary of the American Revolution. No. C256a has continuous design.

Schweitzer, Bach and Score AP105

Designs: No. C257, Albert Einstein (1879-1955), theoretical physicist. No. No. C258, André-Marie Ampère (1775-1836), French physicist. 100fr, Clément Ader (1841-1925), French aviation pioneer. No. C260, Dr. Albert Schweitzer (1875-1965), Medical missionary and musician. No. C261, Sir Alexander Fleming (1881-1955), British bacteriologist, discoverer of penicillin.

1975 **Engr.** ***Perf. 13***

C257 AP105 90fr multi .22 .16
C258 AP105 90fr pur, org & bis .22 .15
C259 AP105 100fr bl, red & lil .25 .16
C260 AP105 150fr grn, bl & dk grn .40 .20
C261 AP105 150fr lil, bl & brick red .40 .20
Nos. C257-C261 (5) 1.49 .87

Issued: #C257, May 26; #C258, Sept. 23; 100fr, Dec. 8; #C260, Jan. 14; #C261, July 21.
For surcharge see No. C358.

Olympic Rings and Globe — AP106

400fr, Montreal Olympic Games' emblem.

1975, Oct.

C262 AP106 350fr pur & bl .70 .40
C263 AP106 400fr blue .80 .45

Pre-Olympic Year 1975.

Nos. C247-C249 Overprinted: "ARRIMAGE / 17 Juil. 1975"

1975, Oct. 20 **Engr.** ***Perf. 13***

C264 AP101 290fr multi .80 .38
C265 AP101 300fr multi .80 .38
C266 AP101 370fr multi 1.00 .55
Nos. C264-C266 (3) 2.60 1.31

Apollo-Soyuz link-up in space, July 17, 1975.

Painting Type of 1974

Designs: 290fr, Visitation, by Ghirlandaio. 300fr, Nativity, Fra Filippo Lippi school. 370fr, Adoration of the Kings, by Velazquez.

1975, Nov. 24 **Litho.** ***Perf. 12½x13***

C267 AP95 290fr multi .80 .38
C268 AP95 300fr multi .80 .42
C269 AP95 370fr multi 1.00 .55
Nos. C267-C269 (3) 2.60 1.35

Christmas 1975.

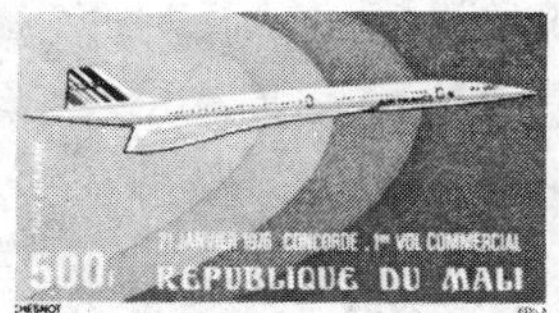

Concorde — AP107

1976, Jan. 12 **Litho.** ***Perf. 13***

C270 AP107 500fr multi 1.40 .90

Concorde supersonic jet, first commercial flight, Jan. 21, 1976.
For overprint see No. C315.

AP108 AP109

1976, Feb. 16 **Litho.** ***Perf. 13***

C271 AP108 120fr Figure skating .35 .16
C272 AP108 420fr Ski jump 1.10 .60
C273 AP108 430fr Slalom 1.20 .60
Nos. C271-C273 (3) 2.65 1.36

12th Winter Olympic Games, Innsbruck, Austria, Feb. 4-15.

1976, Apr. 5 **Litho.** ***Perf. 12½***

Eye examination, WHO emblem.

C274 AP109 130fr multi .35 .18

World Health Day: "Foresight prevents blindness."

Space Ship with Solar Batteries — AP110

Design: 300fr, Astronaut working on orbital space station, vert.

1976, May 10 **Engr.** ***Perf. 13***

C275 AP110 300fr org, dk & lt bl .65 .32
C276 AP110 400fr mag, dk bl & org .80 .45

Futuristic space achievements.

American Eagle, Flag and Liberty Bell — AP111

Designs: 400fr, Revolutionary War naval battle and American eagle. 440fr, Indians on horseback and American eagle, vert.

1976, May 24 **Litho.** ***Perf. 12½***

C277 AP111 100fr multi .25 .16
C278 AP111 400fr multi 1.10 .65
C279 AP111 440fr multi 1.25 .70
Nos. C277-C279 (3) 2.60 1.51

American Bicentennial. Nos. C278-C279 also for Interphil 76, International Philatelic Exhibition, Philadelphia, Pa, May 29-June 6.

Running AP112

Designs (Olympic Rings and): 250fr, Swimming. 300fr, Field ball. 440fr, Soccer.

1976, June 7 **Engr.** ***Perf. 13***

C280 AP112 200fr red brn & blk .55 .25
C281 AP112 250fr multi .65 .38
C282 AP112 300fr multi .80 .42
C283 AP112 440fr multi 1.25 .60
Nos. C280-C283 (4) 3.25 1.65

21st Olympic Games, Montreal, Canada, July 17-Aug. 1.

Cub Scout and Leader — AP113

Designs: 180fr, Scouts tending sick animal, horiz. 200fr, Night hike.

1976, June 14 **Engr.** ***Perf. 13***

C284 AP113 140fr ultra & red brn .38 .30
C285 AP113 180fr dk brn & multi .45 .35
C286 AP113 200fr brn org & vio bl .55 .38
Nos. C284-C286 (3) 1.38 1.03

First African Boy Scout Jamboree, Nigeria.

Mohenjo-Daro, Bull from Wall Relief — AP114

Design: 500fr, Man's head, animals, wall and UNESCO emblem.

1976, Sept. 6 **Engr.** ***Perf. 13***

C287 AP114 400fr blk, bl & pur 1.10 .55
C288 AP114 500fr dk red, bl & grn 1.40 .80

UNESCO campaign to save Mohenjo-Daro excavations.

Europafrica Issue

Freighter, Plane, Map of Europe and Africa — AP115

1976, Sept. 20

C289 AP115 200fr vio brn & bl .55 .35

Nativity, by Taddeo Gaddi — AP116

Paintings: 300fr, Adoration of the Kings, by Hans Memling. 320fr, Nativity, by Carlo Crivelli.

1976, Nov. 8 Litho. ***Perf. 13x12½***

C290 AP116 280fr multi		.70	.38
C291 AP116 300fr multi		.80	.42
C292 AP116 320fr multi		.90	.45
	Nos. C290-C292 (3)	2.40	1.25

Christmas 1976.

Pres. Giscard d'Estaing, Village and Bambara Antelope — AP118

1977, Feb. 13 Photo. ***Perf. 13***

C295 AP118 430fr multi 1.00 .42

Visit of Pres. Valéry Giscard d'Estaing of France, Feb. 13-15.

Elizabeth II and Prince Philip — AP119

Designs: 200fr, Charles de Gaulle, vert. 250fr, Queen Wilhelmina, vert. 300fr, King Baudouin and Queen Fabiola. 480fr, Coronation of Queen Elizabeth II, vert.

REPUBLIQUE DU MALI OPERATION VIKING 20 AOUT 75 4 JUILLET 76 500F POSTE AERIENNE

Viking Flying to Mars — AP117

Design: 1000fr, Viking landing craft on Mars.

1976, Dec. 8 Engr. ***Perf. 13***

C293 AP117 500fr red, brn & bl		1.25	.55
C294 AP117 1000fr multi		2.50	1.25
a. Miniature sheet of 2		4.50	2.50

Operation Viking, US Mars mission. No. C294a contains 2 stamps similar to Nos. C293-C294 in changed colors.

1977, Mar. 21 Litho. ***Perf. 12***

C296 AP119 180fr multi		.45	.25
C297 AP119 200fr multi		.55	.35
C298 AP119 250fr multi		.65	.38
C299 AP119 300fr multi		.80	.45
C300 AP119 480fr multi		1.40	.65
	Nos. C296-C300 (5)	3.85	2.08

Personalities involved in de-colonization.

Newton, Rocket and Apple — AP120

1977, May 7 Engr. ***Perf. 13***

C301 AP120 400fr grn, brn & red 1.20 .55

Isaac Newton (1643-1727), natural philosopher and mathematician, 250th death anniversary.

Charles Lindbergh and Spirit of St. Louis — AP121

430fr, Spirit of St. Louis flying over clouds.

1977, Apr. 4 Litho. ***Perf. 12***

C302 AP121 420fr org & pur	.80	.40
C303 AP121 430fr multi	.85	.40

Charles A. Lindbergh's solo transatlantic flight from New York to Paris, 50th anniversary.

Sassenage Castle, Grenoble — AP122

1977, May 21 Litho. ***Perf. 12½***

C304 AP122 300fr multi .80 .42

Intl. French Language Council, 10th anniv.

Zeppelin No. 1, 1900 — AP123

Designs: 130fr, Graf Zeppelin, 1924. 350fr, Hindenburg aflame at Lakehurst, NJ, 1937. 500fr, Ferdinand von Zeppelin and Graf Zeppelin.

1977, May 30 Engr. ***Perf. 13***

C305 AP123 120fr multi		.35	.18
C306 AP123 130fr multi		.35	.18
C307 AP123 350fr multi		.90	.55
C308 AP123 500fr multi		1.40	.65
	Nos. C305-C308 (4)	3.00	1.56

History of the Zeppelin.

Martin Luther King, American and Swedish Flags — AP124

Design: 600fr, Henri Dunant, Red Cross, Swiss and Swedish flags.

1977, July 4 Engr. ***Perf. 13***

C309 AP124 600fr multi	1.20	.65
C310 AP124 700fr multi	1.40	.70

Nobel Peace Prize recipients.

Soccer — AP125

Designs: 200fr, 3 soccer players, vert. 420fr, 3 soccer players.

1977, Oct. 3 Engr. ***Perf. 13***

C311 AP125 180fr multi		.35	.20
C312 AP125 200fr multi		.40	.25
C313 AP125 420fr multi		.90	.45
	Nos. C311-C313 (3)	1.65	.90

World Soccer Cup Elimination Games.

Mao Tse-tung and COMATEX Hall, Bamako — AP126

1977, Nov. 7 Engr. ***Perf. 13***

C314 AP126 300fr dull red .80 .42

Chairman Mao Tse-tung (1893-1976), first death anniversary.

No. C270 Overprinted in Violet Blue: "PARIS NEW-YORK 22.11.77"

1977, Nov. 22 Litho. ***Perf. 13***

C315 AP107 500fr multi 3.50 1.90

Concorde, first commerical transatlantic flight, Paris to New York.

Virgin and Child, by Rubens AP127

Rubens Paintings: 400fr, Adoration of the Kings. 600fr, Detail from Adoration of the Kings, horiz.

1977, Dec. 5 ***Perf. 12½x12, 12x12½***

C316 AP127 400fr gold & multi		1.10	.60
C317 AP127 500fr gold & multi		1.40	.80
C318 AP127 600fr gold & multi		1.60	.90
	Nos. C316-C318 (3)	4.10	2.30

Christmas 1977, and 400th birth anniversary of Peter Paul Rubens (1577-1640).

Battle of the Amazons, by Rubens — AP128

Rubens Paintings: 300fr, Return from the fields. 500fr, Hercules fighting the Nemean Lion, vert.

Perf. 12x12½, 12½x12

1978, Jan. 16 Litho.

C319 AP128 200fr multi		.55	.35
C320 AP128 300fr multi		.80	.50
C321 AP128 500fr multi		1.40	.80
	Nos. C319-C321 (3)	2.75	1.65

Peter Paul Rubens, 400th birth anniversary.

Schubert Composing "Winterreise" — AP129

Design: 300fr, Schubert and score, vert.

1978, Feb. 13

C322 AP129 300fr multi	.80	.50
C323 AP129 420fr multi	1.20	.60

Franz Schubert (1797-1828), Austrian composer, death sesquicentennial.

Capt. Cook Receiving Hawaiian Delegation — AP130

Design: 300fr, Cook landing on Hawaii. Designs after sketches by John Weber.

1978, Feb. 27 Engr. ***Perf. 13***

C324 AP130 200fr multi	.55	.35
C325 AP130 300fr multi	.80	.42

Capt. James Cook (1728-1779), bicentenary of his arrival in Hawaii.

Soccer — AP131

250fr, One player. 300fr, Two players, horiz.

1978, Mar. 20

C326 AP131 150fr multi		.40	.22
C327 AP131 250fr multi		.65	.40
a. "REPUBLIQUE"		.65	.40
C328 AP131 300fr multi		.80	.42
a. Min. sheet of 3, #C326-C328 + label		1.90	1.50
b. As "a," #C326, C327a, C328			
	Nos. C326-C328 (3)	1.85	1.04

World Soccer Cup Championships, Argentina, 1978, June 1-25.

Nos. C327 and C328a were issued in July to correct the spelling error.

For overprints see Nos. C338-C340.

Jesus with Crown of Thorns, by Dürer AP132

Design: 430fr, Resurrection, by Albrecht Dürer.

1978, Mar. 28
C329 AP132 420fr multi 1.10 .65
C330 AP132 430fr multi 1.20 .65

Easter 1978. See Nos. C359-C361.

Citroen, C3-Trefle, 1922 — AP133

Citroen Cars: 130fr, Croisiere Noire, 1924, tractor. 180fr, B14G, 1927. 200fr, "11" Tractor Avant, 1934.

1978, Apr. 24 Engr. *Perf. 13*
C331 AP133 120fr multi .30 .20
C332 AP133 130fr multi .35 .20
C333 AP133 180fr multi .50 .25
C334 AP133 200fr multi .55 .30
Nos. C331-C334 (4) 1.70 .95

Andre Citroen (1878-1935), automobile designer and manufacturer.

UPU Emblem, World Map, Country Names — AP133a

Design: 130fr, UPU emblem, globe and names of member countries.

1978, May 15
C334A AP133a 120fr multi .32 .16
C335 AP133a 130fr red, grn & emer .35 .20

Centenary of Congress of Paris where General Postal Union became the Universal Postal Union.

Europafrica Issue

Ostrich Incubating Eggs, Syrian Manuscript, 14th Century — AP134

Design: 110fr, Zebra, Miniature by Mansur, Jehangir School, 1620.

1978, July 24 Litho. *Perf. 13x12½*
C336 AP134 100fr multi .25 .16
C337 AP134 110fr multi .30 .18

Nos. C326-C328a Overprinted in Black:

a. CHAMPION / 1978 / ARGENTINE
b. 2e HOLLANDE
c. 3e BRESIL / 4e ITALIE

1978, Aug. 7 Engr. *Perf. 13*
C338 AP131 150fr multi (a) .40 .22
C339 AP131 250fr multi (b) .65 .40
C340 AP131 300fr multi (c) .80 .42
a. Souvenir sheet of 3 1.50 1.50
Nos. C338-C340 (3) 1.85 1.04

Winners, World Soccer Cup Championship, Argentina. Overprints on No. C340a are green including label overprint: FINALE / ARGENTINA 3 HOLLANDE 1.

Elizabeth II in Coronation Robes AP135

Design: 500fr, Coronation coach.

1978, Sept. 18 Litho. *Perf. 12½x12*
C341 AP135 500fr multi 1.00 .65
C342 AP135 1000fr multi 2.00 1.50

Coronation of Queen Elizabeth II, 25th anniv.

US No. C3a and Douglas DC-3 AP136

History of Aviation: 100fr, Belgium No. 252 and Stampe SV-4. 120fr, France No. C48 and Ader's plane No. 3. 130fr, Germany No. C2 and Junker Ju-52. 320fr, Japan No. C25 and Mitsubishi A-6M "Zero."

1978, Oct. 16 Engr. *Perf. 13*
C343 AP136 80fr multi .20 .15
C344 AP136 100fr multi .25 .18
C345 AP136 120fr multi .32 .20
C346 AP136 130fr multi .35 .22
C347 AP136 320fr multi .90 .55
Nos. C343-C347 (5) 2.02 1.30

Annunciation, by Dürer — AP137

Etchings by Dürer: 430fr, Virgin and Child. 500fr, Adoration of the Kings.

1978, Nov. 6
C348 AP137 420fr blk & rose car .85 .45
C349 AP137 430fr ol grn & brn .90 .50
C350 AP137 500fr blk & red 1.00 .65
Nos. C348-C350 (3) 2.75 1.60

Christmas 1978 and 450th death anniversary of Albrecht Dürer (1471-1528), German painter.

Rocket and Trajectory Around Moon — AP138

Design: 300fr, Spaceship circling moon.

1978, Nov. 20 Engr. *Perf. 13*
C351 AP138 200fr multi .80 .55
C352 AP138 300fr multi 1.20 .70

10th anniversary of 1st flight around moon. Nos. C351-C352 printed se-tenant with label between showing earth, moon and US astronauts' names.

Ader's Plane and Concorde — AP139

Designs: 130fr, Wright Flyer A and Concorde. 200fr, Spirit of St. Louis and Concorde.

1979, Jan. 25 Litho. *Perf. 13*
C353 AP139 120fr multi .35 .20
C354 AP139 130fr multi .35 .22
C355 AP139 200fr multi .55 .38
Nos. C353-C355 (3) 1.25 .80

1st supersonic commercial flight, 3rd anniv. For surcharges see Nos. C529-C531.

Philexafrique II-Essen Issue
Common Design Types

Designs: No. C356, Dromedary and Mali No. C26. No. C357, Bird and Lubeck No. 1.

1979, Jan. 29 Litho. *Perf. 13x12½*
C356 CD138 200fr multi .55 .38
C357 CD139 200fr multi .55 .38

Nos. C356-C357 printed se-tenant.

No. C257 Surcharged "1879-1979" 130 F

1979, Mar. 26 Engr. *Perf. 13*
C358 AP105 130fr on 90fr multi .35 .22

Albert Einstein (1879-1955).

Easter Type of 1978

Dürer Etchings: 400fr, Jesus Carrying Cross. 430fr, Crucified Christ. 480fr, Pietà.

1979, Apr. 9
C359 AP132 400fr bl & blk 1.10 .70
C360 AP132 430fr red & blk 1.20 .80
C361 AP132 480fr ultra & blk 1.25 .90
Nos. C359-C361 (3) 3.55 2.40

Easter 1979.

Basketball and Cathedral, Moscow — AP140

430fr, Soccer and St. Basil's Cathedral.

1979, Apr. 17 Litho. *Perf. 13*
C362 AP140 420fr multi 1.10 .75
C363 AP140 430fr multi 1.20 .80

Pre-Olympic Year.

Mali #C92, Apollo Spacecraft AP141

Design: 500fr, Mali No. C176, lift-off.

1979, Oct. 22 Litho. *Perf. 12½x13*
C364 AP141 430fr multi 1.20 .60
C365 AP141 500fr multi 1.40 .70

Apollo 11 moon landing, 10th anniversary.

Capt. Cook, Ship, Kerguelen Island — AP142

Design: 480fr, Capt. Cook, Ship, Hawaii.

1979, Oct. 29 *Perf. 13x12½*
C366 AP142 300fr multi 1.20 .65
C367 AP142 480fr multi 1.40 1.00

Capt. James Cook (1728-1779), explorer, death bicentenary.

David Janowski (1868-1927), Chess Pieces AP143

Chess Pieces and Grand Masters: 140fr, Alexander Alekhine (1892-1946). 200fr, W. Schlage. 300fr, Effim D. Bogoljubow (1889-1952).

1979, Nov. 30 Engr. *Perf. 13*
C368 AP143 100fr red & brn .35 .16
C369 AP143 140fr multi .42 .20
C370 AP143 200fr multi .65 .35
C371 AP143 300fr multi 1.00 .50
Nos. C368-C371 (4) 2.42 1.21

For overprints see Nos. C441-C442.

Adoration of the Kings, by Dürer AP144

Christmas 1979: 400fr, 500fr, Adoration of the Kings by Dürer, diff.

1979, Dec. 10 *Perf. 13x13½*
C372 AP144 300fr brn org & brn .80 .35
C373 AP144 400fr bl & brn 1.10 .42
C374 AP144 500fr dk grn & brn 1.40 .55
Nos. C372-C374 (3) 3.30 1.32

Jet, Map of Africa AP145

1979, Dec. 27 Litho. *Perf. 12½*

C375 AP145 120fr multi .32 .15

ASECNA (Air Safety Board), 20th anniv.

Train, Globe, Rotary Emblem AP146

Rotary International, 75th Anniversary: 250fr, Jet. 430fr, Bamako Club emblem, meeting hall.

1980, Jan. 28 Litho. *Perf. 12½*

C376 AP146 220fr multi .70 .35
C377 AP146 250fr multi .90 .40
C378 AP146 430fr multi 1.50 .60
Nos. C376-C378 (3) 3.10 1.35

Speed Skating, Lake Placid '80 Emblem, Snowflake — AP147

1980, Feb. 11 *Perf. 13*

C379 AP147 200fr shown .55 .22
C380 AP147 300fr Ski jump .80 .35
a. Souvenir sheet of 2 1.40 .65

13th Winter Olympic Games, Lake Placid, NY, Feb. 12-24. No. C380a contains Nos. C379-C380 in changed colors.

Stephenson's Rocket, Mali No. 196 — AP148

Liverpool-Manchester Railroad, 150th Anniversary: 300fr, Stephenson's Rocket, Mali No. 142.

1980, Feb. 25 Engr.

C381 AP148 200fr multi .55 .22
C382 AP148 300fr multi .80 .35

Equestrian, Moscow '80 Emblem — AP149

1980, Mar. 10 Engr. *Perf. 13*

C383 AP149 200fr shown .55 .20
C384 AP149 300fr Yachting .80 .35
C385 AP149 400fr Soccer 1.10 .42
a. Souvenir sheet of 3, #C383-C385 3.00 3.00
Nos. C383-C385 (3) 2.45 .97

22nd Summer Olympic Games, Moscow, July 19-Aug. 3.

For overprints see Nos. C399-C401.

Jesus Carrying Cross, by Maurice Denis AP150

Easter: 500fr, Jesus before Pilate, by Dürer.

1980, Mar. 31

C386 AP150 480fr brn & org red 1.25 .50
C387 AP150 500fr org red & brn 1.40 .55

Kepler, Copernicus and Solar System Diagram — AP151

200fr, Kepler & diagram of earth's orbit, vert.

1980, Apr. 7 Engr. *Perf. 13*

C388 AP151 200fr multi .55 .20
C389 AP151 300fr multi .80 .35

Discovery of Pluto, 50th Anniversary — AP152

1980, Apr. 21

C390 AP152 420fr multi 1.10 .70

Lunokhod I, Russian Flag — AP153

Design: 500fr, Apollo and Soyuz spacecraft, flags of US and Russia.

1980, Apr. 28

C391 AP153 480fr multi 1.25 .50
C392 AP153 500fr multi 1.40 .55

Lunokhod I, 10th anniversary; Apollo-Soyuz space test program, 5th anniversary.

Rochambeau, French Fleet Landing at Newport, R.I. — AP154

French Cooperation in American Revolution: 430fr, Rochambeau and George Washington, eagle.

1980, June 16 Engr. *Perf. 13*

C393 AP154 420fr multi 1.10 .70
C394 AP154 430fr multi 1.20 .70

Jet Flying Around Earth — AP155

Designs: No. C396, Ship, people, attack. No. C397, Astronaut on moon. No. C398, Space craft, scientists, moon. Nos. C395-C396 from "Around the World in 80 Days;" Nos. C397-C398 from "From Earth to Moon."

1980, June 30 Engr. *Perf. 11*

C395 AP155 100fr multi .25 .15
C396 AP155 100fr multi .25 .15
C397 AP155 150fr multi .40 .15
C398 AP155 150fr multi .40 .15
Nos. C395-C398 (4) 1.30
Set value .50

Jules Verne (1828-1905), French science fiction writer. Nos. C395-C398 each printed se-tenant with label showing various space scenes.

Nos. C383-C385a Overprinted:

200fr- CONCOURS COMPLET/ INDIVIDUEL/ROMAN (It.)/ BLINOV (Urss) /SALNIKOV (Urss)

300fr- FINN/RECHARDT (Fin.)/ MAYRHOFER (Autr.)/ BALACHOV (Urss)

400fr- TCHECOSLOVAQUIE/ ALLEMAGNE DE L'EST/URSS

1980, Sept. 8 Engr. *Perf. 13*

C399 AP149 200fr multi .55 .20
C400 AP149 300fr multi .80 .35
C401 AP149 400fr multi 1.10 .42
a. Souvenir sheet of 3 2.50 2.50
Nos. C399-C401 (3) 2.45 .97

Butterfly Type of 1980

1980, Oct. 6 Litho. *Perf. 13x12½*

Size: 48x36mm

C402 A137 420fr *Denaus chrysippus* 1.20 .45

Charles De Gaulle, Map and Colors of France — AP156

1980, Nov. 9 Litho. *Perf. 13½x13*

C403 AP156 420fr shown 1.40 .65
C404 AP156 430fr De Gaulle, cross 1.40 .70

Charles De Gaulle, 10th anniv. of death.

Mali No. 140, Amtrak Train — AP157

Mali Stamps and Trains: 120fr, No. 195, Tokaido, Japan, vert. 200fr, No. 144, Rembrandt, Germany. 480fr, No. 143, TGV-001 France, vert.

1980, Nov. 17 Engr. *Perf. 13*

C405 AP157 120fr multi .32 .15
C406 AP157 130fr multi .35 .15
C407 AP157 200fr multi .55 .20
C408 AP157 480fr multi 1.25 .50
Nos. C405-C408 (4) 2.47 1.00

For overprint see No. C425.

Holy Family, by Lorenzo Lotto — AP158

Christmas 1980 (Paintings): 400fr, Flight to Egypt, by Rembrandt, vert. 500fr, Christmas Night, by Gauguin.

1980, Dec. 1 Litho. *Perf. 13x12½*

C409 AP158 300fr multi .80 .38
C410 AP158 400fr multi 1.10 .42
C411 AP158 500fr multi 1.40 .60
Nos. C409-C411 (3) 3.30 1.40

Self-portrait, by Picasso AP159

1981, Jan. 26 Litho. *Perf. 12½x13*

C412 AP159 1000fr multi 2.50 1.10

Pablo Picasso (1881-1973), birth centenary.

Soccer Players — AP160

Designs: Soccer players.

1981, Feb. 28 *Perf. 13*

C413 AP160 100fr multi .25 .15
C414 AP160 200fr multi .55 .20
C415 AP160 300fr multi .80 .35
Nos. C413-C415 (3) 1.60 .70

Souvenir Sheet

C416 AP160 600fr multi 1.60 .65

World Cup Soccer preliminary games.

Mozart and Instruments — AP161

225th Birth Anniversary of Wolfgang Amadeus Mozart: 430fr, Mozart and instruments, diff.

1981, Mar. 30 Litho. *Perf. 13*

C417 AP161 420fr multi 1.10 .45
C418 AP161 430fr multi 1.20 .50

Jesus Falls on the Way to Calvary, by Raphael AP162

Easter 1981: 600fr, Ecce Homo, by Rembrandt.

1981, Apr. 6 *Perf. 12½x13*
C419 AP162 500fr multi 1.40 .60
C420 AP162 600fr multi 1.60 .65

Alan B. Shepard — AP163 Exploration of Saturn — AP164

Space Anniversaries: No. C422, Yuri Gagarin's flight, 1961. 430fr, Uranus discovery bicentennial, horiz.

1981, Apr. 21 **Litho.** *Perf. 13*
C421 AP163 200fr multi .55 .20
C422 AP163 200fr multi .55 .20
C423 AP164 380fr multi 1.00 .40
C424 AP163 430fr multi 1.20 .50
Nos. C421-C424 (4) 3.30 1.30

No. C408 Overprinted: "26 fevrier 1981 Record du monde de/vitesse-380 km/h."

1981, June 15 **Engr.**
C425 AP157 480fr multi 1.25 .50

New railroad speed record.

US No. 233, Columbus and His Fleet — AP165

475th Death Anniversary of Christopher Columbus (Santa Maria and): 200fr, Spain No. 418, vert. 260fr, Spain No. 421, vert. 300fr, US No. 232.

1981, June 22
C426 AP165 180fr multi .50 .20
C427 AP165 200fr multi .55 .20
C428 AP165 260fr multi .70 .30
C429 AP165 300fr multi .80 .35
Nos. C426-C429 (4) 2.55 1.05

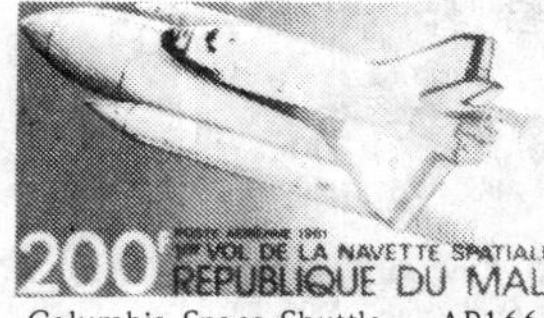

Columbia Space Shuttle — AP166

Designs: Space shuttle.

1981, July 6 **Litho.** *Perf. 13*
C430 AP166 200fr multi .55 .20
C431 AP166 500fr multi 1.40 .50
C432 AP166 600fr multi 1.60 .65
Nos. C430-C432 (3) 3.55 1.35

Souvenir Sheet
Perf. 12
C433 AP166 700fr multi 2.00 .80

For overprint see No. C440.

Harlequin on Horseback AP167

Picasso Birth Cent.: 750fr, Child Holding a Dove.

1981, July 15 *Perf. 12½x13*
C434 AP167 600fr multi 1.60 .65
C435 AP167 750fr multi 2.25 1.00

Prince Charles and Lady Diana, St. Paul's Cathedral AP168

1981, July 20 *Perf. 12½*
C436 AP168 500fr shown 1.40 .50
C437 AP168 700fr Couple, coach 2.00 .80

Royal wedding.

Christmas 1981 AP169

Designs: Virgin and Child paintings.

1981, Nov. 9 **Litho.** *Perf. 12½x13*
C438 AP169 500fr Grunewald 1.40 .50
C439 AP169 700fr Correggio 2.00 .80

See Nos. C451-C452, C464-C466, C475-C477, C488-C489, C511.

No. C433 Overprinted In Blue: "JOE ENGLE / RICHARD TRULY / 2 eme VOL SPATIAL"

1981, Nov. 12 **Litho.** *Perf. 12*
C440 AP166 700fr multi 2.00 .80

Nos. C369, C371 Overprinted with Winners' Names and Dates

1981, Dec. **Engr.** *Perf. 13*
C441 AP143 140fr multi .38 .15
C442 AP143 300fr multi .80 .35

Lewis Carroll (1832-1908) — AP170

Designs: Scenes from Alice in Wonderland.

1982, Jan. 30 **Litho.** *Perf. 12½*
C443 AP170 110fr multi .30 .15
C444 AP170 130fr multi .35 .15
C445 AP170 140fr multi .38 .15
Nos. C443-C445 (3) 1.03 .45

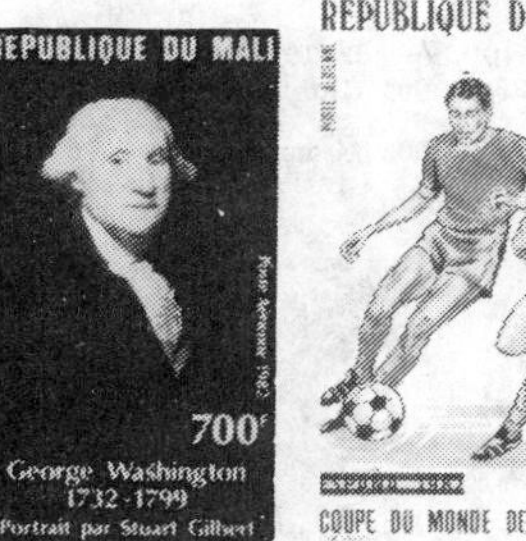

AP171 AP172

1982, Feb. 8 *Perf. 13*
C446 AP171 700fr Portrait, by Gilbert Stuart 2.00 .80

George Washington's Birth, 250th anniv. Incorrectly inscribed "Stuart Gilbert."

1982, Mar. 15 **Litho.** *Perf. 13*

1982 World Cup: Various soccer players.

C447 AP172 220fr multi .60 .22
C448 AP172 420fr multi 1.20 .45
C449 AP172 500fr multi 1.40 .50
Nos. C447-C449 (3) 3.20 1.17

Souvenir Sheet
Perf. 12½
C450 AP172 680fr multi 1.90 .65

For overprints see Nos. C458-C461.

Art Type of 1981

Paintings: 680fr, Transfiguration, by Fra Angelico. 1000fr, Pieta, by Bellini, horiz.

Perf. 12½x13, 13x12½
1982, Apr. 19 **Litho.**
C451 AP169 680fr multi 1.90 .65
C452 AP169 1000fr multi 2.50 1.00

Mali No. O30, France No. 1985 — AP174

1982, June 1 *Perf. 13*
C453 AP174 180fr shown .50 .20
C454 AP174 200fr No. C356 .55 .20

PHILEXFRANCE '82 Intl. Stamp Exhibition, Paris, June 11-21. Nos. C453-C454 se-tenant with label showing show emblem and dates.

Fire Engine, France, 1850 — AP175

Designs: French fire engines.

1982, June 14
C455 AP175 180fr shown .50 .20
C456 AP175 200fr 1921 .55 .22
C457 AP175 270fr 1982 .70 .28
Nos. C455-C457 (3) 1.75 .70

Nos. C447-C450 Overprinted with Finalists' and Scores in Brown, Black, Blue or Red

1982, Aug. 16 **Litho.** *Perf. 13*
C458 AP172 220fr multi (Brn) .60 .22
C459 AP172 420fr multi 1.20 .45
C460 AP172 500fr multi (Bl) 1.40 .50
Nos. C458-C460 (3) 3.20 1.17

Souvenir Sheet
Perf. 12½
C461 AP172 680fr multi (R) 1.90 .65

Italy's victory in 1982 World Cup.

Scouting Year — AP176

1982 *Perf. 12½*
C462 AP176 300fr Tent, Baden-Powell .80 .35
C463 AP176 500fr Salute, emblem 1.40 .50

Art Type of 1981

Boy with Cherries, by Edouard Manet (1832-83).

1982, Oct. 28 **Litho.** *Perf. 12½x13*
C464 AP169 680fr multi 1.90 .65

Art Type of 1981

Madonna and Child Paintings.

1982, Nov. 10
C465 AP169 500fr Titian 1.40 .50
C466 AP169 1000fr Bellini 2.50 1.00

Johann von Goethe (1749-1832), Poet — AP179

1982, Dec. 13 **Engr.** *Perf. 13*
C467 AP179 500fr multi 1.40 .50

Follereau Type of 1974

1983, Jan. 24
C468 AP96 200fr dk brn .55 .16

Vostok VI, 20th Anniv. — AP180 Manned Flight, 200th Anniv. — AP181

1983, Feb. 14 **Litho.** *Perf. 12½*
C469 AP180 400fr Valentina Tereshkova 1.10 .35

1983, Feb. 28 *Perf. 13*
C470 AP181 500fr Eagle transatlantic balloon 1.40 .50
C471 AP181 700fr Montgolfiere 2.00 .90

Pre-Olympic Year — AP182

1983, Mar. 14 Litho. *Perf. 13*

C472 AP182 180fr Soccer .50 .20
C473 AP182 270fr Hurdles .70 .28
C474 AP182 300fr Wind surfing .80 .35
Nos. C472-C474 (3) 2.00 .83

Art Type of 1981

Raphael paintings.

1983, Mar. 28 *Perf. 12½x13*

C475 AP169 400fr Deposition 1.20 .40
C476 AP169 600fr Transfiguration 1.60 .55

Art Type of 1981

Design: Family of Acrobats with Monkey, by Picasso (1881-1973).

1983, Apr. 30 Litho. *Perf. 12½x13*

C477 AP169 680fr multi 1.60 .80

Lions Intl. — AP185

1983, May 9 *Perf. 12½*

C478 Pair 4.00 1.90
a. AP185 700fr shown 2.00 .90
b. AP185 700fr Rotary Intl. 2.00 .90

Challenger Spacecraft — AP186

1983, July 29 Litho. *Perf. 13*

C479 AP186 1000fr multi 2.50 .90

Printed se-tenant with orange red label showing astronaut Sally Ride.

Paris-Dakar Auto Race — AP187

1983, Sept. 5 Litho. *Perf. 12½*

C480 AP187 240fr Mercedes, 1914 .55 .20
C481 AP187 270fr SSK, 1929 .60 .22
C482 AP187 500fr W196, 1954 1.20 .42
Nos. C480-C482 (3) 2.35 .84

Souvenir Sheet

C483 AP187 1000fr Mercedes van 2.50 1.00

For surcharge see No. C506.

Chess Game — AP188

1983, Oct. 24 Engr. *Perf. 13*

C484 AP188 300fr Pawn, bishop .90 .35
C485 AP188 420fr Knight, castle 1.40 .60
C486 AP188 500fr King, Queen 1.60 .60
Nos. C484-C486 (3) 3.90 1.55

Souvenir Sheet

C487 AP188 700fr Various chess pieces 2.00 .80

Art Type of 1981

Raphael Paintings.

1983, Nov. 7 Litho. *Perf. 12½x13*

C488 AP169 700fr Canigiani Madonna 2.00 .80
C489 AP169 800fr Madonna with Lamb 2.50 .90

Portrait of Leopold Zborowski, by Amedeo Modigliani (1884-1920) AP190

1984, Feb. 13 Litho. *Perf. 12½x13*

C490 AP190 700fr multi 2.00 .60

Abraham Lincoln — AP191

Duke Ellington — AP192

1984, Feb. 27 *Perf. 12½*

C491 AP191 400fr Henri Dunant 1.20 .35
C492 AP191 540fr shown 1.60 .50

1984, Mar. 12 *Perf. 13½x13*

C493 AP192 470fr Sidney Bechet 1.50 .40
C494 AP192 500fr shown 1.50 .40

Glider — AP193

1984, Mar. 26

C495 AP193 270fr shown .80 .25
C496 AP193 350fr Hang glider 1.10 .40

1984 Summer Olympics — AP194

1984, Apr. 9 *Perf. 13*

C497 AP194 265fr Weight lifting .80 .22
C498 AP194 440fr Equestrian 1.40 .40
C499 AP194 500fr Hurdles 1.60 .45

Souvenir Sheet

Perf. 12½

C500 AP194 700fr Wind surfing 2.00 .90

For surcharges see Nos. C507-C510.

Easter 1984 — AP195

Paintings; 940fr, Crucifixion, by Rubens, vert. 970fr, Resurrection, by Mantegna.

1984, Apr. 24 Engr.

C501 AP195 940fr multi 3.00 .80
C502 AP195 970fr multi 3.25 .90

Gottlieb Daimler Birth Sesquicentenary — AP196

1984, June 1 Engr. *Perf. 13*

C503 AP196 350fr Mercedes Simplex 1.10 .55
C504 AP196 470fr Mercedes-Benz 370-S 1.50 .70
C505 AP196 485fr 500-SEC 1.60 .80
Nos. C503-C505 (3) 4.20 2.05

No. C480 Overprinted and Surcharged

1984 Litho. *Perf. 12½*

C506 AP187 120fr on 240fr #C480 .32 .16

Nos. C497-C500 Overprinted and Surcharged

1984, Oct. Litho. *Perf. 13*

C507 AP194 135fr on 265fr .40 .15
C508 AP194 220fr on 440fr .60 .20
C509 AP194 250fr on 500fr .70 .20
Nos. C507-C509 (3) 1.70 .55

Souvenir Sheet

C510 AP194 350fr on 700fr .90 .40

Overprints refer to the winners of the events depicted.

Art Type of 1981

Painting: Virgin and Child, by Lorenzo Lotto.

1984, Nov. 20 Litho. *Perf. 12½x13*

C511 AP169 500fr multi 1.40 .42

Audubon Birth Bicentenary — AP198

1985, Apr. 15 Litho. *Perf. 13*

C512 AP198 180fr Kingfisher .45 .16
C513 AP198 300fr Bustard, vert. .70 .25
C514 AP198 470fr Ostrich, vert. 1.20 .40
C515 AP198 540fr Buzzard 1.40 .45
Nos. C512-C515 (4) 3.75 1.26

For surcharge see No. C560, C562, C567.

ASECNA Airlines, 25th Anniv. — AP199

1985, June 10 *Perf. 12½*

C516 AP199 700fr multi 1.90 .60

For surcharge see No. C559.

PHILEXAFRICA Type of 1985

1985, June 24 *Perf. 13*

C517 A183 200fr Boy Scouts, lion .50 .16
C518 A183 200fr Satellite communications .50 .16

Nos. C517-C518 are printed se-tenant with center label picturing map of Africa or UAPT emblem.

Halley's Comet — AP200

1986, Mar. 24 Litho. *Perf. 12½*

C519 AP200 300fr multi 1.10 .38

For surcharge see No. C558.

Statue of Liberty, Cent. — AP201

1986, Apr. 7 *Perf. 13*

C520 AP201 600fr multi 2.25 .70

Gottlieb Daimler Motorcycle — AP202

1986, Apr. 14

C521 AP202 400fr multi 1.50 .50

1st Internal combustion automotive engine, cent.

Paul Robeson (1898-1976), American Actor, Singer — AP203

1986, May 10

C522 AP203 500fr Portrait, Show Boat 2.00 .65

Karl Eberth (1835-1926), Bacteriologist, and Typhoid Bacilli AP204

World Chess Championships AP205

1986, June 7 Litho. *Perf. 12x12½*

C523 AP204 550fr multi 2.00 .65

1986, June 16 *Perf. 12½*

C524 AP205 400fr Chessmen 1.50 .50
C525 AP205 500fr Knight 2.00 .60

Disappearance of Jean Mermoz, 50th Anniv. — AP206

Mermoz and: 150fr, Latecoere-300 seaplane. 600fr, Cams 53 Oiseau Tango, seaplane. 625fr, Flight map, Le Comte de La Vaulx aircraft.

1986, Aug. 18 Litho. *Perf. 13*

C526 AP206 150fr multi .60 .22
C527 AP206 600fr multi 2.50 .85
C528 AP206 625fr multi 2.50 .85
Nos. C526-C528 (3) 5.60 1.92

Nos. C353-C355 Surcharged "1986-10e Anniversaire du ler Vol/Commercial Supersonique" and New Value

1986, Sept. 29

C529 AP139 175fr on 120fr .70 .38
C530 AP139 225fr on 130fr 1.00 .50
C531 AP139 300fr on 200fr 1.10 .60
Nos. C529-C531 (3) 2.80 1.48

Hansen, Leprosy Bacillus, Follereau and Lepers — AP207

1987, Jan. 26 Litho. *Perf. 13*

C532 AP207 500fr multi 2.00 1.00

Gerhard Hansen (1841-1912), Norwegian physician who discovered the leprosy bacillus (1869); Raoul Follereau (1903-1977), philanthropist.

Konrad Adenauer (1876-1967), West German Chancellor — AP208

1987, Mar. 9 Litho. *Perf. 13*

C533 AP208 625fr org, buff & blk 2.25 1.10

Pre-Olympics Year — AP209

Buddha and: 400fr, Runners. 500fr, Soccer players.

1987, Apr. 6 Engr.

C534 AP209 400fr blk & red brn 1.50 .70
C535 AP209 500fr lil rose, ol grn & ol 2.00 1.00

25th Summer Olympics, Seoul, 1988.

Al Jolson in The Jazz Singer — AP210

1987, Apr. 20

C536 AP210 550fr dk red brn & car rose 2.00 1.00

Sound films, 60th anniv.

Albert John Luthuli (1899-1967), 1960 Nobel Peace Prize Winner — AP211

1987, May 26 Engr. *Perf. 13*

C537 AP211 400fr multi 1.50 .75

Service Organizations AP212

1987, June 8 Litho. *Perf. 13*

C538 AP212 500fr Rotary Int'l. 2.00 1.00
C539 AP212 500fr Lions Int'l. 2.00 1.00

Coubertin, Ancient Greek Runners, Contemporary Athletes — AP213

1988, Feb. 14 Litho. *Perf. 13*

C540 AP213 240fr shown 1.10 .60
C541 AP213 400fr 5-ring emblem, stadium 2.00 1.00

125th birth anniv. of Baron Pierre de Coubertin (1863-1937), French educator and sportsman who promulgated revival of the Olympic Games; 1988 Summer Olympics, Seoul.

For surcharge see No. C565

Harlequin, by Pablo Picasso (1881-1973) AP214

1988, Apr. 4 Litho. *Perf. 13*

C542 AP214 600fr multi 4.25 1.15

For surcharge see No. C563.

1st Scheduled Transatlantic Flight of the Concorde (London-New York), 15th Anniv. — AP215

1988, May 2 *Perf. 13*

C543 AP215 500fr multi 3.50 1.75

Home Improvement for a Verdant Mali — AP216

1989, Feb. 6 Litho. *Perf. 12½*

C544 AP216 5fr shown .15 .15
C545 AP216 10fr Furnace, tree, field .15 .15
C546 AP216 25fr like 5fr .18 .15
C547 AP216 100fr like 10fr .70 .35
Set value 1.00 .50

1st Man on the Moon, 20th Anniv. — AP217

1989, Mar. 13 Engr. *Perf. 13*

C548 AP217 300fr multi. 2.10 1.05
C549 AP217 500fr multi, vert. 3.50 1.75

For surcharges see Nos. C561, C564.

French Revolution, Bicent. AP218

1989, July 3 Engr. *Perf. 13*

C550 AP218 400fr Women's march on Versailles 2.35 1.20
C551 AP218 600fr Storming of the Bastille 3.50 1.75

For surcharges see Nos. C566, C568.

World Cup Soccer Championships, Italy — AP219

1990, June 4 Litho. *Perf. 13*

C552 AP219 200fr multi 1.20 .60
C553 AP219 225fr multi, diff. 1.35 .68

Souvenir Sheet

C554 AP219 500fr like #C552 3.00 1.50

No. C552 overprinted in red "ITALIE : 2 / ANGLETERRE : 1"

No. C553 overprinted in red "R.F.A. : 1 / ARGENTINE : 0"

No. C554 overprinted in red in margin "1er : R.F.A. 2eme : ARGENTINE 3eme : ITALIE"

1990

C555 AP219 200fr on #C552 1.20 .60
C556 AP219 225fr on #C553 1.35 .68

Souvenir Sheet

C557 AP219 500fr on #C554 3.00 1.50

#C512-C513, C515-C516, C519, C541-C542, C548-C551 Surcharged Like #579-594

1992, June *Perfs. as Before*

Printing Methods as Before

C558 AP200 20fr on 300fr .16 .15
C559 AP199 20fr on 700fr .16 .15
C560 AP198 30fr on 180fr .24 .15
C561 AP217 30fr on 500fr .24 .15
C562 AP198 100fr on 540fr .80 .40
C563 AP214 100fr on 600fr .80 .40
C564 AP217 150fr on 300fr 1.20 .60
C565 AP213 150fr on 400fr 1.20 .60
C566 AP218 150fr on 400fr 1.20 .60
C567 AP198 200fr on 300fr 1.60 .80
C568 AP218 240fr on 600fr 1.95 1.00
Nos. C558-C568 (11) 9.55 5.00

Size and location of surcharge varies. No. C565 also overprinted "BARCELONE 92."

POSTAGE DUE STAMPS

Bambara Headpiece — D1

Perf. 14x13½

1961, Mar. 18 Engr. Unwmk.

J1 D1 1fr black .15 .15
J2 D1 2fr bright ultra .15 .15
J3 D1 5fr red lilac .15 .15
J4 D1 10fr orange .16 .15
J5 D1 20fr bright green .20 .15
J6 D1 25fr red brown .22 .18
Set value .80 .65

Polyptychus Roseus — D2

Designs: No. J8, Deilephila Nerii. No. J9, Gynanisa maja. No. J10, Bunaea alcinoe. No. J11, Teracolus eris. No. J12, Colotis antevippe. No. J13, Charaxes epijasius. No. J14, Manatha microcera. No. J15, Hypokopelates otraeda. No. J16, Lipaphnaeus leonina. No. J17, Gonimbrasia hecate. No. J18, Lobounaea christyi. No. J19, Hypolimnas misippus. No. J20, Catopsilia florella.

1964, June 1 Photo. *Perf. 11*

Butterflies and Moths in Natural Colors

J7 D2 1fr olive green .15 .15
J8 D2 1fr org & brn .15 .15
a. Pair, #J7-J8 .15 .15
J9 D2 2fr emer & brn .15 .15
J10 D2 2fr emer & brn .15 .15
a. Pair, #J9-J10 .15 .15
J11 D2 3fr rose lil & brn .15 .15
J12 D2 3fr rose lil & brn .15 .15
a. Pair, #J11-J12 .15 .15
J13 D2 5fr blk & rose .15 .15
J14 D2 5fr green .15 .15
a. Pair, #J13-J14 .15 .15
J15 D2 10fr yel, org & blk .15 .15
J16 D2 10fr blue .15 .15
a. Pair, #J15-J16 .15 .15
J17 D2 20fr lt bl & brn .22 .22
J18 D2 20fr lt bl & brn .22 .22
a. Pair, #J17-J18 .45 .45
J19 D2 25fr grn & yel .30 .30
J20 D2 25fr dp grn & blk .30 .30
a. Pair, #J19-J20 .60 .60
Set value (14) 1.80 1.80

Nos. J7-J20 Surcharged

1984 Photo. *Perf. 11*

J21 D2 5fr on 1fr #J7 .15 .15
J22 D2 5fr on 1fr #J8 .15 .15
a. Pair, #J21-J22 .15 .15

No.	Type	Description	Unused	Used
J23	D2	10fr on 2fr #J9	.15	.15
J24	D2	10fr on 2fr #J10	.15	.15
a.		Pair, #J23-J24	.15	.15
J25	D2	15fr on 3fr #J11	.15	.15
J26	D2	15fr on 3fr #J12	.15	.15
a.		Pair, #J25-J26	.15	.15
J27	D2	25fr on 5fr #J13	.15	.15
J28	D2	25fr on 5fr #J14	.15	.15
a.		Pair, #J27-J28	.15	.15
J29	D2	50fr on 10fr #J15	.15	.15
J30	D2	50fr on 10fr #J16	.15	.15
a.		Pair, #J29-J30	.15	.15
J31	D2	100fr on 20fr #J17	.25	.25
J32	D2	100fr on 20fr #J18	.25	.25
a.		Pair, #J31-J32	.50	.50
J33	D2	125fr on 25fr #J19	.35	.35
J34	D2	125fr on 25fr #J20	.35	.35
a.		Pair, #J33-J34	.70	.70
		Set value (14)	1.85	1.85

OFFICIAL STAMPS

Dogon Mask — O1

Mali Coat of Arms — O2

Perf. 14x13½

1961, Mar. 18 Engr. Unwmk.

No.	Type	Description	Unused	Used
O1	O1	1fr gray	.15	.15
O2	O1	2fr red orange	.15	.15
O3	O1	3fr black	.15	.15
O4	O1	5fr light blue	.15	.15
O5	O1	10fr bister brown	.15	.15
O6	O1	25fr brt ultra	.15	.15
O7	O1	30fr car rose	.20	.15
O8	O1	50fr Prus green	.35	.15
O9	O1	85fr red brown	.50	.30
O10	O1	100fr emerald	.65	.35
O11	O1	200fr red lilac	1.20	.75
		Set value	3.25	1.85

1964, June 1 Photo. *Perf. 12½*

National Colors and Arms in Multicolor, Background in Light Green

No.	Type	Description	Unused	Used
O12	O2	1fr green	.15	.15
O13	O2	2fr light vio	.15	.15
O14	O2	3fr gray	.15	.15
O15	O2	5fr lilac rose	.15	.15
O16	O2	10fr bright blue	.15	.15
O17	O2	25fr ocher	.16	.16
O18	O2	30fr dark green	.18	.18
O19	O2	50fr orange	.25	.25
O20	O2	85fr dark brown	.40	.40
O21	O2	100fr red	.50	.40
O22	O2	200fr dk vio bl	1.10	.40
		Set value	2.80	2.00

City Coats of Arms — O3

1981, Sept. Photo. *Perf. 12½x13*

No.	Type	Description	Unused	Used
O23	O3	5fr Gao	.15	.15
O24	O3	15fr Timbuktu	.15	.15
O25	O3	50fr Mopti	.15	.15
O26	O3	180fr Segou	.30	.16
O27	O3	200fr Sikasso	.40	.20
O28	O3	680fr Koulikoro	1.20	.60
O29	O3	700fr Kayes	1.40	.65
O30	O3	1000fr Bamako	2.00	1.00
		Nos. O23-O30 (8)	5.75	3.06

Nos. O23-O30 Surcharged

1984 Photo. *Perf. 12½x13*

No.	Type	Description	Unused	Used
O31	O3	15fr on 5fr	.15	.15
O32	O3	50fr on 15fr	.15	.15
O33	O3	120fr on 50fr	.35	.15
O34	O3	295fr on 180fr	.80	.40
O35	O3	470fr on 200fr	1.25	.60
O36	O3	515fr on 680fr	1.40	.65
O37	O3	845fr on 700fr	2.25	1.10
O38	O3	1225fr on 1000fr	3.50	1.40
		Nos. O31-O38 (8)	9.85	4.60

MALTA

'mȯl-tə

LOCATION — A group of islands in the Mediterranean Sea off the coast of Sicily
GOVT. — Republic within the British Commonwealth
AREA — 122 sq. mi.
POP. — 329,189 (1983)
CAPITAL — Valletta

The former colony includes the islands of Malta, Gozo, and Comino. It became a republic Dec. 13, 1974.

4 Farthings = 1 Penny
12 Pence = 1 Shilling
20 Shillings = 1 Pound
10 Mils = 1 Cent (1972)
100 Cents = 1 Pound (1972)

Catalogue values for unused stamps in this country are for Never Hinged items, beginning with Scott 206 in the regular postage section, Scott B1 in the semi-postal section, Scott C2 in the air post section, and Scott J21 in the postage due section.

Watermark

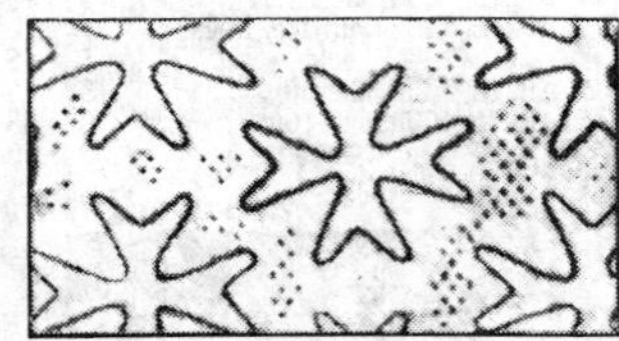

Wmk. 354- Maltese Cross, Multiple

Values for unused stamps are for examples with original gum as defined in the catalogue introduction. Very fine examples of Nos. 1-7 will have perforations touching the frameline on one or more sides due to the narrow spacing of the stamps on the plate. Stamps with perfs clear of the frameline are scarce and will command higher prices.

Queen Victoria
A1 A2

A3 A4

1860-61 Unwmk. Typo. *Perf. 14*

No.	Type	Description	Unused	Used
1	A1	½p buff ('61)	550.00	300.00
2	A1	½p buff, *bluish*	850.00	550.00
a.		Imperf.	*11,000.*	

1863-80 Wmk. 1

No.	Type	Description	Unused	Used
3	A1	½p yellow buff ('75)	60.00	45.00
a.		½p buff	75.00	50.00
b.		½p brown orange ('67)	250.00	75.00
c.		½p orange yel ('80)	110.00	60.00
4	A1	½p golden yel (analine) ('74)	225.00	275.00

1865 *Perf. 12½*

No.	Type	Description	Unused	Used
5	A1	½p buff	75.00	65.00
a.		½p yellow buff	225.00	150.00

1878 *Perf. 14x12½*

No.	Type	Description	Unused	Used
6	A1	½p buff	140.00	80.00
a.		Perf. 12½x14		

1882 Wmk. 2 *Perf. 14*

No.	Type	Description	Unused	Used
7	A1	½p orange	16.00	32.50

1885, Jan. 1

No.	Type	Description	Unused	Used
8	A1	½p green	1.10	.45
9	A2	1p car rose	1.65	.35
a.		1p rose	80.00	25.00
10	A3	2p gray	3.75	1.40
11	A4	2½p ultramarine	30.00	.85
a.		2½p bright ultramarine	30.00	.95
b.		2½p dull blue	42.50	1.65
12	A3	4p brown	8.25	2.75
a.		Imperf., pair	4,750.	*4,750.*
13	A3	1sh violet	30.00	8.25
		Nos. 8-13 (6)	74.75	14.05

For surcharge see No. 20.

Queen Victoria within Maltese Cross — A5

1886 Wmk. 1

No.	Type	Description	Unused	Used
14	A5	5sh rose	110.00	80.00

Gozo Fishing Boat — A6

Ancient Galley — A7

1899, Feb. 4 Engr. Wmk. 2

No.	Type	Description	Unused	Used
15	A6	4½p black brown	10.00	8.75
16	A7	5p brown red	25.00	13.00

See Nos. 42-45.

"Malta" — A8

St. Paul after Shipwreck — A9

1899 Wmk. 1

No.	Type	Description	Unused	Used
17	A8	2sh6p olive gray	37.50	11.00
18	A9	10sh blue black	70.00	55.00

See No. 64. For overprint see No. 85.

Valletta Harbor — A10

1901, Jan. 1 Wmk. 2

No.	Type	Description	Unused	Used
19	A10	1f red brown	.85	.55

See Nos. 28-29.

No. 11 Surcharged in Black **One Penny**

1902, July 4

No.	Type	Description	Unused	Used
20	A4	1p on 2½p ultra	.45	.60
a.		"Pnney"	26.00	*50.00*
b.		Double surcharge	—	4,000.

King Edward VII — A12

1903-04 Typo.

No.	Type	Description	Unused	Used
21	A12	½p dark green	4.25	.60
22	A12	1p car & black	8.75	.25
23	A12	2p gray & red vio	16.00	5.50
24	A12	2½p ultra & brn vio	12.50	2.75
25	A12	3p red vio & gray	.95	.45
26	A12	4p brown & blk ('04)	22.50	12.00
27	A12	1sh violet & gray	12.50	6.50
		Nos. 21-27 (7)	77.45	28.05

1904-11 Wmk. 3

No.	Type	Description	Unused	Used
28	A10	1f red brown ('05)	.90	.20
29	A10	1f dk brown ('10)	.85	.25
30	A12	½p green	1.65	.15
31	A12	1p car & blk ('05)	6.00	.25
32	A12	1p carmine ('07)	.90	.25
33	A12	2p gray & red vio ('05)	4.50	.75
34	A12	2p gray ('11)	1.90	3.50
35	A12	2½p ultra & brn vio	10.00	.60
36	A12	2½p ultra ('11)	3.75	1.65
37	A12	4p brn & blk ('06)	7.50	5.50
38	A12	4p scar & blk, *yel* ('11)	3.25	3.50
39	A12	1sh violet & gray	50.00	2.00
40	A12	1sh blk, *grn* ('11)	5.50	2.00
41	A12	5sh scar & grn, *yel* ('11)	55.00	60.00

Engr.

No.	Type	Description	Unused	Used
42	A6	4½p black brn ('05)	16.00	5.50
43	A6	4½p orange ('11)	3.25	3.00
44	A7	5p red ('04)	18.00	4.50
45	A7	5p ol green ('10)	3.25	3.00
		Nos. 28-45 (18)	192.20	97.10

A13

A15

King George V — A16

1914-21 Typo.

Ordinary Paper

No.	Type	Description	Unused	Used
49	A13	¼p brown	.25	.15
50	A13	½p green	.35	.15
51	A13	1p scarlet ('15)	.60	.15
a.		1p carmine ('14)	.60	.15
52	A13	2p gray ('15)	4.00	2.50
53	A13	2½p ultramarine	.55	.30

Chalky Paper

No.	Type	Description	Unused	Used
54	A15	3p vio, *yel*	3.25	4.25
58	A13	6p dull vio & red vio	6.00	10.00
59	A15	1sh black, *green*	7.00	15.00
a.		1sh black, *bl grn,* ol back	12.50	12.50
b.		1sh black, *emerald* ('21)	7.50	15.00
c.		As "b," olive back	8.00	15.00
60	A16	2sh ultra & dl vio, *bl*	42.50	65.00
61	A16	5sh scar & grn, *yel*	62.50	70.00

Surface-colored Paper

No.	Type	Description	Unused	Used
62	A15	1sh blk, *grn* ('15)	9.00	12.00
		Nos. 49-54,58-62 (11)	136.00	179.50

See Nos. 66-68, 70-72. For overprints see Nos. 77-82, 84.

Valletta Harbor — A17

1915 Engr.

Ordinary Paper

No.	Type	Description	Unused	Used
63	A17	4p black	10.00	6.00

St. Paul
A18

George V
A19

1919

No.	Type	Description	Unused	Used
64	A8	2sh6p olive green	50.00	45.00
65	A18	10sh black	3,250.	*3,700.*
		Revenue cancel		70.00

For overprint see No. 83.

1921-22 Typo. Wmk. 4

Ordinary Paper

No.	Type	Description	Unused	Used
66	A13	¼p brown	.20	.25
67	A13	½p green	1.25	12.00
68	A13	1p rose red	.20	.15
69	A19	2p gray	2.00	.50
70	A13	2½p ultramarine	2.50	15.00

Chalky Paper

71 A13 6p dull vio & red vio 22.50 45.00
72 A16 2sh ultra & dull vio, *bl* 55.00 150.00

Engr.
Ordinary Paper

73 A18 10sh black 275.00 425.00
Nos. 66-73 (8) 358.65 647.90

For overprints and surcharge see Nos. 86-93, 97.

Stamps of 1914-19 Overprinted in Red or Black

1922 **Wmk. 3**

Ordinary Paper
Overprint 21mm

77 A13 ½p green .15 .15
78 A13 2½p ultra 5.00 15.00

Chalky Paper

79 A15 3p violet, *yel* 1.25 8.00
80 A13 6p dull lil & red vio 1.25 8.00
81 A15 1sh black, *emer* 2.75 8.00

Overprint 28mm

82 A16 2sh ultra & dull vio, *bl* (R) 200.00 275.00

Ordinary Paper

83 A8 2sh6p olive grn 18.00 25.00

Chalky Paper

84 A16 5sh scar & grn, *yel* 50.00 70.00
Nos. 77-84 (8) 278.40 409.15

Wmk. 1
Ordinary Paper

85 A9 10sh blue black (R) 175.00 190.00

Same Overprint on Stamps of 1921

1922 **Ordinary Paper** **Wmk. 4**
Overprint 21mm

86 A13 ¼p brown .70 .20
87 A13 ½p green .65 3.00
88 A13 1p rose red .20 .20
89 A19 2p gray .55 .85
90 A13 2½p ultramarine .45 .45

Chalky Paper

91 A13 6p dull vio & red vio 5.00 15.00

Overprint 28mm

92 A16 2sh ultra & dull vio, *bl* (R) 30.00 65.00

Ordinary Paper

93 A18 10sh black (R) 100.00 125.00
Nos. 86-93 (8) 137.55 209.70

No. 69 Surcharged **One Farthing**

1922, Apr. 15

97 A19 1f on 2p gray .15 .15

"Malta" — A20

Britannia and Malta — A21

1922-26 **Typo.**

Chalky Paper

98 A20 ¼p brown .60 .20
99 A20 ½p green .70 .20
100 A20 1p buff & plum .70 .20
101 A20 1p violet ('24) .90 .20
102 A20 1½p org brn ('23) 1.40 .20
103 A20 2p ol brn & turq .90 .20
104 A20 2½p ultra ('26) .90 .45
105 A20 3p ultramarine 1.75 1.40
a. 3p blue 1.75 1.40
106 A20 3p blk, *yel* ('26) 1.00 5.00
107 A20 4p yel & ultra 1.00 1.40
108 A20 6p ol grn & vio 1.75 1.00
109 A21 1sh ol brn & blue 3.00 2.00
110 A21 2sh ultra & ol brn 5.00 8.00
111 A21 2sh6p blk & red vio 7.00 8.00
112 A21 5sh ultra & org 12.50 *25.00*
113 A21 10sh ol brn & gray 45.00 *80.00*

Engr.
Ordinary Paper

114 A20 £1 car red & blk ('25) 95.00 175.00
a. £1 rose car & blk ('22) 95.00 175.00
Nos. 98-114 (17) 179.10 308.45

No. 114a has watermark sideways.

For overprints and surcharges see Nos. 115-129.

No. 105 Surcharged **Two pence halfpenny**

1925, Dec.

115 A20 2½p on 3p ultramarine .50 .65

Stamps of 1922-26 Overprinted **POSTAGE**

1926

116 A20 ¼p brown .20 .20
117 A20 ½p green .20 .20
118 A20 1p violet .20 .20
119 A20 1½p orange brown .25 .20
120 A20 2p ol brn & turq .35 .35
121 A20 2½p ultramarine .35 .25
122 A20 3p black, *yel* .40 .40
a. Inverted overprint 200.00 425.00
123 A20 4p yel & ultra 3.00 7.00
124 A20 6p ol grn & vio 1.25 1.25
125 A21 1sh ol brn & bl 4.00 6.00
126 A21 2sh ultra & ol brown 35.00 90.00
127 A21 2sh6p blk & red vio 8.50 22.50
128 A21 5sh ultra & org 7.50 25.00
129 A21 10sh ol brn & gray 5.50 12.00
Nos. 116-129 (14) 66.70 165.55

George V — A22

Valletta Harbor — A23

St. Publius — A24

Notabile (Mdina) — A25

Gozo Fishing Boat — A26

Statue of Neptune — A27

Ruins at Mnaidra — A28

St. Paul — A29

1926-27 **Typo.** ***Perf. 14½x14***

131 A22 ¼p brown .45 .15
132 A22 ½p green .45 .15
133 A22 1p red 1.10 .20
134 A22 1½p orange brn 1.10 .20
135 A22 2p gray 2.50 2.75
136 A22 2½p blue 2.50 .50
137 A22 3p dark violet 3.00 2.25
138 A22 4p org red & blk 2.50 3.25
139 A22 4½p yel buff & vio 2.50 2.50
140 A22 6p red & violet 2.75 2.50

Engr. ***Perf. 12½***
Inscribed: "Postage"

141 A23 1sh black 4.25 3.25
142 A24 1sh6p green & blk 4.75 *8.00*
143 A25 2sh dp vio & blk 4.75 12.00
144 A26 2sh6p ver & black 9.50 27.50
145 A27 3sh blue & blk 12.00 25.00
146 A28 5sh green & blk 17.50 *40.00*
147 A29 10sh car & blk 47.50 *90.00*
Nos. 131-147 (17) 119.10 *220.20*

See #167-183. For overprints see #148-166.

Stamps and Type of 1926-27 Overprinted in Black **POSTAGE AND REVENUE**

1928 ***Perf. 14½x14***

148 A22 ¼p brown .50 .15
149 A22 ½p green .50 .15
150 A22 1p red 1.10 .35
151 A22 1p orange brown 1.75 1.40
152 A22 1½p yel brown 1.25 .35
153 A22 1½p red 2.75 .15
154 A22 2p gray 2.50 7.00
155 A22 2½p blue .90 .30
156 A22 3p dark violet .90 .40
157 A22 4p org red & blk .90 1.00
158 A22 4½p yel & violet 1.65 1.00
159 A22 6p red & violet 1.65 1.60

Overprinted in Red **POSTAGE AND REVENUE.**

Perf. 12½

160 A23 1sh black 1.65 1.90
161 A24 1sh6p green & blk 3.75 8.00
162 A25 2sh dp vio & blk 14.00 30.00
163 A26 2sh6p ver & black 9.50 20.00
164 A27 3sh ultra & blk 13.00 27.50
165 A28 5sh yel grn & blk 19.00 27.50
166 A29 10sh car rose & black 40.00 80.00
Nos. 148-166 (19) 117.25 208.75

Issued: Nos. 151, 153, Dec. 5; others, Oct. 1.

Types of 1926-27 Issue

1930, Oct. 20 **Typo.** ***Perf. 14½x14***
Inscribed: "Postage & Revenue"

167 A22 ¼p brown .40 .15
168 A22 ½p green .40 .15
169 A22 1p yel brown .50 .15
170 A22 1½p red .55 .15
171 A22 2p gray .80 .50
172 A22 2½p blue 1.65 .25
173 A22 3p dark violet 1.25 .30
174 A22 4p org red & blk 1.00 2.50
175 A22 4½p yel & violet 2.00 1.40
176 A22 6p red & violet 1.65 .70

Engr. ***Perf. 12½***

177 A23 1sh black 6.25 8.00
178 A24 1sh6p green & blk 4.50 11.00
179 A25 2sh dp vio & blk 6.25 14.00
180 A26 2sh6p ver & black 12.00 35.00
181 A27 3sh ultra & blk 18.00 45.00
182 A28 5sh yel grn & blk 22.50 50.00
183 A29 10sh car rose & blk 52.50 95.00
Nos. 167-183 (17) 132.20 264.25

Silver Jubilee Issue
Common Design Type

1935, May 6 ***Perf. 11x12***

184 CD301 ½p green & blk .20 .20
185 CD301 2½p ultra & brn 1.25 1.00
186 CD301 6p ol grn & lt bl 4.50 5.25
187 CD301 1sh brn vio & ind 7.50 10.50
Nos. 184-187 (4) 13.45 16.95
Set, never hinged 25.00

Coronation Issue
Common Design Type
Perf. 13½x14

1937, May 12 **Wmk. 4**

188 CD302 ½p deep green .15 .15
189 CD302 1½p carmine .15 .15
190 CD302 2½p bright ultra .50 .50
Set value .65 .65
Set, never hinged 1.10

Valletta Harbor — A30

Fort St. Angelo — A31

Verdala Palace — A32

Neolithic Ruins — A33

Victoria and Citadel, Gozo — A34

De l'Isle Adam Entering Mdina A35

St. John's Co-Cathedral A36

Mnaidra Temple — A37

Statue of Antonio Manoel de Vilhena — A38

Woman in Faldetta — A39

St. Publius — A40

Mdina Cathedral — A41

Palace Square — A43

Statue of Neptune — A42

St. Paul — A44

1938-43 **Wmk. 4** ***Perf. 12½***

191 A30 1f brown .15 .15
192 A31 ½p green .40 .15
192A A31 ½p chnt ('43) .15 .15
193 A32 1p chestnut 2.50 .20
193A A32 1p grn ('43) .15 .15
194 A33 1½p rose red .25 .15
194A A33 1½p dk gray ('43) .20 .15
195 A34 2p dark gray .90 .75
195A A34 2p rose red ('43) .40 .25
196 A35 2½p blue .90 .60
196A A35 2½p violet ('43) .35 .35
197 A36 3p violet .75 .55
197A A36 3p blue ('43) .40 .20
198 A37 4½p ocher & ol green .30 .30
199 A38 6p rose red & ol green .60 .30
200 A39 1sh black .60 .55
201 A40 1sh6p sage grn & black 4.50 1.00
202 A41 2sh dk bl & lt grn 1.10 1.10
203 A42 2sh6p rose red & black 3.00 3.00

Malta stamps can be mounted in the Scott British Europe album.

204 A43 5sh bl grn & blk 3.75 3.75
205 A44 10sh dp rose & blk 8.75 8.75
Nos. 191-205 (21) 30.10 22.55
Never hinged 47.50

See #236a. For overprints see #208-222.

Catalogue values for unused stamps in this section, from this point to the end of the section, are for Never Hinged items.

Peace Issue
Common Design Type
Inscribed: "Malta" and Crosses

Perf. 13½x14

1946, June 8 Engr. Wmk. 4
206 CD303 1p bright green .15 .15
207 CD303 3p dark ultra .20 .20
Set value .30 .30

Stamps of 1938-43 Overprinted in Black or Carmine

a 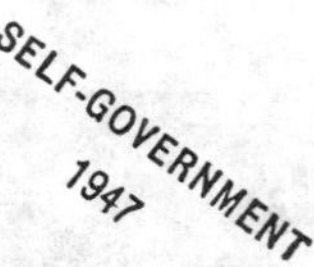

1948, Nov. 25 ***Perf. 12½***
208 A30 1f brown .20 .20
209 A31 ½p chestnut .20 .20
210 A32 1p green .20 .20
211 A33 1½p dk gray (C) .65 .20
212 A34 2p rose red .65 .30
213 A35 2½p violet (C) .70 .30
214 A36 3p blue (C) .25 .20
215 A37 4½p ocher & ol grn 1.75 .90
216 A38 6p rose red & ol green 1.10 .45
217 A39 1sh black 2.00 .65
218 A40 1sh6p sage grn & blk 2.25 1.10
219 A41 2sh dk bl & lt grn (C) 4.25 1.25
220 A42 2sh6p rose red & blk 12.50 2.25
221 A43 5sh bl grn & blk (C) 16.00 4.75
222 A44 10sh dp rose & blk 16.00 16.00
Nos. 208-222 (15) 58.70 28.95

The overprint is smaller on No. 208. It reads from lower left to upper right on Nos. 209 and 221.
See Nos. 235-240.

Silver Wedding Issue
Common Design Types
Inscribed: "Malta" and Crosses

1949, Jan. 4 Photo. ***Perf. 14x14½***
223 CD304 1p dark green .20 .20

Perf. 11½x11

Engr.
224 CD305 £1 dark blue 40.00 30.00

UPU Issue
Common Design Types
Inscribed: "Malta" and Crosses

Perf. 13½, 11x11½

1949, Oct. 10 Engr. Wmk. 4
225 CD306 2½p violet .25 .25
226 CD307 3p indigo .60 .60
227 CD308 6p dp carmine 1.10 1.10
228 CD309 1sh slate 2.25 2.25
Nos. 225-228 (4) 4.20 4.20

Princess Elizabeth — A45

Madonna and Child — A46

1950, Dec. 1 Engr. ***Perf. 12x11½***
229 A45 1p emerald .15 .15
230 A45 3p bright blue .25 .25
231 A45 1sh gray black .55 .55
Nos. 229-231 (3) .95 .95

Visit of Princess Elizabeth.

1951, July 12
232 A46 1p green .15 .15
233 A46 3p purple .20 .15
234 A46 1sh slate black .65 .65
Nos. 232-234 (3) 1.00 .95

700th anniv. of the presentation of the scapular to St. Simon Stock.

Types of 1938-43 Overprinted Type "a" in Red or Black

1953, Jan. 8 Wmk. 4 ***Perf. 12½***
235 A32 1p gray (R) .15 .15
236 A33 1½p green .15 .15
a. Overprint omitted 8,000.
237 A34 2p ocher .25 .20
238 A35 2½p rose red .40 .30
239 A36 3p violet (R) .30 .15
240 A37 4½p ultra & ol grn (R) .65 .50
Nos. 235-240 (6) 1.90 1.45

Coronation Issue
Common Design Type
Inscribed: "Malta" and Crosses

1953, June 3 Engr. ***Perf. 13½x13***
241 CD312 1½p dk green black .25 .15

Type of 1938-43 with Portrait of Queen Elizabeth II Inscribed: "Royal Visit 1954."

1954, May 3 ***Perf. 12½***
242 A36 3p violet .25 .15

Visit of Elizabeth II and the Duke of Edinburgh, 1954.

Central Altarpiece, Collegiate Parish Church, Cospicua — A47

Perf. 14½x13½

1954, Sept. 8 Photo. Wmk. 4
243 A47 1½p bright green .15 .15
244 A47 3p ultramarine .15 .15
245 A47 1sh gray black .50 .50
Nos. 243-245 (3) .80 .80

Cent. of the promulgation of the Dogma of the Immaculate Conception.

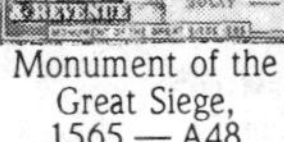

Monument of the Great Siege, 1565 — A48

Auberge de Castille — A49

Designs: ½p, Wignacourt Aqueduct Horse-trough. 1p, Victory Church. 1½p, War Memorial. 2p, Mosta Dome. 3p, King's Scroll. 4½p, Roosevelt's Scroll. 6p, Neolithic Temples at Tarxien. 8p, Vedette. 1sh, Mdina Gate. 1sh6p, Les Gavroches. 2sh, Monument of Christ the King. 2sh6p, Monument of Nicolas Cottoner. 5sh, Raymond Perellos Monument. 10sh, St. Paul. £1, Baptism of Christ.

1956-57 Engr. ***Perf. 11½***
246 A48 ¼p violet .15 .15
247 A48 ½p yel orange .15 .15
248 A48 1p black .15 .15
249 A48 1½p brt green .15 .15
250 A48 2p brown .15 .15
251 A49 2½p orange brown .25 .15
252 A48 3p rose red .15 .15
253 A48 4½p blue .15 .15
254 A49 6p slate blue .15 .15
255 A48 8p olive bister .30 .95
256 A48 1sh purple .50 .38
257 A48 1sh6p Prus green .90 .60
258 A48 2sh olive green 1.65 .95

Perf. 13½x13
259 A48 2sh6p cop brown 3.50 1.25
260 A48 5sh emerald 7.00 4.00
261 A48 10sh dk carmine 32.50 17.50
262 A48 £1 yel brn ('57) 37.50 27.50
Nos. 246-262 (17) 85.30 54.48

See Nos. 296-297.

First George Cross Issue

Symbol of Malta's War Effort — A50

Searchlights over Malta — A51

Design: 1sh, Bombed houses.

Perf. 14x14½, 14½x14

1957, Apr. 15 Photo.

Cross in Silver
263 A50 1½p green .15 .15
264 A51 3p bright red .15 .15
265 A50 1sh dark red brown .40 .35
Set value .60 .55

Award of the George Cross to Malta for its war effort.
See Nos. 269-274.

Symbols of Architecture A52

Designs: 3p, Symbols of Industry, vert. 1sh, Symbols of electronics and chemistry and Technical School, Paola.

Perf. 14½x14, 14x14½

1958, Feb. 15 Wmk. 314
266 A52 1½p dp green & blk .15 .15
267 A52 3p rose red, blk & gray .15 .15
268 A52 1sh gray, blk & lilac .45 .40
Set value .60 .55

Technical education on Malta.

Second George Cross Issue
Types of 1957

1½p, Bombed-out family & searchlights. 3p, Convoy entering harbor. 1sh, Searchlight battery.

Perf. 14½x14, 14x14½

1958, Apr. 15

Cross in Silver
269 A51 1½p black & brt green .15 .15
270 A50 3p black & vermilion .15 .15
271 A51 1sh black & brt lilac .45 .45
Nos. 269-271 (3) .75
Set value .60

Third George Cross Issue
Types of 1957

Designs: 1½p, Air Raid Precautions Organization helping wounded. 3p, Allegory of Malta. 1sh, Mother and child during air raid.

Perf. 14x14½, 14½x14

1959, Apr. 15
272 A50 1½p gold, green & black .15 .15
273 A51 3p gold, lilac & black .15 .15
274 A50 1sh gold, gray & black .65 .65
Nos. 272-274 (3) .95
Set value .80

St. Paul's Shipwreck, Painting in St. Paul's Church, Valletta — A53

Statue of St. Paul, St. Paul's Grotto, Rabat A54

Designs: 3p, Consecration of St. Publius. 6p, St. Paul leaving Malta; painting, St. Paul's Church, Valletta. 1sh, Angel holding tablet with quotations from Acts of the Apostles. 2sh6p, St. Paul and St. Paul's Bay islets.

Wmk. 314

1960, Feb. 9 Photo. ***Perf. 13***
275 A53 1½p bister, brt bl & gold .15 .15
a. Gold dates & crosses omitted 75.00 57.50
276 A53 3p lt blue, red lil & gold .15 .15
277 A53 6p car, gray & gold .30 .20

Perf. 14x14½
278 A54 8p black & gold .50 .40
279 A54 1sh brt cl & gold .65 .50
280 A54 2sh6p brt grnsh bl & gold 3.00 2.25
a. Gold omitted 375.00
Nos. 275-280 (6) 4.75 3.65

19th centenary of St. Paul's shipwreck on Malta.

Stamp of 1860 — A55

Perf. 13x13½

1960, Dec. 1 Engr. Wmk. 314
281 A55 1½p multi .15 .15
282 A55 3p multi .15 .15
283 A55 6p multi .60 .60
Nos. 281-283 (3) .90 .90

Centenary of Malta's first postage stamp.

Fourth George Cross Issue

George Cross A56

Background designs: 3p, Sun and water. 1sh, Maltese crosses.

1961, Apr. 15 Photo. ***Perf. 14½x14***
284 A56 1½p gray, bister & buff .15 .15
285 A56 3p ol gray, lt & dk grnsh blue .15 .15
286 A56 1sh ol green, vio & lil .85 .85
Nos. 284-286 (3) 1.15 1.15

19th anniv. of the award of the George Cross to Malta.

Madonna Damascena — A57

David Bruce and Themistocles Zammit — A58

Designs: 3p, Great Siege Monument by Antonio Sciortino. 6p, Grand Master La Valette (1557-1568). 1sh, Assault on Fort Elmo (old map).

Perf. 12½x12

1962, Sept. 7 **Wmk. 314**

287 A57 2p ultramarine .15 .15
288 A57 3p dark red .15 .15
289 A57 6p olive green .20 .20
290 A57 1sh rose lake .50 .50
Set value .85 .85

Great Siege of 1565 in which the knights of the Order of St. John and the Maltese Christians defeated the Turks.

Freedom from Hunger Issue
Common Design Type

1963, June 4 *Perf. 14x14½*

291 CD314 1sh6p sepia 3.50 3.00

Red Cross Centenary Issue
Common Design Type

1963, Sept. 2 **Litho.** *Perf. 13*

292 CD315 2p black & red .25 .15
293 CD315 1sh6p ultra & red 3.25 3.00

Type of 1956

Designs as before.

1963-64 **Engr.** *Perf. 11½*

296 A48 1p black .75 .45
297 A48 2p brown ('64) 1.25 .75

Perf. 14x13½

1964, Apr. 14 **Photo.** **Wmk. 314**

Design: 1sh6p, Goat and laboratory equipment.

298 A58 2p dl grn, blk & brn .15 .15
a. Black omitted
299 A58 1sh6p rose lake & blk .90 .70

Anti-Brucellosis (Malta fever) Congress of the UN FAO, Valletta, June 8-13.

Nicola Cottoner Attending Sick Man and Congress Emblem — A59

Designs: 6p, Statue of St. Luke and St. Luke's Hospital. 1sh6p, Sacra Infermeria, Valletta.

Perf. 13½x14

1964, Sept. 5 **Wmk. 354**

300 A59 2p multicolored .15 .15
301 A59 6p multicolored .40 .35
302 A59 1sh6p multicolored 1.40 1.25
Nos. 300-302 (3) 1.95 1.75

1st European Cong. of Catholic Physicians, Malta, Sept. 6-10.

Independent State

Dove, Maltese Cross and British Crown — A60

Nativity — A61

Dove, Maltese Cross and: 3p, 1sh6p, Pope's tiara. 6p, 2sh6p, UN Emblem.

Perf. 14½x13½

1964, Sept. 21 **Photo.**

Gold and

303 A60 2p gray ol & red .15 .15
304 A60 3p dk red brn & red .15 .15
305 A60 6p sl blue & red .55 .35
306 A60 1sh ultra & red 1.25 .55
307 A60 1sh6p bl blk & red 3.50 2.50
308 A60 2sh6p vio bl & red 4.75 4.00
Nos. 303-308 (6) 10.35 7.70

Malta's independence.

Perf. 13x13½

1964, Nov. 3 **Wmk. 354**

309 A61 2p magenta & gold .15 .15
310 A61 4p ultra & gold .25 .25
311 A61 8p dp green & gold 1.25 1.10
Nos. 309-311 (3) 1.65 1.50

Cippus, Phoenician and Greek Inscriptions — A62

British Arms, Armory, Valletta A63

Designs (History of Malta): ½p, Neolithic (sculpture of sleeping woman). 1½p, Roman (sculpture). 2p, Proto-Christian (lamp, Roman temple, Chrismon). 2½p, Saracen (tomb, 12th cent.). 3p, Siculo Norman (arch, Palazzo Gatto-Murina, Notabile). 4p, Knights of Malta (lamp base, cross, and armor of knights). 4½p, Maltese navy (16th cent. galleons). 5p, Fortifications. 6p, French occupation (Cathedral of Notabile, cap, fasces). 10p, Naval Arsenal.

1sh, Maltese Corps of the British Army (insignia). 1sh3p, International Eucharistic Congress, 1913 (angels adoring Eucharist and map of Malta). 1sh6p, Self Government, 1921 (Knights of Malta Hall, present assembly seat). 2sh, Civic Council, Gozo (Statue of Livia, Gozo City Hall). 2sh6p, State of Malta (seated woman and George Cross). 3sh, Independence (doves, UN emblem, British crown, and Pope's tiara).

5sh, "HAFMED," (headquarters and insigne of Allied Forces, Mediterranean). 10sh, Map of Mediterranean. £1, Catholicism (Sts. Paul, Publius and Agatha).

Perf. 14x14½, 14½ (A63)

1965-70 **Photo.** **Wmk. 354**

312 A62 ½p violet & yel .15 .15
313 A62 1p multi .15 .15
a. Booklet pane of 6 ('70) .35
314 A62 1½p multi .15 .15
315 A62 2p multi .15 .15
a. Gold omitted 25.00
b. Booklet pane of 6 ('70) .40
316 A62 2½p multi .15 .15
a. Gold ("SARACENIC") omitted 55.00
317 A62 3p multi .15 .15
a. Imperf., pair 250.00
b. Gold (windows) omitted 37.50
318 A62 4p multi .15 .15
a. Black (arms shading) omitted 47.50
b. Silver omitted 45.00
319 A62 4½p multi .15 .15
319A A62 5p multi ('70) .25 .15
b. Booklet pane of 6 ('71) 1.75
320 A62 6p multi .15 .15
a. Black omitted 60.00
b. Silver ("MALTA") omitted 60.00
321 A63 8p multi .15 .15
321A A63 10p multi ('70) .30 .20
322 A63 1sh multi .30 .15
323 A63 1sh3p multi .65 .45
324 A63 1sh6p multi .50 .25
a. Queen's head omitted 225.00
325 A63 2sh multi .65 .45
326 A63 2sh6p multi .75 .50
327 A63 3sh multi .95 .60
328 A63 5sh multi 1.65 1.00
329 A63 10sh multi 3.25 2.50
330 A63 £1 multi 6.00 4.50
a. Pink (shading on figures) omitted 30.00
Nos. 312-330 (21) 16.75 12.25

Issued: 5p, 10p, 8/1/70; others 1/7/65.
For surcharges see Nos. 447-449, 521.

Dante, by Raphael — A64

1965, July 7 **Unwmk.** *Perf. 14*

331 A64 2p dark blue .15 .15
332 A64 6p olive green .20 .20
333 A64 2sh chocolate .80 .70
Nos. 331-333 (3) 1.15 1.05

700th birth anniv. of Dante Alighieri.

Turkish Encampment and Fort St. Michael A65

Blockading Turkish Armada A66

Designs: 3p, Knights and Turks in battle. 8p, Arrival of relief force. 1sh, Trophy, arms of Grandmaster Jean de La Valette. 1sh6p, Allegory of Victory, mural by Calabrese from St. John's Co-Cathedral. 2sh6p, Great Siege victory medal; Jean de La Valette on obverse, David slaying Goliath on reverse.

Perf. 14½x14, 13

1965, Sept. 1 **Photo.** **Wmk. 354**

334 A65 2p ol grn, red & blk .15 .15
335 A65 3p lt gray, red, blk & ol grn .15 .15
336 A66 6p ol grn, red org, cl, blk & gold .30 .25
a. Black omitted 140.00
b. Gold omitted 165.00
337 A65 8p dk bl, red & gold .45 .35
338 A66 1sh bluish blk, red & gold 1.10 .85
339 A65 1sh6p blk, yel brn & red 1.40 1.10
340 A65 2sh6p ol grn, blk, dk brn & red 3.50 3.00
Nos. 334-340 (7) 7.05 5.85

Great Siege (Turks against Malta), 4th cent.

The Three Wise Men — A67

Perf. 11x11½

1965, Oct. 7 **Photo.** **Wmk. 354**

341 A67 1p dk purple & red .15 .15
342 A67 4p dk pur & blue .90 .80
343 A67 1sh3p dk pur & dp mag 1.00 .90
Nos. 341-343 (3) 2.05 1.85

Winston Churchill, Map and Cross of Malta — A68

Winston Churchill: 3p, 1sh6p, Warships in Valletta Harbor and George Cross.

1966, Jan. 24 *Perf. 14½x14*

344 A68 2p black, gold & red .15 .15
345 A68 3p dk grn, gold & black .15 .15
346 A68 1sh dp cl, gold & red .30 .30
a. Gold omitted 225.00
347 A68 1sh6p dk bl, gold & vio .50 .45
Nos. 344-347 (4) 1.10 1.05

Grand Master Jean Parisot de la Valette — A69

Designs: 3p, Pope St. Pius V. 6p, Map of Valletta. 1sh, Francesco Laparelli, Italian architect. 2sh6p, Girolamo Cassar, Maltese architect.

1966, Mar. 28 **Unwmk.** *Perf. 12*

348 A69 2p gold & multi .15 .15
349 A69 3p gold & multi .15 .15
350 A69 6p gold & multi .15 .15
351 A69 1sh gold & multi .20 .15
352 A69 2sh6p gold & multi .55 .55
Set value 1.00 .90

400th anniversary of Valletta.

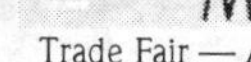

Kennedy — A70

Trade Fair — A71

Perf. 15x14

1966, May 28 **Photo.** **Wmk. 354**

353 A70 3p ol gray, blk & gold .15 .15
354 A70 1sh6p dull bl, blk & gold .35 .35

President John F. Kennedy (1917-1963).

1966, June 16 *Perf. 13x13½*

355 A71 2p multicolored .15 .15
356 A71 8p gray & multi .25 .25
357 A71 2sh6p tan & multi .70 .70
Nos. 355-357 (3) 1.10 1.10

The 10th Malta Trade Fair.

Nativity — A72

George Cross — A73

1966, Oct. 7 **Photo.** **Wmk. 354**

358 A72 1p multicolored .15 .15
359 A72 4p multicolored .15 .15
360 A72 1sh3p multicolored .20 .20
Set value .35 .30

1967, Mar. 1 *Perf. 14½x14*

361 A73 2p multicolored .15 .15
362 A73 4p multicolored .15 .15
363 A73 3sh slate & multi .30 .30
Set value .40 .35

25th anniv. of the award of the George Cross to Malta and Gozo for the war effort.

Crucifixion of St. Peter — A74

Keys, Tiara, Bible, Cross and Sword — A75

Design: 3sh, Beheading of St. Paul.

Perf. 14½, 13½x14

1967, June 28 **Photo.** **Wmk. 354**

364 A74 2p black & brn orange .15 .15
365 A75 8p blk, gold & lt ol grn .15 .15
366 A74 3sh black & brt blue .40 .35
Set value .55 .50

1900th anniv. of the martyrdom of the Apostles Peter and Paul.

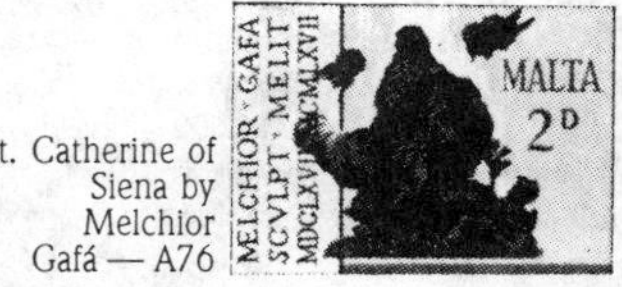

St. Catherine of Siena by Melchior Gafá — A76

Sculptures by Gafá: 4p, St. Thomas from Villanova. 1sh6p, Christ's baptism. 2sh6p, St. John the Baptist.

1967, Aug. 1 *Perf. 13½*

367 A76 2p black, gold, buff & ultra .15 .15
368 A76 4p gold, buff, blk & grn .15 .15
369 A76 1sh6p gold, buff, blk & org brown .15 .15
370 A76 2sh6p black, gold, buff & dp car .30 .30
Set value .55 .50

Melchior Gafá (1635-67), Maltese sculptor.

Ruins of Megalithic Temples, Tarxien — A77

Designs: 6p, Facade of Palazzo Falzon, Notabile. 1sh, Facade of Old Parish Church, Birkirkara. 3sh, Entrance to Auberge de Castille.

1967, Sept. 12 Photo. *Perf. 14½*

371 A77 2p gold, Prus bl & blk .15 .15
372 A77 6p org brn, blk, gray & gold .15 .15
373 A77 1sh gold, ol, ind & blk .15 .15
374 A77 3sh dk car, rose, blk, gray & gold .30 .30
Set value .55 .50

Issued to publicize the 15th Congress of the History of Architecture, Malta, Sept. 12-16.

Nativity
A78 A79

Design: 1sh4p, Angels facing left.

1967, Oct. 20 *Perf. 13½x14*

375 A78 1p slate, gold & red .15 .15
a. Red omitted (stars) 50.00
376 A79 8p slate, gold & red .15 .15
377 A78 1sh4p slate, gold & red .30 .30
a. Triptych, #375-377 .55 .50
Set value .45 .40

Sheets of Nos. 375-377 were arranged in 2 ways: sheets containing 60 stamps of the same denomination arranged tête bêche, and sheets containing 20 triptychs.

Arms of Malta — A80

Designs: 4p, Queen Elizabeth II in the robes of the Order of St. Michael and St. George, vert. 3sh, Queen and map of Malta.

Perf. 14½x14, 14x14½

1967, Nov. 13 Photo. Wmk. 354

378 A80 2p slate & multi .15 .15
379 A80 4p dp claret, blk & gold .15 .15
380 A80 3sh black & gold .30 .30
Set value .45 .45

Visit of Queen Elizabeth II, Nov. 14-17.

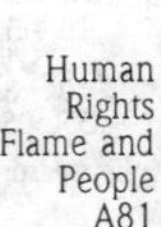

Human Rights Flame and People A81

1968, May 2 Photo. *Perf. 14½*

Size: 40x19mm

381 A81 2p sepia, dp car, blk & gold .15 .15

Perf. 12x12½

Size: 24x24mm

382 A81 6p gray, dk blue, blk & gold .15 .15

Perf. 14½

Size: 40x19mm

383 A81 2sh gray, grnsh blue, blk & gold .25 .20
Set value .40 .35

International Human Rights Year.

Fair Emblem — A82

Perf. 14x14½

1968, June 1 Photo. Wmk. 354

384 A82 4p black & multi .15 .15
385 A82 8p Prus blue & multi .15 .15
386 A82 3sh dp claret & multi .40 .40
Set value .55 .50

12th Malta Intl. Trade Fair, July 1-15.

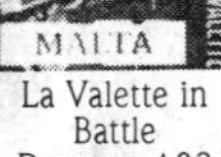

La Valette in Battle Dress — A83

La Valette's Tomb, Church of St. John, Valletta — A84

Designs: 1p, Arms of Order of St. John of Jerusalem and La Valette's arms, horiz. 2sh6p, Putti bearing shield with date of La Valette's death, and map of Malta.

Perf. 13x14, 14x13

1968, Aug. 1 Photo. Wmk. 354

387 A83 1p black & multi .15 .15
388 A83 8p dull blue & multi .15 .15
389 A84 1sh6p blue grn & multi .15 .15
390 A83 2sh6p dp claret & multi .30 .30
Set value .60 .60

400th anniv. of the death of Grand Master Jean de La Valette (1494-1568).

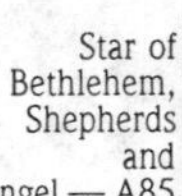

Star of Bethlehem, Shepherds and Angel — A85

8p, Nativity. 1sh4p, The Three Wise Men.

Perf. 14½x14

1968, Oct. 3 Wmk. 354

391 A85 1p multicolored .15 .15
392 A85 8p gray & multi .15 .15
393 A85 1sh4p tan & multi .25 .25
Set value .40 .40

Christmas. Printed in sheets of 60 with alternate rows inverted.

"Agriculture" A86

Mahatma Gandhi A87

Designs: 1sh, Greek medal and FAO emblem. 2sh6p, Woman symbolizing soil care.

1968, Oct. 21 Photo. *Perf. 12½x12*

394 A86 4p ultra & multi .15 .15
395 A86 1sh gray & multi .15 .15
396 A86 2sh6p multicolored .45 .45
Nos. 394-396 (3) .75 .75

6th Regional Congress for Europe of the FAO, Malta, Oct. 28-31.

Perf. 12x12½

1969, Mar. 24 Photo. Wmk. 354

397 A87 1sh6p gold, blk & sepia .35 .32

Birth cent. of Mohandas K. Gandhi (1869-1948), leader in India's struggle for independence.

ILO Emblem — A88

1969, May 26 *Perf. 13½x14½*

398 A88 2p indigo, blue grn & gold .15 .15
399 A88 6p brn blk, red brn & gold .20 .20
Set value .25 .25

50th anniv. of the ILO.

Sea Bed, UN Emblem and Dove A89

Designs: 2p, Robert Samut, bar of music and coat of arms. 10p, Map of Malta and homing birds. 2sh, Grand Master Pinto and arms of Malta University.

1969, July 26 Photo. *Perf. 13½*

400 A89 2p vio blk, blk, gold & red .15 .15
401 A89 5p gray, Prus blue, gold & blk .15 .15
402 A89 10p olive, blk & gold .15 .15
403 A89 2sh dk olive, blk, red & gold .30 .30
Set value .60 .60

Cent. of the birth of Robert Samut, composer of Natl. Anthem (2p); UN resolution on peaceful uses of the sea bed (5p); convention of Maltese emigrants (10p), Aug. 3-16; bicent. of the founding of Malta University (2sh).

June 17, 1919, Uprising Monument A90

"Tourism" A91

Designs: 5p, Maltese flag and 5 doves, horiz. 1sh6p, Dove and emblems of Malta, UN and Council of Euorpe. 2sh6p, Dove and symbols of trade and industry.

Perf. 13x12½

1969, Sept. 20 Photo. Wmk. 354

404 A90 2p black, gray, buff & gold .15 .15
405 A91 5p gray, blk, red & gold .15 .15
406 A91 10p gold, Prus blue, gray & blk .15 .15
407 A91 1sh6p gold, olive & multi .20 .20
408 A91 2sh6p gold, brn ol, gray & blk .40 .40
Set value .80 .80

Fifth anniversary of independence.

St. John the Baptist in Robe of Knight of Malta A92

Mortar and Jars from Infirmary — A93

Designs: 1p, The Beheading of St. John By Caravaggio. 5p, Interior of St. John's Co-Cathedral. 6p, Allegory depicting functions of the Order. 8p, St. Jerome, by Caravaggio. 1sh6p, St. Gerard Receiving Godfrey de Bouillon, 1093, by Antoine de Favray. 2sh, Sacred vestments.

Perf. 14x13 (1p, 8p); 13½x14 (2p, 6p, 1sh6p); 13½ (5p) 12x12½ (10p, 2sh)

1970, Mar. 21 Photo. Wmk. 354

409 A92 1p black & multi .15 .15
410 A92 2p black & multi .15 .15
411 A92 5p black & multi .15 .15
412 A92 6p black & multi .15 .15
413 A92 8p black & multi .15 .15
414 A93 10p black & multi .20 .20
415 A92 1sh6p black & multi .35 .35
416 A93 2sh black & multi .45 .45
Set value 1.50 1.50

13th Council of Europe Art Exhibition in honor of the Order of St. John in Malta, Apr. 2-July 1.

Sizes: 1p, 8p, 54x38mm; 2p, 6p, 44x30mm; 5p, 37x37mm; 10p, 2sh, 60x19mm; 1sh6p, 44x33mm.

EXPO '70 Emblem — A94

1970, May 29 *Perf. 15*

417 A94 2p gold & multi .15 .15
418 A94 5p gold & multi .15 .15
419 A94 3sh gold & multi .45 .45
Set value .55 .55

Issued to publicize EXPO '70 International Exhibition, Osaka, Japan, Mar. 15-Sept. 13.

UN Emblem, Dove, Scales and Symbolic Figure — A95

Perf. 14x14½

1970, Sept. 30 Litho. Wmk. 354

420 A95 2p brown & multi .15 .15
421 A95 5p purple & multi .15 .15
422 A95 2sh6p vio blue & multi .50 .50
Set value .65 .65

25th anniversary of the United Nations.

Books and Quill — A96

Dun Karm, Books and Pens — A97

Perf. 13x14

1971, Mar. 20 Litho. Wmk. 354

423 A96 1sh6p multicolored .20 .20
424 A97 2sh black & multi .30 .30

No. 423 issued in memory of Canon Gian Pietro Francesco Agius Sultana (De Soldanis; 1712-1770), historian and writer; No. 424 for the centenary of the birth of Mgr. Karm Psaila (Dun Karm, 1871-1961), Maltese poet.

Europa Issue, 1971

Common Design Type

1971, May 3 *Perf. 13½x14½*

Size: 32x22mm

425 CD14 2p olive, org & black .15 .15
426 CD14 5p ver, org & black .15 .15
427 CD14 1sh6p gray, org & black .50 .50
Set value .70 .70

St. Joseph, by Giuseppe Cali — A98

Design: 5p, 1sh6p, Statue of Our Lady of Victory. 10p, Like 2p.

Perf. 13x13½

1971, July 24 Litho. Wmk. 354

428	A98	2p	dk blue & multi	.15	.15
429	A98	5p	gray & multi	.15	.15
430	A98	10p	multicolored	.30	.30
431	A98	1sh6p	multicolored	.45	.45
			Nos. 428-431 (4)	1.05	1.05

Centenary (in 1970) of the proclamation of St. Joseph as patron of the Universal Church (2p, 10p), and 50th anniversary of the coronation of the statue of Our Lady of Victory in Senglea, Malta.

Blue Rock Thrush A99

Design: 2p, 1sh6p, Thistle, vert.

Perf. 14x14½, 14½x14

1971, Sept. 18

432	A99	2p	multicolored	.15	.15
433	A99	5p	bister & multi	.15	.15
434	A99	10p	orange & multi	.30	.30
435	A99	1sh6p	bister & multi	.55	.55
			Nos. 432-435 (4)	1.15	1.15

Heart and WHO Emblem A100

1972, Mar. 20 *Perf. 14*

436	A100	2p	yel green & multi	.15	.15
437	A100	10p	lilac & multi	.15	.15
438	A100	2sh6p	lt blue & multi	.55	.55
			Nos. 436-438 (3)	.85	.85

World Health Day, Apr. 7.

Coin Showing Mnara (Lampstand) A101

Sparkles, Symbolic of Communications CD15

Decimal Currency Coins: 2m, Maltese Cross. 3m, Bee and honeycomb. 1c, George Cross. 2c, Penthesilea. 5c, Altar, Megalithic Period. 10c, Grandmaster's Barge, 18th century. 50c, Great Siege Monument, by Antonio Sciortino.

Perf. 14 (16x21mm), 2m, 3m, 2c; Perf. 14½x14 (21x26mm), 5m, 1c, 5c

1972, May 16

439	A101	2m	rose red & multi	.15	.15
440	A101	3m	pink & multi	.15	.15
441	A101	5m	lilac & multi	.15	.15
442	A101	1c	multicolored	.15	.15
443	A101	2c	orange & multi	.15	.15
444	A101	5c	multicolored	.20	.20

Perf. 13½

Size: 27x35mm

445	A101	10c	yellow & multi	.40	.40
446	A101	50c	multicolored	2.00	2.00
			Set value (8)	2.85	2.85

Coins to mark introduction of decimal currency.

Nos. 319A, 321 and 323 Surcharged with New Value and 2 Bars

Perf. 14x14½, 14½

1972, Sept. 30 Photo. Wmk. 354

447	A62	1c3m	on 5p multi	.15	.15
448	A63	3c	on 8p multi	.15	.15
449	A63	5c	on 1sh3p multi	.30	.30
			Set value	.50	.50

Europa Issue 1972

1972, Nov. 11 Litho. *Perf. 13x13½*

450	CD15	1c3m	yellow & multi	.15	.15
451	CD15	3c	multicolored	.20	.20
452	CD15	5c	pink & multi	.30	.30
453	CD15	7c5m	multicolored	.45	.45
			Nos. 450-453 (4)	1.10	1.10

Issued in sheets of 10 plus 2 labels (4x3). Labels are in top row.

Archaeology A103

Woman with Grain, FAO Emblem A104

1973, Mar. 31 Litho. *Perf. 13½*

Size: 22x24mm

454	A103	2m	shown	.15	.15
455	A103	4m	History (knights)	.15	.15
456	A103	5m	Folklore	.15	.15
457	A103	8m	Industry	.15	.15
458	A103	1c	Fishing	.15	.15
459	A103	1c3m	Pottery	.15	.15
460	A103	2c	Agriculture	.15	.15
461	A103	3c	Sport	.15	.15
462	A103	4c	Marina	.15	.15
463	A103	5c	Fiesta	.15	.15
464	A103	7c5m	Regatta	.20	.20
465	A103	10c	Charity (St. Martin)	.30	.30
466	A103	50c	Education	1.25	1.25
467	A103	£1	Religion	2.75	2.75

Perf. 13½x14

Size: 32x27mm

468	A103	£2	Arms of Malta	11.00	11.00
			Nos. 454-468 (15)	17.00	17.00

Europa Issue 1973

Common Design Type

1973, June 2 Unwmk. *Perf. 14*

Size: 36½x19½mm

469	CD16	3c	multicolored	.15	.15
470	CD16	5c	multicolored	.30	.30
471	CD16	7c5m	dk bl & multi	.55	.55
			Nos. 469-471 (3)	1.00	1.00

1973, Oct. 6 Wmk. 354 *Perf. 13½*

Designs: 7c5m, Mother and child, WHO emblem. 10c, Two heads, Human Rights flame.

472	A104	1c3m	yel grn, blk & gold	.15	.15
473	A104	7c5m	ultra, blk & gold	.35	.35
474	A104	10c	claret, blk & gold	.50	.50
			Nos. 472-474 (3)	1.00	1.00

World Food Program, 10th anniv.; WHO, 25th anniv.; Universal Declaration of Human Rights, 25th anniv.

Girolamo Cassar, Architect — A105

Portraits: 3c, Giuseppe Barth, opthalmologist. 5c, Nicolo' Isouard, composer. 7c5m, John Borg, botanist. 10c, Antonio Sciortino, sculptor.

1974, Jan. 12 Litho. *Perf. 14*

475	A105	1c3m	slate green & gold	.15	.15
476	A105	3c	indigo & gold	.15	.15
477	A105	5c	olive gray & gold	.20	.20
478	A105	7c5m	slate blue & gold	.25	.25
479	A105	10c	brn vio & gold	.45	.45
			Nos. 475-479 (5)	1.20	1.20

Prominent Maltese.

Statue of Goddess, 3rd Millenium B.C. A106

Europa (CEPT Emblem and): 3c, Carved door, Cathedral, Mdina, 11th cent, vert. 5c, Silver monstrance, 1689. 7c5m, "Vettina" (statue of nude woman), by Antonio Sciortino (1879-1947), vert.

Perf. 13½x14, 14x13½

1974, July 13

480	A106	1c3m	gray blue, blk & gold	.15	.15
481	A106	3c	ol brn, blk & gold	.20	.20
482	A106	5c	lilac, blk & gold	.35	.35
483	A106	7c5m	dull grn, blk & gold	.70	.70
			Nos. 480-483 (4)	1.40	1.40

Heinrich von Stephan, Coach and Train, UPU Emblem A107

UPU Emblem, von Stephan and: 5c, Paddle steamer and ocean liner. 7c5m, Balloon and jet. 50c, UPU Congress Building, Lausanne, and UPU Headquarters, Bern.

Perf. 13½

1974, Sept. Litho. Wmk. 354

484	A107	1c3m	multicolored	.15	.15
485	A107	5c	multicolored	.20	.20
486	A107	7c5m	multicolored	.30	.30
487	A107	50c	multicolored	1.90	1.90
a.			Souvenir sheet of 4, #484-487	3.25	3.25
			Nos. 484-487 (4)	2.55	2.55

Centenary of Universal Postal Union.

President, Prime Minister, Minister of Justice at Microphone — A108

Designs: 1c3m, President, Prime Minister, Speaker at Swearing-in ceremony. 5c, Flag of Malta.

1975, Mar. 31 *Perf. 14*

488	A108	1c3m	red & multi	.15	.15
489	A108	5c	gray, red & black	.30	.30
490	A108	25c	red & multi	1.25	1.25
			Nos. 488-490 (3)	1.70	1.70

Proclamation of the Republic, Dec. 13, 1974.

IWY Emblem, Mother and Child — A109

Designs: 3c, 20c, Secretary (woman in public life), IWY emblem. 5c, Like 1c3m.

Wmk. 354

1975, May 30 Litho. *Perf. 13*

491	A109	1c3m	violet & gold	.15	.15
492	A109	3c	blue gray & gold	.40	.20
493	A109	5c	olive & gold	.80	.50
494	A109	20c	red brown & gold	3.75	2.50
			Nos. 491-494 (4)	5.10	3.35

International Women's Year.

Allegory of Malta, by Francesco de Mura — A110

Europa: 15c, Judith and Holofernes, by Valentin de Boulogne.

1975, July 15 Litho. *Perf. 14*

495	A110	5c	multicolored	.25	.25
496	A110	15c	multicolored	.95	.95

Floor Plan of Ggantija Complex, 3000 B.C. — A111

Designs: 3c, View of Mdina. 5c, Typical Maltese town. 25c, Fort St. Angelo.

1975, Sept. 16 *Perf. 14*

497	A111	1c3m	black & org	.15	.15
498	A111	3c	org, pur & black	.25	.20
499	A111	5c	gray, black & org	.45	.35
500	A111	25c	org, tan & black	2.75	1.75
			Nos. 497-500 (4)	3.60	2.45

European Architectural Heritage Year.

"Right to Work" — A112

Designs: 5c, Protection of the Environment (Landscape). 25c, Maltese flags.

1975, Dec. 12 Litho. Wmk. 354

501	A112	1c3m	multicolored	.15	.15
502	A112	5c	multicolored	.25	.15
503	A112	25c	multicolored	1.25	.75
			Nos. 501-503 (3)	1.65	1.05

First anniversary of Malta Republic.

Republic Coat of Arms — A113

Perf. 13½x14

1976, Jan. 28 Litho. Wmk. 354

504	A113	£2	black & multi	9.50	9.50

Feast of Sts. Peter and Paul — A114

Designs: 1c3m, "Festa" (flags and fireworks; vert.). 7c5m, Carnival. 10c, Good Friday (Christ carrying cross), vert.

1976, Feb. 26 Litho. *Perf. 14*

505	A114	1c3m	multicolored	.15	.15
506	A114	5c	multicolored	.25	.20
507	A114	7c5m	multicolored	.35	.25
508	A114	10c	multicolored	1.25	.85
			Nos. 505-508 (4)	2.00	1.45

Maltese folk festivals.

Water Polo, Olympic Rings — A115

Olympic Rings and: 5c, Yachting. 30c, Running.

1976, Apr. 28 Litho. *Perf. 13½x14*

509	A115	1c7m	sl green & red	.15	.15
510	A115	5c	dp blue & red	.25	.15
511	A115	30c	sepia & red	1.65	1.25
			Nos. 509-511 (3)	2.05	1.55

21st Olympic Games, Montreal, Canada, July 17-Aug. 1.

Europa A116

1976, July 8 Litho. Wmk. 354

512	A116	7c	Lace-making	.30	.30
513	A116	15c	Stone carving	.70	.65

Grandmaster Nicola Cotoner, Founder — A117

5c, Dissected arm & hand. 7c, Dr. Fra Giuseppe Zammit, 1st professor. 11c, School & balustrade.

1976, Sept. 14 Litho. *Perf. 13½*

514 A117 2c multicolored .15 .15
515 A117 5c multicolored .15 .15
516 A117 7c multicolored .25 .20
517 A117 11c multicolored .80 .65
Nos. 514-517 (4) 1.35 1.15

School of Anatomy and Surgery, Valletta, 300th anniversary.

Armor of Grand Master Jean de La Valette — A118

Suits of Armor: 7c, Grand Master Aloph de Wignacourt. 11c, Grand Commander Jean Jacques de Verdelin.

1977, Jan. 20 Litho. Wmk. 354

518 A118 2c green & multi .15 .15
519 A118 7c brown & multi .30 .25
520 A118 11c ultra & multi .55 .40
Nos. 518-520 (3) 1.00 .80

No. 318 Surcharged with New Value and Bar

1977, Mar. 24 Photo. *Perf. 14x14½*

521 A62 1c7m on 4p multicolored .35 .15

Annunciation, Tapestry after Rubens — A119

Nativity A120

Tapestries after Designs by Rubens: 7c, The Four Evangelists. 20c, Adoration of the Kings. Flemish tapestries commissioned for St. John's Co-Cathedral, Valletta.

Wmk. 354

1977, Mar. 30 Litho. *Perf. 14*

522 A119 2c multicolored .15 .15
523 A119 7c multicolored .30 .25
524 A120 11c multicolored .60 .55
525 A120 20c multicolored 1.10 1.10

1978, Jan. 26

Flemish Tapestries: 2c, Jesus' Entry into Jerusalem, by unknown painter. 7c, Last Supper, by Nicholas Poussin. 11c, Crucifixion, by Rubens. 25c, Resurrection, by Rubens.

526 A120 2c multicolored .15 .15
527 A120 7c multicolored .25 .25
528 A120 11c multicolored .45 .45
529 A120 25c multicolored 1.10 1.10

1979, Jan. 24

Tapestries after Designs by Rubens (Triumph of): 2c, Catholic Church. 7c, Charity. 11c, Faith. 25c, Truth.

530 A119 2c multicolored .15 .15
531 A119 7c multicolored .25 .25
532 A119 11c multicolored .40 .40
533 A119 25c multicolored .95 .95
Nos. 522-533 (12) 5.85 5.75

Consecration of St. John's Co-Cathedral, Valetta, 400th anniv. (#522-533). Peter Paul Rubens (1577-1640; #522-525).

See Nos. 567-569.

Malta Map, Telecommunication — A121

Designs: 1c, 6c, Map of Italy, Sicily, Malta and North Africa, telecommunication tower and waves, vert. 17c, like 8c.

Perf. 14x13½, 13½x14

1977, May 17 Litho. Wmk. 354

535 A121 1c green, red & blk .15 .15
536 A121 6c multicolored .20 .20
537 A121 8c multicolored .35 .35
538 A121 17c purple, red & blk .85 .85
Nos. 535-538 (4) 1.55 1.55

World Telecommunication Day.

View of Ta' L-Isperanza — A122

Europa: 20c, Harbor, Is-Salini.

1977, July Litho. *Perf. 13½*

539 A122 7c multicolored .35 .35
540 A122 20c multicolored .85 .85

Issued in sheets of 10.

Help Given Handicapped Worker — A123

7c, Stonemason & shipbuilder. 20c, Mother holding dead son, & Service to the Republic order, horiz. Sculptures from Workers' Monument.

1977, Oct. 12 Litho. Wmk. 354

541 A123 2c red brown & brn .15 .15
542 A123 7c brown & dk brn .30 .30
543 A123 20c multicolored .90 .90
Nos. 541-543 (3) 1.35 1.35

Tribute to Maltese workers.

Lady on Horseback and Soldier, by Dürer A124

Grand Master Nicola Cotoner Monument A125

Dürer Engravings: 8c, Bagpiper. 17c, Madonna with Long-tailed Monkey.

1978, Mar. 7 *Perf. 14*

544 A124 1c7m dk blue, blk & red .15 .15
545 A124 8c gray, blk & red .35 .35
546 A124 17c dk grn, blk & red .80 .80
Nos. 544-546 (3) 1.30 1.30

Albrecht Dürer (1471-1528), German painter and engraver.

1978, Apr. 26 *Perf. 14x13½*

Europa: 25c, Grand Master Ramon Perellos monument, by Giusepe Mazzuoli. The monument on 7c is believed to be the work of Giovanni Batista Foggini.

547 A125 7c multicolored .30 .30
548 A125 25c multicolored 1.00 1.00

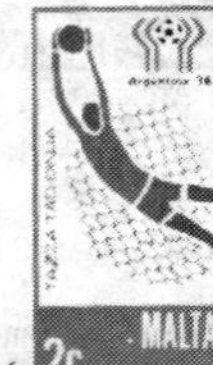

Goalkeeper — A126

Argentina '78 Emblem and: 11c, 15c, different soccer scenes.

Perf. 14x13½

1978, June 6 Litho. Wmk. 354

549 A126 2c multicolored .15 .15
550 A126 11c multicolored .45 .45
551 A126 15c multicolored .75 .75
a. Souvenir sheet of 3, #549-551 1.75 1.75
Nos. 549-551 (3) 1.35 1.35

11th World Cup Soccer Championship, Argentina, June 1-25.

Fishing Boat — A127

Maltese Speronara and AirMalta Fuselage — A128

Designs: 5c, 17c Changing of colors. 7c, 20c, British soldier and oranges. 8c, like 2c.

1979, Mar. 31 *Perf. 14*

552 A127 2c claret & multi .15 .15
553 A127 5c claret & multi .20 .20
554 A127 7c claret & multi .25 .25
555 A127 8c dk blue & multi .35 .35
556 A127 17c dk blue & multi .65 .65
557 A127 20c dk blue & multi .75 .75
Nos. 552-557 (6) 2.35 2.35

End of military agreement between Malta and Great Britain.

1979, May 9

Europa: 25c, Coastal watch tower and radio link tower.

558 A128 7c multicolored .25 .25
559 A128 25c multicolored .95 .95

Children and Globe — A129

Designs: 7c, Children flying kites. 11c, Children in a circle holding hands.

1979, June 13 *Perf. 14x13½, 14*

Size: 20x38mm

560 A129 2c multicolored .15 .15

Size: 27x33mm

561 A129 7c multicolored .30 .30
562 A129 11c multicolored .55 .55
Nos. 560-562 (3) 1.00 1.00

International Year of the Child.

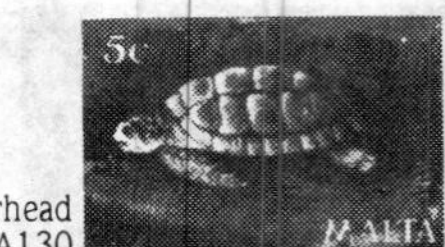

Loggerhead Turtle — A130

Marine Life: 2c, Gibbula nivosa. 7c, Dolphinfish. 25c, Noble pen shell.

1979, Oct. 10 Litho. *Perf. 13½*

563 A130 2c multicolored .15 .15
564 A130 5c multicolored .20 .20
565 A130 7c multicolored .25 .25
566 A130 25c multicolored 1.10 1.10
Nos. 563-566 (4) 1.70 1.70

Tapestry Type of 1977-79

Tapestries after Designs by Rubens: 2c, The Institution of Corpus Domini. 8c, The Destruction of Idolatry. 50c, Portrait of Grand Master Perellos, vert.

1980, Jan. 30 Wmk. 354 *Perf. 14*

567 A120 2c multicolored .15 .15
568 A120 8c multicolored .35 .35

Souvenir Sheet

569 A119 50c multicolored 1.75 1.75

Victoria Citadel, Gozo A131

Monument Restoration (UNESCO Emblem and): 2c5m, Hal Saflieni Catacombs, Paola, 2500 B.C., vert. 6c, Vilhena Palace, Mdina, 18th century, vert. 12c, St. Elmo Fort, Valletta, 16th century.

1980, Feb. 15

570 A131 2c5m multicolored .15 .15
571 A131 6c multicolored .30 .30
572 A131 8c multicolored .40 .40
573 A131 12c multicolored .60 .60
Nos. 570-573 (4) 1.45 1.45

Don Gorg Preca (1880-1962), Founder of Soc. of Christian Doctrine — A132

1980, Apr. 12 Litho. *Perf. 14x13½*

574 A132 2c5m gray violet .15 .15

Ruzar Briffa (1906-1963), Poet, by Vincent Apap — A133

Europa (Vincent Apap Sculpture): 30c, Mikiel Anton Vassalli (1764-1829), freedom fighter and scholar.

1980, Apr. 29 *Perf. 13½x14*

575 A133 8c slate green & dp bis .25 .25
576 A133 30c brown red & olive 1.00 1.00

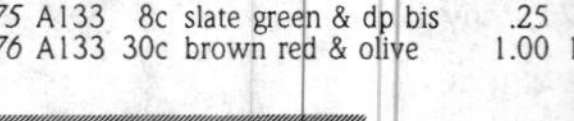

Chess Pieces — A134

Designs: Chess pieces. 30c, vert.

1980, Nov. Litho. *Perf. 14*

577 A134 2c5m multicolored .15 .15
578 A134 8c multicolored .40 .40
579 A134 30c multicolored 1.50 1.50
Nos. 577-579 (3) 2.05 2.05

Chess Olympiad, Valletta, Nov. 20-Dec. 8.

Barn Owl — A135

1981, Jan. 20 Wmk. 354 *Perf. 13½*

580 A135 3c shown .15 .15
581 A135 8c Sardinian warbler .45 .45
582 A135 12c Woodchat shrike .70 .70
583 A135 23c Stormy petrel 1.25 1.25
Nos. 580-583 (4) 2.55 2.55

Europa Issue 1981

Climbing the Gostra (Greasy Pole) — A136

1981, Apr. 28 Litho. *Perf. 14*

584 A136 8c Horse race .35 .35
585 A136 30c shown 1.10 1.10

25th Intl. Fair of Malta, Naxxar, July 1-15 — A137

1981, June 12 *Perf. 13½*

586 A137 4c multicolored .15 .15
587 A137 25c multicolored .95 .95

Disabled Artist — A138

World Food Day — A139

1981, July 17 Litho. *Perf. 13½*

588 A138 3c shown .15 .15
589 A138 35c Boy on crutches 1.25 1.25

Intl. Year of the Disabled.

1981, Oct. 16 Litho. *Perf. 14*

590 A139 8c multicolored .30 .30
591 A139 23c multicolored .90 .90

Men Hauling Building Stone — A140

1981, Oct. 31 Wmk. 354 *Perf. 14*

592 A140 5m shown .15 .15
593 A140 1c Growing cotton .15 .15
594 A140 2c Ship building .15 .15
595 A140 3c Minting coins .15 .15
596 A140 5c Artistic achievements .20 .20
597 A140 6c Fishing .25 .25
598 A140 7c Farming .25 .25
599 A140 8c Quarrying .30 .30
600 A140 10c Grape pressing .35 .35
601 A140 12c Ship repairing .45 .45
602 A140 15c Energy .55 .55
603 A140 20c Communications .75 .75
604 A140 25c Factories .90 .90
605 A140 50c Water drilling 1.65 1.65
606 A140 £1 Sea transport 3.25 3.25
607 A140 £3 Air transport 9.50 9.50
Nos. 592-607 (16) 19.00 19.00

Shipbuilding and Repairing, Tarznar Shipyards — A141

1982, Jan. 29 Litho. *Perf. 13½x14*

608 A141 3c Assembly sheds .15 .15
609 A141 8c Ships in dry dock .35 .35
610 A141 13c Tanker .60 .60
611 A141 27c Tanker, diff. 1.25 1.25
Nos. 608-611 (4) 2.35 2.35

Man and Home for the Elderly A142

1982, Mar. 16 Litho. *Perf. 14*

612 A142 8c shown .30 .30
613 A142 30c Woman, hospital 1.40 1.40

Europa Issue 1982

Redemption of the Islands, 1428 — A143

1982, Apr. 29 Litho. *Perf. 14*

614 A143 8c shown .30 .30
615 A143 30c Declaration of Rights, 1802 1.40 1.40

1982 World Cup — A144

Designs: Various soccer players.

1982, June 11 Litho. *Perf. 14*

616 A144 3c multicolored .15 .15
617 A144 12c multicolored .70 .70
618 A144 15c multicolored .90 .90
a. Souvenir sheet of 3, #616-618 2.25 2.25
Nos. 616-618 (3) 1.75 1.75

Brigantine — A145

1982, Nov. 13 Litho.

619 A145 3c shown .20 .20
619A A145 8c Tartana .60 .60
619B A145 12c Xebec .80 .80
619C A145 20c Speronara 1.40 1.40
Nos. 619-619C (4) 3.00 3.00

See #637-640, 670-673, 686-689, 703-706.

Malta Railway Centenary — A146

1983, Jan. 21 Wmk. 354 *Perf. 14*

620 A146 3c Manning Wardle, 1883 .20 .20
621 A146 13c Black Hawthorn, 1884 .90 .90
622 A146 27c Beyer Peacock, 1895 1.90 1.90
Nos. 620-622 (3) 3.00 3.00

Commonwealth Day — A147

1983, Mar. 14

623 A147 8c Map .30 .30
624 A147 12c Transportation .50 .50
625 A147 15c Beach, vert. .60 .60
626 A147 23c Industry, vert. 1.00 1.00
Nos. 623-626 (4) 2.40 2.40

Europa Issue 1983

Megalithic Temples, Ggantija — A148

Wmk. 354

1983, May 5 Litho. *Perf. 14*

627 A148 8c shown .40 .40
628 A148 30c Fort St. Angelo 1.50 1.50

World Communications Year — A149

Perf. 13½x14

1983, July 14 Litho. Wmk. 354

629 A149 3c Dish antennas .15 .15
630 A149 7c Ships .35 .35
631 A149 13c Trucks .65 .65
632 A149 20c Games emblem 1.00 1.00
Nos. 629-632 (4) 2.15 2.15

25th anniv. of Intl. Maritime Org. (7c); 30th anniv. of Customs Cooperation Council (13c); 9th Mediterranean Games, Casablanca, 9/3-17 (20c).

Monsignor Giuseppe De Piro (1877-1933), Founder of Missionary Society of St. Paul — A150

1983, Sept. 1 Litho. *Perf. 14*

633 A150 3c multicolored .20 .20

40th Anniv. of General Workers' Union A151

1983, Oct. 5 Litho. *Perf. 14x13½*

634 A151 3c Founding rally .15 .15
635 A151 8c Family, workers .40 .40
636 A151 27c Headquarters 1.25 1.25
Nos. 634-636 (3) 1.80 1.80

Maltese Ship Type of 1982

1983, Nov. 17 Litho. *Perf. 14x13½*

637 A145 2c Strangier, 1813 .15 .15
638 A145 12c Tigre 1839 .75 .75
639 A145 13c La Speranza, 1844 .80 .80
640 A145 20c Wignacourt 1844 1.25 1.25
Nos. 637-640 (4) 2.95 2.95

Europa (1959-1984) A152

1984, Apr. 27 Wmk. 354 *Perf. 14*

641 A152 8c multicolored .45 .45
642 A152 30c multicolored 1.50 1.50

Police Force, 170th Anniv. — A153

1984 Summer Olympics — A154

1984, June 14 Litho. *Perf. 14x13½*

643 A153 3c Officer, 1880 .20 .20
644 A153 8c Mounted policeman .60 .60
645 A153 11c Officer on motorcycle .80 .80
646 A153 25c Traffic duty, firemen 1.90 1.90
Nos. 643-646 (4) 3.50 3.50

1984, July 26 Litho. *Perf. 13½x14*

647 A154 7c Running .35 .35
648 A154 12c Gymnastics .55 .55
649 A154 23c Swimming 1.10 1.10
Nos. 647-649 (3) 2.00 2.00

10th Anniv. of Republic — A155

Malta Post Office Cent. — A156

1984, Dec. 12 Litho. Wmk. 354

650 A155 3c Dove on map .20 .20
651 A155 8c Fortress .50 .50
652 A155 30c Hands, flag 1.90 1.90
Nos. 650-652 (3) 2.60 2.60

1985, Jan. 2 Litho. *Perf. 14*

653 A156 3c No. 8 .15 .15
654 A156 8c No. 9 .45 .45
655 A156 12c No. 11 .65 .65
656 A156 20c No. 12 1.10 1.10
a. Souvenir sheet of 4, #653-656 2.50 2.50
Nos. 653-656 (4) 2.35 2.35

International Youth Year — A157

1985, Mar. 7 *Perf. 14x13½, 13½x14*

657 A157 2c shown .15 .15
658 A157 13c Three youths, vert. .75 .75
659 A157 27c Female holding flame 1.50 1.50
Nos. 657-659 (3) 2.40 2.40

Composers — A158

Europa: 8c, Nicolo Baldacchino (1895-1971). 30c, Francesco Azopardi (1748-1809).

1985, Apr. 25 Litho. *Perf. 14*

660 A158 8c multicolored .60 .60
661 A158 30c multicolored 2.25 2.25

Guzeppi Bajada and Manwel Attard, Martyrs A159

Designs: 7c, Karmnu Abela and Wenzu Dyer. 35c, June 7 Uprising Memorial Monument, vert.

1985, June 7 *Perf. 14x14½, 14½x14*

662 A159	3c multicolored	.15	.15
663 A159	7c multicolored	.35	.35
664 A159	35c multicolored	1.90	1.90
	Nos. 662-664 (3)	2.40	2.40

June 7 Uprising, 66th anniv.

UN, 40th Anniv. A160

1985, July 26 *Perf. 13½x14*

665 A160	4c Stylized birds	.25	.25
666 A160	11c Arrows	.65	.65
667 A160	31c Human figures	1.90	1.90
	Nos. 665-667 (3)	2.80	2.80

Famous Men — A161

Portraits: 8c, George Mitrovich (1794-1885), politician and author, novel frontispiece, The Cause of the People of Malta Now Before Parliament. 12c, Pietru Caxaru (1438-1485), scholar, manuscript.

1985, Oct. 3 *Perf. 14*

668 A161	8c multicolored	.60	.60
669 A161	12c multicolored	.90	.90

Ships Type of 1982

1985, Nov. 27

670 A145	3c Scotia paddle steamer, 1844	.30	.30
671 A145	7c Tagliaferro, 1882	.65	.65
672 A145	15c Gleneagles, 1885	1.40	1.40
673 A145	23c L'Isle Adam, 1886	2.25	2.25
	Nos. 670-673 (4)	4.60	4.60

Intl. Peace Year A162

Perf. 14x14½, 13½x14 (#675)

1986, Jan. 28 **Litho.** **Wmk. 354**

674 A162	8c John XXIII Peace Laboratory	.70	.70
675 A162	11c Unity	.95	.95
676 A162	27c Peaceful coexistence	2.25	2.25
	Nos. 674-676 (3)	3.90	3.90

Size of No. 675: 43x27mm.

Europa Issue 1986

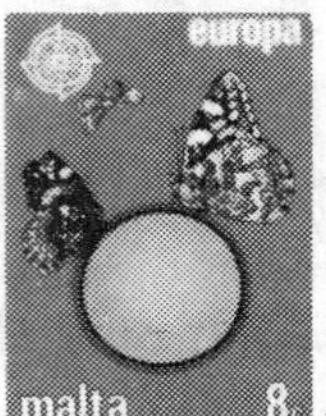
Butterflies — A163

1986, Apr. 3 *Perf. 14½x14*

677 A163	8c shown	.55	.55
678 A163	35c Earth, air, fire and water	2.50	2.50

1986 World Cup Soccer Championships, Mexico — A164

1986, May 30 **Wmk. 354** *Perf. 14*

679 A164	3c Heading the ball	.25	.25
680 A164	7c Goalie catching ball	.60	.60
681 A164	23c Dribbling	1.90	1.90
a.	Souvenir sheet of 3, #679-681	3.00	3.00
	Nos. 679-681 (3)	2.75	2.75

Philanthropists A165

Designs: 2c, Fra Diegu (1831-1902). 3c, Adelaide Cini (1838-1885). 8c, Alfonso Maria Galea (1861-1941). 27c, Vincenzo Bugeja (1820-1890).

1986, Aug. 28 *Perf. 14½x14*

682 A165	2c multicolored	.15	.15
683 A165	3c multicolored	.25	.25
684 A165	8c multicolored	.65	.65
685 A165	27c multicolored	2.25	2.25
	Nos. 682-685 (4)	3.30	3.30

Ships Type of 1982

1986, Nov. 19 **Wmk. 354** *Perf. 14*

686 A145	7c San Paul	.65	.65
687 A145	10c Knight of Malta	.90	.90
688 A145	12c Valetta City	1.10	1.10
689 A145	20c Saver	1.90	1.90
	Nos. 686-689 (4)	4.55	4.55

Malta Ornithological Society, 25th Anniv. — A166

1987, Jan. 26 **Litho.** *Perf. 14*

690 A166	3c Erithacus rubecula	.25	.25
691 A166	8c Falco peregrinus	.70	.70
692 A166	13c Upupa epops	1.10	1.10
693 A166	23c Calonectris diomedea	2.25	2.25
	Nos. 690-693 (4)	4.30	4.30

Nos. 691-692 vert.

Europa Issue 1987

Limestone Buildings — A167

1987, Apr. 15 **Litho.** *Perf. 14½x14*

694 A167	8c Aquasun Lido	.60	.60
695 A167	35c St. Joseph's Church, Manikata	2.75	2.75

Military Uniforms — A168

Uniforms of the Order of St. John of Jerusalem (1530-1798).

1987, June 10 **Wmk. 354** *Perf. 14*

696 A168	3c Soldier, 16th cent.	.25	.25
697 A168	7c Officer, 16th cent.	.65	.65
698 A168	10c Flag bearer, 18th cent.	.90	.90
699 A168	27c General of the galleys, 18th cent	2.50	2.50
	Nos. 696-699 (4)	4.30	4.30

See #723-726, 739-742, 764-767, 774-777.

European Environment Year — A169

Anniversaries and events: 8c, Esperanto movement, cent. 23s, Intl. Year of Shelter for the Homeless.

Perf. 14½x14

1987, Aug. 18 **Wmk. 354**

700 A169	5c shown	.45	.45
701 A169	8c multicolored	.65	.65
702 A169	23c multicolored	1.90	1.90
	Nos. 700-702 (3)	3.00	3.00

Ships Type of 1982

1987, Oct. 16 **Litho.** *Perf. 14*

703 A145	2c Medina, 1969	.20	.20
704 A145	11c Rabat, 1974	1.10	1.10
705 A145	13c Ghawdex, 1979	1.25	1.25
706 A145	20c Pinto, 1987	2.00	2.00
	Nos. 703-706 (4)	4.55	4.55

A170

Designs: 8c, Dr. Arvid Pardo, representative to UN from Malta who proposed the resolution. 12c, UN emblem.

Perf. 14½

1987, Dec. 18 **Litho.** **Wmk. 354**

707 A170	8c multicolored	.65	.65
708 A170	12c multicolored	1.00	1.00

Souvenir Sheet

Perf. 13x13½

709	Sheet of 2	1.75	1.75
a.	A170 8c multicolored	.65	.65
b.	A170 12c multicolored	1.00	1.00

UN resolution for peaceful use of marine resources, 20th anniv. Nos. 709a-709b printed in a continuous design.

Nazju Falzon (1813-1865), Clergyman — A171

Famous men: 3c, Monsignor Sidor Formosa (1851-1931), benefactor of the poor. 4c, Sir Luigi Preziosi (1888-1965), opthalmologist who developed an operation for the treatment of glaucoma. 10c, Father Anastasju Cuschieri (1876-1962), theologian, poet. 25c, Monsignor Pietru Pawl Saydon (1895-1971), translator, commentator on scripture.

Perf. 14½x14

1988, Jan. 23 **Wmk. 354**

710 A171	2c shown	.15	.15
711 A171	3c multicolored	.20	.20
712 A171	4c multicolored	.25	.25
713 A171	10c multicolored	.60	.60
714 A171	25c multicolored	1.50	1.50
	Nos. 710-714 (5)	2.70	2.70

Anniversaries and Events — A172

Designs: 10c, Statue of youth and St. John Bosco in the chapel at St. Patrick's School, Sliema. 12c, Assumption of Our Lady, main altarpiece at Ta' Pinu Sanctuary, Gozo, completed in 1619 by Amodeo Bartolomeo Perugino. 14c, Christ the King monument at the Mall, Floriana, by Antonio Sciortino (1879-1947).

1988, Mar. 5 **Litho.** *Perf. 14*

715 A172	10c multicolored	.65	.65
716 A172	12c multicolored	.80	.80
717 A172	14c multicolored	.95	.95
	Nos. 715-717 (3)	2.40	2.40

St. John Bosco (1815-88), educator (10c); Marian Year (12c); Intl. Eucharistic Congress, Malta, Apr. 24-28, 1913, 75th anniv. (14c).

Land, Sea and Air Transportation — A173

Europa (Transport and communication): 35c, Telecommunications.

1988, Apr. 9 *Perf. 14*

718 A173	10c multicolored	.60	.60
719 A173	35c multicolored	2.25	2.25

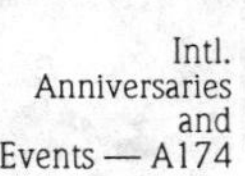
Intl. Anniversaries and Events — A174

Globe picturing hemispheres and: 4c, Red Cross, Red Crescent emblems. 18c, Symbolic design dividing world into north and south regions. 19c, Caduceus, EKG readout.

1988, May 25 **Litho.** *Perf. 14*

720 A174	4c multicolored	.30	.30
721 A174	18c multicolored	1.25	1.25
722 A174	19c multicolored	1.50	1.50
	Nos. 720-722 (3)	3.05	3.05

Intl. Red Cross and Red Crescent Organizations, 125th annivs. (4c); European Public Campaign on North-South Interdependence and Solidarity (18c); WHO, 40th anniv. (19c).

Military Uniforms Type of 1987

Designs: 3c, Light Infantry private, 1800. 4c, Coast Artillery gunner, 1802. 10c, 1st Maltese Provincial Battalion field officer, 1805. 25c, Royal Malta Regiment subaltern, 1809.

1988, July 23 **Litho.** **Wmk. 354**

723 A168	3c multicolored	.25	.25
724 A168	4c multicolored	.30	.30
725 A168	10c multicolored	.75	.75
726 A168	25c multicolored	1.90	1.90
	Nos. 723-726 (4)	3.20	3.20

A175

A176

Perf. 14x13½

1988, Sept. 17 Wmk. 354

727 A175 4c Running .25 .25
728 A175 10c Women's diving .60 .60
729 A175 35c Basketball 2.00 2.00
Nos. 727-729 (3) 2.85 2.85

1988 Summer Olympics, Seoul.

1989, Jan. 28 Litho. *Perf. 13½*

730 A176 2c Commonwealth .15 .15
731 A176 3c Council of Europe .20 .20
732 A176 4c United Nations .25 .25
733 A176 10c Labor .65 .65
734 A176 12c Justice .80 .80

Size: 41x32mm

Perf. 14

735 A176 25c Liberty 1.65 1.65
Nos. 730-735 (6) 3.70 3.70

Natl. independence, 25th anniv.

New Natl. Emblem A177

1989, Mar. 25 *Perf. 14*

736 A177 £1 multicolored 5.75 5.75

Children's Toys — A178

Europa.

1989, May 6

737 A178 10c Kite .75 .75
738 A178 35c Dolls 2.75 2.75

Military Uniforms Type of 1987

Designs: 3c, Officer of the Maltese Veterans, 1815. 4c, Subaltern of the Royal Malta Fencibles, 1839. 10c, Militia private, 1856. 25c, Royal Malta Fencibles Artillery colonel, 1875.

1989, June 24 Litho. Wmk. 354

739 A168 3c multicolored .20 .20
740 A168 4c multicolored .30 .30
741 A168 10c multicolored .70 .70
742 A168 25c multicolored 1.75 1.75
Nos. 739-742 (4) 2.95 2.95

Anniversaries and Events — A179

1989, Oct. 17 Litho. Wmk. 354

743 A179 3c multicolored .20 .20
744 A179 4c multi, diff. .30 .30
745 A179 10c multi, diff. .70 .70
746 A179 14c multi, diff. .95 .95
747 A179 25c multi, diff. 1.65 1.65
Nos. 743-747 (5) 3.80 3.80

UN Declaration on Social Progress and Development, 20th anniv. (3c); signing of the European Social Charter by Malta (4c); Council of Europe, 40th anniv. (10c); Natl. Teachers' Union, 70th anniv. (14c); assembly of the Knights of the Sovereign Military Order of Malta (25c).

Pres. Bush, Map and Gen.-Sec. Gorbachev — A180

1989, Dec. 2 Litho. Wmk. 354

748 A180 10c chalky blue, org & brn .75 .75

US-Soviet summit, Malta, Dec. 2-3.

Europa 1990 — A181

Post offices: 10c, Auberge d'Italie, Valletta, 1574, vert. 35c, Branch P.O., Zebbug, 1987.

1990, Feb. 9

749 A181 10c multicolored .60 .60
750 A181 35c multicolored 2.25 2.25

Anniversaries & Events — A182

1990, Apr. 7

751 A182 3c multi, vert. .20 .20
752 A182 4c shown .25 .25
753 A182 19c multicolored 1.25 1.25
754 A182 20c multi, vert. 1.25 1.25
Nos. 751-754 (4) 2.95 2.95

UNESCO World Literacy Year (3c); subjection of Malta to Count Roger the Norman and subsequent rulers of Sicily, 900th anniv. (4c); 25th anniv. of Malta's membership in the ITU (19c); and 20th Congress of the Union of European Soccer Associations, Malta (20c).

British Poets and Novelists — A183

1990, May 3 *Perf. 13½*

755 A183 4c Samuel Taylor Coleridge .25 .25
756 A183 10c Lord Byron .60 .60
757 A183 12c Sir Walter Scott .75 .75
758 A183 25c William Makepeace Thackeray 1.50 1.50
Nos. 755-758 (4) 3.10 3.10

Visit of Pope John Paul II, May 25-27 — A184

1990, May 25 *Perf. 14*

759 A184 4c St. Paul .25 .25
760 A184 25c Pope John Paul II 1.75 1.75
a. Pair, #759-760 2.00 2.00

World Cup Soccer Championships, Italy — A185

Soccer ball &: 5c, flags. 10c, hands & goal net.

1990, June 8 Wmk. 354

761 A185 5c multicolored .35 .35
762 A185 10c multicolored .65 .65
763 A185 14c multicolored 1.00 1.00
a. Souvenir sheet of 3, #761-763 2.00 2.00
Nos. 761-763 (3) 2.00 2.00

Military Uniforms Type of 1987

Designs: 3c, Captain, Royal Malta Militia, 1889. 4c, Field Officer, Royal Malta Artillery, 1905. 10c, Laborer, Malta Labor Corps, 1915. 25c, Lieutenant, King's Own Malta Regiment of Militia, 1918.

1990, Aug. 25 *Perf. 14*

764 A168 3c multicolored .20 .20
765 A168 4c multicolored .30 .30
766 A168 10c multicolored .70 .70
767 A168 25c multicolored 1.75 1.75
Nos. 764-767 (4) 2.95 2.95

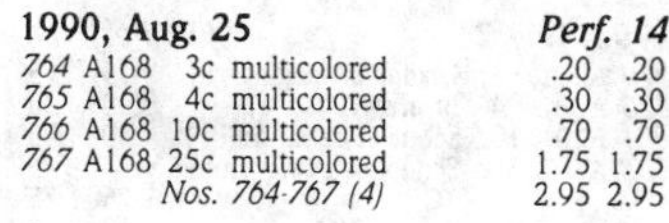

Maltese Philatelic Society, 25th Anniv. A186

1991, Mar. 6 Litho. Wmk. 354

768 A186 10c multicolored .65 .65

Europa — A187

1991, Mar. 16

769 A187 10c Eurostar .65 .65
770 A187 35c Ariane 4, space plane 2.25 2.25

St. Ignatius of Loyola (1491-1556), Founder of Jesuit Order — A188

Designs: 4c, Marie Therese Pisani (1806-1865), Benedictine Nun, vert. 30c, St. John of the Cross (1542-1591), Christian mystic.

1991, Apr. 29 Litho. *Perf. 14*

771 A188 3c multicolored .20 .20
772 A188 4c multicolored .25 .25
773 A188 30c multicoloed 1.90 1.90
Nos. 771-773 (3) 2.35 2.35

Military Uniforms Type of 1987

Colors Officers: 3c, Royal Malta Fencibles, 1860. 10c, Royal Malta Regiment of Militia, 1903. 19c, King's Own Malta Regiment, 1968. 25c, Armed Forces of Malta, 1991.

Wmk. 354

1991, Sept. 23 Litho. *Perf. 14*

774 A168 3c multicolored .20 .20
775 A168 10c multicolored .65 .65
776 A168 19c multicolored 1.25 1.25
777 A168 25c multicolored 1.65 1.65
Nos. 774-777 (4) 3.75 3.75

Union Haddiema Maghqudin, 25th Anniv. — A189

1991, Sept. 23 *Perf. 14x13½*

778 A189 4c multicolored .25 .25

Birds of Prey — A190

1991, Oct. 3 *Perf. 14*

779 A190 4c Pernis apivorus *.50 .50*
780 A190 4c Circus aeruginosus *.50 .50*
781 A190 10c Falco eleonorae *1.00 1.00*
782 A190 10c Falco naumanni *1.00 1.00*
a. Strip of 4, #779-782 *3.00 3.00*

World Wildlife Fund.

Tourism A191

Designs: 1c, Ta' Hagrat neolithic temples, Mgarr. 2c, Cottoner Gate. 3c, St. Michael's Bastion, Valletta. 4c, Spinola Palace, St. Julian's. 5c, Old church, Birkirkara. 10c, Wind surfing, Mellieha Bay. 12c, Boat anchored at Wied iz-Zurrieq. 14c, Mgarr Harbor, Gozo. 20c, Yacht Marina. 50c, Gozo Channel. £1, Statue of Arab Horses, by Sciortino. £2, Independence Monument, by Bonnici, vert.

1991, Dec. 9 *Perf. 13½*

783 A191 1c multicolored .15 .15
784 A191 2c multicolored .15 .15
785 A191 3c multicolored .20 .20
786 A191 4c multicolored .25 .25
787 A191 5c multicolored .30 .30
788 A191 10c multicolored .65 .65
789 A191 12c multicolored .75 .75
790 A191 14c multicolored .85 .85
791 A191 20c multicolored 1.25 1.25
792 A191 50c multicolored 3.25 3.25
793 A191 £1 multicolored 6.25 6.25
794 A191 £2 multicolored 12.50 12.50
Nos. 783-794 (12) 26.55 26.55

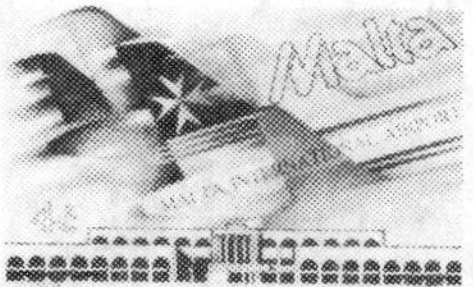

Malta Intl. Airport A192

1992, Feb. 8 *Perf. 14*

795 A192 4c shown .25 .25
796 A192 10c Flags, airport .70 .70

Discovery of America, 500th Anniv. A193

1992, Feb. 20 *Perf. 14x14½*

797 A193 10c Columbus' fleet .65 .65
798 A193 35c Columbus, map 2.25 2.25

Europa.

George Cross, 1942 — A194

George Cross and: 4c, Royal Malta Artillery. 10c, Siege Bell. 50c, Santa Maria convoy entering Grand Harbor.

1992, Apr. 15 *Perf. 14*

799 A194 4c multicolored .30 .30
800 A194 10c multicolored .75 .75
801 A194 50c multicolored 3.75 3.75
Nos. 799-801 (3) 4.80 4.80

1992 Summer Olympics, Barcelona A195

1992, June 24

802 A195	3c Runners		.20	.20
803 A195	10c High jump		.65	.65
804 A195	30c Swimmer		2.00	2.00
	Nos. 802-804 (3)		2.85	2.85

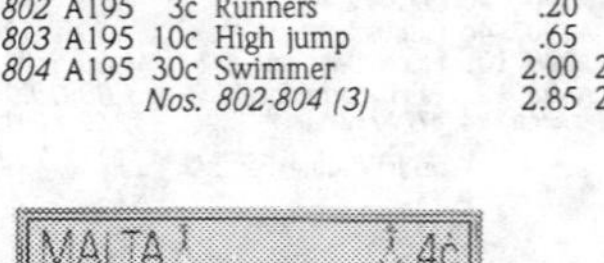

Historic Buildings A196

Designs: 3c, Church of the Flight of the Holy Family into Egypt, vert. 4c, St. John's Co-Cathedral. 19c, Church of the Madonna del Pilar. 25c, Auberge de Provence, vert.

1992, July 5

805 A196	3c blk, gray & buff	.20	.20
806 A196	4c blk, salmon & buff	.30	.30
807 A196	19c blk, green & buff	1.25	1.25
808 A196	25c blk, pink & buff	1.65	1.65
	Nos. 805-808 (4)	3.40	3.40

University of Malta, 400th Anniv. — A197

1992, Nov. 11

809 A197	4c Early building, vert.	.25	.25
810 A197	30c Modern complex	2.00	2.00

Lions Intl., 75th Anniv. — A198

1993, Feb. 4

811 A198	4c We serve	.25	.25
812 A198	50c Sight first campaign	2.50	2.50

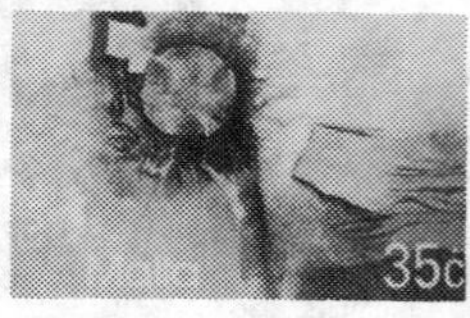

Europa A199

Contemporary paintings by: 10c, Pawl Carbonaro, vert. 35c, Alfred Chircop.

1993, Apr. 7

813 A199	10c multicolored	.60	.60
814 A199	35c multicolored	2.00	2.00

5th Games of Small States of Europe A200

1993, May 4 *Perf. 13½x14*

815 A200	3c Torchbearer	.15	.15
816 A200	4c Cycling	.25	.25
817 A200	10c Tennis	.55	.55
818 A200	35c Sailing	1.90	1.90
a.	Souvenir sheet of 4, #815-818	3.00	3.00
	Nos. 815-818 (4)	2.85	2.85

Boy Scouts and Girl Guides of Malta — A201

1993, July 21 *Perf. 14*

819 A201	3c Leader bandaging girl	.15	.15
820 A201	4c Bronze Cross	.20	.20
821 A201	10c Scout at camp fire	.50	.50
822 A201	35c Scout recieving Bronze Cross	1.75	1.75
	Nos. 819-822 (4)	2.60	2.60

Girl Guides in Malta, 70th anniv. (#819). Award of Bronze Cross for Gallantry to Boy Scouts of Malta, 50th anniv. (#820-822).

A202

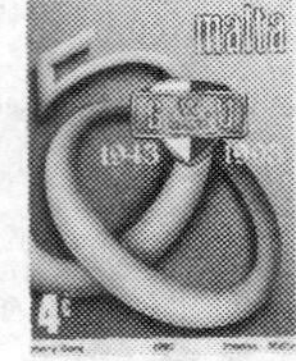

A203

1993, Sept. 23 *Perf. 14½x14*

823 A202	5c Papilio machaon	.25	.25
824 A202	35c Vanessa atalanta	1.90	1.90

1993, Oct. 5 *Perf. 13½*

825 A203	4c multicolored	.25	.25

General Worker's Union, 50th anniv.

Souvenir Sheet

Local Councils — A204

Designs showing various local flags with denominations at: a, UL. b, UR. c, LL. d, LR.

1993, Nov. 20 *Perf. 14½*

826	Sheet of 4	1.10	1.10
a.-d.	A204 5c any single	.25	.25

Dental Assoc. of Malta, 50th Anniv. — A205

Design: 44c, Dental instrument, teeth.

1994, Feb. 12

827 A205	5c multicolored	.25	.25
828 A205	44c multicolored	2.00	2.00

Europa — A206

Designs: 14c, Sir Themistocles Zammit (1864-1935), discoverer of micro-organism causing undulant fever. 30c, Marble candelabrum, 2nd cent. B.C., Natl. Museum of Archaeology, Valletta.

1994, Mar. 29 *Perf. 14*

829 A206	14c multicolored	.80	.80
830 A206	30c multicolored	1.65	1.65

Anniversaries and Events — A207

1994, May 10

831 A207	5c shown	.25	.25
832 A207	9c Crosses	.45	.45
833 A207	14c Farm animals	.70	.70
834 A207	20c Factory worker	1.00	1.00
835 A207	25c Cathedral, vert.	1.25	1.25
	Nos. 831-835 (5)	3.65	3.65

Intl. Year of the Family (#831). Malta Red Cross Society, 3rd anniv. (#832). Agrarian Society, 150th anniv. (#833). ILO, 75th anniv. (#834). St. Paul's Anglican Cathedral, 150th anniv. (#835).

1994 World Cup Soccer Championships, US — A208

1994, June 9

836 A208	5c shown	.25	.25
837 A208	14c Ball, net, map	.70	.70
838 A208	30c Ball, field, map	1.50	1.50
a.	Souvenir sheet of 3, #836-838	2.50	2.50
	Nos. 836-838 (3)	2.45	2.45

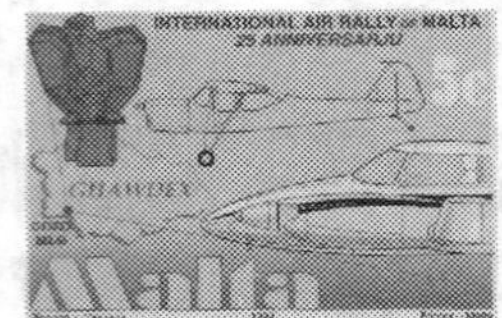

Aviation Anniversaries & Events — A209

Aircraft, related objects: 5c, Trophy, map, Twin Comanche. 14c, Airshow emblem, Phantom jet, demonstration team in silhouette, Alouette helicopter, flag. 20c, Emblem, Avro York, old terminal building, DeHavilland Dove. 25c, Emblem, DeHavilland Comet, new terminal, Airbus 320.

1994, July 2

839 A209	5c multicolored	.25	.25
840 A209	14c multicolored	.80	.80
841 A209	20c multicolored	1.10	1.10
842 A209	25c multicolored	1.40	1.40
	Nos. 839-842 (4)	3.55	3.55

Intl. Air Rally of Malta, 25th anniv. (#839). Malta Intl. Airshow (#840). ICAO, 50th anniv. (#841-842).

First Manned Moon Landing, 25th Anniv. — A210

1994, July 20

843 A210	14c multicolored	.75	.75

Christmas — A211

1994, Oct. 26

844 A211	5c shown	.25	.25

Size: 28x40mm

845 A211	9c +2c Angel in pink	.60	.60
846 A211	14c +3c Madonna & child	.95	.95
847 A211	20c +3c Angel in green	1.25	1.25
	Nos. 844-847 (4)	3.05	3.05

Antique Maltese Silver — A212

Designs: 5c, Ewer, Vilhena period. 14c, Balsamina, Pinto period. 20c, Coffee pot, Pinto period. 25c, Sugar box, Pinto period.

Wmk. 354

1994, Dec. 12 **Litho.** *Perf. 14*

848 A212	5c multicolored	.25	.25
849 A212	14c multicolored	.75	.75
850 A212	20c multicolored	1.10	1.10
851 A212	25c multicolored	1.40	1.40
	Nos. 848-851 (4)	3.50	3.50

Anniversaries & Events — A213

1995, Feb. 27

852 A213	2c multicolored	.15	.15
853 A213	5c multicolored	.25	.25
854 A213	14c multicolored	.75	.75
855 A213	20c multicolored	1.10	1.10
856 A213	25c multicolored	1.40	1.40
	Nos. 852-856 (5)	3.65	3.65

Natl. Assoc. of Pensioners, 25th anniv. (#852). Natl. Youth Council of Malta, 10th anniv. (#853). 4th World Conf. on Women, Beijing (#854). Malta Memorial District Nursing Assoc., 50th anniv. (#855). Louis Pasteur (1822-95) (#856).

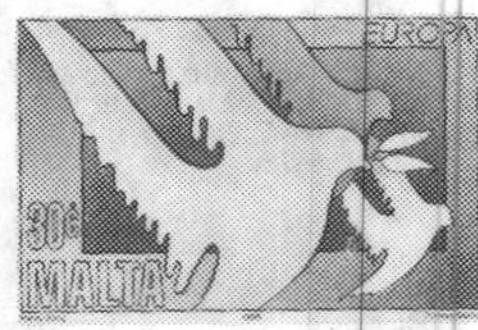

Peace & Freedom A214

Europa: 14c, Hand with olive twig, rainbow, vert. 30c, Doves.

1995, Mar. 29

857 A214	14c multicolored	.75	.75
858 A214	30c multicolored	1.65	1.65

50th Anniversaries — A215

Designs: 5c, End of World War II, ships, planes. 14c, Formation of UN, people joining hands. 35c, FAO, hands holding bowl of wheat, FAO emblem.

1995, Apr. 21

859 A215	5c multicolored	.25	.25
860 A215	14c multicolored	.80	.80
861 A215	35c multi, vert.	2.00	2.00
	Nos. 859-861 (3)	3.05	3.05

Telecommunications & Electricity — A216

1995, June 15

862 A216	2c Light bulb	.15	.15
863 A216	5c Cable, binary numbers	.30	.30
864 A216	9c Satellite dish	.50	.50

865 A216 14c Sun's rays, trees .80 .80
866 A216 20c Telephone, satellite 1.15 1.15
Nos. 862-866 (5) 2.90 2.90

European Nature Conservation Year — A217

1995, July 24

867 A217 5c Ruins, Girna .30 .30
868 A217 14c Podarcis filfolensis .75 .75
869 A217 44c Pina halepensis 2.50 2.50
Nos. 867-869 (3) 3.55 3.55

Antique Clocks — A218

Designs: 1c, Pinto's turret clock. 5c, Michelangelo Sapiano, long case & smaller clock. 14c, Arlogg tal-lira (case) clock. 25c, Maltese sundials.

1995, Oct. 5

870 A218 1c multicolored .15 .15
871 A218 5c multicolored .30 .30
872 A218 14c multicolored .80 .80
873 A218 25c multicolored 1.40 1.40
Nos. 870-873 (4) 2.65 2.65

Christmas — A219

Designs: 5c, Christmas Eve children's procession. 5c+2c, Children carrying manger. 14c+3c, Boy carrying manger, boy with lamp. 25c+3c, Boy with lamp, balcony.
Illustration reduced.

Wmk. 354

1995, Nov. 15 Litho. *Perf. 14*

874 A219 5c multi .30 .30

Size: 26x32mm

875 A219 5c +2c multi .40 .40
876 A219 14c +3c multi 1.00 1.00
877 A219 25c +3c multi 1.65 1.65
Nos. 874-877 (4) 3.35 3.35

Surtax for child welfare organizations.

Child and Youth Welfare Organizations — A220

Silhouettes of youth, children, and: 5c, Maltese cross, Palace of the President. 14c, Fr. Nazzareno Camilleri, St. Patricks' School. 20c, St. Maria of St. Euphrasia Pelletier, convent building. 25c, Globe, children looking at pool.

1996, Feb. 29

878 A220 5c multicolored .30 .30
879 A220 14c multicolored .75 .75
880 A220 20c multicolored 1.10 1.10
881 A220 25c multicolored 1.40 1.40
Nos. 878-881 (4) 3.55 3.55

President's Award, 35th anniv. (#878). Fr. Camilleri, 90th death anniv. (#879). St. Maria, death bicent. (#880). UNICEF, 50th anniv. (#881).

Prehistoric Art A221

Sculptures, pottery from 5000-2500BC: 5c, People, animals. 14c, Two people seated, one with missing head. 20c, Venus figure, vert. 35c, Pitcher, vert.

1996, Mar. 29

882 A221 5c multicolored .30 .30
883 A221 14c multicolored .75 .75
884 A221 20c multicolored 1.10 1.10
885 A221 35c multicolored 1.90 1.90
Nos. 882-885 (4) 4.05 4.05

Famous Women — A222

Europa: 14c, Mabel Strickland (1899-1988). 30c, Inez Soler (1910-1974).

1996, Apr. 24

886 A222 14c multicolored .75 .75
887 A222 30c multicolored 1.65 1.65

Anniversaries and Events — A223

Designs: No. 888, UN, decade against drug abuse. No. 889, Malta Federation of Industry, 50th anniv. 14c, Self-government, 75th anniv. 44c, Guglielmo Marconi, radio, cent.

1996, June 5

888 A223 5c multicolored .30 .30
889 A223 5c multicolored .30 .30
890 A223 14c multicolored .75 .75
891 A223 44c multicolored 2.50 2.50
Nos. 888-891 (4) 3.85 3.85

1996 Summer Olympic Games, Atlanta A224

1996, July 10

892 A224 2c Judo .15 .15
893 A224 5c Running .30 .30
894 A224 14c Swimming .80 .80
895 A224 25c Shooting 1.40 1.40
Nos. 892-895 (4) 2.65 2.65

Paintings, by or of Giuseppe Cali A225

Designs: 5c, Boy cutting wheat. 14c, Dog. 20c, Woman with hoe standing on hillside, vert. 25c, Portrait of Cali, by Dingli, vert.

1996, Aug. 22

896 A225 5c multicolored .30 .30
897 A225 14c multicolored .80 .80
898 A225 20c multicolored 1.10 1.10
899 A225 25c multicolored 1.40 1.40
Nos. 896-899 (4) 3.60 3.60

Buses A226

2c, Tal-Gallarija "Diamond Star" No. 1990. 5c, Stewart "Tom Mix" No. 434. 14c, Diamond T "Verdala" No. 1764. 30c, Front control No. 3495.

Wmk. 354

1996, Sept. 26 Litho. *Perf. 14*

900 A226 2c multicolored .15 .15
901 A226 5c multicolored .30 .30
902 A226 14c multicolored .75 .75
903 A226 30c multicolored 1.75 1.75
Nos. 900-903 (4) 2.95 2.95

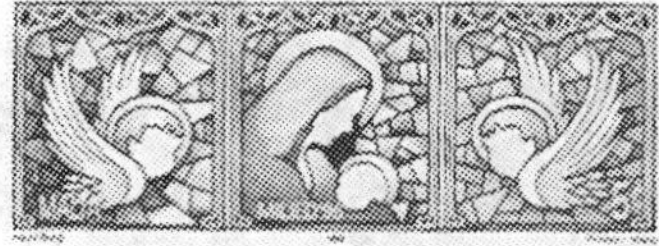

Christmas — A227

Stained glass windows: 5c+2c, Madonna and Child. 14c+3c, Angel flying right. 25c+3c, Angel flying left.

1996, Nov. 7

904 A227 5c shown .30 .30

Size: 26x31mm

905 A227 5c +2c multi .40 .40
906 A227 14c +3c multi .95 .95
907 A227 25c +3c multi 1.50 1.50
Nos. 904-907 (4) 3.15 3.15

City Bicentennials A228

1997, Feb. 20

908 A228 6c Hompesch .30 .30
909 A228 16c Ferdinand .85 .85
910 A228 26c Beland 1.35 1.35
a. Souvenir Sheet of 3, #908-910 2.50 2.50
Nos. 908-910 (3) 2.50 2.50

Treasures of Malta A229

1997, Apr. 11

911 A229 2c Suggetta .15 .15
912 A229 6c Suggetta, diff. .30 .30
913 A229 16c Sedan chair, vert. .80 .80
914 A229 27c Sedan chair, diff., vert. 1.35 1.35
Nos. 911-914 (4) 2.60 2.60

A230 A231

Europa (Stories and Legends): 16c, Man carrying door, figure in front of house (Gahan). 35c, Woman kneeling in prayer, knight on white horse (St. Dimitri).

1997, May 5

915 A230 16c multicolored .85 .85
916 A230 35c multicolored 1.80 1.80

1997, July 10

917 A231 1c multicolored .15 .15
918 A231 16c multicolored .80 .80

Antonio Sciortino (1879-1947), sculptor.

Gozo Cathedral, 300th Anniv. A232

1997, July 10

919 A232 6c multi .30 .30
920 A232 11c multi, diff. .55 .55

Joseph Caleia (1897-1975), Actor — A233

1997, July 10

921 A233 6c multicolored .30 .30
922 A233 22c multi, diff. 1.10 1.10

Pioneers of Freedom — A234

Designs: 6c, Dr. Albert V. Laferla (1887-1943). 16c, Sister Emilie de Vialar (1797-1856). 19c, Msgr. Paolo Pullicino (1815-90). 26c, Msgr. Tommaso Gargallo (c. 1544-1614).

Wmk. 354

1997, Sept. 24 Litho. *Perf. 14*

923 A234 6c multicolored .30 .30
924 A234 16c multicolored .80 .80
925 A234 19c multicolored .95 .95
926 A234 26c multicolored 1.30 1.30
Nos. 923-926 (4) 3.35 3.35

Christmas A235

Designs: 6c, Nativity. 6c+2c, Madonna and Child, vert. 16c+3c, Joseph with donkey, vert. 26c+3c, Shepherd, sheep, vert.

1997, Nov. 12

927 A235 6c multi .30 .30
928 A235 6c +2c multi .40 .40
929 A235 16c +3c multi 1.00 1.00
930 A235 26c +3c multi 1.50 1.50
Nos. 927-930 (4) 3.20 3.20

Victoria Lines, Cent. A236

Designs: 2c, Fort, soldiers in front of wall. 16c, Soldiers with cannon, fort.

1997, Dec. 5

931 A236 2c multicolored .15 .15
932 A236 16c multicolored .80 .80

Self-government, 50th Anniv. — A237

Designs: 6c, Man looking at paper, group of people. 37c, People in line waiting to vote.

1997, Dec. 5

933 A237 6c multicolored .30 .30
934 A237 37c multicolored 1.90 1.90

Treasures of Malta — A238

Designs: No. 935, Vest. No. 936, Portrait of a Woman, by Antoine de Favray (1706-98). No. 937, Portrait of Woman Holding Girl, by de Favray. No. 938, Early woman's costume.
26c, Valletta, city of culture.

1998

935 A238 6c multicolored .30 .30
936 A238 6c multicolored .30 .30
937 A238 16c multicolored .80 .80
938 A238 16c multicolored .80 .80
Nos. 935-938 (4) 2.20 2.20

Souvenir Sheet

Perf. 13x13½

939 A238 26c multicolored 1.30 1.30

No. 939 contains one 39x48mm stamp.

SEMI-POSTAL STAMPS

All semi-postal issues are for Christmas.

Catalogue values for unused stamps in this section are for Never Hinged items.

Angels with Trumpet and Harp, Star of Bethlehem and Mdina Cathedral SP1

Star of Bethlehem and: 1p+1p, Two peasants with tambourine and bagpipe. 1sh6p+3p, Choir boys singing Christmas carols. The background of the 3 stamps together shows the Cathedral of Mdina, Malta, and surrounding countryside.

Perf. 12½

1969, Nov. 8 Wmk. 354 Litho.

B1 SP1 1p +1p multi .15 .15
B2 SP1 5p +1p multi .15 .15
B3 SP1 1sh6p +3p multi .30 .30
a. Triptych, #B1-B3 .50 .50
Set value .45 .45

Nos. B1-B3 were printed each in sheets of 60, and in sheets containing 20 triptychs.

Christmas Eve Procession — SP2

10p+2p, Nativity & Cathedral. 1sh6p+3p, Adoration of the Shepherds & Mdina Cathedral.

1970, Nov. 7 Photo. *Perf. 14x13½*

B4 SP2 1p +½p multi .15 .15
B5 SP2 10p +2p multi .20 .20
B6 SP2 1sh6p +3p multi .45 .45
Nos. B4-B6 (3) .80 .80

Surtax for child welfare organizations.

Angel — SP3

#B8, Madonna & Child. #B9, Shepherd.

1971, Nov. 8 *Perf. 14*

B7 SP3 1p +½p multi .15 .15
B8 SP3 10p +2p multi .25 .25
B9 SP3 1sh6p +3p multi .50 .50
a. Souv. sheet of 3, #B7-B9, perf. 15 1.00 1.00
Nos. B7-B9 (3) .90 .90

1972, Dec. Litho. *Perf. 13½*

Designs: 3c+1c, Angel playing tambourine. 7c5m+1c5m, Angel singing.

B10 SP3 8m +2m dk gray & gold .15 .15
B11 SP3 3c +1c dk purple & gold .20 .20
B12 SP3 7c5m +1c5m slate & gold .50 .50
a. Souvenir sheet of 3, #B10-B12 1.50 1.50
Nos. B10-B12 (3) .85 .85

1973, Nov. 10 Litho. *Perf. 13½*

Designs: 8m+2m, Singers and organ pipes. 3c+1c, Virgin and Child with star. 7c5m+1c5m, Star, candles, buildings, tambourine.

B13 SP3 8m +2m multi .15 .15
B14 SP3 3c +1c multi .30 .30
B15 SP3 7c5m +1c5m multi .80 .80
a. Souvenir sheet of 3, #B13-B15 2.00 2.00
Nos. B13-B15 (3) 1.25 1.25
Nos. B7-B15 (9) 3.00 3.00

Star and Holy Family — SP4

Designs: 3c+1c, Star and two shepherds. 5c+1c, Star and three shepherds. 7c5m+1c5m, Star and Three Kings.

1974, Nov. 22 Litho. *Perf. 14*

B16 SP4 8m +2m multi .15 .15
B17 SP4 3c +1c multi .15 .15
B18 SP4 5c +1c multi .35 .35
B19 SP4 7c5m +1c5m multi .55 .55
Nos. B16-B19 (4) 1.20 1.20

Nativity, by Maestro Alberto — SP5

8m+2m, Shepherds. 7c5m+1c5m, Three Kings.

1975, Nov. 4 *Perf. 13½*

Size: 24x23mm (#B20, B22); 49x23mm (#B21)

B20 SP5 8m +2m multi .15 .15
B21 SP5 3c +1c multi .55 .40
B22 SP5 7c5m +1c5m multi 3.25 2.50
a. Triptych, #B20-B22 4.75 4.75
Nos. B20-B22 (3) 3.95 3.05

Printed singly and as triptychs. Surtax for child welfare.

SP6

Madonna and Saints, by Domenico di Michelino — SP7

Designs (Details of Painting): 5c+1c, Virgin and Child. 7c+1c5m, St. Christopher and Bishop.

1976, Nov. 23 Litho. *Perf. 13½*

B23 SP6 1c +5m multi .15 .15
B24 SP6 5c +1c multi .40 .30
B25 SP6 7c +1c5m multi .70 .65

Perf. 13½x14

B26 SP7 10c +2c multi 1.50 .85
Nos. B23-B26 (4) 2.75 1.95

Nativity SP8

Crèche Figurines: 1c+5m, Annunciation to the Shepherds. 11c+1c5m, Shepherds.

***Perf. 13½x14* Wmk. 354**

1977, Nov. 16

B27 SP8 1c +5m multi .15 .15
B28 SP8 7c +1c multi .25 .25
B29 SP8 11c +1c5m multi .80 .80
a. Triptych, #B27-B29 1.25 1.25
Nos. B27-B29 (3) 1.20 1.20

Nos. B27-B29 printed singly and as triptychs. Surtax was for child welfare.

Christmas Decorations, People and Church — SP9

Designs: 5c+1c, Decorations and angels. 7c+1c5m, Decorations and carolers. 11c+3c, Combined designs of #B30-B32.

1978, Nov. 9 Litho. *Perf. 14*

Size: 24x30mm

B30 SP9 1c +5m multi .15 .15
B31 SP9 5c +1c multi .25 .25
B32 SP9 7c +1c5m multi .35 .35

Perf. 13½

Size: 58x22½mm

B33 SP9 11c +3c multi .65 .65
Nos. B30-B33 (4) 1.40 1.40

Nativity, by Giuseppe Cali — SP10

Designs (Cali Paintings): 5c+1c, 11c+3c, Flight into Egypt. 7c+1c5m, Nativity.

1979, Nov. 14 Litho. *Perf. 14x13½*

B34 SP10 1c +5m multi .15 .15
B35 SP10 5c +1c multi .30 .30
B36 SP10 7c +1c5m multi .40 .40
B37 SP10 11c +3c multi .75 .75
Nos. B34-B37 (4) 1.60 1.60

Nativity, by Anton Inglott (1915-1945) — SP11

Designs (Details of Painting): 2c+5m, Annunciation. 6c+1c, Angel. 8c+1c5m, Holy Family.

1980, Oct. 7 Litho. *Perf. 14x13½*

Size: 20x47mm

B38 SP11 2c +5m multi .15 .15
B39 SP11 6c +1c multi .25 .25
B40 SP11 8c +1c5m multi .30 .30

Perf. 14½x14

Size: 47x39mm

B41 SP11 12c +3c shown .45 .45
Nos. B38-B41 (4) 1.15 1.15

SP12

1981, Nov. 18 Wmk. 354 *Perf. 14*

B42 SP12 2c +1c Children, vert. .15 .15
B43 SP12 8c +2c Procession .35 .35
B44 SP12 20c +3c Service, vert. .95 .95
Nos. B42-B44 (3) 1.45 1.45

SP13

Three Kings Following Star: 2c+1c, Star. 8c+2c, Three Kings. 20c+3c, Entire design.

1982, Oct. 8 Litho. *Perf. 13½*

B45 SP13 2c +1c multi .15 .15
B46 SP13 8c +2c multi .45 .45

Perf. 14

Size: 45x36mm

B47 SP13 20c +3c multi 1.00 1.00
Nos. B45-B47 (3) 1.60 1.60

SP14

Illuminated Manuscripts, Book of Hours, 15th Cent.: 2c+1c, Annunciation. 8c+2c, Nativity. 20c+3c, Three Kings bearing gifts. Surtax was for child welfare.

1983, Sept. 6 Litho. *Perf. 14*

B48 SP14 2c +1c multi .15 .15
B49 SP14 8c +2c multi .55 .55
B50 SP14 20c +3c multi 1.30 1.30
Nos. B48-B50 (3) 2.00 2.00

SP15

Paintings by Peter-Paul Caruana, Church of Our Lady of Porto Salvo, Valletta, 1850: 2c+1c, Visitation, vert. 8c+2c, Epiphany. 20c+3c, Jesus Among the Doctors.

1984, Oct. 5 **Litho.** ***Perf. 14***
B51 SP15 2c +1c multi .15 .15
B52 SP15 8c +2c multi .55 .55
B53 SP15 20c +3c multi 1.25 1.25
Nos. B51-B53 (3) 1.95 1.95

SP16

1985, Oct. 10 **Litho.** ***Perf. 14***
B54 SP16 2c +1c Adoration of the Magi .20 .20
B55 SP16 8c +2c Nativity .70 .70
B56 SP16 20c +3c Trumpeter Angels 1.50 1.50
Nos. B54-B56 (3) 2.40 2.40

Surtax for child welfare organizations.

SP17

Paintings by Giuseppe D'Arena (1633-1719).

1986, Oct. 10 **Wmk. 354** ***Perf. 14½***
B57 SP17 2c +1c The Nativity .25 .25
B58 SP17 8c +2c The Nativity, detail, vert. .80 .80
B59 SP17 20c +3c The Epiphany 1.90 1.90
Nos. B57-B59 (3) 2.95 2.95

Surtax for child welfare organizations.

SP18

Illuminated text from choral books of the Veneranda Assemblea of St. John's Conventual Church, Valletta.

1987, Nov. 6 **Litho.** ***Perf. 14***
B60 SP18 2c +1c Mary's Visit to Elizabeth .25 .25
B61 SP18 8c +2c Nativity .80 .80
B62 SP18 20c +3c Adoration of the Magi 1.75 1.75
Nos. B60-B62 (3) 2.80 2.80

Surtax for child welfare organizations and the handicapped.

SP19

1988, Nov. 5 **Litho.** ***Perf. 14½x14***
B63 SP19 3c +1c Shepherd .25 .25
B64 SP19 10c +2c Nativity .70 .70
B65 SP19 25c +3c Magi 1.65 1.65
Nos. B63-B65 (3) 2.60 2.60

Surtax for child welfare organizations and the handicapped.

SP20

Various angels from frescoes by Mattia Preti in the vault of St. John's Co-Cathedral, Valletta, 1666.

1989, Nov. 11 ***Perf. 14***
B66 SP20 3c +1c multi .25 .25
B67 SP20 10c +2c multi .85 .85
B68 SP20 20c +3c multi 1.50 1.50
Nos. B66-B68 (3) 2.60 2.60

Surtax for child welfare organizations and the handicapped.

SP21 SP22

Creche figures.

1990, Nov. 10
Size: #B70, 41x27mm
B69 SP21 3c +1c Carrying water .25 .25
B70 SP21 10c +2c Nativity .80 .80
B71 SP21 25c +3c Shepherd 1.75 1.75
Nos. B69-B71 (3) 2.80 2.80

Surtax for child welfare organizations.

1991, Nov. 6
B72 SP22 3c +1c Wise men .25 .25
B73 SP22 10c +2c Mary, Joseph, Jesus .75 .75
B74 SP22 25c +3c Shepherds 1.75 1.75
Nos. B72-B74 (3) 2.75 2.75

Surtax for child welfare organizations.

SP23

Paintings from dome spandrels of Mosta Parish Church by Giuseppe Cali (1846-1930): 3c+1c, Nativity scene. 10c+2c, Adoration of the Magi. 25c+3c, Christ among the Elders in the Temple.

1992, Oct. 22
B75 SP23 3c +1c multi .25 .25
B76 SP23 10c +2c multi .80 .80
B77 SP23 25c +3c multi 1.90 1.90
Nos. B75-B77 (3) 2.95 2.95

Surtax for child welfare organizations.

SP24

Designs: 3c+1c, Christ Child in manger. 10c+2c, Christmas tree. 25c+3c, Star.

1993, Nov. 20
B78 SP24 3c +1c multi .20 .20
B79 SP24 10c +2c multi .65 .65
B80 SP24 25c +3c multi 1.50 1.50
Nos. B78-B80 (3) 2.35 2.35

Beginning with No. 845, semi-postal stamps are included with the postage portion of the set.

AIR POST STAMPS

No. 140 Overprinted **AIR MAIL**

Perf. 14½x14
1928, Apr. 1 **Typo.** **Wmk. 4**
C1 A22 6p red & violet 5.50 6.75

Catalogue values for unused stamps in this section, from this point to the end of the section, are for Never Hinged items.

Jet over Valletta — AP1

Designs: 3c, 5c, 20c, 35c, Winged emblem. 7c5m, 25c, like 4c.

Perf. 13½
1974, Mar. **Litho.** **Wmk. 354**
Cross Emblem in Red and Blue
C2 AP1 3c ol brown & gold .15 .15
C3 AP1 4c dk blue & gold .15 .15
C4 AP1 5c dk vio bl & gold .20 .20
C5 AP1 7c5m sl green & gold .30 .30
C6 AP1 20c vio brn & gold .80 .80
C7 AP1 25c slate & gold 1.00 1.00
C8 AP1 35c brown & gold 1.50 1.50
Nos. C2-C8 (7) 4.10 4.10

Jet and Megalithic Temple — AP2

Designs: 7c, 20c, Air Malta Boeing 720B approaching Malta. 11c, 75c, Jumbo jet landing at Luqa Airport. 17c, like 5c.

1978, Oct. 3 **Litho.** ***Perf. 13½***
C9 AP2 5c multicolored .15 .15
C10 AP2 7c multicolored .25 .25
C11 AP2 11c multicolored .40 .40
C12 AP2 17c multicolored .60 .60
C13 AP2 20c multicolored .80 .80
C14 AP2 75c multicolored 2.50 2.50
Nos. C9-C14 (6) 4.70 4.70

Boeing 737, 1984 AP3

1984, Jan. 26 **Wmk. 354** ***Perf. 14***
C15 AP3 7c shown .30 .30
C16 AP3 8c Boeing 720B, 1974 .35 .35
C17 AP3 16c Vickers Vanguard, 1964 .70 .70
C18 AP3 23c Vickers Viscount, 1958 1.10 1.10
C19 AP3 27c Douglas DC3 Dakota, 1948 1.25 1.25
C20 AP3 38c AW Atlanta, 1936 1.75 1.75
C21 AP3 75c Dornier Wal, 1929 3.50 3.50
Nos. C15-C21 (7) 8.95 8.95

POSTAGE DUE STAMPS

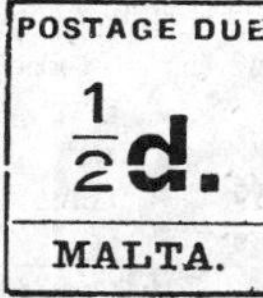

D1

Maltese Cross — D2

1925 **Typeset** **Unwmk.** ***Imperf.***
J1 D1 ½p black, *white* 1.10 3.25
J2 D1 1p black, *white* 2.75 2.25
J3 D1 1½p black, *white* 2.75 3.00
J4 D1 2p black, *white* 4.00 *7.25*
J5 D1 2½p black, *white* 2.50 2.50
a. "2" of "½" omitted 1,200. 1,350.
J6 D1 3p black, *gray* 8.00 *9.50*
J7 D1 4p black, *orange* 4.50 *7.75*
J8 D1 6p black, *orange* 4.50 *11.00*
J9 D1 1sh black, *orange* 6.50 *14.00*
J10 D1 1sh6p black, *orange* 11.00 *40.00*
Nos. J1-J10 (10) 47.60 *100.50*

These stamps were typeset in groups of 42. In each sheet there were four impressions of a group, two of them being inverted and making tete beche pairs.

Forged examples of No. J5a are known.

Wmk. 4 Sideways
1925 **Typo.** ***Perf. 12***
J11 D2 ½p blue green .65 .50
J12 D2 1p violet .65 .40
J13 D2 1½p yellow brown 1.25 1.10
J14 D2 2p gray 4.50 1.40
J15 D2 2½p orange 1.75 1.10
J16 D2 3p dark blue 1.40 1.10
J17 D2 4p olive green 5.00 *7.25*
J18 D2 6p claret 2.50 2.75
J19 D2 1sh gray black 5.50 *8.50*
J20 D2 1sh6p deep rose 7.25 *15.00*
Nos. J11-J20 (10) 30.45 *39.10*

In 1953-57 six values (½p-2p, 3p, 4p) were reissued on chalky paper in slightly different colors.

Catalogue values for unused stamps in this section, from this point to the end of the section, are for Never Hinged items.

1966 **Wmk. 314** ***Perf. 12***
J21 D2 2p sepia 26.00 26.00

1968 **Wmk. 354 Sideways** ***Perf. 12½***
J22 D2 ½p green .15 .15
J23 D2 1p rose violet .15 .15
J24 D2 1½p bister brn .25 .25
J25 D2 2p brown black .45 .45
J26 D2 2½p orange .50 .50
J27 D2 3p Prus blue .60 .60
J28 D2 4p olive .90 .90
J29 D2 6p purple 1.50 1.50
J30 D2 1sh black 1.65 1.65
J31 D2 1sh6p rose car 3.75 3.75
Nos. J22-J31 (10) 9.90 9.90

1967, Nov. 9 ***Perf. 12***
J22a D2 ½p 3.25 3.25
J23a D2 1p 4.50 4.50
J25a D2 2p 6.75 6.75
J28a D2 4p 82.50 *110.00*
Nos. J22a-J28a (4) 97.00 *124.50*

Numeral — D3

Scroll — D4

Perf. 13x13½
1973, Apr. 28 **Litho.** **Wmk. 354**
J32 D3 2m brown .15 .15
J33 D3 3m brown orange .15 .15
J34 D3 5m carmine .15 .15
J35 D3 1c deep green .15 .15
J36 D3 2c black .15 .15
J37 D3 3c olive .15 .15
J38 D3 5c violet blue .30 .30
J39 D3 10c deep magenta .60 .60
Set value 1.35 1.35

Wmk. 354
1993, Jan. 4 **Litho.** ***Perf. 14***
J40 D4 1c brt pink & lt pink .15 .15
J41 D4 2c brt blue & lt blue .15 .15
J42 D4 5c brt grn & lt grn .25 .25
J43 D4 10c org yel & brt yel .50 .50
Nos. J40-J43 (4) 1.05 1.05

WAR TAX STAMPS

Nos. 50, 25 Overprinted **WAR TAX**

1918 **Wmk. 3** ***Perf. 14***
MR1 A13 ½p green .30 .30
Wmk. 2
MR2 A12 3p red violet & gray 3.00 4.00

MANCHUKUO

'man-'chü-'kwō

LOCATION — Covering Manchuria, or China's three northeastern provinces —Fengtien, Kirin and Heilungkiang—plus Jehol province.
GOVT. — Independent state under Japanese influence
AREA — 503,013 sq. mi. (estimated)
POP. — 43,233,954 (est. 1940)
CAPITAL — Hsinking (Changchun)

Manchukuo was formed in 1932 with the assistance of Japan. In 1934 Henry Pu-yi, Chief Executive, was enthroned as Emperor Kang Teh. In 1945, when Japan surrendered to the Allies, the terms included the return of Manchukuo to China. The puppet state was dissolved.

100 Fen = 1 Yuan

Watermarks

Wmk. 141- Horizontal Zigzag Lines

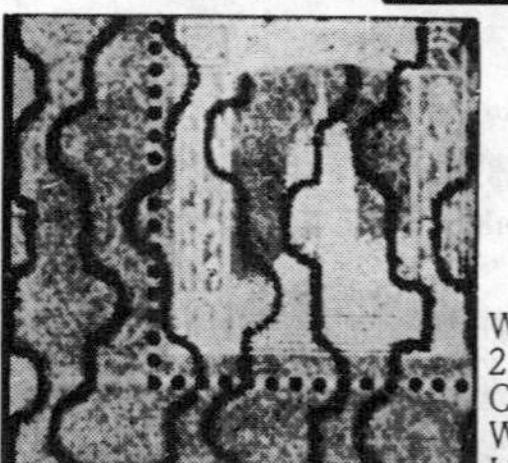

Wmk. 239- Curved Wavy Lines

Wmk. 242- Characters

Pagoda at Liaoyang A1

Chief Executive Henry Pu-yi A2

Five characters in top label.
Inscription reads "Manchu State Postal Administration."

Perf. 13x13½
Lithographed

1932, July 26 — Unwmk.

White Paper

1 A1 ½f gray brown 1.10 .70
2 A1 1f dull red 1.65 .35
3 A1 1½f lilac 5.50 4.00
4 A1 2f slate 6.00 1.00
5 A1 3f dull brown 7.50 5.00
6 A1 4f olive green 2.25 .50
7 A1 5f green 3.00 .55
8 A1 6f rose 9.50 2.50
9 A1 7f gray 3.00 1.00
10 A1 8f ocher 15.00 10.00
11 A1 10f orange 5.50 .50
12 A2 13f dull brown 11.00 7.00
13 A2 15f rose 15.00 3.00
14 A2 16f turquoise grn 27.50 9.00
15 A2 20f gray brown 8.00 1.75
16 A2 30f orange 8.50 2.25
17 A2 50f olive green 16.00 3.25
18 A2 1y violet 37.50 9.00
Nos. 1-18 (18) 183.50 61.35
Set, never hinged 250.00

A local provisional overprint of a horizontal line of four characters in red or black, reading "Chinese Postal Administration," was applied to Nos. 1-18 by followers of Gen. Su Ping-wen, who rebelled against the Manchukuo government in September, 1932. Many counterfeits exist.
See #23-31. For surcharges see #36, 59-61.

Flags, Map and Wreath — A3

Old State Council Building — A4

1933, Mar. 1 — *Perf. 12½*

19 A3 1f orange 5.00 5.00
20 A4 2f dull green 12.50 12.50
21 A3 4f light red 5.00 5.00
22 A4 10f deep blue 32.50 32.50
Nos. 19-22 (4) 55.00 55.00
Set, never hinged 75.00

1st anniv. of the establishing of the State. Nos. 19-22 were printed in sheets of 100 with a special printing in sheets of 20.

Type of 1932
Perf. 13x13½

1934, Feb. Engr. Wmk. 239

Granite Paper

23 A1 ½f dark brown 2.00 1.65
24 A1 1f red brown 2.00 .90
25 A1 1½f dark violet 5.50 1.75
26 A1 2f slate 4.00 1.50
27 A1 3f brown 3.00 .60
28 A1 4f olive brown 25.00 3.50
29 A1 10f deep orange 9.00 1.00
30 A2 15f rose 450.00 200.00
31 A2 1y violet 25.00 10.00
Nos. 23-31 (9) 525.50 220.90

For surcharge see No. 60.

Emperor's Palace — A5

Phoenix — A6

1934, Mar. 1 — *Perf. 12½*

32 A5 1½f orange brown 4.25 4.25
33 A6 3f carmine 4.25 1.75
34 A5 6f green 7.50 7.50
35 A6 10f dark blue 19.00 17.50
Nos. 32-35 (4) 35.00 31.00
Set, never hinged 47.50

Enthronement of Emperor Kang Teh. Nos. 32-35 were printed in sheets of 100, with a special printing in sheets of 20.

No. 6 Surcharged in Black

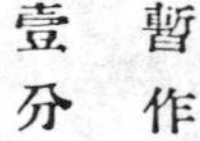

壹 暫
分 作

Perf. 13x13½

1934 Unwmk. White Paper

36 A1 1f on 4f olive grn 5.50 2.50
a. Brown surcharge 37.50 37.50
b. Upper left character of surcharge omitted
c. Inverted surcharge 110.00 110.00

Pagoda at Liaoyang A7

Emperor Kang Teh A8

Six characters in top label instead of five as in 1932-34 issues.
Inscription reads "Manchu Empire Postal Administration."

Perf. 13x13½

1934-36 Wmk. 239 Engr.

Granite Paper

37 A7 ½f brown .50 .35
38 A7 1f red brown 1.00 .30
39 A7 1½f dk violet 1.00 .50
a. Booklet pane of 6 55.00
41 A7 3f brown ('35) .55 .35
a. Booklet pane of 6 65.00
42 A7 5f dk blue ('35) 7.00 1.50
43 A7 5f gray ('36) 3.00 1.25
44 A7 6f rose ('35) 3.00 .60
45 A7 7f dk gray ('36) 2.50 2.00
47 A7 9f red orange ('35) 2.50 .75
50 A8 15f ver ('35) 2.50 .85
51 A8 18f Prus grn ('35) 25.00 4.50
52 A8 20f dk brown ('35) 3.50 .90
53 A8 30f orange brn ('35) 4.50 .90
54 A8 50f ol grn ('35) 5.50 2.00
55 A8 1y dk violet ('35) 20.00 6.00
a. 1y violet 20.00 8.00
Nos. 37-55 (15) 82.05 22.75
Set, never hinged 110.00

4f and 8f, type A7, were prepared but not issued.

1935 Wmk. 242 *Perf. 13x13½*

57 A7 10f deep blue 8.00 1.50
58 A8 13f light brown 10.00 4.50
Set, never hinged 25.00

Nos. 6 and 28 Surcharged in Black

三 暫
分 作

1935 White Paper Unwmk.

59 A1 3f on 4f ol grn 65.00 55.00
Never hinged 85.00

1935 Granite Paper Wmk. 239

60 A1 3f on 4f olive brn 6.50 3.00
Never hinged 9.00

Similar Surcharge on No. 14

1935 White Paper Unwmk.

61 A2 3f on 16f turq grn 15.00 9.00
Never hinged 20.00
Nos. 59-61 (3) 86.50 66.00

Orchid Crest of Manchukuo A9

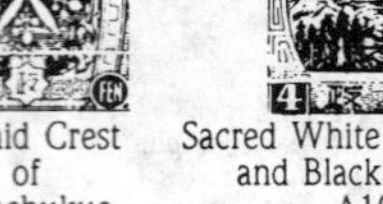

Sacred White Mountains and Black Waters A10

1935, Jan. 1 Litho. Wmk. 141

Granite Paper

62 A9 2f green 3.50 1.40
63 A10 4f dull ol grn 1.50 1.00
64 A9 8f ocher 3.00 2.00
65 A10 12f brown red 11.00 7.00
Nos. 62-65 (4) 19.00 11.40
Set, never hinged 27.50

Nos. 62-65 exist imperforate.

1935 Wmk. 242

66 A9 2f yellow green 3.50 .60
68 A9 8f ocher 6.00 1.65
70 A10 12f brown red 11.00 4.00
Nos. 66-70 (3) 20.50 6.25
Set, never hinged 29.00

Nos. 62-70 issued primarily to pay postage to China, but valid for any postal use.
See Nos. 75-78, 113, 115, 158. For surcharges see Nos. 101, 103-104, 106-109, People's Republic of China No. 2L19.

Mt. Fuji — A11

Phoenix — A12

Perf. 11, 12½ and Compound

1935, Apr. 1 Engr. Wmk. 242

71 A11 1½f dull green 2.25 1.50
72 A12 3f orange 2.25 2.00
a. 3f red orange 6.00 5.00
73 A11 6f dk carmine 5.50 4.75
a. Horiz. pair, imperf. btwn. 200.00
b. Perf. 11x12½ 27.50 27.50
74 A12 10f dark blue 5.50 6.00
a. Perf. 12½x11 22.50 20.00
b. Perf. 12½ 22.50
Nos. 71-74 (4) 15.50 14.25
Set, never hinged 22.00

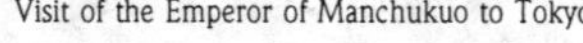

Visit of the Emperor of Manchukuo to Tokyo.

Orchid Crest — A13

Types of A9 & A10
Redrawn and Engraved

1936 Wmk. 242 *Perf. 13x13½*

75 A13 2f lt green .75 .30
76 A10 4f olive green 2.75 .55
77 A13 8f ocher 1.75 .75
78 A10 12f orange brn 37.50 27.50
Nos. 75-78 (4) 42.75 29.10
Set, never hinged 57.50

Unbroken lines of shading in the background of Nos. 76 and 78. Shading has been removed from right and left of the mountains. Nearly all lines have been removed from the lake. There are numerous other alterations in the design.
Issued primarily to pay postage to China, but valid for any postal use.
See #112. For surcharges see #102-106.

Wild Goose over Sea of Japan — A14

Communications Building at Hsinking — A15

Perf. 12x12½, 12½x12

1936, Jan. 26 Wmk. 242

79 A14 1½f black brown 2.50 2.25
80 A15 3f rose lilac 2.50 .55
81 A14 6f carmine rose 6.00 6.00
82 A15 10f blue 7.00 6.50
Nos. 79-82 (4) 18.00 15.30
Set, never hinged 40.00

Postal convention with Japan.

New State Council Building A16

Carting Soybeans A17

North Mausoleum at Mukden A18

Summer Palace at Chengteh A19

1936-37 Wmk. 242 *Perf. 13x13½*

83 A16 ½f brown .40 .15
84 A16 1f red brown .40 .15
85 A16 1½f violet 3.50 2.75
a. Booklet pane of 6 80.00
86 A17 2f lt green ('37) .40 .15
a. Booklet pane of 6 27.50
87 A16 3f chocolate .40 .15
a. Booklet pane of 6 150.00
88 A18 4f lt ol grn ('37) .40 .15
a. Booklet pane of 6 30.00
89 A16 5f gray black 20.00 7.50
90 A17 6f carmine .45 .15
91 A18 7f brown blk .70 .30
92 A18 9f red orange .75 .35
93 A19 10f blue .85 .15
94 A18 12f dp orange ('37) .55 .15
95 A18 13f brown 32.50 32.50
96 A18 15f carmine 1.10 .35
97 A17 20f dk brown 1.10 .35
98 A19 30f chestnut brn 1.10 .35
99 A17 50f olive green 1.50 .50
100 A19 1y violet 3.00 .60
Nos. 83-100 (18) 69.10 46.75
Set, never hinged 105.00

Nos. 83, 84, 86, 88 and 93 are known imperforate but were not regularly issued.
See Nos. 159-163. For overprints see Nos. 140-141, 148-151. For surcharges see People's Republic of China Nos. 2L1-2L2, 2L11-2L18, 2L20-2L37, 2L40-2L52.

暫作貳分五厘
a

暫作五分
b

暫作壹角參分
c

暫作二分五厘
d

1937

Surcharged on No. 66

101 A9 (a) 2½f on 2f 1.75 1.50

Surcharged on Nos. 75, 76 and 78

102 A13 (a) 2½f on 2f 1.75 1.50
103 A10 (b) 5f on 4f 3.00 2.50
104 A10 (c) 13f on 12f 9.00 9.00

Surcharged in Black on Nos. 75, 76 and 70

Space between bottom characters of surcharge 4½mm

105 A13 (d) 2½f on 2f 1.75 1.50
a. Inverted surcharge 110.00 85.00
b. Vert. pair, one without surch. 95.00
106 A10 (b) 5f on 4f 2.50 1.65
107 A10 (c) 13f on 12f 9.00 8.00

Surcharged on No. 70

Space between characters 6½mm

108 A10 (c) 13f on 12f 175.00 150.00

Same Surcharge on No. 63

Space between characters 4½mm

Wmk. 141

109 A10 (b) 5f on 4f 6.00 5.00
Nos. 101-109 (9) 209.75 180.65
Set, never hinged 300.00

Nos. 101-109 were issued primarily to pay postage to China, but were valid for any postal use.

Rising Sun over Manchurian Plain — A20

Composite Picture of Manchurian City — A21

Perf. 12½

1937, Mar. 1 Litho. Unwmk.

110 A20 1½f carmine rose 3.00 3.00
111 A21 3f blue green 3.00 2.00
Set, never hinged 7.50

5th anniv. of the founding of the State of Manchukuo.

Types of 1936

Perf. 13x13½

1937 Wmk. 242 Engr.

112 A13 2½f dk violet .70 .30
113 A10 5f black .25 .20
115 A10 13f dk red brown .45 .30
Nos. 112-115 (3) 1.40 .80
Set, never hinged 1.90

Issued primarily to pay postage to China, but were valid for any postal use.

Pouter Pigeon A22

National Flag and Buildings A23

Perf. 12x12½

1937, Sept. 16 Unwmk.

116 A22 2f dark violet 1.50 1.50
117 A23 4f rose carmine 1.50 1.00
118 A22 10f dark green 3.50 2.00
119 A23 20f dark blue 5.00 5.00
Nos. 116-119 (4) 11.50 9.50
Set, never hinged 15.00

Completion of the national capital, Hsinking, under the first Five-Year Construction Plan.

Map — A24

Dept. of Justice Building — A27

Japanese Residents' Association Building A25

Postal Administration Building — A26

Perf. 12x12½, 13

1937, Dec. 1 Litho. Unwmk.

121 A24 2f dark carmine 1.00 .80
122 A25 4f green 1.75 1.10
123 A25 8f orange 4.00 3.25
124 A26 10f blue 4.00 3.50
125 A27 12f lt violet 5.00 4.50
126 A26 20f lilac brown 5.50 5.00
Nos. 121-126 (6) 21.25 18.15
Set, never hinged 27.50

Issued in commemoration of the abolition of extraterritorial rights within Manchukuo.

New Year Greetings — A28

Map and Cross — A29

1937, Dec. 15 Engr. *Perf. 12x12½*

127 A28 2f dk blue & red 2.00 .55
Never hinged 2.50
a. Double impression of border

Issued to pay postage on New Year's greeting cards.

Wmk. 242

1938, Oct. 15 Litho. *Perf. 13*

128 A29 2f lake & scarlet .70 .60
129 A29 4f slate grn & scar .70 .60
Set, never hinged 1.85

Founding of the Red Cross Soc. in Manchukuo.

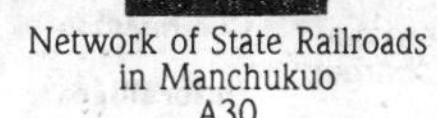

Network of State Railroads in Manchukuo A30

Express Train "Asia" A31

1939, Oct. 21

130 A30 2f dk org, blk & dp bl .90 .80
131 A31 4f dp blue & indigo .90 .80
Set, never hinged 2.75

Attainment of 10,000 kilometers in the railway mileage in Manchuria.

Stork Flying above Mast of Imperial Flagship — A32

1940 Photo. Unwmk.

132 A32 2f brt red violet .20 .20
133 A32 4f brt green .30 .30
Set, never hinged .60

Second visit of Emperor Kang Teh to Emperor Hirohito of Japan.

Census Taker and Map of Manchukuo — A33

Census Form — A34

1940, Sept. 10 Litho. Wmk. 242

134 A33 2f vio brn & org .20 .20
135 A34 4f black & green .30 .25
a. Double impression of green 30.00
Set, never hinged .60

National census starting Oct. 1.

Message of Congratulation from Premier Chang Ching-hui — A35

Dragon Dance A36

1940, Sept. 18 Engr.

136 A35 2f carmine .20 .25
137 A36 4f indigo .30 .35
a. Imperf., pair 90.00
Set, never hinged .60

2600th anniversary of the birth of the Japanese Empire.

Soldier — A37

1941, May 25 Photo. Unwmk.

138 A37 2f deep carmine .25 .25
139 A37 4f bright ultra .30 .30
Set, never hinged .65

Conscription Law, effective June 1, 1941.

Nos. 86 and 88 Overprinted in Red or Blue

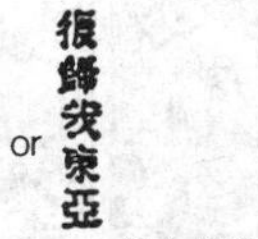

Perf. 13x13½

1942, Feb. 16 Wmk. 242

140 A17 2f lt green (R) .20 .20
141 A18 4f lt olive grn (Bl) .30 .30
Set, never hinged .60

"Return of Singapore to East Asia, 9th year of Kang Teh."

Kengoku Shrine A38

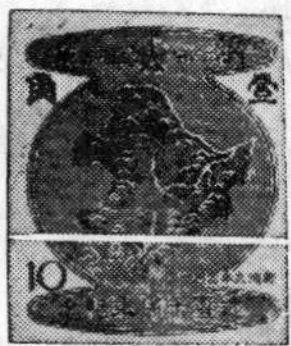

Map of Manchukuo A39

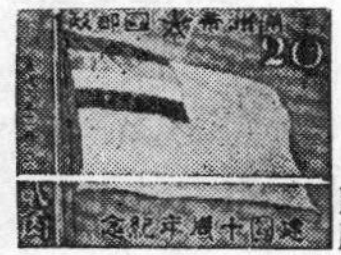

Flag of Manchukuo — A40

Perf. 12x12½, 12½x12

1942, Mar. 1 Engr.

142 A38 2f carmine .30 .30
143 A38 4f lilac .30 .30
144 A39 10f red, *yel* .90 .90
145 A40 20f indigo, *yel* 1.00 1.00
Nos. 142-145 (4) 2.50 2.50
Set, never hinged 3.25

"10th anniv. of Manchukuo, Mar. 1, 1942."

Allegory of National Harmony — A41

Women of Five Races, Dancing — A42

1942, Sept. 15

146 A41 3f orange .30 .30
147 A42 6f light green .45 .45
Set, never hinged 1.00

"10th anniv. of the founding of Manchukuo, Sept. 15, 1942."

Nos. 87 and 90 Overprinted in Green or Blue

1942, Dec. 8 *Perf. 13x13½*

148 A16 3f chocolate (G) .25 .25
149 A17 6f carmine (Bl) .25 .25
Set, never hinged .60

1st anniv. of the "Greater East Asia War." The overprint reads "Asiatic Prosperity Began This Day December 8, 1941."

Nos. 87 and 90 Overprinted in Red or Blue

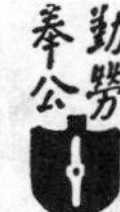

1943, May 1

150 A16 3f chocolate (R) .25 .25
151 A17 6f carmine (Bl) .25 .25
Set, never hinged .60

Proclamation of the labor service law.

Red Cross Nurse Carrying Stretcher A43

Smelting Furnace A44

1943, Oct. 1 Photo.

152 A43 6f green .30 .30
Never hinged .35

5th anniv. of the founding of the Red Cross Society of Manchukuo, Oct. 1, 1938.

1943, Dec. 8 Unwmk. *Perf. 13*

153 A44 6f red brown	.30	.30
Never hinged	.35	

2nd anniv. of the "Greater East Asia War."

Chinese Characters A45

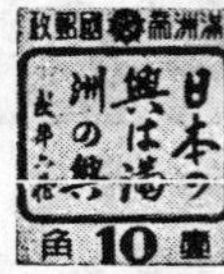
Japanese Characters A46

Perf. 13x13½

1944 Wmk. 242 Litho.

154 A45 10f rose	.75	.75
a. Imperf., vert. pair #154, 155	10.00	
b. Vert. pair #154, 155	1.50	1.50
155 A46 10f rose	.75	.75
156 A45 40f gray green	1.75	1.75
a. Imperf., vert. pair #156, 157	15.00	
b. 40f with 10f vignette, perf.	50.00	45.00
c. 40f with 10f vignette, imperf.	100.00	
d. Vert. pair #156, 157	3.50	3.50
157 A46 40f gray green	1.75	1.75
Nos. 154-157 (4)	5.00	5.00
Set, never hinged	6.75	

"Japan's Progress Is Manchukuo's Progress." Issued as propaganda for the close relationship of Japan and Manchukuo.

Frames of the 10f vignettes have rounded corners, those of the 40f vignettes have indented corners.

Types of 1935 and 1936-37

1944-45 Litho.

158 A10 5f gray black	1.00	1.00
a. Imperf., pair	6.00	
159 A17 6f crimson rose	2.50	2.50
160 A19 10f light blue	4.00	4.00
161 A17 20f brown	1.10	1.65
162 A19 30f buff ('45)	1.40	1.65
163 A19 1y dull lilac	1.65	2.50
Nos. 158-163 (6)	11.65	13.30
Set, never hinged	17.50	

For surcharges see People's Republic of China Nos. 2L1, 2L14, 2L19, 2L24, 2L27, 2L30-2L31, 2L35, 2L37, 2L49, 2L52.

"One Heart, One Soul" — A47

1945, May 2

164 A47 10f red	.30	.30
Never hinged	.40	
a. Imperf., pair	2.25	2.25

Emperor's edict of May 2, 1935, 10th anniv.

AIR POST STAMPS

Sheep Grazing AP1

Railroad Bridge AP2

Wmk. Characters (242)
Perf. 13x13½

1936-37 Engr. Granite Paper

C1 AP1 18f green	12.50	12.50
C2 AP1 19f blue green ('37)	3.00	3.50
C3 AP2 38f blue	12.50	13.00
C4 AP2 39f deep blue ('37)	1.50	1.75
Nos. C1-C4 (4)	29.50	30.75
Set, never hinged	40.00	

MARIANA ISLANDS

ˌmar-ē-ˈa-nə ˈī-ləndz

LOCATION — A group of 14 islands in the West Pacific Ocean, about 1500 miles east of the Philippines.

GOVT. — Possession of Spain, then of Germany
AREA — 246 sq. mi.
POP. — 44,025 (1935)
CAPITAL — Saipan

Until 1899 this group belonged to Spain but in that year all except Guam were ceded to Germany.

100 Centavos = 1 Peso
100 Pfennig = 1 Mark (1899)

Values for unused stamps are for examples with original gum as defined in the catalogue introduction. Very fine examples of Nos. 1-6 will have perforations touching or just cutting into the design. Stamps with perfs clear on all sides and well centered are rare and sell for substantially more.

Issued under Spanish Dominion

King Alfonso XIII — A1

Stamps of the Philippines Handstamped Vertically in Blackish Violet Reading Up or Down

1899, Sept. Unwmk. *Perf. 14*

1 A1 2c dark blue green	425.00	80.00
2 A1 3c dark brown	300.00	75.00
3 A1 5c car rose	425.00	75.00
4 A1 6c dark blue	2,100.	750.00
5 A1 8c gray brown	275.00	75.00
6 A1 15c slate green	1,000.	450.00

Overprint forgeries of Nos. 1-6 exist.

Issued under German Dominion

Stamps of Germany, 1889-90, Overprinted in Black at 56 degree Angle

Perf. 13½x14½

1900, May Unwmk.

11 A9 3pf dark brn	15.00	*35.00*
12 A9 5pf green	20.00	*35.00*
13 A10 10pf carmine	25.00	*40.00*
14 A10 20pf ultra	30.00	*115.00*
15 A10 25pf orange	65.00	*150.00*
b. Inverted overprint	*3,250.*	
16 A10 50pf red brn	75.00	*200.00*
Nos. 11-16 (6)	230.00	*575.00*

Forged cancellations exist on Nos. 11-16, 17-29.

Overprinted at 48 degree Angle

1899, Nov. 18

11a A9 3pf light brown	*1,500.*	*1,600.*
12a A9 5pf green	*2,250.*	*1,100.*
13a A10 10pf carmine	200.00	300.00
14a A10 20pf ultra	200.00	300.00
15a A10 25pf orange	*2,500.*	*2,250.*
16a A10 50pf red brown	*2,500.*	*2,250.*

Kaiser's Yacht "Hohenzollern"
A4 A5

1901, Jan. Typo. *Perf. 14*

17 A4 3pf brown	1.10	1.10
18 A4 5pf green	1.10	1.25
19 A4 10pf carmine	1.10	*4.00*
20 A4 20pf ultra	1.50	*10.00*
21 A4 25pf org & blk, *yel*	1.75	*17.50*
22 A4 30pf org & blk, *sal*	1.75	*17.50*
23 A4 40pf lake & blk	2.25	*17.50*
24 A4 50pf pur & blk, *sal*	2.25	*17.50*
25 A4 80pf lake & blk, *rose*	3.00	*30.00*

Engr.
Perf. 14½x14

26 A5 1m carmine	3.50	*80.00*
27 A5 2m blue	7.50	*100.00*
28 A5 3m blk vio	10.00	*150.00*
29 A5 5m slate & car	175.00	*500.00*
Nos. 17-29 (13)	211.80	

Wmk. Lozenges (125)

1916-19 Typo. *Perf. 14*

30 A4 3pf brown ('19)	1.00	

Engr.
Perf. 14½x14

31 A5 5m slate & carmine	25.00	

Nos. 30 and 31 were never placed in use.

MARIENWERDER

mä-ˈrē-ən-ˌve(ə)rd-ər

LOCATION — Northeastern Germany, bordering on Poland
GOVT. — A district of West Prussia

By the Versailles Treaty the greater portion of West Prussia was ceded to Poland but the district of Marienwerder was allowed a plebiscite which was held in 1920 and resulted in favor of Germany.

100 Pfennig = 1 Mark

Plebiscite Issues

Symbolical of Allied Supervision of the Plebiscite — A1

1920 Unwmk. Litho. *Perf. 11½*

1 A1 5pf green	.45	.35
2 A1 10pf rose red	.40	.30
3 A1 15pf gray	.55	.40
4 A1 20pf brn org	.35	.25
5 A1 25pf deep blue	.75	.55
6 A1 30pf orange	1.25	.85
7 A1 40pf brown	.75	.55
8 A1 50pf violet	.75	.45
9 A1 60pf red brown	4.50	2.75
10 A1 75pf chocolate	1.25	.90
11 A1 1m brn & grn	.90	.70
12 A1 2m dk vio	4.50	3.25
13 A1 3m red	5.25	3.75
14 A1 5m blue & rose	22.50	16.00
Nos. 1-14 (14)	44.15	31.05

These stamps occasionally show parts of two papermakers' watermarks, consisting of the letters "O. B. M." with two stars before and after, or "P. & C. M."

Nos. 1-14 exist imperf.; value for set, $700. Nearly all exist part perf.

Stamps of Germany, 1905-19, Overprinted

Commission
Interalliée
Marienwerder

1920 Wmk. 125 *Perf. 14, 14½*

24 A16 5pf green	15.00	*25.00*
a. Inverted overprint	130.00	*210.00*
26 A16 20pf bl vio	6.00	*10.00*
a. Inverted overprint	80.00	*130.00*
b. Double overprint	80.00	*150.00*
28 A16 50pf vio & blk, *buff*	325.00	*650.00*
29 A16 75pf grn & blk	4.25	*6.00*
a. Inverted overprint	80.00	*100.00*
30 A16 80pf lake & blk, *rose*	85.00	*150.00*
31 A17 1m car rose	90.00	*175.00*
a. Inverted overprint	325.00	*650.00*
Nos. 24-31 (6)	525.25	*1,016.*

Trial impressions were made in red, green and lilac, and with 2½mm instead of 3mm space between the lines of the overprint. These were printed on the 75pf and 80pf. The 1 mark was overprinted with the same words in 3 lines of large sans-serif capitals. All these are essays. Some were passed through the post, apparently with speculative intent.

Stamps of Germany, 1905-18, Surcharged

1 Mark 1
Commission
Interalliée
Marienwerder

32 A22 1m on 2pf gray	20.00	*35.00*
33 A22 2m on 2½pf gray	9.00	*15.00*
a. Inverted surcharge	45.00	*90.00*
34 A16 3m on 3pf brown	12.00	*17.50*
a. Double surcharge	45.00	*90.00*
b. Inverted surcharge	45.00	*90.00*
35 A22 5m on 7½pf org	9.00	*17.50*
a. Inverted surcharge	45.00	*90.00*
b. Double surcharge	45.00	*90.00*
Nos. 32-35 (4)	50.00	*85.00*

There are two types of the letters "M," "C," "i" and "e" and of the numerals "2" and "5" in these surcharges.

Counterfeits exist of Nos. 24-35.

Stamps of Germany, 1920, Overprinted

Commission
Interalliée
Marienwerder

1920, July *Perf. 15x14½*

36 A17 1m red	3.25	*5.00*
37 A17 1.25m green	3.50	*6.00*
38 A17 1.50m yellow brown	3.50	*8.00*
39 A21 2.50m lilac rose	3.25	*5.00*
Nos. 36-39 (4)	13.50	*24.00*

A2

1920 Unwmk. *Perf. 11½*

40 A2 5pf green	2.75	2.00
41 A2 10pf rose red	2.75	2.00
42 A2 15pf gray	12.50	11.00
43 A2 20pf brn org	1.75	1.50
44 A2 25pf dp bl	15.00	12.50
45 A2 30pf orange	1.50	1.00
46 A2 40pf brown	1.00	.55
47 A2 50pf violet	1.75	1.25
48 A2 60pf red brn	5.50	4.00
49 A2 75pf chocolate	6.50	5.50
50 A2 1m brn & grn	1.00	.75
51 A2 2m dk vio	1.50	1.25
52 A2 3m light red	2.00	1.50
53 A2 5m blue & rose	2.75	1.75
Nos. 40-53 (14)	58.25	46.55

MARSHALL ISLANDS

ˈmär-shəl ˈī-ləndz

LOCATION — Two chains of islands in the West Pacific Ocean, about 2,500 miles southeast of Tokyo
GOVT. — Republic
AREA — 70 sq. mi.
POP. — 31,042 (1980)
CAPITAL — Dalap-Uliga-Darrit

The Marshall Islands were German possession from 1885 to 1914. Seized by Japan in 1914, the islands were taken by the US in WW II and became part of the US Trust Territory of the Pacific in 1947. By agreement with the USPS, the islands began issuing their own stamps in 1984, with the USPS continuing to carry the mail to and from the islands.

On Oct. 21, 1986 Marshall Islands became a Federation as a Sovereign State in Compact of Free Association with the US.

100 Pfennig = 1 Mark
100 Cents = 1 Dollar

Catalogue values for unused stamps in this country are for Never Hinged items, beginning with Scott 31 in the regular postage section, and Scott C1 in the airpost section.

Watermark

Wmk. 125-Lozenges

Issued under German Dominion

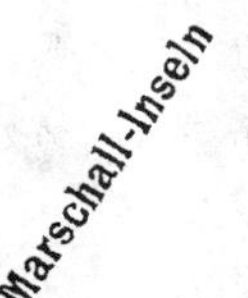

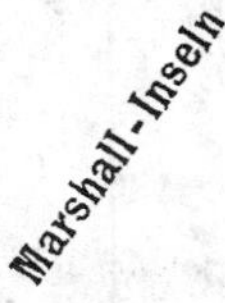

Stamps of Germany Overprinted "Marschall-Inseln" in Black

1897 Unwmk. *Perf.* 13½x14½

1	A9	3pf dk brn	140.00	*550.00*
a.		3pf light brown	*3,500.*	*1,500.*
2	A9	5pf green	125.00	*500.00*
3	A9	10pf carmine	40.00	*90.00*
4	A10	20pf ultra	40.00	*90.00*
5	A10	25pf orange	125.00	
6	A10	50pf red brown	125.00	
		Nos. 1-6 (6)	595.00	

Nos. 5 and 6 were not placed in use, but canceled copies exist.

A small quantity of the 3pf, 5pf, 10pf and 20pf were issued at Jaluit. These have yellowish, dull gum. Later overprintings of Nos. 1-6 were sold only at Berlin, and have white, smooth, shiny gum. No. 1a belongs to the Jaluit issue.

Forged cancellations are found on almost all Marshall Islands stamps.

Overprinted "Marshall-Inseln"

1899-1900

7	A9	3pf dk brn ('00)	4.00	4.75
a.		3pf light brown	110.00	*500.00*
8	A9	5pf green	9.00	7.00
9	A10	10pf car ('00)	11.00	17.00
10	A10	20pf ultra ('00)	17.00	*25.00*
11	A10	25pf orange	20.00	*35.00*
12	A10	50pf red brown	32.50	*50.00*
		Nos. 7-12 (6)	93.50	*138.75*

Kaiser's Yacht "Hohenzollern"
A3 A4

1901 Unwmk. Typo. *Perf.* 14

13	A3	3pf brown	.70	1.50
14	A3	5pf green	.75	1.50
15	A3	10pf carmine	.75	*4.25*
16	A3	20pf ultra	1.10	*8.25*
17	A3	25pf org & blk, *yel*	1.25	*14.00*
18	A3	30pf org & blk, *sal*	1.10	*14.00*
19	A3	40pf lake & blk	1.25	*14.00*
20	A3	50pf pur & blk, *sal*	2.00	*20.00*
21	A3	80pf lake & blk, *rose*	3.00	*40.00*

Engr.

***Perf.* 14½x14**

22	A4	1m carmine	4.00	*67.50*
23	A4	2m blue	5.50	*110.00*
24	A4	3m blk vio	9.00	*175.00*
25	A4	5m slate & car	125.00	*450.00*
		Nos. 13-25 (13)	155.40	

Wmk. Lozenges (125)

1916 Typo. *Perf.* 14

26	A3	3pf brown	.65

Engr.

***Perf.* 14½x14**

27	A4	5m slate & carmine	24.00

Nos. 26 and 27 were never placed in use.

The stamps of Marshall Islands overprinted "G. R. I." and new values in British currency were all used in New Britain and are listed among the issues for that country.

Two unauthorized issues appeared in 1979. The 1st, a set of five for the "Establishment of Government, May 1, 1979," consists of 8c, 15c, 21c, 31c and 75c labels. The 75c is about the size of a postcard. The 2nd, a set of four se-tenant blocks of four 10c labels for the Intl. Year of the Child. This set also exists imperf. and with specimen overprints.

Catalogue values for unused stamps in this section, from this point to the end of the section, are for Never Hinged items.

Inauguration of Postal Service — A5

1984, May 2 Litho. *Perf.* 14x13½

31	A5	20c Outrigger canoe	.45	.45
32	A5	20c Fishnet	.45	.45
33	A5	20c Navigational stick chart	.45	.45
34	A5	20c Islet	.45	.45
a.		Block of 4, #31-34	1.80	1.80

Mili Atoll, Astrolabe — A6

Maps and Navigational Instruments.

1984-85 Litho. *Perf.* 15x14

35	A6	1c shown	.15	.15
36	A6	3c Likiep, Azimuth compass	.15	.15
37	A6	5c Ebon, 16th cent. compass	.15	.15
38	A6	10c Jaluit, anchor buoys	.20	.20
39	A6	13c Ailinginae, Nocturnal	.25	.25
a.		Booklet pane of 10	*8.00*	—
40	A6	14c Wotho Atoll, navigational stick chart	.30	.30
a.		Booklet pane of 10	*7.50*	—
41	A6	20c Kwajalein and Ebeye, stick chart	.40	.40
a.		Booklet pane of 10	*10.00*	—
b.		Bklt. pane, 5 each 13c, 20c	*9.25*	—
42	A6	22c Eniwetok, 18th cent. lodestone storage case	.45	.45
a.		Booklet pane of 10	*9.50*	—
b.		Bklt. pane, 5 each 14c, 22c	*8.50*	—
43	A6	28c Ailinglaplap, printed compass	.55	.55
44	A6	30c Majuro, navigational stick-chart	.60	.60
45	A6	33c Namu, stick chart	.65	.65
46	A6	37c Rongelap, quadrant	.75	.75
47	A6	39c Taka, map compass, 16th cent. sea chart	.80	.80
48	A6	44c Ujelang, chronograph	.90	.90
49	A6	50c Maloelap and Aur, nocturlabe	1.00	1.00
49A	A6	$1 Arno, 16th cent. sector compass	2.00	2.00
		Nos. 35-49A (16)	9.30	9.30

Issue dates: 1c, 3c, 10c, 30c and $1, June 12. 13c, 20c, 28c and 37c. Dec. 19, 1984. 14c, 22c, 33c, 39c, 44c and 50c, June 5, 1985.

See Nos. 107-109.

No. 7 — A7

1984, June 19 *Perf.* 14½x15

50	A7	40c shown	.60	.60
51	A7	40c No. 13	.60	.60
52	A7	40c No. 4	.60	.60
53	A7	40c No. 25	.60	.60
a.		Block of 4, #50-53	2.40	2.40

Philatelic Salon, 19th UPU Congress, Hamburg, June 19-26.

Ausipex '84 A8

Dolphins.

1984, Sept. 5 Litho. *Perf.* 14

54	A8	20c Common	.35	.35
55	A8	20c Risso's	.35	.35
56	A8	20c Spotter	.35	.35
57	A8	20c Bottlenose	.35	.35
a.		Block of 4, #54-57	1.50	1.50

Christmas — A9

Illustration reduced.

1984, Nov. 7 Litho. *Perf.* 14

58	Strip of 4	2.25	2.25
a.-d.	A9 20c any single	.45	.45
e.	Sheet of 16	9.00	

Printed in sheets of 16; background shows text from Marshallese New Testament, giving each stamp on the sheet a different background.

Marshall Islands Constitution, 5th Anniv. — A10

1984, Dec. 19 Litho. *Perf.* 14

59	A10	20c Traditional chief	.40	.40
60	A10	20c Amata Kabua	.40	.40
61	A10	20c Chester Nimitz	.40	.40
62	A10	20c Trygve Lie	.40	.40
a.		Block of 4, #59-62	1.60	1.60

Audubon Bicentenary A11

1985, Feb. 15 Litho. *Perf.* 14

63	A11	22c Forked-tailed Petrel	.60	.60
64	A11	22c Pectoral Sandpiper	.60	.60
a.		Pair, #63-64	1.20	1.20
		Nos. 63-64,C1-C2 (4)	3.00	3.00

Sea Shells — A12

1985, Apr. 17 Litho. *Perf.* 14

65	A12	22c Cymatium lotorium	.45	.45
66	A12	22c Chicoreus cornucervi	.45	.45
67	A12	22c Strombus aurisdanae	.45	.45
68	A12	22c Turbo marmoratus	.45	.45
69	A12	22c Chicoreus palmarosae	.45	.45
a.		Strip of 5, #65-69	2.25	2.25

See Nos. 119-123, 152-156, 216-220.

Decade for Women A13

1985, June 5 Litho. *Perf.* 14

70	A13	22c Native drum	.40	.40
71	A13	22c Palm branches	.40	.40
72	A13	22c Pounding stone	.40	.40
73	A13	22c Ak bird	.40	.40
a.		Block of 4, #70-73	1.65	1.65

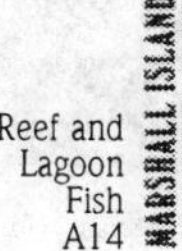

Reef and Lagoon Fish A14

1985, July 15 Litho. *Perf.* 14

74	A14	22c Acanthurus dussumieri	.45	.45
75	A14	22c Adioryx caudimaculatus	.45	.45
76	A14	22c Ostracion meleacaris	.45	.45
77	A14	22c Chaetodon ephippium	.45	.45
a.		Block of 4, #74-77	1.80	1.80

Intl. Youth Year A15

IYY and Alele Nautical Museum emblems and: No. 78, Marshallese youths and Peace Corps volunteers playing basketball. No. 79, Legend teller reciting local history, girl listening to recording. No. 80, Islander explaining navigational stick charts. No. 81, Jabwa stick dance.

1985, Aug. 31 Litho. *Perf.* 14

78	A15	22c multicolored	.45	.45
79	A15	22c multicolored	.45	.45
80	A15	22c multicolored	.45	.45
81	A15	22c multicolored	.45	.45
a.		Block of 4, #78-81	1.80	1.80

1856 American Board of Commissions Stock Certificate for Foreign Missions — A16

Missionary ship Morning Star I: 22c, Launch, Jothan Stetson Shipyard, Chelsea, MA, Aug. 7, 1857. 33c, First voyage, Honolulu to the Marshalls, 1857. 44c, Marshall islanders pulling Morning Star I into Ebon Lagoon, 1857.

TRUST TERRITORIES
Palau • Micronesia • Marshall Is.

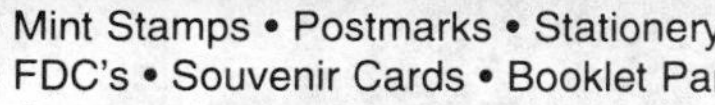

• Mint Stamps • Postmarks • Stationery
• FDC's • Souvenir Cards • Booklet Panes
• Commemorative Panels • Precancels
• German Colony Forerunners

WRITE FOR...
★ FREE PRICELIST ★
Phone/Fax 609-409-9110
MIKE ARMUS
P.O. Box SP-201, Jamesburg, NJ 08831-0201

1985, Oct. 21 Litho. *Perf. 14*
82 A16 14c multicolored .25 .25
83 A16 22c multicolored .45 .45
84 A16 33c multicolored .65 .65
85 A16 44c multicolored .90 .90
Nos. 82-85 (4) 2.25 2.25

Christmas.

US Space Shuttle, Astro Telescope, Halley's Comet — A17

Comet tail and research spacecraft: No. 87, Planet A Space Probe, Japan. No. 88, Giotto spacecraft, European Space Agency. No. 89, INTERCOSMOS Project Vega spacecraft, Russia, France, etc. No. 90, US naval tracking ship, NASA observational aircraft, cameo portrait of Edmond Halley (1656-1742), astronomer. Se-tenant in continuous design.

1985, Nov. 21
86 A17 22c multicolored 1.00 1.00
87 A17 22c multicolored 1.00 1.00
88 A17 22c multicolored 1.00 1.00
89 A17 22c multicolored 1.00 1.00
90 A17 22c multicolored 1.00 1.00
a. Strip of 5, #86-90 5.00 5.00

Marshall Islands 22c

Medicinal Plants A18

1985, Dec. 31 Litho. *Perf. 14*
91 A18 22c Sida fallax .45 .45
92 A18 22c Scaevola frutescens .45 .45
93 A18 22c Guettarda speciosa .45 .45
94 A18 22c Cassytha filiformis .45 .45
a. Block of 4, #91-94 1.90 1.90

Maps Type of 1984

1986-87 *Perf. 15x14, 14 ($10)*
107 A6 $2 Wotje and Erikub, terrestrial globe, 1571 5.00 5.00
108 A6 $5 Bikini, Stick chart 11.00 11.00

Size: 31x31mm
109 A6 $10 Stick chart of the atolls 17.00 17.00
Nos. 107-109 (3) 33.00 33.00

Issued: $2, $5, 3/7/86; $10, 3/31/87.

Marine Invertebrates — A19

1986, Mar. 31 Litho. *Perf. 14½x14*
110 A19 14c Triton's trumpet .35 .35
111 A19 14c Giant clam .35 .35
112 A19 14c Small giant clam .35 .35
113 A19 14c Coconut crab .35 .35
a. Block of 4, #110-113 1.50 1.50

Souvenir Sheet

MARSHALL ISLANDS

Operation Crossroads, Atomic Bomb Tests, 40th Anniv. A21

Designs: No. 115, King Juda, Bikinians sailing tibinal canoe. No. 116, USS Sumner, amphibious DUKW, advance landing. No. 117, Evacuating Bikinians. No. 118, Land reclamation, 1986.

1986, July 1 Litho. *Perf. 14*
115 A21 22c multicolored .45 .45
116 A21 22c multicolored .45 .45
117 A21 22c multicolored .45 .45
118 A21 22c multicolored .45 .45
a. Block of 4, #115-118 1.90 1.90

See No. C7.

Seashells Type of 1985

1986, Aug. 1 Litho. *Perf. 14*
119 A12 22c Ramose murex .45 .45
120 A12 22c Orange spider .45 .45
121 A12 22c Red-mouth frog shell .45 .45
122 A12 22c Laciniate conch .45 .45
123 A12 22c Giant frog shell .45 .45
a. Strip of 5, #119-123 2.25 2.25

Game Fish A22

1986, Sept. 10 Litho.
124 A22 22c Blue marlin .50 .50
125 A22 22c Wahoo .50 .50
126 A22 22c Dolphin fish .50 .50
127 A22 22c Yellowfin tuna .50 .50
a. Block of 4, #124-127 2.00 2.00

Christmas, Intl. Peace Year — A23

1986, Oct. 28 Litho. *Perf. 14*
128 A23 22c United Nations UR .60 .60
129 A23 22c United Nations UL .60 .60
130 A23 22c United Nations LR .60 .60
131 A23 22c United Nations LL .60 .60
a. Block of 4, #128-131 2.50 2.50

See No. C8.

US Whaling Ships — A24

1987, Feb. 20 Litho. *Perf. 14*
132 A24 22c James Arnold, 1854 .50 .50
133 A24 22c General Scott, 1859 .50 .50
134 A24 22c Charles W. Morgan, 1865 .50 .50
135 A24 22c Lucretia, 1884 .50 .50
a. Block of 4, #132-135 2.00 2.00

Historic and Military Flights A25

Designs: No. 136, Charles Lindbergh commemorative medal, Spirit of St. Louis crossing the Atlantic, 1927. No. 137, Lindbergh flying in the Battle of the Marshalls, 1944. No. 138, William Bridgeman flying in the Battle of Kwajalein, 1944. No. 139, Bridgeman testing the Douglas Skyrocket, 1951. No. 140, John Glenn flying in the Battle of the Marshalls. No. 141, Glenn, the first American to orbit the Earth, 1962.

1987, Mar. 12 Litho. *Perf. 14½*
136 A25 33c multicolored .75 .75
137 A25 33c multicolored .75 .75
a. Pair, #136-137 1.50 1.50
138 A25 39c multicolored .80 .80
139 A25 39c multicolored .80 .80
a. Pair, #138-139 1.60 1.60
140 A25 44c multicolored .90 .90
141 A25 44c multicolored .90 .90
a. Pair, #140-141 1.80 1.80
Nos. 136-141 (6) 4.90 4.90

Souvenir Sheet

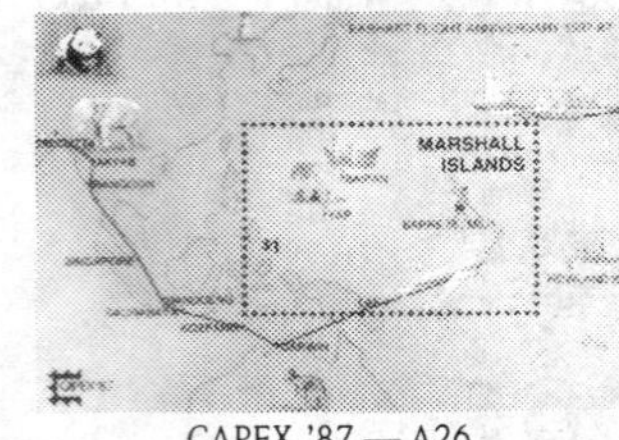

CAPEX '87 — A26

1987, June 15 Litho. *Perf. 14*
142 A26 $1 Map of flight 2.25 2.25

Amelia Earhart (1897-1937), American aviator who died during attempted round-the-world flight, 50th anniv. No. 142 has multicolored margin picturing Earhart's flight pattern from Calcutta, India, to the crash site near Barre Is., Marshall Is.

US Constitution Bicentennial — A27

Excerpts from the Marshall Islands and US Constitutions.

1987, July 16 Litho. *Perf. 14*
143 A27 14c We,... Marshall .35 .35
144 A27 14c National seals .35 .35
145 A27 14c We,... United States .35 .35
a. Triptych, #143-145 1.10 1.10
146 A27 22c All we have... .45 .45
147 A27 22c Flags .45 .45
148 A27 22c to establish... .45 .45
a. Triptych, #146-148 1.40 1.40
149 A27 44c With this Constitution... .90 .90
150 A27 44c Stick chart, Liberty Bell .90 .90
151 A27 44c to promote... .90 .90
a. Triptych, #149-151 2.75 2.75
Nos. 143-151 (9) 5.10 5.10

Triptychs printed in continuous designs.

Seashells Type of 1985

1987, Sept. 1 Litho. *Perf. 14*
152 A12 22c Magnificent cone .50 .50
153 A12 22c Partridge tun .50 .50
154 A12 22c Scorpion spider conch .50 .50
155 A12 22c Hairy triton .50 .50
156 A12 22c Chiragra spider conch .50 .50
a. Strip of 5, #152-156 2.50 2.50

Copra Industry A28

Contest-winning crayon drawings by Amram Enox; design contest sponsored by the Tobular Copra Processing Co.

1987, Dec. 10 Litho. *Perf. 14*
157 A28 44c Planting coconut .75 .75
158 A28 44c Making copra .75 .75
159 A28 44c Bottling coconut oil .75 .75
a. Triptych, #157-159 2.25 2.25

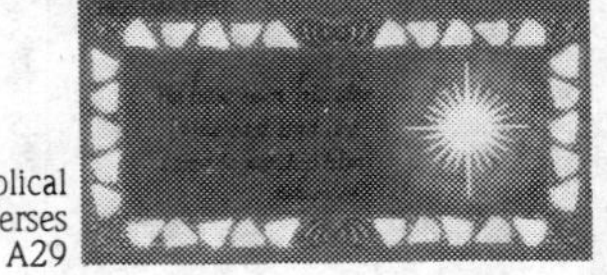

Biblical Verses A29

1987, Dec. 10
160 A29 14c Matthew 2:1 .25 .25
161 A29 22c Luke 2:14 .40 .40
162 A29 33c Psalms 33:3 .60 .60
163 A29 44c Psalms 150:5 .75 .75
Nos. 160-163 (4) 2.00 2.00

Christmas.

Marine Birds — A30

1988, Jan. 27
164 A30 44c Pacific reef herons .75 .75
165 A30 44c Bar-tailed godwit .75 .75
166 A30 44c Masked booby .75 .75
167 A30 44c Northern shoveler .75 .75
a. Block of 4, #164-167 3.00 3.00

Fish — A31 MARSHALL ISLANDS

Perf. 14½x14, 14 (#187)

1988-89 Litho.
168 A31 1c Damselfish .15 .15
169 A31 3c Blackface butterflyfish .15 .15
170 A31 14c Hawkfish .25 .25
a. Booklet pane of 10 3.75 —
171 A31 15c Balloonfish .25 .25
a. Booklet pane of 10 4.50 —
172 A31 17c Trunk fish .30 .30
173 A31 22c Lyretail wrasse .35 .35
a. Booklet pane of 10 5.00 —
b. Bklt. pane of 10 (5 each 14c, 22c) 5.00 —
174 A31 25c Parrotfish .35 .35
a. Booklet pane of 10 7.25 —
b. Bklt. pane of 10 (5 each 15c, 25c) 7.25 —
175 A31 33c White-spotted boxfish .60 .60
176 A31 36c Spotted boxfish .65 .65
177 A31 39c Surgeonfish .75 .75
178 A31 44c Long-snouted butterflyfish .80 .80
179 A31 45c Trumpetfish .80 .80
180 A31 56c Sharp-nosed puffer 1.00 1.00
181 A31 $1 Seahorse 1.90 1.90
182 A31 $2 Ghost pipefish 3.50 3.50
183 A31 $5 Big-spotted triggerfish 8.50 8.50
184 A31 $10 Blue jack ('89) 18.00 18.00
Nos. 168-184 (17) 38.30 38.30

Issued: #170a, 173a, 173b, 3/31/88; 15c, 25c, 36c, 45c, 7/19/; #171a, 174a, 174b, 12/15; $10, 3/31/89; others, 3/17/88.

A32

1988 Summer Olympics, Seoul — A33

Athletes in motion: 15c, Javelin thrower (Nos. 188a-188e as shown). 25c, Runner (Nos. 189a-189e as shown). Illustrations reduced.

1988, June 30 Litho. *Perf. 14*
188 Strip of 5 1.65 1.65
a.-e. A32 15c any single .30 .30
189 Strip of 5 2.25 2.25
a.-e. A33 25c any single .45 .45

Souvenir Sheet

Pacific Voyages of Robert Louis Stevenson — A34

Stick chart of the Marshalls and: a, *Casco* sailing through the Golden Gate. b, At the Needles of Ua-Pu, Marquesas. c, *Equator* departing from Honolulu and Kaiulani, an Hawaian princess. d, Chief's canoe, Majuro Lagoon. e, Bronze medallion, 1887, by Augustus St. Gaudens in the Tate Gallery, London. f, Outrigger canoe and S.S. *Janet Nicoll* in Majuro Lagoon. g, View of Apemama, Gilbert Is. h, Samoan outrigger canoe, Apia Harbor. i, Stevenson riding horse Jack at his estate, Vallima, Samoa.

1988, July 19 Litho. *Perf. 14*

190 Sheet of 9 6.25 4.50
a.-i. A34 25c any single .50 .50

Robert Louis Stevenson (1850-1894), Scottish novelist, poet and essayist.

Colonial Ships and Flags — A35

Designs: No. 191, Galleon *Santa Maria de La Victoria,* 1526, and Spanish "Ragged Cross" ensign in use from 1516 to 1785. No. 192, Transport ships *Charlotte* and *Scarborough,* 1788, and British red ensign, 1707-1800. No. 193, Schooner *Flying Fish,* sloop-of-war *Peacock,* 1841, and U.S. flag, 1837-1845. No. 194, Steamer *Planet,* 1909, and German flag, 1867-1919.

1988, Sept. 2 Litho. *Perf. 14*

191 A35 25c multicolored .50 .50
192 A35 25c multicolored .50 .50
193 A35 25c multicolored .50 .50
194 A35 25c multicolored .50 .50
a. Block of 4, #191-194 2.00 2.00

A36 A37

Christmas: No. 195, Santa Claus riding in sleigh. No. 196, Reindeer, hut and palm trees. No. 197, Reindeer and palm trees. No. 198, Reindeer, palm tree, fish. No. 199, Reindeer and outrigger canoe.

1988, Nov. 7 Litho. *Perf. 14*

195 A36 25c multicolored .50 .50
196 A36 25c multicolored .50 .50
197 A36 25c multicolored .50 .50
198 A36 25c multicolored .50 .50
199 A36 25c multicolored .50 .50
a. Strip of 5, #195-199 2.50 2.50

No. 199a has a continuous design.

1988, Nov. 22 Litho. *Perf. 14*

200 A37 25c Nuclear threat diminished .55 .55
201 A37 25c Signing the Test Ban Treaty .55 .55
202 A37 25c Portrait .55 .55
203 A37 25c US-USSR Hotline .55 .55
204 A37 25c Peace Corps enactment .55 .55
a. Strip of 5, #200-204 2.75 2.75

Tribute to John F. Kennedy. No. 204a has a continuous design.

US Space Shuttle Program and Kwajalein — A38

Designs: No. 205, Launch of *Prime* from Vandenberg Air Force Base downrange to the Kwajalein Missile Range. No. 206, *Prime* X023A/SV-5D lifting body reentering atmosphere. No. 207, Parachute landing and craft recovery off Kwajalein Is. No. 208, Shuttle over island.

1988, Dec. 23 Litho. *Perf. 14*

205 A38 25c multicolored .55 .55
206 A38 25c multicolored .55 .55
207 A38 25c multicolored .55 .55
208 A38 25c multicolored .55 .55
a. Strip of 4, #205-208 2.25 2.25

NASA 30th anniv. and 25th anniv. of the Project PRIME wind tunnel tests.

See No. C21.

Links to Japan A39

Designs: No. 209, Typhoon Monument, Majuro, 1918. No. 210, Seaplane base and railway depot, Djarrej Islet, c. 1940. No. 211, Fishing boats. No. 212, Japanese honeymooners scuba diving, 1988.

1989, Jan. 19 Litho. *Perf. 14*

209 A39 45c multicolored .75 .75
210 A39 45c multicolored .75 .75
211 A39 45c multicolored .75 .75
212 A39 45c multicolored .75 .75
a. Block of 4, #209-212 3.00 3.00

Links to Alaska A40

Paintings by Claire Fejes.

1989, Mar. 31 Litho. *Perf. 14*

213 A40 45c Island Woman .85 .85
214 A40 45c Kotzebue, Alaska .85 .85
215 A40 45c Marshallese Madonna .85 .85
a. Strip of 3, #213-215 2.55 2.55

Printed in sheets of 9.

Seashell Type of 1985

1989, May 15 Litho. *Perf. 14*

216 A12 25c Pontifical miter .50 .50
217 A12 25c Tapestry turban .50 .50
218 A12 25c Flame-mouthed helmet .50 .50
219 A12 25c Prickly Pacific drupe .50 .50
220 A12 25c Blood-mouthed conch .50 .50
a. Strip of 5, #216-220 2.50 2.50

Souvenir Sheet

In Praise of Sovereigns, 1940, by Sanko Inoue — A41

1989, May 15 Litho. *Perf. 14*

221 A41 $1 multicolored 2.00 2.00

Hirohito (1901-89) and enthronement of Akihito as emperor of Japan.

Migrant Birds A42

1989, June 27 Litho. *Perf. 14*

222 A42 45c Wandering tattler .85 .85
223 A42 45c Ruddy turnstone .85 .85
224 A42 45c Pacific golden plover .85 .85
225 A42 45c Sanderling .85 .85
a. Block of 4, #222-225 3.40 3.40

Postal History A43

MARSHALL ISLANDS 25¢

PHILEXFRANCE '89 — A44

Designs: No. 226, Missionary ship *Morning Star V,* 1905, and Marshall Isls. #15 canceled. No. 227, Marshall Isls. #15-16 on registered letter, 1906. No. 228, *Prinz Eitel Friedrich,* 1914, and German sea post cancel. No. 229, Cruiser squadron led by SMS *Scharnhorst,* 1914, and German sea post cancel.

No. 230: a, SMS *Bussard* and German sea post cancel and Germany #32. b, US Type A924 and Marshall Isls. #34a on FDC. c, LST 119 FPO, 1944, US Navy cancel and pair of US #853. d, Mail boat, 1936, cancel and Japan #222. e, Majuro PO f, Marshall Isls. cancel, 1951, and four US #803.

No. 231, Germany #32 and Marshall Isls. cancel, 1889.

1989, July 7

226 A43 45c multicolored .90 .85
227 A43 45c multicolored .90 .85
228 A43 45c multicolored .90 .85
229 A43 45c multicolored .90 .85
a. Block of 4, #226-229 3.75 3.40

Souvenir Sheets

230 Sheet of 6 8.25 8.25
a.-f. A44 25c any single 1.25 1.25
231 A43 $1 multicolored 8.00 3.00

Nos. 230b and 230e are printed in a continuous design.

1st Moon Landing, 20th Anniv. A45

Apollo 11: No. 232, Liftoff. No. 233, Neil Armstrong. No. 234, Lunar module *Eagle.* No. 235, Michael Collins. No. 236, Raising the American flag on the Moon. No. 237, Buzz Aldrin. $1, 1st step on the Moon and "We came in peace for all mankind."

1989, Aug. 1 Litho. *Perf. 13½*

Booklet Stamps

232 A45 25c multicolored 1.50 1.25
233 A45 25c multicolored 1.50 1.25
234 A45 25c multicolored 1.50 1.25
235 A45 25c multicolored 1.50 1.25
236 A45 25c multicolored 1.50 1.25
237 A45 25c multicolored 1.50 1.25

Size: 75x32mm

238 A45 $1 multicolored 8.00 5.00
a. Booklet pane of 7, #232-238 17.00
Nos. 232-238 (7) 17.00 12.50

Decorative inscribed selvage separates No. 238 from Nos. 232-237 and surrounds it like a souvenir sheet margin. Selvage around Nos. 232-237 is plain.

World War II

A46

A47

Anniversaries and events, 1939: #239, Invasion of Poland. #240, Sinking of HMS *Royal Oak.* #241, Invasion of Finland.

Battle of the River Plate: #242, HMS *Exeter,*. #243, HMS *Ajax,*. #244, *Admiral Graf Spee,*. #245, HMNZS *Achilles,*.

1989 Litho. *Perf. 13½*

239 A46 25c W1 (1-1) .60 .45
240 A46 45c W2 (1-1) 1.10 .75
241 A46 45c W3 (1-1) 1.10 .75
242 A46 45c W4 (4-1) 1.10 .75
243 A46 45c W4 (4-2) 1.10 .75
244 A46 45c W4 (4-3) 1.10 .75
245 A46 45c W4 (4-4) 1.10 .75
a. Block of 4, #242-245 4.50 3.00

Issued: #239, 9/1; #240, 10/13; #241, 11/30; #245a, 12/13.

1990

1940: #246, Invasion of Denmark. #247, Invasion of Norway. #248, Katyn Forest Massacre. #249, Bombing of Rotterdam. #250, Invasion of Belgium. #251, Winston Churchill becomes prime minister of England. #252, Evacuation of the British Expeditionary Force at Dunkirk. #253, Evacuation at Dunkirk. #254, Occupation of Paris.

246 A46 25c W5 (2-1) .60 .50
247 A46 25c W5 (2-2) .60 .50
a. Pair, #246-247 1.25 1.00
248 A47 25c W6 (1-1) .50 .50
249 A46 25c W8 (2-1) .50 .50
250 A46 25c W8 (2-2) .50 .50
a. Pair, #249-250 1.00 1.00
251 A46 45c W7 (1-1) 1.10 .90
252 A46 45c W9 (2-1) 1.10 .90
253 A46 45c W9 (2-2) 1.10 .90
a. Pair, #252-253 2.25 1.80
254 A47 45c W10 (1-1) 1.10 .90

Issued: #247a, 4/9; #248, 4/16; #249-251, 5/10; #252-253, 6/4; #254, 6/14.

1990

Designs: #255, Battle of Mers-el-Kebir, 1940. #256, Battles for the Burma Road, 1940-45.

US Destroyers for British bases: #257, HMS Georgetown (ex-USS Maddox). #258, HMS Banff (ex-USCGC Saranac). #259, HMS Buxton (ex-USS Edwards). #260, HMS Rockingham (ex-USS Swasey).

Battle of Britain: #261, Supermarine Spitfire Mark IA. #262, Hawker Hurricane Mark I. #263, Messerschmitt Bf109E. #264, Junkers JU87B-2. #265, Tripartite Pact Signed 1940.

255 A46 25c W11 (1-1) .60 .50
256 A47 25c W12 (1-1) .60 .50
257 A46 45c W13 (4-1) 1.10 .90
258 A46 45c W13 (4-2) 1.10 .90
259 A46 45c W13 (4-3) 1.10 .90
260 A46 45c W13 (4-4) 1.10 .90
a. Block of 4, #257-260 4.50 3.60
261 A46 45c W14 (4-1) 1.10 .90
262 A46 45c W14 (4-2) 1.10 .90
263 A46 45c W14 (4-3) 1.10 .90
264 A46 45c W14 (4-4) 1.10 .90
a. Block of 4, #261-264 4.50 3.60
265 A46 45c W15 1.10 .90

Issued: #255, 7/3; #256, 7/18; #260a, 9/9; #264a, 9/15; #265, 9/27.

1990-91

Designs: #266, Roosevelt elected to third term, 1940. Battle of Taranto: #267, HMS Illustrious. #268, Fairey Swordfish. #269, RM Andrea Doria. #270, RM Conte di Cavour.

Roosevelt's Four Freedoms Speech: #271, Freedom of Speech. #272, Freedom from Want. #273, Freedom of Worship. #274, Freedom From Fear. #275, Battle of Beda Fomm, Feb. 5-7, 1941.

Germany Invades the Balkans: #276, Invasion of Greece. #277, Invasion of Yugoslavia.

Sinking of the Bismarck: #278, HMS Prince of Wales. #279, HMS Hood. #280, Bismarck. #281, Fairey Swordfish. #282, German Invasion of Russia, 1941.

266 A47 25c W16 .60 .50
267 A46 25c W17 (4-1) .60 .50
268 A46 25c W17 (4-2) .60 .50
269 A46 25c W17 (4-3) .60 .50
270 A46 25c W17 (4-4) .60 .50
a. Block of 4, #266-270 2.50 2.00
271 A46 30c W18 (4-1) .75 .60
272 A46 30c W18 (4-2) .75 .60

273 A46 30c W18 (4-3) .75 .60
274 A46 30c W18 (4-4) .75 .60
a. Block of 4, #271-274 3.00 2.40
275 A46 30c Tanks, W19 .75 .60
276 A47 29c W20 (2-1) .75 .60
277 A47 29c W20 (2-2) .75 .60
a. Pair, #276-277 1.50 1.25
278 A46 50c W21 (4-1) 1.25 1.00
279 A46 50c W21 (4-2) 1.25 1.00
280 A46 50c W21 (4-3) 1.25 1.00
281 A46 50c W21 (4-4) 1.25 1.00
a. Block of 4, #278-281 5.00 4.00
282 A46 30c Tanks, W22 .75 .60

Issued: #266, 11/5/90; #270a, 11/11/90; #274a, 1/6/91; #275, 2/5/91; #277a, 4/6/91; #281a, 5/27/91; #282, 6/22/91.

1991

1941 - Declaration of the Atlantic Charter: #283, Pres. Roosevelt and USS Augusta. #284, Churchill and HMS Prince of Wales. #285, Siege of Moscow.
Sinking of USS Reuben James: #286, Reuben James hit by torpedo. #287, German U-562 submarine.
Japanese attack on Pearl Harbor: #288, American warplanes. # 289, Japanese warplanes. #290, USS Arizona. #291, Japanese aircraft carrier Akagi.

283 A47 29c W23 (2-1) .75 .60
284 A47 29c W23 (2-2) .75 .60
a. Pair, #283-284 1.50 1.25
285 A46 29c W24 .75 .60
286 A46 30c W25 (2-1) .75 .60
287 A46 30c W25 (2-1) .75 .60
a. Pair, #286-287 1.50 1.20
288 A47 50c W26 (4-1) 1.25 1.00
a. Revised inscription 4.75 1.00
289 A47 50c W26 (4-2) 1.25 1.00
290 A47 50c W26 (4-3) 1.25 1.00
291 A47 50c W26 (4-4) 1.25 1.00
a. Block of 4, #288-291 5.00 4.00
b. Block of 4, #288a, 289-291 8.50 4.00

Inscriptions read "Peal" on No. 288 and "Pearl" on No. 288a.
Issued: #284a, 8/14; #285, 10/2; #287a, 10/31; #291a, 12/7.

1991-92

1941-42: #292, Japanese capture Guam. #293, Fall of Singapore.
First combat of the Flying Tigers: #294, Curtiss Tomahawk. #295, Mitsubishi Ki-21 on fire.
#296, Fall of Wake Island.
#297, Roosevelt and Churchill at Arcadia Conference. #298, Japanese tank entering Manila. #299, Japanese take Rabaul. #300, Battle of the Java Sea. #301, Rangoon falls to Japanese. #302, Japanese land on New Guinea. #303, MacArthur evacuated from Corregidor. #304, Raid on Saint-Nazaire. #305, Surrender of Bataan / Death March. #306, Doolittle Raid on Tokyo. #307, Fall of Corregidor.

292 A47 29c W27 .75 .60
293 A46 29c W28 .75 .60
294 A46 50c W29 (2-1) 1.25 1.00
295 A46 50c W29 (2-2) 1.25 1.00
a. Pair, #294-295 2.50 2.00
296 A46 29c W30 .75 .60
297 A46 29c W31 .75 .60
298 A46 50c W32 1.25 1.00
299 A46 29c W33 .75 .60
300 A46 29c W34 .75 .60
301 A47 50c W35 1.25 1.00
302 A46 29c W36 .75 .60
303 A46 29c W37 .75 .60
304 A46 29c W38 .75 .60
305 A47 29c W39 .75 .60
306 A47 50c W40 1.25 1.00
307 A46 29c W41 .75 .60

Issued: #292-293, 12/10/91; #295a, 12/20/91; #296, 12/23/91; #297, 1/1/92; #298, 1/2/92; #299, 1/23/92; #300, 2/15/92; #301-302, 3/8/92; #303, 3/11/92; #304, 3/27/92; #305, 4/9/92; #306, 4/18/92; #307, 5/6/92.

1992

1942 - Battle of the Coral Sea: #308, USS Lexington. #309, Japanese Mitsubishi A6M2 Zeros. #310, Douglas SBD Dauntless dive bombers. #311, Japanese carrier Shoho.
Battle of Midway: #312, Japanese aircraft carrier Akagi. #313, US Douglas SBD Dauntless dive bombers. #314, USS Yorktown. #315, Nakajima B5N2 Kate torpedo planes.
#316, Village of Lidice destroyed. #317, Fall of Sevastopol.
Convoy PQ17 destroyed: #318, British merchant ship in convoy. #319, German U-boats.
#320, Marines land on Guadalcanal. #323, Battle of Stalingrad. #324, Battle of Eastern Solomons.
#321, Battle of Savo Island. #322, Dieppe Raid. #325, Battle of Cape Esperance. #326, Battle of El Alamein.
Battle of Barents Sea: #327, HMS Sheffield. #328, Admiral Hipper.

308 A46 50c W42 (4-1) 1.25 1.00
a. Revised inscription 2.00 1.00
309 A46 50c W42 (4-2) 1.25 1.00
a. Revised inscription 2.00 1.00
310 A46 50c W42 (4-3) 1.25 1.00
a. Revised inscription 2.00 1.00
311 A46 50c W42 (4-4) 1.25 1.00
a. Block of 4, #308-311 5.00 4.00
b. Revised inscription 2.00 1.00
c. Block of 4, #308a-310a, 311b 8.50 4.00
312 A46 50c W43 (4-1) 1.25 1.00
313 A46 50c W43 (4-3) 1.25 1.00
314 A46 50c W43 (4-2) 1.25 1.00
315 A46 50c W43 (4-4) 1.25 1.00
a. Block of 4, #312-315 5.00 4.00
316 A46 29c W44 .75 .60
317 A47 29c W45 .75 .60
318 A46 29c W46 (2-1) .75 .60
319 A46 29c W46 (2-2) .75 .60
a. Pair, #318-319 1.50 1.20
320 A46 29c W47 .75 .60
321 A47 29c W48 .75 .60
322 A46 29c W49 .75 .60
323 A47 50c W50 1.25 1.00
324 A46 29c W51 .75 .60
325 A46 50c W52 1.25 1.00
326 A46 29c W53 .75 .60
327 A46 29c W54 (2-1) .75 .60
328 A46 29c W54 (2-2) .75 .60
a. Pair, #327-328 1.50 1.20

Inscription reads "U.S.S. Lexington/Grumman F4F-3 Wildcat" on No. 308a, "Japanese Aichi D3A1 Vals/Nakajima B5N2 Kate" on No. 309a, "U.S. Douglas TBD-1 Devastators" on No. 310a, "Japanese Carrier Shoho/Mitsubishi A6M2 Zeros" on No. 311b.
Issued: #311a, 5/8/92; #315a, 6/4; #316, 6/9/92; #317, 7/4; #319a, 7/5; #320, 8/7; #321, 8/9; #322-323, 8/19; #324, 8/24; #325, 10/11; #326, 10/23; #328a, 12/31.
Vertical pairs, Nos. 312-313 and Nos. 314-315 have continuous designs.
No. 310 incorrectly identifies Douglas TBD torpedo bombers.

1993 Litho. *Perf. 13½*

1943 - #329, Casablanca Conf. #330, Liberation of Kharkov.
Battle of Bismarck Sea: #331, Japanese A6M Zeroes, destroyer Arashio. #332, US P38 Lightnings, Australian Beaufighter. #333, Japanese destroyer Shirayuki. #334, US A-20 Havoc, B-25 Mitchell.
#335, Interception of Admiral Yamamoto.
Battle of Kursk: #336, German Tiger I. #337, Soviet T-34.

329 A46 29c W55 .75 .60
330 A46 29c W56 .75 .60
331 A46 50c W57 (4-1) 1.25 1.00
332 A46 50c W57 (4-2) 1.25 1.00
333 A46 50c W57 (4-3) 1.25 1.00
334 A46 50c W57 (4-4) 1.25 1.00
a. Block of 4, #331-334 5.00 4.00
335 A46 50c W58 1.25 1.00
336 A46 29c W59 (2-1) .85 .60
337 A46 29c W59 (2-2) .85 .60
a. Pair, #336-337 1.70 1.20
Nos. 239-337 (99) 92.85 74.05

Issued: #329, 1/14; #330, 2/16; #334a, 3/3; #335, 4/18; #337a, 7/5.
See #467-524, 562-563.

Christmas A57

Angels playing musical instruments.

1989, Oct. 25 *Perf. 13½*

341 A57 25c Horn .80 .80
342 A57 25c Singing carol .80 .80
343 A57 25c Lute .80 .80
344 A57 25c Lyre .80 .80
a. Block of 4, #341-344 3.25 3.25

Miniature Sheet

Milestones in Space Exploration — A58

Designs: a, Robert Goddard and 1st liquid fuel rocket launch, 1926. b, *Sputnik*, 1st man-made satellite, 1957. c, 1st American satellite, 1958. d, Yuri Gagarin, 1st man in space, 1961. e, John Glenn, 1st American to orbit Earth, 1962. f, Valentina Tereshkova, 1st woman in space, 1963. g, Aleksei Leonov, 1st space walk, 1965. h, Edward White, 1st American to walk in space, 1965. i, Gemini-Titan 6A, 1st rendezvous in space, 1965. j, 1st Soft landing on the Moon, 1966. k, Gemini 8, 1st docking in space, 1966. l, 1st probe of Venus, 1967. m, Apollo 8, 1st manned orbit of the Moon, 1968. n, Apollo 11, 1st man on the Moon, 1969. o, Soyuz 11, 1st space station crew, 1971. p, Apollo 15, 1st manned lunar vehicle, 1971. q, *Skylab 2*, 1st American manned space station, 1973. r, 1st Flyby of Jupiter, 1973. s, Apollo-Soyuz, 1st joint space flight, 1975. t, 1st Landing on Mars, 1976. u, 1st flyby of Saturn, 1979. v, *Columbia*, 1st space shuttle flight, 1981. w, 1st probe beyond the solar system, 1983. x, 1st untethered space walk, 1984. y, Launch of space shuttle *Discovery*, 1988.

1989, Nov. 24 Litho. *Perf. 13½*

345 Sheet of 25 27.50 27.50
a.-y. A58 45c any single .90 .90

No. 345 contains World Stamp Expo '89 emblem on selvage.

Birds
A59 A59a

1990-92 Litho. *Perf. 13½*

346 A59 1c Black noddy .15 .15
347 A59 5c Red-tailed tropic bird .15 .15
348 A59 10c Sanderling .30 .20
349 A59 12c Black-naped tern .40 .25
350 A59 15c Wandering tattler .45 .30
351 A59 20c Bristle-thighed curlew .65 .40
352 A59 23c Northern shoveler .70 .45
353 A59 25c Brown noddy .80 .50
354 A59 27c Sooty tern .85 .55
355 A59 29c Wedge-tailed shearwater .95 .60
356 A59a 29c Northern pintail 1.50 1.00
357 A59 30c Pacific golden plover .95 .60
358 A59 35c Brown booby 1.10 .70
359 A59 36c Red footed booby 1.25 .75
360 A59 40c White tern 1.25 .80
361 A59 50c Great frigate bird 1.65 1.00
a. Min. sheet of 4 (#347, 350, 353, 361) 4.25 2.00
362 A59 52c Great crested tern 1.65 1.00
363 A59 65c Lesser sand plover 2.00 1.25
364 A59 75c Little tern 2.50 1.50
365 A59 $1 Pacific reef heron 3.25 2.00
365A A59 $2 Masked booby 6.25 4.00
Nos. 346-365A (21) 28.75 18.15

No. 361a for ESSEN '90, Germany Apr. 19-22.
Issue dates: 5c, 15c, 25c, 50c, Mar. 8. 30c, 36c, 40c, $1, Oct. 11. No. 361a, Apr. 19. No. 355, 20c, 52c, Feb. 22, 1991. 27c, Mar. 8, 1991. 1c, 12c, 35c, $2, Nov. 6, 1991. No. 356, Feb. 3, 1992. 10c, 23c, 65c, 75c, Apr. 24, 1992.
See Nos. 430-433.

Children's Games A60

1990, Mar. 15

366 A60 25c Lodidean .75 .75
367 A60 25c Lejonjon .75 .75
368 A60 25c Etobobo .75 .75
369 A60 25c Didmakol .75 .75
a. Block of 4, #366-369 3.00 3.00

Penny Black, 150th Anniv. — A61

Designs: No. 370, Penny Black, 1840. No. 371, Essay by James Chalmers. No. 372, Essay by Robert Sievier. No. 373, Essay by Charles Whiting. No. 374, Essay by George Dickinson. No. 375, Medal engraved by William Wyon to celebrate Queen Victoria's first visit to London. $1, Engraver Charles Heath, engraving for master die.

1990, Apr. 6 Booklet Stamps

370 A61 25c multicolored 1.25 1.00
371 A61 25c multicolored 1.25 1.00
372 A61 25c multicolored 1.25 1.00
373 A61 25c multicolored 1.25 1.00
374 A61 25c multicolored 1.25 1.00
375 A61 25c multicolored 1.25 1.00

Size: 73x31mm

376 A61 $1 multicolored 5.25 4.00
a. Booklet pane of 7, #370-376 14.00 —
Nos. 370-376 (7) 12.75 10.00

Decorative inscribed selvage picturing part of a Penny Black proof sheet separates No. 376 from Nos. 370-375 in pane and surrounds it like a souvenir sheet margin. Selvage around Nos. 370-375 is plain.

Endangered Wildlife — A62

Sea Turtles: No. 377, Pacific green turtle hatchlings entering ocean. No. 378, Pacific great turtle under water. No. 379, Hawksbill hatchling, eggs. No. 380, Hawksbill turtle in water.

1990, May 3

377 A62 25c multicolored .75 .75
378 A62 25c multicolored .75 .75
379 A62 25c multicolored .75 .75
380 A62 25c multicolored .75 .75
a. Block of 4, #377-380 3.00 3.00

Stick Chart, Canoe and Flag of the Republic of the Marshall Islands — A63

1990, Sept. 28 *Perf. 11x10½*

381 A63 25c multicolored .85 .60

See #615, US #2507, Micronesia #124-126.

German Reunification — A64

1990, Oct. 3 *Perf. 13½*

382 A64 45c multicolored 1.00 1.00

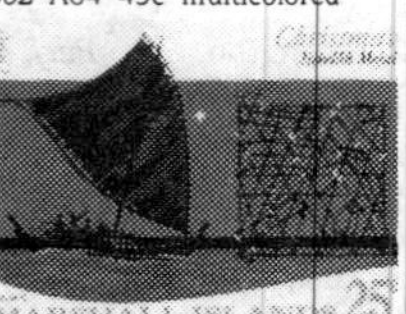

Christmas A65

1990, Oct. 25 Litho. *Perf. 13½*

383 A65 25c Canoe, stick chart .75 .75
384 A65 25c Missionary preaching .75 .75
385 A65 25c Sailors dancing .75 .75
386 A65 25c Youths dancing .75 .75
a. Block of 4, #383-386 3.00 3.00

Breadfruit — A66

1990, Dec. 15 Litho. *Perf. 12x12½*

387	A66	25c Harvesting	.75	.75
388	A66	25c Peeling, slicing	.75	.75
389	A66	25c Preserving	.75	.75
390	A66	25c Kneading dough	.75	.75
a.		Block of 4, #387-390	3.00	3.00

US Space Shuttle Flights, 10th Anniv. A67

1991, Apr. 12 Litho. *Perf. 13½*

391	A67	50c 747 ferry	.90	.90
392	A67	50c Orbital release of LDEF	.90	.90
393	A67	50c Lift-off	.90	.90
394	A67	50c Landing	.90	.90
a.		Block of 4, #391-394	3.75	3.75

Flowers — A68

1991, June 10 Litho. *Perf. 13½*

395	A68	52c Ixora carolinensis	1.10	1.00
396	A68	52c Clerodendrum inerme	1.10	1.00
397	A68	52c Messerchmidia argentea	1.10	1.00
398	A68	52c Vigna marina	1.10	1.00
a.		Miniature sheet of 4, #395-398	4.75	4.00
b.		Block of 4, #395-398, without inscription	4.50	4.00

Phila Nippon '91 (No. 398a). Stamps from miniature sheets inscribed C53A.

Operation Desert Storm — A69

1991, July 4 Litho. *Perf. 13½*

399	A69	29c multicolored	.95	.60

Birds A70

1991, July 16 Booklet Stamps

400	A70	29c Red-footed booby	1.65	.60
401	A70	29c Great frigate bird (7-2)	1.65	.60
402	A70	29c Brown booby	1.65	.60
403	A70	29c White tern	1.65	.60
404	A70	29c Great frigate bird (7-5)	1.65	.60
405	A70	29c Black noddy	1.65	.60

Size: 75x33mm

406	A70	$1 White-tailed tropic bird	9.00	2.00
a.		Booklet pane of 7, #400-406	19.00	—
		Nos. 400-406 (7)	18.90	5.60

Decorative selvage separates No. 406 from Nos. 400-405 and surrounds it like a souvenir sheet margin.

Aircraft of Air Marshall Islands — A71

1991, Sept. 10 Litho. *Perf. 13½*

407	A71	12c Dornier 228	.25	.20
408	A71	29c Douglas DC-8	.65	.50
409	A71	50c Hawker Siddeley 748	1.10	.85
410	A71	50c Saab 2000	1.10	.85
		Nos. 407-410 (4)	3.10	2.40

Admission to United Nations A72

1991, Sept. 24 Litho. *Perf. 11x10½*

411	A72	29c multicolored	.75	.65

Christmas — A73

1991, Oct. 25 *Perf. 13½*

412	A73	30c multicolored	.85	.75

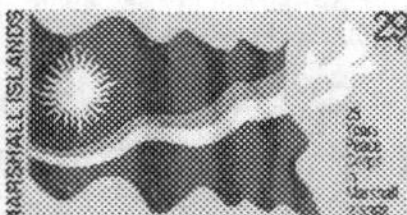

Peace Corps in Marshall Islands, 25th Anniv. — A74

1991, Nov. 26 Litho. *Perf. 11x10½*

413	A74	29c multicolored	.85	.60

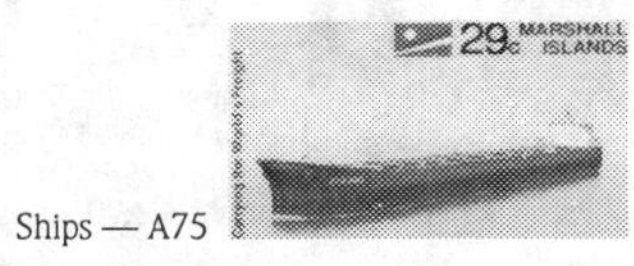

Ships — A75

Designs: No. 414, Bulk cargo carrier, Emlain. No. 415, Tanker, CSK Valiant. No. 416, Patrol boat, Ionmeto. No. 417, Freighter, Micro Pilot.

1992, Feb. 15 Litho. *Perf. 11x10½*

414	A75	29c multicolored	1.10	.45
415	A75	29c multicolored	1.10	.45
416	A75	29c multicolored	1.10	.45
417	A75	29c multicolored	1.10	.45
a.		Strip of 4, #414-417	4.50	2.00

Voyages of Discovery A76

Designs: No. 418, Traditional tipnol. No. 419, Reconstructed Santa Maria. No. 420, Constellation Argo Navis. No. 421, Marshallese sailor, tipnol. No. 422, Columbus, Santa Maria. No. 423, Astronaunt, Argo Navis. $1, Columbus, sailor, and astronaunt.

1992, May 23 Litho. *Perf. 13½*

Booklet Stamps

418	A76	50c multicolored	1.65	1.00
419	A76	50c multicolored	1.65	1.00
420	A76	50c multicolored	1.65	1.00
421	A76	50c multicolored	1.65	1.00
422	A76	50c multicolored	1.65	1.00
423	A76	50c multicolored	1.65	1.00

Size: 75x32mm

424	A76	$1 multicolored	7.00	2.00
a.		Booklet pane of 7, #418-424	17.00	—

Decorative selvage separates No. 424 from Nos. 418-423 and surrounds it like a souvenir sheet margin.

Traditional Handicrafts — A77

1992, Sept. 9 Litho. *Perf. 13½*

425	A77	29c Basket weaving	.70	.60
426	A77	29c Canoe models	.70	.60
427	A77	29c Wood carving	.70	.60
428	A77	29c Fan making	.70	.60
a.		Strip of 4, #425-428	2.80	2.40

Christmas A78

1992, Oct. 29 Litho. *Perf. 11x10½*

429	A78	29c multicolored	.80	.60

Bird Type of 1990

1992, Nov. 10 Litho. *Perf. 13½*

430	A59	9c Whimbrel	.30	.20
431	A59	22c Greater scaup	.70	.45
432	A59	28c Sharp-tailed sandpiper	.85	.55
433	A59	45c Common teal	1.40	.90
		Nos. 430-433 (4)	3.25	2.10

Reef Life — A79

1993, May 26 Litho. *Perf. 13½*

434	A79	50c Butterflyfish	1.25	1.00
435	A79	50c Soldierfish	1.25	1.00
436	A79	50c Damselfish	1.25	1.00
437	A79	50c Filefish	1.25	1.00
438	A79	50c Hawkfish	1.25	1.00
439	A79	50c Surgeonfish	1.25	1.00

Size: 75x33mm

440	A79	$1 Parrotfish	5.50	2.00
a.		Booklet pane of 7, #434-440	13.00	—
		Nos. 434-440 (7)	13.00	8.00

Decorative selvage separates No. 440 from Nos. 434-439 and surrounds it like a souvenir sheet margin.

Ships — A80

Marshallese Sailing Vessels — A81

Designs: 10c, Spanish galleon San Jeronimo. 14c, USCG Fisheries Patrol vessel Cape Corwin. 15c, British merchant ship Britannia. 19c, Island transport Micro Palm. 20c, Dutch ship Eendracht. 23c, Frigate HMS Cornwallis. 24c, US naval schooner Dolphin. 29c, Missionary packet Morning Star. 30c, Russian brig Rurick. 32c, Spanish sailing ship Santa Maria de la Vittoria. 35c, German warship SMS Nautilus. 40c, British brig Nautilus. 45c, Japanese warships Nagara, Isuzu. 46c, Trading schooner Equator. 50c, Aircraft carrier USS Lexington CV-16. 52c, HMS Serpent. 55c, Whaling ship Potomac. 60c, Coast Guard cutter Assateague. 75c, British transport Scarborough. 78c, Whaler Charles W. Morgan. 95c, US steam vessel Tanager. $1, Walap, Eniwetok. $1, Barkentine hospital ship Tole Mour. $2, Walap, Jaluit. $2.90, Marshall Islands fishing vessels. $3, Schooner Victoria. $5, Tipnol, Ailuk. $10, Racing canoes.

Perf. 11x10½ (A80), 13½ (A81)

1993-95 Litho.

441	A80	10c multicolored	.20	.20
442	A80	14c multicolored	.30	.30
443	A80	15c multicolored	.30	.30
444	A80	19c multicolored	.40	.40
445	A80	20c multicolored	.40	.40
446	A80	23c multicolored	.45	.45
447	A80	24c multicolored	.50	.50
448	A80	29c multicolored	.60	.60
449	A80	30c multicolored	.60	.60
450	A80	32c multicolored	.65	.65
451	A80	35c multicolored	.70	.70
452	A80	40c multicolored	.80	.80
453	A80	45c multicolored	.90	.90
454	A80	46c multicolored	.95	.95
455	A80	50c multicolored	1.00	1.00
456	A80	52c multicolored	1.10	1.10
457	A80	55c multicolored	1.10	1.10
458	A80	60c multicolored	1.25	1.25
459	A80	75c multicolored	1.50	1.50
460	A80	78c multicolored	1.65	1.65
461	A80	95c multicolored	1.90	1.90
462	A80	$1 multicolored	2.00	2.00
463	A81	$1 multicolored	2.00	2.00
464	A81	$2 multicolored	4.00	4.00
465	A80	$2.90 multicolored	5.75	5.75
466	A80	$3 multicolored	6.00	6.00
466A	A81	$5 multicolored	10.00	10.00
466B	A81	$10 multicolored	20.00	20.00
		Nos. 441-466B (28)	67.00	67.00

Souvenir Sheet

Stamp Size: 46x26mm

466C	A81	Sheet of 4, #d.-g.	3.75	3.50

Inscription reads "Hong Kong '94 Stamp Exhibition" in Chinese on Nos. 466Cd, 466Cg, and in English on Nos. 466Ce-466Cf.

Issued: 15c, 24c, 29c, 50c, 6/24/93; 10c, 23c, 52c, 75c, 10/14/93; #463, 5/29/93; $2, 8/26. 10c, 30c, 35c, $2.90, 4/19/94; $5, 3/15/94; $10, 8/18/94; 20c, 40c, 45c, 55c, 9/23/94; #466C, 2/18/94; 14c, 46c, 95c, #462, 9/25/95; 32c, 60c, 78c, $3, 5/5/95.

See #605.

World War II Type of 1989

1943 - Invasion of Sicily: #467, Gen. George S. Patton, Jr. #468, Gen. Bernard L. Montgomery. #469, Americans landing at at Licata. #470, British landing south of Syracuse.

Allied bomber raids on Schweinfurt: #471, B-17F Flying Fortresses and Bf-109 fighter. #472, Liberation of Smolensk. #473, Landings at Bougainville. #474, Invasion of Tarawa, 1943. #475, Teheran Conference, 1943.

Battle of North Cape: #476, HMS Duke of York. #477, Scharnhorst.

1944 - #478, Gen. Dwight D. Eisenhower, SHAEF Commander. #479, Invasion of Anzio. #480, Siege of Leningrad lifted. #481, US liberates Marshall Islands. #482, Japanese defeated at Truk. #483, Big Week, US bombing of Germany.

1993-94 Litho. *Perf. 13½*

467	A46	52c W60 (4-1)	1.25	1.10
468	A46	52c W60 (4-2)	1.25	1.10
469	A46	52c W60 (4-3)	1.25	1.10
470	A46	52c W60 (4-4)	1.25	1.10
a.		Block of 4, #467-470	5.25	4.50
471	A46	50c W61	1.25	1.00
472	A47	29c W62	.75	.60
473	A46	29c W63	.75	.60
474	A46	50c W64	1.25	1.00
475	A47	52c W65	1.25	1.10
476	A46	29c W66 (2-1)	.90	.60
477	A46	29c W66 (2-2)	.90	.60
a.		Pair, #476-477	1.80	1.20
478	A46	29c W67	.75	.60
479	A46	50c W68	1.25	1.00
480	A46	52c W69	1.25	1.10
481	A46	29c W70	.75	.60
482	A47	29c W71	.75	.60
483	A46	52c W72	1.25	1.10
		Nos. 467-483 (17)	18.05	14.90

Issued: #467-470, 7/10/93; #471, 8/17/93; #472, 9/25/93; #473, 11/1/93; #474, 11/20/93; #475, 12/1/93; #476-477, 12/26/93; #478, 1/16/94; #479, 1/22/94; #480, 1/27/94; #481, 2/4/94; #482, 2/17/94; #483, 2/20/94.

1994 Litho. *Perf. 13½*

1944 - #484, Lt. Gen. Mark Clark, Rome falls to the Allies.

D-Day-Allied landings in Normandy: #485, Horsa gliders. #486, US P-51B Mustangs, British Hurricanes. #487, German gun defenses. #488, Allied amphibious landing.

#489, V-1 flying bombs strike England. #490, US Marines land on Saipan.

First Battle of the Philippine Sea: #491, Grumman F6F-3 Hellcat.

#492, US liberates Guam. #493, Warsaw uprising. #494, Liberation of Paris. #495, US Marines land on Peliliu. #496, MacArthur returns to the Philippines. #497, Battle of Leyte Gulf.

German battleship Tirpitz sunk: #498, Avro Lancaster. #499, Tirpitz.

Battle of the Bulge: #500, Infantry. #501, Armor. #502, Aviation. #503, Lt. Col. Creighton W. Abrams, Brig. Gen. Anthony C. McAuliffe.

484	A47	50c W73	1.25	1.00
485	A46	75c W74 (4-1)	1.90	1.50
a.		Revised inscription	3.25	1.50
486	A46	75c W74 (4-2)	1.90	1.50
a.		Revised inscription	3.25	1.50
487	A46	75c W74 (4-3)	1.90	1.50
a.		Revised inscription	3.25	1.50
488	A46	75c W74 (4-4)	1.90	1.50
a.		Block of 4, #485-488	7.75	6.00
b.		Block of 4, #485a-487a, 488	12.00	6.00
489	A46	50c W75	1.25	1.00
490	A46	29c W76	.75	.60
491	A46	50c W77	1.25	1.00
492	A46	29c W78	.75	.60
493	A46	50c W79	1.25	1.00
494	A46	50c W80	1.25	1.00
495	A46	29c W81	.75	.60
496	A46	52c W82	1.25	1.00
497	A46	52c multicolored	1.25	1.00

498 A46 50c W84 (2-1) 1.50 1.00
499 A46 50c W84 (2-2) 1.50 1.00
a. Pair, #498-499 3.00 2.00
500 A47 50c W85 (4-1) 1.75 1.00
501 A47 50c W85 (4-2) 1.75 1.00
502 A47 50c W85 (4-3) 1.75 1.00
503 A47 50c W85 (4-4) 1.75 1.00
a. Block of 4, #500-503 7.25 4.00
Nos. 484-503 (20) 28.60 20.80

Inscription reads "Horsa Gliders, Parachute Troops" on #485a, "British Typhoon-1B, U.S. P51B Mustangs" on #486a, "German Gun Defenses, Pointe du Hoc" on #487a.

Issued: #484, 6/4; #485-488, 6/6; #489, 6/13; #490, 6/15; #491, 6/19; #492, 7/21; #493, 8/1; 494, 8/25; #495, 9/15; #496, 10/20; #497, 10/24; #498-499, 11/12; #500-503, 12/16.

1995 Litho. *Perf. 13½*

1945 - #504, Stalin, Churchill, Roosevelt, Yalta Conference. #505, Meissen porcelain, bombing of Dresden, 1945. #506, Iwo Jima invaded by US Marines.

#507, Remagen Bridge taken by US forces.

#508, Okinawa invaded by US forces. #509, Death of Franklin D. Roosevelt.

#510, US/USSR troops meet at Elbe River. #511, Russian troops capture Berlin. #512, Allies liberate concentration camps.

VE Day: #513, German surrender, Rheims. # 514, Times Square, New York. #515, Victory Parade, Moscow. #516, Buckingham Palace, London.

UN Charter signed: #517, 563, US Pres. Harry S Truman, Veteran's Memorial Hall, San Francisco.

#518, Potsdam Conference Convenes. #519, Churchill resigns. #520, B-29 Enola Gay drops atomic bomb on Hiroshima.

V-J Day: #521, Mt. Fuji, ships in Tokyo Bay. #522, USS Missouri. #523, Adm. Nimitz signs surrender document. #524, Japanese delegation.

504 A47 32c W86 .95 .65
505 A47 55c W87 1.70 1.10
506 A47 $1 W88 3.00 2.00
507 A47 32c W89 .95 .65
508 A47 55c W90 1.75 1.10
509 A46 50c W91 1.65 1.00
510 A46 32c W92 1.00 .65
511 A46 60c W93 1.75 1.25
512 A46 55c W94 1.75 1.10
513 A46 75c W95 (4-1) 3.00 1.50
514 A46 75c W95 (4-2) 3.00 1.50
515 A46 75c W95 (4-3) 3.00 1.50
516 A46 75c W95 (4-4) 3.00 1.50
a. Block of 4, #513-516 12.00 6.00
517 A46 32c W96 1.00 .65
518 A46 55c W97 1.75 1.10
519 A47 60c W98 1.75 1.25
520 A46 $1 W99 3.25 2.00
521 A46 75c W100 (4-1) 3.00 1.50
522 A46 75c W100 (4-2) 3.00 1.50
523 A46 75c W100 (4-3) 3.00 1.50
524 A46 75c W100 (4-4) 3.00 1.50
a. Block of 4, #521-524 12.00 6.00
Nos. 504-524 (21) 46.25 26.50

Issued: #504, 2/4/95; #505, 2/13/95; #506, 2/19/95; #507, 3/7/95; #508, 4/1/95; #509, 4/12/95; #516a, 5/8/95; #517, 6/26/95; #518, 7/7/95; #519, 7/26/95; #520, 8/6/95; #524a, 9/2/95.

Souvenir Sheets

Designs: #562a, like #303. #562b, like #496.

1994-95 *Imperf.*
562 Sheet of 2 2.75 2.00
a.-b. A46 50c any single 1.25 1.00
563 A46 $1 like #517 2.75 2.00

No. 563 contains one 80x50mm stamp with UN 50th anniv. emblem.

Issued: #562, 10/20/94; #563, 6/26/95.

Nos. 525-561, 564-566 are unassigned.

Dedication of Capitol Building Complex A82

Designs: No. 567, Capitol building. No. 568, Nitijela (parliament) building. No. 569, Natl. seal, vert. No. 570, Flag over complex, vert.

1993, Aug. 11 Litho. *Perf. 11x10½*
567 A82 29c multi (4-1) .50 .50
568 A82 29c multi (4-2) .50 .50

Perf. 10½x11
569 A82 29c multi (4-3) .50 .50
570 A82 29c multi (4-4) .50 .50
Nos. 567-570 (4) 2.00 2.00

Souvenir Sheet

Christening of Mobil Super Tanker Eagle — A83

1993, Aug. 25 *Perf. 13½*
571 A83 50c multicolored .85 .85

Marshallese Life in 1800's — A84

1993, Sept. 15 Litho. *Perf. 13½*
572 A84 29c Woman, breadfruit (4-1) .60 .60
573 A84 29c Canoes, warrior (4-2) .60 .60
574 A84 29c Young chief (4-3) .60 .60
575 A84 29c Drummer, dancers (4-4) .60 .60
a. Block of 4, #572-575 2.40 2.40

Christmas A85

1993, Oct. 25 Litho. *Perf. 13½*
576 A85 29c multicolored .80 .60

Souvenir Sheet

Constitution, 15th Anniv. — A86

1994, May 1 Litho. *Perf. 13½*
577 A86 $2.90 multicolored 4.25 4.25

Souvenir Sheet

Marshall Islands Postal Service, 10th Anniv. — A87

1994, May 2
578 A87 29c multicolored .65 .60

1994 World Cup Soccer Championships, US — A88

Design: No. 580, Soccer players, diff.

1994, June 17 Litho. *Perf. 13½*
579 A88 50c red & multi (2-1) 2.00 1.00
580 A88 50c blue & multi (2-2) 2.00 1.00
a. Pair, #579-580 4.25 2.00

No. 580a has a continuous design.

Miniature Sheet

Solar System — A89

Mythological characters, symbols: a, Solar system. b, Sun. c, Moon. d, Mercury. e, Venus. f, Earth. g, Mars. h, Jupiter. i, Saturn. j, Uranus. k, Neptune. l, Pluto.

1994, July 20 Litho. *Perf. 13½*
582 A89 50c Sheet of 12, #a.-l. 12.00 12.00

First Manned Moon Landing, 25th Anniv. — A90

Designs: No. 583, First step onto Moon's surface. No. 584, Planting US flag on Moon. No. 585, Astronaut's salute to America, flag. No. 586, Astronaut stepping onto Moon, John F. Kennedy.

1994, July 20
583 A90 75c multi (4-1) 1.10 1.10
584 A90 75c multi (4-2) 1.10 1.10
585 A90 75c multi (4-3) 1.10 1.10
586 A90 75c multi (4-4) 1.10 1.10
a. Block of 4, #583-586 4.50 4.50
b. Souvenir sheet of 4, #583-586 4.50 4.50

Souvenir Sheet

Butterflies A91

1994, Aug. 16 Litho. *Perf. 13½*
587 A91 Sheet of 3 3.75 3.75
a. 29c Meadow argus .60 .60
b. 52c Brown awl 1.10 1.10
c. $1 Great eggfly 2.00 2.00

PHILAKOREA '94.

Christmas — A92

1994, Oct. 28 Litho. *Perf. 13½*
588 A92 29c multicolored .70 .60

Souvenir Sheet

New Year 1995 (Year of the Boar) — A93

Illustration reduced.

1995, Jan. 2 Litho. *Perf. 13½*
589 A93 50c multicolored 1.50 1.00

Marine Life — A94

Designs: a, Meyer's butterflyfish, achilles tang, scuba diver. b, Scuba diver, moorish idols (a, d). c, Pacific green turtle, fairy basslets. d, Fairy basslets, emperor angelfish, orange-fin anemonefish.

1995, Mar. 20 Litho. *Perf. 13½*
590 A94 55c Block of 4, #a.-d. 5.25 4.50

See Nos. 614, 644.

John F. Kennedy (1917-63), 35th Pres. of US — A95

Designs: a, PT-109. b, Taking presidential oath. c, Peace Corps volunteers. d, US aircraft, naval vessels, Cuban Missile Crisis. e, Signing Nuclear Test Ban Treaty. f, Eternal flame, Arlington Natl. Cemetery.

1995, May 29 Litho. *Perf. 13½*
591 A95 55c Strip of 6, #a.-f. 5.25 5.25

Marilyn Monroe (1926-1962), Actress — A96

Various portraits with background color: a, red. b, green. c, orange. d, violet.

1995, June 1 Litho. *Perf. 13½*
592 A96 75c Block of 4, #a.-d. 5.25 5.25

No. 592 was issued in sheets of three blocks.

Cats — A97

Designs: a, Siamese, exotic shorthair. b, American shorthair, Persian. c, Maine coon, Burmese. d, Abyssinian, Himalayan.

1995, July 5 Litho. *Perf. 13½*
593 A97 32c Block of 4, #a.-d. 2.50 2.50

Mir-Space Shuttle Docking & Apollo-Soyuz Link-Up — A98

a, Space station Mir. b, Space shuttle Atlantis. c, Apollo command module. d, Soyuz spacecraft.

1995, June 29 Litho. *Perf. 13½*
594 A98 75c Block of 4, #a.-d. 4.75 4.75

Nos. 594 is a continuous design.

Pacific Game Fish A99

Designs: a, Pacific sailfish. b. Albacore. c, Wahoo. d, Pacific blue marlin. e, Yellowfin tuna. f, Giant trevally. g, Dolphin fish. h, Mako shark.

1995, Aug. 21 Litho. *Perf. 13½*
595 A99 60c Block of 8, #a.-h. 11.00 10.00

Island Legends — A100

Designs: a, Inedel's Magic Kite. b, Lijebake Rescues Her Granddaughter. c, Jebro's Mother Invents the Sail. d, Limajnon Escapes to the Moon.

1995, Aug. 25 Litho. *Perf. 13½*
596 A100 32c Block of 4, #a.-d. + 4 labels 2.50 2.50

See Nos. 612, 643.

Miniature Sheet

Singapore '95 World Stamp Exhibition — A101

Orchids: a, Paphiopedilum armeniacum. b, Masdevallia veitchiana. c, Cattleya francis. d, Cattleya x guatemalensis.

1995, Sept. 1 Litho. *Perf. 13½*
597 A101 32c Sheet of 4, #a.-d. 2.25 2.25

Souvenir Sheet

Intl. Stamp & Coin Expo, Beijing '95 — A102

Illustration reduced.

1995, Sept. 12
598 A102 50c Suzhou Gardens .85 .85

Christmas — A103

1995, Oct. 31 Litho. *Perf. 13½*
599 A103 32c multicolored .55 .55

Miniature Sheet

Jet Fighter Planes — A104

a, Me 262-1a Schwalbe. b, Meteor F.MK8. c, F-80 Shooting Star. d, F-86 Sabre. e, F9F-2 Panther. f, MiG-15. g, F-100 Super Sabre. h, F-102A Delta Dagger. i, F-104 Starfighter. j, MiG-21 MT. k, F8U Crusader. l, F-105 Thunderbird. m, Saab J35 Draken. n, Fiat G91Y. o, F-4 Phantom II. p, Saab JA37 Viggen. q, Mirage F1C. r, F-14 Tomcat. s, F-15 Eagle. t, F-16 Fighting Falcon. u, Tornado F.MK3. v, Sukhoi Su-27UB. w, Mirage 2000C. x, Sea Harrier FRS.MK1. y, F-117 Nighthawk.

1995, Nov. 10
600 A104 32c Sheet of 25, #a.-y. 16.00 16.00

No. 600 was sold in uncut sheets of 6 panes. See Nos. 617, 641.

Yitzhak Rabin (1922-95), Israeli Prime Minister — A105

1995, Nov. 10 Litho. *Perf. 14*
601 A105 32c multicolored .55 .55

No. 601 was issued in sheets of 8.

Souvenir Sheet

New Year 1996 (Year of the Rat) — A106

Illustration reduced.

1996, Jan. 5 Litho. *Perf. 13½*
602 A106 50c multicolored .85 .85

Native Birds A107

Designs: a, Blue-gray noddy. b, Gray-backed tern. c, Masked booby. d, Black-footed albatross.

1996, Feb. 26 Litho. *Perf. 13½*
603 A107 32c Block of 4, #a.-d. 5.25 2.50

Wild Cats — A108

Designs: a, Cheetah. b, Tiger. c, Lion. d, Jaguar.

1996, Mar. 8 Litho. *Perf. 13½*
604 A108 55c Block of 4, #a.-d. 3.75 3.75

Sailing Ship Type of 1993
Miniature Sheet

Designs: a, like #443. b, like #447. c, like #448. d, like #455. e, like #444. f, like #446. g, like #456. h, like #459. i, like #441. j, like #449. k, like #451. l, like #465. m, Malmel outrigger sailing canoe. n, like #445. o, like #452. p, like #453. q, like #457. r, like #450. s, like #458. t, like #460. u, like #466. v, like #442. w, like #454. x, like #459A. y, like #462.

1996, Apr. 18 Litho. *Perf. 11x10½*
605 A80 32c Sheet of 25, #a.-y. 16.00 16.00

Olympic Games, Cent. — A109

First Olympic stamps, Greece: a, #119. b, #124. c, #123. d, #125.

1996, Apr. 27 Litho. *Perf. 12*
606 A109 60c Block of 4, #a.-d. 4.00 4.00

Issued in sheets of 4. A small number were were overprinted in gold in the margin for Olymphilex '96.

Miniature Sheet

History of the Marshall Islands — A110

a, Undersea eruptions form island bases. b, Coral reefs grow. c, Storms bring birds & seeds. d, Early human inhabitants arrive. e, Seen by Spanish explorers, 1527. f, Capt. John Marshall, RN, charts islands, 1788. g, Islands become German protectorate, 1885. h, Japan seizes islands, 1914. i, US troops liberate islands, 1944. j, Bikiniatoll evacuated for nuclear testing, 1946. k, Islands become UN Trust Territory, 1947. l, Independence, 1986.

1996, May 2 Litho. *Perf. 13x12*
607 A110 55c Sheet of 12, #a.-l. 10.50 10.50

Elvis Presley's First #1 Hit, "Heartbreak Hotel," 40th Anniv. — A111

1996, May 5 *Perf. 10½x11*
608 A83 32c multicolored 1.00 .65

Issued in sheets of 20.

Souvenir Sheet

China '96, 9th Asian Intl. Philatelic Exhibition — A112

Design: The Palance Museum, Shenyang. Illustration reduced.

1996, May 17 *Perf. 13½*
609 A112 50c multicolored 1.25 1.00

James Dean (1931-55), Actor — A113

1996, June 1 Litho. *Perf. 10½x11*
610 A113 32c multicolored 1.00 .65

No. 610 was issued in sheets of 20.

First Ford Automobile, Cent. — A114

Designs: a, 1896 Quadricycle. b, 1903 Model A Roadster. c, 1909 Model T Touring Car. d, 1929 Model A Station Wagon. e, 1955 Thunderbird. f, 1964 1/2 Mustang convertible. g, 1995 Explorer. h, 1996 Taurus.

1996, June 4 Litho. *Perf. 13½*
611 A114 60c Sheet of 8, #a.-h. 6.00 6.00

Island Legends Type of 1995

Designs: a, Kijeek An Letao. b, Mennin Jobwodda. c, Wa Kone, Waan Letao. d, Kouj.

1996, July 19
612 A100 32c Block of 4, #a.-d. + 4 labels 2.25 2.25

Steam Locomotives — A115

Designs: a, Pennsylvania K4, US. b, "Big Boy," US. c, Mallard, Great Britain. d, RENFE Class 242, Spain. e, DB Class 01, Germany. f, FS Group 691,

Italy. g, "Royal Hudson," Canada. h, Evening Star, Great Britain. i, SAR 520 Class, Australia. j, SNCF 232.U1, France. k, QJ "Advance Forward," China. l, C62 "Swallow," Japan.

1996, Aug. 23 Litho. *Perf. 13½*
613 A115 55c Sheet of 12, #a.-l. 10.00 10.00

Marine Life Type of 1995

Designs: a, like #590a. b, like #590b. c, like #590c. d, like #590d.

1996, Oct. 21 Litho. *Perf. 13½*
614 A94 32c Block of 4, #a.-d. 1.75 1.75

Taipei '96, 10th Asian Intl. Philatelic Exhibition. Nos. 614a-614b have Chinese inscription, Nos. 614c-614d English.

Stick Chart, Canoe and Flag of the Republic Type of 1990

1996, Oct. 21 *Perf. 11x10½*
615 A63 $3 like No. 381 6.00 6.00

No. 615 inscribed "Free Association United States of America."

Angels from "Madonna and Child with Four Saints," by Rosso Fiorentino A116

1996, Oct. 31 Litho. *Perf. 13½*
616 A116 32c multicolored .55 .55

Christmas.

Legendary Planes Type of 1995

Biplanes: a, JN-3 Jenny. b, SPAD XIII. c, Albatros D.III. d, DH-4 Liberty. e, Fokker Dr.1. f, F-1 Camel. g, Martin MB-2. h, MB-3A Tommy. i, Curtiss TS-1. j, P-1 Hawk. k, Boeing PW-9. l, Douglas 0-2H. m, LB-5 Pirate. n, 02U-1 Corsair. o, F8C Heldiver. p, Boeing F4B-4. q, J6B Gerfalcon. r, Martin BM. s, FF-1 Fifi. t, C.R. 32 Cricket. u, Polikarpov I-15 Gull. v, Mk.1 Swordfish. w, Aichi D1A2. x, Grumman F3F. y, SOC-3 Seagull.

1996, Nov. 1
617 A104 32c Sheet of 25, #a.-y. 16.00 16.00

Native Crafts A117

Designs: a, Fan making. b, Canoe models. c, Carving. d, Basketmaking.

1996, Nov. 7 Litho. *Perf. 11x10½*
618 A117 32c Block of 4, #a.-d. 1.65 1.65

Souvenir Sheet

New Year 1997 (Year of the Ox) — A118

Illustration reduced.

1997, Jan. 7 Litho. *Perf. 13x13½*
619 A118 60c multicolored 1.20 1.20

Marshall Islands stamps can be mounted in the Scott U.S. Trust Territories album.

Amata Kabua (1928-96), President of Marshall Islands — A119

1997, Jan. 27 Litho. *Perf. 13½*
620 A119 32c multicolored .65 .65
621 A119 60c multicolored 1.20 1.20

No. 621 has vertical inscriptions in English.

Elvis Presley (1935-77) A120

Designs: a, "Rocking 50's." b, "Soaring 60's." c, "Sensational 70's."

1997, Jan. 8 Litho. *Perf. 13½*
622 A120 32c Strip of 3, #a.-c. 2.00 2.00

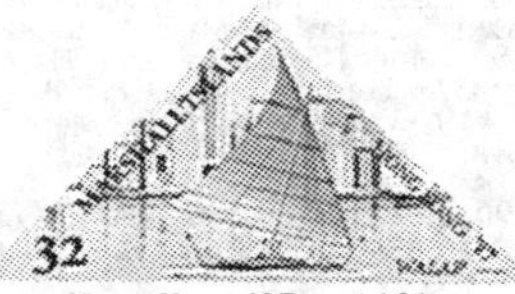

Hong Kong '97 — A121

Hong Kong at sunrise, ships: No. 623: a, Walap. b, Junk.
Hong Kong at night, ships: No. 624: a, Canoe. b, Junk, diff.
Illustration reduced.

1997, Feb. 12 *Perf. 12*
Sheets of 2
623 A121 32c #a.-b. + 3 labels 1.25 1.25
624 A121 32c #a.-b. + 3 labels 1.25 1.25

Christianity in Marshall Islands, 140th Anniv. — A122

Apostles: No. 625: a, Andrew. b, Matthew. c, Philip. d, Simon. e, Thaddeus. f, Thomas. g, Bartholomew. h, John. i, James, the Lesser. j, James, the Greater. k, Paul. l, Peter.
$3, The Last Supper, by Peter Paul Rubens.

1997, Mar. 28 *Perf. 13½*
625 A122 60c Sheet of 12, #a.-l. 14.50 14.50

Souvenir Sheet
Perf. 13x13½
626 A122 $3 multicolored 6.00 6.00

No. 626 contains one 80x50mm stamp.

First Decade of 20th Century — A123

Designs: a, Family of immigrants. b, Dowager Empress, Boxers, China. c, Photography for every man. d, Dr. Walter Reed, mosquito. e, Signund Freud. f, Marconi, wireless transmitter. g, Enrico Caruso, phonograph. h, Wright Brothers, Flyer. i, Einstein. j, HMS Dreadnought. k, San Francisco earthquake, 1906. l, Gandhi, non-violent protestors. m, Picasso. n, Dawn of the automobile age. o, Man, camels, oil derrick amid sand dunes.

1997, Apr. 15 Litho. *Perf. 13½*
627 A123 60c Sheet of 15, #a.-o. 18.00 18.00

See No. 646.

Deng Xiaoping (1904-97), Chinese Leader — A124

1997, Apr. 21
628 A124 60c multicolored 1.20 1.20

Traditional Crafts A125

Designs: Nos. 629a, 630a, Fan making. Nos. 629b, 630b, Canoe models. Nos. 629c, 630c, Wood carving. Nos. 629d, 630d, Basket making.

1997, May 29 Litho. *Perf. 11x10½*
Self-Adhesive
629 A125 32c Block of 4, #a.-d. 2.50 2.50

Serpentine Die Cut Perf. 11
Self-Adhesive
630 A125 32c Strip of 4, #a.-d. 2.50 2.50

No. 629 was issued in sheets of 20 stamps. No. 630 was issued in sheets of 16 stamps. Die cutting does not extend through backing paper on No. 630.

Marshall Islands Stamps, Cent., US Stamps, 150th Anniv. A126

1997, May 29 Litho. *Perf. 13½*
Booklet Stamps
631 A126 50c No. 1 1.00 1.00
632 A126 50c No. 2 1.00 1.00
633 A126 50c No. 3 1.00 1.00
634 A126 50c No. 4 1.00 1.00
635 A126 50c No. 5 1.00 1.00
636 A126 50c No. 6 1.00 1.00
a. Booklet pane, #631-636 6.00

Size: 75x32mm
637 A126 $1 US Nos. 1 & 2 2.00 2.00
a. Booklet pane of 1 2.00
Complete booklet, #636a, #637a 8.00

PACIFIC 97.

Bristle-thighed Curlew — A127

World Wildlife Fund: a, Walking right. b, On tree branch. c, Standing with mouth open. d, In flight.

1997, June 6
638 A127 16c Block or strip of 4, #a.-d. 1.30 1.30

Souvenir Sheet

Bank of China, Hong Kong — A128

Illustration reduced.

1997, July 1 Litho. *Perf. 13½*
639 A128 50c multicolored 1.00 1.00

Canoes A129

Designs: a, Pacific Arts Festival canoe, Walap of Enewetak. b, Large Voyaging canoe, Walap of Jaluit. c. Racing canoe. d, Sailing canoe, Tipnol of Ailuk.

1997, July 10 Litho. *Perf. 13½*
640 A129 32c Block or strip of 4, #a.-d. 2.50 2.50

Legendary Aircraft Type of 1995

Designs: a, C-54 Skymaster. b, B-36 Peacemaker. c, F-86 Sabre. d, B-47 Stratojet. e, C-124 Globemaster II. f, C-121 Constellation. g, B-52 Stratofortress. h, F-100 Super Sabre. i, F-104 Starfighter. j, C-130 Hercules. k, F-105 Thunderchief. l, KC-135 Stratotanker. m, B-58 Hustler. n, F-4 Phanton II. o, T-38 Talon. p, C-141 Star Lifter. q, F-111 Aardvark. r, SR-71 "Blackbird." s, C-5 Galaxy. t, A-10 Thunderbolt II. u, F-15 Eagle. v, F-16 Fighting Falcon. w, F-117 Nighthawk. x, B-2 Spirit. y, C-17 Globemaster III.

1997, July 19
641 A104 32c Sheet of 25, #a.-y. 16.00 16.00

USS Contstitution, Bicent. A130

1997, July 21
642 A130 32c multicolored .65 .65

Island Legends Type of 1995

Designs: a, The Large Pool of Mejit. b, The Beautiful Woman of Kwajalein. c, Sharks and Lowakalle Reef. d, The Demon of Adrie.

1997, Aug. 15 Litho. *Perf. 13½*
643 A100 32c Block of 4, #a.-d.+4 labels 2.50 2.50

Marine Life Type of 1995

Designs: a, Watanabe's angelfish, gray reef shark. b, Raccoon butterflyfish. c, Flame angelfish. d, Square-spot fairy basslets.

1997, Aug. 21
644 A94 60c Block of 4, #a.-d. 4.75 4.75

Diana, Princess of Wales (1961-97) A131

Various portraits, background color: a, violet. b, blue. c, yellow orange.

1997, Sept. 30 Litho. *Perf. 13½*
645 A131 60c Vert. strip of 3, #a.-c. 3.60 3.60

No. 645 was issued in sheets containing 1 vert. strip of 3 #645a, 1 vert. strip of 3 #645b, 1 vert. strip of 3 #645c.

Events of the 20th Century Type of 1997

Events of 1910-1919: a, Women mobilize for equal rights. b, Ernest Rutherford, model of atom. c, Sun Yat-sen. d, Sinking of the Titanic. e, Igor Stravinsky, The Rite of Spring. f, Ford begins assembly line production of autos. g, Archduke Franz Ferdinand, wife Sophie. h, German U-boat sinks Lusitania. i, Soldiers in trenches at Battle of Verdun. j, Patrick Pearse proclaims Irish Republic. k, Jews praying at Wailing Wall. l, Cruiser Aurora. m, Baron Manfred von Richtofen. n, German revolutionary troops, 1918. o, Negotiators write Treaty of Versailles.

1997, Oct. 15 Litho. *Perf. 13½*
646 A123 60c Sheet of 15, #a.-o. 18.00 18.00

Christmas A132

Cherubs from Sistine Madonna, by Raphael: No. 647, With hand under chin. No. 648, With arms folded under chin.

1997, Oct. 25
647 A132 32c multicolored .65 .65
648 A132 32c multicolored .65 .65
a. Pair, #647-648 1.30 1.30

US State-Named Warships — A133

Designs: a.-z., aa.-ax.: USS Alabama-USS Wyoming in alphabetical order. USS Honolulu shown for Hawaii.

1997, Nov. 1
649 A133 20c Sheet of 50 20.00 20.00

Souvenir Sheet

Shanghai 97, Intl. Stamp and Coin Expo — A134

Treasure ship, Ming Dynasty. Illustration reduced.

1997, Nov. 19 Litho. *Perf. 13x13½*
650 A134 50c multicolored 1.00 1.00

Souvenir Sheet

New Year 1998 (Year of the Tiger) — A135

Illustration reduced.

1998, Jan. 2 Litho. *Perf. 13x13½*
651 A135 60c multicolored 1.20 1.20

Elvis Presley's 1968 Television Special A136

Scenes from special: a, shown. b, Red background. c, Elvis in white suit.

1998, Jan. 8 *Perf. 13½*
652 A136 32c Strip of 3, #a.-c. 1.90 1.90

SEMI-POSTAL STAMPS

Sheet of 6

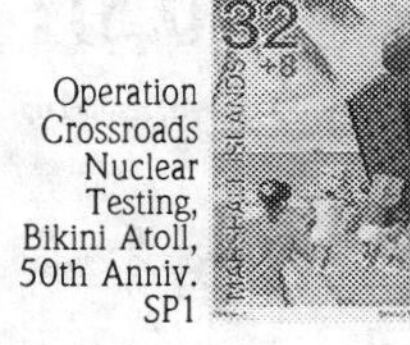

Operation Crossroads Nuclear Testing, Bikini Atoll, 50th Anniv. SP1

Designs: a, Evacuation of Bikinians. b, Navy preparations. c, Able. d, Baker. e, Ghost fleet. f, Effects on Bikinians.

1996, July 1 Litho. *Perf. 13½*
B1 SP1 32c +8c #a.-f. + 6 labels 4.80 4.80

Surtax for the benefit of the people of Bikini.

AIR POST STAMPS

Audubon Type of 1985

1985, Feb. 15 Litho. *Perf. 14*
C1 A11 44c Booby Gannet, vert. .90 .90
C2 A11 44c Esquimaux Curlew, vert. .90 .90
a. Pair, #C1-C2 1.80 1.80

AMERIPEX Type of 1986

Designs: No. C3, Consolidated PBY-5A Catalin Amphibian. No. C4, Grumman SA-16 Albatross. No. C5, McDonnell Douglas DC-6B Super Cloudmaster. No. C6, Boeing &27-100.

1986, May 22 Litho. *Perf. 14*
C3 A20 44c multicolored .95 .95
C4 A20 44c multicolored .95 .95
C5 A20 44c multicolored .95 .95
C6 A20 44c multicolored .95 .95
a. Block of 4, #C3-C6 3.80 3.80

Operation Crossroads Type of 1986
Souvenir Sheet

1986, July 1 Litho. *Perf. 14*
C7 A21 44c USS Saratoga *4.00 4.00*

Statue of Liberty Cent., Intl. Peace Year — AP1

1986, Oct. 28 Litho.
C8 AP1 44c multicolored 1.00 .95

Natl. Girl Scout Movement, 20th Anniv. — AP2

1986, Dec. 8 Litho.
C9 AP2 44c Community service .65 .65
C10 AP2 44c Salute .65 .65
C11 AP2 44c Health care .65 .65
C12 AP2 44c Learning skills .65 .65
a. Block of 4, #C9-C12 2.75 2.75

Girl Scout Movement in the US, 75th anniv. (1912-1987).

Marine Birds — AP3

1987, Jan. 12 Litho. *Perf. 14*
C13 AP3 44c Wedge-tailed shearwater .75 .75
C14 AP3 44c Red-footed booby .75 .75
C15 AP3 44c Red-tailed tropicbird .75 .75
C16 AP3 44c Great frigatebird .75 .75
a. Block of 4, #C13-C16 3.00 3.00

CAPEX '87 — AP4

Last flight of Amelia Earhart: No. C17, Take-off at Lae, New Guinea, July 2, 1937. No. C18, USCG Itasca cutter at Howland Is. No. C19, Purported crash landing of the Electra at Mili Atoll. No. C20, Recovery of the Electra by the Koshu, a Japanese survey ship.

1987, June 15 Litho. *Perf. 14*
C17 AP4 44c multicolored .75 .75
C18 AP4 44c multicolored .75 .75
C19 AP4 44c multicolored .75 .75
C20 AP4 44c multicolored .75 .75
a. Block of 4, #C17-C20 3.00 3.00

Space Shuttle Type of 1988

1988, Dec. 23 Litho. *Perf. 14*
C21 A38 45c Astronaut, shuttle over Rongelap .85 .85

Aircraft — AP5

1989, Apr. 24 Litho. *Perf. 14x14½*
C22 AP5 12c Dornier Do228 .25 .25
a. Booklet pane of 10 3.00 —
C23 AP5 36c Boeing 737 .75 .75
a. Booklet pane of 10 8.00 —
C24 AP5 39c Hawker Siddeley 748 .90 .90
a. Booklet pane of 10 9.00 —
C25 AP5 45c Boeing 727 1.00 1.00
a. Booklet pane of 10 10.00 —
b. Bklt. pane, 5 each 36c, 45c 8.75 —
Nos. C22-C25 (4) 2.90 2.90

MARTINIQUE

ˌmär-tᵊn-ˈēk

LOCATION — Island in the West Indies, southeast of Puerto Rico
GOVT. — French Colony
AREA — 385 sq. mi.
POP. — 261,595 (1946)
CAPITAL — Fort-de-France

Formerly a French colony, Martinique became an integral part of the Republic, acquiring the same status as the departments in metropolitan France, under a law effective Jan. 1, 1947.

100 Centimes = 1 Franc

Catalogue values for unused stamps in this country are for Never Hinged items, beginning with Scott 196 in the regular postage section, Scott C1 in the airpost section, and Scott J37 in the postage due section.

See France Nos. 1278, 1508, French West Africa 70, for stamps inscribed "Martinique."

Stamps of French Colonies 1881-86 Surcharged in Black

MARTINIQUE 5 — Nos. 1, 7
MARTINIQUE 5c — No. 2
MQE 15 c. — No. 3
MQE 15 c. — No. 4
MARTINIQUE 01 — Nos. 5-6, 8
MARTINIQUE 01c. — Nos. 9-20

1886-91 Unwmk. *Perf. 14x13½*
1 A9 5 on 20c 30.00 25.00
a. Double surcharge *425.00 425.00*
2 A9 5c on 20c *11,000. 11,000.*
3 A9 15c on 20c ('87) 125.00 110.00
a. Inverted surcharge *1,400. 1,400.*
4 A9 15c on 20c ('87) 50.00 45.00
a. Inverted surcharge *800.00 800.00*
5 A9 01 on 20c ('88) 7.50 7.50
a. Inverted surcharge *200.00 200.00*
6 A9 05 on 20c 6.00 4.00
7 A9 15 on 20c ('88) 125.00 90.00
c. Inverted surcharge *425.00 425.00*
8 A9 015 on 20c ('87) 30.00 30.00
a. Inverted surcharge *500.00 500.00*
9 A9 01c on 2c ('88) 1.50 1.25
a. Double surcharge *250.00 250.00*
10 A9 01c on 4c ('88) 6.50 1.75
11 A9 05c on 4c ('88) 900.00 800.00
12 A9 05c on 10c ('90) 60.00 30.00
a. Slanting "5" *150.00 110.00*
13 A9 05c on 20c ('88) 12.50 10.00
a. Slanting "5" *60.00 50.00*
b. Inverted surcharge *225.00 190.00*
14 A9 05c on 30c ('91) 15.00 14.00
a. Slanting "5" *70.00 60.00*
15 A9 05c on 35c ('91) 10.00 9.00
a. Slanting "5" *65.00 60.00*
b. Inverted surcharge *175.00 140.00*
16 A9 05c on 40c ('91) 30.00 22.50
a. Slanting "5" *110.00 85.00*
17 A9 15c on 4c ('88) *7,500. 7,000.*
18 A9 15c on 20c ('87) 80.00 50.00
a. Slanting "5" *250.00 225.00*
b. Double surcharge *350.00 350.00*
19 A9 15c on 25c ('90) 12.50 7.50
a. Slanting "5" *75.00 75.00*
b. Inverted surcharge *250.00 250.00*
20 A9 15c on 75c ('91) 125.00 75.00
a. Slanting "5" *300.00 275.00*

French Colonies No. 47 Surcharged

TIMBRE-POSTE
01c.
MARTINIQUE

1891
21 A9 01c on 2c brn, *buff* 5.00 5.00

French Colonies Nos. J5-J9 Surcharged

TIMBRE-POSTE
05c.
MARTINIQUE

1891-92 Black Surcharge *Imperf.*
22 D1 05c on 5c blk ('92) 6.50 5.50
a. Slanting "5" 50.00 35.00
23 D1 05c on 15c blk 5.00 4.00
b. Slanting "5" 40.00 35.00
24 D1 15c on 20c blk 7.50 7.00
a. Inverted surcharge 175.00 175.00
b. Double surcharge 175.00 175.00
25 D1 15c on 30c blk 7.50 7.00
a. Inverted surcharge 175.00 175.00
b. Slanting "5" 40.00 35.00
Nos. 22-25 (4) 26.50 23.50

Red Surcharge
26 D1 05c on 10c blk 5.00 5.00
a. Inverted surcharge 175.00 175.00
27 D1 05c on 15c blk 8.00 8.00
28 D1 15c on 20c blk 25.00 20.00
a. Inverted surcharge 225.00 225.00
Nos. 26-28 (3) 38.00 33.00

French Colonies No. 54 Surcharged in Black

1892
MARTINIQUE
05c.
j

1892
05c.
MARTINIQUE
k

1892 *Perf. 14x13½*
29 A9 (j) 05c on 25c 30.00 30.00
a. Slanting "5" 160.00 160.00
30 A9 (j) 15c on 25c 13.00 13.00
a. Slanting "5" 160.00 160.00
31 A9 (k) 05c on 25c 35.00 30.00
a. "1882" instead of "1892" 325.00 300.00
b. "95" instead of "05" 400.00 350.00
c. Slanting "5" 150.00 150.00
32 A9 (k) 15c on 25c 15.00 13.00
a. "1882" instead of "1892" 275.00 275.00
b. Slanting "5" 90.00 90.00
Nos. 29-32 (4) 93.00 86.00

Navigation and Commerce — A15

1892-1906 Typo. *Perf. 14x13½*
"MARTINIQUE" Colony in Carmine or Blue
33 A15 1c blk, *lil bl* .80 .70
a. "MARTINIQUE" in blue 750.00 750.00
34 A15 2c brn, *buff* .80 .70
35 A15 4c claret, *lav* 1.00 1.00
36 A15 5c grn, *grnsh* 1.25 .50
37 A15 5c yel grn ('99) 1.50 .50
38 A15 10c blk, *lav* 4.75 .75
39 A15 10c red ('99) 1.75 .50
40 A15 15c blue, quadrille paper 20.00 4.25
41 A15 15c gray ('99) 5.50 .80
42 A15 20c red, *grn* 10.00 4.00
43 A15 25c blk, *rose* 10.00 1.00
44 A15 25c blue ('99) 10.00 6.50
45 A15 30c brn, *bis* 20.00 7.00
46 A15 35c blk, *yel* ('06) 9.00 5.00
47 A15 40c red, *straw* 20.00 7.50
48 A15 50c car, *rose* 20.00 9.00
49 A15 50c brn, *az* ('99) 20.00 13.00
50 A15 75c dp vio, *org* 20.00 10.00
51 A15 1fr brnz grn, *straw* 15.00 8.50
52 A15 2fr vio, *rose* ('04) 60.00 55.00
53 A15 5fr lil, *lav* ('03) 75.00 55.00
Nos. 33-53 (21) 326.35 191.20

Perf. 13½x14 stamps are counterfeits.
For surcharges see Nos. 54-61, 101-104.

Stamps of 1892-1903 Surcharged in Black **10c**

1904
54 A15 10c on 30c brn, *bis* 4.50 4.50
a. Double surcharge
55 A15 10c on 5fr lil, *lav* 7.50 7.50

Surcharged

1904
0f10

56 A15 10c on 30c brn, *bis* 10.00 10.00
57 A15 10c on 40c red, *straw* 10.00 10.00
a. Double surcharge 250.00 250.00
58 A15 10c on 50c car, *rose* 10.00 10.00
59 A15 10c on 75c dp vio, *org* 9.50 9.50
60 A15 10c on 1fr brnz grn, *straw* 10.00 10.00
a. Double surcharge 150.00 150.00
61 A15 10c on 5fr lil, *lav* 175.00 175.00
Nos. 54-61 (8) 236.50 236.50

Martinique Woman — A16

Girl Bearing Pineapple in Cane Field — A18

View of Fort-de-France A17

1908-30 Typo.
62 A16 1c red brn & brn .15 .15
63 A16 2c ol grn & brn .15 .15
64 A16 4c vio brn & brn .15 .15
65 A16 5c grn & brn .15 .15
66 A16 5c org & brn ('22) .15 .15
67 A16 10c car & brn .30 .15
68 A16 10c bl grn & grn ('22) .20 .15
69 A16 10c brn vio & rose ('25) .20 .15
70 A16 15c brn vio & rose ('17) .15 .15
71 A16 15c bl grn & gray grn ('25) .20 .15
72 A16 15c dp bl & red org ('27) .65 .65
73 A16 20c vio & brn .65 .45
74 A17 25c bl & brn .65 .15
75 A17 25c org & brn ('22) .15 .15
76 A17 30c brn org & brn .65 .35
77 A17 30c dl red & brn ('22) .15 .15
78 A17 30c rose & ver ('24) .15 .15
79 A17 30c ol brn & brn ('25) .15 .15
80 A17 30c sl bl & bl grn ('27) .65 .65
81 A17 35c vio & brn .35 .25
82 A17 40c gray grn & brn .35 .15
83 A17 45c dk brn & brn .35 .25
84 A17 50c rose & brn .65 .35
85 A17 50c bl & brn ('22) .65 .60
86 A17 50c org & grn ('25) .15 .15
87 A17 60c dk bl & lil rose ('25) .15 .15
88 A17 65c vio & ol brn ('27) .75 .75
89 A17 75c sIATE & brn .70 .30
90 A17 75c ind & dk bl ('25) .15 .15
91 A17 75c org brn & lt bl ('27) 1.25 1.25
92 A17 90c brn red & brt red ('30) 3.00 3.00
93 A18 1fr dl bl & brn .35 .15
94 A18 1fr dk bl ('25) .30 .20
95 A18 1fr ver & ol grn ('27) 1.00 1.00
96 A18 1.10fr vio & dk brn ('28) 1.75 1.75
97 A18 1.50fr ind & ultra ('30) 3.25 3.25
98 A18 2fr gray & brn 2.00 .70
99 A18 3fr red vio ('30) 4.50 4.50
100 A18 5fr org red & brn 5.50 4.50
Nos. 62-100 (39) 32.80 27.75

For surcharges see Nos. 105-128, B1.

Nos. 41, 43, 47 and 53 Surcharged in Carmine or Black

05 **10**

1912, Aug.
101 A15 5c on 15c gray (C) .50 .50
102 A15 5c on 25c blk, *rose* (C) .75 .75
103 A15 10c on 40c red, *straw* .75 .75
104 A15 10c on 5fr lil, *lav* 1.25 1.25
Nos. 101-104 (4) 3.25 3.25

Two spacings between the surcharged numerals are found on Nos. 101 to 104.

Nos. 62, 63, 70 Surcharged **05**

1920, June 15
105 A16 5c on 1c .90 .90
a. Double surcharge 17.00 17.00
b. Inverted surcharge 17.00 17.00
106 A16 10c on 2c .85 .85
a. Inverted surcharge 17.00 17.00
107 A16 25c on 15c .60 .60
a. Double surcharge 27.50 27.50
b. Inverted surcharge 27.50 27.50
Nos. 105-107 (3) 2.35 2.35

No. 70 Surcharged in Various Colors ☰ 0,01 ☰

1922, Dec.
108 A16 1c on 15c (Bk) .15 .15
109 A16 2c on 15c (Bl) .15 .15
110 A16 5c on 15c (R) .15 .15
a. Imperf., pair 65.00
Nos. 108-110 (3) .45 .45

Types of 1908-30 Surcharged **60**

1923-25
111 A17 60c on 75c bl & rose .25 .25
112 A17 65c on 45c ol brn & brn ('25) .60 .60
113 A17 85c on 75c blk & brn (R) ('25) .70 .70
Nos. 111-113 (3) 1.55 1.55

Nos. 63, 73, 76-77, 84-85 Surcharged in Brown **0,01**

Surcharge is horiz. on #114-115, vert. reading up on #116, 119 and down on #117-118.

1924, Feb. 14
114 A16 1c on 2c 1.00 1.00
a. Double surcharge 200.00 200.00
b. Inverted surcharge 45.00 45.00
115 A16 5c on 20c 1.25 1.25
a. Inverted surcharge 45.00 45.00
116 A17 15c on 30c (#76) 6.00 6.00
a. Surcharge reading down 21.00 21.00
117 A17 15c on 30c (#77) 8.00 8.00
a. Surcharge reading up 30.00 30.00
118 A17 25c on 50c (#84) 175.00 175.00
119 A17 25c on 50c (#85) 2.50 2.50
a. Surcharge reading down 22.50 22.50
Nos. 114-119 (6) 193.75 193.75

Stamps and Types of 1908-30 Surcharged with New Value and Bars

1924-27
120 A16 25c on 15c brn vio & rose ('25) .25 .25
121 A18 25c on 2fr gray & brn .20 .20
122 A18 25c on 5fr org red & brn (Bl) .90 .45
123 A17 90c on 75c brn red & red ('27) 1.75 1.40
124 A18 1.25fr on 1fr dk bl ('26) .20 .15
125 A18 1.50fr on 1fr dk bl & ultra ('27) .65 .50
126 A18 3fr on 5fr dl red & grn ('27) 1.25 1.10
127 A18 10fr on 5fr dl grn & dp red ('27) 5.75 5.75
128 A18 20fr on 5fr org brn & red vio ('27) 9.00 8.25
Nos. 120-128 (9) 19.95 18.05

Colonial Exposition Issue
Common Design Types

1931, Apr. 13 Engr. *Perf. 12½*
Name of Country in Black
129 CD70 40c deep green 2.25 2.25
130 CD71 50c violet 2.25 2.25
131 CD72 90c red orange 2.25 2.25
132 CD73 1.50fr dull blue 2.25 2.25
Nos. 129-132 (4) 9.00 9.00

Village of Basse-Pointe A19

Government Palace, Fort-de-France A20

Martinique Women — A21

1933-40 Photo. *Perf. 13½*
133 A19 1c red, *pink* .15 .15
134 A20 2c dull blue .15 .15
135 A20 3c sepia ('40) .15 .15
136 A19 4c olive grn .15 .15
137 A20 5c dp rose .15 .15
138 A19 10c blk, *pink* .15 .15
139 A20 15c blk, *org* .15 .15
140 A21 20c org brn .15 .15
141 A19 25c brn vio .15 .15
142 A20 30c green .15 .15
143 A20 30c lt ultra ('40) .15 .15
144 A21 35c dl grn ('38) .15 .15
145 A21 40c olive brn .15 .15
146 A20 45c dk brn 1.00 1.00
147 A20 45c grn ('40) .20 .20
148 A20 50c red .15 .15
149 A19 55c brn red ('38) .35 .35
150 A19 60c lt bl ('40) .20 .20
151 A21 65c red, *grn* .25 .25
152 A21 70c brt red vio ('40) .20 .20
153 A19 75c dk brn .45 .45
154 A20 80c vio ('38) .15 .15
155 A19 90c carmine 1.00 1.00
156 A19 90c brt red vio ('39) .35 .35
157 A20 1fr blk, *grn* 1.00 .60
158 A20 1fr rose red ('38) .35 .20
159 A21 1.25fr dk vio .35 .15
160 A21 1.25fr dp rose ('39) .35 .35
161 A19 1.40fr lt ultra ('40) .35 .35
162 A20 1.50fr dp bl .35 .15
163 A20 1.60fr chnt ('40) .35 .35
164 A21 1.75fr ol grn 5.00 2.50
165 A21 1.75fr dp bl ('38) .20 .15
166 A19 2fr dk bl, *grn* .20 .15
167 A21 2.25fr blue ('39) .45 .45
168 A19 2.50fr sepia ('40) .50 .50
169 A21 3fr brn vio .15 .15
170 A21 5fr red, *pink* .75 .35
171 A19 10fr dk bl, *bl* .35 .25
172 A20 20fr red, *yel* .80 .45
Nos. 133-172 (40) 17.75
Set value 12.00

For surcharges see Nos. 190-195.

Landing of Bélain d'Esnambuc — A22

Freed Slaves Paying Homage to Victor Schoelcher A23

1935, Oct. 22 Engr. *Perf. 13*
173 A22 40c blk brn 1.00 .90
174 A22 50c dl red 1.00 .90
175 A22 1.50fr ultra 8.00 6.50
176 A23 1.75fr lil rose 6.50 6.50
177 A23 5fr brown 6.50 6.50
178 A23 10fr blue grn 5.50 4.50
Nos. 173-178 (6) 28.50 25.80

Tercentenary of French possessions in the West Indies.

Colonial Arts Exhibition Issue
Common Design Type
Souvenir Sheet

1937 *Imperf.*
179 CD74 3fr brt grn 4.00 4.00

Paris International Exposition Issue
Common Design Types

1937, Apr. 15 *Perf. 13*
180 CD74 20c dp vio .90 .90
181 CD75 30c dk grn .90 .90
182 CD76 40c car rose .90 .90
183 CD77 50c dk brn & blk 1.00 1.00
184 CD78 90c red 1.00 1.00
185 CD79 1.50fr ultra 1.00 1.00
Nos. 180-185 (6) 5.70 5.70

New York World's Fair Issue

Common Design Type

1939, May 10 *Perf. 12½x12*

186	CD82	1.25fr car lake	.60	.60
187	CD82	2.25fr ultra	.60	.60

View of Fort-de-France and Marshal Pétain — A23a

1941 **Engr.** *Perf. 12½x12*

188	A23a	1fr dull lilac	.22
189	A23a	2.50fr blue	.22

Nos. 188-189 were issued by the Vichy government, and were not placed on sale in Martinique.

Nos. 134, 135, 136 and 151 Surcharged with New Values and Bars or Wavy Lines in Red, Black or Blue

1945 *Perf. 13½, 13x13½*

190	A20	1fr on 2c dl bl (R)	.15	.15
191	A19	2fr on 4c ol grn	.20	.20
192	A20	3fr on 2c dl bl (R)	.25	.25
193	A21	5fr on 65c red, *grn*	.45	.45
194	A21	10fr on 65c red, *grn*	.45	.45
195	A20	20fr on 3c sepia (Bl)	.60	.60
		Nos. 190-195 (6)	2.10	2.10

Catalogue values for unused stamps in this section, from this point to the end of the section, are for Never Hinged items.

Eboue Issue

Common Design Type

1945 **Engr.** *Perf. 13*

196	CD91	2fr black	.15	.15
197	CD91	25fr Prussian green	.42	.42

Victor Schoelcher and View of Town of Schoelcher A24

1945 **Unwmk.** **Litho.** *Perf. 11½*

198	A24	10c dp bl vio & ultra	.15	.15
199	A24	30c dk org brn & lt org brn	.15	.15
200	A24	40c grnsh bl & pale bl	.15	.15
201	A24	50c car brn & rose lil	.15	.15
202	A24	60c org yel & yel	.20	.15
203	A24	70c brn & pale brn	.20	.15
204	A24	80c lt bl grn & pale grn	.20	.15
205	A24	1fr bl & lt bl	.20	.15
206	A24	1.20fr rose vio & rose lil	.30	.20
207	A24	1.50fr red org & org	.30	.20
208	A24	2fr blk & gray	.20	.15
209	A24	2.40fr red & pink	1.10	.70
210	A24	3fr pink & pale pink	.20	.15
211	A24	4fr ultra & lt ultra	.35	.15
212	A24	4.50fr yel grn & lt grn	.65	.20
213	A24	5fr org brn & lt org brn	.30	.20
214	A24	10fr dk vio & lil	.65	.30
215	A24	15fr rose car & lil rose	.75	.30
216	A24	20fr ol grn & lt ol grn	1.25	.70
		Nos. 198-216 (19)	7.45	4.45

Martinique Girl — A25

Mountains — A30

Cliffs — A26

Gathering Sugar Cane — A27

Mount Pelée — A28

Tropical Fruit — A29

1947, June 2 **Engr.** *Perf. 13*

217	A25	10c red brown	.15	.15
218	A25	30c deep blue	.15	.15
219	A25	50c olive brown	.15	.15
220	A26	60c dark green	.30	.20
221	A26	1fr red brown	.20	.15
222	A26	1.50fr purple	.35	.25
223	A27	2fr blue green	.75	.40
224	A27	2.50fr blk brn	.65	.35
225	A27	3fr deep blue	.65	.25
226	A28	4fr dk brown	.65	.35
227	A28	5fr dark green	.60	.35
228	A28	6fr lilac rose	.65	.35
229	A29	10fr indigo	1.00	.40
230	A29	15fr red brown	1.25	.75
231	A29	20fr blk brown	1.60	.75
232	A30	25fr violet	1.75	.90
233	A30	40fr blue grren	2.25	1.00
		Nos. 217-233 (17)	13.10	6.90

SEMI-POSTAL STAMPS

Regular Issue of 1908 Surcharged in Red

Perf. 13½x14

1915, May 15 **Unwmk.**

B1	A16	10c + 5c car & brn	1.00	.75

Curie Issue

Common Design Type

1938, Oct. 24 *Perf. 13*

B2	CD80	1.75fr + 50c brt ultra	6.50	6.50

French Revolution Issue

Common Design Type

Photo.; Name & Value Typo. in Black

1939, July 5

B3	CD83	45c + 25c grn	5.00	5.00
B4	CD83	70c + 30c brn	5.00	5.00
B5	CD83	90c + 35c red org	5.00	5.00
B6	CD83	1.25fr + 1fr rose pink	5.00	5.00
B7	CD83	2.25fr + 2fr blue	5.00	5.00
		Nos. B3-B7 (5)	25.00	25.00

Common Design Type and

Colonial Infantry with Machine Gun — SP1

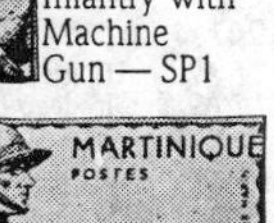

Naval Rifleman SP2

1941 **Photo.** *Perf. 13½*

B8	SP1	1fr + 1fr red	.50
B9	CD86	1.50fr + 3fr maroon	.50
B10	SP2	2.50fr + 1fr blue	.50
		Nos. B8-B10 (3)	1.50

Nos. B8-B10 were issued by the Vichy government, and were not placed on sale in Martinique.

Nos. 188-189 were surcharged "OEUVRES COLONIALES" and surtax (including change of denomination of the 2.50fr to 50c). These were issued in 1944 by the Vichy government, and were not placed on sale in Martinique.

Red Cross Issue

Common Design Type

1944 *Perf. 14½x14*

B11	CD90	5fr + 20fr dark purpler	.40	.30

The surtax was for the French Red Cross and national relief.

AIR POST STAMPS

Catalogue values for unused stamps in this section are for Never Hinged items.

Common Design Type

1945 **Unwmk.** **Photo.** *Perf. 14½x14*

C1	CD87	50fr dark green	1.00	.25
C2	CD87	100fr plum	1.50	.35

Two other values, 8.50fr orange and 18fr red brown, were prepared but not issued. Value, $50 each.

Victory Issue

Common Design Type

1946, May 8 **Engr.** *Perf. 12½*

C3	CD92	8fr indigo	.60	.60

European victory of the Allied Nations in WWII.

Chad to Rhine Issue

Common Design Types

1946, June 6

C4	CD93	5fr orange	.50	.50
C5	CD94	10fr slate grn	.50	.50
C6	CD95	15fr carmine	.60	.60
C7	CD96	20fr chocolate	.60	.60
C8	CD97	25fr deep blue	.75	.75
C9	CD98	50fr gray blk	1.00	1.00
		Nos. C4-C9 (6)	3.95	3.95

Seaplane and Beach Scene — AP1

Plane over Tropic Shore — AP2

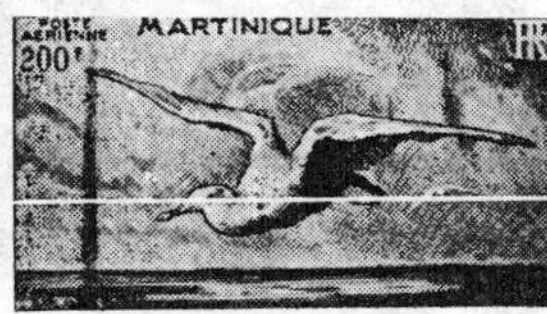

Albatross — AP3

1947, June 2 *Perf. 13*

C10	AP1	50fr dk brn vio	2.50	1.50
C11	AP2	100fr dk bl grn	4.00	2.00
C12	AP3	200fr violet	25.00	15.00
		Nos. C10-C12 (3)	31.50	18.50

AIR POST SEMI-POSTAL STAMPS

Stamps similar to French Guiana type V6 inscribed "Martinique" and stamp of Cameroun type V10 inscribed "Martinique" were issued in 1942 by the Vichy Government, but were not placed on sale in Martinique.

POSTAGE DUE STAMPS

The set of 14 French Colonies postage due stamps (Nos. J1-J14) overprinted "MARTINIQUE" diagonally in red in 1887 was not an official issue.

Postage Due Stamps of France, 1893-1926 Overprinted

MARTINIQUE

1927, Oct. 10 *Perf. 14x13½*

J15	D2	5c light blue	.80	.80
J16	D2	10c brown	1.00	1.00
J17	D2	20c olive green	1.00	1.00
J18	D2	25c rose	1.40	1.40
J19	D2	30c red	1.65	1.65
J20	D2	45c green	1.65	1.65
J21	D2	50c brn violet	3.50	3.50
J22	D2	60c blue green	4.00	4.00
J23	D2	1fr red brown	4.50	4.50
J24	D2	2fr bright vio	6.50	6.50
J25	D2	3fr magenta	7.50	7.50
		Nos. J15-J25 (11)	33.50	33.50

Tropical Fruit — D3

1933, Feb. 15 **Photo.** *Perf. 13½*

J26	D3	5c dk bl, *green*	.25	.25
J27	D3	10c orange brown	.25	.25
J28	D3	20c dk blue	.60	.60
J29	D3	25c red, *pink*	.60	.60
J30	D3	30c dk vio	.40	.40
J31	D3	45c red, *yel*	.25	.25
J32	D3	50c dk brn	.60	.60
J33	D3	60c dl grn	.60	.60
J34	D3	1fr blk, *org*	.75	.75
J35	D3	2fr dp rose	.60	.60
J36	D3	3fr dk blue, *bl*	.60	.60
		Nos. J26-J36 (11)	5.50	5.50

Stamps of type D3 without the "RF" monogram were issued in 1943 by the Vichy Government, but were not placed on sale in Martinique.

Map — D4

1947, June 2 **Engr.** *Perf. 14x13*

J37	D4	10c ultra	.15	.15
J38	D4	30c brt bl grn	.15	.15
J39	D4	50c slate gray	.20	.20
J40	D4	1fr org red	.20	.20
J41	D4	2fr dk vio brn	.40	.40
J42	D4	3fr lilac rose	.40	.40
J43	D4	4fr dk brn	.60	.60
J44	D4	5fr red	.65	.65
J45	D4	10fr black	1.00	1.00
J46	D4	20fr olive grn	1.00	1.00
		Nos. J37-J46 (10)	4.75	4.75

PARCEL POST STAMP

Postage Due Stamp of French Colonies Surcharged in Black

TIMBRE POSTE
5 F.
MARTINIQUE
COLIS POSTAUX

1903, Oct. **Unwmk.** *Imperf.*

Q1	D1	5fr on 60c brn, *buff*	400.00	425.00
a.		Inverted surcharge	*425.00*	*500.00*

MAURITANIA

mȯr-ə-tā-nē-ə

LOCATION — Northwestern Africa, bordering on the Atlantic Ocean
GOVT. — Republic
AREA — 398,000 sq. mi.
POP. — 1,834,500 (est. 1984)
CAPITAL — Nouakchott

The Islamic Republic of Mauritania was proclaimed Nov. 28, 1958.

Stamps of French West Africa were used in the period between the issues of the colony and the republic.

100 Centimes = 1 Franc
Ouguiya ("um") (1973)

Catalogue values for unused stamps in this country are for Never Hinged items, beginning with Scott 116 in the regular postage section, Scott B16 in the semi-postal section, Scott C14 in the airpost section, Scott J19 in the postage due section, and Scott O1 in the official section.

See French West Africa No. 65 for additional stamp inscribed "Mauritanie" and "Afrique Occidentale Francaise."

General Louis Faidherbe — A1

Oil Palms — A2

Dr. Noel Eugène Ballay — A3

Perf. 14x13½

1906-07 Typo. Unwmk.
"Mauritanie" in Red or Blue

1	A1	1c slate	.25	.25
2	A1	2c chocolate	.45	.40
3	A1	4c choc, *gray bl*	.70	.50
4	A1	5c green	.60	.35
5	A1	10c carmine (B)	5.00	2.75
7	A2	20c black, *azure*	12.50	7.50
8	A2	25c blue, *pnksh*	4.00	3.00
9	A2	30c choc, *pnksh*	65.00	40.00
10	A2	35c black, *yellow*	4.00	2.75
11	A2	40c car, *az* (B)	4.00	2.75
12	A2	45c choc, *grnsh* ('07)	4.00	3.25
13	A2	50c deep violet	5.50	3.25
14	A2	75c blue, *org*	4.00	3.25
15	A3	1fr black, *azure*	10.00	10.00
16	A3	2fr blue, *pink*	30.00	30.00
17	A3	5fr car, *straw*(B)	100.00	85.00
		Nos. 1-17 (16)	250.00	195.00

Crossing Desert — A4

1913-38

18	A4	1c brn vio & brn	.15	.15
19	A4	2c black & blue	.15	.15
20	A4	4c violet & blk	.20	.20
21	A4	5c yel grn & bl grn	.30	.30
22	A4	5c brn vio & rose ('22)	.15	.15
23	A4	10c rose & red org	1.00	.80
24	A4	10c yel grn & bl grn ('22)	.15	.15
25	A4	10c lil rose, *bluish* ('25)	.25	.25
26	A4	15c dk brn & blk ('17)	.30	.25
27	A4	20c bis brn & org	.20	.20
28	A4	25c blue & vio	.50	.50
29	A4	25c grn & rose ('22)	.15	.15
30	A4	30c bl grn & rose	.40	.40
31	A4	30c rose & red org ('22)	.60	.60
32	A4	30c black & yel ('26)	.15	.15
33	A4	30c bl grn & yel grn ('28)	.80	.80
34	A4	35c brown & vio	.35	.35
35	A4	35c dp grn & lt grn ('38)	.55	.55
36	A4	40c gray & bl grn	1.50	1.25
37	A4	45c org & bis brn	.70	.70
38	A4	50c brn vio & rose	.35	.35
39	A4	50c dk bl & ultra ('22)	.20	.20
40	A4	50c gray grn & dp bl ('26)	.40	.40
41	A4	60c vio, *pnksh* ('26)	.25	.25
42	A4	65c yel brn & lt bl ('26)	.50	.50
43	A4	75c ultra & brown	.45	.40
44	A4	85c myr grn & lt brn ('26)	.65	.65
45	A4	90c brn red & rose ('30)	.80	.80
46	A4	1fr rose & black	.45	.40
47	A4	1.10fr vio & ver ('28)	6.00	6.00
48	A4	1.25fr dk bl & blk brn ('33)	1.25	1.25
49	A4	1.50fr lt bl & dp bl ('30)	.50	.50
50	A4	1.75fr bl grn & brn red ('33)	.85	.85
51	A4	1.75fr dk bl & ultra ('38)	.65	.65
52	A4	2fr red org & vio	1.00	.70
53	A4	3fr red violet ('30)	1.10	1.10
54	A4	5fr violet & blue	1.65	1.40
		Nos. 18-54 (37)	25.60	24.45

For surcharges see Nos. 55-64, B1-B2.

Stamp and Type of 1913-38 Surcharged

60 **60**

1922-25

55	A4	60c on 75c violet, *pnksh*	.50	.50
56	A4	65c on 15c dk brn & blk ('25)	1.00	1.00
57	A4	85c on 75c ultra & brn ('25)	1.00	1.00
		Nos. 55-57 (3)	2.50	2.50

Stamp and Type of 1913-38 Surcharged with New Value and Bars

1924-27

58	A4	25c on 2fr red org & vio	.55	.55
59	A4	90c on 75c brn red & cer ('27)	1.25	1.25
60	A4	1.25fr on 1fr dk bl & ultra ('26)	.25	.25
61	A4	1.50fr on 1fr bl & dp bl ('27)	.65	.65
62	A4	3fr on 5fr ol brn & red vio ('27)	4.50	4.50
63	A4	10fr on 5fr mag & bl grn ('27)	4.00	4.00
64	A4	20fr on 5fr bl vio & dp org ('27)	4.00	4.00
		Nos. 58-64 (7)	15.20	15.20

Colonial Exposition Issue
Common Design Types

Engr.; Name of Country Typo. in Black
1931, Apr. 13 ***Perf. 12½***

65	CD70	40c deep green	5.00	5.00
66	CD71	50c violet	2.00	2.00
67	CD72	90c red orange	2.00	2.00
68	CD73	1.50fr dull blue	2.00	2.00
		Nos. 65-68 (4)	11.00	11.00

Paris International Exposition Issue
Common Design Types

1937, Apr. 15 ***Perf. 13***

69	CD74	20c deep violet	.75	.75
70	CD75	30c dark green	.75	.75
71	CD76	40c carmine rose	.70	.70
72	CD77	50c dk brn & blk	.70	.70
73	CD78	90c red	.80	.80
74	CD79	1.50fr ultra	.80	.80
		Nos. 69-74 (6)	4.50	4.50

Colonial Arts Exhibition Issue
Common Design Type
Souvenir Sheet

1937 ***Imperf.***

75	CD76	3fr dark blue	3.50	3.50

Camel Rider — A5

Mauri Couple — A8

Mauris on Camels — A6

Family before Tent — A7

1938-40 ***Perf. 13***

76	A5	2c violet blk	.15	.15
77	A5	3c dp ultra	.15	.15
78	A5	4c rose violet	.15	.15
79	A5	5c orange red	.15	.15
80	A5	10c brown car	.15	.15
81	A5	15c dk violet	.15	.15
82	A6	20c red	.20	.20
83	A6	25c deep ultra	.15	.15
84	A6	30c deep brown	.20	.20
85	A6	35c Prus green	.25	.25
86	A6	40c rose car ('40)	.20	.20
87	A6	45c Prus grn ('40)	.20	.20
88	A6	50c purple	.25	.25
89	A7	55c rose violet	.30	.30
90	A7	60c violet ('40)	.25	.25
91	A7	65c deep green	.60	.60
92	A7	70c red ('40)	.45	.45
93	A7	80c deep blue	.85	.85
94	A7	90c rose violet ('39)	.35	.35
95	A7	1fr red	1.00	1.00
96	A7	1fr dp green ('40)	.35	.35
97	A7	1.25fr rose car ('39)	.90	.90
98	A7	1.40fr dp blue ('40)	.35	.35
99	A7	1.50fr violet	.35	.35
99A	A7	1.50fr red brn ('40)	62.50	62.50
100	A7	1.60fr black brn ('40)	.90	.90
101	A8	1.75fr deep ultra	.70	.70
102	A8	2fr rose violet	.50	.50
103	A8	2.25fr dull ultra ('39)	.45	.45
104	A8	2.50fr black brn ('40)	.60	.60
105	A8	3fr deep green	.35	.35
106	A8	5fr scarlet	.60	.60
107	A8	10fr deep brown	.90	.90
108	A8	20fr brown car	.90	.90
		Nos. 76-108 (34)	76.50	76.50

Nos. 91 and 109 surcharged with new values are listed under French West Africa.

For surcharges see Nos. B9-B12.

Caillie Issue
Common Design Type

1939, Apr. 5 Engr. ***Perf. 12½x12***

109	CD81	90c org brn & org	.75	.75
110	CD81	2fr brt violet	.75	.75
111	CD81	2.25fr ultra & dk bl	.75	.75
		Nos. 109-111 (3)	2.25	2.25

New York World's Fair Issue
Common Design Type

1939, May 10

112	CD82	1.25fr carmine lake	.45	.45
113	CD82	2.25fr ultra	.45	.45

Caravan and Marshal Pétain — A9

1941

114	A9	1fr green	.30	
115	A9	2.50fr deep blue	.30	

Nos. 114-115 were issued by the Vichy government, and were not placed on sale in the colony. This also holds true for six stamps of types A5-A7 without "RF," issued in 1943-44.

Catalogue values for unused stamps in this section, from this point to the end of the section, are for Never Hinged items.

Islamic Republic

Camel and Hands Raising Flag — A10

Unwmk.

1960, Jan. 20 Engr. ***Perf. 13***

116	A10	25fr multi, *pink*	.35	.20

Issued to commemorate the proclamation of the Islamic Republic of Mauritania.

Imperforates
Most Mauritania stamps from 1960 onward exist imperforate in issued and trial colors, and also in small presentation sheets in issued colors.

C.C.T.A. Issue
Common Design Type

1960, May 16

117	CD106	25fr bluish grn & ultra	.38	.22

Flag and Map — A11

1960, Dec. 15 Engr. ***Perf. 13***

118	A11	25fr org brn, emer & sepia	.22	.16

Proclamation of independence, Nov. 28, 1960.

Pastoral Well — A12

Scimitar- horned Oryx — A15

Spotted Hyena — A13

Ore Train and Camel Riders — A14

Designs: 50c, 1fr, Well. 2fr, Date harvesting. 3fr, Aoudad. 4fr, Fennecs. 5fr, Millet harvesting. 10fr, Shoemaker. 15fr, Fishing boats. 20fr, Nomad school. 25fr, 30fr, Seated dance. No. 130, Religious student. 60fr, Metalworker.

1960-62 Unwmk. ***Perf. 13***

119	A12	50c mag, yel & brn ('61)	.15	.15
120	A12	1fr brn, yel brn & grn	.15	.15
121	A12	2fr dk brn, bl & grn	.15	.15
122	A13	3fr bl grn, red brn & gray ('61)	.15	.15
123	A13	4fr yel grn & ocher ('61)	.15	.15
124	A12	5fr red, dk brn & yel brn	.15	.15
125	A14	10fr dk bl & org	.15	.15
126	A14	15fr ver, dk brn, grn & bl	.15	.15
127	A14	20fr grn, sl grn & red brn	.22	.15
128	A12	25fr ultra & gray grn ('61)	.25	.15
129	A12	30fr lil, bis & indigo	.30	.15
130	A12	50fr org brn & grn	.60	.20
131	A14	50fr red brn, bl & ol ('62)	.55	.38
132	A12	60fr grn, cl & pur	.65	.20
133	A15	85fr bl, brn & blk ('61)	1.00	.50
		Set value	4.00	1.75

An overprint, "Jeux Olympiques / Rome 1960 / Tokyo 1964," the 5-ring Olympic emblem and a 75fr surcharge were applied to Nos. 126-127 in 1962.

An overprint, "Aide aux Rèfugiès" with uprooted oak emblem, was applied in 1962 to No. 132 and to pink-paper printings of Nos. 129-130.

Other overprints, applied to airmail stamps, are noted after No. C16.

1963, July 6

Designs: 50c, Striped hyena. 1.50fr, Cheetah. 2fr, Guinea baboons. 5fr, Dromedaries. 10fr, Leopard. 15fr, Bongo antelopes. 20fr, Aardvark. 25fr,

Patas monkeys. 30fr, Crested porcupine. 50fr, Dorcas gazelle. 60fr, Common chameleon.

134 A15 50c sl grn, blk & org brn .15 .15
135 A13 1fr ultra, blk & yel .15 .15
136 A15 1.50fr ol grn, brn & bis .15 .15
137 A13 2fr dk brn, grn & dp org .15 .15
138 A15 5fr brn, ultra & bis .15 .15
139 A13 10fr blk & bis .15 .15
140 A13 15fr vio bl & red brn .16 .15
141 A13 20fr dk red brn, dk bl & bis .18 .15
142 A15 25fr brt grn, red brn & ol bis .30 .15
143 A13 30fr dk brn, dk bl & ol bis .40 .15
144 A15 50fr grn, ocher & brn .55 .25
145 A13 60fr dk bl, emer & ocher .80 .45
Set value 2.80 1.30

UN Headquarters, New York, and View of Nouakchott — A15a

1962, June 1 Engr. *Perf. 13*
167 A15a 15fr blk, ultra & cop red .16 .15
168 A15a 25fr cop red, sl grn & ultra .25 .22
169 A15a 85fr dk bl, dl pur & cop red .80 .65
Nos. 167-169 (3) 1.21 1.02

Mauritania's admission to the UN.

African-Malagasy Union Issue
Common Design Type

1962, Sept. 8 Photo. *Perf. 12½x12*
170 CD110 30fr multi .35 .30

Organization Emblem and View of Nouakchott A16

1962, Oct. 15 *Perf. 12½*
171 A16 30fr dk red brn, ultra & brt grn .25 .22

8th Conf. of the Organization to Fight Endemic Diseases, Nouakchott, Oct. 15-18.

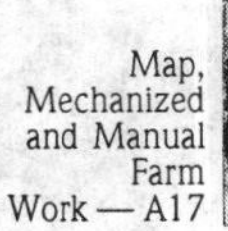

Map, Mechanized and Manual Farm Work — A17

1962, Nov. 28 Engr. *Perf. 13*
172 A17 30fr blk, grn & vio brn .30 .22

2nd anniversary of independence.

People in European and Mauritanian Clothes A18

1962, Dec. 24 Unwmk.
173 A18 25fr multicolored .22 .16

First anniversary of Congress for Unity.

Weather and WMO Symbols — A20

1964, Mar. 23 Unwmk. *Perf. 13*
175 A20 85fr dk brn, dk bl & org 1.25 .80

UN 4th World Meteorological Day, Mar. 23.

IQSY Emblem A21

1964, July 3 Engr.
176 A21 25fr dk bl, red & grn .22 .16

International Quiet Sun Year, 1964-65.

Striped Mullet A22

Designs: 5fr, Mauritanian lobster, vert. 10fr, Royal lobster, vert. 60fr, Maigre fish.

1964, Oct. 5 Engr. *Perf. 13*
177 A22 1fr org brn, dk bl & grn .15 .15
178 A22 5fr org brn, sl grn & choc .15 .15
179 A22 10fr dk bl, bis & sl grn .20 .15
180 A22 60fr dk brn, dp grn & dl bl .60 .45
Set value .94 .70

Cooperation Issue
Common Design Type

1964, Nov. 7 Unwmk. *Perf. 13*
181 CD119 25fr mag, sl grn & dk brn .25 .20

Water Lilies — A23

Tropical Plants: 10fr, Acacia. 20fr, Adenium obesum. 45fr, Caralluma retrospiciens.

1965, Jan. 11 Engr. *Perf. 13*
182 A23 5fr multi .15 .15
183 A23 10fr multi, vert. .15 .15
184 A23 20fr multi .15 .15
185 A23 45fr multi, vert. .35 .25
Set value .68 .54

Hardine A24

Musical Instruments: 8fr, Tobol (drums). 25fr, Tidinit (stringed instruments). 40fr, Musicians.

1965, Mar. 8 *Perf. 13*
186 A24 2fr red brn, brt bl & sep .15 .15
187 A24 8fr red brn, red & brn .15 .15
188 A24 25fr red brn, emer & blk .20 .15
189 A24 40fr vio bl, plum & blk .30 .18
Set value .65 .40

Abraham Lincoln (1809-1865) — A25

1965, Apr. 23 Photo. *Perf. 13x12½*
190 A25 50fr lt ultra & multi .50 .25

Palms at Adrar — A26

Designs: 4fr, Chinguetti mosque, vert. 15fr, Clay pit and donkeys. 60fr, Decorated door, Oualata.

1965, June 14 Engr. *Perf. 13*
191 A26 1fr brn, bl & grn .15 .15
192 A26 4fr dk red, bl & brn .15 .15
193 A26 15fr multi .15 .15
194 A26 60fr grn, dk brn & red brn .55 .35
Set value .75 .50

Issued for tourist publicity.

Tea Service in Inlaid Box — A27

Designs: 7fr, Tobacco pouch and pipe, vert. 25fr, Dagger, vert. 50fr, Mederdra ornamental chest.

1965, Sept. 13 Unwmk. *Perf. 13*
195 A27 3fr gray, choc & ocher .15 .15
196 A27 7fr red lil, Prus bl & org .15 .15
197 A27 25fr blk, org red & brn .16 .15
198 A27 50fr brt grn, brn org & mar .35 .20
Set value .60 .40

Choum Railroad Tunnel — A28

10fr, Nouakchott wharf, ships & anchor, horiz. 85fr, Nouakchott hospital & caduceus, horiz.

1965, Oct. 18 Engr. *Perf. 13*
199 A28 5fr dk brn & brt grn .15 .15
200 A28 10fr dk vio bl, brn red & Prus bl .15 .15
201 A28 30fr brn red, red & red brn .25 .15
202 A28 85fr dp bl, rose cl & lil .65 .40
Set value 1.00 .55

Sculptured Heads — A29

Designs: 30fr, "Music and Dance." 60fr, Movie camera and huts.

1966, Apr. Engr. *Perf. 13*
203 A29 10fr brt grn, blk & brn .15 .15
204 A29 30fr brt bl, red lil & blk .25 .16
205 A29 60fr red, org & dk brn .55 .35
Nos. 203-205 (3) .95 .66

Intl. Negro Arts Festival, Dakar, Senegal, Apr. 1-24.

Mimosa — A30

Myrina Silenus — A31

Flowers: 15fr, Schouwia purpurea. 20fr, Ipomea asarifolia. 25fr, Grewia bicolor. 30fr, Pancratium trianthum. 60fr, Blepharis linariifolia.

1966, Aug. 8 Photo. *Perf. 13x12½*
Flowers in Natural Colors
206 A30 10fr dl bl & dk bl .15 .15
207 A30 15fr dk brn & buff .15 .15
208 A30 20fr grnsh bl & lt bl .20 .15
209 A30 25fr brn & buff .22 .15
210 A30 30fr lil & vio .30 .15
211 A30 60fr grn & pale grn .50 .25
Nos. 206-211 (6) 1.52
Set value .65

1966, Oct. 3 Photo. *Perf. 12x12½*
Various Butterflies
212 A31 5fr buff & multi .15 .15
213 A31 30fr bl grn & multi .35 .15
214 A31 45fr yel grn & multi .50 .16
215 A31 60fr dl bl & multi .65 .30
Nos. 212-215 (4) 1.65
Set value .62

Hunter, Petroglyph from Adrar — A32

Designs: 3fr, Two men fighting, petroglyph from Tenses (Adrar). 30fr, Copper jug, Le Mreyer (Adrar). 50fr, Camel caravan.

1966, Oct. 24 Engr. *Perf. 13*
216 A32 2fr dk brn & brn org .15 .15
217 A32 3fr bl & brn org .15 .15
218 A32 30fr sl grn & dk red .30 .15
219 A32 50fr mag, sl grn & brn .50 .35
Set value .90 .55

Issued for tourist publicity.

UNESCO, 20th Anniv. — A33

1966, Dec. 5 Litho. *Perf. 12½x13*
220 A33 30fr multi .30 .15

Plaza of Three Cultures, Mexico City — A34

Olympic Village, Grenoble A35

Designs: 40fr, Olympic torch and skating rink. 100fr, Olympic Stadium, Mexico City.

1967, Mar. 11 Engr. *Perf. 13*
221 A34 20fr dl bl, brn & sl grn .20 .15
222 A35 30fr dl bl, brn & grn .30 .15
223 A34 40fr brt bl, dk brn & sep .38 .16
224 A35 100fr brn, emer & blk .70 .42
Nos. 221-224 (4) 1.58 .88

Nos. 221 and 223 publicize the 19th Olympic Games, Mexico City; Nos. 222 and 224 the 10th Winter Olympic Games, Grenoble.

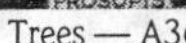

Trees — A36

1967 Jamboree Emblem and Campsite — A37

1967, May 15 Engr. *Perf. 13*
225 A36 10fr Prosopis .15 .15
226 A36 15fr Jujube .15 .15
227 A36 20fr Date palm .16 .15
228 A36 25fr Peltophorum .22 .15
229 A36 30fr Baobob .25 .15
Nos. 225-229 (5) .93
Set value .45

1967, June 5

Design: 90fr, 1967 Jamboree emblem and Mauritanian Boy Scouts, horiz.

230 A37 60fr brn, ultra & slate grn .55 .25
231 A37 90fr dl red, bl & slate grn .80 .38

12th Boy Scout World Jamboree, Farragut State Park, Idaho, Aug. 1-9.

Weavers A38

10fr, Embroiderer, vert. 20fr, Nurse, mother & infant. 30fr, Laundress, vert. 50fr, Seamstresses.

1967, July 3 Engr. *Perf. 13*

232 A38 5fr plum, blk & cl .15 .15
233 A38 10fr plum, brt grn & blk .15 .15
234 A38 20fr brt bl, plum & blk .15 .15
235 A38 30fr dk bl, brn & blk .20 .15
236 A38 50fr plum, sl & blk .35 .16
Set value .80 .45

Progress made by working women.

Cattle and Hypodermic Syringe — A39

1967, Aug. 21 Engr. *Perf. 13*

237 A39 30fr sl grn, brt bl & rose cl .20 .15

Campaign against cattle plague.

Monetary Union Issue
Common Design Type

1967, Nov. 4 Engr. *Perf. 13*

238 CD125 30fr gray & orange .30 .15

Fruit — A40

Human Rights Flame — A41

1967, Dec. 4 Engr. *Perf. 13*

239 A40 1fr Doom palm .15 .15
240 A40 2fr Bito, horiz. .15 .15
241 A40 3fr Baobob .15 .15
242 A40 4fr Jujube, horiz. .15 .15
243 A40 5fr Daye .15 .15
Set value .26 .24

For surcharges see Nos. 323-327.

1968, Jan. 8 Photo. *Perf. 13x12½*

244 A41 30fr brt grn, blk & yel .25 .15
245 A41 50fr brn org, blk & yel .40 .18

International Human Rights Year.

Nouakchott Mosque A42

45fr, Amogjar Pass. 90fr, Cavaliers' Towers.

1968, Apr. 1 Photo. *Perf. 12½x13*

246 A42 30fr multi .20 .15
247 A42 45fr multi .25 .15
248 A42 90fr multi .55 .25
Nos. 246-248 (3) 1.00 .55

For surcharges see Nos. 332-333.

UPU Building, Bern, Globe and Map of Africa — A43

1968, June 3 Engr. *Perf. 13*

249 A43 30fr ver, ultra & olive .20 .15

Mauritania's admission to the UPU.

Symbolic Water Cycle — A44

1968, June 24

250 A44 90fr car, lake, grn & sl grn .55 .30

Hydrological Decade (UNESCO), 1965-74.

Land Yacht Racing — A45

Donkey and Foal — A46

Designs: 40fr, Three land yachts racing, horiz. 60fr, Crew changing wheel of land yacht.

1968, Oct. 7 Engr. *Perf. 13*

251 A45 30fr ultra, org & ocher .20 .15
252 A45 40fr ultra, dp org & plum .25 .15
253 A45 60fr brt grn, dp org & ocher .40 .18
Nos. 251-253 (3) .85 .48

1968, Dec. 16 Photo. *Perf. 13*

Domestic Animals: 10fr, Ewe and lamb. 15fr, Camel and calf. 30fr, Mare and foal. 50fr, Cow and calf. 90fr, Goat and kid.

254 A46 5fr ocher & multi .15 .15
255 A46 10fr multi .15 .15
256 A46 15fr multi .15 .15
257 A46 30fr multi .20 .15
258 A46 50fr pur & multi .30 .15
259 A46 90fr multi .55 .30
Set value 1.25 .70

For surcharge see No. 303.

ILO Emblem and Map — A47

Desert Monitor — A48

1969, Apr. 14 Photo. *Perf. 13x12½*

260 A47 50fr dk & lt bl, pur & org .42 .16

ILO, 50th anniversary.

1969, May 5 Photo. *Perf. 13x12½*

Reptiles: 10fr, Horned viper. 30fr, Common spitting cobra. 60fr, Rock python. 85fr, African crocodile.

261 A48 5fr brn, pink & yel .15 .15
262 A48 10fr brn, lt grn & yel .16 .15
263 A48 30fr dk brn, pink & yel .25 .15
264 A48 60fr dk brn, lt bl & yel .45 .25
265 A48 85fr dk brn, yel & red .65 .45
Nos. 261-265 (5) 1.66 1.15

Lady Beetle Eating Noxious Insects A49

1969, May 26 Engr. *Perf. 13*

266 A49 30fr indigo, grn & maroon .25 .15

Natural protection of date palms.

Development Bank Issue
Common Design Type

1969, Sept. 10 Engr. *Perf. 13*

267 CD130 30fr Prus bl, grn & ocher .22 .15

Pendant — A50

Design: 20fr, Rahla headdress, horiz.

1969, Oct. 13 Engr. *Perf. 13*

268 A50 10fr dk brn, lil & brn .15 .15
269 A50 20fr blk, Prus bl & mag .16 .15
Set value .24 .15

For surcharges see Nos. 309-310.

Desalination Plant — A51

Designs: 15fr, Fishing harbor, Nouadhibou. 30fr, Meat refrigeration plant, Kaedi.

1969, Dec. 1 Engr. *Perf. 13*

270 A51 10fr brt rose lil, dk bl & red brn .15 .15
271 A51 15fr dk car, blk & dp bl .15 .15
272 A51 30fr blk, dk bl & rose brn .20 .15
Set value .36 .25

Issued to publicize economic progress.

Lenin (1870-1924) A52

Sternocera Interrupta A53

1970, Feb. 16 Photo. *Perf. 12x12½*

273 A52 30fr car, lt bl & blk .22 .15

1970, Mar. 16 Engr. *Perf. 13*

Insects: 10fr, Anoplocnemis curvipes. 20fr, Julodis aequinoctialis. 30fr, Thermophilum sexmaculatum marginatum. 40fr, Plocaederus denticornis.

274 A53 5fr red brn, buff & blk .15 .15
275 A53 10fr red brn, yel & brn .15 .15
276 A53 20fr red brn, lil & dk ol .15 .15
277 A53 30fr red brn, grn & vio .20 .15
278 A53 40fr red brn, lt bl & brn .25 .16
Set value .70 .42

For surcharges see Nos. 311-315.

Soccer Players and Hemispheres A54

Hemispheres & various views of soccer play.

1970, May 11 Engr. *Perf. 13*

279 A54 25fr bl, vio bl & dk brn .16 .15
280 A54 30fr vio bl, brn & ol brn .20 .15
281 A54 70fr brt pink, mar & dk brn .40 .22
282 A54 150fr brn red, grn & dk brn .90 .50
Nos. 279-282 (4) 1.66 1.02

9th World Soccer Championships for the Jules Rimet Cup, Mexico City, May 29-June 21.

UPU Headquarters Issue
Common Design Type

1970, May 20 Engr. *Perf. 13*

283 CD133 30fr grn, dk brn & red brn .20 .15

Woman Wearing "Boubou" — A55

Various Traditional Costumes: 30fr, 70fr, Men. 40fr, 50fr, Women.

1970, Sept. 21 Engr. *Perf. 12½x13*

284 A55 10fr red brn & org .15 .15
285 A55 30fr ol, red brn & ind .16 .15
286 A55 40fr red brn, plum & dk brn .25 .15
287 A55 50fr dk brn & brt bl .30 .16
288 A55 70fr bl, brn & dk brn .40 .20
Nos. 284-288 (5) 1.26
Set value .65

People of Various Races — A55a

Design: 40fr, Outstretched hands, vert.

1971, Mar. 22 Engr. *Perf. 13*

288A A55a 30fr brn vio, ol & brt bl .20 .15
288B A55a 40fr brn red, bl & blk .22 .15
Set value .24

Intl. year against racial discrimination.

Gen. Charles de Gaulle (1890-1970), President of France — A56

Design: 100fr, De Gaulle as President.

1971, June 18 Photo. *Perf. 13*

289 A56 40fr gold, blk & grnsh bl .40 .40
290 A56 100fr lt bl, gold & blk 1.10 1.10
a. Souvenir sheet of 2, #289-290 1.90 1.90

Iron Ore Freight Train of Miferma Mines A57 A58

1971, Nov. 8 Photo. *Perf. 12½x12*

291 A57 35fr bl & multi .25 .15
292 A58 100fr bl & multi .70 .40
a. Pair, #291-292 1.00 .90

UNICEF Emblem and Child A59

1971, Dec. 11 Litho. *Perf. 13½*
293 A59 35fr lt ultra, blk & brn .22 .15

UNICEF, 25th anniv.

Samuel F. B. Morse and Telegraph — A60

Designs: 40fr, Relay satellite over globes. 75fr, Alexander Graham Bell.

1972, May 17 Engr. *Perf. 13*
294 A60 35fr lilac, indigo & vio .25 .15
295 A60 40fr bl, ocher & choc .28 .16
296 A60 75fr grn, ol grn & Prus bl .45 .25
Nos. 294-296 (3) .98 .56

4th World Telecommunications Day.
For surcharge see No. 343.

Fossil Spirifer Shell A61

1972, July 31 Litho. *Perf. 12½*
297 A61 25fr shown .16 .15
298 A61 75fr Phacops rana .42 .30

Fossil shells.
For surcharges see Nos. 306, 308.

West African Monetary Union Issue
Common Design Type

1972, Nov. 2 Engr. *Perf. 13*
299 CD136 35fr brn, yel grn & gray .22 .15

Mediterranean Monk Seal and Pup — A63

1973, Feb. 28 Litho. *Perf. 13*
300 A63 40fr multi .30 .16

See #C130. For surcharges see #307, C145.

Food Program Symbols and Emblem A64

1973, Apr. 30 Photo. *Perf. 12x12½*
301 A64 35fr gray bl & multi .22 .15

World Food Program, 10th anniversary.

UPU Monument and Globe — A65

1973, May 28 Engr. *Perf. 13*
302 A65 100fr grn, ocher & bl .65 .50

Universal Postal Union Day.

Currency Change to Ouguiya ("um")
No. 258 Surcharged with New Value, 2 Bars, and Overprinted: "SECHERESSE / SOLIDARITE / AFRICAINE"

1973, Aug. 16 Photo. *Perf. 13*
303 A46 20um on 50fr multi .60 .38

African solidarity in drought emergency.

African Postal Union Issue
Common Design Type

1973, Sept. 12 Engr. *Perf. 13*
304 CD137 20um org, brn & ocher .60 .38

INTERPOL Emblem, Detective, Criminal, Fingerprint A66

1973, Sept. 24
305 A66 15um brn, ver & vio .50 .30

50th anniv. of Intl. Criminal Police Org.

Nos. 297-298, 300 and 268-269 Surcharged with New Value and Two Bars in Ultramarine, Red or Black

1973-74 Litho. *Perf. 12½*
306 A61 5um on 25fr (U) ('74) .16 .15
307 A63 8um on 40fr (R) .25 .15
308 A61 15um on 75fr (U) ('74) .45 .25

Engr.
Perf. 13
309 A50 27um on 10fr (B) ('74) .70 .38
310 A50 28um on 20fr (R) ('74) .80 .42
Nos. 306-310 (5) 2.36 1.35

Nos. 274-278 Surcharged with New Value and Two bars in Violet Blue or Red

1974, July 29 Engr. *Perf. 13*
311 A53 5um on 5fr .16 .15
312 A53 7um on 10fr .22 .15
313 A53 8um on 20fr .22 .16
314 A53 10um on 30fr (R) .35 .20
315 A53 20um on 40fr .65 .40
Nos. 311-315 (5) 1.60 1.06

UPU Emblem and Globes — A67

1974, Aug. 5 Photo. *Perf. 13*
316 A67 30um multi .90 .65
317 A67 50um multi 1.50 .90

Centenary of Universal Postal Union.
For overprints see Nos. 321-322.

5-Ouguiya Coin and Bank Note — A68

Designs: 8um, 10-ouguiya coin. 20um, 20-ouguiya coin. Each design includes picture of different bank note.

1974, Aug. 12 Engr.
318 A68 7um blk, ultra & grn .20 .15
319 A68 8um blk, sl grn & mag .22 .15
320 A68 20um blk, red & bl .60 .35
Nos. 318-320 (3) 1.02
Set value .52

First anniversary of currency reform.

Nos. 316-317 Overprinted in Red: "9 OCTOBRE / 100 ANS D'UNION POSTALE / INTERNATIONALE"

1974, Oct. 9 Photo. *Perf. 13*
321 A67 30um multi .90 .50
322 A67 50um multi 1.50 .65

Centenary of Universal Postal Union.

Nos. 239-243 Surcharged with New Value and Two Bars in Black or Violet Blue

1975, Feb. 14 Engr. *Perf. 13*
323 A40 1um on 5fr multi (B) .15 .15
324 A40 2um on 4fr multi (VB) .15 .15
325 A40 3um on 2fr multi (B) .15 .15
326 A40 10um on 1fr multi (B) .30 .15
327 A40 12um on 3fr multi (VB) .35 .15
Set value .85 .40

Hunters, Rock Carvings — A69

White and Black Men, Map of Europe and Africa — A70

Rock Carvings from Zemmour Cave: 5um, Ostrich. 10um, Elephant, horiz.

1975, May 26 Engr. *Perf. 13*
328 A69 4um lt brn & car .15 .15
329 A69 5um red lil .16 .15
330 A69 10um blue .30 .16
Nos. 328-330 (3) .61
Set value .28

Europafrica Issue

1975, July 7 Engr. *Perf. 13*
331 A70 40um dk brn & red 1.20 .70

Nos. 247-248 Surcharged in Red or Black

15UM

SECHERESSE SOLIDARITE
AFRICAINE

1975, Aug. 25 Photo. *Perf. 12½x13*
332 A42 15um on 45fr (R) .42 .30
333 A42 25um on 90fr .70 .50

African solidarity in drought emergency.

Map of Africa with Mauritania, Akjoujt Blast Furnace, Camel — A71

Fair Emblem — A72

Design: 12um, Snim emblem, furnace, dump truck, excavator.

1975, Sept. 22 Engr. *Perf. 13*
334 A71 10um brt bl, choc & org .30 .16
335 A71 12um brt bl & multi .38 .20

Mining and industry: Somima (Société Minière de Mauritanie) and Snim (Société Nationale Industrielle et Minière).

1975, Oct. 5 Litho. *Perf. 12*
336 A72 10um multi .30 .15

National Nouakchott Fair, Nov. 28-Dec. 7.

Commemorative Medal — A73

Design: 12um, Map of Mauritania, vert.

1975, Nov. 28 Litho. *Perf. 12*
337 A73 10um sil & multi .30 .15
338 A73 12um grn, yel & grn .38 .20

15th anniversary of independence.

Docked Space Ships and Astronauts — A74

Docked Space Ships and: 10um, Soyuz rocket launch.

1975, Dec. 29 Litho. *Perf. 14*
339 A74 8um multi .30 .16
340 A74 10um multi .38 .20
Nos. 339-340,C156-C158 (5) 3.68 1.88

Apollo Soyuz space test project, Russo-American cooperation, launched July 15, link-up July 17, 1975.

French Legion Infantryman A75

Uniform: 10um, Green Mountain Boy.

1976, Jan. 26 *Perf. 13½x14*
341 A75 8um multi .25 .15
342 A75 10um multi .30 .15
Nos. 341-342,C160-C162 (5) 3.80 1.60

American Bicentennial.

10e ANNIVERSAIRE DE LA
CHARTE ARABE DU TRAVAIL

No. 296 Surcharged

12UM

1976, Mar. 1 Engr. *Perf. 13*
343 A60 12um on 75fr multi .35 .16

Arab Labor Charter, 10th anniversary.

Demand, as well as supply, determine a stamp's market value.

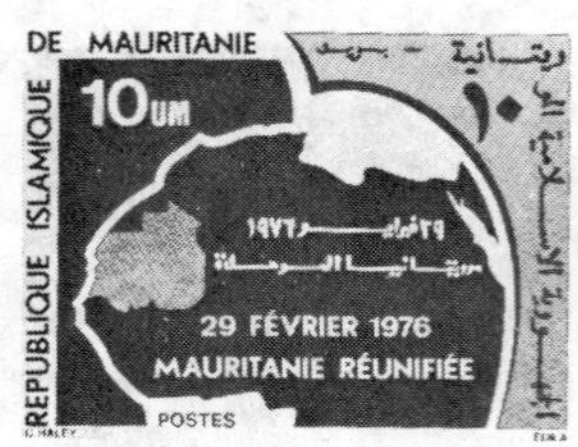

Map of Mauritania with Spanish Sahara Incorporated — A76

1976, Mar. 15 Litho. *Perf. 13x12½*
344 A76 10um grn & multi .30 .16

Reunified Mauritania, Feb. 29, 1976.

LZ-4 over Hangar — A77

75th anniv. of the Zeppelin: 10um, Dr. Hugo Eckener and "Schwaben" (LZ-10). 12um, "Hansa" (LZ-13) over Heligoland. 20um, "Bodensee" (LZ-120) and Dr. Ludwig Dürr.

1976, June 28 Litho. *Perf. 11*
345 A77 5um multi .18 .15
346 A77 10um multi .38 .18
347 A77 12um multi .42 .22
348 A77 20um multi .70 .30
Nos. 345-348,C167-C168 (6) 5.08 2.30

Mohenjo-Daro — A78

1976, Sept. 6 Litho. *Perf. 12*
349 A78 15um multi .42 .20

UNESCO campaign to save Mohenjo-Daro excavations, Pakistan.

A. G. Bell, Telephone and Satellite — A79

1976, Oct. 11 Engr. *Perf. 13*
350 A79 10um bl, car & red .30 .16

Centenary of first telephone call by Alexander Graham Bell, Mar. 10, 1876.

Mohammed Ali Jinnah (1876-1948), Governor General of Pakistan — A80

1976, Dec. 25 Litho. *Perf. 13*
351 A80 10um multi .30 .16

NASA Control Room, Houston — A81

Design: 12um, Viking components, vert.

1977, Feb. 28 *Perf. 14*
352 A81 10um multi .35 .15
353 A81 12um multi .42 .20
Nos. 352-353,C173-C175 (5) 3.97 1.77

Viking Mars project.
For surcharge and overprints see Nos. 425-426, C192-C195.

Jackals — A82

Designs: 5um, Wild rabbits. 12um, Warthogs. 14um, Lions. 15um, Elephants.

1977, Mar. 14 Litho. *Perf. 12½*
354 A82 5um multi .15 .15
355 A82 10um multi .30 .16
356 A82 12um multi .38 .20
357 A82 14um multi .40 .20
358 A82 15um multi .45 .20
Nos. 354-358 (5) 1.68 .91

For surcharge see No. 577.

Irene and Frederic Joliot-Curie, Chemistry — A83

Nobel prize winners: 15um, Emil A. von Bering, medicine.

1977, Apr. 29 Litho. *Perf. 14*
359 A83 12um multi .40 .20
360 A83 15um multi .45 .25
Nos. 359-360,C177-C179 (5) 3.92 1.90

APU Emblem, Member's Flags — A84

1977, May 30 Photo. *Perf. 13*
361 A84 12um multi .38 .20

Arab Postal Union, 25th anniversary.

Oil Lamp — A85

Tegdaoust Pottery: 2um, 4-handled pot. 5um, Large jar. 12um, Jug with filter.

1977, June 13 Engr. *Perf. 13*
362 A85 1um multi .15 .15
363 A85 2um multi .15 .15
364 A85 5um multi .15 .15
365 A85 12um multi .38 .18
Set value .64 .32

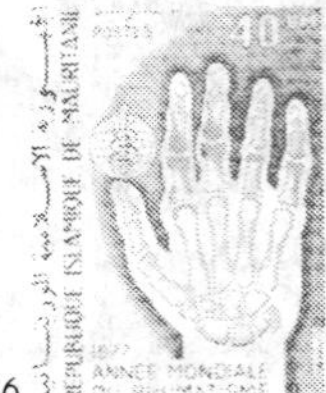

X-ray of Hand — A86

1977, June 27 Engr. *Perf. 12½x13*
366 A86 40um multi 1.20 .65

World Rheumatism Year.

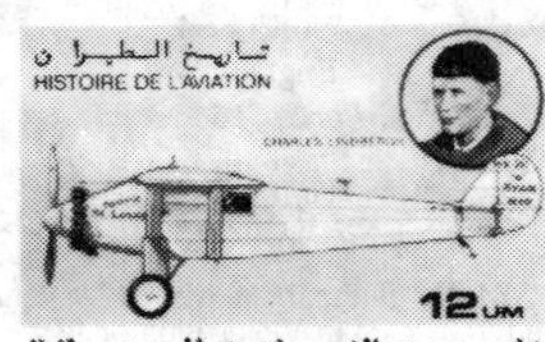

Charles Lindbergh and "Spirit of St. Louis" — A87

History of aviation: 14um, Clement Ader and "Eole!" 15um, Louis Bleriot over channel. 55um, Italo Balbo and seaplanes. 60um, Concorde. 100um, Charles Lindbergh and "Spirit of St. Louis."

1977, Sept. 19
367 A87 12um multi .40 .20
368 A87 14um multi .42 .20
369 A87 15um multi .45 .25
370 A87 55um multi 1.75 .80
371 A87 60um multi 1.90 .90
Nos. 367-371 (5) 4.92 2.35

Souvenir Sheet

372 A87 100um multi 3.00 1.75

Dome of the Rock, Jerusalem — A88

1977, Oct. 31 Litho. *Perf. 12½*
373 A88 12um multi .38 .20
374 A88 14um multi .40 .22

Palestinian fighters and their families.

Soccer and Emblems — A89

Emblems and: 14um, Alf Ramsey and stadium. 15um, Players and goalkeeper.

1977, Dec. 19 Litho. *Perf. 13½*
375 A89 12um multi .40 .18
376 A89 14um multi .45 .22
377 A89 15um multi .50 .22
Nos. 375-377,C182-C183 (5) 4.05 1.77

Elimination Games for World Cup Soccer Championship, Argentina, 1978.
For overprints see Nos. 399-401, C187-C189.

Helen Fourment and her Children, by Rubens — A90

Paintings by Peter Paul Rubens (1577-1640): 14um, Knight in armor. 67um, Three Burghers. 69um, Landscape, horiz. 100um, Rubens with wife and son.

1977, Dec. 26
378 A90 12um multi .40 .18
379 A90 14um multi .45 .25
380 A90 67um multi 2.25 .80
381 A90 69um multi 2.25 .80
Nos. 378-381 (4) 5.35 2.03

Souvenir Sheet

382 A90 100um gold & multi 3.75 1.60

Sable Antelope and Wildlife Fund Emblem — A91

Endangered Animals: 12um, Gazelles, vert. 14um, Manatee. 55um, Aoudad, vert. 60um, Elephant. 100um, Ostrich, vert.

1978, Feb. 28 Litho. *Perf. 13½x14*
383 A91 5um multi .18 .15
384 A91 12um multi .40 .16
385 A91 14um multi .42 .20
386 A91 55um multi 1.75 .62
387 A91 60um multi 1.90 .65
388 A91 100um multi 3.25 1.10
Nos. 383-388 (6) 7.90 2.88

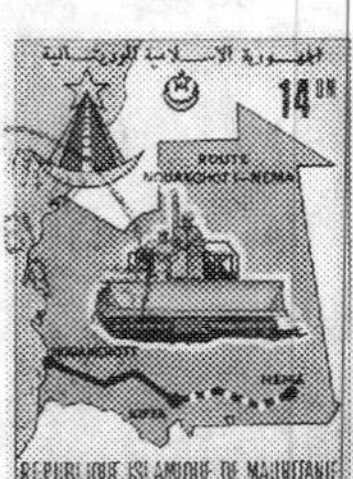

Nouakchott-Nema Road — A91a

1978, June 19 Litho. *Perf. 13*
388A A91a 12um multicolored
388B A91a 14um multicolored

Soccer and Games' Emblem — A92

14um, Rimet Cup. 20um, Soccer ball & F.I.F.A. flag. 50um, Soccer ball & Rimet Cup, horiz.

1978, June 26 Photo. *Perf. 13*

389 A92 12um multi	.40	.16
390 A92 14um multi	.45	.20
391 A92 20um multi	.65	.25
Nos. 389-391 (3)	1.50	.61

Souvenir Sheet

392 A92 50um multi	1.75	1.00

11th World Cup Soccer Championship, Argentina, June 1-25.

Raoul Follereau and St. George Slaying Dragon — A93

1978, Sept. 4 Engr. *Perf. 13*

393 A93 12um brn & dp grn	.40	.16

25th anniversary of the Raoul Follereau Anti-Leprosy Foundation.

Anti-Apartheid Emblem, Fenced-in People — A94

Design: 30um, Anti-Apartheid emblem and free people, vert.

1978, Oct. 9

394 A94 25um bl, red & brn	.80	.38
395 A94 30um grn, bl & brn	1.00	.42

Anti-Apartheid Year.

Charles de Gaulle A95

14um, King Baudouin. 55um, Queen Elizabeth II.

1978, Oct. 16 Litho. *Perf. 12½x12*

396 A95 12um multi	.40	.16
397 A95 14um multi	.45	.20
398 A95 55um multi	1.90	.80
Nos. 396-398 (3)	2.75	1.16

Rulers who helped in de-colonization. No. 398 also commemorates 25th anniversary of coronation of Queen Elizabeth II.

Nos. 375-377 Overprinted in Arabic and French in Silver: "ARGENTINE- / PAYS BAS 3-1"

1978, Dec. 11 Litho. *Perf. 13½*

399 A89 12um multi	.40	.16
400 A89 14um multi	.45	.20
401 A89 15um multi	.50	.20
Nos. 399-401,C187-C188 (5)	4.10	1.71

Argentina's victory in World Cup Soccer Championship 1978.

View of Nouakchott — A96

1978, Dec. 18 Litho. *Perf. 12*

402 A96 12um multi	.40	.16

20th anniversary of Nouakchott.

Flame Emblem — A97

Leather Key Holder — A98

1978, Dec. 26 *Perf. 12½*

403 A97 55um ultra & red	1.90	.80

Universal Declaration of Human Rights, 30th anniv.

1979, Feb. 5 Litho. *Perf. 13½x14*

Leather Craft: 7um, Toothbrush case. 10um, Knife holder.

404 A98 5um multi	.16	.15
405 A98 7um multi	.22	.15
406 A98 10um multi	.35	.16
Nos. 404-406 (3)	.73	
Set value		.35

Farmers at Market, by Dürer — A99

Engravings by Albrecht Durer (1471-1528): 14um, Young Peasant and Wife. 55um, Mercenary with flag. 60um, St. George Slaying Dragon. 100um, Mercenaries, horiz.

Litho.; Red Foil Embossed

1979, May 3 *Perf. 13½x14*

407 A99 12um blk, *buff*	.40	.20
408 A99 14um blk, *buff*	.45	.22
409 A99 55um blk, *buff*	1.90	.90
410 A99 60um blk, *buff*	2.00	1.10
Nos. 407-410 (4)	4.75	2.42

Souvenir Sheet

Perf. 14x13½

411 A99 100um blk, *buff*	3.50	1.60

Buddha, Borobudur Temple and UNESCO Emblem — A100

UNESCO Emblem and: 14um, Hunter on horseback, Carthage. 55um, Caryatid, Acropolis.

1979, May 14 Photo. *Perf. 12½*

412 A100 12um multi	.40	.20
413 A100 14um multi	.45	.22
414 A100 55um multi	1.90	.90
Nos. 412-414 (3)	2.75	1.32

Preservation of art treasures with help from UNESCO.

Paddle Steamer Sirius, Rowland Hill — A101

Sir Rowland Hill (1795-1879), originator of penny postage, and: 14um, Paddle steamer Great Republic. 55um, S.S. Mauritania. 60um, M.S. Stirling Castle. 100um, Mauritania No. 8.

1979, June 4 Litho. *Perf. 13½x14*

415 A101 12um multi	.50	.22
416 A101 14um multi	.65	.30
417 A101 55um multi	2.25	1.20
418 A101 60um multi	2.50	1.40
Nos. 415-418 (4)	5.90	3.12

Souvenir Sheet

419 A101 100um multi	3.50	2.00

Embossed Leather Cushion — A102

30um, Satellite, jet, ship, globe & UPU emblem.

1979, June 8 Litho. *Perf. 12½*

420 A102 12um multi	.40	.22

Engr.

Perf. 13

421 A102 30um multi, vert.	1.00	.55

Philexafrique II, Libreville, Gabon, June 8-17. Nos. 420, 421 each printed in sheets of 10 and 5 labels showing exhibition emblem.

Mother and Children, IYC Emblem — A103

1979, Oct. 2 Litho. *Perf. 12½*

422 A103 12um multi	.40	.20
423 A103 14um multi	.45	.22
424 A103 40um multi	1.40	.65
Nos. 422-424 (3)	2.25	1.07

International Year of the Child

Nos. 352-353 Overprinted in Silver: "ALUNISSAGE / APOLLO XI / JUILLET 1969" and Emblem

1979, Oct. 24 Litho. *Perf. 14*

425 A81 10um multi	.35	.16
426 A81 12um multi	.40	.20
Nos. 425-426,C192-C194 (5)	3.85	1.94

Apollo 11 moon landing, 10th anniversary.

Runner, Moscow '80 Emblem A104

Moscow '80 Emblem and: 14um, 55um, 100um, Running, diff. 60um, Hurdles.

1979, Oct. 26 Litho. *Perf. 13½*

427 A104 12um multi	.40	.20
428 A104 14um multi	.45	.22
429 A104 55um multi	1.90	.90
430 A104 60um multi	2.00	1.00
Nos. 427-430 (4)	4.75	2.32

Souvenir Sheet

431 A104 100um multi	3.50	3.50

Pre-Olympic Year.

Scomberesox Saurus Walbaum — A104a

1979, Nov. 12 Photo. *Perf. 14*

431A A104a 1um shown	.15	.15
431B A104a 5um Trigla lucerna	.16	.15
Set value	.20	.15

Ice Hockey, Lake Placid '80 Emblem A105

Various ice hockey plays.

1979, Dec. 6 Litho. *Perf. 14½*

432 A105 10um multi	.35	.15
433 A105 12um multi	.40	.20
434 A105 14um multi	.45	.25
435 A105 55um multi	1.90	.90
436 A105 60um multi	2.00	1.10
437 A105 100um multi	3.50	1.60
Nos. 432-437 (6)	8.60	4.20

13th Winter Olympic Games. Lake Placid, NY, Feb. 12-24, 1980.

For overprints see Nos. 440-445.

Arab Achievements A106

1980, Mar. 22 Litho. *Perf. 13*

438 A106 12um multi	.40	.20
439 A106 15um multi	.50	.25

Nos. 432-437 Overprinted:

a. Médaille / de bronze / SUÈDE
b. MÉDAILLE / DE BRONZE / SUÈDE
c. Médaille / d'argent / U.R.S.S.
d. MÉDAILLE / D'ARGENT/ U.R.S.S.
e. MÉDAILLE / D'OR / ÉTATS-UNIS
f. Médaille / d'or / ÉTATS-UNIS

1980, June 14 Litho. *Perf. 14½*

440 A105(a) 10um multi	.35	.15
441 A105(b) 12um multi	.40	.20
442 A105(c) 14um multi	.45	.25
443 A105(d) 55um multi	1.90	.90
444 A105(e) 60um multi	2.00	1.10
445 A105(f) 100um multi	3.50	1.75
Nos. 440-445 (6)	8.60	4.35

Equestrian, Olympic Rings — A107

Designs: Equestrian scenes. 10um, 20um, 70um, 100um, vert.

1980, June **Litho.** ***Perf. 14***
446 A107 10um multi .35 .15
447 A107 20um multi .65 .30
448 A107 50um multi 1.60 .70
449 A107 70um multi 2.25 1.00
Nos. 446-449 (4) 4.85 2.15

Souvenir Sheet

450 A107 100um multi 3.50 1.50

22nd Summer Olympic Games, Moscow, July 19-Aug. 3.
For overprints see Nos. 464-468.

Armed Forces Day — A108

1980, July 9 ***Perf. 13x12½***
451 A108 12um multi .40 .20
452 A108 14um multi .45 .25

World Red Cross Day — A109

1980, June 14 ***Perf. 13***
453 A109 20um multi .65 .30

Pilgrimage to Mecca — A110

Design: 50um, Mosque, outside view.

1980
454 A110 10um multi .35 .15
455 A110 50um multi 1.60 .70

Man with Turban, by Rembrandt A111

Rembrandt Paintings: 10um, Self-portrait. 20um, His mother. 70um, His son Titus reading. 100um, Polish knight, horiz.

1980, July **Litho.** ***Perf. 12½***
456 A111 10um multi .35 .15
457 A111 20um multi .65 .30
458 A111 50um multi 1.60 .70
459 A111 70um multi 2.25 1.00
Nos. 456-459 (4) 4.85 2.15

Souvenir Sheet

460 A111 100um multi 3.50 3.50

Tea Time — A112

1980, Mar. 11 **Litho.** ***Perf. 12½***
460A A112 1um multi .15 .15
461 A112 5um multi .16 .15
462 A112 12um multi .40 .20
Set value .60 .32

Arbor Day — A113

1980, Aug. 29
463 A113 12um multi .40 .20

Nos. 446-450 Overprinted with Winner and Country

1980, Oct. **Litho.** ***Perf. 14***
464 A107 10um multi .35 .15
465 A107 20um multi .65 .30
466 A107 50um multi 1.60 .70
467 A107 70um multi 2.25 1.00
Nos. 464-467 (4) 4.85 2.15

Souvenir Sheet

468 A107 100um multi 3.50 1.50

Mastodont Locomotive, 1850 — A114

Designs: Various locomotives.

1980, Nov. ***Perf. 12½***
469 A114 10um shown .35 .15
470 A114 12um Iron ore train .40 .20
471 A114 14um Chicago-Milwaukee line, 1900 .45 .25
472 A114 20um Bury, 1837 .65 .30
473 A114 67um Reseau North line, 1870 2.25 1.00
474 A114 100um Potsdam, 1840 3.50 1.40
Nos. 469-474 (6) 7.60 3.30

20th Anniversary of Independence — A115

1980, Nov. 27 ***Perf. 13***
475 A115 12um multi .40 .20
476 A115 15um multi .50 .22

El Haram Mosque — A116

1981, Apr. 13 **Litho.** ***Perf. 12½***
477 A116 2um shown .15 .15
478 A116 12um Medina Mosque .40 .20
479 A116 14um Chinguetti Mosque .45 .25
Nos. 477-479 (3) 1.00
Set value .50

Hegira, 1500th anniversary.

Prince Charles and Lady Diana, Coach A117

Designs: Coaches.

1981, July 8 **Litho.** ***Perf. 14½***
480 A117 14um multi .35 .35
481 A117 18um multi .45 .45
482 A117 77um multi 1.90 1.10
Nos. 480-482 (3) 2.70 1.90

Souvenir Sheet

483 A117 100um multi 5.00 2.50

Royal wedding.
For overprints see Nos. 518-521.

Intl. Year of the Disabled A119

1981, June 29 **Litho.** ***Perf. 13x13½***
486 A119 12um multi .40 .20

Battle of Yorktown Bicentenary (American Revolution) — A120

1981, Oct. 5 ***Perf. 12½***
487 A120 14um George Washington, vert. .45 .22
488 A120 18um Admiral de Grasse, vert. .60 .30
489 A120 63um Surrender of Cornwallis 2.00 1.10
490 A120 81um Battle of Chesapeake Bay 2.50 1.40
Nos. 487-490 (4) 5.55 3.02

475th Death Anniv. of Christopher Columbus (1451-1506) — A121

1981, Oct. 5
491 A121 19um Pinta .62 .32
492 A121 55um Santa Maria 1.90 .90

World Food Day — A122

Kemal Ataturk Birth Cent. — A123

1981, Oct. 16 ***Perf. 13***
493 A122 19um multi .62 .32

1981, Oct. 29 ***Perf. 12½***
494 A123 63um multi 2.00 1.10

Scouting Year — A124

Designs: Boating scenes. 92um vert.

1982, Jan. 20 **Litho.** ***Perf. 12½***
495 A124 14um multi .45 .22
496 A124 19um multi .62 .32
497 A124 22um multi .70 .40
498 A124 92um multi 3.00 1.25
Nos. 495-498 (4) 4.77 2.19

Souvenir Sheet

Perf. 13

499 A124 100um Baden-Powell, scout 3.50 1.60

75th Anniv. of Grand Prix — A125

Designs: Winners and their Cars.

1982, Jan. 23 ***Perf. 13½***
500 A125 7um Deusenberg, 1921 .22 .15
501 A125 12um Alfa Romeo, 1932 .40 .20
502 A125 14um Juan Fangio, 1949 .45 .22
503 A125 18um Renault, 1979 .60 .30
504 A125 19um Niki Lauda, 1974 .62 .32
Nos. 500-504 (5) 2.29 1.19

Souvenir Sheet

505 A125 100um Race 3.50 1.60

Birds of the Arguin Bank A126

1981, Dec. 17 **Photo.** ***Perf. 13***
506 A126 2um White pelicans .15 .15
507 A126 18um Pink flamingoes .60 .30
Set value .35

Battle of Karameh — A127

1982, Dec. 19 **Litho.**

508 A127 14um Hand holding tattered flag .45 .22

Deluth Turtle — A128

APU, 30th Anniv. — A129

Designs: Sea turtles.

1981, Dec. 21 **Photo.** ***Perf.* 14x13½**

509 A128 1um shown .15 .15
510 A128 3um Green turtle .15 .15
511 A128 4um Shell turtle .15 .15
Set value .28 .16

1982, May 14 **Litho.** ***Perf.* 13**

512 A129 14um org & brn .45 .22

A130 A131

1982, May 17 **Photo.** ***Perf.* 13½x13**

513 A130 21um multi .70 .35

14th World Telecommunications Day.

1982, June 7 **Litho.** ***Perf.* 12½**

514 A131 14um grnsh bl .45 .22

UN Conf. on Human Environment, 10th anniv.

21st Birthday of Princess Diana of Wales — A132

Portraits.

1982, July ***Perf.* 14x13½**

515 A132 21um multi .70 .35
516 A132 77um multi 2.50 1.10

Souvenir Sheet

517 A132 100um multi 3.50 1.60

Nos. 480-483 Overprinted in Blue: "NAISSANCE ROYALE 1982"

1982, Aug. 2 ***Perf.* 14½**

518 A117 14um multi .45 .22
519 A117 18um multi .60 .30
520 A117 77um multi 2.50 1.20
Nos. 518-520 (3) 3.55 1.72

Souvenir Sheet

521 A117 100um multi 3.50 1.60

Birth of Prince William of Wales, June 21.

Manned Flight Bicentenary A133

1982, Dec. 29 **Litho.** ***Perf.* 14**

522 A133 14um Montgolfiere balloon, 1783, vert. .45 .22
523 A133 18um Hydrogen balloon, 1783 .60 .30
524 A133 19um Zeppelin, vert. .62 .32
525 A133 55um Nieuport plane 1.90 .90
526 A133 63um Concorde 2.25 1.10
527 A133 77um Apollo II, vert. 2.50 1.10
Nos. 522-527 (6) 8.32 3.94

Preservation of Ancient Cities — A134

1983, Feb. 16 **Litho.** ***Perf.* 14x14½**

528 A134 14um City Wall, Ouadane .45 .22
529 A134 18um Chinguetti .60 .30
530 A134 24um Staircase, panels, Qualata .80 .42
531 A134 30um Ruins, Tichitt 1.00 .50
Nos. 528-531 (4) 2.85 1.44

World Communications Year — A135

1983, June 21 **Litho.** ***Perf.* 13**

532 A135 14um multi .45 .22

30th Anniv. of Customs Cooperation Council — A136

1983, June 25

533 A136 14um multi .45 .22

Traditional Houses — A137

Ancient Manuscript Page — A138

1983, June 14 **Photo.** ***Perf.* 13½**

534 A137 14um Peule .38 .18
535 A137 18um Toucouleur .50 .25
536 A137 19um Tent .52 .28
Nos. 534-536 (3) 1.40 .71

1983, June 15 **Photo.** ***Perf.* 12½x13**

537 A138 2um shown .15 .15
538 A138 5um Ornamental scrollwork .15 .15
539 A138 7um Sheath .18 .15
Set value .36 .22

Manned Flight Bicentenary — A139

Early Fliers and their Balloons or Dirigibles. 10um, 14um vert.

1983, Oct. 17 **Litho.** ***Perf.* 13½**

540 A139 10um F. Pilatre de Rozier .25 .15
541 A139 14um John Wise .38 .18
542 A139 25um Charles Renard .65 .35
543 A139 100um Henri Julliot 2.50 1.40
Nos. 540-543 (4) 3.78 2.08

Souvenir Sheet

544 A139 100um Joseph Montgolfier 2.50 1.40

No. 544 contains one stamp 47x37mm. Nos. 543-544 airmail.

Mortar — A140

Various prehistoric grinding implements.

1983, Dec. 28 **Litho.** ***Perf.* 13**

545 A140 10um multi .25 .15
546 A140 14um multi .38 .18
547 A140 18um multi .50 .25
Nos. 545-547 (3) 1.13 .58

Pre-Olympics — A141

1983, Dec. 31 **Litho.** ***Perf.* 13½**

548 A141 1um Basketball .15 .15
549 A141 20um Wrestling .25 .15
550 A141 50um Equestrian .65 .35
551 A141 77um Running 1.00 .50
Nos. 548-551 (4) 2.05 1.15

Souvenir Sheet

552 A141 100um Soccer 1.40 .65

No. 552 contains one stamp 41x36mm. Nos. 551-552 airmail.

Scouting Year — A142

Artemis, by Rembrandt — A142a

Events & Annivs.: 14um, Johann Wolfgang von Goethe. 25um, Virgin and Child, by Peter Paul Rubens.

No. 553C illustration reduced.

1984, Jan. 24

553 A142 5um Flag, Baden-Powell .15 .15
553A A142 14um multicolored .22 .15
553B A142 25um multicolored .35 .16
Nos. 553-553B (3) .72 .46

Souvenir Sheet

553C A142a 100um multicolored 1.40 .65

No. 553C is airmail and contains one 42x51mm stamp.

Sand Rose — A143

1984, Mar. **Litho.** ***Perf.* 14**

554 A143 21um multi .28 .15

Inscribed 1982.

Anniversaries and Events A145

1984, Apr. 26

555 A145 10um Albrecht Durer (1471-1528) .15 .15
556 A145 12um Apollo XI, 15th anniv. .16 .15
557 A145 50um Chess .65 .35
Nos. 555-557 (3) .96
Set value .50

1984, Apr. 16 **Litho.** ***Perf.* 13½**

Designs: 77um, Prince Charles, Princess Diana. 100um, Prince Charles, Princess Diana, vert.

557A A145 77um multi 1.50 .70

Miniature Sheet

557B A145 100um multi 2.00 1.00

Nos. 557A-557B airmail.

Fishing Industry A146

1984

558 A146 1um Tuna .15 .15
559 A146 2um Mackerel .15 .15
560 A146 5um Haddock .15 .15
561 A146 14um Black chinchard .18 .15
562 A146 18um Boat building .25 .15
Set value .55 .35

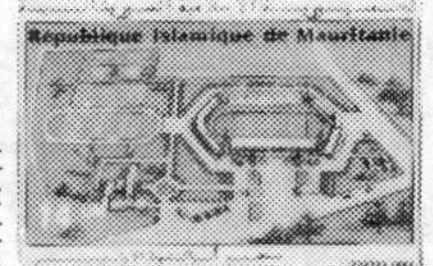

Nouakchott Olympic Complex A148

1984, Sept. 26 **Litho.** ***Perf.* 13½**

569 A148 14um multi .28 .15

Infant Survival Campaign — A149

1984, Sept. 26 Litho. *Perf. 12½*

570 A149 1um Feeding by glass .15 .15
571 A149 4um Breastfeeding .15 .15
572 A149 10um Vaccinating .20 .15
573 A149 14um Weighing .28 .15
Set value .60 .35

Pilgrimage to Mecca — A150

1984, Oct. 3 Litho. *Perf. 13*

574 A150 14um Tents, mosque .28 .15
575 A150 18um Tents, courtyard .38 .18

10th Anniv., West African Union — A151

1984, Nov. Litho. *Perf. 13*

576 A151 14um Map of member nations .28 .15

No. 355 Overprinted "Aide au Sahel 84" and Surcharged

1984 Litho. *Perf. 12½*

577 A82 18um on 10um .38 .18

Issued to publicize drought relief efforts.

Technical & Cultural Cooperation Agency, 15th Anniv. — A152

1985, Mar. 20 Litho. *Perf. 12½*

578 A152 18um Profiles, emblem .35 .16

League of Arab States, 40th Anniv. — A153

1985, May 7 *Perf. 13*

579 A153 14um brt yel grn & blk .28 .15

German Railways 150th Anniv. — A154

Anniversaries and events: 12um, Adler, 1st German locomotive, 1835. 18um, Series 10, 1956, last Fed. German Railways locomotive. 44um, European Music Year, Johann Sebastian Bach, composer, and Angels Making Music, unattributed painting. 77um, George Frideric Handel. 90um, Statue of Liberty, cent., vert. 100um, Queen Mother, 85th birthday, vert.

1985, Sept.

580 A154 12um multi .22 .15
581 A154 18um multi .35 .16
582 A154 44um multi .80 .40
583 A154 77um multi 1.50 .80
584 A154 90um multi 1.60 .80
Nos. 580-584 (5) 4.47 2.31

Souvenir Sheet

585 A154 100um multi 2.00 1.00

World Food Day — A155

1985, Oct. 16 *Perf. 13x12½*

586 A155 18um multi .35 .16

UN Food and Agriculture Org., 40th anniv.

Fight Against Drought — A156

1985 Litho. *Perf. 13*

587 A156 14um Antelope .28 .15
588 A156 18um Oasis .35 .16

Fight Against Desert Encroachment — A157

1985

589 A157 10um Grain harvest, vert. .20 .15
590 A157 14um Brush fire .28 .15
591 A157 18um Planting brush .35 .16
Nos. 589-591 (3) .83
Set value .40

Natl. Independence, 25th Anniv. — A158

1985 *Perf. 15x14½*

592 A158 18um multi .35 .16

Intl. Youth Year A159

1986, Feb. 13 Litho. *Perf. 13*

593 A159 18um Development .15 .15
594 A159 22um Participation .15 .15
595 A159 25um Peace, vert. .15 .15
Set value .35 .18

Toujounine Satellite Station — A160

1986, May 22 Litho. *Perf. 12½*

596 A160 25um multi .15 .15

World Wildlife Fund — A161

Monk seal (Monachus monachus).

1986, June 12 *Perf. 13*

597 A161 2um multi .15 .15
598 A161 5um multi .15 .15
599 A161 10um multi .15 .15
600 A161 18um multi .15 .15
Set value .25 .25

Souvenir Sheet

601 A161 50um multi .28 .15

Weaving — A162

1986, July 20 Litho. *Perf. 12½*

602 A162 18um multi .35 .18

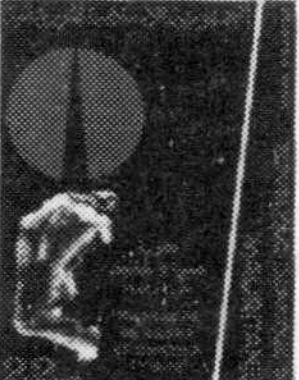

Sabra and Chatila Massacre, 4th Anniv. — A163

1986, Oct. 18

603 A163 22um multi .45 .22

A164

Christopher Columbus — A165

Indians, maps on globe and: 2um, Santa Maria. 22um, Nina. 35um, Pinta. 150um, Columbus.

1986, Oct. 14 Litho. *Perf. 13½*

604 A164 2um multi .15 .15
605 A164 22um multi .65 .32
606 A164 35um multi 1.05 .52
607 A164 150um multi 4.50 2.25
Nos. 604-607 (4) 6.35 3.24

Souvenir Sheet

608 A165 100um Columbus, Earth 3.00 1.50

Nos. 607-608 are airmail.

US Space Shuttle Challenger Explosion, Jan. 28, 1986 — A166

Crew members and: 7um, Space shuttle. 22um, Canadarm. 32um, Sky, moon. 43um, Memorial emblem.

1986, Oct. 14

609 A166 7um multi .22 .15
610 A166 22um multi .65 .32
611 A166 32um multi .95 .48
612 A166 43um multi 1.30 .65
Nos. 609-612 (4) 3.12 1.60

Souvenir Sheet

613 A166 100um Crew, lift-off 3.00 1.50

Nos. 612-613 are airmail.

Fish A167

1986, Oct. 16 *Perf. 13*

614 A167 4um Dorade .15 .15
615 A167 98um Truite de mer 3.00 1.50

See Nos. 631-633.

Birds A168

1986, Oct. 16

616 A168 22um Spatule blanche .65 .32
617 A168 32um Sterne bridee .95 .48

See Nos. 634-635.

World Food Day — A169

1986, Nov. 6 *Perf. 12½*

618 A169 22um multi .65 .32

A170

Halley's Comet — A171

Space probes and portraits: 5um, J.H. Dort, Giotto probe. 18um, Sir William Huggins (1824-1910), English astronomer, and launch of Giotto on Ariane rocket. 26um, E.J. Opik, Giotto and Vega. 80um, F.L. Whipple, Planet-A. 100um, Edmond Halley, Giotto.

1986, Oct. 14 Litho. *Perf. 13½*

619 A170 5um multi .15 .15
620 A170 18um multi .30 .15
621 A170 26um multi .40 .20
622 A170 80um multi 1.25 .60
Nos. 619-622 (4) 2.10 1.10

Souvenir Sheet

623 A171 100um multi 2.00 1.00

Nos. 622-623 are airmail.

Jerusalem Day — A172

1987, May 21 Litho. *Perf. 13½*

624 A172 22um Dome of the Rock .65 .32

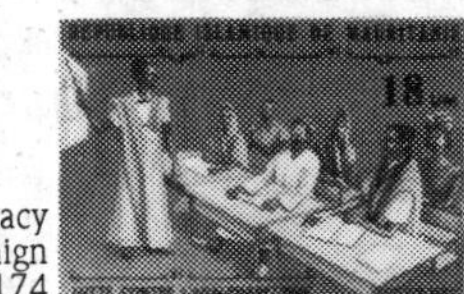

Cordoue Mosque, 1200th Anniv. A173

1987, Sept. 5 Litho. *Perf. 13½*

625 A173 30um multi 1.10 .55

Literacy Campaign A174

1987, Sept. 12

626 A174 18um Classroom .65 .32
627 A174 22um Family reading, vert. .80 .40

World Health Day — A175

1987, Oct. 1 *Perf. 13*

628 A175 18um multi .65 .32

Natl. Population Census A176

1988, Aug. 21 Litho. *Perf. 13½*

629 A176 20um multi .60 .30

WHO, 40th Anniv. — A177

Arab Scouting Movement, 75th Anniv. — A178

1988, Sept. 19 *Perf. 13*

630 A177 30um multi .90 .45

Fish Type of 1986

1988, Sept. 10 Litho. *Perf. 13*

631 A167 1um Rascasse blanche .15 .15
632 A167 7um Baliste .48 .25
633 A167 15um Bonite a ventre raye 1.00 .50
Nos. 631-633 (3) 1.63 .90

Bird Type of 1986

1988, Sept. 15

634 A168 18um Grand cormorant 1.20 .60
635 A168 80um Royal tern 5.40 2.70

1988, Sept. 29 Litho. *Perf. 13*

636 A178 35um multi 1.15 .58

1st Municipal Elections — A179

1988, Nov. 22 *Perf. 13½*

637 A179 20um Men casting ballots .65 .32
638 A179 24um Woman casting ballot .78 .40

Organization of African Unity, 25th Anniv. (in 1988) — A180

Intl. Fund for Agricultural Development, 10th Anniv. (in 1988) — A181

1988, Dec. 7 Litho. *Perf. 13*

639 A180 40um multi 1.30 .65

1988, Dec. 15

640 A181 35um multi 1.15 .58

Autonomy of Nouakchott (Amitie) Port, 1st Anniv. — A182

1988, Dec. 20 Litho. *Perf. 13*

641 A182 24um multi .78 .40

A183

A184

1989, July 7 Litho. *Perf. 13*

642 A183 35um multi 1.10 .55

French Revolution bicent., PHILEXFRANCE '89.

1989, July 17

643 A184 20um multi .60 .30

1990 World Cup Soccer Championships, Italy.

Pilgrimage to Mecca A185

1989, Aug. 26 Litho. *Perf. 13½*

644 A185 20um Mosque .65 .32

African Development Bank, 25th Anniv. — A186

1989, Sept. 2

645 A186 37um lt vio & blk 1.20 .60

Tapestry — A187

1989, Oct. 1 *Perf. 13*

646 A187 50um multicolored 1.60 .80

Locusts, Moths and Ladybugs — A188

1989, Dec. 29

647 A188 2um *Heliothis armigera* .15 .15
648 A188 5um Locust .16 .15
649 A188 6um *Aphis gossypii* .20 .15
650 A188 10um *Agrotis ypsilon* .35 .17
651 A188 20um *Chilo* .68 .35
652 A188 20um Two locusts, egg case .68 .35
653 A188 24um Locusts emerging .80 .40
654 A188 24um *Plitella xylostella* .80 .40
655 A188 30um *Henosepilachna elaterii* 1.00 .50
656 A188 40um Locust flying 1.35 .68
657 A188 42um *Trichoplusia ni* 1.40 .70
658 A188 88um Locust, diff. 2.85 1.45
Nos. 647-658 (12) 10.42 5.45

Revolt — A189

1989, Dec. 8 Litho. *Perf. 13*

659 A189 35um multicolored 1.10 .55

2nd Anniv. of the Palestinian Uprising and 1st anniv. of the declaration of a Palestinian State.

Maghreb Arab Union, 1st Anniv. — A190

Illustration reduced.

1990, Feb. 17 Litho. *Perf. 13½*

660 A190 50um multicolored 1.35 .65

Mineral Resources A191

1990, July 27 *Perf. 11½*

661 A191 60um multicolored 2.00 1.00

Intl. Literacy Year — A192

1990, July 27

662 A192 60um multicolored 1.65 .85

1992 Summer Olympics, Barcelona A193

Litho. & Typo.

1990, Sept. 2 *Perf. $13^1/_2$*

663 A193 5um Equestrian .15 .15
664 A193 50um Archery 1.35 .65
665 A193 60um Hammer throw 1.65 .85
666 A193 75um Field hockey 2.00 1.00
667 A193 90um Handball 2.50 1.25
668 A193 220um Table tennis 6.00 3.00
Nos. 663-668 (6) 13.65 6.90

Souvenir Sheet

669 A193 150um Runner 4.00 2.00

Nos. 668-669 airmail.

A194

A195

1990, July 27 *Perf. $11^1/_2$*

670 A194 50um multicolored 1.35 .65

Multinational Postal School, 20th anniv.

1990, Nov. 21 Litho. *Perf. $11^1/_2$*

671 A195 85um multicolored 3.20 1.60

Declaration of the Palestinian State, 2nd anniv.

1992 Winter Olympics, Albertville A196

1990, Dec. 10 Litho. *Perf. $13^1/_2$*

672 A196 60um Downhill skiing 2.50 1.25
673 A196 75um Cross-country skiing 3.00 1.50
674 A196 90um Ice hockey 3.50 1.75
675 A196 220um Pairs figure skating 8.50 4.25
Nos. 672-675 (4) 17.50 8.75

Souvenir Sheet

676 A196 150um Slalom skiing 6.00 3.00

Nos. 675-676 are airmail.

Release of Nelson Mandela A197

1990, Dec. 10

677 A197 85um multicolored 3.20 1.60

Return of Senegalese Refugees A198

1990, Dec. 10

678 A198 50um Cooking at encampment 1.90 .95
679 A198 75um Women sewing 2.80 1.40
680 A198 85um Drawing water 3.40 1.70
Nos. 678-680 (3) 8.10 4.05

Boy Scouts Observing Nature — A199

Scout: 5um, Picking mushrooms. 50um, Holding mushroom. 60um, Drawing butterfly. 75um, Feeding butterfly. 90um, Photographing butterfly. 220um, Drying mushrooms. No. 687, Using microscope.

1991, Jan. 16 Litho. *Perf. $13^1/_2$*

681 A199 5um multicolored .20 .15
682 A199 50um multicolored 1.90 .95
683 A199 60um multicolored 2.25 1.15
684 A199 75um multicolored 2.80 1.40
685 A199 90um multicolored 3.40 1.70
686 A199 220um multicolored 8.25 4.15
Nos. 681-686 (6) 18.80 9.50

Souvenir Sheet

687 A199 150um multicolored 5.85 2.95

Nos. 684 and 687 are airmail. Nos. 683-685 exist in souvenir sheets of 1.

Independence, 30th Anniv. — A200

1991, Mar. 5

688 A200 50um Satellite dish antennae 1.90 .95
689 A200 60um Container ship 2.25 1.15
690 A200 100um Harvesting rice 3.80 1.90
Nos. 688-690 (3) 7.95 4.00

World Meteorology Day — A201

1991, Mar. 23 *Perf. 14x15*

691 A201 100um multicolored 3.80 1.90

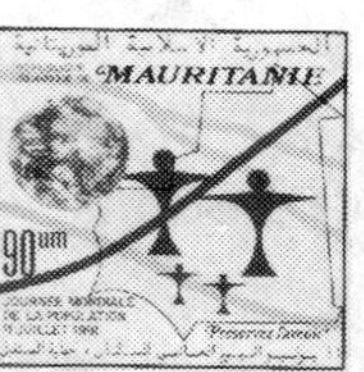

World Population Day — A202

1991, July 27 Litho. *Perf. $13^1/_2$*

692 A202 90um multicolored 3.60 1.80

Domesticated Animals — A203

1991 Litho. *Perf. $13^1/_2$*

693 A203 50um Cats 2.00 1.00
693A A203 60um Dog 2.40 1.20

Campaign Against Blindness A204

1991, Nov. 10 Litho. *Perf. $13^1/_2$*

694 A204 50um multicolored 2.00 1.00

Doctors Without Borders, 20th Anniv. A205

1991 Litho. *Perf. $13^1/_2$*

695 A205 60um multicolored 2.40 1.20

Installation of Central Electric Service (in 1989) A206

1991, Dec. 29 Litho. *Perf. $13^1/_2$*

696 A206 50um multicolored 2.00 1.00

Mineral Exploration, M'Haoudat A207

1993 Litho. *Perf. $13^1/_2$*

697 A207 50um shown 1.90 .95
698 A207 60um Desert landscape 2.25 1.10

1994 Winter Olympics, Lillehammer A208

Intifada, 6th Anniv. A209

1993

699 A208 10um Bobsled .38 .18
700 A208 50um Luge 1.90 .95
701 A208 60um Figure skating 2.25 1.10
702 A208 80um Downhill skiing 3.00 1.50
703 A208 220um Cross-country skiing 8.25 4.00
Nos. 699-703 (5) 15.78 7.73

Souvenir Sheet

704 A208 150um Downhill skiing, diff. 5.75 2.75

No. 704 is airmail.

1993

Design: 60um, Palestinian children, horiz.

705 A209 50um multicolored 1.90 .95
706 A209 60um multicolored 2.25 1.10

Caravans A210

1993

707 A210 50um blue & multi 1.90 .95
708 A210 60um violet & multi 2.25 1.10

1994 World Cup Soccer Championships, US — A211

Designs: 10um, Soldier Field. 50um, Foxboro Stadium. 60um, Robert F. Kennedy Stadium. 90um, Stanford Stadium. 220um, Giants Stadium. 150um, Rose Bowl.

1994 Litho. *Perf. 13*

709 A211 10um multicolored .38 .18
710 A211 50um multicolored 1.90 .95
711 A211 60um multicolored 2.25 1.10
712 A211 90um multicolored 3.25 1.65
713 A211 220um multicolored 8.25 4.00
Nos. 709-713 (5) 16.03 7.88

Souvenir Sheet

714 A211 150um multicolored 5.75 2.75

UN, 50th Anniv. — A212

1995 Litho. *Perf. $11^1/_2$*

715 A212 60um Emblem, #167 1.50 .75

FAO, 50th Anniv. — A213

1995

716 A213 50um Working in field 1.25 .60
717 A213 60um With fishing boat 1.50 .75
718 A213 90um Planting garden 2.25 1.10
Nos. 716-718 (3) 5.00 2.45

SEMI-POSTAL STAMPS

Nos. 23 and 26 Surcharged in Red **+5c**

1915-18 Unwmk. *Perf. $14x13^1/_2$*

B1 A4 10c + 5c rose & red org .45 .45
B2 A4 15c + 5c dk brn & blk ('18) .35 .35

Curie Issue

Common Design Type

1938, Oct. 24 *Perf. 13*

B3 CD80 1.75fr + 50c brt ultra 5.00 5.00

French Revolution Issue

Common Design Type

Photo.; Name and Value Typographed in Black

1939, July 5 Unwmk.

B4 CD83 45c + 25c grn 5.00 5.00
B5 CD83 70c + 30c brn 5.00 5.00
B6 CD83 90c + 35c red org 5.00 5.00
B7 CD83 1.25fr + 1fr rose pink 5.00 5.00
B8 CD83 2.25fr + 2fr bl 5.00 5.00
Nos. B4-B8 (5) 25.00 25.00

Stamps of 1938 Surcharge in Red or Black

SECOURS
+ 1 fr.
NATIONAL

1941

B9 A6 50c + 1fr pur (R) 1.00 1.00
B10 A7 80c + 2fr dp bl (R) 4.00 4.00
B11 A7 1.50fr + 2fr vio (R) 4.00 4.00
B12 A8 2fr + 3fr rose vio (Bk) 4.00 4.00
Nos. B9-B12 (4) 13.00 13.00

Common Design Type and

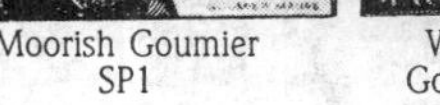

Moorish Goumier SP1

White Goumier SP2

1941 Photo. *Perf. 13½*

B13 SP1 1fr + 1fr red .50
B14 CD86 1.50fr + 3fr claret .50
B15 SP2 2.50fr + 1fr blue .50
Nos. B13-B15 (3) 1.50

Nos. B13-B15 were issued by the Vichy government, and were not placed on sale in the colony.

Nos. 114-115 were surcharged "OEUVRES COLONIALES" and surtax (including change of denomination of the 2.50fr to 50c). These were issued in 1944 by the Vichy government and were not placed on sale in the colony.

Catalogue values for unused stamps in this section, from this point to the end of the section, are for Never Hinged items.

Islamic Republic
Anti-Malaria Issue
Common Design Type

1962, Apr. 7 Engr. *Perf. 12½x12*

B16 CD108 25fr + 5f light olive grn .40 .40

Freedom from Hunger Issue
Common Design Type

1963, Mar. 21 Unwmk. *Perf. 13*

B17 CD112 25fr + 5fr multi .35 .35

Nurse Tending Infant — SP3

1972, May 8 Photo. *Perf. 12½x13*

B18 SP3 35fr + 5fr grn, red & brn .25 .25

Surtax was for Mauritania Red Crescent Society.

AIR POST STAMPS

Common Design Type
Perf. 12½x12

1940, Feb. 8 Engr. Unwmk.

C1 CD85 1.90fr ultra .25 .25
C2 CD85 2.90fr dk red .25 .25
C3 CD85 4.50fr dk gray grn .35 .35
C4 CD85 4.90fr yel bister .70 .70
C5 CD85 6.90fr deep org .70 .70
Nos. C1-C5 (5) 2.25 2.25

Common Design Types

1942

C6 CD88 50c car & bl .15
C7 CD88 1fr brn & blk .20
C8 CD88 2fr dk grn & red brn .20
C9 CD88 3fr dk bl & scar .25
C10 CD88 5fr vio & brn red .30

Frame Engraved, Center Typo.

C11 CD89 10fr ultra, ind & hn .35
a. Center inverted 650.00
C12 CD89 20fr rose car, mag & buff .35
C13 CD89 50fr yel grn, dl grn & org .45 1.00
Nos. C6-C13 (8) 2.25

There is doubt whether Nos. C6-C12 were officially placed in use.

Catalogue values for unused stamps in this section, from this point to the end of the section, are for Never Hinged items.

Islamic Republic

Flamingoes — AP1

Designs: 200fr, African spoonbills. 500fr, Slender-billed gull, horiz.

Unwmk.

1961, June 30 Engr. *Perf. 13*

C14 AP1 100fr red org, brn & ultra 1.40 .90
C15 AP1 200fr red org, sep & sl grn 2.75 1.90
C16 AP1 500fr red org, gray & bl 6.50 3.75
Nos. C14-C16 (3) 10.65 6.55

An overprint, "Europa / CECA / MIFERMA," was applied in carmine to No. C16 in 1962.

The anti-malaria emblem, including slogan "Le Monde contre le Paludisme," was overprinted on Nos. C14-C15 in 1962.

Air Afrique Issue
Common Design Type

1962, Feb. 17

C17 CD107 100fr sl grn, choc & bis 1.00 .65

UN Headquarters, New York; View of Nouakchott — AP2

1962, Oct. 27 Engr. *Perf. 13*

C18 AP2 100fr bluish grn, dk bl & org brn 1.00 .70

Mauritania's admission to the UN.

Plane, Nouakchott Airport — AP3

1963, May 3 Unwmk. *Perf. 13*

C19 AP3 500fr dp bl, gldn brn & slate grn 3.75 2.25

Miferma Open-pit Mine at Zouerate — AP4

Design: 200fr, Ore transport at Port Etienne.

1963, June Photo. *Perf. 13x12*

C20 AP4 100fr multi .65 .35
C21 AP4 200fr multi 1.50 .75

African Postal Union Issue
Common Design Type

1963, Sept. 8 Unwmk. *Perf. 12½*

C22 CD114 85fr blk brn, ocher & red .70 .40

Globe and Telstar — AP5

Design: 150fr, Relay satellite and stars.

1963, Oct. 7 Engr. *Perf. 13*

C23 AP5 50fr yel grn, pur & red brn .50 .30
C24 AP5 150fr red brn & sl grn 1.50 1.00

Communication through space.

Tiros Satellite and Emblem of WMO — AP6

UN Emblem, Doves and Sun — AP7

1963, Nov. 4

C25 AP6 200fr ultra, brn & grn 1.50 .90

Space research for meteorology and navigation.

1963 Air Afrique Issue
Common Design Type

1963, Nov. 19 Photo. *Perf. 13x12*

C26 CD115 25fr multi .30 .18

1963, Dec. 10 Engr. *Perf. 13*

C27 AP7 100fr vio, brn, & dk bl 1.00 .55

Universal Declaration of Human Rights, 15th anniv.

Symbols of Agriculture and Industry — AP8

Lichtenstein's Sand Grouse — AP9

Europafrica Issue

1964, Jan. 6 Photo.

C28 AP8 50fr multi .80 .50

Signing of economic agreement between the European Economic Community and the African and Malgache Union at Yaoundé, Cameroun, July 20, 1963.

1964, Feb. 3 Engr. *Perf. 13*

Birds: 200fr, Long-tailed cormorant. 500fr, Chanting goshawk.

C29 AP9 100fr ocher, ol & dk brn 1.00 .40
C30 AP9 200fr blk, dk bl & brn 1.90 .80
C31 AP9 500fr rose red, grn & sl 4.50 2.00
Nos. C29-C31 (3) 7.40 3.20

Isis, Temple at Philae and Trajan's Kiosk — AP10

1964, Mar. 8 Unwmk. *Perf. 13*

C32 AP10 10fr red brn, Prus bl & blk .25 .18
C33 AP10 25fr red brn, ind & Prus bl .40 .30
C34 AP10 60fr blk brn, Prus bl & red brn .80 .60
Nos. C32-C34 (3) 1.45 1.08

UNESCO world campaign to save historic monuments in Nubia.

Syncom Satellite, Globe — AP11

1964, May 4 Engr.

C35 AP11 100fr red, red brn & ultra 1.00 .60

Issued to publicize space communications.

Horse Race on Bowl — AP12

Sport Designs from Ancient Pottery: 50fr, Runner, vert. 85fr, Wrestlers, vert. 100fr, Charioteer.

1964, Sept. 27 Unwmk. *Perf. 13*

C36 AP12 15fr ol bis & choc .15 .15
C37 AP12 50fr bl & org brn .38 .22
C38 AP12 85fr crim & brn .65 .38
C39 AP12 100fr emer & dk red brn .75 .45
a. Min. sheet of 4, #C36-C39 2.25 2.25
Nos. C36-C39 (4) 1.93 1.20

18th Olympic Games, Tokyo, Oct. 10-25.

Pres. John F. Kennedy (1917-1963) — AP13

1964, Dec. 7 Photo. *Perf. 12½*

C40 AP13 100fr red brn, bl grn & dk brn .75 .65
a. Souv. sheet of 4 3.25 3.25

ITU Emblem, Induction Telegraph and Relay Satellite — AP14

1965, May 17 Engr. *Perf. 13*

C41 AP14 250fr multi 1.90 1.25

ITU, centenary.

Fight Against Cancer — AP15

Winston Churchill — AP16

1965, July 19 Unwmk. *Perf. 13*

C42 AP15 100fr bis, Prus bl & red 1.00 .42

Issued to publicize the fight against cancer.

1965, Dec. 6 Photo. *Perf. 13*

C43 AP16 200fr multi 1.50 .60

Sir Winston Spencer Churchill (1874-1965), statesman and WWII leader.

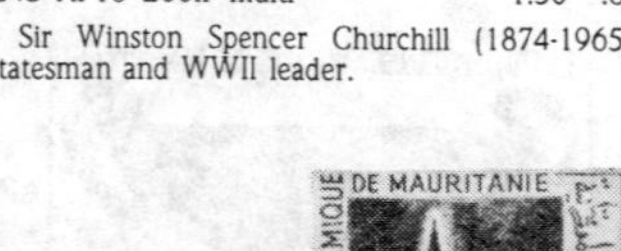

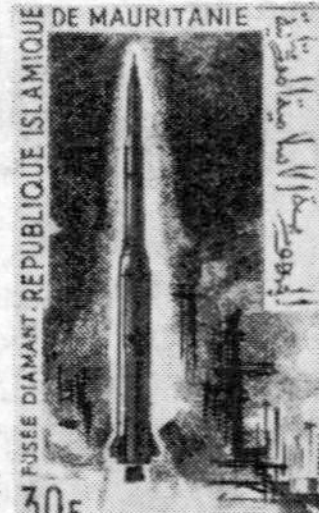

Diamant Rocket Ascending — AP17

French achievements in space: 60fr, Satellite A-1 and earth, horiz. 90fr, Scout rocket and satellite FR-1, horiz.

1966, Feb. 7 Engr. *Perf. 13*

C44 AP17 30fr dp bl, red & grn	.60	.22
C45 AP17 60fr mar, Prus grn & bl	1.10	.40
C46 AP17 90fr dp bl, rose cl & vio	1.40	.65
Nos. C44-C46 (3)	3.10	1.27

Dr. Albert Schweitzer and Clinic — AP18

1966, Feb. 21 Photo. *Perf. 12½*

C47 AP18 50fr multi .50 .22

Schweitzer (1875-1965), medical missionary to Gabon, theologian and musician.

Thomas P. Stafford, Walter M. Schirra and Gemini 6 — AP19

Designs: 100fr, Frank A. Borman, James A. Lovell, Jr., and Gemini 7. 200fr, Pavel Belyayev, Alexei Leonov, Voskhod 2.

1966, Mar. 7 Photo. *Perf. 12½*

C48 AP19 50fr multi	.40	.18
C49 AP19 100fr multi	.70	.35
C50 AP19 200fr multi	1.50	.60
Nos. C48-C50 (3)	2.60	1.13

Issued to honor achievements in space.

Map of Africa and Dove — AP20

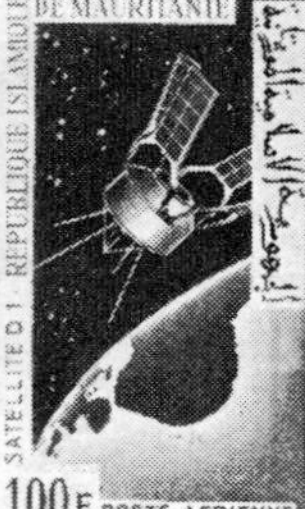

D-1 Satellite over Earth — AP21

1966, May 9 Photo. *Perf. 13*

C51 AP20 100fr red brn, sl & yel grn .90 .38

Organization for African Unity.

1966, June 6 Engr.

C52 AP21 100fr bl, dk pur & ocher 1.90 .42

Launching of the D-1 satellite at Hammaguir, Algeria, Feb. 17, 1966.

Bréguet 14 — AP22

Planes: 100fr, Goliath Farman, and camel caravan. 150fr, Couzinet "Arc-en-Ciel." 200fr, Latécoère 28 hydroplane.

1966, July 4 Engr. *Perf. 13*

C53 AP22 50fr sl bl, dl grn & ol bis	.50	.18
C54 AP22 100fr brt bl, dk grn & dk red brn	.90	.30
C55 AP22 150fr dl brn, Prus bl & saph	1.40	.45
C56 AP22 200fr dk red brn, bl & ind	2.00	.70
Nos. C53-C56 (4)	4.80	1.63

Air Afrique Issue, 1966

Common Design Type

1966, Aug. 31 Photo. *Perf. 13*

C57 CD123 30fr red, blk & gray .30 .15

"The Raft of the Medusa," by Théodore Géricault — AP23

1966, Sept. 5 Photo. *Perf. 12½*

C58 AP23 500fr multi 3.75 2.00

Sinking of the frigate "Medusa" off Mauritania, July 2, 1816.

Symbols of Agriculture and Industry — AP24

1966, Nov. 7 Photo. *Perf. 13x12*

C59 AP24 50fr multi .42 .16

Third anniversary, economic agreement between the European Economic Community and the African and Malgache Union.

Crowned Crane — AP25

Eye, Globe and Rockets — AP26

1967, Apr. 3 *Perf. 12½x13*

C60 AP25 100fr shown	.65	.40
C61 AP25 200fr Common egret	1.40	.60
C62 AP25 500fr Ostrich	3.50	1.60
Nos. C60-C62 (3)	5.55	2.60

For surcharge see No. C129.

1967, May 2 Engr. *Perf. 13*

C63 AP26 250fr brn, Prus bl & blk 1.90 1.00

EXPO '67 Intl. Exhibition, Montreal, Apr. 28-Oct. 27.

Emblem of Atomic Energy Commission AP27

1967, Aug. 7 Engr. *Perf. 13*

C64 AP27 200fr dk red, brt grn & ultra 2.25 1.00

International Atomic Energy Commission.

African Postal Union Issue, 1967

Common Design Type

1967, Sept. 9 Engr. *Perf. 13*

C65 CD124 100fr brn org, vio brn & brt grn .90 .40

Francesca da Rimini, by Ingres AP28

Paintings by and of Ingres: 100fr, Young man's torso. 150fr, "The Iliad" (seated woman). 200fr, Ingres in his Studio, by Alaux. 250fr, "The Odyssey" (seated woman).

1967-68 Photo. *Perf. 12½*

C66 AP28 90fr multi	.90	.42
C67 AP28 100fr multi ('68)	.80	.45
C68 AP28 150fr multi ('68)	1.40	.65
C69 AP28 200fr multi	2.00	.90
C70 AP28 250fr multi ('68)	2.25	1.20
Nos. C66-C70 (5)	7.35	3.62

Jean Dominique Ingres (1780-1867), French painter.

Issued: 90fr, 200fr, 10/2/67; others, 9/2/68. See No. C79.

Konrad Adenauer — AP29

Gymnast — AP30

1968, Feb. 5 Photo. *Perf. 12½*

C71 AP29 100fr org brn, lt bl & blk	.75	.35
a. Souv. sheet of 4	3.00	2.50

Adenauer (1876-1967), chancellor of West Germany (1949-63).

1968, Mar. 4 Engr. *Perf. 13*

Sports: 20fr, Slalom, horiz. 50fr, Ski jump. 100fr, Hurdling, horiz.

C72 AP30 20fr plum, blk & bl	.16	.15
C73 AP30 30fr dl pur, brt grn & brn	.22	.15
C74 AP30 50fr Prus bl, bis & bl grn	.40	.18
C75 AP30 100fr brn, grn & ver	.80	.35
Nos. C72-C75 (4)	1.58	
Set value		.70

1968 Olympic Games.

WHO Emblem, Man and Insects — AP31

1968, May 2 Engr. *Perf. 13*

C76 AP31 150fr red lil, dp bl & org red 1.20 .60

WHO, 20th anniversary.

Martin Luther King — AP32

Design: No. C78, Mahatma Gandhi.

1968, Nov. 4 Photo. *Perf. 12½*

C77 AP32 50fr sl bl, cit & blk	.35	.18
C78 AP32 50fr sl bl, lt bl & blk	.35	.18
a. Souv. sheet of 4, 2 each #C77-C78	1.60	1.60

Issued to honor two apostles of peace.

PHILEXAFRIQUE Issue

Painting Type of 1967

Design: 100fr, The Surprise Letter, by Charles Antoine Coypel.

1968, Dec. 9 Photo. *Perf. 12½*

C79 AP28 100fr multi 1.00 1.00

PHILEXAFRIQUE, Phil. Exhib., Abidjan, Feb. 14-23. Printed with alternating brown red label.

2nd PHILEXAFRIQUE Issue

Common Design Type

50fr, Mauritania #89 & family on jungle trail.

1969, Feb. 14 Engr. *Perf. 13*

C80 CD128 50fr sl grn, vio brn & red brn .55 .55

Napoleon Installed in Council of State, by Louis Charles Couder
AP33

Paintings: 50fr, Napoleon at Council of the 500, by F. Bouchot. 250fr, Farewell at Fontainebleau, by Horace Vernet.

1969, Feb. 24 Photo. *Perf. 12½*

C81 AP33 50fr pur & multi .80 .65
C82 AP33 90fr multi 1.20 1.00
C83 AP33 250fr multi 3.50 2.25
Nos. C81-C83 (3) 5.50 3.90

Napoleon Bonaparte (1769-1821).

Camel, Gazelles, and Tourist Year Emblem — AP34

1969, June 9 Engr. *Perf. 13*

C84 AP34 50fr org, dk brn & lt bl .42 .22

Year of African Tourism.

Dancers and Temple Ruins, Baalbek — AP35

1969, June 16

C85 AP35 100fr Prus bl, ol brn & rose car .65 .35

International Baalbek Festival, Lebanon.

Apollo 8 and Moon Surface — AP36

Embossed on Gold Foil

1969 *Die-cut Perf. 10*

C86 AP36 1000fr gold 10.00 10.00

Man's first flight around the moon, Dec. 21-28, 1968 (US astronauts Col. Frank Borman, Capt. James Lovell and Maj. William Anders).

Mamo Wolde, Ethiopia, Marathon — AP37

Designs: 70fr, Bob Beamon, US, broad jump. 150fr, Vera Caslavska, Czechoslovakia, gymnastics.

1969, July 7 Engr. *Perf. 13*

C87 AP37 30fr multi .20 .15
C88 AP37 70fr multi .42 .20
C89 AP37 150fr multi .90 .55
Nos. C87-C89 (3) 1.52 .90

Issued to honor gold medal winners in the 19th Olympic Games, Mexico City.

Map of London-Istanbul Route — AP38

London to Sydney automobile rally: 20fr, Map showing Ankara to Teheran route, and compass rose. 50fr, Map showing Kandahar to Bombay route, arms of Afghanistan and elephant. 70fr, Map of Australia with Perth to Sydney route, and kangaroo.

1969, Aug. 14 Engr. *Perf. 13*

C90 AP38 10fr multicolored .15 .15
C91 AP38 20fr multicolored .15 .15
C92 AP38 50fr multicolored .35 .15
C93 AP38 70fr multicolored .40 .18
a. Min. sheet of 4, #C90-C93 1.40 1.40
Nos. C90-C93 (4) 1.05
Set value .45

Palette with World Map, Geisha and EXPO '70 Emblem — AP39

EXPO '70 Emblem and: 75fr, Fan & fireworks. 150fr, Stylized bird, map of Japan & boat.

1970, June 15 Photo. *Perf. 12½*

C94 AP39 50fr multi .40 .15
C95 AP39 75fr multi .50 .25
C96 AP39 150fr multi 1.10 .45
Nos. C94-C96 (3) 2.00 .85

Issued to publicize EXPO '70 International Exhibition, Osaka, Japan, Mar. 15-Sept. 13.

UN Emblem, Balloon, Rocket, Farm Woman, Tractor, Old and New Record Players — AP40

1970, June 22 Engr. *Perf. 13*

C97 AP40 100fr ultra, dk brn & grn .70 .42

25th anniversary of the United Nations.

Elliott See (1927-1966), American Astronaut — AP41

Apollo 13 Capsule with Parachutes — AP42

#C99, Vladimir Komarov (1927-67). #C100, Yuri Gagarin (1934-68). #C101, Virgil Grissom (1926-67). #C102, Edward White (1930-67). #C103, Roger Chaffee (1935-67).

1970 Engr. *Perf. 13*

Portrait in Brown

C98 AP41 150fr gray & brt bl 1.00 .42
C99 AP41 150fr gray & org 1.00 .42
C100 AP41 150fr gray & org 1.00 .42
a. Souv. sheet of 3, #C98-C100 4.00 4.00
C101 AP41 150fr ultra & grnsh bl 1.00 .42
C102 AP41 150fr ultra & org 1.00 .42
C103 AP41 150fr ultra & grnsh bl 1.00 .42
a. Souv. sheet of 3, #C101-C103 6.00 6.00
Nos. C98-C103 (6) 6.00 2.52

American and Russian astronauts who died in space explorations.

Gold Embossed

1970, Aug. 17 *Perf. 12½*

C104 AP42 500fr gold, crim & bl 4.00 4.00

Safe return of Apollo 13 crew.

Parliament, Nouakchott, and Coat of Arms — AP43

1970, Nov. 28 Photo. *Perf. 12½*

C105 AP43 100fr multi .65 .35

10th anniversary of Independence.

Hercules Wrestling Antaeus — AP44

1971, Mar. 8 Engr. *Perf. 13*

C106 AP44 100fr red lil, brn & ultra .80 .50

Pre-Olympic Year. Design from a vase decoration by Euphronius.

Gamal Abdel Nasser (1918-1970), President of U.A.R. — AP46

1971, May 10 Photo. *Perf. 12½*

C109 AP46 100fr gold & multi .60 .30

Boy Scout, Emblem and Map of Mauritania — AP47

1971, Aug. 16 Photo. *Perf. 12½*

C110 AP47 35fr yel & multi .20 .15
C111 AP47 40fr pink & multi .22 .16
C112 AP47 100fr multi .60 .35
Nos. C110-C112 (3) 1.02 .66

13th Boy Scout World Jamboree, Asagiri Plain, Japan, Aug. 2-10.

African Postal Union Issue, 1971

Common Design Type

Design: 100fr, Women musicians and UAMPT building, Brazzaville, Congo.

1971, Nov. 13 Photo. *Perf. 13x13½*

C113 CD135 100fr bl & multi .65 .42

Letter and Postal Emblem AP48

1971, Dec. 2 *Perf. 13*

C114 AP48 35fr bis & multi .22 .15

10th anniversary of African Postal Union.

Mosul Monarch, from Book of Songs, c. 1218 — AP49

Designs from Mohammedan Miniatures: 40fr, Prince holding audience, Egypt, 1334. 100fr, Pilgrim caravan, from "Maquamat," Baghdad, 1237.

1972, Jan. 10 Photo. *Perf. 13*

C115 AP49 35fr gold & multi .22 .16
C116 AP49 40fr gray & multi .25 .20
C117 AP49 100fr buff & multi .65 .42
Nos. C115-C117 (3) 1.12 .78

For surcharges see Nos. C140, C143-C144.

Grand Canal, by Canaletto — AP50

Designs: 45fr, Venice Harbor, by Carlevaris, vert. 250fr, Santa Maria della Salute, by Canaletto.

1972, Feb. 14

C118 AP50 45fr gold & multi .20 .15
C119 AP50 100fr gold & multi .45 .25
C120 AP50 250fr gold & multi 1.25 .60
Nos. C118-C120 (3) 1.90 1.00

UNESCO campaign to save Venice.

Hurdles and Olympic Rings — AP51

1972, Apr. 27 Engr. *Perf. 13*

C121 AP51 75fr org, vio brn & blk .35 .16
C122 AP51 100fr Prus bl, vio brn & brn .50 .25
C123 AP51 200fr lake, vio brn & blk 1.00 .40
a. Min. sheet of 3, #C121-C123 1.90 1.90
Nos. C121-C123 (3) 1.85 .81

20th Olympic Games, Munich, Aug. 26-Sept. 11.
For overprints see Nos. C126-C128.

Luna 17 on Moon AP52

Design: 75fr, Luna 16 take-off from moon, vert.

1972, Oct. 9

C124 AP52 75fr vio bl, bis & grn .45 .20
C125 AP52 100fr dl pur, sl & ol bis .65 .35

Russian moon missions, Luna 16, Sept. 12-14, 1970; and Luna 17, Nov. 10-17, 1970.

Nos. C121-C123 Overprinted in Violet Blue or Red:

a. 110m HAIES / MILBURN MEDAILLE D'OR
b. 400m HAIES / AKII-BUA MEDAILLE D'OR
c. 3.000m STEEPLE / KEINO MEDAILLE D'OR

1972, Oct. 16

C126 AP51(a) 75fr multi (VB) .45 .20
C127 AP51(b) 100fr multi (R) .65 .35
C128 AP51(c) 200fr multi (VB) 1.40 .55
Nos. C126-C128 (3) 2.50 1.10

Gold medal winners in 20th Olympic Games: Rod Milburn, US, John Akii-Bua, Uganda, and Kipchoge Keino, Kenya.

No. C62 Surcharged with New Value, Two Bars and: "Apollo XVII / December 1972"

1973, Jan. 29 Photo. *Perf. 12½x13*

C129 AP25 250fr on 500fr multi 1.50 .65

Apollo 17 moon mission, Dec. 7-19, 1972.

Seal Type of Regular Issue

1973, Feb. 28 Litho. *Perf. 13*

C130 A63 135fr Seal's head 1.20 .70

For surcharge see No. C145.

Lion Eating Caiman, by Delacroix — AP53

Painting: 250fr, Lion Eating Boar, by Delacroix.

1973, Mar. 26 Photo. *Perf. 13x12½*

C131 AP53 100fr blk & multi .80 .42
C132 AP53 250fr blk & multi 2.00 1.10

For surcharges see Nos. C148-C149.

Villagers Observing Solar Eclipse — AP54

40fr, Rocket take-off & Concord, vert. 140fr, Scientists with telescopes observing eclipse.

1973, June 20 Engr. *Perf. 13*

C133 AP54 35fr grn & pur .22 .15
C134 AP54 40fr ultra, pur & scar .25 .15
C135 AP54 140fr scar & pur .90 .55
a. Souvenir sheet of 3 2.00 2.00
Nos. C133-C135 (3) 1.37 .85

Solar eclipse, June 30, 1973. No. C135a contains 3 stamps similar to Nos. C133-C135 in changed colors (35fr, 140fr in magenta and violet blue; 40fr in magenta, violet blue and orange).
For surcharges see Nos. C141-C142, C146.

Soccer AP55

1973, Dec. 24 Photo. *Perf. 13*

C136 AP55 7um multi .22 .15
C137 AP55 8um multi .22 .15
C138 AP55 20um multi .65 .42
Nos. C136-C138 (3) 1.09 .72

Souvenir Sheet

C139 AP55 30um multi 1.10 1.10

World Soccer Cup, Munich, 1974.

Nos. C115-C117, C130 and C133-C135 Surcharged with New Value and Two Bars in Red, Black or Ultramarine

1973-74 Photo., Litho. or Engr.

C140 AP49 7um on 35fr (R) ('74) .22 .15
C141 AP54 7um on 35fr (B) .25 .15
C142 AP54 8um on 40fr (B) .25 .16
C143 AP49 8um on 40fr (U) ('74) .25 .16
C144 AP49 20um on 100fr (R) ('74) .70 .42
C145 A63 27um on 135fr (B) .80 .50
C146 AP54 28um on 140fr (B) .95 .55
Nos. C140-C146 (7) 3.42 2.09

Winston Churchill (1874-1965) AP56

Lenin (1870-1924) AP57

1974, June 3 Engr. *Perf. 13*

C147 AP56 40um blk, brn & hn brn 1.00 .60

Nos. C131-C132 Surcharged with New Value and Two Bars in Red

1974, July 15 Photo. *Perf. 13x12½*

C148 AP53 20um on 100fr multi .45 .28
C149 AP53 50um on 250fr multi 1.20 .70

1974, Sept. 16 Engr. *Perf. 13*

C150 AP57 40um slate grn & red 1.00 .60

Women, IWY Emblem AP58

40um, Woman's head and IWY emblems.

1975, June 16 Engr. *Perf. 13*

C151 AP58 12um multi .38 .20
C152 AP58 40um dk brn, lt brn & bl 1.25 .65

International Women's Year.

Albert Schweitzer and Patients Arriving — AP59

1975, Aug. 4 Engr. *Perf. 13*

C153 AP59 60um multi 1.60 1.00

Schweitzer (1875-1965), medical missionary.

Javelin and Olympic Emblem — AP60

Design: 52um, Running and Olympic emblem.

1975, Nov. 17 Engr. *Perf. 13*

C154 AP60 50um sl grn, red & ol 1.50 .80
C155 AP60 52um car, ocher & ultra 1.40 .80

Pre-Olympic Year 1975.

Apollo Soyuz Type, 1975

Docked Space Ships and: 20um, Apollo rocket launch. 50um, Handshake in linked-up cabin. 60um, Apollo splash-down. 100um, Astronauts and Cosmonauts.

1975, Dec. 29 Litho. *Perf. 14*

C156 A74 20um multi .50 .22
C157 A74 50um multi 1.10 .60
C158 A74 60um multi 1.40 .70
Nos. C156-C158 (3) 3.00 1.52

Souvenir Sheet

C159 A74 100um multi 2.40 1.25

American Bicentennial Type, 1976

Uniforms: 20um, French Hussar officer. 50um, 3rd Continental Artillery officer. 60um, French infantry regiment grenadier. 100um, American infantryman.

1976, Jan. 26

C160 A75 20um multi .50 .20
C161 A75 50um multi 1.25 .50
C162 A75 60um multi 1.50 .60
Nos. C160-C162 (3) 3.25 1.30

Souvenir Sheet

C163 A75 100um multi 2.50 1.25

Running and Olympic Rings — AP61

12um, High jump. 52um, Fencing.

1976, June 14 Engr. *Perf. 13*

C164 AP61 10um pur, grn & brn .30 .16
C165 AP61 12um pur, grn & brn .38 .20
C166 AP61 52um pur, grn & brn 1.50 .80
Nos. C164-C166 (3) 2.18 1.16

21st Olympic Games, Montreal, Canada, July 17-Aug. 1.

Zeppelin Type, 1976

Designs: 50um, "Graf Zeppelin" (LZ-127) over US Capitol. 60um, "Hindenburg" (LZ-130) over Swiss Alps. 100um, "Führersland" (LZ-129) over 1936 Olympic stadium.

1976, June 28 Litho. *Perf. 11*

C167 A77 50um multi 1.50 .65
C168 A77 60um multi 1.90 .80

Souvenir Sheet

C169 A77 100um multi 3.25 1.40

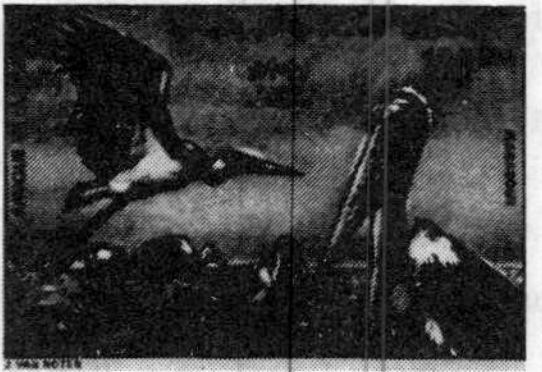
Marabou Storks — AP62

African Birds: 50um, Sacred ibis, vert. 200um, Long-crested eagles, vert.

1976, Sept. 20 Litho. *Perf. 13½*

C170 AP62 50um multi 1.50 .62
C171 AP62 100um multi 3.00 1.40
C172 AP62 200um multi 5.75 2.25
Nos. C170-C172 (3) 10.25 4.27

Viking Type, 1977

Designs: 20um, Viking orbiter in flight to Mars. 50um, Viking "B" in descent to Mars. 60um, Various phases of descent. 100um, Viking lander using probe.

1977, Feb. 28 *Perf. 14*

C173 A81 20um multi .50 .22
C174 A81 50um multi 1.20 .55
C175 A81 60um multi 1.50 .65
Nos. C173-C175 (3) 3.20 1.42

Souvenir Sheet

C176 A81 100um multi 2.50 1.00

For surcharge & overprints see #C192-C195.

Nobel Prize Type, 1977

Designs: 14um, George Bernard Shaw, literature. 55um, Thomas Mann, literature. 60um, International Red Cross Society, peace. 100um, George C. Marshall, peace.

1977, Apr. 29 Litho. *Perf. 14*

C177 A83 14um multi .32 .20
C178 A83 55um multi 1.25 .60
C179 A83 60um multi 1.50 .65
Nos. C177-C179 (3) 3.07 1.45

Souvenir Sheet

C180 A83 100um multi 2.50 1.00

Holy Kaaba AP63

1977, July 25 Litho. *Perf. 12½*

C181 AP63 12um multi .38 .20

Pilgrimage to Mecca.

Soccer Type of 1977

50um, Soccer ball. 60um, Eusebio Ferreira. 100um, Players holding pennants.

1977, Dec. 19 Litho. *Perf. 13½*

C182 A89 50um multi 1.20 .50
C183 A89 60um multi 1.50 .65

Souvenir Sheet

C184 A89 100um multi 2.40 1.00

For overprints see Nos. C187-C189.

Franco-African Co-operation — AP63a

1978, June 7 Embossed *Perf. 10½*

C184A AP63a 250um silver
C184B AP63a 500um gold

Philexafrique II - Essen Issue
Common Design Types

Designs: No. C185, Hyena and Mauritania No. C60. No. C186, Wading bird and Hamburg No. 1.

1978, Nov. 1 Litho. *Perf. 12½*

C185 CD138 20um multi	.65	.35
C186 CD139 20um multi	.65	.35
a. Pair, #C185-C186	1.30	.75

Nos. C182-C184 Overprinted in Arabic and French in Silver: "ARGENTINE- / PAYS BAS 3-1"

1978, Dec. 11 Litho. *Perf. 13½*

C187 A89 50um multi	1.25	.50
C188 A89 60um multi	1.50	.65

Souvenir Sheet

C189 A89 100um multi	2.75	1.25

Argentina's victory in World Cup Soccer Championship 1978.

Flyer A and Prototype Plane — AP64

Design: 40um, Flyer A and supersonic jet.

1979, Jan. 29 Engr. *Perf. 13*

C190 AP64 15um multi	.42	.20
C191 AP64 40um multi	1.10	.55

75th anniversary of first powered flight.

Nos. C173-C176 Overprinted and Surcharged in Silver: "ALUNISSAGE / APOLLO XI / JUILLET 1969" and Emblem

1979, Oct. 24 Litho. *Perf. 14*

C192 A81 14um on 20um multi	.35	.18
C193 A81 50um multi	1.25	.65
C194 A81 60um multi	1.50	.75
Nos. C192-C194 (3)	3.10	1.58

Souvenir Sheet

C195 A81 100um multi	2.75	2.75

Apollo 11 moon landing, 10th anniversary.

Soccer Players — AP65

Designs: Various soccer scenes.

1980, Sept. 29 Litho. *Perf. 12½*

C196 AP65 10um multi	.35	.15
C197 AP65 12um multi	.40	.18
C198 AP65 14um multi	.45	.20
C199 AP65 20um multi	.65	.30
C200 AP65 67um multi	2.25	1.10
Nos. C196-C200 (5)	4.10	1.93

Souvenir Sheet

C201 AP65 100um multi	3.50	1.50

World Soccer Cup 1982.
For overprints see Nos. C212-C217.

Flight of Columbia Space Shuttle — AP66

Designs: Views of Columbia space shuttle.

1981, Apr. 27 Litho. *Perf. 12½*

C202 AP66 12um multi	.40	.20
C203 AP66 20um multi	.65	.30
C204 AP66 50um multi	1.60	.80
C205 AP66 70um multi	2.25	1.20
Nos. C202-C205 (4)	4.90	2.50

Souvenir Sheet

C206 AP66 100um multi	3.50	1.60

Dinard Landscape, by Pablo Picasso — AP67

Picasso Birth Centenary: 12um, Harlequin, vert. 20um, Vase of Flowers, vert. 50um, Three Women at the Well. 100um, Picnic.

1981, June 29 Litho. *Perf. 12½*

C207 AP67 12um multi	.40	.20
C208 AP67 20um multi	.65	.35
C209 AP67 50um multi	1.60	.80
C210 AP67 70um multi	2.25	1.10
C211 AP67 100um multi	3.50	1.60
Nos. C207-C211 (5)	8.40	4.05

Nos. C196-C201 Overprinted in Red with Finalists and Score on 1 or 2 Lines

1982, Sept. 18 Litho. *Perf. 12½*

C212 AP65 10um multi	.35	.15
C213 AP65 12um multi	.40	.18
C214 AP65 14um multi	.45	.20
C215 AP65 20um multi	.65	.30
C216 AP65 67um multi	2.25	1.10
Nos. C212-C216 (5)	4.10	1.93

Souvenir Sheet

C217 AP65 100um multi	3.50	1.50

Italy's victory in 1982 World Cup.

25th Anniv. of Intl. Maritime Org. — AP68

1983, June 18 Litho. *Perf. 12½x13*

C218 AP68 18um multi	.60	.28

Paul Harris, Rotary Founder — AP69

1984, Jan. 20 Litho. *Perf. 13½*

C219 AP69 100um multi	1.40	.65

1984 Summer Olympics — AP70

1984, July 15 Litho. *Perf. 14*

C223 AP70 14um Running, horiz.	.18	.15
C224 AP70 18um Shot put	.25	.15
C225 AP70 19um Hurdles	.25	.15
C226 AP70 44um Javelin	.60	.30
C227 AP70 77um High jump	1.00	.50
Nos. C223-C227 (5)	2.28	1.25

Souvenir Sheet

C228 AP70 100um Hurdles, diff.	1.40	.65

Olympics Winners — AP71

1984, Dec. 20 Litho. *Perf. 13*

C229 AP71 14um Van den Berg, sailboard, Netherlands	.28	.15
C230 AP71 18um Coutts, Finn sailing, N.Z.	.38	.18
C231 AP71 19um 470 class, Spain	.40	.20
C232 AP71 44um Soling, US	.90	.45
Nos. C229-C232 (4)	1.96	.98

Souvenir Sheet

C233 AP71 100um Sailing, US	2.00	1.00

PHILEXAFRICA '85, Lome, Togo — AP72

1985, May 23 Litho. *Perf. 13*

C234 AP72 40um Youths, map, IYY emblem	.70	.40
C235 AP72 40um Oil refinery, Nouadhibou	.70	.40
a. Pair, #C234-C235 + label	1.40	1.00

1985, Nov. 12 *Perf. 13x12½*

C236 AP72 50um Iron mine, train	1.00	.50
C237 AP72 50um Boy reading, herding sheep	1.00	.50
a. Pair, #C236-C237 + label	2.00	1.00

Audubon Birth Bicentenary AP73

1985, Aug. 14

C238 AP73 14um Passeriformes thraupidae	.28	.15
C239 AP73 18um Larus philadelphia	.35	.16
C240 AP73 19um Cyanocitta cristata	.38	.18
C241 AP73 44um Rhyncops nigra	.80	.40
Nos. C238-C241 (4)	1.81	.89

Souvenir Sheet

C242 AP73 100um Anhinga anhinga	2.00	1.00

1st South Atlantic Crossing, 55th Anniv. — AP74

1986, May 19 Litho. *Perf. 13*

C243 AP74 18um Comte de Vaux, 1930	.55	.28
C244 AP74 50um Flight reenactment, 1985	1.50	.75
a. Pair, #C243-C244 + label	2.05	1.05

1986 World Cup Soccer Championships, Mexico — AP75

Various soccer plays.

1986, June 19 Litho. *Perf. 13*

C245 AP75 8um No. 279	.24	.15
C246 AP75 18um No. 280	.55	.28
C247 AP75 22um No. 281	.65	.32
C248 AP75 25um No. 282	.75	.38
C249 AP75 40um Soccer cup	1.20	.60
Nos. C245-C249 (5)	3.39	1.73

Souvenir Sheet

C250 AP75 100um multi	3.00	1.50

Air Africa, 25th Anniv. — AP76

1986, Oct. 6 Litho. *Perf. 13*

C251 AP76 26um multi	.80	.40

1988 Summer Olympics, Seoul — AP77

1987, Aug. 13 Litho. *Perf. 13*

C252 AP77 30um Boxing	.90	.45
C253 AP77 40um Judo	1.20	.60
C254 AP77 50um Fencing	1.50	.75
C255 AP77 75um Wrestling	2.25	1.10
Nos. C252-C255 (4)	5.85	2.90

Souvenir Sheet

C256 AP77 150um Judo, diff.	4.50	2.25

1988 Winter Olympics, Calgary — AP78

1987, Sept.

C257 AP78 30um Women's slalom	.90	.45
C258 AP78 40um Speed skating	1.20	.60
C259 AP78 50um Ice hockey	1.50	.75

C260 AP78 75um Women's downhill skiing 2.25 1.10
Nos. C257-C260 (4) 5.85 2.90

Souvenir Sheet

C261 AP78 150um Men's cross-country skiing 4.50 2.25

For overprints see Nos. C267-C271.

1988 Summer Olympics, Seoul — AP79

1988, Sept. 17 Litho. *Perf. 13*

C262 AP79 20um Hammer throw .60 .30
C263 AP79 24um Discus .72 .35
C264 AP79 30um Shot put .90 .45
C265 AP79 150um Javelin 4.50 4.50
Nos. C262-C265 (4) 6.72 5.60

Souvenir Sheet

C266 AP79 170um Javelin, diff. 5.00 2.50

Nos. C257-C261 Overprinted "Medaille d'or" in Red or Bright Blue and:
a. "Vreni Schneider (Suisse)"
b. "1500 m / Andre Hoffman (R.D.A.)"
c. "U.R.S.S."
d. "Marina Kiehl (R.F.A.)"
e. "15 km / Mikhail Deviatiarov (U.R.S.S.)"

1988, Sept. 18

C267 AP78(a) 30um multi .90 .45
C268 AP78(b) 40um multi (BB) 1.20 .60
C269 AP78(c) 50um multi 1.50 .75
C270 AP78(d) 75um multi 2.25 1.10
Nos. C267-C270 (4) 5.85 2.90

Souvenir Sheet

C271 AP78(e) 150um multi 4.50 2.25

World Cup Soccer Championships, Italy — AP80

Map of Italy and various soccer plays.

1990 Litho. *Perf. 13*

C272 AP80 50um multicolored 1.35 .65
C273 AP80 60um multicolored 1.65 .85
C274 AP80 70um multicolored 1.90 .95
C275 AP80 90um multicolored 2.50 1.25
C276 AP80 150um multicolored 4.00 2.00
Nos. C272-C276 (5) 11.40 5.70

POSTAGE DUE STAMPS

D1

D2

Perf. 14x13½

1906-07 Unwmk. Typo.

J1 D1 5c grn, *grnsh* 2.00 2.00
J2 D1 10c red brn 2.50 2.50
J3 D1 15c dk bl 5.50 4.50
J4 D1 20c blk, *yellow* 6.00 5.50
J5 D1 30c red, *straw* 6.00 6.00
J6 D1 50c violet 10.00 10.00
J7 D1 60c blk, *buff* 7.50 6.50
J8 D1 1fr blk, *pinkish* 11.00 10.00
Nos. J1-J8 (8) 50.50 47.00

Issue dates: 20c, 1906; others 1907.

Regular postage stamps canceled "T" in a triangle were used for postage due.

1914

J9 D2 5c green .15 .15
J10 D2 10c rose .15 .15
J11 D2 15c gray .20 .20
J12 D2 20c brown .20 .20
J13 D2 30c blue .25 .25
J14 D2 50c black .85 .85
J15 D2 60c orange .40 .40
J16 D2 1fr violet .60 .60
Nos. J9-J16 (8) 2.80 2.80

Type of 1914 Issue Surcharged **2F.**

1927, Oct. 10

J17 D2 2fr on 1fr lil rose 1.50 1.50
J18 D2 3fr on 1fr org brn 1.75 1.75

Catalogue values for unused stamps in this section, from this point to the end of the section, are for Never Hinged items.

Islamic Republic

Oualata Motif — D3

Perf. 14x13½

1961, July 1 Typo. Unwmk.

Denominations in Black

J19 D3 1fr plum & org yel .15 .15
J20 D3 2fr red & gray .15 .15
J21 D3 5fr mar & pink .15 .15
J22 D3 10fr dk grn & grn .25 .15
J23 D3 15fr ol & brn org .30 .16
J24 D3 20fr red brn & lt bl .40 .20
J25 D3 25fr grn & vermilion .60 .38
Nos. J19-J25 (7) 2.00
Set value 1.10

Vulture (Ruppell's Griffon) — D4

Birds: #J27, Eurasian crane. #J28, Pink-backed pelican. #J29, Garganey teal. #J30, European golden oriole. #J31, Variable sunbird. #J32, Shoveler ducks. #J33, Great snipe. #J34, Vulturine guinea fowl. #J35, Black stork. #J36, Gray heron. #J37, White stork. #J38, Red-legged partridge. #J39, Paradise whydah. #J40, Sandpiper (little stint). #J41, Sudan bustard.

1963, Sept. 7 Engr. *Perf. 11*

J26 D4 50c blk, yel org & red .15 .15
J27 D4 50c blk, yel org & red .15 .15
a. Pair, #J26-J27 .30 .30
J28 D4 1fr blk, red & yel .15 .15
J29 D4 1fr blk, red & yel .15 .15
a. Pair, #J28-J29 .30 .30
J30 D4 2fr blk, bl grn & yel .15 .15
J31 D4 2fr blk, bl grn & yel .15 .15
a. Pair, #J30-J31 .30 .30
J32 D4 5fr blk, grn & red brn .15 .15
J33 D4 5fr blk, grn & red brn .15 .15
a. Pair, #J32-J33 .30 .30
J34 D4 10fr blk, red & tan .38 .38
J35 D4 10fr blk, red & tan .38 .38
a. Pair, #J34-J35 .80 .80
J36 D4 15fr blk, emer & red .45 .45
J37 D4 15fr blk, emer & red .45 .45
a. Pair, #J36-J37 .90 .90
J38 D4 20fr blk, yel grn & red .70 .70
J39 D4 20fr blk, yel grn & red .70 .70
a. Pair, #J38-J39 1.40 1.40
J40 D4 25fr blk, yel grn & brn 1.00 1.00
J41 D4 25fr blk, yel grn & brn 1.00 1.00
a. Pair, #J40-J41 2.00 2.00
Nos. J26-J41 (16) 6.26 6.26

Ornament D5

1976, May 10 Litho. *Perf. 12½x13*

J42 D5 1um buff & multi .15 .15
J43 D5 3um buff & multi .15 .15
J44 D5 10um buff & multi .38 .38
J45 D5 12um buff & multi .42 .42
J46 D5 20um buff & multi .70 .70
Nos. J42-J46 (5) 1.80 1.80

OFFICIAL STAMPS

Catalogue values for unused stamps in this section are for Never Hinged items.

Islamic Republic

Cross of Trarza — O1

Perf. 14x13½

1961, July 1 Typo. Unwmk.

O1 O1 1fr vio & lilac .15 .15
O2 O1 3fr red & slate .15 .15
O3 O1 5fr grn & brown .15 .15
O4 O1 10fr grn & vio bl .18 .15
O5 O1 15fr blue & org .26 .15
O6 O1 20fr sl grn & emer .30 .15
O7 O1 25fr red org & mar .35 .26
O8 O1 30fr maroon & grn .42 .30
O9 O1 50fr dk red & dk brn .85 .42
O10 O1 100fr orange & blue 1.50 .80
O11 O1 200fr grn & red org 3.00 1.50
Nos. O1-O11 (11) 7.31 4.18

Ornament O2

1976, May 3 Litho. *Perf. 12½x13*

O12 O2 1um black & multi .15 .15
O13 O2 2um black & multi .15 .15
O14 O2 5um black & multi .20 .15
O15 O2 10um black & multi .40 .16
O16 O2 12um black & multi .55 .22
O17 O2 40um black & multi 1.50 .70
O18 O2 50um black & multi 2.00 1.00
Nos. O12-O18 (7) 4.95
Set value 2.20

AIR POST SEMI-POSTAL STAMPS
Stamps of Dahomey types V1, V2, V3 and V4 inscribed "Mauritanie" were issued in 1942 by the Vichy Government, but were not placed on sale in the colony.

MAURITIUS

mȯ-'ri-sh(ē-)əs

LOCATION — Island in the Indian Ocean about 550 miles east of Madagascar
GOVT. — Republic
AREA — 720 sq. mi.
POP. — 969,191 (est. 1983)
CAPITAL — Port Louis

12 Pence = 1 Shilling
100 Cents = 1 Rupee (1878)

The British Crown Colony of Mauritius was granted self-government in 1967 and became an independent state on March 12, 1968.

Nos. 1-6, 14-17 unused are valued without gum.

Nos. 3a-8, 14-15 are printed on fragile paper with natural irregularities which might be mistaken for faults.

Very fine examples of Nos. 22-58 will have perforations touching the design on one or more sides. Examples with perfs clear on four sides are scarce and will sell for more. Inferior copies will sell for much reduced prices.

Catalogue values for unused stamps in this country are for Never Hinged items, beginning with Scott 223 in the regular postage section, Scott J1 in the postage due section.

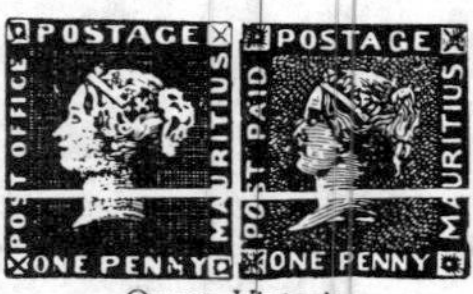

Queen Victoria
A1 A2

1847 Unwmk. Engr. *Imperf.*

1 A1 1p orange *1,100,000. 500,000.*
2 A1 2p dark blue *500,000.*

Nos. 1 and 2 were engraved and printed in Port Louis. There is but one type of each value. The initials "J. B." on the bust are those of the engraver, J. Barnard.

All unused copies of the 2p are in museums. There is one unused copy of the 1p in private hands.

1848

Earliest Impressions

Thick Yellowish Paper

3 A2 1p orange *32,500. 12,500.*
4 A2 2p dark blue *30,000. 13,500.*
d. "PENOE" *55,000. 21,000.*

Early Impressions

Yellowish White Paper

3a A2 1p orange *14,000. 5,250.*
4a A2 2p blue *16,000. 5,750.*
e. "PENOE" *25,000. 9,000.*

Bluish Paper

5 A2 1p orange *15,000. 5,250.*
6 A2 2p blue *16,500. 5,750.*
c. "PENOE" *25,000. 9,000.*

Intermediate Impressions

Yellowish White Paper

3b A2 1p red orange *7,000.* 2,000.
4b A2 2p blue *7,000.* 2,000.
f. "PENOE" *12,500. 4,500.*

Bluish Paper

5a A2 1p red orange *6,750.* 1,900.
6a A2 2p blue *6,500.* 2,000.
d. "PENOE" *12,500. 4,500.*
f. Double impression —

Worn Impressions

Yellowish White Paper

3c A2 1p orange red 2,000. 375.
d. 1p brownish red 2,000. 375.
4c A2 2p blue 2,000. 750.
g. "PENOE" *3,000.* 1,350.

Bluish Paper

5b A2 1p orange red 1,450. 350.
c. 1p brownish red 1,450. 350.
d. Pair, double impression
6b A2 2p blue 2,000. 675.
e. "PENOE" 2,750. 1,350.

Latest Impressions

Yellowish or Grayish Paper

3e A2 1p orange red 1,250. 350.
f. 1p brownish red 1,200. 350.
4h A2 2p blue 1,600. 450.
i. "PENOE" *2,750.* 900.

Bluish Paper

5e A2 1p orange red 1,200. 325.
f. 1p brownish red 1,150. 325.
6g A2 2p blue 1,500. 425.
h. "PENOE" 2,750. 900.

These stamps were printed in sheets of twelve, four rows of three, and each position differs in details. The "PENOE" error is the most pronounced variety on the plates and is from position 7.

The stamps were in use until 1859. Earliest impressions, Nos. 3-4, show the full background of diagonal and vertical lines with the diagonal lines predominant. Early impresions, Nos. 3a-4a, 5-6, show the full background with the vertical lines predominating. As the plate became worn the vertical lines disappeared, giving the intermediate impressions, Nos. 3b-4b, 5a-6a.

Worn impressions, Nos. 3c-4c, 5b-6b, have little background remaining, and latest impressions, Nos.

3e-4h, 5e-6g, have also lost details of the frame and head. The paper of the early impressions is usually rather thick, that of the worn impressions rather thin. Expect fibrous inclusions in the paper of all impressions.

"Britannia"

A3 A4

1849-58

7	A3	red brown, *blue*	7.75
8	A3	blue ('58)	3.00

Nos. 7-8 were never placed in use.

1858-59

9	A3	(4p) green, *bluish*	400.00	190.00
10	A3	(6p) red	20.00	*30.00*
11	A3	(9p) mag ('59)	450.00	150.00

No. 11 was re-issued in Nov. 1862, as a 1p stamp. When used as such it is always canceled "B53." Same value as No. 11 used.

1858 **Black Surcharge**

12	A4	4p green, *bluish*	675.00	325.00

Queen Victoria — A5

Early Impressions

1859, Mar.

14	A5	2p blue, *grayish*	3,250.	1,500.
a.		2p deep blue, *grayish*	4,500.	1,750.
14B	A5	2p blue, *bluish*	3,250.	1,500.
c.		Worn impression	1,000.	400.

Type A5 was engraved by Lapirot, in Port Louis, and was printed locally. There were twelve varieties in the sheet.

A6 A7

1859, Oct.

15	A6	2p blue, *bluish*	*100,000.*	4,000.

No. 15 was printed from the plate of the 1848 issue after it had been entirely re-engraved by Sherwin. It is commonly known as the "fillet head." The plate of the 1p, 1848, was also re-engraved but was never put in use.

1859, Dec. **Litho.**

Laid Paper

16	A7	1p red	4,000.	800.
a.		1p deep red	4,750.	1,400.
17	A7	2p blue	2,000.	425.
a.		2p slate blue	4,500.	650.

Lithographed locally by Dardenne.

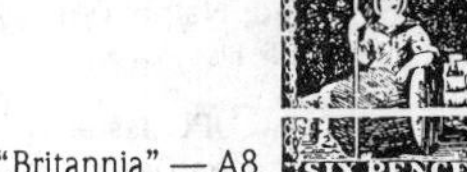

"Britannia" — A8

1859 **Wove Paper** **Engr.** ***Imperf.***

18	A8	6p blue	475.00	27.50
19	A8	1sh vermilion	1,900.	42.50

1861

20	A8	6p gray violet	17.00	22.50
21	A8	1sh green	325.00	75.00

1862 ***Perf. 14 to 16***

22	A8	6p slate	14.00	27.50
23	A8	1sh deep green	1,600.	300.00

A9 A10

1860-63 **Typo.** ***Perf. 14***

24	A9	1p brown lilac	100.00	16.00
25	A9	2p blue	140.00	24.00
26	A9	4p rose	125.00	19.00
27	A9	6p green ('62)	550.00	90.00
28	A9	6p lilac ('63)	150.00	65.00
29	A9	9p dull lilac	70.00	30.00
30	A9	1sh buff ('62)	225.00	50.00
31	A9	1sh green ('63)	500.00	125.00

For surcharges see Nos. 43-45.

1863-72 **Wmk. 1**

32	A9	1p lilac brown	40.00	4.75
a.		1p bister brown	75.00	5.00
33	A9	2p blue	60.00	6.00
a.		Imperf., pair	1,250.	1,700.
34	A9	3p vermilion	35.00	8.25
35	A9	4p rose	67.50	2.00
36	A9	6p lilac ('64)	110.00	21.00
37	A9	6p blue grn ('65)	80.00	3.50
a.		6p yellow green ('65)	100.00	10.00
38	A9	9p green ('72)	95.00	*140.00*
39	A9	1sh org yel ('64)	110.00	11.00
a.		1sh yellow	125.00	13.00
40	A9	1sh blue ('70)	125.00	17.00
41	A9	5sh red violet	140.00	40.00
a.		5sh bright violet	165.00	40.00
		Nos. 32-41 (10)	862.50	253.50

For surcharges see Nos. 48-49, 51-58, 87.

1872

42	A10	10p claret	140.00	25.00

For surcharges see Nos. 46-47.

No. 29 Surcharged in Black or Red:

HALF PENNY — a

½ d HALF PENNY — b

1876 **Unwmk.**

43	A9(a)	½p on 9p	4.75	*7.50*
a.		Inverted surcharge	500.00	
b.		Double surcharge		*1,000.*
44	A9(b)	½p on 9p	*1,200.*	
45	A9(b)	½p on 9p (R)	*775.00*	

Nos. 44 and 45 were never placed in use. No. 45 is valued with perfs cutting into the design.

Stamps of 1863-72 Surcharged in Black:

HALF PENNY — c

One Penny — d

1876-77 **Wmk. 1**

46	A10(a)	½p on 10p claret	1.50	*11.00*
47	A10(c)	½p on 10p cl ('77)	3.50	*22.50*
48	A9(d)	1p on 4p rose ('77)	7.00	10.00
49	A9(d)	1sh on 5sh red vio ('77)	175.00	80.00
a.		1sh on 5sh violet ('77)	190.00	90.00

block newblock=y

A16

Black Surcharge

1878

50	A16	2c claret	5.00	4.25

Stamps and Type of 1863-72 Surcharged in Black

e — 4 CENTS

51	A9	4c on 1p bister brn	7.00	3.50
52	A9	8c on 2p blue	60.00	1.25
53	A9	13c on 3p org red	7.00	17.50
54	A9	17c on 4p rose	110.00	2.00
55	A9	25c on 6p sl blue	140.00	4.50
56	A9	38c on 9p violet	17.00	*40.00*
57	A9	50c on 1sh green	77.50	2.50
58	A9	2r50c on 5sh violet	11.00	9.25
		Nos. 50-58 (9)	434.50	84.75

For surcharge see No. 87.

A18 A19

A20 A21

A22 A23

A24 A25

A26

1879-80 **Wmk. 1**

59	A18	2c red brown ('80)	27.50	10.00
60	A19	4c orange	60.00	3.25
61	A20	8c blue ('80)	12.00	1.40
62	A21	13c slate ('80)	110.00	150.00
63	A22	17c rose ('80)	42.50	4.25
64	A23	25c bister	200.00	7.50
65	A24	38c violet ('80)	125.00	150.00
66	A25	50c green ('80)	3.25	2.00
67	A26	2r50c brn vio ('80)	26.00	*45.00*
		Nos. 59-67 (9)	606.25	373.40

Nos. 59-67 are known imperforate.

For surcharges & overprints see #76-78, 83-86, 122-123.

1882-93 **Wmk. 2**

68	A18	1c violet ('93)	.90	.40
69	A18	2c red brown	26.00	4.50
70	A18	2c green ('85)	1.40	.50
71	A19	4c orange	55.00	2.25
72	A19	4c rose ('85)	2.00	.45
73	A20	8c blue ('91)	1.40	.75
74	A23	25c bister ('83)	4.00	1.65
75	A25	50c dp orange ('87)	26.00	7.50
		Nos. 68-75 (8)	116.70	18.00

For surcharges and overprint see #88-89, 121.

Nos. 63 and Type of 1882 Surcharged in Black:

16 CENTS — f

SIXTEEN CENTS — g

1883 **Wmk. 1**

Surcharge Measures 14x3½mm

76	A22(f)	16c on 17c rose	100.00	45.00
a.		Double surcharge		

Surcharge Measures 15½x3½mm

77	A22(f)	16c on 17c rose	110.00	45.00

Surcharge Measures 15½x2¾mm

78	A22(f)	16c on 17c rose	*225.00*	*92.50*

Wmk. 2

79	A22(g)	16c on 17c rose	50.00	1.25
		Nos. 76-79 (4)	*485.00*	*183.75*

Queen Victoria — A29

1885-94

80	A29	15c orange brown ('92)	2.75	.85
81	A29	15c blue ('94)	5.00	.60
82	A29	16c orange brown	3.25	.75
		Nos. 80-82 (3)	11.00	2.20

For surcharges see Nos. 90, 116.

Various Stamps Surcharged in Black or Red:

2 CENTS — h

2 CENTS — j

1885-87 **Wmk. 1**

83	A24(h)	2c on 38c violet	75.00	30.00
a.		Inverted surcharge	350.00	350.00
b.		Double surcharge	400.00	
c.		Without bar		87.50
84	A21(j)	2c on 13c sl (R) ('87)	30.00	*50.00*
a.		Inverted surcharge	100.00	*125.00*
b.		Double surcharge		375.00
c.		As "b," one on back	*425.00*	

TWO CENTS — k

TWO CENTS — l

1891

85	A22(k)	2c on 17c rose	75.00	75.00
a.		Inverted surcharge	175.00	
b.		Double surcharge	375.00	375.00
86	A24(k)	2c on 38c vio	2.00	4.00
a.		Double surcharge	85.00	
b.		Dbl. surch., one invtd.	85.00	
c.		Inverted surcharge	375.00	
87	A9(e+l)	2c on 38c on 9p vio	1.25	3.25
a.		Double surcharge	375.00	375.00
b.		Inverted surcharge	150.00	
c.		Dbl. surch., one invtd.	75.00	

Wmk. 2

88	A19(k)	2c on 4c rose	.75	.50
a.		Double surcharge	65.00	65.00
b.		Inverted surcharge	65.00	
c.		Dbl. surch., one invtd.	70.00	70.00
		Nos. 85-88 (4)	79.00	82.75

ONE CENT — m

ONE CENT — n

1893, Jan.

89	A18(m)	1c on 2c violet	.75	.50
90	A29(n)	1c on 16c org brown	.75	*2.00*

Coat of Arms — A38

1895-1904 **Wmk. 2**

91	A38	1c lilac & ultra	.70	.75
92	A38	1c gray blk & black	.45	.30
93	A38	2c lilac & orange	1.75	.35
94	A38	2c dull lil & vio	1.00	.20
95	A38	3c lilac	.75	.40
96	A38	3c grn & scar, *yel*	2.50	.60
97	A38	4c lilac & green	3.50	.40
98	A38	4c dull lil & car, *yel*	1.40	.30
99	A38	4c gray green & pur	2.00	1.10
100	A38	4c black & car, *blue*	3.50	.55
101	A38	5c lilac & vio, *buff*	3.75	*47.50*
102	A38	5c lilac & blk, *buff*	1.65	*2.00*
103	A38	6c grn & rose	3.00	3.00
104	A38	6c violet & scar, *red*	1.25	.60
105	A38	8c gray grn & blk, *buff*	1.40	*4.25*
106	A38	12c black & car rose	1.50	1.50
107	A38	15c grn & org	6.50	*5.50*
108	A38	15c blk & ultra, *blue*	35.00	1.10
109	A38	18c gray grn & ultra	6.00	4.50
110	A38	25c grn & car, *grn*	3.25	*9.00*
111	A38	50c green, *yel*	9.25	*22.50*
		Nos. 91-111 (21)	90.10	*106.40*

The 25c is on both ordinary and chalky paper. Ornaments in lower panel omitted on #106-111.

Year of issue: #103, 107, 1899; #92, 94, 98, 1900; #96, 99, 101-102, 104-106, 110-111, 1902; #100, 108, 1904; others, 1895.

See #128-135. For surcharges and overprints see #113, 114, 117-120.

Diamond Jubilee Issue

Arms — A39

1898, May 23 **Wmk. 46**
112 A39 36c brown org & ultra 8.50 12.00

60th year of Queen Victoria's reign.
For surcharge see No. 127.

No. 109 Surcharged in Red — 6 CENTS

1899 **Wmk. 2**
113 A38 6c on 18c .55 .70
a. Inverted surcharge 225.00 150.00

No. 112 Surcharged in Blue — 15 CENTS

Wmk. 46
114 A39 15c on 36c 1.50 1.50
a. Without bar 165.00

Admiral Mahe de La Bourdonnais — A40

1899, Dec. **Engr.** **Wmk. 1**
115 A40 15c ultra 9.25 2.50

Birth bicent. of Admiral Mahe de La Bourdonnais, governor of Mauritius, 1734-46.

No. 82 Surcharged in Black — 4 Cents

1900 **Wmk. 2**
116 A29 4c on 16c orange brown 1.65 5.00

No. 109 Surcharged in Black — 12 CENTS
r

1902
117 A38 12c on 18c grn & ultra 1.25 4.75

Preceding Issues Overprinted in Black — Postage & Revenue.

1902
118 A38 4c lilac & car, *yel* .60 .30
119 A38 6c green & rose .50 2.50
120 A38 15c green & orange .95 .40
121 A23 25c bister 1.10 2.00

Wmk. 1
122 A25 50c green 3.50 1.65
123 A26 2r50c brown violet 62.50 62.50
Nos. 118-123 (6) 69.15 69.35

Coat of Arms — A41

1902 **Wmk. 1**
124 A41 1r blk & car rose 42.50 32.50

Wmk. 2 Sideways
125 A41 2r50c grn & blk, *bl* 13.00 60.00
126 A41 5r blk & car, *red* 45.00 75.00
Nos. 124-126 (3) 100.50 167.50

No. 112 Surcharged type "r" but with longer bar

1902 **Wmk. 46**
127 A39 12c on 36c 1.25 1.50
a. Inverted surcharge 350.00 250.00

Arms Type of 1895-1904

1904-07 **Wmk. 3**

Chalky Paper
128 A38 1c gray blk & black ('07) 6.00 1.75
129 A38 2c dl lil & vio ('05) 9.50 .45
130 A38 3c grn & scar, *yel* 16.00 4.25
131 A38 4c blk & car, *blue* 1.90 .15
132 A38 6c vio & scar, *red* ('06) 1.25 .15
133 A38 15c blk & ultra, *bl* 3.00 .80
135 A38 50c green, *yel* .90 2.00
136 A41 1r black & car rose ('07) 14.00 27.50
Nos. 128-136 (8) 52.55 37.05

The 2c, 4c, 6c also exist on ordinary paper.
Ornaments in lower panel omitted on 15c and 50c.

Arms — A42

Edward VII — A43

1910 **Wmk. 3**

Ordinary Paper
137 A42 1c black 1.50 .15
138 A42 2c brown 2.00 .15
139 A42 3c green 1.75 .15
140 A42 4c ol grn & rose 2.00 .15
141 A43 5c gray & rose 1.25 1.50
142 A42 6c carmine 1.25 .15
143 A42 8c brown orange 2.00 1.00
144 A43 12c gray 1.10 .90
145 A42 15c ultramarine 10.00 .15

Chalky Paper
146 A43 25c blk & scar, *yel* 1.50 6.00
147 A43 50c dull vio & blk 1.50 10.00
148 A43 1r blk, *green* 4.00 5.50
149 A43 2r50c blk & car, *bl* 6.75 32.50
150 A43 5r grn & car, *yel* 22.50 52.50
151 A43 10r grn & car, *grn* 70.00 110.00
Nos. 137-151 (15) 129.10 220.80

Numerals of 12c, 25c and 10r of type A43 are in color on plain tablet.
See Nos. 161-178.

King George V — A44

Die I

For description of dies I and II see back of this section of the Catalogue.
Numeral tablet of 5c, 50c, 1r, 2.50r and 5r of type A44 has lined background with colorless denomination.

1912-22 **Wmk. 3**

Ordinary Paper
152 A44 5c gray & rose 1.00 2.00
153 A44 12c gray 2.50 .35

Chalky Paper
154 A44 25c blk & red, *yel* .35 1.25
a. 25c gray black & red, *yellow*, Die II .50 9.00
155 A44 50c dull vio & blk 21.00 40.00
156 A44 1r black, *emerald*, die II 1.00 5.50
a. 1r black, *emer*, olive back, die I ('21) 6.00 15.00
b. blk, *bl grn*, olive back, die I 1.65 12.00
157 A44 2r50c blk & red, *bl* 13.00 15.00
158 A44 5r grn & red, *yel* 37.50 50.00
a. Die II ('22) 32.50 85.00
159 A44 10r grn & red, *emer*, die II ('21) 20.00 67.50
a. 10r grn & red, *bl grn*, olive back, die I 550.00
b. 10r green & red, *emer*, die I 40.00 80.00
c. 10r grn & red, *emer*, olive back, die I 32.50 80.00
d. 10r grn & red, *grn*, die I 37.50 80.00

Surface-colored Paper
160 A44 25c blk & red, *yel* ('16) .40 11.00
Nos. 152-160 (9) 96.75 192.60

1921-26 **Wmk. 4**

Ordinary Paper
161 A42 1c black .50 .70
162 A42 2c brown .50 .15
163 A42 2c violet, *yel* ('25) .45 .60
164 A42 3c green ('25) 1.65 .50
165 A42 4c ol grn & rose 1.25 1.50
166 A42 4c green .65 .15
167 A42 4c brown ('25) .20 .50
168 A42 6c rose red 6.50 4.00
169 A42 6c violet .35 .15
170 A42 8c brown org ('25) 1.50 7.50
171 A42 10c gray ('22) 1.75 3.00
172 A42 10c rose red ('25) 1.65 .65
173 A42 12c rose red .90 .30
174 A42 12c gray ('25) .50 1.25
175 A42 15c ultramarine 3.50 2.50
176 A42 15c dull blue ('25) .45 .30
177 A42 20c ultra ('22) 1.75 .40
178 A42 20c dull vio ('25) 5.00 6.50
Nos. 161-178 (18) 29.05 30.65

Ornaments in lower panel omitted on #171-178.
For surcharges see Nos. 201-203.

Die II

1922-34

Ordinary Paper
179 A44 1c black .60 .35
180 A44 2c brown .40 .15
181 A44 3c green .45 .20
182 A44 4c olive grn & red ('27) .30 .15
a. Die I ('32) 4.50 20.00
183 A44 4c green, die I ('33) 2.25 .30
184 A44 5c gray & car .60 .15
a. Die I ('32) 2.50 1.65
185 A44 6c olive brn ('28) .50 .50
186 A44 8c orange .45 5.50
187 A44 10c rose red ('26) .80 .15
a. Die I ('32) 3.25 3.75
188 A44 12c gray, small "c" ('22) .25 .30
189 A44 12c gray, "c" larger & thinner ('34) .50 6.50
190 A44 12c rose red .35 2.00
191 A44 15c dk blue ('28) .60 .50
192 A44 20c dull vio .45 .55
193 A44 20c dk blue ('34) 7.50 .75
a. Die I ('27) 8.50 .30
194 A44 25c black & red, *yel* .25 .15
a. Die I ('32) 2.25 17.00

Chalky Paper
195 A44 50c dull vio & blk 6.00 2.75
196 A44 1r blk, *emerald* 1.00 .20
a. Die I ('32) 6.50 14.00
197 A44 2r50c blk & red, *bl* 12.00 5.00
198 A44 5r green & red, *yel* 18.00 47.50
199 A44 10r green & red, *emer* ('28) 40.00 80.00
Nos. 179-199 (21) 93.25 153.65

A45

1924
200 A45 50r lilac & green 750.00 1,350.

Nos. 166, 173, 177 Surcharged — 10 Cents

1925
201 A42 3c on 4c green 1.50 1.50
202 A42 10c on 12c rose red .25 .75
203 A42 15c on 20c ultra .25 .75
Nos. 201-203 (3) 2.00 3.00

Silver Jubilee Issue
Common Design Type

1935, May 6 **Engr.** ***Perf.*** $13^1/_2$***x14***
204 CD301 5c gray black & ultra .25 .15
205 CD301 12c indigo & green .60 .60
206 CD301 20c blue & brown 2.25 1.75
207 CD301 1r brt vio & indigo 22.50 22.50
Nos. 204-207 (4) 25.60 25.00

Coronation Issue
Common Design Type

Perf. $13^1/_2$***x14***

1937, May 12 **Wmk. 4**
208 CD302 5c dark purple .15 .15
209 CD302 12c carmine .15 .15
210 CD302 20c bright ultra .25 .25
Nos. 208-210 (3) .55 .55

King George VI — A46

1938-43 **Typo.** ***Perf. 14***
211 A46 2c gray .20 .15
a. Perf. 15x14 ('43) .60 .15
212 A46 3c rose vio & car 1.25 .40
213 A46 4c green 1.50 .40
214 A46 5c violet 2.75 .25
a. Perf. 15x14 ('43) 16.00 .15
215 A46 10c carmine 1.50 .15
a. Perf. 15x14 ('43) 14.00 .50
216 A46 12c salmon pink .60 .15
a. Perf. 15x14 ('43) 30.00 .50
217 A46 20c blue .60 .15
218 A46 25c maroon 1.75 .15
219 A46 1r brown black 5.75 .40
220 A46 2.50r pale violet 12.75 3.50
221 A46 5r olive green 15.00 10.00
222 A46 10r rose violet 6.75 8.00
Nos. 211-222 (12) 50.40 23.70

Catalogue values for unused stamps in this section, from this point to the end of the section, are for Never Hinged items.

Peace Issue
Common Design Type

Perf. $13^1/_2$***x14***

1946, Nov. 20 **Engr.** **Wmk. 4**
223 CD303 5c lilac .15 .15
224 CD303 20c deep blue .15 .15
Set value .25 .25

"Post Office" Stamp of 1847 — A47

1948, Mar. 22 ***Perf.*** $11^1/_2$
225 A47 5c red vio & orange .15 .15
226 A47 12c green & orange .15 .15
227 A47 20c blue & dp blue .16 .16
228 A47 1r lt red brn & dp blue .60 .60
Nos. 225-228 (4) 1.06 1.06

Cent. of the 1st Mauritius postage stamps.

Silver Wedding Issue
Common Design Types

1948, Oct. 25 **Photo.** ***Perf. 14x14***$^1/_2$
229 CD304 5c violet .15 .15

Perf. $11^1/_2$***x11***

Engraved; Name Typographed
230 CD305 10r lilac rose 9.00 15.50

UPU Issue
Common Design Types

Engr.; Name Typo. on 20c, 35c

Perf. $13^1/_2$***,*** 11***x***$11^1/_2$

1949, Oct. 10 **Wmk. 4**
231 CD306 12c rose carmine .38 .38
232 CD307 20c indigo .42 .42
233 CD308 35c rose violet .50 .50
234 CD309 1r sepia .85 .75
Nos. 231-234 (4) 2.15 2.05

Sugar Factory — A48

Aloe Plant — A49

Designs: 2c, Grand Port. 4c, Tamarind Falls. 5c, Rempart Mountain. 10c, Transporting cane. 12c, Map and dodo. 20c, "Paul et Virginie." 25c, Statue of Mahe La Bourdonnais. 35c, Government House. 50c, Pieter Both Mountain. 1r, Sambar. 2.50r, Port Louis. 5r, Beach scene. 10r, Arms.

Perf. 13½x14½, 14½x13½

1950, July 1 **Photo.**

No.	Type	Description	Unused	Used
235	A48	1c red violet	.15	.15
236	A48	2c cerise	.15	.15
237	A49	3c yel green	.15	.15
238	A49	4c green	.20	.15
239	A48	5c greenish blue	.20	.15
240	A48	10c red	.35	.15
241	A48	12c olive green	.20	.15
242	A49	20c brt ultra	.35	.18
243	A49	25c vio brown	.75	.35
244	A48	35c rose violet	.65	.25
245	A49	50c emerald	1.10	.45
246	A48	1r sepia	3.25	1.25
247	A48	2.50r orange	5.50	2.25
248	A48	5r red brown	8.25	4.00
249	A48	10r gray blue	30.00	7.50
		Nos. 235-249 (15)	51.25	17.28

Coronation Issue

Common Design Type

1953, June 2 **Engr.** *Perf. 13½x13*

No.	Type	Description	Unused	Used
250	CD312	10c dk green & black	.25	.18

Sugar Factory — A50

Tamarind Falls — A51

Designs: 2c, Grand Port. 3c, Aloe plant. 5c, Rempart Mountain. 15c, Museum, Mahebourg. 20c, Statue of Mahe La Bourdonnais. 25c, "Paul et Virginie." 35c, Government House. 50c, Pieter Both Mountain. 60c, Map and dodo. 1r, Sambar. 2.50r, Port Louis. 5r, Beach scene. 10r, Arms.

Perf. 13½x14½, 14½x13½

1953-54 **Photo.** **Wmk. 4**

No.	Type	Description	Unused	Used
251	A50	2c rose car ('54)	.15	.15
252	A51	3c yel green ('54)	.15	.15
253	A50	4c red violet	.20	.15
254	A50	5c grnsh blue ('54)	.20	.15
255	A51	10c dk green	.25	.15
256	A50	15c scarlet	.25	.15
257	A51	20c violet brown	.35	.15
a.		Imperf., pair		
258	A51	25c brt ultra	.50	.15
259	A50	35c rose vio ('54)	.50	.15
260	A51	50c emerald	.90	.20
261	A50	60c gray grn ('54)	2.25	.50
262	A50	1r sepia	1.25	.40
a.		Imperf., pair		
263	A50	2.50r orange ('54)	5.00	2.00
264	A50	5r red brn ('54)	8.50	2.75
265	A50	10r gray blue ('54)	13.00	3.75
		Nos. 251-265 (15)	33.45	10.95

See Nos. 273-275.

King George III and Queen Elizabeth II — A52

Perf. 13½

1961, Jan. 11 **Wmk. 314** **Litho.**

No.	Type	Description	Unused	Used
266	A52	10c dk red & dk brown	.15	.15
267	A52	20c lt blue & dk blue	.18	.18
268	A52	35c org yel & brown	.35	.35
269	A52	1r yel green & dk brn	.75	.75
		Nos. 266-269 (4)	1.43	1.43

Sesquicentenary of postal service under British administration.

Freedom from Hunger Issue

Common Design Type

1963, June 4 **Photo.** *Perf. 14x14½*

No.	Type	Description	Unused	Used
270	CD314	60c lilac	.40	.40

Red Cross Centenary Issue

Common Design Type

1963, Sept. 2 **Litho.** *Perf. 13*

No.	Type	Description	Unused	Used
271	CD315	10c black & red	.15	.15
272	CD315	60c ultra & red	.50	.50

Types of 1953-54

Perf. 14½x13½, 13½x14½

1963-64 **Photo.** **Wmk. 314**

No.	Type	Description	Unused	Used
273	A51	10c dark green ('64)	.15	.15
274	A50	60c gray green ('64)	.90	.90
275	A50	2.50r orange	2.75	2.75
		Nos. 273-275 (3)	3.80	3.80

Gray White-Eye A53

Birds of Mauritius: 3c, Rodriguez fody. 4c, Olive white-eye. 5c, Mauritius paradise flycatcher. 10c, Mauritius fody. 15c, Rose-ringed parakeet. 20c, Cuckoo shrike. 25c, Mauritian kestrel. 35c, Pink pigeon. 50c, Mauritius olivaceous bulbul. 60c, Mauritius blue pigeon. 1r, Dodo. 2.50r, Rodriguez solitaire. 5r, Van den Broeck's red rail. 10r, Broad-billed Mauritian parrot.

Perf. 14½

1965, Mar. 16 **Photo.** **Wmk. 314**

Birds in Natural Colors

No.	Type	Description	Unused	Used
276	A53	2c brt yel & brn	.15	.15
a.		Gray (leg, etc.) omitted	50.00	
277	A53	3c brn & dk brn	.15	.15
a.		Black (eye, beak) omitted	45.00	
278	A53	4c dl rose lil & blk	.15	.15
a.		Rose lilac omitted	30.00	
279	A53	5c gray & ultra	1.40	.15
a.		Wmkd. sideways ('66)	.15	.15
280	A53	10c dl grn & dk brn	.15	.15
281	A53	15c lt gray & dk brn	1.25	.15
a.		Carmine (beak) omitted	45.00	
282	A53	20c pale yel & dk brown	1.25	.15
283	A53	25c gray & brown	2.00	.15
284	A53	35c vio bl & blk	1.65	.15
a.		Wmkd. sideways ('67)	.35	.30
285	A53	50c pale yel & blk	.45	.15
286	A53	60c pale cit & brn	.25	.15
287	A53	1r lt yel grn & blk	2.00	.20
a.		Pale gray (ground) omitted	80.00	
b.		Pale orange omitted	80.00	
288	A53	2.50r pale grn & brn	4.00	5.00
289	A53	5r pale blue & blk	12.00	5.50
290	A53	10r pale grn & ultra	22.50	9.00
		Nos. 276-290 (15)	49.35	21.35

On No. 278 the background was printed in two colors. The rose lilac tint is omitted on No. 278a.

See #327-332. For overprints see #306-320.

ITU Issue

Common Design Type

Perf. 11x11½

1965, May 17 **Litho.** **Wmk. 314**

No.	Type	Description	Unused	Used
291	CD317	10c dp org & apple grn	.15	.15
292	CD317	60c yellow & violet	.45	.35

Intl. Cooperation Year Issue

Common Design Type

1965, Oct. 25 *Perf. 14½*

No.	Type	Description	Unused	Used
293	CD318	10c lt green & claret	.15	.15
294	CD318	60c lt violet & green	.35	.35
		Set value	.43	.43

Churchill Memorial Issue

Common Design Type

1966, Jan. 24 **Photo.** *Perf. 14*

Design in Black, Gold and Carmine Rose

No.	Type	Description	Unused	Used
295	CD319	2c brt blue	.15	.15
296	CD319	10c green	.15	.15
297	CD319	60c brown	.50	.50
298	CD319	1r violet	1.10	1.10
		Nos. 295-298 (4)	1.90	1.90

UNESCO Anniversary Issue

Common Design Type

1966, Dec. 1 **Litho.** *Perf. 14*

No.	Type	Description	Unused	Used
299	CD323	5c "Education"	.15	.15
300	CD323	10c "Science"	.20	.15
301	CD323	60c "Culture"	.75	.60
		Nos. 299-301 (3)	1.10	.90

Red-Tailed Tropic Bird A54

Birds of Mauritius: 10c, Rodriguez bush warbler. 60c, Newton's parakeet. 1r, Mauritius swiftlet.

1967, Sept. 1 **Photo.** *Perf. 14½*

No.	Type	Description	Unused	Used
302	A54	2c lt ultra & multi	.15	.15
303	A54	10c emerald & multi	.15	.15
304	A54	60c salmon & multi	.40	.40
305	A54	1r yellow & multi	.75	.75
		Nos. 302-305 (4)	1.45	1.45

Attainment of self-government, Sept. 1, 1967.

Bird Issue of 1965-67 and Type Overprinted: "SELF GOVERNMENT 1967"

1967, Dec. 1 **Photo.** **Wmk. 314**

No.	Type	Description	Unused	Used
306	A53	2c multicolored	.15	.15
307	A53	3c multicolored	.15	.15
308	A53	4c multicolored	.15	.15
309	A53	5c multicolored	.15	.15
310	A53	10c multicolored	.15	.15
311	A53	15c multicolored	.15	.15
312	A53	20c multicolored	.15	.15
313	A53	25c multicolored	.15	.15
314	A53	35c multicolored	.15	.15
315	A53	50c multicolored	.25	.20
316	A53	60c multicolored	.35	.25
317	A53	1r multicolored	.50	.40
318	A53	2.50r multicolored	1.40	1.40
319	A53	5r multicolored	2.75	2.75
320	A53	10r multicolored	5.50	5.50
		Nos. 306-320 (15)	12.10	11.85

5c, 10c, 35c watermarked sideways.

Independent State

Flag of Mauritius A55

Designs: 3c, 20c, 1r, Dodo emerging from egg and coat of arms.

Perf. 13½x13

1968, Mar. 12 **Litho.** **Unwmk.**

No.	Type	Description	Unused	Used
321	A55	2c brt violet & multi	.15	.15
322	A55	3c red brown & multi	.15	.15
323	A55	15c brown & multi	.15	.15
324	A55	20c multicolored	.15	.15
325	A55	60c dk green & multi	.40	.40
326	A55	1r brt violet & multi	.65	.65
		Set value	1.35	1.35

Independence of Mauritius.

Bird Type of 1965 in Changed Background Colors

Perf. 14½

1968, July 12 **Photo.** **Wmk. 314**

Birds in Natural Colors

No.	Type	Description	Unused	Used
327	A53	2c lemon & brown	.15	.15
328	A53	3c ultra & dk brown	.15	.15
329	A53	15c tan & dk brown	.30	.15
330	A53	20c dull yel & dk brn	.42	.20
331	A53	60c pink & black	1.10	.50
332	A53	1r rose lilac & black	1.90	.90
		Nos. 327-332 (6)	4.02	2.05

Domingue Rescuing Paul and Virginie — A56

Designs: 15c, Paul and Virginie crossing river, vert. 50c, La Bourdonnais visiting Madame de la Tour. 60c, Paul and Virginie, vert. 1r, Departure of Virginie for Europe. 2.50r, Bernardin de St. Pierre, vert. The designs are from old prints illustrating "Paul et Virginie."

Perf. 13½

1968, Dec. 2 **Unwmk.** **Litho.**

No.	Type	Description	Unused	Used
333	A56	2c multicolored	.15	.15
334	A56	15c multicolored	.15	.15
335	A56	50c multicolored	.25	.25
336	A56	60c multicolored	.30	.30
337	A56	1r multicolored	.50	.50
338	A56	2.50r multicolored	1.35	1.35
		Nos. 333-338 (6)	2.70	2.70

Bicent. of the visit of Bernardin de St. Pierre (1737-1814), author of "Paul et Virginie."

Batardé Fish A57

Marine Life: 3c, Red reef crab. 4c, Episcopal miter shell. 5c, Bourse fish. 10c, Starfish. 15c, Sea urchin. 20c, Fiddler crab. 25c, Spiny shrimp. 30c, Single and double harp shells. 35c, Argonaut shell. 40c, Nudibranch (sea-slug). 50c, Violet and orange spider shells. 60c, Blue marlin. 75c, Conus clytospira. 1r, Dorad. 2.50r, Spiny lobster. 5r, Sacré chien rouge fish. 10r, Moonfish.

Wmk. 314 Sideways (#339-344, 351-352), others Upright

1969, Mar. 12 **Photo.** *Perf. 14*

No.	Type	Description	Unused	Used
339	A57	2c pink & multi	.15	.15
340	A57	3c yellow & multi	.15	.15
341	A57	4c multicolored	.15	.15
342	A57	5c lt blue & multi	.15	.15
343	A57	10c salmon & multi	.15	.15
344	A57	15c pale blue & multi	.15	.15
345	A57	20c pale gray & multi	.15	.15
346	A57	25c multicolored	.15	.15
347	A57	30c multicolored	.20	.20
348	A57	35c multicolored	.20	.20
349	A57	40c tan & multi	.25	.25
350	A57	50c lt vio & multi	.35	.30
351	A57	60c ultra & multi	.40	.35
352	A57	75c lemon & multi	.55	.40
353	A57	1r cream & multi	.60	.55
354	A57	2.50r lt vio & multi	2.25	2.25
355	A57	5r multicolored	5.00	5.00
356	A57	10r multicolored	9.00	9.00
		Nos. 339-356 (18)	20.00	19.70

For overprints see Nos. 368-369.

Wmk. 314 Upright (#339a-344a, 351a-352a), others Sideways

1972-74

No.	Type	Description	Unused	Used
339a	A57	2c multi ('74)	.15	.15
340a	A57	3c multi ('74)	.15	.15
341a	A57	4c multi ('74)	.15	.15
342a	A57	5c multi ('74)	.15	.15
343a	A57	10c multicolored	.15	.15
344a	A57	15c multi ('74)	.15	.15
345a	A57	20c multicolored	.15	.15
346a	A57	25c multi ('73)	.15	.15
347a	A57	30c multicolored	.22	.18
348a	A57	35c multicolored	.28	.22
349a	A57	40c multicolored	.30	.30
350a	A57	50c multi ('73)	.30	.30
351a	A57	60c multi ('74)	.38	.32
352a	A57	75c multicolored	.52	.42
353a	A57	1r multicolored	.60	.52
354a	A57	2.50r multi ('73)	1.50	1.40
355a	A57	5r multi ('73)	3.00	2.50
356a	A57	10r multicolored	5.75	5.00
		Nos. 339a-356a (18)	14.05	12.36

1975-77 **Wmk. 373**

No.	Type	Description	Unused	Used
339b	A57	2c multi ('77)	.15	.15
340b	A57	3c multi ('77)	.15	.15
341b	A57	4c multi ('77)	.15	.15
342b	A57	5c multicolored	.15	.15
344b	A57	15c multicolored	.18	.15
345b	A57	20c multi ('76)	.20	.18
346b	A57	25c multicolored	.26	.20
347b	A57	30c multicolored	.30	.26
348b	A57	35c multi ('76)	.30	.26
349b	A57	40c multi ('76)	.32	.30
350b	A57	50c multi ('76)	.40	.32
351b	A57	60c multi ('77)	.52	.42
352b	A57	75c multi ('77)	.52	.48
353b	A57	1r multi ('76)	.80	.75
354b	A57	2.50r multi ('77)	3.25	2.00
355b	A57	5r multicolored	5.50	4.25
356b	A57	10r multicolored	13.00	8.75
		Nos. 339b-356b (17)	26.15	18.92

Gandhi as Law Student in London — A58

Portraits of Gandhi: 15c, as stretcher bearer during Zulu rebellion. 50c, as member of non-violent movement in South Africa (Satyagrahi). 60c, wearing Indian garment at No. 10 Downing Street, London. 1r, wearing turban in Mauritius, 1901. 2.50r, as old man.

1969, July 1 Litho. *Perf. 13½*

357 A58 2c dull org & multi .15 .15
358 A58 15c brt blue & multi .15 .15
359 A58 50c multicolored .18 .18
360 A58 60c brick red & multi .25 .25
361 A58 1r multicolored .50 .50
362 A58 2.50r olive & multi 1.25 1.25
a. Souvenir sheet of 6, #357-362 5.25 5.25
Nos. 357-362 (6) 2.48 2.48

Mohandas K. Gandhi (1869-1948), leader in India's struggle for independence.

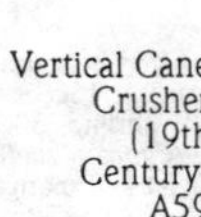

Vertical Cane Crusher (19th Century) A59

Dr. Charles Telfair (1778-1833) — A60

Designs: 15c, The Frangourinier, 18th century cane crusher. 60c, Beau Rivage sugar factory, 1867, painting by Numa Desjardin. 1r, Mon Desert-Alma sugar factory, 1969.

Perf. 11x11½, 11½x11

1969, Dec. 22 Photo. Wmk. 314

363 A59 2c multicolored .15 .15
364 A59 15c multicolored .15 .15
365 A59 60c multicolored .25 .25
366 A59 1r multicolored .38 .38
367 A60 2.50r multicolored .90 .90
a. Souvenir sheet of 5 2.00 2.00
Nos. 363-367 (5) 1.83 1.83

150th anniv. of Telfair's improvements of the sugar industry.

No. 367a contains one each of Nos. 363-367. The 2.50r in the sheet is imperf., the others are perf. 11x11½.

Nos. 351 and 353 Overprinted: "EXPO '70 / OSAKA"

1970, Apr. 7 *Perf. 14*

368 A57 60c ultra & multi .25 .25
369 A57 1r cream & multi .38 .38

EXPO '70 Intl. Exhib., Osaka, Japan, Mar. 15-Sept. 13.

Lufthansa Plane over Mauritius — A61

Design: 25c, Brabant Hotel, Morne Beach, horiz.

1970, May 2 Litho. *Perf. 14*

370 A61 25c multicolored .15 .15
371 A61 50c multicolored .25 .25

Lufthansa's inaugural flight from Mauritius to Frankfurt, Germany, May 2, 1970.

Lenin as Student, by V. Tsigal — A62

Design: 75c, Bust of Lenin.

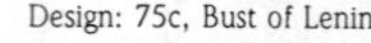

1970, May 15 Photo. *Perf. 12x11½*

372 A62 15c dk slate blue & sil .15 .15
373 A62 75c dk brown & gold .45 .45
Set value .50 .50

Birth cent. of Lenin (1870-1924), Russian communist leader.

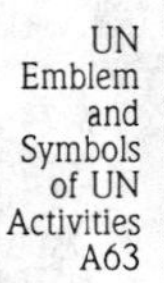

UN Emblem and Symbols of UN Activities A63

1970, Oct. 24 Litho. *Perf. 14*

374 A63 10c blue black & multi .15 .15
375 A63 60c blue black & multi .28 .28
Set value .34 .34

25th anniversary of the United Nations.

Mauritius No. 2, and Post Office before 1870 A64

Designs: 15c, General Post Office Building, 1870-1970. 50c, Mauritius mail coach, 1870. 75c, Port Louis harbor, 1970. 2.50r, Arrival of Pierre André de Suffren de St. Tropez in Port Louis harbor, 1783.

1970, Oct. 15 Litho. *Perf. 14*

376 A64 5c multicolored .15 .15
377 A64 15c multicolored .15 .15
378 A64 50c multicolored .20 .20
379 A64 75c multicolored .30 .30
380 A64 2.50r multicolored 1.00 1.00
a. Souvenir sheet of 5 3.50 3.50
Nos. 376-380 (5) 1.80 1.80

Centenary of the General Post Office and to show the improvements of Port Louis harbor. No. 380a contains one each of Nos. 376-380 and a label showing map of Mauritius.

Waterfall A65

Designs: 15c, Trois Mamelles Mountains. 60c, Beach scene with sailboats. 2.50r, Marine life.

1971, Apr. 12 Litho. *Perf. 14*

381 A65 10c multicolored .15 .15
382 A65 15c multicolored .15 .15
383 A65 60c multicolored .25 .25
384 A65 2.50r multicolored 1.25 1.25
Nos. 381-384 (4) 1.80 1.80

Tourist publicity. Each stamp has a different 6-line message printed in black on back.

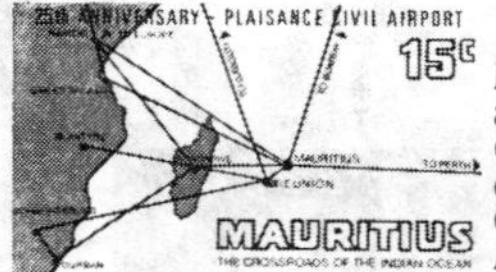

Mauritius at Crossroads of Indian Ocean A66

Designs: 60c, Plane at Plaisance Airport. 1r, Stewardesses on plane ramp. 2.50r, Roland Garros' airplane, Choisy Airfield, 1937.

1971, Oct. 23 Wmk. 314 *Perf. 14½*

385 A66 15c multicolored .15 .15
386 A66 60c multicolored .25 .25
387 A66 1r multicolored .35 .35
388 A66 2.50r multicolored 1.25 1.25
Nos. 385-388 (4) 2.00 2.00

25th anniversary of Plaisance Civil Airport.

Princess Margaret Orthopedic Center A67

Design: 75c, Operating room, National Hospital.

1971, Nov. 2 *Perf. 14x14½*

389 A67 10c multicolored .15 .15
390 A67 75c multicolored .30 .30
Set value .35 .35

3rd Commonwealth Medical Conf., Nov. 1971.

Elizabeth II and Prince Philip A68

Design: 2.50r, Queen Elizabeth II, vert.

1972, Mar. Litho. *Perf. 14½*

391 A68 15c brown & multi .15 .15
392 A68 2.50r ultra & multi 1.75 1.75

Visit of Elizabeth II and Prince Philip.

Port Louis Theater and Masks A69

Design: 1r, Interior view and masks of Comedy and Tragedy.

1972, June 26

393 A69 10c brown & multi .15 .15
394 A69 1r multicolored .30 .30
Set value .35 .35

Sesquicentennial of Port Louis Theater.

Pirate Dhow Entering Tamarind River A70

Perf. 14x14½, 14½x14

1972, Nov. 17 Litho.

395 A70 15c shown .15 .15
396 A70 60c Treasure chest, vert. .40 .40
397 A70 1r Lememe and brig Hirondelle, vert. .80 .80
398 A70 2.50r Robert Surcouf 3.50 3.50
Nos. 395-398 (4) 4.85 4.85

Pirates and privateers.

Mauritius University A71

60c, Tea development plant. 1r, Bank of Mauritius.

1973, Apr. 10 *Perf. 14½*

399 A71 15c green & multi .15 .15
400 A71 60c yellow & multi .20 .20
401 A71 1r red & multi .30 .30
Set value .55 .55

5th anniversary of independence.

OCAM Emblem A72

Design: 2.50r, Handshake, map of Africa; inscriptions in French, vert.

1973, Apr. 25

402 A72 10c multicolored .15 .15
403 A72 2.50r lt blue & multi .90 .90

Conference of the Organisation Commune Africaine, Malgache et Mauricienne (OCAM), Mauritius, Apr. 25-May 6.

WHO Emblem A73

Perf. 14½x14

1973, Nov. 20 Wmk. 314

404 A73 1r green & multi .35 .35

25th anniv. of WHO.

Meteorological Station, Vacoas — A74

1973, Nov. 27

405 A74 75c multicolored .25 .25

Cent. of intl. meteorological cooperation.

Surcouf and Capture of the "Kent" A75

1974, Mar. 21 Litho. *Perf. 14½x14*

406 A75 60c sepia & multi .38 .38

Bicentenary of the birth of Robert Surcouf (1773-1827), French privateer.

Philibert Commerson and Bougainvillaea — A76

1974, Apr. 18 *Perf. 14*

407 A76 2.50r slate green & multi .90 .90

Philibert Commerson (1727-1773), French physician and naturalist.

FAO Emblem, Woman Milking Cow A77

1974, Oct. 23 *Perf. 14½*

408 A77 60c multicolored .25 .25

8th FAO Regional Conference, Aug. 1-17.

Mail Train and UPU Emblem A78

Design: 1r, New General Post Office Building, Port Louis, and UPU emblem.

1974, Dec. 4 Litho. *Perf. 14½*

409 A78 15c multicolored .15 .15
410 A78 1r multicolored .40 .40
Set value .46 .46

Centenary of Universal Postal Union.

Cottage Life, by F. Leroy A79

Paintings: 60c, Milk Seller, by A. Richard, vert. 1r, Entrance to Port Louis Market, by Thuillier. 2.50r, Washerwomen, by Max Boullé, vert.

1975, Mar. 6 — Wmk. 373

411 A79	15c multicolored	.15	.15
412 A79	60c multicolored	.25	.25
413 A79	1r multicolored	.40	.40
414 A79	2.50r multicolored	1.00	1.00
	Nos. 411-414 (4)	1.80	1.80

Artistic views of life on Mauritius.

Mace, Map and Arms of Mauritius, Association Emblem — A80

1975, Nov. 21 — Litho. — Wmk. 373

415 A80	75c multicolored	.25	.25

French-speaking Parliamentary Association, conf.

Woman and Aladdin's Lamp A81

1975, Dec. 5 — Perf. 14½

416 A81	2.50r multicolored	.90	.90

International Women's Year.

Parched Land A82

Drought in Africa: 60c, Map of Africa, carcass and desert, vert.

1976, Feb. 26 — Litho. — Wmk. 373

417 A82	50c vermilion & multi	.18	.18
418 A82	60c blue & multi	.24	.24

Pierre Loti, 1953-1970 A83

Mail Carriers: 15c, Secunder, 1907. 50c, Hindoostan, 1842. 60c, St. Geran, 1740. 2.50r, Maen, 1638.

1976, July 2 — Litho. — Wmk. 373

419 A83	10c multicolored	.15	.15
420 A83	15c multicolored	.15	.15
421 A83	50c multicolored	.25	.25
422 A83	60c multicolored	.30	.30
423 A83	2.50r multicolored	1.50	1.50
a.	Souvenir sheet of 5, #419-423	2.25	2.25
	Nos. 419-423 (5)	2.35	2.35

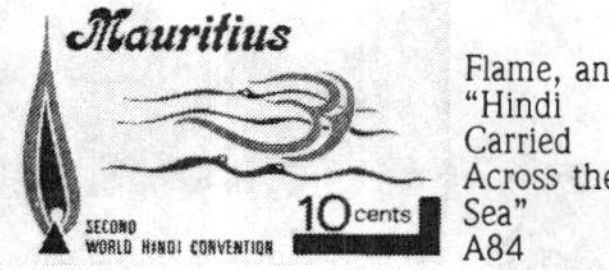

Flame, and "Hindi Carried Across the Sea" A84

Designs: 75c, like 10c. 1.20r, Flame and tablet with Hindi inscription.

1976, Aug. 28 — Perf. 14½x14

424 A84	10c multicolored	.15	.15
425 A84	75c lt blue & multi	.20	.20
426 A84	1.20r multicolored	.35	.35
	Set value	.60	.60

2nd World Hindi Convention.

Commonwealth Emblem, Map of Mauritius — A85

King Priest and Steatite Pectoral — A86

Design: 2.50r, Commonwealth emblem twice.

1976, Sept. 22 — Litho. — Perf. 14x14½

427 A85	1r multicolored	.30	.30
428 A85	2.50r multicolored	.75	.75

22nd Commonwealth Parliamentary Association Conference, Mauritius, Sept. 17-30.

1976, Dec. 15 — Wmk. 373 — Perf. 14

Designs: 1r, House with well, and goblet. 2.50r, Terracotta goddess and necklace.

429 A86	60c multicolored	.15	.15
430 A86	1r multicolored	.30	.30
431 A86	2.50r multicolored	.75	.75
	Nos. 429-431 (3)	1.20	1.20

UNESCO campaign to save Mohenjo-Daro excavations.

Sega Dance A87

1977, Jan. 20 — Litho. — Perf. 13

432 A87	1r multicolored	.25	.25

2nd World Black and African Festival, Lagos, Nigeria, Jan. 15-Feb. 12.

Elizabeth II at Mauritius Legislative Assembly — A88

Designs: 75c, Queen holding scepter and orb. 5r, Presentation of scepter and orb.

1977, Feb. 7 — Perf. 14½x14

433 A88	50c multicolored	.15	.15
434 A88	75c multicolored	.18	.18
435 A88	5r multicolored	1.10	1.10
	Nos. 433-435 (3)	1.43	1.43

25th anniv. of the reign of Elizabeth II.

Hugonia Tomentosa A89

Flowers: 1r, Oehna mauritiana, vert. 1.50r, Dombeya acuntangula. 5r, Trochetia blackburniana, vert.

1977, Sept. 22 — Wmk. 373 — Perf. 14

436 A89	20c multicolored	.15	.15
437 A89	1r multicolored	.35	.35
438 A89	1.50r multicolored	.50	.50
439 A89	5r multicolored	1.50	1.50
a.	Souvenir sheet of 4, #436-439	4.00	4.00
	Nos. 436-439 (4)	2.50	2.50

Twin Otter of Air Mauritius A90

Designs: 50c, Air Mauritius emblem (red-tailed tropic bird) and Twin Otter. 75c, Piper Navajo and Boeing 747. 5r, Air Mauritius Boeing 707 in flight.

1977, Oct. 31 — Litho. — Perf. 14½

440 A90	25c multicolored	.15	.15
441 A90	50c multicolored	.15	.15
442 A90	75c multicolored	.18	.18
443 A90	5r multicolored	1.25	1.25
a.	Souvenir sheet of 4, #440-443	3.50	3.50
	Nos. 440-443 (4)	1.73	1.73

Air Mauritius International Inaugural Flight.

Mauritius, Portuguese Map, 1519 — A91

Dutch Occupation, 1638-1710 — A92

Designs: 20c, Mauritius, map by Van Keulen, c. 1700. 25c, 1st settlement of Rodrigues, 1708. 35c, Proclamation, arrival of French settlers, 1715. 50c, Construction of Port Louis, c. 1736. 60c, Pierre Poivre and nutmeg tree. 70c, Map by Belin, 1763. 75c, First coin minted in Mauritius, 1810. 90c, Naval battle of Grand Port, 1810. 1r, Landing of the British, Nov. 1810. 1.20r, Government House, c. 1840. 1.25r, Invitation with No. 1 and ball of Lady Gomm, 1847. 1.50r, Indian immigration in Mauritius, 1835. 2r, Champ de Mars race course, c. 1870. 3r, Place D'Armes, c. 1880. 5r, Postal card commemorating visit of Prince and Princess of Wales, 1901. 10r, Curepipe College, 1914. 15r, Raising flag of Mauritius, 1968. 25r, Raman Osman, first Governor General and Seewoosagur Ramgoolan, first Prime Minister.

1978, Mar. 12 — Wmk. 373 — Perf. 13½

444 A91	10c multicolored	.15	.15
445 A92	15c multicolored	.15	.15
446 A92	20c multicolored	.15	.15
447 A91	25c multicolored	.15	.15
448 A91	35c multicolored	.15	.15
b.	Perf. 14½, "1986"	.15	.15
449 A92	50c multicolored	.15	.15
450 A91	60c multicolored	.15	.15
451 A92	70c multicolored	.15	.15
452 A91	75c multicolored	.15	.15
453 A92	90c multicolored	.18	.18
454 A92	1r multicolored	.20	.20
455 A92	1.20r multicolored	.25	.25
456 A91	1.25r multicolored	.25	.25
457 A92	1.50r multicolored	.30	.30
458 A92	2r multicolored	.40	.40
459 A92	3r multicolored	.60	.60
460 A92	5r multicolored	1.00	1.00
461 A92	10r multicolored	2.00	2.00
462 A91	15r multicolored	3.00	3.00
463 A92	25r multicolored	5.00	5.00
	Nos. 444-463 (20)	14.53	14.53

Nos. 448, 452, 456, 458 reprinted inscribed 1983; Nos. 444, 447-449, 452, 454, 456, 460 reprinted inscribed 1985.

1985-89 — Wmk. 384 — Perf. 14½

446a A92	20c "1987"	.15	.15
447a A91	25c "1987"	.15	.15
448a A91	35c ('85)	.15	.15
449a A92	50c ('85)	.15	.15
452a A91	75c ('85)	.15	.15
458a A92	2r "1987"	.15	.15
459a A92	3r "1989"	.42	.42
460a A92	5r "1989"	.70	.70
463a A92	25r "1989"	3.45	3.45
	Nos. 446a-463a (9)	5.47	5.47

Issued: 20c, 25c, 2r, 1/11/87; 3r-25r, 1/19/89.

Elizabeth II Coronation Anniv. Issue

Common Design Types

Souvenir Sheet

1978, Apr. 21 — Unwmk. — Perf. 15

464	Sheet of 6	3.25	
a.	CD326 3r Antelope of Bohun	.55	.55
b.	CD327 3r Elizabeth II	.55	.55
c.	CD328 3r Dodo	.55	.55

No. 464 contains 2 se-tenant strips of Nos. 464a-464c, separated by horizontal gutter with commemorative and descriptive inscriptions and showing central part of coronation procession with coach.

Dr. Fleming, WWI Casualty, Bacteria — A93

1r, Microscope & 1st mold growth, 1928. 1.50r, Penicillium notatum, close-up. 5r, Alexander Fleming & nurse administering penicillin.

Perf. 13½

1978, Aug. 3 — Wmk. 373 — Litho.

465 A93	20c multicolored	.15	.15
466 A93	1r multicolored	.20	.20
467 A93	1.50r multicolored	.30	.30
468 A93	5r multicolored	1.75	1.75
a.	Souvenir sheet of 4, #465-468	2.75	2.75
	Nos. 465-468 (4)	2.40	2.40

Discovery of penicillin by Dr. Alexander Fleming, 50th anniversary.

Citrus Butterfly — A94

Wildlife Protection (Wildlife Fund Emblem and): 1r, Geckos. 1.50r, Flying foxes. 5r, Mauritius kestrels.

1978, Sept. 21 — Perf. 13½x14

469 A94	20c multicolored	.50	.50
470 A94	1r multicolored	1.25	1.25
471 A94	1.50r multicolored	2.00	2.00
472 A94	5r multicolored	6.25	6.25
a.	Souvenir sheet of 4, #469-472	18.00	18.00
	Nos. 469-472 (4)	10.00	10.00

Le Reduit — A95

Designs: 15c, Ornate table. 3r, Reduit gardens.

1978, Dec. 21 — Perf. 14½x14

473 A95	15c multicolored	.15	.15
474 A95	75c multicolored	.30	.30
475 A95	3r multicolored	1.00	1.00
	Nos. 473-475 (3)	1.45	1.45

Reconstruction of Chateau Le Reduit, 200th anniversary.

Whitcomb, 1949 A96

Locomotives: 1r, Sir William, 1922. 1.50r, Kitson, 1930. 2r, Garratt, 1927.

1979, Feb. 1 — Perf. 14½

476 A96	20c multicolored	.15	.15
477 A96	1r multicolored	.40	.40
478 A96	1.50r multicolored	.60	.60
479 A96	2r multicolored	.80	.80
a.	Souvenir sheet of 4, #476-479	2.00	2.00
	Nos. 476-479 (4)	1.95	1.95

Father Laval and Crucifix — A97

Designs: 1.50r, Jacques Desire Laval. 5r, Father Laval's sarcophagus, horiz.

1979, Apr. 30 Wmk. 373 *Perf. 14*

480 A97 20c multicolored .15 .15
481 A97 1.50r multicolored .30 .30
482 A97 5r multicolored 1.00 1.00
a. Souvenir sheet of 3, #480-482 1.50 1.50
Nos. 480-482 (3) 1.45 1.45

Beatification of Father Laval (1803-1864), physician and missionary.

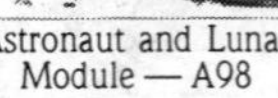

Astronaut and Lunar Module — A98

Rowland Hill and Great Britain No. 23 — A99

Designs: 20c, Neil Armstrong on moon. 5r, Astronaut walking on moon.

Imperf. x Roulette 5

1979, July 20 Litho.

Self-adhesive

483 A98 Souvenir booklet 5.50
a. Bklt. pane of 3 (20c, 5r, 3r) 2.50
b. Bklt. pane of 6 (3 each 20c, 3r) 2.75

10th anniv. of Apollo 11 moon landing. No. 483 contains 2 panes printed on peelable paper backing showing (a) map of moon and (b) details of uniform and spacecraft.

1979, Aug. 29 *Perf. 14½*

Rowland Hill and: 2r, Mauritius No. 261. 3r, Mauritius No. 2. 5r, Mauritius No. 1.

484 A99 25c multicolored .15 .15
485 A99 2r multicolored .40 .40
486 A99 5r multicolored 1.00 1.00
Nos. 484-486 (3) 1.55 1.55

Souvenir Sheet

Imperf

487 A99 3r multicolored .75 .75

Sir Rowland Hill (1795-1879), originator of penny postage. No. 487 contains one stamp.

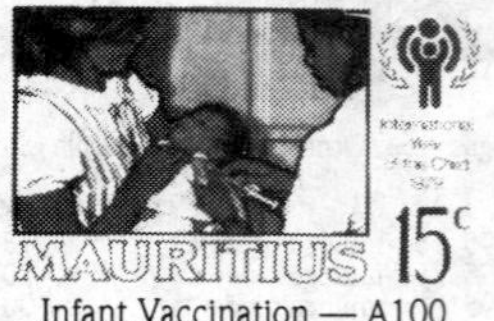

Infant Vaccination — A100

IYC Emblem and: 25c, Children playing. 1r, Coat of arms, vert. 1.50r, Children in laboratory. 3r, Teacher and student working lathe.

Wmk. 373

1979, Oct. 11 Litho. *Perf. 14*

488 A100 15c multicolored .15 .15
489 A100 25c multicolored .15 .15
490 A100 1r multicolored .20 .20
491 A100 1.50r multicolored .30 .30
492 A100 3r multicolored .60 .60
Set value 1.20 1.20

International Year of the Child.

Lienard Obelisk A101

Designs: 25c, Poivre Avenue, 1r, Pandanus. 2r, Giant water lilies, 5r, Mon Plaisir.

1980, Jan. 24 *Perf. 14x14½*

493 A101 20c multicolored .15 .15
494 A101 25c multicolored .15 .15
495 A101 1r multicolored .20 .20
496 A101 2r multicolored .40 .40
497 A101 5r multicolored 1.00 1.00
a. Souvenir sheet of 5, #493-497 1.75 1.75
Nos. 493-497 (5) 1.90 1.90

Pamplemousses Botanical Gardens.

"Emirne," 19th Century, London 1980 Emblem A102

1980, May 6 Litho. *Perf. 14½*

498 A102 25c shown .15 .15
499 A102 1r Boissevain, 1930's .20 .20
500 A102 2r La Boudeuse, 18th cent. .40 .40
501 A102 5r Sea Breeze, 19th cent. 1.00 1.00
Nos. 498-501 (4) 1.75 1.75

London 80 Intl. Stamp Exhib., May 6-14.

Helen Keller Reading Braille — A103

1980, June 27 Litho. *Perf. 14½*

502 A103 25c Blind men weaving baskets .15 .15
503 A103 1r Teacher and deaf girl .25 .25
504 A103 2.50r shown .50 .50
505 A103 5r Keller graduating college 1.00 1.00
Nos. 502-505 (4) 1.90 1.90

Helen Keller (1880-1968), blind and deaf writer and lecturer.

Prime Minister Seewoosagur Ramgoolan, 80th Birthday A104

Litho.; Gold Embossed

1980, Sept. 18 *Perf. 13½*

506 A104 15r multicolored 2.00 2.00

Mauritius Institute, Centenary — A105

1980, Oct. 1 Litho. *Perf. 13*

507 A105 25c shown .15 .15
508 A105 2r Rare Veda copy .40 .40
509 A105 2.50r Rare cone .50 .50
510 A105 5r Landscape, by Henri Harpignies 1.00 1.00
Nos. 507-510 (4) 2.05 2.05

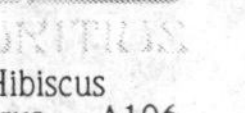

Hibiscus Liliiflorus — A106

Arms of Curepipe — A107

1981, Jan. 15 Litho. *Perf. 14*

511 A106 25c shown .15 .15
512 A106 2r Erythrospermum monticolum .45 .45
513 A106 2.50r Chasalia boryana .55 .55
514 A106 5r Hibiscus columnaris 1.10 1.10
Nos. 511-514 (4) 2.25 2.25

Perf. 13½x13

1981, Apr. 10 Litho. Wmk. 373

Designs: City coats of arms.

515 A107 25c Beau-Bassin / Rose Hill .15 .15
516 A107 1.50r shown .30 .30
517 A107 2r Quatre-Bornes .40 .40
518 A107 2.50r Vacoas/Phoenix .50 .50
519 A107 5r Port Louis 1.00 1.00
a. Souv. sheet of 5, #515-519, perf. 14 2.25 2.25
Nos. 515-519 (5) 2.35 2.35

Royal Wedding Issue

Common Design Type

1981, July 22 Litho. *Perf. 14*

520 CD331 25c Bouquet .15 .15
521 CD331 2.50r Charles .50 .50
522 CD331 10r Couple 2.00 2.00
Nos. 520-522 (3) 2.65 2.65

Emmanuel Anquetil and Guy Rozemont A108

Famous Men: 25c, Remy Ollier, Sookdeo Bissoondoyal. 1.25r, Maurice Cure, Barthelemy Ohsan. 1.50r, Guy Forget, Renganaden Seeneevassen. 2r, Abdul Razak Mohamed, Jules Koenig. 2.50r, Abdoollatiff Mahomed Osman, Dazzi Rama. 5r, Thomas Lewis.

1981, Aug. 13 *Perf. 14½*

523 A108 20c black & red .15 .15
524 A108 25c black & yellow .15 .15
525 A108 1.25r black & green .25 .25
526 A108 1.50r black & vermilion .30 .30
527 A108 2r black & ultra .40 .40
528 A108 2.50r black & red brn .50 .50
529 A108 5r black & blue grn 1.00 1.00
Nos. 523-529 (7) 2.75 2.75

Chinese Pagoda A109

1981, Sept. 16 *Perf. 13½*

530 A109 20c Tamil Women .15 .15
531 A109 2r Swami Sivananda, vert. .40 .40
532 A109 5r shown 1.00 1.00
Nos. 530-532 (3) 1.55 1.55

World Tamil (Hindu sect) Culture Conference, 1980 (20c).

A110

A111

1981, Oct. 26 Litho. *Perf. 14*

533 A110 25c Pottery making .15 .15
534 A110 1.25r Dog grooming .18 .18
535 A110 5r Hiking .75 .75
536 A110 10r Duke of Edinburgh 1.50 1.50
Nos. 533-536 (4) 2.58 2.58

Duke of Edinburgh's Awards, 25th anniv.

1981, Nov. 26 Wmk. 373 *Perf. 14½*

537 A111 25c Holy Ka'aba, Mecca .15 .15
538 A111 2r Prophet's Mosque .40 .40
539 A111 5r Holy Ka'aba, Prophet's Mosque 1.00 1.00
Nos. 537-539 (3) 1.55 1.55

Hegira, 1,500th anniv.

Scouting Year — A112

1982, Feb. 25 Litho. *Perf. 14x14½*

540 A112 25c Emblem .15 .15
541 A112 2r Baden-Powell .35 .35
542 A112 5r Grand howl, sign .85 .85
543 A112 10r Scouts, mountain 1.75 1.75
Nos. 540-543 (4) 3.10 3.10

Darwin Death Centenary A113

1982, Apr. 19 Litho. *Perf. 14*

544 A113 25c Portrait .15 .15
545 A113 2r Telescope .40 .40
546 A113 2.50r Riding elephant .50 .50
547 A113 10r The Beagle 2.00 2.00
Nos. 544-547 (4) 3.05 3.05

Princess Diana Issue

Common Design Type

1982, July 1 Litho. *Perf. 13*

548 CD333 25c Arms .15 .15
549 CD333 2.50r Diana .50 .50
550 CD333 5r Wedding 1.00 1.00
551 CD333 10r Portrait 2.00 2.00
Nos. 548-551 (4) 3.65 3.65

Birth of Prince William of Wales, June 21 — A114

1982, Sept. 22 Litho. *Perf. 14½*

552 A114 2.50r multicolored .60 .60

Issued in sheets of 9.

TB Bacillus Centenary — A115

1982, Dec. 15 *Perf. 14*

553 A115 25c Aphloia theiformis .15 .15
554 A115 1.25r Central Market, Port Louis .24 .24
555 A115 2r Gaertnera psychotrioides .38 .38
556 A115 5r Selaginella deliquescens .85 .85
557 A115 10r Koch 1.90 1.90
Nos. 553-557 (5) 3.52 3.52

A116

1983, Mar. 14 *Perf. 13x13½*

558 A116 25c Flag, arms .15 .15
559 A116 2.50r Satellite view .42 .42
560 A116 5r Sugar cane harvest .85 .85
561 A116 10r Port Louis Harbor 1.75 1.75
Nos. 558-561 (4) 3.17 3.17

Commonwealth Day.

World Communications Year — A117

1983, June 24 **Wmk. 373** *Perf. 14*

562 A117 25c Antique telephone, vert. .15 .15
563 A117 1.25r Early telegraph apparatus .28 .28
564 A117 2r Earth satellite station, vert. .45 .45
565 A117 10r 1st hot air balloon in Mauritius, 1784 2.25 2.25
Nos. 562-565 (4) 3.13 3.13

Namibia Day — A118

1983, Aug. 26

566 A118 25c Map .15 .15
567 A118 2.50r Breaking chains .50 .50
568 A118 5r Family, village 1.00 1.00
569 A118 10r Diamond mining 2.00 2.00
Nos. 566-569 (4) 3.65 3.65

Fishery Resources A119

1983, Oct. 7

570 A119 25c Fish trap, vert. .15 .15
571 A119 1r Fishermen in boat .16 .16
572 A119 5r Game fishing, vert. .80 .80
573 A119 10r Octopus drying 1.75 1.75
Nos. 570-573 (4) 2.86 2.86

Swami Dayananda, Death Centenary — A120

1983, Nov. 3 **Litho.** **Wmk. 373**

574 A120 25c shown .15 .15
575 A120 35c Last meeting with father .15 .15
576 A120 2r Receiving instruction .32 .32
577 A120 5r Demonstrating strength .80 .80
578 A120 10r Religious gathering 1.75 1.75
Nos. 574-578 (5) 3.17 3.17

Adolf von Plevitz (1837-1893), Social Reformer A121

1983, Dec. 8

579 A121 25c shown .15 .15
580 A121 1.25r Government school .42 .42
581 A121 5r Addressing Commission of Enquiry .70 .70
582 A121 10r Indian field workers 1.50 1.50
Nos. 579-582 (4) 2.77 2.77

Mauritius Kestrels A122

1984, Mar. 26 **Wmk. 373** *Perf. 14*

583 A122 25c Courtship chase .15 .15
584 A122 2r Side view, vert. .42 .42
585 A122 2.50r Fledgling .52 .52
586 A122 10r Bird, diff., vert. 2.25 2.25
Nos. 583-586 (4) 3.34 3.34

Lloyd's List Issue
Common Design Type

1984, May 23 **Litho.** *Perf. 14½x14*

587 CD335 25c Tayeb, Port Lewis .15 .15
588 CD335 1r Taher .15 .15
589 CD335 5r East Indiaman Triton .70 .70
590 CD335 10r Astor 1.65 1.65
Nos. 587-590 (4) 2.65 2.65

Palm Trees — A123

Slave Sale — A124

1984, July 23 **Litho.** *Perf. 14*

591 A123 25c Blue latan .15 .15
592 A123 50c Hyophorbe vaughanii .15 .15
593 A123 2.50r Tectiphiala ferox .40 .40
594 A123 5r Round Isld. bottle-palm .80 .80
595 A123 10r Hyophorbe amaricaulis 1.75 1.75
Nos. 591-595 (5) 3.25 3.25

1984, Aug. *Perf. 14½*

596 A124 25c Woman .15 .15
597 A124 1r shown .16 .16
598 A124 2r Family, horiz. .32 .32
599 A124 10r Immigrant arrival, horiz. 1.75 1.75
Nos. 596-599 (4) 2.38 2.38

Alliance Francaise Centenary A125

1984, Sept. 10 *Perf. 14½*

600 A125 25c Production of Faust, 1959 .15 .15
601 A125 1.25r Award ceremony .20 .20
602 A125 5r Headquarters .70 .70
603 A125 10r Lion Mountain 1.50 1.50
Nos. 600-603 (4) 2.55 2.55

Queen Mother 85th Birthday
Common Design Type
Perf. 14½x14

1985, June 7 **Wmk. 384**

604 CD336 25c Portrait, 1926 .15 .15
605 CD336 2r With Princess Margaret .35 .35
606 CD336 5r On Clarence House balcony .90 .90
607 CD336 10r Holding Prince Henry 1.75 1.75
Nos. 604-607 (4) 3.15 3.15

Souvenir Sheet

608 CD336 15r On Royal Barge, reopening Stratford Canal, 1964 2.75 2.75

2nd Annual Indian Ocean Islands Games — A126

Pink Pigeon — A127

1985, Aug. 24 **Wmk. 373** *Perf. 14½*

609 A126 25c High jump .15 .15
610 A126 50c Javelin .15 .15
611 A126 1.25r Cycling .22 .22
612 A126 10r Wind surfing 1.75 1.75
Nos. 609-612 (4) 2.27 2.27

1985, Sept. 2 **Wmk. 384** *Perf. 14*

613 A127 25c Adult and young .15 .15
614 A127 2r Nest site display .65 .65
615 A127 2.50r Nesting .80 .80
616 A127 5r Preening 1.65 1.65
Nos. 613-616 (4) 3.25 3.25

World Wildlife Fund.

World Tourism Org., 10th Anniv. A128

1985, Sept. 20 *Perf. 14½*

617 A128 25c Patates Caverns .15 .15
618 A128 35c Colored Earth, Chamarel .15 .15
619 A128 5r Serpent Island .80 .80
620 A128 10r Coin de Mire Is. 1.75 1.75
Nos. 617-620 (4) 2.85 2.85

Port Louis, 250th Anniv. A129

1985, Nov. 22 *Perf. 13½*

621 A129 25c Old Town Hall .15 .15
622 A129 1r Al-Aqsa Mosque .16 .16
623 A129 2.50r Tamil-speaking Indians, settlement .40 .40
624 A129 10r Port Louis Harbor 1.65 1.65
Nos. 621-624 (4) 2.36 2.36

Halley's Comet A130

1986, Feb. 21 **Wmk. 384** *Perf. 14*

625 A130 25c Halley, map .15 .15
626 A130 1.25r Newton's telescope, 1682 sighting .16 .16
627 A130 3r Mauritius from space .40 .40
628 A130 10r Giotto space probe 1.40 1.40
Nos. 625-628 (4) 2.11 2.11

Queen Elizabeth II 60th Birthday
Common Design Type

Designs: 25c, In uniform, Grenadier Guards, 1942. 75c, Investiture of the Prince of Wales, 1969. 2r, State visit with Prince Philip. 3r, State visit to Germany, 1978. 15r, Visiting Crown Agents' offices, 1983.

1986, Apr. 21 **Litho.** *Perf. 14½x14*

629 CD337 25c scar, black & sil .15 .15
630 CD337 75c ultra & multi .15 .15
631 CD337 2r green & multi .30 .30
632 CD337 3r violet & multi .45 .45
633 CD337 15r rose vio & multi 2.15 2.15
Nos. 629-633 (5) 3.20 3.20

Intl. Events — A131

Orchids — A132

Designs: 25c, World Food Day. 1r, African Regional Industrial Property Organization, 10th anniv. 1.25r, Intl. Peace Year. 10r, 1986 World Cup Soccer Championships.

1986, July 25 **Litho.** *Perf. 14*

634 A131 25c FAO emblem, corn .15 .15
635 A131 1r ARIPO emblem .15 .15
636 A131 1.25r IPY emblem .20 .20
637 A131 10r Athlete, MFA 1.50 1.50
Nos. 634-637 (4) 2.00 2.00

1986, Oct. 3 **Litho.** *Perf. 14½*

638 A132 25c Cryptopus elatus .15 .15
639 A132 2r Jumellea recta .42 .42
640 A132 2.50r Angraecum mauritianum .55 .55
641 A132 10r Bulbophyllum longiflorum 2.25 2.25
Nos. 638-641 (4) 3.37 3.37

Bridges A133

1987, May 22 **Wmk. 373**

642 A133 25c Hesketh Bell .15 .15
643 A133 50c Sir Colville Deverell .15 .15
644 A133 2.50r Cavendish .35 .35
645 A133 5r Tamarin .70 .70
646 A133 10r Grand River North West 1.40 1.40
Nos. 642-646 (5) 2.75 2.75

The Bar, Bicent. A134

Perf. 14x14½

1987, June 2 **Wmk. 384**

647 A134 25c Port Louis Supreme Court .15 .15
648 A134 1r Flacq District Court .15 .15
649 A134 1.25r Statue of Justice .18 .18
650 A134 10r Barristers, 1787-1987 1.40 1.40
Nos. 647-650 (4) 1.88 1.88

Intl. Festival of the Sea — A135

1987, Sept. 5 **Wmk. 373**

651 A135 25c Dodo mascot, vert. .15 .15
652 A135 1.50r Sailboats .22 .22
653 A135 3r Water-skier .42 .42

654 A135 5r Tall ship Svanen, vert. .70 .70
Nos. 651-654 (4) 1.49 1.49

Industrialization — A136

1987, Oct. 30 *Perf. 14*

655 A136 20c Toy .15 .15
656 A136 35c Spinning .15 .15
657 A136 50c Rattan .15 .15
658 A136 2.50r Optical .38 .38
659 A136 10r Stone carving 1.40 1.40
Nos. 655-659 (5) 2.23 2.23

Art & Architecture A137

Designs: 25c, Maison Ouvriere, Intl. Year of Shelter for the Homeless emblem. 1r, Paul et Virginie, a lithograph. 1.25r, Chateau Rosney. 2r, Old Farmhouse, Boulle. 5r, Three Peaks, watercolor.

1988, June 29 Wmk. 384 *Perf. 14½*

660 A137 25c multicolored .15 .15
661 A137 1r gray & black .16 .16
662 A137 1.25r multicolored .20 .20
663 A137 2r multicolored .32 .32
664 A137 5r multicolored .80 .80
Nos. 660-664 (5) 1.63 1.63

Natl. Independence, 20th Anniv. A138

Designs: 25c, University of Mauritius. 75c, Calisthenics at sunset in stadium. 2.50r, Runners, Sir Maurice Rault Stadium. 5r, Air Mauritius jet at gate, Sir Seewoosagur Ramgoolam Intl. Airport. 10r, Gov.-Gen. Veerasamy Ringadoo and Prime Minister Aneerood Jugnauth.

1988, Mar. 11 Wmk. 373 *Perf. 14*

665 A138 25c multicolored .15 .15
666 A138 75c multicolored .15 .15
667 A138 2.50r multicolored .40 .40
668 A138 5r multicolored .80 .80
669 A138 10r multicolored 1.60 1.60
Nos. 665-669 (5) 3.10 3.10

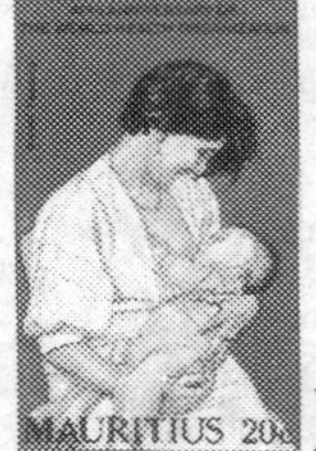
WHO, 40th Anniv. — A139

1988, July 1 Wmk. 373 *Perf. 13½*

670 A139 20c Breast-feeding .15 .15
671 A139 2r Immunization .32 .32
672 A139 3r Nutrition .48 .48
673 A139 10r Emblem 1.55 1.55
Nos. 670-673 (4) 2.50 2.50

Mauritius Commercial Bank, Ltd., 150th Anniv. A140

1988, Sept. 1 Wmk. 373 *Perf. 14*

674 A140 25c Bank, 1981, vert. .15 .15
675 A140 1r Bank, 1897 .15 .15
676 A140 1.25r Coat of arms, vert. .18 .18
677 A140 25r 15-Dollar bank note, 1838 3.65 3.65
Nos. 674-677 (4) 4.13 4.13

1988 Summer Olympics, Seoul — A141

1988, Oct. 1

678 A141 25c shown .15 .15
679 A141 35c Wrestling .15 .15
680 A141 1.50r Running .25 .25
681 A141 10r Swimming 1.55 1.55
Nos. 678-681 (4) 2.10 2.10

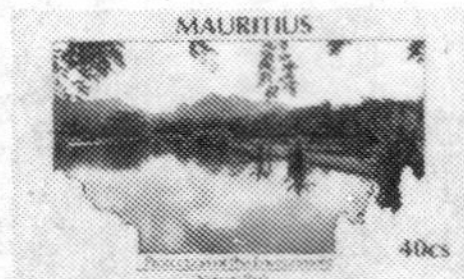

Environmental Protection — A142

Wmk. 384 (20c, 40c, 50c, 1r, 10r), 373 (Others)

1989-96 Litho. *Perf. 14*

682 A142 15c Tropical reef .15 .15
682A A142 20c like #682 .15 .15
683 A142 30c Greenshank .15 .15
684 A142 40c shown .15 .15
a. Wmk. 373 .15 .15
685 A142 50c Round Island, vert. .15 .15
685A A142 60c like #685 .15 .15
686 A142 75c Bassin Blanc .15 .15
688 A142 1r Mangrove, vert. .15 .15
690 A142 1.50r Whimbrel .20 .20
691 A142 2r Le Morne .22 .22
692 A142 3r Fish .45 .45
693 A142 4r Fern tree, vert. .58 .58
694 A142 5r Riviere du Poste Estuary .58 .58
695 A142 6r Ecological scenery, vert. .88 .88
699 A142 10r Phelsuma ornata,vert. 1.45 1.45
700 A142 15r Benares surf 1.75 1.75
701 A142 25r Migratory birds, vert. 3.50 3.50
Nos. 682-701 (17) 10.81 10.81

Issued: 40c, 3r-10r, 3/11/89; #684a, 2/19/91; 50c, 75c, 2r, 5r, 15r, 10/4/91; 20c, 60c, 3/96; others, 11/22/90.

#682, 684a, 693 exist inscribed "1994," #682-683, 699, "1995," #701, "1996," #684, 685A, 699, 701, "1997."

For surcharge see No. 781.

This is an expanding set. Numbers will change if necessary.

A143

A144

French Revolution, Bicent.: 30c, La Tour Sumeire, Place Du Theatre Municipal. 1r, Salle De Spectacle Du Jardin. 8r, Le Comte De Malartic. 15r, Anniv. emblem.

1989, July 14 **Wmk. 373**

702 A143 30c multicolored .15 .15
703 A143 1r multicolored .15 .15
704 A143 8r multicolored 1.10 1.10
705 A143 15r multicolored 2.00 2.00
Nos. 702-705 (4) 3.40 3.40

1989, Oct. 13 *Perf. 14x13½*

Visit of Pope John Paul II: 30c, Cardinal Jean Margeot. 40c, Pope welcoming Prime Minister Aneerood Jugnauth to the Vatican, 1988. 3r, Mother Mary Magdalene of the Cross (1810-1889) and Filles des Marie Chapel, Port Louis, 1864. 6r, St. Francis of Assisi Church, 1756, Pamplemousses. 10r, Pope John Paul II.

706 A144 30c multicolored .15 .15
707 A144 40c multicolored .15 .15
708 A144 3r multicolored .40 .40
709 A144 6r multicolored .80 .80
710 A144 10r multicolored 1.35 1.35
Nos. 706-710 (5) 2.85 2.85

Jawaharlal Nehru, 1st Prime Minister of India A145

Designs: 1.50r, Nehru and Indira, Rajiv and Sanjay Gandhi. 3r, With Mahatma Gandhi. 4r, With Nasser and Tito. 10r, With children.

1989, Oct. 13 Wmk. 384 *Perf. 14*

711 A145 40c shown .15 .15
712 A145 1.50r multicolored .20 .20
713 A145 3r multicolored .40 .40
714 A145 4r multicolored .55 .55
715 A145 10r multicolored 1.35 1.35
Nos. 711-715 (5) 2.65 2.65

Sugar Cane Industry, 350th Anniv. A146

Perf. 13½x14

1990, Jan. 10 Litho. Wmk. 384

716 A146 30c Cutting cane .15 .15
717 A146 40c Refinery, 1867 .15 .15
718 A146 1r Mechanically loading cane .15 .15
719 A146 25r Modern refinery 3.35 3.35
Nos. 716-719 (4) 3.80 3.80

Prime Minister Jugnauth's 60th Birthday A147

Jugnauth: 35c, And symbols of the industrial estate. 40c, At his desk. 1.50r, And stock exchange emblem. 4r, And Gov.-Gen. Ramgoolam. 10r, And Pope John Paul II, map.

Wmk. 373

1990, Mar. 29 Litho. *Perf. 14*

720 A147 35c multicolored .15 .15
721 A147 40c multicolored .15 .15
722 A147 1.50r multicolored .22 .22
723 A147 4r multicolored .55 .55
724 A147 10r multicolored 1.40 1.40
Nos. 720-724 (5) 2.47 2.47

Mauritian Television, 25th Anniv. A148

Anniversaries and Events: 30c, Death of Desjardins, naturalist, 150th anniversary, vert. 6r, Line barracks, 250th anniversary, vert. 8r, Municipality of Curepipe, centenary.

1990, July 5

725 A148 30c lt orange & multi .15 .15
726 A148 35c pink & multi .15 .15
727 A148 6r lt blue & multi .85 .85
728 A148 8r lt green & multi 1.10 1.10
Nos. 725-728 (4) 2.25 2.25

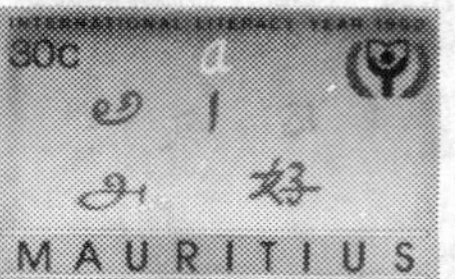

Intl. Literacy Year A149

Wmk. 373

1990, Sept. 28 Litho. *Perf. 14*

729 A149 30c shown .15 .15
730 A149 1r Blind girl printing braille .15 .15
731 A149 3r Globe, open book .42 .42
732 A149 10r Open book, world map 1.40 1.40
Nos. 729-732 (4) 2.12 2.12

Elizabeth & Philip, Birthdays

Common Design Types

Perf. 14½

1991, June 17 Litho. Wmk. 384

733 CD345 8r multicolored .92 .92
734 CD346 8r multicolored .92 .92
a. Pair, #733-734 + label 1.84 1.84

Port Louis, City Incorporation, 25th Anniv. — A150

Anniversaries and Events: 4r, Col. Draper, 150th death anniv., vert. 6r, Joseph Barnard, engraver of first Mauritius stamps, 175th birth anniv., vert. 10r, Spitfire, Mauritius' contribution to Allied war effort, 1939-1945.

Wmk. 373

1991, Aug. 18 Litho. *Perf. 14*

735 A150 40c multicolored .15 .15
736 A150 4r multicolored .45 .45
737 A150 6r multicolored .70 .70
738 A150 10r multicolored 1.15 1.15
Nos. 735-738 (4) 2.45 2.45

Phila Nippon '91 — A151

Butterflies: 40c, Euploea euphon. 3r, Hypolimnas misippus, female. 8r, Papilio manlius. 10r, Hypolimnas misippus, male.

Perf. 14x14½

1991, Nov. 15 Litho. Wmk. 373

739 A151 40c multicolored .15 .15
740 A151 3r multicolored .35 .35
741 A151 8r multicolored .95 .95
742 A151 10r multicolored 1.15 1.15
Nos. 739-742 (4) 2.60 2.60

Flora and Fauna From Island States of Mauritius A152

Designs: 40c, Chelonia mydas, Tromelin. 1r, Ibis, Agalega. 2r, Takamaka flowers, Chagos Archipelago. 15r, Lambis violacea, St. Brandon.

1991, Dec. 13 *Perf. 14*

743 A152 40c multicolored .15 .15
744 A152 1r multicolored .15 .15
745 A152 2r multicolored .22 .22
746 A152 15r multicolored 1.70 1.70
Nos. 743-746 (4) 2.22 2.22

Republic

Proclamation of the Republic of Mauritius — A153

1992, Mar. 12

747 A153 40c President .15 .15
748 A153 4r Prime Minister .45 .45
749 A153 8r Mauritian children .95 .95
750 A153 10r President's flag 1.15 1.15
Nos. 747-750 (4) 2.70 2.70

8th African Track and Field Championships A154

Designs: 40c, Games mascot, Tricolo. 4r, Sir Anerood Jugnauth Stadium, horiz. 5r, High jumper, horiz. 6r, Torch, emblem of games.

1992, June 25 *Perf. 13½*

751	A154	40c multicolored	.15	.15
752	A154	4r multicolored	.45	.45
753	A154	5r multicolored	.58	.58
754	A154	6r multicolored	.70	.70
		Nos. 751-754 (4)	1.88	1.88

Anniversaries and Events — A155

Designs: 40c, Flower, vert. 1r, Swami Krishnanandji Maharaj, vert. 2r, Boy and dog. 3r, Building, flags. 15r, Radio telescope antennae.

1992, Aug. 13

755	A155	40c multicolored	.15	.15
756	A155	1r multicolored	.15	.15
757	A155	2r multicolored	.28	.28
758	A155	3r multicolored	.40	.40
759	A155	15r multicolored	2.00	2.00
		Nos. 755-759 (5)	2.98	2.98

Fleurir Maurice, 25th anniv. (#755). 25th anniv. of Swami Maharaj's arrival (#756). Humane education (#757). Indian Ocean Commission, 10th anniv. (#758). Inauguration of radio telescope project (#759).

Bank of Mauritius, Silver Jubilee A156

Designs: 40c, Bank of Mauritius building, vert. 4r, Dodo gold bullion coin. 8r, First bank note issues. 15r, Foreign exchange reserves 1967-1992.

Perf. 14½x14, 14x14½

1992, Oct. 29 **Litho.** **Wmk. 373**

760	A156	40c multicolored	.15	.15
761	A156	4r multicolored	.52	.52
762	A156	8r multicolored	1.10	1.10
763	A156	15r multicolored	2.00	2.00
		Nos. 760-763 (4)	3.77	3.77

National Day, 25th Anniv. — A157

Designs: 30c, Housing development. 40c, Computer showing gross domestic product. 3r, Flag in shape of map of Mauritius. 4r, Ballot box. 15r, Medal for Grand Commander of the Order of the Star and Key of the Indian Ocean.

1993, Mar. 12 *Perf. 15x14*

764	A157	30c multicolored	.15	.15
765	A157	40c multicolored	.15	.15
766	A157	3r multicolored	.35	.35
767	A157	4r multicolored	.48	.48
768	A157	15r multicolored	1.75	1.75
		Nos. 764-768 (5)	2.88	2.88

Air Mauritius Ltd., 25th Anniv. A158

Designs: 40c, Bell 206B Jet Ranger. 3r, Boeing 747SP. 4r, ATR 42. 10r, Boeing 767-200ER.

1993, June 14 *Perf. 14*

769	A158	40c multicolored	.15	.15
770	A158	3r multicolored	.35	.35
771	A158	4r multicolored	.45	.45
772	A158	10r multicolored	1.15	1.15
a.		Souvenir sheet of 4, #769-772	2.10	2.10
		Nos. 769-772 (4)	2.10	2.10

5th Francophone Summit — A159

Designs: 1r, 1715 Act of French Seizure of Mauritius, 1810 Act of Surrender. 5r, Signs. 6r, Page from Napoleonic Code. 7r, French publications.

1993, Oct. 16

773	A159	1r multicolored	.15	.15
774	A159	5r multicolored	.60	.60
775	A159	6r multicolored	.70	.70
776	A159	7r multicolored	.80	.80
		Nos. 773-776 (4)	2.25	2.25

Telecommunications — A160

Designs: 40c, SS Scotia, cable laying. 3r, Morse code, Morse key. 4r, Signal mountain station. 8r, Communications satellite.

1993, Nov. 25 *Perf. 13*

777	A160	40c multicolored	.15	.15
778	A160	3r multicolored	.35	.35
779	A160	4r multicolored	.50	.50
780	A160	8r multicolored	1.00	1.00
		Nos. 777-780 (4)	2.00	2.00

No. 686 Surcharged

40cs ═

1993, Sept. 15 **Litho.** *Perf. 14*

781	A142	40c on 75c multi	.15	.15

Mammals A161

Perf. 14½

1994, Mar. 9 **Litho.** **Wmk. 384**

782	A161	40c Mongoose	.15	.15
783	A161	2r Hare	.22	.22
784	A161	8r Monkey	.90	.90
785	A161	10r Tenrec	1.10	1.10
		Nos. 782-785 (4)	2.37	2.37

Anniversaries and Events — A162

Designs: 40c, Dr. E. Brown-Sequard (1817-94). 4r, Silhouettes of family. 8r, World Cup trophy, US map. 10r, Control Tower, SSR Intl. Airport.

Wmk. 373

1994, June 16 **Litho.** *Perf. 14*

786	A162	40c multicolored	.15	.15
787	A162	4r multicolored	.45	.45
788	A162	8r multicolored	.90	.90
789	A162	10r multicolored	1.10	1.10
		Nos. 786-789 (4)	2.60	2.60

Intl. Year of the Family (#787). 1994 World Cup Soccer Championships, US (#788). ICAO, 50th anniv. (#789).

Wreck of the St. Geran, 250th Anniv. A163

Wmk. 384

1994, Aug. 18 **Litho.** *Perf. 14*

790	A163	40c Leaving L'Orient	.15	.15
791	A163	5r In rough seas	.55	.55
792	A163	6r Ship's bell	.65	.65
793	A163	10r Relics from ship	1.10	1.10
		Nos. 790-793 (4)	2.45	2.45

Souvenir Sheet

794	A163	15r St. Geran, vert.	1.65	1.65

Children's Paintings of Leisure Activities A164

Designs: 30c, "Ring Around the Rosey." 40c, Playing with balls, jump rope. 8r, Water sports. 10r, "Blindman's Buff."

Perf. 13½

1994, Oct. 25 **Litho.** **Wmk. 373**

795	A164	30c multicolored	.15	.15
796	A164	40c multicolored	.15	.15
797	A164	8r multicolored	.90	.90
798	A164	10r multicolored	1.10	1.10
		Nos. 795-798 (4)	2.30	2.30

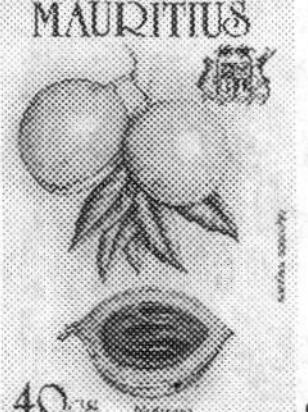

Spices — A165

Perf. 13x14

1995, Mar. 10 **Litho.** **Wmk. 373**

799	A165	40c Nutmeg	.15	.15
800	A165	4r Coriander	.45	.45
801	A165	5r Cloves	.55	.55
802	A165	10r Cardamon	1.10	1.10
		Nos. 799-802 (4)	2.25	2.25

End of World War II

Common Design Type

Designs: No. 803, HMS Mauritius. No. 304, Mauritian servicemen, map of North Africa. No. 305, Catalina, Tombeau Bay.

Wmk. 373

1995, May 8 **Litho.** *Perf. 14*

Size: 35x28mm

803	CD351	5r multicolored	.55	.55
804	CD351	5r multicolored	.55	.55
805	CD351	5r multicolored	.55	.55
		Nos. 803-805 (3)	1.65	1.65

Anniversaries & Events A166

1995, May 8

806	A166	40c multicolored	.15	.15
807	A166	4r multicolored	.45	.45
808	A166	10r multicolored	1.10	1.10
		Nos. 806-808 (3)	1.70	1.70

Construction of Mare Longue Reservoir, 50th anniv. (#806). Construction of Mahebourg-Curepipe Road, bicent. (#807). Great fire of Port Louis, cent. (#808).

A167 A168

Designs: Lighthouses.

Perf. 13x14

1995, Aug. 28 **Litho.** **Wmk. 373**

809	A167	30c Ile Plate	.15	.15
810	A167	40c Pointe aux Caves	.15	.15
811	A167	8r Ile aux Fouquets	.90	.90
812	A167	10r Pointe aux Canonniers	1.10	1.10
a.		Souvenir sheet of 4, #809-812	2.25	2.25
		Nos. 809-812 (4)	2.30	2.30

UN, 50th Anniv.

Common Design Type

Designs: 40c, Silhouettes of children under UNICEF umbrella. 4r, ILO contruction site. 8r, WMO satellite view of hurricane. 10r, Bread, grain representing FAO.

Wmk. 373

1995, Oct. 24 **Litho.** *Perf. 14*

813	CD353	40c multicolored	.15	.15
814	CD353	4r multicolored	.45	.45
815	CD353	8r multicolored	.90	.90
816	CD353	10r multicolored	1.10	1.10
		Nos. 813-816 (4)	2.60	2.60

1995, Dec. 8 **Litho.** *Perf. 13*

817	A168	60c pink & multi	.15	.15
818	A168	4r blue & multi	.45	.45
819	A168	8r yellow & multi	.90	.90
820	A168	10r green & multi	1.10	1.10
		Nos. 817-820 (4)	2.60	2.60

Common Market for Eastern and Southern Africa (COMESA).

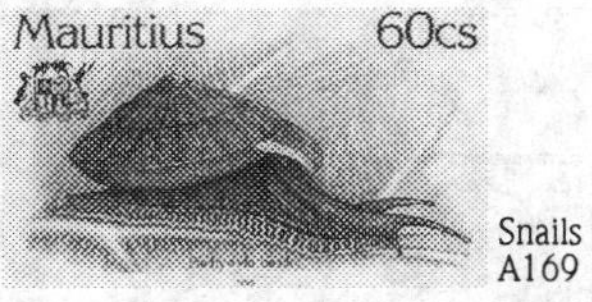

Snails A169

Designs: 60c, Pachystyla bicolor. 4r, Gonidomus pagodus. 5r, Harmogenanina implicata. 10r, Tropidophora eugeniae.

Wmk. 373

1996, Mar. 11 **Litho.** *Perf. 13*

821	A169	60c multicolored	.15	.15
822	A169	4r multicolored	.40	.40
823	A169	5r multicolored	.50	.50
824	A169	10r multicolored	1.00	1.00
		Nos. 821-824 (4)	2.05	2.05

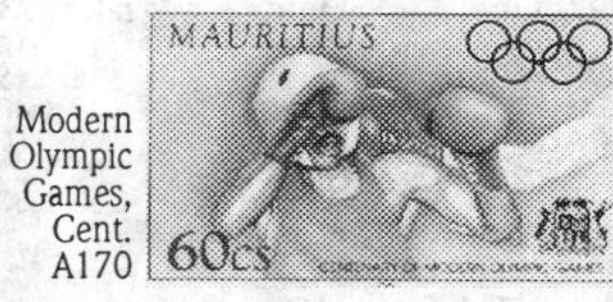

Modern Olympic Games, Cent. A170

Perf. 13½

1996, June 26 **Litho.** **Wmk. 384**

825	A170	60c Boxing	.15	.15
826	A170	4r Badminton	.40	.40
827	A170	5r Basketball	.50	.50
828	A170	10r Table tennis	1.00	1.00
		Nos. 825-828 (4)	2.05	2.05

Ships A171

Wmk. 373

1996, Sept. 30 Litho. *Perf. 14*

829	A171	60c SS Zambezia	.15	.15
830	A171	4r MV Sir Jules	.40	.40
831	A171	5r MV Mauritius	.50	.50
832	A171	10r MS Mauritius Pride	1.00	1.00
a.		Souvenir sheet of 4, #829-832	2.05	2.05
		Nos. 829-832 (4)	2.05	2.05

Post Office Ordinance, 150th Anniv. — A172

Perf. 13½

1996, Dec. 2 Litho. Wmk. 384

833	A172	60c Pillar box	.15	.15
834	A172	4r Early handstamp cancel	.40	.40
835	A172	5r Mobile post office	.50	.50
836	A172	10r Carriole	1.00	1.00
		Nos. 833-836 (4)	2.05	2.05

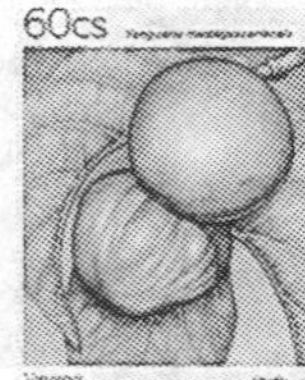

Fruit — A173

Designs: 60c, Vangueria madgascariensis. 4r, Mimusops coriacea. 5r, Syzgium jambos. 10r, Diospyros digyna.

Perf. 14x13½

1997, Mar. 10 Litho. Wmk. 373

837	A173	60c multicolored	.15	.15
838	A173	4r multicolored	.40	.40
839	A173	5r multicolored	.50	.50
840	A173	10r multicolored	1.00	1.00
		Nos. 837-840 (4)	2.05	2.05

Anniversaries and Events — A174

Designs: 60c, Ile de France, Mahé de La Bourdonnais. 1r, Exploration, La Perouse. 4r, Lady Gomm's Ball, Sir William Maynard Gomm. 6r, Skeleton of the Dodo, George Clark. 10r, Professor Brian Abel-Smith.

Perf. 13½

1997, June 9 Litho. Wmk. 373

841	A174	60c multicolored	.15	.15
842	A174	1r multicolored	.15	.15
843	A174	4r multicolored	.40	.40
844	A174	6r multicolored	.60	.60
845	A174	10r multicolored	1.00	1.00
		Nos. 841-845 (5)	2.30	2.30

First Postage Stamps of Mauritius, 150th Anniv. A175

Stamps: 60c, #1. 4r, #2. 5r, #2, #1, gold background. 10r, #1, #2, silver background.
20r, #2, #1 on "The Bordeaux Cover."

Perf. 13½

1997, Sept. 22 Litho. Wmk. 373

846	A175	60c multicolored	.15	.15
847	A175	4r multicolored	.35	.35
a.		Sheet of 12, 7 #846, 5 #847	2.25	2.25
848	A175	5r multicolored	.45	.45
849	A175	10r multicolored	.90	.90
		Nos. 846-849 (4)	1.85	1.85

Souvenir Sheet

850	A175	20r multicolored	1.80	1.80

Booklet Panes and Booklets

846a	Booklet pane of 10	1.00
	Complete booklet, #846a	1.00
847b	Booklet pane of 10	3.50
	Complete booklet, #847b	3.50
848a	Booklet pane of 10	4.50
	Complete booklet, #848a	4.50
849a	Booklet pane of 10	9.00
	Complete booklet, #849a	9.00

Local Occupations — A176

Perf. 14½

1997, Dec. 1 Litho. Wmk. 373

851	A176	60c Wheelwright	.15	.15
852	A176	4r Washerman	.35	.35
853	A176	5r Shipwright	.45	.45
854	A176	15r Quarryman	1.40	1.40
		Nos. 851-854 (4)	2.35	2.35

SPECIAL DELIVERY STAMPS

SD1

1903 Wmk. 1 *Perf. 14*

Red Surcharge

E1	SD1	15c on 15c ultra	9.00	10.00

SD2

SD3

1904

E2	SD2	15c on 15c ultra	15.00	14.00
a.		"INLAND" inverted	175.00	175.00
b.		Inverted "A" in "INLAND"	250.00	250.00
E3	SD3	15c on 15c ultra	8.00	2.00
a.		Double surcharge	175.00	
b.		Inverted surcharge		*175.00*
c.		No period after "c"	150.00	150.00

To make No. E2 the word "INLAND" was printed on No. E1. For No. E3 a new setting of the surcharge was made with different spacing between the words.

SD4

SD5

E4	SD4	15c green & red	5.00	2.50
a.		Double surcharge	150.00	150.00
b.		Inverted surcharge	100.00	100.00
c.		"LNIAND."	125.00	125.00
d.		As "c," double surcharge	*450.00*	
E5	SD5	18c green & black	3.50	5.00
a.		Exclamation point (!) instead of "I" in "FOREIGN"	200.00	

POSTAGE DUE STAMPS

Catalogue values for unused stamps in this section are for Never Hinged items.

Numeral — D1

Perf. 14½x14

1933-54 Typo. Wmk. 4

J1	D1	2c black	.15	.15
J2	D1	4c violet	.15	.15
J3	D1	6c red	.20	*.70*
J4	D1	10c green	.30	*.60*
J5	D1	20c ultramarine	.45	*1.50*
J6	D1	50c dp red lilac ('54)	.90	*2.25*
J7	D1	1r orange ('54)	.90	*3.75*
		Nos. J1-J7 (7)	3.05	*9.10*

1966-68 Wmk. 314 *Perf. 14*

J8	D1	2c black ('67)	.15	.15

Perf. 14½14

J9	D1	4c rose violet ('68)	.15	.15
J10	D1	6c dp orange ('68)	.15	.15
J11	D1	10c yel green ('67)	.15	.15
J12	D1	20c ultramarine	.25	.20
J13	D1	50c dp red lilac ('68)	.65	.35
		Nos. J8-J13 (6)	1.50	1.15

Nos. 445-446, 450, 455, 457, 462 Surcharged "POSTAGE/ DUE" and New Value

Perf. 13½

1982, Oct. 25 Litho. Wmk. 373

J14	A92	10c on 15c multi	.15	.15
J15	A92	20c on 20c multi	.15	.15
J16	A91	50c on 60c multi	.15	.15
J17	A92	1r on 1.20r multi	.20	.20
J18	A92	1.50r on 1.50r multi	.25	.25
J19	A91	5r on 15r multi	.75	.75
		Nos. J14-J19 (6)	1.65	1.65

MAYOTTE

mä-'yät

LOCATION — One of the Comoro Islands situated in the Mozambique Channel midway between Madagascar and Mozambique (Africa)
GOVT. — French Colony
AREA — 140 sq. mi.
POP. — 13,783 (1914)
CAPITAL — Dzaoudzi
See Comoro Islands

100 Centimes = 1 Franc

See France No. 2271 for French stamp inscribed "Mayotte."

Catalogue values for unused stamps in this country are for Never Hinged items, beginning with Scott 75 in the regular postage section, and Scott C1 in the airpost section.

Navigation and Commerce — A1

Perf. 14x13½

1892-1907 Typo. Unwmk.

Name of Colony in Blue or Carmine

1	A1	1c blk, *lil bl*	.40	.40
2	A1	2c brn, *buff*	.50	.50
a.		Name double	275.00	275.00
3	A1	4c claret, *lav*	.70	.60
4	A1	5c grn, *grnsh*	1.50	1.25
5	A1	10c blk, *lavender*	1.90	1.50
6	A1	10c red ('00)	30.00	24.00
7	A1	15c blue, quadrille paper	7.00	4.00
8	A1	15c gray ('00)	57.50	47.50
9	A1	20c red, *grn*	6.00	4.00
10	A1	25c blk, *rose*	4.50	3.50
11	A1	25c blue ('00)	6.00	3.50
12	A1	30c brn, *bis*	9.00	5.50
13	A1	35c blk, *yel*	*3.50*	3.50
14	A1	40c red, *straw*	6.00	5.50
15	A1	45c blk, *gray grn* ('07)	7.00	5.50
16	A1	50c carmine, *rose*	13.00	9.00
17	A1	50c brn, *az* ('00)	10.00	10.00
18	A1	75c dp vio, *org*	13.00	8.00
19	A1	1fr brnz grn, *straw*	10.00	9.00
20	A1	5fr red lil, *lav* ('99)	82.50	65.00
		Nos. 1-20 (20)	270.00	211.75

Perf. 13½x14 stamps are counterfeits.

Issues of 1892-1907 Surcharged in Black or Carmine

05 **10**

1912

22	A1	5c on 2c brn, *buff*	1.25	1.25
23	A1	5c on 4c cl, *lav* (C)	.65	.65
24	A1	5c on 15c bl (C)	.60	.60
25	A1	5c on 20c red, *grn*	.65	.65
26	A1	5c on 25c blk, *rose* (C)	.75	.75
a.		Double surcharge	125.00	
27	A1	5c on 30c brn, *bis* (C)	.70	.70
28	A1	10c on 40c red, *straw*	.70	.70
a.		Double surcharge	175.00	
29	A1	10c on 45c blk, *gray grn* (C)	.70	.70
a.		Double surcharge	175.00	
30	A1	10c on 50c car, *rose*	1.65	1.65
31	A1	10c on 75c dp vio, *org*	.90	.90
32	A1	10c on 1fr brnz grn, *straw*	1.10	1.10
		Nos. 22-32 (11)	9.65	9.65

Two spacings between the surcharged numerals are found on Nos. 22-32.

Nos. 22-32 were available for use in Madagascar and the entire Comoro archipelago.

Stamps of Mayotte were replaced successively by those of Madagascar, Comoro Islands and France.

Catalogue values for unused stamps in this section, from this point to the end of the section, are for Never Hinged items.

Marianne Type of France Ovtpd. "MAYOTTE"

1997, Jan. 2 Engr. *Perf. 13*

75	A1161	10c on No. 2179	.15	.15
76	A1161	20c on No. 2180	.15	.15
77	A1161	50c on No. 2181	.20	.20
78	A1161	1fr on No. 2182	.40	.40
79	A1161	2fr on No. 2331	.80	.80
80	A1161	(2.50fr) on No. 2342	1.00	1.00
81	A1161	2.70fr on No. 2334	1.10	1.10
82	A1161	3.80fr on No. 2337	1.50	1.50
83	A1161	5fr on No. 2194	2.50	2.50
84	A1161	10fr on No. 2195	5.00	5.00
		Nos. 75-84 (10)	12.80	12.80

Ylang Ylang — A5

1997, Jan. 2 Litho. *Perf. 13½x13*

85	A5	2.70fr multicolored	1.25	1.25

Coat of Arms — A6

1997, Jan. 2 *Perf. 13x13½*

86	A6	3fr multicolored	1.50	1.50

Le Banga — A7

1997, May 31 Litho. *Perf. 13*
87 A7 3.80fr multicolored 1.40 1.40

Dzen Dzé Musical Instrument A8

Photo. & Engr.
1997, May 31 *Perf. 12½*
88 A8 5.20fr multicolored 2.00 2.00

Lemur — A9

1997, Aug. 30 Engr. *Perf. 12*
89 A9 3fr red & dk brown 1.10 1.10

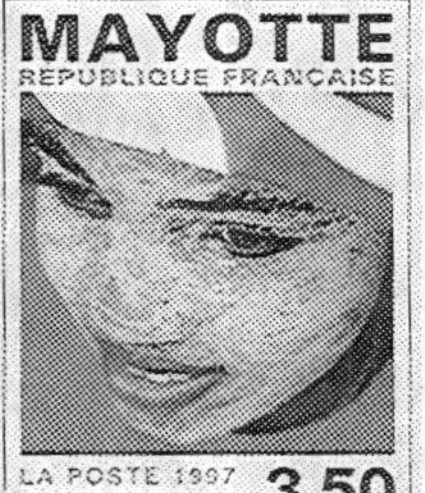

Face of a Woman A10

1997, Aug. 30 Litho. *Perf. 13*
90 A10 3.50fr multicolored 1.25 1.25

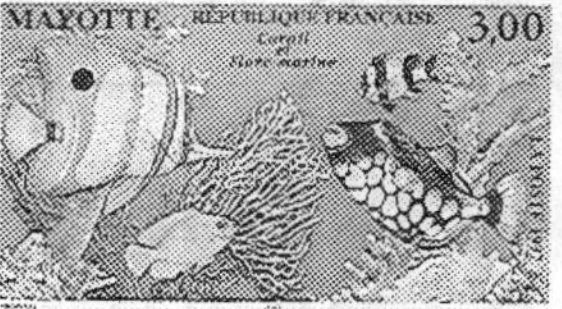

Marine Life — A11

1997, Nov. 29 Litho. *Perf. 13*
91 A11 3fr multicolored 1.10 1.10

AIR POST STAMPS

Catalogue values for unused stamps in this section are for Never Hinged items.

Opening of New Air Terminal — AP1

1997, Mar. 1 Engr. *Perf. 13x12½*
C1 AP1 20fr multicolored 9.00 9.00

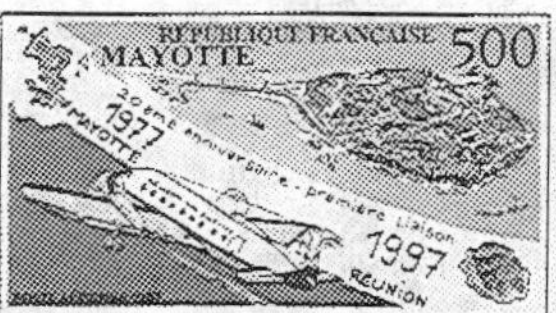

First Mayotte-Réunion Flight, 20th Anniv. — AP2

Photo. & Engr.
1997, Nov. 29 *Perf. 13x12½*
C2 AP2 5fr multicolored 1.75 1.75

MEMEL

'mā–məl

LOCATION — In northern Europe, bordering on the Baltic Sea
GOVT. — Special commission (see below)
AREA — 1099 sq. mi.
POP. — 151,960

Following World War I this territory was detached from Germany and by Treaty of Versailles assigned to the government of a commission of the Allied and Associated Powers (not the League of Nations), which administered it until January, 1923, when it was forcibly occupied by Lithuania. In 1924 Memel became incorporated as a semi-autonomous district of Lithuania with the approval of the Allied Powers and the League of Nations.

100 Pfennig = 1 Mark
100 Centu = 1 Litas (1923)

Stamps of Germany, 1905-20, Overprinted **Memel-gebiet**

Wmk. Lozenges (125)
1920, Aug. 1 *Perf. 14, 14½*

1	A16	5pf green	.35	.35
2	A16	10pf car rose	2.50	5.00
3	A16	10pf orange	.15	.35
4	A22	15pf violet brown	2.50	2.50
5	A16	20pf blue violet	.45	.60
6	A16	30pf org & blk, *buff*	1.25	1.90
7	A16	30pf dull blue	.15	.30
8	A16	40pf lake & blk	.15	.15
9	A16	50pf pur & blk, *buff*	.15	.15
10	A16	60pf olive green	.60	1.75
11	A16	75pf grn & blk	3.00	4.00
12	A16	80pf blue violet	1.00	2.25

Overprinted **Memelgebiet**

13	A17	1m car rose	.25	.45
14	A17	1.25m green	13.00	18.00
15	A17	1.50m yel brn	4.00	6.00
16	A21	2m blue	2.00	2.75
17	A21	2.50m red lilac	11.00	20.00
		Nos. 1-17 (17)	42.50	66.50

Stamps of France, Surcharged in Black

On A22 **MEMEL 5 pfennig**

On A18 **MEMEL 60 pfennig**

1920 Unwmk. *Perf. 14x13½*

18	A22	5pf on 5c green	.15	.15
19	A22	10pf on 10c red	.15	.15
20	A22	20pf on 25c blue	.15	.15
21	A22	30pf on 30c org	.15	.15
22	A22	40pf on 20c red brn	.15	.15
23	A22	50pf on 35c vio	.15	.30
24	A18	60pf on 40c red & pale bl	.25	.40
25	A18	80pf on 45c grn & bl	.20	.20
26	A18	1m on 50c brn & lav	.15	.20
27	A18	1m 25pf on 60c vio & ultra	1.25	1.65
28	A18	2m on 1fr cl & ol grn	.25	.25
29	A18	3m on 5fr bl & buff	15.00	20.00
		Nos. 18-29 (12)	18.00	23.75

For stamps with additional surcharges and overprints see Nos. 43-49, C1-C4.

French Stamps of 1900-20 Surcharged like Nos. 24 to 29 in Red or Black

4 Type I **4** Type II — Four Marks

1920-21 Unwmk. *Perf. 14x13½*

30	A18	3m on 2fr org & pale bl	12.50	20.00
31	A18	4m on 2fr org & pale bl (I) (Bk)	.25	.25
a.		Type II	50.00	*125.00*
32	A18	10m on 5fr bl & buff	2.25	3.25
33	A18	20m on 5fr bl & buff	40.00	40.00
		Nos. 30-33 (4)	55.00	63.50

For stamps with additional overprints see Nos. C5, C19.

New Value with Initial Capital

1921

39	A18	60Pf on 40c red & pale bl	4.00	7.50
40	A18	3M on 60c vio & ultra	1.00	.70
41	A18	10M on 5fr bl & buff	1.00	1.10
42	A18	20M on 45c grn & bl	4.00	6.00
		Nos. 39-42 (4)	10.00	15.30

The surcharged value on No. 40 is in italics.
For stamps with additional overprints see Nos. C6-C7, C18.

Stamps of 1920 Surcharged with Large Numerals in Dark Blue or Red

1921-22

43	A22	15pf on 10pf on 10c	.15	.45
a.		Inverted surcharge	60.00	85.00
44	A22	15pf on 20pf on 25c	.20	.50
a.		Inverted surcharge	60.00	85.00
45	A22	15pf on 50pf on 35c (R)	.15	.30
a.		Inverted surcharge	60.00	85.00
46	A22	60pf on 40pf on 20c	.15	.30
a.		Inverted surcharge	60.00	85.00
47	A18	75pf on 60pf on 40c	.50	.80
48	A18	1.25m on 1m on 50c	.15	.40
49	A18	5.00m on 2m on 1fr	.70	1.25
a.		Inverted surcharge	275.00	300.00
		Nos. 43-49 (7)	2.00	4.00

Stamps of France Surcharged in Black or Red

On A22 **MEMEL 5 Pfennig**

On A18 ***MEMEL* 40 Pfennig**

1922

50	A22	5pf on 5c org	.15	.30
51	A22	10pf on 10c red	.50	2.00
52	A22	10pf on 10c grn	.15	.30
53	A22	15pf on 10c grn	.20	.35
54	A22	20pf on 20c red brn	6.50	7.00
55	A22	20pf on 25c bl	6.50	7.00
56	A22	25pf on 5c org	.15	.15
57	A22	30pf on 30c red	.35	1.50
58	A22	35pf on 35c vio	.15	.15
59	A22	50pf on 50c dl bl	.15	.20
60	A22	75pf on 15c grn	.15	.15
61	A22	75pf on 35c vio	.15	.20
62	A22	1m on 25c blue	.15	.15
63	A22	1¼m on 30c red	.15	.15
64	A22	3m on 5c org	.15	.75
65	A22	6m on 15c grn (R)	.25	.60
66	A22	8m on 30c red	.20	.80

Type A18

67		40pf on 40c red & pale bl	.15	.20
68		80pf on 45c grn & bl	.15	.20
69		1m on 40c red & pale bl	.15	.20
70		1.25m on 60c vio & ultra (R)	.15	.20
71		1.50m on 45c grn & bl (R)	.15	.20
72		2m on 45c grn & bl	.15	.15
73		2m on 1fr cl & ol grn	.15	.20
74		2¼m on 40c red & pale bl	.15	.15
75		2½m on 60c vio & ultra	.20	.35
76		3m on 60c vio & ultra (R)	.45	.70
77		4m on 45c grn & bl	.15	.15
78		5m on 1fr cl & ol grn	.20	.35
79		6m on 60c vio & ultra	.15	.15
80		6m on 2fr org & pale bl	.20	.40
81		9m on 1fr cl & ol grn	.25	.30
82		9m on 5fr bl & buff (R)	.30	.55
83		10m on 45c grn & bl (R)	.20	.45
84		12m on 40c red & pale bl	.25	.35
85		20m on 40c red & pale bl	.20	.45
86		20m on 2fr org & pale bl	.25	.35
87		30m on 60c vio & ultra	.20	.45
88		30m on 5fr dk bl & buff	2.50	6.50
89		40m on 1fr cl & ol grn	.20	.50
90		50m on 2fr org & pale bl	10.00	18.00
91		80m on 2fr org & pale bl (R)	.50	1.75
92		100m on 5fr bl & buff	.30	3.00
		Nos. 50-92 (43)	33.70	58.00

Nos. 59, 60 and 65 are on France type A20.
A 500m on 5fr dark blue and buff was prepared, but not officially issued. Value, $750.
For stamps with additional surcharges and overprints see Nos. 93-99, C8-C17, C20-29C.

Nos. 52, 54, 67, 59 Surcharged "Mark"

1922-23

93	A22	10m on 10pf on 10c	.80	3.50
a.		Double surcharge	125.00	140.00
94	A22	20m on 20pf on 20c	.60	.85
95	A18	40m on 40pf on 40c ('23)	.60	1.40
96	A20	50m on 50pf on 50c	2.00	6.25
		Nos. 93-96 (4)	4.00	12.00

Nos. 72, 61, 70 Surcharged with New Values in Red or Black

1922-23

97	A18	10m on 2m on 45c	1.00	3.00
98	A22	25m on 1m on 25c	1.00	3.00
99	A18	80m on 1.25m on 60c (Bk) ('23)	.50	1.75
		Nos. 97-99 (3)	2.50	7.75

For No. 99 with additional surcharges see Nos. N28-N30.

AIR POST STAMPS

Nos. 24-26, 28, 31, 39-40 Overprinted in Dark Blue

1921, July 6 Unwmk. *Perf. 14x13½*

C1	A18	60pf on 40c	37.50	45.00
C2	A18	80pf on 45c	2.75	3.50
C3	A18	1m on 50c	2.75	3.50
C4	A18	2m on 1fr	2.75	4.00
a.		"Flugpost" inverted	200.00	240.00
C5	A18	4m on 2fr (I)	4.25	6.25
a.		Type II	200.00	240.00

New Value with Initial Capital

C6	A18	60Pf on 40c	3.75	4.75
a.		"Flugpost" inverted	200.00	240.00
C7	A18	3M on 60c	2.75	4.25
a.		"Flugpost" inverted	200.00	225.00
		Nos. C1-C7 (7)	56.50	71.25

The surcharged value on No. C7 is in italics.

Nos. 67-71, 73, 76, 78, 80, 82 Overprinted in Dark Blue

1922, May 12

C8	A18	40pf on 40c	.40	.90
C9	A18	80pf on 45c	.40	.90
C10	A18	1m on 40c	.40	.90
C11	A18	1.25m on 60c	.55	1.50
C12	A18	1.50m on 45c	.55	1.50
C13	A18	2m on 1fr	.55	1.50
C14	A18	3m on 60c	.55	1.50

Memel stamps can be mounted in the Scott Germany album part 2.

C15	A18	5m on 1fr	.85	1.65
C16	A18	6m on 2fr	.85	1.65
C17	A18	9m on 5fr	.85	1.75

Same Overprint On Nos. 40, 31

C18	A18	3M on 60c	150.00	*400.00*
C19	A18	4m on 2fr	.55	1.50
		Nos. C8-C17,C19 (11)	6.50	15.25

Nos. 67, 69-71, 73, 76, 78, 80, 82 Overprinted in Black or Red

FLUGPOST

1922, Oct. 17

C20	A18	40pf on 40c	1.00	*4.50*
C21	A18	1m on 40c	1.00	*4.50*
C22	A18	1.25m on 60c (R)	1.00	*4.50*
C23	A18	1.50m on 45c (R)	1.00	*4.50*
C24	A18	2m on 1fr	1.00	*4.50*
C25	A18	3m on 60c (R)	1.00	*4.50*
C26	A18	4m on 2fr	1.00	*4.50*
C27	A18	5m on 1fr	1.00	*4.50*
C28	A18	6m on 2fr	1.00	*4.50*
C29	A18	9m on 5fr (R)	1.00	*4.50*
		Nos. C20-C29 (10)	10.00	*45.00*

No. C26 is not known without the "FLUGPOST" overprint.

OCCUPATION STAMPS

Issued under Lithuanian Occupation

Surcharged in Various Colors on Unissued Official Stamps of Lithuania Similar to Type O4

Klaipėda
(Memel)
10
Markių
On Nos. N1-N6

KLAIPĖDA
(MEMEL)
25
MARKĖS
On Nos. N7-N11

Memel Printing

1923 Unwmk. Litho. ***Perf. 11***

N1	O4	10m on 5c bl (Bk)	.75	1.50
a.		"Memel" and bars omitted	7.50	*17.00*
N2	O4	25m on 5c bl (R)	.75	1.50
N3	O4	50m on 25c red (Bk)	.75	1.50
N4	O4	100m on 25c red (G)	.75	1.50
N5	O4	400m on 1 l brn (R)	1.00	2.00
N6	O4	500m on 1 l brn (Bl)	1.00	2.00
		Nos. N1-N6 (6)	5.00	10.00

Nos. N1 and N3-N6 exist with double surcharge. Value $50 each.

Kaunas Printing

Black Surcharge

N7	O4	10m on 5c blue	.50	.90
N8	O4	25m on 5c blue	.50	.90
N9	O4	50m on 25c red	.50	.90
N10	O4	100m on 25c red	.65	1.50
N11	O4	400m on 1 l brn	1.00	2.75
		Nos. N7-N11 (5)	3.15	6.95

No. N8 has the value in "Markes," others of the group have it in "Markiu."

For additional surcharge see No. N87.

Surcharged in Various Colors on Unissued Official Stamps of Lithuania Similar to Type O4

KLAIPĖDA
(Memel)
25
MARKĖS

1923

N12	O4	10m on 5c bl (R)	.75	1.50
a.		"Markes" instead of "Markiu"	22.50	50.00
N13	O4	20m on 5c bl (R)	.75	1.50
N14	O4	25m on 25c red (Bl)	.75	1.50
N15	O4	50m on 25c red (Bl)	.85	2.25
a.		Inverted surcharge	40.00	
N16	O4	100m on 1 l brn (Bk)	1.00	2.50
a.		Inverted surcharge	40.00	
N17	O4	200m on 1 l brn (Bk)	1.00	2.50
		Nos. N12-N17 (6)	5.10	11.75

No. N14 has the value in "Markes," others of the group have it in "Markiu."

"Vytis"
O4 O5

1923, Mar.

N18	O4	10m lt brown	.25	.35
N19	O4	20m yellow	.25	.35
N20	O4	25m orange	.25	.35
N21	O4	40m violet	.25	.35
N22	O4	50m yellow grn	.75	.90
N23	O5	100m carmine	.40	.45
N24	O5	300m olive grn	4.00	*45.00*
N25	O5	400m olive brn	.50	.60
N26	O5	500m lilac	4.00	*45.00*
N27	O5	1000m blue	.85	1.50
		Nos. N18-N27 (10)	11.50	*94.85*

No. N20 has the value in "Markes."

For surcharges see Nos. N44-N69, N88-N114.

No. 99 Surcharged in Green

1923, Apr. 13

N28	A18	100m on No. 99	4.00	8.00
N29	A18	400m on No. 99	4.00	8.00
N30	A18	500m on No. 99	4.00	8.00
		Nos. N28-N30 (3)	12.00	24.00

The normal position of the green surcharge is sideways, with the top at the left. It exists reversed on the three stamps.

Ship — O7

Seal — O8

Lighthouse — O9

1923, Apr. 12 **Litho.**

N31	O7	40m olive grn	3.50	8.00
N32	O7	50m brown	3.50	8.00
N33	O7	80m green	3.50	8.00
N34	O7	100m red	3.50	8.00
N35	O8	200m deep blue	3.50	8.00
N36	O8	300m brown	3.50	8.00
N37	O8	400m lilac	3.50	8.00
N38	O8	500m orange	3.50	8.00
N39	O8	600m olive grn	3.50	8.00
N40	O9	800m deep blue	3.50	8.00
N41	O9	1000m lilac	3.50	8.00
N42	O9	2000m red	3.50	8.00
N43	O9	3000m green	3.50	8.00
		Nos. N31-N43 (13)	45.50	104.00

Union of Memel with Lithuania. Forgeries exist.

For surcharges see Nos. N70-N86.

Nos. N20, N24, N26 Surcharged in Various Colors

3
CENTŲ

1923

Thin Figures

N44	O5	2c on 300m (R)	5.00	4.50
N45	O5	3c on 300m (R)	5.00	4.50
N46	O4	10c on 25m (Bk)	5.50	4.50
a.		Double surcharge	65.00	
N47	O4	15c on 25m (Bk)	5.50	4.50
N48	O5	20c on 500m (Bl)	6.50	9.00
N49	O5	30c on 500m (Bk)	5.00	4.50
N50	O5	50c on 500m (G)	12.50	12.50
a.		Inverted surcharge	125.00	
		Nos. N44-N50 (7)	45.00	44.00

Nos. N19, N21-N27 Surcharged:

2 CENT. **1 LITAS**

N51	O4	2c on 20m yellow	2.75	3.25
N52	O4	2c on 50c yel grn	2.75	3.25
N53	O4	3c on 40m violet	3.50	3.25
a.		Double surcharge	65.00	
N54	O5	3c on 300m ol grn	2.00	2.25
a.		Double surcharge	65.00	
N55	O5	5c on 100m carmine	2.75	2.00
N56	O5	5c on 300m ol grn (R)	3.50	4.25
N57	O5	10c on 400m ol brn	6.75	5.00
N58	O5	30c on 500m lilac	4.00	8.00
N59	O5	1 l on 1000m blue	12.00	20.00
		Nos. N51-N59 (9)	40.00	51.25

There are several types of the numerals in these surcharges. Nos. N56 and N58 have "CENT" in short, thick letters, as on Nos. N44 to N50.

Nos. N18-N23, N25, N27 Surcharged

2
CENT.

Thick Figures

N60	O4	2c on 10m lt brn	3.00	*4.50*
N61	O4	2c on 20m yellow	10.00	*75.00*
N62	O4	2c on 50m yel grn	2.50	*6.00*
N63	O4	3c on 10m lt brn	2.50	*6.00*
a.		Double surcharge	60.00	
N64	O4	3c on 40m violet	18.00	*110.00*
N65	O5	5c on 100m carmine	2.00	*6.00*
a.		Double surcharge	60.00	
N66	O5	10c on 400m ol brn	90.00	*300.00*
N67	O4	15c on 25m orange	90.00	*300.00*
N68	O5	50c on 1000m blue	5.00	*5.50*
a.		Double surcharge	60.00	
N69	O5	1 l on 1000m blue	6.00	*10.00*
a.		Double surcharge	90.00	
		Nos. N60-N69 (10)	229.00	*823.00*

No. N69 is surcharged like type "b" in the following group.

Nos. N31-N43 Surcharged:

30 CENT.
a

1 LITAS
b

N70	O7(a)	15c on 40m ol grn	5.00	*11.00*
N71	O7(a)	30c on 50m brown	5.00	*7.00*
N72	O7(a)	30c on 80m green	5.00	*15.00*
N73	O7(a)	30c on 100m red	5.00	*7.00*
N74	O8(a)	50c on 200m dp blue	5.50	*11.00*
N75	O8(a)	50c on 300m brown	5.00	*7.00*
N76	O8(a)	50c on 400m lilac	5.00	*13.00*
N77	O8(a)	50c on 500m orange	4.25	*7.00*
N78	O8(b)	1 l on 600m ol grn	5.00	*11.00*
N79	O9(b)	1 l on 800m dp blue	6.50	*11.00*
N80	O9(b)	1 l on 1000m lilac	6.00	*11.00*
N81	O9(b)	1 l on 2000m red	6.00	*11.00*
N82	O9(b)	1 l on 3000m green	6.50	*11.00*
		Nos. N70-N82 (13)	69.75	*133.00*

These stamps are said to have been issued to commemorate the institution of autonomous government.

Double or inverted surcharges exist on Nos. N71, N75-N77. Value, each $60.

Nos. N32, N34, N36, N38 Surcharged in Green

25
CENT.

1923

N83	O7	15c on 50m brn	275.	*1,500.*
N84	O7	25c on 100m red	150.	*1,000.*
N85	O8	30c on 300m brn	250.	*1,100.*
N86	O8	60c on 500m org	150.	*1,000.*

Surcharges on Nos. N83-N86 are of two types, differing in width of numerals. Values are for stamps with narrow numerals, as illustrated. Stamps with wide numerals sell for two to four times as much.

Nos. N8, N10-N11, N3 Surcharged in Red or Green

15
Centų

N87	O4	10c on 25m on 5c bl (R)	20.00	*35.00*
N88	O4	15c on 100m on 25c red (G)	22.50	*125.00*
a.		Inverted surcharge	150.00	250.00
N89	O4	30c on 400m on 1 l brn (R)	11.00	*25.00*
N90	O4	60c on 50m on 25c red (G)	25.00	*150.00*
		Nos. N87-N90 (4)	78.50	*335.00*

Nos. N18-N22 Surcharged in Green or Red

15
Centų

N91	O4	15c on 10m	6.00	*20.00*
N92	O4	15c on 20m	3.00	*12.00*
N93	O4	15c on 25m	3.50	*13.00*
N94	O4	15c on 40m	3.00	*12.00*
N95	O4	15c on 50m (R)	2.25	*10.00*
N96	O4	25c on 10m	3.75	*10.00*
N97	O4	25c on 20m	3.00	*10.00*
N98	O4	25c on 25m	3.50	*13.00*
N99	O4	25c on 40m	3.00	*16.00*
N100	O4	25c on 50m (R)	2.25	*9.00*
N101	O4	30c on 10m	5.50	*22.50*
N102	O4	30c on 20m	3.00	*13.00*
N103	O4	30c on 25m	3.50	*16.00*
N104	O4	30c on 40m	3.00	*7.00*
N105	O4	30c on 50m (R)	2.25	*9.00*
		Nos. N91-N105 (15)	50.50	*192.50*

Nine stamps between Nos. N95 and N114 exist with inverted surcharge. No. 102 exists with double surcharge.

Nos. N23, N25, N27 Surcharged in Green or Red

15
Centų

N106	O5	15c on 100m	2.50	*10.00*
N107	O5	15c on 400m	2.50	*9.00*
N108	O5	15c on 1000m (R)	60.00	*250.00*
N109	O5	25c on 100m	2.50	*8.50*
N110	O5	25c on 400m	2.50	*8.00*
N111	O5	25c on 1000m (R)	65.00	*300.00*
N112	O5	30c on 100m	2.50	*9.00*
N113	O5	30c on 400m	2.50	*8.00*
N114	O5	30c on 1000m (R)	65.00	*250.00*
		Nos. N106-N114 (9)	205.00	*852.50*

Nos. N96 to N100 and N109 to N111 are surcharged "Centai," the others "Centu."

Excellent counterfeits of all Memel issues exist.

MESOPOTAMIA

ˌme–s(ə–)pə–ˈtā–mē–ə

LOCATION — In Western Asia, bounded on the north by Syria and Turkey, on the east by Persia, on the south by Saudi Arabia and on the west by Trans-Jordan.
GOVT. — A former Turkish Province
AREA — 143,250 (1918) sq. mi.
POP. — 2,849,282 (1920)
CAPITAL — Baghdad

During World War I this territory was occupied by Great Britain. It was recognized as an independent state and placed under British Mandate but in 1932 the Mandate was terminated and the country admitted to membership in the League of Nations as the Kingdom of Iraq. Postage stamps of Iraq are now in use.

16 Annas = 1 Rupee

Watermark

Wmk. 48 - Diagonal Zigzag Lines

Issued under British Occupation

Baghdad Issue

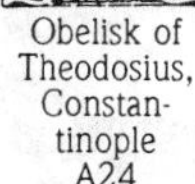

Obelisk of Theodosius, Constantinople
A24

Leander's Tower
A26

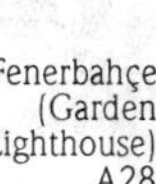

Fenerbahçe (Garden Lighthouse)
A28

Castle of Europe on Bosporus — A29

Mosque of Sultan Ahmed — A30

Stamps of Turkey 1901-16 Surcharged

IN BRITISH BAGHDAD OCCUPATION
½ An

The surcharges were printed from slugs which were arranged to fit the various shapes of the stamps.

1917 Unwmk. *Perf. 12, 13½*

On Turkey Nos. 254, 256, 258-260

No.	Type	Description	Unused	Used
N1	A24	¼a on 2pa red lil	90.00	105.00
a.		"IN BRITISH" omitted	*4,250.*	
N2	A26	¼a on 5pa vio brown	75.00	82.50
a.		"¼ An" omitted	*3,750.*	
N3	A28	½a on 10pa green	525.00	525.00
N4	A29	1a on 20pa red	450.00	400.00
N5	A30	2a on 1pi blue	150.00	165.00
		Nos. N1-N5 (5)	1,290.	1,277.

General Post Office, Constantinople — A22

Mosque of Selim, Adrianople
A23

On Turkey No. 249 with Overprint ب

No.	Type	Description	Unused	Used
N6	A22	2a on 1pi ultra	250.	250.

On Turkey No. 251

No.	Type	Description	Unused	Used
N7	A23	½a on 10pa green	950.	900.

On Turkey Nos. 272-273 with Overprint ★

No.	Type	Description	Unused	Used
N8	A29	1a on 20pa red	250.	250.
a.		"OCCUPATION" omitted	*3,000.*	
N9	A30	2a on 1pi blue	4,000.	4,000.

Old General Post Office, Constantinople — A41

On Turkey Nos. 346-348

No.	Type	Description	Unused	Used
N10	A41	½a on 10pa car	225.00	225.00
N11	A41	1a on 20pa ultra	900.00	750.00
a.		"1 An" omitted	*4,250.*	
N12	A41	2a on 1pi vio & black	57.50	57.50
a.		"BAGHDAD" omitted	*2,500.*	

Tughra, Sultan's Monogram
A17 A18

On Various Issues with Overprint

On Turkey Nos. 297, 300

No.	Type	Description	Unused	Used
N13	A17	¼a on 5pa purple	*2,500.*	
N14	A17	2a on 1pi blue	120.00	120.00

On Turkey No. 306

No.	Type	Description	Unused	Used
N15	A18	1a on 20pa car	300.00	250.00

On Turkey Nos. 329-331

No.	Type	Description	Unused	Used
N16	A22	½a on 10pa bl grn	60.00	60.00
N17	A22	1a on 20pa car rose	275.00	265.00
a.		"1 An" omitted	*2,500.*	*2,500.*
N18	A22	2a on 1pi ultra	115.00	110.00

On Turkey No. 337 With Overprint

No.	Type	Description	Unused	Used
N19	A22	1a on 20pa car rose	*4,000.*	*4,000.*

On Turkey No. P125 with Overprint

and Overprint

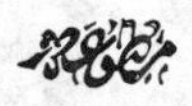

No.	Type	Description	Unused	Used
N20	A17	1a on 20pa car	*4,000.*	*4,000.*

A21

A11

On Turkey Nos. B1, B8 with Overprint

Inscription in crescent is obliterated by another crescent handstamped in violet black on Nos. N21-N27.

No.	Type	Description	Unused	Used
N21	A18	½a on 10pa dull grn	70.00	62.50
a.		"OCCUPATION" omitted	*3,250.*	
N22	A21	1a on 20pa car rose	275.00	200.00

On Semi-Postal Stamps of 1916 with Overprint

On Turkey No. B29

No.	Type	Description	Unused	Used
N23	A21	2a on 1pi ultra	900.00	900.00

On Turkey Nos. B33-B34

No.	Type	Description	Unused	Used
N24	A22	1a on 20pa car rose	90.00	90.00
N25	A22	2a on 1pi ultra	140.00	125.00
a.		"OCCUPATION" omitted	*3,250.*	
b.		"BAGHDAD" omitted	*3,250.*	

On Turkey No. B42

No.	Type	Description	Unused	Used
N26	A41	½a on 10pa car	140.00	140.00
a.		"BAGHDAD" double	*2,000.*	

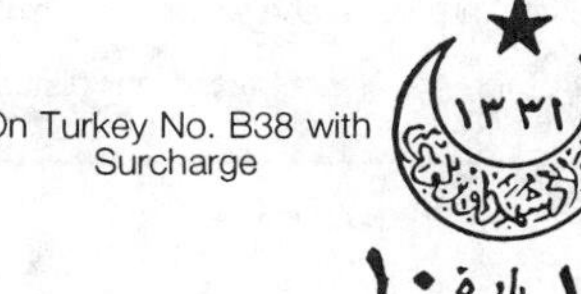

No.	Type	Description	Unused	Used
N27	A11	1a on 10pa on 20pa vio brn	200.00	210.00

Iraq Issue

Monument to the Martyrs of Liberty — A31

Fountains of Suleiman
A32

Cruiser "Hamidie"
A33

Kandili on the Bosporus
A34

War Ministry
A35

Sweet Waters of Europe Park, Constantinople — A36

Mosque of Suleiman
A37

The Bosporus
A38

Sultan Ahmed's Fountain
A39

Turkey Nos. 256, 258-269 Surcharged

IN BRITISH IRAQ OCCUPATION
1An.

1918-20 *Perf. 12*

No.	Type	Description	Unused	Used
N28	A26	¼a on 5pa vio brn	.15	.15
N29	A28	½a on 10pa grn	.15	.15
N30	A29	1a on 20pa red	.15	.15
N31	A26	1½a on 5pa vio brn	.15	.15
N32	A30	2½a on 1pi blue	.15	.15
a.		Inverted surcharge	*3,250.*	
N33	A31	3a on 1½pi car & black	.15	.15
a.		Double surcharge, red & blk	*1,750.*	
N34	A32	4a on 1¾pi slate & red brn	.15	.15
a.		Center inverted		*10,000.*
N35	A33	6a on 2pi grn & black	.35	.25
N36	A34	8a on 2½pi org & ol grn	.30	.20
N37	A35	12a on 5pi dl vio	1.50	.50
N38	A36	1r on 10pi red brown	1.50	.45
N39	A37	2r on 25pi ol grn	6.25	2.00
N40	A38	5r on 50pi car	20.00	8.75
N41	A39	10r on 100pi dp blue	32.50	7.50
		Nos. N28-N41 (14)	63.45	20.70

See #N50-N53. For overprints see #NO1-NO21.

Mosul Issue

A13

A14

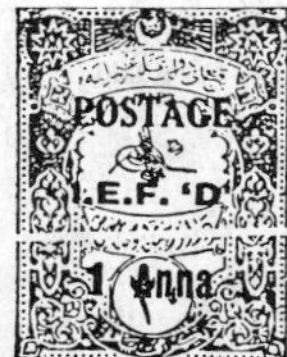

A15

A16

A17

A18

A19

1919 Unwmk. *Perf. 11½, 12*

No.	Type	Description	Unused	Used
N42	A13	½a on 1pi grn & brn red	.85	.50
N43	A14	1a on 20pa *rose*	.85	.50
a.		"POSTAGE" omitted		
N44	A15	1a on 20pa *rose*	3.75	3.75
a.		Double surcharge		

Turkish word at right of tughra ("reshad") is large on No. N43, small on No. N44.

Wmk. Turkish Characters

Perf. 12½

N45	A16	2½a on 1pi vio & yel	.40	.30
N46	A17	3a on 20pa grn & yel	25.00	25.00

Wmk. 48

N47	A17	3a on 20pa green	1.00	.50
N48	A18	4a on 1pi dull vio	2.00	1.40
a.		Double surcharge		
b.		"4" omitted	1,650.	
c.		As "b," double surcharge		
N49	A19	8a on 10pa claret	2.50	2.00
a.		Double surcharge	*500.00*	
b.		Inverted surcharge	*500.00*	
c.		8a on 1pi dull violet	*1,100.*	
		Nos. N42-N49 (8)	36.35	33.95

Value for No. 49c is for copies with the perfs cutting into the design.

Iraq Issue

Types of 1918-20 Issue

1921 **Wmk. 4** *Perf. 12*

N50	A28	½a on 10pa green	.50	.25
N51	A26	1½a on 5pa dp brn	.50	.25
N52	A37	2r on 25pi ol grn	11.00	10.00
		Nos. N50-N52 (3)	12.00	10.50

Type of 1918-20 without "Reshad"

1922 **Unwmk.**

N53	A36	1r on 10pi red brn	110.00	12.50

"Reshad" is the small Turkish word at right of the tughra in circle at top center.

For overprint, see No. NO22.

OFFICIAL STAMPS

Nos. N29-N41 Overprinted:

ON STATE SERVICE

1920 **Unwmk.** *Perf. 12*

NO1	A28	½a on 10pa green	.20	.15
NO2	A29	1a on 20pa red	.25	.15
NO3	A26	1½a on 5pa vio brown	1.10	.35
NO4	A30	2½a on 1pi blue	1.10	.60
NO5	A31	3a on 1½pi car & black	1.10	.40
NO6	A32	4a on 1¾pi sl & red brn	1.65	.50
NO7	A33	6a on 2pi grn & black	1.10	.40
NO8	A34	8a on 2½pi org & ol grn	1.10	.50
NO9	A35	12a on 5pi dull violet	2.75	1.65
NO10	A36	1r on 10pi red brown	2.75	1.10
NO11	A37	2r on 25pi ol green	7.25	8.00
NO12	A38	5r on 50pi car	30.00	15.00
NO13	A39	10r on 100pi dp blue	50.00	19.00
		Nos. NO1-NO13 (13)	100.35	47.80

Same Overprint on Types of Regular Issue of 1918-20

1921-22 **Wmk. 4**

NO14	A28	½a on 10pa green	.15	.15
NO15	A29	1a on 20pa red	.15	.15
NO16	A26	1½a on 5pa dp brn	.30	.30
NO17	A32	4a on 1¾pi gray & red brn	.30	.30
NO18	A33	6a on 2pi grn & black	4.00	3.25
NO19	A34	8a on 2½pi org & yel grn	.80	.55
NO20	A35	12a on 5pi dl vio	3.00	2.75
NO21	A37	2r on 25pi ol grn	22.50	14.00
		Nos. NO14-NO21 (8)	31.20	21.45

Same Overprint on No. N53

1922 **Unwmk.**

NO22	A36	1r on 10pi red brn	12.00	5.00

MEXICO

'mek-si-,kō

LOCATION — Extreme southern part of the North American continent, south of the United States

GOVT. — Republic

AREA — 756,198 sq. mi.

POP. — 76,791,819 (est. 1984)

CAPITAL — Mexico, D.F

8 Reales = 1 Peso

100 Centavos = 1 Peso

Catalogue values for unused stamps in this country are for Never Hinged items, beginning with Scott 792 in the regular postage section, Scott C143 in the airpost section, Scott E8 in the special delivery section, and Scott G4 in the insured letter section.

District Overprints

Nos. 1-149 are overprinted with names of various districts, and sometimes also with district numbers and year dates. Some of the district overprints are rare and command high prices. Values given for Nos. 1-149 are for the more common district overprints.

Watermarks

Wmk. 150- PAPEL SELLADO in Sheet

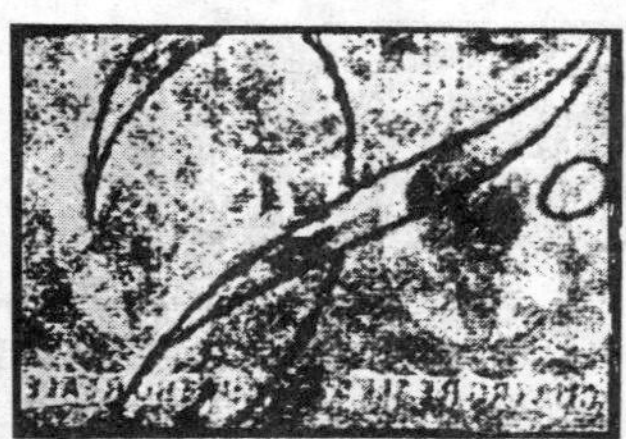

Wmk. 151- R. P. S. in the Sheet (R.P.S. stands for "Renta Papel Sellado")

Wmk. 152- "CORREOS E U M" on Every Horizontal Line of Ten Stamps

Wmk. 153- "R M" Interlaced

Wmk. 154- Eagle and R M

Wmk. 155- SERVICIO POSTAL DE LOS ESTADOS UNIDOS MEXICANOS

Wmk. 156- CORREOS MEXICO

Wmk. 248- SECRETARIA DE HACIENDA MEXICO

Wmk. 260- Lines and SECRETARIA DE HACIENDA MEXICO

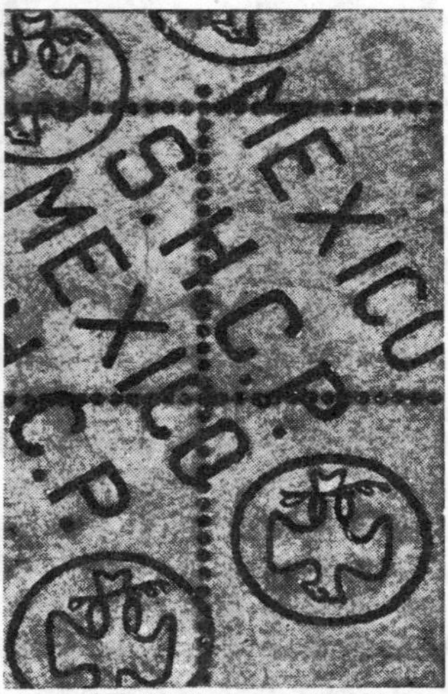

Wmk. 272- "S. H. C. P. MEXICO" and Eagle in Circle

Wmk. 279- GOBIERNO MEXICANO and Eagle in Circle

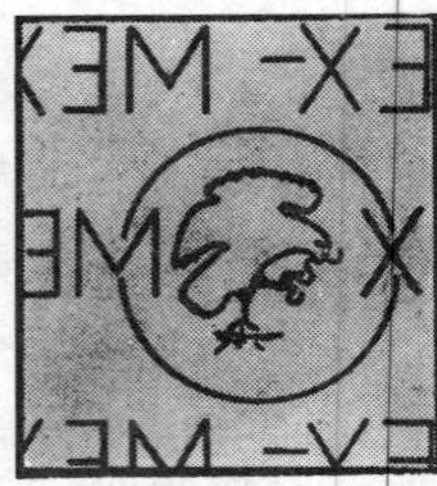

Wmk. 300- MEX-MEX and Eagle in Circle, Multiple (Letters 6mm)

Wmk. 350- MEX and Eagle in Circle, Multiple. Letters 8-9mm

Miguel Hidalgo y Costilla — A1

Handstamped with District Name

1856 **Unwmk.** **Engr.** *Imperf.*

1	A1	½r blue	45.00	25.00
b.		Without overprint	40.00	35.00
c.		Double impression		150.00
2	A1	1r yellow	25.00	3.50
b.		Half used as ½r on cover		*5,000.*
c.		Without overprint	12.50	15.00
d.		1r green (error)		
3	A1	2r yellow grn	25.00	3.00
a.		2r blue green	250.00	50.00
b.		2r emerald	225.00	30.00
c.		Half used as 1r on cover		550.00
d.		Without overprint	35.00	20.00
e.		Printed on both sides (yel green)	200.00	225.00
4	A1	4r red	150.00	75.00
a.		Half used as 2r on cover		250.00
b.		Quarter used as 1r on cover		500.00
c.		Without overprint	125.00	150.00
d.		Three quarters used as 3r on cover		*7,000.*
5	A1	8r red lilac	300.00	175.00
a.		8r violet	225.00	165.00
b.		Without overprint	200.00	200.00
c.		Eighth used as 1r on cover		*2,500.*
d.		Quarter used as 2r on cover		225.00
e.		Half used as 4r on cover		425.00
		Nos. 1-5 (5)	545.00	281.50

The 1r and 2r were printed in sheets of 60 with wide spacing between stamps, and in sheets of 190 or 200 with narrow spacing.

All values have been reprinted, some of them several times. The reprints usually show signs of wear and the impressions are often smudgy. The paper is usually thicker than that of the originals. Reprints are usually on very white paper. Reprints are found with and without overprints and with cancellations made both from the original handstamps and from forged ones.

Counterfeits exist.

See Nos. 6-12. For overprints see Nos. 35-45.

1861

6	A1	½r black, *buff*	45.00	25.00
a.		Without overprint	30.00	35.00
7	A1	1r black, *green*	17.50	5.00
a.		Impression of 2r on back		400.00
b.		Without overprint	5.00	4.50
c.		Printed on both sides		300.00
d.		As "b," blk, *pink* (error)		*7,000.*
f.		Double impression		150.00
8	A1	2r black, *pink*	12.50	2.50
a.		Impression of 1r on back	450.00	
b.		Half used as 1r on cover		350.00
c.		Without overprint	3.00	6.50
d.		Printed on both sides		2,250.
e.		Double impression		100.00
9	A1	4r black, *yellow*	165.00	50.00
a.		Half used as 2r on cover		200.00
b.		Without overprint	45.00	70.00
c.		Quarter used as 1r on cover		325.00
d.		Three-quarters used as 3r on cover		*3,000.*
10	A1	4r dull rose, *yel*	175.00	65.00
a.		Half used as 2r on cover		*500.00*
b.		Without overprint	100.00	125.00
c.		Printed on both sides		*1,500.*
d.		Quarter used as 1r on cover		*500.00*
11	A1	8r black, *red brn*	325.00	200.00
b.		Quarter used as 2r on cover		200.00
c.		Half used as 4r on cover		325.00
d.		Without overprint	100.00	200.00
e.		Three quarters used as 6r on cover		*3,500.*
12	A1	8r grn, *red brn*	450.00	175.00
a.		Half used as 4r on cover		
b.		Without overprint	125.00	160.00

c. Quarter used as 2r on cover
d. Printed on both sides 1,250. 1,250.
Nos. 6-12 (7) 1,190. 522.50

Nos. 6, 9, 10, 11 and 12 have been reprinted. Most reprints of the ½r, 4r and 8r are on vertically grained paper. Originals are on horizontally grained paper. The original ½r stamps are much worn but the reprints are unworn. The paper of the 4r is too deep and rich in color and No. 10 is printed in too bright red.

Reprints of the 8r can only be told by experts. All these reprints are found in fancy colors and with overprints and cancellations as in the 1856 issue.

Counterfeits exist.

Hidalgo — A3

Coat of Arms — A4

With District Name

1864 ***Perf. 12***

14 A3 1r red 600. 1,250.
a. Without District Name .75
15 A3 2r blue 550. 1,000.
a. Without District Name .75
16 A3 4r brown 1,250. 2,400.
a. Without District Name 1.25
b. Vert. pair, imperf. between
17 A3 1p black 2,500. 22,500.
a. Without District Name 2.00

Nos. 14 to 17 were issued with district overprints of Saltillo or Monterrey on the toned paper of 1864. Overprints on the 1867 white paper are fraudulent. Counterfeits and counterfeit cancellations are plentiful. The 1r red with "½" surcharge is bogus.

Overprint of District Name, etc.

1864-66 ***Imperf.***

Five types of overprints:
I - District name only.
II - District name, consignment number and "1864" in large figures.
III - District name, number and "1864" in small figures.
IV - District name, number and "1865."
V - District name, number and "1866."

18 A4 3c brn (IV, V) 1,200. 2,500.
a. Without overprint 650.00
b. Laid paper 3,500. 5,500.
19 A4 ½r brown (I) 300.00 210.00
a. Type II 1,500. 1,000.
b. Without overprint 150.00 500.00
20 A4 ½r lilac (IV) 55.00 45.00
a. Type III 60.00 55.00
b. Type II 110.00 100.00
c. Type V 3,000.
d. ½r gray (V) 65.00 65.00
e. Without overprint 4.00
21 A4 1r blue (IV, V) 13.00 8.00
a. Type III 20.00 12.00
b. Without overprint 2.00
c. Half used as ½r on cover 3,000.
22 A4 1r ultra (I, II) 100.00 27.50
a. Type III 75.00 35.00
b. Without overprint 130.00 120.00
c. Half used as ½r on cover 3,000.
23 A4 2r org (III, IV, V) 4.00 2.50
a. Type II 15.00 3.00
b. Type I 40.00 4.50
c. 2r dp org, without ovpt., early plate 150.00 50.00
d. Without ovpt., late plate 1.25
e. Half used as 1r on cover 1,750.
24 A4 4r grn (III, IV, V) 85.00 35.00
a. Types I, II 120.00 60.00
b. 4r dk grn, without ovpt. 3.50 275.00
d. Half used as 2r on cover 700.00
25 A4 8r red (IV, V) 125.00 75.00
a. Types II, III 150.00 70.00
b. Type I 300.00 100.00
c. 8r dk red, without ovpt. 5.25 500.00
f. Quarter used as 2r on cover 15,000.
g. Three-quarters used as 6r on cover

The 2r printings from the early plates are 25½mm high; those from the late plate, 24½mm.

Varieties listed as "Without overprint" in unused condition are remainders.

Besides the overprints of district name, number and date, Nos. 18-34 often received, in the district offices, additional overprints of numbers and sometimes year dates. Copies with these "sub-consignment numbers" sell for more than stamps without them.

Faked quarterlings and bisects of 1856-64 are plentiful.

The 3c has been reprinted from a die on which the words "TRES CENTAVOS," the outlines of the serpent and some of the background lines have been retouched.

Emperor Maximilian — A5

Overprinted with District Name, Number and Date 1866 or 866; also with Number and Date only, or with Name only

1866 **Litho.**

26 A5 7c lilac gray 60.00 110.00
a. 7c deep gray 85.00 110.00
27 A5 13c blue 24.00 24.00
a. Half used as 7c on cover 5,000.
b. 13c cobalt blue 25.00 25.00
c. Without overprint 80.00
28 A5 25c buff 10.00 6.00
a. Half used as 13c on cover
29 A5 25c orange 10.00 8.50
a. 25c red orange 18.00 13.50
b. 25c red brown 40.00 30.00
c. 25c brown 100.00 45.00
30 A5 50c green 24.00 24.00
Nos. 26-30 (5) 128.00 172.50

Litho. printings have round period after value numerals.

The listing of No. 28a is being re-evaluated. The Catalogue Editors would appreciate any information on the stamp.

Overprinted with District Name, Number and Date 866 or 867; also with Number and Date only

Engr.

31 A5 7c lilac 425.00 5,000.
a. Without overprint 3.25
32 A5 13c blue 7.50 11.00
a. Without overprint 1.25
33 A5 25c orange brown 6.25 9.50
a. Without overprint 1.25
34 A5 50c green 675.00 67.50
a. Without overprint 2.50

See "sub-consignment" note after No. 25.

Engraved printings have square period after value numerals.

Varieties listed as "Without overprint" in unused condition are remainders.

Stamps of 1856-61 Overprinted *Mexico*

1867

35 A1 ½r blk, *buff* 1,500. 1,750.
36 A1 1r blk, *green* 50.00 8.00
37 A1 2r blk, *pink* 20.00 4.00
a. Printed on both sides 140.00
38 A1 4r red, *yel* 300.00 16.00
a. Printed on both sides 150.00
39 A1 4r red 4,000. 1,200.
40 A1 8r blk, *red brn* 1,100. 250.00
41 A1 8r grn, *red brn* 2,500.

Dangerous counterfeits exist of the "Mexico" overprint.

Copies of No. 38 with yellow removed are offered as No. 39.

Same Overprint
Thin Gray Blue Paper
Wmk. 151

42 A1 ½r gray 225.00 150.00
a. Without overprint 175.00 175.00
43 A1 1r blue 375.00 60.00
b. Without overprint 300.00 75.00
44 A1 2r green 70.00 7.00
a. Printed on both sides 900.00
b. Without overprint 75.00 20.00
45 A1 4r rose 1,500. 75.00
a. Without overprint 2,000. 60.00

Reprints of the ½r and 4r exist on watermarked paper. Reprints of ½r and 8r also exist in gray on thick grayish wove paper, unwatermarked.

Hidalgo — A6

Thin Figures of Value, without Period after Numerals

6 CENT. 12 CENT.
25 CENT. 50 CENT.
100 CENT.

Overprinted with District Name, Number and Abbreviated Date

1868 **Unwmk.** **Litho.** ***Imperf.***

46 A6 6c blk, *buff* 35.00 17.50
47 A6 12c blk, *green* 30.00 15.00
a. Period after "12" 50.00
48 A6 25c bl, *pink* 52.50 12.50
a. Without overprint 125.00
49 A6 50c blk, *yellow* 400.00 50.00
50 A6 100c blk, *brown* 600.00 110.00
51 A6 100c brn, *brn* 1,400. 500.00

Perf.

52 A6 6c blk, *buff* 25.00 18.00
a. Without overprint 140.00
b. Period after "6" 70.00
53 A6 12c blk, *green* 25.00 9.00
a. Period after "12" 85.00 30.00
b. Very thick paper 40.00 22.50
c. Without overprint 110.00
54 A6 25c blue, *pink* 55.00 6.00
b. Without overprint 150.00
55 A6 50c blk, *yellow* 325.00 35.00
56 A6 100c blk, *brown* 375.00 90.00
c. Without overprint 350.00
57 A6 100c brn, *brn* 1,000. 300.00
a. Printed on both sides 1,250. 1,000.

Four kinds of perforation are found in the 1868 issue: serrate, square, pin and regular. The narrow spacing between stamps was inadequate for some of these perforation types.

Thick Figures of Value, with Period after Numerals

6. CENT. 12. CENT
25. CENT. 50. CENT.
100. CENT

Overprinted with District Name, Number and Abbreviated Date

Imperf

58 A6 6c blk, *buff* 8.50 4.50
59 A6 12c blk, *green* 3.75 1.25
a. Very thick paper 9.00
c. 12c black, *buff* (error) 500.00 500.00
61 A6 25c blue, *pink* 8.00 .90
a. No period after "25" 100.00
c. Very thick paper 25.00 5.50
d. "85" for "25" 60.00 30.00
e. "35" for "25" 47.50
62 A6 50c blk, *yellow* 125.00 15.00
a. No period after "50" 175.00 25.00
b. 50c blue, *lt pink* (error) 2,500. 1,750.
c. Half used as 25c on cover 1,000.
d. Very thick paper 45.00
64 A6 100c blk, *brown* 125.00 42.50
a. No period after "100" 140.00 47.50
b. Very thick paper 60.00
c. Quarter used as 25c on cover 1,700.
Nos. 58-64 (5) 270.25 64.15

Perf.

65 A6 6c blk, *buff* 37.50 19.00
a. Very thick paper 50.00 30.00
66 A6 12c blk, *green* 5.00 5.00
a. Very thick paper 17.50 13.00
b. 12c black, *buff* (error) 550.00 550.00
68 A6 25c blue, *pink* 18.00 2.00
a. No period after "25" 75.00
c. Thick paper 12.50
d. "85" for "25" 60.00 37.50
69 A6 50c blk, *yellow* 190.00 25.00
a. No period after "50" 200.00 30.00
b. 50c blue, *lt pink* (error) 2,000. 1,500.
c. Thick paper 50.00
70 A6 100c blk, *brown* 190.00 55.00
a. No period after "100" 200.00 62.50
b. Very thick paper 75.00
Nos. 65-70 (5) 440.50 106.00

Postal forgeries of Nos. 58-70 were printed from original plates with district name overprints forged. These include the pelure paper varieties and some thick paper varieties. The "Anotado" handstamp was applied to some of the confiscated forgeries and they were issued, including Nos. 73a and 78a.

Stamps of 1868 Handstamped

Overprinted with District Name, Number and Abbreviated Date
Thick Figures with Period

1872 ***Imperf.***

71 A6 6c blk, *buff* 625.00 650.00
72 A6 12c blk, *green* 65.00 70.00
73 A6 25c bl, *pink* 40.00 45.00
a. Pelure paper 52.50 65.00
b. "85" for "25" 125.00
74 A6 50c blk, *yellow* 800.00 425.00
a. No period after "50" 900.00 450.00

MEXICO
We have an excellent stock of...
• Early Classics
• 20th Century
• Postal History
• Revenues

...for Beginners to Advanced Collectors!
NEW & UP-TO-DATE FREE PRICE LIST
• Send us your Want List •
TOP PRICES PAID FOR
COVERS - CLASSICS - MODERN
Send for our periodic auction lists.
SE HABLA ESPAÑOL
Retail and Wholesale call or write...
GREGG NELSON
Specializing in Mexico For 26 years+
P.O. Box 6382 Santa Rosa, CA 95406
Phone 707-579-5000 • 1-800-609-5009
FAX 707-579-5007
E-mail:GNMEXSTMPS@AOL.COM

MEPSI
Life Member
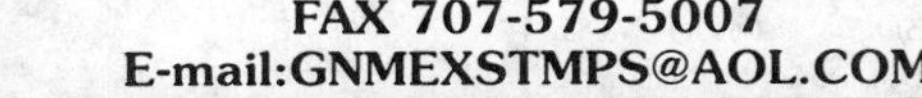

75 A6 100c blk, *brown* 1,200. 1,000.
a. No period after "100" 1,050.

Perf.

76 A6 6c blk, *buff*
77 A6 12c blk, *green* 90.00 80.00
78 A6 25c blue, *pink* 32.50 40.00
a. Pelure paper 65.00 90.00
79 A6 50c blk, *yellow* 850.00 500.00
a. No period after "50" 550.00
80 A6 100c blk, *brown* 1,200.

Counterfeit "Anotado" overprints abound. Genuine cancellations other than Mexico City are unknown. It is recommended that these be purchased accompanied by certificates of authenticity from competent experts.

The stamps of the 1872 issue are found perforated with square holes, pin-perf. 13, 14 or 15, and with serrate perforation.

Counterfeits of the 1868 6c, 12c buff, 50c and 100c (both colors) from new plates have clear, sharp impressions and more facial shading lines than the originals. These counterfeits are found perf. and imperf., with thick and thin numerals, and with the "Anotado" overprint.

Hidalgo — A8

Moiré on White Back
Overprinted with District Name, Number and Abbreviated Date
White Wove Paper

1872 Litho. Wmk. 150 *Imperf.*

81 A8 6c green 70.00 55.00
82 A8 12c blue 42.50 30.00
a. Laid paper
83 A8 25c red 100.00 24.00
a. Laid paper
84 A8 50c yellow 475.00 250.00
a. 50c blue (error) 1,000.
b. Laid paper
c. As "a," without ovpt. 65.00
86 A8 100c gray lilac 325.00 175.00
Nos. 81-86 (5) 1,012. 534.00

Wmk. "LA + F"

81a A8 6c green 200.00 125.00
82b A8 12c blue 150.00 52.50
83b A8 25c red 190.00 42.50
c. Without overprint 250.00
84d A8 50c yellow 1,200. 900.00
86a A8 100c gray lilac 850.00 600.00

1872 Wmk. 150 *Pin-perf.*

87 A8 6c green 400.00 400.00
88 A8 12c blue 60.00 50.00
89 A8 25c red 140.00 45.00
b. Laid paper
90 A8 50c yellow 650.00 325.00
a. 50c blue (error) *500.00 625.00*
b. As "a," without overprint 100.00
92 A8 100c gray lilac 350.00 300.00
Nos. 87-92 (5) 1,600. 1,120.

Wmk. "LA + F"

87a A8 6c green 475.00 400.00
88a A8 12c blue 150.00 150.00
89a A8 25c red 450.00 90.00
90c A8 50c yellow 1,300. 1,000.
92a A8 100c gray lilac 1,000. 625.00

The watermark "LA+F" stands for La Croix Frères, the paper manufacturers, and is in double-lined block capitals 13mm high. A single stamp will show only part of this watermark.

Values for Nos. 87-92a are for examples with visible perfs on all sides.

1872 Unwmk. *Imperf.*

93 A8 6c green 12.50 12.50
a. Without moiré on back, without overprint 60.00 65.00
b. Vertically laid paper 1,300.
c. Bottom label retouched 95.00 90.00
d. Very thick paper 24.00
94 A8 12c blue 2.00 1.65
a. Without moiré on back, without overprint 24.00 35.00
b. Vertically laid paper 350.00 210.00
c. Thin gray bl paper of 1867 (Wmk 151)
95 A8 25c red 6.50 2.00
a. Without moiré on back, without overprint 24.00 35.00
b. Vertically laid paper 450.00 200.00
c. Thin gray bl paper of 1867 (Wmk 151)
96 A8 50c yellow 140.00 30.00
a. 50c orange 140.00 30.00
b. Without moiré on back, without overprint 47.50 65.00
c. Vertically laid paper 2,000.
d. 50c blue (error) 650.00
e. As "d," without overprint 42.50
f. As "e," without moiré on back 65.00
98 A8 100c gray lilac 90.00 47.50
a. 100c lilac 95.00 42.50
b. Without moiré on back, without overprint 47.50 110.00
c. Vertically laid paper 950.00
Nos. 93-98 (5) 251.00 93.65

Counterfeits of these stamps are 24½mm high instead of 24mm. The printing is sharper and more uniform than the genuine. Forged district names and consignment numbers exist.

Pin-perf. and Serrate Perf.

99 A8 6c green 90.00 75.00
100 A8 12c blue 3.50 3.00
a. Vertically laid paper 350.00
b. Horiz. pair, imperf. vert. 100.00 100.00
c. Vert. pair, imperf. between
101 A8 25c red 3.25 1.50
a. Vertically laid paper 450.00
b. Horiz. pair, imperf. vert. 100.00 100.00
102 A8 50c yellow 165.00 50.00
a. 50c orange 165.00 50.00
b. 50c blue (error) 475.00
c. As "b," without overprint 45.00
104 A8 100c lilac 150.00 80.00
a. 100c gray lilac 125.00 80.00
Nos. 99-104 (5) 411.75 209.50

Values for Nos. 99-104a are for examples with visible perfs on all sides.

Hidalgo
A9 A10

A11 A12

A13 A14

Overprinted with District Name and Number and Date; also with Number and Date only
Thick Wove Paper, Some Showing Vertical Ribbing

1874-80 Unwmk. Engr. *Perf. 12*

105 A9 4c org ('80) 12.50 11.00
a. Vert. pair, imperf. btwn. 60.00
b. Without overprint 6.50 12.50
c. Half used as 2c on cover 1,000.
106 A10 5c brown 4.25 2.75
a. Horizontally laid paper 90.00 52.50
b. Imperf., pair 60.00
c. Horiz. pair, imperf. btwn. 47.50
d. Vert. pair, imperf. btwn. 110.00 110.00
e. Without overprint 37.50
f. As "a," wmkd. "LACROIX" 300.00 200.00
107 A11 10c black 2.00 1.25
a. Horizontally laid paper 2.40 2.40
b. Horiz. pair, imperf. btwn. 60.00 60.00
c. Without overprint 27.50 27.50
d. Half used as 5c on cover 600.00
e. Imperf., pair
f. As "a," wmkd. "LACROIX" 60.00 45.00
108 A11 10c org ('78) 2.00 1.25
a. 10c yellow bister 6.00 4.25
b. Imperf., pair
c. Without overprint 55.00 55.00
d. Half used as 5c on cover 100.00
109 A12 25c blue .85 .70
b. Horizontally laid paper 2.10
c. Imperf., pair 42.50 30.00
d. Without overprint 35.00 20.00
e. Horiz. pair, imperf. btwn. 120.00
f. As "b," horiz. pair, imperf. vert. 120.00
g. As "b," wmkd. "LACROIX" 47.50 35.00
h. Printed on both sides
i. Half used as 10c on cover
110 A13 50c green 12.50 12.50
a. Without overprint 47.50
b. Half used as 25c on cover
111 A14 100c carmine 18.00 15.00
a. Imperf., pair 175.00
b. Without overprint 50.00
c. Quarter used as 25c on cover
Nos. 105-111 (7) 52.10 44.45

The "LACROIX" watermark is spelled out "LACROIX FRERES" in 2 lines of block capitals without serifs once to a sheet of horiz. laid paper. 6-12 stamps may have a portion of the wmk.

1875-77 Wmk. 150

112 A10 5c brown 35.00 35.00
113 A11 10c black 35.00 35.00
114 A12 25c blue 32.50 32.50
115 A13 50c green 200.00 200.00
116 A14 100c carmine 165.00 165.00
Nos. 112-116 (5) 467.50 467.50

1881 Unwmk. Thin Wove Paper

117 A9 4c orange 62.50 62.50
a. Without overprint 18.00 18.00
118 A10 5c brown 10.00 6.50
a. Without overprint .50 19.00
b. As "a," vert. pair, imperf. horiz. 150.00
119 A11 10c orange 6.00 3.50
a. Imperf., pair
b. Vert. pair, imperf. horiz. 65.00 65.00
c. Without overprint .75 4.00
d. Vert. pair, imperf. btwn. 65.00 65.00
e. Half used as 5c on cover —
120 A12 25c blue 4.00 2.25
a. Imperf., pair
b. Without overprint .50
c. Double impression 65.00
121 A13 50c green 45.00 40.00
a. Without overprint 4.00 30.00
122 A14 100c carmine 60.00 47.50
a. Without overprint 6.00
Nos. 117-122 (6) 187.50 162.25

The stamps of 1874-81 are found with number and date wide apart, close together or omitted, and in various colors.

The thin paper is fragile and easily damaged. Values for Nos. 117-122 are for undamaged, fine examples.

Benito Juárez — A15

Overprinted with District Name and Number and Date; also with Number and Date only

1879 *Perf. 12*

Thick Wove Paper, Some Showing Vertical Ribbing

123 A15 1c brown 3.75 3.50
a. Without overprint 72.50 140.00
b. 1c gray 17.50 15.00
124 A15 2c dk violet 3.50 3.25
a. Without overprint 75.00 90.00
b. Printed on both sides
c. 2c dark gray 17.00 13.00
125 A15 5c orange 2.25 1.40
a. Without overprint 45.00 65.00
126 A15 10c blue 2.75 2.25
a. Without overprint 50.00 75.00
b. 10c ultra 165.00 165.00
127 A15 25c rose 7.00 8.25
a. Without overprint 1.65
128 A15 50c green 11.00 11.00
a. Without overprint 1.25
b. Printed on both sides 165.00
129 A15 85c violet 19.00 17.00
a. Without overprint 2.50
130 A15 100c black 22.50 19.00
a. Without overprint 2.50
Nos. 123-130 (8) 71.75 65.65

1882

Thin Wove Paper

131 A15 1c brown 40.00 30.00
a. Without overprint 125.00
132 A15 2c dk violet 27.50 21.00
a. 2c slate 37.50 30.00
b. Without overprint 95.00
c. Half used as 1c on cover
133 A15 5c orange 9.00 4.50
a. Without overprint 1.25
b. Half used as 2c on cover
c. As "a," vert. pair, imperf. btwn.
134 A15 10c blue 9.00 4.50
a. Without overprint 1.25
b. Half used as 5c on cover
135 A15 10c brown 9.00
a. Imperf., pair 3.00
136 A15 12c brown 7.50 7.50
a. Without overprint 2.50
b. Imperf., pair 7.50 7.50
c. Half used as 6c on cover
137 A15 18c orange brn 9.00 7.50
a. Horiz. pair, imperf. btwn. 90.00 9.00
b. Without overprint 2.25 12.50
138 A15 24c violet 9.00 7.50
a. Without overprint 2.25 16.00
139 A15 25c rose 45.00 45.00
a. Without overprint 4.50
140 A15 25c orange brn 5.50
141 A15 50c green 42.50 45.00
a. Without overprint 6.25
142 A15 50c yellow 80.00 90.00
a. Without overprint 125.00
143 A15 85c red violet 55.00
144 A15 100c black 60.00 *90.00*
a. Without overprint 4.75
b. Vert. pair, imperf. btwn. 165.00 165.00
145 A15 100c orange 95.00 110.00
a. Without overprint 150.00
Nos. 131-145 (15) 503.00

No. 135, 140 and 143 exist only without overprint. They were never placed in use.

Used values for 50c, 85c and 100c of type A15 are for privately canceled copies. Postally used examples sell for several times as much.

See note on thin paper after No. 122.

A16

Hidalgo — A17

Overprinted with District Name, Number and Abbreviated Date

1882-83

146 A16 2c green 11.00 8.00
a. Without overprint 27.50 18.00
147 A16 3c car lake 11.00 8.00
a. Without overprint 5.25 6.00
148 A16 6c blue ('83) 40.00 30.00
a. Without overprint 27.50 35.00
149 A16 6c ultra 8.50 6.00
a. Without overprint 3.50 3.00
b. Imperf., pair 62.50
Nos. 146-149 (4) 70.50 52.00

See note on thin paper after No. 122.

1884 Wove or Laid Paper *Perf. 12*

150 A17 1c green 4.00 .65
a. Imperf., pair 30.00
b. 1c blue (error) 475.00 450.00
151 A17 2c green 6.00 1.00
a. Imperf., pair 55.00 42.50
b. Half used as 1c on cover
152 A17 3c green 11.00 1.75
a. Imperf., pair 100.00 80.00
b. Horiz. pair, imperf. vert. 65.00
153 A17 4c green 15.00 1.75
a. Imperf., pair 75.00 60.00
b. Half used as 2c on cover 100.00
154 A17 5c green 15.00 1.40
a. Imperf., pair 100.00 80.00
155 A17 6c green 12.50 1.25
a. Imperf., pair 75.00 60.00
156 A17 10c green 15.00 .65
a. Imperf., pair 35.00 27.50
157 A17 12c green 27.50 2.75
a. Vert. pair, imperf. between 75.00 60.00
b. Half used as 6c on cover 90.00
158 A17 20c green 75.00 2.00
a. Diagonal half used as 10c on cover 100.00
b. Imperf., pair 150.00 110.00
159 A17 25c green 130.00 4.00
a. Imperf., pair 240.00 190.00
160 A17 50c green .50 *2.75*
a. Imperf., pair 24.00 20.00
161 A17 1p blue .50 *10.00*
a. Imperf., pair 52.50 42.50
b. Vert. pair, imperf. between
162 A17 2p blue .50 *20.00*
a. Imperf., pair 70.00 55.00
163 A17 5p blue 300.00 170.00
164 A17 10p blue 450.00 190.00
Nos. 150-162 (13) 312.50 *49.95*

Imperforate varieties should be purchased in pairs or larger. Single imperforates are usually trimmed perforated stamps.

Beware of copies of No. 150 that have been chemically changed to resemble No. 150b.

Some values exist perf. 11.

See Nos. 165-173, 230-231.

1885

165 A17 1c pale green 27.50 6.50
166 A17 2c carmine 19.00 3.00
a. Diagonal half used as 1c on cover 75.00
167 A17 3c orange brn 24.00 5.25
a. Imperf., pair 100.00 80.00
168 A17 4c red orange 37.50 16.00
169 A17 5c ultra 24.00 3.25
170 A17 6c dk brown 27.50 5.25
a. Half used as 3c on cover 75.00
171 A17 10c orange 22.50 1.25
a. 10c yellow 22.50 1.25
b. Horiz. pair, imperf. btwn. 100.00 80.00
172 A17 12c olive brn 50.00 8.25
173 A17 25c grnsh blue 175.00 19.00
Nos. 165-173 (9) 407.00 67.75

Numeral of Value — A18

1886 *Perf. 12*

174 A18 1c blue grn 1.65 .55
a. 1c yellow green 1.65 .55
b. Horiz. pair, imperf. btwn. 42.50 32.50
c. Perf. 11 35.00 35.00
175 A18 2c carmine 2.00 .85
a. Horiz. pair, imperf. btwn. 45.00
b. Vert. pair, imperf. between 45.00 45.00
c. Perf. 11 35.00 35.00
d. Half used as 1c on cover 75.00
176 A18 3c lilac 8.00 5.00
177 A18 4c lilac 14.00 3.25
a. Perf. 11 40.00 40.00
178 A18 5c ultra 1.65 .55
a. 5c blue 1.75 .60
179 A18 6c lilac 17.50 2.00
180 A18 10c lilac 17.50 .65
a. Perf. 11 35.00 35.00

181 A18 12c lilac 17.50 10.00
182 A18 20c lilac 125.00 75.00
183 A18 25c lilac 55.00 13.00
Nos. 174-183 (10) 259.80 110.85

Nos. 175, 191, 194B, 196, 202 with blue or black surcharge "Vale 1 Cvo." These were made by the Colima postmaster.

1887
184 A18 3c scarlet 1.40 .40
a. Imperf., pair
185 A18 4c scarlet 5.50 1.50
186 A18 6c scarlet 8.00 1.65
a. Horiz. pair, imperf. btwn. 40.00
187 A18 10c scarlet 2.25 .40
a. Imperf., pair
b. Horiz. pair, imperf. btwn. 35.00
188 A18 20c scarlet 13.50 1.10
a. Horiz. pair, imperf. btwn. 55.00
189 A18 25c scarlet 11.00 2.75
Nos. 184-189 (6) 41.65 7.80

Perf. 6
190 A18 1c blue grn 12.50 9.00
191 A18 2c brown car 17.50 9.00
191A A18 3c scarlet *325.00* 130.00
192 A18 5c ultra 10.00 3.25
a. 5c blue 10.00 3.25
193 A18 10c lilac 10.50 3.25
193A A18 10c brown lilac 9.00 2.25
194 A18 10c scarlet 20.00 11.00

Perf. 6x12
194A A18 1c blue grn 42.50 32.50
194B A18 2c brown car 52.50 42.50
194C A18 3c scarlet 200.00
194D A18 5c ultra 42.50 32.50
194E A18 10c lilac 42.50 37.50
194F A18 10c scarlet 52.50 42.50
194G A18 10c brown lilac 52.50 32.50

Many shades exist.

Paper ruled with blue lines on face or reverse of stamp

1887 ***Perf. 12***
195 A18 1c green 52.50 30.00
196 A18 2c brown car 85.00 32.50
196A A18 3c scarlet
198 A18 5c ultra 85.00 17.50
199 A18 10c scarlet 85.00 16.00

Perf. 6
201 A18 1c green 42.50 13.00
202 A18 2c brown car 42.50 16.00
204 A18 5c ultra 35.00 8.00
205 A18 10c brown lil 30.00 6.50
206 A18 10c scarlet 175.00 25.00
Nos. 201-206 (5) 325.00 68.50

Perf. 6x12
207 A18 1c green 165.00 100.00
208 A18 2c brown car 165.00 100.00
209 A18 5c ultra 165.00 100.00
210 A18 10c brown lil 200.00 85.00
211 A18 10c scarlet 225.00 140.00
Nos. 207-211 (5) 920.00 525.00

1890-95 Wmk. 152 ***Perf. 11 & 12***
Wove or Laid Paper
212 A18 1c yellow grn .45 .25
a. 1c blue green .45 .25
b. Horiz. pair, imperf. btwn. 30.00 30.00
c. Laid paper 2.00 2.00
d. Horiz. pair, imperf. vert. 30.00 30.00
213 A18 2c brown car 1.10 .65
a. 2c carmine 1.10 .50
b. Vert. pair, imperf. btwn. 125.00
c. Imperf., pair 165.00
214 A18 3c vermilion .65 .45
b. Horiz. pair, imperf. between 25.00
215 A18 4c vermilion 2.50 1.65
a. Horiz. pair, imperf. between 65.00
216 A18 5c ultra .45 .35
a. 5c dull blue .65 .45
217 A18 6c vermilion 2.50 2.00
a. Horiz. pair, imperf. btwn. 35.00
218 A18 10c vermilion .25 .25
b. Horiz. or vert. pair, imperf. btwn. 35.00
c. Vert. pair, imperf. horiz. 35.00 35.00
d. Imperf., pair 42.50
219 A18 12c ver ('95) 11.00 12.50
220 A18 20c vermilion 2.00 .85
220A A18 20c dk violet 110.00 125.00
221 A18 25c vermilion 3.25 1.65
Nos. 212-220,221 (10) 24.15 20.60

No. 219 has been reprinted in slightly darker shade than the original.

1892
222 A18 3c orange 3.25 1.65
223 A18 4c orange 3.50 2.00
224 A18 6c orange 4.75 1.65
225 A18 10c orange 25.00 1.65
226 A18 20c orange 42.50 5.00
227 A18 25c orange 13.00 3.50
Nos. 222-227 (6) 92.00 15.45

1892
228 A18 5p carmine 1,000. 700.
229 A18 10p carmine 1,600. 1,000.
230 A17 5p blue green 3,000. 1,000.
231 A17 10p blue green *6,000. 2,500.*

1894 ***Perf. 5½, 6***
232 A18 1c yellow grn 1.75 1.75
233 A18 3c vermilion 6.00 6.00
234 A18 4c vermilion 30.00 20.00
235 A18 5c ultra 9.00 3.25
236 A18 10c vermilion 5.50 2.00
236A A18 20c vermilion 85.00 85.00
237 A18 25c vermilion 42.50 42.50
Nos. 232-237 (7) 179.75 160.50

Perf. 5½x11, 11x5½, Compound and Irregular
238 A18 1c yellow grn 3.50 3.50
238A A18 2c brown car 10.50 10.50
238B A18 3c vermilion 20.00 20.00
238C A18 4c vermilion 35.00 35.00
239 A18 5c ultra 9.00 9.00
a. 5c blue 9.00 9.00
239C A18 6c vermilion 42.50 42.50
240 A18 10c vermilion 14.00 4.00
240A A18 20c vermilion 165.00 100.00
241 A18 25c vermilion 42.50 35.00
Nos. 238-241 (9) 342.00 259.50

The stamps of the 1890 to 1895 issues are also to be found unwatermarked, as part of the sheet frequently escaped the watermark.

Letter Carrier — A20

Mounted Courier with Pack Mule — A21

Statue of Cuauhtémoc A22

Mail Coach A23

Mail Train — A24

Regular or Pin Perf. 12
1895 **Wmk. 152**
Wove or Laid Paper
242 A20 1c green 1.00 .35
a. Vert. pair, imperf. horiz. 75.00
243 A20 2c carmine 1.25 .40
a. Half used as 1c on cover 30.00
244 A20 3c orange brown 1.25 .40
a. Vert. pair, imperf. horiz. 67.50
246 A21 4c orange 4.25 .75
a. 4c orange red 4.25 .75
247 A22 5c ultra 2.25 .20
a. Imperf., pair 35.00 35.00
b. Horiz. or vert. pair, imperf. between 45.00 35.00
e. Half used as 2c on cover 60.00
248 A23 10c lilac rose 1.75 .35
a. Horiz. or vert. pair, imperf. between 52.50
b. Half used as 5c on cover 52.50
249 A21 12c olive brown 22.50 8.00
251 A23 15c brt blue 11.00 1.75
252 A23 20c brown rose 11.00 1.40
b. Half used as 10c on cover 50.00
253 A23 50c purple 35.00 9.50
a. Half used as 25c on cover 75.00
254 A24 1p brown 45.00 24.00
255 A24 5p scarlet 150.00 100.00
256 A24 10p deep blue 250.00 190.00
Nos. 242-256 (13) 536.25 337.10

No. 248 exists in perf. 11.

Perf. 6
242b A20 1c green 32.50 17.50
243b A20 2c carmine 65.00 30.00
244b A20 3c orange brown 50.00 25.00
247c A22 5c ultra 47.50 25.00
248c A23 10c lilac rose 65.00 27.50
249a A21 12c olive brown 60.00 35.00

Perf. 6x12, 12x6 & Compound or Irregular
242c A20 1c green 17.50 10.00
244c A20 3c orange brown 20.00 10.00
246b A21 4c orange 35.00 25.00
247d A22 5c ultra 35.00 25.00
248d A23 10c lilac rose 22.50 10.00
249b A21 12c olive brown 30.00 15.00

251a A23 15c brt blue 35.00 30.00
252a A23 20c brown rose 50.00 35.00
253b A23 50c purple 80.00 50.00

See Nos. 257-291. For overprints see Nos. O10-O48A.

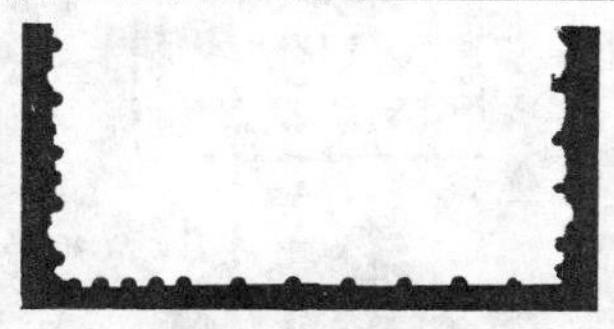

"Irregular" Perfs.
Some copies perf. 6x12, 12x6, 5½x11 and 11x5½ have both perf. 6 and 12 or perf. 5½ and 11 on one or more sides of the stamp. These are known as irregular perfs.

1896-97 **Wmk. 153** ***Perf. 12***
257 A20 1c green 4.00 .45
c. Imperf., pair
258 A20 2c carmine 5.00 .55
a. Horiz. pair, imperf. vert.
259 A20 3c orange brn 5.50 .60
260 A21 4c orange 9.00 .75
c. 4c deep orange 15.00 2.75
261 A22 5c ultra 3.50 .30
a. Imperf., pair 35.00
b. Vert. pair, imperf. btwn. 72.50
262 A21 12c olive brn 65.00 32.50
263 A23 15c brt blue 65.00 5.25
264 A23 20c brown rose 450.00 165.00
265 A23 50c purple 72.50 45.00
266 A24 1p brown 125.00 67.50
267 A24 5p scarlet 400.00 275.00
268 A24 10p dp blue 600.00 325.00
Nos. 257-268 (12) 1,804. 917.90

Perf. 6
257a A20 1c green 15.00 12.50
259a A20 3c orange brown 14.00 10.00
260a A21 4c orange 22.50 12.50
261c A22 5c ultra 65.00 35.00
263a A23 15c bright blue 42.50 20.00

Perf. 6x12, 12x6 and Compound or Irregular
257b A20 1c green 12.50 9.50
258b A20 2c carmine 20.00 12.50
259b A20 3c orange brown 19.00 10.00
260b A21 4c orange 25.00 10.00
261d A22 5c ultra 19.00 10.00
262a A21 12c olive brown 75.00 40.00
263b A23 15c bright blue 150.00 65.00
264a A23 20c brown rose
265a A23 50c purple

1897-98 **Wmk. 154** ***Perf. 12***
269 A20 1c green 6.00 .95
270 A20 2c scarlet 10.00 1.40
271 A21 4c orange 21.00 1.10
a. Horizontal pair, imperf. vertical
272 A22 5c ultra 12.50 .60
a. Imperf., pair 60.00
273 A21 12c olive brown 65.00 13.00
275 A23 15c brt blue 100.00 40.00
276 A23 20c brown rose 70.00 5.50
277 A23 50c purple 110.00 27.50
278 A24 1p brown 150.00 60.00
278A A24 5p scarlet *15,000. 17,500.*
Nos. 269-278 (9) 544.50 150.05

Perf. 6
269a A20 1c green 20.00 12.50
270a A20 2c scarlet 20.00 12.50
272b A22 5c ultra 50.00 20.00
273a A21 12c olive brown 75.00 50.00
276a A23 20c brown rose *600.00*

Perf. 6x12, 12x6 and Compound or Irregular
269b A20 1c green 2.50 *7.00*
270b A20 2c scarlet 2.50 *7.00*
271b A21 4c orange 35.00 12.50
272c A22 5c ultra 22.50 8.00
273b A21 12c olive brown 70.00 30.00
275a A23 15c bright blue 75.00 30.00
276b A23 20c brown rose 100.00 20.00
277a A23 50c purple 80.00 25.00

1898 **Unwmk.** ***Perf. 12***
279 A20 1c green 1.00 .25
a. Horiz. pair, imperf. vert
b. Imperf., pair 60.00
280 A20 2c scarlet 2.25 .35
a. 2c green (error) *350.00*
281 A20 3c orange brn 2.00 .35
a. Imperf., pair 75.00
b. Pair, imperf. between 52.50
282 A21 4c orange 10.50 1.50
b. 4c deep orange 25.00 6.50
283 A22 5c ultra 1.00 .25
a. Imperf., pair 35.00 35.00
b. Pair, imperf. between 80.00
284 A23 10c lilac rose 275.00 110.00
285 A21 12c olive brn 30.00 9.00
a. Imperf., pair 150.00
286 A23 15c brt blue 82.50 4.00
287 A23 20c brown rose 25.00 2.50
a. Imperf., pair 150.00
288 A23 50c purple 65.00 21.00
289 A24 1p brown 75.00 30.00
290 A24 5p carmine rose 450.00 300.00
291 A24 10p deep blue 600.00 400.00
Nos. 279-291 (13) 1,619. 879.20

Perf. 6
279c A20 1c green 42.50 20.00
280b A20 2c scarlet 42.50 9.50
281c A20 3c orange brown 25.00 25.00
283c A22 5c ultra 42.50 9.50
287b A23 20c brown rose 80.00 40.00
291a A24 10p deep blue

Perf. 6x12, 12x6 and Compound or Irregular
279d A20 1c green 19.00 6.00
280c A20 2c scarlet 15.00 5.00
281d A20 3c orange brown 10.00 5.00
282a A21 4c orange 30.00 10.00
283d A22 5c ultra 9.00 4.00
284a A23 10c lilac rose 110.00 75.00
285b A21 12c olive brown 60.00 30.00
286a A23 15c bright blue 40.00 22.50
287c A23 20c brown rose 50.00 25.00
288a A23 50c purple

Forgeries of the 6 and 6x12 perforations of 1895-98 are plentiful.

Coat of Arms
A25 A26

A27

A28

A29

A30

A31

Juanacatlán Falls — A32

View of Mt. Popocatépetl A33

Cathedral, Mexico, D. F. — A34

1899 **Wmk. 155** ***Perf. 14, 15***
294 A25 1c green 1.75 .15
295 A26 2c vermilion 4.25 .25
296 A27 3c orange brn 2.75 .15
297 A28 5c dark blue 4.50 .15
298 A29 10c violet & org 5.75 .35
299 A30 15c lav & claret 7.50 .30
300 A31 20c rose & dk bl 8.50 .40
301 A32 50c red lil & blk 32.50 2.25
a. 50c lilac & black 40.00 2.25
302 A33 1p blue & blk 75.00 3.50
303 A34 5p carmine & blk 225.00 11.00
Nos. 294-303 (10) 367.50 18.50

See Nos. 304-305, 307-309. For overprints see Nos. 420-422, 439-450, 452-454, 482-483, 515-516, 539, 550, O49-O60, O62-O66, O68-O74, O101.

A35

1903
304 A25 1c violet 1.40 .15
a. Booklet pane of 6 55.00

305 A26 2c green 1.90 .15
a. Booklet pane of 6 82.50
306 A35 4c carmine 4.50 .45
307 A28 5c orange 1.10 .15
a. Booklet pane of 6 82.50
308 A29 10c blue & org 4.50 .35
309 A32 50c carmine & blk 72.50 6.00
Nos. 304-309 (6) 85.90 7.25

For overprints see Nos. 451, O61, O67.

Independence Issue

Josefa Ortiz — A36

Leona Vicario — A37

López Rayón — A38

Juan Aldama — A39

Miguel Hidalgo — A40

Ignacio Allende — A41

Epigmenio González — A42

Mariano Abasolo — A43

Declaration of Independence A44

Mass on the Mount of Crosses — A45

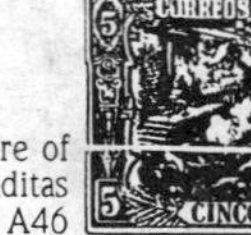
Capture of Granaditas A46

1910 *Perf. 14*
310 A36 1c dull violet .15 .25
a. Booklet pane of 4 40.00
311 A37 2c green .15 .15
a. Booklet pane of 8 40.00
312 A38 3c orange brn .60 .30
313 A39 4c carmine 2.25 .45
314 A40 5c orange .15 .15
a. Booklet pane of 8 27.50
315 A41 10c blue & org 1.40 .25
316 A42 15c gray bl & cl 7.50 .50
317 A43 20c red & bl 4.50 .40
318 A44 50c red brn & blk 11.00 1.65
319 A45 1p blue & blk 13.50 1.90
320 A46 5p car & blk 50.00 5.00
Nos. 310-320 (11) 91.20 11.00

Centenary of the independence of Mexico from Spain.

For overprints and surcharges see Nos. 370-380, 423-433, 455-465, 484-494, 517-538, 540-549, 551-558, 577-590, O75-O85, O102-O112, O191-O192, O195, RA13, Merida 1.

CIVIL WAR ISSUES

During the 1913-16 Civil War, provisional issues with various handstamped overprints were circulated in limited areas.

Sonora

A47

Seal

Typeset in a row of five varieties. Two impressions placed tête bêche (foot to foot) constitute a sheet. The settings show various wrong font and defective letters, "!" for "1" in "1913," etc. The paper occasionally has a manufacturer's watermark.

a

b

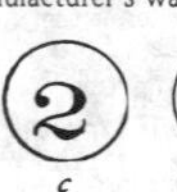
c

d

Four Types of the Numerals.
a- Wide, heavy-faced numerals.
b- Narrow Roman numerals.
c- Wide Roman numerals.
d- Gothic or sans-serif numerals.

Embossed "CONSTITUCIONAL"

1913 Typeset Unwmk. *Perf. 12*
321 A47 (a) 5c black & red 2,500. 650.00
a. "CENTAVOB" *2,750.* *700.00*

Colorless Roulette
322 A47(b) 1c black & red 10.00 12.00
a. With green seal *750.00* *650.00*
323 A47(a) 2c black & red 7.00 7.00
a. With green seal *950.00* *950.00*
324 A47(c) 2c black & red 35.00 35.00
a. With green seal *2,000.* *2,000.*
325 A47(a) 3c black & red 45.00 37.50
a. With green seal *400.00* *400.00*
326 A47(a) 5c black & red 150.00 37.50
a. "CENTAVOB" 175.00 42.50
327 A47(d) 5c black & red 400.00 200.00
a. With green seal 650.00
328 A47(b) 10c black & red 12.50 15.00

Black Roulette
329 A47(d) 5c black & red 75.00 45.00
a. "MARO" 85.00 50.00

Stamps are known with the embossing double or omitted.

The varieties with green seal are from a few sheets embossed "Constitucional" which were in stock at the time the green seal control was adopted.

Without Embossing
With Green Seal
Colorless Roulette
336 A47(b) 1c black & red 5.00 5.00
337 A47(a) 3c black & red 4.50 4.50
a. Imperf. 250.00
338 A47(a) 5c black & red 700.00 200.00
a. "CENTAVOB" *750.00* 225.00
339 A47(b) 10c black & red 3.00 3.00

Colored Roulette
340 A47(d) 5c brnsh blk & red 6.00 3.00
a. 5c lilac brown & red 45.00 11.00
b. Double seal *1,000.* *750.00*
c. Red printing omitted *1,000.*

1913-14 ***Black Roulette***
With Green Seal
341 A47(a) 1c black & red 1.20 1.00
b. "erano" ('14) 60.00 60.00
342 A47(d) 2c black & red 1.20 .90
a. "erano" ('14) 30.00 35.00
343 A47(a) 3c black & red 1.75 1.50
a. "CENTAVO" 25.00 25.00
b. "erano" ('14) 35.00 35.00
344 A47(d) 5c black & red 1.75 1.00
b. Heavy black penetrating roulette 2.75 1.75
c. As "b," "MARO" 7.50 5.00
Nos. 341-344 (4) 5.90 4.40

Stamps without seal are unfinished remainders.

On Nos. 341-344 the rouletting cuts the paper slightly or not at all. On Nos. 344b-344c the rouletting is heavy, cutting deeply into the paper.

1914
345 A47(a) 5c black & red 2.00 1.75
346 A47(b) 10c black & red 1.20 1.20

Coat of Arms — A49

Revenue Stamps Used for Postage

1913 Litho. ***Rouletted 14, 14x7***
347 A49 1c yellow grn 1.50 1.50
a. With coupon 5.00 5.00
348 A49 2c violet 3.00 3.00
a. With coupon 12.00 12.00
349 A49 5c brown .45 .45
a. With coupon 1.25 1.25
350 A49 10c claret 2.00 2.00
a. With coupon 10.00 10.00
351 A49 20c gray grn 2.25 2.75
a. With coupon 15.00 15.00
352 A49 50c ultra 8.00 10.00
a. With coupon 50.00 40.00
353 A49 1p orange 35.00 40.00
a. With coupon 125.00 100.00
Nos. 347-353 (7) 52.20 59.70

For a short time these stamps (called "Ejercitos") were used for postage with coupon attached. Later this was required to be removed unless they were to be used for revenue. Stamps overprinted with district names are revenues. Values above 1p were used for revenue. Imperfs exist of all values, but were not issued.

Many copies do not have gum because of a flood.

Use of typeset Sonora revenue stamps for postage was not authorized or allowed.

Coat of Arms
A50 A51

5c (A50): "CINCO CENTAVOS" 14x2mm

1914 ***Rouletted 9½x14***
354 A50 1c deep blue .45 .45
355 A50 2c yellow grn .60 .35
a. 2c green 3.00 1.75
356 A50 4c blue vio 11.00 2.50
a. Horiz. pair, imperf. btwn. 225.00
357 A50 5c gray grn 11.00 3.00
a. Horiz. pair imperf. btwn. 65.00
358 A50 10c red .45 .45
359 A50 20c yellow brn .60 .60
a. 20c deep brown 2.25 2.25
b. Horiz. pair, imperf. btwn. 225.00
360 A50 50c claret 2.50 3.50
a. Horiz. pair, imperf. btwn. 225.00
361 A50 1p brt violet 14.00 16.00
a. Horiz. pair, imperf. btwn. 200.00
Nos. 354-361 (8) 40.60 26.85

Nos. 354-361 (called "Transitorios") exist imperf. but were not regularly issued.

Many copies do not have gum because of a flood.

See Note after No. 465.

See No. 369. For overprints see Nos. 362-368, 559-565.

Overprinted in Black

Victoria de
TORREON
ABRIL 2-1914

1914
362 A50 1c deep blue 150.00 125.00
363 A50 2c yellow green 175.00 150.00
364 A50 4c blue violet 200.00 250.00
365 A50 5c gray green 18.00 20.00
a. Horiz. pair, imperf. btwn. 425.00
366 A50 10c red 100.00 100.00
367 A50 20c yellow brn *1,750.* *1,750.*
368 A50 50c claret *2,000.* *2,000.*

Values are for copies with design close to, or just touching, the perfs.

Excellent counterfeits of this overprint exist.

Redrawn
"CINCO CENTAVOS" 16x2½mm

1914 *Perf. 12*
369 A51 5c gray green .15 .15

Imperfs are printers' waste.

Regular Issue of 1910 Overprinted in Violet, Magenta, Black or Green

1914 Wmk. 155 *Perf. 14*
370 A36 1c dull violet .70 .60
a. Booklet pane of 4 75.00
371 A37 2c green 1.50 1.25
a. Booklet pane of 8 75.00
372 A38 3c orange brn 1.50 1.25
373 A39 4c carmine 2.50 2.00
374 A40 5c orange .50 .30
a. Booklet pane of 8 60.00
375 A41 10c blue & org 3.00 2.00
376 A42 15c gray bl & cl 5.00 3.00
377 A43 20c red & blue 10.00 6.00
378 A44 50c red brn & blk 12.00 8.00
379 A45 1p blue & blk 25.00 10.00
380 A46 5p carmine & blk 165.00 150.00
Nos. 370-380 (11) 226.70 184.40

Overprinted On Postage Due Stamps of 1908

381 D1 1c blue 14.00 16.00
382 D1 2c blue 14.00 16.00
383 D1 4c blue 14.00 16.00
384 D1 5c blue 14.00 16.00
385 D1 10c blue 14.00 16.00
Nos. 381-385 (5) 70.00 80.00

This overprint is found double, inverted, sideways and in pairs with and without the overprint.

There are two or more types of this overprint.

The Postage Due Stamps and similar groups of them which follow were issued and used as regular postage stamps.

Values are for copies where the overprint is clear enough to be expertised.

Counterfeits abound.

A52

A53

1914 Unwmk. Litho. *Perf. 12*
386 A52 1c pale blue .35 .50
387 A52 2c light green .30 .45
388 A52 3c orange .50 .50
389 A52 5c deep rose .50 .30
390 A52 10c rose .70 .85
391 A52 15c rose lilac 1.20 1.75
392 A52 50c yellow 2.00 2.50
a. 50c ocher 1.75
393 A52 1p violet 8.50 12.00
Nos. 386-393 (8) 14.05 18.85

Nos. 386-393, are known imperforate.

This set is usually called the Denver Issue because it was printed there.

See Note after No. 465.

For overprints and surcharges see Nos. 566-573, 591-592.

Revenue Stamps Used for Postage

1914, July *Perf. 12*
393A A53 1c rose 20.00
393B A53 2c lt green 18.00
393C A53 3c lt orange 20.00
393D A53 5c red 8.00
393E A53 10c gray green 35.00
Nos. 393A-393E (5) 101.00

Nos. 393A-393E were used in the northeast. Values are for examples with postal cancellations.

Unused copies are to be considered as revenues.

Background as A55 — A54

A55

1914 *Imperf.*
Values and Inscriptions in Black
Inscribed "SONORA"
394 A54 1c blue & red .25 .25
a. Double seal
b. Without seal 20.00
395 A54 2c green & org .30 .30
a. Without seal 100.00
396 A54 5c yellow & grn .30 .30
a. 5c orange & green 1.50 1.25
b. Without seal 200.00

397 A54 10c lt bl & red 3.50 1.75
a. 10c blue & red 40.00 15.00
398 A54 20c yellow & grn 1.75 2.00
399 A54 20c orange & bl 15.00 17.50
400 A54 50c green & org 1.25 1.25
Nos. 394-400 (7) 22.35 23.35

Shades. Stamps of type A54 are usually termed the "Coach Seal Issue."

Inscribed "DISTRITO SUR DE LA BAJA CAL"

401 A54 1c yellow & blue 2.00 *30.00*
a. Without seal 50.00
402 A54 2c gray & ol grn 2.50 *25.00*
403 A54 5c olive & rose 2.00 *20.00*
a. Without seal 50.00
404 A54 10c pale red & dl vio 2.00 *20.00*
a. Without seal 50.00
Nos. 401-404 (4) 8.50

Counterfeit cancellations exist.

Inscribed "SONORA"

405 A55 1c blue & red 6.00
a. Without seal 50.00
406 A55 2c green & org .50
407 A55 5c yellow & grn .50 *2.50*
a. Without seal 75.00
408 A55 10c blue & red .50 *2.50*
409 A55 20c yellow & grn 30.00 *15.00*
a. Without seal 50.00
b. Double seal *80.00*
Nos. 405-409 (5) 37.50

With "PLATA" added to the inscription

410 A55 1c blue & red 1.00
a. "PLATA" inverted 60.00
b. Pair, one without "PLATA" 15.00
411 A55 10c blue & red 1.00
412 A55 20c yellow & grn 2.50
a. "PLATA" double 50.00
413 A55 50c gray grn & org 1.75
a. Without seal 1.00
b. As "a," "P" of "PLATA" missing 150.00
Nos. 410-413 (4) 6.25

Stamps of type A55 are termed the "Anvil Seal Issue".
Nos. 394-413 were issued without gum.
Nos. 410-413 were not placed in use.

Oaxaca

Coat of Arms — A56

5c:
Type I - Thick numerals, 2mm wide.
Type II - Thin numerals, 1 1/2mm wide.

Perf. 8 1/2 to 14
1915 Typo. Unwmk.

414 A56 1c dull violet .85 1.25
415 A56 2c emerald 1.50 2.25
a. Inverted numeral 30.00
e. Numeral omitted 35.00
416 A56 3c red brown 2.25 3.50
b. Inverted numeral 24.00
417 A56 5c org (type I) 20.00 25.00
a. Tête bêche pair 60.00 60.00
418 A56 5c org (type II) .50 .75
a. Types I and II in pair 70.00
419 A56 10c blue & car 1.75
Nos. 414-419 (6) 26.85

Many printing errors, imperfs and part perfs exist. Mostly these are printers' waste, private reprints or counterfeits.
Nos. 414-419 printed on backs of post office receipt forms.

Regular Issues of 1899-1910 Overprinted in Black

GOBIERNO $ CONSTITUCIONALISTA

1914 Wmk. 155 *Perf. 14*
On Issues of 1899-1903

420 A28 5c orange
421 A30 15c lav & claret 150.00 150.00
422 A31 20c rose & dk bl *650.00* 400.00

Counterfeits exist.

The listing of No. 420 is being re-evaluated. The Catalogue Editors would appreciate any information on the stamp.

On Issue of 1910

423 A36 1c dull violet .20 .20
424 A37 2c green .25 .25
425 A38 3c orange brown .40 .40
426 A39 4c carmine .50 .50
427 A40 5c orange .15 .15
428 A41 10c blue & orange .25 .25
429 A42 15c gray bl & claret .70 .60
430 A43 20c red & blue .75 .70

Overprinted

GOBIERNO
Y
CONSTITUCIONALISTA

431 A44 50c red brn & blk 1.75 1.50
432 A45 1p blue & blk 7.50 5.00
433 A46 5p carmine & blk 40.00 30.00
Nos. 423-433 (11) 52.45 39.55

In the first setting of the overprint on 1c to 20c, the variety "GONSTITUCIONALISTA" occurs 4 times in each sheet of 100. In the second setting it occurs on the last stamp in each row of 10.

The overprint exists reading downward on Nos. 423-430; inverted on Nos. 431-433; double on Nos. 423-425, 427.

See Note after No. 465.

Postage Due Stamps of 1908 Overprinted

GOBIERNO $ CONSTITUCIONALISTA

434 D1 1c blue 1.75 1.75
435 D1 2c blue 2.00 2.00
436 D1 4c blue 15.00 15.00
437 D1 5c blue 15.00 15.00
438 D1 10c blue 2.50 2.50
a. Double overprint
Nos. 434-438 (5) 36.25 36.25

Preceding Issues Overprinted

This is usually called the "Villa" monogram. Counterfeits abound.

1915

On Issue of 1899

439 A25 1c green *130.00*
440 A26 2c vermilion *130.00*
441 A27 3c orange brn *65.00*
442 A28 5c dark blue *130.00*
443 A29 10c violet & org *130.00*
444 A30 15c lav & claret *130.00*
445 A31 20c rose & bl *130.00*
446 A32 50c red lil & blk *325.00*
447 A33 1p blue & blk *325.00*
448 A34 5p car & blk *650.00*
Nos. 439-448 (10) *2,145.*

On Issue of 1903

449 A25 1c violet *130.00*
450 A26 2c green *130.00*
451 A35 4c carmine *130.00*
452 A28 5c orange 18.00
a. Inverted overprint *27.50*
453 A29 10c blue & org *100.00*
454 A32 50c car & blk *250.00*
Nos. 449-454 (6) *758.00*

In Sept. 1915 Postmaster Hinojosa ordered a special printing of Nos. 439-454 (as valued) for sale to collectors. Earlier a small quantity of Nos. 444-445, 448 and 452-454 was regularly issued. They are hard to distinguish and sell for much more. Counterfeits abound.

On Issue of 1910

455 A36 1c dull violet .85 1.00
456 A37 2c green .40 .60
457 A38 3c orange brown .60 .75
458 A39 4c carmine 4.00 4.50
459 A40 5c orange .20 .20
460 A41 10c blue & orange 7.00 7.50
461 A42 15c gray bl & cl 3.00 4.00
462 A43 20c red & blue 5.50 7.00
463 A44 50c red brn & blk 13.00 14.00
464 A45 1p blue & blk 17.00 20.00
465 A46 5p carmine & blk *150.00*
Nos. 455-464 (10) 51.55 59.55

Nos. 455-465 are known with overprint inverted, double and other variations. Most were ordered by Postmaster General Hinojosa for philtelic purposes. They were sold at a premium. This applies to Nos. 354-361, 386-393, 431-433 with this monogram as well.

Overprinted On Postage Due Stamps of 1908

466 D1 1c blue 9.50 10.00
467 D1 2c blue 9.50 10.00
468 D1 4c blue 9.50 10.00
469 D1 5c blue 9.50 10.00
470 D1 10c blue 9.50 10.00
Nos. 466-470 (5) 47.50 50.00

Nos. 466 to 470 are known with inverted overprint. All other values of the 1899 and 1903 issues exist with this overprint. See note after No. 465.

Issues of 1899-1910 Overprinted

This is called the "Carranza" or small monogram. Counterfeits abound.

On Issues of 1899-1903

482 A28 5c orange 20.00 20.00
483 A30 15c lav & claret 80.00 80.00

On Issue of 1910

484 A36 1c dull violet .70 .70
485 A37 2c green .70 .60
486 A38 3c orange brn .75 .75
487 A39 4c carmine 2.00 2.00
488 A40 5c orange .25 .25
489 A41 10c blue & org 1.50 1.50
a. Double ovpt., one invtd. 25.00
490 A42 15c gray bl & cl 1.50 1.50
491 A43 20c red & blue 1.50 1.50
492 A44 50c red brn & blk 10.00 10.00
493 A45 1p blue & blk 15.00 15.00
494 A46 5p car & blk 150.00 *150.00*
Nos. 484-494 (11) 183.90 *183.80*

All values exist with inverted overprint; all but 5p with double overprint.

Overprinted On Postage Due Stamps of 1908

495 D1 1c blue 11.00 12.00
496 D1 2c blue 11.00 12.00
497 D1 4c blue 11.00 12.00
498 D1 5c blue 11.00 12.00
499 D1 10c blue 11.00 12.00
Nos. 495-499 (5) 55.00 60.00

Nos. 495-499 exist with inverted overprint.

It is stated that, in parts of Mexico occupied by the revolutionary forces, instructions were given to apply a distinguishing overprint to all stamps found in the post offices. This overprint was usually some arrangement or abbreviation of "Gobierno Constitucionalista". Such overprints as were specially authorized or were in general use in large sections of the country are listed. Numerous other handstamped overprints were used in one town or locality. They were essentially military faction control marks necessitated in most instances by the chaotic situation following the split between Villa and Carranza. The fact that some were often struck in a variety of colors and positions suggests the influence of philatelists.

Coat of Arms
A57

Statue of Cuauhtémoc
A58

Ignacio Zaragoza
A59

José María Morelos
A60

Francisco Madero
A61

Benito Juárez
A62

1915 Unwmk. Litho. *Rouletted 14*

500 A57 1c violet .15 .15
501 A58 2c green .25 .20
502 A59 3c brown .50 .25
503 A60 4c carmine .50 .25
504 A61 5c orange .75 .25
505 A62 10c ultra .35 .30
Nos. 500-505 (6) 2.50 1.40

Nos. 500-505 exists imperf.; some exist imperf. vertically or horizontally; some with rouletting and perforation combined. These probably were not regularly issued in these forms.

See Nos. 506-511. For overprints see Nos. O86-O97.

Map of Mexico — A63

Veracruz Lighthouse
A64

Post Office, Mexico, D.F. — A65

TEN CENTAVOS:
Type I - Size 19 1/2x24mm. Crossed lines on coat.
Type II - Size 19x23 1/2mm. Diagonal lines only on coat.

1915-16 *Perf. 12*

506 A57 1c violet .40 .30
507 A58 2c green .40 .30
508 A59 3c brown .50 .30
509 A60 4c carmine .50 .35
a. "CEATRO" 7.50 7.50
510 A61 5c orange .75 .35
511 A62 10c ultra, type I 1.00 .35
a. 10c ultra, type II .50 .25

Engr.

512 A63 40c slate .75 .35
513 A64 1p brown & blk 1.00 .75
a. Inverted center 200.00
514 A65 5p cl & ultra ('16) 10.00 4.00
a. Inverted center 400.00
Nos. 506-514 (9) 15.30 7.05

Nos. 507-508, 510-514, exist imperf; Nos. 513-514 imperf with inverted center. These varieties were not regularly issued.

See Nos. 626-628, 647. For overprints see Nos. O92-O100, O121-O123, O132-O133, O142-O144, O153-O154, O162-O164, O174, O188, O193, O207, O222.

Issues of 1899-1910 Overprinted in Blue, Red or Black

1916 Wmk. 155 *Perf. 14*
On Issues of 1899-1903

515 A28 5c orange (Bl) 85.00 15.00
516 A30 15c lav & cl (Bl) 425.00 425.00

On Issue of 1910

517 A36 1c dull vio (R) 10.00 *10.00*
518 A37 2c green (R) .50 .35
519 A38 3c orange brn (Bl) .55 .35
a. Double overprint 500.00
520 A39 4c carmine (Bl) 6.00 *8.00*
521 A40 5c orange (Bl) .25 .25
a. Double overprint 75.00
522 A41 10c blue & org (R) 1.25 1.50
523 A42 15c gray bl & cl (Bk) 1.75 3.00
524 A43 20c red & bl (Bk) 1.75 3.00
525 A44 50c red brn & blk (R) 8.50 5.00
526 A45 1p blue & blk (R) 15.00 6.50
527 A46 5p car & blk (R) 175.00 175.00
Nos. 517-527 (11) 220.55 212.95

Nos. 519-524 exist with this overprint (called the "Corbata") reading downward and Nos. 525-527 with it inverted. Of these varieties only Nos. 519-521 were regularly issued.

On Nos. 423-430

528 A36 1c dull vio (R) 2.50 4.00
529 A37 2c green (R) .75 .60
530 A38 3c orange brn (Bl) .60 .60
531 A39 4c carmine (Bl) .60 .60
532 A40 5c orange (Bl) 1.00 .30
533 A41 10c blue & org (R) .75 .60
534 A42 15c gray bl & cl (Bk) .80 .80
535 A43 20c red & bl (Bk) .80 .80

On Nos. 431-433 in Red

536 A44 50c red brn & blk 7.50 6.00
537 A45 1p blue & blk 16.00 16.00
538 A46 5p carmine & blk 150.00 140.00
a. Tablet inverted 200.00
Nos. 528-538 (11) 181.30 170.30

Nos. 529 to 535 are known with the overprint reading downward and Nos. 536 to 538 with it inverted.

On No. 482

539 A28 5c orange (Bl) 60.00 *60.00*

On Nos. 484-494

540 A36 1c dull vio (R) 5.00 *5.00*
541 A37 2c green (R) .60 .60
a. Monogram inverted 40.00
542 A38 3c orange brn (Bl) .50 .60
543 A39 4c carmine (Bl) 7.50 9.00
544 A40 5c orange (Bl) .85 .25
545 A41 10c blue & org (R) 1.50 2.00
546 A42 15c gray bl & cl (Bk) 1.25 .60
a. Tablet double *500.00 500.00*
b. Monogram double *500.00*
547 A43 20c red & bl (Bk) 1.20 1.10
548 A44 50c red brn & blk (R) 7.50 9.00
a. Monogram inverted 65.00
b. Tablet inverted 75.00
549 A45 1p blue & blk (R) 11.00 12.00
a. Tablet double 175.00
b. Monogram inverted 60.00
Nos. 539-549 (11) 96.90 *100.15*

Nos. 541-547 exist with overprint reading downward. A few 5p were overprinted for the Post Office collection.

On No. 453

550 A28 5c orange (Bl) 90.00 *90.00*

On Nos. 455-462

551 A36 1c dull vio (R) 11.00 *15.00*
552 A37 2c green (R) 1.50 .90
553 A38 3c org brn (Bl) 3.25 *4.50*
554 A39 4c carmine (Bl) 13.00 *15.00*
555 A40 5c orange (Bl) 4.50 *6.00*
556 A41 10c bl & org (R) 12.00 *14.00*
a. Monogram inverted 125.00
557 A42 15c gray bl & cl (Bk) 12.00 *14.00*
a. Monogram inverted 90.00
558 A43 20c red & bl (Bk) 12.00 *14.00*
a. Monogram inverted 82.50
Nos. 550-558 (9) 159.25 *173.40*

Stamps of 50c, 1p and 5p were overprinted for the Post Office collection but were not regularly issued.

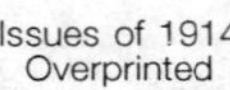

Issues of 1914 Overprinted

On "Transitorio" Issue

Rouletted 9½x14

Unwmk.

559 A50 1c dp blue (R) 24.00 24.00
560 A50 2c yellow grn (R) 12.00 18.00
561 A50 4c blue vio (R) 250.00 200.00
562 A50 10c red (Bl) 2.00 6.00
a. Vertical overprint 125.00
563 A50 20c yellow brn (Bl) 3.00 6.00
564 A50 50c claret (Bl) 15.00 20.00
565 A50 1p violet (Bl) 24.00 24.00
a. Horiz. pair, imperf. btwn.
Nos. 559-565 (7) 330.00 298.00

Overprinted in Blue
On "Denver" Issue
Perf. 12

566 A52 1c pale blue 3.75
567 A52 2c lt green 3.75
568 A52 3c orange .45
569 A52 5c deep rose .45
570 A52 10c rose .45
571 A52 15c rose lilac .45
572 A52 50c yellow 1.10
573 A52 1p violet 9.50
Nos. 566-573 (8) 19.90

Many of the foregoing stamps exist with the "G. P. DE M." overprint printed in other colors than those listed. These "trial color" stamps were not regularly on sale at post offices but were available for postage and used copies are known.

There appears to have been speculation in Nos. 516, 517, 520, 528, 539, 540, 543, 566, and 567. A small quantity of each of these stamps was sold at post offices but subsequently they could be obtained only from officials or their agents at advanced prices.

Venustiano Carranza
A66

Coat of Arms
A67

1916, June 1 **Engr.** ***Perf. 12***

574 A66 10c blue 1.50 1.00
a. Imperf., pair 25.00
575 A66 10c lilac brown 14.00 15.00
a. Imperf., pair 50.00

Entry of Carranza into Mexico, D.F.
Stamps of type A66 with only horizontal lines in the background of the oval are essays.

1916

576 A67 1c lilac .20 .20

Issue of 1910 Surcharged in Various Colors

This overprint is called the "Barril."

1916 **Wmk. 155** ***Perf. 14***

577 A36 5c on 1c dl vio (Br) .50 .50
a. Vertical surcharge 1.25 1.25
b. Double surcharge 150.00
578 A36 10c on 1c dl vio (Bl) .50 .50
a. Double surcharge 100.00
579 A40 20c on 5c org (Br) .50 .50
a. Double surcharge 90.00
580 A40 25c on 5c org (G) .40 .50
581 A37 60c on 2c grn (R) 25.00 20.00
Nos. 577-581 (5) 26.90 22.00

On Nos. 423-424, 427

582 A36 5c on 1c (Br) .50 .50
a. Double tablet, one vertical 100.00
b. Inverted tablet 250.00 250.00
583 A36 10c on 1c (Bl) 1.00 1.00
584 A40 25c on 5c (G) .50 .50
a. Inverted tablet 225.00 225.00
585 A37 60c on 2c (R) 200.00 *275.00*

No. 585 was not regularly issued.
The variety "GONSTITUCIONALISTA" is found on Nos. 582 to 585.

On No. 459

586 A40 25c on 5c org (G) .20 .15

On Nos. 484-485, 488

587 A36 5c on 1c (Br) 15.00 20.00
a. Vertical tablet 100.00 125.00
588 A36 10c on 1c (Bl) 5.00 7.50
589 A40 25c on 5c (G) 1.00 1.50
a. Inverted tablet 225.00
590 A37 60c on 2c (R) 225.00

No. 590 was not regularly issued.

Surcharged on "Denver" Issue of 1914

1916 **Unwmk.** ***Perf. 12***

591 A52 60c on 1c pale bl (Br) 3.00 6.00
592 A52 60c on 2c lt grn (Br) 3.00 6.00
a. Inverted surcharge *750.00*

Postage Due Stamps Surcharged Like Nos. 577-581

1916 **Wmk. 155** ***Perf. 14***

593 D1 5c on 1c blue (Br) 2.50
594 D1 10c on 2c blue (V) 2.50
595 D1 20c on 4c blue (Br) 2.50
596 D1 25c on 5c blue (G) 2.50
597 D1 60c on 10c blue (R) 1.50
598 D1 1p on 1c blue (C) 1.50
599 D1 1p on 2c blue (C) 1.50
600 D1 1p on 4c blue (C) .80 .80
601 D1 1p on 5c blue (C) 2.50
602 D1 1p on 10c blue (C) 2.50
Nos. 593-602 (10) 20.30

There are numerous "trial colors" and "essays" of the overprints and surcharges on Nos. 577 to 602. They were available for postage though not regularly issued.

Postage Due Stamps Surcharged

1916

603 D1 2.50p on 1c blue 1.25 1.25
604 D1 2.50p on 2c blue 10.00
605 D1 2.50p on 4c blue 10.00
606 D1 2.50p on 5c blue 10.00
607 D1 2.50p on 10c blue 10.00
Nos. 603-607 (5) 41.25

Regular Issue

Ignacio Zaragoza
A68

Ildefonso Vázquez
A69

J. M. Pino Suárez
A70

Jesús Carranza
A71

Maclovio Herrera
A72

F. I. Madero
A73

Belisario Domínguez
A74

Aquiles Serdán
A75

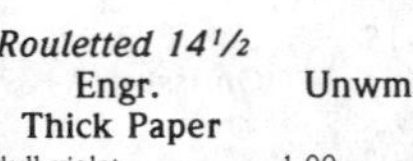

Rouletted 14½

1917-20 **Engr.** **Unwmk.**

Thick Paper

608 A68 1c dull violet 1.00 .50
609 A68 1c gray ('20) 2.50 1.00
a. 1c lilac gray ('20) 1.50 .50
610 A69 2c gray green .75 .30
611 A70 3c bister brn .75 .30
612 A71 4c carmine 1.50 .75
613 A72 5c ultra 2.00 .25
a. Horiz. pair, imperf. btwn. 50.00
b. Imperf., pair 50.00
614 A73 10c blue 3.00 .50
a. Without imprint 5.00 .50
615 A74 20c rose 30.00 1.50
a. 20c brown rose 25.00 .60
616 A75 30c gray brown 75.00 2.50
617 A75 30c gray blk ('20) 80.00 3.00
Nos. 608-617 (10) 196.50 10.60

Perf. 12

Thick or Medium Paper

618 A68 1c dull violet 25.00 25.00
619 A69 2c gray green 7.50 5.00
620 A70 3c bis brn ('17) 125.00 110.00
621 A71 4c carmine *500.00 500.00*
622 A72 5c ultra 4.00 .20
623 A73 10c blue ('17) 4.00 .20
a. Without imprint ('17) 15.00 15.00
624 A74 20c rose ('20) 125.00 2.50
625 A75 30c gray blk ('20) 100.00 1.65

Thin or Medium Paper

626 A63 40c violet 50.00 .75
627 A64 1p blue & blk 40.00 1.50
a. With center of 5p 450.00
b. 1p bl & dark blue (error) 500.00 25.00
c. Vert. pair, imperf. btwn. 250.00
628 A65 5p green & blk 1.25 5.00
a. With violet or red control number 7.50
b. With center of 1p 425.00

The 1, 2, 3, 5 and 10c are known on thin paper perforated. It is stated they were printed for Postal Union and "specimen" purposes.

All values exist imperf; these are not known to have been regularly issued. Nos. 627a and 628b were not regularly issued.

All values except 3c have an imprint.

For overprints and surcharges see Nos. B1-B2, O113-O165.

Meeting of Iturbide and Guerrero
A77

Entering City of Mexico — A78

1921

632 A77 10c blue & brn 15.00 3.00
a. Center inverted *25,000.*
633 A78 10p black brn & blk 20.00 35.00

Commemorating the meeting of Augustin de Iturbide and Vincente Guerrero and the entry into City of Mexico in 1821.

For overprint see No. O194.

"El Salto de Agua," Public Fountain
A79

Pyramid of the Sun at Teotihuacán
A80

Chapultepec Castle
A81

Columbus Monument
A82

Juárez Colonnade, Mexico, D. F. — A83

Monument to Josefa Ortiz de Dominguez
A84

Cuauhtémoc Monument
A85

1923 **Unwmk.** ***Rouletted 14½***

634 A79 2c scarlet 2.00 .20
635 A80 3c bister brn 2.00 .25
636 A81 4c green 2.50 .75
637 A82 5c orange 5.00 .20
638 A83 10c brown 3.75 .15
639 A85 10c claret 3.50 .15
640 A84 20c dk blue 50.00 1.75
641 A85 30c dk green 32.50 2.00
Nos. 634-641 (8) 101.25 5.45

See Nos. 642-646, 650-657, 688-692, 727A, 735A-736. For overprints see Nos. O166-O173, O178-O181, O183-O187, O196-O197, O199-O206, O210, O212-O214, O217-O222.

Communications Building — A87

Palace of Fine Arts (National Theater) — A88

Two types of 1p:
I - Eagle on palace dome.
II - Without eagle.

1923 **Wmk. 156** ***Perf. 12***

642 A79 2c scarlet 10.00 10.00
643 A81 4c green 1.40 .35
644 A82 5c orange 10.00 7.00
645 A85 10c brown lake 12.50 6.00
646 A83 30c dark green .95 .20
647 A63 40c violet 1.25 .25

648 A87 50c olive brn 1.00 .25
649 A88 1p red brn & bl (I) 1.00 1.00
a. Type II 3.00 10.00
Nos. 642-649 (8) 38.10 25.05

Most of Nos. 642-649 are known imperforate or part perforate but probably were not regularly issued.

For overprints see Nos. O175-O176, O189-O190, O208-O209, O223.

1923-34 ***Rouletted 14½***

650 A79 2c scarlet .25 .15
651 A80 3c bis brn ('27) .25 .15
652 A81 4c green 25.00 10.00
653 A82 4c green ('27) .25 .15
654 A82 5c orange .25 .15
655 A85 10c lake .25 .15
656 A84 20c deep blue .75 .30
657 A83 30c dk green ('34) .75 .30
Nos. 650-657 (8) 27.75 11.35

Nos. 650 to 657 inclusive exist imperforate.

Medallion A90

Map of Americas A91

Francisco García y Santos — A92

Post Office, Mexico, D. F. — A93

1926 ***Perf. 12***

658 A90 2c red 2.50 1.00
659 A91 4c green 2.50 1.00
660 A90 5c orange 2.50 .75
661 A91 10c brown red 4.00 1.00
662 A92 20c dk blue 4.00 1.25
663 A92 30c dk green 7.00 4.00
664 A92 40c violet 12.50 3.00
665 A93 1p brown & blue 25.00 10.00
a. 1p red & blue 35.00 15.00
Nos. 658-665 (8) 60.00 22.00

Pan-American Postal Congress.

Nos. 658-665 were also printed in black, on unwatermarked paper, for presentation to delegates to the Universal Postal Congress at London in 1929. Remainders were overprinted in 1929 for use as airmail official stamps, and are listed as Nos. CO3-CO10.

For overprints see Nos. 667-674, 675A-682, CO3-CO10.

Benito Juárez — A94

1926 ***Rouletted 14½***

666 A94 8c orange .30 .15

For overprint see No. O182.

Nos. 658-665 Overprinted

HABILITADO 1930

1930 ***Perf. 12***

667 A90 2c red 4.00 2.25
a. Reading down 15.00 15.00
668 A91 4c green 4.00 2.50
a. Reading down 15.00 15.00
669 A90 5c orange 4.00 2.00
a. Reading down 15.00
b. Double overprint 75.00 75.00
670 A91 10c brown red 7.50 2.50
671 A92 20c dk blue 9.50 3.50
672 A92 30c dk green 8.50 4.00
a. Reading down 10.00 12.00
673 A92 40c violet 12.50 8.50
a. Reading down 47.50
674 A93 1p red brn & bl 11.00 7.00
a. Double overprint 140.00
b. Triple overprint 200.00
Nos. 667-674 (8) 61.00 32.25

Overprint horizontal on 1p.

Arms of Puebla — A95

1931, May 1 **Engr.**

675 A95 10c dk bl & dk brn 3.00 .50

400th anniversary of Puebla.

Nos. 658-665a Overprinted

HABILITADO 1931

1931

675A A90 2c red 800.00
676 A91 4c green 65.00 70.00
677 A90 5c orange 12.00 17.00
678 A91 10c brown red 12.00 14.00
679 A92 20c dk blue 12.00 18.00
680 A92 30c dk green 21.00 25.00
681 A92 40c violet 30.00 35.00
682 A93 1p brown & bl 27.50 35.00
a. 1p red & blue 40.00 45.00
Nos. 676-682 (7) 179.50 214.00

Overprint horizontal on 1p.

Nos. 676 and 682 are not known to have been sold to the public through post offices.

Forgeries of overprint exist.

Bartolomé de las Casas — A96

Emblem of Mexican Society of Geography and Statistics — A97

1933, Mar. 3 **Engr.** ***Rouletted 14½***

683 A96 15c dark blue .20 .15

For overprint see No. O215.

1933, Oct. ***Rouletted 14½***

684 A97 2c deep green 1.50 .60
685 A97 5c dark brown 1.75 .50
686 A97 10c dark blue .75 .15
687 A97 1p dark violet 60.00 65.00
Nos. 684-687 (4) 64.00 66.25

XXI Intl. Congress of Statistics and the 1st centenary of the Mexican Society of Geography and Statistics.

Types of 1923 and PT1

1934 ***Perf. 10½, 11 (4c)***

687A PT1 1c brown 1.00 .30
688 A79 2c scarlet .35 .15
689 A82 4c green .35 .15
690 A85 10c brown lake .35 .15
691 A84 20c dark blue .75 .75
692 A83 30c dk blue grn 1.00 1.25
Nos. 687A-692 (6) 3.80 2.75

See 2nd note after Postal Tax stamp No. RA3.

Indian Archer A99

Indian A100

Woman Decorating Pottery A101

Peon A102

Potter A103

Sculptor A104

Craftsman A105

Offering to the Gods A106

Worshiper — A107

1934, Sept. 1 **Wmk. 156** ***Perf. 10½***

698 A99 5c dk green 1.65 .35
699 A100 10c brown lake 2.00 .60
700 A101 20c ultra 8.00 5.00
701 A102 30c black 14.00 12.00
702 A103 40c black brn 24.00 16.00
703 A104 50c dull blue 45.00 50.00
704 A105 1p brn lake & blk 100.00 47.50
705 A106 5p brn blk & red brn 190.00 200.00
706 A107 10p brown & vio 800.00 900.00
a. Unwatermarked 3,250.
Nos. 698-706 (9) 1,184. 1,231.

National University.

The design of the 1p is wider than the rest of the set. Values are for copies with perfs just touching the design.

See Nos. C54-C61, RA13B.

Yalalteca Indian — A108

Tehuana Indian — A109

Arch of the Revolution — A110

Tower of Los Remedios — A111

Cross of Palenque — A112

Independence Monument — A113

Independence Monument, Puebla A114

Monument to the Heroic Cadets A115

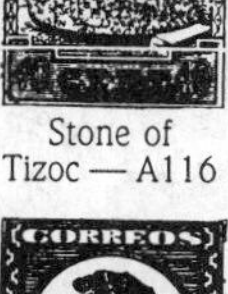

Stone of Tizoc — A116

Ruins of Mitla — A117

Coat of Arms — A118

Charro — A119

Imprint: "Oficina Impresora de Hacienda-Mexico"

1934-40 **Wmk. 156** ***Perf. 10½***

Size: 20x26mm

707 A108 1c orange .65 .15
a. Unwmkd. —
708 A109 2c green .65 .15
a. Unwmkd. 3.75 3.75
709 A110 4c carmine .90 .20
710 A111 5c olive brn .65 .15
a. Unwmkd. 400.00 350.00
711 A112 10c dk blue .80 .15
712 A112 10c violet ('35) 1.25 .15
a. Unwmkd. 200.00 40.00
713 A113 15c lt blue 4.00 .30
714 A114 20c gray green 1.90 .20
a. 20c olive green 2.00 .20
715 A114 20c ultra ('35) 1.40 .15
a. Unwmkd. 150.00
716 A115 30c lake .90 .15
a. Unwmkd. 350.00
716B A115 30c lt ultra ('40) 1.00 .15
717 A116 40c red brown 1.00 .15
718 A117 50c grnsh black .90 .15
a. Imperf., pair 110.00
b. Unwmkd. 375.00
719 A118 1p dk brn & org 2.50 .15
a. Imperf., pair 350.00
720 A119 5p orange & vio 7.75 .75
Nos. 707-720 (15) 26.25
Set value 2.60

No. 718a was not regularly issued.

The existence of No. 707a has been questioned.

See Nos. 729-733, 733B, 735, 784-788, 795A-800A, 837-838, 840-841, 844, 846-851. For overprints see Nos. 728, O224-O232.

Tractor — A120

1935, Apr. 1 **Wmk. 156** ***Perf. 10½***

721 A120 10c violet 4.00 .50

Industrial census of Apr. 10, 1935.

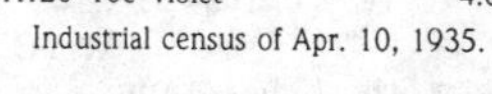

Arms of Chiapas A121

Emiliano Zapata A122

1935, Sept. 14
722 A121 10c dark blue .50 .20
a. Unwmkd. 125.00 100.00

The 111th anniversary of the joining of the state of Chiapas with the federal republic of Mexico. See No. 734.

1935, Nov. 20 **Wmk. 156**
723 A122 10c violet .75 .20

25th anniversary of the Plan of Ayala.

US and Mexico Joined by Highways
A123

Matalote Bridge
A124

View of Nuevo Laredo Highway — A125

1936 **Wmk. 248** ***Perf. 14***
725 A123 5c blue grn & rose .30 .15
726 A124 10c slate bl & blk .50 .15
727 A125 20c brn & dk grn 1.50 1.00
Nos. 725-727,C77-C79 (6) 3.35 2.10

Opening of the Mexico City - Nuevo Laredo Highway.

Monument Type of 1923

1936 **Wmk. 248** **Engr.** ***Perf. 10½***
727A A85 10c brown lake 1,150. 650.00

No. 712 Overprinted in Green

PRIMER CONGRESO
NAL. DE HIGIENE Y
MED. DEL TRABAJO

1936, Dec. 15 **Wmk. 156**
728 A112 10c violet .60 .50

1st National Congress of Industrial Hygiene and Medicine.

Type of 1934
Redrawn size: 17½x21mm
Imprint: "Talleres de Imp. de Est. y Valores-Mexico"

1937 **Photo.** **Wmk. 156** ***Perf. 14***
729 A108 1c orange .60 .15
a. Imperf., pair 12.50
730 A109 2c dull green .60 .15
a. Imperf., pair 12.50
731 A110 4c carmine .90 .15
a. Imperf., pair 12.50
732 A111 5c olive brn .80 .15
a. Unwmkd. 150.00
733 A112 10c violet .70 .15
a. Imperf., pair 10.00
Nos. 729-733 (5) 3.60 .75

The imperfs were not regularly issued.

Types of 1934-35

1937 **Wmk. 260**
Size: 17½x21mm
733B A111 5c olive brown 650.00 185.00

1937 **Engr.** ***Perf. 10½***
734 A121 10c dark blue 15.00 12.00

1937
Size: 20x26mm
735 A112 10c violet 275.00 35.00

Types of 1923

1934-37 **Wmk. 260** ***Perf. 10½***
735A A79 2c scarlet 4,000.
735B A85 10c brown lake

Forged perforations exist.

The listing of No. 735B is being re-evaluated. The Catalogue Editors would appreciate any information on the stamp.

Rouletted 14½
736 A85 10c claret 1,800. 125.

Blacksmith
A126

Revolutionary Soldier
A127

Revolutionary Envoy — A128

Wmk. 156

1938, Mar. 26 **Photo.** ***Perf. 14***
737 A126 5c black & brn .80 .20
738 A127 10c red brown .35 .15
739 A128 20c maroon & org 6.00 1.00
Nos. 737-739,C82-C84 (6) 13.15 4.10

Plan of Guadalupe, 25th anniv.

Arch of the Revolution — A129

Independence Monument — A131

Design: 10c, National Theater.

1938, July 1
740 A129 5c bister brn 1.25 .60
741 A129 5c red brown 2.50 2.25
742 A129 10c orange 14.00 11.00
743 A129 10c chocolate .60 .18
744 A131 20c brown lake 3.50 4.00
745 A131 20c black 18.00 15.00
Nos. 740-745 (6) 39.85 33.03
Nos. 740-745,C85-C90 (12) 82.95 63.28

16th Intl. Congress of Planning & Housing.

Arch of the Revolution
A132

1939, May 1
746 A132 10c Prus blue .65 .20
Nos. 746,C91-C93 (4) 4.75 2.95

New York World's Fair.

Indian — A133

1939, May 17
747 A133 10c red orange .45 .15
Nos. 747,C94-C96 (4) 5.60 2.70

Tulsa World Philatelic Convention.

Juan Zumárraga
A134

First Printing Shop in Mexico, 1539
A135

Design: 10c, Antonio de Mendoza.

1939, Sept. 1 **Engr.** ***Perf. 10½***
748 A134 2c brown blk .75 .25
749 A135 5c green .75 .20
750 A134 10c red brown .25 .15
Nos. 748-750,C97-C99 (6) 3.75 1.60

400th anniversary of printing in Mexico.

View of Taxco
A137

Allegory of Agriculture
A138

10c, Two hands holding symbols of commerce.

1939, Oct. 1 **Photo.** ***Perf. 12x13***
751 A137 2c dark carmine 1.25 .20
752 A138 5c sl grn & gray grn .15 .15
753 A138 10c org brn & buff .15 .15
Nos. 751-753,C100-C102 (6) 6.05 1.70

Census Taking.

"Penny Black" of 1840
A140

Roadside Monument
A141

1940, May ***Perf. 14***
754 A140 5c black & lemon .90 .50
755 A140 10c dark violet .25 .15
756 A140 20c lt blue & car .32 .15
757 A140 1p gray & red org 7.00 4.00
758 A140 5p black & Prus bl 37.50 30.00
Nos. 754-758,C103-C107 (10) 91.07 95.85

Postage stamp centenary.

1940 **Wmk. 156**
759 A141 6c deep green .50 .15

Opening of the highway between Mexico, D. F., and Guadalajara. See Nos. 789, 842.

Vasco de Quiroga
A142

Melchor Ocampo
A143

College Seal — A144

1940, July 15 **Engr.** ***Perf. 10½***
760 A142 2c violet 1.30 .50
761 A143 5c copper red .80 .20
762 A144 10c olive bister .80 .30
a. Imperf., pair 150.00
Nos. 760-762,C108-C110 (6) 5.10 2.50

Founding of the National College of San Nicolas de Hidalgo, 400th anniv.

Coat of Arms of Campeche
A145

1940, Aug. 7 **Photo.** ***Perf. 12x13***
763 A145 10c bis brn & dk car 3.00 1.25
Nos. 763,C111-C113 (4) 10.65 5.70

400th anniversary of the founding of Campeche.

Man at Helm
A146

1940, Dec. 1
764 A146 2c red org & blk 1.65 .60
765 A146 5c peacock bl & red brn 8.00 3.50
766 A146 10c slate grn & dk brn 4.00 .85
Nos. 764-766,C114-C116 (6) 21.05 9.45

Inauguration of Pres. Manuel Avila Camacho.

Alternated Perforations

Nos. 763-766, 774-779, 792-795, 801-804, 806-811, 813-818, C100-C102, C111-C116, C123-C128, C143-C162, C430-C431 have alternating small and large perforations.

Javelin Thrower — A147

1941, Nov. 4 ***Perf. 14***
767 A147 10c dull yellow grn 5.00 .50

National Athletic Games of the Revolution, Nov. 4-20, 1941.

Serpent Columns, Chichén Itzá A148

Mayan Sculpture A149

Coat of Arms of Merída — A150

1942, June 30

768	A148	2c dk olive bis	1.40	.75
769	A149	5c deep orange	2.25	.60
770	A150	10c dark violet	1.65	.25
		Nos. 768-770,C117-C119 (6)	11.55	6.35

400th anniversary of the founding of Merida.

Independence Monument to Hidalgo — A151

Government Palace — A152

View of Guadalajara — A153

1942, Feb. 11 **Engr.** ***Perf. 10x10½***

771	A151	2c bl vio & vio brn	.35	.30
772	A152	5c black & cop red	1.25	.50
773	A153	10c red org & ultra	1.25	.40
		Nos. 771-773,C120-C122 (6)	7.90	4.20

Founding of Guadalajara, 400th anniv.

No. 773 exists imperf on unwatermarked paper as a color proof.

Black Cloud in Orion A154

Designs: 5c, Total solar eclipse. 10c, Spiral galaxy in the "Hunting Dogs."

1942, Feb. 17 **Photo.** ***Perf. 12x13***

774	A154	2c lt vio & indigo	3.00	3.00
775	A154	5c blue & indigo	15.00	2.00
776	A154	10c red org & indigo	9.00	.75
		Nos. 774-776,C123-C125 (6)	61.50	17.25

Astrophysics Congress and the inauguration of an observatory at Tonanzintla, Feb. 17, 1942.

"Mother Earth" A157

Sowing Wheat A158

Western Hemisphere Carrying Torch A159

1942, July 1

777	A157	2c chestnut	2.00	.40
778	A158	5c turq blue	3.50	1.10
779	A159	10c red orange	1.50	.55
		Nos. 777-779,C126-C128 (6)	12.90	5.50

2nd Inter-American Agricultural Conference.

Fuente Academy A160

1942, Nov. 16 ***Perf. 14***

780	A160	10c grnsh black	2.50	.75

75th anniversary of Fuente Academy.

Las Monjas Church A161

Generalissimo Ignacio José de Allende A163

Design: 5c, San Miguel Church.

1943, May 11

781	A161	2c intense blue	1.00	.35
782	A161	5c deep brown	1.10	.30
783	A163	10c dull black	3.50	1.00
		Nos. 781-783,C129-C131 (6)	10.55	5.35

400th anniv. of the founding of San Miguel de Allende.

Types of 1937

1944 **Photo.** **Wmk. 272**

784	A108	1c orange	1.10	.15
785	A109	2c dull green	1.10	.15
786	A110	4c carmine	2.00	.20
787	A111	5c olive brown	1.75	.15
788	A112	10c violet	.90	.15

Type of 1940

789	A141	6c green	.90	.15
		Nos. 784-789 (6)	7.75	.95

"Liberty" — A164

Juan M. de Castorena — A165

1944 **Photo.**

790	A164	12c violet brown	.35	.15

See No. 845.

1944, Oct. 12 **Engr.** ***Perf. 10***

791	A165	12c dark brown	.60	.15

Third Book Fair. See No. C142.

Catalogue values for unused stamps in this section, from this point to the end of the section, are for Never Hinged items.

Hands Holding Globe Showing Western Hemisphere A166

1945, Feb. 27 **Photo.** ***Perf. 12x13***

792	A166	12c dark carmine	.60	.15
793	A166	1p slate green	1.00	.25
794	A166	5p olive brown	5.75	4.50
795	A166	10p black	10.00	8.00
		Nos. 792-795,C143-C147 (9)	41.10	33.60

Inter-American Conf. held at Chapultepec, Feb. 1945.

Types of 1934-40

Perf. 10½

1945-46 **Wmk. 272** **Engr.**

795A	A113	15c lt grnsh bl ('46)	250.00	60.00
796	A114	20c gray grn	2.50	.15
797	A115	30c lt ultra	3.25	.15
798	A116	40c brown	2.50	.20
799	A117	50c grnsh blk	1.65	.20
800	A118	1p dk brn & org	2.50	.20
b.		Imperf., pair		
800A	A119	5p org & vio ('46)	12.00	6.00
		Nos. 795A-800A (7)	274.40	66.90

Theater of Peace, San Luis Potosi A167

Fountain of Diana, the Huntress A168

1945, July 27 **Photo.** ***Perf. 12x13***

801	A167	12c blk & vio brn	.45	.15
802	A167	1p blk & bl gray	.60	.40
803	A167	5p blk & brn lake	5.50	5.00
804	A167	10p blk & grnsh bl	12.50	12.00
		Nos. 801-804,C148-C152 (9)	39.40	35.30

Reconstruction of the Peace Theater (Teatro de la Paz), San Luis Potosi.

1945 ***Perf. 14***

805	A168	3c violet blue	.55	.15

See No. 839.

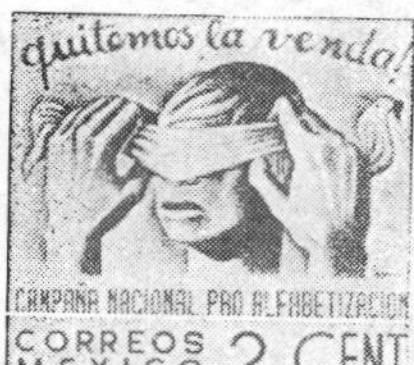
Removing Blindfold A169

1945, Nov. 2 ***Perf. 12x13***

806	A169	2c bluish grn	.40	.20
807	A169	6c orange	.40	.20
808	A169	12c ultra	.40	.20
809	A169	1p olive	.60	.25
810	A169	5p gray & pale rose	3.50	3.00
811	A169	10p bl & yel grn	20.00	20.00
		Nos. 806-811 (6)	25.30	23.85
		Nos. 806-811,C153-C157 (11)	58.85	55.80

Issued to publicize the national literacy campaign.

M. E. de Almanza — A170

1946 ***Perf. 14***

812	A170	8c black	1.25	.25

Martines Enriquez de Almanza, founder of the Mexican posts. See No. 843.

Allegory of World Peace — A171

1946, Apr. 10 ***Perf. 12x13***

813	A171	2c dk olive bis	.35	.20
814	A171	6c red brown	.30	.20
815	A171	12c Prus green	.25	.15
816	A171	1p lt green	.60	.40
817	A171	5p dull red vio	5.00	5.00
818	A171	10p lt ultra	22.50	20.00
		Nos. 813-818 (6)	29.00	25.95
		Nos. 813-818,C158-C162 (11)	48.20	40.65

United Nations.

Arms of Zacatecas A173

Monument to Gen. Gonzalez Ortega A174

Ramón Lopez Velarde A175

Francisco Garcia Salinas A176

Wmk. 279

1946, Sept. 1 **Photo.** ***Perf. 14***

820	A173	2c orange brn	.55	.15
821	A173	12c Prus blue	.25	.15

Engr.

Perf. 10x10½

822 A174 1p lilac rose .70 .20
823 A175 5p red 5.50 3.00
824 A176 10p dk blue & blk 40.00 10.00
Nos. 820-824 (5) 47.00 13.50
Nos. 820-824,C163-C166 (9) 63.10 22.00

400th anniversary of the founding of the city of Zacatecas.

A177

A178

1947 Photo. *Perf. 14*

825 A177 15c Postman .25 .15
a. Imperf., pair 110.00

1947, May 16

10c, F. D. Roosevelt and Stamp of 1st Mexican Issue. 15c, Arms of Mexico and Stamp of 1st US Issue.

826 A178 10c yellow brown 1.65 1.00
827 A178 15c green .25 .15
Nos. 826-827,C167-C169 (5) 4.65 2.30

Cent. Intl. Phil. Exhib., NYC, May 17-25, 1947.

Justo Sierra — A180

Communications Building — A181

Perf. 10x10½, 10½x10

1947, Engr. Wmk. 279

828 A180 10p brown & dl grn 100.00 20.00
829 A181 20p dk green & lil 1.65 2.00

Cadet Francisco Márquez A182

Gen. Manuel Rincón A186

Flag of San Blas Battalion — A188

Designs: 5c, Cadet Fernando Montes de Oca. 10c, Cadet Juan Escutia. 15c, Cadet Agustin Melgar. 1p, Gen. Lucas Balderas.

1947, Sept. 8 Photo. *Perf. 14*

830 A182 2c brown black .45 .15
831 A182 5c red orange .30 .15
832 A182 10c dk brown .25 .15
833 A182 15c dk Prus green .25 .15
834 A186 30c dull olive grn .35 .15

Engr.

Perf. 10x10½

835 A186 1p aqua .45 .45
836 A188 5p dk blue & claret 1.90 1.90
Nos. 830-836 (7) 3.95 3.10
Nos. 830-836,C180-C184 (12) 7.30 5.70

Centenary of the battles of Chapultepec, Churubusco and Molino del Rey.

Types of 1934-46

1947-50 Wmk. 279 Photo. *Perf. 14*

837 A108 1c orange 1.00 .30
a. Imperf., pair 90.00
838 A109 2c dk green .60 .15
839 A168 3c violet blue .60 .15
840 A110 4c dull red 1.90 .15
841 A111 5c olive brown 2.50 .15
842 A141 6c deep green .45 .15
a. Imperf., pair 90.00
843 A170 8c black .35 .15
844 A112 10c violet 1.90 .25
845 A164 12c violet brn 12.00 .75

Types A108 to A112 are in the redrawn size of 1937.

Size: 19x25mm

Engr. *Perf. 10½*

846 A114 20c olive green 1.25 .20
a. 20c green 3.00 .30
847 A115 30c lt ultra 12.00 .40
848 A116 40c red brown 1.40 .25
849 A117 50c green 1.90 .20
a. Imperf., pair 110.00
850 A118 1p dk brn & org 30.00 9.00
851 A119 5p org & vio ('50) 20.00 11.00
Nos. 837-851 (15) 87.85 23.25

Puebla Cathedral — A189

Designs: 3c, Modernistic church, Nuevo Leon. 5c, Modern building, Mexico City. 10c, Convent, Morelos. 15c, Benito Juarez. 30c, Indian dancer, Michoacan. 40c, Stone head, Tabasco. 50c, Carved head, Veracruz. 1p, Convent and carved head, Hidalgo. 5p, Galleon, arms of Campeche. 10p, Francisco I. Madero. 20p, Modern building, Mexico City.

1950-52 Wmk. 279 Photo. *Perf. 14*

856 A189 3c blue vio ('51) .50 .15
857 A189 5c dk red brn .75 .15
858 A189 10c dk green 3.50 .15
859 A189 15c dk green ('51) 1.75 .15
860 A189 20c blue violet 14.00 .15
861 A189 30c red .50 .15
862 A189 40c red orange ('51) 1.00 .15
863 A189 50c blue 1.25 .15

Engr.

864 A189 1p dull brown 4.50 .15
865 A189 5p ultra & bl grn 7.00 4.00
866 A189 10p blk & dp ultra ('52) 7.00 7.00
867 A189 20p purple & grn ('52) 10.00 10.00
Nos. 856-867 (12) 51.75 22.35

See Nos. 875-885, 909, 928-931, 943-952, 1003-1004, 1054-1055, 1072, 1076, 1081, 1090-1091, 1094-1102.

Highway Bridge A190

Symbolical of Construction in 1950 A191

Railroad Laborer A192

Perf. 10½x10, 10x10½

1950, May 5 Engr.

868 A190 15c purple .60 .15
869 A191 20c deep blue .40 .20
Nos. 868-869,C199-C200 (4) 4.25 .75

Completion of the International Highway between Ciudad Juarez and the Guatemala border.

Inscribed: "Ferrocarril del Sureste 1950"

Design: 20c, Map and locomotive.

1950, May 24 *Perf. 10x10½*

870 A192 15c chocolate 1.25 .15
871 A192 20c dp carmine .45 .15
Nos. 870-871,C201-C202 (4) 2.55 .80

Opening of the Southeastern Railroad between Veracruz, Coatzocoalcos and Yucatan, 1950.

Postal Service — A193

Miguel Hidalgo y Costilla — A194

1950, June 25 *Perf. 10x10½*

872 A193 50c purple .40 .15
Nos. 872-872,C203-C204 (3) 1.25 .60

75th anniv. (in 1949) of the UPU.

Wmk. 300

1953, May 8 Photo. *Perf. 14*

873 A194 20c grnsh bl & dk brn 1.75 .25
Nos. 873,C206-C207 (3) 3.55 .65

Bicentenary of birth of Miguel Hidalgo y Costilla. See Nos. C206-C207.

Type of 1950-52

Designs as before.
Two types of 5p:
Type I - Imprint ½mm high and blurred.
Type II - Imprint ¾mm high and clear.

1954-67 Photo. *Perf. 14*

875 A189 5c red brown .50 .15
876 A189 10c green, redrawn .65 .15
a. 10c dark green 2.50 .15
877 A189 15c dk green .40 .15
878 A189 20c bluish blk, white paper, colorless gum ('67) .60 .15
a. 20c dark blue 3.50 .15
879 A189 30c brown red .75 .15
a. 30c redsh brn .75 .15
880 A189 40c red orange 1.50 .15
881 A189 50c lt blue 1.00 .15

Engr.

882 A189 1p olive grn, perf. 11, vert. wmk. ('58) 4.00 .25
a. 1p olive grn, perf. 14 7.00 .20
b. olive brown 12.00 .20
883 A189 5p ultra & bl grn, I 7.00 1.00
a. Type II 400.00 7.00
884 A189 10p sl & dp ultra ('56) 9.00 5.00
a. 10p slate green & ultra 35.00 5.00
885 A189 20p purple & grn 11.00 9.00
a. 20p brn vio & yel grn 75.00 20.00
Nos. 875-885 (11) 36.40 16.30

Nos. 875-881 comes only with watermark vertical, and in various shades. Watermark inverted on Nos. 884, 885.

On No. 876, imprint extends full width of stamp.

Vert. pairs, imperf. horiz. of Nos. 878, 880 are noted after No. 1004.

Aztec Messenger of the Sun A195

Symbolizing Adoption of National Anthem A196

1954, Mar. 6

886 A195 20c rose & bl gray 1.10 .15
Nos. 886,C222-C223 (3) 2.85 .75

7th Central American and Caribbean Games.

1954, Sept. 16 Photo.

887 A196 5c rose lil & dk bl .75 .20
888 A196 20c yel brn & brn vio .90 .20
889 A196 1p gray grn & cerise .65 .40
Nos. 887-889,C224-C226 (6) 3.25 1.45

Centenary of the adoption of Mexico's National Anthem.

Torch-Bearer and Stadium A197

Aztec Designs A198

1955, Mar. 12 Wmk. 300 *Perf. 14*

890 A197 20c dk grn & red brn .85 .20
Nos. 890,C227-C228 (3) 2.35 .80

Second Pan American Games, 1955.

1956, Aug. 1

891 A198 5c "Motion" .50 .15
892 A198 10c Bird .50 .15
893 A198 30c Flowers .40 .15
894 A198 50c Corn .50 .15
895 A198 1p Deer .60 .20
896 A198 5p Man 2.25 2.25
a. Souv. sheet, #891-896, imperf. 50.00 50.00
Nos. 891-896,C229-C234 (12) 7.90 5.15

Centenary of Mexico's 1st postage stamps. No. 896a sold for 15p.

Stamp of 1856 A199

Francisco Zarco A200

1956, Aug. 1

897 A199 30c brn & intense bl .75 .25

Cent. of 1st Mexican Stamp Intl. Philatelic Exhibition, Mexico City, Aug. 16, 1956.

1956-63

Portraits: 25c, 45c, Guillermo Prieto. 60c, Ponciano Arriaga.

897A A200 25c dk brown ('63) .75 .50
898 A200 45c dk blue green .35 .25
899 A200 60c red lilac .35 .35
900 A200 70c violet blue .40 .20
Nos. 897A-900,C236-C237A (7) 4.45 2.55

Centenary of the constitution (in 1957). See Nos. C289, 1075, 1092-1093.

"Mexico" A201

Mexican Eagle and Oil Derrick A202

Design: 1p, National Assembly.

1957, Aug. 31 Photo. *Perf. 14*

901 A201 30c maroon & gold .50 .15
902 A201 1p pale brn & metallic grn .35 .25
Nos. 901-902,C239-C240 (4) 1.70 .80

Constitution, centenary.

1958, Aug. 30 Wmk. 300 *Perf. 14*

Design: 5p, Map of Mexico and refinery.

903 A202 30c lt blue & blk .50 .15
904 A202 5p hn brn & Prus grn 6.00 4.00
Nos. 903-904,C243-C244 (4) 7.15 4.45

20th anniv. of the nationalization of Mexico's oil industry.

UNESCO Building and Eiffel Tower — A203

UN Headquarters, New York — A204

1959, Jan. 20
905 A203 30c dull lilac & blk .50 .15

UNESCO Headquarters opening, Paris, Nov. 9.

1959, Sept. 7 Litho. *Perf. 14*
906 A204 30c org yel & bl .50 .15

Meeting of UNESCO.

Carranza A205

Humboldt Statue A206

1960, Jan. 15 Photo. Wmk. 300
907 A205 30c pale grn & plum .35 .15

Birth centenary of Pres. Venustiano Carranza. See No. C246.

1960, Mar. 16 Wmk. 300 *Perf. 14*
908 A206 40c bis brn & grn .35 .15

Cent. of the death (in 1859) of Alexander von Humboldt, German naturalist and geographer.

Type of 1950-52 Inscribed: "HOMENAJE AL COLECCIONISTA DEL TIMBRE DE MEXICO-JUNIO 1960"

1960, June 8 Engr. Wmk. 300
909 A189 10p lil, brn & grn 50.00 42.50

Visit of the Elmhurst (Ill.) Philatelic Society of Mexico Specialists to Mexico, 25th anniv. See No. C249.

Independence Bell & Monument A207 A208

Designs: 5p, Bell of Dolores and Miguel Hidalgo.

Wmk. 300

1960, Sept. 15 Photo. *Perf. 14*
910 A207 30c grn & rose red 1.00 .15
911 A208 1p dl grn & dk brn .50 .20
912 A208 5p maroon & dk bl 5.00 5.00
Nos. 910-912,C250-C252 (6) 13.45 8.00

150th anniv. of Mexican independence. See US No. 1157.

Agricultural Reform A209

Symbols of Health Education — A210

Designs: 20c, Sailor and Soldier, 1960, and Fighter of 1910. 30c, Electrification. 1p, Political development (schools). 5p, Currency stability (Bank and money).

1960-61 Photo. *Perf. 14*
913 A209 10c sl grn, blk & red org .75 .20
914 A210 15c grn & org brn 2.75 .50
915 A210 20c brt bl & lt brn ('61) 1.00 .15
916 A210 30c vio brn & sep .40 .15
917 A210 1p redsh brn & slate .50 .15
918 A210 5p maroon & gray 6.00 3.50
Nos. 913-918,C253-C256 (10) 15.30 6.45

50th anniversary (in 1960) of the Mexican Revolution.

Tunnel A211

Microscope, Mosquito and Globe A212

1961, Dec. Wmk. 300 *Perf. 14*
919 A211 40c blk & brt grn .40 .15
Nos. 919,C258-C259 (3) 1.20 .45

Opening of the railroad from Chihuahua to the Pacific Ocean.

1962, Apr. 6
920 A212 40c dl bl & maroon .40 .15

WHO drive to eradicate malaria.

President Joao Goulart of Brazil — A213

Insurgent at Marker for Battle of Puebla — A214

Wmk. 300

1962, Apr. 11 Photo. *Perf. 14*
921 A213 40c brown olive 1.00 .25

Visit of Joao Goulart, president of Brazil, to Mexico.

1962, May 5
922 A214 40c sepia & dk grn .35 .15

Centenary of the Battle of May 5 at Puebla and the defeat of French forces by Gen. Ignacio Zaragoza. See No. C260.

Draftsman and Surveyor A215

Plumbline A216

1962, June 11
923 A215 40c slate grn & dk bl .90 .20

25th anniversary of the National Polytechnic Institute. See No. C261.

1962, June 21
924 A216 20c dp blue & blk 1.40 .20

Issued to publicize the importance of mental health.

"Space Needle" and Gear Wheels A217

Globe A218

1962, July 6
925 A217 40c dk grn & gray .35 .15

"Century 21" International Exposition, Seattle, Wash., Apr. 21-Oct. 12.

1962, Oct. 1 *Perf. 14*
926 A218 40c gray & brn .35 .15

1962 meeting of the Inter-American Economic and Social Council. See No. C263.

Pres. Alessandri of Chile A219

Pres. Betancourt of Venezuela A220

1962, Dec. 20 Wmk. 300 *Perf. 14*
927 A219 20c olive black .75 .20

Visit of President Jorge Alessandri Rodriguez of Chile to Mexico, Dec. 17-20.

Type of 1950-52

Designs as before.

Wmk. 300, Vertical

1962-74 Photo. *Perf. 14*
928 A189 1p ol gray ('67) 1.25 .15
a. 1p green 4.00 .20
929 A189 5p dl bl & dk grn 3.50 .75
a. 5p bluish gray & dark green, white paper ('67) 3.50 .50
930 A189 10p gray & bl ('63) 8.50 5.00
a. 10p green & deep blue ('74) 7.50 5.50
931 A189 20p lil & blk ('63) 9.00 7.50
a. Redrawn, white paper 10.00 10.00
Nos. 928-931 (4) 22.25 13.40

No. 928 is on thick, luminescent paper. No. 929 is 20½mm high; No. 929a, 20¾mm. Nos. 931a and 1102 (unwmkd.) have more shading in sky and spots on first floor windows.

1963, Feb. 28 Wmk. 300
932 A220 20c slate .70 .20

Visit of President Romulo Betancourt of Venezuela to Mexico.

Congress Emblem A221

Wheat Emblem A222

1963, Apr. 22 Wmk. 300 *Perf. 14*
933 A221 40c fawn & blk .60 .20

19th International Chamber of Commerce Congress. See No. C271.

1963, June 17 Wmk. 300 *Perf. 14*
934 A222 40c crim & dk bl .60 .20

FAO "Freedom from Hunger" campaign.

Mercado Mountains and Arms of Durango A223

Belisario Dominguez A224

1963, July 13 Photo.
935 A223 20c dk bl & choc .60 .20

400th anniv. of the founding of Durango.

1963, July 13 Photo.
936 A224 20c dk grn & ol gray .60 .20

Centenary of the birth of Belisario Dominguez, revolutionary leader.

Mexico No. 1 — A225

1963, Oct. 9 Wmk. 350 *Perf. 14*
937 A225 1p int blue & brn 1.25 .75

77th Annual Convention of the American Philatelic Society, Mexico City, Oct. 7-13. See No. C274.

Tree of Life A226

José Morelos A227

1963, Oct. 26 Wmk. 350 *Perf. 14*
938 A226 20c dl bl grn & car .40 .20

Centenary of the Intl. Red Cross. See No. C277.

1963, Nov. 9
939 A227 40c grn & dk sl grn .55 .20

150th anniv. of the 1st congress of Anahuac.

Pres. Victor Paz Estenssoro A228

Arms of Sinaloa University A229

1963, Nov. 9 Wmk. 350 *Perf. 14*
940 A228 40c dk brn & dk red brn .60 .20

Visit of President Victor Paz Estenssoro of Bolivia.

1963 Photo.
941 A229 40c slate grn & ol bister .60 .20

90th anniversary of the founding of the University of Sinaloa.

Diesel Train, Rail Cross Section and Globe A230

1963, Nov. 29 Photo.
942 A230 20c black & dk brn .90 .50

11th Pan-American Railroad Congress. See No. C279.

Type of 1950-52

Designs as before.

1963-66 Wmk. 350 Photo. *Perf. 14*

943	A189	5c red brown ('65)	.60	.15
944	A189	10c dk green ('64)	.65	.15
945	A189	15c dk green ('66)	.60	.15
946	A189	20c dark blue	.60	.15
948	A189	40c red orange	.70	.15
949	A189	50c blue ('64)	2.00	.15
950	A189	1p olive grn ('64)	4.00	.15
951	A189	5p dl bl & dk grn ('66)	100.00	30.00
952	A189	10p gray & Prus bl ('65)	35.00	25.00
		Nos. 943-952 (9)	144.15	56.05

The 20c is redrawn; clouds almost eliminated and other slight variations.

"F.S.T.S.E." Emblem A231

Academy of Medicine Emblem A232

1964, Feb. 15
954 A231 20c red org & dk brn .40 .15

25th anniv. (in 1963) of the Civil Service Statute affecting federal employees.

1964, May 18 Wmk. 350 *Perf. 14*
955 A232 20c gold & blk .40 .15

National Academy of Medicine, cent.

José Rizal A233

View of Zacatecas A234

40c, Miguel Lopez de Legaspi, Spanish navigator.

1964, Nov. 10 Photo. *Perf. 14*
956 A233 20c dk bl & dp grn .50 .20
957 A233 40c dk bl & brt vio .60 .20
Nos. 956-957,C300-C301 (4) 6.10 1.75

Issued to honor 400 years of Mexican-Philippine friendship.

1964, Nov. 10 Wmk. 350
958 A234 40c slate grn & red .55 .20

50th anniv. of the capture of Zacatecas.

Col. Gregorio Mendez A235

Morelos Theater, Aguascalientes A236

1964, Nov. 10
959 A235 40c grysh blk & dk brn .50 .20

Cent. of the Battle of Jahuactal, Tabasco.

1965, Jan. 9 Photo. *Perf. 14*
960 A236 20c dl cl & dk gray .35 .15

50th anniversary of the Aguascalientes Convention, Oct. 1-Nov. 9, 1914.

Andrés Manuel del Río — A237

1965, Feb. 19 Wmk. 350 *Perf. 14*
961 A237 30c gray .40 .20

Bicentenary of the birth of Andrés Manuel del Rio, founder of the National School of Mining and discoverer of vanadium.

José Morelos and Constitution — A238

Trees — A239

1965, Apr. 24 Photo. *Perf. 14*
962 A238 40c brt grn & dk red brn .45 .20

Sesquicentennial (in 1964) of the 1st Mexican constitution.

1965, July 14 Wmk. 350 *Perf. 14*
963 A239 20c blue & green .30 .15

Issued to commemorate Tree Day, July 8.

ICY Emblem A240

1965, Sept. 13 Photo.
964 A240 40c olive gray & slate grn .30 .15

International Cooperation Year, 1965.

Athlete with Sling, Clay Figure A241

Design: 40c, Batter. Clay figures on 20c and 40c found in Colima, period 300-650 A.D.

1965, Dec. 17 Wmk. 350 *Perf. 14*
965 A241 20c olive & vio bl .90 .20
966 A241 40c pink & black .30 .15
Nos. 965-966,C309-C311 (5) 3.30 1.15

19th Olympic Games, Mexico, 1968.

José Morelos by Diego Rivera A242

Emiliano Zapata A243

1965, Dec. 22
967 A242 20c lt vio bl & blk .40 .20

José Maria Morelos y Pavon (1765-1815), priest and patriot in 1810 revolution against Spain.

1966, Jan. 10 Photo.

20c, Corn, cotton, bamboo, wheat and cow.

968 A243 20c carmine rose .35 .15
969 A243 40c black .45 .20

50th anniv. of the Agrarian Reform Law.

Mexican Postal Service Emblem A244

Bartolomé de Las Casas A245

1966, June 24 Wmk. 300 *Perf. 14*
970 A244 40c brt green & blk .40 .15
Nos. 970,C314-C315 (3) 1.00
Set value .30

Congress of the Postal Union of the Americas and Spain, UPAE, Mexico City, June 24-July 23.

1966, Aug. 1 Photo. Wmk. 300
971 A245 20c black & buff .40 .15

400th anniv. of the death of Bartolomé de Las Casas (1474-1566), "Apostle of the Indies."

Mechanical Drawings and Cogwheels A246

1966, Aug. 15 Photo. *Perf. 14*
972 A246 20c gray & grn .30 .15

50th anniversary of the founding of the School of Mechanical and Electrical Engineering (ESIME).

FAO Emblem — A247

1966, Sept. 30 Wmk. 300 *Perf. 14*
973 A247 40c green .30 .15

FAO International Rice Year.

Running and Jumping, by Diego Rivera A248

1966, Oct. 15
Size: 35x21mm
974 A248 20c shown .70 .20
975 A248 40c Wrestling .35 .15
a. Souvenir sheet 2.00 2.00
Nos. 974-975,C318-C320 (5) 3.05 1.35

Issued to publicize the 19th Olympic Games, Mexico City, D.F., 1968. No. 975a contains 2 imperf. stamps similar to Nos. 974-975 with simulated perforations. Sold for 90c.

First Page of Constitution A249

Oil Refinery and Pyramid of the Sun A250

Wmk. 300
1967, Feb. 5 Photo. *Perf. 14*
976 A249 40c black .50 .20

50th anniv. of the Constitution. See No. C322.

1967, Apr. 2 Wmk. 300 *Perf. 14*
977 A250 40c lt bl & blk .35 .15

7th Intl. Oil Congress, Mexico City, Sept. 1967.

Nayarit Indian — A251

Wmk. 300
1967, May 1 Photo. *Perf. 14*
978 A251 20c pale grn & blk .30 .15

50th anniversary of Nayarit Statehood.

Degollado Theater, Guadalajara A252

Wmk. 300
1967, June 12 Photo. *Perf. 14*
979 A252 40c pink & black .20 .20

Centenary of the founding of the Degollado Theater, Guadalajara.

Mexican Eagle over Imperial Crown — A253

Perf. 10x10½

1967, June 19 Litho. Wmk. 350

980 A253 20c black & ocher .30 .15

Centenary of the victory of the Mexican republican forces and of the execution of Emperor Maximilian I.

Canoeing A254

Designs: 40c, Basketball. 50c, Hockey. 80c, Bicycling. 2p, Fencing.

Wmk. 300

1967, Oct. 12 Photo. *Perf. 14*

981 A254 20c blue & blk .35 .15
982 A254 40c brick red & blk .30 .15
983 A254 50c brt yel grn & blk .30 .15
a. Souvenir sheet of 3, #981-983, imperf. 2.50 1.50
984 A254 80c brt pur & blk .42 .15
985 A254 2p orange & blk .70 .30
a. Souvenir sheet of 2, #984-985, imperf. 4.00 2.00
Nos. 981-985,C328-C331 (9) 5.27 2.40
Nos. 981-985 (5) 2.07 .90

Issued to publicize the 19th Olympic Games, Mexico City, Oct. 12-27, 1968.

No. 983a sold for 1.50p; No. 985a sold for 3.50p. Both sheets are watermark 350.

See Nos. 990-995, C335-C338.

Artemio de Valle-Arizpe A255

Pedro Moreno A256

1967, Nov. 1 Photo.

986 A255 20c brown & slate .35 .30

Centenary of the Ateneo Fuente, a college at Saltillo, Coahuila.

1967, Nov. 18 Wmk. 300 *Perf. 14*

987 A256 40c blk & lt bl .35 .15

Moreno (1775-1817), revolutionary leader.

Gabino Barreda A257

Staircase, Palace of Mining A258

1968, Jan. 27 Photo. *Perf. 14*

988 A257 40c dk bl & rose claret .40 .15
989 A258 40c blk & bl gray .40 .15

Centenary of the founding of the National Preparatory and Engineering Schools.

Type of Olympic Issue, 1967

20c, Wrestling. 40c, Pentathlon. 50c, Water polo. 80c, Gymnastics. 1p, Boxing. 2p, Pistol shoot.

1968, Mar. 21 Wmk. 300 *Perf. 14*

990 A254 20c olive & blk .40 .15
991 A254 40c red lil & blk .40 .20
992 A254 50c brt green & blk .40 .20
a. Souvenir sheet of 3, #990-992, imperf. 3.00 2.00
993 A254 80c brt pink & blk .45 .25
994 A254 1p org brn & blk 2.25 .50
995 A254 2p gray & blk 2.50 1.50
a. Souvenir sheet of 3, #993-995, imperf. 7.50 4.00
Nos. 990-995,C335-C338 (10) 8.80 4.55

19th Olympic Games, Mexico City, Oct. 12-27. No. 992a sold for 1.50p; No. 995a sold for 5p. Both sheets are watermark 350.

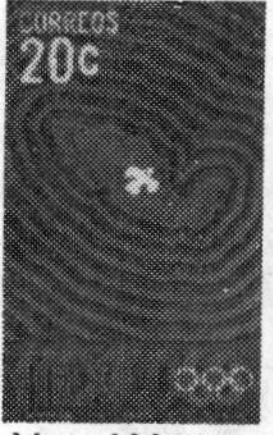

Map of Mexico, Peace Dove — A259

Arms of Veracruz — A261

Symbols of Cultural Events A260

40c, University City Olympic stadium. 50c, Telecommunications tower. 2p, Sports Palace. 10p, Pyramid of the Sun, Teotihuacan, & Olympic torch.

Wmk. 350

1968, Oct. Photo. *Perf. 14*

996 A259 20c blue, yel & grn .25 .15
997 A259 40c multicolored .35 .20
998 A259 50c multicolored .35 .20
a. Souv. sheet of 3, #996-998, imperf. 15.00 10.00
999 A260 2p multicolored 2.00 .50
1000 A260 5p silver & blk 4.00 1.25
a. Souv. sheet of 2, #999-1000, imperf. 15.00 10.00
1001 A259 10p multicolored 3.00 2.00
Nos. 996-1001,C340-C344 (11) 16.75 8.00

19th Olympic Games, Mexico City, Oct. 12-27 (Nos. 996-1000). Arrival of the Olympic torch in Veracruz (No. 1001).

No. 998a sold for 1.50p. No. 1000a sold for 9p.

1969, May 20 Wmk. 350 *Perf. 14*

1002 A261 40c multicolored .35 .15

450th anniv. of the founding of Veracruz.

Type of 1950-52
Coil Stamps
Perf. 11 Vert.

1969 Wmk. 300 Photo.

1003 A189 20c dk blue 2.50 2.00
1004 A189 40c red orange 3.50 3.00

Vert. pairs, imperf. horiz. may be from uncut rolls of coils.

Subway Train — A262

1969, Sept. 4 Wmk. 350 *Perf. 14*

1005 A262 40c multicolored .35 .15

Inauguration of Mexico City subway.

Honeycomb, Bee and ILO Emblem A263

Gen. Allende, by Diego Rivera A264

1969, Oct. 18 Photo. *Perf. 14*

1006 A263 40c multicolored .25 .15

50th anniversary of the ILO.

1969, Nov. 15 Wmk. 350 *Perf. 14*

1007 A264 40c multicolored .25 .15

Gen. Ignacio Allende Unzaga (1769-1811), hero of Mexican independence.

Tourist Issue

Pyramid of Niches at El Tajin, Veracruz, and Dancers Swinging from Pole A265

Anthropology Museum, Mexico City — A266

Deer Dance, Sonora — A267

Designs: No. 1010, View of Puerto Vallarta. No. 1011, Puebla Cathedral. No. 1012, Calle Belaunzaran. No. 1014, Ocotlan Cathedral, horiz.

1969-73 Photo. Wmk. 350

1008 A265 40c shown .45 .15
1009 A266 40c shown ('70) .45 .15
1010 A266 40c Jalisco ('70) .45 .15
1011 A266 40c Puebla ('70) .45 .15
1012 A266 40c Guanajuato ('70) .45 .15

Wmk. 300

1013 A267 40c shown ('73) .25 .15
1014 A267 40c Tlaxcala ('73) .25 .15
Nos. 1008-1014,C354-C358 (12) 6.15 2.40
Nos. 1008-1014 (7) 2.75 1.05

No. 1010 is inscribed "1970" below the design. Copies inscribed "1969" are from an earlier, unissued printing.

Luminescence

Fluorescent stamps include Nos. 1013-1014, 1035, 1038, 1041, 1043-1045, 1047-1050, 1054-1059. (See Luminescence note over No. C527.)

"How Many, Who and What are We?" — A268

40c, "What, How & How Much do we produce?" (horse's head & symbols of agriculture).

1970, Jan. 26 Wmk. 350 *Perf. 14*

1024 A268 20c multicolored .30 .15
1025 A268 40c blue & multi .25 .15

Issued to publicize the 1970 census.

Human Eye and Spectrum A269

1970, Mar. 8 Photo. Wmk. 350

1026 A269 40c multicolored .25 .15

21st International Congress of Ophthalmology, Mexico City, Mar. 8-14.

Helmets of 1920 and 1970 — A270

1970, Apr. 11 Wmk. 350 *Perf. 14*

1027 A270 40c dk car rose, blk & lt brn .20 .15

50th anniversary of the Military College.

José Maria Pino Suarez A271

Coat of Arms of Celaya A272

1970, Apr. 25 Photo.

1028 A271 40c black & multi .20 .15

Centenary of the birth of José Maria Pino Suarez (1869-1913), lawyer, poet and Vice President of Mexico.

1970, Oct. 12 Photo. *Perf. 14*

1029 A272 40c black & multi .20 .15

City of Celaya, 400th anniversary.

Eclipse of Sun — A273

1970, Nov. 11 Wmk. 350 *Perf. 14*

1030 A273 40c black & gray .25 .15

Total eclipse of the sun, Mar. 7, 1970.

Spheres with Dates 1970-1770 A274

1971, June 26 Photo. *Perf. 14*

1031 A274 40c emerald & blk .25 .15

Bicentenary of National Lottery.

Vasco de Quiroga, Mural by O'Gorman A275

1971, July 10 Photo.

1032 A275 40c multicolored .20 .15

500th anniversary of the birth of Vasco de Quiroga (1470-1565), Archbishop of Michoacan, founder of hospitals and schools.

Amado Nervo (1870-1919), Poet — A276

1971, Aug. 7 Wmk. 350 *Perf. 14*
1033 A276 40c multicolored .20 .15

Waves and Transformer A277

1971, Oct. 9
1034 A277 40c blk, lt bl & lt grn .30 .15

50th anniversary of Mexican radio.

Pres. Lazaro Cardenas (1895-1970) — A278

1971, Oct. 19 Wmk. 300
1035 A278 40c blk & pale lil .30 .15

Keyboard and Lara's Signature A279

1971, Nov. 6 Wmk. 350
1036 A279 40c blk, buff & pale bl .30 .15

Agustin Lara (1900-70), composer.

Arms of Monterrey A280

Cardiology Institute and WHO Emblems A281

1971, Dec. 18
1037 A280 40c black & multi .30 .15

375th anniv. of the founding of Monterrey.

1972, Apr. 8 Wmk. 300
1038 A281 40c multicolored .25 .15

"Your heart is your health," World Health Day 1972. See No. C395.

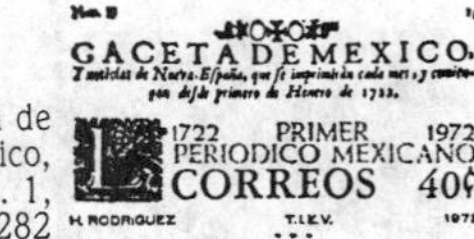

Gaceta de Mexico, Jan. 1, 1722 — A282

1972, June 24 Wmk. 350
1039 A282 40c multicolored .25 .15

250th anniv. of 1st Mexican newspaper.

Lions Intl. Emblem — A283

Sailing Ship Zaragoza — A284

1972, June 28
1040 A283 40c black & multi .25 .15

55th Lions International Convention.

1972, July 1
1041 A284 40c blue & multi .25 .15

75th anniv. of the Naval School of Veracruz.

A285

COLABORADORA FIEL
CORREOS 20¢
MEXICO

A286

Olive tree and branch.

1972, July 18 Wmk. 350 *Perf. 14*
1042 A285 40c lt grn, ocher & blk .25 .15
a. 40c light green, yellow & black 3.00 3.00

Centenary of Chilpancingo as capital of Guerrero State.

1972, Sept. 15 Photo. Wmk. 300

Design: 20c, Margarita Maza de Juárez. 40c, Benito Juárez, by Diego Rivera.

1043 A286 20c pink & multi .40 .15
1044 A286 40c dp yellow & multi .40 .15
Nos. 1043-1044,C403-C405 (5) 1.60
Set value .66

Benito Juárez (1806-1872), revolutionary leader and president of Mexico.

Emperor Justinian I, Mosaic A287

1972, Sept. 30 Wmk. 300
1045 A287 40c multicolored .65 .15

Mexican Bar Association, 50th anniv.

Caravel — A288

Library, Book Year Emblem — A290

Olympic Emblems A289

1972, Oct. 12 Wmk. 350
1046 A288 80c buff, pur & ocher .40 .15

Stamp Day of The Americas.

1972, Dec. 9 Wmk. 300
1047 A289 40c multicolored .35 .15

20th Olympic Games, Munich, Aug. 26-Sept. 11. See Nos. C410-C411.

1972, Dec. 16
1048 A290 40c black & multi .25 .15

International Book Year 1972.

Fish in Clean Water A291

1972, Dec. 16
1049 A291 40c blk & lt bl .40 .15

Anti-pollution campaign. See No. C412.

Metlac Railroad Bridge A292

1973, Feb. 2 *Perf. 14*
1050 A292 40c multicolored .85 .15

Centenary of Mexican railroads.

Cadet — A293

1973, Oct. 11 Photo. Wmk. 300
1051 A293 40c black & multi .45 .15

Sesquicentennial of Military College.

Madero, by Diego Rivera — A294

Antonio Narro — A295

1973, Nov. 9 Wmk. 350 *Perf. 14*
1052 A294 40c multicolored .20 .15

Pres. Francisco I. Madero (1873-1913).

1973, Nov. 9 Photo.
1053 A295 40c steel gray .35 .15

50th anniversary of the Antonio Narro Agriculture School in Saltillo.

Type of 1950-52

Designs as before.

1973 Unwmk. *Perf. 14*
1054 A189 20c blue violet 2.00 1.50
1055 A189 40c red orange 2.00 1.50

Fluorescent printing on back (or on front of 40c) consisting of network pattern and diagonal inscription.

Unsaturated Hydrocarbon Molecule A296

Wmk. 300
1973, Dec. 7 Photo. *Perf. 14*
1056 A296 40c blk, dk car & yel .20 .15

Pointing Hand Emblem of Foreign Trade Institute — A297

1974, Jan. 11 Photo. Wmk. 300
1057 A297 40c dk green & blk .20 .15

Export promotion.

A298

1974, Jan. 18 Litho. Wmk. 300
1058 A298 40c black .20 .15

EXMEX 73 Philatelic Exhibition, Cuernavaca, Apr. 7-15. See No. C424.

Manuel M. Ponce at Keyboard A299

1974, Jan. 18 Photo. Wmk. 300
1059 A299 40c gold & multi .20 .15

Manuel M. Ponce (1882-1948), composer.

Silver Statuette of Mexican Woman — A300

1974, Mar. 23 Photo. *Perf. 14*
1060 A300 40c red & multi .20 .15

First World Silver Fair.

Mariano Azuela A301

1974, Apr. 10 Wmk. 300 *Perf. 14*
1061 A301 40c multicolored .20 .15

Mariano Azuela (1873-1952), writer.

Dancing Dogs, Pre-Columbian — A302

1974, Apr. 10
1062 A302 40c multicolored .20 .15

6th Traveling Dog Exhibition, Mexico City, Nov. 23-Dec. 1.

Aqueduct, Tepotzotlan — A303

1974, July 10 Photo. Wmk. 300
1063 A303 40c brt blue & blk .45 .15

National Engineers' Day, July 1.

Dr. Rodolfo Robles A304

1974, July 19 *Perf. 14*
1064 A304 40c bister & grn .20 .15

25th anniv. of WHO (in 1973).

EXFILMEX 74 Emblem — A305

1974, July 26 *Perf. 13x12*
1065 A305 40c buff, grn & blk .20 .15

EXFILMEX 74, Fifth Inter-American Philatelic Exhibition honoring centenary of Universal Postal Union, Mexico City, Oct. 26-Nov. 3. See No. C429.

Demosthenes — A306

1974, Aug. 2 Photo. *Perf. 14*
1066 A306 20c green & brn .35 .15

2nd Spanish-American Cong. for Reading and Writing Studies, Mexico City, May 7-14.

Map of Chiapas and Head A307

1974, Sept. 14 Wmk. 300 *Perf. 14*
1067 A307 20c black & grn .20 .15

Centenary of Chiapas statehood.

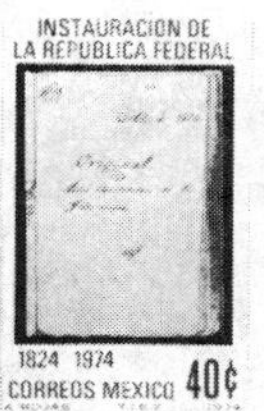

Law of 1824 — A308

Sebastian Lerdo de Tejada — A309

1974, Oct. 11 Wmk. 300
1068 A308 40c gray & grn .20 .15

Sesquicentennial of the establishment of the Federal Republic of Mexico.

1974, Oct. 11 Photo.
1069 A309 40c black & lt bl .20 .15

Centenary of restoration of the Senate.

UPU Monument, Bern A310

1974, Dec. 13 Wmk. 300 *Perf. 14*
1070 A310 40c ultra & org brn .20 .15
Nos. 1070,C437-C438 (3) .60 .45

Cent. of UPU.

Types of 1950-56

Designs (as 1951-56 issues): 2.30p, Guillermo Prieto. 3p, Modernistic church, Nuevo Leon. 50p, Benito Juarez.

1975 Photo. Wmk. 300 *Perf. 14*

No.	Type	Value	Color	Unused	Used
1072	A189	80c	green	.55	.25
1075	A200	2.30p	dp violet bl	.85	.35
1076	A189	3p	brick red	.85	.35
1081	A189	50p	orange & grn	10.00	7.50
			Nos. 1072-1075 (2)	1.40	.60

See No. 1097 for unwmkd. 3p with no shading under "Leon."

Gov. José Maria Mora — A312

1975, Feb. 21 Photo. Wmk. 300
1084 A312 20c yellow & multi .20 .15

Sesquicentennial (in 1974) of establishment of the State of Mexico.

Merchants with Pre-Columbian Goods — A313

1975, Apr. 18 Photo. Unwmk.
1085 A313 80c multicolored .20 .15

Centenary (in 1974) of the National Chamber of Commerce in Mexico City. Design from Florentine Codex.

Juan Aldama, by Diego Rivera A314

1975, June 6 *Perf. 14*
1086 A314 80c multicolored .20 .15

Juan Aldama (1774-1811), officer and patriot, birth bicentenary.

Indians and Eagle on Cactus Destroying Serpent, from Duran Codex A315

1975, Aug. 1 Photo. Unwmk.
1087 A315 80c multicolored .20 .15

650th anniv. of Tenochtitlan (Mexico City).

Julián Carrillo A316

Academy Emblem A317

1975, Sept. 12 Photo. Unwmk.
1088 A316 80c brt grn & red brn .20 .15

Julián Carrillo (1875-1965), violinist and composer, birth centenary.

1975, Sept. 13 *Perf. 14*
1089 A317 80c brown & ocher .20 .15

Cent. of Mexican Academy of Languages.

Types of 1950-56

Designs (as 1950-56 issues): 80c, Indian dancer, Michoacan. 2p, Convent, Morelos.

1975-76 Photo. Unwmk.

No.	Type	Value	Color	Unused	Used
1090	A189	40c	orange	.30	.15
1091	A189	50c	blue	.35	.15
1092	A200	60c	red lilac	.45	.15
1093	A200	70c	violet blue	.40	.15
1094	A189	80c	green	.40	.15
1095	A189	1p	olive green	.40	.15
1096	A189	2p	scarlet	.80	.50
1097	A189	3p	brick red	.80	.50
1099	A189	5p	gray bl & grn	1.75	1.00
1101	A189	10p	grn & dp ultra ('76)	4.00	2.00
1102	A189	20p	lilac & blk ('76)	8.25	4.00
			Nos. 1090-1102 (11)	17.90	8.90

University of Guadalajara A318

1975, Oct. 1 Photo. *Perf. 14*
1107 A318 80c multicolored .20 .15

University of Guadalajara, 50th anniversary.

Road Workers — A319

1975, Oct. 17 Photo. Unwmk.
1108 A319 80c gray grn, grn & blk .20 .15

50 years of road building for progress.

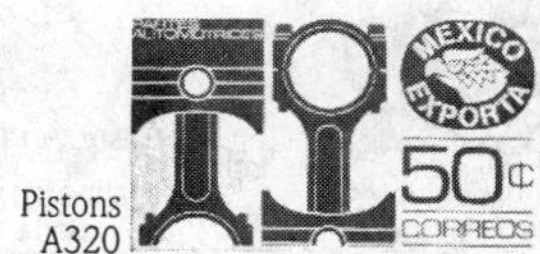

Pistons A320

Designs: Export Emblem and 5c, 6p, Steel pipes. 20c, Chemistry flasks. 40c, Cup of coffee. 80c, Meat cuts marked on steer. 1p, Electrical conductor. 2p, Abalone. 3p, Men's shoes. 4p, Tiles. 5p, Minerals. 7p, 8p, 9p, Overalls. 10p, Tequila. 15p, Honey. 20p, Wrought iron. 25p, Copper vase. 35p, 40p, No. 1133, 80p, Books. No. 1132, Jewelry. 100p, Strawberry. 200p, Citrus fruit. 300p, Motor vehicles. 400p, Circuit board. 500p, Cotton.

Some stamps have a gray burelage;
Type I - Burelage lines run lower left to upper right with arch towards lower right.
Type II - Burelage lines run lower left to upper right with arch towards upper left.

1975-87 Photo. Unwmk. *Perf. 14*

No.	Type	Value	Color	Unused	Used
1109	A320	5c	slate bl ('77)	.15	.15
1110	A320	20c	black ('76)	.15	.15
1111	A320	40c	dk brown ('76)	.50	.20
a.			40c claret brown ('81)	1.00	.25

1112 A320 50c slate, thin paper ('81) .30 .15

a. 50c slate blue ('76) .60 .15

b. 50c black ('83) .60 .15

c. 50c dull blue ('75) .75 .15

1113 A320 80c brt car ('76) .20 .15

a. Perf. 11 .40 .15

b. Perf. 11½x11 .20 .15

c. As "a," thin paper ('81) .75 .25

d. As "b," thin paper ('81) .15 .15

1114 A320 1p vio bl & org ('78) .15 .15

1115 A320 1p lt vio & org ('83) .15 .15

1116 A320 1p black & org ('84) .15 .15

1117 A320 2p grn & brt bl ('81) .15 .15

a. 2p bl grn & dk bl ('76) 1.25 .15

1118 A320 3p red brown .35 .15

a. 3p brn, perf 11½x11 ('82) .30 .15

b. Golden brn, thin paper ('81) .30 .15

1119 A320 4p tan & dk brn ('80) .20 .15

1120 A320 5p gray olive ('78) .20 .15

a. Perf 11½x11 ('84) .15 .15

1121 A320 6p brt orange ('83) .30 .15

a. Perf 11½x11 ('83) .30 .15

b. Perf 11 ('84) 3.25 .15

1121C A320 6p gray, perf. 11½x11 ('84) .15 .15

1122 A320 7p Prus blue ('84) .15 .15

a. 7p blue gray ('84) 5.00 .15

1123 A320 8p bis brn, perf 11½x11 ('84) .15 .15

a. Perf 11 ('84) 2.25 .15

1124 A320 9p dk blue ('84) .15 .15

1125 A320 10p dk & lt grn ('78) .35 .15

a. Thin paper ('81) .65 .30

b. Dk ol grn & yel grn ('86) 2.00 .15

c. Dk ol grn & brt ol grn ('87) .30 .15

1126 A320 15p yel org & red brn ('84) .30 .15

1127 A320 20p black ('78) 1.00 .15

1128 A320 20p dk gray ('84) .15 .15

1129 A320 25p org brn ('84) .40 .15

1130 A320 35p brt cer & yel ('84) .20 .20

1131 A320 40p org brn & lt yel ('84) .30 .20

1132 A320 50p gray, sil, brt vio & pur ('80) 6.00 .75

1133 A320 50p brt bl & lt yel ('83) 1.50 .15

1133A A320 80p pink & gold ('85) 1.65 .35

1134 A320 100p scar & brt grn, I ('83) 1.00 .25

1135 A320 200p emer & yel grn, I ('83) 2.40 .25

a. Emer & lemon, I ('87) 4.00 1.00

b. Emer & yel grn, II ('83) 3.00 .50

1136 A320 300p brt bl & red, I ('83) 1.65 1.00

a. Type II ('87) 25.00 1.00

1137 A320 400p lem & red brn, I ('84) 1.50 .60

1138 A320 500p lt ol grn & yel org, I ('84) 3.00 .50

Nos. 1109-1138 (32) 24.95

Set value 6.40

No. 1125b is 2mm wider than No. 1125. Size of No. 1125b: 37x21mm.

Nos. 1117, 1119, 1126, 1135 exist with one or more colors missing. These were not regularly issued.

See Nos. 1166-1176, 1465-1470A, 1491-1505, 1583-1603, 1763-1776, C486-C508, C594-C603.

Aguascalientes Cathedral A323

Jaime Torres Bodet A324

1975, Nov. 28

1140 A323 50c bl grn & blk .75 .20

400th anniversary of Aguascalientes.

1975, Nov. 28

1141 A324 80c blue & brn .20 .15

Jaime Torres Bodet (1920-1974), writer, director general of UNESCO (1958-1962).

Allegory, by José Clemente Orozco — A325

1975, Dec. 9 ***Perf. 14***

1142 A325 80c multicolored .20 .15

Sesquicentennial of Supreme Court.

The Death of Cuauhtemoc, by Chavez Morado — A326

1975, Dec. 12 **Photo.**

1143 A326 80c multicolored .20 .15

450th anniv. of the death of Cuauhtemoc (1495?-1525), last Aztec emperor.

Netzahualcoyotl (Water God) — A327

1976, Jan. 9 **Unwmk.** ***Perf. 14***

1144 A327 80c blue & vio bl .20 .15

50th anniv. of Mexican irrigation projects.

Arch, Leon A328

1976, Jan. 20

1145 A328 80c dk brn & ocher .20 .15

400th anniversary of León, Guanajuato.

Forest Fire A329

1976, July 8 **Photo.** ***Perf. 14***

1146 A329 80c blk, grn & red .20 .15

Prevent fires!

Hat and Scout Emblem A330

Exhibition Emblem A331

1976, Aug. 24 **Photo.** **Unwmk.**

1147 A330 80c olive & red brn .20 .15

Mexican Boy Scout Assoc., 50th anniv.

1976, Sept. 2

1148 A331 80c black, red & grn .20 .15

Mexico Today and Tomorrow Exhibition.

New Building, Military College A332

1976, Sept. 13 ***Perf. 14***

1149 A332 50c red brn & ocher .20 .15

Military College, new installations.

Dr. Ricardo Vertiz — A333

1976, Sept. 24 **Photo.** ***Perf. 14***

1150 A333 80c blk & redsh brn .20 .15

Our Lady of Light Ophthalmological Hospital, centenary.

National Basilica of Guadeloupe A334

1976, Oct. 12

1151 A334 50c black & ocher .20 .15

Inauguration of the new National Basilica of Our Lady of Guadeloupe.

"40" and Emblem A335

1976, Oct. 28 **Photo.** ***Perf. 14***

1152 A335 80c blk, lt grn & car .20 .15

Natl. Polytechnic Institute, 40th anniv.

Blast Furnace A336

1976, Nov. 4

1153 A336 50c multicolored .20 .15

Inauguration of the Lazaro Cardenas Steel Mill, Las Truchas.

Saltillo Cathedral A337

Electrification A338

1977, July 25 **Photo.** ***Perf. 14***

1154 A337 80c yel & dk brn .20 .15

400th anniversary of the founding of Saltillo.

1977, Aug. 14 **Photo.** ***Perf. 14***

1155 A338 80c multicolored .20 .15

40 years of Mexican development program.

Flags of Spain and Mexico A339

1977, Oct. 8 **Photo.** **Wmk. 300**

1156 A339 50c multicolored .20 .15

1157 A339 80c multicolored .20 .15

Nos. 1156-1157,C537-C539 (5) 1.10

Set value .60

Resumption of diplomatic relations with Spain.

Aquiles Serdan (1877-1910), Martyr of the Revolution — A340

1977, Nov. 18 **Photo.** ***Perf. 14***

1158 A340 80c lt & dk grn & blk .20 .15

Poinsettia A341

1977, Dec. 2 **Wmk. 300** ***Perf. 14***

1159 A341 50c multicolored .15 .15

Christmas 1977.

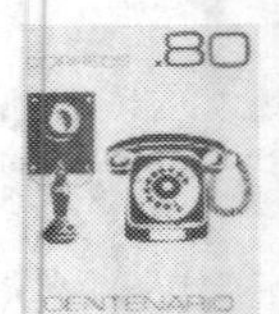

Old and New Telephones — A342

1978, Mar. 15 **Photo.** ***Perf. 14***

1160 A342 80c salmon & maroon .20 .15

Centenary of first telephone in Mexico.

Mexico stamps can be mounted in the annually supplemented Scott Mexico album.

Oil Derrick A343

1978, Mar. 18

1161 A343 80c dp org & mar .20 .15
Nos. 1161,C556-C557 (3) .70 .45

Nationalization of oil industry, 40th anniv.

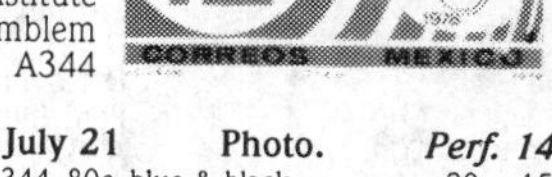
Institute Emblem A344

1978, July 21 Photo. *Perf. 14*

1162 A344 80c blue & black .20 .15
Nos. 1162,C574-C575 (3) .70 .45

Pan-American Institute for Geography and History, 50th anniv.

Dahlias A345

Decorations and Candles A346

1978, Sept. 29 Photo. Wmk. 300

1163 A345 50c shown .20 .15
1164 A345 80c Frangipani .20 .15

See No. 1196.

1978, Nov. 22 Photo. *Perf. 14*

1165 A346 50c multicolored .15 .15

Christmas 1978.

Export Type of 1975

Designs as before. 50p, Jewelry.

1979-81 Photo. Wmk. 300 *Perf. 14*

1166 A320 20c black ('81) .40 .20
1167 A320 50c slate blue .20 .20
a. 50c bluish black .30 .20
1168 A320 80c brt carmine, perf. 11 .75 .20
a. Perf. 14 1.00 .20
1169 A320 1p ultra & org .30 .15
1170 A320 2p brt grn & bl .50 .20
1171 A320 3p dk brown .60 .15
1172 A320 4p tan & dk brn ('80) .75 .20
1173 A320 5p gray olive 1.00 .35
1174 A320 10p dk & lt green 2.75 .75
1175 A320 20p black 2.75 .75
1176 A320 50p gray, sil, brt vio & pur 6.75 2.50
Nos. 1166-1176 (11) 16.75 5.65

A347

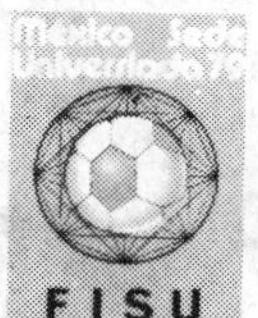
Soccer Ball — A348

1979, Apr. 26 Wmk. 300 *Perf. 14*

1177 A347 80c multicolored .15 .15

Centenary of Hermosillo, Sonora.

1979, June 15 Photo. Wmk. 300

Designs: 80c, Aztec ball player. 1p, Wall painting showing athletes. 5p, Runners, horiz.

1178 A348 50c blue & blk .15 .15
1179 A348 80c multicolored .15 .15
1180 A348 1p multicolored .15 .15
Nos. 1178-1180,C606-C607 (5) .95
Set value .55

Souvenir Sheet

Imperf

1181 A348 5p multicolored 2.00 .80

Universiada '79, World Games, Mexico City, Sept. 1979. No. 1181 has simulated perforations.

Josefa Ortiz de Dominguez, Wife of the Mayor of Queretaro (Miguel Dominguez), 150th Death Anniv. — A349

1979, July 6 *Perf. 14*

1182 A349 80c multicolored .15 .15

Allegory of National Culture, by Alfaro Siqueiros — A350

3p, Conquest of Energy, by Chavez Morado.

1979, July 10

1183 A350 80c multicolored .16 .15
1184 A350 3p multicolored .25 .15
Nos. 1183-1184,C609-C610 (4) .86 .60

National University, 50th anniv. of autonomy.

Emiliano Zapata, by Diego Rivera — A351

1979, Aug. 8 Photo. *Perf. 14*

1185 A351 80c multicolored .20 .15

Emiliano Zapata (1879-1919), revolutionist.

Soccer A352

Designs: 80c, Women's volleyball. 1p, Basketball. 5p, Fencing.

1979, Sept. 2

1186 A352 50c multicolored .15 .15
1187 A352 80c multicolored .15 .15
1188 A352 1p multicolored .15 .15
Nos. 1186-1188,C612-C613 (5) .90
Set value .55

Souvenir Sheet

Imperf

1189 A352 5p multicolored 2.00 .80

Universiada '79 World University Games, Mexico City. No. 1189 has simulated perforations.

Tepoztlan, Morelos — A353

Tourism: No. 1191, Mexcaltitan, Nayarit.

1979, Sept. 28 Photo. *Perf. 14*

1190 A353 80c multicolored .15 .15
1191 A353 80c multicolored .15 .15
Nos. 1190-1191,C615-C616 (4) .70
Set value .40

See Nos. 1274-1277, 1318-1321, 1513-1516.

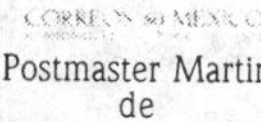
Postmaster Martin de Olivares — A354

Shepherd and Sheep — A355

1979 Wmk. 300 *Perf. 14*

1192 A354 80c multicolored .15 .15

Royal proclamation of mail service in the New World (New Spain), 400th anniversary. See Nos. C618-C620.

1979, Nov. 15

1193 A355 50c multicolored .15 .15

Christmas 1979. See No. C623.

Serpent, Mayan Temple A356

1980, Feb. 16 Photo. *Perf. 14x14½*

1194 A356 80c multicolored .15 .15
Nos. 1194,C625-C626 (3) .65 .50

Pre-Hispanic monuments.

North American Turkey — A357

Tajetes Erecta — A358

Wmk. 300

1980, Mar. 8 Photo. *Perf. 14*

1195 A357 80c multicolored .15 .15
1196 A358 80c multicolored .15 .15
Nos. 1195-1196,C632-C633 (4) .60
Set value .40

See Nos. 1163-1164, 1234-1237.

A359

A360

Designs: 50c, China Poblana (woman's costume), Puebla. 80c, Jarocha, Veracruz.

Wmk. 300

1980, Apr. 26 Photo. *Perf. 14*

1197 A359 50c multicolored .15 .15
1198 A359 80c multicolored .15 .15
Nos. 1197-1198,C636 (3) .50
Set value .25

See Nos. 1231-1233.

1980, June 4 Unwmk.

1200 A360 3p silver & blk .20 .15

10th national census.

Cuauhtemoc (Last Aztec Emperor), 1520, Matritense Codex A361

Pre-Hispanic Art (Leaders): 1.60p, Nezahualcoyotl (1402-1472), governor of Tetzcoco, poet, Azcatitlan Codex. 5.50p, Eight Deer Tiger's Claw (1011-1063), 11th king of Mixtec, Nuttall Codex.

1980, June 21

1201 A361 80c multicolored .15 .15
1202 A361 1.60p multicolored .16 .15
1203 A361 5.50p multicolored .45 .20
Nos. 1201-1203 (3) .76
Set value .40

See Nos. 1285-1287, 1510-1512.

Xipe (Aztec God of Medicine), Bourbon Codex A362

1980, June 29

1204 A362 1.60p multicolored .15 .15

22nd International Biennial Congress of the International College of Surgeons, Mexico City, June 29-July 4.

Moscow '80 Bronze Medal, Emblem, Misha, Olympic Rings — A363

1980, July 19 Photo. *Perf. 14*

1205 A363 1.60p shown .15 .15
1206 A363 3p Silver medal .25 .15
1207 A363 5.50p Gold medal .40 .25
Nos. 1205-1207 (3) .80 .55

22nd Summer Olympic Games, Moscow, July 19-Aug. 3.

Ceremonial Vessel, Tenochtitlan Temple A364

Wmk. 300

1980, Aug. 23 Photo. *Perf. 14*
1208 A364 80c shown .15 .15
1209 A364 1.60p Caracol .15 .15
1210 A364 5.50p Chacmool .30 .15
Nos. 1208-1210 (3) .60
Set value .30

Pre-Columbian Art.

Sacromonte Sanctuary, Amecameca — A365

Colonial Monuments: No. 1212, St. Catherine's Convent, Patzcuaro. No. 1213, Basilica, Cuilapan, vert. No. 1214, Calvary Hermitage, Cuernavaca.

1980, Sept. 26 Photo. *Perf. 14*
1211 A365 2.50p black .20 .15
1212 A365 2.50p black .20 .15
1213 A365 3p black .25 .15
1214 A365 3p black .25 .15
Nos. 1211-1214 (4) .90
Set value .40

See Nos. 1260-1263, 1303-1306, 1338-1341.

Quetzalcoatl (God) — A366

Sinaloa Coat of Arms — A367

1980, Sept. 27
1215 A366 2.50p multicolored .20 .15

World Tourism Conf., Manila, Sept. 27.

1980, Oct. 13
1216 A367 1.60p multicolored .20 .15

Sinaloa state sesquicentennial.

Straw Angel — A368

Christmas 1980: 1.60p, Poinsettias.

1980, Nov. 17 Photo. *Perf. 14*
1217 A368 50c multicolored .15 .15
1218 A368 1.60p multicolored .15 .15
Set value .20

Congress Emblem A369

1980, Dec. 10
1219 A369 1.60p multicolored .15 .15

4th International Civil Justice Congress.

Glass Vase and Animals A370

1980, Dec. 13 Wmk. 300
1220 A370 50c shown .15 .15
1221 A370 1p Poncho .15 .15
1222 A370 3p Wooden mask, 17th century .30 .15
Nos. 1220-1222 (3) .60
Set value .35

See Nos. 1267-1269.

Simon Bolivar, by Paulin Guerin A371

Valentin Gomez Farias — A373

Vicente Guerrero A372

1980, Dec. 17
1223 A371 4p multicolored .40 .25

Simon Bolivar death sesquicentennial.

1981, Feb. 14
1224 A372 80c multicolored .15 .15

Vicente Guerrero (1783-1831), statesman.

1981, Feb. 14
1225 A373 80c brt grn & gray .15 .15

First Latin-American Table Tennis Cup — A374

Wmk. 300

1981, Feb. 27 Photo. *Perf. 14*
1226 A374 4p multicolored .40 .25

Jesus Gonzalez Ortega, Politician, Birth Cent. A375

Gabino Barreda (1818-1881), Physician A376

Wmk. 300

1981, Mar. 10 Photo. *Perf. 14*
1227 A375 80c brn & yel org .15 .15

1981, Feb. 28
1228 A376 80c multicolored .15 .15

Benito Juarez, 175th Birth Anniv. A377

1981, Mar. 21
1229 A377 1.60p multicolored .15 .15

450th Anniv. of Puebla City — A378

1981, Apr. 16 Unwmk.
1230 A378 80c multicolored .15 .15
a. Wmk. 300 1.00 .20

Costume Type of 1980

1981, Apr. 25 Unwmk.
1231 A359 50c Purepecha, Michoacan .15 .15
1232 A359 80c Charra, Jalisco .15 .15
1233 A359 1.60p Mestiza, Yucatan .15 .15
Set value .30 .15

Flora and Fauna Types of 1980

Wmk. 300 (#1235), Unwmkd.

1981, May 30
1234 A357 80c Mimus polyglottos .15 .15
1235 A358 80c Persea americana .15 .15
1236 A357 1.60p Trogon mexicanus .15 .15
1237 A358 1.60p Theobromo cacao .15 .15
Set value .40 .20

Workers' Strike, by David Alfaro Siqueiros A379

1981, June 10 Photo. *Perf. 14*
1238 A379 1.60p multicolored .15 .15

Labor strike martyrs of Cananea, 75th anniv.

Intl. Year of the Disabled A380

1981, July 4 Unwmk. *Perf. 14*
1239 A380 4p multicolored .40 .25

450th Anniv. of Queretaro City — A381

1981, July 25 Unwmk.
1240 A381 80c multicolored .15 .15
a. Wmk. 300 1.00 .15

Alexander Fleming (1881-1955), Discoverer of Penicillin A382

1981, Aug. 1 Unwmk.
1241 A382 5p blue & orange .40 .15

No. 1 A383

1981, Aug. 6
1242 A383 4p multicolored .32 .15
a. Wmk. 300 1.00 .15

125th anniv. of Mexican stamps.

St. Francis Xavier Clavijero, 250th Birth Anniv. — A384

1981, Sept. 9 Unwmk. *Perf. 14*
1243 A384 80c multicolored .15 .15

Union Congress Building Opening — A385

1981, Sept. 10
1244 A385 1.60p red & brt grn .15 .15

1300th Anniv. of Bulgarian State A386

1981, Sept. 19 **Photo.** ***Perf. 14***

1245 A386	1.60p	Desislava, mural, 1259	.15	.15
1246 A386	4p	Thracian gold cup	.30	.15
1247 A386	7p	Horseman	.45	.15
		Nos. 1245-1247 (3)	.90	
		Set value		.35

Pre-Hispanic Art — A387

1981, Sept. 26

1248 A387	80c	Squatting diety	.20	.15
1249 A387	1.60p	Animal head	.30	.15
1250 A387	4p	Fish	.40	.25
		Nos. 1248-1250 (3)	.90	
		Set value		.45

Pablo Picasso (1881-1973) A388

1981, Oct. 5

1251 A388 5p lt ol grn & grn .40 .25

Christmas 1981 — A389

1981, Oct. 15

1252 A389	50c	Shepherd	.15	.15
1253 A389	1.60p	Girl	.20	.15
		Set value		.20

World Food Day — A390

1981, Oct. 16

1254 A390 4p multicolored .30 .20

50th Death Anniv. of Thomas Edison A391

1981, Oct. 18

1255 A391 4p multicolored .30 .20

Intl. Meeting on Cooperation and Development — A392

1981, Oct. 22

1256 A392 4p multicolored .30 .15

Pan-American Railway Congress A393

1981, Oct. 25 **Unwmk.**

1257 A393 1.60p multicolored .15 .15

50th Anniv. of Mexican Sound Movies A394

1981, Nov. 3 **Photo.** ***Perf. 14***

1258 A394 4p multicolored .30 .15

Inauguration of Zip Codes A395

1981, Nov. 12

1259 A395 80c multicolored .15 .15

Colonial Monument Type of 1980

#1260, Mascarones House. #1261, La Merced Order Convent. #1262, Third Order Chapel, Texcoco. #1263, Friar Tembleque Aqueduct, Otumba.

1981, Nov. 28

1260 A365	4p	black	.20	.15
1261 A365	4p	black	.20	.15
1262 A365	5p	black	.20	.15
1263 A365	5p	black	.20	.15
		Nos. 1260-1263 (4)	.80	
		Set value		.40

Martyrs of Rio Blanco, 75th Anniv. A396

1982, Jan. 7 **Photo.** ***Perf. 14***

1264 A396 80c multicolored .15 .15

Death Sesquicentennial of Ignacio Lopez Rayon — A397

1982, Feb. 2

1265 A397 1.60p multicolored .15 .15

75th Anniv. of Postal Headquarters — A398

1982, Feb. 17

1266 A398 4p green & ocher .20 .15

Crafts Type of 1980

1982, Mar. 6 **Photo.** ***Perf. 14***

1267 A370	50c	Huichole art	.15	.15
1268 A370	1p	Ceramic snail	.20	.15
1269 A370	3p	Tiger mask, Madera	.20	.15
		Nos. 1267-1269 (3)	.55	
		Set value		.15

"Use Zip Codes" A399

1982, Mar. 20

1270 A399 80c multicolored .15 .15

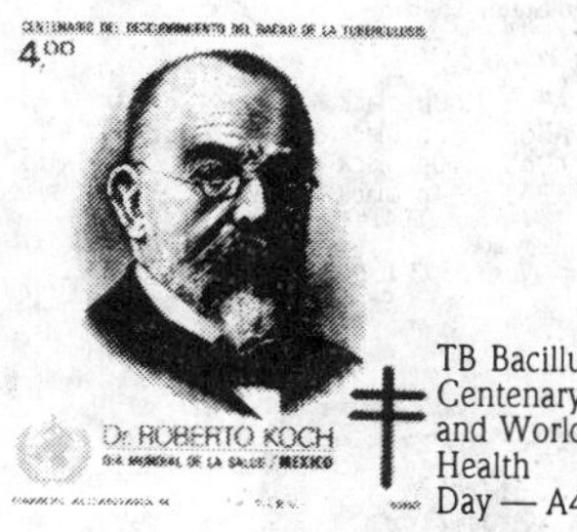

TB Bacillus Centenary and World Health Day — A400

1982, Apr. 7 **Photo.** ***Perf. 14***

1271 A400 4p multicolored .20 .15

50th Anniv. of Military Academy A401

1982, Apr. 15

1272 A401 80c multicolored .15 .15

Oaxaca City, 450th Anniv. — A402

1982, Apr. 25

1273 A402 1.60p multicolored .15 .15

Tourism Type of 1979

Designs: No. 1274, Basaseachic Cascade, Chihuahua. No. 1275, Silence Zone, Durango. No. 1276, Ruins, Maya city of Edzna, Campeche. No. 1277, Olmec sculpture, Tabasco.

1982, May 29 **Photo.** ***Perf. 14***

1274 A353	80c	multicolored	.15	.15
1275 A353	80c	multicolored	.15	.15
1276 A353	1.60p	multicolored	.15	.15
1277 A353	1.60p	multicolored	.15	.15
		Nos. 1274-1277 (4)	.60	
		Set value		.20

1982 World Cup A403

Designs: Various soccer players.

1982, June 13

1278 A403	1.60p	multicolored	.15	.15
1279 A403	4p	multicolored	.20	.15
1280 A403	7p	multicolored	.25	.15
		Nos. 1278-1280 (3)	.60	
		Set value		.15

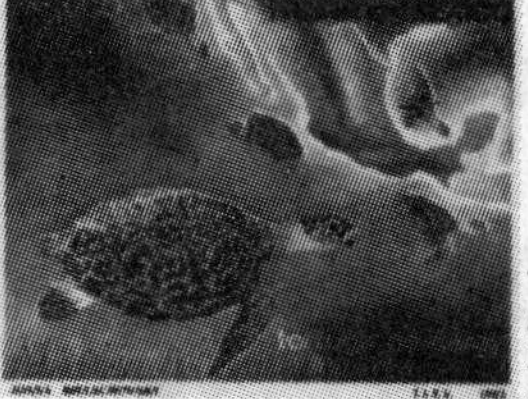

Turtles and Map A404

1982, July 3

1281 A404	1.60p	shown	.20	.15
1282 A404	4p	Gray whales	.25	.15
		Set value		.15

Gen. Vicente Guerrero (1783-1831) — A405

1982, Aug. 10 **Photo.** ***Perf. 14***

1283 A405 80c multicolored .15 .15

2nd UN Conference on Peaceful Uses of Outer Space, Vienna, Aug. 9-21 A406

1982, Aug. 14

1284 A406 4p multicolored .20 .15

Pre-Hispanic Art Type of 1980

Designs: 80c, Tariacuri, founder of Tarasco Kingdom, Chronicle of Michoacan, 16th cent. 1.60p, Acamapichtli, Aztec emperor, 1376-1396, Azcatitlan Codex. 4p, 10-Deer Tiger's Breastplate, wife of Lord 13-Eagle Tlaloc Copal Ball, 12th cent., Nuttal Mixtec Codex.

1982, Sept. 4

1285 A361 80c multicolored .15 .15
1286 A361 1.60p multicolored .20 .15
1287 A361 4p multicolored .25 .15
Nos. 1285-1287 (3) .60
Set value .15

Papaya A407

1982, Sept. 18 Unwmk. *Perf. 14*

1288 A407 80c shown .15 .15
1289 A407 1.60p Corn .20 .15
Set value .15

Florentine Codex Illustrations A408

1982, Oct. 2

1290 A408 80c Astrologer .15 .15
1291 A408 1.60p School .15 .15
1292 A408 4p Musicians .20 .15
Nos. 1290-1292 (3) .50
Set value .15

See Nos. 1520-1522.

Manuel Gamio (1883-1960) Anthropologist — A409

Scientists: No. 1294, Isaac Ochoterena (1855-1950), biologist. No. 1295, Angel Maria Garibay K. (1892-1976), philologist. No. 1296, Manuel Sandoval Vallarta (1899-), nuclear physicist. No. 1297, Guillermo Gonzalez Camarena (b. 1917), electronic engineer.

1982, Oct. 16 Photo. *Perf. 14*

1293 A409 1.60p multicolored .20 .15
1294 A409 1.60p multicolored .20 .15
1295 A409 1.60p multicolored .20 .15
1296 A409 1.60p multicolored .20 .15
1297 A409 1.60p multicolored .20 .15
a. Strip of 5, #1293-1297 1.25 1.25
Set value .25

Natl. Archives Opening, Aug. 27 — A410

1982, Oct. 23 *Perf. 14*

1298 A410 1.60p brt grn & blk .20 .15

Christmas 1982 A411

1982, Oct. 30 *Perf. 14*

1299 A411 50c Dove .15 .15
1300 A411 1.60p Dove, diff. .20 .15
Set value .15

Mexican Food System A412

1982, Nov. 13 Photo. *Perf. 14*

1301 A412 1.60p multicolored .20 .15

Opening of Revolutionary Museum, Chihuahua — A413

1982, Nov. 17 *Perf. 14*

1302 A413 1.60p No. C232 .20 .15

Colonial Monument Type of 1980

Designs: 1.60p, College of Sts. Peter and Paul, Mexico City, 1576. 8p, Convent of Jesus Maria, Mexico City, 1603. 10p, Open Chapel, Tlalmanalco, 1585. 14p, Convent at Actopan, Hidalgo State, 1548.

1982, Nov. 27

1303 A365 1.60p black & gray .20 .15
1304 A365 8p black & gray .30 .15
1305 A365 10p black & gray .30 .15
1306 A365 14p black & gray .40 .15
a. Vert. strip of 4, #1303-1306 + label 15.00 15.00
Nos. 1303-1306 (4) 1.20
Set value .35

Alfonso Garcia Robles, 1982 Nobel Peace Prize Winner A414

1982, Nov. 30 Unwmk. *Perf. 14*

1307 A414 1.60p multicolored .15 .15
1308 A414 14p multicolored .30 .15
Set value .20

Jose Vasconcelos, Philosopher — A415

1982, Dec. 11 *Perf. 14*

1309 A415 1.60p bl & blk .20 .15

World Communications Year — A416

1983, Feb. 12 Photo. *Perf. 14*

1310 A416 16p multicolored .30 .15

First Philatelic Exposition of the Mexican Revolution A417

1983, Mar. 13 Photo. *Perf. 14*

1311 A417 6p No. 326 .20 .15

25th Anniv. of Intl. Maritime Org. — A418

1983, Mar. 17

1312 A418 16p multicolored .35 .20

Year of Constitutional Right to Health Protection — A419

1983, Apr. 7

1313 A419 6p red & olive .20 .15

Society of Geography and Statistics Sesquicentennial — A420

1983, Apr. 18

1314 A420 6p Founder Gomez Farias .20 .15

2nd World Youth Soccer Championships — A421

1983, June 2 Photo. *Perf. 14*

1315 A421 6p green & blk .20 .15
1316 A421 13p red & blk .35 .15
1317 A421 14p blue & blk .35 .15
Nos. 1315-1317 (3) .90
Set value .35

Tourism Type of 1979

Designs: No. 1318, Federal Palace Building, Queretaro. No. 1319, Fountain, San Luis Potosi. 13p, Cable car, Zacatecas. 14p, Mayan stone head, Quintana Roo.

1983, June 24 Photo. *Perf. 14*

1318 A353 6p multicolored .20 .15
1319 A353 6p multicolored .20 .15
1320 A353 13p multicolored .35 .15
1321 A353 14p multicolored .35 .15
a. Vert. strip of 4, #1318-1321 + label 2.75 2.75
Set value .40

Simon Bolivar (1783-1830) — A422

1983, July 14

1322 A422 21p multicolored .40 .20

Angela Peralta, Opera Singer (1845-1883) — A423

1983 Photo. *Perf. 14*

1323 A423 9p multicolored .25 .15

Mexican Flora — A424

1983, Sept. 23 Photo. *Perf. 14*

1324 A424 9p Achras zapota .25 .15
1325 A424 9p Agave atrovirens .25 .15
Set value .20

Mexican Fauna A425

1983, Sept. 23 Photo. *Perf. 14*

1326 A425 9p Boa constrictor imperator .25 .15
1327 A425 9p Papilio machaon .25 .15
Set value .20

Christmas 1983 — A426

1983, Oct. 15 Photo. *Perf. 14*

1328 A426 9p multicolored .20 .15
1329 A426 20p multicolored .30 .20

SISTEMA INTEGRAL DE LAS COMUNICACIONES Y EL TRANSPORTE

SCT

MEXICO 13.00

Integral Communications and Transportation Systems — A427

1983, Oct. 17 Photo. *Perf. 14*

1330 A427 13p brt blue & blk .30 .15

Arte y Ciencia de México
Artistas Contemporaneos

Carlos Chavez (1899-1978), Musician, Composer A428

Contemporary Artists: No. 1332, Francisco Goitia (1882-1960), Painter. No. 1333, Salvador Diaz Miron (1853-1927), Lyrical Poet. No. 1334, Carlos Bracho (1899-1966), Sculptor. No. 1335, Fanny Anitua (1887-1968), Singer.

1983, Nov. 7 Photo. *Perf. 14*

1331 A428 9p brown & multi .25 .15
1332 A428 9p brown & multi .25 .15
1333 A428 9p brown & multi .25 .15
1334 A428 9p brown & multi .25 .15
1335 A428 9p brown & multi .25 .15
a. Horiz. strip of 5, #1331-1335 4.00 4.00
Set value .50

Jose Clemente Orozco (1883-1949), Painter A429

1983, Nov. 23 Photo. *Perf. 14*

1336 A429 9p multicolored .25 .15

35th Anniv. of Human Rights Declaration A430

1983, Dec. 10 *Perf. 14*

1337 A430 20p multicolored .30 .20

Colonial Monument Type of 1980

Designs: 9p, Convent Garden, Malinalco, 16th cent. 20p, Open Chapel, Cuernavaca Cathedral, Morelos. 21p, Tepeji del Rio Convent, Hidalgo. 24p, Atlatlahuacan Convent, Morelos.

1983, Dec. 16 Photo. *Perf. 14*

1338 A365 9p black & gray .30 .15
1339 A365 20p black & gray .40 .20
1340 A365 21p black & gray .40 .20
1341 A365 24p black & gray .40 .25
a. Vert. strip of 4, #1338-1341 + label 4.00 4.00

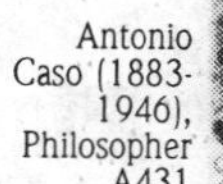

Antonio Caso (1883-1946), Philosopher A431

1983, Dec. 19

Granite Paper

1342 A431 9p multicolored .25 .15

Royal Mining Decree Bicentenary A432

1983, Dec. 21

1343 A432 9p Joaquin Velazquez Leon, reform author .25 .15

Postal Code Centenary A433

1984, Jan. 2 Photo. *Perf. 14*

1344 A433 12p Envelopes .35 .15

Fight Against Polio — A434

1984, Apr. 7 Photo. *Perf. 14*

1345 A434 12p Children dancing .35 .15

Aquatic Birds A435

1984, May 4 Photo. *Perf. 14*

1346 A435 12p Muscovy duck .40 .15
1347 A435 20p Black-bellied whistling tree duck .45 .15
a. Pair, #1346-1347 1.75 1.75
Set value .20

World Dog Exposition, Mexico City — A436

1984, May 27

1348 A436 12p multicolored .35 .15

Natl. Bank of Mexico Centenary — A437

1984, June 2

1349 A437 12p multicolored .35 .15

Forest Protection and Conservation — A438

1984, July 12 Photo. *Perf. 14*

1350 A438 20p Hands holding trees .40 .15

JUEGOS XXIII OLIMPIADA LOS ANGELES,CALIF.'84

MEXICO 14.00

1984 Summer Olympics A439

1984, July 28

1351 A439 14p Shot put .25 .15
1352 A439 20p Equestrian .30 .15
1353 A439 23p Gymnastics .30 .20
1354 A439 24p Diving .30 .20
1355 A439 25p Boxing .30 .20
1356 A439 26p Fencing .30 .20

Size: 56x62mm

Imperf

1357 A439 40p Rings 2.00 .30
Nos. 1351-1357 (7) 3.75 1.40

Mexico-USSR Diplomatic Relations, 60th Anniv. A440

1984, Aug. 4

1358 A440 23p Flags .40 .15

Intl. Population Conference, Aug. 5-14 — A441

1984, Aug. 6

1359 A441 20p UN emblem, hand .40 .15

Economic Culture Fund, 50th Anniv. — A442

1984, Sept. 3

1360 A442 14p multicolored .30 .15

Gen Francisco J. Mugica A443

1984,

1361 A443 14p black & brown .20 .15

Red Cactus, by Sebastian A444

Airline Emblem A445

1984, Sept. 14 Photo. *Perf. 14*

1362 A444 14p multicolored .15 .15
1363 A445 20p blk & org .20 .15

Aeromexico (airline), 50th anniv.

Palace of Fine Arts, 50th Anniv. A446

1984, Sept. 29

1364 A446 14p multicolored .15 .15

275th Anniv. of Chihuahua City — A447

1984, Oct. 12

1365 A447 14p Cathedral exterior detail .15 .15

Coatzacoalcos Bridge Inauguration — A448

1984, Oct. 17 *Perf. 14*

1366 A448 14p Aerial view .15 .15

UN Disarmament Week — A449

1984, Oct. 14 Photo. *Perf. 14*

1367 A449 20p multicolored .20 .15

Christmas 1984 A450

1984, Oct. 31 Photo. *Perf. 14*

1368 A450 14p Toy train & tree .15 .15
1369 A450 20p Pinata breaking .20 .15

Politician-Journalist Ignacio M. Altamirano (1834-1893) — A451

1984, Nov. 13 Photo. *Perf. 14*

1370 A451 14p blk & lt red brn .15 .15

State Audit Office, 160th Anniv. A452

1984, Nov. 16

1371 A452 14p multicolored .15 .15

1986 World Cup Soccer Championships, Mexico — A453

1984, Nov. 19

1372 A453 20p multicolored *.15 .15*
1373 A453 24p multicolored *.20 .15*
a. Pair, #1372-1373 + label *3.50 .40*

Romulo Gallegos (1884-1969), Author and Former Pres. of Venezuela — A454

1984, Dec. 6

1374 A454 20p blue & gray .20 .15

State Registry Office, 125th Anniv. A455

1984, Dec. 13

1375 A455 24p slate blue .25 .20

Natl. Flag, 50th Anniv. A456

1985, Feb. 24

1376 A456 22p multicolored .25 .20

Johann Sebastian Bach — A457

Intl. Youth Year — A458

1985, Mar. 21 Photo. *Perf. 14*

1377 A457 35p dl red brn, gold & blk .25 .20

1985, Mar. 28 Photo. *Perf. 14*

1378 A458 35p rose vio, gold & blk .25 .20

Child Survival Campaign A459

1985, Mar. 28 Photo. *Perf. 14*

1379 A459 36p multicolored .25 .20

Mexican Mint, 450th Anniv. A460

1985, May 11 Photo. *Perf. 14*

1380 A460 35p 1st gold & copper coins .25 .20

Victor Hugo A461

1985, May 22 Photo. *Perf. 14*

1381 A461 35p slate .25 .20

MEXFIL '85 — A462

1985, June 9 Photo. *Perf. 14*

1382 A462 22p No. 5 .15 .15
1383 A462 35p No. 574 .25 .20
1384 A462 36p No. 1081 .25 .20
Nos. 1382-1384 (3) .65 .55

Souvenir Sheet

1985, June 27 *Imperf.*

1385 A462 90p No. 111 on cover 2.00 .35

Morelos Telecommunications Satellite Launch — A463

1985, June 17 *Perf. 14*

1386 A463 22p Shuttle launch .15 .15
1387 A463 36p Ground receiver .20 .20
1388 A463 90p Modes of communication .50 .40
a. Strip of 3, #1386-1388 + 2 labels 3.50 3.50
Nos. 1386-1388 (3) .85 .75

Souvenir Sheet

Imperf

1389 A463 100p multicolored 2.00 .45

Nos. 1386-1388 has continuous design. No. 1389 pictures uninscribed continuous design of Nos. 1386-1388.

9th World Forestry Congress, Mexico City, July 1-9 — A464

1985, July 1 *Perf. 14*

1390 A464 22p Conifer .15 .15
1391 A464 35p Silk-cotton tree .20 .15
1392 A464 36p Mahogany .20 .20
a. Strip of 3, #1390-1392 + 2 labels 3.50 3.50
Nos. 1390-1392 (3) .55
Set value .40

Martin Luis Guzman (1887-1977), Journalist, Politician A465

Contemporary writers: No. 1394, Agustin Yanez (1904-1980), politician. No. 1395, Alfonso Reyes (1889-1959), diplomat. No. 1396, Jose Ruben Romero (1890-1952), diplomat. No. 1397, Artemio de Valle Arizpe (1888-1961), historian.

1985, July 19 *Perf. 14*

1393 A465 22p multicolored .15 .15
1394 A465 22p multicolored .15 .15
1395 A465 22p multicolored .15 .15
1396 A465 22p multicolored .15 .15
1397 A465 22p multicolored .15 .15
a. Strip of 5, #1393-1397 3.50 3.50
Nos. 1393-1397 (5) .75 .75

Heroes of the Mexican Independence, 1810 — A466

1985, Sept. 15

1398 A466 22p Miguel Hidalgo .15 .15
1399 A466 35p Jose Morelos .15 .15
1400 A466 35p Ignacio Allende .15 .15
1401 A466 36p Leona Vicario .20 .20
1402 A466 110p Vicente Guerrero .50 .50
Nos. 1398-1402 (5) 1.15 1.15

Souvenir Sheet

Imperf

1403 A466 90p Bell, church 2.00 .30

175th anniv. of independence from Spanish rule. #1403 contains one 56x49mm stamp.

University of Mexico, 75th Anniv. A467

1985, Sept. 22 Photo. *Perf. 14*

1404 A467 26p San Ildefonso, 1910 .15 .15
1405 A467 26p University emblem .15 .15
1406 A467 40p Rectory, 1985 .25 .20
1407 A467 45p 1st Rector Justo Sierra, crest, 1910 .25 .20
1408 A467 90p Crest, 1985 .50 .40
a. Strip of 5, #1404-1408 7.00 7.00
Nos. 1404-1408 (5) 1.30 1.10

Interamerican Development Bank, 25th Anniv. — A468

1985, Oct. 23 Photo. *Perf. 14*

1409 A468 26p multicolored .15 .15

UN Disarmament Week A469

1985, Oct. 24 *Perf. 14*

1410 A469 36p Guns, doves .20 .15

MEXICO 26.00 UN, 40th Anniv. — A470

1985, Oct. 25 *Perf. 14*

1411 A470 26p Hand, dove .15 .15

Christmas 1985 A471

Children's drawings.

1985, Nov. 15 **Photo.** *Perf. 14*

1412 A471 26p multicolored .15 .15
1413 A471 35p multicolored .15 .15
Set value .25

1910 Revolution, 75th Anniv. A472

1985, Nov. 18 *Perf. 14*

1414 A472 26p Soldadera .15 .15
1415 A472 35p Francisco Villa .15 .15
1416 A472 40p Emiliano Zapata .20 .15
1417 A472 45p Venustiano Carranza .20 .15
1418 A472 110p Francisco Madero .35 .25
Nos. 1414-1418 (5) 1.05 .85

Souvenir Sheet

Imperf

1419 A472 90p Liberty bell 2.00 .30

No. 1419 contains one 48x40mm stamp.

Astronaut, by Sebastian A473

The Watchman, by Federico Silva — A474

Mexican Astronaut, Rodolfo Neri, by Cauduro — A475

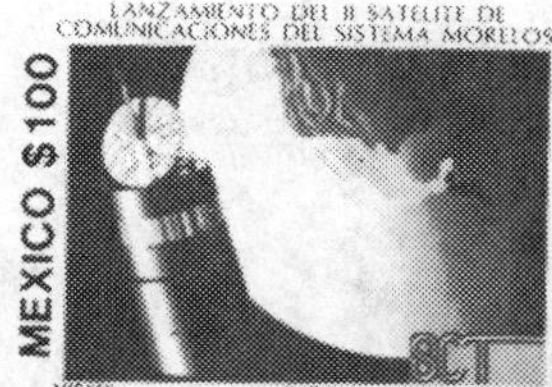

Morelos and Telecommunications Satellite Launch — A476

1985, Nov. 26 *Perf. 14*

1420 A473 26p multicolored .15 .15
1421 A474 35p multicolored .15 .15
1422 A475 45p multicolored .20 .15
Nos. 1420-1422 (3) .50
Set value .40

Miniature Sheet

Imperf

1423 A476 100p multicolored 2.00 .30

1986 World Cup Soccer Championships, Mexico — A477

1985, Dec. 15 **Photo.** *Perf. 14*

1424 A477 26p Olympic Stadium .15 .15
1425 A477 45p Aztec Stadium .20 .15

1st Free Textbook for Primary Education, 25th Anniv. — A478

1985, Dec. 16

1426 A478 26p Book cover .15 .15

Colonial Monuments A479

Landmarks in Mexico City: 26p, College of the Vizcainas, c. 1735. 35p, Palace of the Counts of Heras and Soto. 40p, Palace of the Counts of Calimaya, 16th cent. 45p, San Carlos Academy, 16th cent.

1985, Dec. 27 *Perf. 14*

1427 A479 26p grnsh blk & fawn .15 .15
1428 A479 35p grnsh blk & fawn .20 .15
1429 A479 40p grnsh blk & fawn .20 .15
1430 A479 45p grnsh blk & fawn .20 .15
a. Strip of 4, #1427-1430 + label 4.00 4.00
Nos. 1427-1430 (4) .75
Set value .50

Natl. Polytechnic Institute, 50th Anniv. A480

1986, Feb. 7 *Perf. 14*

1431 A480 40p Luis Enrique Erro Planetarium .15 .15
1432 A480 65p School of Arts & Communications .25 .20
1433 A480 75p Emblem, founders .30 .25
a. Strip of 3, #1431-1433 + 2 labels 7.00 7.00
Nos. 1431-1433 (3) .70 .60

Fruit — A481

1986, Feb. 21 *Perf. 14*

1434 A481 40p Cucurbita pepo .20 .15
1435 A481 65p Nopalea coccinellifera .30 .25

World Health Day — A482

1986, Apr. 7 **Photo.** *Perf. 14*

1436 A482 65p Doll .20 .20

Halley's Comet A483

1986, Apr. 25

1437 A483 90p multicolored .25 .20

Natl. Geology Institute, Cent. A484

1986, May 26

1438 A484 40p multicolored .20 .15

1986 World Cup Soccer Championships — A485

Paintings by Angel Zarraga (1886-1946) and Sergio Guerrero Morales: 30p, Three Soccer Players with Cap. 40p, Portrait of Ramon Novaro. 65p, Dimanche. 70p, Portrait of Ernest Charles Gimpel. 90p, Three Soccer Players. 110p, Poster for 1986 championships, by Morales.

1986, May 31

1439 A485 30p multicolored .15 .15
1440 A485 40p multicolored .20 .15
1441 A485 65p multicolored .30 .20
1442 A485 70p multicolored .30 .20
1443 A485 90p multicolored .35 .30

Size: 120x91mm

Imperf

1444 A485 110p multicolored 2.00 .75
Nos. 1439-1444 (6) 3.30 1.75

Independence War Heroes A486

175th Death anniv. of: 40p, Ignacio Allende (1769-1811). 65p, Juan Aldama (1774-1811). 75p, Mariano Jimenez (1781-1811).

1986, June 26 **Photo.** *Perf. 14*

1445 A486 40p multicolored .15 .15
1446 A486 65p multicolored .25 .20
1447 A486 75p multicolored .25 .20
Nos. 1445-1447 (3) .65 .55

Miguel Hidalgo y Costilla (1753-1811), Mural by Jose Clemente Orozco A487

1986, July 30 **Photo.** *Perf. 14*

1448 A487 40p multicolored .15 .15

Federal Tax Court, 50th Anniv. — A488

Gen. Nicolas Bravo (1786-1854) — A489

1986, Aug. 27 *Perf. 14*

1449 A488 40p gray, bl & blk .15 .15

1986, Sept. 10 *Perf. 14*

1450 A489 40p multicolored .15 .15

Paintings by Diego Rivera — A490

Designs: 50p, Paisaje Zapatista, 1915, vert. 80p, Desnudo con Alcatraces, 1944, vert. 110p, Sueno de una Tarde Dominical en la Alameda Central, 1947-48.

1986, Sept. 26 *Perf. 14*

1451 A490 50p multicolored .15 .15
1452 A490 80p multicolored .25 .20
1453 A490 110p multicolored .35 .25

See Nos. 1571-1573.

Guadalupe Victoria (1786-1843), 1st President — A491

1986, Sept. 29 *Perf. 14*

1454 A491 50p multicolored .15 .15

Natl. Storage Warehouse, 50th Anniv. — A492

1986, Oct. 3

1455 A492 40p multicolored .15 .15

Intl. Post Day — A493

1986, Oct. 9 *Perf. 14*

1456 A493 120p multicolored .25 .20

Natl. Committee Commemorating the 500th Anniv. (1992) of the Meeting of Two Worlds — A494

1986, Oct. 12 *Perf. 14*

1457 A494 50p black & lake .15 .15

15th Pan American Highways Congress, Mexico City — A495

1986, Oct. 17 **Photo.** *Perf. 14*

1458 A495 80p Palacio de Mineria .20 .15

Franz Liszt, Composer, 175th Birth Anniv. — A496

1986, Oct. 22 *Perf. 14*

1459 A496 100p black & brown .25 .20

Intl. Peace Year A497

1986, Oct. 24

1460 A497 80p blk, bl & dk red .20 .15

Interment of Pino Suarez in the Rotunda of Illustrious Men — A498

1986, Nov. 6

1461 A498 50p multicolored .15 .15

Jose Maria Pino Suarez, vice-president of 1st revolutionary government, 1911.

See Nos. 1472, 1475, 1487, 1563.

Christmas — A499

Clay figurines from Tonala, Jalisco.

1986, Nov. 28

1462 A499 50p King .15 .15
1463 A499 80p Angel .15 .15

Diego Rivera (1886-1957), Painter A500

1986, Dec. 4 **Photo.** *Perf. 14*

1464 A500 80p Self-portrait .20 .15

Export Type of 1975

Designs as before and: 60p, Men's shoes. 70p, Copperware. 80p, Denim overalls. 90p, Abalone. 100p, Cup of coffee.

1986-87 **Unwmk.** *Perf. 11½x11*

1465 A320 20p gray .15 .15

Perf. 14

1466 A320 40p pale grn & gold .30 .15

Perf. 11½x11

1467 A320 60p brown .45 .15
1468 A320 70p orange brn .60 .20
a. Perf. 14 1.65 .20

Perf. 14

1469 A320 80p blue .40 .20
1470 A320 90p green & blue .70 .25
1470A A320 100p brown ('88) .40 .20
b. 100p dark brown, perf. 11½x11 ('87) .60 .30
Nos. 1465-1470A (7) 3.00 1.30

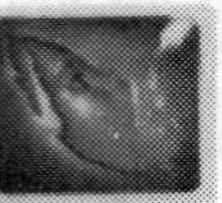

Natl. Polio Vaccination Program, Jan. 24-Mar. 28 — A501

1987, Jan. 20 **Photo.** *Perf. 14*

1471 A501 50p Oral vaccine .15 .15

Rotunda of Illustrious Men Type of 1986

1987, Feb. 4

1472 A498 100p multicolored .30 .25

Jose Maria Iglesias (1823-1891), president in 1876.

Natl. Teachers' College, 100th Anniv. A503

1987, Feb. 24 *Perf. 14*

1473 A503 100p multicolored .30 .25

Exploration of Pima Indian Territory by Eusebio Francisco Kino, 300th Anniv. — A504

1987, Feb. 27 *Perf. 14*

1474 A504 100p multicolored .30 .25

Rotunda of Illustrious Men Type of 1986

1987, Mar. 20 **Photo.** *Perf. 14*

1475 A498 100p Pedro Sainz de Baranda .30 .25

World Health Day, UN Child Survival Program A505

1987, Apr. 7

1476 A505 100p blue & slate blue .30 .25

Autonomous University of Puebla, 50th Anniv. A506

1987, Apr. 23

1477 A506 200p multicolored .50 .35

Battle of Puebla, 125th Anniv. — A507

1987, May 5 **Photo.** *Perf. 14*

1478 A507 100p multicolored .25 .20

METROPOLIS '87 — A508

1987, May 19

1479 A508 310p gray blk, grn & red .65 .45

Cong. of metropolitan areas, Mexico City.

Handicrafts A509

100p, Lacquerware tray, Uruapan, Michoacan. 200p, Blanket, Santa Ana Chiautempan, Tlaxcala. 230p, Lidded jar, Puebla, Pue.

1987, May 29 **Photo.** *Perf. 14*

1480 A509 100p multicolored .25 .15
1481 A509 200p multicolored .45 .35
1482 A509 230p multicolored .50 .40
Nos. 1480-1482 (3) 1.20 .90

Genaro Estrada, (1887-1937) Political Reformer — A510

1987, June 2
1483 A510 100p pale pink, blk & pale rose .25 .20

See Nos. 1509, 1568-1569.

Native Traders, 1961, Mural by P. O'Higgins A511

1987, June 8
1484 A511 100p multicolored .25 .20

Nat'l. Bank of Int'l. Commerce, 50th anniv.

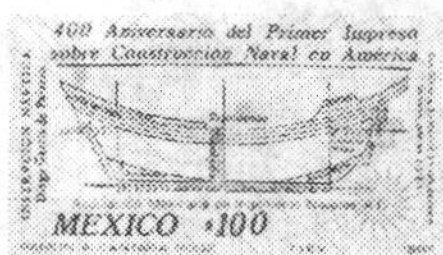

Publication of the 1st Shipbuilding Manual in the Americas, by Diego Garcia Palacio, 400th Anniv. A512

1987, June 15
1485 A512 100p multicolored .25 .20

Nat'l. Food Program, 50th Anniv. A513

1987, June 22
1486 A513 100p multicolored .25 .20

Rotunda of Illustrious Men Type of 1986

1987, June 22
1487 A498 100p multicolored .25 .20

Leandro Valle (1833-1861), jurist.

Paintings by Saturnino Herran (1887-1918) A514

1917 paintings: No. 1488, Self-portrait with Skull. No. 1489, The Offering. No. 1490, Creole Woman with Mantilla.

1987, July 9
1488 A514 100p black & red brn .25 .20
1489 A514 100p multicolored .25 .20
1490 A514 400p multicolored .95 .75
Nos. 1488-1490 (3) 1.45 1.15

Export Type of 1975

Designs: 10p, Meat cuts marked on steer. 20p, Bicycle. 50p, Tomatoes. 300p, Motor vehicle. 500p, Petroleum valves. 600p, Jewelry. 700p, Film. 800p, Construction materials. 900p, Pistons. 1,000p, Agricultural machinery. 2,000p, Wrought iron. 3,000p, Electric wiring. 4,000p, Honey. 5,000p, Cotton.

1987-88 Photo. Unwmk. *Perf. 14*
1491 A320 10p brt carmine .15 .15
1492 A320 20p black & org .15 .15
1493 A320 50p ver & yel grn .45 .15
1494 A320 300p chalky blue & scar, type I .45 .15
1495 A320 300p Prus blue & brt rose .45 .15
a. Thin paper .80 .15
b. Brt blue & brt rose .50 .15
1496 A320 500p dark gray & Prus blue .50 .25
1497 A320 600p multicolored 1.50 .30
a. Thin paper 3.00 .15
1498 A320 700p brt yel grn, dark red & blk 1.00 .35
a. Brt yel grn, lilac rose & blk 1.50 .35
1499 A320 800p dark red brn & golden brn .80 .40
1500 A320 900p black 1.25 .45

Wmk. 300
Granite Paper
Type I Burelage in Gray
1501 A320 1000p dk red & blk 4.00 .75
1502 A320 2000p black 3.25 1.00
1503 A320 3000p gray blk & org 3.00 1.50
1504 A320 4000p yel org & red brn 4.00 2.00
1505 A320 5000p apple grn & org 4.75 2.50
Nos. 1491-1505 (15) 25.70 10.25

Issue years: 10p-50p, 1987; others, 1988.

A515

10th Pan American Games, Indianapolis — A516

Unwmk.
1987, Aug. 7 Photo. *Perf. 14*
1506 A515 100p multicolored .15 .15
1507 A516 200p blk, brt grn & dk red .25 .20

Federal Power Commission, 50th Anniv. A517

1987, Aug. 14 Photo. *Perf. 14*
1508 A517 200p multicolored .30 .25

Art and Science Type of 1987

Design: J.E. Hernandez y Davalos (1827-1893), historian.

1987, Aug. 25 *Perf. 14*
1509 A510 100p buff, blk & dull red brn .15 .15

Pre-Hispanic Art Type of 1980

Designs: 100p, Xolotl (d. 1232), king of Amaquemecan. 200p, Nezahualpilli (1460-1516), king of Texcoco, conqueror. 400p, Motecuhzoma Ilhuicamina (Montezuma I d. 1469), emperor of Tenochtitlan (1440-1469).

1987, Aug. 31 *Perf. 14*
1510 A361 100p multicolored .20 .15
1511 A361 200p multicolored .35 .30
1512 A361 400p multicolored .75 .35
Nos. 1510-1512 (3) 1.30 .80

Tourism Type of 1979

Designs: 100p, Central Public Library, Mexico State. No. 1514, Patzcuaro Harbor, Michoacan. No. 1515, Garcia Caverns, Nuevo Leon. No. 1516, Beach resort, Mazatlan, Sinaloa.

1987 *Perf. 14*
1513 A353 100p multicolored .15 .15
1514 A353 150p multicolored .20 .15
1515 A353 150p multicolored .20 .15
1516 A353 150p multicolored .20 .15
Nos. 1513-1516 (4) .75
Set value .55

Issue dates: 100p, Sept. 11; others, Oct. 19.

Formula 1 Grand Prix Race, Oct. 18 A518

1987, Sept. 11
1517 A518 100p multicolored .15 .15

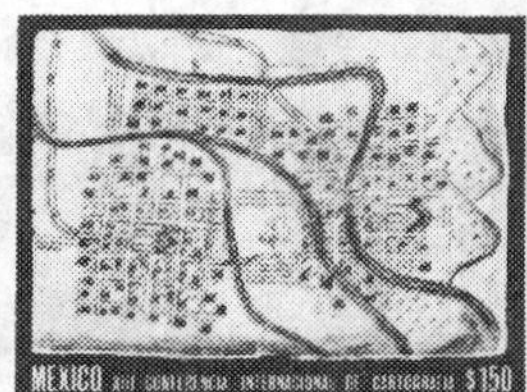

13th Intl. Cartography Conference — A519

1987, Oct. 12
1518 A519 150p Map, 16th cent. .20 .15

Discovery of America, 500th Anniv. (in 1992) A520

Design: Santa Maria, emblem of the Discovery of America Festival to be held in 1992.

1987, Oct. 12 *Perf. 14*
1519 A520 150p multicolored 1.50 .15

For overprint see No. 1698.

Illuminated Codices Type of 1982

Mendocino Codex (c. 1541): No. 1520, Founding of Tenochtitlan by the Aztecs, 1324. No. 1521, Pre-Hispanic wedding. No. 1522, Montezuma's Council.

1987, Nov. 3
1520 A408 150p multicolored .20 .15
1521 A408 150p multicolored .20 .15
1522 A408 150p multicolored .20 .15
Nos. 1520-1522 (3) .60 .45

Christmas 1987 — A521

1987, Nov. 6
1523 A521 150p brt pink .20 .15
1524 A521 150p dull blue .20 .15

World Post Day — A522

Documents: 150p, Ordinance for expediting mail by sea, 1777. 600p, Roster of correspondence transported by coach, 1857.

1987, Nov. 12
1525 A522 150p pale gray & slate gray .20 .15

Size: 129x102mm
Imperf
1526 A522 600p rose lake & yel bis 2.00 .55

Meeting of Eight Latin American Presidents, 1st Anniv. — A523

1987, Nov. 26 *Perf. 14*
1527 A523 250p shown .25 .20
1528 A523 500p Flags, peace doves .50 .40

Dualidad 1964, by Rufino Tamayo (b. 1899) — A524

1987, Dec. 9
1529 A524 150p multicolored .20 .15

Nationalization of Mexican Railroads, 50th Anniv. — A525

1987, Dec. 15
1530 A525 150p Metlac Bridge .20 .15

Antonio Stradivarius (c. 1644-1737), Italian Violin Maker A526

1987, Dec. 18 *Perf. 14*
1531 A526 150p bluish lilac .20 .15

Constitutional Tribunal of the Supreme Court, Plenum Hall, Jan. 15 — A527

Design: Statue of Manuel Rejon, author of the Mexican constitution.

1988, Jan. 15 Photo. *Perf. 14*
1532 A527 300p multicolored .35 .30

Fauna A528

1988, Feb. 29 Photo. *Perf. 14*
1533 A528 300p *Ambystoma mexicanum* .30 .25
1534 A528 300p *Trichechus manatus* .30 .25

A529

Nationalization of the Petroleum Industry, 50th Anniv. — A530

1988, Mar. 18
1535 A529 300p blue & blk .30 .25
1536 A530 300p PEMEX emblem, vert. .30 .25
1537 A530 500p shown .45 .35
Nos. 1535-1537 (3) 1.05 .85

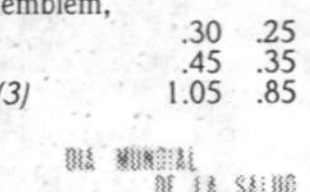

Vaccination, Detroit, 1932, Mural (detail) by Diego Rivera — A531

1988, Apr. 7
1538 A531 300p olive grn & henna brn .35 .25

World Health Day: child immunization.

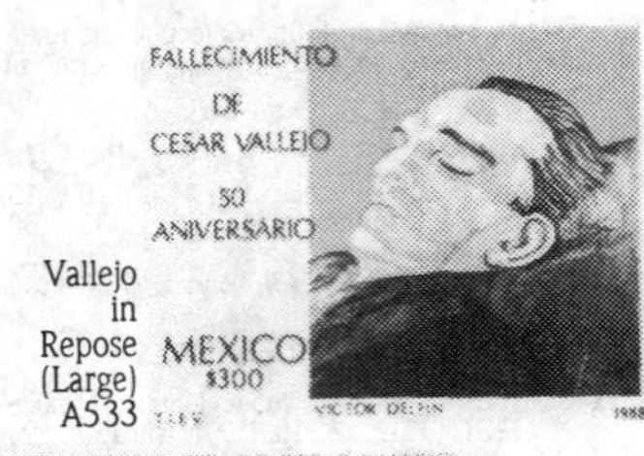

Vallejo in Repose (Large) A533

FALLECIMIENTO DE CESAR VALLEJO 50 ANIVERSARIO

Me moriré en París con aguacero

MEXICO $300

Vallejo in Repose (Small) A534

1988, Apr. 15
1540 A533 300p shown .35 .25
1541 A533 300p Portrait, diff. (large) .35 .25
a. Pair, #1540-1541 + label 3.25 3.25
b. Bklt. pane of 4 (2 each #1540-1541) + label
1542 A534 300p shown .35 .25
1543 A534 300p As #1541 (small) .35 .25
a. Pair, #1542-1543 + label 3.25 3.25
Nos. 1540-1543 (4) 1.40 1.00

Cesar Vallejo (1892-1938), Peruvian poet. Stamps of the same type printed se-tenant in sheets of 20 stamps containing 10 pairs plus 5 labels between inscribed with various Vallejo quotes or commemorative text.

Issue date: No. 1541b, Nov. 9, 1990. Label in No. 1541b is overprinted in red with Mexican Chicagopex '90 souvenir cancel, and had limited distribution.

Sketch of Carlos Pellicer Camara (1897-1977), Poet, by Fontanelly — A535

1988, Apr. 23
1544 A535 300p pale vio, blk & sal .35 .25

MEPSIRREY '88 Philatelic Exhibition, Monterrey, May 27-29 — A536

1988, May 27
1545 A536 300p Youth collectors .35 .25
1546 A536 300p Handstamped cover .35 .25
1547 A536 500p Alfa Planetarium .55 .45
Nos. 1545-1547 (3) 1.25 .95

Mexico-Elmhurst Philatelic Society Intl. (MEPSI).

1988 Formula I Championships, Mexico — A537

Design: Layout of Hermanos Rodriguez race track, Mexico City, and car.

1988, May 28 Photo. *Perf. 14*
1548 A537 500p multicolored .50 .35

A538

Ramon Lopez Velarde (1888-1921), Poet A539

1988, June 15
1549 A538 300p multicolored .30 .25
1550 A539 300p multicolored .30 .25
a. Bklt. pane of 4 + label

Issue date: No. 1550a, Nov. 9, 1990. Label in No. 1550a is overprinted in red with Mexican Chicagopex '90 souvenir cancel, and had limited distribution.

MEXICO $300

PENTATHLON

50 ANIVERSARIO

DEPORTIVO MILITARIZADO UNIVERSITARIO

University Military Pentathlon, 50th Anniv. — A540

1988, July 9 Photo. *Perf. 14*
1551 A540 300p multicolored .30 .25

1st Mexico-Japan Friendship, Commerce and Navigation Treaty, Cent. — A541

1988, Aug. 16
1552 A541 500p multicolored .50 .35

Joint Oceanographic Assembly, Acapulco, Aug. 23-31 — A542

1988, Aug. 23
1553 A542 500p multicolored .50 .35

1988 Summer Olympics, Seoul — A543

1988, Aug. 31 Photo. *Perf. 14*
1554 A543 500p multi .50 .35

Size: 71x55mm
Imperf
1555 A543 700p Emblems, torch 1.00 .60

World Boxing Council, 25th Anniv. A544

1988, Sept. 9
1556 A544 500p multi .50 .35

Intl. Red Cross and Red Crescent Organizations, 125th Annivs. A545

1988, Sept. 23 Photo. *Perf. 14*
1557 A545 300p blk, gray & scar .30 .25

Jose Guadalupe Posada (1852-1913), Painter, Illustrator — A546

1988, Sept. 29
1558 A546 300p sil & blk .30 .25

World Wildlife Fund — A547

Various monarch butterflies, *Danaus plexippus.*

1988, Sept. 30 *Perf. 14*
1559 A547 300p shown 1.00 .25
1560 A547 300p Three adults 1.00 .25
1561 A547 300p Larva, adult, pupa 1.00 .25
1562 A547 300p Five adults 1.00 .25
Nos. 1559-1562 (4) 4.00 1.00

Rotunda of Illustrious Men Type of 1986

Portrait and eternal flame: Manuel Sandoval Vallarta (1899-1977), physicist.

1988, Oct. 5
1563 A498 300p multi .30 .25

World Post Day A548

1988, Oct. 9 *Perf. 14*
1564 A548 500p World map .50 .35

Size: 75x44mm
Imperf
1565 A548 700p Envelope, doves, Earth 2.00 .60

Discovery of America, 500th Anniv. (in 1992) — A549

Illuminations: Aztec painter Tlacuilo from the Mendocine Codex, 1541, and Dominican scribe from the Yanhuitlan Codex, 1541-50.

1988, Oct. 12 *Perf. 14*
1566 A549 500p multi .50 .35

World Food Day — A550

1988, Oct. 15 *Perf. 14*
1567 A550 500p multi .50 .35

Art and Science Type of 1987

#1568, Alfonso Caso (1896-1970), educator, founder of the Natl. Museum of Anthropology. #1569, Vito Alessio Robles (1879-1957), historian.

1988, Oct. 24 *Perf. 14*
1568 A510 300p gray & blk .30 .25
1569 A510 300p pale yel, blk & red brn .30 .25

Act of Independence, 175th Anniv. — A551

1988, Nov. 9
1570 A551 300p claret brn & fawn .30 .25

Art Type of 1986

Paintings by Antonio M. Ruiz (1895-1964): No. 1571, *Parade*, 1936. No. 1572, *La Malinche*, 1939. No. 1573, *Self-portrait*, 1925, vert.

1988, Nov. 21 *Perf. 14*
1571 A490 300p multi .30 .25
1572 A490 300p multi .30 .25
1573 A490 300p multi .30 .25
Nos. 1571-1573 (3) .90 .75

Tempera and Oil Paintings by Jose Reyes (b. 1924) A552

1988, Nov. 25 *Perf. 14*
1574 A552 300p Feast .30 .25
1575 A552 300p Pinata, vert. .30 .25

Christmas.

Municipal Workers' Trade Union, 50th Anniv. A553

1988, Dec. 5 *Perf. 14*
1576 A553 300p pale bister & blk .30 .25

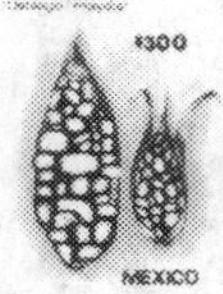

Flora — A554

1988, Dec. 20 *Perf. 14*
1577 A554 300p *Ustilago maydis* .30 .25
1578 A554 300p *Mimosa tenuiflora* .30 .25

Exporta Type of 1975

Designs: 40p, 1400p, Chemistry flasks. 200p, Citrus fruit. 450p, Circuit board. 750p, Film. 950p, Pistons. 1000p, Agricultural machinery. 1100p, Minerals. 1300p, Strawberries. 1500p, Copper vase. 1600p, Steel pipes. 1700p, Tequila. 1900p, Abalone. 2000p, Wrought iron. 2100p, Bicycles. 2500p, Overalls. 5000p, Cotton.

#1588A, 1589, 1592, 1598A, 1599, 1601, 1603 have gray burelage Type I.

1988-92 Photo. Unwmk. *Perf. 14*

1583	A320	40p	black	.20	.15
1584	A320	200p	emer & brt yel	.30	.15
a.			Thin paper	.75	.15
1585	A320	450p	yel bister & lil rose	.50	.25
a.			Thin paper	.75	.25
1586	A320	750p	brt yel grn, dark red & dark gray	1.50	.30
1587	A320	950p	indigo	1.50	.30
a.			Thin paper	1.65	.45
1588	A320	1000p	dark red & blk	1.10	.25
1588A	A320	1000p	dark red & blk, type 1	2.50	.25
1589	A320	1100p	dark gray, type I	1.75	.40
1590	A320	1100p	dark gray	1.65	.40
1591	A320	1300p	red & grn	1.65	.45
1592	A320	1300p	red & grn, type I	1.75	.45
a.			Thin paper	2.25	.45
1593	A320	1400p	black	1.75	.50
1594	A320	1500p	tan	1.75	.60
a.			1500p orange brown	1.75	.60
1595	A320	1600p	red orange	1.65	.55
1596	A320	1700p	dk grn & yel grn	1.65	.60
1597	A320	1900p	bl grn & bl	1.75	.65
1598	A320	2000p	black	2.25	.75
1598A	A320	2000p	black, type 1	2.25	.15
1599	A320	2100p	black & orange, type I	2.50	.85
1600	A320	2100p	black & ver	6.75	.80
1601	A320	2500p	dark blue, type I	2.50	1.00
1602	A320	2500p	slate blue	3.25	.90
1603	A320	5000p	apple grn & org, type I	4.00	1.75
	Nos. 1583-1603 (23)			46.45	12.45

Issued: 40p, 1/5/88; 200p, 2/27/89; 450p, 2/10/89; #1585a, 950p, #1587a, 1589, 3/30/89; 1,000p, 1989; #1590, 1599, 1601, 1991; #1600, 1602, 5000p, 1992; others, 1990.

Graphic Arts Workshop, 50th Anniv. A555

1989, Feb. 9 Photo. *Perf. 14*
1604 A555 450p yel bis, red & blk .45 .35

Coat of Arms and *E Santo Domingo*, the Natl. Hymn — A556

1989, Feb. 27
1605 A556 450p multicolored .45 .35

Dominican Republic independence, 145th anniv.

Intl. Border and Territorial Waters Commission of Mexico and the US, Cent. — A557

1989, Mar. 1
1606 A557 1100p multi 1.10 .80

10th Intl. Book Fair — A558

1989, Mar. 4
1607 A558 450p UNAM School of Engineering .45 .35

Lyricists and Composers Soc., 25th Anniv. A559

1989, Mar. 17
1608 A559 450p multi .45 .35

World Day for the Fight Against AIDS A560

1989, Apr. 7
1609 A560 450p multi .45 .35

Leona Vicario (1779-1842), Heroine of the Independence Movement A561

Alfonso Reyes (1889-1959), Author, Educator A562

1989, Apr. 20 Photo. *Perf. 14*
1610 A561 450p blk, sepia & golden brn .45 .35

1989, May 17
1611 A562 450p multi .45 .35

Formula 1 Grand Prix of Mexico — A563

1989, May 28 *Perf. 14*
1612 A563 450p multi .45 .35

14th Tourism Congress, Acapulco — A564

14th Intl. Gerontology Congress, Mexico — A565

1989, June 11 *Perf. 14*
1613 A564 1100p multi 1.10 .80

1989, June 18

Statue: The god Huehueteotl as an old man bearing the weight of the world on his shoulders.

1614 A565 450p multi .45 .35

Battle of Zacatecas, 75th Anniv. — A566

1989, June 23
1615 A566 450p black .45 .35

Baseball Hall of Fame of Mexico — A567

1989, June 25

1616 A567 550p Umpire, catcher 1.00 .45
1617 A567 550p Batter 1.00 .45
a. Pair, #1616-1617 + label 6.50 6.50

No. 1617a has continuous design.

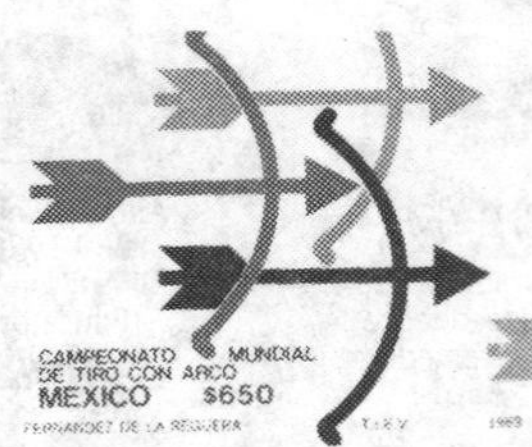

35th World Archery Championships, Lausanne, Switzerland, July 4-8 — A568

1989, July 2

1618 A568 650p Bows and arrows 1.25 .50
1619 A568 650p Arrows, target 1.25 .50
a. Pair, #1618-1619 + label 4.50 4.50

No. 1619a has continuous design.

Tijuana, Cent. A569

1989, July 11 **Photo.** ***Perf. 14***

1620 A569 1100p Municipal arms .90 .70

French Revolution, Bicent. A570

1989, July 14

1621 A570 1300p blue, blk & dark red 1.10 .80

Gen. Francisco Xavier Mina (1789-1817), Independence Hero — A571

1989, Sept. 7

1622 A571 450p green, blk & dark red .40 .30

Natl. Museum of Anthropology, Chapultepec, 25th Anniv. — A572

1989, Sept. 17 ***Perf. 14***

1623 A572 450p multicolored .40 .30

7th Mexico City Marathon — A573

1989, Sept. 24

1624 A573 450p multicolored .40 .30

Printing in America, 450th Anniv. — A574

1989, Sept. 28

1625 A574 450p multicolored .40 .30

World Post Day A575

1989, Oct. 9 **Photo.** ***Perf. 14***

1626 A575 1100p multicolored .85 .65

Sovereign Revolutionary Convention of Aguascalientes, 75th Anniv. — A576

1989, Oct. 10

1627 A576 450p multicolored .35 .25

Exploration and Colonization of the Americas by Europeans A577

1989, Oct. 12

1628 A577 1300p multicolored 1.00 .75

America Issue — A578

UPAE emblem and symbols like those produced on art by pre-Columbian peoples.

1989, Oct. 12

1629 A578 450p shown .35 .25
1630 A578 450p multi, diff., vert. .35 .25

Natl. Tuberculosis Foundation, 50th Anniv. — A579

1989, Nov. 10

1631 A579 450p multicolored .35 .25

Mask of the Bat God, Zapoteca Culture, c. 200-300 A580

1989, Nov. 28

1632 A580 450p multicolored .35 .25

Serfin Commercial Bank of Mexico, 125th Anniv. A581

1989, Nov. 29

1633 A581 450p deep blue, gold & blk .35 .25

Pres. Adolfo Ruiz Cortines (1889-1973) — A582

1989, Dec. 3

1634 A582 450p multicolored .35 .25

Christmas A583

1989, Dec. 11

1635 A583 450p Candlelight vigil .35 .25
1636 A583 450p Man sees star, vert. .35 .25

Natl. Institute of Anthropology and Natural History, 50th Anniv. — A584

1989, Dec. 13

1637 A584 450p dark red, gold & black .35 .25

Nationalization of the Railway System in Mexico, 80th Anniv. — A585

1989

1638 A585 450p multicolored .35 .25

Issue dates for some 1990-1991 issues are based on First Day cancels. Original printings were small. Later printings, made in 1991, were distributed to the stamp trade and seem to be the ones used for "First Day Covers."

Tampico Bridge — A586

1990, Jan. 11 **Photo.** ***Perf. 14***

1639 A586 600p gold, blk & red .45 .30

Eradication of Polio — A587

1990, Feb. 1

1640 A587 700p multicolored .50 .35

Natl. Census A588

1990, Mar. 12

1641 A588 700p lt grn & yel .50 .35

Mexican Philatelic Assoc., 10th Anniv. — A589

1990, Apr. 19
1642 A589 700p multicolored .50 .35

Natl. Archives, Bicentennial — A590

1990, Apr. 24
1643 A590 700p pale violet .50 .35

Intl. Conf. of Advertising Agencies — A591

1990, Apr. 27
1644 A591 700p multicolored .50 .35

Stamp World London '90 — A592

1990, May 3
1645 A592 700p multicolored .50 .35

First Postage Stamps, 150th Anniv. — A593

1990, May 6
1646 A593 700p lake, gold & blk .50 .35

15th Tourism Exposition — A594

1990, May 6
1647 A594 700p multicolored .50 .35

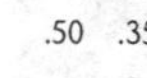

Visit of Pope John Paul II A595

1990, May 6
1648 A595 700p multicolored .50 .35

Health of Young Mothers A596

1990, May 10
1649 A596 700p multicolored .50 .35

Fight Against Smoking — A597

1990, May 31
1650 A597 700p multicolored .50 .35

World Environment Day — A598

1990, June 5
1651 A598 700p multicolored .50 .35

Formula 1 Grand Prix of Mexico A599

1990, June 24
1652 A599 700p grn, red & blk .50 .35

Airport & Auxiliary Services, 25th Anniv. — A600

1990, June 25 Photo. *Perf. 14*
1653 A600 700p multicolored .50 .35

Fight Against Drugs A601

1990, June 26
1654 A601 700p multicolored .50 .35

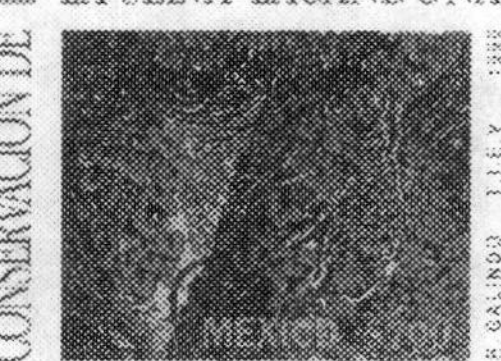

Protection of Rain Forests — A602

1990, July 6
1655 A602 700p multicolored .50 .35

Solidarity with Poor People — A603

1990, Aug. 8
1656 A603 700p multicolored .50 .35

Solidarity is a governmental social program of Pres. Salinas de Gortari. See No. 1704.

Oaxaca Cultural Heritage — A604

1990, Aug. 10
1657 A604 700p multicolored .50 .35

Nature Conservation A605

1990, Aug. 21
1658 A605 700p blk, gray & org .50 .35

Mexican Institute of Petroleum, 25th Anniv. A606

1990, Aug. 23
1659 A606 700p black & blue .50 .35

8th Mexico City Marathon — A607

1990, Aug. 24
1660 A607 700p blk, red & grn .50 .35

University of Colima, 50th Anniv. A608

1990, Sept. 16
1661 A608 700p gray, bister, red & grn .50 .35

Mexico City Advisory Council, Founded in 1929 — A609

1990, Sept. 17
1662 A609 700p sil, yel, blk & org .50 .35

Nationalization of Electric Industry, 30th Anniv. — A610

1990, Sept. 27
1663 A610 700p gray, grn, red & blk .50 .35

City of Campeche, 450th Anniv. A611

1990, Oct. 4
1664 A611 700p multicolored .50 .35

Silvestre Revueltas (1899-1940), Musician A612

1990, Oct. 4
1665 A612 700p multicolored .50 .35

Plan of San Luis, 80th Anniv. A613

1990, Oct. 5
1666 A613 700p multicolored .50 .35

14th World Conference of Supreme Counselors — A614

1990, Oct. 8
1667 A614 1500p vio, sil, gold & grn 1.10 .80

Discovery of America, 498th Anniv. — A615

1990, Oct. 12
1668 A615 700p multicolored .50 .35

Mexican Archaeology, Bicentennial A616

1990, Nov. 18
1669 A616 1500p multicolored 1.10 .80

16th Central American and Caribbean Games — A617

1990, Nov. 20
1670 A617 750p shown .75 .40
1671 A617 750p Mayan ball player .75 .40
1672 A617 750p Mayan ball player, vert. .75 .40
1673 A617 750p Ball court, stone ring, vert. .75 .40
a. Strip of 4, #1670-1673 4.50 4.50
Nos. 1670-1673 (4) 3.00 1.60

Christmas
A618 A619

1990, Dec. 3
1674 A618 700p Poinsettias .50 .35
1675 A619 700p Candles .50 .35

Mexican Canine Federation, 50th Anniv. A620

1990, Dec. 9
1676 A620 700p multicolored .50 .35

World Post Day — A621

1990, Oct. 9 **Photo.** ***Perf. 14***
1677 A621 1500p multicolored 1.10 .80

America Issue A622

#1678, Flowers, galleon. #1679, Galleon, parrot.

1990, Oct. 12
1678 A622 700p multicolored .75 .35
1679 A622 700p multicolored .75 .35
a. Pair, #1678-1679 + blank label 1.65 1.65

No. 1679a has continuous design.

Mexican Brewing Industry, Cent. — A623

1990, Nov. 8 ***Perf. 14***
1680 A623 700p multicolored .50 .35

National Chamber of Industrial Development, 50th Anniv. — A624

1990, Dec. 5 ***Perf. 14***
1681 A624 1500p multicolored 1.10 .80

Naval Secretariat, 50th Anniv. A625

1991 **Photo.** ***Perf. 14***
1682 A625 1000p bl, blk & gold .70 .50

Prevent Transportation Accidents — A626

1991, Jan. 11 **Photo.** ***Perf. 14***
1683 A626 700p multicolored .55 .40

Natl. Consumers Institute, 15th Anniv. — A627

1991, Feb. 11
1684 A627 1000p multicolored .80 .55

Voter Registration A628

1991, Feb. 13 ***Perf. 14***
1685 A628 1000p org, blk & grn .80 .55

Olympic Basketball — A629

1991, Feb. 25 ***Perf. 14***
1686 A629 1000p black & yellow .80 .55

Campaign Against Polio — A630

1991, Mar. 8
1687 A630 1000p multicolored .80 .55

Nos. 1688-1691, 1697 with "NP" and Post Office eagle head logo or just the logo, are specimens.

Childrens' Day for Peace and Development — A631

Health and Family Life — A632

1991, Apr. 16 *Perf. 14*
1688 A631 1000p multicolored .80 .55
Perf. 14x14½
1689 A632 1000p multicolored .80 .55

Mining in Mexico, 500th Anniv. — A633

1991, Apr. 25 *Perf. 14*
1690 A633 1000p multicolored .80 .55

Promotion of Breastfeeding A634

1991, May 10 *Perf. 14*
1691 A634 1000p multicolored .80 .55

16th Tourism Exposition — A635

1991, May 12 *Perf. 14*
1692 A635 1000p brt grn & dk grn .85 .60

Rotary Intl. Convention A636

1991, June 2 *Rouletted 6½*
1693 A636 1000p blue & gold .85 .60

Integrated Communications and Transportation Systems (SCT), Cent. — A637

Designs: No. 1695a, 1000p, Jet landing. b, 1500p, Airport control tower. c, 1000p, FAX machine. d, 1500p, Upper floors, SCT headquarters. e, 1000p, Communications van. f, 1500p, Satellite. g, 1000p, Satellite in orbit, earth. h, 1000p, Boxcars. i, 1500p, Locomotives. j, 1000p, People using telephones. k, 1500p, Lower floors, SCT headquarters. l, 1000p, Hillside road, left section, highway bridge. m, 1500p, Center section, highway bridge. n, 1000p, Right section of bridge. o, 1000p, Cranes loading cargo ship. p, 1500p, Bow of cargo ship. q, 1000p, Television camera. r, 1500p, Bus. s, 1000p, Truck. t, 1500p, Trailers passing through toll plaza. u, 1000p, Bridge construction. Continuous design.

1991, June 11 *Rouletted 6½*
1694 A637 1000p gray & multi 1.00 .60
1695 A637 Block of 21, #a.-u. 45.00 *50.00*

Jaguar A638

1991, June 12 *Perf. 14*
1696 A638 1000p black & orange .85 .60

Conservation of the rain forests.

Formula 1 Grand Prix of Mexico A639

1991, June 16 Litho. *Rouletted 6½*
1697 A639 1000p multicolored .85 .50

No. 1519 Ovptd. in Red 

1991, June 14 Photo. *Perf. 14*
1698 A520 150p multicolored

No. 1698 was available in strips of 5 only in booklets with limited distribution.

Total Solar Eclipse — A640

Designs: No. 1699a, 1000p, Denomination at lower right. b, Globe showing Mexico. c, 1000p, Denomination at lower left. Continuous design.

1991, July 5 *Rouletted 6½*
1699 A640 Strip of 3, #a.-c. 6.50 5.00

A641 A642

1991, July 18
1700 A641 1500p blk, org & yel 1.10 .80

First Latin American Presidential Summit, Guadalajara.

1991, July 31
1701 A642 2000p Solidarity bridge 1.70 1.20

A643 A644

1991, Aug. 22
1702 A643 1000p multicolored .85 .60

Ninth Mexico City marathon.

1991, Aug. 27
1703 A644 1000p blue & silver .85 .60

Federal tax court, 55th anniv.

Solidarity Type of 1990 and

A645

1991 *Perf. 14½x14*
1704 A603 1000p multicolored .85 .60
Rouletted 6½
1705 A645 1000p multicolored .85 .60

Issued: No. 1704, Dec. 17; No. 1705, Sept. 9.

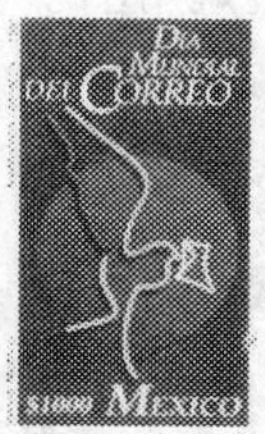

World Post Day — A646

1991, Oct. 9 *Rouletted 6½*
1706 A646 1000p multicolored .85 .60

Voyages of Discovery A647

Discovery of America, 500th Anniv. (in 1992) A648

Design: No. 1708, Sailing ship, storm.

1991, Oct. 12
1707 A647 1000p multicolored 1.00 .60
1708 A647 1000p multicolored 1.00 .60
a. Pair, #1707-1708 2.25 1.20
1709 A648 1000p multicolored 1.50 .60
Nos. 1707-1709 (3) 3.50 1.80

No. 1708a has continuous design. Printed in sheets of 20+5 labels.

A649

Christmas A650

1991, Nov. 26
1710 A649 1000p multicolored .85 .60
1711 A650 1000p multicolored .85 .60

Carlos Merida, Birth Cent. A651

1991, Dec. 2 Photo. *Rouletted 6½*
1712 A651 1000p multicolored .85 .60

Wolfgang Amadeus Mozart, Death Bicent. A652

1991, Dec. 5
1713 A652 1000p multicolored .85 .60

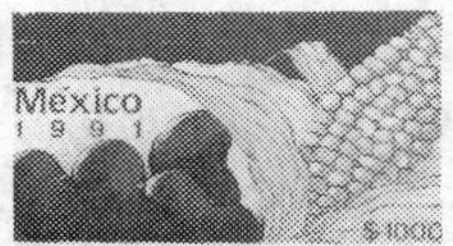

Self-sufficiency in Corn and Bean Production — A653

1991, Dec. 11 Photo. *Rouletted 6½*
1714 A653 1000p multicolored .78 .55

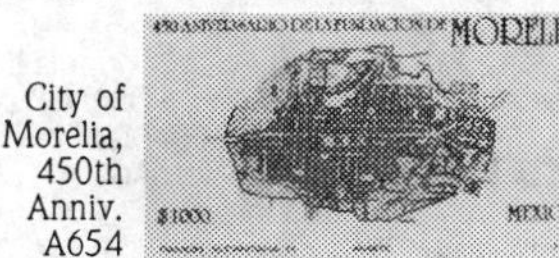

City of Morelia, 450th Anniv. A654

1991, Dec. 13
1715 A654 1000p multicolored .78 .55

Merida, 450th Anniv. A655

1992, Jan. 6 Photo. *Rouletted 6½*
1716 A655 1300p multicolored 1.00 .70

Engineering Education in Mexico, Bicent. A656

1992, Jan. 15
1717 A656 1300p blue & red 1.00 .70

1992 Summer Olympics, Barcelona A657

Design: No. 1719, Stylized Olympic Rings.

1992 Photo. *Rouletted 6½*
1718 A657 2000p multicolored 1.50 1.05
1719 A657 2000p multicolored 1.50 .95

Issued: No. 1718, Feb. 10; No. 1719, Mar. 1.

Guadalajara, 450th Anniv. — A658

Designs: No. 1720a, 1300p, Coat of arms. b, 1300p, Municipal buildings. c, 1300p, Guadalajara Cathedral. d, 1900p, Allegory of the city's founding. e, 1900p, Anniversary emblem.

1992, Feb. 14
1720 A658 Strip of 5, #a.-e. 6.00 4.50

Healthy Child Development — A659

1992, Feb. 26
1721 A659 2000p multicolored 1.50 .95

Formula 1 Grand Prix of Mexico A660

1992, Mar. 22
1722 A660 1300p multicolored 1.00 .65

Introduction of the wheel and domesticated horses to America, 500th anniv.

Telecom '92 — A661

1992, Apr. 6
1723 A661 1300p multicolored 1.00 .65

World Health Day — A662

1992, Apr. 7
1724 A662 1300p blk, red & bl 1.00 .65

War College, 60th Anniv. A663

1992, Apr. 15
1725 A663 1300p multicolored 1.00 .65

Discovery of America, 500th Anniv. A664

Paintings: No. 1726, Inspiration of Christopher Columbus, by Jose Maria Obregon. No. 1727, Meeting of the Races, by Jorge Gonzalez Camarena. No. 1728, Spanish, Indian and Mestizo, from the Natl. Historical Museum. No. 1729, Origin of the Sky, from Selden Codex. No. 1730, Quetzalcoatl and Tezcatlipoca, from Borbonico Codex. No. 1731, Human Culture by Camarena.

1992, Apr. 24 Litho. *Perf. 14*
1726 A664 1300p multicolored 2.00 .65
1727 A664 1300p multicolored 2.00 .65
1728 A664 2000p multicolored 3.00 .95
1729 A664 2000p multicolored 3.00 .95
1730 A664 2000p multicolored 3.00 .95
Nos. 1726-1730 (5) 13.00 4.15

Size: 107x84mm

Imperf

1731 A664 7000p multicolored 15.00 3.25

Granada '92. For overprints see Nos. 1752-1757.

Natl. Medical Center in the 21st Cent. — A665

1992, Apr. 27 Photo. *Rouletted 6½*
1732 A665 1300p multicolored 1.00 .65

Rights of the Child A666

1992, Apr. 30
1733 A666 1300p multicolored 1.00 .65

Midwives in Mexico — A667

1992, May 10
1734 A667 1300p multicolored 1.00 .65

Discovery of America, 500th Anniv. — A668

Illustration reduced.

1992, May 22 Litho. *Imperf.*
1735 A668 7000p multicolored 9.00 3.65

World Columbian Stamp Expo, Chicago.

Notary College of Mexico, Mexico City, Bicent. A669

1992, June 18 Litho. *Rouletted 6½*
1736 A669 1300p multicolored 1.00 .70

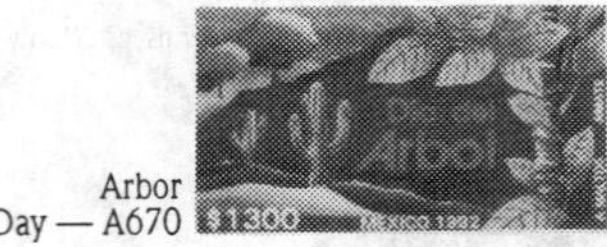

Arbor Day — A670

1992, July 9 *Rouletted 5*
1737 A670 1300p multicolored 1.00 .70

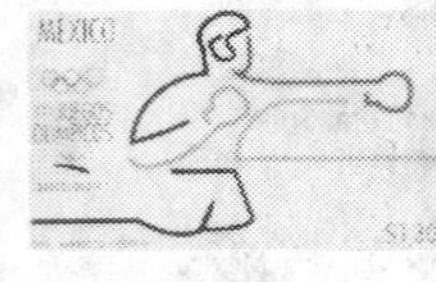

1992 Summer Olympics, Barcelona A671

1992, July 30 *Perf. 14*
1738 A671 1300p Boxing 1.00 .70
1739 A671 1300p Fencing 1.00 .70
1740 A671 1300p High jump 1.00 .70
1741 A671 1300p Gymnastics 1.00 .70
1742 A671 1300p Shooting 1.00 .70
1743 A671 1900p Swimming 2.00 1.00
1744 A671 1900p Running 2.00 1.00
1745 A671 1900p Rowing 2.00 1.00
1746 A671 1900p Soccer 2.00 1.00
1747 A671 2000p Equestrian 2.00 1.10
Nos. 1738-1747 (10) 15.00 8.60

Souvenir Sheet

Perf. 10

1748 A671 7000p Torch bearer 15.00 4.75

10th Intl. Marathon of Mexico City — A672

1992, Aug. 26 Litho. *Rouletted 5*
1749 A672 1300p multicolored 1.00 .65

Solidarity, United for Progress — A673

1992, Sept. 8 *Perf. 10*
1750 A673 1300p multicolored 1.00 .65

Souvenir Sheet

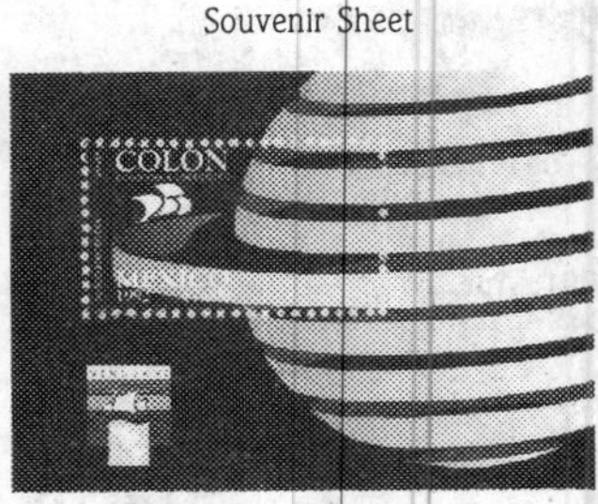

Discovery of America, 500th Anniv. — A674

1992, Sept. 18 *Perf. 10*
1751 A674 7000p multicolored 10.00 3.25

Genoa '92.

Nos. 1726-1731 Ovptd. with emblem of World Columbian Stamp Expo '92, Chicago

1992 Litho. *Perf. 14*
1752 A664 1300p on #1726
1753 A664 1300p on #1727
1754 A664 2000p on #1728
1755 A664 2000p on #1729
1756 A664 2000p on #1730

Size: 107x84mm

Imperf

1757 A664 7000p on #1731

Nos. 1752-1757 were produced in limited quantities and had limited distribution with no advance release information available.

Natl. Council of Radio and Television, 50th Anniv. A675

1992, Oct. 5 Litho. *Perf. 10*
1758 A675 1300p multicolored 1.00 .65

World Post Day A676

1992, Oct. 9 Litho. *Perf. 10*
1759 A676 1300p multicolored 1.00 .65

Communications System of the Americas — A677

1992, Oct. 12
1760 A677 2000p multicolored 2.00 1.00

Discovery of America, 500th Anniv. A678

Designs: No. 1761, Aztec calendar stone. No. 1762, Snake, fish, compass.

1992, Oct. 12

No.	Type	Description	Unused	Used
1761	A678	2000p shown	2.00	1.00
1762	A678	2000p multicolored	2.00	1.00
a.		Pair, #1761-1762	4.50	2.00

Exporta Type of 1975

Designs: 2200p, Cuts of meat marked on steer. 2800p, Chemistry flasks. 3600p, Pistons. 3900p, Petroleum valves. 4000p, Honey. 4800p, Tomatoes. 6000p, Citrus fruit. 7200p, Film.

1992 Photo. *Perf. 14*

No.	Type	Description	Unused	Used
1763	A320	2200p red	1.60	.80
1764	A320	2800p black	2.50	1.00

With Gray Burelage

No.	Type	Description	Unused	Used
1765	A320	3600p blk, I	2.75	1.40
1766	A320	3900p gray & bl, II	3.50	1.50
1767	A320	4000p yel org & red brn, I	3.50	1.40
1768	A320	4800p red & grn, I	4.00	1.75
1768A	A320	4800p red & green, II	8.00	1.75
1769	A320	6000p yel & grn, I	5.00	2.25
1770	A320	7200p grn, red & blk, I	6.00	2.75
		Nos. 1763-1770 (9)	36.85	14.60

San Luis Potosi, 400th Anniv. — A679

1992, Nov. 3 Litho. *Perf. 10*

No.	Type	Description	Unused	Used
1777	A679	1300p multicolored	1.00	.65

Values are for copies with perfs touching the design.

United for Conservation — A680

1992, Nov. 17

No.	Type	Description	Unused	Used
1778	A680	1300p multicolored	1.00	.65

Navy Day — A681

1992, Nov. 23

No.	Type	Description	Unused	Used
1779	A681	1300p multicolored	1.00	.65

Values are for copies with perfs touching the design.

Christmas A682

1300p, Christmas tree, children, pinata, vert.

1992, Nov. 26

No.	Type	Description	Unused	Used
1780	A682	1300p multicolored	1.00	.65
1781	A682	2000p multicolored	2.00	1.00

Tourism in States of Mexico A683

1993-96 Photo. Unwmk. *Perf. 14*

No.	Type	Description	Unused	Used
1782	A683	90c Campeche	.75	.50
1783	A683	1p Guanajuato	.85	.60
1784	A683	1.10p Guanajuato	.85	.25
1785	A683	1.30p Colima	1.00	.70
1786	A683	1.80p Coahuila	.80	.45
1787	A683	1.80p Campeche	.70	.40
1788	A683	1.80p Colima	.70	.40
1789	A683	1.80p Chiapas	.70	.30
1790	A683	1.90p Michoacan, vert.	1.60	1.05
1791	A683	2p Coahuila	1.50	1.10
1792	A683	2p Colima	1.10	.20
1793	A683	2.20p Queretaro	2.00	1.20
1794	A683	2.30p Sinaloa	.85	.35
1795	A683	2.40p Yucatan	1.00	.40
1796	A683	2.50p Sonora	2.50	1.35
1797	A683	2.70p Mexico	1.60	.60
1798	A683	2.80p Zacatecas, vert.	2.75	1.50
1798A	A683	3p Campeche	1.75	.30
1799	A683	3.40p Sinaloa	1.75	.80
1800	A683	3.70p Sinaloa	4.00	1.90
1801	A683	3.80p Yucatan	1.60	.85
1802	A683	4.40p Yucatan	4.50	2.40
1803	A683	4.80p Chiapas	4.75	2.60
1804	A683	6p Mexico	5.00	3.25
1805	A683	6.50p Sonora	3.25	1.50
		Nos. 1782-1805 (25)	1,046.	24.95

A 2nd printing of #1797 exists. This printing appears crude, with missing and misregistered color dots.

Issued: 90c, 1p, 1.30p, 1.90p, #1791, 2.20p, 2.30p, 2.40p, 2.50p, 2.80p, 3.70p, 4.40p, 4.80p, 6p, 1993; 1.10p, 1.80p, 2.70p, 3.40p, 3.80p, 6.50p, 1995; #1792, 3p, 1996.

See Nos. 1958-1980.

A685

A686

Designs: No. 1808, Child's drawing, ball, blocks. No. 1809, Hands.

1993, Jan. 19 Litho. *Perf. 10*

No.	Type	Description	Unused	Used
1807	A685	1.30p Doctor, child	.95	.70
1808	A685	1.30p multicolored	1.00	.75
1809	A685	1.30p multicolored	1.00	.75
1810	A686	1.50p multicolored	1.10	.85
		Nos. 1807-1810 (4)	4.05	3.05

Mexican Social Security Institute, 50th anniv. Medical Services (#1807), Day Nursery Social Security Service (#1808), security and solidarity (#1809).

Issued: 1.50p, Jan. 19. No. 1807, May 11. Nos. 1808-1809, Dec. 7.

Mexican Society of Ophthomolgists, Cent. — A687

1993, Feb. 18 Litho. *Perf. 10*

No.	Type	Description	Unused	Used
1811	A687	1.30p multicolored	.95	.70

Children's Month — A688

1993, Feb. 23

No.	Type	Description	Unused	Used
1812	A688	1.30p multicolored	.95	.70

Mexican Geography and Statistics Society, 160th Anniv. A689

1993, Apr. 19 Litho. *Perf. 10*

No.	Type	Description	Unused	Used
1813	A689	1.30p blue, black & red	.95	.70

Miguel Ramos Arizpe (1776-1843), Proponent of Mexican Federalism — A690

1993, Apr. 28

No.	Type	Description	Unused	Used
1814	A690	1.30p multicolored	.95	.70

Federico Gomez Children's Hospital, 50th Anniv. — A691

1993, Apr. 29

No.	Type	Description	Unused	Used
1815	A691	1.30p multicolored	.95	.70

Health Begins at Home — A692

1993, May 31

No.	Type	Description	Unused	Used
1816	A692	1.30p multicolored	.95	.70

Upper Gulf of California, Nature Preserve A693

1993, June 10 Litho. *Perf. 10*

No.	Type	Description	Unused	Used
1817	A693	1.30p multicolored	.95	.70

Mario Moreno (Cantinflas), Film Actor — A694

1993, June 24 Photo. *Perf. 14*

No.	Type	Description	Unused	Used
1818	A694	1.30p black & blue	.95	.70

See Nos. 1847-1851.

Secretariat of Health, 50th Anniv. A695

Designs: No. 1819, Dr. Maximiliano Ruiz Castaneda. No. 1820, Dr. Bernardo Sepulveda Gutierrez. No. 1821, Dr. Ignacio Chavez Sanchez. No. 1822, Dr. Mario Salazar Mallen. No. 1823, Dr. Gustavo Baz Prada.

1993 Litho. *Perf. 10*

No.	Type	Description	Unused	Used
1819	A695	1.30p multicolored	.95	.70
1820	A695	1.30p multicolored	.95	.70
1821	A695	1.30p multicolored	.95	.70
1822	A695	1.30p multicolored	.95	.70
1823	A695	1.30p multicolored	.95	.70
		Nos. 1819-1823 (5)	4.75	3.50

Issued: #1819, June 29; #1820, July 26; #1821, Aug. 31; #1822, Sept. 23; #1823, Oct. 26.

First Postage Stamps of Brazil, 150th Anniv. A696

1993, July 30

No.	Type	Description	Unused	Used
1824	A696	2p multicolored	1.50	1.15

A697

A698

1993, Aug. 25

No.	Type	Description	Unused	Used
1825	A697	1.30p Runners	.95	.70

11th Intl. Marathon of Mexico City.

1993, Sept. 6

1.30p, Open book, lightning bolt. 2p, Buildings.

No.	Type	Description	Unused	Used
1826	A698	1.30p multicolored	.95	.70
1827	A698	2p multicolored	1.45	1.05
a.		Pair, #1826-1827	2.50	2.00

Monterrey Institute of Technology and Higher Studies, 50th anniv.

Solidarity Week — A699

1993, Sept. 6

No.	Type	Description	Unused	Used
1828	A699	1.30p multicolored	.95	.70

Confederation of Mexican Chambers of Industry, 75th Anniv. A700

1993, Sept. 13 Litho. *Perf. 10*

No.	Type	Description	Unused	Used
1829	A700	1.30p multicolored	.95	.70

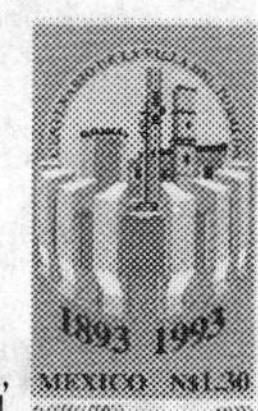

City of Torreon, Cent. — A701

1993, Sept. 15

No.	Type	Description	Unused	Used
1830	A701	1.30p multicolored	.95	.70

Europalia '93 — A702

1993, Sept. 22

No.	Type	Description	Unused	Used
1831	A702	2p multicolored	1.50	1.10

The only foreign revenue stamps listed in this catalogue are those also authorized for prepayment of postage.

A703

A704

1993, Oct. 9
1832 A703 2p multicolored 1.50 1.10

World Post Day.

1993, Oct. 10
1833 A704 1.30p multicolored .95 .70

Guadalupe Victoria (1786-1843), first president of Mexico.

Natl. Civil Protection System — A705

1993, Oct. 13
1834 A705 1.30p multicolored .95 .70

Intl. Day for Reduction of Natural Disasters.

UN Decade for Intl. Law — A706

1993, Oct. 19
1835 A706 2p multicolored 1.50 1.10

20th Natl. Wheelchair Games A707

1993, Oct. 21
1836 A707 1.30p multicolored .95 .70

Jose Peon y Contreras, Poet, 150th Anniv. of Birth — A708

1993, Oct. 22 **Litho.** ***Perf. 10***
1837 A708 1.30p purple & black .95 .70

Endangered Species — A709

1993, Oct. 25 **Litho.** ***Perf. 10***
1838 A709 2p Quetzal 1.50 1.10
1839 A709 2p Pavon, vert. 1.50 1.10

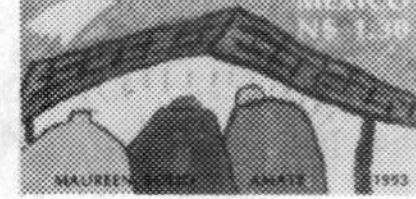
Christmas A710

Designs: No. 1840, Adoration of the Magi. No. 1841, Christmas trees, presents, vert.

1993, Nov. 26 **Litho.** ***Perf. 10***
1840 A710 1.30p multicolored .95 .70
1841 A710 1.30p multicolored .95 .70

Solidarity A711

1993, Nov. 20
1842 A711 1.30p multicolored 1.00 .75

Natl. Preparatory School, 125th Anniv. A712

1993, Dec. 2 **Litho.** ***Perf. 10***
1843 A712 1.30p multicolored 1.00 .75

FSTSE, 55th Anniv. A713

1993, Dec. 6 **Photo.**
1844 A713 1.30p multicolored 1.00 .75

Mescala Bridge A714

1993, Dec. 7
1845 A714 1.30p multicolored 1.00 .75

Highway of the Sun — A715

1993, Dec. 7
1846 A715 1.30p multicolored 1.00 .75

Film Actor Type of 1993

Designs: No. 1847, Pedro Armendariz. No. 1848, Pedro Infante. No. 1849, Jorge Negrete. No. 1850, Maria Felix. No. 1851, Dolores del Rio.

1993, Dec. 9 ***Perf. 14***
1847 A694 1.30p black & light blue 1.00 .75
1848 A694 1.30p black & green 1.00 .75
1849 A694 1.30p black & purple 1.00 .75
1850 A694 1.30p black & orange 1.00 .75
1851 A694 1.30p black & rose 1.00 .75
Nos. 1847-1851 (5) 5.00 3.75

Secretariat of Education, 72nd Anniv. A716

Famous educators: No. 1852, Jose Vasconcelos. No. 1853, Rafael Ramirez Castaneda. No. 1854, Estefania Castaneda Nunez. No. 1855, Moises Saenz Garza. No. 1856, Rosaura Zapata Cano. No. 1857, Gregorio Torres Quintero. No. 1858, Lauro Aguirre Espinosa.

1994, Jan. 26 **Litho.** ***Perf. 10***
1852 A716 1.30p multicolored 1.00 .75
1853 A716 1.30p multicolored 1.00 .75
1854 A716 1.30p multicolored 1.00 .75
1855 A716 1.30p multicolored 1.00 .75
1856 A716 1.30p multicolored 1.00 .75
1857 A716 1.30p multicolored 1.00 .75
1858 A716 1.30p multicolored 1.00 .75
Nos. 1852-1858 (7) 7.00 5.25

Emiliano Zapata, (1879-1919), Revolutionary — A717

1994, Apr. 10 **Litho.** ***Perf. 10***
1859 A717 1.30p multicolored .95 .70

ILO, 75th Anniv. — A718

1994, Apr. 18 ***Perf. 14***
1860 A718 2p multicolored 1.40 1.00

School Construction by CAPFCE, 50th Anniv. A719

1994, Apr. 19
1861 A719 1.30p multicolored .90 .70

Children for Peace — A720

1994, Apr. 28
1862 A720 1.30p multicolored .90 .70

Youth Services A721

1994, May 12 ***Rouletted 12***
1863 A721 1.30p green & black .90 .70

United for Conservation A722

1994, May 6 ***Perf. 10***
1864 A722 1.30p multicolored .90 .70

Rouletting on many of the 1994 issues leaves individual stamps with rough, unattractive edges. Some copies are separated by scissors because of the difficulty in separating stamps.

The gum on many issues is poorly applied, often having a rough feel and appearance, due to air bubbles. Gum may not cover the entire back side.

Serial numbers are found on the back of some copies of No, 1896. These may appear on other stamps.

A723 A724

1994, Apr. 26 ***Rouletted 12***
1865 A723 1.30p Francisco Zuniga .90 .70

1994, May 16 **Litho.** ***Rouletted 13***
1866 A724 2p multicolored 1.40 1.00

34th World Congress of Publicists, Cancun.

World Telecommunications Day — A725

1994, May 17 **Litho.** ***Rouletted 13***
1867 A725 2p multicolored 1.40 .75

ANIERM (Natl. Assoc. of Importers & Exporters of the Republic of Mexico), 50th Anniv. — A726

1994, May 17 ***Rouletted 12½***
1868 A726 1.30p multicolored .90 .70

Yumka Natural Wildlife Center A727

1994, May 21 **Litho.** ***Rouletted 13***
1869 A727 1.30p multicolored .90 .70

City of Zacatecas A728

1994, May 26 ***Rouletted 12½***
1870 A728 1.30p multicolored .90 .70

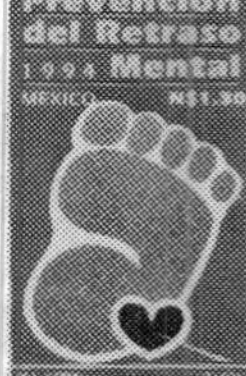
Prevention of Mental Retardation — A729

1994, June 1 **Litho.** ***Perf. 14***
1871 A729 1.30p multicolored .90 .70

Month of the Child.

A730

A731

1994, June 1 Litho. *Perf. 14*
1872 A730 1.30p Mother and child .90 .70

Friendship Hospital.

1994, June 7 *Rouletted 13*

Stylized soccer players: a, Kicking ball. b, Behind net.

1873 A731 2p Pair, #a.-b. 3.25 2.25

1994 World Cup Soccer Championships, US. No. 1873 is a continuous design.

A732

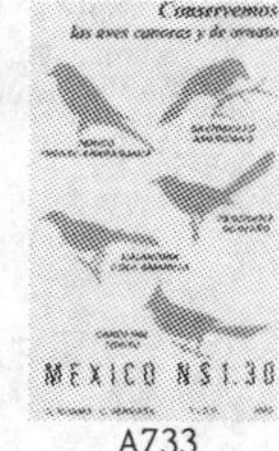

A733

1994, June 8
1874 A732 1.30p multicolored .90 .70

Intl. Fish Fair, Vera Cruz.

1994, June 5 *Perf. 14*

Wildlife conservation: a, Silhouettes of ornamental songbirds (green). b, Silhouettes of cynegetic birds (blue). c, Silhouettes of fierce-looking wildlife (brown). d, Silhouettes of endangered wildlife (red). e, Perico frente-anaranjada. f, Calandria cola amarilla. g, Cardenal torito. h, Sastrecillo americano. i, Cenzontle norteno. j, Guajolote norteno. k, Paloma de ala blanca. l, Pato pijiji de ala blanca. m, Ganso blanco. n, Codorniz de gambel. o, Peregrin falcon. p, Jaguar. q, Jaguarundi. r, Mono saraguato. s, Lobo fino de guadalupe. t, Berrendo peninsular. u, Guacamaya roja. v, Mexican prairie dog. w, Mexican wolf. x, Manati.

1875 A733 1.30p Block of 24 + label 32.50 32.50

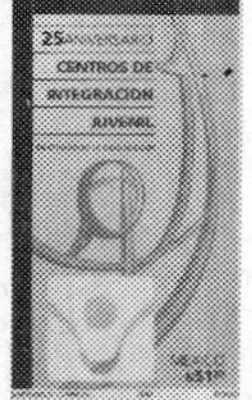

Juvenile Integration Centers, 25th Anniv. — A734

1994, June 29 Litho. *Rouletted 12½*
1876 A734 1.30p multicolored .90 .70

Mexican-Canadian Diplomatic Relations, 50th Anniv. — A735

1994, July 1
1877 A735 2p multicolored 1.40 1.10

Natl. Population Council, 20th Anniv. A736

1994, July 15
1878 A736 1.30p multicolored .90 .70

A737

A738

1994, July 20
1879 A737 2p multicolored 1.40 1.00

Intl. Year of the Family.

Rouletted 12½
1994, Aug. 22 Photo.
1880 A738 1.30p Arbor day .90 .70

A739

A740

1994, July 27
1881 A739 1.30p multicolored .90 .70

12th Mexico City Marathon.

1994, Aug. 1
1882 A740 1.30p Giant panda 1.25 .70

Chapultepec Zoo.

A741

A742

1994, Sept. 5 *Perf. 13x13½*
1883 A741 1.30p multicolored .90 .70

Metro System, 25th anniv.

1994, Sept. 5
1884 A742 1.30p multicolored .90 .70

Economic Cultural Foundation, 60th Anniv..

A743

A744

1994, Sept. 22
1885 A743 1.30p multicolored .90 .70

Don Adolfo Lopez Mateos, 25th Death Anniv.

1994, Sept. 22
1886 A744 1.30p multicolored .90 .70

Solidarity Week.

City University, 40th Anniv. A745

1994, Sept. 21 Litho. *Perf. 13½*
1887 A745 1.30p blue & yellow .90 .70

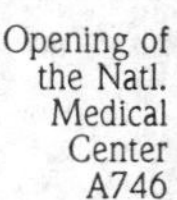

Opening of the Natl. Medical Center A746

1994, Oct. 3
1888 A746 1.30p multicolored .90 .70

Natl. Week of Patriot Symbols A747

1994, Sept. 16
1889 A747 1.30p multicolored .90 .70

Intl. Olympic Committee, Cent. — A748

America Issue — A749

1994, Sept. 29
1890 A748 2p multicolored 1.40 1.00

1994, Oct. 12

Mail delivery vehicles: a, bicycle. b, Railroad cycle.

1891 A749 2p Pair, #a.-b. 2.75 2.00

City of Salvatierra Guanajuato, 350th Anniv. A750

1994, Sept. 12
1892 A750 1.30p multicolored .90 .70

Horses A751

Designs: a, Saddled Aztec racer. b, Light brown quarter horse. c, Black quarter horse. d, Charro on horseback. e, Aztec racer. f, Chinaco riding galloping horse.

1994, Sept. 30 *Perf. 14*
1893 A751 1.30p Block of 6, #a.-f. 5.25 4.00

Issued in sheets of 3 #1893 + 7 labels.

Grandparents' Day — A752

1994, Oct. 15 *Perf. 13½*
1894 A752 1.30p multicolored .90 .70

Palace of Fine Arts, Mexico City, 60th Anniv. A753

1994, Sept. 29 Litho. *Perf. 13½*
1895 A753 1.30p multicolored .90 .70

Antoine de Saint-Exupery (1900-44), Writer — A754

1994, Oct. 6 *Rouletted 13*
1896 A754 2p multicolored 1.40 1.00

World Post Day — A755

1994, Oct. 9 *Perf. 13½*
1897 A755 2p multicolored 1.40 1.00

Natl. Clean Water Program A756

1994, Oct. 17
1898 A756 1.30p multicolored .90 .70

Dr. Jose Luis Mora (1794-1850), Politician — A757

1994, Oct. 27
1899 A757 1.30p multicolored .90 .70

City Theater, Saltillo, 50th Anniv. A758

1994, Nov. 3
1900 A758 1.30p multicolored .90 .70

ICAO, 50th Anniv. A759

1994, Nov. 3
1901 A759 2p multicolored 1.40 1.00

Natl. Museum of Anthropology, 30th Anniv. — A760

Natl. Assoc. of Actors, 60th Anniv. — A761

1994, Nov. 8
1902 A760 1.30p multicolored .90 .70

1994, Nov. 9
1903 A761 1.30p multicolored .90 .70

Ignacio Allende (1769-1811), Independence Hero — A762

1994, Nov. 10
1904 A762 1.30p multicolored .90 .70

Natl. Museum of History, 50th Anniv. — A763

1994, Nov. 22 *Perf. 14*
1905 A763 1.30p multicolored .90 .70

Coahuila Teachers' College, Cent. — A764

Pumas UNAM Soccer Team, 40th Anniv. — A765

1994, Nov. 23 *Perf. 13½*
1906 A764 1.30p multicolored .90 .70

1994, Nov. 23
1907 A765 1.30p blue & gold .90 .70

Christmas A766

1994, Nov. 29
1908 A766 2p shown 1.40 1.00
1909 A766 2p Tree, vert. 1.40 1.00

Chalco Valley Solidarity A767

1994, Nov. 30
1910 A767 1.30p multicolored .90 .70

Sr. Juana Ines de la Cruz (1648-95), Writer — A768

1995, Apr. 17 Litho. *Perf. 13½*
1911 A768 1.80p multicolored .75 .60

Wilhelm Roentgen (1845-1923), Discovery of the X-Ray, Cent. — A769

1995, May 8
1912 A769 2p multicolored .85 .65

A770

A771

1995, May 15
1913 A770 1.80p Ignacio M. Altamirano .75 .60

Teachers' Day.

1995, May 17 *Perf. 14x14½*
1914 A771 2.70p multicolored 1.10 .85

World Telecommunications Day.

A772

A773

1995, May 18 *Perf. 13½*
1915 A772 1.80p multicolored .75 .60

Natl. Institute of Public Administration, 40th anniv.

1995, May 19 *Perf. 14x14½*

Jose Marti (1853-95), Cuban patriot.

1916 A773 2.70p multicolored 1.10 .85

A774

A775

Design: 1.80p, Venustiano Carranza (1859-1920), politician, President of Mexico, 1917-20.

Perf. 13½

1995, May 23
1917 A774 1.80p multicolored .75 .60

1995, June 11
1918 A775 2.70p multicolored 1.10 .85

Natl. Tourist Organization, 20th anniv.

A776

A777

Designs: a, Face becoming skull with pills, needle. b, Person as puppet. c, Faces behind bars.

1995, June 26
1919 A776 1.80p Strip of 3, #a.-c. 2.25 1.75

Intl. Day Against Illegal Drugs.

1995, June 28
1920 A777 1.80p black .75 .60

Lazaro Cardenas (1895-1970), soldier, politician, President of Mexico, 1934-40.

Natl. School for the Blind, 125th Anniv. A778

1995, July 18 Litho. *Perf. 13½*
1921 A778 1.30p sepia & black .45 .35

Migratory Wildlife A781

Designs: a, Danaus plexippus. b, Lasiurus cinereus. c, Anas acuta. d, Ceryle alcyon.

1995, Aug. 15 Litho. *Perf. 13½*
1924 A781 2.70p Block of 4, #a.-d. 4.00 3.25

See Canada Nos. 1563-1567.

13th Mexico City Marathon A782

1995, Aug. 22 Litho. *Perf. 13½*
1925 A782 2.70p multicolored .95 .70

16th Congress of UPAEP — A783

World Post Day — A785

Louis Pasteur (1822-95) — A784

World Food Day — A786

1995, Sept. 15
1926 A783 2.70p multicolored .95 .70

1995, Sept. 26 *Perf. 14*
1927 A784 2.70p multicolored .95 .70

1995, Oct. 9
1928 A785 2.70p multicolored .95 .70

1995, Oct. 16 *Perf. 14x14½*
1929 A786 1.80p multicolored .65 .50

FAO, 50th Anniv. A787

1995, Oct. 16 *Perf. 14*
1930 A787 2.70p multicolored .95 .70

Plutarco Elias Calles (1877-1945), President of Mexico 1924-28 — A788

1995, Oct. 19 *Perf. 13½*
1931 A788 1.80p multicolored .65 .50

Birth of Cuauhtemoc, 500th Anniv. — A789

1995, Oct. 21
1932 A789 1.80p multicolored .65 .50

A790

A791

National Symbols: 1.80p, Natl. flag, Constitution of Apatzingan, words of Natl. Anthem.

1995, Oct. 22
1933 A790 1.80p multicolored .65 .50

1995, Oct. 24 Litho. *Perf. 14½x14*
1934 A791 2.70p multicolored .95 .70

UN, 50th anniv.

Intl. Year of Travel A792

1995, Nov. 14 Litho. *Perf. 13½*
1935 A792 2.70p multicolored .85 .65

Viceregal Gallery of Art Painting, The Holy Family, by Andres de Conchas A793

1995, Nov. 16 *Perf. 14*
1936 A793 1.80p multicolored .55 .40

Famous Generals A794

Designs: No. 1937, Ignacio Zaragoza (1829-62). No. 1938, Sóstenes Rocha (1831-97). No. 1939, Felipe B. Berriozábal (1829-1900). No. 1940, Pedro María Anaya (1795-1854). No. 1941, Leandro Valle (1833-61). No. 1942, Santos Degollado (1811-61).

1995, Nov. 23 *Perf. 13½*

1937 A794	1.80p	yel, blk & bister	.55	.40
1938 A794	1.80p	yel, blk & bister	.55	.40
1939 A794	1.80p	yel, blk & bister	.55	.40
1940 A794	1.80p	yel, blk & bister	.55	.40
1941 A794	1.80p	yel, blk & bister	.55	.40
1942 A794	1.80p	yel, blk & bister	.55	.40
		Nos. 1937-1942 (6)	3.30	2.40

Christmas A795

Children's paintings: 1.80p, Family celebrating Christmas inside house. 2.70p, Adoration of the Magi.

1995, Nov. 27

1943 A795	1.80p	multicolored	.55	.40
1944 A795	2.70p	multicolored	.85	.65
a.		Pair, Nos. 1943-1944	1.40	1.10

Mexican Health Foundation, 10th Anniv. — A796

1995, Nov. 30 **Litho.** *Perf. 14*
1945 A796 1.80p multicolored .60 .45

Wildlife Conservation A797

1995, Dec. 4 *Perf. 14*
1946 A797 1.80p Ocelot .55 .40

Motion Pictures, Cent. — A798

1995, Dec. 12
1947 A798 1.80p violet & black .55 .40

Natl. Library of Education A799

1995, Dec. 13 *Perf. 13½*
1948 A799 1.80p bl grn & yel .55 .40

A800

A801

1995, Dec. 15
1949 A800 1.80p multicolored .55 .40

Natl. Arts and Sciences Awards, 50th anniv.

1995, Dec. 19 *Perf. 14*

Radio personalities: a, Pedro Vargas. b, Agustin Lara. c, Hermanas Aguila. d, Toña "La Negra." e, "Cri-Cri," (F. Gabilondo Soler). f, Emilio Tuero. g, Gonzalo Curiel. h, Lola Beltrán.

1950 A801 1.80p Strip of 8, #a.-h. 4.50 3.30

Natl. Council of Science and Technology, 25th Anniv. A802

1995, Dec. 20 *Perf. 13½*
1951 A802 1.80p multicolored .55 .40

Plaza de Toros, Mexico City, 50th Anniv. A803

Matadors: 1.80p, Silverio Perez, Carlos Arruza, Manolo Martinez. 2.70p, Rodolfo Gaona, Fermin Espinosa "Armillita," Lorenzo Garza.

1996, Feb. 5 **Litho.** *Perf. 13½*

1952 A803	1.80p	multicolored	.55	.40
1953 A803	2.70p	multicolored	.85	.65
a.		Pair, Nos. 1952-1953	1.40	1.10

No. 1953a is a contiunuous design.

Mexican Aviation Day A804

Designs: a, 2.70p, Patrol jet. b, 2.70p, Jet landing, airport terminal. c, 1.80p, Fighter plane, Squadron 201 (1945), map. d, 1.80p, Commercial biplane (1921), commerical jet.

1996, Jan. 20 **Litho.** *Perf. 13½*
1954 A804 Block of 4, #a.-d. 2.75 2.00

Dr. Alfonso Caso (1896-1970), Archaeologist A805

1996, Feb. 1
1955 A805 1.80p multicolored .55 .40

Natl. Consumer Agency, 20th Anniv. A806

1996, Feb. 2 *Perf. 14*
1956 A806 1.80p multicolored .55 .40

Tourism Type of 1993
Denomination Shown As $

1996-97 **Photo.** **Unwmk.** *Perf. 14*

1958	A683	1p	Colima ('97)	.25	.15
1962	A683	1.80p	Chiapas	.45	.20
1964	A683	2p	Colima	.50	.25
1964A	A683	2p	Guanajuato ('97)	.45	.25
1965	A683	2.30p	Chiapas ('97)	.60	.30
1966	A683	2.50p	Queretaro ('97)	.60	.40
1968	A683	2.70p	Mexico	.70	.35
1971	A683	3p	Campeche	.75	.40
1974	A683	3.40p	Sinaloa	.90	.45
1975	A683	3.50p	Mexico ('97)	.90	.60
1976	A683	4p	Michoacan, vert. ('97)	.95	.50
1976A	A683	4.40p	Yucatan ('97)	1.00	.50
1977	A683	5p	Queretaro	1.30	.65
1978	A683	6p	Zacatecas, vert. ('97)	1.40	.70
1979	A683	7p	Sonora ('97)	1.60	.80
1980	A683	8.50p	Mexico ('97)	2.00	1.00
			Nos. 1958-1980 (16)	14.35	7.50

Denomination on #1782-1805 was shown as N$. This is an expanding set. Numbers may change.

Orthopedics Society, 50th Anniv. A807

1996, Apr. 29 **Litho.** *Perf. 13½*
1981 A807 1.80p multicolored .55 .40

Juan Rulfo (1917-86), Writer A808

1996, May 3
1982 A808 1.80p multicolored .55 .40

Natl. Polytechnical Institute, 60th Anniv. A809

1996, May 21
1983 A809 1.80p multicolored .55 .40

A810

A811

Stylized designs: a, 1.80p, Hands reaching toward one another. b, 1.80p, Two people. c, 2.70p, Person seated, person standing.

1996, June 26 **Litho.** *Perf. 13½*
1984 A810 Strip of 3, #a.-c. 1.90 1.40

Decade of United Nations Against Illegal Drug Abuse and Trafficking.

1996, July 19 *Perf. 14x14½*

1996 Summer Olympic Games, Atlanta: a, Women's gymnastics. b, Soccer. c, Marathon race. d, Hurdles. e, Equestrian show jumping.

1985 A811 Strip of 5, #a.-e. 3.60 2.70

Motion Pictures, Cent. A812

1996, Aug. 6 **Litho.** *Perf. 13½*

Color of Film Cells

1986 A812	1.80p	green, ocher & violet	.45	.35
1987 A812	1.80p	purple, green & red	.45	.35
a.		Pair, #1986-1987	.90	.70

Justice Dept., 60th Anniv. A813

1996, Aug. 18
1988 A813 1.80p multicolored .45 .35

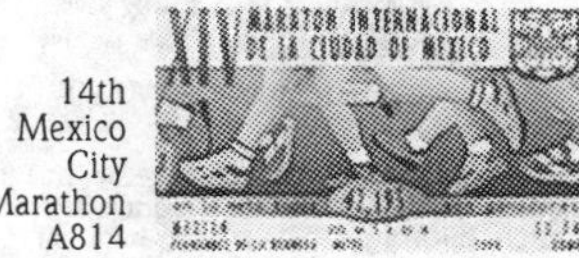

14th Mexico City Marathon A814

1996, Aug. 20
1989 A814 2.70p multicolored .70 .50

City of Zacatecas, 450th Anniv. A815

1996, Sept. 8
1990 A815 1.80p multicolored .45 .35

Natl. Council to Promote Education, 25th Anniv. A816

1996, Sept. 17
1991 A816 1.80p multicolored .45 .35

Souvenir Sheet

City of Monterrey, 400th Anniv. — A817

Illustration reduced.

1996, Sept. 20
1992 A817 7.40p multicolored 1.90 1.40

Family Planning — A818

1996, Sept. 26
1993 A818 1.80p multicolored .45 .35

Independence, 175th Anniv. — A819

1996, Sept. 27
1994 A819 1.80p multicolored .45 .35

Endangered Species — A820

Designs show a wide variety of species, one from each stamp is: a, Aguila arpia. b, Tortola serrana. c, Monarch butterflies. d, Vernado bura. e, Guacamaya roja. f, Quetzal. g, Venado cola blanca. h, Puma. i, Coyote. j, Jaguar. k, Martucha. l, Woodpecker. m, Cuco canelo. n, Lince. o, Oso hormiguero. p, Ocelote. q, Encino. r, Chachalaca. s, Liebre. t, Tapir. u, Crocodile. v, Armadillo. w, Pecari. x, Cacomixtle.

1996, Oct. 2

Sheet of 24

1995 A820 1.80p #a.-x. + label 11.00 8.25

See US No. 3105.

World Post Day — A821

1996, Oct. 9
1996 A821 2.70p multicolored .70 .50

Salvador Zubirán Natl. Nutrition Institute, 50th Anniv. A822

1996, Oct. 12
1997 A822 1.80p multicolored .45 .35

Radio in Mexico, 75th Anniv. — A823

1996, Oct. 13
1998 A823 1.80p multicolored .45 .35

Paintings in Viceregal Gallery A824

Designs: a, 1.80p, Portrait of a Woman, by Baltasar de Echave Ibia. b, 2.70p, Archangel Michael, by Luis Juarez. c, 1.80p, Portrait of young Joaquín Manuel Fernández of Santa Cruz, by Nicolas Rodriguez Xuarez. d, 2.70p. The Virgin of the Apocalypse, by Miguel Cabrera. e, 1.80p, Portrait of Dona Maria Luisa Gonzaga Foncerrada y Labarrieta, by Jose Maria Vazquez.

1996, Oct. 14 *Perf. 14*
1999 A824 Strip of 5, #a.-e. 2.75 2.00

World Food Day — A825

1996, Oct. 31 *Perf. 13½*
2000 A825 2.70p multicolored .70 .50

Mexican Science A826

1996, Sept. 2
2001 A826 1.80p multicolored .45 .35

Intl. Subway Conference A828

1996, Nov. 12 **Litho.** *Perf. 13½*
2003 A828 2.70p multicolored .70 .50

Christmas A829

1996, Nov. 14 **Litho.** *Perf. 13½*
2004 A829 1p Star pinata .25 .15
2005 A829 1.80p Man carrying pinatas .45 .30

Andres Henestrosa, Writer A830

1996, Nov. 23 **Litho.** *Perf. 14*
2006 A830 1.80p multicolored .45 .30

Natl. Cancer Institute, 50th Anniv. A831

1996, Nov. 25 **Litho.** *Perf. 13½*
2007 A831 1.80p multicolored .45 .30

Paisano Program — A832

1996, Nov. 28 **Litho.** *Perf. 13½*
2008 A832 2.70p multicolored .70 .50

David Alfaro Siqueiros (1896-1974), Painter — A833

1996, Dec. 5 **Litho.** *Perf. 13½*
2009 A833 1.80p multicolored .45 .30

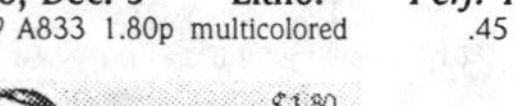

32nd Natl. Assembly of Surgeons A834

Dr. José Ma. Barceló de Villagrán

1996, Dec. 6 **Litho.** *Perf. 13½*
2010 A834 1.80p multicolored .45 .30

Wildlife Conservation A835

1996, Dec. 11 **Litho.** *Perf. 14*
2011 A835 1.80p Black bear, cubs .45 .30

UNICEF, 50th Anniv. A836

1996, Dec. 11 **Litho.** *Perf. 13½*
2012 A836 1.80p multicolored .45 .30

Palafoxiana Library, Puebla, 350th Anniv. — A837

1996, Dec. 17 **Litho.** *Perf. 13½*
2013 A837 1.80p multicolored .45 .30

Natl. Institute of Nuclear Research A838

1996, Dec. 19 **Litho.** *Perf. 13½*
2014 A838 1.80p multicolored .45 .30

A839

A840

1996, Dec. 19 **Litho.** *Perf. 13½*
2015 A839 1.80p multicolored .45 .30

Intl. Day for Preservation of the Ozone Layer.

1996, Dec. 20 **Litho.** *Perf. 13½*
2016 A840 1.80p multicolored .45 .30

Thirty year career of plastic arts sculptor Sebastian.

Mexican Diplomats A841

Design: Isidro Fabela (b. 1882), lawyer, and Genaro Estrada (1887-1977), journalist, politician.

1996, Oct. 24 **Litho.** *Perf. 13½*
2017 A841 1.80p multicolored .45 .30

Carlos Pellicer (1897-1977), Poet, Museum Founder — A842

1997, Jan. 16
2018 A842 2.30p multicolored .60 .40

Andres Eloy Blanco (1896-1955), Poet — A843

1997, Feb. 6 **Litho.** *Perf. 13½*
2019 A843 3.40p multicolored .90 .60

A844

A845

1997, Feb. 10
2020 A844 3.40p multicolored .90 .60

UNESCO Intl. Summit on Education, Confederation of American Educators.

1997, Feb. 14
2021 A845 3.40p multicolored .90 .60

Treaty of Tlatelolco prohibiting nuclear weapons in Latin America & Caribbean.

Souvenir Sheet

Mexican Central Post Office, 90th Anniv. — A846

Illustration reduced.

1997, Feb. 20
2022 A846 7.40p multicolored 1.90 1.25

A847

A848

Generals: No. 2023, Francisco L. Urquizo. No. 2024, Mariano Escobedo. No. 2025, Jacinto B. Trevino Gonzalez. No. 2026, Felipe Angeles. No. 2027, Candido Aguilar Vargas. No. 2028, Joaquin Amaro Dominguez.

1997, Mar. 5
2023 A847 2.30p multicolored .60 .40
2024 A847 2.30p multicolored .60 .40
2025 A847 2.30p multicolored .60 .40
2026 A847 2.30p multicolored .60 .40
2027 A847 2.30p multicolored .60 .40
2028 A847 2.30p multicolored .60 .40
Nos. 2023-2028 (6) 3.60 2.40

1997, Mar. 8
2029 A848 2.30p multicolored .60 .40

Intl. Women's Day.

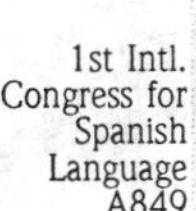

1st Intl. Congress for Spanish Language A849

Painting: Allegory, "La Gramatica," by Juan Correa.

1997, Apr. 7 **Litho.** ***Perf. 13½***
2030 A849 3.40p multicolored .90 .40

Dr. Ignacio Chávez, Pres. of Natl. Academy of Medicine, Birth Cent. A850

1997, Apr. 23
2031 A850 2.30p multicolored .60 .40

Mexican Constitution, 80th Anniv. A851

1997, Apr. 29
2032 A851 2.30p Venusitano Carranza .60 .40

First Edition of "Al Filo Del Agua," by Agustín Yáñez, 50th Anniv. A852

1997, May 9
2033 A852 2.30p multicolored .60 .40

Prof. Rafael Ramírez (1855-1959), Educator — A853

1997, May 12
2034 A853 2.30p green & gray .60 .40

Japanese Emigration to Mexico, Cent. A854

1997, May 12
2035 A854 3.40p multicolored .90 .60

A855

A856

1997, May 31
2036 A855 2.30p multicolored .60 .40

Autonomous University of Baja California, 40th Anniv.

1997, June 26

Intl. Day to Stop Use of Illegal Drugs: a, 2.30p, Dove, clouds, sunlight. b, 3.40p, Man with one hand on bars, one hand raised toward sky. c, 3.40p, Dove in window behind bars.

2037 A856 Strip of 3, #a.-c. + label 2.40 1.60

Sigmund Freud — A857

Naval Military School, Cent. — A858

1997, June 28
2038 A857 2.30p multicolored .60 .40

1997, July 1
2039 A858 2.30p multicolored .60 .40

Natl. Bank of Foreign Commerce, 60th Anniv. A859

1997, July 4 **Litho.** ***Perf. 13½***
2040 A859 3.40p multicolored .90 .60

United for Conservation — A860

1997, July 16
2041 A860 2.30p Vaquita, calf .60 .40

Mexican College of Aviation Pilots, 50th Anniv. A861

1997, July 17
2042 A861 2.30p multicolored .60 .40

15th Mexico City Marathon — A862

1997, Aug. 6
2043 A862 3.40p multicolored .90 .60

Juarez Hospital of Mexico, 150th Anniv. A863

1997, Aug. 18
2044 A863 2.30p multicolored .60 .40

Battles of 1847 — A864

#2045, Battle of Padierna. #2046, Battle of Churubusco. #2047, Battle of Molino del Rey. #2047A, Defense of the Castle of Chapultepec.

1997
2045 A864 2.30p multicolored .60 .40
2046 A864 2.30p multicolored .60 .40
2047 A864 2.30p multicolored .60 .40
2047A A864 2.30p multicolored .60 .40
Nos. 2045-2047A (4) 2.40 1.60

Issued: #2045, 8/19; #2046, 8/20; #2047, 9/8; #2047A, 9/13.

Guillermo Prieto, Poet, Death Cent. — A865

1997, Sept. 3
2048 A865 2.30p multicolored .60 .40

MEXICO

Full Range Stock #1 to Present

NEW ISSUE SERVICE

Classics
Exportas
Folletos
First Day Covers

WRITE or CALL
Ph/Fax: 415-968-4142

J.O. VADEBONCOEUR
1671 Kensington Ave.
Los Altos, CA 94024

MEPSI (Life)

CCNY

A866

A867

1997, Sept. 12 Litho. *Perf. 13½*
2049 A866 3.40p multicolored .85 .60

Battalion of St. Patrick, 150th anniv.
See Ireland No. 1085.

1997, Oct. 6
2050 A867 2.30p multicolored .60 .40

Reproductive health for adolescents month.

Stamp Day — A868

1997, Oct. 9
2051 A868 3.40p multicolored .85 .60

Heinrich von Stephan (1831-97) A869

1997, Oct. 9
2052 A869 3.40p multicolored .85 .60

Manuel Gómez Morin (1897-1949), Politician — A870

1997, Oct. 14
2053 A870 2.30p multicolored .60 .40

Dr. Manuel Gea González General Hospital, 50th Anniv. A871

1997, Oct. 14
2054 A871 2.30p multicolored .60 .40

Mexican Bar Assoc. College of Law, 75th Anniv. — A872

1997, Oct. 30
2055 A872 2.30p multicolored .60 .40

Christmas A873

Children with piñatas: No. 2056, By Ana R. Botello. No. 2057, By Adrián Laris.

1997, Nov. 19
2056 A873 2.30p multicolored .60 .40
2057 A873 2.30p multicolored .60 .40

New Law on Social Security — A874

1997, Dec. 10
2058 A874 2.30p multicolored .60 .40

Central University Hospital, Chihuahua, Cent. A875

1997, Dec. 5 Litho. *Perf. 13½*
2059 A875 2.30p multicolored .55 .40

Dr. Mario Jose Molina Henriquez, 1995 Nobel Prize Recipient in Chemistry A876

1997, Dec. 5
2060 A876 3.40p multicolored .80 .55

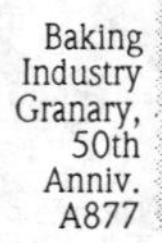

Baking Industry Granary, 50th Anniv. A877

Baked goods and: a, Storage shelves. b, Man working at oven. c, Basic ingredients, man working with dough.

1997, Dec. 10
2061 A877 2.30p Vert. strip of 3, #a.-c. + label 1.60 1.10

A878

A879

Modern Mexican art, by Jose Chavez Morado.

1997, Dec. 19
2062 A878 2.30p multicolored .55 .40

Cervantes Festival, Guanajuato, 45th anniv.

1997, Dec. 20
2063 A879 2.30p multicolored .55 .40

City of Loreto, 300th anniv.

SEMI-POSTAL STAMPS

Nos. 622, 614 Surcharged in Red **✚ 3 ¢**

1918, Dec. 25 Unwmk. *Perf. 12*
B1 A72 5c + 3c ultra 14.00 15.00

Rouletted 14½
B2 A73 10c + 5c blue 17.50 15.00

AIR POST STAMPS

Eagle — AP1

Unwmk.
1922, Apr. 2 Engr. *Perf. 12*
C1 AP1 50c blue & red brn 60.00 40.00
a. 50c dark blue & claret ('29) 90.00 90.00

See #C2-C3. For overprints and surcharges see #C47-C48, CO1-CO2B, CO18-CO19, CO29.

1927, Oct. 13 Wmk. 156
C2 AP1 50c dk bl & red brn .75 .25
a. 50c dark blue & claret ('29) .75 .25
b. Vert. strip of 3, imperf. btwn. 7,500.

The vignettes of Nos. C1a and C2a fluoresce a bright rose red under UV light.

1928
C3 AP1 25c brn car & gray brn .45 .15
C4 AP1 25c dk grn & gray brn .45 .20

On May 3, 1929, certain proofs or essays were sold at the post office in Mexico, D. F. They were printed in different colors from those of the regularly issued stamps. There were 7 varieties perf. and 2 imperf. and a total of 225 copies. They were sold with the understanding that they were for collections but the majority of them were used on air mail sent out that day.

Capt. Emilio Carranza and his Airplane "México Excelsior" AP2

1929, June 19
C5 AP2 5c ol grn & sepia 1.15 .65
C6 AP2 10c sep & brn red 1.30 .70
C7 AP2 15c vio & dk grn 3.00 1.25
C8 AP2 20c brown & blk 1.20 .75
C9 AP2 50c brn red & blk 6.00 2.00
C10 AP2 1p black & brn 12.50 2.75
Nos. C5-C10 (6) 25.15 8.10

1st anniv. of death of Carranza (1905-28).
For overprints see Nos. C29-C36, C40-C44.

Coat of Arms and Airplane AP3

1929-34 *Perf. 11½, 12*
C11 AP3 10c violet .35 .15
C12 AP3 15c carmine 1.35 .20
C13 AP3 20c brown olive 27.50 1.25
C14 AP3 30c gray black .20 .20
C15 AP3 35c blue green .35 .25
a. Imperf., pair 1,200.
C16 AP3 50c red brn ('34) 1.25 .65
C17 AP3 1p blk & dk bl 1.25 .65
C18 AP3 5p claret & dp bl 4.00 3.50
C19 AP3 10p vio & ol brn 6.00 7.00
Nos. C11-C19 (9) 42.25 13.85

1930-32 *Rouletted 13, 13½*
C20 AP3 5c lt blue ('32) .25 .15
C21 AP3 10c violet .25 .15
C22 AP3 15c carmine .35 .15
a. 15c rose carmine .40 .15
C23 AP3 20c brown olive 1.50 .15
a. 20c brown .50 .15
b. 20c yellow brown .50 .15
c. Horiz. pair, imperf. btwn.
C24 AP3 25c violet .95 .80
C25 AP3 50c red brown .90 .75
Nos. C20-C25 (6) 4.20 2.15

Trial impressions of No. C20 were printed in orange but were never sold at post offices.
See Nos. C62-C64, C75. For overprints and surcharges see Nos. C28, C38-C39, C46, C49-C50, CO17, CO20-CO28, CO30.

Plane over Plaza, Mexico City — AP4

1929, Dec. 10 Wmk. 156 *Perf. 12*
C26 AP4 20c black violet 1.25 1.00
C27 AP4 40c slate green 85.00 75.00

Aviation Week, Dec. 10-16.
For overprint see No. CO11.

No. C21 Overprinted in Red

Primer Congreso Nacional de Turismo. México. Abril 20-27 de 1930.

1930, Apr. 20 *Rouletted 13, 13½*
C28 AP3 10c violet 2.00 1.25

National Tourism Congress at Mexico, D. F., Apr. 20-27, 1930.

Nos. C5 and C7 Overprinted **HABILITADO 1930**

1930, Sept. 1 *Perf. 12*
C29 AP2 5c ol grn & sepia 5.50 4.50
a. Double overprint 220.00 250.00
C30 AP2 15c violet & dk grn 9.00 7.75

Nos. C5-C10 Overprinted **HABILITADO Aéreo 1930-1931**

1930, Dec. 18
C31 AP2 5c ol grn & sepia 6.00 6.50
C32 AP2 10c sep & brn red 3.50 4.00
a. Double overprint 50.00 50.00
C33 AP2 15c vio & dk grn 6.50 7.00
C34 AP2 20c brown & blk 7.00 5.50
C35 AP2 50c brn red & blk 14.00 10.00
C36 AP2 1p black & brn 4.00 2.75
Nos. C31-C36 (6) 41.00 35.75

Plane over Flying Field AP5

1931, May 15 Engr. *Perf. 12*
C37 AP5 25c lake 4.00 4.50
a. Imperf., pair 80.00 72.50

Aeronautic Exhibition of the Aero Club of Mexico. Of the 25c, 15c paid air mail postage and 10c went to a fund to improve the Mexico City airport.
For surcharge see No. C45.

Nos. C13 and C23 Surcharged in Red

HABILITADO Quince centavos

1931
C38 AP3 15c on 20c brn ol 32.50 35.00

Rouletted 13, 13½
C39 AP3 15c on 20c brn ol .30 .15
a. Inverted surcharge 150.00
b. Double surcharge 150.00
c. Pair, one without surcharge 350.00

Nos. C5 to C9 Overprinted **HABILITADO AEREO-1932**

1932, July 13 *Perf. 12*
C40 AP2 5c ol grn & sep 6.00 5.00
a. Imperf., pair 50.00 50.00

C41	AP2 10c sep & brn red	5.00	3.00
a.	Imperf., pair	50.00	50.00
C42	AP2 15c vio & bk grn	6.00	4.00
a.	Imperf., pair	50.00	50.00
C43	AP2 20c brn & blk	5.00	2.75
a.	Imperf., pair	50.00	50.00
C44	AP2 50c brn red & blk	35.00	35.00
a.	Imperf., pair	50.00	50.00
	Nos. C40-C44 (5)	57.00	49.75

Death of Capt. Emilio Carranza, 4th anniv.

No. C37 Surcharged VEINTE CENTS 20

1932

C45	AP5 20c on 25c lake	.70	.30
a.	Imperf., pair	72.50	72.50

No. C13 Surcharged HABILITADO TREINTA C 30

C46	AP3 30c on 20c brn ol	30.00	30.00

Similar Surcharge on Nos. C3 and C4

C47	AP1 40c on 25c (#C3)	.90	.90
a.	Inverted surcharge	*1,000.*	
C48	AP1 40c on 25c (#C4)	40.00	40.00

Surcharged on Nos. C23 and C24
Rouletted 13, 13½

C49	AP3 30c on 20c brn ol	.35	.20
a.	Inverted surcharge		*2,750.*
C50	AP3 80c on 25c dl vio	1.80	1.20
	Nos. C45-C50 (6)	73.75	72.60

Palace of Fine Arts — AP6

1933, Oct. 1 — Engr. — *Perf. 12*

C51	AP6 20c dk red & dl vio	3.50	1.40
C52	AP6 30c dk brn & dl vio	6.75	6.00
C53	AP6 1p grnsh blk & dl vio	67.50	70.00
	Nos. C51-C53 (3)	77.75	77.40

21st Intl. Cong. of Statistics and the cent. of the Mexican Soc. of Geography and Statistics.

National University Issue

Nevado de Toluca — AP7

Pyramids of the Sun and Moon — AP8

View of Ajusco AP9

Volcanoes Popocatepetl and Iztaccíhuatl AP10

Bridge over Tepecayo AP11

Chapultepec Fortress AP12

Orizaba Volcano (Citlaltépetl) AP13

Mexican Girl and Aztec Calendar Stone AP14

1934, Sept. 1 — Wmk. 156 — *Perf. 10½*

C54	AP7 20c orange	3.25	2.50
C55	AP8 30c red lilac & vio	6.50	5.50
C56	AP9 50c ol grn & bis brn	7.25	9.00
C57	AP10 75c blk & yel grn	8.50	14.00
C58	AP11 1p blk & pck bl	9.00	9.00
C59	AP12 5p bis brn & dk bl	50.00	85.00
C60	AP13 10p indigo & mar	140.00	175.00
C61	AP14 20p brn & brn lake	875.00	1,000.
	Nos. C54-C61 (8)	1,099.	1,300.

Type of 1929-34

1934-35 — *Perf. 10½, 10½x10*

C62	AP3 20c olive green	.35	.15
a.	20c slate	500.00	500.00
C63	AP3 30c slate	.40	.40
C64	AP3 50c red brn ('35)	2.00	2.00
	Nos. C62-C64 (3)	2.75	2.55

Symbols of Air Service AP15

Tláloc, God of Water (Quetzalcóatl Temple) AP16

Orizaba Volcano (Citlaltépetl) AP17

"Eagle Man" AP18

Symbolical of Flight AP19

Aztec Bird-Man — AP20

Allegory of Flight and Pyramid of the Sun — AP21

"Eagle Man" and Airplanes AP22

Natives Looking at Airplane and Orizaba Volcano — AP23

Imprint: "Oficina Impresora de Hacienda-Mexico"
Perf. 10½x10, 10x10½

1934-35 — Wmk. 156

C65	AP15 5c black	.45	.15
a.	Imperf., pair		
C66	AP16 10c red brown	.90	.15
C67	AP17 15c gray green	1.25	.15
a.	Imperf., pair	*400.00*	
C68	AP18 20c brown car	3.00	.15
a.	20c lake	4.00	.15
b.	Imperf., pair		
C69	AP19 30c brown olive	.70	.15
C70	AP20 40c blue ('35)	1.25	.15
C71	AP21 50c green	2.50	.15
a.	Imperf., pair	275.00	
C72	AP22 1p gray grn & red brn	3.50	.15
C73	AP23 5p dk car & blk	7.25	.70
	Nos. C65-C73 (9)	20.80	
	Set value		1.55

See Nos. C76A, C80, C81, C132-C140, C170-C177A. For overprint see No. C74.

No. C68 Overprinted in Violet

AMELIA EARHART
VUELO
DE BUENA VOLUNTAD
MEXICO
1935

1935, Apr. 16

C74	AP18 20c lake	*3,250.*	*4,000.*

Amelia Earhart's goodwill flight to Mexico.

Arms-Plane Type of 1929-34

1935 — Wmk. 248 — *Perf. 10½x10*

C75	AP3 30c slate	3.00	5.00

Francisco I. Madero AP24

1935, Nov. 20 — Wmk. 156

C76	AP24 20c scarlet	.30	.15

Plan of San Luis, 25th anniv. See No. C76B.

Eagle Man Type of 1934-35

1936 — Wmk. 260

C76A	AP18 20c lake	*4,500.*	60.00

Madero Type of 1935

C76B	AP24 20c scarlet		*12,500.*

Tasquillo Bridge AP25

Corona River Bridge AP26

Bridge on Nuevo Laredo Highway AP27

Wmk. 248

1936, July 1 — Photo. — *Perf. 14*

C77	AP25 10c slate bl & lt bl	.20	.15
C78	AP26 20c dl vio & org	.30	.15
C79	AP27 40c dk bl & dk grn	.55	.50
	Nos. C77-C79 (3)	1.05	.80

Opening of Nuevo Laredo Highway.

Eagle Man Type of 1934-35
Perf. 10½x10

1936, June 18 — Engr. — Unwmk.

C80	AP18 20c brown carmine	6.50	7.00

Imprint: "Talleres de Imp. de Est. y Valores-Mexico"

1937 — Wmk. 156 — Photo. — *Perf. 14*

C81	AP18 20c rose red	1.25	.15
a.	20c brown carmine	1.50	.15
b.	20c dark carmine	2.00	.15
c.	Imperf., pair	37.50	50.00

There are two sizes of watermark 156. No. C81c was not regularly issued.

Cavalryman AP28

Early Biplane over Mountains AP29

Venustiano Carranza on Horseback AP30

1938, Mar. 26

C82	AP28 20c org red & bl	.50	.20
C83	AP29 40c bl & org red	.75	.30
C84	AP30 1p bl & bis brn	4.75	2.25
	Nos. C82-C84 (3)	6.00	2.75

Plan of Guadalupe, 25th anniversary.

The Zócalo and Cathedral, Mexico City — AP31

Designs: Nos. C87, C88, Reconstructed edifices of Chichén Itzá. Nos. C89, C90, View of Acapulco.

1938, July 1

C85	AP31 20c carmine rose	.35	.25
C86	AP31 20c purple	14.00	10.00
C87	AP31 40c brt green	7.75	5.00
C88	AP31 40c dark green	7.00	5.00
C89	AP31 1p light blue	7.00	5.00
C90	AP31 1p slate blue	7.00	5.00
	Nos. C85-C90 (6)	43.10	30.25

16th Intl. Cong. of Planning & Housing.

Statue of José María Morelos AP34

Statue of Pioneer Woman, Ponca City, OK AP35

1939 — Engr. — *Perf. 10½*

C91	AP34 20c green	.70	.50
C92	AP34 40c red violet	2.00	1.25
C93	AP34 1p vio brn & car	1.40	1.00
	Nos. C91-C93 (3)	4.10	2.75

New York World's Fair. Released in New York May 2, in Mexico May 24.

Type of 1939 Overprinted in Cerise

1939, May 23

C93A AP34 20c blue & red 200.00 400.00

Issued for the flight of Francisco Sarabia from Mexico City to New York on May 25.

1939, May 17

C94 AP35 20c gray brown 1.00 .40
C95 AP35 40c slate green 2.50 1.25
C96 AP35 1p violet 1.65 .90
Nos. C94-C96 (3) 5.15 2.55

Tulsa World Philatelic Convention.

First Engraving Made in Mexico, 1544 — AP36

First Work of Legislation Printed in America, 1563 — AP37

Designs: 1p, Reproduction of oldest preserved Mexican printing.

1939, Sept. 7 **Wmk. 156**

C97 AP36 20c slate blue .25 .15
a. Unwmkd. 42.50
C98 AP37 40c slate green .65 .15
a. Imperf., pair 700.00
C99 AP37 1p dk brn & car 1.10 .70
Nos. C97-C99 (3) 2.00 1.00

400th anniversary of printing in Mexico.

Alternated Perforations

Nos. 763-766, 774-779, 792-795, 801-804, 806-811, 813-818, C100-C102, C111-C116, C123-C128, C143-C162, C430-C431 have alternating small and large perforations.

Transportation — AP39

Designs: 40c, Finger counting and factory. 1p, "Seven Censuses."

Perf. 12x13, 13x12

1939, Oct. 2 **Photo.**

C100 AP39 20c dk bl & bl 1.00 .20
C101 AP39 40c red org & org .75 .25
C102 AP39 1p ind & vio bl 2.75 .75
Nos. C100-C102 (3) 4.50 1.20

National Census of 1939-40.

Penny Black Type of Regular Issue, 1940

1940, May ***Perf. 14***

C103 A140 5c blk & dk grn .65 .60
C104 A140 10c bis brn & dp bl .55 .25
C105 A140 20c car & bl vio .40 .20
C106 A140 1p car & choc 3.50 5.00
C107 A140 5p gray grn & red brn 40.00 55.00
Nos. C103-C107 (5) 45.10 61.05

Issue dates: 5c-1p, May 2; 5p, May 15.

Part of Original College at Pátzcuaro AP43

College at Morelia (18th Century) — AP44

College at Morelia (1940) AP45

1940, July 15 **Engr.** ***Perf. 10½***

C108 AP43 20c brt green .45 .20
C109 AP44 40c orange .50 .30
C110 AP45 1p dp pur, red brn & org 1.25 1.00
Nos. C108-C110 (3) 2.20 1.50

400th anniv. of the founding of the National College of San Nicolas de Hidalgo.

Pirate Ship — AP46

Designs: 40c, Castle of San Miguel. 1p, Temple of San Francisco.

Perf. 12x13, 13x12

1940, Aug. 7 **Photo.**

C111 AP46 20c red brn & bis brn 1.15 .70
C112 AP46 40c blk & sl grn 1.50 .75
C113 AP46 1p vio bl & blk 5.00 3.00
Nos. C111-C113 (3) 7.65 4.45

400th anniversary of Campeche.

Inauguration Type of Regular Issue, 1940

1940, Dec. 1 ***Perf. 12x13***

C114 A146 20c gray blk & red org 1.90 1.00
C115 A146 40c chnt brn & dk sl 2.00 1.50
C116 A146 1p brt vio bl & rose 3.50 2.00
Nos. C114-C116 (3) 7.40 4.50

Tower of the Convent of the Nuns — AP50

Casa de Montejo — AP51

Design: 1p, Campanile of Cathedral at Merída.

1942, Jan. 2 ***Perf. 14***

C117 AP50 20c Prus blue 1.50 .75
C118 AP51 40c grnsh blk (C) 2.25 2.00
a. Without overprint 7.50 7.50
C119 AP50 1p carmine 2.50 2.00
Nos. C117-C119 (3) 6.25 4.75

400th anniversary of Merída.

No. C118 bears the overprint "Servicio Aereo" in carmine.

Church of Zapopán AP53

Our Lady of Guadalupe Church AP54

Guadalajara Arms — AP55

1942, Feb. 11 **Engr.** ***Perf. 10½x10***

C120 AP53 20c green & blk 1.65 .75
C121 AP54 40c ol & yel grn 1.75 1.00
C122 AP55 1p purple & sepia 1.65 1.25
Nos. C120-C122 (3) 5.05 3.00

400th anniversary of Guadalajara.

Astrophysics Type of Regular Issue

Designs: 20c, Spiral Galaxy NGC 4594. 40c, Planetary Nebula in Lyra. 1p, Russell Diagrams.

1942, Feb. 17 **Photo.** ***Perf. 12x13***

C123 A154 20c dk grn & ind 12.50 3.00
C124 A154 40c car lake & ind 11.00 4.00
C125 A154 1p orange & blk 11.00 4.50
Nos. C123-C125 (3) 34.50 11.50

Corn AP59

1942, July 1

C126 AP59 20c shown 1.90 .70
C127 AP59 40c Coffee 1.50 .75
C128 AP59 1p Bananas 2.50 2.00
Nos. C126-C128 (3) 5.90 3.45

2nd Inter-American Agricultural Conf.

View of San Miguel de Allende AP62

Designs: 40c, Birthplace of Allende. 1p, Church of Our Lady of Health.

1943, May 18 ***Perf. 14***

C129 AP62 20c dk slate grn .95 .60
C130 AP62 40c purple 1.25 .60
C131 AP62 1p dp carmine 2.75 2.50
Nos. C129-C131 (3) 4.95 3.70

400th anniversary of the founding of San Miguel de Allende.

Types of 1934-35

1944 **Photo.** **Wmk. 272**

C132 AP18 20c brown carmine .75 .15

Perf. 10½x10

1944-46 **Engr.** **Wmk. 272**

C133 AP15 5c black .50 .15
C134 AP16 10c red brn ('45) 1.25 .15
C135 AP17 15c gray grn ('45) .85 .15
C136 AP19 30c brown ol ('45) 12.50 .75
C137 AP20 40c gray bl ('45) 1.10 .20
C138 AP21 50c green .85 .15
C139 AP22 1p gray grn & red brn ('45) 6.00 1.50
C140 AP23 5p dk car & blk ('46) 4.75 2.00
Nos. C133-C140 (8) 27.80 5.05

Symbol of Flight — AP65

Microphone, Book and Camera — AP66

1944 **Photo.** ***Perf. 14***

C141 AP65 25c chestnut brown .35 .15

See No. C185.

1944, Nov. 8 **Wmk. 272**

C142 AP66 25c dull slate grn .65 .15

Issued to commemorate the third Book Fair.

Catalogue values for unused stamps in this section, from this point to the end of the section, are for Never Hinged items.

Globe-in-Hands Type

1945, Feb. 27 ***Perf. 12x13***

C143 A166 25c red orange .35 .15
C144 A166 1p brt green .40 .30
C145 A166 5p indigo 2.50 2.00
C146 A166 10p brt rose 6.50 5.25
C147 A166 20p brt vio bl 14.00 13.00
Nos. C143-C147 (5) 23.75 20.70

Theater Type

1945, July 27

C148 A167 30c slate & ol .25 .15
C149 A167 1p slate & lil .35 .35
C150 A167 5p slate & blk 2.75 2.50
C151 A167 10p sl & lt ultra 5.00 4.25
C152 A167 20p blk & gray grn 12.00 10.50
Nos. C148-C152 (5) 20.35 17.75

Blindfold Type

1945, Nov. 21

C153 A169 30c slate green .20 .20
C154 A169 1p brown red .35 .25
C155 A169 5p red brn & pale bl 3.00 2.50
C156 A169 10p sl blk & pale lil 5.00 5.00
C157 A169 20p grn & lt brn 25.00 24.00
Nos. C153-C157 (5) 33.55 31.95

Torch, Laurel and Flag-decorated ONU — AP70

1946, Apr. 10

C158 AP70 30c chocolate .20 .15
C159 AP70 1p slate grn .35 .30
C160 AP70 5p chnt & dk grn 1.65 1.25
C161 AP70 10p dk brn & chnt 5.00 4.00
C162 AP70 20p sl grn & org red 12.00 9.00
Nos. C158-C162 (5) 19.20 14.70

Issued to honor the United Nations.

Father Margil de Jesus and Plane over Zacatecas AP71

Zacatecas scene and: 1p, Genaro Codina. 5p, Gen. Enrique Estrada. 10p, Fernando Villalpando.

Perf. 10½x10

1946, Sept. 13 **Engr.** **Wmk. 279**

C163 AP71 30c gray .20 .15
C164 AP71 1p brn & Prus grn .40 .35
C165 AP71 5p red & olive 3.00 3.00
C166 AP71 10p Prus grn & dk brn 12.50 5.00
Nos. C163-C166 (4) 16.10 8.50

400th anniversary of Zacatecas.

Franklin D. Roosevelt and Stamp of 1st Mexican Issue AP72

30c, Arms of Mexico & Stamp of 1st US Issue.

1947, May 16 Photo. *Perf. 14*
C167 AP72 25c lt violet bl .90 .50
C168 AP72 30c gray black .60 .25
a. Imperf., pair 325.00
C169 AP72 1p blue & carmine 1.25 .40
Nos. C167-C169 (3) 2.75 1.15

Centenary International Philatelic Exhibition, New York, May 17-25, 1947.

Type of 1934-35

Perf. 10½x10, 10x10½

1947 Engr. Wmk. 279
C170 AP15 5c black 1.50 .15
C171 AP16 10c red brown 3.00 .30
C172 AP17 15c olive grn 3.00 .30
C173 AP19 30c brown ol 2.00 .15
C174 AP20 40c blue gray 2.00 .15
C175 AP21 50c green 12.50 .30
a. Imperf., pair 450.00
C176 AP22 1p gray grn & red brn 3.50 .25
a. Imperf., pair 500.00
C177 AP23 5p red & blk 9.00 1.25
c. 5p dark car & black 200.00 3.00

Perf. 14
C177A AP18 20c brown car 2.75 .50
b. Imperf., pair 250.00
Nos. C170-C177A (9) 39.25 3.35

Emilio Carranza AP74

Douglas DC-4 — AP75

1947, June 25 Engr. *Perf. 10½x10*
C178 AP74 10p red & dk brn 1.75 1.50
a. 10p dark carmine & brown 8.00
C179 AP75 20p bl & red brn 2.75 2.75

Cadet Vincente Suárez AP76

Chapultepec Castle — AP78

Designs: 30c, Lieut. Juan de la Barrera. 1p, Gen. Pedro M. Anaya. 5p, Gen. Antonio de Leon.

1947, Sept. 8 Photo. *Perf. 14*
C180 AP76 25c dull violet .25 .15
C181 AP76 30c blue .25 .15

Engr.

Perf. 10x10½
C182 AP78 50c deep green .35 .15
C183 AP78 1p violet .50 .15
C184 AP78 5p aqua & brn 2.00 2.00
a. Imperf. pair 600.00
Nos. C180-C184 (5) 3.35 2.60

Centenary of the battles of Chapultepec, Churubusco and Molino del Rey.

Flight Symbol Type of 1944

1947 Wmk. 279 Photo. *Perf. 14*
C185 AP65 25c chestnut brn .40 .15
a. Imperf., pair 250.00

Puebla, Dance of the Half Moon AP81

Designs: 5c, Guerrero, Acapulco water-front. 10c, Oaxaca, dance. 20c, Chiapas, musicians (Mayan). 25c, Michoacan, masks. 30c, Cuauhtemoc. 35c, Guerrero, view of Taxco. 40c, San Luis Potosi, head. 50c, Chiapas, bas-relief profile, Mayan culture. 80c, Mexico City University Stadium. 5p, Queretaro, architecture. 10p, Miguel Hidalgo. 20p, Modern building.

Two types of 20p:
Type I - Blue gray part 21¼mm wide. Child's figure touching left edge.
Type II - Blue gray part 21¾mm wide; "LQ" at lower left corner. Child's figure 1mm from left edge.

Imprint: "Talleres de Impresion de Estampillas y Valores-Mexico"

Perf. 10½x10

1950-52 Wmk. 279 Engr.
C186 AP81 5c aqua ('51) .50 .15
C187 AP81 10c brn org ('51) 2.75 .50
C188 AP81 20c carmine 1.25 .15
C189 AP81 25c redsh brown 1.25 .15
C190 AP81 30c olive bister .50 .15
C191 AP81 35c violet 2.75 .15
a. Retouched die 19.00 .30
b. As "a," imperf., pair 300.00
C192 AP81 40c dk gray bl ('51) 2.25 .15
a. Imperf., pair 300.00
C193 AP81 50c green 3.75 .15
C194 AP81 80c claret ('52) 2.25 .50
a. Imperf., pair 300.00
C195 AP81 1p blue gray 1.25 .15
C196 AP81 5p dk brn & org ('51) 5.00 1.00
a. Imperf., pair *1,800.*
C197 AP81 10p blk & aqua ('52) 65.00 20.00
C198 AP81 20p car & bl gray, I ('52) 8.50 9.00
a. Type II 400.00 75.00
Nos. C186-C198 (13) 97.00 32.20

No. C191a: A patch of heavy shading has been added at right of "MEXICO;" lines in sky increased and strengthened. On Nos. C191, C191a, the top of the highest tower is even with the top of the "o" in "Guerrero," and has no frame line at right. No. C220C has frame line at right and tower top is even with "Arquitectura."

Many shades exist of Nos. C186-C198.

See Nos. C208-C221, C249, C265-C268, C285-C288, C290-C298, C347-C349, C422, C444, C446-C450, C471-C480.

Pres. Aleman and Highway Bridging Map of Mexico AP82

Design: 35c, Pres. Juarez and map.

1950, May 21 Engr.
C199 AP82 25c lilac rose 3.00 .25
C200 AP82 35c deep green .25 .15

Completion of the Intl. Highway between Ciudad Juarez and the Guatemala border.

Trains Crossing Isthmus of Tehuantepec AP83

Design: 35c, Pres. Aleman and bridge.

1950, May 24
C201 AP83 25c green .50 .25
C202 AP83 35c ultra .35 .25

Opening of the Southeastern Railroad between Veracruz, Coatzocoalcos and Yucatan, 1950.

Aztec Courier, Plane, Train — AP84

Design: 80c, Symbols of universal postal service.

1950, June 15
C203 AP84 25c red orange .35 .15
C204 AP84 80c blue .50 .30

75th anniv. (in 1949) of the UPU.

Miguel Hidalgo — AP86

Design: 35c, Hidalgo and Mexican Flag.

Wmk. 300

1953, May 8 Photo. *Perf. 14*
C206 AP86 25c gray bl & dk red brn .90 .15
C207 AP86 35c slate green .90 .25

Bicentenary of birth of Miguel Hidalgo y Costilla (1753-1811), priest and revolutionist.

Type of 1950-52

Designs as before.

Imprint: "Talleres de Impresion de Estampillas y Valores-Mexico"

Wmk. 300, Horizontal

1953-56 Engr. *Perf. 10½x10*
C208 AP81 5c aqua .50 .15
C209 AP81 10c orange brn 5.50 .90
a. 10c orange 11.50 2.50
C210 AP81 30c gray olive 18.00 1.25
C211 AP81 40c gray bl ('56) 18.00 1.50
C212 AP81 50c green 250.00 150.00
C213 AP81 80c claret 100.00 10.00
C214 AP81 1p blue gray 3.00 .30
C215 AP81 5p dk brn & org 2.75 .60
C216 AP81 10p black & aqua 6.25 1.25
C217 AP81 20p car & bl gray (II) ('56) 65.00 8.00
Nos. C208-C211,C213-C217 (9) 219.00 23.95

Printed in sheets of 30.

Type of 1950-52

Designs as in 1950-52. 2p, Guerrero, view of Taxco. 2.25p, Michoacan, masks.

Two types of 2p:
I - No dots after "Colonial". Frame line at right broken near top.
II - Three dots in a line after "Colonial". Right frame line unbroken.

Wmk. 300, Vertical

1955-65 *Perf. 11½x11*
C218 AP81 5c bluish grn ('56) .15 .15

Perf. 11
C219 AP81 10c orange brn ('60) .35 .15
a. Perf. 11½x11 1.10 .40
C220 AP81 20c carmine ('60) .35 .15
k. Perf. 11½x11 ('57) 1.65 .15
C220A AP81 25c vio brn, perf. 11½x11 1.75 .15
C220B AP81 30c olive gray ('60) .15 .15
l. Perf. 11½x11 .90 .15
C220C AP81 35c dk vio, perf. 11½x11 .90 .15
C220D AP81 40c slate bl ('60) .35 .15
m. Perf. 11½x11 10.00 .15
C220E AP81 50c green, perf. 11½x11 .90 .15
n. Perf. 11 ('60) 1.10 .15
q. 50c yellow green 1.10 .20
C220F AP81 80c claret ('60) 5.00 .70
o. Perf. 11½x11 5.00 .60
C220G AP81 1p grn gray ('60) 1.10 .30
p. Perf. 11½x11 12.50 .30
C220H AP81 2p dk org brn, II ('63) 1.10 .60
i. 2p lt org brn, perf. 11½x11 ('65) 150.00 40.00
j. 2p org brn, I, perf. 11 8.50 1.25
C221 AP81 2.25p maroon ('63) .65 .70
Nos. C218-C221 (12) 12.75 3.50

Printed in sheets of 45 and 50. Nos. C218-C221 have been re-engraved.

No. C218 has been redrawn and there are many differences. "CTS" measures 7mm; it is 5½mm on No. C208.

Nos. C208-C221 exist in various shades.

For No. C220C, see note after No. C198.

No. C220n was privately overprinted in red: "25vo Aniversario / Primer Cohete Internacional / Reynosa, Mexico-McAllen, U.S.A. / 1936-1961."

Mayan Ball Court and Player — AP87

Design: 35c, Modern Stadium, Mexico.

1954, Mar. 6 Photo. *Perf. 14*
C222 AP87 25c brn & dk bl grn 1.00 .35
C223 AP87 35c dl sl grn & lil rose .75 .25

7th Central American & Caribbean Games.

Allegory AP88

1954, Sept. 15
C224 AP88 25c red brn & dp bl .50 .25
C225 AP88 35c dk bl & vio brn .20 .15
C226 AP88 80c blk & bl grn .25 .25
Nos. C224-C226 (3) .95 .65

Centenary of national anthem.

Aztec God Tezcatlipoca and Map — AP89

Design: 35c, Stadium and map.

1955, Mar. 12
C227 AP89 25c dk Prus grn & red brn .75 .30
C228 AP89 35c carmine & brn .75 .30

2nd Pan American Games, 1955.

Ornaments and Mask, Archeological Era — AP90

Designs: 10c, Virrey Enriquez de Almanza, bell tower and coach, colonial era. 50c, Jose Maria Morelos and cannon, heroic Mexico. 1p, Woman and child and horse back rider, revolutionary Mexico. 1.20p, Sombrero and Spurs, popular Mexico. 5p, Pointing hand and school, modern Mexico.

Perf. 11½x11

1956, Aug. 1 Engr. Wmk. 300
C229 AP90 5c black .40 .15
C230 AP90 10c lt blue .40 .15
C231 AP90 50c violet brn .30 .15
C232 AP90 1p blue gray .40 .15
C233 AP90 1.20p magenta .40 .25
C234 AP90 5p blue grn 1.25 1.25
a. Souv. sheet of 6, #C229-C234, perf. 10½x10 50.00 50.00
Nos. C229-C234 (6) 3.15 2.10

Centenary of Mexico's 1st postage stamps. No. C234a sold for 15 pesos.

Paricutin Volcano AP91

1956, Sept. 5 Photo. *Perf. 14*
C235 AP91 50c dk violet bl .50 .15

20th Intl. Geological Cong., Mexico City.

Valentin Gomez Farias and Melchor Ocampo AP92

1.20p, Leon Guzman and Ignacio Ramirez.

1956-63 Wmk. 300 *Perf. 14*
C236 AP92 15c intense blue .50 .15
C237 AP92 1.20p dk grn & pur .85 .35
b. Dark green omitted 110.00
c. Purple omitted 125.00
C237A AP92 2.75p purple ('63) 1.25 .75
Nos. C236-C237A (3) 2.60 1.25

Centenary of the constitution (in 1957). See Nos. C289, C445, C451, C471A.

Map — AP93

1956, Dec. 1

C238 AP93 25c gray & dk bl .35 .15

Issued to publicize the 4th Inter-American Regional Tourism Congress of the Gulf of Mexico and the Caribbean (in 1955).

Eagle Holding Scales AP94

Design: 1p, Allegorical figure writing the law.

1957, Aug. 31 Photo. *Perf. 14*

C239 AP94 50c metallic red brn & green .35 .15
C240 AP94 1p metallic lilac & ultra .50 .25

Centenary of 1857 Constitution.

Globe, Weights and Measure AP95

1957, Sept. 21

C241 AP95 50c metallic bl & blk .40 .15

Centenary of the adoption of the metric system in Mexico.

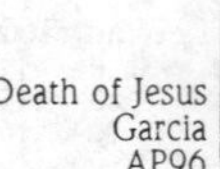

Death of Jesus Garcia AP96

1957, Nov. 7 Wmk. 300 *Perf. 14*

C242 AP96 50c car rose & dk vio .35 .15

50th anniversary of the death of Jesus Garcia, hero of Nacozari.

Oil Industry Symbols AP97

Design: 1p, Derricks at night.

1958, Aug. 30

C243 AP97 50c emerald & blk .25 .15
C244 AP97 1p car & bluish blk .40 .15
Set value .20

20th anniversary of the nationalization of Mexico's oil industry.

Independence Monument Figure AP98

1958, Dec. 15 Engr. *Perf. 11*

C245 AP98 50c gray blue .25 .15

10th anniversary of the signing of the Universal Declaration of Human Rights.

Pres. Venustiano Carranza AP99

1960, Jan. 15 Photo. *Perf. 14*

C246 AP99 50c salmon & dk bl .25 .15

Centenary of the birth of President Venustiano Carranza.

Alberto Braniff's 1910 Plane, Douglas DC-7 and Mexican Airlines Map AP100

1960, May 15 Wmk. 300 *Perf. 14*

C247 AP100 50c lt brn & vio .50 .15
C248 AP100 1p lt brn & bl grn .40 .20

50th anniversary of Mexican aviation.

Type of 1950-52 inscribed: "HOMENAJE AL COLECCIONISTA DEL TIMBRE DE MEXICO-JUNIO 1960"

1960, June 8 Engr. *Perf. 10½x10*

C249 AP81 20p lil, brn & lt grn 75.00 80.00

See note below No. 909.

Flag — AP101

Designs: 1.20p, Bell of Dolores and eagle. 5p, Dolores Church.

Wmk. 300

1960, Sept. 16 Photo. *Perf. 14*

C250 AP101 50c dp grn & brt red .40 .15
C251 AP101 1.20p grnsh bl & dk brn .55 .25
C252 AP101 5p sepia & green 6.00 2.25
Nos. C250-C252 (3) 6.95 2.65

150th anniversary of independence.

Aviation (Douglas DC-8 Airliner) AP102

Designs: 1p, Oil industry. 1.20p, Road development. 5p, Water power (dam).

1960, Nov. 20 Photo. *Perf. 14*

C253 AP102 50c gray bl & blk .40 .15
C254 AP102 1p dk grn & rose car .50 .25
C255 AP102 1.20p dk grn & sep .50 .30
C256 AP102 5p blue & lilac 2.50 1.10
Nos. C253-C256 (4) 3.90 1.80

50th anniversary of Mexican Revolution.

Count de Revillaggigedo — AP103

1960, Dec. 23

C257 AP103 60c dk car & blk .60 .15

80th census and to honor Juan Vicente Güémez Pacheco de Padilla Horcasitas, Count de Revillagigedo, who conducted the 1st census in America, 1793.

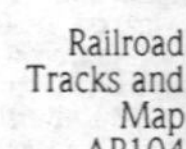

Railroad Tracks and Map AP104

Design: 70c, Railroad bridge.

1961, Nov. Wmk. 300 *Perf. 14*

C258 AP104 60c chlky bl & dk grn .40 .15
C259 AP104 70c dk blue & gray .40 .15

Opening of the railroad from Chihuahua to the Pacific Ocean.

Gen. Ignacio Zaragoza and View of Puebla AP105

1962, May 5

C260 AP105 1p gray grn & slate grn .60 .15

Centenary of the Battle of May 5 at Puebla and the defeat of French forces by Gen. Ignacio Zaragoza.

Laboratory AP106

1962, June 11

C261 AP106 1p olive & vio bl .60 .15

National Polytechnic Institute, 25th anniv.

Pres. John F. Kennedy AP107

1962, June 29

C262 AP107 80c brt blue & car 1.75 .40

Issued to commemorate the visit of President John F. Kennedy to Mexico, June 29-30.

Globe AP108

1962, Oct. 20

C263 AP108 1.20p violet & dk brn .60 .25

Inter-American Economic and Social Council meeting.

Balloon over Mexico City, 1862 — AP109

1962, Dec. 21 Wmk. 300 *Perf. 14*

C264 AP109 80c lt blue & blk 1.65 .60

Cent. of the 1st Mexican balloon ascension by Joaquin de la Cantolla y Rico.

Type of 1950-52

Imprint: "Talleres de Imp. de Est. y Valores-Mexico"

Designs as before.

Wmk. 300, Vertical

1962-72 Photo. *Perf. 14*

Two sizes of 80c:
I - 35½x20mm.
II - 37x20½mm.

C265 AP81 80c cl, I ('63) 1.40 .30
a. Perf. 11½x11, size II ('63) 4.00 .35
b. Perf. 11, size II ('63) 3.50 .30
c. Perf. 11, size I ('72) 2.50 .15
C266 AP81 5p dk brn & yel org 4.00 1.00
C267 AP81 10p blk & lt grn ('63) 7.00 3.75
C268 AP81 20p car & bl gray 15.00 3.50
a. 20p carmine & aqua 17.00 4.75
Nos. C265-C268 (4) 27.40 8.55

Vert. pairs, imperf. horiz. of No. C265, perf. 11, may be from uncut rolls of No. C348.

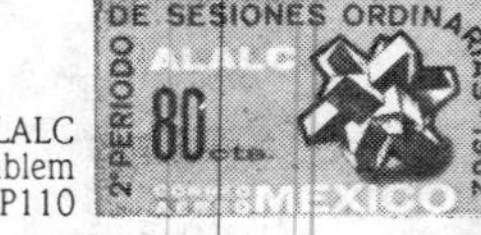

ALALC Emblem AP110

1963, Feb. 15 Wmk. 300

C269 AP110 80c orange & dl pur 1.10 .30

2nd general session of the Latin American Free Trade Assoc. (ALALC), held in 1962.

Mexican Eagle and Refinery AP111

1963, Mar. 23

C270 AP111 80c red org & slate .60 .15

Nationalization of the oil industry, 25th anniv.

Polyconic Map — AP112

1963, Apr. 22 Photo. *Perf. 14*

C271 AP112 80c blue & blk .85 .30

19th Intl. Chamber of Commerce Congress.

EXMEX Emblem and Postmark AP113

1963, Oct. 9 Wmk. 350 *Perf. 14*

C274 AP113 5p rose red 2.75 1.75

77th Annual Convention of the American Philatelic Society, Mexico City, Oct. 7-13.

Marshal Tito — AP114

1963, Oct. 15 Wmk. 350 *Perf. 14*

C275 AP114 2p dk grn & vio 2.00 .70

Visit of Marshal Tito of Yugoslavia.

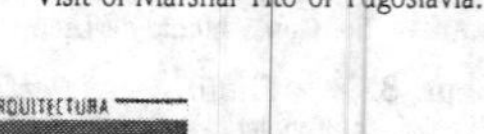

Modern Architecture — AP115

1963, Oct. 19

C276 AP115 80c dk blue & gray .70 .25

Intl. Architects' Convention, Mexico City.

Dove — AP116

1963, Oct. 26
C277 AP116 80c dl bl grn & car 1.25 .35

Centenary of the International Red Cross.

Don Quixote by José Guadalupe Posada
AP117

1963, Nov. 9 Engr. *Perf. 10½x10*
C278 AP117 1.20p black 1.75 .50

50th anniversary of the death of José Guadalupe Posada, satirical artist.

Horse-drawn Rail Coach, Old and New Trains
AP118

Wmk. 350
1963, Nov. 29 Photo. *Perf. 14*
C279 AP118 1.20p violet bl & bl .90 .35

11th Pan-American Railroad Congress.

Eleanor Roosevelt, Flame and UN Emblem
AP119

1964, Feb. 22 Wmk. 350 *Perf. 14*
C280 AP119 80c lt ultra & red .85 .25

15th anniversary (in 1963) of the Universal Declaration of Human Rights and to honor Eleanor Roosevelt.

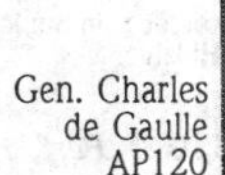

Gen. Charles de Gaulle
AP120

1964, Mar. 16 Photo.
C281 AP120 2p dl vio bl & brn 2.50 .80

Visit of President Charles de Gaulle of France to Mexico, Mar. 16-18.

Pres. John F. Kennedy and Pres. Adolfo López Mateos and Map — AP121

1964, Apr. 11 Photo.
C282 AP121 80c vio bl & gray .85 .25

Ratification of the Chamizal Treaty, returning the Chamizal area of El Paso, Texas, to Mexico, July 18, 1963.

Queen Juliana
AP122

1964, May 8 Wmk. 350 *Perf. 14*
C283 AP122 80c bister & vio bl 1.25 .25

Visit of Queen Juliana of the Netherlands.

Lt. José Azueta and Cadet Virgilio Uribe
AP123

1964, June 18 Wmk. 350 *Perf. 14*
C284 AP123 40c dk brn & blk .55 .15

50th anniversary of the defense of Veracruz (against US Navy).

Types of 1950-62

Designs as before.

Engraved; Photogravure (C296-C298)
Perf. 11 (20c, 40c, 50c, 80c, 2p); 14
1964-73 Wmk. 350

C285 AP81 20c carmine ('71) .80 1.25
C286 AP81 40c gray bl ('71) 125.00 *100.00*
C287 AP81 50c green ('71) .50 .50
C288 AP81 80c claret, I ('73) .50 .50
C289 AP92 1.20p dk grn & pur 6.50 2.50
C290 AP81 2p red brn, II ('71) 1.75 1.40
C296 AP81 5p brn & org ('66) 11.00 9.00
C297 AP81 10p black & aqua 35.00 17.50
C298 AP81 20p car & bl gray 40.00 26.00
Nos. C285-C290,C296-C298 (9) 221.05 *158.65*

National Emblem, Cahill's Butterfly World Map, Sword and Scales of Justice
AP124

1964, July 29 Photo.
C299 AP124 40c sepia & dp bl .60 .15

10th conference of the International Bar Association, Mexico City, July 27-31.

Galleon
AP125

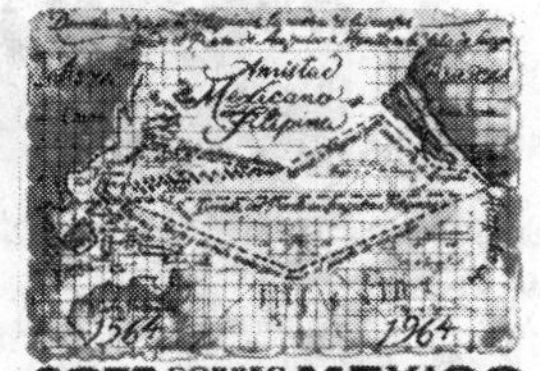

Map Showing 16th Century Voyages Between Mexico and Philippines — AP126

1964, Nov. 10 Wmk. 350 *Perf. 14*
C300 AP125 80c ultra & indigo 2.25 .35
C301 AP126 2.75p brt yel & blk 2.75 1.00

400 years of Mexican-Philippine friendship.

Netzahualcoyotl Dam, Grijalva River — AP127

1965, Feb. 19 Photo. *Perf. 14*
C302 AP127 80c vio gray & dk brn .50 .15

Radio-electric Unit of San Benito, Chiapas
AP128

80c, Microwave tower, Villahermosa, Tabasco.

1965, June 19 Wmk. 350 *Perf. 14*
C303 AP128 80c lt bl & dk bl .65 .30
C304 AP128 1.20p dk grn & blk .70 .30

Centenary of the ITU.

Campfire, Tent and Scout Emblem
AP129

1965, Sept. 27 Photo. *Perf. 14*
C305 AP129 80c lt ultra & vio bl .65 .30

Issued to publicize the 20th World Scout Conference, Mexico City, Sept. 27-Oct. 3.

King Baudouin, Queen Fabiola and Arms of Belgium
AP130

1965, Oct. 18 Wmk. 350 *Perf. 14*
C306 AP130 2p slate grn & dl bl 1.00 .40

Visit of the King and Queen of Belgium.

Mayan Antiquities and Unisphere
AP131

1965, Nov. 9 Photo.
C307 AP131 80c lemon & emerald .50 .20

Issued for the NY World's Fair, 1964-65.

Dante by Raphael — AP132

Perf. 10x10½
1965, Nov. 23 Wmk. 350 Engr.
C308 AP132 2p henna brown 1.25 .65

700th anniv. of the birth of Dante Alighieri.

Runner in Starting Position, Terra Cotta Found in Colima, 300-650 A.D.
AP133

Designs: 1.20p, Chin cultic disk, ball game scoring stone with ball player in center, Mayan culture, c. 500 A.D., found in Chiapas. 2p, Clay sculpture of ball court, players, spectators and temple. Pieces on 80c and 2p from 300-650 A.D.

1965, Dec. 17 Photo. *Perf. 14*
Size: 35x21mm

C309 AP133 80c orange & sl .65 .25
C310 AP133 1.20p bl & vio bl .80 .30
a. Souv. sheet of 4, #965-966, C309-C310, imperf. 1.50 1.50

Size: 43x36mm

C311 AP133 2p brt bl & dk brn .65 .25
a. Souv. sheet, imperf. 1.50 1.50
Nos. C309-C311 (3) 2.10 .80

19th Olympic Games, Mexico, 1968. No. C310a sold for 3.90p. No. C311a sold for 3p.

Nos. C310a and C311a have large watermark of national arms (diameter 54mm) and "SECRETARIA DE HACIENDA Y CREDITO PUBLICO." Issued without gum.

Ruben Dario — AP134

1966, Mar. 17 Wmk. 350 *Perf. 14*
C312 AP134 1.20p sepia .60 .35

Ruben Dario (pen name of Felix Ruben Garcia Sarmiento, 1867-1916), Nicaraguan poet, newspaper correspondent and diplomat.

Father Andres de Urdaneta and Compass Rose
AP135

Perf. 10½x10
1966, June 4 Engr. Wmk. 350
C313 AP135 2.75p bluish blk 1.25 .60

4th centenary of Father Urdaneta's return trip from the Philippines.

UPAE Type of Regular Issue

Designs: 80c, Pennant and post horn. 1.20p, Pennant and UPAE emblem, horiz.

Wmk. 300
1966, June 24 Photo. *Perf. 14*
C314 A244 80c magenta & blk .25 .15
C315 A244 1.20p lt ultra & blk .35 .15
Set value .25

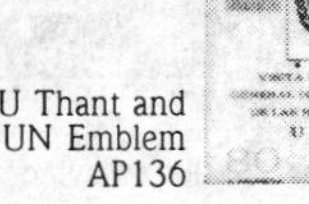

U Thant and UN Emblem
AP136

1966, Aug. 24 Photo. Wmk. 300
C316 AP136 80c black & ultra .75 .20

Visit of U Thant, Secretary General of the UN.

AP137

1966, Aug. 26 *Perf. 14*
C317 AP137 80c green & red .25 .15

Issued to publicize the year of friendship between Mexico and Central America.

Olympic Type of Regular Issue

Designs by Diego Rivera: 80c, Obstacle race. 2.25p, Football. 2.75p, Lighting Olympic torch.

1966, Oct. 15 Wmk. 300 *Perf. 14*
Size: 57x21mm

C318 A248 80c org brn & blk .40 .15
C319 A248 2.25p green & blk .60 .35
C320 A248 2.75p dp pur & blk 1.00 .50
a. Souvenir sheet of 3 3.00 3.00
Nos. C318-C320 (3) 2.00 1.00

Issued to publicize the 19th Olympic Games, Mexico City, D.F., 1968. No. C320a contains 3 imperf. stamps similar to Nos. C318-C320 with simulated perforations. Sold for 8.70p.

UNESCO Emblem
AP138

Litho. & Engr.

1966, Nov. 4 *Perf. 11*
C321 AP138 80c blk, car, brt grn & org .50 .15
a. Perf. 10½ 5.00 2.00
b. Perf. 10½x11 25.00
c. Perf. 11x10½ 12.50 5.00

UNESCO 20th anniv. The 4th color varies from yellow to orange. A number of perforation varieties exist on the perf 11 stamps.

Venustiano Carranza AP139

Tiros Satellite over Earth AP140

1967, Feb. 5 **Photo.** *Perf. 14*
C322 AP139 80c dk red brn & ocher .35 .15

Constitution, 50th anniv. Venustiano Carranza (1859-1920), was president of Mexico 1917-20.

1967, Mar. 23 **Photo.** **Wmk. 300**
C323 AP140 80c blk & dk bl .50 .20

World Meteorological Day, Mar. 23.

Medical School Emblem AP141

Captain Horacio Ruiz Gaviño AP142

1967, July 10 **Wmk. 300** *Perf. 14*
C324 AP141 80c black & ocher .35 .15

Mexican Military Medical School, 50th anniv.

1967, July 17 **Photo.**

Design: 2p, Biplane, horiz.

C325 AP142 80c black & brown .25 .15
C326 AP142 2p black & brown .45 .25

50th anniv. of the 1st Mexican airmail flight, from Pachuca to Mexico City, July 6, 1917.

Marco Polo and ITY Emblem — AP143

1967, Sept. 9 **Wmk. 300** *Perf. 14*
C327 AP143 80c rose cl & blk .25 .15

Issued for International Tourist Year, 1967.

Olympic Games Type of Regular Issue, 1967

Designs: 80c, Diving. 1.20p, Runners. 2p, Weight lifters. 5p, Soccer.

1967, Oct. 12 **Photo.** *Perf. 14*
C328 A254 80c dp lil rose & blk .25 .15
C329 A254 1.20p brt grn & blk .30 .20
a. Souv. sheet of 2, #C328-C329, imperf. 3.00 2.25
C330 A254 2p yellow & blk 1.00 .40
C331 A254 5p olive & blk 1.65 .75
a. Souv. sheet of 2, #C330-C331, imperf. 7.50 4.00
Nos. C328-C331 (4) 3.20 1.50

No. C329a sold for 2.50p; No. C331a sold for 9p. Both sheets are watermark 350.

Heinrich Hertz and James Clerk Maxwell AP144

1967, Nov. 15 **Photo.** **Wmk. 300**
C332 AP144 80c brt grn & blk .30 .15

2nd Intl. Telecommunications Plan Conf., Mexico City, Oct. 30-Nov. 15.

EFIMEX Emblem, Showing Official Stamp of 1884 — AP145

1968, Feb. 24 **Wmk. 300** *Perf. 14*
C333 AP145 80c black & grn .45 .25
C334 AP145 2p black & ver .45 .25

EFIMEX '68, International Philatelic Exhibition, Mexico City, Nov. 1-9, 1968.

Olympic Games Type of Regular Issue, 1967

Designs: 80c, Sailing. 1p, Rowing. 2p, Volleyball. 5p, Equestrian.

1968, Mar. 21 **Photo.** *Perf. 14*
C335 A254 80c ultra & blk .25 .15
C336 A254 1p brt bl grn & blk .30 .20
a. Souv. sheet of 2, #C335-C336, imperf. 3.00 2.00
C337 A254 2p yellow & blk .60 .30
C338 A254 5p red brn & blk 1.25 1.10
a. Souv. sheet of 2, #C337-C338, imperf. 5.00 3.75
Nos. C335-C338 (4) 2.40 1.75

No. C336a sold for 2.40p; No. C338a sold for 9p. Both sheets are watermark 350.

Martin Luther King, Jr. — AP146

1968, June 8 **Photo.** **Wmk. 300**
C339 AP146 80c black & gray .35 .15

Rev. Dr. Martin Luther King, Jr. (1929-1968), American civil rights leader.

Olympic Types of Regular Issue, 1968

Designs: 80c, Peace dove and Olympic rings. 1p, Discobolus. 2p, Olympic medals. 5p, Symbols of Olympic sports events. 10p, Symbolic design for Mexican Olympic Games.

1968, Oct. 12 **Wmk. 350** *Perf. 14*
C340 A259 80c green, lil & org .25 .15
C341 A259 1p green, bl & blk .30 .15
C342 A259 2p multicolored .75 .50
a. Souvenir sheet of 3, #C340-C342, imperf. 15.00 7.50
C343 A260 5p multicolored 3.00 1.40
C344 A260 10p black & multi 2.50 1.50
a. Souvenir sheet of 2, #C343-C344, imperf. 10.00 7.50
Nos. C340-C344 (5) 6.80 3.70

19th Olympic Games, Mexico City, Oct. 12-27. No. C342a sold for 5p. No. C344a sold for 20p.

Souvenir Sheet

EFIMEX Emblem — AP147

1968, Nov. 1 **Photo.** *Imperf.*
C345 AP147 5p black & ultra 3.00 2.25

EFIMEX '68 International philatelic exhibition, Mexico City, Nov. 1-9. No. C345 contains one stamp with simulated perforations.

Father Francisco Palóu (See footnote) AP148

1969, July 16 **Wmk. 350** *Perf. 14*
C346 AP148 80c multicolored .40 .15

Issued to honor Father Junipero Serra (1713-1784), Franciscan missionary, founder of San Diego, Calif. The portrait was intended to be that of Father Serra. By error the head of Father Palóu, his coworker, was taken from a painting (c. 1785) by Mariano Guerrero which also contains a Serra portrait.

Type of 1950-52 Redrawn
Coil Stamps
Wmk. 300 Vert.

1969 **Photo.** *Perf. 11 Vert.*

Imprint: "T.I.E.V."

C347 AP81 20c carmine 2.00 1.25

Imprint: "Talleres de Imp de Est y Valores-Mexico"

C348 AP81 80c claret 2.00 1.25

Imprint: "T.I.E.V."

C349 AP81 1p gray grn 3.00 1.75
Nos. C347-C349 (3) 7.00 4.25

Soccer Ball — AP149

Design: 2p, Foot and soccer ball.

1969, Aug. 16 **Wmk. 350** *Perf. 14*
C350 AP149 80c red & multi .35 .15
C351 AP149 2p green & multi .50 .15

9th World Soccer Championships for the Jules Rimet Cup, Mexico City, May 30-June 21, 1970.

Mahatma Gandhi AP150

Astronaut's Footprint AP151

1969, Sept. 27 **Photo.** *Perf. 14*
C352 AP150 80c multicolored .30 .15

Mohandas K. Gandhi (1869-1948), leader in India's fight for independence.

1969, Oct. 29 **Photo.**
C353 AP151 2p black .50 .25

Man's 1st landing on the moon, July 20, 1969. See note after US No. C76.

Tourist Issue

Type of Regular Issue, 1969-73 and

"Sound and Light" at Pyramid, Teotihuacan AP152

Designs: No. C355, Acapulco Bay. No. C356, El Caracol Observatory, Yucatan. No. C357, Dancer with fruit basket, Oaxaca. No. C358, Sports fishing, Lower California, horiz.

1969-73 **Wmk. 350** *Perf. 14*
C354 AP152 80c shown .90 .30
C355 AP152 80c multicolored .90 .30
C356 AP152 80c multicolored .90 .30

Wmk. 300

C357 A267 80c multicolored .35 .25
C358 A267 80c multicolored .35 .20
Nos. C354-C358 (5) 3.40 1.35

Issue dates: Nos. C354-C356, Nov. 1, 1969. Nos. C357-C358, Mar. 16, 1973.

Red Crosses AP154

1969, Nov. 8 **Photo.** **Wmk. 350**
C370 AP154 80c black & multi .30 .15
a. Red omitted 150.00

50th anniv. of the League of Red Cross Societies.

AP155

AP156

1969, Dec. 6 **Wmk. 350** *Perf. 14*
C371 AP155 80c multicolored .35 .15

Installation of the ground station for communications by satellite at Tulancingo, Hidalgo.

1970, May 31 **Wmk. 350** *Perf. 14*

Design: 80c, Soccer Ball, and Mexican Masks. 2p, Pre-Columbian sculptured heads and soccer ball.

C372 AP156 80c blue & multi .25 .15
C373 AP156 2p multicolored .45 .20

World Soccer Championships for the Jules Rimet Cup, Mexico City, May 30-June 21, 1970. The design of Nos. C372-C373 is continuous.

SPORTMEX '70 Emblem — AP157

1970, June 19 *Rouletted 13*
C374 AP157 2p gray & car 5.00 3.00

SPORTMEX '70 philatelic exposition devoted to sports, especially soccer, on stamps. Mexico City, June 19-28. The 2p stamp of No. C374 is imperf.

Ode to Joy and Beethoven's Signature
AP158

1970, Sept. 26 Wmk. 350 *Perf. 14*

C375 AP158 2p multicolored .50 .25

200th anniversary of the birth of Ludwig van Beethoven (1770-1827), composer.

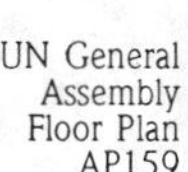

UN General Assembly Floor Plan
AP159

1970, Oct. 24 Photo. *Perf. 14*

C376 AP159 80c multicolored .30 .15

25th anniversary of United Nations.

Isaac Newton
AP160

1971, Feb. 27 Wmk. 350 *Perf. 14*

C377 AP160 2p shown .45 .20
C378 AP160 2p Galileo .45 .20
C379 AP160 2p Johannes Kepler .45 .20
Nos. C377-C379 (3) 1.35 .60

Mayan Warriors, Dresden Codex
AP161

Designs: No. C381, Sister Juana, by Miguel Cabrera (1695-1768). No. C382, José Maria Velasco (1840-1912), self-portrait. No. C383, El Paricutin (volcano), by Gerardo Murillo ("Dr. Atl," 1875-1964). No. C384, Detail of mural, Man in Flames, by José Clemente Orozco (1883-1949).

Imprint includes "1971"

1971, Apr. 24 Photo. Wmk. 350

C380 AP161 80c multicolored .30 .20
C381 AP161 80c multicolored .30 .20
C382 AP161 80c multicolored .30 .20
C383 AP161 80c multicolored .30 .20
C384 AP161 80c multicolored .30 .20
Nos. C380-C384 (5) 1.50 1.00

Mexican art and science through the centuries. See Nos. C396-C400, C417-C421, C439-C443, C513-C517, C527-C531.

Stamps of Venezuela, Mexico and Colombia
AP162

1971, May 22 Photo. Wmk. 350

C385 AP162 80c multicolored .35 .20

EXFILCA 70, 2nd Interamerican Philatelic Exhibition, Caracas, Venezuela, Nov. 27-Dec. 6, 1970.

Francisco Javier Clavijero
AP163

1971, July 10 Wmk. 350 *Perf. 14*

C386 AP163 2p lt ol bis & dk brn .50 .25

Francisco Javier Clavijero (1731-1786), Jesuit and historian, whose remains were returned from Italy to Mexico in 1970.

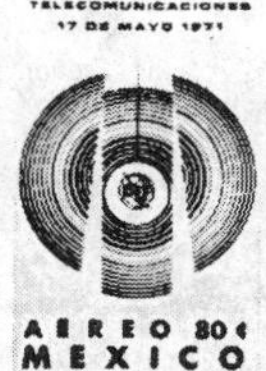

Waves — AP164

Mariano Matamoros, by Diego Rivera — AP165

1971, Aug. 7 Wmk. 350 *Perf. 14*

C387 AP164 80c multicolored .25 .15

3rd World Telecommunications Day, May 17.

1971, Aug. 28 Photo.

C388 AP165 2p multicolored .45 .20

Bicentenary of the birth of Mariano Matamoros (1770-1814), priest and patriot.

Vicente Guerrero
AP166

Circles
AP167

1971, Sept. 27

C389 AP166 2p multicolored .40 .20

Vicente Guerrero (1783-1831), independence leader, president of Mexico. Painting by Juan O'Gorman.

1971, Nov. 4 Wmk. 300

C390 AP167 80c grnsh bl, dk bl & blk .30 .15

25th anniv. of UNESCO.

FILATELIA PARA LA PAZ

Stamps of Venezuela, Mexico, Colombia and Peru
AP168

1971, Nov. 4

C391 AP168 80c multicolored .45 .15

EXFILIMA '71, 3rd Interamerican Philatelic Exhibition, Lima, Peru, Nov. 6-14.

Faces and Hand
AP169

1971, Nov. 29

C392 AP169 2p blk, dk bl & pink .45 .20

5th Congress of Psychiatry, Mexico City, Nov. 28-Dec. 4.

Ex Libris by Albrecht Dürer
AP170

1971, Dec. 18

C393 AP170 2p blk & buff .65 .20

Albrecht Dürer (1471-1528), German painter and engraver.

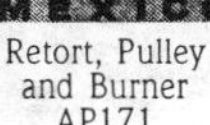

Retort, Pulley and Burner
AP171

Scientists and WHO Emblem
AP172

1972, Feb. 26 Wmk. 300 *Perf. 14*

C394 AP171 2p lilac, blk & yel .35 .15

Anniversary of the National Council on Science and Technology.

1972, Apr. 8

C395 AP172 80c multicolored .25 .15

World Health Day 1972. Stamp shows Willem Einthoven and Frank Wilson.

Art and Science Type of 1971

Designs: No. C396, King Netzahuacoyotl (1402-1472) of Texcoco, art patron. No. C397, Juan Ruiz de Alarcon (c. 1580-1639), lawyer. No. C398, José Joaquin Fernandez de Lizardi (1776-1827), author. No. C399, Ramon Lopez Velarde (1888-1921), writer. No. C400, Enrique Gonzalez Martinez (1871-1952), poet.

Imprint includes "1972"

1972, Apr. 15 Wmk. 350

Black Inscriptions

C396 AP161 80c ocher 1.25 .25
C397 AP161 80c green 1.25 .25
C398 AP161 80c brown 1.25 .25
C399 AP161 80c carmine 1.25 .25
C400 AP161 80c gray blue 1.25 .25
Nos. C396-C400 (5) 6.25 1.25

Mexican art and science through the centuries.

Rotary Emblem
AP173

1972, Apr. 5

C401 AP173 80c multicolored .30 .15

Rotary Intl. in Mexico, 50th anniv.

Tire Treads
AP174

1972, May 11 Wmk. 300

C402 AP174 80c gray & blk .30 .15

74th Assembly of the International Tourism Alliance, Mexico City, May 8-11.

Benito Juárez
AP175

Designs: 80c, Page of Civil Register. 1.20p, Juárez, by Pelegrin Clavé.

1972 Photo. *Perf. 14*

C403 AP175 80c gray bl & blk .20 .15
C404 AP175 1.20p multi .25 .15
C405 AP175 2p yellow & multi .35 .20
Nos. C403-C405 (3) .80 .50

Benito Juárez (1806-1872), revolutionary leader and president of Mexico.

Issue dates: 80c, 2p, July 18; 1.20p, Sept. 15.

Atom Symbol, Olive Branch
AP176

"Over the Waves," by Juventino Rosas
AP177

1972, Oct. 3 Photo. Wmk. 300

C406 AP176 2p gray, bl & blk .40 .15

16th Conference of the Atomic Energy Commission, Mexico City, Sept. 26.

1972, Oct. 16 *Perf. 14*

C407 AP177 80c olive bister .25 .15

28th Intl. Cong. of the Societies of Authors and Composers, Mexico City, Oct. 16-21.

Child with Doll, by Guerrero Galvan, UNICEF Emblem
AP178

1972, Nov. 4

C408 AP178 80c multicolored .75 .20

25th anniv. (in 1971) of UNICEF.

Pedro de Gante, by Rodriguez y Arangorti
AP179

Map of Americas with Tourists' Footprints
AP180

1972, Nov. 22 *Perf. 14*
C409 AP179 2p multicolored .35 .15

Brother Pedro de Gante (Pedro Moor or van der Moere; 1480?-1572), Franciscan brother who founded first school in Mexico, and writer.

Olympic Games Type of Regular Issue, 1972

Designs: 80c, Olympic emblems and stylized soccer game. 2p, Olympic emblems, vert.

1972, Dec. 9 Photo. Wmk. 300
C410 A289 80c green & multi .20 .15
C411 A289 2p yel grn, blk & bl .35 .15
Set value .25

20th Olympic Games, Munich, Aug. 26-Sept. 11.

Anti-pollution Type of Regular Issue

80c, Bird sitting on ornamental capital, vert.

1972, Dec. 16
C412 A291 80c lt blue & blk .25 .20

Anti-pollution campaign.

1972, Dec. 23
C413 AP180 80c black, yel & grn .25 .15

Tourism Year of the Americas.

Mexico #O1, Brazil #992, Colombia #130, Venezuela #22, Peru #C320
AP181

1973, Jan. 19 *Perf. 14*
C414 AP181 80c multicolored .25 .15

4th Interamerican Philatelic Exhibition, EXFILBRA 72, Rio de Janeiro, Brazil, Aug. 26-Sept. 2, 1972.

Aeolus, God of Winds
AP182

1973, Sept. 14 Photo. Wmk. 300
C415 AP182 80c brt pink, blk & bl .60 .20

Cent. of intl. meteorological cooperation.

Nicolaus Copernicus
AP183

San Martin Monument
AP184

Wmk. 300

1973, Oct. 10 Photo. *Perf. 14*
C416 AP183 80c slate green .30 .15

500th anniversary of the birth of Nicolaus Copernicus (1473-1543), Polish astronomer.

Art and Science Type of 1971

Designs: No. C417, Aztec calendar stone. No. C418, Carlos de Sigüenza y Gongora (1645-1700), mathematician, astronomer. No. C419, Francisco Diaz Covarrubias (1833-1889), topographer. No. C420, Joaquin Gallo (1882-1965), geographer, astronomer. No. C421, Luis Enrique Erro (1897-1955), founder of Tonanzintla Observatory.

Imprint includes "1973"

1973, Nov. 21 Wmk. 350
C417 AP161 80c car & sl grn .15 .15
C418 AP161 80c multicolored .15 .15
C419 AP161 80c multicolored .15 .15
C420 AP161 80c multicolored .15 .15
C421 AP161 80c multicolored .15 .15
Nos. C417-C421 (5) .75
Set value .60

Type of 1950-52

Design: Mexico City University Stadium.

Imprint: "Talleres de. Imp. de Est. y Vallores-Mexico"

1973 Unwmk. *Perf. 11*
C422 AP81 80c claret, I 1.25 .95

Fluorescent printing on front or back of stamps consisting of beehive pattern and diagonal inscription.

Wmk. 350

1973, Nov. 9 Photo. *Perf. 14*
C423 AP184 80c orange, indigo & yel .20 .15

Erection of a monument to San Martin in Mexico City, a gift of Argentina.

Palace of Cortes, Cuernavaca
AP185

Wmk. 300

1974, Jan. 18 Litho. *Perf. 14*
C424 AP185 80c black & multi .20 .15

EXMEX 73 Philatelic Exhibition, Cuernavaca, Apr. 7-15.

Gold Brooch, Mochica Culture
AP186

1974, Mar. 6 Photo. Wmk. 300
C425 AP186 80c gold & multi .20 .15

Exhibition of Peruvian gold treasures, Mexico City, 1973-74.

Luggage — AP187

1974, Mar. 22 *Perf. 14*
C426 AP187 80c multicolored .20 .15

16th Convention of the Federation of Latin American Tourist Organizations (COTAL), Acapulco, May 1974.

CEPAL Emblem
AP188

1974, Mar. 22
C427 AP188 80c black & multi .20 .15
a. Red omitted 100.00

25th anniversary (in 1973) of the Economic Commission for Latin America (CEPAL).

"The Enameled Casserole," by Picasso — AP189

1974, Mar. 29 Wmk. 300
C428 AP189 80c multicolored .30 .15

Pablo Ruiz Picasso (1881-1973), painter and sculptor.

EXFILMEX Type of 1974

1974, July 26 *Perf. 13x12*
C429 A305 80c buff, red brn & blk .20 .15

See note after No. 1065.

Biplane — AP190

Perf. 13x12

1974, Aug. 20 Photo. Wmk. 300
C430 AP190 80c shown .15 .15
C431 AP190 2p Jet plane .25 .15
Set value .20

50th anniversary of Mexican Airlines (MEXICANA).

Transmitter and Waves Circling Globe — AP191

1974, Oct. 4 Wmk. 300 *Perf. 14*
C432 AP191 2p multicolored .20 .15

First International Congress of Electric and Electronic Communications, Sept. 17-21.

Volleyball
AP192

1974, Oct. 12 *Perf. 13x12*
C433 AP192 2p orange, bis & blk .20 .15

8th World Volleyball Championship. Perforation holes are of two sizes.

Souvenir Sheet

Mexico #O1, Colombia #130, Venezuela #22, Peru #C320, Brazil #992, Mexico #123 — AP193

Wmk. 300

1974, Oct. 28 Photo. *Imperf.*
C434 AP193 10p multicolored 3.00 1.50

EXFILMEX 74, 5th Inter-American Philatelic Exhibition, Mexico City, Oct. 26-Nov. 3.
Exists with red omitted.

Felipe Carrillo Puerto
AP194

1974, Nov. 8 *Perf. 14*
C435 AP194 80c grn & gldn brn .20 .15

Birth centenary of Felipe Carrillo Puerto (1874-1924), politician and journalist.

Mask, Bat and Catcher's Mitt — AP195

1974, Nov. 29 Wmk. 350 *Perf. 14*
C436 AP195 80c multi .20 .15

Mexican Baseball League, 50th anniversary.

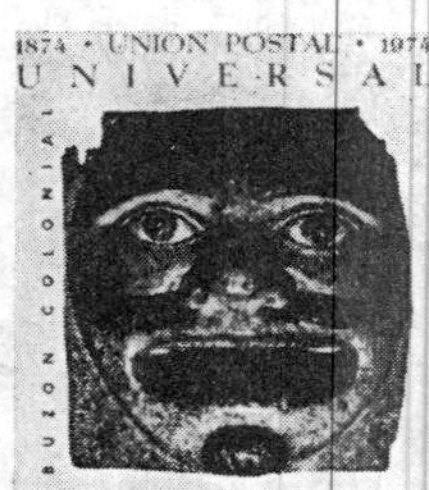

Man's Face, Mailbox, Colonial Period
AP196

Design: 2p, Heinrich von Stephan, contemporary engraving.

1974, Dec. 13 Photo. Wmk. 300

C437	AP196	80c multicolored	.20	.15
C438	AP196	2p green & ocher	.20	.15
		Set value		.25

Centenary of Universal Postal Union.

Art and Science Type of 1971

Designs: No. C439, Mayan mural (8th century), Bonampak, Chiapas. No. C440, First musical score printed in Mexico, 1556. No. C441, Miguel Lerdo de Tejada (1869-1941), composer. No. C442, Silvestre Revueltas (1899-1940), composer (bronze bust). No. C443, Angela Peralta (1845-1883), singer.

Imprint includes "1974"

1974, Dec. 20 Wmk. 300

C439	AP161	80c multi	.15	.15
C440	AP161	80c multi	.15	.15
C441	AP161	80c multi	.15	.15
C442	AP161	80c multi	.15	.15
C443	AP161	80c multi	.15	.15
		Nos. C439-C443 (5)	.75	
		Set value		.60

Types of 1950-56

Designs (as 1950-56 issues): 40c, San Luis Potosi, head. 60c, Leon Guzman and Ignacio Ramirez. 1.60p, Chiapas, Mayan bas-relief. 1.90p, Guerrero, Acapulco waterfront. 4.30p, Oaxaca, dance. 5.20p, Guerrero, view of Taxco. 5.60p, Michoacan, masks. 50p, Valentin Gomez Farias and Melchor Ocampo.

Engraved (40c), Photogravure
Perf. 11 (40c, 1.60p), 14

1975 Wmk. 300

C444	AP81	40c	bluish gray	.25	.15
C445	AP92	60c	yellow grn	.25	.15
C446	AP81	1.60p	red	.90	.15
C447	AP81	1.90p	rose red	.60	.15
C448	AP81	4.30p	ultra	.75	.15
C449	AP81	5.20p	purple	1.10	.40
C450	AP81	5.60p	blue grn	2.25	.50
C451	AP92	50p	dk bl & brick red	13.00	2.50
			Nos. C444-C451 (8)	19.10	4.15

Women's Year Emblem — AP199

1975, Jan. 3 Wmk. 300 *Perf. 14*

C456	AP199	1.60p brt pink & blk	.20	.15

International Women's Year 1975.

Declaration, UN Emblem, Mexican Flag AP200

1975, Feb. 7 Photo. Wmk. 300

C457	AP200	1.60p multi	.15	.15

Declaration of Economic Rights and Duties of Nations.

Balsa Raft "Acali" AP201

1975, Mar. 7 Wmk. 300 *Perf. 14*

C458	AP201	80c multicolored	.20	.15

Trans-Atlantic voyage of the "Acali" from Canary Islands to Yucatan, May-Aug. 1973.

Dr. Miguel Jimenez, by I. Ramirez AP202

Miguel de Cervantes AP203

1975, Mar. 24 Unwmk. *Perf. 14*

C459	AP202	2p multicolored	.20	.15

Fifth World Gastroenterology Congress.

1975, Apr. 26 Photo. Unwmk.

C460	AP203	1.60p bl blk & dk car	.20	.15

Third International Cervantes Festival, Guanajuato, Apr. 26-May 11.

Four-reales Coin, 1675 — AP204

1975, May 2

C461	AP204	1.60p bl, gold & blk	.20	.15

Intl. Numismatic Convention, Mexico City, Mar. 28-30, 1974, and 300th anniv. of 1st coin struck by Mexico City Mint.

Salvador Novo, by Roberto Montenegro AP205

1975, May 9

C462	AP205	1.60p multi	.20	.15

Salvador Novo (1904-1974), author.

Mural, Siqueiros — AP206

1975, May 16

C463	AP206	1.60p multi	.20	.15

David Alfaro Siqueiros (1896-1974), painter.

UN and IWY Emblems AP207

1975, June 19

C464	AP207	1.60p ultra & pink	.20	.15

International Women's Year World Conference, Mexico City, June 19-July 2.

Mexico City Coat of Arms AP208

Unwmk.
1975, Aug. 1 Photo. *Perf. 14*

C465	AP208	1.60p multi	.20	.15

650th anniv. of Tenochtitlan (Mexico City).

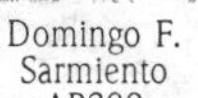
Domingo F. Sarmiento AP209

Teachers' Monument AP210

Unwmk.
1975, Aug. 9 Photo. *Perf. 14*

C466	AP209	1.60p brown & sl grn	.20	.15

1st International Congress of Third World Educators, Acapulco, Aug. 5-9. Domingo Faustino Sarmiento (1811-1888), Argentinian statesman, writer and educator.

1975, Aug. 9

C467	AP210	4.30p green & ocher	.30	.15

Mexican-Lebanese friendship. The monument in Mexico City, by I Naffa al Rozzi, shows Cadmus, a mythical Phoenician, teaching the alphabet.

7th Pan American Games' Emblem AP211

1975, Aug. 29

C468	AP211	1.60p multi	.20	.15

Pan American Games, Mexico City, Oct. 13-26.

Dr. Atl, Self-portrait AP212

Unwmk.
1975, Oct. 3 Photo. *Perf. 14*

C469	AP212	4.30p multi	.30	.15

Geraldo Murillo ("Dr. Atl," 1875-1924), painter and writer, birth centenary.

Globe and Traffic Circle — AP213

1975, Oct. 12

C470	AP213	1.60p bl, blk & gray	.20	.15

15th World Road Congress, Mexico City, Oct. 12-26.

Type of 1950-52

Designs: 40c, San Luis Potosi, head. 80c, Mexico City University stadium. 1p, Puebla, Half Moon dance. 1.60p, Chiapas, Mayan bas-relief. 5p, Queretaro, architecture. 5.60p, Michoacan, masks. 10p, Miguel Hidalgo. 20p, Modern building.

Perf. 11 (40c, 80c, 1p, 1.60p), 14
Engraved (40c, 1p), Photogravure

1975-76 Unwmk.

C471	AP81	40c	bluish gray	.35	.35
C471A	AP92	60c	yellow green	*1,000.*	
C472	AP81	80c	claret, II	.60	.50
C473	AP81	1p	grysh green	1.00	.80
C474	AP81	1.60p	red	1.40	1.00
C476	AP81	5p	dk brn & org ('76)	1.25	1.00
a.			5p dark brown & red orange	2.00	2.00
C477	AP81	5.60p	bluish grn ('76)	4.75	3.25
C479	AP81	10p	black & green	3.50	2.50
C480	AP81	20p	red & dl grn ('76)	6.25	4.00
			Nos. C471,C472-C480 (8)	19.10	13.40

Bicycle and Export Emblem AP214

Designs: Export Emblem and 30c, Copper vase. 80c, Overalls. 1.90p, Oil valves. 2p, Books. 4p, Honey. 4.30p, Strawberry. 5p, Motor vehicles. 5.20p, Farm machinery. 5.60p, Cotton. 20p, Film. 50p, Cotton thread.

1975-82 Unwmk. Photo. *Perf. 14*

C486	AP214	30c copper ('76)	.20	.15
C489	AP214	80c dull blue ('76)	.20	.15
C491	AP214	1.60p black & org	.20	.15
a.		Thin paper ('81)	.30	.15
C492	AP214	1.90p ver & dk grn	.35	.15
C493	AP214	2p ultra & gold ('76)	.50	.15
C495	AP214	4p yel bis & brn ('82)	1.00	.20
C496	AP214	4.30p brt pink & ol	.40	.15
C497	AP214	5p dk bl & ocher ('76)	.50	.20
C498	AP214	5.20p red & blk ('76)	.50	.40
C499	AP214	5.60p yel grn & org ('76)	.20	.20
C503	AP214	20p multi, thin paper ('81)	.75	.20
C508	AP214	50p multi ('82)	3.25	2.00
		Nos. C486-C508 (12)	8.05	4.10

See Nos. C594-C603.

Art and Science Type of 1971

Designs: No. C513, Title page of "Medical History of New Spain," by Francisco Hernandez, 1628. No. C514, Alfonso L. Herrera (1868-1942), biologist. No. C515, Title page, Aztec Herbal, 1552. No. C516, Arturo S. Rosenblueth (1900-1970). No. C517, Alfredo Augusto Duges (1826-1910) French-born naturalist.

Imprint includes "1975"

1975, Nov. 21 Unwmk. *Perf. 14*

C513	AP161	1.60p buff, red & blk	.15	.15
C514	AP161	1.60p vio bl & multi	.15	.15
C515	AP161	1.60p black & multi	.15	.15
C516	AP161	1.60p gray & multi	.15	.15
C517	AP161	1.60p green & multi	.15	.15
		Nos. C513-C517 (5)	.75	
		Set value		.25

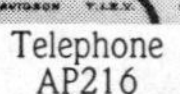

Telephone
AP216

60-peso Gold Coin, Oaxaca, 1917
AP217

1976, Mar. 10 **Photo.**
C518 AP216 1.60p gray & blk .20 .15

Centenary of first telephone call by Alexander Graham Bell, Mar. 10, 1876.

1976, Mar. 25 **Photo.** **Unwmk.**
C519 AP217 1.60p black, ocher & yel .20 .15

4th International Numismatic Convention, Mexico City, March 1976.

Rain God Tlaloc and Calles Dam
AP218

1976, Mar. 29 ***Perf. 14***
C520 AP218 1.60p vio brn & dk grn .20 .15

12th International Great Dams Congress, Mar. 29-Apr. 2.

Perforation Gauge
AP219

1976, May 7 **Photo.** **Unwmk.**
C521 AP219 1.60p blk, red & bl .20 .15

Interphil 76 International Philatelic Exhibition, Philadelphia, Pa., May 29-June 6.

Rainbow over City — AP220

1976, May 31 **Unwmk.** ***Perf. 14***
C522 AP220 1.60p black & multi .20 .15

Habitat, UN Conf. on Human Settlements, Vancouver, Canada, May 31-June 11.

Liberty Bell
AP221

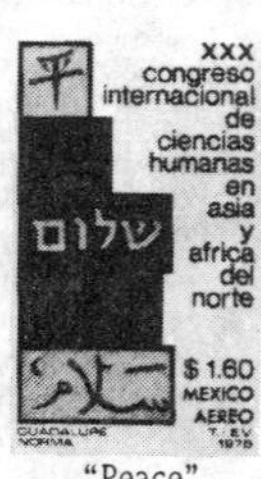

"Peace"
AP222

1976, July 4 **Photo.** ***Perf. 14***
C523 AP221 1.60p ultra & red .20 .15

American Bicentennial.

1976, Aug. 3 **Photo.** ***Perf. 14***

Design: "Peace" written in Chinese, Japanese, Hebrew, Hindi and Arabic.

C524 AP222 1.60p multi .20 .15

30th Intl. Cong. of Science and Humanities of Asia and North Africa, Mexico, Aug. 3-8.

Television Screen
AP223

1976, Aug. 24 **Photo.** **Unwmk.**
C525 AP223 1.60p multi .20 .15

1st Latin-American Forum on Children's Television.

Luminescence

Fluorescent airmail stamps include Nos. C265, C265c, C288, C357-C358, C390-C415, C422-C423.

Airmail stamps issued on both ordinary and fluorescent paper include Nos. C220, C220D-C220E, C220G-C220H, C265b, C266-C268, C286.

Sky, Sun, Water and Earth
AP224

1976, Nov. 8 **Photo.** ***Perf. 14***
C526 AP224 1.60p multi .20 .15

World Conservation Day.

Art and Science Type of 1971

Designs: No. C527, Coatlicue, Mother of Earth, Aztec sculpture. No. C528, El Caballito, statue of Charles IV of Spain, by Manuel Tolsá. No. C529, Chief Tlahuicole, bronze statue by Manuel Vilar. No. C530, Today's God, Money, seated ceramic figure, by L. Ortiz Monasterio. No. C531, Signal, abstract sculpture by Angela Gurria.

Imprint includes "1976"

1976, Dec. 10 **Photo.** ***Perf. 14***

C527	AP161	1.60p	black & yel	.15	.15
C528	AP161	1.60p	black & red brn	.15	.15
C529	AP161	1.60p	black & multi	.15	.15
C530	AP161	1.60p	carmine & multi	.15	.15
C531	AP161	1.60p	carmine & blk	.15	.15
			Nos. C527-C531 (5)	.75	
			Set value		.25

Score for El Pesebre by Casals
AP225

1976, Dec. 29
C532 AP225 4.30p lt bl, blk & brn .35 .15

Pablo Casals (1876-1973), cellist and composer, birth centenary.

Mankind Destroyed by Nuclear Power
AP226

1977, Feb. 14 **Photo.** ***Perf. 14***
C533 AP226 1.60p multi .20 .15
a. Wmk. 300 50.00 40.00

10th anniv. of the Agreement of Tlatelolco, banning nuclear arms in Latin America.

Soccer
AP227

Anniversary Emblem
AP228

1977, Aug. 23 **Wmk. 300** ***Perf. 14***
C534 AP227 1.60p multicolored .20 .15
C535 AP228 4.30p black, bl & yel .30 .15

Mexican Soccer Fed., 50th anniv.

Hands and Scales
AP229

1977, Sept. 28 **Photo.** ***Perf. 14***
C536 AP229 1.60p org, brn & blk .20 .15

Federal Council of Reconciliation and Arbitration, 50th anniversary.

Arms of Mexico and Spain
AP230

1.90p, Maps of Mexico & Spain. 4.30p, Pres. José Lopez Portillo & King Juan Carlos.

1977, Oct. 8 ***Perf. 14***

C537	AP230	1.60p	dull bl & blk	.20	.15
C538	AP230	1.90p	lt grn & maroon	.25	.15
C539	AP230	4.30p	tan, grn & brn	.25	.15
			Nos. C537-C539 (3)	.70	.45

Resumption of diplomatic relations with Spain.

Tlaloc, the Rain God
AP231

Ludwig van Beethoven
AP232

Wmk. 300

1977, Nov. 4 **Photo.** ***Perf. 14***
C540 AP231 1.60p multi .20 .15

National Central Observatory, centenary.

1977, Nov. 12 **Photo.**
C541 AP232 1.60p brt grn & brn .15 .15
C542 AP232 4.30p lilac rose & bl .25 .15

Tractor and Dam
AP233

1977, Nov. 25 **Photo.** ***Perf. 14***
C543 AP233 1.60p multi .20 .15

United Nations Desertification Conference.

Mexico City-Cuernavaca Highway — AP234

1977, Nov. 30
C544 AP234 1.60p multi .20 .15

25th anniversary of first national highway.

Arms of Campeche — AP235

1977, Dec. 3
C545 AP235 1.60p multi .20 .15

200th anniv. of the naming of Campeche.

Congress Emblem
AP236

1977, Dec. 9
C546 AP236 1.60p multi .20 .15

20th World Congress for Education, Hygiene and Recreation, July 18-24, 1977.

Freighter Navimex
AP237

1977, Dec. 16
C547 AP237 1.60p multi .20 .15

60th anniv. of National Merchant Marine.

Mayan Dancer, Jaina — AP238

Pre-Columbian Sculptures: No. C549, Aztec dance god. No. C550, Snake dancer, bas-relief. No. C551, Monte Alban, bas relief. No. C552, Totonaca figurine.

1977, Dec. 26 ***Perf. 14***

C548	AP238	1.60p	sal, blk & car	.15	.15
C549	AP238	1.60p	lt & dk bl & blk	.15	.15
C550	AP238	1.60p	yel, blk & gray	.15	.15
C551	AP238	1.60p	bl grn, blk & grn	.15	.15
C552	AP238	1.60p	gray, blk & red brn	.15	.15
			Nos. C548-C552 (5)	.75	
			Set value		.25

Mexican art.

Tumor Clinic, by David A. Siqueiros — AP239

4.30p, La Raza Medical Center, by Diego Rivera.

1978, Jan. 19 Photo. Wmk. 300

C553 AP239	1.60p multi		.20	.15
C554 AP239	4.30p multi		.30	.15

Mexican Social Security Institute, 35th anniv.

Moorish Fountain — AP240

1978, Mar. 1 Photo. *Perf. 14*

C555 AP240	1.60p multi	.20	.15

Founding of Chiapa de Corzo, Chiapas, 450th anniv.

Oil Industry Type of 1978

Designs: 1.60p, Gen. Lazaro Cardenas. 4.30p, Offshore oil rig.

Wmk. 300

1978, Mar. 18 Photo. *Perf. 14*

C556 A343	1.60p brt bl & lil rose	.20	.15
C557 A343	4.30p bl, brt bl & blk	.30	.15

Oil industry nationalization, 40th anniv.

Arms of Diego de Mazariegos AP241

Wmk. 300

1978, Apr. 3 Photo. *Perf. 14*

C558 AP241	1.60p pink, blk & pur	.20	.15

400th anniversary of the founding of San Cristobal de las Casas, Chiapas, by Diego de Mazariegos.

Blood Pressure Gauge, Map of Mexico AP242

Globe, Snake, Hand Holding Stethoscope AP243

1978, Apr. 30

C559 AP242	1.60p dk bl & car	.20	.15
C560 AP243	4.30p org & dk bl	.30	.15

Drive against hypertension and World Health Day.

X-ABC1 Plane AP244

1978, Mar. 15

C561 AP244	1.60p ultra & multi	.20	.15
C562 AP244	4.30p ultra & multi	.30	.15

1st Mexican airmail route, 50th anniv.

Globe, Cogwheel, UN Emblem — AP245

4.30p, Globe, flags, cogwheel, UN emblem.

1978, Apr. 21

C563 AP245	1.60p multi	.20	.15
C564 AP245	4.30p multi	.30	.15

World Conference on Technical Cooperation of Underdeveloped Countries.

Soccer — AP246

Designs: 1.90p, Goalkeeper catching ball. 4.30p, Soccer player.

Wmk. 300

1978, June 1 Photo. *Perf. 14*

C565 AP246	1.60p multi	.15	.15
C566 AP246	1.90p multi	.15	.15
C567 AP246	4.30p multi	.30	.15
	Nos. C565-C567 (3)	.60	.45

11th World Cup Soccer Championship, Argentina, June 1-25.

Francisco (Pancho) Villa AP247

1978, June 5

C568 AP247	1.60p multi	.20	.15

Pancho Villa (1878-1923), revolutionary leader.

Mexico No. C6, Independence Monument, Washington Monument — A248

1978, June 11

C569 AP248	1.60p ol gray & red	.20	.15

50th anniversary of flight Mexico to Washington by Emilio Carranza (1905-1928).

Woman and Calendar Stone — AP249

Wmk. 300

1978, July 15 Photo. *Perf. 14*

C570 AP249	1.60p rose, blk & brn	.20	.15
C571 AP249	1.90p brt grn, blk & brn	.20	.15
C572 AP249	4.30p org, blk & brn	.30	.15
	Nos. C570-C572 (3)	.70	.45

Miss Universe contest, Acapulco, July 1978.

Alvaro Obregón AP250

1978, July 17

C573 AP250	1.60p multi	.20	.15

Obregón (1880-1928), president of Mexico.

Geographical Institute Type of 1978

Institute emblem in different arrangements.

1978, July 21 Photo. Wmk. 300

C574 A344	1.60p emerald & blk	.20	.15
C575 A344	4.30p ocher & blk	.30	.15

Pan-American Institute for Geography and History, 50th anniversary.

Sun Rising over Ciudad Obregón AP251

1978, Aug. 4 *Perf. 14*

C576 AP251	1.60p multi	.20	.15

Founding of the city of Obregón, 50th anniv.

Mayan Figure, Castle and Pawn — AP252

Aristotle (384-322 B.C.), Philosopher — AP253

1978, Aug. 19 Photo. *Perf. 14*

C577 AP252	1.60p multi	.20	.15
C578 AP252	4.30p multi	.30	.15

World Youth Team Chess Championship, Ajedrez, Aug. 19-Sept. 7.

1978, Aug. 25

Design: 4.30p, Statue of Aristotle.

C579 AP253	1.60p multi	.20	.15
C580 AP253	4.30p multi	.30	.15

Mule Deer AP254

Man's Head, Dove, UN Emblem AP255

1978, Sept. 8 Photo. Wmk. 300

C581 AP254	1.60p shown	.20	.15
C582 AP254	1.60p Ocelot	.30	.15
	Set value		.25

Protected animals.

1978, Sept. 22 *Perf. 14*

4.30p, Woman's head, dove, UN emblem.

C583 AP255	1.60p ver, gray & blk	.20	.15
C584 AP255	4.30p lil, gray & blk	.30	.15

Anti-Apartheid Year.

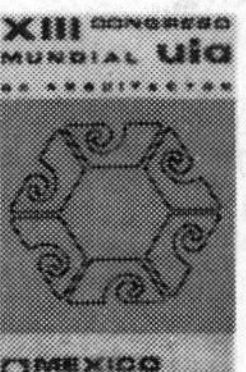

Emblem — AP256

Wmk. 300

1978, Oct. 23 Photo. *Perf. 14*

C585 AP256	1.60p multi	.20	.15

13th Congress of International Union of Architects, Mexico City, Oct. 23-27.

Dr. Rafael Lucio (1819-1886) AP257

Franz Schubert, "Death and the Maiden" AP258

1978, Nov. 13 Wmk. 350

C586 AP257	1.60p yellow grn	.20	.15

11th International Anti-Leprosy Congress.

1978, Nov. 19 Photo. *Perf. 14*

C587 AP258	4.30p brn, grn & blk	.30	.15

Schubert (1797-1828), Austrian composer.

Children, Christmas Decorations AP259

Antonio Vivaldi AP260

Wmk. 350

1978, Nov. 22 Photo. *Perf. 14*

C588 AP259 1.60p multi .20 .15

Christmas 1978.

1978, Dec. 1

C589 AP260 4.30p multi .30 .15

Antonio Vivaldi (1675-1741), Italian violinist and composer.

Wright Brothers' Flyer AP261

Design: 4.30p, Flyer, different view.

1978, Dec. 17

C590 AP261 1.60p multi .20 .15
C591 AP261 4.30p multi .30 .15

75th anniversary of 1st powered flight.

Einstein and his Equation AP262

Wmk. 300

1979, Apr. 20 Photo. *Perf. 14*

C592 AP262 1.60p multi .20 .15

Albert Einstein (1879-1955), theoretical physicist.

Rowland Hill — AP263

1979, Apr. 27

C593 AP263 1.60p multi .20 .15

Sir Rowland Hill (1795-1879), originator of penny postage.

Export Type of 1975

Designs: Export Emblem and 50c, Circuit board. 1.60p, Bicycle. 1.90p, Oil valves. 2.50p, Tomato. 4p, Honey. 5p, Motor vehicles. 10p, Citrus fruit. 50p, Cotton thread.

1979-81 Photo. Wmk. 300

C594 AP214	50c	ocher & red brn	.15	.15
C596 AP214	1.60p	black & org	.35	.15
C597 AP214	1.90p	ver & dk grn ('81)	.45	.40
C599 AP214	2.50p	ver & grn	.15	.15
C600 AP214	4p	yel bis & brn ('81)	.35	.25
C601 AP214	5p	dk bl & dl org	4.00	.50
C602 AP214	10p	grn & yel grn ('81)	.75	.75
C603 AP214	50p	multicolored	5.00	1.50
		Nos. C594-C603 (8)	11.20	3.85

No. C600 exists with brown omitted.

Children, Child's Drawing — AP264

1979, May 16

C604 AP264 1.60p multi .15 .15

International Year of the Child.

Registered Letter from Mexico to Rome, 1880 — AP265

Wmk. 300

1979, June 7 Photo. *Perf. 14*

C605 AP265 1.60p multi .15 .15

MEPSIPEX '79, 3rd Intl. Exhibition of Elmhurst Philatelic Society, Mexico City, June 7-10.

Sports Type of 1979

Designs: 1.60p, Games emblem. 4.30p, Symbolic flame and birds. 10p, Women gymnasts, horiz.

1979, June 15

C606 A348 1.60p multi .20 .15
C607 A348 4.30p multi .30 .15

Souvenir Sheet

Imperf

C608 A348 10p multi 1.00

No. C608 has simulated perforations.

University Type of 1979

Paintings: 1.60p, The Return of Quetzalcoatl, by Chavez Morado. 4.30p, Students Reaching for Culture, by Alfaro Siqueiros.

1979, July 10 *Perf. 14*

C609 A350 1.60p multi .15 .15
C610 A350 4.30p multi .30 .15

Messenger and UPU Emblem AP266

1979, July 27 Photo. Wmk. 300

C611 AP266 1.60p multi .20 .15

Cent. of Mexico's membership in UPU.

Sports Type of 1979

1979, Sept. 2 Wmk. 300 *Perf. 14*

C612 A352 1.60p Tennis .15 .15
C613 A352 5.50p Swimming .30 .15

Souvenir Sheet

Imperf

C614 A352 10p Varios sports 1.10

Tourism Type of 1979

Designs: No. C615, Agua Azul Waterfall, Chiapas. No. C616, King Coliman statue, Colima.

Wmk. 300

1979, Sept. 28 Photo. *Perf. 14*

C615 A353 1.60p multi .20 .15
C616 A353 1.60p multi .20 .15
Set value .25

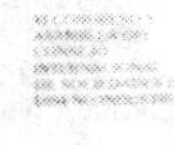

Graphic Design AP267

1979, Oct. 14 Photo. Wmk. 300

C617 AP267 1.60p multi .20 .15

ICSID, 11th Congress and Assembly of the Intl. Industrial Design Council, Oct. 1979.

Mail Service Type of 1979

Designs: 1.60p, Martin Enriquez de Almanza, Viceroy of New Spain. 5.50p, King Philip II of Spain. 10p, Sailing ship, horiz.

1979

C618 A354 1.60p multi .15 .15
C619 A354 5.50p multi .30 .20

Souvenir Sheet

Imperf

C620 A354 10p multi 3.00 1.25

#C620 contains stamp with simulated perfs.

Early Lamp — AP268

1979, Oct. 21 Wmk. 300

C621 AP268 1.60p multi .20 .15

Centenary of invention of electric light.

Union Emblem AP269

Wmk. 300

1979, Nov. 12 Photo. *Perf. 14*

C622 AP269 1.60p multi .20 .15

Latin American Universities Union, 8th general assembly.

Christmas Type of 1979

Design: 1.60p, Girl and Christmas tree.

1979, Nov. 15

C623 A355 1.60p multi .20 .15

Moon Symbol from Mexican Codex AP270

1979, Nov. 30

C624 AP270 2.50p multi .20 .15

Apollo 11 moon landing, 10th anniversary.

Monument Type of 1980

Stone Sculptures: 1.60p, Tlaloc, water god. 5.50p, Coyolxauqui, goddess.

1980, Feb. 16 Photo. *Perf. 14*

C625 A356 1.60p multi .20 .15
C626 A356 5.50p multi .30 .20

16th Century Church, Acolman AP271

16th Century Churches in: No. C628, Actopan Convent. No. C629, Tlayacapan. No. C630, Yanhuitlan. No. C631, Yuriria. No. C628 actually shows Tlayacapan; No. C629, Actopan convent (inscriptions reversed).

1980

C627 AP271 1.60p multi .15 .15
C628 AP271 1.60p multi .15 .15
C629 AP271 1.60p multi .15 .15
C630 AP271 1.60p multi .15 .15
C631 AP271 1.60p multi .15 .15
Nos. C627-C631 (5) .75
Set value .60

Flora and Fauna Types of 1980

1980, Mar. 8 *Perf. 14*

C632 A357 1.60p Flamingo .15 .15
C633 A358 1.60p Vanilla plant .15 .15
Set value .25

Jules Verne AP272

Wmk. 300

1980, Mar. 24 Photo. *Perf. 14*

C634 AP272 5.50p blk & red brn .30 .15

Jules Verne (1828-1905) French science fiction writer.

Skeleton Smoking Cigar, UN Emblem AP273

1980, Apr. 7 *Perf. 14*

C635 AP273 1.60p multi .20 .15

World Health Day/Fight against cigarette smoking.

Costume Type

1980, Apr. 26 *Perf. 14*

C636 A359 1.60p Chiapaneca, Chiapas .20 .15

Items inscribed "MEXICO" and "correo aereo" picturing Emiliano Zapata are not postage stamps.

AIR POST OFFICIAL STAMPS

Nos. C4 and C3 Overprinted in Black or Red **OFICIAL.**

1929 Wmk. 156 *Perf. 12*

CO1 AP1 25c dk grn & gray brn		3.00	3.25
a.	Without period	11.00	11.00
CO2 AP1 25c dk grn & gray brn (R)		2.75	3.75
a.	Without period	13.00	15.00
CO2B AP1 25c brn car & gray brn		7.75	9.50
c.	Without period	17.50	20.00
	Nos. CO1-CO2B (3)	13.50	16.50

Types of Regular Issue of 1926 Overprinted in Red **HABILITADO Servicio Oficial Aereo**

1929, Oct. 15 Unwmk.

CO3	A90	2c black	50.00	60.00
CO4	A91	4c black	50.00	60.00
CO5	A90	5c black	50.00	60.00
CO6	A91	10c black	50.00	60.00
CO7	A92	20c black	50.00	60.00
CO8	A92	30c black	50.00	60.00
CO9	A92	40c black	50.00	60.00
		Nos. CO3-CO9 (7)	350.00	420.00

Horizontal Overprint

CO10 A93 1p black *1,500. 1,500.*

#CO3-CO9 also exist with overprint reading up.

No. C26 Overprinted in Black **OFICIAL.**

1930 **Wmk. 156**

CO11 AP4 20c black violet .85 *1.40*
- *a.* Without period 13.00 *15.00*
- *b.* Inverted overprint 11.00 *15.00*
- *c.* As "a." inverted overprint 140.00

No. CO11 with red overprint is believed not to have been issued for postal purposes.

Plane over Mexico City OA1

1930 **Engr.**

CO12 OA1 20c gray black 5.00 5.00
CO13 OA1 35c lt violet .95 *1.65*
CO14 OA1 40c ol brn & dp bl 1.10 *1.50*
CO15 OA1 70c vio & ol gray 1.10 *1.65*
Nos. CO12-CO15 (4) 8.15 *9.80*

No. CO12 Surcharged in Red

HABILITADO
Quince centavos

1931

CO16 OA1 15c on 20c .70 *1.10*
- *a.* Inverted surcharge 140.00
- *b.* Double surcharge 140.00

No. C20 Overprinted **OFICIAL.**

1932 ***Rouletted 13, 13½***

CO17 AP3 5c light blue .70 *.80*

Air Post Stamps of 1927-32 Overprinted

SERVICIO OFICIAL

On No. C1a

1932 **Unwmk.** ***Perf. 12***

CO18 AP1 50c dk bl & cl 900.00 900.00

On Nos. C2, C2a
Wmk. 156

CO19 AP1 50c dk bl & red brn 1.10 *1.40*
- *a.* 50c dark blue & claret 1.40 *1.65*

See note after No. C2.

On Nos. C11 and C12

1932 ***Perf. 12***

CO20 AP3 10c violet 17.00 20.00
CO21 AP3 15c carmine 250.00 275.00

On Nos. C21 to C23
Rouletted 13, 13½

CO22 AP3 10c violet .30 *.45*
CO23 AP3 15c carmine 1.10 *1.50*
CO24 AP3 20c brn olive 1.10 *1.50*

Nos. C20, C21 C23 and C25 Overprinted **SERVICIO OFICIAL**

1933-34 ***Rouletted 13½***

CO25 AP3 5c light blue .30 *.45*
CO26 AP3 10c violet ('34) .30 *.65*
CO27 AP3 20c brown olive .55 *.85*
CO28 AP3 50c red brn ('34) .70 *1.65*

On No. C2
Perf. 12

CO29 AP1 50c dk bl & red brn 1.10 *1.50*
- *a.* 50c dark blue & claret 1.65 *2.25*

On No. C11
Perf. 12

CO30 AP3 10c violet ('34) 110.00 *140.00*
- *a.* Double overprint *325.00*

Forgeries exist.

SPECIAL DELIVERY STAMPS

Motorcycle Postman SD1

1919 **Unwmk.** **Engr.** ***Perf. 12***

E1 SD1 20c red & black 60.00 2.75

1923 **Wmk. 156**

E2 SD1 20c blk car & blk .30 .25

For overprint see No. E7

Toltec Messenger with Quipu — SD2

1934

E3 SD2 10c brn red & blue .30 .50

Indian Archer — SD3

Imprint: "Oficina Impresora de Hacienda Mexico."

1934 ***Perf. 10x10½***

E4 SD3 10c black violet 1.50 .50

See Nos. E5-E6, E8-E9.

Redrawn

Imprint: "Talleres de Imp. de Est. y Valores-Mexico."

1938-41 **Photo.** ***Perf. 14***

E5 SD3 10c slate violet .75 .25
- *a.* Unwatermarked 50.00

E6 SD3 20c orange red ('41) .50 .15

Imperforate copies of No. E6 were not regularly issued.

No. E2 Overprinted "1940" in Violet

1940 **Engr.** ***Perf. 12***

E7 SD1 20c red & black .40 .20

Catalogue values for unused stamps in this section, from this point to the end of the section, are for Never Hinged items.

Redrawn Archer Type of 1941

1944-47 **Wmk. 272** **Photo.** ***Perf. 14***

E8 SD3 20c orange red 1.40 .25

Wmk. 279

E9 SD3 20c orange red ('47) 1.75 .25

Special Delivery Messenger SD4

Messengers' Hands Transferring Letter — SD5

1950-51 **Photo.** **Wmk. 279**

E10 SD4 25c bright red .35 .15
E11 SD5 60c dk bl grn ('51) 2.00 .95

Redrawn

1951

E12 SD4 25c bright red 35.00 5.00

Sharper Impression, heavier shading; motorcycle sidecar ½mm from "s" of "centavos;" imprint wider, beginning under "n" of "inmediata."

Second Redrawing

1952

E13 SD4 25c bright red 10.00 2.00

Design 35½mm wide (33mm on Nos. E10 and E12); finer lettering at left, and height of letters in imprint reduced 50 per cent; three distinct lines in tires.

Redrawn Type of 1951

1954 **Wmk. 300**

E14 SD4 25c red orange .45 .15

Type of 1951

1954

E15 SD5 60c dk blue grn .55 *1.10*

Hands and Pigeon — SD6

Plane Circling Globe — SD7

1956 **Wmk. 300** **Photo.** ***Perf. 14***

E16 SD6 35c red lilac .25 .15
E17 SD7 80c henna brown .35 *1.40*

1962

E18 SD6 50c green .80 .15
E19 SD7 1.20p dark purple 1.25 *1.40*

1964 **Wmk. 350**

E20 SD6 50c green .65 .15
E21 SD7 1.20p dk purple 1.40 1.00

1973 **Unwmk.**

E22 SD6 50c green 3.50 3.25

Fluorescent printing on front or back consists of beehive pattern and diagonal inscription.

1975 **Wmk. 300**

E23 SD6 2p orange .20 *1.00*
E24 SD7 5p vio bl 1.25 .90

1976 **Unwmk.**

E25 SD6 2p red org .25 .40
E26 SD7 5p dk vio bl .35 1.00

Watch — SD8

1976 **Unwmk.** **Photo.** ***Perf. 14***

E27 SD8 2p org & blk .15 *1.00*

INSURED LETTER STAMPS

Insured Letters — IL1

Registered Mailbag — IL2

Safe — IL3

1935 **Engr.** **Wmk. 156** ***Perf. 10½***

G1 IL1 10c vermilion 1.75 .75
- *a.* Perf. 10x10½

G2 IL2 50c dk bl 1.25 .60
G3 IL3 1p turq grn 1.25 .85
Nos. G1-G3 (3) 4.25 2.20

Nos. G1 and G4 were issued both with and without imprint.

Catalogue values for unused stamps in this section, from this point to the end of the section, are for Never Hinged items.

1944-45 **Wmk. 272** ***Perf. 10x10½***

G4 IL1 10c ver ('45) 9.50 1.50
G5 IL2 50c dk bl 1.40 .50
G6 IL3 1p turq grn 2.50 .65
Nos. G4-G6 (3) 13.40 2.65

1947 **Wmk. 279** ***Perf. 10x10½***

G7 IL1 10c vermilion 8.00 .85
G8 IL2 50c dark blue 10.00 1.50
G9 IL3 1p turq grn 3.50 1.00
Nos. G7-G9 (3) 21.50 3.35

Vault — IL4

1950-51 **Photo.** ***Perf. 14***

G10 IL4 20c blue 2.00 .45
G11 IL4 40c purple .30 .20
G12 IL4 1p yel grn ('51) .65 .50
G13 IL4 5p dk bl & gray grn ('51) 1.00 1.00
G14 IL4 10p car & ultra ('51) 4.00 4.00
Nos. G10-G14 (5) 7.95 6.15

1954-71 **Wmk. 300**

G15 IL4 20c blue ('56) .20 .15
G16 IL4 40c lt pur ('56) .20 .15
G17 IL4 1p yel grn .30 .20
- *a.* Size: 37x20½mm ('71) 1.10 1.10

G18 IL4 5p bl & grn ('59) 1.00 1.00
G19 IL4 10p car & ultra ('63) 4.75 2.50
Nos. G15-G19 (5) 6.45 4.00

No. G17 measures 35x19½mm. Vertical measurement excludes imprint.

1967 **Wmk. 350** ***Perf. 14***

G21 IL4 40c light purple 1.25 1.50
G22 IL4 1p yellow green 1.25 1.50

1975 **Photo.** **Wmk. 300**

G23 IL4 2p lilac rose .30 .30
G24 IL4 20p orange & gray 1.80 3.00

Padlock — IL5

1976-81 **Unwmk.** **Photo.** ***Perf. 14***

G25 IL5 40c black & blue .15 .15
G26 IL5 1p black & blue .15 .15
G26A IL5 2p blk & bl ('81) .15 .15
G27 IL5 5p black & blue .15 .15
G28 IL5 10p black & blue .15 .15
G28A IL5 20p black & blue .30 .30
Set value .65 .65

1979 **Photo.** **Wmk. 300**

G29 IL5 40c black & blue .15 .40
G30 IL5 1p black & blue .15 .20
G31 IL5 5p black & blue .15 .40
G32 IL5 10p black & blue .15 .20
G33 IL5 20p black & blue .50 .65
Nos. G29-G33 (5) 1.10 1.85

Perf. 14½x14

1983-86 Photo. Unwmk.

Size of Lock: 20x31mm

G36 IL5 5p black & blue .45 .40
G37 IL5 10p black & blue .45 .40
G38 IL5 20p black & blue .80 .80
G39 IL5 50p black & blue 1.50 1.50
G40 IL5 100p blk & bl ('86) 1.00 1.00
Nos. G36-G40 (5) 4.20 4.10

This is an expanding set. Numbers will change if necessary.

POSTAGE DUE STAMPS

D1

1908 Engr. Wmk. 155 *Perf. 14*

J1 D1 1c blue 1.00 *3.00*
J2 D1 2c blue 1.00 *3.00*
J3 D1 4c blue 1.00 *3.00*
J4 D1 5c blue 1.00 *3.00*
J5 D1 10c blue 1.00 *3.00*
Nos. J1-J5 (5) 5.00 *15.00*

For overprints and surcharges see Nos. 381-385, 434-438, 466-470, 495-499, 593-607.

PORTE DE MAR STAMPS

These stamps were used to indicate the amount of cash to be paid to the captains of the mail steamers taking outgoing foreign mail.

PM2

PM3

1875 Unwmk. Litho. *Imperf.*

JX9 PM2 2c black .60 *50.00*
a. "5" added to make 25c 12.00 *100.00*
JX10 PM2 10c black .80 *30.00*
JX11 PM2 12c black .80 *50.00*
JX12 PM2 20c black 1.00 *50.00*
JX13 PM2 25c black 3.25 *50.00*
JX14 PM2 35c black 3.25 *60.00*
JX15 PM2 50c black 3.00 *60.00*
JX16 PM2 60c black 3.00 *75.00*
JX17 PM2 75c black 3.50 *75.00*
JX18 PM2 85c black 3.25 *100.00*
JX19 PM2 100c black 4.00 *100.00*
Nos. JX9-JX19 (11) 26.45

Same, Numerals Larger

JX20 PM2 5c black 1.00 *50.00*
JX21 PM2 25c black 1.65 *50.00*
JX22 PM2 35c black 175.00
JX23 PM2 50c black 1.00 *50.00*
JX24 PM2 60c black 65.00
JX25 PM2 100c black .60 *100.00*
Nos. JX20-JX25 (6) 244.25

In Nos. JX9-JX19 the figures of value are 7mm high and "CENTAVOS" is 7½mm long. On Nos. JX20-JX25 the figures of value are 8mm high and "CENTAVOS" is 9½mm long.

Nos. JX9-JX25 exist with overprints of district names.

Counterfeits exist of Nos. JX9-JX31.

1879

JX26 PM3 2c brown .50
JX27 PM3 5c yellow .50
JX28 PM3 10c red .50
JX29 PM3 25c blue .50
JX30 PM3 50c green .50
JX31 PM3 100c violet .50
Nos. JX26-JX31 (6) 3.00

Nos. JX26-JX31 were never put in use.

Nos. JX26-JX31 were printed on paper watermarked "ADMINISTRACION GENERAL DE CORREOS MEXICO." Approximately ¾ of the stamps do not show any of the watermark.

Stamps of this design were never issued. Copies appeared on the market in 1884. Value, set, $22.

All were printed in same sheet of 49 (7x7). Sheet consists of 14 of 10c; 7 each of 25c, 35c, 50c; 4 each of 60c, 85c; 3 each of 75c, 100c. There are four varieties of 10c, two of 25c, 35c and 50c.

OFFICIAL STAMPS

Hidalgo — O1

Wove or Laid Paper

1884-93 Unwmk. Engr. *Perf. 12*

O1 O1 red .70 .50
a. Vert. pair, imperf. betwn. 90.00
O1B O1 scarlet ('85) .70 .50
O2 O1 olive brn ('87) .45 .30
a. Blue ruled lines on paper
O3 O1 orange ('88) 1.25 .45
a. Vert. pair, imperf. betwn. 80.00
b. Perf. 11 10.00 8.00
O4 O1 blue grn ('93) .70 .40
a. Imperf., pair 10.00 8.00
b. Perf. 11 10.00 8.00
Nos. O1-O4 (5) 3.80 2.15

Pin-perf. 6

O5 O1 olive brown ('87) 40.00 16.00

Wmk. "Correos E U M" on every Vertical Line of Ten Stamps (152)

1894 *Perf. 5½*

O6 O1 ultra 1.50 1.40
a. Vert. pair, imperf. horiz. 30.00
b. Imperf., pair 40.00

Perf. 11, 12

O7 O1 ultra .90 .80

Perf. 5½x11, 11x5½

O9 O1 ultra 6.00 4.00
Nos. O6-O9 (3) 8.40 6.20

Regular Issues with Handstamped Overprint in Black **OFICIAL**

1895 *Perf. 12*

O10 A20 1c green 9.00 3.00
O11 A20 2c carmine 10.00 3.00
O12 A20 3c orange brn 9.00 3.00
O13 A21 4c red orange 13.00 6.00
a. 4c orange 21.00 7.00
O14 A22 5c ultra 18.00 6.00
O15 A23 10c lilac rose 16.00 1.50
O16 A21 12c olive brn 35.00 15.00
O17 A23 15c brt blue 21.00 9.00
O18 A23 20c brown rose 21.00 9.00
O19 A23 50c purple 45.00 21.00
O20 A24 1p brown 100.00 45.00
O21 A24 5p scarlet 275.00 125.00
O22 A24 10p deep blue 450.00 250.00
Nos. O10-O22 (13) 1,022. 496.50

Similar stamps with red overprint were not officially placed in use.

Black Overprint

1896-97 Wmk. 153

O23 A20 1c green 30.00 5.00
O24 A20 2c carmine 30.00 6.00
O25 A20 3c orange brn 30.00 6.00
O26 A21 4c red orange 30.00 6.00
a. 4c orange 37.50 11.00
O27 A22 5c ultra 30.00 6.00
O28 A21 12c olive brn 40.00 15.00
O29 A23 15c brt blue 52.50 22.50
O29A A23 50c purple 400.00 400.00
Nos. O23-O29A (8) 642.50 466.50

Black Overprint

1897 Wmk. 154

O30 A20 1c green 52.50 15.00
O31 A20 2c scarlet 45.00 18.00
O33 A21 4c orange 70.00 30.00
O34 A22 5c ultra 52.50 18.00
O35 A21 12c olive brn 70.00 21.00
O36 A23 15c brt blue 90.00 21.00
O37 A23 20c brown rose 60.00 9.00
O38 A23 50c purple 75.00 15.00
O39 A24 1p brown 190.00 60.00
Nos. O30-O39 (9) 705.00 207.00

Black Overprint

1898 Unwmk.

O40 A20 1c green 18.00 4.50
O41 A20 2c scarlet 18.00 4.50
O42 A20 3c orange brn 18.00 4.50
O43 A21 4c orange 30.00 6.00
O44 A22 5c ultra 30.00 10.00
O45 A23 10c lilac rose 400.00 250.00
O46 A21 12c olive brn 65.00 15.00
O47 A23 15c brt blue 65.00 15.00
O48 A23 20c brown rose 110.00 37.50
O48A A23 50c purple 190.00 75.00
O48B A24 10p deep blue —
Nos. O40-O48A (10) 944.00 422.00

Black Overprint

1900 Wmk. 155 *Perf. 14, 15*

O49 A25 1c green 19.00 1.25
O50 A26 2c vermilion 25.00 2.00
O51 A27 3c yellow brn 25.00 1.25
O52 A28 5c dark blue 25.00 2.25
O53 A29 10c violet & org 32.50 2.75
O54 A30 15c lavender & cl 32.00 2.75
O55 A31 20c rose & dk bl 37.50 1.25
O56 A32 50c red lil & blk 75.00 12.50
O57 A33 1p blue & blk 150.00 12.50
O58 A34 5p carmine & blk 325.00 37.50
Nos. O49-O58 (10) 746.00 76.00

Black Overprint

1903

O59 A25 1c violet 17.50 1.90
O60 A26 2c green 17.50 1.90
O61 A35 4c carmine 32.50 1.25
O62 A28 5c orange 32.50 6.25
O63 A29 10c blue & org 35.00 1.90
O64 A32 50c carmine & blk 95.00 12.50
Nos. O59-O64 (6) 230.00 25.70

Regular Issues Overprinted **OFICIAL**

On Issues of 1899-1903

1910

O65 A26 2c green 87.50 3.25
O66 A27 3c orange brn 87.50 2.00
O67 A35 4c carmine 100.00 5.00
O68 A28 5c orange 110.00 25.00
O69 A29 10c blue & org 100.00 1.90
O70 A30 15c lav & claret 115.00 3.25
O71 A31 20c rose & dk bl 135.00 1.50
O72 A32 50c carmine & blk 190.00 17.50
O73 A33 1p blue & blk 350.00 62.50
O74 A34 5p carmine & blk 100.00 62.50
Nos. O65-O74 (10) 1,375. 184.40

On Issue of 1910

1911

O75 A36 1c violet 2.50 2.50
O76 A37 2c green 1.90 1.10
O77 A38 3c orange brn 2.50 1.25
O78 A39 4c carmine 3.75 1.10
O79 A40 5c orange 6.25 3.50
O80 A41 10c blue & org 3.75 1.25
O81 A42 15c gray bl & cl 6.25 4.25
O82 A43 20c red & blue 5.00 1.25
O83 A44 50c red brn & blk 17.50 7.50
O84 A45 1p blue & blk 30.00 12.50
O85 A46 5p carmine & blk 110.00 62.50
Nos. O75-O85 (11) 189.40 98.70

Nos. 500 to 505 Overprinted **OFICIAL**

1915 Unwmk. *Rouletted 14½*

O86 A57 1c violet .50 1.00
O87 A58 2c green .50 1.00
O88 A59 3c brown .60 1.00
O89 A60 4c carmine .50 1.00
O90 A61 5c orange .50 1.00
O91 A62 10c ultra .60 1.00
Nos. O86-O91 (6) 3.20 6.00

All values are known with inverted overprint. All values exist imperforate and part perforate but were not regularly issued in these forms.

On Nos. 506 to 514

1915-16 *Perf. 12*

O92 A57 1c violet .50 1.00
O93 A58 2c green .50 1.00
O94 A59 3c brown .50 1.00
O95 A60 4c carmine .50 1.00
a. "CEATRO" 7.00 15.00
O96 A61 5c orange .50 1.00
O97 A62 10c ultra, type II .50 1.00
a. Double overprint *475.00*
O98 A63 40c slate 4.00 7.25
a. Inverted overprint 12.00 12.50
b. Double overprint 20.00
O99 A64 1p brown & blk 5.00 7.25
a. Inverted overprint 14.00 17.50
O100 A65 5p claret & ultra 30.00 30.00
a. Inverted overprint 40.00
Nos. O92-O100 (9) 42.00 50.50

Nos. O98 and O99 exist imperforate but probably were not issued in that form.

Preceding Issues Overprinted in Red, Blue or Black

On No. O74

1916 Wmk. 155

O101 A34 5p carmine & blk 700.00

On Nos. O75 to O85

O102 A36 1c violet 3.25
O103 A37 2c green .65
O104 A38 3c orange brn (Bl) .85
O105 A39 4c carmine (Bl) 3.50
O106 A40 5c orange (Bl) .85
O107 A41 10c blue & org .85
O108 A42 15c gray bl & cl (Bk) .85
O109 A43 20c red & bl (Bk) .95
O110 A44 50c red brn & blk 100.00
O111 A45 1p blue & blk 5.50
O112 A46 5p carmine & blk *2,500.*
Nos. O102-O111 (10) 117.25

No. O102 with blue overprint is a trial color. Counterfeits exist of Nos. O110, O112.

Nos. 608, 610 to 612, 615 and 616 Overprinted Vertically in Red or Black **OFICIAL**

Thick Paper

1918 Unwmk. *Rouletted 14½*

O113 A68 1c violet (R) 30.00 17.00
O114 A69 2c gray grn (R) 32.50 18.00
O115 A70 3c bis brn (R) 30.00 17.00
O116 A71 4c carmine (Bk) 30.00 18.00
O117 A74 20c rose (Bk) 60.00 47.50
O118 A75 30c gray brn (R) 95.00 85.00

On Nos. 622-623

Medium Paper

Perf. 12

O119 A72 5c ultra (R) 20.00 20.00
O120 A73 10c blue (R) 18.00 12.50
a. Double overprint *200.00* *200.00*
Nos. O113-O120 (8) 315.50 235.00

Overprinted Horizontally in Red **OFICIAL**

On Nos. 626-628

Thin Paper

O121 A63 40c violet (R) 17.00 14.00
O122 A64 1p bl & blk (R) 42.50 35.00
O123 A65 5p grn & blk (R) *270.00* *300.00*
Nos. O121-O123 (3) *329.50* *349.00*

Nos. 608 and 610 to 615 Overprinted Vertically Up in Red or Black **OFICIAL**

Thick Paper

1919 *Rouletted 14½*

O124 A68 1c dull vio (R) 3.00 3.00
a. "OFICIAN" 35.00 40.00
O125 A69 2c gray grn (R) 4.75 1.75
a. "OFICIAN" 35.00 40.00
O126 A70 3c bister brn (R) 7.25 3.00
a. "OFICIAN" 47.50 50.00
O127 A71 4c carmine (Bk) 14.50 6.50
c. "OFICIAN" —
O127A A72 5c ultra 100.00 60.00
b. "OFICIAN" *400.00*
O128 A73 10c blue (R) 4.75 1.25
a. "OFICIAN" 42.50 30.00
O129 A74 20c rose (Bk) 30.00 24.00
a. "OFICIAN" 70.00

On Nos. 618, 622

Perf. 12

O130 A68 1c dull violet (R) 24.00 24.00
a. "OFICIAN" 72.50 50.00
O131 A72 5c ultra (R) 24.00 10.75
a. "OFICIAN" 72.50 50.00

Overprinted Horizontally

On Nos. 626-627

Thin Paper

O132 A63 40c violet (R) 24.00 17.00
O133 A64 1p bl & blk (R) 15.00 12.50
Nos. O124-O133 (11) 251.25 163.75

Nos. 608 to 615 and 617 Overprinted Vertically down in Black, Red or Blue

OFICIAL

Size: 17½x3mm

1921 *Rouletted 14½*

O134 A68 1c gray (Bk) 15.00 6.00
a. 1c dull violet (Bk) 8.50 3.50
O135 A69 2c gray grn (R) 2.50 1.50
O136 A70 3c bis brn (R) 4.25 1.50
O137 A71 4c carmine (Bk) 9.75 7.25
O138 A72 5c ultra (R) 12.50 6.00
O139 A73 10c bl, reading down (R) 16.00 6.00
a. Overprint reading up 30.00 30.00
O140 A74 20c rose (Bl) 24.00 14.00
O141 A75 30c gray blk (R) 12.50 12.50

Overprinted Horizontally On Nos. 626-628

Perf. 12

O142 A63 40c violet (R) 16.00 16.00
O143 A64 1p bl & blk (R) 12.50 12.50
O144 A65 5p grn & blk (Bk) *250.00 250.00*
Nos. O134-O144 (11) *375.00 333.25*

Nos. 609 to 615 Overprinted Vertically Down in Black **OFICIAL.**

1921-30 *Rouletted 14½*

O145 A68 1c gray 2.50 1.25
a. 1c lilac gray .50 .35
O146 A69 2c gray green .90 .30
O147 A70 3c bister brn .40 .30
a. "OFICAL" 24.00 12.50
b. "OIFCIAL" 24.00 12.50
c. Double overprint 72.00
O148 A71 4c carmine 7.50 1.25
O149 A72 5c ultra .50 .30
O150 A73 10c blue .50 .30
a. "OIFCIAL" 25.00
O151 A74 20c brown rose 4.75 4.75
a. 20c rose 2.50 1.25

On No. 625

Perf. 12

O152 A75 30c gray black 7.25 2.50

Overprinted Horizontally On Nos. 626, 628

O153 A63 40c violet 3.50 2.50
a. "OFICAL" 30.00 30.00
b. "OICIFAL" 30.00 30.00
c. Inverted overprint 45.00
O154 A65 5p grn & blk ('30) 125.00 *150.00*
Nos. O145-O154 (10) 152.80 *163.45*

Overprinted Vertically Down in Red On Nos. 609, 610, 611, 613 and 614

1921-24 *Rouletted 14½*

O155 A68 1c lilac .80 .50
O156 A69 2c gray green .75 .45
O157 A70 3c bister brown 2.00 .50
O158 A72 5c ultra .80 .40
O159 A73 10c blue 17.50 1.75
a. Double overprint

On Nos. 624-625

Perf. 12

O160 A74 20c rose 3.75 .80
O161 A75 30c gray black 9.50 2.50

Overprinted Horizontally On Nos. 626-628

O162 A63 40c violet 7.25 3.75
a. Vert. pair, imperf. btwn.
O163 A64 1p blue & blk 17.50 12.50
O164 A65 5p green & blk 110.00 *175.00*

Overprinted Vertically Down in Blue on No. 612

Rouletted 14½

O165 A71 4c carmine 3.50 1.75
Nos. O155-O165 (11) 173.35 *199.90*

Same Overprint Vertically Down in Red or Blue On Nos. 635 and 637

1926-27 *Rouletted 14½*

O166 A80 3c bis brn, ovpt. horiz. (R) 6.00 6.00
a. Period omitted 15.00 15.00
O167 A82 5c orange (R) 14.00 15.00

Same Overprint Vertically Down On Nos. 650, 651, 655 and 656

Wmk. 156

O168 A79 2c scarlet (Bl) 10.00 10.00
a. Overprint reading up 15.00 15.00
O169 A80 3c bis brn, ovpt. horiz. (R) 2.50 2.50
a. Inverted overprint 30.00
O170 A85 10c claret (Bl) 17.50 8.00
O171 A84 20c deep blue (R) 7.00 6.00
a. Overprint reading up 7.00 6.00

Overprinted Horizontally On Nos. 643, 646-649

Perf. 12

O172 A81 4c green (R) 3.00 3.00
O173 A83 30c dk grn (R) 3.00 3.00
O174 A63 40c violet (R) 8.00 8.00
a. Inverted overprint 40.00
O175 A87 50c olive brn (R) .75 .75
a. 50c yellow brown (R) 9.00 9.00
O176 A88 1p red brn & bl (R) 7.50 7.50
Nos. O168-O176 (9) 59.25 48.75

Same Overprint Horizontally on No. 651, Vertically Up on Nos. 650, 653-656, 666, RA1

1927-31 *Rouletted 14½*

O177 PT1 1c brown ('31) .30 .50
O178 A79 2c scarlet .30 .50
a. "OFICAIL" 15.00 15.00
b. Overprint reading down .75 1.00
O179 A80 3c bis brn 1.00 .75
a. "OFICAIL" 20.00 15.00
O180 A82 4c green .75 .55
a. "OFICAIL" 20.00 20.00
b. Overprint reading down 5.00 1.00
O181 A82 5c orange 2.00 1.50
a. Overprint reading down 2.00 1.25
O182 A94 8c orange 6.00 4.00
a. Overprint reading down 3.50 3.00
O183 A85 10c lake 1.00 1.00
a. Overprint reading down 1.00 1.00
O184 A84 20c dark blue 5.00 4.00
a. "OFICAIL" 20.00 20.00
b. Overprint reading down 10.00 10.00
Nos. O177-O184 (8) 16.35 12.80

Overprinted Vertically Up on #O186, Horizontally On Nos. 643 and 645 to 649

1927-33 *Perf. 12*

O185 A81 4c green 3.00 2.50
a. Inverted overprint 15.00 15.00
O186 A85 10c brown lake 27.50 27.50
O187 A83 30c dark green .70 .50
a. Inverted overprint 15.00 15.00
b. Pair, tête bêche overprints 17.50 17.50
c. "OFICAIL" 17.50 17.50
O188 A63 40c violet 6.00 4.00
O189 A87 50c olive brn ('33) 1.75 2.00
O190 A88 1p red brn & bl 12.00 10.00
Nos. O185-O190 (6) 50.95 46.50

The overprint on No. O186 is vertical.

Nos. 320, 628, 633 Overprinted Horizontally **OFICIAL**

On Stamp No. 320

1927-28 **Wmk. 155** *Perf. 14, 15*

O191 A46 5p car & blk (R) 90.00 *125.00*
O192 A46 5p car & blk (Bl) 90.00 *125.00*

Unwmk. *Perf. 12*

O193 A65 5p grn & blk (Bk) 85.00 *125.00*
a. Inverted overprint 120.00 *120.00*
O194 A78 10p blk brn & blk (Bl) 100.00 *150.00*

No. 320 Overprinted Horizontally **OFICIAL.**

Wmk. 155 *Perf. 14*

O195 A46 5p carmine & blk 150.00

Nos. 650 and 655 Overprinted Horizontally **OFICIAL**

1928-29 **Wmk. 156** *Rouletted 14½*

Size: 16x2½mm

O196 A79 2c dull red 9.00 6.00
O197 A85 10c rose lake 14.00 6.00

Nos. RA1, 650-651, 653-656 Overprinted **SERVICIO OFICIAL**

1932-33

O198 PT1 1c brown .30 .50
O199 A79 2c dull red .40 .40
O200 A80 3c bister brn 1.50 1.50
O201 A82 4c green 5.00 4.00
O202 A82 5c orange 6.00 4.00
O203 A85 10c rose lake 1.75 1.50
O204 A84 20c dark blue 7.50 5.00
a. Double overprint *100.00 45.00*
Nos. O198-O204 (7) 22.45 16.90

Nos. 651, 646-649 Overprinted Horizontally **SERVICIO OFICIAL**

1933 *Rouletted 14½*

O205 A80 3c bister brn 1.50 1.50

Perf. 12

O206 A83 30c dk green 4.00 1.50
O207 A63 40c violet 7.50 3.00
O208 A87 50c olive brn 1.25 1.50
a. "OFICIAL OFICIAL" 25.00 25.00
O209 A88 1p red brn & bl, type I 1.50 1.50
a. Type II 1.40 1.75

Overprinted Vertically On No. 656

Rouletted 14½

O210 A84 20c dark blue 9.00 5.00
Nos. O205-O210 (6) 24.75 14.00

Nos. RA1, 651, 653, 654, 683 Overprinted Horizontally **OFICIAL**

1934-37 *Rouletted 14½*

Size: 13x2mm

O211 PT1 1c brown 2.50 3.00
O212 A80 3c bister brn .30 .30
O213 A82 4c green 6.00 5.00
O214 A82 5c orange .30 .30
O215 A96 15c dk blue ('37) .50 .50
Nos. O211-O215 (5) 9.60 9.10

See No. O217a.

Same Overprint on Nos. 687A-692

1934-37 *Perf. 10½*

O216 PT1 1c brown ('37) .50 .60
O217 A79 2c scarlet .50 .75
a. On No. 650 (error) 175.00
b. Double overprint 75.00
O218 A82 4c green ('35) .70 .80
O219 A85 10c brown lake .50 .50
O220 A84 20c dk blue ('37) .60 .60
O221 A83 30c dk bl grn ('37) 1.00 1.00

On Nos. 647 and 649

Perf. 12, 11½x12

O222 A63 40c violet 1.50 1.75
O223 A88 1p red brn & bl (I) 2.50 3.00
a. Type II 2.00 2.00
Nos. O216-O223 (8) 7.80 9.00

On Nos. 707 to 709, 712, 715, 716, 717, 718 and 719

O224 A108 1c orange 1.00 *2.00*
O225 A109 2c green .60 *1.00*
O226 A110 4c carmine .60 *.70*
O227 A112 10c violet .60 *1.25*
O228 A114 20c ultra .80 *1.25*
O229 A115 30c lake 1.00 *2.00*
O230 A116 40c red brown 1.25 *2.00*
O231 A117 50c black 1.40 *1.40*
O232 A118 1p dk brn & org 4.00 *6.00*
Nos. O224-O232 (9) 11.25 *17.60*

PARCEL POST STAMPS

Railroad Train — PP1

1941 **Photo.** **Wmk. 156** *Perf. 14*

Q1 PP1 10c brt rose 2.75 .35
Q2 PP1 20c dk vio bl 1.75 .35

1944-46 **Wmk. 272**

Q3 PP1 10c brt rose 1.75 1.00
Q4 PP1 20c dk vio bl ('46) 5.00 2.50

1947-49 **Wmk. 279**

Q5 PP1 10c brt rose 1.25 .60
Q6 PP1 20c dk vio bl ('49) 1.60 .60

Streamlined Locomotive PP2

1951

Q7 PP2 10c rose pink 2.00 .40
Q8 PP2 20c blue violet 1.75 .70

1954 **Wmk. 300**

Q9 PP2 10c rose pink 1.25 .60
Q10 PP2 20c blue violet 1.25 1.50

POSTAL TAX STAMPS

Morelos Monument — PT1

Rouletted 14½

1925 **Engr.** **Wmk. 156**

RA1 PT1 1c brown .35 .15
a. Imperf. 30.00

1926 *Perf. 12*

RA2 PT1 1c brown .75 *5.00*
a. Booklet pane of 2 12.00

1925 **Unwmk.** *Rouletted 14½*

RA3 PT1 1c brown 25.00 9.00

It was obligatory to add a stamp of type PT1 to the regular postage on every article of domestic mail matter. The money obtained from this source formed a fund to combat a plague of locusts.

In 1931, 1c stamps of type PT1 were discontinued as Postal Tax stamps. It was subsequently used for the payment of postage on drop letters (announcement cards and unsealed circulars) to be delivered in the city of cancellation. See No. 687A.

For overprints see Nos. O177, O198, O211, O216, RA4.

Protección a la Infancia

Mother and Child — PT3

Red Overprint

1929 **Wmk. 156**

RA4 PT1 1c brown .35 .15
a. Overprint reading down 40.00 40.00

There were two settings of this overprint. They may be distinguished by the two lines being spaced 4mm or 6mm apart.

The money from sales of this stamp was devoted to child welfare work.

1929 **Litho.** *Rouletted 13, 13½*

RA5 PT3 1c violet .25 .15

PT4

PT5

1929 **Unwmk.**

Size: 18x24½mm

RA6 PT4 2c deep green .40 .15
RA7 PT4 5c brown .40 .15
a. Imperf., pair 40.00 40.00
Set value .20

For surcharges see Nos. RA10-RA11.

1929 **Size: 19x25¼mm**

Two types of 1c:

Type I - Background lines continue through lettering of top inscription. Denomination circle hangs below second background line. Paper and gum white.

Type II - Background lines cut away behind some letters. Circle rests on second background line. Paper and gum yellowish.

RA8 PT5 1c violet, type I .15 .15
a. Booklet pane of 4 10.00
b. Booklet pane of 2 18.00
c. Type II .40 .15
d. Imperf., pair 35.00 35.00
RA9 PT5 2c deep green .40 .15
a. Imperf., pair 12.00

The use of these stamps, in addition to the regular postage, was compulsory. The money obtained from their sale was used for child welfare work.

For surcharge see No. RA12.

Nos. RA6, RA7, RA9 Surcharged

HABILITADO
$0.01

1930

RA10 PT4 1c on 2c dp grn .75 .40
RA11 PT4 1c on 5c brown 1.00 .60
RA12 PT5 1c on 2c dp grn 2.00 1.00
Nos. RA10-RA12 (3) 3.75 2.00

Used stamps exist with surcharge double or reading down.

No. 423 Overprinted

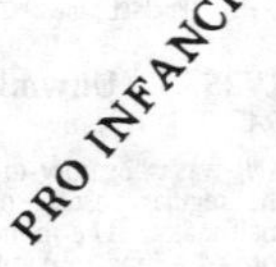

1931, Jan. 30 Wmk. 155 *Perf. 14*

RA13 A36 1c dull violet .30 .40
a. "PRO INFANCIA" double 50.00

Indian Mother and Child — PT6

Mosquito Attacking Man — PT7

Perf. 10½

1934, Sept. 1 Engr. Wmk. 156

RA13B PT6 1c dull orange .20 .15

1939 Photo. Wmk. 156 *Perf. 14*

RA14 PT7 1c Prus blue 1.50 .15
a. Imperf. 3.00 3.00

This stamp was obligatory on all mail, the money being used to aid in a drive against malaria.

See Nos. RA16, RA19.

Miguel Hidalgo y Costilla — PT8

Learning Vowels — PT9

1941

RA15 PT8 1c brt carmine .45 .15

Type of 1939

1944 Wmk. 272 *Perf. 14*

RA16 PT7 1c Prus blue 1.00 .15

1946 Photo. Wmk. 279

RA17 PT9 1c black brown .45 .15
a. 1c green black 1.00 1.00

1947 Wmk. 272

RA18 PT9 1c black brown 50.00 5.00

Type of 1939
Wmk. 279

RA19 PT7 1c Prus blue 3.50 .30

PROVISIONAL ISSUES

During the struggle led by Juarez to expel the Emperor Maximilian, installed June, 1864 by Napoleon III and French troops, a number of towns when free of Imperial forces issued provisional postage stamps. Maximilian was captured and executed June 19, 1867, but provisional issues continued current for a time pending re-establishment of Republican Government.

Campeche

A southern state in Mexico, comprising the western part of the Yucatan peninsula.

A1

White Paper
Numerals in Black

1876 Handstamped *Imperf.*

1 A1 5c gray blue & blue *2,000.*
2 A1 25c gray blue & blue *1,100.*
3 A1 50c gray blue & blue *4,500.*

The stamps printed in blue-black and blue on yellowish paper, formerly listed as issued in 1867, are now known to be an unofficial production of later years. They are reprints, but produced without official sanction.

Chiapas

A southern state in Mexico, bordering on Guatemala and the Pacific Ocean.

A1

1866 Typeset

1 A1 ½r blk, *gray bl* *2,000. 1,300.*
2 A1 1r blk, *lt grn* *850.*
3 A1 2r blk, *rose* *900.*
4 A1 4r blk, *lt buff* *2,000.*
a. Vertical half used as 2r on cover *3,000.*
5 A1 8r blk, *rose* *15,000.*
a. Quarter used as 2r on cover *4,000.*
b. Half used as 4r on cover *5,000.*

Chihuahua

A city of northern Mexico and capital of the State of Chihuahua.

A1

1872 Handstamped

1 A1 12(c) black *1,200.*
2 A1 25(c) black *1,000.*

Cuautla

A town in the state of Morelos.

A1

1867 Handstamped

1 A1 (2r) black *7,000.*

Cuernavaca

A city of Mexico, just south of the capital, and the capital of the State of Morelos.

A1

1867 Handstamped

1 A1 (2r) black *1,500. 1,750.*

The CUERNAVACA district name handstamp was used to cancel the stamp.

Counterfeits exist.

Guadalajara

A city of Mexico and capital of the State of Jalisco.

A1

Dated "1867"
1st Printing
Medium Wove Paper

1867 Handstamped *Imperf.*

1 A1 Medio r blk, *white* 150.00 110.00
2 A1 un r blk, *gray bl* 110.00
3 A1 un r blk, *dk bl* 95.00
4 A1 un r blk, *white* 85.00
5 A1 2r blk, *dk grn* 47.50 21.50
6 A1 2r blk, *white* 85.00
7 A1 4r blk, *rose* 135.00 85.00
a. Half used as 2r on cover 300.00
8 A1 4r blk, *white* 125.00
9 A1 un p blk, *lilac* 145.00 150.00

Serrate Perf.

10 A1 un r blk, *gray bl* 150.00
11 A1 2r blk, *dk grn* 85.00
12 A1 4r blk, *rose* 95.00

2nd Printing
No Period after "2" or "4"
Thin Quadrille Paper
Imperf

13 A1 2r blk, *green* 30.00 20.00
a. Half used as 1r on cover 300.00

Serrate Perf.

14 A1 2r blk, *green* 60.00

Thin Laid Batonné Paper
Imperf

15 A1 2r blk, *green* 45.00 24.00

Serrate Perf.

16 A1 2r blk, *green* 50.00

3rd Printing
Capital "U" in "Un" on 1r, 1p
Period after "2" and "4"
Thin Wove Paper
Imperf

16A A1 Un r blk, *white* 90.00
17 A1 Un r blk, *blue* 60.00
17A A1 Un r blk, *lilac* 85.00
18 A1 2r blk, *rose* 50.00
18A A1 4r blk, *blue*

Serrate Perf.

19 A1 Un r blk, *blue* 100.00

Thin Quadrille Paper
Imperf

20 A1 2r blk, *rose* 42.50 42.50
21 A1 4r blk, *blue* 15.00 30.00
22 A1 4r blk, *white* 65.00
23 A1 Un p blk, *lilac* 15.00 60.00
24 A1 Un p blk, *rose* 65.00

Serrate Perf.

25 A1 Un p blk, *lilac* 150.00
25A A1 Un p blk, *rose* 150.00

Thin Laid Batonné Paper
Imperf

26 A1 Un r blk, *green* 22.50 17.50
27 A1 2r blk, *rose* 27.50 22.50
27A A1 2r blk, *green* 47.50
28 A1 4r blk, *blue* 17.50 42.50
29 A1 4r blk, *white* 65.00
30 A1 Un p blk, *lilac* 30.00 52.50
31 A1 Un p blk, *rose* 65.00

Serrate Perf.

32 A1 Un r blk, *green* 65.00
33 A1 2r blk, *rose* 70.00 *80.00*
34 A1 4r blk, *blue* 100.00

Thin Oblong Quadrille Paper
Imperf

35 A1 Un r blk, *blue* 22.50
36 A1 4r blk, *blue* 175.00

Serrate Perf.

37 A1 Un r blk, *blue* 75.00

4th Printing
Dated "1868"
Wove Paper

1868 *Imperf.*

38 A1 2r blk, *lilac* 30.00 14.00
a. Half used as 1r on cover 325.00
39 A1 2r blk, *rose* 52.50 65.00

Serrate Perf.

40 A1 2r blk, *lilac* 52.50
41 A1 2r blk, *rose* 95.00

Laid Batonné Paper
Imperf

42 A1 un r blk, *green* 12.50 12.50
a. "nu" instead of "un" 80.00
43 A1 2r blk, *lilac* 12.50 12.50

Serrate Perf.

44 A1 un r blk, *green* 70.00 52.50

Quadrille Paper.
Imperf

45 A1 2r blk, *lilac* 25.00 14.00

Serrate Perf.

46 A1 2r blk, *lilac* 65.00 65.00

Laid Paper
Imperf

47 A1 un r blk, *green* 13.00 17.00
a. "nu" instead of "un" 70.00
48 A1 2r blk, *lilac* 32.50 32.50
49 A1 2r blk, *rose* 37.50 37.50

Serrate Perf.

50 A1 un r blk, *green* 55.00
51 A1 2r blk, *rose* 110.00

Counterfeits of Nos. 1-51 abound.

Merida

A city of southeastern Mexico, capital of the State of Yucatan.

Mexico No. 521 Surcharged **25**

1916 Wmk. 155 *Perf. 14*

1 A40 25(c) on 5c org, on cover *500.00*

The G.P.DE.M. overprint reads down.

Authorities consider the Monterrey, Morelia and Patzcuaro stamps to be bogus.

Tlacotalpan

A village in the state of Veracruz.

A1

1856, Oct. Handstamped

1 A1 ½(r) black *10,000.*

REVOLUTIONARY ISSUES

SINALOA

A northern state in Mexico, bordering on the Pacific Ocean. Stamps were issued by a provisional government.

Coat of Arms — A1

1929 Unwmk. Litho. *Perf. 12*

1	A1 10c blk, red & bl	3.00
a.	Tête bêche pair	35.00
2	A1 20c blk, red & gray	3.00

Just as Nos. 1 and 2 were ready to be placed on sale the state was occupied by the Federal forces and the stamps could not be used. At a later date a few copies were canceled by favor.

A recent find included a number of errors or printers waste.

YUCATAN

A southeastern state of Mexico.

Mayan Altar Support — A1

"Casa de Monjas" — A2

Temple of the Tigers — A3

1924 Unwmk. Litho. *Imperf.*

1	A1 5c violet	10.00	15.00
2	A2 10c carmine	40.00	50.00
3	A3 50c olive green	175.00	

Perf. 12

4	A1 5c violet	50.00	60.00
5	A2 10c carmine	50.00	75.00
6	A3 50c olive green	200.00	

Nos. 3 and 6 were not regularly issued.

MICRONESIA, FEDERATED STATES OF

ˌmī–krə–ˈnē–zhə

LOCATION — A group of over 600 islands in the West Pacific Ocean, north of the Equator.
GOVT. — Republic
AREA — 271 sq. miles
POP. — 73,755 (1980)
CAPITAL — Palikir

These islands, also known as the Caroline Islands, were bought by Germany from Spain in 1899. Caroline Islands stamps issued as a German territory are listed in Vol. 2 of this Catalogue. Seized by Japan in 1914, they were taken by the US in WWII and became part of the US Trust Territory of the Pacific in 1947. By agreement with the USPS, the islands began issuing their own stamps in 1984, with the USPS continuing to carry the mail to and from the islands.

On Nov. 3, 1986 Micronesia became a Federation as a Sovereign State in Compact of Free Association with the US.

100 Cents = 1 Dollar

Catalogue values for all unused stamps in this country are for Never Hinged items.

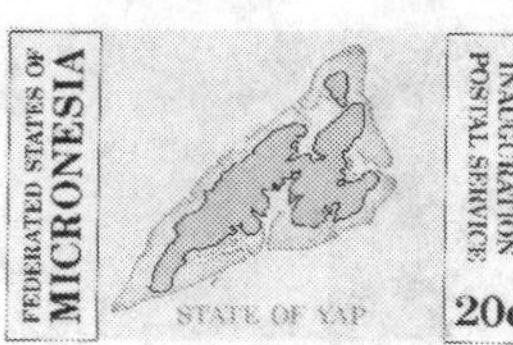

Postal Service Inauguration — A1

1984, July 12 Litho. *Perf. 14*

1	A1 20c Yap	.50	.50
2	A1 20c Truk	.50	.50
3	A1 20c Pohnpei	.50	.50
4	A1 20c Kosrae	.50	.50
a.	Block of 4, #1-4	2.00	2.00

For surcharges see Nos. 48-51.

Fernandez de Quiros — A2

Men's House, Yap — A3

Designs: 1c, 19c, Pedro Fernandez de Quiros, Spanish explorer, first discovered Pohnpei, 1595. 2c, 20c, Louis Duperrey, French explorer. 3c, 30c, Fyedor Lutke, Russian explorer. 4c, 37c, Dumont d'Urville. 10c, Sleeping Lady, Kosrae. 13c, Liduduhriap Waterfall, Pohnpei. 17c, Tonachau Peak, Truk. 50c, Devil mask, Truk. $1, Sokeh's Rock, Pohnpei. $2, Canoes, Kosrae. $5, Stone money, Yap.

1984, July 12 *Perf. 13½x13*

5	A2 1c Prussian blue	.15	.15
6	A2 2c deep claret	.15	.15
7	A2 3c dark blue	.15	.15
8	A2 4c green	.15	.15
9	A3 5c yellow brown	.15	.15
10	A3 10c dark violet	.15	.15
11	A3 13c dark blue	.20	.20
12	A3 17c brown lake	.25	.25
13	A2 19c dark violet	.30	.30
14	A2 20c olive green	.30	.30
15	A2 30c rose lake	.45	.45
16	A2 37c deep violet	.55	.55
17	A3 50c brown	.75	.75
18	A3 $1 olive	1.50	1.50
19	A3 $2 Prussian blue	3.00	3.00
20	A3 $5 brown lake	7.50	7.50
	Nos. 5-20 (16)	15.70	15.70

See #33, 36, 38. For surcharges see #48-51.

Ausipex '84 A4

1984, Sept. 21 Litho. *Perf. 13½*

21	A4 20c Truk Post Office	.45	.45
	Nos. 21,C4-C6 (4)	3.05	3.05

Christmas A5

Child's drawing.

1984, Dec. 20

22	A5 20c Child in manger	.90	.90
	Nos. 22,C7-C9 (4)	4.65	4.65

Ships — A6

1985, Aug. 19

23	A6 22c U.S.S. Jamestown	.55	.55
	Nos. 23,C10-C12 (4)	3.20	3.20

Christmas A7

1985, Oct. 15 Litho. *Perf. 13½*

24	A7 22c Lelu Protestant Church, Kosrae	.80	.60
	Nos. 24,C13-C14 (3)	2.95	2.75

Audubon Birth Bicentenary — A8

1985, Oct. 30 *Perf. 14½*

25	A8 22c Noddy tern	.65	.65
26	A8 22c Turnstone	.65	.65
27	A8 22c Golden plover	.65	.65
28	A8 22c Black-bellied plover	.65	.65
a.	Block of 4, #25-28	2.75	2.75
	Nos. 25-28,C15 (5)	3.60	3.60

Types of 1984 and

Birds — A9

Tall Ship Senyavin A10

Natl. Seal A11

Perf. 13½ (A8a), 13½x13

1985-88 Litho.

31	A9 3c Long-billed white-eye	.15	.15
32	A9 14c Truk monarch	.30	.30
33	A3 15c Liduduhriap Waterfall, Pohnpei	.30	.30
a.	Booklet pane of 10	3.00	—
34	A10 22c bright blue green	.35	.35
35	A9 22c Pohnpei mountain starling	.45	.45
36	A3 25c Tonachau Peak, Truk	.50	.50
a.	Booklet pane of 10	5.00	—
b.	Booklet pane, 5 15c + 5 25c	4.00	—
37	A10 36c ultramarine	.70	.70
38	A3 45c Sleeping Lady, Kosrae	.90	.90
39	A11 $10 bright ultra	15.00	15.00
	Nos. 31-39,C34-C36 (12)	21.65	21.65

Issued: $10, 10/15; #34, 4/14/86; 3c, 14c, #35, 8/1/88; 15c, 25c, 36c, 45c, 9/1/88.

Nan Madol Ruins, Pohnpei A16

1985, Dec. Litho. *Perf. 13½*

45	A16 22c Land of the Sacred Masonry	.60	.60
	Nos. 45,C16-C18 (4)	3.00	3.00

Intl. Peace Year — A17

1986, May 16

46	A17 22c multicolored	.65	.60

Nos. 1-4 Surcharged

1986, May 19 Litho. *Perf. 14*

48	A1 22c on 20c No. 1	.40	.40
49	A1 22c on 20c No. 2	.40	.40
50	A1 22c on 20c No. 3	.40	.40
51	A1 22c on 20c No. 4	.40	.40
a.	Block of 4, #48-51	1.65	1.65

AMERIPEX '86 — A18

Bully Hayes (1829-1877), Buccaneer.

1986, May 22 *Perf. 13½*

52	A18 22c At ship's helm	.50	.50
	Nos. 52,C21-C24 (5)	4.00	4.00

First Passport A19

1986, Nov. 4 Litho. *Perf. 13½*

53	A19 22c multicolored	.60	.60

Christmas — A20

Virgin and child paintings: 5c, Italy, 18th cent. 22c, Germany, 19th cent.

1986, Oct. 15 Litho. *Perf. 14½*

54	A20 5c multicolored	.25	.25
55	A20 22c multicolored	.75	.75
	Nos. 54-55,C26-C27 (4)	3.40	3.40

Anniversaries and Events — A21

1987, June 13 Litho. *Perf. 14½*

56	A21 22c Intl. Year of Shelter for the Homeless	.50	.50
	Nos. 56,C28-C30 (4)	3.20	3.20

Souvenir Sheet

57	A21 $1 CAPEX '87	3.25	3.25

Christmas A22

22c, Archangel Gabriel appearing before Mary.

1987, Nov. 16 Litho. *Perf. 14½*

58	A22 22c multicolored	.60	.60

See Nos. C31-C33.

Colonial Eras — A23

1988, July 20 Litho. *Perf. 13x13½*

59	A23 22c German	.60	.60
60	A23 22c Spanish	.60	.60
61	A23 22c Japanese	.60	.60

62 A23 22c US Trust Territory .60 .60
a. Block of 4, #59-62 2.40 2.40
Nos. 59-62,C37-C38 (6) 4.30 4.30

Printed se-tenant in sheets of 28 plus 4 center labels picturing flags of Spain (UL), Germany (UR), Japan (LL) and the US (LR).

1988 Summer Olympics, Seoul — A24

1988, Sept. 1 Litho. *Perf. 14*

63 A24 25c Running .50 .50
64 A24 25c Women's hurdles .50 .50
a. Pair, #63-64 1.00 1.00
65 A24 45c Basketball .80 .80
66 A24 45c Women's volleyball .80 .80
a. Pair, #65-66 1.65 1.65
Nos. 63-66 (4) 2.60 2.60

Christmas A25

Children decorating tree: No. 67, Two girls, UL of tree. No. 68, Boy, girl, dove, UR of tree. No. 69, Boy, girl, LL of tree. No. 70, Boy, girl, LR of tree. Se-tenant in a continuous design.

1988, Oct. 28 Litho. *Perf. 14*

67 A25 25c multicolored .45 .45
68 A25 25c multicolored .45 .45
69 A25 25c multicolored .45 .45
70 A25 25c multicolored .45 .45
a. Block of 4, #67-70 1.90 1.90

Miniature Sheet

Truk Lagoon State Monument — A26

Designs: a, Sun and stars angelfish. b, School of fish. c, 3 divers. d, Goldenjack. e, Blacktip reef shark. f, 2 schools of fish. g, Squirrelfish. h, Batfish. i, Moorish idols. j, Barracudas. k, Spot banded butterflyfish. l, Three-spotted damselfish. m, Foxface. n, Lionfish. o, Diver. p, Coral. q, Butterflyfish. r, Bivalve, fish, coral.

1988, Dec. 19 Litho. *Perf. 14*

71 Sheet of 18 9.50 9.50
a.-r. A26 25c any single .50 .50

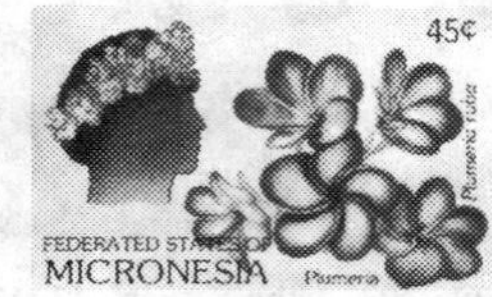

Mwarmwarms — A27

1989, Mar. 31 Litho. *Perf. 14*

72 A27 45c Plumeria .65 .65
73 A27 45c Hibiscus .65 .65
74 A27 45c Jasmine .65 .65
75 A27 45c Bougainvillea .65 .65
a. Block of 4, #72-75 2.75 2.75

Souvenir Sheet

Pheasant and Chrysanthemum, 1830s, by Hiroshige (1797-1858) — A28

1989, May 15 Litho. *Perf. 14½*

76 A28 $1 multicolored 1.65 1.65

Hirohito (1901-1989), emperor of Japan.

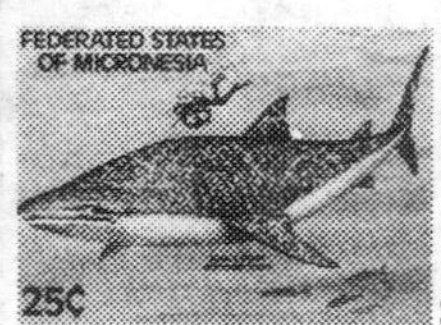

Sharks — A29

1989, July 7

77 A29 25c Whale .40 .40
78 A29 25c Hammerhead .40 .40
a. Pair, #77-78 .80 .80
79 A29 45c Tiger, vert. .75 .75
80 A29 45c Great white, vert. .75 .75
a. Pair, #79-80 1.50 1.50
Nos. 77-80 (4) 2.30 2.30

Miniature Sheet

First Moon Landing, 20th Anniv. — A30

Space achievements: a, X-15 rocket plane, 1959. b, *Explorer 1* launched into orbit, 1958. c, Ed White, 1st American to walk in space, Gemini 4 mission, 1965. d, Apollo 18 command module, 1975. e. Gemini 4 capsule. f, Space shuttle *Challenger,* 1983-86. g, *San Marco 2,* satellite engineered by Italy. h, Soyuz 19 spacecraft, 1975. i, *Columbia* command module and Neil Armstrong taking man's first step onto the Moon during the Apollo 11 mission, 1969.

1989, July 20 Litho. *Perf. 14*

81 A30 Sheet of 9 4.75 4.00
a.-i. 25c any single .45 .40

Earth and Lunar Module, by William Hanson, 1st Art Transported to the Moon — A31

1989, July 20 *Perf. 13½x14*

82 A31 $2.40 multicolored 4.00 3.50

First Moon landing, 20th anniv.

Seashells — A32

1989, Sept. 26 *Perf. 14*

83 A32 1c Horse's hoof .15 .15
84 A32 3c Rare spotted cowrie .15 .15
85 A32 15c Commercial trochus .20 .20
a. Booklet pane of 10 2.75 —
87 A32 20c General cone .30 .30
88 A32 25c Triton's trumpet .40 .40
a. Booklet pane of 10 4.75 —
b. Booklet pane, 5 each 15c, 25c 3.75 —
90 A32 30c Laciniated conch .45 .45
91 A32 36c Red-mouthed olive .55 .55
93 A32 45c Map cowrie .70 .70
95 A32 50c Textile cone .75 .75
100 A32 $1 Orange spider conch 1.75 1.75
101 A32 $2 Golden cowrie 3.50 3.50
102 A32 $5 Episcopal miter 9.00 9.00
Nos. 83-102 (12) 17.90 17.90

Booklet panes issued Sept. 14, 1990.
This is an expanding set. Numbers will change if necessary.

Miniature Sheet

Fruits and Flowers Endemic to Kosrae A33

Designs: a, Orange. b, Lime. c, Tangerine. d, Mango. e, Coconut. f, Breadfruit. g, Sugar cane. h, Thatched dwelling. i, Banana. j, Girl, boy. k, Pineapple picker. l, Taro. m, Hibiscus. n, Ylang ylang. o, White ginger. p, Plumeria. q, Royal poinciana. r, Yellow allamanda.

1989, Nov. 18 Litho. *Perf. 14*

103 Sheet of 18 8.00 8.00
a.-r. A33 25c any single .40 .40

Margin inscribed for World Stamp Expo '89.

Christmas A34

1989, Dec. 14 Litho. *Perf. 14½*

104 A34 25c Heralding angel .40 .40
105 A34 45c Three wise men .80 .80

World Wildlife Fund A35

Micronesian kingfishers and pigeons.

1990, Feb. 19 Litho. *Perf. 14*

106 A35 10c Kingfisher (juvenile) .20 .20
107 A35 15c Kingfisher (adult) .30 .30
108 A35 20c Pigeon .40 .40
109 A35 25c Pigeon, diff. .50 .50
Nos. 106-109 (4) 1.40 1.40

Stamp World London '90 — A36

Exhibition emblem, artifacts and whaling vessels: No. 110, Wooden whale stamp, *Lyra,* 1826. No. 111, Harpoons, *Prudent,* 1827. No. 112, Scrimshaw (whale), *Rhone,* 1851. No. 113, Scrimshaw on whale tooth, *Sussex,* 1843. $1, Whalers at kill.

1990, May 3 Litho. *Perf. 14*

110 A36 45c multicolored .70 .70
111 A36 45c multicolored .70 .70
112 A36 45c multicolored .70 .70
113 A36 45c multicolored .70 .70
a. Block of 4, #110-113 2.80 2.80

Souvenir Sheet

114 A36 $1 multicolored 1.65 1.65

Souvenir Sheet

Penny Black, 150th Anniv. — A37

1990, May 6 *Perf. 14*

115 A37 $1 Great Britain No. 1 1.65 1.65

Main Building — A38

Fr. Hugh Costigan, School Founder — A39

Designs: No. 117, Fr. Costigan, students. No. 119, Fr. Costigan, Isaphu Samuel Hadley. No. 120, New York City Police Badge.

1990, July 31 Litho. *Perf. 14*

116 A38 25c multicolored .40 .40
117 A38 25c multicolored .40 .40
118 A39 25c multicolored .40 .40
119 A38 25c multicolored .40 .40
120 A38 25c multicolored .40 .40
a. Strip of 5, #116-120 2.00 2.00

Pohnpei Agriculture and Trade School, 25th anniversary. Printed in sheets of 15.

Souvenir Sheet

Expo '90, Intl. Garden and Greenery Exposition, Osaka, Japan — A40

1990, July 31 Litho. *Perf. 14*

121 A40 $1 multicolored 1.25 1.25

Loading Mail, Pohnpei Airport, 1990 A41

Pacifica Emblem and: 45c, Japanese mail boat, Truk Lagoon, 1940.

1990, Aug. 24

122 A41 25c multicolored .55 .55
123 A41 45c multicolored 1.00 1.00

Canoe, Flag of Federated States of Micronesia A42

Designs: No. 124, Stick chart, canoe, flag of Marshall Islands. No. 125, Frigate bird, eagle, USS Constitution, flag of US.

1990, Sept. 28 *Perf. 13½*

124 A42 25c multicolored .55 .55
125 A42 25c multicolored .55 .55
126 A42 25c multicolored .55 .55
a. Strip of 3, #124-126 1.65 1.65

Compact of Free Association with the US. Printed in sheets of 15. See #253, US #2506, Marshall Islands #381.

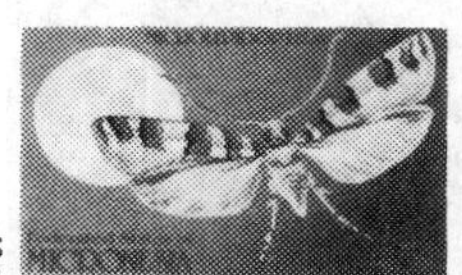

Moths A43

1990, Nov. 10 **Litho.** *Perf. 14*

127 A43 45c Gracillariidae .65 .65
128 A43 45c Yponomeatidae .65 .65
129 A43 45c shown .65 .65
130 A43 45c Cosmopterigidae, diff. .65 .65
a. Block of 4, #127-130 2.75 2.75

Miniature Sheet

Christmas A44

Designs: a, Cherub. b, Star of Bethlehem. c, Cherub blowing horn. d, Goats. e, Nativity scene. f, Children, outrigger canoe. g, Messenger blowing a conch shell. h, Family walking. i, People carrying bundles.

1990, Nov. 19 **Litho.** *Perf. 14*

131 Sheet of 9 3.50 3.50
a.-i. A44 25c any single .40 .40

Souvenir Sheets

New Capital of Micronesia — A45

1991, Jan. 15 **Litho.** *Perf. 14x13½*

132 Sheet of 2 1.40 1.40
a. A45 25c Executive Branch .50 .50
b. A45 45c Legislative, Judicial Branches .90 .90
133 A45 $1 New Capitol 2.00 2.00

Turtles — A46

1991, Mar. 14 **Litho.** *Perf. 14*

134 A46 29c Hawksbill on beach .70 .70
135 A46 29c Green .70 .70
a. Pair, #134-135 1.40 1.40
136 A46 50c Hawksbill 1.10 1.10
137 A46 50c Leatherback 1.10 1.10
a. Pair, #136-137 2.25 2.25
Nos. 134-137 (4) 3.60 3.60

Operation Desert Storm A47

1991, July 30 **Litho.** *Perf. 14*

138 A47 29c Battleship Missouri .50 .50
139 A47 29c Multiple launch rocket system .50 .50
140 A47 29c F-14 Tomcat .50 .50
141 A47 29c E-3 Sentry (AWACS) .50 .50
a. Block of 4, #138-141 2.00 2.00

Size: 51x38mm

142 A47 $2.90 Frigatebird, flag 4.00 4.00
a. Souvenir sheet of 1 4.00 4.00
Nos. 138-142 (5) 6.00 6.00

Miniature Sheets

Phila Nippon '91 — A48

Ukiyo-e prints by Paul Jacoulet (1902-1960): No. 143a, Evening Flowers, Toloas, Truk, 1941. b, The Chief's Daughter, Mogomog, 1953. c, Yagourouh and Mio, Yap, 1938. No. 144a, Yap Beauty and Orchids, 1934. b, The Yellow-eyed Boys, Ohlol, 1940. c, Violet Flowers, Tomil, 1937. $1, First Love, Yap, 1937, horiz.

1991, Sept. **Litho.** *Perf. 14*

143 Sheet of 3 1.25 1.25
a.-c. A48 29c any single .40 .40
144 Sheet of 3 2.25 2.25
a.-c. A48 50c any single .75 .75

Souvenir Sheet

145 A48 $1 multicolored 1.65 1.65

Christmas — A49

Handicraft scenes: 29c, Nativity. 40c, Adoration of the Magi. 50c, Adoration of the Shepherds.

1991, Oct. 30 *Perf. 14x13½*

146 A49 29c multicolored .45 .45
147 A49 40c multicolored .60 .60
148 A49 50c multicolored .75 .75
Nos. 146-148 (3) 1.80 1.80

Pohnpei Rain Forest A50

Designs: a, Pohnpei fruit bat. b, Purple capped fruit-dove. c, Micronesian kingfisher. d. Birdnest fern. e, Island swiftlet. f, Long-billed white-eye. g, Brown noddy. h, Pohnpei lory. i, Pohnpei flycatcher. j, Caroline ground-dove. k, White-tailed tropicbird. l, Micronesian honeyeater. m, Ixora. n, Pohnpei fantail. o, Gray white-eye. p, Blue-faced parrotfinch. q, Cicadabird. r, Green skink.

1991, Nov. 18

149 Sheet of 18 10.00 10.00
a.-r. A50 29c any single .50 .50

Peace Corps — A51

Designs: a, Learning crop planting techniques. b, Education. c, John F. Kennedy. d, Public health nurses. e, Recreation.

1992, Apr. 10 **Litho.** *Perf. 14*

150 A51 29c Strip of 5, #a.-e. 2.25 2.25

Printed in sheets of 15.

Discovery of America, 500th Anniv. — A52

Designs: a, Queen Isabella I. b, Santa Maria. c, Columbus.

1992, May 23 **Litho.** *Perf. 13½*

151 A52 29c Strip of 3, #a.-c. 4.50 3.00

Admission to the UN, First Anniv. — A53

1992, Sept. 24 *Perf. 11x10½*

152 A53 29c multicolored .60 .60
153 A53 50c multicolored 1.00 1.00
a. Souvenir sheet of 2, #152-153 1.60 1.60

Christmas A54

1992, Dec. 4 *Perf. 13½*

154 A54 29c multicolored .60 .60

Pioneers of Flight A55

a, Andrei N. Tupolev. b, John A. Macready. c, Edward V. Rickenbacker. d, Manfred von Richtofen. e, Hugh M. Trenchard. f, Glenn H. Curtiss. g, Charles E. Kingsford-Smith. h, Igor I. Sikorsky.

1993, Apr. 12

155 A55 29c Block of 8, #a.-h. 4.25 4.25

See Nos. 178, 191, 200, 210, 233, 238, 249.

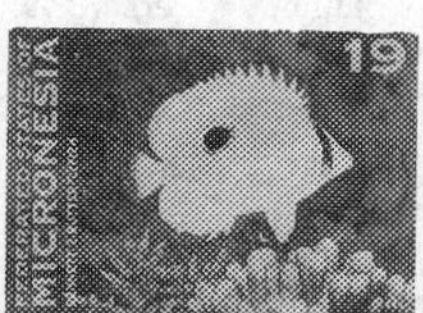

Fish — A56

Designs: 10c, Bigscale soldierfish. 19c, Bennett's butterflyfish. 20c, Peacock grouper. 22c, Great barracuda. 25c, Coral grouper. 29c, Regal angelfish. 30c, Bleeker's parrotfish. 35c, Picassofish. 40c, Mandarinfish. 45c, Bluebanded surgeonfish. 50c, Orange-striped triggerfish. 52c, Palette surgeonfish. 75c, Oriental sweetlips. $1, Zebra moray. $2, Foxface rabbitfish. $2.90, Orangespine unicornfish.

1993-94 **Litho.** *Perf. 13½*

156 A56 10c multicolored .20 .20
157 A56 19c multicolored .40 .40
158 A56 20c multicolored .40 .40
159 A56 22c multicolored .45 .45
160 A56 25c multicolored .50 .50
161 A56 29c multicolored .60 .60
162 A56 30c multicolored .60 .60
162A A56 35c multicolored .70 .70
163 A56 40c multicolored .80 .80
163A A56 45c multicolored .90 .90
164 A56 50c multicolored 1.00 1.00
164A A56 52c multicolored 1.10 1.10
164B A56 75c multicolored 1.50 1.50
165 A56 $1 multicolored 2.00 2.00
166 A56 $2 multicolored 4.00 4.00
167 A56 $2.90 multicolored 6.00 6.00
Nos. 157-167 (15) 20.95 20.95

Issued: 19c, 29c, 50c, $1, 5/14/93; 22c, 30c, 40c, 45c, 8/26/93; 10c, 20c, 35c, $2.90, 5/20/94; 25c, 52c, 75c, $2, 8/5/94.

See Nos. 213-227, 250.

A57

A59

Sailing Ships: a, Great Republic. b, Benjamin F. Packard. c, Stag Hound. d, Herald of the Morning. e, Rainbow. f, Flying Cloud. g, Lightning. h, Sea Witch. i, Columbia. j, New World. k, Young America. l, Courier.

1993, May 21 **Litho.** *Perf. 13½*

168 A57 29c Sheet of 12, #a.-l. 7.00 7.00

1993, July 4 **Litho.** *Perf. 13½*

172 A59 29c multicolored .60 .60

Thomas Jefferson, 250th anniv. of birth.

Pacific Canoes — A60

1993, July 21 **Litho.** *Perf. 13½*

173 A60 29c Yap .60 .60
174 A60 29c Kosrae .60 .60
175 A60 29c Pohnpei .60 .60
176 A60 29c Chuuk .60 .60
a. Block of 4, #173-176 2.40 2.40

Local Leaders — A61

Designs: a, Ambilos Iehsi, (1935-81), educator. b, Andrew Roboman (1905-92), Yap chief. c, Joab N. Sigrah (1932-88), first vice-speaker of Congress. d, Petrus Mailo (1902-71), Chuuk leader.

1993, Sept. 16 **Litho.** *Perf. 13½*

177 A61 29c Strip of 4, #a.-d. 2.35 2.35

See Nos. 204-207.

Pioneers of Flight Type of 1993

Designs: a, Hugh L. Dryden. b, Theodore von Karman. c, Otto Lilienthal. d, Thomas O.M. Sopwith. e, Lawrence B. Sperry. f, Alberto Santos-Dumont. g, Orville Wright. h, Wilbur Wright.

1993, Sept. 25 **Litho.** *Perf. 13½*

178 A55 50c Block of 8, #a.-h. 8.00 8.00

Micronesia stamps can be mounted in the Scott U.S. Trust Territories album.

Tourist Attractions, Pohnpei — A62

1993, Oct. 5

179 A62 29c Kepirohi Falls .60 .60
180 A62 50c Spanish Wall 1.00 1.00

Souvenir Sheet

181 A62 $1 Sokehs Rock 2.00 2.00

No. 181 contains one 80x50mm stamp.
See Nos. 187-189.

Butterflies — A63 Christmas — A64

Designs: No. 182a, Great eggfly female (typical). No. 182b, Great eggfly female (local variant). No. 183a, Monarch. No. 183b, Great eggfly male.

1993, Oct. 20 Litho. *Perf. 13½*

182 A63 29c Pair, #a.-b. 1.25 1.25
183 A63 50c Pair, #a.-b. 2.00 2.00

See No. 190.

1993, Nov. 11

184 A64 29c We Three Kings .60 .60
185 A64 50c Silent Night, Holy Night 1.00 1.00

Miniature Sheet

Yap Culture A65

Designs: a, Baby basket. b, Bamboo raft. c, Baskets, handbag. d, Fruit bat. e, Forest. f, Outrigger canoe. g, Dioscorea yams. h, Mangroves. i, Manta ray. j, Cyrtosperma taro. k, Fish weir. l, Seagrass, fish. m, Taro bowl. n, Thatched house. o, Coral reef. p, Lavalava. q, Dance. r, Stone money.

1993, Dec. 15 Litho. *Perf. 13½x14*

186 A65 29c Sheet of 18, #a.-r. 9.00 9.00

Tourist Attractions Type of 1993

Sites on Kosrae: 29c, Sleeping Lady Mountain. 40c, Walung. 50c, Lelu Ruins.

1994, Feb. 11 Litho. *Perf. 13½*

187 A62 29c multicolored .60 .60
188 A62 40c multicolored .80 .80
189 A62 50c multicolored 1.00 1.00
Nos. 187-189 (3) 2.40 2.40

Butterfly Type of 1993 with Added Inscription

Souvenir Sheet

Designs: a, 29c, like No. 182a. b, 29c, like No. 182b. c, 50c, like No. 183a. d, 50c, like No. 183b.

1994, Feb. 18

190 A63 Sheet of 4, #a.-d. 3.25 3.25

Inscription reads "Hong Kong '94 Stamp Exhibition" in Chinese on Nos. 190a, 190d, and in English on Nos. 190b-190c.
Inscriptions on Nos. 190a-190d are in black.

Pioneers of Flight Type of 1993

Designs: a, Edwin E. Aldrin, Jr. b, Neil A. Armstrong. c, Michael Collins. d, Wernher von Braun. e, Octave Chanute. f, T. Claude Ryan. g, Frank Whittle. h, Waldo D. Waterman.

1994, Mar. 4 Litho. *Perf. 13½*

191 A55 29c Block of 8, #a.-h. 4.25 4.25

1994 Micronesian Games A66

Designs: a, Spearfishing. b, Basketball. c, Coconut husking. d, Tree climbing.

1994, Mar. 26 *Perf. 13½x14*

192 A66 29c Block of 4, #a.-d. 2.50 2.50

Native Costumes — A67

Designs: a, Pohnpei. b, Kosrae. c, Chuuk. d, Yap.

1994, Mar. 31 *Perf. 13½*

193 A67 29c Block of 4, #a.-d. 2.50 2.50

Constitution, 15th Anniv. — A68

1994, May 10 Litho. *Perf. 11x10½*

194 A68 29c multicolored .60 .60

Flowers — A69

Designs: a, Fagraea berteriana. b, Pangium edule. c, Pittosporum ferrugineum. d, Sonneratia caseolaris.

1994, June 6 Litho. *Perf. 13½*

195 A69 29c Strip of 4, #a.-d. 2.50 2.50

1994 World Cup Soccer Championships, US — A70

Design: No. 197, Soccer players, diff.

1994, June 17 Litho. *Perf. 13½*

196 A70 50c red & multi 1.00 1.00
197 A70 50c blue & multi 1.00 1.00
a. Pair, #196-197 2.00 2.00

No. 197a has a continuous design.

Micronesian Postal Service, 10th Anniv. — A71

Stamps: a, #39, 45, 54 (c), 159, 189, 192 (b). b, #58 (d), 151, 161 (d), 176a, 183a (d). c, #4a, 137a, 184 (a), C12 (d), C39, C41. d, #161 (b), 183a (b), 183b, 193, C12, C40, C42.

1994, July 12 Litho. *Perf. 13½*

198 A71 29c Block of 4, #a.-d. 2.50 2.50

No. 198 is a continuous design.

Souvenir Sheet

PHILAKOREA '94 — A72

Dinosaurs: a, 29c, Iguanodons (b). b, 52c, Coelurosaurs (c). c, $1, Camarasaurus.

1994, Aug. 16 Litho. *Perf. 13½*

199 A72 Sheet of 3, #a.-c. 3.75 3.75

Pioneers of Flight Type of 1993

Designs: a, William A. Bishop. b, Karel J. Bossart. c, Marcel Dassault. d, Geoffrey de Havilland. e, Yuri A. Gagarin. f, Alan B. Shepard, Jr. g, John H. Towers. h, Hermann J. Oberth.

1994, Sept. 20 Litho. *Perf. 13½*

200 A55 50c Block of 8, #a.-h. 7.50 7.50

Migratory Birds — A73

Designs: a, Oriental cuckoo. b, Long-tailed cuckoo. c, Short-eared owl. d, Dollarbird.

1994, Oct. 20 Litho. *Perf. 13½*

201 A73 29c Block of 4, #a.-d. 2.50 2.50

Christmas A74

1994, Nov. 2

202 A74 29c Doves .60 .60
203 A74 50c Angels 1.00 1.00

Local Leaders Type of 1993

Pioneers of island unification: No. 204, Johnny Moses (1900-91), Pohnpei. No. 205, Belarmino Hatheylul (1907-93), Yap. No. 206, Anton Ring Buas (1907-79), Chuuk. No. 207, Paliknoa Sigrah (King John) (1875-1957), Kosrae.

1994, Dec. 15 Litho. *Perf. 13½*

204 A61 32c multicolored .65 .65
205 A61 32c multicolored .65 .65
206 A61 32c multicolored .65 .65
207 A61 32c multicolored .65 .65
Nos. 204-207 (4) 2.60 2.60

Souvenir Sheet

New Year 1995 (Year of the Boar) — A75

Illustration reduced.

1995, Jan. 2

208 A75 50c multicolored 1.00 1.00

Chuuk Lagoon A76

Underwater scenes: a, Photographer with light. b, Various species of fish, coral. c, Diver. d, Two gold fish.

1995, Feb. 6

209 A76 32c Block of 4, #a.-d. 2.50 2.50

Pioneers of Flight Type of 1993

Designs: a, Robert H. Goddard. b, Leroy R. Grumman. c, Hugo Junkers. d, James A. Lovell, Jr. e, Louis-Charles Breguet. f, Juan de la Cierva. g, Donald W. Douglas. h, Reginald J. Mitchell.

1995, Mar. 4 Litho. *Perf. 13½*

210 A55 32c Block of 8, #a.-h. 5.25 5.25

Dogs A77

a, West Highland white terrier. b, Welsh springer spaniel. c, Irish setter. d, Old English sheepdog.

1995, Apr. 5 Litho. *Perf. 13½*

211 A77 32c Block of 4, #a.-d. 2.50 2.50

Fish Type of 1993

Designs: 23c, Yellow-fin tuna. 32c, Saddled butterflyfish. 46c, Achilles tang. 55c, Moorish idol. 60c, Skipjack tuna. 78c, Square-spot fairy basslet. 95c, Bluelined snapper. $3, Flame angelfish. $5, Cave grouper.

#227: a, like #157. b, like #161. c, like #164. d, like #165. e, like #159. f. like #162. g, like #163. h, like #163A. i, like #156. j, like #158. k, like #162A. l, like #167. m, like #217. n, like #160. o, like #164A. p, like #164B. q, like #166. r, like #214. s, like #218. t, like #222. u, like #225. v, like #213. w, like #219. x, like #223. y, like #226.

1996 Litho. *Perf. 13½*

213 A56 23c multicolored .45 .45
214 A56 32c multicolored .65 .65
217 A56 46c multicolored .95 .95
218 A56 55c multicolored 1.10 1.10
219 A56 60c multicolored 1.25 1.25
222 A56 78c multicolored 1.50 1.50
223 A56 95c multicolored 1.90 1.90
225 A56 $3 multicolored 6.00 6.00
226 A56 $5 multicolored 10.00 10.00
Nos. 214-226 (8) 23.35 23.35

Miniature Sheet

227 A56 32c Sheet of 25, #a.-y. 16.00 16.00

Issued: 32c, 55c, 78c, $3, 5/15/95. 23c, 60c, 95c, $5, 8/4/95; 46c, 4/10/96.
This is an expanding set. Numbers may change.

Hibiscus — A78

a, Tiliaceus. b, Huegelii. c, Trionum. d, Splendens.

1995, June 1 Litho. *Perf. 13½*

228 A78 32c Strip of 4, #a.-d. 2.50 2.50

No. 228 is a continuous design.

Souvenir Sheet

UN, 50th Anniv. — A79

Illustration reduced.

1995, June 26 Litho. *Perf. 13½*
229 A79 $1 multicolored 2.00 2.00

Miniature Sheet

Singapore '95 — A80

Orchids: a, Paphiopedilum henrietta fujiwara. b, Thunia alba. c, Lycaste virginalis. d, Laeliocattleya prism palette.

1995, Sept. 1 Litho. *Perf. 13½*
230 A80 32c Sheet of 4, #a.-d. 2.60 2.60

End of World War II, 50th Anniv. — A81

US warships: a, USS Portland. b, USS Tillman. c, USS Soley. d, USS Hyman.

1995, Sept. 2
231 A81 60c Block of 4, #a.-d. 5.00 5.00

Souvenir Sheet

Intl. Stamp & Coin Expo, Beijing '95 — A82

Illustration reduced.

1995, Sept. 14
232 A82 50c Temple of Heaven 1.00 1.00

Pioneers of Flight Type of 1993

Designs: a, Hugh C.T. Dowding. b, William Mitchell. c, John K. Northrop. d, Frederick Handley Page. e, Frederick H. Rohr. f, Juan T. Trippe. g, Konstantin E. Tsiolkovsky. h. Ferdinand Graf von Zeppelin.

1995, Sept. 21 Litho. *Perf. 13½*
233 A55 60c Block of 8, #a.-h. 9.50 9.50

Christmas Poinsettias — A83

1995, Oct. 30 Litho. *Perf. 13½*
234 A83 32c gray & multi .65 .65
235 A83 60c bister & multi 1.25 1.25

Yitzhak Rabin (1922-95), Israeli Prime Minister — A84

1995, Nov. 30 Litho. *Perf. 13½*
236 A84 32c multicolored .65 .65

No. 236 was issued in sheets of 8.

Souvenir Sheet

New Year 1996 (Year of the Rat) — A85

Illustration reduced.

1996, Jan. 5 Litho. *Perf. 13½*
237 A85 50c multicolored 1.00 1.00

Pioneers of Flight Type of 1993

Designs: a, James H. Doolittle. b, Claude Dornier. c, Ira C. Eaker. d, Jacob C.H. Ellehammer. e, Henry H. Arnold. f, Louis Blériot. g, William E. Boeing. h, Sydney Camm.

1996, Feb. 21 Litho. *Perf. 13½*
238 A55 32c Block of 8, #a.-h. 5.25 5.25

Tourism in Yap — A86

Designs: a, Meeting house. b, Stone money. c, Churu dancing. d, Traditional canoe.

1996, Mar. 13 Litho. *Perf. 13½*
239 A86 32c Block of 4, #a.-d. 2.50 2.50

Sea Stars A87

Designe: a, Rhinoceros. b, Necklace c, Thick-skinned. d, Blue.

1996, Apr. 26 Litho. *Perf. 12*
240 A87 55c Block of 4, #a.-d. 4.50 4.50

Olympic Games, Cent. — A88

First Olympic stamps, Greece: a, #120. b, #122. c, #121. d, #128.

1996, Apr. 27
241 A88 60c Block of 4, #a.-d. 4.80 4.80

Souvenir Sheet

China '96, 9th Asian Intl. Philatelic Exhibition — A89

Design: The Tarrying Garden, Suzhou. Illustration reduced.

1996, May 15 *Perf. 13x13½*
242 A89 50c multicolored 1.00 1.00

Patrol Boats — A90

1996, May 3 Litho. *Perf. 13½*
243 A90 32c FSS Palikir .65 .65
244 A90 32c FSS Micronesia .65 .65
a. Pair, #243-244 1.30 1.30

No. 244a is a continuous design.

First Ford Automobile, Cent. — A91

Designs: a, 1896 Quadricycle. b, 1917 Model T truck. c, 1928 Model A Tudor Sedan. d, 1932 V-8 Sport Roadster. e, 1941 Lincoln Continental. f, 1953 F-100 Truck. g, 1958 Thunderbird convertible. h, 1996 Mercury Sable.

1996, June 4 *Perf. 13½*
245 A91 55c Sheet of 8, #a.-h. 8.75 8.75

Officer Reza, Member of Natl. Police Drug Enforcement Unit — A93

1996, July 31 Litho. *Perf. 13½*
247 A93 32c multicolored .65 .65

Citrus Fruit — A94

a, Orange. b, Lime. c, Lemon. d, Tangerine.

1996, Aug. 24 Litho. *Perf. 13½*
248 A94 50c Strip of 4, #a.-d. 4.00 4.00

Pioneers of Flight Type of 1993

Designs: a, Gianni Caproni. b, Henri Farman. c, Curtis E. LeMay. d, Grover Loening. e, Sergey P. Korolyov. f, Isaac M. Laddon. g, Glenn L. Martin. h, Alliott Verdon Roe.

1996, Sept. 18
249 A55 60c Block of 8, #a.-h. 9.75 9.75

Fish Type of 1993

Designs: a, like #157. b, like #165. c, like #162A. d, like #218.

1996, Oct. 21 Litho. *Perf. 13½*
250 A56 32c Block of 4, #a.-d. 2.50 2.50

Taipei '96, 10th Asian Intl. Philatelic Exhibition. Nos. 250a, 250d have English inscriptions. Nos. 250b-250c have Chinese inscriptions.

Magi Following Star to Bethlehem A95

1996, Oct. 30 Litho. *Perf. 13½*
251 A95 32c dark blue & multi .65 .65
252 A95 60c blue & multi 1.20 1.20

Christmas.

Canoe, Flag of Federated States of Micronesia Type of 1990

1996, Nov. 3 *Perf. 11x10½*
253 A42 $3 like #124 6.00 6.00

No. 253 inscribed "Free Association United States of America."

FEDERATED STATES OF MICRONESIA 60¢

Deng Xiaoping (1904-97) — A96

Portraits: a, Wearing white-collared shirt. b, Looking left. c, Looking right. d, Wearing hat. $3, Looking left, diff.

1997 Litho. *Perf. 14*
254 A96 60c Sheet of 4, #a.-d. 4.80 4.80

Souvenir Sheet

255 A96 $3 multicolored 6.00 6.00

Souvenir Sheet

Hong Kong — A97

Illustration reduced.

1997
256 A97 $2 multicolored 4.00 4.00

New Year 1997 (Year of the Ox) A98

1997 Litho. *Perf. 14*
257 A98 32c multicolored .65 .65

Souvenir Sheet

258 A98 $2 like #257 4.00 4.00

Return of Hong Kong to China A99

Flowers, Victoria Harbor: a, Melia azedarach. b, Sail from ship, Victoria Peak. c, Sail from ship, dendrobium chrysotoxum. d, Bauhinia blakeana. e, Cassia surattensis, Chinese junk. f, Junk, nelumbo nucifera.
$3, Strongylodon macrobatrys, pagoda.

1997, July 1
259 A99 60c Sheet of 6, #a.-f. 7.25 7.25

Souvenir Sheet

260 A99 $3 multicolored 6.00 6.00

Sea Goddesses of the Pacific — A100

a, Giant serpent, woman holding child, Walutahanga of Melanesia. b, Sailing ship in storm, woman holding lantern, Tien-Hou of China. c, Woman swimming to bottom of sea gathering fish into basket, Lorop of Micronesia. d, Woman swimming to man in canoe, Oto-Hime of Japan. e, Woman holding seashell, Nomoi of Micronesia. f, Three women in canoe, Junkgowa sisters of Australia.

1997 Litho. *Perf. 14*
261 A100 32c Sheet of 6, #a.-f. 3.75 3.75

PACIFIC 97.

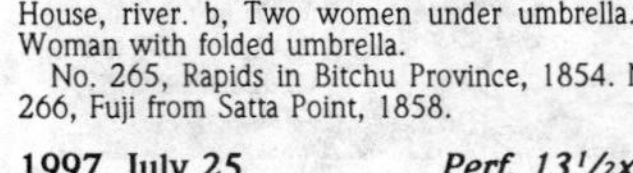

Paintings by Hiroshige (1797-1858) A101

Whirlpools at Naruto in Awa Province, 1857: No. 262: a, Sailboats in distance. b, Island of trees at left. c, Island of trees at right.
Tale of Genji: Viewing the Plum Blossoms, 1852: No. 263: a, Small evergreen trees in front of woman. b, Woman. c, Trees, house in distance with woman.
Snow on the Sumida River, 1847: No. 264: a, House, river. b, Two women under umbrella. c, Woman with folded umbrella.
No. 265, Rapids in Bitchu Province, 1854. No. 266, Fuji from Satta Point, 1858.

1997, July 25 *Perf. 13½x14*
262 A101 20c Sheet of 3, #a.-c. 1.20 1.20
263 A101 50c Sheet of 3, #a.-c. 3.00 3.00
264 A101 60c Sheet of 3, #a.-c. 3.60 3.60

Souvenir Sheets

265-266 A101 $2 each 4.00 4.00

Second Federated States of Micronesia Games A102

a, Tennis. b, Discus. c, Swimming. d, Canoeing.

1997, Aug. 15 Litho. *Perf. 14*
267 A102 32c Block of 4, #a.-d. 2.50 2.50

No. 267 was issued in sheets of 16 stamps.

Elvis Presley (1935-77) — A103

Various portraits.

1997, Aug. 16
268 A103 50c Sheet of 6, #a.-f. 6.00 6.00

Ocean Exploration A104

#269: a, Simon Lake, Argonaut, 1897. b, William Beebe, Bathysphere, 1934. c, Auguste Piccard, Bathyscaphe, 1954. d, Harold Edgerton, deep-sea camera, 1954. e, Jacques Piccard, Trieste, 1960. f, Edwin Link, Man-in-Sea Project, 1962. g, Melvin Fisher, search for treasure, 1971. h, Robert Ballard, Alvin, 1978. i, Sylvia Earle, Deep Rover, 1979.
No. 270, C. Wyville Thomson, deep-sea dredge, vert. No. 271, Shinkai 6500 exploring bottom of sea, vert. No. 272, Jacques-Yves Cousteau, vert.

1997, Oct. 6 Litho. *Perf. 14*
269 A104 32c Sheet of 9, #a.-i. 4.30 4.30

Souvenir Sheets

270-272 A104 $2 each 4.00 4.00

Diana, Princess of Wales (1961-97) A105

1997, Nov. 26 Litho. *Perf. 14*
273 A105 60c multicolored 1.20 1.20

No. 273 was issued in sheets of 6.

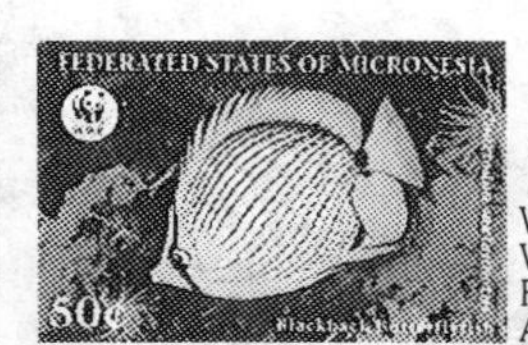

World Wildlife Fund A106

Butterfly fish: a, Blackback. b, Saddled. c, Threadfin. d, Bennett's.

1997, Nov. 24 Litho. *Perf. 14*
274 A106 50c Block of 4, #a.-d. 4.00 4.00

No. 274 was issued in sheets of 16 stamps.

Christmas Paintings — A107

Christ Glorified in the Court of Heaven, by Fra Angelico: No. 275, Angels playing musical instruments. No. 276, Choir of Angels.
A Choir of Angels, by Simon Marmion: No. 277, Two angels blowing long horns. No. 278, One angel blowing horn.

1997, Nov. 25
275 A107 32c multicolored .65 .65
276 A107 32c multicolored .65 .65
a. Horiz. pair, Nos. 275-276 1.30 1.30
277 A107 60c multicolored 1.20 1.20
278 A107 60c multicolored 1.20 1.20
a. Vert. pair, Nos. 277-278 2.40 2.40

Nos. 276a, 278a were each issued in sheets of 8 pairs.

Souvenir Sheets

New Year 1998 (Year of the Tiger) — A108

Illustration reduced.

1998, Jan. 2 Litho. *Perf. 14*
279 A108 50c shown 1.00 1.00
280 A108 50c Chinese toy (face) 1.00 1.00

Souvenir Sheet

Micronesia's Admission to United Nations, 7th Anniv. — A109

Illustration reduced.

1998, Feb. 13 *Perf. 13½*
281 A109 $1 multicolored 2.00 2.00

Winnie the Pooh — A110

No. 282: a, Rabbit. b, Owl. c, Eeyore. d, Kanga and Roo. e, Piglet. f, Tigger. g, Pooh. h, Christopher Robin.
No. 283, Piglet, Pooh, and Tigger. No. 284, Rabbit and Pooh.

1998, Feb. 16 *Perf. 14x14½*
282 A110 32c Sheet of 8, #a.-h. 5.25 5.25

Souvenir Sheets

283-284 A110 $2 each 4.00 4.00

AIR POST STAMPS

Boeing 727, 1968 — AP1

1984, July 12 Litho. *Perf. 13½*
C1 AP1 28c shown .60 .60
C2 AP1 35c SA-16 Albatross, 1960 .80 .80
C3 AP1 40c PBY-5A Catalina, 1951 1.00 1.00
Nos. C1-C3 (3) 2.40 2.40

Ausipex Type of 1984

Ausipex '84 emblem and: 28c, Caroline Islands No. 4. 35c, No. 7. 40c, No. 19.

1984, Sept. 21 Litho. *Perf. 13½*
C4 A4 28c multicolored .65 .65
C5 A4 35c multicolored .85 .85
C6 A4 40c multicolored 1.10 1.10
Nos. C4-C6 (3) 2.60 2.60

Christmas Type

Children's drawings.

1984, Dec. 20
C7 A5 28c Illustrated Christmas text 1.00 1.00
C8 A5 35c Decorated palm tree 1.25 1.25
C9 A5 40c Feast preparation 1.50 1.50
Nos. C7-C9 (3) 3.75 3.75

Ships Type

1985, Aug. 19
C10 A6 33c L'Astrolabe .65 .65
C11 A6 39c La Coquille .90 .90
C12 A6 44c Shenandoah 1.10 1.10
Nos. C10-C12 (3) 2.65 2.65

Christmas Type

1985, Oct. 15 Litho. *Perf. 13½*
C13 A7 33c Dublon Protestant Church .90 .90
C14 A7 44c Pohnpei Catholic Church 1.25 1.25

Audubon Type

1985, Oct. 31 *Perf. 14½*
C15 A8 44c Sooty tern 1.00 1.00

Ruins Type

1985, Dec. Litho. *Perf. 13½*
C16 A16 33c Nan Tauas inner courtyard .70 .70
C17 A16 39c Outer wall .80 .80
C18 A16 44c Tomb .90 .90
Nos. C16-C18 (3) 2.40 2.40

Halley's Comet AP2

1986, May 16
C19 AP2 44c dk bl, bl & blk 1.40 1.25

Return of Nauruans from Truk, 40th Anniv. AP3

1986, May 16
C20 AP3 44c Ship in port 1.40 1.25

AMERIPEX '86 Type

Bully Hayes (1829-1877), buccanneer.

1986, May 22

C21 A18 33c Forging Hawaiian stamp .55 .55
C22 A18 39c Sinking of the Leonora, Kosrae .70 .70
C23 A18 44c Hayes escapes capture .75 .75
C24 A18 75c Biography, by Louis Becke 1.50 1.50
Nos. C21-C24 (4) 3.50 3.50

Souvenir Sheet

C25 A18 $1 Hayes ransoming chief 3.25 3.25

Christmas Type

Virgin and child paintings: 33c, Austria, 19th cent. 44c, Italy, 18th cent., diff.

1986, Oct. 15 Litho. *Perf. 14½*

C26 A20 33c multicolored 1.00 1.00
C27 A20 44c multicolored 1.40 1.40

Anniversaries and Events Type

1987, June 13 Litho. *Perf. 14½*

C28 A21 33c US currency, bicent. .60 .60
C29 A21 39c 1st American in orbit, 25th anniv. 1.00 1.00
C30 A21 44c US Constitution, bicent. 1.10 1.10
Nos. C28-C30 (3) 2.70 2.70

Christmas Type

1987, Nov. 16 Litho. *Perf. 14½*

C31 A22 33c Holy Family .80 .80
C32 A22 39c Shepherds .90 .90
C33 A22 44c Three Wise Men 1.00 1.00
Nos. C31-C33 (3) 2.70 2.70

Bird Type

1988, Aug. 1 Litho. *Perf. 13½*

C34 A9 33c Great truk white-eye .55 .55
C35 A9 44c Blue-faced parrotfinch .70 .70
C36 A9 $1 Yap monarch 1.75 1.75
Nos. C34-C36 (3) 3.00 3.00

Colonial Era Type

1988, July 20 *Perf. 13x13½*

C37 A23 44c Traditional skills (boat-building) .95 .95
C38 A23 44c Modern Micronesia (tourism) .95 .95
a. Pair, #C37-C38 1.90 1.90

Printed se-tenant in sheets of 28 plus 4 center labels picturing flags of Kosrae (UL), Truk (UR), Pohnpei (LL) and Yap ((LR).

Flags of the Federated States of Micronesia AP4

1989, Jan. 19 Litho. *Perf. 13x13½*

C39 AP4 45c Pohnpei .70 .70
C40 AP4 45c Truk .70 .70
C41 AP4 45c Kosrae .70 .70
C42 AP4 45c Yap .70 .70
a. Block of 4, #C39-C42 2.80 2.80

This issue exists with 44c denominations but was not issued.

Aircraft Serving Micronesia — AP5

1990, July 16 Litho. *Perf. 14*

C43 AP5 22c shown .45 .45
C44 AP5 36c multi, diff. .70 .70
C45 AP5 39c multi, diff. .80 .80
C46 AP5 45c multi, diff. .90 .90

1992, Mar. 27

C47 AP5 40c Propeller plane, outrigger canoe .75 .75
C48 AP5 50c Passenger jet, sailboat .90 .90
Nos. C43-C48 (6) 4.50 4.50

Souvenir Sheet

First Manned Moon Landing, 25th Anniv. — AP6

Illustration reduced.

1994, July 20 Litho. *Perf. 13½*

C49 AP6 $2.90 US #C76 4.25 4.25

MIDDLE CONGO

'mi–dᵊl 'käŋ–(,)gō

LOCATION — Western Africa at the Equator, bordering on the Atlantic Ocean
GOVT. — Former French Colony
AREA — 166,069
POP. — 746,805 (1936)
CAPITAL — Brazzaville

In 1910 Middle Congo, formerly a part of French Congo, was declared a separate colony. It was grouped with Gabon and the Ubangi-Shari and Chad Territories and officially designated French Equatorial Africa. This group became a single administrative unit in 1934. See Gabon.

See Congo People's Republic for issues of 1959 onward.

100 Centimes = 1 Franc

See French Equatorial Africa No. 191 for additional stamp inscribed "Moyen Congo" and "Afrique Equatoriale Francaise."

Leopard — A1

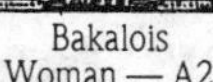

Bakalois Woman — A2 Coconut Grove — A3

Perf. 14x13½

1907-22 Typo. Unwmk.

1 A1 1c ol gray & brn .15 .15
2 A1 2c vio & brn .20 .15
3 A1 4c blue & brn .20 .15
4 A1 5c dk grn & bl .30 .15
5 A1 5c yel & bl ('22) .50 .50
6 A1 10c car & bl .30 .15
7 A1 10c dp grn & bl grn ('22) 1.40 1.40
8 A1 15c brn vio & rose .80 .50
9 A1 20c brown & bl 1.25 .85
10 A2 25c blue & grn .35 .35
11 A2 25c bl grn & gray ('22) .40 .45
12 A2 30c scar & grn .80 .50
13 A2 30c dp rose & rose ('22) .80 .70
14 A2 35c vio brn & bl .50 .50
15 A2 40c dl grn & brn .50 .50
16 A2 45c violet & red 3.00 2.00
17 A2 50c bl grn & red .75 .60
18 A2 50c bl & grn ('22) .75 .70
19 A2 75c brown & bl 4.50 3.00
20 A3 1fr dp grn & vio 6.00 4.00
21 A3 2fr vio & gray grn 5.00 3.25
22 A3 5fr blue & rose 19.00 16.00
Nos. 1-22 (22) 47.45 36.55

For stamps of types A1-A3 in changed colors, see Chad, French Congo and Ubangi-Shari.

For overprints and surcharges see Nos. 23-60, B1-B2.

Stamps and Types of 1907-22 Overprinted in Black, Blue or Red

AFRIQUE EQUATORIALE FRANÇAISE

1924-30

23 A1 1c ol gray & brn .15 .15
24 A1 2c violet & brn .15 .15
25 A1 4c blue & brn .15 .15
26 A1 5c yellow & bl .15 .15
27 A1 10c grn & bl grn (R) .15 .15
28 A1 10c car & gray ('25) .15 .15
29 A1 15c brn vio & rose (Bl) .15 .15
a. Double surcharge 70.00
30 A1 20c brown & blue .15 .15
31 A1 20c bl grn & yel grn ('26) .15 .15
32 A1 20c dp brn & rose lil ('27) .45 .15

Overprinted **AFRIQUE EQUATORIALE FRANÇAISE**

33 A2 25c bl grn & gray .30 .30
34 A2 30c rose & pale rose (Bl) .40 .30
35 A2 30c gray & bl vio (R) ('25) .35 .25
36 A2 30c dk grn & grn ('27) .65 .50
37 A2 35c choc & bl .35 .25
38 A2 40c ol grn & brn .35 .25
39 A2 45c vio & pale red (Bl) .65 .45
a. Inverted overprint 75.00 75.00
40 A2 50c blue & grn (R) .40 .25
41 A2 50c org & blk ('25) .35 .25
a. Without overprint 100.00
42 A2 65c org brn & bl ('27) 1.25 .90
43 A2 75c brown & blue .40 .25
44 A2 90c brn red & pink ('30) 2.00 1.65
45 A3 1fr green & vio .65 .50
a. Double overprint 125.00 110.00
46 A3 1.10fr vio & brn ('28) 2.00 1.25
47 A3 1.50fr ultra & bl ('30) 3.50 2.50
48 A3 2fr vio & gray grn .90 .65
49 A3 3fr red violet ('30) 3.75 3.00
50 A3 5fr blue & rose 2.50 1.50
Nos. 23-50 (28) 22.55 16.50

Nos. 48 and 50 Surcharged with New Values

1924

51 A3 25c on 2fr vio & gray grn .35 .35
52 A3 25c on 5fr bl & rose (Bl) .35 .35

Types of 1924-27 Surcharged with New Values in Black or Red

1925-27

53 A3 65c on 1fr red org & ol brn .50 .50
54 A3 85c on 1fr red org & ol brn .50 .50
55 A2 90c on 75c brn red & rose red ('27) .60 .60
56 A3 1.25fr on 1fr dl bl & ultra (R) .25 .25
57 A3 1.50fr on 1fr ultra & bl ('27) .85 .60
a. New value omitted 80.00
58 A3 3fr on 5fr org brn & dl red ('27) 1.10 .75
a. New value omitted 150.00
59 A3 10fr on 5fr ver & bl grn ('27) 6.00 5.00
60 A3 20fr on 5fr org brn & vio ('27) 7.25 5.25
Nos. 53-60 (8) 17.05 13.45

Bars cover old values on Nos. 56-60.

Colonial Exposition Issue

Common Design Types

1931 Engr. *Perf. 12½*

Name of Country in Black

61 CD70 40c deep green 2.00 1.75
62 CD71 50c violet 1.10 .90
63 CD72 90c red orange 1.40 1.10
64 CD73 1.50fr dull blue 2.00 1.10
Nos. 61-64 (4) 6.50 4.85

Viaduct at Mindouli A4

Pasteur Institute at Brazzaville A5

Government Building, Brazzaville A6

1933 Photo. *Perf. 13½*

65 A4 1c lt brown .15 .15
66 A4 2c dull blue .15 .15
67 A4 4c olive grn .15 .15
68 A4 5c red violet .15 .15
69 A4 10c slate .15 .15
70 A4 15c dk violet .25 .25
71 A4 20c red, *pink* 3.75 2.50
72 A4 25c orange .35 .25
73 A4 30c yellow grn .90 .75
74 A5 40c orange brn .75 .55
75 A5 45c blk, *green* .90 .70
76 A5 50c black violet .55 .40
77 A5 65c brn red, *grn* .60 .50
78 A5 75c black, *pink* 6.00 4.50
79 A5 90c carmine .60 .55
80 A5 1fr dark red .60 .50
81 A5 1.25fr Prus blue .90 .65
82 A5 1.50fr dk blue 3.25 1.65
83 A6 1.75fr dk violet 1.00 .70
84 A6 2fr grnsh blk .80 .70
85 A6 3fr orange 1.75 1.75
86 A6 5fr slate blue 9.00 7.50
87 A6 10fr black 30.00 17.00
88 A6 20fr dark brown 20.00 13.00
Nos. 65-88 (24) 82.70 55.15

SEMI-POSTAL STAMPS

No. 6 Surcharged in Black

1916 Unwmk. *Perf. 14x13½*

B1 A1 10c + 5c car & blue .65 .45
a. Double surcharge 70.00 70.00
b. Inverted surcharge 60.00 60.00

A printing with the surcharge placed lower and more to the left was made and used in Ubangi.

No. 6 Surcharged in Red **+5c**

B2 A1 10c + 5c car & blue .50 .50

POSTAGE DUE STAMPS

MOYEN-CONGO

Postage Due Stamps of France Overprinted

A. E. F.

1928 Unwmk. *Perf. 14x13½*

J1 D2 5c light blue .40 .40
J2 D2 10c gray brn .40 .40
J3 D2 20c olive grn .55 .55
J4 D2 25c brt rose .55 .55
J5 D2 30c lt red .55 .55
J6 D2 45c blue grn .65 .65
J7 D2 50c brown vio .70 .70
J8 D2 60c yellow brn 1.00 1.00
J9 D2 1fr red brn 1.10 1.10
J10 D2 2fr orange red 1.75 1.75
J11 D2 3fr brt violet 3.50 3.50
Nos. J1-J11 (11) 11.15 11.15

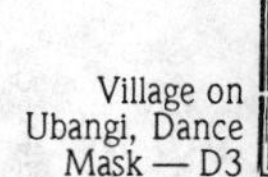

Village on Ubangi, Dance Mask — D3

Steamer on Ubangi River — D4

1930 **Typo.**

J12 D3 5c dp bl & ol .40 .40
J13 D3 10c dp red & brn .60 .60
J14 D3 20c green & brn 1.50 1.50
J15 D3 25c lt bl & brn 2.00 2.00
J16 D3 30c bis brn & Prus bl 3.00 3.00
J17 D3 45c Prus bl & ol 3.00 3.00
J18 D3 50c red vio & brn 3.00 3.00
J19 D3 60c gray lil & bl blk 3.50 3.50
J20 D4 1fr bis brn & bl blk 6.00 6.00
J21 D4 2fr violet & brn 6.50 6.50
J22 D4 3fr dk red & brn 6.50 6.50
Nos. J12-J22 (11) 36.00 36.00

Rubber Trees and Djoué River — D5

1933 **Photo.** ***Perf. 13½***

J23 D5 5c apple green .40 .40
J24 D5 10c dk bl, *bl* .40 .40
J25 D5 20c red, *yel* .55 .55
J26 D5 25c chocolate .55 .55
J27 D5 30c orange red .65 .65
J28 D5 45c dk violet .65 .65
J29 D5 50c gray black 1.25 1.25
J30 D5 60c blk, *orange* 1.75 1.75
J31 D5 1fr brown rose 2.75 2.75
J32 D5 2fr orange yel 3.50 3.50
J33 D5 3fr Prus blue 6.00 6.00
Nos. J23-J33 (11) 18.45 18.45

MOHELI

mō-'ā-lē

LOCATION — One of the Comoro Islands, situated in the Mozambique Channel midway between Madagascar and Mozambique (Africa)
GOVT. — French Colony
AREA — 89 sq. mi.
POP. — 4,000
CAPITAL — Fomboni

See Comoro Islands

100 Centimes = 1 Franc

Navigation and Commerce — A1

Perf. 14x13½

1906-07 **Typo.** **Unwmk.**

Name of Colony in Blue or Carmine

1 A1 1c blk, *lil bl* .85 .80
2 A1 2c brn, *buff* .85 .75
3 A1 4c claret, *lav* 1.40 1.10
4 A1 5c yellow grn 1.40 1.10
5 A1 10c carmine 2.00 1.25
6 A1 20c red, *green* 5.50 2.50
7 A1 25c blue 5.50 3.00
8 A1 30c brn, *bister* 8.50 6.25
9 A1 35c blk, *yellow* 4.50 2.25
10 A1 40c red, *straw* 8.50 4.00
11 A1 45c blk, *gray grn* ('07) 42.50 27.50
12 A1 50c brn, *az* 14.00 7.50
13 A1 75c dp vio, *org* 14.00 10.50
14 A1 1fr brnz grn, *straw* 14.00 7.50
15 A1 2fr vio, *rose* 19.00 17.00
16 A1 5fr lil, *lavender* 82.50 75.00
Nos. 1-16 (16) 225.00 168.00

Perf. 13½x14 stamps are counterfeits.

Issue of 1906-07 Surcharged in Carmine or Black

05 **10**

1912

17 A1 5c on 4c cl, *lav* (C) .60 .60
18 A1 5c on 20c red, *grn* 2.00 2.00
19 A1 5c on 30c brn, *bis* (C) .90 .90
20 A1 10c on 40c red, *straw* .90 .90
21 A1 10c on 45c blk, *gray grn* (C) .90 .90
a. "Moheli" double 250.00
b. "Moheli" triple 250.00
22 A1 10c on 50c brn, *az* (C) 1.25 1.25
Nos. 17-22 (6) 6.55 6.55

Two spacings between the surcharged numerals are found on Nos. 17 to 22.

The stamps of Mohéli were supposed to have been superseded by those of Madagascar, January, 1908. However, Nos. 17-22 were surcharged in 1912 to use up remainders. These were available for use in Madagascar and the entire Comoro archipelago. In 1950 stamps of Comoro Islands came into use.

MOLDOVA

mäl-'dō-və

(Moldavia)

LOCATION — Southeastern Europe, bounded by Romania and the Ukraine
GOVT. — Independent republic, member of the Commonwealth of Independent States
AREA — 13,012 sq. mi.
POP. — 4,300,000 (1989)
CAPITAL — Chisinau

With the breakup of the Soviet Union on Dec. 26, 1991, Moldova and ten former Soviet republics established the Commonwealth of Independent States.

100 Kopecks = 1 Ruble
100 Bani = 1 Leu (1993)

Catalogue values for all unused stamps in this country are for Never Hinged items.

Codrii Nature Preserve A6

1992, Feb. 8 **Litho.** ***Perf. 12***

25 A6 25k multicolored .35

Natl. Arms — A7

1992, May 24 **Photo.** ***Perf. 13½***

26 A7 35k green .15
27 A7 50k red .15
28 A7 65k brown .20
29 A7 1r purple .30
30 A7 1.50r blue .40
Nos. 26-30 (5) 1.20

Birds — A8

She-Wolf Suckling Romulus and Remus — A10

Church of St. Panteleimon, Cent. — A9

Designs: 50k, Merops apiaster. 65k, Oriolus oriolus. 2.50r, Picus viridis. 6r, Coracias garrulus. 7.50r, Upupa epops. 15r, Cuculus canorus.

1992, Aug. 5 **Litho.** ***Perf. 13½x14***

31 A8 50k multicolored .15
32 A8 65k multicolored .15
33 A8 2.50r multicolored .30
34 A8 6r multicolored .75
35 A8 7.50r multicolored 1.00
36 A8 15r multicolored 2.00
Nos. 31-36 (6) 4.35

No. 31 incorrectly inscribed "ariaster."

See Nos. 75-81.

1992, Aug. 10 **Photo.** ***Perf. 11½***

37 A9 1.50r multicolored .30

1992, Aug. 10 ***Perf. 12x11½***

38 A10 5r multicolored .50

Russia Nos. 4598-4599, 5839 Surcharged "MOLDOVA" and New Value in Black or Red

1992, Aug. 31 **Litho.** ***Perf. 12x12½***

39 A2138 2.50r on 4k #4599 .15
40 A2139 6r on 3k #4598 .25
41 A2138 8.50r on 4k #4599 .35
42 A2765 10r on 3k #5839 (R) .45
a. Black surcharge .45
b. Brown red surcharge .45
Nos. 39-42 (4) 1.20

Sheets of #39, 41 had row 5 inverted. On #40 only the 1st 5 stamps of row 5 were inverted. Counterfeit inverts were made using the original plates but with all 100 surcharges inverted. All inverts on #42 are fakes.

Russia Nos. 4596-4598 Surcharged in Black, Green or Red

1992, Oct. 20 **Litho.** ***Perf. 12x12½***

43 A2138 45k on 2k #4597 (G) .15
44 A2138 46k on 2k #4597 .15
45 A2138 63k on 1k #4596 (R) .15
46 A2138 63k on 3k #4598 .15
47 A2138 70k on 1k #4596 (R) .20
50 A2138 4r on 1k #4596 .95
a. Red surcharge .95
Nos. 43-50 (6) 1.75

Nos. 45-46 exist with overprint inverted (6th row of sheet).

1992 Summer Olympics, Barcelona — A11

1992, Oct. 24 **Litho.** ***Perf. 13***

53 A11 35k High jump *1.25*
54 A11 65k Wrestling *1.25*
55 A11 1r Archery *1.25*
56 A11 2.50r Swimming *1.25*
57 A11 10r Equestrian *1.25*
a. Souvenir sheet, #53-57 + label *6.50*
Nos. 53-57 (5) *6.25*

Nos. 55-56 Ovptd. with Name of Medalist, Medal and Olympic Rings in Bronze or Silver

1992, Oct. 24

58 A11 1r "NATALIA VALEEV / bronz" (BR) 1.00
59 A11 2.50r "IURIE BASCATOV / argint" 2.50

Souvenir Sheet

Tudor Casapu, 1992 Weight Lifting Gold Medalist — A12

1992, Oct. 24 ***Perf. 14½***

60 A12 25r multicolored 5.00

Admission of Moldova to UN — A13

Designs: 12r, UN Headquarters at left, Statue of Liberty, UN emblem, Moldovan flag.

1992, Oct. 24 ***Perf. 13***

61 A13 1.30r multicolored .25
62 A13 12r multicolored 1.00

Moldovan Participation in Conference on European Security and Cooperation A14

1992, Oct. 24

63 A14 2.50r Flag, Prague Castle .25
64 A14 25r Helsinki Cathedral, flag 1.25

Traditional Folk Art — A15

1992, Nov. 21 ***Perf. 12x11½***

65 A15 7.50r Rug, pottery .30

Admission of Moldova to UPU — A16

1992, Dec. 26 ***Perf. 12***

66 A16 5r Train, flag, emblem .75
67 A16 10r Plane, flag, emblem 1.50

Discovery of America, 500th Anniv. — A17

1992, Dec. 26 **Litho.** ***Perf. 12***

68 A17 1r Galleon .50
69 A17 6r Carrack 1.50
70 A17 6r Caravel 1.50
a. Pair, #69-70 3.00
Nos. 68-70 (3) 3.50

Souvenir Sheet

71 A17 25r Columbus 7.00

Elaphe Longissima A18

Denominations at: a, UL. b, UR. c, LL. d, LR.

1993, July 3 **Litho.** ***Perf. 13½***

72 A18 3r Block of 4, #a.-d. .75
73 A18 15r Natrix natrix 1.00
74 A18 25r Vipera berus 1.75
Nos. 72-74 (3) 3.50

Bird Type of 1992

1993, July 24 **Litho.** ***Perf. 13x13½***

75 A8 2r like #31 .15
76 A8 3r like #32 .15
77 A8 5r like #33 .15

78 A8 10r like #34 .30
79 A8 15r like #35 .40
80 A8 50r like #36 1.25
81 A8 100r Hirundo rustica 2.50
Nos. 75-81 (7) 4.90

Natl. Arms — A19

1993, Aug. 7 Photo. *Perf. 12x12½*

82 A19 2k blue .15
83 A19 3k purple .15
84 A19 6k green .15
85 A19 10k olive & purple .15
86 A19 15k olive & purple .15
87 A19 20k gray & purple .20
88 A19 30k yellow & purple .30
89 A19 50k pink & purple .45

Size: 21x32½mm

Perf. 12½x12

90 A19 100k multicolored .90
91 A19 250k multicolored 2.00
Nos. 82-91 (10) 4.60

Butterflies — A20

Flowers — A21

1993, Dec. 22 Litho. *Perf. 13*

94 A20 6b Pyrameis atalanta .15
95 A20 10b Papilio machaon .15
96 A20 50b Vanessa jo .60
97 A20 250b Saturnia pavonia 2.75
Nos. 94-97 (4) 3.65

1993, Dec. 25 Litho. *Perf. 13½*

Designs: 6b, Tulipa bibersteiniana. 15b, Convallaria majalis. 25b, Galanthus nivalis. 30b, Paeonia peregrina. 50b, Galanthus plicatus. 90b, Pulsatilla grandis. 250b, Cypripedium calceolus.

98 A21 6b multicolored .15 .15
99 A21 15b multicolored .20 .20
100 A21 25b multicolored .40 .40
101 A21 30b multicolored .50 .50
102 A21 50b multicolored .75 .75
103 A21 90b multicolored 2.00 2.00
Nos. 98-103 (6) 4.00 4.00

Souvenir Sheet

104 A21 250b multicolored 4.00 4.00

No. 104 contains one 30x45mm stamp.

A22

A23

Famous Men: 6b, Dragos Voda. 25b, Bogdan Voda I. 50b, Latcu Voda. 100b, Petru I Musat. 150b, Roman Voda Musat. 200b, Stefan I.

1993, Dec. 29 Litho. *Perf. 13*

105 A22 6b multicolored .15 .15
106 A22 25b multicolored .30 .30
107 A22 50b multicolored .50 .50
108 A22 100b multicolored 1.00 1.00
109 A22 150b multicolored 1.50 1.50
110 A22 200b multicolored 2.00 2.00
Nos. 105-110 (6) 5.45 5.45

1993, Dec. 29 Litho. *Perf. 13*

Europa (Contemporary art): 3b, History of Man, by M. Grecu. 150b, Springtime, by I. Vieru.

111 A23 3b multicolored .50 .50
112 A23 150b multicolored 2.75 2.75

A24

A25

1994, Feb. 12 Litho. *Perf. 13½*

113 A24 3b Biathlete, skiiers .15 .15
114 A24 150b Biathlete, diff. 2.75 2.75

1994 Winter Olympics, Lillehammer.

Russia No. 4596 Surcharged in Dark Blue

1994, Apr. 11 Litho. *Perf. 12x12½*

114A A2138 3b on 1k olive grn .15 .15
114B A2138 25b on 1k olive grn .30 .30
114C A2138 50b on 1k olive grn .60 .60
Nos. 114A-114C (3) 1.05 1.05

1994, June 18 Litho. *Perf. 14*

Europa: 1b, Gemini space mission, Titan II rocket. 45b, Ed White, Gemini IV. 2.50 l, Lunar landing module.

115 A25 1b multicolored .25 .25
116 A25 45b multicolored 1.00 1.00
117 A25 2.50 l multicolored 6.00 6.00
Nos. 115-117 (3) 7.25 7.25

First Manned Moon Landing, 25th anniv.

Natl. Arms — A26

1994 *Perf. 13½x14*

118 A26 1b multicolored .75 .75
119 A26 10b multicolored .15 .15
120 A26 30b multicolored .25 .25
121 A26 38b multicolored .30 .30
122 A26 45b multicolored .35 .35
123 A26 75b multicolored .60 .60
125 A26 1.50 l multicolored 1.10 1.10
126 A26 1.80 l multicolored 1.40 1.40
127 A26 2.50 l multi, size: 23½x29mm 2.00 2.00
128 A26 4.50 l multicolored 3.50 3.50
128A A26 5.40 l multicolored 4.25 4.25

Size: 23½x29mm

128B A26 6.90 l multicolored 5.50 5.50
128C A26 7.20 l multicolored 5.75 5.75
129 A26 13 l multicolored 10.00 10.00
130 A26 24 l multicolored 19.00 19.00
Nos. 118-130 (15) 54.90 54.90

Issued: 1b, 45b, 1.50 l, 4.50 l, 6/11/94; 10b, 20b, 5.40 l, 6.90 l, 13 l, 7/16/94; 38b, 75b, 1.80 l, 2.50 l, 7.20 l, 8/13/94.

This is a expanding set. Numbers may change.

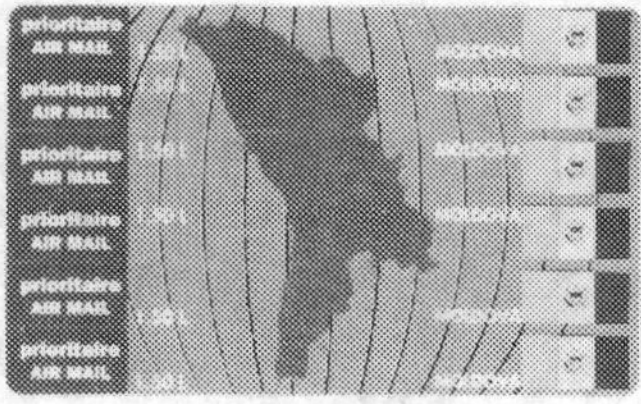

Stamp Card — A27

Designs: 1.50 l, 4.50 l, Map of Moldova.

Rouletted 26 on 2 or 3 Sides

1994, Dec. 22 Litho.

Self-Adhesive

Cards of 6 + 6 labels

131 A27 1.50 l #a.-f., lt vio & multi 7.50
132 A27 4.50 l #a.-f., dp red vio & multi 20.00

Individual stamps measure 70x9mm and have a card backing. Se-tenant labels inscribed "AIR MAIL."

Famous People — A28

Designs: 3b, Maria Cibotari (1910-49), singer. 90b, Dumitru Caraciobanu (1937-80), actor. 150b, Eugeniu Coca (1893-1954), composer. 250b, Igor Vieru (1923-83), actor.

1994, June 30 Litho. *Perf. 13½*

133 A28 3b multicolored .15 .15
134 A28 90b multicolored .60 .60
135 A28 150b multicolored 1.00 1.00
136 A28 250b multicolored 1.75 1.75
Nos. 133-136 (4) 3.50 3.50

Stamp Day A29

Designs: 10b, Designing stamp. 45b, Printing stamps. 2 l, Inspecting finished sheets.

1994, July 22 Litho. *Perf. 14*

137 A29 10b multicolored .25 .25
138 A29 45b multicolored 1.00 1.00
139 A29 2 l multicolored 3.75 3.75
Nos. 137-139 (3) 5.00 5.00

Intl. Olympic Committee, Cent. — A30

1994, Aug. 29 Litho. *Perf. 13½x14*

140 A30 60b Pierre de Coubertin .75 .75
141 A30 1.50 l Olympic rings, symbol 1.90 1.90

Moldova's Entrance into NATO — A31

Intl. Year of the Family — A32

Designs: 60b, Moldova Pres. Mircea Snegur, NATO Secretary General Manfred Worner signing documents. 2.50 l, World map centered on Europe.

1994, Nov. 8 Litho. *Perf. 13½*

142 A31 60b multicolored 1.25 1.25
143 A31 2.50 l multicolored 5.00 5.00

1994, Nov. 26 *Perf. 14*

144 A32 30b Family .75 .75
145 A32 60b Mother breast-feeding 1.50 1.50
146 A32 1.50 l Child painting 3.00 3.00
Nos. 144-146 (3) 5.25 5.25

Moldova stamps can be mounted in the annual Scott Commonwealth of Independent States supplement.

1996 European Soccer Championships, England — A33

Designs: 10b, Handshaking. 40b, Players legs, soccer ball. 1.20 l, Goalie.

No. 150: a, 1.10 l, Soccer federation, German flags. b, 2.20 l, Soccer ball, German, Moldovan flags. c, 2.40 l, Players.

1994, Dec. 10

147 A33 10b multicolored .20 .20
148 A33 40b multicolored .80 .80
149 A33 2.40 l multicolored 5.00 5.00
Nos. 147-149 (3) 6.00 6.00

Souvenir Sheet

150 A33 Sheet of 3, #a.-c. 10.00 10.00

Christmas A34

Mushrooms A35

Paintings of Birth of Christ by: 20b, unknown artist, 18th cent. 3.60 l, Gherasim, 1808.

1994, Dec. 29

151 A34 20b multicolored .30 .30
152 A34 3.60 l multicolored 5.00 5.00

1995, Feb. 8

153 A35 4b Russula virescens .15 .15
154 A35 10b Boletus luridus .40 .40
155 A35 20b Cantherellus cibarius .75 .75
156 A35 90b Leccinum aurantiacum 4.00 4.00
157 A35 1.80 l Leccinum duriusculum 8.00 8.00
Nos. 153-157 (5) 13.30 13.30

European Nature Conservation Year — A36

Designs: 4b, Hieraaetus pennatus. 45b, Capreolus capreolus. 90b, Sus scrofa.

1995, Mar. 18 Litho. *Perf. 14*

158 A36 4b multicolored .25 .25
159 A36 45b multicolored 2.25 2.25
160 A36 90b multicolored 4.50 4.50
Nos. 158-160 (3) 7.00 7.00

Museum of Natural Sciences — A37

Designs: 4b, Jars. 10b+2b, Dinotherium gigantissimum. 1.80 l+30b, Silver coin, 3rd-2nd cent. BC.

1995 Litho. *Perf. 14*

161 A37 4b multicolored .25 .25
162 A37 10b +2b multicolored .75 .75
163 A37 1.80 l +30b multicolored 7.00 7.00
Nos. 161-163 (3) 8.00 8.00

Peace & Freedom A38

Paintings: 10b, May 1945, by Igor Vieru. 40b, Linistea, by Sergiu Cuciuc. 2.20 l, Primavara 1944, by Cuciuc.

1995, May 9 Litho. *Perf. 14*

164	A38	10b multicolored	.25	.25
165	A38	40b multicolored	1.00	1.00
166	A38	2.20 l multicolored	6.00	6.00
		Nos. 164-166 (3)	7.25	7.25

Europa.

Famous People — A39

Designs: 90b, Constantin Stere (1865-1936), writer. 10b, Tamara Ceban (1914-90), musician. 40b, Alexandru Plamadeala (1888-1940), artist. 1.80 l, Lucian Blaga (1895-1961), writer.

1995, June 17 Litho. *Perf. 14*

167	A39	9b dp claret & gray	.50	.50
168	A39	10b brt magenta & gray	.50	.50
169	A39	40b violet & gray	2.00	2.00
170	A39	1.80 l dk green & gray	9.00	9.00
		Nos. 167-170 (4)	12.00	12.00

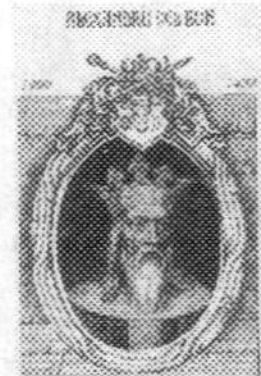

Kings of Moldova — A40

King, years in power: No. 171, Alexandru Cel Bun, 1400-32. No. 172, Petru Aron, 1451-52, 1454-57. No. 173, Stefan Cel Mare, 1457-1504. 45 l, Petru Rares, 1527-38, 1541-46. 90 l, Alexandru Lapusneanu, 1552-61, 1564-68. 1.80 l, Ion Voda Cel Cumplit, 1572-74. 5 l, Stefan Cel Mare, 1457-1504.

1995, July 2 Litho. *Perf. 14*

171	A40	10 b multicolored	.50	.50
172	A40	10 b multicolored	.50	.50
173	A40	10 b multicolored	.50	.50
174	A40	45 b multicolored	2.00	2.00
175	A40	90 b multicolored	4.00	4.00
176	A40	1.80 l multicolored	8.00	8.00
		Nos. 171-176 (6)	15.50	15.50

Souvenir Sheet

177	A40	5 l multicolored	2.50	2.50

No. 177 contains one 24x29mm stamp.

Citadels of Moldova A41

1995, July 29

178	A41	10 b Soroca	.40	.40
179	A41	20 b Tighina	.75	.75
180	A41	60 b Alba	2.50	2.50
181	A41	1.30 l Hotin	5.00	5.00
		Nos. 178-181 (4)	8.65	8.65

A42

UN, 50th Anniv. — A43

Designs inside of stylized eye: No. 182, Devastation of war. No. 183, Fighter plane. No. 184, Prisoner of war.

Nos. 185-186: a, 1. b, 2. c, 3. d, 4. e, 5. f, 6. g, 7. h, 8. i, 9. j, 10.

1995, Oct. 24 Litho. *Perf. 14*

182	A42	10b yellow & multi	.75	.75
183	A42	10b blue & multi	.75	.75
184	A42	1.50 l green & multi	10.00	10.00
		Nos. 182-184 (3)	11.50	11.50

Stamp Cards

Rouletted 15 on 2 or 3 Sides

Self-Adhesive

Cards of 10

185	A43	90b #a.-j.	6.25	6.25
186	A43	1.50 l #a.-j.	10.25	10.25

Background color of stamps gradually shifts from light blue (#1) to dark blue (#10). Each stamp is individually numbered.

A45

A46

Mushrooms: No. 190, Amanita muscaria. No. 191, Boletus satanas. 65b, Amanita phalloides. 1.30 l, Hypholoma fasciculare. 2.40 l, Amanita virosa.

1996, Mar. 23 Litho. *Perf. 14*

190	A45	10b multicolored	.15	.15
191	A45	10b multicolored	.15	.15
192	A45	65b multicolored	1.25	1.25
193	A45	1.30 l multicolored	2.75	2.75
194	A45	2.40 l multicolored	5.00	5.00
		Nos. 190-194 (5)	9.30	9.30

1996, Mar. 30

195	A46	10b Weight lifting	.20	.20
196	A46	20b +5b Judo	.55	.55
197	A46	45b +10b Running	1.25	1.25
198	A46	2.40 l +30b Canoeing	6.00	6.00
		Nos. 195-198 (4)	8.00	8.00

Souvenir Sheet

199	A46	2.20 l Archery	2.50	2.50

1996 Summer Olympic Games, Atlanta.
No. 199 contains one 34x29mm stamp.

Monasteries — A47

1996, Apr. 26

200	A47	10b Rudi, 18th cent.	.15	.15
201	A47	90b Japca, 17th cent.	1.25	1.25
202	A47	1.30 l Curchi, 18th cent.	1.75	1.75
203	A47	2.80 l Saharna, 18th cent.	4.00	4.00
204	A47	4.40 l Capriana, 16th cent.	5.00	5.00
		Nos. 200-204 (5)	12.15	12.15

Birds — A48

Designs: 9b, Gallinula chloropus. 10b, Anser anser. No. 207, Streptopelia turtur. 4.40 l, Anas platyrhynchos.
No. 209, Phasianus colchicus.

1996, May 17

205	A48	9b multicolored	.15	.15
206	A48	10b multicolored	.15	.15
207	A48	2.20 l multicolored	2.50	2.50
208	A48	4.40 l multicolored	5.00	5.00
		Nos. 205-208 (4)	7.80	7.80

Souvenir Sheet

209	A48	2.20 l multicolored	2.00	2.00

Famous Women — A49

Europa: 10b, Elena Alistar (1873-1955), president of women's league. 3.70 l, Marie Curie (1867-1934), chemist, physicist.
2.20 l, Julia Hasdeu (1869-1888), writer.

1996, June 21 Litho. *Perf. 14*

210	A49	10b multicolored	.20	.20
211	A49	3.70 l multicolored	5.00	5.00

Souvenri Sheet

212	A49	2.20 l multicolored	3.00	3.00

Famous Men — A50

#213, Gavriil Banulescu-Bodoni (1746-1821). #214, Mihail Eminescu (1850-69), poet. 2.20 l, Ion Creanga (1837-89). 3.30 l, Vasile Alecsandri (1821-90). 5.40 l, Petru Movila (1596-1646), theologian.
1.80 l, Eminescu, diff., vert.

1996, July 30 Litho. *Perf. 14*

213	A50	10b gray vio & brn	.15	.15
214	A50	10b lt brn & dk brn	.15	.15
215	A50	2.20 l gray & brn	3.00	3.00
216	A50	3.30 l ol & brn	4.50	4.50
217	A50	5.40 l red brn & brn	7.00	7.00
		Nos. 213-217 (5)	14.80	14.80

Souvenir Sheet

218	A50	1.80 l brn	2.25	2.25

City of Chisinau, 560th Anniv. — A51

Building, year erected: 10b, City Hall, 1902. 1.30 l, Palace of Culture, 1911. 2.40 l, Mazarache Church, 1752.

1996, Oct. 6 Litho. *Perf. 14*

219	A51	10b multicolored	.15	.15
220	A51	1.30 l multicolored	2.50	2.50
221	A51	2.40 l multicolored	4.50	4.50
		Nos. 219-221 (3)	7.15	7.15

A52

A53

Christmas: 10b, Children carrying star. 2.20 l+30b, Mother and child in center of star. 2.80 l+50b, Children decorating Christmas tree.

1996, Dec. 12 Litho. *Perf. 14*

222	A52	10b multicolored	.15	.15
223	A52	2.20 l +30b multicolored	2.50	2.50
224	A52	2.80 l +50b multicolored	3.50	3.50
		Nos. 222-224 (3)	6.15	6.15

1997, Jan. 17 Litho. *Perf. 14*

Wines of Moldova.

225	A53	10b Feteasca	.15	.15
226	A53	45b Cabernet-Sauvignon	.65	.65
227	A53	65b Sauvignon	.90	.90
228	A53	3.70 l Rara neagra	5.20	5.20
		Nos. 225-228 (4)	6.90	6.90

Easter — A54

Designs: 3.30b, Colored eggs, grass on plate. 5 l, Basket of eggs, food.

1997, Apr. 25 Litho. *Perf. 13½*

229	A54	10b multicolored	.15	.15
230	A54	3.30 l multicolored	4.00	4.00

Souvenir Sheet

231	A54	5 l multicolored	6.25	6.25

Stories and Legends — A56

Europa: 10b, Man holding up arms, goose flying, arrows from fortress. 2.80 l, Man upside down, church, sun in sky with stars and eye. 5 l, Angel touching flowers during winter.

1997, June 20 Litho. *Perf. 13½*

236	A56	10b multicolored	.15	.15
237	A56	2.80 l multicolored	4.00	4.00

Souvenir Sheet

238	A56	5 l multicolored	6.50	6.50

Red Book Insects — A57

Insects on plants, flowers: 25b, Mantis religiosa. 80b, Ascalphus macaronius scop. 1 l, Calosoma sycophanta. 2.20 l, Liometopum microcephalum.
5 l, Scolia maculata drury.

1997, July 26 Litho. *Perf. 14*

239	A57	25b multicolored	.30	.30
240	A57	80b multicolored	.95	.95
241	A57	1 l multicolored	1.20	1.20
242	A57	2.20 l multicolored	2.60	2.60
		Nos. 239-242 (4)	5.05	5.05

Souvenir Sheet

243	A57	5 l multicolored	6.00	6.00

World Post Day — A58

Designs: 10b, Chisinau post office building, 1997. 2.20 l, Mail coach, Chisinaupost office building. 3.30 l, Heinrich von Stephan (1831-97), vert.

1997 Litho. *Perf. 14*

244	A58	10b multicolored	.15	.15
245	A58	2.20 l multicolored	2.75	2.75
246	A58	3.30 l multicolored	4.25	4.25
		Nos. 244-246 (3)	7.15	7.15

Christmas A59

Designs: 10b, Noul Neamt Monastery. 45b, "Adoration of the Shepherds," Noul Neamt Monastery. 5 l, "Nativity," Natl. Museum of Plastic Arts.

1997 Litho. *Perf. 13½*

247 A59 10b multicolored .15 .15
248 A59 45b multicolored .60 .60
249 A59 5 l multicolored 6.50 6.50
Nos. 247-249 (3) 7.25 7.25

A60

A61

UNESCO World Heritage Sites: 7b, Nicolai Zelinski High School, Tiraspol. No. 251, Railway station, Tighina. No. 252, Cathedral, Balti. 90b, Church, Causeni. 1.30 l, Cathedral, Kagul. 3.30 l, Art Institute, Chisinau.

1997 Litho. *Perf. 14*

250 A60 7b black & lilac .15 .15
251 A60 10b black & red violet .15 .15
252 A60 10b black & grn blue .15 .15
253 A60 90b black & yel org 1.25 1.25
254 A60 1.30 l black & blue 1.75 1.75
255 A60 3.30 l black & gray 4.25 4.25
Nos. 250-255 (6) 7.70 7.70

1997

Princes of Moldova, reign: No. 256, Petru Schiopul (1574-77, 78-79, 82-91). No. 257, Ieremia Movila (1595-1606). 45b, Stefan Tomsa (1611-15, 1621-23). 1.80 l, Radu Mihnea (1616-19, 1623-26). 2.20 l, Miron Barnovschi Movila (1626-29, 1633). 2.80 l, Bogdan Orbul (1504-17). 5 l, Mihai Viteazul, 1600.

256 A61 10b multicolored .15 .15
257 A61 10b multicolored .15 .15
258 A61 45b multicolored .60 .60
259 A61 1.80 l multicolored 2.25 2.25
260 A61 2.20 l multicolored 2.75 2.75
261 A61 2.80 l multicolored 3.50 3.50
Nos. 256-261 (6) 9.40 9.40

Souvenir Sheet

262 A61 5 l multicolored 6.25 6.25

No. 262 contains one 23x29mm stamp.

1998 Winter Olympic Games, Nagano A62

1998

263 A62 10b Slalom skiing .15 .15
264 A62 45b Figure skating .55 .55
265 A62 2.20 l Biathlon 2.75 2.75
Nos. 263-265 (3) 3.45 3.45

AIR POST STAMPS

TU-144 — AP1

1992-93 Litho. *Perf. 12*

C1 AP1 1.75r maroon .50
C2 AP1 2.50r red vio .75
C3 AP1 7.75r blue 2.25
C4 AP1 8.50r blue green 2.50
C5 AP1 25r red brown .35
C6 AP1 45r brown .60
C7 AP1 50r olive green .70
C8 AP1 90r blue 1.25
Nos. C1-C8 (8) 8.90

Issued: #C1-C4, 7/20/92; #C5-C8, 7/24/93.

POSTAGE DUE STAMPS

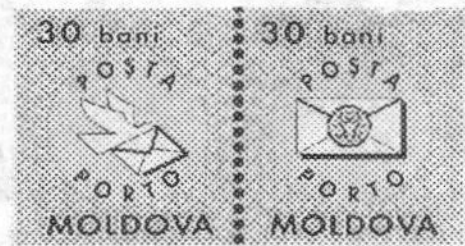

Dove, Envelope — D1

1994, Nov. 12 Litho. *Perf. 14*

J1 D1 30b lt olive & brown .40 .40
J2 D1 40b pale vio & slate .60 .60

In use, Nos. J1-J2 were torn apart, one half being affixed to the postage due item and the other half being pasted into the postman's record book. Values are for unused and canceled-to-order pairs.

MONACO

ˈmä-nə-ˌkō

LOCATION — Southern coast of France, bordering on the Mediterranean Sea
GOVT. — Principality
AREA — 481 acres
POP. — 27,063 (1982)
CAPITAL — Monaco

100 Centimes = 1 Franc

Catalogue values for unused stamps in this country are for Never Hinged items, beginning with Scott 182 in the regular postage section, Scott B51 in the semi-postal section, Scott C2 in the airpost section, Scott CB1 in the airpost semi-postal section, and Scott J28 in the postage due section.

Prince Charles III — A1

Prince Albert I — A2

1885 Unwmk. Typo. *Perf. 14x13½*

1 A1 1c olive green 14.00 12.00
2 A1 2c dull lilac 40.00 20.00
3 A1 5c blue 50.00 25.00
4 A1 10c brown, *straw* 60.00 25.00
5 A1 15c rose 275.00 12.00
6 A1 25c green 500.00 45.00
7 A1 40c slate, *rose* 65.00 30.00
8 A1 75c black, *rose* 200.00 85.00
9 A1 1fr black, *yellow* 1,200. 325.00
10 A1 5fr rose, *green* 2,250. 1,350.

1891-1921

11 A2 1c olive green .55 .55
12 A2 2c dull violet .55 .55
13 A2 5c blue 42.50 3.00
14 A2 5c yellow grn ('01) .55 .30
15 A2 10c brown, *straw* 90.00 9.00
16 A2 10c carmine ('01) 3.00 .40
17 A2 15c rose 150.00 .85
18 A2 15c vio brn, *straw* ('01) 3.00 .60
19 A2 15c gray green ('21) 2.00 1.75
20 A2 25c green 275.00 20.00
21 A2 25c deep blue ('01) 15.00 3.00
22 A2 40c slate, *rose* ('94) 3.00 2.00
23 A2 50c violet, *org* 5.50 3.00
24 A2 75c vio brn, *buff* ('94) 20.00 14.00
a. 75c lilac brown, *buff* 35.00 19.00
25 A2 75c ol brn, *buff* ('21) 20.00 15.00
26 A2 1fr black, *yellow* 20.00 6.00
27 A2 5fr rose, *grn* 90.00 50.00
28 A2 5fr dull violet ('21) 200.00 200.00
29 A2 5fr dark green ('21) 20.00 20.00
Nos. 11-29 (19) 960.65 350.00

The handstamp "OL" in a circle of dots is a cancellation, not an overprint.

See No. 1782. For overprints and surcharges see Nos. 30-35, 57-59, B1.

Stamps of 1901-21 Overprinted or Surcharged:

28 DÉCEMBRE 1920

28 DÉCEMBRE 1920 2f

1921, Mar. 5

30 A2 5c lt green .75 .60
31 A2 75c brown, *buff* 5.50 5.00
32 A2 2fr on 5fr dull vio 45.00 45.00
Nos. 30-32 (3) 51.25 50.60

Issued to commemorate the birth of Princess Antoinette, daughter of Princess Charlotte and Prince Pierre, Comte de Polignac.

Stamps and Type of 1891-1921 Surcharged 25c.

1922

33 A2 20c on 15c gray green 1.50 1.00
34 A2 25c on 10c rose 1.00 .75
35 A2 50c on 1fr black, *yel* 7.00 5.00
Nos. 33-35 (3) 9.50 6.75

Prince Albert I — A5

Oceanographic Museum — A6

"The Rock" of Monaco — A7

Royal Palace — A8

1922-24 Engr. *Perf. 11*

40 A5 25c olive brn 5.00 4.00
41 A6 30c dark green .80 .80
42 A6 30c scarlet ('23) .35 .35
43 A6 50c ultra 3.25 3.25
44 A7 60c black brn .25 .25
45 A7 1fr black, *yellow* .20 .20
46 A7 2fr scarlet .35 .35
47 A8 5fr red brown 32.50 25.00
48 A8 5fr dk green, *lil* ('24) 6.00 6.00
49 A8 10fr carmine 11.00 11.00
Nos. 40-49 (10) 59.70 51.20

Nos. 40-49 exist imperf.

Prince Louis II
A9 A10

St. Dévote Viaduct ("Bridge of Suicides") — A11

1923-24 Engr.

50 A9 10c deep green .40 .40
51 A9 15c car rose ('24) .55 .55
52 A9 20c red brown .35 .35
53 A9 25c violet .35 .35
a. Without engraver's name 18.00 18.00
54 A11 40c orange brn ('24) .50 .50
55 A10 50c ultra .35 .35
Nos. 50-55 (6) 2.50 2.50

The 25c comes in 2 types, one with larger "5" and "c" touching frame of numeral tablet.

Stamps of the 1922-24 issues sometimes show parts of the letters of a papermaker's watermark.

The engraved stamps of type A11 measure 31x21½mm. The typographed stamps of that design measure 36x21½mm.

See #86-88. For surcharges see #95-96.

Stamps and Type of 1891-1921 Surcharged 45

1924, Aug. 5 *Perf. 14x13½*

57 A2 45c on 50c brn ol, *buff* .55 .55
a. Double surcharge 600.00 600.00
58 A2 75c on 1fr blk, *yel* .30 .30
a. Double surcharge 475.00 475.00
59 A2 85c on 5fr dk green .30 .30
a. Double surcharge 525.00 525.00
Nos. 57-59 (3) 1.15 1.15

Grimaldi Family Coat of Arms — A12

Prince Louis II — A13

Louis II — A14

View of Monaco — A15

1924-33 Typo.

60 A12 1c gray black .15 .15
61 A12 2c red brown .15 .15
62 A12 3c brt violet ('33) 1.25 .30
63 A12 5c orange ('26) .25 .25
64 A12 10c blue .15 .15

Approvals

Engraved Proofs Monaco

1985 Type A83
#1500 Prince Rainier III

1986 #1547 Positive Proof
Beau Rivage Ave. Negative Proof

Pencil-signed and/or Plate Proofs.
Printed and released in limited quantities.
Please write for details and price quotes.

FINE STOCK OF MONACO VARIETIES ON HAND FROM THE 1940'S to DATE.

E. JOSEPH McCONNELL, INC.
P.O. Box 683, Monroe, NY 10950
Fax 914-782-0347
Email:mcconn1@warwick.net

65 A13 15c apple green .15 .15
66 A13 15c dull vio ('29) 1.25 .60
67 A13 20c violet .20 .15
68 A13 20c rose .25 .15
69 A13 25c rose .15 .15
70 A13 25c red, *yel* .20 .20
71 A13 30c orange .15 .15
72 A13 40c black brown .20 .15
73 A13 40c lt bl, *bluish* .25 .25
74 A13 45c gray black ('26) .60 .35
75 A14 50c myrtle grn ('25) .20 .20
76 A13 50c brown, *org* .15 .15
77 A14 60c yellow brn ('25) .20 .20
78 A13 60c ol grn, *grnsh* .20 .15
79 A13 75c ol grn, *grnsh* ('26) .40 .25
80 A13 75c car, *straw* ('26) .20 .15
81 A13 75c slate .50 .25
82 A13 80c red, *yel* ('26) .35 .25
83 A13 90c rose, *straw* ('27) 1.50 1.00
84 A13 1.25fr bl, *bluish* ('26) .15 .15
85 A13 1.50fr bl, *bluish* ('27) 3.00 1.25

Size: 36x21½mm

86 A11 1fr blk, *orange* .20 .20
87 A11 1.05fr red violet ('26) .20 .20
88 A11 1.10fr blue grn ('27) 6.50 5.00
89 A15 2fr vio & ol brn ('25) .85 .55
90 A15 3fr rose & ultra, *yel* ('27) 13.00 8.00
91 A15 5fr green & rose ('25) 6.00 4.00
92 A15 10fr yel brn & bl ('25) 15.00 13.00
Nos. 60-92 (33) 53.95 38.25

Nos. 60 to 74 and 76 exist imperforate.
For surcharges see Nos. 93-94, 97-99, C1.

Type of 1924-33 Surcharged with New Value and Bars

1926-31

93 A13 30c on 25c rose .25 .20
94 A13 50c on 60c ol grn, *grnsh* ('28) .80 .25
95 A11 50c on 1.05fr red vio ('28) .60 .40
a. Double surcharge
96 A11 50c on 1.10fr bl grn ('31) 6.50 3.75
97 A13 50c on 1.25fr bl, *bluish* (R) ('28) 1.00 .40
98 A13 1.25fr on 1fr bl, *bluish* .40 .25
99 A15 1.50fr on 2fr vio & ol brn ('28) 3.50 2.75
Nos. 93-99 (7) 13.05 8.00

Princes Charles III, Louis II and Albert I
A17

1928, Feb. 18 **Engr.** *Perf. 11*

100 A17 50c dull carmine .75 .75
101 A17 1.50fr dark blue .75 .75
102 A17 3fr dark violet .75 .75
Nos. 100-102 (3) 2.25 2.25

Nos. 100-102 were sold exclusively at the Intl. Phil. Exhib. at Monte Carlo, Feb., 1928. One set was sold to each purchaser of a ticket of admission to the exhibition which cost 5fr.
Exist imperf. Value, set $20.

Old Watchtower
A20

Royal Palace — A21

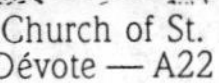

Church of St. Dévote — A22

Prince Louis II — A23

"The Rock" of Monaco
A24

Gardens of Monaco
A25

Fortifications and Harbor — A26

1932-37 *Perf. 13, 14x13½*

110 A20 15c lilac rose .70 .15
111 A20 20c orange brn .70 .15
112 A21 25c olive blk .90 .30
113 A22 30c yellow grn 1.00 .30
114 A23 40c dark brown 2.50 1.25
115 A24 45c brown red 2.50 1.00
a. 45c red 325.00 325.00
116 A23 50c purple 2.50 .75
117 A25 65c blue green 2.50 .45
118 A26 75c deep blue 3.00 1.25
119 A23 90c red 7.50 1.75
120 A22 1fr red brown ('33) 20.00 4.50
121 A26 1.25fr rose lilac 4.50 2.50
122 A23 1.50fr ultra 25.00 6.50
123 A21 1.75fr rose lilac 25.00 6.00
124 A21 1.75fr car rose ('37) 15.00 8.00
125 A24 2fr dark blue 8.00 3.25
126 A20 3fr purple 12.00 6.00
127 A21 3.50fr orange ('35) 35.00 22.50
128 A22 5fr violet 18.00 12.00
129 A21 10fr deep blue 90.00 45.00
130 A25 20fr black 125.00 100.00
Nos. 110-130 (21) 401.30 223.60

Postage Due Stamps of 1925-32 Surcharged or Overprinted in Black:

POSTES
=5

POSTES

1937-38 *Perf. 14x13*

131 D3 5c on 10c violet .70 .70
132 D3 10c violet .70 .70
133 D3 15c on 30c bister .70 .70
134 D3 20c on 30c bister .70 .70
135 D3 25c on 60c red 1.00 1.00
136 D3 30c bister 1.75 1.65
137 D3 40c on 60c red 1.65 1.50
138 D3 50c on 60c red 2.25 2.00
139 D3 65c on 1fr lt bl 1.75 1.75
140 D3 85c on 1fr lt bl 4.25 3.00
141 D3 1fr light blue 5.50 5.00
142 D3 2.15fr on 2fr dl red 6.00 6.00
143 D3 2.25fr on 2fr dl red ('38) 14.00 13.00
144 D3 2.50fr on 2fr dl red ('38) 20.00 18.00
Nos. 131-144 (14) 60.95 55.70

Grimaldi Arms — A27

Prince Louis II — A28

1937-43 **Engr.**

145 A27 1c dk vio brn ('38) .15 .15
146 A27 2c emerald .15 .15
147 A27 3c brt red violet .15 .15
148 A27 5c red .15 .15
149 A27 10c ultra .15 .15
149A A27 10c black ('43) .15 .15
150 A27 15c violet ('39) .90 .75
150A A27 30c dull green ('43) .15 .15
150B A27 40c rose car ('43) .15 .15
150C A27 50c brt violet ('43) .15 .15
151 A28 55c red brown ('38) 2.25 .75
151A A27 60c Prus blue ('43) .15 .15
152 A28 65c violet ('38) 20.00 8.00
153 A28 70c red brown ('39) .15 .15
153A A27 70c red brown ('43) .15 .15
154 A28 90c violet ('39) .25 .25
155 A28 1fr rose red ('38) 6.50 3.00
156 A28 1.25fr rose red ('39) .25 .15
157 A28 1.75fr ultra ('38) 11.00 5.25
158 A28 2.25fr ultra ('39) .25 .15
Nos. 145-158 (20) 43.20 20.10
Set, never hinged 75.00

Nos. 151, 152, 155 and 157 exist imperforate.

Souvenir Sheet

Prince Louis II — A29

1938, Jan. 17 **Unwmk.** ***Imperf.***

159 A29 10fr magenta 25.00 25.00
Never hinged 57.50

"Fête Nationale" Jan. 17, 1938. Size: 99x120mm.

Cathedral of Monaco — A30

St. Nicholas Square — A31

Palace Gate — A32

Palace of Monaco — A34

Panorama of Monaco
A33

Harbor of Monte Carlo — A35

1939-46 *Perf. 13*

160 A30 20c rose lilac .20 .20
161 A31 25c gldn brown .40 .25
162 A32 30c dk blue grn .30 .25
162A A32 30c brown red ('40) .30 .20
163 A31 40c henna brn .60 .35
164 A33 45c brt red vio .30 .25
165 A34 50c dk blue grn .30 .20
166 A32 60c rose carmine .35 .25
166A A32 60c dk green ('40) .30 .25
166B A35 70c brt red vio ('41) .35 .20
167 A35 75c dark green .35 .20
167A A30 80c dull green ('43) .20 .20
168 A34 1fr brown black .35 .20
168A A33 1fr claret ('43) .15 .15
168B A35 1.20fr ultra ('46) .20 .20
168C A34 1.30fr brown blk ('41) .35 .20
168D A31 1.50fr ultra ('46) .35 .35
169 A31 2fr rose violet .35 .25
169A A35 2fr lt ultra ('43) .15 .15
169B A34 2fr green ('46) .15 .15
170 A33 2.50fr red 20.00 11.00
171 A33 2.50fr dp blue ('40) 1.00 .40
172 A35 3fr brown red .40 .20
172A A31 3fr black ('43) .15 .15
172B A30 4fr rose lilac ('46) .35 .35
172C A34 4.50fr brt violet ('43) .15 .15
173 A30 5fr Prus blue 2.00 .40
173A A32 5fr deep green ('43) .15 .15
173B A34 6fr lt violet ('46) .45 .45
174 A33 10fr green 1.40 .35
174A A30 10fr deep blue ('43) .20 .20
174B A35 15fr rose pink ('43) .35 .20
175 A32 20fr brt ultra 1.40 .35
175A A32 20fr sepia ('43) .35 .20
175B A35 25fr blue green ('46) 1.25 .85
Nos. 160-175B (35) 35.60 19.85
Set, never hinged 50.00

See Nos. 214-221, 228-232, 274-275, 319-320, 407-408, 423, 426, 428-429, B36-B50.

Louis II Stadium
A36

1939, Apr. 23 **Engr.**

176 A36 10fr dark green 80.00 80.00
Never hinged 140.00

Inauguration of Louis II Stadium.

Louis II Stadium
A37

1939, Aug. 15

177 A37 40c dull green .80 .80
178 A37 70c brown black .90 .90
179 A37 90c dark violet 1.25 1.25
180 A37 1.25fr copper red 1.50 1.50
181 A37 2.25fr dark blue 2.25 2.25
Nos. 177-181 (5) 6.70 6.70
Set, never hinged 10.00

8th International University Games.

Imperforates

Nearly all Monaco stamps from 1940 onward exist imperforate. Officially 20 sheets, ranging from 25 to 100 subjects, were left imperforate.

Catalogue values for unused stamps in this section, from this point to the end of the section, are for Never Hinged items.

Prince Louis II
A38 A39

1941-46 *Perf. 14x13*

182 A38 40c brown carmine .30 .30
183 A38 80c deep green .30 .30
184 A38 1fr rose violet .15 .15
185 A38 1.20fr green ('42) .15 .15
186 A38 1.50fr rose .15 .15
187 A38 1.50fr violet ('42) .15 .15
187A A38 2fr lt green ('46) .30 .25
188 A38 2.40fr red ('42) .15 .15
189 A38 2.50fr deep ultra .55 .55
190 A38 4fr blue ('42) .15 .15
Set value 1.70 1.65

1943 *Perf. 13*

191 A39 50fr purple .70 .70

Prince Louis II
A40 A41

1946 **Unwmk.** **Engr.** *Perf. 14x13*

192 A40 2.50fr dk blue green .25 .20
193 A40 3fr brt red violet .25 .20
194 A40 6fr brt red .30 .30
195 A40 10fr brt ultra .38 .40

Perf. 13

196 A41 50fr dp Prus green 1.65 1.50
197 A41 100fr red 2.50 2.25
Nos. 192-197 (6) 5.33 4.85

Nos. 196-197 exist imperforate.
See Nos. 222-227, 233-236. For overprints see Nos. C8-C9.

Franklin D. Roosevelt A42

Harbor of Monte Carlo — A43

Palace of Monaco A44

Map of Monaco — A45

Prince Louis II — A46

1946, Dec. 13 Unwmk. *Perf. 13*

198 A42 10c red violet .15 .15
199 A43 30c deep blue .20 .20
200 A44 60c blue black .20 .20
201 A45 1fr sepia .40 .40
202 A45 3fr lt violet .75 .75
Nos. 198-202,B93,C14-C15,CB6 (9) 4.05 3.90

Issued in tribute to the memory of Franklin D. Roosevelt.

1947, May 15

203 A46 10fr dark blue green 1.40 1.40

25th anniv. of the reign of Prince Louis II.
See Nos. B94, C20a.

Hurdler A47

Runner — A48

Designs: 2fr, Discus thrower. 2.50fr, Basketball. 4fr, Swimmer.

1948, July 1 *Perf. 13*

204 A47 50c blue green .25 .25
205 A48 1fr rose brown .25 .25
206 A48 2fr grnsh blue .50 .50
207 A48 2.50fr vermilion .80 .80
208 A48 4fr slate gray 1.00 1.00
Nos. 204-208,CB7-CB10 (9) 62.30 62.30

Issued to publicize Monaco's participation in the 1948 Olympic Games held at Wembley, England, during July and August.

Nymph Salmacis A49

Hercules — A50

Aristaeus — A51

Hyacinthus A52

François J. Bosio and Louis XIV Statue — A53

1948, July 12

209 A49 50c dark green .20 .20
210 A50 1fr red .20 .20
211 A51 2fr deep ultra .25 .25
212 A52 2.50fr deep violet .45 .45
213 A53 4fr purple .65 .65
Nos. 209-213,CB11-CB14 (9) 47.25 47.25

Issued to honor François J. Bosio (1768-1845), sculptor. No. 213 inscribed "J F Bosio."

Scenic Types of 1939

1948 Engr.

214 A30 50c sepia .35 .25
215 A31 60c rose pink .35 .25
216 A32 3fr violet rose .55 .35
217 A31 4fr emerald .55 .35
218 A34 8fr red brown 1.90 .80
219 A34 10fr brown red 3.25 .65
220 A33 20fr carmine rose 1.40 .50
221 A35 25fr gray black 27.50 12.00
Nos. 214-221 (8) 35.85 15.15

Louis II Type of 1946

1948, July *Perf. 14x13*

222 A40 30c black .30 .15
223 A40 5fr orange brown .45 .30
224 A40 6fr purple 1.65 .50
225 A40 10fr orange .45 .30
226 A40 12fr deep carmine 2.50 .75
227 A40 18fr dark blue 5.25 4.50
Nos. 222-227 (6) 10.60 6.50

Scenic Types of 1939

1949 *Perf. 13*

228 A33 5fr blue green .50 .15
229 A35 10fr orange .80 .30
230 A32 25fr blue 15.00 6.00
231 A30 40fr brown red 5.75 2.75
232 A30 50fr purple 3.75 .70
Nos. 228-232 (5) 25.80 9.90

Louis II Type of 1946

1949, Mar. 10 *Perf. 14x13*

233 A40 50c olive .30 .15
234 A40 1fr dk violet bl .25 .25
235 A40 12fr dk slate grn 5.00 2.75
236 A40 15fr brown carmine 5.00 3.25
Nos. 233-236 (4) 10.55 6.40

Hirondelle I — A54

Cactus Plants — A55

Designs: 4fr, Oceanographic Museum. 5fr, Princess Alice II at Spitzbergen. 6fr, Albert I Monument. 10fr, Hirondelle II. 12fr, Albert I whaling. 18fr, Bison.

1949, Mar. 5 *Perf. 13*

237 A54 2fr brt blue .20 .20
238 A55 3fr dark green .20 .20
239 A54 4fr blk brn & bl .30 .30
240 A54 5fr crimson .35 .35
241 A55 6fr dark violet .60 .60
242 A54 10fr black brown .70 .70
243 A54 12fr brt red violet .90 .90
244 A54 18fr dk brn & org brn 2.50 2.50
Nos. 237-244 (8) 5.75 5.75

See Nos. C21-C26.

Palace, Globe and Pigeon — A56

1949-50 Engr. Unwmk.

245 A56 5fr blue green .40 .40
245A A56 10fr orange 3.50 3.50
246 A56 15fr carmine .45 .45
Nos. 245-246,C30-C33 (7) 10.25 10.25

75th anniversary of the UPU.
Nos. 245, 245A and 246 exist imperf.
Issued: 5fr, 15fr, Dec. 27; 10fr, Sept. 12, 1950.

Prince Rainier III
A57 A58

1950, Apr. 11

247 A57 10c red & blk brn .15 .15
248 A57 50c dp yel & dk brn .15 .15
249 A57 1fr purple .25 .25
250 A57 5fr dark green .95 .95
251 A57 15fr carmine 1.75 1.75
252 A57 25fr ultra, ol grn & ind 2.75 2.75
Nos. 247-252,C34-C35 (8) 14.75 14.75

Enthronement of Prince Rainier III.

1950, Apr. Engr. *Perf. 14x13*

253 A58 50c purple .25 .25
254 A58 1fr orange brown .35 .30
255 A58 8fr blue green 4.50 1.75
256 A58 12fr blue 1.50 .65
257 A58 15fr crimson 2.25 .70
Nos. 253-257 (5) 8.85 3.65

1951, Apr. 31 Typo.

258 A58 5fr emerald 6.75 4.25
259 A58 10fr orange 12.00 6.00

See Nos. 276-279.

Statue of Prince Albert I — A59

1951, Apr. 11 Engr. *Perf. 13*

260 A59 15fr deep blue 7.00 5.75

Edmond and Jules de Goncourt A60

1951, Apr. 11

261 A60 15fr violet brown 8.00 6.50

50th anniversary of the foundation of Goncourt Academy.

St. Vincent de Paul A61

Judgment of St. Dévote — A62

Symbolizing Monaco's Adoption of Catholicism — A63

Mosaic of the Immaculate Conception A64

Blessed Rainier of Westphalia — A65

Holy Year, 1951: 50c, Pope Pius XII. 12fr, Prince Rainier III at Prayer. 15fr, St. Nicholas de Patare. 20fr, St. Roman. 25fr, St. Charles Borromée. 40fr, Cross, arms and Roman Coliseum. 50fr, Chapel of St. Dévote.

Inscribed: "Anno Santo"

1951, June 4 Unwmk. *Perf. 13*

262 A61 10c ultra & red .30 .30
263 A61 50c dk rose lake & pur .30 .30
264 A62 1fr brown & dk grn .35 .35
265 A63 2fr vio brn & ver .45 .45
266 A64 5fr blue green .50 .50
267 A63 12fr rose violet .75 .75
268 A63 15fr vermilion 3.50 3.50
269 A63 20fr red brown 5.50 5.50
270 A63 25fr ultra 5.75 5.75
271 A63 40fr dk car rose & pur 7.00 7.00
272 A63 50fr ol grn & dk vio brn 9.00 9.00
273 A65 100fr dk violet brn 25.00 25.00
Nos. 262-273 (12) 58.40 58.40

Scenic Types of 1939-46

1951, Dec. 22 *Perf. 13*

274 A31 3fr deep turq green 1.00 .40
275 A32 30fr slate black 5.25 2.75

Rainier Type of 1950

1951, Dec. 22 *Perf. 14x13*

276 A58 6fr blue green .85 .50
277 A58 8fr orange .90 .60
278 A58 15fr indigo 1.10 .35
279 A58 18fr crimson 3.25 1.50
Nos. 276-279 (4) 6.10 2.95

Monaco stamps can be mounted in the annually supplemented Scott Monaco and French Andorra album.

Radio Monte Carlo — A66

Knight in Armor — A67

1951, Dec. 22 *Perf. 13*

280 A66 1fr blue, car & org .35 .38
281 A66 15fr pur, car & rose vio 1.25 .65
282 A66 30fr indigo & red brn 10.50 2.00
Nos. 280-282 (3) 12.10 3.03

1951, Dec. 22

283 A67 1fr purple 1.25 .48
284 A67 5fr gray black 3.00 1.00
285 A67 8fr deep carmine 5.75 2.75
286 A67 15fr emerald 7.75 5.75
287 A67 30fr slate black 11.00 5.75
Nos. 283-287 (5) 28.75 15.73

See Nos. 328-332, 2025-2026.

Nos. B96-B99a Surcharged with New Values and Bars in Black

1951, Dec. *Perf. 13½x13, Imperf.*

288 SP51 1fr on 10fr + 5fr 7.00 7.00
289 SP52 3fr on 15fr + 5fr 7.00 7.00
290 SP52 5fr on 25fr + 5fr 7.00 7.00
291 SP51 6fr on 40fr + 5fr 7.00 7.00
b. Block of 4, #288-291 30.00 30.00

Gallery of Hercules, Royal Palace — A68

1952, Apr. 26 **Engr.** *Perf. 13*

292 A68 5fr red brn & brn .55 .45
293 A68 15fr purple & lil rose .75 .45
294 A68 30fr indigo & ultra .95 .75
Nos. 292-294 (3) 2.25 1.65

Opening of a philatelic museum at the royal palace, Apr. 26, 1952.

Basketball — A69

Designs: 2fr, Soccer. 3fr, Sailing. 5fr, Cyclist. 8fr, Gymnastics. 15fr, Louis II Stadium.

1953, Feb. 23 **Unwmk.** *Perf. 11*

295 A69 1fr dk purple & mag .25 .20
296 A69 2fr dk grn & sl bl .35 .25
297 A69 3fr blue & lt blue .30 .35
298 A69 5fr dk brn & grnsh blk .70 .35
299 A69 8fr brown lake & red 1.40 .85
300 A69 15fr bl, brn blk & dk grn .85 .60
Nos. 295-300,C36-C39 (10) 43.35 37.60

Issued to publicize Monaco's participation in the Helsinki Olympic Games.

Books, Pens and Proof Pages — A70

1953, June 29 *Perf. 13*

301 A70 5fr dark green .75 .60
302 A70 15fr red brown 1.40 1.00

Publication of a first edition of the unexpurgated diary of Edmond and Jules Goncourt.

Physalia and Laboratory Ship Hirondelle II — A71

1953, June 29

303 A71 2fr Prus green, pur & choc .35 .18
304 A71 5fr dp mag, red & Prus grn .60 .40
305 A71 15fr ultra, vio brn & Prus grn 2.50 1.75
Nos. 303-305 (3) 3.45 2.33

50th anniversary of the discovery of anaphylaxis by Charles Richet and Paul Portier.

Frederic Ozanam — A72

Nun — A73

1954, Apr. 12 **Engr.** *Perf. 13*

306 A72 1fr bright red .20 .15
307 A73 5fr dark blue .50 .35
308 A72 15fr black 1.10 .80
Nos. 306-309 (4) 2.00 1.45

Centenary of the death of Frederic Ozanam, founder of the Society of Saint Vincent de Paul.

Jean Baptiste de la Salle
A74 A75

1954, Apr. 12

309 A74 1fr dark carmine .20 .15
310 A75 5fr black brown .50 .35
311 A74 15fr bright ultra 1.10 .80
Nos. 309-311 (3) 1.80 1.30

Issued to honor Jean Baptiste de la Salle, founder of the Christian Brothers Institute and saint.

A76

A77

Grimaldi Arms — A78

Knight in Armor — A79

Perf. 13½x14, 14x13½

1954, Apr. 12 **Typo.**

Various Forms of Grimaldi Arms in Black and Red or Black, Red and Deep Plum (5fr)

312 A76 50c black & mag .15 .15
313 A77 70c black & aqua .15 .15
314 A76 80c black, red & dk grn .15 .15
315 A77 1fr violet blue .15 .15
316 A77 2fr black & dp org .16 .16
317 A77 3fr black & green .16 .16
318 A78 5fr black & lt grn .22 .22
Set value .80 .80

Scenic Types of 1939-46

1954, Apr. 12 **Engr.** *Perf. 13*

319 A34 25fr bright red 2.00 1.10
320 A31 75fr dark green 17.00 10.00

1954, Apr. 12 **Unwmk.** *Perf. 13*

321 A79 4fr dark red 1.10 .42
322 A79 8fr dark green .90 .80
323 A79 12fr dark purple 4.00 1.40
324 A79 24fr dark maroon 8.50 4.00
Nos. 321-324 (4) 14.50 6.62

Nos. 321-324 were issued precanceled only. Values for precanceled stamps in first column are for those which have not been through the post and have original gum. Values in the second column are for postally used, gumless stamps.

See Nos. 400-404, 430-433, 466-469.

Lambarene Landing, Gabon — A80

Dr. Albert Schweitzer — A81

Design: 15fr, Lambarene hospital.

1955, Jan. 14 *Perf. 11x11½*

325 A80 2fr ol grn, bl grn & ind .20 .15
326 A81 5fr dk grnsh bl & grn 1.10 .80
327 A81 15fr dk bl grn, dp cl & brn blk 2.00 1.50
Nos. 325-327 (3) 3.30 2.45

Issued to honor Dr. Albert Schweitzer, medical missionary. See No. C40.

Knight Type of 1951

1955, Jan. 14 *Perf. 13*

328 A67 5fr purple 1.90 .85
329 A67 6fr red 2.25 1.25
330 A67 8fr red brown 2.50 1.65
331 A67 15fr ultra 6.60 3.75
332 A67 30fr dark green 7.50 4.75
Nos. 328-332 (5) 20.75 12.25

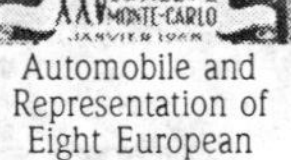
Automobile and Representation of Eight European Cities — A82

Prince Rainier III — A83

1955, Jan. 14 **Unwmk.**

333 A82 100fr dk brown & red 55.00 55.00

25th Monte Carlo Automobile Rally.

1955, June 7 **Engr.** *Perf. 13*

334 A83 6fr green & vio brn .40 .55
335 A83 8fr red & violet .40 .55
336 A83 12fr carmine & green .40 .55
337 A83 15fr purple & blue .85 .30
338 A83 18fr orange & blue .85 .55
339 A83 30fr ultra & gray 11.00 7.75
Nos. 334-339 (6) 13.90 10.25

See Nos. 405-406, 424-425, 427, 462-465, 586, 603-604A, 725-728, 730, 789, 791.

"Five Weeks in a Balloon" — A84

"A Floating City" and Jules Verne — A85

"Michael Strogoff" A86

"Around the World in 80 Days" — A87

USS Nautilus and Verne A88

Designs (Scenes from Jules Verne's Books): 3fr, The House of Vapors. 6fr, The 500 Millions of the Begum. 8fr, The Magnificent Orinoco. 10fr, A Journey to the Center of the Earth. 25fr, Twenty Thousand Leagues under the Sea.

1955, June 7

340 A84 1fr red brn & bl gray .15 .15
341 A85 2fr blue, ind & brn .15 .15
342 A85 3fr red brn, gray & sl .25 .25
343 A86 5fr carmine & blk brn .30 .30
344 A84 6fr blk brn & bluish gray .35 .35
345 A86 8fr ol grn & aqua .50 .50
346 A85 10fr indigo, turq & brn 1.10 1.00
347 A87 15fr rose brn & ver .85 .80
348 A85 25fr bl grn, grn & gray 1.75 1.40
349 A88 30fr violet, turq & blk 4.25 4.25
Nos. 340-349,C45 (11) 33.65 33.15

50th anniv. of the death of Jules Verne.

Virgin by Francois Brea — A89

Blessed Rainier A90

Marian Year: 10fr, Pieta by Louis Brea.

1955, June 7

No.	Type	Description	Unused	Used
350	A89	5fr vio brn, gray & dk grn	.25	.25
351	A89	10fr vio brn, gray & dk grn	.35	.35
352	A90	15fr black brn & org brn	.50	.50
		Nos. 350-352 (3)	1.10	1.10

Rotary Emblem, World Map — A91

1955, June 7

No.	Type	Description	Unused	Used
353	A91	30fr blue & orange	.75	.75

50th anniv. of the founding of Rotary Intl.

George Washington — A92

Franklin D. Roosevelt — A93

Dwight D. Eisenhower — A94

Palace of Monaco, c. 1790 — A95

Palace of Monaco, c. 1750 — A96

Designs: 3fr, Abraham Lincoln. 30fr, Columbus landing in America. 40fr, Prince Rainier III. 100fr, Early Louisiana scene.

1956, Apr. 3 Engr. *Perf. 13*

No.	Type	Description	Unused	Used
354	A92	1fr dark purple	.15	.15
355	A93	2fr claret & dk pur	.15	.15
356	A93	3fr vio & dp ultra	.24	.24
357	A94	5fr brown lake	.40	.40
358	A95	15fr brn blk & vio brn	.75	.75
359	A95	30fr ind, blk & ultra	1.40	1.40
360	A94	40fr dk brn & vio brn	1.50	1.10
361	A96	50fr vermilion	1.75	1.50
362	A96	100fr Prus green	2.00	2.00
a.		Strip of 3, #360-362	5.75	5.50
		Nos. 354-362 (9)	8.34	7.69

5th Intl. Phil. Exhib. (FIPEX), NYC, Apr. 28-May 6, 1956.

Ski Jump, Cortina d'Ampezzo — A97

Design: 30fr, Olympic Scenes.

1956, Apr. 3

No.	Type	Description	Unused	Used
363	A97	15fr brn vio, brn & dk grn	.95	.55
364	A97	30fr red orange	1.50	1.40

Issued to publicize Monaco's participation in the 1956 Olympic Games.

"Glasgow to Monte Carlo" — A98

1956, Apr. 3 Unwmk.

No.	Type	Description	Unused	Used
365	A98	100fr red brn & red	19.00	19.00

The 26th Monte Carlo Automobile Rally.

See Nos. 411, 437, 460, 483, 500, 539, 549, 600, 629.

Princess Grace and Prince Rainier III — A99

1956, Apr. 19 Engr. *Perf. 13*

Portraits in Black

No.	Type	Description	Unused	Used
366	A99	1fr dark green	.15	.15
367	A99	2fr dark carmine	.15	.15
368	A99	3fr ultra	.28	.20
369	A99	5fr brt yellow grn	.35	.22
370	A99	15fr redsh brown	.35	.28
		Nos. 366-370,C46-C48 (8)	5.38	5.10

Wedding of Prince Rainier III to Grace Kelly, Apr. 19, 1956.

Nos. J41-J47, J50-J56 Overprinted with Bars and Surcharged in Indigo, Red or Black

Unwmk.

1956, Apr. 3 Engr. *Perf. 11*

Designs: Early Transportation.

No.	Type	Description	Unused	Used
371	D6	2fr on 4fr (I)	.45	.45
372	D6	3fr (R)	.45	.45
373	D6	5fr on 4fr	.60	.60
374	D6	10fr on 4fr (R)	.75	.75
375	D6	15fr on 5fr (I)	1.50	1.50
376	D6	20fr (R)	2.50	2.50
377	D6	25fr on 20fr	3.25	3.25
378	D6	30fr on 10fr (I)	5.25	5.25
379	D6	40fr on 50fr (R)	6.00	6.00
380	D6	50fr on 100fr	8.50	8.50

Designs: Modern Transportation.

No.	Type	Description	Unused	Used
381	D7	2fr on 4fr (I)	.45	.45
382	D7	3fr (R)	.45	.45
383	D7	5fr on 4fr	.60	.60
384	D7	10fr on 4fr (R)	.75	.75
385	D7	15fr on 5fr (I)	1.50	1.50
386	D7	20fr (R)	2.50	2.50
387	D7	25fr on 20fr	3.25	3.25
388	D7	30fr on 10fr (I)	5.25	5.25
389	D7	40fr on 50fr (R)	6.00	6.00
390	D7	50fr on 100fr	8.50	8.50
		Nos. 371-390,C49-C50 (22)	77.00	77.00

The two types of each value in Nos. 371-390 were printed tête bêche, se-tenant at the base.

Princess Grace — A100

1957, May 11 Engr. *Perf. 13*

No.	Type	Description	Unused	Used
391	A100	1fr blue violet	.15	.15
392	A100	2fr lt olive grn	.25	.25
393	A100	3fr yellow brown	.25	.25
394	A100	5fr magenta	.30	.30
395	A100	15fr pink	.30	.30
396	A100	25fr Prus blue	.65	.40
397	A100	30fr purple	.65	.42
398	A100	50fr scarlet	.95	.42
399	A100	75fr orange	1.25	1.10
		Nos. 391-399 (9)	4.75	3.59

Birth of Princess Caroline of Monaco.

Knight Type of 1954

1957 Unwmk. *Perf. 13*

No.	Type	Description	Unused	Used
400	A79	5fr dark blue	.28	.22
401	A79	10fr yellow green	.28	.15
402	A79	15fr brt orange	.95	.70
403	A79	30fr brt blue	1.25	.80
404	A79	45fr crimson	1.75	1.25
		Nos. 400-404 (5)	4.51	3.12

Nos. 400-404 were issued precanceled only. See note after No. 324.

Types of 1955 and 1939-46

1957

No.	Type	Description	Unused	Used
405	A83	20fr greenish blue	.70	.45
406	A83	35fr red brown	2.25	1.25
407	A33	65fr brt violet	7.00	5.50
408	A30	70fr orange yellow	8.00	7.25
		Nos. 405-408 (4)	17.95	14.45

Princesses Grace and Caroline A101

1958, May 15 Engr. *Perf. 13*

No.	Type	Description	Unused	Used
409	A101	100fr bluish black	5.50	5.50

Birth of Prince Albert Alexander Louis, Mar. 14.

Order of St. Charles — A102

1958, May 15

No.	Type	Description	Unused	Used
410	A102	100fr carmine, grn & bis	1.65	1.65

Centenary of the National Order of St. Charles.

Rally Type of 1956

Design: 100fr, "Munich to Monte Carlo."

1958, May 15

No.	Type	Description	Unused	Used
411	A98	100fr red, green & sepia	6.50	6.00

27th Monte Carlo Automobile Rally.

Virgin Mary, Popes Pius IX and XII — A103

Bernadette Soubirous — A104

Tomb of Bernadette, Nevers A105

Designs: 3fr, Shepherdess Bernadette at Bartres. 5fr, Bouriette kneeling (first miracle). 8fr, Stained glass window showing apparition. 10fr, Empty grotto at Lourdes. 12fr, Grotto with statue and altar. 20fr, Bernadette praying. 35fr, High Altar at St. Peter's during canonization of Bernadette. 50fr, Bernadette, Pope Pius XI, Mgr. Laurence and Abbe Peyramale.

1958, May 15 Unwmk.

No.	Type	Description	Unused	Used
412	A103	1fr lilac gray & vio brn	.15	.15
413	A104	2fr blue & violet	.15	.15
414	A104	3fr green & sepia	.15	.15
415	A104	5fr gray brn & vio bl	.15	.15
416	A104	8fr blk, ol bis & ind	.30	.25
417	A105	10fr multicolored	.28	.25
418	A105	12fr ind, ol bis & ol grn	.30	.25
a.		Strip of 3, #416-418	1.00	.90
419	A104	20fr dk sl grn & rose	.35	.30
420	A104	35fr ol, gray ol & dk sl grn	.45	.35
421	A103	50fr lake, ol grn & ind	.60	.50
422	A105	65fr indigo & grnsh bl	1.00	.65
		Nos. 412-422,C51-C52 (13)	7.38	6.15

Centenary of the apparition of the Virgin Mary at Lourdes.

Sizes: Nos. 413-415, 419-420 26x36mm. No. 416 22x36mm. Nos. 417-418 48x36mm. No. 422 36x26mm.

Types of 1939-46 and 1955

1959 Engr. *Perf. 13*

No.	Type	Description	Unused	Used
423	A32	5fr copper red	1.00	.80
424	A83	25fr orange & blk	1.25	.80
425	A83	30fr dark violet	2.00	1.50
426	A34	35fr dark blue	6.00	2.00
427	A83	50fr bl grn & rose cl	2.75	1.50
428	A31	85fr dk carmine rose	10.00	4.50
429	A33	100fr brt grnsh blue	9.00	6.25
		Nos. 423-429 (7)	32.00	17.35

Knight Type of 1954

1959

No.	Type	Description	Unused	Used
430	A79	8fr deep magenta	.55	.25
431	A79	20fr bright green	1.00	.75
432	A79	40fr chocolate	2.00	.80
433	A79	55fr ultra	3.75	1.65
		Nos. 430-433 (4)	7.30	3.45

Nos. 430-433 were issued precanceled only. See note after No. 324.

Princess Grace Polyclinic — A106

1959, May 16

No.	Type	Description	Unused	Used
434	A106	100fr gray, brn & grn	1.25	1.25

Opening of Princess Grace Hospital.

UNESCO Building, Paris, and Cultural Emblems — A107

50fr, UNESCO Building, children of various races.

1959, May 16

435 A107 25fr multicolored .28 .20
436 A107 50fr ol, bl grn & blk brn .55 .48

Opening of UNESCO Headquarters in Paris, Nov. 3, 1958.

Rally Type of 1956

Design: 100fr, "Athens to Monaco."

1959, May 16

437 A98 100fr vio bl, red & sl grn, *bl* 5.25 5.25

28th Monte Carlo Automobile Rally.

Carnations — A108

Bougainvillea A109

Flowers: 10fr on 3fr, Princess Grace Carnations. 15fr on 1fr, Mimosa, vert. 25fr on 6fr, Geranium, vert. 35fr, Oleander. 50fr, Jasmine. 85fr on 65fr, Lavender. 100fr, Grace de Monaco Rose.

1959, May 16

438 A108 5fr brn, Prus grn & rose car .40 .15
439 A108 10fr on 3fr brn, grn & rose .40 .18
440 A109 15fr on 1fr dk grn & cit .50 .18
441 A109 20fr ol grn & mag .65 .35
442 A109 25fr on 6fr yel grn & red 1.00 .42
443 A109 35fr dk grn & pink 1.25 .80
444 A109 50fr dk brn & dk grn 2.00 1.00
445 A109 85fr on 65fr ol grn & gray vio 2.75 1.75
446 A108 100fr green & pink 3.50 2.00
Nos. 438-446 (9) 12.45 6.83

Nos. 439-440, 442 and 445 were not issued without surcharge.

View of Monaco and Uprooted Oak Emblem — A110

1960, June 1 Unwmk. *Perf. 13*

447 A110 25c bl, olive grn & sepia .20 .20

World Refugee Year, July 1, 1959-June 30, 1960.

Entrance to Oceanographic Museum — A111

Museum and Aquarium — A112

Designs: 15c, Museum conference room. 20c, Arrival of equipment, designed by Prince Albert I. 25c, Research on electrical qualities of cephalopodes. 50c, Albert I and vessels Hirondelle I and Princesse Alice.

1960, June 1 Engr. *Perf. 13*

448 A111 5c blue, sepia & cl .22 .15
449 A112 10c multicolored .40 .28
450 A112 15c sep, ultra & bis .25 .15
451 A112 20c rose lil, blk & bl .48 .22
452 A112 25c grnsh blue 1.00 .75
453 A112 50c lt ultra & brown 1.10 .90
Nos. 448-453 (6) 3.45 2.45

50th anniv. of the inauguration of the Oceanographic Museum of Monaco. See No. 475.

Horse Jumping — A113

Sports: 10c, Women swimmers. 15c, Broad jumper. 20c, Javelin thrower. 25c, Girl figure skater. 50c, Skier.

1960, June 1

454 A113 5c dk brn, car & emer .16 .16
455 A113 10c red brn, bl & grn .20 .20
456 A113 15c dl red brn, ol & mag .20 .20
457 A113 20c black, bl & grn 2.75 2.75
458 A113 25c dk grn & dull pur .70 .70
459 A113 50c dk bl, grnsh bl & dl pur 1.10 1.10
Nos. 454-459 (6) 5.11 5.11

Nos. 454-457 for the 17th Olympic Games, Rome, Aug. 25-Sept. 11; Nos. 458-459 for the 8th Winter Olympic Games, Squaw Valley, Feb. 18-29.

Rally Type of 1956

Design: 25c, "Lisbon to Monte Carlo."

1960, June 1

460 A98 25c bl, brn & car, *bluish* 1.90 1.90

29th Monte Carlo Automobile Rally.

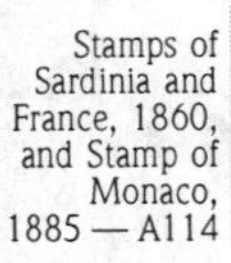

Stamps of Sardinia and France, 1860, and Stamp of Monaco, 1885 — A114

1960, June 1 Engr. & Embossed

461 A114 25c violet, blue & ol .80 .70

75th anniversary of postage stamps of Monaco.

Prince Rainier Type of 1955

1960 Engr. *Perf. 13*

462 A83 25c orange & blk .20 .15
463 A83 30c dark violet .25 .15
464 A83 50c bl grn & rose lil 1.00 .15
465 A83 65c yel brn & slate 5.00 .60
Nos. 462-465 (4) 6.45
Set value .85

Knight Type of 1954

1960

466 A79 8c deep magenta 1.40 .42
467 A79 20c brt green 1.90 .42
468 A79 40c chocolate 2.25 .80
469 A79 55c ultra 4.00 1.25
Nos. 466-469 (4) 9.55 2.89

Nos. 466-469 were issued precanceled only. See note after No. 324.

Sea Horse — A115

#471 Cactus (Cereanee). #472, Cactus (Nopalea dejecta). #473, Scorpion fish, horiz.

1960, June 1

470 A115 15c org brn & sl grn .50 .20
471 A115 15c ol grn, yel & brn .60 .15
472 A115 20c maroon & ol grn .40 .15
473 A115 20c brn, red brn, red & ol .60 .15
Nos. 470-473 (4) 2.10
Set value .54

See Nos. 581-584.

Type of 1960 and

Palace of Monaco A116

Designs: 10c, Type A111 without inscription. 45c, Aerial view of Palace. 85c, Honor court. 1fr, Palace at night.

1960, June 1 Engr.

474 A116 5c green & sepia .15 .15
475 A111 10c dk bl & vio brn .52 .25
476 A116 45c dk bl, sep & grn .85 .25
477 A116 85c slate, gray & bis 4.00 .25
478 A116 1fr dk bl, red brn & sl grn 1.65 .40
Nos. 474-478 (5) 7.17 1.30

See Nos. 585, 602, 729, 731, 731A, 790, 792.

Sphinx of Wadi-es-Sebua — A117

1961, June 3 Unwmk. *Perf. 13*

479 A117 50c choc, dk bl & ocher .80 .80

Issued as publicity to save historic monuments in Nubia.

Murena, Starfish, Sea Urchin, Sea Cucumber and Coral — A118

Medieval Town and Leper — A119

1961, June 3

480 A118 25c vio buff & dk red .22 .20

Issued to commemorate the World Congress of Aquariology, Monaco, Nov. 1960.

1961, June 3

481 A119 25c ol gray, ocher & car .22 .18

Issued to honor the Sovereign Order of the Knights of Malta.

Hand and Ant — A120

1961, June 3

482 A120 25c magenta & dp car .22 .16

Issued to publicize "Respect for Life."

Rally Type of 1956

Design: 1fr, "Stockholm to Monte Carlo."

1961, June 3

483 A98 1fr multicolored 1.50 1.50

30th Monte Carlo Automobile Rally.

Turcat-Mery, 1911 Winner, and 1961 Car — A121

1961, June 3

484 A121 1fr org brn, vio & rose red 1.50 1.25

50th anniv. of the founding of the Monte Carlo Automobile Rally.

Chevrolet, 1912 — A122

Automobiles (pre-1912): 2c, Peugeot. 3c, Fiat. 4c, Mercedes. 5c, Rolls Royce. 10c, Panhard-Levassor. 15c, Renault. 20c, Ford. 25c, Rochet-Schneider. 30c, FN-Herstal. 45c, De Dion Bouton. 50c, Buick. 65c, Delahaye. 1fr, Cadillac.

1961, June 13 Engr.

485 A122 1c org brn, dk brn & grn .15 .15
486 A122 2c org red, dk bl & brn .15 .15
487 A122 3c multicolored .15 .15
488 A122 4c multicolored .15 .15
489 A122 5c ol bis, sl grn & car .15 .15
490 A122 10c brn, sl & red .25 .25
491 A122 15c grnsh bl & dk sl grn .20 .20
492 A122 20c pur, blk & red .30 .30
493 A122 25c dk brn lil & red .40 .40
494 A122 30c ol grn & dl pur .60 .60
495 A122 45c multicolored 1.25 1.25
496 A122 50c brn blk, red & ultra 1.25 1.25

497 A122 65c multicolored 1.25 1.25
498 A122 1fr brt pur, ind & red 2.50 2.50
Nos. 485-498 (14) 8.75 8.75

See Nos. 648-661.

Bugatti, First Winner, and Course — A123

1962, June 6 Unwmk. Perf. 13
499 A123 1fr lilac rose 1.50 1.25

20th Automobile Grand Prix of Monaco.

Rally Type of 1956

Design: 1fr, "Oslo to Monte Carlo."

1962, June 6
500 A98 1fr multicolored 1.40 1.25

31st Monte Carlo Automobile Rally.

Louis XII and Lucien Grimaldi A124

Designs: 50c, Document granting sovereignty. 1fr, Seals of Louis XII and Lucien Grimaldi.

1962, June 6 Engr.
501 A124 25c ver, blk & vio bl .26 .20
502 A124 50c dk bl, brn & mag .26 .20
503 A124 1fr dk brn, grn & car .70 .60
Nos. 501-503 (3) 1.22 1.00

450th anniversary of Monaco's reception of sovereignty from Louis XII.

Mosquito and Swamp A125

1962, June 6
504 A125 1fr brn ol & lt grn .60 .55

WHO drive to eradicate malaria.

Aquatic Stadium at Night A126

1962, June 6
505 A126 10c dk bl, ind & grn .16 .15

Sun, Flowers and Hope Chest A127

1962, June 6
506 A127 20c multicolored .20 .16

Issued to publicize the National Multiple Sclerosis Society of New York.

Wheat Harvest A128

1962, June 6
507 A128 25c dk bl, red brn & brn .15 .15
508 A128 50c ind, ol bis & dk bl grn .25 .25
509 A128 1fr red lil & ol bis .60 .60
Nos. 507-509,C61 (4) 2.25 2.00

Europa. See No. C61.

Blood Donor's Arm and Globe A129

1962, Nov. 15 Engr. Perf. 13
510 A129 1fr dk red, blk & orange .50 .45

3rd International Blood Donors' Congress, Nov. 15-18 at Monaco.

Yellow Wagtails — A130

Birds: 10c, European robins. 15c, European goldfinches. 20c, Blackcaps. 25c, Great spotted woodpeckers. 30c, Nightingale. 45c, Barn owls. 50c, Common starlings. 85c, Red crossbills. 1fr, White storks.

1962, Dec. 12 Unwmk.
511 A130 5c green, sep & yel .18 .18
512 A130 10c bis, dk pur & red .22 .22
513 A130 15c multicolored .30 .30
514 A130 20c mag, grn & blk .35 .30
515 A130 25c multicolored .45 .28
516 A130 30c brn, sl grn & bl .52 .42
517 A130 45c vio & gldn brn .75 .65
518 A130 50c bl grn, blk & yel 1.10 .80
519 A130 85c multicolored 1.40 1.10
520 A130 1fr blk, grn & red 1.65 1.40
Nos. 511-520 (10) 6.92 5.65

Protection of useful birds.

Divers A131

10c, Galeazzi's turret, vert. 25c, Williamson's photosphere, 1914 & bathyscape "Trieste," 1962. 45c, Diving suits. 50c, Diving chamber. 85c, Fulton's "Nautilus," 1800 and modern submarine. 1fr, Alexander the Great's underwater chamber and bathysphere of the N. Y. Zoological Society.

1962, Dec. 12
521 A131 5c bluish grn, vio & blk .15 .15
522 A131 10c multicolored .15 .15
523 A131 25c bis, bluish grn & sl grn .20 .20
524 A131 45c green, ind & blk .30 .30
525 A131 50c cit & dk bl .45 .45
526 A131 85c Prus grn & dk vio bl .60 .60
527 A131 1fr dk bl, dk brn & dk grn 1.00 1.00
Nos. 521-527 (7) 2.85 2.85

Issued in connection with an exhibition at the Oceanographic Museum "Man Under Water," showing ancient and modern methods of underwater exploration.

Dancing Children and UN Emblem — A132

Children on Scales A133

Designs: 10c, Bird feeding nestlings, vert. 20c, Sun shining on children of different races, vert. 25c, Mother and child, vert. 50c, House and child. 95c, African mother and child, vert. 1fr, Prince Albert and Princess Caroline.

1963, May 3 Unwmk. Perf. 13
528 A132 5c ocher, dk red & ultra .15 .15
529 A133 10c vio bl, emer & ol gray .16 .15
530 A133 15c ultra, red & grn .20 .15
531 A133 20c multicolored .20 .15
532 A133 25c blue, brn & pink .20 .20
533 A133 50c multicolored .45 .40
534 A133 95c multicolored .60 .55
535 A132 1fr multicolored 1.10 1.00
Nos. 528-535 (8) 3.06 2.75

Publicizing the UN Children's Charter.

Figurehead with Red Cross, Red Crescent and Red Lion and Sun — A134

1fr, Centenary emblem, Gustave Moynier, Henri Dunant and Gen. Henri Dufour, horiz.

1963, May 3 Engr.
536 A134 50c bluish grn, red & red brn .38 .38
537 A134 1fr blue, sl grn & red .60 .60

Centenary of International Red Cross.

Racing Cars on Monte Carlo Course and Map of Europe A135

1963, May 3
538 A135 50c multicolored .45 .38

European Automobile Grand Prix.

Rally Type of 1956

Design: 1fr, "Warsaw to Monte Carlo."

1963, May 3
539 A98 1fr multicolored 1.40 1.25

32nd Monte Carlo Auto Race.

Lions International Emblem A136

1963, May 3
540 A136 50c bis, lt vio & bl .75 .75

Issued to commemorate the founding of the Lions Club of Monaco, Mar. 24, 1962.

Hôtel des Postes, Paris, and UPU Allegory — A137

1963, May 3
541 A137 50c multicolored .60 .60

1st Intl. Postal Conference, Paris, 1863.

Globe and Telstar A138

1963, May 3
542 A138 50c grn, dk pur & maroon .75 .75

1st television connection of the US and Europe through the Telstar satellite, July 11-12, 1962.

Holy Spirit over St. Peter's and World — A139

1963, May 3
543 A139 1fr grn, red brn & bl .75 .75

Vatican II, the 21st Ecumenical Council of the Roman Catholic Church.

Wheat Emblem and Dove Feeding Nestlings A140

1963, May 3 Engr.
544 A140 1fr multicolored .85 .85

FAO "Freedom from Hunger" campaign.

Henry Ford and 1903 Model A — A141

1963, Dec. 12 Unwmk. Perf. 13
545 A141 20c slate grn & lil rose .38 .32

Centenary of the birth of Henry Ford, American automobile manufacturer.

Bicyle Racer in Town — A142

Design: 50c, Bicyclist on country road.

1963, Dec. 12
546 A142 25c bl, sl grn & red brn .30 .25
547 A142 50c bl, gray grn, & blk brn .38 .38

50th anniv. of the Bicycle Tour de France.

Pierre de Coubertin and Myron's Discobolus A143

1963, Dec. 12

548 A143 1fr dp claret, car & ocher 1.00 .90

Baron Pierre de Coubertin, organizer of the modern Olympic Games, birth cent.

Rally Type of 1956

Design: 1fr, "Paris to Monte Carlo."

1963, Dec. 12

549 A98 1fr multicolored 1.40 1.40

33rd Monte Carlo Automobile Rally.

Children with Stamp Album and UNESCO Emblem A144

1963, Dec. 12

550 A144 50c dp ultra, red & vio .45 .42

International Philatelic and Educational Exposition, Monaco, Nov.-Dec., 1963.

Europa Issue, 1963

Woman, Dove and Lyre — A145

1963, Dec. 12

551 A145 25c brn, grn & car .25 .20
552 A145 50c dk brn, bl & car .48 .38

Wembley Stadium and British Football Association Emblem — A146

Overhead Kick — A147

Soccer Game, Florence, 16th Century A148

Tackle A149

Designs: 3c, Goalkeeper. 4c, Louis II Stadium and emblem of Sports Association of Monaco, with black overprint: "Championnat /1962-1963/Coupe de France." 15c, Soule Game, Brittany, 19th century. 20c, Soccer, England, 1827. 25c, Soccer, England, 1890. 50c, Clearing goal area. 95c, Heading the ball. 1fr, Kicking the ball.

1963, Dec. 12

553 A146 1c green, vio & dk red .15 .15
554 A147 2c black, red & grn .15 .15
555 A147 3c gray ol, org & red .15 .15
556 A146 4c bl, red, grn, pur & blk .15 .15
557 A148 10c dk bl, car & sep .15 .15
558 A148 15c sepia & car .15 .15
559 A148 20c sepia & dk bl .22 .22
560 A148 25c sepia & lilac .22 .22
a. Block of 4 .70 .70
561 A149 30c green, sep & red .45 .45
562 A149 50c sepia, grn & red .52 .52
563 A149 95c sepia, grn & red 1.00 1.00
564 A149 1fr sepia, grn & red 1.25 1.25
a. Block of 4 3.50 3.50
Nos. 553-564 (12) 4.56 4.56

Cent. of British Football Assoc. (organized soccer). No. 556 also for the successes of the soccer team of Monaco, 1962-63 (overprint typographed). No. 556 was not regularly issued without overprint. Value $525.

The 4 stamps of No. 560a are connected by an 1863 soccer ball in red brown; the stamps of No. 564a by a modern soccer ball.

Design from 1914 Rally Post Card — A150

Farman Biplane over Monaco — A151

Designs: 3c, Nieuport monoplane. 4c, Breguet biplane. 5c, Morane-Saulnier monoplane. 10c, Albatros biplane. 15c, Deperdussin monoplane. 20c, Vickers-Vimy biplane and map (Ross Smith's flight London-Port Darwin, 1919). 25c, Douglas Liberty biplane (first American around-the-world flight. 4 planes, 1924). 30c, Savoia S-16 hydroplane (De Pinedo's Rome-Australia-Japan-Rome flight, 1925). 45c, Trimotor Fokker F-7 monoplane (first aerial survey of North Pole, Richard E. Byrd and James Gordon Bennett, 1925). 50c, Spirit of St. Louis (first crossing of Atlantic, New York-Paris, Charles Lindbergh, 1927). 65c, Breguet 19 (Paris-New York, Coste and Bellonte, 1930). 95c, Laté 28 hydroplane (first South Atlantic airmail route, Dakar-Natal, 1930). 1fr, Dornier DO-X, (Germany-Rio de Janeiro, 1930).

1964, May 22 Engr. *Perf. 13*

565 A150 1c green, bl & ol .15 .15
566 A151 2c bl, bis & red brn .15 .15
567 A151 3c olive, grn & bl .15 .15
568 A151 4c red brn, bl & Prus grn .15 .15
569 A151 5c gray ol, vio & mag .15 .15
570 A151 10c violet, bl & ol .15 .15
571 A151 15c blue, org & brn .15 .15
572 A151 20c brt grn, blk & bl .16 .15
573 A151 25c red, bl & ol .20 .15
574 A151 30c bl, sl grn & dp cl .28 .20
575 A151 45c red brn, grnsh bl & blk .48 .32
576 A151 50c purple, ol & bis .60 .45
577 A151 65c steel bl, blk & red .70 .48
578 A151 95c ocher, sl grn & red .96 .65
579 A151 1fr sl grn, bl & vio brn 1.10 .80
Nos. 565-579,C64 (16) 9.03 7.25

50th anniv. of the 1st airplane rally of Monte Carlo. Nos. 565-571 show planes which took part in the 1914 rally, Nos. 572-579 and C64 show important flights from 1919 to 1961.

Ancient Egyptian Message Transmitters and Rocket — A152

1964, May 22 Unwmk.

580 A152 1fr dk bl, indigo & org brn .80 .80

Issued to publicize "PHILATEC", International Philatelic and Postal Techniques Exhibition, Paris, June 5-21, 1964.

Types of 1955-60

1c, Crab (Macrocheira Kampferi), horiz. 2c, Flowering cactus (Selenicereus Gr.). 12c, Shell (Fasciolaria trapezium). 18c, Aloe ciliaris. 70c, Honor court of palace (like #477). 95c, Prince Rainier III.

1964, May 19 *Perf. 13*

581 A115 1c bl grn & dk red .15 .15
582 A115 2c dk grn & multi .15 .15
583 A115 12c vio & brn red .42 .18
584 A115 18c grn, yel & car .55 .15
585 A116 70c lt grn, choc & red org .55 .32
586 A83 95c ultra 1.50 .38
Nos. 581-586 (6) 3.32
Set value 1.05

Rainier III Aquatic Stadium A153

1964-67 Engr. *Perf. 13*

587 A153 10c dk car, rose, bl & blk 1.50 .18
587A A153 15c dk car, rose, brt bl & blk ('67) .65 .18
588 A153 25c dl grn, dk bl & blk .65 .18
589 A153 50c lil, bl grn & blk 1.50 .65
Nos. 587-589 (4) 4.30 1.19

Nos. 587-589 were issued precanceled only. See note after No. 324. The "1962" date has been obliterated with 2 bars. See Nos. 732-734, 793-796, 976-979.

Europa Issue, 1964

Common Design Type

1964, Sept. 12

Size: 22x34½mm

590 CD7 25c brt red, brt grn & dk grn .18 .18
591 CD7 50c ultra, ol bis & dk red brn .45 .45

Weight Lifter — A154

1964, Dec. 3 Unwmk. *Perf. 13*

592 A154 1c shown .15 .15
593 A154 2c Judo .15 .15
594 A154 3c Pole vault .15 .15
595 A154 4c Archery .15 .15
Set value .20 .20

Issued to commemorate the 18th Olympic Games, Tokyo, Oct. 10-25. See No. C65.

Pres. John F. Kennedy and Mercury Capsule — A155

1964, Dec. 3

596 A155 50c brt bl & indigo .65 .65

Pres. John F. Kennedy (1917-63).

Television Set and View of Monte Carlo — A156

1964, Dec. 3

597 A156 50c dk car rose, dk bl & brn .38 .38

Fifth International Television Festival.

Frédéric Mistral, (1830-1914), Provençal Poet — A157

1964, Dec. 3 Engr.

598 A157 1fr gray olive & brn red .45 .45

Scales of Justice and Code — A158

1964, Dec. 3

599 A158 1fr gldn brn & slate grn .60 .60

Universal Declaration of Human Rights.

Rally Type of 1956

Design: 1fr, "Minsk to Monte Carlo."

1964, Dec. 3

600 A98 1fr bl grn, ocher & brn .65 .60

34th Monte Carlo Automobile Rally.

International Football Association Emblem — A159

1964, Dec. 3

601 A159 1fr red, bl & ol bister .70 .70

60th anniv. of FIFA, the Federation Internationale de Football (soccer).

Types of 1955 and 1960

Designs: 40c, Aerial view of palace. 60c, 1.30fr, 2.30fr, Prince Rainier III.

1965-66 Engr. *Perf. 13*

602 A116 40c sl grn, dl cl & brt grn .35 .18
603 A83 60c sl grn & blk .45 .24
604 A83 1.30fr dk red & blk 3.25 .75
604A A83 2.30fr org & rose lil ('66) 1.10 .45
Nos. 602-604A (4) 5.15 1.62

Telstar and Pleumeur-Bodou Relay Station — A160

Alexander Graham Bell and Telephone A161

Designs (ITU Emblem and): 5c, Syncom II and Earth. 10c, Echo II and Earth. 12c, Relay satellite and Earth, vert. 18c, Lunik III and Moon. 50c, Samuel Morse and telegraph. 60c, Edouard Belin, belinograph and newspaper. 70c, Roman signal towers and Chappe telegraph. 95c, Cable laying ships; "The Great Eastern" (British, 1858) and "Alsace" (French, modern). 1fr, Edouard Branly, Guglielmo Marconi and map of English Channel.

1965, May 17

605	A161	5c vio bl & slate grn	.15	.15
606	A161	10c dk bl & sepia	.15	.15
607	A161	12c gray, brn & dk car	.15	.15
608	A161	18c ind, dk car & plum	.15	.15
609	A160	25c vio, ol & rose brn	.15	.15
610	A161	30c dk brn, ol & bis brn	.18	.18
611	A161	50c green & indigo	.24	.24
612	A161	60c dl red brn & brt bl	.26	.26
613	A160	70c brn blk, org & dk bl	.45	.45
614	A160	95c indigo, blk & bl	.55	.55
615	A160	1fr brn, blk & ultra	.80	.80
		Nos. 605-615,C66 (12)	7.48	7.48

International Telecommunication Union, cent.

Europa Issue, 1965

Common Design Type

1965, Sept. 25 Engr. *Perf. 13*

Size: 36x22mm

616	CD8	30c red brn & grn	.18	.18
617	CD8	60c violet & dk car	.40	.40

Palace of Monaco, 18th Century A162

Views of Palace: 12c, From the Bay, 17th century. 18c, Bay with sailboats, 18th century. 30c, From distance, 19th century. 60c, Close-up, 19th century. 1.30fr, Aerial view, 20th century.

1966, Feb. 1 Engr. *Perf. 13*

618	A162	10c vio, dl grn & ind	.15	.15
619	A162	12c bl, bis brn & dk brn	.15	.15
620	A162	18c blk, grn & bl	.15	.15
621	A162	30c vio bl, sep & red brn	.24	.24
622	A162	60c bl, grn & brn	.38	.38
623	A162	1.30fr dk grn & red brn	.75	.75
		Nos. 618-623 (6)	1.82	1.82

750th anniversary of Palace of Monaco.

Dante Alighieri — A163

Designs: 60c, Dante facing Panther of Envy. 70c, Dante and Virgil boating across muddy swamp of 5th Circle. 95c, Dante watching the arrogant and Cross of Salvation. 1fr, Invocation of St. Bernard; Dante and Beatrice.

1966, Feb. 1

624	A163	30c crimson & dp grn	.38	.38
625	A163	60c dl grn, Prus bl & ind	.65	.65
626	A163	70c black, sep & car	.85	.85
627	A163	95c red lilac & blue	1.25	1.25
628	A163	1fr ultra & bluish grn	1.40	1.40
		Nos. 624-628 (5)	4.53	4.53

700th anniv. (in 1965) of the birth of Dante (1265-1321), poet.

Rally Type of 1956

Design: 1fr, "London to Monte Carlo."

1966, Feb. 1

629	A98	1fr purple, red & indigo	.95	.95

The 35th Monte Carlo Automobile Rally.

Nativity by Gerard van Honthorst A164

1966, Feb. 1

630	A164	30c brown	.22	.22

Issued to honor the World Association for the Protection of Children.

Casino, Monte Carlo — A165

View of La Condamine, 1860, and Francois Blanc — A166

Designs: 12c, Prince Charles III, vert. 40c, Charles III monument, Bowling Green Gardens. 60c, Seaside Promenade and Rainier III. 70c, René Blum, Sergei Diaghilev and "Petroushka." 95c, Jules Massenet and Camille Saint-Saens. 1.30fr, Gabriel Fauré and Maurice Ravel.

1966, June 1 Engr. *Perf. 13*

631	A165	12c dp blue, blk & mag	.15	.15
632	A165	25c multicolored	.15	.15
633	A166	30c bl, plum, grn & org	.15	.15
634	A165	40c multicolored	.16	.16
635	A166	60c multicolored	.40	.40
636	A166	70c rose cl & ind	.40	.40
637	A165	95c purple & blk	.60	.60
638	A165	1.30fr brn org, ol bis & brn	1.00	1.00
		Nos. 631-638,C68 (9)	5.51	5.51

Centenary of founding of Monte Carlo.

Europa Issue, 1966

Common Design Type

1966, Sept. 26 Engr. *Perf. 13*

Size: 21½x35½mm

639	CD9	30c orange	.16	.16
640	CD9	60c light green	.32	.32

Prince Albert I, Yachts Hirondelle I and Princesse Alice — A167

1966, Dec. 12 Engr. *Perf. 13*

641	A167	1fr ultra & dk vio brn	.70	.60

1st Intl. Congress of the History of Oceanography, Monaco, Dec. 12-17. Issued in sheets of 10.

Red Chalk Drawing by Domenico Zampieri — A168

Television Screen and Cross over Monaco — A169

1966, Dec. 12

642	A168	30c brt rose & dk brn	.16	.16
643	A168	60c brt bl & yel brn	.26	.26

20th anniv. of UNESCO.

1966, Dec. 12

644	A169	60c dk car rose, lil & red	.28	.18

10th meeting of "UNDA," the International Catholic Association for Radio and Television.

Precontinent III and Divers on Ocean Floor — A170

1966, Dec. 12

645	A170	1fr Prus bl, yel & dk brn	.45	.38

First anniversary of the submarine research station Precontinent III.

WHO Headquarters, Geneva A171

1966, Dec. 12

646	A171	30c dp bl, ol brn & dp bl grn	.15	.15
647	A171	60c dk grn, crim & dk brn	.22	.20

Opening of WHO Headquarters, Geneva.

Automobile Type of 1961

Automobiles (Previous Winners): 1c, Bugatti, 1931. 2c, Alfa Romeo, 1932. 5c, Mercedes, 1936. 10c, Maserati, 1948. 18c, Ferrari, 1955. 20c, Alfa Romeo, 1950. 25c, Maserati, 1957. 30c, Cooper-Climax, 1958. 40c, Lotus-Climax, 1960. 50c, Lotus-Climax, 1961. 60c, Cooper-Climax, 1962. 70c, B.R.M., 1963-66. 1fr, Walter Christie, 1907. 2.30fr, Peugeot, 1910.

1967, Apr. 28 Engr. *Perf. 13x12½*

648	A122	1c ind, red & brt bl	.15	.15
649	A122	2c green, red & blk	.15	.15
650	A122	5c red, ind & gray	.15	.15
651	A122	10c violet, red & ind	.15	.15
652	A122	18c indigo & red	.15	.15
653	A122	20c dk grn, red & ind	.15	.15
654	A122	25c ultra, red & ind	.15	.15
655	A122	30c brown, ind & grn	.20	.15
656	A122	40c car rose, ind & grn	.28	.20
657	A122	50c lilac, ind & grn	.40	.25
658	A122	60c carmine, ind & grn	.55	.35
659	A122	70c dl yel, bl grn & ind	.65	.45
660	A122	1fr brn red, blk & gray	.80	.60
661	A122	2.30fr multicolored	1.75	1.25
		Nos. 648-661,C73 (15)	7.93	6.30

25th Grand Prix of Monaco, May 7.

Dog, Egyptian Statue — A172

1967, Apr. 28 *Perf. 12½x13*

662	A172	30c dk grn, brn & blk	.45	.38

Congress of the International Dog Fanciers Federation, Monaco, Apr. 5-9.

View of Monte Carlo — A173

1967, Apr. 28 *Perf. 13*

663	A173	30c slate grn, brt bl & brn	.25	.18

International Tourist Year, 1967.

Chessboard and Monte Carlo Harbor — A174

1967, Apr. 28

664	A174	60c brt bl, dk pur & blk	.65	.60

International Chess Championships, Monaco, Mar. 19-Apr. 1.

Melvin Jones, View of Monte Carlo and Lions Emblem — A175

1967, Apr. 28

665	A175	60c ultra, slate bl & choc	.42	.32

50th anniversary of Lions International.

Rotary Emblem and View of Monte Carlo — A176

1967, Apr. 28

666	A176	1fr brt bl & lt ol grn	.50	.40

Issued to publicize the Rotary International Convention, Monaco, May 21-26.

EXPO '67 Monaco Pavilion — A177

1967, Apr. 28

667	A177	1fr multicolored	.38	.32

EXPO '67, International Exhibition, Montreal, Apr. 28-Oct. 27, 1967.

Map of Europe A178

1967, Apr. 28

668 A178 1fr choc, lemon & Prus bl .38 .30

Issued to publicize the International Committee for European Migration, CIME.

Europa Issue, 1967

Common Design Type

1967, Apr. 28 *Perf. 12½x13*

669 CD10 30c brt car, rose lil & brt vio .18 .18
670 CD10 60c grn ol & bl grn .35 .32

Skier and Olympic Emblem — A179

1967, Dec. 7 **Engr.** *Perf. 13*

671 A179 2.30fr red brn, gray & brt bl 1.10 .95

10th Winter Olympic Games, Grenoble, France, Feb. 6-18, 1968.

Sounding Line and Map — A180

1967, Dec. 7

672 A180 1fr dk bl, grn & ol .50 .40

9th International Hydrographic Conference, Monte Carlo, April-May, 1967.

Marie Curie, Chemical Apparatus and Atom Symbol — A181

1967, Dec. 7

673 A181 1fr brn, ultra & ol .52 .40

Marie Curie (1867-1934), discoverer of radium and polonium.

Princes of Monaco Issue

Rainier I, by Eugene Charpentier A182

#675, Lucien Grimaldi, by Ambrogio di Predis.

1967, Dec. 7 *Perf. 12x13*

674 A182 1fr multicolored .95 .70
675 A182 1fr multicolored .95 .70

See Nos. 710-711, 735-736, 774-775, 813-814, 860-861, 892-893, 991-992, 1035-1036, 1093, 1135-1136, 1187-1188, 1246-1247, 1302-1303.

Shot Put — A183

Sport: 30c, High jump. 60c, Gymnast on rings. 70c, Water polo. 1fr, Wrestling. 2.30fr, Gymnast.

1968, Apr. 29 **Engr.** *Perf. 13*

676 A183 20c brt bl, grn & brn .15 .15
677 A183 30c vio bl, sep & brn vio .15 .15
678 A183 60c car, brt rose lil & dp bl .24 .24
679 A183 70c ocher, brn org & Prus bl .30 .30
680 A183 1fr brn org, bm & ind .48 .48
681 A183 2.30fr dk car, vio bl & ol 1.00 1.00
Nos. 676-681,C74 (7) 4.32 4.07

19th Olympic Games, Mexico City, Oct. 12-27.

St. Martin and the Beggar A184

1968, Apr. 29

682 A184 2.30fr brn red, Prus bl & blk brn 1.00 .90

Red Cross of Monaco, 20th anniversary.

Anemones, by Raoul Dufy A185

1968, Apr. 29 **Photo.** *Perf. 12x13*

683 A185 1fr lt blue & multi .60 .48

International Flower Show in Monte Carlo. See Nos. 766, 776, 815-816, 829, 865.

Arms of Pope Pius IX and Prince Charles III — A186

St. Nicholas — A187

Designs: 30c, St. Benedict. 60c, Benedictine Monastery, Subiaco (Italy). 1fr, Church of St. Nicholas, Monaco, 13th century, horiz.

Perf. 12½x13, 13x12½

1968, Apr. 29 **Engr.**

684 A186 10c red & brown .15 .15
685 A187 20c sl grn, ocher & car .15 .15
686 A187 30c ultra & ol grn .22 .16
687 A187 60c lt bl, brn & dk grn .30 .30
688 A187 1fr ind, bl & ol bis .55 .45
Nos. 684-688 (5) 1.37 1.21

Centenary of the elevation of St. Nicholas Church to an Abbey *Nullius*, directly subject to the Holy See.

Europa Issue, 1968

Common Design Type

1968, Apr. 29 *Perf. 13*

Size: 36x22mm

689 CD11 30c dp orange & car .20 .15
690 CD11 60c carmine & ultra .30 .18
691 CD11 1fr green & red brn .65 .42
Nos. 689-691 (3) 1.15 .75

Locomotive 030, 1868 — A188

Locomotives and Views: 30c, Type "C"-220, 1898. 60c, Type 230-"C", 1910. 70c, Type 231-"F," 1925. 1fr, Type 241-"A," 1932. 2.30fr, Type "BB," 1968.

1968, Dec. 12 **Engr.** *Perf. 13*

692 A188 20c vio bl, brn & blk .32 .25
693 A188 30c dk ol grn, bl & blk .50 .28
694 A188 60c bl, bis & blk .75 .35
695 A188 70c vio, red brn & blk .90 .55
696 A188 1fr bl, brn red & blk 1.75 1.00
697 A188 2.30fr sal pink, brt bl & blk 3.50 2.50
Nos. 692-697 (6) 7.72 4.93

Centenary of the Nice-Monaco Railroad.

Chateaubriand and Combourg Castle — A189

Scenes from Chateaubriand Novels: 20c, The Genius of Christianity. 25c, René. 30c, The Last Abencerage. 60c, The Martyrs. 2.30fr, Atala.

1968, Dec. 12

698 A189 10c dk grn, grn & pur .15 .15
699 A189 20c brt bl, vio & mag .15 .15
700 A189 25c slate, pur & brn .16 .15
701 A189 30c dp brn, brn & pur .25 .16
702 A189 60c brn red, bl grn & dk brn .32 .30
703 A189 2.30fr dk bl, ol & mag 1.10 .95
Nos. 698-703 (6) 2.13 1.86

Vicomte François René de Chateaubriand (1768-1848), novelist and statesman.

"France" and "Fidelity" by Bosio — A190

François Joseph Bosio (1768-1845), Sculptor — A191

Designs: 25c, Henri IV as a boy. 60c, Louis XIV on horseback, Place des Victoires. 2.30fr, Busts of Louis XVIII, Napoleon I and Charles X.

1968, Dec. 12

704 A190 20c brown .15 .15
705 A191 25c sal pink & dk brn .15 .15
706 A191 30c slate & vio bl .16 .15
707 A191 60c dk ol grn & gray grn .28 .20
708 A190 2.30fr black & slate .90 .70
Nos. 704-708 (5) 1.64 1.35

WHO Emblem — A192

1968, Dec. 12 **Photo.**

709 A192 60c multicolored .30 .25

World Health Organization, 20th anniv.

Princes of Monaco Type of 1967

Designs: 1fr, Charles II (1581-89). 2.30fr, Jeanne Grimaldi (1596-1620).

1968, Dec. 12 **Engr.** *Perf. 12x13*

710 A182 1fr multicolored .42 .42
711 A182 2.30fr multicolored 1.10 1.10

Faust and Mephistopheles — A193

Scenes from "Damnation of Faust" by Berlioz: 10c, Rakoczy March. 25c, Auerbach's Cellar. 30c, Dance of the Sylphs. 40c, Dance of the Sprites. 50c, Faust and Marguerite. 70c, Woods and Meadows. 1fr, The Ride to the Abyss. 1.15fr, Heaven.

1969, Apr. 26 **Engr.** *Perf. 13*

712 A193 10c bl grn, pur & org brn .15 .15
713 A193 20c mag, dk ol & lt brn .15 .15
714 A193 25c ind, brn & mag .15 .15
715 A193 30c yel grn, sl & blk .15 .15
716 A193 40c org red, sl & blk .18 .15
717 A193 50c ol, plum & sl .22 .20
718 A193 70c dp grn, sl & lt brn .35 .28
719 A193 1fr mag, blk & ol bis .48 .40
720 A193 1.15fr Prus bl, blk & ultra .60 .60
Nos. 712-720,C75 (10) 3.68 3.33

Hector Berlioz (1803-69), French composer.

St. Elizabeth and Husband, Louis IV, Landgrave of Thuringia A194

1969, Apr. 26

721 A194 3fr dk red, sl & gray 1.65 1.40

Issued for the Red Cross.

See Nos. 767, 812, 830, 905, 963, 1037, 1094, 1189.

Europa Issue, 1969

Common Design Type

1969, Apr. 26

Size: 36x26mm

722 CD12 40c scarlet & purple .20 .16
723 CD12 70c brt blue & blk .48 .30
724 CD12 1fr yel bis, brn & bl .60 .42
Nos. 722-724 (3) 1.28 .88

Prince Rainier Type of 1955 and Palace Type of 1960

Designs: 80c, Aerial view of Palace. 1.15fr, 1.30fr, Honor Court.

1969-70 **Engr.** ***Perf. 13***

725 A83 40c olive & rose red .24 .18
726 A83 45c slate & ocher .28 .18
727 A83 50c ocher & mar .45 .18
728 A83 70c dk pur & brt vio bl .65 .35
729 A116 80c bl, red brn & grn .70 .35
730 A83 85c dk vio & brt grn .75 .50
731 A116 1.15fr blk, bl & mar 1.10 .70
731A A116 1.30fr ol brn, lt bl & dl grn ('70) .85 .45
Nos. 725-731A (8) 5.02 2.89

Aquatic Stadium Type of 1964-67, "1962" Omitted

1969 **Engr.** ***Perf. 13***

732 A153 22c choc, brt bl & blk .35 .15
733 A153 35c Prus bl, brt bl & blk .35 .28
734 A153 70c black & vio bl .60 .24
Nos. 732-734 (3) 1.30 .67

Nos. 732-734 were issued precanceled only. See note after No. 324.

Princes of Monaco Type of 1967

Designs: 1fr, Honoré II (1604-1662), by Philippe de Champaigne. 3fr, Louise-Hippolyte (1697-1731), by Pierre Gobert.

1969, Nov. 25 **Engr.** ***Perf. 12x13***

735 A182 1fr multicolored .38 .38
736 A182 3fr multicolored 1.10 1.10

Woman's Head, by Leonardo da Vinci — A195

Drawings by Leonardo da Vinci: 40c, Self-portrait. 70c, Head of old man. 80c, Study for head of St. Magdalene. 1.15fr, Man's head. 3fr, Professional soldier.

1969, Nov. 25 ***Perf. 13***

737 A195 30c dull brown .20 .15
738 A195 40c brn & rose red .22 .16
739 A195 70c gray green .30 .22
740 A195 80c dk brown .35 .30
741 A195 1.15fr orange brn .60 .55
742 A195 3fr olive brown 1.50 1.10
Nos. 737-742 (6) 3.17 2.48

Leonardo da Vinci (1452-1519), Florentine painter, sculptor and scientist.

Alphonse Daudet and Scenes from "Letters from My Windmill" — A196

Various Scenes from "Letters from My Windmill" (Lettres de Mon Moulin).

1969, Nov. 25

743 A196 30c blue grn & multi .16 .15
744 A196 40c brn, vio bl & ol .28 .24
745 A196 70c pur, brn & ol gray .32 .30
746 A196 80c sl grn, vio bl & mar .38 .35
747 A196 1.15fr ocher, sep & blk .50 .48
Nos. 743-747 (5) 1.64 1.52

Centenary of publication of "Letters from My Windmill," by Alphonse Daudet (1840-1897).

ILO Emblem A197

1969, Nov. 25 ***Perf. 13x12½***

748 A197 40c dk blue & dk pur .35 .28

50th anniv. of the ILO.

World Map and JCI Emblem A198

1969, Nov. 25

749 A198 40c olive, dk bl & bl .24 .20

25th anniversary of the Junior Chamber of Commerce in Monaco.

Television Camera and View of Monte Carlo — A199

1969, Nov. 25

750 A199 40c red brn, lil & bl .24 .20

10th International Television Festival in 1970.

King Alfonso XIII, Prince Albert I and Underwater Scene — A200

1969, Nov. 25 ***Perf. 12½x13***

751 A200 40c dk brn, blk & grnsh bl .28 .28

50th anniv. of the International Commission for the Scientific Exploration of the Mediterranean.

Congress Building, Princes Albert I and Rainier III — A201

1970, Feb. 21 **Engr.** ***Perf. 13***

752 A201 40c gray & carmine .22 .16

Meeting of the Interparliamentary Union, Monaco, Mar. 30-Apr. 5.

EXPO '70 Emblem, Japanese Scroll — A202

Designs (EXPO '70 Emblem and): 30c, Ibis. 40c, Torii. 70c, Cherry blossoms, horiz. 1.15fr, Palace and arms of Monaco, Osaka Castle and arms, horiz.

1970, Mar. 16

753 A202 20c brn, yel grn & car .15 .15
754 A202 30c brn, yel grn & buff .15 .20
755 A202 40c olive bis & pur .22 .22
756 A202 70c lt gray & red .55 .55
757 A202 1.15fr red & multi .60 .60
Nos. 753-757 (5) 1.67 1.72

Issued to publicize EXPO '70 International Exposition, Osaka, Japan, Mar. 15-Sept. 13.

Harbor Seal Pup — A203

1970, Mar. 16

758 A203 40c red lil, bl & gray .50 .42

Protection of seal pups.

Doberman Pinscher A204

1970, Apr. 25

759 A204 40c ocher & black 1.65 .60

International Dog Show, Monte Carlo, Apr. 25. See No. 996.

Basque Ponies A205

Designs: 30c, Parnassius Apollo butterfly. 50c, Harbor seal in Somme Bay. 80c, Pyrenean chamois, vert. 1fr, Whitetailed sea eagles, vert. 1.15fr, European otter, vert.

1970, May 4

760 A205 30c Prus bl & multi .35 .20
761 A205 40c blue & multi .45 .25
762 A205 50c grnsh bl, bis & brn .65 .25
763 A205 80c gray grn, sl bl & brn .90 .45
764 A205 1fr gray, brown & bis 1.50 .60
765 A205 1.15fr dk brn, lt bl & yel grn 1.75 .70
Nos. 760-765 (6) 5.60 2.45

20th anniversary of the International Federation of Animal Protection.

Flower Type of 1968

Roses and Anemones, by Vincent van Gogh.

1970, May 4 **Photo.** ***Perf. 12x13***

766 A185 3fr black & multi 1.75 1.75

International Flower Show, Monte Carlo.

Red Cross Type of 1969

Design: 3fr, St. Louis giving alms to the poor.

1970, May 4 **Engr.** ***Perf. 13***

767 A194 3fr dk gray, ol gray & slate grn 1.50 1.50

Issued for the Red Cross.

Europa Issue, 1970
Common Design Type

1970, May 4

Size: 26x36mm

768 CD13 40c deep rose lilac .22 .15
769 CD13 80c bright green .45 .28
770 CD13 1fr deep blue .55 .35
Nos. 768-770 (3) 1.22 .78

UPU Headquarters and Monument, Bern — A206

1970, May 4

771 A206 40c brn ol, gray & bl grn .22 .16

New UPU Headquarters in Bern opening.

Plaque and Flag on the Moon, Presidents Kennedy and Nixon — A207

Design: 80c, Astronauts and landing module on moon, and Apollo 11 emblem.

1970, May 4 **Photo.**

772 A207 40c multicolored .28 .24
773 A207 80c multicolored .55 .42

Man's first landing on moon, July 20, 1969. US astronauts Neil A. Armstrong and Col. Edwin E. Aldrin, Jr., with Lt. Col. Michael Collins piloting Apollo 11.

Princes of Monaco Type of 1967

Designs: 1fr, Louis I (1662-1701), by Jean Francois de Troy. 3fr, Charlotte de Gramont (1639-1678), by Sebastian Bourdon.

1970, Dec. 15 **Engr.** ***Perf. 12x13***

774 A182 1fr multicolored .45 .45
775 A182 3fr multicolored 1.25 1.40

Painting Type of 1968

Design: 3fr, Portrait of Dédie, by Amedeo Modigliani (1884-1920).

1970, Dec. 15

776 A185 3fr multicolored 1.00 .70

Beethoven and "Ode to Joy" — A208

1970, Dec. 15

777 A208 1.30fr brown & maroon 1.00 .70

Ludwig van Beethoven (1770-1827), composer.

Dumas and Scene from "Three Musketeers" — A209

Designs: 40c, Henri Rougier and biplane over Monaco. 80c, Alphonse de Lamartine and scenes from his works.

1970, Dec. 15

778 A209 30c blue, brown & gray .15 .15
779 A209 40c blue, sepia & gray .26 .18
780 A209 80c multicolored .35 .22
Nos. 778-780 (3) .76 .55

Alexandre Dumas, père (1802-70), novelist; 1st flight over the Mediterranean by Henri Rougier, 60th anniv.; publication of "Méditations Poétiques" by Alphonse de Lamartine (1790-1869), poet, 150th anniv.

Camargue Horse A210

Horses: 20c, Anglo-Arabian thoroughbred. 30c, French saddle horse. 40c, Lippizaner. 50c, Trotter. 70c, English thoroughbred. 85c, Arabian. 1.15fr, Barbary.

1970, Dec. 15 Engr. *Perf. 13*

781 A210 10c bl, ol bis & dk bl .15 .15
782 A210 20c vio bl, brn & ol .20 .15
783 A210 30c blue, brn & grn .32 .18
784 A210 40c gray, ind & ol bis .45 .25
785 A210 50c blue, dk brn & ol .65 .32
786 A210 70c dk grn, ol brn & red brn .80 .40
787 A210 85c dk grn, ol & sl 1.00 .65
788 A210 1.15fr blue, emer & blk 1.40 .80
Nos. 781-788,C77 (9) 8.22 5.90

Prince Rainier Type of 1955 and Palace Type of 1960

90c, Honor Court. 1.40fr, Aerial view of Palace.

1971 Engr. *Perf. 13*

789 A83 60c plum & blk .75 .35
790 A116 90c dk car, ultra & blk 1.00 .48
791 A83 1.10fr gray & ultra 1.25 .75
792 A116 1.40fr pur, org & grn 1.50 1.10
Nos. 789-792 (4) 4.50 2.68

Aquatic Stadium Type of 1964-67, "1962" Omitted

1971

793 A153 26c pur, ultra & blk .35 .18
794 A153 30c cop red, bl, lil & blk .45 .18
795 A153 45c sl grn, vio bl & blk .70 .24
796 A153 90c ol, Prus bl & blk 1.25 .40
Nos. 793-796 (4) 2.75 1.00

Nos. 793-796 were issued precanceled only. See note after No. 324.

Europa Issue, 1971

Common Design Type

1971, Sept. 6

797 CD14 50c carmine rose .25 .15
798 CD14 80c brt blue .38 .22
799 CD14 1.30fr slate green .90 .32
Nos. 797-799 (3) 1.53 .69

Old Bridge at Sospel — A211

80c, Roquebrune Castle. 1.30fr, Grimaldi Castle. 3fr, Roman Monument, La Turbie, vert. All views in Alpes-Maritimes Department, France.

1971, Sept. 6

800 A211 50c sl grn, bl & ol brn .20 .15
801 A211 80c sl grn, sl & brn .35 .16
802 A211 1.30fr brn, sl grn & red .50 .35
803 A211 3fr brt bl, sl & olive 1.25 .85
Nos. 800-803 (4) 2.30 1.51

Protection of historic monuments.

Theodolite, Underwater Scene and Coast Line — A212

1971, Sept. 6

804 A212 80c blue grn & multi .42 .35

International Hydrographical Bureau, 50th anniv.

Sea Bird Covered with Oil — A213

1971, Sept. 6

805 A213 50c dp blue & indigo .45 .35

Against pollution of the seas.

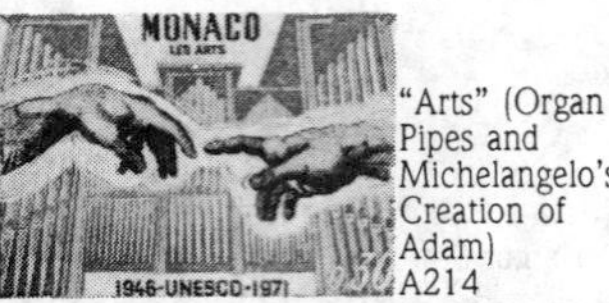

"Arts" (Organ Pipes and Michelangelo's Creation of Adam) A214

"Science" (Alchemist, Radar and Rocket) — A215

Prince Pierre of Monaco — A216

Design: 80c, "Culture" (medieval scholar, book, film and television).

1971, Sept. 6 Engr. *Perf. 13*

806 A214 30c brt bl, pur & brn .15 .15
807 A215 50c slate & brn org .18 .15
808 A214 80c emerald & brn .28 .18

Photo. *Perf. 12½x13*

809 A216 1.30fr gray green .42 .32
Nos. 806-809 (4) 1.03
Set value .66

25th anniv. of UNESCO.

Cocker Spaniel A217

1971, Sept. 6 *Perf. 13x12½*

810 A217 50c multicolored 2.00 1.50

Intl. Dog Show. See Nos. 826, 879, 910.

Hand Holding Blood Donor Emblem A218

1971, Sept. 6 Engr. *Perf. 13*

811 A218 80c red, violet & gray .45 .32

7th International Blood Donors Congress, Monaco, Oct. 21-24.

Red Cross Type of 1969

3fr, St. Vincent de Paul appearing to prisoners.

1971, Sept. 6

812 A194 3fr bl grn, ol grn & dp grn 1.40 1.10

Princes of Monaco Type of 1967

Designs: 1fr, Antoine I (1701-1731), by Hyacinthe Rigaud. 3fr, Marie de Lorraine (1674-1724), French School.

1972, Jan. 18 *Perf. 12x13*

813 A182 1fr multicolored .45 .45
814 A182 3fr multicolored 1.40 1.25

Painting Type of 1968

Designs: 2fr, The Cradle, by Berthe Morisot. 3fr, Clown, by Jean Antoine Watteau.

1972, Jan. 18

815 A185 2fr green & multi 1.10 .95
816 A185 3fr multicolored 1.50 1.25

No. 815 issued for 25th anniv. (in 1971) of UNICEF.

Christ Before Pilate, by Dürer A219

1972, Jan. 18 *Perf. 13*

817 A219 2fr lt brown & blk 1.25 1.00

500th anniv. of the birth of Albrecht Dürer (1471-1528), German painter and engraver.

La Fontaine and Animals — A220

Saint-Saens and "Samson et Dalila" — A221

1.30fr, Charles Baudelaire, nudes and cats.

1972, Jan. 18

818 A220 50c brn, grn & sl grn .35 .24
819 A221 90c dk brn & yel brn .52 .38
820 A220 1.30fr blk, red & vio brn .65 .52
Nos. 819-820 (2) 1.17 .90

350th anniv. of the birth of Jean de La Fontaine (1621-1695), fabulist; 50th anniv. of the death of Camille Saint-Saens (1835-1921), composer; 150th anniv. of the birth of Charles Baudelaire (1821-1867), poet.

Father Christmas — A222

1972, Jan. 18

821 A222 30c bis, slate bl & red .15 .15
822 A222 50c vio brn, grn & red .24 .15
823 A222 90c ocher, indigo & red .40 .22
Nos. 821-823 (3) .79 .52

Christmas 1971.

Battle of Lepanto — A223

1972, Jan. 18

824 A223 1fr dull bl, red & brn .50 .40

400th anniversary of the Battle of Lepanto against the Turks.

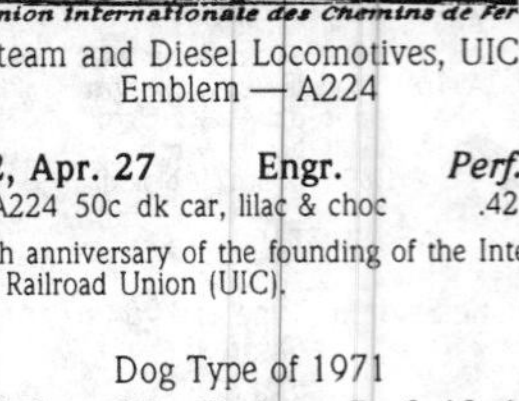

Steam and Diesel Locomotives, UIC Emblem — A224

1972, Apr. 27 Engr. *Perf. 13*

825 A224 50c dk car, lilac & choc .42 .32

50th anniversary of the founding of the International Railroad Union (UIC).

Dog Type of 1971

1972, Apr. 27 Photo. *Perf. 13x12½*

826 A217 60c Great Dane 1.25 .70

International Dog Show.

Serene Landscape, Pollution, Destruction — A225

1972, Apr. 27 Engr. *Perf. 13*

827 A225 90c grn, brn & blk .48 .30

Anti-pollution fight.

Ski Jump, Sapporo '72 Emblem — A226

1972, Apr. 27

828 A226 90c bl grn, dk red & blk .50 .40

11th Winter Olympic Games, Sapporo, Japan, Feb. 3-13.

Flower Type of 1968

Design: 3fr, Flowers in Vase, by Paul Cezanne.

1972, Apr. 27 Photo. *Perf. 12x13*

829 A185 3fr multicolored 1.65 1.10

International Flower Show, Monte Carlo.

Red Cross Type of 1969

3fr, St. Francis of Assisi comforting poor man.

1972, Apr. 27 Engr. *Perf. 13*

830 A194 3fr dk purple & brn 1.65 1.40

For the Red Cross.

Europa Issue 1972

Common Design Type

1972, Apr. 27 *Perf. 12½x13*

Size: 26x36mm

831 CD15 50c vio blue & org .68 .35
832 CD15 90c vio blue & emer 1.25 .80

Church of Sts. John and Paul (detail), by Canaletto A227

Designs: 60c, Church of St. Peter of Castello, by Francesco Guardi. 2fr, St. Mark's Square, by Bernardo Bellotto.

1972, Apr. 27 *Perf. 13*
Sizes: 36x48mm (30c, 2fr); 26½x48mm (60c)

833 A227 30c rose red .24 .20
834 A227 60c brt purple .32 .24
835 A227 2fr Prus blue 1.75 1.25
Nos. 833-835 (3) 2.31 1.69

UNESCO campaign to save Venice.

Dressage A228

Equestrian Events: 90c, Jump over fences. 1.10fr, Jump over wall. 1.40fr, Jump over gates.

1972, Apr. 27

836 A228 60c rose car, vio bl & brn .70 .70
837 A228 90c vio bl, rose car & brn 1.10 1.10
838 A228 1.10fr brn, rose car & vio bl 1.75 1.75
839 A228 1.40fr vio bl, rose car & brn 2.50 2.50
a. Block of 4 + 2 labels 8.00 8.00

20th Olympic Games, Munich, Aug. 26-Sept. 10. Nos. 836-839 printed se-tenant in sheets of 24 stamps and 6 labels.

Auguste Escoffier and his Birthplace A229

1972, May 6 **Engr.** *Perf. 13*

840 A229 45c black & olive .32 .24

125th anniversary of the birth of Georges Auguste Escoffier (1846-1935), French chef.

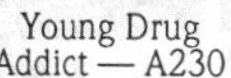

Young Drug Addict — A230

Congress Emblem, Birds and Animals — A231

1972, July 3

841 A230 50c carmine, sep & org .40 .22
842 A230 90c slate grn, sep & ind .60 .38

Fight against drug abuse.

1972, Sept. 25

Designs: 50c, Congress emblem, Neptune, sea, earth and land creatures, horiz. 90c, Globe, land, sea and air creatures.

843 A231 30c ol, brt grn & car .15 .15
844 A231 50c ocher, brn & org brn .25 .15
845 A231 90c org brn, bl & ol .38 .24
Nos. 843-845 (3) .78 .54

17th Intl. Zoology Cong., Monaco, Sept. 24-30.

Arrangement of Lilies and Palm — A232

Designs: Floral arrangements.

1972, Nov. 13 **Photo.** *Perf. 13*

846 A232 30c orange red & multi .24 .15
847 A232 50c multicolored .35 .24
848 A232 90c black & multi .60 .32
Nos. 846-848 (3) 1.19 .71

International Flower Show, Monte Carlo, May, 1973. See Nos. 894-896.

Child and Adoration of the Kings — A233

1972, Nov. 13 **Engr.**

849 A233 30c gray, vio bl & brt pink .15 .15
850 A233 50c dp car, lil & brn .22 .15
851 A233 90c violet bl & pur .45 .24
Nos. 849-851 (3) .82 .54

Christmas 1972.

Louis Bleriot and his Monoplane — A234

Designs: 50c, Roald Amundsen and Antarctic landscape. 90c, Louis Pasteur and laboratory.

1972, Dec. 4

852 A234 30c choc & brt blue .22 .15
853 A234 50c Prus blue & ind .35 .28
854 A234 90c choc & ocher .60 .50
Nos. 852-854 (3) 1.17 .93

Louis Bleriot (1872-1936), French aviation pioneer (30c); Roald Amundsen (1872-1928), Norwegian polar explorer (50c); Louis Pasteur (1822-1895), French chemist and bacteriologist (90c).

Gethsemane, by Giovanni Canavesio A235

Frescoes by Canavesio, 15th century, Chapel of Our Lady of Fountains at La Brique: 50c, Christ Stripped of His Garments. 90c, Christ Carrying the Cross. 1.40fr, Resurrection. 2fr, Crucifixion.

1972, Dec. 4

855 A235 30c bright rose .16 .15
856 A235 50c indigo .28 .22
857 A235 90c slate green .50 .32
858 A235 1.40fr bright red .60 .45
859 A235 2fr purple 1.10 .70
Nos. 855-859 (5) 2.64 1.84

Protection of historic monuments.

Princes of Monaco Type of 1967

1fr, Jacques I, by Nicolas de Largillière. 3fr, Louise Hippolyte (1697-1731), by Jean Baptiste Vanloo.

1972, Dec. 4 *Perf. 12x13*

860 A182 1fr multicolored .60 .35
861 A182 3fr multicolored 1.50 1.25

Girl, Syringe, Addicts A236

1973, Jan. 5 **Engr.** *Perf. 13*

862 A236 50c brt bl, claret & sl grn .24 .15
863 A236 90c orange, lil & emer .52 .38

Fight against drug abuse.

Souvenir Sheet

Sts. Barbara, Dévote and Agatha, by Louis Brea — A237

1973, Apr. 30

864 A237 5fr dull red 10.50 10.50

Red Cross of Monaco, 25th anniv.

Flower Type of 1968

3.50fr, Flowers in Vase, by Ambrosius Bosschaert.

1973, Apr. 30 **Photo.** *Perf. 12x13*

865 A185 3.50fr multicolored 3.00 2.50

International Flower Show, Monte Carlo.

Europa Issue 1973
Common Design Type

1973, Apr. 30 **Engr.** *Perf. 13*
Size: 36x26mm

866 CD16 50c orange 1.40 1.10
867 CD16 90c blue green 2.75 1.65

Molière, Scene from "Le Malade Imaginaire" — A238

Costumed Players and Mask — A239

1973, Apr. 30

868 A238 20c red, vio bl & brn .38 .18

Tricentenary of the death of Molière (1622-1673), French actor and writer.

1973, Apr. 30

869 A239 60c red, lilac & blue .48 .28

5th International Amateur Theater Festival.

Virgin Mary, St. Teresa, Lisieux Basilica — A240

1973, Apr. 30

870 A240 1.40fr indigo, ultra & brn .65 .45

Centenary of the birth of St. Teresa of Lisieux (Thérèse Martin, 1873-1897), Carmelite nun.

Charles Peguy and Cathedral of Chartres — A241

1973, Apr. 30

871 A241 50c dp claret, ol brn & sl .38 .24

Centenary of the birth of Charles Pierre Peguy (1873-1914), French writer.

Colette, Books and Cat — A242

Designs: No. 873, Eugene Ducretet and transmission from Eiffel Tower to Pantheon. 45c, Jean Henri Fabre and insects. 50c, Blaise Pascal, vert. 60c, Radar installation and telegraph wire insulators. No. 877, William Webb Ellis and rugby. No. 878, Sir George Cayley and early model plane.

1973, Apr. 30

872 A242 30c dp org, bl & dk bl .52 .26
873 A242 30c brown & multi .32 .26
874 A242 45c dp blue & multi .52 .32
875 A242 50c vio bl, lil & dk pur .32 .26
876 A242 60c brn, bl blk & brt bl .42 .32
877 A242 90c brown & car rose .65 .42
878 A242 90c red & multi .65 .52
Nos. 872-878 (7) 3.40 2.36

Anniversaries: Colette (1873-1954), French writer (#872); 75th anniv. of 1st Hertzian wave transmission (#873); Fabre (1823-1915), entomologist (45c); Pascal (1623-1662), scientist and philosopher (50c); 5th Intl. Telecommunications Day (60c); Sesquicentennial of the invention of rugby (#877); Cayley (1821-95), aviation pioneer (#878).

Dog Type of 1971

1973, Apr. 30 **Photo.** *Perf. 13x12½*

879 A217 45c German shepherd 6.00 3.00

International Dog Show.

The First Crèche, by Giotto — A243

Paintings of the Nativity by: 45c, School of Filippo Lippi. 50c, Giotto. 1fr, 15th century miniature, vert. 2fr, Fra Angelico, vert.

Perf. 13x12, 12x13

1973, Nov. 12 **Engr.**

880 A243 30c purple .42 .28
881 A243 45c rose magenta .70 .50
882 A243 50c brown orange .85 .60
883 A243 1fr slate green 1.40 1.00
884 A243 2fr olive green 2.25 1.90
Nos. 880-884,C78 (6) 8.87 6.53

750th anniversary of the first crèche assembled by St. Francis of Assisi.

Picnic and View of Monte Carlo — A244

Designs: 20c, Dance around maypole, vert. 30c, "U Brandi" folk dance. 45c, Dance around St. John's fire. 50c, Blessing of the Christmas bread. 60c, Blessing of the sea. 1fr, Good Friday procession.

1973, Nov. 12 *Perf. 13*

885	A244	10c sl grn, dk bl & sep	.15	.15
886	A244	20c blue, ol & lil	.15	.15
887	A244	30c lt grn, bl & brn	.22	.22
888	A244	45c dk brn, vio & red brn	.28	.28
889	A244	50c black, brn & ver	.28	.28
890	A244	60c blue, mag & vio bl	.42	.42
891	A244	1fr ind, vio & ol bis	.70	.70
		Nos. 885-891 (7)	2.20	2.20

Monegasque customs.

Princes of Monaco Type of 1967

Paintings of Charlotte Grimaldi, by Pierre Gobert, 1733: No. 892, in court dress, No. 893, in nun's habit.

1973, Nov. 12 *Perf. 12x13*

892	A182	2fr multicolored	1.25	1.10
893	A182	2fr multicolored	1.25	1.10

Flower Type of 1972

Designs: Floral arrangements.

1973, Nov. 12 **Photo.** *Perf. 13*

894	A232	45c vio blue & multi	.55	.38
895	A232	60c dk brown & multi	.72	.55
896	A232	1fr brown org & multi	1.25	.95
		Nos. 894-896 (3)	2.52	1.88

Intl. Flower Show, Monte Carlo, May 1974.

Children, Syringes, Drug Addicts A245

1973, Nov. 12 **Engr.**

897	A245	50c blue, grn & brn	.28	.22
898	A245	90c red, brn & indigo	.70	.42

Fight against drug abuse.

Souvenir Sheet

1949  1974

RAINIER III
PRINCE DE MONACO

Prince Rainier III — A246

1974, May 8 **Engr.** *Imperf.*

899	A246	10fr black	6.00	6.00

25th anniv. of the accession of Prince Rainier III.

Art from Around the World — A247

King of Rome (Napoleon's Son), by Bosio — A248

70c, Hands holding letters. 1.10fr, Famous buildings, Statue of Liberty and Sphinx.

1974, May 8 *Perf. 13*

900	A247	50c choc & org brn	.22	.18
901	A247	70c aqua & multi	.35	.30
902	A247	1.10fr indigo & multi	.90	.65
		Nos. 900-902 (3)	1.47	1.13

Centenary of the Universal Postal Union.

1974, May 8

Europa: 1.10fr, Madame Elisabeth (sister of Louis XVI), by Francois Josef Bosio.

903	A248	45c slate grn & sep	.85	.65
904	A248	1.10fr brn & ol brn	1.50	1.00
a.		Souv. sheet, 5 #903, 5 #904	20.00	20.00

Red Cross Type of 1969

Design: St. Bernard of Menthon rescuing mountain traveler.

1974, May 8

905	A194	3fr Prus bl & vio brn	1.65	1.25

For the Red Cross.

Henri Farman and Farman Planes A249

Designs: 40c, Guglielmo Marconi, circuit diagram and ships which conducted first tests. 45c, Ernest Duchesne and penicillin. 50c, Fernand Forest and 4-cylinder motor.

1974, May 8

906	A249	30c multicolored	.18	.15
907	A249	40c multicolored	.20	.15
908	A249	45c multicolored	.25	.18
909	A249	50c multicolored	.24	.18
		Nos. 906-909 (4)	.87	.66

Farman (1874-1934), French aviation pioneer; Marconi (1874-1937), Italian inventor; Duchesne (1874-1912), French biologist; Forest (1851-1914), inventor.

Dog Type of 1971

1974, May 8 **Photo.** *Perf. 13x12½*

910	A217	60c Schnauzer	2.25	.85

Intl. Dog Show, Monte Carlo, Apr. 6-7.

Ronsard and Scenes from his Sonnet à Hélène — A250

1974, May 8 **Engr.** *Perf. 13*

911	A250	70c choc & dk car	.42	.32

450th anniversary of the birth of Pierre de Ronsard (1524-1585), French poet.

Winston Churchill — A251

1974, May 8

912	A251	1fr gray & brn	.52	.32

Centenary of the birth of Sir Winston Churchill (1874-1965), statesman.

Palaces of Monaco and Vienna — A252

1974, May 8

913	A252	2fr multicolored	1.00	.85

60th anniversary of the first International Police Congress, Monaco, Apr. 1914.

The Box, by Auguste Renoir A253

Rising Sun, by Claude Monet — A254

Impressionist Paintings: No. 915, Dancing Class, by Edgar Degas. No. 917, Entrance to Voisins Village, by Camille Pissarro. No. 918, House of the Hanged Man, by Paul Cezanne. No. 919, The Flooding of Port Marly, by Alfred Sisley.

Perf. 12x13, 13x12

1974, Nov. 12 **Engr.**

914	A253	1fr multicolored	1.50	1.25
915	A253	1fr multicolored	1.50	1.25
916	A254	2fr multicolored	2.50	1.50
917	A254	2fr multicolored	2.50	1.50
918	A254	2fr multicolored	2.50	1.50
919	A254	2fr multicolored	2.50	1.50
		Nos. 914-919 (6)	13.00	8.50

Trainer and Tigers A255

Prancing Horses — A256

Perf. 13x12½, 12½x13

1974, Nov. 12

920	A255	2c shown	.15	.15
921	A256	3c shown	.15	.15
922	A255	5c Elephants	.15	.15
923	A256	45c Equestrian act	.40	.18
924	A255	70c Clowns	.52	.32
925	A256	1.10fr Jugglers	.90	.65
926	A256	5fr Trapeze act	3.75	2.50
		Nos. 920-926 (7)	6.02	4.10

International Circus Festival.

Honoré II Coin — A257

1974, Nov. 12 *Perf. 13*

927	A257	60c rose red & blk	.45	.32

350th anniversary of coins of Monaco.

Underwater Fauna and Flora — A258

Designs: 45c, Fish, and marine life. 1.10fr, Coral.

1974, Nov. 12 **Photo.** *Perf. 13x12½*

Size: 35x25mm

928	A258	45c multicolored	.65	.45

Size: 48x27mm

Perf. 13

929	A258	70c multicolored	.80	.45
930	A258	1.10fr multicolored	1.10	.80
		Nos. 928-930 (3)	2.55	1.70

Congress of the International Commission for the Scientific Exploration of the Mediterranean, Monaco, Dec. 6-14.

Floral Arrangements
A259 A260

1974, Nov. 12 *Perf. 13x12½*

931	A259	70c multicolored	.60	.35
932	A260	1.10fr multicolored	.85	.48

International Flower Show, Monte Carlo, May 1975. See Nos. 1003-1004, 1084-1085.

Prince Rainier III — A261

1974-78 **Engr.** *Perf. 13*

933	A261	60c slate green	.42	.15
934	A261	80c red	.70	.15
935	A261	80c brt green	.48	.15
936	A261	1fr brown	.85	.42
937	A261	1fr scarlet	.75	.15
938	A261	1fr slate green	.60	.15
939	A261	1.20fr violet bl	1.25	.80
940	A261	1.20fr red	.70	.15
941	A261	1.25fr blue	1.00	.48
942	A261	1.50fr black	.80	.24
943	A261	1.70fr dp blue	.80	.30
944	A261	2fr dk purple	2.25	.80
945	A261	2.10fr olive bister	1.00	.65
946	A261	2.50fr indigo	1.75	.70
947	A261	9fr brt violet	4.25	2.00
		Nos. 933-947 (15)	17.60	7.29

Issued: 60c, #934, 936, 939, 2fr, Dec. 23; #935, 937, 1.25fr, 2.50fr, Jan. 10, 1977; #938, 940, 1.50fr, 1.70fr, 2.10fr, 9fr, Aug. 18, 1978.

See Nos. 1200-1204, 1255-1256.

Monte Carlo Beach A262

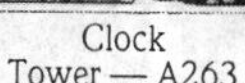

Clock Tower — A263

Prince Albert I Statue and Museum — A264

1974-77

948 A262 25c shown .32 .22
949 A263 50c shown .45 .30
950 A262 1.10fr shown ('77) 1.10 .45
951 A264 1.40fr shown 1.40 .55
952 A262 1.70fr All Saints' Tower 1.75 1.25
953 A263 3fr Fort Antoine 3.75 1.65
954 A262 5.50fr La Condamine (view) 5.50 2.50
Nos. 948-954 (7) 14.27 6.92

Issue dates: 1.10fr, Jan. 10. Others, Dec. 23.
See Nos. 1005-1008, 1030-1033, 1069-1072, 1138-1152.

Haageocereus A265

1974, Dec. 23 Photo. *Perf. 12½x13*

955 A265 10c *shown* .18 .18
956 A265 20c *Matucana* .18 .18
957 A265 30c *Parodia* .32 .25
958 A265 85c *Mediolobivia* .70 .50
959 A265 1.90fr *Matucana* 1.90 1.40
960 A265 4fr *Echinocereus* 3.75 2.00
Nos. 955-960 (6) 7.03 4.51

Plants from Monaco Botanical Gardens.

Europa Issue 1975

Sailor, by Philibert Florence — A266

St. Dévote, by Ludovic Brea — A267

1975, May 13 Engr. *Perf. 13*

961 A266 80c brt red lilac .95 .80
962 A267 1.20fr brt blue 1.25 .90
a. Souv. sheet, 5 each #961-962 18.00 18.00

Red Cross Type of 1969

Design: St. Bernardino of Siena (1380-1444) burying the dead.

1975, May 13

963 A194 4fr pur & Prus bl 2.75 1.75

For the Red Cross.

Carmen, at the Tavern A268

Scenes from Carmen: 30c, Prologue, vert. 80c, The smugglers' hide-out. 1.40fr, Entrance to bull ring.

1975, May 13

964 A268 30c multicolored .16 .15
965 A268 60c multicolored .28 .16
966 A268 80c multicolored .55 .35
967 A268 1.40fr multicolored 1.00 .75
Nos. 964-967 (4) 1.99 1.41

Centenary of first performance of opera Carmen by George Bizet (1838-1875).

Louis de Saint-Simon A269

Albert Schweitzer A270

1975, May 13

968 A269 40c bluish black .40 .32
969 A270 60c black & dull red .48 .40

300th birth anniversary of Louis de Saint-Simon (1675-1755), statesman and writer, and birth centenary of Albert Schweitzer (1875-1965), medical missionary.

ARPHILA 75 Emblem, G Clef — A271

1975, May 13

970 A271 80c sepia & org brn .65 .45

ARPHILA 75 International Philatelic Exhibition, Paris, June 6-16.

Seagull and Rising Sun — A272

1975, May 13 Photo.

971 A272 85c multicolored .55 .45

Oceanexpo 75, International Exhibition, Okinawa, July 20, 1975-Jan. 1976.

Charity Label and "1f" Destroying Cancer A273

1975, May 13 Engr.

972 A273 1fr multicolored .80 .60

Fight against cancer.

Jesus with Crown of Thorns, Holy Year Emblem — A274

1975, May 13

973 A274 1.15fr lilac, bis & ind .85 .60

Holy Year 1975.

Villa Sauber, by Charles Garnier A275

1975, May 13

974 A275 1.20fr multicolored .90 .65

European Architectural Heritage Year 1975.

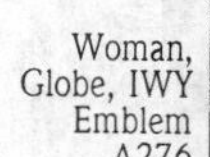

Woman, Globe, IWY Emblem A276

1975, May 13

975 A276 1.20fr multicolored .85 .65

International Women's Year.

Nos. 793-796 Surcharged

1975, Apr. 1 Engr. *Perf. 13*

976 A153 42c on 26c multi 1.25 .70
977 A153 48c on 30c multi 1.90 .90
978 A153 70c on 45c multi 4.25 1.25
979 A153 1.35fr on 90c multi 5.25 1.50
Nos. 976-979 (4) 12.65 4.35

Nos. 976-979 were issued precanceled only. See note after No. 324.

Rolls Royce "Silver Ghost" 1907 — A277

1975, Nov. Engr. *Perf. 13*

980 A277 5c shown .15 .15
981 A277 10c Hispano Suiza, 1926 .15 .15
982 A277 20c Isotta Fraschini, 1928 .20 .18
983 A277 30c Cord L. 29 .35 .25
984 A277 50c Voisin, 1930 .65 .35
985 A277 60c Duesenberg, 1933 .75 .48
986 A277 80c Bugatti, 1938 1.25 .65
987 A277 85c Delahaye, 1940 2.00 1.00
988 A277 1.20fr Cisitalia, 1946 3.00 1.25
989 A277 1.40fr Mercedes Benz, 1955 3.25 2.00
990 A277 5.50fr Lamborghini, 1974 8.00 4.25
Nos. 980-990 (11) 19.75 10.71

Development of the automobile.

Princes of Monaco Type of 1967

Paintings (Unknown Artists): 2fr, Prince Honoré III (1733-1795). 4fr, Princess Catherine de Brignole (1759-1813).

1975, Nov.

991 A182 2fr multicolored 1.25 .90
992 A182 4fr multicolored 2.50 1.50

Caged Dog — A278

Designs: 80c, Cat chased up a tree, vert. 1.20fr, Horses pulling heavy load.

1975, Nov.

993 A278 60c black & brown .75 .52
994 A278 80c black, gray & brn .95 .60
995 A278 1.20fr magenta & sl grn 1.25 .75
Nos. 993-995 (3) 2.95 1.87

125th anniversary of the Grammont (J. P. Delmas Grammont) Law against cruelty to animals.

Dog Type of 1970

1975, Nov.

996 A204 60c Poodle 1.90 1.40

International Dog Show, Monte Carlo.

Maurice Ravel — A279

Clown — A280

Design: 1.20fr, Johann Strauss and dancers.

1975, Nov.

997 A279 60c maroon & sepia .48 .35
998 A279 1.20fr maroon & indigo .90 .70

Maurice Ravel (1875-1937), birth centenary, and Johann Strauss (1804-1849), sesquicentennial of birth, composers.

1975, Nov. Photo. *Perf. 12½x13*

999 A280 80c multicolored .55 .38

2nd Intl. Circus Festival, Monte Carlo, Dec. 1975.

Honoré II Florin, 1640 — A281

1975, Nov. Engr. *Perf. 13*

1000 A281 80c slate & gray .55 .38

See Nos. 1040, 1088, 1234.

Ampère and Ampère Balance A282

1975, Nov.

1001 A282 85c ultra & indigo .52 .38

André Marie Ampère (1775-1836), physicist, birth bicentennial.

Lamentation for the Dead Christ, by Michelangelo A283

1975, Nov.

1002 A283 1.40fr black & ol gray .95 .65

Michelangelo Buonarroti (1475-1564), Italian sculptor, painter and architect.

Flower Types of 1974

Designs: Floral arrangements.

1975, Nov. Photo. *Perf. 13x12½*

1003 A259 60c multicolored .48 .25
1004 A260 80c multicolored .60 .35

Intl. Flower Show, Monte Carlo, May 1976.

Clock Tower Type, 1974

1976, Jan. 26 Engr. *Perf. 13*

1005 A263 50c brown lake .55 .38
1006 A263 60c olive green .65 .52
1007 A263 90c purple 1.00 .75
1008 A263 1.60fr brt blue 1.50 1.40
Nos. 1005-1008 (4) 3.70 3.05

Nos. 1005-1008 were issued precanceled only. See note after No. 324.

Prince Pierre — A284

André Maurois and Colette — A285

Portraits: 25c, Jean and Jerome Tharaud. 30c, Emile Henriot, Marcel Pagnol, Georges Duhamel. 50c, Philippe Heriat, Jules Supervielle, L. Pierard. 60c, Roland Dorgeles, M. Achard, G. Bauer. 80c, Franz Hellens, A. Billy, Msgr. Grente. 1.20fr, Jean Giono, L. Pasteur-Vallery-Radot, M. Garcon.

1976, May 3 Engr. *Perf. 13*

1009 A284	10c	black	.15	.15
1010 A285	20c	red & slate	.15	.15
1011 A285	25c	red, dk bl & blk	.20	.15
1012 A285	30c	brown	.30	.20
1013 A285	50c	brn, red & vio bl	.38	.24
1014 A285	60c	grn, brn & lt brn	.52	.30
1015 A285	80c	black & magenta	.70	.35
1016 A285	1.20fr	blk, vio & cl	1.25	.70
		Nos. 1009-1016 (8)	3.65	2.24

Literary Council of Monaco, 25th anniv.

Dachshunds — A286

1976, May 3 Photo.
1017 A286 60c multicolored 2.00 .65

International Dog Show, Monte Carlo.

Bridge Table, Coast — A287

1976, May 3 Engr.
1018 A287 60c multicolored .52 .35

Fifth Bridge Olympiade, Monte Carlo.

A. G. Bell, Telephone, 1876, Satellite Dish — A288

1976, May 3
1019 A288 80c multicolored .50 .35

Centenary of first telephone call by Alexander Graham Bell, Mar. 10, 1876.

Federation Emblem — A289

1976, May 3
1020 A289 1.20fr multicolored .80 .55

International Federation of Philately (F.I.P.), 50th anniversary.

US Liberty Bell Type of 1926 — A290

1976, May 3
1021 A290 1.70fr carmine & blk 1.25 .95

American Bicentennial.

Fritillaria, by Vincent van Gogh — A291

1976, May 3 Photo. *Perf. 12x13*
1022 A291 3fr multicolored 5.00 3.25

Intl. Flower Show, Monte Carlo, May 1976.

Plate with Lemon Branch — A292

Diving — A293

Europa: 1.20fr, The Peddler, 19th century figurine, and CEPT emblem.

1976, May 3 *Perf. 12½x13*

1023 A292	80c	salmon & multi	.85	.55
1024 A292	1.20fr	ultra & multi	1.25	.70
a.		Souv. sheet of 10, 5 each #1023-1024	16.00	16.00

1976, May 3 Engr. *Perf. 13*

80c, Athlete on parallel bars. 85c, Hammer throw. 1.20fr, Rowing, horiz. 1.70fr, Boxing, horiz.

1025 A293	60c	multicolored	.32	.26
1026 A293	80c	multicolored	.42	.32
1027 A293	85c	multicolored	.52	.42
1028 A293	1.20fr	multicolored	.70	.60
1029 A293	1.70fr	multicolored	1.10	1.00
a.		Souv. sheet of 5, #1025-1029, perf. 14	3.50	3.50
		Nos. 1025-1029 (5)	3.06	2.60

21st Olympic Games, Montreal, Canada, July 17-Aug. 1.

Clock Tower Type, 1974

1976, Sept. 1 Engr. *Perf. 13*

1030 A263	52c	bister	.35	.24
1031 A263	62c	red lilac	.48	.30
1032 A263	95c	scarlet	.70	.50
1033 A263	1.70fr	blue green	1.25	.85
		Nos. 1030-1033 (4)	2.78	1.89

Nos. 1030-1033 were issued precanceled only. See note after No. 324.

Princes of Monaco Type of 1967

Paintings: 2fr, Honoré IV (1815-1819), by Francois Lemoyne. 4fr, Louise d'Aumont-Mazarin (1750-1826), by Marie Verroust.

1976, Nov. 9 *Perf. 12½x13*

1035 A182	2fr	violet brown	1.25	1.00
1036 A182	4fr	multicolored	2.50	1.65

Red Cross Type of 1969

Design: St. Louise de Marillac and children.

1976, Nov. 9 *Perf. 13*
1037 A194 4fr grn, gray & plum 2.25 1.40

St. Vincent de Paul, View of Monaco A294

1976, Nov. 9
1038 A294 60c multicolored .55 .45

St. Vincent de Paul Conference, Monaco, July 31, 1876, centenary.

Marquise de Sevigné — A295

1976, Nov. 9
1039 A295 80c multicolored .42 .28

Marie de Rabutin-Chantal, Marquise de Sevigné (1626-1696), writer.

Coin Type of 1975

Design: 80c, Honoré II 2-gros coin.

1976, Nov. 9
1040 A281 80c grn & steel bl .60 .38

Richard E. Byrd, Roald Amundsen, North Pole — A296

1976, Nov. 9
1041 A296 85c olive, blk & bl .75 .55

1st flights over the North Pole, 50th anniv.

Gulliver Holding King, Queen and Enemy Fleet — A297

1976, Nov. 9
1042 A297 1.20fr indigo, bl & brn .70 .55

250th anniversary of the publication of Gulliver's Travels, by Jonathan Swift.

Child and Christmas Decorations A298

1976, Nov. 9 *Perf. 13x12½*

1043 A298	60c	multicolored	.38	.24
1044 A298	1.20fr	multicolored	.75	.42

Christmas 1976.

"Trapped by Drugs" A299

1976, Nov. 9

1045 A299	80c	grn, ultra & org	.60	.35
1046 A299	1.20fr	red brn, vio & car	.85	.48

Fight against drug abuse.

Floral Arrangement A300

Clown and Circus Acts A301

Design: 1fr, Floral arrangement. Designs by Princess Grace.

1976, Nov. 9 Photo. *Perf. 13½x13*

1047 A300	80c	yellow grn & multi	.60	.30
1048 A300	1fr	lt blue & multi	.85	.40

International Flower Show, Monte Carlo, May 1977. See Nos. 1124-1125, 1191.

1976, Nov. 9
1049 A301 1fr multi .85 .70

3rd Intl. Circus Festival, Dec. 26-30.

L'Hirondelle I — A302

Prince Albert I — A303

Designs (Gouaches by Louis Tinayre): 30c, Crew of L'Hirondelle. 80c, L'Hirondelle in Storm. 1fr, The Helmsman, vert. 1.25fr, L'Hirondelle in Storm. 1.40fr, Shrimp Fishermen in Boat. 1.90fr, Hauling in the Net, vert. 2.50fr, Catching Opah Fish.

1977, May 3 Engr. *Perf. 13*

1050 A302	10c	multicolored	.15	.15
1051 A303	20c	multicolored	.20	.15
1052 A302	30c	multicolored	.30	.18
1053 A302	80c	multicolored	.45	.30
1054 A302	1fr	multicolored	.75	.35
1055 A302	1.25fr	multicolored	.85	.50
1056 A302	1.40fr	multicolored	1.25	.75
1057 A302	1.90fr	multicolored	1.65	1.00
1058 A302	2.50fr	multicolored	2.25	1.50
		Nos. 1050-1058 (9)	7.85	4.88

75th anniversary of publication of "The Career of a Sailor," by Prince Albert I.

See Nos. 1073-1081.

Pyreneean Mountain Dogs — A304

1977, May 3 **Photo.**

1059 A304 80c multicolored 1.40 1.00

International Dog Show, Monte Carlo. See No. 1199.

Motherhood, by Mary Cassatt — A305

1977, May 3 **Engr.**

1060 A305 80c multicolored .55 .40

World Association of the Friends of Children.

Archers, Target and Monte Carlo — A306

1977, May 3

1061 A306 1.10fr multicolored .65 .48

10th Intl. Rainier III Archery Championships.

Spirit of St. Louis and Lindbergh — A307

1977, May 3

1062 A307 1.90fr multicolored 1.10 .85

50th anniversary of first transatlantic flight by Charles Lindbergh.

The Dock at Deauville, by Dufy — A308

1977, May 3 **Photo.**

1063 A308 2fr multicolored 1.90 1.40

Raoul Dufy (1877-1953), painter, birth centenary.

Young Girl, by Rubens — A309

Helmet Tower, Monaco — A310

Rubens Paintings: 1fr, Duke of Buckingham. 1.40fr, Rubens' son Nicolas, 2 years old.

1977, May 3 **Engr.**

1064 A309 80c multicolored .40 .35
1065 A309 1fr multicolored .55 .35
1066 A309 1.40fr multicolored .95 .70
Nos. 1064-1066 (3) 1.90 1.40

Peter Paul Rubens (1577-1640).

1977, May 3

Europa: 1.40fr, St. Michael's Church, Menton.

1067 A310 1fr multicolored .60 .48
1068 A310 1.40fr multicolored 1.25 .70
a. Souv. sheet, 5 each #1067-1068 16.00 16.00

Clock Tower Type of 1974

1977, Apr. 1 **Engr.** *Perf. 13*

1069 A263 54c brt green .38 .32
1070 A263 68c orange .52 .45
1071 A263 1.05fr olive .75 .52
1072 A263 1.85fr brown 1.40 1.00
Nos. 1069-1072 (4) 3.05 2.29

Nos. 1069-1072 were issued precanceled only. See note after No. 324.

Career of a Sailor Types of 1977

Designs (Gouaches by Louis Tinayre): 10c, Yacht Princess Alice II, Kiel harbor. 20c, Laboratory on board ship. 30c, Yacht amidst ice floes. 80c, Crew in arctic outfits. 1fr, Yacht in polar region. 1.25fr, Yacht in snow storm. 1.40fr, Building camp on ice. 1.90fr, Yacht under steam amidst ice floes. 3fr, Yacht passing iceberg.

1977, Nov. **Engr.** *Perf. 13*

1073 A302 10c black & brt bl .15 .15
1074 A302 20c Prus blue .20 .15
1075 A302 30c black & brt bl .25 .18
1076 A303 80c multicolored .45 .30
1077 A302 1fr brt green & blk .65 .35
1078 A302 1.25fr violet, sep & blk .70 .48
1079 A302 1.40fr olive, bl & pur 1.10 .70
1080 A302 1.90fr black & brt bl 1.50 1.00
1081 A302 3fr dk grn, ol & brt bl 2.00 1.50
Nos. 1073-1081 (9) 7.00 4.81

75th anniversary of publication of "The Career of a Sailor," by Prince Albert I.

Santa Claus — A311

1977, Nov.

1082 A311 80c multicolored .40 .24
1083 A311 1.40fr multicolored .65 .40

Christmas 1977.

Flowers Types of 1974

Designs: 80c, Snapdragons and bellflowers. 1fr, Ikebana arrangement.

1977, Nov. **Photo.** *Perf. 13½x13*

1084 A259 80c multicolored .60 .32
1085 A260 1fr multicolored .75 .45

Intl. Flower Show, Monte Carlo, May 1978.

Face (Van Gogh), Syringe, Hallucination Pattern A312

Clown, Flags of Participants A313

1977, Nov. **Engr.** *Perf. 13*

1086 A312 1fr multicolored .75 .45

Fight against drug abuse.

1977, Nov. **Photo.** *Perf. 13½x13*

1087 A313 1fr multicolored .75 .55

Fourth International Circus Festival. Monte Carlo, December 1977.

Coin Type of 1975

Design: 80c, Doubloon of Honoré II, 1648.

1977, Nov. **Engr.** *Perf. 13*

1088 A281 80c lil & brn .60 .45

Mediterranean Landscape and Industrial Pollution — A314

1977, Nov.

1089 A314 1fr multicolored .85 .52

Protection of the Mediterranean. Meeting of the UN Mediterranean Environmental Protection Group, Monte Carlo, Nov. 28-Dec. 6.

Men Spreading Tar, Dr. Guglielminetti, 1903 Car — A315

1977, Nov.

1090 A315 1.10fr multicolored .60 .42

75th anniversary of first tarred roads, invented by Swiss Dr. Guglielminetti.

View of Monaco and Tennis Emblem — A316

First Match at Wimbledon and Stadium — A317

1977, Nov.

1091 A316 1fr multicolored .65 .48
1092 A317 1.40fr multicolored .90 .70

Lawn Tennis Federation of Monaco, 50th anniv. and cent. of 1st intl. tennis match at Wimbledon.

Prince of Monaco Type of 1967

Honoré V (1819-1841), by Marie Verroust.

1977, Nov. *Perf. 12½x13*

1093 A182 6fr multicolored 3.00 2.00

Red Cross Type of 1969

Design: 4fr, St. John Bosco and boys.

1977, Nov. *Perf. 13*

1094 A194 4fr multicolored 2.00 1.40

Nos. 1069-1072 Surcharged

1978, Jan. 17

1095 A263 58c on 54c brt green .45 .35
1096 A263 73c on 68c orange .65 .45
1097 A263 1.15fr on 1.05fr olive .85 .55
1098 A263 2fr on 1.85fr brown 1.50 1.10
Nos. 1095-1098 (4) 3.45 2.45

See note after No. 324.

The Abandoned Ship, from "Mysterious Island" — A318

Illustrations, Novels by Jules Verne: 5c, Shipwreck. 30c, Secret of the Island. 80c, Robur, the Conqueror. 1fr, Master Zacharius. 1.40fr, The Castle in the Carpathians. 1.70fr, The Children of Capt. Grant. 5.50fr, Jules Verne and allegories.

1978, May 2 **Engr.** *Perf. 13*

1099 A318 5c multicolored .15 .15
1100 A318 25c multicolored .15 .15
1101 A318 30c multicolored .20 .15
1102 A318 80c multicolored .40 .28
1103 A318 1fr multicolored .60 .35
1104 A318 1.40fr multicolored .80 .52
1105 A318 1.70fr multicolored 1.10 .70
1106 A318 5.50fr multicolored 3.25 1.65
Nos. 1099-1106 (8) 6.65 3.95

Jules Verne (1828-1905), science fiction writer, birth sesquicentennial.

Congress Center and Monte Carlo — A319

1.40fr, Congress Center, view from the sea.

1978, May 2

1107 A319 1fr multicolored .52 .42
1108 A319 1.40fr multicolored .65 .52

Inauguration of Monaco Congress Center.

Soccer Players and Globe — A320

1978, May 2

1109 A320 1fr multicolored .52 .42

11th World Soccer Cup Championship, Argentina, June 1-25.

Vivaldi and St. Mark's Place, Venice — A321

Control Ship and Grimaldi Palace — A322

1978, May 2

1110 A321 1fr dk brown & red .60 .52

Antonio Vivaldi (1675?-1741), Italian violinist and composer.

1978, May 2

Design: 1fr, Map of coastal area and city emblems, horiz.

Size: 26x36mm

1111 A322 80c multicolored .48 .30

Size: 48x27mm

1112 A322 1fr multicolored .60 .40

Protection of the environment, signing of "Ra Mo Ge" agreement for the protection of the Mediterranean Coast between Saint-Raphael, France, and Genoa, Italy (including Monaco).

Monaco Cathedral — A323

Europa: 1.40fr, View of Principality from East.

1978, May 2 *Perf. 12½x13*

1113 A323 1fr multicolored .70 .42
1114 A323 1.40fr multicolored 1.00 .55
a. Souv. sheet, 5 each #1113-1114 12.00 12.00

Cinderella — A324

Mother Goose Tales: 25c, Puss in Boots. 30c, Sleeping Beauty. 80c, Fairy tale princess. 1fr, Little Red Riding Hood. 1.40fr, Bluebeard. 1.70fr, Tom Thumb. 1.90fr, Riquet with the Tuft of Hair. 2.50fr, The Fairies.

1978, Nov. 8 Engr. *Perf. 13*

1115 A324 5c multicolored .15 .15
1116 A324 25c multicolored .15 .15
1117 A324 30c multicolored .15 .15
1118 A324 80c multicolored .35 .22
1119 A324 1fr multicolored .45 .32
1120 A324 1.40fr multicolored .90 .42
1121 A324 1.70fr multicolored 1.10 .52
1122 A324 1.90fr multicolored 1.10 .65
1123 A324 2.50fr multicolored 1.25 .75
Nos. 1115-1123 (9) 5.60 3.33

Charles Perrault (1628-1703), compiler of Mother Goose Tales.

Flower Type of 1976

Van Gogh Paintings: 1fr, Sunflowers. 1.70fr, Iris.

1978, Nov. 8 Photo. *Perf. 12½x13*

1124 A300 1fr multicolored 1.25 .95
1125 A300 1.70fr multicolored 1.75 1.40

Intl. Flower show, Monte Carlo, May 1979, and 125th birth anniv. of Vincent van Gogh (1853-1890), Dutch painter.

Afghan Hound A325

Design: 1.20fr, Russian wolfhound.

1978, Nov. 8 *Perf. 13x12½*

1126 A325 1fr multicolored 1.25 .90
1127 A325 1.20fr multicolored 1.65 1.10

International Dog Show, Monte Carlo.

Child Holding Gift of Shoes — A326

1978, Nov. 8 Engr. *Perf. 12½x13*

1128 A326 1fr multicolored .52 .40

Christmas 1978.

Catherine and William Booth, Salvation Army Band — A327

1978, Nov. 8 Engr. *Perf. 13*

1129 A327 1.70fr multicolored .80 .70

Centenary of founding of Salvation Army.

Trained Seals A328

Designs: 1fr, Lions, vert. 1.40fr, Equestrian act. 1.90fr, Monkey music band. 2.40fr, Trapeze act.

1978, Nov. 8 *Perf. 13x12½*

1130 A328 80c multicolored .40 .30
1131 A328 1fr multicolored .55 .40
1132 A328 1.40fr multicolored .95 .60
1133 A328 1.90fr multicolored 1.10 .85
1134 A328 2.40fr multicolored 1.50 1.10
Nos. 1130-1134 (5) 4.50 3.25

5th Intl. Circus Festival, Monte Carlo.

Princes of Monaco Type of 1967

Paintings: 2fr, Florestan I (1841-1856), by G. Dauphin. 4fr, Caroline Gilbert de Lametz (1793-1879), by Marie Verroust.

1978, Nov. 8 Engr. *Perf. 12½x13*

1135 A182 2fr multicolored .95 .65
1136 A182 4fr multicolored 2.00 1.25

Souvenir Sheet

Henri Dunant and Battle Scene — A329

1978, Nov. 8 Engr. *Perf. 13*

1137 A329 5fr multicolored 3.25 3.25

Henri Dunant (1828-1910), founder of Red Cross.

View Types of 1974

1978-80

1138 A262 25c All Saints' Tower .18 .18
1139 A262 65c Monte Carlo Beach .35 .35
1140 A263 70c Exotic Garden, cacti ('80) .40 .22
1142 A262 1.10fr Palais de Justice ('80) .52 .22
1144 A263 1.30fr Cathedral .75 .28
1145 A264 1.50fr Prince Albert Statue and Museum ('80) .90 .45
1146 A262 1.80fr La Condamine 1.10 .70
1148 A262 2.30fr Palace ('80) 1.25 .70
1152 A262 6.50fr Monte Carlo Auditorium 3.50 1.90
Nos. 1138-1152 (9) 8.95 5.00

Convention Center, Monte Carlo — A330

1978-79

1154 A330 61c vermilion .42 .20
1155 A330 64c green .38 .24
1156 A330 68c brt blue .30 .20
1157 A330 78c dp rose lilac .55 .26
1158 A330 83c violet blue .42 .26
1159 A330 88c orange .38 .26
1160 A330 1.25fr brown .90 .42
1161 A330 1.30fr purple .75 .45
1162 A330 1.40fr brt yel grn .70 .42
1163 A330 2.10fr violet blue 1.40 .80
1164 A330 2.25fr brown org 1.25 .75
1165 A330 2.35fr lilac rose 1.10 .60
Nos. 1154-1165 (12) 8.55 4.86

Issued precanceled only. See note after No. 324.
Issue dates: 61c, 78c, 1.25fr, 2.10fr, July 10, 1978. Others, 1979.

Souvenir Sheet

Prince Albert — A331

1979, Apr. 30 Engr. *Perf. 12½x13*

1166 A331 10fr multicolored 6.25 6.25

21st birthday of Hereditary Prince Albert.

The Juggler of Notre Dame, by Jules Massenet A332

Designs: 1.20fr, Hans, the Flute Player, by Gaston L. Ganne. 1.50fr, Don Quichotte, by Massenet. 1.70fr, L'Aiglon, by Jacques Ibert and Arthur Honegger, vert. 2.10fr, The Child and the Sorcerer, by Maurice Ravel. 3fr, Monte Carlo Opera and Charles Garnier, architect.

1979, Apr. 30 *Perf. 13*

1167 A332 1fr multicolored .52 .24
1168 A332 1.20fr multicolored .65 .30
1169 A332 1.50fr multicolored .85 .55
1170 A332 1.70fr multicolored 1.25 .70
1171 A332 2.10fr multicolored 1.50 1.10
1172 A332 3fr multicolored 2.00 1.25
Nos. 1167-1172 (6) 6.77 4.14

Centenary of the Salle Garnier, Monte Carlo Opera.

Flower, Bird, Butterfly, IYC Emblem A333

Children's Drawings (IYC Emblem and): 1fr, Horse and child. 1.20fr, Children shaking hands, and heart. 1.50fr, Children of the world for peace. 1.70fr, Children against pollution.

1979, Apr. 30

1173 A333 50c multicolored .24 .15
1174 A333 1fr multicolored .45 .32
1175 A333 1.20fr multicolored .65 .42
1176 A333 1.50fr multicolored .75 .52
1177 A333 1.70fr multicolored 1.10 .65
Nos. 1173-1177 (5) 3.19 2.06

International Year of the Child.

Armed Messenger, 15th-16th Centuries A334

Europa (designs similar to 1960 postage dues); 1.50fr, Felucca, 18th cent. 1.70fr, Arrival of 1st train, Dec. 12, 1868.

1979, Apr. 30

1178 A334 1.20fr multicolored .55 .40
1179 A334 1.50fr multicolored .75 .45
1180 A334 1.70fr multicolored .90 .60
a. Souv. sheet of 6, 2 each #1178-1180, perf. 13x12½ 7.50 7.50
Nos. 1178-1180 (3) 2.20 1.45

Les Biches, by Francis Poulenc A335

Ballets: 1.20fr, Les Matelots, by George Auric. 1.50fr, Le Spectre de la Rose, by Carl Maria Weber, vert. 1.70fr, Gaieté Parisienne, by Jacques Offenbach. 2.10fr, Dance of Salomé, by Richard Strauss, vert. 3fr, Instrumental Music, ceiling decoration of Salle Garnier.

1979, Nov. 12

Size: 26x36mm, 36x26mm

1181 A335 1fr multicolored .55 .22
1182 A335 1.20fr multicolored .70 .35
1183 A335 1.50fr multicolored .95 .55
1184 A335 1.70fr multicolored 1.10 .75
1185 A335 2.10fr multicolored 1.40 1.10

Size: 48x27mm

1186 A335 3fr multicolored 2.00 1.40
Nos. 1181-1186 (6) 6.70 4.37

Salle Garnier, Monte Carlo Opera, cent.

Princes of Monaco Type of 1967

Paintings: 3fr, Charles III (1856-1889). 4fr, Antoinette de Merode (1828-1864).

1979, Nov. 12 *Perf. 12½x13*

1187 A182 3fr multicolored 1.40 1.00
1188 A182 4fr multicolored 1.95 1.40

Red Cross Type of 1969

Design: 5fr, St. Peter Claver preaching to slaves.

1979, Nov. 12 *Perf. 13*

1189 A194 5fr multicolored 2.50 2.00

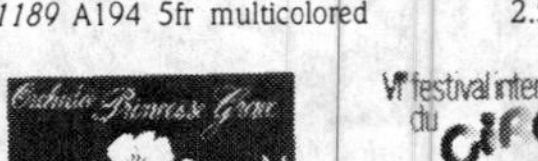

Princess Grace Orchid — A336

Clown Balancing on Globe — A337

1979, Nov. 12 **Photo.**

1190 A336 1fr multicolored .75 .70

Intl. Orchid Exhibition, Monte Carlo, Apr. 1980.

Flower Type of 1976

Design: 1.20fr, Princess Grace rose.

1979, Nov. 12

1191 A300 1.20fr multicolored .65 .55

Intl. Flower Show, Monte Carlo, May 1980.

1979, Nov. 12

1192 A337 1.20fr multicolored .65 .52

6th International Circus Festival, Monte Carlo, Dec. 6-10.

Rowland Hill, Penny Black — A338

1979, Nov. 12 Engr. *Perf. 13*

1193 A338 1.70fr multicolored .70 .52

Sir Rowland Hill (1795-1879), originator of penny postage.

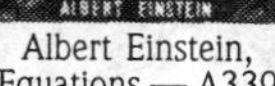

Albert Einstein, Equations — A339

St. Patrick's Cathedral — A340

1979, Nov. 12
1194 A339 1.70fr multicolored .75 .55

Albert Einstein (1879-1955), theoretical physicist.

1979, Nov. 12
1195 A340 2.10fr multicolored 1.00 .75

St. Patrick's Cathedral, New York City, centenary.

Nativity A341

1979, Nov. 12
1196 A341 1.20fr multicolored .60 .26

Christmas 1979.

Bugatti, Monte Carlo, 1929 Winner — A342

1979, Nov. 12
1197 A342 1fr multicolored .60 .40

50th anniv. of Grand Prix auto race, Monte Carlo.

Arms of Charles V and Monaco, View of Monaco — A343

1979, Nov. 12
1198 A343 1.50fr multicolored .65 .45

Emperor Charles V visit to Monaco, 450th anniversary.

Dog Type of 1977

Design: 1.20fr, Setter and pointer.

1979, Nov. 12 **Photo.**
1199 A304 1.20fr multicolored 1.40 .80

International Dog Show, Monte Carlo.

Prince Rainier Type of 1974

1980, Jan. 17 **Engr.** ***Perf. 13***
1200 A261 1.10fr emerald .55 .15
1201 A261 1.30fr rose red .60 .15
1202 A261 1.60fr dk blue gray .75 .18
1203 A261 1.80fr grnsh blue .90 .26
1204 A261 2.30fr red lilac 1.00 .30
Nos. 1200-1204 (5) 3.80 1.04

Chestnut Branch in Spring A344

Designs of 1980, 1981 stamps show chestnut branch. 1982 stamps show peach branch. 1983 stamps show apple branch.

1980-83 **Engr.** ***Perf. 13x12½***
1205 A344 76c shown .40 .28
1206 A344 88c Spring ('81) .40 .28
1207 A344 97c Spring ('82) .45 .28
1208 A344 99c Summer .55 .35
1209 A344 1.05fr Spring ('83) .40 .25
1210 A344 1.14fr Summer ('81) .55 .35
1211 A344 1.25fr Summer ('82) .60 .35
1212 A344 1.35fr Summer ('83) .48 .32
1213 A344 1.60fr Autumn .85 .65
1214 A344 1.84fr Autumn ('81) .85 .65
1215 A344 2.03fr Autumn ('82) 1.10 .60
1216 A344 2.19fr Autumn ('83) .85 .52
1217 A344 2.65fr Winter 1.50 1.10
1218 A344 3.05fr Winter ('81) 1.50 1.10
1219 A344 3.36fr Winter ('82) 1.65 1.10
1220 A344 3.63fr Winter ('83) 1.40 1.10
Nos. 1205-1220 (16) 13.53 9.28

Issued precanceled only. See note after No. 324. See Nos. 1406-1409, 1457-1460.

Gymnast — A345

1980, Apr. 28
1221 A345 1.10fr shown .32 .22
1222 A345 1.30fr Handball .35 .28
1223 A345 1.60fr Shooting .55 .40
1224 A345 1.80fr Volleyball .70 .52
1225 A345 2.30fr Ice hockey .95 .60
1226 A345 4fr Slalom 1.40 1.00
Nos. 1221-1226 (6) 4.27 3.02

22nd Summer Olympic Games, Moscow, July 19-Aug. 3; 13th Winter Olympic Games, Lake Placid, NY, Feb. 12-24.

Colette, Novelist — A346

Europa: 1.80fr, Marcel Pagnol (1895-1974), French playwright.

1980, Apr. 28 ***Perf. 12½x13***
1227 A346 1.30fr multicolored .45 .42
1228 A346 1.80fr multicolored .65 .45
a. Souv. sheet, 5 each #1227-1228 5.00 5.00

The Source, by Ingres A347

1980, Apr. 28
1229 A347 4fr multicolored 2.75 1.90

Jean Auguste Dominique Ingres (1780-1867).

Michel Eyquem de Montaigne A348

Guillaume Apollinaire A349

1980, Apr. 28 ***Perf. 13***
1230 A348 1.30fr multicolored .52 .35

Essays of Montaigne (1533-1592), 400th anniversary of publication.

1980, Apr. 28
1231 A349 1.10fr multicolored .42 .30

Guillaume Apollinaire (1880-1918), French writer.

Paul P. Harris, Chicago Skyline, Rotary Emblem — A350

1980, Apr. 28
1232 A350 1.80fr multicolored .75 .42

Rotary International, 75th anniversary.

Convention Center, Map of Europe, Kiwanis Emblem — A351

1980, Apr. 28
1233 A351 1.30fr multicolored .55 .48

Kiwanis International, European Convention, Monte Carlo, June.

Coin Type of 1975

Design: 1.50fr, Honoré II silver ecu, 1649.

1980, Apr. 28
1234 A281 1.50fr multicolored .65 .52

Lhasa Apso and Shih-Tzu — A352

1980, Apr. 28 **Photo.**
1235 A352 1.30fr multicolored 1.65 1.00

International Dog Show, Monte Carlo.

The Princess and the Pea — A353

Hans Christian Andersen (1805-1875) Fairy Tales: 1.30fr, The Little Mermaid. 1.50fr, The Chimneysweep and the Shepherdess. 1.60fr, The Brave Little Tin Soldier. 1.80fr, The Little Match Girl. 2.30fr, The Nightingale.

1980, Nov. 6 **Engr.** ***Perf. 13***
1236 A353 70c multicolored .25 .18
1237 A353 1.30fr multicolored .38 .24
1238 A353 1.50fr multicolored .60 .20
1239 A353 1.60fr multicolored .75 .55
1240 A353 1.80fr multicolored 1.00 .60
1241 A353 2.30fr multicolored 1.10 .75
Nos. 1236-1241 (6) 4.08 2.52

Women on Balcony, by Van Dongen — A354

Paintings from 1905 Paris Fall Salon: 2fr, The Road, by de Vlaminck. 4fr, Woman Reading, by Matisse. 5fr, Three Women in a Meadow, by André Derain.

1980, Nov. 6 ***Perf. 13x12***
1242 A354 2fr multicolored 1.50 1.25
1243 A354 3fr multicolored 2.50 2.00
1244 A354 4fr multicolored 3.50 2.50
1245 A354 5fr multicolored 4.50 3.50
Nos. 1242-1245 (4) 12.00 9.25

Princes of Monaco Type of 1967

Paintings: No. 1246, Prince Albert I (1848-1922), by Leon Bonnat. No. 1247, Princess Alice (1857-1925), by L. Maeterlinck.

1980, Nov. 6 ***Perf. 12½x13***
1246 A182 4fr multicolored 1.75 1.40
1247 A182 4fr multicolored 1.75 1.40

Sun and Birds, by Perrette Lambert — A355

1980, Nov. 6 ***Perf. 13***
1248 A355 6fr multicolored 2.50 2.25

Red Cross.

7th International Circus Festival — A356

1980, Nov. 6 ***Perf. 13x12½***
1249 A356 1.30fr multicolored .70 .50

Christmas 1980 A357

1980, Nov. 6
1250 A357 1.10fr multicolored .38 .26
1251 A357 2.30fr multicolored .85 .65

Princess Stephanie of Monaco Rose — A358

1980, Nov. 6 Photo. *Perf. 12½x13*

1252 A358 1.30fr shown .60 .48
1253 A358 1.80fr Ikebana .80 .60

International Flower Show, Monte Carlo, May 1981.

Prince Rainier Type of 1974

1980 Engr. *Perf. 13*

1255 A261 1.20fr bright green .52 .20
1256 A261 1.40fr red .75 .15

Issue dates: 1.20fr, Aug. 19; 1.40fr, Aug. 11.

Paramuricea Clavata A359

5c-20c, 40c, 50c, vert.

1980, Nov. 6 *Perf. 13x12½*

1259 A359 5c Spirographis spallanzanii .15 .15
1260 A359 10c Anemonia sulcata .15 .15
1261 A359 15c Leptosammia pruvoti .15 .15
1262 A359 20c Pteroides .18 .15
1263 A359 30c shown .20 .15
1264 A359 40c Alcyonium .25 .15
1265 A359 50c Corallium rubrum .30 .16
1266 A359 60c Caliactis parisitica .55 .16
1267 A359 70c Cerianthus membranaceus .70 .20
1268 A359 1fr Actinia equina .75 .20
1269 A359 2fr Protula 1.40 .35
Nos. 1259-1269 (11) 4.78
Set value 1.50

See Nos. 1316-1321, 1380.

25th Wedding Anniversary of Prince Rainier and Princess Grace — A360

1981, May 4 *Perf. 13*

1270 A360 1.20fr green & blk 1.25 .55
1271 A360 1.40fr carmine & blk 1.50 .55
1272 A360 1.70fr olive grn & blk 1.90 .85
1273 A360 1.80fr brown & blk 2.00 .90
1274 A360 2fr brt blue & blk 2.50 1.25
Nos. 1270-1274 (5) 9.15 4.10

Mozart with his Father and Sister, by Carmontelle — A361

Wolfgang Amadeus Mozart (1756-1791), 225th Birth Anniversary (Paintings): 2fr, Portrait, by Lorenz Vogel (26x36mm). 3.50fr, Conducting his Requiem Two Days Before his Death, by F.C. Baude.

1981, May 4 Engr. *Perf. 13½x13*

1275 A361 2fr multicolored 1.65 1.50
1276 A361 2.50fr multicolored 2.25 2.00
1277 A361 3.50fr multicolored 3.00 2.50
a. Strip of 3, #1275-1277 7.00 6.00

Cross of Palms — A362

Europa (Palm Sunday Traditions): 2fr, Children with palms at benediction.

1981, May 4 *Perf. 12½x13*

1278 A362 1.40fr multicolored .40 .25
1279 A362 2fr multicolored .60 .40
a. Souv. sheet, 5 each #1278-1279 6.00 6.00

European Soccer Cup, 25th Anniversary A363

1981, May 4 *Perf. 13*

1280 A363 2fr black & blue .75 .65

International Year of the Disabled A364

1981, May 4

1281 A364 1.40fr brt grn & bl .52 .38

Monegasque National Pavilion Centenary — A365

1981, May 4

1282 A365 2fr multicolored .85 .70

Oceanographic Institute, Monaco and Museum, Paris — A366

1981, May 4

1283 A366 1.20fr multicolored .52 .38

75th anniversary of the Oceanographic Institute (Monaco-France).

50th Anniversary of the International Hydrographic Bureau — A367

1981, May 4

1284 A367 2.50fr multicolored .90 .80

Rough Collies and Shetland Sheepdogs — A368

1981, May 4 Photo.

1285 A368 1.40fr multicolored 2.50 2.00

International Dog Show, Monte Carlo.

Marine Life Preservation A369

Prince Rainier III and Hereditary Prince Albert A370

1981, Mar. 21 Photo.

1286 A369 1.20fr multicolored .85 .52

1981-84 Engr. *Perf. 13*

1287 A370 1.40fr dark green .80 .15
1288 A370 1.60fr carmine .95 .15
1289 A370 1.60fr olive grn ('82) .70 .15
1290 A370 1.70fr bluish grn ('84) .70 .15
1291 A370 1.80fr magenta ('82) .95 .15
1292 A370 2fr red ('83) 1.00 .15
1293 A370 2.10fr red ('84) .95 .15
1294 A370 2.30fr blue 1.65 .70
1295 A370 2.60fr violet bl ('82) 1.25 .48
1296 A370 2.80fr steel bl ('83) 1.25 .60
1297 A370 3fr sky blue ('84) 1.25 .48
1298 A370 4fr brown 1.50 .40
1299 A370 5.50fr black 1.90 1.10
Nos. 1287-1299 (13) 14.85 4.81

See Nos. 1505-1515.

Hauling Ice Floes, 17th Cent. Map Arctic — A371

1981, Oct. 5

1301 A371 1.50fr multicolored .75 .38

First Intl. Arctic Committee Congress, Rome, Oct. 5-9.

Princes of Monaco Type of 1967

Paintings by P.A. de Laszlo, 1929: 3fr, Prince Louis II. 5fr, Princess Charlotte.

1981, Nov. 5 Engr. *Perf. 12½x13*

1302 A182 3fr multicolored 1.25 .85
1303 A182 5fr multicolored 2.00 1.40

Ettore Bugatti, Auto Designer and Racer, Birth Centenary A372

George Bernard Shaw (1856-1950) A373

1981, Nov. 5 *Perf. 13*

1304 A372 1fr multicolored .55 .45

1981, Nov. 5

Design: 2.50fr, Fernand Leger, painter, birth centenary.

1305 A373 2fr multicolored .90 .65
1306 A373 2.50fr multicolored 1.10 .80

Self-portrait, by Pablo Picasso (1881-1973) A374

#1308, Self-portrait, by Rembrandt (1606-69).

1981, Nov. 5 *Perf. 12½x13*

1307 A374 4fr multicolored 2.00 1.65
1308 A374 4fr multicolored 2.00 1.65

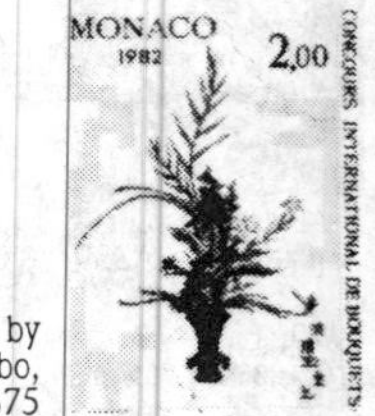

Ikebana, Painting by Ikenobo, 1673 — A375

Intl. Flower Show, Monte Carlo, 1982: 1.40fr, Elegantines, morning glories.

1981, Nov. 5 Photo. *Perf. 12½*

1309 A375 1.40fr multicolored .55 .42
1310 A375 2fr multicolored .85 .65

Catherine Deneuve Rose — A376

1981, Nov. 5 *Perf. 13x12½*

1311 A376 1.80fr multicolored .85 .70

First Intl. Rose Competition, Monte Carlo, June 12-14.

8th Intl. Circus Festival, Monte Carlo, Dec. 10-14 — A377

1981, Nov. 5 Engr. *Perf. 13*

1312 A377 1.40fr multicolored .65 .50

Christmas 1981 — A378

1981, Nov. 5

1313 A378 1.20fr multicolored .50 .42

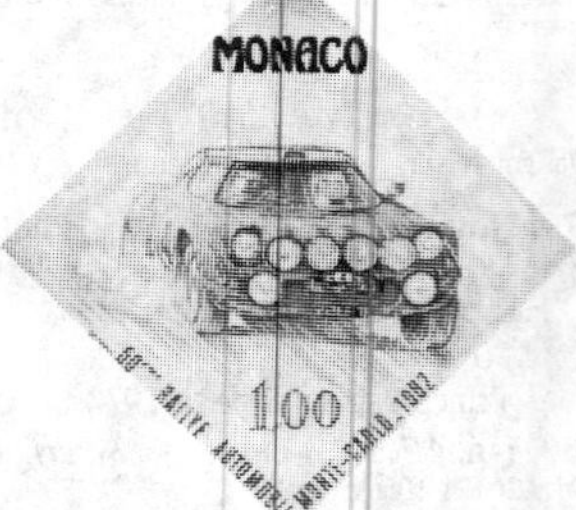

50th Monte Carlo Auto Race — A379

1981, Nov. 5

1314 A379 1fr Lancia-Stratos .42 .30

Souvenir Sheet

Persimmon Branch in Spring A380

1981, Nov. 5 *Perf. 13x12½*
1315 Sheet of 4 5.00 5.00
a. A380 1fr shown .50 .50
b. A380 2fr Summer .95 .95
c. A380 3fr Autumn 1.25 1.25
d. A380 4fr Winter 1.90 1.90

Coral Type of 1980

Exotic Plants. 1.40fr, 1.60fr, 2.30fr vert.

Perf. 12½x13, 13x12½

1981-82 **Photo.**
1316 A359 1.40fr Hoya bella 1.50 .42
1317 A359 1.60fr Bolivicereus sam-aipatanus 1.10 .42
1317A A359 1.80fr Trichocereus grandiflorus 1.40 .85
1318 A359 2.30fr Euphorbia milii 1.25 .75
1319 A359 2.60fr Echinocereus fitchii 1.40 1.10
1320 A359 2.90fr Rebutia heliosa 1.75 1.40
1321 A359 4.10fr Echinopsis multiplex 2.25 1.75
Nos. 1316-1321 (7) 10.65 6.69

Issue dates: 1.80fr, June 7, others Dec. 10.

Miniature Sheet

1982 World Cup A381

Designs: Various soccer players.

1982, May 3 *Perf. 13*
1322 Sheet of 4 4.50 4.50
a. A381 1fr multicolored .48 .48
b. A381 2fr multicolored .80 .80
c. A381 3fr multicolored 1.25 1.25
d. A381 4fr multicolored 1.75 1.75

Mercantour Natl. Park Birds — A382

Europa — A383

1982, May 3 *Perf. 12½x13, 13x12½*
1323 A382 60c Nutcracker .55 .40
1324 A382 70c Black grouse .70 .40
1325 A382 80c Rock partridge .70 .50
1326 A382 90c Wall creeper, horiz. 1.00 .50
1327 A382 1.40fr Ptarmigan, horiz. 1.75 .65
1328 A382 1.60fr Golden eagle 2.50 .65
Nos. 1323-1328 (6) 7.20 3.10

1982, May 3 *Perf. 12½x13*
1329 A383 1.60fr Guelph attacking Fortress of Monaco, 1297 .52 .25
1330 A383 2.30fr Treaty of Peronne, 1641 .80 .38
a. Souv. sheet, 5 each #1329-1330 6.25 6.25

Fontvielle Landfill Project A384

1982, May 3 *Perf. 13x12½*
1331 A384 1.40fr Old coastline .48 .24
1332 A384 1.60fr Landfill site .55 .24
1333 A384 2.30fr Completed site .90 .55
Nos. 1331-1333 (3) 1.93 1.03

Fontvielle Stadium — A385

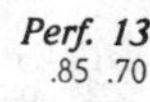

1982, May 3 *Perf. 13*
1334 A385 2.30fr multicolored .85 .70

PHILEXFRANCE '82 Stamp Exhibition, Paris, June 11-21 — A386

1982, May 3
1335 A386 1.40fr multicolored .52 .42

Intl. Dog Show, Monte Carlo A387

1982, May 3 **Photo.** *Perf. 13x12½*
1336 A387 60c Old English sheepdog .95 .35
1337 A387 1fr Briard terrier 1.25 .45

See Nos. 1366, 1431, 1479, 1539, 1676, 1704, 1756, 1806, 1855, 1900, 1940, 1990, 2035.

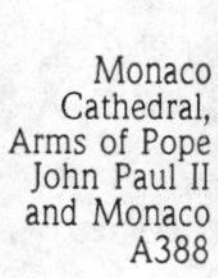

Monaco Cathedral, Arms of Pope John Paul II and Monaco A388

1982, May 3 **Engr.**
1338 A388 1.60fr multicolored .55 .40

Creation of archbishopric of Monaco, July 25, 1981.

800th Birth Anniv. of St. Francis of Assisi — A389

TB Bacillus Cent. — A390

1982, May 3 *Perf. 12½x13*
1339 A389 1.40fr multicolored .55 .45

1982, May 3
1340 A390 1.40fr multicolored .45 .35

Scouting Year — A391

Intl. Hunting Council, 29th Meeting — A392

1982, May 3
1341 A391 1.60fr dk brown & blk .60 .42

1982, June 11 **Photo.** *Perf. 12½*
1342 A392 1.60fr St. Hubert .60 .45

Intl. Bibliophile Assoc. General Assembly — A393

1982, Sept. 30 **Engr.** *Perf. 13*
1343 A393 1.60fr multicolored .50 .35

Monte Carlo and Monaco During the Belle Epoch (1870-1925), by Hubert Clerissi — A394

Photogravure and Engraved

1982, Nov. 8 *Perf. 13x12½*
1344 A394 3fr Casino, 1870 1.25 .80
1345 A394 5fr Palace, 1893 2.25 1.25

See Nos. 1385-1386, 1436-1437, 1488-1489, 1546-1547, 1605-1606, 1638-1639, 1695-1696.

Nicolo Paganini (1782-1840), Composer and Violinist — A395

1.80fr, Anna Pavlova (1881-1931), ballerina. 2.60fr, Igor Stravinsky (1882-1971), composer.

1982, Nov. 8 **Engr.** *Perf. 12½x13*
1346 A395 1.60fr multicolored .75 .50
1347 A395 1.80fr multicolored 1.10 .50
1348 A395 2.60fr multicolored 1.40 .65
Nos. 1346-1348 (3) 3.25 1.65

In a Boat, by Manet (1832-1883) — A396

Design: No. 1350, Les Poissons Noir, by Georges Braque (1882-1963).

Photogravure and Engraved

1982, Nov. 8 *Perf. 13x12½*
1349 A396 4fr multicolored 2.50 1.50
1350 A396 4fr multicolored 2.50 1.50

Intl. Flower Show, Monte Carlo — A397

Designs: Various floral arrangements.

1982, Nov. 8 **Photo.** *Perf. 12½x13*
1351 A397 1.60fr multicolored .70 .42
1352 A397 2.60fr multicolored 1.00 .75

Bouquet — A398

Christmas 1982 — A399

1982 *Perf. 13*
1353 A398 1.60fr multicolored .80 .52

1982, Nov. 8 **Engr.** *Perf. 12½x13*
1354 A399 1.60fr Three Kings .48 .35
1355 A399 1.80fr Holy Family .70 .35
1356 A399 2.60fr Shepherds .90 .48
a. Souv. sheet of 3, #1354-1356 2.50 2.50
Nos. 1354-1356 (3) 2.08 1.18

Intl. Polar Year Centenary — A400

1982, Nov. 8 **Engr.** *Perf. 13*
1358 A400 1.60fr Prince Louis, Discovery .75 .55

Discovery of Greenland Millenium — A401

1982, Nov. 8
1359 A401 1.60fr Erik the Red's longship .70 .52

Death Bimillenium of Virgil — A402

1982, Nov. 8
1360 A402 1.80fr Scene from Aeneid, Book 6 .75 .60

50th Anniv. of Botanical Garden
A403

1983, Feb. 11 Photo. *Perf. 12½x13*

1361 A403 1.80fr Cacti, vert. .65 .35
1362 A403 2fr Exotic plants, vert. .80 .35
1363 A403 2.30fr Intl. exhibits, vert. .80 .65
1364 A403 2.60fr Cave .90 .70
1365 A403 3.30fr Prehistoric Anthropology Museum 1.40 1.00
Nos. 1361-1365 (5) 4.55 3.05

Monte Carlo Dog Show Type

1983, Apr. 13 *Perf. 13x12½*

1366 A387 1.80fr Alaskan malamute 2.25 .85

Souvenir Sheet

Princess Grace (1929-1982) — A405

1983, Apr. 19 Engr. *Perf. 13*

1367 A405 10fr black 7.00 7.00

A406 A407

1983, Apr. 27 *Perf. 12½x13*

1368 A406 1.80fr Montgolfiere balloon flight, 1783 .60 .42
1369 A406 2.60fr Columbia space shuttle .90 .65
a. Souv. sheet, 5 each #1368-1369 7.25 7.25

Europa.

1983, Apr. 27 Engr.

1370 A407 2.60fr St. Charles Borromeo .80 .48

Centenary of St. Charles' Church, Monte Carlo.

Franciscan College Centenary
A408

1983, Apr. 27 *Perf. 13x12½*

1371 A408 2fr Church, medallion .70 .45

Fontvielle Stadium Interior — A409

1983, Apr. 28 *Perf. 13*

1372 A409 2fr multicolored .70 .50

Automobile Centenary — A410

1983, Apr. 27

1373 A410 2.90fr Benz, 1883, Formula One racer .95 .65

Save the Whales Campaign — A411

1983, Apr. 27

1374 A411 3.30fr Blue whale 1.65 .95

World Communications Year — A412

1983, Apr. 27

1375 A412 4fr lil rose & brn vio 1.25 .90

Souvenir Sheet

Fig Branch in Spring
A413

1983, Nov. 9 Engr. *Perf. 13x12½*

1376 Sheet of 4 5.00 5.00
a. A413 1fr shown .45 .45
b. A413 2fr Summer .95 .95
c. A413 3fr Autumn 1.40 1.40
d. A413 4fr Winter 1.75 1.75

Exotic Plant Type of 1980

1983, Nov. 9 Photo. *Perf. 13*

1380 A359 2fr Argyroderma roseum .95 .40

Belle Epoch Type of 1982

Paintings by Hubert Clerissi: 3fr, Thermes Valentia from the Beach, 1902. 5fr, Cafe de Paris and Place du Casino, 1905.

Photogravure and Engraved

1983, Nov. 9 *Perf. 13x12½*

1385 A394 3fr multicolored 1.10 .70
1386 A394 5fr multicolored 1.50 1.10

Portrait of a Young Man, by Raphael (1483-1520)
A414

Passage Cottin, by Maurice Utrillo (1883-1955)
A415

Photogravure and Engraved

1983, Nov. 9 *Perf. 13*

1387 A414 4fr multicolored 1.50 .90
1388 A415 4fr multicolored 1.50 .90

Johannes Brahms (1833-1897), Composer — A416

Design: No. 1390, Giacomo Puccini (1858-1924), composer, scene from Madame Butterfly.

1983, Nov. 9 Engr. *Perf. 13½x13*

1389 A416 3fr multicolored 1.75 .80
1390 A416 3fr multicolored 1.75 .80

9th Intl. Circus Festival, Monte Carlo, Dec. 8-12 — A417

Intl. Flower Show, Monte Carlo — A418

1983, Nov. 9 *Perf. 13*

1391 A417 2fr multicolored .80 .65

1983, Nov. 9 Photo.

1392 A418 1.60fr Pansies, convolvulus, carnations .60 .35
1393 A418 2.60fr Oriental poppies .85 .65

Christmas 1983 — A419

1983, Nov. 9 Photo.

1394 A419 2fr Provencal creche figures .65 .42

Alfred Nobel (1833-1896), Literature Medal
A420

1983, Nov. 9 Engr.

1395 A420 2fr multicolored .65 .42

Sesquicentenary of Society of St. Vincent de Paul — A421

1983, Nov. 9 Engr.

1396 A421 1.80fr F. Ozanam, founder, Paris headquarters .60 .48

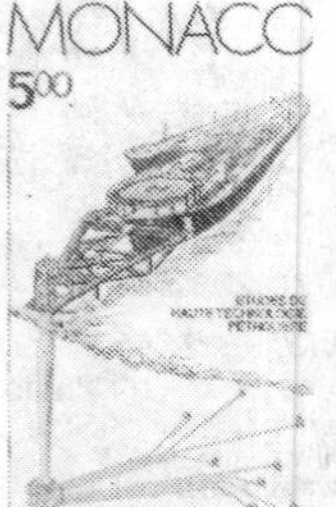

A422 A423

1983, Nov. 9

1397 A422 5fr Offshore petroleum plant 1.50 .95

1983, Nov. 9 Photo. *Perf. 12½x13*

19th cent. figurines, Galea toy collection.

1398 A423 50c Water pipe smoker .16 .15
1399 A423 60c Clown with yo-yo .20 .15
1400 A423 70c Smoking monkey .20 .16
1401 A423 80c Farmer and pig .24 .16
1402 A423 90c Buffalo Bill .30 .20
1403 A423 1fr Snake charmer .35 .15
1404 A423 1.50fr Piano and harp player .45 .30
1405 A423 2fr Girl powdering her face .65 .30
Nos. 1398-1405 (8) 2.55 1.57

Quince Branch in Spring
A424

1984, May 10 Photo. *Perf. 13x12½*

1406 A424 1.14fr shown .35 .25
1407 A424 1.47fr Summer .45 .32
1408 A424 2.38fr Autumn .70 .42
1409 A424 3.95fr Winter 1.40 .85
Nos. 1406-1409 (4) 2.90 1.84

Issued precanceled only. See note after No. 324.

Place de la Visitation, by Hubert Clerissi — A425

Drawings by Hubert Clerissi: 10c, Town Hall. 15c, Rue Basse. 20c, Place Saint-Nicolas. 30c, Quai du Commerce. 40c, Rue des Iris. 3fr, Bandstand. 6fr, Opera House.

1984, May 10 Engr. *Perf. 12½x13*

1410 A425 5c brown .15 .15
1411 A425 10c claret .15 .15
1412 A425 15c violet .15 .15
1413 A425 20c dark blue .15 .15
1414 A425 30c deep blue .15 .15
1415 A425 40c dark green .15 .15
1416 A425 3fr red brown 1.10 .55
1417 A425 6fr yellow green 2.00 1.25
Set value 3.40 2.10

See Nos. 1516-1524, 1750-1755, 1821-1825.

Souvenir Sheet

1984 Los Angeles Olympics — A426

Rhythmic Gymnastics.

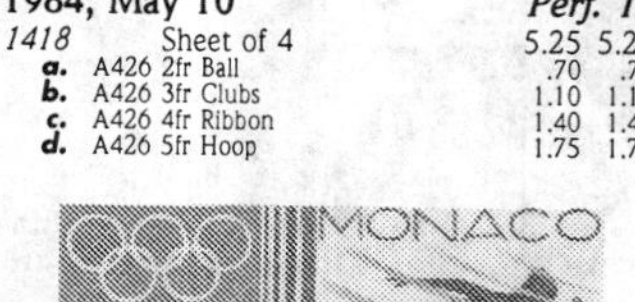

1984, May 10 *Perf. 13*

1418	Sheet of 4	5.25	5.25
a.	A426 2fr Ball	.70	.70
b.	A426 3fr Clubs	1.10	1.10
c.	A426 4fr Ribbon	1.40	1.40
d.	A426 5fr Hoop	1.75	1.75

1984 Winter Olympics — A427

1984, May 10

1422	A427 2fr Rink, speed skater	.65	.48
1423	A427 4fr Skater, snowflake	1.25	.95

Europa (1959-84) A428

1984, May 10 *Perf. 13x12½*

1424	A428 2fr blue	.70	.38
1425	A428 3fr yel grn	.95	.70
a.	Souv. sheet, 4 each #1424-1425	8.00	8.00

Butterflies and Rare Flowers, Mercantour Natl. Park A429

1.60fr, Boloria graeca tendensis, ranunculus montanus. 2fr, Zygaena vesubiana, saxifraga aizoides. 2.80fr, Erebia aethiopella, myosotis alpestris. 3fr, Parnassius phoebus gazeli, rhododendron ferrugineum. 3.60fr, Papilio alexanor, myrrhis odorata. Nos. 1426-1428 vert.

Perf. 12½x13, 13x12½

1984, May 10 **Photo.**

1426	A429 1.60fr multicolored	.70	.25
1427	A429 2fr multicolored	.95	.25
1428	A429 2.80fr multicolored	1.25	.45
1429	A429 3fr multicolored	1.40	.60
1430	A429 3.60fr multicolored	1.90	.90
	Nos. 1426-1430 (5)	6.20	2.45

Monte Carlo Dog Show Type

1984, May 10 *Perf. 13x12½*

1431	A387 1.60fr Auvergne pointer	1.25	.52

A431

A432

1984, May 10 Engr. *Perf. 12½x13*

1432	A431 2fr Statue, rosary, pilgrimage sanctuary	.65	.40

Sanctuary of Our Lady of Laghet.

1984, May 10

1433	A432 2.80fr Stratosphere balloon	1.00	.60
1434	A432 4fr Bathyscaphe	1.50	.85

Auguste Piccard birth centenary.

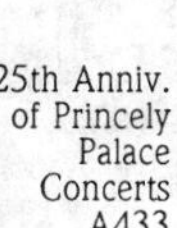

25th Anniv. of Princely Palace Concerts A433

1984, May 10 *Perf. 13x12½*

1435	A433 3.60fr Orchestra	1.00	.60

Belle Epoch Type of 1982

Paintings by Hubert Clerissi: 4fr, Rue Grimaldi, 1908. 5fr, Train Entering Monte Carlo Station, 1910.

Photo. & Engr.

1984, Nov. 8 *Perf. 12½x13*

1436	A394 4fr multicolored	1.10	1.00
1437	A394 5fr multicolored	1.65	1.40

25th Intl. Television Festival, Monte Carlo, Feb. 1985 — A434

1984, Nov. 8 Engr. *Perf. 13*

1438	A434 2.10fr Lights	.60	.35
1439	A434 3fr Golden nymph (prize)	.75	.55

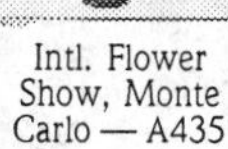

Intl. Flower Show, Monte Carlo — A435

Pharmaceuticals, Cosmetics Industry — A436

1984, Nov. 8 Photo. *Perf. 12½x13*

1440	A435 2.10fr Mixed bouquet	.60	.32
1441	A435 3fr Ikebana	.80	.60

See Nos. 1491-1492, 1552-1553.

1984, Nov. 8 Engr. *Perf. 13*

1442	A436 2.40fr multicolored	1.10	.85

Illustration from Gargantua, by Rabelais — A437

Francois Rabelais (1490-1553), 17th Cent. Drawing A438

1984, Nov. 8 *Perf. 13x12½, 12½x13*

1443	A437 2fr With animals	.70	.52
1444	A437 2fr With sheep of Panurge	.70	.52
1445	A438 4fr multicolored	1.40	1.10
	Nos. 1443-1445 (3)	2.80	2.14

Souvenir Sheet

10th Intl. Circus Festival, Dec. 6-10 — A439

1984, Nov. 8 Photo. *Perf. 13*

1446	A439 5fr Poster	2.75	2.75

La Femme a la Potiche, by Degas A440

1984, Nov. 8 Engr. *Perf. 12x13*

1447	A440 6fr multicolored	2.75	2.50

Christmas 1984 — A441

Figurines from Provence.

1984, Nov. 8 *Perf. 12½x13*

1448	A441 70c Shepherd	.35	.24
1449	A441 1fr Blind man	.40	.30
1450	A441 1.70fr Happy man	.65	.50
1451	A441 2fr Woman spinning	.85	.58
1452	A441 2.10fr Angel	.90	.60
1453	A441 2.40fr Garlic seller	1.10	.70
1454	A441 3fr Drummer	1.25	.85
1455	A441 3.70fr Knife grinder	1.65	1.00
1456	A441 4fr Elderly couple	1.65	1.10
	Nos. 1448-1456 (9)	8.80	5.87

See Nos. 1737-1739, 1766-1768, 1838-1840, 1883-1885, 1919-1921, 1976-1978.

Cherry Tree — A442

1985, Mar. 1 Engr. *Perf. 13*

1457	A442 1.22fr Spring	.45	.22
1458	A442 1.57fr Summer	.52	.30
1459	A442 2.55fr Fall	.90	.45
1460	A442 4.23fr Winter	1.65	.95
	Nos. 1457-1460 (4)	3.52	1.92

Issued precanceled only. See note after No. 324.

No. 1 in Green A443

1985, Mar. 25

1461	A443 1.70fr shown	.60	.42
1462	A443 2.10fr #1 in scarlet	.70	.22
1463	A443 3fr #1 in lt peacock bl	.90	.42
	Nos. 1461-1463 (3)	2.20	1.06

Stamp centenary, Natl. Stamp Exhibition, Dec. 5-8, Monte Carlo.

Europa 1985 — A444

Portraits: 2.10fr Prince Antoine I (1661-1731), Founder of Monaco Palace, music library. 3fr, Jean-Baptiste Lully (1632-1687), composer, violinist, superintendent of music to King Louis XIV.

1985, May 23 *Perf. 12½x13*

1464	A444 2.10fr brt blue	.70	.52
1465	A444 3fr dark carmine	1.00	.85
a.	Souv. sheet, 5 #1464, 5 #1465	10.50	10.50

Flowers in Mercantour Park A444a

Perf. 13x12½, 12½x13

1985, May 23 **Photo.**

1466	A444a 1.70fr Berardia subacaulis	.60	.38
1467	A444a 2.10fr Saxifraga florulenta, vert.	.70	.38
1468	A444a 2.40fr Fritillaria moggridgei, vert.	.75	.70
1469	A444a 3fr Sempervivum allionii, vert.	1.00	.90
1470	A444a 3.60fr Silene cordifolia, vert.	1.25	1.00
1471	A444a 4fr Primula allionii	1.40	1.10
	Nos. 1466-1471 (6)	5.70	4.46

Japanese Medlar A445

1985, May 23 Engr. *Perf. 13x12½*

1472	Sheet of 4	3.25	3.25
a.	A445 1fr Spring	.32	.32
b.	A445 2fr Summer	.65	.65
c.	A445 3fr Autumn	.85	.85
d.	A445 4fr Winter	1.25	1.25

Nadia Boulanger (1887-1979), Musician, Composer, Conductor — A446

Portraits, manuscripts and music: 2.10fr, Georges Auric (1899-1983), composer of film, ballet music, Music Foundation council president.

1985, May 23 *Perf. 13*

1473	A446 1.70fr brown	.55	.48
1474	A446 2.10fr brt ultra	.77	.55

Prince Pierre de Monaco Music Foundation composition prize, 25th anniv.

Natl. Oceanographic Museum, 75th Anniv. — A447

1985, May 23

1475	A447 2.10fr brt bl, grn & blk	.70	.45

Graphs, Fish, Molecular Structures, Lab Apparatus — A448

1985, May 23

1476 A448 3fr dk bl grn, blk & dk rose lil .90 .60

Prince Rainier III Scientific Research Center, 25th anniv.

Intl. Athletic Championships, May 25-26 — A449

1985, May 23

1477 A449 1.70fr Running .52 .30
1478 A449 2.10fr Swimming .70 .35

Opening of Louis II Stadium, May 25.

Monte Carlo Dog Show Type

1985, May 3 Photo. *Perf. 13x12½*

1479 A387 2.10fr Boxer 1.65 .90

Intl. Youth Year — A450

1985, May 23 Engr. *Perf. 13*

1480 A450 3fr fawn, sepia & dp grn .95 .55

Fish, Natl. Oceanographic Museum Aquarium — A451

1985, Aug. 13 Photo. *Perf. 12½x13*

1481 A451 1.80fr Pygoplites diacanthus .75 .40
1482 A451 2.20fr Acanthurus leucosternon .90 .38
1483 A451 3.20fr Chaetodon collare 1.40 .85
1484 A451 3.90fr Balistoides conspicillum 1.50 .90

Size: 40x52mm

Perf. 13

1485 A451 7fr Aquarium 3.00 2.00
Nos. 1481-1485 (5) 7.55 4.53

See Nos. 1560-1561, 1610-1615.

Souvenir Sheet

Transatlantic Yachting Race, Oct. 13 — A452

Yacht classes: a, Catamaran. b, Monocoque. c, Trimaran.

1985, Oct. Engr. *Perf. 13*

1486 Sheet of 3 4.25 4.25
a.-c. A452 4fr. any single 1.25 1.25

Monaco-New York competition.

ITALIA '85, Rome, Oct. 25-Nov. 3 — A453

Design: Exhibition emblem, St. Peter's Cathedral and Temple of Castor ruins.

1985, Oct. 25 *Perf. 13½x13*

1487 A453 4fr int blk, brt grn & red rose 1.40 .80

Belle Epoch Type of 1982

Illustrations by Hubert Clerissi.

Photo. & Engr.

1985, Nov. 7 *Perf. 13x12½*

1488 A394 4fr Port of Monaco, 1912 1.40 1.40
1489 A394 6fr La Gare Vers Avenue, 1920 2.00 2.00

11th Intl. Circus Festival, Dec. 5-9 — A454

1985, Nov. 7 Photo. *Perf. 13*

1490 A454 1.80fr multi .55 .22

Intl. Flower Show Type of 1984

1985, Nov. 7

1491 A435 2.20fr Roses, tulips, jonquils .75 .26
1492 A435 3.20fr Ikebana of chrysanthemums, bryony 1.10 .52

Dated 1986.

Factory, Ship, Fish, Crustaceans — A455

Christmas 1985 — A456

1985, Nov. 7 Engr. *Perf. 13x13½*

1493 A455 2.20fr brt bl, dp brn & dk grnsh bl .75 .38

Monagasque fishing industry, Fontvieille District. See No. 1555.

1985, Nov. 7 Photo. *Perf. 12½x13*

1494 A456 2.20fr multi .75 .25

EUTELSAT Orbiting Earth — A457

1985, Nov. 7 Engr. *Perf. 13*

1495 A457 3fr int blk, dp rose lil & dk bl 1.00 .60

European Telecommunications Satellite Org.

Sacha Guitry (1885-1957), Actor, Dramatist — A458

Authors, composers: 4fr, Brothers Grimm. 5fr, Frederic Chopin and Robert Schumann, composers. 6fr, Johann Sebastian Bach and George Frideric Handel, composers.

1985, Nov. 7

1496 A458 3fr brn blk & gldn brn 1.10 .75
1497 A458 4fr dp rose lil, sep & turq bl 1.50 .95
1498 A458 5fr stl bl, dp bl & grnsh bl 1.65 1.25
1499 A458 6fr blk, brn & stl bl 1.90 1.50
Nos. 1496-1499 (4) 6.15 4.45

Souvenir Sheet

Natl. Postage Stamp Cent. — A459

Altered designs: a, Type A1. b, Type A2. c, Type A13. d, Type A83.

1985, Dec. 5

1500 Sheet of 4 7.75 7.75
a.-d. A459 5fr. any single 1.90 1.90

Rainier and Albert Type of 1981-84

1985-88 Engr. *Perf. 13*

1505 A370 1.80fr brt grn .55 .15
1506 A370 1.90fr ol grn ('86) .58 .30
1507 A370 2fr emer grn ('87) .68 .35
1508 A370 2.20fr red rose .60 .15
1509 A370 2.50fr dk brn .65 .30
1510 A370 3.20fr brt bl .95 .22
1511 A370 3.40fr ind ('86) 1.05 .52
1512 A370 3.60fr dp ultra ('87) 1.20 .60
1513 A370 10fr claret ('86) 2.50 1.50
1514 A370 15fr dk bl grn ('86) 4.75 2.40
1515 A370 20fr brt blue ('88) 7.20 3.60
Nos. 1505-1515 (11) 20.71 10.09

This is an expanding set. Numbers will change if necessary.

Views of Old Monaco Type of 1984

Illustrations by Hubert Clerissi: 50c, Port of Monaco. 60c, St. Charles Church. 70c, Promenade. 80c, Harbor, olive trees. 90c, Quay. 1fr, Palace Square. 2fr, Ships, harbor mouth. 4fr, Monaco Tram Station. 5fr, Mail coach.

1986, Jan. 23

1516 A425 50c red .15 .15
1517 A425 60c Prus blue .15 .15
1518 A425 70c orange .18 .15
1519 A425 80c brt yel grn .20 .18
1520 A425 90c rose violet .32 .20
1521 A425 1fr brt blue .32 .15
1522 A425 2fr black .65 .28
1523 A425 4fr ultramarine 1.40 .55
1524 A425 5fr olive green 1.50 .70
Nos. 1516-1524 (9) 4.87 2.51

Hazel Nut Tree — A460

1986, Feb. 24 Engr. *Perf. 13x12½*

1525 A460 1.28fr Spring .42 .25
1526 A460 1.65fr Summer .52 .38
1527 A460 2.67fr Fall .85 .50
1528 A460 4.44fr Winter 1.50 .85
Nos. 1525-1528 (4) 3.29 1.98

Nos. 1525-1528 known only precanceled. See note after No. 324.

See Nos. 1580-1583, 1616-1619, 1685-1688, 1719-1722, 1809-1812.

Port of Monaco, 18th Cent. — A461

1986, Feb. 24

1529 A461 2.20fr ultra, gray & brown .75 .38

Publication of Annales Monegasques, 10th anniv.

Europa 1986 — A462

1986 World Cup Soccer Championships, Mexico — A463

1986, May 22 Engr. *Perf. 12½x13*

1530 A462 2.20fr Ramoge Nature Protection Treaty .85 .42
1531 A462 3.20fr Natl. marine reserve .95 .65
a. Souv. sheet, 5 each #1530-1531 9.00 9.00

Souvenir Sheet

1986, May 22

1532 Sheet of 2 3.75 3.75
a. A463 5fr Player 1.50 1.50
b. A463 7fr Goalie 2.00 2.00

Ovis Musimon A464

1986, May 22 *Perf. 13x12½*

1533 A464 2.20fr shown .65 .24
1534 A464 2.50fr Capra ibex .70 .35
1535 A464 3.20fr Rupicapra rupicapra 1.00 .35
1536 A464 3.90fr Marmota marmota 1.10 .48
1537 A464 5fr Lepus timidus varronis 1.40 .80
1538 A464 7.20fr Mustela erminea 2.25 1.25
Nos. 1533-1538 (6) 7.10 3.47

Nos. 1536-1538 vert.

Monte Carlo Dog Show Type

1986, May 22 Photo. *Perf. 13x12½*

1539 A387 1.80fr Terriers 2.00 .42

Prince Albert I, Parliament — A465

1986, May 22 *Perf. 13*

1540 A465 2.50fr brn & ol grn .70 .52

First Constitution, 75th anniv.

Serge Diaghilev, Founder — A466

1986, May 22 *Perf. 13*

1541 A466 3.20fr brn blk, carm rose & blk .90 .75

Diaghilev's first permanent ballet company, 75th anniv., and creation of Monte Carlo Ballet Company, 1986.

1st Monte Carlo Auto Rally, 75 Anniv. — A467

Winner Henri Rougier and Turcat-Mery, 1911.

1986, May 22
1542 A467 3.90fr rose magenta & car 1.10 .90

Statue of Liberty, Cent. — A468

1986, May 22
1543 A468 5fr multi 1.40 1.10

Halley's Comet — A469

1986, May 22
1544 A469 10fr Sightings, 1986, 1352 2.75 2.25

AMERIPEX '86, Chicago, May 22-June 1 — A470

1986, May 22
1545 A470 5fr US flag, skyline 1.40 1.10

Belle Epoch Type of 1982

Illustrations by Hubert Clerissi.

Photo. & Engr.

1986, Oct. 28 ***Perf. 12½x13***
1546 A394 6fr Pavilion, 1920, vert. 1.80 .90
1547 A394 7fr Beau Rivage Avenue, 1925, vert. 2.10 1.05

Premiere of El Cid, by Pierre Corneille, 350th Anniv. — A471

1986, Oct. 28 **Engr.** ***Perf. 13***
1548 A471 4fr Scenes 1.20 .60

Franz Liszt, Composer — A472

1986, Oct. 28
1549 A472 5fr dk red brn & brt ultra 1.50 .75

The Olympic Swimmer, 1961, by Emma de Sigaldi A473

1986, Oct. 28 ***Perf. 12½x13***
1550 A473 6fr multi 1.80 .90

Intl. Insurers Congress, Monte Carlo, Sept. 30 — A474

1986, Oct. 28 ***Perf. 13½x13***
1551 A474 3.20fr brn, dp grn & brt bl .95 .48

Intl. Flower Show Type of 1984

Designs: 2.20fr, Bouquet of roses, acidenthera. 3.90fr, Ikebana of lilies, beech branches.

1986, Oct. 28 **Photo.** ***Perf. 12½x13***
1552 A435 2.20fr multi .65 .32
1553 A435 3.90fr multi 1.15 .58

Dated 1987.

A475 A476

1986, Oct. 28 ***Perf. 13***
1554 A475 2.20fr multi .90 .32

12th Intl. Circus Festival, Dec. 4-8.

Industries Type of 1985

Design: 3.90fr, Plastics industry.

1986, Oct. 28 **Engr.**
1555 A455 3.90fr dk red, dk gray & bl grn 1.15 .58

1986, Oct. 28 **Photo.** ***Perf. 12½x13***
1556 A476 1.80fr Holly .55 .28
1557 A476 2.50fr Poinsettia .75 .38

Christmas.

Ascent of Mt. Blanc by J. Balmat and M.G. Paccard, Bicent. — A477

1986, Oct. 28 **Engr.** ***Perf. 13***
1558 A477 5.80fr red, brt bl & slate bl 1.75 .90

Miniature Sheet

Arbutus Tree — A478

1986, Oct. 28 ***Perf. 13x12½***
1559 Sheet of 4 6.00 3.00
 a. A478 3fr Spring 1.00 .50
 b. A478 4fr Summer 1.40 .65
 c. A478 5fr Fall 1.75 .85
 d. A478 6fr Winter 2.00 1.00

See Nos. 1645, 1680, 1736, 1775, 1804, 1852, 1934, 1943.

Aquarium Type of 1985

1986, Sept. 25 **Photo.** ***Perf. 12½x13***
1560 A451 1.90fr like No. 1481 .90 .30
1561 A451 3.40fr like No. 1483 1.65 .52

Prince Rainier III — A479

Villa Miraflores, Seat of the Philatelic Bureau — A480

#1562b, Prince Louis II, founder of the bureau.

1987, Apr. 23 **Engr.** ***Perf. 12½x13***
1562 Strip of 3 5.50 2.75
 a. A479 4fr bright blue 1.35 .68
 b. A479 4fr dark red 1.35 .68
 c. A480 8fr multi 2.70 1.35

Philatelic Bureau, 50th anniv.

See No. 1607.

Louis II Stadium A481

1987, Apr. 23 ***Perf. 13x12½***
1563 A481 2.20fr Exterior .75 .38
1564 A481 3.40fr Interior 1.15 .58
 a. Min. sheet, 5 each #1563-1564 9.50 4.80

Europa 1987.

Insects — A482 St. Devote Parish, Cent. — A483

1987, Apr. 23 **Photo.**
1565 A482 1fr Carabe de solier .42 .22
1566 A482 1.90fr Guepe dorec .75 .35
1567 A482 2fr Cicindele .80 .42
1568 A482 2.20fr Grande aeschne .90 .45
1569 A482 3fr Chrysomele 1.25 .60
1570 A482 3.40fr Grande sauterelle verte 1.40 .65
 Nos. 1565-1570 (6) 5.52 2.69

Nos. 1565, 1567 and 1569 horiz.

1987, Apr. 23 **Engr.** ***Perf. 12½x13***
1571 A483 1.90fr black .65 .32

Monaco Diocese, Cent. — A484

1987, Apr. 23
1572 A484 2.50fr dk yellow grn .85 .42

50th Intl. Dog Show, Monte Carlo A485

1987, Apr. 23 ***Perf. 13x12½***
1573 A485 1.90fr Dog breeds .85 .40
1574 A485 2.70fr Poodle 1.10 .60

Stamp Day — A486

1987, Apr. 23 ***Perf. 13***
1575 A486 2.20fr multi .75 .38

Red Curley Tail, Mobile by Alexander Calder (1898-1976), Sculptor — A487

1987, Apr. 23 **Photo.**
1576 A487 3.70fr multi 1.25 .62

Sculpture Exhibition, Monte Carlo.

2nd Small European Countries Games, May 14-17 — A488

1987, Apr. 23 **Engr.**

1577 A488 3fr Tennis		1.00	.50
1578 A488 5fr Windsurfing		1.70	.85

Miniature Sheet

Grape Vines A489

1987, Apr. 23 ***Perf. 13x12½***

1579 Sheet of 4	6.00	3.00
a. A489 3fr Spring	1.00	.50
b. A489 4fr Summer	1.30	.65
c. A489 5fr Autumn	1.70	.85
d. A489 6fr Winter	2.00	1.00

Four Seasons Type of 1986

Life cycle of the chestnut tree.

1987, Mar. 17 **Engr.** ***Perf. 13x12½***

1580 A460 1.31fr Spring	.45	.22
1581 A460 1.69fr Summer	.55	.28
1582 A460 2.74fr Fall	.90	.45
1583 A460 4.56fr Winter	1.50	.75
Nos. 1580-1583 (4)	3.40	1.70

Nos. 1580-1583 known only precanceled. See note after No. 324.

The Life of St. Devote, Patron Saint of Monaco A490

Text: 4fr, Born in 283, in Quercio, Devote was martyred in Mariana, Corsica. 5fr, Devote's nurse teaches the saint about Christianity.

1987, Nov. 13 **Photo.** ***Perf. 13x12½***

1584 A490 4fr multi	1.30	.65
1585 A490 5fr multi	1.65	.82

Red Cross of Monaco.

See Nos. 1643-1644, 1692-1693, 1714-1715, 1776-1777, 1836-1837.

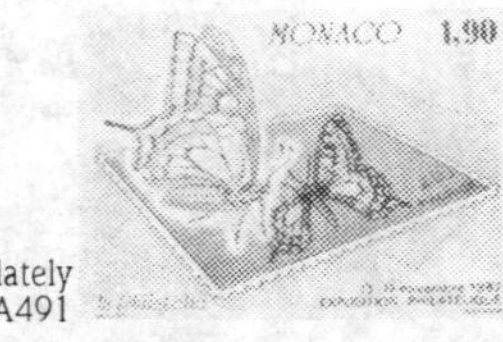

Philately A491

Butterflies and butterflies on simulated stamps.

1987, July 28 **Engr.**

1586 A491 1.90fr brt grn & dk gray	.62	.30
1587 A491 2.20fr rose red & rose lake	.72	.35
1588 A491 2.50fr red lil & vio	.82	.40
1589 A491 3.40fr brt bl & bluish blk	1.15	.58
Nos. 1586-1589 (4)	3.31	1.63

A492 A493

1987, Nov. 13 **Photo.** ***Perf. 12½x13***

1590 A492 2.20fr multi	1.00	.35

13th Int'l. Circus Festival, Monte Carlo, Jan. 28-Feb. 1.

1987, Nov. 13

1591 A493 2.20fr Ikebanas	.72	.35
1592 A493 3.40fr multi, horiz.	1.15	.58

1988 Int'l Flower Show.

Dated 1988. See Nos. 1651, 1749.

Christmas A494

1987, Nov. 13 **Engr.** ***Perf. 13x12½***

1593 A494 2.20fr crimson	.72	.35

5-Franc Prince Honoré V Coin — A495

1987, Nov. 13 ***Perf. 13***

1594 A495 2.50fr scar & dk gray	.82	.40

Recapture of the Mint, 150th anniv.

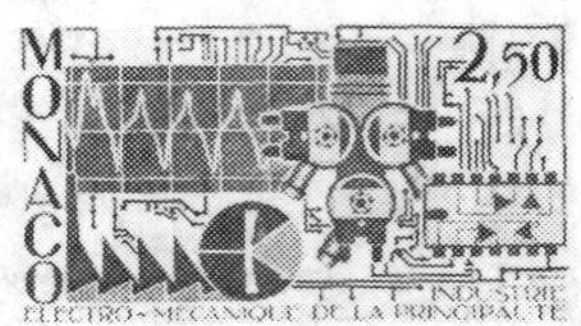

Electronics Industry — A496

1987, Nov. 13

1595 A496 2.50fr henna brn, vio bl & grn	.82	.40

Int'l. Marine Radioactivity Laboratory, 25th Anniv. — A497

Design: Monaco Oceanographic Museum and Int'l. Agency of Atomic Energy, Vienna.

1987, Nov. 13

1596 A497 5fr brt bl, red brn & blk	1.65	.82

Louis Jouvet (b.1887), French Actor — A498

1987, Nov. 16 ***Perf. 13x12½***

1597 A498 3fr black	1.00	.50

A499

1987, Nov. 16

1598 A499 3fr The River Crossing	1.00	.50

Paul and Virginia, by Bernardin de Saint-Pierre, first edition bcent. (in 1988).

Marc Chagall (1887-1985), Painter — A500

1987, Nov. 16 ***Perf. 13***

1599 A500 4fr terra cotta & bl gray	1.30	.65

Jean Jenneret (Le Corbusier, 1887-1965), French Architect — A501

1987, Nov. 16

1600 A501 4fr Architect, Ronchamp Chapel	1.30	.65

Newton's Theory of Gravity, 300th Anniv. — A502

Invention of the Telegraph by Samuel Morse, 150th Anniv. — A503

1987, Nov. 16

1601 A502 4fr magenta & dk bl	1.30	.65
1602 A503 4fr brt vio, turq bl & brn	1.30	.65

Don Juan, Opera by Mozart, Bicent. — A504

Mass of the Dead, by Berlioz — A505

1987, Nov. 16

1603 A504 5fr ind, vio brn & sage grn	1.65	.82
1604 A505 5fr sl grn, vio brn & bl	1.65	.82

Belle Epoch Type of 1982

Illustrations by Hubert Clerissi. 6fr, 7fr vert.

Photo. & Engr.

1987, Nov. 16 ***Perf. 12½x13***

1605 A394 6fr Rampe Major	2.00	1.00
1606 A394 7fr Old Monte Carlo Station	2.35	1.20

Philatelic Bureau Type of 1987

1987, Nov. 13 **Engr.** ***Perf. 12½x13***

1607 Sheet of 3	5.50	5.50
a. A479 4fr blk vio, like #1562a	1.35	1.35
b. A479 4fr blk vio, like #1562b	1.35	1.35
c. A480 8fr blk vio, like #1562c	2.70	2.70

Postage Due Arms Type of 1985

Booklet Stamps

1987-88 **Photo.** ***Perf. 13 on 3 Sides***

Size: 17x23mm

1608 D10 2fr multi ('88)	.72	.35
a. Bklt. pane of 10	7.25	
1609 D10 2.20fr multi	.72	.35
a. Bklt. pane of 10	7.25	

Issued: 2fr, Jan. 15; 2.20fr, Nov. 13.

Aquarium Type of 1985

Perf. 13x12½, 12½x13

1988, Jan. 15 **Photo.**

1610 A451 2fr Bodianus rufus	.72	.35
1611 A451 2.20fr Chelmon rostratus	.80	.40
1612 A451 2.50fr Oxymonacanthus longirostris	.90	.45
1613 A451 3fr Ostracion lentiginosum	1.10	.55
1614 A451 3.70fr Pterois volitans	1.30	.65
1615 A451 7fr Thalassoma lunare, horiz.	2.50	1.25
Nos. 1610-1615 (6)	7.32	3.65

Four Seasons Type of 1986

Life cycle of the pear tree.

1988, Feb. 15 ***Perf. 13x12½***

1616 A460 1.36fr Spring	.50	.25
1617 A460 1.75fr Summer	.65	.32
1618 A460 2.83fr Fall	1.00	.50
1619 A460 4.72fr Winter	1.70	.85
Nos. 1616-1619 (4)	3.85	1.92

Nos. 1616-1619 known only precanceled. See note after No. 324.

Souvenir Sheet

Biathlon, 1988 Winter Olympics, Calgary — A506

1988, Feb. 15 **Litho. & Engr.** ***Perf. 13***

1620 Sheet of 2	6.50	6.50
a. A506 4fr Skiing	2.50	2.50
b. A506 6fr Shooting	4.00	4.00

51st Intl. Dog Show, Monte Carlo — A507

1988, Mar. 30 **Photo.** ***Perf. 12½x13***

1621 A507 3fr Dachshunds	1.50	.75

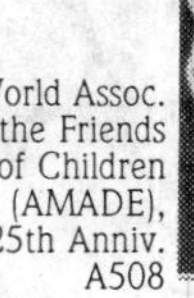

World Assoc. of the Friends of Children (AMADE), 25th Anniv. A508

1988, Mar. 30 **Engr.** ***Perf. 13***

1622 A508 5fr dark vio blue, dark brn & brt olive grn	1.80	.90

Europa 1988 — A509

Transport and communication: 2.20fr, Globe picturing hemispheres, man, brain, telecommunications satellite. 3.60fr, Plane propeller and high-speed locomotive.

1988, Apr. 21 *Perf. 12½x13*
1623 A509 2.20fr multi .80 .40
1624 A509 3.60fr multi 1.30 .65
a. Souv. sheet, 5 each #1623-1624 10.50 10.50

Mushrooms of Mercantour Natl. Park — A510

Perf. 13x12½, 12½x13
1988, May 26 **Photo.**
1625 A510 2fr Leccinum rotundifoliae .75 .38
1626 A510 2.20fr Hygrocybe punicea .85 .42
1627 A510 2.50fr Pholiota flammans .95 .48
1628 A510 2.70fr Lactarius lignyotus 1.00 .45
1629 A510 3fr Cortinarius traganus 1.10 .55
1630 A510 7fr Russula olivacea 2.75 1.40
Nos. 1625-1630 (6) 7.40 3.68

Nos. 1629-1630 vert.

Nautical Soc., Cent. — A511

1988, May 26 **Engr.** *Perf. 13*
1631 A511 2fr dk red, lt blue & dk grn .70 .35

5th Year of Restoration of Our Lady of Laghet Sanctuary — A512

1988, May 26 *Perf. 12½*
1632 A512 5fr multicolored 1.75 .88

World Health Organization, 40th Anniv. A513

1988, May 26 *Perf. 13*
1633 A513 6fr brt blue & lake 2.15 1.10

Intl. Red Cross and Red Crescent Organizations, 125th Annivs. A514

1988, May 26 **Photo.** *Perf. 13x12½*
1634 A514 6fr dull red, blk & gray 2.15 1.10

Jean Monnet (1888-1979), Nobel Peace Prize Winner in 1922 — A515

Maurice Chevalier (1888-1972), Actor — A516

1988, May 26 **Engr.** *Perf. 12½x13*
1635 A515 2fr brt blue, dark olive bister & blk 1.40 .35
1636 A516 2fr blk & dark blue 1.40 .35

1st Crossing of Greenland by Fridtjof Nansen (1861-1930), Cent. — A517

1988, May 26 *Perf. 13*
1637 A517 4fr bright violet 1.40 .70

Belle Epoch Type of 1982

Illustrations by Hubert Clerissi.

Photo. & Engr.
1988, Sept. 8 *Perf. 13x12½*
1638 A394 6fr Packet in Monte Carlo Harbor, 1910 2.00 1.00
1639 A394 7fr Monte Carlo Station, c. 1910 2.50 1.25

Souvenir Sheet

1988 Summer Olympics, Seoul A518

Woman wearing Korean regional costume, Games emblem and event: 2fr, Women's tennis. 3fr, Women's table tennis. 5fr, Women's yachting. 7fr, Women's cycling.

1988, Sept. 8 **Engr.**
1640 Sheet of 4 5.50 5.50
a. A518 2fr blk, light ultra & brown .65 .65
b. A518 3fr blk, light ultra & brown .95 .95
c. A518 5fr blk, light ultra & brown 1.60 1.60
d. A518 7fr blk, light ultra & brown 2.25 2.25

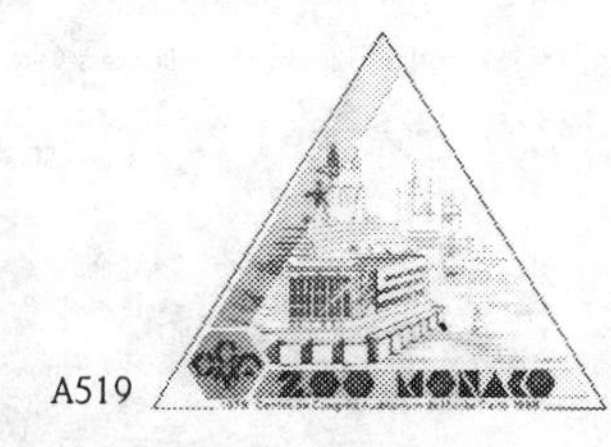

A519

Monte Carlo Congress Center, 10th Anniv. A520

1988, Sept. 8 *Perf. 13*
1641 A519 2fr dark blue grn .68 .35
1642 A520 3fr henna brn 1.00 .50
a. Pair, #1641-1642 1.75 1.00

Monegasque Red Cross Type of 1987

The Life of St. Devote, patron saint of Monaco: 4fr, Devote witnessing the arrival of the governor of Rome. 5fr, Devote and the governor.

1988, Oct. 20 **Photo.** *Perf. 13x12½*
1643 A490 4fr multicolored 1.30 .65
1644 A490 5fr multicolored 1.60 .80

Tree Type of 1986

Life cycle of the olive tree.

1988, Oct. 20 **Engr.** *Perf. 13x12½*
1645 Sheet of 4 6.50 6.50
a. A478 3fr Spring 1.00 1.00
b. A478 4fr Summer 1.50 1.50
c. A478 5fr Fall 1.75 1.75
d. A478 6fr Winter 2.25 2.25

Le Nain and Brothers, Detail of a Painting in the Louvre, by Antoine Le Nain (c. 1588-1648) A521

1988, Oct. 20 *Perf. 12½x13*
1646 A521 5fr ol brn, dull brn & car rose 1.60 .80

Les Grands Archeologues, Bronze Sculpture by Giorgio De Chirico (1888-1978), Italian Painter and Sculptor A522

1988, Oct. 20 *Perf. 13*
1647 A522 5fr ol bis, blk brn & dark bl 1.60 .80

A523

A524

1988, Oct. 20
1648 A523 3fr dull ol & ultra .95 .48

Pierre Carlet de Chamblain de Marivaux (1688-1763), French playwright and novelist.

1988, Oct. 20
1649 A524 3fr grnsh bl, brn & blk .95 .48

Lord Byron (1788-1824), English poet.

14th Intl. Circus Festival, Monte Carlo, Feb. 2-6, 1989 — A525

1988, Oct. 20 **Photo.** *Perf. 12½x13*
1650 A525 2fr multi .65 .32

Intl. Flower Show Type of 1987

1988, Oct. 20
1651 A493 3fr Ikebana .95 .48

22nd Intl. Flower Show and Flower Arranging Contest, Monte Carlo.

Textile Industry (Ready-to-Wear Clothes by Bettina and Le Squadra) — A526

1988, Oct. 20 **Engr.** *Perf. 13*
1652 A526 3fr blk, yel org & dk ol grn .95 .48

Christmas — A527

1988, Oct. 20 **Litho.** *Perf. 12½x13*
1653 A527 2fr black & lemon .65 .32

Petroglyphs, Mercantour Natl. Park — A528

Perf. 13x12½, 12½x13
1989, Feb. 8 **Litho.**
1654 A528 2fr multi .65 .32
1655 A528 2.20fr multi, diff. .72 .35
1656 A528 3fr multi, diff. .98 .50
1657 A528 3.60fr multi, diff. 1.20 .60
1658 A528 4fr multi, diff., vert. 1.30 .65
1659 A528 5fr multi, diff., vert. 1.65 .82
Nos. 1654-1659 (6) 6.50 3.24

Rue des Spelugues — A528a

1989, Feb. 8 **Litho.** *Perf. 13½x13*
Booklet Stamps
1660 A528a 2fr shown .65 .32
b. Booklet pane of 10 6.50
1660A A528a 2.20fr St. Nicolas Place .72 .35
c. Booklet pane of 10 7.25

See Nos. 1702-1703, 1826-1827.

Prince Rainier III — A529

1989-91 **Photo. & Engr.** *Perf. 13*
1661 2fr pale blue grn & Prus grn .65 .16
1662 2.10fr lt blue & Prus blue .75 .18
1663 2.20fr pink & rose brn .72 .18
1664 2.20fr pale greenish bl & greenish bl .80 .40
1665 2.30fr pale pink & car lake .82 .20
1666 2.50fr pale rose & rose lake .90 .45

1667 3.20fr pale blue & brt blue 1.15 .28
1668 3.40fr lt bl & dk bl 1.25 .62
1669 3.60fr lt blue & sapphire 1.20 .30
1670 3.80fr pale pink & dk lil rose 1.35 .32
1671 4fr pale vio & rose vio 1.40 .70
1672 5fr buff & dark vio brn 1.65 .55
1673 15fr pale vio & indigo 4.75 2.40
1673A 20fr pink & rose car 6.80 3.40
1674 25fr pale gray & blk 9.00 4.50
Nos. 1661-1674 (15) 33.19 14.64

Issued: 2fr, #1663, 3.60fr, 5fr, 15fr, 3/14; 2.10fr, 2.30fr, 25fr, 1/11/90; 3.20fr, 3.80fr, 3/15/90; 20fr, 4/26/91; #1664, 2.50fr, 3.40fr, 4fr, 9/24/91.
See Nos. 1790-1799.

5th Magic Grand Prix, Monte Carlo, Mar. 17-19
A530

1989, Mar. 14 Engr. *Perf. 13x12½*
1675 A530 2.20fr multi .75 .35

Dog Show Type of 1982

1989, Mar. 14 Photo.
1676 A387 2.20fr Yorkshire terrier .85 .42

Our Lady of Mercy Soc., 350th Anniv.
A531

1989, Mar. 14 Engr. *Perf. 13*
1677 A531 3fr choc, dark red & blk 1.00 .50

Theater & Film — A532

Designs: 3fr, Jean Cocteau (1889-1963), French writer, artist. 4fr, Charlie Chaplin (1889-1977), English actor, film producer.

1989, Mar. 14
1678 A532 3fr Prus grn, olive grn & dp rose lil 1.00 .50
1679 A532 4fr dk grn, dk vio & dk red 1.30 .65

Tree Type of 1986

Life cycle of the pomegranate tree.

1989, Mar. 14 *Perf. 13x12½*
Miniature Sheet
1680 Sheet of 4 5.90 5.90
a. A478 3fr Spring .98 .98
b. A478 4fr Summer 1.30 1.30
c. A478 5fr Fall 1.65 1.65
d. A478 6fr Winter 1.95 1.95

Values quoted in this catalogue are for stamps graded Very Fine and with no faults. An illustrated guide to grade is provided in the "Catalogue Information" section of the Introduction.

Souvenir Sheet

Reign of Prince Rainier III, 40th Anniv.
A533

1989, May 9 Engr. *Perf. 13*
1681 A533 20fr rose vio 6.00 6.00

Europa 1989 — A534

Children's games.

1989, May 9 *Perf. 12½x13*
1682 A534 2.20fr Marbles .68 .35
1683 A534 3.60fr Jumping rope 1.10 .55
a. Souv. sheet, 5 each #1682-1683 9.00 9.00

Souvenir Sheet

French Revolution, Bicent., PHILEXFRANCE '89 — A535

Designs: a, Liberty. b, Equality. c, Fraternity.

1989, July 7 Engr. *Perf. 12½x13*
1684 A535 Sheet of 3 4.35 4.35
a. 5fr sapphire 1.45 1.45
b. 5fr black 1.45 1.45
c. 5fr dark red 1.45 1.45

Four Seasons Type of 1986

Life cycle of the pear tree.

1989, July 27 Photo. *Perf. 13x12½*
1685 A460 1.39fr like No. 1616 .45 .22
1686 A460 1.79fr like No. 1617 .58 .30
1687 A460 2.90fr like No. 1618 .92 .45
1688 A460 4.84fr like No. 1619 1.55 .78
Nos. 1685-1688 (4) 3.50 1.75

Nos. 1685-1688 known only precanceled. See note after No. 324.

Portrait of the Artist's Mother, by Philibert Florence
A536

Regatta at Molesey, by Alfred Sisley (1839-1899) — A537

Paintings: 8fr, *Enclosed Courtyard, Auvers,* by Paul Cezanne (1839-1906), vert.

Perf. 13, 13x12½ (6fr), 12½x13 (8fr)
1989, Sept. 7 Engr.
1689 A536 4fr olive black 1.40 .70
1690 A537 6fr multi 2.25 1.10
1691 A537 8fr multi 3.00 1.40
Nos. 1689-1691 (3) 6.65 3.20

Birth sesquicentennials of painters.

Monegasque Red Cross Type of 1987

The life of St. Devote, patron saint of Monaco: 4fr, Eutychius refuses to betray Devote to Barbarus and is poisoned. 5fr, Devote is condemned to torture by Barbarus when she refuses to make sacrifices to the Gods.

1989, Sept. 7 Photo. *Perf. 13x12½*
1692 A490 4fr multi 1.20 .60
1693 A490 5fr multi 1.50 .75

Interparliamentary Union, Cent. — A538

1989, Oct. 26 Engr. *Perf. 13*
1694 A538 4fr multi 1.20 .60

Belle Epoch Type of 1982

Illustrations by Hubert Clerissi.

1989, Oct. 26 *Perf. 12½x13*
1695 A394 7fr Ship in Monaco Port 2.25 1.10
1696 A394 8fr Gaming hall, Monte Carlo Casino 2.75 1.40

Souvenir Sheet

Princess Grace Foundation, 25th Anniv. — A539

Designs: a, Princess Grace. b, Princess Caroline.

1989, Oct. 26
1697 Sheet of 2 4.50 4.50
a.-b. A539 5fr any single 2.25 2.25

20th UPU Congress — A540

Design: Views of the Prince of Monaco's palace and the White House.

1989, Oct. 26 *Perf. 13*
1698 A540 6fr multicolored 1.80 .90

A541

A542

1989, Oct. 26 Litho. *Perf. 12½x13*
1699 A541 2fr Poinsettia .65 .32

Christmas.

1989, Dec. 7 Photo. *Perf. 12½x13*
1700 A542 2.20fr multicolored .95 .40

15th Intl. Circus Festival, Monte Carlo, Feb. 1-5, 1990.

Monaco Aid and Presence, 10th Anniv.
A543

1989, Dec. 7 Engr. *Perf. 13x12½*
1701 A543 2.20fr brown & red .95 .40

Avenues Type of 1989

1990, Feb. 8 Litho. *Perf. 13½x13*
1702 A528a 2.10fr The Great Stairs .75 .38
a. Bklt. pane of 10 + 2 labels 7.50
1703 A528a 2.30fr Mayoral Court of Honor .82 .40
a. Bklt. pane of 10 + 2 labels 8.25

Dog Show Type of 1982

1990, Mar. 15 *Perf. 13x12½*
1704 A387 2.30fr Bearded collie .90 .42

Sir Rowland Hill, Great Britain No. 1 — A544

1990, Mar. 15 Engr. *Perf. 13*
1705 A544 5fr royal blue & black 1.80 .90

Penny Black, 150th anniv.

Flowers Named for Members of the Royal Family — A545

1990, Mar. 15 Litho. *Perf. 12½x13*
1706 A545 2fr Princess Grace .72 .35
1707 A545 3fr Prince Rainier III 1.05 .52
1708 A545 3fr Grace Patricia 1.05 .52
1709 A545 4fr Principessa Grace 1.45 .72
1710 A545 5fr Caroline of Monaco 1.75 .90
Nos. 1706-1710 (5) 6.02 3.01

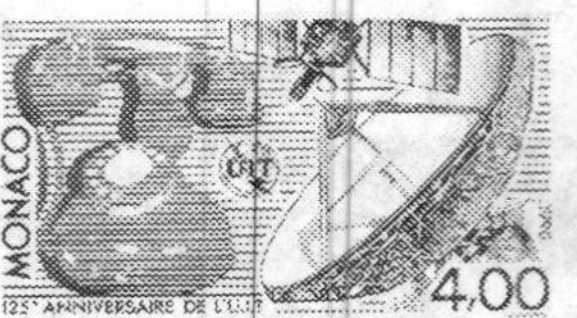

Intl. Telecommunications Union, 125th Anniv. — A546

1990, Mar. 15 Engr. *Perf. 13*
1711 A546 4fr pink, deep vio & dull blue grn 1.45 .72

Antony Noghes (1890-1978), Creator of the Monaco Grand Prix and Monte Carlo Rally — A547

1990, Mar. 15

1712 A547 3fr deep vio, blk & dark red 1.10 .55

A548 A549

1990, Mar. 15

1713 A548 4fr brt pur, sepia & brt blue 1.45 .72

Automobile Club, centenary.

Monegasque Red Cross Type of 1987

The life of St. Devote, patron saint of Monaco: 4fr, Devote tortured to death (whipped). 5fr, Body layed out in a small boat.

1990, Mar. 15 Litho. *Perf. 13x12½*

1714 A490 4fr multicolored 1.45 .72
1715 A490 5fr multicolored 1.75 .88

1990, May 3 Engr. *Perf. 12½x12*

1716 A549 2.30fr multicolored .80 .40
1717 A549 3.70fr multicolored 1.30 .60
a. Souv. sheet, 4 each, perf. 12½x13 8.75 8.75

Europa.

Souvenir Sheet

World Cup Soccer Championships, Italy — A550

1990, May 3 *Perf. 13x12½*

1718 A550 Sheet of 4 7.00 7.00
a. 5fr Players, trophy 1.75 1.75
b. 5fr Player dribbling ball 1.75 1.75
c. 5fr Ball 1.75 1.75
d. 5fr Players, stadium 1.75 1.75

Four Seasons Type of 1986

Life cycle of the plum tree.

1990, Sept. 17 *Perf. 13*

1719 A460 1.46fr Spring .52 .26
1720 A460 1.89fr Summer .65 .32
1721 A460 3.06fr Fall 1.10 .55
1722 A460 5.10fr Winter 1.80 .90
Nos. 1719-1722 (4) 4.07 2.03

Nos. 1719-1722 known only precanceled. See note after No. 324.

Minerals, Mercantour Natl. Park — A551

Perf. 13x12½, 12½x13

1990, Sept. 4 Litho.

1723 A551 2.10fr Anatase .75 .38
1724 A551 2.30fr Albite .80 .40
1725 A551 3.20fr Rutile 1.15 .58
1726 A551 3.80fr Chlorite 1.35 .68
1727 A551 4fr Brookite 1.40 .70
1728 A551 6fr Quartz 2.10 1.05
Nos. 1723-1728 (6) 7.55 3.79

Nos. 1727-1728 vert.

Pierrot Ecrivain — A552

1990, Sept. 4 Engr. *Perf. 12½x13*

1729 A552 3fr dark blue 1.10 .55

Helicopter, Monaco Heliport A553

Design: 5fr, Helicopters, Monte Carlo skyline.

1990, Sept. 4 *Perf. 13*

1730 A553 3fr red, brn & blk 1.10 .55
1731 A553 5fr blk, gray bl & brn 1.80 .90

30th World Congress of Civilian Airports, Monte Carlo.

C. Samuel Hahnemann (1755-1843), Physician — A554

1990, Sept. 4

1732 A554 3fr multicolored 1.10 .55

Homeopathic medicine, bicentennial.

MONACO 500

Jean-Francois Champollion (1790-1832), Egyptologist — A555

1990, Sept. 4

1733 A555 5fr blue & brown 1.80 .90

A556 A558

Design: 6fr, Petanque World Championships.

1990, Sept. 4

1734 A556 2.30fr brt ultra, brn & red .90 .45
1735 A556 6fr brn org, brn & bl 2.25 1.10

Offshore Power Boating World Championships.

Tree Type of 1986
Miniature Sheet

Life cycle of the lemon tree.

1990, Oct. 17 Litho. *Perf. 13x12½*

1736 Sheet of 4 6.75 6.75
a. A478 3fr Spring 1.15 1.15
b. A478 4fr Summer 1.50 1.50
c. A478 5fr Fall 1.90 1.90
e. A478 6fr Winter 2.25 2.25

Type of 1984

1990, Oct. 17 Litho. *Perf. 12½x13*

1737 A441 2.30fr Miller riding donkey .90 .45
1738 A441 3.20fr Woman carrying firewood 1.25 .65
1739 A441 3.80fr Baker 1.50 .75
Nos. 1737-1739 (3) 3.65 1.85

1990, Oct. 17 Engr. *Perf. 12½*

The Cathedral, by Auguste Rodin (1840-1917).

1740 A558 5fr bl & cream 1.90 .95

La Pie by Claude Monet (1840-1926) — A559

1990, Oct. 17 *Perf. 13x12*

1741 A559 7fr multicolored 2.60 1.30

A560 A561

1990, Oct. 17 *Perf. 12½x13*

1742 A560 5fr dark grn & bl 1.90 .95

Peter Ilich Tchaikovsky, composer (1840-1893).

1991, Jan. 2 Photo. *Perf. 13*

1743 A561 2.30fr multicolored .90 .45

16th Intl. Circus Festival, Monte Carlo. See No. 1801.

A562 A563

Migratory birds and their continents: 2fr, Ciconia abdimii, Africa. 3fr, Selasphorus platycercus, America. 4fr, Anas querquedula, Asia. 5fr, Eurystomus orientalis, Australia. 6fr, Merops apiaster, Europe.

1991, Feb. 22 Litho. *Perf. 12½x13*

1744 A562 2fr multicolored .80 .40
1745 A562 3fr multicolored 1.20 .60
1746 A562 4fr multicolored 1.60 .80
1747 A562 5fr multicolored 2.00 1.00
1748 A562 6fr multicolored 2.40 1.20
Nos. 1744-1748 (5) 8.00 4.00

Intl. Symposium on Migratory Birds.

Intl. Flower Show Type of 1987

1991, Feb. 22

1749 A493 3fr Cyclamen 1.20 .60

Views of Old Monaco Type of 1984

Designs: 20c, Cliffs of Monaco, Port de Fontvieille. 40c, Place du Casino. 50c, Place de la Cremaillere. 70c, Prince's Palace. 80c, Avenue du Beau Rivage. 1fr, Place d'Armes.

1991, Feb. 22 Engr.

1750 A425 20c rose violet .15 .15
1751 A425 40c dk green .15 .15
1752 A425 50c claret .20 .15
1753 A425 70c ol green .25 .15
1754 A425 80c ultramarine .30 .15
1755 A425 1fr dk blue .40 .20
Nos. 1750-1755 (6) 1.45
Set value .78

Dog Show Type of 1982

1991, Feb. 22 Litho. *Perf. 12*

1756 A387 2.50fr Schnauzer 1.00 .50

1991, Feb. 22

1757 A563 2.10fr Phytoplankton .85 .42

Oceanographic Museum.

1992 Olympics A564

Design: No. 1758b, Cross country skiiers, diff. No. 1759a, Relay runner receiving baton. No. 1759b, Runner passing baton.

1991, Apr. 26 Engr. *Perf. 13x12½*

1758 Pair 2.80 1.40
a. A564 3fr dark green, blue & olive 1.20 .60
b. A564 4fr dark green, blue & olive 1.60 .80
1759 Pair 3.20 1.60
a. A564 3fr brown & Prussian blue 1.20 .60
b. A564 5fr brown & Prussian blue 2.00 1.00

Nos. 1758 and 1759 have continuous designs.

Europa A565

1991, Apr. 26

1760 A565 2.30fr Eutelsat .90 .45
1761 A565 3.20fr Inmarsat 1.25 .65
a. Min. sheet, 5 ea. #1760-1761 10.75 5.35

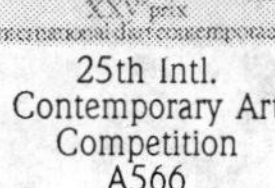

25th Intl. Contemporary Art Competition A566

Prince Pierre Foundation, 25th Anniv. A567

1991, Apr. 26 Engr. *Perf. 12½x13*

1762 A566 4fr multicolored 1.40 .70

1991, Apr. 26

1763 A567 5fr multicolored 1.75 .88

Coral — A568

1991, Apr. 26 Photo. *Perf. 12*

1764 A568 2.20fr shown .75 .38
1765 A568 2.40fr Coral necklace .85 .42

Christmas Type of 1984

1991, Nov. 7 Litho. *Perf. 12*

1766 A441 2.50fr Consul .90 .45
1767 A441 3.50fr Woman from Arles 1.30 .65
1768 A441 4fr Mayor 1.45 .75
Nos. 1766-1768 (3) 3.65 1.85

Conifers, Mercantour Natl. Park — A569

1991, Nov. 7

1769 A569 2.50fr Epicea .90 .45
1770 A569 3.50fr Sapin 1.30 .65
1771 A569 4fr Pin a crochets 1.45 .75
1772 A569 5fr Pin sylvestre, vert. 1.85 .90
1773 A569 6fr Pin cembro 2.20 1.10
1774 A569 7fr Meleze, vert. 2.55 1.30
Nos. 1769-1774 (6) 10.25 5.15

Tree Type of 1986
Miniature Sheet

Life cycle of an orange tree.

1991, Nov. 7 Engr. *Perf. 13x12½*

1775 Sheet of 4 6.60 3.30
a. A478 3fr Spring 1.10 .55
b. A478 4fr Summer 1.45 .75
c. A478 5fr Fall 1.85 .90
d. A478 6fr Winter 2.20 1.10

Monagasque Red Cross Type of 1987

Life of St. Devote, Monaco's Patron Saint: 4.50fr, The Storm is Rising. 5.50fr, Arrival of the Rock of Monaco.

1991, Nov. 7 Photo.

1776 A490 4.50fr multicolored 1.65 .85
1777 A490 5.50fr multicolored 2.00 1.00

Testudo Hermanni A570

1991, Nov. 7 Litho. *Perf. 12*

1778 A570 1.25fr Two crawling right .45 .22
1779 A570 1.25fr Peering from shell .45 .22
1780 A570 1.25fr Walking in grass .45 .22
1781 A570 1.25fr Walking amid plants .45 .22
a. Block or strip of 4, #1778-1781 1.80 .90

Prince Albert I Type of 1891
Miniature Sheet

1991, Nov. 7 Engr. *Perf. 13*

Stamp size: 22½x28mm

1782 Sheet of 3 11.10 5.55
a. A2 10fr dark red 3.70 1.85
b. A2 10fr dark blue green 3.70 1.85
c. A2 10fr deep violet 3.70 1.85

Portrait of Claude Monet by Auguste Renoir A571

1991, Nov. 7 Engr. *Perf. 12½x13*

1783 A571 5fr multicolored 1.80 .90

Treaty of Peronne, 350th Anniv. A572

Portraits by Philippe de Champaigne (1602-1674): 6fr, Honore II (1604-1662), Monaco. 7fr, Louis XIII (1610-1643), France.

1991, Nov. 7

1784 A572 6fr multicolored 2.20 1.10
1785 A572 7fr multicolored 2.55 1.30

Princess Grace Theatre, 10th Anniv. A573

1991, Nov. 7 Litho.

1786 A573 8fr Princess Grace 3.00 1.50

Prince Rainier III Type of 1989

1991-96 Photo. & Engr. *Perf. 13*

1790 A529 2.40fr pale greenish blue & dk Prus bl 1.00 .50
1791 A529 2.70fr pale bl grn, dk bl grn 1.60 .80
1792 A529 2.80fr pale rose & rose lake 1.10 .58
1793 A529 3fr pale red, red brown 1.80 .90
1794 A529 3.70fr pale blue & dk blue 1.50 .80
1795 A529 3.80fr pale blue, dk blue 2.25 1.10
1797 A529 10fr lt bl grn & deep bl grn 3.70 1.85
1799 A529 40fr pale brown & dk brown 16.00 8.25
Nos. 1790-1799 (8) 28.95 14.78

Issued: 10fr, 11/7/91; 2.40fr, 2.80fr, 3.70fr, 40fr, 7/28/93; 2.70fr, 3/18/96. 3fr, 3.80fr, 7/8/96.

See No. 1863b.

This is an expanding set. Numbers will change if necessary.

16th Intl. Circus Festival Type

1992, Jan. 6 Photo. *Perf. 12½x13*

1801 A561 2.50fr multicolored .90 .45

1992 Winter and Summer Olympics, Albertville and Barcelona A574

Designs: 7fr, Two-man bobsled. 8fr, Soccer.

1992, Feb. 7 Engr. *Perf. 13*

1802 A574 7fr multicolored 2.50 1.25
1803 A574 8fr multicolored 2.90 1.45

Tree Type of 1986
Miniature Sheet

Life cycle of a cactus plant.

1992, Apr. 24 Photo. *Perf. 13x12½*

1804 Sheet of 4 7.25 7.25
a. A478 3fr Spring 1.20 1.20
b. A478 4fr Summer 1.60 1.60
c. A478 5fr Fall 2.00 2.00
d. A478 6fr Winter 2.40 2.40

60th Monte Carlo Rally — A575

1992, Mar. 13 Engr. *Perf. 13x12½*

1805 A575 4fr dk bl grn, blk & red 1.45 .75

Intl. Dog Show Type of 1982

1992, Mar. 13 Litho. *Perf. 13x12½*

1806 A387 2.20fr Labrador retriever .80 .40

50th Grand Prix of Monaco A576

1992, Mar. 13 Engr.

1807 A576 2.50fr vio brn, blk & brt bl .90 .45

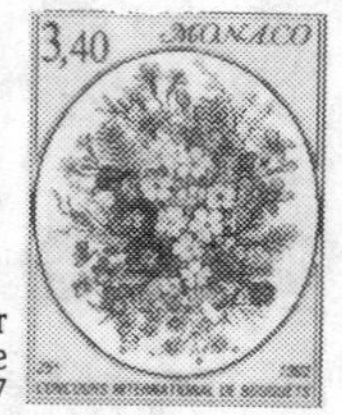

25th Intl. Flower Show, Monte Carlo — A577

1992, Mar. 13 Photo. *Perf. 12½x13*

1808 A577 3.40fr multicolored 1.25 .60

See No. 1848.

Four Seasons Type of 1986

Life cycle of a walnut tree.

1992, Mar. 13 Photo.

1809 A460 1.60fr Spring .58 .28
1810 A460 2.08fr Summer .75 .38
1811 A460 2.98fr Fall 1.10 .55
1812 A460 5.28fr Winter 1.90 .95
Nos. 1809-1812 (4) 4.33 2.16

Nos. 1809-1812 known only precanceled. See the note after No. 324.

Souvenir Sheet

Dolphins A578

1992, Mar. 13

1813 A578 Sheet of 4 8.00 8.00
a. 4fr Steno bredanensis 1.50 1.50
b. 5fr Delphinus delphis 1.80 1.80
c. 6fr Tursiops truncatus 2.20 2.20
d. 7fr Stenella coeruleoalba 2.50 2.50

See Nos. 1853, 1898.

Discovery of America, 500th Anniv. A579

1992, Apr. 24

1814 A579 2.50fr Pinta .90 .45
1815 A579 3.40fr Santa Maria 1.25 .65
1816 A579 4fr Nina 1.45 .75
a. Sheet, 2 each #1814-1816 7.25 7.25
Nos. 1814-1816 (3) 3.60 1.85

Europa.

Ameriflora Intl. Flower Show, Columbus, Ohio — A580

1992, Apr. 24 Litho. *Perf. 12½x13*

1817 A580 4fr Fruits & vegetables 1.45 .75
1818 A580 5fr Vase of flowers 1.80 .90

Columbus Exposition, Genoa '92 — A581

1992, Apr. 24 Engr. *Perf. 13*

1819 A581 6fr multicolored 2.20 1.10

Expo '92, Seville — A582

1992, Apr. 24

1820 A582 7fr multicolored 2.50 1.25

Views of Old Monaco Type of 1984

Illustrations by Hubert Clerissi: 60c, National Council. 90c, Port of Fontvieille. 2fr, Condamine Market. 3fr, Sailing ship. 7fr, Oceanographic Museum.

1992, May 25 Engr. *Perf. 12½x13*

1821 A425 60c dark blue .22 .15
1822 A425 90c violet brown .35 .16
1823 A425 2fr vermilion .75 .38
1824 A425 3fr black 1.15 .58
1825 A425 7fr gray blue & blk 2.70 1.35
Nos. 1821-1825 (5) 5.17 2.62

Avenues Type of 1989

1992, May 25 Litho. *Perf. 13x13½*

Booklet Stamps

1826 A528a 2.20fr Porte Nueve, horiz. .82 .42
a. Bklt. pane of 10 + 2 labels 8.25
1827 A528a 2.50fr Placette Bosio, horiz. .92 .46
a. Bklt. pane of 10 + 2 labels 9.25

Genoa '92 — A583

Roses: 3fr, Christopher Columbus. 4fr, Prince of Monaco.

1992, Sept. 18 Litho. *Perf. 12*

1828 A583 3fr multicolored 1.20 .60
1829 A583 4fr multicolored 1.60 .80

Gypaetus Barbatus, Mercantour Natl. Park — A584

1992, Oct. 20 Engr. *Perf. 13x12½*

1830 A584 2.20fr grn, org & blk .85 .42

Seabus A585

1992, Oct. 20

1831 A585 4fr multicolored 1.55 .78

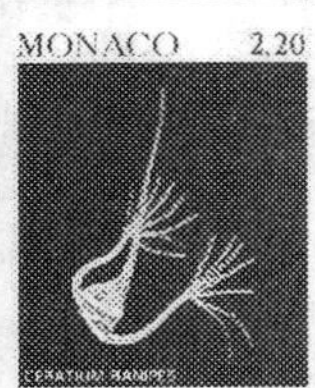

Phytoplankton A586

Designs: 2.20fr, Ceratium ranipes. 2.50fr, Ceratium hexacanthum.

1992, Oct. 20 Litho. *Perf. 12*

1832 A586	2.20fr multicolored	.85	.42
1833 A586	2.50fr multicolored	.95	.48

Baron de Coubertin's Call for Modern Olympics, Cent. — A587

1992, Oct. 20 Engr. *Perf. 13*

1834 A587 10fr blue 3.85 1.90

Chapel of St. Catherine — A588

Prince of Monaco, the Marquisat of Baux-de-Provence.

1992, Oct. 20 Litho. & Engr.

1835 A588 15fr multicolored 5.75 2.85

Monagasque Red Cross Type of 1987

The life of St. Devote, patron saint of Monaco: 6fr, Fire aboard ship. 8fr, Procession of the reliquary.

1992, Oct. 20 Engr.

Size: 48x36mm

1836 A490 6fr multicolored	2.30	1.15
1837 A490 8fr multicolored	3.10	1.55

Christmas Type of 1984

1992, Oct. 20 Litho. *Perf. 12*

1838 A441 2.50fr Basket maker	.95	.48
1839 A441 3.40fr Fishmonger	1.30	.65
1840 A441 5fr Drummer	1.95	.98
Nos. 1838-1840 (3)	4.20	2.11

Miniature Sheet

Postal Museum — A589

1992, Oct. 20 Litho. & Engr. *Perf. 13*

1841 Sheet of 2	8.30	8.30
a. A589 10fr Sardinia Type A4	4.15	4.15
b. A589 10fr France Type A3	4.15	4.15

17th Intl. Circus Festival, Monte Carlo — A590

Birds, Mercantour Natl. Park — A591

1993, Jan. 5 Litho. *Perf. 13½x13*

1842 A590 2.50fr multicolored .90 .45

Perf. 13x12½, 12½x13

1993, Feb. 15 Engr.

Designs: 2fr, Circaetus gallicus, horiz. 3fr, Falco peregrinus, horiz. 4fr, Bubo bubo. 5fr, Pernis apivorus. 6fr, Aegolius funereus.

1843 A591 2fr multicolored	.72	.36
1844 A591 3fr multicolored	1.10	.55
1845 A591 4fr multicolored	1.45	.72
1846 A591 5fr multicolored	1.80	.90
1847 A591 6fr multicolored	2.20	1.10
Nos. 1843-1847 (5)	7.27	3.63

Intl. Flower Show Type of 1992

1993, Mar. 1 Photo. *Perf. 12½x13*

1848 A577 3.40fr multicolored 1.25 .62

10th World Amateur Theater Festival — A592

1993, Mar. 1 Litho. *Perf. 13*

1849 A592 4.20fr multicolored 1.50 .75

A593

A594

1993, Mar. 1 Engr. *Perf. 12½x13*

1850 A593 6fr multicolored 2.20 1.10

Intl. Civil Protection Day

1993, Mar. 24 Engr. *Perf. 13*

1851 A594 5fr Princess Grace 1.80 .90

See US No. 2749.

Tree Type of 1986

Miniature Sheet

Life cycle of an almond tree: a, Spring. b, Summer. c, Autumn. d, Winter.

1993, Mar. 24 Photo. *Perf. 13x12½*

1852 Sheet of 4	7.40	7.40
a.-d. A478 5fr any single	1.85	1.85

Marine Mammals Type of 1992

Miniature Sheet

1993, Mar. 24

1853 Sheet of 4	8.00	8.00
a. A578 4fr Balaenoptera physalus	1.45	1.45
b. A578 5fr Balaenoptera acutorostrata	1.80	1.80
c. A578 6fr Physeter catodon	2.25	2.25
d. A578 7fr Ziphius cavirostris	2.50	2.50

10th Monte Carlo Open Golf Tournament — A595

1993, Mar. 24 Photo. *Perf. 12*

1854 A595 2.20fr multicolored 1.00 .50

Dog Show Type of 1982

1993, Mar. 24 Litho. *Perf. 13x13½*

1855 A387 2.20fr Newfoundland 1.00 .50

10th Biennial of Antique Dealers of Monte Carlo A596

1993, Mar. 24 *Perf. 12*

1856 A596 7fr multicolored 3.15 1.60

Flowering Cacti — A597

1993, May 4 Engr. *Perf. 13x13½*

Booklet Stamps

1857 A597 2.50fr Echinopsis multiplex	1.15	.58
1858 A597 2.50fr Zygocactus truncatus	1.15	.58
1859 A597 2.50fr Echinocereas procumbens	1.15	.58
1860 A597 2.50fr Euphorbia virosa	1.15	.58
a. Booklet pane, 2 each #1857-1860	9.20	
Nos. 1857-1860 (4)	4.60	2.32

See Nos. 1889-1892, 1914-1918, 2007-2009.

Europa A598

1993, May 4 *Perf. 12½x12*

1861 A598 2.50fr Monte Carlo Ballet	1.15	.58
1862 A598 4.20fr Sigaldi sculpture	2.00	1.00
a. Souvenir sheet, 3 each, #1861-1862, perf. 13x12½	9.50	9.50

Souvenir Sheet

Admission to the UN — A599

1993, July 28 Engr. *Perf. 13*

1863 A599 Sheet of 3	10.50	10.50
a. 10fr light blue	3.50	3.50
b. 10fr brown violet (Type A529)	3.50	3.50
c. 10fr brown violet & red	3.50	3.50

Intl. Olympic Committee, 101st Session A600

Perf. 13½x13

1993, Sept. 20 Litho. & Engr.

Booklet Stamps

1864 A600 2.80fr Coat of arms	1.25	.60
1865 A600 2.80fr Bobsledding	1.25	.60
1866 A600 2.80fr Skiing	1.25	.60
1867 A600 2.80fr Sailing	1.25	.60
1868 A600 2.80fr Rowing	1.25	.60
1869 A600 2.80fr Swimming	1.25	.60
1870 A600 2.80fr Cycling	1.25	.60
1871 A600 2.80fr shown	1.25	.60
a. Booklet pane of 8, #1864-1871	10.00	
1872 A600 4.50fr like #1864	2.00	1.00
1873 A600 4.50fr Gymnastics	2.00	1.00
1874 A600 4.50fr Judo	2.00	1.00
1875 A600 4.50fr Fencing	2.00	1.00
1876 A600 4.50fr Hurdles	2.00	1.00
1877 A600 4.50fr Archery	2.00	1.00
1878 A600 4.50fr Weight lifting	2.00	1.00
1879 A600 4.50fr like #1871	2.00	1.00
a. Booklet pane of 8, #1872-1879	16.00	

See No. 1899.

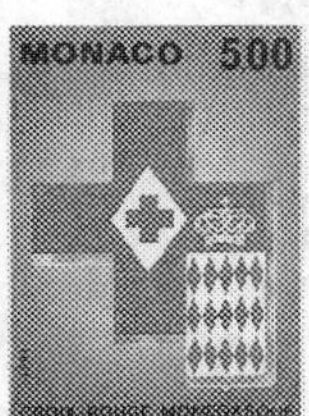

Red Cross of Monaco — A601

Design: 6fr, Red, white crosses.

1993, Nov. 10 Litho. *Perf. 13½x13*

1880 A601 5fr red, black & yellow	1.75	.85
1881 A601 6fr red & black	2.00	1.00

Monaco Philatelic Union, Cent. — A602

1993, Nov. 10 *Perf. 13x13½*

1882 A602 2.40fr multicolored .80 .40

Christmas Type of 1984

1993, Nov. 10 *Perf. 13½x13*

1883 A441 2.80fr Donkey	.95	.48
1884 A441 3.70fr Shepherd	1.25	.60
1885 A441 4.40fr Cow	1.50	.75
Nos. 1883-1885 (3)	3.70	1.83

Edvard Grieg (1843-1907), Composer A603

Joan Miro (1893-1943), Artist — A604

Georges de La Tour (1593-1652), Painter A605

Litho. (#1887), Engr.

1993, Dec. 10 *Perf. 13*

1886 A603 4fr blue 1.40 .70
1887 A604 5fr multicolored 1.75 .85

Perf. 12x13

1888 A605 6fr multicolored 2.00 1.00

Flowering Cacti Type of 1993

1994, Jan. 7 **Engr.** *Perf. 13*

1889 A597 20c like #1857 .15 .15
1890 A597 30c like #1858 .15 .15
1891 A597 40c like #1860 .15 .15
1892 A597 4fr like #1859 1.40 .70
Nos. 1889-1892 (4) 1.85
Set Value .85

18th Intl. Circus Festival, Monte Carlo — A606

Figurines, Natl. Museum — A607

1994, Jan. 7 **Litho.** *Perf. 13½x13*

1893 A606 2.80fr multicolored .95 .48

1994, Jan. 7 **Engr.** *Perf. 12½x13*

Designs: No. 1894, Poet. No. 1895, Japanese geisha. No. 1896, Shepherdess with lamb. No. 1897, Parisian woman.

1894 A607 2.80fr blue .95 .48
1895 A607 2.80fr magenta .95 .48
1896 A607 2.80fr purple .95 .48
1897 A607 2.80fr blue green .95 .48
Nos. 1894-1897 (4) 3.80 1.92

Marine Mammals Type of 1992
Miniature Sheet

1994, Feb. 11 **Photo.** *Perf. 13x12½*

1898 Sheet of 4 7.75 7.75
a. A578 4fr Orcinus orca 1.40 1.40
b. A578 5fr Grampus griseus 1.75 1.75
c. A578 6fr Pseudorca crassidens 2.00 2.00
d. A578 7fr Globicephala melas 2.50 2.50

Intl. Olympic Committee Type of 1993
Souvenir Sheet

1994, Feb. 11 **Engr.** *Perf. 13*

1899 Sheet of 2 7.00 7.00
a. A600 10fr like #1866 3.50 3.50
b. A600 10fr like #1865 3.50 3.50

1994 Winter Olympics, Lillehammer.

Intl. Dog Show Type of 1982

1994, Mar. 14 **Litho.** *Perf. 13x13½*

1900 A387 2.40fr King Charles spaniel .85 .42

27th Intl. Flower Show — A608

1994, Mar. 14 *Perf. 13½x13*

1901 A608 4.40fr Iris 1.50 .75

See Nos. 1941, 1989, 2028.

10th Grand Prix of Magic, Monte Carlo — A609

1994, Mar. 14 **Engr.** *Perf. 13x12½*

1902 A609 5fr lake, black & blue 1.75 .85

25th Conference of the Grand Cordon of French Cuisine A610

1994, Mar. 14 *Perf. 12½*

1903 A610 6fr multicolored 2.00 1.00

Prince Albert I, Research Ship Princess Alice II — A611

Europa: 4.50fr, Opisthoproctus Grimaldii, Eryoneicus Alberti, Oceanographic Museum, Monaco.

1994, May 5 **Engr.** *Perf. 13x12½*

1904 A611 2.80fr multicolored .95 .48
1905 A611 4.50fr multicolored 1.60 .80
a. Miniature sheet, 3 each #1904-1905 7.75 7.75

A612

A613

1994, May 17 **Engr.** *Perf. 12½x12*

1906 A612 3fr multicolored 1.00 .50

Intl. Olympic Committee, Cent.

1994, May 17 **Litho.** *Perf. 13*

1907 A613 6fr multicolored 2.00 1.00

Institute for Preservation of the Sea.

A614 A615

1994, May 17 **Engr.** *Perf. 13*

1908 A614 7fr multicolored 2.50 1.25

Intl. Year of the Family.

1994, May 17 *Perf. 12½x13*

1909 A615 8fr red & black 2.75 1.40

1994 World Cup Soccer Championships, US.

Intl. Amateur Athletic Federation — A616

1994, June 10 *Perf. 13*

1910 A616 8fr multicolored 2.75 1.40

1903 De Dion Bouton A617

1994, Aug. 22 **Engr.** *Perf. 13x12½*

1911 A617 2.80fr lilac, black & brn 1.10 .55

A618

A619

1994, Aug. 22 **Litho.** *Perf. 13*

1912 A618 3fr black, lilac rose & grn 1.25 .62

Intl. Assoc. of Philatelic Catalogue Editors (ASCAT).

1994, Aug. 22

1913 A619 4.40fr blue, red & black 1.65 .82

21st UPU Congress, Seoul, Korea.

Flowering Cacti Type of 1993

1994, Oct. 17 **Engr.** *Perf. 13*

1914 A597 50c Selenicereus grandiflorus .20 .15
1915 A597 60c Opuntia basilaris .24 .15
1916 A597 70c Aloe plicatilis .28 .15
1917 A597 80c Opuntia hybride .30 .15
1918 A597 2fr Aporocactus flagelliformis .80 .40
Nos. 1914-1918 (5) 1.82 1.00

Christmas Type of 1984

1994, Oct. 17 **Litho.** *Perf. 13*

1919 A441 2.80fr Mary 1.10 .55
1920 A441 4.50fr Christ child 1.75 .90
1921 A441 6fr Joseph 2.25 1.10
Nos. 1919-1921 (3) 5.10 2.55

Currency Museum — A620

1994, Oct. 17 **Engr.** *Perf. 12½*

1922 A620 3fr Prince Albert 1.25 .60
1923 A620 4fr Arms of Grimaldi 1.65 .80
1924 A620 7fr Prince Rainier III 2.75 1.40
Nos. 1922-1924 (3) 5.65 2.80

Souvenir Sheet

Perf. 12½x13

1925 Sheet of 3 12.00 12.00
a. A620 10fr like #1922 4.00 4.00
b. A620 10fr like #1923 4.00 4.00
c. A620 10fr like #1924 4.00 4.00

Red Cross Campaigns — A621

Designs: 6fr, Fight against cancer. 8fr, Fight against AIDS.

1994, Oct. 17 **Litho.** *Perf. 13*

1926 A621 6fr lake, blue & black 2.25 1.10
1927 A621 8fr lake, green & black 3.25 1.50

See Nos. 1983-1984.

ICAO, 50th Anniv. A622

Helicopters and: 5fr, Monaco Heliport. 7fr, Monaco skyline.

1994, Oct. 17 **Engr.** *Perf. 13*

1928 A622 5fr multicolored 2.00 1.00
1929 A622 7fr multicolored 2.75 1.40

Voltaire (1694-1778), Writer — A623

Sarah Bernhardt (1844-1923), Actress A624

Publication of Robinson Crusoe, by Daniel Defoe, 275th Anniv. — A625

The Snake Charmer, by Henri Rousseau (1844-1910) — A626

1994, Oct. 17 **Engr.** *Perf. 13*

1930 A623 5fr olive green 2.00 1.00
1931 A624 6fr multicolored 2.25 1.10

Litho.

1932 A625 7fr multicolored 2.75 1.40
1933 A626 9fr multicolored 3.50 1.75
Nos. 1930-1933 (4) 10.50 5.25

Tree Type of 1986
Miniature Sheet

Life cycle of an apricot tree.

1994, Oct. 17 Photo. *Perf. 13x12½*

1934	Sheet of 4	12.00	12.00
a.	A478 6fr Spring	2.25	2.25
b.	A478 7fr Summer	2.75	2.75
c.	A478 8fr Autumn	3.25	3.25
d.	A478 9fr Winter	3.50	3.50

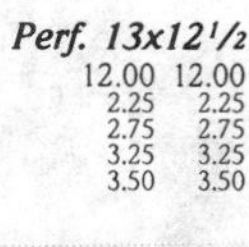

A627

A628

1995, Jan. 3 Litho. *Perf. 13½x13*

1935	A627 2.80fr multicolored	1.20	.60

19th Intl. Circus Festival, Monte Carlo.

1995, Feb. 13 Engr. *Perf. 12½x13*

1936	A628 8fr Prince Albert	3.50	1.75

Monte Carlo Television, 35th festival.

European Nature Conservation Year — A629

1995, Apr. 3 Litho. *Perf. 13x13½*

1937	A629 2.40fr multicolored	1.00	.50

Intl. Special Olympics A630

1995, Apr. 3

1938	A630 3fr multicolored	1.25	.60

Rotary Intl. Convention, Nice — A631

1995, Apr. 3 Engr. *Perf. 13x12½*

1939	A631 4fr blue	1.65	.80

Intl. Dog Show Type of 1982

1995, Apr. 3 Litho. *Perf. 13x13½*

1940	A387 4fr American cocker spaniel	1.65	.80

Intl. Flower Show Type of 1993

1995, Apr. 3 *Perf. 13½x13*

1941	A608 5fr Perroquet tulips	2.25	1.10

European Bonsai Congress A632

1995, Apr. 3 *Perf. 12*

1942	A632 6fr Acer palmatum	2.50	1.25

Tree Type of 1986
Miniature Sheet

Life cycle of a jujube tree.

1995, Apr. 3 Photo. *Perf. 12x12½*

1943	Sheet of 4	9.50	9.50
a.	A478 4fr Spring	1.65	1.65
b.	A478 5fr Summer	2.25	2.25
c.	A478 6fr Fall	2.50	2.50
d.	A478 7fr Winter	3.00	3.00

Peace & Liberty A633

Europa: 2.80fr, Dove with olive branch, Alfred Nobel. 5fr, Chain broken over concentration camp, flowers.

Photo. & Engr.

1995, May 8 *Perf. 12x12½*

1944	A633 2.80fr multicolored	1.10	.55
1945	A633 5fr multicolored	2.00	1.00

50th anniversaries: End of World War II (#1944), liberation of the concentration camps (#1945).

A634 A635

Designs: 5fr, Jean Giono (1895-1970), writer. 6fr, Marcel Pagnol (1895-1974), film producer, writer.

1995, May 8 Engr. *Perf. 12½x13*

1946	A634 5fr multicolored	2.00	1.00
1947	A634 6fr multicolored	2.50	1.25

1995, May 8 Photo. *Perf. 13½x13*

1948	A635 7fr blue	2.75	1.40

Princess Caroline, Pres. of World Assoc. of Friends of Children.

Intl. Council of Wildlife Conservation A636

1995, May 8 Engr. *Perf. 13*

1949	A636 6fr St. Hubert, stag	2.50	1.25

IAAF Track & Field Championships, Louis II Stadium — A637

1995, May 8

1950	A637 7fr multicolored	2.75	1.40

Alps Monument A638

1995, May 8

1951	A638 8fr multicolored	3.25	1.65

Prince Pierre of Monaco (1895-1964) A639

1995, May 8

1952	A639 10fr lake	4.00	2.00

Souvenir Sheet

Stamp & Coin Museum — A640

Designs: a, #927. b, Museum entrance. c, #294. Illustration reduced.

1995, May 8

1953	A640 Sheet of 3, #a.-c.	12.00	12.00
a.-c.	10fr any single	4.00	4.00

St. Anthony of Padua (1195-1231) — A641

1995, Sept. 25 Litho. *Perf. 13½*

1954	A641 2.80fr multicolored	1.25	.60

UN, 50th Anniv. A642

Designs: #1955, 1963a, Soldiers, UN Charter. #1956, 1963b, Grain, child. #1957, 1963c, Childrens' faces. #1958, 1963d, Musical notes, temple of Abu Simbel. #1959, 1963e, UN Security Council. #1960, 1963f, Hand holding grain, field. #1961, 1963g, Letters from various languages. #1962, 1963h, UNESCO Headquarters.

1995, Oct. 24 Engr. *Perf. 13*

1955	A642 2.50fr multicolored	1.00	.50
1956	A642 2.50fr multicolored	1.00	.50
1957	A642 2.50fr multicolored	1.00	.50
1958	A642 2.50fr multicolored	1.00	.50
1959	A642 3fr multicolored	1.25	.65
1960	A642 3fr multicolored	1.25	.65
1961	A642 3fr multicolored	1.25	.65
1962	A642 3fr multicolored	1.25	.65
	Nos. 1955-1962 (8)	9.00	4.60

Miniature Sheet

1963	Sheet of 8	13.00	13.00
a.-d.	A642 3fr any single	1.25	1.25
e.-h.	A642 4.50fr any single	1.90	1.90

A643

A644

Flowers: No. 1964, Rose *Grace of Monaco.* No. 1965, Fuschia *Lakeland Princess.* No. 1966, Carnation *Century of Monte Carlo.* No. 1967, Fuschia *Grace.* No. 1968, Rose *Princess of Monaco.* No. 1969, Alstroemeria *Gracia.* No. 1970, Lily *Princess Grace.* No. 1971, Carnation *Princess Caroline.* No. 1972, Rose *Stephanie of Monaco.* No. 1973, Carnation *Prince Albert.* No. 1974, Sweet pea *Grace of Monaco.* No. 1975, Gerbera *Gracia.*

1995, Oct. 24 Litho. *Perf. 13½*

Booklet Stamps

1964	A643 3fr multicolored	1.25	.65
1965	A643 3fr multicolored	1.25	.65
1966	A643 3fr multicolored	1.25	.65
1967	A643 3fr multicolored	1.25	.65
1968	A643 3fr multicolored	1.25	.65
1969	A643 3fr multicolored	1.25	.65
1970	A643 3fr multicolored	1.25	.65
1971	A643 3fr multicolored	1.25	.65
1972	A643 3fr multicolored	1.25	.65
1973	A643 3fr multicolored	1.25	.65
1974	A643 3fr multicolored	1.25	.65
1975	A643 3fr multicolored	1.25	.65
a.	Bklt. pane, #1964-1975 + 2 labels	15.00	
	Complete booklet, #1975a	15.00	

Christmas Type of 1984

1995, Oct. 24 Litho. *Perf. 13½x13*

1976	A441 3fr Balthazar	1.25	.65
1977	A441 5fr Gaspard	2.25	1.10
1978	A441 6fr Melchior	2.50	1.25
	Nos. 1976-1978 (3)	6.00	3.00

1995, Oct. 24 Engr. *Perf. 13*

1980	A644 4fr green, black & red	1.75	.85

Monagasque Assoc. for Protection of Nature, 20th anniv.

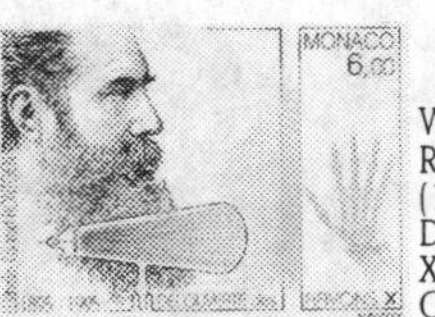

Wilhelm Röntgen (1845-1923), Discovery of X-Rays, Cent. — A645

1995, Oct. 24

1981	A645 6fr multicolored	2.50	1.25

Motion Pictures, Cent. — A646

1995, Oct. 24

1982	A646 7fr dark blue	3.00	1.50

Red Cross Campaigns Type of 1994

Designs: 7fr, World fight against leprosy. 8fr, Drs. Prakash and Mandakini Amte, Indian campaign against leprosy.

1995, Oct. 24 Litho.

1983	A621 7fr multicolored	3.00	1.50
1984	A621 8fr multicolored	3.50	1.75

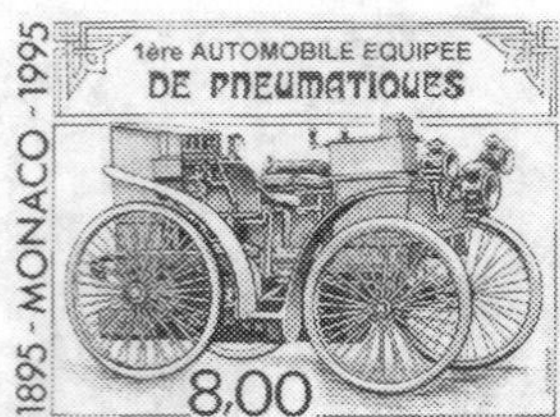

Pneumatic Automobile Tires, Cent. — A647

1995, Oct. 24 **Engr.**
1985 A647 8fr claret & dk purple 3.50 1.75

Springtime, by Sandro Botticelli (1445-1510) — A648

1995, Oct. 24
1986 A648 15fr blue 7.50 3.75
a. Souvenir sheet of 1 7.50 3.75

No. 1986 printed in sheets of 10 + 5 labels.
No. 1986a inscribed in sheet margin as a winner of the 4th World Cup of Stamps, portrait of Botticelli.

20th Intl. Circus Festival, Monte Carlo — A649

1996, Jan. 10 **Litho.** ***Perf. 13***
1987 A649 2.40fr multicolored .95 .50

Magic Festival, Monte Carlo — A650

1996, Jan. 10 **Engr.**
1988 A650 2.80fr black & gray 1.10 .55

Intl. Flower Show Type of 1994

1996, Jan. 26 **Litho.**
1989 A608 3fr Rhododendron 1.20 .60

Intl. Dog Show Type of 1982

1996, Jan. 26
1990 A387 4fr Airedale terrier 1.60 .80

Opening of Chapel of Notre Dame of Miséricorde, 350th Anniv. A651

1996, Jan. 26 **Engr.** ***Perf. 12x13***
1991 A651 6fr multicolored 2.40 1.20

Oceanographic Voyages of Prince Albert I of Monaco and King Charles I of Portugal, Cent. — A652

Designs: 3fr, Fish in sea, net, Prince Albert I holding binoculars, ship. 4.50fr, Ship, King Charles I holding sextant, microscope, sea life.
Illustration reduced.

1996, Feb. 1 **Litho.** ***Perf. 12***
1992 A652 3fr multicolored 1.20 .60
1993 A652 4.50fr multicolored 1.80 .90

See Portugal Nos. 2084-2085.

Prince Rainer III Type of 1974 Inscribed "MUSEE DES TIMBRES ET DES MONNAIES"

1996, Mar. 11 **Engr.** ***Perf. 13***
1994 AP37 10fr purple 4.00 2.00
1995 AP37 15fr henna brown 6.00 3.00
1996 AP37 20fr ultra 8.00 4.00
Nos. 1994-1996 (3) 18.00 9.00

Stamp and Currency Museum.

Princess Grace — A653

1996, Apr. 29
1997 A653 3fr red & brown 1.20 .60

Europa.

RAMOGE Agreement Between France, Italy, Monaco, 20th Anniv. A654

Photo. & Engr.

1996, May 14 ***Perf. 13***
1998 A654 3fr multicolored 1.25 .65

See France #2524, Italy #2077.

Annales Monegasques, 20th Anniv. — A655

Famous people: a, Saint Nicolas of Myra, by Louis Brea. b, Guillaume Apollinaire (1880-1918), poet. c, Jean-Baptiste Francois Bosio (1764-1827), painter. d, Francois-Joseph Bosio (1768-1845), sculptor. e, Hector Berlioz (1803-69), composer. f, Niccolo Machiavelli (1469-1527), writer. g, Sidonie-Gabrielle Colette (1873-1954), writer. h, Michael Montaigne (1533-92), essayist.

1996, May 14 **Engr.** ***Perf. 12½x13***
1999 Sheet of 8 14.50 7.25
a., e. A655 3fr any single 1.20 .60
b., f. A655 4fr any single 1.60 .80
c., g. A655 5fr any single 2.00 1.00
d., h. A655 6fr any single 2.40 1.20

Souvenir Sheet

CHINA '96, 9th Asian Intl. Philatelic Exhibition A656

Designs: a, Chinese acrobats in Monaco. b, Fuling Tomb, Shenyang.

1996, May 14 **Litho.** ***Perf. 13***
2000 Sheet of 2 4.00 2.00
a.-b. A656 5fr any single 2.00 1.00

Introduction of Telephone Area Code 377 for Monaco — A657

1996, June 21 **Engr.** ***Perf. 13***
2001 A657 3fr dk blue 1.80 .90
2002 A657 3.80fr vermilion 2.25 1.10

1996 Summer Olympic Games, Atlanta — A658

1996, July 19 **Litho.** ***Perf. 13½x13***
2003 A658 3fr Javelin, 1896 1.80 .90
2004 A658 3fr Women's softball, 1996 1.80 .90
2005 A658 4.50fr Runners, 1896 2.75 1.40
2006 A658 4.50fr Cycling, 1996 2.75 1.40
Nos. 2003-2006 (4) 9.10 4.60

Flowering Cacti Type of 1993

Designs: 10c, Bromelia brevifolia. 1fr, Stapelia flavirostris. 5fr, Cereus peruvianus.

1996, Sept. 16 **Engr.** ***Perf. 13***
2007 A597 10c multicolored .15 .15
2008 A597 1fr multicolored .40 .20
2009 A597 5fr multicolored 2.00 1.00
Nos. 2007-2009 (3) 2.55 1.35

Tree Type of 1986

Life cycle of thorn (ronce) tree.

1996, Oct. 14 **Photo.** ***Perf. 13***
2010 Sheet of 4 8.50 4.25
a. A478 4fr Spring 1.50 .75
b. A478 5fr Summer 2.00 1.00
c. A478 6fr Fall 2.30 1.15
d. A478 7fr Winter 2.70 1.35

Red Cross Campaigns Type of 1994

Designs: 7fr, Fight against tuberculosis. 8fr, Camille Guérin, Albert-Leon C. Calmette, developers of BCG vaccine against tuberculosis.

1996, Oct. 14
2011 A621 7fr multicolored 2.70 1.35
2012 A621 8fr multicolored 3.10 1.55

UNICEF, 50th Anniv. — A658a

1996, Oct. 14 **Engr.** ***Perf. 12½x13***
2013 A658a 3fr multicolored 1.15 .60

Discovery of the Planet, Neptune, 150th Anniv. — A659

Photo. & Engr.

1996, Oct. 14 ***Perf. 13x12½***
2014 A659 4fr multicolored 1.55 .80

René Descartes (1596-1650), Philosopher, Mathematician — A660

1996, Oct. 14 **Engr.** ***Perf. 13***
2015 A660 5fr blue & carmine 2.00 1.00

Christmas — A661

1996, Oct. 14 **Litho.** ***Perf. 13***
2016 A661 3fr Angel 1.15 .60
2017 A661 6fr Angels 2.30 1.15

Self-Portrait, by Corot (1796-1875) A662

7fr, Self-portrait (detail), by Goya (1746-1828).

Photo. & Engr.

1996, Oct. 14 ***Perf. 12x13***
2018 A662 6fr multicolored 2.30 1.15
2019 A662 7fr multicolored 2.70 1.35

Stamp and Coin Museum — A663

Designs: No. 2020, Printing and engraving stamps. No. 2021, Coins, screw press. 10fr, Front entrance to museum.

1996, Oct. 14 Engr. ***Perf. 13***
2020 A663 5fr dk olive & violet 2.00 1.00
2021 A663 5fr dk olive & dk blue 2.00 1.00
2022 A663 10fr dk olive & dk blue 4.00 2.00
a. Souvenir sheet, #2020-2022 8.00 4.00
Nos. 2020-2022 (3) 8.00 4.00

No. 2022 is 48x36mm.

Grimaldi Dynasty, 700th Anniv. A664

No. 2023: a, Francois Grimaldi, 1297. b, Rainier I, d. 1314. c, Charles I, d. 1357. d, Rainier II, 1350-1407. e, Jean I, 1382-1454. f, Catalan, d. 1457. g, Lambert, d. 1494. h, Jean II, 1468-1505. i, Lucien, 1481-1523. j, Augustin, d. 1532. k, Honoré I, 1522-1581. l, Charles II, 1555-1589. m, Hercule I, 1562-1604.

No. 2024: a, Honoré II (1597-1662). b, Louis I (1642-1701). c, Antoine (1661-1731). d, Louise-Hippolyte (1697-1731). e, Jacques I (1689-1751). f, Honoré III (1720-95). g, Honoré IV (1758-1819). h, Honoré V (1778-1841). i, Florestan I (1785-1856). j, Charles III (1818-89). k, Albert I (1848-1922). l, Louis II (1870-1949). m, Rainier III.

1997 Litho. ***Perf. 13***
2023 Sheet of 14 + 2 labels 25.00 25.00
a. A664 7fr multicolored 2.50 2.50
b.-d. A664 1fr multi, each .35 .35
e, g. A664 2fr multi, each .70 .70
f. A664 9fr multicolored 3.15 3.15
h.-j A664 9fr multi, each 3.15 3.15
k.-m. A664 7fr multi, each 2.50 2.50
2024 Sheet of 13 + 2 labels 26.00 13.00
a.-c. A664 1fr multi, each .35 .35
d. A664 9fr multicolored 3.00 3.00
e. A664 2fr multicolored .70 .70
f.-i. A664 9fr multi, each 3.00 3.00
j.-m. A664 7fr multi, each 2.50 2.50

Portions of the designs on Nos. 2023-2024 were applied by a thermographic process producing a shiny, raised effect.

Issued: #2023, 1/8; #2024, 7/3.

Knight in Armor Type of 1951
Inscribed "1297-1997"

1996-97 Engr. ***Perf. 13***
2025 A67 2.70fr blue, brown & red 1.00 .50

Sheet of 8

2026 2 ea #a.-c., 2025 8.00 8.00
a. A67 2.70fr red 1.00 1.00
b. A67 2.70fr brown 1.00 1.00
c. A67 2.70fr blue 1.00 1.00

Issued: #2025, 12/19/96; #2026, 1/8/97.

Yacht Club of Monaco — A665

1996, Dec. 12 Litho. ***Perf. 13***
2027 A665 3fr multicolored 1.15 .60

Intl. Flower Show Type of 1993

1996, Dec. 19 ***Perf. 13½x13***
2028 A608 3.80fr Camellia 1.50 .75

Tennis Tournaments in Monaco, Cent. — A666

1997, Feb. 1 Litho. ***Perf. 13***
2029 A666 4.60fr multicolored 1.50 .75

Portions of the design on No. 2029 were applied by a thermographic process producing a shiny, raised effect.

For overprint see No. 2049.

A667

A668

1996, Dec. 19 ***Perf. 13½x13***
2030 A667 4.90fr multicolored 1.90 .95

37th Festival of Television in Monte Carlo.

1996, Dec. 19 Litho. ***Perf. 13***
2031 A668 5fr Campanule "Medium" 1.90 .95

Auto Sports in Monaco — A669

1996, Dec. 19 Litho. ***Perf. 13***
2032 A669 3fr multicolored 1.15 .60

Philatelic Events A670

Stamp & Coin Museum and: No. 2033, Pictures, engraving tools, picture on stamps. No. 2034, Stamp, magnifying glass, envelopes.

1996, Dec. 19 Engr. ***Perf. 13***
2033 A670 3fr multicolored 1.15 .60
2034 A670 3fr multicolored 1.15 .60
a. Pair, #2033-2034 2.30 1.20

Monaco Philatelic Office, 60th anniv. (#2033). Monaco Intl. Philatelic Exhibition (#2034).

Dog Show Type of 1982

1996, Dec. 19 Litho. ***Perf. 13x13½***
2035 A387 4.40fr Afghan hound 1.70 .85

21st Intl. Circus Festival, Monte Carlo — A671

1996, Dec. 19 Litho. ***Perf. 13½x13***
2036 A671 3fr multicolored 1.15 .60

Intl. Grand Prix of Philately — A672

1997, Apr. 5 Litho. ***Perf. 13***
2041 A672 4.60fr multicolored 1.60 .80

A673

A674

1997, May 5 ***Perf. 13½x13***
2042 A673 7fr multicolored 2.40 1.20

Red Cross Campaign Against Drug Abuse.

1997, May 5 Engr. ***Perf. 12½x13***

Europa (Stories and Legends): No. 2043, Legend of St. Devote. No. 2044, Port Hercules named for mythological Hercules.

2043 A674 3fr multicolored 1.00 .50
2044 A674 3fr multicolored 1.00 .50
a. Pair, #2043-2044 2.00 1.00

PACIFIC 97 Intl. Philatelic Exhibition A675

Design: US types A2 & A1, Monaco #1995.

1997, May 29 ***Perf. 13x12½***
2045 A675 4.90fr multicolored 1.70 .85

Uniforms of the Carabiniers (Palace Guards) A676

Years uniforms used: 3fr, 1997. 3.50fr, 1750-1853. 5.20fr, 1865-1935.

1997, May 31 Litho. ***Perf. 13x13½***
2046 A676 3fr multicolored 1.00 .50
2047 A676 3.50fr multicolored 1.20 .60
2048 A676 5.20fr multicolored 1.80 .90
Nos. 2046-2048 (3) 4.00 2.00

No. 2029 Ovptd. "M. RIOS"

1997 ***Perf. 13***
2049 A666 4.60fr multicolored 1.60 .80

13th Grand Prix of Magic, Monte Carlo — A677

1997 Litho. ***Perf. 13½x13***
2050 A677 4.40fr multicolored 1.50 .75

Monaco Soccer Assoc., 1996 French Division 1 Champions — A678

1997 ***Perf. 13***
2051 A678 3fr multicolored 1.00 .50

Francois Grimaldi, by Ernando Venanzi A679

9fr, Saint Peter and Saint Paul, by Rubens.

1997, Sept. 8 Engr. ***Perf. 13½x13***
2052 A679 8fr multicolored 2.75 1.40
2053 A679 9fr multicolored 3.00 1.50

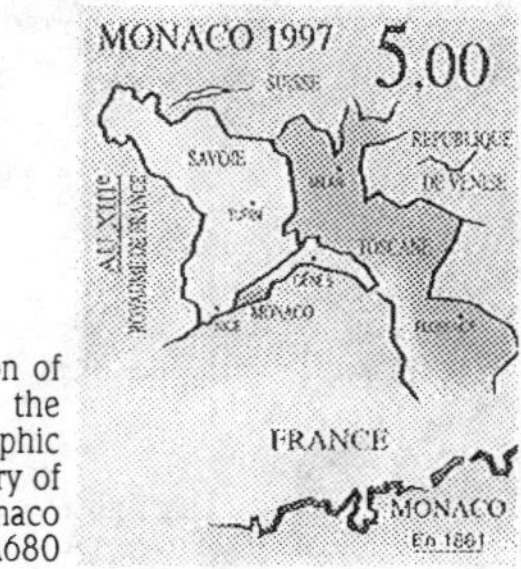

Evolution of the Geographic Territory of Monaco A680

Designs: a, 13th century. b, 15th-19th century. c, Map of western half of Monaco, panoramic view. d, Map of eastern half of Monaco, panoramic view.

1997, Oct. 6 Litho. & Engr. ***Perf. 13***
2054 A680 5fr Sheet of 4, #a.-d. 6.75 3.40

Grimaldi Dynasty, 700th anniv.

49th Session of Intl. Whaling Commission — A681

1997, Oct. 20 Photo. ***Perf. 13x13½***
2055 A681 6.70fr multicolored 2.30 1.15

22nd Intl. Circus Festival, Monte Carlo — A682

1997 Litho. ***Perf. 13½x13***
2057 A682 3fr multicolored 1.00 .50

Princess Charlotte (1898-1977) A683

1997 Engr. ***Perf. 13x12½***
2058 A683 3.80fr brown 1.30 .65

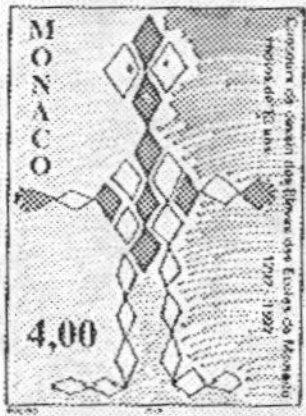
A684

Designs by Monagasque Students
A685

1997 Litho. *Perf. 13½x13, 13x13½*

2059 A684	4fr Under 13 group	1.30	.65
2060 A685	4.50fr Over 13 group	1.50	.75

31st Intl. Flower Show — A686

1997 *Perf. 13½x13*

2061 A686	4.40fr multicolored	1.50	.75

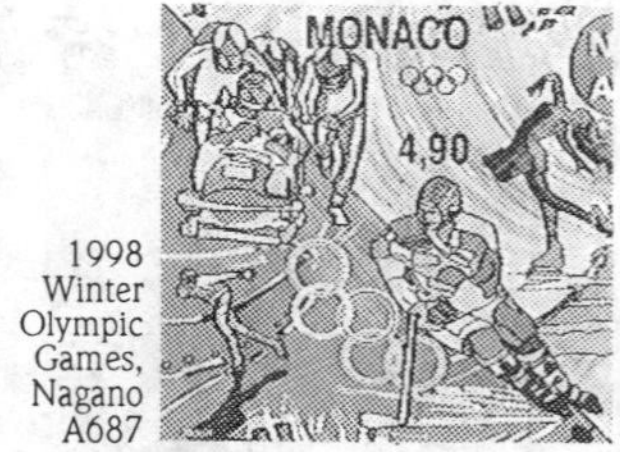
1998 Winter Olympic Games, Nagano
A687

Designs: No. 2062, 4-Man bobsled, speed skating, ice hockey, figure skating. No. 2063, Downhill skiing, biathlon, luge, ski jumping, slalom skiing.

1997 Photo. *Perf. 12½*

2062 A687	4.90fr multicolored	1.60	.80
2063 A687	4.90fr multicolored	1.60	.80
a.	Pair, #2062-2063	3.25	1.60

A688 A689

Moscow '97: Ballet Russes de Monte Carlo.

1997 Photo. *Perf. 13½x13*

2064 A688	5fr multicolored	1.80	.90

1997 Engr. *Perf. 12½x13*

2065 A689	5.20fr red brn & dk grn	1.75	.90

J.L. David (1748-1825), painter.

Keep up to date with all new stamp issues by subscribing to the "Scott Stamp Monthly." Please call 1-800-572-6885 for more information.

Papal Bull for the Parish of Monaco, 750th Anniv.
A690

1997 *Perf. 12½x13*

2066 A690	7.50fr Pope Innocent IV	2.50	1.25

Prince Albert I (1848-1922) — A691

Illustration reduced.

1997 Photo. *Perf. 13x12½*

2067 A691	8fr multicolored	2.70	1.30

38th Television Festival — A692

1998 Litho. *Perf. 13½x13*

2068 A692	4.50fr multicolored	1.80	.90

Marcel Kroenlein Arboretum, 10th Anniv. — A693

1998 Photo. *Perf. 13*

2069 A693	9fr multicolored	3.00	1.50

No. 2069 was issued in sheets of 2.

SEMI-POSTAL STAMPS

No. 16 Surcharged in Red 

1914, Oct. Unwmk. *Perf. 14x13½*

B1 A2	10c + 5c carmine	8.00	5.00

View of Monaco — SP2

1919, Sept. 20 Typo.

B2	SP2	2c + 3c lilac	21.00	21.00
B3	SP2	5c + 5c green	12.00	12.00
B4	SP2	15c + 10c rose	12.00	12.00
B5	SP2	25c + 15c blue	32.50	32.50
B6	SP2	50c + 50c brn, *buff*	125.00	125.00
B7	SP2	1fr + 1fr blk, *yel*	275.00	275.00
B8	SP2	5fr + 5fr dull red	900.00	900.00
		Nos. B2-B8 (7)	1,377.	1,377.

Nos. B4-B8 Surcharged

20 mars
1920
2c + 3c

1920, Mar. 20

B9	SP2	2c + 3c on #B4	30.00	30.00
a.		"c" of "3c" inverted	*1,300.*	*1,300.*
B10	SP2	2c + 3c on #B5	30.00	30.00
a.		"c" of "3c" inverted	*1,300.*	*1,300.*
B11	SP2	2c + 3c on #B6	30.00	30.00
a.		"c" of "3c" inverted	*1,300.*	*1,300.*
B12	SP2	5c + 5c on #B7	30.00	30.00
B13	SP2	5c + 5c on #B8	30.00	30.00

Overprinted **20 mars 1920**

B14	SP2	15c + 10c rose	22.50	22.50
B15	SP2	25c + 15c blue	10.00	10.00
B16	SP2	50c + 50c brown, *buff*	45.00	45.00
B17	SP2	1fr + 1fr black, *yel*	60.00	60.00
B18	SP2	5fr + 5fr red	*5,000.*	*5,000.*
		Nos. B9-B17 (9)	287.50	287.50

Marriage of Princess Charlotte to Prince Pierre, Comte de Polignac.

Palace Gardens SP3

"The Rock" of Monaco SP4

Bay of Monaco SP5

Prince Louis II — SP6

1937, Apr. Engr. *Perf. 13*

B19	SP3	50c + 50c green	2.00	2.00
B20	SP4	90c + 90c carmine	2.00	2.00
B21	SP5	1.50fr + 1.50fr blue	4.00	4.00
B22	SP6	2fr + 2fr violet	9.00	9.00
B23	SP6	5fr + 5fr brn red	67.50	67.50
		Nos. B19-B23 (5)	84.50	84.50

The surtax was used for welfare work.

Pierre and Marie Curie — SP7

Monaco Hospital, Date Palms — SP8

1938, Nov. 15 *Perf. 13*

B24	SP7	65c + 25c dp bl grn	7.00	7.00
B25	SP8	1.75fr + 50c dp ultra	9.00	9.00

B24 and B25 exist imperforate.

The surtax was for the International Union for the Control of Cancer.

Lucien — SP9

Honoré II — SP10

Louis I SP11

Charlotte de Gramont SP12

Antoine I — SP13

Marie de Lorraine — SP14

Jacques I SP15

Louise-Hippolyte SP16

Honoré III — SP17

"The Rock," 18th Century SP18

1939, June 26

B26	SP9	5c + 5c brown blk	1.00	1.00
B27	SP10	10c + 10c rose vio	1.00	1.00
B28	SP11	45c + 15c brt green	3.25	3.25
B29	SP12	70c + 30c brt red vio	6.00	6.00
B30	SP13	90c + 35c violet	7.00	7.00
B31	SP14	1fr + 1fr ultra	17.00	17.00
B32	SP15	2fr + 2fr brn org	18.00	18.00
B33	SP16	2.25fr + 1.25fr Prus bl	25.00	25.00
B34	SP17	3fr + 3fr dp rose	35.00	35.00
B35	SP18	5fr + 5fr red	65.00	65.00
		Nos. B26-B35 (10)	178.25	178.25
		Set, never hinged	350.00	

Types of Regular Issue, 1939 Surcharged in Red

+
+ 1f

1940, Feb. 10	Engr.	Perf. 13	
B36 A30	20c + 1fr violet	2.50	2.50
B37 A31	25c + 1fr dk green	2.50	2.50
B38 A32	30c + 1fr brn red	2.50	2.50
B39 A31	40c + 1fr dk blue	2.50	2.50
B40 A33	45c + 1fr rose car	2.50	2.50
B41 A34	50c + 1fr brown	2.50	2.50
B42 A32	60c + 1fr dk green	2.50	2.50
B43 A35	75c + 1fr brown blk	2.50	2.50
B44 A34	1fr + 1fr scarlet	3.00	3.00
B45 A31	2fr + 1fr indigo	3.00	3.00
B46 A33	2.50fr + 1fr dk green	7.00	7.00
B47 A35	3fr + 1fr dk blue	8.00	8.00
B48 A30	5fr + 1fr brn blk	10.00	10.00
B49 A33	10fr + 5fr lt blue	16.00	16.00
B50 A32	20fr + 5fr brn vio	18.00	18.00
	Nos. B36-B50 (15)	85.00	85.00
	Set, never hinged	165.00	

The surtax was used to purchase ambulances for the French government.

Catalogue values for unused stamps in this section, from this point to the end of the section, are for Never Hinged items.

Symbol of Charity and View of Monaco SP19

Symbol of Charity and View of Monaco — SP20

1941, May 15			
B51 SP19	25c + 25c brt red vio	2.25	2.25
B52 SP20	50c + 25c dk brown	2.25	2.25
B53 SP20	75c + 50c rose vio	2.75	2.75
B54 SP19	1fr + 1fr dk blue	2.75	2.75
B55 SP20	1.50fr + 1.50fr rose red	4.00	4.00
B56 SP19	2fr + 2fr Prus grn	4.00	4.00
B57 SP20	2.50fr + 2fr brt ultra	4.75	4.75
B58 SP19	3fr + 3fr dl red brn	4.75	4.75
B59 SP20	5fr + 5fr dk bl grn	9.00	9.00
B60 SP19	10fr + 8fr brn blk	17.00	17.00
	Nos. B51-B60 (10)	53.50	53.50

The surtax was for various charities.

Rainier Grimaldi — SP21

Designs: 5c, Charles II. 10c, Jeanne Grimaldi. 20c, Charles-August Goyon de Matignon. 30c, Jacques I. 40c, Louise-Hippolyte. 50c, Charlotte Grimaldi. 75c, Marie-Charles Grimaldi. 1fr, Honore III. 1.50fr, Honore IV. 2.50fr, Honore V. 3fr, Florestan I. 5fr, Charles III. 10fr, Albert I. 20fr, Marie-Victoire. Frames differ.

1942, Dec. 10			
B61 SP21	2c + 3c ultra	.30	.30
B62 SP21	5c + 5c org ver	.30	.30
B63 SP21	10c + 5c blk	.30	.30
B64 SP21	20c + 10c brt grn	.30	.30
B65 SP21	30c + 30c brn vio	.30	.30
B66 SP21	40c + 40c rose red	.30	.30
B67 SP21	50c + 50c vio	.30	.30
B68 SP21	75c + 75c brt red vio	.30	.30
B69 SP21	1fr + 1fr dk grn	.30	.30
B70 SP21	1.50fr + 1fr car brn	.30	.30
B71 SP21	2.50fr + 2.50fr pur	4.00	4.00
B72 SP21	3fr + 3fr turq bl	4.25	4.25
B73 SP21	5fr + 5fr sepia	4.25	4.25
B74 SP21	10fr + 5fr rose lil	4.25	4.25
B75 SP21	20fr + 5fr ultra	4.25	4.25
	Nos. B61-B75 (15)	24.00	24.00

Saint Dévote SP36

Procession SP37

Procession SP38

Church of St. Dévote — SP39

Burning of Symbolic Boat — SP40

Blessing of the Sea — SP41

Church of St. Dévote SP42

Trial of St. Barbara — SP43

Arrival of St. Dévote at Monaco — SP44

1944, Jan. 27	Unwmk.	Perf. 13	
B76 SP36	50c + 50c sepia	.25	.25
B77 SP37	70c + 80c dp ultra	.25	.25
B78 SP38	80c + 70c green	.20	.20
B79 SP39	1fr + 1fr rose vio	.20	.20
B80 SP40	1.50fr + 1.50fr red	.35	.35
B81 SP41	2fr + 2fr brn vio	.40	.40
B82 SP42	5fr + 2fr violet	.45	.45
B83 SP43	10fr + 40fr royal bl	.45	.45
B84 SP44	20fr + 60fr chlky bl	4.25	4.25
	Nos. B76-B84 (9)	6.80	6.80

Issued in honor of St. Dévote.

Type SP43 is inscribed "Jugement de Sainte Dévote," but actually shows the trial of St. Barbara in 235 A.D.

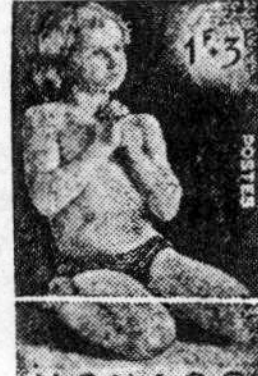

Needy Child — SP45

Nurse and Child — SP46

1946, Feb. 18		Engr.	
B85 SP45	1fr + 3fr dp bl grn	.25	.25
B86 SP45	2fr + 4fr rose pink	.25	.25
B87 SP45	4fr + 6fr dk bl	.25	.25
B88 SP45	5fr + 40fr dk vio	.60	.60
B89 SP45	10fr + 60fr brn red	.70	.70
B90 SP45	15fr + 100fr indigo	.95	.95
	Nos. B85-B90 (6)	3.00	3.00

The surtax was for child welfare.

1946, Feb. 18			
B91 SP46	2fr + 8fr brt blue	.45	.15

The surtax was used for prevention of tuberculosis.

19th Century Steamer and Map — SP47

1946			
B92 SP47	3fr + 2fr deep blue	.45	.16

Stamp Day, June 23, 1946.

Harbor of Monte Carlo — SP48

1946, Dec. 13			
B93 SP48	2fr + 3fr dk bluish grn	.45	.45

Issued in tribute to the memory of Franklin D. Roosevelt. The surtax was for a fund to erect a monument in his honor.

Prince Louis II Type
Souvenir Sheet
Unwmk.

1947, May 15	Engr.	Imperf.	
B94 A46	200fr + 300fr dk red & choc	22.50	22.50

Prince Charles III — SP50

1948, Mar. 6		Perf. 14x13	
B95 SP50	6fr + 4fr dk bl grn, *lt bl*	.25	.25

Issued for Stamp Day, Mar. 6.

Princess Charlotte SP51

Prince Rainier III SP52

Perf. 13½x13, Imperf.

1949, Dec. 27		Engr.	
	Cross Typo. in Red		
B96 SP51	10fr + 5fr red brown	8.75	8.75
B97 SP52	15fr + 5fr brt red	8.75	8.75
B98 SP52	25fr + 5fr dk vio bl	8.75	8.75
B99 SP51	40fr + 5fr dull green	8.75	8.75
a.	Block of 4, #B96-B99	35.00	35.00

Printed in sheets measuring 151x173mm, perf. and imperf., containing 4 of No. B99a.

The surtax was for the Red Cross.

For surcharges see Nos. 288-291.

Hercules Strangling the Lion of Nemea — SP53

Twelve Labors of Hercules: No. B101, Capturing the Erymanthean boar. No. B102, Killing the Hydra of Lerna. No. B103, Killing Stymphalian birds. No. B104, Hercules and the Ceryneian Hind. No. B105, The Augean Stables. No. B106, Hercules and the Cretan Bull. No. B107, Wild horses of Diomedes. No. B108, Hercules and the Oxen of Geryon. No. B109, Hercules and the Belt of Hippolytus. No. B110, Winning the golden apple of Hesperides. No. B111, Battling Cerberus.

1981, Nov. 5	Engr.	Perf. 13	
B100 SP53	2.50fr + 50c multi	1.25	1.25
B101 SP53	3.50fr + 50c multi	1.40	1.40
1982, Nov. 8			
B102 SP53	2.50fr + 50c multi	1.10	1.10
B103 SP53	3.50fr + 50c multi	1.25	1.25
1983, Nov. 9			
B104 SP53	2.50fr + 50c multi	1.10	1.10
B105 SP53	3.50fr + 50c multi	1.25	1.25
1984, Nov. 8			
B106 SP53	3fr + 50c multi	1.25	1.25
B107 SP53	4fr + 50c multi	1.65	1.65
1985, Nov. 7			
B108 SP53	3fr + 70c multi	1.25	.48
B109 SP53	4fr + 80c multi	1.65	.62
1986, Oct. 28			
B110 SP53	3fr + 70c multi	1.25	.42
B111 SP53	4fr + 80c multi	1.50	.55
	Nos. B100-B111 (12)	15.90	12.32

Surtax on #B100-B111 for the Red Cross.

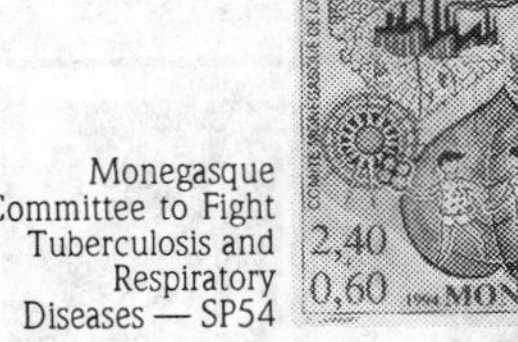

Monegasque Committee to Fight Tuberculosis and Respiratory Diseases — SP54

1994, Mar. 14	Litho.	Perf. 13½x13	
B112 SP54	2.40fr +60c multi	1.00	.50

AIR POST STAMPS

No. 91 Surcharged in Black

1F50

Perf. 14x13½

1933, Aug. 22		Unwmk.	
C1 A15	1.50fr on 5fr	20.00	15.00
a.	Imperf., pair	300.00	

Catalogue values for unused stamps in this section, from this point to the end of the section, are for Never Hinged items.

Plane over Monaco — AP1

Plane Propeller and Buildings — AP2

Pegasus — AP3

Sea Gull — AP4

Plane, Globe and Arms of Monaco AP5

1942, Apr. 15 **Engr.** ***Perf. 13***

C2	AP1	5fr blue green	.25	.25
C3	AP1	10fr ultra	.25	.25
C4	AP2	15fr sepia	.40	.40
C5	AP3	20fr henna brown	.65	.65
C6	AP4	50fr red violet	3.00	1.65
C7	AP5	100fr red & vio brn	2.50	1.65
		Nos. C2-C7 (6)	7.05	4.85

For surcharges see Nos. CB1-CB5.

MONACO Specialist

BUYING AND SELLING

Mint • Used • Imperfs

FDC's • Proofs

Postal Stationery

Postal History

WANT LISTS ALWAYS WELCOME

• TOP PRICES PAID •

Call or Write

DAVID GROSSBLAT

P.O. Box 26387V

Phoenix, AZ 85068

Ph (602) 863-2242

Fax (602) 942-4339

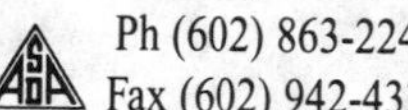

Nos. 196-197 Overprinted in Blue

POSTE AÉRIENNE

1946, May 20

C8	A41	50fr dp Prus green	2.00	2.00
C9	A41	100fr red	3.00	3.00
a.		Inverted overprint	*25,000.*	
b.		Double overprint	*17,000.*	

Douglas DC-3 and Arms — AP6

1946, May 20

C10	AP6	40fr red	.80	.50
C11	AP6	50fr red brown	.90	.70
C12	AP6	100fr dp blue grn	1.40	1.25
C13	AP6	200fr violet	2.25	2.00
		Nos. C10-C13 (4)	5.35	4.45

Exist imperforate. See Nos. C27-C29.

Harbor of Monte Carlo — AP7

Map of Monaco — AP8

1946, Dec. 13

C14	AP7	5fr carmine rose	.45	.45
C15	AP8	10fr violet black	.50	.50

Issued in tribute to the memory of Franklin D. Roosevelt.

Franklin D. Roosevelt Examining his Stamp Collection AP9

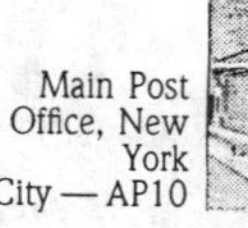

Main Post Office, New York City — AP10

Oceanographic Museum, Monaco — AP11

Harbor of Monte Carlo — AP12

Statue of Liberty and New York City Skyline — AP13

1947, May 15 **Unwmk.**

C16	AP9	50c violet	.65	.65
C17	AP10	1.50fr rose violet	.90	.90
C18	AP11	3fr henna brown	1.00	1.00
C19	AP12	10fr deep blue	4.00	4.00
C20	AP13	15fr rose carmine	4.50	4.50
a.		Strip of 3, #C20, 203, C19	11.00	11.00
		Nos. C16-C20 (5)	11.05	11.05

Monaco's participation in the Centenary Intl. Philatelic Exhibition, NYC, May, 1947.

Crowd Acclaiming Constitution of 1911 — AP14

Anthropological Museum — AP15

Designs: 25fr, Institute of Human Paleontology, Paris. 50fr, Albert I. 100fr, Oceanographic Institute, Paris. 200fr, Albert I medal.

1949, Mar. 5 **Engr.** ***Perf. 13***

C21	AP14	20fr brown red	.70	.70
C22	AP14	25fr indigo	.80	.80
C23	AP15	40fr blue green	1.25	1.25
C24	AP15	50fr black, brn & grn	1.50	1.50
C25	AP15	100fr cerise	5.50	5.50
C26	AP14	200fr deep orange	8.25	8.25
		Nos. C21-C26 (6)	18.00	18.00

Plane-Arms Type of 1946

1949, Mar. 10

C27	AP6	300fr dp ultra & ind	50.00	35.50
C28	AP6	500fr grnsh blk & bl grn	35.00	32.50
C29	AP6	1000fr black & red vio	55.00	42.50
		Nos. C27-C29 (3)	140.00	110.50

UPU Type of Regular Issue

1949-50

C30	A56	25fr deep blue	.60	.60
C31	A56	40fr red brown & sep	.90	.90
C32	A56	50fr dk green & ultra	1.40	1.40
C33	A56	100fr dk car & dk grn	3.00	3.00
		Nos. C30-C33 (4)	5.90	5.90

75th anniv. of the UPU.

Nos. C30-C33 exist imperforate, also No. C30 in deep plum and violet, imperforate.

Issued: 25fr, Dec. 27; others, Sept. 12, 1950.

Rainier Type of Regular Issue

1950, Apr. 11 **Unwmk.**

C34	A57	50fr black & red brn	3.25	3.25
C35	A57	100fr red brn, sep & ind	5.50	5.50

Enthronement of Prince Rainier III.

Runner — AP18

Designs: 50fr, Fencing. 100fr, Target Shooting. 200fr, Olympic Torch.

1953, Feb. 23 ***Perf. 11***

C36	AP18	40fr black	8.25	7.00
C37	AP18	50fr brt purple	8.25	7.00
C38	AP18	100fr dk slate grn	11.00	10.00
C39	AP18	200fr deep carmine	12.00	11.00
		Nos. C36-C39 (4)	39.50	35.00

Issued to publicize Monaco's participation in the Helsinki Olympic Games.

Dr. Albert Schweitzer and Ogowe River Scene, Gabon — AP19

1955, Jan. 14 ***Perf. 13***

C40	AP19	200fr multicolored	30.00	30.00

Dr. Albert Schweitzer, medical missionary.

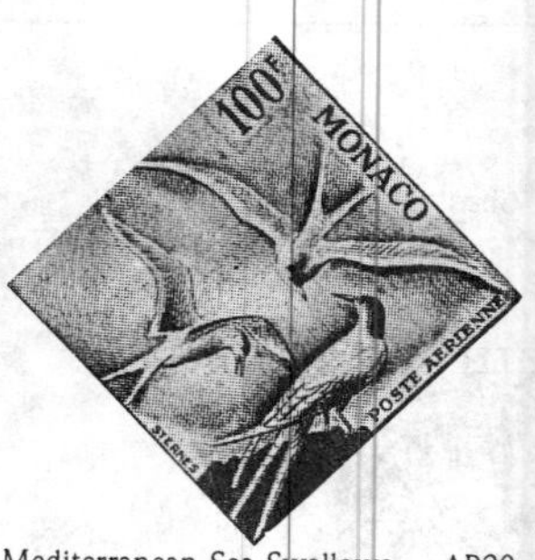

Mediterranean Sea Swallows — AP20

Birds: 200fr, Sea gulls. 500fr, Albatross. 1000fr, Great cormorants.

1955-57 ***Perf. 11***

C41	AP20	100fr dp blue & indigo	21.00	8.00
a.		Perf. 13	20.00	16.00
C42	AP20	200fr blue & black	22.50	10.00
c.		Perf. 13	300.00	125.00
C43	AP20	500fr gray & dk grn	37.50	25.00
		Perf. 13		
C44	AP20	1000fr dk bl grn & blk brn	75.00	50.00
a.		Perf. 11	225.00	165.00
		Nos. C41-C44 (4)	156.00	93.00

Issued: Perf. 11, Jan. 14, 1955; Perf. 13, 1957.

"From the Earth to the Moon" and Jules Verne — AP21

1955, June 7 **Unwmk.**

C45	AP21	200fr dp blue & slate	24.00	24.00

50th anniv. of the death of Jules Verne.

Wedding Type of Regular Issue

1956, Apr. 19 **Engr.**

Portraits in Brown

C46	A99	100fr purple	.60	.60
C47	A99	200fr carmine	1.00	1.00
C48	A99	500fr gray violet	2.50	2.50
		Nos. C46-C48 (3)	4.10	4.10

Wedding of Prince Rainier III to Grace Kelly, Apr. 19, 1956.

Nos. J45 and J54 Surcharged and Overprinted "Poste Aerienne" and bars

1956, Apr. ***Perf. 11***

C49	D6	100fr on 20fr	9.25	9.25
a.		Double surcharge	*425.00*	*425.00*
C50	D7	100fr on 20fr	9.25	9.25
a.		Double surcharge	*425.00*	*425.00*

See footnote after No. 390.

Basilica of Lourdes — AP23

200fr, Pope Pius X and underground basilica.

1958, May 15 Unwmk. *Perf. 13*
C51 AP23 100fr dk bl, grn & gray 1.50 1.10
C52 AP23 200fr red brn & sepia 2.00 1.90

Centenary of the apparition of the Virgin Mary at Lourdes.

Prince Rainier III and Princess Grace — AP24

1959, May 16
C53 AP24 300fr dark purple 7.00 5.50
C54 AP24 500fr blue 12.50 8.25

St. Dévote AP25

1960, June 1 Engr. *Perf. 13*
C55 AP25 2fr green, bl & vio 1.40 .85
C56 AP24 3fr dark purple 32.50 12.00
C57 AP24 5fr blue 32.50 13.00
C58 AP25 10fr green & brown 6.50 3.00
Nos. C55-C58 (4) 72.90 28.85

1961, June 3
C59 AP25 3fr ultra, grn & gray ol 1.75 1.00
C60 AP25 5fr rose carmine 3.50 .50

Europa Issue, 1962

Mercury over Map of Europe AP26

1962, June 6 Unwmk. *Perf. 13*
C61 AP26 2fr dk grn, sl grn & brn 1.25 1.00

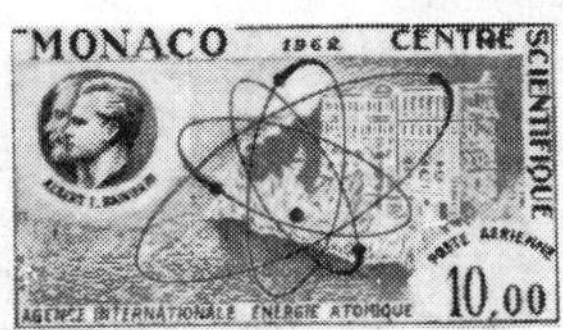

Oceanographic Museum, Atom Symbol and Princes Albert I and Rainier III — AP27

1962, June 6
C62 AP27 10fr violet, bl & bis 6.50 6.00

Establishment of a scientific research center by agreement with the Intl. Atomic Energy Commission.

Roland Garros AP28

1963, Dec. 12 Engr. *Perf. 13*
C63 AP28 2fr dk blue & dk brn 1.25 .95

50th anniversary of the first airplane crossing of the Mediterranean by Roland Garros (1888-1918).

Type of Regular Issue, 1964

Design: 5fr, Convair B-58 Hustler (New York-Paris in 3 hours, 19 minutes, 41 seconds, Maj. William R. Payne, USAF, 1961).

1964, May 22 Unwmk. *Perf. 13*
C64 A151 5fr brown, blk & bl 3.50 3.00

1st airplane rally of Monte Carlo, 50th anniv.

Bobsledding — AP29

1964, Dec. 3 Engr. *Perf. 13*
C65 AP29 5fr multicolored 2.75 2.75

9th Winter Olympic Games, Innsbruck, Austria, Jan. 29-Feb. 9, 1964.

ITU Type of Regular Issue

Design: 10fr, ITU Emblem and Monte Carlo television station on Mount Agel, vert.

1965, May 17 Engr. *Perf. 13*
C66 A161 10fr bis brn, sl grn & bl 4.25 4.25

Princess Grace with Albert Alexander Louis, Caroline and Stephanie — AP30

1966, Feb. 1 Engr. *Perf. 13*
C67 AP30 3fr pur, red brn & Prus bl 2.25 1.75

Birth of Princess Stephanie, Feb. 1, 1965.

Opera House Interior AP31

1966, June 1 Engr. *Perf. 13*
C68 AP31 5fr Prus bl, bis & dk car rose 2.50 2.50

Centenary of founding of Monte Carlo.

Prince Rainier III and Princess Grace — AP32

1966-71 Engr. *Perf. 13*
C69 AP32 2fr pink & slate 1.00 .40
C70 AP32 3fr emerald & slate 2.00 .65
C71 AP32 5fr lt blue & slate 2.50 1.10
C72 AP32 10fr lemon & sl ('67) 4.00 2.75
C72A AP32 20fr orange & brn ('71) 30.00 15.00
Nos. C69-C72A (5) 39.50 19.90

Issue dates: 10fr, Dec. 7, 1967; 20fr, Sept. 6, 1971. Others, Dec. 12, 1966.

Panhard-Phenix, 1895 — AP33

1967, Apr. 28 Engr. *Perf. 13*
C73 AP33 3fr Prus blue & blk 2.25 2.00

25th Grand Prix of Monaco.

Olympic Games Type of Regular Issue

1968, Apr. 29 Engr. *Perf. 13*
C74 A183 3fr Field hockey 2.00 1.75

Berlioz Monument, Monte Carlo — AP34

1969, Apr. 26 Engr. *Perf. 13*
C75 AP34 2fr green, blk & ultra 1.25 1.10

Hector Berlioz (1803-69), French composer.

Napoleon, by Paul Delaroche AP35

1969, Apr. 26 Photo. *Perf. 12x13*
C76 AP35 3fr multicolored 1.50 1.25

Bicentenary of birth of Napoleon I.

Horses, Prehistoric Drawing from Lascaux Cave — AP36

1970, Dec. 15 Engr. *Perf. 13*
C77 AP36 3fr multicolored 3.25 3.00

Nativity Type of Regular Issue

Design: 3fr, Nativity, Flemish School, 15th century, vert.

1973, Nov. 12 Engr. *Perf. 12x13*
C78 A243 3fr Prus green 3.25 2.25

Prince Rainier III — AP37

1974, Dec. 23 Engr. *Perf. 12½x13*
C81 AP37 10fr dark purple 4.00 3.00
C82 AP37 15fr henna brown 6.50 4.50
C83 AP37 20fr ultra 9.50 6.00
Nos. C81-C83 (3) 20.00 13.50

See Nos. 1994-1996.

Prince Rainier and Hereditary Prince Albert — AP38

1982-84 Engr. *Perf. 13x13½*
C84 AP38 5fr deep violet 1.50 .85
C85 AP38 10fr red 3.00 1.65
C86 AP38 15fr dk blue grn 4.50 2.50
C87 AP38 20fr brt blue 5.50 3.25
C88 AP38 30fr brown ('84) 8.50 4.75
Nos. C84-C88 (5) 23.00 13.00

AIR POST SEMI-POSTAL STAMPS

Catalogue values for unused stamps in this section are for Never Hinged items.

Types of 1942 Air Post Stamps Surcharged with New Values and Bars

Unwmk.

1945, Mar. 27 Engr. *Perf. 13*
CB1 AP1 1fr + 4fr on 10fr rose red .25 .25
CB2 AP2 1fr + 4fr on 15fr red brown .25 .25
CB3 AP3 1fr + 4fr on 20fr sepia .25 .25
CB4 AP4 1fr + 4fr on 50fr ultra .25 .25
CB5 AP5 1fr + 4fr on 100fr bright red violet .25 .25
Nos. CB1-CB5 (5) 1.25 1.25

Surtax for the benefit of prisoners of war.

Franklin D. Roosevelt Type

1946, Dec. 13
CB6 A42 15fr + 10fr red .95 .80

The surtax was for a fund to erect a monument in his honor.

1948 Olympic Type

1948, July

CB7 A47 5fr +5fr Rowing 8.00 8.00
CB8 A47 6fr +9fr Skiing 11.50 11.50
CB9 A47 10fr +15fr Tennis 16.00 16.00
CB10 A48 15fr +25fr Sailing 24.00 24.00
Nos. CB7-CB10 (4) 59.50 59.50

Salmacis Nymph SPAP4

Designs similar to regular issue.

1948, July

CB11 A50 5fr + 5fr black blue 9.50 9.50
CB12 A51 6fr + 9fr dk green 11.00 11.00
CB13 A52 10fr + 15fr crimson 12.00 12.00
CB14 SPAP4 15fr + 25fr red brown 13.00 13.00
Nos. CB11-CB14 (4) 45.50 45.50

François J. Bosio (1769-1845), sculptor.

POSTAGE DUE STAMPS

D1

Prince Albert I — D2

Perf. 14x13½

1905-43 Unwmk. Typo.

J1 D1 1c olive green .60 .60
J2 D1 5c green .70 .60
J3 D1 10c rose .60 .60
J4 D1 10c brn ('09) 250.00 100.00
J5 D1 15c vio brn, *straw* 3.00 1.10
J6 D1 20c bis brn, *buff* ('26) .30 .30
J7 D1 30c blue .60 .60
J8 D1 40c red vio ('26) .30 .30
J9 D1 50c brn, *org* 6.25 3.00
J10 D1 50c blue grn ('27) .30 .30
J11 D1 60c gray blk ('26) .55 .55
J12 D1 60c brt vio ('34) 18.00 18.00
J13 D1 1fr red brn, *straw* ('26) .15 .15
J14 D1 2fr red org ('27) 1.25 1.25
J15 D1 3fr mag ('27) 1.25 1.25
J15A D1 5fr ultra ('43) .70 .70
Nos. J1-J15A (16) 284.55 129.30

For surcharge see No. J27.

1910

J16 D2 1c olive green .35 .35
J17 D2 10c light violet .50 .50
J18 D2 30c bister 150.00 125.00

In January, 1917, regular postage stamps overprinted "T" in a triangle were used as postage due stamps.

Nos. J17 and J18 Surcharged **20 c.**

1918

J19 D2 20c on 10c lt vio 4.00 4.00
a. Double surcharge *900.00*
J20 D2 40c on 30c bister 4.00 4.00

D3

1925-32

J21 D3 1c gray green .25 .25
J22 D3 10c violet .25 .25
J23 D3 30c bister .35 .35
J24 D3 60c red .50 .50
J25 D3 1fr lt bl ('32) 55.00 45.00
J26 D3 2fr dull red ('32) 80.00 67.50
Nos. J21-J26 (6) 136.35 113.85

Nos. J25 and J26 have the numerals of value double-lined.

"Recouvrements" stamps were used to recover charges due on undelivered or refused mail which was returned to the sender.

No. J9 Surcharged **1 franc à percevoir**

1925

J27 D1 1fr on 50c brn, *org* .50 .40
a. Double surcharge *650.00*

Catalogue values for unused stamps in this section, from this point to the end of the section, are for Never Hinged items.

D4

D5

1946-57 Engr. *Perf. 14x13, 13*

J28 D4 10c sepia .20 .20
J29 D4 30c dark violet .20 .20
J30 D4 50c deep blue .20 .20
J31 D4 1fr dark green .20 .20
J32 D4 2fr yellow brn .20 .20
J33 D4 3fr brt red vio .25 .25
J34 D4 4fr carmine .40 .40
J35 D5 5fr chocolate .30 .30
J36 D5 10fr deep ultra .55 .55
J37 D5 20fr grnsh blue .60 .60
J38 D5 50fr red vio & red ('50) 50.00 50.00
J38A D5 100fr dk grn & red ('57) 8.75 8.75
Nos. J28-J38A (12) 61.85 61.85

Sailing Vessel — D6

S. S. United States D7

Early Postal Transport (D6): 1fr, Carrier pigeons. 3fr, Old railroad engine. 4fr, Old monoplane. 5fr, Steam automobile. 10fr, daVinci's flying machine. 20fr, Balloon. 50fr, Post rider. 100fr, Old mail coach.

Modern Postal Transport (D7): 1fr, Sikorsky S-51 helicopter. 3fr, Modern locomotive. 4fr, Comet airliner. 5fr, Sabre sports car. 10fr, Rocket. 20fr, Graf Zeppelin. 50fr, Motorcyclist. 100fr, Railroad mail car.

1953-54 *Perf. 11*

J39 D6 1fr dk grn & brt red ('54) .15 .15
a. Pair, Nos. J39, J48 .20 .20
J40 D6 2fr dp ultra & bl grn .20 .20
a. Pair, Nos. J40, J49 .40 .40
J41 D6 3fr Prus grn & brn lake .20 .20
a. Pair, Nos. J41, J50 .40 .40
J42 D6 4fr dk brn & Prus grn .35 .35
a. Pair, Nos. J42, J51 .70 .70
J43 D6 5fr ultra & pur .85 .85
a. Pair, Nos. J43, J52 1.75 1.75
J44 D6 10fr dp ultra & dk bl 9.00 9.00
a. Pair, Nos. J44, J53 18.00 18.00
J45 D6 20fr indigo & pur 3.00 3.00
a. Pair, Nos. J45, J54 6.00 6.00
J46 D6 50fr red & dk brn 8.00 8.00
a. Pair, Nos. J46, J55 16.00 16.00
J47 D6 100fr vio brn & dp grn 16.00 16.00
a. Pair, Nos. J47, J56 32.00 32.00
J48 D7 1fr brt red & dk grn ('54) .15 .15
J49 D7 2fr bl grn & dp ultra .20 .20
J50 D7 3fr brn lake & Prus grn .20 .20
J51 D7 4fr Prus grn & dk brn .35 .35
J52 D7 5fr purple & ultra .85 .85
J53 D7 10fr dk bl & dp ultra 9.00 9.00
J54 D7 20fr purple & indigo 3.00 3.00
J55 D7 50fr dk brn & red 8.00 8.00
J56 D7 100fr dp grn & vio brn 16.00 16.00
Nos. J39-J56 (18) 75.50 75.50

The two types of each value in Nos. J39-J56 were printed tête bêche, se-tenant at the base.

For overprints see Nos. 371-390.

Felucca, 18th Century D8

Designs: 2c, Paddle steamer La Palmaria, 19th century. 5c, Arrival of first train. 10c, Armed messenger, 15th-16th century. 20c, Monaco-Nice courier, 18th century. 30c, "Charles III," 1866. 50c, Courier on horseback, 17th century. 1fr, Diligence, 19th century.

1960-69 Engr. *Perf. 13*

J57 D8 1c bl grn, bis brn & bl .45 .45
J58 D8 2c sl grn, sep & ultra .15 .15
J59 D8 5c grnsh bl, gray & red brn .15 .15
J60 D8 10c vio bl, blk & grn .30 .30
J61 D8 20c blue, brn & grn 1.00 1.00
J62 D8 30c brn, brt grn & brt bl ('69) .55 .55
J63 D8 50c dk bl, brn & sl grn 1.00 1.00
J64 D8 1fr sl grn, bl & brn 1.40 1.40
Nos. J57-J64 (8) 5.00 5.00

Knight in Armor D9

1980-83 Engr. *Perf. 13*

J65 D9 5c red & gray .15 .15
J66 D9 10c salmon & red .15 .15
J67 D9 15c violet & red .15 .15
J68 D9 20c lt green & red .15 .15
J69 D9 30c blue & red .15 .15
J70 D9 40c lt brown & red .20 .20
J71 D9 50c lilac & red .20 .20
J72 D9 1fr black & blue .45 .45
J73 D9 2fr dk brn & org ('82) .75 .75
J74 D9 3fr sl bl & rose car ('83) 1.25 1.25
J75 D9 4fr red & dk grn ('82) 1.40 1.40
J76 D9 5fr magenta & brn ('83) 2.50 2.50
Nos. J65-J76 (12) 7.50 7.50

Nos. J65-J76 printed in horizontal rows with princely coat of arms between stamps. Sold in strips of 3 only.

Issue dates: Nos. J65-J72, Feb. 8; Nos. J73, J75, Feb. 15; Nos. J74, J76, Jan. 3.

Natl. Coat of Arms — D10

1985-86 Photo. *Perf. 13x12½*

J77 D10 5c multicolored .15 .15
J78 D10 10c multicolored .15 .15
J79 D10 15c multicolored .15 .15
J80 D10 20c multicolored .15 .15
J81 D10 30c multicolored .15 .15
J82 D10 40c multicolored .15 .15
J83 D10 50c multicolored ('86) .15 .15
J84 D10 1fr multicolored ('86) .35 .15
J85 D10 2fr multicolored ('86) .65 .30
J86 D10 3fr multicolored .75 .35
J87 D10 4fr multicolored ('86) 1.50 .60
J88 D10 5fr multicolored 1.50 .60
Set value 4.40 2.30

See Nos. 1608-1609.

MONGOLIA

män-ˈgōl-yə

(Mongolian People's Republic)

(Outer Mongolia)

LOCATION — Central Asia, bounded on the north by Siberia, on the west by Sinkiang, on the south and east by China proper and Manchuria
GOVT. — Republic
AREA — 604,250 sq. mi.
POP. — 1,820,000 (est. 1984)
CAPITAL — Ulan Bator

Outer Mongolia, which had long been under Russian influence although nominally a dependency of China, voted at a plebescite on October 20, 1945, to sever all ties with China and become an independent nation. See Tannu Tuva.

100 Cents = 1 Dollar
100 Mung = 1 Tugrik (1926)

Catalogue values for unused stamps in this country are for Never Hinged items, beginning with Scott 149 in the regular postage section, Scott B1 in the semi-postal section, Scott C1 in the airpost section, and Scott CB1 in the airpost semi-postal section.

Watermark

Wmk. 170- Greek Border and Rosettes

Scepter of Indra — A1

A2

1924 Litho. Unwmk. *Perf. 10, 13½*
Surface Tinted Paper

1 A1 1c multi, *bister* 5.00 5.00
2 A1 2c multi, *brnsh* 3.00 3.00
a. Perf. 13½ 15.00 13.00
3 A1 5c multi 25.00 25.00
a. Perf. 10 50.00 50.00
4 A1 10c multi, *gray bl* 10.00 6.00
a. Perf. 10 20.00 6.00
5 A1 20c multi, *gray* 15.00 10.00
6 A1 50c multi, *salmon* 20.00 15.00
7 A1 $1 multi, *yellow* 30.00 25.00
b. Perf. 10 100.00 100.00
Nos. 1-7 (7) 108.00 89.00

These stamps vary in size from 19x25mm (1c) to 30x39mm ($1). They also differ in details of the design.

Errors of perforating and printing exist.

Some quantities of Nos. 1-2, 4-7 were defaced with horizontal perforation across the center.

The 5c exists perf 11½.

Revenue Stamps Handstamp Overprinted "POSTAGE" in Violet

Sizes: 1c to 20c: 22x36mm
50c, $1: 26x43½mm
$5: 30x45½mm

1926 *Perf. 11*

16 A2 1c blue 5.00 5.00
17 A2 2c orange 5.00 5.00
18 A2 5c plum 5.00 5.00

No.	Type	Value / Color	Unused	Used
19	A2	10c green	5.00	5.00
20	A2	20c yel brn	5.00	5.00
21	A2	50c brn & ol grn	150.00	150.00
22	A2	$1 brn & salmon	500.00	275.00
23	A2	$5 red, yel & gray	350.00	175.00
		Nos. 16-23 (8)	*1,025.*	*625.00*

Black Overprint

No.	Type	Value / Color	Unused	Used
16a	A2	1c blue	8.75	8.75
17a	A2	2c orange	8.75	8.75
18a	A2	5c plum	8.75	8.75
19a	A2	10c green	8.75	8.75
20a	A2	20c yellow brown	8.75	8.75
21a	A2	50c brown & olive grn	150.00	125.00
22a	A2	$1 brown & salmon	500.00	300.00
23a	A2	$5 red, yellow & gray		
		Nos. 16a-22a (7)	*693.75*	*468.75*

Red Overprint

No.	Type	Value / Color
16b	A2	1c blue
17b	A2	2c orange
18b	A2	5c plum
19b	A2	10c green
20b	A2	20c yellow brown

The preceding handstamped overprints may be found inverted, double, etc. Counterfeits abound.

For overprints and surcharges see #48-61.

Yin Yang and other Symbols
A3 A4

TYPE I - The pearl above the crescent is solid. The devices in the middle of the stamp are not outlined.

TYPE II - The pearl is open. The devices and panels are all outlined in black.

1926-29 *Perf. 11*

Type I

Size: 22x28mm

No.	Type	Value / Color	Unused	Used
32	A3	5m lilac & blk	6.00	7.50
33	A3	20m blue & blk	7.50	8.00

Type II

Size: 22x29mm

No.	Type	Value / Color	Unused	Used
34	A3	1m yellow & blk	2.50	2.00
35	A3	2m brn org & blk	4.00	3.00
36	A3	5m lilac & blk	5.00	3.00
37	A3	10m lt blue & blk	5.00	2.50
a.		Imperf.		
38	A3	20m dp bl & blk ('29)	7.50	6.00
a.		Imperf.		
39	A3	25m yel grn & blk	6.00	4.00
a.		Imperf.		

Size: 26x34mm

No.	Type	Value / Color	Unused	Used
40	A3	40m lemon & blk	7.50	3.00
41	A3	50m buff & blk	7.50	4.50

Size: 28x37mm

No.	Type	Value / Color	Unused	Used
42	A4	1t brown, grn & blk	20.00	17.50
43	A4	3t red, yel & blk	65.00	50.00
44	A4	5t brn vio, rose & blk	75.00	65.00
		Nos. 32-44 (13)	218.50	176.00

In 1929 a change was made in the perforating machine. Every fourth pin was removed, which left the perforation holes in groups of three with blank spaces between the groups. Nos. 38 and 44A have only this interrupted perforation. Nos. 37 and 39 are found with both perforations.

For overprints and surcharges see #45-47.

Yin Yang and other Symbols — A5

1929

No.	Type	Value / Color	Unused	Used
44A	A5	5m lilac & black	12.50	7.50

See note after No. 44.

Nos. 34, 35, 40 Handstamped With New Values in Black

1930

No.	Type	Value / Color	Unused	Used
45	A3	10m on 1m	12.50	10.00
46	A3	20m on 2m	12.50	10.00
47	A3	25m on 40m	17.50	14.00
		Nos. 45-47 (3)	42.50	34.00

Symbols of Government
A6 A7

Violet Overprint, Handstamped

1931

No.	Type	Value / Color	Unused	Used
48	A6	1c blue	5.50	5.50
a.		Blue overprint	8.00	5.50
49	A6	2c orange	8.00	5.50
50	A6	5c brown vio	8.00	6.50
a.		Blue overprint	8.50	6.00
51	A6	10c green	8.50	6.00
a.		Blue overprint	11.00	9.50
52	A6	20c bister brn	11.00	6.00
53	A6	50c brown & ol yel	65.00	50.00
54	A6	$1 brown & salmon	85.00	67.50
		Nos. 48-54 (7)	191.00	147.00

Revenue Stamps Surcharged in Black, Red or Blue

1931

No.	Type	Value / Color	Unused	Used
59	A7	5m on 5c brn vio (Bk)	12.50	6.00
a.		Inverted surcharge		17.50
b.		Imperf., pair	22.00	22.00
60	A7	10m on 10c green (R)	25.00	12.50
a.		Inverted surcharge	15.00	12.50
b.		Imperf., pair	35.00	35.00
61	A7	20m on 20c bis brn (Bl)	32.50	19.00
a.		Inverted surcharge		18.00
b.		Imperf., pair	55.00	55.00
		Nos. 59-61 (3)	70.00	37.50

On Nos. 59-61, "Postage" is always diagonal, and may read up or down.

Weaver at Loom — A8

Telegrapher A9

Sukhe Bator A10

Lake and Mountains — A11

Designs: 5m, Mongol at lathe. 10m, Government building, Ulan Bator. 15m, Young Mongolian revolutionary. 20m, Studying Latin alphabet. 25m, Mongolian soldier. 50m, Monument to Sukhe Bator. 3t, Sheep shearing. 5t, Camel caravan. 10t, Chasing wild horses.

Perf. 12½x12

1932 **Photo.** **Wmk. 170**

No.	Type	Value / Color	Unused	Used
62	A8	1m brown	.50	.35
63	A9	2m red violet	.50	.35
64	A8	5m indigo	.50	.30
65	A8	10m dull green	.50	.30
66	A9	15m dp brown	.50	.30
67	A9	20m rose red	.50	.30
68	A9	25m dull violet	.50	.30
69	A10	40m gray black	.50	.35
70	A10	50m dull blue	.50	.40

Perf. 11x12

No.	Type	Value / Color	Unused	Used
71	A11	1t dull green	.50	.40
72	A11	3t dull violet	1.50	1.25
73	A11	5t brown	5.00	3.50
74	A11	10t ultra	10.00	7.00
		Nos. 62-74 (13)	21.50	15.10

Used values are for c-t-o's.

Marshal Kharloin Choibalsan — A21

1945 **Unwmk.** *Perf. 12½*

No.	Type	Value / Color	Unused	Used
83	A21	1t black brown	2.75	2.75

Choibalsan — A22

Victory Medal — A24

Sukhe Bator and Choibalsan A23

Designs: #86, Choibalsan as young man. #87, Choibalsan University, Ulan Bator. 1t, Anniversary medal. 2t, Sukhe Bator.

1946, July **Photo.** *Perf. 12½*

No.	Type	Value / Color	Unused	Used
84	A22	30m olive bister	1.40	1.40
85	A23	50m dull purple	2.00	2.00
86	A24	60m black	2.00	2.00
87	A23	60m orange brown	2.50	2.50
88	A24	80m dk orange brn	2.75	2.75
89	A24	1t indigo	5.75	5.75
90	A24	2t deep brown	7.50	7.50
		Nos. 84-90 (7)	23.90	23.90

25th anniversary of independence.

New Housing — A25

School Children — A26

Mongolian Arms and Flag — A27

Sukhe Bator — A28

Flags of Communist Countries — A29

Lenin — A30

Designs: 15m, Altai Hotel. No. 94, State Store. No. 95, Like 30m. 25m, University. 40m, National Theater. 50m, Pedagogical Institute. 60m, Sukhe Bator monument. Sizes of type A25: Nos. 91, 93-94, 98-99, 32½x22mm. 25m, 55x26mm.

1951

No.	Type	Value / Color	Unused	Used
91	A25	5m brn, *pink*	.80	.80
92	A26	10m dp bl, *pink*	1.00	1.00
93	A25	15m grn, *grnsh*	1.00	1.00
94	A25	20m red org	1.40	1.40
95	A27	20m dk bl & multi	1.40	1.40
96	A25	25m bl, *bluish*	1.50	1.50
97	A27	30m red & multi	1.50	1.50
98	A25	40m pur, *pink*	1.50	1.50
99	A25	50m brn, *grysh*	5.50	5.50
100	A28	60m brn blk	5.50	5.50
101	A29	1t multi	5.50	5.50
102	A28	2t dk brn & org brn	6.75	6.75
103	A30	3t multi	14.00	14.00
		Nos. 91-103 (13)	47.35	47.35

30th anniversary of independence.

Choibalsan A31

Choibalsan and Farmer A32

Choibalsan and Sukhe Bator — A33

Designs: No. 108, 30m, Choibalsan and factory worker (47x33mm). 50m, Choibalsan and Young Pioneer. No. 112, 2t, Choibalsan in uniform.

1953, Dec. **Photo.** *Perf. 12½*

No.	Type	Value / Color	Unused	Used
104	A31	15m dull blue	1.00	1.00
105	A32	15m dull green	1.00	1.00
106	A31	20m dull green	1.40	1.40
107	A32	20m sepia	1.50	1.50
108	A32	20m violet blue	1.50	1.50
109	A32	30m dark brown	1.75	1.75
110	A33	50m orange brn	2.00	2.00
111	A33	1t carmine rose	2.00	2.00
112	A31	1t sepia	2.00	2.00
113	A31	2t red	2.00	2.00
114	A33	3t sepia	2.75	2.75
115	A33	5t red	4.00	4.00
		Nos. 104-115 (12)	22.90	22.90

First anniversary of death of Marshal Karloin Choibalsan (1895-1952).

Arms of Mongolia — A34

1954, Mar. **Litho.** ***Perf. 12½***
116 A34 10m carmine 2.00 1.75
117 A34 20m carmine 4.00 2.75
118 A34 30m carmine 2.50 1.90
119 A34 40m carmine 3.50 1.75
120 A34 60m carmine 3.00 1.75
Nos. 116-120 (5) 15.00 9.90

Sukhe Bator and Choibalsan — A35

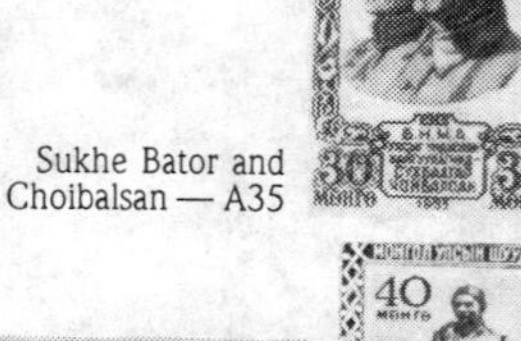

Lake Hubsugul — A36

Guard with Dog — A37

#122, Lenin Statue, Ulan Bator. 50m, Choibalsan University. 1t, Arms and flag of Mongolia.

1955, June **Photo.** ***Perf. 12½***
121 A35 30m green .20 .15
122 A35 30m orange ver .28 .15
123 A36 30m brt blue .20 .15
124 A37 40m dp red lilac .35 .15
125 A36 50m ocher .70 .30
126 A37 1t red & multi 1.50 1.00
Nos. 121-126 (6) 3.23
Set value 1.65

35th anniversary of independence.

1955

Design: 2t, Lenin.

127 A35 2t bright blue 2.50 1.25

85th anniversary of birth of Lenin.

Flags of Communist Countries A38

Arms of Mongolia A39

1955
128 A38 60m blue & multi 1.00 .55

Fight for peace.

1956 **Photo.** ***Perf. 12½***
129 A39 20m dark brown .18 .15
130 A39 30m dark olive .20 .15
131 A39 40m bright blue .28 .20
132 A39 60m blue green .40 .28
133 A39 1t deep carmine .70 .28
Nos. 129-133 (5) 1.76 1.06

Kremlin, Moscow, Train and Sukhe Bator Monument A40

Design: 2t, Flags of Mongolia and USSR.

1956
134 A40 1t dk blue & multi 1.40 .70
135 A40 2t red & multi 2.75 1.00

Establishment of railroad connection between Moscow and Ulan Bator.

Mongolia stamps through 1945 can be mounted in the Scott Soviet Republics album part 1.

Mongolian Arms and Flag — A41

Hunter with Golden Eagle — A42

Wrestlers — A43

Designs: No. 138, 3 children (33x26½mm).

1956, July **Typo.** ***Perf. 9***
136 A41 30m blue 2.00 2.00
137 A42 30m pale brown 8.00 8.00
138 A42 60m orange 9.00 8.00
139 A43 60m yellow green 9.00 8.00
Nos. 136-139 (4) 28.00 26.00

35th anniversary of independence.

Types A41 and A43 without "XXXV"

1958
140 A41 20m red .50 .50
141 A43 50m brown, *pink* 2.75 2.75

Nos. 140-143 were issued both with and without gum.

Poster — A44

Globe and Dove — A45

1958, Mar. **Litho.** ***Perf. 9***
142 A44 30m maroon & salmon 2.25 1.40

13th Congress of Mongolian People's Party.

1958, May
143 A45 60m deep blue 2.00 .85

4th Congress of International Democratic Women's Federation, Vienna, June, 1958. Nos. 142-143 exist imperf.

Yak — A46

No. 144, Pelicans, vert. No. 145, Siberian ibex, vert. No. 147, Yak. No. 148, Camels.

1958, July **Typo.** ***Perf. 9***
144 A46 30m lt blue .70 .35
145 A46 30m brt green .70 .35
146 A46 60m orange 1.00 .50
147 A46 1t blue 2.50 1.00
148 A46 1t rose 2.50 1.00
Nos. 144-148 (5) 7.40 3.20

Shades exist.

Canceled to Order
Some quantity of all issues not printed by the State Printing Works, Ulan Bator, except Nos. 296-303, were canceled to order.
Used values are for c-t-o. Postally used specimens sell for considerably more.

Catalogue values for unused stamps in this section, from this point to the end of the section, are for Never Hinged items.

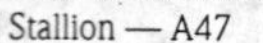

Stallion — A47

Holy Flame (Tulaga) — A48

Designs: 5m, 40m, Goat. 10m, 30m, Ram. 15m, 60m, Stallion. 20m, 50m, Bull. 25m, 1t, Bactrian camel.

Perf. 10½x11½

1958, Nov. 11 **Litho.**
149 A47 5m yellow & brn .15 .15
150 A47 10m lt grn & brn .15 .15
151 A47 15m lilac & brn .15 .15
152 A47 20m lt bl & brn .15 .15
153 A47 25m rose & brn .15 .15
154 A47 30m lilac & pur .15 .15
155 A47 40m lt & dk green .15 .15
156 A47 50m salmon & brn .18 .15
157 A47 60m lt blue & ind .20 .15
158 A47 1t yellow & brn .50 .20
Set value 1.40 .75

1959, May 1 **Litho.** ***Perf. 9***
159 A48 1t multi 1.75 .70

See No. C36.

Archer — A49

Mongol Sports: 5m, Taming wild horse. 10m, Wrestlers. 15m, Horseback riding. 25m, Horse race. 30m, Archers. 70m, Hunting wild horse. 80m, Proclaiming a champion.

1959, June 6 **Photo.** ***Perf. 11***
160 A49 5m multi .15 .15
161 A49 10m multi .15 .15
162 A49 15m multi .15 .15
163 A49 20m multi .15 .15
164 A49 25m multi .18 .15
165 A49 30m multi .18 .15
166 A49 70m multi .35 .15
167 A49 80m multi .55 .24
Set value 1.55 .75

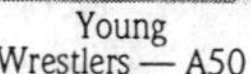

Young Wrestlers — A50

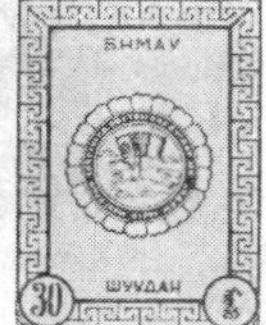

Youth Festival Emblem — A51

Designs: 5m, Young musician, horiz. 20m, Boy on horseback. 25m, Two opera singers. 40m, Young Pioneers with flags, horiz.

Photo.; Litho. (30m)

1959, July ***Perf. 12, 11 (30m)***
168 A50 5m vio bl & rose car .15 .15
169 A50 10m bl grn & brn .15 .15
170 A50 20m claret & grn .15 .15
171 A50 25m green & vio bl .18 .15
172 A51 30m lil & lt bl .18 .15
173 A50 40m green & pur .35 .20
Set value 1.00 .62

Mongolian Youth Festival.
The 30m was printed by State Printing Works, Ulan Bator.
Issue dates: 30m, July 11; others July 10.

"Mongol" in Stylized Uighur Script — A52

"Mongol" in Various Scripts: 40m, Soyombo. 50m, Kalmuck. 60m, Square (Pagspa). 1t, Cyrillic. Printed by State Printing Works, Ulan Bator.

1959, Sept. 1 **Litho.** ***Perf. 11***

Size: 29x42½mm
174 A52 30m black & multi 2.00 2.00
175 A52 40m black & multi 2.00 2.00
176 A52 50m black & multi 2.75 2.75
177 A52 60m black & multi 4.00 4.00

Size: 21x31mm

Perf. 9
178 A52 1t black & multi 8.50 8.50
Nos. 174-178 (5) 19.25 19.25

1st Intl. Mongolian Language Congress.

Battle Emblem A53

Battle Monument A54

1959, Sept. 15 **Photo.** ***Perf. 12½x12***
179 A53 40m yellow, brn & car .24 .15
180 A54 50m multicolored .28 .15
Set value .20

Ha-lo-hsin (Khalka) River Battle, 20th anniv.

Congress Emblem — A55

Printed by State Printing Works, Ulan Bator.

1959, Dec. **Litho.** ***Perf. 11***
181 A55 30m green 1.40 1.40

2nd meeting of rural economy cooperatives of Mongolia.

Sable — A56

Pheasants — A57

1959, Dec. 21 **Photo.** ***Perf. 15, 11x13***
182 A56 5m shown .15 .15
183 A57 10m shown .15 .15
184 A56 15m Muskrat .15 .15
185 A57 20m Otter .15 .15
186 A56 30m Argali .16 .15
187 A57 50m Saigas .35 .20
188 A57 1t Musk deer .70 .38
Set value 1.50 .90

Lunik 3 — A58

50m, Lunik 3 with path around moon, horiz.

1959, Dec. 30 Photo. *Perf. 12*

189 A58 30m violet & yel grn .40 .18
190 A58 50m red, dk bl & grn .60 .20

Lunik 3 Russian moon mission, Oct. 7, 1959.

Motherhood Badge — A59

Flower Emblem — A60

1960, Mar. 8 *Perf. 11, 12½x11½*

191 A59 40m blue & bister .40 .15
192 A60 50m blue, grn & yel .55 .20

International Women's Day.

Lenin — A61

Jacob's-ladder — A62

1960, Apr. 22 Photo. *Perf. 11½x12*

193 A61 40m dk rose car .35 .15
194 A61 50m rose violet .48 .15
Set value .24

90th anniversary, birth of Lenin.

1960, May 31 *Perf. 11½x12*

195 A62 5m Larkspur .15 .15
196 A62 10m Tulips .15 .15
197 A62 15m shown .15 .15
198 A62 20m Globeflowers .15 .15
199 A62 30m Bellflowers .15 .15
200 A62 40m Parnassia .15 .15
201 A62 50m Geranium .20 .18
202 A62 1t Begonia .40 .30
Set value 1.05 .85

For overprints see Nos. 296-303.

Equestrian — A63

Running — A64

1960, Aug. 1 *Perf. 15, 11*

203 A63 5m shown .15 .15
204 A64 10m shown .15 .15
205 A63 15m Diving .15 .15
206 A64 20m Wrestling .15 .15
207 A63 30m Hurdling .18 .15
208 A64 50m Gymnastics, women's .28 .15
209 A63 70m High jump .35 .15
210 A64 1t Discus, women's .70 .28
Nos. 203-210 (8) 2.11
Set value .80

17th Olympic Games, Rome, Aug. 25-Sept. 11.

Red Cross A65

1960, Aug. 29 *Perf. 11*

211 A65 20m blue, red & yel .24 .15

Newspaper "Unen" (Truth) A66

1960, Dec. 19 *Perf. 12x11½*

212 A66 20m red, yel & sl grn .15 .82
213 A66 30m grn, yel & red .20 .15

40th anniversary of Mongolian press.

Golden Orioles — A67

Songbirds: 5m, Rose-colored starling. 10m, Hoopoe. 20m, Black-billed capercaillie. 50m, Oriental broad-billed roller. 70m, Tibetan sandgrouse. 1t, Mandarin duck. (Triangle points down on 5m, 50m, 70m, 1t.)

1961, Jan. 3 *Perf. 11*

214 A67 5m multi .15 .15
215 A67 10m multi .15 .15
216 A67 15m multi .15 .15
217 A67 20m multi .15 .15
218 A67 50m multi .28 .15
219 A67 70m multi .40 .18
220 A67 1t multi .60 .24
Nos. 214-220 (7) 1.88
Set value .80

Federation Emblem A68

Design: 30m, Worker and emblem, vert.

Perf. 11½x12, 12x11½

1961, Jan. 29 Photo.

221 A68 30m dk gray & rose .15 .15
222 A68 50m ultra & red .20 .15
Set value .18

World Federation of Trade Unions, 15th anniv.

Patrice Lumumba (1925-1961), Premier of Congo — A69

1961, Apr. 8 *Perf. 11½x12*

223 A69 30m brown .85 .28
224 A69 50m violet gray 1.75 .40

Bridge — A70

Designs: 10m, Shoemaker. 15m, Department Store, Ulan Bator. 20m, Government building. 30m, State Theater, Ulan Bator. 50m, Machinist. 1t, Modern and old buildings.

1961, Apr. 30 *Perf. 11½x12, 15*

Sizes: 31½x21mm, 59x20mm (20m)

225 A70 5m emerald .15 .15
226 A70 10m blue .15 .15
227 A70 15m rose red .15 .15
228 A70 20m brown .18 .15
229 A70 30m blue .28 .18
230 A70 50m olive green .35 .24
231 A70 1t violet .50 .35
Nos. 225-231 (7) 1.76
Set value 1.05

40th anniversary of independence; modernization of Mongolia.

Yuri Gagarin and Globe — A71

Designs: 20m, Gagarin with rocket, vert. 50m, Gagarin making parachute descent, vert. 1t, Gagarin wearing helmet, globe.

1961, May 31 *Perf. 15*

232 A71 20m multi .20 .15
233 A71 30m multi .28 .15
234 A71 50m multi .50 .18
235 A71 1t multi .70 .45
Nos. 232-235 (4) 1.68 .93

Yuri A. Gagarin, 1st man in space, 4/12/61.

Postman on Reindeer A72

Designs: 15m, No. 241a, Postman on camel. 10m, 20m, Postman with yaks. 25m, No. 241c, Postman with ship. 30m, 50m, Diesel train.

1961, June 5 *Perf. 15*

236 A72 5m multi .15 .15
237 A72 15m multi .15 .15
238 A72 20m multi .15 .15
239 A72 25m multi .18 .15
240 A72 30m multi .24 .18
Nos. 236-240,C1-C3 (8) 2.02
Set value .95

Souvenir Sheet

Perf. 11

241 Sheet of 4 1.25 1.25
a. A72 5m light blue & brown .28 .28
b. A72 10m green, brown & blue .28 .28
c. A72 15m green, violet & brown .28 .28
d. A72 50m violet, green & black .28 .28

40th anniv. of independence; postal modernization. See No. C4b for 25m, perf. 11.

Souvenir Sheet

Ornamental Column — A73

1961, June 20 *Perf. 12*

242 A73 Sheet of 2 + label 2.00 1.75
a. 2t blue, red & gold .85 .85

40th anniversary of the Mongolian People's Revolution. No. 242 contains two No. 242a and label, imperf. between.

Herdsman and Oxen — A74

Designs: Herdsmen and domestic animals (except 1t and No. 252a).

1961, July 10 *Perf. 13*

243 A74 5m Rams .15 .15
244 A74 10m shown .15 .15
245 A74 15m Camels .15 .15
246 A74 20m Pigs and geese .15 .15
247 A74 25m Angora goats .15 .15
248 A74 30m Horses .18 .15
249 A74 40m Sheep .20 .15
250 A74 50m Cows .28 .20
251 A74 1t Combine harvester .48 .35
Set value 1.60 1.15

Souvenir Sheets

Perf. 12

252 Sheet of 3 1.00 1.00
a. A74 5m Combine harvester .28 .28
b. A74 15m Angora goats .28 .28
c. A74 40m Oxen .28 .28
253 Sheet of 3 1.00 1.00
a. A74 10m Pigs and geese .28 .28
b. A74 20m Horses .28 .28
c. A74 30m Cows .28 .28
254 Sheet of 3 1.00 1.00
a. A74 25m Camels .28 .28
b. A74 50m Rams .28 .28
c. A74 1t Sheep .28 .28

40th anniversary of independence. Nos. 252-254 each contain 3 stamps imperf. between.

Horseback Riders — A75

Designs: 5m, Young wrestlers and instructor. 15m, Camel and pony riders. 20m, Falconers. 30m, Skier. 50m, Archers. 1t, Male dancers.

1961, Aug. 10 *Perf. 11*

255 A75 5m multi .15 .15
256 A75 10m multi .15 .15
257 A75 15m multi .15 .15
258 A75 20m multi .15 .15
259 A75 30m multi .18 .15
260 A75 50m multi .35 .15
261 A75 1t multi .50 .24
Set value 1.30 .70

40th anniversary of independence; Mongolian youth sports.

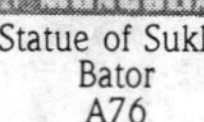

Statue of Sukhe Bator
A76

Arms of Mongolia
A77

Designs: 5m, Mongol youth. 10m, Mongol chieftain. 20m, Singer. 30m, Dancer. 50m, Dombra player. 70m, Musicians. 1t, Gymnast. 5m, 10m, 70m, 1t, horiz.

Perf. 12x11½, 11½x12

1961, Sept. 16

262 A76 5m brt grn & red lil .15 .15
263 A76 10m red & dk bl .15 .15
264 A76 15m bl & lt brn .15 .15
265 A76 20m pur & brt grn .15 .15
266 A76 30m vio bl & car .15 .15
267 A76 50m ol & vio .28 .28
268 A76 70m brt lil rose & ol .38 .38
269 A76 1t dk bl & ver .50 .45
Nos. 262-269 (8) 1.91 1.86

40th anniv. of independence; Mongolian culture.

1961, Nov. 17 *Perf. 11½x12*

270 A77 5m multi .15 .15
271 A77 10m multi .15 .15
272 A77 15m multi .15 .15
273 A77 20m multi .15 .15
274 A77 30m multi .18 .15
275 A77 50m multi .20 .15
276 A77 70m multi .28 .18
277 A77 1t multi .50 .28
Set value 1.50 .88

For surcharge see No. 2144A.

Congress Emblem
A78

1961, Dec. 4 **Litho.** *Perf. 11½*

278 A78 30m vio bl, yel & red .18 .15
279 A78 50m brn, yel & red .24 .18
Set value .28

5th World Congress of Trade Unions, Moscow, Dec. 4-16.

UN Emblem and Arms of Mongolia — A79

10m, Globe, map of Mongolia and dove. 50m, Flags of UN and Mongolia. 60m, UN Headquarters, New York and Parliament, Ulan Bator. 70m, UN assembly, UN and Mongolian flags.

1962, Mar. 15 **Photo.** *Perf. 11*

280 A79 10m gold & multi .15 .15
281 A79 30m gold & multi .15 .15
282 A79 50m gold & multi .20 .15
283 A79 60m gold & multi .40 .18
284 A79 70m gold & multi .60 .35
Nos. 280-284 (5) 1.50
Set value .75

Mongolia's admission to UN.

Soccer — A80

Designs: 10m, Soccer ball, globe and flags. 50m, Soccer players, globe and ball. 60m, Goalkeeper. 70m, Stadium.

1962, May 15 **Litho.** *Perf. 10½*

285 A80 10m multi .15 .15
286 A80 30m multi .15 .15
287 A80 50m multi .18 .15
288 A80 60m multi .35 .18
289 A80 70m multi .50 .20
Nos. 285-289 (5) 1.33
Set value .55

World Soccer Championship, Chile, 5/30-6/17.

D. Natsagdorji
A81

Solidarity Emblem
A82

1962, May 15 **Photo.** *Perf. 15x14½*

290 A81 30m brown .18 .15
291 A81 50m bluish grn .24 .15
Set value .20

Mongolian writers' congress.
For overprints see Nos. 430-431.

Perf. 11½x10½

1962, May 22 **Litho.**

292 A82 20m yel grn & multi .18 .15
293 A82 30m bl & multi .24 .15
Set value .20

Afro-Asian Peoples' solidarity.

Flags of USSR and Mongolia — A83

Perf. 11½x10½

1962, June 25 **Litho.**

294 A83 30m brn & multi .15 .15
295 A83 50m vio bl & multi .20 .15
Set value .20

Mongol-Soviet friendship.

Nos. 195-202 Overprinted

1962, July 20 **Photo.** *Perf. 11½x12*

296 A62 5m multi .15 .15
297 A62 10m multi .15 .15
298 A62 15m multi .20 .20
299 A62 20m multi .20 .20
300 A62 30m multi .24 .24
301 A62 40m multi .30 .30
302 A62 50m multi .48 .48
303 A62 1t multi .75 .75
Nos. 296-303 (8) 2.47 2.47

WHO drive to eradicate malaria.

Military Field Emblem — A84

Designs: 30m, Tablets with inscriptions. 50m, Stone column. 60m, Genghis Khan.

1962, July 20 *Perf. 11½x12*

304 A84 20m blue & multi .70 .70
305 A84 30m red & multi .70 .70
306 A84 50m pink, brn & blk 1.50 1.50
307 A84 60m blue & multi 2.25 2.25
Nos. 304-307 (4) 5.15 5.15

Genghis Khan (1162-1227), Mongol conqueror.
For overprints see Nos. 1846-1849.

River Perch — A85

1962, Dec. 28 *Perf. 11*

308 A85 5m shown .15 .15
309 A85 10m Burbot .15 .15
310 A85 15m Arctic grayling .15 .15
311 A85 20m Shorthorn sculpin .15 .15
312 A85 30m Marine zander .18 .15
313 A85 50m Siberian sturgeon .20 .15
314 A85 70m Waleck's chub minnow .35 .18
315 A85 1.50t Cottocomephorid .55 .30
Set value 1.60 .85

Sukhe Bator (1893-1923), National Hero — A86

1963, Feb. 2 **Photo.** *Perf. 11½x12*

316 A86 30m blue .15 .15
317 A86 60m rose car .20 .15
Set value .20

Laika and Rocket
A87

Designs: 15m, Rocket launching, vert. 25m, Lunik 2, vert. 70m, Andrian G. Nikolayev and Pavel R. Popovich. 1t, Mars rocket.

1963, Apr. 1 **Litho.** *Perf. 12½x12*

Size: 46x32mm

318 A87 5m multicolored .15 .15

Size: 20x68mm

319 A87 15m multicolored .15 .15
320 A87 25m multicolored .24 .15

Size: 46x32mm

321 A87 70m multicolored .38 .20
322 A87 1t multicolored .60 .35
Nos. 318-322 (5) 1.52
Set value .78

Soviet space explorations.

Blood Transfusion — A88

1963, Aug. 15 *Perf. 10½*

323 A88 20m Packing Red Cross parcels .15 .15
324 A88 30m shown .15 .15
325 A88 50m Vaccination .18 .15
326 A88 60m Ambulance service .24 .18
327 A88 1.30t Centenary emblem .50 .40
Nos. 323-327 (5) 1.22
Set value .80

Red Cross centenary.

Karl Marx — A89

Mongolian Woman — A90

1963, Sept. 16 **Photo.** *Perf. 11½x12*

328 A89 30m blue .15 .15
329 A89 60m dk car rose .20 .15
Set value .20

145th anniversary of birth of Karl Marx.

1963, Sept. 26

330 A90 30m blue & multi .18 .15

5th Intl. Women's Cong., Moscow, June 24-29.

Inachis
A91

Designs: Mongolian butterflies.

1963, Nov. 7 **Litho.** *Perf. 11½*

331 A91 5m shown .15 .15
332 A91 10m Gonepteryxrhamni .15 .15
333 A91 15m Aglais urticae .15 .15
334 A91 20m Parnassius apollo .15 .15
335 A91 30m Papilio machaon .20 .15
336 A91 60m Agrodiaetus damon .35 .20
337 A91 1t Limenitis populi .48 .28
Set value 1.38 .85

UNESCO Emblem, Globe and Scales — A92

1963, Dec. 10 **Photo.** *Perf. 12*

338 A92 30m multicolored .18 .15
339 A92 60m multicolored .28 .15
Set value .18

Universal Declaration of Human Rights, 15th anniversary.

Coprinus Comatus — A93

Designs: Mushrooms.

1964, Jan. 1 Litho. *Perf. 10½*

340 A93 5m shown .15 .15
341 A93 10m Lactarius torminosus .15 .15
342 A93 15m Psalliota campestris .15 .15
343 A93 20m Russula delica .15 .15
344 A93 30m Ixocomus granulatus .20 .15
345 A93 50m Lactarius scrobiculatus .24 .18
346 A93 70m Lactarius deliciosus .35 .20
347 A93 1t Ixocomus variegatus .50 .28
Set value 1.60 .95

Souvenir Sheet

Skier — A94

1964, Feb. 12 Photo. *Perf. 12x11½*

348 A94 4t gray 2.00 2.00

9th Winter Olympic Games, Innsbruck, Jan. 29-Feb. 9.

Lenin — A95

1964 Photo. *Perf. 11½x12*

349 A95 30m salmon & multi .48 .15
350 A95 50m blue & multi .55 .15
Set value .20

60th anniversary of Communist Party. Nos. 349-350 printed with alternating label showing Lenin quotation.

Javelin — A96

1964, Apr. 30 Litho. *Perf. 10½*

351 A96 5m Gymnastics, women's .15 .15
352 A96 10m shown .15 .15
353 A96 15m Wrestling .15 .15
354 A96 20m Running, women's .15 .15
355 A96 30m Equestrian .20 .15
356 A96 50m Diving, women's .28 .15
357 A96 60m Bicycling .35 .20
358 A96 1t Olympic Games emblem .60 .28
Set value 1.70 .95

Souvenir Sheet

Perf. 12x11½

359 A96 4t Wrestling 2.50 2.50

18th Olympic Games, Toyko, Oct. 10-25. No. 359 contains one horizontal stamp, 37x27½mm. Issued Sept. 1.

Congress Emblem — A97

1964, Sept. 30 Photo. *Perf. 11*

360 A97 30m multicolored .24 .15

4th Mongolian Women's Congress.

Lunik 1 — A98

Russian Space Research: 10m, Vostok 1 and 2. 15m, Tiros weather satellite, vert. 20m, Cosmos circling earth, vert. 30m, Mars probe, vert. 60m, Luna 4, vert. 80m, Echo 2. 1t, Radar and rockets.

1964, Oct. 30

361 A98 5m multicolored .15 .15
362 A98 10m multicolored .15 .15
363 A98 15m multicolored .15 .15
364 A98 20m multicolored .15 .15
365 A98 30m multicolored .20 .15
366 A98 60m multicolored .24 .15
367 A98 80m multicolored .24 .15
368 A98 1t multicolored .45 .24
Set value 1.50 .70

Rider Carrying Flag — A99

1964, Nov. 26 Photo. *Perf. 11½x12*

369 A99 25m multicolored .20 .15
370 A99 50m multicolored .30 .15
Set value .20

40th anniversary of Mongolian constitution.

Weather Balloon A100

Designs: 5m, Oceanographic exploration. 60m, Northern lights and polar bears. 80m, Gemagnetism. 1t, I.Q.S.Y. emblem and Mercator map.

1965, May 15 Photo. *Perf. 13½*

371 A100 5m gray & multi .15 .15
372 A100 10m grn & multi .15 .15
373 A100 60m blue, blk & pink .20 .15
374 A100 80m citron & multi .40 .20
375 A100 1t brt green & multi .70 .38
Nos. 371-375,C6-C8 (8) 2.10
Set value 1.10

International Quiet Sun Year.

Horses — A101

Designs: Mongolian horses.

1965, Aug. 25 *Perf. 11*

376 A101 5m shown .15 .15
377 A101 10m Falconers .15 .15
378 A101 15m Taming wild horse .15 .15
379 A101 20m Horse race .15 .15
380 A101 30m Hurdles .18 .15
381 A101 60m Wolf hunt .20 .15
382 A101 80m Milking a mare .28 .20
383 A101 1t Mare and foal .45 .30
Set value 1.40 .95

Girl Holding Lambs — A102

1965, Oct. 10 Photo. *Perf. 11*

384 A102 5m shown .15 .15
385 A102 10m Boy and girl drummers .15 .15
386 A102 20m Camp fire .15 .15
387 A102 30m Wrestlers .24 .15
388 A102 50m Emblem .35 .28
Set value .82 .58
Nos. 384-388 (5) 1.04 .88

40th anniv. of Mongolian Youth Org.

Chinese Perch — A103

1965, Nov. 25

389 A103 5m shown .15 .15
390 A103 10m Lenok trout .15 .15
391 A103 15m Siberian sturgeon .15 .15
392 A103 20m Amur salmon .15 .15
393 A103 30m Bagrid catfish .18 .15
394 A103 60m Siluri catfish .24 .15
395 A103 80m Northern pike .35 .18
396 A103 1t River perch .50 .28
Nos. 389-396 (8) 1.87
Set value .90

Marx and Lenin — A104

1965, Dec. 15 *Perf. 11½x12*

397 A104 10m red & blk .15 .15

6th Conference of Postal Ministers of Communist Countries, Peking, June 21-July 15.

Sable — A105

1966, Feb. 15 Photo. *Perf. 12½*

398 A105 5m shown .15 .15
399 A105 10m Fox .15 .15
400 A105 15m Otter, vert. .15 .15
401 A105 20m Cheetah, vert. .15 .15
402 A105 30m Pallas's cat .18 .15
403 A105 60m Stone marten .24 .15
404 A105 80m Ermine, vert. .30 .20
405 A105 1t Woman in mink coat, vert. .50 .28
Set value 1.50 .90

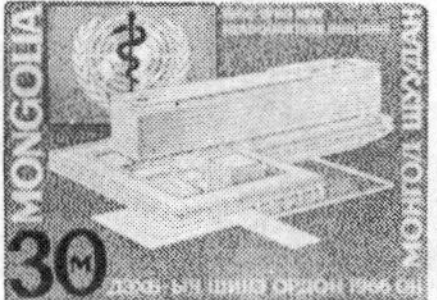

Opening of WHO Headquarters, Geneva A106

1966, May 3 Photo. *Perf. 12x11½*

406 A106 30m bl grn, bl & gold .15 .15
407 A106 50m red, bl & gold .28 .15
Set value .16

For overprints see Nos. 483-484.

Soccer — A107

Designs: 30m, 60m, 80m, Various soccer plays. 1t, British flag and World Soccer Cup emblem. 4t, Wembley Stadium, horiz.

1966, May 31 Photo. *Perf. 11*

408 A107 10m multicolored .15 .15
409 A107 30m multicolored .15 .15
410 A107 60m multicolored .18 .15
411 A107 80m multicolored .30 .18
412 A107 1t multicolored .50 .30
Nos. 408-412 (5) 1.28
Set value .70

Souvenir Sheet

Perf. 12½, Imperf.

413 A107 4t gray & brown 3.50 2.00

World Soccer Championship for Jules Rimet Cup, Wembley, England, July 11-30. No. 413 contains one stamp 61x83mm.

Sukhe Bator, Parliament Building, Ulan Bator A108

1966, June 7 Litho. *Perf. 12x12½*

414 A108 30m red, bl & brn .20 .15

15th Congress of Mongolian Communist Party.

Wrestling — A109

Designs: Various wrestling holds.

1966, June 15 Photo. *Perf. 11½x12*

415 A109 10m multicolored .15 .15
416 A109 30m multicolored .15 .15
417 A109 60m multicolored .24 .15
418 A109 80m multicolored .28 .18
419 A109 1t multicolored .35 .28
Set value 1.00 .68

World Wrestling Championship, Toledo, Spain.

Emblem and Map of Mongolia — A110

Sukhe Bator, Grain and Factories A111

Perf. 11½x12, 12x11½

1966, July 11 **Litho.**
420 A110 30m red & multi .20 .15
421 A111 50m red & multi .30 .18

45th anniversary of independence.
For overprints see Nos. 552-553.

Lilium Tenuifolium A112

1966, Oct. 15 **Photo.** *Perf. 12x11½*
422 A112 5m Physochlaena physaloides .15 .15
423 A112 10m Allium polyrrchizum .15 .15
424 A112 15m shown .15 .15
425 A112 20m Thermopsis lanceolata .15 .15
426 A112 30m Amygdalus mongolica .18 .15
427 A112 60m Caryopteris mongolica .24 .15
428 A112 80m Piptanthus mongolicus .30 .20
429 A112 1t Iris bungei .45 .30
Set value 1.55 .90

Nos. 290-291 Overprinted: "1906/1966"

1966, Oct. 26 **Photo.** *Perf. 15x14½*
430 A81 30m brown .28 .15
431 A81 50m bluish grn .35 .15
Set value .22

60th anniv. of birth of D. Natsagdorji, writer.
50m exists double, one inverted.

Child with Dove — A113

1966, Dec. 2 *Perf. 11½x12, 12x11½*
432 A113 10m shown .15 .15
433 A113 15m Children with reindeer .15 .15
434 A113 20m Boys wrestling, vert. .15 .15
435 A113 30m Horseback riding .20 .15
436 A113 60m Children riding camel, vert. .24 .15
437 A113 80m Child with sheep .35 .15
438 A113 1t Boy archer, vert. .50 .28
Nos. 432-438 (7) 1.74
Set value .80

Children's Day.

Proton 1 — A114

Perf. 11½x12½, 12½x11½

1966, Dec. 28 **Photo.**
439 A114 5m Vostok 2, vert. .15 .15
440 A114 10m shown .15 .15
441 A114 15m Telstar 1, vert. .15 .15
442 A114 20m Molnija 1, vert. .15 .15
443 A114 30m Syncom 3, vert. .18 .15
444 A114 60m Luna 9 .24 .15
445 A114 80m Luna 12, vert. .30 .18
446 A114 1t Mariner 4 .45 .20
Set value 1.55 .90

Space exploration.

Tarbosaurus A115

1967, Mar. 31 *Perf. 12x11½*
447 A115 5m shown .15 .15
448 A115 10m Talarurus .15 .15
449 A115 15m Proceratops .15 .15
450 A115 20m Indricotherium .15 .15
451 A115 30m Saurolophus .18 .15
452 A115 60m Mastodon .20 .15
453 A115 80m Mongolotherium .30 .18
454 A115 1t Mammoth .45 .20
Set value 1.50 .90

Prehistoric animals.

A116

A117

Congress emblem.

1967, June 9 **Litho.** *Perf. 12*
455 A116 30m lt blue & multi .18 .15
456 A116 50m pink & multi .24 .20

9th Youth Festival for Peace and Friendship, Sofia.

1967, Oct. 25 **Litho.** *Perf. 11½x12*

Design: 40m, Sukhe Bator and soldiers. 60m, Lenin and soldiers.

457 A117 40m red & multi .28 .24
458 A117 60m red & multi .35 .28

Russian October Revolution, 50th anniv.

Ice Hockey and Olympic Rings A118

1967, Dec. 29 *Perf. 12x12½*
459 A118 5m Figure skating .15 .15
460 A118 10m Speed skating .15 .15
461 A118 15m shown .15 .15
462 A118 20m Ski jump .18 .15
463 A118 30m Bobsledding .20 .15
464 A118 60m Figure skating, pair .40 .15
465 A118 80m Slalom .55 .24
Nos. 459-465 (7) 1.78
Set value .72

Souvenir Sheet

Perf. 12

466 A118 4t Women's figure skating 2.00 2.00

10th Winter Olympic Games, Grenoble, France, Feb. 6-18.

Bactrian Camels A119

1968, Jan. 15 **Photo.** *Perf. 12*
467 A119 5m shown .15 .15
468 A119 10m Yak .15 .15
469 A119 15m Lamb .18 .15
470 A119 20m Foal .20 .15
471 A119 30m Calf .24 .15
472 A119 60m Bison .30 .15
473 A119 80m Roe deer .38 .18
474 A119 1t Reindeer .55 .28
Nos. 467-474 (8) 2.15
Set value .90

Young animals.

Black Currants A120

Berries: 5m, Rosa acicularis. 15m, Gooseberries. 20m, Malus. 30m, Strawberries. 60m, Ribes altissimum. 80m, Blueberries. 1t, Hippophae rhamnoides.

Lithographed & Engraved

1968, Feb. 15
475 A120 5m blue & ultra .15 .15
476 A120 10m buff & brn .15 .15
477 A120 15m lt grn & grn .15 .15
478 A120 20m yel & red .18 .15
479 A120 30m pink & car .28 .15
480 A120 60m sal & org brn .35 .15
481 A120 80m pale & dl bl .45 .18
482 A120 1t lt yel & red .60 .24
Nos. 475-482 (8) 2.31
Set value .85

Nos. 406-407 Overprinted ДЭХБ 20 ЖИЛ WHO

1968, Apr. 16 **Photo.** *Perf. 12x11½*
483 A106 30m bl grn, bl & gold .18 .15
484 A106 50m red, blue & gold .24 .15
Set value .22

WHO, 20th anniversary.

Human Rights Flame — A121

1968, June 20 **Litho.** *Perf. 12*
485 A121 30m turq & vio bl .15 .15

International Human Rights Year.

"Das Kapital," by Karl Marx A122

Design: 50m, Karl Marx.

1968, July 1 **Litho.** *Perf. 12*
486 A122 30m blue & multi .18 .15
487 A122 50m red & multi .24 .15
Set value .20

Karl Marx (1818-1883).

Artist, by A. Sangatzohyo A123

Paintings: 10m, On Remote Roads, by Sangatzohyo. 15m, Camel calf, by B. Avarzad. 20m, Milk, by Avarzad. 30m, The Bowman, by B. Gombosuren. 80m, Girl Sitting on Yak, by Sangatzohyo. 1.40t, Cagan Dara Eke, by Janaivajara. 4t, Meeting, by Sangatzohyo, horiz.

1968, July 11 **Litho.** *Perf. 12*
488 A123 5m brown & multi .15 .15
489 A123 10m brown & multi .15 .15
490 A123 15m brown & multi .15 .15
491 A123 20m brown & multi .24 .15
492 A123 30m brown & multi .35 .15
493 A123 80m brown & multi .48 .18
494 A123 1.40t brown & multi .70 .35
Nos. 488-494 (7) 2.22
Set value .90

Miniature Sheets

Perf. 11½, Imperf.

495 A123 4t brown & multi 2.25 2.25

Paintings from national museum, Ulan Bator. #495 contains one 54x84mm stamp.

Volleyball A124

Sports (Olympic Rings and): 10m, Wrestling. 15m, Bicycling. 20m, Javelin, women's. 30m, Soccer. 60m, Running. 80m, Gymnastics, women's. 1t, Weight lifting. 4t, Equestrian.

1968, Sept. 1 **Litho.** *Perf. 12*
496 A124 5m multicolored .15 .15
497 A124 10m multicolored .15 .15
498 A124 15m multicolored .15 .15
499 A124 20m multicolored .15 .15
500 A124 30m multicolored .20 .15
501 A124 60m multicolored .28 .15
502 A124 80m multicolored .30 .18
503 A124 1t multicolored .60 .20
Set value 1.75 .78

Souvenir Sheets

Perf. 11½, Imperf.

504 A124 4t orange & multi 2.75 2.75

19th Olympic Games, Mexico City, Oct. 12-27. #504 contains one 52x44mm stamp.

A125

A126

Hammer, spade & cogwheel.

1968, Sept. 17 **Litho.** *Perf. 11½*
505 A125 50m blue & vermilion .15 .15

Industrial development in town of Darhan.

1968, Nov. 6 **Litho.** *Perf. 12*
506 A126 60m turquoise & sepia .18 .15

Maxim Gorki (1868-1936), Russian writer.

Madonna and Child, by Boltraffio
A127

Paintings: 10m, St. Roch Healed by an Angel, by Brescia. 15m, Madonna and Child with St. Anne, by Macchietti. 20m, St. John on Patmos, by Cano. 30m, Lady with Viola da Gamba, by Kupetzky. 80m, Boy, by Amerling. 1.40t, Death of Adonis, by Furini. 4t, Portrait of a Lady, by Renoir.

1968, Nov. 20 Litho. *Perf. 12*

507	A127	5m gray & multi	.15	.15
508	A127	10m gray & multi	.15	.15
509	A127	15m gray & multi	.15	.15
510	A127	20m gray & multi	.20	.15
511	A127	30m gray & multi	.30	.15
512	A127	80m gray & multi	.45	.20
513	A127	1.40t gray & multi	.60	.28
		Nos. 507-513 (7)	2.00	
		Set value		.94

Miniature Sheet

514	A127	4t gray & multi	2.25	2.25

UNESCO, 22nd anniv.

Jesse Owens, US
A128

Olympic Gold Medal Winners: 5m, Paavo Nurmi, Finland. 15m, Fanny Blankers-Koen, Netherlands. 20m, Laszlo Papp, Hungary. 30m, Wilma Rudolph, US. 60m, Boris Sahlin, USSR. 80m, Donald Schollander, US. 1t Akinori Nakayama, Japan. 4t, Jigjidin Munhbat, Mongolia.

1969, Mar. 25 Litho. *Perf. 12*

515	A128	5m multicolored	.15	.15
516	A128	10m multicolored	.15	.15
517	A128	15m multicolored	.15	.15
518	A128	20m multicolored	.15	.15
519	A128	30m multicolored	.15	.15
520	A128	60m multicolored	.15	.15
521	A128	80m multicolored	.28	.24
522	A128	1t multicolored	.60	.28
		Set value	1.30	.85

Souvenir Sheet

523	A128	4t green & multi	2.75	2.75

Bayit Woman
A129

Regional Costumes: 10m, Torgut man. 15m, Dzakhachin woman. 20m, Khalkha woman. 30m, Dariganga woman. 60m, Mingat woman. 80m, Khalkha man. 1t, Bargut woman.

1969, Apr. 20 Litho. *Perf. 12*

524	A129	5m multicolored	.15	.15
525	A129	10m multicolored	.15	.15
526	A129	15m multicolored	.15	.15
527	A129	20m multicolored	.15	.15
528	A129	30m multicolored	.18	.15
529	A129	60m multicolored	.24	.15
530	A129	80m multicolored	.30	.15
531	A129	1t multicolored	.48	.20
		Set value	1.55	.75

Red Cross Emblem and Helicopter — A130

50m, Emblem, Red Cross car and shepherd.

1969, May 15 Litho. *Perf. 12*

532	A130	30m multicolored	.15	.15
533	A130	50m multicolored	.20	.15
		Set value		.22

30th anniversary of Mongolian Red Cross.

Landscape and Edelweiss — A131

Designs: Mongolian landscapes and flowers.

1969, May 20

534	A131	5m shown	.15	.15
535	A131	10m Pinks	.15	.15
536	A131	15m Dianthus superbus	.15	.15
537	A131	20m Geranium	.15	.15
538	A131	30m Dianthus ramosissimus	.18	.15
539	A131	60m Globeflowers	.24	.15
540	A131	80m Delphinium	.28	.20
541	A131	1t Haloxylon	.45	.28
		Set value	1.50	.90

See No. 1105.

Bull Fight, by Tsewegdjaw — A132

Paintings from National Museum: 10m, Fighting Colts, by O. Tsewegdjaw. 15m, Horseman and Herd, by A. Sangatzohyo. 20m, Camel Caravan, by D. Damdinsuren. 30m, On the Steppe, by N. Tsultem. 60m, Milking Mares, by Tsewegdjaw. 80m, Going to School, by B. Avarzad. 1t, After Work, by G. Odon. 4t, Horses, by Damdinsuren.

1969, July 11 Litho. *Perf. 12*

542	A132	5m multicolored	.15	.15
543	A132	10m multicolored	.15	.15
544	A132	15m multicolored	.15	.15
545	A132	20m multicolored	.15	.15
546	A132	30m multicolored	.18	.15
547	A132	60m multicolored	.24	.15
548	A132	80m multicolored	.28	.18
549	A132	1t multicolored	.45	.20
		Set value	1.45	.80

Souvenir Sheet

550	A132	4t multicolored	1.75	1.75

10th anniversary of cooperative movement. No. 550 contains one stamp 65x42mm.

Mongolian Flag and Emblem — A133

1969, Sept. 20 Litho. *Perf. 12*

551	A133	50m multicolored	.18	.15

Battle of Ha-lo-hsin (Khalka) River, 30th anniversary.

Nos. 420-421 Overprinted

ВНМАУ-ыг
түнхагласны
45
жилийн ой
1969—XI—26

Perf. 11½x12, 12x11½

1969, Nov. 26 Photo.

552	A110	30m red & multi	.20	.15
553	A111	50m red & multi	.28	.20

45th anniv. of Mongolian People's Republic.

Mercury 7 — A134

Designs: 5m, Sputnik 3. 10m, Vostok 1. 20m, Voskhod 2. 30m, Apollo 8. 60m, Soyuz 5. 80m, Apollo 12.

1969, Dec. 6 Photo. *Perf. 12x11½*

554	A134	5m multicolored	.15	.15
555	A134	10m multicolored	.15	.15
556	A134	15m multicolored	.15	.15
557	A134	20m multicolored	.18	.15
558	A134	30m multicolored	.28	.15
559	A134	60m multicolored	.38	.18
560	A134	80m multicolored	.55	.20
		Nos. 554-560 (7)	1.84	
		Set value		.65

Souvenir Sheet

561	A134	4t multicolored	2.25	2.25

Space achievements of US and USSR.

Wolf — A135

Designs: 10m, Brown bear. 15m, Lynx. 20m, Wild boar. 30m, Moose. 60m, Bobac marmot. 80m, Argali. 1t, Old wall carpet showing hunter and dog.

1970, Mar. 25 Photo. *Perf. 12*

562	A135	5m multicolored	.15	.15
563	A135	10m multicolored	.15	.15
564	A135	15m multicolored	.15	.15
565	A135	20m multicolored	.15	.15
566	A135	30m multicolored	.15	.15
567	A135	60m multicolored	.24	.15
568	A135	80m multicolored	.35	.18
569	A135	1t multicolored	.45	.28
		Set value	1.55	.90

Lenin and Mongolian Delegation, by Sangatzohyo — A136

Designs: 20m, Lenin, embroidered panel, by Cerenhuu, vert. 1t, Lenin, by Mazhig, vert.

1970, Apr. 22 Photo. & Litho.

570	A136	20m multicolored	.15	.15
571	A136	50m multicolored	.18	.15
572	A136	1t lt bl, blk & red	.35	.18
		Set value	.56	.32

Centenary of the birth of Lenin.

Souvenir Sheet

EXPO '70 Pavilion of Matsushita Electric Co. and Time Capsule — A137

1970, May 26 Photo. *Perf. 12½*

573	A137	4t gold & multi	2.25	2.25

EXPO '70 International Exposition, Osaka, Japan, Mar. 15-Sept. 13.

Sumitomo Fairy Tale Pavilion
A138

1970, June 5 Photo. *Perf. 12x11½*

574	A138	1.50t multicolored	.50	.40

EXPO '70 International Exposition, Osaka. No. 574 printed in sheets of 20 (5x4) with alternating horizontal rows of tabs showing various fairy tales and EXPO '70 emblem.

Soccer, Rimet Cup — A139

Soccer players of various teams in action.

1970, June 20 *Perf. 12½x11½*

575	A139	10m multi	.15	.15
576	A139	20m multi	.15	.15
577	A139	30m multi	.15	.15
578	A139	50m multi	.15	.15
579	A139	60m multi	.20	.15
580	A139	1t multi	.40	.20
581	A139	1.30t multi	.50	.30
		Nos. 575-581 (7)	1.70	
		Set value		.85

Souvenir Sheet

Perf. 12½

582	A139	4t multi	2.00	2.00

World Soccer Championship for Jules Rimet Cup, Mexico City, May 30-June 21. No. 582 contains one stamp 51x37mm.

Old World Buzzard
A140

Birds of Prey: 20m, Tawny owls. 30m, Northern goshawk. 50m, White-tailed sea eagle. 60m, Peregrine falcon. 1t, Old world kestrel. 1.30t, Black kite.

1970, June 30 Litho. *Perf. 12*

583	A140	10m bl & multi	.15	.15
584	A140	20m pink & multi	.15	.15
585	A140	30m yel grn & multi	.15	.15
586	A140	50m bl & multi	.18	.15
587	A140	60m yel & multi	.20	.15
588	A140	1t grn & multi	.35	.24
589	A140	1.30t bl & multi	.50	.28
		Nos. 583-589 (7)	1.68	
		Set value		.90

Russian War Memorial, Berlin — A141

1970, July 11 **Litho.** ***Perf. 12***
590 A141 60m bl & multi .18 .15

25th anniversary of end of World War II.

Bogdo-Gegen Palace — A142

Designs: 10m, Archer. 30m, Horseman. 40m, "White Mother" Goddess. 50m, Girl in national costume. 60m, Lion statue. 70m, Dancer's mask. 80m, Detail from Bogdo-Gegen Palace, Ulan Bator.

1970, Sept. 20 **Litho.** ***Perf. 12***
591 A142 10m multi .15 .15
592 A142 20m multi .15 .15
593 A142 30m multi .18 .15
594 A142 40m multi .20 .15
595 A142 50m multi .28 .20
596 A142 60m multi .35 .28
597 A142 70m multi .40 .35
598 A142 80m multi .50 .40
Nos. 591-598 (8) 2.21 1.83

Nos. 595-598 printed se-tenant in blocks of 4, in sheets of 40.

Souvenir Sheet

Recovery of Apollo 13 Capsule A143

1970, Nov. 1 **Litho.** ***Perf. 12***
599 A143 4t blue & multi 2.00 2.00

Space missions of Apollo 13, Apr. 11-17, and Soyuz 9, June 1-10, 1970.

Mongolian Flag, UN and Education Year Emblems A144

1970, Nov. 7
600 A144 60m multi .40 .18

International Education Year.

Mounted Herald A145

1970, Nov. 7 **Litho.** ***Perf. 12***
601 A145 30m gold & multi .15 .15

50th anniv. of newspaper Unen (Truth).

Apollo 11 Lunar Landing Module — A146

Designs: 10m, Vostok 2 and 3. 20m, Voskhod 2 and space walk. 30m, Gemini 6 and 7 capsules. 50m, Soyuz 4 and 5 docking in space. 60m, Soyuz 6, 7 and 8 group flight. 1t, Apollo 13 with damaged capsule. 1.30t, Luna 16 unmanned moon landing. 4t, Radar ground tracking station.

1971, Feb. 25 **Litho.** ***Perf. 12***
602 A146 10m multi .15 .15
603 A146 20m multi .15 .15
604 A146 30m multi .15 .15
605 A146 50m multi .20 .15
606 A146 60m multi .26 .15
607 A146 80m multi .26 .15
608 A146 1t multi .45 .15
609 A146 1.30t multi .55 .15
Nos. 602-609 (8) 2.17
Set value .65

Souvenir Sheet

610 A146 4t vio bl & multi 2.25 2.25

US and USSR space explorations.

Rider with Mongolian Flag — A147

Designs: 30m, Party meeting. 90m, Lenin with Mongolian leader. 1.20t, Marchers, pictures of Lenin and Marx.

1971, Mar. 1 **Photo.** ***Perf. 12½***
611 A147 30m gold & multi .15 .15
612 A147 60m gold & multi .15 .15
613 A147 90m gold & multi .18 .15
614 A147 1.30t gold & multi .35 .28
Nos. 611-614 (4) .83
Set value .54

Mongolian Revolutionary Party, 50th anniv.

Souvenir Sheet

Lunokhod 1 on Moon — A148

Design: No. 615b, Apollo 14 on moon.

1971, Apr. 15 **Photo.** ***Perf. 14***
615 A148 Sheet of 2 2.00 2.00
a.-b. 2t any single .80 .80

Luna 17 unmanned automated moon mission, Nov. 10-17, 1970, and Apollo 14 moon landing, Jan. 31-Feb. 9, 1971.

Dancer's Mask — A149

Designs: Various masks for dancers.

1971, Apr. 25 **Litho.** ***Perf. 12***
616 A149 10m gold & multi .15 .15
617 A149 20m gold & multi .15 .15
618 A149 30m gold & multi .20 .15
619 A149 50m gold & multi .24 .15
620 A149 60m gold & multi .28 .15
621 A149 1t gold & multi .55 .20
622 A149 1.30t gold & multi .75 .24
Nos. 616-622 (7) 2.32
Set value .75

Red Flag and Emblems A150

1971, May 31 **Photo.** ***Perf. 12x11½***
623 A150 60m bl, red & gold .18 .15

16th Congress of Mongolian Revolutionary Party.

Steam Locomotive — A151

1971, July 11 **Litho.** ***Perf. 12***
624 A151 20m shown .15 .15
625 A151 30m Diesel locomotive .15 .15
626 A151 40m Truck .15 .15
627 A151 50m Automobile .20 .15
628 A151 60m Biplane PO-2 .24 .15
629 A151 80m AN-24 plane .32 .18
630 A151 1t Fishing boat .40 .20
Nos. 624-630 (7) 1.61
Set value .72

50th anniversary of modern transportation.
For overprints see Nos. 850A-850G.

Arms of Mongolia and Soldier — A152

Design: 1.50t, Arms, policeman and child.

1971, July 11 **Litho.** ***Perf. 12***
631 A152 60m multi .15 .15
632 A152 1.50t multi .40 .18
Set value .26

50th anniversary of the people's army and police.

Mongolian Flag and Emblem A153

1971, Aug. 25 **Photo.** ***Perf. 12x11½***
633 A153 60m lt bl & multi .18 .15

International Year Against Racial discrimination.

Flag of Youth Organization — A154

1971, Aug. 25 **Litho.** ***Perf. 12***
634 A154 60m org & multi .20 .15

50th anniversary of Mongolian revolutionary youth organization.

The Woodsman and the Tiger — A155

Designs: Various Mongolian fairy tales.

1971, Sept. 15 **Litho.** ***Perf. 12***
635 A155 10m gold & multi .15 .15
636 A155 20m gold & multi .15 .15
637 A155 30m gold & multi .15 .15
638 A155 50m gold & multi .18 .15
639 A155 60m gold & multi .25 .15
640 A155 80m gold & multi .30 .15
641 A155 1t gold & multi .38 .18
642 A155 1.30t gold & multi .55 .24
Nos. 635-642 (8) 2.11
Set value .88

Bactrian Camel A156

1971, Nov. 1 **Litho.** ***Perf. 12½***
643 A156 20m Yaks .15 .15
644 A156 30m shown .15 .15
645 A156 40m Sheep .15 .15
646 A156 50m Goats .18 .15
647 A156 60m Cattle .28 .18
648 A156 80m Horses .35 .20
649 A156 1t White horse .45 .24
Nos. 643-649 (7) 1.71
Set value .90

Mongolian livestock breeding.

Cross-country Skiing — A157

Designs (Sapporo Olympic Emblem and): 20m, Bobsledding. 30m, Women's figure skating. 50m, Slalom. 60m, Speed skating. 80m, Downhill skiing. 1t, Ice hockey. 1.30t, Figure skating, pairs. 4t, Ski jump.

Perf. 12½x11½

1972, Jan. 20 **Photo.**
650 A157 10m multi .15 .15
651 A157 20m ol & multi .15 .15
652 A157 30m ultra & multi .15 .15
653 A157 50m brt bl & multi .15 .15
654 A157 60m multi .20 .15
655 A157 80m grn & multi .24 .15
656 A157 1t bl & multi .30 .18
657 A157 1.30t vio & multi .38 .24
Set value 1.50 .90

Souvenir Sheet

Perf. 12½

658	A157	4t lt bl & multi	2.00	2.00

11th Winter Olympic Games, Sapporo, Japan, Feb. 3-13.

Taming Wild Horse — A158

Paintings: 20m, Mythological animal in winter. 30m, Lancer on horseback. 50m, Athletes. 60m, Waterfall and horses. 80m, The Wise Musician, by Sarav. 1t, Young musician. 1.30t, Old sage with animals.

1972, Apr. 15 Litho. *Perf. 12*

659	A158	10m multi	.15	.15
660	A158	20m multi	.15	.15
661	A158	30m multi	.15	.15
662	A158	50m multi	.15	.15
663	A158	60m multi	.20	.15
664	A158	80m multi	.24	.15
665	A158	1t multi	.30	.20
666	A158	1.30t multi	.38	.24
		Set value	1.50	.90

Paintings by contemporary artists in Ulan Bator Museum.

Calosoma Fischeri A159

Designs: Various insects.

1972, Apr. 30 Litho. *Perf. 12*

667	A159	10m multi	.15	.15
668	A159	20m multi	.15	.15
669	A159	30m multi	.15	.15
670	A159	50m multi	.15	.15
671	A159	60m multi	.24	.15
672	A159	80m multi	.28	.15
673	A159	1t multi	.35	.20
674	A159	1.30t multi	.40	.24
		Nos. 667-674 (8)	1.87	
		Set value		.90

UN Emblem — A160

1972, Aug. 30 Photo. *Perf. 12*

675	A160	60m multi	.20	.15

ECAFE (UN Economic Commission for Asia and the Far East), 25th anniv.

Slow Lizard — A161

Designs: 15m, Radd's toad. 20m, Pallas's viper. 25m, Toad-headed agamid. 30m, Siberian wood frog. 60m, Przewalski's lizard. 80m, Taphrometopon lineolatum (snake). 1t, Stoliczka's agamid.

1972, Sept. 5 Litho. *Perf. 12*

676	A161	10m multi	.15	.15
677	A161	15m multi	.15	.15
678	A161	20m multi	.15	.15
679	A161	25m multi	.15	.15
680	A161	30m multi	.18	.15
681	A161	60m multi	.28	.15
682	A161	80m multi	.35	.20
683	A161	1t multi	.40	.24
		Nos. 676-683 (8)	1.81	
		Set value		.90

Symbols of Technical Knowledge A162

Design: 60m, University of Mongolia.

1972, Sept. 25

684	A162	50m org & multi	.18	.15
685	A162	60m lil & multi	.20	.15
		Set value		.15

30th anniversary of Mongolian State University.

Virgin and Child with St. John, by Bellini — A163

Paintings by Venetian Masters: 20m, Transfiguration, by Bellini, vert. 30m, Virgin and Child, by Bellini, vert. 50m, Presentation in the Temple, by Bellini. 60m, St. George, by Mantegna, vert. 80m, Departure of St. Ursula, by Carpaccio, vert. 1t, Departure of St. Ursula, by Carpaccio.

1972, Oct. 1

686	A163	10m multi	.15	.15
687	A163	20m multi	.15	.15
688	A163	30m multi	.15	.15
689	A163	50m multi	.20	.15
690	A163	60m multi	.35	.18
691	A163	80m multi	.40	.20
692	A163	1t multi	.55	.24
		Nos. 686-692 (7)	1.95	
		Set value		.95

Save Venice campaign. See No. B3.

Manlay Bator Ramdinsuren A164

Designs: 20m, Ard Ayus, horiz. 50m, Hatan Bator Magsarzhav. 60m, Has Bator, horiz. 1t, Sukhe Bator.

1972, Oct. 20 Litho. *Perf. 12*

693	A164	10m gold & multi	.15	.15
694	A164	20m gold & multi	.15	.15
695	A164	50m gold & multi	.20	.15
696	A164	60m gold & multi	.30	.18
697	A164	1t gold & multi	.40	.28
		Nos. 693-697 (5)	1.20	
		Set value		.68

Paintings of national heroes.

Spasski Tower, Moscow — A165

1972, Nov. 7 Photo. *Perf. 11*

698	A165	60m multi	.20	.15

50th anniversary of USSR. Printed with small label showing arms of USSR.

Mark Spitz, US, Gold Medal — A166

Designs (Medal and): 10m, Ulrike Meyfarth, Germany. 20m, Sawao Kato, Japan. 30m, András Balczó, Hungary. 60m, Lasse Viren, Finland. 80m, Shane Gould, Australia. 1t, Anatoli Bondarchuk, USSR. 4t, Khorloo Baianmunk, Mongolia.

1972, Dec. 15 Photo. *Perf. 12½*

699	A166	5m grn & multi	.15	.15
700	A166	10m ver & multi	.15	.15
701	A166	20m bl & multi	.15	.15
702	A166	30m multi	.20	.15
703	A166	60m lt vio & multi	.28	.15
704	A166	80m ol & multi	.35	.18
705	A166	1t lem & multi	.50	.28
		Nos. 699-705 (7)	1.78	
		Set value		.85

Souvenir Sheet

706	A166	4t red & multi	2.00	2.00

Winners in 20th Olympic Games, Munich.

Chimpanzee on Bicycle A167

Circus Scenes: 10m, Seal playing ball. 15m, Bear riding wheel. 20m, Woman acrobat on camel. 30m, Woman equestrian. 50m, Clown playing flute. 60m, Woman gymnast. 1t, Circus building, Ulan Bator, horiz.

1973, Jan. 29 Litho. *Perf. 12*

707	A167	5m multi	.15	.15
708	A167	10m multi	.15	.15
709	A167	15m multi	.15	.15
710	A167	20m multi	.15	.15
711	A167	30m multi	.18	.15
712	A167	50m multi	.20	.15
713	A167	60m multi	.28	.15
714	A167	1t multi	.38	.24
		Set value	1.40	.80

Postrider — A168

Designs: 60m, Diesel locomotive. 1t, Truck.

1973, Jan. 31 Photo. *Perf. 12*

715	A168	50m brown	.24	.15
716	A168	60m green	.30	.15
717	A168	1t rose claret	.50	.20
		Nos. 715-717,C34 (4)	1.74	
		Set value		.55

Sukhe Bator and Merchants A169

Paintings of Sukhe Bator: 20m, With elders. 50m, Leading partisans. 60m, With revolutionary council. 1t, Receiving deputation, horiz.

1973, Feb. 2 Photo. *Perf. 11½x12*

718	A169	10m gold & multi	.15	.15
719	A169	20m gold & multi	.15	.15
720	A169	50m gold & multi	.18	.15
721	A169	60m gold & multi	.20	.18
722	A169	1t gold & multi	.35	.28
		Nos. 718-722 (5)	1.03	
		Set value		.66

Sukhe Bator (1893-1923).

Nicolaus Copernicus A170

Marx and Lenin A171

Designs: 60m, 2t, Copernicus in laboratory, by Jan Matejko, horiz., 55x35mm. Nos. 725, 726b, Portrait. No. 726a, like 50m.

1973, Mar. Litho. *Perf. 12*

723	A170	50m gold & multi	.18	.15
724	A170	60m gold & multi	.24	.15
725	A170	1t gold & multi	.38	.20
		Nos. 723-725 (3)	.80	.50

Souvenir Sheet

726		Sheet of 3	2.00	2.00
a.	A170	1t multi	.35	.35
b.	A170	1t multi	.35	.35
c.	A170	2t multi	.70	.70

500th anniversary of the birth of Nicolaus Copernicus (1473-1543), Polish astronomer.

1973, July 15 Photo. *Perf. 11½x12*

727	A171	60m gold, car & ultra	.28	.15

9th meeting of postal administrations of socialist countries, Ulan Bator.

Common Shelducks — A172

Designs: Aquatic birds.

1973, Aug. 10 Litho. *Perf. 12x11*

728	A172	5m shown	.15	.15
729	A172	10m Arctic loons	.15	.15
730	A172	15m Bar-headed geese	.15	.15
731	A172	30m Great crested grebe	.18	.15
732	A172	50m Mallards	.24	.15

733 A172 60m Mute swans .30 .20
734 A172 1t Greater scaups .55 .28
Nos. 728-734 (7) 1.72
Set value .88

1973, Aug. 25 Litho. *Perf. 12x11*

Designs: Fur-bearing animals.

735 A172 5m Siberian weasel .15 .15
736 A172 10m Siberian chipmunk .15 .15
737 A172 15m Flying squirrel .15 .15
738 A172 20m Eurasian badger .15 .15
739 A172 30m Eurasian red squirrel .15 .15
740 A172 60m Wolverine .20 .15
741 A172 80m Mink .24 .20
742 A172 1t White hare .30 .24
Set value 1.15 .90

1973, Dec. 15 Litho. *Perf. 12x11*

Designs: Flowers.

743 A172 5m Alpine aster .15 .15
744 A172 10m Mongolian silene .15 .15
745 A172 15m Rosa davurica .15 .15
746 A172 20m Mongolian dandelion .15 .15
747 A172 30m Rhododendron dahuricum .15 .15
748 A172 50m Clematis tangutica .18 .15
749 A172 60m Siberian primula .24 .18
750 A172 1t Pasqueflower .35 .24
Set value 1.20 .90

Globe and Red Flag Emblem — A173

1973, Dec. 10 Photo. *Perf. 12x12½*

751 A173 60m gold, red & blue .28 .15

15th anniversary of the review "Problems of Peace and Socialism," published in Prague.

Limenitis Populi A174

Butterflies: 10m, Arctia hebe. 15m, Rhyparia purpurata. 20m, Catocala pacta. 30m, Isoceras kaszabi. 50m, Celerio costata. 60m, Arctia caja. 1t, Diacrisia sannio.

1974, Jan. 15 Litho. *Perf. 11*

752 A174 5m lil & multi .15 .15
753 A174 10m brn & multi .15 .15
754 A174 15m bl & multi .15 .15
755 A174 20m brn org & multi .15 .15
756 A174 30m lt vio & multi .15 .15
757 A174 50m dl red & multi .20 .16
758 A174 60m yel grn & multi .28 .24
759 A174 1t ultra & multi .40 .30
Set value 1.35 1.00

"Hehe Namshil" by L. Merdorsh A175

Designs (Various Scenes from): 20m, "Sive Hiagt," by D. Luvsansharav. 25m, 80m, 1t, "Edre," by D. Namdag. 30m, "The 3 Khans of Sara-Gol" (legend). 60m, "Amarsana," by B. Damdinsuren. 20m and 30m horizontal.

1974, Feb. 20 Litho. *Perf. 12*

760 A175 15m sil & multi .15 .15
761 A175 20m sil & multi .15 .15
762 A175 25m sil & multi .15 .15
763 A175 30m sil & multi .18 .15
764 A175 60m sil & multi .24 .15
765 A175 80m sil & multi .35 .18
766 A175 1t sil & multi .38 .20
Nos. 760-766 (7) 1.60
Set value .80

Mongolian operas and dramas.

Government Building and Sukhe Bator — A176

1974, Mar. 1 Photo. *Perf. 11*

767 A176 60m gold & multi .20 .15

50th anniv. of renaming capital Ulan Bator.

Juggler A177

10m, Dressage, horiz. 30m, Trained elephant. 40m, Yak pushing ball, horiz. 60m, Acrobats with ring. 80m, Woman acrobat on unicycle.

1974, May 4 Litho. *Perf. 12*

768 A177 10m multi .15 .15
769 A177 20m multi .15 .15
770 A177 30m multi .15 .15
771 A177 40m multi .16 .15
772 A177 60m multi .28 .20
773 A177 80m multi .35 .24
Nos. 768-773,C65 (7) 1.72
Set value 1.00

Mongolian Circus. No. 773 has se-tenant label, with similar design.

Girl on Bronco A178

Children's Activities: 20m, Boy roping calf. 30m, 40m, Boy taming horse (different designs). 60m, Girl with doves. 80m, Wrestling. 1t, Dancing.

1974, June 2 Litho. *Perf. 12*

774 A178 10m dl yel & multi .15 .15
775 A178 20m lt bl & multi .15 .15
776 A178 30m grn & multi .15 .15
777 A178 40m yel & multi .18 .15
778 A178 60m pink & multi .24 .15
779 A178 80m bl & multi .35 .18
780 A178 1t dl bl & multi .38 .20
Set value 1.35 .72

Children's Day.

Archer — A179

National Sports: 20m, Two horsemen fighting for goatskin. 30m, Archer on horseback. 40m, Horse race. 60m, Riding wild horse. 80m, Rider chasing riderless horse. 1t, Boys wrestling.

1974, July 11 Photo. *Perf. 11*

781 A179 10m vio bl & multi .15 .15
782 A179 20m yel & multi .15 .15
783 A179 30m lil & multi .15 .15
784 A179 40m multi .15 .15
785 A179 60m multi .20 .15
786 A179 80m multi .30 .18
787 A179 1t multi .45 .24
Set value 1.30 .76

Nadom, Mongolian national festival.

Grizzly Bear — A180

1974, July Litho. *Perf. 12*

788 A180 10m shown .15 .15
789 A180 20m Common panda .15 .15
790 A180 30m Giant panda .15 .15
791 A180 40m Two brown bears .18 .15
792 A180 60m Sloth bear .28 .15
793 A180 80m Asiatic black bears .40 .18
794 A180 1t Giant brown bear .55 .20
Nos. 788-794 (7) 1.86
Set value .80

Stag in Zuun Araat Wildlife Preserve — A181

1974, Sept. Litho. *Perf. 12*

795 A181 10m shown .15 .15
796 A181 20m Beaver .15 .15
797 A181 30m Leopard .15 .15
798 A181 40m Great black-backed gull .15 .15
799 A181 60m Deer .20 .15
800 A181 80m Mouflon .30 .20
801 A181 1t Deer and entrance to Bogd-uul Preserve .45 .28
Set value 1.30 .90

Protected fauna in Mongolian wildlife preserves.

Buddhist Temple, Bogdo Gegen Palace — A182

Mongolian Architecture: 15m, Buddhist Temple, now Museum. 30m, Entrance to Charity Temple, Ulan Bator. 50m, Mongolian yurta. 80m, Gazebo in convent yard.

1974, Oct. 15 Litho. *Perf. 12*

802 A182 10m bl & multi .15 .15
803 A182 15m multi .15 .15
804 A182 30m grn & multi .15 .15
805 A182 50m multi .24 .15
806 A182 80m yel & multi .40 .24
Set value .88 .56

Spasski Tower, Sukhe Bator Statue — A183

1974, Nov. 26 Photo. *Perf. 11½x12*

807 A183 60m multi .28 .15

Visit of General Secretary Brezhnev and a delegation from the USSR to participate in celebration of 50th anniversary of People's Republic of Mongolia.

Sukhe Bator Proclaiming Republic — A184

Designs: No. 808, "First Constitution," symbolic embroidery. No. 809, Flag over landscape, lane and communications tower.

1974, Nov. 28 Litho.

808 A184 60m multi .28 .15
809 A184 60m multi .28 .15
810 A184 60m multi .28 .15
Nos. 808-810 (3) .84
Set value .30

50th anniv. of People's Republic of Mongolia.

Decanter — A185

Designs: 20m, Silver jar. 30m, Night lamp. 40m, Tea jug. 60m, Candelabra. 80m, Teapot. 1t, Silver bowl on 3-legged stand.

1974, Dec. 1 Photo.

811 A185 10m blue & multi .15 .15
812 A185 20m claret & multi .15 .15
813 A185 30m multi .15 .15
814 A185 40m dp bl & multi .15 .15
815 A185 60m multi .20 .15

No.	Type	Value	Color	Unused	Used
816	A185	80m	grn & multi	.35	.18
817	A185	1t	lilac & multi	.45	.24
			Set value	1.35	.75

Mongolian 19th century goldsmiths' work.

Lapwing (plover) — A186

1974, Dec. Litho. *Perf. 11*

No.	Type	Value	Design	Unused	Used
818	A186	10m	shown	.15	.15
819	A186	20m	Fish	.15	.15
820	A186	30m	Marsh marigolds	.16	.15
821	A186	40m	White pelican	.25	.15
822	A186	60m	Perch	.32	.20
823	A186	80m	Mink	.50	.28
			Nos. 818-823,C66 (7)	2.08	
			Set value		1.10

Water and nature protection.

American Mail Coach, UPU Emblem — A187

Designs (UPU Emblem and): 20m, French two-wheeled coach. 30m, Changing horses, Russian coach. 40m, Swedish caterpillar mail truck. 50m, First Hungarian mail truck. 60m, German Daimler-Benz mail truck. 1t, Mongolian dispatch rider.

1974, Dec. Litho. *Perf. 12*

No.	Type	Value	Color	Unused	Used
824	A187	10m	multi	.15	.15
825	A187	20m	multi	.15	.15
826	A187	30m	multi	.15	.15
827	A187	40m	multi	.18	.15
828	A187	50m	multi	.20	.15
829	A187	60m	multi	.28	.15
830	A187	1t	multi	.45	.24
			Nos. 824-830 (7)	1.56	
			Set value		.80

Cent. of the UPU and Stockholmia 74.

Mongolian Flag, Broken Swastika — A188

1975, May 9 Photo. *Perf. 11½x12*

No.	Type	Value	Color	Unused	Used
832	A188	60m	multi	.28	.15

30th anniversary of the end of World War II and victory over fascism.

Mongolian Woman — A189

1975, May

No.	Type	Value	Color	Unused	Used
833	A189	60m	multi	.28	.15

International Women's Year 1975.

Zygophyllum Xanthoxylon — A190

Medicinal Plants: 20m, Ingarvillea potaninii. 30m, Lancea tibetica. 40m, Jurinea mongolica. 50m, Saussurea involucrata. 60m, Allium mongolicum. 1t, Adonis mongolica.

1975, May 24 Photo. *Perf. 11x11½*

No.	Type	Value	Color	Unused	Used
834	A190	10m	dp org & multi	.15	.15
835	A190	20m	grn & multi	.15	.15
836	A190	30m	yel & multi	.15	.15
837	A190	40m	vio & multi	.15	.15
838	A190	50m	brn & multi	.24	.15
839	A190	60m	bl & multi	.28	.18
840	A190	1t	multi	.48	.28
			Set value	1.35	.88

12th International Botanists' Conference.

Shepherd — A191

Puppet Theater: 20m, Boy on horseback. 30m, Boy and disobedient bull calf. 40m, Little orphan camel's tale. 50m, Boy and obedient little yak. 60m, Boy riding swan. 1t, Children's choir.

1975, June 30 Litho. *Perf. 12*

No.	Type	Value	Color	Unused	Used
841	A191	10m	multi	.15	.15
842	A191	20m	multi	.15	.15
843	A191	30m	multi	.15	.15
844	A191	40m	multi	.15	.15
845	A191	50m	multi	.24	.15
846	A191	60m	multi	.28	.18
847	A191	1t	multi	.48	.28
			Set value	1.35	.88

Pioneers Tending Fruit Tree — A192

60m, Pioneers studying, and flying model plane. 1t, New emblem of Mongolian Pioneers.

1975, July 15 *Perf. 12x11½*

No.	Type	Value	Color	Unused	Used
848	A192	50m	multi	.20	.15
849	A192	60m	multi	.24	.15
850	A192	1t	multi	.35	.24
			Nos. 848-850 (3)	.79	
			Set value		.45

Mongolian Pioneers, 50th anniversary.

Nos. 624-630 Overprinted

Тээвэр—50
1975—7—15

1975, July 15 Litho. *Perf. 12*

No.	Type	Value	Color	Unused	Used
850A	A151	20m	multi	.85	.85
850B	A151	30m	multi	.85	.85
850C	A151	40m	multi	1.25	1.25
850D	A151	50m	multi	1.25	1.25
850E	A151	60m	multi	1.40	1.40
850E	A151	80m	multi	2.00	2.00
850G	A151	1t	multi	2.50	2.50
			Nos. 850A-850G (7)	10.10	10.10

Fifty years of communication.

Golden Eagle Hunting Fox — A193

Hunting Scenes: 20m, Dogs treeing lynx, vert. 30m, Hunter stalking marmots. 40m, Hunter riding reindeer, vert. 50m, Boar hunt. 60m, Trapped wolf, vert. 1t, Bear hunt.

1975, Aug. 25 Litho. *Perf. 12*

No.	Type	Value	Color	Unused	Used
851	A193	10m	multi	.15	.15
852	A193	20m	multi	.20	.15
853	A193	30m	multi	.30	.15
854	A193	40m	multi	.35	.15
855	A193	50m	multi	.45	.18
856	A193	60m	multi	.60	.20
857	A193	1t	multi	1.00	.35
			Nos. 851-857 (7)	3.05	
			Set value		1.00

Hunting in Mongolia.

Mesocottus Haitej — A194

Various Fish: 20m, Pseudaspius lepto cephalus. 30m, Oreoleuciscus potanini. 40m, Tinca tinca. 50m, Coregonus lavaretus pidschian. 60m, Erythroculter mongolicus. 1t, Carassius auratus.

1975, Sept. 15 Photo. *Perf. 11*

No.	Type	Value	Color	Unused	Used
858	A194	10m	multi	.15	.15
859	A194	20m	multi	.15	.15
860	A194	30m	multi	.15	.15
861	A194	40m	bl & multi	.18	.15
862	A194	50m	grn & multi	.28	.18
863	A194	60m	lil & multi	.35	.20
864	A194	1t	vio bl & multi	.55	.35
			Nos. 858-864 (7)	1.81	
			Set value		1.00

Neck and Bow of Musical Instrument (Morin Hur) — A195

National Handicraft: 20m, Saddle. 30m, Silver headgear. 40m, Boots. 50m, Tasseled Woman's cap. 60m, Pipe and tobacco pouch. 1t, Sable cap.

Perf. 11½x12½

1975, Oct. 10 Litho.

No.	Type	Value	Color	Unused	Used
865	A195	10m	multi	.15	.15
866	A195	20m	multi	.15	.15
867	A195	30m	multi	.15	.15
868	A195	40m	multi	.18	.15
869	A195	50m	multi	.28	.18
870	A195	60m	multi	.35	.20
871	A195	1t	multi	.55	.35
			Nos. 865-871 (7)	1.81	
			Set value		1.00

Revolutionists with Flags — A196

1975, Nov. 15 Litho. *Perf. 11½x12*

No.	Type	Value	Color	Unused	Used
872	A196	60m	multi	.28	.15

70th anniversary of Russian Revolution.

Ski Jump, Olympic Games Emblem — A197

Designs (Winter Olympic Games Emblem and): 20m, Ice hockey. 30m, Skiing. 40m, Bobsled. 50m, Biathlon. 60m, Speed skating. 1t, Figure skating, women's. 4t, Skier carrying torch.

Perf. 11½x12½

1975, Dec. 20 Litho.

No.	Type	Value	Color	Unused	Used
873	A197	10m	multi	.15	.15
874	A197	20m	multi	.15	.15
875	A197	30m	brn & multi	.15	.15
876	A197	40m	grn & multi	.18	.15
877	A197	50m	multi	.28	.18
878	A197	60m	ol & multi	.35	.20
879	A197	1t	multi	.55	.35
			Nos. 873-879 (7)	1.81	
			Set value		1.00

Souvenir Sheet

No.	Type	Value	Color	Unused	Used
880	A197	4t	multi	3.00	3.00

12th Winter Olympic Games, Innsbruck, Austria, Feb. 4-15, 1976.

Taming Wild Horse — A198

Mongolian Paintings: 20m, Camel caravan, horiz. 30m, Man playing lute. 40m, Woman adjusting headdress, horiz. 50m, Woman wearing ceremonial costume. 60m, Women fetching water. 1t, Woman musician. 4t, Warrior on horseback.

1975, Nov. 30 *Perf. 12*

No.	Type	Value	Color	Unused	Used
881	A198	10m	brown & multi	.15	.15
882	A198	20m	blue & multi	.15	.15
883	A198	30m	olive & multi	.15	.15
884	A198	40m	lilac & multi	.15	.15
885	A198	50m	blue & multi	.24	.18
886	A198	60m	lilac & multi	.28	.18
887	A198	1t	silver & multi	.48	.30
			Set value	1.40	.95

Souvenir Sheet

No.	Type	Value	Color	Unused	Used
888	A198	4t	bl & multi	1.75	1.75

House of Young Technicians — A199

Designs: 60m, Hotel Ulan Bator. 1t, Museum of the Revolution.

1975, Dec. 30 Photo. *Perf. 12x11½*

893 A199 50m ultra .20 .15
894 A199 60m bl grn .40 .15
895 A199 1t brick red .60 .20
Nos. 893-895 (3) 1.20
Set value .40

Camels in Gobi Desert A200

20m, Horse taming. 30m, Horseback riding. 40m, Pioneers' camp. 60m, Young musician. 80m, Children's festival. 1t, Mongolian wrestling.

1976, June 1 Litho. *Perf. 12*

896 A200 10m multi .15 .15
897 A200 20m multi .15 .15
898 A200 30m multi .15 .15
899 A200 40m multi .20 .15
900 A200 60m multi .35 .15
901 A200 80m multi .48 .24
902 A200 1t multi .60 .28
Nos. 896-902 (7) 2.08
Set value .90

International Children's Day.

Red Star — A201

1976, May 1 Photo. *Perf. 11x12½*

903 A201 60m red, mar & sil .30 .15

17th Congress of the Mongolian People's Revolutionary Party, June 14.

Archery, Montreal Games' Emblem, Canadian Flag — A202

20m, Judo. 30m, Boxing. 40m, Vaulting. 60m, Weight lifting. 80m, High Jump. 1t, Target shooting.

Perf. 12½x11½

1976, May 20 Litho.

904 A202 10m yel & multi .15 .15
905 A202 20m yel & multi .15 .15
906 A202 30m yel & multi .15 .15
907 A202 40m yel & multi .18 .15
908 A202 60m yel & multi .28 .15
909 A202 80m yel & multi .35 .24
910 A202 1t yel & multi .45 .28
Set value 1.45 .90

21st Olympic Games, Montreal, Canada, July 17-Aug. 1. See No. C81.

Partisans A203

Fighter and Sojombo Independence Symbol — A204

Perf. 12x11½, 11½x12

1976, June 15 Litho.

911 A203 60m multi .35 .15
912 A204 60m multi .40 .15

55th anniversary of Mongolia's independence. See No. C82.

Souvenir Sheet

Sukhe Bator Medal — A205

1976, July 11 *Perf. 11½*

913 A205 4t multi 1.75 1.75

Mongolian honors medals.

Osprey A206

Protected Birds: 20m, Griffon vulture. 30m, Bearded lammergeier. 40m, Marsh harrier. 60m, Black vulture. 80m, Golden eagle. 1t, Tawny eagle.

1976, Aug. 16 Litho. *Perf. 12*

914 A206 10m multi .15 .15
915 A206 20m multi .15 .15
916 A206 30m multi .15 .15
917 A206 40m multi .20 .15
918 A206 60m multi .35 .18
919 A206 80m multi .40 .28
920 A206 1t multi .55 .35
Nos. 914-920 (7) 1.95
Set value 1.05

"Nadom" Military Game — A207

Paintings by O. Cevegshava: 10m, Taming Wild Horse, vert. 30m, Hubsugul Lake Harbor. 40m, The Steppe Awakening. 80m, Wrestlers. 1.60t, Yak Descending in Snow, vert.

1976, Sept. Litho. *Perf. 12*

921 A207 10m multi .15 .15
922 A207 20m multi .15 .15
923 A207 30m multi .15 .15
924 A207 40m multi .20 .15
925 A207 80m multi .40 .24
926 A207 1.60t multi .55 .28
Nos. 921-926 (6) 1.60
Set value .78

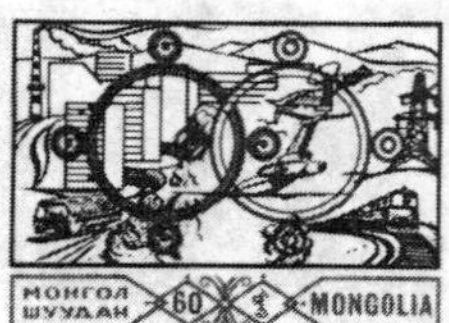

Interlocking Circles, Industry and Transport — A208

1976, Oct. 15 Photo. *Perf. 12x11½*

927 A208 60m brn, bl & red .35 .18

Soviet-Mongolian friendship.

John Naber, US Flag, Gold Medals — A209

Designs: 20m, Nadia Comaneci, Romanian flag. 30m, Kornelia Ender, East German flag. 40m, Mitsuo Tsukahara, Japanese flag. 60m, Gregor Braun, German flag. 80m, Lasse Viren, Finnish flag. 1t, Nikolai Andrianov, Russian flag.

1976, Nov. 30 Litho. *Perf. 12*

928 A209 10m multi .15 .15
929 A209 20m multi .15 .15
930 A209 30m multi .15 .15
931 A209 40m multi .20 .15
932 A209 60m multi .35 .15
933 A209 80m multi .40 .24
934 A209 1t multi .55 .28
Nos. 928-934 (7) 1.95
Set value .90

Gold medal winners, 21st Olympic Games, Montreal. See No. C83.

Stone Tablet on Tortoise A210

Carved Tablet, 6th-8th Centuries A211

1976, Dec. 15 Litho. *Perf. 11½x12*

935 A210 50m brn & lt bl .85 .15
936 A211 60m gray & brt grn 1.25 .15
Set value .24

Intl. Archaeological Conference, Ulan Bator.

R-1 Plane — A212

Designs: Various Mongolian planes.

1976, Dec. 22 *Perf. 12*

937 A212 10m multi .15 .15
938 A212 20m multi .15 .15
939 A212 30m multi .15 .15
940 A212 40m multi .18 .15
941 A212 60m multi .35 .18
942 A212 80m multi .40 .24
943 A212 1t multi .48 .30
Nos. 937-943 (7) 1.86
Set value .95

Dancers — A213

Folk Dances: 20m, 13th century costumes. 30m, West Mongolian dance. 40m, "Ekachi," or horse-dance. 60m, "Bielge," West Mongolian trunk dance. 80m, "Hodak," or friendship dance. 1t, "Dojarka."

1977, Mar. 20 Litho. *Perf. 12½*

944 A213 10m multi .15 .15
945 A213 20m multi .15 .15
946 A213 30m multi .15 .15
947 A213 40m multi .18 .15
948 A213 60m multi .35 .18
949 A213 80m multi .40 .28
950 A213 1t multi .48 .35
Nos. 944-950 (7) 1.86
Set value 1.10

Miniature Sheet

Path of Pioneer from Earth to Jupiter, deflected by Mars — A214

Isaac Newton — A215

1977, Mar. 31 Litho. *Perf. 11½x12*

951 Sheet of 9 2.00 .85
a. A214 60m shown .20 .15
b. A215 60m Apple tree .20 .15
c. A214 60m Sextant and planets .20 .15
d. A214 60m Astronauts in space .20 .15
e. A215 60m shown .20 .15
f. A214 60m Prism and spectrum .20 .15
g. A214 60m Rain falling on earth .20 .15
h. A215 60m Motion of celestial bodies .20 .15
i. A214 60m Pioneer 10 over Jupiter .20 .15

Sir Isaac Newton (1642-1727), English natural philosopher and mathematician.

Nos. 951a-951i arranged in 3 rows of 3. Nos. 951d and 951i inscribed AIR MAIL.

D. Natsagdorji, Writer, and Quotation — A216

Design: No. 953, Grazing horses, landscape, ornament and quotation.

1977 *Perf. 11½x12*

952 A216 60m multi .35 .18
953 A216 60m multi .40 .18

D. Natsagdorji, founder of modern Mongolian literature. Label and vignette separated by simulated perforations.

Primitive Tortoises — A217

Prehistoric Animals: 20m, Ungulate (titanothere). 30m, Flying lizard. 40m, Entelodon (swine). 60m, Antelope. 80m, Hipparion. 1t, Aurochs.

1977, May 7 Photo. *Perf. 12½*

954 A217 10m multi .15 .15
955 A217 20m multi .15 .15
956 A217 30m multi .15 .15
957 A217 40m multi .18 .15
958 A217 60m multi .35 .18
959 A217 80m multi .40 .28
960 A217 1t multi .48 .35
Nos. 954-960 (7) 1.86
Set value 1.10

Souvenir Sheet

Mongolia, Type A2 and Netherlands No. 1 — A218

1977, May 20

961 A218 4t multi 2.00 2.00

AMPHILEX '77 International Philatelic Exhibition, Amsterdam, May 27-June 5. No. 961 contains one 37x52mm stamp.

Boys on Horseback — A219

20m, Girl on horseback. 30m, Hunter on horseback. 40m, Grazing horses. 60m, Mare & foal. 80m, Grazing horse & student. 1t, White stallion.

1977, June 15 Litho. *Perf. 12*

962 A219 10m multi .15 .15
963 A219 20m multi .18 .15
964 A219 30m multi .24 .15
965 A219 40m multi .38 .15
966 A219 60m multi .65 .15
967 A219 80m multi .75 .24
968 A219 1t multi 1.00 .28
Nos. 962-968 (7) 3.35
Set value .90

Copper and Molybdenum Plant, Vehicles — A220

1977, June 15 Litho. *Perf. 12*

969 A220 60m multi .35 .18

Erdenet, a new industrial town.

Bucket Brigade Fighting Fire — A221

Fire Fighting: 20m, Horse-drawn fire pump. 30m, Horse-drawn steam pump. 40m, Men in protective suits fighting forest fire. 60m, Modern foam extinguisher. 80m, Truck and ladder. 1t, Helicopter fighting fire on steppe.

1977, Aug. Litho. *Perf. 12*

970 A221 10m multi .15 .15
971 A221 20m multi .15 .15
972 A221 30m multi .15 .15
973 A221 40m multi .20 .15
974 A221 60m multi .35 .18
975 A221 80m multi .40 .28
976 A221 1t multi .55 .35
Nos. 970-976 (7) 1.95
Set value 1.05

Radar and Molnya Satellite on TV Screen — A222

1977, Sept. 12 Photo. *Perf. 12x11½*

977 A222 60m gray, bl & blk .35 .18

40th anniversary of Technical Institute.

Lenin Museum, Ulan Bator A223

1977, Oct. 1 Litho. *Perf. 12*

978 A223 60m multi .40 .18

Inauguration of Lenin Museum in connection with the 60th anniversary of the Russian October Revolution.

Dove, Globe, Decree of Peace A224

Designs: 50m, Cruiser Aurora and Russian flag, vert. 1.50t, Globe and "Freedom."

Perf. 11½x12, 12x11½

1977, Oct. 1 Photo.

979 A224 50m gold & multi .28 .15
980 A224 60m gold & multi .35 .18
981 A224 1.50t gold & multi .80 .48
Nos. 979-981 (3) 1.43 .81

60th anniversary of the Russian Revolution.

Aporia Crataegi A225

Moths: 20m, Gastropacha quercifolia. 30m, Colias chrysoteme. 40m, Dasychira fascelina. 60m, Malocosoma neustria. 80m, Diacrisia sanno. 1t, Heodes virgaureae.

1977, Sept. 25 Photo. *Perf. 12½*

982 A225 10m multi .15 .15
983 A225 20m multi .15 .15
984 A225 30m multi .18 .15
985 A225 40m multi .24 .15
986 A225 60m multi .38 .18
987 A225 80m multi .48 .28
988 A225 1t multi .60 .35
Nos. 982-988 (7) 2.18
Set value 1.05

Giant Pandas — A226

Pandas: 10m, Eating bamboo, vert. 30m, Female and cub in washtub, vert. 40m, Male and cub playing with bamboo. 60m, Female and cub, vert. 80m, Family. 1t, Male, vert.

1977, Nov. 25 Litho. *Perf. 12*

989 A226 10m multi .15 .15
990 A226 20m multi .15 .15
991 A226 30m multi .15 .15
992 A226 40m multi .20 .15
993 A226 60m multi .35 .18
994 A226 80m multi .40 .28
995 A226 1t multi .55 .35
Nos. 989-995 (7) 1.95
Set value 1.05

Souvenir Sheet

Helen Fourment and her Children, by Rubens — A227

1977, Dec. 5 *Perf. 11½x10½*

996 A227 4t multi 2.25 2.25

Peter Paul Rubens (1577-1640).

Ferrari Racing Car — A228

Experimental Racing Cars: 30m, Ford McLaren. 40m, Madi, USSR. 50m, Mazda. 60m, Porsche. 80m, Russian model car. 1.20t, The Blue Flame, US speed car.

1978, Jan. 28 Litho. *Perf. 12*

997 A228 20m multi .15 .15
998 A228 30m multi .15 .15
999 A228 40m multi .18 .15
1000 A228 50m multi .24 .18
1001 A228 60m multi .28 .20
1002 A228 80m multi .35 .28
1003 A228 1.20t multi .55 .38
Nos. 997-1003 (7) 1.90
Set value 1.25

Boletus Variegatus — A229

Mushrooms: 30m, Russula cyanoxantha. 40m, Boletus aurantiacus. 50m, Boletus scaber. 60m, Russula flava. 80m, Lactarius resimus. 1.20t, Flammula spumosa.

1978, Feb. 28 Photo. *Perf. 11x11½*

1004 A229 20m yel & multi .15 .15
1005 A229 30m yel & multi .15 .15
1006 A229 40m yel & multi .18 .15
1007 A229 50m yel & multi .24 .18
1008 A229 60m yel & multi .30 .20
1009 A229 80m yel & multi .38 .28
1010 A229 1.20t yel & multi .60 .38
Nos. 1004-1010 (7) 2.00
Set value 1.25

Young Couple with Youth Flag — A230

1978, Apr. Litho. *Perf. 11½x12*

1011 A230 60m multi .35 .18

17th Congress of Mongolian Youth Organization, Ulan Bator, Apr. 1978.

Soccer, Sugar Loaf Mountain, Rio de Janeiro, Brazil 1950 Emblem — A231

Designs (Various Soccer Scenes and): 30m, Old Town Tower, Bern, Switzerland, 1954. 40m, Town Hall, Stockholm, Sweden, 1958. 50m, University of Chile, Chile, 1962. 60m, Parliament and Big Ben, London, 1966. 80m, Degolladeo Theater, Guadalajara, Mexico, 1970. 1.20t, Town Hall and TV Tower, Munich, Germany.

1978, Apr. 15 *Perf. 12*

1012 A231 20m multi .15 .15
1013 A231 30m multi .15 .15
1014 A231 40m multi .20 .15
1015 A231 50m multi .28 .15
1016 A231 60m multi .35 .18
1017 A231 80m multi .40 .20
1018 A231 1.20t multi .70 .28
Nos. 1012-1018 (7) 2.23
Set value 1.00

11th World Cup Soccer Championship, Argentina, June 1-25. See No. C109.

Capex Emblem, Eurasian Beaver and Canada #336 — A232

30m, Tibetan sand grouse & Canada #478. 40m, Red-throated loon & Canada #369. 50m, Argali & Canada #324. 60m, Eurasian brown bear & Canada #322. 80m, Moose & Canada #323. 1.20t, Great black-backed gull & Canada #343.

1978, June Litho. *Perf. 12*

1019 A232 20m multi .15 .15
1020 A232 30m multi .15 .15
1021 A232 40m multi .18 .15
1022 A232 50m multi .20 .18
1023 A232 60m multi .28 .20
1024 A232 80m multi .40 .30
1025 A232 1.20t multi .60 .40
Nos. 1019-1025 (7) 1.96
Set value 1.30

CAPEX '78 International Philatelic Exhibition, Toronto, June 9-18. See No. C110.

Marx, Engels and Lenin A233

1978, July 11 Photo. *Perf. 12x11½*

1026 A233 60m gold, blk & red .35 .18

50th anniversary of publication in Prague of "Problems of Peace and Socialism."

Souvenir Sheet

Outdoor Rest, by Amgalan — A234

Paintings by D. Amgalan: No. 1027b, Winter Night (dromedary and people in snow). No. 1027c, Saddling up.

1978, Aug. 10 Litho. *Perf. 12*

1027	Sheet of 3	2.75	2.75
a.-c.	A234 1.50t any single	.80	

Philatelic cooperation between Hungary and Mongolia, 20th anniversary. No. 1027 contains 3 stamps and 3 labels.

Papillon — A235

Dogs: 20m, Black Mongolian sheepdog. 30m, Puli. 40m, St. Bernard. 50m, German shepherd. 60m, Mongolian watchdog. 70m, Samoyed. 80m, Laika (1st dog in space) and rocket. 1.20t, Cocker spaniels and poodle.

1978, Sept. 25 Litho. *Perf. 12*

1028	A235 10m multi	.15	.15
1029	A235 20m multi	.15	.15
1030	A235 30m multi	.15	.15
1031	A235 40m multi	.18	.15
1032	A235 50m multi	.20	.15
1033	A235 60m multi	.24	.15
1034	A235 70m multi	.28	.18
1035	A235 80m multi	.30	.20
1036	A235 1.20t multi	.50	.24
	Nos. 1028-1036 (9)	2.15	
	Set value		1.10

Open Book and Pen — A236

1978, Oct. 20 Photo. *Perf. 12x11½*

1037	A236 60m car & ultra	.35	.18

Mongolian Writers' Association, 50th anniversary.

Souvenir Sheets

Clothed Maya, by Goya — A237

Melancholy, by Dürer — A238

Paintings: No. 1038b, "Ta Matete," by Gauguin. No. 1038c, Bridge at Arles, by Van Gogh.

1978, Oct. 30 Litho. *Perf. 12*

1038	Sheet of 3 + 3 labels	2.75	2.75
a.-c.	A237 1.50t any single	.80	.80

Perf. 11½

1039	A238 4t black	2.25	2.25

Anniversaries of European painters: Francisco Goya; Paul Gauguin; Vincent van Gogh; Albrecht Dürer.

Camel and Calf — A239

Bactrian Camels: 30m, Young camel. 40m, Two camels. 50m, Woman leading pack camel. 60m, Old camel. 80m, Camel pulling cart. 1.20t, Race.

1978, Nov. 30 Litho. *Perf. 12*

1040	A239 20m multi	.15	.15
1041	A239 30m multi	.15	.15
1042	A239 40m multi	.20	.15
1043	A239 50m multi	.24	.15
1044	A239 60m multi	.35	.15
1045	A239 80m multi	.40	.15
1046	A239 1.20t multi	.60	.20
	Nos. 1040-1046 (7)	2.09	
	Set value		.75

Flags of Comecon Members, Globe A240

1979, Jan. 2 Litho. *Perf. 12*

1047	A240 60m multi	.28	.15

30th anniversary of the Council of Mutual Assistance (Comecon).

Silver Tabby — A241

Domestic Cats: 30m, White Persian. 50m, Red Persian. 60m, Cream Persian. 70m, Siamese. 80m, Smoky Persian. 1t, Burmese.

1979, Feb. 10

1048	A241 10m multi	.15	.15
1049	A241 30m multi	.15	.15
1050	A241 50m multi	.20	.15
1051	A241 60m multi	.24	.15
1052	A241 70m multi	.28	.15
1053	A241 80m multi	.35	.18
1054	A241 1t multi	.40	.28
	Nos. 1048-1054 (7)	1.77	
	Set value		.98

Potaninia Mongolica — A242

Flowers: 30m, Sophora alopecuroides. 50m, Halimodendron halodendron. 60m, Forget-me-nots. 70m, Pincushion flower. 80m, Leucanthemum Sibiricum. 1t, Edelweiss.

1979, Mar. 10 Litho. *Perf. 12*

1055	A242 10m multi	.15	.15
1056	A242 30m multi	.15	.15
1057	A242 50m multi	.22	.15
1058	A242 60m multi	.28	.15
1059	A242 70m multi	.30	.15
1060	A242 80m multi	.38	.15
1061	A242 1t multi	.45	.18
	Nos. 1055-1061 (7)	1.93	
	Set value		.75

Finland-Czechoslovakia, Finnish Flag — A243

Ice Hockey Games and 1980 Olympic Emblems: 30m, German Fed. Rep.-Sweden, German flag. 50m, US-Canada, US flag. 60m, USSR-Sweden, Russian flag. 70m, Canada-USSR, Canadian flag. 80m, Swedish goalie and flag. 1t, Czechoslovakia-USSR, Czechoslovak flag.

1979, Apr. 10 Litho. *Perf. 12*

1062	A243 10m multi	.15	.15
1063	A243 30m multi	.15	.15
1064	A243 50m multi	.22	.15
1065	A243 60m multi	.28	.15
1066	A243 70m multi	.35	.15
1067	A243 80m multi	.40	.18
1068	A243 1t multi	.50	.20
	Nos. 1062-1068 (7)	2.05	
	Set value		.82

Ice Hockey World Championship, Moscow, Apr. 14-27.

Lambs — A244

Paintings: 30m, Milking, camels. 50m, Plane bringing supplies in winter. 60m, Herdsmen and horses. 70m, Milkmaids, vert. 80m, Summer Evening (camels). 1t, Landscape with herd. 4t, After the Storm.

Perf. 12x11½, 11½x12

1979, May 3 Litho.

1069	A244 10m multi	.15	.15
1070	A244 30m multi	.15	.15
1071	A244 50m multi	.18	.15
1072	A244 60m multi	.24	.15
1073	A244 70m multi	.32	.15
1074	A244 80m multi	.40	.18
1075	A244 1t multi	.48	.20
	Nos. 1069-1075 (7)	1.92	
	Set value		.82

Souvenir Sheet

1076	A244 4t multi	2.25	2.25

20th anniv. of 1st agricultural cooperative.

Souvenir Sheet

Mongolia No. 4, Bulgaria No. 1, Philaserdica Emblem — A245

Designs (Rowland Hill and): No. 1077b, American mail coach. No. 1077c, Mail car, London-Birmingham railroad, 1838. 1077d, Packet leaving Southampton, Sept. 24, 1842, opening Indian mail service.

1979, May 15 Litho. *Perf. 12*

1077	Sheet of 4, multi	1.75	1.75
a.-d.	A245 1t any single	.38	.38

Philaserdica '79, Sofia, May 18-27, and Rowland Hill (1795-1879), originator of penny postage.

Rocket, Manchester, 1829 — A246

Locomotives: 20m, "Adler" Nuremberg-Furth, 1835. 30m, American engine, 1860. 40m, Ulan Bator-Nalajh run, 1931. 50m, Moscow-Ulan Bator run, 1936. 60m, Moscow-Ulan Bator, 1970. 70m, Tokyo-Osaka run, 1963. 80m, Orleans Aerotrain, 1967. 1.20t, Soviet Rapidity, experimental train.

1979, June 8 Litho. *Perf. 12*

1078	A246 10m multi	.15	.15
1079	A246 20m multi	.15	.15
1080	A246 30m multi	.15	.15
1081	A246 40m multi	.18	.15
1082	A246 50m multi	.20	.15
1083	A246 60m multi	.28	.15
1084	A246 70m multi	.30	.15
1085	A246 80m multi	.35	.15
1086	A246 1.20t multi	.48	.20
	Nos. 1078-1086 (9)	2.24	
	Set value		.85

Intl. Transportation Exhibition, Hamburg. For surcharge see No. 2144B.

Mongolian and Russian Flags — A247

Battle Scene and Emblem — A248

1979, Aug. 10 Photo. *Perf. 11½x12*

1087	A247 60m multi	.28	.15
1088	A248 60m multi	.28	.15
	Set value		.24

Battle of Ha-lo-hsin River, 40th anniversary.

Manuls A249

Wild Cats: 30m, Lynx. 50m, Tigers. 60m, Snow leopards. 70m, Black panthers. 80m, Cheetahs. 1t, Lions.

1979, Sept. 10 Litho. *Perf. 12*

1089	A249 10m multi	.15	.15
1090	A249 30m multi	.15	.15
1091	A249 50m multi	.20	.15
1092	A249 60m multi	.24	.15
1093	A249 70m multi	.28	.15
1094	A249 80m multi	.35	.15
1095	A249 1t multi	.40	.18
	Nos. 1089-1095 (7)	1.77	
	Set value		.72

Souvenir Sheet

Brazil No. 1582 A250

b, Brazil #1144 (Pele). c, Mongolia #C1.

1979, Sept. 15 Litho. *Perf. 11*

1096	Sheet of 3 + 3 labels	2.50	2.50
a.-c.	A250 1.50t any single	.75	.75

Brasiliana '79, 3rd World Thematic Stamp Exhibition, Rio de Janeiro, Sept. 15-23.

Cross-Country Skiing, Lake Placid '80 Emblem — A251

30m, Biathlon. 40m, Ice hockey. 50m, Ski jump. 60m, Downhill skiing. 80m, Speed skating. 1.20t, Bobsledding. 4t, Figure skating.

Perf. 11½x12½

1980, Jan. 20 **Litho.**

1097 A251 20m multi .15 .15
1098 A251 30m multi .16 .15
1099 A251 40m multi .22 .15
1100 A251 50m multi .25 .15
1101 A251 60m multi .35 .15
1102 A251 80m multi .42 .15
1103 A251 1.20t multi .65 .22
Nos. 1097-1103 (7) 2.20
Set value .75

Souvenir Sheet

1104 A251 4t multi 2.75 2.75

13th Winter Olympic Games, Lake Placid, NY, Feb. 12-24.

Flower Type of 1969
Souvenir Sheet

Design: Landscape and edelweiss.

1980, May 5 **Litho.** ***Perf. 11***

1105 A131 4t multi 3.00 3.00

London 1980 Intl. Stamp Exhib., May 6-14. No. 1105 contains one stamp 43x26mm.

Weightlifting, Moscow '80 Emblem — A252

1980, June 2 **Litho.** ***Perf. 12***

1106 A252 20m shown .15 .15
1107 A252 30m Archery .15 .15
1108 A252 40m Gymnast .18 .15
1109 A252 50m Running .20 .15
1110 A252 60m Boxing .24 .15
1111 A252 80m Judo .35 .15
1112 A252 1.20t Bicycling .50 .18
Nos. 1106-1112 (7) 1.77
Set value .66

Souvenir Sheet

1113 A252 4t Wrestling 2.75 2.75

22nd Summer Olympic Games, Moscow, July 19-Aug. 3.

Gold Medal, Swimmer, Moscow '80 Emblem — A253

Gold Medal, Moscow '80 Emblem and Number of Medals won by Top Countries: 30m, Fencing. 50m, Judo. 60m, Track. 80m, Boxing. 1t, Weight lifting. 1.20t, Kayak.

1980, Sept. 15 **Litho.** ***Perf. 12½***

1114 A253 20m multi .15 .15
1115 A253 30m multi .16 .15
1116 A253 50m multi .28 .15
1117 A253 60m multi .32 .15
1118 A253 80m multi .45 .15
1119 A253 1t multi .55 .15
1120 A253 1.20t multi .65 .18
Nos. 1114-1120 (7) 2.56
Set value .75

See No. C144.

A254

A255

1980, Sept. 17 ***Perf. 11½x12***

1121 A254 60m Jumdshaigiin Zedenbal .32 .15
1122 A254 60m Zedenbal, 1941, grn .32 .15
1123 A254 60m Zedenbal, 1979, gray grn .32 .15
1124 A254 60m with Brezhnev, horiz. .32 .15
1125 A254 60m with children .32 .15
1126 A254 60m Sukhe Bator, dk brn .32 .15
1127 A254 60m Choibalsan, ultra .32 .15
Nos. 1121-1127 (7) 2.24
Set value .84

Miniature Sheet

Cosmonauts from various Intercosmos flights: a, A. Gubarjev. b, Czechoslovakia #2222. c, P. Klimuk. d, Poland #2270. e, V. Bykovsky. f, DDR #1947. g, N. Rukavishnikov. h, Bulgaria #2576. i, V. Kubasov. j, Hungary #C417.

1980, Oct. 10 **Litho.** ***Perf. 12***

1128 Sheet of 12 2.50 2.50
a.-j. A255 40m any single .22 .22

Intercosmos cooperative space program.

See No. 1232.

Benz, Germany, 1885 — A256

Antique Cars: 30m, President, Austria-Hungary, 1897. 40m, Armstrong Siddley, 1904. 50m, Russo-Balt, 1909. 60m, Packard, United States, 1909. 80m, Lancia, Italy, 1911. 1.60t, Marne taxi, France, 1914. 4t, Nami-1, Russia, 1927.

1980, Nov. 20 **Litho.** ***Perf. 12½***

1129 A256 20m multi .15 .15
1130 A256 30m multi .16 .15
1131 A256 40m multi .22 .15
1132 A256 50m multi .28 .15
1133 A256 60m multi .32 .15
1134 A256 80m multi .45 .15
1135 A256 1.60t multi .90 .28
Nos. 1129-1135 (7) 2.48
Set value .82

Souvenir Sheet

1136 A256 4t multi 2.50 2.50

Penguins A257

1980, Dec. 1 ***Perf. 12***

1137 A257 20m shown .15 .15
1138 A257 30m Giant blue whale .16 .15
1139 A257 40m Albatross .22 .15
1140 A257 50m Weddell seals .28 .15
1141 A257 60m Emperor penguins .32 .15
1142 A257 70m Skua .38 .15
1143 A257 80m Grampus .45 .15
1144 A257 1.20t Penguins, Soviet plane .65 .18
Nos. 1137-1144 (8) 2.61
Set value .78

Souvenir Sheet

1145 A257 4t World map showing continental drift 2.50 2.50

Antarctic animals and exploration. No. 1145 contains one 44mm circular stamp.

Souvenir Sheet

A258

1980, Dec. 20 **Litho.** ***Perf. 11***

1146 Sheet of 2 2.50 .85
a. A258 2t shown 1.25 .40
b. A258 2t Old Marketplace 1.25 .40

The Shepherd Speaking the Truth, IYC Emblem — A259

IYC Emblem and Nursery Tales: 30m, Above Them the Sky is Always Clear. 40m, Winter's Joys. 50m, Little Musicians. 60m, Happy Birthday. 80m, The First Day of School. 1.20t, May Day. 4t, The Wonder-working Squirrels.

1980, Dec. 29 ***Perf. 12***

1147 A259 20m multi .15 .15
1148 A259 30m multi .16 .15
1149 A259 40m multi .22 .15
1150 A259 50m multi .35 .15
1151 A259 60m multi .40 .15
1152 A259 80m multi .55 .16
1153 A259 1.20t multi .75 .22
Nos. 1147-1153 (7) 2.58
Set value .75

Souvenir Sheet

1154 A259 4t multi 2.50 2.50

Intl. Year of the Child (1979).

60th Anniversary of People's Army — A260

1981, Jan. 31 **Litho.** ***Perf. 12***

1155 A260 60m multi .32 .15

60th Anniversary of People's Revolutionary Party — A261

1981, Feb. 2

1156 A261 60m multi .32 .15

Ice Racing — A262

Designs: Various racing motorcycles.

1981, Feb. 28 ***Perf. 12½***

1157 A262 10m multi .15 .15
1158 A262 20m multi .15 .15
1159 A262 30m multi .16 .15
1160 A262 40m multi .22 .15
1161 A262 50m multi .28 .15
1162 A262 60m multi .32 .15
1163 A262 70m multi .35 .15
1164 A262 80m multi .45 .15
1165 A262 1.20t multi .65 .18
Nos. 1157-1165 (9) 2.73
Set value .82

Cosmonauts Boarding Soyuz 39 — A263

Designs: 30m, Rocket designer Koroljov. 40m, Vostok I, Yuri Gagarin. 50m, Salyut space station. 60m, Satellite photographing earth. 80m, Light crystallization from Salyut spacecraft. 1.20t, Salyut, Kremlin, Sukhe Bator statue. 4t, Soviet and Mongolian cosmonauts.

1981, Mar. 22 **Litho.** ***Perf. 12***

1166 A263 20m multi .15 .15
1167 A263 30m multi .16 .15
1168 A263 40m multi .22 .15
1169 A263 50m multi .28 .15
1170 A263 60m multi .35 .15
1171 A263 80m multi .45 .15
1172 A263 1.20t multi .65 .22
Nos. 1166-1172 (7) 2.26
Set value .75

Souvenir Sheet

Perf. 11½

1173 A263 4t multi 2.50 2.50

Intercosmos cooperative space program (Mongolia-USSR). No. 1173 contains one 29x39mm stamp.

No. 240, Ulan Bator A264

1981, Apr. 28 **Litho.** ***Perf. 12***

1174 Sheet of 4 + 4 labels 2.50 2.50
a. A264 1t shown .55 .20
b. A264 1t Germany #8N4, 8N34 .55 .20
c. A264 1t Austria #B110 .55 .20
d. A264 1t Japan #827 .55 .20

1981 Stamp Exhibitions: Mongolian Natl., Ulan Bator; Naposta, Stuttgart; WIPA, Vienna; Japex, Tokyo.

The Scott International album provides spaces for an extensive representative collection of the world's postage stamps.

Star Shining on Factories and Sheep — A265

1981, May 5
1175 A265 60m multi .32 .15

18th Congress of Revolutionary People's Party, May.

Souvenir Sheet

Statue of Sukhe Bator, Mongolian Flag A266

1981, May 20 *Perf. 12½*
1176 A266 4t multi 2.50 2.50

Mongolian Revolutionary People's Party, 60th anniv.

Sheep Farming (Economic Development) — A267

1981, June 1 *Perf. 12½x11½*
1177 A267 20m shown .15 .15
1178 A267 30m Transportation .16 .15
1179 A267 40m Telecommunications .22 .15
1180 A267 50m Public health service .28 .15
1181 A267 60m Agriculture .35 .15
1182 A267 80m Power plant .45 .15
1183 A267 1.20t Public housing .65 .22
Nos. 1177-1183 (7) 2.26
Set value .75

A268

A269

Souvenir Sheet
Perf. 12½x11½

1981, July 11 **Litho.**
1184 A268 4t multi 2.50 2.50

20th anniv. of UN membership.

1981, Aug. 1 *Perf. 12*

Designs: Sailing ships. 10m, 20m, horiz.

1185 A269 10m Egyptian, 15th cent. BC .15 .15
1186 A269 20m Mediterranean, 9th cent. .15 .15
1187 A269 40m Hansa Cog, 12th cent. .22 .15
1188 A269 50m Venitian, 13th cent. .28 .15
1189 A269 60m Santa Maria .35 .15
1190 A269 80m Endeavor .45 .15

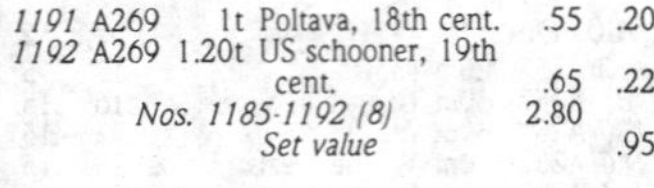
1191 A269 1t Poltava, 18th cent. .55 .20
1192 A269 1.20t US schooner, 19th cent. .65 .22
Nos. 1185-1192 (8) 2.80
Set value .95

Mongolian-USSR Friendship Pact — A270

1981, Sept. 1 *Perf. 11½x12*
1193 A270 60m multi .35 .15

Flora, by Rembrandt A271

1981, Sept. 1 *Perf. 11½x12½*
1194 A271 20m shown .15 .15
1195 A271 30m Hendrickje in the Bed .16 .15
1196 A271 40m Young Woman with Earrings .22 .15
1197 A271 50m Young Girl in the Window .28 .15
1198 A271 60m Hendrickje like Flora .35 .15
1199 A271 80m Saskia with Red Flower .45 .15
1200 A271 1.20t Holy Family with Drape .65 .22
Nos. 1194-1200 (7) 2.26
Set value .75

Souvenir Sheet
1201 A271 4t Self-portrait with Saskia 2.50 2.50

375th birth anniv. of Rembrandt.

Goat (Pawn) A272

Designs: Wood chess pieces.

1981, Sept. 30 **Litho.** *Perf. 12½*
1202 A272 20m shown .15 .15
1203 A272 40m Cart (castle) .22 .15
1204 A272 50m Camel (bishop) .28 .15
1205 A272 60m Horse (knight) .35 .15
1206 A272 80m Lion (queen) .45 .15
1207 A272 1.20t Man and dog (king) .65 .15
Nos. 1202-1207 (6) 2.10
Set value .58

Souvenir Sheet
1208 A272 4t Men playing 2.50 2.50

Camel and Circus Tent A273

1981, Oct. 30 **Litho.** *Perf. 12*
1209 A273 10m shown .15 .15
1210 A273 20m Horsemen .15 .15
1211 A273 40m Wrestlers .22 .15
1212 A273 50m Archers .28 .15
1213 A273 60m Folksinger .35 .15
1214 A273 80m Girl playing jatga .45 .15
1215 A273 1t Ballet dancers .55 .18
1216 A273 1.20t Statue .65 .20
Nos. 1209-1216 (8) 2.80
Set value .85

Wolfgang Amadeus Mozart and Scene from his Magic Flute A274

Composers and Scenes from their Works.

1981, Nov. 16
1217 A274 20m shown .15 .15
1218 A274 30m Beethoven, Fidelio .16 .15
1219 A274 40m Bartok, Miraculous Mandarin .22 .15
1220 A274 50m Verdi, Aida .28 .15
1221 A274 60m Tchaikovsky, Sleeping Beauty .35 .15
1222 A274 80m Dvorak, New World Symphony score .45 .15
1223 A274 1.20t Chopin, piano .65 .20
Nos. 1217-1223 (7) 2.26
Set value .70

Ribbon Weaver A275

Designs: Mongolian women.

Perf. 11½x12½
1981, Dec. 10 **Litho.**
1224 A275 20m multi .15 .15
1225 A275 30m multi .16 .15
1226 A275 40m multi .22 .15
1227 A275 50m multi .28 .15
1228 A275 60m multi .35 .15
1229 A275 80m multi .45 .15
1230 A275 1.20t multi .65 .22
Nos. 1224-1230 (7) 2.26
Set value .75

Souvenir Sheet
1231 A275 4t multi 2.75 2.75

Intercosmos Type of 1980

Designs: a, V. Gorbatko. b, Y. Romanenko. c, V. Dzhanibekov. d, L. Popov. e, Vietnamese stamp. f, Cuban stamp. g, No. 1173. h, Romania No. C241.

1981, Dec. 28 *Perf. 12*
1232 Sheet of 8, multi 2.50 2.50
a.-h. A255 50m, any single .30 .30

Historic Bicycles A276

1982, Mar. 25 **Litho.** *Perf. 11*
1233 A276 10m Germany, 1816 .15 .15
1234 A276 20m Scotland, 1838 .15 .15
1235 A276 40m US, 1866 .22 .15
1236 A276 50m France, 1863 .28 .15
1237 A276 60m "Kangaroo", 1877 .35 .15
1238 A276 80m England, 1870 .45 .15
1239 A276 1t 1878 .55 .20
1240 A276 1.20t Modern bike .65 .22
Nos. 1233-1240 (8) 2.80
Set value .95

Souvenir Sheet
Perf. 12½
1241 A276 4t Racing 2.75 2.75

No. 1241 contains one stamp 47x47mm.

1982 World Cup — A277

1982, Apr. 20 *Perf. 12*
1242 A277 10m Brazil, 1950 .15 .15
1243 A277 20m Switzerland, 1954 .15 .15
1244 A277 40m Sweden, 1958 .22 .15
1245 A277 50m Chile, 1962 .28 .15
1246 A277 60m England, 1966 .35 .15
1247 A277 80m Mexico, 1970 .45 .15
1248 A277 1t Germany, 1974 .55 .20
1249 A277 1.20t Argentina, 1978 .65 .22
Nos. 1242-1249 (8) 2.80
Set value .95

Souvenir Sheet
Perf. 11
1250 A277 4t Spain, 1982 2.50 2.50

No. 1250 contains one stamp 48x48mm.

12th Trade Union Congress, Ulan Bator — A278

Perf. 11½x12½
1982, May 20 **Litho.**
1251 A278 60m multi .35 .15

Souvenir Sheet

PHILEXFRANCE Intl. Stamp Exhibition, Paris, June 11-21 — A279

1982, June 11 *Imperf.*
1252 A279 4t No. B13 design 2.50 2.50

George Dimitrov (1882-1949), First Prime Minister of Bulgaria — A280

1982, June 18 *Perf. 12*
1253 A280 60m gold & blk .35 .15

Chicks — A281

1982, June 25 *Perf. 11*

1254 A281 10m shown .15 .15
1255 A281 20m Colt .15 .15
1256 A281 30m Lamb .16 .15
1257 A281 40m Fawn .22 .15
1258 A281 50m Camel calf .28 .15
1259 A281 60m Kid .35 .15
1260 A281 70m Calf .38 .15
1261 A281 1.20t Young boar .65 .22
Nos. 1254-1261 (8) 2.34
Set value .75

Coal Mining Industry — A282

1982, July 5 *Perf. 12*

1262 A282 60m Mine, truck .35 .15

18th Mongolian Youth Org. Congress — A283

1982, Aug. 14 *Perf. 11½x12*

1263 A283 60m multi .35 .15

Siberian Pine A284

1982, Aug. 16

1264 A284 20m shown .15 .15
1265 A284 30m Abies sibirica .15 .15
1266 A284 40m Populus diversifolia .18 .15
1267 A284 50m Larix sibirica .20 .15
1268 A284 60m Pinus silvestris .28 .15
1269 A284 80m Betula platyphylla .35 .15
1270 A284 1.20t Picea obovata .50 .22
Nos. 1264-1270 (7) 1.81
Set value .75

60th Anniv. of Mongolian Youth Org. — A285

1982, Aug. 30

1271 A285 60m multi .35 .15

Iseki-6500 Tractor, Japan — A286

1982, Oct. 1 **Litho.** *Perf. 12½*

1272 A286 10m shown .15 .15
1273 A286 20m Deutz-DX-230, Germany .15 .15
1274 A286 40m Bonser, Gt. Britain .18 .15
1275 A286 50m Intl.-884, US .22 .15
1276 A286 60m Renault TX-145-14, France .28 .15
1277 A286 80m Belarus-611, USSR .35 .15
1278 A286 1t K-7100, USSR .45 .15
1279 A286 1.20t DT-75, USSR .55 .18
Nos. 1272-1279 (8) 2.33
Set value .70

Scenes from The Foal and The Hare Folktale A287

1983, Jan. 1 **Litho.** *Perf. 14*

1280 A287 10m multi .15
1281 A287 20m multi .15
1282 A287 30m multi .15
1283 A287 40m multi .22
1284 A287 50m multi .26
1285 A287 60m multi .35
1286 A287 70m multi .38
1287 A287 80m multi .42
1288 A287 1.20t multi .70
Nos. 1280-1288 (9) 2.78

Souvenir Sheet

Imperf

1289 A287 7t multi 4.00

No. 1289 contains one stamp 58x58mm.

Scenes from Walt Disney's The Sorcerer's Apprentice — A288

1983, Jan. 1

1290 A288 25m multi .15
1291 A288 35m multi .16
1292 A288 45m multi .24
1293 A288 55m multi .28
1294 A288 65m multi .32
1295 A288 75m multi .35
1296 A288 85m multi .42
1297 A288 1.40t multi .70
1298 A288 2t multi .95
Nos. 1290-1298 (9) 3.57

Souvenir Sheet

1299 A288 7t multi 4.00

Fish, Lake Hevsgel — A289

1982, Nov. 30 *Perf. 12*

1300 A289 20m shown .15
1301 A289 30m Sheep, Zavhan Highlands .15
1302 A289 40m Beaver, Lake Hovd .18
1303 A289 50m Horses, Lake Uvs .22
1304 A289 60m Chamois, Bajanhongor Steppe .28
1305 A289 80m Mounted hunter, eagle, Bajan-Elgij Highlands .35
1306 A289 1.20t Camels, Gobi Desert .55
Nos. 1300-1306 (7) 1.88

Mongolian Skin Tent (Yurt) — A290

1983, Mar. 30 **Litho.** *Perf. 14*

1307 A290 20m Antonov AN-24B plane .15
1308 A290 30m shown .15
1309 A290 40m Deer .18
1310 A290 50m Bighorn sheep .22
1311 A290 60m Eagle .28
1312 A290 80m Museum of the Khans, Ulan Bator .35
1313 A290 1.20t Sukhe Bator monument, Ulan Bator .55
Nos. 1307-1313 (7) 1.88

Souvenir Sheet

90th Birth Anniv. of Sukhe Bator — A291

1983 *Perf. 13x14*

1314 A291 4t multi 2.50

Local Flowers — A292

1983, Feb. 4 **Photo.** *Perf. 13*

1315 A292 20m Rose .15
1316 A292 30m Dahlias .16
1317 A292 40m Tagetes faula .22
1318 A292 50m Narcissus .28
1319 A292 60m Violets .35
1320 A292 80m Tulips .40
1321 A292 1.20t Heliopsis helianthoides .70
Nos. 1315-1321 (7) 2.26

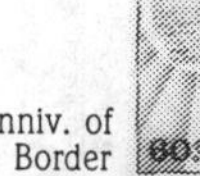

50th Anniv. of Border Forces — A293

1983, Feb. 9 **Litho.** *Perf. 14*

1322 A293 60m multi .35

Souvenir Sheet

BRASILIANA, Philatelic Exhibition — A294

1983, July 10 **Litho.** *Perf. 14*

1323 A294 4t multi 2.50

Karl Marx — A295

1983, Oct. 1 **Litho.** *Perf. 14*

1324 A295 60m gold, dp car & bl .40

18th Party Congress, Ulan Bator — A296

1983, Nov. 1 **Litho.** *Perf. 14*

1325 A296 10m Cattle .15
1326 A296 20m Coal .15
1327 A296 30m Garment .20
1328 A296 40m Agricultural .28
1329 A296 60m Communications .40
1330 A296 80m Transportation .55
1331 A296 1t Educational System .70
Nos. 1325-1331 (7) 2.43

Souvenir Sheet

Sistine Madonna, by Raphael (1483-1520) A297

1983, Dec. 15 **Litho.** *Perf. 14x13½*

1332 A297 4t multi 2.75

A298

Children in Various Activities.

1984, Jan. 1 Photo. *Perf. 13*

1333	A298	10m	multi	.15
1334	A298	20m	multi	.15
1335	A298	30m	multi	.20
1336	A298	40m	multi	.28
1337	A298	50m	multi	.35
1338	A298	70m	multi	.48
1339	A298	1.20t	multi	.80
			Nos. 1333-1339 (7)	2.41

Rodents — A299

Various rodents.

1984, Jan. 15 Litho. *Perf. 13½x13*

1340	A299	20m	multi	.15
1341	A299	30m	multi	.20
1342	A299	40m	multi	.28
1343	A299	50m	multi	.35
1344	A299	60m	multi	.40
1345	A299	80m	multi	.55
1346	A299	1.20t	multi	.80
			Nos. 1340-1346 (7)	2.73

1984 Winter Olympics — A300

1984, Feb. 15 Litho. *Perf. 14*

1347	A300	20m	Bobsledding	.15
1348	A300	30m	Cross-country skiing	.20
1349	A300	40m	Hockey	.28
1350	A300	50m	Speed skating	.35
1351	A300	60m	Downhill skiing	.40
1352	A300	80m	Figure skating	.55
1353	A300	1.20t	Biathlon	.80
			Nos. 1347-1353 (7)	2.73

Souvenir Sheet

1354	A300	4t	Ski jumping	2.75

Size of No. 1354: 134x106mm. Nos. 1347-1352 vert.

Children Feeding Lambs — A301

1984, Mar. 1 Litho. *Perf. 12*

1355	A301	20m	Ice skating	.15
1356	A301	30m	shown	.20
1357	A301	40m	Planting tree	.28
1358	A301	50m	Playing on beach	.35
1359	A301	60m	Carrying pail	.40
1360	A301	80m	Dancing	.55
1361	A301	1.20t	Dancing, diff.	.80
			Nos. 1355-1361 (7)	2.73

Souvenir Sheet

1362	A301	4t	Boy, girl	2.75

No. 1362 contains one stamp 48x46mm.

Mail Car, Communications Emblems — A302

1984, Apr. 15 *Perf. 13½x14*

1363	A302	10m	shown	.15
1364	A302	20m	Earth satellite receiving station	.15
1365	A302	40m	Airplane	.28
1366	A302	50m	Central PO	.35
1367	A302	1t	Radar station	.70
1368	A302	1.20t	Train	.80
			Nos. 1363-1368 (6)	2.43

Souvenir Sheet

Imperf

1369	A302	4t	Dish antenna	2.75

1984 Summer Olympics — A303

1984, June 1 Photo. *Perf. 14*

1370	A303	20m	Gymnastics	.15
1371	A303	30m	Bicycling	.20
1372	A303	40m	Weight lifting	.28
1373	A303	50m	Judo	.35
1374	A303	60m	Archery	.40
1375	A303	80m	Boxing	.55
1376	A303	1.20t	High jump	.80
			Nos. 1370-1376 (7)	2.73

Souvenir Sheet

1377	A303	4t	Wrestling	2.75

Souvenir Sheet

AUSIPEX '84 and ESPANA '84 — A304

1984, May Litho. *Perf. 14*

1378	A304	4t	Jet	2.75

Cuban Revolution, 25th Anniv. — A304a

1984, June 2 Litho. *Perf. 14*

1378A	A304a	60m	multi	.24

State Bank, 60th Anniv. — A304b

1984, Sept. 25 *Perf. 13½x13*

1378B	A304b	60m	Commemorative coins, 1981	.24

Radio Broadcasting in Mongolia, 50th Anniv. — A304c

1984, Sept. 1 Litho. *Perf. 13x13½*

1378C	A304c	60m	multicolored	.75

Scenes from Walt Disney's Mickey and the Beanstalk — A305

1984, Dec. 20 Litho. *Perf. 11*

1379	A305	25m	multi	.15
1380	A305	35m	multi	.15
1381	A305	45m	multi	.20
1382	A305	55m	multi	.24
1383	A305	65m	multi	.28
1384	A305	75m	multi	.30
1385	A305	85m	multi	.35
1386	A305	1.40t	multi	.60
1387	A305	2t	multi	.80
			Nos. 1379-1387 (9)	3.07

Miniature Sheet

Perf. 14

1388	A305	7t	multi	3.75

Fairy Tales — A306

1984, Dec. 20 Litho. *Perf. 13½*

1389	A306	10m	multi	.15
1390	A306	20m	multi	.15
1391	A306	30m	multi	.16
1392	A306	40m	multi	.20
1393	A306	50m	multi	.28
1394	A306	60m	multi	.35
1395	A306	70m	multi	.40
1396	A306	80m	multi	.45
1397	A306	1.20t	multi	.65
			Nos. 1389-1397 (9)	2.79

Miniature Sheet

1398	A306	4t	multi	3.00

Souvenir Sheet

60th Anniv. of Mongolian Stamps — A308

1984, Dec. 20 Litho. *Perf. 14*

1400	A308	4t	No. 1	2.75

Ulan Bator, 60th Anniv. — A309

Mongolian People's Republic, 60th Anniv. — A310

1984, Nov. 26 Litho. *Perf. 13x13½*

1401	A309	60m	multicolored	.75

Perf. 14

1402	A310	60m	multicolored	.75

Mongolian People's Party, 60th Anniv. — A311

1984, Nov. 26 Litho. *Perf. 14*

1403	A311	60m	multi	.35

Native Masks — A312

1984, Dec. 31 Litho. *Perf. 14*

1404	A312	20m	multi	.15
1405	A312	30m	multi	.20
1406	A312	40m	multi	.25
1407	A312	50m	multi	.35
1408	A312	60m	multi	.40
1409	A312	80m	multi	.60
1410	A312	1.20t	multi	.85
			Nos. 1404-1410 (7)	2.80

Souvenir Sheet

1411	A312	4t	multi	2.75

Dogs A313

1984, Dec. 31 Litho. *Perf. 13*

1412	A313	20m	Collie	.15
1413	A313	30m	German Sheepdog	.20
1414	A313	40m	Papillon	.25
1415	A313	50m	Cocker Spaniel	.35
1416	A313	60m	Puppy	.40
1417	A313	80m	Dalmatians	.60
1418	A313	1.20t	Mongolian Sheep-dog	.85
			Nos. 1412-1418 (7)	2.80

Cattle — A314

1985, Jan. *Perf. 14*

1419 A314 20m Shar tarlan .15
1420 A314 30m Bor khaliun .18
1421 A314 40m Sarlag .25
1422 A314 50m Dornod taliin bukh .32
1423 A314 60m Char tarlan .38
1424 A314 80m Nutgiin uulderiin unee .50
1425 A314 1.20t Tsagaan tolgoit .75
Nos. 1419-1425 (7) 2.53

1984 Olympic Winners — A315

Gold medalists: 20m, Gaetan Boucher, Canada, 1500-meter speed skating. 30m, Eirik Kvalfoss, Norway, 10-kilometer biathlon. 40m, Marja-Lissa Haemaelainen, Finland, 5-kilometer Nordic skiing. 50m, Max Julen, Switzerland, men's giant slalom. 60m, Jens Weissflag, German Democratic Republic, 70-meter ski jump. 80m, W. Hoppe and D. Schauerhammer, German Democratic Republic, 2-man bobsled. 1.20t, Elena Valova and Oleg Vassiliev, USSR, pairs figure skating. 4t, USSR, ice hockey. Nos. 1430-1432 vert.

1985, Apr. 25

1426 A315 20m multi .15
1427 A315 30m multi .15
1428 A315 40m multi .20
1429 A315 50m multi .25
1430 A315 60m multi .30
1431 A315 80m multi .40
1432 A315 1.20t multi .60
Nos. 1426-1432 (7) 2.05

Souvenir Sheet

1433 A315 4t multi 2.00

Souvenir Sheet

Girl, Fawn — A316

1985, Apr. 25

1434 A316 4m multi 2.00

Birds — A317

World Youth Festival, Moscow — A318

1985, May 1 *Perf. 12½x13*

1435 A317 20m Ciconia nigra .15
1436 A317 30m Haliaetus albicilla .15
1437 A317 40m Grus leucogeranus .20
1438 A317 50m Paradoxornis heudei .25
1439 A317 60m Grus monahas .30
1440 A317 80m Grus vipio .40
1441 A317 1.20t Buteo lagopus .60
Nos. 1435-1441 (7) 2.05

National Wildlife Preservation Association.

1985, June *Perf. 14*

1442 A318 60m Girls in folk costumes .30

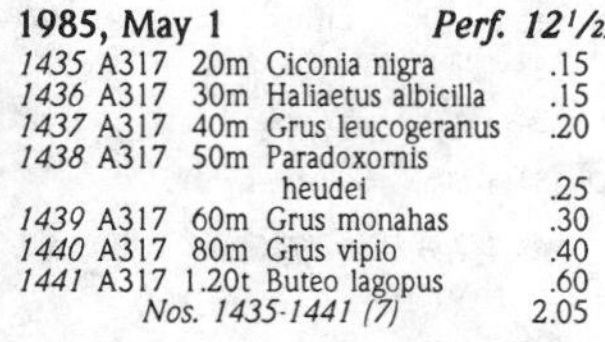
Camelus Bactrianus — A319

Panthera Unicias — A320

Cervus Elaphus — A321

Camels, leopards and deer.

1985

1443 A319 50m Adults, young .25
1444 A319 50m Facing right .25
1445 A319 50m Facing left .25
1446 A319 50m Trotting .25
1447 A320 50m Hunting .25
1448 A320 50m Standing in snow .25
1449 A320 50m Female, young .25
1450 A320 50m Adults .25
1451 A321 50m Fawn .25
1452 A321 50m Doe in woods .25
1453 A321 50m Adult male .25
1454 A321 50m Adults, fawn .25
Nos. 1443-1454 (12) 3.00

#1443-1446 show the World Wildlife Fund emblem, #1447-1454 the Natl. Wildlife Preservation emblem. Issue dates: #1443-1446, July 1; #1447-1454, Aug. 1.

UN, 40th Anniv. — A322

1985, Aug. 1 *Perf. 13½x13*

1455 A322 60m Flags, UN building .30

Indigenous Flowering Plants — A323

1985, Aug. 1 *Perf. 14*

1456 A323 20m Rosa davurica .15
1457 A323 30m Matricaria chamomilla .15
1458 A323 40m Taraxacum officinale .20
1459 A323 50m Saxzifraga hirculus .25
1460 A323 60m Vaccinium vitis idaea .30
1461 A323 80m Sanguisorba officinalis .40
1462 A323 1.20t Plantago major .60
Nos. 1456-1462 (7) 2.05

Souvenir Sheet

1463 A323 4t Hippophae rhamnoides 2.00

A324

A325

1985, Sept. 15 *Perf. 13x13½*

1464 A324 60m Monument .30

Defeat of Nazi Germany, 40th anniv.

1985, Oct. 1 *Perf. 14*

Various soccer plays. No. 1472 horiz.

1465 A325 20m multi .15
1466 A325 30m multi .15
1467 A325 40m multi .20
1468 A325 50m multi .25
1469 A325 60m multi .30
1470 A325 80m multi .40
1471 A325 1.20t multi .60
Nos. 1465-1471 (7) 2.05

Souvenir Sheet

1472 A325 4t multi 2.00

1985 Junior World Soccer Championships, Moscow.

Souvenir Sheet

ITALIA '85 — A326

1985, Oct. 1

1473 A326 4t Horseman 2.00

Conquest of Space — A327

Russian spacecraft.

1985, Nov. 1

1474 A327 20m Soyuz .15
1475 A327 30m Cosmos .15
1476 A327 40m Venera 9 .20
1477 A327 50m Salyut .25
1478 A327 60m Luna 9 .30
1479 A327 80m Train .40
1480 A327 1.20t Dish receiver .60
Nos. 1474-1480 (7) 2.05

Souvenir Sheet

1985, Dec. 15

1481 A327 4t Cosmonaut on space walk 2.00

Mushrooms — A328

1985, Dec. 1 *Perf. 13½*

1482 A328 20m Tricholoma mongolica .15
1483 A328 30m Cantharellus cibarius .15
1484 A328 40m Armillariella mellea .20
1485 A328 50m Amanita caesarea .25
1486 A328 70m Xerocomus badius .35
1487 A328 80m Agaricus silvaticus .40
1488 A328 1.20t Boletus edulis .60
Nos. 1482-1488 (7) 2.10

Souvenir Sheet

Phalacrocorax Penicillatus — A329

1986, Jan. 15 *Perf. 12½x13*

1489 A329 4t multi 3.00

No. 1489 contains one stamp plus 2 labels picturing various bird species.

Young Pioneers A330

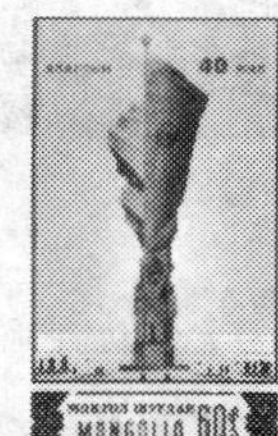

Victory Monument A331

1985, Dec. 31 **Litho.** *Perf. 13x13½*

1490 A330 60m multi .38

1985, Dec. 31 *Perf. 12½x13*

1491 A331 60m multi .38

Victory over Japan ending WWII, 40th anniv.

Natl. Costumes — A332

1986, Mar. 1 **Litho.** *Perf. 14*

Background Color

1492 A332 60m yel grn, shown .20
1493 A332 60m red .20
1494 A332 60m pale yel grn .20
1495 A332 60m violet .20
1496 A332 60m ultra .20
1497 A332 60m bluish grn .20
1498 A332 60m pale org brn .20
Nos. 1492-1498 (7) 1.40

Ernst Thalmann (1886-1944) A333

1986, May 15 Litho. *Perf. 14*

1499 A333 60m gold, redsh brn & dk brn .28

Natl. Revolution, 65th Anniv. — A334

1986, May 15

1500 A334 60m Statue of Sukhe Bator .28

19th Socialist Party Congress — A335

1986, May 15

1501 A335 60m multi .28

1986 World Cup Soccer Championships, Mexico — A336

FIFA emblem and various soccer plays. Nos. 1502-1503, 1505-1508 vert.

1986, May 31

1502 A336 20m multi .15
1503 A336 30m multi .15
1504 A336 40m multi .20
1505 A336 50m multi .24
1506 A336 60m multi .28
1507 A336 80m multi .38
1508 A336 1.20t multi .55
Nos. 1502-1508 (7) 1.95

Souvenir Sheet

1509 A336 4t multi 1.90

Mink, Wildlife Conservation — A337

1986, June 15

1510 A337 60m Spring .35
1511 A337 60m Summer .35
1512 A337 60m Autumn .35
1513 A337 60m Winter .35
Nos. 1510-1513 (4) 1.40

Flowers — A338 Butterflies — A339

1986, June 1 Litho. *Perf. 14*

1514 A338 20m Valeriana officinalis .15
1515 A338 30m Hyoscymus niger .16
1516 A338 40m Ephedra sinica .20
1517 A338 50m Thymus gobica .25
1518 A338 60m Paeonia anomala .30
1519 A338 80m Achilea millefolium .40
1520 A338 1.20t Rhododendron adamsii .60
Nos. 1514-1520 (7) 2.06

1986, Aug. 1 *Perf. 13½*

1521 A339 20m Neptis coenobita .15
1522 A339 30m Colias tycha .20
1523 A339 40m Leptidea amurensis .28
1524 A339 50m Oeneis tarpenledevi .32
1525 A339 60m Mesoacidalia charlotta .40
1526 A339 80m Smerinthus ocellatus .50
1527 A339 1.20t Pericalia matronula .80
Nos. 1521-1527 (7) 2.65

Circus — A340

Animal trainers & acrobats. #1531-1534 vert.

1986, Aug. 1 *Perf. 14*

1528 A340 20m multi .15
1529 A340 30m multi .16
1530 A340 40m multi .20
1531 A340 50m multi .25
1532 A340 60m multi .30
1533 A340 80m multi .40
1534 A340 1.20t multi .60
Nos. 1528-1534 (7) 2.06

Przewalski's Horses — A341

1986, Aug. 1 Litho. *Perf. 14*

1535 A341 50m Two horses, foal .35
1536 A341 50m One facing left, two facing right .35
1537 A341 50m Three facing right .35
1538 A341 50m Four in storm .35
Nos. 1535-1538 (4) 1.40

Pelicans *(Pelecanus)* — A341a

1986, Sept. 1 Litho. *Perf. 14*

1538A A341a 60m *crispus* feeding .58
1538B A341a 60m *crispus* wading .58
1538C A341a 60m *onocrotalus* flying .58
1538D A341a 60m *onocrotalus* on land .58
Nos. 1538A-1538D (4) 2.32

Saiga tatarica mongolica — A341b

1986, Sept. 15

1538E A341b 60m Spring (doe, fawn) .58
1538F A341b 60m Summer (buck, doe) .58
1538G A341b 60m Fall (buck) .58
1538H A341b 60m Winter (buck, doe) .58
Nos. 1538E-1538H (4) 2.32

Musical Instruments — A342

1986, Sept. 4

1539 A342 20m Morin khuur .15
1540 A342 30m Bishguur .20
1541 A342 40m Ever buree .28
1542 A342 50m Shudarga .35
1543 A342 60m Khiil .40
1544 A342 80m Janchir .55
1545 A342 1.20t Jatga .80
Nos. 1539-1545 (7) 2.73

Souvenir Sheet

1546 A342 4t like 20m, vert. 2.75

STOCKHOLMIA '86. Nos. 1539-1543 vert.

Intl. Peace Year — A342a

1986, Sept. 20 Litho. *Perf. 13x13½*

1546A A342a 10m multicolored .75

North American Bird Species — A343

1986, Oct. 1

1547 A343 60m Anthus spinoletta .35
1548 A343 60m Aythya americana .35
1549 A343 60m Bonasa umbellus .35
1550 A343 60m Olor columbianus .35
Nos. 1547-1550 (4) 1.40

Eastern Architecture — A343a

Various two-story buildings.

1986, Oct. 1

Color of Border

1551 A343a 60m dark grn & blk .70
1552 A343a 60m beige & blk .70
1553 A343a 60m apple grn & blk .70
1554 A343a 60m red brn & blk .70
Nos. 1551-1554 (4) 2.80

Classic Automobiles — A344

1986, Oct. 1 Litho. *Perf. 14*

1554A A344 20m 1922 Alfa Romeo RL Sport, Italy .15
1554B A344 30m 1912 Stutz Bearcat, US .24
1554C A344 40m 1902 Mercedes Simplex, Germany .30
1554D A344 50m 1923 Tatra 11, Czechoslovakia .38
1554E A344 60m 1908 Ford Model T, US .45
1554F A344 80m 1905 Vauxhall, England .60
1554G A344 1.20t 1913 Russo-Baltik, Russia .90
Nos. 1554A-1554G (7) 3.02

Souvenir Sheet

1554H A344 4t like 1.20t 3.00

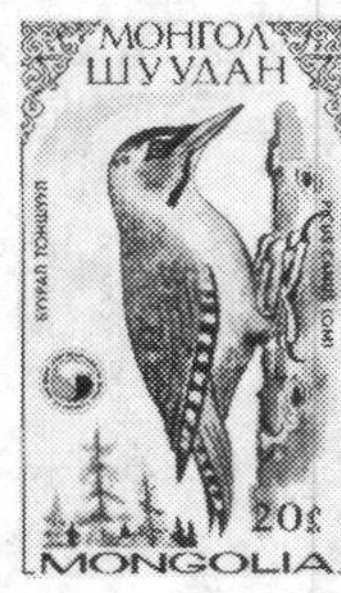

Woodpeckers A344a

1986, Nov. 1

1555 A344a 20m Picus canus .16
1556 A344a 30m Jynx torquilla .24
1557 A344a 40m Dryobates major .32
1558 A344a 50m Dryobates leucotos .40
1559 A344a 60m Dryobates minor .48
1560 A344a 80m Dryocopus martius .65
1561 A344a 1.20t Picoides tridactylus .90
Nos. 1555-1561 (7) 3.15

Souvenir Sheet

1562 A344a 4t Saphopipo noguchi 3.25

Chess Champions — A345

Portraits and chessmen on boards in match-winning configurations. No. 1562H, Chess champions Gary Kasparov, Jose R. Capablanca, Max Euwe, Vassily Smyslow, Mikhail Tal, Tigran Petrosian, Boris Spasski and Bobby Fischer; W. Menchik, L. Rudenko, E. Bykowa and O. Rubzowa.

1986, Nov. 1 *Perf. 14*

1562A A345 20m Steinitz, Austria .15
1562B A345 30m Lasker, Germany .24
1562C A345 40m Alekhine, France .30
1562D A345 50m Botvinnik, USSR .38
1562E A345 60m Karpov, USSR .45
1562F A345 80m N. Gaprindashvili .60
1562G A345 1.20t M. Chiburdanidze .90

Size: 110x100mm

Imperf

1562H A345 4t multi 3.00
Nos. 1562A-1562H (8) 6.02

Souvenir Sheet

Halley's Comet — A346

1986, Nov. 30 Litho. *Perf. 14*

1563 A346 4t multicolored 3.00

Ovis Ammon Ammon — A347

1987, Jan. 1

1564 A347 60m shown .42
1565 A347 60m In the mountains .42
1566 A347 60m Close-up of head .42
1567 A347 60m Male, female, lamb .42
Nos. 1564-1567 (4) 1.68

Children's Activities — A348

1987, Feb. 1

1568 A348 20m Backpacking, hunting butterflies .15
1569 A348 30m Playing with calves .24
1570 A348 40m Chalk-writing on cement .30
1571 A348 50m Playing soccer .38
1572 A348 60m Go-cart, model rocket, boat .45
1573 A348 80m Agriculture .60
1574 A348 1.20t Playing the morin khuur, dancing .90
Nos. 1568-1574 (7) 3.02

Int'l. Peace Year (40m); Child Survival Campaign (50m).

13th Trade Unions Congress — A349

1987, Feb. 15 *Perf. 13½x13*

1575 A349 60m multi .45

Equestrian Sports — A350

1987, Mar. 1

1576 A350 20m Lassoer .15
1577 A350 30m Breaking horse .24
1578 A350 40m Shooting bow .30
1579 A350 50m Race .38
1580 A350 60m Retrieving flags .45
1581 A350 80m Tug-of-war .60
1582 A350 1.20t Racing wolf .90
Nos. 1576-1582 (7) 3.02

Admission into Comecon, 25th Anniv. — A351

1987, Apr. 15 *Perf. 13x13½*

1583 A351 60m multi .45

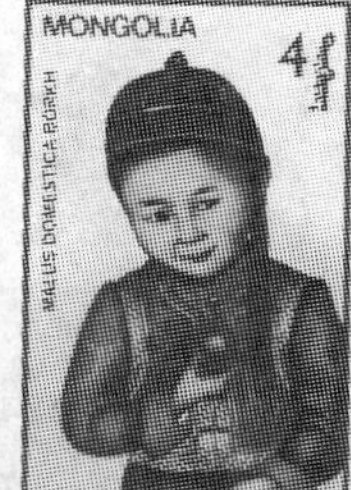

Fruit — A352 A353

1987, June 1 *Perf. 13½*

1584 A352 20m Hippophae rhamnoides .15
1585 A352 30m Ribes nigrum .24
1586 A352 40m Ribes rubrus .30
1587 A352 50m Ribes altissimum .38
1588 A352 60m Rubus sachalinensis .45
1589 A352 80m Padus asiatica .60
1590 A352 1.20t Fragaria orientalis .90
Nos. 1584-1590 (7) 3.02

Souvenir Sheet

Perf. 14

1591 A353 4t Malus domestica 3.00

Soviet-Mongolian Diplomatic Relations, 50th Anniv. — A354

Russian Revolution, 70th Anniv. — A355

1987, July 1 *Perf. 13x13½*

1592 A354 60m multi .55

1987, July 1

1593 A355 60m multi .55

Folk Dances — A356

1987, Aug. 1 *Perf. 14*

1594 A356 20m multi .15
1595 A356 30m multi, diff. .24
1596 A356 40m multi, diff. .30
1597 A356 50m multi, diff. .38
1598 A356 60m multi, diff. .45
1599 A356 80m multi, diff. .60
1600 A356 1.20t multi, diff. .90
Nos. 1594-1600 (7) 3.02

Antiques — A357

Full costume and accessories.

1987, Aug. 10

1601 A357 20m Folk costumes .15
1602 A357 30m Gilded nunchaku .24
1603 A357 40m Brooches .30
1604 A357 50m Draw-string pouch, rice bowl .38
1605 A357 60m Headdress .45
1606 A357 80m Pouches, bottle, pipe .60
1607 A357 1.20t Sash, brooch .90
Nos. 1601-1607 (7) 3.02

Souvenir Sheet

HAFNIA '87 — A358

1987, Aug. 10

1608 A358 4t multi 3.00

Swans — A359

1987, Aug. 15

1609 A359 60m Cygnus olor on land .35
1610 A359 60m Cygnus olor in water .35
1611 A359 60m Cygnus beruickii .35
1612 A359 60m Cygnus beruickii, gunus and olor .35
Nos. 1609-1612 (4) 1.40

Domestic and Wild Cats — A360

1987, Oct. 1 Litho. *Perf. 14*

1613 A360 20m multi, vert. .15
1614 A360 30m multi, vert. .24
1615 A360 40m multi, vert. .30
1616 A360 50m shown .38
1617 A360 60m multi .45
1618 A360 80m multi .60
1619 A360 1.20t multi .90
Nos. 1613-1619 (7) 3.02

Miniature Sheet

1620 A360 4t multi, vert. 3.00

Helicopter — A361

1987, Oct. 3 *Perf. 12½x11½*

1621 A361 20m B-12 .15
1622 A361 30m Westland-WG-30 .24
1623 A361 40m Bell-S-206L .30
1624 A361 50m Kawasaki-369HS .38
1625 A361 60m KA-32 .45
1626 A361 80m MI-17 .60
1627 A361 1.20t MI-10K .90
Nos. 1621-1627 (7) 3.02

Disney Cartoons — A362

The Brave Little Tailor (25m-55m, 2t, No. 1637), and The Celebrated Jumping Frog of Calaveras County (65m-1.40t, No. 1638).

1987, Nov. 23 *Perf. 14*

1628 A362 25m multi .15
1629 A362 35m multi .18
1630 A362 45m multi .22
1631 A362 55m multi .28
1632 A362 65m multi .32
1633 A362 75m multi .38
1634 A362 85m multi .40
1635 A362 1.40t multi .70
1636 A362 2t multi 1.00
Nos. 1628-1636 (9) 3.63

Souvenir Sheets

1637 A362 7t multi 3.25
1638 A362 7t multi 3.25

A363

Tropical Fish — A364

1987, Oct. *Perf. 13x12½, 12½x13*

1639 A363 20m Betta splendens .15
1640 A363 30m Carassius auratus .24
1641 A363 40m Rasbora hengeli .30
1642 A363 50m Aequidens .38
1643 A363 60m Xiphophorus macalatus .45
1644 A363 80m Xiphophorus helleri .60
1645 A363 1.20t Pterophyllum scalare, vert. .90
Nos. 1639-1645 (7) 3.02

Miniature Sheet

Perf. 14

1646 A364 4t Crenuchus spilurus 3.00

19th Communist Party Congress — A365

1987, Dec. *Perf. 14*

1647 A365 60m Family .45
1648 A365 60m Construction .45
1649 A365 60m Jet, harvesting, produce .45
1650 A365 60m Education .45
1651 A365 60m Transportation .45
1652 A365 60m Heavy industry .45
1653 A365 60m Science and technology .45
Nos. 1647-1653 (7) 3.15

Vulpes Vulpes (Fox) — A366

1987, Dec.

1654 A366 60m Adult in snow .45
1655 A366 60m Adult, young .45
1656 A366 60m Adult in field .45
1657 A366 60m Close-up of head .45
Nos. 1654-1657 (4) 1.80

Souvenir Sheet

INTERCOSMOS — A367

1987, Dec. 15 Litho. *Perf. 14*

1658 A367 4t multi 3.00

Souvenir Sheet

PRAGA '88 — A368

1988, Jan. 30

1659 A368 4t 1923 Tatra 11 3.00

Sukhe Bator — A369

1988, Feb. 2 *Perf. 13x13½*

1660 A369 60m multi .60

A370 A371

Roses.

1988, Feb. 20 *Perf. 14*

1661 A370 20m Invitation .15
1662 A370 30m Meilland .24
1663 A370 40m Pascali .30
1664 A370 50m Tropicana .40
1665 A370 60m Wendy cussons .45
1666 A370 80m Blue moon .60
1667 A370 1.20t Diorama .90
Nos. 1661-1667 (7) 3.04

Souvenir Sheet

1668 A370 4t shown 3.00

1988, Apr. 15 *Perf. 12½x13*

1669 A371 60m multi .60

19th Communist Youth Congress.

Puppets — A372

Folk tales.

1988, Apr. 1 Litho. *Perf. 14*

1670 A372 20m Ukhaant Ekhner .20
1671 A372 30m Altan Everte Mungun Turuut .30
1672 A372 40m Aduuchyn Khuu .40
1673 A372 50m Suulenkhuu .45
1674 A372 60m Khonchyn Khuu .60
1675 A372 80m Argat Byatskhan Baatar .80
1676 A372 1.20t Botgochyn Khuu 1.25
Nos. 1670-1676 (7) 4.00

1988 Summer Olympics, Seoul A373

Soviet Space Achievements A374

1988, Feb. 15

1677 A373 20m Judo .15
1678 A373 30m Women's archery .24
1679 A373 40m Weight lifting .30
1680 A373 50m Women's gymnastics .40
1681 A373 60m Cycling .45
1682 A373 80m Running .60
1683 A373 1.20t Wrestling .90
Nos. 1677-1683 (7) 3.04

Souvenir Sheet

1684 A373 4t Boxing 3.00

1988, May 15

1685 A374 20m Cosmos .15
1686 A374 30m Meteor .24
1687 A374 40m Salyut-Soyuz .30
1688 A374 50m Prognoz-6 .40
1689 A374 60m Molniya-1 .45
1690 A374 80m Soyuz .60
1691 A374 1.20t Vostok .90
Nos. 1685-1691 (7) 3.04

Effigies of Buddhist Deities — A375

Various statues.

1988, June 15 Litho. *Perf. 14*

1692 A375 20m multi .15
1693 A375 30m multi, diff. .20
1694 A375 40m multi, diff. .28
1695 A375 50m multi, diff. .35
1696 A375 60m multi, diff. .40
1697 A375 70m multi, diff. .48
1698 A375 80m multi, diff. .55
1699 A375 1.20t multi, diff. .80
Nos. 1692-1699 (8) 3.21

Wildlife Conservation — A376

Eagles, Haliaeetus albicilla. Nos. 1700-1702 vert.

1988, Aug. 1 Litho. *Perf. 14*

1700 A376 60m Eagle facing left, diff. .40
1701 A376 60m Landing on branch .40
1702 A376 60m Facing right .40
1703 A376 60m shown .40
Nos. 1700-1703 (4) 1.60

Souvenir Sheet

Cosmos — A377

1988, Sept. 15 Litho. *Perf. 14*

1704 A377 4t Satellite links 3.25

Opera A378

1988, Oct. 1 Litho. *Perf. 13x12½*

1705 A378 60m multi .90

No. 1705 printed se-tenant with label picturing composer.

Equus hemionus — A380

1988, May 3

1713 A380 60m Mare, foal .58
1714 A380 60m Horse's head .58
1715 A380 60m Horse galloping .58
1716 A380 60m Horses cantering .58
Nos. 1713-1716 (4) 2.32

Winners of the 1988 Winter Olympics, Calgary — A381

1988, July 1

1717 A381 1.50t Matti Nykaenen, Finland .58
1718 A381 1.50t Bonnie Blair, US .58
1719 A381 1.50t Alberto Tomba, Italy .58
1720 A381 1.50t USSR hockey team .58
Nos. 1717-1720 (4) 2.32

Souvenir Sheet

1721 A381 4t Katarina Witt, DDR 2.35

Nos. 1718-1720 vert.

A382 A383

1988, Sept. 1

1722 A382 10m shown .15
1723 A382 20m Horsemanship .20
1724 A382 30m Archery .30
1725 A382 40m Wrestling .40
1726 A382 50m Archery, diff. .50
1727 A382 70m Horsemanship, diff. .70
1728 A382 1.20t Horsemanship, wrestling, archery 1.20
Nos. 1722-1728 (7) 3.45

1988, Dec. 1 *Perf. 13x13½*

1729 A383 60m multicolored .80

Socialism and Peace.

Goats — A384

Various species.

1989, Jan. 15 *Perf. 14*

1730 A384 20m multi .20
1731 A384 30m multi .30
1732 A384 40m multi .40
1733 A384 50m multi .50
1734 A384 60m multi .60
1735 A384 80m multi .75
1736 A384 1.20t multi 1.00
Nos. 1717-1723 (7) 5.02

Souvenir Sheet

1737 A384 4t multi, vert. 3.00

Souvenir Sheet

Child Survival — A385

1989, Jan. 28 Litho. *Perf. 14*
1738 A385 4t Drawing by H. Jargalsuren 3.00

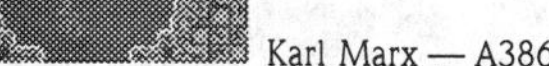

Karl Marx — A386

1989, Feb. 25 Litho. *Perf. 13x13½*
1739 A386 60m multicolored .80

Miniature Sheet

Statue of Sukhe Bator — A387

Mongolian Airline Jet — A388

1989, July 1 *Perf. 14*
1740 Sheet of 3 2.50
a. A387 20m Concorde jet .25
b. A387 60m TGV high-speed train .75
c. A387 1.20t shown 1.50

Souvenir Sheet

1741 A388 4t shown 3.00

PHILEXFRANCE '89, BULGARIA '89.
For overprint see No. 1756.

World War II Memorial — A389

1989, Sept. 2
1742 A389 60m multicolored .80

Cacti — A390

1989, Sept. 7
1743 A390 20m *O. microdasys* .20
1744 A390 30m *E. multipiex* .25
1745 A390 40m *R. tephracanthus* .35
1746 A390 50m *B. haselbergii* .50
1747 A390 60m *G. mihanovichii* .60
1748 A390 80m *C. strausii* .75
1749 A390 1.20t *Horridocactus tuberisvicatus* 1.00
Nos. 1743-1749 (7) 3.65

Souvenir Sheet

1750 A390 4t *Astrophytum ornatum* 3.00

A391 A392

Winners at the 1988 Summer Olympics, Seoul.

1989, Oct. 1
1751 A391 60m Kristin Otto, East Germany .55
1752 A391 60m Florence Griffith-Joyner, US .55
1753 A391 60m Gintaoutas Umaras, USSR .55
1754 A391 60m Stefano Cerioni, Italy .55
Nos. 1751-1754 (4) 2.20

Souvenir Sheet

1755 A391 4t N. Enkhbat, Mongolia 3.00

No. 1740 Overprinted for WORLD STAMP EXPO '89

1989, Nov. 17 Miniature Sheet
1756 Sheet of 3 2.50
a. A387 20m multicolored .25
b. A387 60m multicolored .75
c. A387 1.20t multicolored 1.50

1989, Dec. 1
1757 A392 60m Books, fountain pen .55

Beavers *(Castor fiber birulai)* — A393

1989, Dec. 10
1758 A393 60m Cutting down saplings .55
1759 A393 60m Rolling wood across ground .55
1760 A393 60m Beaver on land, in water .55
1761 A393 60m Beaver and young .55
Nos. 1758-1761 (4) 2.20

Medals and Military Decorations — A394

1989, Dec. 31 *Perf. 13x13½*
1762 A394 60m pink & multi .55
1763 A394 60m lt blue grn & multi .55
1764 A394 60m vio & multi .55
1765 A394 60m org & multi .55
1766 A394 60m brt blue & multi .55
1767 A394 60m ver & multi .55
1768 A394 60m vio blue & multi .55
Nos. 1762-1768 (7) 3.85

Bears and Giant Pandas — A395

1990, Jan. 1 *Perf. 14*
1769 A395 20m *Ursus pruinosis* .20
1770 A395 30m *Ursus arctos syriacus* .30
1771 A395 40m *Ursus thibetanus* .40
1772 A395 50m *Ursus maritimus* .55
1773 A395 60m *Ursus arctos bruinosus* .65
1774 A395 80m *Ailuropus melanoleucus* .85
1775 A395 1.20t *Ursus arctos isabellinus* 1.25
Nos. 1769-1775 (7) 4.20

Souvenir Sheet

1776 A395 4t *Ailuropus melanoleucus*, diff. 4.25

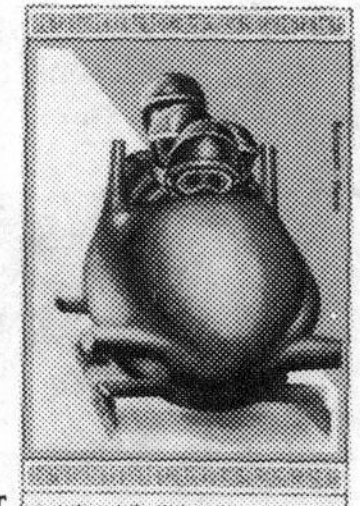

Winter Sports — A396

1990, Jan. 6
1777 A396 20m 4-man bobsled .20
1778 A396 30m Luge .30
1779 A396 40m Women's figure skating .40
1780 A396 50m 1-man bobsled .50
1781 A396 60m Pairs figure skating .60
1782 A396 80m Speed skating .75
1783 A396 1.20t Ice speedway 1.25
Nos. 1777-1783 (7) 4.00

Souvenir Sheet

1784 A396 4t Ice hockey 4.00

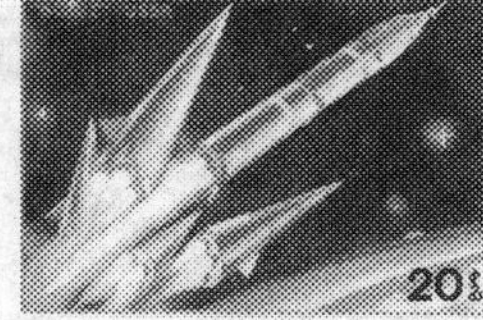

Space Exploration — A397

Rockets and spacecraft: 20m, Soyuz, USSR. 30m, Apollo-Soyuz, US-USSR. 40m, *Columbia* space shuttle, US, vert. 50m, *Hermes*, France. 60m, *Nippon*, Japan, vert. 80m, *Energy*, USSR, vert. 1.20t, *Buran*, USSR, vert. 4t, *Sanger*, West Germany.

1990, Jan. 30
1785 A397 20m shown .20
1786 A397 30m multicolored .30
1787 A397 40m multicolored .40
1788 A397 50m multicolored .50
1789 A397 60m multicolored .60
1790 A397 80m multicolored .75
1791 A397 1.20t multicolored 1.25
Nos. 1785-1791 (7) 4.00

Souvenir Sheet

1792 A397 4t multicolored 4.00

Jawaharlal Nehru, 1st Prime Minister of Independent India — A398

1990, Feb. 10
1793 A398 10m gold, blk & dark red brn .80

Statue of Sukhe Bator — A399

1990, Feb. 27
1794 A399 10m multicolored .80

Mongolian Ballet — A400

Dancers in scenes from various ballets. 40m, 80m, 1.20t vert.

1990, Feb. 28
1795 A400 20m shown .20
1796 A400 30m multi .30
1797 A400 40m multi .40
1798 A400 50m multi .50
1799 A400 60m multi .60
1800 A400 80m multi .75
1801 A400 1.20t multi 1.00
Nos. 1795-1801 (7) 3.75

Automobiles — A401

1990, Mar. 26

1802	A401	20m	Citroen, France	.20
1803	A401	30m	Volvo 760 GLF, Sweden	.30
1804	A401	40m	Honda, Japan	.40
1805	A401	50m	Volga, USSR	.50
1806	A401	60m	Ford Granada, US	.60
1807	A401	80m	BAZ 21099, USSR	.75
1808	A401	1.20t	Mercedes Class 190, West Germany	1.25
			Nos. 1802-1808 (7)	4.00

Souvenir Sheet

1809 A401 4t like 50m 3.00

Lenin — A402

1990, Mar. 27 *Perf. 13x13½*

1810 A402 60m gold, black & ver .80

Unen Newspaper, 70th Anniv. — A403

1990, Apr. 1 *Perf. 14*

1811 A403 60m multicolored .80

End of World War II, 45th Anniv. — A404

1990, Apr. 1

1812 A404 60m multicolored .80

Buddhist Deities (18th-20th Cent. Paintings) — A405

1990, Apr. 1

1813	A405	20m	Damdin Sandub	.22
1814	A405	30m	Pagwa Lama	.32
1815	A405	40m	Chu Lha	.42
1816	A405	50m	Agwanglobsan	.55
1817	A405	60m	Dorje Dags Dan	.65
1818	A405	80m	Wangchikdorje	.85
1819	A405	1.20t	Buddha	1.25
			Nos. 1813-1819 (7)	4.26

Souvenir Sheet

1820 A405 4t Migjed Jang-Rasek 4.25

A406

Aspects of a Cooperative Settlement — A407

Paintings: 20m, Animals on plain, rainbow. 30m, Workers, reindeer, dog, vert. 40m, Two men, mountains, Bactrian camels. 50m, Man, Bactrian camels. 60m, Huts, animal shelter, corral. 60m, Breaking horses, vert. 1.20t, Sheep, shepherd girl on horse. 4t, Wrestling match.

1990, Apr. 1

1821	A406	20m	shown	.22
1822	A406	30m	multicolored	.32
1823	A406	40m	multicolored	.42
1824	A406	50m	multicolored	.55
1825	A406	60m	multicolored	.65
1826	A406	80m	multicolored	.85
1827	A406	1.20t	multicolored	1.25
			Nos. 1821-1827 (7)	4.26

Souvenir Sheet

1828 A407 4t shown 4.25

Scenes from Various Mongolian-made Films — A408

1990, Apr. 1

1829	A408	20m	shown	.22
1830	A408	30m	multi, diff.	.32
1831	A408	40m	multi, diff.	.42
1832	A408	50m	multi, diff.	.55
1833	A408	60m	multi, diff.	.65
1834	A408	80m	multi, diff.	.85
1835	A408	1.20t	multi, diff.	1.25
			Nos. 1829-1835 (7)	4.26

Souvenir Sheet

1836 A408 4t multi, diff., vert. 4.25

Souvenir Sheet

Stamp World London '90 — A409

1990, Apr. 1

1837 A409 4t multicolored 3.00

1990 World Cup Soccer Championships, Italy — A410

Trophy and various athletes.

1990, Apr. 30

1838	A410	20m	multicolored	.20
1839	A410	30m	multicolored	.30
1840	A410	40m	multicolored	.40
1841	A410	50m	multicolored	.50
1842	A410	60m	multicolored	.60
1843	A410	80m	multicolored	.75
1844	A410	1.20t	multicolored	1.25
			Nos. 1838-1844 (7)	4.00

Souvenir Sheet

1845 A410 4t Trophy, vert. 3.00

Nos. 304-307 Ovptd. CHINGGIS KHAN CROWNATION 1189

1990, May 1 Photo. *Perf. 11½x12*

1846	A84	20m	multicolored	*2.50*
1847	A84	30m	multicolored	*3.75*
1848	A84	50m	multicolored	*6.25*
1849	A84	60m	multicolored	*7.50*
			Nos. 1846-1849 (4)	*20.00*

Coronation of Genghis Khan, 800th anniv. (in 1989).

Souvenir Sheet

Genghis Khan — A411

1990, May 8 Litho. *Perf. 13½*

1850 A411 7t multicolored 4.90

Stamp World London '90. Exists imperf. Exists without "Stamp World London '90" and Great Britain No. 1.

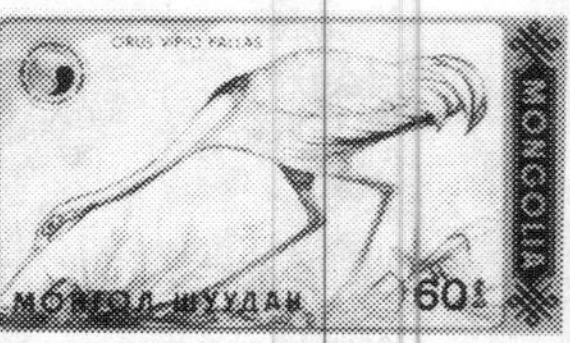

Cranes *(Grus vipio pallas)* — A412

1990, May 23 *Perf. 14*

1851	A412	60m	brt blue & multi	.58
1852	A412	60m	brt rose lil & multi	.58
1853	A412	60m	red lil & multi	.58
1854	A412	60m	car rose & multi	.58
			Nos. 1851-1854 (4)	2.32

Nos. 1853-1854 are vert.

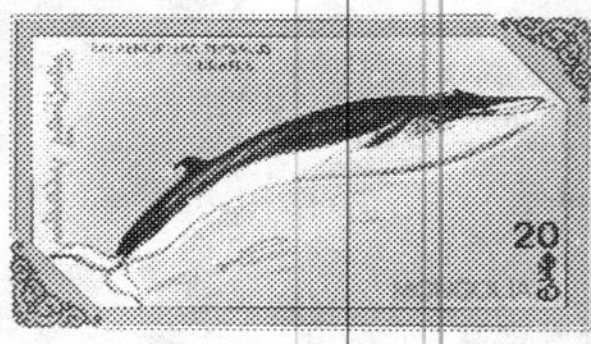

Marine Mammals — A413

1990, June 20 Litho. *Perf. 14*

1855	A413	20m	Balaenoptera physalus	.24
1856	A413	30m	Megaptera novaeangliae	.35
1857	A413	40m	Monodon monoceros	.48
1858	A413	50m	Grampus griseus	.60
1859	A413	60m	Tursiops truncatus	.70
1860	A413	80m	Lagenorhynchus acutius	.95
1861	A413	1.20t	Balaena mysticetus	1.40
			Nos. 1855-1861 (7)	4.72

Souvenir Sheet

1861A A413 4t Killer whale 4.65

Cultural Heritage
A414 A415

1990, Aug. 13 *Perf. 13x12½*

1862	A414	10m	shown	.15
1863	A414	10m	Like No. 1862, arrows at left	.15
1864	A415	40m	Fire ring	.48
1865	A415	60m	Genghis Khan	.70
1866	A414	60m	Tent	.70
1867	A414	60m	Horses	.70
1868	A414	80m	Royal family (green panel)	.95
1869	A414	80m	Royal court (dk bl panel)	.95
a.			Souv. sheet, #1862-1869 + label	5.00
			Nos. 1862-1869 (8)	4.78

20th Party Congress — A416

1990, Mar. 1 Litho. *Perf. 14*

1870 A416 60m multicolored .90

Dinosaurs — A417

1990, Aug. 25

1871 A417 20m shown .25
1872 A417 30m multi, diff. .35
1873 A417 40m multi, diff. .50
1874 A417 50m multi, diff .60
1875 A417 60m multi, vert. .70
1876 A417 80m multi, diff. 1.00

Size: 60x21mm

Perf. 13

1877 A417 1.20t multi, diff. 1.40
Nos. 1871-1877 (7) 4.80

Souvenir Sheet

1878 A417 4t multi, diff. 4.75

Giant Pandas — A418

1990, Aug. 15 Litho. *Perf. 14*

1879 A418 10m Adult on rock, vert. .15
1880 A418 20m Adult, eating, vert. .25
1881 A418 30m Adult and cub, vert. .35
1882 A418 40m shown .50
1883 A418 50m Adult and cub, resting .60
1884 A418 60m Adult, mountains .70
1885 A418 80m Adult and cub, playing 1.00
1886 A418 1.20t Adult, in winter 1.40
Nos. 1879-1886 (8) 4.95

Souvenir Sheet

1887 A418 4t Family 4.70

Pyramids of Egypt — A419

Seven wonders of the ancient world: 20m, Lighthouse of Alexander, vert. 40m, Statue of Zeus, vert. 50m, Colossus of Rhodes, vert. 60m, Mausoleum of Halicarnassus, vert. 80m, Temple of Artemis. 1.20t, Hanging gardens of Babylon, vert. 4t, Pyramids of Egypt, vert.

1990, Sept. 25

1888 A419 20m multicolored .25
1889 A419 30m shown .35
1890 A419 40m multicolored .50
1891 A419 50m multicolored .62
1892 A419 60m multicolored .70
1893 A419 80m multicolored 1.00
1894 A419 1.20t multicolored 1.40
Nos. 1888-1894 (7) 4.82

Souvenir Sheet

1895 A419 4t multicolored 4.65

Moschus Moschiferus — A419a

1990, Sept. 26 Litho. *Perf. 14*

1895A A419a 60m shown .70
1895B A419a 60m In snow .70
1895C A419a 60m Facing left .70
1895D A419a 60m Two, one on ground .70
Nos. 1895A-1895D (4) 2.80

Parrots — A420

1990, Oct. 25 Litho. *Perf. 14*

1896 A420 20m shown .20
1897 A420 30m multi, diff. .30
1898 A420 40m multi, diff. .40
1899 A420 50m multi, diff. .50
1900 A420 60m multi, diff. .60
1901 A420 80m multi, diff. .90
1902 A420 1.20t multi, diff. 1.25
Nos. 1896-1902 (7) 4.15

Souvenir Sheet

1903 A420 4t multi, diff. 3.50

Butterflies — A421

Designs: 20m, Purpurbar. 30m, Grosses nachtpfauenauge. 40m, Grosser C-Falter. 50m, Stachelbeerspanner. 60m, Damenbrett. 80m, Schwalbenschwanz. 1.20t, Aurorafalter. 4t, Linienschwarmer, vert.

1990, Nov. 25 Litho. *Perf. 14*

1904 A421 20m multicolored .25
1905 A421 30m multicolored .35
1906 A421 40m multicolored .50
1907 A421 50m multicolored .60
1908 A421 60m multicolored .70
1909 A421 80m multicolored 1.00
1910 A421 1.20t multicolored 1.50
Nos. 1904-1910 (7) 4.90

Souvenir Sheet

1911 A421 4t multicolored 4.65

Flintstones Visit Mongolia — A422

Designs: 25m, Dino, Bamm-Bamm. 35m, Dino, Bamm-Bamm, diff., vert. 45m, Betty, Wilma, Bamm-Bamm, Pebbles. 55m, Fred, Barney, Dino. 65m, Flintstones & Rubbles. 75m, Bamm-Bamm riding Dino. 85m, Fred, Barney, Bamm-Bamm. 1.40t, Flintstones, Rubbles in car. 2t, Fred, Barney. No. 1921, Wilma, Betty & Bamm-Bamm. No. 1922, Bamm-Bamm, Pebbles riding Dino.

1991, Feb. 10 Litho. *Perf. 14*

1912 A422 25m multicolored .30
1913 A422 35m multicolored .42
1914 A422 45m multicolored .55
1915 A422 55m multicolored .65
1916 A422 65m multicolored .78
1917 A422 75m multicolored .90
1918 A422 85m multicolored 1.00
1919 A422 1.40t multicolored 1.70
1920 A422 2t multicolored 2.40
Nos. 1912-1920 (9) 8.70

Souvenir Sheets

1921 A422 7t multicolored 3.50
1922 A422 7t multicolored 3.50

The Jetsons
A423

Designs: 20m, Jetsons blasting off in spaceship. 25m, Jetsons on planet, horiz. 30m, George, Jane, Elroy & Astro. 40m, George, Judy, Elroy & Astro. 50m, Jetsons in spaceship, horiz. 60m, George, Jane, Elroy & Mr. Spacely, horiz. 70m, George, Elroy wearing jet packs. 80m, Elroy. 1.20t, Elroy, Judy & Astro. No. 1932, Elroy, red flowers. No. 1933, Elroy, blue flowers.

1991, Feb. 10

1923 A423 20m multicolored .25
1924 A423 25m multicolored .30
1925 A423 30m multicolored .35
1926 A423 40m multicolored .50
1927 A423 50m multicolored .60
1928 A423 60m multicolored .70
1929 A423 70m multicolored .85
1930 A423 80m multicolored 1.00
1931 A423 1.20t multicolored 1.50
Nos. 1923-1931 (9) 6.05

Souvenir Sheets

1932 A423 7t multicolored 3.50
1933 A423 7t multicolored 3.50

Mongolian People's Revolutionary Party, 70th Anniv. — A423a

1991, Mar. 1 Litho. *Perf. 14*

1933A A423a 60m multicolored .75

Stamp World London '90
A424 A425

Various birds.

1991, Mar. 3 Litho. *Perf. 14½*

1934 A424 25m multicolored .30
1935 A424 35m multicolored .42
1936 A424 45m multicolored .55
1937 A424 55m multicolored .65
1938 A424 65m multicolored .78
1939 A424 75m multi, horiz. .90
1940 A424 85m multicolored 1.00
1941 A424 1.40t multicolored 1.70
1942 A424 2t multicolored 2.40
Nos. 1934-1942 (9) 8.70

Souvenir Sheets

1943 A424 7t multicolored 3.50
1944 A425 7t multicolored 3.50

Butterflies and Flowers of Mongolia — A426

Designs: 20m, 30m-60m, various butterflies. Others, various flowers.

1991, Mar. 3 Litho. *Perf. 14½*

1945 A426 20m multicolored .25
1946 A426 25m multicolored .30
1947 A426 30m multicolored .35
1948 A426 40m multicolored .48
1949 A426 50m multicolored .60
1950 A426 60m multicolored .70
1951 A426 70m multicolored .80
1952 A426 80m multicolored .95
1953 A426 1.20t multicolored 1.40
Nos. 1945-1953 (9) 5.83

Nos. 1945-1953 and Types Overprinted

EXPO'90

1991, Mar. 3

1954 A426 20m multicolored .25
1955 A426 25m multicolored .30
1956 A426 30m multicolored .35
1957 A426 40m multicolored .48
1958 A426 50m multicolored .60
1959 A426 60m multicolored .70
1960 A426 70m multicolored .80
1961 A426 80m multicolored .95
1962 A426 1.20t multicolored 1.40
Nos. 1954-1962 (9) 5.83

Souvenir Sheets

1963 A426 7t Butterfly 5.35
1964 A426 7t Flower 5.35

Nos. 1963-1964 were not issued without overprint which appears in sheet margin only.

Mongolian People's Army, 70th Anniv. — A426a

1991, Mar. 18 Litho. *Perf. 14*

1964A A426a 60m multicolored .75

Birds — A427

1991, Apr. 1 *Perf. 14*

1965 A427 20m Lururus tetrix .25
1966 A427 30m Tadorna tadorna .35
1967 A427 40m Phasianus colchicus .48
1968 A427 50m Clangula byemalis .60
1969 A427 60m Tetrastes bonasia .70
1970 A427 80m Mergus serrator .95
1971 A427 1.20t Bucephaia clangula 1.40
Nos. 1965-1971 (7) 4.73

Souvenir Sheet

1972 A427 4t Anas crecca, vert. 4.65

Flowers — A428

1991, Apr. 15

1973 A428 20m Dianthus superbus .25
1974 A428 30m Gentiana puenmonanthe .35
1975 A428 40m Taraxacum officinale .48
1976 A428 50m Iris sibrica .60
1977 A428 60m Lilium martagon .70
1978 A428 80m Aster amellus .95
1979 A428 1.20t Cizsium rivulare 1.40
Nos. 1973-1979 (7) 4.73

Souvenir Sheet

1980 A428 4t Campanula persicifolia 4.65

Buddhist Effigies — A429

1991, May 1

1981 A429 20m Defend .25
1982 A429 30m Badmasanhava .35
1983 A429 40m Avalokitecvara .48
1984 A429 50m Buddha .60
1985 A429 60m Mintugwa .70
1986 A429 80m Shyamatara .95
1987 A429 1.20t Samvara 1.40
Nos. 1981-1987 (7) 4.73

Souvenir Sheet

1988 A429 4t Lamidhatara 4.65

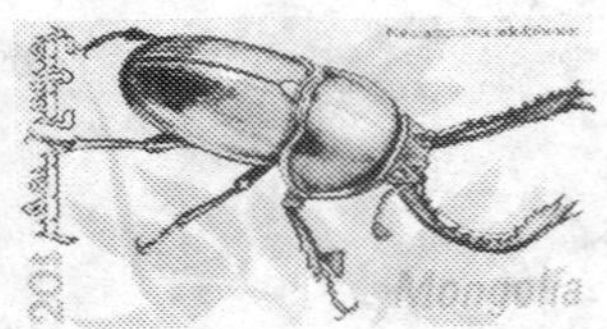

Insects — A430

1991, May 22

1989 A430 20m Neolamprima adolphinae .25
1990 A430 30m Chelorrhina polyphemus .35
1991 A430 40m Coptolabrus coelestis .48
1992 A430 50m Epepeotes togatus .60
1993 A430 60m Cicindela chinensis .70
1994 A430 80m Macrodontia cervicornis .95
1995 A430 1.20t Dynastes hercules 1.40
Nos. 1989-1995 (7) 4.73

African Animals — A431

1991, May 23

1996 A431 20m Zebras .25
1997 A431 30m Cheetah .35
1998 A431 40m Black rhinos .48
1999 A431 50m Giraffe, vert. .60
2000 A431 60m Gorilla .70
2001 A431 80m Elephants .95
2002 A431 1.20t Lion, vert. 1.40
Nos. 1996-2002 (7) 4.73

Souvenir Sheet

2003 A431 4t Gazelle 4.65

No. 1997 is incorrectly spelled "Cheetan."

Exhibition of Meiso Mizuhara's Mongolian Stamp Collection — A432

1991, June **Litho.** ***Perf. 13½***

2004 A432 1.20t multicolored 1.10

Lizards — A433

1991, Oct. 29 ***Perf. 14***

2005 A433 20m Iguana iguana .30
2006 A433 30m Ptychozoon kihli .45
2007 A433 40m Chlamydo- saurus kingii .62
2008 A433 50m Cordylus cordylus .78
2009 A433 60m Basiliscus basilisus .90
2010 A433 80m Tupinambis teguixin 1.25
2011 A433 1.20t Amblyrhynchus cristatus 1.85
Nos. 2005-2011 (7) 6.15

Souvenir Sheet

2012 A433 4t Varanus bengalensis, vert. 4.75

Masks and Costumes — A434

Various masks and costumes.

1991, Oct. 1

2013 A434 35m multicolored .40
2014 A434 45m multicolored .52
2015 A434 55m multicolored .65
2016 A434 65m multicolored .75
2017 A434 85m multicolored 1.00
2018 A434 1.40t multicolored 1.65
2019 A434 2t multicolored 2.35
Nos. 2013-2019 (7) 7.32

Souvenir Sheet

2020 A434 4t multicolored 4.75

Phila Nippon '91 — A435

1991, Oct. 29

2021 A435 1t Pagoda
2022 A435 2t Japanese beauty
2023 A435 3t Mongolian woman
2024 A435 4t Mongolian building

Fantasia, 50th Anniv. A436

Designs: 1.70t, Poster, 1985. 2t, Poster, 1940. 2.30t, Poster, 1982. 2.60t, Poster, 1981. 4.20t, Poster, 1969. 10t, Poster, 1941. 15t, Drawing of Mlle. Upanova, 1940. 16t, Sketch of Mickey as Sorcerer's Apprentice. No. 2033, Mickey as Sorcerer's Apprentice. No. 2034, Dinosaurs from "The Rite of Spring," horiz. No. 2035, Thistles and orchids from "Russian Dance," horiz. No. 2036, Dancing mushrooms from "Chinese Dance," horiz.

Perf. 13½x14, 14x13½

1991, Dec. 31

2025 A436 1.70t multicolored .28
2026 A436 2t multicolored .32
2027 A436 2.30t multicolored .38
2028 A436 2.60t multicolored .42
2029 A436 4.20t multicolored .68
2030 A436 10t multicolored 1.60
2031 A436 15t multicolored 2.40
2032 A436 16t multicolored 2.60
Nos. 2025-2032 (8) 8.68

Souvenir Sheets

2033 A436 30t multicolored 4.80
2034 A436 30t multicolored 4.80
2035 A436 30t multicolored 4.80
2036 A436 30t multicolored 4.80

1992 Winter Olympics, Albertville — A437

1992, Feb. 1 ***Perf. 14***

2037 A437 60m Speed skating, vert. .40
2038 A437 80m Ski jumping, vert. .50
2039 A437 1t Hockey, vert. .60
2040 A437 1.20t Figure skating, vert. .70
2041 A437 1.50t Biathlon .80
2042 A437 2t Downhill skiing .90
2043 A437 2.40t Two-man bobsled 1.00
Nos. 2037-2043 (7) 4.90

Souvenir Sheet

2044 A437 8t Four-man bobsled, vert. 3.00

Dogs — A438

Various breeds of dogs.

1991, Dec. 1 **Litho.** ***Perf. 14***

2045 A438 20m multi .25
2046 A438 30m multi, vert. .35
2047 A438 40m multi, vert. .48
2048 A438 50m multi .58
2049 A438 60m multi .70
2050 A438 80m multi .95
2051 A438 1.20t multi 1.40
Nos. 2045-2051 (7) 4.71

Souvenir Sheet

2052 A438 4t multi 4.70

Cats — A439

Various breeds of cats.

1991, Dec. 27

2053 A439 20m multi .25
2054 A439 30m multi, vert. .35
2055 A439 40m multi .48
2056 A439 50m multi, vert. .58
2057 A439 60m multi, vert. .70
2058 A439 80m multi, vert. .95
2059 A439 1.20t multi, vert. 1.40
Nos. 2053-2059 (7) 4.71

Souvenir Sheet

2060 A439 4t multi 4.70

Alces Alces — A440

1992, May 1 **Litho.** ***Perf. 14***

2061 A440 3t Male .65
2062 A440 3t Two females .65
2063 A440 3t One female, vert. .65
2064 A440 3t Male's head, vert. .65
Nos. 2061-2064 (4) 2.60

Souvenir Sheet

Ferdinand von Zeppelin (1838-1917), Airship Designer — A441

1992, May 1

2065 A441 16t multicolored 4.00

Souvenir Sheets

People and Events — A442

Designs: No. 2066, Pres. Punsalmaagiyn Orchirbat visiting Pres. George Bush at White House. No. 2067, Mother Teresa helping poor in Calcutta. No. 2068, Pope John Paul II at mass. Nos. 2069-2070, Boy Scout blowing bugle.

1992, May 22 ***Perf. 14x13½***

2066 A442 30t silver & multi 4.75

Perf. 14

2067 A442 30t silver & multi 4.75
2068 A442 30t silver & multi 4.75
2069 A442 30t silver & multi 4.75
2070 A442 30t silver & multi 4.75
Nos. 2066-2070 (5) 23.75

Nos. 2067-2070 each contain one 43x28mm stamp. Nos. 2069-2070 exist with gold inscription and border. No. 2069, 17th World Boy Scout Jamboree, Korea. No. 2070, 18th World Boy Scout Jamboree, Netherlands, 1995.

Souvenir Sheet

Discovery of America, 500th Anniv. — A443

Designs: a, Columbus. b, Sailing ship.

1992, May 22
2071 A443 30t Sheet of 2, #a.-b. 9.25

World Columbian Stamp Expo '92, Chicago, Genoa '92.

Miniature Sheets

Railways of the World A444

Designs: No. 2072a, 3t, Tank locomotive, Darjeeling-Himalaya Railway, India. b, 3t, Royal Scot, Great Britain. c, 6t, Bridge on the River Kwai, Burma-Siam Railway. d, 6t, Baltic tank engine, Burma. e, 8t, Baldwin locomotive, Thailand. f, 8t, Western Railway locomotive, Pakistan. g, 16t, P.36 class locomotive, USSR. h, 16t, Shanghai-Beijing Express, China.

Orient Express: No. 2073a, 3t, 1931 Advertising poster. b, 3t, 1928 poster. c, 6t, Dawn departure. d, 6t, Golden Arrow departing Victoria Station. e, 8t, Waiting at station in Yugoslavia. f, 8t, Turn of the century picture of train. g, 16t, Fleche d'Or locomotive approaching Etaples, France. h, 16t, Arrival in Istanbul, Turkey.

No. 2074, New Tokaido line, Japan. No. 2076a, Emblem of Pullman Car Company. b, Emblem of Intl. Wagons-lits Company. No. 2075, TGV, France. No. 2077, Passengers waiting to board Orient Express.

1992, May 24
2072 A444 Sheet of 8, #a.-h. 12.00
2073 A444 Sheet of 8, #a.-h. 12.00

Souvenir Sheets
2074 A444 30t multicolored 4.75
2075 A444 30t multicolored 4.75
2076 A444 30t Sheet of 2, #a.-b. 9.50
2077 A444 30t black & gold 4.75

Nos. 2074-2075 contain one 58x42mm stamp.

Miniature Sheet

Birds — A445

Various birds: a, 3t. b, 3t, Owl. c, 6t, Gull, horiz. d, 6t, horiz. e, 8t. f, 8t, horiz. g, 16t. h, 16t, horiz.

1992, May 24
2078 A445 Sheet of 8, #a.-h. 12.00

Souvenir Sheet
Perf. 14x13½
2079 A445 30t Ducks, 30t in UR 4.75
2080 A445 30t Duck, 30t in LR 4.75

Nos. 2079-2080 contain one 50x38mm stamp.

Miniature Sheet

Butterflies and Moths A446

Various butterflies or moths and: a, 3t, Mountains. b, 3t, Desert. c, 6t, Grass. d, 6t, Lake. e, 8t, Mountain, diff. f, 8t, Flowers. g, 16t, Rocks. h, 16t, Lake, diff.

1992, May 24 ***Perf. 14***
2081 A446 Sheet of 8, #a.-h. 12.00

Souvenir Sheet
Perf. 14x13½
2082 A446 30t pink & multi 4.75
2083 A446 30t blue & multi 4.75

Nos. 2082-2083 contain one 50x38mm stamp.

1992 Summer Olympics, Barcelona — A447

Designs: a, Gold medal. b, Torch.

1992, Jan. 22 **Litho.** ***Perf. 14***
2084 A447 30t Sheet of 2, #a.-b. 9.50

Souvenir Sheet

Genghis Khan — A448

1992, June 15 **Litho.** ***Perf. 14***
2085 A448 16t multicolored

Mushrooms — A449

Designs: 20m, Marasmius oreades. 30m, Boletus luridus. 40m, Hygrophorus marzuelus. 50m, Cantharellus cibarius. 60m, Agaricus campester. 80m, Boletus aereus. 1.20t, Amanita caesarea. 2t, Tricholoma terreum. 4t, Mitrophora hybrida.

1991, June 18 **Litho.** ***Perf. 13***
2086 A449 20m multicolored .18
2087 A449 30m multicolored .28
2088 A449 40m multicolored .35
2089 A449 50m multicolored .45
2090 A449 60m multicolored .55
2091 A449 80m multicolored .70
2092 A449 1.20t multicolored 1.10
2093 A449 2t multicolored 1.80
Nos. 2086-2093 (8) 5.41

Souvenir Sheet
2094 A449 4t multicolored 4.75

Dated 1990. No. 2094 contains one 32x40mm stamp.

Discovery of America, 500th Anniv. — A450

Columbus and: 3t, Two sailing ships. 7t, Natives approaching Santa Maria. 10t, Pinta. 16t, Santa Maria, vert. 30t, Santa Maria, diff. 40t, Santa Maria, dolphins. 50t, Nina.

No. 2102, Ship, vert. No. 2103, Portrait, vert.

1992, Aug. **Litho.** ***Perf. 14***
2095 A450 3t multicolored .16
2096 A450 7t multicolored .40
2097 A450 10t multicolored .55
2098 A450 16t multicolored .90
2099 A450 30t multicolored 1.70
2100 A450 40t multicolored 2.25
2101 A450 50t multicolored 2.75
Nos. 2095-2101 (7) 8.71

Souvenir Sheets
Perf. 13½x14
2102 A450 80t multicolored 4.50
2103 A450 80t multicolored 4.50

Nos. 2102-2103 each contain one 38x52mm stamp.

Miniature Sheet

Butterflies A451

Designs: No. 2104a, 3t, Anthocharis cardamines. b. 8t, Inachis io. c, 10t, Fabriciana adippe. d, 16t, Limenitis reducta. e, 30t, Agrumaenia carniolica. f, 40t, Polyommatus icarus. g, 50t, Parnassius apollo. h, 60t, Saturnia pyri.

No. 2105, Limenitis populi. No. 2106, Heodes virgaureae.

1992, Dec. **Litho.** ***Perf. 14***
2104 A451 Sheet of 8, #a.-h. 10.75

Souvenir Sheets
Perf. 14x13½
2105 A451 80t multicolored 4.00
2106 A451 80t multicolored 4.00

Nos. 2105-2106 each contain one 51x38mm stamp.

1992 Summer Olympics, Barcelona A452

1993, Jan. **Litho.** ***Perf. 13½***
2107 A452 3t Long jump .15
2108 A452 6t Pommel horse .15
2109 A452 8t Boxing .20
2110 A452 16t Wrestling .50
2111 A452 20t Archery, vert. .60
2112 A452 30t Cycling .70
2113 A452 40t Equestrian .80
2114 A452 50t High jump .90
2115 A452 60t Weight lifting 1.00
Nos. 2107-2115 (9) 5.00

Souvenir Sheet
Perf. 15x14
2116 A452 80t Judo 3.00
2117 A452 80t Javelin 3.00

Nos. 2116-2117 contain one 40x30mm stamp.

Miniature Sheet

Birds A453

Designs: No. 2118a, 3t, Tetrae tetrix. b, 8t, Gallinula chloropus. c, 10t, Regulus satrapa. d, 16t, Alcede atthis. e, 30t, Gavia stellata. f, 40t, Ardes cinerea. g, 50t, Upupa epops. h, 60t, Niltava rubeculoides. No. 2119, Gyps fulvus. No. 2120, Podiceps cristatus.

1993, Feb. **Litho.** ***Perf. 14***
2118 A453 Sheet of 8, #a.-h. 12.00

Souvenir Sheets
Perf. 14x13½
2119 A453 80t multicolored 4.35
2120 A453 80t multicolored 4.35

Nos. 2119-2120 each contain one 51x38mm stamp.

Souvenir Sheets

Polska '93 — A454

#2121a, 2122, Copernicus. #2121b, Chopin. #2121c, 2123, Pope John Paul II.

1993, May 1 **Litho.** ***Perf. 13½x14***
2121 A454 30t Sheet of 3, #a.-c. 8.00
2122 A454 80t multicolored 7.25
2123 A454 80t multicolored 7.25
Nos. 2121-2123 (3) 22.50

Animals, Sports, & Transportation — A455

Designs in gold: No. 2124, Cats, dogs. No. 2125, Turtle, bee, wildcat, butterfly. No. 2126, Owl, butterfly, mushroom, dinosaur. Nos. 2127, Chessmen, archer, baseball player, wrestlers, horse and rider. Nos. 2128, Modern transportation.

No. 2129, Dinosaur, whales, butterflies. No. 2130, Mushroom, turtle, flowers.

1993, Jan. 5 **Embossed** ***Perf. 9***
2124-2128 A455 200t Set of 5

Nos. 2124-2128 exist in silver and in either gold or silver imperf. souvenir sheets of 1.

1993, June 1 **Embossed** ***Perf. 8½x9***
Size: 79x53mm
2129 A455 200t silver

Souvenir Sheet
Imperf
Litho. & Embossed
2130 A455 200t gold

No. 2130, Topex '93, Madison, WI. No. 2129 exists in imperf. souvenir sheet of 1. No. 2130 exists in silver.

Souvenir Sheets

Taipei '93 — A456

1993, Aug. 14 **Litho.** ***Perf. 13½x14***
2137 A456 80t Genghis Khan .55
2138 A456 80t Sun Yat-Sen .55

Dirigible Flight Over Ulan Bator — A457

1993, Aug. 27 **Litho.** *Perf. 14*

2139 A457 80t multicolored .55

No. 2139 has a holographic image. Soaking in water may affect the hologram.

Buddhist Deities — A458

Various statues and paintings.

1993, Oct. 3 *Perf. 13½x14*

2140 A458 50t multicolored .35
2141 A458 100t multicolored .70
2142 A458 150t multicolored 1.00
2143 A458 200t multicolored 1.40
a. Miniature sheet of 4 5.75
Nos. 2140-2143 (4) 3.45

Souvenir Sheet

2144 A458 300t multicolored 2.00

Bangkok '93.

Nos. 276 & 1084 Surcharged

XXX 15 тег

1993 *Perfs., Etc. as Before*

2144A A77 8t on 70m #276 .38
2144B A246 15t on 70m #1084 .70

New Year 1994 (Year of the Dog) — A459

Design: No. 2146, Stylized dog running, vert.

Perf. 14x13½, 13½x14

1994, Jan. 10

2145 A459 60t multicolored .42
2146 A459 60t multicolored .42

1994 World Cup Soccer Championships, US — A460

Championship teams: No. 2147, Uruguay, 1930, 1950. No. 2148, Italy, 1954. No. 2149, Brazil, 1959. No. 2150, West Germany, 1954. No. 2151, Argentina, 1978, 1986. No. 2152, Italy, 1938. No. 2153, Brazil, 1962. No. 2154, West Germany, 1974. No. 2155, Brazil, 1970. No. 2156, Italy, 1982. No. 2157, West Germany, 1990.

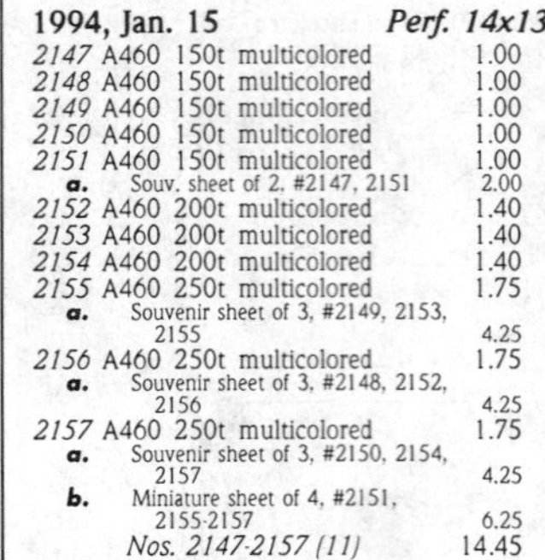

1994, Jan. 15 *Perf. 14x13½*

2147 A460 150t multicolored 1.00
2148 A460 150t multicolored 1.00
2149 A460 150t multicolored 1.00
2150 A460 150t multicolored 1.00
2151 A460 150t multicolored 1.00
a. Souv. sheet of 2, #2147, 2151 2.00
2152 A460 200t multicolored 1.40
2153 A460 200t multicolored 1.40
2154 A460 200t multicolored 1.40
2155 A460 250t multicolored 1.75
a. Souvenir sheet of 3, #2149, 2153, 2155 4.25
2156 A460 250t multicolored 1.75
a. Souvenir sheet of 3, #2148, 2152, 2156 4.25
2157 A460 250t multicolored 1.75
a. Souvenir sheet of 3, #2150, 2154, 2157 4.25
b. Miniature sheet of 4, #2151, 2155-2157 6.25
Nos. 2147-2157 (11) 14.45

Souvenir Sheet

Punsalmaagiin Ochirbat, First President of Mongolia — A461

1994, Apr. 1 *Perf. 14*

2158 A461 150t multicolored 1.00

1994 Winter Olympics, Lillehammer A462

1994, Apr. 10 **Litho.** *Perf. 13½*

2159 A462 50t Biathlon .32
2160 A462 60t Two-man bobsled .38
2161 A462 80t Slalom skiing .50
2162 A462 100t Ski jumping .65
2163 A462 120t Pairs figure skating .75
2164 A462 200t Speed skating 1.25
Nos. 2159-2164 (6) 3.85

Souvenir Sheet

2165 A462 400t Ice hockey 4.25

Souvenir Sheet

Dalai Lama, 1989 Nobel Peace Prize Winner — A463

1994, June 27 **Litho.** *Perf. 13½*

2166 A463 400t multicolored 5.50

A464

People's Army — A465

1994 **Litho.** *Perf. 14*

2167 A464 60m multicolored .90

Souvenir Sheet

2168 A465 4t multicolored 3.50

Miniature Sheet of 18

Wildlife A466

Designs: a, Brown raptor. b, Woodpecker. c, Cranes in flight. d, White raptor. e, Yellow bird on tree branch (i). f, Two birds flying left. g, Raptor perched on rock. h, Two birds flying right. i, Squirrel. j, Dragonfly (f). k, Water bird standing near pond (o). l, Duck in flight over pond. m, Brown bird. n, Ground hog. o, Ladybug on flower. p, Bird's eggs. q, Grasshopper (m). r, Butterfly.

1994, July 15

2169 A466 60m #a.-r. + 2 labels 7.25

First Manned Moon Landing, 25th Anniv. A467

1994, July 20 **Litho.** *Perf. 13½*

2170 A467 200m Trans-lunar injection .70
2171 A467 200m Astronaut on moon .70
2172 A467 200m Space shuttle, earth .70
2173 A467 200m Astronaut, shuttle .70
a. Miniature sheet of 4, #2170-2173 2.80
Nos. 2170-2173 (4) 2.80

Singpex '94 — A468

1994, Aug. 31

2174 A468 300m Butterfly 1.00

Souvenir Sheet

2175 A468 400m Dog *4.00*

New Year 1994 (Year of the Dog).

A469

PHILAKOREA '94 — A470

1994 **Litho.** *Perf. 14*

2176 A469 600m Korea #1749 3.00
2177 A469 600m #433 3.00
2178 A470 600m #1 3.00
2179 A470 600m Korea #1 3.00
Nos. 2176-2179 (4) 12.00

Souvenir Sheets

Perf. 13½x14

2180 A470 400m #5 2.00

Perf. 14

2181 A469 600m Yong Sik Hong 3.00

Issued: No. 2180, 11/23, others, 8/16. No. 2180 contains one 34x46mm stamp.

First Mongolian Stamp, 70th anniv. (#2180).

Dinosaurs — A471

1994, Nov. 30 *Perf. 14*

2182 A471 60m Mammuthus, vert. .40
2183 A471 80m Stegosaurus, vert. .52
2184 A471 100m Talararus .65
2185 A471 120m Gorythosaurus .80
2186 A471 200m Tyrannosaurus 1.25
Nos. 2182-2186 (5) 3.62

Souvenir Sheet

2187 A471 400m Triceratops *4.00*

Nos. 2182-2187 exist in imperf. sheets of 1. No. 2182 is misspelled.

Mongolian-Japanese Friendship — A472

1994, Dec. 15 *Perf. 14x13½*

2188 A472 20m multicolored .15

New Year 1995 (Year of the Boar) — A474

1995, Jan. 1 *Perf. 14x13½, 13½x14*

2190 A474 200m shown .48
2191 A474 200m Boar, diff, vert. .48

A475

Litho. & Typo.

1994, July 25 *Perf. 15x14*

Denomination in Black

2192 A475 10t Flower .15
2193 A475 18t Ram .15
2194 A475 22t Airplane .15
2196 A475 44t like #2193 .28
Set value .52

Dated 1993. This is an expanding set. Numbers may change.

Religious Masked Dancing — A476

Various masked dancers in traditional costumes.

1995, Feb. 25 **Litho.** *Perf. 14*

2201 A476 20t multicolored .15
2202 A476 50t multicolored .28
2203 A476 60t multicolored .35
2204 A476 100t multicolored .60
2205 A476 120t multicolored .70
2206 A476 150t multicolored .85
2207 A476 200t multicolored 1.10
Nos. 2201-2207 (7) 4.03

Souvenir Sheet

2208 A476 400t multicolored 4.00

Saiga Tatarica A477

1995, Mar. 30 **Litho.** *Perf. 14*

2209 A477 40t shown .22
2210 A477 55t Two adults .28
2211 A477 70t One running left .40
2212 A477 200t One up close 1.10
a. Block of 4, #2209-2212 2.00

World Wildlife Fund.

Souvenir Sheet

First Philately & Collections Fair, Hong Kong '95 — A478

Designs: a, Butterfly. b, Flowers.

1995, June 6 **Litho.** *Perf. 14*

2213 A478 200t Sheet of 2, #a.-b. + 2 labels 4.25

Goldfish A479

Designs: 20t, Yellow oranda. 50t, Red and white wen-yu. 60t, Brown oranda with red head. 100t, Calico pearl-scale with phoenix tail. 120t, Red lion-head. 150t, Brown oranda. 200t, Red and white oranda with narial.

400t, White and gold unidentified fish.

1995, Sept. 1 **Litho.** *Perf. 14*

2214-2220 A479 Set of 7 4.25

Souvenir Sheet

2221 A479 400t multicolored 4.25

No. 2221 contains one 50x38mm stamp.

Miniature Sheet

Motion Pictures, Cent. A480

Various portraits of Marilyn Monroe (1926-62): No. 2222a, 60t. b, 80t. c, 100t. d, 120t. e, 150t. f, 200t. g, 250t. h, 300t. i, 350t.

No. 2223, In white-collared blouse. No. 2224, With lion. No. 2225, In black lace dress. No. 2226, In scene from movie, Niagara.

1995, Oct. 20

2222 A480 Sheet of 9, #a.-i. 8.00

Souvenir Sheets

2223 A480 200t multi 3.25
2224-2226 A480 300t each 4.25

Miniature Sheet

UN, 50th Anniv. — A481

Exterior views of UN complexes, Secretaries General: a, Trygve Lie. b, Dag Hammarskjold. c, U Thant. d, Kurt Waldheim. e, Jose Perez de Cuellar. f, Boutros Boutros-Ghali.

1995, Oct. 15

2227 A481 60t Sheet of 9, #a.-f. 4.25

Miniature Sheet

Elvis Presley (1935-77) A482

Various portaits: No. 2228a, 60t. b, 80t. c, 100t. d, 120t. e, 150t. f, 200t. g, 250t. h, 300t. i, 350t.

No. 2229, Wearing yellow sweater. No. 2230, With dancing girl. No. 2231, With guitar. No. 2232, In army uniform, wife Priscilla.

1995, Oct. 20

2228 A482 Sheet of 9, #a.-i. 8.00

Souvenir Sheets

2229 A482 200t multi 3.25
2230 A482 300t multi 5.00
2231-2232 A482 400t each 6.50

Miniature Sheet

X-Men Comic Characters A483

Designs: No. 2233a, 30t, Bishop. b, 50t, Beast. c, 60t, Rogue. d, 70t, Gambit. e, 80t, Cyclops. f, 100t, Storm. g, 200t, Professor X. h, 250t, Wolverine.

No. 2234: a, Wolverine, horiz. b, Magneto, horiz.

1995, Sept. 15

2233 A483 Sheet of 8, #a.-h. 4.25

Souvenir Sheet

2234 A483 250t Sheet of 2, #a.-b. 4.25

New Year 1996 (Year of the Rat) A484

1996, Jan. 1 **Litho.** *Perf. 14*

2235 A484 150t Rat, diff., vert. .80
2236 A484 200t shown 1.00

CHINA '96 — A485

Designs: a, Monument of Sukhe Bator. b, Temple of Heaven, Beijing. c, Migjed Jang-Rasek. d, Great Wall.

1996, Apr. 25 **Litho.** *Perf. 13½x14*

2237 A485 65t Sheet of 4, #a.-d. 8.30

1996 Summer Olympic Games, Atlanta A486

30t, Cycling. 60t, Women's shooting. 80t, Weight lifting. 100t, Boxing. 120t, Women's archery, vert. 150t, Rhythmic gymnastics, vert. 200t, Hurdles, vert. 350t, Equestrian. 400t, Wrestling.

500t, Basketball. 600t, Judo.

1996 **Litho.** *Perf. 14*

2238 A486 30t multicolored .15
2239 A486 60t multicolored .15
2240 A486 80t multicolored .20
2241 A486 100t multicolored .25
2242 A486 120t multicolored .30
2243 A486 150t multicolored .40
2244 A486 200t multicolored .50
2245 A486 350t multicolored .90
2246 A486 400t multicolored 1.00
Nos. 2238-2246 (9) 3.85

Souvenir Sheets

2246A A486 500t multicolored 4.00
2246B A486 600t multicolored 4.75

No. 2246A contains one 37x53mm stamp, No. 2246B one 52x39mm stamp.

Olymphilex '96 (#2246A-2246B).

CAPEX '96 — A487

Designs: a, 350t, No 2. b, 400t, Canada No. 1.

1996 **Litho.** *Perf. 12½*

2247 A487 Sheet of 2, #a.-b. 4.50

No. 2247b is 40x30mm. No. 2247 exists with blue at upper right margin corner and different colored margin picture of CN Tower.

New Year 1997 (Year of the Ox) A488

1997 **Litho.** *Perf. 14*

2248 A488 300t Ox, vert. .75
2249 A488 350t shown .85

Souvenir Sheet

Total Solar Eclipse Over Mongolia, Mar. 9, 1997 — A489

Illustration reduced.

1997 **Litho.** *Perf. 12½*

2250 A489 1000t Map of Mongolia 4.25

Return of Hong Kong to China A490

Designs: 200t, Former Chinese Pres. Deng Xioaping, Queen Elizabeth II. 250t, Chinese Pres. Jiang Zemin and Chief Executive of the Special Administrative Region of Hong Kong, Tung Chee-hwa.

1997 **Litho.** *Perf. 13½*

2251 A490 200t multicolored .80
2252 A490 250t multicolored 1.00
a. Pair, #2251-2252 1.80

Seven Joys A491

Designs: a, Wheel. b, Gem. c, Minister. d, Queen. e, Elephant. f, Horse. g, General.

1997 Litho. *Perf. 11*

2253 A491 200t Sheet of 7, #a.-g., + 2 labels 6.00

Souvenir Sheet

Moscow '97 — A492

Illustration reduced.

1997 *Perf. 12½x11½*

2254 A492 1000t No. 264 4.00

Monument to the Politically Repressed — A493

1997 *Perf. 13x13½*

2255 A493 150t black & gray .95

SEMI-POSTAL STAMPS

Catalogue values for unused stamps in this section are for Never Hinged items.

Vietnamese Mother and Child — SP1

1967, Dec. 22 Photo. *Perf. 12x11½*

B1	SP1	30m + 20m multi	.20	.15
B2	SP1	50m + 30m multi	.30	.20

Solidarity with Vietnam.

Save Venice Type of Regular Issue
Souvenir Sheet

3t+1t, Departure of St. Ursula, by Carpaccio.

1972, Oct. 1 Litho. *Perf. 12*

B3 A163 3t + 1t multi 3.25 3.25

Save Venice Campaign. No. B3 contains one horizontal stamp.

Girl Feeding Lambs — SP2

Designs (UNICEF Emblem and): 20m+5m, Boy playing flute and dancing girl. 30m+5m, Girl chasing butterflies. 40m+5m, Girl with ribbon. 60m+5m, Girl with flowers. 80m+5m, Girl carrying bucket. 1t+5m, Boy going to school.

1977, June 1 Litho. *Perf. 12*

B4	SP2	10m + 5m multi	.15	.15
B5	SP2	20m + 5m multi	.18	.15
B6	SP2	30m + 5m multi	.30	.18
B7	SP2	40m + 5m multi	.40	.25
B8	SP2	60m + 5m multi	.60	.30
B9	SP2	80m + 5m multi	.70	.40
B10	SP2	1t + 5m multi	.90	.55
		Nos. B4-B10 (7)	3.23	1.98

Surtax was for Mongolian Children's Village. See No. CB1.

Boys on Horseback — SP3

Mongolian Children and IYC Emblem: 30m+5m, Raising chickens. 50m+5m, With deer. 60m+5m, With flowers. 70m+5m, Planting tree. 80m+5m, Studying space project. 1t+5m, Dancing. 4t+50m, Girl on horseback.

1979, Jan. 10

B11	SP3	10m + 5m multi	.15	.15
B12	SP3	30m + 5m multi	.18	.15
B13	SP3	50m + 5m multi	.32	.15
B14	SP3	60m + 5m multi	.35	.15
B15	SP3	70m + 5m multi	.45	.22
B16	SP3	80m + 5m multi	.55	.32
B17	SP3	1t + 5m multi	.70	.40
		Nos. B11-B17 (7)	2.70	
		Set value		1.25

Souvenir Sheet

B18 SP3 4t + 50m multi 3.00 3.00

International Year of the Child.

AIR POST STAMPS

Catalogue values for unused stamps in this section are for Never Hinged items.

Postal Modernization Type of Regular Issue

Designs: 10m, 20m, Postman with horses. 25m, Postman with reindeer. 30m, 50m, Plane over map of Mongolia. 1t, Post horn and flag of Mongolia.

1961, June 5 Photo. *Perf. 15*

C1	A72	10m multicolored	.15	.15
C2	A72	50m multicolored	.30	.15
C3	A72	1t multicolored	.70	.40
		Nos. C1-C3 (3)	1.15	
		Set value		.58

Souvenir Sheet
Perf. 11

C4		Sheet of 4	1.00	1.00
a.	A72	20m lt blue grn & multi	.24	.24
b.	A72	25m light blue & multi	.24	.24
c.	A72	30m light green & multi	.24	.24
d.	A72	1t rose carmine & multi	.24	.24

40th anniversary of independence; postal modernization. No. C4b is not inscribed Airmail.

Souvenir Sheet

Austria Type SP55, Austrian and Mongolian Stamps Circling Globe — AP1

1965, May 1 Engr. *Perf. 11½*

C5 AP1 4t brown carmine 2.50 2.50

Vienna Intl. Philatelic Exhibition, WIPA, June 4-13. #C5 contains one 61x38mm stamp.

Weather Satellite — AP2

Designs: 20m, Antarctic exploration. 30m, Space exploration.

1965, May 15 Photo. *Perf. 13½*

C6	AP2	15m lilac, gold & blk	.15	.15
C7	AP2	20m blue & multi	.15	.15
C8	AP2	30m rose & multi	.20	.15
		Nos. C6-C8 (3)	.50	
		Set value		.28

International Quiet Sun Year, 1964-65.

ITU Emblem — AP3

Design: 4t, Communications satellite.

1965, Dec. 20 *Perf. 11½x12*

C9	AP3	30m blue & bister	.15	.15
C10	AP3	50m red & bister	.20	.15
		Set value		.16

Souvenir Sheet
Perf. 11, Imperf.

C11 AP3 4t gold, bl & blk 2.25 2.25

ITU, centenary. No. C11 contains one stamp, 38x51mm.

Souvenir Sheet

Luna 10, Moon and Earth — AP4

1966, July 10 Photo. *Imperf.*

C12 AP4 4t multicolored 2.50 2.50

Luna 10 Russian moon mission, Apr. 3, 1966.

Souvenir Sheet

Astronaut and Landing Module — AP5

1969, Aug. 20 Litho. *Perf. 11½*

C13 AP5 4t ultra & multi 2.50 2.50

Apollo 11 US moon mission, first man landing on moon.

Souvenir Sheet

Apollo 16 — AP6

Perf. 12½x11½

1972, Apr. 16 Photo.

C14 AP6 4t multicolored 2.50 2.50

Apollo 16 moon mission, Apr. 15-27.

Souvenir Sheet

Mongolian Horse — AP7

1972, May 10 Photo. *Perf. 12½*

C15 AP7 4t multicolored 2.50 2.50

Centenary of the discovery of the Przewalski wild horse, bred in captivity in Berlin Zoo.

Telecommunication — AP8

Designs: 30m, Horse breeding. 40m, Train and plane. 50m, Corn and farm machinery. 60m, Red Cross ambulance and hospital. 80m, Actors. 1t, Factories.

1972, July 11 Litho. *Perf. 12*

C16	AP8	20m olive & multi	.15	.15
C17	AP8	30m violet & multi	.15	.15
C18	AP8	40m rose & multi	.15	.15
C19	AP8	50m red & multi	.20	.15
C20	AP8	60m multicolored	.35	.15
C21	AP8	80m lt blue & multi	.35	.18
C22	AP8	1t green & multi	.40	.28
		Nos. C16-C22 (7)	1.75	
		Set value		.88

Mongolian Achievements.

Mongolian Flag, Globe and Radar — AP9

Perf. 12½x11½

1972, July 20 Photo.

C23 AP9 60m olive & multi .28 .18

Intl. Telecommunications Day, May 17, 1972.

Running and Olympic Rings — AP10

Olympic Rings and: 15m, Boxing. 20m, Judo. 25m, High jump. 30m, Rifle shooting. 60m, Wrestling. 80m, Weight lifting. 1t, Mongolian flag and sport emblem. 4t, Woman archer, vert.

Perf. 12½x11½

1972, July 30 **Photo.**

C24 AP10 10m multicolored .15 .15
C25 AP10 15m multicolored .15 .15
C26 AP10 20m multicolored .15 .15
C27 AP10 25m multicolored .18 .15
C28 AP10 30m multicolored .20 .15
C29 AP10 60m multicolored .30 .20
C30 AP10 80m multicolored .38 .24
C31 AP10 1t multicolored .55 .32
Nos. C24-C31 (8) 2.06
Set value 1.10

Souvenir Sheet

Perf. 11½x12½

C32 AP10 4t orange & multi 2.00 2.00

20th Olympic Games, Munich, Aug. 26-Sept. 11.

Dragon and Mariner 2 — AP11

Designs: a, Snake, Mars 1. c, Hare, Soyuz 5. d, Monkey, Explorer 6. e, Cock, Venus 1. f, Rat, Apollo 15. g, Horse, Apollo 8. h, Boar, Cosmos 110. i, Tiger, Gemini 7. j, Sheep, Electron 2. k, Dog, Ariel 2. l, Ram, Venus 4.

1972, Dec. 4 **Photo.** *Perf. 12*

C33 AP11 Sheet of 12 4.00 1.50
a.-f. 60m any single, size: 55x35mm .30 .15
g.-l. 60m any single, size: 35x35mm .30 .15

Space achievements of US and USSR, and signs of Eastern Calendar.

Airliner — AP12

1973, Jan. **Photo.** *Perf. 12*

C34 AP12 1.50t blue .70 .20

Weather Satellite, Earth Station, WMO Emblem — AP13

1973, Feb. **Photo.** *Perf. 12x11½*

C35 AP13 60m multicolored .28 .15

Intl. meteorological cooperation, cent.

Holy Flame Type of 1959
Souvenir Sheet

1973, Apr. 15 **Photo.** *Perf. 12½*

C36 A48 4t gold & multi 1.75 1.75

IBRA München 1973 Intl. Stamp Exhibition, Munich, May 11-20. No. C36 contains one 40x63mm stamp in redrawn design of A48 with simulated perforations and wide gold margin.

Russia No. 3100 — AP14

Designs: Stamps (with mail-connected designs) of participating countries.

1973, July 31 **Litho.** *Perf. 12½*

C37 AP14 30m shown .20 .15
C38 AP14 30m Mongolia #236 .20 .15
C39 AP14 30m Bulgaria #1047 .20 .15
C40 AP14 30m Hungary #B202 .20 .15
C41 AP14 30m Czechoslavia #C72 .20 .15
C42 AP14 30m German Dem. Rep. #369 .20 .15
C43 AP14 30m Cuba #C31 .20 .15
C44 AP14 30m Romania #2280 .20 .15
C45 AP14 30m Poland #802 .20 .15
Nos. C37-C45 (9) 1.80 1.35

Conference of Permanent Committee for Posts and Telecommunications of Council for Economic Aid (COMECON), Ulan Bator, Aug. 1973.

Launching of Soyuz Spacecraft — AP15

1973, Oct. 26 **Litho.** *Perf. 12½*

C46 AP15 5m shown .15 .15
C47 AP15 10m Apollo 8 .15 .15
C48 AP15 15m Soyuz 4 & 5 docking .15 .15
C49 AP15 20m Apollo 11 lunar module .15 .15
C50 AP15 30m Apollo 14 splashdown .30 .15
C51 AP15 50m Soyuz 6, 7 & 8 .35 .16
C52 AP15 60m Apollo 16 moon rover .40 .28
C53 AP15 1t Lunokhod 1 on moon .60 .38
Nos. C46-C53 (8) 2.25
Set value 1.20

Souvenir Sheet

C54 AP15 4t Soyuz and Apollo 2.25 2.25

US and Russian achievements in space.

Comecon Building, Moscow — AP16

1974, Feb. 28 **Photo.** *Perf. 11½x12*

C55 AP16 60m blue & multi .28 .15

25th anniversary of the Council of Mutual Economic Assistance.

Souvenir Sheet

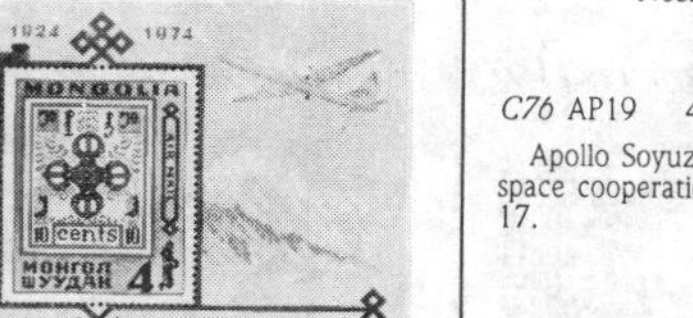

Mongolia No. 4 — AP17

1974, Mar. 15 **Photo.** *Perf. 12½*

C56 AP17 4t multicolored 1.90 1.90

50th anniv. of 1st stamps of Mongolia.

Postrider and UPU Emblem AP18

Designs: UPU emblem and means of transportation.

1974, Apr. **Litho.** *Perf. 12*

C57 AP18 50m shown .35 .18
C58 AP18 50m Reindeer post .35 .18
C59 AP18 50m Mail coach .35 .18
C60 AP18 50m Balloon post .35 .18
C61 AP18 50m Steamship and AN-2 plane .35 .18
C62 AP18 50m Train, truck and city .35 .18
C63 AP18 50m Rocket over North Pole .35 .18
Nos. C57-C63 (7) 2.45 1.26

Souvenir Sheet

C64 AP18 4t Globe and post horn, vert. 2.50 2.50

Centenary of Universal Postal Union.

Circus Type of 1974

Design: 1t, Two women contortionists.

1974, May 4 **Litho.** *Perf. 12*

C65 A177 1t multicolored .48 .30

No. C65 has se-tenant label, with similar design.

Nature Type of Regular Issue

1t, Scientist checking water, globe. 4t, Wild rose.

1974, Dec. **Litho.** *Perf. 11*

C66 A186 1t multicolored .55 .30

Souvenir Sheet

Perf. 12½

C67 A186 4t multicolored 2.25 2.25

UPU Type of 1974
Souvenir Sheet

Design: UPU Emblem, vert.

1974, Dec. *Perf. 11½x12*

C68 A187 4t multicolored 4.00 4.00

Soyuz on Launching Pad, Project Emblem — AP19

Project Emblem and: 20m, Radar and Apollo. 30m, Apollo, Soyuz and earth. 40m, Spacecraft before docking. 50m, Spacecraft after docking. 60m, Soyuz circling earth. 1t, Spacecraft, space station and earth. 4t, Russian and American astronauts.

1975, June 14 **Litho.** *Perf. 12*

C69 AP19 10m blue & multi .15 .15
C70 AP19 20m multicolored .15 .15
C71 AP19 30m sepia & multi .20 .15
C72 AP19 40m silver & multi .24 .15
C73 AP19 50m multicolored .35 .15
C74 AP19 60m multicolored .48 .20
C75 AP19 1t multicolored .60 .30
Nos. C69-C75 (7) 2.17
Set value .90

Souvenir Sheet

C76 AP19 4t black & multi 3.00 3.00

Apollo Soyuz space test project (Russo-American space cooperation), launching July 15; link-up July 17.

Mongolian Mountain Sheep — AP20

1975, Aug. 4 **Litho.** *Perf. 12*

C77 AP20 1.50t multicolored .80 .30

South Asia Tourism Year. No. C77 printed se-tenant with label showing modern hotel, map and stone turtle.

Satellite over Weather Map of Mongolia AP21

1976, Mar. 20 *Perf. 12x11½*

C78 AP21 60m blue & yellow .35 .15

40th anniversary of meteorological service.

Souvenir Sheet

Girl with Books and Flowers — AP22

1976, Mar. 30 *Perf. 12*

C79 AP22 4t multicolored 2.25 2.25

30th anniversary of UNESCO.

Souvenir Sheet

The Wise Musician, by Sarav — AP23

1976, May 3 **Litho.** *Perf. 11½x12½*

C80 AP23 4t multicolored 2.25 2.25

Interphil 76 Phil. Exhib., Philadelphia, Pa., May 29-June 6.

Olympic Games Type of 1976
Souvenir Sheet

1976, May 20 *Perf. 12½x11½*

C81 A202 4t Wrestling 2.25 2.25

Independence Type of 1976

Design: 60m, Progress in agriculture and industry.

1976, June 20 **Litho.** *Perf. 12x11½*

C82 A203 60m multicolored .35 .18

Olympic Medalists Type, 1976
Souvenir Sheet

Design: 4t, Oidov Zeveg, Mongolian flag.

1976, Nov. 30 Litho. *Perf. 11x11½*
C83 A209 4t multicolored 2.00 2.00

Mounting Carrier Rocket with Bell-shaped Gear — AP24

Designs: 20m, Launching of Intercosmos 3. 30m, Marine Observatory Gagarin (ship). 40m, Satellite observation of lunar eclipse. 60m, Observatory with multiple antenna system. 80m, Examination of Van Allen Zone, magnetosphere. 1t, Meteorological earth satellite. 4t, Intercosmos satellite with lines showing participating countries on globe.

1977, June 20 Litho. *Perf. 12*

C84	AP24	10m multicolored	.15	.15
C85	AP24	20m multicolored	.15	.15
C86	AP24	30m multicolored	.18	.15
C87	AP24	40m multicolored	.28	.15
C88	AP24	60m multicolored	.48	.20
C89	AP24	80m multicolored	.60	.28
C90	AP24	1t multicolored	.75	.38
		Nos. C84-C90 (7)	2.59	
		Set value		1.15

Souvenir Sheet
Perf. 12½

C91 AP24 4t multicolored 2.50 2.50

11th anniv. of Intercosmos program, cooperation of 9 socialist countries for space research. No. C91 contains one stamp 58x37mm.

Trade Union Emblem, Factory and Sheep AP25

1977, June *Perf. 12x11½*
C92 AP25 60m multicolored .40 .18

11th Cong. of Mongolian Trade Unions, May 12.

Montgolfier's Balloon — AP26

Dirigibles: 30m, Zeppelin over North Pole, 1931. 40m, Osoaviahim, Russian Arctic cargo. 50m, North, Russian heavy duty cargo. 60m, Aeron-340, Russian planned. 80m, Machinery transport, Russian planned. 1.20t, Flying crane, French planned. 4t, Russia No. C26 (stamp) and Sukhe Bator statue.

1977, Dec. Litho. *Perf. 12*

C93	AP26	20m multicolored	.15	.15
C94	AP26	30m multicolored	.15	.15
C95	AP26	40m multicolored	.20	.15
C96	AP26	50m multicolored	.28	.15
C97	AP26	60m multicolored	.35	.18
C98	AP26	80m multicolored	.40	.24
C99	AP26	1.20t multicolored	.60	.38
		Nos. C93-C99 (7)	2.13	
		Set value		1.20

Souvenir Sheet
Perf. 12½x11½

C100 AP26 4t multicolored 2.00 2.00

History of airships.

A. F. Mozhaiski and his Plane, 1884 — AP27

Designs: 30m, Henry Farman and his plane, 1909. 40m, Geoffrey de Havilland and D. H. 66 Hercules, 1920's. 50m, Charles A. Lindbergh, Spirit of St. Louis and route New York to Paris, 1927. 60m, Mongolian pilots Shagdarsuren and Demberel and plane over Altai Mountains, 1935. 80m, Soviet aviators Chkalov, Baidukov, Beliakov, plane and route Moscow to Vancouver, 1937. 1.20t, A. N. Tupolev, supersonic plane TU 154, route Moscow to Alma-Ata, 1968. 4t, Wilbur and Orville Wright and their plane.

1978, Mar. 25 Litho. *Perf. 12½x11*

C101	AP27	20m multi	.15	.15
C102	AP27	30m multi	.15	.15
C103	AP27	40m multi	.20	.15
C104	AP27	50m multi	.28	.15
C105	AP27	60m multi	.35	.18
C106	AP27	80m multi	.40	.24
C107	AP27	1.20t multi	.70	.38
		Nos. C101-C107 (7)	2.23	
		Set value		1.20

Souvenir Sheet

C108 AP27 4t multi 3.00 3.00

75th anniversary of first powered flight, Wright brothers, 1903.

Soccer Type of 1978
Souvenir Sheet

Design: 4t, Two soccer players.

1978, Apr. 15 *Perf. 11½*
C109 A231 4t multi 2.50 2.50

World Soccer Championships, Argentina 78, June 1-25. #C109 contains 1 45x38mm stamp.

Souvenir Sheet

Canada No. 553 and Mongolia No. 549 — AP28

1978, June Litho. *Perf. 12½*
C110 AP28 4t multi 3.00 3.00

CAPEX '78, Intl. Phil. Exhibition, Toronto, June 9-18.

Map of Cuba, Ship, Plane and Festival Emblem — AP29

1978, July 28 Litho. *Perf. 12*
C111 AP29 1t multicolored .60 .24

11th World Youth Festival, Havana, 7/28-8/5.

Souvenir Sheet

Aleksei Gubarev and Vladimir Remek, PRAGA '78 Emblem — AP30

1978, Sept. 5 Litho. *Perf. 12*
C112 AP30 4t multicolored 3.00 3.00

PRAGA '78 Intl. Phil. Exhib., Prague, Sept. 8-17, and Russian-Czechoslovak space cooperation, Intercosmos.

DDR Flag, TV Tower, Berlin, Satellite — AP31

1979, Oct. 9 Litho. *Perf. 11½x12*
C113 AP31 60m multicolored .35 .15

German Democratic Republic, 30th anniv.

Demoiselle Crane — AP32

Protected Birds: 30m, Hawk warbler. 50m, Ruddy shelduck. 60m, Blue magpie. 70m, Goldfinch. 80m, Titmouse. 1t, Golden oriole.

1979, Oct. 25

C114	AP32	10m multi	.15	.15
C115	AP32	30m multi	.15	.15
C116	AP32	50m multi	.28	.15
C117	AP32	60m multi	.30	.15
C118	AP32	70m multi	.30	.15
C119	AP32	80m multi	.35	.15
C120	AP32	1t multi	.45	.18
		Nos. C114-C120 (7)	1.98	
		Set value		.72

Venera 5 and 6 — AP33

American and Russian Space Missions: 30m, Mariner 5. 50m, Mars 3. 60m, Viking 1 and 2. 70m, Luna 1, 2 and 3. 80m, Lunakhod 2. 1t, Apollo 15. 4t, Apollo 11, astronauts on moon.

Perf. 12½x11½
1979, Nov. 24 Litho.

C121	AP33	10m multi	.15	.15
C122	AP33	30m multi	.16	.15
C123	AP33	50m multi	.28	.15
C124	AP33	60m multi	.32	.15
C125	AP33	70m multi	.38	.15
C126	AP33	80m multi	.45	.15
C127	AP33	1t multi	.55	.18
		Nos. C121-C127 (7)	2.29	
		Set value		.75

Souvenir Sheet

C128 AP33 4t multi 2.50 2.50

Apollo 11 moon landing, 10th anniversary.

Andrena Scita — AP34

Insects: 30m, Paravespula germanica. 40m, Perilampus ruficornis. 50m, Bumblebee. 60m, Honey bee. 80m, Stilbum cyanurum. 1.20t, Ruby tail.

1980, Feb. 25 Litho. *Perf. 11x12*

C129	AP34	20m multi	.15	.15
C130	AP34	30m multi	.16	.15
C131	AP34	40m multi	.25	.15
C132	AP34	50m multi	.40	.15
C133	AP34	60m multi	.45	.15
C134	AP34	80m multi	.60	.25
C135	AP34	1.20t multi	.80	.30
		Nos. C129-C135 (7)	2.81	
		Set value		1.05

Z-526 AFS Stunt Planes, Czechoslovakia — AP35

1980, Aug. 4 Litho. *Perf. 12*

C136	AP35	20m shown	.15	.15
C137	AP35	30m RS-180 "Sportsman," Germany	.20	.15
C138	AP35	40m Yanki-Anu, US	.28	.15
C139	AP35	50m MJ-2 "Tempete," France	.35	.15
C140	AP35	60m "Pits," Canada	.40	.15
C141	AP35	80m "Acrostar," Switzerland	.55	.18
C142	AP35	1.20t JAK-50, USSR	.85	.20
		Nos. C136-C142 (7)	2.78	
		Set value		.78

Souvenir Sheet

C143 AP35 4t JAK-52, USSR 2.00 1.75

10th World Aerobatic Championship, Oshkosh, Wisconsin, Aug. 17-30. No. C143 contains one 50x43mm stamp.

Olympic Type of 1980
Souvenir Sheet

1980, Sept. 15 Litho. *Perf. 12½*
C144 A253 4t Wrestlers 2.00 1.75

J. Davaajav, Mongolian silver medalist, 22nd Summer Olympic Games, Moscow. Inscribed "Los Angeles '84".

AP36

AP37

1980, Dec. 10 Litho. *Perf. 11½x11*
C145 AP36 4t multi 3.00 2.75

Johannes Kepler (1571-1630), German astronomer.

1981, Oct. 5 Litho. *Perf. 12x11½*

Graf Zeppelin and: 20m, Germany #C40, sea eagle. 30m, Germany #C41, polar fox. 40m, Germany #C42, sea ox. 50m, Russia #C26, polar bear. 60m, Russia #C27, snowy owl. 80m, Russia #C28, puffin. 1.20t, Russia #C29, seal. 4t, Icebreaker Maligin.

C146	AP37	20m multi	.15	.15
C147	AP37	30m multi	.18	.15
C148	AP37	40m multi	.28	.15
C149	AP37	50m multi	.35	.15
C150	AP37	60m multi	.40	.15

C151	AP37	80m multi	.50	.15
C152	AP37	1.20t multi	.70	.22
		Nos. C146-C152 (7)	2.56	
		Set value		.75

Souvenir Sheet

C153	AP37	4t multi	2.50	2.50

Graf Zeppelin polar flight, 50th anniv. No. C153 contains one stamp 36x51mm.

ITU Plenipotentiaries Conference, Nairobi, Sept. — AP38

1982, Sept. 27 Litho. *Perf. 12*

C154	AP38	60m Map	.28	.15

2nd UN Conference on Peaceful Uses of Outer Space, Vienna, Aug. 9-21 — AP39

1982, Dec. 15 Litho. *Perf. 12*

C155	AP39	60m Sputnik 1	.28	.15
C156	AP39	60m Sputnik 2	.28	.15
C157	AP39	60m Vostok 1	.28	.15
C158	AP39	60m Venera 8	.28	.15
C159	AP39	60m Vostok 6	.28	.15
C160	AP39	60m Voskhod 2	.28	.15
C161	AP39	60m Apollo II	.28	.15
C162	AP39	60m Soyuz 6	.28	.15
		Nos. C155-C162 (8)	2.24	
		Set value		.65

Souvenir Sheet

Perf. 12½x12

C163	AP39	4t Soyuz 39, Salyut 6	3.00	3.00

Balloon Flight Bicentenary AP40

1982, Dec. 31 *Perf. 11½x12½*

C164	AP40	20m Montgolfiere, 1783	.15	.15
C165	AP40	30m Blanchard, 1785	.15	.15
C166	AP40	40m Royal-Vauzhall, 1836	.20	.15
C167	AP40	50m Oernen, 1897	.24	.15
C168	AP40	60m Gordon Bennett Race, 1906	.35	.15
C169	AP40	80m Paris, 1931	.40	.15
C170	AP40	1.20t USSR-VR-62, 1933	.70	.18
		Nos. C164-C170 (7)	2.19	
		Set value		.60

Souvenir Sheet

C171	AP40	4t Mongolia, 1977	3.00	2.50

Souvenir Sheet

Revolutionary Mongolia Monument — AP41

1983 Litho. *Imperf.*

C172	AP41	4t multi	2.50

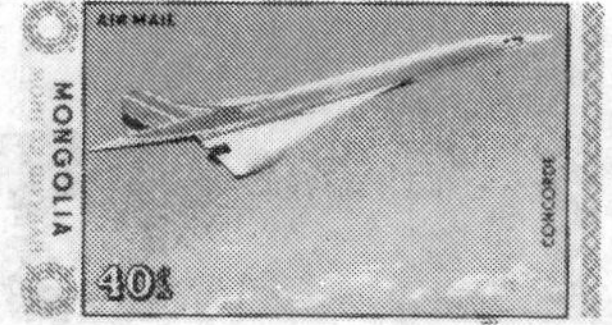

Concorde — AP42

1984, Aug. 15 Litho. *Perf. 14*

C173	AP42	20m DC-10, vert.	.15
C174	AP42	30m Airbus A-300 B-2	.20
C175	AP42	40m shown	.28
C176	AP42	50m Boeing 747	.35
C177	AP42	60m IL-62	.40
C178	AP42	80m TU-154	.55
C179	AP42	1.20t IL-86	.80
		Nos. C173-C179 (7)	2.73

Souvenir Sheet

C180	AP42	4t Yak-42	2.75

1988 Winter Olympics, Calgary — AP43

1988, Jan. 20 Litho. *Perf. 14*

C181	AP43	20m Bobsled	.15
C182	AP43	30m Ski jumping	.22
C183	AP43	40m Downhill skiing	.30
C184	AP43	50m Biathlon	.40
C185	AP43	60m Speed skating	.45
C186	AP43	80m Women's figure skating	.60
C187	AP43	1.20t Ice hockey	.90
		Nos. C181-C187 (7)	3.02

Souvenir sheet

C188	AP43	4t Cross-country skiing	3.00

Souvenir Sheet

Hong Kong '94 — AP44

1994, Feb. 18 Litho. *Perf. 14½x15*

C189	AP44	600t multicolored	4.25

AIR POST SEMI-POSTAL STAMP

Catalogue values for unused stamps in this section are for Never Hinged items.

UNICEF Type of 1977
Souvenir Sheet

Design: 4t+50m, Balloon with Mongolian flag, children and UNICEF emblem.

1977, June 1 Litho. *Perf. 12*

CB1	SP2	4t + 50m multi	2.50	2.50

First balloon flight in Mongolia. Surtax was for Children's Village.

MONTENEGRO

ˌmän-tə-ˈnē-(ˌ)grō

LOCATION — Southern Europe, bordering on the Adriatic Sea
GOVT. — A former Kingdom
AREA — 5,603 sq. mi.
POP. — 516,000 (estimated)
CAPITAL — Cetinje

This kingdom, formerly a Turkish Protectorate, later became independent. On December 1, 1918, Montenegro united with Serbia, Bosnia and Herzegovina, Croatia, Dalmatia and Slovenia to form the Kingdom of the Serbs, Croats and Slovenes which became Yugoslavia in 1929.

100 Novcic = 1 Florin
100 Helera = 1 Kruna (1902)
100 Para = 1 Kruna (1907)
100 Para = 1 Perper (1910)

Canceled to Order
Used values for Nos. 1-110, H1-H5, J1-J26, are for canceled to order stamps. Postally used specimens sell for considerably more.

Watermark

Wmk. 91- "BRIEF-MARKEN" (#1-14) or "ZEITUNGS-MARKEN" (#15-21) in Double-lined Capitals once across sheet

Wmk. 140- Crown

Prince Nicholas I — A1

1874 Typo. Wmk. 91

Early Printings

Perf. 10½ Large Holes, pointed teeth

Narrow Spacing (2-2½mm)

1	A1	2n yellow	55.00	45.00
2	A1	3n green	45.00	40.00
3	A1	5n rose red	45.00	35.00
4	A1	7n lt lilac	45.00	40.00
5	A1	10n blue	110.00	70.00
6	A1	15n yel bister	140.00	90.00
7	A1	25n lilac gray	200.00	165.00
		Nos. 1-7 (7)	640.00	485.00

Middle Printings (1879)

Perf. 12, 12½, 13 and Compound

Narrow spacing

8	A1	2n yellow	10.00	7.00
a.		Perf. 12-13x10½	65.00	65.00
9	A1	3n green	7.50	5.50
10	A1	5n red	7.50	5.50
11	A1	7n rose lilac	7.50	5.50
a.		7n lilac	19.00	14.00
12	A1	10n blue	13.00	11.00
a.		Perf. 12-13x10½	65.00	52.50
13	A1	15n bister brn	19.00	11.00
14	A1	25n gray lilac	25.00	16.00
		Nos. 8-14 (7)	89.50	61.50

Late Printings (1893?)

Perf. 10½, 11½ Small holes, broad teeth

(Perf. 11½ also with pointed teeth)

Narrow and wide spacing (2¾-3½mm)

15	A1	2n yellow	1.75	1.25
a.		Perf. 11 ('94)	25.00	19.00
16	A1	3n green	2.25	1.75
17	A1	5n red	2.25	1.00
18	A1	7n rose	2.25	1.00
a.		Perf. 11 ('94)	9.00	8.50
19	A1	10n blue	2.50	2.25
20	A1	15n brown	2.50	2.25
21	A1	25n brown violet	2.25	2.00
		Nos. 15-21 (7)	15.75	11.50

Dates of issue of the late printings are still being researched.

Types of 1874-93 Overprinted in Black or Red

Пpocлaвa
1493 1893
Штaмнapијe

1893 *Perf. 10½, 11½*

22	A1	2n yellow	40.00	7.50
a.		Perf. 11	*40.00*	*40.00*
23	A1	3n green	2.50	1.50
24	A1	5n red	1.65	.85
25	A1	7n rose	4.25	3.00
a.		Perf. 12	60.00	50.00
b.		7n rose lilac	5.00	3.00
c.		7n lilac, perf. 12	*125.00*	
d.		Perf. 11	*40.00*	*30.00*
26	A1	10n blue	2.50	2.50
27	A1	10n blue (R)	3.25	3.25
28	A1	15n brown	1.65	1.65
a.		Perf. 12	50.00	42.50
29	A1	15n brown (R)	*1,500.*	*1,500.*
30	A1	25n brown violet	3.00	3.00
31	A1	25n brown violet (R)	3.00	3.00
a.		Perf. 12½		*225.00*
		Nos. 22-28,30-31 (9)	61.80	26.25

Introduction of printing to Montenegro, 400th anniversary.

This overprint had many settings. Several values exist with "1494" or "1495" instead of "1493", or with missing letters or numerals due to wearing of the clichés. Double and inverted overprints exist. Some printings were made after 1893 to supply a philatelic demand, but were available for postage.

The 7n with red overprint was not issued.

1894-98 Wmk. 91 *Perf. 10½, 11½*

32	A1	1n gray blue	.20	.15
33	A1	2n emerald ('98)	.20	.15
34	A1	3n carmine rose ('98)	.20	.15
35	A1	5n orange ('98)	1.50	.35
36	A1	7n gray lilac ('98)	.30	.30
37	A1	10n magenta ('98)	.30	.30
38	A1	15n red brown ('98)	.25	.25
39	A1	20n brown orange	.25	.20
40	A1	25n dull blue ('98)	.25	.25
41	A1	30n maroon	.25	.20
42	A1	50n ultra	.30	.25
43	A1	1fl deep green	.50	.50
44	A1	2fl red brown	.75	.75
		Nos. 32-44 (13)	5.25	3.80

Monastery at Cetinje (Royal Mausoleum) A3

Perf. 10½, 11½

1896, Sept. 1 Litho. Unwmk.

45	A3	1n dk blue & bis	.15	.15
46	A3	2n magenta & yel	.25	.25
47	A3	3n org brn & yel grn	.25	.25
48	A3	5n bl grn & bis	.25	.25
49	A3	10n yellow & ultra	.25	.25
50	A3	15n dk blue & grn	.25	.25
a.		Perf. 11½	30.00	30.00
51	A3	20n bl grn & ultra	.25	.25
a.		Perf. 11½	27.50	27.50
52	A3	25n dk blue & yel	.25	.25
53	A3	30n magenta & bis	.25	.25
54	A3	50n red brn & gray bl	.25	.25
55	A3	1fl rose & gray bl	.40	.40
56	A3	2fl brown & black	.40	.40
		Nos. 45-56 (12)	3.20	3.20

Bicentenary of the ruling dynasty, founded by the Vladika, Danilo Petrovich of Nyegosh.

Inverted centers and other errors exist, but experts believe these to be printer's waste.
Perf. 11½ counterfeits are common.

Prince Nicholas I
A4 A5

Perf. 13x13½, 13x12½ (2h, 5h, 50h, 2k, 5k), 12½ (1h, 25h)

1902, July 12

57 A4 1h ultra .20 .20
58 A4 2h rose lilac .20 .20
59 A4 5h green .15 .15
60 A4 10h rose .20 .20
61 A4 25h dull blue .25 .25
62 A4 50h gray green .40 .40
63 A4 1k chocolate .35 .35
64 A4 2k pale brown .45 .45
65 A4 5k buff .60 .60
Nos. 57-65 (9) 2.80 2.80

The 2h black brown and 25h indigo were not issued. The 25h, perf. 12½, probably was never issued.

Constitution Issue

Same Overprinted in Red or Black "Constitution" 15mm

УСТАВ
Constitution
Николаја
1905

1905, Dec. 5

66 A4 1h ultra (R) .15 .15
67 A4 2h rose lilac .15 .15
68 A4 5h green (R) .20 .20
69 A4 10h rose .20 .20
70 A4 25h dull blue (R) .20 .20
71 A4 50h gray green (R) .20 .20
72 A4 1k chocolate (R) .22 .22
73 A4 2k pale brown (R) .40 .40
74 A4 5k buff .50 .50
Nos. 66-74 (9) 2.22 2.22

Overprints in other colors are proofs.

1906

"Constitution" 16½mm

66a A4 1h ultra (R) .15 .15
67a A4 2h rose lilac .15 .15
68a A4 5h green (R) .15 .15
69a A4 10h rose .15 .15
70a A4 25h dull blue (R) .15 .15
71a A4 50h gray green (R) .15 .15
72a A4 1k chocolate (R) .15 .15
73a A4 2k pale brown (R) .25 .25
74a A4 5k buff .50 .50
Nos. 66a-74a (9) 1.80 1.80

Three settings of Nos. 66a-74a containing four types of "YCTAB": I, 9¾mm, II, 11¼mm, III, 10¼mm, IV, 8½mm. Type IV occurs only in one setting, at two positions. Nos. 67a, 69a-74a, H3a exist in type IV.

Two errors occur: "Constitutton" and "Coustitution." Many other varieties including reversed color overprints exist.

Values are for types I and II.

1907, June 1 Engr. *Perf. 12½*

75 A5 1pa ocher .15 .15
76 A5 2pa black .15 .15
77 A5 5pa yellow green .25 .15
78 A5 10pa rose red .25 .15
79 A5 15pa ultra .15 .15
80 A5 20pa red orange .15 .15
81 A5 25pa indigo .15 .15
82 A5 35pa bister brown .20 .15
83 A5 50pa dull violet .30 .20
84 A5 1kr carmine rose .30 .25
85 A5 2kr green .30 .30
86 A5 5kr red brown .40 .35
Nos. 75-86 (12) 2.75 2.30

Many Montenegro stamps exist imperforate or part perforate. Experts believe these to be printer's waste.

King Nicholas I as a Youth — A6

King Nicholas I and Queen Milena — A7

King Nicholas I — A11

Prince Nicholas — A12

Designs: 5pa, 10pa, 35pa, Nicholas in 1910. 15pa, Nicholas in 1878. 20pa, King and Queen, diff.

1910, Aug. 28 Engr.

87 A6 1pa black .15 .15
88 A7 2pa purple brown .15 .15
89 A6 5pa dark green .15 .15
90 A6 10pa carmine .15 .15
91 A6 15pa slate blue .15 .15
92 A7 20pa olive green .15 .15
93 A6 25pa deep blue .15 .15
94 A6 35pa chestnut .20 .20
95 A11 50pa violet .25 .20
96 A11 1per lake .25 .20
97 A11 2per yellow green .50 .30
98 A12 5per pale blue .65 .40
Nos. 87-98 (12) 2.90 2.35

Proclamation of Montenegro as a kingdom, the 50th anniv. of the reign of King Nicholas and the golden wedding celebration of the King and Queen.

King Nicholas I — A13

1913, Apr. 1 Typo.

99 A13 1pa orange .15 .15
100 A13 2pa plum .15 .15
101 A13 5pa deep green .15 .15
102 A13 10pa deep rose .15 .15
103 A13 15pa blue gray .15 .15
104 A13 20pa dark brown .15 .15
105 A13 25pa deep blue .15 .15
106 A13 35pa vermilion .25 .25
107 A13 50pa pale blue .15 .15
108 A13 1per yellow brown .15 .15
109 A13 2per gray violet .20 .20
110 A13 5per yellow green .20 .20
Nos. 99-110 (12) 2.00 2.00

ACKNOWLEDGMENT OF RECEIPT STAMPS

Prince Nicholas I
AR1 AR2

Perf. 10½, 11½

1895 Litho. Wmk. 91

H1 AR1 10n ultra & rose .50 .50

1902 Unwmk. *Perf. 12½*

H2 AR2 25h orange & carmine .50 .50

Constitution Issue

No. H2 Overprinted in Black Like Nos. 66-74

1905

H3 AR2 25h orange & carmine .50 .50
a. "Constitution" 16½mm ('06) .50 .50

See note after 74a.

Nicholas I
AR3 AR4

1907 Engr.

H4 AR3 25pa olive .25 .25

1913 Typo.

H5 AR4 25pa olive green .25 .25

POSTAGE DUE STAMPS

D1

D2

Perf. 10½, 11, 11½

1894 Litho. Wmk. 91

J1 D1 1n red 1.50 1.00
J2 D1 2n yellow green .50 .30
J3 D1 3n orange .40 .30
J4 D1 5n olive green .25 .15
J5 D1 10n violet .25 .15
J6 D1 20n ultra .25 .15
J7 D1 30n emerald .25 .15
J8 D1 50n pale gray grn .25 .15
Nos. J1-J8 (8) 3.65 2.35

1902 Unwmk. *Perf. 12½*

J9 D2 5h orange .15 .15
J10 D2 10h olive green .15 .15
J11 D2 25h dull lilac .15 .15
J12 D2 50h emerald .15 .15
J13 D2 1k pale gray green .15 .15
Nos. J9-J13 (5) .75 .75

Constitution Issue

Postage Due Stamps of 1902 Overprinted in Black or Red Like Nos. 66-74

1905

J14 D2 5h orange .15 .15
J15 D2 10h olive green (R) .15 .15
J16 D2 25h dull lilac .15 .15
J17 D2 50h emerald .15 .15
J18 D2 1k pale gray green .15 .15
Nos. J14-J18 (5) .75 .75

The 10h with "Constitution" 16½mm is not known used. It probably is an essay or fake.

D3

D4

1907 Typo. *Perf. 13x13½*

J19 D3 5pa red brown .15 .15
J20 D3 10pa violet .15 .15
J21 D3 25pa rose .15 .15
J22 D3 50pa green .15 .15
Nos. J19-J22 (4) .60 .60

1913 *Perf. 12½*

J23 D4 5pa gray .15 .15
J24 D4 10pa violet .15 .15
J25 D4 25pa blue gray .15 .15
J26 D4 50pa lilac rose .15 .15
Nos. J23-J26 (4) .60 .60

ISSUED UNDER AUSTRIAN OCCUPATION

Austrian Military Stamps of 1917 Overprinted

K.U.K. MILIT.-VERWALTUNG
MONTENEGRO

1917 Unwmk. *Perf. 12½*

1N1 M1 10h blue 5.75 3.50
1N2 M1 15h car rose 5.75 3.50

Austrian Military Stamps of 1917 Overprinted in Black

Montenegro

1918

1N3 M1 10h blue 35.00
1N4 M1 15h car rose 1.90

Nos. 1N3-1N4 were never placed in use.
This overprint exists on other stamps of Austria and Bosnia and Herzegovina, and in blue or red.

ISSUED UNDER ITALIAN OCCUPATION

Yugoslavia Nos. 142, 144-154 Overprinted

Montenegro
Црна Гора
17-IV-41-XIX

1941 Unwmk. Typo. *Perf. 12½*

2N1 A16 25p black .15 .20
2N2 A16 1d yellow green .15 .20
2N3 A16 1.50d red .15 .20
2N4 A16 2d dp magenta .15 .20
2N5 A16 3d dull red brn .15 .20
2N6 A16 4d ultra .15 .20
2N7 A16 5d dark blue 1.00 1.50
2N8 A16 5.50d dk violet brn 1.00 1.50
2N9 A16 6d slate blue 1.00 1.50
2N10 A16 8d sepia 1.00 1.50
2N11 A16 12d brt violet 1.00 1.50
2N12 A16 16d dull violet 1.00 1.50
2N13 A16 20d blue 100.00 125.00
2N14 A16 30d brt pink 65.00 85.00
Nos. 2N1-2N14 (14) 171.90 220.20

The 25p, 1d, 3d, 6d and 8d exist with inverted overprint.

Stamps of Italy, 1929, Overprinted in Red or Black

ЦРНА ГОРА

1941 Wmk. 140 *Perf. 14*

2N15 A90 5c olive brn (R) .15 *.35*
2N16 A92 10c dark brown .15 *.35*
2N17 A93 15c slate grn (R) .15 *.35*
2N18 A91 20c rose red .15 *.35*
2N19 A94 25c deep green .15 *.35*
2N20 A95 30c olive brn (R) .15 *.35*
2N21 A95 50c purple (R) .15 *.35*
2N22 A94 75c rose red .15 *.35*
2N23 A94 1.25 l deep blue (R) .15 *.35*
Nos. 2N15-2N23 (9) *3.15*
Set value 1.00

Yugoslavia Nos. 144-145, 147-148, 148B, 149-152 Overprinted in Black

Governatorato del Montenegro
Valore
LIRE

1942 Unwmk. Typo. *Perf. 12½*

2N24 A16 1d yellow green .65 .85
2N25 A16 1.50d red 20.00 22.50
2N26 A16 3d dull red brn .65 .85
2N27 A16 4d ultra .65 .85
2N28 A16 5.50d dk vio brn .65 .85
2N29 A16 6d slate blue .65 .85
2N30 A16 8d sepia .65 .85
2N31 A16 12d brt violet .65 .85
2N32 A16 16d dull violet .65 .85
Nos. 2N24-2N32 (9) 25.20 29.30

Yugoslavia Nos. 142 and 146 with this overprint in red were not officially issued.

Red Overprint

2N24a A16 1d .65 *1.65*
2N25a A16 1.50d 20.00 *22.50*
2N26a A16 3d .65 *1.65*
2N27a A16 4d .65 *1.65*
2N28a A16 5.50d .65 *1.65*
2N29a A16 6d .65 *1.65*
2N30a A16 8d .65 *1.65*
2N31a A16 12d .65 *1.65*
2N32a A16 16d .65 *1.65*
Nos. 2N24a-2N32a (9) 25.20 *35.70*

Peter Nyegosh and Mt. Lovchen View — OS1

Mt. Lovchen Scene — OS2

Peter Petrovich Nyegosh — OS3

Designs: 15c, Mountain Church, Eve of Trinity Feast. 20c, Chiefs at Cetinje Monastery. 25c, Folk Dancing at Cetinje Monastery. 50c, Eagle dance. 1.25 l, Chiefs taking loyalty oath. 2 l, Moslem wedding procession. 5 l, Group sitting up with injured standard bearer.

1943, May 9 Unwmk. Photo. Perf. 14.

2N33	OS1	5c	deep violet	.15	.60
2N34	OS2	10c	dull olive grn	.15	.60
2N35	OS1	15c	brown	.15	.60
2N36	OS1	20c	dull orange	.15	.60
2N37	OS1	25c	dull green	.15	.60
2N38	OS1	50c	rose pink	.15	.60
2N39	OS1	1.25 l	sapphire	.30	1.00
2N40	OS1	2 l	blue green	.50	1.50
2N41	OS2	5 l	dark red, *sal*	2.50	5.00
2N42	OS3	20 l	dark violet, *gray*	8.00	10.50
			Nos. 2N33-2N42 (10)	12.20	21.60

Quotations from national poem on backs of stamps.

For overprints and surcharges see Nos. 3N10-3N14, 3NB3-3NB8.

OCCUPATION AIR POST STAMPS

Yugoslavia Nos. C7-C14 Overprinted Like Nos. 2N1-2N14

Perf. 12½, 11½x12½, 12½x11½

1941 Photo. Unwmk.

2NC1	AP6	50p	brown	5.00	6.00
2NC2	AP7	1d	yellow green	2.50	3.00
2NC3	AP8	2d	blue gray	2.50	3.00
2NC4	AP9	2.50d	rose red	5.00	6.00
2NC5	AP6	5d	brown violet	40.00	45.00
2NC6	AP7	10d	brown lake	40.00	45.00
2NC7	AP8	20d	dark green	60.00	65.00
2NC8	AP9	30d	ultra	40.00	45.00
			Nos. 2NC1-2NC8 (8)	195.00	218.00

Italy No. C13 Overprinted in Red Like Nos. 2N15-2N23

1941 Wmk. 140 Perf. 14

2NC9	AP3	50c	olive brown	.15	.50

Yugoslavia Nos. C7-C14 Overprinted in Black

Governatorato del Montenegro Valore in Lire
a

Governatorato del Montenegro Valore in Lire
b

Perf. 12½, 11½x12½, 12½x11½

1942, Jan. 9 Unwmk.

2NC10	AP6(a)	50p	brown	1.25	2.25
2NC11	AP7(a)	1d	yellow grn	1.25	2.25
2NC12	AP8(b)	2d	blue gray	1.25	2.25
2NC13	AP9(b)	2.50d	rose red	1.25	2.25
2NC14	AP6(a)	5d	brown vio	1.25	2.25
2NC15	AP7(a)	10d	brn lake	1.25	2.25
2NC16	AP8(b)	20d	dark green	115.00	115.00
2NC17	AP9(b)	30d	ultra	37.50	37.50
			Nos. 2NC10-2NC17 (8)	160.00	166.00

Nos. 2NC10-2NC17 exist with red overprints. Value, each $80 unused, $90 used.

Governatorato del Montenegro
c

Overprints *a*, *b* or *c* were applied in 1941-42 to the following Yugoslavia stamps under Italian occupation:
a. or *b.* Nos. B120-B123 (4 values) in black and in red.
c. Nos. B116-B119 (4 values) in black and in red.

Cetinje AP1

Mt. Durmitor — AP6

Designs: 1 l, Seacoast. 2 l, Budus. 5 l, Mt. Lovchen. 10 l, Rieka River.

1943 Unwmk. Photo. Perf. 14

2NC18	AP1	50c	brown	.20	.60
2NC19	AP1	1 l	ultra	.20	.60
2NC20	AP1	2 l	rose pink	.40	1.00
2NC21	AP1	5 l	green	.50	1.50
2NC22	AP1	10 l	lake, *rose buff*	2.50	6.00
2NC23	AP6	20 l	indigo, *rose*	8.50	10.50
			Nos. 2NC18-2NC23 (6)	12.30	20.20

For overprints and surcharges see Nos. 3NC1-3NC5, 3NCB1-3NCB6.

OCCUPATION POSTAGE DUE STAMPS

Yugoslavia Nos. J28-J32 Overprinted Like Nos. 2N1-2N14

1941 Unwmk. Typo. Perf. 12½

2NJ1	D4	50p	violet	.24	.50
2NJ2	D4	1d	deep magenta	.24	.50
2NJ3	D4	2d	deep blue	.24	.50
2NJ4	D4	5d	orange	16.00	20.00
2NJ5	D4	10d	chocolate	1.65	3.50
			Nos. 2NJ1-2NJ5 (5)	18.37	25.00

Postage Due Stamps of Italy, 1934, Overprinted in Black Like Nos. 2N15-2N23

1942 Wmk. 140 Perf. 14

2NJ6	D6	10c	blue	.15	.70
2NJ7	D6	20c	rose red	.15	.70
2NJ8	D6	30c	red orange	.15	.70
2NJ9	D6	50c	violet	.15	.70
2NJ10	D7	1 l	red orange	.15	.70
			Nos. 2NJ6-2NJ10 (5)		3.50
			Set value	.60	

ISSUED UNDER GERMAN OCCUPATION

Yugoslavia Nos. 147-148 Surcharged

Deutsche Militaer-Verwaltung Montenegro 0.50 LIRE

1943 Unwmk. Typo. Perf. 12½

3N1	A16	50c on 3d		2.25	12.00
3N2	A16	1 l on 3d		2.25	12.00
3N3	A16	1.50 l on 3d		2.25	12.00
3N4	A16	2 l on 3d		4.50	25.00
3N5	A16	4 l on 3d		4.00	25.00
3N6	A16	5 l on 4d		4.50	25.00
3N7	A16	8 l on 4d		5.50	50.00
3N8	A16	10 l on 4d		11.50	80.00
3N9	A16	20 l on 4d		25.00	165.00
		Nos. 3N1-3N9 (9)		61.75	406.00

Montenegro Nos. 2N37-2N41 Ovptd.

Nationaler Verwaltungsausschuss 10.XI.1943

1943 Photo. Perf. 14

3N10	OS1	25c	dull green	6.50	90.00
3N11	OS1	50c	rose pink	6.50	90.00
3N12	OS1	1.25 l	sapphire	6.50	90.00
3N13	OS1	2 l	blue green	6.50	90.00
3N14	OS2	5 l	dk red, *sal*	230.00	1,700.
			Nos. 3N10-3N14 (5)	256.00	2,060.

Counterfeits exist.

SEMI-POSTAL STAMPS

Yugoslavia Nos. 147-148 Surcharged

Flücht-lingshilfe Montenegro 0.15+0.85 RM.

1944 Unwmk. Typo. Perf. 12½

3NB1	A16	15pf + 85pf on 3d	6.50	90.00
3NB2	A16	15pf + 85pf on 4d	6.50	90.00

Montenegro Nos. 2N37-2N40 Surcharged

Flüchtlingshilfe Montenegro

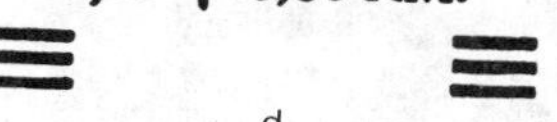
0,15 + 0,85 RM.
d

1944 Photo. Perf. 14

3NB3	OS1	15pf +85pf on 25c	6.00	90.00
3NB4	OS1	15pf +1.35m on 50c	6.50	90.00
3NB5	OS1	25pf +1.75m on 1.25 l	6.50	90.00
3NB6	OS1	25pf +1.75m on 2 l	6.50	90.00
		Nos. 3NB1-3NB6 (6)	38.50	540.00

Surtax on Nos. 3NB1-3NB6 aided refugees.

Montenegro Nos. 2N37-2N38 Surcharged

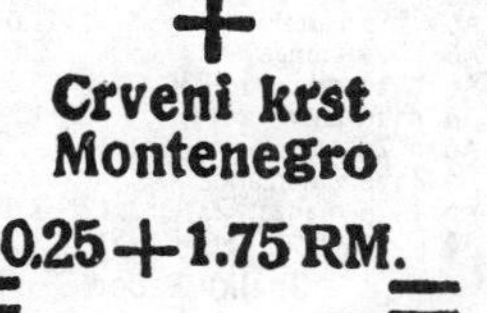
+ Crveni krst Montenegro 0.25+1.75 RM.
e

1944

3NB7	OS1	15pf + 85pf on 25c	6.00	70.00
3NB8	OS1	15pf + 1.35m on 50c	6.00	70.00

Yugoslavia Nos. 147-148 Surcharged

+ Crveni krst Montenegro 0.50+2.50 RM.

Typo. Perf. 12½

3NB9	A16	50pf + 2.50m on 3d	6.00	70.00
3NB10	A16	50pf + 2.50m on 4d	6.00	70.00

The surtax on Nos. 3NB7-3NB10 aided the Montenegro Red Cross.

Montenegro under German Occupation stamps can be mounted in the Scott Germany album part 2.

AIR POST STAMPS

Montenegro Nos. 2NC18-2NC22 Overprinted Like Nos. 3N10-3N14

1943 Unwmk. Photo. Perf. 14

3NC1	AP1	50c	brown	10.00	85.00
3NC2	AP1	1 l	ultra	10.00	85.00
3NC3	AP1	2 l	rose pink	10.00	85.00
3NC4	AP1	5 l	green	10.00	85.00
3NC5	AP1	10 l	lake, *rose buff*	1,400.	15,000.

Counterfeits exist.

AIR POST SEMI-POSTAL STAMPS

Montenegro Nos. 2NC18-2NC20 Surcharged Type "d"

1944 Unwmk. Photo. Perf. 14

3NCB1	AP1	15pf +85pf on 50c	6.50	65.00
3NCB2	AP1	25pf +1.25m on 1 l	6.50	65.00
3NCB3	AP1	50pf +1.50m on 2 l	6.50	65.00
		Nos. 3NCB1-3NCB3 (3)	19.50	195.00

The surtax aided refugees.

Same Surcharged Type "e"

1944

3NCB4	AP1	25pf +1.75m on 50c	6.00	75.00
3NCB5	AP1	25pf +2.75m on 1 l	6.00	75.00
3NCB6	AP1	50pf +2m on 2 l	6.00	75.00
		Nos. 3NCB4-3NCB6 (3)	18.00	225.00

The surtax aided the Montenegro Red Cross.

MONTSERRAT

ˌmän(t)–sə–ˈrat

LOCATION — West Indies southeast of Puerto Rico
GOVT. — British Crown Colony
AREA — 39 sq. mi.
POP. — 12,074 (1980)
CAPITAL — Plymouth

Montserrat was one of the four presidencies of the former Leeward Islands colony until it became a colony itself in 1956.

Montserrat stamps were discontinued in 1890 and resumed in 1903. In the interim, stamps of Leeward Islands were used. In 1903-56, stamps of Montserrat and Leeward Islands were used concurrently.

12 Pence = 1 Shilling
20 Shillings = 1 Pound
100 Cents = 1 Dollar (1951)

Catalogue values for unused stamps in this country are for Never Hinged items, beginning with Scott 104 in the regular postage section, Scott B1 in the semi-postal section, Scott O45 in the officials section.

Watermark

Wmk. 380- "POST OFFICE"

Values for unused stamps are for examples with original gum as defined in the catalogue introduction. Very fine examples of Nos. 1-2, 6 and 11 will have perforations touching the design on at least one side due to the narrow spacing of the stamps on the plates. Stamps with perfs clear of the framelines on all four sides are scarce and will command higher prices.

Stamps of Antigua Overprinted in Black

a MONTSERRAT

1876 Engr. Wmk. 1 *Perf. 14*

1	A1	1p red	22.50	27.50
a.		Vert. or diag. half used as ½p on cover		1,500.
c.		"S" inverted	1,250.	1,250.
2	A1	6p green	55.00	40.00
a.		Vertical half used as 3p on cover		
b.		Vertical third used as 2p on cover		
c.		"S" inverted	1,750.	1,500.
d.		6p blue green	1,200.	
e.		As "d," "S" inverted	*6,500.*	

Some experts consider Nos. 2d, 2e to be from a trial printing.

Queen Victoria — A2

1880 Typo.

3	A2	2½p red brown	225.00	150.00
4	A2	4p blue	140.00	45.00

See Nos. 5, 7-10.

1884 Wmk. 2

5	A2	½p green	2.00	5.00

Antigua No. 18 Overprinted type "a"

1884 Engr.

6	A1	1p rose red	10.00	16.00
a.		Vert. half used as ½p on cover		2,000.
b.		"S" inverted	1,100.	1,100.

Type of 1880

1884-85 Typo.

7	A2	2½p red brown	200.00	90.00
8	A2	2½p ultra ('85)	16.00	17.50
9	A2	4p blue	2,500.	275.00
10	A2	4p red lilac ('85)	4.00	*6.00*

Antigua No. 20 Overprinted type "a"

1884 Engr. *Perf. 12*

11	A1	1p red	70.00	50.00
a.		"S" inverted	2,250.	2,000.
b.		Vert. half used as ½p on cover		1,750.

Symbol of the Colony — A3

King Edward VII — A4

1903 Wmk. 2 Typo. *Perf. 14*

12	A3	½p gray green	1.00	3.50
13	A3	1p car & black	1.00	.35
14	A3	2p brown & black	4.75	9.00
15	A3	2½p ultra & black	1.50	1.50
16	A3	3p dk vio & brn orange	6.00	10.00
17	A3	6p ol grn & vio	7.75	15.00
18	A3	1sh vio & gray grn	10.50	14.00
19	A3	2sh brn org & gray green	17.50	22.50
20	A3	2sh6p blk & gray grn	27.50	*40.00*

Wmk. 1

21	A4	5sh car & black	125.00	*165.00*
		Nos. 12-21 (10)	202.50	*280.85*

1904-08 Wmk. 3

Chalky Paper

22	A3	½p grn & gray grn	.90	1.10
23	A3	1p car & blk ('08)	10.00	*17.50*
24	A3	2p brown & black	.90	2.00
25	A3	2½p ultra & blk ('06)	2.25	*5.75*
26	A3	3p dk vio & brn orange	3.00	3.00
27	A3	6p ol grn & vio	3.00	*6.00*
28	A3	1sh violet & gray grn ('08)	7.00	6.00
29	A3	2sh brn org & gray grn ('08)	24.00	35.00
30	A3	2sh6p blk & gray grn ('08)	35.00	35.00
31	A4	5sh car & blk ('07)	90.00	*110.00*
		Nos. 22-31 (10)	176.05	*221.35*

The ½, 2, 3 and 6p are also on ordinary paper.

1908-13

Ordinary Paper

31A	A3	½p deep green	1.75	.50
32	A3	1p carmine	1.25	.20
33	A3	2p gray	2.50	*6.00*
34	A3	2½p ultramarine	2.50	4.25

Chalky Paper

35	A3	3p vio, *yellow*	1.65	*10.00*
36	A3	6p red vio & gray vio	5.75	*35.00*
37	A3	1sh blk, *green*	7.00	*27.50*
38	A3	2sh bl & vio, *bl*	22.50	*42.50*
39	A3	2sh 6p car & blk, *blue*	27.50	*47.50*
40	A4	5sh grn & scar, *yel*	60.00	80.00

Surface-colored Paper

41	A3	3p vio, *yel* ('13)	3.75	17.50
		Nos. 31A-41 (11)	136.15	*255.95*

King George V
A5 A6

1913

Chalky Paper

42	A5	5sh green & scar, *yel*	80.00	85.00

1916-22 Wmk. 3 *Perf. 14*

Ordinary Paper

43	A6	½p green	.60	1.25
44	A6	1p scarlet	.50	.70
45	A6	2p gray	2.00	*6.00*
46	A6	2½p ultramarine	3.50	*9.00*

Chalky Paper

47	A6	3p violet, *yel*	.90	*3.50*
48	A6	4p blk & red, *yel* ('22)	5.25	*15.00*
49	A6	6p dl vio & red violet	3.00	*10.00*
50	A6	1sh blk, *bl grn*, ol back	3.50	*11.00*
51	A6	2sh vio & ultra, *bl*	10.50	*15.00*
52	A6	2sh 6p blk & red, *bl*	17.50	*32.50*
53	A6	5sh grn & red, *yel*	30.00	*47.50*
		Nos. 43-53 (11)	77.25	*151.45*

For overprints see Nos. MR1-MR3.

1922-29 Wmk. 4

Ordinary Paper

54	A6	¼p brown	.30	2.00
55	A6	½p green ('23)	.20	.25
56	A6	1p dp violet ('23)	.70	.50
57	A6	1p carmine ('29)	1.00	1.10
58	A6	1½p orange	3.00	*7.50*
59	A6	1½p rose red ('23)	.50	*1.75*
60	A6	1½p fawn ('29)	1.00	.40
61	A6	2p gray	.70	*1.25*
62	A6	2½p ultramarine	4.00	1.25
63	A6	2½p orange ('23)	2.50	*10.00*
64	A6	3p ultra ('23)	.70	*5.00*

Chalky Paper

65	A6	3p vio, *yel* ('26)	1.75	*3.50*
66	A6	4p black & red, *yel* ('23)	1.50	*5.00*
67	A6	5p dull vio & ol grn	4.00	*7.75*
68	A6	6p dull vio & red vio ('23)	1.65	*4.50*
69	A6	1sh blk, *emer* ('23)	2.75	*5.00*
70	A6	2sh vio & ultra, *bl*	4.25	*10.00*
71	A6	2sh 6p blk & red, *bl* ('23)	12.00	*17.50*
72	A6	3sh green & vio	12.00	*17.50*
73	A6	4sh black & scar	12.00	*17.50*
74	A6	5sh grn & red, *yel* ('23)	19.00	*30.00*
		Nos. 54-74 (21)	85.50	*149.25*

Tercentenary Issue

New Plymouth and Harbor — A7

1932, Apr. 18 Engr.

75	A7	½p green	.75	.75
76	A7	1p red	.75	.75
77	A7	1½p orange brown	2.00	2.00
78	A7	2p gray	2.25	2.25
79	A7	2½p ultra	2.25	2.25
80	A7	3p orange	4.50	4.00
81	A7	6p violet	7.25	7.75
82	A7	1sh olive green	12.50	14.00
83	A7	2sh6p lilac rose	52.50	57.50
84	A7	5sh dark brown	100.00	110.00
		Nos. 75-84 (10)	169.15	201.25
		Set, never hinged	275.00	

300th anniv. of the colonization of Montserrat.

Silver Jubilee Issue

Common Design Type

1935, May 6 *Perf. 11x12*

85	CD301	1p car & dk blue	1.00	.75
86	CD301	1½p gray blk & ultra	.90	*1.50*
87	CD301	2½p ultra & brn	3.50	*3.00*
88	CD301	1sh brn vio & ind	5.00	*10.00*
		Nos. 85-88 (4)	10.40	*15.25*
		Set, never hinged	22.50	

Coronation Issue

Common Design Type

1937, May 12 *Perf. 13½x14*

89	CD302	1p carmine	.15	.20
90	CD302	1½p brown	.15	.25
91	CD302	2½p bright ultra	.25	.40
		Nos. 89-91 (3)	.55	.85
		Set, never hinged	.90	

Carr's Bay — A8

Sea Island Cotton — A9

Botanic Station — A10

1941-48 *Perf. 14*

92	A8	½p dk grn ('42)	.20	.20
93	A9	1p car ('42)	.20	.20
94	A8	1½p rose vio ('42)	.20	.20
95	A10	2p red orange	.45	.30
96	A9	2½p brt ultra ('43)	.45	.35
97	A8	3p brown ('42)	.55	.40
98	A10	6p dull vio ('42)	.55	.35
99	A8	1sh brn lake ('42)	1.10	.85
100	A10	2sh6p slate bl ('43)	3.75	5.00
101	A8	5sh car rose ('42)	4.00	4.75

Perf. 12

102	A10	10sh blue ('48)	9.00	19.00
103	A8	£1 black ('48)	12.50	26.00
		Nos. 92-103 (12)	32.95	57.60
		Set, never hinged	65.00	

1938, Aug. 2 *Perf. 13*

92a	A8	½p	.15	.15
93a	A8	1p	.15	.15
94a	A8	1½p	2.00	1.65
95a	A10	2p	1.65	1.65
96a	A9	2½p	.30	.40
97a	A8	3p	.40	.50
98a	A10	6p	.35	.40
99a	A8	1sh	2.00	2.00
100a	A10	2sh6p	2.00	2.00
101a	A8	5sh	5.00	*10.00*
		Nos. 92a-101a (10)	14.00	*18.90*
		Set, never hinged	30.00	

Catalogue values for unused stamps in this section, from this point to the end of the section, are for Never Hinged items.

Peace Issue

Common Design Type

1946, Nov. 1 Engr. *Perf. 13½x14*

104	CD303	1½p deep magenta	.15	.15
105	CD303	3p brown	.15	.15
		Set value	.25	.25

Silver Wedding Issue

Common Design Types

1949, Jan. 3 Photo. *Perf. 14x14½*

106	CD304	2½p brt ultra	.15	.15

Engraved; Name Typographed

Perf. 11½x11

107	CD305	5sh rose carmine	6.75	*10.00*

UPU Issue

Common Design Types

Engr.; Name Typo. on 3p and 6p

Perf. 13½, 11x11½

1949, Oct. 10 Wmk. 4

108	CD306	2½p ultramarine	.40	.40
109	CD307	3p chocolate	.55	.55
110	CD308	6p lilac	.65	.65
111	CD309	1sh rose violet	1.00	1.00
		Nos. 108-111 (4)	2.60	2.60

University Issue

Common Design Types

1951, Feb. 16 Engr. *Perf. 14x14½*

112	CD310	3c rose lil & gray blk	.25	.25
113	CD311	12c violet & black	.70	.70

Government House — A11

Designs (portrait at right on 12c, 24c and $2.40): 2c, $1.20, Cotton field. 3c, Map of Presidency. 4c, 24c, Picking tomatoes. 5c, 12c, St. Anthony's Church. 6c, $4.80, Badge of Presidency. 8c, 60c, Cotton ginning.

Perf. 11½x11

1951, Sept. 17 Engr. Wmk. 4

114	A11	1c gray	.15	.15
115	A11	2c green	.20	.20
116	A11	3c orange brown	.15	.15
117	A11	4c rose carmine	.15	.15
118	A11	5c red violet	.20	.20
119	A11	6c dark brown	.25	.25
120	A11	8c dark blue	.35	.35
121	A11	12c red brn & blue	.65	.65
122	A11	24c emer & rose carmine	1.00	1.00
123	A11	60c rose car & gray black	2.00	2.00
124	A11	$1.20 dp bl & emer	6.00	6.00
125	A11	$2.40 dp grn & gray black	7.50	*9.00*
126	A11	$4.80 pur & gray blk	15.00	*20.00*
		Nos. 114-126 (13)	33.60	*40.10*

Coronation Issue

Common Design Type

1953, June 2 *Perf. 13½x13*

127	CD312	2c dark green & black	.20	.20

Type of 1951 with Portrait of Queen Elizabeth II

½c, 3c, "Map of Presidency." 48c, Cotton field.

1953-57 *Perf. 11½x11*

128	A11	½c violet ('56)	.15	.15
129	A11	1c gray black	.15	.15
130	A11	2c green	.15	.15
131	A11	3c orange brown	.40	.40
132	A11	4c rose car ('55)	.15	.15
133	A11	5c red vio ('55)	.15	.15
134	A11	6c dk brown ('55)	.45	.45
135	A11	8c dp ultra ('55)	.20	.20
136	A11	12c red brn & blue ('55)	.20	.20
137	A11	24c emer & rose car ('55)	.45	.45
138	A11	48c rose violet & olive ('57)	1.00	1.00
139	A11	60c rose car & blk ('55)	1.25	1.25
140	A11	$1.20 bl & emer ('55)	2.50	2.50
141	A11	$2.40 dp green & blk ('55)	5.00	5.00
142	A11	$4.80 pur & gray black ('55)	22.50	22.50
		Nos. 128-142 (15)	34.70	34.70

See Nos. 146-149, 156.

West Indies Federation

Common Design Type

Perf. 11½x11

1958, Apr. 22 Engr. Wmk. 314

143	CD313	3c green	.30	.15
144	CD313	6c blue	.40	.30
145	CD313	12c carmine rose	.75	.40
		Nos. 143-145 (3)	1.45	.85

Type of 1953-57

As before, but inscribed: "Map of the Colony" (½c, 3c) "Badge of the Colony" (6c, $4.80).

1958 Wmk. 4 *Perf. 11½x11*

146	A11	½c violet	.15	.15
147	A11	3c orange brown	.15	.15
148	A11	6c dark brown	.20	.20
149	A11	$4.80 pur & gray blk	10.00	*12.00*
		Nos. 146-149 (4)	12.50	*12.50*

Freedom from Hunger Issue
Common Design Type
Perf. 14x14½

1963, June 4 Photo. Wmk. 314
150 CD314 12c lilac .75 .65

Red Cross Centenary Issue
Common Design Type

1963, Sept. 2 Litho. *Perf. 13*
151 CD315 4c black & red .15 .15
152 CD315 12c ultra & red .75 .55

Shakespeare Issue
Common Design Type

1964, Apr. 23 Photo. *Perf. 14x14½*
153 CD316 12c slate blue .35 .25

Type of 1953-57
Perf. 11½x11

1964, Oct. 30 Engr. Wmk. 314
156 A11 2c green .25 .20

ITU Issue
Common Design Type
Perf. 11x11½

1965, May 17 Litho. Wmk. 314
157 CD317 4c ver & lilac .15 .15
158 CD317 48c emer & rose red 1.00 .90

Pineapple — A12

Wmk. 314 Upright

1965, Aug. 16 Photo. *Perf. 15x14*
159 A12 1c shown .15 .15
160 A12 2c Avacado .15 .15
161 A12 3c Soursop .15 .15
162 A12 4c Peppers .15 .15
163 A12 5c Mango .15 .15
164 A12 6c Tomatoes .15 .15
165 A12 8c Guava .15 .15
166 A12 10c Okra .15 .15
167 A12 12c Limes .25 .15
168 A12 20c Oranges .35 .20
169 A12 24c Bananas .55 .25
170 A12 42c Onion 1.10 .80
171 A12 48c Cabbage 1.40 .90
172 A12 60c Papayas 1.50 1.10
173 A12 $1.20 Pumpkin 1.75 1.50
174 A12 $2.40 Sweet potato 4.50 3.50
175 A12 $4.80 Eggplant 9.00 7.25
Nos. 159-175 (17) 21.60 16.85

For surcharges see Nos. 193-198.

1969 Wmk. 314 Sideways
159a A12 1c .15 .15
160a A12 2c .30 .30
161a A12 3c .35 .25
162a A12 4c .50 .25
163a A12 5c .60 .60
166a A12 10c 1.15 1.15
168a A12 20c 1.40 1.40
Nos. 159a-168a (7) 4.45 4.10

Intl. Cooperation Year Issue
Common Design Type

1965, Oct. 25 Litho. *Perf. 14½*
176 CD318 2c lt green & claret .15 .15
177 CD318 12c lt violet & green .40 .40

Churchill Memorial Issue
Common Design Type

1966, Jan. 24 Photo. *Perf. 14*
Design in Black, Gold and Carmine Rose
178 CD319 1c bright blue .15 .15
179 CD319 2c green .15 .15
180 CD319 24c brown .35 .30
181 CD319 42c violet .75 .75
Set value 1.15 1.15

Royal Visit Issue
Common Design Type
Perf. 11x12

1966, Feb. 4 Litho. Wmk. 314
182 CD320 14c violet blue .30 .20
183 CD320 24c dk carmine rose .60 .60

WHO Headquarters Issue
Common Design Type

1966, Sept. 20 Litho. *Perf. 14*
184 CD322 12c multicolored .15 .15
185 CD322 60c multicolored .75 .75

UNESCO Anniversary Issue
Common Design Type

1966, Dec. 1 Litho. *Perf. 14*
186 CD323 4c "Education" .15 .15
a. Orange omitted 50.00
187 CD323 60c "Science" .40 .40
188 CD323 $1.80 "Culture" 1.75 1.75
Nos. 186-188 (3) 2.30 2.30

On No. 186a, the squares of the lowercase letters appear in yellow.

Sailing and ITY Emblem
A13

ITY Emblem and: 15c, Waterfall, Chance Mountain, vert. 16c, Beach scene. 24c, Golfers.

1967, Dec. 29 Photo. Wmk. 314
189 A13 5c multicolored .15 .15
190 A13 15c multicolored .20 .20
191 A13 16c multicolored .25 .25
192 A13 24c multicolored .50 .50
Nos. 189-192 (4) 1.10 1.10

Issued for International Tourist Year.

Nos. 167, 169, 171, 173-175 and Type Surcharged **15c**

1968, May 6 *Perf. 15x14*
193 A12 15c on 12c multi .25 .25
a. Wmkd. sideways ('69) 1.00 1.00
194 A12 25c on 24c multi .40 .40
a. Wmkd. sideways ('69) 1.75 1.75
195 A12 50c on 48c multi .80 .80
a. Wmkd. sideways ('69) 3.50 3.50
196 A12 $1 on $1.20 multi 1.25 1.25
197 A12 $2.50 on $2.40 multi 2.75 2.75
198 A12 $5 on $4.80 multi 5.50 5.50
Nos. 193-198 (6) 10.95 10.95

The surcharge bars are slightly thinner on the "Wmkd. sideways" varieties.

Woman Runner
A14

Designs: 25c, Weight lifter. 50c, Athlete on rings. $1, Runner and Toltec sculptures, vert.

Perf. 14½x14, 14x14½

1968, July 31 Photo. Wmk. 314
199 A14 15c gold, brt grn & rose claret .15 .15
200 A14 25c gold, org & blue .15 .15
201 A14 50c gold, ver & green .25 .25
202 A14 $1 multicolored .55 .55
Nos. 199-202 (4) 1.10 1.10

19th Olympic Games, Mexico City, Oct. 12-27.

Albert T. Marryshow
A15

Portraits and Human Rights Flame: 5c, Alexander Hamilton. 25c, William Wilberforce. 50c, Dag Hammarskjold. $1, Rev. Martin Luther King, Jr.

1968, Dec. 2 Photo. *Perf. 14x14½*
203 A15 5c multicolored .15 .15
204 A15 15c multicolored .15 .15
205 A15 25c multicolored .15 .15
206 A15 50c multicolored .20 .20
207 A15 $1 multicolored .50 .50
Nos. 203-207 (5) 1.15 1.15

International Human Rights Year.

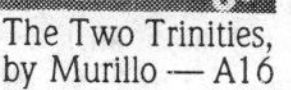

The Two Trinities, by Murillo — A16

Map of Caribbean — A17

Christmas: 15c, 50c, The Adoration of the Magi, by Botticelli.

1968, Dec. 16 *Perf. 14½x14*
208 A16 5c red & multi .15 .15
209 A16 15c dk green & multi .15 .15
210 A16 25c purple & multi .20 .20
211 A16 50c brown & multi .40 .40
Nos. 208-211 (4) .90 .90

1969, May 27 Photo. *Perf. 14*

Design: 35c, 50c, "Strength in Unity," horiz.

212 A17 15c green & multi .15 .15
213 A17 20c brown & multi .15 .15
214 A17 35c dp carmine & multi .25 .25
215 A17 50c multicolored .35 .35
Nos. 212-215 (4) .90 .90

First anniversary of CARIFTA (Caribbean Free Trade Area).

Telephone and Map — A18

Development Projects (Map and): 25c, Book and "New Schools." 50c, Planes (air transport service). $1, Pylon and power lines.

Perf. 13½

1969, July 29 Litho. Wmk. 314
216 A18 15c multicolored .15 .15
217 A18 25c multicolored .15 .15
218 A18 50c multicolored .30 .30
219 A18 $1 multicolored .60 .60
Set value 1.00 1.00

Dolphin
A19

Fish: 15c, Atlantic sailfish. 25c, Blackfin tuna and fishing boat. 40c, Spanish mackerel.

1969, Nov. 1 Photo. *Perf. 13x14*
220 A19 5c multicolored .15 .15
221 A19 15c multicolored .30 .30
222 A19 25c multicolored .60 .60
223 A19 40c multicolored 1.00 1.00
Nos. 220-223 (4) 2.05 2.05

King Caspar, Virgin and Child (Stained-glass Window) — A20

Christmas: 50c, Nativity, by Leonard Limosin, horiz.

Perf. 12½x13, 13x12½

1969, Dec. 10 Litho. Wmk. 314
224 A20 15c violet & multi .15 .15
225 A20 25c red & multi .25 .25
226 A20 50c orange & multi .45 .45
Nos. 224-226 (3) .85 .85

Red Cross and Distribution of Hearing Aids — A21

Red Cross and: 3c, Fund raising sale and invalid. 15c, Car bringing handicapped to work. 20c, Instruction for blind worker.

1970, Apr. 13 Litho. *Perf. 14½*
227 A21 3c multicolored .15 .15
228 A21 4c multicolored .15 .15
229 A21 15c multicolored .25 .25
230 A21 20c multicolored .35 .35
Nos. 227-230 (4) .90 .90

Centenary of British Red Cross Society.

Red-footed Booby
A22

Birds: 2c, Killy hawk, vert. 3c, Frigate bird, vert. 4c, White egret, vert. 5c, Brown pelican, vert. 10c, Bananaquit, vert. 15c, Common ani. 20c, Tropic bird. 25c, Montserrat oriole. 50c, Greenthroated carib, vert. $1, Antillean crested hummingbird. $2.50, Little blue heron, vert. $5, Purple-throated carib. $10, Forest thrush.

Wmk. 314 Upright on Horiz. Stamps, Sideways on Vert. Stamps
Perf. 14x14½, 14½x14

1970-74 Photo.
231 A22 1c yel org & multi .15 .15
232 A22 2c lt vio & multi .15 .15
233 A22 3c multicolored .15 .15
234 A22 4c lt grn & multi .15 .15
235 A22 5c bister & multi .15 .15
236 A22 10c gray & multi .20 .20
237 A22 15c multicolored .30 .30
238 A22 20c rose brn & multi .40 .40
239 A22 25c brown & multi .50 .50
240 A22 50c lt vio & multi 1.00 1.00
241 A22 $1 multicolored 1.75 1.75
242 A22 $2.50 dl bl & multi 4.00 4.00
243 A22 $5 multicolored 8.00 8.00
243A A22 $10 blue & multi 16.00 16.00
Nos. 231-243A (14) 32.90 32.90

Issued: $10, Oct. 30, 1974; others July 2, 1970.
For surcharges and overprints see Nos. 314, 317, 337-339, O1-O4.

Wmk. Sideways on Horiz. Stamps, Upright on Vert. Stamps

1972-74
231a A22 1c multicolored .15 .15
232a A22 2c multicolored .25 .20
233a A22 3c multicolored .25 .20
234a A22 4c multicolored .35 .25
235a A22 5c multicolored .45 .30
237a A22 15c multicolored 1.20 .75
238a A22 20c multicolored 1.75 1.20
239a A22 25c multicolored 2.50 1.50
Nos. 231a-239a (8) 6.90 4.55

Issued: 1c, 2c, 3c, 7/21/72; 5c, 15c, 3/8/73; 20c, 10/2/73; 4c, 2/4/74; 25c, 5/17/74.

"Madonna and Child with Animals," after Dürer — A23

Christmas: 15c, $1, Adoration of the Shepherds, by Domenichino (Domenico Zampieri).

1970, Sept. 21 Litho. *Perf. 14*
244 A23 5c lt blue & multi .15 .15
245 A23 15c red orange & multi .20 .20
246 A23 20c ol green & multi .25 .25
247 A23 $1 multicolored 1.00 1.00
Nos. 244-247 (4) 1.60 1.60

War Memorial, Plymouth A24

Tourist Publicity: 15c, Fort St. George and view of Plymouth. 25c, Beach at Carrs Bay. 50c, Golf Course.

1970, Nov. 30 Litho. *Perf. 14*

248	A24	5c multicolored	.15	.15
249	A24	15c multicolored	.25	.25
250	A24	25c multicolored	.40	.40
251	A24	50c multicolored	.85	.85
a.		Souvenir sheet of 4, #248-251	3.00	3.00
		Nos. 248-251 (4)	1.65	1.65

Girl Guide — A25

"Noli me Tangere," by Orcagna (Andrea di Cione) — A26

Girl Guides' 60th Anniv.: 15c, 25c, Brownie.

1970, Dec. 31

252	A25	10c orange & multi	.15	.15
253	A25	15c lt blue & multi	.20	.20
254	A25	25c lilac & multi	.30	.30
255	A25	40c multicolored	.50	.50
		Nos. 252-255 (4)	1.15	1.15

Perf. 13½x13

1971, Mar. 22 Photo. Wmk. 314

Easter: 5c, 20c, Descent from the Cross, by Jan van Hemessen.

256	A26	5c orange brn & multi	.15	.15
257	A26	15c multicolored	.20	.20
258	A26	20c green & multi	.25	.25
259	A26	40c blue green & multi	.50	.50
		Nos. 256-259 (4)	1.10	1.10

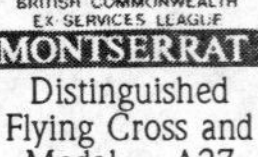

Distinguished Flying Cross and Medal — A27

"Nativity with Saints" (detail), by Romanino — A28

Highest Awards for Military Personnel: 20c, Military Cross and Medal. 40c, Distinguished Service Cross and Medal. $1, Victoria Cross.

Perf. 14½x14

1971, July 8 Litho. Wmk. 314

260	A27	10c gray, vio & silver	.15	.15
261	A27	20c green & multi	.25	.25
262	A27	40c lt bl, dk bl & sil	.45	.45
263	A27	$1 red, dk brn & gold	1.25	1.25
		Nos. 260-263 (4)	2.10	2.10

50th anniversary of the British Commonwealth Ex-services League.

1971, Sept. 16 *Perf. 14x13½*

Christmas (Paintings): 15c, $1, Angels' Choir, by Simon Marmion.

264	A28	5c brown & multi	.15	.15
265	A28	15c emerald & multi	.20	.20
266	A28	20c ultra & multi	.25	.25
267	A28	$1 red & multi	1.50	1.50
		Nos. 264-267 (4)	2.10	2.10

Piper Apache, First Landing at Olveston Airfield — A29

Designs: 10c, Beech Twin Bonanza. 15c, De Havilland Heron. 20c, Britten Norman Islander. 40c, De Havilland Twin Otter. 75c, Hawker Siddeley 748 and stewardesses.

1971, Dec. 16 *Perf. 13½x14*

268	A29	5c multicolored	.15	.15
269	A29	10c multicolored	.30	.30
270	A29	15c multicolored	.45	.45
271	A29	20c multicolored	.65	.65
272	A29	40c multicolored	1.25	1.25
273	A29	75c multicolored	2.00	2.00
a.		Souvenir sheet of 6, #268-273	19.00	19.00
		Nos. 268-273 (6)	4.80	4.80

14th anniversary of Leeward Islands Air Transport (LIAT).

Chapel of Christ in Gethsemane, Coventry Cathedral — A30

Easter: 10c, 75c, The Agony in the Garden, by Giovanni Bellini.

1972, Mar. 9 Litho. *Perf. 13½x13*

274	A30	5c red & multi	.15	.15
275	A30	10c blue & multi	.15	.15
276	A30	20c emerald & multi	.25	.25
277	A30	75c lilac & multi	1.25	1.25
		Nos. 274-277 (4)	1.80	1.80

Iguana A31

Designs: 15c, Spotted ameiva (lizard), vert. 20c, Frog ("mountain chicken"), vert. $1, Redfoot tortoises.

1972, June 8 Litho. *Perf. 14½*

278	A31	15c lilac rose & multi	.45	.45
279	A31	20c black & multi	.55	.55
280	A31	40c blue & multi	1.10	1.10
281	A31	$1 green & multi	2.25	2.25
		Nos. 278-281 (4)	4.35	4.35

Madonna of the Chair, by Raphael — A32

Christmas (Paintings): 35c, Virgin and Child with Cherubs, by Bernardino Fungai. 50c, Magnificat Madonna, by Botticelli. $1, Virgin and Child with St. John and Angel, by Botticelli.

1972, Oct. 18 *Perf. 13½*

282	A32	10c violet & multi	.15	.15
283	A32	35c brt red & multi	.40	.40
284	A32	50c red brown & multi	.70	.70
285	A32	$1 olive & multi	1.50	1.50
		Nos. 282-285 (4)	2.75	2.75

Silver Wedding Issue, 1972

Common Design Type

Design: Queen Elizabeth II, Prince Philip, tomatoes, papayas, limes.

Perf. 14x14½

1972, Nov. 20 Photo. Wmk. 314

286	CD324	35c car rose & multi	.20	.20
287	CD324	$1 ultra & multi	.60	.60

Passionflower A33

Designs: 35c, Passiflora vitifolia. 75c, Passiflora amabilis. $1, Passiflora alata caerulea.

1973, Apr. 9 Litho. *Perf. 14x13½*

288	A33	20c purple & multi	.50	.50
289	A33	35c multicolored	.85	.85
290	A33	75c brt blue & multi	1.25	1.25
291	A33	$1 multicolored	2.25	2.25
		Nos. 288-291 (4)	4.85	4.85

Easter. Black backprinting gives story of passionflower.

Montserrat Monastery, Spain — A34

35c, Columbus aboard ship sighting Montserrat. 60c, Columbus' ship off Montserrat. $1, Arms and map of Montserrat & neighboring islands.

1973, July 16 Litho. *Perf. 13½x14*

292	A34	10c multicolored	.45	.45
293	A34	35c multicolored	1.00	1.00
294	A34	60c multicolored	1.65	1.65
295	A34	$1 multicolored	2.50	2.50
a.		Souvenir sheet of 4, #292-295	25.00	25.00
		Nos. 292-295 (4)	5.60	5.60

480th anniversary of the discovery of Montserrat by Columbus.

Virgin and Child, Studio of David A35

Masqueraders A36

Christmas (Paintings): 35c, Holy Family with St. John, by Jacob Jordaens. 50c, Virgin and Child, by Bellini. 90c, Virgin and Child by Carlo Dolci.

1973, Oct. 15 Litho. *Perf. 14x13½*

296	A35	20c blue & multi	.25	.25
297	A35	35c ol bister & multi	.40	.40
298	A35	50c brt green & multi	.95	.95
299	A35	90c brt rose & multi	1.90	1.90
		Nos. 296-299 (4)	3.50	3.50

Princess Anne's Wedding Issue

Common Design Type

1973, Nov. 14 *Perf. 14*

300	CD325	35c brt green & multi	.20	.20
301	CD325	$1 multicolored	.65	.65

1974, Apr. 8

302	A36	20c Steel band, horiz.	.25	.25
303	A36	35c shown	.60	.60
304	A36	60c Girl weaving	.90	.90
305	A36	$1 University Center, horiz.	1.40	1.40
a.		Souvenir sheet of 4, #302-305	11.00	11.00
		Nos. 302-305 (4)	3.15	3.15

University of the West Indies, 25th anniv. For surcharge see No. 316.

Hands Holding Letters, UPU Emblem A37

Designs: 2c, 5c, $1, Hands and figures from UPU Monument, Bern; UPU emblem. 3c, 50c, like 1c.

1974, July 3 Litho. *Perf. 14*

306	A37	1c violet & multi	.15	.15
307	A37	2c red & black	.15	.15
308	A37	3c olive & multi	.15	.15
309	A37	5c orange & black	.15	.15
310	A37	50c brown & multi	.55	.55
311	A37	$1 grnsh blue & black	1.10	1.10
		Set value	1.85	1.85

Centenary of Universal Postal Union. For surcharges see Nos. 315-318.

Churchill, Parliament, Big Ben — A38

Churchill and Blenheim Palace — A39

Perf. 13x13½

1974, Nov. 30 Unwmk.

312	A38	35c ocher & multi	.20	.20
313	A39	70c brt green & multi	.60	.60
a.		Souvenir sheet of 2, #312-313	1.10	1.10

Sir Winston Churchill (1874-1965).

Nos. 241, 304, 310-311 Surcharged with New Value and Two Bars

Perf. 14x14½, 14

Photo., Litho.

1974, Oct. 2 Wmk. 314

314	A22	2c on $1 multi	.20	.20
315	A37	5c on 50c multi	1.10	1.10
316	A36	10c on 60c multi	3.00	3.00
317	A22	20c on $1 multi	1.00	1.00
a.		One bar in surcharge	2.25	2.25
318	A37	35c on $1 multi	2.25	2.25
		Nos. 314-318 (5)	7.55	7.55

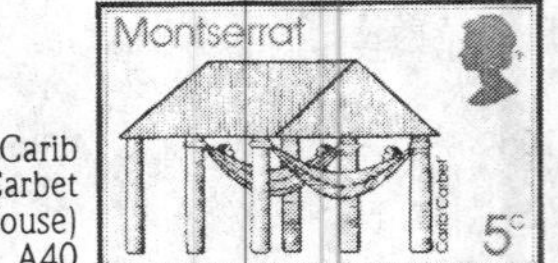

Carib Carbet (House) A40

Carib Artifacts: 20c, Necklace (caracoli). 35c, Club. 70c, Canoe.

Wmk. 314

1975, Mar. 3 Litho. *Perf. 14*

319	A40	5c dk red, ocher & blk	.15	.15
320	A40	20c black, ocher & dk red	.15	.15
321	A40	35c black, dk red & ocher	.30	.30
322	A40	70c ocher, dk red & blk	.55	.55
a.		Souvenir booklet	3.00	
		Nos. 319-322 (4)	1.15	1.15

No. 322a contains 2 self-adhesive panes printed on peelable paper backing with bicolored advertising on back. One pane of 6 contains 3 each similar to Nos. 320-321; the other pane of 4 contains one each similar to Nos. 319-322. Stamps are imperf. x roulette. Panes have commemorative marginal inscription.

One Bitt — A41

Old Local Coinage (1785-1801): 10c, Eighth of a dollar. 35c, Quarter dollars. $2, One dollar.

1975, Sept. 1 Litho. Perf. 14

323 A41 5c ultra, silver & blk .15 .15
324 A41 10c brown org, sil & blk .15 .15
325 A41 35c green, silver & blk .35 .35
326 A41 $2 brt rose, sil & blk 1.75 1.75
a. Souvenir sheet of 4, #323-326 3.00 3.00
Nos. 323-326 (4) 2.40 2.40

Explanation and description of coinage printed in black on back of souvenir sheet.

Montserrat Nos. 1 and 2 — A42

10c, Post Office, Montserrat, & #1a (bisect) with AO8 cancel. 40c, Cover with #1a, 1b. 55c, G.B. #27 with AO8 cancel, & #2. 70c, 2 #1, 1 #1a with AO8 cancels. $1.10, Packet "Antelope" & #2.

1976, Jan. 5 Perf. 13½

327 A42 5c multicolored .15 .15
328 A42 10c multicolored .15 .15
329 A42 40c multicolored .50 .50
330 A42 55c multicolored .65 .65
331 A42 70c multicolored .85 .85
332 A42 $1.10 multicolored 1.25 1.25
a. Souvenir sheet of 6, #327-332 4.50 4.50
Nos. 327-332 (6) 3.55 3.55

Centenary of Montserrat's postage stamps.

Trinity, by Orcagna — A43

Paintings by Orcagna (Andrea di Cione): 40c, Resurrection. 55c, Ascension. $1.10, Pentecost.

Perf. 14x13½

1976, Apr. 5 Litho. Wmk. 373

333 A43 15c multicolored .15 .15
334 A43 40c multicolored .25 .25
335 A43 55c multicolored .30 .30
336 A43 $1.10 multicolored .65 .65
a. Souvenir sheet of 4 2.00 2.00
Nos. 333-336 (4) 1.35 1.35

Easter 1976. Nos. 333-336 were prepared, but not issued in 1975. Stamps are surcharged with new values; date "1975" obliterated with heavy bar. No. 336a contains one each of Nos. 333-336; "1975" in margin obliterated with heavy bar.

Nos. 235-236, 233 Surcharged 2¢

Perf. 14½x14

1976, Apr. 12 Photo. Wmk. 314

337 A22 2c on 5c multi .15 .15
338 A22 30c on 10c multi .65 .65
339 A22 45c on 3c multi 1.10 1.10
Nos. 337-339 (3) 1.90 1.90

For overprints see Nos. O3-O4.

White Frangipani — A44

Designs: Flowering trees of Montserrat.

Perf. 13½x14

1976, July 5 Litho. Wmk. 373

340 A44 1c shown .15 .15
341 A44 2c Cannonball tree .15 .15
342 A44 3c Lignum vitae .15 .15
343 A44 5c Malay apple .15 .15
344 A44 10c Jacaranda .15 .15
345 A44 15c Orchid tree .15 .15
346 A44 20c Manjak .15 .15
347 A44 25c Tamarind .15 .15
348 A44 40c Flame of the Forest .25 .25
349 A44 55c Pink cassia .35 .35
350 A44 70c Long John .45 .45
351 A44 $1 Saman .60 .60
352 A44 $2.50 Immortelle 1.40 1.40
353 A44 $5 Yellow poui 2.75 2.75
354 A44 $10 Flamboyant 6.00 6.00
Nos. 340-354 (15) 13.00 13.00

For surcharges and overprints see Nos. 374-376, 420, 435-440, O10-O44.

Mary and Joseph on Road to Bethlehem — A45

Christmas (Map of Montserrat and): 20c, Shepherds. 55c, Virgin and Child. $1.10, Three Kings.

1976, Oct. 4 Perf. 14½

355 A45 15c vio blue & multi .15 .15
356 A45 20c green & multi .20 .20
357 A45 55c lilac & multi .40 .40
358 A45 $1.10 multicolored .90 .90
a. Souvenir sheet of 4, #355-358 2.50 2.50
Nos. 355-358 (4) 1.65 1.65

Hudson River Review of Opsail 76
A46 A47

Designs: 40c, Raleigh. 75c, HMS Druid (Raleigh attacking Druid, 1776).

1976, Dec. 13 Litho. Perf. 13

359 A46 15c multicolored .20 .20
a. Pair, #359, 362 1.75 1.75
360 A46 40c multicolored .50 .50
361 A47 75c multicolored 1.00 1.00
a. Pair, #360-361 1.50 1.50
362 A47 $1.25 multicolored 1.50 1.50
a. Souvenir sheet of 4, #359-362, perf. 14x13½ 3.75 3.75
Nos. 359-362 (4) 3.20 3.20

American Bicentennial. Nos. 359a and 361a each have continuous designs.

Queen Arriving for 1966 Visit, Yacht Britannia — A48

Designs: 45c, Firing of cannons at Tower of London. $1, The crowning.

1977, Feb. 7

363 A48 30c multicolored .25 .25
364 A48 45c multicolored .35 .35
365 A48 $1 multicolored .90 .90
Nos. 363-365 (3) 1.50 1.50

25th anniv. of the reign of Queen Elizabeth II. #363-365 were issued also in booklet panes of 4.

Epiphyllum Hookeri A49

Flowers of the Night: 15c, Ipomoea alba, vert. 55c, Cereus hexagonus. $1.50, Cestrum nocturnum, vert.

1977, June 1 Litho. Perf. 14

366 A49 15c multicolored .15 .15
367 A49 40c multicolored .40 .40
368 A49 55c multicolored .50 .50
369 A49 $1.50 multicolored 1.50 1.50
a. Souvenir sheet of 4, #366-369 3.50 3.50
Nos. 366-369 (4) 2.55 2.55

Princess Anne at Ground-breaking Ceremony, Glendon Hospital — A50

Designs: 40c, New deep-water jetty, Plymouth. 55c, Glendon Hospital. $1.50, Freighter unloading at new jetty.

1977, Oct. 3 Wmk. 373 Perf. 14½

370 A50 20c multicolored .15 .15
371 A50 40c multicolored .20 .20
372 A50 55c multicolored .35 .35
373 A50 $1.50 multicolored .85 .85
a. Souvenir sheet of 4, #370-373 2.50 2.50
Nos. 370-373 (4) 1.55 1.55

Development.

Nos. 349-350, 352 Surcharged with New Value and Bars and Overprinted: "SILVER JUBILEE 1977 / ROYAL VISIT / TO THE CARIBBEAN"

1977, Oct. Litho. Perf. 13½x14

374 A44 $1 on 55c multi .75 .75
375 A44 $1 on 70c multi .75 .75
376 A44 $1 on $2.50 multi .75 .75
Nos. 374-376 (3) 2.25 2.25

Caribbean visit of Queen Elizabeth II. Surcharge has bars of differing thickness and length. No. 374 has two settings.

"Silent Night, Holy Night" — A51

Christmas Carols and Map of Montserrat: 40c, "We Three Kings of Orient Are." 55c, "I Saw Three Ships Come Sailing In." $2, "Hark the Herald Angels Sing."

1977, Nov. 14 Litho. Perf. 14½

377 A51 5c blue & multi .15 .15
378 A51 40c bister & multi .20 .20
379 A51 55c lt blue & multi .30 .30
380 A51 $2 rose & multi 1.00 1.00
a. Souvenir sheet of 4, #377-380 2.00 2.00
Nos. 377-380 (4) 1.65 1.65

Four-eye Butterflyfish A52

Fish: 40c, French angelfish. 55c, Blue tang. $1.50, Queen triggerfish.

1978, Feb. 27 Wmk. 373 Perf. 14

381 A52 30c multicolored .30 .30
382 A52 40c multicolored .40 .40
383 A52 55c multicolored .55 .55
384 A52 $1.50 multicolored 1.50 1.50
a. Souvenir sheet of 4, #381-384 3.50 3.50
Nos. 381-384 (4) 2.75 2.75

Elizabeth II and St. Paul's, London — A53

Designs: 55c, Chichester Cathedral. $1, Lincoln Cathedral. $2.50, Llandaff Cathedral, Cardiff.

1978, June 2 Perf. 13½

385 A53 40c multicolored .15 .15
386 A53 55c multicolored .25 .25
387 A53 $1 multicolored .40 .40
388 A53 $2.50 multicolored 1.00 1.00
a. Souvenir sheet of 4, #385-388 2.00 2.00
Nos. 385-388 (4) 1.80 1.80

25th anniversary of coronation of Elizabeth II, Defender of the Faith. Nos. 385-388 printed in sheets of 10 stamps and 2 labels.

#385-388 were also issued in booklet panes of 2.

Alpinia — A54 Private, 1796 — A55

Flowering Plants: 55c, Allamanda cathartica. $1, Blue tree petrea. $2, Amaryllis.

1978, Sept. 18 Litho. Perf. 13½x13

389 A54 40c multicolored .25 .25
390 A54 55c multicolored .40 .40
391 A54 $1 multicolored .70 .70
392 A54 $2 multicolored 1.40 1.40
Nos. 389-392 (4) 2.75 2.75

1978, Nov. 20 Litho. Perf. 14½

Uniforms: 40c, Corporal, 1831. 55c, Sergeant, 1837. $1.50, Officer, 1784.

393 A55 30c multicolored .20 .20
394 A55 40c multicolored .25 .25
395 A55 55c multicolored .40 .40
396 A55 $1.50 multicolored 1.10 1.10
a. Souvenir sheet of 4, #393-396 2.00 2.00
Nos. 393-396 (4) 1.95 1.95

See Nos. 401-404.

Cub Scouts A56

Boy Scouts: 55c, Signaling. $1.25, Cooking, vert. $2, Flag folding ceremony, vert.

1979, Apr. 2 Litho. Perf. 14

397 A56 40c multicolored .25 .25
398 A56 55c multicolored .35 .35
399 A56 $1.25 multicolored .80 .80
400 A56 $2 multicolored 1.25 1.25
a. Souvenir sheet of 4, #397-400 3.00 3.00
Nos. 397-400 (4) 2.65 2.65

50th anniversary of Scouting in Montserrat.

Uniform Type of 1978

30c, Private, 1783. 40c, Private, 1819. 55c, Officer, 1819. $2.50, Highlander officer, 1830.

1979, July 4 Wmk. 373 Perf. 14

401 A55 30c multicolored .20 .20
402 A55 40c multicolored .25 .25
403 A55 55c multicolored .30 .30
404 A55 $2.50 multicolored 1.50 1.50
a. Souvenir sheet of 4, #401-404 2.50 2.50
Nos. 401-404 (4) 2.25 2.25

IYC Emblem, Learning to Walk A56a

1979, Sept. 17 Litho. Perf. 13½x14

405 A56a $2 brown org & black .85 .85
a. Souvenir sheet 2.00 2.00

International Year of the Child.

Hill, Penny Black, Montserrat No. 1 — A57

Designs: 55c, UPU Emblem, charter. $1, UPU Emblem, cover. $2, Hill, Post Office regulations.

1979, Oct. 1 *Perf. 14*
406 A57 40c multicolored .15 .15
407 A57 55c multicolored .20 .20
408 A57 $1 multicolored .45 .45
409 A57 $2 multicolored .85 .85
a. Souvenir sheet of 4, #406-409 3.50 3.50
Nos. 406-409 (4) 1.65 1.65

Sir Rowland Hill (1795-1879), originator of penny postage; UPU membership, centenary.

Tree Lizard A58

1980, Feb. 4 **Litho.** *Perf. 14*
410 A58 40c Tree frog .25 .25
411 A58 55c shown .40 .40
412 A58 $1 Crapaud .70 .70
413 A58 $2 Wood slave 1.40 1.40
Nos. 410-413 (4) 2.75 2.75

Marquis of Salisbury, 1817; Postmarks, 1838, London 1980 Emblem A59

Ships or Planes, Stamps of Montserrat: 55c, H.S. 748, #349. #416, La Plata, 1901, type A4. #417, Lady Hawkins, 1929, #84. #418, Avon, 1843, Gt Britain #3. #419, Aeronca, #140.

1980, Apr. 14 **Litho.** *Perf. 14½*
414 A59 40c multicolored .20 .20
415 A59 55c multicolored .30 .30
416 A59 $1.20 multicolored .65 .65
417 A59 $1.20 multicolored .65 .65
418 A59 $1.20 multicolored .65 .65
419 A59 $1.20 multicolored .65 .65
a. Souvenir sheet of 6, #414-419 3.50 3.50
Nos. 414-419 (6) 3.10 3.10

London 1980 Intl. Stamp Exhib., May 6-14.
For surcharges see Nos. 736-740.

No. 352 Overprinted: 75th Anniversary of / Rotary International

1980, July 7 **Litho.** *Perf. 13½x14*
420 A44 $2.50 multicolored 1.25 1.25

Discus Thrower, Stadium, Olympic Rings — A60

Flags of Host Countries: 40c, Greece, 1896; France, 1900; US, 1904. 55c, Great Britain, 1908; Sweden, 1912; Belgium, 1920. 70c, France, 1924; Netherlands, 1928; US, 1932. $1, Germany, 1936; Great Britain, 1948; Finland, 1952. $1.50, Australia, 1956; Italy, 1960; Japan, 1964. $2, Mexico, 1968,; Fed. Rep. of Germany, 1972; Canada, 1976.

1980, July 7 **Litho.** *Perf. 14*
421 A60 40c multicolored .20 .20
422 A60 55c multicolored .25 .25
423 A60 70c multicolored .30 .30
424 A60 $1 multicolored .45 .45
425 A60 $1.50 multicolored .70 .70
426 A60 $2 multicolored .95 .95
427 A60 $2.50 multicolored 1.25 1.25
a. Souv. sheet of 7, #421-427 + 2 labels 4.25
Nos. 421-427 (7) 4.10 4.10

22nd Summer Olympic Games, Moscow, July 19-Aug. 3.

Lady Nelson, 1928 A61

1980 **Litho.** *Perf. 14*
428 A61 40c shown .20 .20
429 A61 55c Chignecto, 1913 .30 .30
430 A61 $1 Solent, 1878 .60 .60
431 A61 $2 Dee, 1841 1.25 1.25
Nos. 428-431 (4) 2.35 2.35

Plume Worm — A62

1980 **Litho.** *Perf. 14*
432 A62 40c shown .45 .45
433 A62 55c Sea fans .60 .60
434 A62 $2 Coral, sponges 2.25 2.25
Nos. 432-434 (3) 3.30 3.30

Nos. 340, 342, 345, 348 Surcharged

1980, Sept. 30 **Litho.** *Perf. 14*
435 A44 5c on 3c (#342) .15 .15
436 A44 35c on 1c (#340) .15 .15
437 A44 35c on 3c (#342) .15 .15
438 A44 35c on 15c (#345) .15 .15
439 A44 55c on 40c (#348) .30 .30
440 A44 $5 on 40c (#348) 2.50 2.50
Nos. 435-440 (6) 3.40 3.40

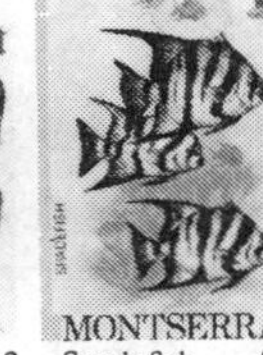

Zebra Butterfly — A63 Spadefish — A64

1981, Feb. 2 **Wmk. 373**
441 A63 50c shown .45 .45
442 A63 65c Tropical checkered skipper .60 .60
443 A63 $1.50 Large orange sulphur 1.25 1.25
444 A63 $2.50 Monarch 2.50 2.50
Nos. 441-444 (4) 4.80 4.80

Perf. 13½

1981, Mar. 20 **Litho.** **Wmk. 373**
445 A64 5c shown .15 .15
446 A64 10c Hogfish .15 .15
447 A64 15c Creole wrasse .15 .15
448 A64 20c Yellow damselfish .15 .15
449 A64 25c Sergeant major .15 .15
450 A64 35c Clown wrasse .20 .15
451 A64 45c Schoolmaster .35 .20
452 A64 55c Striped parrotfish .40 .30
453 A64 65c Bigeye .45 .35
454 A64 75c French grunt .50 .40
455 A64 $1 Rock beauty .70 .50
456 A64 $2 Blue chromis 1.40 1.00
457 A64 $3 Fairy basslet, blueheads 2.25 1.50
458 A64 $5 Cherubfish 3.50 2.50
459 A64 $7.50 Longspine squirrelfish 5.00 3.75
460 A64 $10 Longsnout butterflyfish 6.75 5.00
Nos. 445-460 (16) 19.70 16.40

For surcharges and overprints see Nos. 507-508, 511-512, 515, O45-O55, O95-O97.

Inscribed 1983

1983 **Wmk. 380**
445a A64 5c .15 .15
446a A64 10c .15 .15
449a A64 25c .15 .15
450a A64 35c .25 .25
454a A64 75c .50 .50
455a A64 $1 .65 .65
458a A64 $5 3.25 3.25
460a A64 $10 6.50 6.50
Nos. 445a-460a (8) 11.60 11.60

Fort St. George (National Trust) — A65

1981, May 18 **Wmk. 373** *Perf. 13½*
461 A65 50c shown .25 .25
462 A65 65c Bird Sanctuary, Fox's Bay .35 .35
463 A65 $1.50 The Museum .85 .85
464 A65 $2.50 Bransby Point Battery 1.40 1.40
Nos. 461-464 (4) 2.85 2.85

Prince Charles, Lady Diana, Royal Yacht Charlotte A66

Prince Charles and Lady Diana — A67

Illustration A67 is reduced.

Wmk. 380

1981, July 13 **Litho.** *Perf. 14*
465 A66 90c shown .60 .60
a. Booklet pane of 4, perf. 12 3.00
466 A67 90c shown .60 .60
467 A66 $3 Portsmouth 2.00 2.00
468 A67 $3 like #466 2.00 2.00
a. Booklet pane of 2, perf. 12 5.00
469 A66 $4 Britannia 2.75 2.75
470 A67 $4 like #466 2.75 2.75
Nos. 465-470 (6) 10.70 10.70

Royal wedding. Each denomination issued in sheets of 7 (6 type A66, 1 type A67).
For surcharges and overprints see Nos. 509-510, 513-514, 578-579, O56-O61.

Souvenir Sheet

1981, Dec. *Perf. 12*
471 A67 $5 multicolored 2.75 2.75

50th Anniv. of Airmail Service A68

1981, Aug. 31 **Wmk. 373** *Perf. 14*
472 A68 50c Seaplane, Dorsetshire .35 .35
473 A68 65c Beechcraft Twin Bonanza .45 .45
474 A68 $1.50 DeHaviland Dragon Rapide .95 .95
475 A68 $2.50 Hawker Siddeley Avro 748 1.50 1.50
Nos. 472-475 (4) 3.25 3.25

Methodist Church, Bethel — A69

Christmas (Churches): 65c, St. George's Anglican, Harris. $1.50, St. Peter's Anglican, St. Peter's. $2.50, St. Patrick's Roman Catholic, Plymouth.

1981, Nov. 16 **Litho.** *Perf. 14*
476 A69 50c multicolored .30 .30
477 A69 65c multicolored .40 .40
478 A69 $1.50 multicolored .90 .90
479 A69 $2.50 multicolored 1.50 1.50
a. Souvenir sheet of 4, #476-479 3.50 3.50
Nos. 476-479 (4) 3.10 3.10

Wild Flowers First Discovered on Montserrat A70

1982, Jan. 18 **Litho.** *Perf. 14½*
480 A70 50c Rondeletia buxifolia, vert. .30 .30
481 A70 65c Heliotropium ternatum .40 .40
482 A70 $1.50 Picramnia pentandra, vert. .90 .90
483 A70 $2.50 Diospyros revoluta 1.75 1.75
Nos. 480-483 (4) 3.35 3.35

350th Anniv. of Settlement of Montserrat by Sir Thomas Warner — A70a

Jubilee Type of 1932.

Perf. 14½

1982, Apr. 17 **Litho.** **Wmk. 373**
483A A70a 40c green .25 .25
483B A70a 55c red .35 .35
483C A70a 65c brown .40 .40
483D A70a 75c gray .45 .45
483E A70a 85c ultra .55 .55
483F A70a 95c orange .60 .60
483G A70a $1 purple .65 .65
483H A70a $1.50 olive .95 .95
483I A70a $2 car rose 1.25 1.25
483J A70a $2.50 sepia 1.65 1.65
Nos. 483A-483J (10) 7.10 7.10

A70b A71

1982, June **Wmk. 380** *Perf. 14*
484 A70b 75c Catherine of Aragon, 1501 .40 .40
485 A70b $1 Aragon arms .50 .50
486 A70b $5 Diana 2.75 2.75
Nos. 484-486 (3) 3.65 3.65

21st birthday of Princess Diana, July 1.
For surcharges and overprints see Nos. 574, O62-O64.

1982, Sept. 13 **Litho.** *Perf. 14*
487 A71 $1.50 Scout .95 .95
488 A71 $2.50 Baden-Powell 1.50 1.50

Scouting Year.

Christmas A72

1982, Nov. 18 **Wmk. 373** *Perf. 14*
489 A72 35c Annunciation .20 .20
490 A72 75c Shepherds' vision .45 .45
491 A72 $1.50 Virgin and Child .85 .85
492 A72 $2.50 Flight into Egypt 1.50 1.50
Nos. 489-492 (4) 3.00 3.00

Montserrat stamps can be mounted in the Scott British Leeward Islands album.

Dragonflies — A73

1983, Jan. 19 Litho. *Perf. 13½x14*

493 A73 50c Lepthemis vesiculosa .30 .30
494 A73 65c Orthemis ferruginea .40 .40
495 A73 $1.50 Triacanthagyna trifida 1.00 1.00
496 A73 $2.50 Erythrodiplax umbrata 1.50 1.50
Nos. 493-496 (4) 3.20 3.20

Blue-headed Hummingbird — A74

1983, May 24 Wmk. 373 *Perf. 14*

497 A74 35c shown .50 .50
498 A74 75c Green-throated carib 1.00 1.00
499 A74 $2 Antillean crested hummingbird 2.60 2.60
500 A74 $3 Purple-throated carib 3.75 3.75
Nos. 497-500 (4) 5.70 5.70

The $12 and $30 stamps showing the Montserrat emblem were primarily for revenue purposes.

Manned Flight Bicentenary A76

Designs: 35c, Montgolfiere, 1783, vert. 75c, De Havilland Twin Otter 310, 1981. $1.50, Lockheed Vega's around the world flight, 1933. $2, British R34 airship transatlantic flight, 1919.

1983, Sept. 19 Litho. *Perf. 14*

503 A76 35c multicolored .20 .20
504 A76 75c multicolored .45 .45
505 A76 $1.50 multicolored .85 .85
506 A76 $2 multicolored 1.25 1.25
a. Souvenir sheet of 4, #503-506 3.00 3.00
Nos. 503-506 (4) 2.75 2.75

For surcharges see Nos. 573, 577.

Nos. 449, 446, 467-468, 453-454, 469-470, 456 Surcharged

Wmk. 373 (A64), 380

1983, Aug. 15 Litho. *Perf. 13½x14*

507 A64 40c on 25c multi .45 .45
508 A64 70c on 10c multi .75 .75
509 A66 70c on $3 multi .75 .75
510 A67 70c on $3 multi .75 .75
511 A64 90c on 65c multi 1.00 1.00
512 A64 $1.15 on 75c multi 1.25 1.25
513 A66 $1.15 on $4 multi 1.25 1.25
514 A67 $1.15 on $4 multi 1.25 1.25
515 A64 $1.50 on $2 multi 1.75 1.75
Nos. 507-515 (9) 9.20 9.20

Christmas Carnival 1983 A77

1983, Nov. 18 Wmk. 380 *Perf. 14*

516 A77 55c Clowns .30 .30
517 A77 90c Star Bursts .45 .45
518 A77 $1.15 Flower Girls .65 .65
519 A77 $2 Masqueraders 1.10 1.10
Nos. 516-519 (4) 2.50 2.50

See Nos. 547-550.

Nos. 503-506 were overprinted "INAUGURAL FLIGHT Montserrat - Nevis - St. Kitts." These exist on souvenir covers with first day cancel of Dec. 15, 1983. No announcement of this set was made nor were mint copies generally available.

1984 Summer Olympics — A78

1984, Mar. 6 Litho. *Perf. 14*

520 A78 90c Discobolus .40 .40
521 A78 $1 Torch .45 .45
522 A78 $1.15 Stadium .55 .55
523 A78 $2.50 Flags 1.10 1.10
a. Souvenir sheet of 4, #520-523 3.00 3.00
Nos. 520-523 (4) 2.50 2.50

Cattle Egret — A79

1984, May 11

524 A79 5c shown .15 .15
525 A79 10c Carib grackles .15 .15
526 A79 15c Common gallinule .15 .15
527 A79 20c Brown boobys .15 .15
528 A79 25c Black-whiskered vireos .15 .15
529 A79 40c Scaly-breasted thrashers .25 .25
530 A79 55c Laughing gulls .40 .40
531 A79 70c Glossy ibis .45 .45
532 A79 90c Green heron .65 .65
533 A79 $1 Belted kingfisher .70 .70
534 A79 $1.15 Bananaquits .80 .80
535 A79 $3 Sparrow hawks 2.25 2.25
536 A79 $5 Forest thrush 3.50 3.50
537 A79 $7.50 Black-crowned night heron 5.25 5.25
538 A79 $10 Bridled quail doves 6.75 6.75
Nos. 524-538 (15) 21.75 21.75

For surcharges see Nos. 651-655, 663-666. For overprints see Nos. O65-O78.

Packet Boats A80

1984, July 9 Wmk. 380 *Perf. 14*

539 A80 55c Tagus, 1907 .35 .35
540 A80 90c Cobequid, 1913 .65 .65
541 A80 $1.15 Lady Drake, 1942 .75 .75
542 A80 $2 Factor, 1948 1.40 1.40
a. Souvenir sheet of 4, #539-542 3.50 3.50
Nos. 539-542 (4) 3.15 3.15

Marine Life — A81

1984, Sept. Wmk. 380 *Perf. 14*

543 A81 90c Top shell & hermit crab 1.00 1.00
544 A81 $1.15 Rough file shell 1.25 1.25
545 A81 $1.50 True tulip snail 1.65 1.65
546 A81 $2.50 West Indian fighting conch 3.00 3.00
Nos. 543-546 (4) 4.55 4.55

Christmas Carnival Type of 1983

1984, Nov. 12

547 A77 55c Bull Man .45 .45
548 A77 $1.15 Masquerader Captain .95 .95
549 A77 $1.50 Carnival Queen contestant 1.25 1.25
550 A77 $2.30 Contestant, diff. 2.00 2.00
Nos. 547-550 (4) 4.65 4.65

National Emblems — A82

1985, Feb. 8 Litho. *Perf. 14*

551 A82 $1.15 Mango .65 .65
552 A82 $1.50 Lobster Claw .85 .85
553 A82 $3 Montserrat Oriole 1.75 1.75
Nos. 551-553 (3) 3.25 3.25

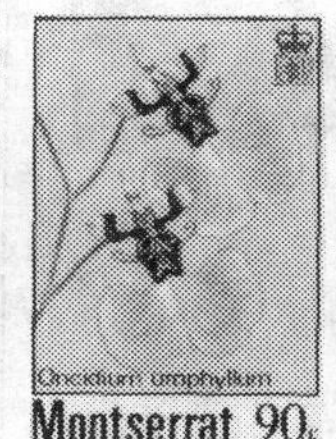

Indigenous Orchids — A83

Queen Mother, 85th Birthday — A84

1985, May 9 Wmk. 380 *Perf. 14*

554 A83 90c Oncidium urophyllum .55 .55
555 A83 $1.15 Epidendrum difforme .75 .75
556 A83 $1.50 Epidendrum ciliare 1.00 1.00
557 A83 $2.50 Brassavola cucullata 1.65 1.65
a. Souvenir sheet of 4, #554-557 5.00 5.00
Nos. 554-557 (4) 3.95 3.95

1985, Aug. 7 Unwmk. *Perf. 12½*

Portraits.

558 A84 55c Facing right .30 .30
559 A84 55c Facing forward .30 .30
560 A84 90c Facing right, diff. .50 .50
561 A84 90c Facing left .50 .50
562 A84 $1.15 Facing right, diff. .60 .60
563 A84 $1.15 Glancing right .60 .60
564 A84 $1.50 Facing right, diff. .80 .80
565 A84 $1.50 Facing left, diff. .80 .80
Nos. 558-565 (8) 4.40 4.40

Souvenir Sheets

566 Sheet of 2 2.50 2.50
a. A84 $2 Facing right, diff. 1.10 1.10
b. A84 $2 Facing forward, diff. 1.10 1.10

1986, Jan. 10

567 Sheet of 2 4.25 4.25
a. A84 $3.50 like #564 2.00 2.00
b. A84 $3.50 like #565 2.00 2.00
568 Sheet of 2 6.75 6.75
a. A84 $6 like #558 3.50 3.50
b. A84 $6 like #559 3.50 3.50

Stamps of the same denomination printed se-tenant. For surcharges see Nos. 575-576.

Cotton Industry A85

1985, Sept. 23 Unwmk. *Perf. 15*

569 A85 90c Cotton plants .45 .45
570 A85 $1 Carding .55 .55
571 A85 $1.15 Automated loom .60 .60
572 A85 $2.50 Hand loom 1.40 1.40
a. Souvenir sheet of 4, #569-572 4.00 4.00
Nos. 569-572 (4) 3.00 3.00

Nos. 504, 485, 562-563, 505, 469-470 Ovptd. or Surcharged "CARIBBEAN ROYAL VISIT 1985" in 2 or 3 Lines

Perf. 14, 12½ ($1.15)

Wmk. as Before

1985, Nov. 14 Litho.

573 A76 75c multicolored 3.50 3.50
574 A64 $1 multicolored 5.00 5.00
575 A84 $1.15 multicolored 5.50 5.50
576 A84 $1.15 multicolored 5.50 5.50
577 A76 $1.50 multicolored 7.00 7.00
578 A66 $1.60 on $4 multi 3.50 3.50
579 A67 $1.60 on $4 multi 12.00 12.00
Nos. 573-579 (7) 42.00 42.00

Nos. 575-576 printed se-tenant. Nos. 578-579 issued in sheets of 7 (6 type A66, 1 type A67). No. 579 surcharged but not overprinted.

Audubon Birth Bicentenary — A86

Illustrations of North American bird species by John J. Audubon.

1985, Nov. 29 Unwmk. *Perf. 12½*

580 A86 15c Black-throated blue warbler .15 .15
581 A86 15c Palm warbler .15 .15
582 A86 30c Bobolink .15 .15
583 A86 30c Lark sparrow .15 .15
584 A86 55c Chipping sparrow .25 .25
585 A86 55c Northern oriole .25 .25
586 A86 $2.50 American goldfinch 1.25 1.25
587 A86 $2.50 Blue grosbeak 1.25 1.25
Nos. 580-587 (8) 3.60 3.60

Stamps of the same denomination printed se-tenant.

Christmas A87

1985, Dec. 2 Wmk. 380 *Perf. 15*

588 A87 70c Angel of the Lord .35 .35
589 A87 $1.15 Three wise men .60 .60
590 A87 $1.50 Caroling, Plymouth War Memorial .75 .75
591 A87 $2.30 Our Lady of Montserrat 1.25 1.25
Nos. 588-591 (4) 2.95 2.95

A set of 8 stamps for the 1986 World Cup was printed but not issued. Copies became available with the liquidation of the printer.

Girl Guides, 50th Anniv. — A88

1986, Apr. 11

592 A88 20c Lord Baden-Powell .15 .15
593 A88 20c Guide saluting .15 .15
594 A88 75c Lady Baden-Powell .50 .50
595 A88 75c Guide cutting hair .50 .50
596 A88 90c Lord and Lady Baden-Powell .60 .60
597 A88 90c Guides in public service .60 .60
598 A88 $1.15 Troop inspection, 1936 .75 .75
599 A88 $1.15 Guides saluting .75 .75
Nos. 592-599 (8) 4.00 4.00

Stamps of same denomination printed se-tenant.

Queen Elizabeth II, 60th Birthday — A89

Various portraits.

1986, Apr. 11 Unwmk. *Perf. 12½*

600 A89 10c multicolored .15 .15
601 A89 $1.50 multicolored .55 .55
602 A89 $3 multicolored 1.10 1.10
603 A89 $6 multi, vert. 2.25 2.25
Nos. 600-603 (4) 4.05 4.05

Souvenir Sheet

604 A89 $8 multicolored 5.00 5.00

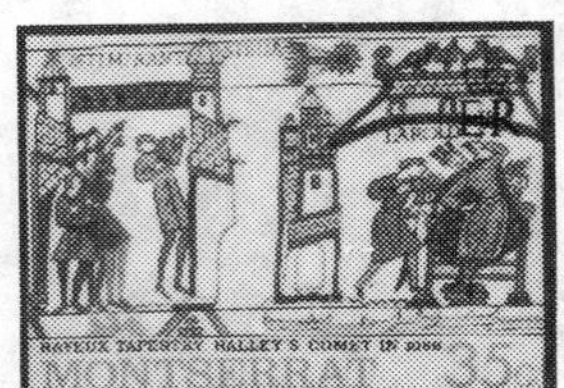

Halley's Comet — A90

Designs: 35c, Bayeux Tapestry (detail), 1066 sighting. 50c, Adoration of the Magi, by Giotto. 70c, Edmond Halley, trajectory diagram, 1531 sighting. $1, Sightings, 1066 and 1910. $1.15, Sighting, 1910. $1.50, Giotto space probe, comet, diagram. $2.30, US Space Telescope, comet. $4, Computer picture of photograph, 1910.

1986, May 9 *Perf. 14*

605 A90 35c multicolored .20 .20
606 A90 50c multicolored .30 .30
607 A90 70c multicolored .40 .40
608 A90 $1 multicolored .55 .55
609 A90 $1.15 multicolored .70 .70
610 A90 $1.50 multicolored .85 .85
611 A90 $2.30 multicolored 1.40 1.40
612 A90 $4 multicolored 2.25 2.25
Nos. 605-612 (8) 6.65 6.65

See Nos. 625-626.

Wedding of Prince Andrew and Sarah Ferguson — A91

Design: No. 613, Andrew, vert. No. 614, Sarah, vert. No. 615, Andrew wearing cowboy hat. No. 616, Sarah wearing fur hat.

Perf. 12½x13, 13x12½

1986, July 23 Litho.

613 A91 70c multicolored .25 .25
614 A91 70c multicolored .25 .25
a. Pair, Nos. 613-614 .50 .50
615 A91 $2 multicolored .75 .75
616 A91 $2 multicolored .75 .75
a. Pair, Nos. 615-616 1.50 1.50
Nos. 613-616 (4) 3.00 3.00

For overprints see Nos. 628-631.

Clipper Ships — A92

1986, Aug. 29 *Perf. 14*

617 A92 90c Antelope, 1793 .80 .80
618 A92 $1.15 Montagu, 1840 .95 .95
619 A92 $1.50 Little Catherine, 1813 1.25 1.25
620 A92 $2.30 Hinchingbrook, 1813 2.00 2.00
a. Souvenir sheet of 4, #617-620 5.00 5.00
Nos. 617-620 (4) 4.40 4.40

Communications — A93

Designs: 70c, Radio Montserrat, near Dagenham. $1.15, Radio Gem ZGM-FM 94, Plymouth. $1.50, Radio Antilles, O'Garro's, $2.30, Cable & Wireless telegraph office, Plymouth.

1986, Sept. 29 Wmk. 380 *Perf. 14*

621 A93 70c multicolored .60 .60
622 A93 $1.15 multicolored .95 .95
623 A93 $1.50 multicolored 1.25 1.25
624 A93 $2.30 multicolored 2.00 2.00
Nos. 621-624 (4) 4.25 4.25

Halley's Comet Type of 1986
Souvenir Sheets

1986, Oct. 10 Unwmk. *Perf. 14*

625 Sheet of 4 4.25 4.25
a. A90 40c like #605 .25 .25
b. A90 $1.75 like #606 1.00 1.00
c. A90 $2 like #607 1.25 1.25
d. A90 $3 like #608 1.75 1.75
626 Sheet of 4 4.25 4.25
a. A90 55c like #609 .30 .30
b. A90 60c like #610 .35 .35
c. A90 80c like #611 .50 .50
d. A90 $5 like #612 3.00 3.00

For overprints see Nos. 656-657.

Souvenir Sheet

Wedding of Prince Andrew and Sarah Ferguson — A94

1986, Oct. 15 *Perf. 13x12½*

627 A94 $10 multicolored 5.50 5.50

Nos. 613-616 Ovptd. in Silver: "Congratulations to T.R.H. The Duke & Duchess of York"

Perf. 12½x13, 13x12½

1986, Nov. 14 Litho.

628 A91 70c No. 613 .55 .55
629 A91 70c No. 614 .55 .55
a. Pair, Nos. 628-629 1.10 1.10
630 A91 $2 No. 615 1.65 1.65
631 A91 $2 No. 616 1.65 1.65
a. Pair, Nos. 630-631 3.30 3.30
Nos. 628-631 (4) 4.00 4.00

Stamps of the same denomination printed tete-beche.

Christmas — A95

1986, Dec. 12 Unwmk. *Perf. 14*

632 A95 70c Christmas rose .50 .50
633 A95 $1.15 Candle flower .85 .85
634 A95 $1.50 Christmas tree kalanchoe 1.25 1.25
635 A95 $2.30 Snow on the mountain 1.90 1.90
a. Souvenir sheet of 4, #632-635, perf. 12x12½ 4.50 4.50
Nos. 632-635 (4) 4.50 4.50

Souvenir Sheets

Statue of Liberty, Cent. — A96

1986, Nov. 18 Litho. *Perf. 14*

636 A96 $3 Statue, pedestal 2.00 2.00
637 A96 $4.50 Head 2.75 2.75
638 A96 $5 Statue, NYC 3.25 3.25
Nos. 636-638 (3) 8.00 8.00

Sailing A97

1986, Dec. 10 *Perf. 15*

639 A97 70c shown .50 .50
640 A97 $1.15 Golf .85 .85
641 A97 $1.50 Plymouth Public Market 1.25 1.25
642 A97 $2.30 Air Studios 1.90 1.90
Nos. 639-642 (4) 4.50 4.50

For surcharge see No. B3.

Sharks A98

1987, Feb. 2 Wmk. 380 *Perf. 14*

643 A98 40c Tiger .35 .35
644 A98 90c Lemon .75 .75
645 A98 $1.15 White .90 .90
646 A98 $3.50 Whale 2.75 2.75
a. Souvenir sheet of 4, #643-646, perf. 12½x12 4.00 4.00
Nos. 643-646 (4) 4.75 4.75

Butterflies — A99

1987, Aug. 10 Wmk. 380 *Perf. 14*

647 A99 90c Straight-line sulpher .85 .85
648 A99 $1.15 Red rim 1.10 1.10
649 A99 $1.50 Hammock skipper 1.40 1.40
650 A99 $2.50 Mimic 2.25 2.25
Nos. 647-650 (4) 5.00 5.00

Nos. 531, 527, 525, 532 and 535 Surcharged

1987, Apr. 6

651 A79 5c on 70c multi .15 .15
652 A79 $1 on 20c multi 1.00 1.00
653 A79 $1.15 on 10c multi 1.25 1.25
654 A79 $1.50 on 90c multi 1.65 1.65
655 A79 $2.30 on $3 multi 2.50 2.50
Nos. 651-655 (5) 6.55 6.55

Nos. 625-626 Ovptd. for CAPEX '87 in Red and Black
Souvenir Sheets

1987, June 13 Unwmk.

656 Sheet of 4, #a.-d. 4.25 4.25
657 Sheet of 4, #a.-d. 4.25 4.25

Orchids A100

1987, Nov. 13 Unwmk. *Perf. 14*

658 A100 90c Oncidium variegatum, vert. .70 .70
659 A100 $1.15 Vanilla planifolia .85 .85
660 A100 $1.50 Gongora quinquenervis, vert. 1.10 1.10
661 A100 $3.50 Brassavola nodosa 2.75 2.75
Nos. 658-661 (4) 5.40 5.40

Souvenir Sheet

662 A100 $5 Oncidium lanceanum 5.50 5.50

Christmas.

Nos. 525, 528-529 and 532 Surcharged "40th Wedding Anniversary / HM Queen Elizabeth II / HRH Duke of Edinburgh / November 1987." and New Value

Wmk. 380

1987, Nov. 20 Litho. *Perf. 14*

663 A79 5c on 90c No. 532 .50 .50
664 A79 $1.15 on 10c No. 525 .65 .65
665 A79 $2.30 on 25c No. 528 1.40 1.40
666 A79 $5 on 40c No. 529 3.00 3.00
Nos. 663-666 (4) 5.55 5.55

Exists spelled "Edingburgh."

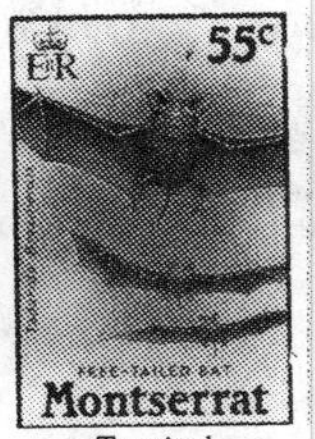

Tropical Bats — A101

Marine Birds — A102

1988, Feb. 8 Wmk. 380 *Perf. 14*

667 A101 55c Free-tailed bat .65 .65
668 A101 90c Fruit bat 1.10 1.10
669 A101 $1.15 Fisherman bat 1.40 1.40
670 A101 $2.30 Fruit bat, diff. 2.75 2.75
Nos. 667-670 (4) 5.90 5.90

Souvenir Sheet

671 A101 $2.50 Funnel-eared bat 3.00 3.00

1988, Apr. 2 Unwmk.

672 A102 90c Magnificent frigatebird .80 .80
673 A102 $1.15 Caribbean elaenia 1.00 1.00
674 A102 $1.50 Glossy ibis 1.25 1.25
675 A102 $3.50 Purple-throated carib 2.75 2.75
Nos. 672-675 (4) 5.80 5.80

Souvenir Sheet

676 A102 $5 Brown pelican 4.00 4.00

Easter.

1988 Summer Olympics, Seoul — A103

Eastern architecture and events: 90c, Women's discus. $1.15, High jump. $3.50, Women's 200-meter and Seoul university building. $5, Single scull rowing, pagoda.

Unwmk.

1988, July 29 Litho. *Perf. 14*

677 A103 90c multicolored .60 .60
678 A103 $1.15 multicolored .65 .65
679 A103 $3.50 multicolored 2.00 2.00
Nos. 677-679 (3) 3.25 3.25

Souvenir Sheet

680 A103 $5 multicolored 3.50 3.50

Sea Shells A104

1988, Aug. 30

681 A104 5c Golden tulip .15 .15
682 A104 10c Little knobby scallop .15 .15
683 A104 15c Sozoni's cone .15 .15
684 A104 20c Globular coral shell .15 .15
685 A104 25c Sundial .20 .20
686 A104 40c King helmet .30 .30
687 A104 55c Channeled turban .40 .40
688 A104 70c True tulip shell .50 .50
689 A104 90c Music volute .65 .65
690 A104 $1 Flame auger .70 .70
691 A104 $1.15 Rooster-tail conch .90 .90
692 A104 $1.50 Queen conch 1.10 1.10
693 A104 $3 Teramachi's slit shell 2.25 2.25
694 A104 $5 Florida crown conch 3.50 3.50

695 A104 $7.50 Beau's murex 5.50 5.50
696 A104 $10 Triton's trumpet 7.50 7.50
Nos. 681-696 (16) 24.10 24.10

For surcharges see Nos. 698-701, 767-770. For overprints see Nos. O79-O94.

University of the West Indies, 40th Anniv. — A105

1988, Oct. 4 Litho. *Perf. 14*
697 A105 $5 multicolored 3.75 3.75

Nos. 687, 690, 693 and 694 Surcharged

HRH PRINCESS
ALEXANDRA'S VISIT
NOVEMBER 1988
40¢

Unwmk.

1988, Nov. 4 Litho. *Perf. 14*
698 A104 40c on 55c No. 687 .35 .35
699 A104 90c on $1 No. 690 .85 .85
700 A104 $1.15 on $3 No. 693 1.10 1.10
701 A104 $1.50 on $5 No. 694 1.35 1.35
Nos. 698-701 (4) 3.00 3.00

Intl. Red Cross, 125th Anniv. A106

1988, Dec. 16
702 A106 $3.50 multicolored 2.00 2.00

Christmas — A107

Birds.

1988, Nov. 28 *Perf. 14x13½*
703 A107 90c Spotted sandpiper .70 .70
704 A107 $1.15 Ruddy turnstone .85 .85
705 A107 $3.50 Red-footed booby 2.75 2.75
Nos. 703-705 (3) 4.30 4.30

Souvenir Sheet

Perf. 13½x14
706 A107 $5 Aububon's shearwater 3.75 3.75

Uniforms — A108

1989, Feb. 24 Litho. *Perf. 14*
707 A108 90c Drum major .70 .70
708 A108 $1.15 Fatigue clothing .85 .85
709 A108 $1.50 Khaki uniform 1.10 1.10
710 A108 $3.50 Dress uniform 2.75 2.75
Nos. 707-710 (4) 5.40 5.40

Souvenir Sheet
711 A108 $5 Cadet (girl), woman 3.75 3.75

Defense Force, 75th anniv.

Easter Lilies A109

1989, Mar. 21 Litho. *Perf. 14*
712 A109 90c Amazon .65 .65
713 A109 $1.15 Salmon blood, vert. .75 .75
714 A109 $1.50 Amaryllis, vert. 1.00 1.00
715 A109 $3.50 Amaryllis, diff., vert. 2.50 2.50
Nos. 712-715 (4) 4.90 4.90

Souvenir Sheet
716 A109 $5 Resurrection, vert. 3.75 3.75

Ships Built in Montserrat — A110

Designs: 90c, Schooner *Morning Prince*, 1942-1948. $1.15, Cargo boat *Western Sun*. $1.50, Cargo boat *Kim G* under construction. $3.50, Cargo and passenger boat MV *Romaris*.

1989, June 30 Litho. *Perf. 13½x14*
717 A110 90c multicolored .60 .60
718 A110 $1.15 multicolored .70 .70
719 A110 $1.50 multicolored .95 .95
720 A110 $3.50 multicolored 2.25 2.25
Nos. 717-720 (4) 4.50 4.50

For surcharges see Nos. B1-B2.

Making of the Film *The Wizard of Oz*, 50th Anniv. A111

1989, Sept. 22 Litho. *Perf. 14*
721 A111 90c Scarecrow .60 .60
722 A111 $1.15 Cowardly Lion .70 .70
723 A111 $1.50 Tin Man .95 .95
724 A111 $3.50 Dorothy 2.25 2.25
Nos. 721-724 (4) 4.50 4.50

Souvenir Sheet
725 A111 $5 shown 3.50 3.50

Nos. 721-724 vert.

1st Moon Landing, 20th Anniv. — A112

Designs: $1.15, Armstrong on ladder, descending from lunar module. $1.50, *Eagle*, astronaut on lunar surface. $3.50, Recovery of command module after splashdown. $5, Astronaut on the Moon, vert.

Perf. 13½x14, 14x13½

1989, Dec. 19 Litho.
726 A112 90c shown .55 .55
727 A112 $1.15 multicolored .65 .65
728 A112 $1.50 multicolored .90 .90
729 A112 $3.50 multicolored 2.00 2.00
Nos. 726-729 (4) 4.10 4.10

Souvenir Sheet
730 A112 $5 multicolored 3.50 3.50

For overprints see Nos. 847-850.

World War II Battle Ships A113

1990, Feb. 12 Litho. *Perf. 14*
731 A113 70c I.J.N. *Yamato* .50 .50
732 A113 $1.15 USS *Arizona* .90 .90
733 A113 $1.50 K.M. *Bismarck* on fire 1.10 1.10
734 A113 $3.50 HMS *Hood* 2.50 2.50
Nos. 731-734 (4) 5.00 5.00

Souvenir Sheet
735 A113 $5 K.M. *Bismarck*, map 4.00 4.00

Nos. 414-418 Surcharged in Bright Rose Lilac

70¢

1990, May 3 *Perf. 14½*
736 A59 70c on 40c #414 .55 .55
737 A59 90c on 55c #415 .70 .70
738 A59 $1 on $1.20 #416 .75 .75
739 A59 $1.15 on $1.20 #417 .90 .90
740 A59 $1.50 on $1.20 #418 1.10 1.10
Nos. 736-740 (5) 4.00 4.00

Stamp World London '90.

Penny Black, 150th Anniv. A114

Designs: 90c, Montserrat #5, General P.O. $1.15, Montserrat #1, postal workers sorting mail, vert. $1.50, Great Britain #1, man and woman mailing letters, vert. $3.50, Great Britain #2, mailman delivering to residence. $5, Chateau Barrack cover of 1836, Great Britain #1, landscape.

1990, June 1 *Perf. 13½x14, 14x13½*
741 A114 90c shown .70 .70
742 A114 $1.15 multicolored .90 .90
743 A114 $1.50 multicolored 1.10 1.10
744 A114 $3.50 multicolored 2.50 2.50
Nos. 741-744 (4) 5.20 5.20

Souvenir Sheet
745 A114 $5 multicolored 3.75 3.75

Stained-glass Windows — A115

1990, Apr. 12 Litho. *Perf. 14x15*
746 Strip of 3 4.50 4.50
a. A115 $1.15 *The Empty Tomb* .85 .85
b. A115 $1.50 *The Ascension* 1.10 1.10
c. A115 $3.50 *Risen Christ with Disciples* 2.50 2.50

Souvenir Sheet
747 A115 $5 *The Crucifixion* 3.75 3.75

World Cup Soccer Championships, Italy — A116

Designs: 90c, Montserrat vs. Antigua. $1.15, US vs. Trinidad. $1.50, Montserrat team. $3.50, West Germany vs. Wales. $5, World Cup trophy.

1990, July 8 Litho. *Perf. 14*
748 A116 90c multicolored .55 .55
749 A116 $1.15 multicolored .75 .75
750 A116 $1.50 multicolored .95 .95
751 A116 $3.50 multicolored 2.25 2.25
Nos. 748-751 (4) 4.50 4.50

Souvenir Sheet
752 A116 $5 multicolored 3.75 3.75

Spinner Dolphin A117

1990, Sept. 25 Litho. *Perf. 14*
753 A117 90c shown .75 .75
754 A117 $1.15 Common dolphin 1.00 1.00
755 A117 $1.50 Striped dolphin 1.25 1.25
756 A117 $3.50 Atlantic spotted dolphin 2.75 2.75
Nos. 753-756 (4) 5.20 5.20

Souvenir Sheet
757 A117 $5 Atlantic white-sided dolphin 4.75 4.75

Fish A118

1991, Feb. 7 Litho. *Perf. 14*
758 A118 90c Spotted goatfish .75 .75
759 A118 $1.15 Cushion starfish 1.00 1.00
760 A118 $1.50 Rock beuaty 1.25 1.25
761 A118 $3.50 French grunt 2.75 2.75
Nos. 758-761 (4) 5.20 5.20

Souvenir Sheet
762 A118 $5 Trunkfish 4.75 4.75

For surcharges and overprints see Nos. O98-O99, O104, O107.

Birds A119

1991, Apr. 17 Litho. *Perf. 14*
763 A119 90c Duck .70 .70
764 A119 $1.15 Hen, chicks .90 .90
765 A119 $1.50 Rooster 1.10 1.10
766 A119 $3.50 Helmeted guinea fowl 2.50 2.50
Nos. 763-766 (4) 5.20 5.20

For surcharges and overprints see Nos. O100, O102, O105, O108.

Nos. 684-685, 692, 695 Surcharged

1991 Litho. *Perf. 14*
767 A104 5c on 20c #684 .15 .15
768 A104 5c on 25c #685 .15 .15
769 A104 $1.15 on $1.50 #692 2.25 2.25
770 A104 $1.15 on $7.50 #695 2.25 2.25
Nos. 767-770 (4) 4.80 4.80

Mushrooms — A120

Lilies — A121

1991, June 13 Litho. *Perf. 14*
771 A120 90c Panaeolus antillarum .60 .60
772 A120 $1.15 Cantharellus cinnabarinus .75 .75
773 A120 $1.50 Gymnopilus chrysopellus 1.00 1.00

774 A120 $2 Psilocybe cubensis 1.40 1.40
775 A120 $3.50 Leptonia caeruleo-capitata 2.25 2.25
Nos. 771-775 (5) 6.00 6.00

1991, Aug. 8
776 A121 90c Red water lily .70 .70
777 A121 $1.15 Shell ginger .85 .85
778 A121 $1.50 Early day lily 1.10 1.10
779 A121 $3.50 Anthurium 2.75 2.75
Nos. 776-779 (4) 5.40 5.40

For surcharges and overprints see Nos. O101, O103, O106, O109.

Frogs and Toads — A122

1991, Oct. 9 Litho. *Perf. 14*
780 A122 $1.15 Tree frog .75 .75
781 A122 $2 Crapaud toad 1.40 1.40
782 A122 $3.50 Mountain chicken 2.25 2.25
Nos. 780-782 (3) 4.40 4.40

Souvenir Sheet
Perf. 14½x14
783 A122 $5 Sheet of 1 4.00 4.00

No. 783 contains one 81x48mm stamp that incorporates designs of Nos. 780-782.

Cats A123

1991, Dec. 5
784 A123 90c Black British shorthair .60 .60
785 A123 $1.15 Seal point siamese .75 .75
786 A123 $1.50 Silver tabby persian 1.00 1.00
787 A123 $2.50 Birman temple cat 1.65 1.65
788 A123 $3.50 Egyptian mau 2.25 2.25
Nos. 784-788 (5) 6.25 6.25

Miniature Sheet

Discovery of America, 500th Anniv. — A124

a, $1.50, Navigating instruments. b, $1.50, Coat of arms, Columbus. c, $1.50, Columbus, Bahamian natives. d, $1.50, Queen Isabella, Columbus with petition. e, $1.50, Exotic birds. f, $1.50, Exotic plants. g, $3.00, Santa Maria, Nina & Pinta.

1992, Jan. 16 Litho. *Perf. 14*
789 A124 Sheet of 7, #a.-g. 8.50 8.50

No. 789g is 85x28mm. See No. 829.

Dinosaurs A125

1992, Aug. 1 Litho. *Perf. 14*
790 A125 $1 Tyrannosaurus .75 .75
791 A125 $1.15 Diplodocus .85 .85
792 A125 $1.50 Apatosaurus 1.10 1.10
793 A125 $3.45 Dimetrodon 2.50 2.50
Nos. 790-793 (4) 5.20 5.20

Souvenir Sheet
794 A125 $4.60 Owen with bone, vert. 4.00 4.00

Sir Richard Owen, cent. of death.

1992 Summer Olympics, Barcelona — A126

1992, Apr. 10
795 A126 $1 Torch bearer .70 .70
796 A126 $1.15 Flags .80 .80
797 A126 $2.30 Olympic flame, map 1.50 1.50
798 A126 $3.60 Various events 2.50 2.50
Nos. 795-798 (4) 5.50 5.50

Montserrat Oriole — A127

1992, June 30 Litho. *Perf. 13½x14*
799 A127 $1 Male .70 .70
800 A127 $1.15 Male, female .80 .80
801 A127 $1.50 Female feeding chicks 1.00 1.00
802 A127 $3.60 Map, male 2.50 2.50
Nos. 799-802 (4) 5.00 5.00

Insects A128

1992, Aug. 20 Litho. *Perf. 15x14*
803 A128 5c Grasshopper .15 .15
804 A128 10c Field cricket .15 .15
805 A128 15c Dragonfly .15 .15
806 A128 20c Red skimmer .15 .15
807 A128 25c Pond skater .20 .20
808 A128 40c Leaf weevil .30 .30
809 A128 55c Leaf cutter ants .40 .40
810 A128 70c Paper wasp .50 .50
811 A128 90c Bee fly .70 .70
812 A128 $1 Lacewing .80 .80
813 A128 $1.15 Orange-barred sulphur .90 .90
814 A128 $1.50 Painted lady 1.10 1.10
815 A128 $3 Bella moth 2.25 2.25
816 A128 $5 Plume moth 3.75 3.75
817 A128 $7.50 White peacock 5.50 5.50
818 A128 $10 Postman 7.50 7.50
Nos. 803-818 (16) 24.50 24.50

For overprints see Nos. 871-872, O110-O125.

Christmas — A129

Designs: $1.15, Adoration of the Magi. $4.60, Angel appearing before shepherds.

1992, Nov. 26 Litho. *Perf. 13½x14*
819 A129 $1.15 multicolored .65 .65
820 A129 $4.60 multicolored 2.75 2.75

Coins and Bank Notes — A130

Designs: $1, One-dollar coin, twenty-dollar notes. $1.15, Ten-cent, twenty-five cent coins, ten-dollar notes. $1.50, Five-cent coin, five-dollar notes. $3.60, One-cent, two-cent coins, one-dollar notes.

1993, Feb. 10 *Perf. 14x13½*
821 A130 $1 multicolored .70 .70
822 A130 $1.15 multicolored .80 .80
823 A130 $1.50 multicolored 1.00 1.00
824 A130 $3.60 multicolored 2.50 2.50
Nos. 821-824 (4) 5.00 5.00

Discovery of America, 500th Anniv. (in 1992) — A131

1993, Mar. 10 Litho. *Perf. 14*
825 A131 $1 Coming ashore .85 .85
826 A131 $2 Natives, ships 1.65 1.65

Organization of East Caribbean States.

Coronation of Queen Elizabeth II, 40th Anniv. — A132

Designs: $1.15, Queen, M.H. Bramble. $4.60, Queen riding in Gold State Coach.

1993, June 2 *Perf. 13½x14*
827 A132 $1.15 multicolored .90 .90
828 A132 $4.60 multicolored 3.50 3.50

Columbus Type of 1992 with Added Text

IRISH CATHOLICS
FROM ST. KITTS AND VIRGINIA
SETTLED ON ISLAND
BETWEEN 1628-1634

a, $1.15, like #789a. b, $1.15, like #789b. c, $1.15, like #789c. d, $1.50, like #789d. e, $1.50, like #789e. f, $1.50, like #789f. g, $3.45, like #789g.

1993, Sept. 7 Litho. *Perf. 14*
829 A124 Sheet of 7, #a.-g. 8.75 8.75

Nos. 829a-829g each have different added text.

Royal Air Force, 75th Anniv.
Common Design Type

Designs: 15c, Boeing Sentry, 1993. 55c, Vickers Valiant, 1962. $1.15, Handley Page Hastings, 1958. $3, 1943 Lockheed Ventura, 1943.

No. 834a, Felixstowe F5, 1921. b, Armstrong Whitworth Atlas, 1934. c, Fairey Gordon, 1935. d, Boulton Paul Overstrand, 1936.

Wmk. 373
1993, Nov. 17 Litho. *Perf. 14*
830 CD350 15c multicolored .15 .15
831 CD350 55c multicolored .50 .50
832 CD350 $1.15 multicolored 1.10 1.10
833 CD350 $3 multicolored 3.00 3.00
Nos. 830-833 (4) 4.75 4.75

Souvenir Sheet
834 CD350 $1.50 Sheet of 4, #a.-d. 5.00 5.00

Beetles A133

Perf. 15x14
1994, Jan. 21 Litho. Unwmk.
835 A133 $1 Ground beetle .75 .75
836 A133 $1.15 Click beetle .90 .90
837 A133 $1.50 Harlequin beetle 1.10 1.10
838 A133 $3.45 Leaf beetle 2.50 2.50
Nos. 835-838 (4) 5.25 5.25

Souvenir Sheet
839 A133 $4.50 Scarab beetle 4.00 4.00

Hibiscus Flowers and Fruits — A134

Designs: 90c, Cotton. $1.15, Sorrel. $1.50, Okra. $3.50, Hibiscus rosa sinensis.

1994, Mar. 22 Litho. *Perf. 14x13½*
840 A134 90c multicolored .70 .70
841 A134 $1.15 multicolored .90 .90
842 A134 $1.50 multicolored 1.10 1.10
843 A134 $3.50 multicolored 2.75 2.75
Nos. 840-843 (4) 5.45 5.45

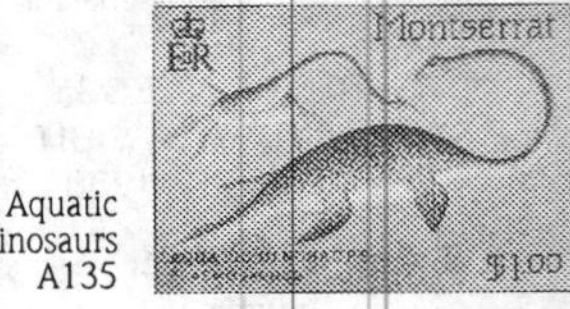
Aquatic Dinosaurs A135

a, $1, Elasmosaurus. b, $1.15, Plesiosaurus. c, $1.50, Nothosaurus. d, $3.45, Mosasaurus.

1994, May 6 Litho. *Perf. 15x14*
844 A135 Strip of 4, #a.-d. 6.50 6.50

1994 World Cup Soccer Championships, US — A136

#845: a, 90c, Montserrat youth soccer. b, $1, 1990 World Cup, US vs. England. c, $1.15, Rose Bowl Stadium, Pasadena, Calif., US. d, $3.45, German team, 1990 World Cup Winners.

#846: a, Jules Rimet. b, Bobby Moore, England Team Captain, 1966. c, Lew Jaschin. d, Sepp Herberger, German trainer.

1994, May 20 *Perf. 14*
845 A136 Vert. strip of 4, #a.-d. 5.00 5.00

Souvenir Sheet
Perf. 14x14½
846 A136 $2 Sheet of 4, #a.-d. 6.00 6.00

No. 845 printed in sheets of 2 strips + 4 labels.

Nos. 726-729 Ovptd. in Red with "Space Anniversaries" and:

40c, "Yuri Gagarin / First man in space / April 12, 1961." $1.15, "First Joint US / Soviet Mission / July 15, 1975." $1.50, "25th Anniversary / First Moon Landing / Apollo XI-July 20, 1994." $2.30, "Columbia / First Space Shuttle / April 12, 1981."

1994, July 20 *Perf. 13½x14*
847 A112 40c on 90c multi .30 .30
848 A112 $1.15 multi .90 .90
849 A112 $1.50 multi 1.10 1.10
850 A112 $2.30 on $3.50 multi 1.75 1.75
Nos. 847-850 (4) 4.05 4.05

Obliterator on Nos. 847, 850 is black.

Wookstock Festival, 25th Anniv. A137

1994, Oct. 20 *Perf. 12½*
851 A137 $1.15 1969 Poster .90 .90

852 A137 $1.50 1994 Poster 1.25 1.25

Souvenir Sheets

853 A137 $4.50 like #851 3.50 3.50
854 A137 $4.50 like #852 3.50 3.50

Sea Vegetation — A138

1995, Feb. 14 ***Perf. 14x15***

855 A138 $1 Sea fan .75 .75
856 A138 $1.15 Sea lily .90 .90
857 A138 $1.50 Sea pen 1.25 1.25
858 A138 $3.45 Sea fern 2.75 2.75
Nos. 855-858 (4) 5.65 5.65

Souvenir Sheet

859 A138 $4.50 Sea rose 3.50 3.50

Miniature Sheet of 9

Motion Pictures, Cent. A139

No. 860: Various portraits of Marilyn Monroe. $6, Marilyn Monroe & Elvis Presley.

1995, June 13 **Litho.** ***Perf. 12½***

860 A139 $1.15 #a.-i. 8.00 8.00

Souvenir Sheet

861 A139 $6 multicolored 4.75 4.75

No. 861 contains one 51x57mm stamp.

Souvenir Sheet of 4

1995 IAAF World Track & Field Championships, Gothenburg, Sweden — A140

a, Jesse Owens, US. b, Eric Lemming, Sweden. c, Rudolf Harbig, Germany. d, Montserrat youth.

1995, Aug. 3 ***Perf. 14***

862 A140 $1.50 #a.-d. 4.75 4.75

End of World War II, 50th Anniv. A141

Scientific achievements based on World War II research: No. 863, Atmospheric sounding experiments using V-2 rockets. No. 864, Space Shuttle Challenger. No. 865, First successful nuclear reactor. No. 866, Calder Hall Atomic Power Station, England. No. 867, Ju88G-7a nightfighter equipped with SN2 radar. No. 868, NATO Boeing E6 AWACS. No. 869, Gloster Meteor III jet aircraft. No. 870, British Airways Concorde.

1995, Aug. 15

863 A141 $1.15 multicolored .90 .90
864 A141 $1.15 multicolored .90 .90
a. Pair, #863-864 1.75 1.75
865 A141 $1.15 multicolored .90 .90
866 A141 $1.15 multicolored .90 .90
a. Pair, #865-866 1.75 1.75
867 A141 $1.50 multicolored 1.25 1.25
868 A141 $1.50 multicolored 1.25 1.25
a. Pair, #867-868 2.50 2.50
869 A141 $1.50 multicolored 1.25 1.25
870 A141 $1.50 multicolored 1.25 1.25
a. Pair, #869-870 2.50 2.50
Nos. 863-870 (8) 8.60 8.60

Nos. 812, 818 Ovptd. 

1995 **Litho.** ***Perf. 15x14***

871 A128 $1 multicolored .75 .75
872 A128 $10 multicolored 7.50 7.50

UN, 50th Anniv. — A142

1995, Sept. 4 **Litho.** ***Perf. 14***

873 A142 $1.15 Food .90 .90
874 A142 $1.50 Education 1.10 1.10
875 A142 $2.30 Health 1.75 1.75
876 A142 $3 Peace 2.25 2.25
Nos. 873-876 (4) 6.00 6.00

Souvenir Sheet

877 A142 $6 Justice 4.50 4.50

Natl. Trust, 25th Anniv. A143

Designs: $1.15, Headquarters building. $1.50, 17th cent. cannon, Bransby Point. $2.30, Painting of original Galways sugar mill, vert. $3, Great Alps Falls, vert.

1995, Nov. 15 **Litho.** ***Perf. 14***

878 A143 $1.15 multicolored .90 .90
879 A143 $1.50 multicolored 1.10 1.10
880 A143 $2.30 multicolored 1.75 1.75
881 A143 $3 multicolored 2.25 2.25
Nos. 878-881 (4) 6.00 6.00

Scavengers of the Sea — A144

1996, Feb. 14 **Litho.** ***Perf. 15x14***

882 A144 $1 Bull shark .75 .75
883 A144 $1.15 Sea mouse .90 .90
884 A144 $1.50 Bristleworm 1.15 1.15
885 A144 $3.45 Prawn xiphocaris 2.60 2.60
Nos. 882-885 (4) 5.40 5.40

Souvenir Sheet

886 A144 $4.50 Man o'war 3.40 3.40

Radio, Cent. (in 1995) A145

Designs: $1.15, Guglielmo Marconi, transmitting equipment, 1901. $1.50, Wireless laboratory, Marconi's yacht, Elettra. $2.30, First transatlantic radio message, Newfoundland, 1901. $3, First air/ground radio station, Croydon, 1920.
$4.50, First radio telescope, Jodrell Bank, Cheshire, England.

1996, Mar. 19 **Litho.** ***Perf. 14***

887 A145 $1.15 multicolored .90 .90
888 A145 $1.50 multicolored 1.15 1.15
889 A145 $2.30 multicolored 1.75 1.75
890 A145 $3 multicolored 2.25 2.25
Nos. 887-890 (4) 6.05 6.05

Souvenir Sheet

891 A145 $4.50 multicolored 3.50 3.50

1996 Summer Olympic Games, Atlanta A146

1896 Medalists: $1.15, Paul Masson, cycling. $1.50, Robert Garrett, discus. $2.30, Spiridon Louis, marathon. $3, John Boland, tennis.

1996, June 24 **Litho.** ***Perf. 14***

892 A146 $1.15 multicolored .90 .90
893 A146 $1.50 multicolored 1.15 1.15
894 A146 $2.30 multicolored 1.75 1.75
895 A146 $3 multicolored 2.25 2.25
Nos. 892-895 (4) 6.05 6.05

Mythical Creatures — A147

1996, Aug. 15 **Litho.** ***Perf. 14***

896 A147 5c Leprechaun .15 .15
897 A147 10c Pegasus .15 .15
898 A147 15c Griffin .15 .15
899 A147 20c Unicorn .15 .15
900 A147 25c Gnome .20 .20
901 A147 40c Mermaid .30 .30
902 A147 55c Cockatrice .40 .40
903 A147 70c Fairy .55 .55
904 A147 90c Goblin .70 .70
905 A147 $1 Faun .75 .75
906 A147 $1.15 Dragon .90 .90
907 A147 $1.50 Giant 1.15 1.15
908 A147 $3 Elf 2.25 2.25
909 A147 $5 Centaur 3.75 3.75
910 A147 $7.50 Phoenix 5.75 5.75
911 A147 $10 Erin 7.50 7.50
Nos. 896-911 (16) 24.80 24.80

For overprints see Nos. O126-O140.

James Dean (1931-55), Actor A148

Various portraits.

1996, June 28 **Litho.** ***Perf. 12½***

912 A148 $1.15 Sheet of 9, #a.-i. 8.00 8.00

Souvenir Sheet

913 A148 $6 multicolored 4.50 4.50

No. 913 contains one 51x57mm stamp.
For overprint see No. 921.

Dancing Bears, Emblem of "The Grateful Dead" — A149

Jerry Garcia A150

Color of bears: No. 914: a, blue violet, green. b, yellow. c, orange, pink.

1996 **Litho.** ***Perf. 12½***

914 A149 $1.15 Strip of 3, #a.-c. 2.60 2.60
915 A150 $6 multicolored 4.50 4.50

For surcharge see No. 928.

Scavenger Birds A151

1997 **Litho.** ***Perf. 14½x14***

916 A151 $1 Turkey vulture .75 .75
917 A151 $1.15 American crow .90 .90
918 A151 $1.50 Great skua 1.10 1.10
919 A151 $3.45 Kittiwake 2.60 2.60
Nos. 916-919 (4) 5.35 5.35

Souvenir Sheet

920 A151 $4.50 King vulture 3.40 3.40

No. 912 Ovptd. 

1997 **Litho.** ***Perf. 12½***

921 A148 $1.15 Sheet of 9, #a.-i. 8.00 8.00

Overprints are placed over vertical perfs separating each column of stamps. Each stamp in the left and right columns has only half the overprint. The stamps in the center column contains two incomplete halves of the overprint. The overprints also appear twice in sheet margin.

Eruption of Mt. Soufriere, Endangered Species — A152

Designs: a, Heavy ash eruption, Plymouth, 1995. b, First pyroclastic flow entering sea. c, Double venting at Castle Peak. d, Mangrove cuckoo. e, Nocturnal lava flow, Soufriere Hills, 1996. f, Antillean crested hummingbird. g, Ash cloud engulfing Plymouth. h, Lava spine extruded, Soufriere Hills, 1996. i, New land created from pyroclastic flows.

1997 ***Perf. 14***

922 A152 $1.50 Sheet of 9, #a.-i. 10.50 10.50

Elvis Presley (1935-77) A153

American rock stars: No. 924, Jimi Hendrix (1942-70). No. 925, Jerry Garcia (1942-95). No. 926, Janis Joplin (1943-70).

1997 Litho. Perf. 12½
923 A153 $1.15 multicolored 1.00 1.00
924 A153 $1.15 multicolored 1.00 1.00
925 A153 $1.15 multicolored 1.00 1.00
926 A153 $1.15 multicolored 1.00 1.00
Nos. 923-926 (4) 4.00 4.00

Abstract Art — A154

1997 Litho. Perf. 12½
927 A154 $1.50 multicolored 1.15 1.15

No. 915 Surcharged in Gold and Black

$1 50

1997 Litho. Perf. 12½
928 A150 $1.50 on $6 multi 1.10 1.10

SEMI-POSTAL STAMPS

Catalogue values for unused stamps in this section, from this point to the end of the section, are for Never Hinged items.

Nos. 719-720 Surcharged

Hurricane Hugo Relief Surcharge $2.50

1989, Oct. 20 Litho. Perf. 13½x14
B1 A110 $1.50 +$2.50 multi 3.00 3.00
B2 A110 $3.50 +$2.50 multi 4.50 4.50

Surcharge for hurricane relief.

No. 642 Surcharged

25TH ANNIVERSARY
1970 1995

+$5 00

1995 Litho. Perf. 15
B3 A97 $2.30 +$5 multi 5.50 5.50

Surcharge for volcano relief.

WAR TAX STAMPS

No. 43 Overprinted in Red or Black WAR STAMP

1917-18 Wmk. 3 Perf. 14
MR1 A6 ½p green (R) .15 .15
MR2 A6 ½p green ('18) .15 .15

Type of Regular Issue of 1919 Overprinted WAR STAMP

1918
MR3 A6 1½p orange & black .25 .25

Denomination on No. MR3 in black on white ground. Two dots under "d."

OFFICIAL STAMPS

Nos. O1-O44 used on Post Office and Philatelic Bureau mail. Not sold to public, used or unused.

Nos. 235-236, 338-339 Overprinted O.H.M.S.

Perf. 12½x14
1976, Apr. 12 Photo. Wmk. 314
O1 A22 5c multicolored 1.90
O2 A22 10c multicolored 2.50
O3 A22 30c on 10c multi 5.00
O4 A22 45c on 3c multi 6.00
Nos. O1-O4 (4) 15.40

Nos. 243-243A also received this overprint.

Nos. 343-347, 349-351, 353 Overprinted

O.H.M.S.

Perf. 13½x14
1976, Oct. 1 Litho. Wmk. 373
O10 A44 5c multicolored .15
O11 A44 10c multicolored .15
O12 A44 15c multicolored .15
O13 A44 20c multicolored .15
O14 A44 25c multicolored .20
O15 A44 55c multicolored .40
O16 A44 70c multicolored .50
O17 A44 $1 multicolored .70
O18 A44 $5 multicolored 3.50
O19 A44 $10 multicolored 7.00
Nos. O10-O19 (10) 12.90

Nos. 343-347, 349-351, 353-354 Overprinted O.H.M.S.

1980, Sept. 30 Perf. 14
O20 A44 5c multicolored .15
O21 A44 10c multicolored .15
O22 A44 15c multicolored .15
O23 A44 20c multicolored .15
O24 A44 25c multicolored .15
O25 A44 55c multicolored .35
O26 A44 70c multicolored .45
O27 A44 $1 multicolored .65
O28 A44 $5 multicolored 3.25
O29 A44 $10 multicolored 6.50
Nos. O20-O29 (10) 11.95

Nos. 341-351, 353-354 Overprinted or Surcharged O.H.M.S.

1980, Sept. 30 Litho. Perf. 14
O30 A44 5c multicolored .15
O31 A44 5c on 3c multi .15
O32 A44 10c multicolored .15
O33 A44 15c multicolored .15
O34 A44 20c multicolored .15
O35 A44 25c multicolored .20
O36 A44 30c on 15c multi .25
O37 A44 35c on 2c multi .40
O38 A44 40c multicolored .30
O39 A44 55c multicolored .45
O40 A44 70c multicolored .60
O41 A44 $1 multicolored .80
O42 A44 $2.50 on 40c multi 2.00
O43 A44 $5 multicolored 4.00
O44 A44 $10 multicolored 8.00
Nos. O30-O44 (15) 17.75

Catalogue values for unused stamps in this section, from this point to the end of the section, are for Never Hinged items.

Fish Issue of 1981 Nos. 445-449, 451, 453, 455, 457-458, 460 Overprinted O.H.M.S.

1981, Mar. 20 Litho. Perf. 13½
O45 A64 5c multicolored .15 .15
O46 A64 10c multicolored .15 .15
O47 A64 15c multicolored .15 .15
O48 A64 20c multicolored .15 .15
O49 A64 25c multicolored .20 .20
O50 A64 45c multicolored .35 .35
O51 A64 65c multicolored .50 .50
O52 A64 $1 multicolored .75 .75
O53 A64 $3 multicolored 2.25 2.25
O54 A64 $5 multicolored 3.75 3.75
O55 A64 $10 multicolored 7.50 7.50
Nos. O45-O55 (11) 15.90 15.90

Nos. 465-470 Surcharged O.H.M.S. 45c

1982, Nov. 17 Litho. Perf. 14
O56 A66 45c on 90c (#465) .30 .30
O57 A67 45c on 90c (#466) .30 .30
O58 A66 75c on $3 (#467) .50 .50
O59 A67 75c on $3 (#468) .50 .50
O60 A66 $1 on $4 (#469) .65 .65
O61 A67 $1 on $4 (#470) .65 .65
Nos. O56-O61 (6) 2.90 2.90

Princess Diana Issue, Nos. 484-486 Overprinted or Surcharged 70¢

O.H.M.S.

1983, Oct. 19 Litho. Perf. 14
O62 A64 70c on 75c (#484) .50 .50
O63 A64 $1 (#485) .70 .70
O64 A64 $1.50 on $5 (#486) 1.00 1.00
Nos. O62-O64 (3) 2.20 2.20

Nos. 524-536, 538 Overprinted OHMS

1985, Apr. 12 Wmk. 380 Perf. 14
O65 A79 5c multicolored .15 .15
O66 A79 10c multicolored .15 .15
O67 A79 15c multicolored .15 .15
O68 A79 20c multicolored .15 .15
O69 A79 25c multicolored .20 .20
O70 A79 40c multicolored .30 .30
O71 A79 55c multicolored .35 .35
O72 A79 70c multicolored .50 .50
O73 A79 90c multicolored .60 .60
O74 A79 $1 multicolored .70 .70
O75 A79 $1.15 multicolored .75 .75
O76 A79 $3 multicolored 2.00 2.00
O77 A79 $5 multicolored 3.50 3.50
O78 A79 $10 multicolored 6.75 6.75
Nos. O65-O78 (14) 16.25 16.25

Nos. 681-694 and 696 Overprinted OHMS

Unwmk.
1989, May 9 Litho. Perf. 14
O79 A104 5c multicolored .15 .15
O80 A104 10c multicolored .15 .15
O81 A104 15c multicolored .15 .15
O82 A104 20c multicolored .15 .15
O83 A104 25c multicolored .20 .20
O84 A104 40c multicolored .30 .30
O85 A104 55c multicolored .45 .45
O86 A104 70c multicolored .55 .55
O87 A104 90c multicolored .65 .65
O88 A104 $1 multicolored .75 .75
O89 A104 $1.15 multicolored .90 .90
O90 A104 $1.50 multicolored 1.10 1.10
O91 A104 $3 multicolored 2.25 2.25
O92 A104 $5 multicolored 3.75 3.75
O94 A104 $10 multicolored 7.50 7.50
Nos. O79-O94 (15) 19.00 19.00

70¢

Nos. 446, 454a and 456 Surcharged

OHMS

1989 Wmk. 373 Perf. 13½
O95 A64 70c on 10c multi .50 .50
O96 A64 $1.15 on 75c multi .90 .90
O97 A64 $1.50 on $2 multi 1.10 1.10
Nos. O95-O97 (3) 2.50 2.50

Nos. 758-761, 763-766, 776-779 Surcharged or Overprinted "OHMS"

1992 Litho. Perf. 14
O98 A118 70c on 90c #758 1.50 1.50
O99 A118 70c on $3.50 #761 1.50 1.50
O100 A119 70c on 90c #763 1.50 1.50
O101 A121 70c on 90c #776 1.50 1.50
O102 A119 $1 on $3.50 #766 2.00 2.00
O103 A121 $1 on $3.50 #779 2.00 2.00
O104 A118 $1.15 on #759 2.25 2.25
O105 A119 $1.15 on #764 2.25 2.25
O106 A121 $1.15 on #777 2.25 2.25
O107 A118 $1.50 on #760 3.00 3.00
O108 A119 $1.50 on #765 3.00 3.00
O109 A121 $1.50 on #778 3.00 3.00
Nos. O98-O109 (12) 25.75 25.75

Nos. 803-816, 818 Ovptd. "OHMS" in Red

1993, Apr. 14 Litho. Perf. 15x14
O110 A128 5c multicolored .15 .15
O111 A128 10c multicolored .15 .15
O112 A128 15c multicolored .15 .15
O113 A128 20c multicolored .15 .15
O114 A128 25c multicolored .20 .20
O115 A128 40c multicolored .30 .30
O116 A128 55c multicolored .45 .45
O117 A128 70c multicolored .55 .55
O118 A128 90c multicolored .65 .65
O119 A128 $1 multicolored .75 .75
O120 A128 $1.15 multicolored .90 .90
O121 A128 $1.50 multicolored 1.10 1.10
O122 A128 $3 multicolored 2.25 2.25
O123 A128 $5 multicolored 3.75 3.75
O125 A128 $10 multicolored 7.50 7.50
Nos. O110-O125 (15) 19.00 19.00

A number has been reserved for an additional value in this set.

Nos. 896-909, 911 Ovptd. "O.H.M.S." In Red

1997 Litho. Perf. 14
O126 A147 5c multicolored .15 .15
O127 A147 10c multicolored .15 .15
O128 A147 15c multicolored .15 .15
O129 A147 20c multicolored .15 .15
O130 A147 25c multicolored .20 .20
O131 A147 40c multicolored .30 .30
O132 A147 55c multicolored .40 .40
O133 A147 70c multicolored .55 .55
O134 A147 90c multicolored .70 .70
O135 A147 $1 multicolored .75 .75
O136 A147 $1.15 multicolored .90 .90
O137 A147 $1.50 multicolored 1.10 1.10
O138 A147 $3 multicolored 2.25 2.25
O139 A147 $5 multicolored 3.75 3.75
O140 A147 $10 multicolored 7.50 7.50
Nos. O126-O140 (15) 19.05 19.05

MOROCCO

mə-'rä-(,)kō

LOCATION — Northwest coast of Africa
GOVT. — Kingdom
AREA — 171,953 sq. mi.
POP. — 21,160,000 (est. 1984)
CAPITAL — Rabat

In 1956 the three zones of Morocco, French, Spanish and Tangier, were united to form an independent nation. Nos. 1-24 and C1-C3 were intended for use only in the southern (French currency) zone. Issues of the northern zone (Spanish currency) are listed after Postage Due stamps.

For earlier issues see French Morocco and Spanish Morocco.

100 Centimes = 1 Franc
100 Centimes = 1 Dirham (1962)

Catalogue values for all unused stamps in this country are for Never Hinged items.

Sultan Mohammed V — A1

Men Reading — A2

1956-57 Unwmk. Engr. Perf. 13
1 A1 5fr brt bl & indigo .15 .15
2 A1 10fr bis brn & choc .15 .15
3 A1 15fr dp grn & magENTA .16 .15
4 A1 25fr purple ('57) .50 .15
5 A1 30fr green ('57) .90 .15
6 A1 50fr rose red ('57) 1.40 .15
7 A1 70fr dk brn & brn red ('57) 2.00 .40
Nos. 1-7 (7) 5.26
Set value .78

For surcharges see Nos. B1-B5, B8-B9.

1956, Nov. 5

Campaign against illiteracy: 15fr, Girls reading. 20fr, Instructor and pupils. 30fr, Old man and child reading. 50fr, Girl pointing out poster.

8	A2	10fr pur & vio	.85	.65
9	A2	15fr car & rose lake	1.10	.70
10	A2	20fr bl grn & grn	1.25	1.25
11	A2	30fr rose lake & brt red	2.00	1.40
12	A2	50fr dp bl & bl	3.50	2.25
		Nos. 8-12 (5)	8.70	6.25

Sultan Mohammed V — A3

Prince Moulay el Hassan — A4

1957, Mar. 2 Photo. *Perf. 13 1/2x13*

13	A3	15fr blue green	.75	.65
14	A3	25fr gray olive	1.00	.65
15	A3	30fr deep rose	1.40	.90
		Nos. 13-15 (3)	3.15	2.20

Anniversary of independence.

1957, July 9 *Perf. 13*

16	A4	15fr blue	.70	.50
17	A4	25fr green	.85	.65
18	A4	30fr car rose	1.40	.90
		Nos. 16-18 (3)	2.95	2.05

Designation of Prince Moulay el Hassan as heir to the throne.

King Mohammed V — A5

1957, Nov. *Perf. 12 1/2*

19	A5	15fr blk & brt grn	.45	.40
20	A5	25fr blk & rose red	.70	.50
21	A5	30fr blk & vio	.75	.65
		Nos. 19-21 (3)	1.90	1.55

Enthronement of Mohammed V, 30th anniv.

Morocco Pavilion, Brussels World's Fair — A6

1958, Apr. 20 Engr. *Perf. 13*

22	A6	15fr brt grnsh bl	.20	.15
23	A6	25fr carmine	.20	.15
24	A6	30fr indigo	.25	.20
		Nos. 22-24 (3)	.65	.50

World's Fair, Brussels.

UNESCO Building, Paris, and Mohammed V — A7

1958, Nov. 23

25	A7	15fr green	.20	.15
26	A7	25fr lake	.20	.15
27	A7	30fr blue	.25	.20
		Nos. 25-27 (3)	.65	.50

UNESCO Headquarters opening, Paris, Nov. 3.

Ben Smin Sanatorium A8

1959, Jan. 18 Unwmk. *Perf. 13*

28	A8	50fr dk brn, car & slate grn	.38	.25

Red Cross-Red Crescent Society.

Mohammed V — A9

Princess Lalla Amina — A10

1959, Aug. 18 Engr. *Perf. 13*

29	A9	15fr dk car rose	.30	.20
30	A9	25fr brt bl	.40	.22
31	A9	45fr dk grn	.45	.30
		Nos. 29-31 (3)	1.15	.72

50th birthday of King Mohammed V.

1959, Nov. 17

32	A10	15fr blue	.20	.15
33	A10	25fr green	.22	.15
34	A10	45fr rose lil	.25	.20
		Nos. 32-34 (3)	.67	.50

Issued for International Children's Week.

Map of Africa and Symbols of Agriculture, Industry and Commerce — A11

1960, Jan. 31 *Perf. 13*

35	A11	45fr vio, ocher & emer	.45	.30

Issued to publicize the meeting of the Economic Commission for Africa, Tangier.

Refugees and Uprooted Oak Emblem A12

45fr, Refugee family and uprooted oak emblem.

1960, Apr. 7 Unwmk. *Perf. 13*

36	A12	15fr ocher, blk & grn	.16	.15
37	A12	45fr blk & grn	.28	.20

World Refugee Year, July 1, 1959-June 30, 1960.

Marrakesh A13

1960, Apr. 25 Engr. *Perf. 13*

38	A13	100fr grn, bl & red brn	.55	.40

900th anniversary of Marrakesh.

Lamp — A14

Wrestlers — A16

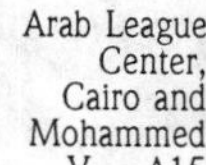

Arab League Center, Cairo and Mohammed V — A15

Designs: 25fr, Fountain and arched door. 30fr, Minaret. 35fr, Ornamented wall. 45fr, Moorish architecture.

1960, May 12 *Perf. 13 1/2*

39	A14	15fr rose lil	.25	.22
40	A14	25fr dk bl	.30	.25
41	A14	30fr org red	.55	.40
42	A14	35fr black	.70	.50
43	A14	45fr yel grn	1.00	.70
		Nos. 39-43 (5)	2.80	2.07

1,100th anniv. of Karaouiyne University, Fez.

1960, June 28 Photo. *Perf. 12 1/2*

44	A15	15fr grn & blk	.15	.15

Opening of the Arab League Center and the Arab Postal Museum, Cairo.

1960, Sept. 26 Engr. *Perf. 13*

Sports: 10fr, Gymnast. 15fr, Bicyclist. 20fr, Weight lifter. 30fr, Runner. 40fr, Boxers. 45fr, Sailboat. 70fr, Fencers.

45	A16	5fr ol, vio bl & plum	.15	.15
46	A16	10fr org brn, bl & brn	.15	.15
47	A16	15fr emer, bl & org brn	.15	.15
48	A16	20fr ultra, ol & brn	.20	.16
49	A16	30fr vio bl, mar & sep	.25	.20
50	A16	40fr grnsh bl, dk pur & red brn	.40	.20
51	A16	45fr grn, plum & ultra	.45	.25
52	A16	70fr dk brn, bl & gray	.70	.30
		Nos. 45-52 (8)	2.45	1.56

17th Olympic Games, Rome, Aug. 25-Sept. 11.

Runner A17

1961, Aug. 30 Unwmk. *Perf. 13*

53	A17	20fr dk grn	.15	.15
54	A17	30fr dk car rose	.25	.15
55	A17	50fr brt bl	.32	.25
		Nos. 53-55 (3)	.72	.55

3rd Pan-Arabic Games, Casablanca.

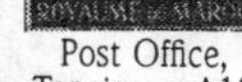
Post Office, Tangier — A18

View of Tangier and Gibraltar — A19

Design: 30fr, Telephone operator.

1961, Dec. 8 Litho. *Perf. 12 1/2*

56	A18	20fr red vio	.20	.16
57	A18	30fr green	.25	.20
57A	A19	90fr lt bl & vio bl	.50	.32
		Nos. 56-57A (3)	.95	.68

Conference of the African Postal and Telecommunications Union, Tangier.

Mohammed V and Map of Africa — A20

Patrice Lumumba and Map of Congo — A21

1962, Jan. 4 Unwmk. *Perf. 11 1/2*

58	A20	20c buff & vio brn	.15	.15
59	A20	30c lt & dk bl	.20	.15
		Set value		.22

1st anniv. of the conference of African heads of state at Casablanca.

1962, Feb. 12 *Perf. 12 1/2*

60	A21	20c bis & blk	.15	.15
61	A21	30c dl red brn & blk	.20	.16
		Set value		.25

1st death anniv. of Patrice Lumumba, Premier of Congo Democratic Republic.

Moroccan Students — A22

Arab League Building, Cairo — A23

1962, Mar. 5 Engr.

62	A22	20fr multi	.20	.15
63	A22	30fr multi	.25	.20
64	A22	90fr gray grn, indigo & brn	.45	.32
		Nos. 62-64 (3)	.90	.67

Issued to honor the nation's students.

1962, Mar. 22 Photo. *Perf. 13 1/2x13*

65	A23	20c red brn	.38	.15

Arab Propaganda Week, 3/22-28. See #146.

Malaria Eradication Emblem and Swamp — A24

Design: 50c, Dagger stabbing mosquito, vert.

1962, Sept. 3 Engr. *Perf. 13*

66	A24	20c dk grn & grnsh blk	.15	.15
67	A24	50c dk grn & mag	.25	.15
		Set value		.22

WHO drive to eradicate malaria.

Fish and Aquarium — A25

1962, Nov. 5 Unwmk. *Perf. 13*

68	A25	20c shown	.25	.16
69	A25	30c Moray eel	.25	.16

Casablanca Aquarium.

Courier and Sherifian Stamp of 1912 — A26

Designs: 30c, Courier on foot and round Sherifian cancellation. 50c, Sultan Hassan I and octagonal cancellation.

1962, Dec. 15 **Unwmk.**

70 A26 20c Prus grn & redsh brn .30 .20
71 A26 30c dk car rose & blk .40 .22
72 A26 50c bl & bister .65 .30
Nos. 70-72 (3) 1.35 .72

Stamp Day; 1st National Stamp Exhibition, Dec. 15-23; 75th anniv. of the Sherifian Post and the 50th anniv. of its reorganization.

Boy Scout — A27

King Hassan II — A28

1962, Aug. 8 **Litho.** ***Perf. 11½***

73 A27 20c vio brn & lt bl .15 .15

5th Arab Boy Scout Jamboree, Rabat.

1962 **Engr.** ***Perf. 13½x13***

75 A28 1c gray olive .15 .15
76 A28 2c violet .15 .15
77 A28 5c black .15 .15
78 A28 10c brn org .15 .15
79 A28 15c Prus grn .15 .15
80 A28 20c purple .16 .15
81 A28 30c dp yel grn .20 .15
82 A28 50c vio brn .40 .15
83 A28 70c deep blue .65 .15
84 A28 80c magenta 1.00 .16
Set value 2.70 .60

"Mazelin" (designer-engraver) reads down on Nos. 75-84. See Nos. 110-114.

King Moulay Ismail — A29

Al Idrissi, Geographer — A30

1963, Mar. 3 ***Perf. 12½***

85 A29 20c sepia .25 .16

Tercentenary of Meknes as Ismaili capital.

1963-66 **Engr.**

Portraits: Nos. 87, 88A, Ibn Batota, explorer. No. 88, Ibn Khaldoun, historian and sociologist.

86 A30 20c dk sl grn .25 .15
87 A30 20c dk car rose .25 .15
88 A30 20c black .25 .15
88A A30 40c dk vio bl ('66) .25 .15
Nos. 86-88A (4) 1.00 .60

Famous medieval men of Morocco (Maghreb). No. 88A also marks the inauguration of the ferry-boat "Ibn Batota" connecting Tangier and Malaga.
Issued: #86-88, 5/7/63; #88A, 7/15/66.

Sugar Beet and Sugar Refinery, Sidi Slimane A31

1963, June 10 **Unwmk.** ***Perf. 13***

89 A31 20c shown .20 .15
90 A31 50c Tuna fisherman, vert. .32 .22

FAO "Freedom from Hunger" campaign.

Heads of Ramses II, Abu Simbel — A32

Designs: 30c, Isis, Kalabsha Temple, vert. 50c, Temple of Philae.

1963, July 15 **Engr.** ***Perf. 11½***

91 A32 20c black .15 .15
92 A32 30c vio, *grysh* .20 .16
93 A32 50c maroon, *buff* .30 .22
Nos. 91-93 (3) .65 .53

Campaign to save historic monuments in Nubia.

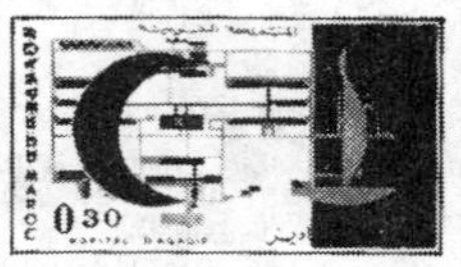

Agadir Before Earthquake A33

Designs: 30c, Like 20c, with "29 Février 1960" and crossed bars added. 50c, Agadir rebuilt.

Engr.; Engr. & Photo. (No. 95)

1963, Oct. 10 ***Perf. 13½x13***

94 A33 20c bl & brn red .22 .20
95 A33 30c bl, brn red & red .30 .22
96 A33 50c bl & brn red .80 .32
Nos. 94-96 (3) 1.32 .74

Issued to publicize the rebuilding of Agadir.

Centenary Emblem and Plan of Agadir Hospital A34

1963, Oct. 28 **Photo.** ***Perf. 12½x13***

97 A34 30c blk, dp car & sil .20 .16

Centenary of the International Red Cross.

Arms of Morocco and Rabat — A35

Flag — A37

Hands Breaking Chain — A36

1963, Nov. 18 ***Perf. 13x12½***

98 A35 20c gold, red, blk & emer .16 .16

Installation of Parliament.

1963, Dec. 10 **Engr.** ***Perf. 13***

99 A36 20c dk brn, grn & org .20 .16

15th anniversary of the Universal Declaration of Human Rights.

1963, Dec. 25 **Photo.** ***Perf. 13x12½***

100 A37 20c blk, dp car & grn .20 .16

Evacuation of all foreign military forces from Moroccan territory.

Moulay Abd-er-Rahman, by Delacroix — A38

1964, Mar. 3 **Engr.** ***Perf. 12x13***

101 A38 1d multi 1.50 1.00

Coronation of King Hassan II, 3rd anniv.

Weather Map of Africa and UN Emblem — A39

Children on Vacation — A40

30c, World map and barometer trace, horiz.

1964, Mar. 23 **Photo.** ***Perf. 11½***

Granite Paper

102 A39 20c multi .20 .16
103 A39 30c multi .25 .20

UN 4th World Meteorological Day. See No. C10.

1964, July 6 **Litho.** ***Perf. 12½***

Design: 30c, Heads of boy and girl, buildings.

104 A40 20c multi .20 .16
105 A40 30c multi .25 .22

Issued for vacation camps for children of P.T.T. employees.

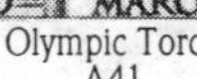

Olympic Torch A41

Cape Spartel Lighthouse, Sultan Mohammed ben Abd-er-Rahman A42

1964, Sept. 22 **Engr.** ***Perf. 13***

106 A41 20c car lake, dk pur & grn .25 .16
107 A41 30c bl, dk grn & red brn .38 .20
108 A41 50c grn, red & brn .50 .25
Nos. 106-108 (3) 1.13 .61

18th Olympic Games, Tokyo, Oct. 10-25.

Perf. 12½x11½

1964, Oct. 15 **Photo.**

109 A42 25c multi .20 .16

Centenary of the Cape Spartel lighthouse.

King Type of 1962

1964-65 **Engr.** ***Perf. 12½x13***

Size: 17x23mm

110 A28 20c purple (redrawn) .38 .25

Perf. 13½x13

Size: 18x22mm

111 A28 25c rose red ('65) .22 .15
112 A28 35c slate ('65) .35 .15
113 A28 40c ultra ('65) .38 .15
114 A28 60c red lilac ('65) .55 .15
Nos. 110-114 (5) 1.88
Set value .45

The Arabic inscription touches the frame on No. 110. "Mazelin" (designer-engraver) reads up on No. 110, down on Nos. 111-114. No. 110 is a coil stamp with red control numbers on the back of some copies.

Iris — A43

Mohammed V Arriving by Plane — A44

1965 **Photo.** ***Perf. 11½***

Granite Paper

115 A43 25c shown .45 .30
116 A43 40c Gladiolus segetum .50 .38
117 A43 60c Capparis spinosa, horiz. .85 .65
Nos. 115-117 (3) 1.80 1.33

Printed in sheets of 10. Five tête-bêche pairs in every sheet; vertical stamps arranged 5x2, horizontal stamps 2x5.
See Nos. 129-131.

1965, Mar. 15 **Litho.** ***Perf. 12½***

118 A44 25c lt bl & dk grn .20 .15

10th anniv. of the return of King Mohammed V from exile and the restoration of the monarchy.

ITU Emblem, Punched-Tape Writer and Telegraph Wires — A45

Design: 40c, ITU emblem, Syncom satellite, radio waves and "ITU" in Morse code.

Perf. 13x14

1965, May 17 **Unwmk.** **Typo.**

119 A45 25c multi .16 .16
120 A45 40c lt bl, dp bl & bis .25 .20

ITU, centenary.

ICY Emblem A46

1965, June 14 **Engr.** ***Perf. 13***

121 A46 25c slate grn .16 .15
122 A46 60c dk car rose .25 .15
Set value .22

International Cooperation Year.

Triton Shell — A47

Designs: No. 124, Varnish shell (pitaria chione). No. 125, Great voluted shell (cymbium neptuni). No. 126, Helmet crab, vert. 40c, Mantis shrimp, vert. 1d, Royal prawn.

1965 **Photo.** ***Perf. 11½***

Granite Paper

123 A47 25c vio & multi .38 .15
124 A47 25c lt bl & multi .38 .15
125 A47 25c org & multi .38 .16
126 A47 25c lt grn & multi .38 .25
127 A47 40c bl & multi .75 .45
128 A47 1d yel & multi 1.00 .65
Nos. 123-128 (6) 3.27 1.81

Printed in sheets of 10. Nos. 126-127 (5x2); others (2x5). Five tête bêche pairs in every sheet.

Flower Type of 1965

Orchids: 25c, Ophrys speculum. 40c, Ophrys fusca. 60c, Ophrys tenthredinifera (front and side view), horiz.

1965, Dec. 13 Photo. *Perf. 11½*
Granite Paper

129 A43 25c yel & multi .25 .22
130 A43 40c dl rose & multi .38 .22
131 A43 60c lt bl & multi .75 .55
Nos. 129-131 (3) 1.38 .99

Note on tête bêche pairs after No. 117 also applies to Nos. 129-131.

Grain — A48

40c, Various citrus fruit. 60c, Olives, horiz.

1966 Photo. *Perf. 11½*
Granite Paper

133 A48 25c blk & bisTER .15 .15
136 A48 40c multi .20 .16
137 A48 60c gray & multi .25 .15
Nos. 133-137 (3) .60
Set value .35

For surcharge see No. 231.

Flag, Map and Dove — A49

1966, Mar. 2 Typo. *Perf. 14x13*
139 A49 25c brt grn & red .15 .15

Tenth anniversary of Independence.

King Hassan II — A50

1966, Mar. 2 Engr. *Perf. 13*
140 A50 25c red, brt grn & indigo .15 .15

Coronation of King Hassan II, 5th anniv.

Cross-country Runner A51

1966, Mar. 20 Engr. *Perf. 13*
141 A51 25c blue green .16 .15

53rd International Cross-country Race.

WHO Headquarters from West — A52

Design: 40c, WHO Headquarters from the East.

1966, May 3 Engr. *Perf. 13*
142 A52 25c rose lil & blk .15 .15
143 A52 40c dp bl & blk .20 .15

Inauguration of the WHO Headquarters, Geneva.

Crown Prince Hassan Kissing Hand of King Mohammed V — A53

Design: 25c, King Hassan II and parachutist.

Perf. 12½x12
1966, May 14 Photo. Unwmk.

144 A53 25c gold & blk .30 .22
145 A53 40c gold & blk .30 .22
a. Strip of 2, #144-145 + label .65 .50

10th anniv. of the Royal Armed Forces.

Type of 1962 Inscribed: "SEMAINE DE LA PALESTINE"

1966, May 16 *Perf. 11x11½*
146 A23 25c slate blue .15 .15

Issued for Palestine Week.

Train — A54

1966, Dec. 19 Photo. *Perf. 13½*
147 A54 25c shown .22 .16
148 A54 40c Ship .30 .20
149 A54 1d Autobus .38 .25
Nos. 147-149 (3) .90 .61

Twaite Shad — A55

Fish: 40c, Plain bonito. 1d, Bluefish, vert.

1967, Feb. 1 Photo. *Perf. 11½*
Granite Paper

150 A55 25c yel & multi .38 .15
151 A55 40c yel & multi .50 .22
152 A55 1d lt grn & multi 1.00 .55
Nos. 150-152 (3) 1.88 .92

Printed tête bêche in sheets of 10. Nos. 150-151 (2x5); No. 152 (5x2).

Ait Aadel Dam A56

1967, Mar. 3 Engr. *Perf. 13*
153 A56 25c sl grn, Prus bl & gray .20 .16
154 A56 40c Prus bl & lt brn .28 .16

Inauguration of Ait Aadel Dam.

Rabat Hilton Hotel, Map of Morocco and Roman Arch — A57

1967, Mar. 3
155 A57 25c brt bl & blk .20 .16
156 A57 1d brt bl & pur .38 .16

Opening of the Rabat Hilton Hotel.

Torch, Globe, Town and Lions Emblem — A58

1967, Apr. 22 Photo. *Perf. 12½*
157 A58 40c gold & saph bl .22 .16
158 A58 1d gold & slate grn .45 .25

Lions International, 50th anniversary.

Three Hands Holding Pickax — A59

1967, July 9 Engr. *Perf. 13*
159 A59 25c slate green .15 .15

Community Development Campaign.

Intl. Tourism Year Emblem A60

1967, Aug. 9 Photo. *Perf. 12½*
160 A60 1d lt ultra & dk bl .38 .25

Arrow and Map of Mediterranean — A61

1967, Sept. 8 *Perf. 13x12*
161 A61 25c dk bl, ultra, red & tan .16 .15
162 A61 40c blk, bl grn, red & tan .20 .15
Set value .24

Mediterranean Games, Tunis, Sept. 8-17.

Steeplechase A62

1967, Oct. 14 Photo. *Perf. 12½*
163 A62 40c yel grn, blk & brt rose lilac .22 .15
164 A62 1d lt ultra, blk & brt rose lilac .32 .22

International Horseshow.

Cotton — A63

Human Rights Flame — A64

1967, Nov. 15 Photo. *Perf. 12½*
165 A63 40c lt bl, grn & yel .22 .15

1968, Jan. 10 Engr. *Perf. 13*
166 A64 25c gray .15 .15
167 A64 1d rose claret .22 .20

International Human Rights Year.

King Hassan II — A65

1968-74 Litho. *Perf. 13*
Portrait in Magenta, Brown and Black
Size: 23x30mm

169 A65 1c cream & blk .15 .15
170 A65 2c lt grnsh bl & blk .15 .15
171 A65 5c lt ol grn & blk .15 .15
172 A65 10c pale rose & blk .15 .15
173 A65 15c gray bl & blk .15 .15
174 A65 20c pink & blk .15 .15
175 A65 25c white & blk .18 .15
176 A65 30c pale rose & blk .20 .15
177 A65 35c bl & blk .22 .25
178 A65 40c gray & blk .22 .15
179 A65 50c lt bl & blk .32 .15
180 A65 60c salmon & blk .85 .15
181 A65 70c gray & blk 2.00 .50
182 A65 75c pale yel ('74) .50 .25
183 A65 80c ocher & blk 1.00 .15

Perf. 13½x14
Size: 26x40mm

184 A65 90c lt bl grn & blk .65 .35
185 A65 1d tan & blk .85 .15
186 A65 2d lt ultra & blk 1.90 .25
187 A65 3d bluish lil & blk 2.75 .45
188 A65 5d apple grn & blk 3.75 1.50
Nos. 169-188 (20) 16.29
Set value 4.40

For overprints & surcharges see #224, B17-B18.

Nurse and Child — A66

Pendant — A67

1968, Apr. 8 Engr. *Perf. 13*
189 A66 25c ultra, red & olive .15 .15
190 A66 40c slate, red & olive .16 .15
Set value .18

WHO, 20th anniv.

1968, May 15 Photo. *Perf. 11½*
191 A67 25c shown .38 .20
192 A67 40c Bracelet .50 .25
a. Pair, #191-192, vertically tête-bêche .90 .90

Moroccan Red Crescent Society.
See Nos. 373-374.

Map of Morocco and Rotary Emblem — A68

1968, May 23 *Perf. 13*
193 A68 40c multi .30 .15
194 A68 1d ultra & multi .45 .22

Rotary Intl. District Conference, Casablanca, May 24-25.

The first value column gives the catalogue value of an unused stamp, the second that of a used stamp.

Ornamental Design — A69

Designs: Various patterns used for sashes.

1968, July 12 Photo. *Perf. 11½*

195 A69 25c multi		.90	.40
196 A69 40c multi		1.10	.50
197 A69 60c multi		1.75	.85
198 A69 1d multi		3.00	1.65
	Nos. 195-198 (4)	6.75	3.40

Berber (Riff), North Morocco — A70

Princess Lalla Meryem — A71

Regional Costumes: 10c, Man from Ait Moussa ou Ali. 15c, Woman from Ait Mouhad. No. 200, Bargeman from Rabat Salé. No. 201, Citadin man. 40c, Citadin woman. 60c, Royal Mokhazni. No. 204, Zemmours man. No. 204A, Man from Meknassa. No. 206, Msouffa woman, Sahara.

1968-74 Litho. *Perf. 13x12½*

198A A70 10c multi ('69)		.45	.32
199 A70 15c yel & multi ('69)		.75	.40
200 A70 25c bis & multi		.75	.45
201 A70 25c tan & multi ('69)		.85	.45
202 A70 40c lt bl & multi		.90	.65
203 A70 60c emer & multi		1.25	.85
204 A70 1d lt bl & multi		1.65	1.10
204A A70 1d gray & multi ('69)		1.50	.75

Perf. 15

205 A70 1d bis & multi		1.40	.90
206 A70 1d grn & multi		1.40	.90
a. Souvenir sheet of 10, #198A-206, perf. 13		13.75	12.50
b. As "a," with red overprint & surcharge		15.00	15.00
	Nos. 198A-206 (10)	10.90	6.77

No. 206a issued June 30, 1970, for the opening of the National P.T.T. Museum, Rabat. Sold for 10d.

No. 206b issued Nov. 22, 1974, for the 8th Cong. of the Intl. Fed. of Blood Donors. Each stamp overprinted vertically "8eme Congres de la F.I.O.D.S." and blood container emblem. Black marginal inscription partially obliterated with lines, new Arabic inscription and price added. Sold for 20d.

1968, Oct. 7 Litho. *Perf. 13½*

Children's Week: 40c, Princess Lalla Asmaa. 1d, Crown Prince Sidi Mohammed.

207 A71 25c red & multi		.30	.15
208 A71 40c yel & multi		.38	.22
209 A71 1d lt bl & multi		.50	.38
	Nos. 207-209 (3)	1.18	.75

Wrestling, Aztec Calendar Stone and Olympic Rings — A72

1968, Oct. 25 Photo. *Perf. 12x11½*

210 A72 15c shown		.15	.15
211 A72 20c Basketball		.15	.15
212 A72 25c Cycling		.22	.20
213 A72 40c Boxing		.25	.16
214 A72 60c Running		.32	.20
215 A72 1d Soccer		.50	.30
	Nos. 210-215 (6)	1.59	1.16

19th Olympic Games, Mexico City, Oct. 12-27.

10 Dirham Coin of Tetuan, 1780 — A73

Women from Zagora — A74

Coins: 25c, Dirham, Agmat, c. 1138 A.D. 40c, Dirham, El Alya (Fes), c. 840 A.D. 60c, Dirham, Marrakesh, c. 1248 A.D.

1968, Dec. 17 Photo. *Perf. 11½*
Granite Paper

216 A73 20c dp plum, sil & blk		.22	.15
217 A73 25c dk rose brn, gold & blk		.32	.22
218 A73 40c dk grn, sil & blk		.55	.30
219 A73 60c dk red, gold & blk		.75	.45
	Nos. 216-219,C16-C17 (6)	10.09	6.37

1969, Jan. 21 Litho. *Perf. 12*

Design: 25c, Women from Ait Adidou.

220 A74 15c multi		.55	.30
221 A74 25c multi		.75	.45
	Nos. 220-221,C15 (3)	2.50	1.30

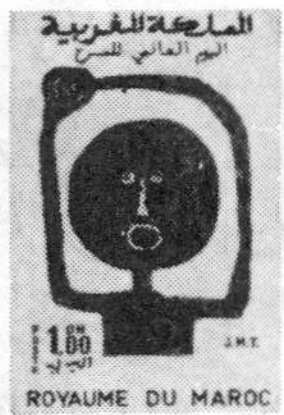
Painting by Belkahya — A75

King Hassan II — A76

1969, Mar. 27 Litho. *Perf. 11½x12*

222 A75 1d lt grnsh bl, blk & brn		.32	.16

International Day of the Theater.

1969, July 9 Photo. *Perf. 11½*

223 A76 1d gold & multi		.55	.22

40th birthday of King Hassan II. A souvenir sheet contains one of No. 223. Size: 75x105mm. Sold for 2.50d.

No. 185 Overprinted

مؤتمر القمة الاسلامي
الرباط ١٠ رجب 1389

1969, Sept. 22 Litho. *Perf. 13*

224 A65 1d tan & multi		2.25	1.90

First Arab Summit Conference, Rabat.

Mahatma Gandhi — A77

1969, Oct. 16 Photo. *Perf. 11½*

225 A77 40c pale vio, blk & gray		.50	.25

Mohandas K. Gandhi (1869-1948), leader in India's struggle for independence.

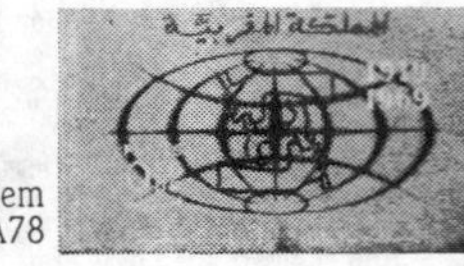
ILO Emblem A78

1969, Oct. 29

226 A78 50c multi		.38	.20

ILO, 50th anniv.

King Hassan II on Way to Prayer — A79

1969, Nov. 20 Photo. *Perf. 11½*

227 A79 1d multi		.50	.25

1st Arab Summit Conference, Rabat, Sept. 1969. For overprint see No. 311.

Spahi Horsemen, by Haram al Glaoui A80

1970, Jan. 23 Engr. *Perf. 12x13*

228 A80 1d multi		.50	.25

Main Sewer, Fez — A81

Guedra Dance, by P. C. Beaubrun — A82

1970, Mar. 23 Litho. *Perf. 12*

229 A81 60c multi		.28	.15

50th Congress of Municipal Engineers, Rabat, Mar. 1970.

1970, Apr. 15

230 A82 40c multi		.38	.20

Folklore Festival, Marrakesh, May 1970.

No. 137 Overprinted "1970", "Census" in Arabic in Red and Surcharged in Black

1970 حصاء

0,25

1970, July 9 Photo. *Perf. 11½*

231 A48 25c on 60c multi		.50	.30

Issued to publicize the 1970 census.

Radar Station at Souk El Arba des Sehoul, and Satellite — A83

Ruddy Shelduck — A84

1970, Aug. 20

232 A83 1d lt ultra & multi		.50	.30

Revolution of King and People, 17th anniv.

1970, Sept. 25 Photo. *Perf. 11½*

233 A84 25c shown		.42	.22
234 A84 40c Houbara bustard		.55	.30

Campaign to save Moroccan wildlife.

Man Reading Book, Intl. Education Year Emblem — A85

1970, Oct. 20 Litho. *Perf. 12x11½*

235 A85 60c dl yel & multi		.50	.25

Symbols of Peace, Justice and Progress — A86

1970, Oct. 27 *Perf. 13½*

236 A86 50c multi		.38	.25

United Nations, 25th anniversary.

Arab League Countries and Emblem — A87

1970, Nov. 13 Photo. *Perf. 11½*

237 A87 50c multi		.38	.25

Arab League, 25th anniversary.

Olive Grove, Tree and Branch — A88

1970, Dec. 3 Litho. *Perf. 12*

238 A88 50c red brn & grn		.45	.28

International Olive Year.

Es Sounna Mosque, Rabat — A89

1971, Jan. 5 Engr. *Perf. 13*

239 A89 60c ol bis, bl & sl grn		.40	.22

Restoration of Es Sounna Mosque, Rabat, built in 1785.

Heart and Horse — A90

1971, Feb. 23 Photo. *Perf. 12x12½*
240 A90 50c blk & multi .35 .18

European heart research week, Feb. 21-28.

Dam and Hassan II — A91

1971, Mar. 3 *Perf. 11½*
241 A91 25c multi .35 .15
a. Souv. sheet of 4 1.50 1.50

Accession of King Hassan II, 10th anniv. No. 241a issued Mar. 24. Sold for 2.50d.

Black and White Hands with Dove and Emblem A92

1971, June 16 Photo. *Perf. 13*
242 A92 50c brn & multi .35 .20

Intl. Year against Racial Discrimination.

Children Around the World — A93

Shah Mohammed Riza Pahlavi of Iran — A94

1971, Oct. 4 Litho. *Perf. 13x14*
243 A93 40c emer & multi .32 .15

International Children's Day.

1971, Oct. 11 Photo. *Perf. 11½*
244 A94 1d bl & multi .30 .22

2500th anniv. of the founding of the Persian empire by Cyrus the Great.

Mausoleum of Mohammed V — A95

Designs: 50c, Mausoleum, close-up view, and Mohammed V. 1d, Decorated interior wall, vert.

1971, Nov. 10 Litho. *Perf. 14*
245 A95 25c multi .15 .15
246 A95 50c multi .20 .15
247 A95 1d multi .40 .25
Nos. 245-247 (3) .75 .55

Soccer Ball and Games Emblem A96

1971, Nov. 30 Photo. *Perf. 13x13½*
248 A96 40c shown .22 .20
249 A96 60c Runner .30 .20

Mediterranean Games, Izmir, Turkey, Oct. 6-17.

Arab Postal Union Emblem A97

1971, Dec. 23 Litho. *Perf. 13x12½*
250 A97 25c dk & lt bl & org .15 .15

25th anniv. of the Conference of Sofar, Lebanon, establishing APU.

Sun over Cultivated Sand Dunes — A98

Torch and Book Year Emblem — A99

1971, Dec. 30 Photo. *Perf. 12½*
251 A98 70c blk, bl & yel .22 .15

Sherifian Phosphate Office (fertilizer production and export), 50th anniversary.

1972, Jan. 12 *Perf. 11½*
252 A99 1d silver & multi .25 .15

International Book Year.

National Lottery — A100

Bridge of Sighs — A101

1972, Feb. 7 Photo. *Perf. 13*
253 A100 25c tan, blk & gold .15 .15

Creation of a national lottery.

1972, Feb. 25

Designs: 50c, St. Mark's Basilica and waves, horiz. 1d, Lion of St. Mark.

254 A101 25c multi .15 .15
255 A101 50c red, blk & buff .15 .15
256 A101 1d lt bl & multi .30 .15
Nos. 254-256 (3) .60
Set value .35

UNESCO campaign to save Venice.

Bridge, Road, Map of Africa A102

1972, Apr. 21 *Perf. 13*
257 A102 75c blue & multi .22 .15

2nd African Road Conf., Rabat, Apr. 17-22.

Morocco No. 223 — A103

1972, Apr. 27 *Perf. 11½*
258 A103 1d lt ultra & multi .30 .20

Stamp Day.

The Engagement of Imilchil, by Tayeb Lahlou — A104

1972, May 26 Litho. *Perf. 13x13½*
259 A104 60c blk & multi .38 .22

Folklore Festival, Marrakesh, May 26-June 4.

Map of Africa, Dove and OAU Emblem — A105

1972, June 12 Photo. *Perf. 11½*
260 A105 25c multi .15 .15

9th Summit Conference of Organization for African Unity, Rabat, June 12-15.

Landscape, Environment Emblem A106

1972, July 20 Photo. *Perf. 12½x12*
261 A106 50c bl & multi .20 .15

UN Conference on Human Environment, Stockholm, June 5-16

Olympic Emblems, Running A107

1972, Aug. 29 Photo. *Perf. 13x13½*
262 A107 25c shown .15 .15
263 A107 50c Wrestling .15 .15
264 A107 75c Soccer .25 .20
265 A107 1d Cycling .32 .22
Nos. 262-265 (4) .87
Set value .60

20th Olympic Games, Munich, Aug. 26-Sept. 11.

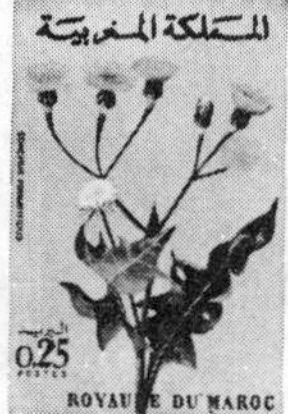
Sow Thistle — A108

Mountain Gazelle — A109

1972, Sept. 15 Litho. *Perf. 14*
266 A108 25c shown .20 .15
267 A108 40c Amberboa crupinoides .25 .20
Set value .28

See No. 305-306.

1972, Sept. 29 Photo. *Perf. 11½*
268 A109 25c shown .22 .20
269 A109 40c Barbary sheep .32 .25

Nos. 266-269 issued for nature protection.

Rabat Rug — A110

Child and UNICEF Emblem — A111

Designs: 25c, High Atlas rug. 70c, Tazenakht rug. 75c, Rabat rug, different pattern.

Perf. 13½ (25fr, 70fr), 11½
1972-73 Photo.
270 A110 25c multi .50 .15
270A A110 50c multi .75 .22
271 A110 70c multi .90 .30
271A A110 75c multi 1.00 .30
Nos. 270-271A (4) 3.15 .97

Issued: 50c, 75c, 10/27; 25c, 70c, 12/28/73.
See Nos. 326-327.

1972, Dec. 20 Photo. *Perf. 13½x13*
272 A111 75c brt grn & bl .22 .15

International Children's Day.

Symbolic Letter Carrier and Stamp — A112

1973, Jan. 30 Photo. *Perf. 13x13½*
273 A112 25c brn & multi .15 .15

Stamp Day.

Weather Map, Northern Hemisphere — A113

1973, Feb. 23 Photo. *Perf. 13*
274 A113 70c silver & multi .25 .16

Intl. meteorological cooperation, cent.

King Hassan II, Coat of Arms — A114

1973-76 Photo. *Perf. 14*
275 A114 1c pale yel & multi .15 .15
276 A114 2c pale bl & multi .15 .15
277 A114 5c pale ol & multi .15 .15
278 A114 10c brn org & multi .15 .15
279 A114 15c vio gray & multi .15 .15
280 A114 20c pink & multi .22 .15
281 A114 25c pale bl & multi .15 .15
282 A114 30c rose & multi .22 .15
283 A114 35c org yel & multi .15 .15
284 A114 40c lt gray & multi 1.50 .25
285 A114 50c ultra & multi .22 .15
286 A114 60c sal & multi .25 .15
287 A114 70c yel grn & multi .20 .15
288 A114 75c lem & multi .38 .15
289 A114 80c multi .25 .20

290 A114 90c brt grn & multi .50 .15
291 A114 1d beige & multi .65 .15
292 A114 2d gray & multi 2.00 .38
293 A114 3d lt lil & multi 2.25 .50
294 A114 5d lt brn & multi ('75) 2.00 .55
294A A114 5d pink & multi ('76) 2.00 .70
Nos. 275-294A (21) 13.69
Set value 3.50

Nos. B26-B27 Surcharged to Obliterate Surtax

مناظرة
الساحة
1973

1973, Mar. 13 *Perf. 11½*
295 SP1 25c multi 1.10 1.10
296 SP1 70c multi 1.10 1.10
a. Pair, #295-296, vertically tête-bêche 2.25 2.25

Tourism Conference 1973. Arabic overprint and date on one line on No. 296.
See Nos. 351-352.

Holy Ka'aba, Mecca, Mosque and Minaret, Rabat A115

1973, May 3 **Photo.** *Perf. 13½x14*
297 A115 25c lt bl & multi .15 .15

Mohammed's 1,403rd birthday.

Roses and M'Gouna A116

1973, May 14 *Perf. 13*
298 A116 25c bl & multi .15 .15

Rose Festival of M'Gouna.

Hands, Torch, OAU Emblem — A117

1973, May 25 **Photo.** *Perf. 14x13*
299 A117 70c deep claret & multi .20 .15

OAU, 10th anniversary.

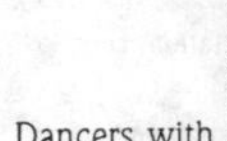

Dancers with Tambourines A118

Design: 1d, Dancer with handbells, Marrakesh Minaret, Atlas Mountain.

1973, May 30 *Perf. 12½x13*
300 A118 50c multi .20 .15
301 A118 1d multi .25 .20

Folklore Festival, Marrakesh.

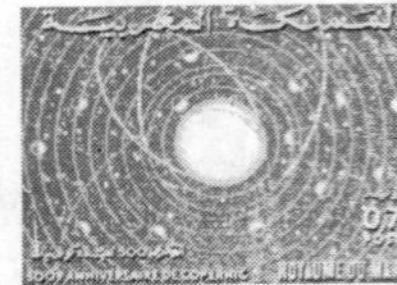

Copernicus A119

1973, June 29 *Perf. 13x13½*
302 A119 70c Heliocentric system .30 .15

Microscope, WHO Emblem, World Map — A120

1973, July 16 **Photo.** *Perf. 13x12½*
303 A120 70c multi .22 .15

WHO, 25th anniversary.

INTERPOL Emblem, Fingerprint A121

1973, Sept. 12 **Photo.** *Perf. 13x13½*
304 A121 70c brn, sil & bl .20 .15

50th anniv. of Intl. Criminal Police Org.

Flower Type of 1972

1973, Oct. 12 **Litho.** *Perf. 14*
305 A108 25c Daisies, horiz. .38 .15
306 A108 1d Thistle .75 .25

Nature protection.

Berber Hyena A122

Design: 50c, Eleonora's falcon, vert.

1973, Nov. 23 **Photo.** *Perf. 14*
307 A122 25c multi .38 .15
308 A122 50c multi .50 .20

Nature protection.

Map and Colors of Morocco, Algeria and Tunisia A123

1973, Dec. 7 *Perf. 13x13½*
309 A123 25c gold & multi .15 .15

Maghreb Committee for Coordination of Posts and Telecommunications.

Fairway and Drive over Water Hazard — A124

Map of Africa, Scales, Human Rights Flame — A125

1974, Feb. 8 **Photo.** *Perf. 14x13*
310 A124 70c multi .30 .20

International Golf Grand Prix for the Hassan II Morocco trophy.

No. 227 Overprinted in Red

المؤتمر الاسلامي - لاهور
1394

1974, Feb. 25 *Perf. 11½*
311 A79 1d multi 1.40 .75

Islamic Conference, Lahore, India, 1974.

1974, Mar. 15 **Photo.** *Perf. 14x13½*
312 A125 70c gold & multi .40 .25

25th anniversary of the Universal Declaration of Human Rights.

Vanadinite — A126

Minaret, Marrakesh Mosque, Rotary Emblem — A127

1974-75 **Photo.** *Perf. 13*
313 A126 25c shown .15 .15
313A A126 50c Aragonite .38 .15
314 A126 70c Erythrine .38 .22
314A A126 1d Agate .75 .16
Nos. 313-314A (4) 1.66 .68

Issued: 25c, 70c, 4/30/74; 50c, 1d, 2/14/75.

1974, May 11 **Photo.** *Perf. 14*
315 A127 70c multi .25 .15

District 173 Rotary International annual meeting, Marrakesh, May 10-12.

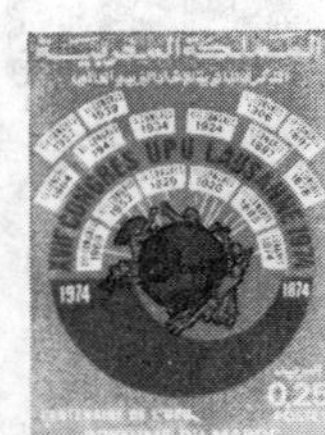

UPU Emblem, Congress Dates — A128

Drummer and Dancers — A129

1d, Scroll with UPU emblem, Lausanne coat of arms & 17th UPU Congress emblem, horiz.

1974, May 30 **Photo.**
316 A128 25c lt grn, org & blk .15 .15
317 A128 1d dk grn & multi .32 .20

Centenary of Universal Postal Union.

1974, June 7 **Photo.** *Perf. 14*

Design: 70c, Knife juggler and women.

318 A129 25c multi .22 .15
319 A129 70c multi .50 .22

National folklore festival, Marrakesh.

Environment Emblem, Polution, Clean Water and Air — A130

1974, June 25 *Perf. 13*
320 A130 25c multi .15 .15

World Environment Day.

Simulated Stamps, Cancel and Magnifier A131

1974, Aug. 2 **Photo.** *Perf. 13*
321 A131 70c sil & multi .22 .15

Stamp Day.

No. J5 Surcharged الاحصاء الفلاحي

1،00

1974, Sept. 25 **Photo.** *Perf. 14*
322 D2 1d on 5c multi .85 .65

Agricultural census.

World Soccer Cup — A132

Double-spurred Francolin — A133

1974, Oct. 11
323 A132 1d brt bl & multi .50 .30

World Cup Soccer Championship, Munich, June 13-July 7.

A stamp similar to No. 323, also issued Oct. 11, has gold inscription: "CHAMPION: R.F.A." in French and Arabic, honoring the German Federal Republic as championship winner. Value $32.50.

Perf. 14x13½, 13½x14

1974, Dec. 5 **Photo.**
324 A133 25c shown .38 .15
325 A133 70c Leopard, horiz. .70 .22

Nature protection.

Zemmour Rug A134

Columbine A135

Design: 1d, Beni Mguilo rug.

1974, Dec 20 *Perf. 13*
326 A134 25c multi .38 .15
327 A134 1d multi .75 .22

See Nos. 349-350, 398-400.

1975 Photo. *Perf. 13½*

No.	Type	Denom.	Design	Unused	Used
328	A135	10c	Daisies	.15	.15
329	A135	25c	Columbine	.20	.15
330	A135	35c	Orange lilies	.22	.15
331	A135	50c	Anemones	.22	.15
332	A135	60c	White starflower	.30	.20
333	A135	70c	Poppies	.32	.22
334	A135	90c	Carnations	.45	.32
335	A135	1d	Pansies	.50	.38
			Nos. 328-335 (8)	2.36	
			Set value		1.50

Issued: 25c, 35c, 70c, 90c, 1/10; others, 4/29.

Water Carrier, by Feu Tayeb Lahlou — A136

1975, Apr. 3 *Perf. 13*

No.	Type	Denom.	Design	Unused	Used
338	A136	1d	multicolored	.65	.30

Stamp Collector, Carrier Pigeon, Globe — A137

Musicians and Dancers — A138

1975, May 21 Photo. *Perf. 13*

No.	Type	Denom.	Design	Unused	Used
339	A137	40c	gold & multi	.15	.15

Stamp Day.

1975, June 12 Photo. *Perf. 14x13½*

No.	Type	Denom.	Design	Unused	Used
340	A138	1d	multicolored	.40	.22

16th Folklore Festival, Marrakesh, 5/30-6/15.

Guitar and Association for the Blind Emblem A139

1975, July 8 *Perf. 13x13½*

No.	Type	Denom.	Design	Unused	Used
341	A139	1d	purple & multi	.38	.15

Week of the Blind.

Animals in Forest — A140

1975, July 25 Photo. *Perf. 13x13½*

No.	Type	Denom.	Design	Unused	Used
342	A140	25c	multicolored	.15	.15

Children's Week.

Games' Emblem, Runner, Weight Lifter — A141

1975, Sept. 4 Photo. *Perf. 13*

No.	Type	Denom.	Design	Unused	Used
343	A141	40c	gold, maroon & buff	.15	.15

7th Mediterranean Games, Algiers, 8/23-9/6.

Bald Ibis A142

1975, Oct. 21 Photo. *Perf. 13*

No.	Type	Denom.	Design	Unused	Used
344	A142	40c	shown	.38	.15
345	A142	1d	Persian lynx, vert.	.55	.30

Nature protection.

King Mohammed V Greeting Crowd, Prince Moulay Hassan at Left — A143

King Hassan II — A144

Design: #348, King Mohammed V wearing fez.

1975, Nov. 21 Photo. *Perf. 13½*

No.	Type	Denom.	Design	Unused	Used
346	A143	40c	blk, sil & dk bl	.20	.15
347	A144	1d	blk, gold & dk bl	.32	.20
348	A144	1d	blk, gold & dk bl	.32	.20
a.			Sheet of 3, #346-348	9.00	9.00

20th anniversary of independence.

Rug Type of 1974

25c, Ouled Besseba. 1d, Ait Ouaouzguid.

1975, Dec. 11

No.	Type	Denom.	Design	Unused	Used
349	A134	25c	red & multi	.38	.25
350	A134	1d	orange & multi	.55	.32

A number of issues have been printed se-tenant in sheets of 10 (5x2) arranged vertically tête bêche.

المسيرة الخضراء
1975

Nos. B29-B30 Surcharged in Green to Obliterate Surtax

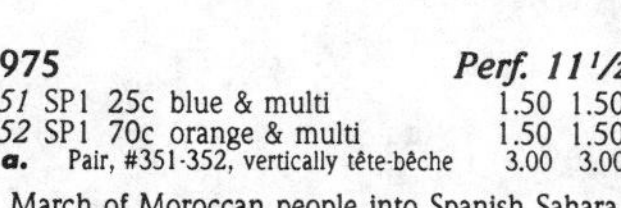

1975 *Perf. 11½*

No.	Type	Denom.	Design	Unused	Used
351	SP1	25c	blue & multi	1.50	1.50
352	SP1	70c	orange & multi	1.50	1.50
a.			Pair, #351-352, vertically tête-bêche	3.00	3.00

March of Moroccan people into Spanish Sahara, Dec. 1975.

"Green March of the People" — A145

Copper Coin, Fez, 1883-84 — A146

1975, Dec. 30 Photo. *Perf. 13½x13*

No.	Type	Denom.	Design	Unused	Used
353	A145	40c	multicolored	.15	.15

March of Moroccan people into Spanish Sahara, Dec. 1975.

1976 Photo. *Perf. 14x13½*

Coins: 15c, 50c, silver coin, Rabat, 1774-75. 35c, 65c, Gold coin, Sabta, 13th-14th centuries. 1d, Square coin, Sabta, 12th-13th centuries.

No.	Type	Denom.	Design	Unused	Used
354	A146	5c	dull rose & multi	.15	.15
355	A146	15c	brown & multi	.15	.15
356	A146	35c	gray & multi	.38	.15
357	A146	40c	ocher & multi	.16	.15
358	A146	50c	ultra & blk	.25	.15
359	A146	65c	yellow & multi	.30	.22
360	A146	1d	multicolored	.40	.25
			Nos. 354-360 (7)	1.79	
			Set value		.98

Issued: #354-356, Apr. 26; #357-360, Jan. 20.

1976, Sept. 9

Designs: Various Moroccan coins.

No.	Type	Denom.	Design	Unused	Used
361	A146	5c	green & multi	.15	.15
362	A146	15c	dp rose & multi	.15	.15
363	A146	20c	lt bl & multi	.18	.15
364	A146	30c	lil rose & multi	.20	.15
365	A146	35c	green & multi	.38	.15
366	A146	70c	orange & multi	.50	.18
			Nos. 361-366 (6)	1.56	
			Set value		.64

See Nos. 403-406A, 524B-524C.

Family — A147

Arch, Ibn Zaidoun Mosque — A148

1976, Feb. 12 *Perf. 14x13½*

No.	Type	Denom.	Design	Unused	Used
367	A147	40c	multicolored	.25	.20

Family planning.

Perf. 13½x14, 14x13½

1976, Feb. 12 Photo.

Design: 40c, Hall, Ibn Zaidoun Mosque, horiz.

No.	Type	Denom.	Design	Unused	Used
368	A148	40c	multicolored	.15	.15
369	A148	65c	multicolored	.25	.20
			Set value		.28

Ibn Zaidoun Mosque, millennium.

Medersa bou Anania, Fez A149

1976, Feb. 26 *Perf. 13x14½*

No.	Type	Denom.	Design	Unused	Used
370	A149	1d	multicolored	.25	.20

Borobudur Temple A150

Design: 40c, Bas-relief, Borobudur.

1976, Mar. 11 Photo. *Perf. 13*

No.	Type	Denom.	Design	Unused	Used
371	A150	40c	multicolored	.15	.15
372	A150	1d	multicolored	.25	.15
			Set value		.24

UNESCO campaign to save Borobudur Temple, Java.

Islamic Conference, 6th Anniv. A151

1976 Litho. *Perf. 13½x13*

No.	Type	Denom.	Design	Unused	Used
372A	A151	1d	Dome of the Rock	3.50	1.25

Jewelry Type of 1968

Designs: 40c, Pendant. 1d, Breastplate.

1976, June 29 Photo. *Perf. 14x13½*

No.	Type	Denom.	Design	Unused	Used
373	A67	40c	blue & multi	.25	.15
374	A67	1d	olive & multi	.38	.20
a.			Pair, #373-374, vertically tête-bêche	.65	.30

Moroccan Red Crescent Society.

Bicentennial Emblem, Flags and Map of US and Morocco — A152

Design: 1d, George Washington, King Hassan, Statue of Liberty and Royal Palace, Rabat, vert.

1976, July 27 Photo. *Perf. 14*

No.	Type	Denom.	Design	Unused	Used
375	A152	40c	multicolored	.20	.15
376	A152	1d	multicolored	.32	.22

American Bicentennial.

Wrestling A153

1976, Aug. 11 *Perf. 13x13½*

No.	Type	Denom.	Design	Unused	Used
377	A153	35c	shown	.15	.15
378	A153	40c	Cycling	.22	.15
379	A153	50c	Boxing	.35	.22
380	A153	1d	Running	.50	.38

21st Olympic Games, Montreal, Canada, July 17-Aug. 1.

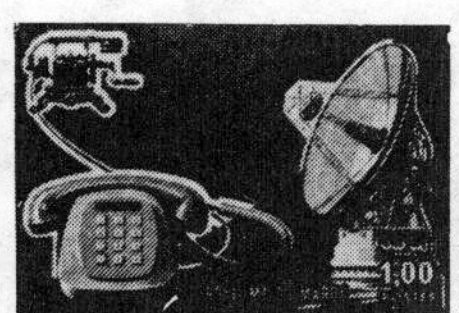

Old and New Telephones, Radar A154

1976, Sept. 29 Photo. *Perf. 14*

No.	Type	Denom.	Design	Unused	Used
381	A154	1d	gold & multi	.30	.15

Centenary of first telephone call by Alexander Graham Bell, Mar. 10, 1876.

Blind Person's Identification A155

1976, Oct. 12 Photo. ***Perf. 13½x14***
382 A155 50c multicolored .16 .15

Week of the Blind.

Chanting Goshawk — A156

1976, Oct. 29 ***Perf. 13x13½***
383 A156 40c shown .45 .15
384 A156 1d Purple gallinule .75 .30

Nature protection.

King Hassan, Star, Torch, Map of Morocco — A157

Africa Cup — A159

Globe and Dove — A158

1976, Nov. 19 Photo. ***Perf. 12½x13***
385 A157 40c multicolored .15 .15

Green March into Spanish Sahara, 1st anniv.

Nos. B34-B35 Overprinted with 2 Bars over Surcharge and 4-line Arabic Inscription

1976, Nov. 29 Photo. ***Perf. 13½***
386 SP1 25c ultra, blk & org .75 .75
387 SP1 70c red, blk & org .90 .90
a. Pair, #386-387, vertically tête-bêche 1.65 1.65

5th African Tuberculosis Conference, Rabat.

1976, Dec. 16 ***Perf. 13***
388 A158 1d blue, blk & red .22 .15

5th Summit Meeting of Non-aligned Countries, Colombo, Aug. 9-19, and 25th anniv. of Org. of Non-aligned Countries.

1976, Dec. 29 Photo. ***Perf. 14***
389 A159 1d multicolored .25 .16

African Soccer Cup.

Letters Circling Globe, Postmark A160

1977, Jan. 24 Photo. ***Perf. 13½***
390 A160 40c multicolored .16 .15

Stamp Day.

Aeonium Arboreum — A161

Malope Trifida — A162

Design: 1d, Hesperolaburnum platyclarpum.

Perf. 13x13½, 14 (A162)

1977, Feb. 22
391 A161 40c multicolored .32 .15
392 A162 50c multicolored .45 .22
393 A161 1d multicolored .55 .22
Nos. 391-393 (3) 1.32 .59

Ornamental Lamps, View of Salé A163

1977, Mar. 24 Photo. ***Perf. 14***
394 A163 40c multicolored .20 .15

Candle procession of Salé.

No. J6 Surcharged in Orange

موسم حب الملوك
1977
0,40

1977, May 11 Photo. ***Perf. 14***
395 D2 40c on 10c multi .32 .20

Cherry Festival.

Map of Arab Countries, Emblem A164

1977, June 2 Photo. ***Perf. 14***
396 A164 50c multicolored .20 .15

5th Congress of Organization of Arab Cities.

APU Emblem, Members' Flags A165

1977, June 20
397 A165 1d multicolored .35 .20

Arab Postal Union, 25th anniversary.

Rug Type of 1974

Designs: 35c, No. 399A, Marmoucha rug, diff. No. 399, Ait Haddou rug. 1d, Salé rug.

Perf. 11½x12, 13½ (#399A)

1977-79 Photo.
398 A134 35c multicolored .25 .15
399 A134 40c multicolored .32 .15
399A A134 40c multicolored .32 .15
400 A134 1d multicolored .45 .22
Nos. 398-400 (4) 1.34
Set value .56

Issued: #399A, 3/8/79; others, 7/21/77.

Cithara — A166

Ali Jinnah and Map of Pakistan — A167

1977, Aug. 18 Photo. ***Perf. 14***
401 A166 1d multi .25 .15

Week of the Blind.

1977, Oct. 10 Photo. ***Perf. 13½x13***
402 A167 70c multi .20 .15

Mohammed Ali Jinnah (1876-1948), first Governor General of Pakistan.

Coin Type of 1976

Designs: Various Moroccan coins.

1977-81 ***Perf. 14x13½***
403 A146 10c gray & multi .15 .15
403A A146 25c ap grn & multi ('81) .15 .15
404 A146 60c dk red & multi ('78) .22 .15
405 A146 75c citron & multi .25 .15
405A A146 80c pale vio & mult ('81) .20 .15
406 A146 2d yel grn & multi .75 .25
406A A146 3d beige & multi ('81) .75 .40
Nos. 403-406A (7) 2.47
Set value 1.00

Marcher with Flag, Map of Morocco and Spanish Sahara — A168

1977, Nov. 6 Photo. ***Perf. 14***
407 A168 1d multi .28 .15

Green March into Spanish Sahara, 2nd anniv.

Chamber of Representatives — A169

1977, Nov. 6 ***Perf. 13½***
408 A169 1d multi .25 .15
a. Souvenir sheet 1.40 1.40

Opening of Chamber of Representatives. No. 408a sold for 3d.

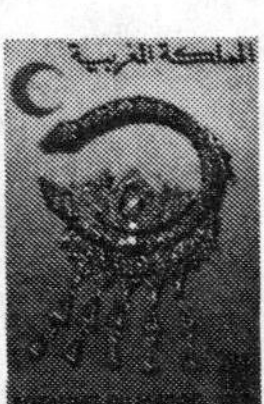

Enameled Silver Brooch — A170

Copper Vessel — A171

1977, Dec. 14 Photo. ***Perf. 11½***
409 A170 1d multi .30 .16

Moroccan Red Crescent Society.

1978, Jan. 5 Photo. ***Perf. 13***

1d, Standing filigree copper bowl with cover.

410 A171 40c gold & multi .25 .15
411 A171 1d gold & multi .45 .20
a. Pair, #410-411, vertically tête-bêche .70 .35
Set value .28

Map of Sahara, Cogwheel Emblem — A172

Covered Jar — A173

1d, Map of North Africa, fish in net, camels.

1978, Feb. 27 Photo. ***Perf. 14***
412 A172 40c multi .15 .15
413 A172 1d multi, horiz .30 .15

Promotion of the Sahara. See Nos. 441-442 for similar stamps overprinted.

1978, Mar. 27 ***Perf. 13½x13***
414 A173 1d shown .38 .22
415 A173 1d Vase .38 .22

Week of the Blind.

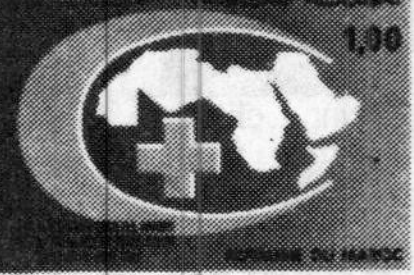

Red Crescent, Red Cross, Arab Countries A174

1978, Apr. 14 ***Perf. 13x13½***
416 A174 1d multi .25 .15

10th Conference of Arab Red Crescent and Red Cross Societies, Apr. 10-15.

View of Fez, Rotary Emblem — A175

1978, Apr. 22 Photo. ***Perf. 14***
417 A175 1d multi .25 .15

Rotary Intl. Meeting, Fez, District 173.

Dome of the Rock, Jerusalem — A176

Folk Dancers and Flutist — A177

1978, May 29 ***Perf. 14½***
418 A176 5c multi .15 .15
419 A176 10c multi .15 .15
Set value .24 .18

Palestinian fighters and their families. For overprints see Nos. 502-502A.

1978, June 15 ***Perf. 13½x13***
420 A177 1d multi .50 .25

National Folklore Festival, Marrakesh.

Sugar Cane Field, and Conveyor Belt
A178

1978, July 24 **Photo.** ***Perf. 13***
421 A178 40c multi .15 .15

Sugar industry.

Games Emblem — A179

Bird, Tree, Tent, Scout Emblem — A180

1978, Aug. 25
422 A179 1d multi .30 .20

World sailing championships.

1978, Sept. 26 **Photo.** ***Perf. 13***
423 A180 40c multi 1.75 .50

Pan-Arab Scout Jamboree, Rabat.

View of Fez
A181

1978, Oct. 10
424 A181 40c multi .15 .15

Moulay Idriss the Great, Festival, Fez.

Flame Emblem — A182

Houses, Agadir — A183

1978, Dec. 21 **Photo.** ***Perf. 14***
425 A182 1d multi .38 .20

30th anniversary of Universal Declaration of Human Rights.

1979, Jan. 25 **Photo.** ***Perf. 12***
426 A183 40c shown .15 .15
427 A183 1d Old Fort, Marrakesh .30 .15

Soccer and Cup
A184

1979, Mar. 2 ***Perf. 13***
428 A184 40c multi .15 .15

Mohammed V Soccer Cup.

Vase — A185

Procession — A186

1979, Mar. 29 **Photo.** ***Perf. 14***
429 A185 1d multi .25 .20

Week of the Blind.

Perf. 13x13½, 13½x13
1979, Apr. 18

1d, Festival, by Mohamed Ben Ali Rbati, horiz.

430 A186 40c multi .15 .15
431 A186 1d multi .30 .20

Brass Containers, Red Crescent
A187

Perf. 13x13½, 13½x13
1979, May 16 **Photo.**
432 A187 40c shown .25 .15
433 A187 1d Heated coffee urn, vert. .50 .20

Red Crescent Society.

Dancers — A188

Silver Dagger — A189

1979, June 1 **Photo.** ***Perf. 13***
434 A188 40c multi .15 .15

National Festival of Marrakech.

1979, June 20 ***Perf. 14***
435 A189 1d multi .30 .15

King Hassan II, 50th Birthday — A190

1979, July 9 **Photo.** ***Perf. 14***
436 A190 1d multi .25 .15

4th Arab Youth Festival, Rabat
A191

1979, July 30 **Photo.** ***Perf. 13½x14***
437 A191 1d multi .25 .15

King Hassan II and Crowd — A192

1979, Aug. 20 ***Perf. 14x13½***
438 A192 1d multi .22 .15

Revolution of the King and the People, 25th anniv.

Intl. Bureau of Education, 50th Anniv. — A193

1979, Sept. 28 **Photo.** ***Perf. 13x13½***
439 A193 1d multi .38 .20

Pilgrimage to Mecca, Mt. Arafat, Holy Ka'aba
A194

1979, Oct. 25 ***Perf. 13½***
440 A194 1d multi .25 .15

No. 413 Redrawn in Smaller Size and Overprinted in Red

استرجاع اقليم وادي الذهب
1979-8-14

1979, Nov. 7 **Litho.** ***Perf. 14***
Size: 33x23mm
441 A172 40c multi .25 .15
442 A172 1d multi .38 .25

Return of Oued Eddahab province, Aug. 14.

Leucanthemum Catanance
A195

Children, Globe, IYC Emblem
A196

1979, Nov. 21 **Photo.** ***Perf. 14½***
443 A195 40c Centaurium .15 .15
444 A195 1d shown .32 .15
Set value .22

1979, Dec. 3 ***Perf. 14***
445 A196 40c multi .65 .25

International Year of the Child.

Otter — A197

Traffic Signs and Road — A198

1979, Dec. 18 ***Perf. 13½x13***
446 A197 40c shown .25 .15
447 A197 1d Redstart .40 .22
Set value .30

1980, Jan. 3 **Photo.** ***Perf. 14***
448 A198 40c shown .15 .15
449 A198 1d Children at curb .20 .15
Set value .16

Fortress
A199

1980, Jan. 29 ***Perf. 13x13½***
450 A199 1d multi .25 .15

Copper Bowl and Lid, Red Crescent — A200

Week of the Blind — A201

Red Crescent Soc.: 70c, Copper kettle, brazier.

1980, Feb. 28 **Photo.** ***Perf. 14***
451 A200 50c multi .20 .15
452 A200 70c multi .28 .15
a. Pair, #451-452, vertically tête-bêche .50 .25

1980, Mar. 19 **Photo.** ***Perf. 14***
453 A201 40c multi .15 .15

Rabat Mechanical Sorting Office
A202

1980, Apr. 17
454 A202 40c multi .15 .15

Stamp Day.

Rotary Intl., 75th Anniv. — A203

Cloth and Leather Goods — A204

1980, May 14 **Photo.** ***Perf. 14***
455 A203 1d multi .22 .15

1980, May 31 **Photo.** ***Perf. 13½x13***
456 A204 1d multi .22 .15

4th Textile and Leather Exhibition, Casablanca, May 2-9.

Set Values
A 15-cent minimum now applies to individual stamps and sets. Where the 15-cent minimum per stamp would increase the value of a set beyond retail, there is a "Set Value" notation giving the retail value of the set.

Gypsum — A205

Falcon — A206

1980, June 19 Photo. ***Perf. 13½x13***
457 A205 40c multi .20 .15

See Nos. 477-478.

1980, July 26 ***Perf. 11½***
458 A206 40c multi .20 .15

Hunting with falcons.

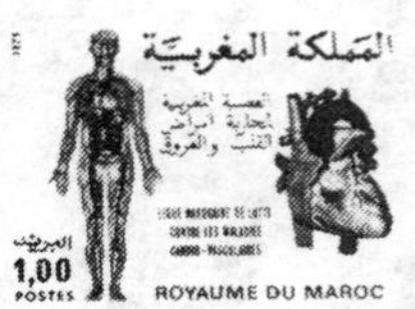

Fight against Heart Disease A207

1980, Aug. 7 Photo. ***Perf. 13x13½***
459 A207 1d multi .30 .15

A208

A210

Ornamental Saddle and Harness — A209

1980, Aug. 18 ***Perf. 14***
460 A208 40c shown .15 .15
461 A208 1d Emblems, diff. .25 .15
Set value .16

United Nations Decade for Women.

1980, Sept. 3 ***Perf. 14½***
462 A209 40c Saddle, harness, diff. .15 .15
463 A209 1d shown .30 .15
Set value .22

1980, Sept. 18
464 A210 40c multi .15 .15

World Meteorological Day.

Hand Holding Dry Gas Pump A211

1980, Oct. 6 Photo. ***Perf. 14***
465 A211 40c Light bulb, gas can .15 .15
466 A211 1d shown .25 .15
Set value .18

Energy conservation.

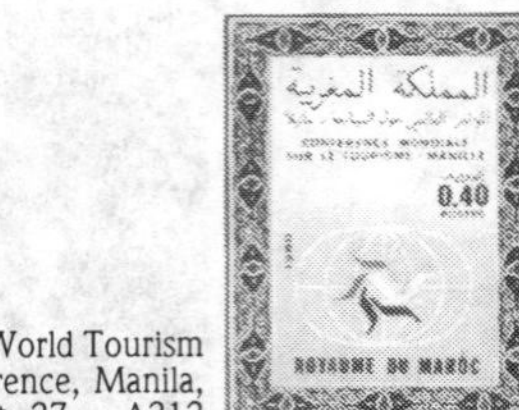

World Tourism Conference, Manila, Sept. 27 — A212

1980, Oct. 22 ***Perf. 11½x12***
467 A212 40c multi .15 .15

Symbolic Tree Rooted in Europe and Africa A213

1980, Oct. 30 ***Perf. 14***
468 A213 1d multi .25 .15

Straits of Gibraltar linking Europe and Africa.

5th Anniversary of the Green March A214

1980, Nov. 6
469 A214 1d multi .22 .15

Holy Ka'aba A215

Senecio Antheuphorbium A216

1980, Nov. 9
470 A215 40c shown .15 .15
471 A215 1d Mecca Mosque .25 .15
a. Souv. sheet of 2, #480-471 1.25
Set value .22

No. 471a sold for 3d.

1980, Dec. 4 ***Perf. 13***
472 A216 50c shown .15 .15
473 A216 1d Periploca laevigata .30 .16
Set value .25

Leaves, by Mahjoubi Aherdan — A217

Nejjarine Fountain, Fes — A218

Design: 40c. Untitled painting by Mahjoubi Aherdan (23x38mm).

1980, Dec. 18 ***Perf. 12***
474 A217 40c multi .15 .15
475 A217 1d multi .25 .15
Set value .22

1981, Jan. 22 ***Perf. 14x13½***
476 A218 40c multi .15 .15

Mineral Type of 1980

1981, Feb. 19 Photo. ***Perf. 13½x13***
477 A205 40c Onyx .16 .15
478 A205 1d Malachite-azurite .35 .20
Set value .28

Inscribed 1980.

King Hassan II — A219

1981, Mar. 2 ***Perf. 14***
479 A219 60c shown .15 .15
480 A219 60c Map of Morocco .15 .15
481 A219 60c King Mohammed V .15 .15
a. Strip of 3, #479-481 .45 .30

25th anniv. of independence.

25th Anniv. of King Hassan II Coronation A220

1981, Mar. 3
482 A220 1.30d multi .30 .20

The Source, by Jillali Gharbaoui — A221

1981, Apr. 8 ***Perf. 13x12½***
483 A221 1.30d multi .30 .20

Anagalis Monelli — A222

Army Badge — A223

1981, Apr. 23 ***Perf. 13***
484 A222 40c shown .15 .15
485 A222 70c Bubonium intricatum .22 .15
Set value .20

1981, May 14 Photo. ***Perf. 14x13½***

Moroccan Armed Forces, 25th Anniv: Nos. 486, 488, King Hassan as army major general.

486 A223 60c Facing right .15 .15
487 A223 60c multi .15 .15
488 A223 60c Facing left .15 .15
a. Strip of 3, #486-488 .45 .30

13th World Telecommunications Day — A224

1981, May 18 ***Perf. 14x13***
489 A224 1.30d multi .25 .16

Hand-painted Plate — A225

22nd Marrakesh Arts Festival — A226

1981, June 5 ***Perf. 14***
490 A225 50c shown .15 .15
491 A225 1.30d Plate, diff. .25 .15
Set value .22

Week of the Blind.

1981, June 18 ***Perf. 13½x13***
492 A226 1.30d multi .30 .20

For overprint see No. 579.

Seboula Dagger, Oujda — A227

Copper Mortar and Pestle, Red Crescent — A228

1981, Sept. 7 Photo. ***Perf. 13½***
493 A227 1.30d multi .25 .16

1981, Sept. 24 ***Perf. 14***
494 A228 60c shown .25 .15
495 A228 1.30d Tripod .40 .16
Set value .25

Intl. Year of the Disabled A229

Iphiclides Feisthamelii A230

1981, Oct. 15 ***Perf. 13½***
496 A229 60c multi .22 .15

1981, Oct. 29 ***Perf. 13½x13***
497 A230 60c shown .20 .15
498 A230 1.30d Zerynthia rumina .40 .22

See Nos. 528-529.

6th Anniv. of Green March — A231

Intl. Palestinian Solidarity Day — A232

1981, Nov. 6 *Perf. 13x13½*
499 A231 1.30d multi .50 .25

1981, Nov. 22 *Perf. 13½x13*
500 A232 60c multi .38 .25

Congress Emblem — A233

1981, Nov. 22 *Perf. 13½*
501 A233 1.30d multi .38 .25

World Federation of Twin Cities, 10th Congress, Casablanca, Nov. 15-18.

Nos. 418-419 Overprinted

مؤتمر القمة العربى
الثانى عشر
فاس 1981

0,40

ROYAUME DU MAROC

1981, Nov. 25 **Photo.** *Perf. 14½*
502 A176 40c on 5c multi 3.00 3.00
502A A176 40c on 10c multi 2.25 2.25

First Anniv. of Mohammed V Airport — A234

King Hassan II — A236

Al Massirah Dam Opening A235

1981, Dec. 8 **Photo.** *Perf. 14x13*
503 A234 1.30d multi .25 .20

1981, Dec. 17 *Perf. 11½*
504 A235 60c multi .15 .15

1981, Dec. 28 *Perf. 13x12½*
505 A236 5c multi .15 .15
506 A236 10c multi .15 .15
507 A236 15c multi .15 .15
508 A236 20c multi .15 .15
509 A236 25c multi .15 .15
510 A236 30c multi .15 .15
511 A236 35c multi .15 .15
512 A236 40c multi .38 .15
513 A236 50c multi .15 .15
514 A236 60c multi .18 .15
515 A236 65c multi .18 .15
516 A236 70c multi .20 .15
517 A236 75c multi .20 .15
518 A236 80c multi .22 .15
519 A236 90c multi .28 .15

1983, Mar. 1 **Photo.** *Perf. 14½*
Size: 25x32mm
520 A236 1d multi .32 .15
521 A236 1.40d multi .38 .15
522 A236 2d multi .45 .15
523 A236 3d multi .65 .20
524 A236 5d multi .85 .40
524A A236 10d multi 1.65 .70
Nos. 505-524A (21) 7.14
Set value 2.40

See Nos. 566-575, 715.

Type of 1976

1979-81 **Photo.** *Perf. 12½*
Size: 18x23mm
524B A146 40c ocher & multi .15 .15
524C A146 50c brt bl, blk & dk brn ('81) .15 .15
d. Bklt. pane of 10 1.25
Set value .20 .15

Equestrian Sports A237

1981, Dec. 29 *Perf. 13x13½*
525 A237 1.30d multi .30 .20

Traditional Carpet Design — A238

1982, Jan. 21
526 A238 50c Glaoua pattern .15 .15
527 A238 1.30d Ouled Besseba pattern .30 .20
Set value .28

Butterfly Type of 1981

1982, Feb. 25 *Perf. 13½x13*
528 A230 60c Celerio oken lineata .15 .15
529 A230 1.30d Mesoacidalia aglaja lyauteyi .32 .22

World Forest Day — A240

Blind Week — A241

1982, Apr. 8 *Perf. 14*
531 A240 40c multi .15 .15

1982, May 10
532 A241 1d Jug .20 .15

Folk Dancers, Rabat — A242

Copper Candlestick, Red Crescent — A243

1982, June 3
533 A242 1.40d multi .25 .16

1982, July 1
534 A243 1.40d multi .25 .16

Women in Traditional Clothing, by M. Mezian — A244

ITU Conf., Nairobi, Sept. — A246

Natl. Census A245

1982, Aug. 16 **Photo.** *Perf. 14*
535 A244 1.40d multi .25 .16

1982, Sept. 6 **Photo.** *Perf. 11½*
536 A245 60c multi .15 .15

1982 *Perf. 13½x13*
537 A246 1.40d multi .25 .15

TB Bacillus Centenary — A247

World Food Day — A248

1982, Sept. 30
538 A247 1.40d multi .25 .15

1982, Oct. 16 *Perf. 14*
539 A248 60c multi .15 .15

Unity Railroad A249

1982, Nov. 6 *Perf. 13x13½*
540 A249 1.40d multi .25 .16

30th Anniv. of Arab Postal Union A250

1982, Nov. 17 *Perf. 14*
541 A250 1.40d multi .25 .15

Intl. Palestinian Solidarity Day — A251

Red Coral, Al-Hoceima — A252

1982, Nov. 29 *Perf. 14*
542 A251 1.40d sil & multi .38 .18

1982, Dec. 20 *Perf. 13½*
543 A252 1.40d multi .25 .15

Stamp Day — A253

Week of the Blind — A254

1983, Jan. 26 *Perf. 13½x13*
544 A253 1.40d Nos. 3, 178 .25 .15

1983, Apr. 20 **Photo.** *Perf. 14*
545 A254 1.40d multi .25 .15

Popular Arts A255

1983, June 27 **Photo.** *Perf. 14*
546 A255 1.40d multi .25 .15

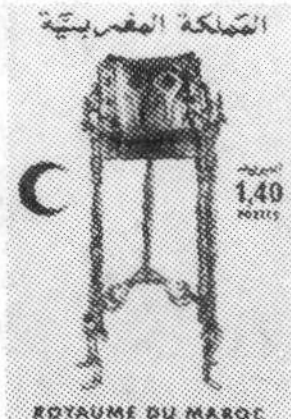
Wrought-Iron Lectern — A256

Moroccan Flora — A258

Economic Commission for Africa, 25th Anniv. A257

1983, July 7 **Litho.** *Perf. 13½*
547 A256 1.40d multi .25 .16

1983, July 18 **Photo.** *Perf. 14*
548 A257 1.40d multi .25 .15

1983, Aug. 1 **Litho.** *Perf. 14*

549 A258 60c Tecoma .15 .15
550 A258 1.40d Strelitzia .25 .15
Set value .34 .22

Kings Mohammed V and Hassan II — A259

1983, Aug. 20 **Litho.** *Perf. 14*

551 A259 80c multi .15 .15
a. Souvenir sheet of 1 .90 .90

King and People's Revolution, 30th Anniv. No. 551a sold for 5 dinars.

Mediterranean Games — A260

Palestinian Solidarity — A262

Touiza A261

1983, Sept. 3 **Photo.** *Perf. 14*

552 A260 80c Stylized sportsmen .15 .15
553 A260 1d Emblem .16 .15
554 A260 2d Stylized runner, horiz. .32 .22
a. Souv. sheet of 3, #552-554, imperf. .90 .90
Nos. 552-554 (3) .63 .52

No. 554a sold for 5d.

1983, Sept. 30 **Photo.** *Perf. 13*

555 A261 80c Tractors .15 .15

1983, Nov. 10 **Photo.** *Perf. 13½x13*

556 A262 80c multi .25 .15

8th Anniv. of the Green March into Spanish Sahara A263

1983, Nov. 17 *Perf. 13x13½*

557 A263 80c multi .15 .15

Ouzoud Waterfall — A264

1983, Nov. 28 *Perf. 14*

558 A264 80c multi .15 .15

Children's Day — A265

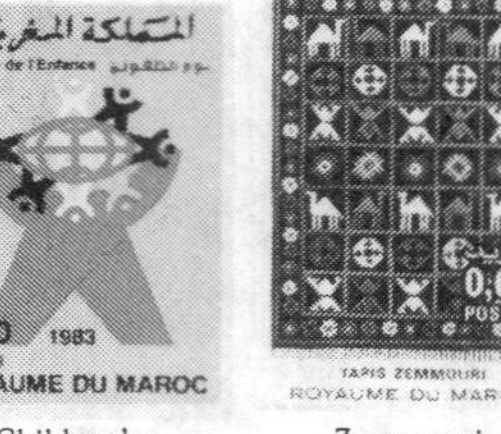

Zemmouri Carpet — A266

1983, Dec. 5 **Photo.** *Perf. 13½x13*

559 A265 2d multi .32 .15

1983, Dec. 15 *Perf. 13½*

Various carpets.

560 A266 60c multi .15 .15
561 A266 1.40d multi .25 .15
Set value .34 .22

World Communications Year — A267

1983, Dec. 20 *Perf. 14*

562 A267 2d multi .32 .15

Twin Cities, Jerusalem and Fez — A268

1984, Jan. 16 **Photo.** *Perf. 13x13½*

563 A268 2d multi .32 .15

Desert Fox — A269

Perf. 11½x12, 12x11½

1984, Feb. 13

564 A269 80c shown .15 .15
565 A269 2d Jumping mouse, vert. .32 .20
Set value .28

King Hassan II Type of 1981

1984-88 **Photo.** *Perf. 14½*

Size: 25x32mm

566	A236	1.20d multi ('88)	.32	.15
567	A236	1.25d multi	.20	.15
568	A236	1.60d multi ('87)	.18	.15
569	A236	2.50d multi ('87)	.28	.15
570	A236	3.60d multi ('88)	1.00	.40
571	A236	4d multi	.65	.25
572	A236	5.20d multi ('88)	1.45	.58
573	A236	6.50d multi ('87)	.70	.28
574	A236	7d multi ('87)	.75	.30
575	A236	8.50d multi ('87)	.90	.35
		Nos. 566-575 (10)	6.43	2.76

Dated 1986: 1.60d, 2.50d, 6.50d, 7d, 8.50d. Issued: 1.20d, 3.60d, 5.20d, Dec. 26, 1988.

39th Anniv. of Arab League A270

1984, May 24 *Perf. 14½x14*

578 A270 2d Emblem .32 .15

No. 492 Overprinted المهرجان 25

1984, June 12 *Perf. 13½x13*

579 A226 1.30d multi .30 .20

25th Anniv. of Marrakesh Arts Festival.

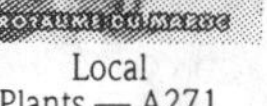
Local Plants — A271

Red Crescent — A273

Week of the Blind — A272

1984, June 13 *Perf. 14*

580 A271 80c Mentha viridis .15 .15
581 A271 2d Aloe .32 .20
Set value .28

See Nos. 602-603.

1984, July 10 *Perf. 13x13½*

582 A272 80c Painted bowl .15 .15

1984, July 16 *Perf. 14*

583 A273 2d Octagonal brass container .32 .20

1984 Summer Olympics — A274

Intl. Child Victims' Day — A275

1984, Aug. 8 *Perf. 13½x13*

584 A274 2d Sports .32 .20

1984, Aug. 22 *Perf. 14*

585 A275 2d Children held by dove .32 .15

UPU Day — A276

World Food Day — A277

1984, Oct. 9 **Photo.** *Perf. 13½*

586 A276 2d multi .50 .25

1984, Oct. 16 *Perf. 14*

587 A277 80c multi .20 .15

Intl. Civil Aviation Org., 40th Anniv. — A278

Green March, 9th Anniv. — A279

1984, Oct. 20 *Perf. 13½*

588 A278 2d multi 1.00 .50

1984, Nov. 6 *Perf. 14*

589 A279 80c Scroll, text .40 .20

Palestinian Solidarity — A281

UN Human Rights Declaration, 36th Anniv. — A282

1984, Nov. 29 *Perf. 13½*

591 A281 2d Arab Revolt flag, 1918-19 1.00 .50

1984, Dec. 10 *Perf. 14*

592 A282 2d multi .65 .35

Native Dogs — A283

UN Child Survival Campaign — A284

1984, Dec. 21 **Photo.** *Perf. 14*

593 A283 80c Aidi .15 .15
594 A283 2d Sloughi .32 .15
Set value .22

1985, Mar. 5 **Photo.** *Perf. 14*

595 A284 80c Growth monitoring .20 .15

1st SOS Children's Village in Morocco — A285

1985, Mar. 11 *Perf. 13x13½*

596 A285 2d multi .50 .25

Sherifian Hand Stamp, 1892 — A287

World Environment Day — A288

1985, Mar. 25 **Photo.** *Perf. 14*
597 A287 2d dl pink, blk & gray .50 .25

Souvenir Sheet
Perf. 13½

598 Sheet of 6 1.25 1.25
a. A287 80c green, black & gray .20 .15
b. A287 80c yellow, black & gray .20 .15
c. A287 80c blue, black & gray .20 .15
d. A287 80c red, black & gray .20 .15
e. A287 80c purple, black & gray .20 .15
f. A287 80c brown, black & gray .20 .15

Stamp Day. #598 sold for 5d.
See #615-616, 633-634, 668-669, 684-685, 701-702, 733-734, 756-757, 790-791, 806-807, 821-822, 835-836.

1985, June 5 *Perf. 13*
599 A288 80c Emblem, ecosystem .20 .15

Susi Dancers from Marrakesh and Kutabia, Minaret — A289

1985, June 7 *Perf. 13x13½*
600 A289 2d multi .50 .25

Folk Arts Festival.

Week of the Blind — A290

Berber Woman — A291

1985, June 24 *Perf. 14*
601 A290 80c Ceramic bowl .20 .15

See type A316.

Flower Type of 1984

1985, July 1
602 A271 80c Bougainvillea .20 .15
603 A271 2d Red hibiscus .50 .25

1985, July 15 *Perf. 14*
604 A291 2d multi .50 .25

Red Crescent Society.

6th Pan-Arab Games — A292

UN, 40th Anniv. — A293

1985 *Perf. 14½x13½*
605 A292 2d Torch, emblem, map .50 .25

1985, Oct. 7 *Perf. 13*
606 A293 2d multi .50 .25

Intl. Youth Year — A294

Green March, 10th Anniv. — A295

1985, Oct. 21
607 A294 2d multi .50 .25

1985, Nov. 6 *Perf. 14½x13½*
608 A295 2d Commemorative medal .50 .25

Palestinian Solidarity — A296

Butterflies — A297

1985, Nov. 29 *Perf. 13½*
609 A296 2d multi .50 .25

1985, Dec. 16 **Photo.** *Perf. 14*
610 A297 80c Euphydryas desfontainii .15 .15
611 A297 2d Colotis evagore .20 .15
Set value .18

Accession of King Hassan II, 25th Anniv. — A298

Perf. 13x13½, 13½x13

1986, Mar. 3 **Litho.**
612 A298 80c Natl. arms, vert. .25 .16
613 A298 2d shown .65 .40
a. Souv. sheet of 2, #612-613, imperf. 1.00 1.00

26th Intl. Military Medicine and Pharmaceutical Congress — A299

1986, Mar. 24 **Photo.** *Perf. 14*
614 A299 2d multi .42 .25

Hand Stamp Type of 1985

Sherifian postal seals of Maghzen-Safi, 1892.

1986, Apr. 7
615 A287 80c orange & blk .18 .15
616 A287 2d green & blk .42 .25

Week of the Blind — A300

1986 World Cup Soccer Championships, Mexico — A301

1986, Apr. 21
617 A300 1d multi .22 .15

1986, May 31 *Perf. 13½*
618 A301 1d Emblems, horiz. .22 .15
619 A301 2d Soccer cup, emblems .42 .25

Red Crescent Soc. — A302

Flowers — A304

Popular Arts A303

1986, June *Perf. 14*
620 A302 2d multi .42 .25

1986, June
621 A303 2d Folk band, dancers .42 .25

1986, July 21 **Photo.** *Perf. 14*
622 A304 1d Warionia saharae .22 .15
623 A304 2d Mandragora autumnalis .42 .25

Intl. Peace Year A305

18th Skydiving Championships A306

1986, Aug. 4 *Perf. 13*
624 A305 2d multi .42 .25

1986, Aug. 18 *Perf. 13½x13*
625 A306 2d multi .42 .25

Horse Week A307

1986, Oct. 10 *Perf. 13*
626 A307 1d multicolored .22 .15

Green March, 11th Anniv. — A308

World Food Day — A309

1986, Nov. 6 **Photo.** *Perf. 14*
627 A308 1d multicolored .22 .15

1986, Nov. 12
628 A309 2d multicolored .42 .25

Aga Khan Architecture Prize — A310

1986, Nov. 24 **Litho.** *Perf. 13*
629 A310 2d multicolored .42 .25

Operation Grain: One Million Hectares — A311

Butterflies — A312

1986, Dec. 8
630 A311 1d multicolored .22 .15

1986, Dec. 22 *Perf. 14*
631 A312 1d Elphinstonia charlonia .22 .15
632 A312 2d Anthocharis belia .42 .25

Hand Stamp Type of 1985

Stamp Day: Sherifian postal seals of Maghzen-Tetouan, 1892.

1987, Jan. 26 **Photo.**
633 A287 1d blue & blk .22 .15
634 A287 2d red & black .42 .25

King Mohammed V, Flag, 1947 A313

1987, Apr. 9 **Photo.** *Perf. 13½x13*
635 A313 1d shown .22 .15
636 A313 1d King Hassan II, 1987 .22 .15
a. Souvenir sheet of 2, Nos. 635-636 .75 .75

Tangiers Conf., 40th anniv. #636a sold for 3d.

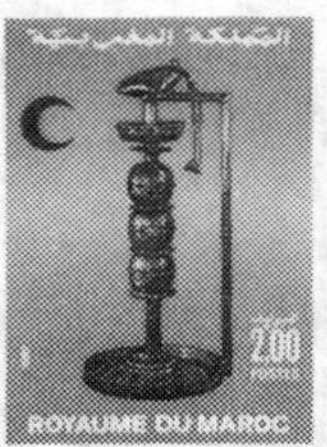
Red Crescent Society — A314

UN Child Survival Campaign — A315

1987, May 1 **Photo.** ***Perf. 14***
637 A314 2d Brass lamp .50 .35

1987, May 25 ***Perf. 12½x13***
638 A315 1d Oral rehydration .25 .18

See Nos. 647, 687.

Week of the Blind — A316

1987, June 8 ***Perf. 14***
639 A316 1d Porcelain cup .25 .18

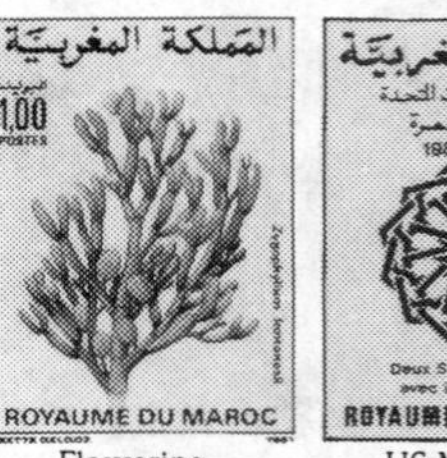
Flowering Plants — A317

US-Morocco Diplomatic Relations, 200th Anniv. — A318

1987, July 6 **Photo.**
640 A317 1d Zygophyllum fontanesii .25 .18
641 A317 2d Otanthus maritimus .50 .35

See Nos. 661-662.

1987, July 22 **Litho & Engr.**
642 A318 1d lt bl, blk & scar .25 .18

See United States No. 2349.

Give Blood — A319

1987, Aug. 20 **Photo.** ***Perf. 13x13½***
643 A319 2d King Hassan II, map .60 .45

Desert Costumes, the Sahara — A320

13th Intl. Cong. on Irrigation and Drainage — A321

1987, Sept. 14 ***Perf. 13***
644 A320 1d Woman from Melhfa .32 .24
645 A320 2d Man from Derraa .65 .48

See Nos. 711-712, 740-741.

1987, Sept. 21
646 A321 1d multi .35 .28

UN Child Survival Type of 1987

1987, Sept. 28
647 A315 1d Universal immunization .35 .28

Congress on Mineral Industries, Marrakesh — A322

Green March, 12th Anniv. — A323

1987, Oct.
648 A322 1d Azurite .32 .24
649 A322 2d Wulfenite .65 .48

See No. 769.

1987, Nov. 6 **Photo.** ***Perf. 14***
650 A323 1d multicolored .30 .22

See Nos. 667, 683, 695, 727, 750, 802, 820, 834.

Royal Armed Forces Social Services Month A324

1987, Nov. 13 ***Perf. 13x12½***
651 A324 1d multicolored .30 .22

Birds — A325

1987, Dec. 1 **Litho.** ***Perf. 14***
652 A325 1d Passer simplex saharae .30 .22
653 A325 2d Alectoris barbara .60 .45

Natl. Postage Stamp 75th Anniv. — A326

Design: Postmark and Sherifian postage stamp (French Morocco) of 1912.

1987, Dec. 31 **Photo.** ***Perf. 14x13½***
654 A326 3d pale lil rose, blk & blue grn .92 .70

Cetiosaurus Mogrebiensis — A327

1988, Jan. 18 **Photo.** ***Perf. 13½***
655 A327 2d multicolored .62 .48

A328

A329

1988, Feb. 16 **Litho.** ***Perf. 14***
656 A328 2d multicolored .62 .45

Intl. Symposium on Mohammed V, Aug. 16-Nov. 20, 1987.

Perf. 14½x13½

1988, Mar. 13 **Photo.**
657 A329 3d multi .85 .75

16th Africa Cup Soccer Championships.

Horse Week A330

1988, Mar. 20 **Litho.** ***Perf. 14***
658 A330 3d multi .85 .75

Intl. Red Cross and Red Crescent Orgs., 125th Annivs. — A331

1988, Apr. 30 **Photo.** ***Perf. 12½x13***
659 A331 3d pink, blk & dark red .85 .65

Week of the Blind — A332

UN Child Survival Campaign — A333

1988, May 25 **Litho.** ***Perf. 14***
660 A332 3d Pottery bottle .85 .65

Flower Type of 1987

1988, June 27 **Litho.** ***Perf. 14***
661 A317 3.60d Citrullus colocynthis .95 .75
662 A317 3.60d Calotropis procera .95 .75

1988, July 18 **Litho.** ***Perf. 12½x13***
663 A333 3d multi .82 .62

1988 Summer Olympics, Seoul — A334

Birds — A335

Perf. 14½x13½

1988, Sept. 19 **Litho.**
664 A334 2d multi .62 .48

1988, Oct. 26 **Litho.** ***Perf. 14***
665 A335 3.60d Grande outarde 1.00 .75
666 A335 3.60d Flamant rose 1.00 .75

Green March Anniv. Type of 1987

1988, Nov. 6
667 A323 2d multi .55 .42

Green March, 13th anniv.

Hand Stamp Type of 1985

Sherifian postal seals of Maghzen-El Jadida, 1892: No. 668, Octagonal. No. 669, Circular.

1988, Nov. 22 **Photo.** ***Perf. 14***
668 A287 3d olive bister & blk .82 .62
669 A287 3d violet & blk .82 .62

Stamp Day.

Housing of the Ksours and Casbahs A336

1989, Jan. 23 ***Perf. 13x13½***
670 A336 2d multi .55 .42

Royal Chess Federation, 25th Anniv. A337

1989, Apr. 17 **Litho.** ***Perf. 14***
671 A337 2d multi .52 .38

Red Crescent Society — A338

Week of the Blind — A339

1989, May 29 **Litho.** ***Perf. 14x13½***
672 A338 2d multi .55 .42

1989, June 12 ***Perf. 14***
673 A339 2d multi .55 .42

A340

A341

1989, July 9 Litho. *Perf. 13x13½*

674 A340 2d multi	.52	.40
675 A340 2d King Hassan II, diff.	.52	.40
a. Souvenir sheet of 2, #674-675, imperf. & embossed	1.30	1.30

King Hassan II, 60th birthday. No. 675a sold for 5d.

1989, Sept. 11 Litho. *Perf. 14*

Flowering plants.

676 A341 2d *Narcissus papyraceus*	.60	.45
677 A341 2d *Cerinthe major*	.60	.45

See Nos. 709-710, 742-743.

World Telecommunications Day — A342

1989, Sept. 25 *Perf. 13x12½*

678 A342 2d multicolored	.60	.45

13th World Congress on Fertility and Sterility — A343

1989, Oct. 6 *Perf. 14*

679 A343 2d multicolored	.60	.45

Birds A344

1989, Oct. 16 *Perf. 14*

680 A344 2d Desert beater	.60	.45
681 A344 3d Gorget lark	.90	.68

Interparliamentary Union, Cent. — A345

1989, Oct. 27

682 A345 2d multicolored	.60	.45

Green March Anniv. Type of 1987

1989, Nov. 6

683 A323 3d multicolored	.90	.68

Green March, 14th anniv.

Hand Stamp Type of 1985

Sherifian postal seals of Maghzen-Casablanca, 1892: 2d, Circular. 3d, Octagonal.

1990, Jan. 15 Photo. *Perf. 14*

684 A287 2d orange & blk	.62	.45
685 A287 3d green & blk	.95	.72

Maghreb Union, 1st Anniv. A346

1990, Feb. 17 *Perf. 13½x14*

686 A346 2d multicolored	.62	.45
a. Souv. sheet of one, perf. 13½	.95	.95

No. 686a sold for 3d.

Child Survival Type of 1987

1990 *Perf. 12½x13*

687 A315 3d Breast feeding	.95	.72

3rd World Olive Day A347

1990, May 14 Litho. *Perf. 14*

688 A347 2d Olive press	.50	.36
689 A347 3d King Hassan II	.75	.55

Week of the Blind A348

1990, May 28 Litho. *Perf. 14*

690 A348 2d multicolored	.70	.52

Red Crescent Society A349

1990, June 11

691 A349 2d multicolored	.50	.36

A350 A353

Birds A351

1990, Sept. 17 Litho. *Perf. 14*

692 A350 3d blk, yel grn & grn	1.10	.82

Intl. Literacy Year

1990, Oct. 26

693 A351 2d Tourterelle, vert.	.70	.52
694 A351 3d Huppe fasciee	1.10	.82

Green March Type of 1987

1990, Nov. 5

695 A323 3d multicolored	1.10	.82

Green March, 15th anniv.

1990, Nov. 18

696 A353 3d multicolored	1.10	.82

Independence, 35th anniv.

Dam A354

1990, Nov. 26

697 A354 3d multicolored	1.10	.82

A355

A357

A356

1990, Dec. 28 Litho. *Perf. 14*

698 A355 3d multicolored	1.00	.75

Royal Academy of Morocco, 10th anniv.

1990, Dec. 31 Litho. *Perf. 13½x13*

Opening of Postal Museum, 20th Anniv.: No. 699, Telegraph machine. No. 700, Horse-drawn mail carriage fording river.

699 A356 2d multicolored	.65	.50
700 A356 3d multicolored	1.00	.75
a. Souv. sheet of 2, #699-700, imperf.	2.15	2.15

No. 700a sold for 6d, has simulated perforations.

Hand Stamp Type of 1985

Sherifian postal seals of Maghzen-Rabat, 1892: 2d, Circular. 3d, Octagonal.

1991, Jan. 25 *Perf. 14*

701 A287 2d ver & blk	.65	.50
702 A287 3d blue & blk	1.00	.75

1991, Feb. 18

703 A357 3d multicolored	1.00	.75

UN Development Program, 40th anniv.

A358

A359

1991, Mar. 3 Litho. *Perf. 14½x13*

704 A358 3d shown	1.00	.75
705 A358 3d Wearing business suit	1.00	.75
a. Souv. sheet of 2, #704-705, imperf.	3.00	2.35

Coronation of King Hassan II, 30th anniv. Nos. 704-705 exist tete beche. No. 705a has simulated perforations and sold for 10d.

1991, Mar. 28 Litho. *Perf. 14*

706 A359 3d multicolored	1.00	.75

Phosphate Mining, 70th anniv.

Week of the Blind — A360

Red Crescent Society — A361

1991, May 15 Photo. *Perf. 14*

707 A360 3d multicolored	1.00	.75

1991, May 27 Litho. *Perf. 14*

708 A361 3d multicolored	.95	.70

Flowering Plants Type of 1989

1991, June 27 Litho. *Perf. 14*

709 A341 3d Pyrus mamorensis	.95	.70
710 A341 3d Cynara humilis	.95	.70

Desert Costumes Type of 1987

Costumes of Ouarzazate.

1991, July 31 Photo.

711 A320 3d Woman	.95	.70
712 A320 3d Man	.95	.70

King Hassan II Type of 1981

1991-96 Photo. *Perf. 14½*

Size: 25x32mm

715 A236 1.35d multicolored	.42	.16
717 A236 1.70d multicolored	.40	.16
722 A236 5.50d multicolored	1.30	1.00
724 A236 20d multicolored	4.50	3.50
Nos. 715-724 (4)	6.62	4.82

Issued: 1.35d, Sept. 2; 1.70d, 1994.

This is an expanding set. Numbers will change if necessary.

A362

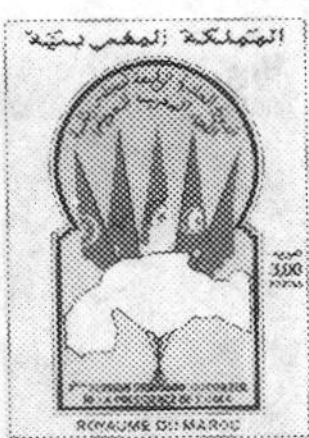
A363

1991, Sept. 23 Litho. *Perf. 14*

725 A362 3d multicolored	.95	.70

19th World Congress on Roads, Marrakesh.

1991, Oct. 30 Litho.

726 A363 3d multicolored	.95	.70

4th Session of the Council of Presidents of the Maghreb Arab Union.

Green March Anniv. Type of 1987

1991, Nov. 6 Photo. *Perf. 14*

727 A323 3d multicolored	.95	.70

Green March, 16th anniv.

Birds — A364

Fight Against AIDS — A365

1991, Nov. 20 Litho. *Perf. 14*

728 A364 3d Merops apiaster	1.00	.80
729 A364 3d Ciconia ciconia	1.00	.80

See Nos. 748-749.

1991, Dec. 16

730 A365 3d multicolored	1.00	.80

Organization of the Islamic Conference, 20th Anniv. — A366

1991, Dec. 16
731 A366 3d multicolored 1.00 .80

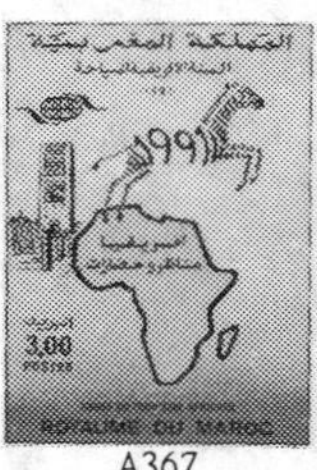
A367

A368

1991 **Litho.** ***Perf. 14***
732 A367 3d multicolored 1.00 .80

African Tourism Year.

Handstamp Type of 1985

Sherifian postal seals of Maghzen-Essaouira, 1892: No. 733, Circular. No. 734, Octagonal.

1992, Jan. 13
733 A287 3d olive & blk 1.00 .80
734 A287 3d purple & blk 1.00 .80

1992, Feb. 17
735 A368 3d multicolored 1.00 .80

Intl. Space Year.

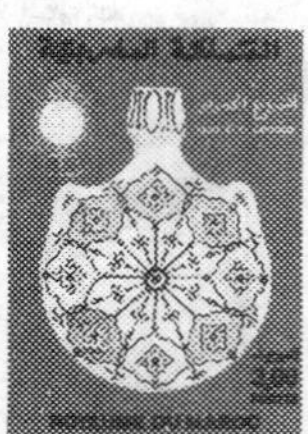
Week of the Blind — A369

Red Crescent Society — A370

1992, Mar. 19 **Photo.** ***Perf. 14***
736 A369 3d multicolored 1.00 .80

1992, Mar. 30
737 A370 3d multicolored 1.00 .80

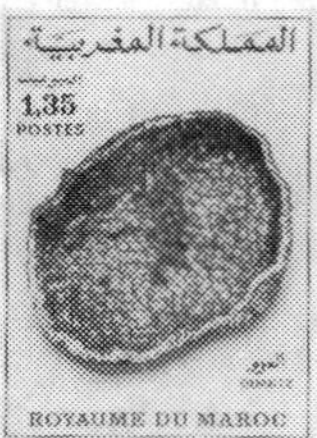
Minerals — A371

A372

1992, May 11 **Litho.** ***Perf. 14***
738 A371 1.35d Quartz .48 .38
739 A371 3.40d Calcite 1.25 1.00

Desert Costumes Type of 1987

Costumes of Tata.

1992, May 25 **Photo.** ***Perf. 14***
740 A320 1.35d Woman .50 .38
741 A320 3.40d Man 1.25 1.00

Flowering Plants Type of 1989

1992, July 13
742 A341 1.35d Campanula afra .50 .38
743 A341 3.40d Thymus broussonetii 1.25 1.00

1992, July 24
744 A372 3.40d multicolored 1.25 1.00

1992 Summer Olympics, Barcelona.

Modes of Transportion and Communications, Map of Africa — A373

1992, Sept. 14 **Litho.** ***Perf. 14***
745 A373 3.40d multicolored .95 .75

Expo '92, Seville — A374

1992, Oct. 12
746 A374 3.40d multicolored .95 .75

Discovery of America, 500th Anniv. A375

1992, Oct. 12
747 A375 3.40d multicolored .95 .75

Bird Type of 1991

1992, Oct. 26 **Litho.** ***Perf. 14***
748 A364 3d Gyps fulvus .82 .65
749 A364 3d Ganga cata, horiz. .82 .65

Green March Anniv. Type of 1987

1992, Nov. 6 **Litho.** ***Perf. 14***
750 A323 3.40d multicolored .95 .75

Green March, 17th anniv.

Sherifian Post, Cent. A377

Designs: 3.40d, Octagonal Sherifian postal seal, scroll, Sultan Moulay Hassan I. 5d, Scroll, various circular and octagonal Sherifian postal seals, Sultan.

1992, Nov. 22 **Litho.** ***Perf. 14***
751 A377 1.35d multicolored .38 .30
752 A377 3.40d multicolored .95 .75

Size: 165x115mm

Imperf

753 A377 5d multicolored 1.40 1.00
Nos. 751-752 (2) 1.33 1.05

Intl. Conference on Nutrition, Rome A378

1992, Dec. 7 **Litho.** ***Perf. 14***
754 A378 3.40d multicolored .95 .75

Al Massira Airport, Agadir — A379

1992, Dec. 21 **Litho.** ***Perf. 14***
755 A379 3.40d multicolored 1.00 .80

Hand Stamp Type of 1985

Sherifian postal seals of Maghzen-Tanger, 1892: 1.70, Circular. 3.80d, Octagonal.

1993, Jan. 29 **Litho.** ***Perf. 14***
756 A287 1.70d green & black .45 .35
757 A287 3.80d orange & black 1.05 .82

Stamp Day.

Week of the Blind A380

1993, Mar. 15 **Litho.** ***Perf. 14***
758 A380 4.40d multicolored 1.25 1.00

World Meteorology Day — A381

1993, Mar. 23
759 A381 4.40d multicolored 1.25 1.00

Red Crescent Society — A382

World Telecommunications Day — A383

1993, Apr. 26 **Litho.** ***Perf. 14***
760 A382 4.40d multicolored 1.25 1.00

1993, June 14
761 A383 4.40d multicolored 1.25 1.00

A384

A385

Argania spinosa.

1993, July 26 **Litho.** ***Perf. 14***
762 A384 1.70d Extracting oil .45 .35
763 A384 4.80d Tree branch 1.25 1.00

1993, Aug. 21
764 A385 4.80d multicolored 1.25 1.00

Prince Sidi Mohammed, 30th birthday.

Inauguration of the Hassan II Mosque — A386

1993, Aug. 30 ***Perf. 13***
765 A386 4.80d multicolored 1.25 1.00

A387

A388

1993, Sept. 30 **Litho.** ***Perf. 14***
766 A387 4.80d multicolored 1.25 1.00

King and People's Revolution, 40th Anniv.

1993, Oct. 15
767 A388 4.80d multicolored 1.25 1.00

World Post Day.

New Islamic University — A389

1993, Nov. 1 **Litho.** ***Perf. 14***
768 A389 4.80d multicolored 1.25 1.00

Green March Anniv. Type of 1987

1993, Nov. 6
769 A323 4.80d multicolored 1.25 1.00

Green March, 18th anniv.

Water Birds A390

1993, Dec. 13 **Litho.** ***Perf. 14***
770 A390 1.70d Sarcelle marbree .38 .30
771 A390 4.80d Foulque a crete 1.10 .85

Manifest of Independence, 50th Anniv. — A391

1994, Mar. 31 **Litho.** ***Perf. 14***
772 A391 4.80d multicolored 1.10 .85

General Agreement on Tariffs and Trade (GATT), 1994 Summit, Marrakech
A392 A393

1994, Apr. 29 Litho. *Perf. 14*
773 A392 1.70d multicolored .38 .28
774 A393 4.80d multicolored 1.10 .80

Week of the Blind — A394

Red Crescent Society — A395

1994, May 9
775 A394 4.80d multicolored 1.10 .85

1994, May 18
776 A395 4.80d multicolored 1.10 .85

Natl. Conference on Children's Rights — A396

1994, May 25
777 A396 1.70d shown .38 .30
778 A396 4.80d Boy, girl under sun 1.10 .85

1994 World Cup Soccer Championships, US — A397

1994, June 17 *Perf. 13*
779 A397 4.80d multicolored 1.10 .85

King Hassan II, 65th Birthday A398

Designs: 1.70d, Wearing business suit. 4.80d, Wearing traditional costume, vert.

1994 *Perf. 13x12½, 12½x13*
780 A398 1.70d multicolored .40 .30
781 A398 4.80d multicolored 1.10 .45

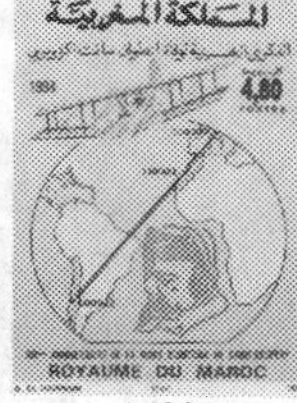

A399 A400

1994 *Perf. 12½x13*
782 A399 4.80d multicolored 1.10 .45

Intl. Olympic Committee, Cent.

1994
783 A400 4.80d multicolored 1.10 .45

Death of Antoine de Saint-Exupery, 50th anniv.

Flowers A401

1994 *Perf. 13x12½, 12½x13*
784 A401 1.70d Chamaelon gummifer .40 .30
785 A401 4.80d Pancratium maritimum, vert. 1.10 .45

Water Birds — A402

1994, Oct. 24 Photo. *Perf. 13x13½*
786 A402 1.70d Courlis a bec grele .38 .28
787 A402 4.80d Goeland d'audouin 1.10 .80

A403 A404

Green March, 19th Anniv.: 4.80d, Marchers, map, inscription.

1994, Nov. 6 Litho. *Perf. 12½*
788 A403 1.70d multicolored .38 .28
789 A403 4.80d multicolored 1.10 .80

Hand Stamp Type of 1985

Sherifan postal seals of Maghzen-Marrakesh: 1.70d, Circular. 4.80d, Octagonal.

1994, Nov. 22 *Perf. 12½*
790 A287 1.70d blue & black .38 .28
791 A287 4.80d vermilion & black 1.10 .80

Stamp Day.

1995, Feb. 27 Litho. *Perf. 13½*
792 A404 4.80d multicolored 1.10 .80

Week of the Blind.

A405 A406

1995 Litho. *Perf. 13½*
793 A405 4.80d multicolored 1.10 .80

Arab League, 50th anniv.

1995, Mar. Litho. *Perf. 13½x13*
794 A406 4.80d multicolored 1.10 .80

Red Crescent Society.

Flowers — A407

Birds — A408

1995, June Litho. *Perf. 13½x13*
795 A407 2d Malva hispanica .48 .35
796 A407 4.80d Phlomis crinita 1.10 .85

1995, Sept. 18 Litho. *Perf. 13½x13*
797 A408 1.70d Coracias garrulus .40 .30
798 A408 4.80d Carduelis carduelis 1.10 .85

See Nos. 818-819, 832-833.

FAO, 50th Anniv. A409

1995, Oct. 16 Photo. *Perf. 13½*
799 A409 4.80d multicolored 1.10 .85

UN, 50th Anniv. A410

Designs: 1.70d, "50," Moroccan, UN flags. 4.80d, Moroccan flag, UN emblem, map of Africa.

1995, Oct. 24 *Perf. 12½*
800 A410 1.70d multicolored .40 .30
801 A410 4.80d multicolored 1.10 .85

Green March Anniv. Type of 1987 and

Green March, 20th Anniv. — A411

1995, Nov. 6 Photo. *Perf. 12½*
802 A323 1.70d multicolored .40 .30
803 A411 4.80d multicolored 1.10 .85

A412 A413

Independence, 40th anniv.: 4.80d, Crown, national flag. 10d, King Mohammed V, crown over flag, King Hassan II.

1995, Nov. 18 Litho. *Perf. 12½*
804 A412 4.80d multicolored 1.10 .85

Size: 112x83mm

Imperf

805 A412 10d multicolored 2.50 2.00

Hand Stamp Type of 1985

Sherifan postal seals of Maghzen-Meknes, 1892: 1.70d, Circular. 4.80d, Octagonal.

1995, Nov. 22 Photo. *Perf. 12½*
806 A287 1.70d olive & black .40 .30
807 A287 4.80d violet & black 1.10 .85

Stamp Day.

1996, Mar. 3 Litho. *Perf. 13½*
808 A413 2d Natl. arms .45 .35
809 A413 5.50d King Hassan II 1.25 .95

Size: 134x86mm

Imperf

810 A413 10d Crown, King 2.25 1.75

Accession of King Hassan II, 35th anniv.

Traditional Crafts — A414

Flowers — A415

1996, Mar. 25 Photo. *Perf. 13½x13*
811 A414 5.50d Pottery 1.30 1.00
812 A414 5.50d Copper 1.30 1.00

1996, Apr. 25
813 A415 2d Cleonia lusitanica .50 .40
814 A415 5.50d Tulipa sylvestris 1.30 1.00

A416 A417

King Hassan II: 2d, In uniform. 5.50d, Wearing traditional headpiece.

1996, May 14 Photo. *Perf. 13x13½*
815 A416 2d multicolored .50 .40
816 A416 5.50d multicolored 1.30 1.00

Royal Armed Forces, 40th anniv.

1996, July 19 Photo. *Perf. 13½x13*
817 A417 5.50d multicolored 1.30 1.00

1996 Summer Olympics, Atlanta.

Bird Type of 1995

1996, Oct. 21 Photo. *Perf. 13½x13*
818 A408 2d Pandion haliaetus .50 .40
819 A408 5.50d Egretta garzetta 1.30 1.00

Green March Anniv. Type of 1987

1996, Nov. 6 Litho. ***Perf. 13½***

820 A323 5.50d multicolored 1.25 1.00

Green March, 21st anniv.

Hand Stamp Type of 1985

Sherifan postal seals of Maghzen-Fes, 1892: 2d, Circular. 5.50d, Octagonal.

1996, Nov. 22 Photo. ***Perf. 13½***

821 A287 2d orange & black .45 .35

822 A287 5.50d green & black 1.25 1.00

Stamp Day.

UNICEF, 50th Anniv. A418

1996, Dec. 11 ***Perf. 13x13½***

823 A418 5.50d multicolored 1.25 1.00

Moroccan Pottery A419

1997, Feb. 24 Photo. ***Perf. 13x13½***

824 A419 5.50d multicolored 1.15 .90

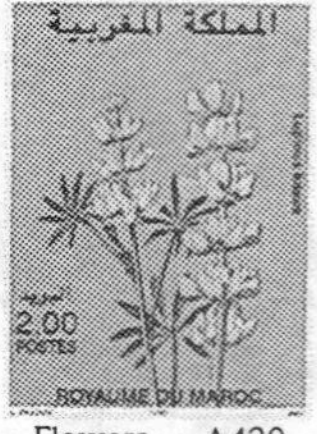

Flowers — A420

A421

1997, Mar. 24 Photo. ***Perf. 13½x13***

825 A420 2d Lupinus luteus .45 .20

826 A420 5.50d Silybum marianum 1.20 .60

1997, Apr. 9 Litho. ***Perf. 13½x13***

Speakers, 1947: No. 827, Crown Prince Hassan. No. 828, Sultan Mohammed V.

827 A421 2d multicolored .45 .20

828 A421 2d multicolored .45 .20

Speech in Tangier by King Hassan II, 50th anniv.

World Reading and Copyright Day — A422

1997, Apr. 23

829 A422 5.50d multicolored 1.20 .60

Intl. Meeting on Ibn Battuta (1304-77?), Traveler and Writer A423

1997, May 9 ***Perf. 13x13½***

830 A423 5.50d multicolored 1.20 .60

Moroccan Copper — A424

1997, July 21 Photo. ***Perf. 13½***

831 A424 5.50d multicolored 1.10 .55

Bird Type of 1995

Designs: 2d, Anthropoides virgo. 5.50d, Parus caeruleus ultramarinus.

1997, Oct. 20 Photo. ***Perf. 13½x13***

832 A408 2d multicolored .45 .20

833 A408 5.50d multicolored 1.15 .60

Green March Anniv. Type of 1987

1997, Nov. 6 ***Perf. 13½***

834 A323 5.50d multicolored 1.15 .60

Hand Stamp Type of 1985

Sherifan postal seals of Maghzen-Larache, 1892: 2d, Circular. 5.50d, Octagonal.

1997 Photo. ***Perf. 13½***

835 A287 2d blue & black .40 .20

836 A287 5.50d vermilion & black 1.15 .60

SEMI-POSTAL STAMPS

Nos. 1-5 Surcharged

+10f

اعانة ضحايا
الزيت المسمومة
اكتوبر 1959

1960, Mar. Unwmk. Engr. ***Perf. 13***

B1 A1 5fr + 10fr brt bl & ind .22 .20

B2 A1 10fr + 10fr bis brn & choc .30 .28

B3 A1 15fr + 10fr dp grn & mag .55 .45

B4 A1 25fr + 15fr purple .65 .55

B5 A1 30fr + 20fr green 1.00 1.00

Nos. B1-B5 (5) 2.72 2.48

The surtax aided families whose members consumed adulterated cooking oil with crippling or fatal results.

French Morocco Nos. 321 and 322 Surcharged

اسبوعا
التضامن
1380
1960
≋
15 + 3f

1960, Sept. 12

B6 A71 15fr + 3fr on 18fr dk grn .32 .32

B7 A71 20fr + 5fr brown lake .50 .50

Nos. 1 and 6 Surcharged in Red or Black

فيضانات
1
9
6
3

≋ 20 + 5

1963, Jan. 28 Engr. ***Perf. 13***

B8 A1 20c + 5c on 5fr brt bl & ind (R) .38 .38

B9 A1 30c + 10c on 50fr rose red .45 .38

The surtax was for flood victims.

Moroccan Brooch — SP1

Design: 40c+10c, Brooch with pendants.

1966, May 23 Photo. ***Perf. 11½***

Granite Paper

B10 SP1 25c + 5c ultra, sil, blk & red .38 .30

B11 SP1 40c + 10c mag, sil, blk, ultra & bl .55 .38

a. Pair, #B10-B11, vertically tête-bêche .95 .70

Meeting in Morocco of the Middle East and North African Red Cross-Red Crescent Seminar. The surtax was for the Moroccan Red Crescent Society.

See Nos. B12-B13, B15-B16, B19-B22, B26-B27, B29-B30, B34-B35.

1967, May 15 Granite Paper

Designs: 60c+5c, Two brooches, by silver drapery. 1d+10c, Two bracelets.

B12 SP1 60c + 5c yel bis & multi .40 .40

a. Pair, vertically tête-bêche .80 .80

B13 SP1 1d + 10c emer & multi .85 .85

a. Pair, vertically tête-bêche 1.70 1.70

Surtax for the Moroccan Red Crescent Society.

Hands Reading Braille and Map of Morocco — SP2

1969, Mar. 21 Photo. ***Perf. 12½***

B14 SP2 25c + 10c multi .15 .15

Week of the Blind, Mar. 21-29.

Jewelry Type of 1966

Designs: 25c+5c, Silver earrings. 40c+10c, Gold ear pendant.

1969, May 9 Photo. ***Perf. 11½***

Granite Paper

B15 SP1 25c + 5c gray grn & multi .38 .30

B16 SP1 40c + 10c tan & multi .55 .38

a. Pair, #B15-B16, vertically tête-bêche .95 .70

50th anniv. of the League of Red Cross Societies. Surtax was for Moroccan Red Crescent Society.

Nos. 173-174 Surcharged

+0²⁵
فيضانات 1970

1970, Feb. 26 Litho. ***Perf. 13***

B17 A65 10c + 25c multi 1.50 1.50

B18 A65 15c + 25c multi 1.50 1.50

The surtax was for flood victims.

Jewelry Type of 1966

Designs: 25c+5c, Necklace with pendants. 50c+10c, Earring with 5 pendants.

1970, May 25 Photo. ***Perf. 11½***

Granite Paper

B19 SP1 25c + 5c gray & multi .40 .38

B20 SP1 50c + 10c brt vio & multi .65 .65

a. Pair, #B19-B20, vertically tête-bêche 1.05 .95

Surtax for Moroccan Red Crescent Society.

1971, May 10

Designs: 25c+5c, Brooch. 40c+10c, Stomacher.

Granite Paper

B21 SP1 25c + 5c gray & multi .30 .30

B22 SP1 40c + 10c yel & multi .45 .38

a. Pair, #B21-B22, vertically tête-bêche .75 .70

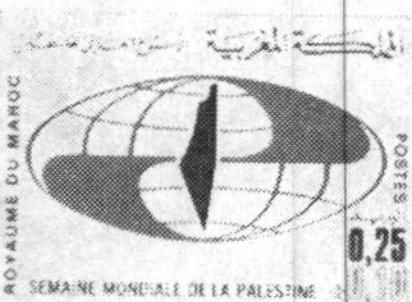

Globe and Map of Palestine SP3

1971, Apr. 30 ***Perf. 13***

B23 SP3 25c + 10c multi .50 .25

Palestine Week, May 3-8.

String Instrument and Bow — SP4

1971, June 28 Photo. ***Perf. 12***

B24 SP4 40c + 10c multi .20 .15

Week of the Blind.

Mizmar (Double Flute) — SP5

1972, Mar. 31 Photo. ***Perf. 13x13½***

B25 SP5 25c + 10c multi .22 .22

Week of the Blind.

Jewelry Type of 1966

Designs: 25c+5c, Jeweled bracelets. 70c+10c, Rectangular pendant with ball drop.

1972, May 8 Photo. ***Perf. 11½***

Granite Paper

B26 SP1 25c + 5c brn & multi .30 .30

B27 SP1 70c + 10c dp grn & multi .45 .38

a. Pair, #B26-B27, vertically tête-bêche .75 .70

For overprints see Nos. 295-296.

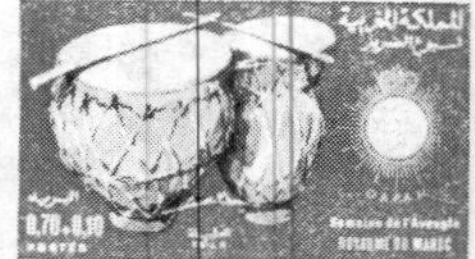

Drums SP6

1973, Mar. 30 Photo. ***Perf. 13x14***

B28 SP6 70c + 10c multi .30 .25

Week of the Blind.

Jewelry Type of 1966

25c+5c, Silver box pendant. 70c+10c, Bracelet.

1973, June 15 Photo. ***Perf. 11½***

B29 SP1 25c + 5c bl & multi .40 .30

B30 SP1 70c + 10c org & multi .50 .38

a. Pair, #B29-B30, vertically tête-bêche .90 .70

Moroccan Red Crescent Society. For overprints see Nos. 351-352.

Pistol — SP7

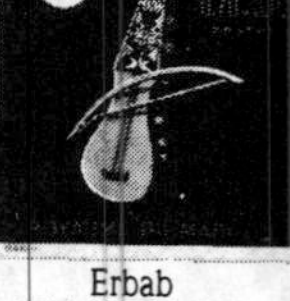

Erbab (Fiddle) — SP8

70c+10c, Decorated antique powder box.

1974, July 8 Photo. *Perf. 14x13½*

No.	Type	Description	Unused	Used
B31	SP7	25c + 5c multi	.30	.30
B32	SP7	70c + 10c multi	.45	.38
a.		Pair, #B31-B32, vertically tête-bêche	.95	.70

Moroccan Red Crescent Society.

1975, Jan. 10 Photo. *Perf. 13*

No.	Type	Description	Unused	Used
B33	SP8	70c + 10c multi	.38	.22

Week of the Blind.

Jewelry Type of 1966

25c+5c, Silver pendant. 70c+10c, Earring.

1975, Mar. 13 Photo. *Perf. 13½*

No.	Type	Description	Unused	Used
B34	SP1	25c + 5c multi	.30	.30
B35	SP1	70c + 10c multi	.45	.38
a.		Pair, #B34-B35, vertically tête-bêche	.75	.70

Moroccan Red Crescent Society. For overprints see #386-387.

AIR POST STAMPS

Sultan's Star over Casablanca AP1

King Hassan II AP2

Unwmk.

1957, May 4 Engr. *Perf. 13*

No.	Type	Description	Unused	Used
C1	AP1	15fr car & brt grn	.55	.50
C2	AP1	25fr brt grnsh bl	1.00	.70
C3	AP1	30fr red brn	1.40	.90
		Nos. C1-C3 (3)	2.95	2.10

Intl. Fair, Casablanca, May 4-19.

1962

No.	Type	Description	Unused	Used
C5	AP2	90c black	.30	.15
C6	AP2	1d rose red	.50	.15
C7	AP2	2d deep blue	.65	.30
C8	AP2	3d dl bl grn	1.10	.65
C9	AP2	5d purple	2.25	.90
		Nos. C5-C9 (5)	4.80	2.15

Meteorological Day Type of Regular Issue

1964, Mar. 23 Photo. *Perf. 11½*

Granite Paper

No.	Type	Description	Unused	Used
C10	A39	90c Anemometer & globe	.40	.30

Intl. Fair, Casablanca, 20th Anniv. AP3

1964, Apr. 30 Photo. *Perf. 12½*

No.	Type	Description	Unused	Used
C11	AP3	1d bl, bis & org	.50	.40

Moroccan Pavilion and Unisphere AP4

1964, May 25 Unwmk. *Perf. 12½*

No.	Type	Description	Unused	Used
C12	AP4	1d dk grn, red & bl	.55	.40

New York World's Fair, 1964-65.

Ramses II and UNESCO Emblem — AP5

Perf. 12x11½

1966, Oct. 3 Litho. & Engr.

No.	Type	Description	Unused	Used
C13	AP5	1d magenta, *yel*	.55	.40

UNESCO, 20th anniv.

Jet Plane AP6

Perf. 12½x13½

1966, Dec. 19 Photo.

No.	Type	Description	Unused	Used
C14	AP6	3d multi	2.25	1.25

Costume Type of Regular Issue

Design: 1d, Women from Ait Ouaouzguit.

1969, Jan. 21 Litho. *Perf. 12*

No.	Type	Description	Unused	Used
C15	A74	1d multi	1.20	.55

Coin Type of Regular Issue, 1968

Coins: 1d, King Mohammed V, 1960. 5d, King Hassan II, 1965.

1969, Mar. 3 Photo. *Perf. 11½*

Granite Paper

No.	Type	Description	Unused	Used
C16	A73	1d brt bl, sil & blk	2.25	1.50
C17	A73	5d vio blk, sil & blk	6.00	3.75

King Hassan II — AP7

1983, Mar. 1 Photo. *Perf. 12*

Granite Paper

No.	Type	Description	Unused	Used
C18	AP7	1.40d multi	.40	.15
C19	AP7	2d multi	.45	.15
C20	AP7	3d multi	.65	.20
C21	AP7	5d multi	1.00	.30
C22	AP7	10d multi	2.00	.65
		Nos. C18-C22 (5)	4.50	1.45

No. C19 Overprinted

الملتقى العالمي الاول
لخطباء الجمعة

1987, Mar. 23 Photo. *Perf. 12*

Granite Paper

No.	Type	Description	Unused	Used
C23	AP7	2d multi	.40	.25

1st World Congress of Friday Preachers, Al Joumouaa.

اتحاد المغرب العربى

No. C18 Overprinted

مراكش– فبراير 89

1989, Mar. 27 Photo. *Perf. 12*

Granite Paper

No.	Type	Description	Unused	Used
C24	AP7	1.40d multi	.40	.20

Maghreb Union, agreement between Morocco, Algeria and Tunisia.

POSTAGE DUE STAMPS

D1

Oranges — D2

1965 Unwmk. Typo. *Perf. 14x13½*

No.	Type	Description	Unused	Used
J1	D1	5c green	.75	.20
J2	D1	10c bister brown	.30	.15
J3	D1	20c red	.45	.15
J4	D1	30c brown black	.75	.20
		Nos. J1-J4 (4)	2.25	.70

See French Morocco Nos. J27-J34, J46-J56.

1974-96 Photo. *Perf. 14*

No.	Type	Description	Unused	Used
J5	D2	5c shown	.15	.15
J6	D2	10c Cherries	.15	.15
J7	D2	20c Grapes	.20	.15
J8	D2	30c Peaches, horiz.	.20	.15
J9	D2	40c Grapes ('78)	.15	.15
J10	D2	60c Peaches, horiz. ('78)	.20	.15
J11	D2	80c Oranges ('78)	.30	.15
J12	D2	1d Apples ('86)	.20	.15
J13	D2	1.20d Cherries ('84)	.25	.15
J14	D2	1.60d Peaches ('85)	.50	.25
J15	D2	2d Strawberries ('86)	.40	.25

Litho.

No.	Type	Description	Unused	Used
J16	D2	5d like #J12 ('96)	1.20	.60
		Nos. J5-J15 (11)	2.70	
		Set value		1.45

For surcharges see Nos. 322, 395.

Type D2 is an expanding set. Numbers will change again if more stamps are added.

NORTHERN ZONE

100 Centimos = 1 Peseta

Sultan Mohammed V — A1

Villa Sanjurjo Harbor A2

Designs: 25c, Polytechnic school. 50c, 10p, Institute of Culture, Tetuan.

Perf. 13x12½, 12½x13

1956, Aug. 23 Photo. Unwmk.

No.	Type	Description	Unused	Used
1	A1	10c deep rose	.15	.15
2	A2	15c yellow brn	.15	.15
3	A2	25c dk bl gray	.15	.15
4	A1	50c dark olive	.15	.15
5	A1	80c brt green	.15	.15
6	A2	2p brt red lil	1.50	1.00
7	A2	3p brt blue	3.25	1.65
8	A1	10p green	11.00	7.00
		Nos. 1-8 (8)	16.50	10.40

Sultan Mohammed V A3 A4

1957, Mar. 2 *Perf. 13½x13*

No.	Type	Description	Unused	Used
9	A3	80c blue green	.20	.15
10	A3	1.50p gray olive	.85	.55
11	A3	3p deep rose	2.75	1.75
		Nos. 9-11 (3)	3.80	2.45

1st anniv. of independence. See Morocco #13-15.

1957 Engr. *Perf. 13*

No.	Type	Description	Unused	Used
12	A4	30c brt bl & indigo	.15	.15
13	A4	70c bis, brn & choc	.15	.15
14	A4	80c brt violet	.55	.15
15	A4	1.50p dp grn & mag	.15	.15
16	A4	3p green	.25	.15
17	A4	7p rose red	1.10	.25
		Nos. 12-17 (6)	2.35	
		Set value		.55

Prince Moulay el Hassan — A5

King Mohammed V — A6

1957, July 15 Photo. *Perf. 13*

No.	Type	Description	Unused	Used
18	A5	80c blue	.20	.15
19	A5	1.50p green	.85	.50
20	A5	3p carmine rose	2.50	1.65
		Nos. 18-20 (3)	3.55	2.30

Nos. 13 and 15 Surcharged in Carmine or Black

ستنتما
15 Cts.

بسيطة
1'20
PESETAS

1957 Engr.

No.	Type	Description	Unused	Used
21	A4	15c on 70c (C)	.20	.15
22	A4	1.20p on 1.50p (Bk)	.50	.20

1957, Nov. Photo. *Perf. 12½*

No.	Type	Description	Unused	Used
23	A6	1.20p blk & brt grn	.25	.20
24	A6	1.80p blk & rose red	.25	.25
25	A6	3p black & violet	.75	.45
		Nos. 23-25 (3)	1.25	.90

Enthronement of Mohammed V, 30th anniv.

NORTHERN ZONE AIR POST STAMPS

Plane over Lau Dam — AP1

Design: 1.40p, 4.80p, Plane over Nekor bridge.

Perf. 12½x13

1956, Dec. 17 Photo. Unwmk.

No.	Type	Description	Unused	Used
C1	AP1	25c rose violet	.15	.15
C2	AP1	1.40p lilac rose	.15	.15
C3	AP1	3.40p org vermilion	.85	.65
C4	AP1	4.80p dull violet	1.40	1.00
		Nos. C1-C4 (4)	2.55	1.95

Keep up to date with all new stamp issues by subscribing to the "Scott Stamp Monthly." Please call 1-800-572-6885 for more information.

MOZAMBIQUE

mō-zəm-'bēk

LOCATION — Southeastern Africa, bordering on the Mozambique Channel
GOVT. — Republic
AREA — 308,642 sq. mi.
POP. — 14,140,000 (est. 1983)
CAPITAL — Maputo

Formerly a Portuguese colony, Mozambique, or Portuguese East Africa, was divided into eight districts: Lourenco Marques, Inhambane, Quelimane, Tete, Mozambique, Zambezia, Nyassa and the Manica and Sofala region formerly administered by the Mozambique Company. At various times the districts issued their own stamps which were eventually replaced by those inscribed "Mocambique."

Mozambique achieved independence June 25, 1975, taking the name People's Republic of Mozambique.

1000 Reis = 1 Milreis
100 Centavos = 1 Escudo (1913)
100 Centavos = 1 Metical (1980)

Catalogue values for unused stamps in this country are for Never Hinged items, beginning with Scott 330 in the regular postage section, Scott C29 in the airpost section, Scott J51 in the postage due section, and Scott RA55 in the postal tax section.

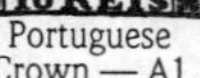

Portuguese Crown — A1

King Luiz — A2

Perf. 12½, 13½

1877-85 Typo. Unwmk.

1 A1 5r black 2.00 1.00
a. Perf. 13½ 3.00 1.65
2 A1 10r yellow 15.00 4.50
3 A1 10r green ('81) 1.50 .60
4 A1 20r bister 1.50 .75
a. Perf. 13½ 3.00 2.00
5 A1 20r rose ('85) 250.00 150.00
6 A1 25r rose .70 .35
a. Perf. 13½ 6.75 1.65
7 A1 25r violet ('85) 3.00 2.00
8 A1 40r blue 25.00 15.00
9 A1 40r yel buff ('81) 2.00 1.65
a. Perf. 12½ 3.50 3.00
10 A1 50r green 70.00 25.00
a. Perf. 13½ 125.00 60.00
11 A1 50r blue ('81) .50 .40
12 A1 100r lilac .70 .50
13 A1 200r orange 1.90 1.40
a. Perf. 12½ 5.25 4.50
14 A1 300r chocolate 2.25 2.00
Nos. 1-4,6-14 (13) 126.05 55.15

The reprints of the 1877-85 issues are printed on a smooth white chalky paper, ungummed, with rough perforation 13½, also on thin white paper, with shiny white gum and clean-cut perforation 13½.

Typographed and Embossed

1886 *Perf. 12½*

15 A2 5r black 1.50 .60
16 A2 10r green 1.50 .70
17 A2 20r rose 2.00 1.50
18 A2 25r dull lilac 9.00 1.40
19 A2 40r chocolate 1.75 .85
20 A2 50r blue 2.25 .50
21 A2 100r yellow brn 2.50 .50
22 A2 200r gray violet 4.25 1.75
23 A2 300r orange 4.50 2.00
Nos. 15-23 (9) 29.25 9.80

Perf. 13½

15a A2 5r 4.00 2.75
16a A2 10r 4.25 2.75
17a A2 20r 13.00 6.00
18a A2 25r 13.00 6.00
19a A2 40r 15.00 9.50
20a A2 50r 16.00 4.50
22a A2 200r 15.00 12.50
Nos. 15a-22a (7) 80.25 44.00

Nos. 15, 18, 19, 20, 21 and 23 have been reprinted. The reprints have shiny white gum and clean-cut perforation 13½. Many of the colors are paler than those of the originals.

For surcharges and overprints see Nos. 23A, 36-44, 46-48, 72-80, 192, P1-P5.

PROVISORIO

No. 19 Surcharged in Black

5 5

1893, Jan. *Perf. 12½*

Without Gum

23A A2 5r on 40r choc 125.00 50.00

There are three varieties of No. 23A:
I - "PROVISORIO" 19mm long, numerals 4½mm high.
II - "PROVISORIO" 19½mm long, numerals 5mm high.
III - "PROVISORIO" 19½mm long, numerals of both sizes.

King Carlos I — A3

1894 Typo. *Perf. 11½, 12½*

24 A3 5r yellow .50 .45
25 A3 10r red lilac .50 .35
26 A3 15r red brown 1.25 .75
27 A3 20r gray lilac 1.25 .50
28 A3 25r blue green 1.25 .20
29 A3 50r lt blue 5.00 1.50
a. Perf. 12½ 7.50 2.00
30 A3 75r rose 1.75 1.25
31 A3 80r yellow grn 3.00 1.40
32 A3 100r brown, *buff* 2.25 1.50
33 A3 150r car, *rose* 11.00 7.25
a. Perf. 11½
34 A3 200r dk blue, *blue* 5.00 3.00
35 A3 300r dk blue, *salmon* 7.00 3.00
Nos. 24-35 (12) 39.75 21.15

Nos. 28 and 31-33 have been reprinted with shiny white gum and clean-cut perf. 13½.

For surcharges and overprints see Nos. 45, 81-92, 193-198, 201-206, 226-228, 238-239.

Stamps of 1886 Overprinted in Red or Black

1195 CENTENARIO ANTONINO 1895

1895, July 1 *Perf. 12½*

Without Gum

36 A2 5r black (R) 8.00 5.50
37 A2 10r green 9.00 6.50
38 A2 20r rose 10.00 6.00
39 A2 25r violet 12.50 6.50
a. Double overprint
40 A2 40r chocolate 14.00 7.50
41 A2 50r blue 15.00 7.50
a. Perf. 13½ 80.00 55.00
42 A2 100r yellow brown 16.00 8.25
43 A2 200r gray violet 25.00 13.00
a. Perf. 13½ 100.00 65.00
44 A2 300r orange 35.00 17.50
Nos. 36-44 (9) 144.50 78.25

Birth of Saint Anthony of Padua, 7th cent.

No. 35 Surcharged in Black

50 réis

1897, Jan. 2 *Perf. 12½*

Without Gum

45 A3 50r on 300r dk bl, *sal* 150.00 40.00

Nos. 17, 19 Surcharged

a

MOCAMBIQUE 2½ REIS

b

MOCAMBIQUE 2½ RÉIS

c

MOÇAMBIQUE 5 RÉIS

1898

Without Gum

46 A2 (a) 2½r on 20r rose 42.50 11.00
47 A2 (b) 2½r on 20r rose 27.50 10.00
a. Inverted surcharge 55.00 45.00
48 A2 (c) 5r on 40r choc 35.00 10.00
a. Inverted surcharge 90.00 45.00
Nos. 46-48 (3) 105.00 31.00

King Carlos I — A4

1898-1903 Typo. *Perf. 11½*

Name and Value in Black except 500r

49 A4 2½r gray .20 .15
50 A4 5r orange .20 .15
51 A4 10r lt green .25 .20
52 A4 15r brown 3.00 1.50
53 A4 15r gray grn ('03) .70 .55
54 A4 20r gray violet .85 .40
55 A4 25r sea green .85 .40
56 A4 25r carmine ('03) .70 .30
57 A4 50r dark blue 1.50 .50
58 A4 50r brown ('03) 2.00 1.50
59 A4 65r dull blue ('03) 15.00 12.00
60 A4 75r rose 7.00 2.75
61 A4 75r red lilac ('03) 3.00 1.75
62 A4 80r violet 6.00 3.25
63 A4 100r dk blue, *bl* 2.00 1.00
64 A4 115r org brn, *pink* ('03) 9.00 5.00
65 A4 130r brown, *straw* ('03) 9.00 5.00
66 A4 150r brown, *straw* 9.00 2.75
67 A4 200r red lilac, *pnksh* 2.00 1.40
68 A4 300r dk blue, *rose* 8.00 3.25
69 A4 400r dl bl, *straw* ('03) 12.00 7.50
70 A4 500r blk & red, *bl* ('01) 15.00 8.00
71 A4 700r vio, *yelsh* ('01) 15.00 9.00
Nos. 49-71 (23) 122.25 68.30

For overprints and surcharges see Nos. 94-113, 200, 207-220.

Stamps of 1886-94 Surcharged

65 RÉIS

1902 *Perf. 12½, 13½*

On Stamps of 1886

Red Surcharge

72 A2 115r on 5r blk 5.00 2.00

Black Surcharge

73 A2 65r on 20r rose 5.00 2.50
a. Double surcharge 50.00 50.00
74 A2 65r on 40r choc 6.00 4.00
75 A2 65r on 200r violet 5.00 1.75
76 A2 115r on 50r blue 2.00 1.00
77 A2 130r on 25r red vio 3.00 .90
78 A2 130r on 300r orange 3.00 .90
79 A2 400r on 10r green 7.50 3.25
80 A2 400r on 100r yel brn 40.00 25.00
Nos. 72-80 (9) 76.50 41.30

The reprints of Nos. 74, 75, 76, 77, 79 and 80 have shiny white gum and clean-cut perforation 13½.

On Stamps of 1894

Perf. 11½

81 A3 65r on 10r red lil 3.00 2.00
82 A3 65r on 15r red brn 3.00 2.00
a. Pair, one without surcharge
83 A3 65r on 20r gray lil 3.00 2.00
84 A3 115r on 5r yel 3.00 2.00
a. Inverted surcharge
85 A3 115r on 25r bl grn 3.00 2.00
86 A3 130r on 75r rose 4.00 2.25
87 A3 130r on 100r brn, *buff* 6.00 5.00
88 A3 130r on 150r car, *rose* 4.00 2.00
89 A3 130r on 200r bl, *bl* 5.00 3.50
90 A3 400r on 50r lt bl 1.00 1.40
91 A3 400r on 80r yel grn 1.00 1.40
92 A3 400r on 300r bl, *sal* 1.00 1.40

On Newspaper Stamp of 1893

Perf. 13½

93 N3 115r on 2½r brn 2.00 2.25
Nos. 81-93 (13) 39.00 29.20

Reprints of No. 87 have shiny white gum and clean-cut perforation 13½.

Overprinted in Black **PROVISORIO**

On Stamps of 1898

Perf. 11½

94 A4 15r brown 2.00 .85
95 A4 25r sea green 2.50 .85
96 A4 50r blue 3.00 1.75
97 A4 75r rose 5.00 2.00
Nos. 94-97 (4) 12.50 5.45

No. 59 Surcharged in Black

50 RÉIS

1905

98 A4 50r on 65r dull blue 3.00 2.00

Stamps of 1898-1903 Overprinted in Carmine or Green

REPUBLICA

1911

99 A4 2½r gray .30 .20
a. Inverted overprint 15.00 15.00
100 A4 5r orange .30 .20
101 A4 10r lt green 2.00 .50
102 A4 15r gray grn .30 .20
103 A4 20r gray vio 2.00 .40
104 A4 25r carmine (G) .30 .15
a. 25r gray violet (error)
105 A4 50r brown .50 .20
106 A4 75r red lilac 1.00 .50
107 A4 100r dk blue, *bl* 1.00 .50
108 A4 115r org brn, *pink* 1.50 .85
109 A4 130r brown, *straw* 1.50 .85
a. Double overprint
110 A4 200r red lil, *pnksh* 3.00 .70
111 A4 400r dull bl, *straw* 3.50 .85
112 A4 500r blk & red, *bl* 4.00 .85
113 A4 700r vio, *straw* 4.50 .85
Nos. 99-113 (15) 25.70 7.80

King Manoel — A5

Overprinted in Carmine or Green

1912 *Perf. 11½x12*

114 A5 2½r violet .15 .15
115 A5 5r black .15 .15
116 A5 10r gray grn .20 .20
117 A5 20r carmine (G) .55 .40
118 A5 25r vio brn .15 .15
119 A5 50r dp blue .50 .35
120 A5 75r bis brn .50 .35
121 A5 100r brn, *lt grn* .50 .35
122 A5 200r dk grn, *sal* 1.00 .70
123 A5 300r black, *azure* 1.00 .70

Perf. 14x15

124 A5 500r ol grn & vio brn 2.00 1.25
Nos. 114-124 (11) 6.70 4.75

Vasco da Gama Issue of Various Portuguese Colonies Common Design Types Surcharged

REPUBLICA MOCAMBIQUE ¼ C.

1913

On Stamps of Macao

125 CD20 ¼c on ½a bl grn 2.00 2.00
126 CD21 ½c on 1a red 2.00 2.00
127 CD22 1c on 2a red vio 2.00 2.00
128 CD23 2½c on 4a yel grn 2.00 2.00
a. Double surcharge 50.00 50.00
129 CD24 5c on 8a dk bl 4.00 4.00
130 CD25 7½c on 12a vio brn 3.00 3.00
131 CD26 10c on 16a bis brn 2.50 2.00
132 CD27 15c on 24a bis 2.50 2.00
Nos. 125-132 (8) 20.00 19.00

On Stamps of Portuguese Africa

133 CD20 ¼c on 2½r bl grn 1.25 1.25
134 CD21 ½c on 5r red 1.25 1.25
135 CD22 1c on 10r red vio 1.25 1.25
a. Inverted surcharge 45.00 45.00
136 CD23 2½c on 25r yel grn 1.25 1.25
137 CD24 5c on 50r dk bl 1.25 1.25
138 CD25 7½c on 75r vio brn 1.75 1.75
139 CD26 10c on 100r bis brn 1.50 1.50
140 CD27 15c on 150r bis 1.50 1.50
Nos. 133-140 (8) 11.00 11.00

On Stamps of Timor

141 CD20 ¼c on ½a bl grn 1.50 1.50
142 CD21 ½c on 1a red 1.50 1.50
143 CD22 1c on 2a red vio 1.50 1.50
144 CD23 2½c on 4a yel grn 1.50 1.50
145 CD24 5c on 8a dk bl 1.50 1.50
146 CD25 7½c on 12a vio brn 3.00 3.00
147 CD26 10c on 16a bis brn 1.50 1.50
148 CD27 15c on 24a bis 2.00 2.00
Nos. 141-148 (8) 14.00 14.00
Nos. 125-148 (24) 45.00 44.00

Ceres — A6

1914-26 Typo. *Perf. 15x14, 12x11½*
Name and Value in Black

149 A6 ¼c olive brown .15 .15
150 A6 ½c black .15 .15
151 A6 1c blue green .15 .15
152 A6 1½c lilac brown .15 .15
153 A6 2c carmine .15 .15
154 A6 2c gray ('26) .20 .20
155 A6 2½c lt vio .15 .15
156 A6 3c org ('21) .15 .15
157 A6 4c pale rose ('21) .15 .15
158 A6 4½c gray ('21) .15 .15
159 A6 5c deep blue .15 .15
160 A6 6c lilac ('21) .15 .15
a. Name and value printed twice
161 A6 7c ultra ('21) .15 .15
162 A6 7½c yel brn .15 .15
163 A6 8c slate .15 .15
164 A6 10c org brn .15 .15
165 A6 12c gray brn ('21) .25 .15
166 A6 12c blue grn ('22) .20 .15
167 A6 15c plum 1.40 1.00
a. Perf. 12x11½ ('30) .65 .35
168 A6 15c brn rose ('22) .15 .15
169 A6 20c yel grn .15 .15
170 A6 24c ultra ('26) 4.50 2.00
171 A6 25c choc ('26) 1.50 1.25
172 A6 30c brown, *grn* 1.10 1.10
173 A6 30c deep green ('21) .40 .15
174 A6 30c gray bl, *pink* ('21) 1.00 1.25
175 A6 40c brn, *pink* 1.25 .85
176 A6 40c turq blue ('22) .80 .30
177 A6 50c org, *salmon* 2.75 3.00
178 A6 50c lt violet ('26) .30 .15
179 A6 60c red brn, *pink* ('21) 1.00 .85
180 A6 60c dk blue ('22) .85 .30
181 A6 60c rose ('26) .70 .25
182 A6 80c dk brn, *bl* ('21) 1.10 .85
183 A6 80c brt rose ('22) .70 .25
184 A6 1e grn, *bl*, perf. 12x11½ ('21) 1.40 .60
a. Perf. 15x14 6.00 2.00
185 A6 1e rose ('21) 1.25 .50
186 A6 1e blue ('26) 1.25 .65
187 A6 2e brt vio, *pink* ('21) 1.40 .60
188 A6 2e dk violet ('22) .70 .35
189 A6 5e buff ('26) 7.25 2.50
190 A6 10e pink ('26) 12.00 5.00
191 A6 20e pale turq ('26) 35.00 17.50
Nos. 149-191 (43) 82.80 44.30

For surcharges see Nos. 232-234, 236-237, 249-250, J46-50.

Stamps of 1902 Overprinted Locally in Carmine — REPUBLICA

1915
On Provisional Stamps of 1902

192 A2 115r on 5r black 150.00 100.00
193 A3 115r on 5r yellow .85 .75
194 A3 115r on 25r bl grn .85 .75
195 A3 130r on 75r rose .85 .75
196 A3 130r on 100r brn, *buff* .85 .75
197 A3 130r on 150r car, *rose* .85 .75
198 A3 130r on 200r bl, *bl* .85 .75
199 N3 115r on 2½r brn .60 .40

On No. 97

200 A4 75r rose 1.50 1.10
Nos. 192-200 (9) 157.20 106.00

Stamps of 1902-05 Overprinted in Carmine — REPUBLICA

1915
On Provisional Stamps of 1902

201 A3 115r on 5r yellow .55 .50
202 A3 115r on 25r bl grn .55 .55
203 A3 130r on 75r rose .55 .55
204 A3 130r on 150r car, *rose* .70 .50
205 A3 130r on 200r bl, *bl* .70 .50
206 A3 115r on 2½r brn .75 .50

On No. 96

207 A4 50r blue .85 .50

On No. 98

208 A4 50r on 65r dull blue .70 .50
Nos. 201-208 (8) 5.35 4.10

Stamps of 1898-1903 Overprinted Locally in Carmine Like Nos. 192-200

1917

209 A4 2½r gray 20.00 17.50
210 A4 15r gray grn 15.00 12.50
211 A4 20r gray vio 15.00 12.50
212 A4 50r brown 14.00 11.00
213 A4 75r red lilac 32.50 25.00
214 A4 100r blue, *bl* 6.00 2.50
215 A4 115r org brn, *pink* 8.00 3.00
216 A4 130r brown, *straw* 7.50 3.00
217 A4 200r red lil, *pnksh* 7.50 2.50
218 A4 400r dull bl, *straw* 7.50 3.00
219 A4 500r blk & red, *bl* 7.00 2.50
220 A4 700r vio, *yelsh* 15.00 6.00
Nos. 209-220 (12) 155.00 101.00

War Tax Stamps of 1916-18 Surcharged — 2½ CENTAVOS

1918 ***Rouletted 7***

221 WT2 2½c on 5c rose 2.50 1.50

Perf. 11, 12

222 WT2 2½c on 5c red 1.10 .70
a. "PETRIA" 2.00 2.00
b. "PEPUBLICA" 2.00 2.00
c. "1910" for "1916" 7.50 4.00

War Tax Stamps of 1916-18 Surcharged — "CORREIOS" 1 C.

1919 ***Perf. 11***

224 WT1 1c on 1c gray grn .75 .40
a. "PEPUBLICA" 4.75 4.00
b. Rouletted 7 300.00 100.00

Perf. 12

225 WT2 1½c on 5c red .40 .35
a. "PETRIA" 3.00 2.00
b. "PEPUBLICA" 3.00 2.50
c. "1910" for "1916" 5.00 3.75

Stamps of 1902 Overprinted Locally in Carmine Like Nos. 192-200

1920

226 A3 400r on 50r lt blue .85 .85
227 A3 400r on 80r yel grn .85 .85
228 A3 400r on 300r bl, *sal* .85 .85
Nos. 226-228 (3) 2.55 2.55

War Tax Stamp of 1918 Surcharged in Green — SEIS CENTAVOS

1920 ***Perf. 12***

229 WT2 6c on 5c red .60 .48
a. "1910" for "1916" 8.00 5.00
b. "PETRIA" 2.50 2.00
c. "PEPUBLICA" 2.50 2.00

Lourenco Marques Nos. 117, 119 Surcharged in Red or Bue — 10 c.

1921 ***Perf. 15x14***

230 A4 10c on ½c blk (R) .55 .40
231 A4 30c on 1½c brn (Bl) .55 .70

Same Surcharge on Mozambique Nos. 150, 152, 155 in Red, Blue or Green

232 A6 10c on ½c blk (R) 1.00 .85
233 A6 30c on 1½c brn (Bl) 1.10 .70
234 A6 60c on 2½c vio (G) 1.50 .80
Nos. 230-234 (5) 4.70 3.45

War Tax Stamp of 1918 Surcharged in Green — 2$00

1921 ***Perf. 12***

235 WT2 2e on 5c red 1.00 .50
a. "PETRIA" 2.50 2.25
b. "PEPUBLICA" 4.25 2.50
c. "1910" for "1916" 8.00 6.50

No. 157 Surcharged — 50 c.

1923 ***Perf. 12x11½***

236 A6 50c on 4c pale rose .85 .55

No. 183 Overprinted in Green — Vasco da Gama 1924

1924

237 A6 80c bright rose .85 .60

4th centenary of the death of Vasco da Gama.

Nos. 90 and 91 Surcharged — República 40 C.

1925 ***Perf. 11½***

238 A3 40c on 400r on 50r .70 .70
239 A3 40c on 400r on 80r .60 .48
a. "a" omitted 42.50 42.50

Postage Due Stamp of 1917 Overprinted in Black and Bars in Red — CORREIOS

1929, Jan. ***Perf. 12***

247 D1 50c gray .85 .55

No. 188 Surcharged — 70 C.

1931 ***Perf. 11½***

249 A6 70c on 2e dk vio .70 .50
250 A6 1.40e on 2e dk vio 1.10 .50

"Portugal" Holding Volume of the "Lusiads" — A7

Wmk. Maltese Cross (232)
1933, July 13 Typo. *Perf. 14*
Value in Red or Black

251 A7 1c bister brn (R) .15 .15
252 A7 5c black brn .15 .15
253 A7 10c dp violet .15 .15
254 A7 15c black (R) .15 .15
255 A7 20c light gray .15 .15
256 A7 30c blue green .15 .15
257 A7 40c orange red .15 .15
258 A7 45c brt blue .40 .15
259 A7 50c dk brown .35 .15
260 A7 60c olive grn .25 .15
261 A7 70c orange brn .20 .15
262 A7 80c emerald .20 .15
263 A7 85c deep rose 1.00 .50
264 A7 1e red brown .75 .25
265 A7 1.40e dk blue (R) 7.00 1.10
266 A7 2e dk violet 2.00 .35
267 A7 5e apple green 3.00 .50
268 A7 10e olive bister 7.00 1.00
269 A7 20e orange 22.50 2.00
Nos. 251-269 (19) 45.70
Set value 6.40

See Nos. 298-299.

Common Design Types pictured following the introduction.

Common Design Types
Perf. 13½x13
1938, Aug. Engr. Unwmk.
Name and Value in Black

270 CD34 1c gray green .15 .15
271 CD34 5c orange brn .15 .15
272 CD34 10c dk carmine .15 .15
273 CD34 15c dk vio brn .15 .15
274 CD34 20c slate .15 .15
275 CD35 30c rose vio .15 .15
276 CD35 35c brt green .30 .15
277 CD35 40c brown .40 .15
278 CD35 50c brt red vio .40 .15
279 CD36 60c gray black .50 .15
280 CD36 70c brown vio .50 .15
281 CD36 80c orange .75 .15
282 CD36 1e red .70 .20
283 CD37 1.75e blue 1.75 .30
284 CD37 2e brown car 1.50 .30
285 CD37 5e olive green 3.50 .50
286 CD38 10e blue vio 9.00 1.00
287 CD38 20e red brown 22.50 1.40
Nos. 270-287 (18) 42.70
Set value 4.80

For surcharges see Nos. 297, 301.

No. 258 Surcharged in Black — 40 centavos

1938, Jan. 16 Wmk. 232 *Perf. 14*

288 A7 40c on 45c brt blue 2.50 1.40

Map of Africa — A7a

Perf. 11½x12
1939, July 17 Litho. Unwmk.

289 A7a 80c vio, *pale rose* 1.50 1.25
290 A7a 1.75e bl, *pale bl* 4.00 2.75
291 A7a 3e grn, *yel grn* 6.00 4.00
292 A7a 20e brn, *buff* 30.00 50.00
Nos. 289-292 (4) 41.50 58.00

Presidential visit.

New Cathedral, Lourenço Marques — A8

Railroad Station — A9

Municipal Hall — A10

1944, Dec. Litho. *Perf. 11½*

293 A8 50c dk brown .70 .40
294 A8 50c dk green .70 .40
295 A9 1.75e ultra 4.00 .85
296 A10 20e dk gray 8.50 .85
Nos. 293-296 (4) 13.90 2.50

4th cent. of the founding of Lourenço Marques. See No. 302. For surcharge see No. 300.

No. 283 Surcharged in Carmine

60 CENTAVOS

1946 **Engr.** *Perf. 13½x13*

No.	Type	Description	Unused	Used
297	CD37	60c on 1.75e blue	.85	.40

Lusiads Type of 1933

1947 **Wmk. 232** **Typo.** *Perf. 14*

Value in Black

No.	Type	Description	Unused	Used
298	A7	35c yellow grn	4.00	2.00
299	A7	1.75e deep blue	4.50	2.00

No. 296 Surcharged in Pink

2$00

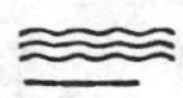

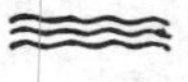

1946 **Unwmk.** *Perf. 11½*

No.	Type	Description	Unused	Used
300	A10	2e on 20e dk gray	1.40	.40

No. 273 Surcharged with New Value and Wavy Lines

Perf. 13½x13

No.	Type	Description	Unused	Used
301	CD34	10c on 15c dk vio brn	.70	.40
a.		Inverted surcharge	30.00	

Cathedral Type of 1944

Commemorative Inscription Omitted

1948 **Litho.** *Perf. 11½*

No.	Type	Description	Unused	Used
302	A8	4.50e brt vermilion	1.40	.38

Antonio Enes — A11

1948, Oct. 4 *Perf. 14*

No.	Type	Description	Unused	Used
303	A11	50c black & cream	1.00	.35
304	A11	5e vio brn & cream	3.00	.85

Birth centenary of Antonio Enes.

Gogogo Peak — A12

Zambezi River Bridge — A13

Zumbo River A14

Waterfall at Nhanhangare A15

Lourenço Marques — A16

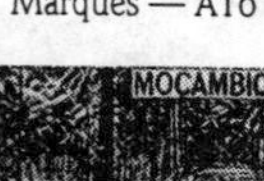

Plantation, Baixa — A17

Pungwe River at Beira — A18

Polana Beach — A19

Lourenço Marques — A20

Malema River — A21

Perf. 13½x13, 13x13½

1948-49 **Typo.** **Unwmk.**

No.	Type	Description	Unused	Used
305	A12	5c orange brn	.25	.15
306	A13	10c violet brn	.25	.15
307	A14	20c dk brown	.25	.15
308	A12	30c plum	.25	.15
309	A14	40c dull green	.25	.15
310	A16	50c slate	.25	.15
311	A15	60c brown car	.25	.15
312	A16	80c violet blk	.25	.15
313	A17	1e carmine	.35	.20
314	A13	1.20e slate gray	.35	.20
315	A18	1.50e dk purple	.50	.20
316	A19	1.75e dk blue ('49)	.75	.25
317	A18	2e brown	.50	.20
318	A20	2.50e dk slate ('49)	1.50	.20
319	A19	3e gray ol ('49)	1.00	.20
320	A15	3.50e olive gray	1.10	.20
321	A17	5e blue grn	1.10	.20
322	A20	10e choc ('49)	2.50	.35
323	A21	15e dp carmine ('49)	7.25	1.75
324	A21	20e orange ('49)	12.00	1.75
		Nos. 305-324 (20)	30.90	6.90

On No. 320 the "$" is reversed.

Lady of Fatima Issue

Common Design Type

1948, Oct. **Litho.** *Perf. 14½*

No.	Type	Description	Unused	Used
325	CD40	50c blue	1.00	.50
326	CD40	1.20e red violet	3.00	1.00
327	CD40	4.50e emerald	8.00	2.00
328	CD40	20e chocolate	14.00	2.50
		Nos. 325-328 (4)	26.00	6.00

Symbols of the UPU — A21a

1949, Apr. 11 *Perf. 14*

No.	Type	Description	Unused	Used
329	A21a	4.50e ultra & pale gray	1.00	.50

75th anniversary of UPU.

Catalogue values for unused stamps in this section, from this point to the end of the section, are for Never Hinged items.

Holy Year Issue

Common Design Types

1950, May *Perf. 13x13½*

No.	Type	Description	Unused	Used
330	CD41	1.50e red orange	.70	.25
331	CD42	3e brt blue	.75	.30

Spotted Triggerfish — A22

Pennant Coral Fish — A22a

Fish: 10c, Golden butterflyfish. 15c, Orange butterflyfish. 20c, Lionfish. 30c, Sharpnose puffer. 40c, Porky filefish. 50c, Dark brown surgeonfish. 1.50e Rainbow wrasse. 2e, Orange-spotted gray-skin. 2.50e, Kasmir snapper. 3e, Convict fish. 3.50e, Stellar triggerfish. 4e, Cornetfish. 4.50e, Vagabond butterflyfish. 5e, Mail-cheeked fish. 6e, Pinnate batfish. 8e, Moorish idol. 9e, Triangulate boxfish. 10e, Flying gurnard. 15e, Redtooth triggerfish. 20e, Striped triggerfish. 30e, Horned cowfish. 50e, Spotted cowfish.

Photogravure and Lithographed

1951 **Unwmk.** *Perf. 14x14½*

Fish in Natural Colors

No.	Type	Description	Unused	Used
332	A22	5c dp yellow	.30	*.75*
333	A22	10c lt blue	.20	*.50*
334	A22	15c yellow	.80	*1.00*
335	A22	20c pale olive	.38	.18
336	A22	30c gray	.38	.18
337	A22	40c pale green	.28	.15
338	A22	50c pale buff	.28	.15
339	A22a	1e aqua	.28	.15
340	A22	1.50e olive	.22	.15
341	A22	2e blue	.30	.18
342	A22	2.50e brnsh lilac	.60	.18
343	A22	3e aqua	.60	.18
344	A22	3.50e olive grn	.60	.18
345	A22	4e blue gray	1.40	1.00
346	A22	4.50e green	.90	.70
347	A22	5e buff	.90	.18
348	A22a	6e salmon pink	.90	.20
349	A22a	8e gray blue	.90	.24
350	A22	9e lilac rose	3.50	.30
351	A22	10e gray lilac	17.00	2.00
352	A22	15e gray	35.00	5.50
353	A22	20e lemon	20.00	3.50
354	A22	30e yellow grn	22.50	4.00
355	A22	50e gray vio	40.00	6.50
		Nos. 332-355 (24)	148.22	28.05

Holy Year Extension Issue

Common Design Type

1951, Oct. **Litho.** *Perf. 14*

No.	Type	Description	Unused	Used
356	CD43	5e carmine & rose	1.75	1.00

Victor Cordon A23

Plane and Ship A24

1951, Oct. *Perf. 11½*

No.	Type	Description	Unused	Used
357	A23	1e dk brown	1.00	.35
358	A23	5e black & slate	4.50	1.00

Centenary of the birth of Victor Cordon, explorer.

Medical Congress Issue

Common Design Type

Design: Miguel Bombarda Hospital.

1952, June 19 **Litho.** *Perf. 13½*

No.	Type	Description	Unused	Used
359	CD44	3e dk bl & brn buff	.85	.35

1952, Sept. 15 **Unwmk.**

No.	Type	Description	Unused	Used
360	A24	1.50e multi	.48	.35

4th African Tourism Congress.

Missionary A25

Papilio Demodocus A26

1953

No.	Type	Description	Unused	Used
361	A25	10c red brn & pale vio	.15	.15
362	A25	1e red brn & pale yel grn	.50	.20
363	A25	5e blk & lt bl	1.40	.35
		Nos. 361-363 (3)	2.05	
		Set value		.60

Exhibition of Sacred Missionary Art, held at Lisbon in 1951.

Canceled to Order

Certain issues, including Nos. 364-383, were canceled to order under Republican administration.

Photogravure and Lithographed

1953, May 28 *Perf. 13x14*

Various Butterflies and Moths in Natural Colors

No.	Type	Description	Unused	Used
364	A26	10c lt blue	.15	.15
365	A26	15c cream	.15	.15
366	A26	20c yellow grn	.20	.15
367	A26	30c lt violet	.20	.15
368	A26	40c brown	.20	.15
369	A26	50c bluish gray	.15	.15
370	A26	80c brt blue	.15	.15
371	A26	1e gray bl	.15	.15
372	A26	1.50e ocher	.22	.15
373	A26	2e orange brn	3.50	.50
374	A26	2.30e blue	3.50	.35
375	A26	2.50e citron	5.25	.35
376	A26	3e lilac rose	1.90	.15
377	A26	4e light blue	.35	.15
378	A26	4.50e orange	.35	.15
379	A26	5e green	.35	.15
380	A26	6e pale vio	.50	.15
381	A26	7.50e buff	4.00	.30
382	A26	10e pink	6.25	.75
383	A26	20e grnsh gray	8.00	.70
		Nos. 364-383 (20)	35.52	
		Set value		4.00
		Set value, CTO		.50

For overprints see Nos. 517, 527.

Stamps of Portugal and Mozambique A27

Stamp of Portugal and Arms of Colonies A27a

1953, July 23 **Litho.** *Perf. 14*

No.	Type	Description	Unused	Used
384	A27	1e multicolored	.55	.40
385	A27	3e multicolored	1.90	.70

Issued in connection with the Lourenço Marques philatelic exhibition, July 1953.

Stamp Centenary Issue

1953 **Photo.** *Perf. 13*

No.	Type	Description	Unused	Used
386	A27a	50c multicolored	.55	.40

Map — A28

1954, Oct. 15 **Litho.**

Color of Colony

No.	Type	Description	Unused	Used
387	A28	10c pale rose lilac	.15	.15
388	A28	20c pale yellow	.15	.15
389	A28	50c lilac	.15	.15
390	A28	1e orange yel	.20	.15
391	A28	2.30e white	.45	.18
392	A28	4e pale salmon	.60	.20
393	A28	10e lt green	1.90	.20
394	A28	20e brown buff	2.50	.35
		Nos. 387-394 (8)	6.10	
		Set value		1.10

For overprints see Nos. 516, 530.

Sao Paulo Issue

Common Design Type

1954, July 2

No.	Type	Description	Unused	Used
395	CD46	3.50e dk gray, cream & ol	.35	.28

Arms of Beira A29

Mousinho de Albuquerque A30

Paper with network as in parenthesis

1954, Dec. 1 *Perf. 13x13½*

Arms in Silver, Gold, Red and Pale Green

396 A29 1.50e dk bl *(bl)* .35 .28
397 A29 3.50e brn *(buff)* .75 .35

Issued to publicize the first philatelic exhibition of Manica and Sofala.

1955, Feb. 1 Litho. *Perf. 11½x12*

2.50e, Statue of Mousinho de Albuquerque.

398 A30 1e gray, blk & buff .60 .35
399 A30 2.50e ol bis, blk & bl .85 .50

100th anniversary of the birth of Mousinho de Albuquerque, statesman.

A31

A32

Eight Races Holding Arms of Portugal

1956, Aug. 4 Unwmk. *Perf. 14½*

Central Design in Multicolored

400 A31 1e pale yellow & multi .28 .20
401 A31 2.50e lt blue & multi .70 .28

Issued to commemorate the visit of President Antonio Oscar de Fragoso Carmona.

1957, Aug. 15 Litho.

402 A32 2.50e View of Beira .48 .28

50th anniversary of the city of Beira.

Brussels Fair Issue

Exhibition Emblems and View — A32a

1958, Oct. 8 Unwmk. *Perf. 14½*

403 A32a 3.50c blk, grn, yel, red & bl .20 .15

Tropical Medicine Congress Issue

Common Design Type

Design: Strophanthus grandiflorus.

1958, Sept. 14 *Perf. 13½*

404 CD47 1.50e sal brn, grn & red 1.25 .70

Caravel — A33

Technical Instruction — A34

1960, June 25 Litho. *Perf. 13½*

405 A33 5e multicolored .32 .15

500th anniversary of the death of Prince Henry the Navigator.

1960, Nov. 21 Unwmk. *Perf. 14½*

406 A34 3e multicolored .40 .28

Commission for Technical Co-operation in Africa South of the Sahara (C.C.T.A.), 10th anniv.

Arms of Lourenço Marques — A35

Arms of various cities of Mozambique.

1961, Jan. 30 Litho. *Perf. 13½*

Arms in Original Colors; Black, Ultramarine and Red Inscriptions

407 A35 5c salmon .15 .15
408 A35 15c pale green .15 .15
409 A35 20c lt vio gray .15 .15
410 A35 30c buff .15 .15
411 A35 50c bluish gray .15 .15
412 A35 1e pale ol .30 .15
413 A35 1.50e lt blue .30 .15
414 A35 2e pale pink .45 .15
415 A35 2.50e lt bl grn 1.00 .15
416 A35 3e beige .60 .20
417 A35 4e yellow .42 .15
418 A35 4.50e pale gray .42 .15
419 A35 5e pale bluish grn .90 .15
420 A35 7.50e rose 1.00 .24
a. "CORREIOS 7$50" omitted
421 A35 10e lt yel grn 1.50 .24
422 A35 20e beige 3.25 .50
423 A35 50e gray 4.75 1.00
Nos. 407-423 (17) 15.64
Set value 3.00

Sports Issue

Common Design Type

Sports: 50c, Water skiing. 1e, Wrestling. 1.50e, Woman gymnast. 2.50e, Field hockey. 4.50e, Women's basketball. 15e, Speedboat racing.

1962, Feb. 10 Unwmk. *Perf. 13½*

Multicolored Designs

424 CD48 50c gray green .15 .15
425 CD48 1e dk gray .70 .35
426 CD48 1.50e pink .40 .15
427 CD48 2.50e buff .45 .15
428 CD48 4.50e gray .70 .40
429 CD48 15e gray green 2.00 1.00
Nos. 424-429 (6) 4.40 2.20

For overprints see Nos. 522, 526, 529.

Anti-Malaria Issue

Common Design Type

Design: Anopheles funestus.

1962, Apr. 5 *Perf. 13½*

430 CD49 2.50e multicolored .60 .35

Mozambique stamps can be mounted in the annually supplemented Scott Portugal album.

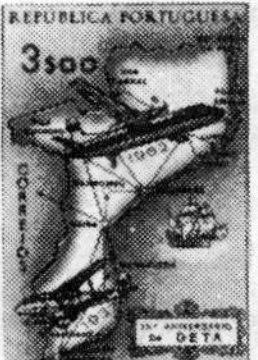
Planes over Mozambique A36

Lourenço Marques 1887 and 1962 A37

1962, Oct. 15 Litho. *Perf. 14½*

431 A36 3e multicolored .35 .20

25th anniversary of DETA airlines.

1962, Nov. 1 *Perf. 13*

432 A37 1e multicolored .28 .15

75th anniversary of Lourenço Marques.

Vasco da Gama Statue and Arms — A38

1963, Apr. 25 Unwmk. *Perf. 14½*

433 A38 3e multicolored .28 .15

Founding of Mozambique City, 200th anniv.

Airline Anniversary Issue

Common Design Type

1963, Oct. 21 Litho. *Perf. 14½*

434 CD50 2.50e brt pink & multi .28 .15

Barque, 1430 — A39

Caravel, 1436 — A40

Development of Sailing Ships: 30c, Lateen-rigged caravel, 1460. 50c, "Sao Gabriel," 1497. 1e, Dom Manuel's ship, 1498. 1.50e, Warship, 1500. 2e, "Flor de la Mar," 1511. 2.50e, Redonda caravel, 1519. 3.50e, 800-ton ship, 1520. 4e, Portuguese India galley, 1521. 4.50e, "Santa Tereza," 1639. 5e, "Nostra Senhora da Conceiçao," 1716. 6e, "Nostra Senhora do Bom Sucesso," 1764. 7.50e, Launch with mortar, 1788. 8e, Brigantine, 1793. 10e, Corvette, 1799. 12.50e, Schooner "Maria Teresa," 1820. 15e, "Vasco da Gama," 1841. 20e, Frigate "Dom Fernando II," 1843. 30e, Training Ship "Sagres," 1924.

1963, Dec. 1 Litho. *Perf. 14½*

435 A39 10c multicolored .15 .15
436 A40 20c multicolored .15 .15
437 A40 30c multicolored .20 .20
438 A40 50c multicolored .20 .20
439 A40 1e multicolored .35 .15
440 A40 1.50e multicolored .20 .15
441 A40 2e multicolored .28 .20
442 A39 2.50e multicolored .50 .15
443 A40 3.50e multicolored .45 .28
444 A39 4e multicolored .60 .15
445 A40 4.50e multicolored 1.10 .22
446 A40 5e multicolored 6.50 .18
447 A39 6e multicolored 1.00 .25
448 A39 7.50e multicolored 1.10 .32
449 A39 8e multicolored 1.10 .32
450 A39 10e multicolored 1.25 .60
451 A39 12.50e multicolored 1.40 .75
452 A39 15e multicolored 1.40 .60
453 A40 20e multicolored 2.00 .70
454 A40 30e multicolored 2.75 1.25
Nos. 435-454 (20) 22.68
Set value 5.35

National Overseas Bank Issue

Modern Bank Building, Luanda — A40a

1964, May 16 *Perf. 13½*

455 A40a 1.50e bl, yel gray & grn .35 .20

National Overseas Bank of Portugal, cent.

Pres. Americo Rodrigues Thomaz — A41

Perf. 13½x12½

1964, July 23 Litho.

456 A41 2.50e multicolored .20 .15

Visit of Pres. Americo Rodrigues Thomaz of Portugal to Mozambique, in July.

Royal Barge of King John V, 1728 — A42

Designs: 35c, Barge of Dom Jose I, 1753. 1e, Customs barge, 1768. 1.50e, Sailor, 1780, vert. 2.50e, Royal barge, 1780. 5e, Barge of Dona Carlota Joaquina, 1790. 9e, Barge of Dom Miguel, 1831.

1964, Dec. 18 Litho. *Perf. 14½*

457 A42 15c multicolored .20 .15
458 A42 35c lt bl & multi .20 .15
459 A42 1e gray & multi .50 .15
460 A42 1.50e gray & multi .30 .15
461 A42 2.50e multicolored .25 .15
462 A42 5e multicolored .30 .15
463 A42 9e multicolored .50 .40
Nos. 457-463 (7) 2.25
Set value .90

ITU Issue

Common Design Type

1965, May 17 Unwmk. *Perf. 14½*

464 CD52 1e yellow & multi .40 .28

National Revolution Issue

Common Design Type

Design: 1e, Beira Railroad Station, and Antonio Enes School.

1966, May 28 Litho. *Perf. 11½*

465 CD53 1e multicolored .20 .20

Harquebusier, 1560 — A42a

Designs: 30c, Harquebusier, 1640. 40c, Infantry soldier, 1777. 50c, Infantry officer, 1777. 80c, Drummer, 1777. 1e, Infantry sergeant, 1777. 2e, Infantry major, 1784. 2.50e, Colonial officer, 1788. 3e, Infantry soldier, 1789. 5e, Colonial bugler, 1801. 10e, Colonial officer, 1807. 15e, Colonial infantry soldier, 1817.

1967, Jan. 12 Photo. *Perf. 14*

466 A42a 20c multicolored .15 .15
467 A42a 30c multicolored .15 .15
468 A42a 40c multicolored .15 .15
469 A42a 50c multicolored .15 .15
470 A42a 80c multicolored .50 .35
471 A42a 1e multicolored .40 .15
472 A42a 2e multicolored .40 .20
473 A42a 2.50e multicolored .65 .28
474 A42a 3e multicolored .50 .20
475 A42a 5e multicolored .65 .28
476 A42a 10e multicolored .85 .35
477 A42a 15e multicolored 1.00 .55
Nos. 466-477 (12) 5.55 2.96

Navy Club Issue
Common Design Type

Designs: 3e, Capt. Azevedo Coutinho and gunboat (stern-wheeler) Tete. 10e, Capt. Joao Roby and gunboat (paddle steamer) Granada.

1967, Jan. 31 Litho. *Perf. 13*

478	CD54	3e	multicolored	.35	.15
479	CD54	10e	multicolored	.75	.40

Virgin's Crown, Presented by Portuguese Women — A43

1967, May 13 Litho. *Perf. 12½x13*

480	A43	50c	multicolored	.15	.15

50th anniversary of the appearance of the Virgin Mary to 3 shepherd children at Fatima.

Cabral Issue

Raising the Cross at Porto Seguro — A44

Designs: 1.50e, First mission to Brazil. 3e, Grace Church, Santarem, vert.

1968, Apr. 22 Litho. *Perf. 14*

481	A44	1e	multicolored	.15	.15
482	A44	1.50e	multicolored	.20	.15
483	A44	3e	multicolored	.30	.20
			Nos. 481-483 (3)	.65	
			Set value		.30

500th birth anniv. of Pedro Alvares Cabral, navigator who took possession of Brazil for Portugal.

Admiral Coutinho Issue
Common Design Type

Design: 70c, Adm. Coutinho and Adm. Gago Coutinho Airport.

1969, Feb. 17 Litho. *Perf. 14*

484	CD55	70c	multicolored	.15	.15

Luiz Vaz de Camoens — A45

Sailing Ship, 1553 — A46

Designs: 1.50e, Map of Mozambique, 1554. 2.50e, Chapel of Our Lady of Baluarte, 1552. 5e, Excerpt from Lusiads about Mozambique (1st Song, 14th Stanza).

Perf. 12½x13, 13x12½

1969, June 10 Litho.

485	A45	15c	multicolored	.15	.15
486	A46	50c	multicolored	.15	.15
487	A45	1.50e	multicolored	.15	.15
488	A46	2.50e	multicolored	.15	.15
489	A45	5e	multicolored	.28	.15
			Set value	.75	.40

400th anniversary of the visit to Mozambique of Luiz Vaz de Camoens (1524-1580), poet.

Vasco da Gama Issue

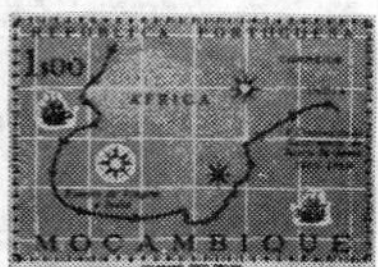

Map Showing Voyage to Mozambique and India — A47

1969, Aug. 29 Litho. *Perf. 14*

490	A47	1e	multicolored	.15	.15

Vasco da Gama (1469-1524), navigator.

Administration Reform Issue
Common Design Type

1969, Sept. 25 Litho. *Perf. 14*

491	CD56	1.50e	multicolored	.15	.15

King Manuel I Issue

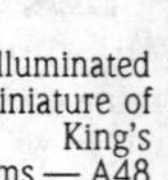

Illuminated Miniature of King's Arms — A48

1969, Dec. 1 Litho. *Perf. 14*

492	A48	80c	multicolored	.15	.15

500th anniversary of the birth of King Manuel I.

Marshal Carmona Issue
Common Design Type

5e, Antonio Oscar Carmona in marshal's uniform.

1970, Nov. 15 Litho. *Perf. 14*

493	CD57	5e	multicolored	.20	.15

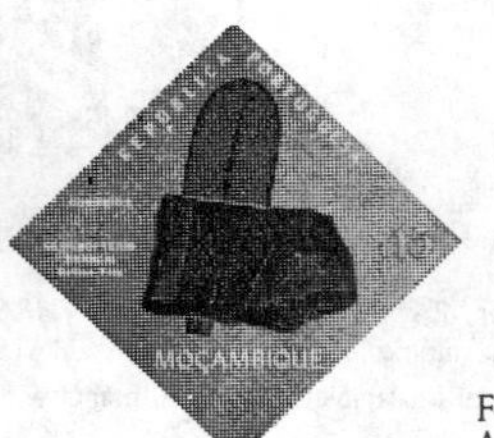

Fossil Fern A49

Fossils and Minerals: 50c, Fossil snail. 1e, Stibnite. 1.50e, Pink beryl. 2e, Dinosaur. 3e, Tantalocolumbite. 3.50e, Verdelite. 4e, Zircon. 10e, Petrified wood.

1971, Jan. 15 Litho. *Perf. 13*

494	A49	15c	gray & multi	.25	.15
495	A49	50c	lt ultra & multi	.25	.15
496	A49	1e	green & multi	.25	.15
497	A49	1.50e	multicolored	.25	.15
498	A49	2e	multicolored	.50	.15
499	A49	3e	lt bl & multi	.50	.15
500	A49	3.50e	lilac & multi	1.00	.20
501	A49	4e	multicolored	1.00	.20
502	A49	10e	dl red & multi	4.00	.50
			Nos. 494-502 (9)	8.00	
			Set value		1.25

For overprints see Nos. 525, 528.

Mozambique Island — A49a

1972, May 25 Litho. *Perf. 13*

503	A49a	4e	ultra & multi	.28	.15

4th centenary of publication of The Lusiads by Luiz Camoens.

Olympic Games Issue
Common Design Type

3e, Hurdles and swimming, Olympic emblem.

1972, June 20 *Perf. 14x13½*

504	CD59	3e	multi	.20	.15

For overprint see No. 523.

Lisbon-Rio de Janeiro Flight Issue
Common Design Type

Design: 1e, "Santa Cruz" over Recife harbor.

1972, Sept. 20 Litho. *Perf. 13½*

505	CD60	1e	multi	.15	.15

Sailboats A50

Designs: Various sailboats.

1973, Aug. 21 Litho. *Perf. 12x11½*

506	A50	1e	multi	.15	.15
507	A50	1.50e	multi	.15	.15
508	A50	3e	multi	.28	.15
			Nos. 506-508 (3)	.58	
			Set value		.25

World Sailing Championships, Vauriens Class, Lourenço Marques, Aug. 21-30.
For overprints see Nos. 519-520, 524.

WMO Centenary Issue
Common Design Type

1973, Dec. 15 Litho. *Perf. 13*

509	CD61	2e	rose red & multi	.20	.15

For overprint see No. 521.

Radar Station A51

1974, June 25 Litho. *Perf. 13*

510	A51	50c	multi	.15	.15

Establishment of satellite communications network via Intelsat among Portugal, Angola and Mozambique.
For overprint see No. 518.

"Bird" Made of Flags of Portugal and Mozambique A52

1975, Jan. Litho. *Perf. 14½*

511	A52	1e	pink & multi	.15	.15
512	A52	1.50e	yel & multi	.15	.15
513	A52	2e	gray & multi	.20	.15
514	A52	3.50e	lem & multi	.28	.15
515	A52	6e	lt bl & multi	.75	.28
a.			Souv. sheet of 5, #511-515 + label	3.50	
			Nos. 511-515 (5)	1.53	
			Set value		.70

Lusaka Agreement, Sept. 7, 1974, which gave Mozambique independence from Portugal, effective June 25, 1975.
No. 515a sold for 25e.
For overprints see Nos. 543-545.

Republic
Issues of 1953-74 Overprinted in Red or Black:

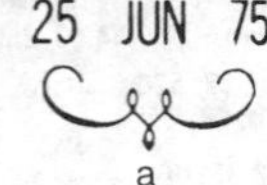

a

INDEPENDÊNCIA
25 JUN 75

b

1975, June 25

516	A28 (a)	10c	(R; #387)	.15	.15
517	A26 (a)	40c	(R; #368)	.15	.15
518	A51 (b)	50c	(B; #510)	.15	.15
519	A50 (b)	1e	(B; #506)	.15	.15
520	A50 (b)	1.50e	(B; #507)	.20	.15
521	CD61 (a)	2e	(B; #509)	.20	.15
522	CD48 (b)	2.50e	(B; #427)	.40	.20
523	CD59 (a)	3e	(R; #504)	.40	.20
524	A50 (b)	3e	(B; #508)	.40	.40
525	A49 (b)	3.50e	(B; #500)	.40	.40
526	CD48 (b)	4.50e	(B; #428)	2.50	1.75
527	A26 (a)	7.50e	(R; #381)	.85	.40
528	A49 (b)	10e	(B; #502)	1.75	.60
529	CD48 (b)	15e	(B; #429)	1.75	.85
530	A28 (a)	20e	(R; #394)	1.00	.60
			Nos. 516-530,C35-C38 (19)	13.60	7.26

Workers, Farmers and Children A53

Designs: 30c, 50c, 2.50e, like 20c. 4.50e, 5e, 10c, 50e, Dancers, workers, armed family.

1975 Litho. *Perf. 12x11½*

531	A53	20c	pink & multi	.15	.15
532	A53	30c	bis & multi	.15	.15
533	A53	50c	bl & multi	.15	.15
534	A53	2.50e	grn & multi	.15	.15
535	A53	4.50e	brn & multi	.18	.15
536	A53	5e	bis & multi	.18	.15
537	A53	10e	bl & multi	.35	.20
538	A53	50e	yel & multi	1.65	.80
a.			Souvenir sheet of 8	3.25	3.25
			Set value	2.60	1.35

No. 538a contains 8 stamps similar to Nos. 531-538 with simulated perforation. Sold for 75e.
For overprint see No. 554.

Farm Woman — A54

1976, Apr. 7 Litho. *Perf. 14½*

539	A54	1e	shown	.15	.15
540	A54	1.50e	Teacher	.16	.16
541	A54	2.50e	Nurse	.25	.25
542	A54	10e	Mother	.50	.35
			Nos. 539-542 (4)	1.06	.91

Day of the Mozambique Woman, Apr. 7.

Nos. 513-515 Overprinted in Red: "PRESIDENTE KENNETH KAUNDA / PRIMEIRA VISITA 20/4/1976"

1976, Apr. 20 Litho. *Perf. 14½*

543	A52	2e	gray & multi	.18	.18
544	A52	3.50e	lem & multi	.30	.30
545	A52	6e	lt bl & multi	.50	.50
			Nos. 543-545 (3)	.98	.98

Visit of President Kaunda of Zambia.

Pres. Machel's Arrival at Maputo — A55

Mozambique No. 1 — A56

Designs: 1e, Independence proclamation ceremony. 2.50e, Pres. Samora Moises Machel taking office. 7.50e, Military parade. 20e, Flame of Unity and festival.

1976, June 25

546	A55	50c	multi	.15	.15
547	A55	1e	multi	.15	.15
548	A55	2.50e	multi	.24	.20
549	A55	7.50e	multi	.40	.24
550	A55	20e	multi	1.00	.50
			Nos. 546-550 (5)	1.94	1.24

First anniversary of independence.

1976, July *Perf. 11½x12*

551	A56	1.50e	ocher & multi	.18	.18
552	A56	6e	red & multi	.35	.28

Centenary of Mozambique postage stamps.

Flag and Weapons — A57

1976, Sept. 25 Litho. *Perf. 14½*

553	A57	3e	multi	.24	.15

Army Day 1976.

No. 534 Overprinted in Silver: "FACIM"

1976 Litho. *Perf. 12x11½*

554	A53	2.50e	multi	.28	.15

FACIM, Industrial Fair.

Bush Baby — A58

Animals: 1e, Honey badger. 1.50e, Pangolin. 2e, Steinbok. 2.50e, Guenon (monkey). 3e, Cape hunting dog. 4e, Cheetah. 5e, Spotted hyena. 7.50e, Wart hog. 8e, Hippopotamus. 10e, Rhinoceros. 15e, Sable antelope. 1e, 2e, 3e, 4e, 7.50e, 8e, 10e horiz.

1977, Jan. Litho. *Perf. 14½*

555	A58	50c multi	.15	.15
556	A58	1e multi	.15	.15
557	A58	1.50e multi	.15	.15
558	A58	2e multi	.15	.15
559	A58	2.50e multi	.18	.15
560	A58	3e multi	.20	.15
561	A58	4e multi	.28	.15
562	A58	5e multi	.35	.15
563	A58	7.50e multi	.50	.20
564	A58	8e multi	.55	.28
565	A58	10e multi	.70	.28
566	A58	15e multi	1.00	.40
		Nos. 555-566 (12)	4.36	
		Set value		2.00

Congress Emblem — A59

Monument in Maputo — A60

Design: 3.50e, Monument in Macheje, site of 2nd Frelimo Congress, horiz.

1977, Feb. 7 *Perf. 14½*

567	A59	3e multi	.20	.20

Perf. 12x11½, 11½x12

568	A60	3.50e multi	.28	.28
569	A60	20e multi	1.00	.35
		Nos. 567-569 (3)	1.48	.83

3rd FRELIMO Party Congress, Maputo, Feb. 3-7.

Women, Child's Design — A61

Worker and Farmer — A62

1977, Apr. 7 Litho. *Perf. 14½*

570	A61	5e dp org & multi	.28	.18
571	A61	15e lt grn & multi	.70	.20

Mozambique Women's Day 1977.

1977, May 1 Litho. *Perf. 14½*

572	A62	5e red, blk & yel	.38	.28

Labor Day.

People, Flags and Rising Sun — A63

1977, June 25 Litho. *Perf. 11½x12*

573	A63	50c multi	.15	.15
574	A63	1.50e multi	.15	.15
575	A63	3e multi	.20	.15
576	A63	15e multi	.70	.20
		Nos. 573-576 (4)	1.20	
		Set value		.48

2nd anniversary of independence.

Bread Palm — A64

1977, Dec. 21 Litho. *Perf. 12x11½*

577	A64	1e shown	.15	.15
578	A64	10e Nyala	.50	.24
		Set value		.30

Nature protection and Stamp Day.

Chariesthes Bella Rufoplagiata — A65

Violet-crested Touraco — A66

Beetles: 1e, Tragocephalus variegata. 1.50e, Monochamus leuconotus. 3e, Prospocera lactator meridionalis. 5e, Dinocephalus ornatus. 10e, Tragiscoschema nigroscriptum maculata.

1978, Jan. 20 Litho. *Perf. 11½x12*

579	A65	50c multi	.15	.15
580	A65	1e multi	.15	.15
581	A65	1.50e multi	.15	.15
582	A65	3e multi	.20	.20
583	A65	5e multi	.35	.35
584	A65	10e multi	.50	.35
		Set value	1.25	1.10

1978, Mar. 20 Litho. *Perf. 11½*

Birds of Mozambique: 1e, Lilac-breasted roller. 1.50e, Weaver. 2.50e, Violet-backed starling. 3e, Peter's twinspot. 15e, European bee-eater.

585	A66	50c multi	.15	.15
586	A66	1e multi	.15	.15
587	A66	1.50e multi	.15	.15
588	A66	2.50e multi	.18	.18
589	A66	3e multi	.20	.20
590	A66	15e multi	.70	.35
		Set value	1.30	.92

Mother and Child, WHO Emblem A67

1978, Apr. 17 *Perf. 12*

591	A67	15e multi	.50	.28

Smallpox eradication campaign.

Crinum Delagoense — A68

No. 1, Canada No. 1 — A69

Flowers of Mozambique: 1e, Gloriosa superba. 1.50e, Eulophia speciosa. 3e, Erithrina humeana. 5e, Astripomoea malvacea. 10e, Kigelia africana.

1978, May 16 *Perf. 11½x12*

592	A68	50c multi	.15	.15
593	A68	1e multi	.15	.15
594	A68	1.50e multi	.15	.15
595	A68	3e multi	.20	.20
596	A68	5e multi	.24	.24
597	A68	10e multi	.48	.28
		Set value	1.12	.92

1978, June 9

598	A69	15e multi	.50	.28

CAPEX Canadian International Philatelic Exhibition, Toronto, Ont., June 9-18.

National Flag — A70

Soldiers, Festival Emblem — A71

1.50e, Coat of arms. 7.50e, Page of Constitution people. 10e, Music band & natl. anthem.

1978, June 25 *Perf. 11½x12*

599	A70	1e multi	.15	.15
600	A70	1.50e multi	.15	.15
601	A70	7.50e multi	.28	.18
602	A70	10e multi	.50	.24
a.		Souvenir sheet of 4	1.75	1.75
		Nos. 599-602 (4)	1.08	
		Set value		.58

3rd anniversary of proclamation of independence. No. 602a contains 4 stamps similar to Nos. 599-602 with simulated perforations. Sold for 30e.

1978, July 28

2.50e, Student. 7.50e, Farmworkers.

603	A71	2.50e multi	.18	.15
604	A71	3e multi	.20	.15
605	A71	7.50e multi	.25	.18
		Nos. 603-605 (3)	.63	.48

11th World Youth Festival, Havana, 7/28-8/5.

Czechoslovakia No. B126 and PRAGA '78 Emblem — A72

1978, Sept. 8 Litho. *Perf. 12x11½*

606	A72	15e multi	.50	.24
a.		Souvenir sheet	2.50	2.50

PRAGA '78 International Philatelic Exhibition, Prague, Sept. 8-17.

No. 606a contains one stamp with simulated perforations. Sold for 30e.

Soccer — A73

Stamp Day: 1.50e, Shotput. 3e, Hurdling. 7.50e, Fieldball. 12.50e, Swimming. 25e, Roller skate hockey.

1978, Dec. 21 Litho. *Perf. 12x11½*

607	A73	50c multi	.15	.15
608	A73	1.50e multi	.15	.15
609	A73	3e multi	.15	.15
610	A73	7.50e multi	.28	.15
611	A73	12.50e multi	.35	.20
612	A73	25e multi	.70	.35
		Nos. 607-612 (6)	1.78	
		Set value		.92

Carrier Pigeon, UPU Emblem A74

1979, Jan. 1 Litho. *Perf. 11x11½*

613	A74	20e multi	.55	.40

Membership in Universal Postal Union.

Soldier Giving Gourd to Woman — A75

Edward Chivambo Mondlane A76

Designs: 3e, Frelimo soldiers. 7.50e, Mozambique children in school.

1979, Feb. 3 *Perf. 11½x11, 11x11½*

614	A75	1e multi	.15	.15
615	A75	3e multi	.20	.15
616	A75	7.50e multi	.28	.15
617	A76	12.50e multi	.55	.20
		Nos. 614-617 (4)	1.18	
		Set value		.55

Dr. Edward Chivambo Mondlane (1920-1969), educator, founder of Frelimo Party.

Shaded Silver Cat — A77

Cats: 1.50e, Manx. 2.50e, English blue. 3e, Turkish. 12.50e, Long-haired Mid-East tabby. 20e, African wild cat.

1979, Mar. 27 Litho. *Perf. 11*

618	A77	50c multi	.15	.15
619	A77	1.50e multi	.15	.15
620	A77	2.50e multi	.15	.15
621	A77	3e multi	.18	.15
622	A77	12.50e multi	.50	.20
623	A77	20e multi	.70	.28
		Nos. 618-623 (6)	1.83	
		Set value		.85

Wrestling and Moscow '80 Emblem — A78

Sport and Moscow '80 Emblem: 2e, Running. 3e, Equestrian. 5e, Canoeing. 10e, High jump. 15e, Archery.

1979, Apr. 24 Litho. *Perf. 11*

624 A78 1e gray grn & blk .15 .15
625 A78 2e brt bl & blk .15 .15
626 A78 3e lt brn & blk .15 .15
627 A78 5e multi .18 .15
628 A78 10e grn & blk .30 .15
629 A78 15e lil rose & blk .50 .18
Nos. 624-629 (6) 1.43
Set value .58

Souvenir Sheet

Imperf

630 A78 30e rose & dk brn 1.75 1.75

22nd Olympic Games, Moscow, July 10-Aug. 3, 1980. No. 630 contains one 47x37mm stamp.

Garden and IYC Emblem A79

Children's Drawings and IYC Emblem: 1.50e, Dancers. 3e, City. 5e, Farmers. 7.50e, Village. 12.50e, Automobiles, train and flowers.

1979, June 1 Litho. *Perf. 11*

631 A79 50c multi .15 .15
632 A79 1.50e multi .15 .15
633 A79 3e multi .15 .15
634 A79 5e multi .15 .15
635 A79 7.50e multi .20 .15
636 A79 12.50e multi .40 .15
Set value 1.00 .55

International Year of the Child.

Flight from Colonialism — A80

Designs: 2e, Founding of FRELIMO and Pres. Eduardo Chivambo Mondlane. 3e, Advance of armed strruggle and death of Mondlane. 7.50e, Final fight for liberation. 15e, Proclamation of victory, Pres. Samora Moises Machel, flag and torch. Designs after mural in Heroes' Square, Maputo. 30e, Building up the country.

1979, June 25

637 A80 50c multi .15 .15
638 A80 2e multi .15 .15
639 A80 3e multi .15 .15
640 A80 7.50e multi .20 .15
641 A80 15e multi .50 .20
b. Strip of 5, #537-641 1.25 1.00
Set value .48

Souvenir Sheet

Imperf

641A A80 30e multi 3.25 3.25

4th anniversary of independence. No. 641A contains one stamp with simulated perforations. No. 641b has continuous design.

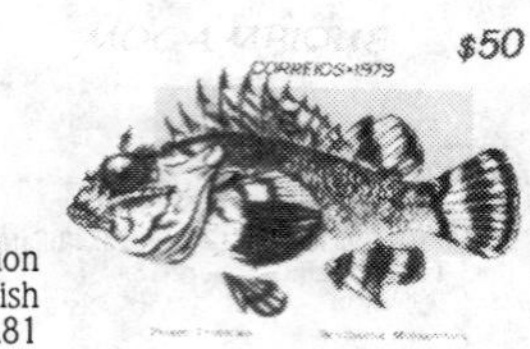

Scorpion Fish A81

Tropical Fish: 1.50e, King fish. 2.50e, Gobius inhaca. 3e, Acanthurus lineatus. 10e, Gobuchthys lemayi. 12.50e, Variola louti.

1979, Aug. 7 Litho. *Perf. 11*

642 A81 50c multi .15 .15
643 A81 1.50e multi .15 .15
644 A81 2.50e multi .18 .15
645 A81 3e multi .20 .15
646 A81 10e multi .50 .15
647 A81 12.50e multi .60 .20
Nos. 642-647 (6) 1.78
Set value .65

For surcharge see No. 1254.

Quartz A82

Mozambique Minerals.

1979, Sept. 10

648 A82 1e shown .15 .15
649 A82 1.50e Beryl .15 .15
650 A82 2.50e Magnetite .18 .15
651 A82 5e Tourmaline .20 .15
652 A82 10e Euxenite .35 .15
653 A82 20e Fluorite .70 .35
Nos. 648-653 (6) 1.73
Set value .82

Citizens Gathering Arms A83

1979, Sept. 25

654 A83 5e multi .28 .15

15th anniversary of independence.

Locomotive — A85

Designs: Historic Locomotives.

1979, Nov. 11 Litho. *Perf. 11*

656 A85 50c multi .15 .15
657 A85 1.50e multi .15 .15
658 A85 3e multi .15 .15
659 A85 7.50e multi .24 .15
660 A85 12.50e multi .35 .18
661 A85 15e multi .50 .20
Nos. 656-661 (6) 1.54
Set value .72

Dalmatian — A86

Perf. 11½x11, 11x11½

1979, Dec. 17 Litho.

662 A86 50c Basenji, vert. .15 .15
663 A86 1.50e shown .15 .15
664 A86 3e Boxer .15 .15
665 A86 7.50e Blue gasconha braco .25 .15
666 A86 12.50e Cocker spaniel .35 .15
667 A86 15e Pointer .50 .18
Nos. 662-667 (6) 1.55
Set value .60

Nireus Lyaeus A87

Butterflies: 1.50e, Amauris ochlea. 2.50e, Pinacopterix eriphia. 5e, Junonia hierta cebrene. 10e, Nephronia argia. 20e, Catacroptera cloanthe.

1979, Dec. 21

668 A87 1e multi .15 .15
669 A87 1.50e multi .15 .15
670 A87 2.50e multi .15 .15
671 A87 5e multi .20 .15
672 A87 10e multi .45 .24
673 A87 20e multi 1.00 .50
Nos. 668-673 (6) 2.10
Set value 1.00

Dermacentor Rhinocerinus, Rhinoceros — A88

Ticks and Animals: 50c, Dermacentor circumguttatus cunhasilvai, elephant. 2.50e, Green tick, giraffe. 3e, Red tick, antelope. 5e, Ambloymma theilerae, cattle. 7.50e, Buffalo tick, buffalo.

1980, Jan. 29 Litho. *Perf. 11½x11*

674 A88 50c multi .15 .15
675 A88 1.50e multi .15 .15
676 A88 2.50e multi .15 .15
677 A88 3e multi .15 .15
678 A88 5e multi .18 .15
679 A88 7.50e multi .24 .15
Set value .85 .58

Ford Hercules, 1950 A89

Public Transportation: 1.50e, Scania Marcopolo, 1978. 3e, Bussing Nag, 1936. 5e, Articulated Ikarus, 1978. 7.50e, Ford taxi, 1929. 12.50e, Fiat 131 taxi, 1978.

1980, Feb. 29 Litho. *Perf. 11*

680 A89 50c multi .15 .15
681 A89 1.50e multi .15 .15
682 A89 3e multi .15 .15
683 A89 5e multi .20 .15
684 A89 7.50e multi .35 .15
685 A89 12.50e multi .50 .15
Nos. 680-685 (6) 1.50
Set value .58

Marx, Engels, and Lenin A90

1980, May 1 Litho. *Perf. 11*

686 A90 10e multi .28 .15

Workers' Day.

"Heads," by Malangatana, London 1980 Emblem — A91

Paintings by Mozambique Artists: 1.50e, Crowded Market, by Moises Simbine. 3e, Heads with Helmets, by Malangatana. 5e, Women with Goods, by Machiana. 7.50e, Crowd with Masks, by Malangatana. 12.50e, Man and Woman with Spear, by Mankeu.

1980, May 6

687 A91 50c multi .15 .15
688 A91 1.50e multi .15 .15
689 A91 3e multi .15 .15
690 A91 5e multi .18 .15
691 A91 7.50e multi .28 .15
692 A91 12.50e multi .50 .15
Nos. 687-692 (6) 1.41
Set value .58

London 1980 Intl. Stamp Exhibition, May 6-14.

World Telecommunications Day — A92

1980, May 17 Litho. *Perf. 12*

693 A92 15e multi .50 .28

Mueda Massacre, 20th Anniv. — A93

People with Weapons and Flag — A94

1980, June 16 Litho. *Perf. 11*

694 A93 15e multi .50 .28

1980, June 25

695 A94 1e Development projects, 1975 .15 .15
696 A94 2e shown .15 .15
697 A94 3e Arms, flags, 1977 .15 .15
698 A94 4e Raised fists, 1978 .20 .15
699 A94 5e Hand holding grain, flags, 1979 .24 .15
700 A94 10e Year banners, 1980 .38 .15
Nos. 695-700 (6) 1.27
Set value .60

Souvenir Sheet

Litho. *Imperf.*

700A A94 30e Soldiers 3.00

5th anniv. of independence. No. 700A contains one stamp with simulated perforations.

Gymnast, Moscow '80 Emblem A95

1980, July 19

701 A95 50c shown .15 .15
702 A95 1.50e Soccer .15 .15
703 A95 2.50e Running .15 .15
704 A95 3e Volleyball .15 .15

705 A95 10e Bicycling .40 .18
706 A95 12.50e Boxing .50 .28
Set value 1.25 .80

22nd Summer Olympic Games, Moscow, July 19-Aug. 3.

Soldier, Map of Southern Africa Showing Zimbabwe — A96

1980, Apr. 18
707 A96 10e multi .28 .15

Establishment of independent Zimbabwe, Apr. 18.

Narina Trogon — A97

1980, July 30 Litho. *Perf. 11*
708 A97 1m shown .15 .15
709 A97 1.50m Crowned crane .15 .15
710 A97 2.50m Red-necked francolin .15 .15
711 A97 5m Ostrich .18 .15
712 A97 7.50m Spur-winged goose .30 .15
713 A97 12.50m Fish eagle .50 .24
Set value 1.20 .75

For surcharge see No. 1255.

First Census, Aug. 1-15 — A98

1980, Aug. 12 *Perf. 11*
714 A98 3.5m multi .15 .15

Brush Fire Control Campaign — A99

1980, Sept. 7
715 A99 3.5m multi .15 .15

Harpa Major — A100

1980, Dec. 12 Litho. *Perf. 11*
716 A100 1m *shown* .15 .15
717 A100 1.50m *Lambis chiragra* .15 .15
718 A100 2.50m *Murex pecten* .15 .15
719 A100 5m *Architectonia perspectiva* .15 .15
720 A100 7.50m *Murex ramosus* .28 .15
721 A100 12.50m *Strombus aurisdinae* .50 .24
Set value 1.12 .68

Pres. Machel and Symbols of Industry and Transportation — A101

Decade of Development, 1981-1990 (Pres. Machel and): 7.50m, Soldiers. 12.50m, Symbols of education.

1981, Jan. 1 Litho. *Perf. 11x11½*
722 A101 3.50m red & bl .15 .15
723 A101 7.50m grn & red brn .30 .15
724 A101 12.50m dk bl & lil rose .48 .15
Nos. 722-724 (3) .93 .45

Bilbao Soccer Stadium, Soccer Player — A102

Designs: Soccer players and various stadiums.

1981, Jan. 30 Litho. *Perf. 11*
725 A102 1m multi .15 .15
726 A102 1.50m multi .15 .15
727 A102 2.50m multi .15 .15
728 A102 5m multi .15 .15
729 A102 7.50m multi .28 .15
730 A102 12.50m multi .50 .20
c. Souvenir sheet of 6 1.25 1.25
Set value 1.12 .65

Souvenir Sheets

Imperf

730A A102 20m multi .85 .85
730B A102 20m multi .85 .85

ESPANA '82 World Cup Soccer Championship. No. 730c contains Nos. 725-730 with simulated perforations. Sizes: No. 730A, 105x85mm; 730B, 141x111mm.

Giraffe — A103

1981, Mar. 3 *Perf. 11*
731 A103 50c shown .15 .15
732 A103 1.50m Tsessebe .15 .15
733 A103 2.50m Aardvark .15 .15
734 A103 3m African python .15 .15
735 A103 5m Loggerhead turtle .18 .15
736 A103 10m Marabou .40 .15
737 A103 12.50m Saddlebill stork .50 .20
738 A103 15m Kori bustard .60 .28
Nos. 731-738 (8) 2.28
Set value 1.12

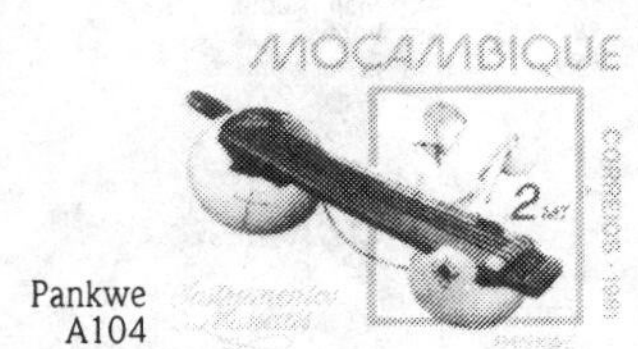
Pankwe — A104

1981, Apr. 8 Litho. *Perf. 11*
739 A104 50c Chitende, vert. .15 .15
740 A104 2m shown .15 .15
741 A104 2.50m Kanyembe, vert. .15 .15
742 A104 7m Nyanga .28 .28
743 A104 10m Likuti and m'petheni .40 .40
Set value .90 .90

International Year of the Disabled — A105

1981, Apr. 18
744 A105 5m multi .20 .15

African Buffalo and Helicopter, Exhibition Emblem — A106

1981, June 14 *Perf. 11*
745 A106 2m shown .15 .15
746 A106 5m Hunters, blue kids .15 .15
747 A106 6m Hunter, impala .18 .15
748 A106 7.50m Hunters shooting .30 .15
749 A106 12.50m Elephants .50 .15
750 A106 20m Trap .80 .30
a. Souv. sheet of 6, #745-750, imperf. 2.50 2.50
Nos. 745-750 (6) 2.08
Set value .80

World Hunting Exhibition, Plovdiv, Bulgaria. No. 750a sold for 60m.

For surcharge see No. 1258.

50-centavo Coin, Obverse and Reverse — A107

Sunflower — A108

First Anniversary of New Currency (Coins on stamps of matching denomination).

1981, June 16
751 A107 50c multi .15 .15
752 A107 1m multi .15 .15
753 A107 2.50m multi .15 .15
754 A107 5m multi .20 .15
755 A107 10m multi .40 .20
756 A107 20m multi .80 .28
a. Souv. sheet of 6, #751-756, imperf. 1.75 1.75
Set value 1.55 .75

No. 756a sold for 40m.

1981, July 24 Litho. *Perf. 14½*
757 A108 50c shown .15 .15
758 A108 1m Cotton .15 .15
759 A108 1.50m Sisal .15 .15
760 A108 2.50m Cashews .15 .15
761 A108 3.50m Tea leaves .15 .15
762 A108 4.50m Sugar cane .20 .15
763 A108 10m Castor-oil plant .40 .15
764 A108 12.50m Coconut .50 .18
765 A108 15m Tobacco leaves .60 .20
766 A108 25m Rice 1.00 .40
767 A108 40m Corn 1.65 .60
768 A108 60m Peanut 2.50 .85
Nos. 757-768 (12) 7.60
Set value 2.75

For surcharges see Nos. 1185, 1216, 1218, 1252.

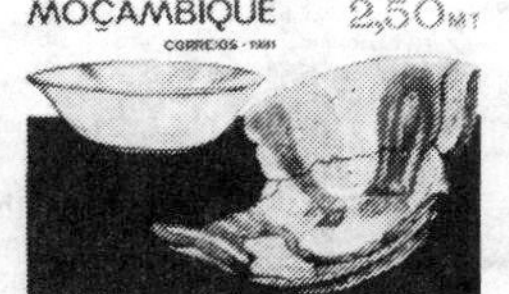
9th Cent. Persian Bowl, Chibuene Excavation Site — A109

1981, Aug. 30 *Perf. 11*
769 A109 1m Manyikeni Museum .15 .15
770 A109 1.50m Hand ax, Massingir Dam .15 .15
771 A109 2.50m shown .15 .15
772 A109 7.50m Pot, Chibuene, 9th cent. .30 .15
773 A109 12.50m Gold beads, Manyikeni .50 .20
774 A109 20m Iron, Manyikeni, 15th cent. .80 .30
Nos. 769-774 (6) 2.05
Set value .80

For surcharge see No. 1213.

Sculptures — A110

1981, Sept. 25 Litho. *Perf. 11*
775 A110 50c Mapiko mask .15 .15
776 A110 1m Suffering woman .15 .15
777 A110 2.50m Mother and child .15 .15
778 A110 3.50m Man making fire .20 .15
779 A110 5m Chietane .50 .28
780 A110 12.50m Chietane, diff. .50 .50
Set value 1.40 1.00

World Food Day — A111

1981, Oct. 16 Litho. *Perf. 11*
781 A111 10m multi .40 .15

Ocean Tanker Matchedje — A112

1981, Nov. 22 Litho. *Perf. 11*
782 A112 50c shown .15 .15
783 A112 1.50m Tugboat Macuti .15 .15
784 A112 3m Prawn trawler Vega 7 .15 .15
785 A112 5m Freighter Linde .20 .15
786 A112 7.50m Ocean freighter Pemba .30 .20
787 A112 12.50m Dredger Rovuma .50 .25
Set value 1.22 .75

Chinaman Crab — A113

1981, Dec. 6
788 A113 50c shown .15 .15
789 A113 1.50m Scylla serrata .15 .15
790 A113 3m White prawn .15 .15
791 A113 7.50m Palinurus delagoae .30 .15
792 A113 12.50m Mantis shrimp .50 .18
793 A113 15m Panulirus ornatus .60 .28
Nos. 788-793 (6) 1.85
Set value .80

For surcharges see Nos. 1214, 1219, 1253.

Hypoxis Multiceps — A114

1981, Dec. 21 **Litho.** ***Perf. 11***
794 A114 1m shown .15 .15
795 A114 1.50m Pelargonium luridum .15 .15
796 A114 2.50m Caralluma melananthera .15 .15
797 A114 7.50m Ansellia gigantea .30 .15
798 A114 12.50m Stapelia leendertsiae .50 .18
799 A114 25m Adenium multiflorium 1.00 .28
Nos. 794-799 (6) 2.25
Set value .75

For surcharges see Nos. 1215, 1217, 1251.

First Anniv. of Posts and Telecommunications Dept. — A115

1982, Jan. 1 **Litho.** ***Perf. 11***
800 A115 6m Phone, globe .25 .15
801 A115 15m Envelope .60 .20

Gasoline Conservation A116

1982, Jan. 25
802 A116 5m Piston .20 .15
803 A116 7.50m Car .30 .15
804 A116 10m Truck .40 .15
Nos. 802-804 (3) .90
Set value .30

Sea Snake A117

1982, Feb. 27 **Litho.** ***Perf. 11***
805 A117 50c shown .15 .15
806 A117 1.50m Mozambique spitting cobra .15 .15
807 A117 3m Savanna vine snake .15 .15
808 A117 6m Black mamba .25 .15
809 A117 15m Boomslang .60 .20
810 A117 20m Bitis arietans .80 .28
Nos. 805-810 (6) 2.10
Set value .78

TB Bacillus Centenary A118

1982, Mar. 15 **Litho.** ***Perf. 11***
811 A118 20m multi .80 .28

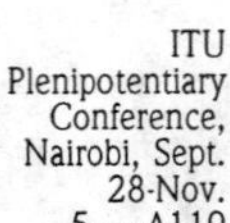

ITU Plenipotentiary Conference, Nairobi, Sept. 28-Nov. 5 — A119

1982, Mar. 31 ***Perf. 13½***
812 A119 20m multi .80 .35

1982 World Cup — A120

Designs: Various soccer players.

1982, Apr. 19 **Litho.** ***Perf. 13½***
813 A120 1.5m multi .15 .15
814 A120 3.5m multi .15 .15
815 A120 7m multi .30 .15
816 A120 10m multi .40 .15
817 A120 20m multi .80 .28
Nos. 813-817 (5) 1.80
Set value .65

Souvenir Sheet

Imperf

818 A120 50m multi 2.00 2.00

Souvenir Sheet

Two Tahitian Women, by Gauguin — A121

1982, June 11 **Litho.** ***Imperf.***
819 A121 35m multi 1.75 1.75

PHILEXFRANCE '82 Intl. Stamp Exhibition, Paris, June 11-21.

Natl. Liberation Front, 20th Anniv. — A122

Vangueria Infausta — A123

1982, June 25 ***Perf. 13***
820 A122 4m Pres. Mondland addressing crowd .16 .15
821 A122 8m Guarded fields .35 .15
822 A122 12m Procession .50 .18
Nos. 820-822 (3) 1.01
Set value .38

1982, Sept. 13 ***Perf. 11***

Designs: Fruits.

823 A123 1m shown .15 .15
824 A123 2m Mimusops caffra .15 .15
825 A123 4m Sclerocarya caffra .16 .15
826 A123 8m Strychnos spinosa .35 .15
827 A123 12m Salacia kraussi .50 .18
828 A123 32m Trichilia emetica 1.40 .40
Nos. 823-828 (6) 2.71
Set value .90

25th Anniv. of Sputnik 1 Flight A124

1982, Oct. 4 **Litho.** ***Perf. 11***
829 A124 1m Sputnik, 1957 .15 .15
830 A124 2m Yuri Gagarin's flight, 1961 .15 .15
831 A124 4m A. Leonov's spacewalk, 1965 .18 .15
832 A124 8m Apollo 11, 1969 .35 .15
833 A124 16m Apollo-Soyuz, 1975 .70 .24
834 A124 20m Salyut-6, 1978 .85 .30
a. Min. sheet of 6, #829-834 2.50 2.50
Nos. 829-834 (6) 2.38
Set value .85

People's Vigilance Day — A125

Caique — A126

1982, Oct. 11 ***Perf. 13½***
835 A125 4m multi .18 .15

1982, Nov. 29

Traditional boats. 4m, 8m, 12m, 16m horiz.

836 A126 1m shown .15 .15
837 A126 2m Machua .15 .15
838 A126 4m Calaua .18 .15
839 A126 8m Chitatarro .35 .15
840 A126 12m Cangaia .50 .18
841 A126 16m Chata (flatboat) .70 .24
Nos. 836-841 (6) 2.03
Set value .72

Marine Life — A127

1982, Dec. 21 **Litho.** ***Perf. 11***
842 A127 1m Ophiomastix venosa .15 .15
843 A127 2m Protoreaster lincki .15 .15
844 A127 4m Tropiometra carinata .18 .15
845 A127 8m Holothuria scabra .35 .18
846 A127 12m Prionocidaris baculosa .50 .18
847 A127 16m Colobocentrotus atnatus .70 .24
Nos. 842-847 (6) 2.03
Set value .80

Frelimo Party 4th Congress A128

1983, Jan. 17
848 A128 4m Map, soldier .18 .15
849 A128 8m Voters .35 .15
850 A128 16m Farm workers .70 .18
Nos. 848-850 (3) 1.23
Set value .38

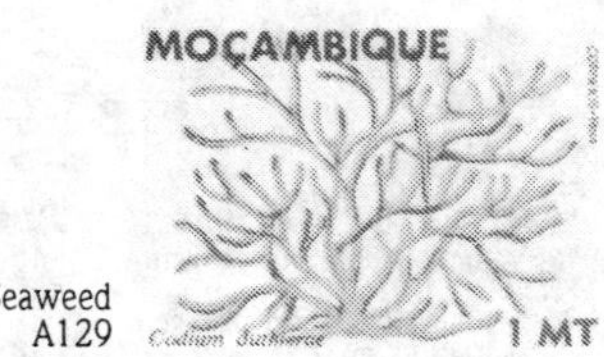

Seaweed A129

1983, Feb. 28 **Litho.** ***Perf. 11***
851 A129 1m Codium duthierae .15 .15
852 A129 2m Halimeda cuncata .15 .15
853 A129 4m Dictyota liturata .18 .15
854 A129 8m Encorachne binghamiae .35 .15
855 A129 12m Laurencia flexuosa .50 .18
856 A129 20m Acrosorium sp. .85 .35
Nos. 851-856 (6) 2.18
Set value .85

1984 Olympic Games, Los Angeles — A130

1983, Mar. 31 **Litho.** ***Perf. 11***
857 A130 1m Diving .15 .15
858 A130 2m Boxing .15 .15
859 A130 4m Basketball .18 .15
860 A130 8m Handball .35 .15
861 A130 12m Volleyball .50 .18
862 A130 16m Running .70 .24
863 A130 20m Sailing .85 .35
Nos. 857-863 (7) 2.88
Set value 1.12

Souvenir Sheet

Imperf

864 A130 50m Discus 2.00 2.00

For surcharge see No. 1257.

Steam Locomotives — A131

1983, Apr. 29 **Litho.** ***Perf. 11***
865 A131 1m 1912 .15 .15
866 A131 2m 1947 .15 .15
867 A131 4m 1923 .18 .15
868 A131 8m 1924 .35 .18
869 A131 16m 1924, diff. .70 .28
870 A131 32m 1950 1.40 .40
Nos. 865-870 (6) 2.93
Set value 1.05

20th Anniv. of Org. of African Unity A132

1983, May 25 **Litho.** ***Perf. 11***
871 A132 4m multi .18 .15

Mammals — A133

1983, May 30
872 A133 1m Petrodromus tetradactylus .15 .15
873 A133 2m Rhabdomys pumilio .15 .15
874 A133 4m Paraxerus vincenti .18 .15
875 A133 8m Cryptomys hottentotus .35 .15
876 A133 12m Pronolagus crassicaudatus .50 .18
877 A133 16m Eidolon helvum .70 .28
Nos. 872-877 (6) 2.03
Set value .78

Souvenir Sheet

Marimba Players — A134

1983, July 29 Litho. *Perf. 11*

878 A134 30m multi 1.50 1.50

BRASILIANA '83 Intl. Stamp Show, Rio de Janeiro, July 29-Aug. 7.

World Communications Year — A135

1983, Aug. 26 Litho. *Perf. 11*

879 A135 8m multi .35 .15

Fishing Techniques A136

1983, Oct. 29 Litho. *Perf. 11*

880 A136 50c Line fishing .15 .15
881 A136 2m Chifonho .15 .15
882 A136 4m Momba .15 .15
883 A136 8m Gamboa .28 .15
884 A136 16m Mono .55 .18
885 A136 20m Lema .70 .28
Nos. 880-885 (6) 1.98
Set value .75

World Communications Year, Stamp Day — A137

1983, Dec. 21 Litho.

886 A137 50c Horn .15 .15
887 A137 1m Drum .15 .15
888 A137 4m Native mail carriers .15 .15
889 A137 8m Boat .28 .15
890 A137 16m Truck .55 .20
891 A137 20m Train .70 .28
Nos. 886-891 (6) 1.98
Set value .75

2nd Anniv. of Mozambique Red Cross (July 10) — A138

1983, Oct. 29 Litho. *Perf. 11*

892 A138 4m Flood relief .15 .15
893 A138 8m Rescue truck .28 .15
894 A138 16m First aid .55 .20
895 A138 32m Field first aid 1.10 .40
Nos. 892-895 (4) 2.08
Set value .75

Olympic Games 1984, Los Angeles — A139

1984, Jan. 2 Litho. *Perf. 11*

896 A139 50c Swimming .15 .15
897 A139 4m Soccer .15 .15
898 A139 8m Hurdles .28 .20
899 A139 16m Basketball .55 .25
900 A139 32m Handball 1.10 .30
901 A139 60m Boxing 2.00 .50
Nos. 896-901 (6) 4.23 1.55

Indigenous Trees — A140

1984, Mar. 30 Litho. *Perf. 11*

902 A140 50c Trichilia emetica .15 .15
903 A140 2m Brachystegia spiciformis .15 .15
904 A140 4m Androstachys johnsonii .15 .15
905 A140 8m Pterocarpus angolensis .16 .15
906 A140 16m Milletia stuhlmannii .32 .20
907 A140 50m Dalbergia melanoxylon 1.00 .40
Set value 1.65 .85

Nkomati Accord, Mar. 16 — A141

1984, Mar. 16

908 A141 4m Dove .15 .15

Natl. Arms A142

909 A142 4m shown .15 .15
910 A142 8m Natl. flag .16 .15
Set value .24 .15

Traditional Dances — A143

1984, May 9

911 A143 4m Makway .15 .15
912 A143 8m Mapiko .16 .15
913 A143 16m Wadjaba .32 .15
Nos. 911-913 (3) .63
Set value .30

LUBRAPEX '84, May 9-17.

Museums and Artifacts A144

50c, Nampula Museum, African carrying water jar, wooden statue. 4m, Museum of Natural History, preserved bird. 8m, Revolution Museum, guerrilla fighter statue. 16m, Colonial Occupation Museum, fort and cannon. 20m, Numismatic Museum, coins. 30m, Palace of St. Paul, char, 19th cent.

1984, June 25

914 A144 50c multi .15 .15
915 A144 4m multi .15 .15
916 A144 8m multi .16 .15
917 A144 16m multi .32 .20
918 A144 20m multi .40 .25
919 A144 30m multi .60 .30
Nos. 914-919 (6) 1.78
Set value 1.00

Freshwater Fish A145

1984, Aug. 24

920 A145 50c Alestes imberi .15 .15
921 A145 4m Labeo congoro .15 .15
922 A145 12m Syndontis zambezensis .40 .20
923 A145 16m Noto branchius zachovii .55 .30
924 A145 40m Barbus paludinosus 1.40 .40
925 A145 60m Barilius zambezensis 2.00 .60
Nos. 920-925 (6) 4.65 1.80

Intl. Fair, Maputo — A145a

1984, Aug. 24 Litho. *Perf. 11*

925A A145a 16m multicolored

Traditional Weapons — A146

1984, Sept. 25

926 A146 50c Knife, cudgel *.18 .15*
927 A146 4m Axes *.25 .15*
928 A146 8m Shield, assagai *.45 .20*
929 A146 16m Bow and arrow *.75 .30*
930 A146 32m Muzzleloader *2.00 .40*
931 A146 50m Assagai, arrow *3.00 .50*
Nos. 926-931 (6) *6.63 1.70*

Natl. Revolution, 20th anniv.
For surcharge see No. 1256.

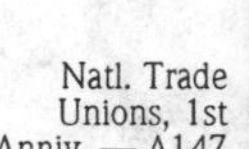

Natl. Trade Unions, 1st Anniv. — A147

1984, Oct. 13 *Perf. 13½*

932 A147 4m Workers, emblem .15 .15

Stamp Day — A149

Cancellations on altered stamps and stationery: 4m, Barue cancel on 1885 20r postal card. 8m, Zumbo cancel on design similar to No. 52. 12m, Mozambique Co. cancel on design similar to Mozambique Company Type API. 16m, Macequece cancel on design similar to Mozambique Company No. 190.

1984, Dec. 21 *Perf. 11½x11*

936 A149 4m multi .15 .15
937 A149 8m multi .28 .15
938 A149 12m multi .40 .20
939 A149 16m multi .55 .25

African Development Bank, 20th Anniv. — A150

1984, Sept. 16 Photo. *Perf. 11½x11*

940 A150 4m multi .15 .15

Apiculture — A151

1985, Feb. 3

941 A151 4m Beekeeper .15 .15
942 A151 8m Bee gathering pollen .15 .15
943 A151 16m Entering nest .22 .15
944 A151 20m Building honeycomb .28 .20
Nos. 941-944 (4) .80
Set value .50

OLYMPHILEX '85, Lausanne — A152

1985, Mar. 18 *Perf. 11*

945 A152 16m Shot putter .22 .15

World Meteorology Day — A153

1985, Mar. 23 Litho. *Perf. 11*

946 A153 4m multi .15 .15

Southern African Development Coordination Conference, 5th Anniv. — A154

1985, Apr. 1

947	A154	4m	Map	.15	.15
948	A154	8m	Map, transmission tower	.15	.15
949	A154	16m	Industry	.22	.15
950	A154	32m	Flags	.45	.20
			Nos. 947-950 (4)	.97	
			Set value		.50

Independence, 10th Anniv. — A155

Colonial resistance battles: 1m, Mujenga, 1896. 4m, Mungari, 1917. 8m, Massangano, 1868. 16m, Marracuene, 1895, and Gungunhana (c. 1840-1906), resistance leader.

1985, June 25 Litho. *Perf. 11*

951	A155	1m	multi	.15	.15
952	A155	4m	multi	.15	.15
953	A155	8m	multi	.15	.15
954	A155	16m	multi	.22	.15
			Set value	.45	.35

UN, 40th Anniv. — A156

1985, June 26

955 A156 16m multi *5.00 5.00*

Traditional Games A157

1985, Aug. 28 Litho. *Perf. 11*

956	A157	50c	Mathacuzana	.15	.15
957	A157	4m	Mudzobo	.18	.18
958	A157	8m	Muravarava	.35	.35
959	A157	16m	N'Tshuwa	.70	.70
			Nos. 956-959 (4)	1.38	1.38

Frogs and Toads A158

1985, Oct. 25 Litho. *Perf. 11*

960	A158	50c	Rana angolensis	.15	.15
961	A158	1m	Hyperolius pictus	.15	.15
962	A158	4m	Ptychadena porosissima	.15	.15
963	A158	8m	Afrixalus formasinii	.15	.15
964	A158	16m	Bufo regularis	.22	.15
965	A158	32m	Hyperolius marmoratus	.45	.25
			Set value	.90	.62

Medicinal Plants — A159

1985, Nov. 28 Litho. *Perf. 11*

966	A159	50c	Aloe ferox	.15	.15
967	A159	1m	Boophone disticha	.15	.15
968	A159	3.50m	Gloriosa superba	.15	.15
969	A159	4m	Cotyledon orbiculata	.15	.15
970	A159	8m	Homeria breyniana	.15	.15
970A	A159	50m	Haemanthus coccineus	.70	.25
			Set value	1.00	.54

Stamp Day A160

Stamps: 1m, Mozambique Company No. 126. 4m, Nyassa Type A6. 8m, Mozambique Company No. 110. 16m, Nyassa No. J2.

1985, Dec. 21

971	A160	1m	multi	.15	.15
972	A160	4m	multi	.15	.15
973	A160	8m	multi	.15	.15
974	A160	16m	multi	.22	.15
			Set value	.45	.35

Halley's Comet — A161

Comet and: 4m, Space probe. 8m, Trajectory diagram. 16m, Newton's telescope, observatory, probe. 30m, Earth.

1986, Jan. 2

975	A161	4m	multi	.15	.15
976	A161	8m	multi	.15	.15
977	A161	16m	multi	.22	.15
978	A161	30m	multi	.45	.25
			Nos. 975-978 (4)	.97	
			Set value		.55

1986 World Cup Soccer Championships, Mexico — A162

Players.

1986, Feb. 28 Litho. *Perf. 11½x11*

979	A162	3m	Vicente	.15	.15
980	A162	4m	Coluna	.15	.15
981	A162	8m	Costa Pereira	.15	.15
982	A162	12m	Hilario	.16	.15
983	A162	16m	Matateu	.22	.20
984	A162	50m	Eusebio	.70	.40
			Set value	1.30	.95

Intl. Peace Year — A163

1986, Mar. 18 *Perf. 11*

985 A163 16m multi .22 .15

Mushrooms A164

1986, Apr. 8

986	A164	4m	Amanita muscaria	.15	.15
987	A164	8m	Lactarius deliciosus	.15	.15
988	A164	16m	Amanita phaloides	.22	.15
989	A164	30m	Tricholoma nudum	.40	.20
			Set value	.78	.50

Souvenir Sheet

Statue of Liberty, Cent. — A165

1986, May 22 *Imperf.*

990 A165 100m multi 1.40 1.40

AMERIPEX '86. #990 has simulated perfs.

Traditional Women's Hair Styles — A166

1986, June Litho. *Perf. 11½x11*

991	A166	1m	Tanzanian	.15	.15
992	A166	4m	Miriam	.15	.15
993	A166	8m	Estrelinhas	.15	.15
994	A166	16m	Toto	.22	.20
			Set value	.45	.42

Marine Mammals A167

1986, Aug. *Perf. 11*

995	A167	1m	Dugongo dugon	.15	.15
996	A167	16m	Delphinus delphis	.15	.15
997	A167	16m	Neobalena marginata	.22	.15
998	A167	50m	Balaenoptera physalus	.70	.25
			Nos. 995-998 (4)	1.22	
			Set value		.50

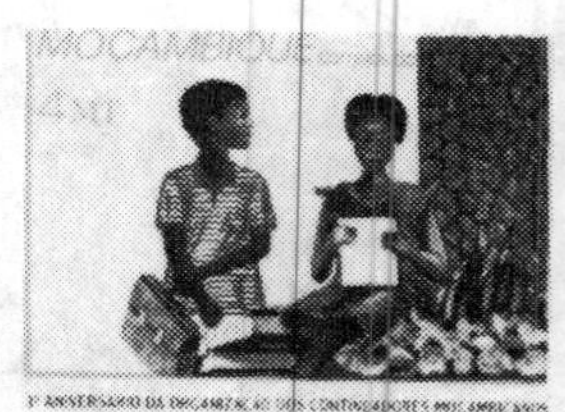
Continuing Youth Education Organization, 1st Anniv. — A168

1986, Sept. 16 Litho. *Perf. 11½x11*

999 A168 4m multi .15 .15

Natl. Savings Campaign — A169

Bank notes, front and back.

1986, Oct. 22 Litho. *Perf. 11½x11*

1000	A169	4m	50m note	.15	.15
1001	A169	8m	100m note	.15	.15
1002	A169	16m	500m note	.22	.15
1003	A169	30m	1000m note	.40	.20
			Set value	.80	.50

Stamp Day A170

Post offices.

1986, Dec. 21 Litho. *Perf. 11*

1004	A170	3m	Quelimane	.15	.15
1005	A170	4m	Maputo	.15	.15
1006	A170	8m	Beira	.15	.15
1007	A170	16m	Nampula	.22	.20
			Set value	45	.50

Minerals
A171

1987, Jan. 2 *Perf. 11x11½*

1008 A171 4m Pyrite .15 .15
1009 A171 8m Emerald .15 .15
1010 A171 12m Agate .16 .15
1011 A171 16m Malachite .22 .20
1012 A171 30m Garnet .40 .25
1013 A171 50m Amethyst .70 .40
Nos. 1008-1013 (6) 1.78 1.30

Frelimo Party, 10th Anniv. — A172

1987, Feb. 3 *Perf. 11*

1014 A172 4m multi .15 .15

Pequenos Libombos Dam — A173

1987, Feb. 17 *Perf. 11½x11*

1015 A173 16m multi .22 .15

World Health Day — A174

1987, Apr. 7 **Litho.** *Perf. 11x11½*

1016 A174 50m multi .70 .25

Birds — A175

1987, Apr. 27 **Litho.** *Perf. 11½x11*

1017 A175 3m Granatina granatina .15 .15
1018 A175 4m Halcyon senegalensis .15 .15
1019 A175 8m Mellittophagus bullockoides .15 .15
1020 A175 12m Perinestes minor .16 .20
1021 A175 16m Coracias naevia mosambica .22 .25
1022 A175 30m Cimmyris neergardi .40 .30
Set value 1.00 1.00

Souvenir Sheet

CAPEX '87, Toronto, June 13-21 — A176

1987, June *Imperf.*

1023 A176 200m multi 2.00 2.00

No. 1023 contains one stamp having simulated perforations.

1988 Summer Olympics, Seoul — A177

1987, May **Litho.** *Perf. 11½x11*

1024 A177 12.50m Soccer players and ball .15 .15
1025 A177 25m Runner's legs .25 .20
1026 A177 50m Volleyball .50 .30
1027 A177 75m Chess .75 .40
1028 A177 100m Basketball 1.00 .50
1029 A177 200m Swimming 2.00 .75
Nos. 1024-1029 (6) 4.65 2.30

Tapestries
A178

1987, Aug. *Perf. 11*

1030 A178 20m Incomplete pattern on loom .15 .15
1031 A178 40m Diamond-shaped pattern .16 .15
1032 A178 80m Landscape pattern .32 .25
1033 A178 200m Oriental pattern .80 .40
Nos. 1030-1033 (4) 1.43 .95

Maputo City
A179

Early Portuguese map of Lourenco Marques.

1987, Nov. 10 **Litho.** *Perf. 11*

1034 A179 20m multi .15 .15

No. 762 Surcharged in Silver and Dark Red **4,00 MT**

1987 **Litho.** *Perf. 14½*

1034A A108 4m on 4.50m multi *2.00 2.00*

1988 Summer Olympics, Seoul — A180

Flowering Plants — A181

1988, Feb. 10 **Litho.** *Perf. 11*

1035 A180 10m Javelin .15 .15
1036 A180 20m Baseball .28 .15
1037 A180 40m Boxing .58 .25
1038 A180 80m Field hockey 1.15 .40
1039 A180 100m Gymnastic rings 1.40 .50
1040 A180 400m Cycling 5.65 1.90
Nos. 1035-1040 (6) 9.21 3.35

Nos. 1036-1040 horiz.

1988, Mar. 18 *Perf. 11½x11*

1041 A181 10m Heamanthus nelsonii .15 .15
1042 A181 20m Crinum polyphyllum .28 .15
1043 A181 40m Boophane disticha .58 .25
1044 A181 80m Cyrtanthus contractus 1.15 .40
1045 A181 100m Nerine angustifolia 1.40 .50
1046 A181 400m Cyrtanthus galpinnii 5.65 1.90
Nos. 1041-1046 (6) 9.21 3.35

World Health Organization, 40th Anniv. — A182

1988, Apr. 7

1047 A182 20m multi .28 .28

Anti-smoking campaign.

Wickerwork — A183

1988, June 16 **Litho.** *Perf. 11*

1048 A183 20m Mat .16 .15
1049 A183 25m Lidded container .20 .15
1050 A183 80m Market basket .62 .20
1051 A183 100m Fan .78 .25
1052 A183 400m Flat basket 3.15 1.00
1053 A183 500m Funnel basket 3.90 1.25
Nos. 1048-1053 (6) 8.81 3.00

Souvenir Sheet

FINLANDIA '88 — A184

1988, June 12 **Litho.** *Imperf.*

1054 A184 500m multi 2.50 1.00

Stamp in No. 1054 has simulated perfs.

Souvenir Sheet

State Visit of Pope John Paul II, Sept. 16-19 — A185

1988 **Litho.** *Perf. 13½*

1055 A185 500m multi 1.50 1.50

Horses
A186

1988, Sept. 20 **Litho.** *Perf. 11*

1056 A186 20m Percheron .20 .15
1057 A186 40m Arab .38 .15
1058 A186 80m Purebred .75 .25
1059 A186 100m Pony .92 .30
Nos. 1056-1059 (4) 2.25 .85

Pres. Samora Machel (1933-1986)
A187

1988, Oct. 19 **Litho.** *Perf. 11*

1060 A187 20m multi .15 .15

Stamp Day — A188

Perf. 11x11½, 11½x11

1988, Dec. 21

1061 A188 20m P.O. trailer .15 .15
1062 A188 40m Mailbox, vert. .20 .15

Ports
A189

1988, Nov. 30 *Perf. 11*

1063 A189 25m Inhambane .15 .15
1064 A189 50m Quelimane, vert. .20 .15
1065 A189 75m Pemba .30 .15
1066 A189 100m Beira .42 .15
1067 A189 250m Nacala, vert. 1.05 .25
1068 A189 500m Maputo 2.05 .50
Nos. 1063-1068 (6) 4.17
Set value 1.00

5th Frelimo Party Congress — A190

1989, Jan. 19

1069	Strip of 5	2.40	1.25
a.	A190 25m Com	.15	.15
b.	A190 50m Axe	.24	.15
c.	A190 75m Abstract shapes	.35	.18
d.	A190 100m 2½ Gearwheels	.48	.24
e.	A190 250m ½ Gearwheel	1.20	.60

Printed se-tenant in a continuous design.

French Revolution Bicent. A191

Designs: 100m, *Storming of the Bastille,* by Thevenin. 250m, *Liberty Guiding the People,* by Delacroix. 500m, *Declaration of the Rights of Man and the Citizen,* a print by Blanchard.

1989, Feb. 16 ***Perf. 11***

1070	A191 100m multi	.30	.15
1071	A191 250m multi	.75	.25

Souvenir Sheet

1072	A191 500m multi	1.50	.75

Eduardo Chivambo Mondlane (1920-1969), Frelimo Party Founder, 20th Death Anniv. — 192

1989, Feb. 3 Litho. ***Perf. 11***

1073	A192 25m blk, gold & dark red	.15	.15

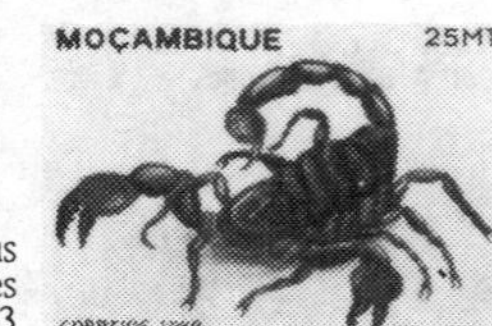

Venomous Species A193

1989, Mar. 23

1074	A193 25m *Pandinus*	.15	.15
1075	A193 50m *Naja haje*	.20	.15
1076	A193 75m *Bombus*	.30	.15
1077	A193 100m *Paraphysa*	.42	.15
1078	A193 250m *Conus marmoreus*	1.05	.25
1079	A193 500m *Pterois volitans*	2.05	.50
	Nos. 1074-1079 (6)	4.17	
	Set value		1.00

Coral A194

1989, May 2 Litho. ***Perf. 11***

1080	A194 25m *Acropora pulchra*	.15	.15
1081	A194 50m *Eunicella papilosa*	.15	.15
1082	A194 100m *Dendrophyla migrantus*	.28	.15
1083	A194 250m *Favia fragum*	.68	.25
	Nos. 1080-1083 (4)	1.26	
	Set value		.40

1990 World Cup Soccer Championships, Italy — A195

Athletes executing various plays.

1989, June 22 Litho. ***Perf. 11½x11***

1084	A195 30m multi	.15	.15
1085	A195 60m multi	.16	.15
1086	A195 125m multi	.32	.15
1087	A195 200m multi	.55	.18
1088	A195 250m multi	.68	.22
1089	A195 500m multi	1.35	.45
	Nos. 1084-1089 (6)	3.21	
	Set value		1.00

Lighthouses A196

1989, July 24 Litho. ***Perf. 11***

1090	A196 30m Macuti	.15	.15
1091	A196 60m Pinda	.16	.15
1092	A196 125m Cape Delgado	.35	.15
1093	A196 200m Isle of Goa	.55	.18
1094	A196 250m Caldeira Point	.68	.22
1095	A196 500m Vilhena	1.35	.45
	Nos. 1090-1095 (6)	3.24	
	Set value		1.00

Filigree Workmanship in Silver A197

1989, Aug. 30 Litho. ***Perf. 11x11½***

1096	A197 30m shown	.15	.15
1097	A197 60m Flower on band	.15	.15
1098	A197 125m Necklace	.32	.15
1099	A197 200m Decorative box	.50	.15
1100	A197 250m Utensils	.62	.22
1101	A197 500m Butterfly	1.25	.45
	Nos. 1096-1101 (6)	2.99	
	Set value		1.00

Natl. Liberation War, 25th Anniv. A198

1989, Sept. 25

1102	A198 30m multicolored	.15	.15

Meteorological Instruments — A199

Designs: 30m, Rain gauge. 60m, Weather system on radar. 125m, Instrument shelter. 200m, Computer monitor and keyboard.

1989, Oct. 12 ***Perf. 11½x11***

1103	A199 30m multicolored	.15	.15
1104	A199 60m multicolored	.15	.15
1105	A199 125m multicolored	.32	.16
1106	A199 200m multicolored	.50	.25
	Nos. 1103-1106 (4)	1.12	.71

Souvenir Sheet

World Stamp Expo '89, Washington, DC — A200

1989, Nov. 17 ***Perf. 13½***

1107	A200 500m Washington Monument	1.25	.75

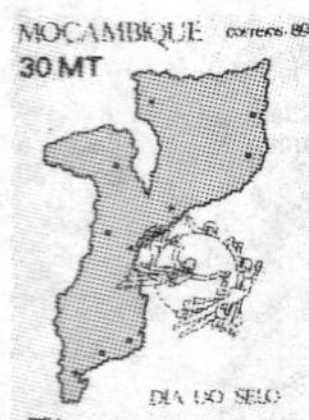

A201 A201a

Stamp Day: Maps and emblems.

1989, Dec. 21 Litho. ***Perf. 11½x11***

1108	A201 30m UPU emblem	.15	.15
1109	A201 60m P.O. emblem	.16	.16
	Set value	.24	.24

1990, Jan. 31 ***Perf. 11½x11***

1109A	A201a 35m multicolored	.15	.15

Southern African Development Coordination Conf. (SADCC), 10th anniv.

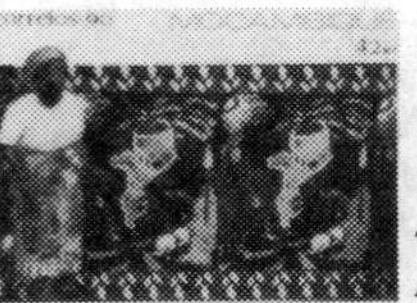

Textile Designs A202

1990, Feb. 28 Litho. ***Perf. 11x11½***

1110	A202 42m multi, diff.	.15	.15
1111	A202 90m multi, diff.	.28	.16
1112	A202 150m multi, diff.	.45	.22
1113	A202 200m multi, diff.	.60	.30
1114	A202 400m multi, diff.	1.20	.60
1115	A202 500m multi, diff.	1.50	.75
	Nos. 1110-1115 (6)	4.18	2.18

Forts — A203

1990, Mar. 20 ***Perf. 11x11½***

1116	A203 45m Sena	.15	.15
1117	A203 90m Santo Antonio	.28	.16
1118	A203 150m Santo Sebastiao	.45	.22
1119	A203 200m Santo Caetano	.60	.30
1120	A203 400m Our Lady of Conceicao	1.20	.60
1121	A203 500m Santo Luis	1.50	.75
	Nos. 1116-1121 (6)	4.18	2.18

Souvenir Sheet

Penny Black, Mozambique No. 1 — A204

1990, May 3 Litho. ***Perf. 11½x11***

1122	A204 1000m red, blk & bl	2.85	1.50

Penny Black, 150th anniversary. Stamp World London '90.

Bank of Mozambique, 15th Anniv. A205

1990, May 17 Litho. ***Perf. 11x11½***

1123	A205 100m multicolored	.30	.16

Natl. Independence, 15th Anniv. — A206

1990, June 25 ***Perf. 11***

1124	A206 42.50m Eduardo Mondlane	.15	.15
1125	A206 150m Samora Machel	.45	.22

Endangered Species A207

1990, Aug. 20 Litho. ***Perf. 11x11½***

1126	A207 42.50m *Ceratotherium simum*	.15	.15
1127	A207 100m Dugong dugong	.30	.16
1128	A207 150m Loxodonta africana	.45	.22
1129	A207 200m Acinonix jubatus	.60	.30
1130	A207 400m Lutra maculicollis	1.20	.60
1131	A207 500m Eretmochelys imbricata	1.45	.70
	Nos. 1126-1131 (6)	4.15	2.13

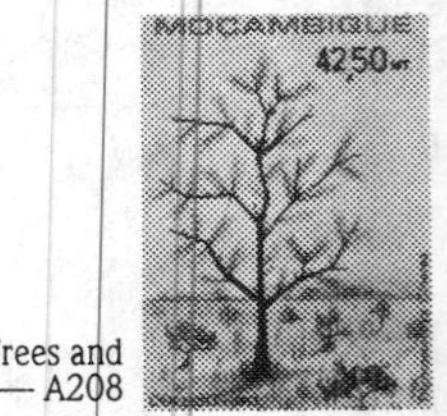

Trees and Plants — A208

1990, Oct. 15 Litho. *Perf. 11½x11*

1132 A208 42.50m Dichrostachys cinerea .15 .15
1133 A208 100m Queimadas .30 .16
1134 A208 150m Casuariana equisetifolia .45 .22
1135 A208 200m Rhizophora muronata .60 .30
1136 A208 400m Estrato herbaceo 1.20 .60
1137 A208 500m Atzelia cuanzensis 1.45 .70
Nos. 1132-1137 (6) 4.15 2.13

A209

A210

Stamp Day: a, Pick-up at letter box. b, Canceling letters. c, Letter carrier. d, Delivery to recipient.

1990, Dec. 21 Litho. *Perf. 11½x11*

1138 Strip of 4 .60 .40
a.-d. A209 42.50m any single .15 .15

1991, Jan. 2

Post Office Dept., 10th Anniv.: #1140, Telecommunications Dept.

1139 A210 50m dk bl, red & blk .20 .15
1140 A210 50m grn, blk & brn .20 .15
Set value .20

Flowers
A211

Alcelaphus Lichtensteini
A212

1991, Feb. 25 Litho. *Perf. 11½x11*

1141 A211 50m Strilitzia reginae .20 .15
1142 A211 125m Anthurium andraeanum .50 .25
1143 A211 250m Zantedeschia pentlandii 1.00 .50
1144 A211 300m Canna indica 1.20 .60
Nos. 1141-1144 (4) 2.90 1.50

1991, Mar. 27 *Perf. 14*

1145 Strip of 4 3.60 1.85
a. A212 50m Two adults .20 .15
b. A212 100m Adult .40 .20
c. A212 250m Adult grazing 1.00 .50
d. A212 500m Nursing calf 2.00 1.00

A213

A214

Fountains of Maputo: 50m, Mpompine. 125m, Chinhambanine. 250m, Sao Pedro-Zaza. 300m, Xipamanine.

1991, Apr. 15 Litho. *Perf. 11½x11*

1146 A213 50m multicolored .15 .15
1147 A213 125m multicolored .28 .15
1148 A213 250m multicolored .55 .28
1149 A213 300m multicolored .65 .32
Nos. 1146-1149 (4) 1.63
Set value .80

1991, May 18 Litho. *Perf. 11½x11*

1150 A214 180m Samale .40 .20
1151 A214 250m Malangatana .55 .30
1152 A214 560m Malangatana, diff. 1.25 .60
Nos. 1150-1152 (3) 2.20 1.10

Paintings by Mozambican artists.

A215

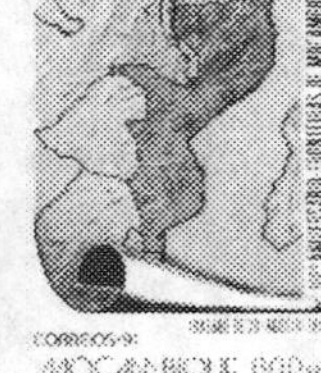

A216

1991, June 25 Litho. *Perf. 11½x11*

1153 A215 10m Swimming .15 .15
1154 A215 50m Roller hockey .15 .15
1155 A215 100m Tennis .22 .15
1156 A215 200m Table tennis .45 .22
1157 A215 500m Running 1.10 .55
1158 A215 1000m Badminton 2.20 1.10
Nos. 1153-1158 (6) 4.27 2.32

1992 Summer Olympics, Barcelona.

1991, Oct. 9 Litho. *Perf. 11½x11*

1159 A216 600m Map of 1890 .85 .42
1160 A216 800m Map of 1891 1.15 .58

British-Portuguese agreement on Mozambique borders, cent.

Souvenir Sheet

Phila Nippon '91 — A217

1991, Nov. 15 Litho. *Perf. 11½x11*

1161 A217 1500m Map of Japan 1.40 1.40

Children's Games — A218

Stained Glass Windows — A219

1991, Dec. 21

1162 A218 40m Jumping rope .15 .15
1163 A218 150m Spinning top .15 .15
1164 A218 400m Marbles .36 .18
1165 A218 900m Hopscotch .82 .40
Nos. 1162-1165 (4) 1.48
Set value .68

1992, Jan. 22

Various designs: a, 40m. b, 150m. c, 400m. d, 900m.

1166 A219 Block of 4, #a.-d. 1.35 .70

A220

A221

Designs: Plants.

1992, Mar. 23 Litho. *Perf. 11½x11*

1167 A220 300m Rhisophora mucronata .52 .28
1168 A220 600m Cymodocea ciliata 1.10 .52
1169 A220 1000m Sophora inhambanensis 1.75 .90
Nos. 1167-1169 (3) 3.37 1.70

1992, May 9

Designs: Traditional tools.

1170 A221 100m Spear, spear-thrower .18 .15
1171 A221 300m Pitch forks .52 .25
1172 A221 500m Hatchet .90 .45
1173 A221 1000m Dagger 1.75 .90
Nos. 1170-1173 (4) 3.35 1.75

Lubrapex '92, Lisbon.

A222

A223

Birds: 150m, Chalcomitra amethystina. 200m, Ceropis senegalensis. 300m, Cossypha natalensis. 400m, Lamprocolius chloropterus. 500m, Malaconotus poliocephalus. 800m, Oriolus auratus.

1992, July 24 Litho. *Perf. 11½x11*

1174 A222 150m multicolored .28 .15
1175 A222 200m multicolored .35 .18
1176 A222 300m multicolored .52 .25
1177 A222 400m multicolored .68 .35
1178 A222 500m multicolored .85 .42
1179 A222 800m multicolored 1.40 .70
Nos. 1174-1179 (6) 4.08 2.05

1992, Aug. 21

1180 A223 150m grn, brn & blk .28 .15

Eduardo Mondlane University, 30th anniv.

A224

A225

Designs: Traditional musical instruments.

1992, Sept. 18

1181 A224 200m Phiane .35 .18
1182 A224 300m Xirupe .52 .25
1183 A224 500m Ngulula .85 .42
1184 A224 1500m Malimba 2.50 1.25
a. Souvenir sheet of 4, #1181-1184, imperf. 4.25 2.10
Nos. 1181-1184 (4) 4.22 2.10

Genoa '92. No. 1184a has simulated perforations.

No. 757 Surcharged

1992, Oct. Litho. *Perf. 14½*

1185 A108 50m on 50c #757 .78 .40

1992, Oct. 16 *Perf. 11½x11*

1186 A225 450m multicolored .75 .38

Intl. Conference on Nutrition.

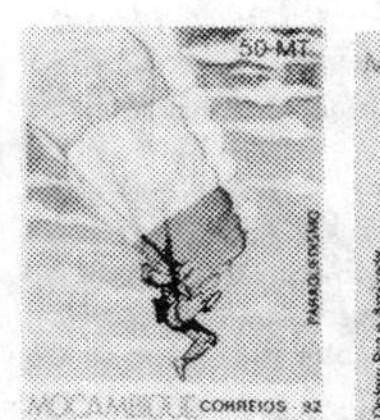

Parachuting — A226

Medals — A227

Various parchutists descending from sky.

1992, Nov. 10 Litho. *Perf. 11½x11*

1187 A226 50m multicolored .15 .15
1188 A226 400m multicolored .65 .32
1189 A226 500m multicolored .78 .38
1190 A226 1500m multicolored 2.35 1.15
Nos. 1187-1190 (4) 3.93 2.00

1993, Feb. 3 Litho. *Perf. 11½x11*

1191 A227 400m Order of Peace & Amity .28 .15
1192 A227 800m Baga moyo .55 .28
1193 A227 1000m Order of Eduardo Mondlane .70 .35
1194 A227 1500m War veterans 1.05 .52
Nos. 1191-1194 (4) 2.58 1.30

Pollution
A228

1993, Apr. 8 *Perf. 11x11½*

1195 A228 200m Deforestation .15 .15
1196 A228 750m Factory smoke .52 .25
1197 A228 1000m Oil spill from ship .70 .35
1198 A228 1500m Automobile exhaust 1.05 .52
Nos. 1195-1198 (4) 2.42 1.27

Natl. Parks — A229

Park, animal, map: 200m, Gorongosa, lion. 800m, Banhine, giraffes. 1000m, Bazaruto, manatees. 1500m, Zinave, ostriches.

1993, May 25 Litho. *Perf. 11x11½*

1199 A229 200m multicolored .15 .15
1200 A229 800m multicolored .58 .28
1201 A229 1000m multicolored .70 .35
1202 A229 1500m multicolored 1.05 .52
Nos. 1199-1202 (4) 2.48 1.30

Natl. Conference on Culture — A230

1993, Sept. 27 Litho. *Perf. 11½x11*

1203 A230 200m multicolored .18 .15

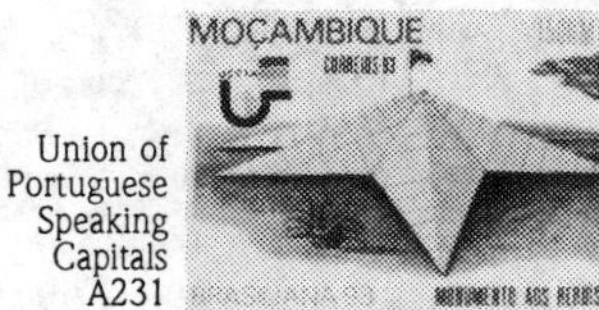

Union of Portuguese Speaking Capitals
A231

1993, July 30 Litho. *Perf. 11x11½*

1204 A231 1500m multicolored 1.75 .85

Brasilana '93.

Forest Plants — A232

Medicinal Plants — A233

Designs: 200m, Cycas cercinalis. 250m, Cycas revoluta. 900m, Encephalartos ferox. 2000m, Equisetum ramosissimum.

1993, Dec. 29 Litho. *Perf. 11½x11*

1205 A232 200m multicolored .15 .15
1206 A232 250m multicolored .15 .15
1207 A232 900m multicolored .55 .28
1208 A232 2000m multicolored 1.25 .60
Nos. 1205-1208 (4) 2.10 1.18

1994 Litho. *Perf. 11½x11*

1209 A233 200m Anacardium occidentale .15 .15
1210 A233 250m Sclerocarya caffra .15 .15
1211 A233 900m Annona senegalensis .55 .28

1212 A233 2000m Crinum de-lagoense 1.25 .65
Nos. 1209-1212 (4) 2.10 1.23

Nos. 763-764, 772, 791-792, 797-798 Surcharged

50,00 MT

1994
Perfs. and Printing Methods as Before

1213 A109 50m on 7.50m #772 .15 .15
1214 A113 50m on 7.50m #791 .15 .15
1215 A114 50m on 7.50m #797 .15 .15
1216 A108 100m on 10m #763 .15 .15
1217 A114 100m on 12.50m #798 .15 .15
1218 A108 200m on 12.50m #764 .15 .15
1219 A113 250m on 12.50m #792 .15 .15
Set value .69 .34

Size and location of surcharge varies. Surcharge on Nos. 1214-1215, 1219 does not contain an obliterator.

PHILAKOREA '94 — A234

Reptiles: 300m, Ichnotropis squamulosa. 500m, Lepidachelys olivacea. 2000m, Prosyma frontalis. 3500m, Rampholeon marshalli. 4000m, Snake eating a lizard.

1994 Litho. *Perf. 11½x11*

1220 A234 300m multicolored .15 .15
1221 A234 500m multicolored .20 .15
1222 A234 2000m multicolored .85 .42
1223 A234 3500m multicolored 1.40 .70
Nos. 1220-1223 (4) 2.60 1.42

Souvenir Sheet

1224 A234 4000m multicolored 1.75 .90

ICAO, 50th Anniv. A235

Designs: 300d, Crop dusting. 500m, Airport terminal. 2000m, Passenger jet in flight. 3500m, Maintenance man inspecting jet engine.

1994 Litho. *Perf. 11x11½*

1225 A235 300m multicolored .18 .15
1226 A235 500m multicolored .30 .15
1227 A235 2000m multicolored 1.25 .60
1228 A235 3500m multicolored 2.00 1.00
Nos. 1225-1228 (4) 3.73 1.90

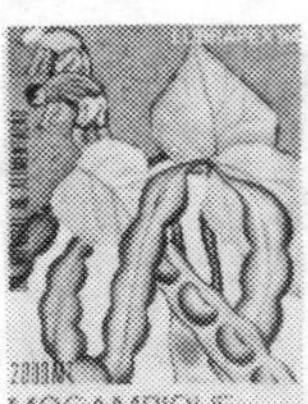

World Food Day — A236

Nat. Elections — A237

1994 *Perf. 11½x11*

1229 A236 2000m multicolored 1.25 .60

Lubrapex '94.

1994

1230 A237 900m multicolored .70 .35

Fight Against Illegal Drugs — A238

Lusaka Accord, 20th Anniv. — A239

Designs: 500m, Couple using drugs. 1000m, Hypodermic needle, couple tied in rope, skeleton. 2000m, Man with drug dependency. 5000m, Dog apprehending man with contraband.

1994

1231 A238 500m multicolored .30 .15
1232 A238 1000m multicolored .60 .30
1233 A238 2000m multicolored 1.25 .60
1234 A238 5000m multicolored 3.00 1.50
Nos. 1231-1234 (4) 5.15 2.55

1994, Nov. 9

1235 A239 1500m multicolored .90 .45

Basketry — A240

Clothing — A241

1995 Litho. *Perf. 11½x11*

1236 A240 250m shown .15 .15
1237 A240 300m Two-handled basket .15 .15
1238 A240 1200m Round purse .55 .28
1239 A240 5000m Purse, diff. 2.25 1.25
Nos. 1236-1239 (4) 3.10 1.83

1995

Various styles of women's traditional clothing.

1240 A241 250m blue & multi .15 .15
1241 A241 300m pink & multi .15 .15
1242 A241 1200m blue & multi .55 .28
1243 A241 5000m red & multi 2.25 1.25
Nos. 1240-1243 (4) 3.10 1.83

A242

A243

Inauguration of Pres. Joaquim A. Chissano, 12/9/94: a, 900m, Natl. arms. b, 5000m, Pres. Chissano. c, 2500m, Natl. flag.

1995 Litho. *Perf. 11½x11*

1244 A242 Strip of 3, #a.-c. 2.25 1.25

No. 1244 has a common inscription across the bottom.

1995 Litho. *Perf. 11½x11, 11x11½*

Wild Animals: 500m, Crassicadautus lombergi. 2000m, Tragelaphus strepsceros, horiz. 3000m, Potamochoerus porcus nyasae, horiz. 5000m, Tragelaphus scriptus.

1245 A243 500m multicolored .15 .15
1246 A243 2000m multicolored .45 .25
1247 A243 3000m multicolored .65 .35
1248 A243 5000m multicolored 1.10 .55
Nos. 1245-1248 (4) 2.35 1.30

FAO, 50th Anniv. — A244

UN, 50th Anniv. — A245

Perf. 11½x11

1995, Oct. 16

1249 A244 5000m multicolored 1.10 .55

1995, Oct. 24

1250 A245 5000m blue & black 1.10 .55

250 MT

Nos. 647, 713, 749, 763 792, 798, 862, 929 Surcharged

Perfs. and Printing Methods as Before
1995

1251 A114 250m on 12.50m #798 .15 .15
1252 A108 300m on 10m #763 .15 .15
1253 A113 500m on 12.50m #792 .15 .15
1254 A81 900m on 12.50m #647 .20 .15
1255 A97 1000m on 12.50m #713 .25 .15
1256 A146 1500m on 16m #929 .35 .15
1257 A130 2000m on 16m #862 .45 .25
1258 A106 2500m on 12.50m #749 .55 .30
Nos. 1251-1258 (8) 2.25
Set value 1.00

UNICEF, 20th Anniv. — A246

1995, Oct. 24 Litho. *Perf. 11½*

1259 A246 5000m multicolored 1.10 .55

Mozambique-South Africa Soccer Match — A247

Various soccer plays.

1996 Litho. *Perf. 11x11½*

1260 A247 1000m multicolored .20 .15
1261 A247 2000m multicolored .40 .20
1262 A247 4000m multicolored .80 .40
1263 A247 6000m multicolored 1.20 .60
Nos. 1260-1263 (4) 2.60 1.35

Masks — A248

Red Cross of Mozambique, 15th Anniv. — A249

Various masks.

1996 Litho. *Perf. 11½x11*

1264 A248 1000m multicolored .20 .15
1265 A248 2000m multicolored .40 .20
1266 A248 4000m multicolored .80 .40
1267 A248 6000m multicolored 1.20 .60
Nos. 1264-1267 (4) 2.60 1.35

1996

1268 A249 5000m multicolored .90 .45

A250 A251

Endangered Wildlife.

1996 Litho. *Perf. 11½x11*

1269 A250 1000m Loxodona africana .20 .15
1270 A250 2000m Ceratotherum simum .40 .20
1271 A250 4000m Panthera pardus .80 .40
1272 A250 6000m Scotopelia peli 1.20 .60
Nos. 1269-1272 (4) 2.60 1.35

1996 Litho. *Perf. 11½x11*

Removal of Land Mines: 2000m, Mine, tripwire across path. 6000m, Warning sign posted. 8000m, Using mine detector. 10,000m, Removing mine.

1273 A251 2000m multicolored .35 .20
1274 A251 6000m multicolored 1.10 .55
1275 A251 8000m multicolored 1.40 .70
1276 A251 10,000m multicolored 1.75 .90
Nos. 1273-1276 (4) 4.60 2.35

A252

A253

Keep the City Clean campaign.

1996 Litho. *Perf. 11½x11*

1277 A252 2000m multicolored .40 .20

1996 Litho. *Perf. 11½x11*

1278 A253 2000m No. 1 .35 .20

Postage stamps of Mozambique, 120th anniv.

Mozambique Boats — A254

1997, Apr. 10 Litho. *Perf. 11x11½*

1279 A254 2000m Mitumbui .35 .20
1280 A254 6000m Muterere 1.10 .55
1281 A254 8000m Lancha 1.40 .70
1282 A254 10,000m Dau 1.75 .90
Nos. 1279-1282 (4) 4.60 2.35

Children's Day — A255

1997, June 1 Litho. *Perf. 11x11½*

1283 A255 2000m multicolored .35 .20

Aquatic Birds — A256

Designs: 2000m, Mycteria ibis. 4000m, Himantopus himantopus. 8000m, Calidris subminuta. 10,000m, Pelecanus onocrotalus.

Perf. 11½x11, 11x11½

1997, June 10

1284	A256	2000m multi, vert.	.35	.20
1285	A256	4000m multi, vert.	.65	.35
1286	A256	8000m multi	1.35	.65
1287	A256	10,000m multi, vert.	1.70	.85
		Nos. 1284-1287 (4)	4.05	2.05

Insects A257

Designs: 2000m, Enaretta conifera. 6000m, Zographus heiroglyphicus. 8000m, Tragiscoschema bertolonii. 10,000m, Tragocephala ducalis.

1997 Litho. *Perf. 11x11½*

1288	A257	2000m multicolored	.35	.20
1289	A257	6000m multicolored	1.00	.50
1290	A257	8000m multicolored	1.40	.70
1291	A257	10,000m multicolored	1.70	.85
a.		Souvenir sheet, #1288-1291	4.50	2.25
		Nos. 1288-1291 (4)	4.45	2.25

Labrapex '97 (#1291a).

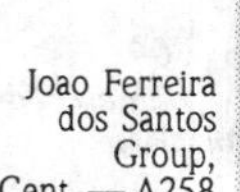

Joao Ferreira dos Santos Group, Cent. — A258

1997 Litho. *Perf. 11x11½*

1292	A258	2000m multi	.40	.20

Protection of the Ozone Layer — A259

1997 Litho. *Perf. 11½x11*

1293	A259	2000m multicolored	.40	.20

SEMI-POSTAL STAMPS

"History" Pointing out to "the Republic" Need for Charity SP1

Nurse Leading Wounded Soldiers SP2

Veteran Relating Experiences SP3

Perf. 11½

1920, Dec. 1 Litho. Unwmk.

B1	SP1	¼c olive	3.50	3.50
B2	SP1	½c olive blk	3.50	3.50
B3	SP1	1c dp bister	3.50	3.50
B4	SP1	2c lilac brn	3.50	3.50
B5	SP1	3c lilac	3.50	3.50
B6	SP1	4c green	3.50	3.50
B7	SP2	5c grnsh blue	3.50	3.50
B8	SP2	6c light blue	3.50	3.50
B9	SP2	7½c red brown	3.50	3.50
B10	SP2	8c lemon	3.50	3.50
B11	SP2	10c gray lilac	3.50	3.50
B12	SP2	12c pink	3.50	3.50
B13	SP3	18c rose	3.50	3.50
B14	SP3	24c vio brn	3.50	3.50
B15	SP3	30c pale ol grn	3.50	3.50
B16	SP3	40c dull red	3.50	3.50
B17	SP3	50c yellow	3.50	3.50
B18	SP3	1e ultra	3.50	3.50
		Nos. B1-B18 (18)	63.00	63.00

Nos. B1-B18 were used Dec. 1, 1920, in place of ordinary stamps. The proceeds were for war victims.

AIR POST STAMPS

Common Design Type

Perf. 13½x13

1938, Aug. Engr. Unwmk.

Name and Value in Black

C1	CD39	10c scarlet	.30	.20
C2	CD39	20c purple	.30	.20
C3	CD39	50c orange	.30	.20
C4	CD39	1e ultra	.40	.30
C5	CD39	2e lilac brn	1.00	.30
C6	CD39	3e dk green	1.75	.40
C7	CD39	5e red brown	2.00	.70
C8	CD39	9e rose car	4.25	.75
C9	CD39	10e magenta	5.50	1.10
		Nos. C1-C9 (9)	15.80	4.15

No. C7 exists with overprint "Exposicao Internacional de Nova York, 1939-1940" and Trylon and Perisphere.

No. C7 Surcharged in Black

3$00

≋ ≋

1946, Nov. 2 *Perf. 13½x13*

C10	CD39	3e on 5e red brn	6.00	1.75
a.		Inverted surcharge		

Plane AP1

1946, Nov. 2 Typo. *Perf. 11½*

Denomination in Black

C11	AP1	1.20e carmine	1.10	.85
C12	AP1	1.60e blue	1.40	.90
C13	AP1	1.70e plum	3.50	1.40
C14	AP1	2.90e brown	3.50	1.90
C15	AP1	3e green	3.00	1.75
		Nos. C11-C15 (5)	12.50	6.80

Inscribed "Taxe perçue" and Denomination in Brown Carmine or Black

1947, May 20

C16	AP1	50c blk (BrC)	.50	.25
C17	AP1	1e pink	.50	.25
C18	AP1	3e green	1.00	.40
C19	AP1	4.50e yel grn	2.50	.75
C20	AP1	5e red brown	2.50	.90
C21	AP1	10e ultra	6.00	1.25
C22	AP1	20e violet	11.00	4.00
C23	AP1	50e orange	15.00	6.00
		Nos. C16-C23 (8)	39.00	13.80

Dangerous counterfeits exist.

Planes Circling Globe — AP2

Oil Refinery, Sonarep — AP3

1949, Mar.

C24	AP2	50c sepia	.30	.15
C25	AP2	1.20e violet	.50	.30
C26	AP2	4.50e dull blue	1.25	.50
C27	AP2	5e blue green	1.75	.50
C28	AP2	20e chocolate	4.00	.85
		Nos. C24-C28 (5)	7.80	2.30

Catalogue values for unused stamps in this section, from this point to the end of the section, are for Never Hinged items.

1963, Mar. 5 Litho. *Perf. 13*

Designs: 2e, Salazar High School, Lourenço Marques. 3.50e, Lourenço Marques harbor. 4.50e, Salazar dam. 5e, Trigo de Morais bridge. 20e, Marcelo Caetano bridge.

C29	AP3	1.50e multi	.60	.15
C30	AP3	2e multi	.30	.15
C31	AP3	3.50e multi	.60	.15
C32	AP3	4.50e multi	.40	.20
C33	AP3	5e multi	.50	.20
C34	AP3	20e multi	1.10	.50
		Nos. C29-C34 (6)	3.50	1.35

Republic

Nos. C31-C34 Overprinted in Red

INDEPENDÊNCIA
25 JUN 75

1975, June 25 Litho. *Perf. 13*

C35	AP3	3.50e multi	.20	.18
C36	AP3	4.50e multi	.35	.18
C37	AP3	5e multi	.85	.20
C38	AP3	20e multi	1.75	.40
		Nos. C35-C38 (4)	3.15	.96

DeHavilland Dragonfly, 1937 AP4

Designs: 1.50m, Junker JU-52-3M, 1938. 3m, Lockheed Lodestar L-18-08, 1940. 7.50m, DeHavilland Dove DH-104, 1948. 10m, Douglas Dakota DC-3, 1956. 12.5m, Fokker Friendship F-27, 1962.

1981, May 14 Litho. *Perf. 11*

C39	AP4	50c multi	.20	.15
C40	AP4	1.50m multi	.20	.15
C41	AP4	3m multi	.20	.15
C42	AP4	7.50m multi	.50	.15
C43	AP4	10m multi	.75	.35
C44	AP4	12.5m multi	1.00	.50
		Nos. C39-C44 (6)	2.85	
		Set value		1.25

Piper Navajo Over Hydroelectric Dam — AP5

Designs: 40m, De Havilland Hornet trainer, 1936. 80m, Boeing 737, Maputo Airport, 1973. 120m, Beechcraft King-Air. 160m, Piper Aztec. 320m, Douglas DC-10, 1982.

1987, Oct. 28 Litho. *Perf. 11*

C45	AP5	20m multi	.15	.15
C46	AP5	40m multi	.15	.15
C47	AP5	80m multi	.30	.20
C48	AP5	120m multi	.50	.25
C49	AP5	160m multi	.65	.35
C50	AP5	320m multi	1.25	.40
		Nos. C45-C50 (6)	3.00	1.50

POSTAGE DUE STAMPS

D1

1904 Unwmk. Typo. *Perf. 11½x12*

Name and Value in Black

J1	D1	5r yellow grn	.40	.20
J2	D1	10r slate	.40	.20
J3	D1	20r yellow brn	.40	.25
J4	D1	30r orange	.75	.60
J5	D1	50r gray brn	.70	.40
J6	D1	60r red brown	3.25	1.65
J7	D1	100r red lilac	2.75	1.65
J8	D1	130r dull blue	1.25	.85
J9	D1	200r carmine	1.75	1.00
J10	D1	500r violet	2.25	1.00
		Nos. J1-J10 (10)	13.90	7.80

See J34-J43. For overprints see Nos. 247, J11-J30.

Same Overprinted in Carmine or Green

1911

J11	D1	5r yellow green	.20	.20
J12	D1	10r slate	.20	.20
J13	D1	20r yellow brn	.28	.20
J14	D1	30r orange	.28	.20
J15	D1	50r gray brown	.40	.30
J16	D1	60r red brown	.50	.35
J17	D1	100r red lilac	.55	.45
J18	D1	130r dull blue	1.10	.80
J19	D1	200r carmine (G)	1.10	.90
J20	D1	500r violet	1.25	.85
		Nos. J11-J20 (10)	5.86	4.45

Nos. J1-J10 Overprinted Locally in Carmine

REPUBLICA

1916

J21	D1	5r yellow grn	3.75	3.00
J22	D1	10r slate	5.00	1.75
J23	D1	20r yellow brn	70.00	52.50
J24	D1	30r orange	15.00	11.00
J25	D1	50r gray brown	67.50	52.50
J26	D1	60r red brown	52.50	40.00
J27	D1	100r red lilac	67.50	50.00
J28	D1	130r dull blue	2.25	2.00
J29	D1	200r carmine	2.50	2.75
J30	D1	500r violet	5.25	4.50
		Nos. J21-J30 (10)	291.25	220.00

War Tax Stamps of 1916 Overprinted Diagonally

PORTEADO

1918 *Rouletted 7*

J31	WT1	1c gray green	.85	.70
J32	WT2	5c rose	.85	.70
a.		Inverted overprint	8.25	7.50

Perf. 11

J33	WT1	1c gray green	.85	.70
a.		"PEPUBLICA"	30.00	30.00
		Nos. J31-J33 (3)	2.55	2.10

Type of 1904 Issue With Value in Centavos

1917 *Perf. 12*

J34	D1	½c yellow green	.15	.15
J35	D1	1c slate	.15	.15
J36	D1	2c orange brown	.15	.15
J37	D1	3c orange	.15	.15
J38	D1	5c gray brown	.15	.15
J39	D1	6c pale brn	.15	.15
J40	D1	10c red violet	.15	.15
J41	D1	13c deep blue	.15	.15
J42	D1	20c rose	.15	.15
J43	D1	50c gray	.18	.18
		Set value	.90	.90

Lourenco Marques Nos. 117, 119 Surcharged in Red

10 C.

PORTEADO

1921

J44 A4 5c on 1/2c blk 1.00 .70
J45 A4 10c on 1 1/2c brn 1.00 .70

Same Surcharge on Mozambique Nos. 151, 155, 157 in Red or Green

J46 A6 6c on 1c bl grn (R) 1.00 .85
J47 A6 20c on 2 1/2c vio (R) .85 .70
J48 A6 50c on 4c rose (G) .85 .70
Nos. J44-J48 (5) 4.70 3.65

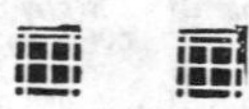

Regular Issues of 1921-22 Surcharged in Black or Red

Porteado

50 C.

1924 *Perf. 12x11 1/2*

J49 A6 20c on 30c ol grn (Bk) .55 .40
a. Perf. 15x14 19.00 4.50
J50 A6 50c on 60c dk bl (R) .85 .55

Catalogue values for unused stamps in this section, from this point to the end of the section, are for Never Hinged items.

Common Design Type

Photo. and Typo.

1952 Unwmk. *Perf. 14*

Numeral in Red Orange or Red; Frame Multicolored

J51 CD45 10c carmine (RO) .15 .15
J52 CD45 30c black brn .15 .15
J53 CD45 50c black .15 .15
J54 CD45 1e violet blue .15 .15
J55 CD45 2e olive green .20 .15
J56 CD45 5e orange brown .50 .28
Set value 1.00 .72

WAR TAX STAMPS

Coats of Arms of Portugal and Mozambique on Columns, Allegorical Figures of History of Portugal and the Republic Holding Scroll with Date of Declaration of War — WT1

Prow of Galley of Discoveries. Left, "Republic" Teaching History of Portugal; Right "History" with Laurels (Victory) and Sword (Symbolical of Declaration of War) — WT2

1916 Unwmk. Litho. *Rouletted 7*

MR1 WT1 1c gray green 2.00 .48
a. Imperf., pair
MR2 WT2 5c rose 2.00 .48
a. Imperf., pair

1918 *Perf. 11, 12*

MR3 WT1 1c gray green .50 .48
a. "PEPUBLICA" 8.50 4.75
MR4 WT2 5c red .70 .60
a. "PETRIA" 2.25 2.25
b. "PEPUBLICA" 2.50 2.25
c. "1910" for "1916" 6.50 5.00
d. Imperf., pair
Nos. MR1-MR4 (4) 5.20 2.04

For surcharges and overprints see Nos. 221-225, 229, 235, J31-J33.

NEWSPAPER STAMPS

No. 19 Surcharged in Black, Red or Blue:

JORNAES JORNAES

2 1/2 REIS 2 1/2 2 1/2
a b

Perf. 11 1/2, 12 1/2, 13 1/2

1893 Unwmk.

P1 A2 (a) 2 1/2r on 40r 200.00 90.00
P2 A2 (a) 5r on 40r 175.00 90.00
P3 A2 (a) 5r on 40r (R) 150.00 75.00
P4 A2 (a) 5r on 40r (Bl) 180.00 75.00
P5 A2 (b) 2 1/2r on 40r 22.50 16.00
Nos. P1-P5 (5) 727.50 346.00

Nos. P1-P5 exist with double surcharge, Nos. P2-P4 with inverted surcharge.

N3

1893 Typo. *Perf. 11 1/2, 13 1/2*

P6 N3 2 1/2r brown .35 .28

For surcharge and overprint see Nos. 93, 199.

No. P6 has been reprinted on chalk-surfaced paper with clean-cut perforation 13 1/2. Value, 50 cents.

POSTAL TAX STAMPS

Pombal Commemorative Issue

Common Design Types

1925 Engr. *Perf. 12 1/2*

RA1 CD28 15c brown & black .30 .24
RA2 CD29 15c brown & black .30 .24
RA3 CD30 15c brown & black .30 .24
Nos. RA1-RA3 (3) .90 .72

Seal of Local Red Cross Society
PT7 PT8

Surcharged in Various Colors

1925 Typo. *Perf. 11 1/2*

RA4 PT7 50c slate & yel (Bk) 1.40 1.40

1926

RA5 PT8 40c slate & yel (Bk) 3.00 3.00
RA6 PT8 50c slate & yel (R) 3.00 3.00
RA7 PT8 60c slate & yel (V) 3.00 3.00
RA8 PT8 80c slate & yel (Br) 3.00 3.00
RA9 PT8 1e slate & yel (Bl) 3.00 3.00
RA10 PT8 2e slate & yel (G) 3.00 3.00
Nos. RA5-RA10 (6) 18.00 18.00

Obligatory on mail certain days of the year. The tax benefited the Cross of the Orient Society.

Type of 1926 Issue

1927

Black Surcharge

RA11 PT8 5c red & yel 3.00 3.00
RA12 PT8 10c green & yel 3.00 3.00
RA13 PT8 20c gray & yel 3.00 3.00
RA14 PT8 30c lt bl & yel 3.00 3.00
RA15 PT8 40c vio & yel 3.00 3.00
RA16 PT8 50c car & yel 3.00 3.00
RA17 PT8 60c brown & yel 3.00 3.00
RA18 PT8 80c blue & yel 3.00 3.00
RA19 PT8 1e olive & yel 3.00 3.00
RA20 PT8 2e yel brn & yel 3.00 3.00
Nos. RA11-RA20 (10) 30.00 30.00

See note after No. RA10.

PT9

1928 Litho.

RA21 PT9 5c grn, yel & blk 4.00 4.00
RA22 PT9 10c sl bl, yel & blk 4.00 4.00
RA23 PT9 20c gray blk, yel & blk 4.00 4.00
RA24 PT9 30c brn rose, yel & blk 4.00 4.00
RA25 PT9 40c cl brn, yel & blk 4.00 4.00
RA26 PT9 50c red org, yel & blk 4.00 4.00
RA27 PT9 60c brn, yel & blk 4.00 4.00
RA28 PT9 80c dk brn, yel & blk 4.00 4.00
RA29 PT9 1e gray, yel & blk 4.00 4.00
RA30 PT9 2e red, yel & blk 4.00 4.00
Nos. RA21-RA30 (10) 40.00 40.00

See note after RA10.

Mother and Children
PT10

Mousinho de Albuquerque
PT11

1929 Photo. *Perf. 14*

RA31 PT10 40c ultra, cl & blk 2.50 2.50

The use of this stamp was compulsory on all correspondence to Portugal and Portuguese Colonies for eight days beginning July 24, 1929.
See Nos.RA39-RA47.

1930-31 *Perf. 14 1/2x14*

Inscribed: "MACONTENE"

RA32 PT11 50c lake, red & gray 3.50 4.00

Inscribed: "COOLELA"

RA33 PT11 50c red vio, red brn & gray 3.50 4.00

Inscribed: "MUJENGA"

RA34 PT11 50c org red, red & gray 3.50 4.00

Inscribed: "CHAIMITE"

RA35 PT11 50c dp grn, bl grn & gray 3.50 4.00

Inscribed: "IBRAHIMO"

RA36 PT11 50c dk bl, blk & gray 3.50 4.00

Inscribed: "MUCUTO-MUNO"

RA37 PT11 50c ultra, blk & gray 3.50 4.00

Inscribed: "NAGUEMA"

RA38 PT11 50c dk vio, lt vio & gray 3.50 4.00
Nos. RA32-RA38 (7) 24.50 28.00

The portrait is that of Mousinho de Albuquerque, the celebrated Portuguese warrior, and the names of seven battles in which he took part appear at the foot of the stamps. The stamps were issued for the memorial fund bearing his name and their use was obligatory on all correspondence posted on eight specific days in the year.

Type of 1929 Issue
Denominations in Black
No. RA40 Without Denomination

1931 *Perf. 14*

RA39 PT10 40c rose & vio 4.00 3.25
RA40 PT10 40c ol grn & vio ('32) 5.00 4.00
RA41 PT10 40c bis brn & rose ('33) 5.00 4.00
RA42 PT10 bl grn & rose ('34) 3.50 2.75
RA43 PT10 40c org & ultra ('36) 5.00 4.00
RA44 PT10 40c choc & ultra ('37) 5.00 4.00
RA45 PT10 40c grn & brn car ('38) 7.00 5.00
RA46 PT10 40c yel & blk ('39) 7.00 5.00
RA47 PT10 40c gray brn ('40) 7.00 5.00
Nos. RA39-RA47 (9) 48.50 37.00

Allegory of Charity — PT12

White Pelican — PT13

1942 Unwmk. Litho. *Perf. 11 1/2*

Denomination in Black

RA48 PT12 50c rose carmine 8.25 1.40

1943-51 *Perf. 11 1/2, 14*

Denomination in Black

RA49 PT13 50c rose carmine 17.00 1.25
RA50 PT13 50c emerald 10.00 1.25
RA51 PT13 50c purple 15.00 1.25
RA52 PT13 50c blue 12.00 1.25
RA53 PT13 50c red brown 50.00 1.25
RA54 PT13 50c olive bister 18.00 1.25
Nos. RA49-RA54 (6) 122.00 7.50

There are two sizes of the numeral on No. RA49.

Catalogue values for unused stamps in this section, from this point to the end of the section, are for Never Hinged items.

Inscribed: "Provincia de Mocambique"

1954-56 *Perf. 14 1/2x14*

RA55 PT13 50c orange 1.40 .28
RA56 PT13 50c olive grn ('56) 1.40 .28
RA57 PT13 50c brown ('56) 1.40 .28
Nos. RA55-RA57 (3) 4.20 .84

No. RA57 Surcharged with New Value and Wavy Lines

1956

RA58 PT13 30c on 50c brown .85 .35

Pelican Type of 1954-56

1958 Litho. *Perf. 14*

Denomination in Black

RA59 PT13 30c yellow .70 .35
RA60 PT13 50c salmon .70 .35

Imprint: "Imprensa Nacional de Mocambique"

1963-64

Denomination Typographed in Black

RA61 PT13 30c yellow ('64) .48 .20
RA62 PT13 50c salmon .35 .20

Women and Children
PT14

Lineman on Pole and Map of Mozambique
PT15

1963-65 Litho. *Perf. 14*

RA63 PT14 50c blk, bis & red .32 .22
RA64 PT14 50c blk, pink & red ('65) .32 .22

See Nos. RA68-RA76.

1965, Apr. 1 Unwmk. *Perf. 14*

30c, Telegraph poles and map of Mozambique.

Size: 23x30mm

RA65 PT15 30c blk, salmon & lil .15 .15

Size: 19x36mm

RA66 PT15 50c blk, bl & sepia .18 .15
RA67 PT15 1e blk, yel & org .18 .15
Set value .42 .24

The tax was for improvement of the telecommunications system. Obligatory on inland mail. A 2.50e in the design of the 30c was issued for use on telegrams.

Type of 1963

1967-70 Litho. *Perf. 14*

RA68 PT14 50c blk, lt yel grn & red .38 .22
RA69 PT14 50c blk, lt bl & red ('69) .40 .18
RA70 PT14 50c blk, buff & brt red ('70) .40 .18
Nos. RA68-RA70 (3) 1.18 .58

1972-73

RA71 PT14 30c blk, lt grn & red .15 .15
RA72 PT14 50c blk, gray & red ('73) 1.00 .18
RA73 PT14 1e blk, bis & red ('73) .20 .15
Nos. RA71-RA73 (3) 1.35
Set value .30

1974-75

RA74 PT14 50c blue, yel & red .15 .15
RA75 PT14 1e blk, gray & ver .85 .15
RA76 PT14 1e blk, lil rose & red ('75) .38 .15
Nos. RA74-RA76 (3) 1.38
Set value .35

POSTAL TAX DUE STAMPS

Pombal Commemorative Issue

Common Design Types

1925 Unwmk. *Perf. 12½*

RAJ1 CD28 30c brown & black .50 .60
RAJ2 CD29 30c brown & black .50 .60
RAJ3 CD30 30c brown & black .50 .60
Nos. RAJ1-RAJ3 (3) 1.50 1.80

MOZAMBIQUE COMPANY

mō-zəm-'bēk 'kəmp-nē

LOCATION — Comprises the territory of Manica and Sofala of the Mozambique Colony in southeastern Africa
GOVT. — A part of the Portuguese Colony of Mozambique
AREA — 51,881 sq. mi.
POP. — 368,447 (1939)
CAPITAL — Beira

The Mozambique Company was chartered by Portugal in 1891 for 50 years. The territory was under direct administration of the Company until July 18, 1941.

1000 Reis = 1 Milreis
100 Centavos = 1 Escudo (1916)

Mozambique Nos. 15-23 Overprinted in Carmine or Black

COMPª DE
MOÇAMBIQUE

1892 Unwmk. *Perf. 12½, 13½*

1 A2 5r black (C) 1.25 .25
a. Pair, one without overprint 22.50 22.50
2 A2 10r green 1.25 .25
3 A2 20r rose 1.25 .25
a. Perf. 13½ 45.00 30.00
4 A2 25r violet 1.50 .35
a. Double overprint 27.50
5 A2 40r chocolate 1.25 .30
a. Double overprint 20.00
6 A2 50r blue 1.50 .25
7 A2 100r yellow brown 1.25 .35
8 A2 200r gray violet 2.50 .45
9 A2 300r orange 3.50 .70
Nos. 1-9 (9) 15.25 3.15

Nos. 1 to 6, 8-9 were reprinted in 1905. These reprints have white gum and clean-cut perf. 13½ and the colors are usually paler than those of the originals.

Company Coat of Arms — A2

Perf. 11½, 12½, 13½

1895-1907 Typo.

Black or Red Numerals

10 A2 2½r olive yellow .25 .25
11 A2 2½r gray ('07) 1.50 1.50
12 A2 5r orange .25 .20
a. Value omitted 10.00
b. Perf. 13½ 2.00 1.10
13 A2 10r red lilac .40 .30
14 A2 10r yel grn ('07) 2.50 .40
a. Value inverted at top of stamp 14.00 10.00
15 A2 15r red brown 1.00 .30
16 A2 15r dk green ('07) 2.50 .40
17 A2 20r gray lilac 1.50 .30
18 A2 25r green .75 .30
a. Perf. 13½ 1.90 1.25
19 A2 25r carmine ('07) 1.75 .60
a. Value omitted 11.00 8.00
20 A2 50r blue .90 .28
21 A2 50r brown ('07) 2.50 .60
a. Value omitted 9.00
22 A2 65r slate blue ('02) .75 .35
23 A2 75r rose .55 .30
24 A2 75r red lilac ('07) 5.00 1.00
25 A2 80r yellow green .35 .30
26 A2 100r brown, *buff* .40 .30
27 A2 100r dk bl, *bl* ('07) 4.00 1.00
28 A2 115r car, *pink* ('04) 1.00 .70
29 A2 115r org brn, *pink* ('07) 6.00 1.40
30 A2 130r grn, *pink* ('04) 1.50 .70
31 A2 130r brn, *yel* ('07) 6.00 1.40
32 A2 150r org brn, *pink* .35 .35
33 A2 200r dk blue, *bl* .35 .35
a. Perf. 13½ 2.00 1.65
34 A2 200r red lil, *pink* ('07) 7.00 1.40
35 A2 300r dk bl, *salmon* .50 .30
a. Perf. 13½ 2.50 1.40
36 A2 400r brn, *bl* ('04) 2.50 .70
37 A2 400r dl bl, *yel* ('07) 8.00 1.90
38 A2 500r blk & red .55 .40
39 A2 500r blk & red, *bl* ('07) 8.00 1.90
a. 500r pur & red, *yel* (error)
40 A2 700r slate, *buff* ('04) 8.50 2.00
41 A2 700r pur, *yel* ('07) 5.00 2.00
42 A2 1000r violet & red .85 .40
Nos. 10-42 (33) 82.95 24.58

#12b, 18a, 33a, 35a were issued without gum.
For overprints & surcharges see #43-107, B1-B7.

Nos. 25 and 6 Surcharged or Overprinted in Red:

PROVISORIO
25
b

PROVISORIO
c

1895 *Perf. 12½, 13½*

43 A2(b) 25r on 80r yel grn 22.50 15.00
44 A2(c) 50r blue 10.00 3.00

Overprint "c" on No. 44 also exists reading from upper left to lower right.

Stamps of 1895 Overprinted in Bister, Orange, Violet, Green, Black or Brown

1498
Centenario
da India
1898

1898 *Perf. 12½, 13½*

Without Gum

45 A2 2½r olive yel (Bi) 5.00 1.50
a. Double overprint *40.00 25.00*
b. Red overprint *60.00 50.00*
46 A2 5r orange (O) 7.00 1.50
47 A2 10r red lilac (V) 7.00 1.50
48 A2 15r red brown (V) 10.00 3.00
a. Red overprint
49 A2 20r gray lilac (V) 10.00 3.00
50 A2 25r green (G) 12.00 3.00
a. Inverted overprint 65.00 40.00
51 A2 50r blue (Bk) 12.00 4.00
a. Inverted overprint 60.00 40.00
52 A2 75r rose (V) 12.50 5.00
a. Inverted overprint 75.00 40.00
b. Red overprint
53 A2 80r yellow grn (G) 17.50 5.00
a. Inverted overprint
54 A2 100r brn, *buff* (Br) 17.50 5.00
55 A2 150r org brn, *pink* (O) 17.50 5.00
a. Inverted overprint 75.00 30.00
b. Double overprint
56 A2 200r dk blue, *bl* (Bk) 16.00 7.50
57 A2 300r dk blue, *sal* (Bk) 20.00 10.00
a. Inverted overprint 60.00 50.00
b. Green overprint
Nos. 45-57 (13) 164.00 55.00

Vasco da Gama's discovery of route to India, 400th anniversary.

No. 57b was prepared but not issued.

Nos. 45 and 49 were also issued with gum.

The "Centenario" overprint on stamps perf. 11½ is forged.

Nos. 23, 12, 17 Surcharged in Black, Carmine or Violet

25
PROVISORIO
e

25
Réis
f

50
RÉIS
g

1899 *Perf. 12½*

59 A2(e) 25r on 75r rose (Bk) 4.00 2.00

1900 *Perf. 12½, 12½x11½*

60 A2(f) 25r on 5r org (C) 1.75 1.25
61 A2(g) 50r on half of 20r gray lil (V) 2.00 1.00
b. Entire stamp 15.00 9.00

No. 61b is perf. 11½ vertically through center.

Stamps of 1895-1907 Overprinted Locally in Carmine or Green

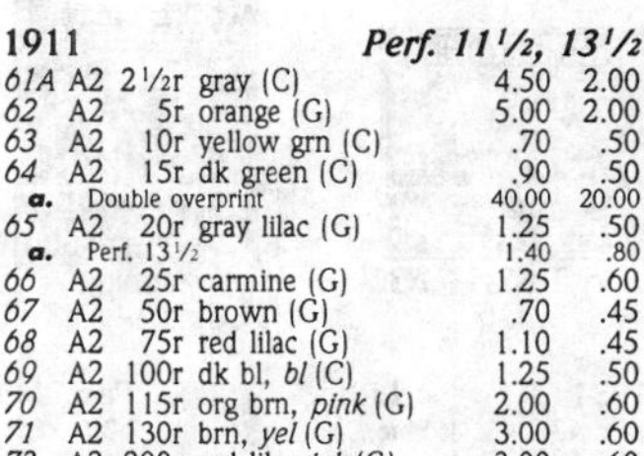

1911 *Perf. 11½, 13½*

61A A2 2½r gray (C) 4.50 2.00
62 A2 5r orange (G) 5.00 2.00
63 A2 10r yellow grn (C) .70 .50
64 A2 15r dk green (C) .90 .50
a. Double overprint 40.00 20.00
65 A2 20r gray lilac (G) 1.25 .50
a. Perf. 13½ 1.40 .80
66 A2 25r carmine (G) 1.25 .60
67 A2 50r brown (C) .70 .45
68 A2 75r red lilac (G) 1.10 .45
69 A2 100r dk bl, *bl* (C) 1.25 .50
70 A2 115r org brn, *pink* (G) 2.00 .60
71 A2 130r brn, *yel* (G) 3.00 .60
72 A2 200r red lil, *pink* (G) 3.00 .60
73 A2 400r dull bl, *yel* (C) 3.00 .60
74 A2 500r blk & red, *bl* (C) 4.00 .95
75 A2 700r pur, *yel* (G) 4.00 .95
Nos. 61A-75 (15) 35.65 11.80

Nos. 63, 67 and 71 exist with inverted overprint; Nos. 63, 72 and 75 with double overprint.

Overprinted in Lisbon in Carmine or Green

1911 *Perf. 11½, 12½*

75B A2 2½r gray .30 .20
76 A2 5r orange .30 .15
77 A2 10r yellow grn .25 .15
78 A2 15r dark green .35 .15
79 A2 20r gray lilac .40 .15
80 A2 25r carmine (G) .35 .15
a. Value inverted at top of stamp 18.00
81 A2 50r brown .70 .15
82 A2 75r red lilac .70 .15
a. Value omitted 15.00
83 A2 100r dk blue, *bl* 1.00 .20
84 A2 115r org brn, *pink* 2.50 .30
85 A2 130r brown, *yel* 3.00 .35
a. Double overprint 30.00
86 A2 200r red lil, *pink* 3.00 .25
87 A2 400r dull bl, *yel* 5.00 .30
88 A2 500r blk & red, *bl* 7.50 .30
89 A2 700r pur, *yel* 5.00 .50
Nos. 75B-89 (15) 30.35 3.45

Nos. 75B-89 Surcharged ¼ C

1916 *Perf. 11½*

90 A2 ¼c on 2½r gray .20 .20
91 A2 ½c on 5r org .20 .20
a. "½c" double 20.00
92 A2 1c on 10r yel grn .40 .20
93 A2 1½c on 15r dk grn .40 .20
a. Imperf., pair 35.00
94 A2 2c on 20r gray lil .50 .20
95 A2 2½c on 25r car 1.00 .25
96 A2 5c on 50r brn .40 .20
a. Imperf., pair 40.00
97 A2 7½c on 75r red lil .65 .20
98 A2 10c on 100r dk bl, *bl* 1.25 .30
a. Inverted surcharge 40.00 40.00
99 A2 11½c on 115r org brn, *pink* 3.50 .35
a. Inverted surcharge 50.00 50.00
100 A2 13c on 130r brn, *yel* 6.50 .30
101 A2 20c on 200r red lil, *pink* 5.50 .30
102 A2 40c on 400r dl bl, *yel* 6.50 .35
103 A2 50c on 500r blk & red, *bl* (R) 8.00 .70
104 A2 70c on 700r pur, *yel* 8.00 .75
Nos. 90-104 (15) 43.00 4.70

Nos. 87 to 89 Surcharged

½
Cent.

1918 *Perf. 11½*

105 A2 ½c on 700r pur, *yel* 2.50 .95
106 A2 2½c on 500r blk & red, *bl* (Bl) 3.50 .95
107 A2 5c on 400r dl bl, *yel* 4.50 .95
Nos. 105-107 (3) 10.50 2.85

Native and Village — A9

Man and Ivory Tusks — A10

Corn — A11

Tapping Rubber Tree — A12

Sugar Refinery — A13

Buzi River Scene — A14

Tobacco Field — A15

View of Beira — A16

Coffee Plantation A17

Orange Tree A18

Cotton Field A19

Sisal Plantation A20

Scene on Beira R. R. — A21

Court House at Beira — A22

Coconut Palm — A23

Mangroves — A24

Cattle — A25

Company Arms — A26

1918-31 Engr. *Perf. 14, 15, 12½*

108 A9	¼c brn & yel grn	.25	.15
109 A9	¼c ol grn & blk ('25)	.20	.15
110 A10	½c black	.25	.15
111 A11	1c green & blk	.25	.15
112 A12	1½c black & grn	.25	.25
113 A13	2c carmine & blk	.25	.15
114 A13	2c ol blk & blk ('25)	.25	.25
115 A14	2½c lilac & blk	.20	.15
116 A11	3c ocher & blk ('23)	.25	.15
117 A15	4c green & brn ('21)	.25	.15
118 A15	4c red & blk ('25)	.20	.15
119 A9	4½c gray & blk ('23)	.20	.20
120 A16	5c blue & blk	.20	.20
121 A17	6c claret & bl ('21)	.80	.30
122 A17	6c lilac & blk ('25)	.25	.20
123 A21	7c ultra & blk ('23)	1.00	.50
124 A18	7½c orange & grn	.75	.30
125 A19	8c violet & blk	.20	.20
126 A20	10c red org & blk	.20	.15
128 A19	12c brown & blk ('23)	.70	.35
129 A19	12c bl grn & blk ('25)	1.40	.35
130 A21	15c carmine & blk	.40	.30
131 A22	20c dp green & blk	.35	.20
132 A23	30c red brn & blk	3.50	.70
133 A23	30c gray grn & blk ('25)	1.65	.25
134 A23	30c bl grn & blk ('31)	3.50	.40
135 A24	40c yel grn & blk	.85	.45
136 A24	40c grnsh bl & blk ('25)	.70	.30
137 A25	50c orange & blk	2.25	.75
138 A25	50c lt vio & blk ('25)	2.25	.45
139 A25	60c rose & brn ('23)	1.50	.50
140 A20	80c ultra & brn ('23)	2.25	.70
141 A20	80c car & blk ('25)	.70	.35
142 A26	1e dk green & blk	2.25	.45
143 A26	1e blue & blk ('25)	2.25	.35
144 A16	2e rose & vio ('23)	5.00	.70
145 A16	2e lilac & blk ('25)	4.00	.45
	Nos. 108-145 (37)	41.70	11.90

Shades exist of several denominations.
For surcharges see Nos. 146-154, RA1.

Nos. 132, 142, 115, 120, 131, 135, 125, 137 Surcharged with New Values in Red, Blue, Violet or Black:

Um e meio Centavo h — **4 Cent.** i

Seis Centavos j

1920 *Perf. 14, 15*

146 A23(h)	½c on 30c (Bk)	6.00	4.50
147 A26(h)	½c on 1e (R)	6.00	4.50
148 A14(h)	1½c on 2½c (Bl)	4.00	2.25
149 A16(h)	1½c on 5c (V)	4.00	3.50
150 A14(h)	2c on 2½c (R)	1.75	1.75
151 A22(i)	4c on 20c (V)	7.50	4.50
152 A24(i)	4c on 40c (V)	8.50	5.00
153 A19(j)	6c on 8c (R)	8.00	5.50
154 A25(j)	6c on 50c (Bk)	9.00	5.50
	Nos. 146-154 (9)	54.75	37.00

The surcharge on No. 148 is placed vertically between two bars. On No. 154 the two words of the surcharge are 13mm apart.

Native — A27

View of Beira — A28

Tapping Rubber Tree — A29

Picking Tea — A30

Zambezi River — A31

1925-31 Engr. *Perf. 12*

155 A27	24c ultra & blk	1.00	.50
156 A28	25c choc & ultra	1.00	.50
157 A27	85c brn red & blk ('31)	.85	.45
158 A28	1.40e dl bl & blk ('31)	.85	.45
159 A29	5e yel brn & ultra	1.25	.30
160 A30	10e rose & blk	1.75	.75
161 A31	20e green & blk	1.75	.75
	Nos. 155-161 (7)	8.45	3.70

Ivory Tusks — A32

Panning Gold — A33

1931 Litho. *Perf. 14*

162 A32	45c lt blue	2.00	.85
163 A33	70c yellow brn	1.40	.35

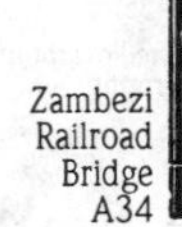

Zambezi Railroad Bridge A34

1935 Engr. *Perf. 12½*

164 A34	1e dk blue & blk	2.00	1.40

Opening of a new bridge over the Zambezi River.

Airplane over Beira — A35

1935

165 A35	5c blue & blk	.45	.35
166 A35	10c red org & blk	.45	.35
a.	Square pair, imperf. between	50.00	
167 A35	15c red & blk	.45	.35
a.	Square pair, imperf. between	50.00	
168 A35	20c yel grn & blk	.45	.35
169 A35	30c green & blk	.45	.35
170 A35	40c gray bl & blk	.45	.35
171 A35	45c blue & blk	.45	.35
172 A35	50c violet & blk	.45	.35
a.	Square pair, imperf. btwn.	60.00	
173 A35	60c carmine & brn	.60	.35
174 A35	80c carmine & blk	.60	.35
	Nos. 165-174 (10)	4.80	3.50

Issued to commemorate the opening of the Blantyre-Beira Salisbury air service.

Giraffe — A36

Thatched Huts — A37

Rock Python A41

Coconut Palms A50

Zambezi Railroad Bridge A52

Sena Gate — A53

Company Arms — A54

Designs: 10c, Dhow. 15c, St. Caetano Fortress, Sofala. 20c, Zebra. 40c, Black rhinoceros. 45c, Lion. 50c, Crocodile. 60c, Leopard. 70c, Mozambique woman. 80c, Hippopotami. 85c, Vasco da Gama's flagship. 1e, Man in canoe. 2e, Greater kudu.

1937, May 16 *Perf. 12½*

175 A36	1c yel grn & vio	.15	*.20*
176 A37	5c blue & yel grn	.15	*.15*
177 A36	10c ver & ultra	.15	*.15*
178 A37	15c carmine & blk	.15	*.15*
179 A36	20c green & ultra	.15	*.15*
180 A41	30c dk grn & ind	.15	*.30*
181 A41	40c gray bl & blk	.15	*.30*
182 A41	45c blue & brn	.15	*.30*
183 A41	50c dk vio & emer	.15	*.30*
184 A37	60c carmine & bl	.15	*.15*
185 A36	70c yel brn & pale grn	.15	*.15*
186 A37	80c car & pale grn	.40	.30
187 A41	85c org red & blk	.40	.40
188 A41	1e dp bl & blk	.30	.15
189 A50	1.40e dk bl & pale grn	.30	.15
190 A41	2e pale lilac & brn	.70	.15
191 A52	5e yel brn & bl	1.00	*.70*
192 A53	10e carmine & blk	2.00	1.40
193 A54	20e grn & brn vio	2.50	2.75
	Nos. 175-193 (19)	9.25	8.30

Stamps of 1937 Overprinted in Red or Black

28-VII-1939
Visita Presidencial

1939, Aug. 28

194 A41	30c dk grn & ind (R)	1.50	.85
195 A41	40c gray bl & blk (R)	1.50	.85
196 A41	45c blue & brn (Bk)	1.50	.85
197 A41	50c dk vio & emer (R)	2.00	1.00
198 A41	85c org red & blk (Bk)	2.00	1.00
199 A41	1e dp bl & blk (R)	1.75	1.25
200 A41	2e pale lil & brn (Bk)	2.50	1.65
	Nos. 194-200 (7)	12.75	7.45

Visit of the President of Portugal to Beira in 1939.

King Alfonso Henriques A55

King John IV A56

1940, Feb. 16 Typo. *Perf. 11½x12*

201 A55	1.75e blue & lt blue	.70	.70

800th anniv. of Portuguese independence.

1941 Engr. *Perf. 12½*

202 A56	40c gray grn & blk	.30	.20
203 A56	50c dk vio & brt grn	.30	.20
204 A56	60c brt car & dp bl	.30	.20
205 A56	70c brn org & dk grn	.30	.20
206 A56	80c car & dp grn	.30	.20
207 A56	1e dk bl & blk	.30	.20
	Nos. 202-207 (6)	1.80	1.20

300th anniv. of the restoration of the Portuguese Monarchy.

Mozambique Company's charter terminated July 18th, 1941 after which date its stamps were superseded by those of the territory of Mozambique.

SEMI-POSTAL STAMPS

Lisbon Issue of 1911 Overprinted in Red

31.7.17.

1917 Unwmk. *Perf. 11½*

B1	A2	2½r gray	7.50	*10.50*
a.		Double overprint	75.00	*75.00*
B2	A2	10r yellow grn	8.75	*15.00*
B3	A2	20r gray lilac	12.00	*20.00*
B4	A2	50r brown	20.00	*25.00*
B5	A2	75r red lilac	65.00	*70.00*
B6	A2	100r dk blue, *bl*	65.00	*70.00*
B7	A2	700r purple, *yel*	165.00	*225.00*
		Nos. B1-B7 (7)	343.25	*435.50*

Nos. B1-B7 were used on July 31, 1917, in place of ordinary stamps. The proceeds were given to the Red Cross.

AIR POST STAMPS

Airplane over Beira — AP1

1935 Unwmk. Engr. *Perf. 12½*

C1 AP1	5c blue & blk	.15	.15
C2 AP1	10c org red & blk	.15	.15
C3 AP1	15c red & blk	.15	.15
C4 AP1	20c yel grn & blk	.15	.15
C5 AP1	30c green & blk	.15	.15
C6 AP1	40c gray bl & blk	.15	.15
C7 AP1	45c blue & blk	.15	.15
C8 AP1	50c dk vio & blk	.40	.15
C9 AP1	60c car & brn	.40	.15
C10 AP1	80c car & blk	.50	.15
C11 AP1	1e blue & blk	.50	.15
C12 AP1	2e mauve & blk	1.25	.25
C13 AP1	5e bis brn & bl	1.25	.40
C14 AP1	10e car & blk	1.40	.60
C15 AP1	20e bl grn & blk	2.75	.85
	Set value	6.50	2.75

POSTAGE DUE STAMPS

D1

1906 Unwmk. Typo. ***Perf. 11½x12***
Denominations in Black

J1 D1 5r yellow grn .70 .30
J2 D1 10r slate .70 .30
J3 D1 20r yellow brn 1.25 .30
J4 D1 30r orange 1.50 1.00
J5 D1 50r gray brown 1.50 1.00
J6 D1 60r red brown 22.50 9.00
J7 D1 100r red lilac 4.00 2.50
J8 D1 130r dull blue 32.50 12.00
J9 D1 200r carmine 13.00 4.00
J10 D1 500r violet 18.00 5.00
Nos. J1-J10 (10) 95.65 35.40

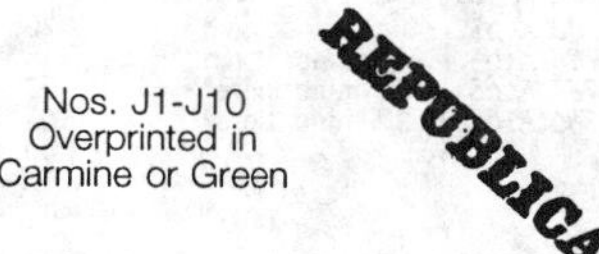

Nos. J1-J10 Overprinted in Carmine or Green

1911

J11 D1 5r yellow grn .15 .15
J12 D1 10r slate .15 .15
J13 D1 20r yellow brn .15 .15
J14 D1 30r orange .20 .15
J15 D1 50r gray brown .30 .20
J16 D1 60r red brown .40 .30
J17 D1 100r red lilac .40 .30
J18 D1 130r dull blue 2.00 1.00
J19 D1 200r carmine (G) 1.25 .85
J20 D1 500r violet 2.50 1.00
Nos. J11-J20 (10) 7.50 4.25

D2

Company Arms — D3

1916 Typo.
With Value in Centavos in Black

J21 D2 ½c yellow grn .30 .20
J22 D2 1c slate .30 .20
J23 D2 2c orange brn .30 .20
J24 D2 3c orange .60 .25
J25 D2 5c gray brown .60 .25
J26 D2 6c pale brown .60 .25
J27 D2 10c red lilac .60 .30
J28 D2 13c gray blue .90 .55
J29 D2 20c rose 1.25 .65
J30 D2 50c gray 3.00 .85
Nos. J21-J30 (10) 8.45 3.70

Perf. 11½, 13½, 14 to 15½
1919 Engr.

J31 D3 ½c green .15 .15
J32 D3 1c slate .15 .15
J33 D3 2c red brown .15 .15
J34 D3 3c orange .15 .15
J35 D3 5c gray brown .20 .20
J36 D3 6c lt brown .45 .45
J37 D3 10c lilac rose .45 .45
J38 D3 13c dull blue .45 .45
J39 D3 20c rose .45 .45
J40 D3 50c gray .45 .45
Nos. J31-J40 (10) 3.05 3.05

NEWSPAPER STAMP

Newspaper Stamp of Mozambique Overprinted Like Nos. 1-9

1894 Unwmk. ***Perf. 11½***

P1 N3 2½r brown .50 .40
a. Inverted overprint 30.00 30.00
b. Perf. 12½ .85 .50

Reprints are on stout white paper with clean-cut perf. 13½. Value $1.

POSTAL TAX STAMPS

Assistencia
Publica

No. 116 Surcharged in Black

2 Ctvos. 2

1932 ***Perf. 12½***

RA1 A11 2c on 3c org & blk 1.40 *2.00*

Charity — PT2

1933 Litho. ***Perf. 11***

RA2 PT2 2c magenta & blk 1.00 *2.00*

PT3 PT4

1940 Unwmk. ***Perf. 10½***

RA3 PT3 2c black & ultra 15.00 *16.00*

1941

RA4 PT4 2c black & brt red 15.00 *16.00*

NAMIBIA

nə-'mi-bē-ə

LOCATION — In southwestern Africa between Angola and South Africa, bordering on the Atlantic Ocean
GOVT. — Republic
AREA — 318,261 sq. mi.
POP. — 1,372,475 (1989)
CAPITAL — Windhoek

Formerly South West Africa.

100 Cents = 1 Rand
100 Cents = 1 Dollar (1993)

Catalogue values for unused stamps in this country are for Never Hinged items.

Pres. Sam Nujoma, Map and Natl. Flag — A137

Perf. 14½x14, 14x14½
1990, Mar. 21 Litho. Unwmk.

659 A137 18c shown .40 .40
660 A137 45c Dove, map, hands unchained, vert. 1.25 1.25
661 A137 60c Flag, map 1.90 1.90
Nos. 659-661 (3) 2.80 2.80

Independence from South Africa.

Sights of Namibia A138

1990, Apr. 26 ***Perf. 14½x14***

662 A138 18c Fish River Canyon .25 .25
663 A138 35c Quiver-tree Forest .85 .85
664 A138 45c Tsaris Mountains 1.00 1.00
665 A138 60c Dolerite Hills 1.40 1.40
a. Souvenir sheet of 1 5.25 5.25
Nos. 662-665 (4) 2.55 2.55

No. 665a publicizies the 150th anniv. of the Penny Black. Sold for 1.50r.

Architectural Development of Windhoek A139

Designs: 18c, Early central business area. 35c, Modern central business area. 45c, First municipal building. 60c, Current municipal building.

1990, July 26 ***Perf. 14½x14***

666 A139 18c multicolored .30 .30
667 A139 35c multicolored .50 .50
668 A139 45c multicolored .65 .65
669 A139 60c multicolored .90 .90
Nos. 666-669 (4) 1.60 1.60

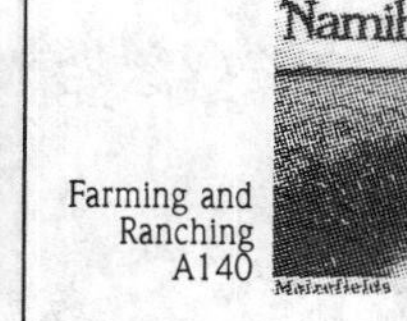

Farming and Ranching A140

1990, Oct. 11 ***Perf. 14½x14***

670 A140 20c Cornfields .20 .20
671 A140 35c Sanga cattle .55 .55
672 A140 50c Damara sheep .70 .70
673 A140 65c Irrigation .90 .90
Nos. 670-673 (4) 2.35 2.35

Gypsum A141

Oranjemund Alluvial Diamond Mine A142

1991, Jan. 2 ***Perf. 14½x14***

674 A141 1c shown .15 .15
675 A141 2c Flourite .15 .15
676 A141 5c Mimetite .15 .15
677 A141 10c Azurite .15 .15
679 A141 20c Dioptase .15 .15
680 A142 25c shown .20 .20
681 A142 30c Tsumeb mine .20 .20
682 A142 35c Rosh Pinah mine .25 .25
683 A141 40c Diamond .30 .30
684 A142 50c Uis mine .40 .40
685 A141 65c Boltwoodite .55 .55
686 A142 1r Rossing mine .80 .80
687 A141 1.50r Wolfenite 1.25 1.25
688 A141 2r Gold 1.65 1.65
689 A141 5r Willemite 4.00 4.00
Nos. 674-689 (15) 9.70 9.70

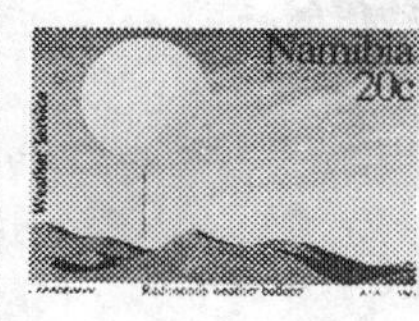

Namibian Weather Service, Cent. — A143

1991, Feb. 2 ***Perf. 14½x14***

690 A143 20c Weather balloon .20 .20
691 A143 35c Sunshine recorder .55 .55
692 A143 50c Measuring equipment .70 .70
693 A143 65c Gobabeb weather station .90 .90
Nos. 690-693 (4) 2.35 2.35

Mountain Zebra — A144

1991, Apr. 18 ***Perf. 14½x14***

694 A144 20c Four zebras .45 .45
695 A144 25c Mother suckling foal 1.00 1.00
696 A144 45c Three zebras 1.75 1.75
697 A144 60c Two zebras 2.50 2.50
Nos. 694-697 (4) 5.05 5.05

Mountains A145

1991, July 18 ***Perf. 14½x14***

698 A145 20c Karas .35 .35
699 A145 25c Gamsberg .50 .50
700 A145 45c Brukkaros .80 .80
701 A145 60c Erongo 1.25 1.25
Nos. 698-701 (4) 1.75 1.75

Tourist Camps — A146

Designs: 20c, Bernabe De la Bat Tourist Camp, Waterberg. 25c, Von Bach Recreation Resort. 45c, Gross Barmen Hot Springs. 60c, Namutoni Rest Camp.

1991, Oct. 24 ***Perf. 14½x14***

702 A146 20c multicolored .35 .35
703 A146 25c multicolored .40 .40
704 A146 45c multicolored .75 .75
705 A146 60c multicolored 1.00 1.00
Nos. 702-705 (4) 1.90 1.90

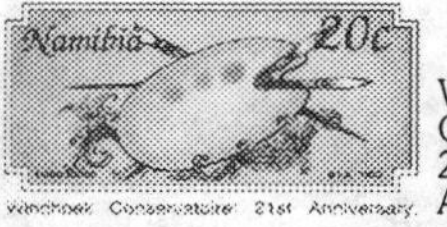

Windhoek Conservatoir, 21st Anniv. A147

Designs: 20c, Artist's palette, brushes. 25c, French horn, neck of violin. 45c, Pan pipes, masks of Comedy and Tragedy, lyre. 60c, Ballet pas de deux.

1992, Jan. 30 ***Perf. 14x14½***

706 A147 20c multicolored .20 .20
707 A147 25c multicolored .35 .35
708 A147 45c multicolored .60 .60
709 A147 60c multicolored .90 .90
Nos. 706-709 (4) 1.70 1.70

Freshwater Fish — A148

1992, Apr. 16 ***Perf. 14½x14***

710 A148 20c Blue kurper .15 .15
711 A148 25c Yellow fish .40 .40
712 A148 45c Carp .70 .70
713 A148 60c Catfish 1.00 1.00
Nos. 710-713 (4) 2.25 2.25

Views of Swakopmund A149

1992, July 2 ***Perf. 14½x14***

714 A149 20c Jetty .15 .15
715 A149 25c Swimming pool .40 .40
716 A149 45c State House, lighthouse .70 .70
717 A149 60c Palm beach 1.00 1.00
a. Souvenir sheet of 4, #714-717 2.50 2.50
Nos. 714-717 (4) 2.25 2.25

1992 Summer Olympics, Barcelona A150

1992, July 24 *Perf. 14½x14*

718 A150 20c Runners .30 .30
719 A150 25c Flag, emblem .40 .40
720 A150 45c Swimmers .75 .75
721 A150 60c Olympic stadium 1.10 1.10
a. Souvenir sheet of 4, #718-721 2.50 2.50
Nos. 718-721 (4) 1.70 1.70

No. 721a sold for 2r.

Disabled Workers — A151

Designs: 20c, Wrapping cucumbers. 25c, Finishing a woven mat. 45c, At a spinning wheel. 60c, Cleaning potted plants.

1992, Sept. 10 *Perf. 14x14½*

722 A151 20c multicolored .25 .25
723 A151 25c multicolored .40 .40
724 A151 45c multicolored .65 .65
725 A151 60c multicolored .75 .75
Nos. 722-725 (4) 1.55 1.55

Endangered Animals A152

1993, Feb. 25 *Perf. 14½x14*

726 A152 20c Loxodonta africana .30 .30
727 A152 25c Tragelaphus spekei .40 .40
728 A152 45c Diceros bicornis .70 .70
729 A152 60c Lycaon pictus .90 .90
a. Souvenir sheet of 4, #726-729 2.50 2.50
Nos. 726-729 (4) 1.30 1.30

Namibia Nature Foundation. No. 729a sold for 2.10r.

Arrival of Simmentaler Cattle in Namibia, Cent. — A153

1993, Apr. 16 *Perf. 14½x14*

730 A153 20c Cows and calves .25 .25
731 A153 25c Cow and calf .30 .30
732 A153 45c Head of stud bull .50 .50
733 A153 60c Arrival on boat, 1893 .65 .65
Nos. 730-733 (4) 1.30 1.30

A souvenir sheet of one No. 732 has inscription for National Philatelic Exhibition. Sold for 3r.

Namib Desert — A154

1993, June 4 *Perf. 14½x14*

734 A154 30c Sossusvlei .30 .30
735 A154 40c Blutkuppe .40 .40
736 A154 65c Homeb .65 .65
737 A154 85c Moon landscape .85 .85
Nos. 734-737 (4) 1.90 1.90

SOS Children's Village — A155

1993, Aug. 6 **Litho.** *Perf. 14*

738 A155 30c Happiness .30 .30
739 A155 40c A loving family .45 .45
740 A155 65c Home sweet home .70 .70
741 A155 85c My village .90 .90
Nos. 738-741 (4) 1.90 1.90

A156

Type A

Butterflies: 5c, Charaxes jasius saturnus. 10c, Acraea anemosa. 20c, Papilio nireus lyaeus. 30c, Junonia octavia sesamus. (35c), Graphium antheus. 40c, Hypolimnas misippus. 50c, Physcaeneura panda. 65c, Charaxes candiope. 85c, Junonia hierta cebrene. 90c, Colotis celimene pholoe. $1, Cacyreus dicksoni. $2, Charaxes bohemani. $2.50, Stugeta bowkeri tearei. $5, Byblia anvatara acheloia.

Type A: On the two long sides, two oval holes equal in width to three perf holes start at the third perf hole from each end of the stamp. The distance between the oval holes is filled by normal perf holes.

1993-94 *Perf. 14x14½*

742 A156 5c multicolored .15 .15
743 A156 10c multicolored .15 .15
744 A156 20c multicolored .15 .15
745 A156 30c multicolored .20 .20
745A A156 (35c) multicolored .25 .25
746 A156 40c multicolored .30 .30
747 A156 50c multicolored .35 .35
748 A156 65c multicolored .45 .45
749 A156 85c multicolored .60 .60
750 A156 90c multicolored .65 .65
751 A156 $1 multicolored .70 .70
752 A156 $2 multicolored 1.40 1.40
753 A156 $2.50 multicolored 1.75 1.75
754 A156 $5 multicolored 3.50 3.50
Nos. 742-754 (14) 10.60 10.60

No. 745A is inscribed "STANDARDISED MAIL" and sold for 35c when issued.

Issued: No. 745A, 4/8/94; others, 10/1/93.

Perf. 14½x15 Syncopated Type A

1997

742a A156 5c multicolored .15 .15
747a A156 50c multicolored .35 .35

Issued: Nos. 742a, 747a, 3/3/97.

Coastal Angling A157

1994, Feb. 4 **Litho.** *Perf. 14*

755 A157 30c Blacktail .30 .30
756 A157 40c Kob .40 .40
757 A157 65c Steenbras .65 .65
758 A157 85c Galjoen .85 .85
a. Souvenir sheet of 4, #755-758 2.25 2.25
Nos. 755-758 (4) 1.70 1.70

Incorporation of Walvis Bay into Namibia A158

1994, Mar. 1

759 A158 30c Quay .30 .30
760 A158 65c Aerial view .60 .60
761 A158 85c Map of Namibia .80 .80
Nos. 759-761 (3) 1.40 1.40

A159

A160

Flowers: 35c, Adenolobus pechuelii. 40c, Hibiscus elliottiae. 65c, Pelargonium cortusifolium. 85c, Hoodia macrantha.

1994, Apr. 8 **Litho.** *Perf. 14*

762 A159 35c multicolored .30 .30
763 A159 40c multicolored .35 .35
764 A159 65c multicolored .55 .55
765 A159 85c multicolored .75 .75
Nos. 762-765 (4) 1.60 1.60

1994, June 3 **Litho.** *Perf. 14*

Storks of Etosha.

766 A160 35c Yellowbilled .25 .25
767 A160 40c Abdim's .30 .30
768 A160 80c Openbilled .60 .60
769 A160 $1.10 White .85 .85
Nos. 766-769 (4) 1.50 1.50

Trains A161

1994, Aug. 5 **Litho.** *Perf. 13½x14*

770 A161 35c Steam railcar .30 .30
771 A161 70c Class Krauss .60 .60
772 A161 80c Class 24 .70 .70
773 A161 $1.10 Class 7C .95 .95
Nos. 770-773 (4) 1.70 1.70

Railways in Namibia, Cent. A162

Locomotives: 35c, Prince Edward, 1st in service. 70c, Ex-German SWA 2-8-0 tank. 80c, Class 8. $1.10, Class 33 400 diesel electric.

1995, Mar. 8 **Litho.** *Perf. 14*

774 A162 35c multicolored .20 .20
775 A162 70c multicolored .40 .40
776 A162 80c multicolored .50 .50
777 A162 $1.10 multicolored .65 .65
a. Souvenir sheet of 4, #774-777 2.00 2.00
Nos. 774-777 (4) 1.75 1.75

No. 777a sold for $3.50.

A163 A164

1995, Mar. 21 **Litho.** *Perf. 14*

778 A163 (35c) multicolored .20 .20

Independence, 5th anniv. No. 778 is inscribed "STANDARDISED MAIL" and sold for 35c on day of issue.

1995, May 24 **Litho.** *Perf. 14*

Fossils: 40c, Geochelone stromeri. 80c, Diamantornis wardi. 90c, Prohyrax hendeyi. $1.20, Crocodylus lloydi.

779 A164 40c multicolored .20 .20
780 A164 80c multicolored .45 .45
a. Souvenir sheet of 1 .45 .45
781 A164 90c multicolored .50 .50
782 A164 $1.20 multicolored .65 .65
Nos. 779-782 (4) 1.80 1.80

No. 780a is a continuous design.

Finnish Mission, 125th Anniv. A165

Designs: 40c, Mission church, Martti Rautanen (1845-1926). 80c, Albin Savola (1867-1934), Oniipa printing press. 90c, Oxwagon, Karl Emanuel August Weikkolin (1842-91). $1.20, Dr. Selma Raino (1873-1939), Onandjokwe Hospital.

1995, July 10 **Litho.** *Perf. 14*

783 A165 40c multicolored .20 .20
784 A165 80c multicolored .45 .45
785 A165 90c multicolored .50 .50
786 A165 $1.20 multicolored .65 .65
Nos. 783-786 (4) 1.80 1.80

Traditional Adornments — A166

1995, Aug. 16 **Litho.** *Perf. 14½x14*

787 A166 40c Ivory buttons .25 .25
788 A166 80c Conus shell .50 .50
789 A166 90c Cowrie shells .55 .55
790 A166 $1.20 Shell button .75 .75
Nos. 787-790 (4) 2.05 2.05

Souvenir Sheet

Singapore '95 — A167

Illustration reduced.

1995, Sept. 10 **Litho.** *Perf. 14*

791 A167 $1.20 Phacochoerus aethiopicus .75 .75

UN, 50th Anniv. — A168

1995, Oct. 24

792 A168 40c blue & black .25 .25

Tourism A169

1996, Apr. 1 **Litho.** *Perf. 15x14*

793 A169 (45c) Bogenfels Arch .25 .25
794 A169 90c Ruacana Falls .50 .50
795 A169 $1 Epupa Falls .55 .55
796 A169 $1.30 Wild horses .75 .75
Nos. 793-796 (4) 2.05 2.05

No. 793 is inscribed "Standardised Mail" and sold for 45c on day of issue.

Catholic Missions in Namibia A170

50c, Döbra Education and Training Centre. 95c, Heirachabis. $1, Windhoek St. Mary's Cathedral. $1.30, Ovamboland Old Church & School.

1996, May 27 Litho. *Perf. 15x14*

797 A170 50c multicolored .30 .30
798 A170 95c multicolored .50 .50
799 A170 $1 multicolored .55 .55
800 A170 $1.30 multicolored .75 .75
Nos. 797-800 (4) 2.10 2.10

Souvenir Sheet

CAPEX 96 — A171

Illustration reduced.

1996, June 8 Litho. *Perf. 14½x14*

801 A171 $1.30 African lynx .75 .75

UNICEF, 50th Anniv. A172

Designs: (45c), Children have rights. $1.30, Educate the girl.

1996, June 14 Litho. *Perf. 15x14*

802 A172 (45c) multicolored .25 .25
803 A172 $1.30 multicolored .75 .75

No. 802 is inscribed "Standard Postage" and sold for 45c on day of issue.

1996 Summer Olympic Games, Atlanta A173

1996, June 27

804 A173 (45c) Boxing .25 .25
805 A173 90c Cycling .50 .50
806 A173 $1 Swimming .55 .55
807 A173 $1.30 Running .75 .75
Nos. 804-807 (4) 2.05 2.05

No. 804 is inscribed "Standard Postage" and sold for 45c on day of issue.

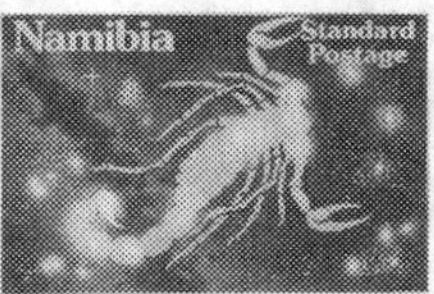

Constellations — A174

Designs: (45c), Scorpio. 90c, Sagittarius. $1, Southern Cross. $1.30, Orion.

1996, Sept. 12 Litho. *Perf. 15x14*

808 A174 (45c) multicolored .25 .25
809 A174 90c multicolored .45 .45
810 A174 $1 multicolored .50 .50
a. Souvenir sheet of 1 .50 .50
811 A174 $1.30 multicolored .70 .70
Nos. 808-811 (4) 1.90 1.90

No. 808 is inscribed "Standard Postage" and sold for 45c on day of issue.

No. 810a exists inscribed "Reprint February 17, 1997. Sold in aid of organized philately N$3.50."

Early Pastoral Pottery — A175

Designs: (45c), Urn-shaped storage vessel. 90c, Globular storage vessel. $1, Bag-shaped cooking vessel. $1.30, Large storage vessel.

1996, Oct. 17 *Perf. 14x15*

812 A175 (45c) multicolored .25 .25
813 A175 90c multicolored .45 .45
814 A175 $1 multicolored .50 .50
815 A175 $1.30 multicolored .70 .70
Nos. 812-815 (4) 1.90 1.90

No. 812 is inscribed "Standard Postage" and sold for 45c on day of issue.

Ancient //Khauxa!nas Ruins, near Karasburg — A176

Various views of stone wall.

1997, Feb. 6 Litho. *Perf. 15x14*

816 A176 (45c) multicolored .20 .20
817 A176 $1 multicolored .45 .45
818 A176 $1.10 multicolored .50 .50
819 A176 $1.50 multicolored .70 .70
Nos. 816-819 (4) 1.85 1.85

No. 816 is inscribed "Standard Postage" and sold for 45c on day of issue.

A177 A178

1997, Apr. 8 Litho. *Perf. 14x14½*

820 A177 $2 multicolored 1.25 1.25

Heinrich Von Stephen (1831-97), founder of UPU.

1997, May 15 Litho. *Perf. 14x14½*

Jackass Penguins.

821 A178 (45c) shown .25 .25
822 A178 $1 Nesting .50 .50
823 A178 $1.10 With young .55 .55
824 A178 $1.50 Swimming .75 .75
Nos. 821-824 (4) 2.05 2.05

World Wildlife Fund. No. 821 is inscribed "Standard Postage" and sold for 45c on day of issue.

Wild Cats A179

1997, June 12 Litho. *Perf. 14½x14*

825 A179 (45c) Felis caracal .25 .25
826 A179 $1 Felis lybica .50 .50
827 A179 $1.10 Felis serval .55 .55
828 A179 $1.50 Felis nigripes .75 .75
Nos. 825-828 (4) 2.05 2.05

No. 825 is inscribed "Standard Postage" and sold for 45c on day of issue. A souvenir sheet containing a $5 stamp like #828 exists.

Helmeted Guineafowl A180

1997, June 5 *Perf. 14½x14*

829 A180 $1.20 multicolored .65 .65

A181 A182

Baskets: 50c, Collecting bag. 90c, Powder basket. $1.20, Fruit basket. $2, Grain basket.

1997, July 8 Litho. *Perf. 14x14½*

830 A181 50c multicolored .25 .25
831 A181 90c multicolored .40 .40
832 A181 $1.20 multicolored .55 .55
833 A181 $2 multicolored .90 .90
Nos. 830-833 (4) 2.10 2.10

Perf. 14x14½ Syncopated Type A

1997

Cinderella Waxbill.

Booklet Stamps

834 A182 50c shown .25 .25
835 A182 60c Blackchecked waxbill .30 .30
a. Booklet pane, 5 each #835-836 2.75
Complete booklet, #835a 2.75

A183

Greetings Stamps A184

Flowers: No. 836, Catophractes alexandri. No. 837, Crinun paludosum. No. 838, Gloriosa superba. No. 839, Tribulus zeyheri. No. 840, Aptosimum pubescens.

Helmeted guineafowl: No. 841, In bed. No. 842, Holding flowers. No. 843, As music conductor. No. 844, Prepared to travel. No. 845, Wearing heart necklace.

1997, July 11 Litho. *Perf. 14x13½*

Booklet Stamps

836 A183 (45c) multicolored .25 .25
837 A183 (45c) multicolored .25 .25
838 A183 (45c) multicolored .25 .25
839 A183 (45c) multicolored .25 .25
840 A183 (45c) multicolored .25 .25
a. Booklet pane, 2 each #836-840 + 10 labels 2.50
Complete booklet, #840a 2.50
841 A184 50c multicolored .25 .25
842 A184 50c multicolored .25 .25
843 A184 50c multicolored .25 .25
844 A184 $1 multicolored .50 .50
845 A184 $1 multicolored .50 .50
a. Booklet pane, 2 each #841-845 + 10 labels 3.50
Complete booklet, #845a 3.50

Nos. 836-840 are inscribed "Standard Postage" and sold for 45c on day of issued.

Namibian Veterinary Assoc., 50th Anniv. — A185

1997, Sept. 12 *Perf. 14*

846 A185 $1.50 multicolored .70 .70

Souvenir Sheet

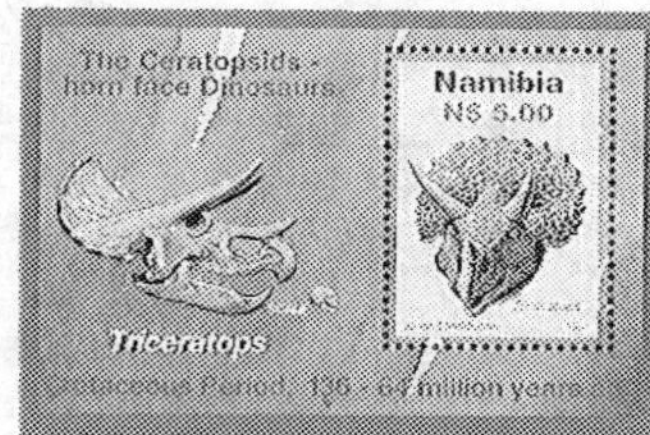

Triceratops — A186

Illustration reduced.

1997, Sept. 27 Litho. *Perf. 13*

847 A186 $5 multicolored 2.25 2.25

World Post Day — A187 Trees — A188

1997, Oct. 9 Litho. *Perf. 14x15*

848 A187 (45c) multicolored .25 .25

No. 848 is inscribed "Standard Postage" and sold for 45c on day of issue.

1997, Oct. 10

849 A188 (45c) False mopane .25 .25
850 A188 $1 Ana tree .45 .45
851 A188 $1.10 Shepherd's tree .50 .50
852 A188 $1.50 Kiaat .70 .70
Nos. 849-852 (4) 1.90 1.90

No. 849 is inscribed "Standard Postage" and sold for 45c on day of issue.

Fauna and Flora — A189

1997, Nov. 3 Litho. *Perf. 13½*

853 A189 5c Flame lily .15 .15
854 A189 10c Bushman poison .15 .15
855 A189 20c Camel's foot .15 .15
856 A189 30c Western rhigozum .15 .15
857 A189 40c Bluecheeked bee-eater .20 .20
858 A189 (45c) Rosyfaced lovebird .25 .25
859 A189 50c Laughing dove .25 .25
860 A189 60c Lappetfaced vulture .30 .30
861 A189 90c Yellowbilled hornbill .50 .50
862 A189 $1 Lilacbreasted roller .45 .45
863 A189 $1.10 Hippopotamus .55 .55
864 A189 ($1.20) Leopard .60 .60
865 A189 $1.20 Giraffe .60 .60
866 A189 $1.50 Elephant .70 .70
867 A189 $2 Lion .95 .95
868 A189 $4 Buffalo 1.90 1.90
869 A189 $5 Black rhinoceros 2.40 2.40
870 A189 $10 Cheetah 4.75 4.75
a. Booklet pane, 1 ea #853-870 15.00
Complete booklet, #870a 15.00
Nos. 853-870 (18) 15.05 15.05

No. 858 is inscribed "Standard Postage" and sold for 45c on day issue. No. 864 is inscribed "Postcard Rate" and sold for $1.20 on day of issue.

Christmas A190

Various pictures of a helmeted guineafowl.

1997, Nov. 3 *Perf. 13x12½*

871 A190 (45c) multicolored .25 .25
872 A190 $1 multicolored .45 .45
873 A190 $1.10 multicolored .50 .50
874 A190 $1.50 multicolored .60 .60
Nos. 872-875 (4) 3.95 3.95

Souvenir Sheet

875 A190 $5 multi, vert. 2.40 2.40

No. 871 is inscribed "Standard Postage" and sold for 45c on day of issue.

A191

A192

1997, Nov. 27 *Perf. 14x15*

876 A191 (45c) multicolored .25 .25

John Muafangejo (1943-87), artist. No. 876 is inscribed "Standard Postage" and sold for 45c on day of issue.

1998, Jan. 15

877 A192 (50c) brown & gray .25 .25

Gabriel B. Taapopi (1911-85). No. 877 is inscribed "Standard Postage" and sold for 50c on day of issue.

Large Wild Cats — A193

Designs: $1.20, Panthera pardus. $1.90, Panthera leo, female carrying young. $2, Panthera leo, male. $2.50, Acinonyx jubatus.

1998, Jan. 26 *Perf. 13x12½*

878 A193 $1.20 multicolored .60 .60
879 A193 $1.90 multicolored .95 .95
880 A193 $2 multicolored 1.00 1.00
881 A193 $2.50 multicolored 1.25 1.25
a. Souvenir sheet, #878-881 3.80 3.80
Nos. 878-881 (4) 3.80 3.80

Narra Plant — A194

1998, Feb. 9 *Perf. 12½x13*

882 A194 $2.40 multicolored 1.20 1.20

NATAL

nə-'tal

LOCATION — Southern coast of Africa, bordering on the Indian Ocean
GOVT. — British Crown Colony
AREA — 35,284 sq. mi.
POP. — 1,206,386 (1908)
CAPITAL — Pietermaritzburg

Natal united with Cape of Good Hope, Orange Free State and the Transvaal in 1910 to form the Union of South Africa.

12 Pence = 1 Shilling
20 Shillings = 1 Pound

Values for Nos. 1-7 are for examples with complete margins and free from damage. Unused values for No. 8 on are for stamps with original gum as defined in the catalogue introduction. Very fine examples of Nos. 8-49, 61-63 and 79 will have perforations touching the design on one or more sides due to the narrow spacing of the stamps on the plates. Stamps with perfs clear of the design on all four sides are scarce and will command higher prices.

Watermark

Wmk. 5 - Small Star

Crown and V R (Victoria Regina)
A2

Crown and Laurel — A3

A4

A5

Colorless Embossing

1857 Unwmk. *Imperf.*

1 A1 3p *rose* 500.
a. Tete beche pair *15,000.*
2 A2 6p *green* 1,200.
a. Diagonal half used as 3p on cover *10,000.*
3 A3 9p *blue* *9,000.*
4 A4 1sh *buff* *7,500.*

1858

5 A5 1p *blue* 1,200.
6 A5 1p *rose* 1,850.
a. No. 1 embossed over No. 6 —
7 A5 1p *buff* 1,000.

Reprints: The paper is slightly glazed, the embossing sharper and the colors as follows: 1p pale blue, deep blue, carmine rose or yellow; 3p pale rose or carmine rose; 6p bright green or yellow green; 1sh pale buff or pale yellow. Bogus cancellations are found on the reprints.

The stamps printed on surface-colored paper are revenue stamps with trimmed perforations.

Queen Victoria
A6 A7

1860 Engr. *Perf. 14*

8 A6 1p rose 125.00 70.00
9 A6 3p blue 140.00 40.00

1863 *Perf. 13*

10 A6 1p carmine lake 75.00 22.50

1861 *Clean-cut Perf. 14 to 16*

11 A6 3p blue 175.00 65.00

1862 *Rough Perf. 14 to 16*

12 A6 3p blue 90.00 30.00
a. Imperf., pair *1,750.*
b. Imperf. horiz. or vert., pair *2,250.*
13 A6 6p gray 135.00 47.50

1862 Wmk. 5

14 A6 1p rose 125.00 55.00

Imperforate copies of the 1p and 3p on paper watermarked small star are proofs.

1864 Wmk. 1 *Perf. 12½*

15 A6 1p carmine red 75.00 30.00
a. 1p brown red 110.00 35.00
b. Imperf.
16 A6 6p violet 37.50 25.00
a. 6p dull violet 55.00 15.00

1867 Typo. *Perf. 14*

17 A7 1sh green 130.00 25.00

For types A6 and A7 overprinted or surcharged see Nos. 18-50, 61-63, 76, 79.

Stamps of 1860-67 Overprinted: **Postage.**

1869

Overprint 12¾mm

18 A6 1p rose red (#15) 250.00 60.00
a. Double overprint 700.00
19 A6 3p blue (#12) 400.00 82.50
19A A6 3p blue (#9) 400.00
19B A6 3p blue (#11) 500.00 200.00
20 A6 6p violet (#16) 400.00 60.00
21 A7 1sh green (#17) 650.00

Same Overprint 13¾mm

22 A6 1p rose red (#15) 450.00 165.00
23 A6 3p blue (#12) 1,000. 235.00
a. Inverted overprint
23B A6 3p blue (#9)
23C A6 3p blue (#11)
24 A6 6p violet (#16) 900.00 120.00
25 A7 1sh green (#17) *1,400.*

Same Overprint 14½ to 15½mm

26 A6 1p rose red (#15) 450.00 140.00
27 A6 3p blue (#12) 200.00
27A A6 3p blue (#11) 250.00
27B A6 3p blue (#9)
28 A6 6p violet (#16) 900.00 75.00
29 A7 1sh green (#17) *1,350.*

Overprinted **POSTAGE.**

30 A6 1p rose red (#15) 70.00 25.00
a. 1p carmine red 120.00 25.00
b. Inverted overprint
31 A6 3p blue (#12) 140.00 40.00
a. Double overprint 550.00
31B A6 3p blue (#11) 110.00 37.50
31C A6 3p blue (#9) 225.00 50.00
32 A6 6p violet (#16) 100.00 42.50
33 A7 1sh green (#17) 165.00 55.00

Overprinted POSTAGE

34 A6 1p rose red (#15) 225.00 50.00
35 A6 3p blue (#12) 350.00 75.00
35A A6 3p blue (#11) 400.00 190.00
35B A6 3p blue (#9) *1,100.* *475.00*
36 A6 6p violet (#16) 325.00 50.00
a. Inverted overprint
37 A7 1sh green (#17) *1,000.*

Overprinted in Black or Red POSTAGE POSTAGE

1870-73 Wmk. 1 *Perf. 12½*

38 A6 1p red 60.00 12.00
39 A6 3p ultra (R) ('72) 60.00 12.00
40 A6 6p lilac ('73) 120.00 24.00
Nos. 38-40 (3) 240.00 48.00

Overprinted in Red, Black or Green

1870 *Perf. 14*

41 A7 1sh green (R) *3,000.*
42 A7 1sh green (Bk) *2,100.* *1,100.*
a. Double overprint *3,250.* *1,400.*
43 A7 1sh green (G) 45.00 10.00

See No. 76.

Type of 1867 Overprinted POSTAGE

1873

44 A7 1sh brown lilac 110.00 18.00

No. 44 without overprint is a revenue.

Type of 1864 Overprinted POSTAGE POSTAGE

1874 *Perf. 12½*

45 A6 1p rose red 165.00 55.00
a. Double overprint

Overprinted POSTAGE

1875

46 A6 1p rose red 80.00 40.00
a. 1p carmine 80.00 50.00
b. Double overprint 500.00 400.00

Overprinted POSTAGE

Overprint 14½mm

1875 *Perf. 12½*

47 A6 1p yellow 70.00 70.00
48 A6 1p rose red 70.00 45.00
a. Inverted overprint 650.00 400.00
49 A6 6p violet 50.00 5.00
a. Inverted overprint 600.00 175.00
b. Double overprint 525.00

Perf. 14

50 A7 1sh green 80.00 5.00
a. Double overprint 300.00
Nos. 47-50 (4) 270.00 125.00

The 1p yellow without overprint is a revenue.

A8

A9

A10

A11

Queen Victoria — A12

1874-78 Typo. Wmk. 1 *Perf. 14*

51 A8 1p rose 20.00 1.90
52 A9 3p ultramarine 80.00 13.00
a. Perf. 14x12½ 1,400. 900.00
53 A10 4p brown ('78) 85.00 10.00
54 A11 6p violet 30.00 5.50

Perf. 15½x15

55 A12 5sh claret 165.00 70.00

Perf. 14

56 A12 5sh claret ('78) 125.00 30.00
57 A12 5sh rose ('78) 50.00 25.00

Perf. 12½

58 A10 4p brown ('78) 325.00 60.00

See Nos. 65-71. For types A8-A10 surcharged see Nos. 59-60, 72-73, 77, 80.

Surcharged in Black:

POSTAGE

HALF ½ (n) ½ No. 60 Half-penny (o)

1877 *Perf. 14*

59 A8(n) ½p on 1p rose 20.00 *60.00*
a. Double surcharge "1/2"
60 A8(n) ½p on 1p rose 47.50 *80.00*

The "1/2" only of No. 60 is illustrated. Surcharge "n" exists in 3 or more types each of the large "1/2" (No. 59) and the small "1/2" (No. 60). "HALF" and "½" were overprinted separately; "½" may be above, below or overlapping.

Perf. 12½

61 A6(o) ½p on 1p yel 8.00 10.00
a. Double surcharge 250.00 175.00
b. Inverted surcharge 250.00 175.00
c. Pair, one without surcharge 1,000. 900.00
d. "POTAGE" 200.00 175.00
e. "POSAGE" 200.00
f. "POSTAGE" omitted 1,100.
62 A6(o) 1p on 6p vio 45.00 8.00
a. "POSTAGE" omitted
b. "POTAGE" 275.00 150.00
63 A6(o) 1p on 6p rose 85.00 27.50
a. Inverted surcharge 275.00
b. Double surcharge 225.00
c. Dbl. surch., one inverted 250.00 190.00
d. Triple surch., one invtd.
e. Quadruple surcharge 350.00 190.00
f. "POTAGE" 375.00
Nos. 61-63 (3) 138.00 45.50

No. 63 without overprint is a revenue.

A14

1880 **Typo.** *Perf. 14*

64 A14 ½p blue green 9.00 12.00
a. Vertical pair, imperf. between

1882-89 **Wmk. Crown and CA (2)**

65 A14 ½p blue green ('84) 85.00 15.00
66 A14 ½p gray green ('84) .75 .25
67 A8 1p rose ('84) 1.10 .15
68 A9 3p ultra ('84) 90.00 16.00
69 A9 3p gray ('89) 2.50 1.00
70 A10 4p brown 2.75 .60
71 A11 6p violet 3.00 .75
Nos. 65-71 (7) 185.10 33.75

Surcharged in Black:

ONE HALF-PENNY. (p) TWO PENCE (q)

1885-86

72 A8(p) ½p on 1p rose 15.00 11.00
73 A9(q) 2p on 3p gray ('86) 18.00 6.00

A17

A20

1887

74 A17 2p olive green, die B 2.00 .90
a. Die A 24.00 .90

For explanation of dies A and B see back of this section of the Catalogue.

Type of 1867 Overprinted Type "g" in Red

1888

76 A7 1sh orange 3.25 .80
a. Double overprint

Surcharged in Black TWOPENCE HALFPENNY

1891

77 A10 2½p on 4p brown 10.00 8.00
a. "PENGE" 50.00 *60.00*
b. "PENN" 300.00 175.00
c. Double surcharge 250.00 165.00
d. Inverted surcharge 325.00 250.00

1891, June

78 A20 2½p ultramarine 3.25 .75

Surcharged in Red or Black:

POSTAGE.

Half-Penny (No. 79) HALF (No. 80)

1895, Mar. **Wmk. 1** *Perf. 12½*

79 A6 ½p on 6p vio (R) 1.10 *2.50*
a. "Ealf" 18.00 *22.50*
b. "Penny" 16.00 *20.00*
c. Double surcharge, one vertical 300.00

Stamps with fancy "P," "T" or "A" in surcharge sell for twice as much.

Wmk. 2 *Perf. 14*

80 A8 ½p on 1p rose (Bk) .65 .75
a. Pair, one without and the other with double surcharge

King Edward VII
A23 A24

1902-03 **Typo.** **Wmk. 2** *Perf. 14*

81 A23 ½p blue green .60 .15
82 A23 1p rose 1.10 .15
83 A23 1½p blk & blue grn 1.10 .85
84 A23 2p ol grn & scar .70 .20
85 A23 2½p ultramarine .90 2.50
86 A23 3p gray & red vio .70 .35
87 A23 4p brown & scar 2.50 7.50
88 A23 5p org & black 1.10 2.50
89 A23 6p mar & bl grn 1.10 .90
90 A23 1sh pale bl & dp rose 3.00 1.00
91 A23 2sh vio & bl grn 42.50 8.00
92 A23 2sh6p red violet 30.00 9.50
93 A23 4sh yel & dp rose 52.50 47.50

Wmk. 1

94 A24 5sh car lake & dk blue 18.00 7.50
95 A24 10sh brn & dp rose 45.00 25.00
96 A24 £1 ultra & blk 125.00 40.00
97 A24 £1 10sh vio & bl green 250.00 65.00
Revenue cancel 5.00
98 A24 £5 black & vio *1,750.* *325.00*
Revenue cancel 11.00
99 A24 £10 org & green *7,000.*
Revenue cancel 82.50
100 A24 £20 green & car *11,500.*
Revenue cancel 140.00
Nos. 81-96 (16) 325.80 153.60

1904-08 **Wmk. 3**

101 A23 ½p blue green 2.50 .15
102 A23 1p rose 2.50 .15
a. Booklet pane of 6
b. Booklet pane of 5 + 1 label
103 A23 2p ol green & scar 3.50 2.75
104 A23 4p brn & scar 2.25 .85
105 A23 5p org & blk ('08) 2.25 3.00
106 A23 1sh pale bl & dp rose 47.50 5.00
107 A23 2sh vio & bl grn 40.00 22.50
108 A23 2sh6p red violet 32.50 25.00
109 A24 £1 10sh vio & org brn, chalky paper 1,000.
Revenue cancel 18.00
Nos. 101-108 (8) 133.00 59.40

A25

A26

1908-09

110 A25 6p red violet 4.50 1.75
111 A25 1sh black, *green* 5.00 1.75
112 A25 2sh bl & vio, *bl* 17.50 3.25
113 A25 2sh6p red & blk, *bl* 27.50 2.75
114 A26 5sh red & grn, *yellow* 17.50 10.50
115 A26 10sh red & grn, *green* 50.00 50.00
116 A26 £1 blk & vio, *red* 300.00 165.00
Nos. 110-115 (6) 122.00 70.00

OFFICIAL STAMPS

Nos. 101-103, 106 and Type A23 Overprinted OFFICIAL

1904 **Wmk. 3** *Perf. 14*

O1 A23 ½p blue green 3.50 .60
O2 A23 1p rose 1.75 .60
O3 A23 2p ol grn & scar 16.00 8.00
O4 A23 3p gray & red vio 8.00 *5.00*
O5 A23 6p mar & bl grn 35.00 30.00
O6 A23 1sh pale bl & dp rose 85.00 *125.00*
Nos. O1-O6 (6) 149.25 *169.20*

Stamps of Natal were replaced by those of the Union of South Africa.

NAURU

nä-'ü-(,)rü

LOCATION — An island on the Equator in the west central Pacific Ocean, midway between the Marshall and Solomon Islands.
GOVT. — Republic
AREA — 8½ sq. mi.
POP. — 8,421 (est. 1983)
CAPITAL — None. Parliament House is in Yaren District.

The island, a German possession, was captured by Australian forces in 1914 and, following World War I, was mandated to the British Empire. It was administered jointly by Great Britain, Australia and New Zealand.

In 1947 Nauru was placed under United Nations trusteeship, administered by Australia. On January 31, 1968, Nauru became a republic.

See North West Pacific Islands.

12 Pence = 1 Shilling
100 Cents = 1 Dollar (1966)

Catalogue values for unused stamps in this country are for Never Hinged items, beginning with Scott 39.

Great Britain Stamps of 1912-13 Overprinted at Bottom of Stamp NAURU

1916-23 **Wmk. 33** *Perf. 14½x14*

1 A82 ½p green .35 *1.00*
2 A83 1p scarlet .45 *1.10*
3 A84 1½p red brn ('23) 67.50 *90.00*
4 A85 2p org (die I) .80 *1.65*
a. 2p deep orange (die II) ('23) 55.00 *80.00*
6 A86 2½p ultra 1.65 *3.50*
7 A87 3p violet 2.25 *4.25*
8 A88 4p slate green 2.25 *6.00*
a. Double overprint
9 A89 5p yel brown 3.25 *8.00*
10 A89 6p dull violet 4.00 *9.50*
11 A90 9p black brown 8.00 *17.50*
12 A90 1sh bister 9.50 *17.50*
Nos. 1-12 (11) 100.00 *160.00*

Overprinted NAURU

Wmk. 34 *Perf. 11x12*

13 A91 2sh6p light brown 70.00 100.00
a. 2sh6p black brown 550.00 600.00
14 A91 5sh carmine 175.00 185.00
a. 5sh rose carmine 2,500. 2,500.
15 A91 10sh lt blue (R) 375.00 *425.00*
a. 10sh indigo blue *6,500.* *6,000.*

Same Ovpt. on Great Britain No. 179

1920

16 A91 2sh6p gray brown 90.00 *150.00*
Nos. 13-16 (4) 710.00 *860.00*
Nos. 1-16 (15) 810.00 *1,020.*

Overprint Centered

1923

1a A82 ½p 4.00 *50.00*
2a A83 1p 22.50 *40.00*
3a A84 1½p 30.00 *50.00*
4b A85 2p As No. 4a 42.50 *75.00*
Nos. 1a-4b (4) 99.00 *215.00*

On Nos. 1-12 "NAURU" is usually 12¾mm wide and at the foot of the stamp. In 1923 four values were overprinted with the word 13½mm wide and across the middle of the stamp.

Freighter — A1 George VI — A2

1924-47 **Unwmk.** **Engr.** *Perf. 11*

17 A1 ½p orange brown 1.00 1.90
a. Perf. 14 ('47) 1.10 *4.75*
18 A1 1p green 1.40 1.90
19 A1 1½p red 1.00 1.00
20 A1 2p orange 1.65 *5.25*
21 A1 2½p blue .90 *2.50*
a. Horiz. pair, imperf. between
22 A1 3p grnsh gray ('37) 2.00 *5.50*
a. 3p pale blue 2.75 *6.25*
23 A1 4p olive green 3.50 *5.75*
24 A1 5p dk brown 2.25 2.75
25 A1 6p dark violet 3.00 2.50
26 A1 9p brown olive 4.50 *13.00*
27 A1 1sh brown red 4.50 1.90
28 A1 2sh6p slate green 25.00 20.00
29 A1 5sh claret 35.00 *35.00*
30 A1 10sh yellow 80.00 *65.00*
Nos. 17-30 (14) 165.70 *163.95*

In 1937 new printings of Nos. 17-30 were made on glazed-surface paper in slighly different shades.

Stamps of Type A1 Overprinted in Black HIS MAJESTY'S JUBILEE. 1910-1935

1935, July 12 **Glazed Paper** *Perf. 11*

31 A1 1½p red .55 .65
32 A1 2p orange 1.25 1.50
33 A1 2½p blue 2.50 2.75
34 A1 1sh brown red 7.00 *8.25*
Set, never hinged 18.00
Nos. 31-34 (4) 11.30 *13.15*

25th anniv. of the reign of George V.

1937, May 10 **Engr.**

35 A2 1½p salmon rose .20 .20
36 A2 2p dull orange .20 .30
37 A2 2½p blue .20 .20
38 A2 1sh brown violet .45 .45
Nos. 35-38 (4) 1.05 1.15
Set, never hinged 1.90

Coronation of George VI & Elizabeth.

Catalogue values for unused stamps in this section, from this point to the end of the section, are for Never Hinged items.

Casting Throw-net — A3

Anibare Bay — A4

3½p, Loading phosphate. 4p, Frigate bird. 6p, Nauruan canoe. 9p, Meeting house (domaneab). 1sh, Palms. 2sh6p, Buada lagoon. 5sh, Map.

1954, Feb. 6 *Perf. 14½x14, 14x14½*

39 A3 ½p purple .15 .15
40 A4 1p green .15 .15
41 A3 3½p red .35 .25
42 A3 4p deep blue .45 .30
43 A3 6p orange .50 .35
44 A3 9p brown lake .95 .50
45 A4 1sh dk rose violet 1.00 .65
46 A3 2sh6p dk gray green 5.00 3.00
47 A4 5sh lilac rose 10.50 5.50
Nos. 39-47 (9) 19.05 10.85

See Nos. 58-71.

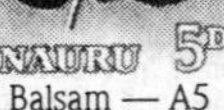

Balsam — A5 Black Lizard — A6

Capparis — A7 Coral Pinnacles — A8

White Tern — A9

Designs: 2p, Micronesian pigeon, vert. 3p, Poison nut flower. 3sh3p, Nightingale reed warbler.

Perf. 13½, Perf. 14½x13½ (10p), Perf. 14½ (2sh3p)
Photo.; Engraved (10p, 2sh3p)

1963-65 Unwmk.

49 A9 2p multi ('65) .20 .15
50 A6 3p red org, sl grn & yel ('64) .30 .25
51 A5 5p gray, bl grn & yellow .75 .50
52 A6 8p green & black 1.50 .65
53 A7 10p black ('64) 2.00 1.10
54 A9 1sh3p ap grn, blk & Prus bl ('65) 3.00 2.00
55 A8 2sh3p vio blue ('64) 3.75 2.50
56 A6 3sh3p lt yel, bl, brn & blk ('65) 7.50 5.00
Nos. 49-56 (8) 19.00 12.15

Issue dates: 5p, Apr. 22. 8p, July 1. 3p, 10p, 2sh3p, Apr. 16. 2p, 1sh3p, 3sh3p, May 3.

"Simpson and His Donkey" by Wallace Anderson — A9a

Perf. 13½x13

1965, Apr. 14 Photo. Unwmk.

57 A9a 5p brt green, sepia & blk .75 .75

See note after Australia No. 387.

Types of 1954-65
Values in Cents and Dollars

Designs: 1c, Anibare Bay. 2c, Casting throw-net. 3c, Loading phosphate. 4c, Balsam. 5c, Palms. 7c, Black lizard. 8c, Capparis. 10c, Frigate bird. 15c, White tern. 25c, Coral pinnacles. 30c, Poison nut flower. 35c, Reed warbler. 50c, Micronesian pigeon, vert. $1, Map.

Engr.; Photo. (4c, 7c, 15c, 30c-50c)

1966 ***Perf. 14½x14, 14x14½***

58 A4 1c dark blue .15 .15
59 A3 2c claret .15 .15
60 A3 3c green .15 .15
61 A5 4c lilac, grn & yel .15 .15
62 A4 5c violet blue .20 .15
63 A6 7c fawn & black .20 .20
64 A7 8c olive green .25 .20
65 A3 10c dark red .30 .25
66 A9 15c ap grn, blk & Prus blue .35 .30
67 A3 25c sepia .70 .55
68 A6 30c brick red, sl grn, & yellow .90 .75
69 A6 35c lt yel, bl, brn & black 1.40 1.25
70 A9 50c yel, bluish blk & brown 1.75 1.75
71 A4 $1 claret 3.75 3.00
Nos. 58-71 (14) 10.40 9.00

The engraved stamps are luminescent.

Issued: 2c, 3c, 5c, 15c, 25c, 35c, 5/25; others, 2/14.

Republic

Nos. 58-71 Overprinted in Red, Black or Orange
"REPUBLIC / OF / NAURU"

1968

72 A4 1c dark blue (R) .15 .15
73 A3 2c claret .15 .15
74 A3 3c green .15 .15
75 A5 4c lilac, grn & yel .15 .15
76 A4 5c violet blue (O) .15 .15
77 A6 7c fawn & blk (R) .15 .15
78 A7 8c olive green (R) .15 .15
79 A3 10c dark red .20 .20
80 A9 15c ap grn, blk & Prus blue 2.00 2.00
81 A3 25c sepia (R) .60 .60
82 A6 30c brick red, sl grn & yellow .95 .70
83 A6 35c multicolored 1.25 .95
84 A9 50c yel, bluish blk & brown 1.50 1.50
85 A4 $1 claret 2.75 2.75
Nos. 72-85 (14) 10.30 9.75

Issued: 4c, 7c, 30c, 35c, May 15; others, Jan 31.

Nauru Woman Watching Rising Sun — A10

Planting Seedling and Map of Nauru — A11

Perf. 13x13½

1968, Sept. 11 Photo. Unwmk.

86 A10 5c multicolored .15 .15
87 A11 10c brt blue, blk & green .30 .30

Independence of Nauru.

Flag of Nauru — A12

1969, Jan. 31 Litho. ***Perf. 13½***

88 A12 15c dk vio blue, yel & org .40 .40

For overprint see No. 90.

Commission Emblem and Nauru — A13

1972, Feb. 7 Litho. ***Perf. 14½x14***

89 A13 25c blue, yellow & black .85 .85

South Pacific Commission, 25th anniv.

No. 88 Overprinted in Gold:

Independence 1968-1973

1973, Jan. 31 ***Perf. 13½***

90 A12 15c multicolored .35 .35

Fifth anniversary of independence.

Lotus (Ekwenababae) A14

Map of Nauru, Artifacts A15

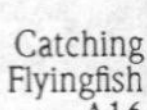

Catching Flyingfish A16

Designs: 2c, Kauwe iud. 3c, Rimone. 4c, Denea. 5c, Beach morning-glory. 7c, Golden butterflyfish. 10c, Nauruan ball game (itsibweb). 15c, Nauruan wrestling. 20c, Snaring frigate birds. 25c, Nauruan girl with flower garland. 30c, Men catching noddies. 50c, Frigate birds.

1973 Litho. ***Perf. 13½x14***

91 A14 1c pale yellow & multi .15 .15
92 A14 2c pale ocher & multi .15 .15
93 A14 3c pale violet & multi .15 .15
94 A14 4c pale green & multi .15 .15
95 A14 5c pale blue & multi .15 .15

Perf. 14½x14, 14x14½

96 A16 7c blue & multi .20 .20
97 A16 8c black & multi .25 .25
98 A16 10c multicolored .30 .30
99 A15 15c green & multi .35 .35
100 A15 20c blue & multi .40 .40
101 A15 25c yellow & multi .45 .45
102 A16 30c multicolored .60 .60
103 A16 50c multicolored 1.10 1.10
104 A15 $1 blue & multi 2.25 2.25
Nos. 91-104 (14) 6.65 6.65

Issue dates: Nos. 97-100, May 23; Nos. 96, 101-103, July 25; others Mar. 28, 1973.

Cooperative Store — A17

Eigigu, the Girl in the Moon — A18

Design: 25c, Timothy Detudamo and cooperative store emblem.

1973, Dec. 20 Litho. ***Perf. 14½x14***

105 A17 5c multicolored .30 .25
106 A17 25c multicolored 1.10 .90
107 A18 50c multicolored 2.50 2.50
Nos. 105-107 (3) 3.90 3.65

50th anniversary of Nauru Cooperative Society, founded by Timothy Detudamo.

"Eigamoiya" — A19

10c, Phosphate mining. 15c, "Nauru Chief" plane over Nauru. 25c, Nauru chieftain with frigate-bird headdress. 35c, Capt. J. Fearn, sailing ship "Hunter" & map of Nauru. 50c, "Hunter" off Nauru.

Perf. 13x13½, 13½x13

1974, May 21 Litho.
Sizes: 70x22mm (7c, 35c, 50c); 33x20mm (10c, 15c, 25c)

108 A19 7c multicolored .25 .15
109 A19 10c multicolored .35 .25
110 A19 15c multicolored .60 .45
111 A19 25c multicolored 1.75 1.40
112 A19 35c multicolored 6.00 5.25
113 A19 50c multicolored 5.75 5.00
Nos. 108-113 (6) 14.70 12.50

175th anniversary of Nauru's first contact with the outside world.

Map of Nauru — A20

Post Office — A21

UPU Emblem and: 20c, Mailman on motorcycle. $1, Flag of Nauru and UPU Building, Bern, vert.

1974, July 23 Litho. ***Perf. 14***

114 A20 5c multicolored .15 .15

Perf. 13½x13, 13x13½

115 A21 8c multicolored .15 .15
116 A21 20c multicolored .55 .40
117 A21 $1 multicolored 3.25 3.00
a. Souv. sheet of 4, #114-117, imperf. 7.50 6.50
Nos. 114-117 (4) 4.10 3.70

Cent. of the UPU.

Rev. P. A. Delaporte — A22

1974, Dec. 10 Litho. ***Perf. 14½***

118 A22 15c brt pink & multi .60 .45
119 A22 20c blue & multi 1.10 1.10

Christmas 1974. Delaporte, a German-born American missionary, took Christianity to Nauru and translated the New Testament into Nauruan.

Nauru, Grain, Albert Ellis, Phosphate Rock — A23

Designs: 7c, Phosphate mining and coolie carrying load. 15c, Electric freight train, tugs and ship. 25c, Excavator, cantilever and truck.

1975, July 23 Litho. ***Perf. 14½x14***

120 A23 5c multicolored .15 .15
121 A23 7c multicolored .20 .20
122 A23 15c multicolored .95 .75
123 A23 25c multicolored 1.50 1.10
Nos. 120-123 (4) 2.80 2.20

75th anniv. of discovery of phosphate (5c); 70th anniv. of Pacific Phosphate Co. Mining Agreement (7c); 50th anniv. of British Phosphate Commissioners (15c); 5th anniv. of Nauru Phosphate Corp. (25c).

Melanesian Outrigger and Map of SPC's Area — A24

1975, Sept. 1 Litho. ***Perf. 14x14½***

124 A24 20c Micronesian outrigger .70 .50
125 A24 20c Polynesian double hull .70 .50
126 A24 20c shown .70 .50
127 A24 20c Polynesian outrigger .70 .50
a. Block of 4, #124-127 3.00 3.00
Nos. 124-127 (4) 2.80 2.00

South Pacific Commission Conference, Nauru, Sept. 29-Oct. 10.

New Civic Center A25

Design: 50c, "Domaneab" (meeting house) and flags of participating nations.

1975, Sept. 29 Litho. ***Perf. 14½***

128 A25 30c multicolored .70 .70
129 A25 50c multicolored 1.25 1.25

South Pacific Commission Conference, Nauru, Sept. 29-Oct. 10.

Virgin Mary, Stained-glass Window — A26

Christmas: 7c, 15c, "Suffer little children to come unto me," stained-glass window, Orro Protestant Church. 25c, like 5c, Yaren Catholic Church.

1975, Nov. 7 Litho. *Perf. 14½*

130 A26 5c gray blue & multi .15 .15
131 A26 7c green & multi .15 .15
132 A26 15c brown & multi .40 .40
133 A26 25c lilac & multi .65 .65
Nos. 130-133 (4) 1.35 1.35

Frangipani Forming Lei Around Nauru A27

Designs: 14c, Hand crowning Nauru with lei. 25c, Reed warbler, birds flying from Truk to Nauru. 40c, Reunion of islanders in Boar Harbor.

1976, Jan. 31 Litho. *Perf. 14½*

134 A27 10c green & multi .15 .15
135 A27 14c violet & multi .15 .15
136 A27 25c red & multi .30 .30
137 A27 40c blue & multi .55 .55
Nos. 134-137 (4) 1.15 1.15

30th anniversary of the return of the islanders from Japanese internment on Truk.

Nauru Nos. 7 and 11 A28

Designs: 15c, Nauru Nos. 10 and 12. 25c, Nauru No. 13. 50c, Nauru No. 14, "Specimen."

1976, May 6 Litho. *Perf. 13½x14*

138 A28 10c multicolored .20 .15
139 A28 15c multicolored .30 .25
140 A28 25c multicolored .45 .40
141 A28 50c multicolored .95 .90
Nos. 138-141 (4) 1.90 1.70

60th anniv. of Nauru's 1st postage stamps.

Nauru Shipping and Pandanus — A29

Designs: 20c, Air Nauru Boeing 737 and Fokker F28, and tournefortia argentea. 30c, Earth satellite station and thespesia populnea. 40c, Area produce and cordia subcordata.

1976, July 26 Litho. *Perf. 13½x14*

142 A29 10c multicolored .20 .15
143 A29 20c multicolored .35 .30
144 A29 30c multicolored .50 .45
145 A29 40c multicolored .80 .55
Nos. 142-145 (4) 1.85 1.45

7th South Pacific Forum, Nauru, July 1976.

Nauruan Children's Choir
A30 A31

20c, Angels. Designs after children's paintings.

1976, Nov. Litho. *Perf. 14x13½*

146 A30 15c multicolored .40 .40
147 A31 15c multicolored .40 .40
a. Pair, #146-147 .80 .80
148 A30 20c multicolored .50 .50
149 A31 20c multicolored .50 .50
a. Pair, #148-149 1.10 1.00
Nos. 146-149 (4) 1.80 1.80

Christmas.

Nauru House, Melbourne, and Coral Pinnacles — A32

Cable-laying Ship Anglia, 1902 — A33

30c, Nauru House and Melbourne skyline.

1977, Apr. 14 Photo. *Perf. 14½*

150 A32 15c multicolored .45 .40
151 A32 30c multicolored .95 .85

Opening of Nauru House in Melbourne, Australia.
For surcharges see Nos. 161-164.

1977, Sept. 7 Photo. *Perf. 14½*

Designs: 15c, Nauru radar station. 20c, Stern of Anglia. 25c, Radar antenna.

152 A33 7c multicolored .15 .15
153 A33 15c multicolored .25 .25
154 A33 20c multicolored .40 .30
155 A33 25c multicolored .50 .40
Nos. 152-155 (4) 1.30 1.10

1st transpacific cable, 75th anniv., and 1st artificial earth satellite, 20th anniv.

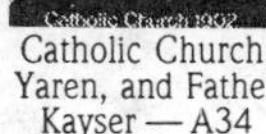

Catholic Church, Yaren, and Father Kayser — A34

Coat of Arms of Nauru — A35

Designs: 25c, Congregational Church, Orro. 30c, Catholic Church, Arubo.

1977, Oct. Photo. *Perf. 14½*

156 A34 15c multicolored .20 .20
157 A34 25c multicolored .35 .35
158 A34 30c multicolored .40 .40
Nos. 156-158 (3) .95 .95

Christmas, and 55th anniversary of first Roman Catholic Church on Nauru.

1978, Jan. 31 Litho. *Perf. 14½*

159 A35 15c blue & multi .20 .15
160 A35 60c emerald & multi .80 .70

10th anniversary of independence.

Nos. 150-151 Surcharged with New Value and Two Bars

1978, Apr. Photo. *Perf. 14½*

161 A32 4c on 15c multi 3.50 3.50
162 A32 5c on 15c multi 3.50 3.50
163 A32 8c on 30c multi 3.50 3.50
164 A32 10c on 30c multi 3.50 3.50
Nos. 161-164 (4) 14.00 14.00

Girls Catching Fish in Buada Lagoon A36

Designs: 1c, Fisherman and family collecting shellfish. 2c, Pigs foraging near coral reef. 3c, Gnarled tree and birds. 4c, Girl catching fish with hands. 5c, Bird catching fish. 10c, Ijuw Lagoon. 15c, Young girl and coral formation. 20c, Reef pinnacles, Anibare Bay. 25c, Pinnacles, Meneng shore. 30c, Frigate bird. 32c, Coconut palm and noddies. 40c, Iwiyi, wading bird. 50c, Frigate birds. $1, Pinnacles, Topside. $2, Newly uncovered pinnacles, Topside. $5, Old pinnacles, Topside.

1978-79 Photo. *Perf. 14½*

165 A36 1c multicolored .15 .15
166 A36 2c multicolored .15 .15
167 A36 3c multicolored .15 .15
168 A36 4c multicolored .15 .15
169 A36 5c multicolored .15 .15
170 A36 7c multicolored .15 .15
171 A36 10c multicolored .15 .15
172 A36 15c multicolored .20 .25
173 A36 20c multicolored .25 .30
174 A36 25c multicolored .30 .35
175 A36 30c multicolored .35 .45
176 A36 32c multicolored .40 .50
177 A36 40c multicolored .45 .55
178 A36 50c multicolored .60 .70
179 A36 $1 multicolored 1.10 1.40
180 A36 $2 multicolored 2.25 2.75
181 A36 $5 multicolored 6.50 7.00
Nos. 165-181 (17) 13.45 15.30

Issued: #166-169, 6/6/79; others, 5/1978.

"APU" — A37

Mother and Child — A38

1978, Aug. 28 Litho. *Perf. 13½*

182 A37 15c multicolored 1.00 .90
183 A37 20c gold, blk & dk blue 1.25 1.10

14th General Assembly of Asian Parliamentary Union, Nauru, Aug. 28-Sept. 1. On sale during conference only.

1978, Nov. 1 Litho. *Perf. 14*

Christmas: 15c, 20c, Angel over the Pacific, horiz. 30c, like 7c.

184 A38 7c multicolored .15 .15
185 A38 15c multicolored .20 .20
186 A38 20c multicolored .25 .25
187 A38 30c multicolored .40 .40
Nos. 184-187 (4) 1.00 1.00

Lord Baden-Powell and Cub Scout — A39

30c, Boy Scout. 50c, Explorer.

1978, Dec. 1 Litho. *Perf. 14*

188 A39 20c multicolored .30 .30
189 A39 30c multicolored .40 .40
190 A39 50c multicolored .70 .70
Nos. 188-190 (3) 1.40 1.40

70th anniversary of 1st Scout Troop.

Flyer A over Nauru Airfield A40

Designs: No. 192, "Southern Cross" and Boeing 727. No. 193, "Southern Cross" and Boeing 737. 30c, Wright Flyer over Nauru.

1979, Jan. *Perf. 14½*

191 A40 10c multicolored .20 .20
192 A40 15c multicolored .30 .30
193 A40 15c multicolored .30 .30
a. Pair, #192-193 .60 .60
194 A40 30c multicolored .60 .60
Nos. 191-194 (4) 1.40 1.40

1st powered flight, 75th anniv. and Kingsford Smith's US-Australia and Australia-New Zealand flights, 50th anniv.
Nos. 192-193 printed checkerwise.

Rowland Hill, Marshall Islands No. 15 with Nauru Cancel A41

1979, Feb. 27 Litho. *Perf. 14½*

195 A41 5c shown .15 .15
196 A41 15c Nauru No. 15 .15 .15
197 A41 60c Nauru No. 160 .70 .70
a. Souvenir sheet of 3, #195-197 1.25 1.25
Nos. 195-197 (3) 1.00 1.00

Sir Rowland Hill (1795-1879), originator of penny postage.

Dish Antenna, Earth Station, ITU Emblem A42

ITU Emblem and: 32c, Woman operating Telex machine. 40c, Radio beacon operator.

1979, Aug. Litho. *Perf. 14½*

198 A42 7c multicolored .15 .15
199 A42 32c multicolored .40 .40
200 A42 40c multicolored .50 .50
Nos. 198-200 (3) 1.05 1.05

Intl. Radio Consultative Committee (CCIR) of the ITU, 50th anniv.

Nauruan Girl — A43

IYC Emblem, Nauruan Children: 15c, Boy. 25c, 32c, 50c, Girls, diff.

1979, Oct. 3 Litho. *Perf. 14½*

201 A43 8c multicolored .15 .15
202 A43 15c multicolored .15 .15
203 A43 25c multicolored .25 .25
204 A43 32c multicolored .30 .30
205 A43 50c multicolored .45 .45
a. Strip of 5, #201-205 1.25 1.25

International Year of the Child.

Star, Scroll, Ekwenababa Flower — A44

Star and Flowers: 15c, Milos. 20c, Denea. 30c, Morning glories.

1979, Nov. 14 Litho. *Perf. 14½*

206 A44 7c multicolored .15 .15
207 A44 15c multicolored .20 .20
208 A44 20c multicolored .25 .25
209 A44 30c multicolored .40 .40
Nos. 206-209 (4) 1.00 1.00

Christmas.

Nauruan Plane over Melbourne — A45

Air Nauru, 10th Anniversary (Plane Over): 20c, Tarawa. 25c, Hong Kong. 30c, Auckland.

1980, Feb. 28 Litho. *Perf. 14½*

210 A45 15c multicolored .25 .25
211 A45 20c multicolored .30 .30
212 A45 25c multicolored .40 .40
213 A45 30c multicolored .50 .50
Nos. 210-213 (4) 1.45 1.45

Early Steam Locomotive A46

1980, May 6 Litho. *Perf. 15*

214 A46 8c shown	.15	.15
215 A46 32c Electric locomotive	.40	.40
216 A46 60c Clyde diesel-hydraulic locomotive	.75	.75
a. Souvenir sheet of 3, #214-216	1.75	1.75
Nos. 214-216 (3)	1.30	1.30

Nauru Phosphate Corp., 10th anniv. No. 216a also for London 1980 Intl. Stamp Exhibition, May 6-14; Penny Black, 140th anniv.

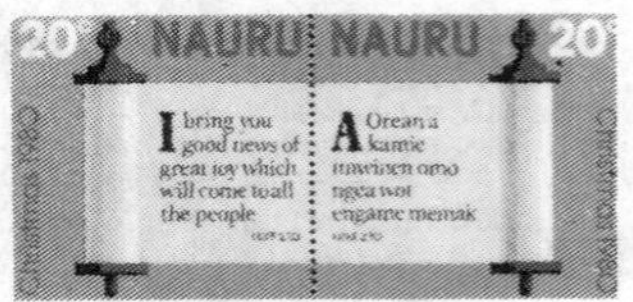

Christmas 1980

A47 A48

Designs: 30c, "Glory to God in the Highest . . ." in English and Nauruan.

1980, Sept. 24 Litho. *Perf. 15*

217 A47 20c multicolored	.25	.25
218 A48 20c multicolored	.25	.25
a. Pair, #217-218	.50	.50
219 A47 30c multicolored	.35	.35
220 A48 30c multicolored	.35	.35
a. Pair, #219-220	.75	.75
Nos. 217-220 (4)	1.20	1.20

See Nos. 236-239.

Flags of Nauru, Australia, Gt. Britain and New Zealand, UN Emblem — A49

1980, Dec. 20 Litho. *Perf. 14½*

221 A49 25c shown	.30	.30

Size: 72x22mm

Perf. 14

222 A49 30c UN Trusteeship Council	.35	.35
223 A49 50c 1968 independence ceremony	.55	.55
Nos. 221-223 (3)	1.20	1.20

UN de-colonization declaration, 20th anniv.

No. 222 printed se-tenant with label showing flags of UN and Nauru, issued Feb. 11, 1981.

Timothy Detudamo (Former Head Chief), Domaneab (Meeting House) — A50

1981, Feb. Litho. *Perf. 14½*

224 A50 20c shown	.25	.25
225 A50 30c Raymond Gadabu	.35	.35
226 A50 50c Hammer DeRoburt	.65	.65
Nos. 224-226 (3)	1.25	1.25

Legislative Council, 30th anniversary.

Casting Net by Hand A51

1981 Litho. *Perf. 12*

227 A51 8c shown	.15	.15
228 A51 20c Ancient canoe	.25	.25
229 A51 32c Powered boat	.45	.45
230 A51 40c Fishing vessel	.65	.65
a. Souvenir sheet of 4, #230	2.00	2.00
Nos. 227-230 (4)	1.50	1.50

Bank of Nauru, 5th Anniv. A52

1981, July 21 Litho. *Perf. 14x14½*

231 A52 $1 multicolored	1.25	1.25

ESCAP Secy. Maramis Delivering Inaugural Speech — A53

1981, Oct. 24 Litho. *Perf. 14½*

232 A53 15c shown	.15	.15
233 A53 20c Maramis, Pres. de Robert	.25	.25
234 A53 25c Plaque	.30	.30
235 A53 30c Raising UN flag	.35	.35
Nos. 232-235 (4)	1.05	1.05

UN Day and first anniv. of Economic and Social Commission for Asia and Pacific (ESCAP) liason office in Nauru.

Christmas Type of 1980

Christmas (Biblical Scriptures in English and Nauruan): 20c, "His Name Shall Be Called Emmanuel." 30c, "To You is Born This Day . . ."

1981, Nov. 14 Litho. *Perf. 14½*

236 A47 20c multicolored	.25	.25
237 A48 20c multicolored	.25	.25
a. Pair, #236-237	.50	.50
238 A47 30c multicolored	.35	.35
239 A48 30c multicolored	.35	.35
a. Pair, #238-239	.70	.70
Nos. 236-239 (4)	1.20	1.20

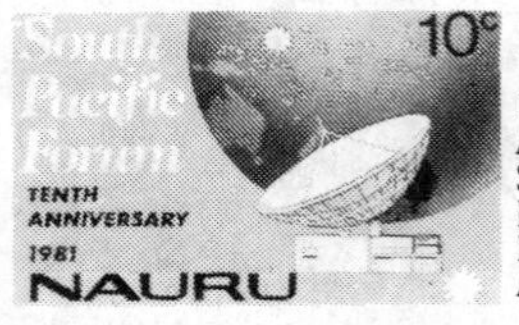

10th Anniv. of South Pacific Forum A54

1981, Dec. 9 Litho. *Perf. 13½x14*

240 A54 10c Globe, dish antenna	.15	.15
241 A54 20c Ship	.30	.30
242 A54 30c Jet	.45	.45
243 A54 40c Produce	.60	.60
Nos. 240-243 (4)	1.50	1.50

Scouting Year — A55

1982, Feb. 23 Litho. *Perf. 14*

244 A55 7c Carrying packages	.15	.15
245 A55 8c Scouts, life preserver, vert.	.15	.15
246 A55 15c Pottery making, vert.	.20	.20
247 A55 20c Inspection	.30	.30
248 A55 25c Scout, cub	.40	.40
249 A55 40c Troop	.60	.60
a. Souv. sheet of 6, #244-249, imperf.	2.00	2.00
Nos. 244-249 (6)	1.80	1.80

A56

Ocean Thermal Energy Conversion — A57

Designs: No. 250, Plant under construction. No. 251, Completed plant.

1982, June 10 Litho. *Perf. 13½*

250 Pair	.90	.90
a.-b. A56 25c any single	.45	.45
251 Pair	1.40	1.40
a.-b. A56 40c any single	.70	.70

75th Anniv. of Phosphate Industry A58

1982, Oct. 11 Litho. *Perf. 14*

252 A58 5c Freighter Fido, 1907	.15	.15
253 A58 10c Locomotive Nellie, 1907	.25	.25
254 A58 30c Modern Clyde diesel train, 1982	.55	.55
255 A58 60c Flagship Eigamoiya, 1969	1.10	1.10
Nos. 252-255 (4)	2.05	2.05

Souvenir Sheet

256 A58 $1 Freighters	2.00	2.00

ANPEX '82 Natl. Stamp Exhibition, Brisbane, Australia, Nos. 252-255 se-tenant with labels describing stamp. No. 256 contains one 68x27mm stamp.

Visit of Queen Elizabeth II and Prince Philip A59

1982, Oct. 21 *Perf. 14½*

257 A59 20c Elizabeth, vert.	.25	.25
258 A59 50c Philip, vert.	.70	.70
259 A59 $1 Couple	1.40	1.40
Nos. 257-259 (3)	2.35	2.35

Christmas A60

Clergymen: 20c, Father Bernard Lahn, Catholic Mission Church. 30c, Rev. Itubwa Amram, Orro Central Church. 40c, Pastor James Aingimea, Tsiminita Memorial Church, Denigomodu. 50c, Bishop Paul Mea, Diocese of Tarawa-Nauru-Tuvalu.

1982, Nov. 17

260 A60 20c multicolored	.25	.25
261 A60 30c multicolored	.40	.40
262 A60 40c multicolored	.55	.55
263 A60 50c multicolored	.70	.70
Nos. 260-263 (4)	1.90	1.90

15th Anniv. of Independence — A61

1983, Mar. 23 Wmk. 373 *Perf. 14½*

264 A61 15c Speaker of Parliament, vert.	.25	.25
265 A61 20c People's Court, vert.	.35	.35
266 A61 30c Law Courts	.50	.50
267 A61 50c Parliament	.85	.85
Nos. 264-267 (4)	1.95	1.95

World Communications Year — A62

1983, May. 11 Litho. *Perf. 14*

268 A62 5c Earth Satellite Staion NZ	.15	.15
269 A62 10c Omni-directional Range Installation	.15	.15
270 A62 20c Fixed-station ambulance driver	.30	.30
271 A62 25c Radio Nauru broadcaster	.40	.40
272 A62 40c Air mail service	.60	.60
Nos. 268-272 (5)	1.60	1.60

Angam Day (Homecoming) — A63

Perf. 14x13½

1983, Sept. 14 Litho. Wmk. 373

273 A63 15c MV Trinza arriving	.20	.20

Size: 25x40mm

Perf. 14

274 A63 20c Elsie Agio in exile	.30	.30
275 A63 30c Baby on scale	.45	.45
276 A63 40c Children	.60	.60
Nos. 273-276 (4)	1.55	1.55

Christmas A64

Designs: 5c, The Holy Virgin, the Holy Child and St. John, School of Raphael. 15c, The Mystical Betrothal of St. Catherine with Jesus, School of Paolo Veronese. 50c, Madonna on the Throne Surrounded by Angels, School of Seville.

Perf. 14½x14, 14x14½

1983, Nov. 16 Litho. Wmk. 373

277 A64 5c multi, vert.	.15	.15
278 A64 15c multi, vert.	.20	.20
279 A64 50c multicolored	.65	.65
Nos. 277-279 (3)	1.00	1.00

Lloyd's List Issue

Common Design Type

1984, May 23 Litho. *Perf. 14½x14*

280 CD335 20c Ocean Queen	.35	.35
281 CD335 25c Enna G.	.45	.45
282 CD335 30c Baron Minto loading phosphate	.60	.60
283 CD335 40c Triadic, 1940	.75	.75
Nos. 280-283 (4)	2.15	2.15

1984 UPU Congress — A65

1984, June 4 Wmk. 373 *Perf. 14*

284 A65 $1 No. 117	1.40	1.40

Coastal Scene A66

Perf. 13½x14, 14x13½

1984, Sept. 21

285 A66 1c shown	.15	.15
286 A66 3c Woman, vert.	.15	.15
287 A66 5c Fishing vessel	.15	.15
288 A66 10c Golfer	.20	.20
289 A66 15c Phosphate excavation, vert.	.25	.25
290 A66 20c Surveyor, vert.	.35	.35
291 A66 25c Air Nauru jet	.45	.45
292 A66 30c Elderly man, vert.	.50	.50
293 A66 40c Social service	.70	.70
294 A66 50c Fishing, vert.	.85	.85
295 A66 $1 Tennis, vert.	1.75	1.75
296 A66 $2 Lagoon Anabar	3.50	3.50
Nos. 285-296 (12)	9.00	9.00

For surcharges see Nos. 425-427.

Local Butterflies A67

1984, July 24 *Perf. 14*

297 A67 25c Common eggfly (female)	.50	.50
298 A67 30c Common eggfly (male)	.60	.60
299 A67 50c Wanderer (female)	1.00	1.00
Nos. 297-299 (3)	2.10	2.10

Christmas A68

1984, Nov. 14

300 A68 30c Buada Chapel, vert.	.55	.55
301 A68 40c Detudamo Memorial Church, vert.	.70	.70
302 A68 50c Candle-light service	.90	.90
Nos. 300-302 (3)	2.15	2.15

Air Nauru, 15th Anniv. A69

1985, Feb. 26 **Wmk. 373** *Perf. 14*

303 A69 20c Jet	.35	.35
304 A69 30c Crew, vert.	.55	.55
305 A69 40c Fokker F28 over Nauru	.70	.70
306 A69 50c Cargo handling, vert.	.90	.90
Nos. 303-306 (4)	2.50	2.50

Nauru Phosphate Corp., 15th Anniv. A70

1985, July 31

307 A70 20c Open-cut mining	.40	.40
308 A70 25c Rail transport	.50	.50
309 A70 30c Phosphate drying plant	.60	.60
310 A70 50c Early steam engine	1.00	1.00
Nos. 307-310 (4)	2.50	2.50

Christmas — A71

1985, Oct.

311 A71 50c Canoe	1.25	1.25
312 A71 50c Mother and child	1.25	1.25
a. Pair, #311-312	2.50	2.50

No. 312a has a continuous design.

Audubon Birth Bicentenary A72

Illustrations of the brown noddy by John J. Audubon.

1985, Dec. 31

313 A72 10c Adult and young	.30	.30
314 A72 20c Flying	.60	.60
315 A72 30c Two adults	.75	.75
316 A72 50c Adult	1.25	1.25
Nos. 313-316 (4)	2.90	2.90

Early Transportation — A73

1986, Mar. 5 **Wmk. 384**

317 A73 15c Douglas motorcycle	.35	.35
318 A73 20c Truck	.45	.45
319 A73 30c German steam locomotive, 1910	.70	.70
320 A73 40c Baby Austin	1.00	1.00
Nos. 317-320 (4)	2.50	2.50

Bank of Nauru, 10th Anniv. A74

Winning drawings of children's competition.

1986, July 21 **Litho.** *Perf. 14*

321 A74 20c multicolored	.35	.35
322 A74 25c multicolored	.45	.45
323 A74 30c multicolored	.55	.55
324 A74 40c multicolored	.75	.75
Nos. 321-324 (4)	2.10	2.10

Flowers — A75

1986, Sept. 30 **Wmk. 384**

325 A75 20c Plumeria rubra	.45	.45
326 A75 25c Tristellateia australis	.55	.55
327 A75 30c Bougainvillea cultivar	.65	.65
328 A75 40c Delonix regia	.85	.85
Nos. 325-328 (4)	2.50	2.50

Christmas A76

1986, Dec. 8 **Wmk. 373**

329 A76 20c Men caroling	.40	.40
330 A76 $1 Carolers, invalid	1.90	1.90

Tribal Dances — A77

1987, Jan. 31

331 A77 20c Girls	.35	.35
332 A77 30c Men and women	.50	.50
333 A77 50c Boy, vert.	.90	.90
Nos. 331-333 (3)	1.75	1.75

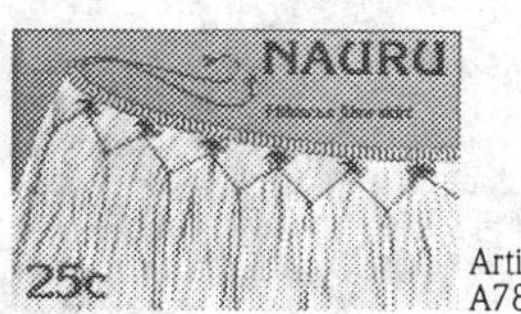

Artifacts A78

1987, July 30 *Perf. 14*

334 A78 25c Hibiscus-fiber skirt	.45	.45
335 A78 30c Headband, necklaces	.50	.50
336 A78 45c Necklaces	.80	.80
337 A78 60c Pandanus-leaf fan	1.00	1.00
Nos. 334-337 (4)	2.75	2.75

World Post Day — A79

Perf. 14½x14

1987, Oct. 9 **Litho.** **Wmk. 384**

338 A79 40c UPU emblem, airmail label	1.00	1.00

Souvenir Sheet

1987, Oct. 20 *Imperf.*

339 A79 $1 Emblem, vert.	3.00	3.00

Nauru Congregational Church, Cent. — A80

Perf. 13x13½

1987, Nov. 5 **Wmk. 373**

340 A80 40c multicolored	.75	.75

Island Christmas Celebration A81

1987, Nov. 27 **Wmk. 384** *Perf. 14*

341 A81 20c shown	.35	.35
342 A81 $1 Sign on building	2.00	2.00

A82

Natl. Independence, 20th Anniv. — A83

Heraldic elements independent of or as part of the natl. arms: 25c, Phosphate mining and shipping. 40c, Tomano flower, vert. 55c, Frigate bird, vert. $1, Natl. arms.

Perf. 13½x14, 14x13½

1988, May 16 **Unwmk.**

343 A82 25c multicolored	.60	.60
344 A82 40c multicolored	.90	.90
345 A82 55c multicolored	1.25	1.25

Perf. 13

346 A83 $1 multicolored	2.10	2.10
Nos. 343-346 (4)	4.85	4.85

Nauru Post Office, 80th Anniv. A84

30c, Nauru highlighted on German map of the Marshall Islands, & canceled Marshall Islands #25. 50c, Letter mailed from Nauru to Dresden & post office, 1908. 70c, Post office, 1988, & Nauru #348 canceled on airmail cover.

1988, July 14 **Wmk. 384** *Perf. 14*

347 A84 30c multicolored	.55	.55
348 A84 50c multicolored	.90	.90
349 A84 70c multicolored	1.25	1.25
Nos. 347-349 (3)	2.70	2.70

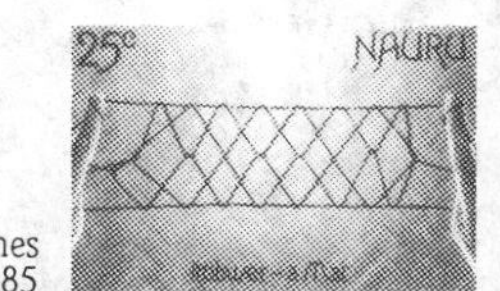

String Games A85

1988, Aug. 1 **Unwmk.** *Perf. 13½x14*

350 A85 25c Mat	.30	.30
351 A85 40c The Pursuer	.50	.50
352 A85 55c Holding Up the Sky	.75	.75
353 A85 80c Manujie's Sword	1.10	1.10
Nos. 350-353 (4)	2.65	2.65

UPU, Cent. — A86

1988, Oct. 1 *Perf. 13½x14*

354 A86 $1 multicolored	1.50	1.50

Hark! The Herald Angels Sing, by Charles Wesley (1703-91) A87

1988, Nov. 28 *Perf. 13½*

355 A87 20c "Hark..."	.35	.35
356 A87 60c "Glory to..."	1.00	1.00
357 A87 $1 "Peace on Earth"	1.75	1.75
Nos. 355-357 (3)	3.10	3.10

A88

Christmas — A89

1989, Nov. 19 *Perf. 14x15*

358 A88 15c NIC emblem	.25	.25
359 A88 50c APT, ITU emblems	.75	.75
360 A88 $1 Mounted photograph	1.50	1.50
361 A88 $2 UPU emblem, US Capitol	3.25	3.25
Nos. 358-361 (4)	5.75	5.75

Annivs. and events: Nauru Insurance Corp., 15th Anniv. (15c). World Telecommunications Day and 10th anniv of the Asia-Pacific Telecommunity (50c); Photography 150th anniv. ($1); and 20th UPU Congress, Washington, DC ($2).

1989, Dec. 15 **Litho.** *Perf. 14x15*

362 A89 20c shown	.40	.40
363 A89 $1 Children opening gifts	1.65	1.65

A90

A91

Legend of Eigigu, The Girl in the Moon: 25c, Eigigu works while sisters play, rocket lift-off. 30c, Eigigu climbing tree, capsule in lunar orbit. 50c, Eigigu stealing from blind woman, lunar module on moon. $1, Eigigu with husband, Maramen (the moon), astronaut stepping on moon.

1989, Dec. 22 **Litho.** *Perf. 14x15*

364 A90 25c multicolored	*2.00*	*2.00*
365 A90 30c multicolored	*2.25*	*2.25*
366 A90 50c multicolored	*4.00*	*4.00*
367 A90 $1 multicolored	*7.50*	*7.50*
Nos. 364-367 (4)	*15.75*	*15.75*

Limited supplies of Nos. 364-367 were available through agent.

1990, July 3 **Litho.** *Perf. 14x15*

368 A91 50c Mining by hand	.90	.90
369 A91 $1 Mechanized extraction	1.75	1.75

Nauru Phosphate Corp., 20th anniv.

Christmas — A92 A93

1990, Nov. 26 Litho. *Perf. 14*
370 A92 25c Children .75 .75
371 A92 25c Telling Christmas story .75 .75
a. Pair, #370-371 1.50 1.50

1990, Dec. 24 Litho. *Perf. 14x15*
372 A93 25c Woman with baby .40 .40
373 A93 30c Weaving flowers .50 .50
374 A93 50c Listening to storm .85 .85
375 A93 $1 Couple 1.65 1.65
Nos. 372-375 (4) 3.40 3.40

Legend of Eoiyepiang, Daughter of Thunder and Lightning.

Flowers — A94

1991, July 15 Litho. *Perf. 14½*
380 A94 15c Oleander .25 .25
381 A94 20c Lily .30 .30
382 A94 25c Passion Flower .40 .40
383 A94 30c Lily, diff. .45 .45
384 A94 35c Caesalpinia .55 .55
385 A94 40c Clerodendron .60 .60
387 A94 45c Bauhina pinnata .70 .70
388 A94 50c Hibiscus, vert. .75 .75
389 A94 75c Apocynaceae 1.10 1.10
390 A94 $1 Bindweed, vert. 1.50 1.50
391 A94 $2 Tristellateia, vert. 3.00 3.00
392 A94 $3 Impala lily, vert. 4.75 4.75
Nos. 380-392 (12) 14.35 14.35

This is an expanding set. Numbers will change if necessary.

Souvenir Sheet

Christmas — A95

1991, Dec. 12 Litho. *Perf. 14*
395 A95 $2 Stained glass window 3.75 3.75

Asian Development Bank, 25th Meeting A96

1992, May 4 Litho. *Perf. 14x14½*
396 A96 $1.50 multicolored 2.25 2.25

Christmas A97

Children's drawings: 45c, Christmas trees, flags and balloons. 60c, Santa in sleigh, reindeer on flag.

1992, Nov. 23 Litho. *Perf. 14½x14*
397 A97 45c multicolored .70 .70
398 A97 60c multicolored .90 .90

Hammer DeRoburt (1922-1992) A98

1993, Jan. 31 Litho. *Perf. 14x14½*
399 A98 $1 multicolored 1.65 1.65

Independence, 25th anniv.

Constitution Day, 15th Anniv. — A99

1993, May 17 Litho. *Perf. 14x14½*
400 A99 70c Runners 1.00 1.00
401 A99 80c Declaration of Republic 1.10 1.10

24th South Pacific Forum — A100

1993, Aug. 9 Litho. *Perf. 14½x14*
402 A100 60c Seabirds .80 .80
403 A100 60c Birds, dolphin .80 .80
404 A100 60c Coral, fish .80 .80
405 A100 60c Fish, coral, diff. .80 .80
a. Block of 4, #402-405 3.25 3.25
b. Souvenir sheet of 4, #402-405 6.00 6.00

No. 405a is a continuous design.

Christmas — A101

Designs: 55c, "Peace on earth..." 65c, "Hark the Herald Angels Sing."

1993, Nov. 29 Litho. *Perf. 14½x14*
406 A101 55c multicolored .75 .75
407 A101 65c multicolored .90 .90

Child's Best Friend — A102

1994, Feb. 10 Litho. *Perf. 14*
408 A102 $1 Girls, dogs 1.25 1.25
409 A102 $1 Boys, dogs 1.25 1.25
a. Pair, #408-409 2.50 2.50
b. Souvenir sheet of 2, #408-409 2.75 2.75
c. As "b," ovptd. in sheet margin 2.75 2.75
d. As "b," ovptd. in sheet margin 3.75 3.75

No. 409c ovptd. with Hong Kong '94 emblem.
No. 409d ovptd. with SINGPEX '94 emblem in gold.
Issued: #409c, 2/18/94; #409d, 8/31/94.

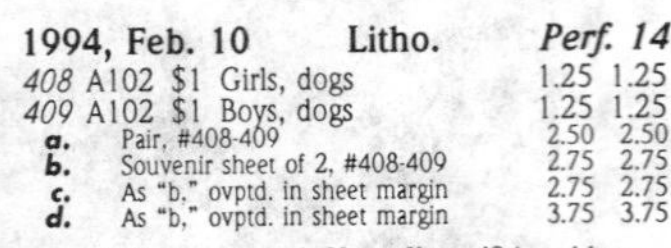

15th Commonwealth Games, Victoria — A103

1994, Sept. 8 Litho. *Perf. 14x14½*
410 A103 $1.50 Weight lifting 2.25 2.25

ICAO, 50th Anniv. — A104

55c, Emblems. 65c, Nauru Intl. Airport. 80c, DVOR navigational aid. $1, Airport fire engines.

1994, Dec. 14
411 A104 55c multicolored .80 .80
412 A104 65c multicolored 1.00 1.00
413 A104 80c multicolored 1.25 1.25
414 A104 $1 multicolored 1.50 1.50
a. Souvenir sheet of 4, #411-414 4.50 4.50
Nos. 411-414 (4) 4.55 4.55

United Nations, 50th Anniv. A105

1995, Jan. 1 *Perf. 14x14½*
415 A105 75c Natl. flag 1.10 1.10
416 A105 75c Natl. coat of arms 1.10 1.10
417 A105 75c Canoe, UN emblem 1.10 1.10
418 A105 75c Jet, ship, UN emblem 1.10 1.10
a. Block of 4, #415-418 4.50 4.50
b. Souvenir sheet of 4, #415-418 4.50 4.50

Nos. 417-418 are a continuous design.

Christmas — A106

1994, Nov. 20 Litho. *Perf. 14½x14*
419 A106 65c shown 1.00 1.00
420 A106 75c Star over Bethlehem 1.10 1.10

Membership in Intl. Olympic Committee A107

1994, Dec. 27 *Perf. 14x14½*
421 A107 50c multicolored .75 .75

Nauru Phosphate Corporation, 25th Anniv. A108

Designs: No. 422, Signing of Phosphate Agreement, June 15, 1967. No. 423, Nauru Pres. Bernard Dowiyogo, Australian Prime Minister Paul Keating at signing Nauru-Australia Compact of Settlement. $2, Mining phosphate.

1995, July 1 Litho. *Perf. 14x15*
422 A108 60c multicolored .90 .90
423 A108 60c multicolored .90 .90
a. Pair, #422-423 1.80 1.80

Souvenir Sheet

424 A108 $2 multicolored 3.00 3.00

No. 291 Surcharged

at Beijing

50c

1995 Litho. *Perf. 13½x14*
Overprinted:
425 A66 50c on 25c "at Beijing" .75 .75
426 A66 $1 on 25c "at Singapore" 1.50 1.50
427 A66 $1 on 25c "at Jakarta" 1.50 1.50
a. Strip of 3, #425-427 3.75 3.75

UN, 50th Anniv. A109

Designs: 75c, Nauru coastline. $1.50, UN headquarters, US, aerial view of Nauru.

1995, Oct. 24 Litho. *Perf. 14*
428 A109 75c multicolored 1.10 1.10
429 A109 $1.50 multicolored 2.20 2.20

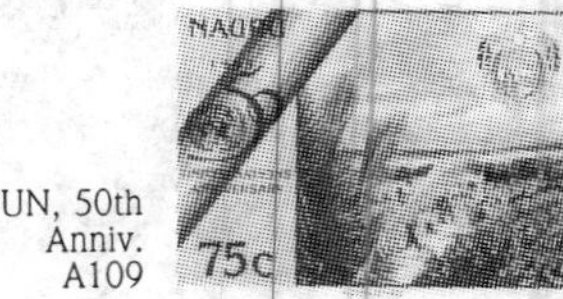

Christmas — A110

1995, Dec. 7 Litho. *Perf. 14*
430 A110 60c Seeking the Way .90 .90
431 A110 70c Finding the Way 1.05 1.05
a. Pair, #430-431 2.00 2.00

Return From Truk, 50th Anniv. A111

1996, Jan. 31 *Perf. 12*
432 A111 75c multicolored 1.10 1.10
433 A111 $1.25 multicolored 1.90 1.90
a. Souvenir sheet of 2, #432-433 3.25 3.25

Souvenir Sheet

Nanjing Stone Carving, Keeping off the Evils — A112

Illustration reduced.

1996, Mar. 20 Litho. *Perf. 12*
434 A112 45c multicolored .70 .70

CHINA '96, 9th Asian Intl. Philatelic Exhibition.

End of World War II, 50th Anniv. — A113

Designs: 75c, Children playing on old cannon. $1.50, Girls making flower leis in front of pillbox.

1996, Sept. 13 Litho. *Perf. 14x13½*

435 A113 75c multicolored 1.20 1.20
436 A113 $1.50 multicolored 2.40 2.40
a. Pair, Nos. 435-436 + label 3.60 3.60

1996 Summer Olympic Games, Atlanta A114

Discobolus and: 40c, Running pictograph, vert. 50c, Weight lifting pictograph, vert. 60c, Weight lifter. $1, Runner.

Perf. 13½x14, 14x13½

1996, July 21 Litho.

437 A114 40c multicolored .65 .65
438 A114 50c multicolored .80 .80
439 A114 60c multicolored .95 .95
440 A114 $1 multicolored 1.60 1.60
Nos. 437-440 (4) 4.00 4.00

Christmas A115

Designs: 50c, Candles, angel with trumpet, nativity. 70c, Angel, candles, map, fauna.

1996, Dec. 16 Litho. *Perf. 14*

441 A115 50c multicolored .80 .80
442 A115 70c multicolored 1.15 1.15

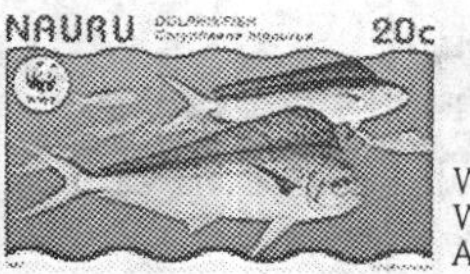

World Wildlife Fund A116

Fish: a, 20c, Dolphinfish. b, 30c, Wahoo. c, 40c, Pacific sailfish. d, 50c, Yellowfin tuna.

1997, Feb. 12 Litho. *Perf. 11½*

443 A116 Strip of 4, #a.-d. 2.20 2.20

A117

A118

Giant Buddha (various statues): a, 1c. b, 2c. c, 5c. d, 10c. e, 12c. f, 15c. g, 25c.

1997, Feb. 12 *Perf. 14*

444 A117 Sheet of 7, #a.-g. 1.40 1.40

Hong Kong '97, Hong Kong's return to China. No. 444g is 60x80mm.

1997 Litho. *Perf. 13½*

Designs: 80c, Engagement portrait. $1.20, 50th Wedding anniversary portrait.

445 A118 80c multicolored 1.15 1.15
446 A118 $1.20 multicolored 1.75 1.75
a. Souvenir sheet, #445-446 2.90 2.90

Queen Elizabeth II and Prince Philip, 50th wedding anniv.

Christmas A119

1997 Litho. *Perf. 13½*

447 A119 60c Monument .80 .80
448 A119 80c Church 1.10 1.10

Nauru Congregational Church, 110th anniv.

SEMI-POSTAL STAMP

Miniature Sheet of 4

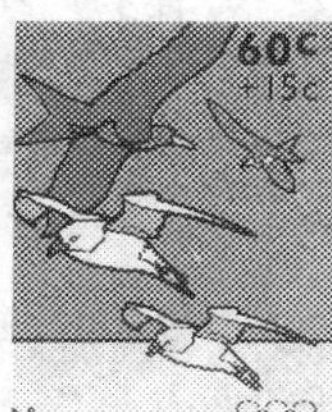

1996 Summer Olympics, Atlanta — SP1

Designs: a, Birds, denomination UR. b, Birds, denomination UL. c, 4 dolphins. d, 2 dolphins.

1995, Sept. 1 Litho. *Perf. 12*

B1 SP1 60c +15c, #a.-d. 4.50 4.50

Surcharge for sports development in Nauru.

NEPAL

nə-'pȯl

LOCATION — In the Himalaya Mountains between India and Tibet
GOVT. — Kingdom
AREA — 56,136 sq. mi.
POP. — 16,100,000 (est. 1982)
CAPITAL — Kathmandu

Although an independent state, Nepal's close political and economic ties with India make it advisable to include its stamps in this section. The stamps were valid only in Nepal and India until April 1959, when they became valid to all parts of the world.

4 Pice = 1 Anna
64 Pice = 16 Annas = 1 Rupee
100 Paisa = 1 Rupee (1958)

Catalogue values for unused stamps in this country are for Never Hinged items, beginning with Scott 103 in the regular postage section, Scott C1 in the air post section and Scott O1 in the officials section.

Nos. 1-24, 29A were issued without gum.

Sripech and Crossed Khukris — A1

Siva's Bow and Two Khukris — A2

1881 Typo. Unwmk. *Pin-perf.*
European Wove Paper

1 A1 1a ultramarine 175.00 *300.00*
2 A1 2a purple 250.00 200.00
a. Tete beche pair
3 A1 4a green 250.00 *400.00*

Imperf

4 A1 1a blue 105.00 110.00
5 A1 2a purple 130.00 130.00
a. Tete beche pair
6 A1 4a green 165.00 60.00

1886 Native Wove Paper *Imperf.*

7 A1 1a ultramarine 15.00 8.00
a. Tete beche pair *125.00 175.00*
8 A1 2a violet 17.50 10.00
a. Tete beche pair *150.00 200.00*
9 A1 4a green 45.00 12.00
a. Tete beche pair *200.00 250.00*
Nos. 7-9 (3) 77.50 30.00

Used values for Nos. 9-49 are for telegraph cancels.

1899-1917 *Imperf.*
Native Wove Paper

10 A2 ½a black 11.00 .50
a. Tete beche pair *200.00* 1.75
11 A2 ½a red orange ('17) *1,000.* —
a. Tete beche pair

Pin-perf.

12 A2 ½a black 20.00
a. Tete beche pair *150.00*

No. 11 is known postally used on six covers.

Type of 1881

1898-1904 *Imperf.*

13 A1 1a pale blue 12.50 6.00
a. 1a bluish green 50.00 50.00
b. Tete beche pair *150.00 150.00*
14 A1 2a gray violet 25.00 10.00
a. Tete beche pair *250.00 300.00*
15 A1 2a claret ('17) 30.00 12.00
a. Tete beche pair *275.00 325.00*
16 A1 2a brown ('17) 10.00
a. Tete beche pair 25.00
17 A1 4a dull green 10.00 15.00
a. Tete beche pair 70.00 *400.00*
b. Cliche of 1a in plate of 4a ('04) *300.00*
Nos. 13-17 (5) 87.50 43.00

#17b has the recut frame of the 1904 issue. #17b probably was used only on telegraph/telephone forms.

Pin-perf.

18 A1 1a pale blue 17.50 10.00
a. Tete beche pair *100.00 150.00*
19 A1 2a gray violet 25.00 12.00
a. Tete beche pair *200.00 225.00*
20 A1 2a claret ('17) 8.75 6.00
a. Tete beche pair 45.00 32.50
21 A1 2a brown 7.50
a. Tete beche pair 45.00
22 A1 4a dull green 50.00 18.00
a. Tete beche pair *400.00 450.00*

Frame Recut on All Cliches, Fewer Lines

1903-04 Native Wove Paper *Imperf.*

23 A1 1a bright blue 10.00
a. Tete beche pair 50.00

Pin-perf.

24 A1 1a bright blue 15.00
a. Tete beche pair *100.00*

No. 23 exists on European wove paper.

Siva Mahadeva — A3

A4

1907 Engr. *Perf. 13½*
European Wove Paper

26 A3 2p brown .90 .60
27 A3 4p green 1.50 .95
28 A3 8p carmine 6.25 .95
29 A3 16p violet 10.50 1.50
Nos. 26-29 (4) 19.15 4.00

Type A3 has five characters in bottom panel, reading "Gurkha Sirkar." Date divided in lower corners is "1964." Outer side panels carry denomination (also on A5).

1917-18 *Imperf.*

29A A4 1a bright blue 10.00 1.00
b. 1a indigo 20.00 1.00
c. Pin-perf.

No. 29A may not have been used postally.

In 1917 a telegraph system was started and remainder stocks and further printings of designs A1 and A2 were used to pay telegrams fees. Design A4 was designed for telegraph use but was valid for postal use. After 1929 design A3 was used for telegrams. The usual telegraph cancellation is crescent-shaped.

Type of 1907 Redrawn

A5

Nine characters in bottom panel reading "Nepal Sirkar"

1929 *Perf. 14, 14½*
Size: 24¾x18¾mm

30 A5 2p dark brown .55 .30
31 A5 4p green .85 .30
32 A5 8p deep red .95 .35
33 A5 16p dark red vio 1.65 .65
34 A5 24p orange yellow 2.50 1.25
35 A5 32p dark ultra 2.75 1.50

Size: 26x19½mm

36 A5 1r orange red 4.25 3.75

Size: 28x21mm

37 A5 5r brown & black 17.00 22.50
Nos. 30-37 (8) 30.50 30.60

On Nos. 30-37 the date divided in lower corners is "1986."

Type of 1929 Redrawn

Date characters in Lower Corners read "1992"

1935 Unwmk. Engr. *Perf. 14*

38 A5 2p dark brown 2.50 .45
39 A5 4p green 3.50 .35
40 A5 8p bright red 35.00 6.50
41 A5 16p dk red violet 7.25 .95
42 A5 24p orange yellow 8.25 1.00
43 A5 32p dark ultra 18.00 3.25
Nos. 38-43 (6) 74.50 12.50

Redrawn Type of 1935

Perf. 11, 11x11½, 12x11½

1941-46 Typo.

44 A5 2p black brown .65 .40
a. 2p green (error) 1.00
45 A5 4p bright green .65 .48
46 A5 8p rose red .90 .20

NEPAL
TIBET
BHUTAN
SIKKIM

POSTAL AUCTIONS
(Consignments Accepted)

• Stamps and Postal History
• Special Offers
• Want Lists Welcomed

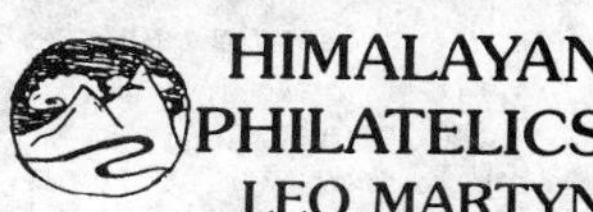
HIMALAYAN PHILATELICS
LEO MARTYN
P.O. Box 49263
Los Angeles, CA 90049-0263
U.S.A.
PH/FAX (310) 476-2608
E-mail:
Himalayan@worldnet.att.net

Member: APS (25 years)
Nepal and Tibet Philatelic Study Circle
The India Study Circle for Philately

47 A5 16p chocolate ('42) 2.75 2.25
48 A5 24p orange ('46) 3.25 2.75
49 A5 32p deep blue ('46) 7.25 6.25

Size: 29x19½mm

50 A5 1r henna brown ('46) 15.00 12.50
Nos. 44-50 (7) 30.45 24.83

Exist imperf. vert. or horiz.

Swayambhunath Stupa — A6

Temple of Krishna — A7

View of Kathmandu — A8

Pashupati (Siva Mahadeva) A9

Designs: 4p, Temple of Pashupati. 6p, Tri-Chundra College. 8p, Mahabuddha Temple. 24p, Guhesworl Temple, Patan. 32p, The 22 Fountains, Balaju.

Perf. 13½x14, 13½, 14

1949, Oct. 1 Litho. Unwmk.

51 A6 2p brown
52 A6 4p green
53 A6 6p rose pink
54 A6 8p vermilion
55 A7 16p rose lake
56 A8 20p blue
57 A8 24p carmine
58 A8 32p ultramarine
59 A9 1r red orange
Nos. 51-59 (9) 30.00 20.00

King Tribhuvana Bir Bikram — A10

1954, Apr. 15 Unwmk. *Perf. 14*

Size: 18x22mm

60 A10 2p chocolate .15 .15
61 A10 4p green .15 .18
62 A10 6p rose .16 .22
63 A10 8p violet .18 .22
64 A10 12p red orange .28 .40

Size: 25½x29½mm

65 A10 16p red brown .35 .60
66 A10 20p car rose .42 .70
67 A10 24p rose lake .70 1.10
68 A10 32p ultramarine .85 1.40
69 A10 50p rose pink 1.10 *2.00*
70 A10 1r vermilion 1.75 *4.00*
71 A10 2r orange 4.00 *8.00*
Nos. 60-71 (12) 10.09 *18.97*

Map of Nepal — A11

1954, Apr. 15

Size: 29½x17½mm

72 A11 2p chocolate .22 .15
73 A11 4p green .25 .15
74 A11 6p rose .42 .15
75 A11 8p violet .50 .18
76 A11 12p red orange .85 .28

Size: 38x21½mm

77 A11 16p red brown 1.10 .50
78 A11 20p car rose 1.25 .55
79 A11 24p rose lake 1.25 .55
80 A11 32p ultramarine 1.65 .80
81 A11 50p rose pink 2.50 1.10
82 A11 1r vermilion 5.00 4.00
83 A11 2r orange 10.00 11.00
Nos. 72-83 (12) 24.99 19.41

Planting Rice — A12

Throne — A13

Hanuman Gate — A14

King Mahendra Bir Bikram and Queen Ratna — A15

Design: 8p, Ceremonial arch and elephant.

Perf. 13½x14, 11½, 13½, 14

Litho., Photo. (6p)

1956 Granite Paper Unwmk.

84 A12 4p green .15 *.35*
85 A13 6p crimson & org .15 *.35*
86 A12 8p light violet .15 *.55*
87 A14 24p carmine rose .32 *1.40*
88 A15 1r brown red 27.50 *72.50*
Nos. 84-88 (5) 28.27 *75.15*

Coronation of King Mahendra Bir Bikram and Queen Ratna Rajya Lakshmi.

Mountain Village and UN Emblem A16

1956, Dec. 14 Litho. *Perf. 13½*

89 A16 12p ultra & orange 1.00 .70

1st anniv. of Nepal's admission to the UN.

Crown of Nepal — A17

Lumbini Temple — A18

Perf. 13½x14

1957, June 22 Unwmk.

Size: 18x22mm

90 A17 2p dull red brown .18 *.55*
91 A17 4p light green .18 *.55*
92 A17 6p pink .20 *.60*
93 A17 8p light violet .28 *1.10*
94 A17 12p orange vermilion .35 *1.00*

Size: 25½x30mm

95 A17 16p red brown .42 .30
96 A17 20p deep pink .55 .35
97 A17 24p brt car rose .70 .45
98 A17 32p ultramarine .85 .60
99 A17 50p rose red 1.40 1.10
100 A17 1r brown orange 2.50 *4.25*
101 A17 2r orange 5.00 *9.00*
Nos. 90-101 (12) 12.61 *19.85*

1958, Dec. 10 Typo. *Perf. 11*

Without Gum

102 A18 6p yellow .15 .15

10th anniversary of Universal Declaration of Human Rights. Exists imperf.

Catalogue values for unused stamps in this section, from this point to the end of the section, are for Never Hinged items.

Map and Flag — A19

1959, Feb. 18 Engr. *Perf. 14½*

103 A19 6p carmine & light green .15 .15

First general elections in Nepal.

Statue of Vishnu, Changu Narayan — A20

Krishna Conquering Black Serpent — A21

Designs: 4p, Nepalese glacier. 6p, Golden Gate, Bhaktapur. 8p, Nepalese musk deer. 12p, Rhinoceros. 16p, 20p, 24p, 32p, 50p, Nyatapola Temple, Bhatgaon. 1r, 2r, Himalayan impeyan pheasant. 5r, Satyr tragopan.

Perf. 13½x14, 14x13½

1959-60 Litho. Unwmk.

Size: 18x22mm

104 A20 1p chocolate .15 .15
105 A21 2p gray violet .15 .15
106 A20 4p light ultra .15 .15
107 A20 6p vermilion .15 .15
108 A21 8p sepia .15 .15
109 A21 12p greenish gray .15 .15

Size: 25½x30mm

110 A20 16p brown & lt vio .15 .15
111 A20 20p blue & dull rose .28 .15
112 A20 24p green & pink .18 .15
113 A20 32p brt vio & ultra .28 .16
114 A20 50p rose red & grn .55 .20
115 A20 1r redsh brn & bl 6.50 2.25
116 A20 2r rose lil & ultra 1.90 .90
117 A20 5r vio & rose red ('60) 22.50 10.00
Nos. 104-117 (14) 33.24 14.86

Nepal's admission to the UPU.

Spinning Wheel — A22

King Mahendra — A23

1959, Apr. 10 Typo. *Perf. 11*

118 A22 2p dark red brown .15 .15

Issued to promote development of cottage industries. Exists imperf.

1959, Apr. 14

119 A23 12p bluish black .15 .15

Nepal's admission to UPU. Exists imperf. and ungummed.

King Mahendra Opening Parliament — A24

1959, July 1 Unwmk. *Perf. 10½*

120 A24 6p deep carmine .15 .15

First session of Parliament. Exists imperf.

Sri Pashupati Nath — A25

King Mahendra — A26

1959, Nov. 19 *Perf. 11*

Size: 18x24½mm

121 A25 4p dp yellow green .15 .15

Size: 20½x28mm

122 A25 8p carmine .18 .15

Size: 24½x33mm

123 A25 1r light blue .70 .32
Nos. 121-123 (3) 1.03
Set value .42

Renovation of Sri Pashupati Temple. Nos. 121-123 exist imperf. between.

1960, June 11 Photo. *Perf. 14*

Size: 25x30mm

124 A26 1r red lilac .70 .28

King Mahendra's 40th birthday. See Nos. 147-151A. For overprint see No. O15.

Children, Temple and Mt. Everest — A27

Mount Everest — A28

1960 Typo. *Perf. 11*

125 A27 6p dark blue 5.00 3.50

1st Children's Day, Mar. 1, 1960. Printed in sheets of four. Exists imperf.; value $25 unused.

1960-61 Photo. *Perf. 14*

Himalaya mountain peaks: 5p, Machha Puchhre. 40p, Mansalu.

126 A28 5p claret & brown ('61) .15 .15
127 A28 10p ultra & rose lilac .15 .15
128 A28 40p violet & red brn ('61) .24 .20
Set value .39 .32

King Tribhuvana A29

King Mahendra A30

1961, Feb. 18 *Perf. 13x13½*

129 A29 10p red brown & orange .15 .15

Tenth Democracy Day.

1961, June 11 *Perf. 14x14½*

130 A30 6p emerald .15 .15
131 A30 12p ultramarine .15 .15
132 A30 50p carmine rose .18 .15
133 A30 1r brown .42 .35
Set value .72 .60

King Mahendra's 41st birthday.

Prince Gyanendra Canceling Stamps — A31

Malaria Eradication Emblem and Temple — A32

1961 Typo. *Perf. 11*

134 A31 12p orange 20.00 8.75

Children's Day, Mar. 1, 1961. Exists imperf. Value, $75.

1962, Apr. 7 Litho. *Perf. 13x13½*

Design: 1r, Emblem and Nepalese flag.

135 A32 12p blue & lt blue .15 .15
136 A32 1r magenta & orange .35 .35
Set value .42 .40

WHO drive to eradicate malaria.

King Mahendra A33

1962, June 11 Unwmk. *Perf. 13*

137 A33 10p slate blue .15 .15
138 A33 15p brown .15 .15
139 A33 45p dull red brown .28 .18
140 A33 1r olive gray .55 .38
Nos. 137-140 (4) 1.13
Set value .68

King Mahendra's 42nd birthday.

Bhanu Bhakta Acharya A34

King Mahendra A35

10p, Moti Ram Bhatta. 40p, Shambu Prasad.

1962 Photo. *Perf. 14x14*

141 A34 5p orange brown .15 .15
142 A34 10p deep aqua .15 .15
143 A34 40p olive bister .15 .15
Set value .22 .22

Issued to honor Nepalese poets.

Mahendra Type of 1960 and Type A35

1962-66 *Perf. 14½x14*

144 A35 1p car rose .15 .15
145 A35 2p brt blue .15 .15
145A A35 3p gray ('66) .15 .15
146 A35 5p golden brown .15 .15

Perf. 14x14½

Size: 21½x38mm

147 A26 10p rose claret .15 .15
148 A26 40p brown .15 .15
149 A26 75p blue green 2.50 2.50

Perf. 14

Size: 25x30mm

150 A26 2r red orange .70 .45
151 A26 5r gray green 2.00 1.00
151A A26 10r violet ('66) 3.75 3.50
Nos. 144-151A (10) 9.85 8.35

See No. 199. For overprints see Nos. O12-O14.

Blackboard, Book and UN Emblem A36

1963, Jan. 6 *Perf. 14½x14*

152 A36 10p dark gray .15 .15
153 A36 15p brown .15 .15
154 A36 50p violet blue .28 .20
Set value .43 .33

UNESCO "Education for All" campaign.

Five-pointed Star and Hands Holding Lamps — A37

Man, Tractor and Wheat — A38

Unwmk.

1963, Feb. 19 Photo. *Perf. 13*

155 A37 5p blue .15 .15
156 A37 10p reddish brown .15 .15
157 A37 50p rose lilac .18 .15
158 A37 1r blue green .35 .20
Set value .65 .40

Panchayat System and National Day.

1963, Mar. 21 *Perf. 14x14½*

159 A38 10p orange .15 .15
160 A38 15p dark ultra .15 .15
161 A38 50p green .15 .15
162 A38 1r brown .18 .18
Set value .37 .37

FAO "Freedom from Hunger" campaign.

Map of Nepal and Hand — A39

1963, Apr. 14 Unwmk. *Perf. 13*

163 A39 10p green .15 .15
164 A39 15p claret .15 .15
165 A39 50p slate .18 .15
166 A39 1r violet blue .35 .18
Set value .64 .36

Rastriya Panchayat system.

King Mahendra — A40

1963, June 11 *Perf. 13*

167 A40 5p violet .15 .15
168 A40 10p brown orange .15 .15
169 A40 15p dull green .15 .15
Set value .20 .20

King Mahendra's 43rd birthday.

East-West Highway on Map of Nepal and King Mahendra A41

1964, Feb. 19 Photo. *Perf. 13*

170 A41 10p blue & dp orange .15 .15
171 A41 15p dk blue & dp orange .15 .15
172 A41 50p dk green & redsh brown .18 .18
Set value .28 .28

Issued to publicize the East-West Highway as "The Prosperity of the Country."

King Mahendra Speaking Before Microphone A42

Crown Prince Birendra A43

1964, June 11 *Perf. 14*

173 A42 1p brown olive .15 .15
174 A42 2p gray .15 .15
175 A42 2r golden brown .75 .55
Set value .87 .67

King Mahendra's 44th birthday.

Perf. 14x14½

1964, Dec. 28 Photo. Unwmk.

176 A43 10p dark green .15 .15
177 A43 15p brown .24 .15
Set value .17

19th birthday (coming of age) of Crown Prince Birendra Bir Bikram Shah Deva.

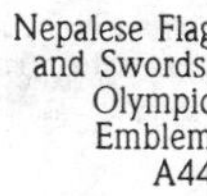

Nepalese Flag and Swords, Olympic Emblem A44

1964, Dec. 31 Litho. *Perf. 13x13½*

178 A44 10p red & ultra .15 .15

18th Olympic Games, Tokyo, Oct. 10-25.

Farmer Plowing — A45

Family — A46

Designs: 5p, Grain. 10p, Chemical plant.

1965 Photo. *Perf. 13½*

179 A45 2p brt green & black .15 .15
180 A45 5p pale yel green & brn .15 .15
181 A45 10p gray & purple .15 .15
182 A46 15p yellow & brown .15 .15
Set value .34 .24

Issued to publicize land reform.
The 2p also exists on light green paper.
Issue dates: 15p, Feb. 10; others, Dec. 16.

Mail Circling Globe — A47

1965, Apr. 13 *Perf. 14½x14*

183 A47 15p rose lilac .15 .15

Issued for Nepalese New Year.

King Mahendra — A48

Perf. 14x14½

1965, June 11 Photo. Unwmk.

184 A48 50p rose violet .30 .15

King Mahendra's 45th birthday.

Victims of Revolution, 1939-40 A49

1965, June 11 *Perf. 13*

185 A49 15p bright green .15 .15

The men executed by the Rana Government 1939-40 were: Shukra Raj Shastri, Dasharath Chand, Dharma Bhakta and Ganga Lal Shresta.

ITU Emblem A50

Devkota A51

1965, Sept. 15 Photo. *Perf. 13*

186 A50 15p deep plum & black .15 .15

Cent. of the ITU.

1965, Oct. 14 *Perf. 14x14½*

187 A51 15p red brown .15 .15

Lakshmi Prasad Devkota (1908-1959), poet.

ICY Emblem — A52

Engr. and Litho.

1965, Oct. 24 *Perf. 11½x12*

188 A52 1r multicolored .45 .25

International Cooperation Year.

Nepalese Flag and King — A53

1966, Feb. 18 Photo. *Perf. 14½x14*

189 A53 15p deep blue & red .15 .15

Issued for Democracy Day.

Siva, Parvati and Pashupati Temple — A54

1966, Feb. 18 *Perf. 14*

190 A54 15p violet .15 .15

Hindu festival Maha Sivaratri.

Emblem — A55

Perf. 14½x14

1966, June 10 Photo. Unwmk.

191 A55 15p dk green & orange .15 .15

National Philatelic Exhib., June 10-16.

King Mahendra
A56

Kanti Rajya
Lakshmi
A57

1966, June 11 *Perf. 13x13¹/₂*

192 A56 15p yellow & vio brown .15 .15

Issued for King Mahendra's 46th birthday.

1966, July 5 Photo. *Perf. 14x14¹/₂*

193 A57 15p golden brown .15 .15

60th birthday of Queen Mother Kanti Rajya Lakshmi.

Queen Ratna Rajya Lakshmi Devi Shah — A58

1966, Aug. 19 Photo. *Perf. 13*

194 A58 15p yellow & brown .15 .15

Issued for Children's Day.

Krishna with Consort Radha and Flute — A59

1966, Sept. 7

195 A59 15p dk purple & yellow .15 .15

Krishnastami 2023, the birthday of Krishna.

King Mahendra A60

1966, Oct. 1 Photo. *Perf. 14¹/₂x14*

196 A60 50p slate green & dp car .45 .20

Issued to commemorate the official recognition of the Nepalese Red Cross.

Opening of WHO Headquarters Building, Geneva — A61

Lekhnath Paudyal — A62

1966, Nov. 11 Photo. *Perf. 14*

197 A61 1r purple .60 .30

1966, Dec. 29 Photo. *Perf. 14*

198 A62 15p dull violet blue .15 .15

Lekhnath Paudyal (1884-1966), poet.

King Type of 1962

1967, Feb. 10 Photo. *Perf. 14¹/₂x14*

199 A35 75p blue green .28 .24

Rama and Sita — A63

Buddha — A64

1967, Apr. 18 Litho. *Perf. 14*

200 A63 15p brown & yellow .15 .15

Rama Navami 2024, the birthday of Rama.

1967, May 23 Photo. *Perf. 13¹/₂x13*

201 A64 75p orange & purple .30 .30

2,511th birthday of Buddha.

King Mahendra Addressing Crowd and Himalayas — A65

1967, June 11 *Perf. 13*

202 A65 15p dk brown & lt blue .15 .15

King Mahendra's 47th birthday.

Queen Ratna among Children — A66

1967, Aug. 20 Photo. *Perf. 13*

203 A66 15p pale yel & dp brown .15 .15

Issued for Children's Day on the birthday of Queen Ratna Rajya Lakshmi Devi Shah.

Durbar Square, Bhaktapur A67

5p, Ama Dablam Mountain and ITY emblem.

1967, Oct. 24 *Perf. 13¹/₂x14*

Size: 29¹/₂x21mm

204 A67 5p violet .15 .15

Perf. 14¹/₂x14

Size: 37¹/₂x19¹/₂mm

205 A67 65p brown .30 .30

Set value .35 .35

Intl. Tourist Year, 1967. See No. C2.

Official Reading Proclamation A68

1967, Dec. 16 Litho. *Perf. 13*

206 A68 15p multicolored .15 .15

"Back to the Villages" campaign.

Crown Prince Birendra, Boy Scouts and Scout Emblem A69

1967, Dec. 29 Photo. *Perf. 14¹/₂x14*

207 A69 15p ultramarine .15 .15

60th anniv. of Boy Scouts.

Prithvi Narayan A70

Arms of Nepal A71

1968, Jan. 11 *Perf. 14x14¹/₂*

208 A70 15p blue & rose .15 .15

Rajah Prithvi Narayan (1779-1839), founder of modern Nepal.

1968, Feb. 19 Photo. *Perf. 14x14¹/₂*

209 A71 15p crimson & dk blue .20 .15

Issued for National Day.

WHO Emblem and Flag of Nepal — A72

1968, Mar. 25 *Perf. 13*

210 A72 1.20r dull yel, red & ultra .60 .32

World Health Day (UN WHO).

Goddess Sita and Shrine A73

1968, May 6 Photo. *Perf. 14¹/₂x14*

211 A73 15p violet & org brown .15 .15

King Mahendra, Pheasant and Himalayas A74

1968, June 11 Photo. *Perf. 13¹/₂*

212 A74 15p multicolored .15 .15

King Mahendra's 48th birthday.

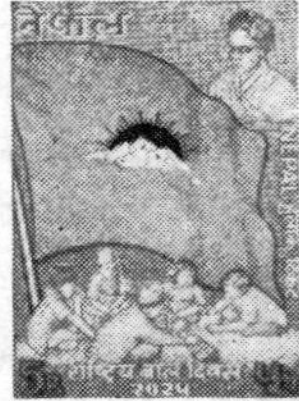

Flag, Children and Queen Ratna — A75

1968, Aug. 19 Litho. *Perf. 13x13¹/₂*

213 A75 5p blue grn, yel & ver .15 .15

Fourth National Children's Day.

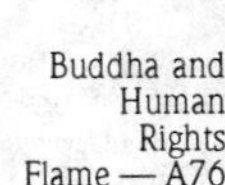

Buddha and Human Rights Flame — A76

1968, Dec. 10 Photo. *Perf. 14¹/₂x14*

214 A76 1r dk green & red .45 .20

International Human Rights Year.

Young People Dancing Around Flag — A77

1968, Dec. 28 Photo. *Perf. 14¹/₂x14*

215 A77 25p violet blue .15 .15

23rd birthday of Crown Prince Birendra, which is celebrated as Youth Festival.

UN Building, Nepalese and UN Flags — A78

Amsu Varma — A79

1969, Jan. 1 *Perf. 13¹/₂x13*

216 A78 1r multicolored .45 .20

Issued to commemorate Nepal's admission to the UN Security Council for 1969-1970.

1969, Apr. 13 Photo. *Perf. 14x14¹/₂*

Portraits: 25p, Ram Shah. 50p, Bhimsen Thapa.

217 A79 15p green & purple .15 .15

218 A79 25p blue green .15 .15

219 A79 50p orange brown .30 .18

Nos. 217-219 (3) .60

Set value .32

Amsu Varma, 7th cent. ruler and reformer; Ram Shah, 17th cent. ruler and reformer, and Bhimsen Thapa, 18-19th cent. administrator and reformer.

ILO Emblem A80

1969, May 1 Photo. *Perf. 14¹/₂x14*

220 A80 1r car rose, blk & lt brown .60 .35

50th anniv. of the ILO.

King Mahendra — A81

1969, June 20 *Perf. 13¹/₂x13*

221 A81 25p gold & multi .15 .15

King Mahendra's 49th birthday (50th by Oriental count). Issuance delayed from June 11 to 20.

King Tribhuvana and Wives A82

1969, July 1 *Perf. 14¹/₂x14*

222 A82 25p yellow & ol gray .15 .15

64th anniv. of the birth of King Tribhuvana.

Queen Ratna & Child Playing — A83

Rhododendron & Himalayas — A84

1969, Aug. 20 Photo. *Perf. 14x14¹/₂*

223 A83 25p gray & rose car	.15	.15

5th Natl. Children's Day and to for the 41st birthday of Queen Ratna Rajya Lakshmi Devi Shah.

1969, Sept. 17 Photo. *Perf. 13¹/₂*

Flowers: No. 225, Narcissus. No. 226, Marigold. No. 227, Poinsettia.

224 A84 25p lt blue & multi	.28	.24
225 A84 25p brown red & multi	.28	.24
226 A84 25p black & multi	.28	.24
227 A84 25p multicolored	.28	.24
a. Block of 4, #224-227	1.15	1.15

Durga, Goddess of Victory — A85

Crown Prince Birendra and Princess Aishwarya — A86

1969, Oct. 17 Photo. *Perf. 14x14¹/₂*

228 A85 15p black & orange	.15	.15
229 A85 50p black, bis brn & vio	.20	.15
Set value	.29	.15

Issued to celebrate the Dasain Festival.

1970, Feb. 27 Photo. *Perf. 13¹/₂*

230 A86 25p multicolored	.15	.15

Wedding of Crown Prince Birendra Bir Bikram Shah Deva and Crown Princess Aishwarya Rajya Lakshmi Devi Rana, Feb. 27-28.

Agricultural Products, Cow, Fish — A87

1970, Mar. 21 Litho. *Perf. 12¹/₂*

231 A87 25p multicolored	.15	.15

Issued to publicize the Agricultural Year.

Bal Bhadra Kunwar A88

1970, Apr. 13 Photo. *Perf. 14¹/₂x14*

232 A88 1r ol bister & red lilac	.30	.24

Bal Bhadra Kunwar, leader in the 1814 battle of Kalanga against British forces.

King Mahendra, Mountain Peak and Crown — A89

1970, June 11 Litho. *Perf. 11¹/₂*

233 A89 50p gold & multi	.15	.15

King Mahendra's 50th birthday.

Gosainkund A90

Lakes: 25p, Phewa Tal. 1r, Rara Daha.

1970, June 11 Photo. *Perf. 13¹/₂*

234 A90 5p dull yellow & multi	.15	.15
235 A90 25p gray & multi	.15	.15
236 A90 1r pink & multi	.30	.28
Set value	.44	.40

A.P.Y. Emblem A91

1970, July 1 *Perf. 14¹/₂x14*

237 A91 1r dark blue & blue	.30	.24

Asian Productivity Year 1970.

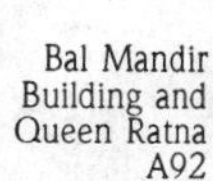
Bal Mandir Building and Queen Ratna A92

1970, Aug. 20 Photo. *Perf. 14¹/₂x14*

238 A92 25p gray & bister brn	.15	.15

Issued for Children's Day. The Bal Mandir Building in Taulihawa is the headquarters of the National Children's Organization.

New UPU Headquarters, Bern — A93

1970, Oct. 9 Photo. *Perf. 14¹/₂x14*

239 A93 2.50r ocher & sepia	.60	.60

UN Flag — A94

1970, Oct. 24 Photo. *Perf. 14¹/₂x14*

240 A94 25p blue & brown	.15	.15

25th anniversary of the United Nations.

Royal Palace and Square, Patan A95

Designs: 25p, Bodhnath stupa, near Kathmandu, vert. 1r, Gauri Shankar, holy mountain.

Perf. 11x11¹/₂, 11¹/₂x11

1970, Dec. 28 Litho.

241 A95 15p multicolored	.15	.15
242 A95 25p multicolored	.15	.15
243 A95 1r multicolored	.35	.28
Set value	.50	.40

Crown Prince Birendra's 25th birthday.

Statue of Harihar (Vishnu-Siva) — A96

1971, Jan. 26 Photo. *Perf. 14x14¹/₂*

244 A96 25p bister brn & black	.15	.15

Torch and Target — A97

1971, Mar. 21 Photo. *Perf. 13¹/₂x13*

245 A97 1r bluish gray & dp orange	.35	.24

Intl. year against racial discrimination.

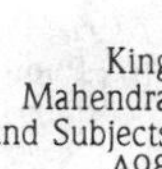
King Mahendra and Subjects A98

1971, June 11 Photo. *Perf. 14¹/₂x14*

246 A98 25p dull purple & blue	.15	.15

King Mahendra's 51st birthday.

Sweta Bhairab (Siva) — A99

Sculptures of Siva: 25p, Manhankal Bhairab. 50p, Kal Bhairab.

1971, July 11 *Perf. 13x13¹/₂*

247 A99 15p orange brown & black	.15	.15
248 A99 25p lt green & black	.15	.15
249 A99 50p blue & black	.24	.15
Set value	.43	.27

Queen Ratna Receiving Garland A100

1971, Aug. 20 Photo. *Perf. 11¹/₂*

Granite Paper

250 A100 25p gray & multi	.15	.15

Children's Day, Queen Ratna's birthday.

Map and Flag of Iran, Flag of Nepal A101

1971, Oct. 14

Granite Paper

251 A101 1r pink & multi	.45	.28

2500th anniversary of the founding of the Persian empire by Cyrus the Great.

UNICEF Emblem, Mother and Child A102

1971, Dec. 11 *Perf. 14¹/₂x14*

252 A102 1r gray blue	.45	.28

25th anniversary of UNICEF.

Everest A103

Himalayan Peaks: 1r, Kangchenjunga. 1.80r, Annapurna I.

1971, Dec. 28 *Perf. 13¹/₂x13*

253 A103 25p blue & brown	.15	.15
254 A103 1r dp blue & brown	.30	.20
255 A103 1.80r blue & yel brown	.60	.45
Nos. 253-255 (3)	1.05	.80

"Visit Nepal."

Royal Standard — A104

Araniko and White Dagoba, Peking — A105

1972, Feb. 19 Photo. *Perf. 13*

256 A104 25p dark red & black	.15	.15

National Day.

1972, Apr. 13 Litho. *Perf. 13*

257 A105 15p lt blue & ol gray	.15	.15

Araniko, a 14th century Nepalese architect, who built the White Dagoba at the Miaoying Monastery, Peking, 1348.

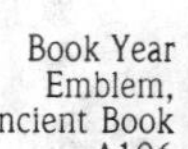
Book Year Emblem, Ancient Book A106

1972, Sept. 8 Photo. *Perf. 14¹/₂x14*

258 A106 2p ocher & brown	.15	.15
259 A106 5p tan & black	.15	.15
260 A106 1r blue & black	.30	.24
Set value	.40	.34

International Book Year.

Heart and WHO Emblem — A107

1972, Nov. 6 Photo. *Perf. 13x13¹/₂*

261 A107 25p dull grn & claret	.15	.15

"Your heart is your health," World Health Month.

King Mahendra (1920-1972) — A108

1972, Dec. 15 Photo. *Perf. 13¹/₂x13*

262 A108 25p brown & black	.15	.15

King Birendra — A109

Northern Border Costume — A110

1972, Dec. 28 Photo. *Perf. 13x13½*

263 A109 50p ocher & purple .18 .15

King Birendra's 27th birthday.

1973, Feb. 18 Photo. *Perf. 13*

Nepalese Costumes: 50p, Hill dwellers. 75p, Kathmandu Valley couple. 1r, Inner Terai couple.

264 A110 25p dull lilac & multi .15 .15
265 A110 50p lemon & multi .15 .15
266 A110 75p multicolored .18 .15
267 A110 1r multicolored .24 .18
a. Block of 4, #264-267 .65 .60

National Day.

Babu Ram Acharya (1888-1972), Historian — A111

1973, Mar. 12 Photo. *Perf. 13*

268 A111 25p olive gray & car .15 .15

Nepalese Family and Home A112

1973, Apr. 7 Photo. *Perf. 14½x14*

269 A112 1r Prus blue & ocher .50 .30

25th anniv. of the WHO.

Lumbini Garden, Birthplace of Buddha — A113

1973, May 17 Photo. *Perf. 13x13½*

270 A113 25p shown .15 .15
271 A113 75p Mt. Makalu .20 .15
272 A113 1r Gorkha Village .30 .20
Nos. 270-272 (3) .65
Set value .40

FAO Emblem, Women Farmers A114

1973, June 29 Photo. *Perf. 14½x14*

273 A114 10p dark gray & violet .15 .15

World food program, 10th anniversary.

INTERPOL Headquarters and Emblem A115

1973, Sept. 3

274 A115 25p bister & blue .15 .15

50th anniversary of the International Criminal Police Organization (INTERPOL).

Shom Nath Sigdyal (1884-1972), Scholar — A116

1973, Oct. 5 Photo. *Perf. 13x13½*

275 A116 1.25r violet blue .32 .24

Cow — A117

1973, Oct. 25 Photo. *Perf. 13½x13*

276 A117 2p shown .15 .15
277 A117 3.25r Yak .75 .75
Set value .80 .80

Festival of Lights (Tihar).

King Birendra — A118

Perf. 13, 13½x14, 15x14½

1973-74 Photo.

278 A118 5p dark brown .15 .15
279 A118 15p ol brn & dk brn ('74) .15 .15
280 A118 1r reddish brn & dk brn ('74) .30 .24
Set value .47 .38

King Birendra's 28th birthday.

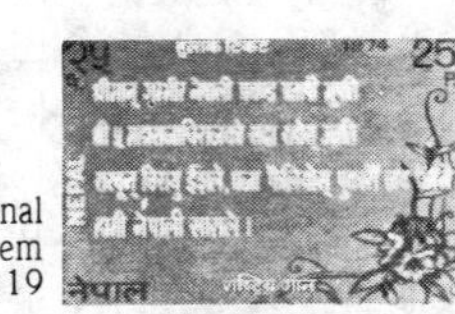

National Anthem A119

Natl. Day: 1r, Score of national anthem.

1974, Feb. 18 Photo. *Perf. 13½x13*

281 A119 25p rose carmine .15 .15
282 A119 1r deep green .24 .24
Set value .29 .29

King Janak on Throne — A120

1974, Apr. 14 Litho. *Perf. 13½*

283 A120 2.50r multicolored .75 .60

Children's Village and SOS Emblem — A121

1974, May 20 Litho. *Perf. 13½x13*

284 A121 25p ultra & red .15 .15

25th anniv. of SOS Children's Village Intl.

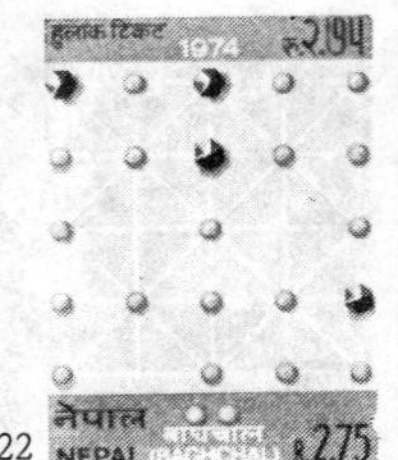

Baghchal — A122

1974, July 1 Litho. *Perf. 13*

285 A122 2p Soccer .15 .15
286 A122 2.75r shown .75 .60
Set value .80 .65

Popular Nepalese games.

WPY Emblem — A123

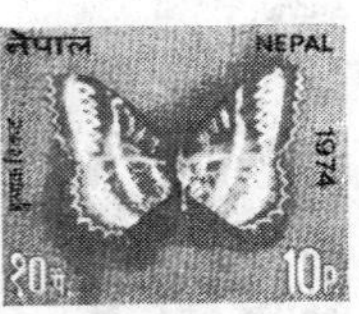

UPU Monument, Bern — A124

1974, Aug. 19 Litho. *Perf. 13*

287 A123 5p ocher & blue .15 .15

World Population Year.

1974, Oct. 9 Litho. *Perf. 13*

288 A124 1r olive & black .24 .18

Centenary of Universal Postal Union.

Butterfly — A125

Designs: Nepalese butterflies.

1974, Oct. 16

289 A125 10p lt brown & multi .15 .15
290 A125 15p lt blue & multi .15 .15
291 A125 1.25r multicolored .35 .28
292 A125 1.75r buff & multi .60 .45
Set value 1.00 .82

King Birendra A126

Muktinath A127

Peacock Window A128

1974, Dec. 28 Litho. *Perf. 13½x13*

293 A126 25p gray green & black .15 .15

King Birendra's 29th birthday.

Perf. 13x13½, 13½x13

1974, Dec. 31

294 A127 25p multicolored .15 .15
295 A128 1r multicolored .30 .18
Set value .36 .23

Tourist publicity.

Guheswari Temple — A129

Pashupati Temple — A131

Rara — A130

King Birendra and Queen Aishwarya — A132

Designs: 1r, Throne. 1.25r, Royal Palace.

1975, Feb. 24 Litho. *Perf. 13x13½*

296 A129 25p multicolored .15 .15

Photo.

Perf. 14½x14

297 A130 50p multicolored .15 .15

Granite Paper

Perf. 11½, 11 (A131)

298 A132 1r olive & multi .24 .18
299 A132 1.25r multicolored .30 .22
300 A131 1.75r multicolored .35 .30
301 A132 2.75r gold & multi .60 .50
a. Souvenir sheet of 3 1.25 1.25
Nos. 296-301 (6) 1.79 1.50

Coronation of King Birendra, Feb. 24, 1975. No. 301a contains 3 imperf. stamps similar to Nos. 298-299, 301 and label with inscription.

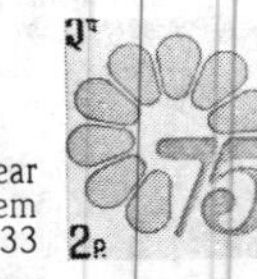

Tourist Year Emblem A133

Swayambhunath Stupa, Kathmandu — A134

Perf. 12½x13½, 13½x12½

1975, May 25 Litho.

302 A133 2p yellow & multi .15 .15
303 A134 25p violet & black .15 .15
Set value .15 .15

South Asia Tourism Year.

Tiger A135

1975, July 17 Litho. *Perf. 13*

304 A135 2p shown .15 .15
305 A135 5p Deer, vert. .15 .15
306 A135 1r Panda .28 .18
Set value .38 .28

Wildlife conservation.

Queen Aishwarya and IWY Emblem — A136

1975, Nov. 8 Litho. *Perf. 13*
307 A136 1r lt blue & multi .30 .18

International Women's Year.

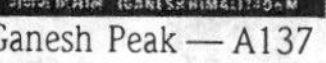
Ganesh Peak — A137

Rupse Falls — A138

Kumari, Living Goddess of Nepal — A139

1975, Dec. 16 Litho. *Perf. 13½*
308 A137 2p multicolored .15 .15
309 A138 25p multicolored .15 .15
310 A139 50p multicolored .24 .15
Set value .40 .26

Tourist publicity.

King Birendra — A140

1975, Dec. 28 Photo. *Perf. 13*
311 A140 25p rose lilac & red lilac .15 .15

King Birendra's 30th birthday.

Flag and Map of Nepal — A141

1976, Feb. 19 Litho. *Perf. 13*
312 A141 2.50r dark blue & red .45 .45

National or Democracy Day.

Rice Cultivation — A142

1976, Apr. 11 Litho. *Perf. 13*
313 A142 25p multicolored .15 .15

Agricultural development.

Flags of Nepal and Colombo Plan — A143

Runner — A144

1976, July 1 Photo. *Perf. 13x13½*
314 A143 1r multicolored .24 .18

Colombo Plan, 25th anniversary.

1976, July 31 Photo. *Perf. 13x13½*
315 A144 3.25r black & ultra .45 .45

21st Olympic Games, Montreal, Canada, July 17-Aug. 1.

Dove and Map of South East Asia — A145

1976, Aug. 17 Litho. *Perf. 13½*
316 A145 5r bister, black & ultra .75 .75

5th Summit Conference of Non-aligned Countries, Colombo, Sri Lanka, Aug. 9-19.

Folk Dances A146

1976, Sept. 27 Litho. *Perf. 13½x13*
317 A146 10p Lakha mask .15 .15
318 A146 15p Maruni .15 .15
319 A146 30p Jhangad .15 .15
320 A146 1r Sebru .30 .20
Set value .48 .35

Nepalese Lily — A147

King Birendra — A148

Flowers: No. 322, Meconopsis grandis. No. 323, Cardiocrinum giganteum, horiz. No. 324, Megacodon stylophorus, horiz.

1976-77 Litho. *Perf. 13*
321 A147 30p lt ultra & multi .15 .15
322 A147 30p brown & multi ('77) .15 .15
323 A147 30p violet & multi ('77) .15 .15
324 A147 30p green & multi ('77) .15 .15
Set value .24 .20

Issue dates: Nov. 7, 1976, Jan. 24, 1977.

1976, Dec. 28 Photo. *Perf. 14*
325 A148 5p green .15 .15
326 A148 30p multicolored .15 .15
Set value .15 .15

King Birendra's 31st birthday.

Bell and American Bicentennial Emblem A149

1976, Dec. 31 Litho. *Perf. 13½*
327 A149 10r multicolored 1.75 1.75

American Bicentennial.

Warrior Kazi Amar Singh Thapa, Natl. Hero — A150

1977, Feb. 18 Photo. *Perf. 13x13½*
328 A150 10p multicolored .15 .15

Terracotta Figurine, Kapilavastu Excavations A151

Asoka Pillar, Lumbini A152

1977, May 3 Photo. *Perf. 14½x14*
329 A151 30p dark violet .15 .15
330 A152 5r green & brown .90 .90

Tourist publicity.

Cheer Pheasant A153

Birds of Nepal: 5p, Great pied hornbill, vert. 1r, Green magpie. 2.30r, Nepalese laughing thrush, vert.

1977, Sept. 17 Photo. *Perf. 13*
331 A153 5p multicolored .15 .15
332 A153 15p multicolored .15 .15
333 A153 1r multicolored .18 .18
334 A153 2.30r multicolored .40 .40
Set value .68 .68

Tukuche Peak, Nepalese Police Flag — A154

1977, Oct. 2
335 A154 1.25r multicolored .22 .22

Ascent of Tukuche, Himalaya Mountains, by Nepalese police team, first anniversary.

Scout Emblem, Map of Nepal — A155

1977, Nov. 7 Litho. *Perf. 13½*
336 A155 3.50r multicolored .65 .65

Boy Scouts of Nepal, 25th anniversary.

Dhanwantari, Health Goddess — A156

1977, Nov. 9 Photo. *Perf. 13*
337 A156 30p bluish green .15 .15

Health Day.

Flags, Map of Nepal — A157

King Birendra — A158

1977, Dec. 5 Photo. *Perf. 13½*
338 A157 1r multicolored .18 .18

Colombo Plan, 26th Consultative Meeting, Kathmandu, Nov. 29-Dec. 7.

1977, Dec. 28
339 A158 5p olive .15 .15
340 A158 1r red brown .18 .18
Set value .22 .22

King Birendra's 32nd birthday.

Post Office Seal, New Post Office A159

75p, Post Office date stamp & new Post Office.

1978, Apr. 14 Photo. *Perf. 14½x14*
341 A159 25p orange brown & black .15 .15
342 A159 75p bister & black .15 .15
Set value .18 .18

Centenary of Nepalese postal service.

Mt. Everest A160

Design: 4r, Mt. Everest, different view.

1978, May 29 Photo. *Perf. 13½x13*
343 A160 2.30r red brown & slate .40 .40
344 A160 4r green & violet blue .70 .70

1st ascent of Mt. Everest, 25th anniv.

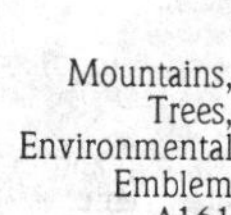

Mountains, Trees, Environmental Emblem A161

1978, June 5
345 A161 1r blue green & orange .18 .18

World Environment Day, June 5.

Queen Mother Ratna — A162

1978, Aug. 20 Photo. *Perf. 14*
346 A162 2.30r olive gray .40 .40

Queen Mother Ratna, 50th birthday.

Trisula River Rapids — A163

Tourist Publicity: 50p, Nepalese window. 1r, Dancer, Mahakali dance, vert.

1978, Sept. 15 Litho. *Perf. 14*

347 A163 10p multicolored .15 .15
348 A163 50p multicolored .15 .15
349 A163 1r multicolored .18 .18
Set value .32 .32

Human Rights Emblem — A164

1978, Oct. 10 Litho. *Perf. 13½*

350 A164 25p red brown & red .15 .15
351 A164 1r dark blue & red .18 .18
Set value .26 .26

Universal Declaration of Human Rights, 30th anniversary.

Choerospondias Axillaris — A165

Designs: 1r, Castanopsis indica, vert. 1.25r, Elaeocarpus sphaericus.

1978, Oct. 31 Photo. *Perf. 13*

352 A165 5p multicolored .15 .15
353 A165 1r multicolored .18 .18
354 A165 1.25r multicolored .22 .22
Set value .45 .45

King Birendra — A166

1978, Dec. 17 *Perf. 13½x14*

355 A166 30p brown & indigo .15 .15
356 A166 2r violet & black .35 .35
Set value .40 .40

King Birendra's 33rd birthday.

Kamroop and Patan Temples and Deity — A167

Red Machhindra Chariot — A168

Perf. 14½x14, 13½

1979 Photo., Litho.

357 A167 75p claret & olive .15 .15
358 A168 1.25r multicolored .22 .22

Red Machhindra Nath Festival, Lalitpur (Patan). Issue dates: 75p, Apr. 27; 1.25r, July 25.

Bas-relief — A169

Tree Planting — A170

1979, May 12 Photo. *Perf. 13*

359 A169 1r yellow & brown .18 .18

Lumbini Year.

1979, June 29 Photo. *Perf. 13x13½*

360 A170 2.30r multicolored .40 .40

Afforestation campaign.

Children with Flag, IYC Emblem — A172

1979, Aug. 20 *Perf. 13½*

362 A172 1r light brown .18 .18

Intl. Year of the Child; Natl. Children's Day.

Mount Pabil — A173

Tourism: 50p, Swargadwari Temple. 1.25r, Altar with statues of Shiva and Parbati.

1979, Sept. 26 Photo. *Perf. 13½x13*

363 A173 30p dk blue green .15 .15
364 A173 50p multicolored .15 .15
365 A173 1.25r multicolored .22 .22
Set value .37 .37

Northern Shrike — A174

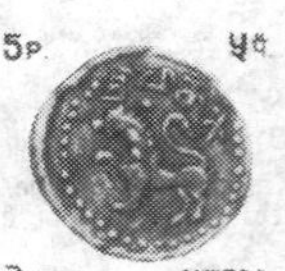

Coin, Lichhavi Period, Obverse — A175

Malla Period, Obverse — A175a

Shaw Period, Obverse — A175b

Perf. 14½x13½

1979, Nov. 22 Photo.

366 A174 10p shown .15 .15
367 A174 10r Aethopyga ignicauda 2.00 2.00

Intl. World Pheasant Assoc. Symposium, Kathmandu, Nov. 21-23. See No. C7.

1979, Dec. 16 Photo. *Perf. 15*

Ancient Coins: No. 369, Lichhavi Period, reverse. No. 371, Malla Period, reverse. No. 373, Shah Period, reverse.

368 A175 5p brown & brown org .15 .15
369 A175 5p brown & brown org .15 .15
a. Pair, #368-369 .15 .15
370 A175a 15p dark blue .15 .15
371 A175a 15p dark blue .15 .15
a. Pair, #370-371 .15 .15
372 A175b 1r slate blue .18 .18
373 A175b 1r slate blue .18 .18
a. Pair, #372-373 .36 .36
Set value .50 .50

King Birendra A176

Ban-Ganga Dam A177

1979, Dec. 28 Litho. *Perf. 14*

374 A176 25p multicolored .15 .15
375 A177 2.30r multicolored .42 .42
Set value .46 .46

King Birendra's 34th birthday.

Samyak Pooja Festival A178

1980, Jan. 15 *Perf. 13½*

376 A178 30p violet brown & gray .15 .15

Holy Basil — A179

1980, Mar. 24 Photo. *Perf. 14x14½*

377 A179 5p shown .15 .15
378 A179 30p Himalayan valerian .15 .15
379 A179 1r Nepalese pepper .18 .18
380 A179 2.30r Himalayan rhubarb .42 .42
Set value .70 .70

Gyandil Das — A180

Nepalese Writers: 30p, Shddhi Das Amatya. 1r, Pahal Man Singh Snwar. 2.30r, Jay Prithibi Bahadur Singh.

1980, Apr. 13 *Perf. 13½x13*

381 A180 5p bister & rose lilac .15 .15
382 A180 30p vio brn & lt red brn .15 .15
383 A180 1r blue & olive gray .18 .18
384 A180 2.30r ol green & dk blue .42 .42
Set value .70 .70

Jwalaji Dailekh (Temple), Holy Flame — A181

Temple Statue — A182

1980, Sept. 14 Litho. *Perf. 14½*

385 A181 10p shown .15 .15
386 A181 1r Godavari Pond .18 .18
387 A181 5r Mt. Dhaulagiri .90 .90
Nos. 385-387 (3) 1.23 1.23

1980, Oct. 29 *Perf. 14x13½*

388 A182 25r multicolored 4.50 4.50

World Tourism Conf., Manila, Sept. 27.

King Birendra's 35th Birthday — A183

1980, Dec. 28 Litho. *Perf. 14*

389 A183 1r multicolored .18 .18

International Year of the Disabled A184

1981, Jan. 1

390 A184 5r multicolored .90 .90

Nepal Rastra Bank, 25th Anniv. — A185

1981, Apr. 26 Litho. *Perf. 14*

391 A185 1.75r multicolored .32 .32

A186

A187

1981, July 16

392 A186 10p No. 1 .15 .15
393 A186 40p No. 2 .15 .15
394 A186 3.40r No. 3 .60 .60
a. Souvenir sheet of 3, #392-394 .75 .75
Set value .72 .72

Nepalese stamp cent.

1981, Oct. 30 Litho. *Perf. 14*

395 A187 1.75r multicolored .32 .32

Intl. Hotel Assoc., 70th council meeting, Kathmandu.

Stamp Centenary A188

King Birendra's 36th Birthday A189

1981, Dec. 27 Litho. *Perf. 14*

396 A188 40p multicolored .15 .15

Nepal '81 Stamp Exhibition, Kathmandu, Dec. 27-31.

1981, Dec. 28

397 A189 1r multicolored .18 .18

Hrishikesh, Buddhist Stone Carving, Ridi — A190

1981, Dec. 30

398 A190	5p shown	.15	.15
399 A190	25p Tripurasundari Pavilion, Baitadi	.15	.15
400 A190	2r Mt. Langtang Lirung	.35	.35
	Set value	.45	.45

Royal Nepal Academy, 25th Anniv. — A191

Balakrishna Sama — A192

1982, June 23 **Litho.** ***Perf. 14***

401 A191 40p multicolored .15 .15

1982, July 21 ***Perf. 13½***

402 A192 1r multicolored .18 .18

Dish Antenna, Satellite — A193

Mt. Nuptse — A194

1982, Nov. 7 **Litho.** ***Perf. 14***

403 A193 5r multicolored .90 .90

1982, Nov. 18 ***Perf. 13½***

Intl. Union of Alpinists Assoc., 50th Anniv. (Himalaya Peaks): b, Mt. Lhotse (31x31mm). c, Mt. Everest (40x31mm). Continuous design.

404	Strip of 3	1.00	1.00
a.	A194 25p multicolored	.15	.15
b.	A194 2r multicolored	.35	.35
c.	A194 3r multicolored	.55	.55

9th Asian Games — A195

1982, Nov. 19 ***Perf. 14***

405 A195 3.40r multicolored .65 .65

Kulekhani Hydro-electric Plant — A196

1982, Dec. 2 ***Perf. 13½***

406 A196 2r Lake, dam .35 .35

A197

A198

1982, Dec. 28 ***Perf. 12½***

407 A197 5p multicolored .15 .15

King Birendra's 37th birthday.

1983, June 15 **Litho.** ***Perf. 14***

408 A198 50p multicolored .15 .15

25th anniv. of Nepal Industrial Development Co.

25th Anniv. of Royal Nepal Airlines — A199

1983, Aug. 1 ***Perf. 13½***

409 A199 1r multicolored .15 .15

World Communications Year — A200

1983, Oct. 30 **Litho.** ***Perf. 12***

410 A200 10p multicolored .15 .15

A201

A202

Musical instruments.

1983, Nov. 3

411 A201	5p Sarangi	.15	.15
412 A201	10p Kwota	.15	.15
413 A201	50p Narashinga	.15	.15
414 A201	1r Murchunga	.15	.15
	Set value	.20	.20

1983, Dec. 20

415 A202 4.50r multicolored .38 .38

Chakrapani Chalise (1883-1957), national anthem composer and poet.

King Birendra's 38th Birthday — A203

1983, Dec. 28 ***Perf. 14***

416 A203 5r multicolored .42 .42

Temple, Barahkshetra A204

1983, Dec. 30 ***Perf. 14***

417 A204	1r shown	.15	.15
418 A204	2.20r Triveni pilgrimage site	.20	.20
419 A204	6r Mt. Cho-oyu	.50	.50
	Nos. 417-419 (3)	.85	.85

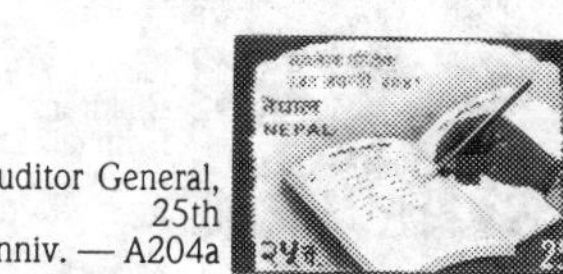

Auditor General, 25th Anniv. — A204a

1984, June 28 **Litho.** ***Perf. 14***

419A A204a 25p Open ledger .15 .15

A205

A206

1984, July 1 **Litho.** ***Perf. 14***

420 A205 5r Transmission tower .42 .42

Asia-Pacific Broadcasting Union, 20th anniv.

1984, July 8

421 A206 50p University emblem .15 .15

Tribhuvan University, 25th anniv.

A207

A208

1984, Aug. 5

422 A207 10r Boxing .85 .85

1984 Summer Olympic Games, Los Angeles.

1984, Sept. 18

423 A208 1r multicolored .15 .15

Family Planning Assoc., 25th anniv.

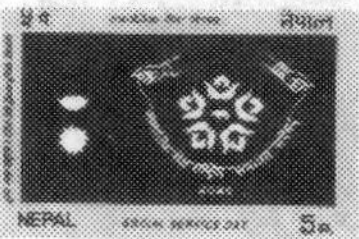

Social Services Day — A209

1984, Sept. 24

424 A209 5p multicolored .15 .15

Wildlife — A210

1984, Nov. 30

425 A210	10p Gavialis gangeticus	.15	.15
426 A210	25p Panthera uncia	.15	.15
427 A210	50p Antilope cervicapra	.15	.15
	Set value	.15	.15

Chhinna Masta Bhagvati Temple and Goddess Sakhandeshwari Devi, Statue — A211

Designs: 10p, Lord Vishu the Giant, Yajna Ceremony on Bali, bas-relief, A. D. 467, vert. 5r, Mt. Api, Himalayas, vert.

1984, Dec. 21

428 A211	10p multicolored	.15	.15
429 A211	1r multicolored	.15	.15
430 A211	5r multicolored	.42	.42
	Set value	.56	.56

King Birendra, 39th Birthday — A212

1984, Dec. 28

431 A212 1r multicolored .15 .15

Sagarmatha Natl. Park — A213

1985, May 6

432 A213 10r Mt. Everest, wildlife .85 .85

King Mahendra Trust Congress for Nature Conservation, May 6-11.

Illustration from Shiva Dharma Purana, 13th Cent. Book — A214

Design: Maheshware, Lord Shiva, with brahma and vishnu. #433b, left person sitting on wall. #433d, left person on throne.

1985, May 30

433	Strip of 5	.24	.24
a.-e.	A214 50p any single	.15	.15
f.	Strip of 5, imperf within	1.50	

#433 has a continuous design. Sizes: #433a, 433e, 26x22mm; #433b, 433d, 24x22mm; #433c, 17x22mm.

UN, 40th Anniv. — A215

1985, Oct. 24 **Litho.** ***Perf. 13½x14***

434 A215 5r multicolored .30 .30

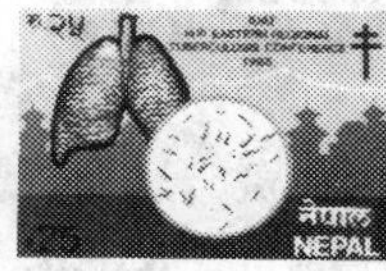

14th Eastern Regional Tuberculosis Conference A216

1985, Nov. 25

435 A216 25r multicolored 1.50 1.50

First South Asian Regional Cooperation Summit A217

1985, Dec. 8 ***Perf. 14***

436 A217 5r Flags .30 .30

Temple of Jaleshwar, Mohottary Underwater Project A218

1985, Dec. 15 **Litho.** ***Perf. 14x13½***

437 A218	10p shown	.15	.15
438 A218	1r Temple of Shaileshwari, Doti	.15	.15
439 A218	2r Lake Phoksundo, Dolpa	.15	.15
	Set value	.22	.22

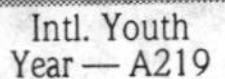

Intl. Youth Year — A219

Devi Ghat Hydro-electric Dam Project — A220

1985, Dec. 21 *Perf. 14*
440 A219 1r multicolored .15 .15

1985, Dec. 28 **Litho.** *Perf. 14*
441 A220 2r multicolored .15 .15

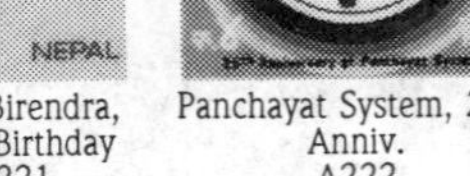

King Birendra, 40th Birthday A221

Panchayat System, 25th Anniv. A222

1985, Dec. 28
442 A221 50p Portrait .15 .15

1986, Apr. 10 *Perf. 13½*
443 A222 4r multicolored .24 .24

Pharping Hydroelectric Station, 75th Anniv. A223

1986, Oct. 9 **Litho.** *Perf. 14x13½*
444 A223 15p multicolored .15 .15

Architecture, Artifacts — A224

1986, Oct. 9 **Photo.** *Perf. 13x13½*
445 A224 5p Pashupati Temple .15 .15
446 A224 10p Lumbini Fort .15 .15
446A A224 50p like 5p ('87) .15 .15
447 A224 1r Crown of Nepal .15 .15
Set value .20 .20

No. 446A issued Apr. 14.

Asian Productivity Org., 25th Anniv. — A225

1986, Oct. 26 **Litho.** *Perf. 13½x14*
448 A225 1r multicolored .15 .15

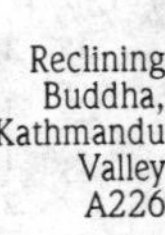

Reclining Buddha, Kathmandu Valley A226

Mt. Pumori, Khumbu Range — A227

Perf. 14, 13½x13
1986, Oct. 26 **Litho.**
449 A226 60p multicolored .15 .15
450 A227 8r multicolored .48 .48
Set value .52 .52

King Birendra, 41st Birthday — A228

Intl. Peace Year — A229

1986, Dec. 28 **Litho.** *Perf. 13x13½*
451 A228 1r multicolored .15 .15

1986, Dec. 28 *Perf. 14*
452 A229 10r multicolored .75 .75

Social Service Natl. Coordination Council, 10th Anniv. — A230

1987, Sept. 22 **Litho.** *Perf. 13½*
453 A230 1r Natl. flag, emblem .15 .15

Birth of Buddha A231

Design: Asoka Pillar, enlargement of commemorative text and bas-relief of birth.

1987, Oct. 28 *Perf. 14*
454 A231 4r multicolored .45 .45

First Natl. Boy Scout Jamboree, Kathmandu A232

1987, Oct. 28 **Litho.** *Perf. 14*
455 A232 1r multicolored .15 .15

A233

A234

1987, Nov. 2
456 A233 60p gold & lake .15 .15

3rd SAARC (Southeast Asian Assoc. for Regional Cooperation) Summit Conference, Kathmandu.

1987, Nov. 10
457 A234 4r multicolored .45 .45

Rastriya Samachar Samiti nNatl. news agency), 25th anniv.

Intl. Year of Shelter for the Homeless A235

1987, Dec. 21 **Litho.** *Perf. 14*
458 A235 5r multicolored .85 .85

Kashthamandap Temple, Kathmandu A236

Surya Bikram Gyawali (b. 1898), Historian A237

1987, Dec. 21 **Photo.** *Perf. 13½x13*
459 A236 25p multicolored .15 .15

1987, Dec. 21 *Perf. 13x13½*
460 A237 60p multicolored .15 .15

King Birendra, 42nd Birthday — A238

Perf. 14½x13½
1987, Dec. 28 **Litho.**
461 A238 25p multicolored .15 .15

Mount Kanjiroba A239

1987, Dec. 30 *Perf. 14*
462 A239 10r multicolored 1.70 1.70

Crown Prince Dipendra's 18th Birthday — A240

Nepal Bank, Ltd., 50th Anniv. — A241

1988, Mar. 28 **Litho.** *Perf. 14*
463 A240 1r multicolored .20 .20

1988, Apr. 8
464 A241 2r multicolored .38 .38

Kanti Childrens' Hospital, 25th Anniv. A242

1988, Apr. 8
465 A242 60p multicolored .15 .15

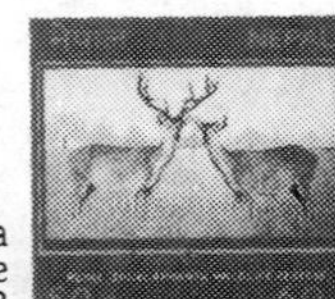

Royal Shuklaphanta Wildlife Reserve — A243

1988, Apr. 8
466 A243 60p Swamp deer .15 .15

A244

A245

1988, Aug. 20 **Litho.** *Perf. 14x13½*
467 A244 5r multicolored .95 .95

Queen Mother Ratna Rajya Laxmi Devi Shah, 60th birthday.

1988, Sept. 12 **Litho.** *Perf. 14x13½*
468 A245 1r dull fawn & dark red .18 .18

Nepal Red Cross, 25th anniv.

Bindhyabasini, Pokhara — A246

1988, Oct. 16 **Litho.** *Perf. 14½*
469 A246 15p multicolored .15 .15

A247

A248

1988, Dec. 28 **Litho.** *Perf. 14*
470 A247 4r multicolored .72 .72

King Birendra, 43rd birthday.

1989, Mar. 3 **Litho.** *Perf. 13½x14*
471 A248 1r Temple .18 .18

Pashupati Area Development Trust.

SAARC Year — A249

A250

1989, Dec. 8 *Perf. 13x13½*
472 A249 60p multicolored .15 .15

Combating Drug Abuse & Trafficking.

1989, Oct. 5 *Perf. 14*
473 A250 4r violet, brt green & blk .52 .52

Asia-Pacific Telecommunity, 10th anniv.

King Birendra, 44th Birthday A251

Perf. 13½x14½
1989, Dec. 28 **Litho.**
474 A251 2r multicolored .28 .28

Child Survival — A252

Design: Oral rehydration therapy, immunization, breast-feeding and growth monitoring.

1989, Dec. 31 *Perf. 13½*
475 A252 1r multicolored .18 .18

Rara Natl. Park — A253

1989, Dec. 31 *Perf. 14½x15*
476 A253 4r multicolored .50 .50

Mt. Ama Dablam — A254

1989, Dec. 31 *Perf. 14*
477 A254 5r multicolored .62 .62

A255

A257

Temple of the Goddess Manakamana, Gorkha — A256

1990, Jan. 3
478 A255 1r multicolored .15 .15

Crown Prince Dipendra investiture, Jan. 3.

1990, Apr. 12 Litho. *Perf. 14½*
479 A256 60p deep blue & black .15 .15

1990, Aug. 20 Litho. *Perf. 14*
480 A257 1r multicolored .15 .15

Nepal Children's Organization, 25th anniv.

A258

A259

1990, Sept. 13 Litho. *Perf. 14x13½*
481 A258 60p orange, blue & red .15 .15

Bir Hospital, cent.

1990, Oct. 9 *Perf. 14½*
482 A259 4r multicolored .55 .55

Asian-Pacific Postal Training Center, 20th anniv.

SAARC Year of the Girl Child — A260

1990, Dec. 24 Litho. *Perf. 14½*
483 A260 4.60r multicolored .65 .65

Bageshwori Temple, Nepalganj A261

Mt. Saipal — A262

1990, Dec. 24 *Perf. 13½*
484 A261 1r multicolored .15 .15
485 A262 5r multicolored .70 .70

B.P. Koirala (1914-82) — A263

King Birendra, 45th Birthday — A264

1990, Dec. 31 *Perf. 14*
486 A263 60p red, orange brn & blk .15 .15

1990, Dec. 28
487 A264 2r multicolored .22 .22

Royal Chitwan Natl. Park — A265

1991, Feb. 10 Litho. *Perf. 14½*
488 A265 4r multicolored .45 .45

Restoration of Multiparty Democracy, 1st Anniv. — A266

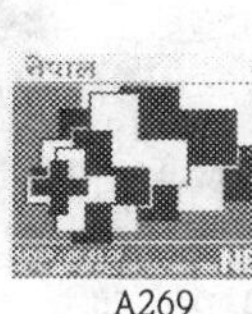
Natl. Census — A267

1991, Apr. 9 Litho. *Perf. 14*
489 A266 1r multicolored .15 .15

1991, May 3 *Perf. 14x13½*
490 A267 60p multicolored .15 .15

A268

A269

1991, Aug. 15 *Perf. 14½x13½*
491 A268 3r multicolored .30 .30

Federation of Nepalese Chambers of Commerce and Industry, 25th anniv.

1991, Sept. 4 Litho. *Perf. 14*
492 A269 60p gray & red .15 .15

Nepal Junior Red Cross, 25th anniv.

Re-establishment of Parliament, 1st Session — A270

1991, Sept. 10 *Perf. 14½*
493 A270 1r multicolored .16 .16

Constitution Day — A271

1991, Nov. 9 Litho. *Perf. 15x14*
494 A271 50p multicolored .15 .15

Mt. Kumbhakarna A272

1991, Oct. Litho. *Perf. 13½x14*
495 A272 4.60r multicolored .55 .55

Vivaha Mandap — A274

SAARC Year of Shelter — A275

1991, Dec. 11 *Perf. 11½*
497 A274 1r multicolored .18 .18

1991, Dec. 28 *Perf. 13½x14*
498 A275 9r multicolored .95 .95

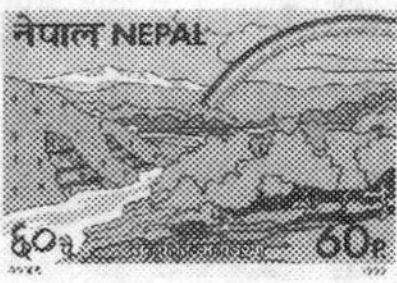
King Birendra, 46th Birthday — A276

1991, Dec. 28 *Perf. 14x13½*
499 A276 8r multicolored .90 .90

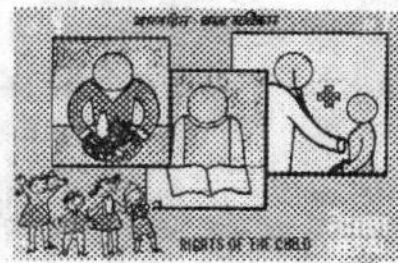
Nepal Philatelic Society, 25th Anniv. — A277

1992, July 11 Litho. *Perf. 13*
500 A277 4r multicolored .38 .38

Protect the Environment A278

1992, Oct. 24 Litho. *Perf. 12½x13*
501 A278 60p multicolored .15 .15

Rights of the Child — A279

1992, Oct. 24 *Perf. 13½x13*
502 A279 1r multicolored .18 .18

A280

A281

Temples: 75p, Thakurdwara. 1r, Namo Buddha. 2r, Narijhowa. 11r, Dantakali.

1992, Nov. 10 *Perf. 14*
503 A280 75p multicolored .15 .15
504 A280 1r multicolored .18 .18
505 A280 2r multicolored .38 .38
506 A280 11r multicolored 2.00 2.00
Nos. 503-506 (4) 2.71 2.71

No. 506 is airmail.

1992, Dec. 20 Photo. *Perf. 13x13½*
507 A281 40p brown & green .15 .15

Agricultural Development Bank, 25th anniv.

Birds — A282

Designs: 1r, Pin-tailed green pigeon. 3r, Bohemian waxwing. 25r, Rufous-tailed finch lark.

1992, Dec. 20 Litho. *Perf. 11½*

508	A282	1r multicolored	.18	.18
509	A282	3r multicolored	.55	.55
510	A282	25r multicolored	4.50	4.50
		Nos. 508-510 (3)	5.23	5.23

King Birendra, 47th Birthday A283

1992, Dec. 28 *Perf. 12½x13*

511 A283 7r multicolored 1.25 1.25

Poets A284

1992 Summer Olympics, Barcelona A285

Designs: No. 512, Pandit Kulchandra Gautam. No. 513, Chittadhar Hridaya. No. 514, Vidyapati. No. 515, Teongsi Sirijunga.

1992, Dec. 31 *Perf. 11½*

512	A284	1r blue & multi	.18	.18
513	A284	1r brown & multi	.18	.18
514	A284	1r tan & multi	.18	.18
515	A284	1r gray & multi	.18	.18
		Nos. 512-515 (4)	.72	.72

1992, Dec. 31

516 A285 25r multicolored 4.50 4.50

Fish — A286

Designs: 25p, Tor putitora. 1r, Schizothorax plagiostomus. 5r, Anguilla bengalensis, temple of Chhabdi Barahi. 10r, Psilorhynchus pseudecheneis.

1993, Aug. 6 Litho. *Perf. 11½*
Granite Paper

517	A286	25p multicolored	.15	.15
518	A286	1r multicolored	.15	.15
519	A286	5r multicolored	.35	.35
520	A286	10r multicolored	.75	.75
a.		Souvenir sheet of 4, #517-520	1.20	1.20
		Set value	1.20	1.20

World AIDS Day — A287

1993, Dec. 1 Litho. *Perf. 13½x14½*

521 A287 1r multicolored .15 .15

Tanka Prasad Acharga — A288

1993, Dec. 2 *Perf. 13½*

522	A288	25p shown	.15	.15
523	A288	1r Sungdare Sherpa	.15	.15
524	A288	7r Siddhi Charan Shrestha	.50	.50
525	A288	15r Falgunand	1.10	1.10
		Set value	1.65	1.65

Holy Places — A289

Designs: 1.50r, Halesi Mahadev, Khotang. 5r, Devghat, Tanahun. 8r, Bagh Bhairab, Kirtipur.

Perf. 13½x14½

1993, Dec. 28 Litho.

526	A289	1.50r multicolored	.15	.15
527	A289	5r multicolored	.35	.35
528	A289	8r multicolored	.60	.60
		Nos. 526-528 (3)	1.10	1.10

Tourism A290

Designs: 5r, Tushahiti Sundari Chowk, Patan. 8r, White water rafting.

1993, Dec. 28

529	A290	5r multicolored	.35	.35
530	A290	8r multicolored	.60	.60

King Birendra, 48th Birthday — A291

1993, Dec. 28 *Perf. 14*

531 A291 10r multicolored .70 .70

Large Building, Courtyard A293

Pagoda, Courtyard A293a

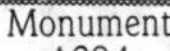
Monument A294

Arms A295

Fort — A296

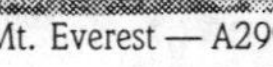
Mt. Everest — A299

Pagoda (Nyata Pola) A300

Map of Nepal A301

Design: 50p, Pagoda, vert.

Perf. 14½, 12, (#533A, 538, 540)
Photo., Litho. (#533A, 538, 540)

1994-96

533	A293	10p green	.15	.15
533A	A293a	10p claret & black	.15	.15
534	A294	20p violet brown	.15	.15
535	A295	25p carmine	.15	.15
536	A296	30p slate	.15	.15
537	A293	50p dark blue	.15	.15
538	A293a	50p black & claret	.15	.15
539	A299	1r multicolored	.15	.15
539A	A300	1r blue & claret	.15	.15

Perf. 14½x13½

540	A301	5r multicolored	.35	.35
		Set value	1.00	1.00

Issued: 20p, 25p, 30p, 5/17/94; #539, 7/6/94; 5r, 9/22/94; #533, 537, 1995; #533A, 538, 539A, 10/9/96. This is an expanding set. Numbers may change.

Pasang Lhamu Sherpa (1960-1993) A304

1994, Sept 2 Litho. *Perf. 14*

544 A304 10r multicolored .70 .70

Stop Smoking Campaign A305

1994, Sept. 26 *Perf. 13½x14*

545 A305 1r multicolored .15 .15

Methods of Transporting Mail — A306

1994, Oct. 9 *Perf. 13x13½*

546 A306 1.50r multicolored .15 .15

Traditional Weapons A307

Designs: No. 547a, Daggers, scabbards. b, Yataghans. c, Sabers, shield. d, Carved stone daggers.

1994, Oct. 9 *Perf. 14*

547 A307 5r Block of 4, #a.-d. 1.50 1.50

ILO, 75th Anniv. A308

1994, Oct. 9 *Perf. 13*

548 A308 15r blue & bister 1.10 1.10

World Food Day — A309

1994, Oct. 23 *Perf. 14*

549 A309 25r multicolored 1.75 1.75

A310

A311

Orchids: a, Dendrobium densiflorum. b, Coelogyne flaccida. c, Cymbidium devonianum. d, Coelogyne corymbosa.

1994, Nov. 7 *Perf. 14x13½*

550 A310 10r Block of 4, #a.-d. 3.00 3.00

1994, Dec. 5 *Perf. 12½x13*

551 A311 9r green & red .70 .70

Intl. Year of the Family.

A312

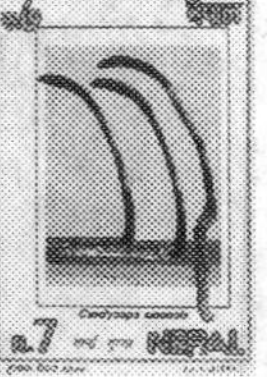
Mushrooms — A313

1994, Dec. 7

552 A312 11r blue & bister .80 .80

ICAO, 50th anniv.

1994, Dec. 20 *Perf. 14*

553	A313	7r Cordyceps sinensis	.60	.60
554	A313	7r Morchella conica	.60	.60
555	A313	7r Amanita caesarea	.60	.60
556	A313	7r Russula nepalensis	.60	.60
		Nos. 553-556 (4)	2.40	2.40

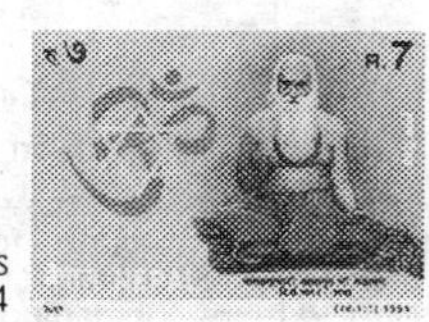

Famous Men — A314

Designs: 1r, Dharanidhar Koirala, poet. 2r, Narayan Gopal Guruwacharya, singer. 6r, Bahadur Shah, military leader, vert. 7r, Balaguru Shadananda, religious leader.

Perf. 13¹/₂x14, 14x13¹/₂

1994, Dec. 23

557 A314 1r multicolored .15 .15
558 A314 2r multicolored .15 .15
559 A314 6r multicolored .45 .45
560 A314 7r multicolored .50 .50
Nos. 557-560 (4) 1.25 1.25

King Birendra, 49th Birthday A315

1994, Dec. 28 ***Perf. 14***

561 A315 9r multicolored .70 .70

Tilicho Lake, Manang A316

Design: 11r, Taleju Temple, Katmandou, vert.

Perf. 13¹/₂x14, 14x13¹/₂

1994, Dec. 28

562 A316 9r multicolored .70 .70
563 A316 11r multicolored .80 .80

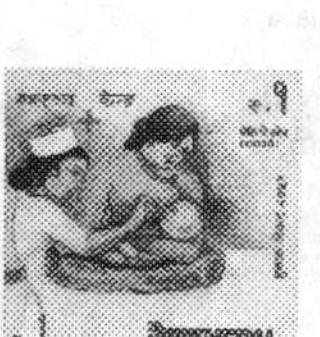

A317

A318

Care of Children: #564: a, Vaccination. b, Education. c, Playground activities. d, Stamp collecting.

1994, Dec. 30 ***Perf. 14***

564 A317 1r Block of 4, #a.-d. .32 .32

1995, June 23 Litho. ***Perf. 14x13¹/₂***

565 A318 2r red & black .15 .15

Fight against cancer.

A319

A320

Famous People: a, Bhim Nidhi Tiwari, writer. b, Yuddha Prasad Mishra, writer. c, Chandra Man Singh Maskey, artist. d, Parijat, writer.

1995, July 11 ***Perf. 14***

566 A319 3r Block of 4, #a.-d. .85 .85

1995, Sept. 1 Litho. ***Perf. 14x13¹/₂***

Famous Men: 15p, Bhakti Thapa, warrior. 1r, Madan Bhandari, politician. 4r, Prakash Raj Kaphley, human rights activist.

567 A320 15p multicolored .15 .15
568 A320 1r multicolored .15 .15
569 A320 4r multicolored .30 .30
Set value .40 .40

Animals A321

Designs: a, Bos gaurus. b, Felis lynx. c, Macaca assamensis. d, Hyaena hyaena.

1995, Sept. 1 Litho. ***Perf. 12***

570 A321 10p Block of 4, #a.-d. 2.75 2.75

Tourism A322

Designs: 1r, Bhimeshwor Temple, Dolakha, vert. 5r, Ugra Tara Temple, Dadeldhura. 7r, Mt. Nampa. 18r, Thanka art, Nrity Aswora, vert.

Perf. 14x13¹/₂, 13¹/₂x14

1995, Nov. 8 **Litho.**

574 A322 1r multicolored .15 .15
575 A322 5r multicolored .35 .35
576 A322 7r multicolored .50 .50

Size: 26x39mm

577 A322 18r multicolored 1.25 1.25
Nos. 574-577 (4) 2.25 2.25

FAO, 50th Anniv. — A323

1995, Oct. 16 Litho. ***Perf. 13¹/₂x14***

578 A323 7r multicolored .45 .45

UN, 50th Anniv. A324

1995, Oct. 22 Litho. ***Perf. 11¹/₂***

Granite Paper

579 A324 50r multicolored 3.25 3.25

Lumbini, Birth Place of Gautama Buddha — A325

1995, Dec. 23 Litho. ***Perf. 14***

580 A325 20r multicolored 1.40 1.40

King Birendra, 50th Birthday
A326 A327

1995, Dec. 28 ***Perf. 12***

Granite Paper (No. 581)

581 A326 1r multicolored .15 .15

Perf. 13x13¹/₂

582 A327 12r multicolored .85 .85

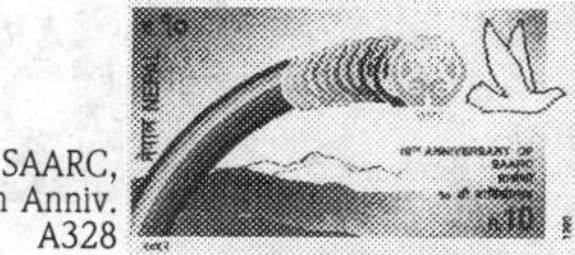

SAARC, 10th Anniv. A328

1995, Dec. 28 ***Perf. 13¹/₂***

583 A328 10r multicolored .70 .70

Karnali Bridge — A329

1996, May 13 Litho. ***Perf. 14***

584 A329 7r multicolored .50 .50

1996 Summer Olympic Games, Atlanta — A330

1996, Oct. 9 Photo. ***Perf. 12***

Granite Paper

585 A330 7r multicolored .45 .45

Kaji Kalu Pande — A331

Hem Raj Sharma, Grammarian — A332

Designs: No. 587, Pushpa Lal Shrestha. No. 589, Padma Prasad Bhattarai, scholar, philosopher. No. 590, Suvarna Shamsher Rana. No. 591, Bhawani Bhikshu, novelist, writer.

Perf. 13¹/₂x14, 14x13¹/₂

1996, Aug. 6 **Litho.**

586 A331 75p multicolored .15 .15
587 A331 1r multicolored .15 .15
588 A332 1r multicolored .15 .15
589 A332 3r multicolored .20 .20
590 A331 5r multicolored .30 .30
591 A332 5r multicolored .30 .30
Set Value 1.00 1.00

See Nos. 614-615.

Asoka Pillar, Lumbini — A333

1996, Dec. 1 Litho. ***Perf. 11¹/₂***

592 A333 12r multicolored .85 .85

Tourism A334

Designs: 1r, Arjun Dhara, Jhapa. 2r, Palace of Nuwakot. 8r, Traditional Gaijatra, Bhaktapur. 10r, Begnash Lake, Kaski.

1996, Nov. 20 Litho. ***Perf. 14***

593 A334 1r multicolored .15 .15
594 A334 2r multicolored .15 .15
595 A334 8r multicolored .50 .50
596 A334 10r multicolored .65 .65
Nos. 593-596 (4) 1.45 1.45

Butterflies and Birds — A335

Designs: a, Krishna pea-cock butterfly. b, Great Himalayan barbet. c, Sarus crane. d, Northern jungleqeen butterfly.

1996, Nov. 20 Litho. ***Perf. 14***

597 A335 5r Block of 4, #a.-d. 1.30 1.30

Annapurna Mountain Range — A336

Designs: a, Annapurna South, Annapurna I. b, Machhapuchhre, Annapurna III. c, Annapurna IV, Annapurna II.

1996, Dec. 28 Litho. ***Perf. 14***

601 A336 18r Strip of 3, #a.-c. 3.50 3.50

King Birendra, 51st Birthday — A337

1996, Dec. 28 Photo. ***Perf. 12***

Granite Paper

602 A337 10r multicolored .65 .65

Accession of King Birendra to Throne, 25th Anniv. A338

1997, Feb. 1 Litho. ***Perf. 14***

603 A338 2r multicolored .20 .20

Nepal Postal Service — A339

1997, Apr. 12 **Litho.** ***Perf. 14***

604 A339 2r brown & red .20 .20

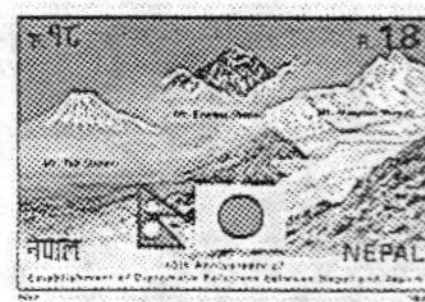

Nepalese-Japanese Diplomatic Relations, 40th Anniv. — A340

1997, Apr. 6 **Photo.** ***Perf. 12***

605 A340 18r multicolored 1.15 1.15

Visit Nepal '98 — A341

2r, Emblem. 10r, Upper Mustang. 18r, Rafting Sunkoshi. 20r, Changunarayan (Bhaktapur), vert.

1997, July 6 **Litho.** ***Perf. 14***

606 A341 2r multicolored .15 .15
607 A341 10r multicolored .65 .65
608 A341 18r multicolored 1.15 1.15
609 A341 20r multicolored 1.30 1.30
Nos. 606-608 (3) 1.95 1.95

A342 A343

Traditional costumes.

1997, Sept. 30 **Litho.** ***Perf. 14***

610 A342 5r Rana Tharu .30 .30
611 A342 5r Gurung .30 .30
612 A342 5r Chepang .30 .30
Nos. 610-612 (3) .90 .90

1997, Sept. 30 ***Perf. 11½***

613 A343 20r multicolored 1.25 1.25

Diplomatic relations between Nepal and US, 50th anniv.

Personality Type of 1996

Designs: No. 614, Riddhi Bahadur Malla, writer. No. 615, Dr. K.I. Singh, political leader.

1997, Nov. 6 **Litho.** ***Perf. 11½***

614 A332 2r multicolored .15 .15
615 A332 2r multicolored .15 .15

Traditional Technology
A344 A345

#616, Janto (grinder), horiz. #617, Dhiki, horiz. #618, Okhal. #619, Kol (oil mill).

1997, Sept. **Litho.** ***Perf. 14***

616 A344 5r multicolored .30 .30
617 A344 5r multicolored .30 .30
618 A344 5r multicolored .30 .30
619 A345 5r multicolored .30 .30
Nos. 616-619 (4) 1.20 1.20

Flowers A346

40p, Jasminum gracile. 1r, Callistephus chinensis. 2r, Manglietia insignis. 15r, Luculia gratissima.

1997, Oct.

620 A346 40p multicolored .15 .15
621 A346 1r multicolored .15 .15
622 A346 2r multicolored .15 .15
623 A346 15r multicolored .85 .85
Set value 1.00 1.00

King Birendra, 52nd Birthday — A347

1997, Dec. 29 **Photo.** ***Perf. 11½***

624 A347 10r multicolored .60 .60

AIR POST STAMPS

Catalogue values for unused stamps in this section are for Never Hinged items.

Bird over Kathmandu — AP1

Rough Perf 11½

1958, Oct. 16 **Typo.** **Unwmk.**

Without Gum

C1 AP1 10p dark blue .15 .15

Plane over Kathmandu AP2

1967, Oct. 24 **Photo.** ***Perf. 13½x13***

C2 AP2 1.80r multicolored .75 .60

International Tourist Year.

God Akash Bhairab and Nepal Airlines Emblem AP3

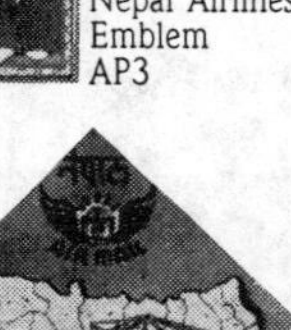

Map of Nepal with Airlines Network AP4

Design: 2.50r, Plane over Himalayas.

Perf. 14½x14, 13 (65p)

1968, July 1 **Photo.**

C3 AP3 15p blue & bis brn .15 .15
C4 AP4 65p violet blue .18 .15
C5 AP3 2.50r dp blue & scar .60 .45
Set value .82 .65

10th anniv. of the Royal Nepal Airlines Corp.

Flyer and Jet — AP5

1978, Dec. 12 **Photo.** ***Perf. 13***

C6 AP5 2.30r blue & ocher .42 .42

75th anniversary of 1st powered flight.

Pheasant Type of 1979

1979, Nov. 22 **Photo.** ***Perf. 14½x14***

C7 A174 3.50r Impeyan pheasant, horiz. 2.00 1.00

OFFICIAL STAMPS

Catalogue values for unused stamps in this section are for Never Hinged items.

Soldiers and Arms of Nepal — O1

Perf. 13½

1959, Nov. 1 **Litho.** **Unwmk.**

Size: 29x17½mm

O1 O1 2p reddish brown .15 .15
O2 O1 4p yel green .15 .15
O3 O1 6p salmon pink .15 .15
O4 O1 8p brt violet .15 .15
O5 O1 12p red orange .18 .15

Size: 37½x21½mm

O6 O1 16p red brown .24 .15
O7 O1 24p carmine .30 .15
O8 O1 32p rose car .45 .15
O9 O1 50p ultramarine .60 .15
O10 O1 1r rose red 1.25 .18
O11 O1 2r orange 2.75 .30
Nos. O1-O11 (11) 6.37
Set value 1.00

Nos. 144-146 and 124 Overprinted in Black **काज सरकारी**

1960-62 **Photo.** ***Perf. 14½x14***

Overprint 12½mm Long

O12 A35 1p carmine rose ('62) .15 .15
O13 A35 2p bright blue ('62) .15 .15
O14 A35 5p golden brown ('62) .15 .15
Set value .27 .27

Perf. 14

Overprint 14½mm Long

O15 A26 1r red lilac .18

The overprint, "Kaj Sarkari" in Devanagari characters means "Service." Five other denominations, 10p, 40p, 75p, 2r and 5r, were similarly overprinted but not issued. A few exist on 1960 first day covers.

In 1983 substantial quantities of the set of nine values were sold as remainders by the Post Office at face value (under $1 for the set).

NETHERLANDS

'ne-thər-lən(d)z

(Holland)

LOCATION — Northwestern Europe, bordering on the North Sea
GOVT. — Kingdom
AREA — 13,203 sq. mi.
POP. — 14,394,589 (1984)
CAPITAL — Amsterdam

100 Cents = 1 Gulden
(Guilder or Florin)

Catalogue values for unused stamps in this country are for Never Hinged items, beginning with Scott 216 in the regular postage section, Scott B123 in the semi-postal section, Scott C13 in the airpost section, Scott J80 in the postage due section, and Scott O44 in the official section.

Values for unused stamps are for examples with original gum as defined in the catalogue introduction. Very fine examples of Nos. 4-12 will have perforations touching the frameline on one or more sides due to the narrow spacing of the stamps on the plates. Stamps with perfs clear on all four sides are very scarce and command higher prices.

Watermarks

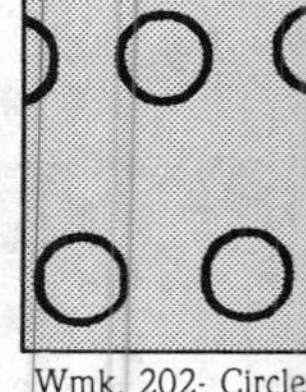

Wmk. 158 Wmk. 202- Circles

King William III
A1 A2

Wmk. 158

1852, Jan. 1 **Engr.** ***Imperf.***

1 A1 5c blue 400.00 32.50
a. 5c light blue 475.00 32.50
b. 5c steel blue 1,200. 95.00
c. 5c dark blue 475.00 37.50
2 A1 10c lake 475.00 24.00
3 A1 15c orange 950.00 110.00

In 1895 the 10c was privately reprinted in several colors on unwatermarked paper by Joh. A. Moesman, whose name appears on the back.

1864 **Unwmk.** ***Perf. 12½x12***

4 A2 5c blue 325.00 17.50
5 A2 10c lake 400.00 7.00
6 A2 15c orange 1,100. 90.00
a. 15c yellow 1,100. 85.00

The paper varies considerably in thickness. It is sometimes slightly bluish, also vertically ribbed.

William III — A3

Coat of Arms — A4

Perf. 12½x12, 13, 13½, 14 and Compound

1867

7 A3 5c ultra 75.00 1.40
8 A3 10c lake 140.00 2.25
9 A3 15c orange brn 625.00 32.50
10 A3 20c dk green 550.00 24.00
11 A3 25c dk violet 2,100. 110.00
12 A3 50c gold 2,275. 150.00

The paper of Nos. 7-22 sometimes has an accidental bluish tinge of varying strength. During its manufacture a chemical whitener (bluing agent) was added in varying quantities. No particular printing was made on bluish paper.

Two varieties of numerals in each value, differing chiefly in the thickness.

Oxidized copies of the 50c are worth much less. Imperforate varieties of Nos. 7-12 are proofs.

1869 *Perf. 10½x10*
7c A3 5c ultra 150.00 8.00
8c A3 10c lake 225.00 3.50
9c A3 15c orange brown 2,500. 700.00
10c A3 20c dark green 1,200. 110.00

1869-71 **Typo.** *Perf. 13½, 14*
17 A4 ½c red brown ('71) 25.00 2.25
c. Perf. 14 2,275. 875.00
18 A4 1c black 225.00 75.00
19 A4 1c green 10.50 1.25
c. Perf. 14 27.50 5.75
20 A4 1½c rose 135.00 80.00
b. Perf. 14 145.00 80.00
21 A4 2c buff 52.50 10.50
c. Perf. 14 55.00 10.50
22 A4 2½c violet ('70) 500.00 52.50
c. Perf. 14 775.00 375.00

Imperforate varieties are proofs.

A5

A6

Perf. 12½, 13, 13½, 13x14, 14, 12½x12 and 11½x12

1872-88
23 A5 5c ultra 10.00 .30
a. 5c blue 10.00 .40
24 A5 7½c red brn ('88) 37.50 20.00
25 A5 10c rose 57.50 1.00
26 A5 12½c gray ('75) 67.50 1.75
27 A5 15c brn org 375.00 5.25
28 A5 20c green 425.00 5.00
29 A5 22½c dk grn ('88) 75.00 45.00
30 A5 25c dull vio 550.00 3.50
31 A5 50c bister 675.00 9.50
32 A5 1g gray vio ('88) 525.00 30.00
33 A6 2g50c rose & ultra 950.00 100.00

Imperforate varieties are proofs.

Numeral of Value — A7

HALF CENT:
Type I - Fraction bar 8 to 8½mm long.
Type II - Fraction bar 9mm long and thinner.

Perf. 12½, 13½, 14, 12½x12, 11½x12

1876-94
34 A7 ½c rose, II 12.50 .30
a. ½c rose, I 14.00 .60
c. Laid paper 47.50
d. Perf. 14, I 1,250. 625.00
35 A7 1c emer grn ('94) 2.25 .15
b. As "c," laid paper 62.50 4.75
c. 1c green 9.50 .20
36 A7 2c olive yel ('94) 35.00 3.50
a. 2c yellow 70.00 2.75
37 A7 2½c violet ('94) 15.00 .30
b. 2½c dark violet ('94) 19.00 .50
c. 2½c lilac 110.00 .90
d. Laid paper
Nos. 34-37 (4) 64.75 4.25

Imperforate varieties are proofs.

Princess Wilhelmina
A8 A9

1891-94 *Perf. 12½*
40 A8 3c orange ('94) 10.00 1.25
a. 3c orange yellow ('92) 12.50 1.25
41 A8 5c lt ultra ('94) 3.50 .30
a. 5c dull blue 4.50 .30
42 A8 7½c brown ('94) 21.00 4.50
a. 7½c red brown 32.50 4.50
43 A8 10c brt rose ('94) 25.00 .80
a. 10c brick red 60.00 2.75
44 A8 12½c bluish gray ('94) 25.00 1.00
a. 12½c gray 50.00 1.25
45 A8 15c yel brn ('94) 62.50 4.75
a. 15c orange brown 92.50 4.75
46 A8 20c green ('94) 67.50 2.50
a. 20c yellow green 90.00 2.75
47 A8 22½c dk grn ('94) 35.00 12.50
a. 22½c deep blue green 60.00 12.50
48 A8 25c dl vio ('94) 115.00 4.25
a. 25c dark violet 125.00 4.25
49 A8 50c yel brn ('94) 600.00 17.00
a. 50c bister 750.00 30.00
50 A8 1g gray vio 675.00 67.50

The paper used in 1891-93 was white, rough and somewhat opaque. In 1894, a thinner, smooth and sometimes transparent paper was introduced.
The 5c orange was privately produced.

1893-96 *Perf. 11½x11*
51 A9 50c emer & yel brn ('96) 80.00 8.50
a. Perf. 11 3,000. 225.00
52 A9 1g brn & ol grn ('96) 225.00 25.00
a. Perf. 11 275.00 70.00
53 A9 2g 50c brt rose & ultra 475.00 135.00
a. 2g 50c lil rose & ultra, perf. 11 575.00 145.00
b. Perf. 11½ 575.00 175.00

Perf. 11
54 A9 5g brnz grn & red brn ('96) 750.00 375.00

A10

Queen Wilhelmina — A11

Perf. 12½, 11½, 11½x11, 11x11½

1898-1924
55 A10 ½c violet .50 .20
56 A10 1c red 1.00 .15
b. Imperf., pair 2,000.
57 A10 1½c ultra ('08) 5.00 4.75
58 A10 1½c dp blue ('13) 3.25 .30
59 A10 2c yellow brn 4.25 .20
60 A10 2½c deep green 3.75 .20
b. Imperf., pair 6,000.
61 A11 3c orange 15.00 3.50
62 A11 3c pale ol grn ('01) 1.25 .20
63 A11 4c claret ('21) 1.75 1.00
64 A11 4½c violet ('19) 4.25 4.25
65 A11 5c car rose 1.75 .15
66 A11 7½c brown .70 .20
a. Tête bêche pair ('24) 90.00 80.00
67 A11 10c gray lilac 7.00 .20
68 A11 12½c blue 3.75 .30
69 A11 15c yellow brn 90.00 3.50
70 A11 15c bl & car ('08) 7.00 .20
71 A11 17½c vio ('06) 55.00 13.00
73 A11 17½c ultra & brn ('10) 17.00 .75
74 A11 20c yellow green 110.00 .75
75 A11 20c ol grn & gray ('08) 11.50 .50
76 A11 22½c brn & ol grn 10.00 .50
77 A11 25c carmine & blue 9.00 .30
78 A11 30c lil & vio brn ('17) 26.50 .30
79 A11 40c grn & org ('20) 37.50 .90
80 A11 50c brnz grn & red brn 90.00 1.00
81 A11 50c gray & vio ('14) 77.50 .90
a. Perf. 11½x11 77.50 13.00
82 A11 60c ol grn & grn ('20) 37.50 1.25
a. Perf. 11½ 225.00 35.00
Nos. 55-82 (27) 631.70 39.45

See Nos. 107-112. For overprints and surcharges see Nos. 102-102, 106, 117-123, 135-136, O1-O8.

A12

Type I

Type II

Type I - The figure "1" is 3¾mm high and 2¾mm wide.
Type II - The figure "1" is 3½mm high and 2½mm wide, it is also thinner than in type I.

Perf. 11, 11x11½, 11½, 11½x11

1898-1905 **Engr.**
83 A12 1g dk grn, II ('99) 55.00 .40
a. 1g dark green, I ('98) 180.00 75.00
84 A12 2½g brn lil ('99) 100.00 3.50
85 A12 5g claret ('99) 250.00 5.50
86 A12 10g orange ('05) 825.00 700.00

For surcharge see No. 104.

Admiral M. A. de Ruyter and Fleet — A13

King William I — A14

1907, Mar. 23 **Typo.** *Perf. 12x12½*
87 A13 ½c blue 1.65 .75
88 A13 1c claret 3.25 2.50
89 A13 2½c vermilion 5.50 2.00
Nos. 87-89 (3) 10.40 5.25

De Ruyter (1607-1676), naval hero.
For surcharges see Nos. J29-J41.

Perf. 11½, 11½x11

1913, Nov. 29 **Engr.**

Designs: 2½c, 12½c, 1g, King William I. 3c, 20c, 2½g, King William II. 5c, 25c, 5g, King William III. 10c, 50c, 10g, Queen Wilhelmina.

90 A14 2½c green, *grn* .65 .60
91 A14 3c buff, *straw* .90 .75
92 A14 5c rose red, *sal* .80 .40
93 A14 10c gray blk 3.00 1.50
94 A14 12½c dp blue, *bl* 2.25 1.50
95 A14 20c orange brn 13.00 5.75
96 A14 25c pale blue 13.00 5.75
97 A14 50c yellow grn 25.00 20.00
98 A14 1g claret 42.50 12.00
a. Perf. 11½ 65.00 16.00
99 A14 2½g dull violet 110.00 35.00
100 A14 5g yel, *straw* 250.00 37.50
101 A14 10g red, *straw* 625.00 600.00
Nos. 90-101 (12) 1,086. 720.75
Set, never hinged 2,750.

Centenary of Dutch independence.
For surcharge see No. 105.

No. 78 Surcharged in Red or Black

Veertig Cent — a
Zestig Cent — b

1919, Dec. 1 *Perf. 12½*
102 A11 (a) 40c on 30c (R) 25.00 3.50
103 A11 (b) 60c on 30c (Bk) 22.50 3.50
Set, never hinged 150.00

Nos. 86 and 101 Surcharged in Black 2.50

1920, Aug. 17 *Perf. 11, 11½*
104 A12 2.50g on 10g 140.00 95.00
Never hinged 300.00
105 A14 2.50g on 10g 140.00 77.50
Never hinged 325.00

No. 64 Surcharged in Red —4C—

1921, Mar. 1 **Typo.** *Perf. 12½*
106 A11 4c on 4½c vio 4.50 1.65
Never hinged 9.00

A17

1921-22 **Typo.** *Perf. 12½*
107 A17 5c green ('22) 9.00 .15
108 A17 12½c vermilion ('22) 20.00 1.75
109 A17 20c blue 30.00 .20
Nos. 107-109 (3) 59.00 2.10
Set, never hinged 225.00

Queen Type of 1898-99, 10c Redrawn

1922 *Perf. 12½*
110 A11 10c gray 32.50 .15
Never hinged 85.00

Imperf
111 A11 5c car rose 5.75 5.75
Never hinged 15.00
112 A11 10c gray 6.75 6.75
Never hinged 16.00
Nos. 110-112 (3) 45.00 12.65

In redrawn 10c the horizontal lines behind the Queen's head are wider apart.

Orange Tree and Lion of Brabant A18

Post Horn and Lion A19

Numeral of Value — A20

1923, Mar. 9 *Perf. 12½*
113 A18 1c dark violet .60 .65
114 A18 2c orange 6.75 .15
115 A19 2½c bluish green 2.00 .50
116 A20 4c deep blue 1.40 .65
Nos. 113-116 (4) 10.75 1.95
Set, never hinged 20.00

Nos. 56, 58, 62, 65, 68, 73, 76 Surcharged in Various Colors

c

d

1923, July *Perf. 12½, 11½x11, 11½*
117 A10(c) 2c on 1c (Bl) .50 .15
118 A10(c) 2c on 1½c (Bk) .50 .15
119 A11(d) 10c on 3c (Br) 4.75 .15
120 A11(d) 10c on 5c (Bk) 9.00 .60

THE NETHERLANDS
NETHERLANDS INDIES
CURAÇAO - SURINAM
I HAVE ASSISTED MANY COLLECTORS,
FROM BEGINNER TO SPECIALIST.
LET ME KNOW HOW I MAY HELP YOU.
BUYING - SELLING - APPRAISALS
R. JANNING - Philately of The Netherlands
FAX OR PHONE 760-321-0843
P. O. BOX 1284, Cathedral City, CA 92235-1284
Website: http://members.aol.com/nethstamp/stamps.html
E-mail: janningnet@aol.com

121 A11(d) 10c on 12½c (R) 8.00 1.00
122 A11(d) 10c on 17½c (R) 4.25 4.25
a. Perf. 11½ 1,750. 900.00
b. Perf. 11½x11 3.25 4.00
123 A11(d) 10c on 22½c (R) 4.25 4.25
a. Perf. 11½ 3.25 4.00
b. Perf. 11½x11 3.25 4.00
Nos. 117-123 (7) 31.25 10.55
Set, never hinged 70.00

Queen Wilhelmina
A21 A22

Perf. 11, 11½, 12, 12½ and Compound

1923, Oct. **Engr.**
124 A22 2c myrtle green .15 .15
a. Vert. pair, imperf. between 2,250.
125 A21 5c green .15 .15
a. Vert. pair, imperf. between 2,000.
126 A22 7½ carmine .20 .15
127 A22 10c vermilion .45 .15
a. Vert. pair, imperf. between 600.00 650.00
128 A22 20c ultra 3.50 .65
129 A22 25c yellow 3.75 1.00
130 A22 35c orange 5.50 2.25
131 A22 50c black 15.00 .50
132 A21 1g red 30.00 6.50
133 A21 2½g black 200.00 175.00
134 A21 5g dark blue 200.00 140.00
Nos. 124-134 (11) 458.70 326.50
Set, never hinged 1,100.

25th anniv. of the assumption as monarch of the Netherlands by Queen Wilhelmina at the age of 18.

Nos. 119, 73 Overprinted in Red "DIENSTZEGEL PORTEN AANTEEKENRECHT; No. 73 with New Value in Blue

1923 **Typo.** ***Perf. 12½***
135 A11 10c on 3c 1.25 1.10
Never hinged 9.00
136 A11 1g on 17½c 67.50 14.00
Never hinged 190.00
a. Perf. 11½ 95.00 37.50
b. Perf. 11½x11 80.00 25.00

Stamps with red surcharge were prepared for use as Officials but were not issued.

Queen Wilhelmina — A23

1924, Sept. 6 **Photo.** ***Perf. 12½***
137 A23 10c slate green 32.50 32.50
Never hinged 57.50
138 A23 15c gray black 40.00 40.00
Never hinged 65.00
139 A23 35c brown orange 32.50 32.50
Never hinged 57.50
Nos. 137-139 (3) 105.00 105.00

These stamps were available solely to visitors to the International Philatelic Exhibition at The Hague and were not obtainable at regular post offices.

See Nos. 147-160, 172-193. For overprints and surcharge see Nos. 194, O11, O13-O15.

Ship in Distress
A23a

Lifeboat
A23b

1924, Sept. 15 **Litho.** ***Perf. 11½***
140 A23a 2c black brn 2.75 1.75
Never hinged 6.00
141 A23b 10c orange brn 6.00 1.50
Never hinged 20.00

Centenary of Royal Dutch Lifeboat Society.

Type A23 and

Gull — A24

1924-26 ***Perf. 12½***
142 A24 1c deep red .50 .70
143 A24 2c red orange 2.25 .15
144 A24 2½c deep green 2.50 .85
145 A24 3c yellow grn ('25) 12.50 .90
146 A24 4c dp ultra 3.00 .75

Photo.

147 A23 5c dull green 3.50 .70
148 A23 6c orange brn ('25) .65 .50
149 A23 7½c orange ('25) .35 .15
150 A23 9c org red & blk ('26) 1.50 1.25
151 A23 10c red 1.25 .35
152 A23 12½c deep rose 1.75 .35
153 A23 15c ultra 6.00 .40
154 A23 20c dp blue ('25) 10.00 .60
155 A23 25c olive bis ('25) 22.50 .85
156 A23 30c violet 13.00 .70
157 A23 35c olive brn ('25) 30.00 6.50
158 A23 40c dp brown 30.00 .70
159 A23 50c blue green ('25) 60.00 .60
160 A23 60c dk violet ('25) 27.50 .85
Nos. 142-160 (19) 228.75 17.85
Set, never hinged 1,000.

See Nos. 164-171, 243A-243Q. For overprints and surcharges see Nos. 226-243, O9-O10.

Syncopated Perforations

Type A

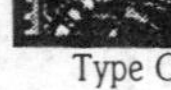

Type C

Type B

These special "syncopated" or "interrupted" perforations, devised for coil stamps, are found on Nos. 142-156, 158-160, 164-166, 168-185, 187-193 and certain semipostals of 1925-33, between Nos. B9 and B69. There are four types:

A. On two shorter sides, groups of four holes separated by blank spaces equal in width to two or three holes.

B. As "A," but on all four sides.

C. On two shorter sides, end holes are omitted.

D. Four-hole sequence on horiz. sides, three-hole on vert. sides.

1925-26 ***Syncopated, Type A (2 Sides)***
142a A24 1c deep red .75 .55
143a A24 2c red orange 3.00 1.90
144a A24 2½c deep green 3.00 .80
145a A24 3c yellow green 20.00 22.50
146a A24 4c deep ultra 2.50 1.90
147a A23 5c dull green 6.00 2.50
148a A23 6c orange brown 125.00 100.00
149a A23 7½c orange 1.00 .70
150a A23 9c org red & blk 2.00 1.25
151a A23 10c red 12.00 3.00
152a A23 12½c deep rose 2.00 1.10
153a A23 15c ultra 75.00 5.50
154a A23 20c deep blue 11.00 4.00
155a A23 25c olive bister 47.50 50.00
156a A23 30c violet 16.00 10.00
158a A23 40c deep brown 50.00 40.00
159a A23 50c blue green 62.50 20.00
160a A23 60c dark violet 30.00 11.00
Nos. 142a-160a (18) 469.25 276.70
Set, never hinged 1,000.

A25

1925-27 **Engr.** ***Perf. 11½, 12½***
161 A25 1g ultra 8.00 .45
Never hinged 25.00
162 A25 2½g car ('27) 80.00 4.50
Never hinged 200.00
163 A25 5g gray blk 150.00 2.75
Never hinged 375.00
Nos. 161-163 (3) 238.00 7.70

Types of 1924-26 Issue

Perf. 12½, 13½x12½, 12½x13½

1926-39 **Wmk. 202** **Litho.**
164 A24 ½c gray ('28) 1.00 1.10
165 A24 1c dp red ('27) .15 .15
166 A24 1½c red vio ('28) 1.25 .15
c. "CEN" for "CENT" 165.00 300.00
c. Never hinged 300.00
167 A24 1½c gray ('35) .15 .15
a. 1½c dark gray .15 .15
168 A24 2c dp org .15 .15
a. 2c red orange .15 .15
169 A24 2½c green ('27) 3.00 .15
170 A24 3c yellow grn ('27) .15 .15
171 A24 4c dp ultra ('27) .15 .15

Photo.

172 A23 5c dp green .15 .15
173 A23 6c org brn ('27) .15 .15
174 A23 7½c dk vio ('27) 4.00 .15
175 A23 7½c red ('28) .15 .15
176 A23 9c org red & blk ('28) 11.00 14.00
b. Value omitted 13,000.
177 A23 10c red 1.40 .15
178 A23 10c dl vio ('29) 2.75 .15
179 A23 12½c dp rose ('27) 42.50 5.00
180 A23 12½c ultra ('28) .30 .15
181 A23 15c ultra 8.00 .25
182 A23 15c orange ('29) 1.00 .15
183 A23 20c dp blue ('28) 8.00 .15
184 A23 21c ol brn ('31) 27.50 1.00
185 A23 22½c ol brn ('27) 8.00 3.50
186 A23 22½c dp org ('39) 17.00 22.50
187 A23 25c ol bis ('27) 5.00 .15
188 A23 27½c gray ('28) 5.00 1.00
189 A23 30c violet 5.50 .15
190 A23 35c olive brn 70.00 16.00
191 A23 40c dp brown 10.00 .25
192 A23 50c blue grn 5.50 .25
193 A23 60c black ('29) 30.00 1.00
Nos. 164-193 (30) 268.90 68.55
Set, never hinged 1,000.

Syncopated, Type A (2 Sides), 12½

1926-27
168b A24 2c deep orange .40 .40
170a A24 3c yellow green .60 .60
171a A24 4c deep ultra .60 .60
172a A23 5c deep green .70 .60
173a A23 6c orange brown .40 .45
174a A23 7½c dark violet 4.50 2.00
177a A23 10c red 1.00 .85
181a A23 15c ultra 7.00 3.00
185a A23 22½c olive brown 7.00 2.50
187a A23 25c olive bister 20.00 18.00
189a A23 30c violet 19.00 12.00
190a A23 35c olive brown 77.50 22.50
191a A23 40c deep brown 50.00 40.00
Nos. 168b-191a (13) 188.70 103.50
Set, never hinged 360.00

1928 ***Syncopated, Type B (4 Sides)***
164a A24 ½c gray .80 .65
165a A24 1c deep red .30 .30
166a A24 1½c red violet .80 .25
168c A24 2c deep orange 1.00 .60
169a A24 2½c green 2.75 .20
170b A24 3c yellow green .75 .75
171b A24 4c deep ultra .75 .65
172b A23 5c deep green 1.00 .75
173b A23 6c orange brown .75 .50
174b A23 7½c dark violet 4.25 2.00
175a A23 7½c red .25 .25
176a A23 9c org red & blk 10.00 12.50
178a A23 10c dull violet 5.25 5.00
179a A23 12½c deep rose 80.00 80.00
180a A23 12½c ultra 1.40 .40
181b A23 15c ultra 9.00 2.00
182a A23 15c orange .75 .30
183a A23 20c deep blue 7.00 3.00
187b A23 25c olive bister 17.00 10.00
188a A23 27½c gray 4.50 2.00
189b A23 30c violet 15.00 8.00
191b A23 40c deep brown 35.00 22.50
192a A23 50c blue green 55.00 45.00
193a A23 60c black 45.00 22.50
Nos. 164a-193a (24) 298.30 220.10
Set, never hinged 600.00

Syncopated, Type C (2 Sides, Corners Only)

1930
164b A24 ½c gray 1.00 .70
165b A24 1c deep red 1.00 .40
166b A24 1½c red violet .90 .25
168d A24 2c deep orange .80 .70
169b A24 2½c green 2.75 .25
170c A24 3c yellow green 1.10 .50
171c A24 4c deep ultra .50 .25
172c A23 5c deep green .70 .70
173c A23 6c orange brown .70 .70
178b A23 10c dull violet 8.00 7.00
183b A23 20c deep blue 7.75 3.75
184a A23 21c olive brown 25.00 9.00
189c A23 30c violet 12.00 7.00
192b A23 50c blue green 45.00 45.00
Nos. 164b-192b (14) 107.20 76.20
Set, never hinged 225.00

1927

Syncopated, Type D (3 Holes Vert., 4 Holes Horiz.)

174c A23 7½c dark violet 2,750. 2,100.
Never hinged 3,750.

No. 185 Surcharged in Red

21

1929, Nov. 11 ***Perf. 12½***
194 A23 21c on 22½c ol brn 20.00 1.75
Never hinged 60.00

Queen Wilhelmina — A26

1931, Oct. **Photo.** ***Perf. 12½***
195 A26 70c dk bl & red 22.50 .60
Never hinged 110.00
a. Perf. 14½x13½ ('39) 26.00 10.00
Never hinged 125.00

See No. 201.

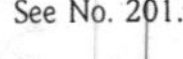

Arms of the House of Orange — A27

William I, Portrait by Goltzius — A28

Designs: 6c, Portrait of William I by Van Key. 12½c, Portrait attributed to Moro.

1933, Apr. 1 **Unwmk.** **Engr.**
196 A27 1½c black .50 .15
197 A28 5c dark green 1.40 .30
198 A28 6c dull violet 3.50 .15
199 A28 12½c deep blue 15.00 3.25
Nos. 196-199 (4) 20.40 3.85
Set, never hinged 70.00

400th anniv. of the birth of William I, Count of Nassau and Prince of Orange, frequently referred to as William the Silent.

Star, Dove and Sword — A31

1933, May 18 **Photo.** **Wmk. 202**
200 A31 12½c dp ultra 8.00 .45
Never hinged 35.00

For overprint see No. O12.

Queen Wilhelmina Design of 1931

Queen Wilhelmina and ships.

Perf. 14½x13½

1933, July 26 **Wmk. 202**
201 A26 80c Prus bl & red 90.00 3.50
Never hinged 375.00

Willemstad Harbor — A33

Van Walbeeck's Ship — A34

Perf. 14x12½

1934, July 2 **Engr.** **Unwmk.**
202 A33 6c violet blk 3.00 .15
203 A34 12½c dull blue 17.00 3.25
Set, never hinged 90.00

Tercentenary of Curacao.

Minerva — A35

Design: 12½c, Gisbertus Voetius.

Perf. 12½

1936, May 15 Photo. Wmk. 202

No.	Type	Value	Color	Unused	Used
204	A35	6c	brown lake	1.90	.25
205	A35	12½c	indigo	3.75	3.25
			Set, never hinged	20.00	

300th anniversary of the founding of the University at Utrecht.

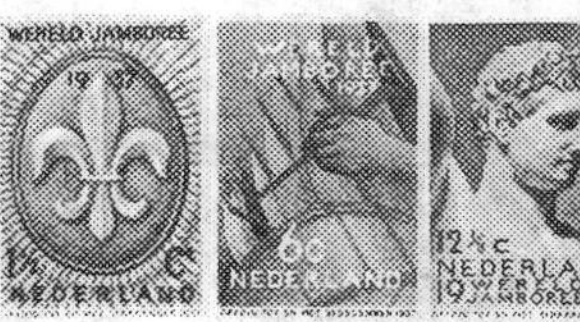

A37 A38 A39

1937, Apr. 1 *Perf. 14½x13½*

No.	Type	Value	Color	Unused	Used
206	A37	1½c	Boy Scout Emblem	.20	.15
207	A38	6c	"Assembly"	1.00	.15
208	A39	12½c	Mercury	2.75	1.00
			Nos. 206-208 (3)	3.95	1.30
			Set, never hinged	12.00	

Fifth Boy Scout World Jamboree, Vogelenzang, Netherlands, July 31-Aug. 13, 1937.

Wilhelmina A40

St. Willibrord A41

1938, Aug. 27 *Perf. 12½x12*

No.	Type	Value	Color	Unused	Used
209	A40	1½c	black	.15	.15
210	A40	5c	red orange	.20	.15
211	A40	12½c	royal blue	3.00	1.25
			Nos. 209-211 (3)	3.35	1.55
			Set, never hinged	13.00	

Reign of Queen Wilhelmina, 40th anniv.

Perf. 12½x14

1939, June 15 Engr. Unwmk.

Design: 12½c, St. Willibrord as older man.

No.	Type	Value	Color	Unused	Used
212	A41	5c	dk slate grn	.75	.15
213	A41	12½c	slate blue	4.00	2.50
			Set, never hinged	16.00	

12th centenary of the death of St. Willibrord.

Woodburning Engine — A43

Queen Wilhelmina — A45

Design: 12½c, Streamlined electric car.

Perf. 14½x13½

1939, Sept. 1 Photo. Wmk. 202

No.	Type	Value	Color	Unused	Used
214	A43	5c	dk slate grn	1.00	.15
215	A43	12½c	dark blue	8.00	3.50
			Set, never hinged	22.00	

Centenary of Dutch Railroads.

Catalogue values for unused stamps in this section, from this point to the end of the section, are for Never Hinged items.

1940-47 *Perf. 13½x12½*

No.	Type	Value	Color	Unused	Used
216	A45	5c	dk green	.15	.15
216B	A45	6c	hn brn ('47)	.55	.25
217	A45	7½c	brt red	.15	.15
218	A45	10c	brt red vio	.15	.15
219	A45	12½c	sapphire	.15	.15
220	A45	15c	light blue	.15	.15
220B	A45	17½c	slate bl ('46)	1.25	.80
221	A45	20c	purple	.35	.15
222	A45	22½c	olive grn	1.25	.60
223	A45	25c	rose brn	.35	.15
224	A45	30c	bister	.80	.40
225	A45	40c	brt green	1.25	.60
225A	A45	50c	orange ('46)	9.50	.75
225B	A45	60c	pur brn ('46)	9.00	2.75
			Nos. 216-225B (14)	25.05	7.20

Imperf. copies of Nos. 216, 218-220 were released through philatelic channels during the German occupation, but were never issued at any post office. Value, set, $1.

For overprints see Nos. O16-O24.

Type of 1924-26 Surcharged in Black or Blue

Perf. 12½x13½

1940, Oct. Photo. Wmk. 202

No.	Type	Value	Color	Unused	Used
226	A24	2½c	on 3c ver	2.00	.15
227	A24	5c	on 3c lt grn	.15	.15
228	A24	7½c	on 3c ver	.15	.15
a.			Pair, #226, 228	4.00	1.50
229	A24	10c	on 3c lt grn	.15	.15
230	A24	12½c	on 3c lt bl (Bl)	.30	.20
231	A24	17½c	on 3c lt grn	.60	.65
232	A24	20c	on 3c lt grn	.40	.15
233	A24	22½c	on 3c lt grn	.80	.85
234	A24	25c	on 3c lt grn	.50	.20
235	A24	30c	on 3c lt grn	.65	.30
236	A24	40c	on 3c lt grn	.80	.60
237	A24	50c	on 3c lt grn	.70	.40
238	A24	60c	on 3c lt grn	1.65	.85
239	A24	70c	on 3c lt grn	3.75	1.75
240	A24	80c	on 3c lt grn	5.50	4.00
241	A24	1g	on 3c lt grn	35.00	32.50
242	A24	2.50g	on 3c lt grn	40.00	37.50
243	A24	5g	on 3c lt grn	37.50	35.00
			Nos. 226-243 (18)	130.60	115.55
			Set, hinged	70.00	

No. 228a is from coils.

Gull Type of 1924-26

1941

No.	Type	Value	Color	Unused	Used
243A	A24	2½c	dk green	1.25	.35
b.			Booklet pane of 6	10.00	
243C	A24	5c	brt green	.15	.15
243E	A24	7½c	henna	.15	.15
r.			Pair, #243A, 243E	1.00	1.00
243G	A24	10c	brt violet	.15	.15
243H	A24	12½c	ultra	.15	.15
243J	A24	15c	lt blue	.15	.15
243K	A24	17½c	red org	.15	.15
243L	A24	20c	lt violet	.20	.20
243M	A24	22½c	dk ol grn	.15	.15
243N	A24	25c	lake	.15	.20
243O	A24	30c	olive	3.50	.20
243P	A24	40c	emerald	.15	.20
243Q	A24	50c	orange brn	.15	.20
			Nos. 243A-243Q (13)	6.45	2.40

No. 243r is from coils.

Post Horn and Lion — A46

Gold Surcharge

1943, Jan. 15 Photo. *Perf. 12½x12*

No.	Type	Value	Color	Unused	Used
244	A46	10c	on 2½c yel	.30	.25
a.			Surcharge omitted	6,000.	6,500.

Founding of the European Union of Posts and Telegraphs at Vienna, Oct. 19, 1942. Surcharge reads: "Europeesche P T T Vereeniging 19 October 1942 10 Cent."

Sea Horse — A47

Triple-crown Tree — A48

Admiral M. A. de Ruyter — A54

Designs: 2c, Swans. 2½c, Tree of Life. 3c, Tree with snake roots. 4c, Man on horseback. 5c, Prancing white horses. 10c, Johan Evertsen. 12½c, Martin Tromp. 15c, Piet Hein. 17½c, Willem van Ghent. 20c, Witte de With. 22½c, Cornelis Evertsen. 25c, Tjerk de Vries. 30c, Cornelis Tromp. 40c, Cornelis Evertsen De Jongste.

Perf. 12x12½, 12½x12

1943-44 Photo. Wmk. 202

No.	Type	Value	Color	Unused	Used
245	A47	1c	black	.15	.15
246	A48	1½c	rose lake	.15	.15
247	A47	2c	dk blue	.15	.15
248	A48	2½c	dk blue grn	.15	.15
249	A47	3c	copper red	.15	.15
250	A48	4c	black brown	.15	.15
251	A47	5c	dull yel grn	.15	.15
			Unwmk.		
252	A54	7½c	henna brn	.15	.15
a.			Thinner numerals and letters ('44)	.15	.15
253	A54	10c	dk green	.15	.15
254	A54	12½c	blue	.15	.15
255	A54	15c	dull lilac	.15	.15
256	A54	17½c	slate ('44)	.15	.15
257	A54	20c	dull brown	.15	.15
258	A54	22½c	org red	.15	.25
259	A54	25c	vio rose ('44)	.35	.55
260	A54	30c	cobalt bl ('44)	.15	.20
			Engr.		
261	A54	40c	bluish blk	.15	.20
			Nos. 245-261 (17)	2.75	3.15

In 1944, 200,000 copies of No. 247 were privately punched with a cross and printed on the back with a number and the words "Prijs 15 Cent toeslag ten bate Ned. Roode Kruis." These were sold at an exhibition, the surtax going to the Red Cross. The Dutch post office tolerated these stamps.

Soldier — A64

S. S. "Nieuw Amsterdam" — A65

Pilot — A66

Cruiser "De Ruyter" — A67

Queen Wilhelmina — A68

Perf. 12, 12½

1944-46 Unwmk. Engr.

No.	Type	Value	Color	Unused	Used
262	A64	1½c	black	.15	.15
263	A65	2½c	yellow grn	.15	.15
264	A66	3c	dull red brn	.15	.15
265	A67	5c	dk blue	.15	.15
266	A68	7½c	vermilion	.15	.15
267	A68	10c	yellow org	.15	.20
268	A68	12½c	ultra	.15	.20
269	A68	15c	dl red brn ('46)	1.40	4.50
270	A68	17½c	gray grn ('46)	1.00	2.50
271	A68	20c	violet	.15	.30
272	A68	22½c	rose red ('46)	.55	1.00
273	A68	25c	brn org ('46)	2.00	2.75
274	A68	30c	blue grn	.15	.20
275	A68	40c	dk vio brn ('46)	2.00	4.50
276	A68	50c	red vio ('46)	1.10	2.00
			Nos. 262-276 (15)	9.40	18.90

These stamps were used on board Dutch war and merchant ships until Netherlands' liberation.

Lion and Dragon — A69

Queen Wilhelmina — A70

1945, July 14 *Perf. 12½x14*

No.	Type	Value	Color	Unused	Used
277	A69	7½c	red orange	.15	.15

Netherlands' liberation or "rising again."

1946 Engr. *Perf. 13½x14*

No.	Type	Value	Color	Unused	Used
278	A70	1g	dark blue	1.00	.20
279	A70	2½g	brick red	125.00	7.00
280	A70	5g	dk olive grn	125.00	21.00
281	A70	10g	dk purple	125.00	26.00
			Nos. 278-281 (4)	376.00	54.20
			Set, hinged	200.00	

A71

Perf. 12½x13½

1946-47 Wmk. 202 Photo.

No.	Type	Value	Color	Unused	Used
282	A71	1c	dark red	.15	.15
283	A71	2c	ultra	.15	.15
284	A71	2½c	dp orange ('47)	8.75	1.65
285	A71	4c	olive green	.35	.15
			Nos. 282-285 (4)	9.40	2.10

The 1c was reissued in 1969 on phosphorescent paper in booklet pane No. 345b. The 4c was reissued on fluorescent paper in 1962.

The 2c was issued in coils in 1972. Every fifth stamp has black control number on back.

See Nos. 340-343A, 404-406.

Queen Wilhelmina
A72 A73

1947-48 *Perf. 13½x12½*

No.	Type	Value	Color	Unused	Used
286	A72	5c	olive green ('48)	1.00	.15
287	A72	6c	brown black	.35	.15
288	A72	7½c	dp red brn ('48)	.35	.15
289	A72	10c	brt red vio	.75	.15
290	A72	12½c	scarlet ('48)	.75	.40
291	A72	15c	purple	6.50	.15
292	A72	20c	deep blue	7.50	.15
293	A72	22½c	ol brn ('48)	.75	.55
294	A72	25c	ultra	15.00	.15
295	A72	30c	dp orange	15.00	.25
296	A72	35c	dk blue grn	6.00	.45
297	A72	40c	henna brown	19.00	.45
			Engr.		
298	A73	45c	deep blue ('48)	24.00	12.00
299	A73	50c	brown ('48)	20.00	.30
300	A73	60c	red ('48)	21.00	2.25
			Nos. 286-300 (15)	137.95	17.70
			Set, hinged	60.00	

For surcharge see No. 330.

Type of 1947

1948 Photo.

No.	Type	Value	Color	Unused	Used
301	A72	6c	gray blue	.25	.15

Queen Wilhelmina A74

Queen Juliana A75

Perf. 12½x14

1948, Aug. 30 Engr. Unwmk.

No.	Type	Value	Color	Unused	Used
302	A74	10c	vermilion	.15	.15
303	A74	20c	deep blue	1.65	1.50

50th anniv. of the reign of Queen Wilhelmina.

Perf. 14x13

1948, Sept. 7 Photo. Wmk. 202

304 A75 10c dark brown .90 .15
305 A75 20c ultra 1.75 .60

Investiture of Queen Juliana, Sept. 6, 1948.

Queen Juliana
A76 A77

1949 *Perf. 13½x12½*

306 A76 5c olive green .55 .15
307 A76 6c gray blue .30 .15
308 A76 10c deep orange .30 .15
309 A76 12c orange red 1.50 1.00
310 A76 15c olive brown 3.25 .15
311 A76 20c brt blue 3.00 .15
312 A76 25c orange brn 9.50 .15
313 A76 30c violet 7.50 .15
314 A76 35c gray 13.00 .20
315 A76 40c red violet 27.50 .20
316 A76 45c red orange 1.40 1.00
317 A76 50c blue green 7.50 .20
318 A76 60c red brown 11.00 .20
Nos. 306-318 (13) 86.30 3.85

See No. 325-327. For surcharge see No. B248.

1949 Unwmk. Engr. *Perf. 12½x12*

319 A77 1g rose red 3.50 .15
320 A77 2½g black brn 200.00 1.00
321 A77 5g orange brn 425.00 2.50
322 A77 10g dk vio brn 350.00 12.00
Nos. 319-322 (4) 978.50 15.65
Set, hinged 400.00

Two types exist of No. 321.

Post Horns Entwined — A78

Janus Dousa — A79

Perf. 11½x12½

1949, Oct. 1 Photo. Wmk. 202

323 A78 10c brown red .15 .15
324 A78 20c dull blue 9.50 2.75

75th anniversary of the UPU.

Juliana Type of 1949

1950-51 *Perf. 13½x12½*

325 A76 12c scarlet ('51) 6.00 .60
326 A76 45c violet brn 42.50 .30
327 A76 75c car rose ('51) 85.00 1.25
Nos. 325-327 (3) 133.50 2.15

1950, Oct. 3 *Perf. 11½x13*

Design: 20c, Jan van Hout.

328 A79 10c olive brown 3.75 .20
329 A79 20c deep blue 4.25 1.65

375th anniversary of the founding of the University of Leyden.

No. 288 Surcharged with New Value

1950, May *Perf. 13½x12½*

330 A72 6c on 7½c dp red brn 2.00 .15

Miner — A80

Perf. 12x12½

1952, Apr. 16 Engr. Unwmk.

331 A80 10c dark blue 2.50 .15

50th anniversary of the founding of Netherlands' mining and chemical industry.

Telegraph Poles and Train of 1852 — A81

Designs: 6c, Radio towers. 10c, Mail Delivery 1852. 20c, Modern postman.

1952, June 28 *Perf. 13x14*

332 A81 2c gray violet .40 .20
333 A81 6c vermilion .45 .35
334 A81 10c green .65 .20
335 A81 20c gray blue 5.50 2.75
Nos. 332-335 (4) 7.00 3.50

Centenary of Dutch postage stamps and of the telegraph service.

1952, June 28

336 A81 2c chocolate 13.00 17.00
337 A81 6c dk bluish grn 13.00 17.00
338 A81 10c brown carmine 13.00 17.00
339 A81 20c violet blue 13.00 17.00
Nos. 336-339 (4) 52.00 68.00

Nos. 336 to 339 sold for 1.38g, which included the price of admission to the International Postage Stamp Centenary Exhibition, Utrecht.

Numeral Type of 1946-47

Perf. 12½x13½

1953-57 Wmk. 202 Photo.

340 A71 3c dp org brn .15 .15
341 A71 5c orange .15 .15
342 A71 6c gray ('54) .25 .15
343 A71 7c red org .15 .15
343A A71 8c brt lil ('57) .15 .15
Set value .65 .40

The 5c and 7c perf. on 3 sides, and with watermark vertical, are from booklet panes Nos. 346a-346b. The 5c perf. on 3 sides, with wmk. horiz., is from No. 349a.

In 1972 the 5c was printed on phosphorescent paper.

Queen Juliana
A82 A83

1953-71 Wmk. 202 *Perf. 13½x12½*

344 A82 10c dk red brn .15 .15
a. Bklt. pane of 6 (1 #344 + 5 #346C)('65) 5.00
345 A82 12c dk Prus grn ('54) .15 .15
a. Bklt. pane of 7 + label (5 #345 + 2 #347)('67) 5.50
b. Bklt. pane, 4 #282 + 8 #345 ('69) 12.50
346 A82 15c dp carmine .15 .15
a. Bklt. pane of 8 (2 #341 in vert. pair + 6 #346)('64) 17.00
b. Bklt. pane of 12 (10 #343 + 2 #346)('64) 12.50
e. Bklt. pane of 8 (2 #341 in horiz. pair + 6 #346)('70) 9.00
346C A82 18c dull bl ('65) .30 .15
d. Bklt. pane of 10 (8 #343A + 2 #346C)('65) 4.50
347 A82 20c dk gray .15 .15
b. Bklt. pane of 5 + label ('66) 4.00
347A A82 24c olive ('63) .32 .15
348 A82 25c deep blue .15 .15
349 A82 30c deep orange .38 .15
a. Bklt. pane of 5 + label (2 #341 + 3 #349)('71) 22.50
350 A82 35c dk ol brn ('54) .95 .15
351 A82 37c aqua ('58) .55 .15
352 A82 40c dk slate .26 .15
353 A82 45c scarlet .42 .15
354 A82 50c dk bl grn .32 .15
355 A82 60c brown bister .32 .15
356 A82 62c dl red lil ('58) 4.50 4.00
357 A82 70c blue ('57) .45 .15
358 A82 75c deep plum .45 .15
359 A82 80c brt vio ('58) .52 .15
360 A82 85c brt bl grn ('56) .70 .15
360A A82 95c org brn ('67) 1.40 .26
Nos. 344-360A (20) 12.59
Set value 5.65

Coils of the 12, 15, 20, 25, 30, 40, 45, 50, 60, 70, 75 and 80c were issued in 1972. Black control number on back of every fifth stamp.

Watermark is vertical on some stamps from booklet panes.

Some booklet panes, Nos. 344a, 347b, 349a, etc., have a large selvage the size of four or six stamps, with printed inscription and sometimes illustration.

Phosphorescent paper was introduced in 1967 for the 12, 15, 20 and 45c; in 1969 for the 25c, and in 1971 for the 30, 40, 50, 60, 70, 75 and 80c.

Of the booklet panes, Nos. 345a, 345b, 346d, 346e and 347b were issued on both ordinary and phosphorescent paper, and No. 349a only on phosphorescent paper.

See No. 407. For surcharge see No. 374.

Perf. 12½x12

1954-57 Unwmk. Engr.

361 A83 1g vermilion 2.75 .15
362 A83 2½g dk green ('55) 9.00 .15
363 A83 5g black ('55) 2.25 .30
364 A83 10g vio bl ('57) 16.00 1.25
Nos. 361-364 (4) 30.00 1.85

St. Boniface — A84

Queen Juliana — A84a

1954, June 16

365 A84 10c blue 2.25 .15

1200th anniversary of the death of St. Boniface.

Perf. 13½

1954, Dec. 15 Photo. Wmk. 202

366 A84a 10c scarlet .80 .15

Issued to publicize the Charter of the Kingdom, adopted December 15, 1954.

Flaming Sword — A85

"Rebuilding Europe" — A86

1955, May 4 *Perf. 12½x12*

367 A85 10c crimson 1.10 .15

10th anniv. of Netherlands' liberation.

1956, Sept. 15 Unwmk. *Perf. 13x14*

368 A86 10c rose brn & blk .75 .15
369 A86 25c brt bl & blk 37.50 2.25

Europa. Issued to symbolize the cooperation among the six countries comprising the Coal and Steel Community.

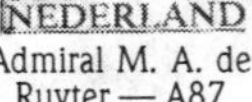

Admiral M. A. de Ruyter — A87

"United Europe" — A88

Design: 30c, Flagship "De Zeven Provincien."

1957, July 2 Engr. *Perf. 12½x12*

370 A87 10c orange .40 .15
371 A87 30c dk blue 4.50 1.75

Adm. M. A. de Ruyter (1607-1676).

1957, Sept. 16 Photo. *Perf. 13x14*

372 A88 10c blk, gray & ultra .85 .15
373 A88 30c dull grn & ultra 7.00 1.50

United Europe for peace and prosperity.

No. 344 Surcharged in Silver with New Value and Bars

Perf. 13½x12½

1958, May 16 Photo. Wmk. 202

374 A82 12c on 10c 1.10 .15
a. Double surcharge 450.00 450.00
b. Inverted surcharge 450.00 450.00

Europa Issue, 1958

Common Design Type

Perf. 13x14

1958, Sept. 13 Litho. Unwmk.

Size: 22x33mm

375 CD1 12c org ver & blue .25 .15
376 CD1 30c blue & red 1.00 1.10

NATO Emblem — A89

1959, Apr. 3 *Perf. 12½x12*

377 A89 12c yel org & blue .15 .15
378 A89 30c red & blue .65 .80

10th anniversary of NATO.

Europa Issue, 1959.

Common Design Type

1959, Sept. 19 *Perf. 13x14*

Size: 22x33mm

379 CD2 12c crimson .40 .15
380 CD2 30c yellow grn 2.25 1.75

Douglas DC-8 and World Map — A90

J. C. Schroeder van der Kolk — A91

Design: 30c, Douglas DC-8 in flight.

1959, Oct. 5 Engr. *Perf. 14x13*

381 A90 12c carmine & ultra .25 .15
382 A90 30c dp blue & dp grn 1.10 1.40

40th anniversary of the founding of KLM, Royal Dutch Airlines.

Perf. 12½x12

1960, July 18 Unwmk.

Design: 30c, Johannes Wier.

383 A91 12c red .25 .15
384 A91 30c dark blue 4.75 2.25

Issued to publicize Mental Health Year and to honor Schroeder van der Kolk and Johannes Wier, pioneers of mental health.

Europa Issue, 1960

Common Design Type

1960, Sept. 19 Photo. *Perf. 12x12½*

Size: 27x21mm

385 CD3 12c car rose & org .25 .20
386 CD3 30c dk blue & yel 2.75 1.90

1st anniv. of CEPT. Spokes symbolize 19 founding members of Conference.

Europa Issue, 1961

Common Design Type

1961, Sept. 18 *Perf. 14x13*

Size: 32½x21½mm

387 CD4 12c golden brown .15 .15
388 CD4 30c Prus blue .24 .20
Set value .28

Queen Juliana and Prince Bernhard — A92

Telephone Dial — A93

Perf. 14x13

1962, Jan. 5 Unwmk. Photo.

389 A92 12c dk red .20 .15
390 A92 30c dk green 1.75 1.00

Silver wedding anniversary of Queen Juliana and Prince Bernhard.

1962, May 22 *Perf. 13x14, 14x13*

Designs: 12c, Map showing telephone network. 30c, Arch and dial, horiz.

391	A93	4c brown red & blk	.20	.15
392	A93	12c brown ol & blk	.32	.15
393	A93	30c black, bis & Prus bl	2.00	1.50
		Nos. 391-393 (3)	2.52	1.80

Completion of the automation of the Netherlands telephone network.

Europa Issue, 1962

Common Design Type

1962, Sept. 17 *Perf. 14x13*

Size: 33x22mm

394	CD5	12c lemon, yel & blk	.20	.15
395	CD5	30c blue, yel & blk	.95	.75

Polder with Canals and Windmills — A94

Design: 4c, Cooling towers, Limburg State Coal Mines. 10c, Dredging in Delta.

Perf. 12½x13½

1962-66 **Wmk. 202** **Photo.**

399	A94	4c dk blue ('63)	.20	.15
401	A94	6c grn & dk grn	.70	.15
403	A94	10c dp claret ('63)	.20	.15
a.		Booklet pane of 10 ('66)	4.00	
		Nos. 399-403 (3)	1.10	
		Set value		.24

The 10c was issued in coils in 1972. Every fifth stamp has black control number on back.

See No. 461b.

Types of 1946 and 1953

1962-73 **Unwmk.**

Phosphorescent Paper

404	A71	4c olive green	.60	.20
405	A71	5c orange ('73)	.40	.15
406	A71	8c bright lilac	13.00	12.00
407	A82	12c dk Prus green	.75	.40
		Nos. 404-407 (4)	14.75	12.75

The 5c is from booklets and has the phosphor on the front only.

Issue dates: 5c, Jan. 12; others Aug. 27.

See Nos. 460d, 461c, 461d and 463a.

Wheat Emblem and Globe — A95

Inscription in Circle — A96

1963, Mar. 21 **Photo.** *Perf. 14x13*

413	A95	12c dl bl, dk bl & yel	.15	.15
414	A95	30c dl car, rose & yel	1.10	.95

FAO "Freedom from Hunger" campaign.

Perf. 13x14

1963, May 7 **Unwmk.** **Litho.**

415	A96	30c brt blue, blk & grn	1.40	1.00

1st Intl. Postal Conf., Paris, cent.

Europa Issue, 1963

Common Design Type

1963, Sept. 16 **Photo.** *Perf. 14x13*

Size: 33x22mm

416	CD6	12c red brown & yel	.15	.15
417	CD6	30c Prus green & yel	1.40	1.40

Prince William of Orange Landing at Scheveningen — A97

Designs: 12c, G. K. van Hogendorp, A. F. J. A. Graaf van der Duyn van Maasdam and L. Graaf van Limburg Stirum, Dutch leaders, 1813. 30c, Prince William taking oath of allegiance.

1963, Nov. 18 **Photo.** *Perf. 12x12½*

Size: 27½x27½mm

418	A97	4c dull bl, blk & brn	.15	.15
419	A97	5c dk grn, blk & red	.15	.15
420	A97	12c olive & blk	.15	.15
421	A97	30c maroon & blk	.60	.55
		Set value	.84	.78

150th anniversary of the founding of the Kingdom of the Netherlands.

Knights' Hall, The Hague A98

Arms of Groningen University A99

1964, Jan. 9 *Perf. 14x13*

422	A98	12c olive & blk	.15	.15

500th anniversary of the meeting of the States-General (Parliament).

1964, June 16 **Engr.** *Perf. 12½x12*

Design: 30c, Initials "AG" and crown.

423	A99	12c slate	.15	.15
424	A99	30c yellow brown	.20	.20

350th anniv. of the University of Groningen.

Railroad Light Signal — A100

Design: 40c, Electric locomotive.

1964, July 28 **Photo.** *Perf. 14x13*

425	A100	15c black & brt grn	.15	.15
426	A100	40c black & yellow	.90	.55

125th anniv. of the Netherlands railroads.

Bible, Chrismon and Dove — A101

1964, Aug. 25 **Unwmk.**

427	A101	15c brown red	.15	.15

150th anniversary of the founding of the Netherlands Bible Society.

Europa Issue, 1964

Common Design Type

1964, Sept. 14 **Photo.** *Perf. 13x14*

Size: 22x33mm

428	CD7	15c dp olive grn	.15	.15
429	CD7	20c yellow brown	.32	.32

Benelux Issue

King Baudouin, Queen Juliana and Grand Duchess Charlotte A101a

1964, Oct. 12 *Perf. 14x13*

Size: 33x22mm

430	A101a	15c purple & buff	.15	.15

20th anniversary of the signing of the customs union of Belgium, Netherlands and Luxembourg.

Queen Juliana — A102

"Killed in Action" and "Destroyed Town" — A103

1964, Dec. 15 **Photo.** *Perf. 13x14*

431	A102	15c green	.15	.15

10th anniversary of the Charter of the Kingdom of the Netherlands.

1965, Apr. 6 **Photo.** *Perf. 12x12½*

Statues: 15c, "Docker" Amsterdam, and "Killed in Action" Waalwijk. 40c, "Destroyed Town" Rotterdam, and "Docker" Amsterdam.

432	A103	7c black & dk red	.15	.15
433	A103	15c black & dk olive	.15	.15
434	A103	40c black & dk red	.85	.60
		Set value	1.00	.75

Resistance movement of World War II.

Knight Class IV, Order of William A104

ITU Emblem A105

1965, Apr. 29 *Perf. 13x14*

435	A104	1g gray	.90	.75

150th anniversary of the establishment of the Military Order of William.

1965, May 17 **Litho.** *Perf. 14x13*

436	A105	20c dull bl & tan	.18	.15
437	A105	40c tan & dull bl	.40	.32

Centenary of the International Telecommunication Union.

Europa Issue, 1965

Common Design Type

1965, Sept. 27 **Photo.**

Size: 33x22mm

438	CD8	18c org brn, dk red & blk	.15	.15
439	CD8	20c sapphire, brn & blk	.28	.16
		Set value		.24

Marines of 1665 and 1965 — A106

1965, Dec. 10 **Engr.** *Perf. 13x14*

440	A106	18c dk vio bl & car	.15	.15

Netherlands Marine Corps, 300th anniv.

Europa Issue, 1966

Common Design Type

1966, Sept. 26 **Photo.** *Perf. 13x14*

Size: 22x33mm

441	CD9	20c citron	.15	.15
442	CD9	40c dull blue	.25	.16
		Set value		.24

Assembly Hall, Delft University A107

1967, Jan. 5 **Litho.** *Perf. 14x13*

443	A107	20c lemon & sepia	.15	.15

125th anniversary of the founding of the Delft University of Technology.

Europa Issue, 1967

Common Design Type

Perf. 13x14

1967, May 2 **Unwmk.** **Photo.**

Ordinary Paper

Size: 22x32½mm

444	CD10	20c dull blue	.50	.20
445	CD10	45c dull vio brn	1.50	.80

Wmk. 202

446	CD10	20c dull blue	1.00	.25
447	CD10	45c dull vio brn	1.50	.95
		Nos. 444-447 (4)	4.50	2.20

Nos. 446-447 are on phosphorescent paper.

Stamp of 1852, #1 — A108

1967, May 8 **Engr.** **Unwmk.**

448	A108	20c shown	2.25	2.25
449	A108	25c No. 5	2.25	2.25
450	A108	75c No. 10	2.25	2.25
		Nos. 448-450 (3)	6.75	6.75

AMPHILEX 67, Amsterdam, May 11-21. Sold only in complete sets together with a 2.50g admission ticket to Amsterdam Philatelic Exhibition. Issued in sheets of 10 (5x2).

Coins and Punched Card — A109

1968, Jan. 16 **Photo.** *Perf. 14x13*

451	A109	20c ver, blk & dl yel	.20	.15

50th anniversary of the postal checking service.

Luminescence

All commemorative issues from No. 451 to No. 511 are printed on phosphorescent paper except No. 478 which is printed with phosphorescent ink, and Nos. 490-492. Some later issues are tagged.

Europa Issue, 1968

Common Design Type

1968, Apr. 29 **Photo.** *Perf. 14x13*

Size: 32½x22mm

452	CD11	20c deep blue	.35	.15
453	CD11	45c crimson	1.10	.85

National Anthem — A110

Fokker F.2, 1919, and Friendship F.29 — A111

1968, Aug. 27 **Litho.** *Perf. 13x14*

454	A110	20c gray, org, car & dk bl	.25	.15

400th anniversary of the national anthem "Wilhelmus van Nassouwe."

1968, Oct. 1 Photo. *Perf. 14x13*

Planes: 12c, Wright A, 1909, and Cessna sports plane. 45c, De Havilland DH-9, 1919, and Douglas DC-9.

455 A111 12c crim, pink & blk .15 .15
456 A111 20c brt grn, bl grn & blk .15 .15
457 A111 45c brt bl, lt grn & blk 1.40 1.10
Nos. 455-457 (3) 1.70 1.40

50th anniv. of the founding in 1919 of Royal Dutch Airlines and the Royal Netherlands Aircraft Factories Fokker, and the 60th anniv. in 1967 of the Royal Netherlands Aeronautical Assoc.

"iao" — A112

Design is made up of 28 minute lines, each reading "1919 internationale arbeids-organisatie 1969".

1969, Feb. 25 Engr. *Perf. 14x13*

458 A112 25c brick red & blk .45 .15
459 A112 45c ultra & blue 1.00 .65

International Labor Organization, 50th anniv.

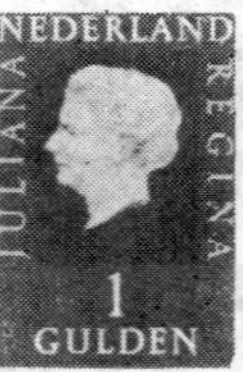

Queen Juliana
A113 A114

Perf. 13½ horiz. x 12½ on one vert. side

1969-75 Photo.

460 A113 25c orange ver 3.00 .32
a. Bklt. pane of 4 + 2 labels 12.50
460B A113 25c dull red ('73) 2.00 .15
c. Booklet pane of 6 (#460B + 5 #461A) 27.50
d. Booklet pane of 12 (5 #405 + 7 #460B) 16.00

Perf. 13x12½

461 A113 30c choc ('72) .48 .15
d. Bklt. pane of 10 (4 #405 + 6 #461 + 2 labels)('74) 6.50
461A A113 35c grnsh bl ('72) .48 .15
b. Bklt. pane of 5 (3 #403, 2 #461A + label)('72) 25.00
c. Bklt. pane of 10 (5 #405 + 5 #461A + 2 labels)('75) 4.50
462 A113 40c car rose ('72) .48 .15
a. Bklt. pane of 5 + label ('73) 7.50
463 A113 45c ultra ('72) .48 .15
a. Bklt. pane of 8 (4 #405 + 4 #463) ('74) 4.00
464 A113 50c lilac ('72) .48 .15
a. Bklt. pane of 4 + 2 labels ('75) 3.00
465 A113 60c slate bl ('72) .55 .15
a. Bklt. pane of 5 + label ('80) 3.00
466 A113 70c bister ('72) .65 .15
467 A113 75c green ('72) .65 .15
468 A113 80c red org ('72) .70 .15
468A A113 90c gray ('75) .80 .18

Perf. 13x14

469 A114 1g yel green .90 .15
470 A114 1.25g maroon 1.10 .15
471 A114 1.50g yel bis ('71) 1.25 .15
471A A114 2g dp rose lil ('72) 1.75 .15
472 A114 2.50g grnsh bl 2.00 .15
473 A114 5g gray ('70) 4.25 .20
474 A114 10g vio bl ('70) 8.50 1.50
Nos. 460-474 (19) 30.50
Set value 3.75

Both 25c stamps issued only in booklets.

Printings were both ordinary and phosphorescent paper for Nos. 460, 460a, 469, 471-474.

Coil printings were issued later for Nos. 461, 462-471. Black control number on back of every fifth stamp.

Booklet panes have a large selvage the size of 4 or 6 stamps, with printed inscription.

See No. 542.

Europa Issue, 1969
Common Design Type

1969, Apr. 28 Photo. *Perf. 14x13*
Size: 33½x22mm

475 CD12 25c dark blue 1.25 .15
476 CD12 45c red 2.00 1.90

A114a

A115

Möbius strip in Benelux colors.

1969, Sept. 8 Photo. *Perf. 13x14*

477 A114a 25c multicolored .40 .15

25th anniversary of the signing of the customs union of Belgium, Netherlands and Luxembourg.

Photo. & Engr.
1969, Sept. 30 *Perf. 13x14*

478 A115 25c yellow grn & maroon .40 .15

Desiderius Erasmus (1469-1536), scholar.

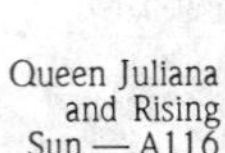

Queen Juliana and Rising Sun — A116

1969, Dec. 15 Photo. *Perf. 14x13*

479 A116 25c blue & multi .32 .15

15th anniversary of the Charter of the Kingdom of the Netherlands.

Prof. E. M. Meijers
A117

1970, Jan. 13 Photo. *Perf. 14x13*

480 A117 25c blue, vio bl & grn .38 .15

Issued to publicize the new Civil Code and to honor Prof. Meijers, who prepared it.

Dutch Pavilion, EXPO '70 — A118

1970, Mar. 10 Photo. *Perf. 14x13*

481 A118 25c multicolored .32 .15

EXPO '70 International Exposition, Osaka, Japan, Mar. 15-Sept. 13.

"V" for Victory — A119

1970, Apr. 21 Photo. *Perf. 13x14*

482 A119 12c red, ultra, brn ol & lt bl 1.10 .15

25th anniv. of liberation from the Germans.

Europa Issue, 1970
Common Design Type

1970, May 4 Photo. *Perf. 14x13*
Size: 32½x21½mm

483 CD13 25c carmine .45 .15
484 CD13 45c dk blue 2.00 2.00

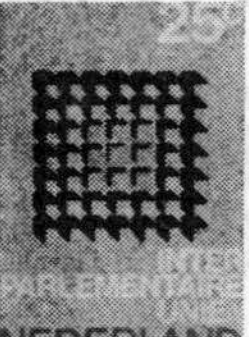

Panels — A120

Globe — A121

1970, June 23 Photo. *Perf. 13x14*

485 A120 25c gray, blk & brt yel grn .45 .15
486 A121 45c ultra, blk & pur 1.00 .85

#485 publicizes the meeting of the interparliamentary Union; #486 the UN 25th anniv.

Punch Cards — A122

1971, Feb. 16 Photo. *Perf. 14x13*

487 A122 15c dp rose lilac .22 .15

14th national census, 1971.

Europa Issue, 1971
Common Design Type

1971, May 3 Photo. *Perf. 14x13*
Size: 33x22mm

488 CD14 25c lil rose, yel & blk .30 .15
489 CD14 45c ultra, yel & blk 2.25 1.25

No. 488 was issued in coils and sheets. In the coils every fifth stamp has a black control number on the back.

Prince Bernhard, Fokker F27, Boeing 747
B — A123

Designs: 15c, Stylized carnation (Prince Bernhard Fund). 20c, Giant Panda (World Wildlife Fund). 15c, 20c horiz.

Photo., Litho. (20c)
1971, June 29 *Perf. 13x14*

490 A123 15c black & yellow .30 .15
491 A123 20c multicolored .50 .20
492 A123 25c multicolored .65 .15
Nos. 490-492,B475 (4) 3.95 3.00
Set value .40

60th birthday of Prince Bernhard. See No. B475.

Map of Delta — A124

1972, Feb. 15 Photo. *Perf. 14x13*

493 A124 20c bl, grn, blk & red .42 .15

Publicity for the Delta plan, a project to shorten the coastline and to build roads.

Europa Issue 1972
Common Design Type

1972, May 52 Photo. *Perf. 13x14*
Size: 22x33mm

494 CD15 30c blue & bis 1.00 .15
495 CD15 45c orange & bis 1.75 1.50

No. 494 was issued in coils and sheets. In the coils every fifth stamp has a black control number on the back.

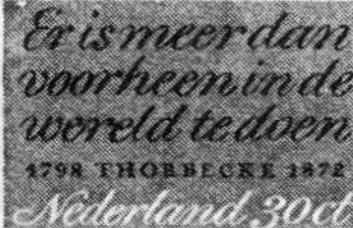

Thorbecke Quotation
A126

1972, June 2 Photo. *Perf. 14x13*

496 A126 30c lt ultra & blk .45 .15

Jan Rudolf Thorbecke (1798-1872), statesman, who said: "There is more to be done in the world than ever before."

Dutch Flag — A127

1972 *Perf. 13x14*

497 A127 20c blue & multi .75 .15
498 A127 25c blue & multi 2.50 .15

400th anniversary of the Dutch flag.
Issue dates: 20c, July 4; 25c, Nov. 1.

Woman Hurdler
A128

Designs: 30c, Woman swimmer. 45c, Bicycling.

1972, July 11 *Perf. 14x13*

499 A128 20c multicolored .30 .15
500 A128 30c crimson & multi .35 .15
501 A128 45c violet & multi 1.40 1.10

20th Olympic Games, Munich, Aug. 26-Sept. 11.

Red Cross — A129
Tulips — A130

1972, Aug. 15 Photo. *Perf. 13x14*

502 A129 5c red .15 .15
Nos. 502,B485-B488 (5) 3.95 2.95

Netherlands Red Cross.

1973, Mar. 20 Photo. *Perf. 14x13*

503 A130 25c rose, brt grn & blk 1.50 .15

Dutch flower and bulb exports.

Europa Issue 1973
Common Design Type

1973, May 1 Photo. *Perf. 14x13*
Size: 32½x22mm

504 CD16 35c bright blue .50 .15
505 CD16 50c purple 1.50 .90

Hockey
A132

Woman Gymnast
A133

Antenna, Burum — A134

Rainbow, Measures A135

Photo. (25c, 35c); Litho. (30c, 50c)

1973, July 31 *Perf. 13x14, 14x13*

506 A132 25c black & green .25 .15
507 A133 30c gray & multi 2.50 .55
508 A134 35c blue & multi .30 .15
509 A135 50c blue & multi .70 .65
Nos. 506-509 (4) 3.75 1.50

Netherlands Hockey Assoc., 75th anniv. (25c); Rhythmical Gymnastics World Championship, Rotterdam (30c); inauguration of satellite ground station at Burum (35c); cent. of intl. meteorological cooperation (50c).

Queen Juliana, Dutch and House of Orange Colors — A136

Engr. & Photo.

1973, Sept. 4 *Perf. 13x12*

510 A136 40c silver & multi .60 .15

25th anniversary of reign of Queen Juliana.

Chain with Open Link — A137

1973, Oct. 16 **Photo.** *Perf. 13x14*

511 A137 40c grn, blk, gold & sil 2.75 .15

Development Corporation.

Nature and Environment — A138

1974, Feb. 19 **Photo.** *Perf. 13x14*

512 A138 Strip of 3 6.00 5.25
a. 25c Bird of prey 1.65 .52
b. 25c Tree 1.65 .52
c. 25c Fisherman in boat and frog 1.65 .52

75th anniv. of the Netherlands Assoc. for the Protection of Birds and of the State Forestry Service.

Soccer Ball — A139

Tennis Ball — A140

Perf. 14x13, 13x14

1974, June 5 **Photo.**

513 A139 25c multicolored .35 .15
514 A140 40c multicolored .40 .15

World Cup Soccer Championship, Munich, June 13-July 7 (25c) and 75th anniversary of the Royal Dutch Lawn Tennis Association (40c).

Cattle — A141

Pierced Crab under Lens — A142

Shipwreck Seen Through Binoculars — A143

1974, July 30 *Perf. 13x14*

515 A141 25c multicolored 11.00 1.75
516 A142 25c salmon pink & multi .16 .16
517 A143 40c dk violet & multi .24 .15
Nos. 515-517 (3) 11.40 2.06

Cent. of the Netherlands Cattle Herdbook Soc. (#515); 25th anniv. of Queen Wilhelmina Fund (for cancer research) (#516); sesquicentennial of Royal Dutch Lifeboat Soc. (#517).

BENELUX Issue

"BENELUX" A143a

1974, Sept. 10 **Photo.** *Perf. 14x13*

518 A143a 30c bl grn, dk grn & lt bl .45 .15

30th anniv. of the signing of the customs union of Belgium, Netherlands and Luxembourg.

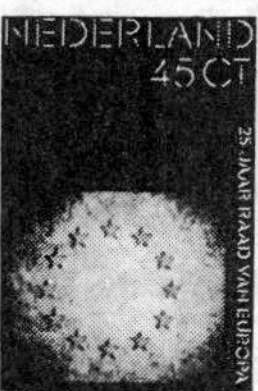

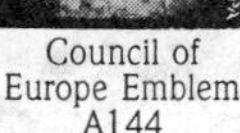
Council of Europe Emblem A144

NATO Emblem and Sea Gull A145

1974, Sept. 10 *Perf. 13x14*

519 A144 45c black, bl & yel .45 .15
520 A145 45c dk blue & silver .70 .15

25th anniv. of Council of Europe (No. 519) and of North Atlantic Treaty Organization (No. 520).

Letters and Hands, Papier-maché Sculpture — A146

1974, Oct. 9

521 A146 60c purple & multi .80 .50

Centenary of Universal Postal Union.

People and Map of Dam Square — A147

Brain with Window Symbolizing Free Thought — A148

Design: No. 523, Portuguese Synagogue and map of Mr. Visser Square. 35c, No. 526, like No. 522.

1975 **Photo.** *Perf. 13x14*

522 A147 30c multicolored .35 .15
523 A147 30c multicolored .30 .20
524 A147 35c multicolored .45 .15
525 A148 45c dp blue & multi .38 .20
Nos. 522-525 (4) 1.48 .70

Coil Stamps

Perf. 13 Horiz.

526 A147 30c multicolored .42 .20
527 A147 35c multicolored .60 .20

700th anniv. of Amsterdam (No. 522); 300th anniv. of the Portuguese Synagogue in Amsterdam (No. 523) and 400th anniv. of the founding of the University of Leyden and the beginning of higher education in the Netherlands (No. 525).

Issue dates: Nos. 522-523, 525-526, Feb. 26; Nos. 524, 527, Apr. 1.

Eye Looking over Barbed Wire — A149

1975, Apr. 29 **Photo.** *Perf. 13x14*

528 A149 35c black & carmine .45 .15

Liberation of the Netherlands from Nazi occupation, 30th anniversary.

Company Emblem and "Stad Middelburg" A150

1975, May 21 **Photo.** *Perf. 14x13*

529 A150 35c multicolored .30 .15

Zeeland Steamship Company, centenary.

Albert Schweitzer in Boat — A151

1975, May 21

530 A151 50c multicolored .40 .15

Albert Schweitzer (1875-1965), medical missionary.

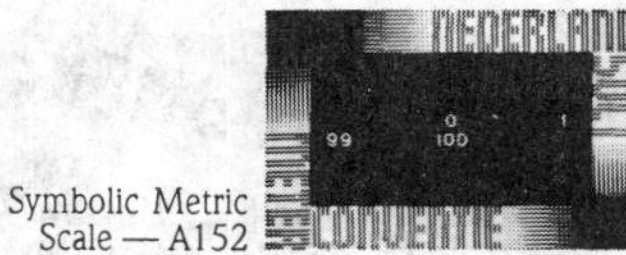

Symbolic Metric Scale — A152

1975, July 29 **Litho.** *Perf. 14x13*

531 A152 50c multicolored .40 .15

Cent. of Intl. Meter Convention, Paris, 1875.

Playing Card with Woman, Man, Pigeons, Pens — A153

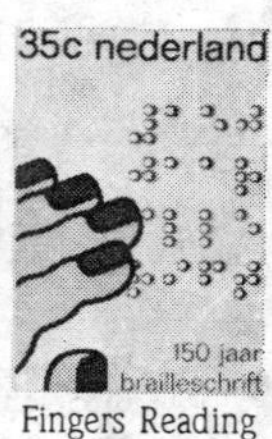

Fingers Reading Braille — A154

1975, July 29 *Perf. 13x14*

532 A153 35c multicolored .30 .15

International Women's Year 1975.

1975, Oct. 7 **Photo.** *Perf. 13x14*

533 A154 35c multicolored .30 .15

Sesquicentennial of the invention of Braille system of writing for the blind by Louis Braille (1809-1852).

Rubbings of 25¢ Coins — A155

1975, Oct. 7 *Perf. 14x13*

534 A155 50c green, blk & bl .40 .15

To publicize the importance of saving.

Lottery Ticket, 18th Century A156

1976, Feb. 3 **Photo.** *Perf. 14x13*

535 A156 35c multicolored .25 .15

250th anniversary of National Lottery.

Queen Type of 1969 and

A157

1976-86 **Photo.** *Perf. 12½x13½*

536 A157 5c gray .15 .15
Booklet Panes
a. (3 #536, 2 #537, 3 #542) 3.00
b. (4 #536, 2 #537, 4 #539 + 2 labels) 3.25
c. (#536, 2 #537, 5 #542) 3.00
d. (4 #536, 7 #539 + label) 3.00
e. (2 #536, 2 #540, 4 #541) 3.00
f. (5 #536, 2 #537, 2 #540, 3 #542) + 2 labels 4.00
g. (1 #536, 2 #537, 5 #543) ('86) 3.00
537 A157 10c ultra .15 .15
538 A157 25c violet .18 .15
539 A157 40c sepia .28 .15
540 A157 45c brt blue .35 .15
541 A157 50c lil rose ('80) .42 .15
a. Bklt. pane, 5 each #537, 541 + 2 labels 2.50
542 A113 55c carmine .50 .15
543 A157 55c brt grn ('81) .45 .20
544 A157 60c apple grn ('81) .45 .20
545 A157 65c dk red brn ('86) .60 .60
Nos. 536-545 (10) 3.53
Set value 1.50

Compare No. 544 with No. 791. No. 542 also issued in coils with control number on the back of every 5th stamp.

Coil Stamps

1976-86 *Perf. 13½ Vert.*

546 A157 5c slate gray .15 .15
547 A157 10c ultra .15 .15
548 A157 25c violet .18 .15
549 A157 40c sepia ('77) .38 .15
550 A157 45c brt blue .40 .15
551 A157 50c brt rose ('79) .50 .20
552 A157 55c brt grn ('81) .50 .20
553 A157 60c apple grn ('81) .50 .20
554 A157 65c dk red brn ('86) .60 .60
Nos. 546-554 (9) 3.36
Set value 1.60

See Nos. 772, 774, 786, 788, 791.

De Ruyter Statue, Flushing A158

1976, Apr. 22 Photo. *Perf. 14x13*
555 A158 55c multicolored .55 .15

Adm. Michiel Adriaenszon de Ruyter (1607-1676), Dutch naval hero, 300th death anniversary.

Van Prinsterer and Page — A159

1976, May 19 Photo. *Perf. 14x13*
556 A159 55c multicolored .55 .15

Guillaume Groen van Prinsterer (1801-1876), statesman and historian.

Women Waving American Flags — A160

Design is from a 220-year old permanent wooden calendar from Ameland Island.

1976, May 25 Litho.
557 A160 75c multicolored .70 .55

American Bicentennial.

Marchers A161

1976, June 15 Photo. *Perf. 14x13*
558 A161 40c multicolored .35 .15

Nijmegen 4-day march, 60th anniversary.

A number of stamps issued from 1970 on appear to have parts of the designs misregistered, blurry, or look off-center. These stamps are deliberately designed that way. Most prominent examples are Nos. 559, 582, 602, 656, 711-712, 721, B638-B640, B662-B667.

Runners A162

1976, June 15 Litho.
Tagged
559 A162 55c multicolored .90 .15

Royal Dutch Athletic Soc., 75th anniv.

Printing: One Communicating with Many — A163

1976, Sept. 2 Photo. *Perf. 13x14*
560 A163 45c blue & red .35 .15

Netherlands Printers Organization, 75th anniv.

Sailing Ship and City — A164

Design: 75c, Sea gull over coast.

1976, Sept. 2 Litho. *Perf. 14x13*
Tagged
561 A164 40c bister, red & bl .35 .15
562 A164 75c ultra, yel & red .65 .40

Zuider Zee Project, the conversion of water areas into land.

Radiation of Heat and Light — A165

Ballot and Pencil — A166

Perf. 13x14, 14x13
1977, Jan. 25 Photo.
563 A165 40c multicolored .28 .15
564 A166 45c black, red & ocher .48 .15
Set value .24

Coil Stamps
Perf. 13 Horiz.
565 A165 40c multicolored .28 .15
Perf. 13 Vert.
566 A166 45c multicolored .35 .15

Publicity for wise use of energy (40c) and forthcoming elections (45c). Nos. 565-566 have black control number on back of every 5th stamp.

For overprint see No. 569.

Spinoza — A167

1977, Feb. 21 Photo. *Perf. 13x14*
567 A167 75c multicolored .60 .40

Baruch Spinoza (1632-1677), philosopher, 300th death anniversary.

Delft Bible Text, Old Type, Electronic "a" — A168

1977, Mar. 8 *Perf. 14x13*
568 A168 55c ocher & black .45 .20

Delft Bible (Old Testament), oldest book printed in Dutch, 500th anniversary. Printed in sheets of 50 se-tenant with label inscribed with description of stamp design and purpose.

No. 564 Overprinted in Blue **25 MEI'77**

1977, Apr. 15 Photo. *Perf. 14x13*
569 A166 45c multicolored .50 .15

Elections of May 25.

Kaleidoscope of Activities — A169

1977, June 9 Litho. *Perf. 13x14*
570 A169 55c multicolored .40 .15

Netherlands Society for Industry and Commerce, bicentenary.

Man in Wheelchair Looking at Obstacles A170

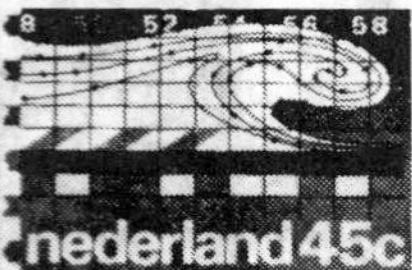

Engineer's Diagram of Water Currents A171

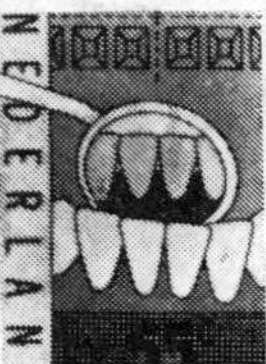

Teeth, Dentist's Mirror — A172

1977, Sept. 6 Photo. *Perf. 14x13*
571 A170 40c multicolored .30 .15
Litho.
572 A171 45c multicolored .30 .15
Perf. 13x14
573 A172 55c multicolored .40 .15
Nos. 571-573 (3) 1.00 .45

50th anniversaries of AVO (Actio vincit omnia), an organization to help the handicapped (40c), and of Delft Hydraulic Laboratory (45c); centenary of Dentists' Training in the Netherlands (55c).

"Postcode" A173

1978, Mar. 14 Photo. *Perf. 14x13*
574 A173 40c dk blue & red .30 .15
575 A173 45c red, dk & lt bl .30 .15
Set value .24

Introduction of new postal code.

European Human Rights Treaty — A174

Haarlem City Hall — A175

1978, May 2 Photo. *Perf. 13x14*
576 A174 45c gray, blue & blk .32 .15

European Treaty of Human Rights, 25th anniv.

Europa Issue

1978, May 2
577 A175 55c multicolored .60 .15

Chess Board and Move Diagram — A176

Korfball — A177

1978, June 1 Photo. *Perf. 13x14*
578 A176 40c multicolored .30 .15
Litho.
579 A177 45c red & vio bl .30 .15

18th IBM Chess Tournament, Amsterdam, July 12, and 75th anniversary of korfball in the Netherlands.

Man Pointing to his Kidney — A178

Heart, Torch, Gauge and Clouds — A179

1978, Aug. 22 Photo. *Perf. 13x13½*
580 A178 40c multicolored .30 .15
Perf. 13x14
581 A179 45c multicolored .30 .15

Importance of kidney transplants and drive against hypertension.

Epaulettes, Military Academy — A180

1978, Sept. 12 Photo. *Perf. 13x14*
582 A180 55c multicolored .40 .15

Royal Military Academy, sesquicentennial. Printed in continuous design in sheets of 100 (10x10).

Verkade as Hamlet A181

1978, Oct. 17 Photo. *Perf. 14x13*
583 A181 45c multicolored .30 .15

Eduard Rutger Verkade (1878-1961), actor and producer.

Clasped Hands and Arrows — A182

1979, Jan. 23 Engr. *Perf. 13x14*
584 A182 55c blue .40 .15

Union of Utrecht, 400th anniversary.

European Parliament A183

1979, Feb. 20 Litho. *Perf. 13½x13*

585 A183 45c blue, blk & red .35 .15

European Parliament, first direct elections, June 7-10.

Queen Juliana A184

1979, Mar. 13 Photo. *Perf. 13½x14*

586 A184 55c multicolored .48 .20

70th birthday of Queen Juliana.

A185

A186

Europa: 55c, Dutch Stamps and magnifying glass. 75c, Hand on Morse key, and ship at sea.

1979, May 2 Litho. *Perf. 13x13½*

587 A185 55c multicolored .45 .20

588 A185 75c multicolored .60 .40

1979, June 5 Litho. *Perf. 13x14*

Map of Netherlands with chamber locations.

589 A186 45c multicolored .35 .15

Netherlands Chambers of Commerce and 175th anniversary of Maastricht Chamber.

Soccer — A187

1979, Aug. 28 Litho. *Perf. 14x13*

590 A187 45c multicolored .30 .15

Centenary of soccer in the Netherlands.

Suffragettes — A188

1979, Aug. 28 Photo. *Perf. 13x14*

591 A188 55c multicolored .40 .15

Voting right for women, 60th anniversary.

Inscribed Tympanum and Architrave A189

1979, Oct. 2 Photo. *Perf. 14x13*

592 A189 40c multicolored .30 .15

Joost van den Vondel (1587-1679), Dutch poet and dramatist.

"Gay Company," Tile Floor — A190

1979, Oct. 2

593 A190 45c multicolored .30 .15

Jan Steen (1626-1679), Dutch painter.

Alexander de Savorin Lohman (1837-1924) — A191

Politicians: 50c, Pieter Jelles Troelstra (1860-1930), Social Democratic Workmen's Party leader. 60c, Pieter Jacobus Oud (1886-1968), mayor of Rotterdam.

1980, Mar. 4 Photo. *Perf. 13x13½*

594 A191 45c multicolored .24 .15

595 A191 50c multicolored .32 .15

596 A191 60c multicolored .50 .15

Nos. 594-596 (3) 1.06

Set value .36

British Bomber Dropping Food, Dutch Flag — A192

Anne Frank — A193

Perf. 13x14, 14x13

1980, Apr. 25 Photo.

597 A192 45c multicolored .30 .15

598 A193 60c multicolored .40 .15

Set value .22

35th anniv. of liberation from the Germans.

Queen Beatrix, Palace — A194

1980, Apr. 30 *Perf. 13x14, 13x13½*

599 A194 60c multicolored .42 .20

Installation of Queen Beatrix.

See No. 608.

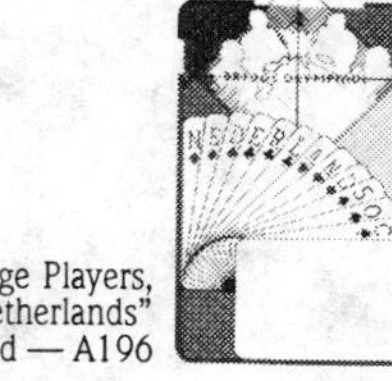

Boy and Girl Inspecting Stamp — A195

1980, May 1 *Perf. 14x13*

600 A195 50c multicolored .32 .25

Youth philately; NVPH Stamp Show, s'Gravenhagen, May 1-3 and JUPOSTEX Stamp Exhibition, Eindhoven, May 23-27. No. 600 printed se-tenant with label.

Bridge Players, "Netherlands" Hand — A196

1980, June 3 Litho. *Perf. 13x14*

601 A196 50c multicolored .32 .15

6th Bridge Olympiad, Valkenburg, 9/27-10/11.

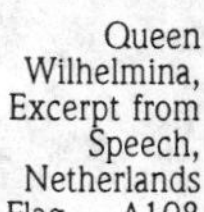

Truck Transport A197

1980, Aug. 26 Photo. *Perf. 13½x13*

602 A197 50c shown .32 .15

603 A197 60c Two-axle railway hopper truck .42 .15

604 A197 80c Inland navigation barge .60 .32

Nos. 602-604 (3) 1.34 .62

Queen Wilhelmina, Excerpt from Speech, Netherlands Flag — A198

1980, Sept. 23 Litho. *Perf. 13½x13*

605 A198 60c shown .42 .15

606 A198 80c Winston Churchill, British flag .60 .32

Europa.

Abraham Kuyper, University Emblem, "100" — A199

1980, Oct. 14 Litho. *Perf. 13½x13*

607 A199 50c multicolored .35 .15

Free University centennial (founded by Kuyper).

Queen Beatrix Type of 1980

Perf. 13x13½, 13x14

1981, Jan. 6 Photo.

608 A194 65c multicolored .50 .15

Parcel — A200

Designs: 55c, Dish antenna and telephone. 65c, Bank books.

1981, May 19 Litho. *Perf. 13½x13*

609 A200 45c multicolored .30 .18

610 A200 55c multicolored .38 .18

611 A200 65c multicolored .50 .18

a. Souvenir sheet of 3, #609-611 1.25 1.25

Centenaries: Parcel Post Service (45c); Public telephone service (55c); National Savings Bank (65c).

Huis ten Bosch (Royal Palace), The Hague — A201

1981, June 16 Litho. *Perf. 13½x13*

612 A201 55c multicolored .38 .15

Europa Issue 1981

Carillon A202

1981, Sept. 1 Litho. *Perf. 13½x13*

613 A202 45c shown .30 .18

614 A202 65c Barrel organ .50 .18

450th Anniv. of Council of State — A203

1981, Oct. 1 Photo. *Perf. 13½x13*

615 A203 65c multi .50 .15

Excavator and Ship's Screw (Exports) A204

1981, Oct. 20 Photo. *Perf. 13½x13*

616 A204 45c shown .30 .15

617 A204 55c Cast iron component, scale .35 .15

618 A204 60c Tomato, lettuce .42 .15

619 A204 65c Egg, cheese .45 .15

Nos. 616-619 (4) 1.52

Set value .48

Queen Beatrix — A205

1981-86 Photo. *Perf. 13½x12½*

620	65c tan & blk	.65	.15
621	70c lt vio & blk ('82)	1.25	.15
a.	Bklt. pane (4 #536, 4 #621) ('85)	4.00	
622	75c pale pink & blk ('82)	.75	.15
a.	Bklt. pane of 4 ('86)	3.00	
623	90c lt grn & blk ('82)	1.75	.15
624	1g lt vio & blk ('82)	1.00	.15
625	1.40g pale grn & blk ('82)	2.50	.15
626	2g lem & blk ('82)	1.75	.15
627	3g pale vio & blk ('82)	2.75	.25
628	4g brt yel grn & blk ('82)	4.00	.25
629	5g lt grnsh bl & blk ('82)	5.00	.25
630	6.50g lt lil rose & blk ('82)	5.00	.25
631	7g pale bl & blk ('86)	7.50	.25
	Nos. 620-631 (12)	33.90	2.30

Coil Stamps

Perf. 13½ Horiz.

632	70c lt vio & blk ('82)	1.25	.25
633	75c pale pink & blk ('86)	.75	.25
634	1g lt vio & blk ('82)	1.00	.25
635	2g lem & blk ('82)	1.75	.25
636	6.50g lt lil rose & blk ('82)	7.50	.25
637	7g pale bl & blk ('86)	6.75	.25
	Nos. 632-637 (6)	19.00	1.50

See Nos. 685-699.

University of Amsterdam, 350th Anniv. — A206

1982, Jan. 14 Litho. *Perf. 13½x13*

638 A206 65c multi .45 .15

Netherlands stamps can be mounted in the annually supplemented Scott Netherlands album.

Royal Dutch Skating Assoc. Centenary — A207

1982, Feb. 26 Litho. *Perf. 13x13½*

639 A207 45c multi .32 .22

Bicentenary of US-Netherlands Diplomatic Relations A208

1982, Apr. 20 Photo. *Perf. 13½x13*

640 A208 50c multi .32 .22
641 A208 65c multi .45 .22

See US No. 2003.

Sandwich Tern and Eider Duck, Waddenzee A209

1982, June 8 Litho. *Perf. 13½x13*

642 A209 50c shown .32 .22
643 A209 70c Barnacle geese .45 .22

Dutch Road Safety Assoc, 50th Anniv. — A210

Europa 1982 — A211

1982, Aug. 24 Photo. *Perf. 13x14*

644 A210 60c multi .45 .25

1982, Sept. 16 Litho. *Perf. 13x13½*

Fortification Layouts.

645 A211 50c Enkhuizen, 1590 .38 .15
646 A211 70c Coevorden, 1680 .50 .15
Set value .24

Royal Palace, Dam Square, Amsterdam — A212

1982, Oct. 5 Litho. *Perf. 13x13½*

647 A212 50c Facade, cross-section .38 .20
648 A212 60c Aerial view .45 .25

Royal Dutch Touring Club Centenary A213

1983, Mar. 1 Litho. *Perf. 13½x13*

649 A213 70c multi .50 .25

A214

A215

Europa: 50c, Netherlands Newspaper Publishers Assoc., 75th anniv. 70c, Launching of European Telecommunication Satellite Org. ECS F-1 rocket, June 3.

1983, May 17 Litho. *Perf. 13x13½*

650 A214 50c multi .38 .18
651 A214 70c multi .50 .20

1983, June 21 Litho. *Perf. 13x13½*

De Stijl ("The Style") Modern Art Movement, 1917-31: 50c, Composition 1922, by P. Mondriaan. 65c, Maison Particuliere contra Construction, by C. van Eesteren and T. van Doesburg.

652 A215 50c multi .38 .20
653 A215 65c multi .45 .25

Symbolic Separation of Church — A216

1983, Oct. 11 Litho. *Perf. 13x13½*

654 A216 70c multi .50 .25

Martin Luther (1483-1546).

2nd European Parliament Election, June 14 — A217

1984, Mar. 13 Litho. *Perf. 13½x13*

655 A217 70c multicolored .45 .18

St. Servatius (d. 384) — A218

1984, May 8 Photo. *Perf. 13x14*

656 A218 60c Statue, 1732 .60 .15

Europa (1959-84) A219

1984, May 22 *Perf. 13½x13*

657 A219 50c blue .45 .15
a. Perf. 14x13 *10.00 1.00*
658 A219 70c yellow green .70 .18
a. Perf. 14x13 *10.00 1.00*

Perf. 14x13 stamps are coils. Every fifth stamp has a control number on the back.

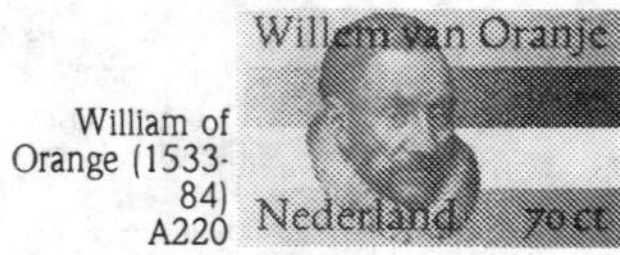

William of Orange (1533-84) A220

1984, July 10 Photo. *Perf. 14x13*

659 A220 70c multicolored .70 .18

World Wildlife Fund — A221

1984, Sept. 18 Litho. *Perf. 14x13*

660 A221 70c Pandas, globe .65 .18

11th Intl. Small Business Congress, Amsterdam, Oct. 24-26 — A222

1984, Oct. 23 Litho. *Perf. 13x13½*

661 A222 60c Graph, leaf .60 .15

Guide Dog Fund — A223

Photogravure and Engraved

1985, Jan. 22 *Perf. 14x13*

662 A223 60c Sunny, first guide dog .60 .15

A224

Tourism A224a

1985, Feb. 26 Photo.

663 A224 50c multicolored .50 .15
664 A224a 70c multicolored .75 .15

Cent. of the Tourist office "Geuldal," and 50th anniv. of the Natl. Park "De Hoge Veluwe."

Liberation from German Forces, 40th Anniv. — A225

Designs: 50c, Jewish star, mastheads of underground newspapers, resistance fighter. 60c, Allied supply air drop, masthead of The Flying Dutchman, Polish soldier at Arnhem. 65c, Liberation Day in Amsterdam, masthead, first edition of Het Parool (underground newspaper), American cemetary at Margraten. 70c, Dutch women in Japanese prison camp, Japanese occupation currency, building of the Burma Railway.

1985, May 5 Photo. *Perf. 14x13*

665 A225 50c blk, buff & red .50 .15
666 A225 60c blk, buff & brt bl .60 .15
667 A225 65c blk, buff & org .60 .15
668 A225 70c blk, buff & brt grn .70 .18
Nos. 665-668 (4) 2.40 .63

WWII resistance effort (1940-1945) and liberation of Europe, 1945.

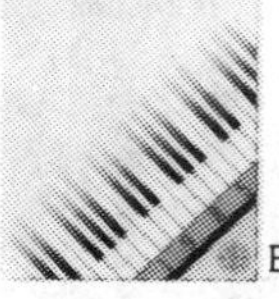
Europa '85 — A226

1985, June 4 Litho. *Perf. 13x13½*

669 A226 50c Piano keyboard .75 .15
670 A226 70c Stylized organ pipes 1.00 .18

Natl. Museum of Fine Arts, Amsterdam, Cent. — A227

Anniversaries and events: 60c, Nautical College, Amsterdam, bicent. 70c, SAIL-85, Amsterdam.

1985, July 2 Photo. *Perf. 13½x13*

671 A227 50c Museum in 1885, 1985 .50 .15
672 A227 60c Students training .60 .15

Perf. 14x13

673 A227 70c Sailboat rigging .70 .18
Nos. 671-673 (3) 1.80 .48

Wildlife Conservation A228

Designs: 50c, Porpoise, statistical graph. 70c, Seal, molecular structure models.

1985, Sept. 10 Litho. *Perf. 13½x13*

674 A228 50c multicolored .50 .15
675 A228 70c multicolored .70 .18

Penal Code, Cent. — A229

Amsterdam Datum Ordinance, 300th Anniv. — A230

Lithographed, Photogravure (60c)

1986, Jan. 21 *Perf. 14x13*

676 A229 50c Text .52 .15
677 A230 60c Elevation gauge .60 .15

Sexbierum Windmill Test Station Inauguration A231

1986, Mar. 4 Litho. *Perf. 14x13*

678 A231 70c multicolored .70 .18

Het Loo Palace Gardens, Apeldorn — A232

1986, May 13 Litho. *Perf. 13x14*

679 A232 50c shown .55 .15

Photo.

680 A232 70c Air and soil pollution .70 .18

Europa 1986.

Utrecht Cathedral A233

Willem Drees (1886-), Statesman A234

1986, June 10 Photo. *Perf. 13x14*
681 A233 50c shown .48 .15
682 A233 60c German House, c.1350 .55 .15

Perf. 14x13
683 A233 70c Utrecht University charter, horiz. .65 .18
Nos. 681-683 (3) 1.68 .48

Cathedral restoration, 1986. Heemschut Conservation. Soc., 75th anniv. Utrecht University, 350th anniv.

1986, July 1 Litho. *Perf. 13x13½*
684 A234 55c multicolored .52 .15

Queen Type of 1981

1986-90 Photo. *Perf. 13½x12½*
685 A205 1.20g citron & blk 1.10 .15
686 A205 1.50g lt rose vio & blk 1.40 .15
688 A205 2.50g tan & blk 2.25 .15
694 A205 7.50g lt grn & blk 6.50 .75
Nos. 685-694 (4) 11.25 1.20

Coil Stamps

Perf. 13½ Horiz.
697 A205 1.50g lt rose vio & blk 1.40 .15
699 A205 2.50g tan & blk 2.25 .15

Issue dates: Nos. 685, 688, 699, Sept. 23. Nos. 686, 697, Aug. 19. 7.50g, May 29, 1990.

This is an expanding set. Numbers will change if necessary.

Billiards — A235

Perf. 14x13, 13x14

1986, Sept. 9 Photo.
705 A235 75c shown .70 .58
706 A235 75c Checkers, vert. .70 .58

Royal Dutch Billiards Assoc., Checkers Association, 75th annivs.

Delta Project Completion A236

1986, Oct. 7 Photo. *Perf. 14x13*
708 A236 65c Storm-surge barrier .70 .15
709 A236 75c Barrier withstanding flood .75 .15

Princess Juliana and Prince Bernhard, 50th Wedding Anniv. — A237

1987, Jan. 6 Photo. *Perf. 13x14*
710 A237 75c multicolored .75 .15

Intl. Year of Shelter for the Homeless A238

Designs: 75c, Salvation Army, cent.

1987, Feb. 10 Photo. *Perf. 14x13*
711 A238 65c multicolored .60 .15
712 A238 75c multicolored .70 .15

Dutch Literature A239

Authors: 55c, Eduard Douwes Dekker (1820-1887) and De Harmonie Club, Batavia. 75c, Constantijn Huygens (1596-1687) and Scheveningseweg, The Hague.

1987, Mar. 10 Litho. *Perf. 13½x13*
713 A239 55c multicolored .52 .15
714 A239 75c multicolored .70 .15
Set value .24

Europa 1987 — A240

Modern architecture: 55c, Scheveningen Dance Theater, designed by Rem Koolhaas. 75c, Montessori School, Amsterdam, designed by Herman Hertzberger.

1987, May 12 Litho. *Perf. 14x13*
715 A240 55c multicolored .55 .15
716 A240 75c multicolored .80 .15

Produce Auction at Broeck op Langedijk, 1887 — A241

Designs: 65c, Field in Groningen Province, signatures of society founders. 75c, Auction, bidding, price indicator, 1987.

1987, June 16 Photo. *Perf. 14x13*
717 A241 55c shown .55 .15
718 A241 65c multicolored .65 .15
719 A241 75c multicolored .80 .15
Nos. 717-719 (3) 2.00
Set value .36

Sale of produce by auction in the Netherlands, cent., and Groningen Agricultural Society, 150th anniv. (No. 718).

Union of the Netherlands Municipalities, 75th Anniv. — A242

1987, Oct. 6 Litho. *Perf. 13x14*
720 A242 75c multicolored .80 .15

Noordeinde Palace, The Hague — A243

1987, Oct. 27 Photo. *Perf. 14x13*
721 A243 65c multicolored .65 .15

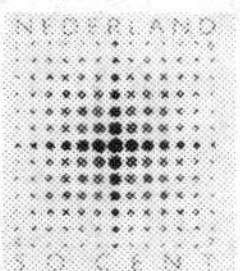

A244

Booklet Stamps

Perf. 13½x13 on 3 Sides

1987, Dec. 1 Photo.
722 A244 50c dk ultra, emer & dk red .50 .15
723 A244 50c dk red, dk ultra & yel .50 .15
724 A244 50c dk ultra, yel & dk red .50 .15
725 A244 50c dk red, emer & yel .50 .15
726 A244 50c emer, dk red & dk ultra .50 .15
a. Bklt. pane of 20, 4 each #722-726 10.50
Nos. 722-726 (5) 2.50 .75

Netherlands Cancer Institute, 75th Anniv. — A246

1988, Apr. 19 Litho. *Perf. 13½x13*
728 A246 75c multicolored .80 .16

Europa 1988 — A247

Modern transportation meeting ecological requirements: 55c, Cyclist, rural scenery, chemical formulas, vert. 75c, Cyclists seen through car-door mirror.

1988, May 17 Litho. *Perf. 13x13½*
729 A247 55c multicolored .60 .15

Perf. 13½x13
730 A247 75c multicolored .80 .20

Coronation of William III and Mary Stuart, King and Queen of England, 300th Anniv. (in 1989) — A248

Designs: 65c, Prism splitting light as discovered by Sir Isaac Newton, planet Saturn as observed by Christian Huygens, and pendulum clock, c. 1688. 75c, William of Orange (1650-1702) and Mary II (1662-1694).

1988, June 14 *Perf. 14x13*
731 A248 65c multicolored .70 .18
732 A248 75c multicolored .80 .20

Arrival of Dutch William in England, 300th anniv.

Modern Art — A249

Paintings by artists belonging to Cobra: 55c, *Cobra Cat,* 1950, by Appel. 65c, *Stag Beetle,* 1948, by Corneille. 75c, *Fallen Horse,* 1950, by Constant.

1988, July 5 Litho. *Perf. 13½x13*
733 A249 55c multicolored .55 .15
734 A249 65c multicolored .65 .16
735 A249 75c multicolored .75 .18
Nos. 733-735 (3) 1.95 .49

Each stamp printed se-tenant with label picturing the featured artist's signature.

Cobra, an intl. organization established in 1948 by expressionist artists from Copenhagen, Brussels and Amsterdam.

Australia Bicentennial — A250

1988, Aug. 30 Photo. *Perf. 13x14*
736 A250 75c multicolored .72 .18

Erasmus University, Rotterdam, 75th Anniv. — A251

Amsterdam Concertgebouw and Orchestra, Cent. — A252

1988, Sept. 27 Litho. *Perf. 13x13½*
737 A251 75c dk green & green .72 .18
738 A252 75c bright violet .72 .18

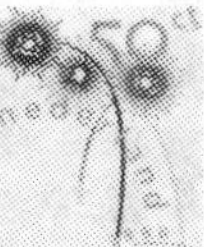

Holiday Greetings — A253

Perf. 13½x12½

1988, Dec. 1 Photo.
739 A253 50c multicolored .52 .15

"Holland," etc.

Stamps inscribed "Holland," "Stadspost," etc., are private issues. In some cases overprints or surcharges on Netherlands stamps may be created.

Privatization of the Netherlands Postal Service — A254

Design: Mailbox, sorting machine, mailbag, mailman, telephone key pad, fiber optics cable, microwave transmitter and telephone handset.

Perf. 13x13½

1989, Jan. 3 Litho. & Engr.
740 A254 75c multicolored .78 .20

Dutch Trade Unions — A255

1989, Feb. 7 Litho. *Perf. 13x13½*
741 A255 55c shown .55 .15

Photo.

Perf. 13x14
742 A255 75c Hands, mouths .72 .15

NATO, 40th Anniv. — A256

1989, Mar. 14 Litho. *Perf. 14x13*
743 A256 75c multicolored .75 .20

Europa 1989 — A257

Children's games (string telephone): 55c, Boy. 75c Girl.

1989, May 9 Litho. *Perf. 13½x13*

744 A257 55c multicolored .55 .15
745 A257 75c multicolored .75 .20

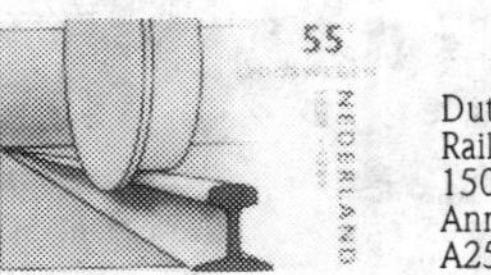

Dutch Railways, 150th Anniv. A258

1989, June 20 Litho. *Perf. 13½x13*

746 A258 55c Rails .55 .15
747 A258 65c Trains .65 .16

Perf. 14x13

748 A258 75c Passengers .75 .20
Nos. 746-748 (3) 1.95 .51

Royal Dutch Soccer Assoc., Cent. — A259

Treaty of London, 150th Anniv. — A260

1989, Sept. 5 Photo. *Perf. 13x14*

749 A259 75c multicolored .72 .18

1989, Oct. 2 Litho. *Perf. 13x14*

750 A260 75c Map of Limburg Provinces .72 .18

See Belgium No. 1327.

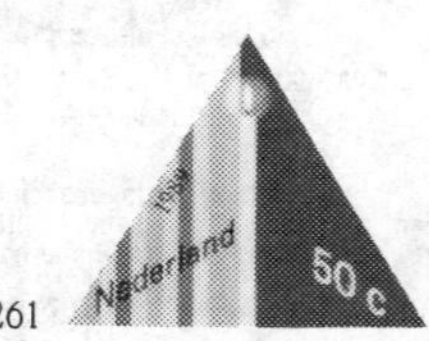

A261

Perf. 13x13x13½

1989, Nov. 30 Photo.

751 A261 50c multicolored .48 .15

Sold only in sheets of 20.

Anniversaries A262

Vincent van Gogh (1853-1890) A263

Designs: 65c, Leiden coat of arms (tulip), and layout of the Hortus Botanicus in 1601. 75c, Assessing work conditions (clock, sky, wooden floor), horiz.

1990, Feb. 6 Litho. *Perf. 13x13½*

752 A262 65c multicolored .70 .18

Perf. 13½x13

753 A262 75c multicolored .80 .22

Hortus Botanicus, Leiden, 400th anniv. (65c); Labor Inspectorate, cent. (75c).

1990, Mar. 6 *Perf. 13x13½*

Details of works by van Gogh: 55c, *Self-portrait*, pencil sketch, 1886-87. 75c, *The Green Vineyard*, painting, 1888.

754 A263 55c multicolored .58 .16
755 A263 75c multicolored .80 .22

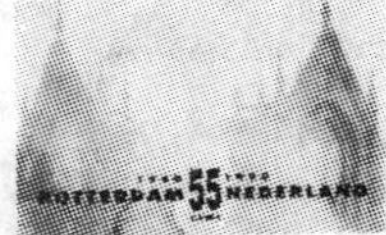

Rotterdam Reconstruction A264

1990, May 8 Litho. *Perf. 13½x13*

756 A264 55c shown .58 .16
757 A264 65c Diagram .70 .18
758 A264 75c Modern bldgs. .80 .22
Nos. 756-758 (3) 2.08 .56

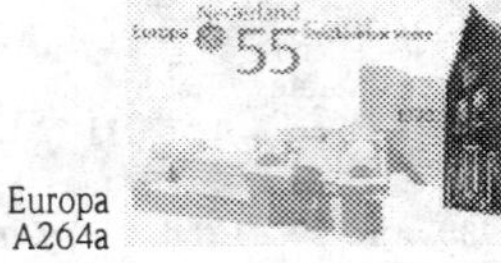

Europa A264a

Post offices.

1990, June 12

759 A264a 55c Veere .58 .16
760 A264a 75c Groningen .80 .22

Dutch East India Co. Ships — A265

Sail '90 — A266

1990, July 3 *Perf. 13x13½*

761 A265 65c multicolored .70 .18
762 A266 75c multicolored .80 .22

Queens of the House of Orange A267

1990, Sept. 5 Litho. *Perf. 13½*

763 A267 150c multicolored 1.60 .60

Century of rule by Queens Emma, Wilhelmina, Juliana and Beatrix.

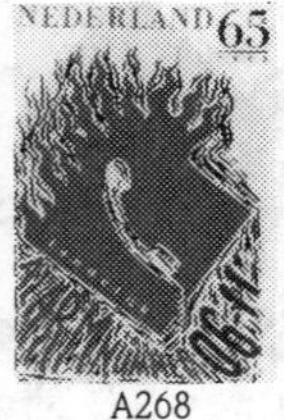

A268

A269

1990, Oct. 9 Photo. *Perf. 13x14*

764 A268 65c multicolored .70 .18

Natl. emergency phone number.

1990, Nov. 29 Photo. *Perf. 14*

765 A269 50c multicolored .55 .15

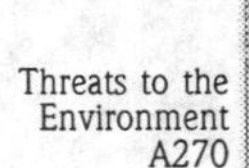

Threats to the Environment A270

1991, Jan. 30 Litho. *Perf. 13½x13*

766 A270 55c Air pollution .60 .15
767 A270 65c Water pollution .70 .15
768 A270 75c Soil pollution .80 .16
Nos. 766-768 (3) 2.10 .46

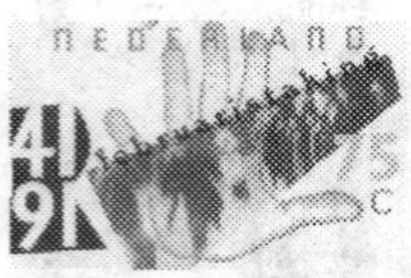

General Strike, 50th Anniv. A271

1991, Feb. 25 Photo. *Perf. 14x13*

769 A271 75c multicolored .80 .16

Queen Beatrix and Prince Claus, 25th Wedding Anniv. A272

1991, Mar. 11 Litho. *Perf. 13½x13*

770 A272 75c shown .82 .20
771 A272 75c Riding horses .82 .20
a. Pair, #770-771 1.65 .40

Numeral Type of 1976 and

Queen Beatrix — A273

Syncopated Type E

Type E: On the two longer sides, groups of six holes separated by an elliptical perforation equal in width to three holes.

Perf. 12½x13½, 13½x12½

1991-94 Photo.

772	A157	70c gray violet	.75	.18
a.		Booklet pane, 5 each #537, 772	4.50	
773	A273	75c green	.75	.15
a.		Bklt. pane of 4 + 2 labels	3.25	
774	A157	80c red lilac	.85	.20
774A	A273	80c red brown	.85	.20
b.		Booklet pane of 5 + label	4.25	
		Complete booklet, #774Ab	4.25	
775	A273	90c blue	.90	.22
776	A273	1g purple	1.10	.28
777	A273	1.30g gray blue	1.50	.38
778	A273	1.40g gray olive	1.60	.40
779	A273	1.60g magenta	1.70	.40
780	A273	2g yellow brown	2.25	.55
781	A273	2.50g red lilac	3.25	.80
782	A273	3g blue	3.50	.85
783	A273	5g brown red	5.75	1.50

Perf. 14x13, Syncopated Type E

784	A273	7.50g purple	10.50	2.75
785	A273	10g green	11.50	3.00
		Nos. 772-785 (15)	46.75	11.86

Coil Stamps

Perf. 13½ Vert. (A157), Horiz. (A273)

786	A157	70c gray violet	.75	.18
787	A273	75c green	.80	.15
788	A157	80c red lilac	.85	.20
789	A273	80c red brown	.85	.20
790	A273	1.60g magenta	1.70	.40
		Nos. 786-790 (5)	4.95	1.13

Booklet Stamp

Perf. 12½x13½

791	A157	60c lemon	.62	.15
a.		Bklt. pane, 2 #791, 4 #772	4.25	

Issued: 75c, 3/14/91; 60c, 70c, #774, 1.60g, 6/25/91; #774A, 789, 1.30g, 1.40g, 9/3/91; 1g, 2g, 3g, 5g, 11/11/92; 90c, 2/2/93; 2.50g, 9/7/93; 10g, 11/29/93; 7.50g, 11/28/94.

See #912.

A274

A276

A275

Designs: 55c, Gerard Philips, carbon filament experiments, 1890. 65c, Electrical wiring. 75c, Laser video disk experiment.

Perf. 13x14, 14x13

1991, May 15 Photo.

792 A274 55c multicolored .60 .15
793 A275 65c multicolored .72 .18
794 A274 75c multicolored .82 .20
Nos. 792-794 (3) 2.14 .53

Philips Electronics, cent. (Nos. 792, 794). Netherlands Normalization Institute, 75th anniv. (No. 793).

1991, June 11 Litho. *Perf. 13x13½*

Europa: 75c, Ladders to another world.

795 A276 55c multicolored .60 .15
796 A276 75c multicolored .82 .20

Nijmegen Four Days Marches, 75th Anniv. — A277

1991, July 9 Photo. *Perf. 14x13*

797 A277 80c multicolored .85 .20

Dutch Nobel Prize Winners A278

Designs: 60c, Jacobus H. Van't Hoff, chemistry, 1901. 70c, Pieter Zeeman, physics, 1902. 80c, Tobias M. C. Asser, peace, 1911.

1991, Sept. 3 *Perf. 14x13*

798 A278 60c multicolored .62 .15
799 A278 70c multicolored .75 .18
800 A278 80c multicolored .85 .20
Nos. 798-800 (3) 2.22 .53

Public Libraries, Cent. — A279

1991, Oct. 1 Litho. *Perf. 13½x13*

801 A279 70c Children reading .80 .16
802 A279 80c Books .90 .18

A280

1991, Nov. 28 Photo. *Perf. 14*

803 A280 55c multicolored .65 .16

Delft University of Technology, Sesquicent. A281

New Civil Code — A282

1992, Jan. 7 Litho. *Perf. 13½x13*
804 A281 60c multicolored .70 .18
805 A282 80c multicolored .95 .25

A283

A284

1992 Olympics, Albertville and Barcelona: No. 806a, Volleyball, rowing. b, Shotput, rowing. c, Speedskating, rowing. d, Field hockey.

1992, Feb. 4 *Perf. 13x14*
Souvenir Sheet
806 A283 80c Sheet of 4, #a.-d. 3.60 3.60

1992, Feb. 25 Litho. *Perf. 13x12½*
807 A284 70c Tulips .85 .22

Photo.
Perf. 13x14
808 A284 80c Map 1.00 .25

Expo '92, Seville.

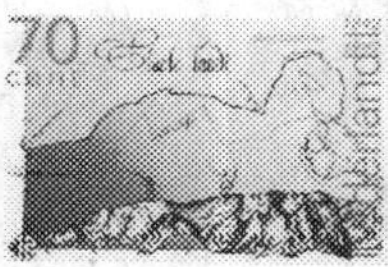

Discovery of New Zealand and Tasmania by Abel Tasman, 350th Anniv. — A285

1992, Mar. 12 Photo. *Perf. 14x13*
809 A285 70c multicolored .85 .22

A286

A287

1992, Apr. 28 Litho. *Perf. 13x13½*
810 A286 60c multicolored .75 .18
811 A287 80c multicolored 1.00 .25

Royal Assoc. of Netherlands Architects, 150th Anniv. (#810). Opening of Building for Lower House of States General (#811).

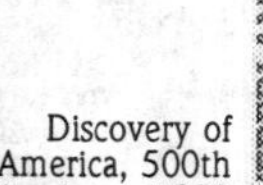

Discovery of America, 500th Anniv. — A288

Perf. 13½x13, 13x13½
1992, May 12 Litho.
812 A288 60c Globe, Columbus .68 .18
813 A288 80c Sailing ship, vert. .95 .22

Europa. On normally centered stamps the white border appears at the left side of No. 813.

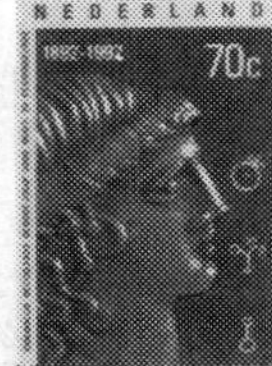

Royal Netherlands Numismatics Society, Cent. — A289

1992, May 19 Photo. *Perf. 13x14*
814 A289 70c multicolored .85 .22

Netherlands Pediatrics Society, Cent. — A290

1992, June 16 Litho. *Perf. 13½x13*
815 A290 80c multicolored 1.00 .25

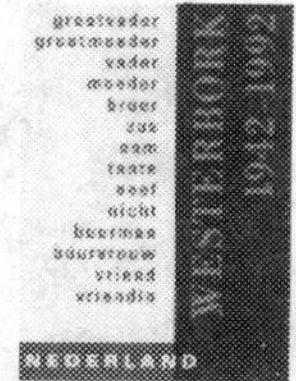

First Deportation Train from Westerbork Concentration Camp, 50th Anniv. — A291

1992, Aug. 25 *Perf. 13x13½*
816 A291 70c multicolored .85 .22

Single European Market A292

1992, Oct. 6 *Perf. 13½x13*
817 A292 80c multicolored 1.00 .25

Queen Beatrix, 12½Years Since Investiture — A293

1992, Oct. 30 *Perf. 13x13½*
818 A293 80c multicolored 1.00 .25

Christmas Rose — A294

1992, Nov. 30 Photo. *Perf. 14*
819 A294 55c Red flower .60 .15
820 A294 55c Silver flower .60 .15
a. Pair, #819-820 1.20 .25

Netherlands Cycle and Motor Industry Assoc. (RAI), Cent. — A295

Designs: 70c, Couple riding bicycle. 80c, Early automobile.

1993, Jan. 5 Litho. *Perf. 13½x13*
821 A295 70c multicolored .78 .15
822 A295 80c black & yellow .90 .18

Greetings Stamps A296

Geometric shapes.

1993, Feb. 2 Photo. *Perf. 14x13½*
823 A296 70c multi .82 .15
824 A296 70c multi, diff. .82 .15
a. Tete-beche pair, #823-824 1.65 .25

Mouth-to-mouth Resuscitation A297

Royal Horse Artillery Lead Driver, Horses A298

Leaf, Insect Pests — A299

1993, Feb. 16 Litho. *Perf. 13x13½*
825 A297 70c multicolored .78 .15
826 A298 80c multicolored .90 .18
827 A299 80c multicolored .90 .18
Nos. 825-827 (3) 2.58 .51

Royal Netherlands First Aid Assoc., cent. (#825). Royal Horse Artillery, bicent. (#826). University of Agriculture, 75th anniv. (#827).

On No. 826, normally centered stamps show design extending to top and right sides only.

Royal Dutch Notaries' Assoc., 150th Anniv. — A300

Litho. & Engr.
1993, Mar. 2 *Perf. 14x13*
828 A300 80c Top half of emblem .90 .18
829 A300 80c Bottom half of emblem .90 .18
a. Pair, #828-829 1.80 .36

No. 829a has continuous design.

Butterflies A301

Designs: 70c, Pearl-bordered fritillary (Zilvervlek). 80c, Large tortoiseshell (Grote vos). 90c, Large white (Koolwitje). 160c, Polyommatus icarus.

1993, Mar. 23 Photo.
830 A301 70c black & multi .78 .15
831 A301 80c yellow & multi .90 .18
832 A301 90c green & multi 1.00 .20
Nos. 830-832 (3) 2.68 .53

Souvenir Sheet
833 A301 160c red & multi 1.75 1.75

On normally centered stamps the white border appears at the right side.

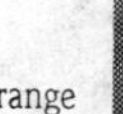

Radio Orange A302

Designs: No. 834, Woman broadcasting. No. 835, Man listening.

1993, May 5 Photo. *Perf. 14x13*
834 A302 80c orange red & purple .95 .18
835 A302 80c purple & orange red .95 .18
a. Pair, #834-835 1.90 .38

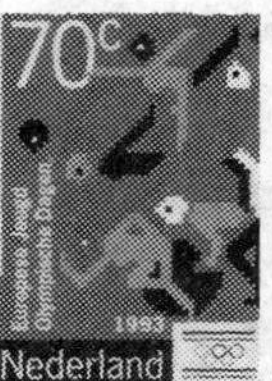

European Youth Olympic Days — A303

Symbols of Olympic sports.

1993, June 1 *Perf. 13x14*
836 A303 70c blue & multi .85 .15
837 A303 80c yellow & multi .95 .18

Europa A304

Contemporary sculpture by: 70c, Wessel Couzijn. 80c, Per Kirkeby. 160c, Naum Gabo, vert.

Perf. 13½x13, 13x13½
1993, July 6 Litho.
838 A304 70c black, blue & green .85 .15
839 A304 80c black, red & yellow .95 .18
840 A304 160c black, blue & purple 1.90 .36
Nos. 838-840 (3) 3.70 .69

Dutch Nobel Prize Winners — A305

Designs: 70c, J.D. van der Waals, physics, 1910. 80c, Willem Einthoven, medicine, 1924. 90c, Christiaan Eijkman, medicine, 1929.

1993, Sept. 7 Litho. *Perf. 13x13½*
841 A305 70c multicolored .85 .15
842 A305 80c multicolored .95 .18
843 A305 90c multicolored 1.10 .22
Nos. 841-843 (3) 2.90 .55

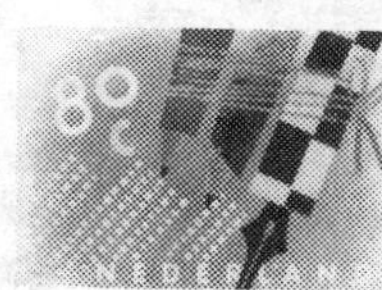

Letter Writing Day — A306

1993, Sept. 14 Photo. *Perf. 14x13*
844 A306 80c Pencils, pen .95 .22
845 A306 80c Envelope, contents .95 .22
a. Pair, #844-845 1.90 .45

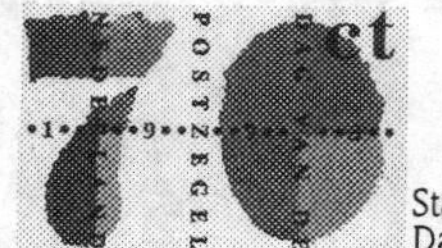

Stamp Day — A307

1993, Oct. 8 Litho. *Perf. 13½x13*
846 A307 70c shown .80 .20
847 A307 80c Dove with envelope .95 .22

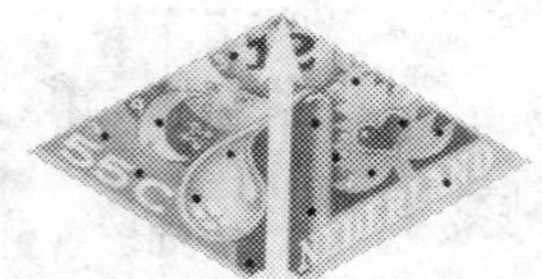

December Stamps — A308

Clock hand pointing to "12:" and: No. 848, Star, candle, Christmas tree. No. 849, Fireworks.

1993, Nov. 29 Photo. *Perf. 12*

848 A308 55c blue & multi	.60	.15
849 A308 55c red & multi	.60	.15
a. Pair, #848-849	1.20	.15

Issued in sheets of 20, 10 each #848-849 + label. Each stamp contains perforations placed within the design to resemble snowflakes.

Piet Mondrian (1872-1944), Painter A309

Details from paintings: 70c, The Red Mill. 80c, Rhomboid with Yellow Lines. 90c, Broadway Boogie Woogie.

1994, Feb. 1 Litho. *Perf. 13½x13*

850 A309 70c multicolored	.80	.20
851 A309 80c multicolored	.95	.22
852 A309 90c multicolored	1.10	.25
Nos. 850-852 (3)	2.85	.67

Wild Flowers A310

1994, Mar. 15 Photo. *Perf. 14]x13*

853 A310 70c Downy rose	.80	.20
854 A310 80c Daisy	.95	.22
855 A310 90c Woods forget-me-not	1.10	.25
Nos. 853-855 (3)	2.85	.67

Souvenir Sheet

856 A310 160c Fire lily croceum	3.00	2.25

Dutch Aviation, 75th Anniv. A311

1994, Apr. 6 Litho. *Perf. 13½x13*

857 A311 80c KLM	.95	.22
858 A311 80c Fokker	.95	.22
859 A311 80c NLR	.95	.22
Nos. 857-859 (3)	2.85	.66

Planetarium, Designed by Eise Eisinga — A312

Design: 90c, Television image of moon landing, footprint on moon.

1994, May 5 Photo. *Perf. 13x14*

860 A312 80c multicolored	.90	.20
861 A312 90c multicolored	1.00	.25

First manned moon landing, 25th anniv. (#861).

1994 World Cup Soccer Championships, US — A313

1994, June 1

862 A313 80c multicolored	.90	.20

No. 862 printed with se-tenant label.

Stock Exchange Floor, Initials KPN — A314

1994, June 13 Litho. *Perf. 13½*

863 A314 80c multicolored	.90	.20

Offering of shares in Royal PTT Netherlands NV (KPN).

Bicycle, Car, Road Sign — A315

80c, Silhouettes of horses, riders, carriage.

1994, June 14 Photo. *Perf. 14x13*

864 A315 70c multicolored	.85	.18

Litho.

Perf. 13½x13

865 A315 80c multicolored	.90	.20

First road signs placed by Dutch motoring assoc. (ANWB), cent. (#864). World Equestrian Games, The Hague (#865).

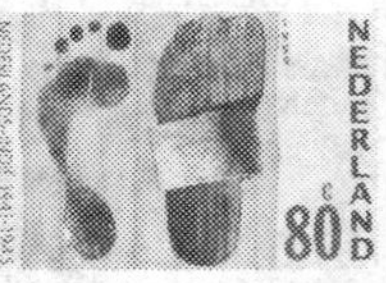

War in Dutch East Indies (1941-45) A316

Operation Market Garden (1944) — A316a

Perf. 14x13, 13x14

1994, Aug. 15 Photo.

866 A316 80c multicolored	1.00	.25
867 A316a 90c multicolored	1.10	.28

Lighthouses A317

Designs: 70c, Brandaris, Terschelling Island. 80c, Ameland Island, vert. 90c, Vlieland Island, vert.

Perf. 13½x13, 13x13½

1994, Sept. 13 Litho.

868 A317 70c multicolored	.90	.22
869 A317 80c multicolored	1.00	.25
870 A317 90c multicolored	1.10	.28
Nos. 868-870 (3)	3.00	.75

December Stamps — A318

1994, Nov. 28 Photo. *Perf. 13½*

871 A318 55c Snowflake, tree	.65	.15
872 A318 55c Candle, star	.65	.15
a. Pair, #871-872	1.30	.30
b. Min. sheet, 10 #872a + label	13.00	

One stamp in #872a is rotated 90 degrees to the other stamp.

Cow, Dutch Products A319

1995, Jan 2 Photo. *Perf. 14x13½*

873 A319 100c multicolored	1.25	.30

Hendrik Nicolaas Werkman (1882-1945), Printer — A320

Mesdag Museum Restoration A321

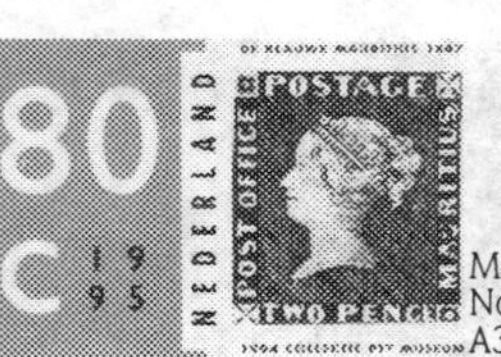

Mauritius No. 2 A322

1995, Jan. 17 Litho. *Perf. 14x13½*

874 A320 80c multicolored	1.00	.25
875 A321 80c multicolored	1.00	.25

Litho. & Engr.

Perf. 13½x14

876 A322 80c multicolored	1.00	.25
Nos. 874-876 (3)	3.00	.75

Acquisition of Mauritius No. 2 by Netherlands PTT Museum (#876).

Motion Pictures, Cent. — A323

70c, Joris Iven, documentary film maker. 80c, Scene from film, "Turkish Delight," 1972.

1995, Feb. 28 Photo. *Perf. 14x13*

877 A323 70c multicolored	.90	.22
878 A323 80c multicolored	1.00	.25

Mahler Festival — A324

Design: 80c, Gustav Mahler, (1860-1911), composer, 7th Symphony score.

1995, Mar. 21 Litho. *Perf. 13½x13*

879 A324 80c blue & black	1.00	.25

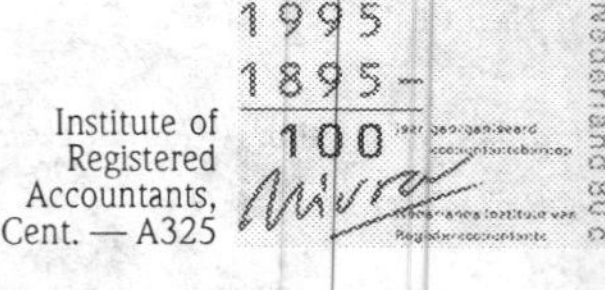

Institute of Registered Accountants, Cent. — A325

Assoc. of Building Contractors, Cent. — A326

1995, Mar. 28

880 A325 80c multicolored	1.00	.20
881 A326 80c multicolored	1.00	.20

50th Anniversaries — A327

Designs: No. 882, End of World War II, "45, 95" No. 883, Liberation of the Netherlands, "40, 45." No. 884, Founding of the UN, "50."

1995, May 3 Litho. *Perf. 13x13½*

882 A327 80c multicolored	1.00	.20
883 A327 80c multicolored	1.00	.20
884 A327 80c multicolored	1.00	.20
Nos. 882-884 (3)	3.00	.60

Signs of the Zodiac, Birthday Cake — A328

1995, May 22 Photo. *Perf. 14x13½*

885 A328 70c multicolored	.90	.18

18th World Boy Scout Jamboree — A329

Sail Amsterdam '95 — A330

Perf. 13x13½, 13½x13

1995, June 6 Litho.

886 A329 70c multicolored	.90	.18
887 A330 80c multicolored	1.00	.20

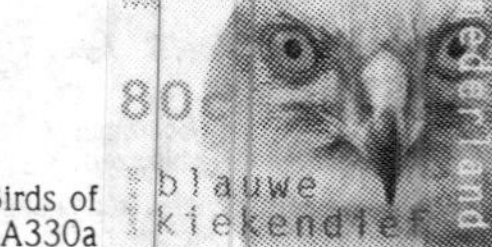

Birds of Prey — A330a

Perf. 13x14, 14x13

1995, Sept. 5 Photo.

888 A330a 70c Kestrel, vert. .90 .20
889 A330a 80c Hen harrier 1.00 .20
890 A330a 100c Red kite 1.25 .25
Nos. 888-890 (3) 3.15 .65

Souvenir Sheet

891 A330a 160c Honey buzzard 2.00 2.00

Nobel Prize Winners A331

Designs: No. 892, F. Zernike, physics, 1953. No. 893, P.J.W. Debye, chemistry, 1936. No. 894, J. Tinbergen, economics, 1969.

1995, Sept. 26 Litho. *Perf. 13½x13*

892 A331 80c green & multi 1.00 .20
893 A331 80c blue & multi 1.00 .20
894 A331 80c red & multi 1.00 .20
Nos. 892-894 (3) 3.00 .60

Dutch Cabaret, Cent. A332

Designs: 70c, Eduard Jacobs (1868-1914), Jean-Louis Pisuisse (1880-1927). 80c, Wim Kan (1911-83), Freek de Jonge (b. 1944).

1995, Oct. 17 Litho. *Perf. 13½x14*

895 A332 70c multicolored .90 .20
896 A332 80c multicolored 1.00 .20

Queen Beatrix Type of 1991

1995 Photo. *Perf. 13½ Horiz.*

Coil Stamp

912 A273 1g gray violet .95 .25

Issued: 1g, 10/5/95.
This is an expanding set. Numbers may change.

December Stamps — A333

Serpentine Die Cut 12½x13

1995, Nov. 27

Self-Adhesive

916 A333 55c Children, star .70 .15
917 A333 55c Children, stars .70 .15
a. air, Nos. 916-917 1.40

Issued in sheets of 20, checkerboard style.

Paintings by Johannes Vermeer (1632-75) — A334

Entire paintings or details: 70c, A Lady Writing a Letter, with Her Maid. 80c, The Love Letter. 100c, A Woman in Blue Reading a Letter.

1996, Feb. 27 Litho. *Perf. 13x13½*

918 A334 70c multicolored .85 .15
919 A334 80c multicolored .95 .20
920 A334 100c multicolored 1.20 .25
a. Souvenir sheet, Nos. 918-920 3.00 .60
Nos. 918-920 (3) 3.00 .60

Spring Flowers A335

Designs: 70c, Daffodil bulb, garden tools. 80c, Closeup of woman, tulip. 100c, Snake's head (fritillaria). 160c, Crocuses.

1996, Mar. 21 Litho. *Perf. 13½x13*

921 A335 70c multicolored .85 .15
922 A335 80c multicolored .95 .20
923 A335 100c multicolored 1.20 .25
Nos. 921-923 (3) 3.00 .60

Souvenir Sheet

924 A335 160c multicolored 1.90 .40

A336 A337

1996, Apr. 1 *Perf. 13x13½*

925 A336 70c Moving stamp .85 .15

No. 925 was sold in sheets of 20. See #951.

1996, May 14 Litho. *Perf. 13½x13*

Mr. Olivier B. Bommel, by Marten Toonder: a, O.B. Bommel goes on holiday. b, O.B. Bommel receives letter.

926 Sheet of 2 + 2 labels 1.80 1.80
a. A337 70c multicolored .85 .85
b. A337 80c multicolored .95 .95

Comic strips, cent.

Vacations A338

Scene, flower: No. 927, Beach, sunflower. No. 928, Cyclists, gerbera. 80c, Gables in Amsterdam, cornflower. 100c, Windmills at "Zaanse Schans" open air museum, anemone.

1996, May 31

927 A338 70c multicolored .85 .15
928 A338 70c multicolored .85 .15
929 A338 80c multicolored .95 .20
930 A338 100c multicolored 1.20 .25
Nos. 927-930 (4) 3.85 .75

Province of North Brabant, Bicent. A339

1996, June 13 Litho. *Perf. 13½x13*

931 A339 80c multicolored .90 .20

Sporting Events A340

Designs: 70c, Lighting the Olympic Torch, 1996 Summer Olympic Games, Atlanta. 80c, Tour de France cycling race. 100c, Euro '96 Soccer Championships, Wembley Stadium, England. 160c, Olympic rings, track sports, Atlanta stadium.

1996, June 25

932 A340 70c multicolored .80 .20
933 A340 80c multicolored .90 .25
934 A340 100c multicolored 1.10 .30
935 A340 160c multicolored 1.80 .45
Nos. 932-935 (4) 4.60 1.20

Erasmus Bridge, Rotterdam A341

UNICEF, 50th Anniv. A342

Designs: No. 936, Martinus Nijhoff Bridge over Waal River, horiz. No. 938, Wijker Tunnel under North Sea Canal, horiz.

1996, Aug. 6 *Perf. 13½x13, 13x13½*

936 A341 80c multicolored .90 .25
937 A341 80c shown .90 .25
938 A341 80c multicolored .90 .25
Nos. 936-938 (3) 2.70 .75

1996, Sept. 3 *Perf. 13x13½*

Designs: 70c, School children from Ghana. 80c, Girl from Ghana with tray on head.

939 A342 70c multicolored .80 .20
940 A342 80c multicolored .90 .25

Sesame Street in Netherlands, 20th Anniv. — A343

70c, Bert & Ernie. 80c, Pino, Ieiemienie & Tommie.

1996, Sept. 3 *Perf. 13½x13*

941 A343 70c multicolored .80 .20
942 A343 80c multicolored .90 .25

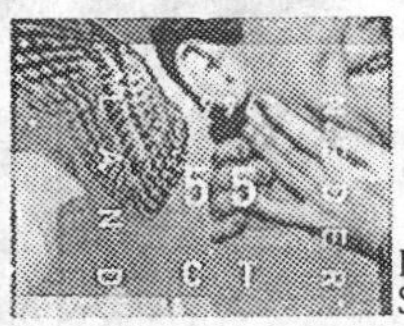

Voyages of Discovery A344

Voyages of: 70c, Petrus Plancius (1552-1622), cartographer. #944, Willem Barents (d. 1597). #945, Cornelis de Houtman (1540-99). 100c, Mahu en De Cordes (1598-1600).

1996, Oct. 1

943 A344 70c multicolored .80 .20
944 A344 80c multicolored .90 .25
945 A344 80c multicolored .90 .25
946 A344 100c multicolored 1.15 .30
Nos. 943-946 (4) 3.75 1.00

December Stamps — A345

Collage of faces, hands: No. 947, Wing, ear, hands. No. 948, Mouth, two faces. No. 949, Woman with eyes closed, hand. No. 950, Eyes, face with mouth open.

Serpentine Die Cut 9 Horiz.

1996, Nov. 26

Self-Adhesive

947 A345 55c multicolored .65 .15
948 A345 55c multicolored .65 .15
949 A345 55c red violet & multi .65 .15
950 A345 55c blue & multi .65 .15
a. Block or strip of 4, #947-950 2.60

Issued in sheets of 20.

Moving Stamp Type of 1996

1997, Jan. 2 Photo. *Die Cut Perf. 13*

Self-Adhesive

951 A336 80c like No. 925 .90 .25

No. 951 sold in panes of 20.

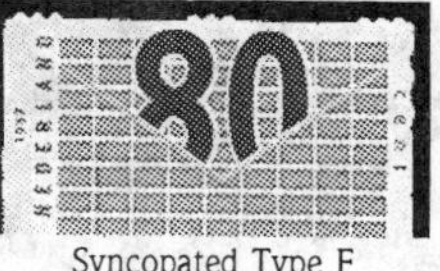

Business Stamps A346

Syncopated Type F

Type F: On the top, groups of two holes separated by rectangular perforations equal in width to eight holes.

Geometric designs.

Sawtooth Die Cut 13½, Syncopated Type F (on 1 Side)

1997, Jan. 2

Self-Adhesive

Coil Stamps

952 A346 80c pink & multi .90 .25
953 A346 160c green & multi 1.80 .50

Cross-Country Skating Championships A347

1997, Jan. 4 Photo. *Perf. 14x13*

954 A347 80c multicolored .90 .25

Surprise Stamps — A348

Inscriptions beneath scratch-off heart-shaped panels: b, Schrijf me. c, Groetjes. d, Ik hou van je. e, Tot gauw. f, Ik denk aan je. g, XXX-jes. h, Ik mis je. i, Geintje. j, Zomaar. k, Wanneer?

1997, Jan. 21 *Perf. 14x13½*

955 Sheet of 10 9.00 2.50
a. A348 80c Any single, unscratched heart .90 .25
b.-k. A348 80c Any single, scratched heart .25

Unused value for #955a is with attached selvage. Inscriptions are shown in selvage beside each stamp.

Nature and Environment A349

1997, Feb. 25 Litho. *Perf. 13½x13*

956 A349 80c Pony .90 .25
957 A349 100c Cow 1.15 .30

Souvenir Sheet

958 A349 160c Sheep 1.80 .45

Suske & Wiske Comic Strip Characters A350

Designs: No. 959, Suske, Wiske, Tante Sidonia, and Lambik. No. 960a, Jerome making exclamation.

997, Mar. 18 Litho. *Perf. 13½x12½*

959 A350 80c multicolored .85 .20

Souvenir Sheet

960 Sheet of 2, #959, 960a 1.70 .45
a. A350 80c violet & red .85 .20

A351

Greetings Stamps A352

Designs: No. 961, Birthday cake. No. 962, Amaryllis surrounded by cup of coffee, two glasses of wine, hand writing card, candlelight.

1997, May 6 Photo. *Perf. 14x13½*
961 A351 80c multicolored .85 .20
962 A352 80c multicolored .85 .20

Marshall Plan, 50th Anniv. — A353

Designs: No. 963, Map of Europe. No. 964, Flag, quotation from George C. Marshall.

1997, May 6 Litho. *Perf. 13½x13*
963 A353 80c multicolored .85 .20
964 A353 80c multicolored .85 .20
a. Pair, #963-964 1.70 .40

R E K E N K A M E R
5 5 0 J A A R ' 9 7
R E C H T M A T I G
& D O E L M A T I G
8 0 C T = 8 0 C T
N E D E R L A N D

Court of Audit, 50th Anniv. — A354

1997, May 27 *Perf. 13½x13*
965 A354 80c multicolored .85 .20

European Council of Ministers Meeting, Amsterdam A355

1997, June 17 Litho. *Perf. 13½*
966 A355 100c multicolored 1.20 .30

Water Recreation A356

1997, July 1 *Perf. 13½x13*
967 A356 80c Swimming, row boat 1.00 .25
968 A356 1g Sailboats 1.25 .30

Royal Institute of Engineers, 150th Anniv. — A357

1997, Aug. 5
969 A357 80c multicolored 1.00 .25

Netherlands Asthma Center, Cent. — A358

1997, Aug. 5
970 A358 80c multicolored 1.00 .25

Horticultural Education at Florens College, Aalsmeer, Cent. — A359

1997, Aug. 5
971 A359 80c multicolored 1.00 .25

Franz Schubert (1797-1828), Composer A360

1997, Aug. 5
972 A360 80c multicolored 1.00 .25

A361

Youth Stamps — A362

1997, Sept. 2
973 A361 80c multicolored 1.00 .25
974 A362 80c multicolored 1.00 .25

Birth Announcement Stamp — A363

Die Cut Perf. 13½x13
1997, Oct. 7 Photo.
Self-Adhesive
975 A363 80c multicolored .90 .25

SEMI-POSTAL STAMPS

Design Symbolical of the Four Chief Means for Combating Tuberculosis: Light, Water, Air and Food — SP1

Perf. 12½
1906, Dec. 21 Typo. Unwmk.
B1 SP1 1c (+1c) rose red 3.00 2.00
B2 SP1 3c (+3c) pale ol grn 30.00 22.50
B3 SP1 5c (+5c) gray 30.00 9.00
Nos. B1-B3 (3) 63.00 33.50
Set, never hinged 275.00

Surtax aided the Society for the Prevention of Tuberculosis.

Nos. B1-B3 canceled-to-order "AMSTERDAM 31.07 10-12 N," sell at $2 a set.

Symbolical of Charity — SP2

SP3

1923, Dec. 15 *Perf. 11½*
B4 SP2 2c (+5c) vio bl 15.00 14.00
B5 SP3 10c (+5c) org red 15.00 14.00
Set, never hinged 95.00

The surtax was for the benefit of charity.

Allegory, Charity Protecting Child — SP6

1924, Dec. 15 Photo. *Perf. 12½*
B6 SP6 2c (+2c) emer .90 1.40
B7 SP6 7½c (+3½c) dk brn 5.00 5.00
B8 SP6 10c (+2½c) vermilion 4.00 .85
Nos. B6-B9 (5) 38.25 8.10
Set, never hinged 27.50

These stamps were sold at a premium over face value for the benefit of Child Welfare Societies.

Arms of North Brabant SP7

Arms of Gelderland SP8

Arms of South Holland — SP9

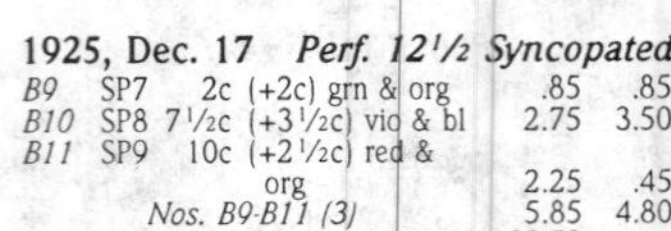

1925, Dec. 17 *Perf. 12½ Syncopated*
B9 SP7 2c (+2c) grn & org .85 .85
B10 SP8 7½c (+3½c) vio & bl 2.75 3.50
B11 SP9 10c (+2½c) red & org 2.25 .45
Nos. B9-B11 (3) 5.85 4.80
Set, never hinged 22.50

Surtax went to Child Welfare Societies.
See note before No. 142a.

Syncopated Perfs., Type A
B9a SP7 2c (+2c) 6.75 6.75
B10a SP8 7½c (+3½c) 20.00 22.50
B11a SP9 10c (+2½c) 55.00 47.50
Nos. B9a-B11a (3) 81.75 76.75
Set, never hinged 260.00

Arms of Utrecht SP10

Arms of Zeeland SP11

Arms of North Holland SP12

Arms of Friesland SP13

1926, Dec. 1 Wmk. 202 *Perf. 12½*
B12 SP10 2c (+2c) sil & red .40 .40
B13 SP11 5c (+3c) grn & gray bl .95 .85
B14 SP12 10c (+3c) red & gold 1.90 .30
B15 SP13 15c (+3c) ultra & yel 4.75 4.00
Nos. B12-B15 (4) 8.00 5.55
Set, never hinged 30.00

The surtax on these stamps was devoted to Child Welfare Societies.

Syncopated Perfs., Type A
B12a SP10 2c (+2c) 3.00 3.00
B13a SP11 5c (+3c) 6.00 6.50
B14a SP12 10c (+3c) 12.00 6.50
B15a SP13 15c (+3c) 15.00 16.00
Nos. B12a-B15a (4) 36.00 32.00
Set, never hinged 90.00

King William III — SP14

Red Cross and Doves — SP18

Designs: 3c, Queen Emma. 5c, Prince Consort Henry. 7½c, Queen Wilhelmina.

Perf. 11½, 11½x12 B
1927, June Photo. Unwmk.
B16 SP14 2c (+2c) scar 1.65 1.65
Engr.
B17 SP14 3c (+2c) dp grn 4.75 6.50
B18 SP14 5c (+3c) slate bl .50 .35
Photo.
B19 SP14 7½c (+3½c) ultra 4.00 1.50
B20 SP18 15c (+5c) ultra & red 8.00 8.00
Nos. B16-B20 (5) 18.90 18.00
Set, never hinged 50.00

60th anniversary of the Netherlands Red Cross Society. The surtaxes in parentheses were for the benefit of the Society.

Arms of Drenthe SP19

Arms of Groningen SP20

FRANK P. GEIGER
PHILATELISTS
NETHERLANDS
CURACAO • ANTILLES • ARUBA • INDIES • UNTEA • SURINAME
We maintain an fabulous stock of Never Hinged, Hinged and Used complete sets, singles, booklets, coils syncopated perforation issues, perforation varieties, missing colors (mostly not mentioned in Scott Catalogue), booklet combination, FDC's, covers, proofs, and literature. We are eager buyers of everything related to Netherland & Colonies Philately. We sell more; we buy more, we pay more! Some raities in stock today: Scott 122a, 174c, 176b! Our Price Lists are available for $2 (deductible from an order). Please indicate your areas of interest as our stock includes Netherlands & Colonies, Western Europe, Eastern Europe, CEPT, Scandinavia, US, UN, Canada, British Commonwealth, Japan, China, Indonesia, Topical Rarities, World-Wide Year Sets and Never Hinged Collection.
WE BUY EVERYTHING!
From Afars to West Irian, we are eager, serious buiyers of collections, dealer stocks, better sets, rarities, covers, booklets, etc. For further information write or call:
BUYING HOTLINE: 201-236-8122

Since 1969
FAX 201-236-8133 website:www.worldstamps.com
OVER 30 YEARS OF PROFESSIONAL EXPERIENCE
242 W. Saddle River Rd., Ste. 2, Saddle River, NJ 07458

Arms of Limburg SP21

Arms of Overijssel SP22

1927, Dec. 15 Wmk. 202 *Perf. 12½*

B21 SP19 2c (+2c) dp rose & vio .30 .30
B22 SP20 5c (+3c) ol grn & yel 1.10 1.25
B23 SP21 7½c (+3½c) red & blk 2.75 .35
B24 SP22 15c (+3c) ultra & org brn 4.00 4.00
Nos. B21-B24 (4) 8.15 5.90
Set, never hinged 30.00

The surtax on these stamps was for the benefit of Child Welfare Societies.

Syncopated Perfs., Type A

B21a SP19 2c (+2c) 1.65 1.65
B22a SP20 5c (+3c) 3.00 2.75
B23a SP21 7½c (+3½c) 4.75 1.75
B24a SP22 15c (+3c) 10.00 8.00
Nos. B21a-B24a (4) 19.40 14.15
Set, never hinged 55.00

Rowing — SP23

Fencing — SP24

Soccer SP25

Yachting SP26

Putting the Shot SP27

Running SP28

Riding — SP29

Boxing — SP30

Perf. 11½, 12, 11½x12, 12x11½

1928, Mar. 27 Litho.

B25 SP23 1½c (+1c) dk grn 1.50 .50
B26 SP24 2c (+1c) red vio 2.00 1.00
B27 SP25 3c (+1c) green 2.00 .80
B28 SP26 5c (+1c) lt bl 2.50 .80
B29 SP27 7½c (+2½c) org 2.50 1.00
B30 SP28 10c (+2c) scarlet 6.00 4.00
B31 SP29 15c (+2c) dk bl 6.00 2.75
B32 SP30 30c (+3c) dk brn 18.00 22.50
Nos. B25-B32 (8) 40.50 33.35
Set, never hinged 165.00

The surtax on these stamps was used to help defray the expenses of the Olympic Games of 1928.

Jean Pierre Minckelers SP31

Child on Dolphin SP35

Designs: 5c, Hermann Boerhaave. 7½c, Hendrik Antoon Lorentz. 12½c, Christian Huygens.

1928, Dec. 10 Photo. *Perf. 12x12½*

B33 SP31 1½c (+1½c) vio .40 .35
B34 SP31 5c (+3c) grn .75 .60

Perf. 12

B35 SP31 7½c (+2½c) ver 2.25 .25
a. Perf. 12x12½ 4.75 .70
Never hinged 11.00
B36 SP31 12½c (+3½c) ultra 8.50 6.50
a. Perf. 12x12½ 77.50 7.75
Never hinged 175.00
Nos. B33-B36 (4) 11.90 7.70
Set, never hinged 40.00

The surtax on these stamps was for the benefit of Child Welfare Societies.

1929, Dec. 10 Litho. *Perf. 12½*

B37 SP35 1½c (+1½c) gray 1.25 .45
B38 SP35 5c (+3c) blue grn 2.25 .75
B39 SP35 6c (+4c) scarlet 1.40 .35
B40 SP35 12½c (+3½c) dk bl 12.00 12.00
Nos. B37-B40 (4) 16.90 13.55
Set, never hinged 60.00

Surtax for child welfare.

Syncopated Perfs., Type B

B37a SP35 1½c (+1½c) 1.75 .75
B38a SP35 5c (+3c) 3.00 .75
B39a SP35 6c (+4c) 2.50 .75
B40a SP35 12½c (+3½c) 13.00 10.50
Nos. B37a-B40a (4) 20.25 12.75
Set, never hinged 57.50

Rembrandt and His "Cloth Merchants of Amsterdam" SP36

"Spring" SP37

Perf. 11½

1930, Feb. 15 Engr. Unwmk.

B41 SP36 5c (+5c) bl grn 5.50 5.50
B42 SP36 6c (+5c) gray blk 3.50 3.50
B43 SP36 12½c (+5c) dp bl 6.50 6.50
Nos. B41-B43 (3) 15.50 15.50
Set, never hinged 62.50

Surtax for the benefit of the Rembrandt Soc.

1930, Dec. 10 *Perf. 12½*

5c, Summer. 6c, Autumn. 12½c, Winter.

B44 SP37 1½c (+1½c) lt red .95 .45
B45 SP37 5c (+3c) gray grn 1.50 .70
B46 SP37 6c (+4c) claret 1.40 .25
B47 SP37 12½c (+3½c) lt ultra 11.00 8.00
Nos. B44-B47 (4) 14.85 9.40
Set, never hinged 65.00

Surtax was for Child Welfare work.

Syncopated Perfs., Type C

B44a SP37 1½c (+1½c) 2.25 1.10
B45a SP37 5c (+3c) 2.25 1.10
B46a SP37 6c (+4c) 2.25 1.10
B47a SP37 12½c (+3½c) 15.00 12.00
Nos. B44a-B47a (4) 21.75 15.30
Set, never hinged 50.00

Stained Glass Window and Detail of Repair Method SP41

Deaf Mute Learning Lip Reading SP43

6c, Gouda Church and repair of window frame.

Perf. 12½

1931, Oct. 1 Photo. Wmk. 202

B48 SP41 1½c (+1½c) bl grn 12.00 12.00
B49 SP41 6c (+4c) car rose 19.00 17.00
Set, never hinged 95.00

1931, Dec. 10 *Perf. 12½*

Designs: 5c, Imbecile child. 6c, Blind girl learning to read Braille. 12½c, Child victim of malnutrition.

B50 SP43 1½c (+1½c) ver & ultra 1.25 .55
B51 SP43 5c (+3c) Prus bl & vio 1.90 1.00
B52 SP43 6c (+4c) vio & grn 1.50 .50
B53 SP43 12½c (+3½c) ultra & dp org 22.50 20.00
Nos. B50-B53 (4) 27.15 22.05
Set, never hinged 100.00

The surtax was for Child Welfare work.

Syncopated Perfs., Type C

B50a SP43 1½c (+1½c) 1.75 1.10
B51a SP43 5c (+3c) 4.75 1.40
B52a SP43 6c (+4c) 4.75 1.40
B53a SP43 12½c (+3½c) 26.00 17.50
Nos. B50a-B53a (4) 37.25 21.40
Set, never hinged 87.50

Windmill and Dikes — SP47

Furze and Boy — SP51

Designs: 6c, Council House, Zierikzee. 7½c, Drawbridge. 12½c, Flower fields.

1932, May 23 *Perf. 12½*

B54 SP47 2½c (+1½c) turq grn & blk 4.00 2.50
B55 SP47 6c (+4c) gray blk & blk 7.75 2.50
B56 SP47 7½c (+3½c) brt red & blk 26.00 16.50
B57 SP47 12½c (+2½c) ultra & blk 30.00 19.00
Nos. B54-B57 (4) 67.75 40.50
Set, never hinged 250.00

The surtax was for the benefit of the National Tourist Association.

1932, Dec. 10 *Perf. 12½*

Designs (Heads of children and flowers typifying the seasons): 5c, Cornflower. 6c, Sunflower. 12½c, Christmas rose.

B58 SP51 1½c (+1½c) brn & yel 1.40 .45
B59 SP51 5c (+3c) red org & ultra 1.40 .70
B60 SP51 6c (+4c) dk grn & ocher 1.40 .45
B61 SP51 12½c (+3½c) ocher & ultra 25.00 18.00
Nos. B58-B61 (4) 29.20 19.60
Set, never hinged 100.00

The surtax aided Child Welfare Societies.

Syncopated Perfs., Type C

B58a SP51 1½c (+1½c) 2.50 1.25
B59a SP51 5c (+3c) 3.00 1.25
B60a SP51 6c (+4c) 3.00 1.25
B61a SP51 12½c (+3½c) 30.00 21.00
Nos. B58a-B61a (4) 38.50 24.75
Set, never hinged 95.00

Monument at Den Helder SP55

The "Hope," A Church and Hospital Ship SP56

Lifeboat in a Storm SP57

Dutch Sailor and Sailors' Home SP58

1933, June 10 *Perf. 14½x13½*

B62 SP55 1½c (+1½c) dp red 1.40 .80
B63 SP56 5c (+3c) bl grn & red org 8.50 1.25
B64 SP57 6c (+4c) dp grn 13.00 1.25
B65 SP58 12½c (+3½c) ultra 19.00 15.00
Nos. B62-B65 (4) 41.90 18.30
Set, never hinged 140.00

The surtax was for the aid of Sailors' Homes.

Child Carrying the Star of Hope, Symbolical of Christmas Cheer — SP59

1933, Dec. 11 *Perf. 12½*

B66 SP59 1½c (+1½c) sl & org brn 1.25 .45
B67 SP59 5c (+3c) dk brn & ocher 1.65 .65
B68 SP59 6c (+4c) bl grn & gold 1.90 .55
B69 SP59 12½c (+3½c) dk bl & sil 19.00 16.00
Nos. B66-B69 (4) 23.80 17.65
Set, never hinged 90.00

The surtax aided Child Welfare Societies.

Syncopated Perfs., Type C

B66a SP59 1½c (+1½c) 1.50 .75
B67a SP59 5c (+3c) 2.25 .75
B68a SP59 6c (+4c) 3.00 .75
B69a SP59 12½c (+3½c) 22.50 19.00
Nos. B66a-B69a (4) 29.25 21.25
Set, never hinged 75.00

Queen Wilhelmina SP60

Princess Juliana SP61

Perf. 12½

1934, Apr. 28 Engr. Unwmk.

B70 SP60 5c (+4c) dk vio 10.00 2.25
B71 SP61 6c (+5c) blue 9.25 4.25
Set, never hinged 67.50

The surtax was for the benefit of the Anti-Depression Committee.

Dowager Queen Emma SP62

Poor Child SP63

1934, Oct. 1 *Perf. 13x14*

B72 SP62 6c (+2c) blue 9.50 1.40
Never hinged 40.00

Surtax for the Fight Tuberculosis Society.

Perf. 13½x13

1934, Dec. 10 Photo. Wmk. 202

B73 SP63 1½c (+1½c) olive 1.00 .45
B74 SP63 5c (+3c) rose red 1.40 .90
B75 SP63 6c (+4c) bl grn 1.40 .20
B76 SP63 12½c (+3½c) ultra 18.00 15.00
Nos. B73-B76 (4) 21.80 16.55
Set, never hinged 85.00

The surtax aided child welfare.

Henri D. Guyot SP64

A. J. M. Diepenbrock SP65

F. C. Donders SP66

J. P. Sweelinck SP67

Perf. 12½ x 12, 12

1935, June Engr. Unwmk.

B77 SP64 1½c (+1½c) dk car 1.00 1.50
B78 SP65 5c (+3c) blk brn 2.50 3.50
B79 SP66 6c (+4c) myr grn 3.00 .30
B80 SP67 12½c (+3½c) dp bl 17.50 4.00
Nos. B77-B80 (4) 24.00 9.30
Set, never hinged 110.00

Surtax for social and cultural projects.

Netherlands Map, DC-3 Planes' Shadows
SP68

Girl Picking Apple
SP69

Perf. 14x13

1935, Oct. 16 Photo. Wmk. 202

B81 SP68 6c (+4c) brn 25.00 9.00
Never hinged 80.00

Surtax for Natl. Aviation.

1935, Dec. 4 *Perf. 14½x13½*

B82 SP69 1½c (+1½c) crim .40 .30
B83 SP69 5c (+3c) dk yel grn 1.25 1.10
B84 SP69 6c (+4c) blk brn 1.25 .30
B85 SP69 12½c (+3½c) ultra 19.00 6.75
Nos. B82-B85 (4) 21.90 8.45
Set, never hinged 90.00

The surtax aided child welfare.

H. Kamerlingh Onnes — SP70

Dr. A. S. Talma — SP71

Msgr. Hjam Schaepman
SP72

Desiderius Erasmus
SP73

Perf. 12½x12

1936, May 1 Engr. Unwmk.

B86 SP70 1½c (+1½c) brn blk .80 .75
B87 SP71 5c (+3c) dl grn 4.00 3.50
B88 SP72 6c (+4c) dk red 1.25 .35
B89 SP73 12½c (+3½c) dl bl 11.00 2.50
Nos. B86-B89 (4) 17.05 7.10
Set, never hinged 70.00

Surtax for social and cultural projects.

Cherub — SP74

Perf. 14½x13½

1936, Dec. 1 Photo. Wmk. 202

B90 SP74 1½c (+1½c) lil gray .45 .30
B91 SP74 5c (+3c) turq grn 1.50 .85
B92 SP74 6c (+4c) dp red brn 1.50 .26
B93 SP74 12½c (+3½c) ind 10.50 3.25
Nos. B90-B93 (4) 13.95 4.66
Set, never hinged 55.00

The surtax aided child welfare.

Jacob Maris — SP75

Franciscus de la Boe Sylvius — SP76

Joost van den Vondel
SP77

Anthony van Leeuwenhoek
SP78

Perf. 12½x12

1937, June 1 Engr. Unwmk.

B94 SP75 1½c (+1½c) blk brn .35 .30
B95 SP76 5c (+3c) dl grn 4.00 2.50
B96 SP77 6c (+4c) brn vio .75 .15
B97 SP78 12½c (+3½c) dl bl 6.00 1.00
Nos. B94-B97 (4) 11.10 3.95
Set, never hinged 40.00

Surtax for social and cultural projects.

"The Laughing Child" after Frans Hals — SP79

Perf. 14½x13½

1937, Dec. 1 Photo. Wmk. 202

B98 SP79 1½c (+1½c) blk .15 .15
B99 SP79 3c (+2c) grn 1.00 1.00
B100 SP79 4c (+2c) hn brn .45 .30
B101 SP79 5c (+3c) bl grn .40 .15
B102 SP79 12½c (+3½c) dk bl 5.00 1.40
Nos. B98-B102 (5) 7.00 3.00
Set, never hinged 35.00

The surtax aided child welfare.

Marnix van Sint Aldegonde — SP80

Otto Gerhard Heldring — SP81

Maria Tesselschade
SP82

Hermann Boerhaave
SP84

Harmenszoon Rembrandt van Rijn — SP83

Perf. 12½x12

1938, May 16 Engr. Unwmk.

B103 SP80 1½c (+1½c) sep .35 .60
B104 SP81 3c (+2c) dk grn .40 .35
B105 SP82 4c (+2c) rose lake 1.25 1.65
B106 SP83 5c (+3c) dk sl grn 1.50 .25
B107 SP84 12½c (+3½c) dl bl 8.50 1.10
Nos. B103-B107 (5) 12.00 3.95
Set, never hinged 35.00

The surtax was for the benefit of cultural and social relief.

Child with Flowers, Bird and Fish — SP85

Perf. 14½x13½

1938, Dec. 1 Photo. Wmk. 202

B108 SP85 1½c (+1½c) blk .15 .15
B109 SP85 3c (+2c) mar .30 .15
B110 SP85 4c (+2c) dk bl grn .60 .80
B111 SP85 5c (+3c) hn brn .25 .15
B112 SP85 12½c (+3½c) dp bl 9.00 1.75
Nos. B108-B112 (5) 10.30 3.00
Set, never hinged 35.00

The surtax aided child welfare.

Matthijs Maris — SP86

Anton Mauve — SP87

Gerard van Swieten
SP88

Nikolaas Beets
SP89

Peter Stuyvesant — SP90

Perf. 12½x12

1939, May 1 Engr. Unwmk.

B113 SP86 1½c (+1½c) sepia .60 .60
B114 SP87 2½c (+2½c) gray grn 3.00 2.75
B115 SP88 3c (+3c) ver .80 1.00
B116 SP89 5c (+3c) dk sl grn 2.00 .30
B117 SP90 12½c (+3½c) indigo 5.00 .85
Nos. B113-B117 (5) 11.40 5.50
Set, never hinged 40.00

The surtax was for the benefit of cultural and social relief.

Child Carrying Cornucopia — SP91

Perf. 14½x13½

1939, Dec. 1 Photo. Wmk. 202

B118 SP91 1½c (+1½c) blk .15 .15
B119 SP91 2½c (+2½c) dk ol grn 3.75 2.00
B120 SP91 3c (+3c) hn brn .40 .15
B121 SP91 5c (+3c) dk grn .85 .15
B122 SP91 12½c (+3½c) dk bl 4.00 1.00
Nos. B118-B122 (5) 9.15 3.45
Set, never hinged 40.00

The surtax was used for destitute children.

Catalogue values for unused stamps in this section, from this point to the end of the section, are for Never Hinged items.

Vincent van Gogh
SP92

E. J. Potgieter
SP93

Petrus Camper
SP94

Jan Steen
SP95

Joseph Scaliger — SP96

Perf. 12½x12

1940, May 11 Engr. Unwmk.

B123 SP92 1½c +1½c brn blk 1.90 .25
B124 SP93 2½c +2½c dk grn 6.00 1.40
B125 SP94 3c +3c car 3.75 1.10
B126 SP95 5c +3c dp grn 7.75 .25
a. Booklet pane of 4 250.00
B127 SP96 12½c +3½c dp bl 6.75 .80

Surtax for social and cultural projects.

Type of 1940 Surcharged in Black **7½ +2½**

1940, Sept. 7

B128 SP95 7½c +2½c on 5c +3c dk red .50 .25
Nos. B123-B128 (6) 26.65 4.05

Child with Flowers and Doll — SP97

Perf. 14½x13½

1940, Dec. 2 Photo. Wmk. 202

B129 SP97 1½c +1½c dl bl gray .65 .15
B130 SP97 2½c +2½c dp ol 2.50 .50
B131 SP97 4c +3c royal bl 2.50 .65
B132 SP97 5c +3c dk bl grn 2.50 .15
B133 SP97 7½c +3½c hn .65 .15
Nos. B129-B133 (5) 8.80 1.60

The surtax was used for destitute children.

Dr. Antonius Mathijsen
SP98

Dr. Jan Ingenhousz
SP99

Aagje Deken
SP100

Johannes Bosboom
SP101

A. C. W. Staring — SP102

Perf. 12½x12

1941, May 29 Engr. Unwmk.

B134	SP98	1½c	+1½c blk brn	.80	.20
B135	SP99	2½c	+2½c dk sl grn	.80	.20
B136	SP100	4c	+3c red	.80	.20
B137	SP101	5c	+3c slate grn	.80	.20
B138	SP102	7½c	+3½c rose vio	.80	.20
	Nos. B134-B138 (5)			4.00	1.00

The surtax was for cultural and social relief.

Rembrandt's Painting of Titus, His Son — SP103

Perf. 14½x13½

1941, Dec. 1 Photo. Wmk. 202

B139	SP103	1½c	+1½c vio blk	.30	.15
B140	SP103	2½c	+2½c dk ol	.30	.15
B141	SP103	4c	+3c royal blue	.30	.15
B142	SP103	5c	+3c dp grn	.30	.15
B143	SP103	7½c	+3½c dp henna brn	.30	.15
	Nos. B139-B143 (5)			1.50	
	Set value				.60

The surtax aided child welfare.

Legionary

SP104 SP105

1942, Nov. 1 *Perf. 12½x12, 12x12½*

B144	SP104	7½c	+2½c dk red	1.00	1.00
a.	Sheet of 10			90.00	100.00
B145	SP106	12½c	+87½c ultra	7.00	10.00
a.	Sheet of 4			75.00	125.00

The surtax aided the Netherlands Legion.

#B144a, B145a measure 155x111mm and 94x94mm respectively.

19th Century Mail Cart — SP108

1943, Oct. 9 Unwmk. *Perf. 12x12½*

B148	SP108	7½c	+7½c henna brn	.15	.15

Issued to commemorate Stamp Day.

Child and House — SP109

#B150, Mother & Child. #B151, Mother $ Children. #B152, Child Carrying Sheaf of Wheat. #B153, Mother & Children, diff.

Perf. 12½x12

1944, Mar. 6 Wmk. 202

B149	SP109	1½c	+3½c dl blk	.15	.15
B150	SP109	4c	+3½ rose lake	.15	.15
B151	SP109	5c	+5c dk bl grn	.15	.15
B152	SP109	7½c	+7½c dp hn brn	.15	.15
B153	SP109	10c	+40c royal blue	.15	.15
	Set value			.50	.50

The surtax aided National Social Service and winter relief.

Child
SP114

Fortuna
SP115

Perf. 14½x13½

1945, Dec. 1 Photo.

B154	SP114	1½c	+2½c gray	.20	.15
B155	SP114	2½c	+3½c dk bl grn	.20	.15
B156	SP114	5c	+5c brn red	.20	.15
B157	SP114	7½c	+4½c red	.20	.15
B158	SP114	12½c	+5½c brt bl	.20	.15
	Nos. B154-B158 (5)			1.00	
	Set value				.60

The surtax was for Child Welfare.

Perf. 12½x12

1946, May 1 Engr. Unwmk.

B159	SP115	1½c	+3½c brn blk	.45	.15
B160	SP115	2½c	+5c dl grn	.60	.32
B161	SP115	5c	+10c dk vio	.65	.40
B162	SP115	7½c	+15c car lake	.45	.15
B163	SP115	12½c	+37½c dk bl	.75	.30
	Nos. B159-B163 (5)			2.90	1.32

The surtax was for victims of World War II.

Princess Irene
SP116

Child on Merry-go-round
SP119

Designs: Nos. B165, B167, Princess Margriet. Nos. B168-B169, Princess Beatrix.

1946, Sept. 16

B164	SP116	1½c	+1½c blk brn	.50	.42
B165	SP116	2½c	+1½c bl grn	.50	.42
B166	SP116	4c	+2c magenta	.52	.42
B167	SP116	5c	+2c brown	.52	.42
B168	SP116	7½c	+2½c red	.50	.15
B169	SP116	12½c	+7½c dk bl	.50	.42
	Nos. B164-B169 (6)			3.04	2.25

The surtax was for child welfare and anti-tuberculosis work.

1946, Dec. 2 Photo. Wmk. 202

B170	SP119	2c	+2c lil gray	.42	.20
B171	SP119	4c	+2c dk grn	.42	.20
B172	SP119	7½c	+2½c brt red	.42	.20
B173	SP119	10c	+5c dp plum	.42	.15
B174	SP119	20c	+5c dp bl	.42	.28
	Nos. B170-B174 (5)			2.10	1.03

The surtax was for child welfare.

Dr. Hendrik van Deventer
SP120

Peter Cornelisz Hooft
SP121

Johan de Witt — SP122

Jean F. van Royen — SP123

Hugo de Groot — SP124

1947, Aug. 1 Engr. Unwmk.

B175	SP120	2c	+2c dark red	.60	.25
B176	SP121	4c	+2c dk green	1.25	.42
B177	SP122	7½c	+2½c dk pur brn	1.90	.42
B178	SP123	10c	+5c brown	1.40	.15
B179	SP124	20c	+5c dk blue	1.10	.42
	Nos. B175-B179 (5)			6.25	1.66

The surtax was for social and cultural purposes.

Children
SP125

Infant
SP126

1947, Dec. 1 Photo. *Perf. 13x14*

B180	SP125	2c	+2c red brn	.15	.15
B181	SP126	4c	+2c bl grn	1.25	.40
B182	SP126	7½c	+2½c sepia	1.25	.55
B183	SP126	10c	+5c dk red	.75	.15
B184	SP125	20c	+5c dk blue	1.25	.65
	Nos. B180-B184 (5)			4.65	1.90

The surtax was for child welfare.

Hall of Knights, The Hague — SP127

Boy in Kayak — SP128

Designs: 6c+4c, Royal Palace, Amsterdam. 10c+5c, Kneuterdyk Palace, The Hague. 20c+5c, New Church, Amsterdam.

1948, June 17 Engr. *Perf. 13½x14*

B185	SP127	2c	+2c dk brn	1.50	.25
B186	SP127	6c	+4c grn	1.50	.25
B187	SP127	10c	+5c brt red	1.25	.15
B188	SP127	20c	+5c deep blue	1.50	.65
	Nos. B185-B188 (4)			5.75	1.30

The surtax was for cultural and social purposes.

1948, Nov. 15 Photo. *Perf. 13x14*

Designs: 5c+3c, Swimming. 6c+4c, Sledding. 10c+5c, Swinging. 20c+8c, Figure skating.

B189	SP128	2c	+2c yel grn	.15	.15
B190	SP128	5c	+3c dk bl grn	2.00	.65
B191	SP128	6c	+4c gray	.85	.15
B192	SP128	10c	+5c red	.15	.15
B193	SP128	20c	+8c blue	2.25	.65
	Nos. B189-B193 (5)			5.40	1.75

The surtax was for child welfare.

Beach Terrace — SP129

Boy and Girl Hikers — SP130

Campers
SP131

Reaping — SP132

Sailboats
SP133

1949, May 2 Wmk. 202 *Perf. 14x13*

B194	SP129	2c	+2c bl & org yel	.90	.15
B195	SP130	5c	+3c bl & yel	1.50	1.00
B196	SP131	6c	+4c dk bl grn	1.50	.30
B197	SP132	10c	+5c bl & org yel	2.50	.15
B198	SP133	20c	+5c blue	1.75	1.25
	Nos. B194-B198 (5)			8.15	2.85

The surtax was for cultural and social purposes.

Hands Reaching for Sunflower
SP134

"Autumn"
SP135

Perf. 14½x13½

1949, Aug. 1 Photo. Unwmk.

Flower in Yellow

B199	SP134	2c	+3c gray	1.10	.20
B200	SP134	6c	+4c red brown	.70	.32
B201	SP134	10c	+5c brt blue	2.25	.20
B202	SP134	30c	+10c dk brown	6.25	2.00
	Nos. B199-B202 (4)			10.30	2.72

The surtax was for the Red Cross and for Indonesia Relief work.

1949, Nov. 14 Engr. *Perf. 13x14*

Designs: 5c+3c, "Summer." 6c+4c, "Spring." 10c+5c, "Winter." 20c+7c, "New Year."

B203	SP135	2c	+3c brown	.15	.15
B204	SP135	5c	+3c red	3.25	.95
B205	SP135	6c	+4c dull green	1.10	.20
B206	SP135	10c	+5c gray	.22	.15
B207	SP135	20c	+7c blue	3.50	.85
	Nos. B203-B207 (5)			8.22	2.30

The surtax was for child welfare.

Figure from PTT Monument, The Hague
SP136

Grain Binder
SP137

Designs: 4c+2c, Dike repairs. 5c+3c, Apartment House, Rotterdam. 10c+5c, Bridge section being towed. 20c+5c, Canal freighter.

1950, May 2 *Perf. 12½x12, 12x12½*

B208	SP136	2c	+2c dk brown	1.50	.75
B209	SP136	4c	+2c dk green	13.00	8.00
B210	SP136	5c	+3c sepia	6.75	2.50
B211	SP137	6c	+4c purple	3.00	.70
B212	SP137	10c	+5c blue gray	3.00	.25
B213	SP137	20c	+5c deep blue	13.00	9.50
	Nos. B208-B213 (6)			40.25	21.70

The surtax was for social and cultural works.

Church Ruins and Good Samaritan
SP138

Baby and Bees
SP139

1950, July 17 Photo. *Perf. 12½x12*

B214 SP138 2c +2c ol brn 3.00 1.25
B215 SP138 5c +3c brn red 16.00 *13.00*
B216 SP138 6c +4c dp grn 9.50 1.50
B217 SP138 10c +5c brt lil rose 10.00 .30
B218 SP138 20c +5c ultra 22.50 *24.00*
Nos. B214-B218 (5) 61.00 *40.05*

The surtax was for the restoration of ruined churches.

1950, Nov. 13 *Perf. 13x12*

Designs: 5c+3c, Boy and rooster. 6c+4c, Girl feeding birds. 10c+5c, Boy and fish. 20c+7c, Girl, butterfly and toad.

B219 SP139 2c +3c car .15 .15
B220 SP139 5c +3c ol grn 7.00 3.00
B221 SP139 6c +4c dk bl grn 2.00 .65
B222 SP139 10c +5c lilac .15 .15
B223 SP139 20c +7c blue 13.00 8.00
Nos. B219-B223 (5) 22.30 11.95

The surtax was to aid needy children.

Hillenraad Castle — SP140

Bergh Castle — SP141

Castles: 6c+4c, Hernen. 10c+5c, Rechteren. 20c+5c, Moermond.

Perf. 12x12½, 12½x12

1951, May 15 Engr. Unwmk.

B224 SP140 2c +2c purple 3.00 1.50
B225 SP141 5c +3c dk red 8.00 7.75
B226 SP140 6c +4c dk brown 1.40 1.25
B227 SP141 10c +5c dk green 3.00 .60
B228 SP141 20c +5c dp blue 7.00 *7.75*
Nos. B224-B228 (5) 22.40 *18.85*

The surtax was for cultural, medical and social purposes.

Girl and Windmill SP142

Jan van Riebeeck SP143

Designs: 5c+3c, Boy and building construction. 6c+4c, Fisherboy and net. 10c+5c, Boy, chimneys and steelwork. 20c+7c, Girl and apartment house.

1951, Nov. 12 Photo. *Perf. 13x14*

B229 SP142 2c +3c dp green .25 .15
B230 SP142 5c +3c sl vio 5.25 2.75
B231 SP142 6c +4c dk brown 5.25 .15
B232 SP142 10c +5c red brown .20 .15
B233 SP142 20c +7c dp bl 7.00 *4.50*
Nos. B229-B233 (5) 17.95 *7.70*

The surtax was for child welfare.

1952, Mar. *Perf. 12½x12*

B234 SP143 2c +3c dk gray 2.75 2.50
B235 SP143 6c +4c dk bl grn 6.50 6.00
B236 SP143 10c +5c brt red 7.00 4.50
B237 SP143 20c +5c brt blue 2.75 2.50
Nos. B234-B237 (4) 19.00 15.50

Tercentenary of Van Riebeeck's landing in South Africa. Surtax was for Van Riebeeck monument fund.

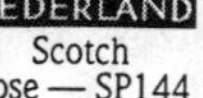

Scotch Rose — SP144

Girl and Dog — SP145

Designs: 5c+3c, Marsh marigold. 6c+4c, Tulip. 10c+5c, Ox-eye daisy. 20c+5c, Cornflower.

1952, May 1

B238 SP144 2c +2c cer & dl grn .65 .40
B239 SP144 5c +3c dp grn & yel .95 .65
B240 SP144 6c +4c red & dl grn 1.25 .30
B241 SP144 10c +5c org yel & dl grn 1.40 .15
B242 SP144 20c +5c bl & dl grn 12.50 7.50
Nos. B238-B242 (5) 16.75 9.00

The surtax was for social, cultural and medical purposes.

Perf. 12x12½

1952, Nov. 17 Unwmk.

2c+3c, Boy & goat. 5c+3c, Girl on donkey. 10c+5c, Boy & kitten. 20c+7c, Boy & rabbit.

Design in Black

B243 SP145 2c +3c olive .15 .15
B244 SP145 5c +3c dp rose .90 .45
B245 SP145 6c +4c aqua 1.90 .28
B246 SP145 10c +5c org yel .15 .15
B247 SP145 20c +7c blue 6.75 4.75
Nos. B243-B247 (5) 9.85 5.78

The surtax was for child welfare.

No. 308 Surcharged in Black

19 53

10c +10
WATERSNOOD

Perf. 13½x13

1953, Feb. 10 Wmk. 202

B248 A76 10c +10c org yel .40 .15

The surtax was for flood relief.

Hyacinth SP146

Red Cross on Shield SP147

Designs: 5c+3c, African Marigold. 6c+4c, Daffodil. 10c+5c, Anemone. 20c+5c, Iris.

1953, May 1 Unwmk. *Perf. 12½x12*

B249 SP146 2c +2c vio & grn .55 .25
B250 SP146 5c +3c dp org & grn .85 .75
B251 SP146 6c +4c grn & yel 1.10 .40
B252 SP146 10c +5c dk red & grn 2.10 .15
B253 SP146 20c +5c dp ultra & grn 11.50 11.00
Nos. B249-B253 (5) 16.10 12.55

The surtax was for social, cultural and medical purposes.

1953, Aug. 24 Engr.

Designs: 6c+4c, Man holding lantern. 7c+5c, Worker and ambulance at flood. 10c+5c, Nurse giving blood transfusion. 25c+8c, Red Cross flags.

Cross in Red

B254 SP147 2c +3c dk ol .55 .20
B255 SP147 6c +4c dk vio brn 2.25 1.90
B256 SP147 7c +5c dk gray grn 1.10 .25
B257 SP147 10c +5c red .85 .15
B258 SP147 25c +8c dp bl 5.75 3.75
Nos. B254-B258 (5) 10.50 6.25

The surtax was for the Red Cross.

Spade, Flag, Bucket and Girl's Head — SP148

Designs: Head of child and: 5c+3c, Apple. 7c+5c, Pigeon. 10c+5c, Sailboat. 25c+8c, Tulip.

1953, Nov. 16 Litho. *Perf. 12x12½*

B259 SP148 2c +3c yel & bl gray .20 .15
B260 SP148 5c +3c ap grn & brn car 1.50 .60
B261 SP148 7c +5c lt bl & sep 3.25 .70
B262 SP148 10c +5c ol bis & lil .20 .15
B263 SP148 25c +8c pink & bl grn 12.00 7.75
Nos. B259-B263 (5) 17.15 9.35

The surtax was for child welfare.

Martinus Nijhoff, Poet — SP149

Boy Flying Model Plane — SP150

5c+3c, Willem Pijper, composer. 7c+5c, H. P. Berlage, architect. 10c+5c, Johan Huizinga, historian. 25c+8c, Vincent van Gogh, painter.

1954, May 1 Photo. *Perf. 12½x12*

B264 SP149 2c +3c dp bl 1.90 1.10
B265 SP149 5c +3c ol brn .90 .45
B266 SP149 7c +5c dk red 2.75 .95
B267 SP149 10c +5c dl grn 6.00 .15
B268 SP149 25c +8c plum 11.00 *9.50*
Nos. B264-B268 (5) 22.55 *12.15*

The surtax was for social and cultural purposes.

1954, Aug. 23 *Perf. 12½x12*

Portrait: 10c+4c, Albert E. Plesman.

B269 SP150 2c +2c ol grn .80 .50
B270 SP150 10c +4c dk gray bl 2.75 .50

The surtax was for the Netherlands Aviation Foundation.

Children Making Paper Chains SP151

Girl Brushing Teeth SP152

7c+5c, Boy sailing toy boat. 10c+5c, Nurse drying child. 25c+8c, Young convalescent, drawing.

Perf. 12x12½, 12½x12

1954, Nov. 15

B271 SP151 2c +3c brn .15 .15
B272 SP152 5c +3c ol grn .70 .35
B273 SP152 7c +5c gray bl 1.00 .30
B274 SP152 10c +5c brn red .15 .15
B275 SP151 25c +8c dp bl 7.50 5.00
Nos. B271-B275 (5) 9.50 5.95

The surtax was for child welfare.

Factory, Rotterdam SP153

Amsterdam Stock Exchange SP154

5c+3c, Post office, The Hague. 10c+5c, Town hall, Hilversum. 25c+8c, Office building, The Hague.

1955, Apr. 25 Engr.

B276 SP153 2c +3c brnsh bis .95 .95
B277 SP153 5c +3c bl grn .35 .20
B278 SP154 7c +5c rose brn .95 .95
B279 SP153 10c +5c steel bl 1.40 .15
B280 SP153 25c +8c choc 11.00 *7.00*
Nos. B276-B280 (5) 14.65 *9.25*

The surtax was for social and cultural purposes.

Microscope and Crab — SP155

Willem van Loon by Dirck Santvoort — SP156

1955, Aug. 15 Photo. *Perf. 12½x12*

Crab in Red

B281 SP155 2c +3c dk gray .70 .40
B282 SP155 5c +3c dk grn .42 .25
B283 SP155 7c +5c dk vio .90 .50
B284 SP155 10c +5c dk bl .90 .15
B285 SP155 25c +8c olive 6.00 4.75
Nos. B281-B285 (5) 8.92 6.05

The surtax was for cancer research.

1955, Nov. 14 Unwmk.

Portraits: 5+3c, Boy by Jacob Adriaanszoon Backer. 7+5c, Girl by unknown artist. 10+5c, Philips Huygens by Adriaan Hanneman. 25+8c, Constantijn Huygens by Adriaan Hanneman.

B286 SP156 2c +3c dk grn .15 .15
B287 SP156 5c +3c dp car .38 .38
B288 SP156 7c +5c dl red brn 1.75 .45
B289 SP156 10c +5c dp bl .15 .15
B290 SP156 25c +8c purple 8.00 5.75
Nos. B286-B290 (5) 10.43 6.88

The surtax was for child welfare.

Farmer Wearing High Cap SP157

Sailboat SP158

Rembrandt Etchings: 5c+3c, Young Tobias with Angel. 7c+5c, Persian Wearing Fur Cap. 10c+5c, Old Blind Tobias. 25c+8c, Self-portrait of 1639.

1956, Apr. 23 Engr. *Perf. 13½x14*

B291 SP157 2c +3c bluish blk 2.25 *4.25*
B292 SP157 5c +3c ol grn 1.10 1.40
B293 SP157 7c +5c brown 3.50 *4.25*
B294 SP157 10c +5c dk grn 13.00 .25
B295 SP157 25c +8c redsh brn 16.00 *17.00*
Nos. B291-B295 (5) 35.85 *27.15*

350th anniv. of the birth of Rembrandt van Rijn. Surtax for social and cultural purposes.

1956, Aug. 27 Litho. *Perf. 12½x12*

Designs: 5c+3c, Woman runner. 7c+5c, Amphora depicting runners. 10c+5c, Field hockey. 25c+8c, Waterpolo player.

B296 SP158 2c +3c brt bl & blk .30 .25
B297 SP158 5c +3c dl yel & blk .30 .25
B298 SP158 7c +5c red brn & blk 1.10 .80
B299 SP158 10c +5c gray & blk 1.50 .80
B300 SP158 25c +8c brt grn & blk 6.25 *6.25*
Nos. B296-B300 (5) 9.45 *8.35*

16th Olympic Games at Melbourne, Nov. 22-Dec. 8, 1956.

The surtax was for the benefit of the Netherlands Olympic Committee.

Boy by Jan van Scorel — SP159

Motor Freighter — SP160

Children's Portraits: 5c+3c, Boy, 1563. 7c+5c, Girl, 1563. 10c+5c, Girl, 1590. 25c+8c, Eechie Pieters, 1592.

1956, Nov. 12 Photo. Unwmk.

B301 SP159 2c +3c blk vio .15 .15
B302 SP159 5c +3c ol grn .50 .30
B303 SP159 7c +5c brn vio 1.90 .50
B304 SP159 10c +5c dp red .15 .15
B305 SP159 25c +8c dk bl 5.25 2.75
Nos. B301-B305 (5) 7.95 3.85

The surtax was for child welfare.

1957, May 13 Photo. *Perf. 14x13*

Ships: 6c+4c, Coaster. 7c+5c, "Willem Barendsz." 10c+8c, Trawler. 30c+8c, S. S. "Nieuw Amsterdam."

B306 SP160 4c +3c brt bl .90 .95
B307 SP160 6c +4c brt vio .55 .40
B308 SP160 7c +5c dk car rose 1.10 .85

B309 SP160 10c +8c grn 1.50 .15
B310 SP160 30c +8c choc 5.00 *4.00*
Nos. B306-B310 (5) 9.05 *6.35*

The surtax was for social and cultural purposes.

White Pelican Feeding Young
SP161

Girl by B. J. Blommers
SP162

Designs: 6c+4c, Vacation ship, "Castle of Staverden." 7c+5c, Cross and dates: 1867-1957. 10c+8c, Cross and laurel wreath. 30c+8c, Globe and Cross.

1957, Aug. 19 Litho. *Perf. 12x12½*
Cross in Red

B311 SP161 4c +3c bl & red .60 .65
B312 SP161 6c +4c dk grn .50 .30
B313 SP161 7c +5c dk grn & pink .70 .40
B314 SP161 10c +8c yel org .70 .15
B315 SP161 30c +8c vio bl 2.75 *2.75*
Nos. B311-B315 (5) 5.25 *4.25*

90th anniversary of the founding of the Netherlands Red Cross.

1957, Nov. 18 Photo. *Perf. 12½x12*

Girls' Portraits by: 6c+4c, William B. Tholen. 8c+4c, Jan Sluyters. 12c+9c, Matthijs Maris. 30c+9c, Cornelis Kruseman.

B316 SP162 4c +4c dp car .15 .15
B317 SP162 6c +4c ol grn 1.65 .50
B318 SP162 8c +4c gray 1.90 1.00
B319 SP162 12c +9c dp claret .15 .15
B320 SP162 30c +9c dk bl 5.75 5.00
Nos. B316-B320 (5) 9.60 6.80

The surtax was for child welfare.

Woman from Walcheren, Zeeland
SP163

Girl on Stilts and Boy on Tricycle
SP164

Regional Costumes: 6c+4c, Marken. 8c+4c, Scheveningen. 12c+9c, Friesland. 30c+9c, Volendam.

1958, Apr. 28 Photo. Unwmk.

B321 SP163 4c +4c blue .50 .40
B322 SP163 6c +4c bister .75 .60
B323 SP163 8c +4c dk car rose 2.25 1.25
B324 SP163 12c +9c org brn .80 .20
B325 SP163 30c +9c vio 4.75 *5.00*
Nos. B321-B325 (5) 9.05 *7.45*

Surtax for social and cultural purposes.

1958, Nov. 17 Litho.

Children's Games: 6c+4c, Boy and girl on scooters. 8c+4c, Leapfrog. 12c+9c, Roller skating. 30c+9c, Boy in toy car and girl jumping rope.

B326 SP164 4c +4c lt bl .15 .15
B327 SP164 6c +4c dp red 1.10 .65
B328 SP164 8c +4c brt bl grn 1.10 .65
B329 SP164 12c +9c red org .15 .15
B330 SP164 30c +9c dk bl 3.50 3.25
Nos. B326-B330 (5) 6.00 4.85

The surtax was for child welfare.

Tugs and Caisson
SP165

Designs: 6c+4c, Dredger. 8c+4c, Laborers making fascine mattresses. 12c+9c, Grab cranes. 30c+9c, Sand spouter.

1959, May 11 *Perf. 14x13*

B331 SP165 4c +4c dk bl, *bl grn* .80 .80
B332 SP165 6c +4c red org, *gray* .90 .60
B333 SP165 8c +4c bl vio, *lt bl* 1.40 .90
B334 SP165 12c +9c bl grn, *brt yel* 2.75 .15
B335 SP165 30c +9c dk brn, *brick red* 5.00 *5.00*
Nos. B331-B335 (5) 10.85 *7.45*

Issued to publicize the endless struggle to keep the sea out and the land dry.

The surtax was for social and cultural purposes.

Child in Playpen
SP166

Refugee Woman
SP167

Designs: 6c+4c, Playing Indian. 8c+4c, Child feeding geese. 12c+9c, Children crossing street. 30c+9c, Doing homework.

1959, Nov. 16 *Perf. 12½x12*

B336 SP166 4c +4c dp rose & dk bl .15 .15
B337 SP166 6c +4c red brn & emer 1.65 .85
B338 SP166 8c +4c red & bl 1.65 1.00
B339 SP166 12c +9c grnsh bl, org & gray .15 .15
B340 SP166 30c +9c yel & bl 3.00 2.50
Nos. B336-B340 (5) 6.60 4.65

The surtax was for child welfare.

1960, Apr. 7 Photo. *Perf. 13x14*

B341 SP167 12c +8c dp claret .48 .30
B342 SP167 30c +10c dk ol grn 2.50 1.75

Issued to publicize World Refugee Year, July 1, 1959-June 30, 1960. The surtax was for aid to refugees.

Tulip
SP168

Girl from Marken
SP169

Flowers: 6c+4c, Gorse. 8c+4c, White waterlily, horiz. 12c+8c, Red poppy. 30c+10c, Blue sea holly.

Perf. 12½x12, 12x12½
1960, May 23 Unwmk.

B343 SP168 4c +4c gray, grn & red .80 .40
B344 SP168 6c +4c sal, grn & yel .60 .30
B345 SP168 8c +4c multi 1.75 .85
B346 SP168 12c +8c dl org, red & grn 1.75 .30
B347 SP168 30c +10c yel, grn & ultra 6.25 4.50
Nos. B343-B347 (5) 11.15 6.35

The surtax was for child welfare.

1960, Nov. 14 *Perf. 12½x12*

Regional Costumes: 6c+4c, Volendam. 8c+4c, Bunschoten. 12c+9c, Hindeloopen. 30c+9c, Huizen.

B348 SP169 4c +4c multi .16 .15
B349 SP169 6c +4c multi 1.10 .80
B350 SP169 8c +4c multi 3.50 1.10
B351 SP169 12c +9c multi .16 .15
B352 SP169 30c +9c multi 6.00 3.50
Nos. B348-B352 (5) 10.92 5.70

The surtax was for child welfare.

Herring Gull
SP170

St. Nicholas on his Horse
SP171

Birds: 6c+4c, Oystercatcher, horiz. 8c+4c, Curlew. 12c+8c, Avocet, horiz. 30c+10c, Lapwing.

Perf. 12½x12, 12x12½
1961, Apr. 24 Litho. Unwmk.

B353 SP170 4c +4c yel & grnsh gray .85 .85
B354 SP170 6c +4c fawn & blk .40 .20
B355 SP170 8c +4c ol & red brn .85 .70
B356 SP170 12c +8c lt bl & gray 1.75 .20
B357 SP170 30c +10c grn & blk 3.50 2.75
Nos. B353-B357 (5) 7.35 4.70

The surtax was for social and cultural purposes.

1961, Nov. 13 *Perf. 12½x12*

Holiday folklore: 6c+4c, Epiphany. 8c+4c, Palm Sunday. 12c+9c, Whitsun bride, Pentecost. 30c+9c, Martinmas.

B358 SP171 4c +4c brt red .15 .15
B359 SP171 6c +4c brt bl 1.10 .85
B360 SP171 8c +4c olive 1.10 .85
B361 SP171 12c +9c dp grn .15 .15
B362 SP171 30c +9c dp org 3.00 2.00
Nos. B358-B362 (5) 5.50 4.00

The surtax was for child welfare.

Christian Huygens' Pendulum Clock by van Ceulen
SP172

Children Cooking
SP173

Designs: 4c+4c, Cat, Roman sculpture, horiz. 6c+4c, Fossil Ammonite. 12c+ 8c, Figurehead from admiralty ship model. 30c+10c, Guardsmen Hendrick van Berckenrode and Jacob van Lourensz, by Frans Hals, horiz.

Perf. 14x13, 13x14
1962, Apr. 27 Photo.

B363 SP172 4c +4c ol grn 1.00 .85
B364 SP172 6c +4c gray .50 .40
B365 SP172 8c +4c dp claret 1.10 .85
B366 SP172 12c +8c olive bis 1.10 .20
B367 SP172 30c +10c bl blk 1.25 1.25
Nos. B363-B367 (5) 4.95 3.55

The surtax was for social and cultural purposes. Issued to publicize the International Congress of Museum Experts, July 4-11.

1962, Nov. 12 *Perf. 12½x12*

Children's Activities: 6c+4c, Bicycling. 8c+4c, Watering flowers. 12c+9c, Feeding chickens. 30c+9c, Music making.

B368 SP173 4c +4c red .15 .15
B369 SP173 6c +4c yel bis 1.25 .30
B370 SP173 8c +4c ultra 1.50 .85
B371 SP173 12c +9c dp grn .15 .15
B372 SP173 30c +9c dk car rose 2.50 1.90
Nos. B368-B372 (5) 5.55 3.35

The surtax was for child welfare.

Gallery Windmill
SP174

Roadside First Aid Station
SP175

Windmills: 6c+4c, North Holland polder mill. 8c+4c, South Holland polder mill, horiz. 12c+8c, Post mill. 30c+10c, Wip mill.

Perf. 13x14, 14x13
1963, Apr. 24 Litho. Unwmk.

B373 SP174 4c +4c dk bl 1.00 .75
B374 SP174 6c +4c dk pur 1.00 .75
B375 SP174 8c +4c dk grn 1.25 .90
B376 SP174 12c +8c blk 2.00 .25
B377 SP174 30c +10c dk car 2.00 1.75
Nos. B373-B377 (5) 7.25 4.40

The surtax was for social and cultural purposes.

1963, Aug. 20 *Perf. 14x13*

Designs: 6c+4c, Book collection box. 8c+4c, Crosses. 12c+9c, International aid to Africans. 30c+9c, First aid team.

B378 SP175 4c +4c dk bl & red .35 .20
B379 SP175 6c +4c dl pur & red .24 .20
B380 SP175 8c +4c blk & red .85 .50
B381 SP175 12c +9c red brn & red .50 .15
B382 SP175 30c +9c yel grn & red 1.50 1.00
Nos. B378-B382 (5) 3.44 2.05

Centenary of the International Red Cross. The surtax went to the Netherlands Red Cross.

"Aunt Lucy Sat on a Goosey"
SP176

Seeing-Eye Dog
SP177

Nursery Rhymes: 6c+4c, "In the Hague there lives a count." 8c+4c, "One day I passed a puppet's fair." 12c+9c, "Storky, storky, Billy Spoon." 30c+9c, "Ride on in a little buggy."

1963, Nov. 12 Litho. *Perf. 13x14*

B383 SP176 4c +4c grnsh bl & dk bl .15 .15
B384 SP176 6c +4c org red & sl grn .70 .45
B385 SP176 8c +4c dl grn & dk brn 1.00 .45
B386 SP176 12c +9c yel & dk pur .15 .15
B387 SP176 30c +9c rose & dk bl 1.75 1.25
Nos. B383-B387 (5) 3.75 2.45

The surtax was for mentally and physically handicapped children.

1964, Apr. 21 *Perf. 12x12½*

Designs: 8c+5c, Three red deer. 12c+9c, Three kittens. 30c+9c, European bison and young.

B388 SP177 5c +5c gray ol, red & blk .35 .20
B389 SP177 8c +5c dk red, pale brn & blk .35 .15
B390 SP177 12c +9c dl yel, blk & gray .35 .15
B391 SP177 30c +9c bl, gray & blk .55 .38
Nos. B388-B391 (4) 1.60 .88

The surtax was for social and cultural purposes.

Child Painting
SP178

View of Veere
SP179

"Artistic and Creative Activities of Children": 10c+5c, Ballet dancing. 15c+10c, Girl playing the flute. 20c+10c, Little Red Riding Hood (masquerading children). 40c+15c, Boy with hammer at work bench.

Perf. 13x14
1964, Nov. 17 Photo. Unwmk.

B392 SP178 7c +3c lt ol grn & bl .45 .32
B393 SP178 10c +5c red, brt pink & grn .35 .25
B394 SP178 15c +10c yel bis, blk & yel .15 .15
B395 SP178 20c +10c brt pink, brn & red .45 .25
B396 SP178 40c +15c bl & yel grn .75 .48
Nos. B392-B396 (5) 2.15 1.45

The surtax was for child welfare.

1965, June 1 Litho. *Perf. 14x13*

Views: 10c+6c, Thorn. 18c+12c, Dordrecht. 20c+10c, Staveren. 40c+10c, Medemblik.

B397 SP179 8c +6c yel & blk .35 .15
B398 SP179 10c +6c grnsh bl & blk .35 .25
B399 SP179 18c +12c sal & blk .35 .15
B400 SP179 20c +10c bl & blk .35 .25
B401 SP179 40c +10c ap grn & blk .60 .40
Nos. B397-B401 (5) 2.00 1.20

The surtax was for social and cultural purposes.

Child — SP180

Designs by Children: 10c+6c, Ship. 18c+12c, Woman, vert. 20c+10c, Child, lake and swan. 40c+10c, Tractor.

Perf. 14x13, 13x14

1965, Nov. 16 **Photo.**

B402 SP180 8c +6c multi .15 .15
B403 SP180 10c +6c multi .45 .38
B404 SP180 18c +12c multi .15 .15
a. Min. sheet of 11, 5 #B402, 6 #B404 + label 20.00 18.00
B405 SP180 20c +10c multi .48 .38
B406 SP180 40c +10c multi .80 .45
Nos. B402-B406 (5) 2.03 1.51

The surtax was for child welfare.

"Help them to a safe haven" — SP181

1966, Jan. 31 **Photo.** ***Perf. 14x13***

B407 SP181 18c +7c blk & org yel .40 .18
B408 SP181 40c +20c blk & red .40 .15
a. Min. sheet of 3, #B407, 2 #B408 4.00 3.00

The surtax was for the Intergovernmental Committee for European Migration (ICEM). The message on the stamps was given and signed by Queen Juliana.

Inkwell, Goose Quill and Book — SP182

Designs: 12c+8c, Fragment of Gysbert Japicx manuscript. 20c+10c, Knight on horseback, miniature from "Roman van Walewein" manuscript, 1350. 25c+10c, Initial "D" from "Ferguut" manuscript, 1350. 40c+20c, Print shop, 16th century woodcut.

1966, May 3 ***Perf. 13x14***

B409 SP182 10c +5c multi .32 .30
B410 SP182 12c +8c multi .35 .32
B411 SP182 20c +10c multi .45 .40
B412 SP182 25c +10c multi .48 .42
B413 SP182 40c +20c multi .55 .50
Nos. B409-B413 (5) 2.15 1.94

Gysbert Japicx (1603-1666), Friesian poet, and the 200th anniversary of the founding of the Netherlands Literary Society.

The surtax was for social and cultural purposes.

Infant — SP183

Designs: 12c+8c, Daughter of the painter S. C. Lixenberg. 20c+10c, Boy swimming. 25c+10c, Dominga Blazer, daughter of Carel Blazer, photographer of this set. 40c+20c, Boy and horse.

1966, Nov. 15 **Photo.** ***Perf. 14x13***

B414 SP183 10c +5c dp org & bl .15 .15
B415 SP183 12c +8c ap grn & red .15 .15
B416 SP183 20c +10c brt bl & red .15 .15
a. Min. sheet of 12, 4 #B414, 5 #B415, 3 #B416 3.00 3.00
B417 SP183 25c +10c brt rose lil & dk bl .80 .75
B418 SP183 40c +20c dp car & dk grn .70 .65
Nos. B414-B418 (5) 1.95 1.85

The surtax was for child welfare.

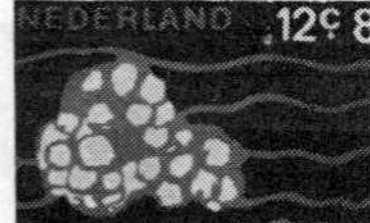

Whelk Eggs — SP184

15c+10c, Whelk. 20c+10c, Mussel with acorn shells. 25c+10c, Jellyfish. 45c+20c, Crab.

1967, Apr. 11 **Unwmk.** **Litho.**

B419 SP184 12c +8c ol grn & tan .28 .25
B420 SP184 15c +10c lt bl, ultra & blk .28 .25
B421 SP184 20c +10c gray, blk & red .28 .15
B422 SP184 25c +10c brn car, plum & ol brn .55 .52
B423 SP184 45c +20c multi .70 .65
Nos. B419-B423 (5) 2.09 1.82

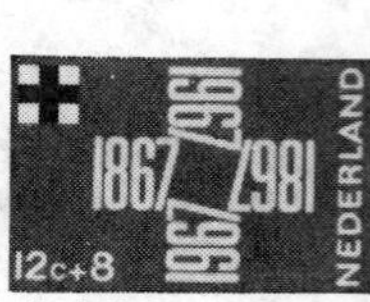

Red Cross and Dates Forming Cross SP185

"Lullaby for the Little Porcupine" SP186

15c+10c, Crosses. 20c+10c, Initials "NRK" forming cross. 25c+10c, Maltese cross and crosses. 45c+20c, "100" forming cross.

1967, Aug. 8 ***Perf. 14x13***

B424 SP185 12c +8c dl bl & red .30 .24
B425 SP185 15c +10c red .38 .35
B426 SP185 20c +10c ol & red .28 .15
B427 SP185 25c +10c ol grn & red .38 .35
B428 SP185 45c +20c gray & red .70 .48
Nos. B424-B428 (5) 2.04 1.57

Centenary of the Dutch Red Cross.

1967, Nov. 7 **Litho.** ***Perf. 13x14***

Nursery Rhymes: 15c+10c, "Little Whistling Kettle." 20c+10c, "Dikkertje Dap and the Giraffe." 25c+10c, "The Nicest Flowers." 45c+20c, "Pippeljoentje, the Little Bear."

B429 SP186 12c +8c multi .15 .15
B430 SP186 15c +10c multi .15 .15
B431 SP186 20c +10c multi .15 .15
a. Min. sheet of 10, 3 #B429, 4 #B430, 3 #B431 4.25 4.25
B432 SP186 25c +10c multi .85 .75
B433 SP186 45c +20c multi 1.00 .75
Nos. B429-B433 (5) 2.30 1.95

The surtax was for child welfare.

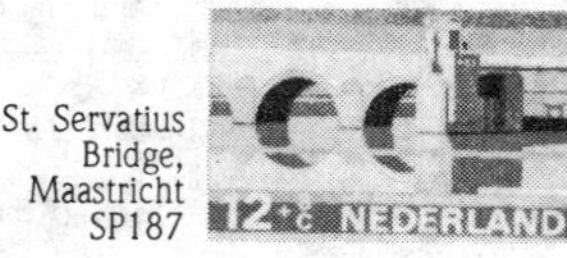

St. Servatius Bridge, Maastricht SP187

Bridges: 15c+10c, Narrow Bridge, Amsterdam. 20c+10c, Railroad Bridge, Culenborg. 25c+10c, Van Brienenoord Bridge, Rotterdam. 45c+20c, Zeeland Bridge, Schelde Estuary.

1968, Apr. 9 **Photo.** ***Perf. 14x13***

B434 SP187 12c +8c green .65 .85
B435 SP187 15c +10c ol brn .75 .90
B436 SP187 20c +10c rose red .65 .25
B437 SP187 25c +10c gray .65 .85
B438 SP187 45c +20c ultra 1.00 1.25
Nos. B434-B438 (5) 3.70 4.10

Goblin — SP188

Fairy Tale Characters: 15c+10c, Giant. 20c+10c, Witch. 25c+10c, Dragon. 45c+20c, Magician.

1968, Nov. 12 **Photo.** ***Perf. 14x13***

B439 SP188 12c +8c grn, pink & blk .15 .15
B440 SP188 15c +10c bl, pink & blk .15 .15
B441 SP188 20c +10c bl, emer & blk .15 .15
a. Min. sheet of 10, 3 #B439, 4 #B440, 3 #B441 8.00 8.00
B442 SP188 25c +10c org red, org & blk 2.00 1.90
B443 SP188 45c +20c yel, org & blk 1.90 1.90
Nos. B439-B443 (5) 4.35 4.25

The surtax was for child welfare.

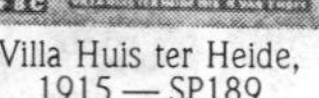

Villa Huis ter Heide, 1915 — SP189

Stylized Crab — SP190

Contemporary Architecture: 15c+10c, House, Utrecht, 1924. 20c+10c, First open-air school, Amsterdam, 1960. 25c+10c, Burgweeshuis (orphanage), Amsterdam, 1960. 45c+20c, Netherlands Congress Building, The Hague, 1969.

1969, Apr. 15 **Photo.** ***Perf. 14x13***

B444 SP189 12c +8c lt brn & sl .85 .85
B445 SP189 15c +10c bl, gray & red .85 1.10
B446 SP189 20c +10c vio & blk .85 1.10
B447 SP189 25c +10c grn & gray 1.00 .52
B448 SP189 45c +20c gray, bl & yel 1.10 1.25
Nos. B444-B448 (5) 4.65 4.82

Surtax for social and cultural purposes.

1969, Aug. 12 **Photo.** ***Perf. 13x14***

B449 SP190 12c +8c vio 1.00 1.10
B450 SP190 25c +10c org 1.40 .55
B451 SP190 45c +20c bl grn 1.75 2.50
Nos. B449-B451 (3) 4.15 4.15

20th anniv. of the Queen Wilhelmina Fund. The surtax was for cancer research.

Child with Violin — SP191

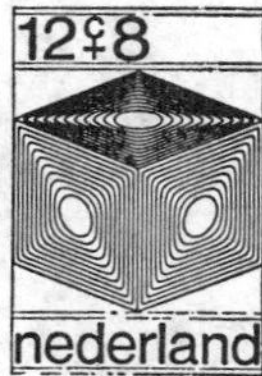

Isometric Projection from Circle to Square — SP192

Designs: 12c+8c, Child with flute. 20c+10c, Child with drum. 25c+10c, Three children singing, horiz. 45c+20c, Two girls dancing, horiz.

1969, Nov. 11 ***Perf. 13x14, 14x13***

B452 SP191 12c +8c ultra, blk & yel .25 .15
B453 SP191 15c +10c blk & red .25 .15
B454 SP191 20c +10c red, blk & yel 2.00 1.75
B455 SP191 25c +10c yel, blk & red .32 .15
a. Min. sheet of 10, 4 #B452, 4 #B453, 2 #B455 8.75 7.25
B456 SP191 45c +20c grn, blk & red 2.75 2.75
Nos. B452-B456 (5) 5.57 4.95

The surtax was for child welfare.

Lithographed and Engraved

1970, Apr. 7 ***Perf. 13x14***

Designs made by Computer: 15c+10c, Parallel planes in a cube. 20c+10c, Two overlapping scales. 25c+10c, Transition phases of concentric circles with increasing diameters. 45c+20c, Four spirals.

B457 SP192 12c +8c yel & blk 1.25 1.75
B458 SP192 15c +10c sil & blk 1.25 1.50
B459 SP192 20c +10c blk 1.25 1.40
B460 SP192 25c +10c brt bl & blk 1.25 .70
B461 SP192 45c +20c sil & white 1.25 1.75
Nos. B457-B461 (5) 6.25 7.10

Surtax for social and cultural purposes.

Bleeding Heart — SP193

Toy Block — SP194

1970, July 28 **Photo.** ***Perf. 13x14***

B462 SP193 12c +8c org yel, red & blk .90 1.10
B463 SP193 25c +10c pink, red & blk .90 .55
B464 SP193 45c +20c brt grn, red & blk .90 1.10
Nos. B462-B464 (3) 2.70 2.75

The surtax was for the Netherlands Heart Foundation.

1970, Nov. 10 **Photo.** ***Perf. 13x14***

B465 SP194 12c +8c bl, vio bl & grn .15 .15
B466 SP194 15c +10c grn, bl & yel 1.75 2.00
B467 SP194 20c +10c lil rose, red & vio bl 1.75 2.00
B468 SP194 25c +10c red, yel & lil rose .25 .15
a. Min. sheet of 11, 9 #B465, 2 #B468 + label 14.00 14.00
B469 SP194 45c +20c gray & blk 2.25 2.50
Nos. B465-B469 (5) 6.15 6.80

The surtax was for child welfare.

St. Paul SP195

Detail from Borobudur SP196

Designs: 15c+10c, "50" and people. 25c+10c, Joachim and Ann. 30c+15c, John the Baptist and the Scribes. 45c+20c, St. Anne. The sculptures are wood, 15th century, and in Dutch museums.

1971, Apr. 20 **Litho.** ***Perf. 13x14***

B470 SP195 15c +10c multi 1.75 1.40

Lithographed and Photogravure

B471 SP195 20c +10c gray, grn & blk 1.40 1.40
B472 SP195 25c +10c buff, org & blk 1.40 .55
B473 SP195 30c +15c gray, bl & blk 1.75 1.50
B474 SP195 45c +20c pink, ver & blk 1.75 1.50
Nos. B470-B474 (5) 8.05 6.35

50th anniversary of the Federation of Netherlands Universities for Adult Education.

1971, June 29 **Litho.** ***Perf. 13x14***

B475 SP196 45c +20c pur, yel & blk 2.50 2.50

60th birthday of Prince Bernhard. Surtax for Save Borobudur Temple Fund.

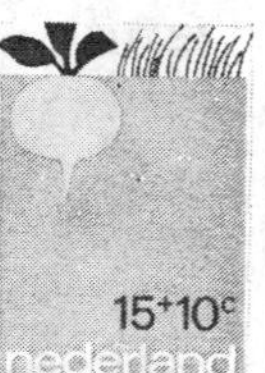

"Earth" SP197

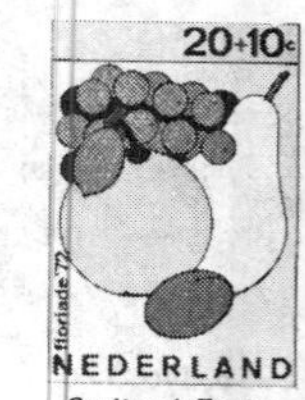

Stylized Fruits SP198

Designs: 20c+10c, "Air" (butterfly). 25c+10c, "Sun," horiz. 30c+15c, "Moon," horiz. 45c+20c, "Water" (child looking at reflection).

Perf. 13x14, 14x13

1971, Nov. 9 **Photo.**

B476 SP197 15c +10c blk, lil & org .15 .15
B477 SP197 20c +10c yel, blk & rose lil .55 .42
B478 SP197 25c +10c multi .42 .15
a. Min. sheet of 9, 6 #B476, #B477, 2 #B478 11.00 10.00
B479 SP197 30c +15c bl, blk & pur 1.50 .55
B480 SP197 45c +20c grn, blk & bl 2.50 2.50
Nos. B476-B480 (5) 5.12 3.77

The surtax was for child welfare.

Luminescence

Some semipostal issues from Nos. B481-B484 onward are on phosphorescent paper.

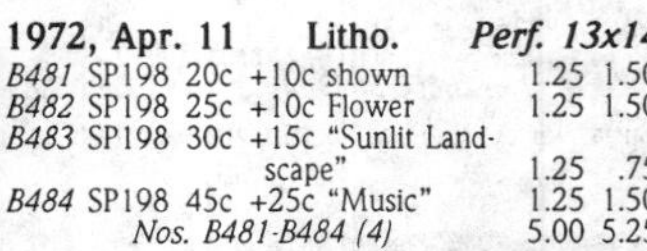

1972, Apr. 11 Litho. *Perf. 13x14*

B481 SP198 20c +10c shown 1.25 1.50
B482 SP198 25c +10c Flower 1.25 1.50
B483 SP198 30c +15c "Sunlit Landscape" 1.25 .75
B484 SP198 45c +25c "Music" 1.25 1.50
Nos. B481-B484 (4) 5.00 5.25

Summer festivals: Nos. B481-B482 publicize the Floriade, flower festival; Nos. B483-B484 the Holland Festival of Arts.

Red Cross, First Aid SP199

Prince Willem-Alexander SP200

Designs (Red Cross and): 25c+10c, Blood bank. 30c+15c, Disaster relief. 45c+25c, Child care.

1972, Aug. 15 *Perf. 13x14*

B485 SP199 20c +10c brt pink & red .80 .45
B486 SP199 25c +10c org & red .95 .80
B487 SP199 30c +15c blk & red .95 .30
B488 SP199 45c +25c ultra & red 1.10 1.25
Nos. B485-B488 (4) 3.80 2.80

Surtax for the Netherlands Red Cross.

Perf. 13x14, 14x13

1972, Nov. 7 Photo.

Photographs of Dutch Princes: 30c+10c, Johan Friso. 35c+15c, Constantijn. 50c+20c, Johan Friso, Constantijn and Willem-Alexander. All are horizontal.

B489 SP200 25c +15c multi .28 .15
B490 SP200 30c +10c multi 1.10 .90
B491 SP200 35c +15c multi 1.10 .15
a. Min. sheet of 7, 4 #B489, #B490, 2 #B491 + label 7.75 7.50
B492 SP200 50c +20c multi 2.50 2.50
Nos. B489-B492 (4) 4.98 3.70

Surtax was for child welfare.

"W. A. Scholten," 1874 — SP201

Ships: 25c+15c, Flagship "De Seven Provincien," 1673, vert. 35c+15c, "Veendam," 1923. 50c+20c, Zuider Zee fish well boat, 17th century, vert.

1973, Apr. 10 Litho.

B493 SP201 25c +15c multi 1.75 1.40
B494 SP201 30c +10c multi 1.75 1.40
B495 SP201 35c +15c multi 1.75 .90
B496 SP201 50c +20c multi 1.75 1.40
Nos. B493-B496 (4) 7.00 5.10

Tercentenary of the Battle of Kijkduin and centenary of the Holland-America Line.
Surtax for social and cultural purposes.

Chessboard — SP202

Games: 30c+10c, Tick-tack-toe. 40c+20c, Labyrinth. 50c+20c, Dominoes.

1973, Nov. 13 Photo. *Perf. 13x14*

B497 SP202 25c +15c multi .60 .28
B498 SP202 30c +10c multi 1.10 .70
B499 SP202 40c +20c multi 1.10 .15
a. Min. sheet of 6, 2 #B497, #B498, 3 #B499 10.00 9.00
B500 SP202 50c +20c multi 2.00 2.00
Nos. B497-B500 (4) 4.80 3.13

Surtax was for child welfare.

Music Bands SP203

Herman Heijermans SP204

Designs: 30c+10c, Ballet dancers and traffic lights. 50c+20c, Kniertje, the fisher woman, from play by Heijermans.

1974, Apr. 23 Litho. *Perf. 13x14*

B501 SP203 25c +15c multi .95 .95
B502 SP203 30c +10c multi .95 .95

Photo.

B503 SP204 40c +20c multi .95 .45
B504 SP204 50c +20c multi .95 .95
Nos. B501-B504 (4) 3.80 3.30

Surtax was for various social and cultural institutions.

Boy with Hoop — SP205

Designs: 35c+20c, Girl and infant. 45c+20c, Two girls. 60c+20c, Girl sitting on balustrade. Designs are from turn-of-the-century photographs.

1974, Nov. 12 Photo. *Perf. 13x14*

B505 SP205 30c +15c brown .38 .30
B506 SP205 35c +20c maroon .50 .45
B507 SP205 45c +20c black brn .60 .18
a. Min. sheet of 6, 4 #B505, #B506, #B507 4.50 4.50
B508 SP205 60c +20c indigo 1.25 1.40
Nos. B505-B508 (4) 2.73 2.33

Surtax was for child welfare.

Beguinage, Amsterdam SP206

Cooper's Gate, Middelburg SP207

Designs: 35c+20c, St. Hubertus Hunting Lodge, horiz. 60c+20c, Orvelte Village, horiz.

Perf. 14x13, 13x14

1975, Apr. 4 Litho.

B509 SP206 35c +20c multi .65 .55
B510 SP206 40c +15c multi .65 .70
B511 SP207 50c +20c multi .80 .55
B512 SP207 60c +20c multi 1.10 .70
Nos. B509-B512 (4) 3.20 2.50

European Architectural Heritage Year 1975. Surtax was for various social and cultural institutions.

Orphans, Sculpture, 1785 — SP208

40c+15c, Milkmaid, 17th cent. 50c+25c, Aymon's 4 sons on steed Bayard, 17th cent. 60c+25c, Life at orphanage, 1557. All designs are after ornamental stones from various buildings.

1975, Nov. 11 Photo. *Perf. 14x13*

B513 SP208 35c +15c multi .28 .15
B514 SP208 40c +15c multi .55 .55
B515 SP208 50c +25c multi .42 .15
a. Min. sheet of 5, 3 #B513, 2 #B515 + label 3.00 3.00
B516 SP208 60c +25c multi .90 .90
Nos. B513-B516 (4) 2.15 1.75

Surtax was for child welfare.

Hedgehog SP209

Book with "ABC" and Grain; Open Field — SP210

Green Frog and Spawn — SP212

People and Initials of Social Security Acts — SP211

Perf. 14x13, 13x14

1976, Apr. 6 Litho.

B517 SP209 40c +20c multi .50 .50
B518 SP210 45c +20c multi .50 .38

Photo.

B519 SP211 55c +20c multi .80 .38
B520 SP212 75c +25c multi .80 .65
Nos. B517-B520 (4) 2.60 1.91

Surtax for various social and cultural institutions. #B517, B520 for wildlife protection; #B518 cent. of agricultural education and 175th anniv. of elementary education legislation; #B519 75th anniv. of social legislation and the Social Insurance Bank.

Patient Surrounded by Caring Hands — SP213

Netherlands No. 41 — SP214

1976, Sept. 2 Litho. *Perf. 13x14*

B521 SP213 55c +25c multi .60 .60

Dutch Anti-Rheumatism Assoc., 50th anniv.

1976, Oct. 8 Litho. *Perf. 13x14*

Designs: No. B523, #64. No. B524, #155. No. B525, #294. No. B526, #220.

B522 SP214 55c +55c multi .85 1.00
B523 SP214 55c +55c multi .85 1.00
B524 SP214 55c +55c multi .85 1.00
a. Strip of 3, #B522-B524 3.00 3.00

Photo.

B525 SP214 75c +75c multi .85 1.00
B526 SP214 75c +75c multi .85 1.00
a. Pair, #B525-B526 1.75 2.00
Nos. B522-B526 (5) 4.25 5.00

Amphilex 77 Philatelic Exhibition, Amsterdam, May 26-June 5, 1977. No. B526a printed checkerwise.
See Nos. B535-B538.

Soccer — SP215

Designs (Children's Drawings): 45c+20c, Sailboat. 55c+20c, Elephant. 75c+25c, Mobile home.

1976, Nov. 16 Photo. *Perf. 14x13*

B527 SP215 40c +20c multi .35 .15
B528 SP215 45c +20c multi .35 .20
B529 SP215 55c +20c multi .35 .15
a. Min. sheet of 6, 2 each #B527-B529 3.00 3.00
B530 SP215 75c +25c multi .90 .85
Nos. B527-B530 (4) 1.95 1.35

Surtax was for child welfare.

Hot Room, Thermal Bath, Heerlen SP216

Designs: 45c+20c, Altar of Goddess Nehalennia, 200 A.D., Eastern Scheldt. 55c+20c, Part of oaken ship, Zwammerdam. 75c+25c, Helmet with face, Waal River at Nijmegen.

1977, Apr. 19 Photo. *Perf. 14x13*

B531 SP216 40c +20c multi .35 .35
B532 SP216 45c +20c multi .35 .35
B533 SP216 55c +20c multi .35 .35
B534 SP216 75c +25c multi .50 .50
Nos. B531-B534 (4) 1.55 1.55

Archaeological finds of Roman period.
Surtax for various social and cultural institutions.

Type of 1976

Designs: No. B535, Netherlands #83. No. B536, Netherlands #128. No. B537, Netherlands #211. No. B538, Netherlands #302.

1977, May 26 Litho. *Perf. 13x14*

B535 SP214 55c +45c multi .55 .55
B536 SP214 55c +45c multi .55 .55
a. Pair, #B535-B536 1.10 1.10
B537 SP214 55c +45c multi .55 .55
B538 SP214 55c +45c multi .55 .55
a. Souv. sheet of 2, #B535, B538 1.25 1.25
b. Pair, #B537-B538 1.10 1.10
Nos. B535-B538 (4) 2.20 2.20

Amphilex 77 International Philatelic Exhibition, Amsterdam May 26-June 5. No. B538a sold at Exhibition only.

Risk of Drowning — SP217

Childhood Dangers: 45c+20c, Poisoning. 55c+20c, Following ball into street. 75c+ 25c, Playing with matches.

1977, Nov. 15 Photo. *Perf. 13x14*

B539 SP217 40c +20c multi .24 .16
B540 SP217 45c +20c multi .24 .16
B541 SP217 55c +20c multi .30 .16
a. Min. sheet of 6, 2 each #B539-B541 2.50 2.50
B542 SP217 75c +25c multi .75 .75
Nos. B539-B542 (4) 1.53 1.23

Surtax was for child welfare.

Anna Maria van Schuurman SP218

Delft Plate SP219

Designs: 45c+20c, Part of letter written by author Belle van Zuylen (1740-1805). 75c+25c, Makkum dish with dog.

1978, Apr. 11 Litho. *Perf. 13x14*

B543 SP218 40c +20c multi .32 .32
B544 SP218 45c +20c multi .32 .32

Photo.

B545 SP219 55c +20c multi .35 .24
B546 SP219 75c +25c multi .48 .48
Nos. B543-B546 (4) 1.47 1.36

Dutch authors and pottery products.

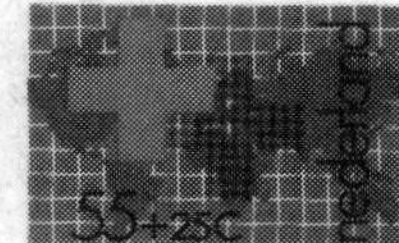

Red Cross and World Map — SP220

1978, Aug. 22 Photo. *Perf. 14x13*
B547 SP220 55c +25c multi .45 .32
a. Souvenir sheet of 3 1.75 1.50

Surtax was for Dutch Red Cross.

Boy Ringing Doorbell SP221

Designs: 45c+20c, Child reading book. 55c+20c, Boy writing "30x Children for Children," vert. 75c+25c, Girl at blackboard, arithmetic lesson.

Perf. 14x13, 13x14

1978, Nov. 14 Photo.
B548 SP221 40c +20c multi .28 .15
B549 SP221 45c +20c multi .30 .15
B550 SP221 55c +20c multi .32 .15
a. Min. sheet of 6, 2 each #B548-B550 2.25 2.25
B551 SP221 75c +25c multi .60 .60
Nos. B548-B551 (4) 1.50 1.05

Surtax was for child welfare.

Psalm Trilogy, by Jurriaan Andriessen SP222

Birth of Christ (detail) Stained-glass Window SP223

Designs: 45c+20c, Amsterdam Toonkunst Choir. 75c+25c, William of Orange, stained-glass window, 1603. Windows from St. John's Church, Gouda.

1979, Apr. 3 Photo. *Perf. 13x14*
B552 SP222 40c +20c multi .30 .25
B553 SP222 45c +20c multi .30 .25
B554 SP223 55c +20c multi .35 .25
B555 SP223 75c +25c multi .50 .48
Nos. B552-B555 (4) 1.45 1.23

Surtax for social and cultural purposes.

Child Sleeping Under Blanket SP224

Designs: 45c+20c, Infant. 55c+20c, African boy, vert. 75c+25c, Children, vert.

1979, Nov. 13 *Perf. 14x13, 13x14*
B556 SP224 40c +20c blk, red & yel .30 .15
B557 SP224 45c +20c blk & red .30 .15
B558 SP224 55c +20c blk & yel .38 .15
a. Min. sheet, 2 each #B556-B558 2.00 2.00
B559 SP224 75c +25c blk, ultra & red .60 .60
Nos. B556-B559 (4) 1.58 1.05

Surtax was for child welfare (in conjuction with International Year of the Child).

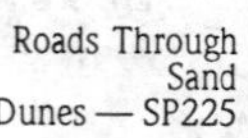

Roads Through Sand Dunes — SP225

Designs: 50c+20c, Park mansion vert. 60c+25c, Sailing. 80c+35c, Bicycling, moorlands.

Perf. 14x13, 13x14

1980, Apr. 15 Litho.
B560 SP225 45c +20c multi .28 .28
B561 SP225 50c +20c multi .35 .28
B562 SP225 60c +25c multi .42 .22
B563 SP225 80c +35c multi .52 .52
Nos. B560-B563 (4) 1.57 1.30

Society for the Promotion of Nature Preserves, 75th anniv. Surtax for social and cultural purposes.

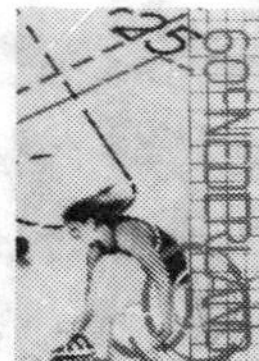

Wheelchair Basketball — SP226

1980, June 3 Litho. *Perf. 13x14*
B564 SP226 60c +25c multi .48 .20

Olympics for the Disabled, Arnhem and Veenendaal, June 21-July 5. Surtax was for National Sports for the Handicapped Fund.

Harlequin and Girl Standing in Open Book — SP227

Designs: 50c+20c, Boy on flying book, vert. 60c+30c, Boy reading King of Frogs, vert. 80c+30c, Boy "engrossed" in book.

Perf. 14x13, 13x14

1980, Nov. 11 Photo.
B565 SP227 45c +20c multi .30 .22
B566 SP227 50c +20c multi .35 .35
B567 SP227 60c +30c multi .42 .22
a. Min. sheet of 5, 2 #B565, 3 #B567 + label 2.00 2.00
B568 SP227 80c +30c multi .52 .52
Nos. B565-B568 (4) 1.59 1.31

Surtax was for child welfare.

Salt Marsh with Outlet Ditch at Low Tide — SP228

Designs: 55c+25c, Dike. 60c+25c, Land drainage. 65c+30c, Cultivated land.

1981, Apr. 7 Photo. *Perf. 13x14*
B569 SP228 45c +20c multi .30 .30
B570 SP228 55c +25c multi .38 .38
B571 SP228 60c +25c multi .42 .42
B572 SP228 65c +30c multi .55 .55
Nos. B569-B572 (4) 1.65 1.65

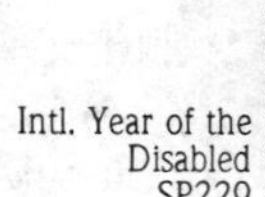

Intl. Year of the Disabled SP229

Perf. 14x13, 13x14

1981, Nov. 10 Photo.
B573 SP229 45c +25c multi .32 .25
B574 SP229 55c +20c multi, vert .35 .32
B575 SP229 60c +25c multi, vert. .38 .38
B576 SP229 65c +30c multi .45 .38
a. Min. sheet of 5, 3 #B573, 2 #B576 + label 2.00 1.50
Nos. B573-B576 (4) 1.50 1.33

Surtax was for child welfare.

Floriade '82, Amsterdam, Apr. — SP230

1982, Apr. 7 Litho. *Perf. 13½x13*
B577 SP230 50c +20c shown .40 .40
B578 SP230 60c +25c Anemones .45 .45
B579 SP230 65c +25c Roses .52 .52
B580 SP230 70c +30c African violets .55 .55
Nos. B577-B580 (4) 1.92 1.92

Surtax was for culture and social welfare institutions.

Birds on Child's Head — SP231

Children and Animals: 60c+20c, Boy and cat. 65c+20c, Boy and rabbit. 70c+30c, Boy and bird.

1982, Nov. 16 Photo. *Perf. 13x14*
B581 SP231 50c +30c multi .45 .45
B582 SP231 60c +20c multi .45 .45
a. Min. sheet of 5, 4 #B581, #B582 2.75 2.75
B583 SP231 65c +20c multi .50 .50
B584 SP231 70c +30c multi .55 .55
Nos. B581-B584 (4) 1.95 1.95

Surtax was for child welfare.

Johan van Oldenbarneveldt (1547-1619), Statesman, by J. Houbraken SP232

Paintings: 60c+25c, Willem Jansz Blaeu (1571-1638), cartographer, by Thomas de Keijser. 65c+25c, Hugo de Groot (1583-1645), statesman, by J. van Ravesteyn. 70c+30c, Portrait of Saskia van Uylenburch, by Rembrandt (1606-1669).

1983, Apr. 19 Photo. *Perf. 14x13*
B585 SP232 50c +20c multi .45 .45
B586 SP232 60c +25c multi .50 .50
B587 SP232 65c +25c multi .60 .60
B588 SP232 70c +30c multi .65 .65
Nos. B585-B588 (4) 2.20 2.20

Surtax was for cultural and social welfare institutions.

Red Cross Workers — SP233

Designs: 60c+20c, Principles. 65c+25c, Sociomedical work. 70c+30c, Peace.

1983, Aug. 30 Photo. *Perf. 13x14*
B589 SP233 50c +25c multi .50 .50
B590 SP233 60c +20c multi .55 .55
B591 SP233 65c +25c multi .65 .65
B592 SP233 70c +30c multi .70 .70
a. Bklt. pane, 4 #B589, 2 #B592 6.00
Nos. B589-B592 (4) 2.40 2.40

Surtax was for Red Cross.

Children's Christmas SP235

1983, Nov. 16 Photo. *Perf. 14x13*
B596 SP235 50c +10c Ox & donkey .42 .42
B597 SP235 50c +25c Snowman .50 .50
B598 SP235 60c +30c Stars .60 .60
B599 SP235 70c +30c Epiphany .70 .70
a. Min. sheet, 4 #B597, 2 #B599 3.25 3.25
Nos. B596-B599 (4) 2.22 2.22

Surtax was for Child Welfare.

Eurasian Lapwings SP236

Birds: 60c+25c, Ruffs. 65c+25c, Redshanks, vert. 70c+30c, Black-tailed godwits, vert.

1984, Apr. 3 *Perf. 14x13, 13x14*
B600 SP236 50c +20c multi .55 .55
B601 SP236 60c +25c multi .70 .70
B602 SP236 65c +25c multi .75 .75

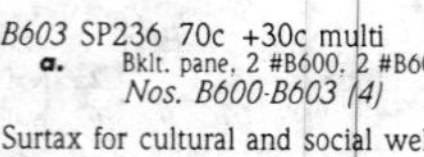

B603 SP236 70c +30c multi .85 .85
a. Bklt. pane, 2 #B600, 2 #B603 3.25
Nos. B600-B603 (4) 2.85 2.85

Surtax for cultural and social welfare institutions.

FILACENTO '84 — SP237

Centenary of Organized Philately: 50c+20c, Eye, magnifying glass (36x25mm). 60c+25c, Cover, 1909 (34½x25mm). 70c+30c, Stamp club meeting, 1949 (34½x24mm).

1984, June 13 Litho. *Perf. 14x13*
B604 SP237 50c +20c multi .60 .60
B605 SP237 60c +25c multi .70 .70
B606 SP237 70c +30c multi .90 .90
a. Souv. sheet of 3, #B604-B606 2.25 2.25
Nos. B604-B606 (3) 2.20 2.20

No. B606a issued Sept. 5, 1984.

Comic Strips — SP238

1984, Nov. 14 Litho. *Perf. 13x13½*
B607 SP238 50c +25c Music lesson .60 .60
B608 SP238 60c +20c Dentist .65 .65
B609 SP238 65c +25c Plumber .70 .70
B610 SP238 70c +30c King .80 .80
a. Min. sheet, 4 #B607, 2 #B610 4.00 4.00
Nos. B607-B610 (4) 2.75 2.75

Surtax was for child welfare.

Winterswijk Synagogue, Holy Arc — SP239

Religious architecture: 50+20c, St. Martin's Church, Zaltbommel, vert. 65+25c, Village Congregational Church, Bolsward, vert. 70+30c, St. John's Cathedral, 'S-Hertogenbosch, detail of buttress.

Perf. 13x14, 14x13

1985, Mar. 26 Photo.
B611 SP239 50c +20c gray & brt bl .65 .65
B612 SP239 60c +25c dk red brn, Prus bl & pck bl .75 .75
B613 SP239 65c +25c sl bl, red brn & gray ol .80 .80
B614 SP239 70c +30c gray, brt bl & bis .90 .90
a. Bklt. pane, 2 #B611, 2 #B614 3.75
Nos. B611-B614 (4) 3.10 3.10

Surtax for social and cultural purposes.

Traffic Safety — SP240

1985, Nov. 13 Photo. *Perf. 13x14*
B615 SP240 50c +25c Photograph, lock, key .75 .75
B616 SP240 60c +20c Boy, target .80 .80
B617 SP240 65c +20c Girl, hazard triangle .90 .90
B618 SP240 70c +30c Boy, traffic sign 1.00 1.00
a. Souv. sheet, 4 #B615, 2 #B618 5.00 5.00
Nos. B615-B618 (4) 3.45 3.45

Surtax was for child welfare organizations.

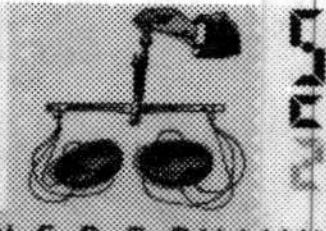

Antique Measuring Instruments SP241

Perf. 13½x13, 13x13½

1986, Apr. 8 **Litho.**

B619	SP241 50c +20c Balance	.65	.65
B620	SP241 60c +25c Clock mechanism	.85	.85
B621	SP241 65c +25c Barometer	.90	.90
B622	SP241 70c +30c Jacob's staff	.95	.95
a.	Bklt. pane, 2 each #B619, B622	4.75	
	Nos. B619-B622 (4)	3.35	3.35

Nos. B620-B621 vert.

Youth and Culture SP242

1986, Nov. 12 **Litho.** *Perf. 14x13*

B623	SP242 55c +25c Music	.80	.80

Perf. 13½x13

B624	SP242 65c +35c Visual arts	.95	.95
B625	SP242 75c +35c Theater	1.00	1.00
a.	Min. sheet of 5, #B623, 2 each #B624-B625, perf. 14x13	5.00	
	Nos. B623-B625 (3)	2.75	2.75

Surtax for child welfare organizations.

Traditional Industries SP243

Designs: 55c+30c, Steam pumping station, Nijkerk. 65c+35c, Water tower, Deventer. 75c+35c, Brass foundry, Joure.

1987, Apr. 7 **Photo.** *Perf. 14x13*

B626	SP243 55c +30c multi	.70	.70
B627	SP243 65c +35c multi	.80	.80
B628	SP243 75c +35c multi	.90	.90
a.	Bklt. pane, 2 #B626, 2 #B628	3.50	
	Nos. B626-B628 (3)	2.40	2.40

Surtax for social and cultural welfare organizations.

Red Cross — SP244

1987, Sept. 1 **Photo.** *Perf. 14x13*

B629	SP244 55c +30c multi	.70	.70
B630	SP244 65c +35c multi, diff.	.80	.80
B631	SP244 75c +35c multi, diff.	.90	.90
a.	Bklt. pane, 2 #B629, 2 #B631	3.75	
	Nos. B629-B631 (3)	2.40	2.40

Surtax for nat'l. Red Cross.

Youth and Professions SP245

Perf. 13x14, 14x13

1987, Nov. 11 **Photo.**

B632	SP245 55c +25c Woodcutter, vert.	.80	.80
B633	SP245 65c +35c Sailor	.95	.95
B634	SP245 75c +35c Pilot	1.00	1.00
a.	Miniature sheet of 5, #B632, 2 #B633, 2 #B634	4.75	4.75
	Nos. B632-B634 (3)	2.75	2.75

Surtax for child welfare organizations.

FILACEPT '88, October 18, The Hague SP246

Designs: 55c +55c, Narcissus cyclamineus and poem "I call you flowers," by Jan Hanlo. No. B636, Rosa gallica versicolor. No. B637, Eryngium maritimum and map of The Hague from 1270.

1988, Feb. 23 **Litho.** *Perf. 13½x13*

B635	SP246 55c +55c multi	1.10	1.10
B636	SP246 75c +70c multi	1.40	1.40
B637	SP246 75c +70c multi	1.40	1.40
a.	Souv. sheet of 3 + 3 labels, #B635-B637	4.00	4.00
	Nos. B635-B637 (3)	3.90	3.90

Surtax helped finance exhibition.
No. B637a issued Oct. 18, 1988.

Man and the Zoo — SP247

Perf. 14x13, 13x14

1988, Mar. 22 **Photo.**

B638	SP247 55c +30c Equus quagga quagga	.80	.80
B639	SP247 65c +35c Carribean sea cow	.95	.95
B640	SP247 75c +35c Sam the orangutan, vert.	1.10	1.10
a.	Bklt. pane, 2 #B638, 2 #B640	3.75	
	Nos. B638-B640 (3)	2.85	2.85

Natural Artis Magistra zoological soc., 150th anniv. Surtax for social and cultural welfare organizations.

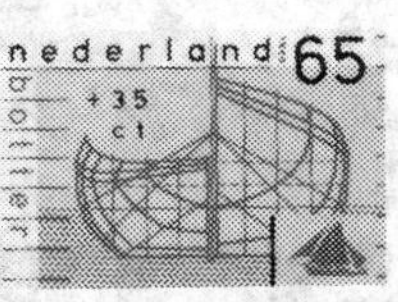

Royal Dutch Swimming Federation, Cent. SP248

Children's drawings on the theme "Children and Water."

1988, Nov. 16 **Photo.** *Perf. 14x13*

B641	SP248 55c +25c Rain	.82	.82
B642	SP248 65c +35c Getting Ready for the Race	1.00	1.00
B643	SP248 75c +35c Swimming Test	1.15	1.15
a.	Souv. sheet of 5, #B641, 2 each #B642-B643	5.15	5.15
	Nos. B641-B643 (3)	2.97	2.97

Surtax to benefit child welfare organizations.

Ships — SP249

Designs: No. B644, Pleasure yacht (boyer), vert. No. B645, Zuiderzee fishing boat (smack). No. B646, Clipper.

Perf. 13x14, 14x13

1989, Apr. 11 **Photo.**

B644	SP249 55c +30c multi	.85	.85
B645	SP249 65c +35c multi	.98	.98
B646	SP249 75c +35c multi	1.05	1.05
a.	Bklt. pane, #B644-B645, 2 #B646	4.00	
	Nos. B644-B646 (3)	2.88	2.88

Surtax for social and cultural organizations.

Children's Rights — SP250

1989, Nov. 8 **Litho.** *Perf. 13½x13*

B647	SP250 55c +25c Housing	.75	.75
B648	SP250 65c +35c Food	.95	.95
B649	SP250 75c +35c Education	1.05	1.05
a.	Min. sheet of 5, #B647, 2 each #B648-B649	5.00	5.00
	Nos. B647-B649 (3)	2.75	2.75

UN Declaration of Children's Rights, 30th anniv. Surtax for child welfare.

Summer Weather SP251

Perf. 14x13, 13x14

1990, Apr. 3 **Photo.**

B650	SP251 55c +30c Girl, flowers	.90	.90
B651	SP251 65c +35c Clouds, isobars, vert.	1.05	1.05
B652	SP251 75c +35c Weather map, vert.	1.15	1.15
a.	Bklt. pane, 2 #B650-B651, 2 #B652	4.25	
	Nos. B650-B652 (3)	3.10	3.10

Surtax for social & cultual welfare organizations.

Children's Hobbies SP252

1990, Nov. 7 **Litho.** *Perf. 13½x13*

B653	SP252 55c +25c Riding	.85	.85
B654	SP252 65c +35c Computers	1.05	1.05
B655	SP252 75c +35c Philately	1.20	1.20
a.	Souv. sheet of 5, #B653, 2 each #B654-B655	5.35	
	Nos. B653-B655 (3)	3.10	3.10

Surtax for child welfare.

Dutch Farms SP253

55c+30c, Frisian farm, Wartena. 65c+35c, Guelders T-style farm, Kesteren. 75c+35c, Closed construction farm, Nuth (Limburg).

1991, Apr. 16 **Litho.** *Perf. 13½x13*

B656	SP253 55c +30c multi	.95	.25
a.	Photo.	.95	.25
B657	SP253 65c +35c multi	1.10	.28
B658	SP253 75c +35c multi	1.20	.30
a.	Photo.	1.20	.30
b.	Bklt. pane, 2 #B656a, 3 #B658a	5.50	
	Nos. B656-B658 (3)	3.25	.83

Surtax for social and cultural welfare organizations.

Children Playing SP254

1991, Nov. 6 **Litho.** *Perf. 13½x13*

B659	SP254 60c +30c Doll, robot	1.05	.26
a.	Photo., perf. 14x13½	1.05	.26
B660	SP254 70c +35c Cycle race	1.20	.30
B661	SP254 80c +40c Hide and seek	1.40	.35
a.	Photo., perf. 14x13½	1.40	.35
b.	Min. sheet, 4 #B659a, 2 #B661a	7.00	
	Nos. B659-B661 (3)	3.65	.91

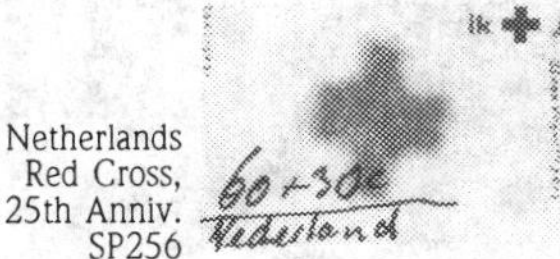

Floriade 1992, World Horticultural Exhibition SP255

Various plants and flowers.

1992, Apr. 7 **Litho.** *Perf. 13½x13*

B662	SP255 60c +30c multi	1.10	.28
a.	Photo., perf. 14x13½	1.10	.28
B663	SP255 70c +35c multi	1.30	.32
a.	Photo., perf. 14x13½	1.30	.32
B664	SP255 80c +40c multi	1.50	.38
a.	Photo., perf. 14x13½	1.50	.38
b.	Booklet pane of 6, 3 #B662a, 2 #B663a, #B664a	7.50	
	Nos. B662-B664 (3)	3.90	.98

Surtax for social and cultural welfare organizations.
Stamps in No. 664b are tete-beche (1 pair of B662a, 1 pair of B663a, 1 pair of B662a and B664a).

Netherlands Red Cross, 125th Anniv. SP256

1992, Sept. 8 **Litho.** *Perf. 13½x13*

B665	SP256 60c +30c Shadow of cross	1.10	.28
a.	Photo., perf. 14 on 3 sides	1.10	.28
B666	SP256 70c +35c Aiding victim	1.25	.30
a.	Photo., perf. 14 on 3 sides	1.25	.30
B667	SP256 80c +40c Red cross on bandage	1.35	.35
a.	Photo., perf. 14 on 3 sides	1.35	.35
b.	Bklt. pane, 3 #B665a, 2 #B666a, 1 #B667a	7.25	
	Nos. B665-B667 (3)	3.70	.93

On normally centered stamps, the white border appears on the top, bottom and right sides only.

Children Making Music — SP257

Senior Citizens — SP258

1992, Nov. 11 **Litho.** *Perf. 13x13½*

B668	SP257 60c +30c Saxophone player	1.05	.28
a.	Photo., perf. 13½x14	1.05	.28
B669	SP257 70c +35c Piano player	1.20	.30
a.	Photo., perf. 13½x14	1.20	.30
B670	SP257 80c +40c Bass player	1.40	.35
a.	Photo., perf. 13½x14	1.40	.35
b.	Souvenir sheet, 3 #B668a, 2 #B669a, #B670a	7.00	
	Nos. B668-B670 (3)	3.65	.93

1993, Apr. 20 **Litho.** *Perf. 13x13½*

B671	SP258 70c +35c shown	1.25	.32
a.	Photo., perf. 13½x14	1.25	.32
B672	SP258 70c +35c couple	1.25	.32
a.	Photo., perf. 13½x14	1.25	.32
B673	SP258 80c +40c woman	1.40	.35
a.	Photo., perf. 13½x14	1.40	.35
b.	Booklet pane, 1 #B671a, 2 #B672a, 3 #B673a	9.25	
	Complete booklet, #B673b	9.25	
	Nos. B671-B673 (3)	3.90	.99

Children and the Media SP259

Designs: No. B674, Child wearing newspaper hat. No. B675, Elephant wearing earphones. 80c + 40c, Television, child's legs.

1993, Nov. 17 **Litho.** *Perf. 13½x13*

B674	SP259 70c +35c multi	1.25	.30
a.	Photo., perf. 14x13½	1.25	.30
B675	SP259 70c +35c multi	1.25	.30
a.	Photo., perf. 14x13½	1.25	.30
B676	SP259 80c +40c multi	1.40	.35
a.	Photo., perf. 14x13½	1.40	.35
b.	Souv. sheet, 2 each #B674a-B676a	8.00	
	Nos. B674-B676 (3)	3.90	.95

FEPAPOST '94 — SP260

Birds: 70c+60c, Branta leucopsis. 80c+70c, Luscinia svecica. 90c+80c, Anas querquedula.

1994, Feb. 22 **Litho.** *Perf. 14x13*

B677	SP260 70c +60c multi	1.50	.38
B678	SP260 80c +70c multi	1.75	.45
B679	SP260 90c +80c multi	2.00	.50
a.	Souvenir sheet, #B677-B679 + 3 labels, perf. 13½x13	5.25	
	Nos. B677-B679 (3)	5.25	1.33

Issued: No. B679a, 10/17/94.

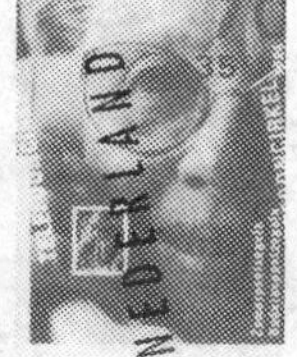

Senior Citizens — SP261

Designs: 80c+40c, Man talking on telephone seen from behind. 90c+35c, Man in suit talking on telephone.

1994, Apr. 26 Litho. *Perf. 13x13½*

B680 SP261 70c +35c shown 1.25 .30
a. Photo., perf. 13½x14 1.25 .30
B681 SP261 80c +40c multi 1.40 .35
a. Photo., perf. 13½x14 1.40 .35
B682 SP261 90c +35c multi 1.50 .38
a. Photo., perf. 13½x14 1.50 .38
b. Booklet pane, 2 #B680a, 3 #B681a, #B682a 8.25
Nos. B680-B682 (3) 4.15 1.03

Child Welfare Stamps SP262

Designs: 70c+35c, Holding ladder for woman painting. 80c+40c, Helping to balance woman picking cherries, vert. 90c+35c, Supporting boy on top of play house, vert.

Perf. 13½x13, 13x13½

1994, Nov. 9 Litho.

B683 SP262 70c +35c multi 1.25 .30
B684 SP262 80c +40c multi 1.40 .35
B685 SP262 90c +35c multi 1.50 .38
a. SP262 Miniature sheet, 2 #B683, 3 #B684, 1 #B685, perf. 13x14 9.00
Nos. B683-B685 (3) 4.15 1.03

Senior Citizens SP263

Designs: 70c+35c, Indonesia #1422 on postcard. 80c+40c, Couple seen in bus mirror. 100c+45c, Grandparents, child at zoo.

1995, Apr. 11 Litho. *Perf. 13½x13*

B686 SP263 70c +35c multi 1.40 .35
B687 SP263 80c +40c multi 1.50 .38
B688 SP263 100c +45c multi 1.90 .50
a. Miniature sheet, 2 #B686, 3 #B687, 1 #B688 9.50
Nos. B686-B688 (3) 4.80 1.23

Child Welfare Stamps SP264

Computer drawings by children: 70c+35c, Dino, by S. Stegeman. 80c+40c, The School Teacher, by L. Ensing, vert. 100c+50c, Children and Colors, by M. Jansen.

Perf. 13½x13, 13x13½

1995, Nov. 15 Litho.

B689 SP264 70c +35c multi 1.25 .25
B690 SP264 80c +40c multi 1.50 .40
B691 SP264 100c +50c multi 1.90 .45
a. Souvenir sheet of 6, 2 #B689, 3 #B690, 1 #B691 9.75 2.00
Nos. B689-B691 (3) 4.65 1.10

Senior Citizens SP265

1996, Apr. 23 Litho. *Perf. 13½x13*

B692 SP265 70c +35c Swimming 1.25 .25
B693 SP265 80c +40c Babysitting 1.40 .40
B694 SP265 100c +50c Playing piano 1.75 .45
a. Sheet of 6, 2 #B692, 3 #B693, 1 #B694, perf. 13x12½ 8.00 2.00
Nos. B692-B694 (3) 4.40 1.10

Child Welfare Stamps — SP266

Designs: 70c+35c, Baby, books. No. B696, Boy, toys. No. B697, Girl, tools.

1996, Nov. 6 Litho. *Perf. 13x13½*

B695 SP266 70c +35 multi 1.20 .30
B696 SP266 80c +40c multi 1.35 .35
B697 SP266 80c +40c multi 1.35 .35
a. Sheet of 2 each, #B695-B697 7.80 1.90
Nos. B695-B697 (3) 3.90 1.00

Senior Citizens SP267

Designs: No. B698, Rose in full bloom. No. B699, Stem of rose. No. B700, Rose bud.

1997, Apr. 15 Litho. *Perf. 13½x13*

B698 SP267 80c +40c multi 1.25 .30
B699 SP267 80c +40c multi 1.25 .30
B700 SP267 80c +40c multi 1.25 .30
a. Souvenir sheet, 2 each #B698-B700 7.50 1.90
Nos. B698-B700 (3) 3.75 .90

Netherlands Red Cross — SP268

1997, May 27 Litho. *Perf. 13x13½*

B701 SP268 80c +40c multi 1.25 .30

Children's Fairy Tales — SP269

Designs: No. B702, Hunter with wolf, from "Little Red Riding Hood." No. B703, Dropping loaves of bread, from "Tom Thumb." No. B704, Man opening bottle, from "Genie in the Bottle."

1997, Nov. 12 Litho. *Perf. 13½x13*

B702 SP269 80c +40c multi 1.30 .35
B703 SP269 80c +40c multi 1.30 .35
B704 SP269 80c +40c multi 1.30 .35
a. Souvenir sheet of 2 each, #B702-B704 7.80 2.25
Nos. B702-B704 (3) 3.90 1.05

AIR POST STAMPS

Stylized Seagull — AP1

Perf. 12½

1921, May 1 Unwmk. Typo.

C1 AP1 10c red 1.25 1.50
C2 AP1 15c yellow grn 6.25 2.50
C3 AP1 60c dp blue 19.00 .25
Nos. C1-C3 (3) 26.50 4.25
Set, never hinged 190.00

Nos. C1-C3 were used to pay airmail fee charged by the carrier, KLM.

Lt. G. A. Koppen — AP2

Capt. Jan van der Hoop — AP3

Wmk. Circles (202)

1928, Aug. 20 Litho. *Perf. 12*

C4 AP2 40c orange red .25 .25
C5 AP3 75c blue green .25 .25
Set, never hinged 1.25

Mercury AP4

Queen Wilhelmina AP5

Perf. 11½

1929, July 16 Unwmk. Engr.

C6 AP4 1½g gray 2.50 1.65
C7 AP4 4½g carmine 1.75 3.00
C8 AP4 7½g blue green 24.00 4.50
Nos. C6-C8 (3) 28.25 9.15
Set, never hinged 70.00

Perf. 12½, 14x13

1931, Sept. 24 Photo. Wmk. 202

C9 AP5 36c org red & dk bl 10.00 .60
Never hinged 70.00

Fokker Pander — AP6

1933, Oct. 9 *Perf. 12½*

C10 AP6 30c dark green .40 .60
Never hinged .80

Nos. C10-C12 were issued for use on special flights.

Crow in Flight — AP7

1938-53 *Perf. 13x14*

C11 AP7 12½c dk blue & gray .35 .25
C12 AP7 25c dk bl & gray ('53) 1.50 1.50
Set, never hinged 3.75

Catalogue values for unused stamps in this section, from this point to the end of the section, are for Never Hinged items.

Seagull — AP8

Airplane — AP9

Perf. 13x14

1951, Nov. 12 Engr. Unwmk.

C13 AP8 15g gray 230.00 85.00
C14 AP8 25g blue gray 230.00 85.00
Set, hinged 260.00

1966, Sept. 2 Litho. *Perf. 14x13*

C15 AP9 25c gray, blk & bl .35 .35

Issued for use on special flights.

AP10

1980, May 13 Photo. *Perf. 13x14*

C16 AP10 1g multicolored .90 .90

MARINE INSURANCE STAMPS

Floating Safe Attracting Gulls — MI1

Floating Safe with Night Flare — MI2

Fantasy of Floating Safe — MI3

Perf. 11½

1921, Feb. 2 Unwmk. Engr.

GY1 MI1 15c slate grn 4.25 *37.50*
GY2 MI1 60c car rose 4.25 *42.50*
GY3 MI1 75c gray brn 6.50 *52.50*
GY4 MI2 1.50g dk blue 65.00 *425.00*
GY5 MI2 2.25g org brn 110.00 *550.00*
GY6 MI3 4½g black 165.00 *675.00*
GY7 MI3 7½g red 250.00 *925.00*
Nos. GY1-GY7 (7) 605.00 *2,707.*
Set, never hinged 1,500.

POSTAGE DUE STAMPS

Postage due types of Netherlands were also used for Curacao, Netherlands Indies and Surinam in different colors.

D1

D2

Perf. 12½x12, 13

1870, May 15 Typo. Unwmk.

J1 D1 5c brown, *org* 72.50 15.00
J2 D1 10c violet, *bl* 150.00 20.00

Type I - 34 loops. "T" of "BETALEN" over center of loop; top branch of "E" of "TE" shorter than lower branch.

Type II - 33 loops. "T" of "BETALEN" between two loops.

Type III - 32 loops. "T" of "BETALEN" slightly to the left of loop; top branch of first "E" of "BETALEN" shorter than lower branch.

Type IV - 37 loops. Letters of "PORT" larger than in the other three types.

Imperforate varieties are proofs.

Perf. 11½x12, 12½x12, 12½, 13½

1881-87

Value in Black

J3 D2 1c lt blue (III) 11.00 11.00
a. Type I 15.00 18.00
b. Type II 20.00 20.00
c. Type IV 47.50 52.50
J4 D2 1½c lt blue (III) 15.00 15.00
a. Type I 18.00 18.00
b. Type II 24.00 24.00
c. Type IV 75.00 75.00
J5 D2 2½c lt blue (III) 37.50 5.00
a. Type I 45.00 5.50
b. Type II 55.00 6.00
c. Type IV 200.00 125.00
J6 D2 5c lt blue (III) ('87) 140.00 3.50
a. Type I 165.00 4.50
b. Type II 190.00 5.25
c. Type IV 1,750. 325.00

J7 D2 10c lt blue (III) ('87) 140.00 4.00
a. Type I 165.00 4.50
b. Type II 190.00 5.00
c. Type IV 2,500. 375.00
J8 D2 12½c lt blue (III) 140.00 35.00
a. Type I 165.00 40.00
b. Type II 190.00 45.00
c. Type IV 475.00 140.00
J9 D2 15c lt blue (III) 125.00 4.00
a. Type I 150.00 4.50
b. Type II 175.00 5.00
c. Type IV 175.00 25.00
J10 D2 20c lt blue (III) 30.00 4.00
a. Type I 47.50 4.25
b. Type II 50.00 5.50
c. Type IV 137.50 27.50
J11 D2 25c lt blue (III) 300.00 3.50
a. Type I 325.00 3.00
b. Type II 400.00 4.50
c. Type IV 600.00 190.00

Value in Red

J12 D2 1g lt blue (III) 110.00 30.00
a. Type I 110.00 37.50
b. Type II 150.00 40.00
c. Type IV 250.00 75.00
Nos. J3-J12 (10) 1,048. 115.00

See Nos. J13-J26, J44-J60. For surcharges see Nos. J27-J28, J42-J43, J72-J75.

1896-1910 *Perf. 12½*

Value in Black

J13 D2 ½c dk bl (I) ('01) .15 .15
J14 D2 1c dk blue (I) 1.65 .20
a. Type III 2.50 3.25
J15 D2 1½c dk blue (I) .60 .30
a. Type III 2.50 2.50
J16 D2 2½c dk blue (I) 1.50 .30
a. Type III 3.25 .40
J17 D2 3c dk bl (I) ('10) 1.65 1.10
J18 D2 4c dk bl (I) ('09) 1.65 2.25
J19 D2 5c dk blue (I) 13.00 .30
a. Type III 16.00 .30
J20 D2 6½c dk bl (I) ('07) 45.00 45.00
J21 D2 7½c dk bl (I) ('04) 1.65 .55
J22 D2 10c dk blue (I) 35.00 .40
a. Type III 52.50 1.50
J23 D2 12½c dk blue (I) 30.00 1.00
a. Type III 45.00 3.50
J24 D2 15c dk blue (I) 35.00 .90
a. Type III 55.00 1.00
J25 D2 20c dk blue (I) 20.00 8.00
a. Type III 20.00 8.75
J26 D2 25c dk blue (I) 45.00 .75
a. Type III 50.00 1.00
Nos. J13-J26 (14) 231.85 61.20

Surcharged in Black **50 CENT**

1906, Jan. 10 *Perf. 12½*

J27 D2 50c on 1g lt bl (III) 125.00 110.00
a. 50c on 1g light blue (I) 165.00 140.00
b. 50c on 1g light blue (II) 175.00 150.00

Surcharged in Red **6½**

1906, Oct. 6

J28 D2 6½c on 20c dk bl (I) 5.50 5.00

PORTZEGEL

Nos. 87-89 Surcharged

CENT

1907, Nov. 1

J29 A13 ½c on 1c claret 1.25 1.25
J30 A13 1c on 1c claret .50 .50
J31 A13 1½c on 1c claret .50 .50
J32 A13 2½c on 1c claret 1.25 1.25
J33 A13 5c on 2½c ver 1.40 .40
J34 A13 6½c on 2½c ver 3.50 3.50
J35 A13 7½c on ½c blue 2.00 1.25
J36 A13 10c on ½c blue 1.75 .75
J37 A13 12½c on ½c blue 5.00 4.75
J38 A13 15c on 2½c ver 6.00 4.00
J39 A13 25c on ½c blue 9.00 8.50
J40 A13 50c on ½c blue 42.50 40.00
J41 A13 1g on ½c blue 60.00 55.00
Nos. J29-J41 (13) 134.65 121.65

Two printings of the above surcharges were made. Some values show differences in the setting of the fractions; others are practically impossible to distinguish.

No. J20 Surcharged in Red

1909, June

J42 D2 4c on 6½c dark blue 5.50 5.00
Never hinged 20.00

No. J12 Surcharged in Black **3 CENT**

1910, July 11

J43 D2 3c on 1g lt bl, type III 30.00 27.50
Never hinged 100.00
a. Type I 37.50 40.00
Never hinged 110.00
b. Type II 40.00 40.00
Never hinged 125.00

Type I

1912-21 *Perf. 12½, 13½x13*

Value in Color of Stamp

J44 D2 ½c pale ultra .15 .15
J45 D2 1c pale ultra ('13) .15 .15
J46 D2 1½c pale ultra ('15) 1.10 .90
J47 D2 2½c pale ultra .15 .15
J48 D2 3c pale ultra .40 .40
J49 D2 4c pale ultra ('13) .15 .15
J50 D2 4½c pale ultra ('16) 5.25 5.00
J51 D2 5c pale ultra .15 .15
J52 D2 5½c pale ultra ('16) 5.00 5.00
J53 D2 7c pale ultra ('21) 2.25 2.25
J54 D2 7½c pale ultra ('13) 2.50 1.00
J55 D2 10c pale ultra ('13) .15 .15
J56 D2 12½c pale ultra ('13) .15 .15
J57 D2 15c pale ultra ('13) .15 .15
J58 D2 20c pale ultra ('20) .15 .15
J59 D2 25c pale ultra ('17) 80.00 .60
J60 D2 50c pale ultra ('20) .40 .15
Nos. J44-J60 (17) 98.25 16.65
Set, never hinged 225.00

D3

Perf. 12½, 13½x12½

1921-38 **Typo.**

J61 D3 3c pale ultra ('28) .15 .15
J62 D3 6c pale ultra ('27) .15 .15
J63 D3 7c pale ultra ('28) .15 .15
J64 D3 7½c pale ultra ('26) .25 .15
J65 D3 8c pale ultra ('38) .15 .15
J66 D3 9c pale ultra ('30) .15 .15
J67 D3 11c ultra ('21) 13.00 3.50
J68 D3 12c pale ultra ('28) .15 .15
J69 D3 25c pale ultra ('25) .15 .15
J70 D3 30c pale ultra ('35) .25 .15
J71 D3 1g ver ('21) .70 .15
Nos. J61-J71 (11) 15.25
Set, never hinged 40.00
Set value 4.50

Stamps of 1912-21 Surcharged

1923, Dec. *Perf. 12½*

J72 D2 1c on 3c ultra .50 .50
J73 D2 2½c on 7c ultra .50 .45
J74 D2 25c on 1½c ultra 8.00 .40
J75 D2 25c on 7½c ultra 8.00 .35
Nos. J72-J75 (4) 17.00 1.70
Set, never hinged 45.00

TE BETALEN

Nos. 56, 58, 62, 65 Surcharged

PORT

1924, Aug.

J76 A11 4c on 3c olive grn 1.10 1.10
J77 A10 5c on 1c red .40 .15
a. Surcharge reading down 550.00 550.00
J78 A10 10c on 1½c blue .95 .15
a. Tête bêche pair 8.50 8.50
J79 A11 12½c on 5c carmine .95 .15
a. Tête bêche pair 10.00 10.00
Nos. J76-J79 (4) 3.40 1.55

The 11c on 22½c and 15c on 17½c exist. These were used by the postal service for accounting of parcel post fees.

Catalogue values for unused stamps in this section, from this point to the end of the section, are for Never Hinged items.

D5

Perf. 13½x12½

1947-58 **Wmk. 202** **Photo.**

J80 D5 1c light blue ('48) .15 .15
J81 D5 3c light blue ('48) .40 .15
J82 D5 4c light blue 12.00 .90
J83 D5 5c light blue ('48) .45 .15
J84 D5 6c light blue ('50) .30 .35
J85 D5 7c light blue .15 .25
J86 D5 8c light blue ('48) .15 .25
J87 D5 10c light blue .15 .15
J88 D5 11c light blue .35 .45
J89 D5 12c light blue ('48) .55 1.10
J90 D5 14c light blue ('53) .90 .90
J91 D5 15c light blue .35 .15
J92 D5 16c light blue .80 1.25
J93 D5 20c light blue .35 .15
J94 D5 24c light blue ('57) 1.25 1.40
J95 D5 25c light blue ('48) .45 .15
J96 D5 26c light blue ('58) 1.90 1.75
J97 D5 30c light blue ('48) .60 .15
J98 D5 35c light blue .65 .15
J99 D5 40c light blue .75 .15
J100 D5 50c light blue ('48) .80 .15
J101 D5 60c light blue ('58) 1.00 .45
J102 D5 85c light blue ('50) 17.00 .45
J103 D5 90c light blue ('56) 2.75 .45
J104 D5 95c light blue ('57) 2.75 .60
J105 D5 1g carmine ('48) 2.50 .15
J106 D5 1.75g carmine ('57) 5.50 .40
Nos. J80-J106 (27) 54.95 12.75

OFFICIAL STAMPS

Regular Issues of 1898-1908 Overprinted **ARMENWET**

1913 **Typo.** **Unwmk.** *Perf. 12½*

O1 A10 1c red 4.00 2.00
O2 A10 1½c ultra 1.00 1.65
O3 A10 2c yellow brn 7.00 7.00
O4 A10 2½c dp green 16.00 12.00
O5 A11 3c olive grn 4.00 1.00
O6 A11 5c carmine rose 4.00 4.50
O7 A11 10c gray lilac 35.00 37.50
Nos. O1-O7 (7) 71.00 65.65

Same Overprint in Red on No. 58

1919

O8 A10 1½c deep blue (R) 90.00 110.00

Nos. O1 to O8 were used to defray the postage on matter relating to the Poor Laws.
Counterfeit overprints exist.

For the International Court of Justice

Regular Issue of 1926-33 Overprinted in Gold **COURPER MANENTE DJUSTICE EJ INTER-NATIONALE**

1934 **Wmk. 202** *Perf. 12½*

O9 A24 1½c red violet .60
O10 A24 2½c deep green .60
O11 A23 7½c red 1.10
O12 A31 12½c deep ultra 32.50
O13 A23 15c orange 1.25
O14 A23 30c violet 2.00
a. Perf. 13½x12½ 2.00
Nos. O9-O14 (6) 38.05

Same Overprint on No. 180 in Gold

1937 *Perf. 13½x12½*

O15 A23 12½c ultra 16.00

"Mint" Officials

Nos. O9-O15, O20-O43 were sold to the public only canceled. Uncanceled, they were obtainable only by favor of an official or from UPU specimen copies.

Same on Regular Issue of 1940 Overprinted in Gold

1940 *Perf. 13½x12½*

O16 A45 7½c bright red 16.00 8.75
O17 A45 12½c sapphire 16.00 8.75
O18 A45 15c lt blue 16.00 8.75
O19 A45 30c bister 16.00 8.75
Nos. O16-O19 (4) 64.00 35.00

Nos. 217 to 219, 221 and 223 Overprinted in Gold **COUR INTER NATIONALE DE JUSTICE**

1947

O20 A45 7½c bright red 1.10
O21 A45 10c brt red violet 1.10
O22 A45 12½c sapphire 1.10
O23 A45 20c purple 1.10
O24 A45 25c rose brown 1.10
Nos. O20-O24 (5) 5.00

O1

Perf. 14½x13½

1950 **Unwmk.** **Photo.**

O25 O1 2c ultra 8.75
O26 O1 4c olive green 8.75

Palace of Peace, The Hague — O2

Queen Juliana — O3

1951-58 *Perf. 12½x12*

O27 O2 2c red brown .40
O28 O2 3c ultra ('53) .40
O29 O2 4c deep green .40
O30 O2 5c olive brn ('53) .40
O31 O2 6c olive grn ('53) .80
O32 O2 7c red ('53) .60

Engr.

O33 O3 6c brown vio 5.50
O34 O3 10c dull green .15
O35 O3 12c rose red .75
O36 O3 15c rose brn ('53) .15
O37 O3 20c dull blue .15
O38 O3 25c violet brn .15
O39 O3 30c rose lil ('58) .35
O40 O3 1g slate gray .80
Nos. O27-O40 (14) 10.38

1977, May **Photo.** *Perf. 12½x12*

O41 O2 40c brt grnsh blue .50
O42 O2 45c brick red .50
O43 O2 50c brt rose lilac .50
Nos. O41-O43 (3) 1.50

Catalogue values for unused stamps in this section, from this point to the end of the section, are for Never Hinged items.

Peace Palace, The Hague — O4

Design: 5g, 7g, Palm, sun, column.

1989, Oct. 24 **Litho.** *Perf. 13x14*

O44 O4 55c black & pink .52 .55
O45 O4 75c black & yellow .70 .70

Litho. & Engr.

O46 O4 7g multicolored 6.50 6.50
Nos. O44-O46 (3) 7.72 7.75

1990, Oct. 23 **Litho.**

O47 O4 65c black & bl grn .75 .75
O48 O4 1g black & org 1.10 1.10
O49 O4 1.50g black & bl 1.60 1.60

Litho. & Engr.

O50 O4 5g multicolored 5.50 5.50
Nos. O47-O50 (4) 8.95 8.95

1991-94 **Litho.**

O51 O4 5c black & org yel .15 .15
O52 O4 10c black & blue .15 .15
O53 O4 25c black & red .30 .30
O54 O4 50c black & yel grn .60 .60
O55 O4 60c black & bister .75 .75
O56 O4 70c black & gray blue .90 .90

O57	O4	80c black & gray grn	1.00	1.00
O58	O4	1.60g black & rose brown	2.00	2.00
		Nos. O44-O58 (15)	22.52	22.55

Issued: 1.60g, 11/28/94; other, 10/22/91.

This is an expanding set. Numbers will change when complete.

NETHERLANDS ANTILLES

'ne-thər-lən(d)z an-'ti-lēz

(Curaçao)

LOCATION — Two groups of islands about 500 miles apart in the West Indies, north of Venezuela

AREA — 383 sq. mi.

POP. — 260,000 (est. 1983)

CAPITAL — Willemstad

Formerly a colony, Curaçao, Netherlands Antilles became an integral part of the Kingdom of the Netherlands under the Constitution of 1954. On Jan. 1, 1986, the island of Aruba achieved a separate status within the Kingdom and began issuing its own stamps.

100 Cents = 1 Gulden

Catalogue values for unused stamps in this country are for Never Hinged items, beginning with Scott 164 in the regular postage section, Scott B1 in the semi-postal section, Scott C18 in the airpost section, Scott CB9 in the airpost semi-postal section, and Scott J41 in the postage due section.

Values for unused examples of Nos. 1-44 are for stamps without gum.

Watermark

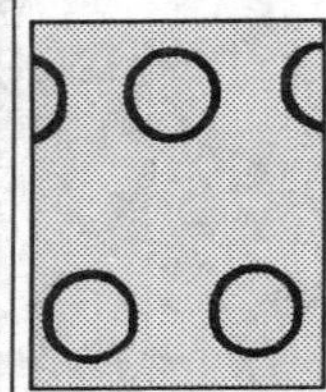

Wmk. 202- Circles

Netherlands & Colonies

Wanted:

All mint stamps NH or Hinged, Set or singles. 1873-1955 especially needed.

- Quantities okay
- Good Collections
- Better Used stamps
- Unusual covers, postal history & specialized material.
- All other Netherlands & Colonies . Top Prices Paid!

We Sell:

Want Lists invited 1850- date!

Netherlands NH

1958-1997 $959.00 (All normally issued stamps & S/S)

1-800-9-4-STAMP (1-800-947-8267

Henry Gitner Philatelists, Inc.

P.O. Box 3077-S

Middletown, NY 10940

Toll Free: 1-800-947-8267

Fax: 914-343-0068

Email: hgitner@hgitner.com

http://www.hgitner.com

Philately - The Quiet Excitement!

King William III
A1

Numeral
A2

Regular Perf. 11½, 12½, 11½x12, 12½x12, 13½x13, 14

1873-79 Typo. Unwmk.

1	A1	2½c green	5.00	8.00
2	A1	3c bister	55.00	*110.00*
3	A1	5c rose	10.00	11.00
4	A1	10c ultra	60.00	15.00
5	A1	25c brown orange	42.50	7.50
6	A1	50c violet	1.75	2.50
7	A1	2.50g bis & pur ('79)	35.00	30.00
		Nos. 1-7 (7)	209.25	*184.00*

See bluish paper note with Netherlands #7-22.

The gulden denominations, Nos. 7 and 12, are of larger size.

See 8-12. For surcharges see #18, 25-26.

Perf. 14, Small Holes

1b	A1	2½c	12.00	15.00
2b	A1	3c	60.00	*140.00*
3b	A1	5c	14.00	21.00
4b	A1	10c	72.50	80.00
5b	A1	25c	65.00	45.00
6b	A1	50c	26.00	30.00
		Nos. 1b-6b (6)	249.50	*331.00*

"Small hole" varieties have the spaces between the holes wider than the diameter of the holes.

1886-89 *Perf. 11½, 12½, 12½x12*

8	A1	12½c yellow	95.00	45.00
9	A1	15c olive ('89)	25.00	16.00
10	A1	30c pearl gray ('89)	32.50	40.00
11	A1	60c olive bis ('89)	45.00	12.50
12	A1	1.50g lt & dk bl ('89)	100.00	80.00
		Nos. 7-12 (12)	582.00	554.50

Nos. 1-12 were issued without gum until 1890. Imperfs. are proofs.

1889 *Perf. 12½*

13	A2	1c gray	.85	1.00
14	A2	2c violet	.70	1.25
15	A2	2½c green	4.50	3.00
16	A2	3c bister	5.00	4.50
17	A2	5c rose	21.00	1.75
		Nos. 13-17 (5)	32.05	11.50

King William III
A3

Queen Wilhelmina
A4

Black Surcharge, Handstamped

1891 *Perf. 12½x12*

Without Gum

18	A3	25c on 30c pearl gray	15.00	14.00

No. 18 exists with dbl. surch., value $225, and with invtd. surch., value $275.

1892-96 *Perf. 12½*

19	A4	10c ultra ('95)	1.25	1.25
20	A4	12½c green	26.00	6.25
21	A4	15c rose ('93)	2.50	2.50
22	A4	25c brown orange	100.00	5.50
23	A4	30c gray ('96)	2.50	*5.50*
		Nos. 19-23 (5)	132.25	21.00

A5

A6

Magenta Surcharge, Handstamped

1895 *Perf. 12½, 13½x13*

25	A5	2½c on 10c ultra	11.00	7.00

Perf. 12½x12

Black Surcharge, Handstamped

26	A6	2½c on 30c gray	125.00	5.00

Nos. 25-26 exist with surcharge double or inverted.

No. 26 and No. 25, perf. 13½x13, were issued without gum.

25 C^T^

CURAÇAO

Nos. 27, 29

Queen Wilhelmina — A8

1902, Jan. 1 *Perf. 12½*

Netherlands Nos. 77, 84, 68 Surcharged in Black

27	A7	25c on 25c car & bl	1.40	1.50

1901, May 1 Engr. *Perf. 11½x11*

28	A8	1.50g on 2.50g brn lil	15.00	17.00

1902, Mar. 1 Typo. *Perf. 12½*

29	A7	12½c on 12½c blue	25.00	7.00

A9

A10

1904-08

30	A9	1c olive green	1.40	.90
31	A9	2c yellow brown	12.00	3.00
32	A9	2½c blue green	4.00	.35
33	A9	3c orange	7.50	4.00
34	A9	5c rose red	7.00	.35
35	A9	7½c gray ('08)	27.50	6.00
36	A10	10c slate	11.00	3.00
37	A10	12½c deep blue	1.25	.50
38	A10	15c brown	14.00	10.00
39	A10	22½c brn & ol ('08)	14.00	8.50
40	A10	25c violet	14.00	1.90
41	A10	30c brown orange	32.50	13.00
42	A10	50c red brown	27.50	8.25
		Nos. 30-42 (13)	173.65	59.75

Queen Wilhelmina — A11

1906, Nov. 1 Engr. *Perf. 11½*

Without Gum

43	A11	1½g red brown	35.00	25.00
44	A11	2½g slate blue	35.00	24.00

A12

Netherlands Antilles stamps can be mounted in the annually supplemented Scott Netherlands album.

Queen Wilhelmina
A13 A14

Perf. 12½, 11, 11½, 11x11½

1915-33 Typo.

45	A12	½c lilac ('20)	.90	1.10
46	A12	1c olive green	.25	.15
47	A12	1½c blue ('20)	.15	.15
48	A12	2c yellow brn	1.25	1.40
49	A12	2½c green	1.10	.20
50	A12	3c yellow	1.50	1.50
51	A12	3c green ('26)	2.25	2.50
52	A12	5c rose	1.40	.15
53	A12	5c green ('22)	2.50	2.75
54	A12	5c lilac ('26)	1.10	.15
55	A12	7½c drab	1.50	.32
56	A12	7½c bister ('20)	1.10	.15
57	A12	10c lilac ('22)	4.25	4.50
58	A12	10c rose ('26)	4.25	1.25
59	A13	10c car rose	13.00	3.00
60	A13	12½c blue	1.50	.50
61	A13	12½c red ('22)	1.40	1.65
62	A13	15c olive grn	.45	.65
63	A13	15c lt blue ('26)	3.00	2.50
64	A13	20c blue ('22)	6.00	3.00
65	A13	20c olive grn ('26)	1.65	2.25
66	A13	22½c orange	1.40	2.25
67	A13	25c red violet	3.25	.90
68	A13	30c slate	3.00	.65
69	A13	35c sl & red ('22)	3.25	4.25

Perf. 11½x11, 11½, 12½, 11

Engr.

70	A14	50c green	3.25	.20
71	A14	1½g violet	13.00	11.00
72	A14	2½g carmine	22.50	20.00
a.		Perf. 12½ ('33)	140.00	*300.00*
		Nos. 45-72 (28)	100.15	69.07

Some stamps of 1915 were also issued without gum.

For surcharges see #74, 107-108, C1-C3.

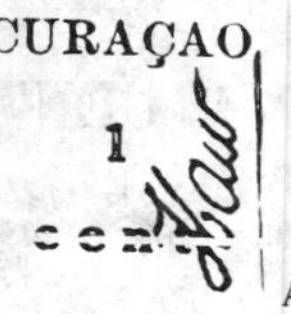

A15

Laid Paper, without Gum

1918, July 16 Typo. *Perf. 12*

73	A15	1c black, *buff*	6.75	3.75

"HAW" are the initials of Postmaster H. A. Willemsen.

No. 60 Surcharged in Black **5 CENT**

1918, Sept. 1 *Perf. 12½*

74	A13	5c on 12½c blue	3.75	2.00
a.		"5" 2½mm wide	60.00	32.50
b.		Double surcharge		700.00

The "5" of No. 74 is 3mm wide. Illustration shows No. 74a surcharge.

Queen Wilhelmina
A16 A17

1923 Engr. *Perf. 11½, 11x11½*

75	A16	5c green	1.00	2.00
76	A16	7½c olive grn	1.25	1.65
77	A16	10c car rose	1.75	2.00
78	A16	20c indigo	2.50	3.50
a.		Perf. 11x11½	3.25	4.25
79	A16	1g brown vio	30.00	19.00
80	A16	2½g gray black	70.00	*170.00*
81	A16	5g brown	90.00	*200.00*
a.		Perf. 11x11½	625.00	
		Nos. 75-81 (7)	196.50	*398.15*

25th anniv. of the assumption of the government of the Netherlands by Queen Wilhelmina, at the age of 18.

Nos. 80-81 with clear cancel between Aug. 1, 1923 and Apr. 30, 1924, sell for considerably more.

Types of Netherlands Marine Insurance Stamps, Inscribed "CURACAO" Surcharged in Black

FRANKEER
= ZEGEL =
10
CENT

1927, Oct. 3

87	MI1	3c on 15c dk green	.25	.30
88	MI1	10c on 60c car rose	.25	.45
89	MI1	12½c on 75c gray brn	.25	.45
90	MI2	15c on 1.50g dk bl	3.00	2.50
a.		Double surcharge	500.00	
91	MI2	25c on 2.25g org brn	6.50	6.25
92	MI3	30c on 4½g black	13.00	11.00
93	MI3	50c on 7½g red	7.50	7.25
		Nos. 87-93 (7)	30.75	28.20

Nos. 90, 91 and 92 have "FRANKEERZEGEL" in one line of small capitals. Nos. 90 and 91 have a heavy bar across the top of the stamp.

1928-30 Engr. *Perf. 11½, 12½*

95	A17	6c orange red ('30)	1.50	.40
a.		Booklet pane of 6		
96	A17	7½c orange red	.60	.45
97	A17	10c carmine	1.50	.35
98	A17	12½c red brown	1.50	1.00
a.		Booklet pane of 6		
99	A17	15c dark blue	1.50	.35
a.		Booklet pane of 6		
100	A17	20c blue black	5.75	.55
101	A17	21c yellow grn ('30)	9.25	14.00
102	A17	25c brown vio	3.50	1.40
103	A17	27½c black ('30)	12.00	14.00
104	A17	30c deep green	5.75	.55
105	A17	35c brnsh black	2.00	1.75
		Nos. 95-105 (11)	44.85	34.80

No. 96 Surcharged in Black with Bars over Original Value **6 ct.**

1929, Nov. 1

106	A17	6c on 7½c org red	1.40	1.00
a.		Inverted surcharge	275.00	260.00

No. 51 Surcharged in Red **2 ½**

1931, Mar. 1 Typo. *Perf. 12½*

107	A12	2½c on 3c green	1.10	1.10

No. 49 Surcharged in Red **1½**

1932, Oct. 29

108	A12	1½c on 2½c grn	3.50	3.50

Prince William I, Portrait by Van Key — A18

1933 Photo. *Perf. 12½*

109	A18	6c deep orange	1.75	1.40

400th birth anniv. of Prince William I, Count of Nassau and Prince of Orange, frequently referred to as William the Silent.

Willem Usselinx — A19

Van Walbeeck's Ship — A22

Designs: 2½c, 5c, 6c, Frederik Hendrik. 10c, 12½c, 15c, Jacob Binckes. 27½c, 30c, 50c, Cornelis Evertsen the Younger. 1.50g, 2.50g, Louis Brion.

1934, Jan. 1 Engr. *Perf. 12½*

110	A19	1c black	1.00	1.25
111	A19	1½c dull violet	.75	.30
112	A19	2c orange	1.00	1.25
113	A19	2½c dull green	.85	1.25
114	A19	5c black brn	.85	.85
115	A19	6c violet bl	.75	.25
116	A19	10c lake	2.00	1.00
117	A19	12½c bister brn	6.50	7.00
118	A19	15c blue	1.65	1.00
119	A22	20c black	3.00	2.00
120	A22	21c brown	11.00	13.00
121	A22	25c dull green	11.00	11.00
122	A19	27½c brown vio	14.00	16.00
123	A19	30c scarlet	11.00	5.25
124	A19	50c orange	11.00	8.25
125	A19	1.50g indigo	47.50	50.00
126	A19	2.50g yellow grn	52.50	47.50
		Nos. 110-126 (17)	176.35	167.15

3rd centenary of the founding of the colony.

Numeral A25

Queen Wilhelmina A26

1936, Aug. 1 Litho. *Perf. 13½x13*

Size: 18x22mm

127	A25	1c brown black	.15	.15
128	A25	1½c deep ultra	.25	.15
129	A25	2c orange	.25	.25
130	A25	2½c green	.20	.20
131	A25	5c scarlet	.35	.15

Engr.

Perf. 12½

Size: 20¼x30½mm

132	A26	6c brown vio	.45	.15
133	A26	10c orange red	.85	.15
134	A26	12½c dk bl grn	1.50	.95
135	A26	15c dark blue	1.25	.60
136	A26	20c orange yel	1.25	.60
137	A26	21c dk gray	2.25	2.25
138	A26	25c brown lake	1.50	.75
139	A26	27½c violet brn	2.50	2.75
140	A26	30c olive brn	.60	.15

Perf. 13x14

Size: 22x33mm

141	A26	50c dull yel grn	3.00	.15
a.		Perf. 14	50.00	.25
142	A26	1.50g black brn	18.00	13.00
a.		Perf. 14	40.00	20.00
143	A26	2.50g rose lake	16.00	11.00
a.		Perf. 14	16.00	11.00
		Nos. 127-143 (17)	50.35	33.40

See Nos. 147-151. For surcharges see Nos. B1-B3.

Queen Wilhelmina — A27

Perf. 12½x12

1938, Aug. 27 Photo. Wmk. 202

144	A27	1½c dull purple	.15	.22
145	A27	6c red orange	.80	.75
146	A27	15c royal blue	1.50	1.25
		Nos. 144-146 (3)	2.45	2.22

Reign of Queen Wilhelmina, 40th anniv.

Numeral Type of 1936 and

Queen Wilhelmina — A28

1941-42 Unwmk. Litho. *Perf. 12½*

Thick Paper

Size: 17¾x22mm

147	A25	1c gray brn ('42)	1.50	1.25
148	A25	1½c dull blue ('42)	9.00	.15
149	A25	2c lt orange ('42)	8.00	4.00
150	A25	2½c green ('42)	1.00	.15
151	A25	5c crimson ('42)	1.00	.15

Photo.

Perf. 12½, 13

Size: 18½x23mm

152	A28	6c rose violet	2.00	2.00
153	A28	10c red orange	1.50	1.00
154	A28	12½c lt green	2.00	.90
155	A28	15c brt ultra	4.00	2.00
156	A28	20c orange	1.10	.55
157	A28	21c gray	2.25	1.75
158	A28	25c brown lake	2.25	1.65
159	A28	27½c deep brown	3.25	3.25
160	A28	30c olive bis	9.00	3.00

Size: 21x26½mm

161	A28	50c olive grn ('42)	12.00	.15
162	A28	1½g gray ol ('42)	17.00	1.75
163	A28	2½g rose lake ('42)	16.00	1.25
		Nos. 147-163 (17)	92.85	24.95

Imperfs. are proofs.

See Nos. 174-187.

Catalogue values for unused stamps in this section, from this point to the end of the section, are for Never Hinged items.

Bonaire — A29

St. Eustatius — A30

Designs: 2c, View of Saba. 2½c, St. Maarten. 5c, Aruba. 6c, Curaçao.

Perf. 13x13½, 13½x13

1943, Feb. 1 Engr. Unwmk.

164	A29	1c rose vio & org brn	.15	.15
165	A30	1½c dp bl & yel grn	.15	.15
166	A29	2c sl blk & org brn	.42	.25
167	A29	2½c grn & org	.18	.18
168	A29	5c red & slate blk	.80	.15
169	A29	6c rose lil & lt bl	.50	.45
		Nos. 164-169 (6)	2.20	1.33

Royal Family — A35

1943, Nov. 8 *Perf. 13½x13*

170	A35	1½c deep orange	.15	.15
171	A35	2½c red	.15	.15
172	A35	6c black	.75	.45
173	A35	10c deep blue	.75	.60
		Nos. 170-173 (4)	1.80	1.35

Princess Margriet Francisca of the Netherlands.

Wilhelmina Type of 1941

1947 Photo. *Perf. 13½x13*

Size: 18x22mm

174	A28	6c brown vio	1.50	2.00
175	A28	10c orange red	1.50	2.00
176	A28	12½c dk blue grn	1.50	2.00
177	A28	15c dark blue	1.50	2.00
178	A28	20c orange yel	1.50	3.00
179	A28	21c dark gray	1.75	2.25
180	A28	25c brown lake	.15	.15
181	A28	27½c chocolate	1.50	1.40
182	A28	30c olive bister	1.65	1.00
183	A28	50c dull yel grn	2.00	.15

Perf. 13½x14

Engr.

Size: 25x31¼mm

184	A28	1½g dark brown	.90	.90
185	A28	2½g rose lake	22.50	7.00
186	A28	5g olive green	90.00	110.00
187	A28	10g red orange	115.00	190.00
		Nos. 174-187 (14)	242.95	323.85

Used values for Nos. 186-187 are for genuinely canceled copies clearly dated before the end of 1949.

Queen Wilhelmina
A36 A37

1948 Unwmk. Photo. *Perf. 13½x13*

188	A36	6c dk vio brn	1.00	1.00
189	A36	10c scarlet	1.00	1.40
190	A36	12½c dk blue grn	1.00	.90
191	A36	15c deep blue	1.00	1.10
192	A36	20c red orange	1.00	2.00
193	A36	21c black	1.00	2.00
194	A36	25c brt red vio	.50	.15
195	A36	27½c henna brn	18.00	17.00
196	A36	30c olive brown	15.00	1.25
197	A36	50c olive green	14.00	.30

Perf. 12½x12

Engr.

198	A37	1.50g chocolate	22.50	6.00
		Nos. 188-198 (11)	76.00	33.10

Queen Wilhelmina A38

Queen Juliana A39

1948, Aug. 30 *Perf. 13x14*

199	A38	6c vermilion	.45	.45
200	A38	12½c deep blue	.45	.45

Reign of Queen Wilhelmina, 50th anniv.

Perf. 14x13½

1948, Oct. 18 Photo. Wmk. 202

201	A39	6c red brown	.35	.35
202	A39	12½c dark green	.35	.35

Investiture of Queen Juliana, Sept. 6, 1948. Nos. 201-202 were issued in Netherlands Sept. 6.

Ship of Ojeda — A40

Alonso de Ojeda — A41

Perf. 14x13, 13x14

1949, July 26 Photo. Unwmk.

203	A40	6c olive green	2.50	1.75
204	A41	12½c brown red	3.25	3.00
205	A40	15c ultra	3.25	2.00
		Nos. 203-205 (3)	9.00	6.75

450th anniversary of the discovery of Curaçao by Alonso de Ojeda, 1499.

Post Horns Entwined — A42

1949, Oct. 3 *Perf. 12x12½*

206	A42	6c brown red	3.50	2.00
207	A42	25c dull blue	3.50	.95

UPU, 75th anniversary.

A43

Queen Juliana
A44 A45

1950-79 Photo. *Perf. 13x13½*

208	A43	1c	red brown	.15	.15
209	A43	1½c	blue	.15	.15
210	A43	2c	orange	.15	.15
211	A43	2½c	green	.60	.15
212	A43	3c	purple	.15	.15
212A	A43	4c	yel grn ('59)	.32	.30
213	A43	5c	dark red	.15	.15
			Perf. 13½x13		
214	A44	6c	deep plum	.65	.15
215	A44	7½c	red brn ('54)	3.50	.15
216	A44	10c	red	1.10	.15
a.			Redrawn ('79)	.15	.15
217	A44	12½c	dk green	1.40	.15
218	A44	15c	deep blue	1.40	.15
a.			Redrawn ('79)	.15	.15
219	A44	20c	orange	1.65	.15
a.			Redrawn ('79)	.18	.15
220	A44	21c	black	1.65	1.25
221	A44	22½c	blue grn ('54)	4.50	.15
222	A44	25c	violet	2.00	.15
a.			Redrawn ('79)	.22	.15
223	A44	27½c	henna brn	3.75	1.50
224	A44	30c	olive brown	7.00	.15
225	A44	50c	olive green	7.00	.15
			Perf. 12½x12		
			Engr.		
226	A45	1½g	slate grn	35.00	.20
227	A45	2½g	black brn	35.00	.75
228	A45	5g	rose red	52.50	8.50
229	A45	10g	dk vio brn	165.00	45.00
			Nos. 208-229 (23)	324.77	59.90

Nos. 216a, 218a, 219a and 222a are from booklets Nos. 427a and 428a. Background design is sharper and stamps have one or two straight edges.

See Nos. 427-429. For surcharge see No. B20.

Fort Beekenburg — A46

Perf. 13½x12½

1953, June 16 Photo.

230 A46 22½c olive brown 3.00 .32

Founding of Fort Beekenburg, 250th anniv.

Beach at Aruba — A47

1954, May 1 *Perf. 11x11½*

231 A47 15c dk bl, sal & dp bl 3.25 2.00

3rd congress of the Caribbean Tourist Assoc., Aruba, May 3-6.

Queen Juliana — A48

1954, Dec. 15 *Perf. 13½*

232 A48 7½c olive green .70 .60

Charter of the Kingdom, adopted Dec. 15, 1954. See Netherlands #366 & Surinam #264.

Beach — A49

Petroleum Refinery, Aruba — A50

1955, Dec. 5 Litho. *Perf. 12*

233 A49 15c chnt, bl & emer 2.25 1.75
234 A50 25c chnt, bl & emer 2.50 2.00

Caribbean Commission, 21st meeting, Aruba.

St. Annabaai Harbor and Flags — A51

1956, Dec. 6 Unwmk. *Perf. 14x13*

235 A51 15c lt bl, blk & red .28 .28

Caribbean Commission, 10th anniversary.

Man Watching Rising Sun — A52

1957, Mar. 14 Photo. *Perf. 11x11½*

236 A52 15c brown, blk & yel .28 .28

1st Caribbean Mental Health Conference, Aruba, Mar. 14-19.

Tourism — A53

1957, July 1 Litho. *Perf. 14x13*

237 A53 7½c Saba .32 .32
238 A53 15c St. Maarten .32 .32
239 A53 25c St. Eustatius .32 .32
Nos. 237-239 (3) .96 .96

Curaçao Intercontinental Hotel — A54

1957, Oct. 12 *Perf. 14x13*

240 A54 15c lt ultra .28 .28

Intercontinental Hotel, Willemstad, opening.

Map of Curaçao — A55

1957, Dec. 10 *Perf. 14x13½*

241 A55 15c indigo & lt bl .60 .55

International Geophysical Year.

Flamingoes, Bonaire — A56

Designs: 7½c, 8c, 25c, 1½g, Old buildings, Curaçao. 10c, 5g, Extinct volcano and palms, Saba. 15c, 30c, 1g, Fort Willem III, Aruba. 20c, 35c, De Ruyter obelisk, St. Eustatius. 12c, 40c, 2½g, Town Hall, St. Maarten.

1958-59 Litho. *Perf. 14x13*

Size: 33x22mm

242	A56	6c	lt ol grn & pink	2.00	.15
243	A56	7½c	red brn & org	.15	.15
244	A56	8c	dk bl & org ('59)	.15	.15
245	A56	10c	gray & org yel	.15	.15
246	A56	12c	bluish grn & gray ('59)	.15	.15
247	A56	15c	grn & lt ultra	.15	.15
a.			15c green & lilac	.15	.15
248	A56	20c	crim & gray	.16	.15
249	A56	25c	Prus bl & yel grn	.20	.15
250	A56	30c	brn & bl grn	.22	.15
251	A56	35c	gray & rose ('59)	.28	.15
252	A56	40c	mag & grn	.30	.15
253	A56	50c	grysh brn & pink	.35	.15
254	A56	1g	brt red & gray	.75	.15
255	A56	1½g	rose vio & pale brn	1.10	.18
256	A56	2½g	blue & citron	1.25	.38
257	A56	5g	lt red brn & rose lil	3.75	.75
			Nos. 242-257 (16)	11.11	
			Set value		2.50

See Nos. 340-348, 400-403. For surcharge see No. B58.

Globe — A57

1958, Oct. 16 *Perf. 11x11½*

258 A57 7½c blue & lake .15 .15
259 A57 15c red & ultra .28 .28

50th anniv. of the Netherlands Antilles Radio and Telegraph Administration.

Hotel Aruba Caribbean A58

1959, July 18 *Perf. 14x13*

260 A58 15c multi .28 .28

Opening of the Hotel Aruba Caribbean, Aruba.

Sea Water Distillation Plant — A59

1959, Oct. 16 Photo. *Perf. 14x13*

261 A59 20c bright blue .32 .32

Opening of sea water distillation plant at Balashi, Aruba.

Netherlands Antilles Flag — A60

1959, Dec. 14 Litho. *Perf. 13½*

262 A60 10c ultra & red .28 .28
263 A60 20c ultra, yel & red .28 .28
264 A60 25c ultra, grn & red .28 .28
Nos. 262-264 (3) .84 .84

5th anniv. of the new constitution (Charter of the Kingdom).

Fokker "Snip" and Map of Caribbean — A61

Designs: 20c, Globe showing route flown, and plane. 25c, Map of Atlantic ocean and view of Willemstad. 35c, Map of Atlantic ocean and plane on Aruba airfield.

1959, Dec. 22 Unwmk. *Perf. 14x13*

265 A61 10c yel, lt & dk bl .32 .28
266 A61 20c yel, lt & dk bl .32 .28
267 A61 25c yel, lt & dk bl .32 .15
268 A61 35c yel, lt & dk bl .32 .40
Nos. 265-268 (4) 1.28 1.11

25th anniv. of Netherlands-Curaçao air service.

Msgr. Martinus J. Niewindt — A62

1960, Jan. 12 Photo. *Perf. 13½*

269 A62 10c deep claret .32 .32
270 A62 20c deep violet .48 .48
271 A62 25c olive green .32 .32
Nos. 269-271 (3) 1.12 1.12

Death centenary of Monsignor Niewindt, first apostolic vicar for Curaçao.

Worker, Flag and Factories — A63

1960, Apr. 29 *Perf. 12½x13½*

272 A63 20c multi .32 .32

Issued for Labor Day, May 1, 1960.

US Brig "Andrea Doria" and Gun at Fort Orange, St. Eustatius A64

1961, Nov. 16 Litho. *Perf. 14x13½*

273 A64 20c bl, red, grn & blk .50 .50

185th anniversary of first salute by a foreign power to the US flag flown by an American ship.

Queen Juliana and Prince Bernhard A64a

1962, Jan. 31 Photo. *Perf. 14x13*

274 A64a 10c deep orange .15 .15
275 A64a 25c deep blue .20 .20

Silver wedding anniversary of Queen Juliana and Prince Bernhard.

Benta Player — A65

Designs: 6c, Corn masher. 20c, Petji kerchief. 25c, "Jaja" (nurse) with child, sculpture.

Perf. 12½x13½

1962, Mar. 14 Photo.

276 A65 6c red brn & yel .15 .15
277 A65 10c multicolored .18 .15
278 A65 20c crim, ind & brt grn .30 .28
279 A65 25c brt grn, brn & gray .32 .28
a. Souvenir sheet of 4, #276-279 1.25 1.25
Nos. 276-279 (4) .95 .86

Emblem of Family Relationship A66

Design: 25c, Emblem of mental health (cross).

1963, Apr. 17 Litho. *Perf. 14x13½*

280	A66	20c dk blue & ocher	.28	.28
281	A66	25c blue & red	.28	.28

Fourth Caribbean Conference for Mental Health, Curaçao, Apr. 17-23.

Dove with Olive Branch — A67

1963, July 1 Unwmk. *Perf. 14x13*

282	A67	25c org yel & dk brn	.22	.22

Centenary of emancipation of the slaves.

Hotel Bonaire — A68

1963, Aug. 31 *Perf. 14x13*

283	A68	20c dk red brown	.22	.22

Opening of Hotel Bonaire on Bonaire.

Prince William of Orange Taking Oath of Allegiance — A69

1963, Nov. 21 Photo. *Perf. 13½x14*

284	A69	25c green, blk & rose	.22	.22

150th anniversary of the founding of the Kingdom of the Netherlands.

Chemical Equipment A70

1963, Dec. 10 Litho. *Perf. 14x13½*

285	A70	20c bl grn, brt yel grn & red	.32	.32

Opening of chemical factories on Aruba.

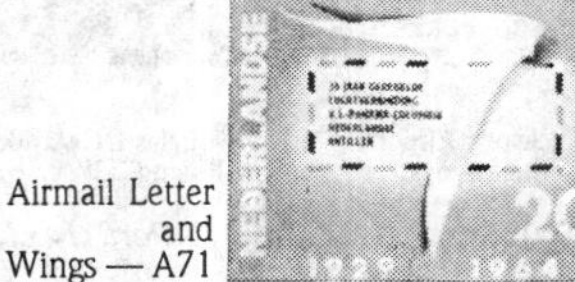

Airmail Letter and Wings — A71

Design: 25c, Map of Caribbean, Miami-Curaçao route and planes of 1929 and 1964.

1964, June 22 Photo. *Perf. 11x11½*

286	A71	20c lt bl, red & ultra	.28	.28
287	A71	25c lt grn, bl, red & blk	.28	.28

35th anniversary of the first regular Curaçao airmail service.

Map of the Caribbean A72

1964, Nov. 30 Litho. Unwmk.

288	A72	20c ultra, org & dk red	.22	.22

5th meeting of the Caribbean Council, Curaçao, Nov. 30-Dec. 4.

Netherlands Antilles Flags, Map of Curaçao and Crest — A73

1964, Dec. 14 Litho. *Perf. 11½x11*

289	A73	25c lt bl & multi	.22	.22

10th anniversary of the Charter of the Kingdom of the Netherlands. The flags, shaped like seagulls, represent the six islands comprising the Netherlands Antilles.

Princess Beatrix — A74

1965, Feb. 22 Photo. *Perf. 13½x14*

290	A74	25c brick red	.28	.28

Visit of Princess Beatrix of Netherlands.

ITU Emblem, Old and New Communication Equipment — A75

1965, May 17 Litho. *Perf. 13½*

291	A75	10c brt bl & dk bl	.15	.15

ITU, centenary.

Shell Refinery, Curaçao A76

10c, Catalytic cracking installation, vert. 25c, Workers operating manifold, primary distillation plant, vert.

Perf. 13½x14, 14x13½

1965, June 22 Photo.

292	A76	10c blk, red & yel	.15	.15
293	A76	20c multi	.15	.15
294	A76	25c multi	.22	.22
		Nos. 292-294 (3)	.52	.52

50th anniv. of the oil industry in Curaçao.

Floating Market, Curaçao — A77

Designs (flag and): 2c, Divi-divi tree and Haystack Mountain, Aruba. 3c, Lace, Saba. 4c, Flamingoes, Bonaire. 5c, Church ruins, St. Eustatius. 6c, Lobster, St. Maarten.

1965, Aug. 25 Litho. *Perf. 14x13*

295	A77	1c lt grn, ultra & red	.15	.15
296	A77	2c yel, ultra & red	.15	.15
297	A77	3c chlky bl, ultra & red	.15	.15
298	A77	4c org, ultra & red	.15	.15
299	A77	5c lt bl, ultra & red	.15	.15
300	A77	6c pink, ultra & red	.15	.15
		Set value	.36	.36

Marine Guarding Beach — A78

1965, Dec. 10 Photo. *Perf. 13x10½*

301	A78	25c multi	.15	.15

300th anniv. of the Netherlands Marine Corps.

Budgerigars, Wedding Rings and Initials — A79

1966, Mar. 10 Photo. *Perf. 13½x14*

302	A79	25c gray & multi	.15	.15

Issued to commemorate the marriage of Princess Beatrix and Claus van Amsberg.

M. A. de Ruyter and Map of St. Eustatius A80

1966, June 19 Photo. *Perf. 13½*

303	A80	25c vio, ocher & lt bl	.15	.15

Visit of Adm. Michiel Adriaanszoon de Ruyter (1607-1676) to St. Eustatius, 1666.

Liberal Arts and Grammar — A81

Designs: 10c, Rhetoric and dialectic. 20c, Arithmetic and geometry. 25c, Astronomy and music.

Perf. 13½x12½

1966, Sept. 19 Litho. Unwmk.

304	A81	6c yel, bl & blk	.15	.15
305	A81	10c yel grn, red & blk	.15	.15
306	A81	20c bl, yel & blk	.15	.15
307	A81	25c red, yel grn & blk	.15	.15
		Set value	.38	.38

25th anniversary of secondary education.

Cruiser — A82

Ships: 10c, Sailing ship. 20c, Tanker. 25c, Passenger ship.

Perf. 13½x14

1967, Mar. 29 Litho. Unwmk.

308	A82	6c lt & dk grn	.15	.15
309	A82	10c org & brn	.15	.15
310	A82	20c sep & brn	.15	.15
311	A82	25c chlky bl & dk bl	.16	.15
		Set value	.44	.44

60th anniv. of *Onze Vloot* (Our Fleet), an organization which publicizes the Dutch navy and merchant marine and helps seamen.

Manuel Carlos Piar (1777-1817), Independence Hero — A83

Discobolus after Myron — A84

1967, Apr. 26 Photo. *Perf. 14x13*

312	A83	20c red & blk	.15	.15

1968, Feb. 19 Litho. *Perf. 13x14*

Designs: 10c, Hand holding torch, and Olympic rings. 25c, Stadium, doves and Olympic rings.

313	A84	10c multi	.20	.20
314	A84	20c dk brn, ol & yel	.20	.20
315	A84	25c bl, dk bl & brt yel grn	.20	.20
		Nos. 313-315 (3)	.60	.60

19th Olympic Games, Mexico City, Oct. 12-27.

Friendship 500 — A84a

Designs: 20c, Beechcraft Queen Air. 25c, Friendship and DC-9.

1968, Dec. 3 Litho. *Perf. 14x13*

315A	A84a	10c dl yel, blk & brt bl	.22	.22
315B	A84a	20c tan, blk & brt bl	.22	.22
315C	A84a	25c sal pink, blk & brt bl	.22	.22
		Nos. 315A-315C (3)	.66	.66

Dutch Antillean Airlines (ALM).

Map of Bonaire, Radio Mast and Waves — A85

Code of Law — A86

1969, Mar. 6 *Perf. 14x13½*

316	A85	25c bl, emer & blk	.22	.22

Opening of the relay station of the Dutch World Broadcasting System on Bonaire.

Perf. 12½x13½

1969, May 19 Photo.

Designs: 25c, Scales of Justice.

317	A86	20c dk grn, yel grn & gold	.22	.22
318	A86	25c vio bl, bl & gold	.22	.22

Court of Justice, centenary.

ILO Emblem, Cactus and House — A87

1969, Aug. 25 Litho. *Perf. 14x13*

319	A87	10c bl & blk	.15	.15
320	A87	25c dk red & blk	.15	.16

ILO, 50th anniversary.

Queen Juliana and Rising Sun — A87a

1969, Dec. 12 Photo. *Perf. 14x13*

321	A87a	25c bl & multi	.22	.22

15th anniv. of the Charter of the Kingdom of the Netherlands. Phosphorescent paper.

Radio Bonaire Studio and Transmitter A88

Design: 15c, Radio waves and cross set against land, sea and air.

1970, Feb. 5 Photo. *Perf. 12½x13½*

322 A88 10c multi .15 .15
323 A88 15c multi .15 .16

5th anniv. of the opening of the Trans World Missionary Radio Station, Bonaire.

Altar, St. Anna's Church, Otraband 1752 — A89

20c, Interior, Synagogue at Punda, 1732, horiz. 25c, Pulpit, Fort Church, Fort Amsterdam, 1769.

Perf. 13½x14, 14x13½

1970, May 12 Photo.

324 A89 10c gold & multi .20 .20
325 A89 20c gold & multi .20 .20
326 A89 25c gold & multi .20 .20
Nos. 324-326 (3) .60 .60

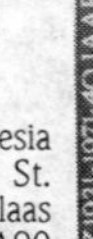

St. Theresia Church, St. Nicolaas A90

1971, Feb. 9 Litho. *Perf. 14x13½*

327 A90 20c dl bl, gray & rose .22 .22

40th anniversary of the Parish of St. Theresia at St. Nicolaas, Aruba.

A91

A91a

1971, Feb. 24 *Perf. 13½x14*

328 A91 25c Lions emblem .28 .28

Lions Club in the Netherlands Antilles, 25th anniversary.

1971, June 29 Photo. *Perf. 13x14*

Prince Bernhard, Fokker F27, Boeing 747B.

329 A91a 45c multi .40 .40

60th birthday of Prince Bernhard.

Pedro Luis Brion (1782-1821), Naval Commander in Fight for South American Independence A92

1971, Sept. 27 Photo. *Perf. 13x12½*

330 A92 40c multi .28 .28

Flamingoes, Bonaire — A93

Ship in Dry Dock — A94

Designs: 1c, Queen Emma Bridge, Curaçao. 2c, The Bottom, Saba. 4c, Water tower, Aruba. 5c, Fort Amsterdam, St. Maarten. 6c, Fort Orange, St. Eustatius.

1972, Jan. 17 Litho. *Perf. 13½x14*

331 A93 1c yel & multi .15 .15
332 A93 2c yel grn & multi .15 .15
333 A93 3c dp org & multi .15 .15
334 A93 4c brt bl & multi .15 .15
335 A93 5c red org & multi .15 .15
336 A93 6c lil rose & multi .15 .15
Set value .36 .36

1972, Apr. 7 *Perf. 14x13½*

337 A94 30c bl gray & multi .28 .28

Inauguration of large dry dock facilities in Willemstad.

Juan Enrique Irausquin A95

Costa Gomez A96

1972, June 20 Photo. *Perf. 13x14*

338 A95 30c deep orange .28 .28

Irausquin (1904-1962), financier and patriot.

1972, Oct. 27 Litho.

339 A96 30c yel grn & blk .28 .28

Moises Frumencio da Costa Gomez (1907-1966), lawyer, legislator, patriot.

Island Series Type of 1958-59

Designs: 45c, 85c, Extinct volcano and palms, Saba. 55c, 90c, De Ruyter obelisk, St. Eustatius. 65c, 75c, 10g, Flamingoes, Bonaire. 70c, Fort Willem III, Aruba. 95c, Town Hall, St. Maarten.

1973, Feb. 12 Litho. *Perf. 14x13*

Size: 33x22mm

340 A56 45c vio bl & lt bl .32 .15
341 A56 55c dk car rose & emer .42 .18
342 A56 65c green & pink .48 .22
343 A56 70c gray vio & org .50 .25
344 A56 75c brt lilac & salmon .55 .28
345 A56 85c brn ol & apple grn .60 .30
346 A56 90c blue & ocher .70 .35
347 A56 95c orange & yellow .70 .38
348 A56 10g brt ultra & salmon 7.00 3.75
Nos. 340-348 (9) 11.27 5.86

Mailman — A97

Designs: 15c, King William III from 1873 issue. 30c, Emblem of Netherlands Antilles postal service.

1973, May 23 Photo. *Perf. 13x14*

349 A97 15c lil, gold & vio .28 .22
350 A97 20c dk grn & multi .32 .28
351 A97 30c org & multi .32 .28
Nos. 349-351 (3) .92 .78

Centenary of first stamps of Netherlands Antilles.

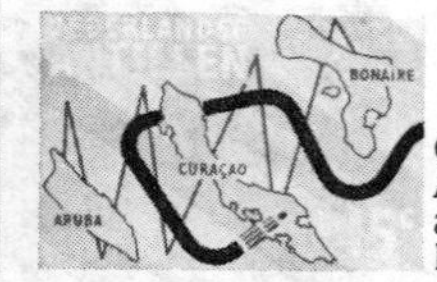

Cable Linking Aruba, Curaçao and Bonaire — A98

30c, 6 stars symbolizing the islands, cable. 45c, Saba, St. Maarten and St. Eustatius linked by cable.

1973, June 20 Litho. *Perf. 14x13*

352 A98 15c multi .32 .32
353 A98 30c multi .32 .32
354 A98 45c multi .32 .23
a. Souvenir sheet of 3, #352-354 2.00 1.50
Nos. 352-354 (3) .96 .87

Inauguration of the inter-island submarine cable.

Queen Juliana, Netherlands Antilles and House of Orange Colors — A99a

Engr. & Photo.

1973, Sept. 4 *Perf. 12½x12*

355 A99a 15c silver & multi .40 .40

25th anniversary of reign of Queen Juliana.

Jan Hendrik Albert Eman — A99

Lionel Bernard Scott — A100

1973, Oct. 17 Litho. *Perf. 13x14*

356 A99 30c lt yel grn & blk .28 .28

Eman (1888-1957), founder of the People's Party in Aruba, member of Antillean Parliament.

1974, Jan. 28

357 A100 30c lt bl & multi .28 .28

Scott (1897-1966), architect and statesman.

Family at Supper — A101

Designs: 12c, Parents watching children at play. 15c, Mother and daughter sewing, father and son gardening.

1974, Feb. 18 Litho. *Perf. 13x14*

358 A101 6c bl & multi .15 .15
359 A101 12c bis & multi .22 .20
360 A101 15c grn & multi .28 .22
Set value .56 .48

Planned parenthood and World Population Year.

Desulphurization Plant, Lago — A102

Designs: 30c, Distillation plant. 45c, Lago refinery at night.

1974, Aug. 12 Litho. *Perf. 14x13*

361 A102 15c lt bl, blk & yel .28 .28
362 A102 30c lt bl, blk & yel .28 .28
363 A102 45c dk brn & multi .28 .28
Nos. 361-363 (3) .84 .84

Oil industry in Aruba, 50th anniversary.

UPU Emblem — A103

1974, Oct. 9 Litho. *Perf. 13x14*

364 A103 15c yel grn, blk & gold .32 .32
365 A103 30c bl, blk & gold .32 .32

Centenary of Universal Postal Union.

Queen Emma Bridge — A104

Willemstad Bridges: 30c, Queen Juliana Bridge. 40c, Queen Wilhelmina Bridge.

1975, Feb. 5 Litho. *Perf. 14x13*

366 A104 20c ultra & multi .32 .32
367 A104 30c ultra & multi .32 .32
368 A104 40c ultra & multi .40 .40
Nos. 366-368 (3) 1.04 1.04

Dedication of new Queen Juliana Bridge spanning Curaçao Harbor.

Salt Crystals A105

Designs: 20c, Solar salt pond. 40c, Map of Bonaire and location of solar salt pond, vert.

Perf. 14x13, 13x14

1975, Apr. 24 Litho.

369 A105 15c multi .32 .32
370 A105 20c multi .32 .32
371 A105 40c multi .40 .32
Nos. 369-371 (3) 1.04 .96

Bonaire's salt industry.

Aruba Airport, 1935 and Fokker F-18 — A106

30c, Aruba Airport, 1950, & Douglas DC-9. 40c, New Princess Beatrix Airport & Boeing 727.

1975, June 19 Litho. *Perf. 14x13*

372 A106 15c vio & multi .28 .22
373 A106 30c blk & multi .32 .28
374 A106 40c yel & multi .32 .32
Nos. 372-374 (3) .92 .82

40th anniversary of Aruba Airport.

International Women's Year Emblem A107

12c, "Women's role in social development." 20c, Embryos within female & male symbols.

1975, Aug. 1 Photo. *Perf. 14x13*

375 A107 6c multi .15 .15
376 A107 12c multi .28 .22
377 A107 20c multi .32 .28
Nos. 375-377 (3) .75 .65

International Women's Year 1975.

Beach, Aruba — A108

Tourist Publicity: No. 379, Beach pavilion and boat, Bonaire. No. 380, Table Mountain and Spanish Water, Curaçao.

1976, June 21 Litho. *Perf. 14x13*

378	A108	40c blue & multi	.40	.40
379	A108	40c blue & multi	.40	.40
380	A108	40c blue & multi	.40	.40
		Nos. 378-380 (3)	1.20	1.20

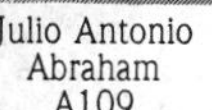

Julio Antonio Abraham A109

Dike and Produce A110

1976, Aug. 10 Photo. *Perf. 13x14*

381	A109	30c tan & claret	.32	.32

Julio Antonio Abraham (1909-1960), founder of Democratic Party of Bonaire.

1976, Sept. 21 Litho.

382	A110	15c shown	.28	.22
383	A110	35c Cattle	.40	.32
384	A110	45c Fish	.40	.40
		Nos. 382-384 (3)	1.08	.94

Agriculture, husbandry and fishing in Netherlands Antilles.

Plaque, Fort Oranje Memorial A111

Designs: 40c, Andrea Doria in St. Eustatius harbor receiving salute. 55c, Johannes de Graaff, Governor of St. Eustatius, holding Declaration of Independence.

1976, Nov. 16 Litho. *Perf. 14x13*

385	A111	25c multi	.55	.32
386	A111	40c multi	.90	.32
387	A111	55c multi	.60	.55
		Nos. 385-387 (3)	2.05	1.19

First gun salute to US flag, St. Eustatius, Nov. 16, 1776.

Dancer with Cactus Headdress A112

Bird Petroglyph, Aruba A113

Carnival: 35c, Woman in feather costume. 40c, Woman in pompadour costume.

1977, Jan. 20 Litho. *Perf. 13x14*

388	A112	25c multi	.40	.32
389	A112	35c multi	.40	.32
390	A112	40c multi	.40	.32
		Nos. 388-390 (3)	1.20	.96

1977, Mar. 29

Indian Petroglyphs: 35c, Loops and spiral, Savonet Plantation, Curaçao. 40c, Tortoise, Onima, Bonaire.

391	A113	25c red & multi	.32	.28
392	A113	35c brn & multi	.32	.32
393	A113	40c yel & multi	.40	.32
		Nos. 391-393 (3)	1.04	.92

A114 A115

Tropical Trees: 25c, Cordia Sebestena. 40c, East Indian walnut, vert. 55c, Tamarind.

1977, July 20 *Perf. 14x13, 13x14*

394	A114	25c blk & multi	.32	.28
395	A114	40c blk & multi	.40	.32
396	A114	55c blk & multi	.48	.48
		Nos. 394-396 (3)	1.20	1.08

1977, Sept. 27 Litho. *Perf. 13x14*

Designs: 20c, Chimes, Spritzer & Fuhrmann Building. 40c, Globe with Western Hemisphere and sun over Curaçao. 55c, Diamond ring and flag of Netherlands Antilles.

397	A115	20c brt grn & multi	.32	.28
398	A115	40c yel & multi	.40	.40
399	A115	55c bl & multi	.48	.48
		Nos. 397-399 (3)	1.20	1.16

Spritzer & Fuhrmann, jewelers of Netherlands Antilles, 50th anniversary.

Type of 1958-59

Designs: 20c, 35c, 55c, De Ruyter obelisk, St. Eustatius. 40c, Town Hall, St. Maarten.

Perf. 13½ Horiz.

1977, Nov. 30 Photo.

Size: 39x22mm

400	A56	20c crim & gray	.70	.50
a.		Bklt. pane of 6 (2 #400, 4 #402)	5.25	
401	A56	35c gray & rose	1.10	.80
a.		Bklt. pane of 4 (1 #401, 3 #403)	6.00	
402	A56	40c magenta & grn	.70	.50
403	A56	55c dk car rose & emer	1.10	1.10
		Nos. 400-403 (4)	3.60	2.90

Nos. 400-403 issued in booklets only. No. 400a has label with red inscription in size of 3 stamps; No. 401a has label with dark carmine rose inscription in size of 2 stamps.

Winding Road, Map of Saba — A116

Tourism: 35c, Ruins of Synagogue, map of St. Eustatius. 40c, Greatbay, Map of St. Maarten.

1977, Nov. 30 Litho. *Perf. 14x13*

404	A116	25c multi	.15	.15
405	A116	35c multi	.15	.15
406	A116	40c multi	.22	.22
		Set value	.42	.42

Tete-beche gutter pairs exist.

Treasure Chest — A117

Designs: 20c, Logo of Netherlands Antilles Bank. 40c, Safe deposit door.

1978, Feb. 7 Litho. *Perf. 14x13*

407	A117	15c brt & dk bl	.15	.15
408	A117	20c org & gold	.15	.15
409	A117	40c brt & dk grn	.15	.15
		Set value	.28	.28

Bank of Netherlands Antilles, 150th anniv. Tete-beche gutter pairs exist.

Flamboyant A118

Polythysana Rubrescens A119

Flowers: 25c, Erythrina velutina. 40c, Guaiacum officinale, horiz. 55c, Gliricidia sepium, horiz.

Perf. 13x14, 14x13

1978, May 31 Litho.

410	A118	15c multi	.15	.15
411	A118	25c multi	.22	.20
412	A118	40c multi	.28	.25
413	A118	55c multi	.32	.32
		Nos. 410-413 (4)	.97	.92

1978, June 20 *Perf. 13x14*

Butterflies: 25c, Caligo eurilochus. 35c, Prepona omphale amesis. 40c, Morpho aega.

414	A119	15c multi	.15	.15
415	A119	25c multi	.22	.20
416	A119	35c multi	.28	.25
417	A119	40c multi	.32	.32
		Nos. 414-417 (4)	.97	.92

"Conserve Energy" — A120

1978, Aug. 31 Litho. *Perf. 13x14*

418	A120	15c org & blk	.15	.15
419	A120	20c dp grn & blk	.18	.15
420	A120	40c dk red & blk	.30	.30
		Nos. 418-420 (3)	.63	.60

Morse Ship-to-Shore Service — A121

Designs: 40c, Ship-to-shore telex service. 55c, Future radar-satellite service, vert.

Perf. 14x13, 13x14

1978, Oct. 16 Litho.

421	A121	20c multi	.22	.22
422	A121	40c multi	.28	.28
423	A121	55c multi	.40	.40
		Nos. 421-423 (3)	.90	.90

70th anniversary of ship-to-shore communications.

Villa Maria Waterworks A122

35c, Leonard B. Smith, vert. 40c, Opening of Queen Emma Bridge, Willemstadt, 1888.

1978, Dec. 13

424	A122	25c multi	.18	.16
425	A122	35c multi	.22	.20
426	A122	40c multi	.30	.25
		Nos. 424-426 (3)	.70	.61

L. B. Smith, engineer, 80th death anniv.

Queen Juliana Type of 1950

1979, Jan. 11 Photo. *Perf. 13½x13*

427	A44	5c dp yel	.15	.15
a.		Bklt. pane of 10 (4 #427, 1 #216a, 2 #222a, 3 #429)	3.00	
428	A44	30c brown	.25	.15
a.		Bklt. pane of 10 (1 #428, 4 #218a, 3 #219a, 2 #222a)	3.00	
429	A44	40c brt bl	.32	.15
		Nos. 427-429 (3)	.72	
		Set value		.20

Nos. 427-429 issued in booklets only. Nos. 427a-428a have 2 labels and selvages the size of 6 stamps. Background design of booklet stamps sharper than 1950 issue. All stamps have 1 or 2 straight edges.

Goat and Conference Emblem A123

75c, Horse & map of Curaçao. 150c, Cattle, Netherlands Antilles flag, UN & Conf. emblems.

1979, Apr. 18 Litho. *Perf. 14x13*

437	A123	50c multi	.28	.28
438	A123	75c multi	.40	.40
439	A123	150c multi	.75	.75
a.		Souv. sheet of 3, perf. 13½x13	1.50	1.50
		Nos. 437-439 (3)	1.43	1.43

12th Inter-American Meeting at Ministerial Level on Foot and Mouth Disease and Zoonosis Control, Curaçao, Apr. 17-20. No. 439a contains Nos. 437-439 in changed colors.

Dutch Colonial Soldier, Emblem — A124

1979, July 4 Litho. *Perf. 13x14*

440	A124	1g multi	.55	.52
		Nos. 440,B166-B167 (3)	1.11	1.03

Netherlands Antilles Volunteer Corps, 50th anniv.

A125 A126

Flowering Trees: 25c, Casearia Tremula. 40c, Cordia cylindro-stachya. 1.50g, Melochia tomentosa.

1979, Sept. 3 Litho. *Perf. 13x14*

441	A125	25c multi	.18	.18
442	A125	40c multi	.28	.28
443	A125	1.50g multi	.75	.75
		Nos. 441-443 (3)	1.21	1.21

1979, Dec. 6 Litho. *Perf. 13x14*

Designs: 65c, Dove and Netherlands flag. 1.50g, Dove and Netherlands Antilles flag.

444	A126	65c multi	.48	.40
445	A126	1.50g multi	.80	.80

Constitution, 25th anniversary.

Map of Aruba, Foundation Emblem A127

Design: 1g, Foundation headquarters, Aruba.

1979, Dec. 18 *Perf. 14x13*

446	A127	95c multi	.60	.60
447	A127	1g multi	.70	.70

Cultural Foundation Center, Aruba, 30th anniv.

Cupola, 1910, Fort Church — A128

1980, Jan. 9 *Perf. 13x14*

448	A128	100c multi	.60	.60
		Nos. 448,B172-B173 (3)	1.23	1.23

Fort Church, Curaçao, 210th anniv. (1979).

Rotary Emblem A129

Designs: 50c, Globe and cogwheels. 85c, Cogwheel and Rotary emblem.

1980, Feb. 22 Litho. *Perf. 14x13*

449 A129 45c multi .25 .25
450 A129 50c multi .30 .30
451 A129 85c multi .48 .48
a. Souvenir sheet of 3, #449-451, perf. 13½x13 1.10 1.10
b. Strip of 3, #449-451 1.05 1.05

Rotary Intl., 75th anniv. No. 451a has continuous design.

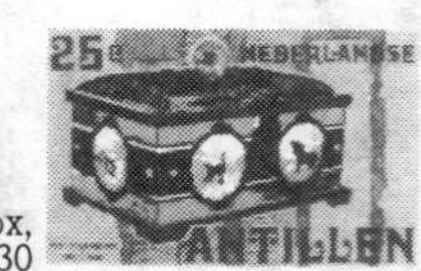

Coin Box, 1905 — A130

Post Office Savings Bank of Netherlands Antilles, 75th Anniversary: 150c, Coin box, 1980.

1980, Apr. 2 Litho. *Perf. 14x13*

452 A130 25c multi .18 .18
453 A130 150c multi .90 .90

Netherlands Antilles No. 200, Arms — A131

1980, Apr. 29 Photo.

454 A131 25c shown .15 .15
455 A131 60c No. 290, royal crown .32 .32
a. Bklt. pane of 5 + 3 labels (#428, 2 #454, 2 #455) 3.00

Abdication of Queen Juliana of the Netherlands. Tete-beche gutter pairs exist.

Sir Rowland Hill (1795-1879), Originator of Penny Postage — A132

1980, May 6 Litho.

456 A132 45c shown .28 .28
457 A132 60c London 1980 emblem .32 .32
458 A132 1g Airmail label .70 .70
a. Souv. sheet of 3, perf. 13½x14 1.40 1.40
Nos. 456-458 (3) 1.30 1.30

London 1980 Intl. Stamp Exhibition, May 6-14. No. 458a contains Nos. 456-458 in changed colors.

Leptotila Verreauxi A133

1980, Sept. 3 Litho. *Perf. 14x13*

459 A133 25c shown .28 .25
460 A133 60c Mockingbird .55 .55
461 A133 85c Coereba flaveola .75 .75
Nos. 459-461 (3) 1.58 1.55

Rudolf Theodorus Palm — A134

Alliance Mission Emblem, Map of Aruba — A135

1981, Jan. 27 Litho. *Perf. 13x14*

462 A134 60c shown .40 .38
463 A134 1g Score, hand playing piano .75 .70

Palm, composer, birth centenary.

1981, Mar. 24 *Perf. 14x13*

464 A135 30c shown .22 .22
465 A135 50c Curaçao .40 .32
466 A135 1g Bonaire map .75 .70
Nos. 464-466 (3) 1.37 1.24

Evangelical Alliance Mission anniversaries: 35th in Aruba, 50th in Curaçao, 30th in Bonaire.

St. Elisabeth's Hospital, 125th Anniv. — A136

1981, June 24 Litho. *Perf. 14x13*

467 A136 60c Gateway .40 .40
468 A136 1.50g shown 1.00 1.00

Oregano Blossom A137

Ship Pilot Service Cent. A138

1981, Nov. 24 Litho. *Perf. 13x14*

469 A137 45c shown .30 .30
470 A137 70c Flaira .52 .52
471 A137 100c Welisali .70 .70
Nos. 469-471 (3) 1.52 1.52

1982, Jan. 13 Litho. *Perf. 13x14*

Designs: Various ships.

472 A138 70c multi .55 .55
473 A138 85c multi .60 .60
474 A138 1g multi .70 .70
Nos. 472-474 (3) 1.85 1.85

A139

A140

1982, Mar. 15 Litho. *Perf. 13x14*

475 A139 75c Altar .60 .60
476 A139 85c Building .60 .60
477 A139 150c Pulpit 1.00 1.00
Nos. 475-477 (3) 2.20 2.20

Community Mikve Israel-Emanuel Synagogue, 250th anniv.

1982, Apr. 21 Litho. *Perf. 13x14*

478 A140 75c Flags, Peter Stuyvesant .70 .70
a. Souvenir sheet .75 .75

US-Netherlands diplomatic relations bicentenary.

A141

A142

1982, May 5

479 A141 35c Radar screen .28 .28
480 A141 75c Control tower .60 .60
481 A141 150c Antenna 1.00 1.00
Nos. 479-481 (3) 1.88 1.88

Intl. Air Traffic Controllers' Year.

1982, June 9 Litho. *Perf. 13x14*

482 A142 45c Emblem .32 .32
483 A142 85c Mail bag .60 .60
484 A142 150c Flags of France, Neth. Ant. 1.10 1.00
a. Souvenir sheet of 3, #482-484 2.25 2.25
Nos. 482-484 (3) 2.02 1.92

PHILEXFRANCE '82 Stamp Exhibition, Paris, June 11-21.

Brown Chromis A143

1982, Sept. 15 Litho. *Perf. 14x13*

485 A143 35c shown .48 .48
486 A143 75c Spotted trunkfish 1.00 1.00
487 A143 85c Blue tang 1.10 1.10
488 A143 100c French angelfish 1.40 1.40
Nos. 485-488 (4) 3.98 3.98

Natural Bridge, Aruba — A144

1983, Apr. 12 Litho. *Perf. 14x13*

489 A144 35c shown .32 .32
490 A144 45c Lac-Bay, Bonaire .40 .40
491 A144 100c Willemstad, Curaçao .90 .90
Nos. 489-491 (3) 1.62 1.62

World Communications Year — A145

1983, May 17 Litho. *Perf. 13x14*

492 A145 1g multi .90 .90
a. Souvenir sheet .95 .95

BRASILIANA '83 — A146

Fruit Tree — A147

1983, June 29 Litho. *Perf. 13x14*

493 A146 45c Ship, postal building, Waaigat .48 .48
494 A146 55c Flags, emblem .55 .55
495 A146 100c Governor's Palace, Sugar Loaf Mt. .95 .95
a. Souvenir sheet of 3, #493-495 2.25 2.25
Nos. 493-495 (3) 1.98 1.98

1983, Sept. 13 Litho. *Perf. 13x14*

496 A147 45c Mangifera indica .70 .70
497 A147 55c Malpighia punicifolia .80 .80
498 A147 100c Citrus aurantifolia 1.40 1.40
Nos. 496-498 (3) 2.90 2.90

Local Government Buildings A148

1983, Dec. 20 Litho. *Perf. 14x13*

499 A148 20c Saba .20 .20
500 A148 25c St. Eustatius .22 .22
501 A148 30c St. Maarten .28 .28
502 A148 35c Aruba .30 .30
503 A148 45c Bonaire .38 .38
a. Perf. 13½ horiz. ('86) .20 .20
504 A148 55c Curaçao .48 .48
a. Perf. 13½ horiz. ('86) .25 .25
b. Bklt. pane of 4 + label (2 #503a, 504a) ('86) 1.75
Nos. 499-504 (6) 1.86 1.86

See Nos. 515-520, 543A-555.

Amigoe di Curaçao Newspaper Centenary A149

1984, Jan. 5 Litho.

505 A149 45c Copy programming .40 .40
506 A149 55c Printing press .48 .48
507 A149 85c Man reading newspaper .90 .90
Nos. 505-507 (3) 1.78 1.78

40th Anniv. of Intl. Civil Aviation Org. — A150

Various emblems.

1984, Feb. 28 Litho. *Perf. 14x13*

508 A150 25c Winair .20 .20
509 A150 45c ICAO .40 .40
510 A150 55c ALM .50 .50
511 A150 100c Plane .90 .90
Nos. 508-511 (4) 2.00 2.00

Chamber of Commerce and Industry Centenary — A151

1984, May 29 Litho. *Perf. 13½*

512 A151 45c Bonnet maker .60 .60
513 A151 55c Emblem .60 .60
514 A151 100c River, bridge, boat .95 .95
Nos. 512-514 (3) 2.15 2.15

Govt. Building Type of 1983

1984, June 26 Litho. *Perf. 14x13*

515 A148 60c like 20c .55 .55
516 A148 65c like 25c .60 .60
517 A148 75c like 30c .75 .75
518 A148 85c like 35c .85 .85
519 A148 90c like 45c .90 .90
520 A148 95c like 55c 1.00 1.00
Nos. 515-520 (6) 4.65 4.65

For surcharges see Nos. B306-B307.

Local Birds — A152

1984, Sept. 18 Litho. *Perf. 14x13*

521 A152 45c Tiaris bicolor .85 .85
522 A152 55c Zonotrichia capensis 1.10 1.10
523 A152 150c Chlorostilbon melanisugus 2.25 2.25
Nos. 521-523 (3) 4.20 4.20

Eleanor Roosevelt (1884-1962) — A153

1984, Oct. 11 Litho. *Perf. 13x14*

524 A153 45c At Hyde Park .48 .48
525 A153 85c Portrait .80 .80
526 A153 100c Reading to children .90 .90
Nos. 524-526 (3) 2.18 2.18

Tete-beche gutter pairs exist.

Flamingos — A154

Curaçao Masonic Lodge Bicent. — A155

1985, Jan. 9 Litho. *Perf. 14x13*

527	A154	25c Adult pullets	.55	.55
528	A154	45c Juveniles	.90	.90
529	A154	55c Adults wading	1.10	1.10
530	A154	100c Adults flying	1.65	1.65
		Nos. 527-530 (4)	4.20	4.20

1985, Feb. 21 Litho. *Perf. 13x14*

531	A155	45c Compass, sun, moon and stars	.50	.50
532	A155	55c Doorway, columns and 5 steps	.70	.70
533	A155	100c Star, 7 steps	1.10	1.10
		Nos. 531-533 (3)	2.30	2.30

UN, 40th Anniv. — A156

1985, June 5 Litho. *Perf. 14x13*

534	A156	55c multi	.60	.60
535	A156	1g multi	1.00	1.00

Papiamentu, Language of the Antilles — A157

45c, Pierre Lauffer (1920-1981), author and poem Patria. 55c, Waves of Papiamentu.

1985, Sept. 4 Litho. *Perf. 14x13*

536	A157	45c multi	.45	.45
537	A157	55c multi	.60	.60

Tete-beche gutter pairs exist.

Flora — A158

1985, Nov. 6 *Perf. 13x14*

538	A158	5c Calotropis procera	.15	.15
539	A158	10c Capparis flexuosa	.22	.22
540	A158	20c Mimosa distachya	.28	.28
541	A158	45c Ipomoea nil	.60	.60
542	A158	55c Heliotropium ternatum	.70	.70
543	A158	1.50g Ipomoea incarnata	2.00	2.00
		Nos. 538-543 (6)	3.95	3.95

Govt. Building Type of 1983

1985-89 *Perf. 14x13*

543A	A148	70c like 20c ('88)	.55	.55
543B	A148	85c like 45c ('88)	.60	.60
544	A148	1g like 20c	.85	.85
545	A148	1.50g like 25c	1.10	1.10
546	A148	2.50g like 30c ('86)	2.25	2.00
551	A148	5g like 45c ('86)	4.00	3.50
554	A148	10g like 55c ('87)	7.50	7.50
555	A148	15g like 20c ('89)	13.00	13.00
		Nos. 543A-555 (8)	29.85	29.10

Issued: 70c, 85c, 3/16; 1g, 1.50g, 12/4; 2.50g, 1/8; 5g, 12/3; 10g, 5/20; 15g, 2/8.
For surcharge see No. B308.
This is an expanding set. Numbers will change if necessary.

Curaçao Town Hall, 125th Anniv. A159

1986, Jan. 8 *Perf. 14x13, 13x14*

561	A159	5c Town Hall	.15	.15
562	A159	15c State room, vert.	.18	.18
563	A159	25c Court room	.25	.25
564	A159	55c Entrance, vert.	.52	.52
		Nos. 561-564 (4)	1.10	1.10

Amnesty Intl., 25th Anniv. — A160

1986, May 28 Litho. *Perf. 14x13*

565	A160	45c Prisoner chained	.40	.40
566	A160	55c Peace bird imprisoned	.50	.50
567	A160	100c Prisoner behind bars	.90	.90
		Nos. 565-567 (3)	1.80	1.80

Mailboxes A161

Perf. 14x13, 13x14

1986, Sept. 3 Litho.

568	A161	10c PO mailbox	.15	.15
569	A161	25c Steel mailbox	.22	.22
570	A161	45c Mailbox on brick wall	.35	.35
571	A161	55c Pillar box	.42	.42
		Nos. 568-571 (4)	1.14	1.14

Nos. 569-571 vert.

Friars of Tilburg in the Antilles, Cent. — A162

10c, Brother Mauritius Vliegendehond, residence, 1886. 45c, Monsignor Ferdinand Kieckens, St. Thomas College, Roodeweg. 55c, Father F.S. de Beer, 1st general-superior, & college courtyard.

1986, Nov. 13 Litho. *Perf. 13x14*

572	A162	10c multi	.15	.15
573	A162	45c multi	.35	.35
574	A162	55c multi	.42	.42
		Nos. 572-574 (3)	.92	.92

Princess Juliana & Prince Bernhard, 50th Wedding Anniv. — A163

Maduro Holding, Inc., Sesquicent. — A164

1987, Jan. 7 Litho. *Perf. 13x14*

575	A163	1.35g multi	1.10	1.10
a.		Souvenir sheet	1.25	1.25

1987, Jan. 26

576	A164	70c Expansion map	.48	.48
577	A164	85c Corporate divisions	.60	.60
578	A164	1.55g S.E.L. Maduro, founder	1.10	1.10
		Nos. 576-578 (3)	2.18	2.18

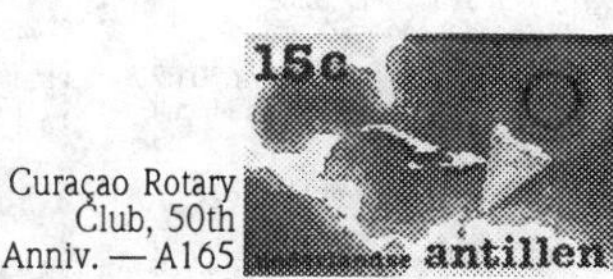

Curaçao Rotary Club, 50th Anniv. — A165

1987, Apr. 2 Litho. *Perf. 14x13*

579	A165	15c Map of the Antilles	.20	.20
580	A165	50c Rotary headquarters	.42	.42
581	A165	65c Map of Curaçao	.52	.52
		Nos. 579-581 (3)	1.14	1.14

Bolivar-Curaçao Friendship, 175th Anniv. — A166

60c, Octagon, residence of Simon Bolivar in Curaçao. 70c, Bolivarian Soc. Headquarters, 1949, Willemstad. 80c, Octagon interior (bedroom). 90c, Manual Carlos Piar, Simon Bolivar (1783-1830) & Pedro Luis Brion.

1987, July 24 Litho. *Perf. 14x13*

582	A166	60c multi	.42	.42
583	A166	70c multi	.52	.52
584	A166	80c multi	.55	.55
585	A166	90c multi	.65	.65
		Nos. 582-585 (4)	2.14	2.14

Bolivarian Society, 50th anniv. (70c, 90c).

Antilles Natl. Parks Foundation, 25th Anniv. — A167

1987, Dec. 1 Litho. *Perf. 14x13*

586	A167	70c Phaethon lepturus	.65	.65
587	A167	85c Odocoileus virginianus curassavicus	.80	.80
588	A167	1.55g Iguana iguana	1.50	1.50
		Nos. 586-588 (3)	2.95	2.95

The Curaçao Courant, 175th Anniv. A168

Designs: 55c, 19th Cent. printing press, lead type. 70c, Keyboard, modern press.

1987, Dec. 11

589	A168	55c multi	.48	.48
590	A168	70c multi	.60	.60

Mijnmaatschappij Phosphate Mining Co., Curaçao, 75th Anniv. — A169

1988, Jan. 21

591	A169	40c William Godden, founder	.30	.30
592	A169	105c Processing plant	.80	.80
593	A169	155c Tafelberg	1.25	1.25
		Nos. 591-593 (3)	2.35	2.35

States of the Netherlands Antilles, 50th Anniv. — A170

Designs: 65c, John Horris Sprockel, 1st president, and natl. colors, crest. 70c, Development of state elections, women's suffrage. 155c, Natl. colors, crest, constellation representing the 5 islands and separation of Aruba.

1988, Apr. 5 Litho.

594	A170	65c multi	.50	.50
595	A170	70c multi	.52	.52
596	A170	155c multi	1.10	1.10
		Nos. 594-596 (3)	2.12	2.12

Abolition of Slavery, 125th Anniv. — A171

1988, July 1 Litho. *Perf. 14x13*

597	A171	155c shown	1.25	1.25
598	A171	190c Slave Wall, Curaçao	1.40	1.40

3rd Conference for Great Cities of the Americas, Curaçao, Aug. 24-27 — A172

1988, Aug. 24 Litho.

599	A172	80c shown	.60	.60
600	A172	155c Bridge, globe	1.25	1.25

Interamerican Foundation of Cities conference on building bridges between peoples.

Charles Ernst Barend Hellmund (1896-1952) A173

Cacti A174

Men and women who initiated community development: 65c, Atthelo Maud Edwards Jackson (1901-1970). 90c, Nicolaas Debrot (1902-1981). 120c, William Charles De La Try Ellis (1881-1977).

1988, Sept. 20 *Perf. 13x14*

601	A173	55c multi	.42	.42
602	A173	65c multi	.50	.50
603	A173	90c multi	.65	.65
604	A173	120c multi	.85	.85
		Nos. 601-604 (4)	2.42	2.42

Tete-beche gutter pairs exist.

1988, Dec. 13 Litho. *Perf. 13x14*

605	A174	55c Cereus hexagonus	.58	.58
606	A174	115c Melocactus	1.20	1.20
607	A174	125c Opuntia wentiana	1.30	1.30
		Nos. 605-607 (3)	3.08	3.08

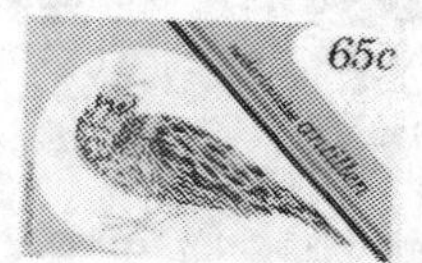

Wildlife Protection and Curaçao Foundation for the Prevention of Cruelty to Animals A175

1989, Mar. 9 Litho. *Perf. 14x13*

608	A175	65c Crested quail	.65	.65
609	A175	115c Dogs, cats	1.15	1.15

Cruise Ships at St. Maarten and Curaçao A176

1989, May 8 Litho.

610	A176	70c Great Bay Harbor	.55	.55
611	A176	155c St. Annabay	1.25	1.25

Tourism.

A177

A178

Social and Political Figures: 40c, Paula Clementina Dorner (1901-1969), teacher. 55c, John Aniceto de Jongh (1885-1951), pharmacist, Parliament member. 90c, Jacobo Palm (1887-1982), composer. 120c, Abraham Mendes Chumaceiro (1841-1902), political reformer.

1989, Sept. 20 Litho. *Perf. 13x14*

612	A177	40c multi	.35	.35
613	A177	55c multi	.45	.45
614	A177	90c multi	.80	.80
615	A177	120c multi	1.10	1.10
		Nos. 612-615 (4)	2.70	2.70

1989, Nov. 7 **Litho.**

616 A178 30c 7 Symptoms of cancer .30 .30
617 A178 60c Radiation treatment .58 .58
618 A178 80c Fund emblem, healthy person .75 .75
Nos. 616-618 (3) 1.63 1.63

Queen Wilhelmina Fund, 40th anniv. Nos. 616-618 printed se-tenant with inscribed labels.

Souvenir Sheet

World Stamp Expo '89 and 20th UPU Congress, Washington, DC — A179

Designs: 70c, Monument, St. Eustatius, where the sovereignty of the US was 1st recognized by a foreign officer, Nov. 16, 1776. 155c, Peter Stuyvesant, flags representing bicent. of US-Antilles diplomatic relations, vert. 250c, 9-Gun salute of the *Andrea Doria*.

1989, Nov. 17 **Litho.** ***Perf. 13***

619 Sheet of 3 3.75 3.75
a. A179 70c multicolored .55 .55
b. A179 155c multicolored 1.25 1.25
c. A179 250c multicolored 1.75 1.75

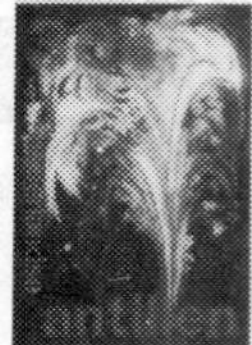

A180

A181

1989, Dec. 1 ***Perf. 13½x14***

620 A180 30c Fireworks .22 .22
621 A180 100c Ornaments on tree .75 .75

Christmas 1989 and New Year 1990. Nos. 620-621 printed se-tenant with labels inscribed "Merry X-mas and Happy New Year" in four languages.

1990, Jan. 31 **Litho.** ***Perf. 13x14***

Flowering plants.

622 A181 30c *Tephrosia cinerea* .22 .22
623 A181 55c *Erithalis fruticosa* .40 .40
624 A181 65c *Evolvulus antillanus* .50 .50
625 A181 70c *Jacquinia arborea* .55 .55
626 A181 125c *Tournefortia gnaphalodes* 1.00 1.00
627 A181 155c *Sesuvium portulacastrum* 1.10 1.10
Nos. 622-627 (6) 3.77 3.77

Dominican Nuns in the Netherlands Antilles, Cent. — A182

10c, Nurse, flag, map. 55c, St. Rose Hospital and St. Martin's Home. 60c, St. Joseph School.

1990, May 7 **Litho.** ***Perf. 14x13***

628 A182 10c multicolored .16 .16
629 A182 55c multicolored .62 .62
630 A182 60c multicolored .70 .70
Nos. 628-630 (3) 1.48 1.48

A183

A184

Poets: 40c, Carlos Alberto Nicolaas-Perez (1915-1989). 60c, Evert Stephanus Jordanus Kruythoff (1893-1967). 80c, John De Pool (1873-1947). 150c, Joseph Sickman Corsen (1853-1911).

1990, Aug. 8 **Litho.** ***Perf. 13x14***

631 A183 40c multicolored .46 .46
632 A183 60c multicolored .70 .70
633 A183 80c multicolored .95 .95
634 A183 150c multicolored 1.75 1.75
Nos. 631-634 (4) 3.86 3.86

1990, Sept. 5 ***Perf. 13x14***

Netherlands queens.

635 A184 100c Emma 1.15 1.15
636 A184 100c Wilhelmina 1.15 1.15
637 A184 100c Juliana 1.15 1.15
638 A184 100c Beatrix 1.15 1.15
Nos. 635-638 (4) 4.60 4.60

Souvenir Sheet

Perf. 14x13

639 A184 250c Four Queens, horiz. 2.85 2.85

Oil Refining in Curaçao, 75th Anniv. — A185

1990, Oct. 1 **Litho.** ***Perf. 14x13***

640 A185 100c multicolored 1.15 1.15

Christmas — A186

1990, Dec. 5 **Litho.** ***Perf. 13½x14***

641 A186 30c Gifts .35 .35
642 A186 100c shown 1.15 1.15

25th anniv. of Bon Bisina Project (No. 641). Nos. 641-642 each printed with se-tenant label showing holiday greetings.

Express Mail Service, 5th Anniv. — A187

1991, Jan. 16 **Litho.** ***Perf. 14x13***

643 A187 20g multicolored 24.00 24.00

Fish — A188

Designs: 10c, Scuba diver, French grunt. 40c, Spotted trunkfish. 55c, Coppersweeper. 75c, Skindiver, yellow goatfish. 100c, Blackbar soldierfish.

1991, Mar. 13 ***Perf. 13x14***

644 A188 10c multicolored .15 .15
645 A188 40c multicolored .50 .50
646 A188 55c multicolored .65 .65
647 A188 75c multicolored .90 .90
648 A188 100c multicolored 1.20 1.20
Nos. 644-648 (5) 3.40 3.40

Greetings A189

1991, May 8 ***Perf. 14x13***

649 A189 30c Good luck .35 .35
650 A189 30c Thank you .35 .35
651 A189 30c Love you .35 .35
652 A189 30c Happy day .35 .35
653 A189 30c Get well soon .35 .35
654 A189 30c Happy birthday .35 .35
Nos. 649-654 (6) 2.10 2.10

Lighthouses — A190

1991, June 19 **Litho.** ***Perf. 13x14***

655 A190 30c Westpoint, Curaçao .35 .35
656 A190 70c Willem's Tower, Bonaire .85 .85
657 A190 115c Little Curaçao, Curaçao 1.40 1.40
Nos. 655-657 (3) 2.60 2.60

Peter Stuyvesant College, 50th Anniv. — A191

Espamer '91 — A192

1991, July 5 ***Perf. 14x13, 13x14***

658 A191 65c multicolored .78 .78
659 A192 125c multicolored 1.50 1.50

Christmas — A193

A194

1991, Dec. 2 **Litho.** ***Perf. 13½x14***

660 A193 30c shown .35 .35
661 A193 100c Angel, shepherds 1.10 1.10

Nos. 660-661 printed with se-tenant labels.

Litho. & Typo.

1991, Dec. 16 ***Perf. 13x14***

662 A194 30c J. A. Correa .35 .35
663 A194 70c "75," coat of arms .85 .85
664 A194 155c I. H. Capriles 1.85 1.85
a. Strip of 3, #662-664 3.05 3.05

Maduro and Curiel's Bank NV, 75th anniv.

Odocoileus Virginianus A195

1992, Jan. 29 **Litho.** ***Perf. 14x13***

666 A195 5c Fawn .15 .15
667 A195 10c Two does .15 .15
668 A195 30c Buck .35 .35
669 A195 40c Buck & doe in water .45 .45
670 A195 200c Buck drinking 2.20 2.20
671 A195 355c Buck, diff. 4.00 4.00
Nos. 666-671 (6) 7.30 7.30

World Wildlife Fund. Nos. 670-671 are airmail and do not have the WWF emblem.

Souvenir Sheet

Discovery of America, 500th Anniv. — A196

Designs: a, 250c, Alhambra, Granada, Spain. b, 500c, Carthusian Monastery, Seville, Spain.

1992, Apr. 1 **Litho.** ***Perf. 14x13***

672 A196 Sheet of 2, #a.-b. 9.00 9.00

#672a, Granada '92. #672b, Expo '92, Seville.

Discovery of America, 500th Anniv. — A197

250c, Sailing ship. 500c, Map, Columbus.

1992, May 13 **Litho.** ***Perf. 14x13***

673 A197 250c multicolored 3.00 3.00
674 A197 500c multicolored 6.00 6.00

World Columbian Stamp Expo '92, Chicago.

Container Terminal, Curaçao A198

1992, June 26

675 A198 80c multi .95 .95
676 A198 125c multi, diff. 1.50 1.50

Famous People — A199

Designs: 30c, Angela Altagracia de Lannoy-Willems (1913-1983), politician and social activist. 40c, Lodewijk Daniel Gerharts (1901-1983), politician and promoter of tourism for Bonaire. 55c, Cyrus Wilberforce Wathey (1901-1969), businessman and philanthropist. 70c, Christiaan Winkel (1899-1962), deputy governor of Netherlands Antilles. 100c, Franciscan Nuns of Roosendaal, educational and charitable group, 150th anniversary of arrival in Curaçao.

1992, Sept. 1 **Litho.** ***Perf. 13x14***

677 A199 30c tan, grn & blk .38 .38
678 A199 40c tan, blue & blk .48 .48
679 A199 55c tan, yel org & blk .65 .65
680 A199 70c tan, lake & blk .85 .85
681 A199 100c tan, blue & blk 1.25 1.25
Nos. 677-681 (5) 3.61 3.61

Queen Beatrix's 1992 Visit — A200

Designs: 70c, Queen in white hat, Prince Claus. 100c, Queen signing jubilee register. 175c, Queen in black hat, Prince Claus, native girl.

1992, Nov. 9 **Litho.** ***Perf. 14x13***

682 A200 70c multicolored .90 .90
683 A200 100c multicolored 1.25 1.25
684 A200 175c multicolored 2.20 2.20
Nos. 682-684 (3) 4.35 4.35

Queen Beatrix's accession to the throne, 12½ year anniv. (#683).

Christmas A201

Perf. 14x13½, 13½x14

1992, Dec. 1 **Litho.**

685 A201 30c Nativity scene .35 .35
686 A201 100c Mary, Joseph, vert. 1.20 1.20

No. 686 printed with se-tenant label.

Flowers — A202

1993, Feb. 3 Litho. *Perf. 13x14*
687 A202 75c Hibiscus .95 .95
688 A202 90c Helianthus annuus 1.10 1.10
689 A202 175c Ixora 2.20 2.20
690 A202 195c Rosea 2.40 2.40
Nos. 687-690 (4) 6.65 6.65

Anniversaries A203

Map of islands and: 65c, Airplane, air routes. 75c, Natl. Laboratory, scientist using microscope. 90c, Airplane at Princess Juliana Intl. Airport. 175c, Yellow and white crosses.

1993, Mar. 9 *Perf. 14x13*
691 A203 65c multicolored .80 .80
692 A203 75c multicolored .95 .95
693 A203 90c multicolored 1.25 1.25
694 A203 175c multicolored 2.25 2.25
Nos. 691-694 (4) 5.25 5.25

Princess Juliana Intl. Airport, 50th anniv. (#691, 693). Natl. Laboratory, 75th anniv. (#692). Princess Margaret White/Yellow Cross Foundation for District Nursing, 50th anniv. (#694).

Dogs — A204

1993, May 26 Litho. *Perf. 13x14*
695 A204 65c Pekingese .80 .80
696 A204 90c Poodle 1.10 1.10
697 A204 100c Pomeranian 1.25 1.25
698 A204 175c Papillon 2.15 2.15
Nos. 695-698 (4) 5.30 5.30

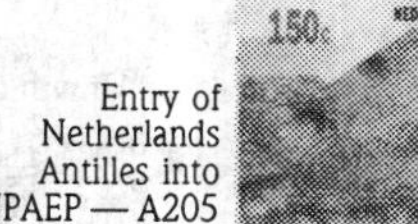

Entry of Netherlands Antilles into UPAEP — A205

Designs: 150c, Indian cave painting, Bonaire. 200c, Emblem of Brasiliana '93, flag of Netherlands Antilles. 250c, Map of Central and South America, Netherlands Antilles, Spain, and Portugal, document being signed.

1993, July 15 Litho. *Perf. 14x13*
699 A205 150c multicolored 1.90 1.90
700 A205 200c multicolored 2.50 2.50
701 A205 250c multicolored 3.15 3.15
Nos. 699-701 (3) 7.55 7.55

Brasiliana '93 (#700).

Contemporary Art — A206

1993, July 23 Litho. *Perf. 13x14*
702 A206 90c silver & multi 1.10 1.10
703 A206 150c gold & multi 1.90 1.90

US Consulate General in Netherlands Antilles, Bicent. — A207

1993, Nov. 16 Litho. *Perf. 14x13*
704 A207 65c American Consulate .80 .80
705 A207 90c Coats of Arms 1.10 1.10
706 A207 175c Eagle in flight 2.25 2.25
Nos. 704-706 (3) 4.15 4.15

Christmas — A208

Designs: 30c, Mosaic of mother and child. 115c, Painting of Mary holding Christ.

1993, Dec. 1 *Perf. 13x14*
707 A208 30c multicolored .35 .35
708 A208 115c multicolored 1.40 1.40

Dogs — A209

1994, Feb. 2 Litho. *Perf. 14x13*
709 A209 65c Basset .80 .80
710 A209 75c Pit bull terrier .95 .95
711 A209 90c Cocker spaniel 1.10 1.10
712 A209 175c Chow 2.25 2.25
Nos. 709-712 (4) 5.10 5.10

Birds — A210

A211

1994, Mar. 2 Litho. *Perf. 13x14*
713 A210 50c Polyborus plancus .60 .60
714 A210 95c Pavo muticus 1.10 1.10
715 A210 100c Ara macao 1.25 1.25
716 A210 125c Icterus icterus 1.50 1.50
Nos. 713-716 (4) 4.45 4.45

1994, Apr. 8

Famous People: 65c, Joseph Husurell Lake (1925-76), politician, journalist. 75c, Efrain Jonckheer (1917-87), diplomat. 100c, Michiel Martinus Romer (1865-1937), educator. 175c, Carel Nicolaas Winkel (1882-1973), public official, social worker.

717 A211 65c green, olive & black .80 .80
718 A211 75c lt brown, brown & black .95 .95
719 A211 100c blue, green & black 1.25 1.25
720 A211 175c tan, brown & black 2.25 2.25
Nos. 717-720 (4) 5.25 5.25

A212

A213

1994 World Cup Soccer Championships, US: 90c, Socks, soccer shoes, horiz. 150c, Shoe, ball. 175c, Whistle, horiz.

Perf. 14x13, 13x14
1994, May 4 Litho.
721 A212 90c multicolored 1.10 1.10
722 A212 150c multicolored 1.90 1.90
723 A212 175c multicolored 2.25 2.25
Nos. 721-723 (3) 5.25 5.25

1994, June 1 Litho. *Perf. 13x14*

ILO, 75th Anniv.: 90c, Declaration, chair, gavel. 110c, "75" over heart. 200c, Wind-blown tree.

724 A213 90c multicolored 1.10 1.10
725 A213 110c multicolored 1.40 1.40
726 A213 200c multicolored 2.50 2.50
Nos. 724-726 (3) 5.00 5.00

Wildlife A214

Designs: 10c, Ware-wara, blenchi, parakeet, dolphin. 35c, Dolphin, pelican, troupial. 50c, Iguana, fish, lobster, sea hedgehog. 125c, Sea hedgehog, sea apple, fish, turtle, flamingos, ducks.

1994, Aug. 4 Litho. *Perf. 14x13*
727 A214 10c multicolored .15 .15
728 A214 35c multicolored .45 .45
729 A214 50c multicolored .65 .65
730 A214 125c multicolored 1.65 1.65
a. Souvenir sheet, #727-730 2.75 2.75
Nos. 727-730 (4) 2.90 2.90

PHILAKOREA '94 (#730a).

FEPAPOST '94 — A215

Designs: 2.50g, Netherlands #277. 5g, #109.

1994, Oct. 5 Litho. *Perf. 14x13*
731 A215 2.50g multicolored 2.75 2.75
732 A215 5g multicolored 5.50 5.50
a. Souv. sheet of 2, #731-732, perf. 13½x13 8.25 8.25

Christmas A216

1994, Dec. 1 Litho. *Perf. 14x13*
733 A216 30c shown .32 .32
734 A216 115c Hands holding earth 1.25 1.25

Curaçao Carnivals A217

Carnival scene and: 125c, Buildings, Willemstad. 175c, Floating market. 250c, House with thatched roof.

1995, Jan. 19 Litho. *Perf. 14x13*
735 A217 125c multicolored 1.40 1.40
736 A217 175c multicolored 2.00 2.00
737 A217 250c multicolored 2.75 2.75
Nos. 735-737 (3) 6.15 6.15

Mgr. Verriet Institute for Physically Handicapped, 50th Anniv. — A218

Design: 90c, Cedric Virginie, handicapped worker at Public Library.

1995, Feb. 2 Litho. *Perf. 13x14*
738 A218 65c multicolored .75 .75
739 A218 90c multicolored 1.00 1.00

Dogs — A219

1995, Mar. 29 Litho. *Perf. 14x13*
740 A219 75c Doberman .85 .85
741 A219 85c Shepherd .95 .95
742 A219 100c Bouvier 1.10 1.10
743 A219 175c St. Bernard 2.00 2.00
Nos. 740-743 (4) 4.90 4.90

Flags, Coats of Arms of Island Territories A220

10c, Bonaire. 35c, Curaçao. 50c, St. Maarten. 65c, Saba. 75c, St. Eustatius, natl. flag, coat of arms. 90c, Flags of territories, natl. coat of arms.

1995, June 30 Litho. *Perf. 14x13*
744 A220 10c multicolored .15 .15
745 A220 35c multicolored .40 .40
746 A220 50c multicolored .55 .55
747 A220 65c multicolored .75 .75
748 A220 75c multicolored .85 .85
749 A220 90c multicolored 1.00 1.00
Nos. 744-749 (6) 3.70 3.70

Domestic Cats — A221

Designs: 25c, Siamese sealpoint. 60c, Maine coon. 65c, Egyptian silver mau. 90c, Angora. 150c, Persian blue smoke.

1995, Sept. 29 Litho. *Perf. 13x14*
750 A221 25c multicolored .30 .30
751 A221 60c multicolored .65 .65
752 A221 65c multicolored .75 .75
753 A221 90c multicolored 1.00 1.00
754 A221 150c multicolored 1.65 1.65
Nos. 750-754 (5) 4.35 4.35

Christmas and New Year — A222

Designs: 30c, Three Magi following star. 115c, Fireworks above houses, Handelskade.

1995, Dec. 1 Litho. *Perf. 13½x13*
755 A222 30c multicolored .35 .35
756 A222 115c multicolored 1.25 1.25

Nos. 755-756 each printed with se-tenant label.

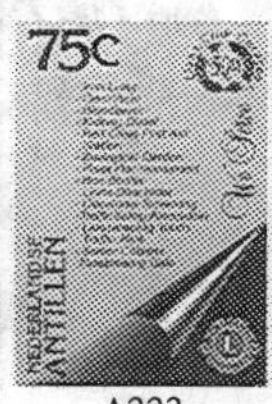

A223

A224

Curaçao Lions Club, 50th Anniv.: 75c, List of services to community. 105c, Seal. 250c, Hands clasp.

1996, Feb. 26 Litho. *Perf. 13x14*
757 A223 75c multicolored .85 .85
758 A223 105c multicolored 1.20 1.20
759 A223 250c multicolored 2.75 2.75
Nos. 757-759 (3) 4.80 4.80

1996, Apr. 12 Litho. *Perf. 13x14*
760 A224 85c shown .95 .95
761 A224 175c Telegraph key 2.00 2.00

Radio, cent.

A225 A226

1996, Apr. 12

762 A225 60c shown .70 .70
763 A225 75c Tornado, sun .80 .80

Dr. David Ricardo Capriles Clinic, 60th anniv.

1996, May 8 Litho. *Perf. 13x14*

764 A226 85c shown .95 .95
765 A226 225c Bible 2.50 2.50

Translation of the Bible into Papiamentu.

CAPEX '96 — A227

Butterflies: 5c, Agraulis vanillae. 110c, Callithea philotima. 300c, Parthenos sylvia. 750c, Euphaedra francina.

1996, June 5 Litho. *Perf. 14x13*

766 A227 5c multicolored .15 .15
767 A227 110c multicolored 1.25 1.25
768 A227 300c multicolored 3.50 3.50
a. Souvenir sheet of 2, #767-768 4.75 4.75
769 A227 750c multicolored 8.50 8.50
Nos. 766-769 (4) 13.40 13.40

Famous Antillean Personalities A228

Designs: 40c, Mary Gertrude Johnson Hassel (1853-1939), introduced drawn thread (Spanish work) to Saba. 50c, Cornelis Marten (Papa Cornes) (1749-1852), spiritual care giver on Bonaire. 75c, Phelippi Benito Chakutoe (1891-1967), union leader. 85c, Christiaan Josef Hendrikus Engels (1907-80), physician, painter, pianist, poet.

1996, Aug. 21 Litho. *Perf. 14x13*

770 A228 40c orange & black .45 .45
771 A228 50c green & black .55 .55
772 A228 75c brown & black .85 .85
773 A228 85c blue & black .95 .95
Nos. 770-773 (4) 2.80 2.80

Horses — A229

1996, Sept. 26 Litho. *Perf. 14x13*

774 A229 110c Shire 1.25 1.25
775 A229 225c Shetland pony 2.50 2.50
776 A229 275c Thoroughbred 3.00 3.00
777 A229 350c Przewalski 3.90 3.90
Nos. 774-777 (4) 10.65 10.65

Christmas — A230

Designs: 35c, Money bag, straw hat, candy cane, gifts, poinsettias, star. 150c, Santa Claus.

Serpentine Die Cut 13x13½

1996, Dec. 2 Litho.

Self-Adhesive

778 A230 35c multicolored .40 .40
779 A230 150c multicolored 1.70 1.70

Mushrooms A231

40c, Galerina autumnalis. 50c, Amanita virosa. 75c, Boletus edulis. 175c, Amanita muscaria.

1997, Feb. 19 Litho. *Perf. 14x13*

780 A231 40c multicolored .45 .45
781 A231 50c multicolored .55 .55
782 A231 75c multicolored .85 .85
783 A231 175c multicolored 2.00 2.00
Nos. 780-783 (4) 3.85 3.85

Birds — A232 Greetings Stamps — A233

5c, Melopsittacus undulatus. 25c, Cacatua leadbeateri leadbeateri. 50c, Amazona barbadensis. 75c, Ardea purperea. 85c, Chrysolampis mosquitus. 100c, Balearica pavonina. 110c, Pyrocephalus rubinus. 125c, Phoenicopteurus ruber. 200c, Pandion haliaetus. 225c, Ramphastos sulfuratus.

1997, Mar. 26 Litho. *Perf. 13x14*

784 A232 5c multicolored .15 .15
785 A232 25c multicolored .30 .30
786 A232 50c multicolored .55 .55
787 A232 75c multicolored .90 .90
788 A232 85c multicolored .95 .95
789 A232 100c multicolored 1.10 1.10
790 A232 110c multicolored 1.25 1.25
791 A232 125c multicolored 1.40 1.40
792 A232 200c multicolored 2.25 2.25
793 A232 225c multicolored 2.50 2.50
Nos. 784-793 (10) 11.35 11.35

1997, Apr. 16

794 A233 40c Love .45 .45
795 A233 75c Positivism .85 .85
796 A233 85c Mother's Day .95 .95
797 A233 100c Correspondence 1.10 1.10
798 A233 110c Success 1.25 1.25
799 A233 225c Congratulations 2.65 2.65
Nos. 794-799 (6) 7.25 7.25

Perf. 13x14 on 3 Sides

1997, Apr. 16 Litho.

#799A, like #794. #799B, Correspondence in 3 languages. #799C, Positivism, flower, sun. #799D, like #795. #799E, Success, rising sun. 85c, like #796. 100c, like #797. #799H, like #798. #799I, Love, silhouette of couple. 225c, like #799.

Booklet Stamps

Size: 21x25mm

799A A233 40c multicolored .50 .50
799B A233 40c multicolored .50 .50
799C A233 75c multicolored .95 .95
799D A233 75c multicolored .95 .95
799E A233 75c multicolored .95 .95
799F A233 85c multicolored 1.10 1.10
799G A233 100c multicolored 1.25 1.25
799H A233 110c multicolored 1.40 1.40
799I A233 110c multicolored 1.40 1.40
799J A233 225c multicolored 2.75 2.75
k. Booklet pane of 10, #799A-799J + label 11.75
Complete booklet, #799k 11.75

Stamps arranged in booklet out of Scott order.

Signs of the Chinese Calendar A234

Stylized designs.

1997, May 19 Litho. *Perf. 14x13*

800 A234 5c Rat .15 .15
801 A234 5c Ox .15 .15
802 A234 5c Tiger .15 .15
803 A234 40c Rabbit .45 .45
804 A234 40c Dragon .45 .45
805 A234 40c Snake .45 .45
806 A234 75c Horse .85 .85
807 A234 75c Goat .85 .85
808 A234 75c Monkey .85 .85
809 A234 100c Rooster 1.10 1.10
810 A234 100c Dog 1.10 1.10
811 A234 100c Pig 1.10 1.10
a. Souvenir sheet of 12, #800-811 7.75 7.75
Nos. 800-811 (12) 7.65 7.65

No. 811a for PACIFIC 97. Issued: 5/19/97.

Coins — A235

1997, Aug. 6 *Perf. 13x14*

812 A235 85c Plaka, 2½ cent 1.10 1.10
813 A235 175c Stuiver, 5 cent 2.20 2.20
814 A235 225c Fuèrtè, 2½ gulden 2.75 2.75
Nos. 812-814 (3) 6.05 6.05

Shanghai '97, Intl. Stamp Exhibition
A236 A237

15c, Nampu Grand Bridge, Shanghai. 40c, Giant panda, horiz. 75c, Tiger, New Year 1998.
90c, Buildings in downtown Shanghai.

Perf. 14x13, 13x14

1997, Nov. 19 Litho.

815 A236 15c multicolored .20 .20
816 A237 40c multicolored .45 .45
817 A237 75c multicolored .85 .85
Nos. 815-817 (3) 1.50 1.50

Souvenir Sheet

818 A236 90c multicolored 1.00 1.00

A238 A239

Christmas and New Year: 35c, Left panel of triptych from Roman Catholic Church, Willemstad. 150c, Champagne bottle being opened, calendar.

1997, Dec. 1 *Perf. 13x14*

819 A238 35c multicolored .40 .40
820 A238 150c multicolored 1.75 1.75

1998, Feb. 26 Litho. *Perf. 13x14*

Total Solar Eclipse, Curacao: 85c, Sun partially covered by moon's shadow. 110c, Outer edge of sun showing beyond moon's shadow. 225c, Total solar eclipse.
750c, Hologram of the eclipse.

821 A239 85c multicolored .95 .95
822 A239 110c multicolored 1.25 1.25
823 A239 225c multicolored 2.50 2.50
Nos. 821-823 (3) 4.70 4.70

Souvenir Sheet

824 A239 750c multicolored 9.00 9.00

No. 824 contains a hologram which may be damaged by soaking.

SEMI-POSTAL STAMPS

Catalogue values for unused stamps in this section are for Never Hinged items.

NIWIN

Nos. 132, 133 and 135 Surcharged in Black

1½ ct.
+ 2½ ct.

1947, Dec. 1 Unwmk. *Perf. 12½*

B1 A26 1½c + 2½c on 6c .90 .80
B2 A26 2½c + 5c on 10c .90 .80
B3 A26 5c + 7½c on 15c .90 .80
Nos. B1-B3 (3) 2.70 2.40

The surtax was for the National Inspanning Welzijnszorg in Nederlandsch Indie, relief organization for Netherlands Indies.

Curaçao Children
SP1 SP2

Design: Nos. B6, B9, Girl.

1948, Nov. 3 Photo. *Perf. 12½x12*

B4 SP1 6c + 10c ol brn 2.25 1.75
B5 SP2 10c + 15c brt red 2.25 1.75
B6 SP2 12½c + 20c Prus grn 2.25 1.75
B7 SP1 15c + 25c brt bl 2.25 1.75
B8 SP2 20c + 30c red brn 2.25 1.75
B9 SP2 25c + 35c purple 2.25 1.75
Nos. B4-B9 (6) 13.50 10.50

The surtax was for child welfare and the White/Yellow Cross Foundation.

Leapfrog — SP4 Ship and Gull — SP5

Designs: 5c+2½c, Flying kite. 6c+2½c, Girls swinging. 12½c+5c, "London Bridge." 25c+10c, Rolling hoops.

Perf. 14½x13½

1951, Aug. 16 Unwmk.

B10 SP4 1½c + 1c pur 1.75 2.10
B11 SP4 5c + 2½c brn 10.00 4.50
B12 SP4 6c + 2½c blue 10.00 4.50
B13 SP4 12½c + 5c red 10.00 4.50
B14 SP4 25c + 10c dl grn 10.00 4.00
Nos. B10-B14 (5) 41.75 19.60

The surtax was for child welfare.

1952, July 16 *Perf. 13x14*

Designs: 6c+4c, Sailor and lighthouse. 12½c+7c, Prow of sailboat. 15c+10c, Ships. 25c+15c, Ship, compass and anchor.

B15 SP5 1½c + 1c dk grn 1.00 1.10
B16 SP5 6c + 4c choc 8.00 3.25
B17 SP5 12½c + 7c red vio 8.00 3.50
B18 SP5 15c + 10c dp bl 10.00 4.25
B19 SP5 25c + 15c red 9.00 3.25
Nos. B15-B19 (5) 36.00 15.35

The surtax was for the seamen's welfare fund.

22½ Ct. +7½ Ct.

No. 226 Surcharged in Black

WATERSNOOD
NEDERLAND
1953

1953, Feb. 21

B20 A45 22½c + 7½c on 1½g .90 1.00

The surtax was for flood relief in the Netherlands.

Tribulus Cistoides — SP6

Flowers: 7½c+5c, Yellow hibiscus. 15c+5c, Oleander. 22½c+7½c, Cactus. 25c+10c, Red hibiscus.

1955, May 17 Photo. *Perf. 14x13*
Flowers in Natural Colors

B21 SP6	1½c + 1c bl grn & dk bl	.30	.35
B22 SP6	7½c + 5c dp ultra	2.50	1.75
B23 SP6	15c + 5c ol grn	2.50	1.90
B24 SP6	22½c + 7½c dk bl	2.50	1.75
B25 SP6	25c + 10c ind & gray	2.50	1.90
	Nos. B21-B25 (5)	10.30	7.65

The surtax was for child welfare.

Prince Bernhard and Queen Juliana — SP7

1955, Oct. 19 *Perf. 11x12*

B26 SP7	7½c + 2½c rose brn	.15	.15
B27 SP7	22½c + 7½c dp bl	.80	.80

Royal visit to the Netherlands Antilles, Oct. 1955. Surtax paid for a gift.

Lord Baden-Powell SP8

1957, Feb. 22 *Perf. 14x13½*

B28 SP8	6c + 1½c org yel	.40	.40
B29 SP8	7½c + 2½c dp grn	.40	.40
B30 SP8	15c + 5c red	.40	.40
	Nos. B28-B30 (3)	1.20	1.20

50th anniv. of the Boy Scout movement.

Soccer Player — SP9

Map of Central America and the Caribbean SP10

Designs: 15c+5c, Goalkeeper catching ball. 22½c+7½c, Men playing soccer.

1957, Aug. 6 *Perf. 12x11, 11x12*

B31 SP9	6c + 2½c org	.40	.55
B32 SP10	7½c + 5c dk red	.80	.90
B33 SP9	15c + 5c brt bl grn	.90	.90
B34 SP9	22½c + 7½c brt bl	.90	.70
	Nos. B31-B34 (4)	3.00	3.05

8th Central American and Caribbean Soccer Championships, Aug. 11-25.
Surtax was for organizing costs.

American Kestrel — SP11

Flag and Map — SP12

Birds: 7½+1½c, Yellow oriole. 15+2½c, Common ground doves. 22½+2½c, Brown-throated parakeet.

1958, Apr. 15 Photo. *Perf. 13½x14*

B35 SP11	2½c + 1c multi	.22	.22
B36 SP11	7½c + 1½c multi	.70	.60
B37 SP11	15c + 2½c multi	.80	.80
B38 SP11	22½c + 2½c multi	.90	.70
	Nos. B35-B38 (4)	2.62	2.32

The surtax was for child welfare.

1958, Dec. 1 Litho. *Perf. 13½*
Cross in Red

B39 SP12	6c + 2c red brn	.28	.28
B40 SP12	7½c + 2½c bl grn	.40	.40
B41 SP12	15c + 5c org yel	.40	.40
B42 SP12	22½c + 7½c blue	.40	.40
	Nos. B39-B42 (4)	1.48	1.48

The surtax was for the Red Cross.

Community House, Zeeland SP13

Historic buildings: 7½c+2½c, Molenplein. 15c+5c, Saba, vert. 22½c+7½c, Scharlooburg. 25c+7½c, Community House, Brievengat.

Perf. 14x13½, 13½x14
1959, Sept. 16 Litho.

B43 SP13	6c + 1½c multi	.80	.70
B44 SP13	7½c + 2½c multi	.80	.80
B45 SP13	15c + 5c multi	.80	.80
B46 SP13	22½c + 7½c multi	.80	.80
B47 SP13	25c + 7½c multi	.80	.80
	Nos. B43-B47 (5)	4.00	3.90

The surtax went to the Foundation for the Preservation of Historical Monuments.

Fish — SP14

Designs. 10c+2c, SCUBA diver with spear gun, vert. 25c+5c, Two fish.

1960, Aug. 24 Photo. *Perf. 13½*

B48 SP14	10c + 2c sapphire	.80	.80
B49 SP14	20c + 3c multi	1.10	1.10
B50 SP14	25c + 5c blk, brt pink & dk bl	1.10	1.10
	Nos. B48-B50 (3)	3.00	3.00

The surtax was for the fight against cancer.

Infant — SP15

Designs: 10c+3c, Girl and doll. 20c+6c, Boy on beach. 25c+8c, Children in school.

1961, July 24 Litho. *Perf. 13½x14*
Designs in Black

B51 SP15	6c + 2c lt yel grn	.20	.20
B52 SP15	10c + 3c rose red	.20	.20
B53 SP15	20c + 6c yellow	.20	.20
B54 SP15	25c + 8c orange	.20	.20
	Nos. B51-B54 (4)	.80	.80

The surtax was for child welfare.

Globe and Knight — SP16

1962, May 2 *Perf. 13½x14½*

B55 SP16	10c + 5c green	.60	.55
B56 SP16	20c + 10c carmine	.60	.55
B57 SP16	25c + 10c dk bl	.60	.55
	Nos. B55-B57 (3)	1.80	1.65

Intl. Candidates Chess Tournament, Willemstad, May-June.

No. 248 Surcharged

TEGEN DE HONGER
+10c

1963, Mar. 21

B58 A56	20c + 10c crimson & gray	.40	.40

FAO "Freedom from Hunger" campaign.

Child and Flowers SP17

Bougainvillea SP18

Designs: 6c+3c, Three girls and flowers, horiz. 10c+5c, Girl with ball and trees, horiz. 20c+10c, Three boys with flags, horiz. 25c+12c, Singing boy.

Perf. 14½x13½, 13½x14½
1963, Oct. 23 Photo. Unwmk.

B59 SP17	5c + 2c multi	.22	.22
B60 SP17	6c + 3c multi	.22	.22
B61 SP17	10c + 5c multi	.22	.22
B62 SP17	20c + 10c multi	.22	.22
B63 SP17	25c + 12c multi	.22	.22
	Nos. B59-B63 (5)	1.10	1.10

Surtax for child welfare.

1964, Oct. 21 *Perf. 14x13*

Designs: 10c+5c, Wild rose. 20c+10c, Chalice flower. 25c+11c, Bellisima.

Flowers in Natural Colors

B64 SP18	6c + 3c bl vio & blk	.15	.15
B65 SP18	10c + 5c yel brn, yel & blk	.15	.15
B66 SP18	20c + 10c dull red & blk	.15	.15
B67 SP18	25c + 11c citron & brn	.15	.15
	Nos. B64-B67 (4)	.60	.60

The surtax was for child welfare.

Sea Anemones and Star Coral — SP19

Corals: 6c+3c, Blue cup sponges. 10c+5c, Green cup sponges. 25c+11c, Basket sponge, knobbed brain coral and reef fish.

1965, Nov. 10 Photo. *Perf. 14x13½*

B68 SP19	6c + 3c multi	.15	.15
B69 SP19	10c + 5c multi	.15	.15
B70 SP19	20c + 10c multi	.15	.15
B71 SP19	25c + 11c multi	.20	.20
	Set value	.55	.55

The surtax was for child welfare.

ICEM Type of Netherlands

1966, Jan. 31 Photo. *Perf. 14x13*

B72 SP181	35c + 15c brn & dl yel	.20	.20

The surtax was for the Intergovernmental Committee for European Migration (ICEM). The message on the stamps was given and signed by Queen Juliana.

Girl Cooking SP20

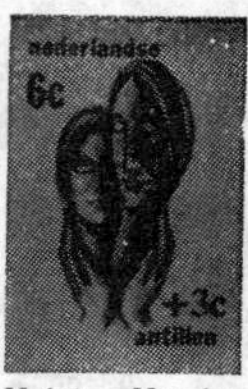

Helping Hands Supporting Women SP21

Youth at Work: 10c+5c, Nurse's aide with infant. 20c+10c, Young metalworker. 25c+11c, Girl ironing.

1966, Nov. 15 *Perf. 13½*

B73 SP20	6c + 3c multi	.15	.15
B74 SP20	10c + 5c multi	.15	.15
B75 SP20	20c + 10c multi	.15	.15
B76 SP20	25c + 11c multi	.20	.20
	Set value	.46	.46

The surtax was for child welfare.

1967, July 4 Litho. *Perf. 13x14*

B77 SP21	6c + 3c bl & blk	.15	.15
B78 SP21	10c + 5c brt pink & blk	.15	.15
B79 SP21	20c + 19c lilac	.15	.15
B80 SP21	25c + 11c dk bl	.15	.15
	Set value	.44	.44

The surtax was for various social and cultural institutions.

Nanzi the Spider and the Tiger — SP22

Nanzi Stories (Folklore): 6c+3c, Princess Longnose, vert. 10c+5c, The Turtle and the Monkey. 25c+11c, Adventure of Shon Arey.

Perf. 14x13, 13x14
1967, Nov. 15 Photo.

B81 SP22	6c + 3c dk red, pink & org	.15	.15
B82 SP22	10c + 5c vio bl & org	.15	.15
B83 SP22	20c + 10c grn & org	.18	.18
B84 SP22	25c + 11c brt bl & org	.18	.18
	Nos. B81-B84 (4)	.66	.66

The surtax was for child welfare.

Lintendans (Dance) and Koeoekoe House — SP23

1968, May 29 Litho. *Perf. 14x13*

B85 SP23	10c + 5c multi	.15	.15
B86 SP23	15c + 5c multi	.15	.15
B87 SP23	20c + 10c multi	.15	.15
B88 SP23	25c + 10c multi	.15	.15
	Nos. B85-B88 (4)	.60	.60

The surtax was for various social and cultural institutions.

Boy and Pet Cat — SP24

Designs: 6c+3c, Boy and goat. 10c+5c, Girl and poodle. 25c+11c, Girl and duckling.

1968, Nov. 13 Photo. *Perf. 13½*

B89 SP24	6c + 3c multi	.15	.15
B90 SP24	10c + 5c multi	.15	.15
B91 SP24	20c + 10c multi	.18	.18
B92 SP24	25c + 11c multi	.18	.18
	Nos. B89-B92 (4)	.66	.66

The surtax was for child welfare.

Carnival Headpiece — SP25

Designs (Folklore): 15c+5c, Harvest-home festival. 20c+10c, Feast of St. John (dancers and cock). 25c+10c, "Dande" New Year's celebration.

1969, July 23 Litho. *Perf. 13½*

B93	SP25	10c + 5c multi	.22	.22
B94	SP25	15c + 5c multi	.22	.22
B95	SP25	20c + 10c multi	.32	.32
B96	SP25	25c + 10c multi	.32	.32
		Nos. B93-B96 (4)	1.08	1.08

The surtax was for various social and cultural institutions.

Boy Playing Guitar — SP26

Designs: 10c+5c, Girl with English flute. 20c+10c, Boy playing the marimula. 25c+11c, Girl playing the piano.

1969, Nov. 3 Litho. *Perf. 14x13*

B97	SP26	6c + 3c org & vio	.20	.20
B98	SP26	10c + 5c yel & brt grn	.28	.28
B99	SP26	20c + 10c bl & car	.28	.28
B100	SP26	25c + 11c pink & brn	.32	.32
		Nos. B97-B100 (4)	1.08	1.08

The surtax was for child welfare.

Printing Press and Quill — SP27

Mother and Child — SP28

Mass Media: 15c+5c, Filmstrip and reels. 20c+10c, Horn and radio mast. 25c+10c, Television antenna and eye focused on globe.

1970, July 14 Litho. *Perf. 13½*

B101	SP27	10c + 5c multi	.32	.32
B102	SP27	15c + 5c multi	.32	.32
B103	SP27	20c + 10c multi	.32	.32
B104	SP27	25c + 10c multi	.32	.32
		Nos. B101-B104 (4)	1.28	1.28

The surtax was for various social and cultural institutions.

1970, Nov. 16 *Perf. 13½x14*

Designs: 10c+5c, Girl holding piggy bank. 20c+10c, Boys wrestling (Judokas). 25c+11c, Youth carrying small boy on his shoulders.

B105	SP28	6c + 3c multi	.50	.50
B106	SP28	10c + 5c multi	.50	.50
B107	SP28	20c + 10c multi	.50	.50
B108	SP28	25c + 11c multi	.50	.50
		Nos. B105-B108 (4)	2.00	2.00

The surtax was for child welfare.

Charcoal Burner — SP29

Kitchen Utensils: 15c+5c, Earthenware vessel for water. 20c+10c, Baking oven. 25c+10c, Soup plate, stirrer and kneading stick.

1971, May 12 *Perf. 14x13½*

B109	SP29	10c + 5c multi	.40	.40
B110	SP29	15c + 5c multi	.40	.40
B111	SP29	20c + 10c multi	.40	.40
B112	SP29	25c + 10c multi	.40	.40
		Nos. B109-B112 (4)	1.60	1.60

Surtax was for various social and cultural institutions.

Homemade Dolls and Comb — SP30

Homemade Toys: 20c+10c, Carts. 30c+15c, Musical top made from calabash.

1971, Nov. 16 *Perf. 13½x14*

B113	SP30	15c + 5c multi	.48	.48
B114	SP30	20c + 10c multi	.48	.48
B115	SP30	30c + 15c multi	.48	.48
		Nos. B113-B115 (3)	1.44	1.44

Surtax was for child welfare.

Steel Band — SP31

Designs: 20c+10c, Harvest festival (Seu). 30c+15c, Tambu dancers.

1972, May 16

B116	SP31	15c + 5c multi	.60	.60
B117	SP31	20c + 10c multi	.60	.60
B118	SP31	30c + 15c multi	.60	.60
		Nos. B116-B118 (3)	1.80	1.80

Surtax was for various social and cultural institutions.

Child at Play on Ground SP32

Designs: 20c+10c, Child playing in water. 30c+15c, Child throwing ball into air.

1972, Nov. 14 Litho. *Perf. 14x13*

B119	SP32	15c + 5c multi	.70	.70
B120	SP32	20c + 10c multi	.70	.70
B121	SP32	30c + 15c multi	.70	.70
		Nos. B119-B121 (3)	2.10	2.10

Surtax was for child welfare.

Pedestrian Crossing, Traffic Sign — SP33

Designs: 15c+7c, School crossing. 40c+20c, Traffic light, road and car.

1973, Apr. 9 Litho. *Perf. 13x14*

B122	SP33	12c + 6c multi	.60	.60
B123	SP33	15c + 7c multi	.60	.60
B124	SP33	40c + 20c multi	.60	.60
		Nos. B122-B124 (3)	1.80	1.80

Surtax was for various social and cultural institutions.

"1948-73" SP34

20c+10c, Children. 30c+15c, Mother & child.

1973, Nov. 19 Litho. *Perf. 14x13*

B125	SP34	15c + 5c multi	.70	.70
B126	SP34	20c + 10c multi	.70	.70
a.		Min. sheet, 2 each #B125-B126	3.00	3.00
B127	SP34	30c + 15c multi	1.10	1.10
		Nos. B125-B127 (3)	2.50	2.50

Child Welfare semi-postal stamps, 25th anniv.

Girl Combing her Hair — SP35

15c+7c, Young people listening to rock music. 40c+20c, Drummer, symbolizing rock music.

1974, Apr. 9 Litho. *Perf. 14x13*

B128	SP35	12c + 6c multi	.80	.80
B129	SP35	15c + 7c multi	.80	.80
B130	SP35	40c + 20c multi	.80	.80
		Nos. B128-B130 (3)	2.40	2.40

Surtax was for various social and cultural institutions.

Child, Saw and Score — SP36

Designs: 20c+10c, Footprints in circle. 30c+15c, Moon and sun. Each design includes score of a children's song.

1974, Nov. 12 Litho. *Perf. 13x14*

B131	SP36	15c + 5c multi	.60	.60
B132	SP36	20c + 10c multi	.60	.60
B133	SP36	30c + 15c multi	.60	.60
		Nos. B131-B133 (3)	1.80	1.80

Surtax was for child welfare.

Carved Stone Grid, Flower Pot SP37

Jewish Tombstone, Mordecai's Procession SP38

Design: 40c+20c, Ornamental stone from facade of Jewish House, 1728.

1975, Mar. 21 Litho. *Perf. 13x14*

B134	SP37	12c + 6c multi	.60	.60
B135	SP38	15c + 7c multi	.60	.60
B136	SP37	40c + 20c multi	.60	.60
		Nos. B134-B136 (3)	1.80	1.80

Surtax was for various social and cultural institutions.

Children Building Curaçao Windmill SP39

Designs: 20c+10c, Girl molding clay animal. 30c+15c, Children drawing picture.

1975, Nov. 12 Litho. *Perf. 14x13*

B137	SP39	15c + 5c multi	.55	.55
B138	SP39	20c + 10c multi	.55	.55
B139	SP39	30c + 15c multi	.55	.55
		Nos. B137-B139 (3)	1.65	1.65

Surtax was for child welfare.

Carrying a Child — SP40

Designs: Different ways of carrying a child. 40c+18c is vertical.

Perf. 14x13, 13x14

1976, Oct. 4 Litho.

B140	SP40	20c + 10c multi	.45	.45
B141	SP40	25c + 12c multi	.45	.45
B142	SP40	40c + 18c multi	.45	.45
		Nos. B140-B142 (3)	1.35	1.35

Surtax was for child welfare.

Composite: Aces of Hearts, Clubs, Diamonds and Spades — SP41

Designs: 25c+12c, "King" and inscription. 40c+18c, Hand holding cards; map of Aruba as ace of hearts, horiz.

Perf. 13x14, 14x13

1977, May 6 Litho.

B143	SP41	20c + 10c red & blk	.32	.28
B144	SP41	25c + 12c multi	.32	.32
a.		Min. sheet, 2 each #B143-B144	1.40	1.10
B145	SP41	40c + 18c multi	.48	.48
		Nos. B143-B145 (3)	1.12	1.08

Central American and Caribbean Bridge Championships, Aruba.

Souvenir Sheet

1977, May 26 *Perf. 13½x14*

B146	SP41	Sheet of 3	2.75 2.50

Amphilex 77 International Philatelic Exhibition, Amsterdam, May 26-June 5. No. B146 contains 3 stamps similar to Nos. B143-B145 with bright green background.

Children and Toys — SP42

Designs: Children playing with fantasy animals.

1977, Oct. 25 Litho. *Perf. 14x13*

B147	SP42	15c + 5c multi	.28	.22
B148	SP42	20c + 10c multi	.32	.32
B149	SP42	25c + 12c multi	.38	.38
B150	SP42	40c + 18c multi	.48	.42
a.		Min. sheet, 2 each #B148, B150	1.75	1.65
		Nos. B147-B150 (4)	1.46	1.34

Surtax was for child welfare.

Water Skiing — SP43

Roller Skating — SP45

Red Cross — SP44

Designs: 20c+10c, Sailing. 25c+12c, Soccer. 40c+18c, Baseball.

1978, Mar. 31 Litho. *Perf. 13x14*

B151 SP43 15c + 5c multi .15 .15
B152 SP43 20c + 10c multi .15 .15
B153 SP43 25c + 12c multi .15 .15
B154 SP43 40c + 18c multi .22 .22
Set value .56 .56

Surtax was for sports. Tete-beche gutter pairs exist.

1978, Sept. 19 Litho. *Perf. 14x13*

B155 SP44 55c + 25c red & blk .22 .22
a. Souv. sheet of 3, perf. 13½x13 1.65 1.65

Henri Dunant (1828-1910), founder of Red Cross. Surtax for the Red Cross.
Tete-beche gutter pairs exist.

1978, Nov. 7 Litho. *Perf. 13x14*

Children's Activities: 20c+10c, Kite flying. 25c+12c, Playing marbles. 40c+ 18c, Bicycling.

B156 SP45 15c + 5c multi .32 .28
B157 SP45 20c + 10c multi .40 .32
a. Min. sheet, 2 each #B156-B157 1.75 1.50
B158 SP45 25c + 12c multi .40 .38
B159 SP45 40c + 18c multi .48 .45
Nos. B156-B159 (4) 1.60 1.43

Surtax was for child welfare.

Carnival King — SP46

Regatta Emblem — SP47

25th Aruba Carnival: 75c+20c, Carnival Queen and coat of arms.

1979, Feb. 20 Litho. *Perf. 13x14*

B160 SP46 40c + 10c multi .38 .30
B161 SP46 75c + 20c multi .55 .52

Perf. 13x14, 14x13

1979, May 16 Litho.

Designs: 35c+10c, Race. 40c+15c, Globe and yacht, horiz. 55c+25c, Yacht, birds and sun.

B162 SP47 15c + 5c multi .15 .15
B163 SP47 35c + 10c multi .25 .25
B164 SP47 40c + 15c multi .32 .32
B165 SP47 55c + 25c multi .40 .40
a. Souv. sheet of 4, #B162-B165 1.10 1.10
Nos. B162-B165 (4) 1.12 1.12

12th International Sailing Regatta, Bonaire. #B164 in souvenir sheet is perf 13x14.

Volunteer Corps Type, 1979

15c+10c, Soldiers, 1929 and 1979. 40c+20c, Soldier guarding oil refinery, Guard emblem.

1979, July 4 Litho. *Perf. 13x14*

B166 A124 15c + 10c multi .18 .16
B167 A124 40c + 20c multi .38 .35

Girls Reading Book, IYC Emblem SP48

Volleyball, Olympic Rings SP49

IYC Emblem and Children's Drawings: 25c+12c, Infant and cat. 35c+15c, Girls walking under palm trees. 50c+20c, Children wearing adult clothing.

1979, Oct. 24 Litho. *Perf. 13x14*

B168 SP48 20c + 10c multi .20 .20
B169 SP48 25c + 12c multi .30 .28
B170 SP48 35c + 15c multi .38 .32
a. Souv. sheet, 2 #B168, 2 #B170 1.25 1.20
B171 SP48 50c + 20c multi .48 .48
Nos. B168-B171 (4) 1.36 1.28

International Year of the Child. Surtax for child welfare.

Fort Church Type of 1980

Designs: 20c+10c, Brass chandelier, 1909, horiz. 50c+25c, Pipe organ.

Perf. 14x13, 13x14

1980, Jan. 9 Litho.

B172 A128 20c + 10c multi .18 .18
B173 A128 50c + 25c multi .45 .45

1980, June 25 Litho. *Perf. 13x14*

Designs: 25c+10c, Woman gymnast. 30c+15c, Male gymnast. 60c+25c, Basketball.

B174 SP49 25c + 10c multi .18 .18
B175 SP49 30c + 15c multi .30 .30
B176 SP49 45c + 20c multi .38 .35
B177 SP49 60c + 25c multi .50 .45
a. Souvenir sheet of 6, 3 each #B174, B177, perf. 14x13½ 2.25 1.90
Nos. B174-B177 (4) 1.36 1.28

22nd Summer Olympic Games, Moscow, July 19-Aug. 3.

St. Maarten Landscape SP50

Children's Drawings: 30c+15c, House in Bonaire. 40c+20c, Child at blackboard. 60c+25c, Cancers, vert.

Perf. 14x13, 13x14

1980, Oct. 22 Litho.

B178 SP50 25c + 10c multi .28 .24
B179 SP50 30c + 15c multi .35 .32
B180 SP50 40c + 20c multi .40 .38
B181 SP50 60c + 25c multi .50 .48
a. Souvenir sheet of 6+ 4 labels, 3 each #B178, B181 2.50 2.25
Nos. B178-B181 (4) 1.53 1.42

Surtax was for child welfare.
#B178 in souvenir sheet is perf 13x14.

Girl Using Sign Language SP51

Tennis Player SP52

Designs: 25c+10c, Blind woman. 30c+15c, Man in wheelchair. 45c+20c, Infant in walker.

1981, Apr. 7 Litho. *Perf. 13x14*

B182 SP51 25c + 10c multi .25 .25
B183 SP51 30c + 15c multi .32 .32
B184 SP51 45c + 20c multi .55 .55
B185 SP51 60c + 25c multi .60 .60
Nos. B182-B185 (4) 1.72 1.72

International Year of the Disabled. Surtax was for handicapped children.

1981, May 27 Litho. *Perf. 13x14*

B186 SP52 30c + 15c shown .35 .35
B187 SP52 50c + 20c Diving .55 .55
B188 SP52 70c + 25c Boxing .75 .75
a. Min. sheet of 3, #B186-B188 1.75 1.75
Nos. B186-B188 (3) 1.65 1.65

Surtax was for sporting events.

Den Mother and Cub Scout — SP53

Scouting in Netherlands Antilles, 50th Anniv.: 70c+25c, van der Maarel, national founder. 1g+50c, Ronde Klip (headquarters).

1981, Sept. 16 Litho. *Perf. 14x13*

B189 SP53 45c + 20c multi .60 .60
B190 SP53 70c + 25c multi .80 .80
B191 SP53 1g + 50c multi 1.25 1.25
a. Min. sheet of 3, #B189-B191, perf. 13½x13 2.75 2.50
Nos. B189-B191 (3) 2.65 2.65

Surtax was for various social and cultural institutions.

Girl and Teddy Bear — SP54

Designs: 35c+15c, Mother and child. 45c+20c, Two children. 55c+25c, Boy and cat.

1981, Oct. 21 Litho. *Perf. 13x14*

B192 SP54 35c + 15c multi .32 .32
B193 SP54 45c + 20c multi .48 .48
B194 SP54 55c + 25c multi .60 .60
B195 SP54 85c + 40c multi .90 .90
a. Min. sheet of 4, #B192-B195 2.50 2.50
Nos. B192-B195 (4) 2.30 2.30

Surtax for child welfare.

Fencing — SP55

1982, Feb. 17 Litho. *Perf. 14x13*

B196 SP55 35c + 15c shown .32 .32
B197 SP55 45c + 20c Judo .50 .50
B198 SP55 70c + 35c Soccer .80 .80
a. Miniature sheet of 2 + label 1.75 1.75
B199 SP55 85c + 40c Bicycling .90 .90
Nos. B196-B199 (4) 2.52 2.52

Surtax was for sporting events.

Girl Playing Accordion SP56

1982, Oct. 20 Litho.

B200 SP56 35c + 15c shown .40 .40
B201 SP56 75c + 35c Guitar .90 .90
B202 SP56 85c + 40c Violin 1.00 1.00
a. Min. sheet of 3, #B200-B202 2.50 2.50
Nos. B200-B202 (3) 2.30 2.30

Surtax for child welfare.

Traditional House, Saba — SP57

1982, Nov. 17 Litho.

B203 SP57 35c + 15c shown .40 .40
B204 SP57 75c + 35c Aruba .90 .90
B205 SP57 85c + 40c Curaçao 1.00 1.00
a. Souv. sheet of 3, #B203-B205 2.50 2.50
Nos. B203-B205 (3) 2.30 2.30

Surtax was for various social and cultural institutions.

High Jump SP58

1983, Feb. 22 Litho.

B206 SP58 35c + 15c shown .32 .32
B207 SP58 45c + 20c Weight lifting .60 .60
B208 SP58 85c + 40c Wind surfing 1.00 1.00
Nos. B206-B208 (3) 1.92 1.92

Surtax was for sporting events.

Child with Lizard — SP59

Pre-Columbian Artifacts — SP60

1983, Oct. 18 Litho. *Perf. 13x14*

B209 SP59 45c + 20c shown .60 .60
B210 SP59 55c + 25c Child with insects .75 .75
B211 SP59 100c + 50c Child with animal 1.40 1.40
a. Souv. sheet of 3, #B209-B211 2.75 2.75
Nos. B209-B211 (3) 2.75 2.75

Surtax was for Childrens' Charity.

1983, Nov. 22 Litho. *Perf. 13x14*

B212 SP60 45c + 20c multi .70 .70
B213 SP60 55c + 25c multi .80 .80
B214 SP60 85c + 40c multi 1.00 1.00
B215 SP60 100c + 50c multi 1.40 1.40
Nos. B212-B215 (4) 3.90 3.90

Curaçao Baseball Federation, 50th Anniv. — SP61

1984, Mar. 27 Litho. *Perf. 14x13*

B216 SP61 25c + 10c Catching .65 .65
B217 SP61 45c + 20c Batting 1.25 1.25
B218 SP61 55c + 25c Pitching 1.65 1.65
B219 SP61 85c + 40c Running 1.90 1.90
a. Min. sheet of 3, #B217-B219 5.00 5.00
Nos. B216-B219 (4) 5.45 5.45

Surtax was for baseball fed., 1984 Olympics.

Microphones, Radio — SP62

Designs: 55c+25c, Radio, record player. 100c+50c, Record players.

1984, Apr. 24 Litho. *Perf. 14x13*

B220 SP62 45c + 20c multi .75 .75
B221 SP62 55c + 25c multi 1.00 1.00
B222 SP62 100c + 50c multi 1.25 1.25
Nos. B220-B222 (3) 3.00 3.00

Surtax was for social and cultural institutions.

Boy Reading — SP63

Designs: 55c+25c, Parents reading to children. 100c+50c, Family worship.

1984, Nov. 7 Litho. *Perf. 13x14*

B223 SP63 45c + 20c multi .70 .70
B224 SP63 55c + 25c multi 1.00 1.00
B225 SP63 100c + 50c multi 1.25 1.25
a. Souv. sheet of 3, #B223-B225 3.25 3.25
Nos. B223-B225 (3) 2.95 2.95

Surtax was for children's charity.

Soccer Players — SP64

1985, Mar. 27 Litho. *Perf. 14x13*

B226 SP64 10c + 5c multi .22 .22
B227 SP64 15c + 5c multi .25 .25
B228 SP64 45c + 20c multi .70 .70

B229 SP64 55c + 25c multi .90 .90
B230 SP64 85c + 40c multi 1.25 1.25
Nos. B226-B230 (5) 3.32 3.32

The surtax was for sporting events.

Intl. Youth Year — SP65

1985, Apr. 29 **Litho.**
B231 SP65 45c + 20c Youth, computer keyboard .75 .75
B232 SP65 55c + 25c Girl listening to music 1.00 1.00
B233 SP65 100c + 50c Youth breakdancing 1.50 1.50
Nos. B231-B233 (3) 3.25 3.25

Surtax for youth, social and cultural organizations.

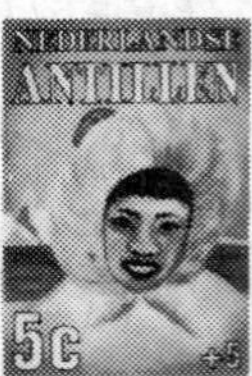

Children — SP66

1985, Oct. 16 **Litho.** ***Perf. 13x14***
B234 SP66 5c + 5c Eskimo .18 .18
B235 SP66 10c + 5c African .20 .20
B236 SP66 25c + 10c Asian .42 .42
B237 SP66 45c + 20c Dutch .70 .70
B238 SP66 55c + 25c American Indian .80 .80
a. Souv. sheet of 3, #B236-B238 2.00 2.00
Nos. B234-B238 (5) 2.30 2.30

Surtax for child welfare.

Sports SP67

Handicrafts SP68

1986, Feb. 19 **Litho.** ***Perf. 13x14***
B239 SP67 15c + 5c Running .18 .18
B240 SP67 25c + 10c Horse racing .38 .38
B241 SP67 45c + 20c Car racing .65 .65
B242 SP67 55c + 25c Soccer .75 .75
Nos. B239-B242 (4) 1.96 1.96

Surtax for the natl. Sports Federation.

1986, Apr. 29
B243 SP68 30c + 15c Painting .40 .40
B244 SP68 45c + 20c Sculpting .55 .55
B245 SP68 55c + 25c Ceramics .70 .70
Nos. B243-B245 (3) 1.65 1.65

Surtax for Curaçao Social & Cultural Care.

Sports SP69

Social and Cultural Programs SP70

1986, Oct. 15 **Litho.** ***Perf. 13x14***
B246 SP69 20c + 10c Soccer .26 .26
B247 SP69 25c + 15c Tennis .35 .35
B248 SP69 45c + 20c Judo .52 .52
B249 SP69 55c + 25c Baseball .65 .65
a. Min. sheet of 2, #B248-B249 1.25 1.25
Nos. B246-B249 (4) 1.78 1.78

Surtax for the natl. Sports Foundation.

1987, Mar. 11 **Litho.**
B250 SP70 35c + 15c Musicians .38 .38
B251 SP70 45c + 25c Handicapped .50 .50
B252 SP70 85c + 40c Pavilion .95 .95
Nos. B250-B252 (3) 1.83 1.83

Surtax for the Jong Wacht (Youth Guard) and the natl. Red Cross.

Boy in Various Stages of Growth — SP71

1987, Oct. 21 **Litho.** ***Perf. 14x13***
B253 SP71 40c +15c Infant .45 .45
B254 SP71 55c +25c Toddler .60 .60
B255 SP71 115c +50c Boy 1.25 1.25
a. Souv. sheet of 3, #B253-B255 2.50 2.50
Nos. B253-B255 (3) 2.30 2.30

Surtax benefited Child Care programs.

Queen Emma Bridge, Cent. — SP72

Designs: 55c+25c, Bridge, vert. 115c+55c, View of Willemstad Harbor and quay. 190c+60c, Flags of the Netherlands, Antilles and United States, Leonard B. Smith, engineer.

1988, May 9 ***Perf. 13x14, 14x13***
B256 SP72 55c +25c multi .60 .60
B257 SP72 115c +55c multi 1.25 1.25
B258 SP72 190c +60c multi 1.75 1.75
Nos. B256-B258 (3) 3.60 3.60

Surtax for social and cultural purposes.

Youth Care Campaign SP73

1988, Oct. 26 **Litho.** ***Perf. 14x13***
B259 SP73 55c +25c Girl, television .60 .60
B260 SP73 65c +30c Boy, portable stereo .70 .70
B261 SP73 115c +55c Girl, computer 1.25 1.25
a. Souv. sheet of 3, #B259-B261 2.50 2.50
Nos. B259-B261 (3) 2.55 2.55

Surtax for child welfare.

Curaçao Stamp Assoc., 50th Anniv. — SP75

Designs: 30c+10c, Type A25 and No. 461 under magnifying glass. 55c+20c, Simulated stamp (learning to use tongs). 80c+30c, Barn owl, album, magnifying glass, tongs.

1989, Jan. 18 **Litho.** ***Perf. 13x14***
B264 SP75 30c +10c multi .30 .30
B265 SP75 55c +20c multi .55 .55
B266 SP75 80c +30c multi .75 .75
a. Strip of 3, #B264-B266 1.60 1.60

No. B266a has a continuous design. Surtaxed for welfare organizations.

Child and Nature — SP76

1989, Oct. 25 **Litho.** ***Perf. 14x13***
B267 SP76 40c +15c Girl, boy, tree .35 .35
B268 SP76 65c +30c Playing on beach .70 .70
B269 SP76 115c +55c Father and child 1.25 1.25
Nos. B267-B269 (3) 2.30 2.30

Souvenir Sheet

B270 SP76 155c +75c At the beach, diff. 1.65 1.65

Surtax for child welfare.

Natl. Girl Scout Movement, 60th Anniv. — SP77

Totolika, 60th Anniv. — SP78

Natl. Boy Scout Movement, 60th Anniv. — SP79

1990, Mar. 7 **Litho.** ***Perf. 13x14***
B271 SP77 30c +10c multi .35 .35
B272 SP78 40c +15c multi .45 .45
B273 SP79 155c +65c multi 1.75 1.75
Nos. B271-B273 (3) 2.55 2.55

Parents' and Friends Association of Persons with a Mental Handicap (Totolika).
Surtax for social and cultural purposes.

SP80

SP81

1990, June 13 **Litho.** ***Perf. 13x14***
B274 SP80 65c +30c multi .90 .90

Sport Unie Brion Trappers Soccer Club. Exists in tete-beche gutter pairs.

1990, June 13
B275 SP81 115c +55c multi 1.60 1.60

Anti-drug campaign. Exists in tete-beche gutter pairs.

Youth Care Campaign SP82

1990, Oct. 31 **Litho.** ***Perf. 14x13***
B276 SP82 30c +5c Bees, flowers .40 .40
B277 SP82 55c +10c Dolphins .72 .72
B278 SP82 65c +15c Donkey, bicycle .90 .90
B279 SP82 100c +20c Goat, house 1.35 1.35
B280 SP82 115c +25c Rabbit 1.60 1.60
B281 SP82 155c +55c Lizard, moon 2.35 2.35
Nos. B276-B281 (6) 7.32 7.32

Surtax for child welfare.
See Nos. B285-B288.

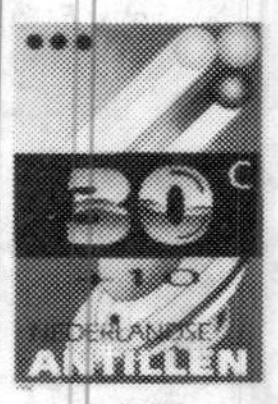

Social and Cultural Care — SP83

Designs: 30c+10c, Youth philately. 65c+25c, St. Vincentius Brass Band, 50th anniv. 155c+55c, Curaçao Community Center Federation.

1991, Apr. 3 **Litho.** ***Perf. 14x13***
B282 SP83 30c +10c multi .50 .50
B283 SP83 65c +25c multi 1.10 1.10
B284 SP83 155c +55c multi 2.55 2.55
Nos. B282-B284 (3) 4.15 4.15

Youth Care Campaign Type of 1990

Fight illiteracy: 40c+15c, Octopus holding numbers and letters. 65c+30c, Birds, blackboard. 155c+65c, Turtle telling time. No. B288a, Owl, flag. b, Books, bookworms. c, Seahorse.

1991, Oct. 31 **Litho.** ***Perf. 14x13***
B285 SP82 40c +15c multi .60 .60
B286 SP82 65c +30c multi 1.00 1.00
B287 SP82 155c +65c multi 2.35 2.35
Nos. B285-B287 (3) 3.95 3.95

Souvenir Sheet

Imperf

B288 Sheet of 3 4.25 4.25
a. SP82 55c +25c multi .90 .90
b. SP82 100c +35c multi 1.50 1.50
c. SP82 115c +50c multi 1.85 1.85

Surtax for child welfare.

SP84

SP85

1992 Summer Olympics, Barcelona: a, 30c + 10c, Triangle and oval. b, 55c + 25c, Globe showing location of Netherland Antilles, flag. c, 115c + 55c, Emblem of Netherlands Antilles Olympic Committee.

1992, Mar. 4 **Litho.** ***Perf. 13x14***
B289 SP84 Strip of 3, #a.-c. 3.50 3.50

Netherlands Antilles Olympic Committee, 60th Anniv.

1992, Oct. 28 **Litho.** ***Perf. 13x14***
B290 SP85 30c +10c Spaceship .48 .48
B291 SP85 70c +30c Robot 1.20 1.20
B292 SP85 100c +40c Extraterrestrial 1.70 1.70
Nos. B290-B292 (3) 3.38 3.38

Souvenir Sheet

B293 SP85 155c +70c Extraterrestrial, diff. 2.75 2.75

Surtax for child welfare.

SP86

Designs: 65c+25c, Fire safety, child playing with blocks. 90c+35c, Child fastening auto safety belt, vert. 175c+75c, Child wearing flotation equipment while swimming. 35c+15c, Alert child studying.

Perf. 14x13, 13x14

1993, Oct. 27 **Litho.**
B294 SP86 65c +25c multi 1.10 1.10
B295 SP86 90c +35c multi 1.50 1.50
B296 SP86 175c +75c multi 3.00 3.00
Nos. B294-B296 (3) 5.60 5.60

Souvenir Sheet

Perf. 13½x13

B297 SP86 35c +15c Sheet of 5 + label 3.00 3.00

Surtax for child welfare.

Intl. Year of the Family — SP87

1994, Oct. 26 Litho. *Perf. 13x14*

No.	Design	Description	Unused	Used
B298	SP87	35c +15c Woman, baby	.55	.55
B299	SP87	65c +25c Daughter, father	1.00	1.00
B300	SP87	90c +35c Grandparents	1.40	1.40
		Nos. B298-B300 (3)	2.95	2.95

Souvenir Sheet

No.	Design	Description	Unused	Used
B301	SP87	175c +75c Intl. emblem	2.75	2.75

Surtax for the benefit of the Antillean Youth Care Federation.

Slave Rebellion in Curaçao, Bicent. SP88

Designs: 30c+10c, Monument, bird with outstretched wings. 45c+15c, Bird, bell tower.

1995, Aug. 17 Litho. *Perf. 14x13*

No.	Design	Description	Unused	Used
B302	SP88	30c +10c multi	.45	.45
B303	SP88	45c +15c multi	.65	.65

Youth Philately SP89

Stamp drawings by children from: 65c+25c, Curaçao, Bonaire. 75c+35c, St. Maarten, St. Eustatius, Saba.

1995, Aug. 17

No.	Design	Description	Unused	Used
B304	SP89	65c +25c multi	1.00	1.00
B305	SP89	75c +35c multi	1.25	1.25

Nos. 516-517, 544 Surcharged in Red Brown

ORKAAN LUIS +65c

1995, Sept. 22 Litho. *Perf. 14x13*

No.	Design	Description	Unused	Used
B306	A148	65c +65c on #516	1.65	1.65
B307	A148	75c +75c on #517	1.90	1.90
B308	A148	1g +1g on #544	2.50	2.50
		Nos. B306-B308 (3)	6.05	6.05

Surcharge for hurricane relief.

Promotion of Children's Good Deeds — SP91

Designs: 35c+15c, Helping elderly across street. 65c+25c, Reading newspaper to blind person. 90c+35c, Caring for younger sibling. 175c+75c, Giving flowers to sick person.

1995, Oct. 25 Litho. *Perf. 14x13*

No.	Design	Description	Unused	Used
B309	SP91	35c +15c multi	.55	.55
B310	SP91	65c +25c multi	1.00	1.00
B311	SP91	90c +35c multi	1.40	1.40
B312	SP91	175c +75c multi	2.75	2.75
		Nos. B309-B312 (4)	5.70	5.70

Surtax for various youth organizations.

UNICEF, 50th Anniv. — SP92

Designs: 40c+15c, Child wandering streets. 75c+25c, Child labor in Asia. 110c+45c, Child in wartime (former Yugoslavia), vert. 225c+100c, Caribbean poverty, vert.

Perf. 14x13, 13x14

1996, Oct. 23 Litho.

No.	Design	Description	Unused	Used
B313	SP92	40c +15c multi	.60	.60
B314	SP92	75c +25c multi	1.10	1.10
B315	SP92	110c +45c multi	1.75	1.75
B316	SP92	225c +100c multi	3.60	3.60
		Nos. B313-B316 (4)	7.05	7.05

Social and Cultrual Care Stamps — SP93

Designs: 40c+15c, Curaçao Foundation for the cure and resettlement of ex-prisoners, 50th anniv. 75c+30c, ABVO (General Union of Public Servants), 60th anniv. 85+40c, 110c+50c, Red Cross Corps section, Curaçao, 65th anniv.

1997, Jan. 16 Litho. *Perf. 13x14*

No.	Design	Description	Unused	Used
B317	SP93	40c +15c multi	.60	.60
B318	SP93	75c +30c multi	.25	.25
B319	SP93	85c +40c multi	1.40	1.40
B320	SP93	110 +50c multi	1.60	1.60
		Nos. B317-B320 (4)	3.85	3.85

Youth Care — SP94

Musical notes, musical instruments: 40c+15c, Drums. 75c+25c, Piano. 110c+45c, Flute. 225c+100c, Guitar.

1997, Oct. 22 Litho. *Perf. 14x13*

No.	Design	Description	Unused	Used
B321	SP94	40c +15c multi	.60	.60
B322	SP94	75c +25c multi	1.10	1.10
B323	SP94	110c +45c multi	1.75	1.75
B324	SP94	225c +100c multi	3.60	3.60
		Nos. B321-B324 (4)	7.05	7.05

Social and Cultural Care — SP95

Designs: No. B325, Curacao Museum, 50th anniv. No. B326, Seawater Desalination, 70th anniv. 75c+25c, Water area, Lac Cai Bonaire, vert. 85c+40c, Water area, Klein-Bonaire, vert.

Perf. 14x13, 13x14

1998, Mar. 9 Litho.

No.	Design	Description	Unused	Used
B325	SP95	40c +15c multi	.60	.60
B326	SP95	40c +15c multi	.60	.60
B327	SP95	75c +25c multi	1.10	1.10
B328	SP95	85c +40c multi	1.40	1.40
		Nos. B325-B328 (4)	3.70	3.70

AIR POST STAMPS

Regular Issues of 1915-22 Surcharged in Black

LUCHTPOST

1 gld.

Perf. 12½

1929, July 6 Typo. Unwmk.

No.	Design	Description	Unused	Used
C1	A13	50c on 12½c red	13.00	13.00
C2	A13	1g on 20c blue	13.00	13.00
C3	A13	2g on 15c ol grn	42.50	47.50
		Nos. C1-C3 (3)	68.50	73.50

Excellent forgeries exist.

Allegory, "Flight" — AP1

1931-39 Engr.

No.	Design	Description	Unused	Used
C4	AP1	10c Prus grn ('34)	.15	.15
C5	AP1	15c dull blue ('38)	.25	.15
C6	AP1	20c red	.75	.25
C7	AP1	25c gray ('38)	.75	.60
C8	AP1	30c yellow ('39)	.30	.30
C9	AP1	35c dull blue	.80	.90
C10	AP1	40c green	.60	.40
C11	AP1	45c orange	2.25	2.25
C12	AP1	50c lake ('38)	.75	.50
C13	AP1	60c brown vio	.60	.35
C14	AP1	70c black	6.50	2.50
C15	AP1	1.40g brown	4.25	5.25
C16	AP1	2.80g bister	5.00	5.50
		Nos. C4-C16 (13)	22.95	19.10

No. C6 Surcharged in Black

10 CT

1934, Aug. 25

No.	Design	Description	Unused	Used
C17	AP1	10c on 20c red	19.00	17.00

Catalogue values for unused stamps in this section, from this point to the end of the section, are for Never Hinged items.

Map of the Atlantic — AP2

Plane over Islands — AP3

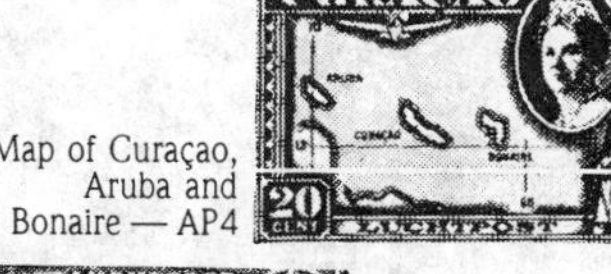

Map of Curaçao, Aruba and Bonaire — AP4

Planes — AP5

Plane — AP6

1942, Oct. 20 *Perf. 13x13½*

No.	Design	Description	Unused	Used
C18	AP2	10c grn & bl	.15	.15
C19	AP3	15c rose car & yel grn	.20	.15
C20	AP4	20c red brn & grn	.25	.35
C21	AP5	25c dp ultra & org brn	.15	.15
C22	AP6	30c red & lt vio	.30	.30
C23	AP2	35c dk vio & ol grn	.45	.30
C24	AP3	40c gray ol & chnt	.50	.40
C25	AP4	45c dk red & blk	.35	.35
C26	AP5	50c vio & blk	.85	.15
C27	AP6	60c lt yel brn & dl bl	.85	.60
C28	AP2	70c red brn & Prus bl	1.10	.60
C29	AP3	1.40g bl vio & sl grn	6.75	1.40
C30	AP4	2.80g int bl & lt bl	8.50	3.00
C31	AP5	5g rose lake & sl grn	15.00	10.50
C32	AP6	10g grn & red brn	20.00	18.00
		Nos. C18-C32 (15)	55.40	36.40

For surcharges see Nos. CB9-CB12.

Plane and Post Horn — AP7

DC-4 above Waves — AP8

1947 Photo. *Perf. 12½x12*

No.	Design	Description	Unused	Used
C32A	AP7	6c gray black	.15	.15
C33	AP7	10c deep red	.15	.15
C33A	AP7	12½c plum	.30	.15
C34	AP7	15c deep blue	.30	.20
C35	AP7	20c dl yel grn	.35	.25
C36	AP7	25c orange yel	.35	.15
C37	AP7	30c lilac gray	.50	.35
C38	AP7	35c orange red	.60	.50
C39	AP7	40c blue grn	.70	.60
C40	AP7	45c brt violet	.85	.75
C41	AP7	50c carmine	1.25	.65
C42	AP7	60c brt blue	2.50	1.00
C43	AP7	70c brown	2.50	1.00

Engr.

Perf. 12x12½

No.	Design	Description	Unused	Used
C44	AP8	1.50g black	1.25	.50
C45	AP8	2.50g dk carmine	10.00	2.75
C46	AP8	5g green	20.00	6.50
C47	AP8	7.50g dk blue	60.00	50.00
C48	AP8	10g dk red vio	45.00	12.00
C49	AP8	15g red orange	72.50	60.00
C50	AP8	25g chocolate	60.00	50.00
		Nos. C32A-C50 (20)	279.25	187.65

AIR POST SEMI-POSTAL STAMPS

Flags of the Netherlands and the House of Orange with Inscription "Netherlands Shall Rise Again" SPAP1

Engr. & Photo.

1941, Dec. 11 Unwmk. *Perf. 12*

No.	Design	Description	Unused	Used
CB1	SPAP1	10c + 10c multi	5.25	5.25
CB2	SPAP1	15c + 25c multi	19.00	19.00
CB3	SPAP1	20c + 25c multi	19.00	19.00
CB4	SPAP1	25c + 25c multi	19.00	19.00
CB5	SPAP1	30c + 50c multi	19.00	19.00
CB6	SPAP1	35c + 50c multi	19.00	19.00
CB7	SPAP1	40c + 50c multi	19.00	19.00
CB8	SPAP1	50c +100c multi	19.00	19.00
		Nos. CB1-CB8 (8)	138.25	138.25

The surtax was used by the Prince Bernhard Committee to purchase war material for the Netherlands' fighting forces in Great Britain.

Catalogue values for unused stamps in this section, from this point to the end of the section, are for Never Hinged items.

Nos. C29-C32 Surcharged in Black

50 ct. + 75 ct

1943, Dec. 1 *Perf. 13x13½*

No.	Design	Description	Unused	Used
CB9	AP3	40c + 50c on 1.40g	5.25	4.25
CB10	AP4	45c + 50c on 2.80g	5.25	4.25
CB11	AP5	50c + 75c on 5g	5.25	4.25
CB12	AP6	60c + 100c on 10g	5.25	4.25
		Nos. CB9-CB12 (4)	21.00	17.00

The surtax was for the benefit of prisoners of war. These stamps were not sold to the public in the normal manner. All were sold in sets by advance subscription, the majority to philatelic speculators.

On No. CB9 overprint reads: "Voor / Krijgsgevangenen."

Princess Juliana — SPAP2

Engr. & Photo.

1944, Aug. 16 *Perf. 12*

Frame in carmine & deep blue, cross in carmine

No.	Design	Description	Unused	Used
CB13	SPAP2	10c + 10c lt brn	1.90	1.50
CB14	SPAP2	15c + 25c turq grn	1.75	1.50
CB15	SPAP2	20c + 25c dk ol gray	1.75	1.50
CB16	SPAP2	25c + 25c slate	1.75	1.50
CB17	SPAP2	30c + 50c sepia	1.75	1.50
CB18	SPAP2	35c + 50c chnt	1.75	1.50
CB19	SPAP2	40c + 50c grn	1.75	1.50
CB20	SPAP2	50c + 100c dk vio	1.90	1.65
		Nos. CB13-CB20 (8)	14.30	12.15

The surtax was for the Red Cross.

Map of Netherlands Indies
SPAP3

Map of Netherlands
SPAP4

Photo. & Typo.

1946, July 1 *Perf. 11x11½*

No.	Type	Denomination	Unused	Used
CB21	SPAP3	10c + 10c	.75	.75
CB22	SPAP3	15c + 25c	.85	.75
CB23	SPAP3	20c + 25c	.85	.75
CB24	SPAP3	25c + 25c	.85	.75
CB25	SPAP3	30c + 50c	.85	1.00
a.		Double impression of denomination	400.00	400.00
CB26	SPAP3	35c + 50c	.85	1.00
CB27	SPAP3	40c + 75c	.85	1.10
CB28	SPAP3	50c + 100c	.85	1.10
CB29	SPAP4	10c + 10c	.75	.75
CB30	SPAP4	15c + 25c	.85	.75
CB31	SPAP4	20c + 25c	.85	.75
CB32	SPAP4	25c + 25c	.85	.75
CB33	SPAP4	30c + 50c	.85	1.00
CB34	SPAP4	35c + 50c	.85	1.00
CB35	SPAP4	40c + 75c	.85	1.10
CB36	SPAP4	50c + 100c	.85	1.10
		Nos. CB21-CB36 (16)	13.40	14.40

The surtax on Nos. CB21 to CB36 was for the National Relief Fund.

POSTAGE DUE STAMPS

D1

D2

Type I - 34 loops. "T" of *"BETALEN"* over center of loop, top branch of "E" of *"TE"* shorter than lower branch.

Type II - 33 loops. "T" of *"BETALEN"* over center of two loops.

Type III - 32 loops. "T" of *"BETALEN"* slightly to the left of loop, top of first "E" of *"BETALEN"* shorter than lower branch.

Value in Black

1889 Unwmk. Typo. *Perf. 12½*

Type III

No.	Type	Denomination	Unused	Used
J1	D1	2½c green	2.50	3.25
J2	D1	5c green	1.50	1.75
J3	D1	10c green	30.00	27.50
J4	D1	12½c green	375.00	200.00
J5	D1	15c green	20.00	17.00
J6	D1	20c green	9.00	9.00
J7	D1	25c green	190.00	150.00
J8	D1	30c green	10.00	9.00
J9	D1	40c green	10.00	9.00
J10	D1	50c green	40.00	37.50

Nos. J1-J10 were issued without gum.

Type I

No.	Type	Denomination	Unused	Used
J1a	D1	2½c	3.00	4.00
J2a	D1	5c	40.00	35.00
J3a	D1	10c	35.00	35.00
J4a	D1	12½c	375.00	200.00
J5a	D1	15c	21.00	19.00
J6a	D1	20c	65.00	65.00
J7a	D1	25c	600.00	350.00
J8a	D1	30c	75.00	75.00
J9a	D1	40c	75.00	75.00
J10a	D1	50c	45.00	40.00

Type II

No.	Type	Denomination	Unused	Used
J1b	D1	2½c	5.00	4.75
J2b	D1	5c	200.00	150.00
J3b	D1	10c	40.00	37.50
J4b	D1	12½c	400.00	250.00
J5b	D1	15c	25.00	20.00
J6b	D1	20c	425.00	425.00
J7b	D1	25c	*1,600.*	*1,600.*
J8b	D1	30c	400.00	400.00
J9b	D1	40c	400.00	400.00
J10b	D1	50c	47.50	45.00

Value in Black

1892-98 *Perf. 12½*

No.	Type	Denomination	Unused	Used
J11	D2	2½c green (III)	.25	.20
J12	D2	5c green (III)	.60	.45
J13	D2	10c green (III)	1.50	.40
J14	D2	12½c green (III)	1.65	.60
J15	D2	15c green (III) ('95)	2.50	1.10
J17	D2	25c green (III)	1.25	.95
		Nos. J11-J17 (6)	7.75	3.70

Type I

No.	Type	Denomination	Unused	Used
J11a	D2	2½c	.50	.50
J12a	D2	5c	2.50	2.50
J13a	D2	10c	2.75	2.00
J14a	D2	12½c	2.00	1.40
J16	D2	20c green ('95)	3.50	1.40
J17a	D2	25c	1.50	1.50
J18	D2	30c green ('95)	25.00	13.00
J19	D2	40c green ('95)	25.00	15.00
J20	D2	50c green ('95)	30.00	15.00

Type II

No.	Type	Denomination	Unused	Used
J11b	D2	2½c	20.00	20.00
J12b	D2	5c	1.00	1.00
J13b	D2	10c	1.75	1.10
J14b	D2	12½c	9.00	8.00
J17b	D2	25c	*12.50*	*12.50*
		Nos. J11b-J17b (5)	44.25	42.60

Type I

On Yellowish or White Paper

Value in Color of Stamp

1915 *Perf. 12½, 13½x12½*

No.	Type	Denomination	Unused	Used
J21	D2	2½c green	1.00	.95
J22	D2	5c green	1.00	.95
J23	D2	10c green	.90	.80
J24	D2	12½c green	1.25	1.10
J25	D2	15c green	1.90	2.00
J26	D2	20c green	1.00	1.75
J27	D2	25c green	.35	.20
J28	D2	30c green	3.00	3.25
J29	D2	40c green	3.00	3.25
J30	D2	50c green	2.50	3.00
		Nos. J21-J30 (10)	15.90	17.25

1944 *Perf. 11½*

No.	Type	Denomination	Unused	Used
J23a	D2	10c yellow green	20.00	18.00
J24a	D2	12½c yellow green	20.00	10.00
J27a	D2	25c yellow green	40.00	1.00
		Nos. J23a-J27a (3)	80.00	29.00

Type of 1915

Type I

Value in Color of Stamp

Perf. 13½x13

1948-49 Unwmk. Photo.

No.	Type	Denomination	Unused	Used
J31	D2	2½c blue green ('48)	1.75	1.10
J32	D2	5c blue green ('48)	1.75	1.10
J33	D2	10c blue green	15.00	10.00
J34	D2	12½c blue green	16.00	1.75
J35	D2	15c blue green	27.50	16.00
J36	D2	20c blue green	25.00	16.00
J37	D2	25c blue green	1.75	.35
J38	D2	30c blue green	27.50	21.00
J39	D2	40c blue green	27.50	21.00
J40	D2	50c blue green	27.50	16.00
		Nos. J31-J40 (10)	171.25	104.30

Catalogue values for unused stamps in this section, from this point to the end of the section, are for Never Hinged items.

D3

1953-59 Photo.

No.	Type	Denomination	Unused	Used
J41	D3	1c dk blue grn ('59)	.15	.15
J42	D3	2½c dk blue grn	.50	.45
J43	D3	5c dk blue grn	.15	.15
J44	D3	6c dk blue grn ('59)	.45	.30
J45	D3	7c dk blue grn ('59)	.45	.30
J46	D3	8c dk blue grn ('59)	.45	.30
J47	D3	9c dk blue grn ('59)	.45	.30
J48	D3	10c dk blue grn	.22	.15
J49	D3	12½c dk blue grn	.22	.15
J50	D3	15c dk blue grn	.30	.18
J51	D3	20c dk blue grn	.30	.30
J52	D3	25c dk blue grn	.45	.15
J53	D3	30c dk blue grn	1.10	.90
J54	D3	35c dk blue grn ('59)	1.25	.90
J55	D3	40c dk blue grn	1.10	.90
J56	D3	45c dk blue grn ('59)	1.25	.90
J57	D3	50c dk blue grn	1.10	.65
		Nos. J41-J57 (17)	9.89	7.13

NETHERLANDS INDIES

'ne-thər-lən(d)z 'in-dēs

(Dutch Indies, Indonesia)

LOCATION — East Indies
GOVT. — Dutch colony
AREA — 735,268 sq. mi.
POP. — 76,000,000 (estimated 1949)
CAPITAL — Jakarta (formerly Batavia)

Netherlands Indies consisted of the islands of Sumatra, Java, the Lesser Sundas, Madura, two thirds of Borneo, Celebes, the Moluccas, western New Guinea and many small islands.

Netherlands Indies changed its name to Indonesia in 1948. The Netherlands transferred sovereignty on Dec. 28, 1949, to the Republic of the United States of Indonesia (see "Indonesia"), except for the western part of New Guinea (see "Netherlands New Guinea"). The Republic of Indonesia was proclaimed Aug. 15, 1950.

100 Cents = 1 Gulden
100 Sen = 1 Rupiah (1949)

Catalogue values for unused stamps in this country are for Never Hinged items, beginning with Scott 250 in the regular postage section, Scott B57 in the semi-postal section, and Scott J43 in the postage due section.

Values for unused stamps are for examples with original gum as defined in the catalogue introduction. Very fine examples of No. 2 will have perforations touching the frameline on one or more sides due to the narrow spacing of the stamps on the plates. Stamps with perfs clear of the framelines on all four sides are scarce and will command higher prices.

Watermarks

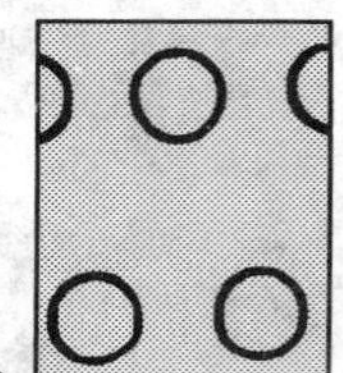

Wmk. 202- Circles

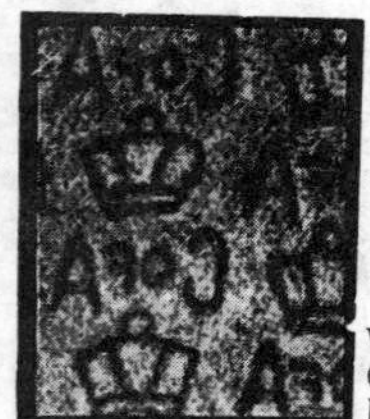

Wmk. 228- Small Crown and C of A Multiple

King William III
A1 A2

1864, Apr. 1 Unwmk. Engr. *Imperf.*

No.	Type	Denomination	Unused	Used
1	A1	10c lake	250.00	140.00

1868 *Perf. 12½x12*

No.	Type	Denomination	Unused	Used
2	A1	10c lake	800.00	150.00

Privately perforated examples of No. 1 sometimes are mistaken for No. 2.

Perf. 11½x12, 12½, 12½x12, 13x14, 13½, 14, 13½x14

1870-88 Typo.

ONE CENT:
Type I - "CENT" 6mm long.
Type II - "CENT" 7½mm long.

No.	Type	Denomination	Unused	Used
3	A2	1c sl grn, type I	6.00	4.50
a.		Perf. 13x14, small holes	10.00	8.00
4	A2	1c sl grn, type II	2.75	1.75
5	A2	2c red brown	6.00	4.00
a.		2c fawn	6.00	4.00
6	A2	2c violet brn	100.00	90.00
7	A2	2½c orange	37.50	24.00
8	A2	5c pale green	55.00	4.00
a.		Perf. 14, small holes	60.00	4.00
b.		Perf. 13x14, small holes	50.00	5.00
9	A2	10c orange brn	14.00	.15
a.		Perf. 14, small holes	24.00	.80
b.		Perf. 13x14, small holes	35.00	.80
10	A2	12½c gray	4.00	1.50
a.		Perf. 12½x12		1,000.
11	A2	15c bister	18.00	1.25
a.		Perf. 13x14, small holes	27.50	1.75
12	A2	20c ultra	87.50	2.50
a.		Perf. 14, small holes	87.50	2.50
b.		Perf. 13x14, small holes	87.50	2.75
13	A2	25c dk violet	14.00	.55
b.		Perf. 13x14, small holes	25.00	2.50
c.		Perf. 14, large holes	450.00	100.00
14	A2	30c green	27.50	3.25
15	A2	50c carmine	18.00	1.50
a.		Perf. 14, small holes	22.50	1.50
b.		Perf. 13x14, small holes	17.00	1.50
c.		Perf. 14, large holes	25.00	2.50
16	A2	2.50g green & vio	85.00	13.00
b.		Perf. 14, small holes	85.00	13.00
c.		Perf. 14, large holes	85.00	13.00
		Nos. 3-16 (14)	475.25	151.95

Imperforate examples of Nos. 3-16 are proofs. The 1c red brown and 2c yellow are believed to be bogus.

"Small hole" varieties have the spaces between the holes wider than the diameter of the holes.

Numeral of Value
A3

Queen Wilhelmina
A4

1883-90 *Perf. 12½*

No.	Type	Denomination	Unused	Used
17	A3	1c slate grn ('88)	.75	.15
a.		Perf. 12½x12	1.10	.65
18	A3	2c brown ('84)	.75	.15
a.		Perf. 12½x12	.75	.30
b.		Perf. 11½x12	65.00	22.50
19	A3	2½c yellow	.75	.65
a.		Perf. 12½x12	1.25	.75
b.		Perf. 11½x12	12.00	4.75
20	A3	3c lilac ('90)	.85	.15
21	A3	5c green ('87)	30.00	20.00
22	A3	5c ultra ('90)	9.00	.15
		Nos. 17-22 (6)	42.10	21.25

For surcharges and overprint see Nos. 46-47, O4.

1892-97 *Perf. 12½*

No.	Type	Denomination	Unused	Used
23	A4	10c orange brn ('95)	3.75	.15
24	A4	12½c gray ('97)	7.50	12.50
25	A4	15c bister ('95)	12.00	1.25
26	A4	20c ultra ('93)	27.50	1.25
27	A4	25c violet	27.50	1.25
28	A4	30c green ('94)	37.50	1.75
29	A4	50c carmine ('93)	25.00	1.25
30	A4	2.50g org brn & ultra	110.00	27.50
		Nos. 23-30 (8)	250.75	46.90

For overprints see Nos. O21-O27.

Netherlands #67-69, 74, 77, 80, 84
Surcharged in Black

10 C^T

NED.-INDIE **NED.-INDIË**

1900, July 1

No.	Type	Denomination	Unused	Used
31	A11	10c on 10c gray lil	1.40	.15
32	A11	12½c on 12½c blue	2.25	.55
33	A11	15c on 15c yel brn	2.50	.30
34	A11	20c on 20c yel grn	13.00	.60
35	A11	25c on 25c car & bl	13.00	.70
36	A11	50c on 50c brnz grn & red brn	22.50	.90

1902 *Perf. 11½x11*

No.	Type	Denomination	Unused	Used
37	A12	2.50g on 2½g brn lil	45.00	11.00
a.		Perf. 11	50.00	12.50
		Nos. 31-37 (7)	99.65	14.20

A6

1902-09 *Perf. 12½*

No.	Type	Denomination	Unused	Used
38	A6	½c violet	.35	.15
39	A6	1c olive grn	.35	.15
a.		Booklet pane of 6		
40	A6	2c yellow brn	2.75	.20
41	A6	2½c green	1.75	.15
a.		Booklet pane of 6		
42	A6	3c orange	1.75	1.10
43	A6	4c ultra ('09)	11.00	9.00
44	A6	5c rose red	4.25	.15
a.		Booklet pane of 6		
45	A6	7½c gray ('08)	2.25	.28
		Nos. 38-45 (8)	24.45	11.18

For overprints see Nos. 63-69, 81-87, O1-O9.

Nos. 18, 20 Surcharged

½ 2½

1902
46 A3 ½c on 2c yel brn .20 .20
a. Double surcharge 175.00 150.00
47 A3 2½c on 3c violet .25 .25

Queen Wilhelmina
A9 A10

1903-08
48 A9 10c slate 1.00 .15
a. Booklet pane of 6
49 A9 12½c deep blue ('06) 1.50 .15
a. Booklet pane of 6
50 A9 15c chocolate 7.25 ('06) 2.00
a. Ovptd. with 2 horiz. bars 1.50 .75
51 A9 17½c bister ('08) 3.00 .15
52 A9 20c grnsh slate 1.50 1.50
53 A9 20c olive grn ('05) 20.00 .15
54 A9 22½c brn & ol grn ('08) 3.75 .15
55 A9 25c violet ('04) 9.00 .15
56 A9 30c orange brn 25.00 .15
57 A9 50c red brown ('04) 19.00 .15
Nos. 48-57 (10) 91.00 4.70

For overprints and surcharges see Nos. 58, 70-78, 88-96, 139, O10-O18.

No. 52 Surcharged in Black

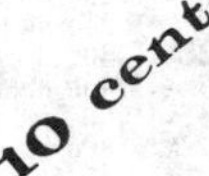

1905, July 6
58 A9 10c on 20c grnsh slate 1.90 1.25

1905-12 Engr. *Perf. 11x11½*
59 A10 1g dull lilac ('06) 42.50 .25
a. Perf. 11½x11 42.50 .40
b. Perf. 11 52.50 3.50
60 A10 1g dl lil, *bl* ('12) 45.00 6.50
a. Perf. 11 55.00 57.50
61 A10 2½g slate bl ('05) 52.50 1.50
a. Perf. 11½ 52.50 1.65
b. Perf. 11½x11 60.00 1.65
c. Perf. 11 675.00
62 A10 2½g sl bl, *bl* ('12) 65.00 32.50
a. Perf. 11 75.00 75.00
Nos. 59-62 (4) 205.00 40.75

Sheets of Nos. 60 & 62 were soaked in an indigo solution.

For overprints and surcharge see Nos. 79-80, 97-98, 140, O19-O20.

Previous Issues Overprinted BUITEN BEZIT.

1908, July 1
63 A6 ½c violet .25 .25
64 A6 1c olive grn .35 .25
65 A6 2c yellow brn 1.50 2.00
66 A6 2½c green .75 .20
67 A6 3c orange .65 1.10
68 A6 5c rose red 2.25 .40
69 A6 7½c gray 2.50 2.25
70 A9 10c slate .55 .20
71 A9 12½c dp blue 8.25 2.00
72 A9 15c choc (#50a) 3.75 2.00
73 A9 17½c bister 1.40 .95
74 A9 20c olive grn 7.50 1.40
75 A9 22½c brn & ol grn 5.75 3.50
76 A9 25c violet 5.75 .30
77 A9 30c orange brn 16.00 1.90
78 A9 50c red brown 7.00 .70
79 A10 1g dull lilac 52.50 3.75
80 A10 2½g slate blue 80.00 57.50
Nos. 63-80 (18) 196.70 80.65

The above stamps were overprinted for use in the territory outside of Java and Madura, stamps overprinted "Java" being used in these latter places.

The 15c is overprinted, in addition, with two horizontal lines, 2½mm apart.

The overprint also exists on #59a-59b. Same values.

Overprint Reading Down
63a A6 ½c .55 *3.25*
64a A6 1c .55 *2.50*
65a A6 2c 2.25 *4.50*
66a A6 2½c .95 *3.00*
67a A6 3c 15.00 *40.00*
68a A6 5c 2.25 *2.50*
70a A9 10c .65 *1.90*
71a A9 12½c 4.50 *8.00*
72a A9 15c 25.00 *62.50*
74a A9 20c 7.25 8.00
75a A9 22½c *1,400* *1,400.*
76a A9 25c 5.50 7.25
77a A9 30c 11.00 15.00
78a A9 50c 7.50 9.00
79a A10 1g 175.00 225.00
80a A10 2½g *2,250.* *2,500.*

Overprinted **JAVA.**

1908, July 1
81 A6 ½c violet .20 .20
a. Inverted overprint .55 *2.25*
b. Double overprint 450.00
82 A6 1c olive grn .25 .25
a. Inverted overprint .45 *2.75*
83 A6 2c yellow brn 1.75 1.75
a. Inverted overprint 1.50 *6.00*
84 A6 2½c green .90 .20
a. Inverted overprint 2.00 *3.25*
85 A6 3c orange .75 .75
a. Inverted overprint 17.00 22.50
86 A6 5c rose red 2.25 .15
a. Inverted overprint 1.50 2.50
87 A6 7½c gray 1.90 1.75
88 A9 10c slate .55 .15
a. Inverted overprint .55 *2.00*
89 A9 12½c deep blue 2.00 .55
a. Inverted overprint 2.75 5.00
b. Dbl. ovpt., one inverted 125.00 125.00
90 A9 15c choc (on No. 50a) 3.00 2.50
a. Inverted overprint 2.75 *9.00*
91 A9 17½c bister 1.50 .65
92 A9 20c olive grn 9.25 .75
a. Inverted overprint 9.00 10.00
93 A9 22½c brn & ol grn 4.00 2.00
94 A9 25c violet 4.00 .30
a. Inverted overprint 4.50 *9.00*
95 A9 30c orange brn 24.00 2.00
a. Inverted overprint 18.00 26.00
96 A9 50c red brown 15.00 .55
a. Inverted overprint 12.00 19.00
97 A10 1g dull lilac 37.50 2.25
a. Inverted overprint 150.00 150.00
b. Perf. 11 47.50 4.00
98 A10 2½g slate blue 57.50 40.00
a. Inverted overprint *2,250.* *2,500.*
Nos. 81-98 (18) 166.30 56.75

A11

Queen Wilhelmina
A12 A13

Typo., Litho. (#114A)

1912-40 *Perf. 12½*
101 A11 ½c lt vio .15 .15
102 A11 1c olive grn .15 .15
103 A11 2c yellow brn .40 .15
104 A11 2c gray blk ('30) .40 .15
105 A11 2½c green 1.25 .15
106 A11 2½c lt red ('22) .25 .15
107 A11 3c yellow .45 .15
108 A11 3c green ('29) .70 .15
109 A11 4c ultra .65 .25
110 A11 4c dp grn ('28) 1.25 .20
111 A11 4c yellow ('30) 8.50 4.00
112 A11 5c rose 1.10 .15
113 A11 5c green ('22) .90 .15
114 A11 5c chlky bl ('28) .55 .15
114A A11 5c ultra ('40) .85 .15
115 A11 7½c bister .40 .15
116 A11 10c lilac ('22) .95 .15
117 A12 10c car rose ('14) .75 .15
118 A12 12½c dull bl ('14) .95 .15
119 A12 12½c red ('22) .95 .15
120 A12 15c blue ('29) 7.50 .15
121 A12 17½c red brn ('15) .95 .15
122 A12 20c green ('15) 1.75 .15
123 A12 20c blue ('22) 1.75 .15
124 A12 20c orange ('32) 13.00 .15
125 A12 22½c orange ('15) 1.75 .45
126 A12 25c red vio ('15) 1.75 .15
127 A12 30c slate ('15) 1.90 .15
128 A12 32½c vio & red ('22) 1.90 .15
129 A12 35c org brn ('29) 8.50 .60
130 A12 40c green ('22) 1.90 .15

Perf. 11½
Engr.
131 A13 50c green ('13) 4.00 .15
a. Perf. 11x11½ 4.25 .15
b. Perf. 12½ 4.25 .30
132 A13 60c dp blue ('22) 4.75 .15
133 A13 80c orange ('22) 4.00 .15
134 A13 1g brown ('13) 3.00 .15
a. Perf. 11x11½ 3.50 .15
135 A13 1.75g dk vio, p. 12½ ('31) 15.00 1.90
136 A13 2½g carmine ('13) 12.50 .40
a. Perf. 11x11½ 13.00 .65
b. Perf. 12½ 14.00 .60
Nos. 101-136 (37) 107.45 12.30

For surcharges and overprints see Nos. 137-138, 144-150, 102a-123a, 158, 194-195, B1-B3, C1-C5.

Water Soluble Ink

Some values of types A11 and A12 and late printings of types A6 and A9 are in soluble ink. The design disappears when immersed in water.

Nos. 105, 109, 54, 59 Surcharged

½ 1 17½
30 CENT

1917-18 Typo. *Perf. 12½*
137 A11 ½c on 2½c .30 .30
138 A11 1c on 4c ('18) .55 .55
139 A9 17½c on 22½c ('18) 1.25 .55
a. Inverted surcharge 350.00 425.00

Perf. 11x11½
140 A10 30c on 1g ('18) 7.00 1.65
a. Perf. 11½x11 110.00 42.50
Nos. 137-140 (4) 9.10 3.05

Nos. 121, 125, 131, 134 Surcharged in Red or Blue

12½ CENT — 40 CENT
On A12 — On A13

Two types of 32½c on 50c:
I - Surcharge bars spaced as in illustration.
II - Bars more closely spaced.

1922, Jan. *Perf. 12½*
144 A12 12½c on 17½c (R) .30 .15
145 A12 12½c on 22½c (R) .40 .15
146 A12 20c on 22½c (Bl) .40 .15

Perf. 11½, 11x11½
147 A13 32½c on 50c (Bl) (I, perf. 11½) 1.25 .15
a. Type II, perf. 11½ 10.00 .15
b. Type I, perf. 11x11½ 1,000. 6.00
c. Type II, perf. 11x11½ 19.00 1.00
148 A13 40c on 50c (R) 3.75 .45
149 A13 60c on 1g (Bl) 6.00 .40
150 A13 80c on 1g (R) 6.75 .90
Nos. 144-150 (7) 18.85 2.35

Stamps of 1912-22 Overprinted in Red, Blue, Green or Black

3de N.I. JAARBEURS — BANDOENG 1922
a

3de N. I. JAARBEURS
BANDOENG 1922
b

1922, Sept. 18 Typo. *Perf. 12½*
102a A11(a) 1c ol grn (R) 5.75 4.75
103a A11(a) 2c yel brn (Bl) 5.75 4.75
106a A11(a) 2½c lt red (G) 47.50 52.50
107a A11(a) 3c yellow (R) 5.75 5.75
109a A11(a) 4c ultra (R) 32.50 30.00
113a A11(a) 5c green (R) 11.00 8.25
115a A11(a) 7½c drab (Bl) 7.50 4.75
116a A11(a) 10c lilac (Bk) 57.50 67.50
145a A12(b) 12½c on 22½c org (Bl) 5.75 5.75
121a A12(b) 17½c red brn (Bk) 3.75 4.75
123a A12(b) 20c blue (Bk) 5.75 4.75
Nos. 102a-123a (11) 188.50 193.50

Issued to publicize the 3rd Netherlands Indies Industrial Fair at Bandoeng, Java. On No. 145a the overprint is vertical.

Nos. 102a-123a were sold at a premium for 3, 4, 5, 6, 8, 9, 10, 12½, 15, 20 and 22½ cents respectively.

Queen Wilhelmina
A15

Prince William I, Portrait by Van Key
A16

1923, Aug. 31 Engr. *Perf. 11½*
151 A15 5c myrtle green .15 .15
a. Perf. 11½x11 350.00 110.00
b. Perf. 11x11½ 4.50 .55
152 A15 12½c rose .18 .15
a. Perf. 11x11½ 1.25 .18
b. Perf. 11½x11 1.75 .25
153 A15 20c dark blue .35 .15
a. Perf. 11½x11 3.25 .40
154 A15 50c red orange 1.40 .60
a. Perf. 11x11½ 6.50 1.25
b. Perf. 11½x11 2.00 .90
c. Perf. 11 4.50 .85
155 A15 1g brown vio 2.75 .38
a. Perf. 11½x11 7.50 .80
156 A15 2½g gray black 22.50 8.75
157 A15 5g orange brown 90.00 87.50
Nos. 151-157 (7) 117.33 97.68

25th anniversary of the assumption of the government of the Netherlands by Queen Wilhelmina, at the age of 18.

No. 123 Surcharged 12½

1930, Dec. 13 Typo. *Perf. 12½*
158 A12 12½c on 20c bl (R) .32 .15
a. Inverted surcharge 375.00 475.00

1933, Apr. 18 Photo.
163 A16 12½c deep orange 1.25 .18

400th anniv. of the birth of Prince William I, Count of Nassau and Prince of Orange, frequently referred to as William the Silent.

Rice Field Scene
A17

Queen Wilhelmina
A18

Queen Wilhelmina — A19

1933-37 Unwmk. *Perf. 12x12½*
164 A17 1c lilac gray ('34) .20 .15
165 A17 2c plum ('34) .20 .15
166 A17 2½c bister ('34) .20 .15
167 A17 3c yellow grn ('34) .20 .15
168 A17 3½c dark gray ('37) .15 .15
169 A17 4c dk olive ('34) .85 .15
170 A17 5c ultra ('34) .15 .15
171 A17 7½c violet ('34) 1.25 .15
172 A17 10c ver ('34) 1.75 .15
173 A18 10c ver ('37) .25 .15
174 A18 12½c dp org ('34) .25 .15
a. 12½c light orange, perf. 12½ ('33) 6.25 .35
175 A18 15c ultra ('34) .25 .15
176 A18 20c plum ('34) .38 .15
177 A18 25c blue grn ('34) 1.75 .15
178 A18 30c lilac gray ('34) 2.75 .15
179 A18 32½c bister ('34) 7.50 6.50
180 A18 35c violet ('34) 4.25 .95
181 A18 40c yel grn ('34) 2.50 .15
182 A18 42½c yellow ('34) 2.50 .18

1934, Jan 16 *Perf. 12½*
183 A19 50c lilac gray 3.25 .18
184 A19 60c ultra 4.00 .45
185 A19 80c vermilion 4.00 .55
186 A19 1g violet 6.25 .38

187	A19	1.75g yellow grn	16.00	11.00
188	A19	2.50g plum	19.00	1.25
		Nos. 164-188 (25)	79.83	23.84

See Nos. 200-225. For overprints and surcharges see Nos. 271-276, B48, B57.

Water Soluble Ink

Nos. 164-188 and the first printing of No. 163 have soluble ink and the design disappears when immersed in water.

Nos. C6-C7, C14, C9-C10 Surcharged in

a

b

1934 Typo. *Perf. 12½x11½, 12½*

189	AP1(a)	2c on 10c	.28	.45
190	AP1(a)	2c on 20c	.18	.18
191	AP3(b)	2c on 30c	.38	.60
192	AP1(a)	42½c on 75c	4.25	.28
193	AP1(a)	42½c on 1.50g	4.25	.38
		Nos. 189-193 (5)	9.34	1.89

Nos. 127-128 Surcharged with New Value in Red or Black

1937, Sept. *Perf. 12½*

194	A12	10c on 30c (R)	2.50	.25
a.		Double surcharge	675.00	
195	A12	10c on 32½c (Bk)	2.75	.28

Wilhelmina — A20

Perf. 12½x12

1938, Aug. 30 Photo. Wmk. 202

196	A20	2c dull purple	.15	.15
197	A20	10c car lake	.15	.15
198	A20	15c royal blue	1.25	.75
199	A20	20c red orange	.48	.28
		Nos. 196-199 (4)	2.03	1.33

40th anniv. of the reign of Queen Wilhelmina.

Types of 1933-37

1938-40 Photo. *Perf. 12½x12*

200	A17	1c lilac gray ('39)	.28	.80
201	A17	2c plum ('39)	.15	.15
202	A17	2½c bister ('39)	.48	.48
203	A17	3c yellow grn ('39)	1.50	1.25
205	A17	4c gray ol ('39)	1.50	1.25
206	A17	5c ultra ('39)	.15	.15
a.		Perf. 12x12½	1.25	.15
207	A17	7½c violet ('39)	2.50	1.00
208	A18	10c ver ('39)	.15	.15
210	A18	15c ultra ('39)	.15	.15
211	A18	20c plum ('39)	.18	.15
a.		Perf. 12x12½	1.25	.18
212	A18	25c blue grn ('39)	25.00	24.00
213	A18	30c lilac gray ('39)	6.50	.80
215	A18	35c violet ('39)	2.75	.65
216	A18	40c dp yel grn ('40)	5.00	.20

Perf. 12½

218	A19	50c lilac gray ('40)	275.00	
219	A19	60c ultra ('39)	10.50	1.25
220	A19	80c ver ('39)	62.50	26.00
221	A19	1g violet ('39)	27.50	.85
223	A19	2g Prus green	27.50	14.00
225	A19	5g yellow brn	25.00	6.00
		Nos. 200-216,219-225 (19)	199.29	79.28

The note following No. 188 applies also to this issue.

The 50c was sold only at the philatelic window in Amsterdam.

War Dance of Nias Island — A23

Legong Dancer of Bali — A24

Wayang Wong Dancer of Java — A25

Padjogé Dancer, Southern Celebes — A26

Dyak Dancer of Borneo — A27

1941 Unwmk. *Perf. 12½*

228	A23	2½c rose violet	.15	.20
229	A24	3c green	.16	.48
230	A25	4c olive green	.15	.45
231	A26	5c blue	.15	.15
232	A27	7½c dark violet	.50	.15
		Nos. 228-232 (5)	1.11	1.43

See Nos. 279-280, 293, N38.

Imperfs. are printers waste.

Queen Wilhelmina

A28 A28a

1941 *Perf. 12½*

Size: 18x22¾mm

234	A28	10c red orange	.15	.15
a.		Perf. 13½	.40	.40
235	A28	15c ultra	1.50	1.25
236	A28	17½c orange	.40	.60
237	A28	20c plum	21.00	35.00
238	A28	25c Prus green	30.00	47.50
239	A28	30c olive bis	1.90	1.10
240	A28	35c purple	95.00	325.00
241	A28	40c yellow grn	8.00	2.50

Perf. 13½

Size: 20½x26mm

242	A28	50c car lake	2.00	.68
243	A28	60c ultra	1.65	.58
244	A28	80c red orange	1.90	.95
245	A28	1g purple	2.00	.28
246	A28	2g Prus green	10.00	1.10
247	A28	5g bis, perf. 12½	250.00	675.00
248	A28	10g green	30.00	15.00

Size: 26x32mm

249	A28a	25g orange	175.00	125.00
		Nos. 234-249 (16)	630.50	1,231.

Nos. 242-246 come with pin-perf 13½.

T%he 10c comes in two types: 1¼mm between "10" and "CENT," and 1¾mm.

For overprints and surcharge see Nos. 276-278, J43-J46.

Catalogue values for unused stamps in this section, from this point to the end of the section, are for Never Hinged items.

Rice Fields — A29

Barge on Java Lake — A30

University of Medicine, Batavia — A31

Palms on Shore — A32

Plane over Bromo Volcano — A33

Queen Wilhelmina

A34 A35

1945-46, Oct. 1 Engr. *Perf. 12*

250	A29	1c green	.22	.18
251	A30	2c rose lilac	.22	.30
252	A31	2½c dull lilac	.22	.15
253	A32	5c blue	.15	.15
254	A33	7½c olive gray	.48	.15
255	A34	10c red brown	.15	.15
256	A34	15c dark blue	.15	.15
257	A34	17½c rose lake	.15	.20
258	A34	20c sepia	.15	.15
259	A34	30c slate gray	.28	.15
260	A35	60c gray black	.65	.15
261	A35	1g blue green	1.10	.18
262	A35	2½g red orange	3.75	.52
		Nos. 250-262 (13)	7.67	2.58

For surcharge see No. 304.

Issued: 15c, 1946, others 10/1/45.

Railway Viaduct Near Soekaboemi — A36

Dam and Power Station — A37

Palm Tree and Menangkabau House — A38

Huts on Piles — A39

Buddhist Stupas — A40

Perf. 14½x14

1946 Typo. Wmk. 228

263	A36	1c dark green	.15	.15
264	A37	2c black brown	.15	.15
265	A38	2½c scarlet	.18	.15
266	A39	5c indigo	.15	.15
267	A40	7½c ultra	.18	.15
		Set value	.65	.52

Nos. 265, 267, 263 Surcharged

1947, Sept. 25

268	A38	3c on 2½c scar	.15	.15
269	A40	3c on 7½c ultra	.15	.15
a.		Double surcharge	150.00	150.00
270	A36	4c on 1c dk green	.15	.18
		Nos. 268-270 (3)	.45	
		Set value		.32

No. 219 Surcharged with New Value and Bars in Red

1947, Sept. 25 Wmk. 202 *Perf. 12½*

271	A19	45c on 60c ultra	1.25	1.25

Nos. 212, 218 and 220 Overprinted "1947" in Red or Black

1947, Sept. 25 *Perf. 12½x12, 12½*

272	A18	25c blue green (R)	.18	.15
a.		Unwmkd.		125.00
273	A19	50c lilac gray (R)	.75	.25
274	A19	80c vermilion	1.10	.75
a.		Unwmkd.	500.00	140.00
		Nos. 272-274 (3)	2.03	1.15

Bar above "1947" on No. 274.

Nos. 174, 241, 247 and Type of 1941 Overprinted "1947" in Black

Perf. 12½, 12½x12 (2g)

1947, Sept. 25 Unwmk.

275	A18	12½c deep orange	.15	.15
276	A28	40c yellow green	.38	.15
277	A28	2g Prus green	3.75	.50
278	A28	5g bister	11.00	7.50
		Nos. 275-278 (4)	15.28	8.30

The overprint is vertical on #276-278.

Dancer Types of 1941, 1945

1948, May 13 Litho. *Perf. 12½*

279	OS21	3c rose red	.15	.15
280	A24	4c dull olive grn	.15	.15
		Set value	.24	.24

Queen Wilhelmina — A41

1948 Photo. *Perf. 12½*

Size: 18x22mm

281	A41	15c red orange	.60	.80
282	A41	20c brt blue	.15	.15
283	A41	25c dk green	.18	.15
284	A41	40c dp yellow grn	.18	.15
285	A41	45c plum	.38	.60
286	A41	50c red brown	.22	.15
287	A41	80c brt red	.30	.15

Perf. 13

Size: 20½x26mm

288	A41	1g deep violet	.22	.15
a.		Perf. 12½ x 12	.75	.38
289	A41	10g green	30.00	8.25
290	A41	25g orange	62.50	45.00
		Nos. 281-290 (10)	94.73	55.55

See #201-202. For overprints see #294-303.

Wilhelmina Type of 1948 Inscribed: "1898 1948"

1948, Aug. 31 *Perf. 12½x12*

Size: 21x26½mm

291	A41	15c orange	.28	.20
292	A41	20c ultra	.28	.16

Reign of Queen Wilhelmina, 50th anniv.

Dancer Type of 1941

1948, Sept. Photo. *Perf. 12½*

293	A27	7½c olive bister	.70	.80

Juliana Type of Netherlands 1948

Perf. 14½x13½

1948, Sept. 25 Wmk. 202

293A	A75	15c red orange	.30	.20
293B	A75	20c deep ultra	.30	.16

Investiture of Queen Juliana, Sept. 6, 1948.

Indonesia

Nos. 281 to 287 Overprinted in Black

INDONESIA

Two types of overprint:

I - Shiny ink, bar 1.8mm wide. By G. C. T. van Dorp & Co.

II - Dull ink, bar 2.2mm. By G. Kolff & Co.

1948 *Perf. 12½*

294	A41	15c red orange (I)	.60	.15
a.		Type II	.55	.15
295	A41	20c bright blue (I)	.16	.15
a.		Type II	.16	.15
296	A41	25c dark green (I)	.22	.15
a.		Type II	.15	.15
297	A41	40c dp yel grn (I)	.22	.15
298	A41	45c plum ('49) (II)	.80	.70
299	A41	50c red brn ('49) (II)	.18	.15
300	A41	80c bright red (I)	.65	.15
a.		Type II	.65	.15

Nos. 288-290 Overprinted in Black

INDONESIA

Two or Three Bars
Perf. 12½x12

301 A41 1g deep violet .55 .15
a. Perf. 13 .95 .15

Perf. 13

302 A41 10g green 50.00 6.25
303 A41 25g orange 60.00 47.50
Nos. 294-303 (10) 113.38 55.50

Same Overprint in Black on No. 262

1949 Engr. *Perf. 12*
Bars 28½mm long

304 A35 2½g red orange 14.00 5.50

A42

Tjandi Puntadewa Temple Entrance, East Java — A43

Detail, Temple of the Dead, Bedjuning, Bali A44

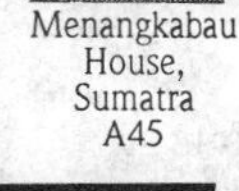
Menangkabau House, Sumatra A45

Toradja House, Celebes — A46

Globe and Arms of Bern — A48

Designs: 5r, 10r, 25r, Temple entrance.

Perf. 12½, 11½

1949 Unwmk. Photo.

307 A42 1s gray .20 .15
a. Perf. 11½ .40 .20
308 A42 2s claret .25 .15
a. Perf. 11½ 5.00 14.00
309 A42 2½s olive brown .20 .15
a. Perf. 11½ .25 .20
310 A42 3s rose pink .25 .15
a. Perf. 11½ 1.10 .75
311 A42 4s green .32 .50
312 A42 5s blue .15 .15
a. Perf. 11½ 1.00 .20
313 A42 7½s dark green .38 .15
a. Perf. 11½ 1.00 .75
314 A42 10s violet .16 .15
a. Perf. 11½ 375.00
315 A42 12½s brt red .32 .15
a. Perf. 11½ 4.00 4.00
316 A43 15s rose red .25 .15
a. Perf. 12½ .30 .15
317 A43 20s gray black .25 .15
a. Perf. 12½ .30 .75
318 A43 25s ultra .30 .15
319 A44 30s brt red .30 .15
320 A44 40s gray green .32 .15
321 A44 45s claret .32 .25
a. Perf. 12½ 2.75 .50
322 A45 50s orange brn .32 .15
323 A45 60s brown .38 .15
324 A45 80s scarlet .32 .15
a. Perf. 12½ 4.00 .25

The 4s is perf. 12½. The 25s, 30s, 40s, 50s, 60s come both 12½ and 11½, same values.

Perf. 12½

325 A46 1r purple .22 .15
326 A46 2r gray green 2.00 .15
327 A46 3r red violet 21.00 .15
328 A46 5r dk brown 21.00 .15
329 A46 10r gray 42.50 .22
330 A46 25r orange brn .22 .25
Nos. 307-330 (24) 91.93
Set value 3.25

1949, Oct. 1 *Perf. 12½*

331 A48 15s bright red .70 .35
332 A48 25s ultra .70 .25

75th anniv. of UPU.

See Indonesia (republic) for subsequent listings.

SEMI-POSTAL STAMPS

Regular Issue of 1912-14 Surcharged in Carmine

+ 5 cts

1915, June 10 Unwmk. *Perf. 12½*

B1 A11 1c + 5c ol grn 4.50 4.50
B2 A11 5c + 5c rose 4.50 4.50
B3 A12 10c + 5c rose 7.25 7.25
Nos. B1-B3 (3) 16.25 16.25

Surtax for the Red Cross.

Bali Temple SP1

Watchtower SP2

Menangkabau Compound SP3

Borobudur Temple, Java — SP4

Perf. 11½x11, 11x11½

1930, Dec. 1 Photo.

B4 SP1 2c (+ 1c) vio & brn 1.00 .80
B5 SP2 5c (+ 2½c) dk grn & brn 4.75 2.50
B6 SP3 12½c (+ 2½c) dp red & brn 3.25 .50
B7 SP4 15c (+ 5c) ultra & brn 5.75 5.75
Nos. B4-B7 (4) 14.75 9.55

Surtax for youth care.

Farmer and Carabao — SP5

5c, Fishermen. 12½c, Dancers. 15c, Musicians.

1931, Dec. 1 Engr. *Perf. 12½*

B8 SP5 2c (+ 1c) olive bis 3.00 2.00
B9 SP5 5c (+ 2½c) bl grn 4.25 3.75
B10 SP5 12½c (+ 2½c) dp red 3.25 .55
B11 SP5 15c (+ 5c) dl bl 8.25 7.00
Nos. B8-B11 (4) 18.75 13.30

The surtax was for the aid of the Leper Colony at Salatiga.

Weaving — SP9

5c, Plaiting rattan. 12½c, Woman batik dyer. 15c, Coppersmith.

1932, Dec. 1 Photo. *Perf. 12½*

B12 SP9 2c (+ 1c) dp vio & bis .40 .38
B13 SP9 5c (+ 2½c) dp grn & bis 2.50 2.00
B14 SP9 12½c (+ 2½c) brt rose & bis .80 .28
B15 SP9 15c (+ 5c) bl & bis 3.25 3.00
Nos. B12-B15 (4) 6.95 5.66

The surtax was donated to the Salvation Army.

Woman and Lotus — SP13

Designs: 5c, "The Light that Shows the Way." 12½c, YMCA emblem. 15c, Jobless man.

1933, Dec. 1 *Perf. 12½*

B16 SP13 2c (+ 1c) red vio & ol bis .65 .28
B17 SP13 5c (+ 2½c) grn & ol bis 2.25 1.90
B18 SP13 12½c (+ 2½c) ver & ol bis 2.50 .28
B19 SP13 15c (+ 5c) bl & ol bis 2.75 2.00
Nos. B16-B19 (4) 8.15 4.46

The surtax was for the Amsterdam Young Men's Society for Relief of the Poor in Netherlands Indies.

Dowager Queen Emma — SP17

A Pioneer at Work — SP18

1934, Sept. 15 *Perf. 13x14*

B20 SP17 12½c (+ 2½c) blk brn 1.25 .45

Issued in memory of the late Dowager Queen Emma of Netherlands. The surtax was for the Anti-Tuberculosis Society.

1935 *Perf. 12½*

Designs: 5c, Cavalryman rescuing wounded native. 12½c, Artilleryman under fire. 15c, Bugler.

B21 SP18 2c (+ 1c) plum & ol bis 1.25 1.00
B22 SP18 5c (+ 2½c) grn & ol bis 3.25 2.25
B23 SP18 12½c (+ 2½c) red org & ol bis 3.25 .22
B24 SP18 15c (+ 5c) brt bl & ol bis 4.50 4.50
Nos. B21-B24 (4) 12.25 7.97

The surtax was for the Indies Committee of the Christian Military Association for the East and West Indies.

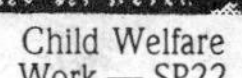
Child Welfare Work — SP22

Boy Scouts — SP23

1936, Dec. 1 Size: 23x20mm

B25 SP22 2c (+ 1c) plum 1.00 .60

Size: 30x26½mm

B26 SP22 5c (+ 2½c) gray vio 1.25 1.10
B27 SP22 7½c (+ 2½c) dk vio 1.25 1.25
B28 SP22 12½c (+ 2½c) red org 1.25 .28
B29 SP22 15c (+5c) brt bl 2.00 1.75
Nos. B25-B29 (5) 6.75 4.98

Surtax for Salvation Army.

1937, May 1

B30 SP23 7½c + 2½c dk ol brn 1.25 1.00
B31 SP23 12½c + 2½c rose car 1.25 .50

Fifth Boy Scout World Jamboree, Vogelenzang, Netherlands, July 31-Aug. 13, 1937. Surtax for Netherlands Indies Scout Association.

Sifting Rice — SP24

Designs: 3½c, Mother and children. 7½c, Plowing with carabao team. 10c, Carabao team and cart. 20c, Native couple.

1937, Dec. 1

B32 SP24 2c (+ 1c) dk brn & org 1.10 .80
B33 SP24 3½c (+ 1½c) gray 1.10 .80
B34 SP24 7½c (+ 2½c) Prus grn & org 1.25 .95
B35 SP24 10c (+ 2½c) car & org 1.25 .18
B36 SP24 20c (+ 5c) brt bl 1.25 1.10
Nos. B32-B36 (5) 5.95 3.83

Surtax for the Public Relief Fund for indigenous poor.

Modern Plane — SP28

Design: 20c, Plane nose facing left.

Perf. 12½

1938, Oct. 15 Photo. Wmk. 202

B36A SP28 17½c (+5c) olive brn .85 .85
B36B SP28 20c (+5c) slate .85 .55

10th anniversary of the Dutch East Indies Royal Air Lines (K. N. I. L. M.).

Surtax for the Aviation Fund in the Netherlands Indies.

Nun and Child
SP29 SP30

Designs: 7½c, Nurse examining child's arm. 10c, Nurse bathing baby. 20c, Nun bandaging child's head.

1938, Dec. 1 Wmk. 202 *Perf. 12½*

B37 SP29 2c (+ 1c) vio .60 .45

Perf. 11½x12

B38 SP30 3½c (+ 1½c) brt grn 1.00 .90

Perf. 12x11½

B39 SP30 7½c (+ 2½c) cop red .80 .85
B40 SP30 10c (+ 2½c) ver .90 .18
B41 SP30 20c (+ 5c) brt ultra 1.00 .95
Nos. B37-B41 (5) 4.30 3.33

The surtax was for the Central Mission Bureau in Batavia.

Social Workers SP34

Indonesian Nurse Tending Patient SP35

European Nurse Tending Patient — SP36

Perf. 13x11½, 11½x13

1939, Dec. 1 Photo.

B42 SP34 2c (+ 1c) purple .22 .16
B43 SP35 3½c (+ 1½c) bl grn & pale bl grn .32 .22
B44 SP34 7½c (+ 2½c) cop brn .22 .18
B45 SP35 10c (+ 2½c) scar & pink 1.40 .80
B46 SP36 10c (+ 2½c) scar 1.40 .80
B47 SP36 20c (+ 5c) dk bl .40 .35
Nos. B42-B47 (6) 3.96 2.51

No. B44 shows native social workers.

Nos. B45 and B46 were issued se-tenant vertically and horizontally. The surtax was used for the Bureau of Social Service.

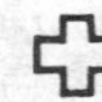

No. 174 Surcharged in Brown

10+5 ct

1940, Dec. 2 Unwmk. *Perf. 12x12½*

B48 A18 10c + 5c on 12½c dp org 1.10 .40

SP37

SP38

Netherlands coat of arms and inscription "Netherlands Shall Rise Again"

1941, May 10 Litho. *Perf. 12½*

B49 SP37 5c + 5c multi .15 .15
B50 SP37 10c + 10c multi .22 .15
B51 SP37 1g + 1g multi 9.00 6.75
Nos. B49-B51 (3) 9.37 7.05

The surtax was used to purchase fighter planes for Dutch pilots fighting with the Royal Air Force in Great Britain.

1941, Sept. 22 Photo.

Designs: 2c, Doctor and child, 3½c, Rice eater. 7½c, Nurse and patient. 10c, Nurse and children. 15c, Basket weaver.

B52 SP38 2c (+ 1c) yel grn .60 .55
B53 SP38 3½c (+ 1½c) vio brn 4.00 3.50
B54 SP38 7½c (+ 2½c) vio 3.25 2.75
B55 SP38 10c (+ 2½c) dk red .90 .18
B56 SP38 15c (+ 5c) saph 9.50 6.00
Nos. B52-B56 (5) 18.25 12.98

The surtax was used for various charities.

Catalogue values for unused stamps in this section, from this point to the end of the section, are for Never Hinged items.

No. 208 Surcharged in Black

Perf. 12½x12

1948, Feb. 2 Wmk. 202

B57 A18 15c + 10c on 10c .15 .15
a. Inverted surcharge 210.00 210.00

The surtax was for war victims and other charitable purposes.

AIR POST STAMPS

LUCHTPOST

Regular Issues of 1913-1923 Surcharged and New Values in Black or Blue

Perf. 12½, 11½

1928, Sept. 20 Unwmk.

C1 A12 10c on 12½c red 1.00 1.00
C2 A12 20c on 25c red vio 2.25 2.25
C3 A13 40c on 80c org 1.90 1.50
C4 A13 75c on 1g brn (Bl) .90 .55
C5 A13 1½g on 2½g car 6.25 5.50
Nos. C1-C5 (5) 12.30 10.80

On Nos. C4 and C5 there are stars over the original values and the airplane is of different shape. On No. C3 there are no bars under "OST."

Planes over Temple — AP1

1928, Dec. 1 Litho. *Perf. 12½x11½*

C6 AP1 10c red violet .30 .15
C7 AP1 20c brown .85 .55
C8 AP1 40c rose 1.00 .55
C9 AP1 75c green 2.25 .15
C10 AP1 1.50g orange 4.00 .45
Nos. C6-C10 (5) 8.40 1.85

For surcharges see Nos. 189-190, 192-193, C11-C12, C17.

No. C8 Surcharged in Black or Green

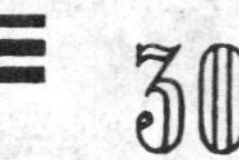

1930-32

C11 AP1 30c on 40c rose .90 .15
C12 AP1 30c on 40c rose (G) ('32) 1.25 .15

Pilot at Controls of Plane — AP2

1931, Apr. 1 Photo. *Perf. 12½*

C13 AP2 1g blue & brown 11.00 11.00

Issued for the first air mail flight from Java to Australia.

Landscape and Garudas — AP3

1931, May

C14 AP3 30c red violet 2.25 .15
C15 AP3 4½g bright blue 8.00 3.00
C16 AP3 7½g yellow green 10.00 3.25
Nos. C14-C16 (3) 20.25 6.40

For surcharge see No. 191.

No. C10 Surcharged in Blue

1932, July 21 *Perf. 12½x11½*

C17 AP1 50c on 1.50g org 2.50 .40
a. Inverted surcharge *1,800. 2,000.*

Airplane AP4

1933, Oct. 18 Photo. *Perf. 12½*

C18 AP4 30c deep blue 1.50 1.50

MARINE INSURANCE STAMPS

Floating Safe Attracting Gulls — MI1

Floating Safe with Night Flare — MI2

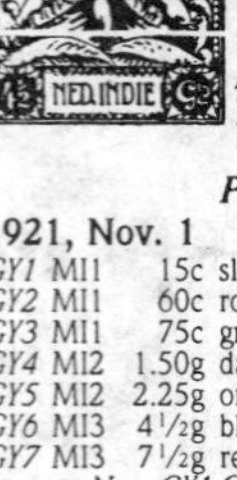

Artistic Fantasy of Floating Safe — MI3

Perf. 11½

1921, Nov. 1 Unwmk. Engr.

GY1 MI1 15c slate green 1.90 *30.00*
GY2 MI1 60c rose 3.75 *45.00*
GY3 MI1 75c gray brn 3.75 *50.00*
GY4 MI2 1.50g dark blue 22.50 *225.00*
GY5 MI2 2.25g org brn 30.00 *300.00*
GY6 MI3 4½g black 57.50 *500.00*
GY7 MI3 7½g red 67.50 *575.00*
Nos. GY1-GY7 (7) 186.90 *1,725.*

POSTAGE DUE STAMPS

Aangebragt per Land-Mail.
Te betalen port duiten.
BATAVIA,

D1

Aangebragt per Land-Mail.
Te betalen port *f* koper.
BATAVIA,

D2

1845-46 Unwmk. Typeset *Imperf.*
Bluish Paper

J1 D1 black ('46) *1,400.*
J2 D2 black *1,400.*
a. "Maill" instead of "Mail" *3,200.*

D3

Perf. 12½x12, 13x14, 10½x12

1874 Typo.

J3 D3 5c ocher 250.00 225.00
J4 D3 10c green, *yel* 100.00 85.00
J5 D3 15c ocher, *org* 18.00 15.00
a. Perf. 11½x12 35.00 35.00
J6 D3 20c green, *blue* 30.00 10.00
a. Perf. 11½x12 65.00 19.00
Nos. J3-J6 (4) 398.00 335.00

D4

D5

Type I - 34 loops. "T" of "Betalen" over center of loop, top branch of "E" of "Te" shorter than lower branch.

Type II - 33 loops. "T" of "Betalen" over center of two loops.

Type III - 32 loops. "T" of "Betalen" slightly to the left of loop, top branch of first "E" of "Betalen" shorter than lower branch.

Type IV - 37 loops and letters of "PORT" larger than in the other three types.

Value in Black

Perf. 11½x12, 12½, 12½x12, 13½

1882-88

Type III

J7 D4 2½c carmine .40 1.10
J8 D4 5c carmine .20 .40
J9 D4 10c carmine 2.50 3.00
J10 D4 15c carmine 3.00 3.00
J11 D4 20c carmine 82.50 .50
J12 D4 30c carmine 1.75 2.50
J13 D4 40c carmine 1.25 2.00
J14 D4 50c deep salmon .75 .60
J15 D4 75c carmine .45 .50
Nos. J7-J15 (9) 92.80 13.60

Type I

J7a D4 2½c carmine .40 1.10
J8a D4 5c carmine .25 .45
J9a D4 10c carmine 3.25 4.00
J10a D4 15c carmine 3.25 3.50
J11a D4 20c carmine 95.00 .50
J12a D4 30c carmine 3.25 4.00
J13a D4 40c carmine 1.40 2.00
J14a D4 50c deep salmon .80 .60
J15a D4 75c carmine .50 .60
Nos. J7a-J15a (9) 108.10 16.75

Type II

J7b D4 2½c carmine .50 1.40
J8b D4 5c carmine .30 .50
J9b D4 10c carmine 3.50 4.50
J10b D4 15c carmine 3.75 4.00
J11b D4 20c carmine 110.00 .65
J12b D4 30c carmine 7.00 7.50
J13b D4 40c carmine 1.50 2.50
J14b D4 50c deep salmon .85 .75
J15b D4 75c carmine .65 .85
Nos. J7b-J15b (9) 128.05 22.65

Type IV

J7c D4 2½c carmine 2.25 3.00
J8c D4 5c carmine 1.00 1.75
J9c D4 10c carmine 20.00 24.00
J10c D4 15c carmine 13.00 14.00
J11c D4 20c carmine 200.00 5.00
J13c D4 40c carmine 2.50 3.50
J14c D4 50c deep salmon 9.00 14.00
J15c D4 75c carmine 1.25 2.50
Nos. J7c-J15c (8) 249.00 67.75

1892-95 *Perf. 12½*

Type I

J16 D5 10c carmine 2.25 .30
J17 D5 15c carmine ('95) 12.00 1.75
J18 D5 20c carmine 2.00 .20
Nos. J16-J18 (3) 16.25 2.25

Type III

J16a D5 10c dull red 2.75 2.00
J18a D5 20c dull red 3.75 1.40

Type II

J16b D5 10c dull red 13.00 13.00
J18b D5 20c dull red 18.00 6.50

1906-09

Type I

J19 D5 2½c carmine ('08) .50 .30
J20 D5 5c carmine ('09) 2.25 .15
J21 D5 30c carmine 17.50 5.75
J22 D5 40c carmine ('09) 12.50 1.50
J23 D5 50c carmine ('09) 8.50 .90
J24 D5 75c carmine ('09) 17.00 4.00
Nos. J19-J24 (6) 58.25 12.60

Value in Color of Stamp

1913-39 *Perf. 12½*

J25 D5 1c salmon ('39) .15 *1.25*
J26 D5 2½c salmon .15 .15
J27 D5 3½c salmon ('39) .15 *1.25*
J28 D5 5c salmon .15 .15
J29 D5 7½c salmon ('22) .15 .15
J30 D5 10c salmon .15 .15
J31 D5 12½c salmon ('22) 2.75 .15
J32 D5 15c salmon 2.75 .15
J33 D5 20c salmon .16 .15
J34 D5 25c salmon ('22) .18 .15
J35 D5 30c salmon .20 .20
J36 D5 37½c salmon ('30) 18.00 19.00
J37 D5 40c salmon .20 .15
J38 D5 50c salmon 1.40 .15
J39 D5 75c salmon 2.50 .18
Nos. J25-J39 (15) 29.04 23.38

Thick White Paper
Invisible Gum
Numerals Slightly Larger

1941 Litho. *Perf. 12½*

J25a D5 1c light red .60 *2.00*
J28a D5 5c light red .65 1.00
J30a D5 10c light red 10.50 10.00
J32a D5 15c light red 1.00 1.00
J33a D5 20c light red .80 .80
J35a D5 30c light red 1.25 1.00
J37a D5 40c light red 1.00 .80
Nos. J25a-J37a (7) 15.80 16.60

No. J36 Surcharged with New Value

1937, Oct. 1 Unwmk. *Perf. 12½*

J40 D5 20c on 37½c salmon .24 .30

D6

D7

1939-40

J41 D6 1g salmon 4.50 6.50
J42 D6 1g blue ('40) .20 *3.00*
a. 1g lt bl, thick paper, invisible gum .65 .80

Catalogue values for unused stamps in this section, from this point to the end of the section, are for Never Hinged items.

TE BETALEN

Nos. 234, 237 and 241 Surcharged or Overprinted in Black

PORT

1946, Mar. 11			Photo.	
J43	A28	2½c on 10c red org	.60	.55
J44	A28	10c red orange	1.25	1.10
J45	A28	20c plum	6.25	3.50
J46	A28	40c yellow green	60.00	45.00
		Nos. J43-J46 (4)	68.10	50.15

Perf. 14½x14

1946, Aug. 14		Wmk. 228	Typo.	
J47	D7	1c purple	1.00	1.40
J48	D7	2½c brn org	3.50	2.00
J49	D7	3½c ultra	1.00	1.40
J50	D7	5c red orange	1.00	1.40
J51	D7	7½c Prus green	1.00	1.40
J52	D7	10c deep magenta	1.00	1.40
J53	D7	20c light ultra	1.00	1.40
J54	D7	25c olive	1.50	2.00
J55	D7	30c red brown	1.50	2.00
J56	D7	40c yellow grn	2.25	1.50
J57	D7	50c yellow	2.25	1.50
J58	D7	75c aqua	2.25	1.50
J59	D7	100c apple green	2.25	1.50
		Nos. J47-J59 (13)	21.50	20.40

1948	Litho.	Unwmk.	*Perf. 12½*	
J59A	D7	2½c brown orange	.75	1.50

OFFICIAL STAMPS

Regular Issues of 1883-1909 Overprinted

Perf. 12½

1911, Oct. 1		Typo.	Unwmk.	
O1	A6	½c violet	.15	.30
O2	A6	1c olive grn	.15	.15
O3	A6	2c yellow brn	.15	.15
O4	A3	2½c yellow	.75	.75
O5	A6	2½c blue grn	1.40	1.25
O6	A6	3c orange	.40	.40
O7	A6	4c ultra	.15	.15
O8	A6	5c rose red	.80	.80
b.		Double overprint		*325.00*
O9	A6	7½c gray	2.75	2.75
O10	A9	10c slate	.15	.15
O11	A9	12½c deep blue	2.00	2.25
O12	A9	15c chocolate	.65	.65
a.		Overprinted with two bars	32.50	
b.		As "a," "Dienst" inverted	52.50	
O13	A9	17½c bister	2.75	2.50
O14	A9	20c olive grn	.60	.50
O15	A9	22½c brn & ol grn	3.50	3.00
O16	A9	25c violet	2.00	2.00
O17	A9	30c orange brn	.90	.60
O18	A9	50c red brown	12.00	7.00
O19	A10	1g dull lilac	3.00	1.25
O20	A10	2½g slate blue	27.50	30.00
		Nos. O1-O20 (20)	61.75	

The overprint reads diagonally downward on Nos. O1-O3 and O5-O9.

Overprint Inverted

O1a	A6	½c	45.00	*125.00*
O2a	A6	1c	3.00	*19.00*
O3a	A6	2c	3.00	*20.00*
O5a	A6	2½c	9.00	*30.00*
O6a	A6	3c	110.00	*40.00*
O8a	A6	5c	3.00	*20.00*
O10a	A9	10c	3.00	*7.00*
O11a	A9	12½c	32.50	*55.00*
O14a	A9	20c	175.00	70.00
O16a	A9	25c	*1,250.*	*1,000.*
O17a	A9	30c	225.00	140.00
O18a	A9	50c	32.50	32.50
O19a	A10	1g	*525.00*	*850.00*
O20a	A10	2½g	225.00	*625.00*

Regular Issue of 1892-1894 Overprinted

1911, Oct. 1				
O21	A4	10c orange brn	1.25	.60
O22	A4	12½c gray	2.75	4.75
O23	A4	15c bister	2.75	2.25
O24	A4	20c blue	2.50	.90
O25	A4	25c lilac	9.00	8.00
O26	A4	50c carmine	2.00	.80
O27	A4	2.50g org brn & bl	45.00	45.00
		Nos. O21-O27 (7)	65.25	62.30

Inverted Overprints

O21a	A4	10c	9.25	*32.50*
O22a	A4	12½c	275.00	275.00
O23a	A4	15c	300.00	300.00
O24a	A4	20c	80.00	90.00
O25a	A4	25c	425.00	425.00
O26a	A4	50c	9.25	*85.00*
O27a	A4	2.50g	500.00	800.00

OCCUPATION STAMPS

Issued under Japanese Occupation

During the Japanese occupation of the Netherlands Indies, 1942-45, the occupation forces applied a great variety of overprints to supplies of Netherlands Indies stamps of 1933-42. A few typical examples are shown above.

Most of these overprinted stamps were for use in limited areas, such as Java, Sumatra, Bangka and Billiton, etc. The anchor overprints were applied by the Japanese naval authorities for areas under their control.

For a time, stamps of Straits Settlements and some of the Malayan states, with Japanese overprints, were used in Sumatra and the Riouw archipelago. Stamps of Japan without overprint were also used in the Netherlands Indies during the occupation.

For Use in Java and Sumatra

100 Sen (Cents) = 1 Rupee (Gulden)

Globe Showing Japanese Empire — OS1

Farmer Plowing Rice Field — OS2

Mt. Semeru, Java's Highest Active Volcano — OS3

Bantam Bay, Northwest Java — OS4

Values in Sen

Perf. 12½

1943, Mar. 9		Unwmk.	Litho.	
N1	OS1	2s red brown	1.25	4.25
N2	OS2	3½s carmine	1.25	1.25
N3	OS3	5s green	1.25	1.25
N4	OS4	10s light blue	14.00	2.50
		Nos. N1-N4 (4)	17.75	9.25

Issued to mark the anniversary of Japan's "Victory" in Java.

For Use in Java (also Sumatra, Borneo and Malaya)

Javanese Dancer — OS5

Javanese Puppet — OS6

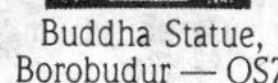

Buddha Statue, Borobudur — OS7

Map of Java — OS8

Sacred Dancer of Djokja Palace, and Borobudur — OS9

Bird of Vishnu, Map of Java and Mt. Semeru — OS10

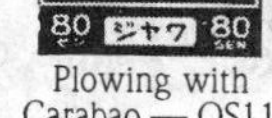

Plowing with Carabao — OS11

Terraced Rice Fields — OS12

Values in Cents, Sen or Rupees

1943-44		Unwmk.	*Perf. 12½*	
N5	OS5	3½c rose red	1.10	.80
N6	OS6	5s yellow grn	1.10	.80
N7	OS7	10c dk blue	1.10	.60
N8	OS8	20c gray olive	1.40	1.40
N9	OS9	40c rose lilac	3.50	3.25
N10	OS10	60c red orange	5.00	1.65
N11	OS11	80s fawn ('44)	11.00	5.50
N12	OS12	1r violet ('44)	42.50	11.50
		Nos. N5-N12 (8)	66.70	25.50

Indies Soldier — OS13

1943, Apr.				
N13	OS13	3½c rose	11.00	15.00
N14	OS13	10c blue	55.00	9.50

Issued to commemorate reaching the postal savings goal of 5,000,000 gulden.

For Use in Sumatra

Batta Tribal House — OS14

Menangkabau House — OS15

Plowing with Carabao — OS16

Nias Island Scene — OS17

Carabao Canyon — OS18

1943		Unwmk.	*Perf. 12½*	
N15	OS14	1c olive green	.55	.30
N16	OS14	2c brt yel brn	.55	.30
N17	OS14	3c bluish green	.55	.30
N18	OS15	3½c rose red	2.50	.30
N19	OS15	4c ultra	2.75	.55
N20	OS15	5c red orange	.80	.30
N21	OS16	10c blue gray	.80	.30
N22	OS16	20c orange brn	1.10	.40
N23	OS17	30c red violet	1.10	.80
N24	OS17	40c dull brown	10.00	2.50
N25	OS18	50c bister brn	10.00	2.50
N26	OS18	1r lt blue vio	52.50	10.50
		Nos. N15-N26 (12)	83.20	19.05

For Use in the Lesser Sunda Islands, Molucca Archipelago and Districts of Celebes and South Borneo Controlled by the Japanese Navy

Japanese Flag, Island Scene — OS19

Mt. Fuji, Kite, Flag, Map of East Indies — OS20

Values in Cents and Gulden

1943		Wmk. 257	Typo.	*Perf. 13*
N27	OS19	2c brown	.40	*15.00*
N28	OS19	3c yellow grn	.40	*15.00*
N29	OS19	3½c brown org	3.25	*15.00*
N30	OS19	5c blue	.40	*15.00*
N31	OS19	10c carmine	.40	*15.00*
N32	OS19	15c ultra	.60	*15.00*
N33	OS19	20c dull violet	.80	*15.00*
		Engr.		
N34	OS20	25c orange	5.50	*15.00*
N35	OS20	30c blue	7.75	*10.00*
N36	OS20	50c slate green	9.25	*25.00*
N37	OS20	1g brown lilac	47.50	*45.00*
		Nos. N27-N37 (11)	76.25	*200.00*

Issued under Nationalist Occupation

Menari Dancer of Amboina — OS21

Perf. 12½

1945, Aug.		Photo.	Unwmk.	
N38	OS21	2c carmine	.15	.35

This stamp was prepared in 1941 or 1942 by Netherlands Indies authorities as an addition to the 1941 "dancers" set, but was issued in 1945 by the Nationalists (Indonesian Republic). It was not recognized by the Dutch. Exists imperforate.

NETHERLANDS NEW GUINEA

'ne–thər–lən(d)z 'nü 'gi–nē

(Dutch New Guinea)

LOCATION — Western half of New Guinea, southwest Pacific Ocean
GOVT. — Former Overseas Territory of the Netherlands
AREA — 151,789 sq. mi.
POP. — 730,000 (est. 1958)
CAPITAL — Hollandia

Netherlands New Guinea came under temporary United Nations administration Oct. 1, 1962, when stamps of this territory overprinted "UNTEA" were introduced to replace issues of Netherlands New Guinea. See West New Guinea (West Irian) in Vol. 6.

100 Cents = 1 Gulden

Catalogue values for all unused stamps in this country are for Never Hinged items.

A1

Queen Juliana

A2 A3

Perf. 12½x13½

1950-52 Unwmk. Photo.

No.	Type	Description	Unused	Used
1	A1	1c slate blue	.15	.15
2	A1	2c deep org	.15	.15
3	A1	2½c olive brn	.15	.15
4	A1	3c deep plum	1.65	1.25
5	A1	4c blue grn	1.65	1.10
6	A1	5c ultra	3.25	.15
7	A1	7½c org brown	.35	.15
8	A1	10c purple	1.75	.15
9	A1	12½c crimson	1.75	1.40

Perf. 13½x12½

No.	Type	Description	Unused	Used
10	A2	15c brown org	1.25	.55
11	A2	20c blue	.35	.15
12	A2	25c orange red	.35	.15
13	A2	30c dp blue ('52)	7.25	.30
14	A2	40c blue grn	.75	.15
15	A2	45c brown ('52)	3.50	.50
16	A2	50c deep orange	.75	.15
17	A2	55c brown blk ('52)	6.25	.55
18	A2	80c purple	7.25	3.00

Engr. *Perf. 12½x12*

No.	Type	Description	Unused	Used
19	A3	1g red	11.00	.15
20	A3	2g yellow brn ('52)	9.00	1.25
21	A3	5g dk olive grn	12.00	1.00
		Nos. 1-21 (21)	70.55	12.55

For surcharges see Nos. B1-B3.

Bird of Paradise — A4

Queen Victoria Crowned Pigeon — A5

Queen Juliana — A6

10c, 15c, 20c, Bird of Paradise with raised wings.

Photo.; Litho. (Nos. 24, 26, 28)

1954-60 *Perf. 12½x12*

No.	Type	Description	Unused	Used
22	A4	1c ver & yel ('58)	.15	.15
23	A4	5c choc & yel	.15	.15
24	A5	7c org red, bl & brn vio ('59)	.15	.20
25	A4	10c aqua & red brn	.15	.15
26	A5	12c grn, bl & brn vio ('59)	.15	.20
27	A4	15c dp yel & red brn	.15	.15
28	A5	17c brn vio & bl ('59)	.15	.15
29	A4	20c lt bl grn & red brn ('56)	.50	.30
30	A6	25c red	.15	.15
31	A6	30c deep blue	.15	.15
32	A6	40c dp orange ('60)	1.75	1.75
33	A6	45c dk olive ('58)	.65	.65
34	A6	55c dk blue grn	.45	.15
35	A6	80c dl gray vio	.80	.30
36	A6	85c dk vio brn ('56)	.90	.45
37	A6	1g plum ('59)	4.50	2.00
		Nos. 22-37 (16)	10.90	7.05

Stamps overprinted "UNTEA" are listed under West New Guinea in Vol. 6.

For surcharges see Nos. B4-B6.

Papuan Watching Helicopter — A7

Mourning Woman — A8

1959, Apr. 10 Photo. *Perf. 11½x11*

No.	Type	Description	Unused	Used
38	A7	55c red brown & blue	.85	.65

1959 expedition to the Star Mountains of New Guinea.

1960, Apr. 7 Unwmk. *Perf. 13x14*

No.	Type	Description	Unused	Used
39	A8	25c blue	.40	.40
40	A8	30c yellow bister	.40	.50

World Refugee Year, July 1, 1959-June 30, 1960.

Council Building A9

1961, Apr. 5 Litho. *Perf. 11x11½*

No.	Type	Description	Unused	Used
41	A9	25c bluish green	.20	.25
42	A9	30c rose	.20	.25

Inauguration of the New Council.

School Children Crossing Street — A10

Design: 30c, Men looking at traffic sign.

1962, Mar. 16 Photo. *Perf. 14x13*

No.	Type	Description	Unused	Used
43	A10	25c dp blue & red	.20	.25
44	A10	30c brt green & red	.20	.25

Need for road safety.

Queen Juliana and Prince Bernhard — A11

1962, Apr. 28 Unwmk. *Perf. 14x13*

No.	Type	Description	Unused	Used
45	A11	55c olive brown	.25	.30

Silver wedding anniv.

Tropical Beach A12

Design: 30c, Palm trees on beach.

1962, July 18 *Perf. 14x13*

No.	Type	Description	Unused	Used
46	A12	25c multicolored	.20	.25
47	A12	30c multicolored	.20	.25

5th So. Pacific Conf., Pago Pago, July 1962.

SEMI-POSTAL STAMPS

Regular Issue of 1950-52 Surcharged in Black

hulp
nederland
1953
+ 5 ct

Perf. 12½x13½

1953, Feb. 9 Unwmk. Photo.

No.	Type	Description	Unused	Used
B1	A1	5c + 5c ultra	9.00	9.00

Perf. 13½x12½

No.	Type	Description	Unused	Used
B2	A2	15c + 10c brn org	9.00	9.00
B3	A2	25c + 10c org red	9.00	9.00
		Nos. B1-B3 (3)	27.00	27.00

The tax was for flood relief work in the Netherlands.

Nos. 23, 25, 27 Surcharged in Red

1955, Nov. 1 *Perf. 12½x12*

No.	Type	Description	Unused	Used
B4	A4	5c + 5c	.90	.90
B5	A4	10c + 10c	.90	.90
B6	A4	15c + 10c	.90	.90
		Nos. B4-B6 (3)	2.70	2.70

The surtax was for the Red Cross.

Leprosarium — SP1

Papuan Girl and Beach Scene — SP2

10c+5c, 30c+10c, Young Papuan and huts.

Perf. 12x12½

1956, Dec. 15 Unwmk. Photo.

No.	Type	Description	Unused	Used
B7	SP1	5c + 5c dk slate grn	.75	.75
B8	SP1	10c + 5c brn violet	.75	.75
B9	SP1	25c + 10c brt blue	.75	.75
B10	SP1	30c + 10c ocher	.75	.75
		Nos. B7-B10 (4)	3.00	3.00

The surtax was for the fight against leprosy.

1957, Oct. 1 *Perf. 12½x12*

10c+5c, 30c+10c, Papuan boy and pile dwelling.

No.	Type	Description	Unused	Used
B11	SP2	5c + 5c maroon	.65	.65
B12	SP2	10c + 5c slate grn	.65	.65
B13	SP2	25c + 10c brown	.65	.65
B14	SP2	30c + 10c dark blue	.65	.65
		Nos. B11-B14 (4)	2.60	2.60

The surtax was to fight infant mortality.

Ancestral Image, North Coast New Guinea — SP3

Bignonia — SP4

Design: 10c+5c, 30c+10c, Bowl in form of human figure, Asmat-Papua.

1958, Oct. 1 Litho. *Perf. 12½x12*

No.	Type	Description	Unused	Used
B15	SP3	5c + 5c bl, blk & red	.75	.75
B16	SP3	10c + 5c rose lake, blk, red & yel	.75	.75
B17	SP3	25c + 10c bl grn, blk & red	.75	.75
B18	SP3	30c + 10c ol gray, blk, red & yel	.75	.75
		Nos. B15-B18 (4)	3.00	3.00

The surtax was for the Red Cross.

1959, Nov. 16 Photo. *Perf. 12½x13*

Flowers: 10c+5c, Orchid. 25c+10c, Rhododendron. 30c+10c, Gesneriacea.

No.	Type	Description	Unused	Used
B19	SP4	5c + 5c car rose & grn	.50	.35
B20	SP4	10c + 5c ol, yel & lil	.50	.35
B21	SP4	25c + 10c red, org & grn	.50	.45
B22	SP4	30c + 10c vio & grn	.50	.45
		Nos. B19-B22 (4)	2.00	1.60

Birdwing — SP5

Various Butterflies.

Perf. 13x12½

1960, Sept. 1 Unwmk. Litho.

No.	Type	Description	Unused	Used
B23	SP5	5c + 5c lt bl, blk, emer & yel	.65	.65
B24	SP5	10c + 5c sal, blk & bl	.65	.65
B25	SP5	25c + 10c yel, blk & org red	.75	.70
B26	SP5	30c + 10c lt grn, brn & yel	.75	.70
		Nos. B23-B26 (4)	2.80	2.70

Surtax for social care.

Rhinoceros Beetle and Coconut Palm Leaf — SP6

Beetles & leaves of host plants: 10c+5c, Ectocemus 10-maculatus Montri, a primitive weevil. 25c+10c, Stag beetle. 30c+10c, Tortoise beetle.

1961, Sept. 15 *Perf. 13x12½*

Beetles in Natural Colors

No.	Type	Description	Unused	Used
B27	SP6	5c + 5c deep org	.20	.25
B28	SP6	10c + 5c lt ultra	.20	.25
B29	SP6	25c + 10c citron	.25	.30
B30	SP6	30c + 10c green	.30	.35
		Nos. B27-B30 (4)	.95	1.15

Surtax for social care.

Crab — SP7

Designs: 10c+5c, Lobster, vert. 25c+10c, Spiny lobster, vert. 30c+10c, Shrimp.

Perf. 14x13, 13x14

1962, Sept. 17 Unwmk.

No.	Type	Description	Unused	Used
B31	SP7	5c + 5c red, grn, brn & yel	.15	.15
B32	SP7	10c + 5c Prus bl & yel	.15	.15
B33	SP7	25c + 10c multicolored	.20	.20
B34	SP7	30c + 10c bl, org red & yel	.20	.25
		Nos. B31-B34 (4)	.70	.75

The surtax on Nos. B19-B34 went to various social works organizations.

POSTAGE DUE STAMPS

D1

Perf. 13½x12½

1957 Photo. Unwmk.

No.	Type	Description	Unused	Used
J1	D1	1c vermilion	.15	.15
J2	D1	5c vermilion	.35	.75
J3	D1	10c vermilion	1.10	1.50
J4	D1	25c vermilion	1.65	.55
J5	D1	40c vermilion	1.65	.65
J6	D1	1g blue	2.00	2.25
		Nos. J1-J6 (6)	6.90	5.85

NEVIS

'nē–vəs

LOCATION — West Indies, southeast of Puerto Rico

GOVT. — A former presidency of the Leeward Islands Colony (British)

AREA — 50 sq. mi.

POP. — 9,800 (1990)

CAPITAL — Charlestown

Nevis stamps were discontinued in 1890 and replaced by those of the Leeward Islands. From 1903 to 1956 stamps of St. Kitts-Nevis and Leeward Islands were used concurrently. From 1956 to 1980 stamps of St. Kitts-Nevis were used. While still a part of St. Kitts-Nevis, Nevis started issuing stamps in 1980.

See Leeward Islands and St. Kitts-Nevis.

12 Pence = 1 Shilling

100 Cents = 1 Dollar

Catalogue values for unused stamps in this country are for Never Hinged items, beginning with Scott 100 in the regular postage section and Scott O1 in the officials section.

Unused examples of Nos. 1-8 almost always have no original gum, and they are valued without gum. These stamps with original gum are worth more. Other issues are valued with original gum as defined in the catalogue introduction. Very fine examples of Nos. 1-8, will have perforations touching the design on at least one side due to the narrow spacing of the stamps on the plates. Stamps with perfs clear of the design on all four sides are scarce and will command higher prices.

Medicinal Spring
A1 A2

A3 A4

1861 Unwmk. Engr. *Perf. 13*

Bluish Wove Paper

1 A1 1p lake rose 225.00 110.00
2 A2 4p dull rose 825.00 275.00
3 A3 6p gray 475.00 275.00
4 A4 1sh green 950.00 250.00

Grayish Wove Paper

5 A1 1p lake rose 45.00 35.00
6 A2 4p dull rose 75.00 55.00
7 A3 6p lilac gray 70.00 40.00
8 A4 1sh green 150.00 50.00

1867 White Wove Paper *Perf. 15*

9 A1 1p red 30.00 25.00
10 A2 4p orange 95.00 20.00
11 A4 1sh yellow green 850.00 120.00
12 A4 1sh blue green 150.00 30.00

Laid Paper

13 A4 1sh yel green 16,500. *3,750.*
Manuscript cancel 900.00

No. 13 values are for copies with design cut into on one or two sides.

1876 Litho.

Wove Paper

14 A1 1p rose 15.00 12.50
14A A1 1p red 25.00 18.00
b. 1p vermilion 25.00 18.00
c. Imperf., pair 360.00
d. Half used as ½p on cover 1,350.
15 A2 4p orange 175.00 30.00
a. Imperf.
b. Vert. pair, imperf. between *2,500.*
16 A3 6p olive gray 200.00 190.00
17 A4 1sh gray green 55.00 80.00
a. 1sh dark green 60.00 90.00
b. Horiz. strip of 3, perf. all around & imperf. btwn. *4,000.*

Perf. 11½

18 A1 1p vermilion 37.50 47.50
a. Horiz. pair, imperf. btwn.
b. Half used as ½p on cover 1,350.
c. Imperf., pair 225.00
Nos. 14-18 (6) 507.50 378.00

Queen Victoria — A5

1879-80 Typo. Wmk. 1 *Perf. 14*

19 A5 1p violet ('80) 40.00 27.50
a. Diagonal half used as ½p on cover 900.00
20 A5 2½p red brown 85.00 80.00

1882-90 Wmk. Crown and CA (2)

21 A5 ½p green ('83) 2.50 6.00
22 A5 1p violet 80.00 22.50
a. Half used as ½p on cover 700.00
23 A5 1p rose ('84) 3.00 3.25
24 A5 2½p red brown 90.00 50.00
25 A5 2½p ultra ('84) 10.00 7.50
26 A5 4p blue 300.00 45.00
27 A5 4p gray ('84) 4.50 3.50
28 A5 6p green ('83) 350.00 *350.00*
29 A5 6p brown org ('86) 17.00 45.00
30 A5 1sh violet ('90) 85.00 175.00
Nos. 21-30 (10) 942.00 *707.75*

Half of No. 22 Surcharged in Black or Violet — NEVIS. ½d

1883

31 A5 ½p on half of 1p *1,200.* 30.00
a. Double surcharge 450.00
b. Unsevered pair *1,750.* 225.00
32 A5 ½p on half of 1p (V) *1,250.* 30.00
a. Double surcharge 450.00

Surcharge reads up or down.

Catalogue values for unused stamps in this section, from this point to the end of the section, are for Never Hinged items.

St. Kitts-Nevis Nos. 357-369 Ovptd.

Perf. 14½x14

1980, June 23 Litho. Wmk. 373

100 A61 5c multicolored .15 .15
101 A61 10c multicolored .15 .15
102 A61 12c multicolored .15 .15
103 A61 15c multicolored .15 .15
104 A61 25c multicolored .15 .15
105 A61 30c multicolored .20 .20
106 A61 40c multicolored .30 .30
107 A61 45c multicolored .30 .30
108 A61 50c multicolored .30 .30
109 A61 55c multicolored .35 .35
110 A61 $1 multicolored .60 .60
111 A61 $5 multicolored 3.00 3.00
112 A61 $10 multicolored 6.00 6.00
Nos. 100-112 (13) 11.80 11.80

The bars cover "St. Christopher" and "Anguilla."
The 25c and $1 also come on unwatermarked paper.

80th Birthday of Queen Mother Elizabeth — A6

1980, Sept. 4 *Perf. 14*

113 A6 $2 multicolored .50 .50

Ships and Boats A6a

1980, Oct. 8

114 A6a 5c Nevis lighter .15 .15
115 A6a 30c Local fishing boat .15 .15
116 A6a 55c *Caona* .30 .30

Size: 38x52mm

117 A6a $3 Windjammer's S.V. *Polynesia* 1.65 1.65
a. Perf. 12½x12 1.65 1.65
b. Booklet pane of 3 #117a 5.00
Nos. 114-117 (4) 2.25 2.25

No. 117b separated into three parts by roulettes running vert. through the margin surrounding the stamps. For overprint see No. 538.

Christmas A7

Landmarks A8

A9

1980, Nov. 20 *Perf. 14*

118 A7 5c Mother and child .15 .15
119 A7 30c Heralding angel .15 .15
120 A7 $2.50 Three kings 1.50 1.50
Nos. 118-120 (3) 1.80 1.80

1981, Feb. 5

121 A8 5c Charlestown Pier .15 .15
122 A8 10c Court House & Library .15 .15
123 A9 15c New River Mill .15 .15
124 A9 20c Nelson Museum .15 .15
125 A9 25c St. James' Parish Church .15 .15
126 A9 30c Nevis Lane .15 .15
127 A9 40c Zetland Plantation .20 .20
128 A9 45c Nisbet Plantation .25 .25
129 A9 50c Pinney's Beach .25 .25
130 A9 55c Eva Wilkin's Studio .30 .30
131 A9 $1 Nevis at dawn .55 .55
132 A9 $2.50 Ft. Charles ruins 1.40 1.40
133 A9 $5 Old Bath House 2.75 2.75
134 A9 $10 Nisbet's Beach 5.50 5.50
Nos. 121-134 (14) 12.10 12.10

Nos. 121-134 exist inscribed "Questa 1982," issued June 9, 1982. Same values.
For surcharges see Nos. 169-181.

Prince Charles, Lady Diana, Royal Yacht Charlotte A9a

Prince Charles and Lady Diana — A9b

Illustration A9b is greatly reduced.

1981, June 23 Wmk. 373 *Perf. 14*

135 A9a 55c Couple, *Royal Caroline* .25 .25
a. Bklt. pane of 4, perf. 12, unwmkd. 1.10 1.10
136 A9b 55c Couple .30 .30
137 A9a $2 Couple, *Royal Sovereign* .95 .95
138 A9b $2 like No. 136 .95 .95
a. Bklt. pane of 2, perf. 12, unwmkd. 2.00 2.00
139 A9a $5 Couple, HMY *Britannia* 2.25 2.25
140 A9b $5 like No. 136 2.25 2.25
Nos. 135-140 (6) 6.95 6.95

Souvenir Sheet

1981, Dec. 14 *Perf. 12*

141 A9b $4.50 like No. 136 3.25 3.25

Stamps of the same denomination issued in sheets of 7 (6 type A9a and 1 type A9b).
For surcharges see Nos. 453-454.

Butterflies — A10

1982, Feb. 16 *Perf. 14*

142 A10 5c Zebra .15 .15
143 A10 30c Malachite .20 .20
144 A10 55c Southern dagger tail .35 .35
145 A10 $2 Large orange sulphur 1.40 1.40
Nos. 142-145 (4) 2.10 2.10

For overprint see No. 452.

1983, June 8

146 A10 30c Tropical chequered skipper .20 .20
147 A10 55c Caribbean buckeye, vert. .40 .40
148 A10 $1.10 Common long-tailed skipper, vert. .80 .80
149 A10 $2 Mimic 1.50 1.50
Nos. 146-149 (4) 2.90 2.90

21st Birthday of Princess Diana, July 1 — A11

1982, June 22 *Perf. 13½x14*

150 A11 30c Caroline of Brunswick .15 .15
151 A11 55c Brunswick arms .35 .35
152 A11 $5 Diana 3.00 3.00
Nos. 150-152 (3) 3.50 3.50

For surcharge see No. 449.

Nos. 150-152 Overprinted "ROYAL BABY"

1982, July 12

153 A11 30c multicolored .15 .15
154 A11 55c multicolored .35 .35
155 A11 $5 multicolored 3.00 3.00
Nos. 153-155 (3) 3.50 3.50

Birth of Prince William of Wales, June 21.

Scouting, 75th Anniv. — A12

1982, Aug. 18

156 A12 5c Cycling .20 .15
157 A12 30c Running .30 .20
158 A12 $2.50 Building campfire 1.90 1.90
Nos. 156-158 (3) 2.40 2.25

For overprints see Nos. 447, 455.

Christmas — A13

Illustrations by youths. Nos. 159-160 vert.

Perf. 13½x14, 14x13½

1982, Oct. 20

159 A13 15c Eugene Seabrookes .15 .15
160 A13 30c Kharenzabeth Glasgow .15 .15
161 A13 $1.50 David Grant .90 .90
162 A13 $2.50 Leonard Huggins 1.50 1.50
Nos. 159-162 (4) 2.70 2.70

Coral — A14

1983, Jan. 12 *Perf. 14*

163 A14 15c Tube sponge .15 .15
164 A14 30c Stinging coral .20 .20
165 A14 55c Flower coral .40 .40
166 A14 $3 Sea rod, red fire sponge 2.25 2.25
a. Souvenir sheet of 4, #163-166 3.00 3.00
Nos. 163-166 (4) 3.00 3.00

For overprints see Nos. 446, 448.

Commonwealth Day — A15

1983, Mar. 14

167 A15 55c HMS *Boreas* off Nevis .30 .30
168 A15 $2 Lord Nelson, *Boreas* 1.25 1.25

Nos. 121 and 123-134 Ovptd.

INDEPENDENCE 1983 — No. 169
INDEPENDENCE 1983 — No. 170-181

1983, Sept. 23

169 A8 5c multicolored .15 .15
a. Overprint larger with serifed letters
170 A9 15c multicolored .15 .15
171 A9 20c multicolored .15 .15
172 A9 25c multicolored .15 .15
173 A9 30c multicolored .18 .18
174 A9 40c multicolored .25 .25
175 A9 45c multicolored .20 .25
176 A9 50c multicolored .30 .30
177 A9 55c multicolored .25 .30
178 A9 $1 multicolored .60 .60
179 A9 $2.50 multicolored 1.50 1.50
180 A9 $5 multicolored 2.75 3.00
181 A9 $10 multicolored 5.00 6.00
Nos. 169-181 (13) 11.63 12.98

Nos. 169 has 1982 inscription, 170-181 have 1983 inscription. Nos. 169a, 170-174, 177-181 exist without date inscription.

1st Manned Flight, Bicent. A16

Designs: 10c, Montgolfier Balloon, 1783, vert. 45c, Lindbergh's Sikorsky S-38 carrying mail, 1929. 50c, Beechcraft Twin Bonanza. $2.50, Sea Harrier, 1st operational V/STOL fighter.

1983, Sept. 28 **Wmk. 380**

182 A16 10c multicolored .15 .15
183 A16 45c multicolored .28 .28
184 A16 50c multicolored .32 .32
185 A16 $2.50 multicolored 1.50 1.50
a. Souvenir sheet of 4, #182-185 2.25 2.25
Nos. 182-185 (4) 2.25 2.25

Christmas A17

1983, Nov. 7

186 A17 5c Nativity .15 .15
187 A17 30c Shepherds, flock .20 .20
188 A17 55c Angels .35 .35
189 A17 $3 Youths 2.00 2.00
a. Souvenir sheet of 4, #186-189 2.75 2.75
Nos. 186-189 (4) 2.70 2.70

Leaders of the World
Large quantities of some Leaders of the World issues were sold at a fraction of face value when the printer was liquidated.

A18

A19

Leaders of the World: Locomotives.

1983-86 Litho. Unwmk. *Perf. 12½*
Pairs, Types A18-A19

190 1c 1882 Class Wee Bogie, UK .15 .15
191 5c 1968 JNR Class EF81, Japan .15 .15
192 5c 1878 Snowdon Ranger, UK .15 .15
193 10c 1927 P.O. Class 5500, France .15 .15
194 15c 1859 Connor Single Class .15 .15
195 30c 1904 Large Belpaire Passenger, UK .20 .20
196 30c 1829 Stourbridge Lion, US .20 .20
197 45c 1934 Cock O' The North .30 .30
198 55c 1945 County of Oxford, GB .35 .35
199 60c 1940 SNCF Class 240P, France .40 .40
200 60c 1851 Comet, UK .40 .40
201 60c 1904 County Class, UK .40 .40
202 60c 1926 JNR Class 7000, Japan .40 .40
203 75c 1877 Nord L'Outrance, France .50 .50
204 75c 1919 CM St.P&P Bipolar, US .50 .50
205 75c 1897 Palatinate Railway Class P3, Germany .50 .50
206 90c 1908 Class 8H, UK .60 .60
207 $1 1927 King George V .70 .70
208 $1 1951 Britannia .70 .70
209 $1 1924 Pendennis Castle .70 .70
210 $1 1960 Evening Star .70 .70
211 $1 1934 Stanier Class 5, GB .70 .70
212 $1 1946 Winston Churchill Battle of Britain .70 .70
213 $1 1935 Mallard A4 .70 .70
214 $1 1899 Q.R. Class PB-15, Australia .70 .70
215 $1 1836 C&St.L Dorchester, Canada .70 .70
216 $1.50 1953 U.P. Gas Turbine, US 1.00 1.00
217 $1.50 1969 U.P. Centennial Class, US 1.00 1.00
218 $2 1866 No. 23 Class A, UK 1.25 1.25
219 $2 1955 NY, NH & HR FL9, US 1.25 1.25
220 $2 1837 B&O Lafayette, US 1.25 1.25
221 $2.50 1964 JNR Shin-Kansen, Japan 2.25 2.25
222 $2.50 1928 DRG Class 64, Germany 2.25 2.25
223 $3 1882 D&RGR Class C-16, US 2.25 2.25
Nos. 190-223 (34) 24.30 24.30

Issued: #190, 200, 205, 218, Apr. 26, 1985; #191, 193, 199, 221, Oct. 29, 1984; #192, 195, 201, 203, 214, 222, July 26, 1985; #194, 197, 202, 204, 215, 217, 220, 223, Oct. 1, 1986; #196, 203, 216, 219, Jan. 30, 1986; #198, 206-213, Nov. 10, 1983.

British Monarchs, Scenes from History
A20 A21

1984

258 A20 5c Boer War .15 .15
259 A21 5c Queen Victoria .15 .15
260 A20 5c Signing of the Magna Carta .15 .15
261 A21 5c King John .15 .15
262 A20 50c Victoria, diff. .18 .18
263 A21 50c Osborne House .18 .18
264 A20 55c John, diff. .20 .20
265 A21 55c Newark Castle, Nottinghamshire .20 .20
266 A20 60c Battle of Dettingen .22 .22
267 A21 60c King George II .22 .22
268 A20 75c George II, diff. .28 .28
269 A21 75c Bank of England, 1732 .28 .28
270 A20 $1 George II's coat of arms .38 .38
271 A21 $1 George II, diff. .38 .38
272 A20 $2 John's coat of arms .75 .75
273 A21 $2 John, diff. .75 .75
274 A20 $3 Victoria's coat of arms 1.25 1.25
275 A21 $3 Victoria, diff. 1.25 1.25
Nos. 258-275 (18) 7.12 7.12

Issue dates: Nos. 258-259, 262-263, 266-271 and 274-275, Apr. 11; others, Nov. 20.

Nos. 258-259, 260-261 and stamps of the same denomination printed se-tenant in continuous designs.

Tourism A22

1984, May 16 **Wmk. 380** *Perf. 14*

276 A22 55c Golden Rock Inn .50 .50
277 A22 55c Rest Haven Inn .50 .50
278 A22 55c Cliffdwellers Hotel .50 .50
279 A22 55c Pinney's Beach Hotel .50 .50
Nos. 276-279 (4) 2.00 2.00

1985, Feb. 12

280 A22 $1.20 Croney's Old Manor Hotel .80 .80
281 A22 $1.20 Montpelier Plantation Inn .80 .80
282 A22 $1.20 Nisbet's Plantation Inn .80 .80
283 A22 $1.20 Zetland Plantation Inn .80 .80
Nos. 280-283 (4) 3.20 3.20

A $15 stamp picturing the seal of the colony was issued June 8, 1984. While issued for revenue purposes it was valid for postal use.

A23

A24

Leaders of the World: Classic cars.

1984-86 Unwmk. *Perf. 12½*
Pairs, Types A23-A24

285 1c 1932 Cadillac V16 Fleetwood Convertible, US .15 .15
286 1c 1935 Delahaye Type 35 Cabriolet, France .15 .15
287 5c 1916 Packard Twin Six Touring Car, US .15 .15
288 5c 1929 Lagonda Speed Model Touring Car, GB .15 .15
289 5c 1958 Ferrari Testarossa, Italy .15 .15
290 10c 1934 Voisin Aerodyne, France .15 .15
291 10c 1912 Sunbeam Coupe De L'Auto, GB .15 .15
292 10c 1936 Adler Trumpf, Germany .15 .15
293 15c 1886 Daimler 2-Cylinder, Germany .15 .15
294 15c 1930 Riley Brooklands Nine, UK .15 .15
295 30c 1967 Jaguar E-Type 4.2 Liter, GB .20 .20
296 35c 1970 Porsche 911 S Targa, Germany .25 .25
297 35c 1948 Cisitalia Pinnifarina Coupe, Italy .25 .25
298 45c 1885 Benz Three-wheeler, Germany .30 .30
299 45c 1966 Alfa Romeo GTA, Italy .30 .30
300 50c 1947 Volkswagen Beetle, Germany .35 .35
301 50c 1963 Buick Riviera .35 .35
302 55c 1947 MG TC, GB .40 .40
303 60c 1960 Cooper Climax, UK .40 .40
304 60c 1957 Maserati Tipo 250F, Italy .40 .40
305 60c 1913 Pierce Arrow Type 66, US .40 .40
306 75c 1904 Ford 999, US .50 .50
307 75c 1980 Porsche 928S, Germany .50 .50
308 75c 1910 Oldsmobile Limited, US .50 .50
309 $1 1951 Jaguar C-Type, UK .65 .65
310 $1 1928 Willys-Knight 66A, US .65 .65
311 $1.15 1933 MG K3 Magnette, GB .75 .75
312 $1.50 1937 Lincoln Zephyr, US 1.00 1.00
313 $1.50 1937 ERA 1.5 l B Type, UK 1.00 1.00
314 $1.75 1953 Studebaker Starliner, US 1.15 1.15
315 $2 1926 Pontiac 2-door, US 1.35 1.35
316 $2.50 1966 Cobra Roadster 289, US 1.75 1.75
317 $2.50 1930 MG M-Type Midget, UK 1.75 1.75
318 $3 1966 Aston Martin DB6 Hardtop, GB 2.00 2.00
319 $3 1932 Pierce Arrow V12, US 2.00 2.00
320 $3 1971 Rolls Royce Corniche, UK 2.00 2.00
321 $3 1953 Chevrolet Corvette, US 2.00 2.00
322 $3 1919 Cunningham V-8, US 2.00 2.00
Nos. 285-322 (38) 26.65 26.65

Issued: #285, 287, 293, 296, 298, 302, 316, 318, 7/25/84; #286, 289-290, 301, 303, 306, 317, 320, 2/20/85; #288, 295, 300, 319, 10/23/84; #291, 297, 307, 311-312, 315, 10/4/85; #292, 303, 308-309, 313, 321, 1/30/86; #294, 299, 305, 310, 314, 322, 8/15/86.

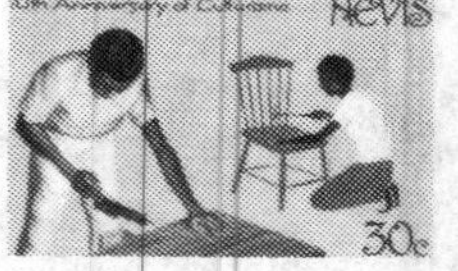

Culturama Carnival, 10th Anniv. A24a

Wmk. 380
1984, Aug. 1 **Litho.** *Perf. 14*

361 A24a 30c Carpentry .18 .18
362 A24a 55c Weaving mats and baskets .32 .32
363 A24a $1 Ceramics .60 .60
364 A24a $3 Carnival queen, folk dancers 1.75 1.75
Nos. 361-364 (4) 2.85 2.85

Flowers — A24b

1984, Aug. 8

365 A24b 5c Yellow bell .15 .15
366 A24b 10c Plumbago .15 .15
367 A24b 15c Flamboyant .15 .15
368 A24b 20c Eyelash orchid .15 .15
369 A24b 30c Bougainvillea .16 .16
370 A24b 40c Hibiscus .20 .20
371 A24b 50c Night-blooming cereus .28 .28
372 A24b 55c Yellow mahoe .30 .30
373 A24b 60c Spider lily .32 .32
374 A24b 75c Scarlet cordia .40 .40
375 A24b $1 Shell ginger .55 .55
376 A24b $3 Blue petrea 1.65 1.65

377 A24b $5 Coral hibiscus 2.75 2.75
378 A24b $10 Passion flower 5.50 5.50
Nos. 365-378 (14) 12.71 12.71

Nos. 368 and 370 were reissued on July 23, 1986 with date inscription. Values for those two stamps are for the 1986 printing.

Independence of St. Kitts and Nevis, 1st Anniv. — A26

1984, Sept. 18
379 A26 15c Picking cotton .15 .15
380 A26 55c Hamilton House .32 .32
381 A26 $1.10 Self-sufficiency in food production .65 .65
382 A26 $3 Pinney's Beach 1.75 1.75
Nos. 379-382 (4) 2.87 2.87

Leaders of the World
A27 A28

Cricket players and team emblems (Type A27) and match scenes (Type A28).

1984 Unwmk. *Perf. 12½*
Pairs, Types A27-A28
383 . 5c C.P. Mead, England .15 .15
384 . 5c J.D. Love, Yorkshire .15 .15
385 . 15c S.J. Dennis, Yorkshire .15 .15
386 . 25c J.B. Statham, England .15 .15
387 . 55c Sir Learie Constantine, West Indies .22 .22
388 . 55c B.W. Luckhurst, Kent .22 .22
389 . $2.50 Sir Leonard Hutton, England 1.00 1.00
390 . $2.50 B.L. D'Oliveira, England 1.00 1.00
Nos. 383-390 (8) 3.04 3.04

Issued: #383, 386, 389, Oct. 23; others, Nov. 20.

Christmas
A29

Musicians from local bands: 15c, Flutist and drummer of the Honeybees Band. 40c, Guitar and barhow players of the Canary Birds Band. 60c, Shell All Stars steel band. $3, Choir, organist, St. John's Church, Fig Tree.

1984, Nov. 2 Wmk. 380 *Perf. 14*
399 A29 15c multicolored .15 .15
400 A29 40c multicolored .25 .25
401 A29 60c multicolored .38 .38
402 A29 $3 multicolored 1.90 1.90
Nos. 399-402 (4) 2.68 2.68

Birds
A30

1985, Mar. 19
403 A30 20c Broad-winged hawk .15 .15
404 A30 40c Red-tailed hawk .28 .28
405 A30 60c Little blue heron .42 .42
406 A30 $3 Great white heron 2.00 2.00
Nos. 403-406 (4) 2.85 2.85

Leaders of the World — A31

Birds.

1985 Unwmk. *Perf. 12½*
407 A31 1c Painted bunting .15 .15
408 A31 1c Golden-crowned kinglet .15 .15
409 A31 5c Eastern bluebird .15 .15
410 A31 5c Northern cardinal .15 .15
411 A31 40c Common flicker .15 .15
412 A31 40c Western tanager .15 .15
413 A31 55c Belted kingfisher .20 .20
414 A31 55c Mangrove cuckoo .20 .20
415 A31 60c Yellow warbler .22 .22
416 A31 60c Cerulean warbler .22 .22
417 A31 60c Sage thrasher .22 .22
418 A31 60c Evening grosbeak .22 .22
419 A31 $2 Burrowing owl 1.25 1.25
420 A31 $2 Long-eared owl 1.25 1.25
421 A31 $2.50 Blackburnian warbler 1.50 1.50
422 A31 $2.50 Northern oriole 1.50 1.50
Nos. 407-422 (16) 7.68 7.68

Birth bicent. of ornithologist John J. Audubon.

Issue dates: Nos. 407-408, 411-412, 417-418 and 421-422, June 3; others, Mar. 25. Nos. 415-416, 417-418 and stamps of the same denomination printed se-tenant in continuous designs.

Girl Guides, 75th Anniv. — A32

Queen Mother Elizabeth — A33

1985, June 17 Wmk. 380 *Perf. 14*
423 A32 15c Troop, horiz. .15 .15
424 A32 60c Uniforms, 1910, 1985 .40 .40
425 A32 $1 Lord and Lady Baden-Powell .65 .65
426 A32 $3 Princess Margaret 2.00 2.00
Nos. 423-426 (4) 3.20 3.20

1985, July 31 Unwmk. *Perf. 12½*
427 A33 45c Black hat, white plume .30 .30
428 A33 45c Blue hat, pink feathers .30 .30
429 A33 75c Blue hat .52 .52
430 A33 75c Tiara .52 .52
431 A33 $1.20 Violet & blue hat .85 .85
432 A33 $1.20 Blue hat .85 .85
433 A33 $1.50 Light blue hat 1.00 1.00
434 A33 $1.50 Black hat 1.00 1.00
Nos. 427-434 (8) 5.34 5.34

Souvenir Sheets
435 Sheet of 2 3.00 3.00
a. A33 $2 As a child, c. 1910 1.50 1.50
b. A33 $2 Queen consort, c. 1945 1.50 1.50

1985, Dec. 27
436 Sheet of 2 3.00 3.00
a. A33 $3.50 similar to No. 427 1.40 1.40
b. A33 $3.50 similar to No. 428 1.40 1.40
437 Sheet of 2 5.00 5.00
a. A33 $6 like No. 433 2.50 2.50
b. A33 $6 like No. 434 2.50 2.50

Stamps of the same denomination printed se-tenant in continuous designs.

For overprints see Nos. 450-451.

Great Western Railway, 150th Anniv.
A34 A35

Railway engineers (Type A34) and their achievements (Type A35). Stamps of the same denomination printed se-tenant in continuous designs.

1985, Aug. 31
438 A34 25c Isambard Brunel .15 .15
439 A35 25c Royal Albert Bridge, 1859 .15 .15
440 A34 50c William Dean .28 .28
441 A35 50c *Lord of the Isles,* 1895 .28 .28
442 A35 $1 *Lode Star,* 1907 .55 .55
443 A34 $1 G.J. Churchward .55 .55
444 A35 $2.50 Pendennis Castle Class, 1924 1.50 1.50
445 A34 $2.50 C.B. Collett 1.50 1.50
Nos. 438-445 (8) 4.96 4.96

Nos. 163, 157, 164, 151, 427-428, 144, 139-140 and 158 Ovptd. or Surcharged "CARIBBEAN ROYAL VISIT 1985" in 2 or 3 Lines

Perf. 14, 12½ (45c)
1985, Oct. 23 Wmk. as Before
446 A14 15c No. 163 .15 .15
447 A12 30c No. 157 .30 .30
448 A14 30c No. 164 .30 .30
449 A11 40c on 55c No. 151 .40 .40
450 A33 45c No. 427 .45 .45
451 A33 45c No. 428 .45 .45
452 A10 55c No. 144 .55 .55
453 A9a $1.50 on $5 No. 139 1.50 1.50
454 A9b $1.50 on $5 No. 140 1.50 1.50
455 A12 $2.50 No. 158 2.50 2.50
Nos. 446-455 (10) 8.10 8.10

#450-451 printed se-tenant. #453-454 issued in sheets of 7 (6 type A9a, 1 type A9b).

Christmas
A36

Anglican, Roman Catholic and Methodist churches.

1985, Nov. 5 Wmk. 380 *Perf. 15*
456 A36 10c St. Paul's, Charlestown .15 .15
457 A36 40c St. Theresa, Charlestown .28 .28
458 A36 60c Methodist Church, Gingerland .42 .42
459 A36 $3 St. Thomas, Lowland 2.00 2.00
Nos. 456-459 (4) 2.85 2.85

Spitfire Fighter Plane, 50th Anniv. — A37

1986, Mar. 24 Unwmk. *Perf. 12½*
460 A37 $1 Prototype K.5054, 1936 .35 .35
461 A37 $2.50 Mk.1A, 1940 .90 .90
462 A37 $3 Mk.XII, 1944 1.00 1.00
463 A37 $4 Mk.XXIV, 1948 1.50 1.50
Nos. 460-463 (4) 3.75 3.75

Souvenir Sheet
464 A37 $6 Seafire Mk.III 4.00 4.00

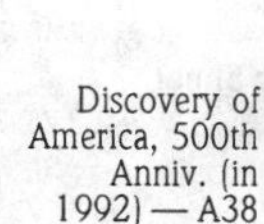

Discovery of America, 500th Anniv. (in 1992) — A38

1986, Apr. 11
465 A38 75c American Indian .42 .42
466 A38 75c Columbus trading with Indians .42 .42
467 A38 $1.75 Columbus's coat of arms 1.00 1.00
468 A38 $1.75 Breadfruit 1.00 1.00
469 A38 $2.50 Galleons 1.50 1.50
470 A38 $2.50 Columbus 1.50 1.50
Nos. 465-470 (6) 5.84 5.84

Souvenir Sheet
471 A38 $6 Columbus, diff. 3.50 3.50

Stamps of the same denomination printed se-tenant in continuous designs picturing various maps of Columbus's voyages.

Queen Elizabeth II, 60th Birthday — A39

Various portraits. Illustration reduced.

1986, Apr. 21
472 A39 5c multicolored .15 .15
473 A39 75c multicolored .30 .30
474 A39 $2 multicolored .75 .75
475 A39 $8 multi, vert. 3.00 3.00
Nos. 472-475 (4) 4.20 4.20

Souvenir Sheet
476 A39 $10 multicolored 7.50 7.50

1986 World Cup Soccer Championships, Mexico — A40

Perf. 15, 12½ (75c, $1, $1.75, $6)
1986, May 16
Size of 75c, $1, $1.75, $6: 56x35½mm
477 A40 1c Character trademark .15 .15
478 A40 2c Brazilian player .15 .15
479 A40 5c Danish player .15 .15
480 A40 10c Brazilian, diff. .15 .15
481 A40 20c Denmark vs. Spain .15 .15
482 A40 30c Paraguay vs. Chile .20 .20
483 A40 60c Italy vs. W. Germany .42 .42
484 A40 75c Danish team .50 .50
485 A40 $1 Paraguayan team .70 .70
486 A40 $1.75 Brazilian team 1.25 1.25
487 A40 $3 Italy vs. England 2.00 2.00
488 A40 $6 Italian team 4.00 4.00
Nos. 477-488 (12) 9.82 9.82

Souvenir Sheets
Perf. 12½
489 A40 $1.50 like $1.75 1.25 1.25
490 A40 $2 like $6 1.50 1.50
Perf. 15
491 A40 $2 like 20c 1.50 1.50
492 A40 $2.50 like 60c 2.00 2.00
493 A40 $4 like 30c 3.00 3.00

Nos. 478-483 and 487 vert.

Local Industry
A41

1986, July 18 Wmk. 380 *Perf. 14*
494 A41 15c Textile .15 .15
495 A41 40c Carpentry .25 .25
496 A41 $1.20 Agriculture .75 .75
497 A41 $3 Fishing 1.90 1.90
Nos. 494-497 (4) 3.05 3.05

Nevis stamps can be mounted in the Scott British Leeward Islands album.

A42

Wedding of Prince Andrew and Sarah Ferguson — A43

1986, July 23 Unwmk. *Perf. 12½*

498 A42	60c	Andrew, vert.	.20	.20
499 A42	60c	Sarah, vert.	.20	.20
500 A42	$2	Andrew at the races	.65	.65
501 A42	$2	Andrew in Africa	.65	.65
		Nos. 498-501 (4)	1.70	1.70

Souvenir Sheet

502 A43 $10 Couple on Balcony 4.75 4.75

Stamps of the same denomination printed se-tenant in pairs existing in vert. and horiz. format.

For overprints see Nos. 521-524.

Coral — A44

1986, Sept. 8 Wmk. 380 *Perf. 15*

503 A44	15c	Gorgonia	.15	.15
504 A44	60c	Fire coral	.38	.38
505 A44	$2	Elkhorn coral	1.25	1.25
506 A44	$3	Feather star	1.90	1.90
		Nos. 503-506 (4)	3.68	3.68

A45

Statue of Liberty, Cent. — A46

1986, Oct. 28 Unwmk. *Perf. 14*

507 A45	15c	Statue, World Trade Center	.15	.15
508 A45	25c	Statue, tall ship	.15	.15
509 A45	40c	Under renovation (front)	.25	.25
510 A45	60c	Renovation (side)	.38	.38
511 A45	75c	Statue, Operation Sail	.50	.50
512 A45	$1	Tall ship, horiz.	.65	.65
513 A45	$1.50	Renovation (arm, head)	.95	.95
514 A45	$2	Ship flying Liberty flag	1.25	1.25
515 A45	$2.50	Statue, Manhattan	1.50	1.50
516 A45	$3	Workers on scaffold	1.90	1.90
		Nos. 507-516 (10)	7.68	7.68

Souvenir Sheets

517 A46	$3.50	Statue at dusk	2.25	2.25
518 A46	$4	Head	2.50	2.50
519 A46	$4.50	Torch struck by lightning	2.75	2.75
520 A46	$5	Torch, blazing sun	3.00	3.00

Nos. 498-501 Ovptd. "Congratulations to T.R.H. The Duke & Duchess of York"

1986, Nov. 17 *Perf. 12½*

521 A42	60c	No. 498	.28	.28
522 A42	60c	No. 499	.28	.28
523 A42	$2	No. 500	1.00	1.00
524 A42	$2	No. 501	1.00	1.00
		Nos. 521-524 (4)	2.56	2.56

Stamps of the same denomination printed se-tenant in pairs existing in horiz. and vert. format.

Sports A47

1986, Nov. 21 *Perf. 14*

525 A47	10c	Sailing	.15	.15
526 A47	25c	Netball	.20	.20
527 A47	$2	Cricket	1.50	1.50
528 A47	$3	Basketball	2.25	2.25
		Nos. 525-528 (4)	4.10	4.10

Christmas A48

Churches: 10c, St. George's Anglican Church, Gingerland. 40c, Methodist Church, Fountain. $1, Charlestown Methodist Church. $5, Wesleyan Holiness Church, Brown Hill.

1986, Dec. 8

529 A48	10c	multicolored	.15	.15
530 A48	40c	multicolored	.30	.30
531 A48	$1	multicolored	.75	.75
532 A48	$5	multicolored	3.75	3.75
		Nos. 529-532 (4)	4.95	4.95

US Constitution A49

Christening of the Hamilton, 1788 A50

US Constitution, bicent. and 230th anniv. of the birth of Alexander Hamilton: 40c, Alexander Hamilton, Hamilton House. 60c, Hamilton. $2, George Washington and members of the 1st presidential cabinet.

1987, Jan. 11

533 A49	15c	shown	.15	.15
534 A49	40c	multicolored	.30	.30
535 A49	60c	multicolored	.45	.45
536 A49	$2	multicolored	1.50	1.50
		Nos. 533-536 (4)	2.40	2.40

Souvenir Sheet

537 A50 $5 shown 3.75 3.75

No. 117 Overprinted

America's Cup
1987 Winners
'Stars & Stripes'

1987, Feb. 20 Wmk. 373

538 A6a $3 multicolored 2.25 2.25

Wedding of Capt. Horatio Nelson and Frances Nisbet, Bicent. A51

1987, Mar. 11 Wmk. 380

539 A51	15c	Fig Tree Church	.15	.15
540 A51	60c	Frances Nisbet	.45	.45
541 A51	$1	HMS *Boreas*	.75	.75
542 A51	$3	Capt. Nelson	2.25	2.25
		Nos. 539-542 (4)	3.60	3.60

Souvenir Sheet

543 Sheet of 2, #542, 543a 4.50 4.50
a. A51 $3 like No. 540 2.25 2.25

Coney Butterfish — A52

1987, July 22 Unwmk. *Perf. 15*

544 A52	60c	Queen angelfish	.45	.45
545 A52	60c	Blue angelfish	.45	.45
546 A52	$1	Blue thum	.75	.75
547 A52	$1	Red thum	.75	.75
548 A52	$1.50	Red hind	1.15	1.15
549 A52	$1.50	Rock hind	1.15	1.15
550 A52	$2.50	shown	1.90	1.90
551 A52	$2.50	Coney butterfish, diff.	1.90	1.90
		Nos. 544-551 (8)	8.50	8.50

Stamps of the same denomination printed se-tenant.

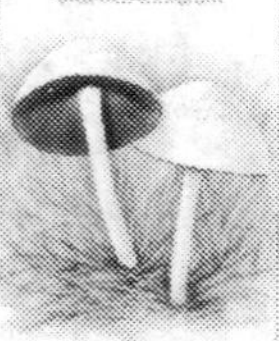

Mushrooms — A53

1987, Oct. 16 Wmk. 384 *Perf. 14*

552 A53	15c	*Panaeolus antillarum*	.15	.15
553 A53	50c	*Pycnoporus sanguineus*	.38	.38
554 A53	$2	*Gymnopilus chrysopellus*	1.50	1.50
555 A53	$3	*Cantharellus cinnabarinus*	2.25	2.25
		Nos. 552-555 (4)	4.28	4.28

Christmas A54

1987, Dec. 4 *Perf. 14½*

556 A54	10c	Rag doll	.15	.15
557 A54	40c	Coconut boat	.30	.30
558 A54	$1.20	Sandbox cart	.90	.90
559 A54	$5	Two-wheeled cart	3.75	3.75
		Nos. 556-559 (4)	5.10	5.10

Sea Shells — A55

1988, Feb. 15 *Perf. 14x14½*

560 A55	15c	Hawk-wing conch	.15	.15
561 A55	40c	Roostertail conch	.30	.30
562 A55	60c	Emperor helmet	.45	.45
563 A55	$2	Queen conch	1.50	1.50
564 A55	$3	King helmet	2.25	2.25
		Nos. 560-564 (5)	4.65	4.65

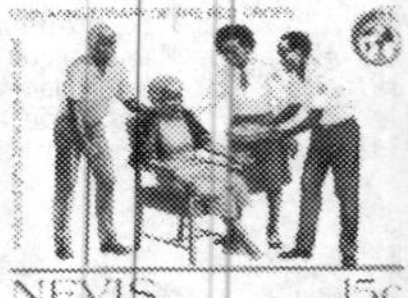

Intl. Red Cross and Red Crescent Organizations, 125th Annivs. A56

Activities: 15c, Visiting the sick and the elderly. 40c, First aid training. 60c, Wheelchairs for the disabled. $5, Disaster relief.

1988, June 20 *Perf. 14½x14*

565 A56	15c	multicolored	.15	.15
566 A56	40c	multicolored	.30	.30
567 A56	60c	multicolored	.45	.45
568 A56	$5	multicolored	3.75	3.75
		Nos. 565-568 (4)	4.65	4.65

A57 A58

1988, Aug. 26 *Perf. 14*

569 Strip of 4 4.75 4.75
a. A57 10c Runner at starting block .15 .15
b. A57 $1.20 Leaving block .90 .90
c. A57 $2 Full stride 1.50 1.50
d. A57 $3 Crossing finish line 2.25 2.25
e. Souvenir sheet of 4, #569a-569d 4.75 4.75

1988 Summer Olympics, Seoul. Printed se-tenant in a continuous design. Stamps in No. 569e are 23½x36½.

1988, Sept. 19 Wmk. 373 *Perf. 14½*

570 A58 $5 multicolored 3.75 3.75

Independence, 5th anniv.

Lloyds of London
Common Design Type

Designs: 15c, Act of Parliament incorporating Lloyds, 1871. 60c, *Cunard Countess* in Nevis Harbor, horiz. $2.50, Space shuttle, deployment of satellite in space, horiz. $3, *Viking Princess* on fire in the Caribbean, 1966.

1988, Oct. 31 Wmk. 384 *Perf. 14*

571 CD341	15c	multicolored	.15	.15
572 CD341	60c	multicolored	.45	.45
573 CD341	$2.50	multicolored	1.50	1.50
574 CD341	$3	multicolored	2.25	2.25
		Nos. 571-574 (4)	4.35	4.35

Christmas Flowers — A59

1988, Nov. 7 *Perf. 14½*

575 A59	15c	Poinsettia	.15	.15
576 A59	40c	Tiger claws	.30	.30
577 A59	60c	Sorrel flower	.45	.45
578 A59	$1	Christmas candle	.75	.75
579 A59	$5	Snow bush	3.75	3.75
		Nos. 575-579 (5)	5.40	5.40

Battle of Frigate Bay, 1782 — A60

Exhibition emblem & maps. #580a-580c in a continuous design. Illustration reduced.

1989, Apr. 17 *Perf. 14*

580 A60 Strip of 3 2.80 2.80
a. 50c multicolored .38 .38
b. $1.20 multicolored .90 .90
c. $2 multicolored 1.50 1.50

Size: 34x47mm

Perf. 14x13½

581 A60 $3 Map of Nevis, 1764 2.25 2.25

French revolution bicent., PHILEXFRANCE '89.

Nocturnal Insects and Frogs — A61

1989, May 15

582 A61 10c Cicada .15 .15
583 A61 40c Grasshopper .30 .30
584 A61 60c Cricket .45 .45
585 A61 $5 Tree frog 3.75 3.75
a. Souvenir sheet of 4, #582-585 4.60 4.60
Nos. 582-585 (4) 4.65 4.65

Moon Landing, 20th Anniv.

Common Design Type

Apollo 12: 15c, Vehicle Assembly Building, Kennedy Space Center. 40c, Crew members Charles Conrad Jr., Richard Gordon and Alan Bean. $2, Mission emblem. $3, Moon operation in the Sun's glare. $6, Buzz Aldrin deploying passive seismic experiment package on the lunar surface, Apollo 11 mission.

1989, July 20 *Perf. 14x13½*

Size of Nos. 587-588: 29x29mm

586 CD342 15c multicolored .15 .15
587 CD342 40c multicolored .30 .30
588 CD342 $2 multicolored 1.50 1.50
589 CD342 $3 multicolored 2.25 2.25
Nos. 586-589 (4) 4.20 4.20

Souvenir Sheet

590 CD342 $6 multicolored 4.50 4.50

Queen Conchs *(Strombus gigas)* — A62

1990, Jan. 31

591 A62 10c shown .15 .15
592 A62 40c Conch, diff .30 .30
593 A62 60c Conch, diff .45 .45
594 A62 $1 Conch, diff .75 .75
Nos. 591-594 (4) 1.65 1.65

Souvenir Sheet

595 A62 $5 Fish and coral 3.75 3.75

World Wildlife Fund.

Wyon Portrait of Victoria — A63

Perf. 14x15

1990, May 3 **Litho.** **Unwmk.**

596 A63 15c shown .15 .15
597 A63 40c Engine-turned background .30 .30
598 A63 60c Heath's engraving .45 .45
599 A63 $4 Inscriptions added 3.00 3.00
Nos. 596-599 (4) 3.90 3.90

Souvenir Sheet

600 A63 $5 Completed design 3.75 3.75

Penny Black, 150th anniv. No. 600 for Stamp World London '90.

A64

1990, May 3 *Perf. 13½*

601 A64 15c brown .15 .15
602 A64 40c deep green .30 .30
603 A64 60c violet .45 .45
604 A64 $4 bright ultra 3.00 3.00
Nos. 601-604 (4) 3.90 3.90

Souvenir Sheet

605 A64 $5 gray, lake & buff 3.75 3.75

Penny Black 150th anniversary and commemoration of the Thurn & Taxis postal service.

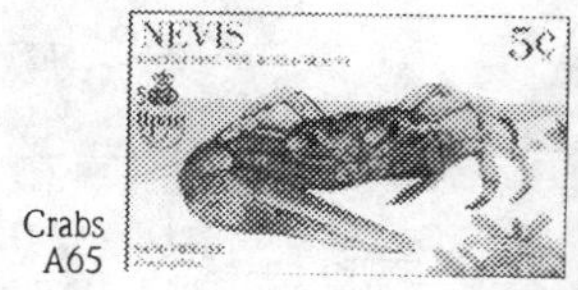

Crabs A65

Designs include UPAE and discovery of America anniversary emblems.

1990, June 25 **Litho.** *Perf. 14*

606 A65 5c Sand fiddler .15 .15
607 A65 15c Great land crab .15 .15
608 A65 20c Blue crab .15 .15
609 A65 40c Stone crab .30 .30
610 A65 60c Mountain crab .45 .45
611 A65 $2 Sargassum crab 1.50 1.50
612 A65 $3 Yellow box crab 2.25 2.25
613 A65 $4 Spiny spider crab 3.00 3.00
Nos. 606-613 (8) 7.95 7.95

Souvenir Sheets

614 A65 $5 Wharf crab 3.75 3.75
615 A65 $5 Sally lightfoot 3.75 3.75

Queen Mother 90th Birthday
A66 A67

1990, July 5

616 A66 $2 shown 1.50 1.50
617 A67 $2 shown 1.50 1.50
618 A66 $2 Queen Consort, diff. 1.50 1.50
a. Strip of 3, #616-618 4.50 4.50

Souvenir Sheet

619 A67 $6 Coronation Portrait, diff. 4.75 4.75

Nos. 616-618 printed in sheet of 9.

A68

A69

Players from participating countries.

1990, Oct. 1 **Litho.** *Perf. 14*

620 A68 10c Cameroun .15 .15
621 A68 25c Czechoslovakia .18 .18
622 A68 $2.50 England 1.90 1.90
623 A68 $5 West Germany 3.75 3.75
Nos. 620-623 (4) 5.98 5.98

Souvenir Sheets

624 A68 $5 Spain 3.75 3.75
625 A68 $5 Argentina 3.75 3.75

World Cup Soccer Championships, Italy.

Unwmk.

1990, Nov. 19 **Litho.** *Perf. 14*

Christmas (Orchids): 10c, Cattleya deckeri. 15c, Epidendrum ciliare. 20c, Epidendrum fragrans. 40c, Epidendrum ibaguense. 60c, Epidendrum latifolium. $1.20, Maxillaria conferta. $2, Epidendrum strobiliferum. $3, Brassavola cucullata. $5, Rodriguezia lanceolata.

626 A69 10c multicolored .15 .15
627 A69 15c multicolored .15 .15
628 A69 20c multicolored .15 .15
629 A69 40c multicolored .30 .30
630 A69 60c multicolored .45 .45
631 A69 $1.20 multicolored .90 .90
632 A69 $2 multicolored 1.50 1.50
633 A69 $3 multicolored 2.25 2.25
Nos. 626-633 (8) 5.85 5.85

Souvenir Sheet

634 A69 $5 multicolored 3.75 3.75

Peter Paul Rubens (1577-1640), Painter — A70

Details from The Feast of Achelous: 10c, Pitchers. 40c, Woman at table. 60c, Two women. $4, Achelous feasting. $5, Complete painting, horiz.

1991, Jan. 14 **Litho.** *Perf. 13½*

635 A70 10c multicolored .15 .15
636 A70 40c multicolored .30 .30
637 A70 60c multicolored .45 .45
638 A70 $4 multicolored 3.00 3.00
Nos. 635-638 (4) 3.90 3.90

Souvenir Sheet

639 A70 $5 multicolored 3.75 3.75

Butterflies A71

1991-92 *Perf. 14*

640 A71 5c Gulf fritillary .15 .15
641 A71 10c Orion .15 .15
642 A71 15c Dagger wing .15 .15
643 A71 20c Red anartia .15 .15
644 A71 25c Caribbean buckeye .18 .18
645 A71 40c Zebra .30 .30
646 A71 50c Southern dagger tail .38 .38
647 A71 60c Silver spot .45 .45
648 A71 75c Doris .55 .55
648A A71 80c like #647 .60 .60
649 A71 $1 Mimic .75 .75
650 A71 $3 Monarch 2.25 2.25
651 A71 $5 Small blue grecian 3.75 3.75
652 A71 $10 Tiger 7.50 7.50
653 A71 $20 Flambeau 15.00 15.00
Nos. 640-653 (15) 32.31 32.31

Issue dates: #648A, 1992. Others, Mar. 1, 1991. Nos. 640-646, 648-653 exist dated 1992. Nos. 640-641, 644, 646, 648A exist dated 1994.

For overprints see Nos. O41-O54.

Space Exploration-Discovery Voyages — A72

1991, Apr. 22 **Litho.** *Perf. 14*

654 A72 15c Viking Mars lander .15 .15
655 A72 40c Apollo 11 lift-off .30 .30
656 A72 60c Skylab .45 .45
657 A72 75c Salyut 6 .55 .55
658 A72 $1 Voyager 1 .75 .75
659 A72 $2 Venera 7 1.50 1.50
660 A72 $4 Gemini 4 3.00 3.00
661 A72 $5 Luna 3 3.75 3.75
Nos. 654-661 (8) 10.45 10.45

Souvenir Sheet

662 A72 $6 Sailing ship, vert. 4.50 4.50
663 A72 $6 Columbus' landfall 4.50 4.50

Discovery of America, 500th anniv. (in 1992) (No. 663).

Miniature Sheet

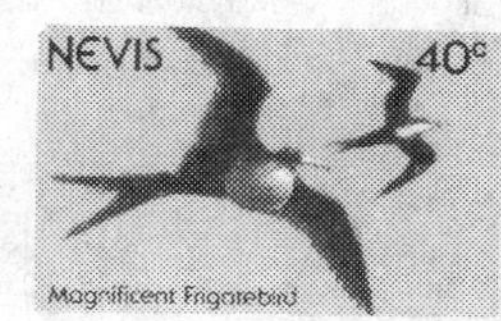

Birds A73

Designs: a, Magnificent frigatebird. b, Roseate tern. c, Red-tailed hawk. d, Zenaida dove. e, Bananaquit. f, American kestrel. g, Grey kingbird. h, Prothonotary warbler. i, Blue-hooded euphonia. j, Antillean crested hummingbird. k, White-tailed tropicbird. l, Yellow-bellied sapsucker. m, Green-throated carib. n, Purple-throated carib. o, Black-bellied tree duck. p, Ringed kingfisher. q, Burrowing owl. r, Ruddy turnstone. s, Great white heron. t, Yellow-crowned night heron.

1991, May 28

664 A73 40c Sheet of 20, #a.-t. 6.00 6.00

Souvenir Sheet

665 A73 $6 Great egret 4.50 4.50

Royal Family Birthday, Anniversary

Common Design Type

1991, July 5 **Litho.** *Perf. 14*

666 CD347 10c multicolored .15 .15
667 CD347 15c multicolored .15 .15
668 CD347 40c multicolored .30 .30
669 CD347 50c multicolored .38 .38
670 CD347 $1 multicolored .75 .75
671 CD347 $2 multicolored 1.50 1.50
672 CD347 $4 multicolored 3.00 3.00
673 CD347 $5 multicolored 3.75 3.75
Nos. 666-673 (8) 9.98 9.98

Souvenir Sheets

674 CD347 $5 Elizabeth, Philip 3.75 3.75
675 CD347 $5 Charles, Diana & family 3.75 3.75

10c, 50c, $1, Nos. 673, 675, Charles and Diana, 10th Wedding Anniv. Others, Queen Elizabeth II 65th birthday.

Japanese Trains A74

Locomotives: 10c, C62 Steam, vert. 15c, C56 Steam. 40c, Streamlined C55, steam. 60c, Class 1400 Steam. $1, Class 485 bonnet type rail diesel car, vert. $2, C61 Steam, vert. $3, Class 485 express train. $4, Class 7000 electric train. No. 684, D51 Steam. No. 685, Hikari bullet train.

1991, Aug. 12

676 A74 10c multicolored .15 .15
677 A74 15c multicolored .15 .15
678 A74 40c multicolored .30 .30
679 A74 60c multicolored .45 .45
680 A74 $1 multicolored .75 .75
681 A74 $2 multicolored 1.50 1.50
682 A74 $3 multicolored 2.25 2.25
683 A74 $4 multicolored 3.00 3.00
Nos. 676-683 (8) 8.55 8.55

Souvenir Sheets

684 A74 $5 multicolored 3.75 3.75
685 A74 $5 multicolored 3.75 3.75

Phila Nippon '91.

Christmas A75

Paintings by Albrecht Durer: 10c, Mary Being Crowned by an Angel. 40c, Mary with the Pear. 60c, Mary in a Halo. $3, Mary with the Crown of Stars and Scepter. No. 690, The Holy Family. No. 691, Mary at the Yard Gate.

1991, Dec. 20 Litho. *Perf. 13½*

686 A75	10c yel green & blk		.15	.15
687 A75	40c org brown & blk		.30	.30
688 A75	60c blue & black		.45	.45
689 A75	$3 brt magenta & blk		2.25	2.25
	Nos. 686-689 (4)		3.15	3.15

Souvenir Sheets

690 A75	$6 black	4.50	4.50
691 A75	$6 black	4.50	4.50

A76

A77

Mushrooms: 15c, Marasmius haematocephalus. 40c, Psilocybe cubensis. 60c, Hygrocybe acutoconica. 75c, Hygrocybe occidentalis. $1, Boletellus cubensis. $2, Gymnopilus chrysopellus. $4, Cantharellus cinnabarinus. $5, Chlorophyllum molybdites. No. 700, Our Lady of the Snows (8 mushrooms). No. 701, Our Lady of the Snows (4 mushrooms), diff.

1991, Dec. 20 Litho. *Perf. 14*

692 A76	15c multicolored	.15	.15
693 A76	40c multicolored	.30	.30
694 A76	60c multicolored	.45	.45
695 A76	75c multicolored	.55	.55
696 A76	$1 multicolored	.75	.75
697 A76	$2 multicolored	1.50	1.50
698 A76	$4 multicolored	3.00	3.00
699 A76	$5 multicolored	3.75	3.75
	Nos. 692-699 (8)	10.45	10.45

Souvenir Sheet

700 A76	$6 multicolored	4.50	4.50
701 A76	$6 multicolored	4.50	4.50

Queen Elizabeth II's Accession to the Throne, 40th Anniv.

Common Design Type

1992, Feb. 26 Litho. *Perf. 14*

702 CD348	10c multicolored	.15	.15
703 CD348	40c multicolored	.30	.30
704 CD348	$1 multicolored	.75	.75
705 CD348	$5 multicolored	3.75	3.75
	Nos. 702-705 (4)	4.95	4.95

Souvenir Sheets

706 CD348	$6 Queen, people on beach	4.50	4.50
707 CD348	$6 Queen, seashell	4.50	4.50

1992, May 7 Litho. *Perf. 14*

Gold medalists: 20c, Monique Knol, France, cycling. 25c, Roger Kingdom, US, 110-meter hurdles. 50c, Yugoslavia, water polo. 80c, Anja Fichtel, West Germany, foil. $1, Said Aouita, Morocco, 5000-meters. $1.50, Yuri Sedykh, USSR, hammer throw. $3, Yelena Shushunova, USSR, gymnastics. $5, Vladimir Artemov, USSR, gymnastics. No. 716, Florence Griffith-Joyner, US, 100-meter dash. No. 717, Naim Suleymanoglu, Turkey, weight lifting.

708 A77	20c multicolored	.15	.15
709 A77	25c multicolored	.18	.18
710 A77	50c multicolored	.38	.38
711 A77	80c multicolored	.60	.60
712 A77	$1 multicolored	.75	.75
713 A77	$1.50 multicolored	1.15	1.15
714 A77	$3 multicolored	2.25	2.25
715 A77	$5 multicolored	3.75	3.75
	Nos. 708-715 (8)	9.21	9.21

Souvenir Sheets

716 A77	$6 multicolored	4.50	4.50
717 A77	$6 multicolored	4.50	4.50

1992 Summer Olympics, Barcelona. All athletes except those on $1 and $1.50 won gold medals in 1988. No. 715 incorrectly spelled "Valimir."

Spanish Art — A78

Designs: 20c, Landscape, by Mariano Fortuny, vert. 25c, Dona Juana la Loca, by Francisco Pradilla Ortiz. 50c, Idyll, by Fortuny, vert. 80c, Old Man in the Sun, by Fortuny, vert. $1, $2, The Painter's Children in the Japanese Salon (different details), vert., by Fortuny. $3, Still Life (Sea Bream and Oranges), by Luis Eugenio Melendez. $5, Still Life (Box of Sweets, Pastry, and Other Objects), by Melendez, vert. No. 726, Moroccans by Fortuny. No. 727, Bullfight, by Fortuny.

Perf. 13x13½, 13½x13

1992, June 1 Litho.

718 A78	20c multicolored	.15	.15
719 A78	25c multicolored	.18	.18
720 A78	50c multicolored	.38	.38
721 A78	80c multicolored	.60	.60
722 A78	$1 multicolored	.75	.75
723 A78	$2 multicolored	1.50	1.50
724 A78	$3 multicolored	2.25	2.25
725 A78	$5 multicolored	3.70	3.70
	Nos. 718-725 (8)	9.51	9.51

Size: 120x95mm

Imperf

726 A78	$6 multicolored	4.50	4.50
727 A78	$6 multicolored	4.50	4.50

Granada '92.

A79

A80

1992, July 6 *Perf. 14*

728 A79	20c Early compass	.15	.15
729 A79	50c Manatee	.38	.38
730 A79	80c Green turtle	.60	.60
731 A79	$1.50 Santa Maria	1.15	1.15
732 A79	$3 Queen Isabella	2.30	2.30
733 A79	$5 Pineapple	3.80	3.80
	Nos. 728-733 (6)	8.38	8.38

Souvenir Sheets

734 A79	$6 Storm petrel, horiz.	4.50	4.50
735 A79	$6 Pepper, horiz.	4.50	4.50

Discovery of America, 500th anniv. World Columbian Stamp Expo '92, Chicago.

1992, Aug. 24 *Perf. 14½*

736 A80	$1 Coming ashore	.75	.75
737 A80	$2 Natives, ships	1.50	1.50

Discovery of America, 500th anniv. Organization of East Caribbean States.

Wolfgang Amadeus Mozart, Bicent. of Death (in 1991) — A81

1992, Oct. Litho. *Perf. 14*

738 A81	$3 multicolored	2.25	2.25

Souvenir Sheet

739 A81	$6 Don Giovanni	4.50	4.50

Mickey's Portrait Gallery — A82

1992, Nov. 9 Litho. *Perf. 13½x14*

740 A82	10c Minnie Mouse, 1930	.15	.15
741 A82	15c Mickey Mouse	.15	.15
742 A82	40c Donald Duck	.30	.30
743 A82	80c Mickey Mouse, 1930	.60	.60
744 A82	$1 Daisy Duck	.75	.75
745 A82	$2 Pluto	1.50	1.50
746 A82	$4 Goofy	3.00	3.00
747 A82	$5 Goofy, 1932	3.75	3.75
	Nos. 740-747 (8)	10.20	10.20

Souvenir Sheet

Perf. 14x13½

748 A82	$6 Plane Crazy	4.50	4.50
749 A82	$6 Mickey, Home Sweet Home, horiz.	4.50	4.50

Christmas A83

Details or entire paintings: 20c, The Virgin and Child Between Two Saints, by Giovanni Bellini. 40c, The Virgin and Child Surrounded by Four Angels, by Master of the Castello Nativity. 50c, Virgin and Child Surrounded by Angels with St. Frediano and St. Augustine, by Fra Filippo Lippi. 80c, The Virgin and Child Between St. Peter and St. Sebastian, by Giovanni Bellini. $1, The Virgin and Child with St. Julian and St. Nicholas of Myra, by Lorenzo Di Credi. $2, Saint Bernardino and a Female Saint Presenting a Donor to Virgin and Child, by Francesco Bissolo. $4, Madonna and Child with Four Cherubs, Ascribed to Barthel Bruyn. $5, The Virgin and Child, by Quentin Metsys. No. 758, The Virgin and Child Surrounded by Two Angels, by Perugino. No. 759, Madonna and Child with the Infant St. John and Archangel Gabriel, by Sandro Botticelli.

1992, Nov. 16 Litho. *Perf. 13½x14*

750 A83	20c multicolored	.15	.15
751 A83	40c multicolored	.30	.30
752 A83	50c multicolored	.38	.38
753 A83	80c multicolored	.60	.60
754 A83	$1 multicolored	.75	.75
755 A83	$2 multicolored	1.50	1.50
756 A83	$4 multicolored	2.25	2.25
757 A83	$5 multicolored	3.75	3.75
	Nos. 750-757 (8)	9.68	9.68

Souvenir Sheet

758 A83	$6 multicolored	4.50	4.50
759 A83	$6 multicolored	4.50	4.50

Empire State Building, New York City — A84

1992, Oct. 28 Litho. *Perf. 14*

760 A84	$6 multicolored	4.50	4.50

Postage Stamp Mega Event '92, New York City.

A85

A89

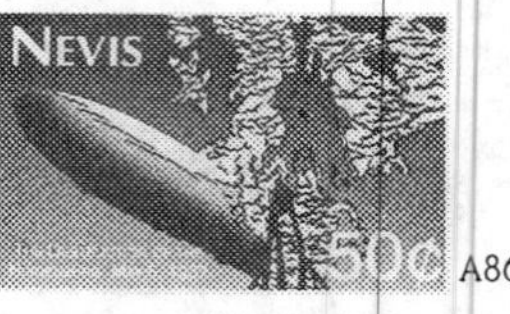

A86

A87

A88

A90

A93

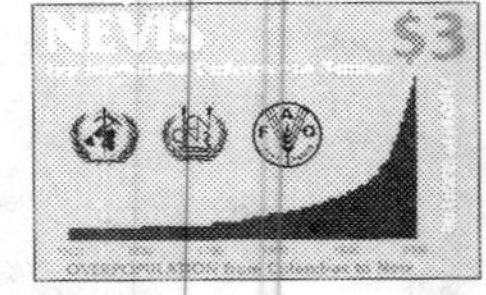

A91

Anniversaries and Events — A92

Designs: 15c, Japanese launch vehicle H-2. 50c, Hindenburg on fire, 1937. 75c, Charles de Gaulle, Konrad Adenauer. No. 764, Horatio Nelson Museum, Nevis. No. 765, Red Cross emblem, Nevis. No. 766, America's Cup yacht *Resolute*, 1920, vert. No. 767, St. Thomas Anglican Church. No. 768, Care Bear, butterfly and flower. No. 770, Blue whale. No. 771, WHO, ICN, FAO emblems, graph showing population growth, vert. No. 772, Lion, Lion's Intl. emblem. No. 773, John F. Kennedy, Adenauer. No. 774, Lebaudy, first flying machine with mechanical engine. No. 775, Soviet Energia launch vehicle SL-17.

Elvis Presley: No. 776a, Portrait. b, With guitar. c, With microphone.

Details or entire paintings, by Georges de La Tour: No. 777a, The Cheater (left). b, The Cheater (center). c, The Cheater (right). d, St. Joseph, the Carpenter. e, Saint Thomas. f, Adoration of the Shepherds (left). g, Adoration of the Shepherds (right). h, La Madeleine a La Veilleuse.

No. 778, Care Bear, palm tree, vert. No. 779, Manned maneuvering unit in space. No. 780, Count Zeppelin taking off from Goppingen for Friedrichshafen. No. 781, Adenauer. No. 782,

America's Cup yacht. No. 783, The Angel Departing from the Family of Tobias, by Rembrandt.

1993 Litho. *Perf. 14*

761	A85	15c	multicolored	.15	.15
762	A86	50c	multicolored	.38	.38
763	A87	75c	multicolored	.58	.58
764	A88	80c	multicolored	.60	.60
765	A88	80c	multicolored	.60	.60
766	A89	80c	multicolored	.60	.60
767	A88	80c	multicolored	.58	.58
768	A90	80c	multicolored	.60	.60
770	A88	$1	multicolored	.75	.75
771	A91	$3	multicolored	2.25	2.25
772	A85	$3	multicolored	2.25	2.25
773	A87	$5	multicolored	3.75	3.75
774	A86	$5	multicolored	3.75	3.75
775	A85	$5	multicolored	3.75	3.75

Perf. 14

776	A92	$1	Strip of 3, #a.-c.	2.25	2.25
			Nos. 761-776 (15)	22.84	22.84

Miniature Sheet

Perf. 12

777	A93	$1	Sheet of 8, #a.-h. + label	6.00	6.00

Souvenir Sheets

Perf. 14

778	A90	$2	multicolored	1.50	1.50
779	A85	$6	multicolored	4.50	4.50
780	A86	$6	multicolored	4.50	4.50
781	A87	$6	multicolored	4.50	4.50
782	A89	$6	multicolored	4.50	4.50

Perf. $14^1/_2$

783	A92	$6	multicolored	4.50	4.50

Intl. Space Year (#761, 775, 779). Count Zeppelin, 75th anniv. of death (#762, 774, 780). Konrad Adenauer, 25th anniv. of death (#763, 773, 781). Anglican Church in Nevis, 150th anniv. Opening of Horatio Nelson Museum (#764). Nevis and St. Kitts Red Cross, 50th anniv. (#765). America's Cup yacht race (#766, 782). (#767). Lions Intl., 75th anniv. (#772). Earth Summit, Rio de Janeiro (#768, 770, 778). Intl. Conference on Nutrition, Rome (#771). Elvis Presley, 15th death anniv. (in 1992) (#776). Louvre Art Museum, bicent. (#777, 783).

Nos. 779-781 have continuous designs.

No. 783 contains one 55x89mm stamp.

Issue dates: No. 767, Mar. Others, Jan. 14.

Tropical Flowers — A94

1993, Mar. 26 Litho. *Perf. 14*

784	A94	10c	Frangipani	.15	.15
785	A94	25c	Bougainvillea	.18	.18
786	A94	50c	Allamanda	.38	.38
787	A94	80c	Anthurium	.60	.60
788	A94	$1	Ixora	.75	.75
789	A94	$2	Hibiscus	1.50	1.50
790	A94	$4	Shrimp plant	2.95	2.95
791	A94	$5	Coral vine	3.70	3.70
			Nos. 784-791 (8)	10.21	10.21

Souvenir Sheets

792	A94	$6	Lantana	4.50	4.50
793	A94	$6	Petrea	4.50	4.50

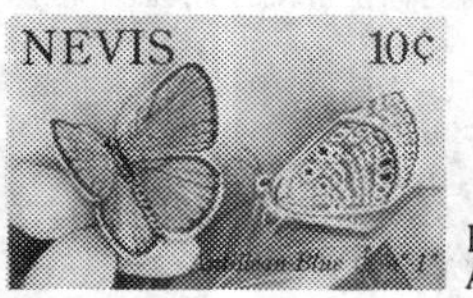

Butterflies A95

1993, May 17 Litho. *Perf. 14*

794	A95	10c	Antillean blue	.15	.15
795	A95	25c	Cuban crescentspot	.18	.18
796	A95	50c	Ruddy daggerwing	.38	.38
797	A95	80c	Little yellow	.60	.60
798	A95	$1	Atala	.75	.75
799	A95	$1.50	Orange-barred giant sulphur	1.15	1.15
800	A95	$4	Tropic queen	3.00	3.00
801	A95	$5	Malachite	3.75	3.75
			Nos. 794-801 (8)	9.96	9.96

Souvenir Sheets

802	A95	$6	Polydamas swallowtail	4.50	4.50
a.			Ovptd. in sheet margin	4.50	4.50
803	A95	$6	West Indian Buckeye	4.50	4.50
a.			Ovptd. in sheet margin	4.50	4.50

Location of Hong Kong '94 emblem on Nos. 802a-803a varies.

Nos. 802a, 803a issued Feb. 18, 1994.

Miniature Sheet

Coronation of Queen Elizabeth II, 40th Anniv. — A96

Designs: a, 10c, Official coronation photograph. b, 80c, Queen, wearing Imperial Crown of State. c, $2, Queen, sitting on throne during ceremony. d, $4, Prince Charles kissing mother's hand.

$6, Portrait, "Riding on Worcran in the Great Park at Windsor," by Susan Crawford, 1977.

1993, June 2 Litho. *Perf. $13^1/_2$x14*

804	A96	Sheet, 2 each #a.-d.	10.50	10.50

Souvenir Sheet

Perf. 14

805	A96	$6 multicolored	4.50	4.50

No. 805 contains one 28x42mm stamp.

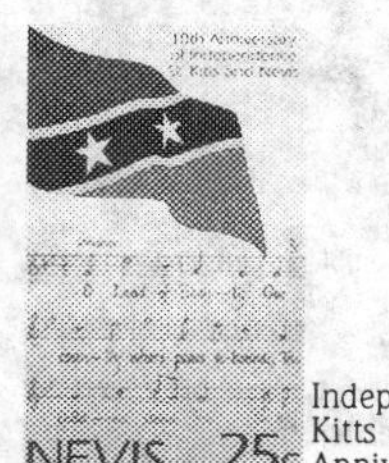

Independence of St. Kitts and Nevis, 10th Anniv. — A97

Designs: 25c, Natl. flag, anthem. 80c, Brown pelican, map of St. Kitts and Nevis.

1993, Sept. 19 Litho. *Perf. $13^1/_2$*

807	A97	25c	multicolored	.18	.18
808	A97	80c	multicolored	.60	.60

1994 World Cup Soccer Championships, US — A98

Soccer players: 10c, Garaba, Hungary; Platini, France. 25c, Maradona, Argentina; Bergomi, Italy. 50c, Fernandez, France; Rats, Russia. 80c, Munoz, Spain. $1, Elkjaer, Denmark; Goicoechea, Spain. $2, Coelho, Brazil; Tigana, France. $3, Troglio, Argentina; Alejnikov, Russia. No. 816, $5, Karas, Poland; Costa, Brazil.

No. 817, Belloumi, Algeria. No. 818, Steven, England, vert.

1993, Nov. 9 Litho. *Perf. 14*

809-816	A98	Set of 8	10.00	10.00

Souvenir Sheets

817-818	A98	$5 each	3.75	3.75

Christmas A99

Works by Albrecht Durer: 20c, Annunciation of Mary. 40c, The Nativity. 50c, Holy Family on a Grassy Bank. 80c, The Presentation of Christ in the Temple. $1, Virgin in Glory on the Crescent. $1.60, The Nativity, diff. $3, Madonna and Child. $5, The Presentation of Christ in the Temple (detail).

No. 827, Mary with Child and the Long-Tailed Monkey, by Durer. No. 828, The Rest on the Flight into Egypt, by Fragonard, horiz.

1993, Nov. 30 *Perf. 13*

819-826	A99	Set of 8	10.00	10.00

Souvenir Sheets

827-828	A99	$6 each	4.50	4.50

Tuff Mickey — A100

Disney's Mickey Mouse playing: 10c, Basketball. 50c, Volleyball. $1, Soccer. $5, Boxing.

No. 837, $6, Tug-of-war. No. 838, Ringing carnival bell with hammer, vert.

Disney's Minnie Mouse: 25c, Welcome to my island, vert. 80c, Sunny and snappy, vert. $1.50, Happy hoopin', vert. $4, Jumping for joy, vert.

Perf. $14x13^1/_2$, $13^1/_2x14$

1994, Mar. 15 Litho.

829	A100	10c	multicolored	.15	.15
830	A100	25c	multicolored	.18	.18
831	A100	50c	multicolored	.38	.38
832	A100	80c	multicolored	.60	.60
833	A100	$1	multicolored	.75	.75
834	A100	$1.50	multicolored	1.10	1.10
835	A100	$4	multicolored	3.00	3.00
836	A100	$5	multicolored	3.75	3.75
			Nos. 829-836 (8)	9.91	9.91

Souvenir Sheets

837	A100	$6	multicolored	4.50	4.50
838	A100	$6	multicolored	4.50	4.50

Hummel Figurines — A101

Designs: 5c, Umbrella Girl. 25c, For Father. 50c, Apple Tree Girl. 80c, March Winds. $1, Have the Sun in Your Heart. $1.60, Blue Belle. $2, Winter Fun. $5, Apple Tree Boy.

1994, Apr. 6 Litho. *Perf. 14*

839-846	A101	Set of 8	8.50	8.50
845a		Souv. sheet of 4, #839, 843-845	3.50	3.50
846a		Souv. sheet of 4, #840-842, 846	5.00	5.00

Beekeeping A102

Designs: 50c, Beekeeper cutting wild nest of bees. 80c, Group of beekeepers, 1987. $1.60, Decapping frames of honey. $3, Queen bee rearing.

$6, Queen bee, worker bees, woman extracting honey.

1994, June 13 Litho. *Perf. 14*

847-850	A102	Set of 4	4.50	4.50

Souvenir Sheet

851	A102	$6 multicolored	4.50	4.50

Miniature Sheet

Cats A103

Designs: a, Blue point Himalayan. b, Black & white Persian. c, Cream Persian. d, Red Persian. e, Persian. f, Persian black smoke. g, Chocolate smoke Persian. h, Black Persian.

No. 853, Brown tabby Persian. No. 854, Silver tabby Persian.

1994, July 20

852	A103	80c Sheet of 8, #a.-h.	4.75	4.75

Souvenir Sheets

853-854	A103	$6 each	4.50	4.50

Marine Life A104

Marine Life A104a

Designs: 10c, Striped burrfish. 25c, Black coral, white & yellow, vert. 40c, Black coral, white & red, vert. 50c, Black coral, yellow & green, vert. 80c, Black coral, spiral-shaped, vert. $1, Blue-striped grunt. $1.60, Blue angelfish. $3, Cocoa damselfish.

No. 864a, Flameback angelfish. b, Reef bass. c, Honey gregory. d, Saddle squirrelfish. e, Cobalt chromis. f, Cleaner goby. g, Slendertail cardinalfish. h, Royal gramma.

No. 865, Sailfish, vert. No. 866, Blue marlin.

1994, July 25 Litho. *Perf. 14*

856-863	A104	Set of 8	5.75	5.75
860a		Strip of 4, #857-860	1.50	1.50
860b		Min. sheet, 3 each #857-860	4.50	4.50

Miniature Sheet of 8

864	A104a	50c #a.-h.	3.00	3.00
i.		Ovptd. in sheet margin	3.00	3.00

Souvenir Sheets

865-866	A104a	$6 each	4.50	4.50

Nos. 857-860, World Wildlife Fund. No. 864i overprinted in sheet margin with PHILAKOREA '94 emblem.

Issued: #864i, 8/16; #860b, 7/25.

Local Architecture — A105

Designs: 25c, Residence, Barnes Ghaut Village. 50c, House above grocery store, Newcastle. $1, Treasury Building, Charlestown. $5, House above supermarket, Charlestown. $6, Apartment houses.

1994, Aug. 22

867-870	A105	Set of 4	5.00	5.00

Souvenir Sheet

871	A105	$6 multicolored	4.50	4.50

Order of the Caribbean Community — A106

First award recipients: 25c, William Demas, economist, Trinidad and Tobago. 50c, Sir Shridath Ramphal, statesman, Guyana. $1, Derek Walcott, writer, Nobel Laureate, St. Lucia.

1994, Sept. 1

872-874	A106	Set of 3	1.25	1.25

Miniature Sheet of 8

PHILAKOREA '94 — A107

Folding screen, longevity symbols embroidered on silk, Late Choson Dynasty: a, #1. b, #2. c, #3. d, #4. e, #5. f, #6. g, #7. h, #8.

1994 Litho. Perf. 14
875 A107 50c #a.-h. 3.00 3.00

Christmas — A108

Different details from paintings: 20c, 40c, 50c, $5, The Virgin Mary as Queen of Heaven, by Jan Provost. 80c, $1, $1.60, $3, Adoration of the Magi, by Workshop of Hugo van der Goes.

No. 884, The Virgin Mary as Queen of Heaven (complete). $6, Adoration of the Magi (complete).

1994, Dec. 1 Litho. Perf. 14
876-883 A108 Set of 8 9.50 9.50

Souvenir Sheets

884 A108 $5 multicolored 3.75 3.75
885 A108 $6 multicolored 4.50 4.50

Disney Valentines — A109

Designs: 10c, Mickey, Minnie. 25c, Donald, Daisy. 50c, Pluto, Fifi. 80c, Clarabelle, Horace Horsecollar. $1, Pluto, Figaro. $1.50, Polly, Peter Penguin. $4, Prunella Pullet, Hick Rooster. $5, Jenny Wren, Cock Robin.

No. 894, Minnie, vert. No. 895, Daisy, vert.

1995, Feb. 14 Litho. Perf. 14x13½
886-893 A109 Set of 8 9.25 9.25

Souvenir Sheets
Perf. 13½x14

894-895 A109 $6 each 4.50 4.50

Birds — A110

Designs: 50c, Hooded merganser. 80c, Green-backed heron. $2, Double crested cormorant. $3, Ruddy duck.

Hummingbirds: No. 900a, Rufous-breasted hermit. b, Purple-throated carib. c, Green mango. d, Bahama woodstar. e, Hispaniolan emerald. f, Antillean crested. g, Green-throated carib. h, Antillean mango. i, Vervian. j, Jamaican mango. k, Cuban emerald. l, Blue-headed.

No. 901, Black skimmer. No. 902, Snowy plover.

1995, Mar. 30 Litho. Perf. 14
896-899 A110 Set of 4 4.75 4.75

Miniature Sheet of 12

900 A110 50c #a.-l. 4.50 4.50

Souvenir Sheets

901-902 A110 $6 each 4.50 4.50

Dogs A111

Designs: 25c, Pointer. 50c, Old Danish pointer. $1, German short-haired pointer. $2, English setter.

No. 907a, Irish setter. b, Weimaraner. c, Gordon setter. d, Britanny spaniel. e, American cocker spaniel. f, English cocker spaniel. g, Labrador retriever. h, Golden retriever. i, Flat-coated retriever.

#908, Bloodhound. #909, German shepherd.

1995, May 23 Litho. Perf. 14
903-906 A111 Set of 4 2.75 2.75

Miniature Sheet of 9

907 A111 80c #a.-i. 5.50 5.50

Souvenir Sheets

908-909 A111 $6 each 4.50 4.50

Cacti — A112

Designs: 40c, Schulumbergera truncata. 50c, Echinocereus pectinatus. 80c, Mammillaria zelmaniana alba. $1.60, Lobivia hertriehiana. $2, Hamatocactus setispinus. $3, Astrophytum myriostigma.

No. 916, Opuntia robusta. No. 917, Rhipsalidopsis gaertneri.

1995, June 20 Litho. Perf. 14
910-915 A112 Set of 6 6.00 6.00

Souvenir Sheets

916-917 A112 $6 each 4.50 4.50

Miniature Sheets of 6 or 8

End of World War II, 50th Anniv. A113

Famous World War II Personalities: No. 918: a, Clark Gable. b, Audie Murphy. c, Glenn Miller. d, Joe Louis. e, Jimmy Doolittle. f, John Hersey. g, John F. Kennedy. h, Jimmy Stewart.

Planes: No. 919: a, F4F Wildcat. b, F4U-1A Corsair. c, Vought SB2U Vindicator. d, F6-F Hellcat. e, SDB Dauntless. f, TBF-1 Avenger.

No. 920, Jimmy Doolittle, vert. No. 921, Fighter plane landing on aircraft carrier.

1995, July 20
918 A113 $1.25 #a.-h. + label 7.50 7.50
919 A113 $2 #a.-f. + label 9.25 9.25

Souvenir Sheets

920-921 A113 $6 each 4.50 4.50

UN, 50th Anniv. — A114

People of various races: No. 922a, $1.25, Two men, child. b, $1.60, Man wearing turban, man with beard, woman. c, $3, Two men in business suits, woman.

$6, Nelson Mandela.

1995, July 20 Litho. Perf. 14
922 A114 Strip of 3, #a.-c. 4.50 4.50

Souvenir Sheet

923 A114 $6 multicolored 4.50 4.50

No. 922 is a continuous design.

1995 Boy Scout Jamboree, Holland A115

Scouts in various activities: No. 924a, $1, Two wearing backpacks. b, $2, One holding rope, one wearing backpack. c, $4, One crossing rope bridge, one looking at map, natl. flag.

$6, Scout in kayak.

1995, July 20
924 A115 Strip of 3, #a.-c. 5.25 5.25

Souvenir Sheet

925 A115 $6 multicolored 4.50 4.50

No. 924 is a continuous design.

Rotary Intl., 90th Anniv. A116

Designs: $5, Rotary emblem, natl. flag.
$6, Rotary emblem, beach.

1995, July 20
926 A116 $5 multicolored 3.75 3.75

Souvenir Sheet

927 A116 $6 multicolored 4.50 4.50

Queen Mother, 95th Birthday A117

No. 928: a, Drawing. b, Pink hat. c, Formal portrait. d, Green blue hat.

$6, Wearing crown jewels.

1995, July 20 Perf. 13½x14
928 A117 $1.50 Block or strip of 4, #a.-d. 4.50 4.50

Souvenir Sheet

928E A117 $6 multicolored 4.50 4.50

No. 928 was issued in sheets of 2.

A118 A119

FAO, 50th anniv.: No. 929a, 40c, Woman with tan sari over head. b, $2, FAO emblem, two infants. c, $3, Woman with blue sari over head.

$6, Man with hands around hoe handle.

1995, July 20 Perf. 14
929 A118 Strip of 3, #a.-c. 4.50 4.50

Souvenir Sheet

930 A118 $6 multicolored 4.50 4.50

No. 929 is a continuous design.

1995, July 20

Nobel Prize recipients: No. 931: a, Emil A. von Behring, medicine, 1901. b, Wilhelm Roentgen, physics, 1901. c, Paul J.L. Heyse, literature, 1910. d, Le Duc Tho, peace, 1973. e, Yasunari Kawabata, 1968. f, Tsung-Dao Lee, physics, 1957. g, Werner Hesisenberg, physics, 1932. h, Johannes Stark, physics, 1919. i, Wilhelm Wien, physics, 1911.

$6, Kenzaburo Oe, literature, 1994.

Miniature Sheet of 9

931 A119 $1.25 #a.-i. 8.50 8.50

Souvenir Sheet

932 A119 $6 multicolored 4.50 4.50

Souvenir Sheet

American Eagle Service, 10th Anniv. — A120

Designs: a, 80c, President's Club Emblem. b, $3, Airplane over beach. Illustration reduced.

1995, Aug. 28 Litho. Perf. 14
933 A120 Sheet of 2, #a.-b. 3.00 3.00

Miniature Sheet of 16

Marine Life A121

No. 934: a, Great egrets. b, 17th cent. ship. c, Marlin. d, Herring gulls. e, Nassau groupers. f, Manta ray. g, Leopard shark, hammerhead shark. h, Hourglass dolphins. i, Spanish hogfish. j, Jellyfish, sea horses. k, Angel fish. l, Hawsbill turtle. m, Octopus vulgaris (i, j, m). n, Moray eel (o). o, Queen angelfish, butterflyfish. p, Ghost crab, sea star.

No. 935, Nassau grouper. No. 936, Queen angelfish, vert.

1995, Sept. 1
934 A121 50c #a.-p. 6.00 6.00

Souvenir Sheets

935-936 A121 $5 each 3.75 3.75

Singapore '95 (#935-936).

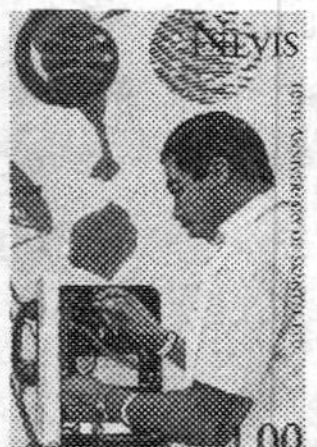

Natl. Telephone Co., SKANTEL Ltd., 10th Anniv. — A122

Designs: $1, Repairman working on telephone. $1.50, Company sign on building.

$5, Front of SKANTEL's Nevis office, horiz.

1995, Oct. 23 Litho. *Perf. 14*
937 A122 $1 multicolored .75 .75
938 A122 $1.50 multicolored 1.10 1.10

Souvenir Sheet

939 A122 $5 multicolored 3.75 3.75

Christmas Paintings, by Duccio di Buoninsegna (1250-1318) A123

Details or entire paintings: 20c, Rucellai Madonna and Child. 50c, Border angel from Rucellai Madonna facing left. 80c, Madonna and Child. $1, The Annuniciation. $1.60, Madonna and Child. $3, Border angel from Rucellai Madonna facing right.

No. 946, Nativity with Prophets Isiah and Ezekiel. No. 947, Crevole Madonna.

1995, Dec. 1 Litho. *Perf. 13½x14*
940-945 A123 Set of 6 5.50 5.50

Souvenir Sheets

946 A123 $5 multicolored 3.75 3.75
947 A123 $6 multicolored 4.50 4.50

Four Seasons Resort, 5th Anniv. A124

Designs: 25c, Beach, resort buildings. 50c, Sailboats on beach. 80c, Golf course. $2, Premier Simeon Daniel laying cornerstone.

$6, Lounge chair on beach, sunset.

1996, Feb. 14 Litho. *Perf. 14*
948-951 A124 Set of 4 2.75 2.75

Souvenir Sheet

952 A124 $6 multicolored 4.50 4.50

New Year 1996 (Year of the Rat) — A125

Rat, various plant life, with olive margin: Nos. 953: a, Looking up at butterfly. b, Crawling left. c, Looking up at horsefly. d, Looking up at dragonfly.

Nos. 954a-954d: like Nos. 953a-953d, with yellow brown margin.

$3, Berries above rat.

1996, Feb, 28
953 A125 $1 Block of 4, #a.-d. 3.00 3.00

Miniature Sheet

954 A125 $1 Sheet of 4, #a.-d. 3.00 3.00

Souvenir Sheet

955 A125 $3 multicolored 2.25 2.25

No. 953 was issued in sheets of 16 stamps.

Pagodas of China A126

#956: a, Qian Qing Gong, 1420, Beijing. b, Qi Nian Dian, Temple of Heaven, Beijing. c, Zhongnanhai, Beijing. d, Da Zing Hall, Shenyang Palace. e, Temple of the Sleeping Buddha, Beijing. f, Huang Qiong Yu, Alter of Heaven, Beijing. g, Grand Bell Temple, Beijing. h, Imperial Palace, Beijing. i, Pu Tuo Temple.

$6, Summer Palace of emperor Wan Yan-liang, 1153, Beijing, vert.

1996, May 15 Litho. *Perf. 14*
956 A126 $1 Sheet of 9, #a.-i. 6.75 6.75

Souvenir Sheet

957 A126 $6 multicolored 4.50 4.50

CHINA '96, 9th Asian Intl. Philatelic Exhibition (#956).

Queen Elizabeth II, 70th Birthday A127

Queen wearing: a, Blue dress, pearls. b, Formal white dress. c, Purple dress, hat.

$6, In uniform at trooping of the color.

1996, May 15 Litho. *Perf. 13½x14*
958 A127 $2 Strip of 3, #a.-c. 3.60 3.60

Souvenir Sheet

959 A127 $6 multicolored 4.50 4.50

No. 958 was issued in sheets of 9 stamps with each strip in a different order.

1996 Summer Olympic Games, Atlanta A128

Designs: 25c, Ancient Greek athletes boxing. 50c, Mark Spitz, gold medalist, swimming, 1972. 80c, Siegbert Horn, kayak singles gold medalist, 1972. $3, Siegestor Triumphal Arch, Munich, vert.

Pictures inside gold medals: No. 964, vert.: a, Jim Thorpe. b, Glenn Morris. c, Bob Mathias. d, Rafer Johnson. e, Bill Toomey. f, Nikolay Avilov. g, Bruce Jenner. h, Daley Thompson. i, Christian Schenk.

No. 965, Willi Holdorf, vert. No. 966, Hans-Joachim Walde, silver medal, vert.

1996, May 28 *Perf. 14*
960-963 A128 Set of 4 3.50 3.50
964 A128 $1 Sheet of 9, #a.-i. 6.75 6.75

Souvenir Sheets

965-966 A128 $5 each 3.80 3.80

Olymphilex '96 (#965).

UNESCO, 50th Anniv. — A129

Designs: 25c, Cave paintings, Tassili N'Ajjer, Algeria. $2, Tikal National Park, Guatemala, vert. $3, Temple of Hera at Samos, Greece.

$6, Pueblo, Taos, US.

1996 Litho. *Perf. 14*
967-969 A129 Set of 3 4.25 4.25

Souvenir Sheet

970 A129 $6 multicolored 4.50 4.50

UNICEF, 50th Anniv. A130

Designs: 25c, Children reading book. 50c, Girl receiving innoculation. $4, Faces of young people.

$6, Girl, vert.

1996
971-973 A130 Set of 3 4.40 4.40

Souvenir Sheet

974 A130 $6 multicolored 4.50 4.50

Disney's Sweethearts — A131

Designs: a, Pocahontas, John Smith, Flit. b, Mowgli, The Girl, Kaa. c, Belle, Beast, Mrs. Potts, Chip. d, Cinderella, Prince Charming, Jaq. e, Pinocchio, Dutch Girl Marionette, Jiminy Cricket. f, Grace Martin, Henry Coy. g, Snow White, Prince. h, Aladdin, Jasmine, Abu. i, Pecos Bill, Slue Foot Sue.

No. 977, Sleeping Beauty, Prince Phillip, vert. No. 978, Ariel, Eric.

Perf. 14x13½, 13½x14

1996, June 17 Litho.
975 A131 $2 Sheet of 9, #a.-i. 13.50 13.50

Souvenir Sheets

977-978 A131 $6 each 4.50 4.50

A number has been reserved for an additional sheet with this set.

American Academy of Ophthalmology, Cent. — A132

1996, July 1 Litho. *Perf. 14*
979 A132 $5 multicolored 3.75 3.75

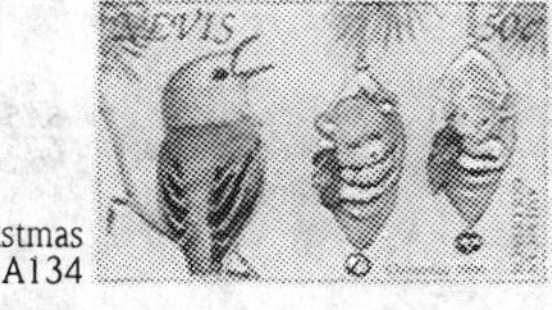

Flowers — A133

Designs: 25c, Rothmannia longiflora. 50c, Gloriosa simplex. $2, Catharanthus roseus. $3, Plumbago auriculata.

No. 984: a, Monodora myristica. b, Giraffa camelopardalis. c, Adansonia digitata. d, Ansellia gigantea. e, Geissorhiza rochensis. f, Arctotis venusta. g, Gladiohis cardinalis. h, Eucomis bicolor. i, Protea obtusifolia.

$5, Stelitzia reginae.

1996, Sept. 24 Litho. *Perf. 14*
980-983 A133 Set of 4 4.30 4.30
984 A133 $1 Sheet of 9, #a.-i. 6.75 6.75

Souvenir Sheet

985 A133 $5 multicolored 3.75 3.75

Christmas A134

Designs: 25c, Western meadowlark, vert. 50c, American goldfinch. 80c, Santa in sleigh, reindeer. $1, Western meadowlark, diff., vert. $1.60, Mockingbird, vert. $5, Yellow-rumped caleque.

No. 992, Macaw. No. 993, Vermilion flycatcher.

1996, Dec. 2 Litho. *Perf. 14*
986-991 A134 Set of 6 6.75 6.75

Souvenir Sheets

992-993 A134 $6 each 4.50 4.50

New Year 1997 (Year of the Ox) — A135

Painting, "Five Oxen," by Han Huang: a, 50c. b, 80c. c, $1.60. d, $2.

1997, Jan. 16 Litho. *Perf. 14x15*
994 A135 Sheet of 4, #a.-d. + label 3.75 3.75

A136

A137

Pandas: a, Eating leaves on branch. b, Face, eating. c, Paws holding object. d, Hanging upside down. e, Lying between tree branch. f, Climbing tree.

$5, Mother, cub.

1997, Feb. 12 Litho. *Perf. 14*
995 A136 $1.60 Sheet of 6, #a.-f. 7.25 7.25

Souvenir Sheet

996 A136 $5 multicolored 3.75 3.75

Hong Kong '97.

1997, May 1 Litho. *Perf. 14*

Cricket Players: 25c, Elquemedo Willet. 80c, Stuart Williams. $2, Keith Arthurton.

No. 1000, Willet, Arthurton, Williams, 1990 Nevis team. No. 1001, Williams, Arthurton, 1994 West Indies team, vert.

997-999 A137 Set of 3 2.25 2.25

Souvenir Sheets

1000-1001 A137 $5 each 3.75 3.75

Queen Elizabeth II, Prince Philip, 50th Wedding Anniv. A138

No. 1002: a, Queen Elizabeth II. b, Royal arms. c, Prince, Queen in red hat. d, Queen in blue coat, Prince. e, Caernarfon Castle. f, Prince Philip.

$5, Queen wearing crown.

1997, May 29 Litho. *Perf. 14*
1002 A138 $1 Sheet of 6, #a.-f. 4.50 4.50

Souvenir Sheet

1003 A138 $5 multicolored 3.75 3.75

Paintings by Hiroshige (1797-1858) A139

No. 1004: a, Scattered Pines, Tone River. b, Nakagawa River Mouth. c, Niijuku Ferry. d, Horie and Nekozane. e, View of Konodai and the Tone

River. f, Maple Trees at Mama, Tekona Shrine & Bridge.
No. 1005, Mitsumata Wakarenofuchi. No. 1006, Moto-Hachinan Shrine, Sunamura.

1997, May 29 *Perf. 13½x14*
1004 A139 $1.60 Sheet of 6, #a.-f. 7.25 7.25

Souvenir Sheets

1005-1006 A139 $6 each 4.50 4.50

Paul Harris (1868-1947), Founder of Rotary Intl. — A140

$2, Literacy promotion, portrait of Harris.
$5, Rotary Village Corps coaching soccer for youths in Chile.

1997, May 29 *Perf. 14*
1007 A140 $2 multicolored 1.50 1.50

Souvenir Sheet

1008 A140 $5 multicolored 3.75 3.75

Heinrich von Stephan (1831-97) A141

No. 1009: a, Russian Reindeer Post, 1859. b, Von Stephan, UPU emblem. c, Steamboat, City of Cairo, 1800's.
$5, Portrait of Von Stephan, Bavarian postal messenger, 1640.

1997, May 29
1009 A141 $1.60 Sheet of 3, #a.-c. 3.50 3.50

Souvenir Sheet

1010 A141 $5 multicolored 3.75 3.75

PACIFIC 97.

Butterflies and Moths A142

10c, Crimson speckled. 25c, Purple emperor. 50c, Regent skipper. 80c, Provence burnet moth. $1, Common wall butterfly. $4, Cruiser butterfly.
No. 1017: a, Red-lined geometrid. b, Boisduval's autumnal moth. c, Blue pansy. d, Common clubtail. e, Tufted jungle queen. f, Lesser marbled fritillary. g, Peacock royal. h, Emperor gum moth. i, Orange swallow-tailed moth.
No. 1018, Jersey tiger. No. 1019, Japanese emperor.

1997, May 12 **Litho.** *Perf. 14*
1011-1016 A142 Set of 6 5.00 5.00
1017 A142 $1 Sheet of 9, #a.-i. 6.75 6.75

Souvenir Sheets

1018-1019 A142 $5 each 3.75 3.75

Souvenir Sheet

Mother Goose A143

1997, May 29
1020 A143 $5 Boy, two pigeons 3.75 3.75

Golf Courses of the World A144

Designs: a, Augusta National, US. b, Cabo Del Sol, Mexico. c, Cypress Point, US. d, Lost City, South Africa. e, Moscow Country Club, Russia. f, New South Wales, Australia. g, Royal Montreal, Canada. h, St. Andrews, Scotland. i, Four Seasons Resort, Nevis.

1997, July 15
1021 A144 $1 Sheet of 9, #a.-i. 6.75 6.75

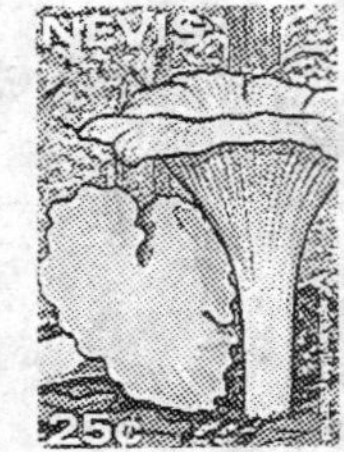

Mushrooms — A145

Designs: 25c, Cantharellus cibarius. 50c, Stropharia aeruginosa. $3, Lactarius turpis. $4, Entoloma Jypeatum.
No. 1026: a, Suillus luteus. b, Amanita musearia. c, Lactarius rufus. d, Amanita rubescens. e, Armillaria mellea. f, Russula sardonia.
No. 1027: a, Boletus edulis. b, Pholiota lenta. c, Cortinarius bolaris. d, Coprinus picaceus. e, Amanita phalloides. f, Cystolepiota aspera.
No. 1028, Gymnopilus junonius. No. 1029, Galerina mutabilis, philiota auriuella.

1997, Aug. 12 **Litho.** *Perf. 13*
1022-1025 A145 Set of 4 6.00 6.00

Sheets of 6

1026 A145 80c #a.-f. 3.75 3.75
1027 A145 $1 #a.-f. 4.50 4.50

Souvenir Sheets

1028-1029 A145 $5 each 3.75 3.75

Diana, Princess of Wales (1961-97) — A146

Various portraits.

1997, Sept. 19 **Litho.** *Perf. 14*
1030 A146 $1 Sheet of 9, #a.-i. 6.75 6.75

Trains A147

Designs: 10c, New Pacific type, Victorian Government Railways, Australia. 50c, Express locomotive, Imperial Government Railways, Japan. 80c, Turbine driven locomotive, London, Midland & Scottish Railway. $1, Electric passenger & freight locomotive, Swiss Federal Railways. $2, 3 cylinder compound express locomotive, London, Midland, Scottish Railway. $3, Express locomotive Kestrel, Great Northern Railway, Ireland.
No. 1037: a, 2-8-2 Mikado, Sudan Government Railways. b, Mohammed Ali El Kebir locomotive, Egyptian State Railways. c, "Schools" class locomotive, Southern Railway. d, Drum Battery Train, Great Southern Railways, Ireland. e, "Pacific" express locomotive, German State Railways. f, Mixed traffic locomotive, Canton-Hankow Railway, China.
No. 1038, "King" class express, Great Western Railway. No. 1039, High pressure locomotive, London, Midland and Scottish Railway.

1997, Sept. 29 **Litho.** *Perf. 14*
1031-1036 A147 Set of 6 5.75 5.75
1037 A147 $1.50 Sheet of 6, #a.-f. 6.75 6.75

Souvenir Sheets

1038-1039 A147 $5 each 3.75 3.75

Christmas — A148

Entire paintings or details: 20c, 25c, Diff. details from Selection of Angels, by Durer. 50c, Andromeda and Perseus, by Rubens. 80c, $1.60, Diff. details from Harmony, by Raphael. $5, Holy Trinity, by Raphael.
No. 1046, Ezekiel's Vision, by Raphael, horiz. No. 1047, Study Muse, by Rapahel, horiz.

1997, Nov. 26 **Litho.** *Perf. 14*
1040-1045 A148 Set of 6 6.25 6.25

Souvenir Sheets

1046-1047 A148 $5 each 3.75 3.75

New Year 1998 (Year of the Tiger) A149

Tigers: No. 1048: a, Jumping right. b, Looking back over shoulder. c, Jumping left. d, Looking forward.
No. 1049, Tiger, vert.

1998, Jan. 19 **Litho.** *Perf. 14*
1048 A149 80c Sheet of 4, #a.-d. 3.00 3.00

Souvenir Sheet

1049 A149 $2 multicolored 1.50 1.50

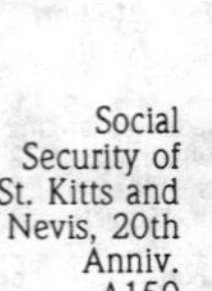

Social Security of St. Kitts and Nevis, 20th Anniv. A150

Designs: 30c, Logo, vert. $1.20, Front of Social Security building.
$6, Social Security staff, Charlestown, Nevis.

1998, Feb. 2 **Litho.** *Perf. 13*
1050 A150 30c multicolored .25 .25
1051 A150 $1.20 multicolored .90 .90

Souvenir Sheet

Perf. 13½x13

1052 A150 $6 multicolored 4.50 4.50

No. 1052 contains one 56x36mm stamp.

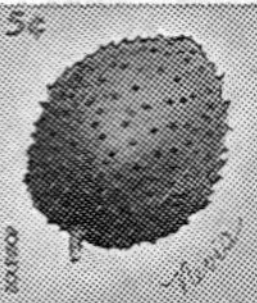

Fruit — A151

1998, Mar. 9 *Perf. 14*
1053 A151 5c Soursop .15 .15
1054 A151 10c Carambola .15 .15
1055 A151 25c Guava .20 .20
1056 A151 30c Papaya .25 .25
1057 A151 50c Mango .40 .40
1058 A151 60c Golden apple .45 .45
1059 A151 80c Pineapple .60 .60
1060 A151 90c Watermelon .70 .70
1061 A151 $1 Bananas .75 .75
1062 A151 $1.80 Orange 1.40 1.40
1063 A151 $3 Honeydew 2.25 2.25
1064 A151 $5 Cantaloupe 3.75 3.75
1065 A151 $10 Pomegranate 7.50 7.50
1066 A151 $20 Cashew 15.00 15.00
Nos. 1053-1066 (14) 33.55 33.55

OFFICIAL STAMPS

Catalogue values for unused stamps in this section are for Never Hinged items.

Nos. 103-112 Ovptd. "OFFICIAL"

Perf. 14½x14

1980, July 30 **Litho.** **Wmk. 373**
O1 A61 15c multicolored .15 .15
O2 A61 25c multicolored .15 .15
O3 A61 30c multicolored .15 .15
O4 A61 40c multicolored .18 .18
O5 A61 45c multicolored .22 .22
O6 A61 50c multicolored .22 .22
O7 A61 55c multicolored .25 .25
O8 A61 $1 multicolored .45 .45
O9 A61 $5 multicolored 2.25 2.25
O10 A61 $10 multicolored 4.50 4.50
Nos. O1-O10 (10) 8.52 8.52

Inverted or double overprints exist on some denominations.

Nos. 123-134 Ovptd. "OFFICIAL"

1981, Mar. *Perf. 14*
O11 A9 15c multicolored .15 .15
O12 A9 20c multicolored .15 .15
O13 A9 25c multicolored .15 .15
O14 A9 30c multicolored .15 .15
O15 A9 40c multicolored .15 .15
O16 A9 45c multicolored .16 .16
O17 A9 50c multicolored .18 .18
O18 A9 55c multicolored .20 .20
O19 A9 $1 multicolored .35 .35
O20 A9 $2.50 multicolored .90 .90
O21 A9 $5 multicolored 1.90 1.90
O22 A9 $10 multicolored 3.75 3.75
Nos. O11-O22 (12) 8.19 8.19

Nos. 135-140 Ovptd. or Surcharged "OFFICIAL" in Blue or Black

1983, Feb. 2
O23 A66 45c on $2 #137 .32 .32
O24 A67 45c on $2 #138 .32 .32
O25 A66 55c #135 .40 .40
O26 A67 55c #136 .40 .40
O27 A66 $1.10 on $5 #139 (Bk) .80 .80
O28 A67 $1.10 on $5 #140 (Bk) .80 .80
Nos. O23-O28 (6) 3.04 3.04

Inverted or double overprints exist on some denominations.

Nos. 367-378 Ovptd. "OFFICIAL"

1985, Jan. 2 **Wmk. 380**
O29 A25 15c multicolored .15 .15
O30 A25 20c multicolored .15 .15
O31 A25 30c multicolored .16 .16
O32 A25 40c multicolored .22 .22
O33 A25 50c multicolored .28 .28
O34 A25 55c multicolored .30 .30
O35 A25 60c multicolored .32 .32
O36 A25 75c multicolored .42 .42
O37 A25 $1 multicolored .55 .55
O38 A25 $3 multicolored 1.65 1.65
O39 A25 $5 multicolored 2.75 2.75
O40 A25 $10 multicolored 5.50 5.50
Nos. O29-O40 (12) 12.45 12.45

Nos. 640-646, 648-653 Ovptd. "OFFICIAL"

1993 **Litho.** *Perf. 14*
O41 A71 5c multicolored .15 .15
O42 A71 10c multicolored .15 .15
O43 A71 15c multicolored .15 .15
O44 A71 20c multicolored .15 .15
O45 A71 25c multicolored .18 .18
O46 A71 40c multicolored .30 .30
O47 A71 50c multicolored .38 .38
O48 A71 75c multicolored .55 .55
O49 A71 80c multicolored .60 .60
O50 A71 $1 multicolored .75 .75
O51 A71 $3 multicolored 2.25 2.25
O52 A71 $5 multicolored 3.75 3.75
O53 A71 $10 multicolored 7.50 7.50
O54 A71 $20 multicolored 15.00 15.00
Nos. O41-O54 (14) 31.86 31.86

Dated "1992."

New Britain stamps can be mounted in the Scott Australian Dependencies album.

NEW BRITAIN

'nü 'bri-tᵊn

LOCATION — South Pacific Ocean, northeast of New Guinea
GOVT. — Australian military government
AREA — 13,000 sq. mi. (approx.)
POP. — 50,600 (approx.)
CAPITAL — Rabaul

The island Neu-Pommern, a part of former German New Guinea, was captured during World War I by Australian troops and named New Britain. Following the war it was mandated to Australia and designated a part of the Mandated Territory of New Guinea. See German New Guinea, North West Pacific Islands and New Guinea.

12 Pence = 1 Shilling

Kaiser's Yacht "The Hohenzollern"
A3 A4

Stamps of German New Guinea, 1900, Surcharged
First Setting

Surcharge lines spaced 6mm on 1p-8p, 4mm on 1sh-5sh.

Perf. 14, 14½

1914, Oct. 17 Unwmk.

1 A3 1p on 3pf brown 225.00 225.00
2 A3 1p on 5pf green 25.00 35.00
3 A3 2p on 10pf car *50.00* *75.00*
4 A3 2p on 20pf ultra 25.00 40.00
 a. "2d." dbl., "G.R.I." omitted 1,600.
 b. Inverted surcharge —
5 A3 2½p on 10pf car 65.00 *125.00*
6 A3 2½p on 20pf ultra 67.50 *125.00*
 a. Inverted surcharge
7 A3 3p on 25pf org & blk, *yel* 155.00 165.00
8 A3 3p on 30pf org & blk, *sal* 175.00 190.00
 a. Double surcharge *3,250.* *3,000.*
 b. Triple surcharge
9 A3 4p on 40pf lake & black 200.00 *250.00*
 a. Double surcharge 850.00 1,250.
 b. Inverted surcharge *3,000.*
 c. "4d." omitted
10 A3 5p on 50pf pur & blk, *sal* 375.00 500.00
 a. Double surcharge *3,250.*
11 A3 8p on 80pf lake & blk, *rose* 500.00 700.00
 a. No period after "8d" *1,500.*
12 A4 1sh on 1m car 1,250. *1,450.*
13 A4 2sh on 2m blue 1,500. *1,750.*
14 A4 3sh on 3m blk vio 3,750. 3,750.
15 A4 5sh on 5m slate & car 4,500. *5,500.*
 a. No period after "I" — —

"G.R.I." stands for Georgius Rex Imperator.

Second Setting

Surcharge lines spaced 5mm on 1p-8p, 5½mm on 1sh-5sh.

1914, Dec. 16

16 A3 1p on 3pf brown 40.00 40.00
 a. Double surcharge 300.00 *425.00*
 b. "1" omitted 315.00
 c. As "b," double surcharge 375.00 *475.00*
 d. Inverted surcharge 800.00 *1,250.*
 e. "4" for "1" —
 f. Small "1" 200.00
17 A3 1p on 5pf green 14.00 20.00
 a. Double surcharge 700.00
 b. "G. I. R." 2,750. *3,250.*
 c. "d" inverted 750.00
 d. No periods after "G R I" —
 e. Small "1" 90.00 125.00
 f. "1d" double —
 g. No period after "1d"
 h. Triple surcharge
18 A3 2p on 10pf car 20.00 25.00
 a. Double surcharge 3,250. —
 b. Dbl. surch., one inverted 1,750.
 c. Surcharged "G. I. R., 3d" *4,150.*
 d. Surcharged "1d" 2,250. 1,750.
 e. Period before "G" *2,000.*
 f. No period after "2d" 100.00 150.00
 g. Inverted surcharge
 h. "2d" double, one inverted
 i. "1d" on "2d" —
 j. Pair, #18, 20 —
19 A3 2p on 20pf ultra 25.00 30.00
 a. Double surcharge 775.00 *1,400.*
 b. Double surch., one inverted 1,000. *1,300.*
 c. "R" inverted *1,500.*
 d. Surcharged "1d" 3,000. 3,000.
 f. Inverted surcharge 1,750. *2,500.*
 g. "1d" on "2d" *8,750.*
 h. Pair, one without surcharge
 i. Pair, #19, 21 — —
20 A3 2½p on 10pf car 125.00 275.00
21 A3 2½p on 20pf ultra 1,000. 1,300.
 a. Double surcharge, one invtd.
 b. "2½" triple
 c. Surcharged "3d"
22 A3 3p on 25pf org & blk, *yel* 90.00 110.00
 a. Double surcharge 2,000. *2,750.*
 b. Inverted surcharge 2,000 *2,750.*
 c. "G. R. I." only
 d. "G. I. R." 1,100. 1,100.
 e. Pair, one without surcharge —
 f. Surcharged "G. I. R., 5d"
23 A3 3p on 30pf org & blk, *sal* 75.00 90.00
 a. Double surcharge 850.00 *1,250.*
 b. Double surcharge, one invtd. 1,000. *1,400.*
 c. "d" inverted 550.00
 d. Surcharged "1d" 2,750. —
 e. Triple surcharge
 g. Double inverted surcharge 2,250. *3,000.*
 h. Pair, one without surcharge *3,000.*
24 A3 4p on 40pf lake & blk 90.00 110.00
 a. Double surcharge 700.00 700.00
 b. Double surcharge, one invtd. 1,250. 1,250.
 e. Surcharged "1d" 1,500.
 f. "1" on "4"
25 A3 5p on 50pf pur & blk, *sal* 145.00 150.00
 a. Double surcharge 1,000.
 b. Double surcharge, one invtd. 1,500. *3,000.*
 c. "5" omitted 550.00
 d. Inverted surcharge 1,500.
 e. Double inverted surcharge 2,000. *3,000.*
 f. "G. I. R."
26 A3 8p on 80pf lake & blk, *rose* 425.00 375.00
 a. Double surcharge 1,400. *1,500.*
 b. Double surcharge, one invtd. 1,400. *1,500.*
 c. Triple surcharge 1,400. *1,750.*
 d. No period after "8d"
 e. Inverted surcharge 2,250. *3,000.*
 f. Surcharged "3d" 3,500.
27 A4 1sh on 1m car 1,500. *2,000.*
28 A4 2sh on 2m bl 2,000. *3,000.*
 a. Surcharged "5s"
 b. Double surcharge
29 A4 3sh on 3m blk vio 2,750. *4,500.*
 a. No periods after "R I"
 b. "G.R.I." double —
29C A4 5sh on 5m sl & car 10,000. *12,500.*
 d. No periods after "R I"
 e. Surcharged "1s"

Same Surcharge on Stamps of Marshall Islands

1914

30 A3 1p on 3pf brown 40.00 45.00
 a. Inverted surcharge 1,350.
31 A3 1p on 5pf green 45.00 45.00
 a. Double surcharge 750.00 *1,500.*
 b. No period after "d"
 c. Inverted surcharge 900.00
32 A3 2p on 10pf car 13.50 24.00
 a. Double surcharge 700.00 *1,250.*
 b. Double surcharge, one invtd. 850.00 *1,250.*
 c. Surcharge sideways 2,500.
 d. No period after "2d"
 e. No period after "G" 450.00
33 A3 2p on 20 pf ultra 15.00 24.00
 a. No period after "d" 35.00 *75.00*
 b. Double surcharge 750.00 —
 c. Double surcharge, one invtd. 1,450. —
 d. Inverted surcharge — —
 e. "I" omitted
34 A3 3p on 25pf org & blk, *yel* 325.00 325.00
 a. Double surcharge 975.00 *1,400.*
 b. Double surcharge, one invtd. 1,100.
 c. No period after "d" 550.00 600.00
 d. Inverted surcharge 2,000.
35 A3 3p on 30pf org & blk, *sal* 375.00 375.00
 a. No period after "d" 550.00 600.00
 b. Inverted surcharge — —
 c. Double surcharge 1,500.
 d. Double surcharge, one invtd.
36 A3 4p on 40pf lake & blk 90.00 100.00
 a. No period after "d" 225.00 *325.00*
 b. Double surcharge 1,250. *1,750.*
 c. "4d" omitted
 d. "1d" on "4d"
 e. No period after "R"
 f. Inverted surcharge 1,400.
 g. Surcharged "1d" 3,000.
37 A3 5p on 50pf pur & blk, *sal* 110.00 140.00
 a. "d" omitted 950.00
 b. Double surcharge 1,750.
 c. "5d" double 475.00
38 A3 8p on 80pf lake & blk, *rose* 500.00 425.00
 a. Inverted surcharge —
 b. Double surcharge 1,750.
 c. Double surcharge, one invtd. —
 d. Triple surcharge
39 A4 1sh on 1m car 1,400. *2,250.*
 a. Double surcharge —
 b. Dbl. surch., one with "s1" for "1s"
 c. No period after "I" 2,250.
40 A4 2sh on 2m blue 1,250. 1,450.
 a. Double surcharge, one invtd. *6,000.*
 b. Double surcharge —
 c. Large "S"
 d. No period after "I" 1,750. *2,500.*
41 A4 3sh on 3m blk vio 2,500. *3,250.*
 a. Double surcharge —
 b. No period after "I" 3,250.
 c. No period after "R I" 2,900.
 d. Inverted surcharge
42 A4 5sh on 5m sl & car *8,000.* *5,500.*
 a. Double surcharge, one invtd. *10,000.*

See Nos. 44-45.

A5

Surcharged in Black on Registration Label

1914 *Perf. 12*

43 A5 3p black & red (Rabaul) 125.00 *160.00*
 a. "Friedrich Wilhelmshaven" 150.00 *300.00*
 b. "Herbertshohe" 175.00 *350.00*
 c. "Kawieng" 225.00 *300.00*
 d. "Kieta" 375.00 *475.00*
 e. "Manus" 200.00 *400.00*
 f. Double surcharge (Rabaul) 1,000. *1,400.*
 g. As "c," double surcharge *1,250.*
 h. As "e," double surcharge *1,750.*
 i. As "d," pair, one without surcharge *4,750.*

Nos. 43a, 43c and 43e exist with town name in letters with serifs. The varieties Deutsch-Neuguinea, Deutsch Neu-Guinea, etc., are known.

Nos. 32-33 Surcharged with Large "1"

1915

44 A3 1p on 2p on 10pf 175. 150.
 a. "1" double —
 b. "1" inverted — —
45 A3 1p on 2p on 20pf 3,000. 1,900.
 a. "1" inverted — —

The stamps of Marshall Islands surcharged "G. R. I." and new values in British currency were all used in New Britain and are therefore listed here.

OFFICIAL STAMPS

O1

German New Guinea Nos. 7-8 Surcharged

1915 Unwmk. *Perf. 14*

O1 O1 1p on 3pf brown 25.00 *60.00*
 a. Double surcharge 1,400.
O2 O1 1p on 5pf green 75.00 *125.00*

NEW CALEDONIA

'nü ˌka-lə-'dō-nyə

LOCATION — Island in the South Pacific Ocean, east of Queensland, Australia
GOVT. — French Overseas Territory
AREA — 7,375 sq. mi.
POP. — 147,200 (est. 1984)
CAPITAL — Noumea

Dependencies of New Caledonia are the Loyalty Islands, Isle of Pines, Huon Islands and Chesterfield Islands.

100 Centimes = 1 Franc

Catalogue values for unused stamps in this country are for Never Hinged items, beginning with Scott 252 in the regular postage section, Scott B13 in the semi-postal section, Scott C14 in the airpost section, Scott J32 in the postage due section, and Scott O1 in the official section.

Watermark

Wmk. 385

Napoleon III — A1

1859 Unwmk. Litho. ***Imperf.***
Without Gum

1 A1 10c black 175.00

Fifty varieties. Counterfeits abound.
See No. 315.

Type of French Colonies, 1877 Surcharged in Black:

NCE 5 — Nos. 2-5
N C E 5 — Nos. 6-7

1881-83

2 A8 5c on 40c red, *straw* ('82) 250.00 250.00
 a. Inverted surcharge 900.00 900.00
3 A8 05c on 40c red, *straw* ('83) 16.00 16.00
4 A8 25c on 35c dp vio, *yel* 200.00 175.00
 a. Inverted surcharge 550.00 550.00
5 A8 25c on 75c rose car, *rose* ('82) 275.00 275.00
 a. Inverted surcharge 600.00 600.00

1883-84

6 A8 5c on 40c red, *straw* ('84) 12.00 12.00
 a. Inverted surcharge 12.00 12.00
7 A8 5c on 75c rose car, *rose* ('83) 27.50 27.50
 a. Inverted surcharge 35.00 35.00

In type "a" surcharge, the narrower-spaced letters measure 14½mm, and an early printing of No. 4 measures 13½mm. Type "b" letters measure 18mm.

French Colonies No. 59 Surcharged in Black:

N. C. E. 5c. — No. 8
N. C. E. 5c. — Nos. 9-10

1886 *Perf. 14x13½*

8 A9 5c on 1fr 11.00 11.00
 a. Inverted surcharge 20.00 20.00
9 A9 5c on 1fr 11.00 11.00
 b. Inverted surcharge 25.00 25.00

French Colonies No. 29 Surcharged
Imperf

10 A8 5c on 1fr *7,250.* *7,250.*

Types of French Colonies, 1877-86, Surcharged in Black:

N.-C. E. 10 c. — Nos. 11, 13

No. 12

1891-92 ***Imperf.***

11 A8 10c on 40c red, *straw* ('92) 16.00 14.00
 a. Inverted surcharge 25.00 25.00
 b. Double surcharge 40.00 40.00
 c. No period after "10c" 20.00 16.00

Perf. 14x13½

12 A9 10c on 30c brn, *bis* 8.75 8.75
 a. Inverted surcharge 10.00 10.00
 b. Double surcharge 25.00 25.00
 c. Double surcharge, inverted 30.00 25.00
13 A9 10c on 40c red, *straw* ('92) 9.00 9.00
 a. Inverted surcharge 10.00 10.00
 b. No period after "10c" 10.00 10.00
 c. Double surcharge 25.00 25.00
 Nos. 11-13 (3) 33.75 31.75

Variety "double surcharge, one inverted" exists on Nos. 11-13. Value same as for "double surcharge."

Types of French Colonies, 1877-86, Handstamped in Black

g

1892 *Imperf.*

16 A8 20c red, *grn* 250.00 250.00
17 A8 35c vio, *org* 45.00 45.00
18 A8 40c red, *straw*
19 A8 1fr brnz grn, *straw* 175.00 175.00

The 1c, 2c, 4c and 75c of type A8 are believed not to have been officially made or actually used.

1892 *Perf. 14x13½*

23 A9 5c grn, *grnsh* 8.00 7.50
24 A9 10c blk, *lavender* 75.00 40.00
25 A9 15c blue 50.00 25.00
26 A9 20c red, *grn* 50.00 30.00
27 A9 25c yel, *straw* 9.00 7.50
28 A9 25c blk, *rose* 55.00 8.00
29 A9 30c brn, *bis* 42.50 37.50
30 A9 35c vio, *org* 140.00 100.00
32 A9 75c car, *rose* 100.00 85.00
33 A9 1fr brnz grn, *straw* 90.00 80.00
Nos. 23-33 (10) 619.50 420.50

The note following No. 19 also applies to the 1c, 2c, 4c and 40c of type A9.

Surcharged in Blue or Black

h

1892-93 *Imperf.*

34 A8 10c on 1fr brnz grn, *straw* (Bl) *3,500. 2,750.*

Perf. 14x13½

35 A9 5c on 20c red, *grn* (Bk) 12.50 8.00
a. Inverted surcharge 55.00 52.50
b. Double surcharge inverted
36 A9 5c on 75c car, *rose* (Bk) 9.00 5.75
a. Inverted surcharge 55.00 52.50
37 A9 5c on 75c car, *rose* (Bl) 8.00 5.00
a. Inverted surcharge 55.00 52.50
38 A9 10c on 1fr brnz grn, *straw* (Bk) 8.00 5.50
a. Inverted surcharge 325.00 325.00
39 A9 10c on 1fr brnz grn, *straw* (Bl) 10.00 10.00
a. Inverted surcharge 55.00 52.50
Nos. 35-39 (5) 47.50 34.25

Navigation and Commerce — A12

1892-1904 **Typo.** *Perf. 14x13½*

Name of Colony in Blue or Carmine

40 A12 1c blk, *blue* .35 .30
41 A12 2c brn, *buff* .65 .45
42 A12 4c claret, *lav* .85 .80
43 A12 5c grn, *grnsh* 1.25 .80
44 A12 5c yel grn ('00) .80 .65
45 A12 10c blk, *lavender* 3.50 2.50
46 A12 10c rose red ('00) 4.00 1.00
47 A12 15c bl, quadrille paper 11.00 .75
48 A12 15c gray ('00) 6.00 1.00
49 A12 20c red, *grn* 8.50 6.00
50 A12 25c blk, *rose* 12.00 3.25
51 A12 25c blue ('00) 9.50 5.50
52 A12 30c brn, *bis* 10.00 5.75
53 A12 40c red, *straw* 10.00 8.25
54 A12 50c car, *rose* 35.00 20.00
55 A12 50c brn, *az* (name in car) ('00) 62.50 45.00
56 A12 50c brn, *az* (name in bl) ('04) 32.50 27.50
57 A12 75c vio, *org* 17.00 11.00
58 A12 1fr brnz grn, *straw* 21.00 13.00
Nos. 40-58 (19) 246.40 153.50

Perf. 13½x14 stamps are counterfeits.
For overprints and surcharges see Nos. 59-87, 117-121.

Nos. 41-42, 52, 57-58, 53 Surcharged in Black:

N:C.E. (15) — j
N.-C.E. 5 — k

1900-01

59 A12 (h) 5c on 2c ('01) 10.00 9.00
a. Double surcharge 80.00 80.00
b. Inverted surcharge 80.00 80.00
60 A12 (h) 5c on 4c 1.75 1.75
a. Inverted surcharge 50.00 50.00
b. Double surcharge 50.00 50.00
61 A12 (j) 15c on 30c 2.50 2.50
a. Inverted surcharge 40.00 40.00
b. Double surcharge 40.00 40.00
62 A12 (j) 15c on 75c ('01) 8.25 7.00
a. Pair, one without surcharge
b. Inverted surcharge 90.00 90.00
c. Double surcharge 90.00 90.00
63 A12 (j) 15c on 1fr ('01) 12.00 11.00
a. Double surcharge 90.00 90.00
b. Inverted surcharge 90.00 90.00
Nos. 59-63 (5) 34.50 31.25

1902

64 A12 (k) 5c on 30c 5.00 5.00
a. Inverted surcharge 22.50 22.50
65 A12 (k) 15c on 40c 4.00 4.00
a. Inverted surcharge 22.50 22.50

Jubilee Issue

Stamps of 1892-1900 Overprinted in Blue, Red, Black or Gold

1903

66 A12 1c blk, *lil bl* (Bl) .90 .80
a. Inverted overprint *165.00 165.00*
67 A12 2c brn, *buff* (Bl) 2.50 2.00
68 A12 4c cl, *lav* (Bl) 3.50 2.00
a. Double overprint *200.00 200.00*
69 A12 5c dk grn, *grnsh* (R) 3.25 2.00
70 A12 5c yel grn (R) 5.00 4.00
71 A12 10c blk, *lav* (R) 10.00 6.00
72 A12 10c blk, *lav* (double G & Bk) 6.00 5.00
73 A12 15c gray (R) 6.00 3.00
74 A12 20c red, *grn* (Bl) 11.00 10.00
75 A12 25c blk, *rose* (Bl) 11.00 10.00
a. Double overprint
76 A12 30c brn, *bis* (R) 13.00 11.00
77 A12 40c red, *straw* (Bl) 20.00 15.00
78 A12 50c car, *rose* (Bl) 32.50 20.00
a. Pair, one without overprint
79 A12 75c vio, *org* (Bk) 55.00 47.50
a. Dbl. ovpt. in blk and red *325.00 325.00*
80 A12 1fr brnz grn, *straw* (Bl) 70.00 60.00
a. Dbl. ovpt., one in red *325.00 300.00*
Nos. 66-80 (15) 249.65 198.30

With Additional Surcharge of New Value in Blue

81 A12 1c on 2c #67 .50 .50
a. Numeral double *60.00 60.00*
b. Numeral only
82 A12 2c on 4c #68 1.25 1.25
83 A12 4c on 5c #69 1.25 1.25
a. Small "4" *400.00 400.00*
84 A12 4c on 5c #70 1.75 1.75
a. Pair, one without numeral
85 A12 10c on 15c #73 1.75 1.75
86 A12 15c on 20c #74 2.00 2.00
87 A12 20c on 25c #75 3.50 3.50
Nos. 81-87 (7) 12.00 12.00

50 years of French occupation.
Surcharge on Nos. 81-83, 85-86 is horizontal, reading down.
There are three types of numeral on No. 83. The numeral on No. 84 is identical with that of No. 83a except that its position is upright.
Nos. 66-87 are known with "I" of "TENAIRE" missing.

Kagu
A16

Landscape
A17

Ship — A18

1905-28 **Typo.** *Perf. 14x13½*

88 A16 1c blk, *green* .15 .15
89 A16 2c red brown .20 .20
90 A16 4c bl, *org* .30 .30
91 A16 5c pale green .30 .30
92 A16 5c dl bl ('21) .15 .15
93 A16 10c carmine 1.00 .80
94 A16 10c green ('21) .50 .50
95 A16 10c red, *pink* ('25) .35 .35
96 A16 15c violet .40 .30
97 A17 20c brown .30 .30
98 A17 25c blue, *grn* .30 .30
99 A17 25c red, *yel* ('21) .30 .30
100 A17 30c brn, *org* .30 .30
101 A17 30c dp rose ('21) 1.00 1.00
102 A17 30c org ('25) .30 .30
103 A17 35c blk, *yellow* .35 .35
104 A17 40c car, *grn* .80 .70
105 A17 45c vio brn, *lav* .45 .45
106 A17 50c car, *org* 1.75 1.25
107 A17 50c dk bl ('21) 1.00 1.00
108 A17 50c gray ('25) .50 .50
109 A17 65c dp bl ('28) .35 .35
110 A17 75c ol grn, *straw* .30 .30
111 A17 75c bl, *bluish* ('25) .45 .45
112 A17 75c violet ('27) .65 .65
113 A18 1fr bl, *yel grn* .80 .50
114 A18 1fr dp bl ('25) 1.10 1.10
115 A18 2fr car, *bl* 1.75 1.40
116 A18 5fr blk, *straw* 4.25 3.75
Nos. 88-116 (29) 20.35 18.30

See Nos. 311, 317a. For surcharges see Nos. 122-135, B1-B3, Q1-Q3.

Stamps of 1892-1904 Surcharged in Carmine or Black

05 10

1912

117 A12 5c on 15c gray (C) .30 .30
a. Inverted surcharge 100.00 100.00
118 A12 5c on 20c red, *grn* .60 .60
119 A12 5c on 30c brn, *bis* (C) .60 .60
120 A12 10c on 40c red, *straw* 1.25 1.25
121 A12 10c on 50c brn, *az* (C) 1.25 1.25
Nos. 117-121 (5) 4.00 4.00

Two spacings between the surcharged numerals are found on Nos. 117 to 121.

No. 96 Surcharged in Brown

5 CENTIMES

1918

122 A16 5c on 15c violet .60 .60
a. Double surcharge 40.00 40.00
b. Inverted surcharge 22.50 22.50

The color of the surcharge on No. 122 varies from red to dark brown.

No. 96 Surcharged

0,05 =

1922

123 A16 5c on 15c vio (R) .30 .30
a. Double surcharge 40.00 40.00

Stamps and Types of 1905-28 Surcharged New Value and Bars in Red or Black

60 =

1924-27

124 A16 25c on 15c vio .30 .30
a. Double surcharge 40.00
125 A18 25c on 2fr car, *bl* .40 .40
126 A18 25c on 5fr blk, *straw* .40 .40
a. Double surcharge 60.00 60.00
127 A17 60c on 75c bl grn (R) .30 .30
128 A17 65c on 45c red brn 1.10 1.10
129 A17 85c on 45c red brn 1.10 1.10
130 A17 90c on 75c dp rose .45 .45
131 A18 1.25fr on 1fr dp bl (R) .35 .35
132 A18 1.50fr on 1fr dp bl, *bl* .90 .90
133 A18 3fr on 5fr red vio .90 .90
134 A18 10fr on 5fr ol, *lav* (R) 4.50 4.50
135 A18 20fr on 5fr vio rose, *org* 8.75 8.75
Nos. 124-135 (12) 19.45 19.45

Issue years: Nos. 125-127, 1924. Nos. 124, 128-129, 1925. Nos. 131, 134, 1926. Nos. 130, 132-133, 135, 1927.

Bay of Palétuviers Point — A19

Landscape with Chief's House — A20

Admiral de Bougainville and Count de La Pérouse
A21

1928-40 **Typo.**

136 A19 1c brn vio & ind .15 .15
137 A19 2c dk brn & yel grn .15 .15
137B A19 3c brn vio & ind .20 .20
138 A19 4c org & Prus grn .15 .15
139 A19 5c Prus bl & dp ol .30 .30
140 A19 10c gray lil & dk brn .15 .15
141 A19 15c yel brn & dp bl .30 .30
142 A19 20c brn red & dk brn .30 .30
143 A19 25c dk grn & dk brn .40 .30
144 A20 30c gray grn & bl grn .30 .20
145 A20 35c blk & brt vio .30 .20
146 A20 40c brt red & olvn .20 .20
147 A20 45c dp bl & red org .80 .55
147A A20 45c bl grn & dl grn .60 .60
148 A20 50c vio & brn .30 .30
149 A20 55c vio bl & car 2.25 1.25
150 A20 60c vio bl & car .30 .30
151 A20 65c org brn & bl .55 .50
152 A20 70c dp rose & brn .30 .30
153 A20 75c Prus bl & ol gray .80 .40
154 A20 80c red brn & grn .40 .40
155 A20 85c grn & brn 1.00 .60
156 A20 90c dp red & brt red .50 .40
157 A20 90c ol grn & rose red .50 .50
158 A21 1fr dp ol & sal red 4.00 2.00
159 A21 1fr rose red & dk car .90 .80
160 A21 1fr brn red & grn .40 .40
161 A21 1.10fr dp grn & brn 8.00 7.00
162 A21 1.25fr brn red & grn .70 .50
163 A21 1.25fr rose red & dk car .50 .50
164 A21 1.40fr dk bl & red org .50 .50
165 A21 1.50fr dp bl & bl .40 .40
166 A21 1.60fr dp grn & brn .70 .70
167 A21 1.75fr dk bl & red org .40 .40
168 A21 1.75fr violet bl .50 .50
169 A21 2fr red org & brn .30 .30
170 A21 2.25fr vio bl .50 .50
171 A21 2.50fr brn & lt brn .80 .80
172 A21 3fr mag & brn .40 .40
173 A21 5fr dk bl & brn .50 .50
174 A21 10fr vio & brn, *pnksh* .80 .80
175 A21 20fr red & brn, *yel* 1.65 1.50
Nos. 136-175 (42) 33.15 27.20

The 35c in Prussian green and dark green without overprint is listed as Wallis and Futuna No. 53a.
Issue years: 35c, 70c, 85c, #162, 167, 1933; 55c, 80c, #159, 168, 1938; #157, 163, 2.25fr, 1939; 3c, 1.40fr, 1.60fr, 2.50fr, 147A, 160, 1940; others, 1928.
For overprints see #180-207, 217-251, Q4-Q6.

Colonial Exposition Issue
Common Design Types

1931 **Engr.** *Perf. 12½*

Country Name Typo. in Black

176 CD70 40c dp green 2.50 2.50
177 CD71 50c violet 2.50 2.50
178 CD72 90c red orange 2.50 2.50
179 CD73 1.50fr dull blue 2.50 2.50
Nos. 176-179 (4) 10.00 10.00

Paris-Nouméa Flight Issue
Regular Issue of 1928 Overprinted:

1932 *Perf. 14x13½*

180 A20 40c brt red & olvn 325.00 325.00
181 A20 50c vio & brn 325.00 325.00

Arrival on Apr. 5, 1932 at Nouméa, of the French aviators, Verneilh, Dévé and Munch.
Excellent forgeries exist of #180-181.

Types of 1928-33 Overprinted in Black or Red:

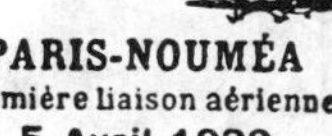

PARIS-NOUMÉA
Première liaison aérienne
5 Avril 1932

1933

182 A19	1c red vio & dl bl	4.25	4.25
183 A19	2c dk brn & yel grn	4.25	4.25
184 A19	4c dl org & Prus bl	4.25	4.25
185 A19	5c Prus grn & ol (R)	4.25	4.25
186 A19	10c gray lil & dk brn (R)	4.25	4.25
187 A19	15c yel brn & dp bl (R)	4.25	4.25
188 A19	20c brn red & dk brn	4.25	4.25
189 A19	25c dk grn & dk brn (R)	4.25	4.25
190 A20	30c gray grn & bl grn (R)	4.25	4.25
191 A20	35c blk & lt vio	4.25	4.25
192 A20	40c brt red & olvn	4.25	4.25
193 A20	45c dp bl & red org	4.25	4.25
194 A20	50c vio & brn	4.25	4.25
195 A20	70c dp rose & brn	4.25	4.25
196 A20	75c Prus bl & ol gray (R)	4.25	4.25
197 A20	85c grn & brn	4.25	4.25
198 A20	90c dp red & brt red	4.25	4.25
199 A21	1fr dp ol & sal red	4.25	4.25
200 A21	1.25fr brn red & grn	4.25	4.25
201 A21	1.50fr dp bl & bl (R)	5.00	5.00
202 A21	1.75fr dk bl & red org	5.00	5.00
203 A21	2fr red org & brn	5.50	5.50
204 A21	3fr mag & brn	5.50	5.50
205 A21	5fr dk bl & brn (R)	5.50	5.50
206 A21	10fr vio & brn, *pnksh*	5.50	5.50
207 A21	20fr red & brn, *yel*	5.50	5.50
	Nos. 182-207 (26)	118.25	118.25

1st anniv., Paris-Noumea flight. Plane centered on Nos. 190-207.

Paris International Exposition Issue
Common Design Types

1937 Engr. *Perf. 13*

208 CD74	20c dp vio	.60	.60
209 CD75	30c dk grn	.60	.60
210 CD76	40c car rose	.65	.65
211 CD77	50c dk brn & bl	.65	.65
212 CD78	90c red	.65	.65
213 CD79	1.50fr ultra	.65	.65
	Nos. 208-213 (6)	3.80	3.80

Colonial Arts Exhibition Issue
Souvenir Sheet
Common Design Type

1937 *Imperf.*

214 CD78 3fr sepia 7.50 7.50

New York World's Fair Issue
Common Design Type

1939 *Perf. 12½x12*

215 CD82	1.25fr car lake	1.25	1.25
216 CD82	2.25fr ultra	1.25	1.25

Nouméa Roadstead and Marshal Pétain A21a

1941 Engr. *Perf. 12½x12*

216A A21a	1fr bluish grn	.65	
216B A21a	2.50fr dk blue	.65	

Nos. 216A-216B were issued by the Vichy government and were not placed on sale in the colony.

A 10c, type A19, without "RF," and a 60c, type A20, without "REPUBLIQUE FRANCAISE," were also issued by the Vichy government and not placed on sale in New Caledonia.

Types of 1928-40 Overprinted in Black **France Libre**

1941 *Perf. 14x13½*

217 A19	1c red vio & dl bl	9.00	9.00
218 A19	2c dk brn & yel grn	9.00	9.00
219 A19	3c brn vio & ind	9.00	9.00
220 A19	4c dl org & Prus bl	9.00	9.00
221 A19	5c Prus bl & dp ol	9.00	9.00
222 A19	10c gray lil & dk brn	9.00	9.00
223 A19	15c yel brn & dp bl	9.00	9.00
224 A19	20c brn red & dk brn	9.00	9.00
225 A19	25c dk grn & dk brn	9.00	9.00
226 A20	30c gray grn & bl grn	9.00	9.00
227 A20	35c blk & brt vio	9.00	9.00
228 A20	40c brt red & olvn	9.00	9.00
229 A20	45c bl grn & dl grn	9.00	9.00
230 A20	50c vio & brn	9.00	9.00
231 A20	55c vio bl & car	9.00	9.00
232 A20	60c vio bl & car	9.00	9.00
233 A20	65c org brn & bl	9.00	9.00
234 A20	70c dp rose & brn	9.00	9.00
235 A20	75c Prus bl & ol gray	9.00	9.00
236 A20	80c red brn & grn	9.00	9.00
237 A20	85c grn & brn	10.00	10.00
238 A20	90c dp red & brt red	10.00	10.00
239 A21	1fr rose red & dk car	10.00	10.00
240 A21	1.25fr brn red & grn	10.00	10.00
241 A21	1.40fr dk bl & red org	10.00	10.00
242 A21	1.50fr dp bl & bl	10.00	10.00
243 A21	1.60fr dp grn & brn	10.00	10.00
244 A21	1.75fr dk bl & red org	10.00	10.00
245 A21	2fr red org & brn	10.00	10.00
246 A21	2.25fr vio bl	10.00	10.00
247 A21	2.50fr brn & lt brn	11.00	11.00
248 A21	3fr mag & brn	11.00	11.00
249 A21	5fr dk bl & brn	11.00	11.00
250 A21	10fr vio & brn, *pnksh*	11.00	11.00
251 A21	20fr red & brn, *yel*	11.00	11.00
	Nos. 217-251 (35)	335.00	335.00

Issued to note this colony's affiliation with the "Free France" movement.

Catalogue values for unused stamps in this section, from this point to the end of the section, are for Never Hinged items.

Kagu — A22

1942 Photo. *Perf. 14½x14*

252 A22	5c brown	.15	.15
253 A22	10c dk gray bl	.20	.20
254 A22	25c emerald	.20	.20
255 A22	30c red org	.30	.30
256 A22	40c dk slate grn	.30	.30
257 A22	80c dl red brn	.40	.40
258 A22	1fr rose vio	.40	.40
259 A22	1.50fr red	.40	.40
260 A22	2fr gray blk	.60	.60
261 A22	2.50fr brt ultra	.60	.60
262 A22	4fr dl vio	.50	.50
263 A22	5fr bister	.60	.60
264 A22	10fr dp brn	.85	.85
265 A22	20fr dp grn	1.50	1.50
	Nos. 252-265 (14)	7.00	7.00

Stamps of 1942 Surcharged in Carmine or Black **60 c. =**

1945-46 Unwmk. *Perf. 14½x14*

266 A22	50c on 5c (C) ('46)	.45	.45
267 A22	60c on 5c (C)	.45	.45
268 A22	70c on 5c (C)	.45	.45
269 A22	1.20fr on 5c (C)	.20	.20
270 A22	2.40fr on 25c	.20	.20
271 A22	3fr on 25c ('46)	.20	.20
272 A22	4.50fr on 25c	.45	.45
273 A22	15fr on 2.50fr (C)	.85	.85
	Nos. 266-273 (8)	3.25	3.25

Eboue Issue
Common Design Type

1945 Engr. *Perf. 13*

274 CD91	2fr black	.30	.30
275 CD91	25fr Prus grn	.85	.85

Kagus — A23

Ducos Sanatorium A24

Porcupine Isle — A25

Nickel Foundry A26

"Towers of Notre Dame" — A27

Chieftain's House — A28

1948 Unwmk. Photo. *Perf. 13½x13*

276 A23	10c yel & brn	.15	.15
277 A23	30c grn & brn	.15	.15
278 A23	40c org & brn	.15	.15
279 A24	50c pink & brn	.30	.30
280 A24	60c yel & brn	.30	.30
281 A24	80c lt grn & bl grn	.30	.30
282 A25	1fr brn, pur & org	.30	.30
283 A25	1.20fr pale gray, brn & bl	.30	.30
284 A25	1.50fr cream, dk bl & yel	.40	.30
285 A26	2fr pck grn & brn	.40	.30
286 A26	2.40fr ver & dp rose	.40	.30
287 A26	3fr org & pur	4.00	.80
288 A26	4fr bl & dk bl	.95	.45
289 A27	5fr ver & pur	1.25	.55
290 A27	6fr yel & brn	1.50	.80
291 A27	10fr org & dk bl	1.50	.65
292 A28	15fr brn & gray	1.50	.95
293 A28	20fr pur & yel	1.50	.95
294 A28	25fr dk bl & org	2.00	1.75
	Nos. 276-294 (19)	17.35	9.75

Military Medal Issue
Common Design Type

1952 Engr. & Typo. *Perf. 13*

295 CD101 2fr multi 2.00 2.00

Admiral Bruni d'Entrecasteaux and his Two Frigates — A29

Designs: 2fr, Msgr. Douarre and Cathedral of Nouméa. 6fr, Admiral Dumont d'Urville and map. 13fr, Admiral Auguste Febvrier-Despointes and Nouméa roadstead.

1953, Sept. 24 Engr.

296 A29	1.50fr org brn & dp claret	3.75	2.25
297 A29	2fr ind & aqua	3.00	2.00
298 A29	6fr dk brn, bl & car	5.50	3.00
299 A29	13fr bl grn & dk grnsh bl	6.25	3.75
	Nos. 296-299 (4)	18.50	11.00

Centenary of the presence of the French in New Caledonia.

"Towers of Notre Dame" — A30

Coffee — A31

1955, Nov. 21 Unwmk. *Perf. 13*

300 A30	2.50fr dk brn, ultra & grn	.75	.45
301 A30	3fr grn, ultra & red brn	3.75	2.00
302 A31	9fr vio bl & indigo	1.50	.45
	Nos. 300-302 (3)	6.00	2.90

FIDES Issue
Common Design Type

1956, Oct. 22 Engr. *Perf. 13x12½*

303 CD103 3fr Dumbea Dam .90 .50

Flower Issue
Common Design Type

Designs: 4fr, Xanthostemon. 15fr, Hibiscus.

1958, July 7 Photo. *Perf. 12x12½*

304 CD104	4fr multi	1.25	.60
305 CD104	15fr grn, red & yel	2.75	.90

Imperforates

Most stamps of New Caledonia from 1958 onward exist imperforate, in trial colors, or in small presentation sheets in which the stamps are printed in changed colors.

Human Rights Issue
Common Design Type

1958, Dec. 10 Engr. *Perf. 13*

306 CD105 7fr car & dk bl .75 .45

Brachyrus Zebra — A32

Lienardella Fasciata A33

Designs: 10fr, Claucus and Spirographe. 26fr, Fluorescent corals.

1959, Mar. 21 Engr. *Perf. 13*

307 A32	1fr lil gray & red brn	.40	.30
308 A33	3fr bl, grn & red	.45	.25
309 A32	10fr dk brn, Prus bl & org brn	1.10	.60
310 A33	26fr multi	2.50	1.75
	Nos. 307-310 (4)	4.45	2.90

Types of 1859, 1905 and

Girl Operating Check Writer — A34

Telephone Receiver and Exchange A35

Port-de-France (Nouméa) in 1859 — A36

Designs: 9fr, Wayside mailbox and mail bus, vert. 33fr, like 19fr without stamps.

Perf. 13½x13, 13

1960, May 20 Unwmk.

311 A16	4fr red	.50	.30
312 A34	5fr claret & org brn	.50	.30
313 A36	9fr dk grn & brn	.50	.40
314 A35	12fr bl & blk	.60	.45
315 A1	13fr slate blue	2.00	.90
316 A36	19fr bl grn, dl grn & red	2.00	.65
317 A36	33fr Prus bl & dl red	2.25	1.25
a.	Souv. sheet of 3, #315, 311, 317 + label	5.50	5.50
	Nos. 311-317 (7)	8.35	4.25

Cent. of postal service and stamps in New Caledonia.

No. 317a has label between 4fr and 33fr stamps.

Melanesian Sailing Canoes A37

Designs: 4fr, Spear fisherman, vert. 5fr, Sail Rock and sailboats, Noumea.

1962, July 2 Engr. *Perf. 13*

318	A37	2fr slate grn, ultra & brn	.65	.30
319	A37	4fr brn, car & grn	.75	.30
320	A37	5fr sepia, grn & bl	1.10	.45
		Nos. 318-320 (3)	2.50	1.05

See Nos. C29-C32.

Map of Australia and South Pacific — A37a

1962, July 18 Photo. *Perf. 13x12*

321	A37a	15fr multi	1.10	.55

Fifth South Pacific Conf., Pago Pago, 1962.

Air Currents over Map of New Caledonia and South Pacific, Barograph and Compass Rose — A38

1962, Nov. 5 *Perf. 12x12½*

322	A38	50fr multi	4.50	3.00

3rd regional assembly of the World Meteorological Association, Noumea, November 1962.

Wheat Emblem and Globe — A38a

1963, Mar. 21 Engr. *Perf. 13*

323	A38a	17fr choc & dk bl	1.25	.70

FAO "Freedom from Hunger" campaign.

Relay Race — A39

Perf. 12½

1963, Aug. 29 Unwmk. Photo.

324	A39	1fr shown	.40	.30
325	A39	7fr Tennis	.75	.40
326	A39	10fr Soccer	1.10	.75
327	A39	27fr Javelin	2.25	1.75
		Nos. 324-327 (4)	4.50	3.20

South Pacific Games, Suva, Aug. 29-Sept. 7.

Red Cross Centenary Issue

Common Design Type

1963 Sept. 2 Engr. *Perf. 13*

328	CD113	37fr bl, gray & car	3.00	2.25

Human Rights Issue

Common Design Type

1963, Dec. 10 Unwmk. *Perf. 13*

329	CD117	50fr sl grn & dp claret	3.50	2.50

Bikkia Fritillarioides A40

Sea Squirts A41

Flowers: 1fr, Freycinettia Sp. 3fr, Xanthostemon Francii. 4fr, Psidiomyrtus locellatus. 5fr, Callistemon suberosum. 7fr, Montrouziera sphaeroidea, horiz. 10fr, Ixora collina, horiz. 17fr, Deplanchea speciosa.

Photogravure; Lithographed (2fr, 3fr)

1964-65 *Perf. 13x12½*

330	A40	1fr multi	.45	.35
331	A40	2fr multi	.60	.35
332	A40	3fr multi	.90	.45
333	A40	4fr multi ('65)	1.50	.75
334	A40	5fr multi ('65)	1.65	.85
335	A40	7fr multi	3.75	1.40
336	A40	10fr multi	3.75	1.40
337	A40	17fr multi	6.00	4.00
		Nos. 330-337 (8)	18.60	9.55

1964-65 Engr. *Perf. 13*

Design: 10fr, Alcyonium catalai. 17fr, Shrimp (hymenocera elegans).

338	A41	7fr dk bl, org & brn	.75	.60
339	A41	10fr dk red & dk vio bl ('65)	1.10	.50
340	A41	17fr dk bl, mag & grn	1.90	1.40
		Nos. 338-340 (3)	3.75	2.50

Nouméa Aquarium. See Nos. C41-C43.

Philatec Issue

Common Design Type

1964, Apr. 9 Unwmk. *Perf. 13*

341	CD118	40fr dk vio, grn & choc	4.00	3.50

De Gaulle's 1940 Poster "A Tous les Francais" A42

1965, Sept. 20 Engr. *Perf. 13*

342	A42	20fr red, bl & blk	5.00	2.75

25th anniv. of the rallying of the Free French.

Amedee Lighthouse A43

Games' Emblem A44

1965, Nov. 25

343	A43	8fr dk vio bl, bis & grn	.65	.35

Centenary of the Amedee lighthouse.

1966, Feb. 28 Engr. *Perf. 13*

344	A44	8fr dk red, brt bl & blk	.40	.25

2nd So. Pacific Games, Nouméa, Dec. 1966.

Red-throated Parrot Finch — A45

Design: 3fr, Giant imperial pigeon.

1966, Oct. 10 Litho. *Perf. 13x12½*

Size: 22x37mm

345	A45	1fr green & multi	.70	.55
346	A45	3fr citron & multi	1.40	.85

See #361-366, 380-381, C48-C49A, C70-C71.

Dancers and UNESCO Emblem A46

1966, Nov. 4 Engr. *Perf. 13*

347	A46	16fr pur, ocher & grn	.55	.40

20th anniv. of UNESCO.

High Jump and Games' Emblem A47

1966, Dec. 8 Engr. *Perf. 13*

348	A47	17fr shown	1.25	.50
349	A47	20fr Hurdling	2.00	.85
350	A47	40fr Running	2.50	1.65
351	A47	100fr Swimming	5.00	2.75
a.		Souv. sheet of 4, #348-351 + label	15.00	9.00
		Nos. 348-351 (4)	10.75	5.75

2nd So. Pacific Games, Nouméa, Dec. 8-18.

Lekine Cliffs — A48

1967, Jan. 14 Engr. *Perf. 13*

352	A48	17fr brt grn, ultra & sl grn	.75	.40

Magenta Stadium, Nouméa A49

Design: 20fr, Fish hatchery, Nouméa.

1967, June 5 Photo. *Perf. 12x13*

353	A49	10fr multi	1.00	.75
354	A49	20fr multi	2.25	1.25

ITY Emblem, Beach at Nouméa A50

1967, June 19 Engr. *Perf. 13*

355	A50	30fr multi	3.00	2.00

Issued for International Tourist Year, 1967.

19th Century Mailman A51

1967, July 12

356	A51	7fr dk car, bl grn & brn	.50	.40

Issued for Stamp Day.

Papilio Montrouzieri A52

Butterflies: 9fr, Polyura clitarchus. 13fr, 15fr, Hypolimnas bolina, male and female respectively.

1967-68 Engr. *Perf. 13*

Size: 36x22mm

357	A52	7fr lt grn, blk & ultra	.95	.60
358	A52	9fr brn, lil & ind ('68)	1.40	.85
359	A52	13fr vio bl, brn org & dk brn	2.00	1.25
360	A52	15fr dk brn, bl & yel	3.00	2.00
		Nos. 357-360,C51-C53 (7)	23.35	13.70

Issued: 9fr, 3/26/68; others, 8/10/67.

Bird Type of 1966

Birds: 1fr, New Caledonian grass warbler. 2fr, New Caledonia whistler. 3fr, New Caledonia white-throated pigeon. 4fr, Kagus. 5fr, Crested parakeet. 10fr, Crow honey-eater.

1967-68 Photo. *Perf. 13x12½*

Size: 22x37mm

361	A45	1fr multi	.95	.25
362	A45	2fr multi	1.25	.30
363	A45	3fr multi	1.25	.40
364	A45	4fr grn & multi	2.00	.60
365	A45	5fr lt yel & multi	3.50	.70
366	A45	10fr pink & multi	8.50	1.75
		Nos. 361-366 (6)	17.45	4.00

Issued: #364-366, 12/16/67; others 5/14/68.

WHO Anniversary Issue

Common Design Type

1968, May 4 Engr. *Perf. 13*

367	CD126	20fr mar, vio & dk bl grn	1.25	.90

Ferrying Mail Truck Across Tontouta River, 1900 — A53

1968, July 1 Engr. *Perf. 13*

368	A53	9fr dk red brn, grn & ultra	1.00	.50

Issued for Stamp Day, 1968.

Human Rights Year Issue

Common Design Type

1968, Aug. 10 Engr. *Perf. 13*

369	CD127	12fr sl grn, dp car & org yel	.75	.55

Conus Geographus A54

1968, Nov. 9 Engr. *Perf. 13*

Size: 36x22mm

370	A54	10fr dk brn, brt bl & gray	1.10	.65
		Nos. 370,C58-C60 (4)	12.10	6.15

Car on Road — A55

1968, Dec. 26 Engr. *Perf. 13*
371 A55 25fr dp bl, sl grn & hn brn 2.50 1.10

2nd Automobile Safari of New Caledonia.

Cattle Dip — A56

1969, May 10 Engr. *Perf. 13*
Size: 36x22mm
372 A56 9fr shown .70 .55
373 A56 25fr Cattle branding 2.25 .85
Nos. 372-373,C64 (3) 6.45 3.40

Cattle breeding in New Caledonia.

Murex Haustellum A57

Sea Shells: 5fr, Venus comb. 15fr, Murex ramosus.

1969, June 21 Engr. *Perf. 13*
Size: 35½x22mm
374 A57 2fr ver, bl & brn 1.25 1.00
375 A57 5fr dl red, pur & beige 1.75 1.40
376 A57 15fr ver, dl grn & gray 6.00 2.75
Nos. 374-376,C65 (4) 25.00 13.15

Judo — A58

1969, Aug. 7 Engr. *Perf. 13*
Size: 36x22mm
377 A58 19fr shown 2.00 1.00
378 A58 20fr Boxers 2.00 1.00
Nos. 377-378,C66-C67 (4) 8.75 4.90

3rd South Pacific Games, Port Moresby, Papua and New Guinea, Aug. 13-23.

ILO Issue
Common Design Type

1969, Nov. 24 Engr. *Perf. 13*
379 CD131 12fr org, brn vio & brn .60 .40

Bird Type of 1966

Birds: 15fr, Friarbird. 30fr, Sacred kingfisher.

1970, Feb. 19 Photo. *Perf. 13*
Size: 22x37mm
380 A45 15fr yel grn & multi 2.50 1.10
381 A45 30fr pale salmon & multi 3.75 1.90
Nos. 380-381,C70-C71 (4) 17.25 8.40

UPU Headquarters Issue
Common Design Type

1970, May 20 Engr. *Perf. 13*
382 CD133 12fr brn, gray & dk car .70 .55

Porcelain Sieve Shell — A59

Designs: 1fr, Strombus epidromis linne, vert. No. 385, Strombus variabilis swainson, vert. 21fr, Mole porcelain shell.

1970
Size: 22x36mm, 36x22mm
383 A59 1fr brt grn & multi .55 .30
384 A59 10fr rose & multi 1.40 .55
385 A59 10fr blk & multi 1.40 .55
386 A59 21fr bl grn, brn & dk brn 2.75 1.00
Nos. 383-386,C73-C76 (8) 20.10 10.30

See Nos. 395-396, C89-C90.

Packet Ship "Natal," 1883 — A60

1970, July 23 Engr. *Perf. 13*
387 A60 9fr Prus bl, blk & brt grn .80 .45

Issued for Stamp Day.

Dumbea Railroad Post Office — A61

1971, Mar. 13 Engr. *Perf. 13*
388 A61 10fr red, slate grn & blk 1.25 .75

Stamp Day, 1971.

Racing Yachts — A62

1971, Apr. 17 Engr. *Perf. 13*
389 A62 16fr bl, Prus bl & sl grn 4.00 3.00

Third sailing cruise from Whangarei, New Zealand, to Nouméa.

Morse Recorder, Communications Satellite — A63

1971, May 17 Engr. *Perf. 13*
390 A63 19fr red, lake & org .85 .40

3rd World Telecommunications Day.

Weight Lifting — A64

1971, June 24 Engr. *Perf. 13*
391 A64 11fr shown 1.00 .50
392 A64 23fr Basketball 2.00 .75
Nos. 391-392,C82-C83 (4) 9.50 4.40

4th South Pacific Games, Papeete, French Polynesia, Sept. 8-19.

De Gaulle Issue
Common Design Type

Designs: 34fr, Gen. de Gaulle, 1940. 100fr, Pres. de Gaulle, 1970.

1971, Nov. 9
393 CD134 34fr dk pur & blk 3.00 1.90
394 CD134 100fr dk pur & blk 7.00 5.00

Sea Shell Type of 1970

Designs: 1fr, Scorpion conch, vert. 3fr, Common spider conch., vert.

1972, Mar. 4 Engr. *Perf. 13*
Size: 22x36mm
395 A59 1fr vio & dk brn .30 .20
396 A59 3fr grn & ocher .40 .30
Nos. 395-396,C89-C90 (4) 6.45 3.50

Carved Wooden Pillow — A66

Chamber of Commerce Emblem — A67

1972-73 Photo. *Perf. 12½x13*
397 A66 1fr Doorpost, Goa ('73) .35 .20
398 A66 2fr shown .35 .30
399 A66 5fr Monstrance .60 .40
400 A66 12fr Tchamba mask 1.75 .75
Nos. 397-400,C102-C103 (6) 5.05 3.15

Objects from Nouméa Museum.

1972, Dec. 16
401 A67 12fr blk, yel & brt bl .80 .50

10th anniversary of the Junior Chamber of Commerce.

Tchamba Mask — A68

Black-back Butterflyfish (Day) — A69

1973, Mar. 15 Engr. *Perf. 13*
402 A68 12fr lilac 1.25 .85
a. Booklet pane of 5 10.00

No. 402 issued in booklets only.
See No. C99.

1973, June 23 Photo. *Perf. 13x12½*
403 A69 8fr shown .95 .60
404 A69 14fr same fish (night) 1.40 .85
Nos. 403-404,C105 (3) 5.35 3.20

Nouméa Aquarium.

Emblem A70

1973, July 21 *Perf. 13*
405 A70 20fr grn, yel & vio bl .80 .45

School Coordinating Office, 10th anniv.

"Nature Protection" — A72

1974, June 22 Photo. *Perf. 13x12½*
406 A72 7fr multi .45 .30

Scorched Landscape — A73

Calanthe Veratrifolia — A74

1975, Feb. 3 Photo. *Perf. 13*
407 A73 20fr multi .60 .50

"Prevent brush fires."

1975, May 30 Photo. *Perf. 13*

Design: 11fr, Liperanthus gigas.

408 A74 8fr pur & multi .70 .40
409 A74 11fr dk bl & multi .85 .50
Nos. 408-409,C125 (3) 4.30 2.65

Orchids. See Nos. 425-426.

Festival Emblem — A75

1975, Sept. 6 Photo. *Perf. 12½x13*
410 A75 12fr ultra, org & yel .40 .30

Melanesia 2000 Festival.

Birds in Flight A76

Georges Pompidou A77

1975, Oct. 18 Photo. *Perf. 13½x13*
411 A76 5fr ocher, yel & blk .32 .20

Nouméa Ornithological Society, 10th anniversary.

1975, Dec. 6 Engr. *Perf. 13*
412 A77 26fr dk grn, blk & sl .90 .45

Pompidou (1911-74), president of France.

Brown Booby — A78

Sea Birds: 2fr, Blue-faced booby. 8fr, Red-footed booby, vert.

Perf. 13x12½, 12½x13
1976, Feb. 21 Photo.
413 A78 1fr multi .20 .15
414 A78 2fr multi .30 .20
415 A78 8fr multi .75 .40
Nos. 413-415 (3) 1.25 .75

Festival Emblem A79

1976, Mar. 13 Litho. *Perf. 12½*
416 A79 27fr bl, org & blk .80 .45

Rotorua 1976, South Pacific Arts Festival, New Zealand.

Lion and Lions Emblem — A80

1976, Mar. 13 Photo. *Perf. 12½x13*
417 A80 49fr multi 1.40 1.10

Lions Club of Nouméa, 15th anniversary.

Music Pavilion — A81

Design: 30fr, Fountain, vert.

1976, July 3 Litho. *Perf. 12½*
418 A81 25fr multi .55 .40
419 A81 30fr blue & multi .75 .50

Old Nouméa.

Polluted Shore — A82

1976, Aug. 21 Photo. *Perf. 13*
420 A82 20fr dp bl & multi .60 .45

Nature protection.

South Pacific People — A83

1976, Oct. 23 Photo. *Perf. 13*
421 A83 20fr bl & multi .75 .45

16th South Pacific Commission Conference, Nouméa, Oct. 1976.

Giant Grasshopper A84

1977, Feb. 21 Engr. *Perf. 13*
422 A84 26fr shown 1.00 .85
423 A84 31fr Beetle and larvae 1.25 .85

Ground Satellite Station, Nouméa — A85

1977, Apr. 16 Litho. *Perf. 13*
424 A85 29fr multi .80 .50

Orchid Type of 1975

Designs: 22fr, Phajus daenikeri. 44fr, Dendrobium finetianum.

1977, May 23 Photo. *Perf. 13*
425 A74 22fr brn & multi 1.25 .75
426 A74 44fr bl & multi 2.25 1.00

Mask, Palms, "Stamps" — A86

1977, June 25 Photo. *Perf. 13*
427 A86 35fr multi .80 .70

Philately in school, Philatelic Exhibition, La Perouse Lyceum, Nouméa.

Trees — A87

1977, July 16 Photo. *Perf. 13*
428 A87 20fr multi .85 .55

Nature protection.

Congress Emblem — A88

1977, Aug. 6 Photo. *Perf. 13*
429 A88 200fr multi 6.25 3.50

French Junior Economic Chambers Congress, Nouméa.

Young Frigate Bird — A89

22fr, Terns, horiz. 40fr, Sooty terns, horiz.

1977-78 Photo. *Perf. 13*
430 A89 16fr multi 1.40 .85
431 A89 22fr multi 1.75 1.25
432 A89 40fr multi 2.50 1.40
Nos. 430-432,C138 (4) 7.90 4.60

Issued: 16fr, 9/17/77; 22fr, 40fr, 2/11/78.

Mare and Foal — A90

1977, Nov. 19 Engr. *Perf. 13*
433 A90 5fr multi .40 .25

10th anniversary of the Society for Promotion of Caledonian Horses.

Araucaria Montana — A91

Halityle Regularis — A92

1978, Mar. 17 Photo. *Perf. 12½x13*
434 A91 16fr multi .55 .35

See No. C149.

1978, May 20 Photo. *Perf. 13*
436 A92 10fr vio bl & multi .35 .25

Nouméa Aquarium.

Stylized Turtle and Globe — A93

1978, May 20
437 A93 30fr multi .85 .70

Protection of the turtle.

Flying Fox — A94

1978, June 10
438 A94 20fr multi .85 .60

Nature protection.

Maurice Leenhardt — A95

Soccer Player, League Emblem — A96

1978, Aug. 16 Engr. *Perf. 13*
439 A95 37fr multi 1.00 .80

Pastor Maurice Leenhardt (1878-1954).

1978, Nov. 4 Photo. *Perf. 13*
440 A96 26fr multi .70 .45

New Caledonia Soccer League, 50th anniversary.

Lifu Island — A97

1978, Dec. 9 Litho. *Perf. 13*
441 A97 33fr multi 1.00 .65

Petroglyph, Mère — A98

Map of Ouvea — A99

1979, Jan. 27 Engr. *Perf. 13*
442 A98 10fr brick red .40 .30

Perf. 12½x13, 13x12½
1979, Feb. 17 Photo.

Design: 31fr, Map of Mare Island, horiz.

443 A99 11fr multi .35 .30
444 A99 31fr multi .60 .45

House at Artillery Point — A100

1979, Apr. 28 Photo. *Perf. 13*
445 A100 20fr multi .65 .50

Auguste Escoffier — A101

1979, July 21 Engr. *Perf. 12½x13*
446 A101 24fr multi .65 .50

Auguste Escoffier Hotel School.

Regatta and Games Emblem A102

1979, Aug. 11 Photo. *Perf. 13*
447 A102 16fr multi .65 .35

6th South Pacific Games, Suva, Fiji, Aug. 27-Sept. 8.

Agathis Ovata A103

1979, Oct. 6 Photo. *Perf. 13x12½*
448 A103 5fr *shown* .25 .15
449 A103 34fr *Cyathea intermedia* .70 .50

Pouembout Rodeo A104

1979, Oct. 27 Engr. *Perf. 13x12½*
450 A104 12fr multi .45 .30

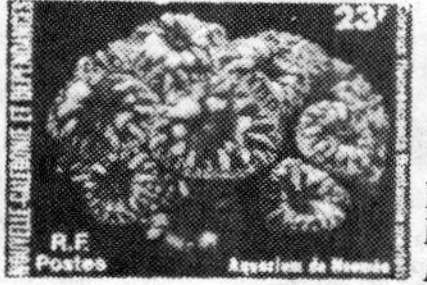
Bantamia Merleti A105

1979, Dec. 1 Photo. *Perf. 13x11½*
451 A105 23fr multi .60 .40

Fluorescent corals from Nouméa Aquarium.

Map of Pine Tree Island, Fishermen with Nets — A106

1980, Jan. 12 Photo. *Perf. 13x12½*
452 A106 23fr multi .45 .30

Hibbertia Virotii A107

1980, Apr. 19 Photo. *Perf. 13x12½*
453 A107 11fr shown .35 .20
454 A107 12fr Grevillea meisneri .35 .20

Philately at School — A108

1980, May 10 Litho. *Perf. 12½*
455 A108 30fr multi .60 .40

Prevention of Traffic Accidents A109

1980, July 5 Photo. *Perf. 13x12½*
456 A109 15fr multi .35 .20

Parribacus Caledonicus A110

Noumea Aquarium Crustacea: 8fr, Panulirus versicolor.

1980, Aug. 23 Litho. *Perf. 13x13½*
457 A110 5fr multi .15 .15
458 A110 8fr multi .25 .15

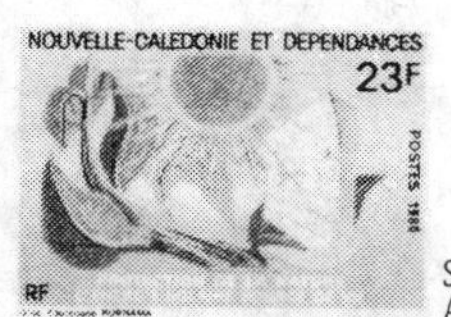
Solar Energy A111

1980, Oct. 11 Photo. *Perf. 13x12½*
459 A111 23fr multi .45 .25

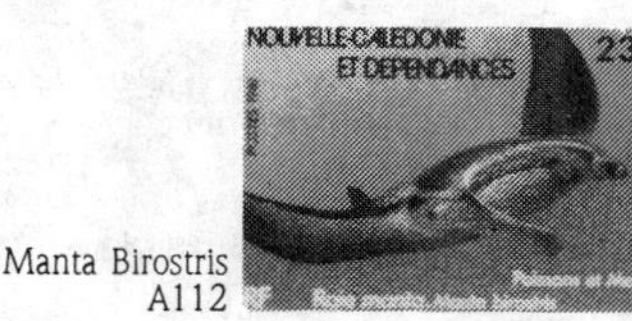
Manta Birostris A112

1981, Feb. 18 Photo. *Perf. 13x12½*
460 A112 23fr shown .45 .20
461 A112 25fr Carcharhinus amblyrhnchos .50 .25

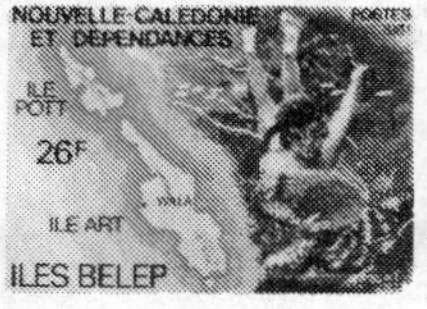
Belep Islands A113

1981, May 4
462 A113 26fr multi .55 .30

Cypraea Stolida A114

1981, June 17 Photo. *Perf. 13*
463 A114 1fr Cymbiola rossiniana, vert. .15 .15
464 A114 2fr Connus floccatus, vert. .15 .15
465 A114 13fr shown .25 .15
Set value .35 .25

See Nos. 470-471.

Corvette Constantine, 1854 A115

1981, July 22 Engr. *Perf. 13*
466 A115 10fr shown .22 .15
467 A115 25fr Aviso le Phoque, 1853 .45 .18

See Nos. 476-477.

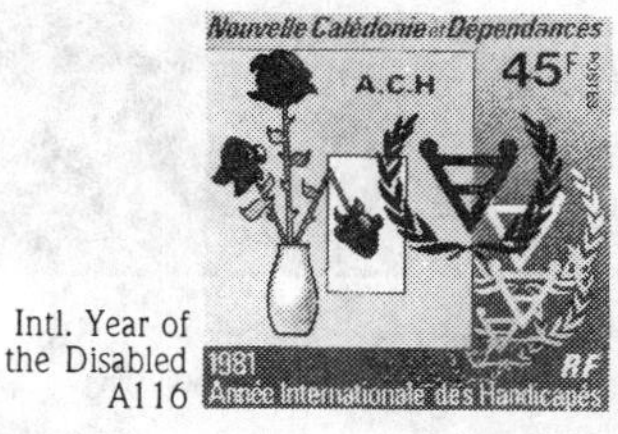
Intl. Year of the Disabled A116

1981, Sept. 2 Litho. *Perf. 12½*
468 A116 45fr multi .85 .48

Nature Preservation — A117

1981, Nov. 7 Photo. *Perf. 13*
469 A117 28fr multi .50 .24

Marine Life Type of 1981

1982, Jan. 20 Photo. *Perf. 13x13½*
470 A114 13fr Calappa calappa .22 .15
471 A114 25fr Etisus splendidus .45 .18

Chalcantite A118

1982, Mar. 17 Photo. *Perf. 13x13½*
472 A118 15fr shown .28 .15
473 A118 30fr Anortnosite .55 .20

Melaleuca Quinquenervia — A119

1982, June 23 Photo. *Perf. 13*
474 A119 20fr Savannah trees, vert. .38 .18
475 A119 29fr shown .55 .18

Ship Type of 1981

1982, July 7 Engr.
476 A115 44fr Barque Le Cher .75 .35
477 A115 59fr Naval dispatch vessel Kersaint 1.00 .55

Ateou Tribe Traditional House — A120

Grey's Ptilope — A121

1982, Oct. 13 Photo. *Perf. 13½x13*
478 A120 52fr multi .85 .35

1982, Nov. 6
479 A121 32fr shown .60 .24
480 A121 35fr Caledonian loriquet .65 .24

Central Education Coordination Office — A122

1982, Nov. 27 Litho. *Perf. 13½x13*
481 A122 48fr Boat .75 .28

Bernheim Library, Noumea — A123

1982, Dec. 15 Engr. *Perf. 13*
482 A123 36fr multi .60 .28

Caledonian Orchids A123a

1983, Feb. 2 Photo. *Perf. 13x13½*
482A A123a 10fr Dendrobium oppositifolium .15 .15
482B A123a 15fr Dendrobium munificum .20 .15
482C A123a 29fr Dendrobium fractiflexum .40 .20
Nos. 482A-482C (3) .75 .50

Xanthostemon Aurantiacum — A124

1983, Mar. 23 Litho. *Perf. 13*
483 A124 1fr Crinum asiaticum .15 .15
484 A124 2fr Xanthostemon aurantiacum .15 .15
485 A124 4fr Metrosideros demonstrans, vert. .15 .15
Set value .15 .15

25th Anniv. of Posts and Telecommunications Dept. — A125

Telephones and post offices.

1983, Apr. 30 Litho. *Perf. 13*

486 A125 30fr multicolored .50 .24
487 A125 40fr multicolored .60 .28
488 A125 50fr multicolored .85 .35
a. Souvenir sheet of 3 2.50 2.50
b. Strip of 3, #486-488 2.00 1.00

No. 488a contains Nos. 486-488 with changed background colors.

Local Snakes — A126

1983, June 22 Photo. *Perf. 13*

489 A126 31fr Laticauda laticauda .55 .24
490 A126 33fr Laticauda colubrina .60 .28

A127

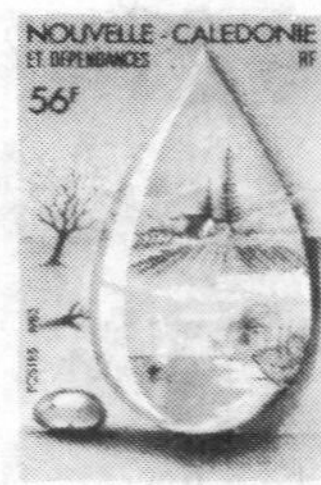

A128

1983, Aug. 10 Engr.

491 A127 16fr Volleyball .25 .15

7th South Pacific Games, Sept.

1983, Sept. 8 Photo. *Perf. 12½*

492 A128 56fr multi .70 .40

Nature protection.

Birds of Prey A129

1983, Nov. 16 Litho. *Perf. 13*

493 A129 34fr Tyto Alba Lifuensis, vert. .40 .26
494 A129 37fr Pandion Haliaetus .45 .30

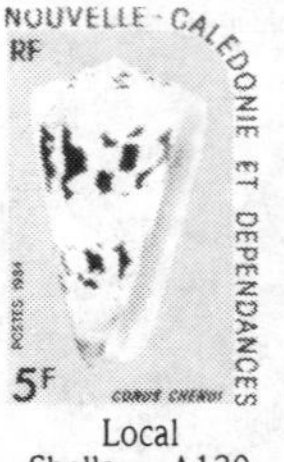

Local Shells — A130

Arms of Noumea — A132

Steamers A131

1984, Jan. 11 Litho. & Engr.

495 A130 5fr Conus chenui .15 .15
496 A130 15fr Conus moluccensis .28 .15
497 A130 20fr Conus optimus .30 .28
Nos. 495-497 (3) .73
Set value .36

See Nos. 521-522.

1984, Feb. 8 Engr.

498 A131 18fr St. Joseph .25 .20
499 A131 31fr St. Antoine .45 .32

1984, Apr. 11 Litho. *Perf. 12½x13*

500 A132 35fr multi .50 .38

See No. 546, 607, C214.

Environmental Preservation — A133

1984, May 23 *Perf. 13*

501 A133 65fr Island scene .60 .45

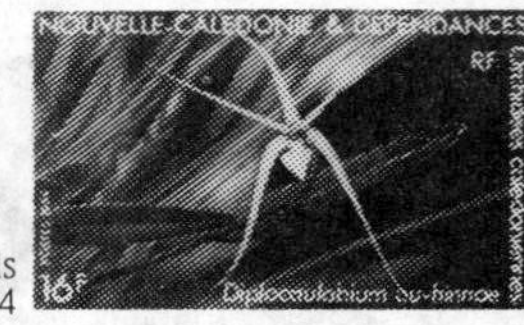

Orchids A134

1984, July 18 Litho. *Perf. 12*

502 A134 16fr Diplocaulobium ou-hinnae .22 .15
503 A134 38fr Acianthus atepalus .48 .30

Cent. of Public Schooling A135

Kagu A137

1984, Oct. 11 Litho. *Perf. 13½x13*

504 A135 59fr Schoolhouse .60 .28

1985-86 Engr. *Perf. 13*

511 A137 1fr brt bl .15 .15
512 A137 2fr green .15 .15
513 A137 3fr brt org .15 .15
514 A137 4fr brt grn .15 .15
515 A137 5fr dp rose lil .15 .15
516 A137 35fr crimson .28 .15
517 A137 38fr vermilion .30 .15
518 A137 40fr brt rose ('86) .40 .20
Set value 1.20 .70

Issue dates: 1fr, 2fr, 5fr, 38fr, May 22. 3fr, 4fr, 35fr, Feb. 13. 40fr, July 30.
See types A179, A179a.

Sea Shell Type of 1984

Lithographed and Engraved

1985, Feb. 27 *Perf. 13*

521 A130 55fr Conus bullatus .42 .20
522 A130 72fr Conus lamberti .55 .28

25th World Meteorological Day — A138

1985, Mar. 20 Litho.

523 A138 17fr Radio communication, storm .20 .15

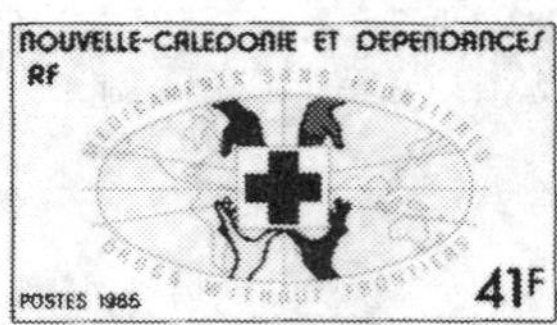

Red Cross, Medicine Without Frontiers — A139

1985, Apr. 10 *Perf. 12½*

524 A139 41fr multi .35 .15

Electronic Railway Switching Center Inauguration — A140

1985, Apr. 24

525 A140 70fr E 10 B installation .70 .38

Marguerite La Foa Suspension Bridge A141

1985, May 10 Engr. *Perf. 13*

526 A141 44fr brt bl & red brn .45 .18

Historical Preservation Association.

Le Cagou Philatelic Society — A142

1985, June 15 Litho.

527 A142 220fr multi 1.75 .85
a. Souvenir sheet, perf. 12½ 1.90 1.90

No. 527a sold for 230fr.

4th Pacific Arts Festival — A143

1985, July 3 *Perf. 13½*

Black Overprint

528 A143 55fr multi .52 .25
529 A143 75fr multi .75 .35

Not issued without overprint. Festival was transferred to French Polynesia.

Intl. Youth Year — A144

1985, July 24 Litho. *Perf. 13*

530 A144 59fr multi .60 .30

Amedee Lighthouse Electrification A145

1985, Aug. 13

531 A145 89fr multi .85 .42

Environmental Conservation A146

1985, Sept. 18

532 A146 100fr Planting trees 1.00 .50

Birds — A147

1985, Dec. 18 *Perf. 12½*

533 A147 50fr Poule sultane .50 .25
534 A147 60fr Merle caledonien .60 .32

Noumea Aquarium A148

1986, Feb. 19 Litho. *Perf. 12½x13*

535 A148 10fr Pomacanthus imperator .15 .15
536 A148 17fr Rhinopias aphanes .20 .15
Set value .16

Kanumera Bay, Isle of Pines — A149

1986, Mar. 26 Litho. *Perf. 12½*

537 A149 50fr shown .60 .30
538 A149 55fr Inland village .68 .35

See Nos. 547-548, 617-618.

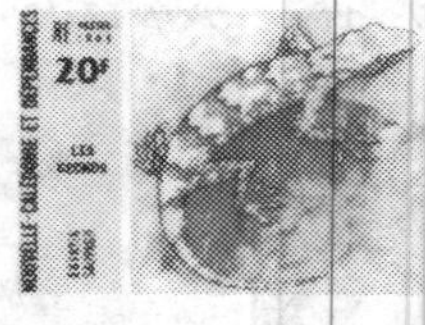

Geckos A150

1986, Apr. 16 *Perf. 12½x13*

539 A150 20fr Bavayia sauvagii .25 .15
540 A150 45fr Rhacodactylus leachianus .55 .30

1986 World Cup Soccer Championships, Mexico — A151

1986, May 28 *Perf. 13*

541 A151 60fr multi .75 .38

1st Pharmacy in New Caledonia, 120th Anniv. — A152

1986, June 25 Litho. *Perf. 13*
542 A152 80fr multi .95 .48

Orchids A153

1986, July 16 *Perf. 12½x13*
543 A153 44fr Coelogynae licastioides .45 .22
544 A153 58fr Calanthe langei .60 .30

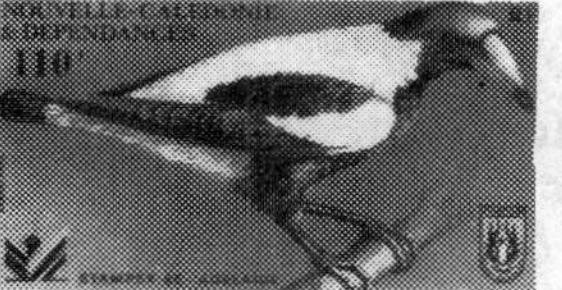

STAMPEX '86, Adelaide — A154

1986, Aug. 4 *Perf. 12½*
545 A154 110fr Bird 1.25 .65

Arms Type of 1984

1986, Oct. 11 Litho. *Perf. 13½*
546 A132 94fr Mont Dore 1.10 .55

Landscape Type of 1986

1986, Oct. 29 Litho. *Perf. 12½*
547 A149 40fr West landscape, vert. .45 .24
548 A149 76fr South Landscape .95 .52

Flowers

A156

Niponthes vieillardi, Syzygium ngayense, Archidendropsis Paivana, Scavola balansae.

1986, Nov. 12 *Perf. 12½*
549 A156 73fr multi .90 .45

Nature Protection Assoc..

A157

A159

A158

1986, Nov. 26 *Perf. 13x12½*
550 A157 350fr Emblem 4.25 2.00

Noumea Lions Club, 25th anniv.

1986, Dec. 23 Litho. *Perf. 13*

Paintings: 74fr, Moret Point, by A. Sisley. 140fr, Butterfly Chase, by B. Morisot.

551 A158 74fr multi .75 .38
552 A158 140fr multi 1.40 .70

1987, Jan. 28 *Perf. 13½*
553 A159 30fr Challenge France .38 .18
554 A159 70fr French Kiss .90 .45

America's Cup.

Plants, Butterflies A160

Designs: 46fr, Anona squamosa, Graphium gelon. 54fr, Albizzia granulosa, Polyura gamma.

1987, Feb. 25 Litho. *Perf. 13x12½*
555 A160 46fr multi .60 .30
556 A160 54fr multi .65 .32

Pirogues A161

1987, May 13 Engr. *Perf. 13x12½*
557 A161 72fr from Isle of Pines .80 .40
558 A161 90fr from Ouvea .90 .45

New Town Hall, Mont Dore — A162

1987, May 23 Litho. *Perf. 12½x13*
559 A162 92fr multi 1.10 .55

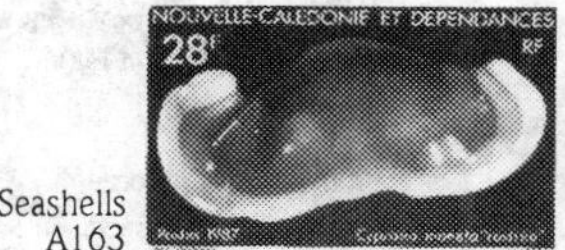

Seashells A163

1987, June 24 *Perf. 13*
560 A163 28fr Cypraea moneta .35 .16
561 A163 36fr Cypraea martini .45 .25

A164

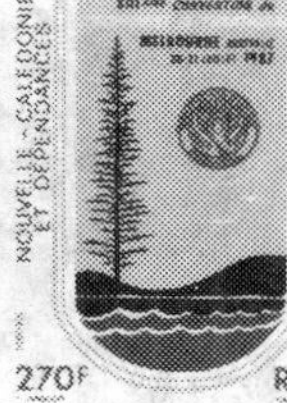

A165

1987, July 8 *Perf. 12½x13*
562 A164 40fr multi .52 .26

8th South Pacific Games.

1987, July 22 *Perf. 13½*
563 A165 270fr multi 3.50 1.75

Soroptimist Int'l. 13th Convention, Melbourne, July 26-31.

Birds — A166

1987, Aug. 26 *Perf. 13*
564 A166 18fr Zosterops xanthochroa .26 .15
565 A166 21fr Falco peregrinus nesiotes, vert. .28 .15
Set value .21

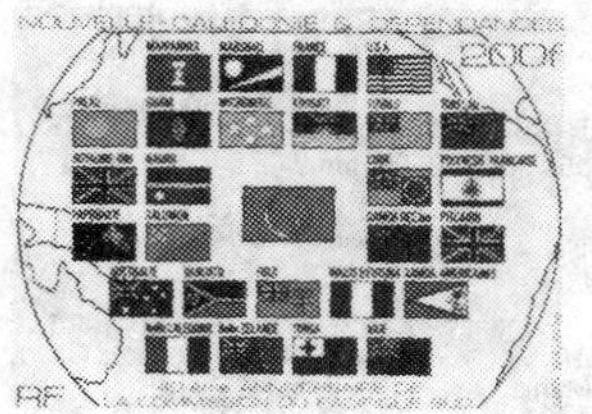

South Pacific Commission, 40th Anniv. — A167

1987, Oct. 14 Litho. *Perf. 13*
566 A167 200fr multi 2.75 1.40

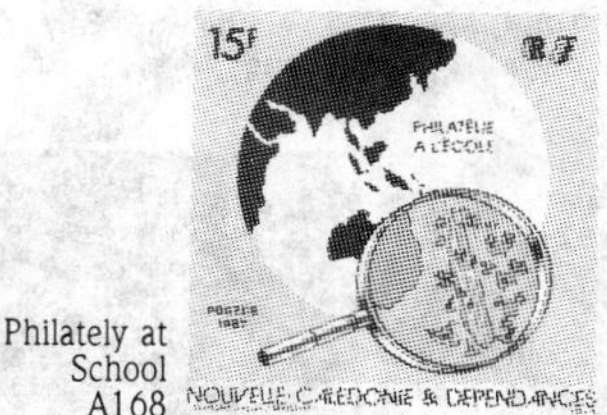

Philately at School A168

1987, Oct. 21 *Perf. 12½*
567 A168 15fr multi .20 .15

8th South Pacific Games, Noumea — A169

1987, Dec. 5 Litho. *Perf. 12½*
568 A169 20fr Golf .28 .15
569 A169 30fr Rugby .40 .20
570 A169 100fr Long jump 1.40 .70
Nos. 568-570 (3) 2.08 1.05

Map, Ships, La Perouse — A170

1988, Feb. 10 Engr. *Perf. 13*
571 A170 36fr dark rose lil .48 .24

Disappearance of La Perouse expedition, 200th anniv., and Jean-Francois de Galaup (1741-1788), Comte de La Perouse.

French University of the South Pacific at Noumea and Papeete A171

1988, Feb. 24 Litho. *Perf. 13x12½*
572 A171 400fr multi 5.25 2.75

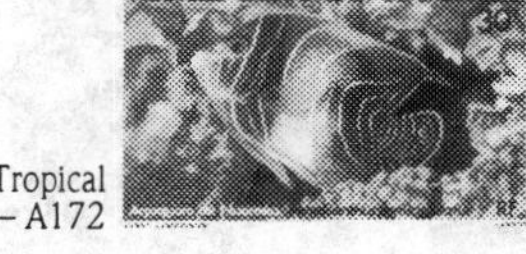

Tropical Fish — A172

1988, Mar. 23 Litho. *Perf. 13*
573 A172 30fr Pomacanthus semicirculatus .38 .20
574 A172 46fr Glyphidodontops cyaneus .60 .30

Intl. Red Cross and Red Crescent Organizations, 125th Annivs. A173

1988, Apr. 27
575 A173 300fr multi 3.75 1.50

Regional Housing A174

Designs: 19fr, Mwaringou, Canala Region, vert. 21fr, Nathalo, Lifou.

1988, Apr. 13 Engr. *Perf. 13*
576 A174 19fr emer grn, brt blue & red brn .24 .15
577 A174 21fr brt blue, emer grn & red brn .28 .15

Medicinal Plants A175

1988, May 18 Litho. *Perf. 13x12½*
578 A175 28fr *Ochrosia elliptica* .38 .20
579 A175 64fr *Rauvolfia levenetii* .85 .42

No. 579 is airmail.

Living Fossils — A176

1988, June 13 *Perf. 13*
580 A176 51fr *Gymnocrinus richeri* .70 .35

Bourail Museum and Historical Soc. — A177

1988, June 25 Litho. *Perf. 13*
581 A177 120fr multi 1.50 .75

SYDPEX '88 — A178

Designs: No. 582, La Perouse aboard *La Boussole,* gazing through spyglass at the First Fleet in Botany Bay, Jan. 24, 1788. No. 583, Capt. Phillip and crew ashore on Botany Bay watching the approach of La Perouse's ships *La Boussole* and *L'Astrolabe.*

1988, July 30 Litho. *Perf. 13x12½*

582 A178 42fr multi .50 .25
583 A178 42fr multi .50 .25
a. Souvenir sheet of 2, #582-583, perf. 13x13½ 1.40 1.40
b. Strip of 2, #582-583 + label 1.00 .50

No. 583a sold for 120fr.

Kagu

A179 A179a

1988-90 Engr. *Perf. 13*

584	A179	1fr bright blue	.15	.15
585	A179	2fr green	.15	.15
586	A179	3fr bright orange	.15	.15
587	A179	4fr bright green	.15	.15
588	A179	5fr deep rose lilac	.15	.15
589	A179	28fr orange	.55	.28
590	A179	40fr bright rose	.50	.25
		Set value	1.35	.75

Issued: 40fr, 8/11/88; 1fr, 4fr, 1/25/89; 2fr, 3fr, 5fr, 4/19/89; 28fr, 1/15/90.
See Type A137.

1990-93 Engr. *Perf. 13*

591	A179a	1fr bright blue	.15	.15
592	A179a	2fr bright green	.15	.15
593	A179a	3fr brt yel org	.15	.15
594	A179a	4fr dark green	.15	.15
595	A179a	5fr bright violet	.15	.15
596	A179a	9fr blue black	.20	.15
597	A179a	12fr orange	.28	.15
598	A179a	40fr lilac rose	.95	.48
599	A179a	50fr red	1.20	.60
		Nos. 591-599 (9)	3.38	
		Set value		1.50

Issued: 50fr, 9/6/90; 1fr-5fr, 1/9/91; 40fr, 1/16/92; 9fr, 12fr, 1/25/93.
See Type A137 and Nos. 675, 683. For surcharge see No. 685.

1988 Summer Olympics, Seoul — A180

1988, Sept. 15 *Perf. 12½x12*

600 A180 150fr multi 1.50 .75

Pasteur Institute, Noumea, Cent. — A181

1988, Sept. 29 Engr. *Perf. 13*

601 A181 100fr blk, brt ultra & dark red 1.50 .75

Writers — A182

1988, Oct. 15 Engr. *Perf. 13*

602 A182 72fr Georges Baudoux (1870-1949) 1.35 .68
603 A182 73fr Jean Mariotti (1901-1975) 1.40 .70

No. 603 is airmail.

WHO, 40th Anniv. A183

1988, Nov. 16 Litho. *Perf. 13x12½*

604 A183 250fr multi 4.75 2.40

Art Type of 1984 Without "ET DEPENDANCES"

Paintings by artists of the Pacific: 54fr, *Land of Men*, by L. Bunckley. 92fr, *The Latin Quarter*, by Marik.

1988, Dec. 7

605 AP113 54fr multi 1.05 .52
606 AP113 92fr multi 1.75 .88

Arms Type of 1984 Without "ET DEPENDANCES"

1989, Feb. 22 Litho. *Perf. 13½*

607 A132 200fr Koumac 3.65 1.85

Indigenous Flora A184

1989, Mar. 22 Litho. *Perf. 13½*

608 A184 80fr *Parasitaxus ustus*, vert. 1.55 .78
609 A184 90fr *Tristaniopsis guillainii* 1.75 .88

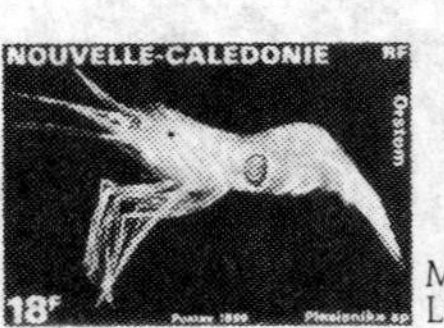

Marine Life — A185

1989, May 17 Litho. *Perf. 12½x13*

610 A185 18fr *Plesionika* .38 .20
611 A185 66fr *Ocosia apia* 1.35 .68
612 A185 110fr *Latiaxis* 2.25 1.25
Nos. 610-612 (3) 3.98 2.13

See Nos. 652-653.

French Revolution, Bicent. — A186

1989, July 7 Litho. *Perf. 13½*

613 A186 40fr Liberty .72 .35
614 A186 58fr Equality 1.05 .52
615 A186 76fr Fraternity 1.35 .68
Nos. 613-615 (3) 3.12 1.55

Souvenir Sheet

616 A186 180fr Liberty, Equality, Fraternity 3.25 3.25

Nos. 614-616 are airmail.

Landscape Type of 1986 Without "ET DEPENDANCES"

1989, Aug. 23 Litho. *Perf. 13*

617 A149 64fr La Poule rookery, Hienghene 1.10 .55
618 A149 180fr Ouaieme ferry 3.00 1.50

No. 617 is airmail.

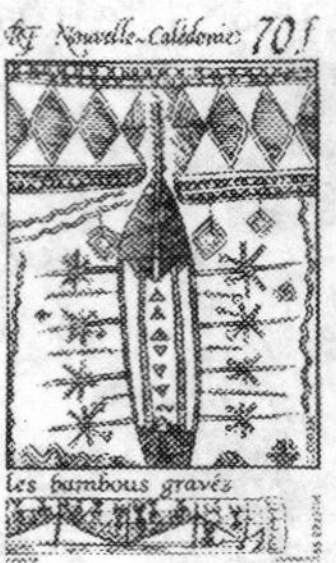

A187 A188

Perf. 12½x13

1989, Sept. 27 Litho. & Engr.

619 A187 70fr Carved bamboo 1.20 .60

See No. C216.

1989, Oct. 25 Litho. *Perf. 13*

620 A188 350fr multicolored 6.00 3.00

Hobie-Cat 14 10th World Championships, Nov. 3, Noumea.

Natl. Historical Soc., 20th Anniv. — A189

Cover of *Moeurs: Superstitions of New Caledonians*, cover of book on Melanesian oral literature and historians G. Pisier, R.P. Neyret and A. Surleau.

1989, Nov. 3 Engr.

621 A189 74fr brown & black 1.30 .65

Ft. Teremba — A190

1989, Nov. 18 Engr.

622 A190 100fr bl grn & dk org 1.75 .88

Marguerite Historical Preservation Soc.

Impressionist Paintings A191

Designs: 130fr, *The Escape of Rochefort*, by Manet. 270fr, *Self-portrait*, by Courbet.

1989, Dec. 6 Litho. *Perf. 13½*

623 A191 130fr multicolored 2.25 1.15
624 A191 270fr multicolored 4.50 2.25

Fr. Patrick O'Reilly (1900-1988), Writer — A192

1990, Jan. 24 Engr. *Perf. 13x13½*

625 A192 170fr blk & plum 3.25 1.65

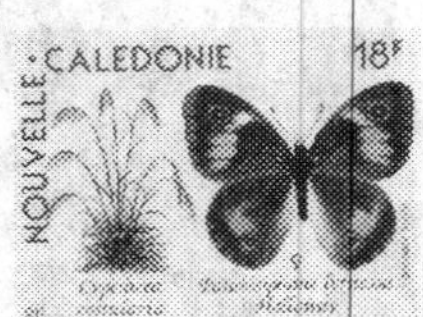

Grasses and Butterflies A193

Various *Cyperacea costularia* and *Paratisiphone lyrnessa:* 18fr, Female. 50fr, Female, diff. 94fr, Male.

1990, Jan. 21 Litho. *Perf. 13½*

626 A193 18fr shown .35 .18
627 A193 50fr multicolored .95 .48
628 A193 94fr multicolored 1.75 .88
Nos. 626-628 (3) 3.05 1.54

Nos. 626 and 628 are airmail.

A194 A195

1990, Mar. 16 Engr. *Perf. 12½x13*

629 A194 85fr Kanakan money 1.60 .80
630 A194 140fr money, diff. 2.65 1.35

1990, Mar. 16 Litho. *Perf. 13x13½*

631 A195 230fr multicolored 4.35 2.20

Jade and mother of pearl exhibition, New Caledonian Museum.

Noumea Aquarium A196

Perf. 13x12½, 12½x13

1990, Apr. 25

632 A196 10fr *Phyllidia ocellata* .20 .15
633 A196 42fr *Chromodoris kuniei*, vert. .88 .45

Petroglyphs — A197

1990, July 11 Engr. *Perf. 13*

634 A197 40fr Neounda .78 .40
635 A197 58fr Kassducou 1.10 .55

No. 635 is airmail.

Meeting Center of the Pacific — A198

1990, July 25 Litho. *Perf. 13*
636 A198 320fr multicolored 6.25 3.10

World Cup Soccer Championships, Italy — A199

1990, May 30 Litho. *Perf. 13*
637 A199 240fr multicolored 5.25 2.60

Flowers A200

1990, Nov. 7 *Perf. 13x12½*
638 A200 105fr Gardenia aubryi 1.00 .50
639 A200 130fr Hibbertia baudouinii 1.20 .60

La Maison Celieres by M. Petron A201

365fr, Le Mont-Dore de Jade by C. Degroiselle.

1990, Dec. 5 *Perf. 12½*
640 A201 110fr multicolored 2.60 1.30
641 A201 365fr multicolored 8.75 4.35

No. 640 is airmail.

Writers — A202

Designs: #642, Louise Michel (1830-1905). #643, Charles B. Nething (1867-1947).

1991, Mar. 20 Engr. *Perf. 13*
642 A202 125fr rose lil & bl 2.75 1.40
643 A202 125fr brn & bl 2.75 1.40
a. Pair, #642-643 + label 5.50 2.80

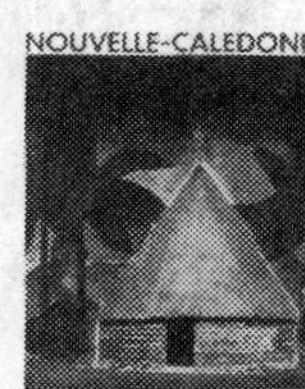

Native Huts — A203

1991, May 15 Litho. *Perf. 12*
644 A203 12fr Houailou .25 .15
645 A203 35fr Hienghene .75 .38

Maps of the Provinces A204

1991, June 17 Litho. *Perf. 13½*
646 A204 45fr Northern .95 .48
647 A204 45fr Island .95 .48
648 A204 45fr Southern .95 .48
a. Strip of 3, #646-648 2.85 1.42

Orchids — A205

1991, July 24 Litho. *Perf. 13*
649 A205 55fr Dendrobium biflorum 1.15 .62
650 A205 70fr Dendrobium closterium 1.45 .72

French Institute of Scientific Research — A206

1991, Aug. 26
651 A206 170fr multicolored 3.50 1.75

Marine Life Type of 1989

1991, Aug. 26 Litho. *Perf. 12*
652 A185 60fr Monocentris japonicus 1.25 .65
653 A185 100fr Tristigenys niphonia 2.10 1.05

9th South Pacific Games, Papua New Guinea A207

1991, Sept. 6 *Perf. 12½*
654 A207 170fr multicolored 3.50 1.75

Vietnamese in New Caledonia, Cent. — A208

1991, Sept. 8 Engr. *Perf. 13x12½*
655 A208 300fr multicolored 7.00 3.50

Lions Club of New Caledonia, 30th Anniv. — A209

1991, Oct. 5 Litho. *Perf. 12½*
656 A209 192fr multicolored 4.25 2.10

First Commercial Harvesting of Sandalwood, 150th Anniv. — A210

1991, Oct. 23 Engr. *Perf. 13*
657 A210 200fr multicolored 4.25 2.10

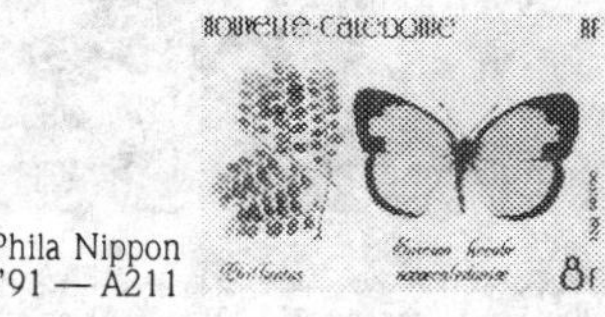

Phila Nippon '91 — A211

Plants and butterflies: 8fr, Phillantus, Eurema hecabe. 15fr, Pipturus incanus, Hypolimnas octocula. 20fr, Stachytarpheta urticaefolia, Precis villida. 26fr, Malaisia scandens, Cyrestis telamon.

Butterflies: No. 662a, Cyrestis telamon, vert. b, Hypolimnas octocula, vert. c, Eurema hecabe, vert. d, Precis villida, vert.

1991, Nov. 16 Litho. *Perf. 12½*
658 A211 8fr multicolored .20 .15
659 A211 15fr multicolored .38 .18
660 A211 20fr multicolored .50 .25
661 A211 26fr multicolored .65 .32
a. Strip of 4, #658-661 + label 1.70 .85

Souvenir Sheet

662 A211 75fr Sheet of 4, #a.-d. 7.00 7.00

Central Bank for Economic Cooperation, 50th Anniv. — A212

Designs: No. 663, Nickel processing plant, dam. No. 664, Private home, tourist hotels.

1991, Dec. 2 Litho. *Perf. 13*
663 A212 76fr multicolored 2.60 1.30
664 A212 76fr multicolored 2.60 1.30
a. Pair, #663-664 + label 5.20 2.60

Preservation of Nature — A213

1992, Mar. 25 Litho. *Perf. 13*
665 A213 15fr Madeleine waterfalls .35 .18
a. Souv. sheet, perf. 12½ 3.35 3.35

No. 665a sold for 150fr.

Immigration of First Japanese to New Caledonia, Cent. — A214

1992, May 11 Litho. *Perf. 13x12½*
666 A214 95fr yellow & multi 2.40 1.20
667 A214 95fr gray & multi 2.40 1.20
a. Pair, #666-667 + label 4.80 2.40

Arrival of American Armed Forces, 50th Anniv. — A215

1992, Aug. 13
668 A215 50fr multicolored 1.25 .60

Lagoon Protection — A216

1993, Feb. 23 Litho. *Perf. 13*
669 A216 120fr multicolored 2.80 1.40

Kagu Type of 1990

1993-94 Engr. *Perf. 13*
675 A179a 55fr red 1.20 .60
676 A179a (60fr) claret 1.25 .60

Self-Adhesive

Litho.

Die Cut Perf. 10

681 A179a 5fr bright lilac .15 .15
a. Bklt. pane, 8+8, gutter btwn. 1.75
683 A179a 55fr red 1.20 .60
a. Bklt. pane, 8+8, gutter btwn. 19.25

Issued: Nos. 675, 683, 4/7/93; No. 676, 1/27/94; No. 681, 2/94.

No. 676 sold for 60fr on day of issue.

By their nature, Nos. 681a, 683a are complete booklets. The peelable paper backing serves as a booklet cover.

This is an expanding set. Numbers may change.

55F

No. 599 Surcharged

1993 Engr. *Perf. 13*
685 A179a 55fr on 50fr red 1.25 .60

Philately in School — A217

1993, Apr. 7 Litho. *Perf. 13½*
686 A217 25fr multicolored .55 .28

For overprint see No. 690.

Miniature Sheet

Town Coats of Arms A218

Designs: a, Bourail. b, Noumea. c, Canala. d, Kone. e, Paita. f, Dumbea. g, Koumac. h, Ponerhouen. i, Kaamoo Hyehen. j, Mont Dore. k, Thio. l, Kaala-Gomen. m, Touho.

1993, Dec. 10 Litho. *Perf. 13½*
687 A218 70fr Sheet of 13, #a.-m., + 2 labels 19.00 19.00

Souvenir Sheet

Hong Kong '94 — A219

Wildlife: a, Panda. b, Kagu.

1994, Feb. 18 Litho. *Perf. 13*
688 A219 105fr Sheet of 2, #a.-b. 4.50 2.25

First Postal Delivery Route, 50th Anniv. — A220

1994, Apr. 28 Engr. *Perf. 13*
689 A220 15fr multicolored .35 .18

No. 686 Ovptd. in Blue

PHILEXJEUNES'94
GRENOBLE

22-24 AVRIL

1994, Apr. 22 Litho. *Perf. 13½*
690 A217 25fr multicolored .52 .25

Headquarters of New Caledonian Post Office — A222

1994, June 25 Litho. *Perf. 13½x13*

691	Strip of 4, #a.-d.	6.50	3.25
a.	A222 30fr 1859	.65	.32
b.	A222 60fr 1936	1.30	.65
c.	A222 90fr 1967	1.90	.95
d.	A222 120fr 1993	2.50	1.25

Pacific Sculpture — A223

Chambeyronia Macrocarpa — A224

1994, June 25 Litho. *Perf. 13x13½*
693 A223 60fr multicolored 1.25 .60

1994, July 7 Litho. *Perf. 13x13½*
694 A224 90fr multicolored 1.90 .95

Stag — A227

1994, Aug. 4 Litho. *Perf. 13½*
697 A227 150fr multicolored 3.25 1.65

Jacques Nervat, Writer — A228

1994, Sept. 15 *Perf. 13x13½*
698 A228 175fr multicolored 3.75 1.90

Frigate Nivose A229

Designs: No. 699, 30fr, Ship at sea. No. 700, 30fr, Ship along shore. No. 701, 30fr, Ship docked. No. 702, 60fr, Painting of frigate, map of island, ship's crest. No. 703, 60fr, Ship's bell. No. 704, 60fr, Sailor looking at ship.

1994, Oct. 7 Litho. *Perf. 13½*

Booklet Stamps

699	A229	30fr multicolored	.60	.30
700	A229	30fr multicolored	.60	.30
701	A229	30fr multicolored	.60	.30
702	A229	60fr multicolored	1.25	.65
703	A229	60fr multicolored	1.25	.65
704	A229	60fr multicolored	1.25	.65
a.		Booklet pane, #699-704	5.50	
		Booklet, 4 #704a	22.50	

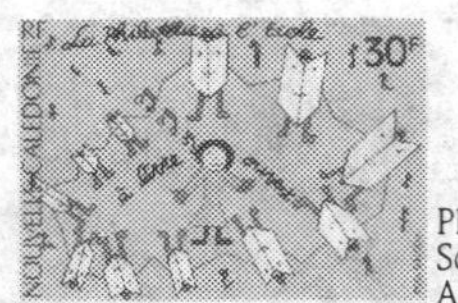

Philately at School A230

1994, Nov. 4 Litho. *Perf. 13½*
705 A230 30fr multicolored .60 .30

For overprint see No. 749

Christmas — A231

Top of bell starts below: a, Second "o." b, Third "e." c, "a." d, "C." e, Second "e."

1994, Dec. 17

706	Strip of 5	3.00	1.50
a.-e.	A231 30fr Any single	.50	.30

Nos. 706a-706e differ in location of the red ball, yellow bell and statue. No.706 is designed for stereoscopic viewing.

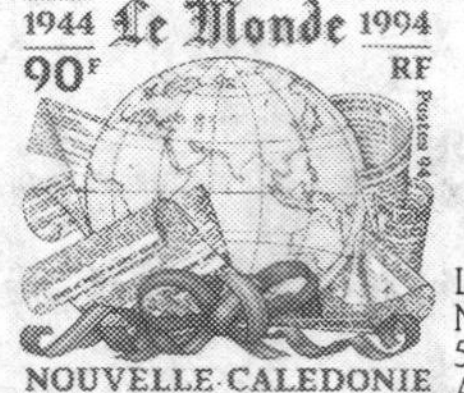

Le Monde Newspaper, 50th Anniv. A232

1994, Dec. 17
707 A232 90fr multicolored 1.75 .90

Louis Pasteur (1822-95) — A233

1995, Feb. 13 Litho. *Perf. 13*
708 A233 120fr No. 601 2.50 1.25

Charles de Gaulle (1890-1970) — A234

Litho. & Embossed

1995, Mar. 29 *Perf. 13*
709 A234 1000fr blue & gold 20.00 10.00

Teacher's Training College for the French Territories in the Pacific — A235

1995, Apr. 25 Litho. *Perf. 13*
710 A235 100fr multicolored 2.00 1.00

Sylviornis Neo-Caledonia, Fossil Bird — A236

1995, May 16 Litho. *Perf. 13x13½*
711 A236 60fr multicolored 1.25 .65

10th Sunshine Triathlon — A237

1995, May 26 Engr. *Perf. 13x12½*
712 A237 60fr multicolored 1.25 .65

Creation of the CFP Franc, 1945 — A238

Top of tree at left points to: a, Second "e." b, Second "l." c, First "l." d, First "e."

1995, June 8 Litho. *Perf. 13x13½*
713 A238 10fr Strip of 4, #a.-d. .80 .40

Nos. 713a-713d show coin rotating clockwise with trees, hut at different locations. No. 713 is designed for stereoscopic viewing.

1st New Caledonian Deputy in French Natl. Assembly, 50th Anniv. A239

1995, June 8 *Perf. 13½*
714 A239 60fr multicolored 1.25 .65

End of World War II, 50th Anniv. A240

1995, June 8 *Perf. 13x13½*
715 A240 90fr multicolored 1.90 .95

UN, 50th Anniv. A241

1995, June 8
716 A241 90fr multicolored 1.90 .95

Sebertia Acuminata A242

1995, July 29 Litho. *Perf. 13x13½*
717 A242 60fr multicolored 1.40 .70

Singapore '95 — A243

Sea birds: 5fr, Anous stolidus. 10fr, Larus novaehollandiae. 20fr, Sterna dougallii. 35fr, Pandion haliaetus. 65fr, Sula sula. 125fr, Fregata minor.

1995, Aug. 24 Litho. *Perf. 13x13½*

718	A243	5fr multicolored	.15	.15
719	A243	10fr multicolored	.25	.15
720	A243	20fr multicolored	.45	.20
721	A243	35fr multicolored	.80	.40
722	A243	65fr multicolored	1.50	.75
723	A243	125fr multicolored	3.00	1.50
a.		Souvenir sheet, #718-723 + label	6.25	6.25
		Nos. 718-723 (6)	6.15	3.15

10th South Pacific Games A244

1995, Aug. 24
724 A244 90fr multicolored 2.00 1.00

Sculpture, The Lizard Man, by Dick Bone — A248

1995, Oct. 25 **Litho.** *Perf. 13*
730 A248 65fr multicolored 1.50 .75

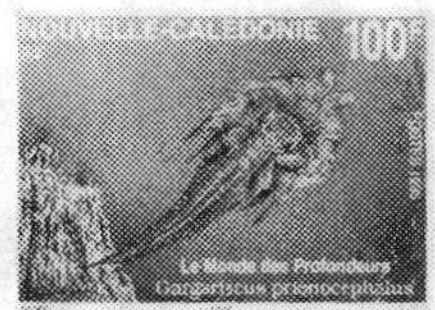
Gargariscus Prionocephalus — A249

1995, Dec. 15 **Litho.** *Perf. 13*
731 A249 100fr multicolored 2.25 2.25

Francis Carco (1886-1958), Poet & Novelist A250

1995, Nov. 16 **Litho.** *Perf. 13x13½*
732 A250 95fr multicolored 2.25 1.10

Ancient Pottery — A251

1996, Apr. 12 **Litho.** *Perf. 13*
733 A251 65fr multicolored 1.50 .75

Endemic Rubiaceous Plants A252

Designs: 65fr, Captaincookia margaretae. 95fr, Ixora cauliflora.

1996, Apr. 17
734 A252 65fr multicolored 1.50 .75
735 A252 95fr multicolored 2.25 1.10

7th VA'A (Outrigger Canoe) World Championship, Noumea, New Caledonia — A253

Designs: a, 30fr, Islander standing on shore with early version of canoe. b, 65fr, Early single-hull canoe with islanders. c, 95fr, Early catamaran, people rowing. d, 125fr, Modern racing canoe.

1996, May 10 **Litho.** *Perf. 13*
736 A253 Strip of 4, #a.-d. 6.50 3.25

No. 736 is a continuous design.

CHINA '96 — A254

Marine life: 25fr, Halieutaea stellata. 40fr, Perotrochus deforgesi. 65fr, Mursia musorstomia. 125fr, Metacrinus levii.

1996, May 18
737 A254 25fr multicolored .55 .25
738 A254 40fr multicolored .85 .40
739 A254 65fr multicolored 1.40 .70
740 A254 125fr multicolored 2.65 1.30
Nos. 737-740 (4) 5.45 2.65

Nos. 737-740 were each issued in sheets of 10 + 5 labels.

On Nos. 737-740 portions of the design were applied by a thermographic process producing a shiny, raised effect.

737a Booklet pane of 6 3.30
738a Booklet pane of 6 5.00
739a Booklet pane of 6 8.50
740a Booklet pane of 6 16.00
Complete booklet, #737a-740a 32.50

CAPEX '96 — A255

Orchids: 5fr, Sarcochilus koghiensis. 10fr, Phaius robertsii. 25fr, Megastylis montana. 65fr, Dendrobium macrophyllum. 95fr, Dendrobium virotii. 125fr, Ephemerantha comata.

1996, June 26 **Litho.** *Perf. 13*
741 A255 5fr multicolored .15 .15
742 A255 10fr multicolored .20 .15
743 A255 25fr multicolored .50 .25
744 A255 65fr multicolored 1.25 .65
745 A255 95fr multicolored 1.75 .90
746 A255 125fr multicolored 2.25 1.10
a. Booklet pane of 6, #741-746 6.00
Souvenir booklet, 4 #746a 24.00
Nos. 741-746 (6) 6.10 3.20

Nos. 741-746 were each issued in sheets of 10 + 5 labels.

No. 705 Ovptd. with UNICEF Emblem in Blue

1996, Sept. 12 **Litho.** *Perf. 13½*
749 A230 30fr multicolored .70 .35

UNICEF, 50th anniv.

Ordination of the First Melanesian Priests A258

1996, Oct. 9 **Litho.** *Perf. 13*
750 A258 160fr multicolored 3.75 1.90

Portions of the design on No. 750 were applied by a thermographic process producing a shiny, raised effect.

7th Festival of South Pacific Arts — A259

Designs: 100fr, Dancer, face carving. 105fr, Wood carvings of women. 200fr, Painting by Paul Boi. 500fr, Gaica Dance, Lifou.

1996, Oct. 9
751 A259 100fr multicolored 2.25 1.10
752 A259 105fr multicolored 2.40 1.25
753 A259 200fr multicolored 4.60 2.30
754 A259 500fr multicolored 11.50 5.75
Nos. 751-754 (4) 20.75 10.40

No. 751 is airmail.

French Pres. Francois Mitterrand (1916-96) — A260

1997, Mar. 14 **Litho.** *Perf. 13*
755 A260 1000fr multicolored 22.00 11.00

Alphonse Daudet (1840-97), Writer — A261

Designs: No. 756, "Letters from a Windmill." No. 757, "Le Petit Chose." No. 758, "Tartarin of Tarascon." No. 759, Daudet writing.

1997, May 14 *Perf. 13*
756 A261 65fr multicolored 1.45 1.45
757 A261 65fr multicolored 1.45 1.45
758 A261 65fr multicolored 1.45 1.45
759 A261 65fr multicolored 1.45 1.45
a. Souvenir sheet, #756-759 5.80 5.80

Henri La Fleur, First Senator of New Caledonia — A262

1997, June 12 **Litho.** *Perf. 13*
760 A262 105fr multicolored 2.00 2.00

Insects A263

Designs: a, Tectocoris diophthalmus. b, Kanakia gigas. c, Aenetus cohici.

1997, June 24 **Litho.** *Perf. 13x12½*
761 A263 65fr Strip of 3, #a.-c. 4.30 4.30

Jacques Iekawe (1946-92), First Melanesian Prefect — A264

1997, July 24 **Litho.** *Perf. 13*
762 A264 250fr multicolored 5.50 5.50

Kagu — A265

1997, Aug. 13 **Engr.** *Perf. 13*
763 A265 95fr blue 2.10 2.10

Se Nos. 772-773.

Horse Racing A266

1997, Sept. 20 **Litho.** *Perf. 13*
764 A266 65fr Harness racing 1.40 1.40
765 A266 65fr Thoroughbred racing 1.40 1.40

Early Engraving of "View of Port de France" (Noumea) — A267

Photo. & Engr.

1997, Sept. 22 *Perf. 13x12½*
766 A267 95fr multicolored 2.10 2.10

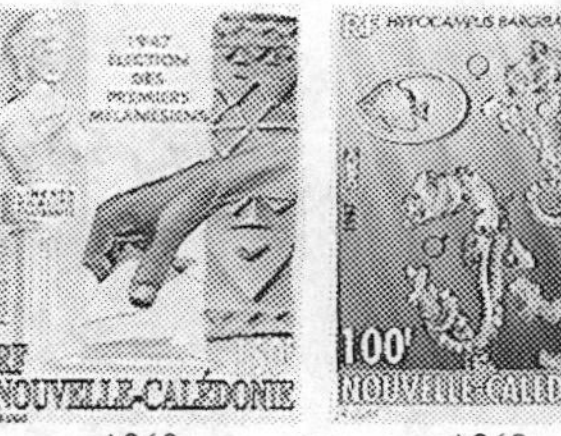
A268 A269

1997, Sept. 22 **Litho.** *Perf. 13*
767 A268 150fr multicolored 3.30 3.30

First Melanesian election, 50th anniv.

1997, Nov. 3 **Litho.** *Perf. 13½x13*
768 A269 100fr Hippocampus Bargibanti 2.25 2.25

5th World Conference on Fish of the Indo-Pacific. Issued in sheets of 10+5 labels.

South Pacific Arts — A270

Designs: a, Doka wood carvings. b, Beizam dance mask. c, Abstract painting of primative life by Yvette Bouquet.

1997, Nov. 3 *Perf. 13*
769 A270 100fr Strip of 3, #a.-c. 6.60 6.60

Christmas A271

Designs: 95fr, Santa on surfboard pulled by dolphins. 100fr, Dolphin with banner in mouth.

1997, Nov. 17

770 A271 95fr multicolored 2.10 2.10
771 A271 100fr multicolored 2.20 2.20

Nos. 770-771 issued in sheets of 10+5 labels.

Kagu Type of 1997

1997-98 **Engr.** ***Perf. 13***

772 A265 30fr orange .65 .65
773 A265 (70fr) red 1.50 1.50

Issued: 30fr, 1997; (70fr), 1/2/98.

Mushrooms — A272

#774, Lentinus tuber-regium. #775, Volvaria bombycina. #776, Morchella anteridiformis.

1998, Jan. 22 **Litho.** ***Perf. 13***

774 A272 70fr multicolored 1.50 1.50
775 A272 70fr multicolored 1.50 1.50
776 A272 70fr multicolored 1.50 1.50
Nos. 774-776 (3) 4.50 4.50

SEMI-POSTAL STAMPS

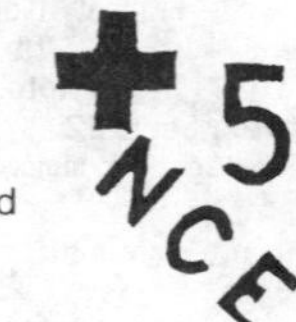

No. 93 Surcharged

1915 **Unwmk.** ***Perf. 14x13½***

B1 A16 10c + 5c carmine .70 .70
a. Inverted surcharge 35.00 35.00
b. Cross omitted 35.00 35.00

Regular Issue of 1905 Surcharged

1917

B2 A16 10c + 5c rose .60 .60
a. Double surcharge 45.00 45.00
B3 A16 15c + 5c violet .50 .50

Curie Issue
Common Design Type

1938, Oct. 24 ***Perf. 13***

B4 CD80 1.75fr + 50c brt ultra 7.50 7.50

French Revolution Issue
Common Design Type

1939, July 5 **Photo.**
Name and Value Typo. in Black

B5 CD83 45c + 25c green 6.00 6.00
B6 CD83 70c + 30c brown 6.00 6.00
B7 CD83 90c + 35c red org 6.00 6.00
B8 CD83 1.25fr + 1fr rose pink 6.00 6.00
B9 CD83 2.25fr + 2fr blue 6.00 6.00
Nos. B5-B9 (5) 30.00 30.00

Common Design Type and

Dumont d'Urville's ship, "Zélée" — SP2

New Caledonian Militiaman SP3

1941 **Photo.** ***Perf. 13½***

B10 SP2 1fr + 1fr red .65
B11 CD86 1.50fr + 3fr maroon .65
B12 SP3 2.50fr + 1fr dk blue .65
Nos. B10-B12 (3) 1.95

Nos. B10-B12 were issued by the Vichy government and were not placed on sale in the colony.

In 1944 Nos. 216A-216B were surcharged "OEUVRES COLONIALES" and surtax (including change of denomination of the 2.50fr to 50c). These were issued by the Vichy government and not placed on sale in New Caledonia.

Catalogue values for unused stamps in this section, from this point to the end of the section, are for Never Hinged items.

Red Cross Issue
Common Design Type

1944 ***Perf. 14½x14***

B13 CD90 5fr + 20fr brt scar .45 .45

The surtax was for the French Red Cross and national relief.

Tropical Medicine Issue
Common Design Type

1950, May 15 **Engr.** ***Perf. 13***

B14 CD100 10fr + 2fr red brn & sepia 2.00 2.00

The surtax was for charitable work.

AIR POST STAMPS

Seaplane Over Pacific Ocean — AP1

1938-40 **Unwmk.** **Engr.** ***Perf. 13***

C1 AP1 65c deep violet .40 .40
a. "65c" omitted 110.00
C2 AP1 4.50fr red .60 .60
C3 AP1 7fr dk bl grn ('40) .40 .40
C4 AP1 9fr ultra 1.50 1.50
C5 AP1 20fr dk orange ('40) .85 .85
C6 AP1 50fr black ('40) 1.75 1.75
Nos. C1-C6 (6) 5.50 5.50

V4

Stamps of type AP1, without "RF" monogram, and stamp of the design shown above were issued in 1942 to 1944 by the Vichy Government, but were not placed on sale in the colony.

Common Design Type

1942 **Unwmk.** ***Perf. 14½x14***

C7 CD87 1fr dk orange .30 .25
C8 CD87 1.50fr brt red .30 .25
C9 CD87 5fr brown red .30 .25
C10 CD87 10fr black .60 .45
C11 CD87 25fr ultra .70 .60
C12 CD87 50fr dk green 1.00 .70
C13 CD87 100fr plum 1.25 1.00
Nos. C7-C13 (7) 4.45 3.50

Catalogue values for unused stamps in this section, from this point to the end of the section, are for Never Hinged items.

Victory Issue
Common Design Type

1946, May 8 **Engr.** ***Perf. 12½***

C14 CD92 8fr brt ultra .75 .75

Chad to Rhine Issue
Common Design Types

1946, June 6

C15 CD93 5fr black 1.00 .80
C16 CD94 10fr carmine 1.00 .80
C17 CD95 15fr dk blue 1.10 .90
C18 CD96 20fr orange brn 1.10 .90
C19 CD97 25fr olive grn 1.50 1.40
C20 CD98 50fr dk rose vio 2.00 1.75
Nos. C15-C20 (6) 7.70 6.55

St. Vincent Bay — AP2

Planes over Islands — AP3

View of Nouméa — AP4

Perf. 13x12½, 12½x13

1948, Mar. 1 **Photo.** **Unwmk.**

C21 AP2 50fr org & rose vio 3.00 2.50
C22 AP3 100fr bl grn & sl bl 6.00 2.75
C23 AP4 200fr brown & yel 11.00 6.00
Nos. C21-C23 (3) 20.00 11.25

UPU Issue
Common Design Type

1949, July 4 **Engr.** ***Perf. 13***

C24 CD99 10fr multicolored 4.00 1.75

Liberation Issue
Common Design Type

1954, June 6

C25 CD102 3fr indigo & ultra 1.90 1.65

Conveyor for Nickel Ore — AP5

1955, Nov. 21 **Unwmk.** ***Perf. 13***

C26 AP5 14fr indigo & sepia 2.00 .70

Rock Formations, Bourail — AP6

1959, Mar. 23

C27 AP6 200fr lt bl, brn & grn 20.00 9.00

Yaté Dam — AP7

1959, Sept. 20 **Engr.**

C28 AP7 50fr grn, brt bl & sepia 4.00 2.75

Dedication of Yaté Dam.

Fisherman with Throw-net — AP8

Skin Diver Shooting Bumphead Surgeonfish — AP9

Designs: 20fr, Nautilus shell. 100fr, Yaté rock.

1962 **Unwmk.** ***Perf. 13***

C29 AP8 15fr red, Prus grn & sep 2.50 1.25
C30 AP9 20fr dk sl grn & org ver 3.50 2.00
C31 AP9 25fr red brn, gray & bl 5.00 2.00
C32 AP9 100fr dk brn, dk bl & sl grn 14.00 7.50
Nos. C29-C32 (4) 25.00 12.75

Telstar Issue
Common Design Type

1962, Dec. 4 **Unwmk.** ***Perf. 13***

C33 CD111 200fr dk bl, choc & grnsh bl 20.00 10.00

Nickel Mining, Houailou — AP10

1964, May 14 **Photo.**

C34 AP10 30fr multi 2.00 1.25

Isle of Pines AP11

1964, Dec. 7 **Engr.** ***Perf. 13***

C35 AP11 50fr dk bl, sl grn & choc 2.25 1.50

Phyllobranchus — AP12

Design: 27fr, Paracanthurus teuthis (fish).

1964, Dec. 17 **Photo.**

C36 AP12 27fr red brn, yel, dp bl & blk 4.00 2.00
C37 AP12 37fr bl, brn & yel 5.00 3.00

Issued to publicize the Nouméa Aquarium.

Greco-Roman Wrestling — AP13

1964, Dec. 28 **Engr.**

C38 AP13 10fr brt grn, pink & blk 12.50 8.00

18th Olympic Games, Tokyo, Oct. 10-25.

Nimbus Weather Satellite over New Caledonia — AP14

1965, Mar. 23 **Photo.** ***Perf. 13x12½***

C39 AP14 9fr multi 2.00 1.50

Fifth World Meteorological Day.

ITU Issue
Common Design Type

1965, May 17 **Engr.** ***Perf. 13***

C40 CD120 40fr lt bl, lil rose & lt brn 5.00 4.25

Coris Angulata (Young Fish) — AP15

15fr, Adolescent fish. 25fr, Adult fish.

1965, Dec. 6 **Engr.** ***Perf. 13***

C41 AP15 13fr red org, ol bis & blk 2.25 1.00
C42 AP15 15fr ind, sl grn & bis 3.50 1.50
C43 AP15 25fr ind & yel grn 6.00 4.00
Nos. C41-C43 (3) 11.75 6.50

Issued to publicize the Nouméa Aquarium.

French Satellite A-1 Issue
Common Design Type

Designs: 8fr, Diamant rocket and launching installations. 12fr, A-1 satellite.

1966, Jan. 10 **Engr.** ***Perf. 13***

C44 CD121 8fr rose brn, ultra & Prus bl 2.00 1.10
C45 CD121 12fr ultra, Prus bl & rose brn 2.50 1.90
a. Strip of 2, #C44-C45 + label 4.50 3.00

French Satellite D-1 Issue
Common Design Type

1966, May 16 **Engr.** ***Perf. 13***

C46 CD122 10fr dl bl, ocher & sep 1.25 1.10

Port-de-France, 1866 — AP16

1966, June 2

C47 AP16 30fr dk red, bl & ind 2.25 1.90

Port-de-France changing name to Nouméa, cent.

Bird Type of Regular Issue

Designs: 27fr, Uvea crested parakeet. 37fr, Scarlet honey eater. 50fr, Two cloven-feathered doves.

1966-68 **Photo.** ***Perf. 13***
Size: 26x46mm

C48 A45 27fr pink & multi 4.50 3.00
C49 A45 37fr grn & multi 6.50 4.00

Size: 27x48mm

C49A A45 50fr multi ('68) 7.50 4.00
Nos. C48-C49A (3) 18.50 11.00

Issued: 27fr, 37fr, Oct. 10; 50fr, May 14.

Sailboats and Map of New Caledonia-New Zealand Route — AP17

1967, Apr. 15 **Engr.** ***Perf. 13***

C50 AP17 25fr brt grn, dp ultra & red 2.25 1.50

2nd sailboat race from Whangarei, New Zealand, to Nouméa, New Caledonia.

Butterfly Type of Regular Issue

Butterflies: 19fr, Danaus plexippus. 29fr, Hippotion celerio. 85fr, Delias elipsis.

1967-68 **Engr.** ***Perf. 13***
Size: 48x27mm

C51 A52 19fr multi ('68) 3.00 1.75
C52 A52 29fr multi ('68) 3.50 2.50
C53 A52 85fr red, dk brn & yel 9.50 4.75
Nos. C51-C53 (3) 16.00 9.00

Issued: 85fr, Aug. 10; others, Mar. 26.

Jules Garnier, Garnierite and Mine — AP18

1967, Oct. 9 **Engr.** ***Perf. 13***

C54 AP18 70fr bl gray, brn & yel grn 2.75 2.00

Discovery of garnierite (nickel ore), cent.

Lifu Island AP19

1967, Oct. 28 **Photo.** ***Perf. 13***

C55 AP19 200fr multi 6.00 4.00

Skier, Snowflake and Olympic Emblem — AP20

1967, Nov. 16 **Engr.** ***Perf. 13***

C56 AP20 100fr brn red, sl grn & brt bl 8.00 4.50

10th Winter Olympic Games, Grenoble, France, Feb. 6-18, 1968.

Sea Shell Type of Regular Issue

Designs: 39fr, Conus lienardi. 40fr, Conus cabriti. 70fr, Conus coccineus.

1968, Nov. 9 **Engr.** ***Perf. 13***

C58 A54 39fr bl grn, brn & gray 2.50 1.25
C59 A54 40fr blk, brn red & ol 2.50 1.25
C60 A54 70fr brn, pur & gray 6.00 3.00
Nos. C58-C60 (3) 11.00 5.50

Maré Dancers — AP21

1968, Nov. 20 **Engr.** ***Perf. 13***

C61 AP21 60fr grn, ultra & hn brn 3.50 2.25

World Map and Caudron C 600 "Aiglon" — AP22

1969, Mar. 24 **Engr.** ***Perf. 13***

C62 AP22 29fr lil, dk bl & dk car 2.00 1.40

Stamp Day and honoring the 1st flight from Nouméa to Paris of Henri Martinet & Paul Klein, Mar. 24, 1939.

Concorde Issue
Common Design Type

1969, Apr. 17 **Engr.** ***Perf. 13***

C63 CD129 100fr sl grn & brt grn 14.00 10.00

Cattle Type of Regular Issue

Design: 50fr, Cowboy and herd.

1969, May 10 **Engr.** ***Perf. 13***
Size: 48x27mm

C64 A56 50fr sl grn, dk brn & red brn 3.50 2.00

Shell Type of Regular Issue, 1969

Design: 100fr, Black murex.

1969, June 21 **Engr.** ***Perf. 13***
Size: 48x27mm

C65 A57 100fr lake, bl & blk 16.00 8.00

Sports Type of 1969

30fr, Woman diver. 39fr, Shot put, vert.

1969, Aug. 7 **Engr.** ***Perf. 13***
Size: 48x27mm, 27x48mm

C66 A58 30fr dk brn, bl & blk 2.00 1.25
C67 A58 39fr dk ol, brt grn & ol 2.75 1.65

Napoleon in Coronation Robes, by François P. Gerard AP23

1969, Oct. 2 **Photo.** ***Perf. 12½x12***

C68 AP23 40fr lil & multi 8.50 5.50

200th birth anniv. of Napoleon Bonaparte (1769-1821).

Air France Plane over Outrigger Canoe — AP24

1969, Oct. 2 **Engr.** ***Perf. 13***

C69 AP24 50fr slate grn, sky bl & choc 2.50 2.00

20th anniversary of the inauguration of the Nouméa to Paris airline.

Bird Type of Regular Issue, 1966.

39fr, Emerald doves. 100fr, Whistling kite.

1970, Feb. 19 **Photo.** ***Perf. 13***
Size: 27x48mm

C70 A45 39fr multi 3.00 1.40
C71 A45 100fr lt bl & multi 8.00 4.00

Planes Circling Globe and Paris-Nouméa Route — AP25

1970, May 6 **Engr.** ***Perf. 13***

C72 AP25 200fr vio, org brn & grnsh bl 9.00 6.00

10th anniversary of the Paris to Nouméa flight: "French Wings Around the World."

Shell Type of Regular Issue

Designs: 22fr, Strombus sinautus humphrey, vert. 33fr, Argus porcelain shell. 34fr, Strombus vomer, vert. 60fr, Card porcelain shell.

1970 **Engr.** ***Perf. 13***
Size: 27x48mm, 48x27mm

C73 A59 22fr bl & multi 2.00 1.40
C74 A59 33fr brn & gray bl 3.00 1.75
C75 A59 34fr pur & multi 3.00 1.75
C76 A59 60fr lt grn & brn 6.00 3.00
Nos. C73-C76 (4) 14.00 7.90

See Nos. C89-C90.

Bicyclists on Map of New Caledonia — AP26

1970, Aug. 20 **Engr.** ***Perf. 13***

C77 AP26 40fr bl, ultra & choc 1.75 1.25

The 4th Bicycling Race of New Caledonia.

Mt. Fuji and Monorail Train — AP27

Design: 45fr, Map of Japan and Buddha statue.

1970, Sept. 3 **Photo.** ***Perf. 13x12½***

C78 AP27 20fr blk, bl & yel grn 1.10 .65
C79 AP27 45fr mar, lt bl & ol 1.90 .90

EXPO '70 International Exposition, Osaka, Japan, Mar. 15-Sept. 13.

Racing Yachts AP28

1971, Feb. 23 Engr. *Perf. 13*
C80 AP28 20fr grn, blk & ver 1.25 .65

First challenge in New Zealand waters for the One Ton Cup ocean race.

Lt. Col. Broche and Map of Mediterranean — AP29

1971, May 5 Photo. *Perf. 12½*
C81 AP29 60fr multi 3.50 2.50

30th anniversary of Battalion of the Pacific.

Pole Vault AP30

1971, June 24 Engr. *Perf. 13*
C82 AP30 25fr shown 1.75 .90
C83 AP30 100fr Archery 4.75 2.25

4th South Pacific Games, Papeete, French Polynesia, Sept. 8-19.

Port de Plaisance, Nouméa — AP31

1971, Sept. 27 Photo. *Perf. 13*
C84 AP31 200fr multi 10.00 6.00

Golden Eagle and Pilot's Leaflet — AP32

1971, Nov. 20 Engr. *Perf. 13*
C85 AP32 90fr dk brn, org & ind 4.50 2.50

40th anniversary of the first flight from New Caledonia to Australia with Victor Roffey piloting the Golden Eagle.

Skiing and Sapporo '72 Emblem — AP33

1972, Jan. 22 Engr. *Perf. 13*
C86 AP33 50fr brt bl, car & sl grn 3.50 2.25

11th Winter Olympic Games, Sapporo, Japan, Feb. 3-13.

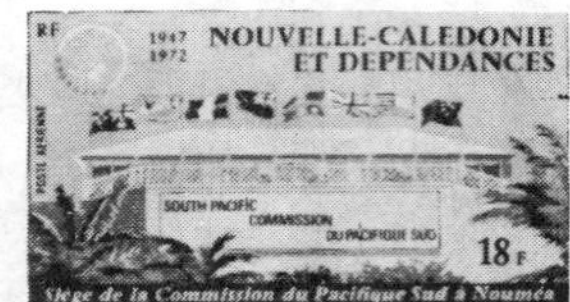
South Pacific Commission Headquarters, Nouméa — AP34

1972, Feb. 5 Photo.
C87 AP34 18fr bl & multi 1.00 .65

South Pacific Commission, 25th anniv.

St. Mark's Basilica, Venice — AP35

1972, Feb. 5 Engr.
C88 AP35 20fr lt grn, bl & grn 2.00 1.25

UNESCO campaign to save Venice.

Shell Type of Regular Issue, 1970

Designs: 25fr, Orange spider conch, vert. 50fr, Chiragra spider conch, vert.

1972, Mar. 4 Engr. *Perf. 13*
Size: 27x48mm
C89 A59 25fr dp car & dk brn 2.25 1.10
C90 A59 50fr grn, brn & rose car 3.50 1.90

Breguet F-ALMV and Globe — AP36

1972, Apr. 5 Engr. *Perf. 13*
C91 AP36 110fr brt rose lil, bl & grn 8.00 5.00

40th anniversary of the first Paris-Nouméa flight, Mar. 9-Apr. 5, 1932.

Round House and Festival Emblem — AP37

1972, May 13
C92 AP37 24fr org, bl & brn 2.00 1.50

So. Pacific Festival of Arts, Fiji, May 6-20.

Hurdles and Olympic Rings AP38

1972, Sept. 2 Engr. *Perf. 13*
C93 AP38 72fr vio, bl & red lil 4.00 2.25

20th Olympic Games, Munich, Aug. 26-Sept. 11.

New Post Office, Noumea — AP39

1972, Nov. 25 Engr. *Perf. 13*
C94 AP39 23fr brn, brt bl & grn 1.25 .55

Molière and Scenes from Plays — AP40

1973, Feb. 24 Engr. *Perf. 13*
C95 AP40 50fr multi 3.00 1.50

300th anniversary of the death of Molière (Jean Baptiste Poquelin, 1622-1673), French actor and playwright.

Woodlands — AP41

Designs: 18fr, Palm trees on coast, vert. 21fr, Waterfall, vert.

1973, Feb. 24 Photo.
C96 AP41 11fr gold & multi .90 .65
C97 AP41 18fr gold & multi 1.75 .75
C98 AP41 21fr gold & multi 2.25 .95
Nos. C96-C98 (3) 4.90 2.35

Concorde — AP42

1973, Mar. 15 Engr. *Perf. 13*
C99 AP42 23fr blue 2.75 2.00
a. Booklet pane of 5 25.00

No. C99 issued in booklets only.

El Kantara in Panama Canal — AP43

1973, Mar. 24 Engr. *Perf. 13*
C100 AP43 60fr brn, yel grn & blk 3.50 2.00

50th anniversary of steamship connection Marseilles to Nouméa through Panama Canal.

Sun, Earth, Wind God and Satellite — AP44

1973, Mar. 24
C101 AP44 80fr multi 3.00 1.65

Centenary of international meteorological cooperation and 13th World Meteorological Day.

Museum Type of Regular Issue

Designs: 16fr, Carved arrows and arrowhead. 40fr, Carved entrance to chief's house.

1973, Apr. 30 Photo. *Perf. 12½x13*
C102 A66 16fr multi .60 .50
C103 A66 40fr multi 1.40 1.00

DC-10 over Map of Route Paris to Nouméa — AP45

1973, May 19 Engr. *Perf. 13*
C104 AP45 100fr brn, ultra & sl grn 5.00 3.50

First direct flight by DC-10, Nouméa to Paris.

Fish Type of Regular Issue

Design: 32fr, Old and young olive surgeonfish.

1973, June 23 Photo. *Perf. 13x12½*
C105 A69 32fr multi 3.00 1.75

Coach, 1880 — AP46

1973, Sept. 22 Engr. *Perf. 13*
C106 AP46 15fr choc, bl & sl grn .85 .55

Stamp Day 1973.

Landscape — AP47

West Coast Landscapes: 8fr, Rocky path, vert. 26fr, Trees on shore.

1974, Feb. 23 Photo. *Perf. 13*
C107 AP47 8fr gold & multi .60 .25
C108 AP47 22fr gold & multi 1.10 .45
C109 AP47 26fr gold & multi 1.65 .65
Nos. C107-C109 (3) 3.35 1.35

Anse-Vata, Scientific Center, Nouméa — AP48

1974, Mar. 23 Photo. *Perf. 13x12½*
C110 AP48 50fr multi 1.75 .80

Ovula Ovum
AP49

1974, Mar. 23

C111 AP49 3fr *shown* .30 .15
C112 AP49 32fr *Hydatina* 2.00 .65
C113 AP49 37fr *Dolium perdix* 2.75 1.00
Nos. C111-C113 (3) 5.05 1.80

Nouméa Aquarium.

Capt. Cook, Map of Grande Terre and "Endeavour" — AP50

Designs: 25fr, Jean F. de la Perouse, his ship and map of Grande Terre. 28fr, French sailor, 18th century, on board ship, vert. 30fr, Antoine R. J. d'Entrecasteaux, ship and map. 36fr, Dumont d'Urville, ship and map of Loyalty Islands.

1974, Sept. 4 Engr. *Perf. 13*

C114 AP50 20fr multi .65 .25
C115 AP50 25fr multi .65 .45
C116 AP50 28fr multi .85 .45
C117 AP50 30fr multi 1.00 .55
C118 AP50 36fr multi 1.10 .85
Nos. C114-C118 (5) 4.25 2.55

Discovery and exploration of New Caledonia and Loyalty Islands.

UPU Emblem and Symbolic Design — AP51

1974, Oct. 9 Engr. *Perf. 13*

C119 AP51 95fr multi 3.00 2.00

Centenary of Universal Postal Union.

Abstract Design — AP52

1974, Oct. 26 Photo. *Perf. 13*

C120 AP52 80fr bl, blk & org 2.50 1.25

ARPHILA 75, Philatelic Exhibition, Paris, June 6-16, 1975.

Hôtel Chateau-Royal, Nouméa — AP53

1975, Jan. 20 Photo. *Perf. 13*

C121 AP53 22fr multi .85 .50

Cricket
AP54

Designs: 25fr, Bougna ceremony (food offering). 31fr, Pilou dance.

1975, Mar. 24 Photo. *Perf. 13*

C122 AP54 3fr bl & multi .32 .15
C123 AP54 25fr ol grn & multi .65 .35
C124 AP54 31fr yel grn & multi 1.00 .45
Nos. C122-C124 (3) 1.97 .95

Tourist publicity.

Orchid Type of 1975

Design: 42fr, Eriaxis rigida.

1975, May 30

C125 A74 42fr grn & multi 2.75 1.75

Globe as "Flower" with "Stamps" and leaves — AP55

1975, June 7 Engr. *Perf. 13*

C126 AP55 105fr multi 3.25 2.00

ARPHILA 75 International Philatelic Exhibition, Paris, June 6-16.

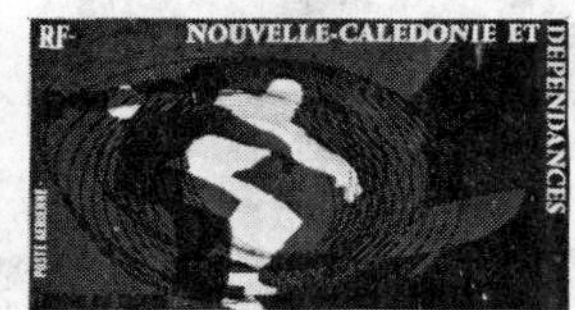

Discus and Games' Emblem — AP56

Design: 50fr, Volleyball and Games' emblem.

1975, Aug. 23 Photo. *Perf. 13x12½*

C127 AP56 24fr emer, pur & dk bl .50 .40
C128 AP56 50fr multi 1.40 .85

5th South Pacific Games, Guam, Aug. 1-10.

Concorde — AP57

1976, Jan. 21 Engr. *Perf. 13*

C129 AP57 147fr car & ultra 5.50 4.00

First commercial flight of supersonic jet Concorde, Paris-Rio de Janeiro, Jan. 21.

For surcharge see No. C141.

Telephones 1876 and 1976, Satellite — AP58

1976, Mar. 10 Photo. *Perf. 13*

C130 AP58 36fr multi 1.10 .55

Centenary of first telephone call by Alexander Graham Bell, Mar. 10, 1876.

Battle Scene — AP59

1976, June 14 Engr. *Perf. 13*

C131 AP59 24fr red brn & ver .75 .55

American Bicentennial.

Runners and Maple Leaf — AP60

1976, July 24 Engr. *Perf. 13*

C132 AP60 33fr car, vio & brn 1.10 .55

21st Olympic Games, Montreal, Canada, July 17-Aug. 1.

Whimsical Bird as Student and Collector
AP61

1976, Aug. 21 Photo.

C133 AP61 42fr multi 1.40 1.00

Philately in School, Philatelic Exhibition in La Perouse Lyceum, Nouméa.

Old City Hall, Nouméa — AP62

Design: 125fr, New City Hall, Nouméa.

1976, Oct. 22 Photo. *Perf. 13*

C134 AP62 75fr multi 2.50 1.40
C135 AP62 125fr multi 3.50 2.00

Lagoon, Women and Festival Symbols
AP63

1977, Jan. 15 Photo. *Perf. 13x12½*

C136 AP63 11fr multi .45 .28

Summer Festival 1977, Nouméa.

Training Children in Toy Cars — AP64

1977, Mar. 12 Litho. *Perf. 13*

C137 AP64 50fr multi 1.40 1.00

Road safety training.

Bird Type of 1977

Design: 42fr, Male frigate bird, horiz.

1977, Sept. 17 Photo. *Perf. 13*

C138 A89 42fr multi 2.25 1.10

Magenta Airport and Routes — AP65

Design: 57fr, La Tontouta airport.

1977, Oct. 22 Litho. *Perf. 13*

C139 AP65 24fr multi .55 .40
C140 AP65 57fr multi 1.65 .65

No. C129 Surcharged in Violet Blue: "22.11.77 PARIS NEW YORK"

1977, Nov. 22 Engr. *Perf. 13*

C141 AP57 147fr car & ultra 6.50 5.50

Concorde, 1st commercial flight Paris-NY.

Old Nouméa, by H. Didonna — AP66

Valley of the Settlers, by Jean Kreber — AP67

1977, Nov. 26 Photo. *Perf. 13*

C142 AP66 41fr gold & multi 1.25 .55

Engr.

C143 AP67 42fr yel brn & dk brn 1.25 .55

"Underwater Carnival," Aubusson Tapestry — AP68

1978, June 17 Photo. *Perf. 13*

C144 AP68 105fr multi 2.50 1.40

"The Hare and the Tortoise" — AP69

1978, Aug. 19 Photo. ***Perf. 13x13½***
C145 AP69 35fr multi 1.25 .75

School philately.

Bourail School Children, Map and Conus Shell — AP70

1978, Sept. 30 Engr. ***Perf. 13***
C146 AP70 41fr multi 1.10 .55

Promotion of topical philately in Bourail public schools.

Old and New Candles — AP71

1978, Oct. 21 Photo. ***Perf. 13***
C147 AP71 36fr multi .75 .45

Third Caledonian Senior Citizens' Day.

Faubourg Blanchot, by Lacouture — AP72

1978, Nov. 25 Photo. ***Perf. 13***
C148 AP72 24fr multi .85 .60

Type of 1978

Design: 42fr, Amyema scandens, horiz.

1978, Mar. 17 ***Perf. 13x12½***
C149 A91 42fr multi 2.00 .90

Orbiting Weather Satellites, WMO Emblem AP73

1979, Mar. 24 Photo. ***Perf. 13***
C150 AP73 53fr multi .90 .55

First world-wide satellite system in the atmosphere.

Ships and Emblem — AP74

1979, Mar. 31 Engr.
C151 AP74 49fr multi .95 .50

Chamber of Commerce and Industry, centenary.

Child's Drawing, IYC Emblem AP75

1979, Apr. 21 Photo. ***Perf. 13***
C152 AP75 35fr multi .80 .52

International Year of the Child.

Surf Casting AP76

Design: 30fr, Swordfish fishing.

1979, May 26 Litho. ***Perf. 12½***
C153 AP76 29fr multi .85 .55
C154 AP76 30fr multi 1.00 .65

Port-de-France, 1854, and de Montravel — AP77

1979, June 16 Engr. ***Perf. 13***
C155 AP77 75fr multi 1.75 1.00

125th anniversary of Noumea, formerly Port-de-France, founded by L. Tardy de Montravel.

The Eel Queen, Kanaka Legend — AP78

1979, July 7 Photo. ***Perf. 13***
C156 AP78 42fr multi 1.50 1.00

Nature protection.

Map of New Caledonia, Postmark, Five Races — AP79

1979, Aug. 18 Photo. ***Perf. 13***
C157 AP79 27fr multi .50 .30

New Caledonian youth and philately.

Orstom Center, Noumea, Orstom Emblem — AP80

1979, Sept. 17 Photo. ***Perf. 13***
C158 AP80 25fr multi .45 .28

Old Post Office, Noumea, New Caledonia No. 1, Hill — AP81

1979, Nov. 17 Engr.
C159 AP81 150fr multi 3.50 2.25

Sir Rowland Hill (1795-1879), originator of penny postage.

Pirogue AP82

1980, Jan. 26 Engr. ***Perf. 13***
C160 AP82 45fr multi 1.00 .70

Rotary Intl., 75th Anniv. — AP83

1980, Feb. 23 Photo. ***Perf. 13***
C161 AP83 100fr multi 2.50 1.75

Man Holding Dolphinfish AP84

1980, Oct. 11 Photo. ***Perf. 13x12½***
C162 AP84 34fr shown .85 .55
C163 AP84 39fr Fishermen, sail fish, vert. 1.00 .65

Coral Seas Air Rally AP85

1980, June 7 Engr. ***Perf. 13***
C164 AP85 31fr multi .85 .65

Carved Alligator, Boat — AP86

1980, June 21 Photo.
C165 AP86 27fr multi .60 .40

South Pacific Arts Festival, Port Moresby, Papua New Guinea.

New Caledonian Kiwanis, 10th Anniversary — AP87

1980, Sept. 10 Photo. ***Perf. 13***
C166 AP87 50fr multi 1.00 .65

View of Old Noumea — AP88

1980, Oct. 25 Photo. ***Perf. 13½***
C167 AP88 33fr multi .65 .48

Charles de Gaulle, 10th Anniversary of Death — AP89

1980, Nov. 15 Engr. ***Perf. 13***
C168 AP89 120fr multi 3.00 2.00

Fluorescent Coral, Noumea Aquarium AP90

1980, Dec. 13 Photo. ***Perf. 13x13½***
C169 AP90 60fr multi 1.25 .70

Xeronema Moorei AP91

1981, Mar. 18 Photo. ***Perf. 13x12½***
C170 AP91 38fr shown .75 .40
C171 AP91 51fr Geissois pruinosa .95 .40

Yuri Gagarin and Vostok I — AP92

20th Anniversary of First Space Flights: 155fr, Alan B. Shepard, Freedom 7.

1981, Apr. 8 Engr. *Perf. 13*

C172 AP92 64fr multi 1.40 .85
C173 AP92 155fr multi 3.00 1.75
a. Souv. sheet of 2, #C172-C173 5.25 5.25

No. C173a sold for 225fr.

40th Anniv. of Departure of Pacific Batallion — AP93

1981, May 5 Photo. *Perf. 13*

C174 AP93 29fr multi .70 .55

Ecinometra Mathaei AP94

1981, Aug. 5 Photo. *Perf. 13x13½*

C175 AP94 38fr shown .65 .35
C176 AP94 51fr Prionocidaris verticillata .85 .48

No. 4, Post Office Building AP95

1981, Sept. 16 Photo. *Perf. 13x13½*

C177 AP95 41fr multi .75 .48

Stamp Day.

Old Noumea Latin Quarter — AP96

1981, Oct. 14 Photo. *Perf. 13½*

C178 AP96 43fr multi .75 .48

New Caledonia to Australia Airmail Flight by Victor Roffey, 50th Anniv. AP97

1981, Nov. 21 Engr. *Perf. 13*

C179 AP97 37fr multi .70 .40

Rousette AP98

1982, Feb. 17 Engr. *Perf. 13*

C180 AP98 38fr shown .65 .35
C181 AP98 51fr Kagu .85 .48

See Nos. C188B-C188C.

50th Anniv. of Paris-Noumea Flight — AP99

1982, Apr. 5 Engr. *Perf. 13*

C182 AP99 250fr Pilots, map, plane 4.50 2.50

Scouting Year — AP100

1982, Apr. 21 Photo. *Perf. 13½x13*

C183 AP100 40fr multi .70 .40

PHILEXFRANCE '82 Intl. Stamp Show, Paris, June 11-21 — AP101

1982, May 12 Engr. *Perf. 13*

C184 AP101 150fr multi 2.50 2.00

1982 World Cup AP102

1982, June 9 Photo. *Perf. 13x13½*

C185 AP102 74fr multi 1.25 .70

French Overseas Possessions Week, Sept. 18-25 AP103

1982, Sept. 17 *Perf. 13x12½*

C186 AP103 100fr Map, kagu, citizens 1.75 .85

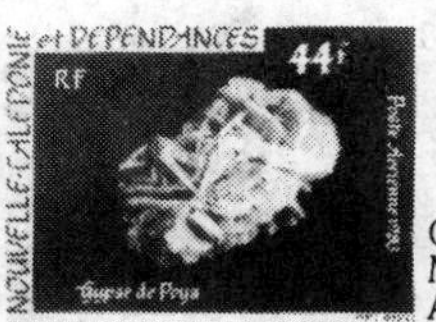
Gypsum, Poya Mines AP104

1983, Jan. 15 Photo. *Perf. 13x13½*

C187 AP104 44fr shown .55 .30
C188 AP104 59fr Silica gel, Kone mine .70 .35

World Communications Year — AP104a

Design: WCY emblem, map, globe.

1983, Mar. 9 Litho. *Perf. 13*

C188A AP104a 170fr multi 2.25 1.10

Aircraft Type of 1982

1983, July 6 Engr. *Perf. 13*

C188B AP98 46fr Pou-du-Ciel .80 .50
C188C AP98 61fr L'Aiglon Caudron .85 .60

Temple and Dancers — AP105

1983, July 20 Litho. *Perf. 12½x12*

C189 AP105 47fr multi .85 .55

BANGKOK '83 Intl. Stamp Show, Aug. 4-13.

Oueholle Tribe, Straw Hut — AP106

1983, Sept. 8 Litho. *Perf. 13*

C190 AP106 76fr multi 1.10 .75

Loyalty Islander by the Shore, by R. Mascart AP107

Paintings: 350fr, The Guitarist from Mare Island, by P. Neilly.

1983, Dec. 7 Photo. *Perf. 13*

C191 AP107 100fr multi 1.10 .75
C192 AP107 350fr multi 4.00 2.75

Noumea Aquarium Fish — AP108

1984, Mar. 7 Photo. *Perf. 13*

C193 AP108 46fr Amphiprion clarkii .50 .35
C194 AP108 61fr Centropyge bicolor .70 .50

Local Plants — AP109

1984, Apr. 25 Litho. *Perf. 12½x13*

C195 AP109 51fr Araucaria columnaris .65 .32
C196 AP109 67fr Pritchardiopsis jeanneneyi .85 .42

1984 Summer Olympics — AP110

1984, June 20 Photo. *Perf. 13½x13*

C197 AP110 50fr Swimming .55 .40
C198 AP110 83fr Wind surfing .95 .70
C199 AP110 200fr Running 2.25 1.40
Nos. C197-C199 (3) 3.75 2.50

Ausipex '84 — AP111

Army Day — AP112

1984, Sept. 21 Engr. *Perf. 13*

C200 AP111 150fr Exhibition Hall 2.00 1.40
a. Souvenir sheet 2.25 2.25

Se-tenant with label showing exhibition emblem. No. C200a contains No. C200 in changed colors.

1984, Oct. 28 Litho. *Perf. 13½x13*

C201 AP112 51fr multi .60 .32

Woman Fishing for Crabs, by Mme. Bonnet de Larbogne — AP113

Painting: 300fr, Cook Discovering New Caledonia, by Pilioko.

1984, Nov. 8 Litho. *Perf. 13x12½*

C202 AP113 120fr multi 1.50 .70
C203 AP113 300fr multi 3.50 1.75

See Nos. 605-606.

Transpac Dragon Rapide, Map AP114

1985, Oct. 2 Litho. *Perf. 13½*

C204 AP114 80fr multi .80 .40

Internal air services, 30th anniv.

UN, 40th Anniv. AP115

Perf. 12½x13

1985, Oct. 25 Wmk. 385

C205 AP115 250fr multi 2.25 1.10

Jules Garnier High School AP116

1985, Nov. 13 Unwmk. *Perf. 13*

C206 AP116 400fr multi 3.75 1.90

Paris-Noumea Scheduled Flights, 30th Anniv. — AP117

1986, Jan. 6

C207 AP117 72fr multi .75 .38

Nou Island Livestock Warehouse — AP118

1986, June 14 Engr. *Perf. 13*

C208 AP118 230fr Prus bl, sep & brn 2.75 1.40

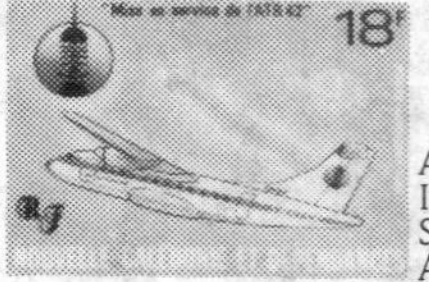

ATR-42 Inaugural Service AP119

1986, Aug. 13 Litho. *Perf. 12½x13*

C209 AP119 18fr multi .20 .10

STOCKHOLMIA '86 — AP120

1986, Aug. 29 Engr. *Perf. 13*

C210 AP120 108fr No. 1 1.25 .65

Natl. Assoc. of Amateur Radio Operators, 25th Anniv. AP121

1987, Jan. 7 Litho. *Perf. 12½*

C211 AP121 64fr multi .80 .40

Nature Conservation, Fight Noise Pollution AP122

1987, Mar. 25 Litho. *Perf. 13x12½*

C212 AP122 150fr multi 1.90 1.00

French Cricket Federation AP123

1987, Nov. 25 Litho. *Perf. 12½*

C213 AP123 94fr multi 1.40 .75

Arms Type of 1984

1988, Jan. 13 *Perf. 12½x13*

C214 A132 76fr Dumbea 1.00 .50

Rotary Intl. Anti-Polio Campaign — AP124

1988, Oct. 26 Litho. *Perf. 13½*

C215 AP124 220fr multi 4.00 2.00

Bamboo Type of 1989

Perf. 12½x13

1989, Sept. 27 Litho. & Engr.

C216 A187 44fr multi .80 .40

De Gaulle's Call For French Resistance, 50th Anniv. AP125

1990, June 20 Litho. *Perf. 12½*

C217 AP125 160fr multicolored 3.50 1.75

Military Cemetery, New Zealand — AP126

Auckland 1990: #C219, Brigadier William Walter Dove.

1990, Aug. 24 *Perf. 13*

C218 AP126 80fr multi 1.60 .80

C219 AP126 80fr multi 1.60 .80

a. Pair, #C218-C219 + label 3.25 1.60

Souvenir Sheet

New Zealand 1990 — AP126a

1990, Aug. 25 Litho. *Perf. 13x12½*

C219B AP126a 150fr multi 3.50 1.75

Crustaceans — AP127

1990, Oct. 17 Litho. *Perf. 12½x13*

C220 AP127 30fr Munidopsis sp. Orstom .60 .30

C221 AP127 60fr Lyreidius tridentatus 1.20 .60

30th South Pacific Conference — AP128

1990, Oct. 29 Litho. *Perf. 13*

C222 AP128 85fr multicolored 2.10 1.05

Gen. Charles de Gaulle (1890-1970) AP129

1990, Nov. 21 Engr. *Perf. 13*

C223 AP129 410fr dk blue 10.00 5.00

Scenic Views — AP130

1991, Feb. 13 Litho. *Perf. 13*

C224 AP130 36fr Fayawa-Ouvea Bay .90 .45

C225 AP130 90fr shown 2.20 1.10

See No. C246.

New Caledonian Cricket Players by Marcel Moutouh — AP131

Design: 435fr, Saint Louis by Janine Goetz.

1991, Dec. 18 *Perf. 13x12½*

C226 AP131 130fr multicolored 3.00 1.50

C227 AP131 435fr multicolored 10.00 5.00

See Nos. C236, C242, C260.

Blue River Nature Park — AP132

Illustration reduced.

1992, Feb. 6 Litho. *Perf. 12½*

C228 AP132 400fr multicolored 9.25 4.65

a. Souvenir sheet of 1 10.50 5.25

No. C228a sold for 450fr.

Native Pottery — AP133

Photo. & Engr.

1992, Apr. 9 *Perf. 12½x13*

C229 AP133 25fr black & orange .53 .28

Expo '92, Seville AP134

1992, Apr. 25 Litho. *Perf. 13*

C230 AP134 10fr multicolored .25 .15

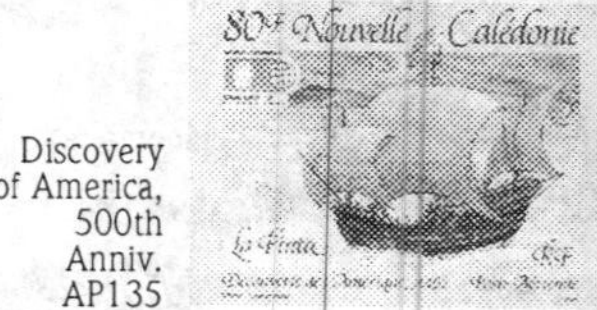

Discovery of America, 500th Anniv. AP135

#C234: a, Erik the Red, Viking longship. b, Columbus, coat of arms. c, Amerigo Vespucci.

1992, May 22 Litho. *Perf. 13½*

C231 AP135 80fr Pinta 2.00 1.00

C232 AP135 80fr Santa Maria 2.00 1.00

C233 AP135 80fr Nina 2.00 1.00

a. Strip of 3, #C231-C233 6.00 3.00

b. Bklt. pane of 3, #C231-C233 6.00 3.00

Souvenir Sheet

Perf. 12½

C234 AP135 110fr Sheet of 3, #a.-c. 9.00 4.50

World Columbian Stamp Expo '92, Chicago. No. C234 sold for 360fr.

1992 Summer Olympics, Barcelona — AP136

1992, July 25 *Perf. 13*

C235 AP136 260fr Synchronized swimming 6.35 3.20

Painters of the Pacific Type of 1991

Design: 205fr, Wahpa, by Paul Mascart

1992, Sept. 28 Litho. *Perf. 12½x13*

C236 AP131 205fr multicolored 5.00 2.50

Australian Bouvier — AP138

1992, Oct. 4 *Perf. 12*
C237 AP138 175fr multicolored 4.10 2.05

Exploration of New Caledonian Coast by Chevalier d'Entrecasteaux, Bicent. — AP139

1992, Nov. 18 Engr. *Perf. 13*
C238 AP139 110fr bl grn, ocher & olive grn 2.50 1.25

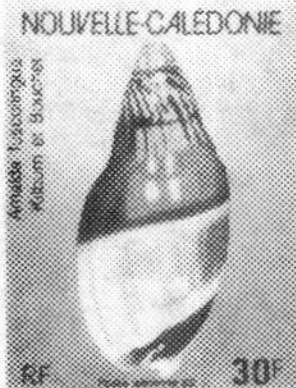
Shells — AP140

AP141

1992, Nov. 26 Litho. *Perf. 13½x13*
C239 AP140 30fr Amalda fuscolingua .70 .35
C240 AP140 50fr Cassis abbotti 1.15 .58

The vignettes on Nos. C239-C240 were applied by a thermographic process, producing a shiny, raised effect.

1992, Dec. 9 Litho. *Perf. 13½*

Comic Strip Characters from "La Brousse en Folie," by Bernard Berger: a, Dede. b. Torton Marcel in Mimine II. c, Tathan. d, Joinville.

C241 AP141 80fr Strip of 4, #a.-d. 7.20 3.60

Painters of the Pacific Type of 1991

Design: 150fr, Noumea, 1890, by Gaston Roullet (1847-1925).

1993, Mar. 25 Litho. *Perf. 13x12½*
C242 AP131 150fr multicolored 3.50 1.75

Extraction of Attar from Niaouli Flowers (Melaleuca Quinquenervia), Cent. — AP142

1993, Apr. 28 *Perf. 13*
C243 AP142 85fr multicolored 1.90 .95

Nicolaus Copernicus (1473-1543) — AP143

1993, May 5 Engr. *Perf. 13*
C244 AP143 110fr multicolored 2.50 1.25

Polska '93.

Noumea Temple, Cent. AP144

1993, June 16 Litho. *Perf. 12½x13*
C245 AP144 400fr multicolored 9.00 4.50

Scenic Views Type of 1991

1993, July 8 Litho. *Perf. 13*
C246 AP130 85fr Malabou 2.00 1.00

Little Train of Thio — AP145

1993, July 24 Engr. *Perf. 13*
C247 AP145 115fr multicolored 2.50 1.25

AP146

AP147

1993, Aug. 18 Litho.
C248 AP146 100fr multicolored 2.00 1.00

Henri Rochefort (1831-1913), writer.

1993, Oct. 1 *Perf. 13½*

Bangkok '93: No. C249, Vanda coerulea. No. C250, Megastylis paradoxa. 140fr, Royal Palace, Bangkok, horiz.

C249 AP147 30fr multicolored .65 .32
C250 AP147 30fr multicolored .65 .32

Souvenir Sheet
Perf. 13

C251 AP147 140fr multicolored 3.00 1.50

No. C251 contains one 52x40mm stamp.

Air Caledonia, 10th Anniv. — AP148

1993, Oct. 9 *Perf. 13*
C252 AP148 85fr multicolored 1.85 .95

New Caledonia-Australia Telephone Cable, Cent. — AP149

1993, Oct. 15 Engr. *Perf. 13x12½*
C253 AP149 200fr blue & black 4.25 2.00

Oxpleurodon Orbiculatus AP150

1993, Oct. 15 Litho. *Perf. 13½*
C254 AP150 250fr multicolored 5.25 2.75

Portions of the design on No. C254 were applied by a thermographic process producing a shiny, raised effect.

Tontouta Airport, Noumea, 25th Anniv. — AP151

1993, Nov. 21 Litho. *Perf. 13*
C255 AP151 90fr multicolored 1.90 .95

Christmas — AP152

1993, Dec. 10 Litho.
C256 AP152 120fr multicolored 2.50 1.25

Portions of the design on No. C256 were applied by a thermographic process producing a shiny, raised effect.

New Year 1994 (Year of the Dog) AP153

1994, Feb. 18 Litho. *Perf. 13*
C257 AP153 60fr multicolored 1.25 .65

Hong Kong '94.

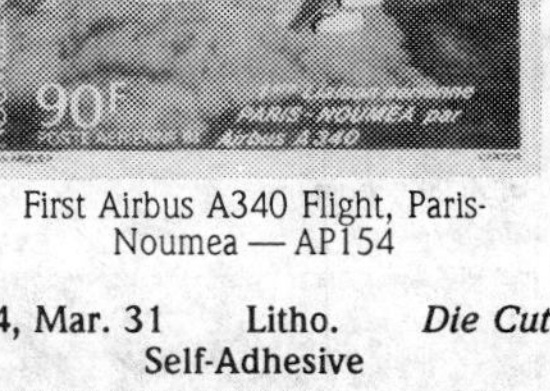
First Airbus A340 Flight, Paris-Noumea — AP154

1994, Mar. 31 Litho. *Die Cut 8*
Self-Adhesive
C258 AP154 90fr multicolored 2.00 1.00

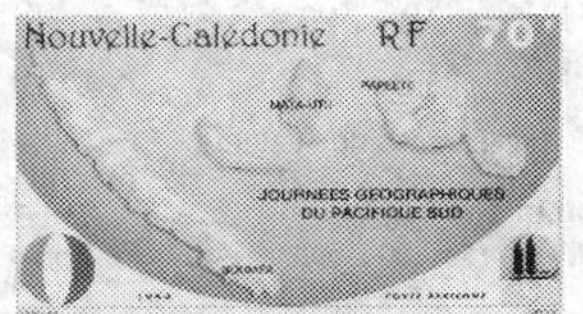
South Pacific Geography Day — AP155

1994, May 10 Litho. *Perf. 13*
C259 AP155 70fr multicolored 1.40 .70

See Wallis and Futuna No. C177.

Painters of the Pacific Type of 1991

Design: 120fr, Legende du Poulpe, by Micheline Neporon.

1994, June 25 Litho. *Perf. 13*
C260 AP131 120fr multicolored 2.50 1.25

Pottery, Museum of Noumea — AP156

1994, July 7 Litho. *Perf. 12½x13*
C261 AP156 95fr multicolored 2.00 1.00

1994 World Cup Soccer Championships, US — AP156a

1994, July 12 Litho. *Perf. 13*
C261A AP156a 105fr multicolored 2.00 1.00

Intl. Year of the Family AP157

PHILAKOREA '94 — AP158

Korean cuisine: No. C263a, Rice, celery, carrots, peppers. b, Lettuce, cabbage, garlic. c, Onions. d, Shrimp, oysters.

1994, Aug. 17 *Perf. 13½x13*
C262 AP157 60fr multicolored 1.25 .62

Souvenir Sheet

Perf. 12½

C263 Sheet of 4 3.00 3.00
a.-d. AP158 35fr any single .75 .75

Research Ship Atalante — AP159

1994, Aug. 26 *Perf. 13*
C264 AP159 120fr multicolored 2.50 1.25

Masons in New Caledonia, 125th Anniv. — AP160

1994, Sept. 16 *Perf. 13*
C265 AP160 350fr multicolored 7.25 3.75

Participation in First European Stamp Show — AP161

1994, Oct. 15 **Litho.** *Perf. 13*
C266 AP161 90fr Island 1.75 .85
C267 AP161 90fr Herding cattle 1.75 .85
a. Pair, #C266-C267 + label 3.50 1.70

ORSTOM, 50th Anniv. — AP162

1994, Nov. 5 **Photo.** *Perf. 13*
C268 AP162 95fr multicolored 1.90 .95

Tiebaghi Mine — AP163

1994, Nov. 24 **Litho.**
C269 AP163 90fr multicolored 1.75 .90

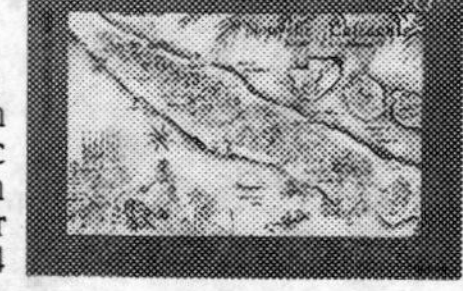

South Pacific Tourism Year AP164

1995, Mar. 16 **Litho.** *Perf. 13½*
C270 AP164 90fr multicolored 1.75 .90

35th South Pacific Conference, Noumea — AP165

1995, Oct. 25 **Litho.** *Perf. 13*
C271 AP165 500fr multicolored 11.50 4.75

Kanak Dances AP166

1995, Dec. 8 **Litho.** *Perf. 13x13½*
C272 AP166 95fr Ouaré 2.25 1.25
C273 AP166 100fr Pothé 2.25 1.25

Mekosuchus Inexpactatus AP167

1996, Feb. 23 **Litho.** *Perf. 13x13½*
C274 AP167 125fr multicolored 2.75 1.40

Indonesian Centenary — AP168

1996, July 22
C275 AP168 130fr multicolored 3.00 3.00

Louis Brauquier (1900-76), Writer — AP169

1996, Aug. 7 **Litho.** *Perf. 12½*
C276 AP169 95fr multicolored 2.20 1.10

Ile Nou Ground Station, 20th Anniv. AP170

125fr, Guglielmo Marconi, telegraph wires.

1996, Sept. 26 **Litho.** *Perf. 13*
C277 AP170 95f multicolored 2.25 1.10
C278 AP170 125fr multicolored 2.75 1.40
a. Pair, #C277-C278 + label 5.00 2.50

Radio, cent. (#C278).

Regional Views — AP171

1996, Nov. 7 **Litho.** *Perf. 13*
C279 AP171 95fr Great reef 2.20 1.10
C280 AP171 95fr Mount Koghi 2.20 1.10
a. Pair, #C279-C280 + label 4.40 2.20

50th Autumn Philatelic Salon.

Christmas — AP172

1996, Nov. 26 *Perf. 13½x13*
C281 AP172 95fr multicolored 2.20 1.10

Horned Turtle Meiolania AP173

1997, Jan. 8 **Litho.** *Perf. 13*
C282 AP173 95fr multicolored 2.20 1.10

Portions of the design were applied by a thermographic process producing a shiny, raised effect.

South Pacific Commission, 50th Anniv. AP174

1997, Feb. 7 **Litho.** *Perf. 13X13½*
C283 AP174 100fr multicolored 2.20 1.10

Hong Kong '97 — AP175

New Year 1997 (Year of the Ox): No. C285a, Water buffalo pulling plow. b, Cattle in pasture.

1997, Feb. 12 *Perf. 13*
C284 AP175 95fr multicolored 2.20 1.10

Perf. 13x13½

C285 AP175 75fr Sheet of 2, #a.-b. 3.30 1.65

No. C285 contains two 40x30mm stamps.

Melanesian Pottery — AP176

Lapita pottery c. 1200-1000 B.C.: No. C286, With stylized faces. No. C287, With labyrinth pattern.

1997, May 14 **Litho.** *Perf. 13*
C286 AP176 95fr multicolored 2.25 2.25
C287 AP176 95fr multicolored 2.25 2.25

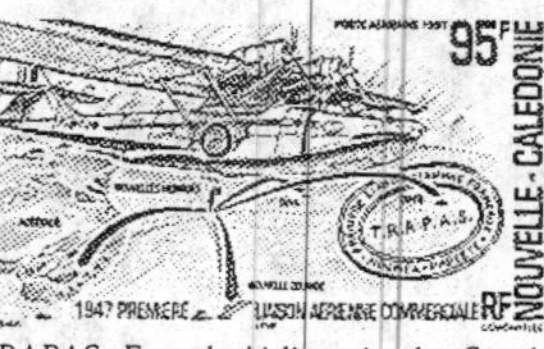

TRAPAS, French Airlines in the South Pacific, 1947-50 — AP177

Airplane, emblem, map showing: a, Australia, New Herbrides, Suva, Tahiti, New Zealand. b, Koumac, Poindimie, Noumea, Isle of Pines.

Photo. & Engr.

1997, Aug. 12 *Perf. 13*
C288 AP177 95fr multicolored 2.10 2.10
C289 AP177 95fr multicolored 2.10 2.10
a. Pair, #C288-C289 4.25 4.25

AIR POST SEMI-POSTAL STAMP

French Revolution Issue

Common Design Type

Unwmk.

1939, July 5 **Photo.** *Perf. 13*

Name and Value Typo. in Orange

CB1 CD83 4.50fr + 4fr brn blk 12.00 12.00

V5

Stamps of the design shown above and stamp of Cameroun type V10 inscribed "Nlle Calédonie" were issued in 1942 by the Vichy Government, but were not placed on sale in the colony.

POSTAGE DUE STAMPS

For a short time in 1894, 5, 10, 15, 20, 25 and 30c postage stamps (Nos. 43, 45, 47, 49, 50 and 52) were overprinted with a "T" in an inverted triangle and used as Postage Due stamps.

French Colonies Postage Due Stamps Overprinted in Carmine, Blue or Silver

1903 Unwmk. *Imperf.*

No.	Type	Description	Unused	Used
J1	D1	5c blue (C)	1.50	1.50
J2	D1	10c brown (C)	5.00	4.00
J3	D1	15c yel grn (C)	13.00	5.00
J4	D1	30c carmine (Bl)	8.00	6.50
J5	D1	50c violet (Bl)	40.00	10.00
J6	D1	60c brn, *buff* (Bl)	160.00	37.50
J7	D1	1fr rose, *buff* (S)	20.00	10.00
J8	D1	2fr red brn (Bl)	700.00	700.00
		Nos. J1-J8 (8)	947.50	774.50

Nos. J1 to J8 are known with the "I" in "TENAIRE" missing.

Fifty years of French occupation.

Men Poling Boat — D2

Malayan Sambar — D3

1906 Typo. *Perf. 13½x14*

No.	Type	Description	Unused	Used
J9	D2	5c ultra, *azure*	.25	.25
J10	D2	10c vio brn, *buff*	.35	.35
J11	D2	15c grn, *greenish*	.35	.35
J12	D2	20c blk, *yellow*	.35	.35
J13	D2	30c carmine	.50	.50
J14	D2	50c ultra, *buff*	1.10	1.10
J15	D2	60c brn, *azure*	.90	.90
J16	D2	1fr dk grn, *straw*	1.25	1.25
		Nos. J9-J16 (8)	5.05	5.05

Type of 1906 Issue Surcharged **2F. =**

1926-27

No.	Type	Description	Unused	Used
J17	D2	2fr on 1fr vio	2.00	2.00
J18	D2	3fr on 1fr org brn	2.00	2.00

1928 Typo.

No.	Type	Description	Unused	Used
J19	D3	2c sl bl & dp brn	.15	.15
J20	D3	4c brn red & bl grn	.30	.30
J21	D3	5c red org & bl blk	.30	.30
J22	D3	10c mag & Prus bl	.30	.30
J23	D3	15c dl grn & scar	.30	.30
J24	D3	20c mar & ol grn	.60	.60
J25	D3	25c bis brn & sl bl	.40	.40
J26	D3	30c bl grn & ol grn	.60	.60
J27	D3	50c lt brn & dk red	.80	.80
J28	D3	60c mag & brt rose	.80	.80
J29	D3	1fr dl bl & Prus grn	1.00	1.00
J30	D3	2fr dk red & ol grn	1.25	1.25
J31	D3	3fr violet & brn	1.75	1.75
		Nos. J19-J31 (13)	8.55	8.55

Catalogue values for unused stamps in this section, from this point to the end of the section, are for Never Hinged items.

D4

Bat — D5

1948 Unwmk. Photo. *Perf. 13*

No.	Type	Description	Unused	Used
J32	D4	10c violet	.15	.15
J33	D4	30c brown	.15	.15
J34	D4	50c blue green	.15	.15
J35	D4	1fr orange	.15	.15
J36	D4	2fr red violet	.15	.15
J37	D4	3fr red brown	.15	.15
J38	D4	4fr dull blue	.28	.28
J39	D4	5fr henna brown	.40	.40
J40	D4	10fr slate green	.60	.60
J41	D4	20fr violet blue	1.25	1.25
		Nos. J32-J41 (10)	3.43	3.43

1983 Litho. *Perf. 13*

No.	Type	Description	Unused	Used
J42	D5	1fr multi	.15	.15
J43	D5	2fr multi	.15	.15
J44	D5	3fr multi	.15	.15
J45	D5	4fr multi	.15	.15
J46	D5	5fr multi	.15	.15
J47	D5	10fr multi	.22	.22
J48	D5	20fr multi	.42	.42
J49	D5	40fr multi	.85	.85
J50	D5	50fr multi	1.00	1.00
		Nos. J42-J50 (9)	3.24	3.24

MILITARY STAMPS

Stamps of the above types, although issued by officials, were unauthorized and practically a private speculation.

OFFICIAL STAMPS

Catalogue values for unused stamps in this section are for Never Hinged items.

Ancestor Pole — O1

Carved Wooden Pillow — O2

Various carved ancestor poles.

1959 Unwmk. Typo. *Perf. 14x13*

No.	Type	Description	Unused	Used
O1	O1	1fr org yel	.28	.15
O2	O1	3fr lt bl grn	.28	.15
O3	O1	4fr purple	.35	.20
O4	O1	5fr ultra	.45	.24
O5	O1	9fr black	.50	.35
O6	O1	10fr brt vio	.65	.35
O7	O1	13fr yel grn	.75	.48
O8	O1	15fr lt bl	.85	.70
O9	O1	24fr red lilac	1.00	.85
O10	O1	26fr deep org	1.25	1.00
O11	O1	50fr green	3.00	1.50
O12	O1	100fr chocolate	6.00	3.00
O13	O1	200fr red	11.00	5.25
		Nos. O1-O13 (13)	26.36	14.22

1973-87 Photo. *Perf. 13*

Vignette: Green, Red Brown (2, 29, 31, 35, 38, 65, 76fr), Brown (40fr), Blue (58fr)

No.	Type	Description	Unused	Used
O14	O2	1fr yellow	.15	.15
O14A	O2	2fr green ('87)	.15	.15
O15	O2	3fr tan	.20	.15
O16	O2	4fr pale violet	.20	.15
O17	O2	5fr lilac rose	.28	.15
O18	O2	9fr light blue	.35	.20
O19	O2	10fr orange	.35	.24
O20	O2	11fr bright lilac	.18	.15
O21	O2	12fr bl grn ('76)	.50	.35
O22	O2	15fr green ('76)	.24	.15
O23	O2	20fr rose ('76)	.28	.15
O24	O2	23fr red ('80)	.28	.15
O25	O2	24fr Prus bl ('76)	.32	.15
O25A	O2	25fr gray ('81)	.32	.15
O26	O2	26fr yellow ('76)	.35	.18
O26A	O2	29fr dl grn ('83)	.30	.15
O26B	O2	31fr yellow ('82)	.32	.16
O26C	O2	35fr yellow ('84)	.48	.24
O27	O2	36fr dp lil rose ('76)	.50	.20
O27A	O2	38fr tan	.28	.15
O27B	O2	40fr blue ('87)	.52	.28
O28	O2	42fr bister ('76)	.60	.35
O29	O2	50fr blue ('76)	.70	.60
O29A	O2	58fr blue grn ('87)	.75	.48
O29B	O2	65fr lilac ('84)	.75	.30
O29C	O2	76fr brt yel ('87)	1.10	.52
O30	O2	100fr red ('76)	1.40	1.00
O31	O2	200fr orange ('76)	2.75	1.50
		Nos. O14-O31 (28)	14.60	8.55

This is an expanding set. Numbers will change when complete.

PARCEL POST STAMPS

Type of Regular Issue of 1905-28 Surcharged or Overprinted

50

Colis Postaux

1926 Unwmk. *Perf. 14x13½*

No.	Type	Description	Unused	Used
Q1	A18	50c on 5fr olive, *lav*	.70	.70
Q2	A18	1fr deep blue	1.00	1.00
Q3	A18	2fr car, *bluish*	1.25	1.25
		Nos. Q1-Q3 (3)	2.95	2.95

Regular Issue of 1928 Overprinted:

Colis Postaux

1930

No.	Type	Description	Unused	Used
Q4	A20	50c violet & brown	.70	.70
Q5	A21	1fr dp ol & sal red	.80	.80
Q6	A21	2fr red org & brn	1.25	1.25
		Nos. Q4-Q6 (3)	2.75	2.75

NEW GUINEA

'nü 'gi-nē

LOCATION — On an island of the same name in the South Pacific Ocean, north of Australia.
GOVT. — Mandate administered by Australia
AREA — 93,000 sq. mi.
POP. — 675,369 (1940)
CAPITAL — Rabaul

The territory occupies the northeastern part of the island and includes New Britain and other nearby islands. It was formerly a German possession and should not be confused with British New Guinea (Papua) which is in the southeastern part of the same island, nor Netherlands New Guinea (Vol. 4). For previous issues see German New Guinea, New Britain, North West Pacific Islands. Issues for 1952 and later are listed under Papua.

12 Pence = 1 Shilling
20 Shillings = 1 Pound

Native Huts — A1

Bird of Paradise — A2

1925-28 Engr. *Perf. 11*

No.	Type	Description	Unused	Used
1	A1	½p orange	1.00	2.00
2	A1	1p yellow green	1.10	2.25
3	A1	1½p vermilion ('26)	1.90	1.75
4	A1	2p claret	2.75	1.65
5	A1	3p deep blue	4.50	3.25
6	A1	4p olive green	10.00	14.00
7	A1	6p yel bister ('28)	6.50	40.00
a.		6p light brown	18.00	40.00
b.		6p olive bister ('27)	8.00	35.00
8	A1	9p deep violet	13.00	35.00
9	A1	1sh gray green	13.00	20.00
10	A1	2sh red brown	22.50	35.00
11	A1	5sh olive bister	30.00	60.00
12	A1	10sh dull rose	95.00	90.00
13	A1	£1 grnsh gray	200.00	250.00
		Nos. 1-13 (13)	401.25	554.90

For overprints see Nos. C1-C13, O1-O9.

1931, Aug. 2

No.	Type	Description	Unused	Used
18	A2	1p light green	.65	2.00
19	A2	1½p red	2.50	4.00
20	A2	2p violet brown	1.40	3.00
21	A2	3p deep blue	1.40	7.50
22	A2	4p olive green	3.00	5.00
23	A2	5p slate green	3.00	8.00
24	A2	6p bister	3.00	9.00
25	A2	9p dull violet	3.75	12.50
26	A2	1sh bluish gray	4.00	12.50
27	A2	2sh red brown	7.50	22.50
28	A2	5sh olive brown	30.00	42.50
29	A2	10sh rose red	72.50	85.00
30	A2	£1 gray	110.00	140.00
		Nos. 18-30 (13)	242.70	353.50

10th anniversary of Australian Mandate.
For overprints see #C14-C27, O12-O22.

Type of 1931 without date scrolls

1932-34 *Perf. 11*

No.	Type	Description	Unused	Used
31	A2	1p light green	.45	.25
32	A2	1½p violet brown	.90	4.50
33	A2	2p red	.50	.45
34	A2	2½p dp green ('34)	4.25	10.00
35	A2	3p gray blue	.90	.75
36	A2	3½p magenta ('34)	9.00	10.50
37	A2	4p olive green	.90	2.00
38	A2	5p slate green	.90	.75
39	A2	6p bister	1.00	2.50
40	A2	9p dull violet	6.50	12.50
41	A2	1sh bluish gray	4.25	7.50
42	A2	2sh red brown	4.25	10.00
43	A2	5sh olive brown	22.50	37.50
44	A2	10sh rose red	70.00	80.00
45	A2	£1 gray	95.00	100.00
		Nos. 31-45 (15)	221.30	279.20

For overprints see #46-47, C28-C43, O23-O35.

Silver Jubilee Issue

Stamps of 1932-34 Overprinted **HIS MAJESTY'S JUBILEE. 1910 — 1935**

1935, June 27

Glazed Paper

No.	Type	Description	Unused	Used
46	A2	1p light green	.75	.75
47	A2	2p red	1.00	.75

King George VI — A3

1937, May 18 Engr.

No.	Type	Description	Unused	Used
48	A3	2p salmon rose	.20	.20
49	A3	3p blue	.20	.20
50	A3	5p green	.35	.30
51	A3	1sh brown violet	.60	.50
		Nos. 48-51 (4)	1.35	1.20

Coronation of George VI and Queen Elizabeth.

AIR POST STAMPS

Regular Issues of 1925-28 Overprinted

1931, June *Perf. 11*

No.	Type	Description	Unused	Used
C1	A1	½p orange	.35	.95
C2	A1	1p yellow green	.45	1.25
C3	A1	1½p vermilion	.85	2.75
C4	A1	2p claret	1.75	4.00
C5	A1	3p deep blue	2.75	3.00
C6	A1	4p olive green	3.75	4.00
C7	A1	6p light brown	3.75	4.00
C8	A1	9p deep violet	5.25	5.50
C9	A1	1sh gray green	6.50	7.00
C10	A1	2sh red brown	11.50	12.00
C11	A1	5sh ol bister	26.00	35.00
C12	A1	10sh light red	55.00	72.50
C13	A1	£1 grnsh gray	135.00	150.00
		Nos. C1-C13 (13)	252.90	301.95

Type of Regular Issue of 1931 and Nos. 18-30 Overprinted

AIR MAIL

1931, Aug.

No.	Type	Description	Unused	Used
C14	A2	½p orange	.35	.35
C15	A2	1p light green	.55	.55
C16	A2	1½p red	1.90	1.90
C17	A2	2p violet brown	1.90	2.00
C18	A2	3p deep blue	2.25	2.25
C19	A2	4p olive green	2.75	2.75
C20	A2	5p slate green	3.00	3.00
C21	A2	6p bister	4.00	4.50
C22	A2	9p dull violet	4.50	4.50
C23	A2	1sh bluish gray	5.00	5.00
C24	A2	2sh red brown	8.00	5.50
C25	A2	5sh olive brown	25.00	17.50
C26	A2	10sh rose red	65.00	75.00
C27	A2	£1 gray	140.00	175.00
		Nos. C14-C27 (14)	264.20	299.80

10th anniversary of Australian Mandate.

Same Overprint on Type of Regular Issue of 1932-34 and Nos. 31-45

1932-34 *Perf. 11*

No.	Type	Description	Unused	Used
C28	A2	½p orange	.25	.30
C29	A2	1p light green	.25	.30
C30	A2	1½p violet brown	.50	.65
C31	A2	2p red	1.00	1.25
C32	A2	2½p dp green ('34)	2.00	2.50
C33	A2	3p gray blue	1.50	2.00
C34	A2	3½p magenta ('34)	2.00	2.50
C35	A2	4p olive green	2.25	2.75
C36	A2	5p slate green	3.75	5.00
C37	A2	6p bister	3.75	5.50

C38 A2 9p dull violet 4.25 6.00
C39 A2 1sh bluish gray 2.50 3.50
C40 A2 2sh red brown 8.00 13.00
C41 A2 5sh olive brown 19.00 25.00
C42 A2 10sh rose red 67.50 100.00
C43 A2 £1 gray 87.50 67.50
Nos. C28-C43 (16) 206.00 237.75

No. C28 exists without overprint, but is believed not to have been issued in this condition.

Plane over Bulolo Goldfield AP1

1935, May 1 Engr. Unwmk.

C44 AP1 £2 violet 175.00 150.00
C45 AP1 £5 green 650.00 300.00

AP2

1939, Mar. 1

C46 AP2 ½p orange 1.10 3.00
C47 AP2 1p green 1.75 1.75
C48 AP2 1½p vio brown .75 4.00
C49 AP2 2p red orange 3.50 2.50
C50 AP2 3p dark blue 4.25 11.00
C51 AP2 4p ol bister 3.00 8.00
C52 AP2 5p slate grn 2.75 2.50
C53 AP2 6p bister brn 7.00 10.00
C54 AP2 9p dl violet 7.00 17.00
C55 AP2 1sh sage green 8.00 14.00
C56 AP2 2sh car lake 27.50 35.00
C57 AP2 5sh ol brown 55.00 80.00
C58 AP2 10sh rose red 175.00 150.00
C59 AP2 £1 grnsh gray 60.00 90.00
Nos. C46-C59 (14) 356.60 428.75

OFFICIAL STAMPS

Regular Issue of 1925 Overprinted

1925-29 Unwmk. *Perf. 11*

O1 A1 1p yellow green .60 3.50
O2 A1 1½p vermilion ('29) 6.50 15.00
O3 A1 2p claret .90 3.25
O4 A1 3p deep blue 2.25 5.50
O5 A1 4p olive green 2.75 7.50
O6 A1 6p yel bister ('29) 5.75 35.00
a. 6p olive bister 5.75 35.00
O7 A1 9p deep violet 7.50 35.00
O8 A1 1sh gray green 11.00 35.00
O9 A1 2sh red brown 21.00 70.00
Nos. O1-O9 (9) 58.25 209.75

Nos. 18-28 Overprinted **O S**

1931, Aug. 2

O12 A2 1p light green 1.10 2.75
O13 A2 1½p red 1.50 4.50
O14 A2 2p violet brown 2.75 4.50
O15 A2 3p deep blue 3.25 6.50
O16 A2 4p olive green 4.50 8.25
O17 A2 5p slate green 4.50 10.00
O18 A2 6p bister 5.50 11.00
O19 A2 9p dull violet 6.50 16.00
O20 A2 1sh bluish gray 8.50 17.50
O21 A2 2sh red brown 22.50 45.00
O22 A2 5sh olive brown 100.00 150.00
Nos. O12-O22 (11) 160.60 276.00

10th anniversary of Australian Mandate.

Same Overprint on Nos. 31-43

1932-34

O23 A2 1p light green 2.50 2.75
O24 A2 1½p violet brown 2.50 10.00
O25 A2 2p red 2.50 2.25
O26 A2 2½p dp green ('34) 2.50 6.00
O27 A2 3p gray blue 5.00 15.00
O28 A2 3½p magenta ('34) 2.50 9.00
O29 A2 4p olive green 4.25 12.00
O30 A2 5p slate green 4.25 12.00
O31 A2 6p bister 5.00 25.00
O32 A2 9p dull violet 9.00 35.00
O33 A2 1sh bluish gray 13.00 25.00
O34 A2 2sh red brown 32.50 75.00
O35 A2 5sh olive brown 110.00 150.00
Nos. O23-O35 (13) 195.50 379.00

NEW HEBRIDES, BRITISH

'nü 'he-brə-,dēz

LOCATION — A group of islands in the South Pacific Ocean northeast of New Caledonia
GOVT. — Condominium under the joint administration of Great Britain and France
AREA — 5,790 sq. mi.
POP. — 100,000 (est. 1976)
CAPITAL — Vila (Port-Vila)

Stamps were issued by both Great Britain and France. In 1911 a joint issue bore the coats of arms of both countries. The British stamps bore the arms of Great Britain and the value in British currency on the right and the French arms and value at the left. On the French stamps the positions were reversed. After World War II when the franc dropped in value, both series were sold for their value in francs.

New Hebrides became the independent state of Vanuatu in 1980.

12 Pence = 1 Shilling
100 Centimes = 1 Franc
100 Centimes = 1 Hebrides Franc (FNH) (1977)

French issues (inscribed "Nouvelles Hebrides") follow after No. J20.

Catalogue values for unused stamps in this country are for Never Hinged items, beginning with Scott 62 in the regular postage section, Scott J11 in the postage due section.

British Issues

Stamps of Fiji, 1903-06, Overprinted

NEW HEBRIDES CONDOMINIUM.

1908-09 Wmk. 2 *Perf. 14*

Colored Bar Covers "FIJI" on #2-6, 9

1 A22 ½p gray green ('09) 47.50 47.50
2 A22 2p vio & orange 1.25 1.25
3 A22 2½p vio & ultra, *bl* 1.25 1.25
4 A22 5p vio & green 3.25 3.25
5 A22 6p vio & car rose 3.25 3.25
6 A22 1sh grn & car rose 150.00 200.00
Nos. 1-6 (6) 206.50 256.50

Wmk. Multiple Crown and CA (3)

7 A22 ½p gray green .75 5.00
8 A22 1p carmine .50 1.00
a. Pair, one without overprint 4,750.
9 A22 1sh grn & car rose ('09) 15.00 14.00
Nos. 7-9 (3) 16.25 20.00

Nos. 2-6, 9 are on chalk-surfaced paper.

Stamps of Fiji, 1904-11, Overprinted in Black or Red

NEW HEBRIDES CONDOMINIUM

1910, Dec. 15

10 A22 ½p green 3.50 15.00
11 A22 1p carmine 6.00 7.50
12 A22 2p gray 1.00 1.75
13 A22 2½p ultra 1.25 2.00
14 A22 5p violet & ol grn 1.65 3.50
15 A22 6p violet 2.50 5.00
16 A22 1sh black, *grn* (R) 3.50 6.50
Nos. 10-16 (7) 19.40 41.25

Nos. 14-16 are on chalk-surfaced paper.

Native Idols — A1

1911, July 25 Engr. Wmk. 3

17 A1 ½p pale green .60 1.00
18 A1 1p red 1.65 .80
19 A1 2p gray 3.50 2.75
20 A1 2½p ultramarine 2.25 2.75
21 A1 5p olive green 1.90 2.00
22 A1 6p claret 2.75 2.25
23 A1 1sh black, *green* 3.00 6.50
24 A1 2sh violet, *blue* 13.50 15.00
25 A1 5sh green, *yel* 27.50 40.00
Nos. 17-25 (9) 56.65 73.05

See Nos. 33-37. For surcharges see Nos. 26-29, 38-39, French Issues No. 36.

Surcharged **1d.**

1920-21

26 A1 1p on 5p ol green ('21) 14.00 32.50
a. Inverted surcharge 1,400.
27 A1 1p on 1sh black, *grn* 4.00 9.00
28 A1 1p on 2sh violet, *blue* 2.50 9.00
29 A1 1p on 5sh green, *yel* 2.50 9.00

On French Issue No. 16

30 A2 2p on 40c red, *yel* ('21) 2.25 9.00
Nos. 26-30 (5) 25.25 68.50

On French Issue No. 27

Wmk. R F in Sheet

31 A2 2p on 40c red, *yel* ('21) 165.00 350.00

The letters "R.F." are the initials of "Republique Francaise." They are large double-lined Roman capitals, about 120mm high. About one-fourth of the stamps in each sheet show portions of the watermark, the other stamps are without watermark.

No. 26a is considered by some to be printers' waste.

Type of 1911 Issue

1921, Oct. Wmk. 4

33 A1 1p rose red 3.00 8.00
34 A1 2p gray 4.00 10.00
37 A1 6p claret 9.25 25.00
Nos. 33-37 (3) 16.25 43.00

For surcharge see No. 40.

Stamps of 1911-21 Surcharged with New Values as in 1920-21

1924, May 1 Wmk. 3

38 A1 1p on ½p pale green 1.75 6.00
39 A1 5p on 2½p ultra 4.50 5.00
a. Inverted surcharge 1,200.

Wmk. 4

40 A1 3p on 1p rose red 4.00 9.00
Nos. 38-40 (3) 10.25 20.00

No. 39a is considered by some to be printers' waste.

A3

The values at the lower right denote the currency and amount for which the stamps were to be sold. The English stamps could be bought at the French post office in French money.

1925 Engr.

41 A3 ½p (5c) black .50 2.00
42 A3 1p (10c) green .60 2.00
43 A3 2p (20c) grnsh gray .65 1.75
44 A3 2½p (25c) brown 1.00 2.00
45 A3 5p (50c) ultra 2.00 3.00
46 A3 6p (60c) claret 2.50 7.50
47 A3 1sh (1.25fr) black, *grn* 2.50 9.00
48 A3 2sh (2.50fr) vio, *bl* 6.50 12.50
49 A3 5sh (6.25fr) grn, *yel* 8.00 17.50
Nos. 41-49 (9) 24.25 57.25

Beach Scene — A5

1938, June 1 Wmk. 4 *Perf. 12*

50 A5 5c green 1.25 .80
51 A5 10c dark orange .90 1.00
52 A5 15c violet 1.25 1.00
53 A5 20c rose red 1.10 1.30
54 A5 25c brown 1.10 1.30
55 A5 30c dark blue 1.25 1.65
56 A5 40c olive green 3.50 2.50
57 A5 50c brown vio 1.65 2.50
58 A5 1fr car, *emerald* 4.25 5.75
59 A5 2fr dk blue, *emer* 21.50 12.00
60 A5 5fr red, *yellow* 55.00 45.00
61 A5 10fr violet, *blue* 95.00 75.00
Nos. 50-61 (12) 187.75 149.80

Catalogue values for unused stamps in this section, from this point to the end of the section, are for Never Hinged items.

UPU Issue
Common Design Type

1949, Oct. 10 Engr. *Perf. 13½*

62 CD309 10c red orange .40 .40
63 CD309 15c violet .40 .40
64 CD309 30c violet blue .75 .50
65 CD309 50c rose violet 1.25 1.00
Nos. 62-65 (4) 2.80 2.30

Outrigger Canoes with Sails — A6

Designs: 25c, 30c, 40c and 50c, Native Carving. 1fr, 2fr and 5fr, Island couple.

1953, Apr. 30 *Perf. 12½*

66 A6 5c green .20 .20
67 A6 10c red .20 .15
68 A6 15c yellow .30 .20
69 A6 20c ultramarine .30 .30
70 A6 25c olive .50 .40
71 A6 30c light brown .60 .50
72 A6 40c black brown .90 .80
73 A6 50c violet 1.00 .90
74 A6 1fr deep orange 2.00 1.75
75 A6 2fr red violet 6.00 10.00
76 A6 5fr scarlet 15.00 18.00
Nos. 66-76 (11) 27.00 33.20

Coronation Issue
Common Design Type

1953, June 2 *Perf. 13½x13*

77 CD312 10c car & black .75 .75

Discovery of New Hebrides, 1606 — A7

20c, 50c, Britannia, Marianne, Flags & Mask.

Perf. 14½x14

1956, Oct. 20 Photo. Wmk. 4

78 A7 5c emerald .15 .15
79 A7 10c crimson .15 .15
80 A7 20c ultramarine .25 .25
81 A7 50c purple .65 .65
Nos. 78-81 (4) 1.20 1.20

50th anniv. of the establishment of the Anglo-French Condominium.

Port Vila and Iririki Islet — A8

Designs: 25c, 30c, 40c, 50c, Tropical river and spear fisherman. 1fr, 2fr, 5fr, Woman drinking from coconut (inscribed: "Franco-British Alliance 4th March 1947").

1957, Sept. 3 Engr. *Perf. 13½x13*

82 A8 5c green .15 .15
83 A8 10c red .15 .15
84 A8 15c orange yellow .25 .15
85 A8 20c ultramarine .30 .20
86 A8 25c olive .35 .25
87 A8 30c light brown .45 .40
88 A8 40c sepia .70 .50
89 A8 50c violet .95 .65
90 A8 1fr orange 1.90 1.25
91 A8 2fr rose lilac 5.50 2.50
92 A8 5fr black 12.00 5.50
Nos. 82-92 (11) 22.70 11.70

Freedom from Hunger Issue
Common Design Type

Perf. 14x14½

1963, Sept. 2 Photo. Wmk. 314

93 CD314 60c green 1.00 .70

Red Cross Centenary Issue
Common Design Type with Royal Cipher and "RF" Replacing Queen's Portrait

1963, Sept. 2 Litho. *Perf. 13*

94 CD315 15c black & red .35 .20
95 CD315 45c ultra & red .90 .70

Copra Industry — A9

Designs: 5c, Manganese loading, Forari Wharf. 10c, Cacao. 20c, Map of New Hebrides, tuna, marlin, ships. 25c, Striped triggerfish. 30c, Pearly nautilus (mollusk). 40c, 60c, Turkeyfish. 50c, Lined tang (fish). 1fr, Cardinal honey-eater and hibiscus. 2fr, Buff-bellied flycatcher. 3fr, Thicket warbler. 5fr, White-collared kingfisher.

Wmk. 314 (10c, 20c, 40c, 60c, 3fr); Unwmkd. (others)
Perf. 12½ (10c, 20c, 40c, 60c); 14 (3fr); 13 (others)
Photo. (10c, 20c, 40c, 60c, 3fr); Engraved (others)

1963-67

96 A9 5c Prus bl & cl ('66) .20 .15
97 A9 10c brt grn, org brn & dk brn ('65) .20 .15
98 A9 15c dk pur, yel & brn .25 .25
99 A9 20c brt blue, gray & cit ('65) .30 .25
100 A9 25c vio, rose lil & org brn ('66) .55 .50
101 A9 30c lilac, brn & cit .80 .75
102 A9 40c dk bl & ver ('65) 1.10 1.10
103 A9 50c Prus bl, yel & green .90 .80
103A A9 60c dk bl & ver ('67) 1.50 1.25
104 A9 1fr blue grn, blk & red ('66) 2.25 2.25
105 A9 2fr ol, blk & brn 3.25 3.00
106 A9 3fr org grn, brt grn & blk ('65) 8.50 7.50
107 A9 5fr indigo, dp bl & gray ('67) 16.00 15.00
Nos. 96-107 (13) 35.80 32.95

For surcharge see No. 141.

ITU Emblem CD317

Perf. 11x11½

1965, May 17 Litho. Wmk. 314

108 CD317 15c ver & ol bister .20 .15
109 CD317 60c ultra & ver .80 .60

Cent. of the ITU.

Intl. Cooperation Year Issue
Common Design Type with Royal Cipher and "RF" Replacing Queen's Portrait

1965, Sept. 24 *Perf. 14½*

110 CD318 5c blue grn & claret .15 .15
111 CD318 55c lt violet & green .65 .65

Churchill Memorial Issue
Common Design Type with Royal Cipher and "RF" Replacing Queen's Portrait

1966, Jan. 24 Photo. *Perf. 14*

112 CD319 5c multicolored .15 .15
113 CD319 15c multicolored .30 .20
114 CD319 25c multicolored .65 .35
115 CD319 30c multicolored .95 .65
Nos. 112-115 (4) 2.05 1.35

World Cup Soccer Issue
Common Design Type with Royal Cipher and "RF" Replacing Queen's Portrait

1966, July 1 Litho. *Perf. 14*

116 CD321 20c multicolored .30 .30
117 CD321 40c multicolored .70 .70

WHO Headquarters Issue
Common Design Type with Royal Cipher and "RF" Replacing Queen's Portrait

1966, Sept. 20 Litho. *Perf. 14*

118 CD322 25c multicolored .25 .25
119 CD322 60c multicolored .65 .65

UNESCO Anniversary Issue
Common Design Type with Royal Cipher and "RF" Replacing Queen's Portrait

1966, Dec. 1 Litho. *Perf. 14*

120 CD323 15c "Education" .25 .25
121 CD323 30c "Science" .50 .50
122 CD323 45c "Culture" .80 .80
Nos. 120-122 (3) 1.55 1.55

Coast Watchers — A11

Designs: 25c, Map of South Pacific war zone, US Marine and Australian soldier. 60c, Australian cruiser Canberra. 1fr, Flying fortress taking off from Bauer Field, and view of Vila.

Perf. 14x13

1967, Sept. 26 Photo. Wmk. 314

123 A11 15c lt blue & multi .15 .15
124 A11 25c yellow & multi .35 .35
125 A11 60c multicolored .80 .80
126 A11 1fr pale salmon & multi 1.40 1.40
Nos. 123-126 (4) 2.70 2.70

25th anniv. of the Allied Forces' campaign in the South Pacific War Zone.

Globe and World Map — A12

Designs: 25c, Ships La Boudeuse and L'Etoile and map of Bougainville Strait. 60c, Louis Antoine de Bougainville, ship's figurehead and bougainvillaea.

1968, May 23 Engr. *Perf. 13*

127 A12 15c ver, emer & dull vio .15 .15
128 A12 25c ultra, olive & brn .30 .30
129 A12 60c magenta, grn & brn .55 .55
Nos. 127-129 (3) 1.00 1.00

200th anniv. of Louis Antoine de Bougainville's (1729-1811) voyage around the world.

Concorde Airliner A13

Design: 60c, Concorde, sideview.

1968, Oct. 9 Litho. *Perf. 14x13½*

130 A13 25c vio bl, red & lt bl 1.10 .75
131 A13 60c red, ultra & black 1.90 1.25

Development of the Concorde supersonic airliner, a joint Anglo-French project to produce a high speed plane.

Kauri Pine — A14

Perf. 14x14½

1969, June 30 Wmk. 314

132 A14 20c brown & multi .25 .25

New Hebrides timber industry. Issued in sheets of 9 (3x3) on simulated wood grain background.

Relay Race, French and British Flags — A15

Design: 1fr, Runner at right.

Perf. 12½x13

1969, Aug. 13 Photo. Unwmk.

133 A15 25c ultra, car, brn & gold .20 .20
134 A15 1fr brn, car, ultra & gold .90 .90

3rd South Pacific Games, Port Moresby, Papua and New Guinea, Aug. 13-23.

Land Diver, Pentecost Island — A16

Designs: 15c, Diver in starting position on tower. 1fr, Diver nearing ground.

Perf. 12½

1969, Oct. 15 Wmk. 314 Litho.

135 A16 15c yellow & multi .15 .15
136 A16 25c pink & multi .30 .30
137 A16 1fr gray & multi 1.10 1.10
Nos. 135-137 (3) 1.55 1.55

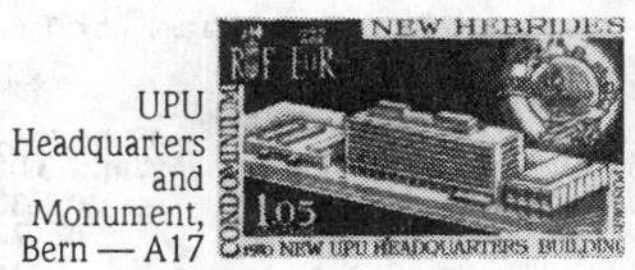

UPU Headquarters and Monument, Bern — A17

Unwmk.

1970, May 20 Engr. *Perf. 13*

138 A17 1.05fr org, lilac & slate .95 .95

Opening of the new UPU Headquarters, Bern.

Charles de Gaulle — A18

1970, July 20 Photo. *Perf. 13*

139 A18 65c brown & multi .65 .65
140 A18 1.10fr dp blue & multi 1.40 1.40

30th anniv. of the rallying to the Free French.
For overprints see Nos. 144-145.

No. 99 Surcharged

1970, Oct. 15 Wmk. 314 *Perf. 12½*

141 A9 35c on 20c multi .60 .60

Virgin and Child, by Giovanni Bellini — A19

Christmas: 50c, Virgin and Child, by Giovanni Cima.

Perf. 14½x14

1970, Nov. 30 Litho. Wmk. 314

142 A19 15c tan & multi .15 .15
143 A19 50c lt green & multi .45 .45

Nos. 139-140 Overprinted with 2 Black Vertical Bars and Gold Inscription: "1890-1970 / IN MEMORIAM / 9-11-70"

Unwmk.

1971, Jan. 19 Photo. *Perf. 13*

144 A18 65c brown & multi .60 .60
145 A18 1.10fr dp blue & multi 1.10 1.10

In memory of Gen. Charles de Gaulle (1890-1970), President of France.

Soccer A20

Design: 65c, Basketball, vert.

1971, July 13 Photo. *Perf. 12½*

146 A20 20c multicolored .20 .20
147 A20 65c multicolored .60 .60

4th South Pacific Games, Papeete, French Polynesia, Sept. 8-19.

Kauri Pine, Cone and Arms of Royal Society — A21

Perf. 14½x14

1971, Sept. 7 Litho. Wmk. 314

148 A21 65c multicolored .75 .75

Royal Society of London for the Advancement of Science expedition to study vegetation and fauna, July 1-October.

Adoration of the Shepherds, by Louis Le Nain — A22

Design: 50c, Adoration of the Shepherds, by Jacopo Tintoretto.

1971, Nov. 23 *Perf. 14x13½*

149 A22 25c lt green & multi .25 .25
150 A22 50c lt blue & multi .60 .60

Christmas. See Nos. 167-168.

Drover Mk III A23

Airplanes: 25c, Sandringham seaplane. 30c, Dragon Rapide. 65c, Caravelle.

Perf. 13½x13

1972, Feb. 29 Photo. Unwmk.

151 A23	20c lt green & multi		.35	.35
152 A23	25c ultra & multi		.40	.40
153 A23	30c orange & multi		.60	.60
154 A23	65c dk blue & multi		1.40	1.40
	Nos. 151-154 (4)		2.75	2.75

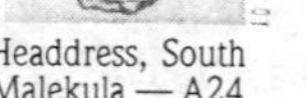

Headdress, South Malekula — A24

Baker's Pigeon — A25

Artifacts: 15c, Slit gong and carved figure, North Ambrym. 1fr, Carved figures, North Ambrym. 3fr, Ceremonial headdress, South Malekula.

Birds: 20c, Red-headed parrot-finch. 35c, Chestnut-bellied kingfisher. 2fr, Green palm lorikeet.

Sea shells: 25c, Cribraria fischeri. 30c, Oliva rubrolabiata. 65c, Strombus plicatus. 5fr, Turbo marmoratus.

1972, July 24 Photo. *Perf. 12½x13*

155 A24	5c plum & multi	.15	.15
156 A25	10c blue & multi	.15	.20
157 A24	15c red & multi	.30	.35
158 A25	20c org brown & multi	.40	.45
159 A24	25c dp blue & multi	.55	.70
160 A24	30c dk green & multi	.70	.75
161 A25	35c gray bl & multi	.80	.90
162 A24	65c dk green & multi	1.40	3.00
163 A24	1fr orange & multi	2.25	2.50
164 A25	2fr multicolored	4.00	3.75
165 A24	3fr yellow & multi	6.00	5.50
166 A24	5fr pink & multi	10.00	11.00
	Nos. 155-166 (12)	26.70	29.25

For overprints and surcharges see #181-182, 217-228.

Christmas Type of 1971

Designs: 25c, Adoration of the Magi (detail), by Bartholomaeus Spranger. 70c, Virgin and Child, by Jan Provoost.

Perf. 14x13½

1972, Sept. 25 Litho. Wmk. 314

167 A22	25c lt green & multi	.20	.20
168 A22	70c lt blue & multi	.60	.60

Silver Wedding Issue, 1972

Common Design Type

Design: Elizabeth II and Prince Philip.

1972, Nov. 20 Photo. *Perf. 14x14½*

169 CD324	35c vio black & multi	.20	.20
170 CD324	65c olive & multi	.40	.40

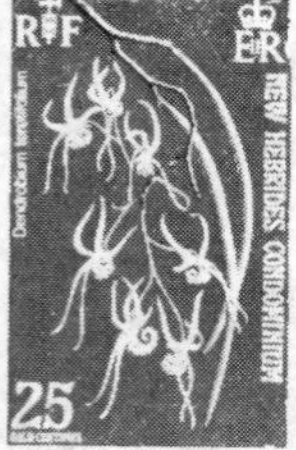

Dendrobium Teretifolium A26

New Wharf, Vila A27

Orchids: 30c, Ephemerantha comata. 35c, Spathoglottis petri. 65c, Dendrobium mohlianum.

1973, Feb. 26 Litho. *Perf. 14*

171 A26	25c blue vio & multi	.45	.35
172 A26	30c multicolored	.55	.45
173 A26	35c violet & multi	.65	.55
174 A26	65c dk green & multi	1.40	1.10
	Nos. 171-174 (4)	3.05	2.45

1973, May 14 Wmk. 314

Design: 70c, New wharf, horiz.

175 A27	25c multicolored	.15	.15
176 A27	70c multicolored	.55	.55

New wharf at Vila, finished Nov. 1972.

Wild Horses, Tanna Island — A28

Perf. 13x12½

1973, Aug. 13 Photo. Unwmk.

177 A28	35c shown	.45	.45
178 A28	70c Yasur Volcano, Tanna	1.50	1.25

Mother and Child, by Marcel Moutouh — A29

Christmas: 70c, Star over Lagoon, by Tatin d'Avesnieres.

Perf. 14x13½

1973, Nov. 19 Litho. Wmk. 314

179 A29	35c tan & multi	.30	.30
180 A29	70c lilac rose & multi	.70	.70

Nos. 161 and 164 Overprinted in Red or Black: "ROYAL VISIT / 1974"

Perf. 12½x13

1974, Feb. 11 Photo. Unwmk.

181 A25	35c multicolored (R)	.20	.20
182 A25	2fr multicolored (B)	1.25	1.25

Visit of British Royal Family, Feb. 11-12.

Pacific Dove — A30

Designs: 35c, Night swallowtail. 70c, Green sea turtle. 1.15fr, Flying fox.

1974, Feb. 11 *Perf. 13x12½*

183 A30	25c gray & multi	.85	.60
184 A30	35c gray & multi	1.25	.85
185 A30	70c gray & multi	2.25	1.65
186 A30	1.15fr gray & multi	2.50	2.25
	Nos. 183-186 (4)	6.85	5.35

Nature conservation.

Old Post Office, Vila — A31

Design: 70c, New Post Office.

1974, May 6 Unwmk. *Perf. 12*

187 A31	35c blue & multi	.40	.40
188 A31	70c red & multi	.80	.80
a.	Pair, #187-188	1.25	1.25

Opening of New Post Office, May, 1974.

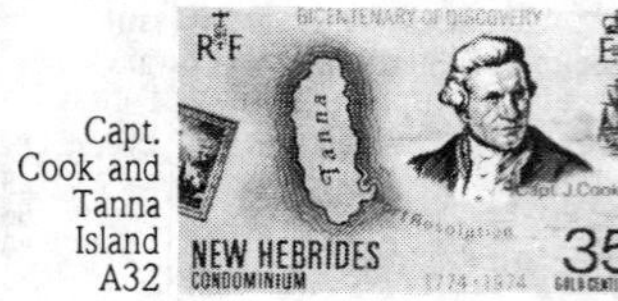

Capt. Cook and Tanna Island A32

Designs: No. 190, William Wales, and boat landing on island. No. 191, William Hodges painting islanders and landscape. 1.15fr, Capt. Cook, "Resolution" and map of New Hebrides.

Wmk. 314

1974, Aug. 1 Litho. *Perf. 13*

Size: 40x25mm

189 A32	35c multicolored	1.65	.75
190 A32	35c multicolored	1.65	.75
191 A32	35c multicolored	1.65	.75
a.	Strip of 3, #189-191	5.00	3.00

Perf. 11

Size: 58x34mm

192 A32	1.15fr lilac & multi	3.50	3.00
	Nos. 189-192 (4)	8.45	5.25

Bicentenary of the discovery of the New Hebrides by Capt. Cook. No. 191a has continuous design.

Exchange of Letters, UPU Emblem A33

Perf. 13x12½

1974, Oct. 9 Photo. Unwmk.

193 A33	70c multicolored	.50	.50

Centenary of Universal Postal Union.

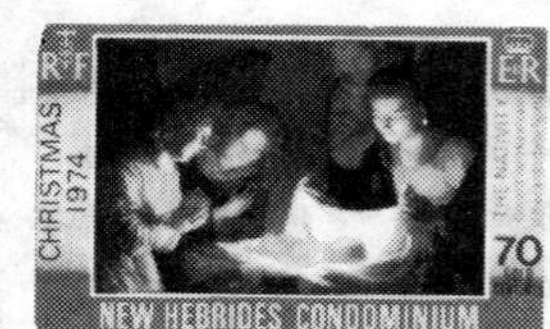

Nativity, by Gerard van Honthorst — A34

Christmas: 35c, Adoration of the Kings, by Velazquez, vert.

Perf. 13½

1974, Nov. 14 Litho. Wmk. 314

194 A34	35c multicolored	.30	.30
195 A34	70c multicolored	.60	.60

Charolais Bull — A35

1975, Apr. 29 Engr. *Perf. 13*

196 A35	10fr multicolored	10.00	12.00

For surcharge see No. 229.

A36

A37

1975, Aug. 5 Litho. *Perf. 14x13½*

197 A36	25c Kayak race	.15	.15
198 A36	35c Camp cooks	.25	.25
199 A36	1fr Map makers	.65	.65
200 A36	5fr Fishermen	5.25	5.00
	Nos. 197-200 (4)	6.30	6.05

Nordjamb 75, 14th Boy Scout Jamboree, Lillehammer, Norway, July 29-Aug. 7.

Perf. 14½x14

1975, Nov. 11 Litho. Wmk. 373

Christmas (After Michelangelo): 35c, Pitti Madonna. 70c, Bruges Madonna. 2.50fr, Taddei Madonna.

201 A37	35c ol green & multi	.20	.20
202 A37	70c brown & multi	.45	.45
203 A37	2.50fr blue & multi	1.50	1.50
	Nos. 201-203 (3)	2.15	2.15

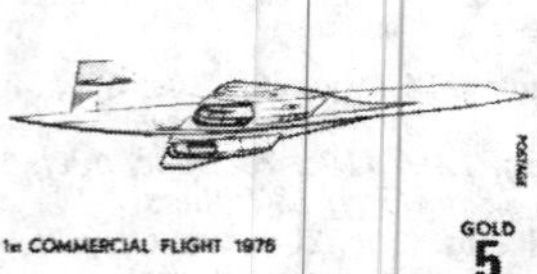

Concorde, British Airways Colors and Emblem — A38

Unwmk.

1976, Jan. 30 Typo. *Perf. 13*

204 A38	5fr blue & multi	11.00	8.50

First commercial flight of supersonic jet Concorde from London to Bahrain, Jan. 21.

Telephones, 1876 and 1976 — A39

Designs: 70c, Alexander Graham Bell. 1.15fr, Nouméa earth station and satellite.

1976, Mar. 31 Photo. *Perf. 13*

205 A39	25c black, car & blue	.15	.15
206 A39	70c black & multi	.40	.40
207 A39	1.15fr black, org & vio bl	.75	.75
	Nos. 205-207 (3)	1.30	1.30

Centenary of first telephone call by Alexander Graham Bell, Mar. 10, 1876.

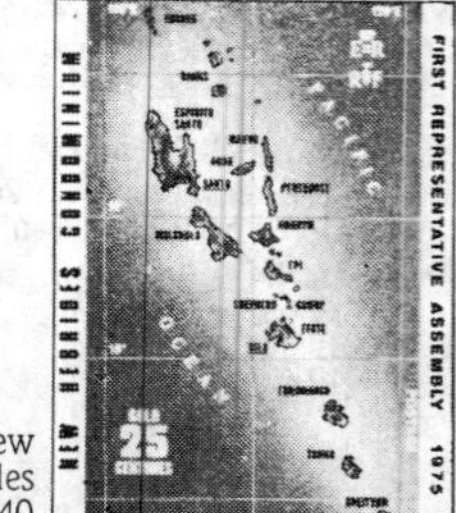

Map of New Hebrides A40

View of Santo — A41

Design: 2fr, View of Vila.

1976, June 29 Photo. *Perf. 13*

208 A40	25c blue & multi	.15	.15
209 A41	1fr multicolored	.55	.55
210 A41	2fr multicolored	1.25	1.25
	Nos. 208-210 (3)	1.95	1.95

Opening of First Representative Assembly, June 29 (25c); first Santo Municipal Council (1fr); first Vila Municipal Council (2fr).

Flight into Egypt, by Francisco Vieira Lusitano — A42

Christmas (Portuguese 16th Cent. Paintings): 70c, Adoration of the Shepherds. 2.50fr, Adoration of the Kings.

Wmk. 373

1976, Nov. 8 Litho. *Perf. 14*

211 A42 35c purple & multi .20 .20
212 A42 70c blue & multi .40 .40
213 A42 2.50fr lt green & multi 1.40 1.40
Nos. 211-213 (3) 2.00 2.00

Queen's Visit, 1974 — A43

70c, Imperial state crown. 2fr, The blessing.

1977, Feb. 7 *Perf. 14x13½*

214 A43 35c lt green & multi .15 .15
215 A43 70c blue & multi .30 .30
216 A43 2fr pink & multi .80 .80
Nos. 214-216 (3) 1.25 1.25

25th anniv. of the reign of Elizabeth II.

Nos. 155-166, 196 Surcharged with New Value, "FNH" and Bars

Perf. 12½x13

1977, July 1 Photo. Unwmk.

217 A24 5fr on 5c multi .15 .15
218 A25 10fr on 10c multi .30 .30
219 A24 15fr on 15c multi .45 .45
220 A25 20fr on 20c multi .55 .55
221 A24 25fr on 25c multi .70 .70
222 A24 30fr on 30c multi .90 .90
223 A25 35fr on 35c multi 1.10 1.10
224 A24 40fr on 65c multi 1.25 1.25
225 A24 50fr on 1fr multi 2.00 2.00
226 A25 70fr on 2fr multi 3.50 3.50
227 A24 100fr on 3fr multi 5.00 5.00
228 A24 200fr on 5fr multi 6.50 6.50

Wmk. 314

Engr. *Perf. 13*

229 A35 500fr on 10fr multi 14.00 14.00
Nos. 217-229 (13) 36.40 36.40

Nos. 217-229 were surcharged in Paris. Eleven denominations were surcharged later in Vila with slightly larger, different letters and different bars; nine were sold at post offices.

Erromango and Kaori Tree — A44

Tempi Madonna, by Raphael — A45

Designs: 10fr, Archipelago and man making copra. 15fr, Espiritu Santo Island and cattle. 20fr, Efate Island and Post Office, Vila. 25fr, Malakula Island and headdresses. 30fr, Aoba and Maewo Islands and pig tusks. 35fr, Pentecost Island and land diving. 40fr, Tanna Island and Prophet John Frum's Red Cross. 50fr, Shepherd Island and canoe with sail. 70fr, Banks Island and dancers. 100fr, Ambrym Island and carvings. 200fr, Aneityum Island and decorated baskets. 500fr, Torres Islands and fishing with bow and arrow.

1977-78 Wmk. 373 Litho. *Perf. 14*

238 A44 5fr multicolored .15 .15
239 A44 10fr multicolored .15 .15
240 A44 15fr multicolored .20 .20
241 A44 20fr multicolored .25 .25
242 A44 25fr multicolored .35 .35
243 A44 30fr multicolored .45 .45
244 A44 35fr multicolored .50 .50
245 A44 40fr multicolored .55 .55
246 A44 50fr multicolored .65 .65
247 A44 70fr multicolored 1.00 1.00
248 A44 100fr multicolored 1.50 1.50
249 A44 200fr multicolored 3.25 3.25
250 A44 500fr multicolored 7.00 7.00
Nos. 238-250 (13) 16.00 16.00

Issue dates: 5fr, 20fr, 50fr, 100fr, 200fr, Sept. 7; 15fr, 25fr, 30fr, 40fr, Nov. 23, 1977; 10fr, 35fr, 70fr, 500fr, May 9, 1978.

1977, Dec. 8 Litho. *Perf. 12*

Christmas: 15fr, Virgin and Child, by Gerard David. 30fr, Virgin and Child, by Pompeo Batoni.

251 A45 10fr multicolored .20 .20
252 A45 15fr multicolored .25 .25
253 A45 30fr multicolored .55 .55
Nos. 251-253 (3) 1.00 1.00

British Airways Concorde over New York City — A46

Designs: 20fr, British Airways Concorde over London. 30fr, Air France Concorde over Washington. 40fr, Air France Concorde over Paris.

1978, May 9 Wmk. 373 *Perf. 14*

254 A46 10fr multicolored .50 .20
255 A46 20fr multicolored .75 .40
256 A46 30fr multicolored 1.25 .60
257 A46 40fr multicolored 1.50 .80
Nos. 254-257 (4) 4.00 2.00

Concorde, 1st commercial flight, Paris to NYC.

Elizabeth II Coronation Anniversary Issue

Common Design Types

Souvenir Sheet

1978, June 2 Unwmk. *Perf. 15*

258 Sheet of 6 4.50 4.50
a. CD326 40fr White horse of Hanover .70 .70
b. CD327 40fr Elizabeth II .70 .70
c. CD328 40fr Gallic cock .70 .70

No. 258 contains 2 se-tenant strips of Nos. 258a-258c, separated by horizontal gutter with commemorative and descriptive inscriptions and showing central part of coronation procession with coach.

Virgin and Child, by Dürer — A47

Dürer Paintings: 15fr, Virgin and Child with St. Anne. 30fr, Virgin and Child with Goldfinch. 40fr, Virgin and Child with Pear.

Perf. 14x13½

1978, Dec. 1 Litho. Wmk. 373

259 A47 10fr multicolored .20 .20
260 A47 15fr multicolored .25 .25
261 A47 30fr multicolored .50 .50
262 A47 40fr multicolored .80 .80
Nos. 259-262 (4) 1.75 1.75

Christmas and 450th death anniv. of Albrecht Dürer (1471-1528), German painter.

Type of 1976 Surcharged with New Value, Bars over Denomination and Inscription at Right. Longitude changed to "166E."

1979, Jan. 11 Photo. *Perf. 13*

263 A40 10fr on 25c bl & multi .20 .20
264 A40 40fr on 25c lt grn & multi .80 .80

1st anniv. of Internal Self-Government.

New Hebrides No. 50 — A48

Rowland Hill and New Hebrides Stamps: 20fr, No. 136. 40fr, No. 43.

1979, Sept. 10 Litho. *Perf. 14*

265 A48 10fr multicolored .15 .15
266 A48 20fr multicolored .25 .25
a. Souvenir sheet of 2 .60 .60
267 A48 40fr multicolored .60 .60
Nos. 265-267 (3) 1.00 1.00

Sir Rowland Hill (1795-1879), originator of penny postage. No. 266a contains New Hebrides, British, No. 266, and French, No. 286; margin shows Mulready envelope.

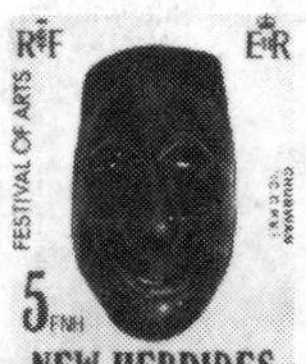

Arts Festival — A49

Designs: 10fr, Clubs and spears. 20fr, Ritual puppet. 40fr, Headdress.

1979, Nov. 16 Wmk. 373 *Perf. 14*

268 A49 5fr multicolored .15 .15
269 A49 10fr multicolored .15 .15
270 A49 20fr multicolored .30 .30
271 A49 40fr multicolored .50 .50
Nos. 268-271 (4) 1.10 1.10

Church, IYC Emblem A50

IYC Emblem, Children's Drawings: 10fr, Father Christmas. 20fr, Cross and Bible, vert. 40fr, Stars, candle and Santa Claus, vert.

1979, Dec. 4 *Perf. 13x13½*

272 A50 5fr multicolored .15 .15
273 A50 10fr multicolored .15 .15
274 A50 20fr multicolored .30 .30
275 A50 40fr multicolored .45 .45
Nos. 272-275 (4) 1.05 1.05

Christmas; Intl. Year of the Child.

White-bellied Honeyeater — A51

1980, Feb. 27 Litho. *Perf. 14*

276 A51 10fr shown .45 .20
277 A51 20fr Scarlet robins .65 .40
278 A51 30fr Yellow white-eyes 1.00 .55
279 A51 40fr Fan-tailed brush cuckoo 1.25 .75
Nos. 276-279 (4) 3.35 1.90

New Hebrides stamps were replaced in 1980 by these of Vanuatu.

POSTAGE DUE STAMPS

British Issues

Type of 1925 Overprinted **POSTAGE DUE**

1925, June Engr. Wmk. 4 *Perf. 14*

J1 A3 1p (10c) green 37.50 1.50
J2 A3 2p (10c) gray 45.00 1.75
J3 A3 3p (30c) carmine 50.00 1.75
J4 A3 5p (50c) ultra 55.00 4.00
J5 A3 10p (1fr) car, *blue* 67.50 5.00
Nos. J1-J5 (5) 255.00 14.00

Values for Nos. J1-J5 are for toned copies.

Regular Stamps of 1938 Overprinted in Black **POSTAGE DUE**

1938, June 1 *Perf. 12*

J6 A5 5c green 9.50 *27.50*
J7 A5 10c dark orange 10.00 *27.50*
J8 A5 20c rose red 11.00 *35.00*
J9 A5 40c olive green 15.00 *45.00*
J10 A5 1fr car, *emerald* 30.00 *62.50*
Nos. J6-J10 (5) 75.50 *197.50*

Catalogue values for unused stamps in this section, from this point to the end of the section, are for Never Hinged items.

Regular Stamps of 1953 Overprinted in Black **POSTAGE DUE.**

1953, Apr. 30 *Perf. 12½*

J11 A6 5c green 1.25 *3.25*
J12 A6 10c red 1.50 *4.50*
J13 A6 20c ultramarine 4.00 *10.00*
J14 A6 40c black brown 8.50 *25.00*
J15 A6 1fr deep orange 10.00 *30.00*
Nos. J11-J15 (5) 25.25 *72.75*

Same on Nos. 82-83, 85, 88 and 90

1957, Sept. 3 *Perf. 13½x13*

J16 A8 5c green .20 *.50*
J17 A8 10c red .35 *.90*
J18 A8 20c ultramarine .80 *1.25*
J19 A8 40c sepia 2.25 *2.75*
J20 A8 1fr orange 4.25 *6.50*
Nos. J16-J20 (5) 7.85 *11.90*

NEW HEBRIDES, FRENCH

'nü 'he–brə–ˌdēz

LOCATION — A group of islands in the South Pacific Ocean lying north of New Caledonia
GOVT. — Condominium under the joint administration of Great Britain and France
AREA — 5,790 sq. mi.
POP. — 100,000 (est. 1976)
CAPITAL — Port-Vila (Vila)

Postage stamps are issued by both Great Britain and France. In 1911 a joint issue was made bearing the coats of arms of both countries. The British stamps bore the coat of arms of Great Britain and the value in British currency on the right and the French coat of arms and values at the left. On the French stamps the positions were reversed. This resulted in some confusion when the value of the French franc decreased following World War I but the situation was corrected by arranging that both series of stamps be sold for their value as expressed in French currency.

12 Pence = 1 Shilling
100 Centimes = 1 Franc
New Hebrides Franc (FNH) — 1977

Catalogue values for unused stamps in this country are for Never Hinged items, beginning with Scott 79 in the regular postage section, Scott J16 in the postage due section.

French Issues

Stamps of New Caledonia, 1905, Overprinted in Black or Red

NOUVELLES

HÉBRIDES

Nos. 1-4

NOUVELLES-HEBRIDES

No. 5

1908 Unwmk. *Perf. 14x13½*

1 A16 5c green 2.50 2.50
2 A16 10c rose 3.00 3.00
3 A17 25c blue, *grnsh* (R) 4.00 4.00

No.	Type	Description	Unused	Used
4	A17	50c carmine, org	5.00	5.00
5	A18	1fr bl, yel grn (R)	10.00	10.00
		Nos. 1-5 (5)	24.50	24.50

For overprints and surcharges see #6-10, 33-35.

Stamps of 1908 with Additional Overprint **CONDOMINIUM**

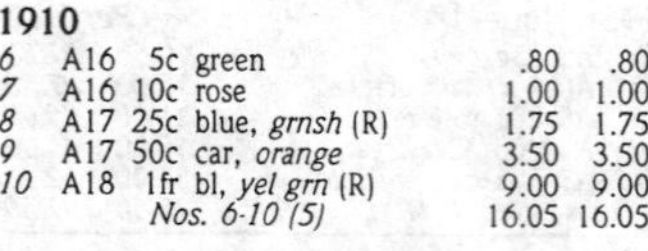

1910

No.	Type	Description	Unused	Used
6	A16	5c green	.80	.80
7	A16	10c rose	1.00	1.00
8	A17	25c blue, grnsh (R)	1.75	1.75
9	A17	50c car, orange	3.50	3.50
10	A18	1fr bl, yel grn (R)	9.00	9.00
		Nos. 6-10 (5)	16.05	16.05

A2

Wmk. 3

1911, July 12 Engr. Perf. 14

No.	Type	Description	Unused	Used
11	A2	5c pale green	.40	.40
12	A2	10c red	.40	.40
13	A2	20c gray	1.65	1.65
14	A2	25c ultramarine	2.00	2.00
15	A2	30c vio, yellow	3.00	3.00
16	A2	40c red, yellow	3.00	3.00
17	A2	50c olive green	3.00	3.00
18	A2	75c brn orange	4.00	4.00
19	A2	1fr brn red, bl	2.25	2.25
20	A2	2fr violet	5.00	5.00
21	A2	5fr brn red, grn	10.00	10.00
		Nos. 11-21 (11)	34.70	34.70

For surcharges see Nos. 36-37, 43 and British issue No. 30.

1912 Wmk. R F in Sheet

No.	Type	Description	Unused	Used
22	A2	5c pale green	1.25	1.25
23	A2	10c red	1.25	1.25
24	A2	20c gray	1.65	1.65
25	A2	25c ultramarine	1.65	1.65
26	A2	30c vio, yellow	1.75	1.75
27	A2	40c red, yellow	15.00	15.00
28	A2	50c olive green	7.00	7.00
29	A2	75c brn orange	7.00	7.00
30	A2	1fr brn red, bl	3.50	3.50
31	A2	2fr violet	7.00	7.00
32	A2	5fr brn red, grn	12.00	12.00
		Nos. 22-32 (11)	59.05	59.05

In the watermark, "R F" (République Française initials) are large double-lined Roman capitals, about 120mm high. About one-fourth of the stamps in each sheet show parts of the watermark. The other stamps are without watermark.

For surcharges see Nos. 38-42 and British issue No. 31.

Nos. 9 and 8 Surcharged **5c.**

1920 Unwmk. Perf. 14x13½

No.	Type	Description	Unused	Used
33	A17	5c on 50c red, org	2.00	2.00
34	A17	10c on 25c bl, grnsh	1.00	1.00

Same Surcharge on No. 4

No.	Type	Description	Unused	Used
35	A17	5c on 50c red, org	800.00	950.00

British Issue No. 21 and French Issue No. 15 Surcharged **10c.**

1921 Wmk. 3 Perf. 14

No.	Type	Description	Unused	Used
36	A1	10c on 5p ol grn	7.50	7.50
37	A2	20c on 30c vio, yel	10.00	10.00

Nos. 27 and 26 Surcharged **05c.**

1921 Wmk. R F in Sheet

No.	Type	Description	Unused	Used
38	A2	5c on 40c red, yel	20.00	20.00
39	A2	20c on 30c vio, yel	10.00	10.00

Stamps of 1910-12 Surcharged with New Values as in 1920-21

1924

No.	Type	Description	Unused	Used
40	A2	10c on 5c pale grn	1.00	1.00
41	A2	30c on 10c red	1.00	1.00
42	A2	50c on 25c ultra	2.00	2.00

Wmk. 3

No.	Type	Description	Unused	Used
43	A2	50c on 25c ultra	7.00	7.00
		Nos. 40-43 (4)	11.00	11.00

A4

The values at the lower right denote the currency and amount for which the stamps were to be sold. The stamps could be purchased at the French post office and used to pay postage at the English rates.

1925 Engr. Wmk. R F in Sheet

No.	Type	Description	Unused	Used
44	A4	5c (½p) black	.70	.70
45	A4	10c (1p) green	.50	.50
46	A4	20c (2p) grnsh gray	.50	.50
47	A4	25c (2½p) brown	.50	.50
48	A4	30c (3p) carmine	.50	.50
49	A4	40c (4p) car, org	.80	.80
50	A4	50c (5p) ultra	1.00	1.00
51	A4	75c (7½p) bis brn	1.50	1.50
52	A4	1fr (10p) car, blue	2.50	2.50
53	A4	2fr (1sh 8p) gray vio	2.50	2.50
54	A4	5fr (4sh) car, grnsh	6.00	6.00
		Nos. 44-54 (11)	17.00	17.00

For overprints see Nos. J1-J5.

Beach Scene — A6

1938 Perf. 12

No.	Type	Description	Unused	Used
55	A6	5c green	.55	.55
56	A6	10c dark orange	.55	.55
57	A6	15c violet	.55	.55
58	A6	20c rose red	.55	.55
59	A6	25c brown	.85	.85
60	A6	30c dark blue	.85	.85
61	A6	40c olive grn	1.25	1.25
62	A6	50c brown violet	1.25	1.25
63	A6	1fr dk car, grn	2.25	2.25
64	A6	2fr blue, grn	5.00	5.00
65	A6	5fr red, yellow	19.00	19.00
66	A6	10fr vio, blue	37.50	37.50
		Nos. 55-66 (12)	70.15	70.15

For overprints see Nos. 67-78, J6-J15.

Stamps of 1938 Overprinted in Black

France Libre

1941

No.	Type	Description	Unused	Used
67	A6	5c green	6.00	6.00
68	A6	10c dark orange	6.00	6.00
69	A6	15c violet	6.00	6.00
70	A6	20c rose red	6.50	6.50
71	A6	25c brown	6.75	6.75
72	A6	30c dark blue	6.75	6.75
73	A6	40c olive green	6.75	6.75
74	A6	50c brn violet	6.75	6.75
75	A6	1fr dk car, grn	8.50	8.50
76	A6	2fr blue, grn	8.50	8.50
77	A6	5fr red, yellow	10.50	10.50
78	A6	10fr vio, blue	16.00	16.00
		Nos. 67-78 (12)	95.00	95.00

Catalogue values for unused stamps in this section, from this point to the end of the section, are for Never Hinged items.

UPU Monument, Bern — A7

Wmk. RF in Sheet

1949 Engr. Perf. 13½x14

No.	Type	Description	Unused	Used
79	A7	10c red orange	.80	.80
80	A7	15c violet	1.00	1.00
81	A7	30c violet blue	1.40	1.40
82	A7	50c rose violet	2.75	2.75
		Nos. 79-82 (4)	5.95	5.95

75th anniv. of the UPU.

Some stamps in each sheet show part of the watermark; others show none.

Outrigger Canoes with Sails — A8

5c, 10c, 15c, 20c, Canoes with sails. 25c, 30c, 40c, 50c, Native carving. 1fr, 2fr, 5fr, Natives.

1953 Perf. 12½

No.	Type	Description	Unused	Used
83	A8	5c green	.25	.25
84	A8	10c red	.40	.40
85	A8	15c yellow	.40	.40
86	A8	20c ultramarine	.70	.70
87	A8	25c olive	.70	.70
88	A8	30c light brown	1.00	1.00
89	A8	40c black brown	1.00	1.00
90	A8	50c violet	1.25	1.25
91	A8	1fr deep orange	3.00	3.00
92	A8	2fr red violet	10.50	10.50
93	A8	5fr scarlet	16.00	16.00
		Nos. 83-93 (11)	35.20	35.20

For overprints see Nos. J16-J20.

Discovery of New Hebrides, 1606 — A9

20c, 50c, Britannia, Marianne, Flags and Mask.

1956 Unwmk. Photo. Perf. 14½x14

No.	Type	Description	Unused	Used
94	A9	5c emerald	.60	.60
95	A9	10c crimson	.60	.60
96	A9	20c ultramarine	.80	.80
97	A9	50c purple	2.50	2.50
		Nos. 94-97 (4)	4.50	4.50

50th anniv. of the establishment of the Anglo-French Condominium.

Port Vila and Iririki Islet — A10

Designs: 25c, 30c, 40c, 50c, Tropical river and spear fisherman. 1fr, 2fr, 5fr, Woman drinking from coconut (inscribed: "Alliance Franco-Britannique 4 Mars 1947").

Wmk. RF in Sheet

1957 Engr. Perf. 13½x13

No.	Type	Description	Unused	Used
98	A10	5c green	.30	.30
99	A10	10c red	.40	.40
100	A10	15c orange yel	.55	.55
101	A10	20c ultramarine	.55	.55
102	A10	25c olive	.55	.55
103	A10	30c light brown	.80	.80
104	A10	40c sepia	.95	.95
105	A10	50c violet	1.50	1.50
106	A10	1fr orange	3.00	3.00
107	A10	2fr rose lilac	7.00	7.00
108	A10	5fr black	14.00	14.00
		Nos. 98-108 (11)	29.60	29.60

For overprints see Nos. J21-J25.

Wheat Emblem and Globe A10a

1963, Sept. 2 Unwmk. Perf. 13

No.	Type	Description	Unused	Used
109	A10a	60c org brn & slate grn	2.00	2.00

FAO "Freedom from Hunger" campaign.

Centenary Emblem — A11

1963, Sept. 2 Unwmk.

No.	Type	Description	Unused	Used
110	A11	15c org, gray & car	.80	.80
111	A11	45c bis, gray & car	1.50	1.50

Centenary of International Red Cross.

Copra Industry A12

Designs: 5c, Manganese loading, Forari Wharf. 10c, Cacao. 20c, Map of New Hebrides, tuna, marlin and ships. 25c, Striped triggerfish. 30c, Nautilus. 40c, 60c, Turkeyfish (pterois volitans). 50c, Lined tang (fish). 1fr, Cardinal honeyeater and hibiscus. 2fr, Buff-bellied flycatcher. 3fr, Thicket warbler. 5fr, White-collared kingfisher.

Perf. 12½ (10c, 20c, 40c, 60c); 14 (3fr); 13 (others)

Photo. (10c, 20c, 40c, 60c, 3fr); Engr. (others)

1963-67 Unwmk.

No.	Type	Description	Unused	Used
112	A12	5c Prus bl & cl ('66)	.40	.40
113	A12	10c brt grn, org brn & dk brn ("RF" at left) ('65)	1.40	.90
114	A12	15c dk pur, yel & brn	.28	.28
115	A12	20c brt bl, gray & cit ("RF" at left) ('65)	1.90	1.40
116	A12	25c vio, rose lil & org brn ('66)	.55	.55
117	A12	30c lil, brn & citron	.65	.65
118	A12	40c dk bl & ver ('65)	3.25	2.25
119	A12	50c Prus bl, yel & grn	.90	.90
119A	A12	60c dk bl & ver ('67)	1.10	.90
120	A12	1fr bl grn, blk & red ('66)	2.00	2.00
121	A12	2fr ol, blk & brn	4.50	4.50
122	A12	3fr org brn, brt grn & blk ("RF" at left) ('65)	9.00	6.50
123	A12	5fr ind, dp bl & gray ('67)	10.00	10.00
		Nos. 112-123 (13)	35.93	31.23

See #146-148. For surcharge see #160.

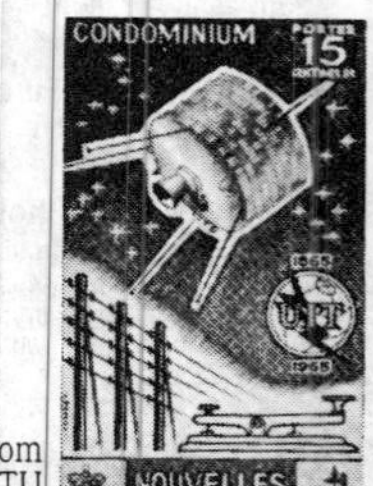
Telegraph, Syncom Satellite and ITU Emblem — A13

1965, May 17 Unwmk. Perf. 13

No.	Type	Description	Unused	Used
124	A13	15c dk red brn, brt bl & emer	1.50	.75
125	A13	60c Prus grn, mag & sl	3.00	1.50

ITU, centenary.

ICY Emblem A14

1965, Oct. 24 Litho. Perf. 14½

No.	Type	Description	Unused	Used
126	A14	5c blue grn & claret	.35	.35
127	A14	55c lt violet & grn	.90	.90

International Cooperation Year.

Winston Churchill and St. Paul's, London, During Air Attack A15

1966, Jan. 24 Photo. *Perf. 14*

Design in Black, Gold and Carmine Rose

128 A15 5c brt blue .20 .20
129 A15 15c green .25 .25
130 A15 25c brown .55 .55
131 A15 30c violet 1.00 1.00
Nos. 128-131 (4) 2.00 2.00

Soccer Player and Rimet Cup A16

1966, July 1 Litho. *Perf. 14*

132 A16 20c multicolored .60 .60
133 A16 40c multicolored .70 .70

World Cup Soccer Championship, Wembley, England, July 11-30.

Inauguration of WHO Headquarters, Geneva — A17

1966, Sept. 20 Litho. *Perf. 14*

134 A17 25c multicolored .60 .60
135 A17 60c multicolored .80 .80

"Education" — A18

UNESCO, 20th anniv.: 30c, "Science" (retort and grain). 45c, "Culture" (lyre and columns).

1966, Dec. 1 Litho. *Perf. 14*

136 A18 15c dp org, yel & dl vio .40 .40
137 A18 30c vio, dk ol grn & yel .65 .65
138 A18 45c yel, magenta & blk .90 .90
Nos. 136-138 (3) 1.95 1.95

US Marine, Australian Soldier and Map of South Pacific War Zone — A19

Designs: 15c, The coast watchers. 60c, Australian cruiser Canberra. 1fr, Flying fortress taking off from Bauer Field, and view of Vila.

Perf. 14x13

1967, Sept. 26 Photo. Unwmk.

139 A19 15c lt blue & multi .40 .40
140 A19 25c yellow & multi .55 .55
141 A19 60c multicolored .80 .80
142 A19 1fr pale salmon & multi 1.50 1.50
Nos. 139-142 (4) 3.25 3.25

25th anniv. of the Allied Forces' campaign in the South Pacific War Zone.

L. A. de Bougainville, Ship's Figurehead and Bougainvillea A20

15c, Globe & world map. 25c, Ships La Boudeuse & L'Etoile & map of Bougainville Strait.

1968, May 23 Engr. *Perf. 13*

143 A20 15c ver, emer & dl vio .22 .22
144 A20 25c ultra, ol & brn .45 .45
145 A20 60c mag, grn & brn .80 .80
Nos. 143-145 (3) 1.47 1.47

200th anniv. of Louis Antoine de Bougainville's (1729-1811) voyage around the world.

Type of 1963-67 Redrawn, "E II R" at left, "RF" at Right

Designs as before.

1968, Aug. 5 Photo. *Perf. 12½*

146 A12 10c brt grn, org brn & dk brn .30 .30
147 A12 20c brt bl, gray & citron .42 .42

Perf. 14

148 A12 3fr org brn, brt grn & blk 3.50 3.50
Nos. 146-148 (3) 4.22 4.22

On Nos. 113, 115 and 122 "RF" is at left and "E II R" is at right.

For surcharge see No. 160.

Concorde Supersonic Airliner A21

Design: 25c, Concorde seen from above.

1968, Oct. 9 Litho. *Perf. 14x13½*

149 A21 25c vio bl, red & lt bl 2.25 2.00
150 A21 60c red, ultra & blk 4.00 3.50

Development of the Concorde supersonic airliner, a joint Anglo-French project.

Kauri Pine — A22 Land Diver at Start, Pentecost Island — A24

Relay Race, British and French Flags A23

1969, June 30 *Perf. 14½x14*

151 A22 20c brown & multi .40 .40

New Hebrides timber industry. Issued in sheets of 9 (3x3) on simulated wood grain background.

1969, Aug. 13 Photo. *Perf. 12½x13*

152 A23 25c shown .75 .75
153 A23 1fr Runner at right 1.25 1.25

3rd South Pacific Games, Port Moresby, Papua and New Guinea, Aug. 13-23.

1969, Oct. 15 Litho. *Perf. 12½*

154 A24 15c shown .35 .35
155 A24 25c Diver in mid-air .45 .45
156 A24 1fr Diver near ground 2.00 2.00
Nos. 154-156 (3) 2.80 2.80

Land divers of Pentecost Island.

UPU Headquarters and Monument, Bern — A25

1970, May 20 Engr. *Perf. 13*

157 A25 1.05fr org, lilac & slate 1.20 1.20

New UPU Headquarters, Bern.

Charles de Gaulle — A26

1970, July 20 Photo. *Perf. 13*

158 A26 65c brown & multi 1.20 1.20
159 A26 1.10fr dp blue & multi 2.25 2.25

Rallying of the Free French, 30th anniv.

For overprints see Nos. 163-164.

No. 147 Surcharged

1970, Oct. 15 Photo. *Perf. 12½*

160 A12 35c on 20c multi .80 .80

Virgin and Child, by Giovanni Bellini — A27

50c, Virgin and Child, by Giovanni Cima.

1970, Nov. 30 Litho. *Perf. 14½x14*

161 A27 15c tan & multi .35 .22
162 A27 50c lt grn & multi .62 .45

Christmas. See Nos. 186-187.

Nos. 158-159 Overprinted "1890-1970 / IN MEMORIAM / 9-11-70" in Gold, 2 Vertical Bars in Black

1971, Jan. 19 Photo. *Perf. 13*

163 A26 65c brown & multi .80 .80
164 A26 1.10fr dp blue & multi 2.00 2.00

In memory of Gen. Charles de Gaulle (1890-1970), President of France.

Soccer A28

Design: 65c, Basketball, vert.

1971, July 13 Photo. *Perf. 12½*

165 A28 20c multicolored .40 .40
166 A28 65c multicolored .90 .70

4th South Pacific Games, Papeete, French Polynesia, Sept. 8-19.

Breadfruit Tree and Fruit, Society Arms — A29

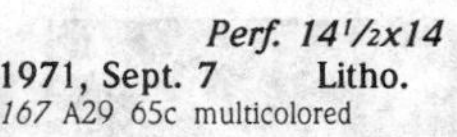
Perf. 14½x14

1971, Sept. 7 Litho. Unwmk.

167 A29 65c multicolored .80 .65

Expedition of the Royal Society of London for the Advancement of Science to study vegetation and fauna, July 1-October.

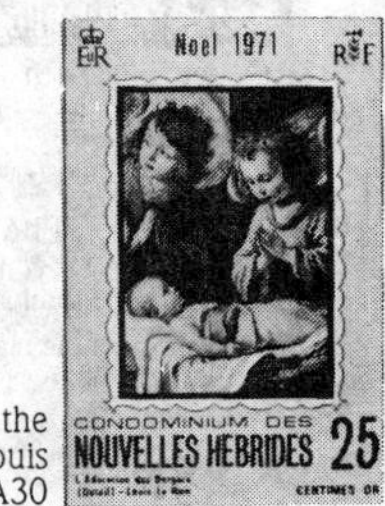

Adoration of the Shepherds, by Louis Le Nain — A30

Christmas: 50c, Adoration of the Shepherds, by Jacopo Tintoretto.

1971, Nov. 23 *Perf. 14x13½*

168 A30 25c lt green & multi .45 .35
169 A30 50c lt blue & multi .65 .60

Drover Mk III A31

Airplanes: 25c, Sandringham seaplane. 30c, Dragon Rapide. 65c, Caravelle.

1972, Feb. 29 Photo. *Perf. 13½x13*

170 A31 20c lt green & multi .45 .35
171 A31 25c ultra & multi .55 .40
172 A31 30c orange & multi .75 .60
173 A31 65c dk blue & multi 2.25 1.75
Nos. 170-173 (4) 4.00 3.10

Headdress, South Malekula — A32 Baker's Pigeon — A33

Artifacts: 15c, Slit gong and carved figure, North Ambrym. 1fr, Carved figures, North Ambrym. 3fr, Ceremonial headdress, South Malekula.

Birds: 20c, Red-headed parrot-finch. 35c, Chestnut-bellied kingfisher. 2fr, Green palm lorikeet.

Sea Shells: 25c, Cribraria fischeri. 30c, Oliva rubrolabiata. 65c, Strombus plicatus. 5fr, Turbo marmoratus.

1972, July 24 Photo. *Perf. 12½x13*

174 A32 5c plum & multi .15 .15
175 A33 10c blue & multi .15 .15
176 A32 15c red & multi .25 .20
177 A33 20c org brn & multi .30 .20
178 A32 25c dp blue & multi .40 .25
179 A32 30c dk green & multi .45 .30
180 A33 35c gray bl & multi .70 .45
181 A32 65c dk green & multi .90 .70
182 A32 1fr orange & multi 1.90 1.25
183 A33 2fr multicolored 3.25 1.75
184 A32 3fr yellow & multi 5.25 2.75
185 A32 5fr pink & multi 11.00 6.00
Nos. 174-185 (12) 24.70 14.15

For overprints see Nos. 200-201.

Christmas Type of 1970

Christmas: 25c, Adoration of the Magi (detail), by Bartholomaeus Spranger. 70c, Virgin and Child, by Jan Provoost.

1972, Sept. 25 Litho. *Perf. 14x13½*

186 A27 25c lt green & multi .45 .40
187 A27 70c lt blue & multi .65 .62

Queen Elizabeth II and Prince Philip — A34

Perf. 14x14½

1972, Nov. 20 Photo. Wmk. 314

188 A34 35c violet blk & multi		.35	.28
189 A34 65c olive & multi		.65	.45

25th anniversary of the marriage of Queen Elizabeth II and Prince Philip.

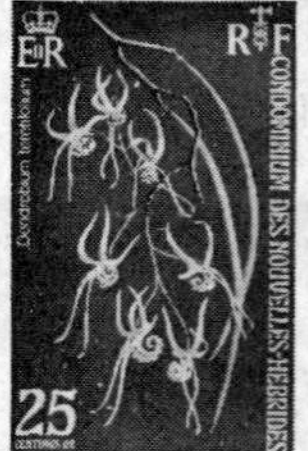

Dendrobium Teretifolium A35

New Wharf, Vila A36

Orchids: 30c, Ephemerantha comata. 35c, Spathoglottis petri. 65c, Dendrobium mohlianum.

Unwmk.

1973, Feb. 26 Litho. *Perf. 14*

190 A35 25c blue vio & multi	.32	.25
191 A35 30c multicolored	.45	.42
192 A35 35c violet & multi	.65	.50
193 A35 65c dk green & multi	1.75	1.50
Nos. 190-193 (4)	3.17	2.67

1973, May 14 Litho. *Perf. 14*

194 A36 25c shown	.60	.40
195 A36 70c New Wharf, horiz.	1.25	1.00

New wharf at Vila, completed Nov. 1972.

Wild Horses, Tanna — A37

Design: 70c, Yasur Volcano, Tanna.

1973, Aug. 13 Photo. *Perf. 13x13½*

196 A37 35c multicolored	.65	.60
197 A37 70c multicolored	1.40	1.10

Mother and Child, by Marcel Moutouh — A38

Christmas: 70c, Star over Lagoon, by Tatin D'Avesnieres.

1973, Nov. 19 Litho. *Perf. 14x13½*

198 A38 35c tan & multi	.45	.28
199 A38 70c lil rose & multi	.65	.60

Nos. 180, 183 Overprinted in Red or Black: "VISITE ROYALE / 1974"

1974, Feb. 11 Photo. *Perf. 12½x13*

200 A33 35c multi (R)	.40	.25
201 A33 2fr multi (B)	1.65	1.25

Visit of British Royal Family, Feb. 15-16.

Pacific Dove — A39

Designs: 35c, Night swallowtail. 70c, Green sea turtle. 1.15fr, Flying fox.

1974, Feb. 11 *Perf. 13x12½*

202 A39 25c gray & multi	.42	.40
203 A39 35c gray & multi	1.00	.55
204 A39 70c gray & multi	1.65	1.25
205 A39 1.15fr gray & multi	2.25	1.75
Nos. 202-205 (4)	5.32	3.95

Nature conservation.

Old Post Office, Vila A40

Design: 70c, New Post Office.

Unwmk.

1974, May 6 Photo. *Perf. 12*

206 A40 35c blue & multi	.45	.32
207 A40 70c red & multi	.65	.65
a. Pair, #206-207	1.10	1.00

Opening of New Post Office, May, 1974.

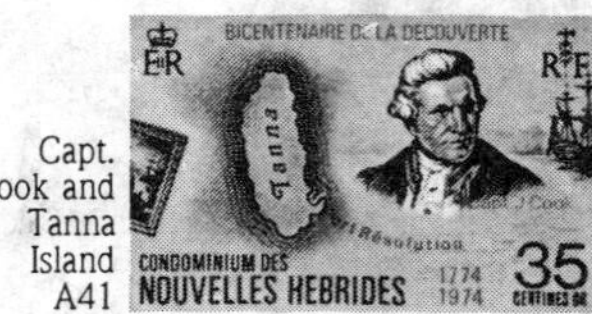

Capt. Cook and Tanna Island A41

Designs: No. 209, William Wales and boat landing on island. No. 210, William Hodges painting islanders and landscape. 1.15fr, Capt. Cook, "Resolution" and map of New Hebrides.

1974, Aug. 1 Litho. *Perf. 13*

Size: 40x25mm

208 A41 35c multicolored	1.25	.90
209 A41 35c multicolored	1.25	.90
210 A41 35c multicolored	1.25	.90
a. Strip of 3, #208-210	3.75	2.75

Size: 58x34mm

Perf. 11

211 A41 1.15fr lilac & multi	3.00	1.90

Bicentenary of the discovery of the New Hebrides by Capt. James Cook.

No. 210a has a continuous design.

Exchange of Letters, UPU Emblem A42

1974, Oct. 9 Photo. *Perf. 13x12½*

212 A42 70c multicolored	.62	.60

Centenary of Universal Postal Union.

Nativity, by Gerard Van Honthorst — A43

Christmas: 35c, Adoration of the Kings, by Velazquez, vert.

1974, Nov. 14 Litho. *Perf. 13½*

213 A43 35c multicolored	.40	.35
214 A43 70c multicolored	.60	.55

Charolais Bull — A44

1975, Apr. 29 Engr. *Perf. 13*

215 A44 10fr multicolored	14.00	10.00

Nordjamb Emblem, Kayaks A45

Pitti Madonna, by Michelangelo A46

1975, Aug. 5 Litho. *Perf. 14x13½*

216 A45 25c shown	.50	.30
217 A45 35c Camp cooks	.50	.42
218 A45 1fr Map makers	1.25	.75
219 A45 5fr Fishermen	7.00	4.75
Nos. 216-219 (4)	9.25	6.22

Nordjamb 75, 14th Boy Scout Jamboree, Lillehammer, Norway, July 29-Aug. 7.

1975, Nov. 11 Litho. *Perf. 14½x14*

Christmas (After Michelangelo): 70c, Bruges Madonna. 2.50fr, Taddei Madonna.

220 A46 35c multicolored	.40	.28
221 A46 70c brown & multi	.62	.45
222 A46 2.50fr blue & multi	2.25	1.90
Nos. 220-222 (3)	3.27	2.63

Concorde, Air France Colors and Emblem — A47

1976, Jan. 30 Typo. *Perf. 13*

223 A47 5fr blue & multi	10.00	6.50

1st commercial flight of supersonic jet Concorde from Paris to Rio, Jan. 21.

Telephones, 1876 and 1976 — A48

Designs: 70c, Alexander Graham Bell. 1.15fr, Nouméa Earth Station and satellite.

1976, Mar. 31 Photo. *Perf. 13*

224 A48 25c black, car & bl	.35	.28
225 A48 70c black & multi	.65	.55
226 A48 1.15fr blk, org & vio bl	1.40	.90
Nos. 224-226 (3)	2.40	1.73

Centenary of first telephone call by Alexander Graham Bell, Mar. 10, 1876.

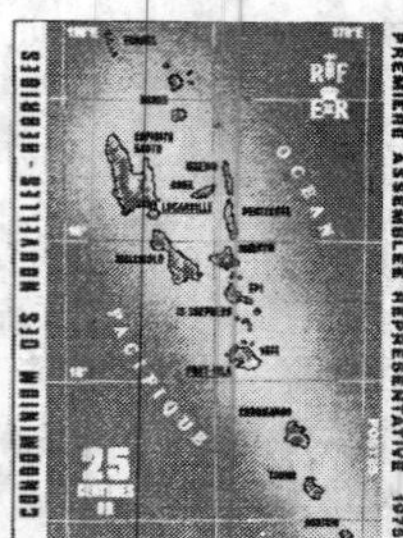

Map of New Hebrides A49

View of Luganville (Santo) — A50

Design: 2fr, View of Vila.

1976, June 29 Unwmk. *Perf. 13*

227 A49 25c blue & multi	.45	.28
228 A50 1fr multicolored	1.25	.65
229 A50 2fr multicolored	3.00	1.60
Nos. 227-229 (3)	4.70	2.53

Opening of first Representative Assembly, June 29, 1976 (25c); first Luganville (Santo) Municipal Council (1fr); first Vila Municipal Council (2fr).

Nos. 228-229 exist with lower inscription reading "Premiere Assemblée Representative 1975" instead of "Premiere Municipalite de Luganville" on 1fr and "Premiere Municipalite de Port-Vila" on 2fr.

Flight into Egypt, by Francisco Vieira Lusitano — A51

Portuguese 16th Cent. Paintings: 70c, Adoration of the Shepherds. 2.50fr, Adoration of the Kings.

1976, Nov. 8 Litho. *Perf. 14*

230 A51 35c purple & multi	.45	.35
231 A51 70c blue & multi	.65	.60
232 A51 2.50fr multicolored	2.50	2.00
Nos. 230-232 (3)	3.60	2.95

Christmas 1976.

Queen's Visit, 1974 — A52

70c, Imperial State crown. 2fr, The blessing.

1977, Feb. 7 Litho. *Perf. 14x13½*

233 A52 35c lt green & multi	.35	.22
234 A52 70c blue & multi	.60	.40
235 A52 2fr pink & multi	1.60	1.40
Nos. 233-235 (3)	2.55	2.02

Reign of Queen Elizabeth II, 25th anniv.

Nos. 174-185, 215 Surcharged with New Value, "FNH" and Bars

1977, July 1 Photo. *Perf. 12½x13*

236 A32 5fr on 5c multi	.22	.22
237 A33 10fr on 10c multi	.35	.35
238 A32 15fr on 15c multi	.55	.55
239 A33 20fr on 20c multi	.60	.50
240 A32 25fr on 25c multi	.80	.80
241 A32 30fr on 30c multi	1.10	1.10
242 A33 35fr on 35c multi	1.10	1.10
243 A32 40fr on 65c multi	1.50	1.50
244 A32 50fr on 1fr multi	2.50	2.50
245 A33 70fr on 2fr multi	4.50	4.50

246 A32 100fr on 3fr multi 6.25 6.25
247 A32 200fr on 5fr multi 11.00 11.00

Engr.

Perf. 13

248 A44 500fr on 10fr multi 25.00 25.00
Nos. 236-248 (13) 55.47 55.37

Surcharged in Paris. Later all except 20fr were surcharged in Vila with slightly different letters and different bars. Of these 12, the 50fr, 70fr and 100fr were reported to have been sold only at the philatelic bureau.

Espiritu Santo and Cattle — A53

Tempi Madonna, by Raphael — A54

Designs: 5fr, Erromango Island and Kaori tree. 10fr, Archipelago and man making copra. 20fr, Efate Island and Post Office, Vila. 25fr, Malakula Island and headdresses. 30fr, Aoba and Maewo Islands and pig tusks. 35fr, Pentecost Island and land diving. 40fr, Tanna Island and Prophet John Frum's Red Cross. 50fr, Shepherd Island and canoe with sail. 70fr, Banks Island and dancers. 100fr, Ambrym Island and carvings. 200fr, Aneityum Island and decorated baskets. 500fr, Torres Islands and fishing with bow and arrow.

1977-78 Litho. *Perf. 14*

258 A53 5fr multicolored .20 .20
259 A53 10fr multicolored .25 .22
260 A53 15fr multicolored .32 .28
261 A53 20fr multicolored .45 .32
262 A53 25fr multicolored .50 .35
263 A53 30fr multicolored .55 .48
264 A53 35fr multicolored .65 .50
265 A53 40fr multicolored .80 .55
266 A53 50fr multicolored .90 .70
267 A53 70fr multicolored 1.25 1.00
268 A53 100fr multicolored 2.25 1.50
269 A53 200fr multicolored 5.00 3.50
270 A53 500fr multicolored 11.00 8.75
Nos. 258-270 (13) 24.12 18.35

Issued: 5fr, 20fr, 50fr, 100fr, 200fr, 9/7/77; 15fr, 25fr, 30fr, 40fr, 11/23/77; 10fr, 35fr, 70fr, 500fr, 5/9/78.

1977, Dec. 8 Litho. *Perf. 12*

Christmas: 15fr, Virgin and Child, by Gerard David. 30fr, Virgin and Child, by Pompeo Batoni.

271 A54 10fr multicolored .30 .25
272 A54 15fr multicolored .38 .32
273 A54 30fr multicolored .80 .70
Nos. 271-273 (3) 1.48 1.27

British Airways Concorde over New York — A55

Designs: 20fr, British Airways Concorde over London. 30fr, Air France Concorde over Washington. 40fr, Air France Concorde over Paris.

1978, May 9 Litho. *Perf. 14*

274 A55 10fr multicolored .60 .40
275 A55 20fr multicolored 1.00 .70
276 A55 30fr multicolored 1.40 1.10
277 A55 40fr multicolored 2.00 1.50
Nos. 274-277 (4) 5.00 3.70

Souvenir Sheet

White Horse of Hanover — A56

Elizabeth II — A57

Design: No. 278c, Gallic cock.

1978, June 2 Litho. *Perf. 15*

278 Sheet of 6 6.00 6.00
a. A56 40fr greenish blue & multi .85 .85
b. A57 40fr greenish blue & multi .85 .85
c. A56 40fr greenish blue & multi .85 .85

25th anniversary of coronation of Queen Elizabeth II. No. 278 contains 2 se-tenant strips of Nos. 278a-278c, separated by horizontal gutter with commemorative and descriptive inscriptions and showing central part of coronation procession with coach.

Virgin and Child, by Dürer — A58

Christmas, Paintings by Albrecht Durer (1471-1528): 15fr, Virgin and Child with St. Anne. 30fr, Virgin and Child with Goldfinch. 40fr, Virgin and Child with Pear.

1978, Dec. 1 Litho. *Perf. 14x13½*

279 A58 10fr multicolored .25 .25
280 A58 15fr multicolored .35 .35
281 A58 30fr multicolored .60 .55
282 A58 40fr multicolored 1.00 .80
Nos. 279-282 (4) 2.20 1.95

Type of 1976 Surcharged with New Value, Bars over Old Denomination and Inscription at Right. Longitude changed to "166E."

1979, Jan. 11 Photo. *Perf. 13*

283 A49 10fr on 25c bl & multi .40 .28
284 A49 40fr on 25c lt grn & multi 1.10 .80

First anniv. of Internal Self-Government.

New Hebrides No. 155 and Hill Statue A59

Rowland Hill and New Hebrides Stamps: 10fr, No. 55. 40fr, No. 46.

1979, Sept. 10 Litho. *Perf. 14*

285 A59 10fr multicolored .22 .16
286 A59 20fr multicolored .45 .35
287 A59 40fr multicolored .80 .62
Nos. 285-287 (3) 1.47 1.13

Sir Rowland Hill (1795-1879), originator of penny postage. A souvenir sheet containing No. 286 and British issue No. 266 is listed as No. 266a under New Hebrides, British issues.

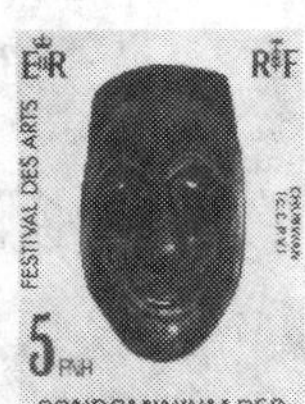

Arts Festival — A60

Designs: 10fr, Clubs and spears. 20fr, Ritual puppet. 40fr, Headdress.

1979, Nov. 16 Litho. *Perf. 14*

288 A60 5fr multicolored .20 .20
289 A60 10fr multicolored .28 .22
290 A60 20fr multicolored .50 .38
291 A60 40fr multicolored 1.00 .62
Nos. 288-291 (4) 1.98 1.42

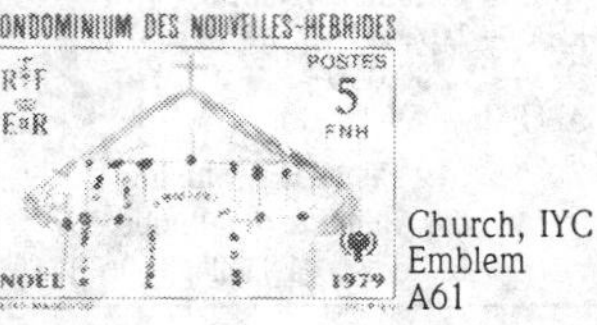

Church, IYC Emblem A61

IYC Emblem, Children's Drawings: 10fr, Father Christmas. 20fr, Cross and Bible, vert. 40fr, Stars, candle and Santa Claus, vert.

1979, Dec. 4 *Perf. 13x13½*

292 A61 5fr multicolored .20 .20
293 A61 10fr multicolored .28 .22
294 A61 20fr multicolored .50 .35
295 A61 40fr multicolored 1.00 .62
Nos. 292-295 (4) 1.98 1.39

Christmas; Intl. Year of the Child.

White-bellied Honeyeater — A62

1980, Feb. 27 Litho. *Perf. 14*

296 A62 10fr shown .40 .40
297 A62 20fr Scarlet robins .60 .60
298 A62 30fr Yellow white-eyes 1.00 1.00
299 A62 40fr Fan-tailed brush cuckoo 1.50 1.50
Nos. 296-299 (4) 3.50 3.50

Stamps of Vanuatu replaced those of New Hebrides in 1980.

POSTAGE DUE STAMPS

French Issues

Nos. 45-46, 48, 50, 52 Overprinted **CHIFFRE TAXE**

1925 Wmk. R F in Sheet *Perf. 14*

J1 A4 10c green 40.00 4.00
J2 A4 20c greenish gray 40.00 4.00
J3 A4 30c carmine 40.00 4.00
J4 A4 50c ultramarine 40.00 4.00
J5 A4 1fr carmine, *blue* 40.00 4.00
Nos. J1-J5 (5) 200.00 20.00

Nos. 55-56, 58, 61, 63 Overprinted **CHIFFRE TAXE**

1938 *Perf. 12*

J6 A6 5c green 2.00 2.00
J7 A6 10c dark orange 2.00 2.00
J8 A6 20c rose red 3.00 3.00
J9 A6 40c olive green 6.25 6.25
J10 A6 1fr dark car, *green* 9.50 9.50
Nos. J6-J10 (5) 22.75 22.75

Nos. J6-J10 Overprinted like Nos. 67-78

1941

J11 A6 5c green 7.50 7.50
J12 A6 10c dark orange 7.50 7.50
J13 A6 20c rose red 7.50 7.50
J14 A6 40c olive green 7.50 7.50
J15 A6 1fr dk car, *green* 7.50 7.50
Nos. J11-J15 (5) 37.50 37.50

Catalogue values for unused stamps in this section, from this point to the end of the section, are for Never Hinged items.

Nos. 83-84, 86, 89, 91 Overprinted "TIMBRE-TAXE"

1953 Unwmk. *Perf. 12½*

J16 A8 5c green .80 .80
J17 A8 10c red 1.25 1.25
J18 A8 20c ultramarine 2.50 2.50
J19 A8 40c black brown 5.50 5.50
J20 A8 1fr deep orange 8.00 8.00
Nos. J16-J20 (5) 18.05 18.05

Nos. 98-99, 101, 104, 106 Overprinted "TIMBRE-TAXE"

Wmk. R F in Sheet

1957 Engr. *Perf. 13½x13*

J21 A10 5c green .60 .60
J22 A10 10c red .75 .75
J23 A10 20c ultramarine 1.00 1.00
J24 A10 40c sepia 3.50 3.50
J25 A10 1fr orange 8.00 8.00
Nos. J21-J25 (5) 13.85 13.85

NEW REPUBLIC

'nü ri-'pə-blik

LOCATION — In South Africa, located in the northern part of the present province of Natal
GOVT. — A former Republic
CAPITAL — Vryheid

New Republic was created in 1884 by Boer adventurers from Transvaal who proclaimed Dinizulu king of Zululand and claimed as their reward a large tract of country as their own, which they called New Republic. This area was excepted when Great Britain annexed Zululand in 1887, but New Republic became a part of Transvaal in 1888 and was included in the Union of South Africa.

12 Pence = 1 Shilling
20 Shillings = 1 Pound

New Republic stamps were individually handstamped on gummed and perforated sheets of paper. Naturally many of the impressions are misaligned and touch or intersect the perforations. Values are for stamps with good color and, for Nos. 37-64, sharp embossing. The alignment does not materially alter the value of the stamp.

A1

A2

Handstamped

1886 Unwmk. *Perf. 11½*

1 A1 1p violet, *yel* 9.00 11.00
1A A1 1p black, *yel* 3,250.
2 A1 2p violet, *yel* 9.00 12.50
a. Without date
b. Tête bêche pair
3 A1 3p violet, *yel* 22.50
a. Double impression
4 A1 4p violet, *yel* 32.50
a. Without date
5 A1 6p violet, *yel* 30.00
a. Double impression
6 A1 9p violet, *yel* 27.50
7 A1 1sh violet, *yel* 75.00
a. "1/S" 475.00
8 A1 1/6 violet, *yel* 75.00
a. Without date
b. "1sh6p" 475.00
9 A1 2sh violet, *yel* 35.00
a. Tête bêche pair 550.00
10 A1 2sh6p violet, *yel* 95.00
a. Without date
b. "2/6" 135.00
11 A1 4sh violet, *yel* 425.00
12 A1 5sh violet, *yel* 30.00 30.00
a. Without date
13 A1 5/6 violet, *yel* 35.00 35.00
a. "5sh6p" 150.00
14 A1 7sh6p violet, *yel* 90.00
a. "7/6" 150.00
15 A1 10sh violet, *yel* 90.00 90.00
16 A1 10sh6p violet, *yel* 175.00
16A A1 13sh violet, *yel* 400.00
17 A1 £1 violet, *yel* 125.00
18 A1 30sh violet, *yel* 90.00
a. Tête bêche pair 700.00

Granite Paper

19 A1 1p violet, *gray* 12.00 13.00
20 A1 2p violet, *gray* 12.00 13.00
a. Without "ZUID AFRIKA"
21 A1 3p violet, *gray* 15.00 17.50
a. Tête bêche pair 275.00
22 A1 4p violet, *gray* 12.50 17.50
23 A1 6p violet, *gray* 25.00 22.50
24 A1 9p violet, *gray* 30.00
25 A1 1sh violet, *gray* 27.50 27.50
a. Tête bêche pair 700.00

26 A1 1sh6p violet, *gray* 40.00
a. Tête bêche pair 600.00
b. "1/6" 140.00
27 A1 2sh violet, *gray* 110.00
28 A1 2sh6p violet, *gray* 150.00
a. "2/6" 175.00
29 A1 4sh violet, *gray* 200.00
30 A1 5sh6p violet, *gray* 165.00
a. "5/6" 190.00
31 A1 7sh6p violet, *gray* 190.00
32 A1 10sh violet, *gray* 190.00 225.00
a. Tête bêche pair 500.00
32B A1 10sh 6p vio, *gray* 185.00
c. Without date
33 A1 12sh violet, *gray* 275.00
34 A1 13sh violet, *gray* 400.00
35 A1 £1 violet, *gray* 250.00
36 A1 30sh violet, *gray* 250.00

Same with Embossed Arms

37 A1 1p violet, *yel* 13.00 14.00
a. Arms inverted 25.00 25.00
b. Arms tête bêche, pair 105.00 125.00
38 A1 2p violet, *yel* 13.00 14.00
a. Arms inverted 25.00 27.50
39 A1 4p violet, *yel* 18.00 18.00
a. Arms inverted 100.00 75.00
b. Arms tête bêche, pair 275.00
40 A1 6p violet, *yel* 35.00

Granite Paper

41 A1 1p violet, *gray* 13.00 15.00
a. Imperf. vert., pair
b. Arms inverted 30.00 35.00
c. Arms tête bêche, pair
42 A1 2p violet, *gray* 13.00 15.00
a. Imperf. horiz., pair
b. Arms inverted 45.00
c. Arms tête bêche, pair

There were several printings of the above stamps and the date upon them varies from "JAN 86" and "7 JAN 86" to "20 JAN 87."

Nos. 7, 8, 10, 13, 14, 26, 28 and 30 have the denomination expressed in two ways. Example: "1s 6d" or "1/6."

1887 Arms Embossed

43 A2 3p violet, *yel* 13.00 13.00
a. Arms inverted 24.00 24.00
b. Tête bêche pair 360.00
c. Imperf. vert., pair
d. Arms omitted
e. Arms tête bêche, pair
44 A2 4p violet, *yel* 12.50 12.50
a. Arms inverted 27.50 27.50
45 A2 6p violet, *yel* 11.00 11.00
a. Arms inverted 52.50 52.50
b. Arms omitted 200.00
c. Arms tête bêche, pair 315.00
46 A2 9p violet, *yel* 11.00 11.00
47 A2 1sh violet, *yel* 13.00 13.00
a. Arms inverted 65.00
b. Arms omitted 55.00
48 A2 1sh6p violet, *yel* 16.00 12.00
49 A2 2sh violet, *yel* 24.00 24.00
a. Arms inverted 75.00
b. Arms omitted 100.00 100.00
50 A2 2sh6p violet, *yel* 21.00 21.00
a. Arms inverted 24.00 24.00
50B A2 3sh violet, *yel* 42.50 42.50
c. Arms inverted 47.50 47.50
51 A2 4sh violet, *yel* 12.00 12.00
a. Arms omitted
52 A2 5sh violet, *yel* 12.00 12.00
a. Imperf. vert., pair
b. Arms inverted 90.00
53 A2 5sh6p violet, *yel* 12.00 12.00
54 A2 7sh6p violet, *yel* 18.00 18.00
a. Arms inverted 80.00
b. Arms tête bêche, pair
55 A2 10sh violet, *yel* 12.00 12.00
a. Arms inverted 21.00 21.00
b. Arms omitted 75.00 75.00
c. Imperf. vert., pair
d. Arms tête bêche, pair 210.00
56 A2 10sh6p violet, *yel* 20.00 20.00
a. Imperf. vert., pair
b. Arms inverted
c. Arms omitted
57 A2 £1 violet, *yel* 50.00 50.00
a. Arms inverted 52.50
b. Tête bêche pair 475.00 475.00
58 A2 30sh violet, *yel* 100.00 100.00

Granite Paper

59 A2 1p violet, *gray* 12.50 12.50
a. Arms omitted 110.00 110.00
b. Arms inverted 21.00 21.00
c. Imperf. vert., pair
d. Tête bêche pair 300.00
60 A2 2p violet, *gray* 8.00 8.00
a. Arms omitted 100.00 100.00
b. Arms inverted 22.50 22.50
c. Tête bêche pair 450.00
61 A2 3p violet, *gray* 12.00 12.00
a. Arms inverted 65.00 65.00
b. Tête bêche pair 465.00
62 A2 4p violet, *gray* 12.00 12.00
a. Arms inverted 85.00 85.00
b. Tête bêche pair 450.00
63 A2 6p violet, *gray* 12.00 12.00
a. Arms inverted 100.00 100.00
64 A2 1sh6p violet, *gray* 13.00 13.00
a. Arms inverted
Nos. 59-64 (6) 69.50 69.50

These stamps were valid only in New Republic.

All these stamps may have been valid for postage but bona-fide canceled specimens of any but the 1p and 2p stamps are quite rare.

NEW ZEALAND

'nü 'zē–lənd

LOCATION — Group of islands in the south Pacific Ocean, southeast of Australia
GOVT. — Self-governing dominion of the British Commonwealth
AREA — 107,241 sq. mi.
POP. — 3,230,000 (est. 1983)
CAPITAL — Wellington

12 Pence = 1 Shilling
20 Shillings = 1 Pound
100 Cents = 1 Dollar (1967)

Catalogue values for unused stamps in this country are for Never Hinged items, beginning with Scott 246 in the regular postage section, Scott AR99 in the postal-fiscal section, Scott B9 in the semi-postal section, Scott J21 in the postage due section, Scott O92 in the officials section, Scott OY29 in the Life Insurance Department section, and Scott L1 in Ross Dependency.

Watermarks

Wmk. 6- Large Star

Wmk. 59- N Z

Wmk. 60- Lozenges

This watermark includes the vertical word "INVICTA" once in each quarter of the sheet.

Wmk. 61- N Z and Star Close Together

Wmk. 62- N Z and Star Wide Apart

On watermark 61 the margins of the sheets are watermarked "NEW ZEALAND POSTAGE" and parts of the double-lined letters of these words are frequently found on the stamps. It occasionally happens that a stamp shows no watermark whatever.

Wmk. 63- Double-lined N Z and Star

Wmk. 64- Small Star Only

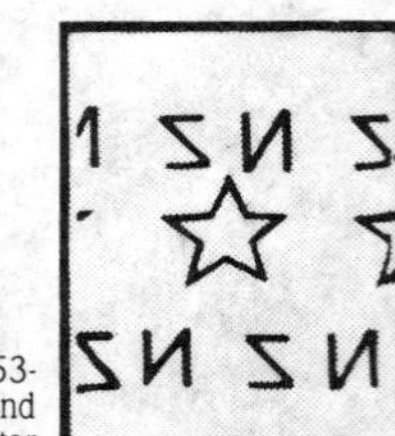
Wmk. 253- Multiple N Z and Star

Values for unused stamps are for examples with original gum as defined in the catalogue introduction.

Very fine examples of the perforated issues between Nos. 7a-69, AR1-AR30, J1-J11, OY1-OY9 and P1-P4 will have perforations touching the framelines or design on one or more sides due to the narrow spacing of the stamps on the plates and imperfect perforating methods.

The rouletted and serrate rouletted stamps of the same period rarely have complete roulettes and are valued as sound and showing partial roulettes. Stamps with complete roulettes range from very scarce to very rare, are seldom traded, and command great premiums.

Victoria — A1

London Print

1855, July 18 Engr. Wmk. 6 *Imperf.*

White Paper

1 A1 1p dull carmine *27,500.* *8,500.*

Blued Paper

2 A1 2p deep blue *12,500.* 500.
3 A1 1sh yellow green *22,500.* *4,500.*
a. Half used as 6p on cover *18,000.*

The blueing was caused by chemical action in the printing process. Stamps which appear to be on white paper are believed to be items where the blueing has later disappeared.

Auckland Print

1855-58 Blue Paper Unwmk.

4 A1 1p orange red 5,500. 1,000.
5 A1 2p blue ('56) 2,000. 250.
6 A1 1sh green ('58) *20,000.* 2,500.
a. Half used as 6p on cover *12,500.*

Nos. 4-6 may be found with parts of the papermaker's name in double-lined letters.

1857-61 Unwmk.

Thin Hard or Thick Soft White Paper

7 A1 1p orange ('58) 1,200. 350.
e. Wmk. 6 ('57) *16,000.*
8 A1 2p blue ('58) 700. 175.
9 A1 6p brown ('59) 900. 300.
e. 6p bister brown ('59) 1,800. 450.
f. 6p chestnut ('59) 2,250. 500.
10 A1 1sh blue green ('61) 6,000. 1,100.
e. 1sh emerald 6,000. 1,100.

No. 7e is identical to a shade of No. 11. The only currently known examples are a pair on a cover front. To qualify as No. 7e, a stamp must have a cancellation prior to 1862.

1859 *Pin Rouletted 9-10*

7a A1 1p dull orange 4,250.
8a A1 2p blue 3,000.
9a A1 6p brown 3,500.
10a A1 1sh greenish blue 5,000.

1859 *Serrate Rouletted 16, 18*

7b A1 1p dull orange 3,500.
8b A1 2p blue 2,500.
9b A1 6p brown 2,500.
g. 6p chestnut 5,250.
10b A1 1sh greenish blue 4,500.

Value for No. 10b is for a damaged stamp.

1859 *Rouletted 7*

7c A1 1p dull orange *5,000.* 3,000.
f. Pair, imperf between —
8c A1 2p blue *6,500.* 2,500.
9c A1 6p brown *4,250.* 2,000.
10c A1 1sh greensh blue *7,500.* 4,000.

1862 *Perf. 13*

7d A1 1p orange vermilion —
8d A1 2p blue 3,500. 2,000.
9d A1 6p brown *6,000.*

1862-63 Wmk. 6 *Imperf.*

11 A1 1p orange ver 375.00 140.00
d. 1p carmine vermilion ('63) 375.00 140.00
e. 1p vermilion 375.00 140.00
12 A1 2p blue 300.00 65.00
d. 2p slate blue 1,250. 215.00
13 A1 3p brown lilac ('63) 375.00 100.00
14 A1 6p red brown ('63) 500.00 65.00
d. 6p black brown 700.00 85.00
e. 6p brown ('63) 700.00 90.00
15 A1 1sh yellow green 800.00 150.00
d. 1sh deep green 850.00 150.00

See No. 7e.

1862 *Pin Rouletted 9-10*

12a A1 2p deep blue
14a A1 6p black brown 2,000.

1862 *Serrate Rouletted 16, 18*

11b A1 1p orange vermilion 1,250.
12b A1 2p blue 1,150.
13b A1 3p lilac brown 1,600.
14b A1 6p black brown 2,000.
15b A1 1sh yellow green 2,500.

1862 *Rouletted 7*

11c A1 1p vermilion 2,000. 500.
12c A1 2p blue 1,400. 400.
13c A1 3p brown lilac 1,600. 600.
14c A1 6p red brown 1,600. 350.
15c A1 1sh yellow green 2,500. 500.

The 1p, 2p, 6p and 1sh come in two or more shades.

1863 *Perf. 13*

16 A1 1p carmine ver 450.00 150.00
17 A1 2p blue 225.00 40.00
18 A1 3p brown lilac 500.00 140.00
19 A1 6p red brown 500.00 45.00
20 A1 1sh yellow green 600.00 150.00

The 1p, 2p, 6p and 1sh come in two or more shades.

1862 Unwmk. *Imperf.*

Pelure Paper

21 A1 1p vermilion 4,250. 1,100.
b. Rouletted 7 2,750.
22 A1 2p pale dull ultra 2,500. 600.
c. 2p gray blue 2,500. 600.
23 A1 3p brown lilac *25,000.*
24 A1 6p black brown 1,000. 250.
b. Rouletted 7 2,000. 350.
c. Serrate perf. 15 3,250.
25 A1 1sh deep yel green 4,750. 700.
b. 1sh deep green 4,750. 400.
c. Rouletted 7 4,250. 1,000.

No. 23 was never placed in use.

1863 *Perf. 13*

21a A1 1p vermilion 7,500. 3,750.
22a A1 2p gray blue 3,500. 400.
b. 2p pale dull ultramarine 3,500. 400.
24a A1 6p black brown 3,000. 225.
25a A1 1sh deep green 4,500. 1,000.

1863 Unwmk. *Imperf.*

Thick White Paper

26 A1 2p dull dark blue 2,000. 650.
a. Perf. 13 1,400. 400.

Nos. 26 and 26a differ from 8 and 8d by a white patch of wear at right of head.

1864 Wmk. 59 *Imperf.*

27 A1 1p carmine ver 750. 175.
28 A1 2p blue 700. 150.
29 A1 6p red brown 1,750. 425.
30 A1 1sh green 850. 250.

1864 *Rouletted 7*

27a A1 1p carmine vermilion 3,000.
28a A1 2p blue 800.
29a A1 6p deep red brown 3,000.
30a A1 1sh green 850.

1864 *Perf. 12½*

27B A1 1p carmine ver 2,750.
28B A1 2p blue 200.00 40.00
29B A1 6p red brown 225.00 30.00
30B A1 1sh dp yel green 2,000.

1864 *Perf. 13*

27C A1 1p carmine ver 5,500. 3,500.
28C A1 2p blue 575. 225.
30C A1 1sh yellow green 1,400. 500.
d. Horiz. pair, imperf. btwn. 8,000.

1864-71 Wmk. 6 *Perf. 12½*

31 A1 1p vermilion 65.00 20.00
a. 1p orange ('71) 125.00 40.00
32 A1 2p blue 85.00 15.00
a. 2p blue, worn plate 70.00 15.00
b. Horiz. pair, imperf. btwn. (#32) *1,500.*
c. Perf. 10x12½ 5,000.
d. Imperf., pair (#32) 1,150. 1,150.

33 A1 3p lilac 65.00 22.50
a. 3p mauve 200.00 45.00
b. Imperf., pair (#33) 1,500. 950.00
c. As "a", imperf., pair 1,250. 1,000.
d. 3p brown lilac *1,250.* *250.00*
34 A1 4p deep rose ('65) 1,750. 250.00
35 A1 4p yellow ('65) 80.00 40.00
a. 4p orange yellow *2,250.* 900.00
36 A1 6p red brown 75.00 15.00
a. 6p brown 90.00 15.00
b. Horiz. pair, imperf. btwn.
37 A1 1sh pale yel green 100.00 45.00
a. 1sh yellow green 100.00 45.00
b. 1sh green 400.00 125.00

The 1p, 2p and 6p come in two or more shades.

Imperforate examples of the 1p pale orange, worn plate; 2p dull blue and 6p dull chocolate brown are reprints. Value, each $100.

1871 Wmk. 6 *Perf. 10*
38 A1 1p deep brown 375.00 60.00

1871 *Perf. 12½*
39 A1 1p brown 90.00 25.00
a. Imperf. 1,000.
40 A1 2p orange 65.00 20.00
a. 2p vermilion 80.00 25.00
b. Imperf., pair 1,250.
41 A1 6p blue 70.00 25.00
Nos. 39-41 (3) 225.00 70.00

Shades exist.

1871 *Perf. 10x12½*
42 A1 1p brown 90.00 25.00
43 A1 2p orange 90.00 22.50
44 A1 6p blue 600.00 200.00
Nos. 42-44 (3) 780.00 247.50

The 6p usually has only one side perf. 10, the 1p and 2p more rarely so.
Shades exist.

1872 Wmk. 59 *Perf. 12½*
45 A1 1p brown 2,500.
46 A1 2p vermilion 300.00 90.00

1872 Unwmk. *Perf. 12½*
47 A1 1p brown 275.00 45.00
48 A1 2p vermilion 55.00 30.00
49 A1 4p yellow orange 125.00 *400.00*

The watermark "T.H. SAUNDERS" in double-line capitals falls on 16 of the 240 stamps in a sheet. The 1p and 2p also are known with script "WT & CO" watermark.

1872 Wmk. 60
50 A1 2p vermilion *4,000.* 600.

A2 A3 A4

A5 A6 A7

Perf. 10x12½, 11½, 12, 12½

1874 Typo. Wmk. 62
51 A2 1p violet 50.00 2.00
a. Bluish paper 75.00 25.00
b. Imperf. 475.00
52 A3 2p rose 40.00 1.25
a. Bluish paper 250.00 50.00
53 A4 3p brown 70.00 35.00
a. Bluish paper 200.00 60.00
54 A5 4p claret 200.00 55.00
a. Bluish paper 400.00 105.00
55 A6 6p blue 140.00 9.00
a. Bluish paper 275.00 75.00
56 A7 1sh green 400.00 22.50
a. Bluish paper 800.00 150.00
Nos. 51-56 (6) 900.00 124.75

1875 Wmk. 6 *Perf. 12½*
57 A2 1p violet 625.00 175.00
58 A3 2p rose 325.00 45.00

A8

1878 Wmk. 62 *Perf. 12x11½*
59 A8 2sh deep rose 300.00 350.00
60 A8 5sh gray 325.00 250.00

No. 60 has numeral "5" in each of the four spandrels.

A9 A10 A11

A12

A13

A14

A15

Perf. 10, 11, 11½, 12, 12½ and Compound

1882
61 A9 1p rose 4.00 .20
a. Vert. pair, imperf. horiz. *475.00*
b. Perf. 12x11½ 30.00 7.00
c. Perf. 12½ 200.00 110.00
62 A10 2p violet 8.75 3.00
a. Vert. pair, imperf. btwn. *450.00*
b. Perf. 12½ 200.00 110.00
63 A11 3p orange 35.00 3.50
a. 3p yellow 35.00 3.50
64 A12 4p blue green 37.50 3.50
a. Perf. 10x11 52.50 7.00
65 A13 6p brown 45.00 3.50
66 A14 8p blue 65.00 35.00
67 A15 1sh red brown 70.00 6.00
Nos. 61-67 (7) 265.25 54.70

See #87. For overprints see #O1-O2, O5, O7-O8.

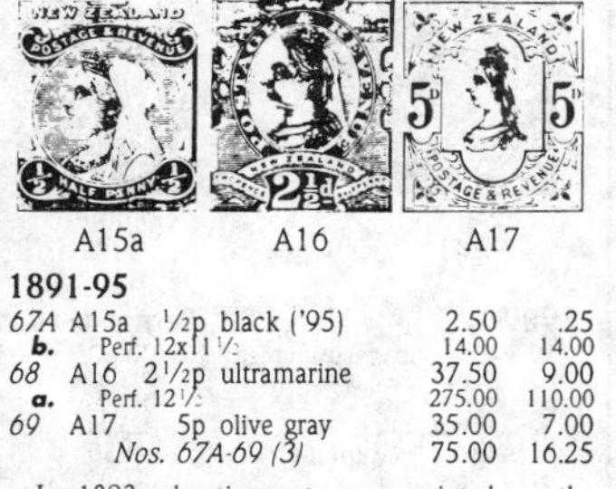

A15a A16 A17

1891-95
67A A15a ½p black ('95) 2.50 .25
b. Perf. 12x11½ 14.00 14.00
68 A16 2½p ultramarine 37.50 9.00
a. Perf. 12½ 275.00 110.00
69 A17 5p olive gray 35.00 7.00
Nos. 67A-69 (3) 75.00 16.25

In 1893 advertisements were printed on the backs of Nos. 61-67, 68-69.
See #86C. For overprints see #O3-O4, O9.

Mt. Cook — A18

Lake Taupo — A19

Pembroke Peak — A20

Mt. Earnslaw, Lake Wakatipu — A21

Mt. Earnslaw, Lake Wakatipu — A22

Huia, Sacred Birds — A23

White Terrace, Rotomahana A24

Otira Gorge and Mt. Ruapehu A25

Kiwi — A26

Maori Canoe — A27

Pink Terrace, Rotomahana — A28

Kea & Kaka (Hawk-billed Parrots) — A29

Milford Sound — A30

Mt. Cook — A31

Perf. 12 to 16

1898, Apr. 5 Engr. Unwmk.
70 A18 ½p lilac gray 3.50 .40
a. Horiz. or vert. pair, imperf. btwn. 650.00 600.00
71 A19 1p yel brn & bl 2.50 .25
a. Horiz. pair, imperf. btwn. 550.00 550.00
72 A20 2p rose brown 21.00 .15
a. Horiz. pair, imperf. vert. 550.00 550.00
73 A21 2½p bl *(Wakitipu)* 6.50 *15.00*
74 A22 2½p bl *(Wakatipu)* 13.00 2.50
a. Vert. pair, imperf. horiz.
75 A23 3p orange brn 20.00 7.00
76 A24 4p rose 11.00 10.00
77 A25 5p red brown 26.00 10.00
a. 5p violet brown 45.00 *100.00*
78 A26 6p green 45.00 20.00
79 A27 8p dull blue 35.00 20.00
80 A28 9p lilac 30.00 20.00
81 A29 1sh dull red 50.00 16.00
82 A30 2sh blue green 85.00 70.00
a. Vert. pair, imperf. btwn. 1,000.
83 A31 5sh vermilion 200.00 180.00
Revenue cancel 25.00
Nos. 70-83 (14) 548.50 371.30

See Nos. 84, 88-89, 91-98, 99B, 102, 104, 106-107, 111-112, 114-121, 126-128. For overprint see No. O10.

The 5sh stamps are often found with revenue cancellations that are embossed or show a crown on the top of a circle. These are worth much less.

A32 A33 A34

1900 Wmk. 63 *Perf. 11*
Thick Soft Wove Paper
84 A18 ½p green 5.00 .40
85 A32 1p carmine rose 6.00 .15
a. 1p lake 10.00 2.50
86 A33 2p red violet 6.50 .35
a. Vert. pair, imperf. horiz. 550.00 550.00
b. Horiz. pair, imperf. vert.
Nos. 84-86 (3) 17.50 .90

Nos. 84 and 86 are re-engravings of Nos. 70 and 72 and are slightly smaller.
See No. 110.

1899-1900 Wmk. 63
86C A15a ½p black ('00) 8.00 5.00
87 A10 2p violet ('00) 17.00 3.50

NEW ZEALAND
BUYING, SELLING, APPRAISALS.
RARE AND CLASSIC STAMPS, POSTAL HISTORY, PROOFS.
For the Best Services in Classic Stamps and Postal History contact the RECOGNIZED LEADERS IN THE FIELD.
Excellent stock of classic material for most countries of the World also available.
THE CLASSIC COLLECTOR
LIANE & SERGIO SISMONDO
Ph. 315-422-2331, Fax 315-422-2956
10035 Carousel Center Drive
Syracuse, NY 13290-0001
CANADIAN OFFICE: P.O. Box 6277, Station J, Ottawa, Canada K2A 1T4, Ph. 613-722-1621, Fax: 613-728-7305

For Elusive Items of Pre-1960 BRITISH COMMONWEALTH
Aron R. Halberstam Philatelists Ltd.
P.O. Box 150168
Van Brunt Station
Brooklyn, NY 11215-0168
Phone 718-788-3978
TOLL FREE 1-800-343-1303
FAX 718-965-3099
Visa, MasterCard, American Express accepted on all orders.

Send for our free price list or send us your want lists.
We are also eager buyers of collections and accumulations of British Commonwealth as well as Worldwide.
Member ASDA – APS

Unwmk.

No.	Type	Description	Unused	Used
88	A22	2½p blue	12.50	2.00
a.		Vert. pair, imperf. horiz.	550.00	550.00
89	A23	3p org brown	22.50	2.00
a.		Horiz. pair, imperf. vert.	450.00	450.00
b.		Horiz. pair, imperf. btwn.	450.00	450.00
90	A34	4p yel brn & bl ('00)	8.00	2.50
a.		Imperf.		
b.		Double impression of center		
91	A25	5p red brown	17.00	4.00
a.		5p violet brown	16.00	1.75
92	A26	6p green	50.00	50.00
a.		Imperf.		
93	A26	6p rose ('00)	35.00	4.00
a.		6p carmine	25.00	4.00
b.		Double impression	475.00	475.00
c.		Imperf., pair	165.00	165.00
d.		Horiz. pair, imperf. vert.	300.00	300.00
94	A27	8p dark blue	17.50	11.00
95	A28	9p red lilac	25.00	11.00
96	A29	1sh red	45.00	8.00
97	A30	2sh blue green	75.00	30.00
98	A31	5sh vermilion	175.00	165.00
		Nos. 86C-98 (13)	507.50	298.00

See #113. For overprints see #O11-O15.

The 5sh stamps are often found with revenue cancellations that are embossed or show a crown on the top of a circle. These are worth much less.

"Commerce" — A35

1901, Jan. 1 Unwmk. ***Perf. 12 to 16***

No.	Type	Description	Unused	Used
99	A35	1p carmine	8.00	3.00

Universal Penny Postage.

See Nos. 100, 103, 105, 108, 129. For overprint see No. O16. Compare design A35 with A42.

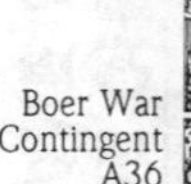

Boer War Contingent A36

Perf. 14, 11x14, 14x11

1901 Wmk. 63

Thick Soft Paper

No.	Type	Description	Unused	Used
99B	A18	½p green	10.00	3.00

Perf. 11, 14 and Compound

No.	Type	Description	Unused	Used
100	A35	1p carmine	6.50	.50
a.		Horiz. pair, imperf. vert.	300.00	300.00
101	A36	1½p brown org	8.00	4.50
a.		Vert. pair, imperf. horiz.	525.00	525.00
b.		Imperf., pair	650.00	650.00
		Nos. 99B-101 (3)	24.50	8.00

No. 101 was issued to honor the New Zealand forces in the South African War.

See No. 109.

Thin Hard Paper

No.	Type	Description	Unused	Used
102	A18	½p green	25.00	16.00
103	A35	1p carmine	19.00	6.25
a.		Horiz. pair, imperf. vert.	300.00	

1902 Unwmk.

No.	Type	Description	Unused	Used
104	A18	½p green	10.00	3.00
105	A35	1p carmine	15.00	2.00

1902 ***Perf. 11***

Thin White Wove Paper

No.	Type	Description	Unused	Used
106	A26	6p rose red	32.50	4.00
a.		Watermarked letters	65.00	45.00

The sheets of No. 106 are watermarked with the words "LISBON SUPERFINE" in two lines, covering ten stamps.

Perf. 11, 14, 11x14, 14x13, 14x14½

1902-07 Wmk. 61

No.	Type	Description	Unused	Used
107	A18	½p green	3.00	.15
a.		Horiz. pair, imperf. vert.	200.00	200.00
108	A35	1p carmine	12.00	.25
a.		1p rose carmine	12.00	.25
b.		Imperf., pair	200.00	200.00
c.		Imperf. x serrate perf.	175.00	175.00
d.		Imperf. horiz. or vert. pair	200.00	200.00
f.		Booklet pane of 6	165.00	
109	A36	1½p brown org ('07)	13.00	*35.00*
110	A33	2p dull vio ('03)	5.50	.25
a.		Horiz. pair, imperf. vert.	325.00	325.00
b.		Vert. pair, imperf. horiz.	325.00	325.00
111	A22	2½p blue	8.50	1.65
112	A23	3p org brown	16.00	1.00
113	A34	4p yel brn & bl	7.00	1.25
a.		Horiz. pair, imperf. vert.	325.00	325.00
b.		Center inverted		
114	A25	5p red brown	16.00	4.00
a.		5p violet brown	15.00	3.50
115	A26	6p rose red	30.00	4.00
a.		6p rose	30.00	4.00
b.		6p pink	30.00	4.00
c.		6p brick red	30.00	4.00
d.		Horiz. pair, imperf. vert.	350.00	350.00
116	A27	8p deep blue	22.50	5.00
117	A28	9p red violet	22.50	5.00
118	A29	1sh scarlet	10.50	1.50
a.		1sh orange red	12.00	1.75
b.		1sh brown red	13.00	1.50
119	A30	2sh blue green	45.00	16.00
120	A31	5sh vermilion	175.00	165.00
		Nos. 107-120 (14)	386.50	240.05

Wmk. 61 is normally sideways on 3p, 5p, 6p, 8p and 1sh.

See No. 129. For overprints see Nos. O17-O22.

The 5sh stamps are often found with revenue cancellations that are embossed or show a crown on the top of a circle. These are worth much less.

In 1908 a quantity of the 1p carmine was overprinted "King Edward VII Land" and taken on a Shackleton expedition to the Antarctic. Because of the weather Shackleton landed at Victoria Land instead. The stamp was never sold to the public at face value. See No. 121a.

Similar conditions prevailed for the 1909-12 ½p green and 1p carmine overprinted "VICTORIA LAND." See Nos. 130d-131d.

1903 Unwmk. ***Perf. 11***

Laid Paper

No.	Type	Description	Unused	Used
121	A30	2sh blue green	350.00	175.00

No. 108a Overprinted in Green: "King Edward VII Land" in Two Lines Reading Up

1908, Jan. 15 ***Perf. 14***

No.	Type	Description	Unused	Used
121a	A35	1p rose carmine	350.00	40.00

See note after No. 120.

Christchurch Exhibition Issue

Arrival of the Maoris A37

Maori Art — A38

Landing of Capt. Cook — A39

Annexation of New Zealand A40

1906, Nov. Wmk. 61 Typo. ***Perf. 14***

No.	Type	Description	Unused	Used
122	A37	½p emerald	10.00	*15.00*
123	A38	1p vermilion	10.00	10.00
a.		1p claret	*6,000.*	*10,000.*
124	A39	3p blue & brown	50.00	75.00
125	A40	6p gray grn & rose	125.00	125.00
		Nos. 122-125 (4)	195.00	225.00

Value for No. 123a is for a fine copy.

Designs of 1902-07 Issue, but smaller

Perf. 14, 14x13, 14x14½

1907-08 Engr.

No.	Type	Description	Unused	Used
126	A23	3p orange brown	*30.00*	5.50
127	A26	6p carmine rose	*32.50*	2.75
128	A29	1sh orange red	*110.00*	14.00
		Nos. 126-128 (3)	*172.50*	22.25

The small stamps are about 21mm high, those of 1898-1902 about 23mm.

Type of 1902 Redrawn

1908 Typo. ***Perf. 14x14½***

No.	Type	Description	Unused	Used
129	A35	1p carmine	20.00	1.00

REDRAWN, 1p: The lines of shading in the globe are diagonal and the other lines of the design are generally thicker than on No. 108.

Edward VII A41

"Commerce" A42

1909-12 ***Perf. 14x14½***

No.	Type	Description	Unused	Used
130	A41	½p yellow green	3.00	.15
a.		Booklet pane of 6	*225.00*	
b.		Booklet pane 5 + label	*650.00*	
c.		Imperf., pair	225.00	
131	A42	1p carmine	.50	.15
a.		Imperf., pair	250.00	250.00
b.		Booklet pane of 6	100.00	

Perf. 14x14½, 14x13½, 14

Engr.

Various Frames

No.	Type	Description	Unused	Used
132	A41	2p mauve	14.00	1.25
133	A41	3p orange brown	19.00	.35
134	A41	4p red orange	17.00	16.00
135	A41	4p yellow ('12)	10.00	3.50
136	A41	5p red brown	14.00	1.25
137	A41	6p carmine rose	21.00	.32
138	A41	8p deep blue	10.00	.40
139	A41	1sh vermilion	35.00	2.00
		Nos. 130-139 (10)	143.50	25.37

Nos. 133, 136-138 exist in vert. pairs with perf. 14x13½ on top and perf. 14x14½ on the bottom. These sell for a premium.

See #177. For overprint see Cook Islands #49.

Nos. 130-131 Overprinted in Black: "VICTORIA LAND" in Two Lines

1911-13

No.	Type	Description	Unused	Used
130d	A41	½p yellow green	*500.00*	*500.00*
131d	A42	1p carmine	60.00	60.00

See note after No. 120.

Issue dates: 1p, Feb. 9; ½p, Jan. 18, 1913.

Stamps of 1909 Overprinted in Black: "AUCKLAND EXHIBITION, 1913," in Three Lines

1913

No.	Type	Description	Unused	Used
130e	A41	½p yellow green	26.00	*27.50*
131e	A42	1p carmine	16.00	*21.00*
133e	A41	3p orange brown	135.00	*160.00*
137e	A41	6p carmine rose	150.00	*210.00*
		Nos. 130e-137e (4)	327.00	*418.50*

This issue was valid only within New Zealand and to Australia from Dec. 1, 1913, to Feb. 28, 1914. The Auckland Stamp Collectors Club inspired this issue.

King George V — A43

1915 Typo. ***Perf. 14x15***

No.	Type	Description	Unused	Used
144	A43	½p yellow green	.85	.15
b.		Booklet pane of 6	*140.00*	

See Nos. 163-164, 176, 178. For overprints see No. MR1, Cook Islands No. 40.

A44 A45

Perf. 14x14½, 14x13½

1915-22 Engr.

No.	Type	Description	Unused	Used
145	A44	1½p gray	1.25	.65
146	A45	2p purple	9.00	13.00
147	A45	2p org yel ('16)	7.50	6.50
148	A44	2½p dull blue	4.25	1.90
149	A45	3p violet brown	5.50	.25
150	A45	4p orange yellow	6.50	*15.00*
151	A45	4p purple ('16)	7.50	.15
a.		Imperf., pair	*1,500.*	
b.		Horiz. pair, imperf. vert.		
152	A44	4½p dark green	14.00	10.50
153	A45	5p light blue ('21)	7.00	.70
a.		Imperf., pair	150.00	
154	A45	6p carmine rose	5.50	.25
a.		Horiz. pair, imperf. vert.		
155	A44	7½p red brown	16.00	16.00
156	A45	8p blue ('21)	15.00	15.00
157	A45	8p red brown ('22)	21.00	2.00
158	A45	9p olive green	13.00	2.25
a.		Imperf., pair	*825.00*	
159	A45	1sh vermilion	15.00	1.25
a.		Imperf., pair	400.00	
		Nos. 145-159 (15)	148.00	85.40

Nos. 145-156, 158-159 exist in vert. pairs with perf 14x13½ on top and perf 14x14½ on the bottom. These sell for a premium. No. 157 only comes perf 14x13½.

For overprints see Cook Islands Nos. 53-60.

A46

A47

1916-19 Typo. ***Perf. 14x15, 14***

No.	Type	Description	Unused	Used
160	A46	1½p gray black	10.00	.35
161	A47	1½p gray black	9.00	.15
162	A47	1½p brown orange ('18)	3.25	.15
163	A43	2p yellow	2.00	.15
164	A43	3p chocolate ('19)	6.00	.80
		Nos. 160-164 (5)	30.25	1.60

The engr. stamps have a background of geometric lathe-work; the typo. stamps have a background of crossed dotted lines.

Type A43 has three diamonds at each side of the crown, type A46 has two, and type A47 has one.

In 1916 the 1½, 2, 3 and 6p of the 1915-16 issue and the 8p of the 1909 issue were printed on paper intended for the long rectangular stamps of the 1902-07 issue. In this paper the watermarks are set wide apart, so that the smaller stamps often show only a small part of the watermark or miss it altogether.

For overprints see Cook Islands #50-52.

IF YOU COLLECT...
NEW ZEALAND
... you need our bimonthly pricelists, featuring New Zealand, Canada, Great Britain, Australia, Ireland, Newfoundland, and United States.
Call 800-842-5305 (USA) or 800-437-8036 (Canada) to request our mailings, or write...
THE PERF GAUGE
P.O. Box 2648
Inverness, FL 34451-2648

Victory Issue

"Peace" and British Lion — A48

Peace and Lion — A49

Maori Chief — A50

British Lion A51

"Victory" A52

King George V, Lion and Maori Fern at Sides — A53

1920, Jan. 27 *Perf. 14*

165 A48	½p	yellow green	1.25	1.00
166 A49	1p	carmine	4.00	.25
167 A50	1½p	brown orange	3.00	.20
168 A51	3p	black brown	12.50	10.00
169 A52	6p	purple	11.00	*12.50*
170 A53	1sh	vermilion	22.50	*32.50*
		Nos. 165-170 (6)	54.25	*56.45*

No. 165 Surcharged in Red

2d. 2d.

TWOPENCE

1922, Mar.

174 A48 2p on ½p yellow green	2.00	.40

Map of New Zealand — A54

1923 **Typo.** *Perf. 14x15*

175 A54 1p carmine rose	1.25	.15

Restoration of Penny Postage. The paper varies from thin to thick.

Types of 1909-15

N Z and Star printed on back in blue

1925 **Unwmk.** *Perf. 14x14½*

176 A43	½p	yellow green	1.65	1.00
177 A42	1p	carmine	2.25	.90
178 A43	2p	yellow	15.00	*25.00*
		Nos. 176-178 (3)	18.90	*26.90*

Exhibition Buildings A55

1925, Nov. 17 **Wmk. 61**

Surface Tinted Paper

179 A55	½p	yel green, *grnsh*	2.50	*8.25*
180 A55	1p	car rose, *pink*	2.50	*5.75*
181 A55	4p	red violet, *lilac*	32.50	*60.00*
		Nos. 179-181 (3)	37.50	*74.00*

Dunedin Exhibition.

George V in Admiral's Uniform A56

In Field Marshal's Uniform A57

1926 *Perf. 14, 14½x14*

182 A56	2sh	blue	40.00	14.00
a.		2sh dark blue	45.00	19.00
183 A56	3sh	violet	90.00	70.00
a.		3sh deep violet	90.00	70.00

Perf. 14, 14x14½

184 A57	1p	rose red	.60	.15
a.		Booklet pane of 6	75.00	
b.		Imperf., pair	75.00	
		Nos. 182-184 (3)	130.60	84.15

For overprints see Cook Islands Nos. 74-75.

Pied Fantail and Clematis — A58

Kiwi and Cabbage Palm — A59

Maori Woman Cooking in Boiling Spring — A60

Maori Council House (Whare) — A61

Mt. Cook and Mountain Lilies — A62

Maori Girl Wearing Tiki — A63

Mitre Peak — A64

Striped Marlin A65

Harvesting — A66

Tuatara Lizard — A67

Maori Panel from Door — A68

Tui or Parson Bird — A69

Capt. Cook Landing at Poverty Bay — A70

Mt. Egmont, North Island — A71

Perf. 14x14½, 14x13½, 13½x14, 13½

1935, May 1 **Engr.** **Wmk. 61**

185	A58	½p	bright green	.40	.15
186	A59	1p	copper red	.40	.15
186A	A59	1p	copper red, re-engraved	13.00	3.75
b.			Booklet pane of 6 + ad labels	*80.00*	
187	A60	1½p	red brown	1.25	1.90
188	A61	2p	red orange	2.00	.15
189	A62	2½p	dk gray & dk brown	4.00	1.90
190	A63	3p	chocolate	4.50	.40
191	A64	4p	black brn & blk	1.25	.65
192	A65	5p	violet blue	7.00	2.25
193	A66	6p	red	8.50	1.75
194	A67	8p	dark brown	4.50	3.25

Litho.

Size: 18x21¼mm

195	A68	9p	black & scarlet	10.00	3.50

Engr.

196	A69	1sh	dk sl green	7.50	1.40
197	A70	2sh	olive green	30.00	2.50
198	A71	3sh	yel brn & brn black	18.00	9.50
			Nos. 185-198 (15)	112.30	33.20
			Set, never hinged	190.00	

On No. 186A, the horizontal lines in the sky are much darker.

The 2½p, 5p, 2sh and 3sh are perf. 13½ vertically; perf. 14 horizontally with alternate rows mixed perf. 14 and 13.

See Nos. 203-216, 244-245.

Silver Jubilee Issue

Queen Mary and King George V A72

1935, May 7 *Perf. 11x11½*

199 A72	½p	blue green	.25	.15
200 A72	1p	dark car rose	.20	.15
201 A72	6p	vermilion	16.00	*25.00*
		Nos. 199-201 (3)	16.45	*25.30*
		Set, never hinged	25.00	

25th anniv. of the reign of King George V.

Types of 1935

Perf. 12½ to 15 and Compound

1936-41 **Wmk. 253**

203	A58	½p	bright green	.25	.15
204	A59	1p	copper red	.45	.15
205	A60	1½p	red brown	1.90	1.65
206	A61	2p	red orange	.15	.15
a.			Perf. 14	1.00	.35
b.			Perf. 14x15	1.25	.35
207	A62	2½p	dk gray & dk brn	1.00	1.25
208	A63	3p	chocolate	7.00	.60
209	A64	4p	black brn & blk	1.25	.20
210	A65	5p	violet blue	1.40	.60
211	A66	6p	red	.45	.20
212	A67	8p	dark brown	1.40	.15

Litho.

Size: 18x21½mm

213	A68	9p	gray & scarlet	13.00	7.00
a.			9p black & scarlet	15.00	1.75

Engr.

214	A69	1sh	dark slate grn	1.75	.25
215	A70	2sh	olive green	7.75	.55
a.			Perf. 13½x14	27.50	.80
216	A71	3sh	yel brn & blk brn	8.50	.70
a.			Perf. 12½ ('41)	9.00	2.25
			Nos. 203-216 (14)	46.25	13.60
			Set, never hinged	85.00	

Wool Industry A73

Butter Industry A74

Sheep Farming A75

Apple Industry A76

Shipping A77

1936, Oct. 1 **Wmk. 61** *Perf. 11*

218 A73	½p	deep green	.15	.15
219 A74	1p	red	.15	.15
220 A75	2½p	deep blue	1.65	2.75
221 A76	4p	dark purple	1.25	1.90
222 A77	6p	red brown	1.40	1.65
		Nos. 218-222 (5)	4.60	6.60
		Set, never hinged	5.00	

Congress of the Chambers of Commerce of the British Empire held in New Zealand.

Queen Elizabeth and King George VI A78

Perf. 13½x13

1937, May 13 **Wmk. 253**

223 A78	1p	rose carmine	.15	.15
224 A78	2½p	dark blue	.20	.50
225 A78	6p	vermilion	.65	.75
		Nos. 223-225 (3)	1.00	1.40
		Set, never hinged	2.25	

Coronation of George VI and Elizabeth.

A79

A80

1938-44 **Engr.** *Perf. 13½*

226	A79	½p	emerald	.45	.15
226B	A79	½p	brown org ('41)	.15	.15
227	A79	1p	rose red	.60	.15
227A	A79	1p	lt blue grn ('41)	.15	.15
228	A80	1½p	violet brown	7.75	1.65
228B	A80	1½p	red ('44)	.15	.15
228C	A80	3p	blue ('41)	.15	.15
			Nos. 226-228C (7)	9.40	2.55
			Set, never hinged	18.00	

See Nos. 258-264. For surcharges see Nos. 242-243, 279, 285.

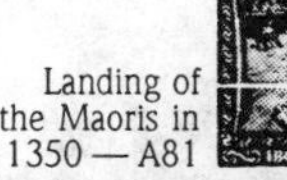

Landing of the Maoris in 1350 — A81

Captain Cook, His Map of New Zealand, 1769, H.M.S. Endeavour A82

Victoria, Edward VII, George V, Edward VIII and George VI — A83

Abel Tasman, Ship, and Chart of West Coast of New Zealand A84

Treaty of Waitangi, 1840 — A85

Pioneer Settlers Landing on Petone Beach, 1840 — A86

The Progress of Transport A87

H.M.S. "Britomart" at Akaroa — A88

Route of Ship Carrying First Shipment of Frozen Mutton to England — A89

Maori Council A90

Gold Mining in 1861 and Modern Gold Dredge A91

Giant Kauri — A92

Perf. 13½x13, 13x13½, 14x13½

1940, Jan. 2 Engr. Wmk. 253

No.	Type	Value	Color	Unused	Used
229	A81	½p	dk blue green	.15	.15
230	A82	1p	scarlet & sepia	.20	.15
231	A83	1½p	brt vio & ultra	.35	.15
232	A84	2p	black brown & Prussian green	.25	.15
233	A85	2½p	dk bl & myr grn	.35	.35
234	A86	3p	dp plum & dk violet	1.90	.30
235	A87	4p	dk red vio & vio brn	1.90	1.00
236	A88	5p	brown & lt bl	2.25	1.75
237	A89	6p	vio & brt grn	2.25	.65
238	A90	7p	org red & black	2.00	*4.00*
239	A90	8p	org red & black	3.25	1.65
240	A91	9p	dp org & olive	5.50	2.50
241	A92	1sh	dk sl grn & ol	5.75	4.50
			Nos. 229-241 (13)	26.10	17.30
			Set, never hinged	60.00	

Centenary of British sovereignty established by the treaty of Waitangi.

Imperfs of #229-241 exist. These probably are plate proofs.

For surcharge see No. 246.

Stamps of 1938 Surcharged with New Values in Black

1941 Wmk. 253 *Perf. 13½*

No.	Type	Value	Description	Unused	Used
242	A79	1p	on ½p emerald	.20	.15
243	A80	2p	on 1½p violet brn	.15	.15
			Set value		.15
			Set, never hinged	.75	

Type of 1935 Redrawn

1941 Typo. Wmk. 61 *Perf. 14x15*

Size: 17¼x20¼mm

No.	Type	Value	Color	Unused	Used
244	A68	9p	int black & scarlet	65.00	15.00

Wmk. 253

No.	Type	Value	Color	Unused	Used
245	A68	9p	int black & scarlet	4.00	3.50
			Set, never hinged	95.00	

Catalogue values for unused stamps in this section, from this point to the end of the section, are for Never Hinged items.

No 231 Surcharged in Black

TENPENCE

1944 *Perf. 13½x13*

No.	Type	Value	Description	Unused	Used
246	A83	10p	on 1½p brt vio & ultra	.45	.45

Peace Issue

Lake Matheson A93

Parliament House, Wellington — A94

St. Paul's Cathedral, London — A95

The Royal Family — A96

Badge of Royal New Zealand Air Force — A97

New Zealand Army Overseas Badge — A98

Badge of Royal Navy — A99

New Zealand Coat of Arms — A100

Knight, Window of Wellington Boys' College — A101

Natl. Memorial Campanile, Wellington — A103

Southern Alps and Chapel Altar A102

Engr.; Photo. (1½p, 1sh)

Perf. 13x13½, 13½x13

1946, Apr. 1 Wmk. 253

No.	Type	Value	Color	Unused	Used
247	A93	½p	choc & dk bl grn	.15	.15
248	A94	1p	emerald	.15	.15
249	A95	1½p	scarlet	.15	.15
250	A96	2p	rose violet	.15	.15
251	A97	3p	dk grn & ultra	.15	.15
252	A98	4p	brn org & ol grn	.18	.15
253	A99	5p	ultra & blue grn	.15	.15
254	A100	6p	org red & red brn	.20	.15
255	A101	8p	brown lake & blk	.22	.18
256	A102	9p	black & brt bl	.22	.26
257	A103	1sh	gray black	.50	.26
			Set value	1.75	1.34

Return to peace at the close of WWII.

Imperfs exist from the printer's archives.

George VI Type of 1938 and

King George VI — A104

1947 Engr. *Perf. 13½*

No.	Type	Value	Color	Unused	Used
258	A80	2p	orange	.15	.15
260	A80	4p	rose lilac	.38	.30
261	A80	5p	gray	.80	.15
262	A80	6p	rose carmine	.45	.15
263	A80	8p	deep violet	1.10	.15
264	A80	9p	chocolate	1.50	.15

Perf. 14

No.	Type	Value	Color	Unused	Used
265	A104	1sh	dk car rose & chnt	1.40	.15
266	A104	1sh3p	ultra & chnt	1.75	.15
267	A104	2sh	dk grn & brn org	3.25	.25
268	A104	3sh	gray blk & chnt	4.25	1.65
			Nos. 258-268 (10)	15.03	3.25

Nos. 265-267 have watermark either upright or sideways. On No. 268 watermark is always sideways.

"John Wickliffe" and "Philip Laing" A105

Cromwell, Otago A106

First Church, Dunedin — A107

University of Otago A108

1948, Feb. 23 *Perf. 13½*

No.	Type	Value	Color	Unused	Used
269	A105	1p	green & blue	.15	.15
270	A106	2p	brown & green	.15	.15
271	A107	3p	violet	.15	.15
272	A108	6p	lilac rose & gray blk	.15	.16
			Set value	.35	.40

Otago Province settlement, cent.

A Royal Visit set of four was prepared but not issued. Copies of the 3p have appeared on the stamp market.

A109

Cathedral at Christchurch — A110

"They Passed this Way" — A111

Wmk. 253

1950, July 28 Typo. *Perf. 14*

Black Surcharge

No.	Type	Value	Color	Unused	Used
273	A109	1½p	rose red	.15	.15

See No. 367.

1950, Nov. 20 Engr. *Perf. 13x13½*

Designs: 3p, John Robert Godley. 6p, Canterbury University College. 1sh, View of Timaru.

No.	Type	Value	Color	Unused	Used
274	A110	1p	blue grn & blue	.15	.15
275	A111	2p	car & red org	.15	.15
276	A110	3p	indigo & blue	.15	.15
277	A111	6p	brown & blue	.20	.20
278	A111	1sh	claret & blue	.65	.65
			Set value	1.12	1.10

Centenary of the founding of Canterbury Provincial District.

Imperfs of #274-278 exist.

No. 227A Surcharged in Black

1952, Dec. *Perf. 13½*

No.	Type	Value	Description	Unused	Used
279	A79	3p	on 1p lt blue green	.15	.15

Coronation Issue

Buckingham Palace and Elizabeth II A112

Queen Elizabeth II — A113

Westminster Abbey — A114

Designs: 4p, Queen Elizabeth and state coach. 1sh6p, Crown and royal scepter.

Perf. 13x12½, 14x14½ (3p, 8p)

Engr., Photo. (3p, 8p)

1953, May 25

No.	Type	Value	Color	Unused	Used
280	A112	2p	ultramarine	.15	.15
281	A113	3p	brown	.20	.15
282	A112	4p	carmine	.60	.35
283	A114	8p	slate black	.80	.70
284	A112	1sh6p	vio blue & pur	1.50	1.50
			Nos. 280-284 (5)	3.25	2.85

No. 226B Surcharged in Black

1953, Sept. *Perf. 13½*

No.	Type	Value	Description	Unused	Used
285	A79	1p	on ½p brown orange	.15	.15

Queen Elizabeth II — A115

Queen Elizabeth II and Duke of Edinburgh A116

Perf. 12½x13½, 13½x13

1953, Dec. 9 Engr.

286 A115 3p lilac .15 .15
287 A116 4p deep blue .20 .20
Set value .30 .24

Visit of Queen Elizabeth II and the Duke of Edinburgh.

A117

A118

A119

1953-57 *Perf. 13½*

288 A117 ½p gray .15 .15
289 A117 1p orange .15 .15
290 A117 1½p rose brown .20 .15
291 A117 2p blue green .15 .15
292 A117 3p red .15 .15
293 A117 4p blue .20 .15
294 A117 6p rose violet .45 .15
295 A117 8p rose car .40 .15
296 A118 9p emerald & org brn .50 .15
297 A118 1sh car & blk 1.25 .15
298 A118 1sh6p blue & blk 1.25 .15
298A A118 1sh9p org & blk 3.75 .55
298B A119 2sh6p redsh brn 30.00 4.75
299 A119 3sh blue green 10.50 .55
300 A119 5sh rose car 17.50 3.00
301 A119 10sh vio blue 30.00 22.50
Nos. 288-301 (16) 96.60 33.00

The 1½p was issued in 1953; 1sh9p and 2sh6p in 1957; all others in 1954.

No. 298A exists on both ordinary and chalky paper.

Two dies of the 1sh differ in shading on the sleeve.

Imperfs of #298B-301 and tete-beche pairs of #301 and 312 exist from the printer's archives.

See #306-312. For surcharge see #320.

Maori Mailman A120

Queen Elizabeth II A121

Douglas DC-3 A122

Perf. 13½ (2p), 14 (3p), 13 (4p)

1955, July 18 Wmk. 253

302 A120 2p deep green & brown .15 .15
303 A121 3p claret .15 .15
304 A122 4p ultra & black .45 .45
Nos. 302-304 (3) .75
Set value .50

Cent. of New Zealand's 1st postage stamps.

Type of 1953-54 Redrawn

1955-59 Wmk. 253 *Perf. 13½*

306 A117 1p orange ('56) .15 .15
307 A117 1½p rose brown .50 .15
308 A117 2p blue green ('56) .20 .15
309 A117 3p vermilion ('56) 1.00 .15
310 A117 4p blue ('58) 3.50 .45
311 A117 6p violet 3.50 .45
312 A117 8p brown red ('59) 8.50 8.50
Nos. 306-312 (7) 17.35 10.00

The numeral has been enlarged and the ornament in the lower right corner omitted.

Nos. 306, 308-310 exist on both ordinary and chalky paper.

Imperfs exist.

For surcharges see Nos. 319, 354.

Whalers of Foveaux Strait A123

"Agriculture" with Cow and Sheep A124

Notornis (Takahe) — A125

1956, Jan. *Perf. 13x12½, 13 (8p)*

313 A123 2p deep green .15 .15
314 A124 3p sepia .15 .15
315 A125 8p car & blue vio 1.50 1.25
Nos. 313-315 (3) 1.80 1.55

Southland centennial.

Lamb and Map of New Zealand — A126

Lamb, S. S. "Dunedin" and Refrigeration Ship — A127

Perf. 14x14½, 14½x14

1957, Feb. 15 Photo.

316 A126 4p bright blue 1.00 .70
317 A127 8p brick red 1.75 1.50

New Zealand Meat Export Trade, 75th anniv.

Sir Truby King — A128

Nelson Diocese Seal — A129a

Sir Charles Kingsford-Smith and "Southern Cross" — A129

1957, May 14 Engr. *Perf. 13*

318 A128 3p rose red .20 .15

Plunket Society, 50th anniversary.

Imperfs exist. These probably are plate proofs.

Nos. 307, 290 Surcharged

1958, Jan. 15 *Perf. 13½*

319 A117 2p on 1½p (#307) .20 .15
a. Small surcharge .20 .15
320 A117 2p on 1½p (#290) 140.00 *200.00*

Surcharge measures 9½mm vert. on Nos. 319-320; 9mm on No. 319a. Diameter of dot 4½mm on Nos. 319-320; 3¾mm on No. 319a.

The small surcharge exists on No. 290.

Counterfeits exist.

Perf. 14x14½

1958, Aug. 27 Engr. Wmk. 253

321 A129 6p brt violet blue .35 .35

1st air crossing of the Tasman Sea, 30th anniv.

See Australia No. 310.

1958, Sept. 29 *Perf. 13*

322 A129a 3p carmine rose .20 .15

Centenary of Nelson City.

Imperfs exist. These probably are plate proofs.

Statue of "Pania," Napier — A130

Gannet Sanctuary, Cape Kidnappers A131

Design: 8p, Maori shearing sheep.

Perf. 13½x14½, 14½x14

1958, Nov. 3 Photo. Wmk. 253

323 A130 2p yellow green .15 .15
324 A131 3p ultramarine .15 .15
325 A130 8p red brown 2.25 1.50
Nos. 323-325 (3) 2.55 1.80

Centenary of Hawkes Bay province.

Jamboree Kiwi Badge — A132

1959, Jan. 5 Engr. *Perf. 13*

326 A132 3p car rose & brown .25 .15

Pan-Pacific Scout Jamboree, Auckland, Jan. 3-10.

"Endeavour" at Ship Cove A133

Designs: 3p, Shipping wool at Wairau bar, 1857. 8p, Salt Industry, Grassmere.

1959, Mar. 2 Photo. *Perf. 14½x14*

327 A133 2p green .15 .15
328 A133 3p dark blue .15 .15
329 A133 8p brown 2.50 2.50
Nos. 327-329 (3) 2.80 2.80

Centenary of Marlborough Province.

The Explorer — A134

Westland Centennial: 3p, The Gold Digger. 8p, The Pioneer Woman.

1960, May 16 *Perf. 14x14½*

330 A134 2p green .15 .15
331 A134 3p orange .15 .15
332 A134 8p gray 2.25 1.75
Nos. 330-332 (3) 2.55 2.05

Kaka Beak Flower — A135

Timber Industry — A136

Tiki — A137

Maori Rock Drawing — A138

Butter Making A139

Designs: ½p, Manuka flower. 1p, Karaka flower. 2½p, Titoki flower. 3p, Kowhai flower. 4p, Hibiscus. 5p, Mountain daisy. 6p, Clematis. 7p, Koromiko flower. 8p, Rata flower. 9p, Flag. 1sh3p, Rainbow trout. 1sh9p, Plane spraying farmland. 3sh, Ngauruhoe Volcano, Tongariro National Park. 5sh, Sutherland Falls. 10sh, Tasman Glacier, Mount Cook. £1, Pohutu Geyser.

Perf. 14½x14, 14x14½

1960-66 Photo. Wmk. 253

333 A135 ½p dp car, grn & pale bl .15 .15
b. Green omitted 70.00
c. Pale blue omitted 55.00
334 A135 1p brn, org & grn .15 .15
b. Orange omitted 150.00
c. Perf. 14½x13, wmkd. sideways 1.75 1.75
335 A135 2p grn, rose car, blk & yel .15 .15
b. Black omitted 200.00
c. Yellow omitted 225.00
336 A135 2½p blk, grn, red & brn .25 .15
a. Brown omitted 50.00
b. Green & red omitted 160.00
c. Green omitted 75.00
d. Red omitted 90.00
337 A135 3p Prus bl, yel, brn & grn .15 .15
b. Yellow omitted 45.00
c. Brown omitted 45.00
d. Green omitted 45.00
e. Perf. 14½x13, wmkd. sideways 2.00 2.00
338 A135 4p bl, grn, yel & lilac .20 .15
a. Yellow omitted 100.00
b. Lilac omitted 45.00
339 A135 5p pur, blk, yel & grn .25 .15
a. Yellow omitted 125.00
340 A135 6p dp grn, lt grn & lil .25 .15
a. Light green omitted 60.00
b. Lilac omitted 70.00
340C A135 7p pink, red, grn & yel .40 .60
341 A135 8p gray, grn, pink & yel .40 .15
342 A136 9p ultra & car .60 .16
a. Carmine omitted 150.00
343 A136 1sh green & brn .45 .15
344 A137 1sh3p bl, brn & carmine .85 .15
a. Carmine omitted 150.00
345 A137 1sh6p org brn & olive grn .95 .18
346 A136 1sh9p pale brown 5.75 .40
347 A138 2sh buff & blk 1.65 .16
348 A139 2sh6p red brn & yellow 3.25 .42
a. Yellow omitted 275.00
349 A139 3sh gray brown 28.00 1.40
350 A138 5sh dark green 7.50 .65
351 A139 10sh blue 6.50 3.50
352 A138 £1 magenta 14.00 9.25
Nos. 333-352 (21) 71.85 18.37

Nos. 334c and 337e were issued in coils.

Only on chalky paper: 2½p, 5p, 7p. On ordinary and chalky paper: 1p, 3p, 4p, 6p, 1sh9p, 2sh, 3sh, 5sh, 10sh. Others on ordinary paper only.

Issued: 2p, 4p, 1sh, 1sh3p, 1sh6p, 1sh9p, 2sh, 2sh6p, 3sh, 5sh, 10sh, £1, 7/11/60; ½p, 1p, 3p, 6p, 8p, 9p, 9/1/60; 2½p, 11/1/61; 5p, 5/14/62; 7p, 3/16/66; #334c, 11/63; #337e, 10/3/63.

See Nos. 360-361, 382-404.

Adoration of the Shepherds, by Rembrandt
A140

Perf. 11½x12

1960, Nov. 1 Wmk. 253

353 A140 2p dp brown & red, *cream* 1.00 .15
a. Red omitted 450.00 250.00

Christmas. See No. 355.

No. 309 Surcharged with New Value and Bars

Two types of surcharge:
Type I - "2½d" is 5½mm wide.
Type II - "2½d" is 5mm wide.

1961, Sept. 1 Engr. *Perf. 13½*

354 A117 2½p on 3p vermilion, I .25 .15
a. Type II .25 .15

Type of 1960

Christmas: 2½p, Adoration of the Magi, by Dürer.

1961, Oct. 16 Photo. *Perf. 14½x14*
Size: 30x34mm

355 A140 2½p multicolored .90 .20

Morse Key and Port Hills, Lyttelton, 1862
A141

Design: 8p, Teleprinter and tape, 1962.

1962, June 1 Wmk. 253

356 A141 3p dk brown & green .15 .15
a. Green omitted
357 A141 8p dk red & gray 1.90 1.90
a. Imperf., pair 900.00
b. Gray omitted 300.00

Centenary of the New Zealand telegraph.

Madonna in Prayer by Sassoferrato — A142

1962, Oct. 15 *Perf. 14½x14*

358 A142 2½p multicolored .60 .15

Christmas.

Holy Family by Titian — A143

1963, Oct. 14 Photo. *Perf. 12½*

359 A143 2½p multicolored .18 .15
a. Imperf., pair *225.00*
b. Yellow omitted *400.00*

Christmas.

Types of 1960-62

Designs: 1sh9p, Plane spraying farmland. 3sh, Ngauruhoe volcano, Tongariro National Park.

1963-64 *Perf. 14½x14*

360 A136 1sh9p brt blue, grn & yel 2.75 .55
361 A139 3sh blue, green & bister 5.00 1.10

Issued: 1sh9p, 11/4/63; 3sh, 4/1/64.

Old and New Engines
A144

Design: 1sh9p, Express train and Mt. Ruapehu.

1963, Nov. 25 *Perf. 14*

362 A144 3p multicolored .15 .15
a. Blue (sky) omitted *300.00*
363 A144 1sh9p bl, blk, yel & carmine 3.50 3.50
a. Carmine (value) omitted *750.00*

Centenary of New Zealand Railways.

Cable Around World and Under Sea — A144a

1963, Dec. 3 Unwmk. *Perf. 13½*

364 A144a 8p yel, car, blk & bl 1.90 1.90

Opening of the Commonwealth Pacific (telephone) cable service (COMPAC).
See Australia No. 381.

Map of New Zealand and Steering Wheel
A145

Perf. 14½x14

1964, May 1 Wmk. 253

365 A145 3p multicolored .18 .15

National Road Safety Campaign.

Rev. Samuel Marsden Conducting First Christian Service, Rangihoua Bay, Christmas 1814
A146

1964, Oct. 12 *Perf. 14x13½*

366 A146 2½p multicolored .22 .15

Christmas.

Postal-Fiscal Type of 1950

1964, Dec. 14 Typo. *Perf. 14*
Black Surcharge

367 A109 7p rose red .38 .52

ANZAC Issue

Anzac Cove, Gallipoli
A147

Design: 5p, Anzac Cove and poppy.

Perf. 12½

1965, Apr. 14 Unwmk. Photo.

368 A147 4p light brown .15 .15
369 A147 5p green & red .35 .35
Set value .41

50th anniv. of the landing of the Australian and New Zealand Army Corps, ANZAC, at Gallipoli, Turkey, Apr. 25, 1915.

ITU Emblem, Old and New Communication Equipment — A148

Perf. 14½x14

1965, May 17 Photo. Wmk. 253

370 A148 9p lt brown & dk blue .60 .60

Centenary of the ITU.

Sir Winston Spencer Churchill (1874-1965) — A148a

1965, May 24 Unwmk. *Perf. 13½*

371 A148a 7p lt blue, gray & blk .48 .48

See Australia No. 389.

Provincial Council Building, Wellington
A149

Perf. 14½x14

1965, July 26 Photo. Wmk. 253

372 A149 4p multicolored .25 .15

Centenary of the establishment of Wellington as seat of government. The design is from a water color by L. B. Temple, 1867.

ICY Emblem
A150

1965, Sept. 28 Litho. *Perf. 14*

373 A150 4p ol bister & dk red .22 .15

International Cooperation Year.

"The Two Trinities" by Murillo — A151

1965, Oct. 11 Photo. *Perf. 13½x14*

374 A151 3p multicolored .22 .15
a. Gold omitted 900.00

Christmas.

Parliament House, Wellington and Commonwealth Parliamentary Association Emblem — A152

Designs: 4p, Arms of New Zealand and Queen Elizabeth II. 2sh, Wellington from Mt. Victoria.

1965, Nov. 30 Unwmk. *Perf. 14*

375 A152 4p multicolored .28 .15
a. Blue omitted *500.00*
376 A152 9p multicolored .95 1.00
377 A152 2sh multicolored 5.50 5.00
Nos. 375-377 (3) 6.73 6.15

11th Commonwealth Parliamentary Assoc. Conf.

Scout Emblem, Maori Pattern — A153

Virgin with Child, by Carlo Maratta — A154

Perf. 14x14½

1966, Jan. 5 Photo. Wmk. 253

378 A153 4p green & gold .22 .15
a. Gold omitted *500.00*

4th National Scout Jamboree, Trentham.

1966, Oct. 3 Wmk. 253 *Perf. 14*

379 A154 3p multicolored .25 .15

Christmas.

Queens Victoria and Elizabeth II — A155

New Zealand PO Savings Bank cent.: 9p, Reverse of half sovereign, 1867, and 1967 dollar.

Perf. 14x14½

1967, Feb. 3 Photo. Wmk. 253

380 A155 4p plum, gold & black .15 .15
381 A155 9p dk grn, bl, blk, sil & gold .45 .45

Decimal Currency

Types of 1960-62

Designs: ½c, Manuka flower. 1c, Karaka flower. 2c, Kaka beak flower. 2½c, Kowhai flower. 3c, Hibiscus. 4c, Mountain daisy. 5c, Clematis. 6c, Koromiko flower. 7c, Rata flower. 7½c, Brown trout. 8c, Flag. 10c, Timber industry. 15c, Tiki. 20c, Maori rock drawing. 25c, Butter making. 28c, Fox Glacier, Westland National Park. 30c, Ngauruhoe Volcano, Tongarino National Park. 50c, Sutherland Falls. $1, Tasman Glacier, Mount Cook. $2, Pohutu Geyser.

Wmk. 253, Unwmkd. (#400)

1967-70 Photo. *Various Perfs.*

382 A135 ½c multicolored .24 .18
383 A135 1c multicolored .15 .15
a. Booklet pane of 5 + label 2.25
384 A135 2c multicolored .24 .15
385 A135 2½c multicolored .15 .16
386 A135 3c multicolored .15 .15
387 A135 4c multicolored .32 .25
388 A135 5c multicolored .28 .15
389 A135 6c multicolored .38 .15
390 A135 7c multicolored .55 .42
391 A137 7½c multicolored .70 .45
392 A136 8c ultra & car .38 .18
393 A136 10c green & brown .55 .30
394 A137 15c org brn & slate grn .85 .38
395 A137 15c grn, sl grn & red ('68) .85 .55
396 A138 20c buff & black 1.65 .22
397 A139 25c brown & yel 2.25 1.40
398 A138 28c multi ('68) 1.75 .42
399 A139 30c multicolored 3.75 .65
400 A139 30c multi ('70) 11.00 4.25
401 A138 50c dark green 3.50 .55
402 A139 $1 blue 21.00 4.25
403 A138 $2 magenta 18.00 20.00
404 A138 $2 multi ('68) 32.50 21.00
Nos. 382-404 (23) 101.19 56.36

Perf. 13½x14: ½c to 3c, 5c, 7c. Perf. 14½x14: 4c, 6c, 8c, 10c, 25c, 30c, $1. Perf. 13½: 7½c. Perf. 14x14½: 15c, 20c, 28c, $2.

Issued: 7½c, 8/29/67; #395, 3/19/68; 28c, 7/30/68; #404, 12/10/68; #400, 1970; others, 7/10/67.

The 7½c was issued to commemorate the centenary of the brown trout's introduction to New Zealand, and retained as part of the regular series.

No. 395 has been redrawn. The "c" on No. 395 lacks serif; No. 394 has serif.

Adoration of the Shepherds, by Poussin — A156

Sir James Hector — A157

Perf. 13½x14

1967, Oct. 3 Photo. Wmk. 253

405 A156 2½c multicolored	.18	.15

Christmas.

1967, Oct. 10 Litho. *Perf. 14*

Design: 4c, Mt. Aspiring, aurora australis and Southern Cross.

406 A157 4c multicolored	.20	.15
407 A157 8c multicolored	.50	.48

Centenary of the Royal Society of New Zealand to Promote Science.

Maori Bible — A158

1968, Apr. 23 Litho. *Perf. 13½*

408 A158 3c multicolored	.25	.18
a. Gold omitted	*100.00*	

Publication of the Bible in Maori, cent.

Soldiers of Two Eras and Tank — A159

10c, Airmen of two eras, insigne & plane. 28c, Sailors of two eras, insigne & battleships.

1968, May 7 *Perf. 14x13½*

409 A159 4c multicolored	.15	.15
410 A159 10c multicolored	.40	.40
411 A159 28c multicolored	2.50	2.50
Nos. 409-411 (3)	3.05	3.05

Issued to honor the Armed Services.

"Universal Suffrage" — A160

Human Rights Flame — A161

Perf. 13½

1968, Sept. 19 Photo. Unwmk.

412 A160 3c ol grn, lt bl & grn	.15	.15
413 A161 10c dp grn, yel & red	.60	.60

75th anniv. of universal suffrage in New Zealand; Intl. Human Rights Year.

Adoration of the Holy Child, by Gerard van Honthorst A162

Perf. 14x14½

1968, Oct. 1 Wmk. 253

414 A162 2½c multicolored	.25	.15

Christmas.

Romney Marsh Sheep and Woolmark on Carpet A163

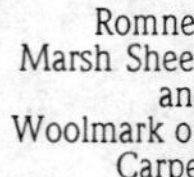

Designs: 7c, Trawler and catch. 8c, Apples and orchard. 10c, Radiata pines and stacked lumber. 20c, Cargo hoist and grazing cattle. 25c, Dairy farm in Taranaki, Mt. Egmont and crated dairy products.

Wmk. 253 (10c, 18c, 25c); others Unwmkd.

Perf. 13½; 14½x14 (10c, 25c)

1968-69 Litho.; Photo. (10c, 25c)

415 A163 7c multi ('69)	1.00	.95
416 A163 8c multi ('69)	1.10	1.10
417 A163 10c multicolored	1.10	.28
418 A163 18c multi ('69)	2.50	.45
419 A163 20c multi ('69)	2.00	.30
420 A163 25c multicolored	4.50	1.00
Nos. 415-420 (6)	12.20	4.08

ILO Emblem A164

Perf. 14½x14

1969, Feb. 11 Photo. Wmk. 253

421 A164 7c scarlet & black	.75	.75

50th anniv. of the ILO.

Law Society Coat of Arms A165

Otago University A166

Designs: 3c, Supreme Court Building, Auckland, horiz. 18c, "Justice" from memorial window of the University of Canterbury Hall, Christchurch.

1969, Apr. 8 Litho. *Perf. 13½*

422 A165 3c multicolored	.15	.15
423 A165 10c multicolored	.60	.55
424 A165 18c multicolored	1.25	2.00
Nos. 422-424 (3)	2.00	2.70

Centenary of New Zealand Law Society.

1969, June 3

Design: 10c, Conferring degree and arms of the University, horiz.

425 A166 3c multicolored	.15	.15
426 A166 10c multicolored	1.00	.90

Centenary of the University of Otago.

Oldest House in New Zealand, Kerikeri A167

Design: 6c, Bay of Islands.

1969, Aug. 18 Litho. Wmk. 253

427 A167 4c multicolored	.50	.50
428 A167 6c multicolored	1.10	1.10

Early European settlements in New Zealand on the 150th anniv. of the founding of Kerikeri, the oldest existing European settlement.

Nativity, by Federico Fiori — A168

Perf. 13½x14

1969, Oct. 1 Photo. Wmk. 253

429 A168 2½c multicolored	.22	.15

Unwmk.

430 A168 2½c multicolored	.22	.16

Christmas.

Capt. Cook, Transit of Venus and Octant A169

Designs: 6c, Joseph Banks and bark Endeavour. 18c, Dr. Daniel Solander and matata branch (rhabdothamnus solandri). 28c, Queen Elizabeth II and map showing Cook's chart of 1769.

1969, Oct. 9 *Perf. 14½x14*

431 A169 4c dk bl, blk & brt rose	.30	.32
432 A169 6c sl grn & choc	1.25	1.40
433 A169 18c choc, sl grn & black	2.50	2.50
434 A169 28c dk ultra, blk & brt rose	5.00	7.00
a. Souvenir sheet of 4, #431-434	26.00	26.00
Nos. 431-434 (4)	9.05	11.22

Cook's landing in New Zealand, bicent.

Child Drinking Milk, and Cattle A170

Design: 7c, Wheat and child with empty bowl.

1969, Nov. 18 Photo. *Perf. 13*

435 A170 7c multicolored	1.50	1.40
436 A170 8c multicolored	1.50	1.40

25th anniv. of CORSO (Council of Organizations for Relief Services Overseas).

Cardigan Bay — A171

1970, Jan. 28 Unwmk. *Perf. 11½*

Granite Paper

437 A171 10c multicolored	.65	.50

Return to New Zealand from the US of Cardigan Bay, 1st standard bred light-harness race horse to win a million dollars in stake money.

Glade Copper Butterfly — A172

Scarlet Parrotfish — A173

New Zealand Coat of Arms and Queen Elizabeth II — A174

Maori Fishhook A175

Egmont National Park — A176

Hauraki Gulf Maritime Park — A177

Designs: 1c, Red admiral butterfly. 2c, Tussock butterfly. 2½c, Magpie moth. 3c, Lichen moth. 4c, Puriri moth. 6c, Sea horses. 7c, Leatherjackets (fish). 7½c, Garfish. 8c, John dory (fish). 18c, Maori club. 20c, Maori tattoo pattern. 30c, Mt. Cook National Park (chamois). 50c, Abel Tasman National Park. $1, Geothermal power plant. $2, Helicopter over field, molecule (agricultural technology).

1970-71 Wmk. 253 *Perf. 13½x13*

438 A172 ½c ultra & multi	.30	.16
439 A172 1c dp bis & multi	.18	.15
a. Bklt. pane of 3 + 3 labels ('71)	1.75	
440 A172 2c ol grn & multi	.20	.15
441 A172 2½c yellow & multi	.20	.15
442 A172 3c brown & multi	.25	.15
443 A172 4c dk brown & multi	.20	.15
444 A173 5c dk green & multi	.38	.15
445 A173 6c dp car & multi	.38	.15
446 A173 7c brn red & multi	.42	.16
447 A173 7½c dk vio & multi	.95	1.00
448 A173 8c blue grn & multi	.55	.15

Perf. 14½x14

449 A174 10c dk bl, sil, red & ultra	.42	.18

Perf. 14x13, 13x14

450 A175 15c brick red, sal & blk ('71)	1.65	.25
451 A177 18c yel grn, blk & red brn ('71)	2.00	.25
452 A175 20c yel brn & blk ('71)	3.00	.22

Perf. 13½x12½

Unwmk.

453 A176 23c bl, grn & blk ('71)	.52	.52

Litho.

Perf. 13½

454 A177 25c gray & multi ('71)	2.25	.22
a. Perf. 14 ('76)	.75	.25
455 A177 30c tan & multi ('71)	.50	.50
a. Perf. 14 ('76)	.90	.38

Photo.

Perf. 13½x12½

456 A176 50c sl grn & multi ('71)	.65	.25

Perf. 11½

Granite Paper

457 A175 $1 light ultra & multi ('71)	1.40	.50
458 A175 $2 ol & multi ('71)	3.25	1.50
Nos. 438-458 (21)	19.65	6.91

The 10c for the visit of Queen Elizabeth II, Prince Philip and Princess Anne.

Issued: 10c, 3/12/70; ½c-4c, 9/2/70; 5c-8c, 11/4/70; 15c-20c, 1/20/71; 25c-50c, 9/1/71; $1-$2, 4/14/71; 23c, 12/1/71.

See #533-546. For surcharge see #480.

EXPO '70 Emblem, Geyser Restaurant A178

Designs: 8c, EXPO '70 emblem and New Zealand Pavilion. 18c, EXPO '70 emblem and bush walk (part of N.Z. exhibit).

Perf. 13x13½

1970, Apr. 8 Photo. Unwmk.

459 A178 7c multicolored	1.10	1.10
460 A178 8c multicolored	1.10	1.10
461 A178 18c multicolored	2.00	2.00
Nos. 459-461 (3)	4.20	4.20

EXPO '70 Intl. Expo., Osaka, Japan.

UN Headquarters, New York — A179

UN, 25th anniv.: 10c, Plowing toward the sun and "25" with laurel.

1970, June 24 Litho. *Perf. 13½*

462 A179 3c multicolored .15 .15
463 A179 10c yellow & red .75 .75

Adoration, by Correggio — A180

Tower, Catholic Church, Sockburn A181

Christmas: 3c, Holy Family, stained glass window, First Presbyterian Church, Invercargill.

1970, Oct. 1 Unwmk. *Perf. 12½*

464 A180 2½c multicolored .15 .15
465 A180 3c multicolored .15 .22
a. Green omitted 200.00
466 A181 10c silver, org & blk .95 .95
Nos. 464-466 (3) 1.25 1.32

Chatham Islands Mollymawk A182

1970, Dec. 2 Photo. *Perf. 13x13½*

467 A182 1c Chatham Islands lily .15 .15
468 A182 2c shown .28 .28

G Clef, Emblem and Spinning Wheel A183

Rotary Emblem and Map of New Zealand A184

1971, Feb. 10 Photo. *Perf. 13x13½*

469 A183 4c multicolored .22 .22
470 A184 10c lemon, dk blue & gold .60 .60

50th anniv. of Country Women's Inst. (4c) and Rotary Intl. in New Zealand (10c).

Ocean Racer A185

8c, One Ton Cup and blueprint of racing yacht.

1971, Mar. 3 Litho. *Perf. 13½x13*

471 A185 5c blue, blk & red .35 .35
472 A185 8c ultra & black .85 1.00

First challenge in New Zealand waters for the One Ton Cup ocean race.

Coats of Arms — A186

1971, May 12 Photo. *Perf. 13x13½*

473 A186 3c Palmerston North .15 .15
474 A186 4c Auckland .28 .28
475 A186 5c Invercargill .48 .48
Nos. 473-475 (3) .91 .91

Centenary of New Zealand cities.

Map of Antarctica A187

1971, June 9 Photo. *Perf. 13x13½*

476 A187 6c dk blue, pur & grn 2.00 2.00

10th anniv. of the Antarctic Treaty pledging peaceful uses of and scientific cooperation in Antarctica.

Child on Swing — A188

1971, June 9 *Perf. 13½x13*

477 188 7c yellow & multi 1.10 1.50

25th anniv. of UNICEF.

Opening of New Zealand's 1st Satellite Earth Station near Warkworth — A189

1971, July 14 *Perf. 11½*

478 A189 8c Radar Station .95 1.10
479 A189 10c Satellite .95 1.50

No. 441 Surcharged

4c

1971 Wmk. 253 *Perf. 13½x13*

480 A172 4c on 2½c multi .38 .15
a. Narrow bars .25 .16

Surcharge typographed on No. 480, photogravure or typographed on No. 480a.

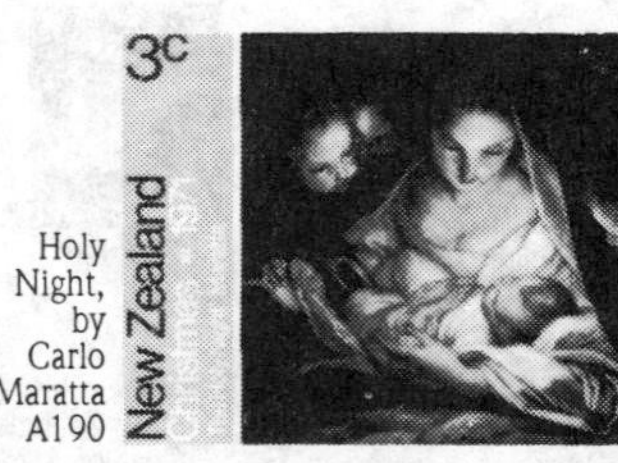

Holy Night, by Carlo Maratta A190

The Three Kings A191

World Rose Convention A192

Christmas: 4c, Annunciation, stained glass window, St. Luke's Anglican Church, Havelock North.

Perf. 13x13½

1971, Oct. 6 Photo. Unwmk.

481 A190 3c orange & multi .15 .15
482 A191 4c multicolored .15 .15
483 A191 10c dk blue & multi .95 .95
Nos. 481-483 (3) 1.25 1.25

1971, Nov. 3 *Perf. 11½*

484 A192 2c Tiffany rose .15 .15
485 A192 5c Peace rose .38 .30
486 A192 8c Chrysler Imperial rose .70 .70
Nos. 484-486 (3) 1.23 1.15

Rutherford and Alpha Particles Passing Atomic Nucleus A193

7c, Lord Rutherford, by Sir Oswald Birley, and formula of disintegration of nitrogen atom.

1971, Dec. 1 Litho. *Perf. 13½x13*

487 A193 1c gray & multi .15 .15
488 A193 7c multicolored .90 .90

Centenary of the birth of Ernest Lord Rutherford (1871-1937), physicist.

Benz, 1895 — A194

Vintage Cars: 4c, Oldsmobile, 1904. 5c, Model T Ford, 1914. 6c, Cadillac service car, 1915. 8c, Chrysler, 1924. 10c, Austin 7, 1923.

1972, Feb. 2 *Perf. 14x14½*

489 A194 3c brn, car & multi .16 .16
490 A194 4c brt lilac & multi .16 .16
491 A194 5c lilac rose & multi .35 .50
492 A194 6c gray grn & multi .65 .90
493 A194 8c vio blue & multi 1.00 1.00
494 A194 10c sepia & multi 1.65 1.65
Nos. 489-494 (6) 3.97 4.37

13th International Vintage Car Rally, New Zealand, Feb. 1972.

Asian-Oceanic Postal Union A195

Designs: 3c, Wanganui City arms and Drurie Hill tower, vert. 5c, De Havilland DH89 and Boeing 737 planes, vert. 8c, French frigate and Maori palisade at Moturoa, vert. 10c, Stone cairn at Kaeo (site of first Methodist mission).

1972, Apr. 5 *Perf. 13x14, 14x13*

495 A195 3c violet & multi .15 .15
496 A195 4c brn org, blk & brn .16 .16
497 A195 5c blue & multi .25 .25
498 A195 8c green & multi 1.75 2.00
499 A195 10c olive, yel & blk 2.10 2.50
Nos. 495-499 (5) 4.41 5.06

Cent. of Council government at Wanganui (3c); 10th anniv. of Asian-Oceanic Postal Union (4c); 25th anniv. of Nat. Airways Corp. (5c); bicent. of the landing by Marion du Fresne at the Bay of Islands (8c); 150th anniv. of the Methodist Church in New Zealand (10c).

Black Scree Cotula — A196

Madonna and Child, by Murillo — A197

Alpine Plants: 6c, North Is. edelweiss. 8c, Haast's buttercup. 10c, Brown mountain daisy.

1972, June 7 Litho. *Perf. 13x14*

500 A196 4c orange & multi .32 .22
501 A196 6c dp blue & multi .90 1.00
502 A196 8c rose lilac & multi 1.10 1.50
503 A196 10c yel green & multi 3.25 3.25
Nos. 500-503 (4) 5.57 5.97

1972, Oct. 4 Photo. *Perf. 11½*

Christmas: 5c, Resurrection, stained-glass window, St. John's Methodist Church, Levin. 10c, Pohutukawa (New Zealand's Christmas flower).

504 A197 3c gray & multi .15 .15
505 A197 5c gray & multi .20 .20
506 A197 10c gray & multi 1.10 1.10
Nos. 504-506 (3) 1.45 1.45

New Zealand Lakes — A198

1972, Dec. 6 Photo. Unwmk.

507 A198 6c Waikaremoana 1.10 1.10
508 A198 8c Hayes 1.50 2.00
509 A198 18c Wakatipu 3.75 3.75
510 A198 23c Rotomahana 4.00 5.00
Nos. 507-510 (4) 10.35 11.85

Old Pollen Street A199

Coal Mining and Landscape A200

Cloister, University of Canterbury A201

Forest, Birds and Lake — A202

Rowing and Olympic Emblems A203

Progress Chart A204

1973, Feb. 7 Litho. *Perf. 13½x13*

511 A199 3c ocher & multi .15 .15
512 A200 4c blue & multi .20 .15
513 A201 5c multicolored .32 .30
514 A202 6c blue & multi 1.00 1.10
515 A203 8c multicolored 1.25 1.25
516 A204 10c blue & multi 1.65 1.50
Nos. 511-516 (6) 4.57 4.45

Centenaries of Thames and Westport Boroughs (3c, 4c); centenary of the Univ. of Canterbury, Christchurch (5c); 50th anniv. of Royal Forest and Bird Protection Soc. (6c); success of New Zealand rowing team at 20th Olympic Games (8c); 25th anniv. of the Economic Commission for Asia and the Far East (ECAFE, 10c).

Class W Locomotive, 1889 — A205

New Zealand Steam Locomotives: 4c, Class X, 1908. 5c, "Passchendaele" Ab Class. 10c, Ja Class, last steam locomotive.

1973, Apr. 4 Litho. *Perf. 14½*

517 A205 3c lt green & multi .45 .15
518 A205 4c lil rose & multi .60 .25
519 A205 5c lt blue & multi .80 .60
520 A205 10c cream & multi 2.50 3.00
Nos. 517-520 (4) 4.35 4.00

Maori Woman and Child, by Hodgkins A206

Christmas in New Zealand A207

Paintings by Frances Hodgkins: 8c, The Hill Top. 10c, Barn in Picardy. 18c, Self-portrait, Still Life.

1973, June 6 Photo. *Perf. 12x11½*

521 A206 5c multicolored .35 .35
522 A206 8c multicolored 1.25 1.25
523 A206 10c multicolored 1.40 1.40
524 A206 18c multicolored 2.00 2.00
Nos. 521-524 (4) 5.00 5.00

1973, Oct. 3 Photo. *Perf. 12½x13½*

Christmas: 3c, Tempi Madonna, by Raphael. 5c, Three Kings, stained-glass window, St. Theresa's R.C. Church, Auckland.

525 A207 3c gold & multi .15 .15
526 A207 5c gold & multi .25 .15
527 A207 10c gold & multi .95 .95
Nos. 525-527 (3) 1.35 1.25

Mitre Peak — A208

Hurdles and Games' Emblem — A209

Perf. 13x13½, 13½x13

1973, Dec. 5 Photo.

528 A208 6c shown .65 .60
529 A208 8c Mt. Ngauruhoe 1.10 1.50
530 A208 18c Mt. Sefton, horiz. 1.75 2.00
531 A208 23c Burnett Range, horiz. 2.75 2.75
Nos. 528-531 (4) 6.25 6.85

Types of 1970-71

Designs as before.

Perf. 13½x13

1973-76 Photo. Unwmk.

533 A172 1c multi ('74) .40 .15
534 A172 2c multicolored .35 .20
536 A172 3c multi ('75) .45 .20
537 A172 4c multicolored .35 .15
538 A173 5c multi ('75) .70 .25
539 A173 6c multi ('74) .70 .30
540 A173 7c multi ('75) 3.75 .95
542 A173 8c multi ('75) 4.50 .65

Perf. 14x13½

543 A174 10c multicolored .60 .15

Perf. 13x14, 14x13

544 A175 15c multi ('76) .70 .15
545 A177 18c multi ('75) .70 .30
546 A175 20c yel brn & blk ('75) .70 .25
Nos. 533-546 (12) 13.90 3.70

Issued: 2c, 10c, 6/73; 1c, 4c, 6c, 9/7/73; 5c, 1973; 3c, 7c, 8c, 18c, 20c, 1974; 15c, 8/2/76.

For surcharges see Nos. 630-631.

1974, Jan. 9 Litho. *Perf. 13x13½*

Designs: 5c, Paraplegic ballplayer. 10c, Bicycling. 18c, Rifle shooting. 23c, Lawn bowling. 4c, 10c, 18c and 23c stamps also show Commonwealth Games' emblem.

547 A209 4c yellow & multi .15 .15
548 A209 5c violet & black .18 .18
549 A209 10c brt red & multi .40 .40
550 A209 18c brown & multi .80 .80
551 A209 23c yel green & multi 1.10 1.10
Nos. 547-551 (5) 2.63 2.63

10th British Commonwealth Games, Christchurch, Jan. 24-Feb. 2. No. 548 publicizes the 4th Paraplegic Games, Dunedin, Jan. 10-20.

Souvenir Sheet

New Zealand Day — A210

Illustration reduced.

1974, Feb. 6 Litho. *Perf. 13*

552 A210 Sheet of 5 2.00 2.00
a. 4c Treaty House, Waitangi .25 .25
b. 4c Parliament extension buildings .25 .25
c. 4c Signing Treaty of Waitangi .25 .25
d. 4c Queen Elizabeth II .25 .25
e. 4c Integrated school .25 .25

New Zealand Day (Waitangi Day). No. 552 has marginal inscription and imprint.

"Spirit of Napier" Fountain — A211

Clock Tower, Bern — A212

Design: 8c, UPU emblem.

1974, Apr. 3 Photo. *Perf. 11½*

553 A211 4c blue green & multi .15 .15
554 A212 5c brown & multi .18 .18
555 A212 8c lemon & multi 1.10 1.10
Nos. 553-555 (3) 1.43 1.43

Centenaries of Napier (4c); UPU (5c, 8c).

Boeing Seaplane, 1919 A213

Designs: 4c, Lockheed Electra, 1937. 5c, Bristol freighter, 1958. 23c, Empire S30 flying boat, 1940.

1974, June 5 Litho. *Perf. 14x13*

556 A213 3c multicolored .22 .15
557 A213 4c multicolored .20 .15
558 A213 5c multicolored .35 .40
559 A213 23c multicolored 2.50 2.50
Nos. 556-559 (4) 3.27 3.20

Development of New Zealand's air transport.

Adoration of the Kings, by Conrad Witz — A214

Christmas: 5c, Angels, stained glass window, St. Paul's Church, Wellington. 10c, Christmas lily (lilium candidum).

1974, Oct. 2 Photo. *Perf. 11½*

Granite Paper

560 A214 3c olive & multi .15 .15
561 A214 5c lilac & multi .22 .22
562 A214 10c orange & multi 1.00 .60
Nos. 560-562 (3) 1.37 .97

Offshore Islands — A215

1974, Dec. 4 Photo. *Perf. 13½x13*

563 A215 6c Great Barrier .28 .28
564 A215 8c Stewart .75 .75
565 A215 18c White 1.25 1.25
566 A215 23c The Brothers 1.90 1.90
Nos. 563-566 (4) 4.18 4.18

Child Using Walker A216

Farm Woman and Children A217

IWY Symbol A218

Otago Medical School A219

1975, Feb. 5 Litho. *Perf. 13½x13*

567 A216 3c orange & multi .15 .15
568 A217 5c green & multi .20 .16
569 A218 10c blue & multi .60 .50
570 A219 18c multicolored 1.00 .80
Nos. 567-570 (4) 1.95 1.61

New Zealand Crippled Children's Soc., 40th anniv. (3c); Women's Division Federated Farmers of N. Z., 50th anniv. (5c); IWY (10c); Otago Medical School cent. (18c).

Scow "Lake Erie," 1873 A220

Historic Sailing Ships: 5c, Schooner "Herald," 1826. 8c, Brigantine "New Zealander," 1828. 10c, Topsail schooner "Jessie Kelly," 1866. 18c, Barque "Tory," 1834. 23c, Clipper "Rangitiki," 1863.

1975, Apr. 2 Litho. *Perf. 13½x13*

571 A220 4c vermilion & blk .15 .15
572 A220 5c grnsh blue & blk .20 .15
573 A220 8c yellow & black .50 .50
574 A220 10c yellow grn & blk .50 .60
575 A220 18c brown & black 1.25 .95
576 A220 23c dull lilac & blk 1.50 1.25
Nos. 571-576 (6) 4.10 3.60

State Forest Parks — A221

1975, June 4 Photo. *Perf. 13½x13*

577 A221 6c Lake Sumner .40 .40
578 A221 8c North West Nelson .75 1.00
579 A221 18c Kaweka 1.50 1.40
580 A221 23c Coromandel 2.00 1.75
Nos. 577-580 (4) 4.65 4.55

Virgin and Child, by Zanobi Machiavelli (1418-1479) — A222

Stained Glass Window, Greendale Methodist/Presbyterian Church — A223

Christmas: 10c, Medieval ships and doves.

Perf. 13½x14, 14x13½

1975, Oct. 1 Photo.

581 A222 3c multicolored .16 .15
582 A223 5c multicolored .22 .16
583 A223 10c multicolored .95 .65
Nos. 581-583 (3) 1.33 .96

Sterling Silver — A224

Roses: 2c, Lilli Marlene. 3c, Queen Elizabeth. 4c, Super star. 5c, Diamond jubilee. 6c, Cresset. 7c, Michele Meilland. 8c, Josephine Bruce. 9c, Iceberg.

1975, Nov. 26 Photo. *Perf. 14½x14*

584 A224 1c multicolored .15 .15
585 A224 2c orange & multi .15 .15
586 A224 3c ultra & multi .15 .15
a. Perf. 14½ ('79) .15 .15
587 A224 4c purple & multi .15 .15
588 A224 5c brown & multi .15 .15
589 A224 6c multicolored ('76) .15 .15
a. Perf. 14½ .35 .22
590 A224 7c multicolored ('76) .15 .15
a. Perf. 14½ 1.40 .90
591 A224 8c yellow & multi ('76) .18 .15
a. Perf. 14½ 1.10 .22
592 A224 9c blue & multi .15 .15
Set value .90 .80

For surcharges see Nos. 693, 695, 718.

Family and Mothers' League Emblem A225

Designs: 7c, "Weight, measure, temperature and capacity." 8c, 1st emigrant ship "William Bryan" and Mt. Egmont. 10c, Maori and Caucasian women and YWCA emblem. 25c, Telecommunications network on Goode's equal area projection.

1976, Feb. 4 Litho. *Perf. 14*

593 A225 6c olive & multi .18 .15
594 A225 7c lilac & multi .20 .18
595 A225 8c red & multi .25 .20
596 A225 10c yellow & multi .32 .30
597 A225 25c tan & multi .80 .80
Nos. 593-597 (5) 1.75 1.63

League of Mothers of New Zealand, 50th anniv. (6c); Metric conversion, 1976 (7c); cent. of New Plymouth (8c); YWCA in New Zealand, 50th anniv. (10c); cent. of link into intl. telecommunications network (25c).

Gig — A226

Farm Vehicles: 7c, Thornycroft truck. 8c, Scandi wagon. 9c, Traction engine. 10c, Wool wagon. 25c, One-horse cart.

1976, Apr. 7 Litho. *Perf. 14x13½*

598 A226 6c dk olive & multi .16 .16
599 A226 7c gray & multi .20 .15
600 A226 8c dk blue & multi .50 .30
601 A226 9c maroon & multi .40 .45
602 A226 10c brown & multi .42 .50
603 A226 25c multicolored 1.40 1.25
Nos. 598-603 (6) 3.08 2.81

Purakaunui Falls — A227

Nativity, Carved Ivory, Spain, 16th Century — A228

Waterfalls: 14c, Marakopa Falls. 15c, Bridal Veil Falls. 16c, Papakorito Falls.

1976, June 2 Photo. *Perf. 11½*

604 A227 10c blue & multi .35 .16
605 A227 14c lilac & multi .75 .80
606 A227 15c ocher & multi .75 .80
607 A227 16c multicolored .95 .85
Nos. 604-607 (4) 2.80 2.61

Perf. 14x14½, 14½x14

1976, Oct. 6 Photo.

Christmas: 11c, Risen Christ, St. Joseph's Church, Grey Lynn, Auckland, horiz. 18c, "Hark the Herald Angels Sing," horiz.

608 A228 7c ocher & multi .15 .15
609 A228 11c ocher & multi .40 .50
610 A228 18c ocher & multi 1.00 .80
Nos. 608-610 (3) 1.55 1.45

Maripi (Carved Wooden Knife) — A229

Maori Artifacts: 12c, Putorino, carved flute. 13c, Wahaika, hardwood club. 14c, Kotiate, violin-shaped weapon.

1976, Nov. 24 Photo. *Perf. 11½*

Granite Paper

611 A229 11c multicolored .20 .15
612 A229 12c multicolored .20 .15
613 A229 13c multicolored .22 .15
614 A229 14c multicolored .24 .15
Nos. 611-614 (4) .86 .60

Arms of Hamilton A230

Automobile Assoc. Emblem A231

Designs: No. 616, Arms of Gisborne. No. 617, Arms of Masterton. No. 619, Emblem of Royal Australasian College of Surgeons.

1977, Jan. 19 Litho. *Perf. 13x13½*

615 A230 8c multicolored .32 .20
616 A230 8c multicolored .32 .20
617 A230 8c multicolored .32 .20
a. Strip of 3, #615-617 1.00 1.00
618 A231 10c multicolored .42 .32
619 A230 10c multicolored .42 .32
a. Pair, #618-619 .90 .75
Nos. 615-619 (5) 1.80 1.24

Centenaries of Hamilton, Gisborne and Masterton (cities); 75th anniv. of the New Zealand Automobile Assoc. and 50th anniv. of the Royal Australasian College of Surgeons.

Souvenir Sheet

Queen Elizabeth II, 1976 — A232

Designs: Various portraits.

1977, Feb. Photo. *Perf. 14x14½*

620 Sheet of 5 1.40 1.40
a.-e. A232 8c single stamp .15 .15
f. Sheet imperf.

25th anniv. of the reign of Elizabeth II.

Physical Education, Maori Culture — A233

Education Dept., Geography, Science — A234

#623, Special school for the deaf; kindergarten. #624, Language class. #625, Home economics, correspondence school, teacher training.

1977, Apr. 6 Litho. *Perf. 13x13½*

621 A233 8c multicolored .50 .50
622 A234 8c multicolored .50 .50
623 A233 8c multicolored .50 .50
624 A234 8c multicolored .50 .50
625 A233 8c multicolored .50 .50
a. Strip of 5, #621-625 3.50 3.50
Nos. 621-625 (5) 2.50 2.50

Cent. of Education Act, establishing Dept. of Education.

Karitane Beach — A235

Seascapes and beach scenes: 16c, Ocean Beach, Mount Maunganui. 18c, Piha Beach. 30c, Kaikoura Coast.

1977, June 1 Photo. *Perf. 14½*

626 A235 10c multicolored .15 .22
627 A235 16c multicolored .32 .32
628 A235 18c multicolored .40 .60
629 A235 30c multicolored .65 .35
Nos. 626-629 (4) 1.52 1.49

Nos. 536-537 Surcharged with New Value and Heavy Bar

1977 Unwmk. *Perf. 13½x13*

630 A172 7c on 3c multicolored .38 .38
631 A172 8c on 4c multicolored .38 .38

Holy Family, by Correggio A236

Window, St. Michael's and All Angels Church — A237

Partridge in a Pear Tree — A238

1977, Oct. 5 Photo. *Perf. 11½*

632 A236 7c multicolored .16 .16
633 A237 16c multicolored .45 .35
634 A238 23c multicolored .70 .52
Nos. 632-634 (3) 1.31 1.03

Christmas.

Merryweather Manual Pump, 1860 — A239

Fire Fighting Equipment: 11c, 2-wheel hose reel and ladder, 1880. 12c, Shand Mason Steam Fire Engine, 1873. 23c, Chemical fire engine, 1888.

1977, Dec. 7 Litho. *Perf. 14x13½*

635 A239 10c multicolored .16 .16
636 A239 11c multicolored .28 .28
637 A239 12c multicolored .35 .30
638 A239 23c multicolored .55 .55
Nos. 635-638 (4) 1.34 1.29

A240

A240a

Parliament Building, Wellington — A241

A242

1977-82 Photo. *Perf. 14½*

648 A240 10c ultra & multi .15 .15
a. Perf. 14½x14 .80 .32

Perf. 14½x14

649 A240a 24c blue & lt green .30 .16
a. Perf. 13x12½ .45 .16

Perf. 13

650 A241 $5 multicolored 5.00 5.00
Nos. 648-650 (3) 5.45 5.31

Issued: #648, 2/79; #648b, 12/7/77; $5, 12/2/81; #649, 4/1/82; #649a, 12/13/82.

For surcharge see #694.

Coil Stamps

1978 Photo. *Perf. 13½x13*

651 A242 1c red lilac .15 .15
652 A242 2c orange .15 .15
653 A242 5c brown .15 .15

Perf. 14½x14

654 A242 10c ultramarine .20 .15
Set value .40 .35

Issue dates: 10c, May 3. Others, June 9.

Ashburton A244

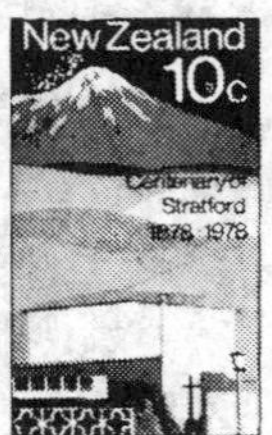

Stratford A245

Old Telephone — A246

Bay of Islands A247

1978, Feb. 1 Litho. *Perf. 14*

656 A244 10c multicolored .20 .16
657 A245 10c multicolored .20 .16
a. Pair, #656-657 .45 .45
658 A246 12c multicolored .28 .28
659 A247 20c multicolored .45 .35
Nos. 656-659 (4) 1.13 .95

Cent. of the cities of Ashburton, Stratford, the NZ Telephone Co. and Bay of Islands County.

Students and Ivey Hall — A248

Maui Gas Drilling Platform — A249

Designs: 12c, Grazing sheep. 15c, Mechanical fertilization. 16c, Furrow, plow and tractor. 20c, Combine harvester. 30c, Grazing cattle.

1978, Apr. 26 *Perf. 14½*

660 A248 10c multicolored .24 .24
661 A248 12c multicolored .28 .28
662 A248 15c multicolored .30 .30
663 A248 16c multicolored .30 .30
664 A248 20c multicolored .42 .42
665 A248 30c multicolored .65 .65
Nos. 660-665 (6) 2.19 2.19

Cent. of Lincoln Univ. College of Agriculture.

1978, June 7 Litho. *Perf. 13½x14*

The sea and its resources: 15c, Fishing boat. 20c, Map of New Zealand and 200-mile limit. 23c, Whale and bottle-nosed dolphins. 35c, Kingfish, snapper, grouper and squid.

666 A249 12c multicolored .24 .18
667 A249 15c multicolored .28 .24
668 A249 20c multicolored .32 .28
669 A249 23c multicolored .40 .32
670 A249 35c multicolored .70 .50
Nos. 666-670 (5) 1.94 1.52

All Saints Church, Howick A250

Christmas: 7c, Holy Family, by El Greco, vert. 23c, Beach scene.

1978, Oct. 4 Photo. *Perf. 11½*

671 A250 7c gold & multi .18 .18
672 A250 16c gold & multi .45 .45
673 A250 23c gold & multi .60 .60
Nos. 671-673 (3) 1.23 1.23

Paua (Haliotis Iris) — A251

Julius Vogel — A252

Sea Shells: 30c, Toheroa (paphies ventricosa). 40c, Coarse dosinia (dosinia anus). 50c, Spiny murex (poirieria zelandica).

1978, Nov. 29 Photo. *Perf. 13x12½*

674 A251 20c multicolored .30 .20
675 A251 30c multicolored .45 .30
676 A251 40c multicolored .55 .45
677 A251 50c multicolored .70 .55
Nos. 674-677 (4) 2.00 1.50

See Nos. 696-697.

1979, Feb. 7 Litho. *Perf. 13x13½*

Portraits: No. 679, George Grey. No. 680, Richard John Seddon.

678 A252 10c light & dark brown .38 .30
679 A252 10c light & dark brown .38 .30
680 A252 10c light & dark brown .38 .30
a. Strip of 3, #678-680 1.25 1.25

19th cent. NZ statesmen.

Riverlands Cottage, Blenheim A253

Early NZ Architecture: 12c, Mission House, Waimate North, 1831-32. 15c, The Elms, Anglican

Church Mission, Tauranga, 1847. 20c, Provincial Council Buildings, Christchurch, 1859.

1979, Apr. 4 *Perf. 13½x13*

681 A253 10c multicolored .15 .15
682 A253 12c multicolored .20 .30
683 A253 15c black & gray .25 .35
684 A253 20c multicolored .32 .40
Nos. 681-684 (4) .92 1.20

Whangaroa Harbor — A254

Small Harbors: 20c, Kawau Island. 23c, Akaroa Harbor, vert. 35c, Picton Harbor, vert.

Perf. 13x13½, 13½x13

1979, June 6 **Photo.**

685 A254 15c multicolored .22 .22
686 A254 20c multicolored .30 .30
687 A254 23c multicolored .32 .32
688 A254 35c multicolored .52 .30
Nos. 685-688 (4) 1.36 1.14

IYC — A255

1979, June 6 **Litho.** *Perf. 14*

689 A255 10c Children playing .25 .20

Virgin and Child, by Lorenzo Ghiberti — A256

Christmas: 25c, Christ Church, Russell, 1835. 35c, Pohutukawa ("Christmas") tree.

1979, Oct. 3 **Photo.** *Perf. 11½*

690 A256 10c multicolored .15 .15
691 A256 25c multicolored .35 .30
692 A256 35c multicolored .45 .42
Nos. 690-692 (3) .95 .87

Nos. 591a, 648 and 589a Surcharged

Perf. 14½, 14½x14 (14c)

1979, Sept.

693 A224 4c on 8c multi .15 .15
694 A240 14c on 10c multi .20 .15
695 A224 17c on 6c multi .25 .15
Nos. 693-695 (3) .60
Set value .32

Shell Type of 1978

Sea Shells: $1, Scallop (pecten novaezelandiae). $2, Circular saw (astraea heliotropium).

1979, Nov. 26 **Photo.** *Perf. 13x12½*

696 A251 $1 multicolored 1.50 .15
697 A251 $2 multicolored 3.00 1.00

Debating Chamber, House of Parliament — A257

1979, Nov. 26 **Litho.** *Perf. 14x13½*

698 A257 14c shown .18 .18
699 A257 20c Mace, black rod .45 .50
700 A257 30c Wall hanging .75 .60
Nos. 698-700 (3) 1.38 1.28

25th Commonwealth Parliamentary Conference, Wellington, Nov. 26-Dec. 2.

NZ No. 1 A258

1980, Feb. 7 **Litho.** *Perf. 14x13½*

701 A258 14c shown .35 .35
702 A258 14c No. 2 .35 .35
703 A258 14c No. 3 .35 .35
a. Souvenir sheet of 3, #701-703 2.75 2.75
b. Strip of 3, #701-703 1.10 1.10

NZ postage stamps, 125th anniv. No. 703a publicizes Zeapex '80 Intl. Stamp Exhib., Auckland, Aug. 23-31; it sold for 52c, of which 10c went to exhib. fund.

Maori Wood Carving, Tudor Towers A259

Earina Autumnalis and Thelymitra Venosa A260

Tractor Plowing, Golden Plow Trophy A261

1980, Feb. 7 *Perf. 14½*

704 A259 17c multicolored .24 .24
705 A260 25c multicolored .35 .35
706 A261 30c multicolored .45 .45
Nos. 704-706 (3) 1.04 1.04

Rotorua cent.; Intl. Orchid Conf., Auckland, Oct.; World Plowing Championship, Christchurch, May.

Ewelme Cottage, Parnell, 1864 A262

Early NZ Architecture: 17c, Broadgreen, Nelson, 1855. 25c, Courthouse, Oamaru, 1822, 30c, Government Buildings, Wellington, 1877.

1980, Apr. 2 **Litho.** *Perf. 13½x13*

707 A262 14c multicolored .18 .18
708 A262 17c multicolored .22 .22
709 A262 25c green & black .32 .32
710 A262 30c multicolored .45 .50
Nos. 707-710 (4) 1.17 1.22

Harbors — A263

1980, June 4 **Photo.** *Perf. 13x13½*

711 A263 25c Auckland .30 .40
712 A263 30c Wellington .35 .35
713 A263 35c Lyttelton .40 .40
714 A263 50c Port Chalmers .60 .60
Nos. 711-714 (4) 1.65 1.75

Madonna and Child with Cherubim, by Andrea della Robbia — A264

1980, Oct. 1 **Photo.** *Perf. 12*

715 A264 10c shown .15 .15
716 A264 25c St. Mary's Church, New Plymouth .32 .32
717 A264 35c Picnic .45 .45
Nos. 715-717 (3) .92 .92

Christmas.

No. 590 Surcharged

1980, Sept. 29 **Photo.** *Perf. 14½x14*

718 A224 20c on 7c multicolored .80 .16

Te Heu Heu Tukino IV, Ngati Tuwharetoa Tribal Chief — A265

Maori Leaders: 25c, Te Hau-Takiri Wharepapa. 35c, Princess Te Puea Herangi. 45, Apirana Ngata. 60c, Hakopa Te Ata-o-tu.

1980, Nov. 26 *Perf. 13*

719 A265 15c multicolored .20 .20
720 A265 25c multicolored .32 .32
721 A265 35c multicolored .45 .45
722 A265 45c multicolored .50 .50
723 A265 60c multicolored .85 .85
Nos. 719-723 (5) 2.32 2.32

Henry A. Feilding, Borough Emblem A266

1981, Feb. 4 **Litho.** *Perf. 14½*

724 A266 20c multicolored .28 .28

Borough of Feilding centenary.

IYD A267

1981, Feb. 4

725 A267 25c orange & black .35 .35

Family and Dog — A268

1981, Apr. 1 **Litho.** *Perf. 13*

726 A268 20c shown .25 .15
727 A268 25c Grandparents .32 .32
728 A268 30c Parents reading to children .40 .30
729 A268 35c Family outing .45 .45
Nos. 726-729 (4) 1.42 1.22

Shotover River — A269

1981, June 3 **Photo.** *Perf. 13½*

730 A269 30c Kaiauai River, vert. .40 .30
731 A269 35c Mangahao River, vert. .45 .55
732 A269 40c shown .52 .52
733 A269 60c Cleddau River .85 .50
Nos. 730-733 (4) 2.22 1.87

Prince Charles and Lady Diana A270

1981, July 29 **Litho.** *Perf. 14½*

734 A270 20c shown .40 .40
735 A270 20c St. Paul's Cathedral .40 .40
a. Pair, #734-735 .80 .80

Royal Wedding.

Golden Tainui — A271

Christmas: 14c, Madonna and Child, by Marco d'Oggiono, 15th cent. 30c, St. John's Church, Wakefield.

1981, Oct. **Photo.** *Perf. 11½*

Granite Paper

736 A271 14c multicolored .18 .18
737 A271 30c multicolored .40 .40
738 A271 40c multicolored .52 .52
Nos. 736-738 (3) 1.10 1.10

SPCA Centenary A272

Intl. Science Year A273

Centenaries: No. 739, Tauranga. No. 740, Hawera. 30c, Frozen meat exports.

1982, Feb. 3 **Litho.** *Perf. 14½*

739 A272 20c multicolored .28 .16
740 A272 20c multicolored .28 .16
a. Pair, #739-740 .60 .40
741 A272 25c multicolored .35 .35
742 A272 30c multicolored .45 .45
743 A273 35c multicolored .50 .50
Nos. 739-743 (5) 1.86 1.62

Alberton Farmhouse, Auckland, 1867 A274

1982, Apr. 7 **Litho.**

744 A274 20c shown .24 .24
745 A274 25c Caccia Birch, Palmerston North, 1893 .30 .30
746 A274 30c Dunedin Railway Station, 1904 .50 .50
747 A274 35c PO, Ophir, 1886 .80 .50
Nos. 744-747 (4) 1.84 1.54

Summer, Kaiteriteri A275

1982, June 2 **Photo.** *Perf. 13½*

748 A275 35c shown .50 .50
749 A275 40c Autumn, Queenstown .55 .55
750 A275 45c Winter, Mt. Ngauruhoe .60 .60
751 A275 70c Spring, Wairarapa 1.00 1.00
Nos. 748-751 (4) 2.65 2.65

Madonna with Child and Two Angels, by Piero di Cosimo — A276

Christmas: 35c, Rangiatea Maori Church, Otaki. 45c, Surf life-saving patrol.

1982, Oct. 6 Photo. *Perf. 14*

752 A276 18c multicolored .20 .20
753 A276 35c multicolored .65 .42
754 A276 45c multicolored .75 .70
Nos. 752-754 (3) 1.60 1.32

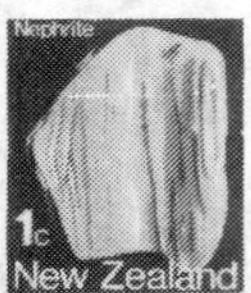

Nephrite
A277

Fruit Export
A278

Native Birds — A279

1982-83 Litho.

755 A277 1c shown .15 .15
a. Perf 13x12½ .80
756 A277 2c Agate .15 .15
a. Perf 13x12½ 1.50
757 A277 3c Iron pyrites .15 .15
758 A277 4c Amethyst .15 .15
759 A277 5c Carnelian .15 .15
760 A277 9c Native sulphur .20 .20
761 A278 10c Grapes .15 .15
762 A278 20c Citrus fruit .25 .25
763 A278 30c Nectarines .40 .30
764 A278 40c Apples .50 .40
765 A278 50c Kiwifruit .65 .15
Set value 2.40 1.60

Issue dates: A277, Dec. 1; A278, Dec. 7, 1983.

1985-89 *Perf. 14½*

766 A279 30c Kakapo .50 .15
767 A279 45c Falcon .95 .50
768 A279 $1 Kokako 1.25 .15
769 A279 $2 Black Robin 2.75 1.10
a. Souvenir sheet of one 4.50 4.50
770 A279 $3 Stitchbird 3.00 1.50
770A A279 $4 Saddleback 4.00 2.00
Nos. 766-770A (6) 12.45 5.40

No. 769a for PHILEXFRANCE '89 and has margin picturing progressive proofs of No. 769. No. 769a sold for $3.50.

Issued: $1, $2, Apr. 24; $3, $4, Apr. 23, 1986; 30c, 45c, May 1, 1986; No. 769a, July 7, 1989.

See Nos. 830-835, 918C-935C.

Salvation Army in NZ Cent. — A280

Univ. of Auckland Cent. — A281

NZ-Australia Closer Economic Relationship Agreement — A282

Introduction of Rainbow Trout Cent. — A283

WCY — A284

Perf. 14, 14x13½ (35c)

1983, Feb. 2 Litho.

771 A280 24c multicolored .30 .15
772 A281 30c multicolored .35 .35
773 A282 35c multicolored .40 .40
774 A283 40c multicolored .50 .50
775 A284 45c multicolored .55 .55
Nos. 771-775 (5) 2.10 1.95

A285

1983, Mar. 14 Litho. *Perf. 14*

776 A285 24c Queen Elizabeth II .30 .30
777 A285 35c Maori rock painting .40 .40
778 A285 40c Wool industry logos .50 .50
779 A285 45c Arms .55 .55
Nos. 776-779 (4) 1.75 1.75

Commonwealth Day.

Island Bay, by Rita Angus (1908-1970) — A286

Landscapes.

1983, Apr. 6 Litho. *Perf. 14½*

780 A286 24c shown .30 .30
781 A286 30c Central Otago .40 .40
782 A286 35c Wanaka .45 .45
783 A286 45c Tree, Greymouth .60 .60
Nos. 780-783 (4) 1.75 1.75

Lake Matheson
A287

Perf. 13½x13, 13x13½

1983, June 1 Photo.

784 A287 35c Mt. Egmont, vert. .45 .45
785 A287 40c Cooks Bay, vert. .55 .55
786 A287 45c shown .60 .60
787 A287 70c Lake Alexandrina .90 .90
Nos. 784-787 (4) 2.50 2.50

Christmas 1983 — A288

1983, Oct. 5 Photo. *Perf. 12*

788 A288 18c Holy Family of the Oak Tree, by Raphael .20 .20
789 A288 35c St. Patrick's Church, Greymouth .40 .40
790 A288 45c Star, poinsettias .55 .55
Nos. 788-790 (3) 1.15 1.15

Antarctic Research A289

1984, Feb. 1 Litho. *Perf. 13½x13*

791 A289 24c Geology .30 .15
792 A289 40c Biology .50 .50
793 A289 58c Glaciology .75 .75
794 A289 70c Meteorology .90 .90
a. Souvenir sheet of 4, #791-794 3.00
Nos. 791-794 (4) 2.45 2.30

Ferry Mountaineer, Lake Wakatipu, 1879 — A290

1984, Apr. 4 Litho. *Perf. 13½*

795 A290 24c shown .30 .15
796 A290 40c Waikana, Otago Harbor, 1909 .50 .50
797 A290 58c Britannia, Waitemata Harbor, 1885 .75 .75
798 A290 70c Wakatere, Firth of Thames, 1896 1.00 .90
Nos. 795-798 (4) 2.55 2.30

Skier, Mount Hutt — A291

1984, June 6 Litho. *Perf. 13½x13*

799 A291 35c shown .35 .15
800 A291 40c Coronet Peak .40 .40
801 A291 45c Turoa .50 .50
802 A291 70c Whakapapa .75 .60
Nos. 799-802 (4) 2.00 1.65

Hamilton's Frog A292

1984, July 11 *Perf. 13½*

803 A292 24c shown .35 .30
804 A292 24c Great barrier skink .35 .30
a. Pair, #803-804 .70 .70
805 A292 30c Harlequin gecko .50 .40
806 A292 58c Otago skink .85 .70
807 A292 70c Gold-striped gecko 1.10 1.10
Nos. 803-807 (5) 3.15 2.80

No. 804a has continuous design.

Christmas — A293

Designs: 18c, Adoration of the Shepherds, by Lorenzo Di Credi. 35c, Old St. Paul's Church, Wellington, vert. 45c, Bell, vert.

Perf. 13½x14, 14x13½

1984, Sept. 26 Photo.

808 A293 18c multicolored .25 .25
809 A293 35c multicolored .45 .45
810 A293 45c multicolored .60 .60
Nos. 808-810 (3) 1.30 1.30

Military History A294

1984, Nov. 7 Litho. *Perf. 15x14*

811 A294 24c South Africa, 1901 .30 .30
812 A294 40c France, 1917 .50 .50
813 A294 58c North Africa, 1942 .80 .80
814 A294 70c Korea & Southeast Asia, 1950-72 .95 .95
a. Souvenir sheet of 4, #811-814 2.75 2.75
Nos. 811-814 (4) 2.55 2.55

St. John Ambulance Assoc. Cent. in NZ — A295

1985, Jan. 16 Litho. *Perf. 14*

815 A295 24c multicolored .35 .15
816 A295 30c multicolored .40 .40
817 A295 40c multicolored .55 .55
Nos. 815-817 (3) 1.30 1.10

Early Transportation — A296

1985, Mar. 6 Litho. *Perf. 13½*

818 A296 24c Nelson Horse Tram, 1862 .35 .35
819 A296 30c Graham's Town-Steam, 1871 .40 .40
820 A296 35c Dunedin Cable Car, 1881 .45 .45
821 A296 40c Auckland Electric, 1902 .50 .50
822 A296 45c Wellington Electric, 1904 .60 .60
823 A296 58c Christchurch Electric, 1905 .75 1.00
Nos. 818-823 (6) 3.05 3.30

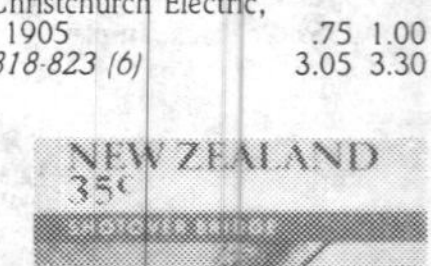

Bridges A297

1985, June 12 Photo. *Perf. 11½*

824 A297 35c Shotover .40 .35
825 A297 40c Alexandra .45 .40
826 A297 45c So. Rangitikei .65 .45
827 A297 70c Twin Bridges 1.25 .70
Nos. 824-827 (4) 2.75 1.90

Bird Type of 1985 and

Elizabeth II — A298

1985-89 Litho. *Perf. 14½x14*

828 A298 25c multicolored .50 .15
829 A298 35c multicolored .60 .45

Perf. 14½

830 A279 40c Blue duck .60 .20
831 A279 60c Brown teal .65 .65
832 A279 70c Paradise shelduck .75 .95
a. Souvenir sheet of 1 7.00 7.00
835 A279 $5 Takahe 6.00 3.75
Nos. 828-835 (6) 9.10 6.15

Size of 70c, 22x27mm.

No. 832a for World Stamp Expo '89. Sold for $1.50.

Issued: 25c, 35c, 7/1/85; 40c, 60c, 2/2/87; 70c, 6/7/88; $5, 4/20/88; #832a, 11/17/89.

Christmas — A301

Carol "Silent Night, Holy Night," by Joseph Mohr (1792-1848), Austrian clergyman.

Perf. 13½x12½

1985, Sept. 18 **Litho.**

836 A301 18c Stable .20 .20
837 A301 40c Shepherds .40 .40
838 A301 50c Angels .50 .50
Nos. 836-838 (3) 1.10 1.10

Navy Ships A302

1985, Nov. 6 **Litho.** *Perf. 13½*

839 A302 25c Philomel, 1914-1947 .35 .25
840 A302 45c Achilles, 1936-1946 .75 .65
841 A302 60c Rotoiti, 1949-1965 1.10 .95
842 A302 75c Canterbury, 1971- 1.25 1.10
a. Souvenir sheet of 4, #839-842 4.50 4.50
Nos. 839-842 (4) 3.45 2.95

Police Force Act, Cent. — A303

Designs: a, Radio operators, 1940-1985. b, Mounted policeman, 1890, forensic specialist in mobile lab, 1985. c, Police station, 1895, policewoman and badge, 1985. d, 1920 motorcycle, 1940s car, modern patrol cars and graphologist. e, Original Mt. Cook Training Center and modern Police College, Poriria.

1986, Jan. 15 *Perf. 14½x14*

843 Strip of 5 1.40 1.40
a.-e. A303 25c any single .25 .25

Intl. Peace Year A304

1986, Mar. 5 *Perf. 13½x13*

844 A304 25c Tree .30 .30
845 A304 25c Dove .30 .30
a. Pair, #844-845 .60 .60

Motorcycles A305

1986, Mar. 5

846 A305 35c 1920 Indian Power Plus .40 .40
847 A305 45c 1927 Norton CS1 .50 .50
848 A305 60c 1930 BSA Sloper 1.00 .80
849 A305 75c 1915 Triumph Model H 1.00 1.00
Nos. 846-849 (4) 2.90 2.70

Knight's Point — A306

1986, June 11 **Litho.** *Perf. 14*

850 A306 55c shown .65 .65
851 A306 60c Beck's Bay .70 .70
852 A306 65c Doubtless Bay .75 .75
853 A306 80c Wainui Bay .90 .90
a. Miniature sheet of one 1.50 1.50
Nos. 850-853 (4) 3.00 3.00

No. 853a sold for $1.20. Surtax benefited the "NZ 1990" executive committee.

No. 853a exists with Stockholmia '86 emblem.

The Twelve Days of Christmas — A307

1986, Sept. 17 **Photo.** *Perf. 14½*

854 A307 25c First day .30 .20
855 A307 55c Second .65 .65
856 A307 65c Third .80 .80
Nos. 854-856 (3) 1.75 1.65

Music — A308

Tourism — A309

1986, Nov. 5 **Litho.** *Perf. 14½x14*

857 A308 30c Conductor .30 .30
858 A308 60c Brass band .55 .55
859 A308 80c Highland pipe band .75 .75
860 A308 $1 Country music .90 .90
Nos. 857-860 (4) 2.50 2.50

1987, Jan. 14 *Perf. 14½x14*

861 A309 60c Boating .60 .60
862 A309 70c Aviation .70 .70
863 A309 80c Camping .75 .75
864 A309 85c Windsurfing .80 .80
865 A309 $1.05 Mountain climbing 1.25 1.25
866 A309 $1.30 White water rafting 1.40 1.40
Nos. 861-866 (6) 5.50 5.50

Blue Water Classics A310

1987, Feb. 2 *Perf. 14x14½*

867 A310 40c Southern Cross Cup .45 .45
868 A310 80c Admiral's Cup .90 .90
869 A310 $1.05 Kenwood Cup 1.20 1.20
870 A310 $1.30 America's Cup 1.45 1.45
Nos. 867-870 (4) 4.00 4.00

Vesting Day A311

a, Motor vehicles, plane. b, Train, bicycle.

1987, Apr. 1 **Litho.** *Perf. 13½*

871 Pair 1.00 1.00
a.-b. A311 40c any single .48 .48

Establishment of NZ Post Ltd., Apr. 1, replacing the NZ PO.

Royal NZ Air Force, 50th Anniv. A312

Designs: 40c, Avro 626, Wigram Airfield, c. 1937. 70c, P-40 Kittyhawks. 80c, Sunderland seaplane. 85c, A4 Skyhawks.

1987, Apr. 15 *Perf. 14x14½*

872 A312 40c multicolored .50 .50
873 A312 70c multicolored .80 .80
874 A312 80c multicolored .95 .95
875 A312 85c multicolored 1.00 1.00
a. Souvenir sheet of 4, #872-875 4.75 4.75
Nos. 872-875 (4) 3.25 3.25

No. 875a with Capex '87 overprint in sheet margin was sold only at the New Zealand P. O. booth at the show.

Natl. Parks System, Cent. — A313

1987, June 17 **Litho.** *Perf. 14½*

876 A313 70c Urewera .95 .50
877 A313 80c Mt. Cook 1.10 .60
878 A313 85c Fiordland 1.10 .70
879 A313 $1.30 Tongariro 1.65 .75
a. Souvenir sheet of one 2.25 2.25
Nos. 876-879 (4) 4.80 2.55

No. 879a sold for $1.70 to benefit the NZ 1990 World Phil. Exhib., Auckland.

Christmas Carols — A314

Maori Fiber Art — A315

1987, Sept. 16 **Litho.** *Perf. 14x14½*

880 A314 35c Hark! The Herald Angels Sing .45 .45
881 A314 70c Away in a Manger .85 .85
882 A314 85c We Three Kings of Orient Are 1.05 1.05
Nos. 880-882 (3) 2.35 2.35

1987, Nov. 4 **Litho.** *Perf. 12*

883 A315 40c Knot .45 .45
884 A315 60c Binding .65 .65
885 A315 80c Plait .90 .90
886 A315 85c Flax fiber .95 .95
Nos. 883-886 (4) 2.95 2.95

Royal Phil. Soc. of NZ, Cent. A316

Portrait of Queen Victoria by Chalon — A317

Queen Elizabeth II and: No. 887, No. 61 (blue background). No. 888, No. 62 (red background).

1988, Jan. 13 *Perf. 14x14½*

887 A316 40c multicolored .45 .45
888 A316 40c multicolored .45 .45
a. Pair, #887-888 .90 .90

Souvenir Sheet

889 A317 $1 multicolored 1.10 1.10

No. 889 exists overprinted in the margin with the SYDPEX 88 emblem.

NZ Electrification, Cent. — A318

1988, Jan. 13 *Perf. 14x14½*

890 A318 40c Geothermal .50 .50
891 A318 60c Thermal .55 .55
892 A318 70c Gas .60 .60
893 A318 80c Hydroelectric .95 .95
Nos. 890-893 (4) 2.60 2.60

Maori Rafter Paintings — A319

1988, Mar. 2 **Litho.** *Perf. 14½*

894 A319 40c Mangopare .48 .48
895 A319 40c Koru .48 .48
896 A319 40c Raupunga .48 .48
897 A319 60c Koiri .70 .70
Nos. 894-897 (4) 2.14 2.14

Greetings Messages — A320

Landscapes — A321

1988, May 18 **Litho.** *Perf. 13½x13*

Booklet Stamps

898 A320 40c Good luck .55 .55
899 A320 40c Keeping in touch .55 .55
900 A320 40c Happy birthday .55 .55

Size: 41x27mm

901 A320 40c Congratulations .55 .55
902 A320 40c Get well soon .55 .55
a. Bklt. pane of 5, #898-902 2.75

1988, June 8 *Perf. 14½*

903 A321 70c Milford Track .60 .60
904 A321 80c Heaphy Track .75 .75
905 A321 85c Copland Track .85 .85
906 A321 $1.30 Routeburn Track 1.40 .90
a. Miniature sheet of one 2.00 2.00
Nos. 903-906 (4) 3.60 3.10

No. 906a sold for $1.70 to benefit the exhibition.

NEW ZEALAND 1990
Souvenir Sheets

Four souvenir sheets were sold by the New Zealand post to benefit NEW ZEALAND 1990 World Stamp Exhibition. They each contain three $1 and one $2 "stamps" picturing antarctic scenes. They are not valid for postage.

Australia Bicentennial A322

Caricature: Kiwi and koala around campfire.

1988, June 21

907 A322 40c multicolored .55 .52

See Australia No. 1086.

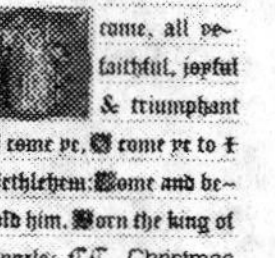

Christmas Carols — A323

Illuminated manuscripts: 35c, O, Come All Ye Faithful, by John Francis Wade, 1742. 70c, Hark! the Herald Angels Sing. 80c, Ding Dong! Merrily on High. 85c, The First Noel, first published in Davies & Gilbert's Some Ancient Christmas Carols, 1832.

1988, Sept. 14 **Litho.** *Perf. 14½*

908 A323 35c multicolored .42 .42
909 A323 70c multicolored .85 .85
910 A323 80c multicolored .95 .95
911 A323 85c multicolored 1.00 .70
Nos. 908-911 (4) 3.22 2.92

New Zealand Heritage A324

The Land. Paintings by 19th cent. artists: 40c, Lake Pukaki, 1862, by John Gully. 60c, On the Grass Plain Below Lake Arthur, 1846, by William Fox. 70c, View of Auckland, 1873, by John Hoyte. 80c, Mt. Egmont from the Southward, 1840, by Charles Heaphy. $1.05, Anakiwa, Queen Charlotte Sound, 1871, by John Kinder. $1.30, White Terraces, Lake Rotomahana, 1880, by Charles Barraud.

1988, Oct. 5 Litho. *Perf. 14x14½*

912 A324 40c multicolored .45 .45
913 A324 60c multicolored .65 .65
914 A324 70c multicolored .80 .80
915 A324 80c multicolored .90 .90
916 A324 $1.05 multicolored 1.10 1.10
917 A324 $1.30 multicolored 1.40 1.40
Nos. 912-917 (6) 5.30 5.30

Treaty of Waitangi, 150th anniv. (in 1990).

Kiwi — A325

1988, Oct. 19 Engr. *Perf. 14½*

918 A325 $1 green 3.00 2.50
a. Booklet pane of 6 14.00
b. Litho. 1.25 1.25

Value is for copy with surrounding selvage. No. 918 issued in booklets only.
No. 918b is from No. 1161a.
See Nos. 1027, 1161, 1445.

Bird Type of 1985

1988-95 Litho. *Perf. 14½x14*

Sizes: $10, 26x31½mm, Others, 22x27mm

918C A279 5c Spotless crake .15 .15
919 A279 10c Banded dotterel .15 .15
920 A279 20c Yellowhead .25 .20
921 A279 30c Silvereye .40 .25
922 A279 40c Brown kiwi .52 .30
922A A279 45c Rock wren .52 .25
b. Booklet pane of 10 5.20
923 A279 50c Kingfisher .65 .35
924 A279 60c Spotted shag .78 .78
a. Sheet of 8, #918C, 919-922, 922A, 923-924 3.00 3.00
925 A279 80c Fiordland crested penguin 1.05 1.05
925A A279 80c New Zealand falcon .85 .85
b. Booklet pane of 10 8.50
c. Perf. 12 on 3 sides 1.00 1.00
d. As "c," booklet pane of 10 10.00
Complete booklet, #925d 10.00
926 A279 90c South Is. robin 1.20 1.20
935 A279 $10 Little spotted kiwi 12.00 6.00
d. Souv. sheet of 1 12.50 12.50

Self-Adhesive

Die Cut Perf 11½

935A A279 40c like #922 .48 .48
935B A279 45c like #922A .52 .52

Die Cut Perf 10½x11

935C A279 45c like #922A .45 .45
Nos. 918C-935C (15) 19.97 12.98

No. 935C has a darker blue background than No. 935B and has perf "teeth" at the corners while No. 935B does not. Perf "teeth" on the top and left side are staggered to line up with perf "holes" on the bottom and right on No. 935C. "Teeth" line up with "teeth" on No. 935B.
PHILAKOREA '94 (#924a). POST'X 95 Postal Exhibition (#935d).
No. 925A comes in booklets only.
Issued: $10, 4/19/89; #935A, 4/17/91; 5c, #922A, 935B, 7/1/91; #935C, 1991; #925A, 3/31/93; #924a, 8/16/94; #935d, 2/3/95; others, 11/2/88.
This is an expanding set. Numbers will change if necessary.

Whales of the Southern Oceans A326

1988, Nov. 2 Litho. *Perf. 13½*

936 A326 60c Humpback .80 .70
937 A326 70c Killer 1.00 1.00
938 A326 80c Southern right 1.25 1.25
939 A326 85c Blue 1.25 1.25
940 A326 $1.05 Southern bottlenose 2.00 1.50
941 A326 $1.30 Sperm 2.25 1.90
Nos. 936-941 (6) 8.55 7.60

Wildflowers A327

1989, Jan. 18 Litho. *Perf. 14½*

942 A327 40c Clover .55 .55
943 A327 60c Lotus .82 .82
944 A327 70c Montbretia .95 .95
945 A327 80c Wild ginger 1.10 1.10
Nos. 942-945 (4) 3.42 3.42

Authors — A328

Portraits: 40c, Katherine Mansfield (1888-1923). 60c, James K. Baxter (1926-1972). 70c, Bruce Mason (1921-1982). 80c, Ngaio Marsh (1899-1982).

1989, Mar. 1 Litho. *Perf. 12½*

946 A328 40c multicolored .52 .52
947 A328 60c multicolored .78 .78
948 A328 70c multicolored .90 .90
949 A328 80c multicolored 1.05 1.05
Nos. 946-949 (4) 3.25 3.25

New Zealand Heritage A329

The people.

1989, May 17 *Perf. 14x14½*

950 A329 40c Moriori .52 .52
951 A329 60c Prospectors .78 .78
952 A329 70c Land settlers .92 .92
953 A329 80c Whalers 1.05 1.05
954 A329 $1.05 Missionaries 1.40 1.40
955 A329 $1.30 Maori 1.70 1.70
Nos. 950-955 (6) 6.37 6.37

Trees — A330 Christmas — A331

1989, June 7

956 A330 80c Kahikatea 1.05 1.05
957 A330 85c Rimu 1.10 1.10
958 A330 $1.05 Totara 1.40 1.40
959 A330 $1.30 Kauri 1.70 1.70
a. Miniature sheet of one 2.35 2.35
Nos. 956-959 (4) 5.25 5.25

No. 959a sold for $1.80. Surtax benefited the "NZ 1990" executive committee.

1989, Sept. 13 Litho. *Perf. 14½*

Star of Bethlehem illuminating settings: 35c, View of One Tree Hill from a bedroom window. 65c, A shepherd overlooking snow-capped mountains. 80c, Boats in harbor. $1, Earth.

960 A331 35c multicolored .42 .42
a. Booklet pane of 10 4.25
961 A331 65c multicolored .80 .80
962 A331 80c multicolored .98 .98
963 A331 $1 multicolored 1.20 1.20
Nos. 960-963 (4) 3.40 3.40

New Zealand Heritage A332

The sea.

1989, Oct. 11 Litho. *Perf. 14x14½*

964 A332 40c Windsurfing .48 .48
965 A332 60c Fishing .72 .72
966 A332 65c Swordfish .78 .78
967 A332 80c Harbor .95 .95
968 A332 $1 Gulls over coast 1.20 1.20
969 A332 $1.50 Container ship 1.80 1.80
Nos. 964-969 (6) 5.93 5.93

14th Commonwealth Games, Auckland, Jan. 24-Feb. 3, 1990 — A333

1989, Nov. 8 *Perf. 14½*

970 A333 40c Emblem .50 .50
971 A333 40c Goldie character trademark .50 .50
a. Souvenir sheet of 2, #970-971, sailboats ('90) 1.00 1.00
b. As "a," stadium ('90) 1.00 1.00
972 A333 40c Gymnastics .50 .50
973 A333 50c Weight lifting .60 .60
974 A333 65c Swimming .80 .80
975 A333 80c Cycling .95 .95
976 A333 $1 Lawn bowling 1.25 1.25
977 A333 $1.80 Hurdles 2.25 2.25
Nos. 970-977 (8) 7.35 7.35

Air New Zealand, 50th Anniv. A334

1990, Jan. 17 *Perf. 13½x14½*

978 A334 80c multicolored .95 .95

Souvenir Sheet

Treaty of Waitangi, 150th Anniv. — A335

Painting by Leonard Mitchell: a, Maori chief signing the treaty. b, Chief Hone Heke shaking hand of Lt.-Gov. William Hobson.

1990, Jan. 17 *Perf. 13½*

979 A335 Sheet of 2 1.10 1.10
a.-b. 40c any single .55 .55

New Zealand Heritage A336

The Ships.

1990, Mar. 7 Litho. *Perf. 14x14½*

980 A336 40c Polynesian double-hulled canoe, c. 1000 .48 .48
981 A336 50c *Endeavour* .60 .60
a. Souvenir sheet of 1 8.75 8.75
982 A336 60c *Tory* .70 .70
983 A336 80c *Crusader* .95 .95
984 A336 $1 *Edwin Fox* 1.20 1.20
985 A336 $1.50 *Arawa* 1.75 1.75
Nos. 980-985 (6) 5.68 5.68

No. 981a for Stamp World London '90. Sold for $1.30. Issued May 3.

Miniature Sheet

Orchids — A337

Designs: a, Sun. b, Spider. c, Winika. d, Greenhood. e, Odd-leaved ordhid.

1990, Apr. 18 Litho. *Perf. 14½*

986 Sheet of 5 7.50 7.50
a.-d. A337 40c any single 1.25 1.25
e. A337 80c multicolored 2.25 2.25

No. 986 sold for $4.90. Surcharge for the intl. stamp exhibition, Auckland, Aug. 24-Sept 2. Imperf. sheets were available only in season tickets which were sold for $25.

New Zealand Heritage A338

The Achievers: 40c, Grace Neill (1846-1926), nurse, journalist. 50c, Jean Batten (1909-1982), aviator. 60c, Katherine Sheppard (1848-1934), social worker. 80c, Richard Pearse (1877-1953), inventor. $1, Gov.-Gen. Bernard Freyberg (1889-1963). $1.50, Peter Buck (1877-1951), cabinet minister.

1990, May 16 Litho. *Perf. 14x14½*

987 A338 40c multicolored .48 .48
988 A338 50c multicolored .60 .60
989 A338 60c multicolored .70 .70
990 A338 80c multicolored .95 .95
991 A338 $1 multicolored 1.20 1.20
992 A338 $1.50 multicolored 1.75 1.75
Nos. 987-992 (6) 5.68 5.68

Akaroa Harbor — A339

Early Settlements: $1, Durie Hill, Wanganui River. $1.50, Mt. Victoria, Wellington. $1.80, Rangitoto Island, Takapuna Beach, Auckland.

1990, June 13 Litho. *Perf. 14½*

993 A339 80c multicolored .95 .95
994 A339 $1 multicolored 1.15 1.15
995 A339 $1.50 multicolored 1.75 1.75
996 A339 $1.80 multicolored 2.10 2.10
a. Souvenir sheet of 1 2.75 2.75
Nos. 993-996 (4) 5.95 5.95

No. 996a sold for $2.30. Surtax for world philatelic expo, New Zealand '90.

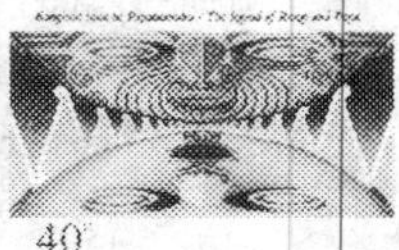

New Zealand Heritage A340

The Maori: 40c, Legend of Rangi and Papa. 50c, Maori feather cloak. 60c, Song. 80c, Maori tattoo. $1, War canoe prow. $1.50, Maori war dance.

1990, Aug. 24 Litho. *Perf. 14*

997 A340 40c multi .45 .45
998 A340 50c multi .60 .60
999 A340 60c multi .70 .70

1000 A340 80c multi .95 .95
1001 A340 $1 multi 1.20 1.20
1002 A340 $1.50 multi 1.75 1.75
Nos. 997-1002 (6) 5.65 5.65

Souvenir Sheet

First Postage Stamps, 150th Anniv. — A341

Designs: a, Victoria. b, Edward VII. c, George V. d, Edward VIII. e, George VI. f, Elizabeth II.

1990, Aug. 29 Engr. *Perf. 14½x14*
1003 A341 40c Sheet of 6 2.80 2.80
a.-f. any single .45 .45

Christmas A342

Various angels.

1990, Sept. 12 Litho. *Perf. 14*
1004 A342 40c multicolored .45 .45
1005 A342 $1 multicolored 1.15 1.15
1006 A342 $1.50 multicolored 1.75 1.75
1007 A342 $1.80 multicolored 2.10 2.10
Nos. 1004-1007 (4) 5.45 5.45

Antarctic Petrel — A343

Sheep — A344

1990, Nov. 7 *Perf. 13½x13*
1008 A343 40c shown .55 .55
1009 A343 50c Wilson's storm petrel .75 .75
1010 A343 60c Snow petrel .85 .85
1011 A343 80c Antarctic fulmar 1.10 1.10
1012 A343 100c Chinstrap penguin 1.50 1.50
1013 A343 150c Emperor penguin 2.25 2.25
Nos. 1008-1013 (6) 7.00 7.00

1991, Jan. 23 Litho. *Perf. 14½*
1014 A344 40c Coopworth .48 .48
1015 A344 60c Perendale .75 .75
1016 A344 80c Corriedale 1.00 1.00
1017 A344 $1 Drysdale 1.25 1.25
1018 A344 $1.50 South Suffolk 1.85 1.85
1019 A344 $1.80 Romney 2.25 2.25
Nos. 1014-1019 (6) 7.58 7.58

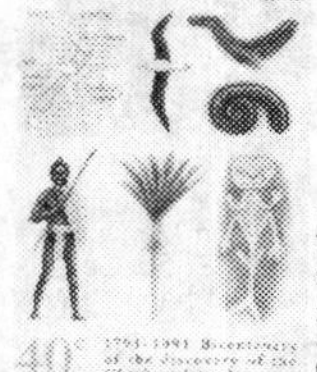

Map, Royal Albatross, Designs from Moriori House, Moriori Man, Nikau Palm, Tree Carving — A345

Design: 80c, Map, sailing ship, carving, petroglyph, Moriori house, Tommy Solomon, last full-blooded Moriori.

1991, Mar. 6 Litho. *Perf. 13½*
1020 A345 40c shown .48 .48
1021 A345 80c multicolored 1.00 1.00

Discovery of the Chatham Islands, Bicent.

New Zealand Football (Soccer) Assoc., Cent. A346

Designs: a, Goal. b, 5 players, referee.

1991, Mar. 6
1022 Pair 2.00 2.00
a.-b. A346 80c any single 1.00 1.00

Tuatara — A347

Designs: No. 1023, Juvenile. No. 1024, In burrow. No. 1025, Female. No. 1026, Male.

1991, Apr. 17 Litho. *Perf. 14½*
Denomination Color
1023 A347 40c gray blue .48 .48
1024 A347 40c dark brown .48 .48
1025 A347 40c olive green .48 .48
1026 A347 40c orange brown .48 .48
Nos. 1023-1026 (4) 1.92 1.92

Kiwi Type of 1988

1991, Apr. 17 Engr. *Perf. 14½*
1027 A325 $1 red 1.20 1.20
a. Litho. 1.25 1.25

Value is for copy with surrounding selvage. No. 1027a is from No. 1161a.

Happy Birthday — A348

Thinking of You — A349

1991, May 15 Litho. *Perf. 14x13½*
Size of Nos. 1031-1032, 1036-1037: 41x27mm
1028 A348 40c Clown face .65 .65
1029 A348 40c Balloons .65 .65
1030 A348 40c Birthday hat .65 .65
1031 A348 40c Present .65 .65
1032 A348 40c Cake & candles .65 .65
a. Bklt. pane of 5, #1028-1032 3.25
1033 A349 40c shown .65 .65
1034 A349 40c Cat, slippers .65 .65
1035 A349 40c Cat, alarm clock .65 .65
1036 A349 40c Cat looking out window .65 .65
1037 A349 40c Cat walking by door .65 .65
a. Bklt. pane of 5, #1033-1037 3.25

See Nos. 1044-1053.

Rock Formations A350

1991, June 12 Litho. *Perf. 14½*
1038 A350 40c Punakaiki Rocks .45 .45
1039 A350 50c Moeraki Boulders .55 .55
1040 A350 80c Organ Pipes .85 .85
1041 A350 $1 Castle Hill 1.10 1.10
1042 A350 $1.50 Te Kaukau Point 1.60 1.60
1043 A350 $1.80 Ahuriri River Clay Cliffs 2.00 2.00
Nos. 1038-1043 (6) 6.55 6.55

Greetings Types

1991, July 1 Litho. *Perf. 14x13½*
Size of Nos. 1047-1048, 1052-1053: 41x27mm
1044 A348 45c like #1028 .65 .65
1045 A348 45c like #1029 .65 .65
1046 A348 45c like #1030 .65 .65
1047 A348 45c like #1031 .65 .65
1048 A348 45c like #1032 .65 .65
a. Bklt. pane of 5, #1044-1048 3.25
1049 A349 45c like #1033 .65 .65
1050 A349 45c like #1034 .65 .65
1051 A349 45c like #1035 .65 .65
1052 A349 45c like #1036 .65 .65
1053 A349 45c like #1037 .65 .65
a. Bklt. pane of 5, #1049-1053 3.25

1991 Rugby World Cup — A351

Christmas — A352

1991, Aug. 21 Litho. *Perf. 14½x14*
1054 A351 80c Children's .95 .95
1055 A351 $1 Women's 1.20 1.20
1056 A351 $1.50 Senior 1.80 1.80
1057 A351 $1.80 All Blacks 2.10 2.10
a. Souvenir sheet of 1 2.50 2.50
Nos. 1054-1057 (4) 6.05 6.05

No. 1057a sold for $2.40 to benefit philatelic trust for hobby support.

1991, Sept. 18 Litho. *Perf. 13½x14*
1058 A352 45c Shepherds .52 .52
1059 A352 45c Wise men, camels .52 .52
1060 A352 45c Mary, Baby Jesus .52 .52
1061 A352 45c Wise man, gift .52 .52
a. Block of 4, #1058-1061 2.10 2.10
1062 A352 65c Star .75 .75
1063 A352 $1 Crown 1.15 1.15
1064 A352 $1.50 Angel 1.75 1.75
Nos. 1058-1064 (7) 5.73 5.73

Butterflies — A354

1991-95 Litho. *Perf. 14½*
1075 A354 $1 Forest ringlet 1.15 1.15
a. Perf. 14x14½ 1.30 1.30
b. Booklet pane of 5 + 5 labels 6.50
Complete booklet, #1075b 6.50
1076 A354 $2 Southern blue 2.30 2.30
1077 A354 $3 Yellow admiral 3.50 3.50
a. Souvenir sheet of 1 3.50 3.50
1078 A354 $4 Common copper 5.00 5.00
1079 A354 $5 Red admiral 6.25 6.25
Nos. 1075-1079 (5) 18.20 18.20

No. 1077a issued later for Phila Nippon '91.
Issued: $1-$3, 11/6/91; $4-$5, 1/25/95; #1075b, 9/1/95.
This is an expanding set. Numbers will change if necessary.

Mount Cook — A356

Die Stamped & Engr.
1994 Wmk. 387 *Perf. 14½x15*
1084 A356 $20 gold & blue 22.50 22.50

Issued: $20, Feb. 18, 1994. This is an expanding set. Number may change.

1992 America's Cup Competition A357

1992, Jan. 22 Litho. *Perf. 14x14½*
1085 A357 45c KZ7 Kiwi Magic, 1987 .52 .52
1086 A357 80c KZ1 New Zealand, 1988 .95 .95
1087 A357 $1 America, 1851 1.15 1.15
1088 A357 $1.50 New Zealand, 1992 1.75 1.75
Nos. 1085-1088 (4) 4.37 4.37

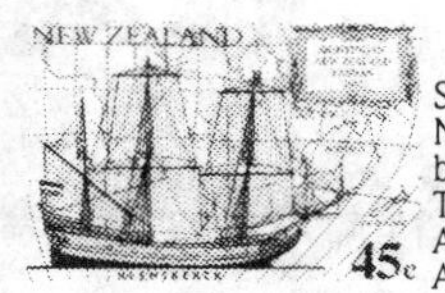

Sighting of New Zealand by Abel Tasman, 350th Anniv. A358

1992, Mar. 12 *Perf. 13½x14½*
1089 A358 45c Heemskerck .52 .45
1090 A358 80c Zeehaen .95 .95
1091 A358 $1 Santa Maria 1.15 1.15
1092 A358 $1.50 Pinta and Nina 1.75 1.75
a. Souvenir sheet of 2, #1091-1092, Perf. 14x14½ 4.00 4.00
Nos. 1089-1092 (4) 4.37 4.30

Discovery of America, 500th anniv. (#1091-1092).
Issue date: No. 1092a, May 22. World Columbian Stamp Expo (#1092a).

1992 Summer Olympics, Barcelona A359

1992, Apr. 3 Litho. *Perf. 13½*
1093 A359 45c Runners .52 .45

Antarctic Seals — A360

1992, Apr. 8 *Perf. 14x13½*
1094 A360 45c Weddell seal .52 .52
1095 A360 50c Crabeater seal .58 .58
1096 A360 65c Leopard seal .75 .75
1097 A360 80c Ross seal .95 .95
1098 A360 $1 Southern elephant seal 1.15 1.15
1099 A360 $1.80 Hooker's sea lion 2.10 2.10
Nos. 1094-1099 (6) 6.05 6.05

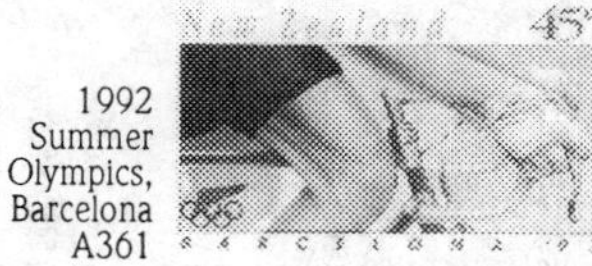

1992 Summer Olympics, Barcelona A361

1992, May 13 Litho. *Perf. 13½*
1100 A361 45c Cycling .45 .45
1101 A361 80c Archery .80 .80
1102 A361 $1 Equestrian 1.00 1.00
1103 A361 $1.50 Board sailing 1.50 1.50
a. Souvenir sheet of 4, #1100-1103, perf 14x14½ 3.50 3.50
b. No. 1103a overprinted 3.50 3.50
Nos. 1100-1103 (4) 3.75 3.75

No. 1103b overprint consists of World Columbian Stamp Expo emblem in sheet margin. Issue date: No. 1103b, May 22.

Glaciers A362

1992, June 12
1104 A362 45c Glacier ice .45 .45
1105 A362 50c Tasman glacier .50 .50
1106 A362 80c Snowball glacier .80 .80
1107 A362 $1 Brewster glacier 1.00 1.00
1108 A362 $1.50 Fox glacier 1.50 1.50
1109 A362 $1.80 Franz Josef glacier 1.80 1.80
Nos. 1104-1109 (6) 6.05 6.05

Camellias — A363

1992, July 8 *Perf. 14½*

1110 A363 45c Grand finale .45 .45
1111 A363 50c Showa-no-sakae .50 .50
1112 A363 80c Sugar dream .80 .80
1113 A363 $1 Night rider 1.00 1.00
1114 A363 $1.50 E.G. Waterhouse 1.50 1.50
1115 A363 $1.80 Dr. Clifford Parks 1.80 1.80
Nos. 1110-1115 (6) 6.05 6.05

Scenic Views of New Zealand — A364

1992, Sept. 1 Litho. *Perf. 14x14½*

Booklet Stamps

1116 A364 45c Tree, hills .45 .45
1117 A364 45c Hills, stream .45 .45
1118 A364 45c Hills, mountain tops .45 .45
1119 A364 45c Glacier .45 .45
1120 A364 45c Trees, green hills .45 .45
1121 A364 45c Tree branch, rapids .45 .45
1122 A364 45c Rocky shoreline .45 .45
1123 A364 45c Fjord .45 .45
1124 A364 45c Glacial runoff .45 .45
1125 A364 45c Vegetation, stream .45 .45
a. Bklt. pane of 10, #1116-1125 4.50

No. 1125a has continous design.

A365 A366

Christmas: No. 1126, Two reindeer over village. No. 1127, Two reindeer pulling Santa's sleigh. No. 1128, Christmas tree in window. No. 1129, Two children looking out window. 65c, Fireplace, stockings. $1, Church. $1.50, People beneath pohutukawa tree at beach.

1992, Sept. 16 *Perf. 14½*

1126 A365 45c multicolored .45 .45
1127 A365 45c multicolored .45 .45
1128 A365 45c multicolored .45 .45
1129 A365 45c multicolored .45 .45
a. Block of 4, #1126-1129 1.80 1.80
1130 A365 65c multicolored .65 .65
1131 A365 $1 multicolored 1.00 1.00
1132 A365 $1.50 multicolored 1.50 1.50
Nos. 1126-1132 (7) 4.95 4.95

No. 1129a has continous design.

1992, Nov. 4 Litho. *Perf. 13½*

The Emerging Years: The 1920s: 45c, Flaming youth. 50c, Birth of broadcasting. 80c, All Blacks rugby player. $1, The swaggie. $1.50, Motorcar brings freedom. $1.80, Arrival of the air age.

1133 A366 45c multicolored .45 .45
1134 A366 50c multicolored .50 .50
1135 A366 80c multicolored .80 .80
1136 A366 $1 multicolored 1.00 1.00
1137 A366 $1.50 multicolored 1.50 1.50
1138 A366 $1.80 multicolored 1.80 1.80
Nos. 1133-1138 (6) 6.05 6.05

Royal Doulton Ceramics A367

45c, Character jug, "Old Charley." 50c, Plate from "Bunnykins" series. 80c, Maori art tea ware. $1, Hand painted "Ophelia" plate. $1.50, Burslem figurine of St. George. $1.80, Salt glazed vase.

1993, Jan. 20 Litho. *Perf. 13*

1139 A367 45c multicolored .45 .45
1140 A367 50c multicolored .50 .50
1141 A367 80c multicolored .80 .80
1142 A367 $1 multicolored 1.00 1.00
1143 A367 $1.50 multicolored 1.50 1.50
1144 A367 $1.80 multicolored 1.80 1.80
a. Souvenir sheet of 1 1.80 1.80
Nos. 1139-1144 (6) 6.05 6.05

A368 A369

The Emerging Years: The 1930's: 45c, Buttons and bows, the new femininity. 50c, The Great Depression. 80c, Race horse, Phar Lap. $1, State housing. $1.50, Free milk for schools. $1.80, The talkies.

1993, Feb. 17 Litho. *Perf. 14½x14*

1145 A368 45c multicolored .45 .45
1146 A368 50c multicolored .50 .50
1147 A368 80c multicolored .80 .80
1148 A368 $1 multicolored 1.00 1.00
1149 A368 $1.50 multicolored 1.50 1.50
1150 A368 $1.80 multicolored 1.80 1.80
Nos. 1145-1150 (6) 6.05 6.05

1993, Mar. 31 Litho. *Perf. 13½*

1151 A369 45c First vote .45 .45
1152 A369 80c War work .80 .80
1153 A369 $1 Child care 1.00 1.00
1154 A369 $1.50 Contemporary women 1.50 1.50
Nos. 1151-1154 (4) 3.75 3.75

Woman Suffrage, cent.

Thermal Wonders A370

45c, Champagne Pool. 50c, Boiling mud, Rotorua. 80c, Emerald Pool. $1, Hakereteke Falls. $1.50, Warbrick Terrace. $1.80, Pohutu Geyser.

1993, May 5 Litho. *Perf. 12*

1155 A370 45c multicolored .48 .48
1156 A370 50c multicolored .55 .55
1157 A370 80c multicolored .85 .85
1158 A370 $1 multicolored 1.10 1.10
1159 A370 $1.50 multicolored 1.60 1.60
1160 A370 $1.80 multicolored 1.95 1.95
a. Souvenir sheet of 1 2.00 2.00
Nos. 1155-1160 (6) 6.53 6.53

No. 1160a inscribed with Bangkok '93 emblem in sheet margin. Issue date: No. 1160a, Oct. 1.

Kiwi Type of 1988

1993, June 9 Engr. *Perf. 14½*

1161 A325 $1 blue 1.10 1.10
a. Souv. sheet of 3, #916b, 1027a, 1161 6.50 6.50
b. Litho. 1.25 1.25
c. Souv. sheet of 3, #918b, 1027a, 1161b 3.50 3.50

Taipei '93, Asian Intl. Stamp Exhibition (#1164a), Hong Kong '94 (#1161c).
Value is for copy with surrounding selvage.
Issued: #1161a, 8/14/93; #1161c, 2/18/94.

Species Unique to New Zealand A371

Designs: No. 1162a, Yellow-eyed penguin, Hector's dolphin, New Zealand fur seal. b, Taiko, Mt. Cook lily, blue duck. c, Giant snail, rock wren, Hamilton's frog. d, Kaka, Chatham Island pigeon, giant weta.
No. 1163, Tusked weta.

1993, June 9 Litho. *Perf. 14x14½*

1162 A371 45c Block of 4, #a.-d. 1.95 1.95

Perf. 13½

1163 A371 45c multicolored .48 .48

World Wildlife Fund.

Christmas A372 Fish A373

Christmas designs: No. 1164, Flowers from pohutukawa tree, denomination at UL. No. 1165, Like #1164, denomination at UR. No. 1166, Present with yellow ribbon, denomination at LL. No. 1167, Present with red ribbon, denomination at LR. $1.00, Ornaments, cracker, sailboats. $1.50, Wreath, sailboats, present.

1993, Sept. 1 Litho. *Perf. 14½x14*

1164 A372 45c multicolored .48 .48
1165 A372 45c multicolored .48 .48
1166 A372 45c multicolored .48 .48
1167 A372 45c multicolored .48 .48
a. Block of 4, #1165-1167 2.00 2.00
1168 A372 $1 multicolored 1.10 1.10
1169 A372 $1.50 multicolored 1.65 1.65
Nos. 1164-1169 (6) 4.67 4.67

Booklet Stamps

Perf. 12

1164a A372 45c multicolored .48 .48
1165a A372 45c multicolored .48 .48
1166a A372 45c multicolored .48 .48
1167b A372 45c multicolored .48 .48
c. Booklet pane, 3 each #1164a-1165a, 2 each #1166a, 1167b 5.00

At least one edge of No. 1167c is guillotined.

1993, Sept. 1 *Perf. 13½*

Designs: No. 1170, Paua (#1175). No. 1171, Greenshell mussels. No. 1172, Terakihi (#1171). No. 1173, Salmon (#1172). No. 1174, Southern bluefin tuna, albacore tuna, kahawai (#1173). No. 1175, Rock lobster (#1171). No. 1176, Snapper (#1177). No. 1177, Groper (#1178). No. 1178, Orange roughy (#1179). No. 1179, Squid, hoki, oreo dory (#1173, #1174, #1178).

Booklet Stamps

1170 A373 45c multicolored .48 .48
1171 A373 45c multicolored .48 .48
1172 A373 45c multicolored .48 .48
1173 A373 45c multicolored .48 .48
1174 A373 45c multicolored .48 .48
1175 A373 45c multicolored .48 .48
1176 A373 45c multicolored .48 .48
1177 A373 45c multicolored .48 .48
1178 A373 45c multicolored .48 .48
1179 A373 45c multicolored .48 .48
a. Booklet pane of 10, #1170-1179 + 2 labels 5.00

Nos. 1179a has continuous design.

Dinosaurs — A374 The 1940s — A375

1993, Oct. 1

1180 A374 45c Sauropod .48 .48
1181 A374 80c Pterosaur .90 .90
1182 A374 $1 Ankylosaur 1.10 1.10
1183 A374 $1.20 Mauisaurus 1.25 1.25
1184 A374 $1.50 Carnosaur 1.65 1.65
a. Souvenir sheet of 1, perf. 14½x14 1.65 1.65
b. As "a," inscribed with Bangkok '93 emblem 1.65 1.65
Nos. 1180-1184 (5) 5.38 5.38

Booklet Stamp

Size: 25½x23½mm

Perf. 12

1185 A374 45c Carnosaur, sauropod .48 .48
a. Booklet pane of 10 + 2 labels 4.75 4.75

1993, Nov. 3 Litho. *Perf. 14*

Designs: 45c, New Zealand at war. 50c, Crop dusting. 80c, State produces hydroelectricity. $1, New Zealand Marching Assoc. $1.50, The American invasion. $1.80, Victory.

1186 A375 45c multicolored .50 .50
1187 A375 50c multicolored .55 .55
1188 A375 80c multicolored .90 .90
1189 A375 $1 multicolored 1.10 1.10
1190 A375 $1.50 multicolored 1.65 1.65
1191 A375 $1.80 multicolored 2.00 2.00
Nos. 1186-1191 (6) 6.70 6.70

Outdoor Adventure Sports — A376

1994, Jan. 19 Litho. *Perf. 12*

1192 A376 45c Bungy jumping .50 .50
1193 A376 80c Trout fishing .90 .90
1194 A376 $1 Jet boating, horiz. 1.10 1.10
1195 A376 $1.50 Tramping 1.65 1.65
1196 A376 $1.80 Heli-skiing 2.00 2.00
a. Souvenir sheet of 1 2.00 2.00
Nos. 1192-1196 (5) 6.15 6.15

No. 1196a inscribed in sheet margin with Hong Kong '94 emblem and text in English and Chinese. Issue date: No. 1196a, Feb. 18.

White Water Rafting — A377

1994, Jan. 19 Litho. *Perf. 12*

Booklet Stamp

1197 A377 45c multicolored .52 .52
a. Booklet pane of 10 + 4 labels 5.25

Whitbread Trans-Global Yacht Race — A378

1994, Jan. 19 *Perf. 15*

1198 A378 $1 Endeavour 1.10 1.10

Used value is for stamp with complete selvage.

The 1950's — A379

Designs: 45c, Rock and roll. 80c, Conquest of Mt. Everest. $1, Aunt Daisy, "Good Morning Everybody." $1.20, Royal visit, 1953. $1.50, Opo, the Friendly Dolphin. $1.80, The Coat Hanger (Auckland Harbor Bridge.)

1994, Mar. 24 Litho. *Perf. 14*

1199 A379 45c multicolored .50 .50
1200 A379 80c multicolored .90 .90
1201 A379 $1 multicolored 1.10 1.10
1202 A379 $1.20 multicolored 1.40 1.40
1203 A379 $1.50 multicolored 1.65 1.65
1204 A379 $1.80 multicolored 2.00 2.00
Nos. 1199-1204 (6) 7.55 7.55

Scenic Views of the Four Seasons A380

Designs: 45c, Winter, Mt. Cook, Mt. Cook lily. 70c, Spring, Lake Hawea, kowhai flower. $1.50, Summer, Opononi, pohutukawa flower. $1.80, Autumn, Mt. Cook, Lake Pukaki, puriri flower.

1994, Apr. 27 *Perf. 12*

1205	A380	45c multicolored	.50	.50
1206	A380	70c multicolored	.80	.80
1207	A380	$1.50 multicolored	1.65	1.65
1208	A380	$1.80 multicolored	2.00	2.00
a.		Strip of 4, #1205-1208	5.00	5.00

Paua Shell — A381

Pavlova Dessert A382

Jandals — A383 Bush Shirt — A384

Buzzy Bee Toy — A385

Kiwi Fruit — A386

Kiwiana: No. 1211, Hokey pokey ice cream. No. 1212, Fish and chips. No. 1216, Black singlet, gumboots. No. 1217, Rugby shoes, ball.

1994, Apr. 27 **Litho.** *Perf. 12*

Booklet Stamps

1209	A381	45c multicolored	.52	.52
1210	A382	45c multicolored	.52	.52
1211	A381	45c multicolored	.52	.52
1212	A382	45c multicolored	.52	.52
1213	A383	45c multicolored	.52	.52
1214	A384	45c multicolored	.52	.52
1215	A385	45c multicolored	.52	.52
1216	A384	45c multicolored	.52	.52
1217	A385	45c multicolored	.52	.52
1218	A386	45c multicolored	.52	.52
a.		Booklet pane of 10, #1209-1218	5.25	

Maori Myths — A387

Designs: 45c, Maui pulls up Te Ika (the fish). 80c, Rona is snatched up by Marama (moon). $1, Maui attacks Tuna (eel). $1.20, Tane separates Rangi (sky) and Papa (earth). $1.50, Matakauri slays Giant of Wakatipu. $1.80, Panenehu shows Koura (crayfish) to Tangaroa.

1994, June 8 *Perf. 13*

1219	A387	45c multicolored	.50	.50
1220	A387	80c multicolored	.95	.95
1221	A387	$1 multicolored	1.10	1.10
1222	A387	$1.20 multicolored	1.40	1.40
1223	A387	$1.50 multicolored	1.75	1.75
1224	A387	$1.80 multicolored	2.00	2.00
		Nos. 1219-1224 (6)	7.70	7.70

First Manned Moon Landing, 25th Anniv. — A388

1994, July 20 **Litho.** *Perf. 12*

1225	A388	$1.50 multicolored	1.65	1.65

No. 1225 has a holographic image. Soaking in water may affect the hologram.

People Reaching People — A389

Die Cut Perf. 11

1994, July 20 **Photo.**

Self-Adhesive

1226	A389	45c multicolored	.50	.50

See No. 1311.

Wild Animals A390

1994, Aug. 16 **Litho.** *Perf. 14*

1227	A390	45c Hippopotamus	.50	.50
1228	A390	45c Spider monkey	.50	.50
1229	A390	45c Giant panda	.50	.50
1230	A390	45c Polar bear	.50	.50
1231	A390	45c African elephant	.50	.50
1232	A390	45c White rhinoceros	.50	.50
1233	A390	45c African lion	.50	.50
1234	A390	45c Plains zebra	.50	.50
1235	A390	45c Giraffe	.50	.50
1236	A390	45c Siberian tiger	.50	.50
a.		Block of 10, #1227-1236	5.00	5.00
b.		Souvenir sheet of 6, #1229-1231, 1233, 1235-1236	3.00	3.00

PHILAKOREA '94 (#1236b). Nos. 1227-1236 printed in sheets of 100. Because of the design of these sheets, blocks or strips of Nos. 1227-1236 exist in 10 different arrangements. Value assigned to No. 1236a applies to all arrangements.

Cricket in New Zealand, Cent. — A392

Christmas A391

Designs: No. 1237, Children, Nativity scene. 70c, Magi, father, child. 80c, Carolers, stained glass window. $1, Carolers, Christmas tree. $1.50, Children, candles. $1.80, Father, mother, infant.

No. 1243, Children, Christmas tree, Santa.

1994, Sept. 21 **Litho.** *Perf. 14*

1237	A391	45c multicolored	.55	.55
1238	A391	70c multicolored	.85	.85
1239	A391	80c multicolored	1.00	1.00
1240	A391	$1 multicolored	1.25	1.25
a.		Souvenir sheet, 1 each #1237-1240	3.75	3.75
1241	A391	$1.50 multicolored	1.90	1.90
1242	A391	$1.80 multicolored	2.25	2.25
		Nos. 1237-1242 (6)	7.80	7.80

Booklet Stamp

Size: 30x25mm

1243	A391	45c multicolored	.55	.55
a.		Booklet pane of 10	5.50	

Beach Cricket — A393

1994, Nov. 2 *Perf. 13½*

1244	A392	45c Batting	.55	.55
1245	A392	80c Bowling	1.00	1.00
1246	A392	$1 Wicketkeeping	1.25	1.25
1247	A392	$1.80 Fielding	2.25	2.25
		Nos. 1244-1247 (4)	5.05	5.05

Perf. 12

1248	A393	45c Bklt. pane of 10	5.50	5.50
a.-j.		Any single	.55	.55

New Zealand at Night A394

1995, Feb. 22 **Litho.** *Perf. 12*

1249	A394	45c Auckland	.55	.55
1250	A394	80c Wellington	1.00	1.00
1251	A394	$1 Christchurch	1.25	1.25
1252	A394	$1.20 Dunedin	1.50	1.50
1253	A394	$1.50 Rotorua	1.90	1.90
1254	A394	$1.80 Queenstown	2.25	2.25
a.		Souvenir sheet of 6, #1249-1254	9.00	9.00
		Nos. 1249-1254 (6)	8.45	8.45

Singapore '95, Jakarta '95 (#1254a). Issued: No. 1254a, 9/1/95.

A395

A396

Golf courses.

1995, Mar. 22 **Litho.** *Perf. 14*

1255	A395	45c Waitangi	.58	.58
1256	A395	80c New Plymouth	1.00	1.00
1257	A395	$1.20 Rotorua	1.50	1.50
1258	A395	$1.80 Queenstown	2.25	2.25
		Nos. 1255-1258 (4)	5.33	5.33

1995, Mar. 22

Environmental Protection: No. 1259, Native fauna, flora. No. 1260, Plant native trees, shrubs. No. 1261, Protect marine mammals. No. 1262, Conserve power, water. No. 1263, Enjoy natural environment. No. 1264, Control animal pests. No. 1265, Eliminate noxious plants. No. 1266, Return undersized catches. No. 1267, Control air, water quality. No. 1268, Dispose of trash properly.

1259	A396	45c multicolored	.58	.58
1260	A396	45c multicolored	.58	.58
1261	A396	45c multicolored	.58	.58
1262	A396	45c multicolored	.58	.58
1263	A396	45c multicolored	.58	.58
1264	A396	45c multicolored	.58	.58
1265	A396	45c multicolored	.58	.58
1266	A396	45c multicolored	.58	.58
1267	A396	45c multicolored	.58	.58
1268	A396	45c multicolored	.58	.58
a.		Booklet pane, #1259-1268	5.80	
		Complete booklet, #1268a	5.80	

New Zealand stamps can be mounted in the annual Scott New Zealand supplement.

Maori Language — A397

Designs: 45c, Treasured Language Nest. 70c, Sing to awaken the spirit. 80c, Acquire knowledge through stories. $1, The welcoming call. $1.50, Recite the genealogies that link people. $1.80, Tell the lore of the people.

1995, May 3 **Litho.** *Perf. 13½*

1269	A397	45c multicolored	.60	.60
1270	A397	70c multicolored	.95	.95
1271	A397	80c multicolored	1.10	1.10
1272	A397	$1 multicolored	1.40	1.40
1273	A397	$1.50 multicolored	2.00	2.00
1274	A397	$1.80 multicolored	2.50	2.50
		Nos. 1269-1274 (6)	8.55	8.55

Asian Development Bank, 28th Meeting of the Board of Governors, Auckland A398

Design: $1.50, Pacific Basin Economic Council, 28th Intl. Meeting, Auckland.

1995, May 3

1275	A398	$1 Map shown	1.40	1.40
1276	A398	$1.50 Map of Pacific	2.00	2.00

Team New Zealand, 1995 America's Cup Winner — A399

1995, May 16 *Perf. 12*

1277	A399	45c Black Magic yacht	.60	.60

Rugby League, Cent. A400

Designs: No. 1278, Club Rugby League, Lion Red Cup. No. 1282, Trans Tasman. $1.00, Mini League. $1.50, George Smith, Albert Baskerville, Early Rugby League. $1.80, Intl. Rugby League, Courtney Intl. Goodwill Trophy.

1995, July 26 **Litho.** *Perf. 14*

1278	A400	45c multicolored	.60	.60
1279	A400	$1 multicolored	1.40	1.40
1280	A400	$1.50 multicolored	2.00	2.00
1281	A400	$1.80 multicolored	2.50	2.50
a.		Souvenir sheet of 1	2.50	2.50
		Nos. 1278-1281 (4)	6.50	6.50

Booklet Stamp

Perf. 12 on 3 Sides

1282	A400	45c multicolored	.60	.60
a.		Booklet pane of 10	6.00	
		Complete booklet, #1282a	6.00	

Farm Animals — A401

1995 **Litho.** *Perf. 14x14½*

Booklet Stamps

1283	A401	40c Sheep	.55	.55
1284	A401	40c Deer	.55	.55
1285	A401	40c Horses	.55	.55
1286	A401	40c Cattle	.55	.55
1287	A401	40c Goats	.55	.55

1288 A401 40c Turkey .55 .55
1289 A401 40c Ducks .55 .55
1290 A401 40c Chickens .55 .55
1291 A401 40c Pigs .55 .55
1292 A401 40c Border collie .55 .55
a. Booklet pane of 10, #1283-1292 5.50
Complete booklet 5.50
1293 A401 45c Sheep .60 .60
1294 A401 45c Deer .60 .60
1295 A401 45c Horses .60 .60
1296 A401 45c Cattle .60 .60
1297 A401 45c Goats .60 .60
1298 A401 45c Turkey .60 .60
1299 A401 45c Ducks .60 .60
1300 A401 45c Chickens .60 .60
1301 A401 45c Pigs .60 .60
1302 A401 45c Border collie .60 .60
a. Booklet pane of 10, #1293-1302 6.00
Complete booklet, #1302a 6.00
b. Souvenir sheet of 5, #1298-1302, perf. 12 3.00 3.00
Nos. 1283-1302 (20) 11.50 11.50

Singapore '95 (#1302b).
Issued: #1302a, 9/1/95; #1292a, 10/2/95.

Christmas — A402

Stained glass windows: 40c, 45c, Archangel Gabriel. No. 1309A, Angel with trumpet. 70c, Mary. 80c, Shepherds. $1, Madonna and Child. $1.50, Two wise men. $1.80, One wise man.

1995 *Perf. 12*
1303 A402 40c multicolored .55 .55
1304 A402 45c multicolored .60 .60
1305 A402 70c multicolored .90 .90
1306 A402 80c multicolored 1.00 1.00
1307 A402 $1 multicolored 1.30 1.30
1308 A402 $1.50 multicolored 2.00 2.00
1309 A402 $1.80 multicolored 2.40 2.40

Booklet Stamp
Size: 25x30mm
Perf. 14½x14

1309A A402 40c multicolored .55 .55
b. Booklet pane of 10 5.50
Complete booklet, #1309b 5.50
Nos. 1303-1309A (8) 9.30 9.30

Issued: 45c-$1.80, 9/1; #1303, 10/2; #1309A, 11/9.

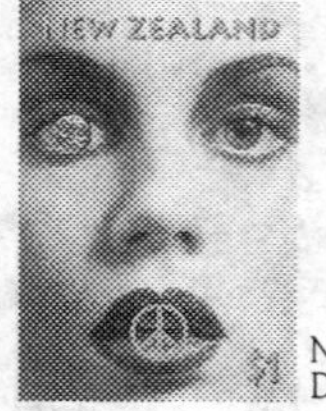

Nuclear Disarmament — A403

1995, Sept. 1 Litho. *Perf. 13½*
1310 A403 $1 multicolored 1.40 1.40

People Reaching People Type of 1994
1995, Oct. 2 Photo. ***Die Cut Perf. 11***
Self-Adhesive
1311 A389 40c multicolored .55 .55

Mitre Peak — A404

UN, 50th Anniv. — A405

1995, Oct. 2 Litho. *Perf. 13½*
1312 A404 40c multicolored .55 .55
a. Perf 12 .55 .55
b. As "a," miniature sheet of 10 5.50

Southpex '96 Stamp Show (No. 1312a).

See Nos. 1345-1360, 1405, 1412.

1995, Oct. 4 *Perf. 14½*
1313 A405 $1.80 multicolored 2.40 2.40

Famous Living New Zealanders — A406

Person, career field: 40c, Dame Kiri Te Kanawa, performing arts. 80c, Charles Upham, service, business, development. $1, Barry Crump, fine arts, literature. $1.20, Sir Brian Barratt-Boyes, science, medicine, education. $1.50, Dame Whina Cooper, community leader, social campaigner. $1.80, Sir Richard Hadlee, sports.

1995, Oct. 4 *Perf. 12*
1314 A406 40c multicolored .55 .55
1315 A406 80c multicolored 1.10 1.10
1316 A406 $1 multicolored 1.40 1.40
1317 A406 $1.20 multicolored 1.65 1.65
1318 A406 $1.50 multicolored 2.00 2.00
1319 A406 $1.80 multicolored 2.40 2.40
Nos. 1314-1319 (6) 9.10 9.10

Nos. 1314-1319 issued with se-tenant tab inscribed "STAMP / MONTH / OCTOBER / 1995."

Commonwealth Heads of Government Meeting, Auckland — A407

Designs: 40c, Fern, sky, globe, $1.80, Fern, sea, national flag.

1995, Nov. 9 Litho. *Perf. 14*
1320 A407 40c multicolored .55 .55
1321 A407 $1.80 multicolored 2.40 2.40

Racehorses A408

1996, Jan. 24 Litho. *Perf. 13½x14*
1322 A408 40c Kiwi .55 .55
1323 A408 80c Rough Habit 1.10 1.10
1324 A408 $1 Blossom Lady 1.30 1.30
1325 A408 $1.20 Il Vicolo 1.60 1.60
1326 A408 $1.50 Horlicks 2.00 2.00
1327 A408 $1.80 Bonecrusher 2.40 2.40
Nos. 1322-1327 (6) 8.95 8.95

Booklet
1328 A408 Souvenir bklt. 18.00

#1328 contains one booklet pane of #1322-1327 and individual panes of 1 each #1322-1327.

Maori Crafts — A409

1996, Feb. 21 Litho. *Perf. 14x13½*
1329 A409 40c Basket .55 .55
1330 A409 80c Weapon 1.10 1.10
1331 A409 $1 Embroidery 1.30 1.30
1332 A409 $1.20 Greenstone 1.60 1.60
1333 A409 $1.50 Gourd 2.00 2.00
a. Souvenir sheet of 3, #1329, 1330, 1333, perf. 13 3.65 3.65
1334 A409 $1.80 Cloak 2.40 2.40
Nos. 1329-1334 (6) 8.95 8.95

No. 1333a for Hong Kong '97. Issued 2/12/97.

Seashore — A410

Designs: No. 1335, Black-backed gull. No. 1336, Sea cucumber, spiny starfish. No. 1337, Common shrimp. No. 1338, Gaudy nudibranch. No. 1339, Large rock crab, clingfish. No. 1340, Snake skin chiton, red rock crab. No. 1341, Estuarine triplefin, cat's eye shell. No. 1342, Cushion star, sea horse. No. 1343, Blue-eyed triplefin, yaldwyn's triplefin. No. 1344, Common octopus.

1996, Feb. 21 *Perf. 14x14½*
Booklet Stamps
1335 A410 40c multicolored .55 .55
1336 A410 40c multicolored .55 .55
1337 A410 40c multicolored .55 .55
1338 A410 40c multicolored .55 .55
1339 A410 40c multicolored .55 .55
1340 A410 40c multicolored .55 .55
1341 A410 40c multicolored .55 .55
1342 A410 40c multicolored .55 .55
1343 A410 40c multicolored .55 .55
1344 A410 40c multicolored .55 .55
a. Booklet pane, Nos. 1335-1344 5.50
Complete booklet, No. 1344a 5.50

No. 1344a has a continuous design.

Scenic Views Type of 1995

5c, Mt. Cook, horiz. 10c, Champagne Pool, horiz. 20c, Cape Reinga, horiz. 30c, Mackenzie Country, horiz. 50c, Mt. Ngauruhoe, horiz. 60c, Lake Wanaka. 70c, Giant Kauri-Tane Mahuta. 80c, Doubtful Sound. 90c, Waitomo Limestone Cave.

No. 1354, Tory Channel, Marlborough Sounds. No. 1355, Lake Wakatipu. No. 1356, Lake Matheson. No. 1357, Fox Glacier. No. 1358, Mt. Egmont, Taranaki. No. 1359, Piercy Island, Bay of Islands. No. 1354-1359 horiz.

1996, Mar. 27 Litho. *Perf. 13½*
1345 A404 5c multicolored .15 .15
1346 A404 10c multicolored .15 .15
1347 A404 20c multicolored .25 .25
1348 A404 30c multicolored .40 .40
1349 A404 50c multicolored .70 .70
a. Souv. sheet of 4, #1346-1349 1.50 1.50
1350 A404 60c multicolored .80 .80
1351 A404 70c multicolored .95 .95
1352 A404 80c multicolored 1.10 1.10
1353 A404 90c multicolored 1.20 1.20
a. Souv. sheet of 4, #1350-1353 4.00 4.00
Nos. 1345-1353 (9) 5.70 5.70

CHINA '96 (#1349a). CAPEX '96 (#1353a.)
See No. 1404.

Die Cut Perf. 11½
1996, May 1 **Litho.**
Size: 26x21mm
Self-Adhesive
1354 A404 40c multicolored .55 .55
1355 A404 40c multicolored .55 .55
1356 A404 40c multicolored .55 .55
1357 A404 40c multicolored .55 .55
1358 A404 40c multicolored .55 .55
1359 A404 40c multicolored .55 .55
a. Strip of 6, Nos. 1354-1359 3.30 3.30

Serpentine Die Cut 11½
1996, Aug. 7 **Litho.**
Size: 33x22mm
Self-Adhesive

Design: $1, Pohutukawa tree, horiz.

1360 A404 $1 multicolored 1.40 1.40
a. Booklet pane of 5 7.00

By its nature No. 1360a is a complete booklet. The peelable paper backing serves as a booklet cover. The outside of the cover contains 5 peelable international airpost labels.

Rescue Services — A411

40c, Fire service, ambulance. 80c, Civil defense. $1, Air sea rescue. $1.50, Air ambulance, rescue helicopter. $1.80, Mountain rescue, Red Cross.

1996, Mar. 27 *Perf. 14½x15*
1361 A411 40c multicolored .55 .55
1362 A411 80c multicolored 1.10 1.10
1363 A411 $1 multicolored 1.30 1.30
1364 A411 $1.50 multicolored 2.00 2.00
1365 A411 $1.80 multicolored 2.40 2.40
Nos. 1361-1365 (5) 7.35 7.35

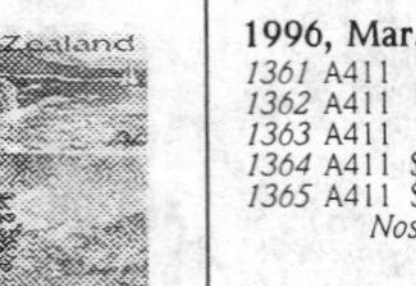

Wildlife A412

Designs: 40c, Yellow-eyed penguin, vert. 80c, Royal albatross. $1, White heron. $1.20, Sperm whale. $1.50, Fur seal, vert. $1.80, Bottlenose dolphin, vert.

1996, May 1 Litho. *Perf. 14*
1366 A412 40c multicolored .55 .55
1367 A412 80c multicolored 1.10 1.10
1368 A412 $1 multicolored 1.40 1.40
1369 A412 $1.20 multicolored 1.65 1.65
1370 A412 $1.50 multicolored 2.00 2.00
a. Sheet of 2, #1368, 1370 3.50 3.50
1371 A412 $1.80 multicolored 2.50 2.50
a. Sheet of 2, #1367, 1371 3.60 3.60
Nos. 1366-1371 (6) 9.20 9.20

No. 1370a for CHINA '96. Issued May 18.
No. 1371a for Taipei '96. Issued Oct. 2.

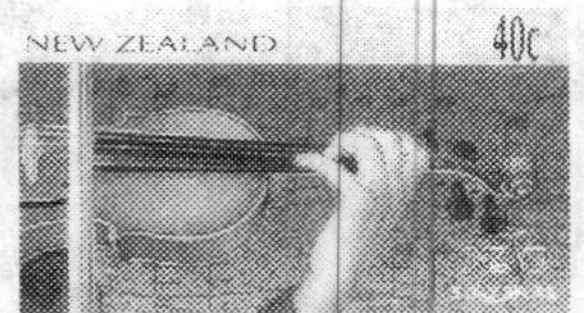

New Zealand Symphony Orchestra, 50th Anniv. — A413

1996, July 10 Litho. *Perf. 15x14½*
1372 A413 40c Violin .55 .55
1373 A413 80c French horn 1.10 1.10

1996 Summer Olympics, Atlanta A414

1996, July 10 *Perf. 14½*
1374 A414 40c Swimming .55 .55
1375 A414 80c Cycling 1.10 1.10
1376 A414 $1 Athletics 1.40 1.40
1377 A414 $1.50 Rowing 2.00 2.00
1378 A414 $1.80 Yachting 2.50 2.50
Nos. 1374-1378 (5) 7.55 7.55

Used value is for stamp with complete selvage.
See No. 1383.

A415

A416

Motion pictures, cent.: 40c, Hinemoa. 80c, Broken Barrier. $1.50, Goodbye Pork Pie. $1.80, Once Were Warriors.

1996, Aug. 7 Litho. *Perf. 14½x15*

1379 A415 40c multicolored .55 .55
1380 A415 80c multicolored 1.10 1.10
1381 A415 $1.50 multicolored 2.00 2.00
1382 A415 $1.80 multicolored 2.50 2.50
Nos. 1379-1382 (4) 6.15 6.15

Nos. 1379-1382 are printed se-tenant with scratch and win labels for a contest available to New Zealand residents.

1996 Summer Olympics Type

Design: Danyon Loader, swimmer, Blyth Tait, horseman, 1996 gold medalists from New Zealand.

1996, Aug. 28 Litho. *Perf. 14½*

1383 A414 40c multicolored .55 .55

Used value is for stamp with complete selvage. Leaves in selvage printed in six different patterns.

1996, Sept. 4 *Perf. 12*

1384 A416 40c Beehive ballot box .55 .55

Mixed member proportional election, 1966. No. 1384 was issued in sheets of 10.

Christmas A417

Scenes from the Christmas story: No. 1385, Following the star. 70c, Shepherd finding baby in manger. 80c, Angel's announcement to shepherd. $1, The Nativity. $1.50, Journey to Bethlehem. $1.80, The annunciation.

No. 1391, Adoration of the Magi. No. 1392, Heavenly host praising God.

1996, Sept. 4 *Perf. 14*

1385 A417 40c multicolored .55 .55
1386 A417 70c multicolored 1.00 1.00
1387 A417 80c multicolored 1.10 1.10
1388 A417 $1 multicolored 1.40 1.40
1389 A417 $1.50 multicolored 2.00 2.00
1390 A417 $1.80 multicolored 2.50 2.50
Nos. 1385-1390 (6) 8.55 8.55

Size: 29x24mm

Self-Adhesive

Serpentine Die Cut 11½

1391 A417 40c multicolored .55 .55
a. Booklet pane 10 5.50
1392 A417 40c multicolored .55 .55

By its nature No. 1391a is a complete booklet. The peelable paper backing serves as a booklet cover.

Extinct Birds A418

1996, Oct. 2 Litho. *Perf. 13½*

1393 A418 40c Adzebill .55 .55
1394 A418 80c Laughing owl 1.10 1.10
1395 A418 $1 Piopio 1.40 1.40
1396 A418 $1.20 Huia 1.70 1.70
1397 A418 $1.50 Giant eagle 2.10 2.10
1398 A418 $1.80 Giant moa 2.50 2.50
a. Souvenir sheet 2.50 2.50
b. As "a," with added inscription 2.50 2.50
Nos. 1393-1398 (6) 9.35 9.35

Size: 29x24mm

Self-Adhesive

Serpentine Die Cut 11½

1399 A418 40c Stout-legged wren .55 .55
a. Booklet pane of 10 5.50

Inscriptions on backs of Nos. 1393-1398 describe each species. By its nature No. 1399a is a complete booklet. The peelable backing serves as a booklet cover.

No. 1398b contains Taipei '96 exhibition emblem in sheet margin.

Scenic Gardens — A419

Designs: 40c, Seymour Square Gardens, Blenheim. 80c, Pukekura Park Gardens, New Plymouth. $1, Wintergarden, Auckland. $1.50, Botanic Gardens, Chrishchurch. $1.80, Marine Parade Gardens, Napier.

1996, Nov. 13 Litho. *Perf. 13½*

1400 A419 40c multicolored .55 .55
1401 A419 80c multicolored 1.10 1.10
1402 A419 $1 multicolored 1.40 1.40
1403 A419 $1.50 multicolored 2.10 2.10
1404 A419 $1.80 multicolored 2.50 2.50
Nos. 1400-1404 (5) 7.65 7.65

New Zealand Post produced and distributed three souvenir sheets as rewards for purchases made from the post office during 1996. The sheets were not available through normal philatelic channels. The sheets are inscribed "NEW ZEALAND POST / Best of 1996" and the Stamp Points emblem. Each sheet contains 3 stamps; #1327, 1365, 1334; #1378, 1382, 1371; #1390, 1404, 1398.

Scenic Views Type of 1995

Serpentine Die Cut 11½

1996, Nov. 1 Litho.

Size: 26x21mm

Self-Adhesive

1405 A404 80c like No. 1352 1.10 1.10
a. Booklet pane of 10 11.00

By its nature No. 1405a is a complete booklet. The peelable paper backing serves as a booklet cover. The outside of the cover contains 10 peelable international airpost labels.

Cattle — A420

1997, Jan. 15 *Perf. 14x14½*

1406 A420 40c Holstein-Friesian .55 .55
1407 A420 80c Jersey 1.10 1.10
1408 A420 $1 Simmental 1.40 1.40
1409 A420 $1.20 Ayrshire 1.70 1.70
1410 A420 $1.50 Angus 2.10 2.10
a. Souvenir sheet of 3, #1407, 1408, 1410 4.60 4.60
1411 A420 $1.80 Hereford 2.50 2.50
Nos. 1406-1411 (6) 9.35 9.35

No. 1410a for Hong Kong '97. Issued 2/12/97.

Scenic Views Type of 1995

1997, Feb. 12 Litho. *Perf. 13½*

Size: 37x32mm

1412 A404 $10 Mt. Ruapehu 13.75 13.75

Discoverers — A421

1997, Feb. 12 *Perf. 14*

1413 A421 40c James Cook .55 .55
1414 A421 80c Kupe 1.10 1.10
1415 A421 $1 Maui, vert. 1.40 1.40
1416 A421 $1.20 Jean de Surville, vert. 1.70 1.70
1417 A421 $1.50 Dumont d'Urville 2.10 2.10
1418 A421 $1.80 Abel Tasman 2.50 2.50
Nos. 1413-1418 (6) 9.35 9.35

"Wackiest Letterboxes" — A422

Serpentine Die Cut 11½

1997, Mar. 19 Litho.

Self-Adhesive

Booklet Stamps

1419 A422 40c Log house .55 .55
1420 A422 40c Owl .55 .55
1421 A422 40c Whale .55 .55
1422 A422 40c "Kilroy is Back" .55 .55
1423 A422 40c House of twigs .55 .55
1424 A422 40c Scottish piper .55 .55
1425 A422 40c Diving helmet .55 .55
1426 A422 40c Airplane .55 .55
1427 A422 40c Water faucet .55 .55
1428 A422 40c Painted buildings .55 .55
a. Booklet pane of 10, #1419-1428 5.50

By its nature No. 1428a is a complete booklet. The peelable paper backing serves as a booklet cover.

Vineyards A423

1997, Mar. 19 *Perf. 14*

1429 A423 40c Central Otago .55 .55
a. Booklet pane of 1 .55
1430 A423 80c Hawke's Bay 1.10 1.10
a. Booklet pane of 1 1.10
1431 A423 $1 Marlborough 1.40 1.40
a. Booklet pane of 1 1.40
1432 A423 $1.20 Canterbury, Waipara 1.70 1.70
a. Booklet pane of 1 1.70
1433 A423 $1.50 Gisborne 2.00 2.00
a. Booklet pane of 1 2.00
b. Souvenir sheet of 3, #1429, 1431, 1433 4.00 4.00
1434 A423 $1.80 Auckland, Waiheke 2.50 2.50
a. Booklet pane of 1 2.50
b. Booklet pane, 1 each #1429-1434 9.25
Complete booklet, #1429a, 1430a, 1431a, 1432a, 1433a, 1434a, 1434b 18.50
Nos. 1429-1434 (6) 9.25 9.25

No. 1433a for PACIFIC 97. Issued: 5/29.

Pigeon Mail Service, Cent. — A424

Design: 1899 local stamp.

1997, May 7 Litho. *Perf. 14*

1435 A424 40c red .55 .55
1436 A424 80c blue 1.10 1.10
a. Souvenir sheet, 2 ea #1435-1436 3.30
b. As "a," diff. inscription 3.30

No. 1436a for PACIFIC 97. Issued: 5/29.

No. 1436b was inscribed in sheet margin for AUPEX '97 National Stamp Exhibition, Auckland. Issued 11/13.

Paintings by Colin McCahon (1919-87) A425

Designs: 40c, The Promised Land, 1948. $1, Six Days in Nelson and Canterbury, 1950. $1.50, Northland Panels, 1958. $1.80, Moby Dick is sighted off Muriwai Beach, 1972.

1997, May 7

1437 A425 40c multicolored .55 .55
1438 A425 $1 multicolored 1.40 1.40
1439 A425 $1.50 multicolored 2.10 2.10
1440 A425 $1.80 multicolored 2.50 2.50
Nos. 1437-1440 (4) 6.55 6.55

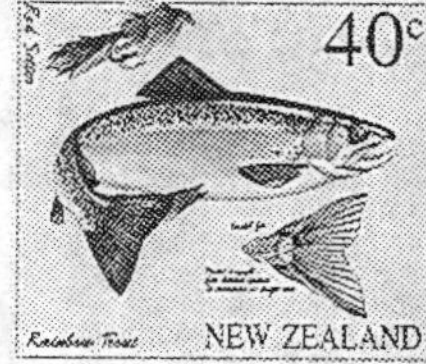

Fly Fishing A426

Designs: 40c, Red setter fly, rainbow trout. $1, Grey ghost fly, sea-run brown trout. $1.50, Twilight beauty fly, brook trout. $1.80, Hare & copper fly, brown trout.

1997, June 18 Litho. *Perf. 13*

1441 A426 40c multicolored .55 .55
1442 A426 $1 multicolored 1.40 1.40
1443 A426 $1.50 multicolored 2.10 2.10
1444 A426 $1.80 multicolored 2.50 2.50
Nos. 1441-1444 (4) 6.55 6.55

Kiwi Type of 1988

1997, Aug. 6 Litho. *Perf. 14½*

1445 A325 $1 violet 1.30 1.30

Value is for copy with surrounding selvage.

Scenic Trains A426a

Name of train, area scene, map of train route: 40c, Overlander, Paremata, Wellington, Wellington-Auckland. 80c, Trans-Alpine, Southern Alps, Christchurch-Greymouth. $1, Southerner, Canterbury, Invercargill-Christchurch. $1.20, Coastal Pacific, Kaikoura Coast, Christchurch-Picton. $1.50, Bay Express, Central Hawke's Bay, Wellington-Napier. $1.80, Kaimai Express, Tauranga Harbor, Tauranga-Auckland.

1997, Aug. 6 *Perf. 14x14½*

1446 A426a 40c multicolored .50 .50
1447 A426a 80c multicolored 1.00 1.00
1448 A426a $1 multicolored 1.30 1.30
1449 A426a $1.20 multicolored 1.50 1.50
1450 A426a $1.50 multicolored 1.90 1.90
1451 A426a $1.80 multicolored 2.30 2.30
Nos. 1446-1451 (6) 8.50 8.50

Christmas — A427 CHRISTMAS 1997

Scenes from first Christian service, Rangihoua Bay, and words from Christmas carol, "Te Harinui:" No. 1452, Samuel Marsden's ship, Active. 70c, Marsden preaching from pulpit. 80c, Marsden extending hand to local chiefs. $1, Mother, children from Rangihoua. $1.50, Maori and Pakeha hands, Marsden's memorial cross. $1.80, Pohutukawa flowers, Rangihoua Bay. No. 1458, Cross marking spot of service, flowers, bay.

1997, Sept. 3 Litho. *Perf. 14*

1452 A427 40c multicolored .50 .50
1453 A427 70c multicolored .90 .90
1454 A427 80c multicolored 1.00 1.00
1455 A427 $1 multicolored 1.30 1.30
1456 A427 $1.50 multicolored 1.90 1.90
1457 A427 $1.80 multicolored 2.30 2.30
a. Block of 6, #1452-1457 8.00 8.00
Nos. 1452-1457 (6) 7.90 7.90

Self-Adhesive

Size: 30x24mm

Serpentine Die Cut 10

1458 A427 40c multicolored .50 .50
a. Booklet pane of 10 5.00

By its nature No. 1458a is a complete booklet. The peelable paper backing serves as a booklet cover.

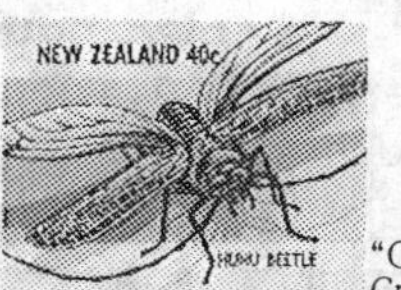

"Creepy Crawlies" — A428

Serpentine Die Cut 11

1997, Oct. 1 **Litho.**

Booklet Stamps

1459 A428 40c	Huhu beetle	.50	.50
1460 A428 40c	Giant land snail	.50	.50
1461 A428 40c	Giant weta	.50	.50
1462 A428 40c	Giant dragonfly	.50	.50
1463 A428 40c	Peripatus	.50	.50
1464 A428 40c	Cicada	.50	.50
1465 A428 40c	Puriri moth	.50	.50
1466 A428 40c	Veined slug	.50	.50
1467 A428 40c	Katipo	.50	.50
1468 A428 40c	Flaxweevil	.50	.50
a.	Booklet pane, #1459-1468	5.00	

By its nature No. 1468a is a complete booklet. The peelable paper backing serves as a booklet cover.

China-New Zealand Stamp Expo — A429

1997, Oct. 9 *Perf. 14*

1469 A429 40c	Rosa rugosa	.50	.50
1470 A429 40c	Aotearoa-New Zealand	.50	.50
a.	Pair, #1469-1470	1.00	1.00
b.	Souvenir sheet, #1470a	1.00	1.00
c.	As "b," diff. inscription	1.00	1.00

No. 1470c inscribed in gold and black in sheet margin for Shanghai 1997 Intl. Stamp & Coin Expo. Issued: 11/19/97.

See People's Republic of China Nos. 2797-2798.

Queen Elizabeth II and Prince Philip, 50th Wedding Anniv. — A430

1997, Nov. 12 **Litho.** *Perf. 12*

1471 A430 40c	multicolored	.50	.50

Issued in sheets of 10.

Cartoonists — A431

"Kiwis Taking on the World:" 40c, Kiwi flying on bee, by Garrick Tremain. $1, Kiwi using world as egg and having it for breakfast, by Jim Hubbard. $1.50, Kiwi in yacht race against the world, by Eric Heath. $1.80, Man with chain saw, trees on mountainside cut as peace symbol, by Burton Silver.

1997, Nov. 12 *Perf. 14*

1472 A431 40c	multicolored	.50	.50
1473 A431 $1	multicolored	1.25	1.25
1474 A431 $1.50	multicolored	1.90	1.90
1475 A431 $1.80	multicolored	2.25	2.25
	Nos. 1472-1475 (4)	5.90	5.90

Performing Arts — A432

NEW ZEALAND COLLECTORS...
FILL THOSE ANNOYING GAPS!
We carry an excellent stock of New Zealand sets, and are happy to supply odd values from sets, mint or used.

PACIFIC ISLANDS
We have an extensive range of mint sets from the
British Pacific Islands

DUNEDIN STAMP CENTRE
P.O. Box 776, (32 Hanover St.)
Dunedin, New Zealand
Telephone +64-3-477-6128
FAX +64-3-479-2718
E-mail dnstamp@es.co.nz

SEND US $2 (cash or mint stamps) FOR AN AIRMAIL COPY OF OUR CURRENT PRICELIST OF NEW ZEALAND AND PACIFIC

Dealer inquiries welcome
Member: NZSDA, PTS, ASDA (NY), ASDA (Mel.)

Established 1968

1998, Jan. 14 **Litho.** *Perf. 13½*

1476 A432 40c	Modern dance	.45	.45
a.	Booklet pane of 1	.45	
1477 A432 80c	Music	.95	.95
a.	Booklet pane of 1	.95	
1478 A432 $1.20	Theater	1.40	1.40
a.	Booklet pane of 1	1.40	
1479 A432 $1.50	Song	1.75	1.75
a.	Booklet pane of 1	1.75	
1480 A432 $1	Opera	1.20	1.20
a.	Booklet pane of 1	1.20	
1481 A432 $1.80	Ballet	2.10	2.10
a.	Booklet pane of 1	2.10	
b.	Booklet pane of 6, #1476-1481	7.75	
	Complete booklet, 1 each #1476a-1481a, 1481b	15.50	
	Nos. 1476-1481 (6)	7.85	7.85

Museum of New Zealand Te Papa Tongarewa — A433

1998, Feb. 11 **Litho.** *Perf. 14*

1482 A433 40c	People at entrance	.45	.45
1483 A433 $1.80	Waterfront location	2.10	2.10

Domestic Cats — A434

A435

1998, Feb. 11 *Perf. 13½*

1484 A434 40c	Moggy	.45	.45
1485 A434 80c	Burmese	.90	.90
1486 A434 $1	Birman	1.20	1.20
1487 A434 $1.20	British blue	1.40	1.40
1488 A434 $1.50	Persian	1.75	1.75
1489 A434 $1.80	Siamese	2.10	2.10
a.	Souvenir sheet of 3, #1484, #1486, #1489	3.75	3.75
	Nos. 1484-1489 (6)	7.80	7.80

1998, Mar. 18 **Litho.** *Perf. 13½*

Memorial Statues: 40c, "With Great Respect to the Mehmetcik, Gallipoli" (Turkish soldier carrying wounded ANZAC). $1.80, "Mother with Children," Natl. War Memorial, Wellington.

1490 A435 40c	multicolored	.45	.45
1491 A435 $1.80	multicolored	2.10	2.10

See Turkey Nos.

New Zealand's Multi-cultural Society — A436

Designs: 40c, The Maori. 80c, British/European settlers, 1840-1914. $1, Fortune seekers, 1800-1920. $1.20, Post-war British/European migrants, 1945-70. $1.50, Pacific Islanders, from 1960. $1.80, Asian arrivals, 1980s-90s.

1998, Mar. 18 *Perf. 14*

1492 A436 40c	multicolored	.45	.45
1493 A436 80c	multicolored	.90	.90
1494 A436 $1	multicolored	1.10	1.10
1495 A436 $1.20	multicolored	1.40	1.40
1496 A436 $1.50	multicolored	1.70	1.70
1497 A436 $1.80	multicolored	2.00	2.00
	Nos. 1492-1497 (6)	7.55	7.55

POSTAL-FISCAL

In 1881 fiscal stamps of New Zealand of denominations over one shilling were made acceptable for postal duty. Values for canceled stamps are for postal cancellations. Denominations above £5 appear to have been used primarily for fiscal purposes.

Queen Victoria
PF1 PF2

Perf. 11, 12, 12½

1882 **Typo.** **Wmk. 62**

AR1 PF1	2sh	blue	60.00	3.50
AR2 PF1	2sh6p	dk brown	80.00	4.25
AR3 PF1	3sh	violet	125.00	5.00
AR4 PF1	4sh	brown vio	165.00	8.00
AR5 PF1	4sh	red brown	165.00	11.00
AR6 PF1	5sh	green	90.00	11.00
AR7 PF1	6sh	rose	165.00	25.00
AR8 PF1	7sh	ultra	180.00	37.50
AR9 PF1	7sh6p	ol gray	275.00	42.50
AR10 PF1	8sh	dull blue	225.00	37.50
AR11 PF1	9sh	org red	275.00	45.00
AR12 PF1	10sh	red brown	250.00	14.00

1882-90

AR13 PF2	15sh	dk grn	475.00	25.00
AR15 PF2	£1	rose	400.00	40.00
AR16 PF2	25sh	blue		50.00
AR17 PF2	30sh	brown		35.00
AR18 PF2	£1 15sh	yellow		165.00
AR19 PF2	£2	purple		55.00

PF3

PF4

AR20 PF3	£2 10sh	red brown		75.00
AR21 PF3	£3	yel green		50.00
AR22 PF3	£3 10sh	rose		210.00
AR23 PF3	£4	ultramarine		175.00
AR24 PF3	£4 10sh	olive brown		210.00
AR25 PF3	£5	dark blue		25.00
AR26 PF4	£6	orange red		100.00
AR27 PF4	£7	brown red		100.00
AR28 PF4	£8	green		100.00
AR29 PF4	£9	rose		165.00
AR30 PF4	£10	blue		65.00

With "COUNTERPART" at Bottom

1901

AR31 PF1	2sh6p	brown	250.00	175.00

Perf. 11, 14, 14½x14

1903-15 **Wmk. 61**

AR32 PF1	2sh	blue ('07)	40.00	4.50
AR33 PF1	2sh6p	brown	40.00	4.50
AR34 PF1	3sh	violet	70.00	5.00
AR35 PF1	4sh	brown red	75.00	7.00
AR36 PF1	5sh	green ('06)	70.00	7.00
AR37 PF1	6sh	rose	140.00	14.00
AR38 PF1	7sh	dull blue	150.00	17.00
AR39 PF1	7sh6p	ol gray ('06)	300.00	55.00
AR40 PF1	8sh	dark blue	150.00	25.00
AR41 PF1	9sh	dl org ('06)	185.00	42.50
AR42 PF1	10sh	dp claret	215.00	12.00
AR43 PF2	15sh	blue grn	275.00	32.50
AR44 PF2	£1	rose	350.00	35.00

Perf. 14½

AR45 PF2	£2	deep vio ('25)	500.00	57.50
a.		Perf. 14	525.00	57.50
		Nos. AR32-AR45 (14)	2,560.	318.50

For overprints see Cook Islands Nos. 67-71.

Coat of Arms — PF5

1931-39 *Perf. 14*

Type PF5

AR46	1sh3p lemon	10.00	5.75
AR47	1sh3p orange ('32)	3.25	.75
AR48	2sh6p brown	8.00	.80
AR49	4sh dull red ('32)	10.00	.95
AR50	5sh green	15.00	2.25
AR51	6sh brt rose ('32)	17.50	7.00
AR52	7sh gray blue	22.50	5.00
AR53	7sh6p olive gray ('32)	42.50	40.00
AR54	8sh dark blue	15.00	9.00
AR55	9sh brn org	30.00	25.00
AR56	10sh dark car	12.00	4.00
AR57	12sh6p brn vio ('35)	140.00	140.00
AR58	15sh ol grn ('32)	50.00	16.00
AR59	£1 pink ('32)	50.00	12.50
AR60	25sh turq bl ('38)	200.00	225.00
AR61	30sh dk brn ('36)	250.00	125.00
AR62	35sh yellow ('37)	2,100.	2,100.
AR63	£2 violet ('33)	250.00	47.50
AR64	£2 10sh dark red ('36)	200.00	200.00
AR65	£3 light grn ('32)	275.00	80.00
AR66	£3 10sh rose ('39)	1,000.	750.00
AR67	£4 light blue	275.00	75.00
AR68	£4 10sh dk ol gray ('39)	1,250.	1,000.
AR69	£5 dk blue ('32)	400.00	125.00

For overprints see Cook Islands Nos. 80-83.

No. AR62 Surcharged in Black **35/-**

1939 *Perf. 14*

AR70	PF5 35sh on 35sh yel	300.00	250.00

Type PF5 Surcharged in Black

1940 **Wmk. 61**

AR71	3sh6p on 3sh6p dl green	10.00	4.00
AR72	5sh6p on 5sh6p rose lilac	17.50	12.00
AR73	11sh on 11sh pale yellow	80.00	55.00
AR74	22sh on 22sh scarlet	125.00	100.00
	Nos. AR71-AR74 (4)	232.50	171.00

Type of 1931

1940-58 **Wmk. 253** *Perf. 14*

Type PF5

AR75	1sh3p orange	1.90	.35
AR76	2sh6p brown	5.50	.20
AR77	4sh dull red	6.50	.50
AR78	5sh green	8.50	.75
AR79	6sh brt rose	13.00	2.00
AR80	7sh gray bl	16.00	4.50
AR81	7sh6p ol gray ('50)	42.50	65.00
AR82	8sh dk blue	30.00	6.00
AR83	9sh orange ('46)	20.00	6.00
AR84	10sh dk carmine	16.00	1.25
AR85	15sh olive ('45)	27.50	10.50
AR86	£1 pink('45)	25.00	3.50
a.	Perf. 14x13½ ('58)	27.50	15.00
AR87	25sh blue ('46)	200.00	200.00
AR88	30sh choc ('46)	165.00	65.00
AR89	£2 violet ('46)	57.50	18.00
AR90	£2 10sh dk red ('51)	190.00	150.00
AR91	£3 lt grn ('46)	60.00	27.50
AR92	£3 10sh rose ('48)	1,250.	900.00
AR93	£4 lt blue ('52)	125.00	35.00
AR94	£5 dk blue ('40)	125.00	40.00

Type PF5 Surcharged in Black

1942-45 **Wmk. 253**

AR95	3sh6p on 3sh6p grn	9.50	6.50
AR96	5sh6p on 5sh6p rose lil ('44)	14.00	7.00
AR97	11sh on 11sh yel	37.50	24.00
AR98	22sh on 22sh car ('45)	165.00	125.00
	Nos. AR95-AR98 (4)	226.00	162.50

Catalogue values for unused stamps in this section, from this point to the end of the section, are for Never Hinged items.

Type of 1931 Redrawn Surcharged in Black

1953 **Typo.**

AR99	PF5 3sh6p on 3sh6p green	30.00	30.00

Denomination of basic stamp is in small, sans-serif capitals without period after "sixpence."

Type of 1931

1955 **Wmk. 253** *Perf. 14*

Denomination in Black

AR100	PF5 1sh3p orange	2.25	.40

1956 **Denomination in Blue**

AR101	PF5 1sh3p orange yel	10.00	10.00

1967, July 10 *Perf. 14*

AR102	PF5 $4 purple	4.50	2.50
AR103	PF5 $6 green	6.75	5.00
AR104	PF5 $8 light blue	9.00	8.00
AR105	PF5 $10 dark blue	12.00	10.00
	Nos. AR102-AR105 (4)	32.25	25.50

1987 **Unwmk.**

AR103a	PF5 $6 green	7.25	7.25
AR104a	PF5 $8 light blue	9.50	9.50
AR105a	PF5 $10 dark blue	12.00	12.00
	Nos. AR103a-AR105a (3)	28.75	28.75

SEMI-POSTAL STAMPS

Nurse

SP1 SP2

Inscribed: "Help Stamp out Tuberculosis, 1929"

Wmk. 61

1929, Dec. 11 **Typo.** *Perf. 14*

B1	SP1 1p + 1p scarlet	10.00	12.50

Inscribed: "Help Promote Health, 1930"

1930, Oct. 29

B2	SP2 1p + 1p scarlet	20.00	20.00

Boy — SP3

Hygeia, Goddess of Health — SP4

1931, Oct. 31 *Perf. 14½x14*

B3	SP3 1p + 1p scarlet	75.00	72.50
B4	SP3 2p + 1p dark blue	75.00	67.50

1932, Nov. 18 **Engr.** *Perf. 14*

B5	SP4 1p + 1p carmine	25.00	25.00
	Never hinged	40.00	

Road to Health — SP5

Crusader — SP6

1933, Nov. 8

B6	SP5 1p + 1p carmine	10.00	11.00
	Never hinged	19.00	

1934, Oct. 25 *Perf. 14x13½*

B7	SP6 1p + 1p dark carmine	8.00	8.00
	Never hinged	12.00	

Child at Bathing Beach — SP7

Anzac — SP8

1935, Sept. 30 *Perf. 11*

B8	SP7 1p + 1p scarlet	1.90	2.00
	Never hinged	3.75	

Catalogue values for unused stamps in this section, from this point to the end of the section, are for Never Hinged items.

1936, Apr. 27

B9	SP8 ½p + ½p green	.50	.50
B10	SP8 1p + 1p red	.50	.50

21st anniv. of Anzac landing at Gallipoli.

"Health" SP9

1936, Nov. 2

B11	SP9 1p + 1p red	2.00	1.50

Boy Hiker — SP10

Children at Play — SP11

1937, Oct. 1

B12	SP10 1p + 1p red	2.50	2.25

Perf. 14x13½

1938, Oct. 1 **Wmk. 253**

B13	SP11 1p + 1p red	2.00	1.25

Children at Play — SP12

Children in Swing — SP13

1939, Oct. 16 **Wmk. 61** *Perf. 11½*

Black Surcharge

B14	SP12 1p on ½p + ½p grn	2.75	2.75
B15	SP12 2p on 1p + 1p scar	2.75	2.75

1940, Oct. 1

B16	SP12 1p + ½p green	3.50	3.50
B17	SP12 2p + 1p org brown	4.00	4.00

The surtax was used to help maintain children's health camps.

Semi-Postal Stamps of 1940, Overprinted in Black "1941"

1941, Oct. 4 *Perf. 11½*

B18	SP12 1p + ½p green	.90	.90
B19	SP12 2p + 1p org brown	1.20	1.20

1942, Oct. 1 **Engr.**

B20	SP13 1p + ½p green	.50	.50
B21	SP13 2p + 1p dp org brown	.60	.60

Imperf plate proofs on card exist for #B22-B27, B32-B33, B38-B39, B46-B48, B59-B60. Imperfs exist for B44-B45, B49-B51. These are from the printer's archives.

Princess Margaret Rose — SP14

Design: 2p+1p, Princess Elizabeth.

1943, Oct. 1 **Wmk. 253** *Perf. 12*

B22	SP14 1p + ½p dark green	.15	.15
a.	Vert. pair, imperf. between		
B23	SP14 2p + 1p red brown	.20	.20
a.	Vert. pair, imperf. between		

Princesses Margaret Rose and Elizabeth SP16

1944, Oct. 9 *Perf. 13½*

B24	SP16 1p + ½p blue green	.15	.15
B25	SP16 2p + 1p chalky blue	.18	.18
	Set value	.28	.28

Peter Pan Statue, London SP17

Statue of Eros, London SP19

Soldier Helping Child over Stile — SP18

1945, Oct. 1

B26	SP17 1p + ½p gray green & bister brown	.15	.15
B27	SP17 2p + 1p car & olive bis	.15	.15
	Set value	.25	.25

1946, Oct. 24 *Perf. 13½x13*

B28	SP18 1p + ½p dk grn & org brn	.15	.15
B29	SP18 2p + 1p dk brn & org brn	.15	.15
	Set value	.22	.22

1947, Oct. 1 **Engr.** *Perf. 13x13½*

B30	SP19 1p + ½p deep green	.15	.15
B31	SP19 2p + 1p deep carmine	.15	.15
	Set value	.22	.22

Children's Health Camp SP20

1948, Oct. 1 *Perf. 13½x13*

B32	SP20 1p + ½p blue grn & ultra	.15	.15
B33	SP20 2p + 1p red & dk brown	.15	.15
	Set value	.22	.20

Nurse and Child — SP21

Princess Elizabeth and Prince Charles — SP22

1949, Oct. 3 **Photo.** *Perf. 14x14½*

B34	SP21 1p + ½p deep green	.15	.15
B35	SP21 2p + 1p ultramarine	.15	.15
	Set value	.25	.22

1950, Oct. 2

B36	SP22 1p + ½p green	.15	.15
B37	SP22 2p + 1p violet brown	.15	.15
	Set value	.25	.22

Racing Yachts SP23

Perf. 13½x13

1951, Nov. 1 **Engr.** **Wmk. 253**

B38	SP23 1½p + ½p red & yellow	.15	.15
B39	SP23 2p + 1p dp green & yel	.15	.15
	Set value	.24	.24

Princess Anne — SP24

Prince Charles — SP25

Perf. 14x14¹/₂

1952, Oct. 1 Wmk. 253 Photo.

B40 SP24	1¹/₂p + ¹/₂p crimson	.15	.15
B41 SP25	2p + 1p brown	.20	.15

Girl Guides Marching SP26

Boy Scouts at Camp SP27

1953, Oct. 7

B42 SP26	1¹/₂p + ¹/₂p bright blue	.15	.15
B43 SP27	2p + 1p deep green	.24	.15

The border of No. B43 consists of Morse code reading "Health" at top and bottom and "New Zealand" on each side. On No. B42 the top border line is replaced by "Health" in Morse code.

Young Mountain Climber Studying Map — SP28

1954, Oct. 4 Engr. *Perf. 13¹/₂*

B44 SP28	1¹/₂p + ¹/₂p pur & brown	.16	.15
B45 SP28	2p + 1p vio gray & brn	.20	.16

Child's Head — SP29

Children Picking Apples — SP30

1955, Oct. 3 Wmk. 253 *Perf. 13*

B46 SP29	1¹/₂p + ¹/₂p brn org & sep	.15	.15
B47 SP29	2p + 1p grn & org brn	.18	.15
B48 SP29	3p + 1p car & sepia	.22	.20
	Nos. B46-B48 (3)	.55	
	Set value		.40

1956, Sept. 24

B49 SP30	1¹/₂p + ¹/₂p chocolate	.15	.15
B50 SP30	2p + 1p blue green	.16	.15
B51 SP30	3p + 1p dark carmine	.18	.16
	Nos. B49-B51 (3)	.49	
	Set value		.34

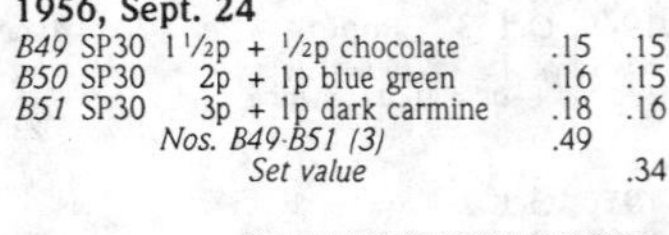

Life-Saving Team — SP31

Design: 3p+1p, Children playing and boy in canoe.

1957, Sept. 25 *Perf. 13¹/₂*

B52 SP31	2p + 1p emer & blk	.22	.18
a.	Miniature sheet of 6	5.75	5.75
B53 SP31	3p + 1p car & ultra	.22	.18
a.	Miniature sheet of 6	5.75	5.75

The watermark is sideways on Nos. B52a and B53a. In a second printing, the watermark is upright; values double.

Girls' Life Brigade Cadet — SP32

Design: 3p+1p, Bugler, Boys' Brigade.

1958, Aug. 20 Photo. *Perf. 14x14¹/₂*

B54 SP32	2p + 1p green	.15	.15
a.	Miniature sheet of 6	5.75	5.75
B55 SP32	3p + 1p ultramarine	.15	.15
a.	Miniature sheet of 6	5.75	5.75

75th anniv. of the founding of the Boys' Brigade.

The surtax on this and other preceding semi-postals was for the maintenance of children's health camps.

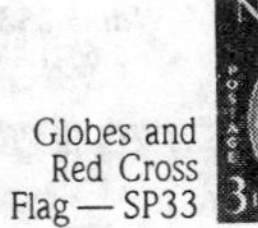

Globes and Red Cross Flag — SP33

1959, June 3 *Perf. 14¹/₂x14*

B56 SP33	3p + 1p ultra & car	.25	.15
a.	Red Cross omitted	*1,200.*	

The surtax was for the Red Cross.

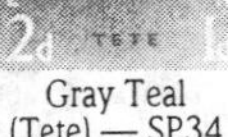

Gray Teal (Tete) — SP34

Sacred Kingfisher (Kotare) — SP35

Design: 3p+1p, Pied stilt (Poaka).

1959, Sept. 16 *Perf. 14x14¹/₂*

B57 SP34	2p + 1p pink, black, yellow & gray	.16	.15
a.	Miniature sheet of 6	6.50	6.50
B58 SP34	3p + 1p blue, black & pink	.16	.15
a.	Miniature sheet of 6	6.50	6.50
b.	Pink omitted	*150.00*	*50.00*

1960, Aug. 10 Engr. *Perf. 13x13¹/₂*

Design: 3p+1p, NZ pigeon (Kereru).

B59 SP35	2p + 1p grnsh blue & sepia	.30	.25
a.	Min. sheet of 6, perf. 11¹/₂x11	12.00	12.00
B60 SP35	3p + 1p org & sepia	.38	.30
a.	Min. sheet of 6, perf. 11¹/₂x11	12.00	12.00

Type of 1959

Birds: 2p+1p, Great white egret (kotuku). 3p+1p, NZ falcon (karearea).

1961, Aug. 2 Wmk. 253

B61 SP34	2p + 1p pale lil & blk	.24	.20
a.	Miniature sheet of 6	9.00	9.00
B62 SP34	3p + 1p yellow green & black brown	.30	.28
a.	Miniature sheet of 6	9.00	9.00

Type of 1959

Birds: 2¹/₂p+1p, Red-fronted parakeet (kakariki). 3p+1p, Saddleback (tieke).

1962, Oct. 3 Photo. *Perf. 15x14*

B63 SP34	2¹/₂p + 1p lt bl, blk, grn & org	.22	.20
a.	Miniature sheet of 6	10.00	10.00
B64 SP34	3p + 1p salmon, blk, grn & org	.25	.22
a.	Miniature sheet of 6	10.00	10.00
b.	Orange omitted		

Prince Andrew SP36

Red-billed Gull (Tarapunga) SP37

Design: 3p+1p, Prince without book.

1963, Aug. 7 Engr. *Perf. 14*

B65 SP36	2¹/₂p + 1p ultramarine	.18	.15
a.	Miniature sheet of 6	8.50	8.50
B66 SP36	3p + 1p rose car	.22	.15
a.	Miniature sheet of 6	8.50	8.50

1964, Aug. 5 Photo. *Perf. 14*

Design: 3p+1p, Blue penguin (korora).

B67 SP37	2¹/₂p + 1p lt bl, pale yel, red & blk	.28	.18
a.	Miniature sheet of 8	20.00	20.00
b.	Red omitted		
c.	Yellow omitted		
B68 SP37	3p + 1p blue, yellow & black	.32	.28
a.	Miniature sheet of 8	20.00	20.00

Kaka — SP38

Bellbird & Bough of Kowhai Tree — SP39

Design: 4p+1p, Fantail (piwakawaka).

1965, Aug. 4 *Perf. 14x14¹/₂*

B69 SP38	3p + 1p gray, red, brn & yellow	.22	.18
a.	Miniature sheet of 6	11.50	11.50
B70 SP38	4p + 1p yel, blk, emerald & brown	.25	.22
a.	Miniature sheet of 6	11.50	11.50

1966, Aug. 3 Photo. Wmk. 253

Design: 4p+1p, Flightless rail (weka) and fern.

B71 SP39	3p + 1p lt bl & multi	.18	.15
a.	Miniature sheet of 6	7.50	7.50
B72 SP39	4p + 1p lt grn & multi	.24	.20
a.	Miniature sheet of 6	7.50	7.50
b.	Brown omitted		

National Team Rugby Player and Boy — SP40

Design: 3c+1c, Man and boy placing ball for place kick, horiz.

1967, Aug. 2 *Perf. 14¹/₂x14, 14x14¹/₂*

B73 SP40	2¹/₂c + 1c multicolored	.18	.15
a.	Miniature sheet of 6	7.75	7.75
B74 SP40	3c + 1c multicolored	.20	.18
a.	Miniature sheet of 6	7.75	7.75

Boy Running and Olympic Rings — SP41

Design: 3c+1c, Girl swimming and Olympic rings.

1968, Aug. 7 *Perf. 14¹/₂x14*

B75 SP41	2¹/₂c + 1c multicolored	.15	.15
a.	Miniature sheet of 6	7.50	7.50
B76 SP41	3c + 1c multicolored	.18	.15
a.	Miniature sheet of 6	7.50	7.50

Boys Playing Cricket — SP42

Dr. Elizabeth Gunn — SP43

Design: 3c+1c, playing cricket.

Perf. 13¹/₂x13, 13x13¹/₂

1969, Aug. 6 Litho. Unwmk.

B77 SP42	2¹/₂c + 1c multicolored	.15	.15
a.	Miniature sheet of 6	8.00	8.00
B78 SP42	3c + 1c multicolored	.18	.15
a.	Miniature sheet of 6	8.00	8.00
B79 SP43	4c + 1c multicolored	2.00	2.00
	Nos. B77-B79 (3)	2.33	

50th anniv. of Children's Health Camps, founded by Dr. Elizabeth Gunn.

Boys Playing Soccer SP44

Design: 2¹/₂c+1c, Girls playing basketball, vert.

1970, Aug. 5 Unwmk. *Perf. 13¹/₂*

B80 SP44	2¹/₂c + 1c multicolored	.20	.18
a.	Miniature sheet of 6	7.75	7.75
B81 SP44	3c + 1c multicolored	.22	.20
a.	Miniature sheet of 6	7.75	7.75

Hygienist and Child SP45

Designs: 3c+1c, Girls playing hockey. 4c+1c, Boys playing hockey.

1971, Aug. 4 Litho. *Perf. 13¹/₂*

B82 SP45	3c + 1c multicolored	.25	.22
a.	Miniature sheet of 6	8.00	8.00
B83 SP45	4c + 1c multicolored	.30	.25
a.	Miniature sheet of 6	8.00	8.00
B84 SP45	5c + 1c multicolored	.65	.65
	Nos. B82-B84 (3)	1.20	

50th anniv. of School Dental Service (No. B84).

Boy Playing Tennis — SP46

Prince Edward — SP47

Design: 4c+1c, Girl playing tennis.

1972, Aug. 2 Litho. *Perf. 13x13¹/₂*

B85 SP46	3c + 1c gray & lt brn	.24	.20
a.	Miniature sheet of 6	9.25	9.25
B86 SP46	4c + 1c brown, yellow & gray	.24	.20
a.	Miniature sheet of 6	9.25	9.25

1973, Aug. 1 Photo.

B87 SP47	3c + 1c green & brown	.24	.20
a.	Miniature sheet of 6	8.25	8.25
B88 SP47	4c + 1c dk red & blk	.24	.20
a.	Miniature sheet of 6	8.25	8.25

Children with Cat and Dog — SP48

Designs: 4c+1c, Girl with dogs and cat. 5c+1c, Children and dogs.

1974, Aug. 7 Litho. *Perf. 13½x14*

B89 SP48 3c + 1c multicolored	.20	.16
B90 SP48 4c + 1c multicolored	.28	.24
a. Miniature sheet of 10	22.50	22.50
B91 SP48 5c + 1c multicolored	.90	.90
Nos. B89-B91 (3)	1.38	1.30

Girl Feeding Lamb SP49

Designs: 4c+1c, Boy with hen and chicks. 5c+1c, Boy with duck and duckling.

1975, Aug. 6 Litho. *Perf. 14x13½*

B92 SP49 3c + 1c multicolored	.20	.16
B93 SP49 4c + 1c multicolored	.24	.20
a. Miniature sheet of 10	18.00	18.00
B94 SP49 5c + 1c multicolored	.60	.60
Nos. B92-B94 (3)	1.04	.96

Boy and Piebald Pony — SP50

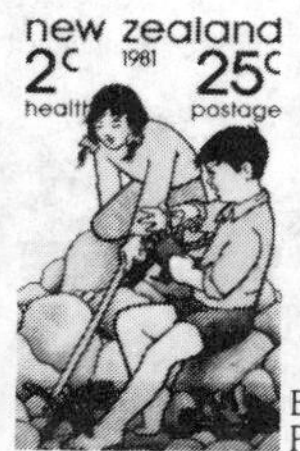

Girl and Bluebird — SP51

Designs: 8c+1c, Farm girl and calf. 10c+1c, 2 girls watching nest-bound thrush.

1976, Aug. 4 Litho. *Perf. 13½x14*

B95 SP50 7c + 1c multicolored	.25	.25
B96 SP50 8c + 1c multicolored	.30	.30
B97 SP50 10c + 1c multicolored	.52	.52
a. Miniature sheet, 2 each #B95-B97	7.25	7.25
Nos. B95-B97 (3)	1.07	1.07

1977, Aug. 3 Litho. *Perf. 13½x14*

8c+2c, Boy & frog. 10c+2c, Girl & butterfly.

B98 SP51 7c + 2c multi	.20	.15
B99 SP51 8c + 2c multi	.24	.20
B100 SP51 10c + 2c multi	.30	.30
a. Miniature sheet of 6	4.25	4.25
Nos. B98-B100 (3)	.74	.65

No. B100a contains 2 each of Nos. B98-B100 in 2 strips of continuous design.

NZ No. B1 — SP52

Heart Surgery — SP53

1978, Aug. 2 Litho. *Perf. 13½x14*

B101 SP52 10c + 2c multi	.32	.32
B102 SP53 12c + 2c multi	.35	.35
a. Min. sheet, 3 each #B101-B102	4.50	4.50

50th Health Stamp issue (No. B101) and National Heart Foundation (No. B102).

Demoiselle Fish — SP54

Designs: No. B104, Sea urchin. 12c+2c, Underwater photographer and red mullet, vert.

Perf. 13½x13, 13x13½

1979, July 25

B103 SP54 10c + 2c multi	.20	.16
B104 SP54 10c + 2c multi	.20	.16
a. Pair, #B103-B104	.40	.40
B105 SP54 12c + 2c multi	.28	.28
a. Min. sheet, 2 each #B103-B105	3.50	3.50
Nos. B103-B105 (3)	.68	.60

Children Wharf Fishing SP55

1980, Aug. 6 Litho. *Perf. 13½x13*

B106 SP55 14c + 2c shown	.22	.22
B107 SP55 14c + 2c Surfcasting	.22	.22
a. Pair, #B106-B107	.45	.45
B108 SP55 17c + 2c Underwater fishing	.28	.28
a. Min. sheet, 2 each #B106-B108	2.10	2.10
Nos. B106-B108 (3)	.72	.72

Boy and Girl at Rock Pool — SP56

1981, Aug. 5 Litho. *Perf. 14½*

B109 SP56 20c + 2c Girl, starfish	.35	.35
B110 SP56 20c + 2c Boy fishing	.35	.35
a. Pair, #B109-B110	.70	.70
B111 SP56 25c + 2c shown	.40	.40
a. Min. sheet, 2 each #B109-B111	2.00	2.00
Nos. B109-B111 (3)	1.10	1.10

Labrador — SP57

Persian Cat — SP58

1982, Aug. 4 Litho. *Perf. 13x13½*

B112 SP57 24c + 2c shown	.35	.35
B113 SP57 24c + 2c Border collie	.35	.35
a. Pair, #B112-B113	.70	.70
B114 SP57 30c + 2c Cocker spaniel	.45	.45
a. Min. sheet, 2 each #B112-B114, perf. 14x13½	2.50	2.50
Nos. B112-B114 (3)	1.15	1.15

1983, Aug. 3 Litho. *Perf. 14½*

B115 SP58 24 + 2c Tabby	.35	.35
B116 SP58 24 + 2c Siamese	.35	.35
a. Pair, #B115-B116	.70	.70
B117 SP58 30 + 2c shown	.45	.45
a. Min. sheet, 2 each #B115-B117	2.50	2.50
Nos. B115-B117 (3)	1.15	1.15

Clydesdales — SP59

1984, Aug. 1 Litho. *Perf. 13½x13*

B118 SP59 24c + 2c shown	.34	.34
B119 SP59 24c + 2c Shetlands	.34	.34
a. Pair, #B118-B119	.70	.70
B120 SP59 30c + 2c Thoroughbreds	.42	.42
a. Min. sheet, 2 each #B118-B120	2.25	2.25
Nos. B118-B120 (3)	1.10	1.10

Health — SP60

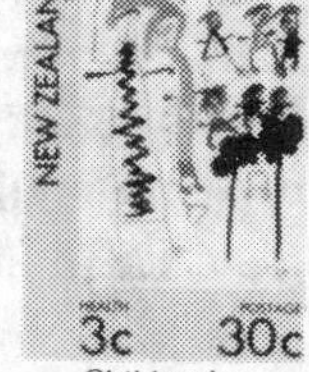

Children's Drawings — SP61

Princess Diana and: No. B121, Prince William. No. B122, Prince Henry. No. B123, Princes Charles, William and Henry.

1985, July 31 Litho. *Perf. 13½*

B121 SP60 25c + 2c multi	.28	.28
B122 SP60 25c + 2c multi	.28	.28
a. Pair, #B121-B122	.60	.60
B123 SP60 35c + 2c multi	.38	.38
a. Min. sheet, 2 each #B121-B123	2.00	2.00
Nos. B121-B123 (3)	.94	.94

Surtax for children's health camps.

1986, July 30 Litho. *Perf. 14½x14*

B124 SP61 30c + 3c shown	.38	.38
B125 SP61 30c + 3c Children playing	.38	.38
a. Pair, #B124-B125	.80	.80
B126 SP61 45c + 3c Skipping rope, horiz.	.55	.55
a. Min. sheet, 2 each #B124-B126	2.75	2.75
Nos. B124-B126 (3)	1.31	1.31

Surtax for children's health camps.

No. B126a exists with Stockholmia '86 emblem.

Children's Drawings SP62

1987, July 29 Litho. *Perf. 14½*

B127 SP62 40c + 3c shown	.52	.52
B128 SP62 40c + 3c Swimming	.52	.52
a. Pair, #B127-B128	1.10	1.10
B129 SP62 60c + 3c Riding horse, vert.	.75	.75
a. Min. sheet, 2 each #B127-B129	3.75	3.75
Nos. B127-B129 (3)	1.79	1.79

Surtax benefited children's health camps.

1988 Summer Olympics, Seoul — SP63

1988, July 27 Litho. *Perf. 14½*

B130 SP63 40c + 3c Swimming	.60	.60
B131 SP63 60c + 3c Running	.88	.88
B132 SP63 70c + 3c Rowing	1.00	1.00
B133 SP63 80c + 3c Equestrian	1.15	1.15
a. Souvenir sheet of 4, #B130-B133	3.75	3.75
Nos. B130-B133 (4)	3.63	3.63

Children's Health — SP64

Designs: No. B134, Duke and Duchess of York, Princess Beatrice. No. B135, Duchess, princess. No. B136, Princess.

1989, July 23

B134 SP64 40c + 3c multi	.55	.55
B135 SP64 40c + 3c multi	.55	.55
a. Pair, #B134-B135	1.25	1.25
B136 SP64 80c + 3c multi	1.05	1.05
a. Min. sheet, 2 each #B134-B136	4.30	4.30
Nos. B134-B136 (3)	2.15	2.15

Athletes — SP65

40c+5c, Jack Lovelock (1910-1949), runner. 80c+5c, George Nepia (1905-1986), rugby player.

1990, July 25 Litho. *Perf. 14½x14*

B137 SP65 40c +5c multi	.50	.50
B138 SP65 80c +5c multi	1.00	1.00
a. Min. sheet, 2 each #B137-B138	3.00	3.00

Hector's Dolphin — SP66

1991, July 24 Litho. *Perf. 14½*

B139 SP66 45c +5c 3 swimming	.55	.55
B140 SP66 80c +5c 2 jumping	.90	.90
a. Souvenir sheet, 2 each #B139-B140	2.90	2.90

Surtax benefited children's health camps.

Anthony F. Wilding (1883-1915), Tennis Player — SP67

Design: No. B142, C.S. "Stewie" Dempster (1903-1974), cricket player.

1992, Aug. 12 Litho. *Perf. 14x13½*

B141 SP67 45c +5c multi	.50	.50
B142 SP67 80c +5c multi	.85	.85
a. Souv. sheet, 2 each #B141-B142, perf. 14½	2.70	2.70

Surtax for children's health camps.

SP68

SP69

1993, July 21 Litho. *Perf. 13½x14*

B143 SP68 45c +5c Boy, puppy	.55	.55
B144 SP68 80c +5c Girl, kitten	.95	.95
a. Souvenir sheet, 2 each #B143-B144, perf. 14½	3.00	3.00
b. As "a," inscribed in sheet margin	3.00	3.00

Surtax for children's health camps.

No. B144b inscribed with "TAIPEI '93" emblem.

Issue date: No. B144b, Aug. 14.

1994, July 20 Litho. *Perf. 14*

Children's Health Camps, 75th Anniv.: No. B145, #B15, Children playing with ball. No. B146, #B34, Nurse holding child. No. B147, #B79, Children reading. 80c+5c, #B4, Boy.

B145 SP69 45c +5c multi	.60	.60
B146 SP69 45c +5c multi	.60	.60
B147 SP69 45c +5c multi	.60	.60
B148 SP69 80c +5c multi	1.00	1.00
a. Souvenir sheet of 4, #B145-B148	2.80	2.80
Nos. B145-B148 (4)	2.80	2.80

Surtax for children's health camps.

Children's Health Camps SP70

Designs: 45c+5c, Boy on skateboard. 80c+5c, Child on bicycle.

1995, June 21 Litho. *Perf. 14½*

B149 SP70 45c +5c multi .65 .65
B150 SP70 80c +5c multi 1.25 1.25
a. Souvenir sheet, 2 each #B149-B150 3.75 3.75
b. As "a," with added inscription 3.75 3.75

No. B150b inscribed with Stampex '95 emblem in sheet margin.

Surtax for children's health camps.

SP71

SP72

Children's Health: Nos. B151, B153, Infant buckled into child safety seat. 80c, Child holding adult's hand on pedestrian crossing.

1996, June 5 Litho. *Perf. 14x13½*

B151 SP71 40c +5c multi .60 .60
B152 SP71 80c +5c multi 1.15 1.15
a. Souvenir sheet, 2 each Nos. B151-B152, perf. 14x14½ 3.50 3.50
b. As "a" with added inscription 3.50 3.50

Self-Adhesive

Serpentine Die Cut 11½

B153 SP71 40c +5c multi .60 .60

No. B152b inscribed with CAPEX '96 emblem in sheet margin.

Original Design

1996, June 5 Litho. *Perf. 14x13½*

B154 SP72 40c +5c multi *1,700.* —

Self-Adhesive

Serpentine Die Cut 11½

B155 SP72 40c +5c multi —

Nos. B154 and B155 were withdrawn before issue by New Zealand Post. Slightly over 1,000 copies of No. B154 and 500 copies of No. B155 were sold in error by two post offices within three days of June 5. A total of 402 copies of the souvenir sheet containing No. B154 were made available by the printer, but none were sold at post offices.

The stamps were withdrawn because the inclusion of the stuffed animal indicated that the infant was improperly belted into the vehicle.

Children's Health SP73

Children's designs of "Healthy Living:" No. B156, Child on beach. No. B157, Child riding horse on waterfront. 80c+5c, Mosaic of person collecting fruit from tree.

1997, June 18 Litho. *Perf. 14*

B156 SP73 40c +5c multi .60 .60
B157 SP73 80c +5c multi 1.15 1.15
a. Souvenir sheet, 1 each Nos. B156-B157, B158a 2.40 2.40

Self-Adhesive

Serpentine Die Cut 10½

B158 SP72 40c +5c multi .60 .60
a. Perf. 14 .60 .60

AIR POST STAMPS

Plane over Lake Manapouri AP1

Perf. 14x14½

1931, Nov. 10 Typo. Wmk. 61

C1 AP1 3p chocolate 18.00 12.50
a. Perf. 14x15 200.00 *425.00*
C2 AP1 4p dark violet 20.00 24.00
C3 AP1 7p orange 21.00 15.00
Nos. C1-C3 (3) 59.00 51.50

Most copies of No. C1a are poorly centered.

Type of 1931 Surcharged in Red **FIVE PENCE**

1931, Dec. 18 *Perf. 14x14½*

C4 AP1 5p on 3p yel green 12.00 8.00

Type of 1931 Overprinted in Dark Blue

TRANS-TASMAN AIR MAIL "FAITH IN AUSTRALIA."

1934, Feb. 17

C5 AP1 7p bright blue 25.00 25.00

1st official air mail flight between NZ and Australia.

Airplane over Landing Field — AP2

1935, May 4 Engr. *Perf. 14*

C6 AP2 1p rose carmine .55 .28
C7 AP2 3p dark violet 1.40 1.25
C8 AP2 6p gray blue 2.25 1.80
Nos. C6-C8 (3) 4.20 3.33
Set, never hinged 17.00

SPECIAL DELIVERY STAMPS

SD1

1903-26 Typo. Wmk. 61 *Perf. 14x15*

E1 SD1 6p purple & red ('26) 30.00 20.00
a. 6p violet & red, perf. 11 32.50 17.50

Mail Car — SD2

1939, Aug. 16 Engr. *Perf. 14*

E2 SD2 6p violet 1.50 2.25
Never hinged 2.00

POSTAGE DUE STAMPS

D1

D2

Wmk. 62

1899, Dec. 1 Typo. *Perf. 11*

J1 D1 ½p green & red 4.50 *7.00*
a. No period after "D" 37.50 37.50
J2 D1 1p green & red 8.00 2.00
J3 D1 2p green & red 16.00 2.50
J4 D1 3p green & red 14.00 2.75
J5 D1 4p green & red 15.00 6.50
J6 D1 5p green & red 19.00 19.00
J7 D1 6p green & red 27.50 22.50
J8 D1 8p green & red 72.50 *110.00*
J9 D1 10p green & red 77.50 *175.00*
J10 D1 1sh green & red 72.50 55.00
J11 D1 2sh green & red 125.00 *250.00*
Nos. J1-J11 (11) 451.50 652.25

Nos. J1-J11 may be found with N. Z. and D. varying in size.

1902, Feb. 28 Unwmk.

J12 D2 ½p gray grn & red 2.50 3.50

Wmk. 61

J13 D2 ½p gray grn & red 1.40 1.25
J14 D2 1p gray grn & red 8.25 3.75
J15 D2 2p gray grn & red 160.00 160.00

1904-28 *Perf. 14, 14x14½*

J16 D2 ½p green & car 2.25 1.75
J17 D2 1p green & car 1.25 .40
J18 D2 2p green & car 4.50 .80
J19 D2 3p grn & rose ('28) 18.00 19.00
Nos. J16-J19 (4) 26.00 21.95

N Z and Star printed on the back in Blue

1925 Unwmk. *Perf. 14x14½, 14x15*

J20 D2 ½p green & rose 2.50 *12.50*
J21 D2 2p green & rose 4.00 *9.50*

Catalogue values for unused stamps in this section, from this point to the end of the section, are for Never Hinged items.

D3

1939 Wmk. 61 Typo. *Perf. 15x14*

J22 D3 ½p turquoise green 5.00 *3.00*
J23 D3 1p rose pink .70 .35
J24 D3 2p ultramarine 6.50 2.00
J25 D3 3p brown orange 16.00 6.50
Nos. J22-J25 (4) 28.20 11.85

1945-49 Wmk. 253

J27 D3 1p rose pink ('49) 1.00 1.00
J28 D3 2p ultramarine ('47) 2.00 2.00
J29 D3 3p brown orange 11.00 7.00
Nos. J27-J29 (3) 14.00 10.00

The use of postage due stamps was discontinued in Sept., 1951.

WAR TAX STAMP

No. 144 Overprinted in Black

★ ★ WAR STAMP

Perf. 14x14½

1915, Sept. 24 Wmk. 61

MR1 A43 ½p green .50 .15

OFFICIAL STAMPS

Regular Issues Ovptd. "O. P. S. O." Handstamped on Stamps of 1882-92

1892 Wmk. 62 *Perf as Before*

Rose or Magenta Handstamp

O1 A9 1p rose *325.*
O2 A10 2p violet *475.*
O3 A16 2½p ultramarine *275.*
O4 A17 5p olive gray *475.*
O5 A13 6p brown *550.*

Violet Handstamp

O6 N1 ½p rose *625.*
O7 A9 1p rose *210.*
O8 A10 2p violet

Handstamped on No. 67A in Rose

1899 *Perf. 10, 10x11, 11*

O9 A15a ½p black *210.*

Handstamped on No. 79 in Violet

Unwmk. *Perf. 14, 15*

O10 A27 8p dull blue *550.*

Handstamped on Stamps of 1899-1900 in Violet

1902 *Perf. 11*

O11 A22 2½p blue *500.*
O12 A23 3p org brown *500.*
O13 A25 5p red brown *400.*
O14 A27 8p dark blue *385.*

Green Handstamp

O15 A25 5p red brown *385.*

Handstamped on Stamp of 1901 in Violet

Wmk. 63 *Perf. 11, 14*

O16 A35 1p carmine *250.*

Handstamped on Stamps of 1902-07 in Violet or Magenta

1905-07 Wmk. 61

O17 A18 ½p green *250.*
O18 A35 1p carmine *250.*
O19 A22 2½p blue *300.*
O20 A25 5p red brown
O21 A27 8p deep blue
O22 A30 2sh blue green *1,000.*

The "O. P. S. O." handstamp is usually struck diagonally, reading up, but on No. O19 it also occurs horizontally. The letters stand for "On Public Service Only."

Overprinted in Black **OFFICIAL.**

On Stamps of 1902-07

1907 *Perf. 14, 14x13, 14x14½*

O23 A18 ½p green 7.50 .65
O24 A35 1p carmine 8.00 .40
a. Booklet pane of 6 60.00
O25 A33 2p violet 7.50 1.10
O26 A23 3p orange brn 35.00 2.50
O27 A26 6p carmine rose 105.00 14.00
a. Horiz. pair, imperf. vert. *1,000.*
O28 A29 1sh brown red 80.00 16.00
O29 A30 2sh blue green 70.00 30.00
a. Horiz. pair, imperf. vert. *1,500.*
O30 A31 5sh vermilion 175.00 150.00
Nos. O23-O30 (8) 488.00 214.65

On No. 127

Perf. 14x13, 14x14½

O31 A26 6p carmine rose 175.00 35.00

On No. 129

1909 *Perf. 14x14½*

O32 A35 1p car (redrawn) 57.50 .60

On Nos. 130-131, 133, 137, 139

1910 *Perf. 14, 14x13½, 14x14½*

O33 A41 ½p yellow green 1.90 .15
O34 A42 1p carmine 1.10 .15
O35 A41 3p orange brown 10.00 1.75
O36 A41 6p carmine rose 15.00 2.75
O37 A41 1sh vermilion 25.00 8.25
Nos. O33-O37 (5) 53.00 13.05

On Postal-Fiscal Stamps No. AR32, AR36, AR44

1911-14

O38 PF1 2sh blue ('14) 18.00 20.00
O39 PF1 5sh green ('13) 72.50 52.50
O40 PF2 £1 rose 525.00 450.00
Nos. O38-O40 (3) 615.50 522.50

On Stamps of 1909-19

Perf. 14x13½, 14x14½

1915-19 Typo.

O41 A43 ½p green .95 .15
O42 A46 1½p gray black ('16) 8.50 1.00
O43 A47 1½p gray black ('16) 3.75 .20
O44 A47 1½p brown org ('19) 3.00 .15
O45 A43 2p yellow ('17) 1.10 .15
O46 A43 3p chocolate ('19) 4.75 .15

Engr.

O47 A45 3p vio brn ('16) 2.00 .85
O48 A45 6p car rose ('16) 1.50 .32
O49 A41 8p dp bl (R) ('16) 12.00 *20.00*
O50 A45 1sh vermilion ('16) 7.75 2.75
a. 1sh orange 7.75 2.75
Nos. O41-O50 (10) 45.30 *25.72*

On No. 157

1922

O51 A45 8p red brown 100.00 90.00

On Nos. 151, 158

1925

O52 A45 4p purple 15.00 1.00
O53 A45 9p olive green 35.00 25.00

On No. 177

1925 *Perf. 14x14½*

O54 A42 1p carmine 3.25 5.00

On Nos. 184, 182

1927-28 Wmk. 61 *Perf. 14, 14½x14*

O55 A57 1p rose red 1.25 .15
O56 A56 2sh blue 70.00 35.00

On No. AR50

1933 *Perf. 14*

O57 PF5 5sh green 275.00 275.00

Nos. 186, 187, 196 Overprinted in Black ***Official***

1936 *Perf. 14x13½, 13½x14, 14*
O58 A59 1p copper red 1.75 .15
O59 A60 1½p red brown 9.50 11.00
O60 A69 1sh dark slate grn 5.50 7.50
Nos. O58-O60 (3) 16.75 18.65

Same Overprint Horizontally in Black or Green on Stamps of 1936

Perf. 12½, 13½, 13x13½, 14x13½, 13½x14, 14

1936-42 **Wmk. 253**
O61 A58 ½p brt grn ('37) 1.65 1.90
O62 A59 1p copper red 1.25 .30
O63 A60 1½p red brown 2.50 2.50
O64 A61 2p red org ('38) .85 .20
a. Perf. 12½ ('42) 140.00 47.50
O65 A62 2½p dk gray & dk brown 5.75 9.50
O66 A63 3p choc ('38) 24.00 1.90
O67 A64 4p blk brn & blk 2.50 .65
O68 A66 6p red ('37) 2.50 1.25
O68B A67 8p dp brn ('42) 6.25 4.75
O69 A68 9p black & scar (G) ('38) 65.00 25.00
O70 A69 1sh dk slate grn 6.25 .95

Overprint Vertical
O71 A70 2sh ol grn ('37) 16.00 5.00
Nos. O61-O71 (12) 134.50 53.90

Same Overprint Horizontally in Black on Nos. 226, 227, 228

1938
O72 A79 ½p emerald 6.25 1.65
O73 A79 1p rose red 8.00 .30
O74 A80 1½p violet brn 40.00 10.00
Nos. O72-O74 (3) 54.25 11.95

Same Overprint on No. AR50

1938 **Wmk. 61** *Perf. 14*
O75 PF5 5sh green 17.00 16.00

Nos. 229-235, 237, 239-241 Overprinted in Red or Black **Official**

Perf. 13½x13, 13x13½, 14x13½

1940 **Wmk. 253**
O76 A81 ½p dk bl grn (R) .65 .35
a. "ff" joined 20.00 18.00
O77 A82 1p scar & sepia 1.50 .15
a. "ff" joined 20.00 18.00
O78 A83 1½p brt vio & ultra 1.25 *2.00*
O79 A84 2p black brn & Prus green 1.50 .15
a. "ff" joined 20.00 18.00
O80 A85 2½p dk bl & myr grn 1.50 3.50
a. "ff" joined 20.00 18.00
O81 A86 3p deep plum & dark vio (R) 5.00 .95
a. "ff" joined 20.00 18.00
O82 A87 4p dark red vio & violet brn 12.50 1.90
a. "ff" joined 24.00 24.00
O83 A89 6p vio & brt grn 12.50 1.90
a. "ff" joined 30.00 24.00
O84 A90 8p org red & blk 12.50 12.50
a. "ff" joined 30.00 24.00
O85 A91 9p dp org & olive 6.25 5.00
O86 A92 1sh dk sl grn & ol 37.50 5.75
Nos. O76-O86 (11) 92.65 34.15

Nos. 227A, 228C Overprinted in Black *Official*

1941 **Wmk. 253** *Perf. 13½*
O88 A79 1p light blue green .30 .15
O89 A80 3p blue .75 .15
Set value .25

Same Overprint on No. 245

1944 *Perf. 14x15*

Size: 17¼x20¼mm
O90 A68 9p int black & scar 12.00 18.00

Same Overprint on No. AR78

Perf. 14
O91 PF5 5sh green 7.75 5.00

Catalogue values for unused stamps in this section, from this point to the end of the section, are for Never Hinged items.

Same Ovpt. on Stamps of 1941-47

1946-51 *Perf. 13½, 14*
O92 A79 ½p brn org ('46) 1.75 .55
O92B A80 1½p red 6.25 .65
O93 A80 2p orange .85 .15
O94 A80 4p rose lilac 4.00 .70
O95 A80 6p rose carmine 7.00 .60
O96 A80 8p deep violet 8.50 3.50
O97 A80 9p chocolate 13.00 6.50
O98 A104 1sh dk car rose & chestnut 12.00 .70
O99 A104 2sh dk green & brown org 9.00 11.00
Nos. O92-O99 (9) 62.35 24.35

Queen Elizabeth II — O1

Perf. 13½x13

1954, Mar. 1 **Engr.** **Wmk. 253**
O100 O1 1p orange .20 .15
O101 O1 1½p rose brown 1.25 1.25
O102 O1 2p green .60 .15
O103 O1 3p red .40 .15
O104 O1 4p blue .65 .15
O105 O1 9p rose carmine 1.40 .20
O106 O1 1sh rose violet 2.25 .45
Nos. O100-O106 (7) 6.75 2.50

Exist imperf.

Nos. O102, O101 Surcharged with New Value and Dots

1959-61
O107 O1 2½p on 2p green ('61) 1.00 .60
O108 O1 6p on 1½p rose brn 1.50 .85

Exist imperf.

1963, Mar. 1
O109 O1 2½p dark olive 2.00 1.00
O111 O1 3sh slate 32.50 32.50

Exist imperf.

LIFE INSURANCE

Lighthouses
LI1 LI2

Perf. 10, 11, 10x11, 12x11½

1891, Jan. 2 **Typo.** **Wmk. 62**
OY1 LI1 ½p purple 65.00 2.00
OY2 LI1 1p blue 60.00 .45
OY3 LI1 2p red brown 80.00 1.50
OY4 LI1 3p chocolate 275.00 22.50
OY5 LI1 6p green 375.00 55.00
OY6 LI1 1sh rose pink 725.00 140.00
Nos. OY1-OY6 (6) 1,580. 221.45

Stamps from outside rows of the sheets sometimes lack watermark.

Perf. 11, 14x11, 14

1903-04 **Wmk. 61**
OY7 LI1 ½p purple 42.50 2.25
OY8 LI1 1p blue 67.50 .85
OY9 LI1 2p red brown 65.00 25.00
Nos. OY7-OY9 (3) 175.00 28.10

1905-32 *Perf. 11, 14, 14x14½*
OY10 LI2 ½p yel grn ('13) 2.00 .50
OY11 LI2 ½p green ('32) 1.75 1.40
OY12 LI2 1p blue 200.00 25.00
OY13 LI2 1p dp rose ('13) 11.00 .50
OY14 LI2 1p scarlet ('31) 5.00 .50
OY15 LI2 1½p gray ('17) 25.00 3.00
OY16 LI2 1½p brn org ('19) 1.50 1.00
OY17 LI2 2p red brown 1,800. 125.00
OY18 LI2 2p violet ('13) 25.00 12.50
OY19 LI2 2p yellow ('21) 4.50 2.00
OY20 LI2 3p ocher ('13) 22.50 15.00
OY21 LI2 3p choc ('31) 11.00 8.00
OY22 LI2 6p carmine rose ('13) 19.00 17.50
OY23 LI2 6p pink ('31) 15.00 15.00
Nos. OY10-OY23 (14) 2,143. 226.90

#OY15, OY16 have "POSTAGE" at each side.
Stamps from outside rows of the sheets sometimes lack watermark.

1946-47 **Wmk. 253** *Perf. 14x15*
OY24 LI2 ½p yel grn ('47) 1.90 1.90
OY25 LI2 1p scarlet 2.00 1.40
OY26 LI2 2p yellow 2.25 1.40
OY27 LI2 3p chocolate 11.00 13.00
OY28 LI2 6p pink ('47) 6.50 10.00
Nos. OY24-OY28 (5) 23.65 27.70
Set, never hinged 30.00

Catalogue values for unused stamps in this section, from this point to the end of the section, are for Never Hinged items.

New Zealand Lighthouses

Castlepoint
LI3

Taiaroa — LI4

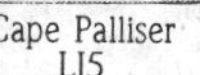

Cape Palliser
LI5

Cape Campbell
LI6

Eddystone (England)
LI7

Stephens Island
LI8

The Brothers — LI9

Cape Brett — LI10

Perf. 13½x13, 13x13½

1947-65 **Engr.** **Wmk. 253**
OY29 LI3 ½p dk grn & red orange 2.50 1.75
OY30 LI4 1p dk ol grn & blue .30 .35
OY31 LI5 2p int bl & gray .35 .20
OY32 LI6 2½p ultra & blk ('63) 7.50 5.50
OY33 LI7 3p red vio & bl 1.00 .22
OY34 LI8 4p dk brn & org 3.00 .90
a. Wmkd. sideways ('65) 9.00 7.00
OY35 LI9 6p dk brn & bl 2.20 1.40
OY36 LI10 1sh red brn & bl 2.00 1.40
Nos. OY29-OY36 (8) 18.85 11.72

Set first issued Aug. 1, 1947.
Exist imperf.

Nos. OY30, OY32-OY33, OY34a, OY35-OY36 and Types Surcharged

1c

2c

Perf. 13½x13, 13x13½

1967-68 **Engr.** **Wmk. 253**
OY37 LI4 1c on 1p dk ol grn & lt bl 1.75 1.65
a. Wmkd. upright ('68) 2.00 1.40
OY38 LI6 2c on 2½p ultra & black 6.00 5.00
OY39 LI7 2½c on 3p, wmkd. upright 2.75 1.90
a. Watermarked sideways ('68) 3.00 3.25
OY40 LI8 3c on 4p dk brn & orange 4.00 3.50
OY41 LI9 5c on 6p dk brn & blue 3.50 4.00
OY42 LI10 10c on 1sh red brn & bl, wmkd. sideways 2.50 3.25
a. Watermarked upright 7.00 7.00
Nos. OY37-OY42 (6) 20.50 19.30

The surcharge is different on each stamp and is adjusted to obliterate old denomination. One dot only on 2½c.
Set first issued July 10, 1967.

Moeraki Point Lighthouse — LI11

Lighthouses: 2½c, Puysegur Point, horiz. 3c, Baring Head. 4c, Cape Egmont, horiz. 8c, East Cape. 10c, Farewell Spit. 15c, Dog Island.

Perf. 13x13½, 13½x13, 14 (8c, 10c)

1969-76 **Litho.** **Unwmk.**
OY43 LI11 ½c pur, bl & yel 1.75 1.75
OY44 LI11 2½c yel, ultra & grn 1.10 .50
OY45 LI11 3c yellow & brown .15 .20
OY46 LI11 4c lt ultra & ocher .15 .20
OY47 LI11 8c multicolored .25 .40
OY48 LI11 10c multicolored .30 .30
OY49 LI11 15c multicolored 2.75 1.40
a. Perf. 14 ('78) .42 .45
Nos. OY43-OY49 (7) 6.45 4.75

Cent. of Government Life Insurance Office.
Issued: #OY47-OY48, 11/17/76; others 3/27/69.

No. OY44 Surcharged with New Value and 4 Diagonal Bars

Perf. 13½x13

1978, Mar. 8 **Litho.** **Wmk. 253**
OY50 LI11 25c on 2½c multi .75 .75

Lighthouse LI12

1981, June 3 **Litho.** *Perf. 14½*
OY51 LI12 5c multicolored .15 .15
OY52 LI12 10c multicolored .15 .15
OY53 LI12 20c multicolored .25 .25
OY54 LI12 30c multicolored .40 .40
OY55 LI12 40c multicolored .52 .52
OY56 LI12 50c multicolored .65 .65
Nos. OY51-OY56 (6) 2.12 2.12

Government Life Insurance Stamps have been discontinued.

NEWSPAPER STAMPS

Queen Victoria — N1

Wmk. 59

1873, Jan. 1 **Typo.** *Perf. 10*
P1 N1 ½p rose 40.00 12.50
a. Perf. 12½x10 125.00 62.50
b. Perf. 12½ 125.00 47.50

The "N Z" watermark (illustrated over No. 27) is widely spaced and intended for larger stamps. About a third of the stamps in each sheet are unwatermarked. They are worth a slight premium.
For overprint, see No. O6.

1875, Jan. **Wmk. 64** *Perf. 12½*
P3 N1 ½p rose 7.50 .65
a. Pair, imperf. between 750.00 375.00
b. Perf. 12 50.00 4.50

1892 **Wmk. 62** *Perf. 12½*
P4 N1 ½p bright rose 2.00 .25
a. Unwatermarked 10.00 4.50

ROSS DEPENDENCY

Catalogue values for unused stamps in this section are for Never Hinged items.

H.M.S. Erebus and Mount Erebus — A1

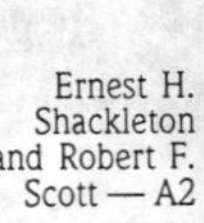

Ernest H. Shackleton and Robert F. Scott — A2

Map Showing Location of Ross Dependency A3

Queen Elizabeth II A4

Perf. 14, 13 (A4)

1957, Jan. 11 Engr. Wmk. 253

No.	Type	Denomination / Color	Unused	Used
L1	A1	3p dark blue	1.75	1.75
L2	A2	4p dark carmine	2.00	1.90
L3	A3	8p ultra & car rose	2.50	1.90
L4	A4	1sh6p dull violet	4.50	3.50
		Nos. L1-L4 (4)	10.75	9.05

1967, July 10

No.	Type	Denomination / Color	Unused	Used
L5	A1	2c dark blue	6.50	4.50
L6	A2	3c dark carmine	6.50	4.50
L7	A3	7c ultra & car rose	7.75	5.25
L8	A4	15c dull violet	16.00	10.50
		Nos. L5-L8 (4)	36.75	24.75

Skua — A5

Scott Base — A6

Designs: 4c, Hercules plane unloading at Williams Field. 5c, Shackleton's hut, Cape Royds. 8c, Naval supply ship Endeavour unloading. 18c, Tabular ice floe.

Perf. 13x13½

1972, Jan. 18 Litho. Unwmk.

No.	Type	Denomination / Color	Unused	Used
L9	A5	3c lt bl, blk & gray	.55	.50
L10	A5	4c black & violet	.45	.42
L11	A5	5c rose lil, blk & gray	.50	.45
L12	A5	8c blk, dk gray & brn	.80	.75

Perf. 14x13½

No.	Type	Denomination / Color	Unused	Used
L13	A6	10c slate grn, brt grn & blk ('79)	.65	.60
a.		Perf. 14½x14	.45	.45
L14	A6	18c pur & black ('79)	1.25	1.10
a.		Perf. 14½x14	1.10	1.10
		Nos. L9-L14 (6)	4.20	3.82

25th Anniv. of Scott Base — A7

1982, Jan. 20 Litho. Perf. 15½

No.	Type	Denomination / Color	Unused	Used
L15	A7	5c Adelie penguins	.15	.15
L16	A7	10c Tracked vehicles	.15	.15
L17	A7	20c shown	.18	.16
L18	A7	30c Field party, Upper Taylor Valley	.45	.40
L19	A7	40c Vanda Station	.75	.70
L20	A7	50c Scott's hut, Cape Evans, 1911	.90	.85
		Nos. L15-L20 (6)	2.58	2.41

Wildlife — A8

1994-95 Litho. Perf. 13½

No.	Type	Denomination / Color	Unused	Used
L21	A8	5c South polar skua	.15	.15
L22	A8	10c Snow petrel chick	.15	.15
L23	A8	20c Black-browed albatross	.25	.25
L23A	A8	40c like No. 24	.55	.55
L24	A8	45c Emperor penguins	.55	.55
L25	A8	50c Chinstrap penguins	.60	.60
L26	A8	70c Adelie penguins	.85	.85
L27	A8	80c Elephant seals	1.00	1.00
L28	A8	$1 Leopard seal	1.25	1.25
L29	A8	$2 Weddell seal	2.50	2.50
L30	A8	$3 Crabeater seal pup	3.75	3.75
		Nos. L21-L30 (11)	11.60	11.60

Issued: 40c, 10/2/95; others, 11/2/94.

Antarctic Explorers A9

Explorer, ships: 40c, James Cook, Resolution & Adventure. 80c, James Clark Ross, Erebus & Terror. $1, Roald Amundsen, Fram. $1.20, Robert Falcon Scott, Terra Nova. $1.50, Ernest Henry Shackleton, Endurance. $1.80, Richard Evelyn Byrd, Floyd Bennett (airplane).

1995, Nov. 9 Litho. Perf. 14½

No.	Type	Denomination / Color	Unused	Used
L31	A9	40c multicolored	.55	.55
L32	A9	80c multicolored	1.10	1.10
L33	A9	$1 multicolored	1.40	1.40
L34	A9	$1.20 multicolored	1.65	1.65
L35	A9	$1.50 multicolored	2.00	2.00
L36	A9	$1.80 multicolored	2.40	2.40
		Nos. L31-L36 (6)	9.10	9.10

Antarctic Landscapes A10

Designs: 40c, Inside ice cave, vert. 80c, Base of glacier, vert. $1, Glacier ice fall, vert. $1.20, Climbers on crater rim. $1.50, Pressure ridges. $1.80, Fumarole ice tower.

1996, Nov. 13 Litho. Perf. 14

No.	Type	Denomination / Color	Unused	Used
L37	A10	40c multicolored	.55	.55
L38	A10	80c multicolored	1.10	1.10
L39	A10	$1 multicolored	1.40	1.40
L40	A10	$1.20 multicolored	1.70	1.70
L41	A10	$1.50 multicolored	2.10	2.10
L42	A10	$1.80 multicolored	2.50	2.50
		Nos. L37-L42 (6)	9.35	9.35

Antarctic Sea Birds — A11

1997, Nov. 12 Litho. Perf. 14

No.	Type	Denomination / Color	Unused	Used
L43	A11	40c Snow petrel	.50	.50
L44	A11	80c Cape petrel	1.00	1.00
L45	A11	$1 Antarctic prion	1.25	1.25
L46	A11	$1.20 Antarctic fulmar	1.50	1.50
L47	A11	$1.50 Antarctic petrel	1.90	1.90
L48	A11	$1.80 Antarctic tern	2.25	2.25
a.		Block of 6, #L43-L48	8.50	8.50

World Wildlife Fund.

NICARAGUA

ˌni-kə-ˈrä-gwə

LOCATION — Central America, between Honduras and Costa Rica
GOVT. — Republic
AREA — 57,143 sq. mi.
POP. — 2,908,000 (est. 1984)
CAPITAL — Managua

100 Centavos = 1 Peso
100 Centavos = 1 Córdoba (1913)

Catalogue values for unused stamps in this country are for Never Hinged items, beginning with Scott 689 in the regular postage section, Scott C261 in the airpost section, Scott CO37 in the airpost official section, and Scott RA60 in the postal tax section.

Watermarks

Wmk. 117- Liberty Cap

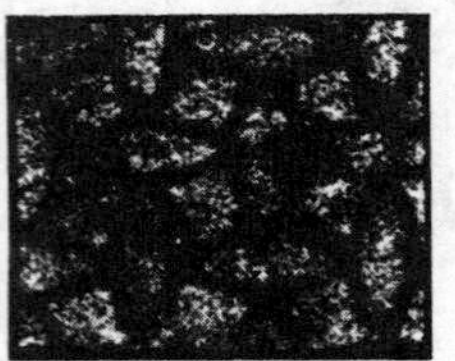
Wmk. 209- Multiple Ovals

Liberty Cap on Mountain Peak; From Seal of Country — A1

A2

A3

Unwmk.

1862, Dec. 2 Engr. Perf. 12

Yellowish Paper

No.	Type	Denomination / Color	Unused	Used
1	A1	2c dark blue	75.00	20.00
2	A1	5c black	150.00	60.00

Values are for copies without gum. Copies with gum sell for more. Nos. 1-2 were canceled only by pen.

See No. C509.

1869-71

White Paper

No.	Type	Denomination / Color	Unused	Used
3	A1	1c bister ('71)	3.00	1.25
4	A1	2c blue	3.00	1.25
5	A1	5c black	55.00	1.00
6	A2	10c vermilion	4.00	1.75
7	A3	25c green	7.50	4.00
		Nos. 3-7 (5)	72.50	9.25

1878-80 Rouletted 8½

No.	Type	Denomination / Color	Unused	Used
8	A1	1c brown	2.00	1.25
9	A1	2c blue	2.00	1.25
10	A1	5c black	12.50	1.00
11	A2	10c ver ('80)	2.50	1.50
12	A3	25c green ('79)	2.50	4.00
		Nos. 8-12 (5)	21.50	9.00

Most values exist on thicker soft paper.

Stamps with letter/numeral cancellations other than "3 G," "6 M," "9 C" sell for more.

Nos. 3-12 were reprinted in 1892. The corresponding values of the two series are printed in the same shades which is not usually true of the originals. They are, however, similar to some of the original shades and the only certain test is comparison. Originals have thin white gum; reprints have rather thick yellowish gum. Value 50c each.

Seal of Nicaragua — A4

Locomotive and Telegraph Key — A5

1882 Engr. Perf. 12

No.	Type	Denomination / Color	Unused	Used
13	A4	1c green	.20	.25
14	A4	2c carmine	.20	.25
15	A4	5c blue	.20	.25
16	A4	10c dull violet	.25	.75
17	A4	15c yellow	.60	17.50
18	A4	20c slate gray	.90	5.00
19	A4	50c dull violet	1.25	10.00
		Nos. 13-19 (7)	3.60	

Used Values

of Nos. 13-120 are for stamps with genuine cancellations applied while the stamps were valid. Various counterfeit cancellations exist.

1890 Engr.

No.	Type	Denomination / Color	Unused	Used
20	A5	1c yellow brown	.20	.25
21	A5	2c vermilion	.20	.25
22	A5	5c deep blue	.20	.25
23	A5	10c lilac gray	.20	.25
24	A5	20c red	.20	1.75
25	A5	50c purple	.20	5.00
26	A5	1p brown	.25	8.50
27	A5	2p dark green	.25	9.00
28	A5	5p lake	.25	
29	A5	10p orange	.25	
		Nos. 20-29 (10)	2.20	

The issues of 1890-1899 were printed by the Hamilton Bank Note Co., New York, to the order of N. F. Seebeck who held a contract for stamps with the government of Nicaragua. Reprints were made, for sale to collectors, of the 1896, 1897 and 1898, postage, postage due and official stamps. See notes following those issues.

For overprints see Nos. O1-O10.

Goddess of Plenty — A6

Columbus Sighting Land — A7

1891 Litho.

No.	Type	Denomination / Color	Unused	Used
30	A6	1c yellow brn	.25	.35
31	A6	2c red	.25	.35
32	A6	5c dk blue	.25	.25
33	A6	10c slate	.25	.50
34	A6	20c plum	.25	2.00
35	A6	50c purple	.25	5.00
36	A6	1p black brn	.25	5.00
37	A6	2p green	.25	8.50
38	A6	5p brown red	.25	
39	A6	10p orange	.25	
		Nos. 30-39 (10)	2.50	

For overprints see Nos. O11-O20.

1892 Engr.

No.	Type	Denomination / Color	Unused	Used
40	A7	1c yellow brn	.20	.25
41	A7	2c vermilion	.20	.20
42	A7	5c dk blue	.20	.20
43	A7	10c slate	.20	.25
44	A7	20c plum	.20	2.00
45	A7	50c purple	.20	7.00
46	A7	1p brown	.20	7.00
47	A7	2p blue grn	.20	8.50
48	A7	5p rose lake	.20	
49	A7	10p orange	.20	
		Nos. 40-49 (10)	2.00	

Commemorative of the 400th anniversary of the discovery of America by Columbus.

Stamps of the 1892 design were printed in other colors than those listed and overprinted "Telegrafos". The 1c blue, 10c orange, 20c slate, 50c plum and 2p vermilion are telegraph stamps which did not receive the overprint.

For overprints see Nos. O21-O30.

Ross Dependency stamps can be mounted in the annual Scott New Zealand supplement.

Arms
A8

"Victory"
A9

1893			Engr.	
51	A8	1c yellow brn	.20	.20
52	A8	2c vermilion	.20	.20
53	A8	5c dk blue	.20	.20
54	A8	10c slate	.20	.25
55	A8	20c dull red	.20	*1.50*
56	A8	50c violet	.20	*4.00*
57	A8	1p dk brown	.20	*7.00*
58	A8	2p blue green	.20	*8.50*
59	A8	5p rose lake	.20	
60	A8	10p orange	.20	
		Nos. 51-60 (10)	2.00	

The 1c blue and 2c dark brown are telegraph stamps which did not receive the "Telegrafos" overprint.

For overprints see Nos. O31-O41.

1894			Engr.	
61	A9	1c yellow brn	.20	.25
62	A9	2c vermilion	.20	.30
63	A9	5c dp blue	.20	.25
64	A9	10c slate	.20	.30
65	A9	20c lake	.20	*1.75*
66	A9	50c purple	.20	*4.00*
67	A9	1p brown	.20	*7.00*
68	A9	2p green	.20	*12.50*
69	A9	5p brown red	.20	*15.00*
70	A9	10p orange	.20	
		Nos. 61-70 (10)	2.00	

Specialists believe the 25c yellow green, type A9, is a telegraph denomination never issued for postal purposes. Stamps in other colors are telegraph stamps without the usual "Telegrafos" overprint.

There was little use of No. 70. Canceled copies are c-t-o or faked cancels.

For overprints see Nos. O42-O51.

Coat of Arms
A10

Map of Nicaragua
A11

1895			Engr.	
71	A10	1c yellow brn	.20	.30
72	A10	2c vermilion	.20	.30
73	A10	5c deep blue	.20	.25
74	A10	10c slate	.20	.25
75	A10	20c claret	.20	*.75*
76	A10	50c dl violet	3.00	*5.00*
77	A10	1p dk brown	.20	*5.00*
78	A10	2p dp green	.20	*8.00*
79	A10	5p brown red	.20	*11.00*
80	A10	10p orange	.20	
		Nos. 71-80 (10)	4.80	

Frames of Nos. 71-80 differ for each denomination.

A 50c violet blue exists. Its status is questioned. Value 20c.

There was little use of No. 80. Canceled copies are c-t-o or faked cancels.

For overprints see Nos. O52-O71.

1896			Engr.	
81	A11	1c violet	.30	*1.00*
82	A11	2c blue grn	.30	*.50*
83	A11	5c brt rose	.30	*.30*
84	A11	10c blue	.50	*.50*
85	A11	20c bister brn	3.00	*4.00*
86	A11	50c blue gray	.60	*8.00*
87	A11	1p black	.75	*11.00*
88	A11	2p claret	.75	*15.00*
89	A11	5p deep blue	.75	*15.00*
		Nos. 81-89 (9)	7.25	

See italic note after No. 109M.

For overprints see Nos. O82-O117.

Wmk. 117				
89A	A11	1c violet	3.75	.90
89B	A11	2c bl grn	3.75	1.25
89C	A11	5c brt rose	15.00	.30
89D	A11	10c blue	25.00	.90
89E	A11	20c bis brn	3.75	4.25
89F	A11	50c bl gray	42.50	*9.00*
89G	A11	1p black	37.50	*12.50*
89H	A11	2p claret		*18.50*
89I	A11	5p dp bl		*40.00*

Same, dated 1897

1897		Engr.	Unwmk.	
90	A11	1c violet	.50	.50
91	A11	2c bl grn	.50	.62
92	A11	5c brt rose	.50	.32
93	A11	10c blue	6.25	.75
94	A11	20c bis brn	2.50	*3.75*
95	A11	50c bl gray	9.00	*9.50*
96	A11	1p black	9.00	*15.00*
97	A11	2p claret	20.00	*19.00*
98	A11	5p dp bl	20.00	*42.50*
		Nos. 90-98 (9)	68.25	*91.94*

See italic note after No. 109M.

Wmk. 117				
98A	A11	1c violet	14.00	.50
98B	A11	2c bl grn	14.00	.50
98C	A11	5c brt rose	20.00	.38
98D	A11	10c blue	22.50	.90
98E	A11	20c bis brn	3.75	4.25
98F	A11	50c bl gray	22.50	*8.00*
98G	A11	1p black	25.00	*16.00*
98H	A11	2p claret	25.00	*25.00*
98I	A11	5p dp bl	125.00	*50.00*
		Nos. 98A-98I (9)	271.75	*105.53*

Coat of Arms of "Republic of Central America" — A12

1898		Engr.	Wmk. 117	
99	A12	1c brown	.25	.38
100	A12	2c slate	.25	.38
101	A12	4c red brown	.25	.50
102	A12	5c olive green	40.00	22.50
103	A12	10c violet	15.00	.62
104	A12	15c ultra	.40	1.50
105	A12	20c blue	10.00	2.00
106	A12	50c yellow	10.00	*9.50*
107	A12	1p violet blue	.40	*16.00*
108	A12	2p brown	19.00	*22.50*
109	A12	5p orange	25.00	*32.50*
		Nos. 99-109 (11)	120.55	*108.38*

Unwmk.				
109A	A12	1c brown	1.25	.32
109B	A12	2c slate	1.25	
109D	A12	4c red brown	2.25	.62
109E	A12	5c olive green	25.00	.15
109G	A12	10c violet	25.00	.62
109H	A12	15c ultra	25.00	
109I	A12	20c blue	25.00	
109J	A12	50c yellow	25.00	
109K	A12	1p deep ultra	25.00	
109L	A12	2p olive brown	25.00	
109M	A12	5p orange	25.00	
		Nos. 109A-109M (11)	204.75	

The paper of Nos. 109A to 109M is slightly thicker and more opaque than that of Nos. 81 to 89 and 90 to 98. The 5c and 10c also exist on very thin, semi-transparent paper.

Many reprints of Nos. 81-98, 98F-98H, 99-109M are on thick, porous paper, with and without watermark. The watermark is sideways. Paper of the originals is thinner for Nos. 81-109 but thicker for Nos. 109A-109M. Value 15 cents each.

In addition, reprints of Nos. 81-89 and 90-98 exist on thin paper, but with shades differing slightly from those of originals.

For overprints see Nos. O118-O128.

"Justice"
A13

Mt. Momotombo
A14

1899			Litho.	
110	A13	1c gray grn	.15	*.35*
111	A13	2c brown	.15	*.25*
112	A13	4c dp rose	.35	*.40*
113	A13	5c dp bl	.20	*.25*
114	A13	10c buff	.20	*.30*
115	A13	15c chocolate	.20	*.65*
116	A13	20c dk grn	.35	*.75*
117	A13	50c brt rose	.20	*3.00*
118	A13	1p red	.20	*8.50*
119	A13	2p violet	.20	*20.00*
120	A13	5p lt bl	.20	*25.00*
		Nos. 110-120 (11)	2.40	

Nos. 110-120 exist imperf. and in horizontal pairs imperf. between.

Nos. 110-111, 113 exist perf 6x12 due to defective perforating equipment.

For overprints see Nos. O129-O139.

Imprint: "American Bank Note Co. NY"

1900, Jan. 1			Engr.	
121	A14	1c plum	.50	.15
122	A14	2c vermilion	.50	.15
123	A14	3c green	.75	.25
124	A14	4c ol grn	1.00	.25
125	A14	5c dk bl	4.00	.20
126	A14	6c car rose	14.00	5.00
127	A14	10c violet	7.00	.25
128	A14	15c ultra	8.00	.65
129	A14	20c brown	8.00	.65
130	A14	50c lake	7.00	1.10
131	A14	1p yellow	12.00	4.00
132	A14	2p salmon	10.00	2.25
133	A14	5p black	10.00	3.00
		Nos. 121-133 (13)	82.75	17.90

Used values for #123, 126, 130-133 are for canceled to order copies.

See Nos. 159-161. For overprints and surcharges see Nos. 134-136, 144-151, 162-163, 175-178, O150-O154, 1L1-1L13, 1L16-1L19, 1L20, 2L1-2L10, 2L16-2L24, 2L36-2L39.

Nos. 131-133 Surcharged in Black or Red

1901

2 Cent.

1901, Mar. 5				
134	A14	2c on 1p yel	5.00	3.00
a.		Bar below date	14.00	8.00
b.		Inverted surcharge		16.50
c.		Double surcharge		27.50
135	A14	10c on 5p blk (R)	6.50	4.50
a.		Bar below date	14.00	8.00
136	A14	20c on 2p salmon	7.50	7.50
a.		Bar below date	14.00	10.00
		Nos. 134-136 (3)	19.00	15.00

A 2c surcharge on No. 121, the 1c plum, was not put on sale, nor postally used.

The 2c on 1p yellow without ornaments is a reprint.

Postage Due Stamps of 1900 Overprinted in Black or Gold

Correos

1901

1901, Mar.				
137	D3	1c plum	4.50	3.50
138	D3	2c vermilion	4.50	3.50
139	D3	5c dk bl	6.00	3.50
140	D3	10c pur (G)	8.50	5.00
a.		Double overprint	14.00	14.00
141	D3	20c org brn	10.00	6.50
142	D3	30c dk grn	10.00	6.50
143	D3	50c lake	8.50	4.00
a.		"1091" for "1901"	16.00	16.00
b.		"Correo"	37.50	
		Nos. 137-143 (7)	52.00	32.50

In 1904 an imitation of this overprint was made to fill a dealer's order. The date is at top and "Correos" at bottom. The overprint is printed in black, sideways on the 1c and 2c and upright on the 5c and 10c. Some copies of the 2c were further surcharged "1 Centavo." None of these stamps was ever regularly used.

3 Cent.

Nos. 126, 131-133 Surcharged

1901

Black Surcharge

1901, Oct. 20				
144	A14	3c on 6c rose	6.00	5.00
a.		Bar below value	7.00	5.50
b.		Inverted surcharge	8.00	8.00
c.		Double surcharge	8.00	8.00
d.		Double surch., one inverted	25.00	25.00
145	A14	4c on 6c rose	5.00	4.00
a.		Bar below value	5.50	4.50
b.		"1 cent" instead of "4 cent"	8.00	8.00
c.		Double surcharge	20.00	20.00
146	A14	5c on 1p yellow	5.00	4.00
a.		Three bars below value	6.00	4.50
b.		Ornaments at each side of "1901"	6.00	4.50
c.		Double surcharge, one in red	15.00	15.00
147	A14	10c on 2p salmon	5.50	4.00
a.		Inverted surcharge	12.50	12.50
b.		Double surcharge		

Blue Surcharge

148	A14	3c on 6c rose	6.00	4.50
a.		Bar below value	7.00	5.50
b.		Double surcharge	8.00	8.00
149	A14	4c on 6c rose	6.50	5.00
a.		Bar below value	7.50	7.50
b.		"1 cent" instead of "4 cent"	10.00	10.00
c.		Inverted surcharge	20.00	20.00

Red Surcharge

150	A14	5c on 1p yellow	7.50	6.50
a.		Three bars below value	9.00	7.00
b.		Ornaments at each side of "1901"	9.00	7.00
c.		Inverted surcharge	12.00	12.00
d.		Double surcharge, inverted	17.50	17.50
151	A14	20c on 5p black	5.00	3.50
a.		Inverted surcharge	16.00	16.00
b.		Double surcharge	22.50	22.50
c.		Triple surcharge		
		Nos. 144-151 (8)	46.50	36.50

In 1904 a series was surcharged as above, but with "Centavos" spelled out. About the same time No. 122 was surcharged "1 cent." and "1901," "1902" or "1904." All of these surcharges were made to fill a dealer's order and none of the stamps was regularly issued or used.

1901

Postage Due Stamps of 1900 Overprinted in Black

Correos

1901, Oct.				
152	D3	1c red violet	1.00	.40
a.		Ornaments at each side of the stamp	1.10	.65
b.		Ornaments at each side of "1901"	1.10	.65
c.		"Correos" in italics	1.50	1.50
d.		Double overprint	14.00	14.00
153	D3	2c vermilion	.75	.40
a.		Double overprint	8.50	5.50
154	D3	5c dark blue	1.00	.60
a.		Double overprint, one inverted		
b.		Double overprint	7.00	7.00
155	D3	10c purple	1.00	.60
b.		Double overprint	10.00	10.00
c.		Double overprint, one inverted	12.00	12.00
156	D3	20c org brn	1.25	1.25
b.		Double overprint	7.00	7.00
157	D3	30c dk grn	1.00	1.10
a.		Double overprint	9.00	9.00
b.		Inverted overprint	19.00	19.00
158	D3	50c lake	1.00	1.10
a.		Triple overprint	25.00	25.00
b.		Double overprint	16.50	16.50
		Nos. 152-158 (7)	7.00	5.45

One stamp in each group of 25 has the 2nd "o" of "Correos" italic. Value twice normal.

Momotombo Type of 1900
Without Imprint

1902		Litho.	*Perf. 14*	
159	A14	5c blue	.50	.25
a.		Imperf., pair	3.75	
160	A14	5c carmine	.50	.20
a.		Imperf., pair	3.75	
161	A14	10c violet	1.50	.20
a.		Imperf., pair	3.75	
		Nos. 159-161 (3)	2.50	.65

No. 161 was privately surcharged 6c, 1p and 5p in black in 1903.

15 cvos.

Nos. 121 and 122 Surcharged in Black

1902

1902, Oct.			*Perf. 12*	
162	A14	15c on 2c ver	2.00	.75
a.		Double surcharge	32.50	
b.		Blue surcharge	90.00	
163	A14	30c on 1c plum	1.00	2.25
a.		Double surcharge	9.00	
b.		Inverted surcharge	27.50	

Counterfeits of No. 163 exist in slightly smaller type.

President José Santos Zelaya — A15

1903, Jan.			Engr.	
167	A15	1c emer & blk	.35	.50
168	A15	2c rose & blk	.70	.50
169	A15	5c ultra & blk	.35	.50
170	A15	10c yel & blk	.35	.85
171	A15	15c lake & blk	.60	2.00
172	A15	20c vio & blk	.60	2.00
173	A15	50c ol & blk	.60	5.00
174	A15	1p red brn & blk	.60	6.00
		Nos. 167-174 (8)	4.15	17.35

10th anniv. of 1st election of Pres. Zelaya.

The so-called color errors-1c orange yellow and black, 2c ultramarine and black, 5c lake and black and 10c emerald and black-were also delivered to postal authorities. They were intended for official use though not issued as such. Value, $4 each.

Vale ¢ 5

Nos. 175-176

15 Centcvos

No. 177b

No. 161 Surcharged with New Values in Blue

1904-05

175 A14 5c on 10c vio ('05) 1.75 .25
- *a.* Inverted surcharge 2.00 1.40
- *b.* Without ornaments 2.00 .70
- *c.* Character for "cents" inverted 1.75 .40
- *d.* As "b," inverted
- *e.* As "c," inverted 2.75 2.75
- *f.* Double surcharge 8.00 8.00
- *g.* "5" omitted 2.75 2.75

176 A14 15c on 10c vio ('05) .30 .30
- *a.* Inverted surcharge 1.40 1.40
- *b.* Without ornaments 1.40 1.40
- *c.* Character for "cents" inverted 1.10 1.10
- *d.* As "b," inverted
- *e.* As "c," inverted 1.75 1.75
- *f.* Imperf. 6.50
- *h.* As "a," imperf. 9.00 9.00
- *i.* Double surcharge 14.00 14.00

177 A14 15c on 10c vio 4.50 2.75
- *a.* Inverted surcharge 6.00 6.00
- *b.* "Centcvos" 6.00 4.50
- *c.* "5" of "15" omitted 7.50
- *d.* As "b," inverted 8.50 8.50
- *e.* Double surcharge 11.00 11.00
- *f.* Double surcharge, inverted 13.00 13.00
- *g.* Imperf., pair 9.00 9.00

Nos. 175-177 (3) 6.55 3.30

There are two settings of the surcharge on No. 175. In the 1st the character for "cents" and the figure "5" are 2mm apart and in the 2nd 4mm.

The 2c vermilion, No. 122, with surcharge "1 cent. / 1904" was not issued.

No. 161 Surcharged in Black **5 CENTS.**

1905, June

178 A14 5c on 10c violet .60 .35
- *a.* Inverted surcharge 2.75 2.75
- *b.* Double surcharge 4.50 4.50
- *c.* Surcharge in blue 13.00

Coat of Arms — A18

Imprint: "American Bank Note Co. NY"

1905, July 25 **Engr.** ***Perf. 12***

179 A18 1c green .30 .20
180 A18 2c car rose .30 .20
181 A18 3c violet .45 .25
182 A18 4c org red .45 .25
183 A18 5c blue .45 .15
184 A18 6c slate .60 .40
185 A18 10c yel brn .85 .25
186 A18 15c brn olive .75 .35
187 A18 20c lake .60 .30
188 A18 50c orange 3.00 1.50
189 A18 1p black 1.50 1.50
190 A18 2p dk grn 1.50 2.00
191 A18 5p violet 1.75 2.50
Nos. 179-191 (13) 12.50 9.85

See Nos. 202-208, 237-248. For overprints and surcharges see Nos. 193-201, 212-216, 235-236, 249-265, O187-O198, O210-O222, 1L21-1L62, 1L73-1L95, 1LO1-1LO3, 2L26-2L35, 2L42-2L46, 2L48-2L72, 2LO1-2LO4.

Nos. 179-184 and 191 Surcharged in Black or Red Reading Up or Down **Vale 10¢**

1906-08

193 A18 10c on 2c car rose (up) 7.00 4.00
- *a.* Surcharge reading down 13.00 13.00

194 A18 10c on 3c vio (up) .60 .20
- *a.* "c" normal 2.75 1.35
- *b.* Double surcharge 4.50 4.50
- *c.* Double surch., up and down 7.00 5.00
- *d.* Pair, one without surcharge 9.50
- *e.* Surcharge reading down .30 .20

195 A18 10c on 4c org red (up) ('08) *35.00 20.00*
- *a.* Surcharge reading down *32.50 22.50*

196 A18 15c on 1c grn (up) .60 .30
- *a.* Double surcharge 7.50 7.50
- *b.* Dbl. surch., one reading down 11.00 11.00
- *c.* Surcharge reading down .40 .25

197 A18 20c on 2c car rose (down) ('07) .50 .30
- *a.* Double surcharge 13.00 13.00
- *b.* Surcharge reading up 37.50 32.00
- *c.* "V" omitted 10.00 10.00

198 A18 20c on 5c bl (down) .75 .50
- *a.* Surcharge reading up 35.00

199 A18 50c on 6c sl (R) (down) .60 .50
- *a.* Double surcharge
- *b.* Surcharge reading up 30.00 30.00
- *c.* Yellow brown surcharge .60 .40

200 A18 1p on 5p vio (down) ('07) 42.50 25.00
Nos. 193-200 (8) *87.55 50.80*

There are several settings of these surcharges and many varieties in the shapes of the figures, the spacing, etc.

Surcharged in Red Vertically Reading Up **Vale 35 cts.**

1908, May

201 A18 35c on 6c slate 3.00 2.25
- *a.* Double surcharge (R) 25.00
- *b.* Double surcharge (R + Bk) 65.00
- *c.* Carmine surcharge 3.00 2.25

Arms Type of 1905

Imprint: "Waterlow & Sons, Ltd."

1907, Feb. ***Perf. 14 to 15***

202 A18 1c green .70 .40
203 A18 2c rose .80 .25
204 A18 4c brn org 2.00 .30
205 A18 10c yel brn 3.00 .25
206 A18 15c brn olive 4.50 .90
207 A18 20c lake 8.00 1.25
208 A18 50c orange 11.00 4.25
Nos. 202-208 (7) 30.00 7.60

Nos. 202-204, 207-208 Surcharged in Black or Blue (Bl) Reading Down **Vale 10 ¢**

1907-08

212 A18 10c on 2c rose 1.50 .50
- *a.* Double surcharge 10.00
- *b.* "Vale" only 22.50
- *c.* Surcharge reading up 14.00 6.50

213 A18 10c on 4c brn org (up) ('08) 2.25 .85
- *a.* Double surcharge 10.00
- *b.* Surcharge reading down 5.50

214 A18 10c on 20c lake ('08) 3.25 1.40
- *b.* Surcharge reading up 80.00

215 A18 10c on 50c org (Bl) ('08) 2.00 .60
216 A18 15c on 1c grn ('08) 32.50 4.00
Nos. 212-216 (5) 41.50 7.35

Several settings of this surcharge provide varieties of numeral font, spacing, etc.

Revenue Stamps Overprinted "CORREO-1908" — A19

1908, June

217 A19 5c yel & blk .60 .40
- *a.* "CORROE" 2.75 2.75
- *b.* Overprint reading down 7.00
- *c.* Double overprint 13.00

218 A19 10c lt bl & blk .50 .25
- *a.* Double overprint 4.50 4.50
- *b.* Overprint reading down .50 .25
- *c.* Double overprint, up and down 13.00 13.00

219 A19 1p yel brn & blk .50 *2.00*
- *a.* "CORROE" 7.50 7.50

220 A19 2p pearl gray & blk .50 *2.50*
- *a.* "CORROE" 10.00 10.00

Nos. 217-220 (4) 2.10 5.15

Remainders of Nos. 219-220 were sold.

Revenue Stamps Surcharged Vertically Reading Up in Red, Blue, Green or Orange ***CORREO–1908* VALE 2 ₵**

221 A19 1c on 5c yel & blk (R) .40 .25
- *a.* "1008" 1.50 1.50
- *b.* "8908" 1.50 1.50
- *c.* Surcharge reading down 4.00 4.00
- *d.* Double surcharge 4.00 4.00

222 A19 2c on 5c yel & blk (Bl) .50 .30
- *b.* "ORREO" 1.75 1.75
- *c.* "1008" 1.75 1.75
- *d.* "8908" 1.75 1.75
- *f.* Double surcharge 7.00 7.00
- *g.* Double surcharge, one inverted 7.00 7.00
- *h.* Surcharge reading down 9.00 9.00

223 A19 4c on 5c yel & blk (G) .65 .35
- *a.* "ORREO" 2.50 2.50
- *b.* "1008" 2.00 2.00
- *c.* "8908" 2.00 2.00

224 A19 15c on 50c ol & blk (R) .60 .40
- *a.* "1008" 4.00 4.00
- *b.* "8908" 4.00 4.00
- *c.* Surcharge reading down 10.00 10.00

225 A19 35c on 50c ol & blk (O) 4.00 1.00
- *a.* Double surcharge, one inverted 12.00 12.00
- *b.* Surcharge reading down 12.00 12.00
- *c.* Double surcharge, one in black

Nos. 221-225 (5) 6.15 2.30

For surcharges and overprints see Nos. 225D-225H, 230-234, 266-278, 1L63-1L72A, 1L96-1L106, 2L47.

Revenue Stamps Surcharged Vertically Reading Up in Blue, Black or Orange ***CORREOS–1908* VALE 2 ₵**

1908, Nov.

225D A19 2c on 5c yel & blk (Bl) 20.00 12.50
- *e.* "9c" instead of "2c" 75.00 75.00

225F A19 10c on 50c ol & blk (Bk) *850.00 325.00*
- *g.* Double surcharge *425.00*

225H A19 35c on 50c ol & blk (O) 17.50 10.00

In this setting there are three types of the character for "cents."

CORREOS—1908

VALE 4 ₵

CORREOS—1908

Revenue Stamps Overprinted or Surcharged in Various Colors

1908, Dec.

226 2c org (Bk) 3.50 2.00
- *a.* Double overprint 6.00 6.00
- *b.* Overprint reading up 5.00 5.00

227 4c on 2c org (Bk) 1.75 .90
- *a.* Surcharge reading up 5.00 5.00
- *b.* Blue surcharge 80.00 80.00

228 5c on 2c org (Bl) 1.50 .60
- *a.* Surcharge reading up 6.00 6.00

229 10c on 2c org (G) 1.50 .30
- *a.* "1988" for "1908" 4.00 3.00
- *b.* Surcharge reading up 5.00 5.00
- *c.* "c" inverted 4.00 4.00
- *d.* Double surcharge 7.50

Nos. 226-229 (4) 8.25 3.80

Two printings of No. 229 exist. In the first, the initial of "VALE" is a small capital, and in the second a large capital.

The overprint "Correos-1908." 35mm long, handstamped on 1c blue revenue stamp of type A20, is private and fraudulent.

Revenue Stamps Surcharged in Various Colors ***CORREOS 1909* VALE 10 ₵**

1909, Feb.

Color: Olive & Black

230 A19 1c on 50c (V) 4.00 1.65
231 A19 2c on 50c (Br) 7.00 3.00
232 A19 4c on 50c (G) 7.00 3.00
233 A19 5c on 50c (C) 4.00 1.75
- *a.* Double surcharge 12.50 12.50

234 A19 10c on 50c (Bk) 1.10 .75
Nos. 230-234 (5) 23.10 10.15

Nos. 230 to 234 are found with three types of the character for "cents."

Nos. 190 and 191 Surcharged in Black **VALE 10 ₵**

1909, Mar. ***Perf. 12***

235 A18 10c on 2p dk grn 20.00 12.00
236 A18 10c on 5p vio *100.00 70.00*

There are three types of the character for "cents."

Arms Type of 1905

Imprint: "American Bank Note Co. NY"

1909, Mar.

237 A18 1c yel grn .35 .20
238 A18 2c vermilion .35 .20
239 A18 3c red org .35 .20
240 A18 4c violet .35 .20
241 A18 5c dp bl .35 .20
242 A18 6c gray brn 3.00 1.50
243 A18 10c lake .85 .15
244 A18 15c black .85 .15
245 A18 20c brn olive .85 .15
246 A18 50c dp grn 1.25 .40
247 A18 1p yellow 1.25 .40
248 A18 2p car rose 1.00 .40
Nos. 237-248 (12) 10.80 4.15

Nos. 239 and 244, Surcharged in Black or Red **VALE 2 ₵**

1910, July

249 A18 2c on 3c red org 2.75 1.10
250 A18 10c on 15c blk (R) 1.25 .30
- *a.* "VLEA" 3.50 2.00
- *b.* Double surcharge 17.50 17.50

There are two types of the character for "cents."

Nos. 239, 244, 245 Surcharged in Black or Red **VALE 2 c**

1910

252 A18 2c on 3c (Bk) 1.50 1.25
- *a.* Double surcharge 6.00 6.00
- *b.* Pair, one without surcharge
- *c.* "Vale" omitted 10.00 10.00

254 A18 5c on 20c (R) .40 .30
- *a.* Double surcharge (R) 6.00 5.00
- *b.* Inverted surcharge (R) 3.50 2.50
- *c.* Black surcharge 100.00
- *d.* Double surcharge (Bk) 135.00
- *e.* Inverted surcharge (Bk) 110.00

255 A18 10c on 15c (Bk) .90 .30
- *a.* "c" omitted 2.00 1.10
- *b.* "10c" omitted 2.50 1.50
- *c.* Inverted surcharge 4.00 4.00
- *d.* Double surcharge 6.00 6.00
- *e.* Double surch., one inverted 12.00

Nos. 252-255 (3) 2.80 1.85

There are several minor varieties in this setting, such as italic "L" and "E" and fancy "V" in "VALE," small italic "C," and italic "I" for "1" in "10."

Nos. 239, 244, 246 and 247, Surcharged in Black ***Vale 2 cts.***

1910, Dec. 10

256 A18 2c on 3c red org .90 .50
- *a.* Without period 1.00 .75
- *b.* Inverted surcharge 6.00 6.00
- *c.* Double surcharge 6.00 6.00

257 A18 10c on 15c blk 2.00 .75
- *a.* Without period 3.50 1.25
- *b.* Double surcharge 3.50 3.00
- *c.* Inverted surcharge 5.00 5.00

258 A18 10c on 50c dp grn 1.25 .40
- *a.* Without period 1.50 .75
- *b.* Double surcharge 3.00 3.00
- *c.* Inverted surcharge 3.00 3.00

259 A18 10c on 1p yel .90 .40
- *a.* Without period 1.25 .75
- *b.* Double surcharge 3.00 3.00

Nos. 256-259 (4) 5.05 2.05

The 15c on 50c deep green is a telegraph stamp.

Nos. 240, 244-248 Surcharged in Black ***Vale 2 cts.***

Surcharge as on Nos. 256-259 but lines wider apart.

1911, Mar.

260 A18 2c on 4c vio .30 .20
- *a.* Without period .35 .30
- *b.* Double surcharge 3.50 3.00
- *c.* Double surcharge, inverted 4.00 4.00
- *d.* Double surcharge, one inverted 3.50 3.50
- *e.* Inverted surcharge 7.50 7.50

261 A18 5c on 20c brn ol .30 .20
- *a.* Without period .60 .50
- *b.* Double surcharge 2.50 2.50
- *c.* Inverted surcharge 2.50 2.00
- *d.* Double surcharge, one inverted 6.00 6.00

262 A18 10c on 15c blk .40 .20
- *a.* Without period 1.00 .50
- *b.* "Yale" 12.00 12.00
- *c.* Double surcharge 3.00 3.00
- *d.* Inverted surcharge 3.00 3.00
- *e.* Double surch., one inverted 5.00 4.00
- *f.* Double surch., both inverted 12.00 12.00

263 A18 10c on 50c dp grn .25 .20
- *a.* Without period 1.00 .50
- *b.* Double surcharge 3.00 2.50

c. Double surcharge, one inverted 5.00 4.00
d. Inverted surcharge 5.00 5.00
264 A18 10c on 1p yel 1.50 .40
a. Without period 2.00 1.50
b. Double surcharge 4.00 4.00
c. Double surcharge, one inverted 7.50
265 A18 10c on 2p car rose .60 .50
a. Without period 2.00 1.50
b. Double surcharge 2.50 2.50
c. Double surcharge, one inverted 6.00 6.00
d. Inverted surcharge 6.00 6.00
Nos. 260-265 (6) 3.35 1.70

Revenue Stamps Surcharged in Black

Correos
02 cts
1911

1911, Apr. 10 *Perf. 14 to 15*

266 A19 2c on 5p dl bl 1.00 1.25
a. Without period 1.25 1.50
b. Double surcharge 2.50 2.00
267 A19 2c on 5p ultra .35 .40
a. Without period .75 1.25
b. Double surcharge 3.50
268 A19 5c on 10p pink .75 .40
a. Without period 1.50 1.00
b. "cte" for "cts" 1.50 1.00
c. Double surcharge 4.00 4.00
d. Inverted surcharge 2.50 2.50
269 A19 10c on 25c lilac .40 .25
a. Without period 1.00 .75
b. "cte" for "cts" 1.25 1.00
c. Inverted surcharge 4.00 4.00
d. Double surcharge 2.50 2.50
e. Double surcharge, one inverted 4.00 4.00
270 A19 10c on 2p gray .40 .25
a. Without period 1.00 .75
b. "cte" for "cts" 1.25 1.00
c. Double surcharge 5.00 5.00
d. Double surcharge, one inverted 4.00 3.00
271 A19 35c on 1p brown .40 .30
a. Without period 1.00 .75
b. "cte" for "cts" 1.25 1.00
c. "Corre" 1.50 1.50
d. Double surcharge 2.50 2.50
e. Double surcharge, one inverted 2.50 2.50
f. Double surcharge inverted 3.00 3.00
g. Inverted surcharge 5.00
Nos. 266-271 (6) 3.30 2.85

These surcharges are in settings of twenty-five. One stamp in each setting has a large square period after "cts" and two have no period. One of the 2c has no space between "02" and "cts" and one 5c has a small thin "s" in "Correos."

Surcharged in Black

CORREOS
05 cts.
1911

1911, June

272 A19 5c on 2p gray 1.50 1.00
a. Inverted surcharge 6.00 5.00

In this setting one stamp has a large square period and another has a thick up-right "c" in "cts."

Surcharged in Black

VALE
05 cts
POSTAL
de 1911

1911, June 12

273 A19 5c on 25c lilac 1.50 1.25
274 A19 5c on 50c ol grn 5.00 5.00
275 A19 5c on 5p blue 7.00 7.00
276 A19 5c on 5p ultra 6.00 6.00
a. Inverted surcharge
277 A19 5c on 50p ver 5.00 5.00
278 A19 10c on 50c ol grn 1.50 .50
Nos. 273-278 (6) 26.00 24.75

This setting has the large square period and the thick "c" in "cts." Many of the stamps have no period after "cts." Owing to broken type and defective impressions letters sometimes appear to be omitted.

A21

Revenue Stamps Surcharged on the Back in Black:

Vale **05 cts.** **CORREO** **DE 1911**
a

Vale **05 cts** **CORREO** **DE 1911**
b

Railroad coupon tax stamps (1st class red and 2nd class blue) are the basic stamps of Nos. 279-294. They were first surcharged for revenue use in 1903 in two types: I- "Timbre Fiscal" and "ctvs." II- "TIMBRE FISCAL" and "cents" (originally intended for use in Bluefields).

1911, July

279 A21 (a) 2c on 5c on 2 bl .25 .30
a. New value in yellow on face 6.00 6.00
b. New value in black on face 5.00 5.00
c. New value in red on face 60.00
d. Inverted surcharge .75
e. Double surch., one inverted 7.50 7.50
f. "TIMBRE FISCAL" in black .75 .75
280 A21 (b) 2c on 5c on 2 bl .25 .30
a. New value in yellow on face 3.00 3.00
b. New value in black on face 4.00 4.00
c. New value in red on face 60.00
d. Inverted surcharge .90 1.00
e. Double surch., one inverted 7.50 7.50
f. "TIMBRE FISCAL" in black 1.00 1.00
281 A21 (a) 5c on 5c on 2 bl .20 .15
a. Inverted surcharge .50 .35
b. "TIMBRE FISCAL" in black 1.00 1.00
c. New value in yellow on face
282 A21 (b) 5c on 5c on 2 bl .25 .20
a. Inverted surcharge .40 .35
b. "TIMBRE FISCAL" in black 1.00 1.00
c. New value in yellow on face
283 A21 (a) 10c on 5c on 2 bl .20 .20
a. Inverted surcharge .75 .50
b. "TIMBRE FISCAL" in black 1.00 1.00
c. New value in yellow on face 60.00
d. Double surcharge 6.00 6.00
284 A21 (b) 10c on 5c on 2 bl .20 .20
a. Inverted surcharge .75 .50
b. "TIMBRE FISCAL" in black 1.00 1.00
c. Double surcharge 6.00 6.00
d. New value in yellow on face 65.00
285 A21 (a) 15c on 10c on 1 red .25 .25
a. Inverted surcharge 1.00 1.25
b. "Timbre Fiscal" double 5.00
286 A21 (b) 15c on 10c on 1 red .35 .35
a. Inverted surcharge 1.00 1.00
b. "Timbre Fiscal" double 5.00
Nos. 279-286 (8) 1.95 1.95

These surcharges are in settings of 20. For listing, they are separated into small and large figures, but there are many other varieties due to type and arrangement.

The colored surcharges on the face of the stamps were trial printings. These were then surcharged in black on the reverse. The olive yellow surcharge on the face of the 2c was later applied to prevent use as a 5c revenue stamps. Other colors known on the face are orange and green. Forgeries exist.

For overprints and surcharges see Nos. 287-294, O223-O244, 1L107-1L108.

Surcharged on the Face in Black

CORREO
02 centavos

1911, Oct.

287 A21 2c on 10c on 1 red 6.50 6.50
a. Inverted surcharge 1.40 1.40
b. Double surcharge 10.00 10.00
288 A21 20c on 10c on 1 red 4.50 4.50
a. Inverted surcharge 5.25 5.00
289 A21 50c on 10c on 1 red 5.25 4.50
a. Inverted surcharge 10.00 10.00
Nos. 287-289 (3) 16.25 15.50

There are two varieties of the figures "2" and "5" in this setting.

Surcharged on the Back in Black

Vale
10 cts.
CORREO DE
1911

1911, Nov.

289B A21 5c on 10c on 1 red 37.50
c. Inverted surcharge 20.00
289D A21 10c on 10c on 1 red 12.50
e. Inverted surcharge 24.00

Surcharged on the Face

Correo
Vale
2 cts.
1911

1911, Dec.

Dark Blue Postal Surcharge

290 A21 2c on 10c on 1 red .25 .20
a. Inverted surcharge 2.50 2.50
b. Double surcharge 5.00 5.00
291 A21 5c on 10c on 1 red .30 .20
a. Double surcharge 2.50 2.50
b. Inverted surcharge 2.50 2.50
292 A21 10c on 10c on 1 red .35 .20
a. Inverted surcharge 2.50 2.50
b. Double surcharge 2.50 2.50
c. "TIMBRE FISCAL" on back 3.50 3.50

Black Postal Surcharge

293 A21 10c on 10c on 1 red 1.50 1.00
a. Inverted surcharge 7.00 7.00
b. New value surch. on back 12.00 12.00

Red Postal Surcharge

293C A21 5c on 5c on 2 blue 1.40 1.25
d. "TIMBRE FISCAL" in black 2.50 1.75
e. "5" omitted 3.75 3.75
f. Inverted surcharge 4.75 4.75
Nos. 290-293C (5) 3.80 2.85

Bar Overprinted on No. O234 in Dark Blue

Correo ~~oficial~~
Vale
10 cts.
1911

294 A21 10c on 10c on 1 red 1.25 1.00
a. Inverted surcharge 2.50 2.50
b. Bar at foot of stamp 5.00 5.00

Nos. 290-294 each have three varieties of the numerals in the surcharge.

"Liberty"
A22

Coat of Arms
A23

1912, Jan. **Engr.** *Perf. 14, 15*

295 A22 1c yel grn .30 .15
296 A22 2c carmine .40 .15
297 A22 3c yel brn .30 .20
298 A22 4c brn vio .30 .15
299 A22 5c blue & blk .25 .15
300 A22 6c olive bister .30 .80
301 A22 10c red brn .25 .15
302 A22 15c vio .25 .15
303 A22 20c red .25 .15
304 A22 25c blue grn & blk .30 .20
305 A23 35c grn & chnt 2.00 1.50
306 A22 50c lt blue 1.00 .40
307 A22 1p org 1.40 2.00
308 A22 2p dark blue grn 1.50 2.25
309 A22 5p blk 3.50 3.50
Nos. 295-309 (15) 12.30 11.90

For overprints and surcharges see Nos. 310-324, 337A-348, 395-396, O245-O259.

No. 305 Surcharged in Violet

Vale 15 cts.
Correos-1913.

1913, Mar.

310 A23 15c on 35c .40 .25
a. "ats" for "cts" 6.00 6.00

Stamps of 1912 Surcharged in Red or Black

VALE
medio
centavo
de córdoba
1913

1913-14

311 A22 ½c on 3c yel brn (R) .40 .35
a. "Corooba" 2.50 2.50
b. "do" for "de" 2.50 2.50
c. Inverted surcharge 22.50
312 A22 ½c on 15c vio (R) .25 .20
a. "Corooba" 1.00 1.00
b. "do" for "de" 1.25 1.25
313 A22 ½c on 1p org .25 .20
a. "VALB" 1.50 1.00
b. "ALE" 4.00 3.50
c. "LE" 6.00 5.00
d. "VALE" omitted 3.50 3.50
314 A22 1c on 3c yel brn .75 .60
315 A22 1c on 4c brn vio .25 .20
316 A22 1c on 50c lt blue .25 .20
317 A22 1c on 5p blk .25 .20
318 A22 2c on 4c brn vio .35 .25
a. "do" for "de" 1.25 1.25
319 A22 2c on 20c red 3.50 4.50
a. "do" for "de" 17.50 12.50
320 A22 2c on 25c blue grn & blk .35 .20
a. "do" for "de" 3.50 2.50
321 A23 2c on 35c grn & chnt .25 .40
a. "9131" 3.00 2.00
b. "do" for "de" 2.50 2.00
322 A22 2c on 50c lt blue .25 .20
a. "do" for "de" 1.25 1.25
323 A22 2c on 2p dark blue grn .20 .15
a. "VALB" 1.25 .75
b. "ALE" 2.50 1.25
c. "VALE" omitted 6.00
d. "VALE" and "dos" omitted 6.00
324 A22 3c on 6c olive bis .20 .15
a. "VALB" 35.00
Nos. 311-324 (14) 7.50 7.80

Nos. 311, 312 surcharged in black were not regularly issued.

Surcharged on Zelaya Issue of 1912

325 Z2 ½c on 2c ver .60 .45
a. "Corooba" 1.25 1.25
b. "do" for "de" 1.25 1.25
326 Z2 1c on 3c org brn .50 .20
327 Z2 1c on 4c car .50 .20
328 Z2 1c on 6c red brn .40 .20
329 Z2 1c on 20c dark vio .50 .20
330 Z2 1c on 25c grn & blk .50 .20
331 Z2 2c on 1c yel grn ('14) 6.75 1.25
a. "Centavos" 7.50 1.50
332 Z2 2c on 25c grn & blk 2.25 3.00
333 Z2 5c on 35c brn & blk .40 .20
334 Z2 5c on 50c ol grn .40 .20
a. Double surcharge 22.50
335 Z2 6c on 1p org .40 .20
336 Z2 10c on 2p org brn .40 .20
337 Z2 1p on 5p dk bl grn .40 .40
Nos. 325-337 (13) 14.00 6.90

On No. 331 the surcharge has a space of 2½mm between "Vale" and "dos."

Space between "Vale" and "dos" 2½mm instead of 1mm "de Cordoba" in different type.

1914, Feb.

337A A22 2c on 4c brn vio 27.50 4.00
b. "Ccntavos" 12.00
337C A22 2c on 20c red 13.00 1.25
d. "Ccntavos" 4.00
337E A22 2c on 25c bl grn & blk 6.00
f. "Ccntavos" 12.00
337G A23 2c on 35c grn & chnt 8.50
h. "Ccntavos" 15.00
337I A22 2c on 50c lt bl 22.00 4.00
j. "Ccntavos" 10.00

No. 310 with Additional Surcharge

medio
cvo. Córdoba

1913, Dec.

337K A23 ½c on 15c on 35c 200.00

The word "Medio" is usually in heavy-faced, shaded letters. It is also in thinner, unshaded letters and in letters from both fonts mixed.

No. 310 Surcharged in Black and Violet

½ ct. Cordoba
Correos 1913.

338 A23 ½c on 15c on 35c .20 .15
a. Double surcharge 3.50
b. Inverted surcharge 3.50
c. Surcharged on No. 305 12.00
339 A23 1c on 15c on 35c .25 .20
a. Double surcharge 4.00

Official Stamps of 1912 Surcharged

VALE
₡ 0.01

1914, Feb.

340 A22 1c on 25c lt bl .40 .25
a. Double surcharge 9.00
341 A23 1c on 35c lt bl .40 .25
a. "0.10" for "0.01" 10.00 10.00
341B A22 1c on 50c lt bl 160.00
342 A22 1c on 1p lt bl .25 .20
342A A22 2c on 20c lt bl 160.00 110.00
b. "0.12" for "0.02"
343 A22 2c on 50c lt bl .40 .20
a. "0.12" for "0.02" 75.00
344 A22 2c on 2p lt bl .40 .20
345 A22 2c on 5p lt bl 185.00
346 A22 5c on 5p lt bl .25 .20

Red Surcharge

347 A22 5c on 1p lt bl 55.00
348 A22 5c on 5p lt bl 450.00

National Palace, Managua — A24 León Cathedral — A25

Various Frames

1914, May 13 Engr. *Perf. 12*

349 A24 ½c lt blue .85 .20
350 A24 1c dk green .85 .15
351 A25 2c red orange .85 .15
352 A24 3c red brown 1.25 .30
353 A25 4c scarlet 1.25 .40
354 A24 5c gray black .45 .15
355 A25 6c black brn 9.00 5.50
356 A25 10c orange yel .85 .20
357 A24 15c dp violet 5.75 2.00
358 A25 20c slate 11.00 5.50
359 A24 25c orange 1.50 .45
360 A25 50c pale blue 1.40 .40
Nos. 349-360 (12) 35.00 15.40

In 1924 the 5c, 10c, 25c, 50c were issued in slightly larger size, 27x22¾mm. The original set was 26x22½mm.

No. 356 with overprint "Union Panamericana 1890-1940" in green is of private origin.

See Nos. 408-415, 483-495, 513-523, 652-664. For overprints and surcharges see Nos. 361-394, 397-400, 416-419, 427-479, 500, 540-548, 580-586, 600-648, 671-673, 684-685, C1-C3, C9-C13, C49-C66, C92-C105, C121-C134, C147-C149, C155-C163, C174-C185, CO1-CO24, O260-O294, O296-O319, O332-O376, RA1-RA5, RA10-RA11, RA26-RA35, RA39-RA40, RA44, RA47, RA52.

No. 355 Surcharged in Black — VALE 5 cts de Córdoba 1915

1915, Sept.

361 A25 5c on 6c blk brn 1.50 .40
a. Double surcharge 7.00 7.00

Stamps of 1914 Surcharged in Black or Red — Vale 1 centavo de córdoba

New Value in Figures

1918-19

362 A24 1c on 3c red brn 6.50 2.25
a. Double surch., one invtd. 12.50
363 A25 2c on 4c scarlet 32.50 22.50
364 A24 5c on 15c dp vio (R) 7.50 1.50
a. Double surcharge 12.00
364C A24 5c on 15c dp vio 350.00

Surcharged in Black — VALE por 2 centavos de Córdoba

365 A25 2c on 20c slate 110.00 55.00
a. "ppr" for "por" 120.00
b. Double surcharge 90.00 30.00
c. "Cordobo" 150.00 110.00
365D A25 5c on 20c slate 325.00 120.00
e. Double surcharge (Bk + R) 250.00
f. "Cordobo" 200.00

The surcharge on No. 365 is in blue black, and that on No. 365D usually has an admixture of red. Used only at Bluefields and Rama.

Surcharged in Black, Red or Violet — Vale medio centavo de córdoba

New Value in Words

366 A25 ½c on 6c blk brn 4.00 1.50
a. "Meio" 15.00
b. Double surcharge 12.00
367 A25 ½c on 10c yellow 2.50 .30
a. "Val" for "Vale" 3.00
b. "Codoba" 3.00
c. Inverted surcharge 5.00
d. Double surch., one inverted 10.00
368 A24 ½c on 15c dp vio 2.50 .60
a. Double surcharge 7.50
b. "Codoba" 4.00
c. "Meio" 6.00
369 A24 ½c on 25c orange 5.00 2.00
a. Double surcharge 8.00
b. Double surch., one inverted 6.00
370 A25 ½c on 50c pale bl 2.50 .30
a. "Meio" 6.00
b. Double surcharge 5.00
c. Double surch., one inverted 7.00
371 A25 ½c on 50c pale bl (R) 4.50 1.50
a. Double surcharge 10.00
372 A24 1c on 3c red brown 3.00 .30
a. Double surcharge 3.50
373 A25 1c on 6c blk brn 12.50 3.50
a. Double surcharge 9.00
374 A25 1c on 10c yellow 24.00 8.00
a. "nu" for "un" 22.50
375 A24 1c on 15c dp vio 4.50 .75
a. Double surcharge 10.00
b. "Codoba" 6.00
376 A25 1c on 20c slate 110.00 55.00
a. Black surch. normal and red surch. invtd. 80.00
b. Double surch., red & black 90.00
c. Blue surcharge 110.00
377 A25 1c on 20c sl (V) 110.00 42.50
a. Double surcharge (V + Bk) 80.00
378 A25 1c on 20c sl (R) 2.50 .30
a. Double surch., one inverted
b. "Val" for "Vale" 3.50 3.00
379 A24 1c on 25c orange 4.50 1.00
a. Double surcharge 11.00
380 A25 1c on 50c pale bl 14.00 4.50
a. Double surcharge 17.50
381 A25 2c on 4c scarlet 3.50 .30
a. Double surcharge 10.00
b. "centavo" 5.00
c. "Val" for "Vale"
382 A25 2c on 6c blk brn 24.00 8.00
a. "Centavoss"
b. "Cordobas"
383 A25 2c on 10c yellow 24.00 4.50
a. "centavo"
384 A25 2c on 20c sl (R) 13.00 3.25
a. "pe" for "de" 15.00
b. Double surch., red & blk 27.50
c. "centavo" 12.00
d. Double surcharge (R) 17.50
385 A24 2c on 25c orange 5.50 .40
a. "Vle" for "Vale" 7.50
b. "Codoba" 7.50
c. Inverted surcharge 10.00
386 A25 5c on 6c blk brn 10.00 4.25
a. Double surcharge 13.50
387 A24 5c on 15c dp vio 3.50 .60
a. "cincoun" for "cinco" 15.00
b. "Vle" for "Vale" 12.50
c. "Codoba" 12.50
Nos. 366-387 (22) 389.50 143.35

No. 378 is surcharged in light red and brown red: the latter color is frequently offered as the violet surcharge (No. 377).

Official Stamps of 1915 Surcharged in Black or Blue — Vale dos centavos de cordoba

1919-21

388 A24 1c on 25c lt blue 1.50 .25
a. Double surcharge 10.00
b. Inverted surcharge 12.00
389 A25 2c on 50c lt blue 1.50 .25
a. "centavo" 4.00 4.00
b. Double surcharge 12.00
390 A25 10c on 20c lt blue 1.40 .40
a. "centovos" 5.00 5.00
b. Double surcharge 8.00
390F A25 10c on 20c lt bl (Bl) 65.00
Nos. 388-390 (3) 4.40 .90

There are numerous varieties of omitted, inverted and italic letters in the foregoing surcharges.

No. 358 Surcharged in Black — VALE 5 Centavos

Types of the numerals:

2 (I), 2 (II), 2 (III)

2 (IV), 2 (V), 2 (VI), 2 (VII), 2 (VIII)

5 (I), 5 (II), 5 (III), 5 (IV)

5 (V), 5 (VI), 5 (VII), 5 (VIII)

1919, May

391 A25 2c on 20c (I) 160.00 110.00
a. Type II
b. Type III
c. Type IV
d. Type VI
e. Type VIII
392 A25 5c on 20c (I) 110.00 40.00
a. Type II 110.00 45.00
b. Type III 120.00 50.00
c. Type IV 125.00 50.00
d. Type V 140.00 60.00
e. Type VI 140.00 60.00
f. Type VII 400.00 250.00
h. Double surch., one inverted

No. 358 Surcharged in Black — VALE 2 Cents

393 A25 2 Cents on 20c (I) 135.00
a. Type II
b. Type III
c. Type IV
d. Type V
e. Type VI
f. Type VII
393G A25 5 Cents on 20c sl, (VIII) 135.00 55.00

Nos. 391-393G used only at Bluefields and Rama.

No. 351 Surcharged in Black — Vale un centavo de córdoba

1920, Jan.

394 A25 1c on 2c red org 1.50 .25
a. Inverted surcharge
b. Double surcharge

«Particular»

Official Stamps of 1912 Overprinted in Carmine

1921, Mar.

395 A22 1c lt blue 1.50 .60
a. "Parricular" 5.00 5.00
b. Inverted overprint 10.00
396 A22 5c lt blue 1.50 .40
a. "Parricular" 5.00 5.00

Official Stamps of 1915 Surcharged in Carmine — Vale un centavo de córdoba

1921, May

397 A25 ½c on 2c light blue .50 .20
a. "Mddio" 2.50 2.50
398 A25 ½c on 4c light blue 1.25 .20
a. "Mddio" 2.50 2.50
399 A24 1c on 3c light blue 1.25 .30
Nos. 397-399 (3) 3.00 .70

No. 354 Surcharged in Red — Vale medio centavo

1921, Aug.

400 A24 ½c on 5c gray blk .75 .75

Trial printings of this stamp were surcharged in yellow, black and red, and yellow and red. Some of these were used for postage.

Gen. Manuel José Arce — A26

José Cecilio del Valle — A27

Miguel Larreinaga A28

Gen. Fernando Chamorro A29

Gen. Máximo Jérez A30

Gen. Pedro Joaquín Chamorro A31

Rubén Darío — A32

1921, Sept. Engr.

401 A26 ½c lt bl & blk 1.00 1.00
402 A27 1c grn & blk 1.00 1.00
403 A28 2c rose red & blk 1.00 1.00
404 A29 5c ultra & blk 1.00 1.00
405 A30 10c org & blk 1.00 1.00
406 A31 25c yel & blk 1.00 1.00
407 A32 50c vio & blk 1.00 1.00
Nos. 401-407 (7) 7.00 7.00

Centenary of independence.

For overprints and surcharges see Nos. 420-421, RA12-RA16, RA19-RA23.

Types of 1914 Issue
Various Frames

1922

408 A24 ½c green .20 .15
409 A24 1c violet .20 .15
410 A25 2c car rose .20 .15
411 A24 3c ol gray .30 .15
411A A25 4c vermilion .35 .25
412 A25 6c red brn .20 .15
413 A24 15c brown .35 .15
414 A25 20c bis brn .50 .20
415 A25 1cor blk brn .90 .50
Nos. 408-415 (9) 3.20 1.85

In 1924 Nos. 408-415 were issued in slightly larger size, 27x22¾mm. The original set was 26x22½mm.

Nos. 408, 410 exist with signature controls. See note before No. 600. Same values.

No. 356 Surcharged in Black — Vale 0.01 de córdoba

1922, Nov.

416 A25 1c on 10c org yel 1.00 .35
417 A25 2c on 10c org yel 1.00 .25

Nos. 354 and 356 Surcharged in Red — Vale 2 centavos de córdoba

1923, Jan.

418 A24 1c on 5c gray blk 1.25 .20
419 A25 2c on 10c org yel 1.25 .20
a. Inverted surcharge

Nos. 401 and 402 Overprinted in Red — Sello Postal

1923

420 A26 ½c lt blue & blk 7.50 7.50
421 A27 1c green & blk 2.50 .85
a. Double overprint 7.50

Francisco Hernández de Córdoba — A33

1924 Engr.

422 A33 1c deep green 1.50 .30
423 A33 2c carmine rose 1.50 .30
424 A33 5c deep blue 1.00 .30
425 A33 10c bister brn 1.00 .60
Nos. 422-425 (4) 5.00 1.50

Founding of León & Granada, 400th anniv.

For overprint & surcharges see #499, 536, O295.

Stamps of 1914-22 Overprinted — Resello 1927

Black, Red or Blue Overprint

1927, May 3

427 A24 ½c green (Bk) .25 .20
428 A24 1c violet (R) .20 .15
a. Double overprint 3.00
428B A24 1c violet (Bk) 85.00 55.00
429 A25 2c car rose (Bk) .20 .15
a. Inverted overprint 5.00
b. Double overprint 5.00
430 A24 3c ol gray (Bk) 1.25 1.25
a. Inverted overprint 5.00
b. Double overprint 6.00
c. Double ovpt., one inverted 9.00 7.00
430D A24 3c ol gray (Bl) 8.00 3.25
431 A25 4c ver (Bk) 16.00 13.00
a. Inverted overprint 30.00
432 A24 5c gray blk (R) 1.25 .30
a. Inverted overprint 7.50
432B A24 5c gray blk (Bk) .75 .25
c. Double ovpt., one inverted 8.00
d. Double overprint 8.00

433 A25 6c red brn (Bk) 13.00 11.00
a. Inverted overprint 17.50
b. Double overprint
434 A25 10c yellow (Bl) .65 .40
a. Double overprint 12.50
b. Double ovpt., one inverted 10.00
435 A24 15c brown (Bk) 6.00 2.50
436 A25 20c bis brn (Bk) 6.00 2.50
a. Double overprint 17.50
437 A24 25c orange (Bk) 27.50 5.00
438 A25 50c pale bl (Bk) 7.50 3.00
439 A25 1cor blk brn (Bk) 15.00 9.00
Nos. 427-439 (16) 188.55 106.95

Most stamps of this group exist with tall "1" in "1927." Counterfeits exist of normal stamps and errors of Nos. 427-478.

Violet Overprint

1927, May 19

440 A24 ½c green .15 .15
a. Inverted overprint 2.00 2.00
b. Double overprint 2.00 2.00
441 A24 1c violet .20 .15
a. Double overprint 2.00 2.00
442 A25 2c car rose .15 .15
a. Double overprint 2.00 2.00
b. "1927" double 5.00
d. Double ovpt., one inverted 2.00 2.00
443 A24 3c ol gray .25 .15
a. Inverted overprint 6.00
b. Overprinted "1927" only 12.00
c. Double ovpt., one inverted 9.00
444 A25 4c vermilion 37.50 27.50
a. Inverted overprint 75.00
445 A24 5c gray blk 1.00 .25
a. Double overprint, one inverted 6.00
446 A25 6c red brn 37.50 27.50
a. Inverted overprint 75.00
447 A25 10c yellow .35 .20
a. Double overprint 2.00 2.00
448 A24 15c brown .75 .30
a. Double overprint 5.00
b. Double overprint, one inverted 8.00
449 A25 20c bis brn .35 .20
a. Double overprint
450 A24 25c orange .40 .20
451 A25 50c pale bl .40 .20
a. Double ovpt., one inverted 4.00 4.00
452 A25 1cor blk brn .75 .20
a. Double overprint 3.00
b. "1927" double 5.00
c. Double ovpt., one inverted 6.00
Nos. 440-452 (13) 79.75 57.15

Stamps of 1914-22 Overprinted in Violet **Resello 1928**

1928, Jan. 3

453 A24 ½c green .25 .20
a. Double overprint 3.00
b. Double overprint, one inverted 4.00
454 A24 1c violet .15 .15
a. Inverted overprint 2.00
b. Double overprint 2.00
c. Double ovpt., overprint, one inverted 2.00
d. "928" for "1928" 2.50
455 A25 2c car rose .20 .15
a. Inverted overprint 2.00
b. Double overprint 2.00
c. "1928" omitted 5.00
d. "928" for "1928" 2.50
e. As "d," inverted
f. "19" for "1928"
456 A24 3c ol gray .40 .15
457 A25 4c vermilion .20 .15
458 A24 5c gray blk .20 .15
a. Double overprint 5.00
b. Double overprint, one inverted 5.00
459 A25 6c red brn .20 .15
460 A25 10c yellow .25 .15
a. Double overprint 2.50
c. Inverted overprint
461 A24 15c brown .35 .25
462 A25 20c bis brn .50 .25
a. Double overprint
463 A24 25c orange .75 .25
a. Double overprint, one inverted 4.00
464 A25 50c pale bl 1.25 .15
465 A25 1cor blk brn 1.25 .35
Nos. 453-465 (13) 5.95 2.50

Stamps of 1914-22 Overprinted in Violet **Correos 1928**

1928, June 11

466 A24 ½c green .20 .15
467 A24 1c violet .15 .15
a. "928" omitted
469 A24 3c ol gray .75 .25
a. Double overprint 6.00
470 A25 4c vermilion .35 .15
471 A24 5c gray blk .25 .20
a. Double overprint 4.00
472 A25 6c red brn .40 .20
a. Double overprint 5.00
473 A25 10c yellow .50 .20
474 A24 15c brown 1.75 .20
a. Double overprint
475 A25 20c bis brn 2.00 .20
476 A24 25c orange 2.00 .25
a. Double overprint, one inverted 6.00
477 A25 50c pale bl 2.00 .25
478 A25 1cor blk brn 5.00 2.50
a. Double overprint 10.00
Nos. 466-478 (12) 15.35 4.70

No. 410 with above overprint in black was not regularly issued.

No. 470 with Additional Surcharge in Violet **Vale 2 Cts.**

1928

479 A25 2c on 4c ver 1.25 .35
a. Double surcharge 9.00

A34

Inscribed: "Timbre Telegrafico" Red Surcharge

1928

480 A34 1c on 5c bl & blk .30 .20
a. Double surcharge 5.00
b. Double surcharge, one inverted
481 A34 2c on 5c bl & blk .30 .20
a. Double surcharge 5.00
482 A34 3c on 5c bl & blk .30 .20
Nos. 480-482 (3) .90 .60

Stamps similar to Nos. 481-482, but with surcharge in black and with basic stamp inscribed "Timbre Fiscal," are of private origin.

See designs A36, A37, A44, PT1, PT4, PT6, PT7.

Types of 1914 Issue Various Frames

1928

483 A24 ½c org red .40 .15
484 A24 1c orange .40 .15
485 A25 2c green .40 .15
486 A24 3c dp vio .40 .25
487 A25 4c brown .40 .25
488 A24 5c yellow .40 .20
489 A25 6c lt bl .40 .25
490 A25 10c dk bl .90 .20
491 A24 15c car rose 1.40 .50
492 A25 20c dk grn 1.40 .50
493 A24 25c blk brn 27.50 6.00
494 A25 50c bis brn 3.25 1.00
495 A25 1cor dl vio 6.25 3.00
Nos. 483-495 (13) 43.50 12.60

No. 425 Overprinted in Violet **Correos 1928**

1929

499 A33 10c bis brn .75 .60

No. 408 Overprinted in Red

Correos 1929

1929

500 A24 ½c green (R) .25 .20
a. Inverted overprint 2.50
b. Double overprint 2.50
c. Double overprint, one inverted 3.50

A36

A37

Ovptd. Horiz. in Black "R. de T." Surcharged Vert. in Red

1929

504 A36 1c on 5c bl & blk (R) .25 .20
a. Inverted surcharge 3.00
b. Surcharged "0.10" for "0.01" 3.00
c. "0.0" instead of "0.01" 5.00
509 A36 2c on 5c bl & blk (R) .20 .15
a. Double surcharge 2.50
b. Double surcharge, one inverted 3.50
c. Inverted surcharge 5.00

Overprinted Horizontally in Black "R. de C." Surcharged Vertically in Red

510 A36 2c on 5c bl & blk (R) 22.50 1.25
a. Dbl. surcharge, one inverted 25.00

Surcharged in Red

511 A37 1c on 10c dk grn & blk (R) .25 .20
a. Double surcharge
512 A37 2c on 5c bl & blk (R) .25 .15
Nos. 504-512 (5) 23.45 1.95

The varieties tall "1" in "0.01" and "O$" for "C$" are found in this surcharge.

Nos. 500, 504, 509-512 and RA38 were surcharged in red and sold in large quantities to the public. Surcharges in various other colors were distributed only to a favored few and not regularly sold at the post offices.

Types of 1914 Issue Various Frames

1929-31

513 A24 1c ol grn .15 .15
514 A24 3c lt bl .30 .15
515 A25 4c dk bl ('31) .30 .20
516 A24 5c ol brn .40 .15
517 A25 6c bis brn ('31) .50 .30
518 A25 10c lt brn ('31) .60 .20
519 A24 15c org red ('31) .90 .25
520 A25 20c org ('31) 1.20 .35
521 A24 25c dk vio .25 .15
522 A25 50c grn ('31) .50 .20
523 A25 1cor yel ('31) 4.50 1.25
Nos. 513-523 (11) 9.60 3.35

Nos. 513-523 exist with signature controls. See note before No. 600. Same values.

New Post Office at Managua — A38

1930, Sept. 15 **Engr.**

525 A38 ½c olive gray 1.20 1.20
526 A38 1c carmine 1.20 1.20
527 A38 2c red org .90 .90
528 A38 3c orange 1.75 1.75
529 A38 4c yellow 1.75 1.75
530 A38 5c ol grn 2.25 2.25
531 A38 6c bl grn 2.25 2.25
532 A38 10c black 2.75 2.75
533 A38 25c dp bl 5.50 5.50
534 A38 50c ultra 9.00 9.00
535 A38 1cor dp vio 25.00 25.00
Nos. 525-535 (11) 53.55 53.55

Opening of the new general post office at Managua. The stamps were on sale on day of issuance and for an emergency in April, 1931.

No. 499 Surcharged in Black and Red **C$ 0.02 1931**

1931, May 29

536 A33 2c on 10c bis brn .50 1.60
a. Red surcharge omitted 2.50
b. Red surcharge double 5.00
c. Red surcharge inverted 3.50
d. Red surcharge double, one invtd.

Surcharge exists in brown.

Types of 1914-31 Issue Overprinted **1931**

1931, June 11

540 A24 ½c green .35 .15
a. Double overprint .80
b. Double ovpt., one inverted 1.40
c. Inverted overprint .80
541 A24 1c ol grn .35 .15
a. Double overprint .80
b. Double ovpt., one inverted 1.40
c. Inverted overprint
542 A25 2c car rose .35 .15
a. Double overprint .80
b. Double ovpt., both inverted 2.50
c. Inverted overprint 1.40
543 A24 3c lt bl .35 .15
a. Double overprint .80
b. Double ovpt., one inverted 1.40
c. Inverted overprint 1.40
544 A24 5c yellow 3.50 2.25
545 A24 5c ol brn 1.00 .16
a. Double overprint 4.50
b. Inverted overprint 4.50
546 A24 15c org red 1.20 .40
a. Double overprint 3.50
547 A24 25c blk brn 10.00 6.50
a. Double overprint 11.00 7.00
b. Inverted overprint 11.00 7.00
548 A24 25c dk vio 4.00 2.50
a. Double overprint 6.50
Nos. 540-548 (9) 21.10 12.41

Counterfeits exist of the scarcer values. The 4c brown and 6c light blue with this overprint are bogus.

Managua P.O. Before and After Earthquake A40

1932, Jan. 1 **Litho.** ***Perf. 11½***

Soft porous paper, Without gum

556 A40 ½c emerald 1.50
557 A40 1c yel brn 1.90
558 A40 2c dp car 1.50
559 A40 3c ultra 1.50
560 A40 4c dp ultra 1.50
561 A40 5c yel brn 1.60
562 A40 6c gray brn 1.60
563 A40 10c yel brn 2.50
564 A40 15c dl rose 3.75
565 A40 20c orange 3.50
566 A40 25c dk vio 2.50
567 A40 50c emerald 2.50
568 A40 1cor yellow 6.25
Nos. 556-568 (13) 32.10

Issued in commemoration of the earthquake at Managua, Mar. 31, 1931. The stamps were on sale on Jan. 1, 1932, only. The money received from this sale was for the reconstruction of the Post Office building and for the improvement of the postal service. Many shades exist.

Sheets of 10.

Reprints are on thin hard paper and do not have the faint horiz. ribbing that is on the front or back of the originals. Fake cancels abound. Value 75 cents each.

See Nos. C20-C24. For overprints and surcharges see Nos. C32-C43, C47-C48.

Rivas Railroad Issue

"Fill" at El Nacascolo — A41

1c, Wharf at San Jorge. 5c, Rivas Station. 10c, San Juan del Sur. 15c, Train at Rivas Station.

1932, Dec. 17 **Litho.** ***Perf. 12***

Soft porous paper

570 A41 1c yellow 16.50
a. 1c ocher 18.00
571 A41 2c carmine 16.50
572 A41 5c blk brn 16.50
573 A41 10c chocolate 16.50
574 A41 15c yellow 16.50
a. 15c deep orange 18.00
Nos. 570-574 (5) 82.50

Inauguration of the railroad from San Jorge to San Juan del Sur. On sale only on Dec. 17, 1932.

Sheets of 4, without gum. See #C67-C71.

Reprints exist on thin hard paper and do not have the faint horiz. ribbing that is on the front or back of the originals. Value, $5 each.

Leon-Sauce Railroad Issue

Bridge No. 2 at Santa Lucia A42

Designs: 1c, Environs of El Sauce. 5c, Santa Lucia. 10c, Works at Km. 64. 15c, Rock cut at Santa Lucia.

1932, Dec. 30 ***Perf. 12***

Soft porous paper

575 A42 1c orange 16.50
576 A42 2c carmine 16.50
577 A42 5c blk brn 16.50

578 A42 10c brown 16.50
579 A42 15c orange 16.50
Nos. 575-579 (5) 82.50

Inauguration of the railroad from Leon to El Sauce. On sale only on Dec. 30, 1932.

Sheets of 4, without gum. See #C72-C76.

Reprints exist on thin hard paper and do not have the faint horiz. ribbing that is on the front or back of the originals. Value $5 each.

Nos. 514-515, 543 Surcharged in Red — **Vale un centavo**

1932, Dec. 10
580 A24 1c on 3c lt bl (514) .35 .15
  a. Double surcharge 3.50
581 A24 1c on 3c lt bl (543) 4.00 3.50
582 A25 2c on 4c dk bl (515) .25 .15
  a. Double surcharge 2.50
Nos. 580-582 (3) 4.60 3.80

Nos. 514, 516, 545 and 518 Surcharged in Black or Red — **Resello 1933 Vale Un Centavo**

1933
583 A24 1c on 3c lt bl (Bk) (514) .16 .15
  a. "Censavo" 4.00 2.25
  b. Double surcharge, one inverted 4.00
584 A24 1c on 5c ol brn (R) (516) .16 .15
  a. Inverted surcharge
  b. Double surcharge
585 A24 1c on 5c ol brn (R) (545) 6.50 5.00
  a. Red surcharge double 12.00
586 A25 2c on 10c lt brn (Bk) (518) .16 .15
  a. Double surcharge 4.00 2.50
  b. Inverted surcharge 3.50 3.50
  c. Double surcharge, one inverted 4.00 2.50
Nos. 583-586 (4) 6.98 5.45

On No. 586 "Vale Dos" measures 13mm and 14mm.

No. 583 with green surcharge and No. 586 with red surcharge are bogus.

Flag of the Race Issue

Flag with Three Crosses for Three Ships of Columbus — A43

1933, Aug. 3 Litho. *Rouletted 9*
Without gum
587 A43 ½c emerald 1.75 1.75
588 A43 1c green 1.50 1.50
589 A43 2c red 1.50 1.50
590 A43 3c dp rose 1.50 1.50
591 A43 4c orange 1.50 1.50
592 A43 5c yellow 1.75 1.75
593 A43 10c dp brn 1.75 1.75
594 A43 15c dk brn 1.75 1.75
595 A43 20c vio bl 1.75 1.75
596 A43 25c dl bl 1.75 1.75
597 A43 30c violet 4.50 4.50
598 A43 50c red vio 4.50 4.50
599 A43 1cor ol brn 4.50 4.50
Nos. 587-599 (13) 30.00 30.00

Commemorating the raising of the symbolical "Flag of the Race"; also the 441st anniversary of the sailing of Columbus for the New World, Aug. 3, 1492. Printed in sheets of 10.

See Nos. C77-C87, O320-O331.

In October, 1933, various postage, airmail and official stamps of current issues were overprinted with facsimile signatures of the Minister of Public Works and the Postmaster-General. These overprints are control marks.

Nos. 410 and 513 Overprinted in Black — **Resello 1935**

1935 *Perf. 12*
600 A24 1c ol grn .15 .15
  a. Inverted overprint 1.40 1.60
  b. Double overprint 1.40 1.60
  c. Double overprint, one inverted 1.60 1.60
601 A25 2c car rose .15 .15
  a. Inverted overprint 1.60
  b. Double overprint 1.60
  c. Double overprint, one inverted 1.60
  d. Double overprint, both inverted 2.50 2.25
Set value .24 .15

No. 517 Surcharged in Red as in 1932

1936, June
602 A25 ½c on 6c bis brn .35 .15
  a. "Ccentavo" .80 .80
  b. Double surcharge 3.50 3.50

Regular Issues of 1929-35 Overprinted in Blue — RESELLO-1935

1935, Dec.
603 A25 ½c on 6c bis brn .65 .15
604 A24 1c ol grn (#600) .80 .15
605 A25 2c car rose (#601) .80 .15
  a. Black overprint inverted 6.00
606 A24 3c lt bl .80 .22
607 A24 5c ol brn 1.00 .25
608 A25 10c lt brn 1.60 .80
Nos. 603-608 (6) 5.65 1.72

Nos. 606-608 have signature control overprint. See note before No. 600.

Same Overprint in Red

1936, Jan.
609 A24 ½c dk grn .16 .15
610 A25 ½c on 6c bis brn (602) .15 .15
  a. Double surch., one inverted 6.00 6.00
611 A24 1c ol grn (513) .22 .15
612 A24 1c ol grn (600) .25 .15
613 A25 2c car rose (410) .50 .15
614 A25 2c car rose (601) .25 .15
  a. Black overprint inverted 2.50 2.50
  b. Black ovpt. double, one invtd. 3.50 3.50
615 A24 3c lt bl .25 .15
616 A25 4c dk bl .25 .15
617 A24 5c ol brn .22 .15
618 A25 6c bis brn .25 .15
619 A25 10c lt brn .50 .16
620 A24 15c org red .15 .15
621 A25 20c orange .80 .22
622 A24 25c dk vio .25 .15
623 A25 50c green .35 .20
624 A25 1cor yellow .40 .25
Nos. 609-624 (16) 4.95
Set value 1.95

Red or blue "Resello 1935" overprint may be found inverted or double. Red and blue overprints on same stamp are bogus.

Nos. 615-624 have signature control overprint. See note before No. 600.

Regular Issues of 1922-29 Overprinted in Carmine

1936, May
625 A24 ½c green .15 .15
626 A24 1c olive green .16 .15
627 A25 2c carmine rose .50 .15
628 A24 3c light blue .16 .15
Nos. 625-628 (4) .97
Set value .35

No. 628 has signature control overprint. See note before No. 600.

Nos. 514, 516 Surcharged in Black — **Resello 1936 Vale Un Centavo**

1936, June
629 A24 1c on 3c lt bl .15 .15
  a. "1396" for "1936" 1.00 1.00
  b. "Un" omitted 1.40 1.40
  c. Inverted surcharge 1.60 1.60
  d. Double surcharge 1.60 1.60
630 A24 2c on 5c ol brn .15 .15
  a. "1396" for "1936" 1.40 1.40
  b. Double surcharge 3.50 3.50
Set value .20

Regular Issues of 1929-31 Surcharged in Black or Red — **1936 Vale Un Centavo**

1936
631 A24 ½c on 15c org red (R) .16 .15
  a. Double surcharge 4.00
632 A25 1c on 4c dk bl (Bk) .22 .15
633 A24 1c on 5c ol brn (Bk) .22 .16
634 A25 1c on 6c bis brn (Bk) .40 .16
  a. "1939" instead of "1936" 2.50 1.60
635 A24 1c on 15c org red (Bk) .22 .16
  a. "1939" instead of "1936" 2.50 1.60
636 A25 1c on 20c org (Bk) .16 .15
  a. "1939" intead of "1936" 2.50 1.60
  b. Double surcharge 4.00
637 A25 1c on 20c org (R) .16 .15
638 A25 2c on 10c lt brn (Bk) .25 .16
639 A24 2c on 15c org red (Bk) 1.00 .80
640 A25 2c on 20c org (Bk) .50 .25
641 A24 2c on 25c dk vio (R) .35 .16
642 A24 2c on 25c dk vio (Bk) .35 .16
  a. "1939" instead of "1936" 2.50 1.60
643 A25 2c on 50c grn (Bk) .35 .22
  a. "1939" instead of "1936" 2.50 1.60
644 A25 2c on 1 cor yel (Bk) .35 .22
  a. "1939" instead of "1936" 2.50 1.60
645 A25 3c on 4c dk bl (Bk) .65 .50
  a. "1939" instead of "1936" 2.50 1.60
  b. "s" of "Centavos" omitted and "r" of "Tres" inverted 2.50
Nos. 631-645 (15) 5.34 3.55

Nos. 634, 639, 643-644 exist with and without signature controls. Same values, except for No. 639, which is rare without the signature control. Nos. 635-636, 642, 645 do not have signature controls. Others have signature controls only. See note before No. 600.

Regular Issues of 1929-31 Overprinted in Black — **Resello 1936**

1936, Aug.
646 A24 3c lt bl .35 .20
647 A24 5c ol brn .25 .15
648 A25 10c lt brn .50 .35
Nos. 646-648 (3) 1.10 .70

No. 648 bears script control mark.

A44

Surcharged in Red

1936, Oct. 19
649 A44 1c on 5c grn & blk .20 .15
650 A44 2c on 5c grn & blk .20 .15
Set value .15

Types of 1914

1937, Jan. 1 **Engr.**
652 A24 ½c black .15 .15
653 A24 1c car rose .15 .15
654 A25 2c dp bl .15 .15
655 A24 3c chocolate .15 .15
656 A25 4c yellow .16 .15
657 A24 5c org red .15 .15
658 A25 6c dl vio .16 .15
659 A25 10c ol grn .16 .15
660 A24 15c green .15 .15
661 A25 20c red brn .25 .15
663 A25 50c brown .35 .15
664 A25 1cor ultra .60 .22
Nos. 652-664 (12) 2.58
Set value 1.25

See note after No. 360.

Mail Carrier — A45

Designs: 1c, Mule carrying mail. 2c, Mail coach. 3c, Sailboat. 5c, Steamship. 7½c, Train.

1937, Dec. Litho. *Perf. 11*
665 A45 ½c green .15 .15
666 A45 1c magenta .15 .15
667 A45 2c brown .15 .15
668 A45 3c purple .15 .15
669 A45 5c blue .15 .15
670 A45 7½c red org .55 .35
Nos. 665-670 (6) 1.30
Set value .75

75th anniv. of the postal service in Nicaragua.

Nos. 665-670 were also issued in sheets of 4, value, set of sheets, $7.

The miniature sheets are ungummed, and also exist imperf. and part-perf.

Nos. 662, 663 and 664 Surcharged in Red — **Vale Tres Centavos 1938**

1938 *Perf. 12*
671 A24 3c on 25c org .15 .15
672 A25 5c on 50c brn .24 .15
  a. "e" of "Vale" omitted 1.60 1.00
673 A25 6c on 1cor ultra .15 .15
Set value .48 .25

No. 672 has a script signature control and the surcharge is in three lines.

Dario Park — A46

1939, Jan. **Engr.** *Perf. 12½*
674 A46 1½c yel grn .15 .15
675 A46 2c dp rose .15 .15
676 A46 3c brt bl .15 .15
677 A46 6c brn org .15 .15
678 A46 7½c dp grn .15 .15
679 A46 10c blk brn .20 .15
680 A46 15c orange .20 .15
681 A46 25c lt vio .20 .15
682 A46 50c brt yel grn .16 .15
683 A46 1cor yellow .65 .40
Nos. 674-683 (10) 2.16
Set value 1.10

Nos. 660 and 661 Surcharged in Red — **Vale un Centavo 1939**

1939 *Perf. 12*
684 A24 1c on 15c grn .15 .15
  a. Inverted surcharge 2.00 2.00
685 A25 1c on 20c red brn .15 .15
Set value .17 .15

No. C236 Surcharged in Carmine — **Servicio ordinario Vale Diez Centavos de Córdoba**

1941 **Unwmk.** *Perf. 12*
686 AP14 10c on 1c brt grn .15 .15
  a. Double surcharge 10.00 2.50
  b. Inverted surcharge 10.00 2.50

Rubén Darío — A47

1941, Dec. **Engr.** *Perf. 12½*
687 A47 10c red .35 .15
Nos. 687,C257-C260 (5) 1.95 1.05

25th anniversary of the death of Rubén Darío, poet and writer.

No. C236 Surcharged in Carmine — **Servicio Ordinario Vale Diez Centavos**

1943 *Perf. 12*
688 AP14 10c on 1c brt grn 4.00 .15
  a. Inverted surcharge 10.00
  b. Double surcharge 10.00

Catalogue values for unused stamps in this section, from this point to the end of the section, are for Never Hinged items.

"Victory" — A48

Columbus and Lighthouse — A49

1943, Dec. 8 **Engr.**
689 A48 10c vio & cerise .15 .15
690 A48 30c org brn & cerise .15 .15
Set value .21 .15

2nd anniv. of Nicaragua's declaration of war against the Axis. See Nos. C261-C262.

1945, Sept. 1 **Unwmk.** ***Perf. 12½***
691 A49 4c dk grn & blk .20 .20
692 A49 6c org & blk .25 .25
693 A49 8c dp rose & blk .35 .35
694 A49 10c bl & blk .40 .40
Nos. 691-694,C266-C271 (10) 6.10 5.35

Issued in honor of the discovery of America by Columbus and the Columbus Lighthouse near Ciudad Trujillo, Dominican Republic.

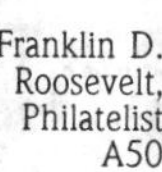

Franklin D. Roosevelt, Philatelist A50

Roosevelt Signing Declaration of War Against Japan — A51

8c, F. D. Roosevelt, Winston Churchill. 16c, Gen. Henri Giraud, Roosevelt, de Gaulle & Churchill. 32c, Stalin, Roosevelt, Churchill. 50c, Sculptured head of Roosevelt.

Engraved, Center Photogravure
1946, June 15 **Unwmk.** ***Perf. 12½***
Frame in Black
695 A50 4c sl grn .16 .16
696 A50 8c violet .28 .28
697 A51 10c ultra .32 .32
698 A50 16c rose red .40 .40
699 A50 32c org brn .28 .28
700 A51 50c gray .28 .28
Nos. 695-700 (6) 1.72 1.72

Issued to honor US Pres. Franklin D. Roosevelt (1882-1945). See Nos. C272-C276.

Metropolitan Cathedral, Managua — A56

Designs: 5c, Sanitation Building. 6c, Municipal Building. 10c, Projected Provincial Seminary. 75c, Communications Building.

1947, Jan. 10
Frame in Black
701 A56 4c carmine .15 .15
702 A56 5c blue .15 .15
703 A56 6c green .20 .16
704 A56 10c olive .20 .16
705 A56 75c golden brn .30 .28
Nos. 701-705 (5) 1.00 .90

Centenary of the founding of the city of Managua. See Nos. C277-C282.

San Cristóbal Volcano — A61

Designs: 3c, Tomb of Rubén Dario. 4c, Grandstand. 5c, Soldiers' monument. 6c, Sugar cane. 8c, Tropical fruit. 10c, Cotton industry. 20c, Horse race. 30c, Nicaraguan coffee. 50c, Steer. 1cor, Agriculture.

Engraved, Center Photogravure
1947, Aug. 29
Frame in Black
706 A61 2c orange .16 .15
707 A61 3c violet .15 .15
708 A61 4c gray .22 .15
709 A61 5c rose car .55 .22
710 A61 6c green .32 .15
711 A61 8c org brn .38 .15
712 A61 10c red .55 .22
713 A61 20c brt ultra 1.90 .48
714 A61 30c rose lilac 1.50 .48
715 A61 50c dp claret 3.25 .95
716 A61 1cor brn org 1.10 .48
Nos. 706-716 (11) 10.08 3.58

The frames differ for each denomination. For surcharge see No. 769.

Softball A62

Boy Scout, Badge and Flag — A63

Designs: 3c, Pole vault. 4c, Diving. 5c, Bicycling. 10c, Proposed stadium. 15c, Baseball. 25c, Boxing. 35c, Basketball. 40c, Regatta. 60c, Table tennis. 1 cor, Soccer. 2 cor, Tennis.

1949, July 15 **Photo.** ***Perf. 12***
717 A62 1c henna brn .15 .15
718 A63 2c ultra .75 .20
719 A63 3c bl grn .30 .15
720 A62 4c dp claret .20 .15
721 A63 5c orange .50 .15
722 A62 10c emerald .50 .15
723 A62 15c cerise .75 .18
724 A63 25c brt bl .75 .20
725 A63 35c olive grn 1.25 .25
726 A62 40c violet 1.75 .30
727 A62 60c olive gray 2.00 .40
728 A62 1cor scarlet 2.50 1.25
729 A62 2cor red vio 4.50 2.50
Nos. 717-729 (13) 15.90 6.03

10th World Series of Amateur Baseball, 1948.
Each denomination was also issued in a souvenir sheet containing four stamps and marginal inscriptions. Value, set of 13 sheets, $100.
See Nos. C296-C308.

Rowland Hill — A64

Designs: 25c, Heinrich von Stephan. 75c, UPU Monument. 80c, Congress medal, obverse. 4cor, as 80c, reverse.

1950, Nov. 23 **Engr.** ***Perf. 13***
Frame in Black
730 A64 20c car lake .15 .15
731 A64 25c yel grn .15 .15
732 A64 75c ultra .48 .18
733 A64 80c green .22 .22
734 A64 4cor blue .90 .80
Nos. 730-734 (5) 1.90 1.50

75th anniv. (in 1949) of the UPU.
Each denomination was also issued in a souvenir sheet containing four stamps and marginal inscriptions. Size: 115x123mm. Value, set of 5 sheets, $30.
See #C309-C315, CO45-CO50. For surcharge see #771.

Queen Isabella I — A65

Ships of Columbus — A66

Designs: 98c, Santa Maria. 1.20cor, Map. 1.76cor, Portrait facing left.

1952, June 25 ***Perf. 11½***
735 A65 10c lil rose .15 .15
736 A66 96c dp ultra .75 .75
737 A65 98c carmine .75 .75
738 A65 1.20cor brown .90 .90
739 A65 1.76cor red vio 1.25 1.25
a. Souv. sheet of 5, #735-739 3.75 3.75
Nos. 735-739 (5) 3.80 3.80

Queen Isabella I of Spain, 500th birth anniv. See Nos. C316-C320.

ODECA Flag — A67

Designs: 5c, Map of Central America. 6c, Arms of ODECA. 15c, Presidents of Five Central American Republics. 50c, ODECA Charter and Flags.

1953, Apr. 15 ***Perf. 13½x14***
740 A67 4c dk bl .15 .15
741 A67 5c emerald .15 .15
742 A67 6c lt brn .15 .15
743 A67 15c lt ol grn .15 .15
744 A67 50c blk brn .15 .15
Set value .55 .35

Founding of the Organization of the Central American States (ODECA).
See #C326-C338. For surcharge see #767.

Pres. Carlos Solorzano — A68

Presidents: 6c, Diego Manuel Chamorro. 8c, Adolfo Diaz. 15c, Gen. Anastasio Somoza. 50c, Gen. Emiliano Chamorro.

Engr. (frames); Photo. (heads)
1953, June 25 ***Perf. 12½***
Heads in Gray Black
745 A68 4c dk car rose .15 .15
746 A68 6c dp ultra .15 .15
747 A68 8c brown .15 .15
748 A68 15c car rose .15 .15
749 A68 50c bl grn .18 .15
Set value .45 .35

See Nos. C326-C338. For surcharges see Nos. 768, 853.

Sculptor and UN Emblem — A69

Capt. Dean L. Ray, USAF — A70

4c, Arms of Nicaragua. 5c, Globe. 15c, Candle & Charter. 1cor, Flags of Nicaragua & UN.

Perf. 13½
1954, Apr. 30 **Engr.** **Unwmk.**
750 A69 3c olive .15 .15
751 A69 4c ol grn .15 .15
752 A69 5c emerald .18 .15
753 A69 15c dp grn .90 .18
754 A69 1cor bl grn .75 .30
Nos. 750-754 (5) 2.13
Set value .70

UN Organization. See Nos. C339-C345.

Engraved; Center Photogravure
1954, Nov. 5 ***Perf. 13***

Designs: 2c, Sabre jet plane. 3c, Plane, type A-20. 4c, B-24 bomber. 5c, Plane, type AT-6. 15c, Gen. Anastasio Somoza. 1cor, Air Force emblem.

Frame in Black
755 A70 1c gray .15 .15
756 A70 2c gray .15 .15
757 A70 3c dk gray grn .15 .15
758 A70 4c orange .15 .15
759 A70 5c emerald .15 .15
760 A70 15c aqua .15 .15
761 A70 1cor purple .20 .15
Set value .55 .40

National Air Force. See Nos. C346-C352.

Rotary Slogans and Wreath — A71

Map of the World and Rotary Emblem — A72

20c, Handclasp, Rotary emblem & globe. 35c, Flags of Nicaragua & Rotary. 90c, Paul P. Harris.

1955, Aug. 30 **Photo.** ***Perf. 11½***
Granite Paper.
762 A71 15c dp org .15 .15
763 A71 20c dk olive grn .15 .15
764 A71 35c red vio .15 .15
765 A72 40c carmine .20 .20
766 A71 90c blk & gray .35 .35
a. Souv. sheet of 5, #762-766 4.25 4.25
Nos. 762-766 (5) 1.00 1.00

50th anniversary of Rotary International.
See Nos. C353-C362. For surcharges see Nos. 770, 772, 876.

Issues of 1947-55 Surcharged in Various Colors

Conmemoración
Exposición Nacional
Febrero 4-16, 1956
₡ 0.15

Perf. 13½x14, 12½, 11½, 13
Engraved, Photogravure
1956, Feb. 4 **Unwmk.**
767 A67 5c on 6c lt brn .15 .15
768 A68 5c on 6c ultra & gray blk (Ult) .15 .15
769 A61 5c on 8c blk & org brn .15 .15
770 A71 15c on 35c red vio (G) .15 .15
771 A64 15c on 80c blk & grn .15 .15
772 A71 15c on 90c blk & gray (Bl) .15 .15
Set value .62 .48

Spacing of surcharge varies to fit shape of stamps.
Issued to commemorate the National Exhibition, Feb. 4-16, 1956. See Nos. C363-C366.

Gen. Máximo Jerez — A73

Battle of San Jacinto — A74

10c, Gen. Fernando Chamorro. 25c, Burning of Granada. 50c, Gen. José Dolores Estrada.

Perf. 12½x12, 12, 12½
1956, Sept. 14 **Engr.**
773 A73 5c brown .15 .15
774 A73 10c dk car rose .15 .15
775 A74 15c bl gray .15 .15
776 A74 25c brt red .25 .18
777 A73 50c brt red vio .30 .20
Set value .84 .58

National War, cent. See Nos. C367-C371.

Boy Scout — A75

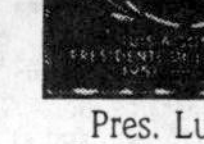
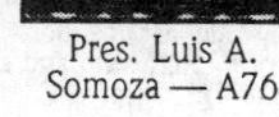

Pres. Luis A. Somoza — A76

Designs: 15c, Cub Scout. 20c, Boy Scout. 25c, Lord Baden-Powell. 50c, Joseph A. Harrison.

Perf. 13½x14

1957, Apr. 9 Photo. Unwmk.

778 A75 10c vio & ol .15 .15
779 A75 15c dp plum & gray blk .15 .15
780 A75 20c ultra & brn .15 .15
781 A75 25c dl red brn & dp bluish grn .15 .15
782 A75 50c red & ol .20 .16
a. Souv. sheet of 5, #778-782 2.50 2.50
Set value .65 .45

Centenary of the birth of Lord Baden-Powell, founder of the Boy Scouts.
See #C377-C386. For surcharge see #C754.

1957, July 2 *Perf. 14x13½*

Portrait in Dark Brown

783 A76 10c brt red .15 .15
784 A76 15c dp bl .15 .15
785 A76 35c rose vio .22 .15
786 A76 50c brown .30 .18
787 A76 75c gray grn .65 .55
Nos. 783-787 (5) 1.47
Set value 1.00

President Luis A. Somoza. See #C387-C391.

Managua Cathedral A77

Bishop Pereira y Castellon — A78

Designs: 15c, Archbishop Lezcano y Ortega. 20c, Leon Cathedral. 50c, De la Merced Church, Granada. 1cor, Father Mariano Dubon.

Perf. 13½x14, 14x13½

1957, July 12

Centers in Olive Gray

788 A77 5c dl grn .15 .15
789 A78 10c dk pur .15 .15
790 A78 15c dk bl .15 .15
791 A77 20c dk brn .15 .15
792 A77 50c dk sl grn .16 .15
793 A78 1cor dk vio .30 .28
Set value .70 .60

Issued in honor of the Catholic Church in Nicaragua. See Nos. C392-C397.

M. S. Honduras A79

5c, Gen. Anastasio Somoza & freighter. 6c, M. S. Guatemala. 10c, M. S. Salvador. 15c, Ship between globes. 50c, Globes & ship.

1957, Oct. 15 Litho. *Perf. 14*

794 A79 4c grn, bl & blk .15 .15
795 A79 5c multi .15 .15
796 A79 6c red, bl & blk .15 .15
797 A79 10c brn, bl grn & blk .15 .15
798 A79 15c dk car, ultra & ol brn .24 .15
799 A79 50c vio, bl & mar .40 .26
Set value 1.00 .65

Issued to honor Nicaragua's Merchant Marine. See Nos. C398-C403. For surcharge see No. C691.

Melvin Jones and Lions Emblem A80

Designs: 5c, Arms of Central American Republics. 20c, Dr. Teodoro A. Arias. 50c, Edward G. Barry. 75c, Motto and emblem. 1.50 cor, Map of Central America.

1958, May 8 Unwmk. *Perf. 14*

Emblem in Yellow, Red and Blue

800 A80 5c bl & multi .15 .15
801 A80 10c bl & org .15 .15
802 A80 20c bl & olive .15 .15
803 A80 50c bl & lilac .25 .20
804 A80 75c bl & pink .35 .25
805 A80 1.50cor bl, gray ol & sal .60 .45
a. Souv. sheet of 6, #800-805 2.50 2.50
Nos. 800-805 (6) 1.65
Set value 1.10

17th convention of Lions Intl. of Central America, May, 1958.
See #C410-C415. For surcharge see #C686.

St. Jean Baptiste De La Salle — A81

UN Emblem and Globe — A82

Christian Brothers: 5c, Arms of La Salle. 10c, School, Managua, horiz. 20c, Bro. Carlos. 50c, Bro. Antonio. 75c, Bro. Julio. 1cor, Bro. Argeo.

1958, July 13 Photo. *Perf. 14*

806 A81 5c car, bl & yel .15 .15
807 A81 10c emer, blk & ultra .15 .15
808 A81 15c red brn, bis & blk .15 .15
809 A81 20c car, bis & blk .15 .15
810 A81 50c org, bis & brn blk .16 .15
811 A81 75c bl, lt grn & dk brn .24 .20
812 A81 1cor vio, bis & grnsh blk .32 .32
Set value .95 .85

See Nos. C416-C423. For surcharges see Nos. C539A, C755-C756.

1958, Dec. 15 Litho. *Perf. 11½*

15c, UNESCO building. 25c, 45c, "UNESCO." 40c, UNESCO building and Eiffel tower.

813 A82 10c brt pink & bl .15 .15
814 A82 15c bl & brt pink .15 .15
815 A82 25c grn & brn .15 .15
816 A82 40c red org & blk .15 .15
817 A82 45c dk bl & rose lil .15 .15
818 A82 50c brn & grn .15 .15
a. Min. sheet of 6, #813-818 .45 .45
Set value .45 .35

Opening of UNESCO Headquarters in Paris, Nov. 3. See Nos. C424-C429.

Pope John XXIII and Cardinal Spellman — A83

Abraham Lincoln — A84

Designs: 10c, Spellman coat of arms. 15c, Cardinal Spellman. 20c, Human rosary and Cardinal, horiz. 25c, Cardinal with Ruben Dario order.

1959, Nov. 26 Unwmk. *Perf. 12½*

819 A83 5c grnsh bl & brn .15 .15
820 A83 10c yel, bl & car .15 .15
821 A83 15c dk grn, blk & dk car .15 .15
822 A83 20c yel, dk bl & grn .15 .15
823 A83 25c ultra, vio & mag .15 .15
a. Min. sheet of 5, #819-823, perf. or imperf. .35 .35
Set value .30 .25

Cardinal Spellman's visit to Managua, Feb. 1958. See Nos. C430-C436. For surcharges see Nos. C638, C747, C752.

1960, Jan. Engr. *Perf. 13x13½*

Center in Black

824 A84 5c dp car .15 .15
825 A84 10c green .15 .15
826 A84 15c dp org .15 .15
827 A84 1cor plum .20 .15
828 A84 2cor ultra .35 .30
a. Souv. sheet of 5, #824-828, imperf. .90 .90
Set value .70 .60

150th anniversary of the birth of Abraham Lincoln. See Nos. C437-C442. For surcharges see Nos. C637, C680, C753.

Nos. 824-828 Overprinted in Red — ✠ Resello

1960, Sept. 19

Center in Black

829 A84 5c dp car .15 .15
830 A84 10c green .15 .15
831 A84 15c dp org .15 .15
832 A84 1cor plum .22 .20
833 A84 2cor ultra .50 .42
Set value .85 .75

Issued for the Red Cross to aid earthquake victims in Chile. For overprints and surcharges see Nos. C446-C451, C500, C539.

Gen. Tomas Martinez and Pres. Luis A. Somoza — A85

Arms of Nueva Segovia — A86

5c, Official decrees. 10c, Two envelopes.

Perf. 13½

1961, Aug. 29 Unwmk. Litho.

834 A85 5c grnsh bl & lt brn .15 .15
835 A85 10c grn & lt brn .15 .15
836 A85 15c pink & brn .15 .15
Set value .17 .15

Cent. (in 1960) of the postal rates regulation.

1962, Nov. 22 *Perf. 12½x13*

Coats of Arms: 3c, León. 4c, Managua. 5c, Granada. 6c, Rivas.

Arms in Original Colors; Black Inscriptions

837 A86 2c pink .15 .15
838 A86 3c lt bl .15 .15
839 A86 4c pale lil .15 .15
840 A86 5c yellow .15 .15
841 A86 6c buff .15 .15
Set value .25 .25

See #C510-C514. For surcharge see #854.

No. RA73 Overprinted in Red: "CORREOS"

1964 Photo. *Perf. 11½*

842 PT13 5c gray, red & org .15 .15
a. Inverted overprint

Nos. RA66-RA75 Overprinted

1965 Photo. *Perf. 11½*

Orchids in Natural Colors

843 PT13 5c pale lil & grn .30
844 PT13 5c yel & grn .30
845 PT13 5c pink & grn .30
846 PT13 5c pale vio & grn .30
847 PT13 5c lt grnsh bl & red .30
848 PT13 5c buff & lil .30
849 PT13 5c yel grn & brn .30
850 PT13 5c gray & red .30
851 PT13 5c lt bl & dk bl .30
852 PT13 5c lt grn & brn .30
Nos. 843-852 (10) 3.00

7th Central American Scout Camporee at El Coyotete. This overprint was also applied to each stamp on souvenir sheet No. C386a.
Use of Nos. 843-852 for postage was authorized by official decree.

Nos. 746 and 841 Surcharged with New Value and "RESELLO"

1968, May Engr. *Perf. 12½*

853 A68 5c on 6c dp ultra & gray blk .50 .50

Litho. *Perf. 12½x13*

854 A86 5c on 6c multi .50 .50

Nos. RA66-RA67, RA69 and RA71 Overprinted — CORREO

1969 Photo. *Perf. 11½*

Orchids in Natural Colors

855 PT13 5c pale lil & grn .50 .50
856 PT13 5c yel & grn .50 .50
857 PT13 5c pale vio & grn .50 .50
858 PT13 5c buff & lil .50 .50
Nos. 855-858 (4) 2.00 2.00

Nos. RA66-RA75 Overprinted — O. I. T. 1919 - 1969

1969 Photo. *Perf. 11½*

Orchids in Natural Colors

859 PT13 5c pale lil & grn .20 .20
860 PT13 5c yel & grn .20 .20
861 PT13 5c pink & grn .20 .20
862 PT13 5c pale vio & grn .20 .20
863 PT13 5c lt grnsh bl & red .20 .20
864 PT13 5c buff & lil .20 .20
865 PT13 5c yel grn & brn .20 .20
866 PT13 5c gray & red .20 .20
867 PT13 5c lt & dk bl .20 .20
868 PT13 5c lt grn & brn .20 .20
Nos. 859-868 (10) 2.00 2.00

International Labor Organization, 50th anniv.

Pelé, Brazil — A87

Soccer Players: 10c, Ferenc Puskás, Hungary. 15c, Sir Stanley Matthews, England. 40c, Alfredo di Stefano, Argentina. 2cor, Giacinto Facchetti, Italy. 3cor, Lev Yashin, USSR. 5cor, Franz Beckenbauer, West Germany.

1970, May 11 Litho. *Perf. 13½*

869 A87 5c multi .15 .15
870 A87 10c multi .15 .15
871 A87 15c multi .15 .15
872 A87 40c multi .25 .18
873 A87 2cor multi .90 .75
874 A87 3cor multi 1.25 .90
875 A87 5cor multi 1.25 1.25
Nos. 869-875,C712-C716 (12) 7.40 6.23

Issued to honor the winners of the 1970 poll for the International Soccer Hall of Fame. Names of players and their achievements printed in black on back of stamps.
For surcharges and overprint see Nos. 899-900, C786-C788.

No. 766 Surcharged with New Value and Overprinted "RESELLO" and Bar Through Old Denomination

1971, Mar. Photo. *Perf. 11*

876 A71 30c on 90c blk & gray

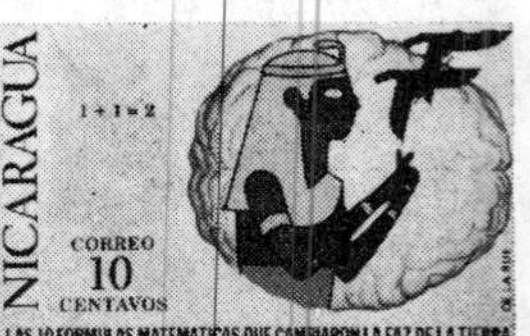

Egyptian Using Fingers to Count — A88

Symbolic Designs of Scientific Formulas: 15c, Newton's law (gravity). 20c, Einstein's theory (relativity). 1cor, Tsiolkovski's law (speed of rockets). 2cor, Maxwell's law (electromagnetism).

1971, May 15 Litho. *Perf. 13½*

877 A88 10c lt bl & multi .15 .15
878 A88 15c lt bl & multi .15 .15
879 A88 20c lt bl & multi .20 .20

880 A88	1cor lt bl & multi	.65	.60
881 A88	2cor lt bl & multi	1.50	1.25
	Nos. 877-881,C761-C765 (10)	4.83	3.96

Mathematical equations which changed the world. On the back of each stamp is a descriptive paragraph.

Symbols of Civilization, Peace Emblem with Globe — A89

1971, Sept. 6 Litho. *Perf. 14*

882 A89	10c blk & bl	.15	.15
883 A89	15c vio bl, bl & blk	.15	.15
884 A89	20c brn bl & blk	.20	.20
885 A89	40c emer, bl & blk	.30	.30
886 A89	50c mag, bl & blk	.40	.40
887 A89	80c org, bl & blk	.60	.60
888 A89	1cor ol, bl & blk	.75	.75
889 A89	2cor vio, bl & blk	1.50	1.50
	Nos. 882-889 (8)	4.05	4.05

"Is there a formula for peace?" issue.

Moses with Tablets of the Law, by Rembrandt A90

The Ten Commandments (Paintings): 15c, Moses and the Burning Bush, by Botticelli (I). 20c, Jephthah's Daughter, by Degas, (II), horiz. 30c, St. Vincent Ferrer Preaching in Verona, by Domenico Morone (III). 35c, The Nakedness of Noah, by Michelangelo (IV), horiz. 40c, Cain and Abel, by Francesco Trevisani (V), horiz. 50c, Potiphar's wife, by Rembrandt (VI). 60c, Isaac Blessing Jacob, by Gerbrand van den Eeckhout (VII), horiz. 75c, Susanna and the Elders, by Rubens (VIII), horiz.

1971, Nov. 1 *Perf. 11*

890 A90	10c ocher & multi	.15	.15
891 A90	15c ocher & multi	.15	.15
892 A90	20c ocher & multi	.15	.15
893 A90	30c ocher & multi	.18	.18
894 A90	35c ocher & multi	.24	.24
895 A90	40c ocher & multi	.24	.24
896 A90	50c ocher & multi	.35	.35
897 A90	60c ocher & multi	.48	.48
898 A90	75c ocher & multi	.75	.75
	Nos. 890-898,C776-C777 (11)	5.09	3.94

Descriptive inscriptions printed in gray on back of stamps.

Nos. 873-874 Surcharged

OLIMPIADAS MUNICH 1972

1972, Mar. 20 Litho. *Perf. 13½*

899 A87	40c on 2cor multi	.15	.15
900 A87	50c on 3cor multi	.20	.15
	Nos. 899-900,C786-C788 (5)	1.75	1.60

20th Olympic Games, Munich, Aug. 26-Sept. 10.

Nos. RA66-RA69, RA71-RA74 Overprinted in Blue **CORREO**

1972, July 29 Photo. *Perf. 11½*
Granite Paper

901 PT13	5c (#RA66)	.25	.25
902 PT13	5c (#RA67)	.25	.25
903 PT13	5c (#RA68)	.25	.25
904 PT13	5c (#RA69)	.25	.25
905 PT13	5c (#RA71)	.25	.25
906 PT13	5c (#RA72)	.25	.25
907 PT13	5c (#RA73)	.25	.25
908 PT13	5c (#RA74)	.25	.25
	Nos. 901-908 (8)	2.00	2.00

Gown by Givenchy, Paris — A91

1973, July 26 Litho. *Perf. 13½*

909 A91	1cor shown	.30	.24
910 A91	2cor Hartnell, London	.55	.52
911 A91	5cor Balmain, Paris	1.40	1.20
	Set value, #909-911, C839-C844	2.75	2.35

Gowns by famous designers, modeled by Nicaraguan women. Inscriptions on back printed on top of gum give description of gown in Spanish and English.

Nos. 909-911 in perf. 11, see No. C844a.

Christmas A92

Designs: 2c, 5c, Virginia O'Hanlon writing letter, father. 3c, 15c, letter. 4c, 20c, Virginia, father reading letter.

1973, Nov. 15 Litho. *Perf. 15*

912 A92	2c multicolored	.15	
913 A92	3c multicolored	.15	
914 A92	4c multicolored	.15	
915 A92	5c multicolored	.15	
916 A92	15c multicolored	.15	
917 A92	20c multicolored	.15	
	Set value, #912-917, C846-C848	2.30	

Sir Winston Churchill (1874-1965) A93

Designs: 2c, Churchill speaking. 3c, Military planning. 4c, Cigar, lamp. 5c, Churchill with Roosevert and Stalin. 10c, Churchill walking ashore from landing craft.

1974, Apr. 30 *Perf. 14½*

918 A93	2c multicolored	.15	
919 A93	3c multicolored	.15	
920 A93	4c multicolored	.15	
921 A93	5c multicolored	.15	
922 A93	10c multicolored	.15	
	Set value, #918-922, C849-C850	3.25	

World Cup Soccer Championships, Munich — A94

Scenes from previous World Cup Championships with flags and scores of finalists.

1974, May 8 *Perf. 14½*

923 A94	1c 1930	.15	
924 A94	2c 1934	.15	
925 A94	3c 1938	.15	
926 A94	4c 1950	.15	
927 A94	5c 1954	.15	
928 A94	10c 1958	.15	
929 A94	15c 1962	.15	
930 A94	20c 1966	.15	
931 A94	25c 1970	.15	
	Set value, #923-931, C853	3.25	

For overprint see No. C856.

A95

A96

Wild Flowers and Cacti: 2c, Hollyhocks. 3c, Paguira insignis. 4c, Morning glory. 5c, Pereschia autumnalis. 10c, Cultivated morning glory. 15c, Hibiscus. 20c, Pagoda tree blossoms.

1974, June 11 Litho. *Perf. 14*

932 A95	2c grn & multi	.15	.15
933 A95	3c grn & multi	.15	.15
934 A95	4c grn & multi	.15	.15
935 A95	5c grn & multi	.15	.15
936 A95	10c grn & multi	.15	.15
937 A95	15c grn & multi	.15	.15
938 A95	20c grn & multi	.15	.15
	Set value, #932-938, C854-C855	1.25	1.10

1974, July 10 *Perf. 14½*

Nicaraguan stamps,

939 A96	2c No. 670	.15	
940 A96	3c No. 669	.15	
941 A96	4c No. C110, horiz.	.15	
942 A96	5c No. 667	.15	
943 A96	10c No. 666	.15	
944 A96	20c No. 665	.15	
	Set value, #934-944, C855A-C855C	2.75	

UPU, Cent.

Four-toed Anteater A97

Designs: 2c, Puma. 3c, Raccoon. 4c, Ocelot. 5c, Kinkajou. 10c, Coypu. 15c, Peccary. 20c, Tapir.

1974, Sept. 10 Litho. *Perf. 14½*

946 A97	1c multi	.15	.15
947 A97	2c multi	.15	.15
948 A97	3c multi	.15	.15
949 A97	4c multi	.15	.15
950 A97	5c multi	.15	.15
951 A97	10c multi	.15	.15
952 A97	15c multi	.15	.15
953 A97	20c multi	.15	.15
	Set value, #946-953, C857-C858	2.10	1.85

Wild animals from San Diego and London Zoos.

Prophet Zacharias, by Michelangelo — A98

Works of Michelangelo: 2c, The Last Judgment. 3c, The Creation of Adam, horiz. 4c, Sistine Chapel. 5c, Moses. 10c, Mouscron Madonna. 15c, David. 20c, Doni Madonna.

1974, Dec. 15

954 A98	1c dp rose & multi	.15	.15
955 A98	2c yel & multi	.15	.15
956 A98	3c sal & multi	.15	.15
957 A98	4c bl & multi	.15	.15
958 A98	5c tan & multi	.15	.15
959 A98	10c multi	.15	.15
960 A98	15c multi	.15	.15
961 A98	20c bl & multi	.15	.15
	Set value, #954-961, C859-C862	1.50	1.40

Christmas 1974 and 500th birth anniversary of Michelangelo Buonarroti (1475-1564), Italian painter, sculptor and architect.

Giovanni Martinelli, Othello — A99

Opera Singers and Scores: 2c, Tito Gobbi, Simone Boccanegra. 3c, Lotte Lehmann, Der Rosenkavalier. 4c, Lauritz Melchior, Parsifal. 5c, Nellie Melba, La Traviata. 15c, Jussi Bjoerling, La Bohème. 20c, Birgit Nilsson, Turandot.

1975, Jan. 22 *Perf. 14x13½*

962 A99	1c rose lil & multi	.15	.15
963 A99	2c brt bl & multi	.15	.15
964 A99	3c yel & multi	.15	.15
965 A99	4c dl bl & multi	.15	.15
966 A99	5c org & multi	.15	.15
967 A99	15c lake & multi	.15	.15
968 A99	20c gray & multi	.15	.15
	Set value, #962-968, C863-C870	3.00	1.60

Famous opera singers.

Jesus Condemned A100

The Spirit of 76, by Archibald M. Willard A101

Stations of the Cross: 2c, Jesus Carries the Cross. 3c, Jesus falls the first time. 4c, Jesus meets his mother. 5c, Simon of Cyrene carries the Cross. 15c, St. Veronica wipes Jesus' face. 20c, Jesus falls the second time. 25c, Jesus meets the women of Jerusalem. 35c, Jesus falls the third time. Designs from Leon Cathedral.

1975, Mar. 20 *Perf. 14½*

969 A100	1c ultra & multi	.15	.15
970 A100	2c ultra & multi	.15	.15
971 A100	3c ultra & multi	.15	.15
972 A100	4c ultra & multi	.15	.15
973 A100	5c ultra & multi	.15	.15
974 A100	15c ultra & multi	.15	.15
975 A100	20c ultra & multi	.15	.15
976 A100	25c ultra & multi	.15	.15
977 A100	35c ultra & multi	.15	.15
	Set value, #969-977, C871-C875	1.80	1.60

Easter 1975.

1975, Apr. 16 *Perf. 14*

Designs: 2c, Pitt Addressing Parliament, by K. A. Hickel. 3c, The Midnight Ride of Paul Revere, horiz. 4c, Statue of George III Demolished, by W. Walcutt, horiz. 5c, Boston Massacre. 10c, Colonial coin and seal, horiz. 15c, Boston Tea Party, horiz. 20c, Thomas Jefferson, by Rembrandt Peale. 25c, Benjamin Franklin, by Charles Willson Peale. 30c, Signing Declaration of Independence, by John Trumbull, horiz. 35c, Surrender of Cornwallis, by Trumbull, horiz.

978 A101	1c tan & multi	.15	.15
979 A101	2c tan & multi	.15	.15
980 A101	3c tan & multi	.15	.15
981 A101	4c tan & multi	.15	.15
982 A101	5c tan & multi	.15	.15
983 A101	10c tan & multi	.15	.15
984 A101	15c tan & multi	.15	.15
985 A101	20c tan & multi	.15	.15
986 A101	25c tan & multi	.15	.15
987 A101	30c tan & multi	.16	.15

988 A101 35c tan & multi .20 .18
Set value, #978-988, C876-C879 4.20 3.80

American Bicentennial.

Scouts Saluting Flag, Scout Emblems A102

2c, Two-men canoe. 3c, Scouts of various races shaking hands. 4c, Scout cooking. 5c, Entrance to Camp Nicaragua. 20c, Group discussion.

1975, Aug. 15 *Perf. 14½*

989 A102 1c multi .15 .15
990 A102 2c multi .15 .15
991 A102 3c multi .15 .15
992 A102 4c multi .15 .15
993 A102 5c multi .15 .15
994 A102 20c multi .15 .15
Set value, #989-994, C880-C883 1.90 1.70

Nordjamb 75, 14th World Boy Scout Jamboree, Lillehammer, Norway, July 29-Aug. 7.

Pres. Somoza, Map and Arms of Nicaragua — A103

1975, Sept. 10 *Perf. 14*

995 A103 20c multi .15 .15
996 A103 40c org & multi .15 .15
Nos. 995-996,C884-C886 (5) 6.50 5.28

Reelection of Pres. Anastasio Somoza D.

King's College Choir, Cambridge — A104

Famous Choirs: 2c, Einsiedeln Abbey. 3c, Regensburg. 4c, Vienna Choir Boys. 5c, Sistine Chapel. 15c, Westminster Cathedral. 20c, Mormon Tabernacle.

1975, Nov. 15 *Perf. 14½*

997 A104 1c silver & multi .15 .15
998 A104 2c silver & multi .15 .15
999 A104 3c silver & multi .15 .15
1000 A104 4c silver & multi .15 .15
1001 A104 5c silver & multi .15 .15
1002 A104 15c silver & multi .15 .15
1003 A104 20c silver & multi .15 .15
Set value, #997-1003, C887-C890 1.90 1.70

Christmas 1975.

The Chess Players, by Ludovico Carracci A105

History of Chess: 2c, Arabs Playing Chess, by Delacroix. 3c, Cardinals Playing Chess, by Victor Marais-Milton. 4c, Albrecht V of Bavaria and Anne of Austria Playing Chess, by Hans Muelich, vert. 5c, Chess Players, Persian manuscript, 14th century. 10c, Origin of Chess, Indian miniature, 17th century. 15c, Napoleon Playing Chess at Schönbrunn, by Antoni Uniechowski, vert. 20c, The Chess Game, by J. E. Hummel.

1976, Jan. 8 *Perf. 14½*

1004 A105 1c brn & multi .15 .15
1005 A105 2c lt vio & multi .15 .15
1006 A105 3c ocher & multi .15 .15
1007 A105 4c multi .15 .15
1008 A105 5c multi .15 .15
1009 A105 10c multi .15 .15
1010 A105 15c blue & multi .15 .15
1011 A105 20c ocher & multi .15 .15
Set value, #1004-1011, C891-C893 2.90 2.30

Olympic Rings, Danish Crew — A107

Winners, Rowing and Sculling Events: 2c, East Germany, 1972. 3c, Italy, 1968. 4c, Great Britain, 1936. 5c, France, 1952. 35c, US, 1920, vert.

1976, Sept. 7 **Litho.** *Perf. 14*

1022 A107 1c blue & multi .15 .15
1023 A107 2c blue & multi .15 .15
1024 A107 3c blue & multi .15 .15
1025 A107 4c blue & multi .15 .15
1026 A107 5c blue & multi .15 .15
1027 A107 35c blue & multi .15 .15
Nos. 1022-1027,C902-C905 (10) 5.98 5.13

The Smoke Signal, by Frederic Remington — A108

#1029, Space Signal Monitoring Center. #1030, Candlelight. #1031, Edison's laboratory & light bulb. #1032, Agriculture, 1776. #1033, Agriculture, 1976. #1034, Harvard College, 1726. #1035, Harvard University, 1976. #1036, Horse-drawn carriage. #1037, Boeing 747.

1976, May 25 **Litho.** *Perf. 13½*

1028 A108 1c gray & multi .15 .15
1029 A108 1c gray & multi .15 .15
a. Pair, #1028-1029 .15 .15
1030 A108 2c gray & multi .15 .15
1031 A108 2c gray & multi .15 .15
a. Pair, #1030-1031 .15 .15
1032 A108 3c gray & multi .15 .15
1033 A108 3c gray & multi .15 .15
a. Pair, #1032-1033 .15 .15
1034 A108 4c gray & multi .15 .15
1035 A108 4c gray & multi .15 .15
a. Pair, #1034-1035 .15 .15
1036 A108 5c gray & multi .15 .15
1037 A108 5c gray & multi .15 .15
a. Pair, #1036-1037 .15 .15
Set value, #1028-1037, C907-C912 3.30 2.35

American Bicentennial, 200 years of progress.

Mauritius No. 2 — A109

Rare Stamps: 2c, Western Australia #3a. 3c, Mauritius #1. 4c, Jamaica #83a. 5c, US #C3a. 10c, Basel #3L1. 25c, Canada #387a.

1976, Dec. *Perf. 14*

1038 A109 1c multi .15 .15
1039 A109 2c multi .15 .15
1040 A109 3c multi .15 .15
1041 A109 4c multi .15 .15
1042 A109 5c multi .15 .15
1043 A109 10c multi .15 .15
1044 A109 25c multi .15 .15
Set value. #1038-1044, C913-C917 2.85 2.60

Back inscriptions printed on top of gum describe illustrated stamp.

Zeppelin in Flight A110

1c, Zeppelin in hangar. 3c, Giffard's dirigible airship, 1852. 4c, Zeppelin on raising stilts coming out of hangar. 5c, Zeppelin ready for take-off.

1977, Oct. 31 **Litho.** *Perf. 14½*

1045 A110 1c multi .15 .15
1046 A110 2c multi .15 .15
1047 A110 3c multi .15 .15
1048 A110 4c multi .15 .15
1049 A110 5c multi .15 .15
Nos. 1045-1049,C921-C924 (9) 4.23
Set value 2.75

75th anniversary of Zeppelin.

Lindbergh, Map of Nicaragua A111

2c, Spirit of St. Louis, map of Nicaragua. 3c, Lindbergh, vert. 4c, Spirit of St. Louis & NYC-Paris route. 5c, Lindbergh & Spirit of St. Louis. 20c, Lindbergh, NYC-Paris route & plane.

1977, Nov. 30

1050 A111 1c multi .15 .15
1051 A111 2c multi .15 .15
1052 A111 3c multi .15 .15
1053 A111 4c multi .15 .15
1054 A111 5c multi .15 .15
1055 A111 20c multi .15 .15
Nos. 1050-1055,C926-C929 (10) 3.61
Set value 2.40

Charles A. Lindbergh's solo transatlantic flight from New York to Paris, 50th anniversary.

Clara and Snowflakes — A112

Nutcracker Suite: 1c, Christmas party. 2c, Dancing dolls. 4c, Snowflake and prince. 5c, Snowflake dance. 15c, Sugarplum fairy and prince. 40c, Waltz of the flowers. 90c, Chinese tea dance. 1cor, Bonbonnière. 10cor, Arabian coffee dance.

1977, Dec. 12

1056 A112 1c multi .15 .15
1057 A112 2c multi .15 .15
1058 A112 3c multi .15 .15
1059 A112 4c multi .15 .15
1060 A112 5c multi .15 .15
1061 A112 15c multi .15 .15
1062 A112 40c multi .15 .15
1063 A112 90c multi .20 .20
1064 A112 1cor multi .28 .20
1065 A112 10cor multi 2.25 2.00
Set value 3.00 2.70

Christmas 1977. See No. C931.

Mr. and Mrs. Andrews, by Gainsborough — A113

Paintings: 2c, Giovanna Bacelli, by Gainsborough. 3c, Blue Boy by Gainsborough. 4c, Francis I, by Titian. 5c, Charles V in Battle of Muhlberg, by Titian. 25c, Sacred Love, by Titian.

1978, Jan. 11 **Litho.** *Perf. 14½*

1066 A113 1c multi .15 .15
1067 A113 2c multi .15 .15
1068 A113 3c multi .15 .15
1069 A113 4c multi .15 .15
1070 A113 5c multi .15 .15
1071 A113 25c multi .15 .15
Set value, #1066-1071, C932-C933 3.25 2.75

Thomas Gainsborough (1727-1788), 250th birth anniv.; Titian (1477-1576), 500th birth anniv.

Gothic Portal, Lower Church, Assisi — A114

Designs: 2c, St. Francis preaching to the birds. 3c, St. Francis, painting. 4c, St. Francis and Franciscan saints, 15th century tapestry. 5c, Portiuncola, cell of St. Francis, now in church of St. Mary of the Angels, Assisi. 15c, Blessing of St. Francis for Brother Leo (parchment). 25c, Stained-glass window, Upper Church of St. Francis, Assisi.

1978, Feb. 23 **Litho.** *Perf. 14½*

1072 A114 1c red & multi .15 .15
1073 A114 2c brt grn & multi .15 .15
1074 A114 3c bl grn & multi .15 .15
1075 A114 4c ultra & multi .15 .15
1076 A114 5c rose & multi .15 .15
1077 A114 15c yel & multi .15 .15
1078 A114 25c ocher & multi .15 .15
Set value, #1072-1078, C935-C936 2.35 2.15

St. Francis of Assisi (1182-1266), 750th anniversary of his canonization, and in honor of Our Lady of the Immaculate Conception, patron saint of Nicaragua.

Passenger and Freight Locomotives — A115

Locomotives: 2c, Lightweight freight. 3c, American. 4c, Heavy freight Baldwin. 5c, Light freight and passenger Baldwin. 15c, Presidential coach.

1978, Apr. 7 **Litho.** *Perf. 14½*

1079 A115 1c lil & multi .15 .15
1080 A115 2c rose lil & multi .15 .15
1081 A115 3c bl & multi .15 .15
1082 A115 4c ol & multi .15 .15
1083 A115 5c yel & multi .15 .15
1084 A115 15c dp org & multi .15 .15
Set value, #1079-1084, C938-C940 3.60 3.35

Centenary of Nicaraguan railroads.

Michael Strogoff, by Jules Verne — A116

Jules Verne Books: 2c, The Mysterious Island. 3c, Journey to the Center of the Earth (battle of the sea monsters). 4c, Five Weeks in a Balloon.

1978, Aug. **Litho.** *Perf. 14½*

1085 A116 1c multi .15 .15
1086 A116 2c multi .15 .15
1087 A116 3c multi .15 .15
1088 A116 4c multi .15 .15
Nos. 1085-1088,C942-C943 (6) 2.55
Set value 1.90

Jules Verne (1828-1905), science fiction writer.

Montgolfier Balloon — A117

1c, Icarus. 3c, Wright Brothers' Flyer A. 4c, Orville Wright at control of Flyer, 1908.

Perf. 14½, horiz.

1978, Sept. 29 **Litho.**

1089 A117 1c multi, horiz. .15 .15
1090 A117 2c multi .15 .15
1091 A117 3c multi, horiz. .15 .15
1092 A117 4c multi .15 .15
Set value, #1089-1092, C945-C946 1.70 1.30

History of aviation & 75th anniv. of 1st powered flight.

Ernst Ocwirk and Alfredo Di Stefano — A118

St. Peter, by Goya — A119

Soccer Players: 25c, Ralf Edstroem and Oswaldo Piazza.

1978, Oct. 25 **Litho.** ***Perf. 13½x14***

1093 A118 20c multicolored .15 .15
1094 A118 25c multicolored .15 .15
Nos. 1093-1094,C948-C949 (4) 1.45
Set value 1.05

11th World Soccer Cup Championship, Argentina, June 1-25. See No. C950.

1978, Dec. 12 **Litho.** ***Perf. 13½x14***

Paintings: 15c, St. Gregory, by Goya.

1095 A119 10c multi .15 .15
1096 A119 15c multi .15 .15
Nos. 1095-1096,C951-C952 (4) 2.12 1.65

Christmas 1978. See No. C953.

San Cristobal Volcano and Map — A120

Designs: No. 1098, Lake Cosiguina. No. 1099, Telica Volcano. No. 1100, Lake Jiloa.

1978, Dec. 29 ***Perf. 14x13½***

1097 A120 5c multi .15 .15
1098 A120 5c multi .15 .15
a. Pair, #1097-1098 .25 .25
1099 A120 20c multi .15 .15
1100 A120 20c multi .15 .15
a. Pair, #1099-1100 .25 .25
Nos. 1097-1100,C954-C961 (12) 5.42
Set value 3.35

Volcanos, lakes and their locations.

1980 Overprints

The editors are still gathering data on the 1980 overprints for the listing of these issues.

Souvenir Sheet

Quetzal — A121

1981, May 18 **Litho.** ***Perf. 13***

1101 A121 10cor multi 1.75 1.25

WIPA 1981 Phil. Exhib., Vienna, May 22-31.

1982 World Cup A122

Designs: Various soccer players and stadiums.

1981, June 25 ***Perf. 12x12½***

1102 A122 5c multi .15 .15
1103 A122 20c multi .15 .15
1104 A122 25c multi .15 .15
1105 A122 30c multi .15 .15
1106 A122 50c multi .15 .15
1107 A122 4cor multi .45 .26
1108 A122 5cor multi .52 .32
1109 A122 10cor multi 1.10 .65
Set value 2.30 1.30

Souvenir Sheet

Perf. 13

1110 A122 10cor multi 1.40 1.00

2nd Anniv. of Revolution — A123

1981, July 19 ***Perf. 12½x12***

1111 A123 50c Adult education .15 .15
Nos. 1111,C973-C975 (4) 1.67 1.02

20th Anniv. of the FSLN A124

1981, July 23

1112 A124 50c Armed citizen .15 .15

See No. C976.

Postal Union of Spain and the Americas, 12th Congress, Managua — A125

1981, Aug. 10

1113 A125 50c Mailman .15 .15
Nos. 1113,C977-C979 (4) 1.27

Aquatic Flowers (Nymphaea...) A126

1981, Sept. 15 ***Perf. 12½***

1114 A126 50c Capensis .15 .15
1115 A126 1cor Daubenyana .15 .15
1116 A126 1.20cor Marliacea .22 .15
1117 A126 1.80cor GT Moore .35 .15
1118 A126 2cor Lotus .35 .15
1119 A126 2.50cor BG Berry .50 .28
Nos. 1114-1119,C981 (7) 3.12 1.93

Tropical Fish A127

1981, Oct. 19

1120 A127 50c Cheirodon axelrodi .15 .15
1121 A127 1cor Poecilia reticulata .18 .15
1122 A127 1.85cor Anostomus anostomus .35 .18
1123 A127 2.10cor Corydoras arcuatus .42 .20
1124 A127 2.50cor Cynolebias nigripinnis .48 .28
Nos. 1120-1124,C983-C984 (7) 2.61 1.54

Dryocopus Lineatus — A128

1981, Nov. 30 ***Perf. 12½***

1125 A128 50c shown .15 .15
1126 A128 1.20cor Ramphastos sulfuratus, horiz. .26 .15
1127 A128 1.80cor Aratinga finschi, horiz. .40 .22
1128 A128 2cor Ara macao .40 .26
Nos. 1125-1128,C986-C988 (7) 3.29 1.97

Space Communications A129

Designs: Various communications satellites.

1981, Dec. 15 ***Perf. 13x12½***

1129 A129 50c multi .15 .15
1130 A129 1cor multi .15 .15
1131 A129 1.50cor multi .25 .15
1132 A129 2cor multi .30 .20
Nos. 1129-1132,C989-C991 (7) 2.30 1.50

Vaporcito 93 A130

1981, Dec. 30 ***Perf. 12½***

1133 A130 50c shown .15 .15
1134 A130 1cor Vulcan Iron Works, 1946 .20 .15
1135 A130 1.20cor 1911 .25 .15
1136 A130 1.80cor Hoist & Derriel, 1909 .38 .20
1137 A130 2cor U-10B, 1956 .38 .25
1138 A130 2.50cor Ferrobus, 1945 .38 .30
Nos. 1133-1138,C992 (7) 2.74 1.75

1982 World Cup — A131

Designs: Various soccer players. 3.50cor horiz.

1982, Jan. 25

1139 A131 5c multi .15 .15
1140 A131 20c multi .15 .15
1141 A131 25c multi .15 .15
1142 A131 2.50cor multi .42 .34
1143 A131 3.50cor multi .55 .35
Nos. 1139-1143,C993-C994 (7) 3.15
Set value 1.80

Cocker Spaniels A132

1982, Feb. 18

1144 A132 5c shown .15 .15
1145 A132 20c German shepherds .15 .15
1146 A132 25c English setters .15 .15
1147 A132 2.50cor Brittany spaniels .45 .28
Nos. 1144-1147,C996-C998 (7) 2.73
Set value 1.40

Dynamine Myrrhina A133

1982, Mar. 26

1148 A133 50c shown .15 .15
1149 A133 1.20cor Eunica alcmena .24 .15
1150 A133 1.50cor Callizona acesta .28 .16
1151 A133 2cor Adelpha leuceria .35 .24
Nos. 1148-1151,C1000-C1002 (7) 2.50 1.63

Satellite — A134

Designs: Various satellites. 5c, 50c, 1.50cor, 2.50cor horiz.

1982, Apr. 12

1152 A134 5c multi .15 .15
1153 A134 15c multi .15 .15
1154 A134 50c multi .15 .15
1155 A134 1.50cor multi .26 .16
1156 A134 2.50cor multi .45 .26
Nos. 1152-1156,C1003-C1004 (7) 2.71
Set value 1.45

UPU Membership Centenary — A135

1982, May 1 **Litho.** ***Perf. 13***

1157 A135 50c Mail coach .15 .15
1158 A135 1.20cor Ship .16 .15
Nos. 1157-1158,C1005-C1006 (4) 1.79 1.22

14th Central American and Caribbean Games (Cuba '82) — A136

1982, May 13

1159 A136 10c Bicycling, vert. .15 .15
1160 A136 15c Swimming .15 .15
1161 A136 25c Basketball, vert. .15 .15
1162 A136 50c Weight lifting, vert. .15 .15
Set value, #1159-1162, C1007-C1009 2.45 1.50

3rd Anniv. of Revolution — A137

1982, July 19

1163 A137 50c multi .15 .15
Nos. 1163,C1012-C1014 (4) 2.13 1.35

George Washington (1732-1799) A138

19th Century Paintings. 1cor horiz. Size of 50c: 45x35mm.

Perf. 13x12½, 12½x13

1982, June 20 **Litho.**

1164 A138 50c Mount Vernon .15 .15
1165 A138 1cor Signing the Constitution .20 .15
1166 A138 2cor Riding through Trenton .38 .25
Nos. 1164-1166,C1015-C1018 (7) 3.23 2.10

Flower Arrangement, by R. Penalba — A139

Paintings: 50c, Masked Dancers, by M. Garcia, horiz. 1cor, The Couple, by R. Perez. 1.20cor, Canales Valley, by A. Mejias, horiz. 1.85cor, Portrait of Mrs. Castellon, by T. Jerez. 2cor, Street Vendors, by L. Cerrato. 10cor, Cock Fight, by Gallos P. Ortiz.

1982, Aug. 17 ***Perf. 13***

1167 A139 25c multi .15 .15
1168 A139 50c multi .15 .15
1169 A139 1cor multi .18 .15
1170 A139 1.20cor multi .20 .15
1171 A139 1.85cor multi .32 .20
1172 A139 2cor multi .32 .20
Nos. 1167-1172,C1019 (7) 2.57
Set value 1.45

Souvenir Sheet

1173 A139 10cor multi 1.65 1.00

No. 1173 contains one 36x28mm stamp.

George Dimitrov, First Pres. of Bulgaria — A140

1982, Sept. 9

1174 A140 50c Lenin, Dimitrov, 1921 .15 .15
Nos. 1174,C1020-C1021 (3) 1.13 .77

26th Anniv. of End of Dictatorship — A141

1982, Sept. 21 ***Perf. 13x12½***

1175 A141 50c Ausberto Narvaez .15 .15
1176 A141 2.50cor Cornelio Silva .52 .30
Nos. 1175-1176,C1022-C1023 (4) 2.27 1.43

Ruins, Leon Viejo A142

1982, Sept. 25 ***Perf. 13***

1177 A142 50c shown .15 .15
1178 A142 1cor Ruben Dario Theater and Park .15 .15
1179 A142 1.20cor Independence Plaza, Granada .18 .15
1180 A142 1.80cor Corn Island .28 .16
1181 A142 2cor Santiago Volcano crater, Masaya .30 .18
Nos. 1177-1181,C1024-C1025 (7) 1.72
Set value 1.10

Karl Marx (1818-1883) — A143

1982, Oct. 4 ***Perf. 12½***

1182 A143 1cor Marx, birthplace .18 .15

Se-tenant with label showing Communist Manifesto titlepage. See No. C1026.

World Food Day (Oct. 16) A144

1982, Oct. 10 ***Perf. 13***

1183 A144 50c Picking fruit .15 .15
1184 A144 1cor Farm workers, vert. .15 .15
1185 A144 2cor Cutting sugar cane .30 .25
1186 A144 10cor Emblems 1.50 1.20
Nos. 1183-1186 (4) 2.10 1.75

Discovery of America, 490th Anniv. A145

1982, Oct. 12 ***Perf. 12½x13***

1187 A145 50c Santa Maria .15 .15
1188 A145 1cor Nina .22 .15
1189 A145 1.50cor Pinta .32 .20
1190 A145 2cor Columbus, fleet .42 .28
Nos. 1187-1190,C1027-C1029 (7) 3.28 2.14

A146 A147

1982, Nov. 13 ***Perf. 12½***

1191 A146 50c Lobelia laxiflora .15 .15
1192 A146 1.20cor Bombacopsis quinata .25 .15
1193 A146 1.80cor Mimosa albida .38 .22
1194 A146 2cor Epidendrum alatum .38 .25
Nos. 1191-1194,C1031-C1033 (7) 2.81 1.76

1982, Dec. 10 ***Perf. 13***

1195 A147 10c Coral snake .15 .15
1196 A147 50c Iguana, horiz. .15 .15
1197 A147 2cor Lachesis muta, horiz. .38 .25
Nos. 1195-1197,C1034-C1037 (7) 2.78 1.82

Telecommunications Day — A148

1982, Dec. 12 **Litho.** ***Perf. 12½***

1198 A148 50c Radio transmission station .15 .15
1199 A148 1cor Telcor building, Managua .16 .15
Set value .25 .15

50c airmail.

Jose Marti, Cuban Independence Hero, 130th Birth Anniv. — A149

1983, Jan. 28 ***Perf. 13***

1200 A149 1cor multi .25 .15

Boxing — A150 Local Flowers — A151

1983, Jan. 31 ***Perf. 12½***

1201 A150 50c shown .15 .15
1202 A150 1cor Gymnast .15 .15
1203 A150 1.50cor Running .20 .15
1204 A150 2cor Weightlifting .25 .16
1205 A150 4cor Women's discus .65 .35
1206 A150 5cor Basketball .80 .40
1207 A150 6cor Bicycling 1.00 .50
Nos. 1201-1207 (7) 3.20 1.86

Souvenir Sheet

Perf. 13

1208 A150 15cor Sailing 2.25 1.20

23rd Olympic Games, Los Angeles, July 28-Aug. 12, 1984. Nos. 1205-1208 airmail. No. 1208 contains one 31x39mm stamp.

1983, Feb. 5 ***Perf. 12½***

1209 A151 1cor Bixa orellana .16 .15
1210 A151 1cor Brassavola nodosa .16 .15
1211 A151 1cor Cattleya lueddemaniana .16 .15
1212 A151 1cor Cochlospermum spec. .16 .15
1213 A151 1cor Hibiscus rosa-sinensis .16 .15
1214 A151 1cor Laella spec. .16 .15
1215 A151 1cor Malvaviscus arboreus .16 .15
1216 A151 1cor Neomarica coerulea .16 .15
1217 A151 1cor Plumeria rubra .16 .15
1218 A151 1cor Senecio spec. .16 .15
1219 A151 1cor Sobralla macrantha .16 .15
1220 A151 1cor Stachytarpheta indica .16 .15
1221 A151 1cor Tabebula ochraceae .16 .15
1222 A151 1cor Tagetes erecta .16 .15
1223 A151 1cor Tecoma stans .16 .15
1224 A151 1cor Thumbergia alata .16 .15
Nos. 1209-1224 (16) 2.56
Set value 1.25

See Nos. 1515-1530, 1592-1607, 1828-1843.

Visit of Pope John Paul II A152

1983, Mar. 4 ***Perf. 13***

1225 A152 50c Peace banner .15 .15
1226 A152 1cor Map, girl picking coffee beans .24 .15
1227 A152 4cor Pres. Rafael Rivas, Pope .95 .60
1228 A152 7cor Pope, Managua Cathedral 1.65 .95
Nos. 1225-1228 (4) 2.99 1.85

Souvenir Sheet

1229 A152 15cor Pope, vert. 3.25 1.75

Nos. 1227-1229 airmail. No. 1229 contains one 31x39mm stamp.

Nocturnal Moths A153

1983, Mar. 10

1230 A153 15c Xilophanes chiron .15 .15
1231 A153 50c Protoparce ochus .15 .15
1232 A153 65c Pholus lasbruscae .15 .15
1233 A153 1cor Amphypterus gannascus .16 .15
1234 A153 1.50cor Pholus licaon .20 .15
1235 A153 2cor Agrius cingulata .35 .16
1236 A153 10cor Rothschildia jurulla, vert. 1.50 .75
Nos. 1230-1236 (7) 2.66
Set value 1.20

No. 1236 airmail.

26th Anniv. of the Anti-Somoza Movement — A154

Various monuments and churches. 2cor, 4cor vert. 4cor airmail.

1983, Mar. 25 ***Perf. 12½***

1237 A154 50c Church of Subtiava, Leon .15 .15
1238 A154 1cor La Immaculata Castle, Rio San Juan .16 .15

1239 A154 2cor La Recoleccion Church, Leon .35 .16
1240 A154 4cor Ruben Dario monument, Managua .65 .35
Nos. 1237-1240 (4) 1.31
Set value .64

Railroad Cars A155

1983, Apr. 15

1241 A155 15c Passenger .15 .15
1242 A155 65c Freight .15 .15
1243 A155 1cor Tank .15 .15
1244 A155 1.50cor Ore .20 .15
1245 A155 4cor Passenger, diff. .55 .30
1246 A155 5cor Flat .70 .35
1247 A155 7cor Rail bus .95 .48
Nos. 1241-1247 (7) 2.85
Set value 1.35

Nos. 1245-1247 airmail.

Red Cross Flood Rescue A156

1983, May 8 ***Perf. 13***

1248 A156 50c shown .15 .15
1249 A156 1cor Putting patient in ambulance .18 .15
1250 A156 4cor 1972 earthquake & fire rescue .65 .38
1251 A156 5cor Nurse examining soldier, 1979 Liberation War .70 .42
Nos. 1248-1251 (4) 1.68 1.10

4cor, 5cor airmail. 4cor vert.

World Communications Year — A157

1983, May 17

1252 A157 1cor multi .18 .15

4th Anniv. of Revolution — A159

1983, July 19 **Litho.** ***Perf. 12½***

1261 A159 1cor Port of Corinto .16 .15
1262 A159 2cor Telecommunications Bldg., Leon .38 .16
Set value .25

Founders of FSLN (Sandinista Party) — A160

1983, July 23 **Litho.** ***Perf. 13***

1263 A160 50c multi .15 .15
1264 A160 1cor multi .16 .15
1265 A160 4cor multi, vert. .60 .35
Nos. 1263-1265 (3) .91
Set value .48

No. 1265, airmail, 33x44mm.

Simon Bolivar, 200th Birth Anniv. A161

1983, July 24 **Litho.** ***Perf. 12½***

1266 A161 50c Bolivar and Sandino .15 .15
1267 A161 1cor Bolivar on horseback, vert. .15 .15
Set value .24 .15

14th Winter Olympic Games, Sarajevo, Yugoslavia, Feb. 8-19, 1984 — A162

1983, Aug. 5 **Litho.** ***Perf. 13***

1268 A162 50c Speed skating .15 .15
1269 A162 1cor Slalom .15 .15
1270 A162 1.50cor Luge .20 .15
1271 A162 2cor Ski jumping .35 .16
1272 A162 4cor Ice dancing .60 .35
1273 A162 5cor Skiing .70 .40
1274 A162 6cor Biathlon .90 .50
Nos. 1268-1274 (7) 3.05 1.86

Souvenir Sheet

1983, Aug. 25 **Litho.** ***Perf. 13***

1275 A162 15cor Hockey 2.50 1.40

No. 1275 contains one 39x32mm stamp. Nos. 1272-1275 airmail.

Chess Moves — A163

Archaeological Finds — A164

1983, Aug. 20 **Litho.** ***Perf. 13***

1276 A163 15c Pawn .15 .15
1277 A163 65c Knight .15 .15
1278 A163 1cor Bishop .15 .15
1279 A163 2cor Castle .35 .16
1280 A163 4cor Queen .60 .35
1281 A163 5cor King .70 .40
1282 A163 7cor Player 1.00 .55
Nos. 1276-1282 (7) 3.10
Set value 1.60

Nos. 1280-1282 airmail.

1983, Aug. 20 ***Perf. 13x12½***

1283 A164 50c Stone figurine .15 .15
1284 A164 1cor Covered dish .15 .15
1285 A164 2cor Vase .35 .16
1286 A164 4cor Platter .60 .35
Nos. 1283-1286 (4) 1.25
Set value .64

No. 1286 airmail.

Madonna of the Chair, by Raphael (1483-1517) A165

Paintings: 1cor, The Eszterhazy Madonna. 1.50cor, Sistine Madonna. 2cor, Madonna of the Linnet. 4cor, Madonna of the Meadow. 5cor, La Belle Jardiniere. 6cor, Adoration of the Kings. 15cor, Madonna de Foligno. 4, 5, 6, 15cor airmail.

1983, Sept. 15

1287 A165 50c multi .15 .15
1288 A165 1cor multi .15 .15
1289 A165 1.50cor multi .20 .15
1290 A165 2cor multi .35 .16
1291 A165 4cor multi .60 .35
1292 A165 5cor multi .70 .40
1293 A165 6cor multi .90 .48
Nos. 1287-1293 (7) 3.05 1.84

Souvenir Sheet

1984, Sept. 15 **Litho.** ***Perf. 13***

1293A A165 15cor multi 2.25 1.25

Mining Industry Nationalization — A166

1983, Oct. 2 ***Perf. 13***

1294 A166 1cor Pouring molten metal .16 .15
1295 A166 4cor Mine headstock, workers .60 .40

4cor airmail.

Ship-to-Shore Communications — A167

1983, Oct. 7 ***Perf. 12½***

1296 A167 1cor shown .16 .15
1297 A167 4cor Radio tower, view .60 .40

FRACAP '83, Federation of Central American and Panamanian Radio Amateurs Cong., Oct. 7-9.

Agrarian Reform — A168

1983, Oct. 16

1298 A168 1cor Tobacco .15 .15
1299 A168 2cor Cotton .35 .15
1300 A168 4cor Corn .60 .25
1301 A168 5cor Sugar cane .70 .35
1302 A168 6cor Cattle .90 .40
1303 A168 7cor Rice paddy 1.00 .45
1304 A168 8cor Coffee beans 1.20 .55
1305 A168 10cor Bananas 1.50 .65
Nos. 1298-1305 (8) 6.40 2.95

See Nos. 1531-1538, 1608-1615.

Fire Engine A169

Various Fire Engines.

1983, Oct. 17 ***Perf. 13***

1306 A169 50c multi .15 .15
1307 A169 1cor multi .15 .15
1308 A169 1.50cor multi .20 .15
1309 A169 2cor multi .35 .16
1310 A169 4cor multi .60 .35
1311 A169 5cor multi .70 .40
1312 A169 6cor multi .90 .48
Nos. 1306-1312 (7) 3.05 1.84

Nos. 1308-1311 airmail.

Nicaraguan-Cuban Solidarity — A170

1983, Oct. 24

1313 A170 1cor José Marti, Gen. Sandino .16 .15
1314 A170 4cor Education, health, industry .60 .40

4cor airmail.

A171

A172

Christmas (Adoration of the Kings Paintings by): 50c, Hugo van der Goes. 1 cor, Ghirlandaio. 2cor, El Greco. 7cor, Konrad von Soest. 7cor airmail.

1983, Dec. 1

1315 A171 50c multi .15 .15
1316 A171 1cor multi .15 .15
1317 A171 2cor multi .28 .15
1318 A171 7cor multi .90 .42
Set value 1.30 .66

1984, Jan. 10

1319 A172 50c Biathlon .15 .15
1320 A172 50c Bobsledding .15 .15
1321 A172 1cor Speed skating .15 .15
1322 A172 1cor Slalom .15 .15
1323 A172 4cor Downhill skiing .65 .35
1324 A172 5cor Ice dancing .80 .40
1325 A172 10cor Ski jumping 1.40 .75
Nos. 1319-1325 (7) 3.45
Set value 1.75

Souvenir Sheet

1326 A172 15cor Hockey 2.50 1.50

1984 Winter Olympics. No. 1326 contains one 31x39mm stamp. Nos. 1323-1326 airmail.

Domestic Cats A173

1984, Feb. 15 ***Perf. 12½***

1327 A173 50c Chinchilla .15 .15
1328 A173 50c Long-haired Angel .15 .15
1329 A173 1cor Red tabby .18 .15

1330	A173	2cor Tortoiseshell	.38	.18
1331	A173	3cor Siamese	.32	.28
1332	A173	4cor Blue Burmese	.70	.38
1333	A173	7cor Silver long-haired	1.25	.60
		Nos. 1327-1333 (7)	3.13	
		Set value		1.55

Nos. 1331, 1333 airmail.

Augusto Cesar Sandino (d. 1934) — A174

1984, Feb. 21

1334	A174	1cor Arms	.16	.15
1335	A174	4cor Portrait	.60	.40

4cor airmail.

Intl. Women's Day — A175

1984, Mar. 8

1336	A175	1cor Blanca Arauz	.15	.15

Bee-pollinated Flowers — A176

1984, Mar. 20

1337	A176	50c Poinsettia	.15	.15
1338	A176	50c Sunflower	.15	.15
1339	A176	1cor Antigonan leptopus	.16	.15
1340	A176	1cor Cassia alata	.16	.15
1341	A176	3cor Bidens pilosa	.42	.25
1342	A176	4cor Althea rosea	.60	.35
1343	A176	5cor Rivea corymbosa	.70	.40
		Nos. 1337-1343 (7)	2.34	
		Set value		1.25

Nos. 1341-1343 airmail.

Space Annivs. — A177

1984, Apr. 20

1344	A177	50c Soyuz 6,7,8, 1969	.15	.15
1345	A177	50c Soyuz 6,7,8, diff.	.15	.15
1346	A177	1cor Apollo 11, 1969	.15	.15
1347	A177	2cor Luna 1, 1959	.35	.16
1348	A177	3cor Luna 2, 1959	.50	.25
1349	A177	4cor Luna 3, 1959	.65	.35
1350	A177	9cor Painting by Koroliov, 1934	1.40	.50
		Nos. 1344-1350 (7)	3.35	
		Set value		1.40

Nos. 1348-1350 airmail.

Noli Me Tangere, by Correggio — A178

1984, May 17 Litho. *Perf. 12½*

1351	A178	50c shown	.15	.15
1352	A178	50c Madonna of San Girolamo	.15	.15
1353	A178	1cor Allegory of the Virtues	.15	.15
1354	A178	2cor Allegory of Placer	.35	.16
1355	A178	3cor Ganimedes	.50	.25
1356	A178	5cor Danae	.80	.40
1357	A178	8cor Leda	1.20	.65
		Nos. 1351-1357 (7)	3.30	
		Set value		1.60

Souvenir Sheet

1358	A178	15cor St. John the Evangelist	2.25	1.20

No. 1358 contains one 31x39mm stamp. Nos. 1355-1358 airmail.

Vintage Cars A179

1984, May 18

1359	A179	1cor Abadal, 1914	.15	.15
1360	A179	1cor Daimler, 1886, vert.	.15	.15
1361	A179	2cor Ford, 1903, vert.	.35	.16
1362	A179	2cor Renault, 1899, vert.	.35	.16
1363	A179	3cor Rolls Royce, 1910	.50	.25
1364	A179	4cor Metallurgique, 1907	.65	.35
1365	A179	7cor Bugatti Mode 40	1.10	.55
		Nos. 1359-1365 (7)	3.25	1.77

Birth sesquicentennial of Gottlieb Daimler. Nos. 1363-1365 airmail.

1984 Summer Olympics — A180

1984, July 6

1366	A180	50c Volleyball	.15	.15
1367	A180	50c Basketball	.15	.15
1368	A180	1cor Field hockey	.15	.15
1369	A180	2cor Tennis	.35	.16
1370	A180	3cor Soccer	.50	.25
1371	A180	4cor Water polo	.65	.35
1372	A180	9cor Net ball	1.40	.70
		Nos. 1366-1372 (7)	3.35	
		Set value		1.60

Souvenir Sheet

Perf. 13

1373	A180	15cor Baseball	2.25	1.20

No. 1373 contains one 40x31mm stamp. Nos. 1370-1373 airmail and horiz.

5th Anniv. of Revolution A181

1984, July 19

1374	A181	50c Construction	.15	.15
1375	A181	1cor Transportation	.16	.15
1376	A181	4cor Agriculture	.65	.35
1377	A181	7cor Govt. building	1.20	.55
		Nos. 1374-1377 (4)	2.16	
		Set value		1.00

Nos. 1376-1377 airmail.

UNESCO Nature Conservation Campaign A182

1984, Aug. 3 *Perf. 12½x13, 13x12½*

1378	A182	50c Children dependent on nature	.15	.15
1379	A182	1cor Forest	.15	.15
1380	A182	2cor River	.35	.16
1381	A182	10cor Seedlings, field, vert.	1.50	.80
		Nos. 1378-1381 (4)	2.15	
		Set value		1.05

No. 1381 airmail.

Nicaraguan Red Cross, 50th Anniv. — A183

1984, Sept. 16 *Perf. 12½x12*

1382	A183	1cor Air ambulance	.16	.15
1383	A183	7cor Battle field	1.00	.55

No. 1383 airmail.

History of Baseball — A184

Portraits and national colors: #1384, Ventura Escalante, Dominican Republic. #1385, Daniel Herrera, Mexico. #1386, Adalberto Herrera, Venezuela. #1387, Roberto Clemente, Puerto Rico. #1388, Carlos Colas, Cuba. #1389, Stanley Cayasso, Nicaragua. #1390, Babe Ruth, US.

1984, Oct. 25 Litho. *Perf. 12½*

1384	A184	50c multi	.15	.15
1385	A184	50c multi	.15	.15
1386	A184	1cor multi	.16	.15
1387	A184	1cor multi	.16	.15
1388	A184	3cor multi	.50	.20
1389	A184	4cor multi	.65	.25
1390	A184	5cor multi	.80	.35
		Nos. 1384-1390 (7)	2.57	
		Set value		1.00

Nos. 1388-1390 are airmail.

Tapirus Bairdii A185

1984, Dec. 28 *Perf. 13*

1391	A185	25c In water	.15	.15
1392	A185	25c In field	.15	.15
1393	A185	3cor Baring teeth	.40	.20
1394	A185	4cor Female and young	.55	.25
		Set value	1.00	.50

Wildlife conservation. Nos. 1393-1394 are airmail. Compare with type A202.

1986 World Cup Soccer Championships, Mexico — A186

Evolution of soccer.

1985, Jan. 20

1395	A186	50c 1314	.15	.15
1396	A186	50c 1500	.15	.15
1397	A186	1cor 1846	.15	.15
1398	A186	1cor 1872	.15	.15
1399	A186	2cor 1883	.20	.15
1400	A186	4cor 1890	.40	.20
1401	A186	6cor 1953	.60	.30
		Set value (7)	1.50	.75

Souvenir Sheet

Perf. 12½

1402	A186	10cor 1985	1.20	.80

Nos. 1399-1402 are airmail. No. 1402 contains one 40x32mm stamp.

Mushrooms — A187

1985, Feb. 20

1403	A187	50c Boletus calopus	.15	.15
1404	A187	50c Strobilomyces retisporus	.15	.15
1405	A187	1cor Boletus luridus	.15	.15
1406	A187	1cor Xerocomus illudens	.15	.15
1407	A187	4cor Gyrodon merulioides	.50	.20
1408	A187	5cor Tylopilus plumbeoviolaceus	.60	.25
1409	A187	8cor Gyroporus castaneus	1.00	.40
		Nos. 1403-1409 (7)	2.70	
		Set value		1.00

Nos. 1406-1409 are airmail.

Postal Union of the Americas and Spain, 13th Congress A188

UPAE emblem and: 1cor, Chasqui, mail runner and map of Realejo-Nicaragua route. 7cor, Monoplane and Nicaraguan air network.

1985, Mar. 11 *Perf. 12½x13*

1410	A188	1cor multi	.15	.15
1411	A188	7cor multi	.70	.38

No. 1411 is airmail.

City Railway Engine A189

Various locomotives.

1985, Apr. 5 *Perf. 12½*

1412	A189	1cor Electric	.15	.15
1413	A189	1cor Steam	.15	.15
1414	A189	9cor shown	.52	.25
1415	A189	9cor shown	.52	.25
1416	A189	15cor steam, diff.	.85	.42
1417	A189	21cor steam, diff.	1.25	.35
		Nos. 1412-1417 (6)	3.44	1.57

Souvenir Sheet

Perf. 13

1418	A189	42cor steam, diff.	3.25	1.90

German Railroads, 150th Anniv. #1418 also for 100th anniv. of Nicaraguan railroads. #1418 contains one 40x32mm stamp. #1414-1418 are airmail.

Motorcycle Cent. — A190

1985, Apr. 30 Litho. *Perf. 12½*

1419 A190 50c F.N., 1928 .15 .15
1420 A190 50c Douglas, 1928 .15 .15
1421 A190 1cor Puch, 1938 .15 .15
1422 A190 2cor Wanderer, 1939 .20 .15
1423 A190 4cor Honda, 1949 .40 .20
1424 A190 5cor BMW, 1984 .50 .25
1425 A190 7cor Honda, 1984 .70 .38
Nos. 1419-1425 (7) 2.25
Set value 1.00

Nos. 1419-1425 se-tenant with labels picturing manufacturers' trademarks. Nos. 1422-1425 are airmail.

Flowers — A194

1985, May 20 Litho. *Perf. 13*

1454 A194 50c Metelea quirosii .15 .15
1455 A194 50c Ipomea nil .15 .15
1456 A194 1cor Lysichitum americanum .18 .15
1457 A194 2cor Clusia sp. .36 .18
1458 A194 4cor Vanilla planifolia .72 .36
1459 A194 7cor Stemmadenia obovata 1.25 .62
a. Min. sheet of 6, #1454-1459 2.75
Nos. 1454-1459 (6) 2.81
Set value 1.35

Nos. 1457-1459 are airmail.
Stamps in No. 1459a do not have white border.

End of World War II, 40th Anniv. — A195

1985, May *Perf. 12x12½, 12½x12*

1460 A195 9.50cor German army surrenders .38 .18
1461 A195 28cor Nuremberg trials, horiz. 1.10 .52

No. 1461 is airmail.

Lenin, 115th Birth Anniv. — A196

Design: 21cor, Lenin speaking to workers.

1985, June Litho. *Perf. 12x12½*

1462 A196 4cor multicolored .40 .20
1463 A196 21cor multicolored 2.25 1.10

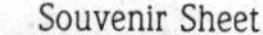
Souvenir Sheet

Argentina '85 — A197

1985, June 5 Litho. *Perf. 13*

1464 A197 75cor multicolored 4.25 2.00

World Stamp Exposition.

Birds — A198

1985, Aug. 25

1465 A198 50c Ring-neck pheasant .15 .15
1466 A198 50c Chicken .15 .15
1467 A198 1cor Guinea hen .20 .15
1468 A198 2cor Goose .40 .20
1469 A198 6cor Turkey 1.25 .60
1470 A198 8cor Duck 1.65 .80
Nos. 1465-1470 (6) 3.80 2.05

Intl. Music Year A199

1985, Sept. 1

1471 A199 1cor Luis A. Delgadillo, vert. .15 .15
1472 A199 1cor shown .15 .15
1473 A199 9cor Parade .60 .30
1474 A199 9cor Managua Cathedral .60 .30
1475 A199 15cor Masked dancer .95 .48
1476 A199 21cor Parade, diff. 1.25 .65
Nos. 1471-1476 (6) 3.70 2.03

Nos. 1473-1476 are airmail.

Natl. Fire Brigade, 6th Anniv. A200

1985, Oct. 18

1477 A200 1cor Fire station .15 .15
1478 A200 1cor Fire truck .15 .15
1479 A200 1cor shown .15 .15
1480 A200 3cor Ambulance .20 .15
1481 A200 9cor Airport fire truck .60 .30
1482 A200 15cor Waterfront fire 1.00 .50
1483 A200 21cor Hose team, fire 1.40 .75
a. Min. sheet of 7, #1474-1483 + 2 labels 3.75
Nos. 1477-1483 (7) 3.65
Set value 1.70

Stamps from No. 1483a have orange borders. Nos. 1480-1483 are airmail.

Halley's Comet — A201

1985, Nov. 26

1484 A201 1cor Edmond Halley .15 .15
1485 A201 3cor Map of comet's track, 1910 .16 .15
1486 A201 3cor Tycho Brahe's observatory .16 .15
1487 A201 9cor Astrolabe, map .50 .24
1488 A201 15cor Telescopes .80 .40
1489 A201 21cor Telescope designs 1.25 .60
Nos. 1484-1489 (6) 3.02 1.69

Nos. 1487-1489 are airmail.

Tapirus Bairdii A202

1985, Dec. 30

1490 A202 1cor Eating .15 .15
1491 A202 3cor Drinking .32 .16
1492 A202 5cor Grazing in field .50 .25
1493 A202 9cor With young .95 .45
Nos. 1490-1493 (4) 1.92 1.01

Nos. 1491-1493 are airmail.

Roses — A203

1986, Jan. 15 *Perf. 12½*

1494 A203 1cor Spinosissima .15 .15
1495 A203 1cor Canina .15 .15
1496 A203 3cor Eglanteria .15 .15
1497 A203 5cor Rubrifolia .15 .15
1498 A203 9cor Foetida .20 .15
1499 A203 100cor Rugosa 2.25 1.10
Nos. 1494-1499 (6) 3.05
Set value 1.25

Nos. 1497-1499 are airmail.

Birds — A204 A205

1986, Feb. 10 *Perf. 13x12½*

1500 A204 1cor Colibri topacio .15 .15
1501 A204 3cor Paraulata picodorado .15 .15
1502 A204 3cor Troupial .15 .15
1503 A204 5cor Vereron pintado .15 .15
1504 A204 10cor Tordo ruisenor .24 .15
1505 A204 21cor Buho real .50 .26
1506 A204 75cor Gran kiskadee 1.75 .90
Nos. 1500-1506 (7) 3.09
Set value 1.45

Nos. 1504-1506 are airmail.

1986, Mar. 20 *Perf. 12½*

World Cup Soccer Championships, Mexico: Soccer players and pre-Columbian artifacts. No. 1514, Player's foot, ball.

Shirt Colors

1507 A205 1cor blue & yel .15 .15
1508 A205 1cor yel & green .15 .15
1509 A205 3cor blue & white .15 .15
1510 A205 3cor red & white .15 .15
1511 A205 5cor red .15 .15
1512 A205 9cor blk & yel .15 .15
1513 A205 100cor red & grn 2.00 1.10
Nos. 1507-1513 (7) 2.90
Set value 1.35

Souvenir Sheet

Perf. 13

1514 A205 100cor multicolored 2.50 1.25

Nos. 1509-1514 are airmail.

Flower Type of 1983

1986, Mar. Litho. *Perf. 12½*

1515 A151 5cor like #1209 .35 .15
1516 A151 5cor like #1210 .35 .15
1517 A151 5cor like #1211 .35 .15
1518 A151 5cor like #1212 .35 .15
1519 A151 5cor like #1213 .35 .15
1520 A151 5cor like #1214 .35 .15
1521 A151 5cor like #1215 .35 .15
1522 A151 5cor like #1216 .35 .15
1523 A151 5cor like #1217 .35 .15
1524 A151 5cor like #1218 .35 .15
1525 A151 5cor like #1219 .35 .15
1526 A151 5cor like #1220 .35 .15
1527 A151 5cor like #1221 .35 .15
1528 A151 5cor like #1222 .35 .15
1529 A151 5cor like #1223 .35 .15
1530 A151 5cor like #1224 .35 .15
Nos. 1515-1530 (16) 5.60
Set value 2.00

Agrarian Reform Type of 1983

1986, Apr. 15 *Perf. 12½*

1531 A168 1cor dk brown .15 .15
1532 A168 9cor purple .20 .15
1533 A168 15cor rose violet .32 .16
1534 A168 21cor dk car rose .45 .22
1535 A168 33cor orange .75 .35
1536 A168 42cor green .95 .45
1537 A168 50cor brown 1.10 .55
1538 A168 100cor blue 2.25 1.10
Nos. 1531-1538 (8) 6.17 3.13

Writers A207

1986, Apr. 23 *Perf. 12½x13*

1539 A207 1cor Alfonso Cortes .15 .15
1540 A207 3cor Salomon de la Selva .15 .15
1541 A207 3cor Azarias H. Pallais .15 .15
1542 A207 5cor Ruben Dario .15 .15
1543 A207 9cor Pablo Neruda .22 .15
1544 A207 15cor Alfonso Reyes .35 .18
1545 A207 100cor Pedro Henriquez Urena 2.25 1.10
Nos. 1539-1545 (7) 3.42
Set value 1.55

Nos. 1544-1545 are airmail.

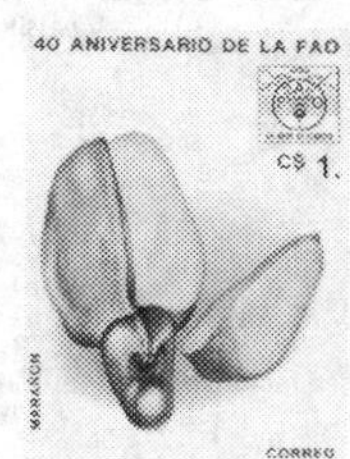

Nuts — A208

1986, June 20 *Perf. 12x12½*

1546 A208 1cor Maranon (cashew) .15 .15
1547 A208 1cor Zapote .15 .15
1548 A208 3cor Pitahaya .15 .15
1549 A208 3cor Granadilla .15 .15
1550 A208 5cor Anona .15 .15

1551 A208 21cor Melocoton (star-fruit) .50 .25
1552 A208 100cor Mamey 2.25 1.10
Set value 3.10 1.55

FAO, 40th Anniv. Nos. 1550-1552 are airmail.

Lockheed L-1011 Tristar A209

Airplanes: No. 1554, YAK 40. No. 1555, BAC 1-11. No. 1556, Boeing 747. 9cor, A-300. 15cor, TU-154. No. 1559, Concorde, vert. No. 1560, Fairchild 340.

1986, Aug. 22 *Perf. 12½*

1553 A209 1cor multicolored .15 .15
1554 A209 1cor multicolored .15 .15
1555 A209 3cor multicolored .15 .15
1556 A209 3cor multicolored .15 .15
1557 A209 9cor multicolored .22 .15
1558 A209 15cor multicolored .35 .20
1559 A209 100cor multicolored 2.25 1.10
Set value 3.10 1.55

Souvenir Sheet

Perf. 13

1560 A209 100cor multicolored 2.50 1.25

Stockholmia '86. No. 1560 contains one 40x32mm stamp.
Nos. 1557-1560 airmail.

A210

A210a

Discovery of America, 500th Anniv. (in 1992) — A210b

1986, Oct. 12 *Perf. 12½x12*

1561 A210 1cor shown .15 .15
1562 A210 1cor 2 of Columbus' ships .15 .15
a. Pair, #1561-1562 .15 .15
b. Souv. sheet of 2, #1561-1562 .15 .15

Perf. 12x12½

1563 A210a 9cor Juan de la Cosa .20 .15
1564 A210a 9cor Columbus .20 .15
a. Pair, #1563-1564 .40 .20
1565 A210b 21cor Ferdinand, Isabella .50 .25
1566 A210b 100cor Columbus before throne 2.25 1.10
a. Pair, #1565-1566 2.75 1.35
b. Souv. sheet of 4, #1563-1566 3.25 1.55
Nos. 1561-1566 (6) 3.45 1.95

Nos. 1563-1566 are airmail. Nos. 1564a, 1566a have continuous design.

Butterflies — A211

1986, Dec. 12 *Perf. 12½*

1567 A211 10cor Theritas coronata .24 .15
1568 A211 15cor Charayes nitebis .35 .18
1569 A211 15cor Salamis cacta .35 .18
1570 A211 15cor Papilio maacki .35 .18
1571 A211 25cor Euphaedro cyparissa .60 .30
1572 A211 25cor Palaeochrysophonus hippothoe .60 .30
1573 A211 30cor Ritra aurea .70 .35
Nos. 1567-1573 (7) 3.19 1.64

Nos. 1568-1573 are airmail.

Ruben Dario Order of Cultural Independence A212

Dario Order Winning Writers: No. 1574, Ernesto Mejia Sanchez. No. 1575, Fernando Gordillo C. No. 1576, Francisco Perez Estrada. 30cor, Julio Cortazar. 60cor, Enrique Fernandez Morales.

1987, Jan. 18 **Litho.** *Perf. 13*

1574 A212 10cor multicolored .22 .15
1575 A212 10cor multicolored .22 .15
1576 A212 10cor multicolored .22 .15
1577 A212 15cor multicolored .32 .16
1578 A212 30cor multicolored .65 .32
1579 A212 60cor multicolored 1.25 .65
a. Strip of 6, #1574-1579 2.90 1.50
b. Min. sheet of 6, #1574-1579 2.90 2.90

1988 Winter Olympics, Calgary — A213

#1580, Speed skating. #1581, Ice hockey. #1582, Women's figure skating. #1583, Ski jumping. 20cor, Biathalon. 30cor, Slalom skiing. 40cor, Downhill skiing. 110cor, Ice hockey, diff., horiz.

1987, Feb. 3 *Perf. 13*

1580 A213 10cor multi .22 .15
1581 A213 10cor multi .22 .15
1582 A213 15cor multi .30 .15
1583 A213 15cor multi .30 .15
1584 A213 20cor multi .40 .20
1585 A213 30cor multi .60 .30
1586 A213 40cor multi .85 .42
Nos. 1580-1586 (7) 2.89 1.52

Souvenir Sheet

Perf. 12½

1587 A213 110cor multi 2.25 2.25

Nos. 1582-1587 are airmail. No. 1587 contains one 40x32mm stamp.

Children's Welfare Campaign — A214

1987, Mar. 18 *Perf. 13*

1588 A214 10cor Growth & development .25 .15
1589 A214 25cor Vaccination .60 .30
1590 A214 30cor Rehydration .75 .35
1591 A214 50cor Breastfeeding 1.25 .60
Nos. 1588-1591 (4) 2.85 1.40

Nos. 1589-1591 are airmail.

Flower Type of 1983

1987, Mar. 25 *Perf. 12½*

1592 A151 10cor Bixa orellana .20 .15
1593 A151 10cor Brassavola nodosa .20 .15
1594 A151 10cor Cattleya lueddemanniana .20 .15
1595 A151 10cor Cochlospermum spec. .20 .15
1596 A151 10cor Hibiscus rosa-sinensis .20 .15
1597 A151 10cor Laelia spec. .20 .15
1598 A151 10cor Malvaviscus arboreus .20 .15
1599 A151 10cor Neomarica coerulea .20 .15
1600 A151 10cor Plumeria rubra .20 .15
1601 A151 10cor Senecio spec. .20 .15
1602 A151 10cor Sobralia macrantha .20 .15
1603 A151 10cor Stachytarpheta indica .20 .15
1604 A151 10cor Tabebula ochraceae .20 .15
1605 A151 10cor Tagetes erecta .20 .15
1606 A151 10cor Tecoma stans .20 .15
1607 A151 10cor Thumbergia alata .20 .15
Nos. 1592-1607 (16) 3.20
Set value 1.70

Agrarian Reform Type of 1983 Inscribed "1987"

Designs: No. 1608, Tobacco. No. 1609, Cotton. 15cor, Corn. 25cor, Sugar. 30cor, Cattle. 50cor, Coffee Beans. 60cor, Rice. 100cor, Bananas.

1987, Mar. 25 *Perf. 12½*

1608 A168 10cor dk brown .28 .15
1609 A168 10cor purple .28 .15
1610 A168 15cor rose violet .45 .22
1611 A168 25cor dk car rose .70 .35
1612 A168 30cor orange .85 .45
1613 A168 50cor brown 1.40 .65
1614 A168 60cor green 1.75 .90
1615 A168 100cor blue 2.75 1.40
Nos. 1608-1615 (8) 8.46 4.27

77th Interparliamentary Conf., Managua — A215

1987, Apr. 27

1616 A215 10cor multicolored .18 .15

Prehistoric Creatures — A216

1987, May 25 *Perf. 13*

1617 A216 10cor Mammoth .18 .15
1618 A216 10cor Dimetrodon .18 .15
1619 A216 10cor Triceratops .18 .15
1620 A216 15cor Dinichthys .22 .15
1621 A216 15cor Uintaterium .22 .15
1622 A216 30cor Pteranodon .55 .25
1623 A216 40cor Tilosaurus .75 .32
Nos. 1617-1623 (7) 2.28 1.32

Nos. 1620-1623 are airmail.

CAPEX '87 — A217

Various tennis players in action.

1987, June 2 *Perf. 13*

1624 A217 10cor Male player .20 .15
1625 A217 10cor Female player .20 .15
1626 A217 15cor Player at net .30 .15
1627 A217 15cor Female player, diff. .30 .15
1628 A217 20cor multi .35 .20
1629 A217 30cor multi .60 .30
1630 A217 40cor multi .90 .40
Nos. 1624-1630 (7) 2.85 1.50

Souvenir Sheet

Perf. 12½

1631 A217 110cor Doubles partners, vert. 2.25 2.25

Nos. 1626-1631 are airmail. No. 1631 contains one 32x40mm stamp.

Dogs — A218

1987, June 25 *Perf. 13*

1632 A218 10cor Doberman pinscher .20 .15
1633 A218 10cor Bull Mastiff .20 .15
1634 A218 15cor Japanese Spaniel .30 .15
1635 A218 15cor Keeshond .30 .15
1636 A218 20cor Chihuahua .40 .20
1637 A218 30cor St. Bernard .60 .30
1638 A218 40cor West Gotha spitz .85 .40
Nos. 1632-1638 (7) 2.85 1.50

Nos. 1634-1638 are airmail.

Cacti A219

1987, July 25 *Perf. 12½*

1639 A219 10cor Lophocereus schottii .20 .15
1640 A219 10cor Opuntia acanthocarpa .20 .15
1641 A219 10cor Echinocereus engelmanii .20 .15
1642 A219 20cor Lemaireocereus thurberi .40 .20
1643 A219 20cor Saguaros .40 .20
1644 A219 30cor Opuntia fulgida .60 .30
1645 A219 50cor Opuntia ficus 1.00 .50
Nos. 1639-1645 (7) 3.00 1.65

Nos. 1642-1645 are airmail.

10th Pan American Games, Indianapolis — A220

1987, Aug. 7 *Perf. 13*

1646 A220 10cor High jump .20 .15
1647 A220 10cor Volleyball .20 .15
1648 A220 15cor Sprinter .30 .22
1649 A220 15cor Gymnastics .30 .22
1650 A220 20cor Baseball .42 .30
1651 A220 30cor Synchronized swimming .60 .45
1652 A220 40cor Weightlifting .85 .60
Nos. 1646-1652 (7) 2.87 2.09

Souvenir Sheet

1653 A220 110cor Rhythmic gymnastics 2.25 2.25

Nos. 1648-1653 are airmail. No. 1653 contains one 32x40mm stamp. Nos. 1651-1653 are vert.

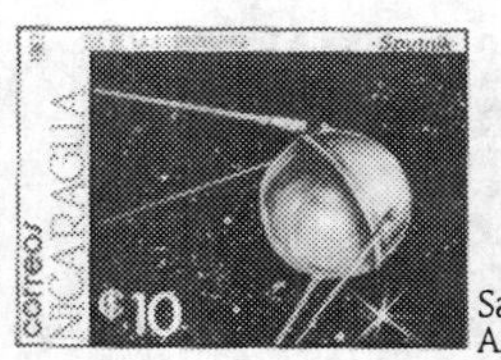

Satellites A221

1987, Oct. 4

No.	Type	Description	Unused	Used
1654	A221	10cor Sputnik	.20	.15
1655	A221	10cor Cosmos	.20	.15
1656	A221	15cor Proton	.30	.15
1657	A221	25cor Meteor	.50	.22
1658	A221	25cor Luna	.50	.22
1659	A221	30cor Electron	.60	.30
1660	A221	50cor Mars 1	.90	.50
		Nos. 1654-1660 (7)	3.20	1.69

Cosmonauts' Day. Nos. 1656-1660 are airmail.

Fish — A222

Designs: No. 1661, Tarpon atlanticus. No. 1662, Cichlasoma managuense. No. 1663, Atractoteus tropicus. No. 1664, Astyana fasciatus. No. 1665, Cichlasoma citrimellum. 20cor, Cichlosoma dowi. 50cor, Caracharhinus nicaraguensis.

1987, Oct. 18 *Perf. 12½*

No.	Type	Description	Unused	Used
1661	A222	10cor multicolored	.20	.15
1662	A222	10cor multicolored	.20	.15
1663	A222	10cor multicolored	.20	.15
1664	A222	15cor multicolored	.30	.15
1665	A222	15cor multicolored	.30	.15
1666	A222	20cor multicolored	.40	.20
1667	A222	50cor multicolored	1.00	.50
		Nos. 1661-1667 (7)	2.60	1.45

Nos. 1663-1667 are airmail.

October Revolution, 70th Anniv. — A223

Designs: 30cor, Cruiser Aurora, horiz. 50cor, USSR natl. arms.

1987, Nov. 7 *Perf. 13*

No.	Type	Description	Unused	Used
1668	A223	10cor multicolored	.22	.15
1669	A223	30cor multicolored	.60	.35
1670	A223	50cor multicolored	1.00	.60
		Nos. 1668-1670 (3)	1.82	1.10

Nos. 1669-1670 are airmail.

Christmas Paintings by L. Saenz — A224

1987, Nov. 15 *Perf. 13*

No.	Type	Description	Unused	Used
1671	A224	10cor Nativity	.15	.15
1672	A224	20cor Adoration of the Magi	.30	.15
1673	A224	25cor Adoration of the Magi, diff.	.35	.18
1674	A224	50cor Nativity, diff.	.75	.35
		Nos. 1671-1674 (4)	1.55	.83

1988 Winter Olymmpics, Calgary — A225

1988, Jan. 30 **Litho.** *Perf. 12½*

No.	Type	Description	Unused	Used
1675	A225	10cor Biathlon	.18	.15
1676	A225	10cor Cross-country skiing, vert.	.18	.15
1677	A225	15cor Hockey, vert.	.35	.15
1678	A225	20cor Women's figure skating, vert.	.50	.20
1679	A225	25cor Slalom skiing, vert.	.65	.30
1680	A225	30cor Ski jumping	.75	.40
1681	A225	40cor Men's downhill skiing, vert.	1.00	.50
		Nos. 1675-1681 (7)	3.61	1.85

Souvenir Sheet

Perf. 13

No.	Type	Description	Unused	Used
1682	A225	100cor Pairs figure skating	2.00	2.00

Nos. 1675-1681 printed with se-tenant label showing Canadian flag and wildlife.
No. 1682 contains one 40x32mm stamp.

Nicaraguan Journalists Assoc., 10th Anniv. — A226

Design: 5cor, Churches of St. Francis Xavier and Fatima, and speaker addressing journalists, horiz.

1988, Feb. 10

No.	Type	Description	Unused	Used
1683	A226	1cor shown	.15	.15
1684	A226	5cor multicolored	.75	.40

No. 1684 is airmail.

1988 Summer Olympics, Seoul — A227

1988, Feb. 28

No.	Type	Description	Unused	Used
1685	A227	10cor Gymnastics	.18	.15
1686	A227	10cor Basketball	.18	.15
1687	A227	15cor Volleyball	.35	.15
1688	A227	20cor Long jump	.50	.20
1689	A227	25cor Soccer	.65	.25
1690	A227	30cor Water polo	.75	.40
1691	A227	40cor Boxing	1.00	.50
		Nos. 1685-1691 (7)	3.61	1.80

Souvenir Sheet

No.	Type	Description	Unused	Used
1692	A227	100cor Baseball	2.00	2.00

No. 1692 contains one 40x32mm stamp.

European Soccer Championships, Essen — A228

Designs: Various soccer players in action.

Perf. 13x12½, 12½x13

1988, Apr. 14

No.	Type	Description	Unused	Used
1693	A228	50c multicolored	.15	.15
1694	A228	1cor multicolored	.15	.15
1695	A228	2cor multi, vert.	.25	.15
1696	A228	3cor multi, vert.	.40	.22
1697	A228	4cor multi, vert.	.55	.25
1698	A228	5cor multi, vert.	.75	.35
1699	A228	6cor multicolored	.85	.40
		Nos. 1693-1699 (7)	3.10	1.67

Souvenir Sheet

Perf. 13

No.	Type	Description	Unused	Used
1700	A228	15cor multi, vert.	2.00	2.00

Nos. 1695-1700 are airmail. No. 1700 contains one 32x40mm stamp.

Sandanista Revolution, 9th Anniv. — A229

1988, July 19 *Perf. 13*

No.	Type	Description	Unused	Used
1701	A229	1cor shown	.15	.15
1702	A229	5cor Volcanoes, dove	.60	.30

No. 1702 is airmail.

Animals — A230

1988, Mar. 3 *Perf. 13x12½*

No.	Type	Description	Unused	Used
1703	A230	10c Bear, cub	.15	.15
1704	A230	15c Lion, cubs	.15	.15
1705	A230	25c Spaniel, pups	.15	.15
1706	A230	50c Wild boars	.15	.15
1707	A230	4cor Cheetah, cubs	.85	.35
1708	A230	7cor Hyenas	1.25	.70
1709	A230	8cor Fox, kit	1.50	.80
		Nos. 1703-1709 (7)	4.20	2.45

Souvenir Sheet

Perf. 12½

No.	Type	Description	Unused	Used
1710	A230	15cor House cat, kittens, vert.	2.00	1.65

Nos. 1707-1710 are airmail. No. 1710 contains one 32x40mm stamp.

Helicopters — A231

Illustration reduced.

1988, June 1 *Perf. 12½x12*

No.	Type	Description	Unused	Used
1711	A231	4cor B-206B-JRIII	.15	.15
1712	A231	12cor BK-117A-3	.20	.15
1713	A231	16cor B-360	.28	.15
1714	A231	20cor 109-MRII	.35	.18
1715	A231	24cor S-61	.42	.20
1716	A231	28cor SA-365N-D2	.50	.25
1717	A231	56cor S-76	1.00	.50
		Nos. 1711-1717 (7)	2.90	1.58

Souvenir Sheet

Perf. 13

No.	Type	Description	Unused	Used
1718	A231	120cor NH-90	2.50	2.50

Nos. 1712-1718 are airmail. No. 1718 contains one 40x32mm stamp.

Shells — A232

1988, Sept. 20 *Perf. 13*

No.	Type	Description	Unused	Used
1719	A232	4cor Strombus pugilis	.15	.15
1720	A232	12cor Polymita picta	.24	.15
1721	A232	16cor Architectonica maximum	.32	.16
1722	A232	20cor Pectens laqueatus	.40	.20
1723	A232	24cor Guildfordia triumphans	.50	.24
1724	A232	28cor Ranella pustulosa	.55	.32
1725	A232	50cor Trochus maculatus	1.00	.50
		Nos. 1719-1725 (7)	3.16	1.72

Nos. 1720-1725 are airmail.

Insects — A233

1988, Nov. 10

No.	Type	Description	Unused	Used
1726	A233	4cor Chrysina macropus	.15	.15
1727	A233	12cor Plusiotis victoriana	.25	.15
1728	A233	16cor Ceratotrupes bolivari	.35	.16
1729	A233	20cor Gymnetosoma stellata	.45	.20
1730	A233	24cor Euphoria lineoligera	.55	.25
1731	A233	28cor Euphoria candezei	.60	.30
1732	A233	50cor Sulcophanaeus chryseicollis	1.10	.50
		Nos. 1726-1732 (7)	3.45	1.71

Nos. 1727-1732 are airmail.

Heroes of the Revolution — A234

Designs: 4cor, Casimiro Sotelo Montenegro. 12cor, Ricardo Morales Aviles. 16cor, Silvio Mayorga Delgado. 20cor, Pedro Arauz Palacios. 24cor, Oscar A. Turcios Chavarrias. 28cor, Julio C. Buitrago Urroz. 50cor, Jose B. Escobar Perez. 100cor, Eduardo E. Contreras Escobar.

1988, Aug. 27 *Perf. 12½x12*

No.	Type	Description	Unused	Used
1733	A234	4cor sky blue	.15	.15
1734	A234	12cor red lilac	.24	.15
1735	A234	16cor yel grn	.32	.16
1736	A234	20cor org brown	.40	.20
1737	A234	24cor brown	.45	.24
1738	A234	28cor purple	.55	.32
1739	A234	50cor henna brown	.95	.50
1740	A234	100cor plum	1.90	.95
		Nos. 1733-1740 (8)	4.96	2.67

Nos. 1734-1740 are airmail.

Flowers — A235

Designs: 4cor, Acacia baileyana. 12cor, Anigozanthos manglesii. 16cor, Telopia speciosissima. 20cor, Eucalyptus ficifolia. 24cor, Boronia heterophylla. 28cor, Callistemon speciosus. 30cor, Nymphaea caerulea, horiz. 50cor, Clianthus formosus.

1988, Aug. 30 *Perf. 13*

No.	Type	Description	Unused	Used
1741	A235	4cor multicolored	.15	.15
1742	A235	12cor multicolored	.24	.15
1743	A235	16cor multicolored	.32	.16
1744	A235	20cor multicolored	.40	.20
1745	A235	24cor multicolored	.45	.24
1746	A235	28cor multicolored	.55	.48
1747	A235	30cor multicolored	.60	.30
1748	A235	50cor multicolored	1.00	.45
		Nos. 1741-1748 (8)	3.71	2.13

Nos. 1742-1748 are airmail.

A236 A237

Pre-Columbian Art: 4cor, Zapotec funeral urn. 12cor, Mochica ceramic kneeling man. 16cor, Mochica ceramic head. 20cor, Taina ceramic vase. 28cor, Nazca cup, horiz. 100cor, Inca pipe, horiz. 120cor, Aztec ceramic vessel, horiz.

Perf. 12x12¹/₂, 12¹/₂x12

1988, Oct. 12

1749 A236 4cor multicolored .15 .15
1750 A236 12cor multicolored .24 .15
1751 A236 16cor multicolored .32 .16
1752 A236 20cor multicolored .40 .20
1753 A236 28cor multicolored .55 .28
1754 A236 100cor multicolored 1.90 1.00
Nos. 1749-1754 (6) 3.56 1.94

Souvenir Sheet

Perf. 13x13¹/₂

1755 A236 120cor multicolored 2.25 1.10

Discovery of America, 500th anniv. (in 1992). Nos. 1750-1755 are airmail. Nos. 1749-1754 printed with se-tenant label. No. 1755 contains one 40x32mm stamp.

1988, Oct. 12 ***Perf. 12x12¹/₂***

1756 A237 25cor Ruben Dario .45 .20

Publication of "Blue," centenary. Printed se-tenant with label.

Tourism A238

1989, Feb. 5 ***Perf. 12¹/₂x12***

1757 A238 4cor Pochomil .15 .15
1758 A238 12cor Granada .24 .16
1759 A238 20cor Olof Palme Convention Center .40 .20
1760 A238 24cor Masaya Volcano Natl. Park .45 .24
1761 A238 28cor La Boquita .55 .25
1762 A238 30cor Xiloa .60 .25
1763 A238 50cor Hotels of Managua 1.00 .45
Nos. 1757-1763 (7) 3.39 1.70

Souvenir Sheet

Perf. 13

1764 A238 160cor Montelimar 2.00 2.00

Nos. 1758-1764 are airmail. No. 1764 contains one 40x32mm stamp.

French Revolution, Bicentennial A240

Designs: 50cor, Procession of the Estates General, Versailles. 300cor, Oath of the Tennis Court. 600cor, 14th of July, vert. 1000cor, Dancing Around the Liberty Tree. 2000cor, Liberty Guiding the People, vert. 3000cor, Storming the Bastille. 5000cor, Lafayette Swearing Allegiance to the Constitution, vert. 9000cor, La Marsiellaise, vert.

Perf. 12¹/₂x13 (50cor), 13x12¹/₂ (600, 2000cor), 12¹/₂

1989, July 14

Sizes: 50cor, 40x25mm

600cor, 2000cor, 33x44mm

1773 A240 50cor multicolored .15 .15
1774 A240 300cor shown .15 .15
1775 A240 600cor multicolored .16 .15
1776 A240 1000cor multicolored .28 .15
1777 A240 2000cor multicolored .55 .28
1778 A240 3000cor multicolored .90 .42
1779 A240 5000cor multicolored 1.40 .65
Nos. 1773-1779 (7) 3.59 1.95

Souvenir Sheet

Perf. 12¹/₂

1780 A240 9000cor multicolored 2.25 2.25

Philexfrance '89. #1774-1780 are airmail. #1780 contains one 32x40mm stamp.

Currency Reform

Currency reform took place Mar. 4, 1990. Until stamps in the new currency were issued, mail was to be handstamped "Franqueo Pagado," (Postage Paid). Stamps were not used again until Apr. 25, 1991. The following four sets were sold by the post office but were not valid for postage.

Ships

Stamp World London '90: 500cor, *Director.* 1000cor, *Independence.* 3000cor, *Orizaba.* 5000cor, SS *Lewis.* 10,000cor, *Golden Rule.* 30,000cor, *Santiago de Cuba.* 75,000cor, *Bahia de Corinto.* 100,000cor, *North Star.*

1990, Apr. 3 ***Perf. 12¹/₂x12***

500cor-100,000cor

Souvenir Sheet

Perf. 12¹/₂

75,000cor

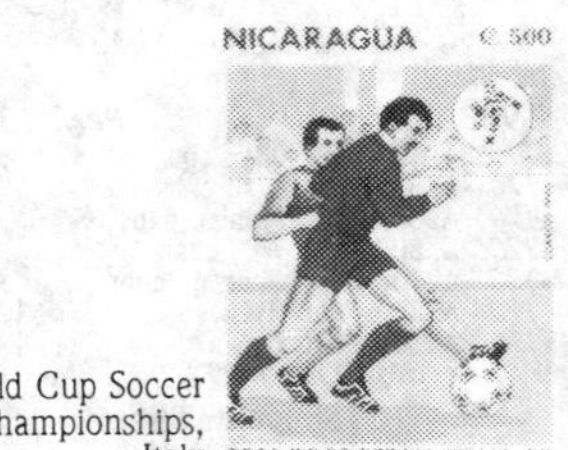

World Cup Soccer Championships, Italy

Designs: Various soccer players in action.

1990, Apr. 30 ***Perf. 13***

500cor-100,000cor

Souvenir Sheet

Perf. 12¹/₂

75,000cor

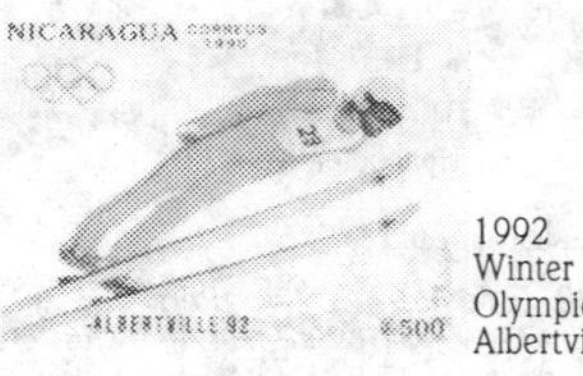

1992 Winter Olympics, Albertville

Designs: 500cor, Ski jumping. 1000cor, Downhill skiing. 3000cor, Figure skating, vert. 5000cor, Speed skating, vert. 10,000cor, Biathlon, vert. 30,000cor, Cross country skiing, vert. 75,000cor, Two-man bobsled, vert. 100,000cor, Ice hockey, vert.

1990, July 25 ***Perf. 13***

500cor-100,000cor

Souvenir Sheet

Perf. 12¹/₂

75,000cor

1992 Summer Olympics, Barcelona

Designs: 500cor, Javelin. 1000cor, Steeplechase. 3000cor, Handball. 5000cor, Basketball. 10,000cor, Gymnastics. 30,000cor, Cycling. 75,000cor, Soccer. 100,000cor, Boxing, horiz.

1990, Aug. 10 ***Perf. 13***

500cor-100,000cor

Souvenir Sheet

75,000cor

Birds A245

Designs: No. 1813, Apteryx owenii. No. 1814, Notornis mantelli. 10c, Cyanoramphus novaezelandiae. 20c, Gallirallus australis. 30c, Rhynochetos jubatus, vert. 60c, Nestor notabilis. 70c, Strigops habroptilus. 1.50cor, Cygnus atratus.

1990, Aug. 14 **Litho.** ***Perf. 12¹/₂***

1813 A245 5c multicolored .15 .15
1814 A245 5c multicolored .15 .15
1815 A245 10c multicolored .20 .15
1816 A245 20c multicolored .42 .20
1817 A245 30c multicolored .65 .32
1818 A245 60c multicolored 1.30 .65
1819 A245 70c multicolored 1.50 .75
Nos. 1813-1819 (7) 4.37 2.37

Souvenir Sheet

1820 A245 1.50cor multicolored 3.25 1.60

New Zealand '90, Intl. Philatelic Exhibition.

Fauna A246

1990, Oct. 10

1821 A246 5c Panthera onca .15 .15
1822 A246 5c Felis pardalis, vert. .15 .15
1823 A246 10c Atelles geoffrogi, vert. .20 .15
1824 A246 20c Tapirus bairdi .42 .20
1825 A246 30c Dasypus novencintus .65 .32
1826 A246 60c Canis latrans 1.30 .65
1827 A246 70c Choloepus hoffmanni 1.50 .75
Nos. 1821-1827 (7) 4.37 2.37

FAO, 45th anniv.

Flower Type of 1983 Redrawn Without Date

1991, Apr. 24 **Litho.** ***Perf. 14x13¹/₂***

Size: 19x22mm

1828 A151 1cor like #1220 .40 .15
1829 A151 2cor like #1212 .80 .15
1830 A151 3cor like #1218 1.20 .15
1831 A151 4cor like #1219 1.60 .15
1832 A151 5cor like #1217 2.00 .15
1833 A151 6cor like #1210 2.40 .15
1834 A151 7cor like #1216 2.80 .15
1835 A151 8cor like #1215 3.20 .15
1836 A151 9cor like #1211 3.60 .15
1837 A151 10cor like #1221 4.00 .15
1838 A151 11cor like #1214 4.40 .15
1839 A151 12cor like #1222 4.80 .15
1840 A151 13cor like #1213 5.20 .15
1841 A151 14cor like #1224 5.60 .15
1842 A151 15cor like #1223 6.00 .15
1843 A151 16cor like #1209 6.40 .15
Nos. 1828-1843 (16) 54.40
Set value 1.25

Dr. Pedro Joaquin Chamorro — A247

1991, Apr. 25 ***Perf. 14¹/₂x14***

1844 A247 2.25cor multicolored .90 .45

1990 World Cup Soccer Championships, Italy — A248

Designs: No. 1845, Two players. No. 1846, Four players, vert. 50c, Two players, referee. 1cor, Germany, five players, vert. 1.50cor, One player, vert. 3cor, Argentina, five players, vert. 3.50cor, Italian players. 7.50cor, German team with trophy.

Perf. 14x14¹/₂, 14¹/₂x14

1991, July 16

1845 A248 25c multicolored .15 .15
1846 A248 25c multicolored .15 .15
1847 A248 50c multicolored .20 .15
1848 A248 1cor multicolored .40 .20
1849 A248 1.50cor multicolored .60 .30
1850 A248 3cor multicolored 1.20 .60
1851 A248 3.50cor multicolored 1.40 .70
Nos. 1845-1851 (7) 4.10 2.25

Souvenir Sheet

1852 A248 7.50cor multicolored 3.00 1.50
a. Overprinted in sheet margin ('93) 3.15 1.60

No. 1852a overprint reads "COPA DE FOOTBALL / U.S.A. '94."

Butterflies — A249

Designs: No. 1853, Prepona praeneste. No. 1854, Anartia fatima. 50c, Eryphanis aesacus. 1cor, Heliconius melpomene. 1.50cor, Chlosyne janais. 3cor, Marpesia iole. 3.50cor, Metamorpha epaphus. 7.50cor, Morpho peleides.

1991, July 16 ***Perf. 14¹/₂x14***

1853 A249 25c multicolored .15 .15
1854 A249 25c multicolored .15 .15
1855 A249 50c multicolored .20 .15
1856 A249 1cor multicolored .40 .20
1857 A249 1.50cor multicolored .60 .30
1858 A249 3cor multicolored 1.20 .60
1859 A249 3.50cor multicolored 1.40 .70
Nos. 1853-1859 (7) 4.10 2.25

Souvenir Sheet

1860 A249 7.50cor multicolored 3.00 1.50

Miniature Sheet

Fauna of Rainforest — A250

Designs: a, Yellow-headed amazon. b, Toucan. c, Scarlet macaw (lapa roja). d, Quetzal. e, Spider monkey (mono arana). f, Capuchin monkey. g, Sloth (cucala). h, Oropendola. i, Violet sabrewing (colibri violeta). j, Tamandua. k, Jaguarundi. l, Boa constrictor. m, Iguana. n, Jaguar. o, White-necked jacobin. p, Doxocopa clothilda. q, Dismorphia deione. r, Golden arrow-poison frog (rana venenosa). s, Callithomia hezia. t, Chameleon.

1991, Aug. 7 **Litho.** ***Perf. 14x14¹/₂***

1861 A250 2.25cor Sheet of 20, #a.-t. 19.00 9.50

America Issue — A251

1991, Oct. 12 *Perf. 14½x14*
1862 A251 2.25cor Concepcion volcano .95 .48

Orchids A252

Designs: No. 1863, Isochilus major. No. 1864, Cycnoches ventricosum. 50c, Vanilla odorata. 1cor, Helleriella nicaraguensis. 1.50cor, Barkeria spectabilis. 3cor, Maxillaria hedwigae. 3.50cor, Cattleya aurantiaca. 7.50cor, Psygmorchis pusilla, vert.

1991 **Litho.** *Perf. 14x14½*
1863 A252 25c multicolored .15 .15
1864 A252 25c multicolored .15 .15
1865 A252 50c multicolored .16 .15
1866 A252 1cor multicolored .32 .16
1867 A252 1.50cor multicolored .48 .24
1868 A252 3cor multicolored .95 .48
1869 A252 3.50cor multicolored 1.10 .55
Nos. 1863-1869 (7) 3.31 1.88

Souvenir Sheet
Perf. 14½x14
1870 A252 7.50cor multicolored 3.00 1.50

Locomotives of South America — A253

Birds — A254

Various steam locomotives.

1991, Apr. 21 *Perf. 14½x14*
1871 A253 25c Bolivia .15 .15
1872 A253 25c Peru .15 .15
1873 A253 50c Argentina .16 .15
1874 A253 1.50cor Chile .48 .24
1875 A253 2cor Colombia .65 .32
1876 A253 3cor Brazil .95 .48
1877 A253 3.50cor Paraguay 1.10 .55
Nos. 1871-1877 (7) 3.64 2.04

Souvenir Sheets
1878 A253 7.50cor Nicaragua 2.50 1.25
1879 A253 7.50cor Guatemala 2.50 1.25

1991 *Perf. 14½x14, 14x14½*

Designs: 50c, Eumomota superciliosa. 75c, Trogon collaris. 1cor, Electron platyrhynchum. 1.50cor, Teleonema filicauda. 1.75cor, Tangara chilensis, horiz. No. 1885, Pharomachrus mocino. No. 1886, Phlegopsis nigromaculata. No. 1887, Hylophylax naevioides, horiz. No. 1888, Aulacorhynchus haematopygius, horiz.

1880 A254 50c multicolored .16 .15
1881 A254 75c multicolored .24 .15
1882 A254 1cor multicolored .32 .16
1883 A254 1.50cor multicolored .48 .24
1884 A254 1.75cor multicolored .55 .28
1885 A254 2.25cor multicolored .75 .35
1886 A254 2.25cor multicolored .75 .35
Nos. 1880-1886 (7) 3.25 1.68

Souvenir Sheets
1887 A254 7.50cor multicolored 2.50 1.25
1888 A254 7.50cor multicolored 2.50 1.25

Paintings by Vincent Van Gogh — A255

Designs: No. 1889, Head of a Peasant Woman Wearing a Bonnet. No. 1890, One-Eyed Man. 50c, Self-Portrait. 1cor, Vase with Carnations and Other Flowers. 1.50cor, Vase with Zinnias and Geraniums. 3cor, Portrait of Pere Tanguy. 3.50cor, Portrait of a Man, horiz. 7.50cor, Path Lined with Poplars, horiz.

1991 *Perf. 14x13½, 13½x14*
1889 A255 25c multicolored .15 .15
1890 A255 25c multicolored .15 .15
1891 A255 50c multicolored .16 .15
1892 A255 1cor multicolored .32 .16
1893 A255 1.50cor multicolored .48 .24
1894 A255 3cor multicolored .95 .48
1895 A255 3.50cor multicolored 1.10 .55
Nos. 1889-1895 (7) 3.31 1.88

Size: 128x102mm
Imperf
1896 A255 7.50cor multicolored 2.50 1.25

Phila Nippon '91 A256

Designs: 25c, Golden Hall. 50c, Phoenix Hall. 1cor, Bunraku puppet head. 1.50cor, Japanese cranes. 2.50cor, Himeji Castle. 3cor, Statue of the Guardian. 3.50cor, Kabuki warrior. 7.50cor, Vase.

1991 *Perf. 14x14½*
1897 A256 25c multicolored .15 .15
1898 A256 50c multicolored .16 .15
1899 A256 1cor multicolored .32 .16
1900 A256 1.50cor multicolored .48 .24
1901 A256 2.50cor multicolored .80 .40
1902 A256 3cor multicolored .95 .48
1903 A256 3.50cor multicolored 1.10 .55
Nos. 1897-1903 (7) 3.96 2.13

Souvenir Sheet
1904 A256 7.50cor multicolored 2.50 1.25

Inscriptions are switched on 50c and 2.50cor.

Child's Drawing A257

1991
1905 A257 2.25cor multicolored .72 .36

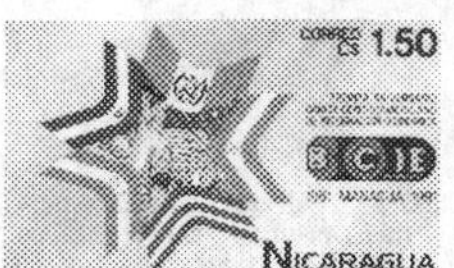

Central American Bank of Economic Integration, 30th Anniv. A258

1991, Aug. 1 **Litho.** *Perf. 14*
1906 A258 1.50cor multicolored .65 .52

No. 1906 printed with se-tenant label.

Discovery of America, 500th Anniv. (in 1992) — A259

1991, Oct. 12 *Perf. 14½x14*
1907 A259 2.25cor Columbus' fleet .95 .75

Swiss Confederation, 700th Anniv. (in 1991) — A260

1992, Aug. 1 **Litho.** *Perf. 14x14½*
1908 A260 2.25cor black & red .95 .75

Contemporary Art — A261

Designs: No. 1909, Pitcher, by Jose Ortiz. No. 1910, Black jar, by Lorenza Pineda Cooperative, vert. 50c, Vase, by Elio Gutierrez, vert. 1cor, Christ on Cross, by Jose de Los Santos, vert. 1.50cor, Sculpture of family, by Erasmo Moya, vert. 3cor, Bird and fish, by Silvio Chavarria Cooperative. 3.50cor, Filigree jar, by Maria de Los Angeles Bermudez, vert. 7.50cor, Masks by Jose Flores.

Perf. 14x14½, 14½x14
1992, Sept. 17 **Litho.**
1909 A261 25c multicolored .15 .15
1910 A261 25c multicolored .15 .15
1911 A261 50c multicolored .22 .15
1912 A261 1cor multicolored .45 .22
1913 A261 1.50cor multicolored .65 .32
1914 A261 3cor multicolored 1.30 .65
1915 A261 3.50cor multicolored 1.50 .75
Nos. 1909-1915 (7) 4.42 2.39

Imperf
Size: 100x70mm
1916 A261 7.50cor multicolored 3.25 1.60

Miniature Sheet

Fauna and Flora of Rainforest — A262

Designs: a, Colibri magnifico (b). b, Aguila arpia (f). c, Orchids. d, Toucan, Mariposa morpho. e, Quetzal (i). f, Guardabarranco (g, k). g, Mono aullador (howler monkey). h, Perezoso (sloth). i, Mono ardilla (squirrel monkey). j, Guacamaya (macaw) (n). k, Boa esmeralda, Tanagra escarlata (emerald boa, scarlet tanager). l, Rana flecha venenosa (arrow frog). m, Jaguar. n, Oso hormiguero (anteater) (o). o, Ocelot. p, Coati.

1992, Nov. 12 *Perf. 14½x14*
1917 A262 1.50cor Sheet of 16, #a.-p. 10.00 5.00

1992 Winter Olympics, Albertville A263

Perf. 14x14½, 14½x14
1992, Sept. 17
1918 A263 25c Ice hockey .15 .15
1919 A263 25c 4-man bobsled .15 .15
1920 A263 50c Combined slalom, vert. .22 .15
1921 A263 1cor Speed skating .45 .22
1922 A263 1.50cor Cross-country skiing .65 .32
1923 A263 3cor Double luge 1.35 .65
1924 A263 3.50cor Ski jumping, vert. 1.50 .75
Nos. 1918-1924 (7) 4.47 2.39

Imperf
Size: 100x70mm
1925 A263 7.50cor Slalom 3.15 1.60
a. Overprinted ('93) 3.15 1.60

No. 1925a overprint reads "JUEGOS PRE OLIMPICOS DE INVIERNO / LILLEHAMMER, NORUEGA."

1992 Summer Olympics, Barcelona A264

Perf. 14x14½, 14½x14
1992, Sept. 17 **Litho.**
1926 A264 25c Javelin .15 .15
1927 A264 25c Fencing .15 .15
1928 A264 50c Basketball .22 .15
1929 A264 1.50cor 1500-meter race .65 .32
1930 A264 2cor Long jump .85 .42
1931 A264 3cor Women's 10,000-meter race 1.25 .65
1932 A264 3.50cor Equestrian 1.50 .75
Nos. 1926-1932 (7) 4.77 2.59

Imperf
Size: 100x70mm
1933 A264 7.50cor Canoeing 3.15 1.60
a. Overprinted ('93) 3.15 1.60

Nos. 1927-1932 are vert. Dated 1991.
No. 1933a overprint reads "JUEGOS PRE OLIMPICOS DE VERANO / ATLANTA, GA. / ESTADOS UNIDOS DE AMERICA."

Father R. M. Fabretto and Children A265

1992, Nov. 12 **Litho.** *Perf. 14x14½*
1934 A265 2.25cor multicolored .95 .48

Nicaraguan Natives, by Claudia Gordillo A266

1992, Nov. 12
1935 A266 2.25cor black & brown .95 .48

Nicaraguan Caciques, by Milton Jose Cruz A267

1992, Nov. 12
1936 A267 2.25cor multicolored .95 .48

Contemporary Paintings — A268

Paintings by: No. 1937, Alberto Ycaza, vert. No. 1938, Alejandro Arostegui, vert. 50c, Bernard Dreyfus. 1.50cor, Orlando Sobalvarro. 2cor, Hugo Palma. 3cor, Omar D'Leon. 3.50cor, Carlos Montenegro, vert. 7.50cor, Federico Nordalm.

1992 *Perf. 14½x14, 14x14½*
1937 A268 25c multicolored .15 .15
1938 A268 25c multicolored .15 .15
1939 A268 50c multicolored .22 .15
1940 A268 1.50cor multicolored .65 .32
1941 A268 2cor multicolored .85 .42
1942 A268 3cor multicolored 1.25 .65
1943 A268 3.50cor multicolored 1.50 .75
Nos. 1937-1943 (7) 4.77 2.59

Imperf
Size: 100x70mm
1944 A268 7.50cor multicolored 3.15 1.60

Monument to Columbus, Rivas — A269

Catholic Religion in Nicaragua, 460th Anniv. — A270

1993, Mar. 22 *Perf. 14½x14*

1945 A269 2.25cor multicolored .95 .48

UPAEP issue. Dated 1992.

1993, Mar. 22

Designs: 25c, Eucharistic gonfalon. 50c, Statue of Virgin Mary. 1cor, Document, 1792-93. 1.50cor, Baptismal font. 2cor, Statue of Madonna and Child. 2.25cor, Monsignor Diego Alvarez Osario. 3cor, Christ on cross.

1946	A270	25c	multicolored	.15	.15
1947	A270	50c	multicolored	.22	.15
1948	A270	1cor	multicolored	.42	.20
1949	A270	1.50cor	multicolored	.65	.32
1950	A270	2cor	multicolored	.85	.42
1951	A270	2.25cor	multicolored	.95	.48
1952	A270	3cor	multicolored	1.25	.65
			Nos. 1946-1952 (7)	4.49	2.37

Dated 1992.

A271 A272

Archdiocese of Managua: a, 3cor, Cathedral of the Immaculate Conception. b, 4cor, Cross, map.

1993, Apr. 30

1953 A271 Pair, #a.-b. 3.00 1.50

Dated 1992.

1994, Jan. 28 **Litho.** *Perf. 14*

Player, country: 50c, Brolin, Sweden. No. 1955, Karas, Poland; Costa, Brazil. No. 1956, Bossis, Platini, France. 1.50cor, Schumacher, Germany. 2cor, Zubizarreta, Spain. 2.50cor, Matthaeus, Germany; Maradona, Argentina. 3.50cor, Robson, England; Santos, Portugal. 10cor, Biyik, Cameroun; Valderrama, Colombia.

1954	A272	50c	multicolored	.22	.15
1955	A272	1cor	multicolored	.42	.22
1956	A272	1cor	multicolored	.42	.22
1957	A272	1.50cor	multicolored	.65	.32
1958	A272	2cor	multicolored	.85	.42
1959	A272	2.50cor	multicolored	1.10	.55
1960	A272	3.50cor	multicolored	1.50	.75
			Nos. 1954-1960 (7)	5.16	2.63

Souvenir Sheet

1961 A272 10cor multicolored 4.25 2.00

1994 World Cup Soccer Championships, US.

Sonatina, by Alma Iris Prez — A272a

1993, Oct. 29 **Litho.** *Perf. 13½x14*

1961A A272a 3cor multicolored 1.00 1.00

Miniature Sheet

Butterfly Fish — A273

Designs: a, Chaetodon lunula. b, Chaetodon rainfordi. c, Chaetodon reticulatus. d, Chaetodon auriga. e, Heniochus acuminatus. f, Coradion fulvocinctus. g, Chaetodon speculum. h, Chaetodon lineolatus. i, Chaetodon bennetti. j, Chaetodon melanotus. k, Chaetodon aureus. l. Chaetodon ephippium. m, Hemitaurichthys polylepis. n, Chaetodon semeion. o, Chaetodon kleinii. p, Chelmon rostratus.

1993, Nov. 18 **Litho.** *Perf. 14*

1962 A273 1.50cor Sheet of 16, #a.-p. 10.00 5.00

q. Inscribed with Bangkok '93 emblem in sheet margin 10.00 5.00

r. Inscribed with Indopex '93 emblem in sheet margin 10.00 5.00

Issue date: No. 1962, Nov. 1, 1993.

No. 1962 inscribed with Taipei '93 emblem in sheet margin.

1994 Winter Olympics, Lillehammer, 1996 Summer Olympics, Atlanta A274

1993, Nov. 18

1963	A274	25c	Downhill skiing	.15	.15
1964	A274	25c	Four-man bobsled	.15	.15
1965	A274	25c	Swimming	.15	.15
1966	A274	25c	Diving	.15	.15
1967	A274	50c	Speed skating	.22	.15
1968	A274	50c	Race walking	.22	.15
1969	A274	1cor	Hurdles	.42	.20
1970	A274	1.50cor	Ski jumping	.65	.32
1971	A274	1.50cor	Women's gymnastics	.65	.32
1972	A274	2cor	Women's figure skating	.85	.42
1973	A274	3cor	Pairs figure skating	1.25	.65
1974	A274	3cor	Javelin	1.25	.65
1975	A274	3.50cor	Biathlon	1.50	.75
1976	A274	3.50cor	Running	1.50	.75
			Nos. 1963-1976 (14)	9.11	4.96

Souvenir Sheets

1977 A274 7.50cor Torch, hands 3.25 1.50

1978 A274 7.50cor Flags 3.25 1.50

1994 Winter Olympics (#1963-1964, 1967, 1970, 1972-1973, 1975, 1978). Others, 1996 Summer Olympics.

Pan-American Health Organization, 90th Anniv. — A275

1993, June 16 *Perf. 14½*

1979 A275 3cor multicolored 1.25 .65

Organization of American States, 23rd General Assembly — A276

1993, June 7 *Perf. 13½x14*

1980 A276 3cor multicolored 1.25 .65

Christmas — A276a

Paintings: 1cor, Holy Family, by unknown painter. 4cor, Birth of Christ, by Lezamon.

1994, Feb. 23 **Litho.** *Perf. 13½x14*

1980A A276a 1cor multicolored .35 .18

1980B A276a 4cor multicolored 1.40 .70

Miniature Sheet

Fauna and Flora of Rainforest — A277

Designs: a, Bromeliacae. b, Tilmatura dupontii. c, Anolis biporcatus (b). d, Fulgara laternaria. e, Bradypus. f, Spizaetus ornatus. g, Cotinga amabilis. h, Bothrops schlegelii. i, Odontoglossum. j, Agalychnis callidryas. k, Heliconius spaho. l, Passiflora vitifolia.

No. 1982, Dasyprocta punctata. No. 1983, Melinaea lilis.

1994, Jan. 20 *Perf. 14*

1981 A277 2cor Sheet of 12, #a.-l. 10.00 5.00

Souvenir Sheets

1982 A277 10cor multicolored 3.50 1.75

1983 A277 10cor multicolored 3.50 1.75

Miniature Sheet

Hong Kong '94 — A278

Butterflies: a, Callicore patelina. b, Chlosyne narva. c, Anteos maerula. d, Marpesia petreus. e, Pierella helvetia. f, Eurytides epidaus. g, Heliconius doris. h, Smyrna blomfildia. i, Eueides lybia. j, Adelpha heraclea. k, Heliconius hecale. l, Parides montezuma. m, Morpho polyphemus. n, Eresia alsina. o, Prepona omphale. p, Morpho granadensis.

1994, Feb. 18 **Litho.** *Perf. 14*

1984 A278 1.50cor Sheet of 16 8.25 4.00

Miniature Sheet

Astronomers — A279

Copernicus and: a, Satellite. b, Tycho Brahe (1546-1601), making observations. c, Galileo probe, Galileo. d, Isaac Newton, Newton telescope. e, Giotto probe to Halley's comet, Edmund Halley. f, James Bradley (1693-1762), Grenwich Observatory. g, 1793 telescope, William Herschel (1738-1822). h, John Goodricke (1764-86), stellar eclipse. i, Gottingen observatory, Karl Fredrich Gauss (1777-1855). j, Friedrich Bessell (1784-1846), astronomical instrument. k, Harvard College Observatory, William Granch (1783-1859). l, George B. Airy (1801-92), stellar disc. m, Lowell Observatory, Flagstaff, Arizona, Percival Lowell (1855-1916). n, George A. Halle (1868-1938), solar spectrograph. o, Space telescope, Edwin Hubble (1889-1953). p, Gerard Kuiper (1905-73), Uranus' moon Miranda.

10cor, Nicolas Copernicus, interstellar probe.

1994, Apr. 4

1985 A279 1.50cor Sheet of 16 8.25 4.00

Souvenir Sheet

1986 A279 10cor multicolored 3.50 1.75

Miniature Sheet

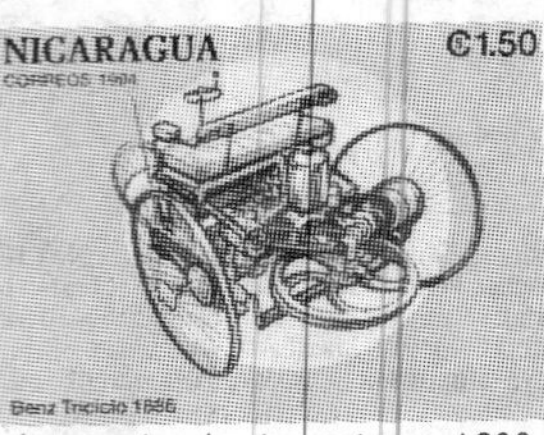

Automotive Anniversaries — A280

Designs: a, 1886 Benz three-wheel car. b, 1909 Benz Blitzen. c, 1923 Mercedes Benz 24/100/140. d, 1928 Mercedes Benz SSK. e, 1934 Mercedes Benz Cabriolet 500k. f, 1949 Mercedes Benz 170S. g, 1954 Mercedes Benz W196. h, 1954 Mercedes Benz 300SL. i, 1896 Ford four-wheel car. j, 1920 Ford taxi. k, 1928 Ford Roadster. l, 1932 Ford V-8. m, 1937 Ford 78 (V-8). n, 1939 Ford 91 Deluxe Tudor Sedan. o, 1946 Ford V-8 Sedan Coupe. p, 1958 Ford Custom 300.

10cor, Henry Ford (1863-1947), 1903 Ford Model A; Karl Benz (1844-1929), 1897 Benz 5CH.

1994, Apr. 5

1987 A280 1.50cor Sheet of 16 8.25 4.00

Souvenir Sheet

1988 A280 10cor multicolored 3.50 1.75

First Benz four-wheeled vehicle, cent. (Nos. 1987a-1987h). First Ford gasoline engine, cent. (Nos. 1987i-1987p).

Miniature Sheet

Graf Zeppelin A281

Graf Zeppelin and: a, Dr. Hugo Eckener, Count Zeppelin (inside cabin). b, New York City, 1928. c, Tokyo, 1929. d, San Simeon, California, 1929. e, Col. Charles Lindbergh, Dr. Hugo Eckener, 1929. f, Moscow, 1930. g, Paris, 1930. h, Cairo, 1931. i, Arctic waters. j, Rio de Janeiro, 1932. k, London, 1935. l, St. Peter's Basilica, Vatican City. m, Swiss Alps. n, Brandenburg Gate. o, Eckener in control room. p, Ernest A. Lehman, DO-X.

No. 1990, Graf Zeppelin, Count Zeppelin. No. 1991, Zeppelin, Eckener.

1994, Apr. 6

1989 A281 1.50cor Sheet of 16 8.25 4.00

Souvenir Sheets

1990 A281 10cor multicolored 3.50 1.75

1991 A281 10cor multicolored 3.50 1.75

Dr. Hugo Eckener (1868-1954) (#1991).

Contemporary Crafts — A282

Designs: No. 1992, 50c, Basket weaving, by Rosalia Sevilla, horiz. No. 1993, 50c, Wood carving, by Julio Lopez. No. 1994, 1cor, Woman carrying sack, by Indiana Robleto. No. 1995, 1cor, Church, by Auxiliadora Bush. 2.50cor, Carving, by Jose de Los Santos. 3cor, Costumed doll with horse's head, by Ines Gutierrez de Chong. 4cor, Ceramic container, by Elio Gutierrez.

10cor, Metate, by Saul Carballo.

Perf. 13½x14, 14x13½

1994, Feb. 15 **Litho.**

1992-1998 A282 Set of 7 4.25 2.00

Imperf

Size: 96x66mm

1999 A282 10cor multicolored 3.25 1.65

Dated 1993.

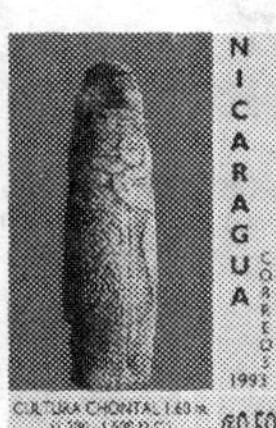

Stone Carvings, Chontal Culture — A283

Color of inscription tablet: #2000, 50c, Yellow. #2001, 50c, Yellow brown. #2002, 1cor, Green. #2003, 1cor, Yellow green. 2.50cor, Greenish blue. 3cor, Blue. 4cor, Grey green.

10cor, Two stone totems seen against landscape painting.

1994, Feb. 23 *Perf. 14*

2000-2006 A283 Set of 7 4.25 2.00

Imperf

Size: 96x66mm

2007 A283 10cor multicolored 3.25 1.65

Dated 1993.

Contemporary Art — A284

Designs: No. 2008, 50c, Lady Embroidering, by Guillermo Rivas Navas. No. 2009, 50c, Virgin of Nicaragua, by Cella Lacayo. No. 2010, 1cor, The Dance, by June Beer. No. 2011, 1cor, Song of Peace, by Alejandro Canales. 2.50cor, Fruits, by Genaro Lugo, horiz. 3cor, Figures and Fragments, by Leonel Vanegas. 4cor, Eruption of Volcano of Water, by Asilia Guillen, horiz.

10cor, Still life, by Alejandro Alonso Rochi.

Perf. 14x13½, 13½x14

1994, Mar. 15

2008-2014 A284 Set of 7 4.25 2.00

Imperf

Size: 96x66mm

2015 A284 10cor multicolored 3.25 1.65

Dated 1993.

Prominent Nicaraguan Philatelists — A285

Designs: 1cor, Gabriel Horvilleur (1907-91). 3cor, Jose S. Cuadra A. (1932-92). 4cor, Alfredo Pertz (1864-1948).

1994, Apr. 18 Litho. *Perf. 14*

2016-2018 A285 Set of 3 2.75 1.40

Dated 1993.

First Tree Conference of Nicaragua A286

1994, June 5 *Perf. 14x13½*

2019 A286 4cor multicolored 1.40 .70

Souvenir Sheets

Reported Alien Sightings — A287

Design, location: No. 2020, July 21, 1991, Missouri. No. 2021, July 28, 1965, Argentina. No. 2022, Aug. 21, 1955, Kentucky. No. 2023, Oct. 25, 1973, Pennsylvania. No. 2024, Sept. 19, 1961, New Hampshire. No. 2025, Nov. 7, 1989, Kansas. No. 2026, Sept. 26, 1976, Grand Canary Island. No. 2027, May 8, 1973, Texas.

1994, May 25 Litho. *Perf. 14*

2020-2027 A287 60cor each 21.00 21.00

Sacred Art — A288

Designs: No. 2028, 50c, Pulpit, Cathedral of Leon. No. 2029, 50c, Statue of Saint Ann, Chinandega Parish. No. 2030, 1cor, Statue of St. Joseph, San Pedro Parish, Rivas. No. 2031, 1cor, Statue of St. James, Jinotepe Parish. 2.50cor, Chalice, Subtiava Temple, Leon. 3cor, Processional cross, Nequinohoma Parish, Masaya. 4cor, Crucifix, Temple of Miracles, Managua.

10cor, Silver frontal, San Pedro Parish, Rivas.

1994, July 11 Litho. *Perf. 14*

2028-2035 A288 Set of 7 4.25 2.25

Size: 96x66mm

Imperf

2036 A288 10cor multicolored 3.50 1.75

A289 A290

1994, July 4 Litho. *Perf. 14*

2037 A289 3cor multicolored 1.00 1.00

Intl. Conference of New or Restored Democracies.

1994, Aug. 2

2038 A290 4cor multicolored 1.50 1.50

32nd World Amateur Baseball Championships.

Miniature Sheet of 8

PHILAKOREA '94 — A291

Designs: a, Soraksan. b, Statue of Kim Yu-Shin. c, Solitary Rock. d, Waterfall, Hallasan Valley. e, Mirukpong and Pisondae. f, Chonbuldong Valley. g, Bridge of the Seven Nymphs. h, Piryong Falls.

No. 2040, Boy on first birthday, gifts of fruit.

1994, Aug. 16

2039 A291 1.50cor #a.-h. 4.00 4.00

Souvenir Sheet

2040 A291 10cor multicolored 3.00 3.00

Miniature Sheet of 16

Dinosaurs A292

Designs: a, Tyrannosaurus rex. b, Plateosaurus (f-g). c, Pteranodon (b). d, Camarasaurus (c). e, Euplocephalus. f, Sacuanjoche. g, Deinonychus (h). h, Chasmosaurus (d). i, Dimorphodon. j, Ametriorhynchids (i). k, Ichthyosaurus (j). l, Pterapsis, Compsognathus. m, Cephalopod. n, Archelon (o). o, Griphognatus, Gyroptychius. p, Plesiosaur (o), Navtiloid.

1994, Sept. 1

2041 A292 1.50cor #a.-p. 8.50 8.50

Miniature Sheet of 8

1994 World Cup Soccer Championships, US — A293

Players: a, Rai. b, Freddy Rincon. c, Luis Garcia. d, Thomas Dooley. e, Franco Baresi. f, Tony Meola. g, Enzo Francescoli. h, Roy Wegerle.

No. 2043, Faustino Asprilla. No. 2044, Adolfo Valencia, horiz.

1994, Sept. 19

2042 A293 3cor #a.-h. 7.50 7.50

Souvenir Sheets

2043-2044 A293 10cor each 3.00 3.00

Miniature Sheet of 6

D-Day, 50th Anniv. A294

Designs: a, British fighter plane. b, C-47 transports dropping paratroopers. c, HMS Mauritius bombards Houlgate. d, Mulberry artificial harbor. e, Churchill tank. f, Landing craft approaching beach.

1994, Sept. 26

2045 A294 3cor #a.-f. 6.00 6.00

Ruben Dario National Theater, 25th Anniv. A295

1994, Sept. 30

2046 A295 3cor multicolored 1.00 1.00

Intl. Olympic Committee, Cent. A296 A297

Gold Medalists: No. 2047, Cassius Clay (Muhammad Ali), boxing, 1960. No. 2048, Renate Stecher, track, 1972, 1976. 10cor, Claudia Pechstein, speed skating, 1994.

1994, Oct. 3

2047 A296 3.50cor multicolored 1.25 1.25

2048 A296 3.50cor multicolored 1.25 1.25

Souvenir Sheet

2049 A297 10cor multicolored 3.25 3.25

La Carreta Nagua, by Erick Joanello Montoya A298

1994, Oct. 19

2050 A298 4cor multicolored 1.25 1.25

Miniature Sheet of 12

Motion Pictures, Cent. — A299

Film, director: a, The Kid, Charlie Chaplin. b, Citizen Kane, Orson Welles. c, Lawrence of Arabia, David Lean. d, Ivan the Terrible, Sergei Eisenstein. e, Metropolis, Fritz Lang. f, The Ten Commandments, Cecil B. DeMille. g, Gandhi, Richard Attenborough. h, Casablanca, Michael Curtis. i, Platoon, Oliver Stone. j, The Godfather, Francis Ford Coppola. k, 2001: A Space Odyssey, Stanley Kubrick. l, The Ocean Depths, Jean Renoir.

No. 2052, Gone With the Wind, Victor Fleming.

1994

2051 A299 2cor #a.-l. 8.00 8.00

Souvenir Sheet

2052 A299 15cor multicolored 5.00 5.00

Miniature Sheet of 16

Wildlife A300

Designs: a, Nyticorax nyticorax. b, Ara macao. c, Bulbulcus ibis. d, Coragyps atratus. e, Epicrates cenchria. f, Cyanerpes cyaneus. g, Ortalis vetula. h, Bradypus griseus. i, Felis onca. j, Anhinga anhinga. k, Tapirus bairdi. l, Myrmecophaga jubata. m, Iguana iguana. n, Chelydra serpentina. o, Dendrocygna autumnalis. p, Felis paradalis.

1994

2053 A300 2cor #a.-p. 10.50 10.50

Miniature Sheet of 8

First Manned Moon Landing, 25th Anniv. — A301

Designs: a, Docking command, lunar modules. b, Lift-off. c, Entering lunar orbit. d, Footprint on moon. e, Separation of first stage. f, Trans-lunar insertion. g, Lander descending toward moon. h, Astronaut on moon.

No. 2055, Astronaut saluting, flag. No. 2056, Astronauts in quarantine, horiz.

1994

2054 A301 3cor #a.-h. 8.00 8.00

Souvenir Sheets

2055-2056 A301 10cor each 3.25 3.25

Nos. 2055-2056 contain 29x47mm stamps.

Contemporary Art — A302

Paintings by Rodrigo Penalba: 50c, Discovery of America. 1cor, Portrait of Maurice. 1.50cor, Portrait of Franco. 2cor, Portrait of Mimi Hammer. 2.50cor, Seated Woman. 3cor, Still Life, horiz. 4cor, Portrait of Maria Augusta. 15cor, Entrance to Anticoli.

1994

2057-2063 A302 Set of 7 4.75 4.75

Size: 66x96mm

Imperf

2064 A302 15cor multicolored 4.75 4.75

Miniature Sheet of 16

Domestic Cats — A303

Designs: a, Chocolate point Himalayan. b, Red Somalian. c, American long hair. d, Russian blue. e, Scottish folded ear. f, Persian chinchilla. g, Egyptian mau. h, Manx blue cream. i, Burmese blue Malaysian. j, Balinesian seal point. k, Oriental long-haired blue. l, Persian chinchilla cameo. m, Angora. n, Siamese. o, Burmese seal point. p, Mixed red.

15cor, Golden shoulder Persian.

1994, Dec. 20 Litho. *Perf. 14*

2065 A303 1.50cor #a.-p. 8.00 8.00

Souvenir Sheet

2066 A303 15cor multicolored 5.00 5.00

No. 2066 contains one 38x51mm stamp.

Wild Fowl A304

Penelopina nigra: No. 2067a, 50c, Male, female on tree branch. b, 1cor, Head of male, male on tree branch. c, 2.50cor, Head of female, female on tree branch. d, 3cor, Male spreading wings, female. No. 2068, Heads of male, female.

No. 2069, Anhinga anhinga.

1994, Dec. 20 Litho. *Perf. 14*

2067 A304 Vert. strip of 4, #a.-d. 2.25 2.25

Souvenir Sheets

2068-2069 A304 15cor each 4.75 4.75

World Wildlife Fund (#2067).

No. 2067 was issued in minature sheets of 3 strips.

Sculpture — A305

Designs: 50c, Truth, by Aparicio Arthola. 1cor, Owl, by Orlando Sobalvarro. 1.50cor, Small Music Player, by Noel Flores Castro. 2cor, Exodus II, by Miguel Angel Abarca. 2.50cor, Raza, by Fernando Saravia. 3cor, Dolor Incognito, by Edith Gron. 4cor, Heron, by Ernesto Cardenal.

No. 2077, 15cor, Atlante, by Jorge Navas Cordonero. No. 2078, 15cor, Motherhood, by Rodrigo Penalba.

1995, Feb. 23 Litho. *Perf. 14½*

2070-2076 A305 Set of 7 4.50 4.50

Size: 66x96mm

Imperf

2077-2078 A305 each 4.50 4.50

Historic Landmarks A306

Designs: 50c, Animas Chapel, Granada, vert. 1cor, San Francisco Convent, Granada. 1.50cor, Santiago Tower, Leon, vert. 2cor, Santa Ana Church, Nindiri. 2.50cor, Santa Ana Church, Nandaime, vert. 3cor, Lion Gate, Granada. 4cor, Castle of the Immaculate Conception, Rio San Juan.

15cor, Hacienda San Jacinto, Managua.

1995 Litho. *Perf. 14*

2079-2085 A306 Set of 7 4.50 4.50

Size: 96x66mm

2086 A306 15cor multicolored 4.50 4.50

Miniature Sheets of 9

Korean Baseball Championships A307

LG Twins: No. 2087a, D.H. Han. b, Y.S. Kim. c, J.H. Yoo. d, Y.B. Seo. e, Team logo. f, J.H. Park. g, S.H. Lee. h, D.S. Kim. i, J.H. Kim.

Samsung Lions: No. 2088a, J.L. Ryu. b, S.Y. Kim. c, S.R. Kim. d, B.C. Dong. e, Team logo. f, K.W. Kang. g, C.S. Park. h, J.H. Yang. i, T.H. Kim.

SBW Raiders: No. 2089a, H.J. Park. b, K.J. Cho. c, K.T. Kim. d, W.H. Kim. e, Team logo. f, I.H. Baik. g, S.K. Park. h, K.L. Kim. i, J.S. Park.

Doosan OB Bears: No. 2090a, M.S. Lee. b, C.S. Park. c, H.S. Lim. d, K.W. Kim. e, Team logo. f, J.S. Kim. g, T.H. Kim. h, H.S. Kim. i, S.J. Kim.

Pacific Dolphins: No. 2091a, M.W. Jung. b, K.K. Kim. c, H.J. Kim. d, M.T. Chung. e, Team logo. f, B.W. An. g, D.G. Yoon. h, S.D. Choi. i, D.K. Kim.

Hanwha Eagles: No. 2092a, J.H. Jang. b, Y.D. Han. c, K.D. Lee. d, J.S. Park. e, Team logo. f, M.C. Jeong. g, J.W. Song. h, J.G. Kang. i, D.S. Koo.

Lotte Giants: No. 2093a, H.K. Yoon. b, D.H. Park. c, H.K. Joo. d, E.G. Kim. e, Team logo. f, J.T. Park. g, P.S. Kong. h, J.S. Yeom. i, M.H. Kim.

Haitai Tigers: No. 2094a, D.Y. Sun. b, J.B. Lee. c, J.S. Kim. d, S.H. Kim. e, Team logo. f, G.C. Lee. g, G.H. Cho. h, S.H. Kim. i, S.C. Lee.

1995, Mar. 25 Litho. *Perf. 14*

2087-2094 A307 3.50cor #a.-i., each 9.50 9.50

Nature Paintings — A308

Designs: 1cor, Advancing Forward, by Maria Jose Zamora. 2cor, Natural Death, by Rafael Castellon. 4cor, Captives of Water, by Alvaro Gutierrez.

1995, Apr. 4 Litho. *Perf. 14*

2095-2097 A308 Set of 3 2.25 2.25

British-Nicaragua Expedition, San Juan River — A309

1995, May 5

2098 A309 4cor multicolored 1.25 1.25

Boaco Festival A310

1995, May 10

2099 A310 4cor multicolored 1.25 1.25

Printed with se-tenant label.

Contemporary Paintings, by Armando Morales — A311

Designs: 50c, Ferry Boat. 1cor, Oliverio Castañeda, vert. 1.50cor, Sitting Nude, vert. 2cor, Señoritas at the Port of Cabeza. 2.50cor, The Automobile and Company, vert. 3cor, Bullfight, vert. 4cor, Still life.

15cor, Woman Sleeping.

1995 Litho. *Perf. 14*

2100-2106 A311 Set 7 4.50 4.50

Size: 96x66mm

2107 A311 15cor multicolored 4.50 4.50

Louis Pasteur (1822-95) — A312

1995, Sept. 28 Litho. *Perf. 14*

2108 A312 4cor multicolored 1.25 1.25

First Place in Childrens' Painting Contest A313

Nature scene, by Brenda Jarquin Gutierrez.

1995, Oct. 9

2109 A313 3cor multicolored .90 .90

Miniature Sheet

Animals A314

No. 2110: a, Crocodile. b, Opossum. c, Zahina. d, Guardatinale. e, Frog. f, Iguana. g, Macaw. h, Capybara. i, Vampire bat.

No. 2111, Jaguar, vert. No. 2112, Eagle, vert.

1995

2110 A314 2.50cor Sheet of 9, #a.-i. 6.75 6.75

Souvenir Sheets

2111-2112 A314 15cor each 4.50 4.50

Issued: #2112, 4/15; #2110-2111, 10/9.

FAO, 50th Anniv. — A315

UN, 50th Anniv. — A316

1995, Oct. 16

2113 A315 4cor multicolored 1.25 1.25

1995, Oct. 31

No. 2114: a, 3cor, UN flag, doves, rainbow. b, 4cor, Rainbow, lion, lamb. c, 5cor, Rainbow, dove on soldier's helmet.

No. 2115, Children holding hands under sun, dove.

2114 A316 Strip of 3, #a.-c. 3.75 3.75

Souvenir Sheet

2115 A316 10cor multicolored 3.00 3.00

No. 2114 is a continuous design.

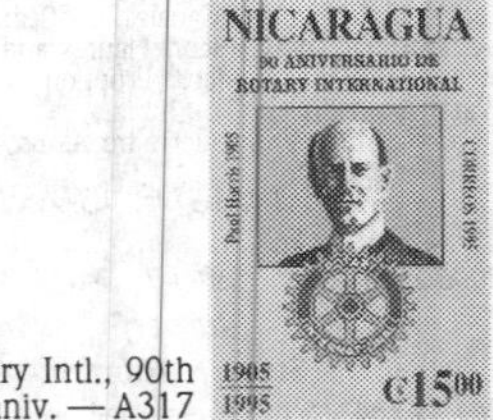

Rotary Intl., 90th Anniv. — A317

1995, Nov. 17

2116 A317 15cor Paul Harris, logo 4.50 4.50

Souvenir Sheet

2117 A317 25cor Old, new logos 7.50 7.50

Miniature Sheet of 12

Butterflies, Moths — A318

No. 2118: a, Cyrestis camillus. b, Salamis cacta. c, Charaxes castor. d, Danaus formosa. e, Graphium ridleyanus. f, Hewitsonia boisduvali. g, Charaxes zoolina. h, Kallima cymodoce i, Precis westermanni. j, Papilo antimachus. k, Cymothoe sangaris. l, Papilio zalmoxis.

No. 2119, Danaus formosa, vert.

1995, Nov. 17

2118 A318 2.50cor #a.-l. 9.00 9.00

Souvenir Sheet

2119 A318 15cor multicolored 4.50 4.50

Miniature Sheet

1996 Summer Olympics, Atlanta — A319

Designs: No. 2120a, Michael Jordan. b, Heike Henkel. c, Linford Christie. d, Vitaly Chtcherbo. e, Heike Drechsler. f, Mark Tewksbury.

Pierre de Coubertin and: No. 2121, Javelin thrower, horiz. No. 2122, Runner.

1995, Dec. 1 Litho. *Perf. 14*

2120 A319 5cor Sheet of 6, #a.-f. 9.00 9.00

Souvenir Sheets

2121-2122 A319 20cor each 6.00 6.00

John Lennon (1940-80) — A320

1995, Dec. 8

2123 A320 2cor multicolored .60 .60

Issued in sheets of 16.

Trains A321

Designs: No. 2124, Mombasa mail train, Uganda. No. 2125, Steam locomotive, East Africa. No. 2126, Electric locomotive, South Africa. No. 2127, Beyer-Garrat steam locomotive, South Africa. No. 2128 Beyer-Garrat steam locomotive, Rhodesia. No. 2129, Class 30 steam locomotive, East Africa.

Steam locomotives: No. 2130a, New York Central & Hudson River RR 4-4-0, #999, US. b, Australian Class 638, 4-6-2, Pacific. c, Baldwin 2-10-2, Bolivia. d, Vulcan 4-8-4, China. e, Paris-Orleans 4-6-2 Pacific, France. f, Class 062, 4-6-4, Japan.

No. 2131, Siberian cargo train. No. 2132, Midland 4-4-0 train, Great Britain. No. 2133, Soviet steam locomotive.

1995, Dec. 11

2124-2129 A321 2cor Set of 6 3.75 3.75

Miniature Sheet

2130 A321 4cor Sheet of 6, #a.-f. 7.25 7.25

Souvenir Sheets

2131-2133 A321 15cor each 4.50 4.50

#2131-2133 each contain 1 85x28mm stamp.

Miniature Sheets of 9 and 12

Nobel Prize Fund Established, Cent. — A322

Recipients: No. 2134a, Otto Meyerhof, medicine, 1922. b, Léon Bourgeois, peace, 1920. c, James Franck, physics, 1925. d, Leo Esaki, physics, 1973. e, Miguel Angel Asturias, literature, 1967. f, Henri Bergson, literature, 1927. g, Friedrich Bergius, chemistry, 1931. h, Klaus von Klitzing, physics, 1985. i, Eisaku Sato, Japan, peace, 1974.

No. 2135: a, Wilhelm C. Roentgen, physics, 1901. b, Theodor Mommsen, literature, 1902. c, Philipp E.A. von Lenard, physics, 1905. d, Walther H. Nernst, chemistry, 1920. e, Hans Spemann, medicine, 1935. f, Jean Paul Sartre, literature, 1964. g, T.S. Eliot, literature, 1948. h, Albert Camus, literature, 1957. i, Ludwig Quidde, peace, 1927. j, Werner Heisenberg, physics, 1932. k, Joseph Brodsky, literature, 1987. l, Carl von Ossietzky, peace, 1935.

No. 2136, Sin-itiro Tomonaga, physics, 1965. No. 2137, Johannes Stark, physics, 1919. No. 2138, Oscar Arias Sánchez, peace, 1987.

1995, Dec. 11

2134 A322 2.50cor #a.-i. 6.75 6.75
2135 A322 2.50cor #a.-l. 9.00 9.00

Souvenir Sheets

2136-2138 A322 15cor each 4.50 4.50

Miniature Sheets

Orchids A323

#2139: a, Cattleya dowinana. b, Odontoglossum maculatum. c, Barkeria lindleyana. d, Rossioglossum grnde. e, Brassavpia digbyana. f, Miltonia schroederiana. g, Ondidium ornithorhynchum. h, Odontoglossum cervantesii. i, Chysis tricostata.

#2140: a, Lycaste auburn. b, Lemboglossum cordatum. c, Cyrtochilum macranthum. d, Miltassia Aztec "Nalo." e, Masdevaltia ignea. f, Oncidium sniffen "Jennifer Dauro." g, Brassolaeliocattleya Alma Kee. h, Ascocenda blue boy. i, Phalaenopsis.

#2141, Odontoglossum uro-skinneri.

1995, Dec. 15

2139 A323 2.50cor Sheet of 9, #a.-i. 6.75 6.75
2140 A323 3cor Sheet of 9, #a.-i. 8.25 8.25

Souvenir Sheet

2141 A323 15cor multicolored 4.50 4.50

Miniature Sheet

World War II, 50th Anniv. A324

Designs: No. 2142a: Patton's troops crossing the Rhine. b, Churchill, Roosevelt, and Stalin at Yalta. c, US flag being raised at Iwo Jima. d, Marine infantry taking possession of Okinawa. e, US troops greeting Russian troops at Torgau. f, Liberation of concentration camps. g, Signing UN Charter, June 1945. h, Ships arriving at Tokyo after war's end.

10cor, German Bf-109 fighter plane.

1996, Jan. 24 Litho. *Perf. 14*

2142 A324 3cor Sheet of 8, #a.-h. + label 7.25 7.25

Souvenir Sheet

2143 A324 10cor multicolored 3.00 3.00

Miniature Sheet

Exotic Birds — A325

a, Paradisiaea apoda. b, Dryocopus galeatus. c, Psarisomus dalhousiae (g). d, Psarocolius montezuma. e, Halcyon pileata. f, Calocitta formosa. g, Ara chloroptera. h, Platycercus eximius. i, Polyplectron emphanum. j, Cariama cristata. k, Opisthocomus hoatzin. l, Coracias cyanogaster.

10cor, Dryocopus galeatus.

1996, Feb. 1

2144 A325 2cor Sheet of 12, #a.-l. 7.25 7.25

Souvenir Sheet

2145 A325 10cor multicolored 3.00 3.00

Town of Rivas, 275th Anniv. A326

1995 Litho. *Perf. 14*

2146 A326 3cor multicolored .90 .90

Printed se-tenant with label.

Christmas A327

1995

2147 A327 4cor multicolored 1.20 1.20

Miniature Sheet of 12

20th Century Writers — A328

Writer, country flag: a, C. Drummond de Andrade (1902-87), Brazil. b, Cesar Vallejo (1892-1938), Peru. c, J. Luis Borges (1899-1986), Argentina. d, James Joyce (1882-1941), Italy. e, Marcel Proust (1871-1922), France. f, William Faulkner (1897-1962), US. g, Vladmir Maiakovski (1893-1930), Russia. h, Ezra Pound (1885-1972), US. i, Franz Kafka (1883-1924), Czechoslovakia. j, T.S. Eliot (188-1965), United Kingdom. k, Rainer Rilke (1875-1926), Austria. l, Federico G. Lorca (1898-1936), Spain.

1995, Oct. 15 *Perf. 14½x14*

2148 A328 3cor #a.-l. 11.00 11.00

Miniature Sheets of 9

Classic Sailing Ships A329

Ship, origin: No. 2149a, Mayflower, England. b, Young America, US. c, Preussen, Germany. d, Lateen-rigged pirate ship, Caribbean Sea. e, Cutty Sark, England. f, Square-rigged pirate ship, Caribbean Sea. g, Galeón, Spain. h, The Sun King, France. i, Santa Maria, Spain.

No. 2150a, HMS Bounty, England. b, The President, US. c, Prince William, Holland. d, Flying Cloud, US. e, Markab, Nile River, Egypt. f, Europa, Holland. g, Vasa, Sweden. h, Foochow junk, China. i, San Gabriel, Portugal.

No. 2151, Passat, Germany. No. 2152, Japanese junk, vert.

1996, Jan. 10 Litho. *Perf. 14*

2149-2150 A329 2.50cor #a.-i., each 6.75 6.75

Souvenir Sheets

2151-2152 A329 15cor each 4.50 4.50

Visit of Pope John Paul II — A330

1996, Feb. 7

2153 A330 5cor multicolored 1.50 1.50

Puppies — A331

Various breeds: No. 2154, 1cor, Holding red leash in mouth. No. 2155, 1cor, With red bandanna around neck. No. 2156, 2cor, Spaniel playing with ball. No. 2157, 2cor, With dog biscuit in mouth. No. 2158, 3cor, Akita. No. 2159, 3cor, Bull dog. No. 2160, 4cor, With newspaper in mouth. No. 2161, 4cor, Dalmatian with cat.

No. 2162, Bending down on front paws. No. 2163, Poodle.

1996, Mar. 6

2154-2161 A331 Set of 8 7.25 7.25

Souvenir Sheets

2162-2163 A331 16cor each 4.75 4.75

Miniature Sheet

Famous Women — A332

Designs: No. 2164a, Indira Gandhi. b, Mme. Chiang Kai-shek. c, Mother Teresa. d, Marie Curie. e, Margaret Thatcher. f, Eleanor Roosevelt. g, Eva Perón. h, Golda Meir. i, Violeta Barrios de Chamorro.

No. 2165, Jacqueline Kennedy Onassis, vert. No. 2166, Aung San Suu Kyi, vert. No. 2167, Valentina Tereshkova, vert.

1996, Mar. 8 *Perf. 14x13½*

2164 A332 2.50cor Sheet of 9, #a.-i. 6.75 6.75

Souvenir Sheets

Perf. 13½x14

2165-2167 A332 15cor each 4.50 4.50

Miniature Sheet

Members of Baseball's Hall of Fame — A333

Player, year inducted: No. 2168a, Gehrig, 1944. b, Hornsby, 1946. c, Mike Schmidt, 1995. d, Wagner, 1936. e, Cobb, 1936. f, Clemente, 1973. g, Ruth, 1936. h, Bench, 1987. i, Seaver, 1993.

10cor, Reggie Jackson, 1993.

1996, Mar. 15 Litho. *Perf. 13½x14*

2168 A333 4cor Sheet of 9, #a.-i. 11.00 11.00

Souvenir Sheet

2169 A333 10cor multicolored 9.25 9.25

1996 Summer Olympics, Atlanta — A334

Designs: 1cor, Takehide Nakatani, Japan. 2cor, Olympic Stadium, Tokyo, 1964. 3cor, Al Oerter, US, vert. 10cor, Discus thrower from ancient games.

Gold medal winners in boxing, vert: No. 2174a, Andrew Maynard, US. b, Rudi Fink, Germany. c,

Peter Lessov, Bulgaria. d, Angel Herrera, Cuba. e, Patrizio Oliva, Italy. f, Armando Martinez, Cuba. g, Slobodan Kacar, Yugoslavia. h, Teofilo Stevenson, Cuba. i, George Foreman, US.

Events: No. 2175a, Basketball. b, Baseball. c, Boxing. d, Long jump. e, Judo. f, Team handball. g, Volleyball. h, Water polo. i, Tennis.

25cor, Cassius Clay (Mohammed Ali), US.

1996, Mar. 28 *Perf. 14*
2170-2173 A334 Set of 4 4.75 4.75

Miniature Sheets of 9

2174-2175 A334 2.50cor #a.-i., each 6.75 6.75

Souvenir Sheet

2176 A334 25cor multicolored 7.50 7.50

Race Horses A335

Carousel Horses — A336

Race horses: 1cor, "Wave." 2cor, "Charming Traveler." 2.50cor, "Noble Vagabond." No. 2180, 3cor, "Golden Dancer," vert. No. 2181, 3cor, "Wave Runner." No. 2182, 4cor, "Ebony Champion." No. 2183, 4cor, "Wave Tamer."

Antique carousel horses: No. 2184a, Persian light infantry horse, 18th cent. b, Italian parade horse, 15th cent. c, German armored horse, 15th cent. d, Turkish light infantry horse, 17th cent.

16cor, "Proud Heart." 25cor, German armored horse, 16th cent.

1996, Apr. 15
2177-2183 A335 Set of 7 6.00 6.00
2184 A336 2cor Sheet of 4, #a.-d. 2.50 2.50

Souvenir Sheets

2185 A335 16cor multicolored 4.75 4.75
2186 A336 25cor multicolored 7.50 7.50

Marine Life A337

No. 218: 7a, Butterflyfish (d). b, Barracuda (a). c, Manatee. d, Jellyfish. e, Octopus (b, d, f, g, h). f, Small yellow-striped fish. g, Lemon shark. h, Striped fish. i, Red fish.

No. 2188: a, Reef shark. b, Diver, hammerhead shark (c, e). c, Moray eel (f). d, Macrela ojos de caballo (a, b, e). e, Hammerhead shark. f, Butterflyfish. g, Mediterranean grouper. h, Octopus, diff. i, Manta ray.

No. 2189, Angel fish. No. 2190, Saddleback butterflyfish.

1996, Apr. 29 **Litho.** *Perf. 14*

Sheets of 9

2187-2188 A337 2.50cor #a.-i., each 7.25 7.25

Souvenir Sheets

2189-2190 A337 20cor each 6.50 6.50

Chinese Lunar Calendar A338

Year signs: a, Rat. b, Ox. c, Tiger. d, Hare. e, Dragon. f, Snake. g, Horse. h, Sheep. i, Monkey. j, Rooster. k, Dog. l, Boar.

1996, May 6
2191 A338 2cor Sheet of 12, #a.-l. 6.50 6.50

China'96.

Central American Integration System (SICA) A339

1996 *Perf. 14½*
2192 A339 5cor multicolored 1.60 1.60

20th Century Events A340

a, Russian revolution, 1917. b, Chinese revolution, 1945. c, Creation of the UN, 1945. d, Tearing down the Berlin Wall, 1989. e, World War I, vert. f, Creation of the State of Israel, 1948, vert. g, World War II, vert. h, 2nd Vatican Council, 1962-65, vert. i, Atom bombing of Hiroshima, 1945. j, Viet Nam War, 1962-73. k, Persian Gulf War, 1991. l, End of Apartheid, 1991.

1996 *Perf. 14*
2193 A340 3cor Sheet of 12, #a.-l. + label 11.50 11.50

Souvenir Sheet

New Year 1997 (Year of the Ox) — A341

Illustration reduced.

1996 **Litho.** *Perf. 15x14*
2194 A341 10cor multicolored 3.00 3.00

Wuhan Huanghelou — A342

1996, May 20 **Litho.** *Perf. 14*
2195 A342 4cor multicolored 1.20 1.20

China '96. No. 2195 was not available until March 1997.

AIR POST STAMPS

Counterfeits exist of almost all scarce surcharges among Nos. C1-C66.

Regular Issues of 1914-28 Overprinted in Red

Correo Aéreo
1929
P.A.A.

1929, May 15 **Unwmk.** *Perf. 12*
C1 A24 25c orange 1.75 1.75
a. Double overprint, one inverted 50.00
b. Inverted overprint 50.00
c. Double overprint 50.00
C2 A24 25c blk brn 2.25 2.25
a. Double overprint, one inverted 50.00
b. Double overprint 50.00
c. Inverted overprint 30.00

There are numerous varieties in the setting of the overprint. The most important are: Large "1" in "1929" and large "A" in "Aereo" and "P. A. A."

Similar Overprint on Regular Issue of 1929 in Red

1929, June
C3 A24 25c dk vio 1.25 .75
a. Double overprint 50.00
b. Inverted overprint 50.00
c. Double overprint, one inverted 50.00
Nos. C1-C3 (3) 5.25 4.75

The stamps in the bottom row of the sheet have the letters "P. A. A." larger than usual.

Similar overprints, some including an airplane, have been applied to postage issues of 1914-20, officials of 1926 and Nos. 401-407. These are, at best, essays.

Airplanes over Mt. Momotombo AP1

1929, Dec. 15 **Engr.**
C4 AP1 25c olive blk .50 .40
C5 AP1 50c blk brn .75 .75
C6 AP1 1cor org red 1.00 1.00
Nos. C4-C6 (3) 2.25 2.15

See Nos. C18-C19, C164-C168. For surcharges and overprints see Nos. C7-C8, C14-C17, C25-C31, C106-C120, C135-C146, C150-C154, C169-C173, CO25-CO29.

No. C4 Surcharged in Red or Black

Vale
C$ 0.15

1930, May 15
C7 AP1 15c on 25c ol blk (R) .50 .40
a. "$" inverted 3.50
b. Double surcharge (R + Bk) 7.00
c. As "b," red normal, blk invtd. 7.00
d. Double red surch., one inverted 7.00
C8 AP1 20c on 25c ol blk (Bk) .75 .60
a. "$" inverted 7.00
b. Inverted surcharge 15.00

Nos. C1, C2 and C3 Surcharged in Green

Vale C$ 0.15
1931

1931, June 7
C9 A24 15c on 25c org 50.00 50.00
C10 A24 15c on 25c blk brn 100.00 100.00
C11 A24 15c on 25c dk vio 15.00 15.00
c. Inverted surcharge 30.00
C12 A24 20c on 25c dk vio 10.00 10.00
c. Inverted surcharge 50.00
d. Double surcharge 50.00
C13 A24 20c on 25c blk brn *375.00*

No. C13 was not regularly issued.

"1391"

C9a A24 15c on 25c
C10a A24 15c on 25c
C11a A24 15c on 25c 60.00
d. As "a," inverted 400.00
C12a A24 20c on 25c 25.00
e. As "a," inverted 400.00
g. As "a," double 400.00
C13a A24 20c on 25c

"1921"

C9b A24 15c on 25c
C10b A24 15c on 25c 400.00
C11b A24 15c on 25c 60.00
e. As "b," inverted 400.00
C12b A24 20c on 25c 25.00
f. As "b," inverted 400.00
h. As "b," double 400.00
C13b A24 20c on 25c

Nos. C8, C4-C6 Surcharged in Blue

1931
C$ 0.15

1931, June
C14 AP1 15c on 20c on 25c 9.00 9.00
b. Blue surcharge inverted 25.00
c. "$" in blk, surch. invtd. 50.00
d. Blue surch. dbl., one invtd. 25.00
C15 AP1 15c on 25c 5.50 5.50
b. Blue surcharge inverted 25.00
c. Double surch., one invtd. 25.00
C16 AP1 15c on 50c 40.00 40.00
C17 AP1 15c on 1cor 100.00 100.00
Nos. C14-C17 (4) 154.50 154.50

"1391"

C14a AP1 15c on 20c on 25c 50.00
C15a AP1 15c on 25c 30.00
C16a AP1 15c on 50c 80.00
C17a AP1 15c on 1cor 225.00
Nos. C14a-C17a (4) 385.00

Momotombo Type of 1929

1931, July 8
C18 AP1 15c deep violet .16 .15
C19 AP1 20c deep green .42 .38

Managua Post Office Before and After Earthquake AP2

Without gum, Soft porous paper

1932, Jan. 1 **Litho.** *Perf. 11*
C20 AP2 15c lilac 1.50 *1.20*
a. 15c violet 22.50
b. Vert. pair, imperf. btwn. 22.50
C21 AP2 20c emerald 1.90
b. Horizontal pair, imperf. between 27.50
C22 AP2 25c yel brn 6.50
b. Vertical pair, imperf. between 60.00
C23 AP2 50c yel brn 8.00
C24 AP2 1cor dp car 12.00
a. Vert. or horiz. pair, imperf. btwn. 80.00
Nos. C20-C24 (5) 29.90

Sheets of 10. See note after No. 568.

For overprint and surcharges see #C44-C46.

Reprints: see note following No. 568. Value $1 each.

Nos. C5 and C6 Surcharged in Red or Black

Vale C$ 0.30

1932, July 12 *Perf. 12*
C25 AP1 30c on 50c (Bk) 1.50 1.50
a. "Valc" 25.00
b. Double surcharge 15.00
c. Double surch., one inverted 15.00
d. Period omitted after "O" 25.00
e. As "a," double 300.00
C26 AP1 35c on 50c (R) 1.50 1.50
a. "Valc" 30.00
b. Double surcharge 12.00
c. Double surch., one inverted 12.00
d. As "a," double 300.00
C27 AP1 35c on 50c (Bk) 35.00 35.00
a. "Valc" 250.00
C28 AP1 40c on 1cor (Bk) 1.75 1.75
a. "Valc" 25.00
b. Double surcharge 15.00
c. Double surch., one inverted 15.00
d. Inverted surcharge 15.00
e. As "a," inverted 300.00
f. As "a," double 300.00
C29 AP1 55c on 1cor (R) 1.75 1.75
a. "Valc" 25.00
b. Double surcharge 12.00
c. Double surch., one inverted 12.00
d. Inverted surcharge 12.00
e. As "a," inverted 300.00
f. As "a," double 300.00
Nos. C25-C29 (5) 41.50 41.50

No. C18 Overprinted in Red

Semana Correo Aéreo
Internacional
11-17 Septiembre 1932

1932, Sept. 11
C30 AP1 15c dp vio 70.00 70.00
a. "Aerreo" 150.00 150.00
b. Invtd. "m" in "Septiembre" 150.00

International Air Mail Week.

No. C6 Surcharged

Inauguracion Interior
12 Octubre 1932
Vale C$ 0.08

1932, Oct. 12
C31 AP1 8c on 1 cor org red 20.00 20.00
a. "1232" 30.00 30.00
b. 2nd "u" of "Inauguration" invtd. 30.00 30.00

Inauguration of airmail service to the interior.

Regular Issue of 1932 Overprinted in Red

Correo Aéreo Interior
1932

1932, Oct. 24 *Perf. 11½*

Without Gum

C32 A40 1c yel brn	20.00	20.00
a. Inverted overprint	125.00	125.00
C33 A40 2c carmine	20.00	20.00
a. Inverted overprint	125.00	125.00
b. Double overprint	100.00	100.00
C34 A40 3c ultra	9.50	9.50
a. Inverted overprint	150.00	150.00
b. As "a," vert. pair, imperf. btwn.	500.00	
C35 A40 4c dp ultra	9.50	9.50
a. Inverted overprint	125.00	125.00
b. Double overprint	100.00	100.00
c. Vert. or horiz. pair, imperf. btwn.	300.00	
C36 A40 5c yel brn	9.50	9.50
a. Inverted overprint	125.00	125.00
b. Vert. pair, imperf. btwn.	75.00	
C37 A40 6c gray brn	9.50	9.50
a. Inverted overprint	100.00	100.00
C38 A40 50c green	9.00	9.00
a. Inverted overprint	125.00	125.00
C39 A40 1cor yellow	9.50	9.50
a. Inverted overprint	125.00	125.00
b. Horiz. pair, imperf. btwn.	200.00	
Nos. C32-C39 (8)	96.50	96.50

Nos. 564, C20-C21 exist overprinted as C32-C39. The editors believe they were not regularly issued.

Surcharged in Red

Correo Aéreo Interior
1932
Vale ₡ 0.16

1932, Oct. 24

C40 A40 8c on 10c yel brn	9.00	9.00
a. Inverted surcharge	125.00	125.00
C41 A40 16c on 20c org	9.00	9.00
a. Inverted surcharge	125.00	125.00
C42 A40 24c on 25c dp vio	9.00	9.00
a. Inverted surcharge	125.00	125.00
b. Horiz. pair, imperf. vert.	300.00	

Surcharged in Red as No. C40 but without the word "Vale"

C43 A40 8c on 10c yel brn	45.00	45.00
a. Inverted surcharge	125.00	125.00
b. Horiz. pair, imperf. vert.	300.00	

No. C22 Overprinted in Red

Interior—1932

1932, Oct. 24

C44 AP2 25c yel brn	8.00	8.00
a. Inverted overprint	125.00	125.00

Nos. C23 and C24 Surcharged in Red

Interior—1932

Vale ₡ 0.32

1932, Oct. 24

C45 AP2 32c on 50c yel brn	9.50	9.50
a. Inverted surcharge	125.00	125.00
b. "Interior-1932" inverted	150.00	150.00
c. "Vale $0.32" inverted	150.00	150.00
d. Horiz. pair, imperf. btwn.	200.00	
C46 AP2 40c on 1cor car	7.00	7.00
a. Inverted surcharge	125.00	125.00
b. "Vale $0.40" inverted	200.00	200.00

Nos. 557-558 Overprinted in Black like Nos. C32 to C39

1932, Nov. 16

C47 A40 1c yel brn	25.00	22.50
a. "1232"	45.00	45.00
b. Inverted overprint	125.00	125.00
c. Double ovpt., one invtd.	125.00	125.00
d. As "a," inverted	500.00	
C48 A40 2c dp car	20.00	17.50
a. "1232"	45.00	45.00
b. Inverted overprint	125.00	125.00
c. As "a," inverted	500.00	

Excellent counterfeits exist of Nos. C27, C30-C48. Forged overprints and surcharges as on Nos. C32-C48 exist on reprints of Nos. C20-C24.

Regular Issue of 1914-32 Surcharged in Black

Correo Aéreo
Interior-1932
Vale ₡ 0.01

1932 *Perf. 12*

C49 A25 1c on 2c brt rose	.35	.30
C50 A24 2c on 3c lt bl	.35	.30
C51 A25 3c on 4c dk bl	.35	.30
C52 A24 4c on 5c gray brn	.35	.30
C53 A25 5c on 6c ol brn	.35	.30
C54 A25 6c on 10c lt brn	.35	.30
a. Double surcharge	25.00	
C55 A24 8c on 15c org red	.35	.30
C56 A25 16c on 20c org	.35	.35
C57 A24 24c on 25c dk vio	1.40	1.00
C58 A25 25c on 25c dk vio	1.40	1.00
a. Double surcharge	25.00	
C59 A25 32c on 50c grn	1.40	1.25
C60 A25 40vc on 50c grn	1.60	1.40
C61 A25 50c on 1cor yel	2.25	2.25
C62 A25 1cor on 1cor yel	3.00	3.00
Nos. C49-C62 (14)	13.85	12.35

Nos. C49-C62 exist with inverted surcharge.

In addition to C49 to C62, four other stamps, Type A25, exist with this surcharge:
40c on 50c bister brown, black surcharge.
1cor on 2c bright rose, black surcharge.
1cor on 1cor yellow, red surcharge.
1cor on 1cor dull violet, black surcharge.
The editors believe they were not regularly issued.

Surcharged on Nos. 548, 547

1932

C65 A24 24c on 25c dk vio	45.00	45.00
C66 A24 25c on 25c blk brn	50.00	50.00

Counterfeits of Nos. C65 and C66 are plentiful.

Rivas Railroad Issue

La Chocolata Cut — AP3

El Nacascola — AP4

Designs: 25c, Cuesta cut. 50c, Mole of San Juan del Sur. 1cor, View of El Estero.

1932, Dec. **Litho.**

Soft porous paper

C67 AP3 15c dk vio	20.00	
C68 AP4 20c bl grn	20.00	
C69 AP4 25c dk brn	20.00	
C70 AP4 50c blk brn	20.00	
C71 AP4 1cor rose red	20.00	
Nos. C67-C71 (5)	100.00	

Inauguration of the railroad from San Jorge to San Juan del Sur, Dec. 18, 1932. Printed in sheets of 4, without gum.

Reprints: see note following No. 574. Value, $6 each.

Leon-Sauce Railroad Issue

"Fill" at Santa Lucia River AP5

Designs: 15c, Bridge at Santa Lucia. 25c, Malpaicillo Station. 50c, Panoramic view. 1cor, San Andres.

1932, Dec. 30

Soft porous paper

C72 AP5 15c purple	20.00	
C73 AP5 20c bl grn	20.00	
C74 AP5 25c dk brn	20.00	
C75 AP5 50c blk brn	20.00	
C76 AP5 1cor rose red	20.00	
Nos. C72-C76 (5)	100.00	

Inauguration of the railroad from Leon to El Sauce, Dec. 30, 1932. Sheets of 4, without gum.

Reprints: see note following No. 579. Value, $6 each.

Flag of the Race Issue

1933, Aug. 3 **Litho.** ***Rouletted 9***

Without gum

C77 A43 1c dk brn	1.50	1.50
C78 A43 2c red vio	1.50	1.50
C79 A43 4c violet	2.50	2.25
C80 A43 5c dl bl	2.25	2.25
C81 A43 6c vio bl	2.25	2.25
C82 A43 8c dp brn	.70	.70
C83 A43 15c ol brn	.70	.70
C84 A43 20c yellow	2.25	2.25
a. Horiz. pair, imperf. btwn.	15.00	
b. Horiz. pair, imperf. vert.	15.00	
C85 A43 25c orange	2.25	2.25
C86 A43 50c rose	2.25	2.25
C87 A43 1cor green	11.00	11.00
Nos. C77-C87 (11)	29.15	28.90

See note after No. 599. Printed in sheets of 10.

Reprints exist, shades differ from postage and official stamps.

Imperf., Pairs

C78a A43 2c	14.00
C79a A43 4c	10.00
C81a A43 6c	10.00
C82a A43 8c	10.00
C83a A43 15c	10.00
C87a A43 1cor	30.00

AP7

1933, Nov. ***Perf. 12***

C88 AP7 10c bis brn	1.50	1.50
a. Vert. pair, imperf. between	35.00	
C89 AP7 15c violet	1.20	1.20
a. Vert. pair, imperf. between	37.50	
C90 AP7 25c red	1.40	1.40
a. Horiz. pair, imperf. between	22.50	
C91 AP7 50c dp bl	1.50	1.50
Nos. C88-C91 (4)	5.60	5.60

Intl. Air Post Week, Nov. 6-11, 1933. Printed in sheets of 4. Counterfeits exist.

Stamps and Types of 1928-31 Surcharged in Black

Correo Aéreo
Interior
Vale ₡ 0.01

1933, Nov. 3

C92 A25 1c on 2c grn	.15	.15
C93 A24 2c on 3c ol gray	.15	.15
C94 A25 3c on 4c car rose	.15	.15
C95 A24 4c on 5c lt bl	.15	.15
C96 A25 5c on 6c dk bl	.15	.15
C97 A25 6c on 10c ol brn	.15	.15
C98 A24 8c on 15c bis brn	.20	.15
C99 A25 16c on 20c brn	.16	.15
C100 A24 24c on 25c ver	.15	.15
C101 A24 25c on 25c org	.22	.16
C102 A25 32c on 50c vio	.20	.20
C103 A25 40c on 50c grn	.20	.15
C104 A25 50c on 1cor yel	.16	.15
C105 A25 1cor on 1cor org red	.35	.22
Set value	2.20	1.75

Nos. C100, C102-C105 exist without script control overprint. Value, each $1.50.

Type of Air Post Stamps of 1929 Surcharged in Black

Vale ₡ 0.30

1933, Oct. 28

C106 AP1 30c on 50c org red	.22	.15
C107 AP1 35c on 50c lt bl	.25	.16
C108 AP1 40c on 1cor yel	.40	.16
C109 AP1 55c on 1cor grn	.30	.22
Nos. C106-C109 (4)	1.17	.69

No. C19 Surcharged in Red

Servicio
Centroamericano
Vale 10 centavos

1934, Mar. 31

C110 AP1 10c on 20c grn	.30	.25
a. Inverted surcharge	15.00	
b. Double surcharge, one inverted	15.00	
c. "Ceutroamericano"	10.00	

No. C110 with black surcharge is believed to be of private origin.

No. C4 Surcharged in Red

Servicio
Centroamericano
Vale 10 centavos

1935, Aug.

C111 AP1 10c on 25c ol blk	.25	.25
a. Small "v" in "vale" (R)	5.00	
b. "centrvos" (R)	5.00	
c. Double surcharge (R)	25.00	
d. Inverted surcharge (R)	25.00	
g. As "a," inverted	400.00	
h. As "a," double	400.00	

No. C111 with blue surcharge is believed to be private origin.

The editors do not recognize the Nicaraguan air post stamps overprinted in red "VALIDO 1935" in two lines and with or without script control marks as having been issued primarily for postal purposes.

Nos C4-C6, C18-C19 Overprinted Vertically in Blue, Reading Up:

1935-36

C112 AP1 15c dp vio	1.00	1.00
C113 AP1 20c dp grn	1.75	1.75
C114 AP1 25c ol blk	2.25	2.25
C115 AP1 50c blk brn	5.00	5.00
C116 AP1 1cor org red	40.00	40.00
Nos. C112-C116 (5)	50.00	50.00

Same Overprint on Nos. C106-C109 Reading Up or Down

C117 AP1 30c on 50c org red	1.50	1.40
C118 AP1 35c on 50c lt bl	6.50	6.50
C119 AP1 40c on 1cor yel	6.50	6.50
C120 AP1 55c on 1cor grn	6.50	6.50
Nos. C117-C120 (4)	21.00	20.90
Nos. C112-C120 (9)	71.00	70.90

Same Overprint in Red on Nos. C92-C105

1936

C121 A25 1c on 2c grn	.15	.15
C122 A24 2c on 3c ol gray	.16	.16
C123 A25 3c on 4c car rose	.16	.16
C124 A24 4c on 5c lt bl	.16	.16
C125 A25 5c on 6c dk bl	.16	.16
C126 A25 6c on 10c ol brn	.16	.16
C127 A24 8c on 15c bis brn	.16	.16
C128 A25 16c on 20c brn	.25	.25
C129 A24 24c on 25c ver	.35	.28
C130 A24 25c on 25c org	.22	.22
C131 A25 32c on 50c vio	.16	.16
C132 A25 40c on 50c grn	.55	.50
C133 A25 50c on 1cor yel	.40	.25
C134 A25 1cor on 1cor org red	1.40	.65
Nos. C121-C134 (14)	4.44	3.42

Nos. C121 to C134 are handstamped with script control mark.

Overprint Reading Down on No. C110

C135 AP1 10c on 20c grn	*350.00*	

This stamp has been extensively counterfeited.

Overprinted in Red on Nos. C4 to C6, C18 and C19

C136 AP1 15c dp vio	.55	.15
C137 AP1 20c dp grn	.65	.60
C138 AP1 25c ol blk	.65	.55
C139 AP1 50c blk brn	.55	.55
C140 AP1 1cor org red	1.10	.55

On Nos. C106 to C109

C141 AP1 30c on 50c org red	.65	.60
C142 AP1 35c on 50c lt bl	.65	.42
C143 AP1 40c on 1cor yel	.65	.55
C144 AP1 55c on 1cor grn	.65	.50

Same Overprint in Red or Blue on No. C111 Reading Up or Down

C145 AP1 10c on 25c, down	.55	.45
a. "Centrvos"	25.00	
C146 AP1 10c on 25c (Bl), up	1.20	1.00
a. "Centrvos"	25.00	
Nos. C136-C146 (11)	7.85	5.92

Overprint on No. C145 is at right, on No. C146 in center.

Nos. C92, C93 and C98 Overprinted in Black

Resello
1936

1936

C147 A25 1c on 2c grn .20 .16
C148 A24 2c on 3c ol gray .15 .15
a. "Resello 1936" dbl., one invtd. 2.50
C149 A24 8c on 15c bis brn .22 .22
Nos. C147-C149 (3) .57 .53

With script control handstamp.

Nos. C5 and C6 Surcharged in Red

1936

Vale

Quince Centavos

1936, Nov. 26

C150 AP1 15c on 50c blk brn .20 .16
C151 AP1 15c on 1cor org red .20 .16

Nos. C18 and C19 Overprinted in Carmine

1936, July 2

C152 AP1 15c dp vio .35 .16
C153 AP1 20c dp grn .35 .25

Overprint reading up or down.

No. C4 Surcharged and Overprinted in Red

Servicio Centroamericano Vale diez centavos

and

RESELLO 1935

C154 AP1 10c on 25c olive blk .30 .30
a. Surch. and ovpt. inverted 3.50

Same Overprint in Carmine on Nos. C92 to C99

C155 A25 1c on 2c green .15 .15
C156 A24 2c on 3c olive gray .65 .65
C157 A25 3c on 4c car rose .15 .15
C158 A24 4c on 5c light blue .15 .15
C159 A25 5c on 6c dark blue .15 .15
C160 A25 6c on 10c olive brn .15 .15
C161 A24 8c on 15c bister brn .15 .15
C162 A25 16c on 20c brown .15 .15
Set value 1.40 1.40

No. 518 Overprinted in Black

Correo Aéreo Centro-Americano Resello 1936

C163 A25 10c lt brn .16 .16
a. Overprint inverted 2.25
b. Double overprint 2.25

Two fonts are found in the sheet of #C163.

Momotombo Type of 1929

1937

C164 AP1 15c yel org .15 .15
C165 AP1 20c org red .15 .15
C166 AP1 25c black .15 .15
C167 AP1 50c violet .22 .15
C168 AP1 1cor orange .55 .15
Nos. C164-C168 (5) 1.22
Set value .42

Surcharged in Black **Vale ₡ 0.30**

1937

C169 AP1 30c on 50c car rose .16 .15
C170 AP1 35c on 50c olive grn .20 .15
C171 AP1 40c on 1cor green .22 .15
C172 AP1 55c on 1cor blue .20 .20
Nos. C169-C172 (4) .78
Set value .42

No. C168 Surcharged in Violet

Servicio Centroamericano Vale Diez Centavos

1937 Unwmk. *Perf. 12*

C173 AP1 10c on 1cor org .15 .15
a. "Centauos" 10.00

No. C98 with Additional Overprint "1937"

C174 A24 8c on 15c bis brn .45 .15
a. "1937" double 6.50

Nos. C92-C102 with Additional Overprint in Blue reading "HABILITADO 1937"

C175 A25 1c on 2c grn .15 .15
a. Blue overprint double 2.50
C176 A24 2c on 3c ol gray .15 .15
a. Double surch., one inverted 2.50
C177 A25 3c on 4c car rose .15 .15
C178 A24 4c on 5c lt bl .15 .15
C179 A25 5c on 6c dk bl .15 .15
C180 A25 6c on 10c ol brn .15 .15
C181 A24 8c on 15c bis brn .15 .15
a. "Habilitado 1937" double 3.50
C182 A25 16c on 20c brn .16 .16
a. Double surcharge 2.50
C183 A24 24c on 25c ver .16 .16
C184 A24 25c on 25c org .22 .20
C185 A25 32c on 50c vio .22 .22
Set value, #C175-C185 1.25 1.10

Map of Nicaragua AP8

For Foreign Postage

1937, July 30 Engr.

C186 AP8 10c green .15 .15
C187 AP8 15c dp bl .15 .15
C188 AP8 20c yellow .20 .16
C189 AP8 25c bl vio .20 .16
C190 AP8 30c rose car .22 .20
C191 AP8 50c org yel .35 .20
C192 AP8 1cor ol grn .70 .55
Nos. C186-C192 (7) 1.97 1.57

Presidential Palace AP9

For Domestic Postage

C193 AP9 1c rose car .15 .15
C194 AP9 2c dp bl .15 .15
C195 AP9 3c ol grn .15 .15
C196 AP9 4c black .15 .15
C197 AP9 5c dk vio .15 .15
C198 AP9 6c chocolate .15 .15
C199 AP9 8c bl vio .15 .15
C200 AP9 16c org yel .22 .20
C201 AP9 24c yellow .15 .15
C202 AP9 25c yel grn .25 .20
Set value 1.32 1.00

No. C201 with green overprint "Union Panamericana 1890-1940" is of private origin.

Managua AP10

Designs: 15c, Presidential Palace. 20c, Map of South America. 25c, Map of Central America. 30c, Map of North America. 35c, Lagoon of Tiscapa, Managua. 40c, Road Scene. 45c, Park. 50c, Another park. 55c, Scene in San Juan del Sur. 75c, Tipitapa River. 1cor, Landscape.

Wmk. 209

1937, Sept. 17 Typo. *Perf. 11*

Center in Dark Blue

C203 AP10 10c yel grn 1.60 1.20
C204 AP10 15c orange 1.60 1.40
C205 AP10 20c red 1.00 1.00
C206 AP10 25c vio brn 1.00 1.00
C207 AP10 30c bl grn 1.00 1.00
a. Great Lakes omitted 40.00 40.00
C208 AP10 35c lemon .50 .45
C209 AP10 40c green .40 .38
C210 AP10 45c brt vio .40 .35
C211 AP10 50c rose lil .40 .35
a. Vert. pair, imperf. btwn. 140.00
C212 AP10 55c lt bl .40 .35
C213 AP10 75c gray grn .40 .35

Center in Brown Red

C214 AP10 1cor dk bl 1.00 .50
Nos. C203-C214 (12) 9.70 8.33

150th anniv. of the Constitution of the US.

Diriangen — AP11

Designs: 4c, 10c, Nicarao. 5c, 15c, Bartolomé de Las Casas. 8c, 20c, Columbus.

For Domestic Postage

Without gum

1937, Oct. 12 Unwmk. *Perf. 11*

C215 AP11 1c green .15 .15
C216 AP11 4c brn car .15 .15
C217 AP11 5c dk vio .15 .15
a. Without imprint .40
C218 AP11 8c dp bl .15 .15
a. Without imprint .50

For Foreign Postage

Wmk. 209

With Gum

C219 AP11 10c lt brn .15 .15
C220 AP11 15c pale bl .15 .15
a. Without imprint 1.00
C221 AP11 20c pale rose .16 .15
Set value, #C215-C221 .75 .65

Nos. C215-C221 printed in sheets of 4.

Imperf., Pairs

C215a AP11 1c .16 .16
C216a AP11 4c .20 .20
C217b AP11 5c .20 .20
C217c AP11 5c Without imprint
C218b AP11 8c .20
C218c AP11 8c Without imprint
C219a AP11 10c .20 .20
C220b AP11 15c .22 .22
C220c AP11 15c Without imprint
C221a AP11 20c .35 .35

Gen. Tomas Martinez — AP11a

Design: 10c-50c, Gen. Anastasio Somoza.

For Domestic Postage

Without Gum

Perf. 11½, Imperf.

1938, Jan. 18 Typo. Unwmk.

Center in Black

C221B AP11a 1c orange .20 .20
C221C AP11a 5c red vio .20 .20
C221D AP11a 8c dk bl .22 .22
C221E AP11a 16c brown .25 .25
f. Sheet of 4, 1c, 5c, 8c, 16c 1.25 1.25

For Foreign Postage

C221G AP11a 10c green .22 .20
C221H AP11a 15c dk bl .25 .25
C221J AP11a 25c violet .42 .40
C221K AP11a 50c carmine .50 .45
m. Sheet of 4, 10c, 15c, 25c, 50c 2.00 2.00
Nos. C221B-C221K (8) 2.26 2.17

75th anniv. of postal service in Nicaragua. Printed in sheets of four.

Stamps of type AP11a exist in changed colors and with inverted centers, double centers and frames printed on the back. These varieties were private fabrications.

Lake Managua AP12

President Anastasio Somoza — AP13

For Domestic Postage

1939 Unwmk. Engr. *Perf. 12½*

C222 AP12 2c dp bl .15 .15
C223 AP12 3c green .15 .15
C224 AP12 8c pale lil .15 .15
C225 AP12 16c orange .15 .15
C226 AP12 24c yellow .15 .15
C227 AP12 32c dk grn .16 .15
C228 AP12 50c dp rose .16 .15

For Foreign Postage

C229 AP13 10c dk brn .15 .15
C230 AP13 15c dk bl .15 .15
C231 AP13 20c org yel .15 .16
C232 AP13 25c dk pur .15 .15
C233 AP13 30c lake .16 .16
C234 AP13 50c dp org .25 .20
C235 AP13 1cor dk ol grn .40 .35
Set value, #C222-C235 2.10 1.90

For Domestic Postage

Will Rogers and View of Managua AP14

Designs: 2c, Rogers standing beside plane. 3c, Leaving airport office. 4c, Rogers and US Marines. 5c, Managua after earthquake.

1939, Mar. 31 Engr. *Perf. 12*

C236 AP14 1c brt grn .15 .15
C237 AP14 2c org red .15 .15
C238 AP14 3c lt ultra .15 .15
C239 AP14 4c dk bl .15 .15
C240 AP14 5c rose car .15 .15
Set value .28 .25

Will Rogers' flight to Managua after the earthquake, Mar. 31, 1931.

For surcharges see Nos. 686, 688.

Pres. Anastasio Somoza in US House of Representatives — AP19

President Somoza and US Capitol AP20

President Somoza, Tower of the Sun and Trylon and Perisphere AP21

For Domestic Postage

1940, Feb. 1

C241 AP19 4c red brn .15 .15
C242 AP20 8c blk brn .15 .15
C243 AP19 16c grnsh bl .15 .15
C244 AP20 20c brt plum .50 .30
C245 AP21 32c scarlet .16 .16

For Foreign Postage

C246 AP19 25c dp bl .20 .15
C247 AP19 30c black .20 .15
C248 AP20 50c rose pink .45 .38
C249 AP21 60c green .50 .30
C250 AP19 65c dk vio brn .50 .20
C251 AP19 90c ol grn .65 .30
C252 AP21 1cor violet 1.00 .55
Nos. C241-C252 (12) 4.61
Set value 2.50

Visit of Pres. Somoza to US in 1939.

For surcharge see No. C636.

L. S. Rowe, Statue of Liberty, Nicaraguan Coastline, Flags of 21 American Republics, US Shield and Arms of Nicaragua — AP22

1940, Aug. 2 Engr. *Perf. 12½*

C253 AP22 1.25cor multi .65 .60

50th anniversary of Pan American Union.
For overprint see No. C493.

First Nicaraguan Postage Stamp and Sir Rowland Hill AP23

1941, Apr. 4

C254 AP23 2cor brown 2.50 .80
C255 AP23 3cor dk bl 8.25 1.40
C256 AP23 5cor carmine 22.50 3.50
Nos. C254-C256 (3) 33.25 5.70

Centenary of the first postage stamp.
Nos. C254-C256 imperf. are proofs.

Rubén Darío AP24

1941, Dec. 23

C257 AP24 20c pale lil .25 .18
C258 AP24 35c yel grn .30 .20
C259 AP24 40c org yel .40 .22
C260 AP24 60c lt bl .65 .30
Nos. C257-C260 (4) 1.60 .90

25th anniversary of the death of Rubén Darío, poet and writer.

Catalogue values for unused stamps in this section, from this point to the end of the section, are for Never Hinged items.

Victory Type

1943, Dec. 8 *Perf. 12*

C261 A48 40c dk bl grn & cer .20 .15
C262 A48 60c lt bl & cer .30 .15
Set value .15

Red Cross — AP26 Cross and Globes — AP27

Red Cross Workers AP28

1944, Oct. 12 Engr.

C263 AP26 25c red lil & car .65 .30
C264 AP27 50c ol brn & car 1.00 .55
C265 AP28 1cor dk bl grn & car 2.00 2.00
Nos. C263-C265 (3) 3.65 2.85

International Red Cross Society, 80th anniv.

Caravels of Columbus and Columbus Lighthouse AP29

Landing of Columbus AP30

1945, Sept. 1 *Perf. 12½*

C266 AP29 20c dp grn & gray .15 .15
C267 AP29 35c dk car & blk .35 .30
C268 AP29 75c ol grn & rose pink .45 .40
C269 AP29 90c brick red & aqua .80 .75
C270 AP29 1cor blk & pale bl .90 .30
C271 AP30 2.50cor dk bl & car rose 2.25 2.25
Nos. C266-C271 (6) 4.90 4.15

Issued in honor of the discovery of America by Columbus and the Columbus Lighthouse near Ciudad Trujillo, Dominican Republic.

Roosevelt Types

Designs: 25c, Franklin D. Roosevelt and Winston Churchill. 75c, Roosevelt signing declaration of war against Japan. 1cor, Gen. Henri Giraud, Roosevelt, Gen. Charles de Gaulle and Churchill. 3cor, Stalin, Roosevelt and Churchill. 5cor, Sculptured head of Roosevelt.

Engraved, Center Photogravure
1946, June 15 *Perf. 12½*
Frame in Black

C272 A50 25c orange .15 .15
a. Horiz. pair, imperf. btwn. 225.00
b. Imperf., pair 175.00
C273 A51 75c carmine .25 .25
a. Imperf., pair 175.00
C274 A50 1cor dark green .40 .40
C275 A50 3cor violet 3.75 3.75
C276 A51 5cor greenish blue 5.00 5.00
Nos. C272-C276 (5) 9.55 9.55

Issued to honor Franklin D. Roosevelt.

Projected Provincial Seminary — AP36

Designs: 20c, Communications Building. 35c, Sanitation Building. 90c, National Bank. 1cor, Municipal Building. 2.50cor, National Palace.

1947, Jan. 10
Frame in Black

C277 AP36 5c violet .15 .15
a. Imperf., pair 125.00
C278 AP36 20c gray grn .15 .15
C279 AP36 35c orange .20 .18
C280 AP36 90c red lil .40 .30
C281 AP36 1cor brown .60 .45
C282 AP36 2.50cor rose lil 1.75 1.50
Nos. C277-C282 (6) 3.25 2.73

City of Managua centenary.

Rubén Darío Monument — AP42

Designs: 6c, Tapir. 8c, Stone Highway. 10c, Genizaro Dam. 20c, Detail of Dario Monument. 25c, Sulphurous Lake of Nejapa. 35c, Mercedes Airport. 50c, Prinzapolka River delta. 1cor, Tipitapa Spa. 1.50cor, Tipitapa River. 5cor, United States Embassy. 10cor, Indian fruit vendor. 25cor, Franklin D. Roosevelt Monument.

Engraved, Center Photogravure
1947, Aug. 29 Unwmk. *Perf. 12½*

C283 AP42 5c dk bl grn & rose car .15 .15
C284 AP42 6c blk & yel .15 .15
C285 AP42 8c car & ol .15 .15
C286 AP42 10c brn & bl .18 .15
C287 AP42 20c bl vio & org .30 .30
C288 AP42 25c brn red & emer .35 .35
C289 AP42 35c gray & bis .30 .30
C290 AP42 50c pur & sep .25 .25
C291 AP42 1cor blk & lil rose .75 .75
C292 AP42 1.50cor red brn & aqua .80 .80
C293 AP42 5cor choc & car rose 6.25 6.25
C294 AP42 10cor vio & dk brn 5.00 5.00
C295 AP42 25cor dk bl grn & yel 10.00 10.00
Nos. C283-C295 (13) 24.63 24.60

The frames differ for each denomination.
For surcharge see No. C750.

Tennis — AP43

Designs: 2c, Soccer. 3c, Table tennis. 4c, Proposed stadium. 5c, Regatta. 15c, Basketball. 25c, Boxing. 30c, Baseball. 40c, Bicycling. 75c, Diving. 1cor, Pole vault. 2cor, Boy Scouts. 5cor, Softball.

1949, July Photo. *Perf. 12*

C296 AP43 1c cerise .15 .15
C297 AP43 2c ol gray .15 .15
C298 AP43 3c scarlet .15 .15
C299 AP43 4c dk bl gray .15 .15
C300 AP43 5c aqua .30 .15
C301 AP43 15c bl grn .90 .15
C302 AP43 25c red vio 2.00 .30
C303 AP43 30c red brn 1.75 .30
C304 AP43 40c violet .45 .30
C305 AP43 75c magenta 4.50 2.75
C306 AP43 1cor lt bl 5.00 1.35
C307 AP43 2cor brn ol 2.00 1.75
C308 AP43 5cor lt grn 2.25 2.25
a. Set of 13 souv. sheets of 4 125.00 125.00
Nos. C296-C308 (13) 19.75 9.90

10th World Series of Amateur Baseball, 1948.

Rowland Hill — AP44

Designs: 20c, Heinrich von Stephan. 25c, First UPU Bldg. 30c, UPU Bldg., Bern. 85c, UPU Monument. 1.10cor, Congress medal, obverse. 2.14cor, as 1.10cor, reverse.

1950, Nov. 23 Engr. *Perf. 13*
Frames in Black

C309 AP44 16c cerise .15 .15
C310 AP44 20c orange .15 .15
C311 AP44 25c gray .20 .20
C312 AP44 30c cerise .30 .15
C313 AP44 85c dk bl grn .65 .65
C314 AP44 1.10cor chnt brn .50 .45
C315 AP44 2.14cor ol grn 2.25 2.25
Nos. C309-C315 (7) 4.20 4.00

75th anniv. (in 1949) of the UPU.
Each denomination was also issued in a souvenir sheet containing four stamps and marginal inscriptions. Size: 126x114mm. Value, set of 7 sheets, $35.
For surcharges see Nos. C501, C758.

Queen Isabela I Type

Designs: 2.30cor, Portrait facing left. 2.80cor, Map. 3cor, Santa Maria. 3.30cor, Columbus' ships. 3.60cor, Portrait facing right.

1952, June 25 Unwmk. *Perf. 11½*

C316 A65 2.30cor rose car 2.00 2.00
C317 A65 2.80cor red org 1.75 1.75
C318 A65 3cor green 2.00 2.00
C319 A66 3.30cor lt bl 2.00 2.00
C320 A65 3.60cor yel grn 2.25 2.25
a. Souv. sheet of 5, #C316-C320 10.00 10.00
Nos. C316-C320 (5) 10.00 10.00

For overprint see No. C445.

Arms of ODECA — AP47

Designs: 25c, ODECA Flag. 30c, Presidents of five Central American countries. 60c, ODECA Charter and Flags. 1cor, Map of Central America.

1953, Apr. 15 *Perf. 13½x14*

C321 AP47 20c red lil .15 .15
C322 AP47 25c lt bl .15 .15
C323 AP47 30c sepia .20 .15
C324 AP47 60c dk bl grn .30 .25
C325 AP47 1cor dk vio .70 .65
Nos. C321-C325 (5) 1.50 1.35

Founding of the Organization of Central American States (ODECA).

Leonardo Arguello — AP48

Presidents: 5c, Gen. Jose Maria Moncada. 20c, Juan Bautista Sacasa. 25c, Gen. Jose Santos Zelaya. 30c, Gen. Anastasio Somoza. 35c, Gen. Tomas Martinez. 40c, Fernando Guzman. 45c, Vicente Cuadra. 50c, Pedro Joaquin Chamorro. 60c, Gen. Joaquin Zavala. 85c, Adan Cardenas. 1.10cor, Evaristo Carazo. 1.20cor, Roberto Sacasa.

Engraved (frames); Photogravure (heads)
1953, June 25 *Perf. 12½*
Heads in Gray Black

C326 AP48 4c dp car .15 .15
C327 AP48 5c dp org .15 .15
C328 AP48 20c dk Prus bl .15 .15
C329 AP48 25c blue .15 .15
C330 AP48 30c red brn .15 .15
C331 AP48 35c dp grn .18 .18
C332 AP48 40c dk vio brn .22 .18
C333 AP48 45c olive .22 .22
C334 AP48 50c carmine .28 .15
C335 AP48 60c ultra .30 .22
C336 AP48 85c brown .38 .35
C337 AP48 1.10cor purple .45 .45
C338 AP48 1.20cor ol bis .45 .45
Set value 2.80 2.40

For surcharges see Nos. C363-C364, C757.

Torch and UN Emblem — AP49 Capt. Dean L. Ray, USAF — AP50

Designs: 4c, Raised hands. 5c, Candle and charter. 30c, Flags of Nicaragua and UN. 2cor, Globe. 3cor, Arms of Nicaragua. 5cor, Type A69 inscribed "Aereo."

1954, Apr. 30 Engr. *Perf. 13½*

C339 AP49 3c rose pink .15 .15
C340 AP49 4c dp org .15 .15
C341 AP49 5c red .15 .15
C342 AP49 30c cerise 1.00 .20
C343 AP49 2cor magenta 1.35 1.00
C344 AP49 3cor org brn 2.50 1.75
C345 AP49 5cor brn vio 3.00 2.25
Nos. C339-C345 (7) 8.30 5.65

Honoring the United Nations.
For overprint & surcharge see #C366, C443.

Engraved; Center Photogravure
1954, Nov. 5 *Perf. 13*

Designs: 15c, Sabre jet plane. 20c, Air Force emblem. 25c, National Air Force hangars. 30c, Gen. A. Somoza. 50c, AT-6's in formation. 1cor, Plane, type P-38.

Frame in Black

C346 AP50 10c gray .15 .15
C347 AP50 15c gray .15 .15
C348 AP50 20c claret .15 .15
C349 AP50 25c red .15 .15
C350 AP50 30c ultra .15 .15
C351 AP50 50c blue .45 .45
C352 AP50 1cor green .35 .22
Set value 1.25 .95

Issued to honor the National Air Force.

Rotary Intl. Type

Designs: 1c, 1cor, Paul P. Harris. 2c, 50c, Handclasp, Rotary emblem and globe. 3c, 45c, Map of world and Rotary emblem. 4c, 30c, Rotary slogans and wreath. 5c, 25c, Flags of Nicaragua and Rotary.

Perf. 11½
1955, Aug. 30 Unwmk. Photo.
Granite Paper

C353 A71 1c vermilion .15 .15
C354 A71 2c ultra .15 .15
C355 A72 3c pck grn .15 .15
C356 A71 4c violet .15 .15
C357 A71 5c org brn .15 .15
C358 A71 25c brt grnsh bl .20 .18

C359	A71	30c dl pur	.15	.15
C360	A72	45c lil rose	.35	.30
C361	A71	50c lt bl grn	.25	.20
C362	A71	1cor ultra	.35	.35
a.		Souv. sheet of 5, #C358-C362	9.50	9.50
		Set value	1.50	1.35

Rotary International, 50th anniversary.
For surcharge see No. C365.

Nos. C331, C333, C360, C345 Surcharged in Green or Black

Conmemoración Exposición Nacional Febrero 4-16, 1956 ₡ 0.15

Engraved, Photogravure

1956, Feb. 4 *Perf. 13½x13, 11½*

C363	AP48	30c on 35c (G)	.20	.18
C364	AP48	30c on 45c (G)	.20	.18
C365	A72	30c on 45c	.20	.15
C366	AP49	2cor on 5cor	.80	.75
		Nos. C363-C366 (4)	1.40	1.26

National Exhibition, Feb. 4-16, 1956.
See note after No. 772.

Gen. Jose D. Estrada — AP53

The Stoning of Andres Castro — AP54

Designs: 1.50 cor, Emanuel Mongalo. 2.50 cor, Battle of Rivas. 10 cor, Com. Hiram Paulding.

1956, Sept. 14 **Engr.** *Perf. 12½*

C367	AP53	30c dk car rose	.15	.15
C368	AP54	60c chocolate	.15	.15
C369	AP53	1.50cor green	.30	.30
C370	AP54	2.50cor dk ultra	.50	.50
C371	AP53	10cor red org	2.00	2.00
		Nos. C367-C371 (5)	3.10	3.10

Centenary of the National War.
For overprint and surcharge see #C444, C751.

President Somoza — AP55

1957, Feb. 1 **Photo.** *Perf. 14x13½*
Various Frames: Centers in Black

C372	AP55	15c gray blk	.15	.15
C373	AP55	30c indigo	.20	.20
C374	AP55	2cor purple	1.00	1.00
C375	AP55	3cor dk grn	2.00	2.00
C376	AP55	5cor dk brn	3.25	3.25
		Nos. C372-C376 (5)	6.60	6.60

President Anastasio Somoza, 1896-1956.

Type of Regular Issue and

Handshake and Globe — AP56

Designs: 4c, Scout emblem, globe and Lord Baden-Powell. 5c, Cub Scout. 6c, Crossed flags and Scout emblem. 8c, Scout symbols. 30c, Joseph A. Harrison. 40c, Pres. Somoza receiving decoration at first Central American Camporee. 75c, Explorer Scout. 85c, Boy Scout. 1cor, Lord Baden-Powell.

1957, Apr. 9 **Unwmk.** *Perf. 13½x14*

C377	AP56	3c red org & ol	.15	.15
C378	A75	4c dk brn & dk Prus grn	.15	.15
C379	A75	5c grn & brn	.15	.15
C380	A75	6c pur & ol	.15	.15
C381	A75	8c grnsh blk & red	.15	.15
C382	A75	30c Prus grn & gray	.15	.15
C383	AP56	40c dk bl & grysh blk	.15	.15
C384	A75	75c mar & brn	.20	.20
C385	A75	85c red & gray	.22	.22
C386	A75	1cor dl red brn & sl grn	.30	.28
a.		Souv. sheet of 5, #C382-C386, imperf.	2.50	2.50
		Set value	1.50	1.45

Centenary of the birth of Lord Baden-Powell, founder of the Boy Scouts.
No. C386a with each stamp overprinted "CAMPOREE SCOUT 1965" was issued in 1965 along with Nos. 843-852.
For surcharge see No. C754.

Pres. Luis A. Somoza — AP57

1957, July 2 *Perf. 14x13½*
Portrait in Dark Brown

C387	AP57	20c dp bl	.15	.15
C388	AP57	25c lil rose	.15	.15
C389	AP57	30c blk brn	.15	.15
C390	AP57	40c grnsh bl	.20	.20
C391	AP57	2cor brt vio	1.25	1.25
		Nos. C387-C391 (5)	1.90	1.90

Issued to honor President Luis A. Somoza.

Church Types of Regular Issue

Designs: 30c, Archbishop Lezcano y Ortega. 60c, Managua Cathedral. 75c, Bishop Pereira y Castellon. 90c, Leon Cathedral. 1.50cor, De la Merced Church, Granada. 2cor, Father Mariano Dubon.

1957, July 16 **Unwmk.**
Centers in Olive Gray

C392	A78	30c dk grn	.15	.15
C393	A77	60c chocolate	.15	.15
C394	A78	75c dk bl	.20	.20
C395	A77	90c brt red	.28	.28
C396	A77	1.50cor Prus grn	.40	.40
C397	A78	2cor brt pur	.60	.60
		Nos. C392-C397 (6)	1.78	1.78

Merchant Marine Type of 1957

Designs: 25c, M. S. Managua. 30c, Ship's wheel and map. 50c, Pennants. 60c, M. S. Costa Rica. 1 cor, M. S. Nicarao. 2.50 cor, Flag, globe & ship.

1957, Oct. 24 **Litho.** *Perf. 14*

C398	A79	25c ultra grysh bl & gray	.15	.15
C399	A79	30c red brn, gray & yel	.15	.15
C400	A79	50c vio, ol gray & bl	.30	.30
C401	A79	60c lake, grnsh bl & blk	.35	.35
C402	A79	1cor crim, brt bl & blk	.48	.48
C403	A79	2.50cor blk, bl & red brn	1.50	1.50
		Nos. C398-C403 (6)	2.93	2.93

For surcharge see No. C691.

Fair Emblem — AP58

Designs: 30c, 2cor, Arms of Nicaragua. 45c, 10cor, Pavilion of Nicaragua, Brussels.

1958, Apr. 17 **Unwmk.** *Perf. 14*

C404	AP58	25c bluish grn, blk & yel	.15	.15
C405	AP58	30c multi	.15	.15
C406	AP58	45c bis, bl & blk	.15	.15
C407	AP58	1cor pale brn, lt bl & blk	.18	.18
C408	AP58	2cor multi	.32	.32
C409	AP58	10cor pale bl, lil & brn	1.65	1.65
a.		Souv. sheet of 6, #C404-C409	7.50	7.50
		Nos. C404-C409 (6)	2.60	2.60

World's Fair, Brussels, Apr. 17-Oct. 19.

Lions Type of Regular Issue

Designs: 30c, Dr. Teodoro A. Arias. 60c, Arms of Central American Republics. 90c, Edward G. Barry. 1.25cor, Melvin Jones. 2cor, Motto and emblem. 3cor, Map of Central America.

1958, May 8 **Litho.**
Emblem in Yellow, Red and Blue

C410	A80	30c bl & org	.15	.15
C411	A80	60c multi	.25	.20
C412	A80	90c blue	.35	.30
C413	A80	1.25cor bl & ol	.45	.40
C414	A80	2cor bl & grn	.80	.70
C415	A80	3cor bl, lil & pink	1.25	1.10
a.		Souv. sheet of 6, #C410-C415	4.25	4.25
		Nos. C410-C415 (6)	3.25	2.85

For surcharge see No. C686.

Christian Brothers Type of 1958

Designs: 30c, Arms of La Salle. 60c, School, Managua, horiz 85c, St. Jean Baptiste De La Salle. 90c, Bro. Carlos. 1.25cor, Bro. Julio. 1.50cor, Bro. Antonio. 1.75cor, Bro. Argeo. 2cor, Bro. Eugenio.

1958, July 13 **Photo.** *Perf. 14*

C416	A81	30c bl, car & yel	.15	.15
C417	A81	60c gray, brn & lil	.28	.24
C418	A81	85c red, bl & grnsh blk	.32	.28
C419	A81	90c ol grn, ocher & blk	.40	.36
C420	A81	1.25cor car, ocher & blk	.55	.52
C421	A81	1.50cor lt grn, gray & vio blk	.65	.55
C422	A81	1.75cor brn, bl & grnsh blk	.70	.65
C423	A81	2cor ol grn, gray & vio blk	1.00	1.00
		Nos. C416-C423 (8)	4.05	3.75

For surcharges see Nos. C539A, C755-C756.

UNESCO Building, Paris — AP59

75c, 5cor, "UNESCO." 90c, 3cor, UNESCO building, Eiffel tower. 1cor, Emblem, globe.

Perf. 11½

1958, Dec. 15 **Unwmk.** **Litho.**

C424	AP59	60c brt pink & bl	.15	.15
C425	AP59	75c grn & red brn	.15	.15
C426	AP59	90c lt brn & grn	.18	.15
C427	AP59	1cor ultra & brt pink	.20	.20
C428	AP59	3cor gray & org	.65	.65
C429	AP59	5cor rose lil & dk bl	1.00	.95
a.		Min. sheet of 6, #C424-C429	2.50	2.50
		Nos. C424-C429 (6)	2.33	2.25

UNESCO Headquarters Opening in Paris, Nov. 3.
For overprints see Nos. C494-C499.

Type of Regular Issue, 1959 and

Nicaraguan, Papal and US Flags AP60

Designs: 35c, Pope John XXIII and Cardinal Spellman. 1cor, Spellman coat of arms. 1.05cor, Cardinal Spellman. 1.50cor, Human rosary and Cardinal, horiz. 2cor, Cardinal with Ruben Dario order.

1959, Nov. 26 *Perf. 12½*

C430	AP60	30c vio bl, yel & red	.15	.15
C431	A83	35c dp org & grnsh blk	.15	.15
C432	A83	1cor yel, bl & car	.22	.22
C433	A83	1.05cor red, blk & dk car	.28	.28
C434	A83	1.50cor dk bl & yel	.30	.30
C435	A83	2cor multi	.40	.40
C436	AP60	5cor multi	1.25	.90
a.		Min. sheet of 7, #C430-C436, perf. or imperf.	3.75	3.75
		Nos. C430-C436 (7)	2.75	2.40

Visit of Cardinal Spellman to Managua, Feb. 1958.
For surcharges see #C538, C638, C747, C752.

Type of Lincoln Regular Issue and

AP61

Perf. 13x13½, 13½x13

1960, Jan. 21 **Engr.** **Unwmk.**
Portrait in Black

C437	A84	30c indigo	.15	.15
C438	A84	35c brt car	.15	.15
C439	A84	70c plum	.15	.15
C440	A84	1.05cor emerald	.22	.22
C441	A84	1.50cor violet	.30	.30
C442	AP61	5cor int blk & bis	.90	.90
a.		Souv. sheet of 6, #C437-C442, imperf.	3.00	3.00
		Nos. C437-C442 (6)	1.87	1.87

150th anniv. of the birth of Abraham Lincoln.
For overprints and surcharges see Nos. C446-C451, C500, C539, C637, C680, C753.

Nos. C343, C370 and C318 Overprinted: "X Aniversario Club Filatelico S.J.-C.R."

1960, July 4 **Engr.**

C443	AP49	2cor magenta	.65	.70
C444	AP54	2.50cor dk ultra	.65	.75
C445	A65	3cor green	.85	1.10
		Nos. C443-C445 (3)	2.15	2.55

10th anniversary of the Philatelic Club of San Jose, Costa Rica.

Nos. C437-C442 Overprinted in Red

✠ Resello

Perf. 13x13½, 13½x13

1960, Sept. 19 **Unwmk.**
Center in Black

C446	A84	30c indigo	.20	.16
C447	A84	35c brt car	.16	.15
C448	A84	70c plum	.16	.16
C449	A84	1.05cor emerald	.22	.22
C450	A84	1.50cor violet	.38	.35
C451	AP61	5cor int blk & bis	1.10	1.10
		Nos. C446-C451 (6)	2.22	2.14

Issued for the Red Cross to aid earthquake victims in Chile. The overprint on No. C451 is horizontal and always inverted.

People and World Refugee Year Emblem AP62

Design: 5cor, Crosses, globe and WRY emblem.

1961, Jan. 2 **Litho.** *Perf. 11x11½*

C452	AP62	2cor multi	.30	.30
C453	AP62	5cor multi	.65	.65
a.		Souv. sheet of 2, #C452-C453	2.50	2.50

World Refugee Year, July 1, 1959-June 30, 1960.

AP63

Consular Service Stamps Surcharged "Correo Aéreo" and New Denomination in Red, Black or Blue

Unwmk.

1961, Feb. 21 **Engr.** *Perf. 12*
Red Marginal Number

C454	AP63	20c on 50c dp bl (R)	.15	.15
C455	AP63	20c on 1cor grnsh blk (R)	.15	.15
C456	AP63	20c on 2cor grn (R)	.15	.15
C457	AP63	20c on 3cor dk car	.15	.15
C458	AP63	20c on 5cor org (Bl)	.15	.15
C459	AP63	20c on 10cor vio (R)	.15	.15
C460	AP63	20c on 20cor red brn (R)	.15	.15
C461	AP63	20c on 50cor brn (R)	.15	.15
C462	AP63	20c on 100cor mag	.15	.15
		Set value	.72	.54

See Nos. CO51-CO59, RA63-RA64.

Charles L. Mullins, Anastasio Somoza and Franklin D. Roosevelt
AP64

Standard Bearers with Flags of Nicaragua and Academy — AP65

Designs: 25c, 70c, Flags of Nicaragua and Academy. 30c, 1.05cor, Directors of Academy: Fred T. Cruse, LeRoy Bartlett, Jr., John F. Greco, Anastasio Somoza Debayle, Francisco Boza, Elias Monge. 40c, 2cor, Academy Emblem. 45c, 5cor, Anastasio Somoza Debayle and Luis Somoza Debayle.

Perf. 11x11½, 11½x11

1961, Feb. 24 Litho. Unwmk.

C463	AP64	20c rose lil, gray & buff	.15	.15
C464	AP65	25c bl, red & blk	.15	.15
C465	AP64	30c bl, gray & yel	.15	.15
C466	AP65	35c multi	.15	.15
C467	AP65	40c multi	.15	.15
C468	AP64	45c pink, gray & buff	.15	.15
a.		Min. sheet of 6, #C463-C468, imperf.	.40	.40
C469	AP64	60c brn, gray & buff	.15	.15
C470	AP65	70c multi	.15	.15
C471	AP64	1.05cor lil, gray & yel	.15	.15
C472	AP65	1.50cor multi	.18	.18
C473	AP65	2cor multi	.26	.25
C474	AP64	5cor gray & buff	.70	.55
a.		Min. sheet of 6, #C469-C474, imperf.	1.65	1.65
		Set value	1.80	1.65

20th anniversary (in 1959) of the founding of the Military Academy of Nicaragua.

In 1977, Nos. C468a and C474a were overprinted in black: "1927-1977 50 ANIVERSARIO / Guardia Nacional de Nicaragua." Value, $4.

For surcharges see Nos. C692, C748, C759.

Emblem of Junior Chamber of Commerce — AP66

Designs: 2c, 15c, Globe showing map of Americas, horiz. 4c, 35c, Globe and initials, horiz. 5c, 70c, Chamber credo. 6c, 1.05cor, Handclasp. 10c, 5cor, Regional map.

Perf. 11x11½, 11½x11

1961, May 16 Unwmk.

C475	AP66	2c multi	.15	.15
C476	AP66	3c yel & blk	.15	.15
C477	AP66	4c multi	.15	.15
C478	AP66	5c crim & blk	.15	.15
C479	AP66	6c brn, yel & blk	.15	.15
C480	AP66	10c red org, blk & bl	.15	.15
C481	AP66	15c bl, blk & grn	.15	.15
C482	AP66	30c bl & blk	.15	.15
C483	AP66	35c multi	.15	.15
C484	AP66	70c yel, blk & crim	.15	.15
C485	AP66	1.05cor multi	.15	.15
C486	AP66	5cor multi	.55	.55
		Set value	1.25	1.15

13th Regional Congress of the Junior Chamber of Commerce of Nicaragua and the Intl. Junior Chamber of Commerce.

The imperforates of Nos. C475-C486 were not authorized.

For overprints and surcharges see Nos. C504-C508, C537, C634, C687, C749.

Rigoberto Cabezas — AP67

Map of Mosquito Territory and View of Cartago
AP68

Designs: 45c, Newspaper. 70c, Building. 2cor, Cabezas quotation. 10cor, Map of lower Nicaragua with Masaya area.

1961, Aug. 29 Litho. *Perf. 13½*

C487	AP67	20c org & dk bl	.15	.15
C488	AP68	40c lt bl & claret	.15	.15
C489	AP68	45c citron & brn	.15	.15
C490	AP68	70c beige & grn	.15	.15
C491	AP68	2cor pink & dk bl	.32	.22
C492	AP68	10cor grnsh bl & cl	1.40	1.10
		Nos. C487-C492 (6)	2.32	1.92

Centenary of the birth of Rigoberto Cabezas, who acquired the Mosquito Territory (Atlantic Littoral) for Nicaragua.

No. C253 Overprinted in Red: "Convención Filatélica-Centro-América-Panama-San Salvador-27 Julio 1961"

1961, Aug. 23 Engr. *Perf. 12½*

C493	AP22	1.25cor multi	.42	.42
a.		Inverted overprint	75.00	

Central American Philatelic Convention, San Salvador, July 27.

Nos. C424-C429 Overprinted in Red: "Homenaje a Hammarskjold Sept. 18-1961"

1961 Litho. *Perf. 11½*

C494	AP59	60c brt pink & bl	.25	.25
C495	AP59	75c grn & red brn	.28	.28
C496	AP59	90c lt brn & grn	.30	.30
C497	AP59	1cor ultra & brt pink	.32	.32
C498	AP59	3cor gray & org	.65	.65
C499	AP59	5cor rose lil & dk bl	1.75	1.75
		Nos. C494-C499 (6)	3.55	3.55

Issued in memory of Dag Hammarskjold, Secretary General of the United Nations, 1953-61.

RESELLO

Nos. C314 and C440 Surcharged in Red

₡ 1.00

Perf. 13x13½, 13

1962, Jan. 20 Engr.

C500	A84	1cor on 1.05cor	.20	.18
C501	AP44	1cor on 1.10cor	.20	.18

UNESCO Emblem and Crowd — AP69

Design: 5cor, UNESCO and UN Emblems.

Unwmk.

1962, Feb. 26 Photo. *Perf. 12*

C502	AP69	2cor multi	.28	.25
C503	AP69	5cor multi	.70	.70
a.		Souv. sheet of 2, #C502-C503, imperf.	1.25	1.25

15th anniv. (in 1961) of UNESCO.

Nos. C480 and C483-C486 Overprinted

Perf. 11x11½, 11½x11

1962, July Litho.

C504	AP66	10c multi	.22	.20
C505	AP66	35c multi	.30	.20
C506	AP66	70c multi	.38	.30
C507	AP66	1.05cor multi	.50	.45
C508	AP66	5cor multi	.85	1.40
		Nos. C504-C508 (5)	2.25	2.55

WHO drive to eradicate malaria.

Souvenir Sheet

Stamps and Postmarks of 1862 — AP69a

1962, Sept. 9 Litho. *Imperf.*

C509	AP69a	7cor multi	2.50	2.50

Cent. of Nicaraguan postage stamps.

Arms Type of Regular Issue, 1962

Coats of Arms: 30c, Nueva Segovia. 50c, León. 1cor, Managua. 2cor, Granada. 5cor, Rivas.

1962, Nov. 22 *Perf. 12½x13*

Arms in Original Colors; Black Inscriptions

C510	A86	30c rose	.15	.15
C511	A86	50c salmon	.15	.15
C512	A86	1cor lt grn	.15	.15
C513	A86	2cor gray	.32	.28
C514	A86	5cor lt bl	.85	.75
		Nos. C510-C514 (5)	1.62	
		Set value		1.25

Liberty Bell
AP70

1963, May 15 Litho. *Perf. 13x12*

C515	AP70	30c lt bl, blk & ol bis	.15	.15

Sesquicentennial of the 1st Nicaraguan declaration of Independence (in 1961).

Paulist Brother Comforting Boy — AP71

Map of Central America — AP72

Designs: 60c, Nun comforting girl. 2cor, St. Vincent de Paul and St. Louisa de Marillac, horiz.

1963, May 15 Photo. *Perf. 13½*

C516	AP71	60c gray & ocher	.15	.15
C517	AP71	1cor salmon & blk	.25	.22
C518	AP71	2cor crimson & blk	.50	.50
		Nos. C516-C518 (3)	.90	.87

300th anniv. of the deaths of St. Vincent de Paul and St. Louisa de Marillac (in 1960).

Lithographed and Engraved

1963, Aug. 2 Unwmk. *Perf. 12*

C519	AP72	1cor bl & yel	.20	.15

Issued to honor the Federation of Central American Philatelic Societies.

Cross over World
AP73

Wheat and Map of Nicaragua
AP74

1963, Aug. 6

C520	AP73	20c yel & red	.15	.15

Vatican II, the 21st Ecumenical Council of the Roman Catholic Church.

1963, Aug. 6

Design: 25c, Dead tree on parched earth.

C521	AP74	10c lt grn & grn	.15	.15
C522	AP74	25c yel & dk brn	.15	.15
		Set value	.15	.15

FAO "Freedom from Hunger" campaign.

Boxing — AP75

Flags of Central American States — AP75a

Lithographed and Engraved

1963, Dec. 12 Unwmk. *Perf. 12*

C523	AP75	2c shown	.15	.15
C524	AP75	3c Running	.15	.15
C525	AP75	4c Underwater	.15	.15
C526	AP75	5c Soccer	.15	.15
C527	AP75	6c Baseball	.15	.15
C528	AP75	10c Tennis	.15	.15
C529	AP75	15c Bicycling	.15	.15
C530	AP75	20c Motorcycling	.15	.15
C531	AP75	35c Chess	.22	.22
C532	AP75	60c Deep-sea fishing	.28	.28
C533	AP75	1cor Table tennis	.42	.42
C534	AP75	2cor Basketball	.80	.80
C535	AP75	5cor Golf	2.00	2.00
		Set value	4.25	4.25

Publicizing the 1964 Olympic Games.

For overprints and surcharge see Nos. C553-C558, C635.

Central American Independence Issue

1964, Sept. 15 Litho. *Perf. 13x13½*

Size: 27x43mm

C536	AP75a	40c multi	.25	.25

Nos. C479, C430, C437 and C416 Surcharged in Black or Red

Resello ₡ 0.15 — a

RESELLO ₡ 0.20 — b

1964 Litho. *Perf. 11½x11*

C537	AP66	5c on 6c	.25	.15

Perf. 12½

C538	AP60	10c on 30c	.50	.15

Engr.

Perf. 13x13½

C539	A84	15c on 30c (R)	.65	.15

Photo.

Perf. 14

C539A	A81	20c on 30c	.15	.15
		Nos. C537-C539A (4)	1.55	
		Set value		.20

Floating Red Cross Station — AP76

Designs: 5c, Alliance for Progress emblem, vert. 15c, Highway. 20c, Plowing with tractors, and sun. 25c, Housing development. 30c, Presidents Somoza and Kennedy and World Bank Chairman Eugene Black. 35c, Adult education. 40c, Smokestacks.

1964, Oct. 15 Litho. *Perf. 12*

C540 AP76 5c yel, brt bl, grn & gray .15 .15
C541 AP76 10c multi .15 .15
C542 AP76 15c multi .15 .15
C543 AP76 20c org brn, yel & blk .15 .15
C544 AP76 25c multi .15 .15
C545 AP76 30c dk bl, blk & brn .15 .15
C546 AP76 35c lil rose, dk red & blk .18 .15
C547 AP76 40c dp car, blk & yel .22 .15
Set value .90 .52

Alliance for Progress.
For surcharges see Nos. C677, C693.

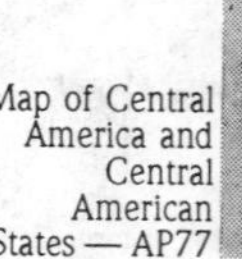

Map of Central America and Central American States — AP77

Designs (Map of Central America and): 25c, Grain. 40c, Cogwheels. 50c, Heads of cattle.

1964, Nov. 30 Litho. *Perf. 12*

C548 AP77 15c ultra & multi .15 .15
C549 AP77 25c multi .15 .15
C550 AP77 40c multi .15 .15
C551 AP77 50c multi .15 .15
Set value .36 .30

Central American Common Market.
For surcharge see No. C678.

Nos. C523-C525, C527 and C533-C534 Overprinted: "OLIMPIADAS / TOKYO-1964"

Lithographed and Engraved

1964, Dec. 19 Unwmk. *Perf. 12*

C553 AP75 2c multi .15 .15
C554 AP75 3c multi .15 .15
C555 AP75 4c multi .15 .15
C556 AP75 6c multi .15 .15
C557 AP75 1cor multi 2.00 2.00
C558 AP75 2cor multi 2.50 2.50
Nos. C553-C558 (6) 5.10 5.10

18th Olympic Games, Tokyo, Oct. 10-25.

Blood Transfusion AP78

Stele AP79

Designs: 20c, Volunteers and priest rescuing wounded man. 40c, Landscape during storm. 10cor, Red Cross over map of Nicaragua.

1965, Jan. 28 Litho. *Perf. 12*

C559 AP78 20c yel, blk & red .15 .15
C560 AP78 25c red, blk & ol bis .15 .15
C561 AP78 40c grn, blk & red .15 .15
C562 AP78 10cor multi 1.75 1.10
Set value 1.90 1.20

Centenary (in 1963) of the Intl. Red Cross.

Perf. 13½x13, 13x13½

1965, Mar. 24 Litho. Unwmk.

Antique Indian artifacts: 5c, Three jadeite statuettes, horiz. 15c, Dog, horiz. 20c, Talamanca pendant. 25c, Decorated pottery bowl and vase, horiz. 30c, Stone pestle and mortar on animal base. 35c, Three statuettes, horiz. 40c, Idol on animal pedestal. 50c, Decorated pottery bowl and vase. 60c, Vase and metate (tripod bowl), horiz. 1cor, Metate.

Black Margin and Inscription

C563 AP79 5c yel & multi .15 .15
C564 AP79 10c multi .15 .15
C565 AP79 15c multi .15 .15
C566 AP79 20c sal & dk brn .15 .15
C567 AP79 25c lil & multi .15 .15
C568 AP79 30c lt grn & multi .15 .15
C569 AP79 35c multi .15 .15
C570 AP79 40c cit & multi .15 .15
C571 AP79 50c ocher & multi .15 .15
C572 AP79 60c multi .15 .15
C573 AP79 1cor car & multi .30 .15
Set value (11) .95 .55

For surcharges see Nos. C596-597, C679, C688-C690.

Pres. John F. Kennedy (1917-63) — AP80

Photogravure & Lithographed

1965, Apr. 28 *Perf. 12½x13½*

C574 AP80 35c blk & brt grn .20 .15
C575 AP80 75c blk & brt pink .35 .20
C576 AP80 1.10cor blk & dk bl .50 .40
C577 AP80 2cor blk & yel brn 1.25 1.00
Nos. C574-C577 (4) 2.30 1.75
Set of 4 souvenir sheets 5.00 5.00

Nos. C574-C577 each exist in souvenir sheets containing one imperf. block of 4.
For surcharge see No. C760.

Andrés Bello — AP81

1965, Oct. 15 Litho. *Perf. 14*

C578 AP81 10c dk brn & red brn .15 .15
C579 AP81 15c ind & lt bl .15 .15
C580 AP81 45c blk & dl lil .15 .15
C581 AP81 80c blk & yel grn .15 .15
C582 AP81 1cor dk brn & yel .18 .15
C583 AP81 2cor blk & gray .32 .30
Set value .80 .70

Centenary of the death of Andrés Bello (1780?-1864), Venezuelan writer and educator.

Winston Churchill AP82

Pope John XXIII AP83

Winston Churchill: 35c, 1cor, Broadcasting, horiz. 60c, 3cor, On military inspection. 75c, As young officer.

1966, Feb. 7 Unwmk. *Perf. 14*

C584 AP82 20c cer & blk .15 .15
C585 AP82 35c dk ol grn & blk .15 .15
C586 AP82 60c brn & blk .16 .15
C587 AP82 75c rose red .20 .16
C588 AP82 1cor vio blk .28 .25
C589 AP82 2cor lil & blk .55 .50
a. Souv. sheet of 4 1.40 1.40
C590 AP82 3cor ind & blk .85 .70
Nos. C584-C590 (7) 2.34 2.06

Sir Winston Spencer Churchill (1874-1965), statesman and World War II leader.
No. C589a contains four imperf. stamps similar to Nos. C586-C589 with simulated perforations.

1966, Dec. 15 Litho. *Perf. 13*

Designs: 35c, Pope Paul VI. 1cor, Archbishop Gonzalez y Robleto. 2cor, St. Peter's, Rome. 3cor, Arms of Pope John XXIII and St. Peter's.

C591 AP83 20c multi .15 .15
C592 AP83 35c multi .15 .15
C593 AP83 1cor multi .22 .18
C594 AP83 2cor multi .42 .35
C595 AP83 3cor multi .65 .50
Nos. C591-C595 (5) 1.59 1.33

Closing of the Ecumenical Council, Vatican II.

RESELLO

Nos. C571-C572 Surcharged in Red

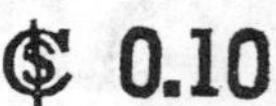

1967 *Perf. 13x13½, 13½x13*

C596 AP79 10c on 50c multi .15 .15
C597 AP79 15c on 60c multi .15 .15
Set value .15 .15

Rubén Dario and Birthplace — AP84

Portrait and: 10c, Monument, Managua. 20c, Leon Cathedral, site of Dario's tomb. 40c, Centaurs. 75c, Swans. 1cor, Roman triumphal march. 2cor, St. Francis and the Wolf. 5cor, "Faith" defeating "Death."

1967, Jan. 18 Litho. *Perf. 13*

C598 AP84 5c lt brn, tan & blk .15 .15
C599 AP84 10c org, pale org & blk .15 .15
C600 AP84 20c vio, lt bl & blk .15 .15
C601 AP84 40c grn, dk grn & blk .15 .15
a. Souv. sheet of 4, #C598-C601 .50 .50
C602 AP84 75c ultra, pale bl & blk .15 .15
C603 AP84 1cor red, pale red & blk .18 .15
C604 AP84 2cor rose pink, car & blk .32 .28
C605 AP84 5cor dp ultra, vio bl, & blk .75 .65
a. Souv. sheet of 4, #C602-C605 3.50 3.50
Set value (8) 1.60 1.35

Rubén Dario (pen name of Felix Rubén Garcia Sarmiento, 1867-1916), poet, newspaper correspondent and diplomat.
Sheets were issued perf. and imperf.

Megalura Peleus AP85

Designs: Various butterflies. 5c, 10c, 30c, 35c, 50c and 1cor are vertical.

1967, Apr. 20 Litho. *Perf. 14*

C606 AP85 5c multi .15 .15
C607 AP85 10c multi .15 .15
C608 AP85 15c multi .15 .15
C609 AP85 20c multi .15 .15
C610 AP85 25c multi .15 .15
C611 AP85 30c multi .15 .15
C612 AP85 35c multi .20 .15
C613 AP85 40c multi .20 .15
C614 AP85 50c multi .25 .15
C615 AP85 60c multi .25 .15
C616 AP85 1cor multi .40 .22
C617 AP85 2cor multi .75 .45
Set value (12) 2.50 1.50

Com. James McDivitt and Maj. Edward H. White AP86

Gemini 4 Space Flight: 10c, 40c, Rocket launching and astronauts. 15c, 75c, Edward H. White walking in space. 20c, 1cor, Recovery of capsule.

1967, Sept. 20 Litho. *Perf. 13*

C618 AP86 5c red & multi .15 .15
C619 AP86 10c org & multi .15 .15
C620 AP86 15c multi .15 .15
C621 AP86 20c multi .15 .15
C622 AP86 35c ol & multi .15 .15
C623 AP86 40c ultra & multi .15 .15
C624 AP86 75c brn & multi .18 .18
C625 AP86 1cor multi .22 .22
Set value (8) .75 .75

Saquanjoche, National Flower of Nicaragua — AP87

Presidents of Nicaragua and Mexico — AP88

National Flowers: No. C626, White nun orchid, Guatemala. No. C627, Rose, Honduras. No. C629, Maquilishuat, Salvador. No. C630, Purple guaria orchid, Costa Rica.

1967, Nov. 22 Litho. *Perf. 13½*

C626 AP87 40c multi .15 .15
C627 AP87 40c multi .15 .15
C628 AP87 40c multi .15 .15
C629 AP87 40c multi .15 .15
C630 AP87 40c multi .15 .15
a. Strip of 5, #C626-C630 .75 .50
Set value .25

5th anniversary of the General Treaty for Central American Economic Integration.

1968, Feb. 28 Litho. *Perf. 12½*

Designs: 40c Pres. Gustavo Diáz Ordaz of Mexico and Pres. René Schick of Nicaragua signing statement, horiz. 1cor, President Diáz.

C631 AP88 20c black .15 .15
C632 AP88 40c slate grn .15 .15
C633 AP88 1cor dp brn .22 .15
Set value .40 .22

Issued to commemorate the visit of the President of Mexico, Gustavo Diáz Ordaz.

Nos. C479, C527, C242, C440 and C434 Surcharged "Resello" and New Value in Black, Red (#C637) or Yellow (#C638)

1968, May Litho.; Engr.

C634 AP66 5c on 6c multi .15 .15
C635 AP75 5c on 6c multi .15 .15
C636 AP20 5c on 8c blk brn .15 .15
C637 A84 1cor on 1.05cor emer & blk .15 .15
C638 A83 1cor on 1.50cor dk bl & yel .15 .15
Set value .45 .38

Mangos — AP89

1968, May 15 Litho. *Perf. 14*

C639 AP89 5c shown .15 .15
C640 AP89 10c Pineapples .15 .15
C641 AP89 15c Orange .15 .15
C642 AP89 20c Papaya .15 .15
C643 AP89 30c Bananas .15 .15
C644 AP89 35c Avocado .15 .15
C645 AP89 50c Watermelon .15 .15
C646 AP89 75c Cashews .25 .15
C647 AP89 1cor Sapodilla .38 .22
C648 AP89 2cor Cacao .75 .45
Set value (10) 1.90 1.15

The Last Judgment, by Michelangelo AP90

Paintings: 10c, The Crucifixion, by Fra Angelo, horiz. 35c, Madonna with Child and St. John, by Raphael. 2cor, The Disrobing of Christ, by El Greco. 3cor, The Immaculate Conception, by Murillo. 5cor, Christ of St. John of the Cross, by Salvador Dali.

1968, July 22 Litho. *Perf. 12½*
C649 AP90 10c gold & multi .15 .15
C650 AP90 15c gold & multi .15 .15
C651 AP90 35c gold & multi .15 .15
C652 AP90 2cor gold & multi .45 .40
C653 AP90 3cor gold & multi .65 .55
Set value 1.25 1.10

Miniature Sheet
C654 AP90 5cor gold & multi 2.75 2.75

Nos. C649-C652 Overprinted: "Visita de S.S. Paulo VI C.E. de Bogota 1968"

1968, Oct. 25 Litho. *Perf. 12½*
C655 AP90 10c gold & multi .15 .15
C656 AP90 15c gold & multi .15 .15
C657 AP90 35c gold & multi .15 .15
C658 AP90 2cor gold & multi .50 .45
Set value .68 .60

Visit of Pope Paul VI to Bogota, Colombia, Aug. 22-24. The overprint has 3 lines on the 10c stamp and 5 lines on others.

Basketball — AP91

Sports: 15c, Fencing, horiz. 20c, Diving. 35c, Running. 50c, Hurdling, horiz. 75c, Weight lifting. 1cor, Boxing, horiz. 2cor, Soccer.

1968, Nov. 28 Litho. *Perf. 14*
C659 AP91 10c multi .15 .15
C660 AP91 15c org red, blk & gray .15 .15
C661 AP91 20c multi .15 .15
C662 AP91 35c multi .15 .15
C663 AP91 50c multi .15 .15
C664 AP91 75c multi .18 .18
C665 AP91 1cor yel & multi .30 .30
C666 AP91 2cor gray & multi .80 .80
a. Souv. sheet of 4, #C663-C666 1.75 1.75
Set value (8) 1.55 1.55

19th Olympic Games, Mexico City, Oct. 12-27.

Cichlasoma Citrinellum — AP92

Fish: 15c, Cichlasoma nicaraguensis. 20c, Carp. 30c, Gar (lepisosteus tropicus). 35c, Swordfish. 50c, Phylipnus dormitor, vert. 75c, Tarpon atlanticus, vert. 1cor, Eulamia nicaraguensis, vert. 2cor, Sailfish, vert. 3cor, Sawfish, vert.

Perf. 13½x13, 13x13½
1969, Mar. 12 Litho.
C667 AP92 10c vio bl & multi .15 .15
C668 AP92 15c org & multi .15 .15
C669 AP92 20c grn & multi .15 .15
C670 AP92 30c pur & multi .15 .15
C671 AP92 35c yel & multi .15 .15
C672 AP92 50c brn & multi .15 .15
C673 AP92 75c ultra & multi .15 .15
C674 AP92 1cor org & multi .20 .15
C675 AP92 2cor dk bl & multi .40 .25
C676 AP92 3cor multi .65 .42
a. Min. sheet of 4, #C673-C676 1.75 1.75
Set value (10) 1.70 1.10

Nos. C544, C549, C567 and C439 Surcharged in Black or Red

RESELLO
C$ 0.10

1969, Mar. Litho. *Perf. 12, 13½x13*
C677 AP76 10c on 25c multi .15 .15
C678 AP77 10c on 25c multi .15 .15
C679 AP79 15c on 25c multi .15 .15

Engr.
C680 A84 50c on 70c (R) .15 .15
Set value .25 .22

Size of 50c surcharge: 11½x9mm.

View, Exhibition Tower and Emblem — AP93

1969, May 30 Litho. *Perf. 13½x13*
C681 AP93 30c dk vio bl & red .15 .15
C682 AP93 35c blk & red .15 .15
C683 AP93 75c car rose & vio bl .15 .15
C684 AP93 1cor dp plum & blk .25 .15
C685 AP93 2cor dk brn & blk .45 .35
a. Souv. sheet of 4, #C681-C682, C684-C685 1.25 1.25
Set value .92 .65

HEMISFAIR 1968 Exhibition.

Nos. C410, C482, C567-C569, C399, C465, C546 Surcharged in Black or Red

RESELLO
C$ 0.20

1969 Litho. *Perfs. as before*
C686 A80 10c on 30c multi .15 .15
C687 AP66 10c on 30c bl & blk (R) .15 .15
C688 AP79 10c on 25c multi .15 .15
C689 AP79 10c on 30c multi .15 .15
C690 AP79 15c on 35c multi (R) .15 .15
C691 A79 20c on 30c multi .15 .15
C692 AP64 20c on 30c multi .15 .15
C693 AP76 20c on 35c multi .15 .15
Set value (8) .40 .40

Fishing AP94

Products of Nicaragua: 5c, Minerals (miner). 15c, Bananas. 20c, Timber (truck). 35c, Coffee. 40c, Sugar cane. 60c, Cotton. 75c, Rice and corn. 1cor, Tobacco. 2cor, Meat.

1969, Sept. 22 Litho. *Perf. 13x13½*
C694 AP94 5c gold & multi .15 .15
C695 AP94 10c gold & multi .15 .15
C696 AP94 15c gold & multi .15 .15
C697 AP94 20c gold & multi .15 .15
C698 AP94 35c gold & multi .15 .15
C699 AP94 40c gold & multi .15 .15
C700 AP94 60c gold & multi .15 .15
C701 AP94 75c gold & multi .15 .15
C702 AP94 1cor gold & multi .20 .15
C703 AP94 2cor gold & multi .42 .25
Set value (10) 1.20 .75

Woman Carrying Jar, Conference Emblem — AP95

1970, Feb. 26 Litho. *Perf. 13½x14*
C704 AP95 10c multi .15 .15
C705 AP95 15c grn & multi .15 .15
C706 AP95 20c ultra & multi .15 .15
C707 AP95 35c multi .15 .15
C708 AP95 50c multi .20 .15
C709 AP95 75c multi .25 .18
C710 AP95 1cor lil & multi .45 .25
C711 AP95 2cor multi .85 .50
Nos. C704-C711 (8) 2.35
Set value 1.20

Issued to publicize the 8th Inter-American Conference on Savings and Loans.

Soccer Type of Regular Issue and

Flags of Participating Nations, World Cup, 1970 — AP96

Soccer Players: 20c, Djalma Santos, Brazil. 80c, Billy Wright, England. 4cor, Jozef Bozsik, Hungary. 5cor, Bobby Charlton, England.

1970, May 11 Litho. *Perf. 13½*
C712 A87 20c multi .15 .15
C713 A87 80c multi .22 .18
C714 AP96 1cor multi .28 .22
C715 A87 4cor multi 1.25 .90
C716 A87 5cor multi 1.40 1.25
Nos. C712-C716 (5) 3.30 2.70

Issued to honor the winners of the 1970 poll for the International Soccer Hall of Fame. No. C714 also publicizes the 9th World Soccer Championships for the Jules Rimet Cup, Mexico City, May 30-June 21, 1970.

Names of players and their achievements printed in black on back of stamps.

For overprint and surcharges see Nos. C786-788.

EXPO Emblem, Mt. Fuji and Torii — AP97

1970, July 5 Litho. *Perf. 13½x14*
C717 AP97 25c multi .15 .15
C718 AP97 30c multi .15 .15
C719 AP97 35c multi .15 .15
C720 AP97 75c multi .22 .15
C721 AP97 1.50cor multi .42 .30
C722 AP97 3cor multi .75 .75
a. Souv. sheet of 3, #C720-C722, imperf. 1.00 1.00
Nos. C717-C722 (6) 1.84
Set value 1.35

EXPO '70 International Exhibition, Osaka, Japan, Mar. 15-Sept. 13, 1970.

Moon Landing, Apollo 11 Emblem and Nicaragua Flag — AP98

Designs (Apollo 11 Emblem, Nicaragua Flag and): 40c, 75c, Moon surface and landing capsule. 60c, 1cor, Astronaut planting US flag.

1970, Aug. 12 Litho. *Perf. 14*
C723 AP98 35c multi .15 .15
C724 AP98 40c multi .15 .15
C725 AP98 60c pink & multi .18 .15
C726 AP98 75c yel & multi .22 .15
C727 AP98 1cor vio & multi .38 .18
C728 AP98 2cor org & multi .65 .38
Nos. C723-C728 (6) 1.73
Set value .90

Man's 1st landing on the moon, July 20, 1969. See note after US No. C76.

Franklin D. Roosevelt AP99

Annunciation, by Matthias Grunewald AP100

Roosevelt Portraits: 15c, 1cor, as stamp collector. 20c, 50c, 2cor, Full face.

1970, Oct. 12
C729 AP99 10c blk & bluish blk .15 .15
C730 AP99 15c blk & brn vio .15 .15
C731 AP99 20c blk & ol grn .15 .15
C732 AP99 35c blk & brn vio .15 .15
C733 AP99 50c brown .15 .15
C734 AP99 75c blue .15 .15
C735 AP99 1cor rose red .18 .15
C736 AP99 2cor black .38 .25
Set value (8) 1.00 .70

Franklin Delano Roosevelt (1882-1945).

1970, Dec. 1 Litho. *Perf. 14*

Paintings: No. C737, like 15c. No. C738, 20c, Nativity, by El Greco. No. C739, 35c, Adoration of the Magi, by Albrecht Dürer No. C740, 75c, Virgin and Child, by J. van Hemessen. No. C741, 1cor, Holy Shepherd, Portuguese School, 16th century.

C737 AP100 10c multi .15 .15
C738 AP100 10c multi .15 .15
C739 AP100 10c multi .15 .15
C740 AP100 10c multi .15 .15
C741 AP100 10c multi .15 .15
C742 AP100 15c multi .15 .15
C743 AP100 20c multi .15 .15
C744 AP100 35c multi .15 .15
C745 AP100 75c multi .18 .15
C746 AP100 1cor multi .22 .15
Set value (10) .80 .60

Christmas 1970. Nos. C737-C741 printed se-tenant.

Issues of 1947-67 Surcharged

RESELLO
C$ 0.15

1971, Mar.
C747 A83 10c on 1.05cor, #C433 .28 .28
C748 AP64 10c on 1.05cor, #C471 .28 .28
C749 AP66 10c on 1.05cor, #C485 .28 .28
C750 AP42 15c on 1.50cor, #C292 .42 .42
C751 AP53 15c on 1.50cor, #C369 .42 .42
C752 A83 15c on 1.50cor, #C434 .42 .42
C753 A84 15c on 1.50cor, #C441 .42 .42
C754 A75 20c on 85c, #C385 .55 .55
C755 A81 20c on 85c, #C418 .55 .55
C756 A81 25c on 90c, #C419 .70 .70
C757 AP48 30c on 1.10cor, #C337 .85 .85
C758 AP44 40c on 1.10cor, #C314 1.10 1.10
C759 AP65 40c on 1.50cor, #C472 1.10 1.10
C760 AP80 1cor on 1.10cor, #C576 2.75 2.75
Nos. C747-C760 (14) 10.12 10.12

The arrangement of the surcharge differs on each stamp.

Mathematics Type of Regular Issue

Symbolic Designs of Scientific Formulae: 25c, Napier's law (logarithms). 30c, Pythagorean theorem (length of sides of right-angled triangle). 40c, Boltzman's equation (movement of gases). 1cor, Broglie's law (motion of particles of matter). 2cor, Archimedes' principle (displacement of mass).

1971, May 15 Litho. *Perf. 13½*
C761 A88 25c lt bl & multi .15 .15
C762 A88 30c lt bl & multi .18 .16
C763 A88 40c lt bl & multi .25 .20
C764 A88 1cor lt bl & multi .60 .35
C765 A88 2cor lt bl & multi 1.00 .75
Nos. C761-C765 (5) 2.18 1.61

On the back of each stamp is a descriptive paragraph.

Montezuma Oropendola — AP101

Birds: 15c, Turquoise-browed motmot. 20c, Magpie-jay. 25c, Scissor-tailed flycatchers. 30c, Spot-breasted oriole, horiz. 35c, Rufous-naped wren. 40c, Great kiskadee. 75c, Red-legged honeycreeper, horiz. 1cor, Great-tailed grackle, horiz. 2cor, Belted kingfisher.

1971, Oct. 15 Litho. *Perf. 14*
C766 AP101 10c multi .15 .15
C767 AP101 15c multi .15 .15
C768 AP101 20c gray & multi .15 .15

C769 AP101 25c multi .15 .15
C770 AP101 30c multi .15 .15
C771 AP101 35c multi .15 .15
C772 AP101 40c multi .15 .15
C773 AP101 75c yel & multi .25 .15
C774 AP101 1cor org & multi .30 .18
C775 AP101 2cor org & multi .65 .32
Set value (10) 1.75 .95

Ten Commandments Type of Regular Issue

Designs: 1cor, Bathsheba at her Bath, by Rembrandt (IX). 2cor, Naboth's Vineyard, by James Smetham (X).

1971, Nov. 1 *Perf. 11*
C776 A90 1cor ocher & multi .90 .45
C777 A90 2cor ocher & multi 1.50 .80

Descriptive inscriptions printed in gray on back of stamps.

U Thant, Anastasio Somoza, UN Emblem AP102

1972, Feb. 15 *Perf. 14x13½*
C778 AP102 10c pink & mar .15 .15
C779 AP102 15c green .15 .15
C780 AP102 20c blue .15 .15
C781 AP102 25c rose claret .15 .15
C782 AP102 30c org & brn .15 .15
C783 AP102 40c gray & sl grn .15 .15
C784 AP102 1cor ol grn .22 .15
C785 AP102 2cor brown .45 .25
Set value (8) 1.00 .65

25th anniv. of the United Nations (in 1970).

Nos. C713, C715, C716 Surcharged or Overprinted Like Nos. 899-900

1972, Mar. 20 **Litho.** *Perf. 13½*
C786 A87 20c on 80c multi .15 .15
C787 A87 60c on 4cor multi .15 .15
C788 A87 5cor multi 1.10 1.00
Nos. C786-C788 (3) 1.40 1.30

20th Olympic Games, Munich, Aug. 26-Sept. 11.

Ceramic Figure, Map of Nicaragua AP103

Pre-Columbian ceramics (700-1200 A.D.) found at sites indicated on map of Nicaragua.

1972, Sept. 16 **Litho.** *Perf. 14x13½*
C789 AP103 10c blue & multi .15 .15
C790 AP103 15c blue & multi .15 .15
C791 AP103 20c blue & multi .15 .15
C792 AP103 25c blue & multi .15 .15
C793 AP103 30c blue & multi .15 .15
C794 AP103 35c blue & multi .15 .15
C795 AP103 40c blue & multi .15 .15
C796 AP103 50c blue & multi .15 .15
C797 AP103 60c blue & multi .15 .15
C798 AP103 80c blue & multi .15 .15
C799 AP103 1cor blue & multi .20 .15
C800 AP103 2cor blue & multi .38 .25
Set value (12) 1.20 .90

Lord Peter Wimsey, by Dorothy L. Sayers AP104

Designs (Book and): 10c, Philip Marlowe, by Raymond Chandler. 15c, Sam Spade, by Dashiell Hammett. 20c, Perry Mason, by Erle S. Gardner. 25c, Nero Wolfe, by Rex Stout. 35c, Auguste Dupin, by Edgar Allan Poe. 40c, Ellery Queen, by Frederick Dannay and Manfred B. Lee. 50c, Father Brown, by G. K. Chesterton. 60c, Charlie Chan, by Earl Derr Biggers. 80c, Inspector Maigret, by Georges Simenon. 1cor, Hercule Poirot, by Agatha Christie. 2cor, Sherlock Holmes, by A. Conan Doyle.

1972, Nov. 13 **Litho.** *Perf. 14x13½*
C801 AP104 5c blue & multi .15 .15
C802 AP104 10c blue & multi .15 .15
C803 AP104 15c blue & multi .15 .15
C804 AP104 20c blue & multi .15 .15
C805 AP104 25c blue & multi .16 .16
C806 AP104 35c blue & multi .22 .22
C807 AP104 40c blue & multi .25 .25
C808 AP104 50c blue & multi .32 .32
C809 AP104 60c blue & multi .38 .38
C810 AP104 80c blue & multi .50 .50
C811 AP104 1cor blue & multi .65 .65
C812 AP104 2cor blue & multi 1.25 1.25
Nos. C801-C812 (12) 4.33 4.33

50th anniv. of INTERPOL, intl. police organization. Designs show famous fictional detectives. Inscriptions on back, printed on top of gum, give thumbnail sketch of character and author.

Shepherds Following Star — AP105

Legend of the Christmas Rose: 15c, Adoration of the kings and shepherds. 20c, Shepherd girl alone crying. 35c, Angel appears to girl. 40c, Christmas rose (Helleborus niger). 60c, Girl thanks angel. 80c, Girl and Holy Family. 1cor, Girl presents rose to Christ Child. 2cor, Adoration.

1972, Dec. 20
C813 AP105 10c multi .15 .15
C814 AP105 15c multi .15 .15
C815 AP105 20c multi .15 .15
C816 AP105 35c multi .15 .15
C817 AP105 40c multi .15 .15
C818 AP105 60c multi .15 .15
C819 AP105 80c multi .16 .15
C820 AP105 1cor multi .18 .16
C821 AP105 2cor multi .35 .32
a. Souv. sheet of 9, #C813-C821 1.10 1.10
Set value 1.00 .90

Christmas 1972.

No. C821a exists with red marginal overprint, "TERREMOTO DESASTRE," for the Managua earthquake of Dec. 22-23, 1972. It was sold abroad, starting in Jan. 1973.

Sir Walter Raleigh, Patent to Settle New World — AP106

Events and Quotations from Contemporary Illustrations: 15c, Mayflower Compact, 1620. 20c, Acquittal of Peter Zenger, 1735, vert. 25c, William Pitt, 1766, vert. 30c, British revenue stamp for use in America No. RM31, vert. 35c, "Join or Die" serpent, 1768. 40c, Boston Massacre and State House, 1770, vert. 50c, Boston Tea Party and 3p coin, 1774. 60c, Patrick Henry, 1775, vert. 75c, Battle scene ("Our cause is just, our union is perfect," 1775). 80c, Declaration of Independence, 1776. 1cor, Liberty Bell, Philadelphia. 2cor, Seal of US, 1782, vert.

1973, Feb. 22 **Photo.** *Perf. 13½*
C822 AP106 10c olive & multi .15 .15
C823 AP106 15c olive & multi .15 .15
C824 AP106 20c olive & multi .15 .15
C825 AP106 25c olive & multi .15 .15
C826 AP106 30c olive & multi .20 .15
C827 AP106 35c ol, gold & blk .35 .20
C828 AP106 40c olive & multi .35 .20
C829 AP106 50c olive & multi .35 .35
C830 AP106 60c olive & multi .40 .35
C831 AP106 75c olive & multi .50 .40
C832 AP106 80c olive & multi .50 .40
C833 AP106 1cor olive & multi .80 .50
C834 AP106 2cor olive & multi 1.50 1.00
Nos. C822-C834 (13) 5.55 4.15

Inscriptions on back, printed on top of gum, give brief description of subject and event.

Baseball, Player and Map of Nicaragua — AP107

1973, May 25 **Litho.** *Perf. 13½x14*
C835 AP107 15c lil & multi .15 .15
C836 AP107 20c multi .15 .15
C837 AP107 40c multi .15 .15
C838 AP107 10cor multi 1.75 1.50
a. Souvenir sheet of 4 2.50 2.50
Nos. C835-C838 (4) 2.20
Set value 1.65

20th International Baseball Championships, Managua, Nov. 15-Dec. 5, 1972. No. C838a contains 4 stamps similar to Nos. C835-C838 with changed background colors (15c, olive; 20c, gray; 40c, lt. green; 10cor, lilac), and 5 labels.

Fashion Type of 1973

1973, July 26 **Litho.** *Perf. 13½*
C839 A91 10c Lourdes Nicaragua .15 .15
C840 A91 15c Halston, New York .15 .15
C841 A91 20c Pino Lancetti, Rome .15 .15
C842 A91 35c Madame Ges, Paris .15 .15
C843 A91 40c Irene Galitzine, Rome .15 .15
C844 A91 80c Pedro Rodriguez, Barcelona .18 .15
a. Souv. sheet of 9, #909-911, C839-C844, perf. 11 + 3 labels 3.00 3.00
Set value .50 .42

Inscriptions on back printed on top of gum give description of gown in Spanish and English.

Type of Air Post Semi-Postal Issue

Design: 2cor, Pediatric surgery.

1973, Sept. 25
C845 SPAP1 2cor multi .40 .35
Set value, #C845, CB1-CB11 1.60 1.35

Planned Children's Hospital. Inscription on back, printed on top of gum gives brief description of subject shown.

Christmas Type

1cor, Virginia O'Hanlon writing letter, father. 2cor, Letter. 4cor, Virginia, father reading letter.

1973, Nov. 15 **Litho.** *Perf. 15*
C846 A92 1cor multicolored .30
C847 A92 2cor multicolored .55
C848 A92 4cor multicolored 1.10
a. Souvenir sheet of 3, #C846-C848, perf. 14½ 3.75
Nos. C846-C848 (3) 1.95

Churchill Type

#C851, Silhouette, Parliament. #C852, Silhouette, #10 Downing St. 5cor, Showing "V" sign. 6cor, "Bulldog" Churchill protecting England.

1974, Apr. 30 *Perf. 14½*
C849 A93 5cor multicolored 1.40
C850 A93 6cor multicolored 1.70

Souvenir Sheets

Perf. 15

C851 A93 4cor blk, org & bl 1.10
C852 A93 4cor blk, org, & grn 1.10

Nos. C851-C852 contain one 28x42mm stamp.

World Cup Type

Scenes from previous World Cup Championships with flags and scores of finalists.

1974, May 8 *Perf. 14½*
C853 A94 10cor Flags of participants 2.80

Souvenir Sheets

C853A A94 4cor like No. 928 1.10
C853B A94 5cor like No. 930 1.40

For overprint see No. C856.

Flower Type of 1974

Wild Flowers and Cacti: 1 cor, Centrosema. 3 cor, Night-blooming cereus.

1974, June 11 **Litho.** *Perf. 14*
C854 A95 1cor green & multi .20 .18
C855 A95 3cor green & multi .65 .55

Nicaraguan Stamps Type

1974, July 10 *Perf. 14½*
C855A A96 40c #835 .20
C855B A96 3cor #C313, horiz. .90
C855C A96 5cor #734 1.40
Nos. C855A-C855C (3) 2.50

Souvenir Sheet

Imperf

C855D Sheet of 3 2.05
e. A96 1cor #665 .30
f. A96 2cor #C110, horiz. .55
g. A96 4cor Globe, stars 1.20

UPU, Cent.

No. C853 Ovptd. **TRIUMFADOR ALEMANIA OCCIDENTAL**

1974, July 12
C856 A94 10cor Flags 2.80

Animal Type of 1974

Designs: 3cor, Colorado deer. 5cor, Jaguar.

1974, Sept. 10 **Litho.** *Perf. 14½*
C857 A97 3cor multi .65 .55
C858 A97 5cor multi 1.00 .90

Christmas Type of 1974

Works of Michelangelo: 40c, Madonna of the Stairs. 80c, Pitti Madonna. 2cor, Pietà. 5cor, Self-portrait.

1974, Dec. 15
C859 A98 40c multi .15 .15
C860 A98 80c multi .15 .15
C861 A98 2cor multi .28 .25
C862 A98 5cor multi .70 .65
Nos. C859-C862 (4) 1.28 1.20

An imperf. souvenir sheet exists containing 2cor and 5cor stamps.

Opera Type of 1975

Opera Singers and Scores: 25c, Rosa Ponselle, Norma. 35c, Giuseppe de Luca, Rigoletto. 40c, Joan Sutherland, La Figlia del Reggimento. 50c, Ezio Pinza, Don Giovanni. 60c, Kirsten Flagstad, Tristan and Isolde. 80c, Maria Callas, Tosca. 2cor, Fyodor Chaliapin, Boris Godunov. 5cor, Enrico Caruso, La Juive.

1975, Jan. 22 *Perf. 14x13½*
C863 A99 25c grn & multi .15 .15
C864 A99 35c multi .15 .15
C865 A99 40c multi .15 .15
C866 A99 50c org & multi .15 .15
C867 A99 60c rose & multi .18 .15
C868 A99 80c lake & multi .25 .15
C869 A99 2cor sep & multi .50 .25
C870 A99 5cor multi 1.25 .65
a. Souvenir sheet of 3 2.50
Nos. C863-C870 (8) 2.78
Set value 1.25

No. C870a contains one each of Nos. C869-C870 and a 1cor with design and colors of No. C868. Exists imperf.

Easter Type of 1975

Stations of the Cross: 40c, Jesus stripped of his clothes. 50c, Jesus nailed to the Cross. 80c, Jesus dies on the Cross. 1cor, Descent from the Cross. 5cor, Jesus laid in the tomb.

1975, Mar. 20 *Perf. 14½*
C871 A100 40c ultra & multi .15 .15
C872 A100 50c ultra & multi .15 .15
C873 A100 80c ultra & multi .15 .15
C874 A100 1cor ultra & multi .16 .15
C875 A100 5cor ultra & multi .90 .80
Nos. C871-C875 (5) 1.51
Set value 1.15

American Bicentennial Type of 1975

Designs: 40c, Washington's Farewell, 1783. 50c, Washington Addressing Continental Congress by J. B. Stearns. 2cor, Washington Arriving for Inauguration. 5cor, Statue of Liberty and flags of 1776 and 1976. 40c, 50c, 2cor, horiz.

1975, Apr. 16 *Perf. 14*
C876 A101 40c tan & multi .18 .15
C877 A101 50c tan & multi .25 .18
C878 A101 2cor tan & multi .80 .75
C879 A101 5cor tan & multi 2.00 1.90
Nos. C876-C879 (4) 3.23 2.98

Perf. and imperf. 7cor souv. sheets exist.

Nordjamb 75 Type of 1975

Designs (Scout and Nordjamb Emblems and): 35c, Camp. 40c, Scout musicians. 1cor, Campfire. 10cor, Lord Baden-Powell.

1975, Aug. 15 *Perf. 14½*
C880 A102 35c multi .15 .15
C881 A102 40c multi .15 .15
C882 A102 1cor multi .15 .15
C883 A102 10cor multi 1.40 1.25
Nos. C880-C883 (4) 1.85
Set value 1.45

Two airmail souvenir sheets of 2 exist. One, perf., contains 2cor and 3cor with designs of Nos. 992 and 990. The other, imperf., contains 2cor and 3cor with designs of Nos. 993 and C882. Size: 125x101mm.

Pres. Somoza Type of 1975

1975, Sept. 10 *Perf. 14*
C884 A103 1cor vio & multi .20 .18
C885 A103 10cor bl & multi 2.00 1.80
C886 A103 20cor multi 4.00 3.00
Nos. C884-C886 (3) 6.20 4.98

Choir Type of 1975

Famous Choirs: 50c, Montserrat Abbey. 1cor, St. Florian Choir Boys. 2cor, Choir Boys of the Wooden Cross, vert. 5cor, Boys and Pope Paul VI (Pueri Cantores International Federation).

1975, Nov. 15 *Perf. 14½*
C887 A104 50c sil & multi .15 .15
C888 A104 1cor sil & multi .20 .16
C889 A104 2cor sil & multi .35 .32
C890 A104 5cor sil & multi 1.00 .85
Nos. C887-C890 (4) 1.70 1.48

A 10cor imperf. souvenir sheet exists (Oberndorf Memorial Chapel Choir and score of "Holy Night-Silent Night").

Chess Type of 1976

Designs: 40c, The Chess Players, by Thomas Eakins. 2cor, Bobby Fischer and Boris Spasski in Reykjavik, 1972. 5cor, Shakespeare and Ben Johnson Playing Chess, by Karel van Mander.

1976, Jan. 8 *Perf. 14½*
C891 A105 40c multi .16 .15
C892 A105 2cor vio & multi .75 .50
C893 A105 5cor multi 1.50 1.25
Nos. C891-C893 (3) 2.41 1.90

A souvenir sheet contains one each of Nos. C892-C893, perf. and imperf. Size: 143x67mm.

Olympic Winner Type 1976

Winners, Rowing and Sculling Events: 55c, USSR, 1956, 1960, 1964, vert. 70c, New Zealand, 1972, vert. 90c, New Zealand, 1968. 10cor, Women's rowing crew, US, 1976, vert. 20cor, US, 1956.

1976, Sept. 7 Litho. *Perf. 14*
C902 A107 55c bl & multi .18 .15
C903 A107 70c bl & multi .18 .15
C904 A107 90c bl & multi .22 .18
C905 A107 20cor bl & multi 4.50 3.75
Nos. C902-C905 (4) 5.08 4.23

Souvenir Sheet

C906 A107 10cor multi 1.65

No. C906 for the 1st participation of women in Olympic rowing events, size of stamp: 37x50mm.

The overprint "Republica Democratica Alemana Vencedor en 1976" was applied in 1976 to No. C905 in black in 3 lines and to the margin of No. C906 in gold in 2 lines.

Bicentennial Type of 1976

Designs (American Bicentennial Emblem and): No. C907, Philadelphia, 1776. No. C908, Washington, 1976. No. C909, John Paul Jones' ships. No. C910, Atomic submarine. No. C911, Wagon train. No. C912, Diesel train.

1976, May 25 Litho. *Perf. 13½*
C907 A108 80c multi .18 .15
C908 A108 80c multi .18 .15
a. Pair, #C907-C908 .36 .30
C909 A108 2.75cor multi .50 .38
C910 A108 2.75cor multi .50 .38
a. Pair, #C909-C910 1.00 .80
C911 A108 4cor multi .65 .50
C912 A108 4cor multi .65 .50
a. Pair, #C911-C912 1.30 1.00
Nos. C907-C912 (6) 2.66 2.06

A souvenir sheet contains two 10cor stamps showing George Washington and Gerald R. Ford with their families. Size: 140x111mm.

Rare Stamps Type of 1976

Rare Stamps: 40c, Hawaii #1. 1cor, Great Britain #1. 2cor, British Guiana #13. 5cor, Honduras #C12. 10cor, Newfoundland #C1.

1976, Dec. *Perf. 14*
C913 A109 40c multi .15 .15
C914 A109 1cor multi .15 .15
C915 A109 2cor multi .28 .25
C916 A109 5cor multi .70 .65
C917 A109 10cor multi 1.40 1.25
Nos. C913-C917 (5) 2.68 2.45

Inscriptions on back printed on top of gum give description of illustrated stamp. A 4cor imperf. souvenir sheet shows 1881 Great Britain-Nicaragua combination cover. Size: 140x101mm.

Olga Nuñez de Saballos — AP108

Designs: 1cor, Josefa Toledo de Aguerri. 10cor, Hope Portocarrero de Somoza.

1977, Feb. Litho. *Perf. 13½*
C918 AP108 35c multi .15 .15
C919 AP108 1cor red & multi .20 .18
C920 AP108 10cor multi 2.00 1.75
Nos. C918-C920 (3) 2.35 2.08

Famous Nicaraguan women and for International Women's Year (in 1975).

Zeppelin Type of 1977

Designs: 35c, Ville de Paris airship. 70c, Zeppelin "Schwaben." 3cor, Zeppelin in flight. 10cor, Vickers "Mayfly" before take-off. 20cor, Zeppelin with leadlines extended.

1977, Oct. 31 Litho. *Perf. 14½*
C921 A110 35c multi .15 .15
C922 A110 70c multi .18 .15
C923 A110 3cor multi .65 .50
C924 A110 10cor multi 2.50 1.75
Nos. C921-C924 (4) 3.48 2.55

Souvenir Sheet

C925 A110 20cor multi 4.50 2.75

Lindbergh Type of 1977

Designs: 55c, Lindbergh's plane approaching Nicaraguan airfield, 1928. 80c, Spirit of St. Louis and map of New York-Paris route. 2cor, Plane flying off Nicaragua's Pacific Coast. 10cor, Lindbergh flying past Momotombo Volcano on way to Managua. 20cor, Spirit of St. Louis.

1977, Nov. 30
C926 A111 55c multi .15 .15
C927 A111 80c multi .16 .15
C928 A111 2cor multi .40 .32
C929 A111 10cor multi 2.00 1.65
Nos. C926-C929 (4) 2.71 2.27

Souvenir Sheet

C930 A111 20cor multi 4.50 3.50

Christmas Type of 1977
Souvenir Sheet

Design: 20cor, Finale of Nutcracker Suite.

1977, Dec. 12
C931 A112 20cor multi 4.50 4.50

Painting Type of 1978

Rubens Paintings: 5cor, Hippopotamus and Crocodile Hunt. 100cor, Duke de Lerma on Horseback. 20cor, Self-portrait.

1978, Jan. 11 Litho. *Perf. 14½*
C932 A113 5cor multi 1.00 .85
C933 A113 10cor multi 2.00 1.65

Souvenir Sheet

C934 A113 20cor multi 4.75 4.00

Peter Paul Rubens (1577-1640), 400th birth anniversary.

St. Francis Type of 1978

Designs: 80c, St. Francis and the wolf. 10cor, St. Francis, painting. 20cor, Our Lady of Conception, statue in Church of El Viejo.

1978, Feb. 23 Litho. *Perf. 14½*
C935 A114 80c lt brn & multi .16 .15
C936 A114 10cor bl & multi 1.90 1.75

Souvenir Sheet

C937 A114 20cor multi 3.50

Railroad Type of 1978

Locomotives: 35c, Light-weight American. 4cor, Heavy Baldwin. 10cor, Juniata, 13-ton. 20cor, Map of route system.

1978, Apr. 7 Litho. *Perf. 14½*
C938 A115 35c lt grn & multi .15 .15
C939 A115 4cor dp org & multi .90 .75
C940 A115 10cor cit & multi 2.00 1.90
Nos. C938-C940 (3) 3.05 2.80

Souvenir Sheet

C941 A115 20cor multi 3.50

Jules Verne Type of 1978

Designs: 90c, 20,000 Leagues under the Sea. 10cor, Around the World in 80 Days. 20cor, From the Earth to the Moon.

1978, Aug. Litho. *Perf. 14½*
C942 A116 90c multi .20 .15
C943 A116 10cor multi 1.75 1.50

Souvenir Sheet

C944 A116 20cor multi 5.00

Aviation History Type of 1978

Designs: 55c, Igor Sikorsky in his helicopter, 1913, horiz. 10cor, Space shuttle, horiz. 20cor, Flyer III, horiz.

1978, Sept. 29 Litho. *Perf. 14½*
C945 A117 55c multi .15 .15
C946 A117 10cor multi 1.40 1.00

Souvenir Sheet

C947 A117 20cor multi 5.00

Soccer Type of 1978

Soccer Players: 50c, Denis Law and Franz Beckenbauer. 5cor, Dino Zoff and Pelé. 20cor, Dominique Rocheteau and Johan Neeskens.

1978, Oct. 25 Litho. *Perf. 13½x14*
C948 A118 50c multi .15 .15
C949 A118 5cor multi 1.00 .85

Souvenir Sheet

C950 A118 20cor multi 4.50

Christmas Type of 1978

Paintings: 3cor, Apostles John and Peter, by Dürer. 10cor, Apostles Paul and Mark, by Dürer. 20cor, Virgin and Child with Garlands, by Dürer.

1978, Dec. 12 Litho. *Perf. 13½x14*
C951 A119 3cor multi .42 .35
C952 A119 10cor multi 1.40 1.00

Souvenir Sheet

C953 A119 20cor multi 3.50

Volcano Type of 1978

Designs: No. C954, Cerro Negro Volcano. No. C955, Lake Masaya. No. C956, Momotombo Volcano. No. C957, Lake Asososca. No. C958, Mombacho Volcano. No. C959, Lake Apoyo. No. C960, Concepcion Volcano. No. C961, Lake Tiscapa.

1978, Dec. 29 *Perf. 14x13½*
C954 A120 35c multi .15 .15
C955 A120 35c multi .15 .15
C956 A120 90c multi .16 .15
C957 A120 90c multi .16 .15
C958 A120 1cor multi .20 .15
C959 A120 1cor multi .20 .15
C960 A120 10cor multi 1.90 1.35
C961 A120 10cor multi 1.90 1.35
Nos. C954-C961 (8) 4.82 3.60

Stamps of same denomination printed se-tenant in sheets of 40.

Bernardo O'Higgins — AP109

1979, Mar. 7 Litho. *Perf. 14*
C962 AP109 20cor multi 4.25 3.25

Bernardo O'Higgins (1778-1842), Chilean soldier and statesman.

Red Ginger and Rubythroated Hummingbird — AP110

Designs: 55c, Orchid. 70c, Poinsettia. 80c, Flower and bees. 2cor, Lignum vitae and blue morpho butterfly. 4cor, Cattleya.

1979, Apr. 6 Litho. *Perf. 14x13½*
C963 AP110 50c multi .15 .15
C964 AP110 55c multi .15 .15
C965 AP110 70c multi .16 .15
C966 AP110 80c multi .16 .15
C967 AP110 2cor multi .35 .28
C968 AP110 4cor multi .70 .52
Nos. C963-C968 (6) 1.67
Set value 1.00

Revolution Type of 1981

1981, July 19 Litho. *Perf. 12½x12*
C973 A123 2.10cor March .30 .15
C974 A123 3cor Construction .42 .24
C975 A123 6cor Health programs .80 .48
Nos. C973-C975 (3) 1.52 .87

FSLN Type of 1981

1981, July 23
C976 A124 4cor Founder .55 .35

Postal Union Type of 1981

1981, Aug. 10
C977 A125 2.10cor Pony express .22 .15
C978 A125 3cor Headquarters .30 .18
C979 A125 6cor Members' flags .60 .35
Nos. C977-C979 (3) 1.12 .68

1300th Anniv. of Bulgaria — AP112

1981, Sept. 2 *Imperf.*
C980 AP112 10cor multi 1.25 1.00

Size: 96x70mm.

Aquatic Flower Type of 1981

1981, Sept. 15 *Perf. 12½*
C981 A126 10cor Nymphaea gladstoniana 1.40 .90

Souvenir Sheet

Panda Bear — AP113

1981, Oct. 9 *Perf. 13*
C982 AP113 10cor multi 1.25 1.00

Philatokyo Stamp Exhibition, Tokyo.

Tropical Fish Type of 1981

1981, Oct. 19 *Perf. 12½*
C983 A127 3.50cor Pterolebias longipinnis .48 .28
C984 A127 4cor Xiphophorus helleri .55 .30

Souvenir Sheet

Frigate — AP114

1981, Nov. 2 *Perf. 13*
C985 AP114 10cor multi 1.40 .85

Espamer '81 Stamp Exhibition, Buenos Aires, Nov. 13-22.

Bird Type of 1981

1981, Nov. 30 *Perf. 12½*
C986 A128 3cor Trogon massena .48 .26
C987 A128 4cor Campylo-pterus hemileucurus, horiz. .65 .38
C988 A128 6cor Momotus momota .95 .55
Nos. C986-C988 (3) 2.08 1.19

Satellite Type of 1981

1981, Dec. 15 *Perf. 13x12½*
C989 A129 3cor multi .35 .22
C990 A129 4cor multi .50 .28
C991 A129 5cor multi .60 .35
Nos. C989-C991 (3) 1.45 .85

Railroad Type of 1981

1981, Dec. 30 *Perf. 12½*
C992 A130 6cor Ferrobus, 1967 1.00 .55

World Cup Type of 1982

1982, Jan. 25
C993 A131 4cor multi .48 .30
C994 A131 10cor multi, horiz. 1.25 .80

Souvenir Sheet
Perf. 13

C995 A131 10cor multi 1.65 1.10

No. C995 contains one 39x31mm stamp.

Dog Type of 1982

1982, Feb. 18

C996 A132 3cor Boxers .45 .28
C997 A132 3.50cor Pointers .48 .28
C998 A132 6cor Collies .90 .50
Nos. C996-C998 (3) 1.83 1.06

Intl. ITU Congress AP115

1982, Mar. 12

C999 AP115 25cor multi 3.25 2.25

Butterfly Type of 1982

1982, Mar. 26

C1000 A133 3cor Parides iphidamas .45 .28
C1001 A133 3.50cor Consul hippona .48 .30
C1002 A133 4cor Morpho peleides .55 .35
Nos. C1000-C1002 (3) 1.48 .93

Satellite Type of 1982

1982, Apr. 12

C1003 A134 5cor multi, horiz. .65 .40
C1004 A134 6cor multi .90 .48

UPU Type of 1982

1982, May 1 **Litho.** ***Perf. 13***

C1005 A135 3.50cor Train .38 .22
C1006 A135 10cor Jet 1.10 .70

Sports Type of 1982

1982, May 13

C1007 A136 2.50cor Women's volleyball, vert. .38 .22
C1008 A136 3cor Boxing .45 .30
C1009 A136 9cor Soccer 1.40 .80
Nos. C1007-C1009 (3) 2.23 1.32

Souvenir Sheet

C1010 A136 10cor Baseball, vert. 1.50 .80

No. C1010 contains one 29x36mm stamp.

Souvenir Sheet

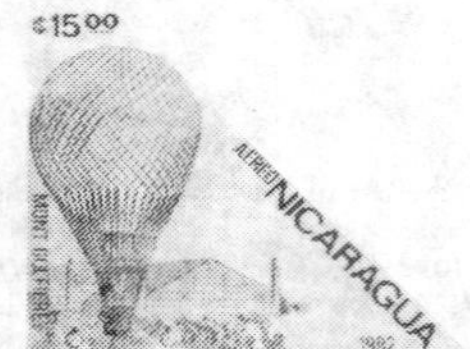

PHILEXFRANCE '82 Intl. Stamp Exhibition, Paris, June 11-21 — AP116

1982, June 9 ***Perf. 13x12½***

C1011 AP116 15cor multi 1.65 1.00

Revolution Type of 1982

Designs: Symbolic doves. 2.50cor, 4cor vert.

1982, July 19 ***Perf. 13***

C1012 A137 2.50cor multi .38 .22
C1013 A137 4cor multi .60 .38
C1014 A137 6cor multi 1.00 .60
Nos. C1012-C1014 (3) 1.98 1.20

Washington Type of 1982

Perf. 12½x13, 13x12½

1982, June 20 **Litho.**

C1015 A138 2.50cor Crossing the Delaware, horiz. .38 .22
C1016 A138 3.50cor At Valley Forge, horiz. .52 .35
C1017 A138 4cor Battle of Trenton .60 .38
C1018 A138 6cor Washington in Princeton 1.00 .60
Nos. C1016-C1018 (3) 2.12 1.33

Painting Type of 1982

1982, Aug. 17 ***Perf. 13***

C1019 A139 9cor Seated Woman, by A. Morales 1.25 .80

Dimitrov Type of 1982

1982, Sept. 9

C1020 A140 2.50cor Dimitrov, Yikov, Sofia, 1946 .38 .24
C1021 A140 4cor Portrait, flag .60 .38

Dictatorship Type of 1982

1982, Sept. 21 ***Perf. 13x12½***

C1022 A141 4cor Rigoberto Lopez Perez .60 .38
C1023 A141 6cor Edwin Castro 1.00 .60

Tourism Type of 1982

1982, Sept. 25 ***Perf. 13***

C1024 A142 2.50cor Coyotepe Fortress, Masaya .28 .16
C1025 A142 3.50cor Velazquez Park, Managua .38 .24

Marx Type of 1982

1982, Oct. 4 ***Perf. 12½***

C1026 A143 4cor Marx, Highgate Monument .55 .35

Discovery of America Type of 1982

1982, Oct. 12 ***Perf. 12½x13***

C1027 A145 2.50cor Trans-atlantic voyage .42 .24
C1028 A145 4cor Landing of Columbus .65 .42
C1029 A145 7cor Death of Columbus 1.10 .70
Nos. C1027-C1029 (3) 2.17 1.36

Souvenir Sheet

Perf. 13

C1030 A145 10cor Columbus' fleet 1.65 1.00

No. C1030 contains one 31x39mm stamp.

Flower Type of 1982

1982, Nov. 13 ***Perf. 12½***

C1031 A146 2.50cor Pasiflora foetida .38 .22
C1032 A146 3.50cor Clitoria sp. .52 .32
C1033 A146 5cor Russelia sarmentosa .75 .45
Nos. C1031-C1033 (3) 1.65 .99

Reptile Type of 1982

1982, Dec. 10 ***Perf. 13***

C1034 A147 2.50cor Turtle, horiz. .38 .22
C1035 A147 3cor Boa constrictor .45 .28
C1036 A147 3.50cor Crocodile, horiz. .52 .32
C1037 A147 5cor Sistrurus catenatus, horiz. .75 .45
Nos. C1034-C1037 (4) 2.10 1.27

Non-aligned States Conference, Jan. 12-14 — AP117

1983, Jan. 10 **Litho.** ***Perf. 12½x13***

C1038 AP117 4cor multi .60 .38

Geothermal Electricity Generating Plant, Momotombo Volcano — AP118

1983, Feb. 25 ***Perf. 13***

C1039 AP118 2.50cor multi .38 .22

Souvenir Sheet

TEMBAL '83 Philatelic Exhibition, Basel, Switzerland AP119

1983, May 21 **Litho.** ***Perf. 13***

C1040 AP119 15cor Chamoix 2.25 1.25

Souvenir Sheet

1st Nicaraguan Philatelic Exhibition AP120

1983, July 17 **Litho.** ***Perf. 13***

C1041 AP120 10cor Nicaragua Airlines jet 2.25 1.25

Armed Forces — AP121

1983, Sept. 2 **Litho.** ***Perf. 13***

C1042 AP121 4cor Frontier guards, watch dog .42 .26

Souvenir Sheet

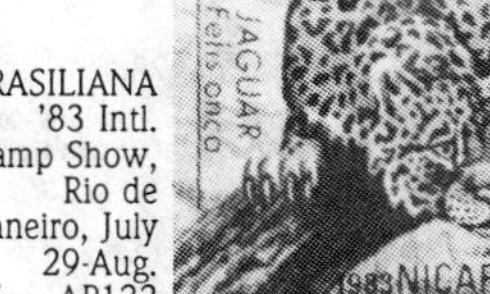

BRASILIANA '83 Intl. Stamp Show, Rio de Janeiro, July 29-Aug. 7 — AP122

1983

C1043 AP122 15cor Jaguar 2.25 1.25

Cuban Revolution, 25th Anniv. — AP122a

1984, Jan. 1 **Litho.** ***Perf. 13***

C1043A AP122a 4cor shown .60 .32
C1043B AP122a 6cor Castro, Guevara, flag .95 .45

Souvenir Sheet

Cardinal Infante Don Fernando, by Diego Velazquez — AP123

1984, May 2 **Litho.** ***Perf. 13***

C1044 AP123 15cor multi 1.75 1.00

ESPANA '84.

Souvenir Sheet

Hamburg '84 AP124

1984, June 19 **Litho.** ***Perf. 13***

C1045 AP124 15cor Dirigible 1.75 .90

1984 UPU Congress AP125

1984, June 24 ***Perf. 12½***

C1046 AP125 15cor Mail transport 1.75 .90

Souvenir Sheet

Expofilnic '84 (2nd Natl. Stamp Exhibition) AP126

1984, July 15

C1047 AP126 15cor Communications Museum 1.75 .90

Souvenir Sheet

Ausipex '84 — AP127

1984, Sept. 21

C1048 AP127 15cor Explorer ship 1.75 .90

Souvenir Sheet

OLYMPHILEX '85 — AP128

1985, Mar. 18 **Litho.** ***Perf. 12½***

C1049 AP128 15cor Bicycle race 1.10 .60

Souvenir Sheet

ESPAMER '85, Havana, Mar. 19-24 — AP129

1985, Mar. 19

C1050 AP129 10cor Crocodylus rhombifer .75 .38

Victory of Sandanista Revolution, 6th Anniv. AP134

1985, July 19 **Litho.** *Perf. 12½*

C1125 AP134 9cor Soldier, flag	.90	.58
C1126 AP134 9cor Sugar mill	.90	.58

Benjamin Zeledon, Birth Cent. — AP135

1985, Oct. 4 **Litho.** *Perf. 12½*

C1127 AP135 15cor multicolored	.75	.38

Henri Dunant (1828-1910), Founder of Red Cross — AP136

1985, Oct. 10 *Perf. 12½x12*

C1128 AP136 3cor shown	.18	.15
C1129 AP136 15cor Dunant, air ambulance	.90	.45
a. Pair, #C1128-C1129 + label	1.10	.55

Nicaraguan Stamps, 125th Anniv. AP137

1986, May 22 *Perf. 12½x13*

C1130 AP137 30cor No. C1	.65	.32
C1131 AP137 40cor No. 174	.85	.42
C1132 AP137 50cor No. 48	1.10	.52
C1133 AP137 100cor No. 1	2.00	1.10
Nos. C1130-C1133 (4)	4.60	2.36

Intl. Peace Year — AP138

1986, July 19 *Perf. 12½*

C1134 AP138 5cor shown	.15	.15
C1135 AP138 10cor Globe, dove	.25	.15
Set value		.20

Carlos Fonseca, 10th Death Anniv. — AP139

1986, Aug. 11 **Litho.** *Perf. 12½*

C1136 AP139 15cor multicolored	.32	.20

Formation of the Sandinista Front, 25th anniv.

AP140 AP141

1986, Nov. 20 *Perf. 13*

C1137 AP140 15cor Rhinoceros	.32	.16
C1138 AP140 15cor Zebra	.32	.16
C1139 AP140 25cor Elephant	.55	.28
C1140 AP140 25cor Giraffe	.55	.28
C1141 AP140 50cor Mandrill	1.10	.55
C1142 AP140 50cor Tiger	1.10	.55
Nos. C1137-C1142 (6)	3.94	1.98

1986, Dec. 20 *Perf. 13*

World Cup Soccer Championships, Mexico: Various soccer players and natl. flags.

Shirt Colors

C1143 AP141 10cor blue	.22	.15
C1144 AP141 10cor blk & white	.22	.15
C1145 AP141 10cor blue & white	.22	.15
C1146 AP141 15cor pink & white	.35	.18
C1147 AP141 15cor grn & blk	.35	.18
C1148 AP141 25cor blk & white, red	.55	.28
C1149 AP141 50cor grn & yel, red, horiz.	1.10	.55
Nos. C1143-C1149 (7)	3.01	1.64

Souvenir Sheet

Perf. 12½

C1150 AP141 100cor blk & white, bl & white	2.75	1.10

Vassil Levski, 150th Birth Anniv. — AP142

1987, Apr. 18 *Perf. 13*

C1151 AP142 30cor multicolored	.70	.32

Intl. Year of Shelter for the Homeless AP143

1987, Aug. 2

C1152 AP143 20cor multicolored	.45	.22
C1153 AP143 30cor Housing, diff.	.70	.35

Souvenir Sheet

Berlin, 750th Anniv. — AP144

1987, Sept. 25 **Litho.** *Perf. 13*

C1154 AP144 130cor multi	1.40	.70

Discovery of America, 500th Anniv. (in 1992) — AP145

1987, Oct. 12 *Perf. 13*

C1155 AP145 15cor Indian village	.32	.16
C1156 AP145 15cor Sailing ships	.32	.16
C1157 AP145 20cor Battle in village	.42	.22
C1158 AP145 30cor Battle, prisoners	.65	.32
C1159 AP145 40cor Spanish town	.85	.42
C1160 AP145 50cor Cathedral	1.00	.52
a. Min. sheet of 6, #C1155-C1160	3.75	3.75
Nos. C1155-C1160 (6)	3.56	1.80

Cuban Revolution, 30th Anniv. AP146

1989, Jan. 1 *Perf. 13*

C1161 AP146 20cor multicolored	.45	.22

AP147 AP148

Designs: Various soccer players in action.

1989, Feb. 20 *Perf. 13x12½*

C1162 AP147 100cor multi	.15	.15
C1163 AP147 200cor multi	.15	.15
C1164 AP147 600cor multi	.16	.15
C1165 AP147 1000cor multi	.26	.15
C1166 AP147 2000cor multi	.52	.46
C1167 AP147 3000cor multi	.80	.40
C1168 AP147 5000cor multi	1.25	.65
Nos. C1162-C1168 (7)	3.29	2.11

Souvenir Sheet

Perf. 13

C1169 AP147 9000cor multi	2.25	2.25

World Cup Soccer Championships, Italy. No. C1169 contains one 32x40mm stamp.

1989, July 19 *Perf. 13*

Design: 9000cor, Concepcion Volcano.

C1170 AP148 300cor multi	.15	.15

Souvenir Sheet

C1171 AP148 9000cor multi	2.25	2.25

Sandinista Revolution, 10th Anniv. No. C1171 contains one 40x32mm stamp.

AP149 AP150

Birds: 100cor, Anhinga anhinga. 200cor, Elanoides forficatus. 600cor, Eumomota superciliosa. 1000cor, Setophaga picta. 2000cor, Taraba major, horiz. 3000cor, Onychorhynchus mexicanus. 5000cor, Myrmotherula axillaris, horiz. 9000cor, Amazona ochrocephala.

Perf. 13x12½, 12½x13

1989, July 18

C1172 AP149 100cor multi	.15	.15
C1173 AP149 200cor multi	.15	.15
C1174 AP149 600cor multi	.18	.15
C1175 AP149 1000cor multi	.30	.15
C1176 AP149 2000cor multi	.60	.30
C1177 AP149 3000cor multi	.90	.45
C1178 AP149 5000cor multi	1.50	.75
Nos. C1172-C1178 (7)	3.78	2.10

Souvenir Sheet

Perf. 13

C1179 AP149 9000cor multi	1.65	1.65

Brasiliana '89. No. C1179 contains one 32x40mm stamp.

1989, Mar. 25 *Perf. 13*

Designs: 50cor, Downhill skiing. 300cor, Ice hockey. 600cor, Ski jumping. 1000cor, Pairs figure skating. 2000cor, Biathalon. 3000cor, Slalom skiing. 5000cor, Cross country skiing. 9000cor, Two-man luge.

C1180 AP150 50cor multi	.15	.15
C1181 AP150 300cor multi	.15	.15
C1182 AP150 600cor multi	.15	.15
C1183 AP150 1000cor multi	.15	.15
C1184 AP150 2000cor multi	.20	.15
C1185 AP150 3000cor multi	.30	.15
C1186 AP150 5000cor multi	.48	.24
Set value	1.20	.65

Souvenir Sheet

C1187 AP150 9000cor multi	.88	.45

1992 Winter Olympics, Albertville. No. C1187 contains one 32x40mm stamp.

AP151 AP152

Designs: 100cor, Water polo. 200cor, Running. 600cor, Diving. 1000cor, Gymnastics. 2000cor, Weight lifting. 3000cor, Volleyball. 5000cor, Wrestling. 9000cor, Field hockey.

1989, Apr. 23

C1188 AP151 100cor multi	.15	.15
C1189 AP151 200cor multi	.15	.15
C1190 AP151 600cor multi	.15	.15
C1191 AP151 1000cor multi	.15	.15
C1192 AP151 2000cor multi	.20	.15
C1193 AP151 3000cor multi	.30	.15
C1194 AP151 5000cor multi	.50	.25
Set value	1.20	.60

Souvenir Sheet

C1195 AP151 9000cor multi	.88	.45

1992 Summer Olympics, Barcelona.

No. C1195 contains one 32x40mm stamp.

1989, Oct. 12

C1196 AP152 2000cor Vase	.68	.32

Discovery of America, 500th Anniv. (in 1992).

Currency Reform

Currency reform took place Mar. 4, 1990. Until stamps in the new currency were issued, mail was to be hand-stamped "Franqueo Pagado," (Postage Paid). Stamps were not used again until Apr. 25, 1991. The following set was sold by the post office but was not valid for postage.

Mushrooms

Designs: 500cor, Morchella esculenta. 1000cor, Boletus edulis. 5000cor, Lactarius deliciosus. 10,000cor, Panellus stipticus. 20,000cor, Craterellus cornucopioides. 40,000cor, Cantharellus cibarius. 50,000cor, Armillariella mellea.

1990, July 15 *Perf. 13*

500cor-50,000cor

AIR POST SEMI-POSTAL STAMPS

Mrs. Somoza and Children's Hospital — SPAP1

Designs: 5c+5c, Children and weight chart. 15c+5c, Incubator and Da Vinci's "Child in Womb." 20c+5c, Smallpox vaccination. 30c+5c, Water purification. 35c+5c, 1cor+50c, like 10c+5c. 50c+10c, Antibiotics. 60c+15c, Malaria control. 70c+10c, Laboratory. 80c+20c, Gastroenteritis (sick and well babies).

1973, Sept. 25 Litho. *Perf. 13½x14*

CB1	SPAP1 5c + 5c multi	.15	.15
CB2	SPAP1 10c + 5c multi	.15	.15
CB3	SPAP1 15c + 5c multi	.15	.15
CB4	SPAP1 20c + 5c multi	.15	.15
CB5	SPAP1 30c + 5c multi	.15	.15
CB6	SPAP1 35c + 5c multi	.15	.15
CB7	SPAP1 50c + 10c multi	.15	.15
CB8	SPAP1 60c + 15c multi	.15	.15
CB9	SPAP1 70c + 10c multi	.15	.15
CB10	SPAP1 80c + 20c multi	.20	.18
CB11	SPAP1 1cor + 50c multi	.30	.25
	Set value	1.20	1.00

The surtax was for hospital building fund. See No. C845. Inscriptions on back, printed on top of gum give brief description of subjects shown.

AIR POST OFFICIAL STAMPS

OA1

"Typewritten" Overprint on #O293

1929, Aug. Unwmk. *Perf. 12*

CO1 OA1 25c orange	50.00	45.00

Excellent counterfeits of No. CO1 are plentiful.

Official Stamps of 1926 Overprinted in Dark Blue

Correo Aéreo

1929, Sept. 15

CO2 A24 25c orange	.50	.50
a. Inverted overprint	25.00	
b. Double overprint	25.00	
CO3 A25 50c pale bl	.75	.75
a. Inverted overprint	25.00	
b. Double overprint	25.00	
c. Double overprint, one inverted	25.00	

Nos. 519-523 Overprinted in Black

Correo Aéreo
OFICIAL

1932, Feb.

CO4 A24 15c org red	.40	.40
a. Inverted overprint	25.00	
b. Double overprint	25.00	
c. Double overprint, one invtd.	25.00	
CO5 A25 20c orange	.45	.45
a. Double overprint	25.00	
CO6 A24 25c dk vio	.45	.45
CO7 A25 50c green	.55	.55
CO8 A25 1cor yellow	1.00	1.00
Nos. CO4-CO8 (5)	2.85	2.85

Nos. CO4-CO5, CO7-CO8 exist with signature control overprint. Value, each, $2.50.

Overprinted on Stamp No. 547

CO9 A24 25c blk brn	42.50	42.50

The varieties "OFICAL", "OFIAIAL" and "CORROE" occur in the setting and are found on each stamp of the series.

Counterfeits of No. CO9 are plentiful.

Stamp No. CO4 with overprint "1931" in addition is believed to be of private origin.

Type of Regular Issue of 1914 Overprinted Like Nos. CO4-CO8

1933

CO10 A24 25c olive	.15	.15
CO11 A25 50c ol grn	.22	.22
CO12 A25 1cor org red	.40	.40

On Stamps of 1914-28

CO13 A24 15c dp vio	.15	.15
CO14 A25 20c dp grn	.15	.15
Nos. CO10-CO14 (5)	1.07	1.07

Nos. CO10-CO14 exist without signature control mark. Value, each $2.50.

Air Post Official Stamps of 1932-33 Overprinted in Blue

RESELLO 1935

1935

CO15 A24 15c dp vio	1.00	.80
CO16 A25 20c dp grn	2.00	1.60
CO17 A24 25c olive	3.00	2.50
CO18 A25 50c ol grn	35.00	30.00
CO19 A25 1cor org red	40.00	37.50
Nos. CO15-CO19 (5)	81.00	72.40

Overprinted in Red

CO20 A24 15c dp vio	.25	.22
CO21 A25 20c dp grn	.25	.22
CO22 A24 25c olive	.25	.25
CO23 A25 50c ol grn	.80	.80
CO24 A25 1cor org red	.80	.80
Nos. CO20-CO24 (5)	2.35	2.29

Nos. CO15 to CO24 are handstamped with script control mark. Counterfeits of blue overprint are plentiful.

The editors do not recognize the Nicaraguan air post Official stamps overprinted in red "VALIDO 1935" in two lines and with or without script control marks as having been issued primarily for postal purposes.

Nos. C164-C168 Overprinted in Black

1937

CO25 AP1 15c yel org	.80	.55
CO26 AP1 20c org red	.80	.60
CO27 AP1 25c black	.80	.70
CO28 AP1 50c violet	.80	.70
CO29 AP1 1cor orange	.80	.70
Nos. CO25-CO29 (5)	4.00	3.25

Pres. Anastasio Somoza — OA2

1939, Feb. 7 Engr. *Perf. 12½*

CO30 OA2 10c brown	.25	.25
CO31 OA2 15c dk bl	.25	.25
CO32 OA2 20c yellow	.25	.25
CO33 OA2 25c dk pur	.25	.25
CO34 OA2 30c lake	.25	.25
CO35 OA2 50c dp org	.65	.65
CO36 OA2 1cor dk ol grn	1.20	1.20
Nos. CO30-CO36 (7)	3.10	3.10

Catalogue values for unused stamps in this section, from this point to the end of the section, are for Never Hinged items.

Mercedes Airport OA3

Designs: 10c, Sulphurous Lake of Nejapa. 15c, Ruben Dario Monument. 20c, Tapir. 25c, Genizaro Dam. 50c, Tipitapa Spa. 1cor, Stone Highway. 2.50cor, Franklin D. Roosevelt Monument.

Engraved, Center Photogravure
1947, Aug. 29
Various Frames in Black

CO37 OA3 5c org brn	.15	.15
CO38 OA3 10c blue	.20	.20
CO39 OA3 15c violet	.15	.15
CO40 OA3 20c red org	.20	.15
CO41 OA3 25c blue	.15	.15
CO42 OA3 50c car rose	.20	.20
CO43 OA3 1cor slate	.45	.45
CO44 OA3 2.50cor red brn	1.25	1.25
Nos. CO37-CO44 (8)	2.75	2.70

Rowland Hill — OA4

Designs: 10c, Heinrich von Stephan. 25c, 1st UPU Bldg. 50c, UPU Bldg., Bern. 1cor, UPU Monument. 2.60cor, Congress medal, reverse.

1950, Nov. 23 Engr. *Perf. 13*
Frames in Black

CO45 OA4 5c rose vio	.15	.15
CO46 OA4 10c dp grn	.15	.15
CO47 OA4 25c rose vio	.15	.15
CO48 OA4 50c dp org	.15	.15
CO49 OA4 1cor ultra	.28	.28
CO50 OA4 2.60cor gray blk	2.25	2.00
Nos. CO45-CO50 (6)	3.13	2.88

75th anniv. (in 1949) of the UPU.

Each denomination was also issued in a souvenir sheet containing four stamps and marginal inscriptions. Size: 121x96mm. Value, set of 6 sheets, $35.

Consular Service Stamps Surcharged "Oficial Aéreo" and New Denomination in Red, Black or Blue

1961, Nov. Unwmk. Engr. *Perf. 12*
Red Marginal Number

CO51 AP63 10c on 1cor grnsh blk (R)	.15	.15
CO52 AP63 15c on 20cor red brn (R)	.15	.15
CO53 AP63 20c on 100cor mag	.15	.15
CO54 AP63 25c on 50c dp bl (R)	.15	.15
CO55 AP63 35c on 50cor brn (R)	.15	.15
CO56 AP63 50c on 3cor dk car	.15	.15
CO57 AP63 1cor on 2cor grn (R)	.20	.20
CO58 AP63 2cor on 5cor org (Bl)	.42	.42
CO59 AP63 5cor on 10cor vio (R)	1.00	1.00
Set value	2.10	2.05

POSTAGE DUE STAMPS

D1

D2

1896 Unwmk. Engr. *Perf. 12*

J1 D1 1c orange	.50	*1.25*
J2 D1 2c orange	.50	*1.25*
J3 D1 5c orange	.50	*1.25*
J4 D1 10c orange	.50	*1.25*
J5 D1 20c orange	.50	*1.25*
J6 D1 30c orange	.50	*1.25*
J7 D1 50c orange	.50	*1.50*
Nos. J1-J7 (7)	3.50	*9.00*

Wmk. 117

J8 D1 1c orange	1.00	*1.50*
J9 D1 2c orange	1.00	*1.50*
J10 D1 5c orange	1.00	*1.50*
J11 D1 10c orange	1.00	*1.50*
J12 D1 20c orange	1.25	*1.50*
J13 D1 30c orange	1.00	*1.50*
J14 D1 50c orange	1.00	*1.50*
Nos. J8-J14 (7)	7.25	*10.50*

1897 Unwmk.

J15 D1 1c violet	.50	*1.50*
J16 D1 2c violet	.50	*1.50*
J17 D1 5c violet	.50	*1.50*
J18 D1 10c violet	.50	*1.50*
J19 D1 20c violet	1.25	*2.00*
J20 D1 30c violet	.50	*1.50*
J21 D1 50c violet	.50	*1.50*
Nos. J15-J21 (7)	4.25	*11.00*

Wmk. 117

J22 D1 1c violet	.50	*1.50*
J23 D1 2c violet	.50	*1.50*
J24 D1 5c violet	.50	*1.50*
J25 D1 10c violet	.50	*1.50*
J26 D1 20c violet	1.00	*2.00*
J27 D1 30c violet	.50	*1.50*
J28 D1 50c violet	.50	*1.50*
Nos. J22-J28 (7)	4.00	*11.00*

Reprints of Nos. J8-J28 are on thick, porous paper. Color of 1896 reprints, reddish orange; or 1897 reprints, reddish violet. On watermarked reprints, liberty cap is sideways. Value 25c each.

1898 Litho. Unwmk.

J29 D2 1c blue green	.15	*2.00*
J30 D2 2c blue green	.15	*2.00*
J31 D2 5c blue green	.15	*2.00*
J32 D2 10c blue green	.15	*2.00*
J33 D2 20c blue green	.15	*2.00*
J34 D2 30c blue green	.15	*2.00*
J35 D2 50c blue green	.15	*2.00*
Nos. J29-J35 (7)	1.05	

1899

J36 D2 1c carmine	.15	*2.00*
J37 D2 2c carmine	.15	*2.00*
J38 D2 5c carmine	.15	*2.00*
J39 D2 10c carmine	.15	*2.00*
J40 D2 20c carmine	.15	*2.00*
J41 D2 50c carmine	.15	*2.00*
Set value	.60	

Some denominations are found in se-tenant pairs.

Various counterfeit cancellations exist on #J1-J41.

D3

1900 Engr.

J42 D3 1c plum	1.00
J43 D3 2c vermilion	1.00
J44 D3 5c dk bl	1.00
J45 D3 10c purple	1.00
J46 D3 20c org brn	1.00
J47 D3 30c dk grn	2.00
J48 D3 50c lake	2.00
Nos. J42-J48 (7)	9.00

Nos. J42-J48 were not issued without postage overprint. For overprints see Nos. 137-143, 152-158, O72-O81, 2L11-2L15, 2L25, 2L40-2L41.

OFFICIAL STAMPS

Types of Postage Stamps Overprinted in Red Diagonally Reading up

FRANQUEO OFICIAL

1890 Unwmk. Engr. *Perf. 12*

No.	Type	Value	Unused	Used
O1	A5	1c ultra	.15	.35
O2	A5	2c ultra	.15	.35
O3	A5	5c ultra	.15	.35
O4	A5	10c ultra	.15	.40
O5	A5	20c ultra	.15	.75
O6	A5	50c ultra	.15	.75
O7	A5	1p ultra	.15	1.25
O8	A5	2p ultra	.15	1.50
O9	A5	5p ultra	.15	2.50
O10	A5	10p ultra	.15	3.25
		Nos. O1-O10 (10)	1.50	

All values of the 1890 issue are known without overprint and most of them with inverted or double overprint, or without overprint and imperforate. There is no evidence that they were issued in these forms.

Official stamps of 1890-1899 are scarce with genuine cancellations. Forged cancellations are plentiful.

Overprinted Vertically Reading Up

1891 Litho.

No.	Type	Value	Unused	Used
O11	A6	1c green	.15	.35
O12	A6	2c green	.15	.35
O13	A6	5c green	.15	.35
O14	A6	10c green	.15	.35
O15	A6	20c green	.15	.75
O16	A6	50c green	.15	1.25
O17	A6	1p green	.15	1.50
O18	A6	2p green	.15	1.50
O19	A6	5p green	.15	2.50
O20	A6	10p green	.15	4.00
		Nos. O11-O20 (10)	1.50	

All values of this issue except the 2c and 5p exist without overprint and several with double overprint. They are not known to have been issued in this form.

Many of the denominations may be found in se-tenant pairs.

Overprinted in Dark Blue

FRANQUEO OFICIAL

1892 Engr.

No.	Type	Value	Unused	Used
O21	A7	1c yellow brown	.15	.35
O22	A7	2c yellow brown	.15	.35
O23	A7	5c yellow brown	.15	.35
O24	A7	10c yellow brown	.15	.35
O25	A7	20c yellow brown	.15	.75
O26	A7	50c yellow brown	.15	1.00
O27	A7	1p yellow brown	.15	1.50
O28	A7	2p yellow brown	.15	2.00
O29	A7	5p yellow brown	.15	3.00
O30	A7	10p yellow brown	.15	4.00
		Nos. O21-O30 (10)	1.50	

The 2c and 1p are known without overprint and several values exist with double or inverted overprint. These probably were not regularly issued.

Commemorative of the 400th anniversary of the discovery of America by Christopher Columbus.

Overprinted in Red

FRANQUEO OFICIAL

1893 Engr.

No.	Type	Value	Unused	Used
O31	A8	1c slate	.15	.35
O32	A8	2c slate	.15	.35
O33	A8	5c slate	.15	.35
O34	A8	10c slate	.15	.35
O35	A8	20c slate	.15	.50
O36	A8	25c slate	.15	
O37	A8	50c slate	.15	.85
O38	A8	1p slate	.15	1.50
O39	A8	2p slate	.15	2.00
O40	A8	5p slate	.15	3.00
O41	A8	10p slate	.15	4.00
		Nos. O31-O41 (11)	1.65	

The 2, 5, 10, 20, 25, 50c and 5p are known without overprint but probably were not regularly issued. Some values exist with double or inverted overprints.

Overprinted in Black

FRANQUEO OFICIAL

1894

No.	Type	Value	Unused	Used
O42	A9	1c orange	.30	.35
O43	A9	2c orange	.30	.35
O44	A9	5c orange	.30	.35
O45	A9	10c orange	.30	.35
O46	A9	20c orange	.30	.50
O47	A9	50c orange	.30	.75
O48	A9	1p orange	.30	1.50
O49	A9	2p orange	.30	2.00
O50	A9	5p orange	2.00	3.00
O51	A9	10p orange	2.00	4.00
		Nos. O42-O51 (10)	6.40	13.15

Reprints are yellow.

1895

Overprinted in Blue

No.	Type	Value	Unused	Used
O52	A10	1c green	.15	.35
O53	A10	2c green	.15	.35
O54	A10	5c green	.15	.35
O55	A10	10c green	.15	.35
O56	A10	20c green	.15	.50
O57	A10	50c green	.15	1.00
O58	A10	1p green	.15	1.50
O59	A10	2p green	.15	2.00
O60	A10	5p green	.15	3.00
O61	A10	10p green	.15	4.00
		Nos. O52-O61 (10)	1.50	

Wmk. 117

No.	Type	Value
O62	A10	1c green
O63	A10	2c green
O64	A10	5c green
O65	A10	10c green
O66	A10	20c green
O67	A10	50c green
O68	A10	1p green
O69	A10	2p green
O70	A10	5p green
O71	A10	10p green

Nos. O62-O71 probably exist only as reprints. Value, each 15 cents.

Postage Due Stamps of Same Date Handstamped in Violet

Franqueo Oficial

1896 Unwmk.

No.	Type	Value	Unused
O72	D1	1c orange	7.00
O73	D1	2c orange	7.00
O74	D1	5c orange	5.00
O75	D1	10c orange	5.00
O76	D1	20c orange	5.00
		Nos. O72-O76 (5)	29.00

Wmk. 117

No.	Type	Value	Unused
O77	D1	1c orange	7.00
O78	D1	2c orange	7.00
O79	D1	5c orange	4.00
O80	D1	10c orange	4.00
O81	D1	20c orange	4.00
		Nos. O77-O81 (5)	26.00

Nos. O72-O81 were handstamped in rows of five. Several handstamps were used, one of which had the variety "Oftcial." Most varieties are known inverted and double.

Forgeries exist.

Types of Postage Stamps Overprinted in Red

1896 Unwmk.

No.	Type	Value	Unused	Used
O82	A11	1c red	2.50	3.00
O83	A11	2c red	2.50	3.00
O84	A11	5c red	2.50	3.00
O85	A11	10c red	2.50	3.00
O86	A11	20c red	3.00	3.00
O87	A11	50c red	5.00	5.00
O88	A11	1p red	12.00	12.00
O89	A11	2p red	12.00	12.00
O90	A11	5p red	16.00	16.00
		Nos. O82-O90 (9)	58.00	60.00

Wmk. 117

No.	Type	Value	Unused	Used
O91	A11	1c red	3.00	3.50
O92	A11	2c red	3.00	3.50
O93	A11	5c red	3.00	3.50
O94	A11	10c red	3.00	3.50
O95	A11	20c red	5.00	5.00
O96	A11	50c red	3.00	5.00
O97	A11	1p red	14.00	14.00
O98	A11	2p red	16.50	16.50
O99	A11	5p red	25.00	25.00
		Nos. O91-O99 (9)	75.50	79.50

Used values for Nos. O88-O90, O97-O99 are for CTO copies. Postally used copies are not known.

Same, Dated 1897

1897 Unwmk.

No.	Type	Value	Unused	Used
O100	A11	1c red	3.00	3.00
O101	A11	2c red	3.00	3.00
O102	A11	5c red	3.00	2.50
O103	A11	10c red	3.00	3.00
O104	A11	20c red	3.00	4.00
O105	A11	50c red	5.00	5.00
O106	A11	1p red	12.00	12.00
O107	A11	2p red	12.00	12.00
O108	A11	5p red	16.00	16.00
		Nos. O100-O108 (9)	60.00	60.50

Wmk. 117

No.	Type	Value	Unused	Used
O109	A11	1c red	5.00	5.00
O110	A11	2c red	5.00	5.00
O111	A11	5c red	5.00	5.00
O112	A11	10c red	10.00	10.00
O113	A11	20c red	10.00	10.00
O114	A11	50c red	12.00	12.00
O115	A11	1p red	20.00	20.00
O116	A11	2p red	20.00	20.00
O117	A11	5p red	20.00	20.00
		Nos. O109-O117 (9)	107.00	107.00

Reprints of Nos. O82-O117 are described in notes after No. 109M. Value 15c each.

Used values for Nos. O106-O108, O115-O117 are for CTO copies. Postally used copies are not known.

Overprinted in Blue

1898 Unwmk.

No.	Type	Value	Unused	Used
O118	A12	1c carmine	3.25	3.25
O119	A12	2c carmine	3.25	3.25
O120	A12	4c carmine	3.25	3.25
O121	A12	5c carmine	2.50	2.50
O122	A12	10c carmine	4.00	4.00
O123	A12	15c carmine	6.00	6.00
O124	A12	20c carmine	6.00	6.00
O125	A12	50c carmine	8.50	8.50
O126	A12	1p carmine	11.00	11.00
O127	A12	2p carmine	11.00	11.00
O128	A12	5p carmine	11.00	11.00
		Nos. O118-O128 (11)	69.75	69.75

Stamps of this set with sideways watermark 117 or with black overprint are reprints. Value 25c each.

Used values for Nos. O126-O128 are for CTO copies. Postally used copies are not known.

Overprinted in Dark Blue

1899

No.	Type	Value	Unused	Used
O129	A13	1c gray grn	.15	1.00
O130	A13	2c bis brn	.15	1.00
O131	A13	4c lake	.15	1.00
O132	A13	5c dk bl	.15	.50
O133	A13	10c buff	.15	1.00
O134	A13	15c chocolate	.15	2.00
O135	A13	20c dk grn	.15	3.00
O136	A13	50c car rose	.15	3.00
O137	A13	1p red	.15	10.00
O138	A13	2p violet	.15	10.00
O139	A13	5p lt bl	.15	15.00
		Set value	1.10	

Counterfeit cancellations on Nos. O129-O139 are plentiful.

"Justice" — O5

1900 Engr.

No.	Type	Value	Unused	Used
O140	O5	1c plum	.60	.60
O141	O5	2c vermilion	.50	.50
O142	O5	4c ol grn	.60	.60
O143	O5	5c dk bl	1.25	.45
O144	O5	10c purple	1.25	.35
O145	O5	20c brown	.90	.35
O146	O5	50c lake	1.25	.50
O147	O5	1p ultra	3.50	2.50
O148	O5	2p brn org	4.00	4.00
O149	O5	5p grnsh blk	5.00	5.00
		Nos. O140-O149 (10)	18.85	14.85

For surcharges see Nos. O155-O157.

Nos. 123, 161 Surcharged in Black

1 1

OFICIAL

1 Centavo

1903 *Perf. 12, 14*

No.	Type	Value	Unused	Used
O150	A14	1c on 10c violet	.25	.30
a.		"Centovo"	1.00	
b.		"Contavo"	1.00	
c.		With ornaments	.30	
d.		Inverted surcharge	1.00	
e.		"1" omitted at upper left	2.00	
O151	A14	2c on 3c green	.30	.40
a.		"Centovos"	1.00	
b.		"Contavos"	1.00	
c.		With ornaments	.35	
d.		Inverted surcharge	1.00	
O152	A14	4c on 3c green	1.25	1.25
a.		"Centovos"	2.50	
b.		"Contavos"	2.50	
c.		With ornaments	2.50	
d.		Inverted surcharge		
O153	A14	4c on 10c violet	1.25	1.25
a.		"Centovos"	2.50	
b.		"Contavos"	2.50	
c.		With ornaments	2.00	
d.		Inverted surcharge		
O154	A14	5c on 3c green	.15	.18
a.		"Centovos"	1.00	
b.		"Contavos"	1.00	
c.		With ornaments	.30	
d.		Double surcharge	2.00	
e.		Inverted surcharge		
		Nos. O150-O154 (5)	3.20	3.38

These surcharges are set up to cover 25 stamps. Some of the settings have bars or pieces of fancy border type below "OFICIAL." There are 5 varieties on #O150, 3 on #O151, 1 each on #O152, O153, O154.

In 1904 #O151 was reprinted to fill a dealer's order. This printing lacks the small figure at the upper right. It includes the variety "OFICILA." At the same time the same setting was printed in carmine on official stamps of 1900, 1c on 10c violet and 2c on 1p ultramarine. Also the 1, 2 and 5p official stamps of 1900 were surcharged with new values and the dates 1901 or 1902 in various colors, inverted, etc. It is doubtful if any of these varieties were ever in Nicaragua and certain that none of them ever did legitimate postal duty.

10 10

No. O145 Surcharged in Black

10 Ctvs.

1904 *Perf. 12*

No.	Type	Value	Unused	Used
O155	O5	10c on 20c brn	.20	.20
a.		No period after "Ctvs"	1.00	.75
O156	O5	30c on 20c brn	.20	.20
O157	O5	50c on 20c brn	.50	.35
a.		Lower "50" omitted	2.50	2.50
b.		Upper figures omitted	2.50	2.50
c.		Top left and lower figures omitted	3.50	3.50
		Nos. O155-O157 (3)	.90	.75

Coat of Arms — O6

1905, July 25 Engr.

No.	Type	Value	Unused	Used
O158	O6	1c green	.25	.25
O159	O6	2c rose	.25	.25
O160	O6	5c blue	.25	.25
O161	O6	10c yel brn	.25	.25
O162	O6	20c orange	.25	.25
O163	O6	50c brn ol	.25	.25
O164	O6	1p lake	.25	.25
O165	O6	2p violet	.25	.25
O166	O6	5p gray blk	.25	.25
		Nos. O158-O166 (9)	2.25	2.25

Surcharged Vertically Up or Down

Vale 10c

1907

No.	Type	Value	Unused	Used
O167	O6	10c on 1c grn	.75	.75
O168	O6	10c on 2c rose	25.00	22.50
O169	O6	20c on 2c rose	22.50	17.50
O170	O6	50c on 1c grn	1.50	1.50
O171	O6	50c on 2c rose	22.50	12.50

Surcharged

Vale $ 1.00

No.	Type	Value	Unused	Used
O172	O6	1p on 2c rose	1.50	1.50
O173	O6	2p on 2c rose	1.50	1.50
O174	O6	3p on 2c rose	1.50	1.50
O175	O6	4p on 2c rose		
O176	O6	4p on 5c blue	2.25	2.25

The setting for this surcharge includes various letters from wrong fonts, the figure "1" for "I" in "Vale" and an "I" for "1" in "$1.00."

Surcharged

Vale 20 cts

No.	Type	Value	Unused	Used
O177	O6	20c on 1c green	1.00	1.00
a.		Double surcharge	5.00	5.00
		Nos. O167-O174,O176-O177 (10)	80.00	62.50

The preceding surcharges are vertical, reading both up and down.

O7

Revenue Stamps Surcharged

1907 *Perf. 14 to 15*

O178 O7 10c on 2c org (Bk) .15 .15
O179 O7 35c on 1c bl (R) .15 .15
a. Inverted surcharge 3.00 3.00
O180 O7 70c on 1c bl (V) .15 .15
a. Inverted surcharge 3.00 3.00
O181 O7 70c on 1c bl (O) .15 .15
a. Inverted surcharge 3.00 3.00
O182 O7 1p on 2c org (G) .15 .15
a. Inverted surcharge 2.50 2.50
O183 O7 2p on 2c org (Br) .15 .15
O184 O7 3p on 5c brn (Bl) .15 .15
O185 O7 4p on 5c brn (G) .20 .20
a. Double surcharge 3.00 3.00
O186 O7 5p on 5c brn (G) .20 .20
a. Inverted surcharge 3.50 3.50
Nos. O178-O186 (9) 1.45 1.45

Letters and figures from several fonts were mixed in these surcharges.

See Nos. O199-O209.

No. 202 Surcharged — OFICIAL — 10 cvs —

1907, Nov.

Black or Blue Black Surcharge

O187 A18 10c on 1c grn 15.00 13.00
O188 A18 15c on 1c grn 15.00 13.00
O189 A18 20c on 1c grn 15.00 13.00
O190 A18 50c on 1c grn 15.00 13.00

Red Surcharge

O191 A18 1(un)p on 1c grn 14.00 13.00
O192 A18 2(dos)p on 1c grn 14.00 13.00
Nos. O187-O192 (6) 88.00 78.00

No. 181 Surcharged — OFICIAL VALE 10 ₵

1908 **Yellow Surcharge** *Perf. 12*

O193 A18 10c on 3c vio 15.00 15.00
O194 A18 15c on 3c vio 15.00 15.00
O195 A18 20c on 3c vio 15.00 15.00
O196 A18 35c on 3c vio 15.00 15.00
O197 A18 50c on 3c vio 15.00 15.00
Nos. O193-O197 (5) 75.00 75.00

Black Surcharge

O198 A18 35c on 3c vio 60.00 60.00

Revenue Stamps Surcharged like 1907 Issue
Dated "1908"

1908 *Perf. 14 to 15*

O199 O7 10c on 1c bl (V) .75 .50
a. Inverted surcharge 3.50 3.50
O200 O7 35c on 1c bl (Bk) .75 .50
a. Inverted surcharge 3.50 3.50
b. Double surcharge 4.00 4.00
O201 O7 50c on 1c bl (R) .75 .50
O202 O7 1p on 1c bl (Br) 37.50 37.50
a. Inverted surcharge 65.00 65.00
O203 O7 2p on 1c bl (G) .90 .75
O204 O7 10c on 2c org (Bk) 1.10 .65
O205 O7 35c on 2c org (R) 1.10 .65
a. Double surcharge 3.50
O206 O7 50c on 2c org (Bk) 1.10 .65
O207 O7 70c on 2c org (Bl) 1.10 .65
O208 O7 1p on 2c org (G) 1.10 .65
O209 O7 2p on 2c org (Br) 1.10 .65
Nos. O199-O209 (11) 47.25 43.65

There are several minor varieties in the figures, etc., in these surcharges.

Nos. 243-248 Overprinted in Black — OFICIAL

1909 *Perf. 12*

O210 A18 10c lake .20 .15
a. Double overprint 2.50 2.50
O211 A18 15c black .60 .50
O212 A18 20c brn ol 1.00 .75
O213 A18 50c dp grn 1.50 1.00
O214 A18 1p yellow 1.75 1.25
O215 A18 2p car rose 2.75 2.00
Nos. O210-O215 (6) 7.80 5.65

Overprinted in Black — OFICIAL

1910

O216 A18 15c black 1.50 1.25
a. Double overprint 4.00 4.00
O217 A18 20c brn ol 2.50 2.00
O218 A18 50c dp grn 2.50 2.00
O219 A18 1p yellow 2.75 2.50
a. Inverted overprint 7.50 7.50
O220 A18 2p car rose 4.00 3.00
Nos. O216-O220 (5) 13.25 10.75

Nos. 239-240 Surcharged in Black — OFICIAL *Vale* 10 *cts.*

1911

O221 A18 5c on 3c red org 6.00 6.00
O222 A18 10c on 4c vio 5.00 5.00
a. Double surcharge 10.00 10.00
b. Pair, one without new value 20.00

Railroad Stamps Surcharged in Black — Correo oficial Vale 10 cts.

1911, Nov. *Perf. 14 to 15*

O223 A21 10c on 1 red 3.00 3.00
a. Inverted surcharge 4.50
b. Double surcharge 4.50
O224 A21 15c on 1 red 3.00 3.00
a. Inverted surcharge 5.00
b. Double surcharge 4.50
O225 A21 20c on 1 red 3.00 3.00
a. Inverted surcharge 5.00
O226 A21 50c on 1 red 3.75 3.75
a. Inverted surcharge 4.50
O227 A21 1p on 1 red 5.00 7.00
a. Inverted surcharge 6.00
O228 A21 2p on 1 red 5.50 10.00
a. Inverted surcharge 7.50
b. Double surcharge 7.50
Nos. O223-O228 (6) 23.25 29.75

Surcharged in Black — CORREO OFICIAL 15 centavos

1911, Nov.

O229 A21 10c on 1 red 22.50
O230 A21 15c on 1 red 22.50
O231 A21 20c on 1 red 22.50
O232 A21 50c on 1 red 16.00
Nos. O229-O232 (4) 83.50

Surcharged in Black — Correo oficial Vale 5 cts. 1911

1911, Dec.

O233 A21 5c on 1 red 4.50 6.00
a. Double surcharge 7.50
b. Inverted surcharge 7.50
c. "5" omitted 6.00
O234 A21 10c on 1 red 5.50 7.00
O235 A21 15c on 1 red 6.00 7.50
O236 A21 20c on 1 red 6.50 8.50
O237 A21 50c on 1 red 7.50 10.00
Nos. O233-O237 (5) 30.00 39.00

Nos. O233 to O237 have a surcharge on the back like Nos. 285 and 286 with "15 cts" obliterated by a heavy bar.

Surcharged Vertically in Black — Correo Oficial 1912 85 cvs.

1912

O238 A21 5c on 1 red 8.00 8.00
O239 A21 10c on 1 red 8.00 8.00
O240 A21 15c on 1 red 8.00 8.00
O241 A21 20c on 1 red 8.00 8.00
O242 A21 35c on 1 red 8.00 8.00
O243 A21 50c on 1 red 8.00 8.00
O244 A21 1p on 1 red 8.00 8.00
Nos. O238-O244 (7) 56.00 56.00

Nos. O238 to O244 are printed on Nos. 285 and 286 but the surcharge on the back is obliterated by a vertical bar.

Types of Regular Issue of 1912 Overprinted in Black — OFICIAL

1912 *Perf. 12*

O245 A22 1c light blue .15 .15
O246 A22 2c light blue .15 .15
O247 A22 3c light blue .15 .15
O248 A22 4c light blue .15 .15
O249 A22 5c light blue .15 .15
O250 A22 6c light blue .15 .15
O251 A22 10c light blue .15 .15
O252 A22 15c light blue .15 .15
O253 A22 20c light blue .15 .15
O254 A22 25c light blue .20 .20
O255 A22 35c light blue .25 .25
O256 A22 50c light blue 1.50 1.50
O257 A22 1p light blue .30 .30
O258 A22 2p light blue .35 .35
O259 A22 5p light blue .50 .50
Set value 3.85 3.85

On the 35c the overprint is 15½mm wide, on the other values it is 13mm.

Types of Regular Issue of 1914 Overprinted in Black — OFICIAL

1915, May

O260 A24 1c light blue .15 .15
O261 A25 2c light blue .15 .15
O262 A24 3c light blue .20 .15
O263 A25 4c light blue .15 .15
O264 A24 5c light blue .15 .15
O265 A25 6c light blue .15 .15
O266 A25 10c light blue .15 .15
O267 A24 15c light blue .20 .20
O268 A25 20c light blue .20 .20
O269 A24 25c light blue .30 .30
O270 A25 50c light blue .60 .60
Nos. O260-O270 (11) 2.40 2.35

Regular Issues of 1914-22 Overprinted in Red — Oficial

1925

O271 A24 ½c dp grn .15 .15
a. Double overprint 2.50 2.50
O272 A24 1c violet .15 .15
O273 A25 2c car rose .15 .15
O274 A24 3c ol grn .15 .15
O275 A25 4c vermilion .15 .15
a. Double overprint 2.50 2.50
O276 A24 5c black .15 .15
a. Double overprint 2.50 2.50
O277 A25 6c red brn .25 .25
O278 A25 10c yellow .35 .35
a. Double overprint 3.50 3.50
O279 A24 15c red brn .40 .40
O280 A25 20c bis brn .50 .50
O281 A24 25c orange .60 .60
a. Inverted overprint 4.00 4.00
O282 A25 50c pale bl .75 .75
a. Double overprint 5.00 5.00
Nos. O271-O282 (12) 3.75 3.75

Type II overprint has "f" and "i" separated. Comes on Nos. O272-O274 and O276.

Regular Issues of 1914-22 Overprinted in Black — OFICIAL

1926

O283 A24 ½c dk grn .15 .15
O284 A24 1c dp vio .15 .15
O285 A25 2c car rose .15 .15
O286 A24 3c ol gray .15 .15
O287 A25 4c vermilion .15 .15
O288 A24 5c gray blk .15 .15
O289 A25 6c red brn .15 .15
O290 A25 10c yellow .15 .15
O291 A24 15c dp brn .15 .15
O292 A25 20c bis brn .15 .15
O293 A24 25c orange .15 .18
O294 A25 50c pale bl .25 .25
Set value 1.30 1.30

No. 499 Surcharged in Black — OFICIAL ₡ 0.05 1931

1931

O295 A33 5c on 10c bis brn .20 .20

Nos. 517-518 Overprinted in Red — OFICIAL

1931

O296 A25 6c bis brn .20 .20
O297 A25 10c lt brn .20 .20

Nos. 541, 543, 545 With Additional Overprint in Black — 1931

O298 A24 1c ol grn .16 .16
O299 A24 3c lt bl .16 .16
a. "OFICIAL" inverted .80 .80
O300 A24 5c gray brn .16 .16
a. "1931" double .80 .80
Nos. O298-O300 (3) .48 .48

Regular Issues of 1914-31 Overprinted in Black — OFICIAL

1932, Feb. 6

O301 A24 1c ol grn .15 .15
a. Double overprint 1.40 1.40
O302 A25 2c brt rose .15 .15
a. Double overprint 1.40 1.40
O303 A24 3c lt bl .15 .15
a. Double overprint .50 .50
O304 A25 4c dk bl .15 .15
O305 A24 5c ol brn .15 .15
O306 A25 6c bis brn .20 .15
a. Double overprint 2.00 2.00
O307 A25 10c lt brn .30 .20
O308 A24 15c org red .40 .22
a. Double overprint 2.25 2.25
O309 A25 20c orange .65 .35
O310 A24 25c dk vio 2.00 .50
O311 A25 50c green .15 .15
O312 A25 1cor yellow .20 .20
Nos. O301-O312 (12) 4.65 2.52

With Additional Overprint in Black — 1931

1932, Feb. 6

O313 A24 1c ol grn 5.50 5.50
O314 A25 2c brt rose 6.50 6.50
a. Double overprint 8.25 8.25
O315 A24 3c lt bl 5.00 5.00
O316 A24 5c ol brn 5.00 5.00
O317 A24 15c org red .65 .65
O318 A24 25c blk brn .65 .65
O319 A24 25c dk vio 1.50 1.50
Nos. O313-O319 (7) 24.80 24.80

The variety "OFIAIAL" occurs once in each sheet of Nos. O301 to O319 inclusive.

Flag of the Race Issue

1933, Aug. 9 **Litho.** *Rouletted 9*

Without gum

O320 A43 1c orange 1.00 1.00
O321 A43 2c yellow 1.00 1.00
O322 A43 3c dk brn 1.00 1.00
O323 A43 4c dp brn 1.00 1.00
O324 A43 5c gray brn 1.00 1.00
O325 A43 6c dp ultra 1.20 1.20
O326 A43 10c dp vio 1.20 1.20
O327 A43 15c red vio 1.20 1.20
O328 A43 20c dp grn 1.20 1.20
O329 A43 25c green 2.00 2.00
O330 A43 50c carmine 2.50 2.50
O331 A43 1cor red 4.00 4.00
Nos. O320-O331 (12) 18.30 18.30

See note after No. 599.

Reprints of Nos. O320-O331 exist.

A 25c dull blue exists. Its status is questioned.

Regular Issue of 1914-31 Overprinted in Red — OFICIAL

1933, Nov. *Perf. 12*

O332 A24 1c ol grn .15 .15
O333 A25 2c brt rose .15 .15
O334 A24 3c lt bl .15 .15
O335 A25 4c dk bl .15 .15
O336 A24 5c ol brn .15 .15
O337 A25 6c bis brn .15 .15
O338 A25 10c lt brn .15 .15
O339 A24 15c red org .15 .15
O340 A25 20c orange .15 .15
O341 A24 25c dk vio .15 .15
O342 A25 50c green .16 .16
O343 A25 1cor yellow .35 .20
Set value 1.00 .90

Nos. O332-O343 exist with or without signature control overprint. Values are the same.

Official Stamps of 1933 Overprinted as Nos. CO15-CO19 in Blue

1935, Dec.

O344 A24 1c ol grn .65 .42
O345 A25 2c brt rose .65 .50
O346 A24 3c lt bl 1.60 .50
O347 A25 4c dk bl 1.60 1.60
O348 A24 5c ol brn 1.60 1.60
O349 A25 6c bis brn 2.00 2.00
O350 A25 10c lt brn 2.00 2.00
O351 A24 15c org red 28.00 28.00
O352 A25 20c orange 28.00 28.00
O353 A24 25c dk vio 28.00 28.00

O354 A25 50c green 28.00 28.00
O355 A25 1cor yellow 28.00 28.00
Nos. O344-O355 (12) 150.10 148.62

Nos. O344-O355 have signature control overprints. Counterfeits of overprint abound.

Same Overprinted in Red

1936, Jan.

O356 A24 1c ol grn .15 .15
O357 A25 2c brt rose .15 .15
O358 A24 3c lt bl .15 .15
a. Double overprint
O359 A25 4c dk bl .15 .15
O360 A24 5c ol brn .15 .15
O361 A25 6c bis brn .15 .15
O362 A25 10c lt brn .15 .15
O363 A24 15c org red .15 .15
O364 A25 20c orange .15 .15
O365 A24 25c dk vio .15 .15
O366 A25 50c green .16 .16
O367 A25 1cor yellow .35 .35
Set value 1.35 1.35

Have signature control overprints.

Nos. 653 to 655, 657, 659 660, 662 to 664 Overprinted in Black

1937

O368 A24 1c car rose .20 .16
O369 A25 2c dp bl .20 .16
O370 A24 3c chocolate .25 .22
O371 A24 5c org red .35 .25
O372 A25 10c ol grn .65 .40
O373 A24 15c green .80 .50
O374 A24 25c orange 1.00 .65
O375 A25 50c brown 1.40 .80
O376 A25 1cor ultra 2.50 1.20
Nos. O368-O376 (9) 7.35 4.34

Islands of the Great Lake — O9

1939, Jan. **Engr.** ***Perf. 12½***

O377 O9 2c rose red .15 .15
O378 O9 3c lt bl .15 .15
O379 O9 6c brn org .15 .15
O380 O9 7½c dp grn .15 .15
O381 O9 10c blk brn .15 .15
O382 O9 15c orange .15 .15
O383 O9 25c dk vio .25 .25
O384 O9 50c brt yel grn .40 .40
Set value 1.25 1.25

POSTAL TAX STAMPS

Official Stamps of 1915 Surcharged in Black

Vale
un centavo
R de C

1921, July **Unwmk.** ***Perf. 12***

RA1 A24 1c on 5c lt bl 1.50 .60
RA2 A25 1c on 6c lt bl .65 .20
a. Double surcharge, one inverted
RA3 A25 1c on 10c lt bl 1.00 .25
a. Double surcharge 3.50 3.50
RA4 A24 1c on 15c lt bl 1.50 .25
a. Double surcharge, one inverted 5.00 5.00
Nos. RA1-RA4 (4) 4.65 1.30

"R de C" signifies "Reconstruccion de Comunicaciones." The stamps were intended to provide a fund for rebuilding the General Post Office which was burned in April, 1921. One stamp was required on each letter or parcel, in addition to the regular postage. In the setting of one hundred there are five stamps with antique "C" and twenty-one with "R" and "C" smaller than in the illustration. One or more stamps in the setting have a dotted bar, as illustrated over No. 388, instead of the double bar.

The use of the "R de C" stamps for the payment of regular postage was not permitted.

Official Stamp of 1915 Overprinted in Black

«Particular»
R de C

1921, July

RA5 A24 1c light blue 6.00 1.75

This stamp is known with the dotted bar as illustrated over No. 388, instead of the double bar.

Coat of Arms — PT1

PT2

1921, Sept.

Red Surcharge

RA6 PT1 1c on 1c ver & blk .15 .15
RA7 PT1 1c on 2c grn & blk .15 .15
a. Double surcharge 3.00 3.00
b. Double surcharge, one inverted 4.00 4.00
RA8 PT1 1c on 4c org & blk .15 .15
a. Double surcharge 4.00 4.00
RA9 PT1 1c on 15c dk bl & blk .15 .15
a. Double surcharge 3.00 3.00
Nos. RA6-RA9 (4) .60
Set value .40

1922, Feb.

Black Surcharge

RA10 PT2 1c on 10c yellow .15 .15
a. Period after "de" .50 .40
b. Double surcharge 2.00 2.00
c. Double inverted surcharge 3.75 3.75
d. Inverted surcharge 3.00 3.00
e. Without period after "C" 1.00 1.00

No. 409 Overprinted in Black **R. de C.**

1922

RA11 A24 1c violet .16 .15
a. Double overprint 2.00 2.00

This stamp with the overprint in red is a trial printing.

Nos. 402, 404-407 Surcharged in Black

R. de C.
Vale
un centavo

1922, June

RA12 A27 1c on 1c grn & blk .75 .75
RA13 A29 1c on 5c ultra & blk .75 .75
RA14 A30 1c on 10c org & blk .75 .40
RA15 A31 1c on 25c yel & blk .75 .30
a. Inverted surcharge 5.00 5.00
RA16 A32 1c on 50c vio & blk .30 .25
a. Double surcharge 4.00 4.00
Nos. RA12-RA16 (5) 3.30 2.45

PT3

Surcharge in Red or Dark Blue

1922, Oct. ***Perf. 11½***

RA17 PT3 1c yellow (R) .15 .15
a. No period after "C" 1.00 1.00
RA18 PT3 1c violet (DBl) .15 .15
a. No period after "C" 1.00 1.00
Set value .24 .20

Surcharge is inverted on 22 out of 50 of No. RA17, 23 out of 50 of No. RA18.

Nos. 403-407 Surcharged in Black

R. de C.
Vale
un centavo
de córdoba

1923 ***Perf. 12***

RA19 A28 1c on 2c rose red & black .50 .45
RA20 A29 1c on 5c ultra & blk .55 .15
RA21 A30 1c on 10c org & blk .25 .20
RA22 A31 1c on 25c yel & blk .35 .30
RA23 A32 1c on 50c vio & blk .25 .15
Nos. RA19-RA23 (5) 1.90 1.25

The variety no period after "R" occurs twice on each sheet.

Red Surcharge

Wmk. Coat of Arms in Sheet

Perf. 11½

RA24 PT3 1c pale blue .15 .15

Unwmk.

Type of 1921 Issue

Without Surcharge of New Value

RA25 PT1 1c ver & blk .15 .15
a. Double overprint, one inverted 3.00 3.00

No. 409 Overprinted in Blue **R. de C. 1924**

1924

RA26 A24 1c violet .20 .15
a. Double overprint 8.00 8.00

There are two settings of the overprint on No. RA26, with "1924" 5½mm or 6½mm wide.

No. 409 Overprinted in Blue **R. de C. 1925**

1925

RA27 A24 1c violet .15 .15

No. 409 Overprinted in Blue **R. de C.**

1926

RA28 A24 1c violet .25 .15

No. RA28 Overprinted in Various Colors **Resello 1927**

1927

RA29 A24 1c vio (R) .15 .15
a. Double overprint (R) 2.00 2.00
b. Inverted overprint (R) 3.00 3.00
RA30 A24 1c vio (V) .15 .15
a. Double overprint 2.50 2.50
b. Inverted overprint 2.50 2.50
RA31 A24 1c vio (Bl) .15 .15
a. Double overprint 5.00 5.00
RA32 A24 1c vio (Bk) .15 .15
a. Double ovpt., one invtd. 4.25 4.25
b. Double overprint 4.25 4.25

Same Overprint on No. RA27

RA33 A24 1c vio (Bk) 15.00 10.00
Nos. RA29-RA33 (5) 15.60 10.60

No. RA28 Overprinted in Violet **Resello 1928**

1928

RA34 A24 1c violet .15 .15
a. Double overprint 2.00 2.00
b. "928" 1.00 1.00

Similar to No. RA34 but 8mm space between "Resello" and "1928"

Black Overprint

RA35 A24 1c violet .40 .15
a. "1828" 2.00 2.00

PT4

Inscribed "Timbre Telegrafico"
Horiz. Surch. in Black,
Vert. Surch. in Red

RA36 PT4 1c on 5c bl & blk .60 .15
a. Comma after "R" 1.25 1.25
b. No period after "R" 1.25 1.25
c. No periods after "R" and "C" 1.25 1.25

("CORREOS" at right) — PT5

PT6

1928 **Engr.** ***Perf. 12***

RA37 PT5 1c plum .25 .15

See Nos. RA41-RA43. For overprints see Nos. RA45-RA46, RA48-RA51.

1929

Surcharged in Red

RA38 PT6 1c on 5c bl & blk .15 .15
a. Inverted surcharge 3.00 3.00
b. Double surcharge 2.00 2.00
c. Double surcharge, one inverted 2.00 2.00
d. Period after "de" 1.25 1.25
e. Comma after "R" 1.25 1.25

See note after No. 512.

Regular Issue of 1928 Overprinted in Blue **R. de C.**

RA39 A24 1c red orange .15 .15

No. RA39 exists both with and without signature control overprint.

An additional overprint, "1929" in black or blue on No. RA39, is fraudulent.

No. 513 Overprinted in Red **R. de C.**

1929

RA40 A24 1c ol grn .20 .15
a. Double overprint .75 .75

No. RA40 is known with overprint in black, and with overprint inverted. These varieties were not regularly issued, but copies have been canceled by favor.

Type of 1928 Issue

Inscribed at right "COMUNICACIONES"

1930-37

RA41 PT5 1c carmine .20 .15
RA42 PT5 1c orange ('33) .15 .15
RA43 PT5 1c green ('37) .15 .15
Nos. RA41-RA43 (3) .50
Set value .18

No. RA42 has signature control. See note before No. 600.

No. RA39 Overprinted in Black **1931**

1931

RA44 A24 1c red orange .15 .15
a. "1931" double overprint .35 .35
b. "1931" double ovpt., one invtd. .42 .42

No. RA44 exists with signature control overprint. See note before No. 600. Value is the same.

No. RA42 Overprinted Vertically, up or down, in Black **Resello 1935**

1935

RA45 PT5 1c orange .15 .15
a. Double overprint 1.00 1.00
b. Double ovpt., one inverted

No. RA45 and RA45a Overprinted Vertically, Reading Down, in Blue

RA46 PT5 1c orange .50 .15
a. Black overprint double 2.00 2.00

Same Overprint in Red on Nos. RA39, RA42 and RA45

RA47 A24 1c red org (#RA39) *37.50*
RA48 PT5 1c org (#RA42) .20 .15
RA49 PT5 1c org (#RA45) .20 .15
a. Black overprint double .80 .80

Overprint is horizontal on No. RA47 and vertical, reading down, on Nos. RA48-RA49.

No. RA48 exists with signature control overprint. See note before No. 600. Same values.

No. RA42 Overprinted Vertically, Reading Down, in Carmine

RESELLO 1935

1935 Unwmk. *Perf. 12*
RA50 PT5 1c orange .20 .15

No. RA45 with Additional Overprint "1936", Vertically, Reading Down, in Red

1936
RA51 PT5 1c orange .50 .16

No. RA39 with Additional Overprint "1936" in Red

RA52 A24 1c red orange .50 .16

No. RA52 exists only with script control mark.

PT7

Vertical Surcharge in Red

1936
RA53 PT7 1c on 5c grn & blk .15 .15
a. "Cenavo" 1.40 1.40
b. "Centavos" 1.40 1.40

Horizontal Surcharge in Red

RA54 PT7 1c on 5c grn & blk .15 .15
a. Double surcharge 1.40 1.40
Set value .16

Baseball Player — PT8

1937 Typo. *Perf. 11*
RA55 PT8 1c carmine .35 .15
RA56 PT8 1c yellow .35 .15
RA57 PT8 1c blue .35 .15
RA58 PT8 1c green .35 .15
b. Sheet of 4, #RA55-RA58 3.00 3.00
Nos. RA55-RA58 (4) 1.40
Set value .44

Issued for the benefit of the Central American Caribbean Games of 1937.

Control mark in red is variously placed. See dark oval below "OLIMPICO" in illustration.

Tête bêche Pairs

RA55a PT8 1c .75 .75
RA56a PT8 1c .75 .75
RA57a PT8 1c .75 .75
RA58a PT8 1c .75 .75
Nos. RA55a-RA58a (4) 3.00 3.00

Catalogue values for unused stamps in this section, from this point to the end of the section, are for Never Hinged items.

Proposed Natl. Stadium, Managua — PT9

PT10

1949 Photo. *Perf. 12*
RA60 PT9 5c greenish blue .25 .15
a. Souvenir sheet of 4 3.75 3.75

10th World Series of Amateur Baseball, 1948. The tax was used toward the erection of a national stadium at Managua.

Type Similar to 1949, with "Correos" omitted

1952
RA61 PT9 5c magenta .25 .15

The tax was used toward the erection of a national stadium at Managua.

1956 Engr. *Perf. 12½x12*
RA62 PT10 5c deep ultra .15 .15

The tax was used for social welfare.

PT11

Jesus and Children — PT12

Surcharged in Red or Black

1959 Unwmk. *Perf. 12*
Red Marginal Number

RA63 PT11 5c on 50c vio bl (R) .15 .15
RA64 PT11 5c on 50c vio bl (B) .15 .15
Set value .24 .15

Nos. RA63-RA64 are surcharged on consular revenue stamps. Surcharge reads "Sobre Tasa Postal CO.O5." Vertical surcharge on No. RA63, horizontal on No. RA64.

1959 Photo. *Perf. 16*
RA65 PT12 5c ultra .15 .15

Hexisia Bidentata — PT13

Orchids: No. RA67, Schomburgkia tibicinus. No. RA68, Stanhopea ecornuta. No. RA69, Lycaste macrophylla. No. RA70, Maxillaria tenuifolia. No. RA71, Cattleya skinneri. No. RA72, Cycnoches egertonianum. No. RA73, Bletia roezlii. No. RA74, Sobralia pleiantha. No. RA75, Oncidium cebolleta and ascendens.

1962, Feb. Photo. *Perf. 11½*
Granite Paper
Orchids in Natural Colors

RA66 PT13 5c pale lil & grn .15 .15
RA67 PT13 5c yel & grn .15 .15
RA68 PT13 5c pink & grn .15 .15
RA69 PT13 5c pale vio & grn .15 .15
RA70 PT13 5c lt grnsh bl & red .15 .15
RA71 PT13 5c buff & lil .15 .15
RA72 PT13 5c yel grn & brn .15 .15
RA73 PT13 5c gray & red .15 .15
RA74 PT13 5c lt bl & dk bl .15 .15
RA75 PT13 5c lt grn & brn .15 .15
Set value .80 .80

For overprints see #842-852, 855-868, 901-908.

PROVINCE OF ZELAYA

(Bluefields)

A province of Nicaragua lying along the eastern coast. Special postage stamps for this section were made necessary because for a period two currencies, which differed materially in value, were in use in Nicaragua. Silver money was used in Zelaya and Cabo Gracias a Dios while the rest of Nicaragua used paper money. Later the money of the entire country was placed on a gold basis.

Dangerous counterfeits exist of most of the Bluefields overprints.

Regular Issues of 1900-05 Handstamped in Black (4 or more types)

B
Dpto Zelaya.

1904-05 Unwmk. *Perf. 12, 14*
On Engraved Stamps of 1900

1L1 A14 1c plum 1.50 .75
1L2 A14 2c vermilion 1.50 .75
1L3 A14 3c green 1.90 1.50
1L4 A14 4c ol grn 11.00 11.00
1L5 A14 15c ultra 3.00 1.90
1L6 A14 20c brown 3.00 1.90
1L7 A14 50c lake 10.50 7.50
1L8 A14 1p yellow 21.00
1L9 A14 2p salmon 30.00
1L10 A14 5p black 37.50
Nos. 1L1-1L10 (10) 120.90
Nos. 1L1-1L7 (7) 25.30

On Lithographed Stamps of 1902

1L11 A14 5c blue 3.00 .75
1L12 A14 5c carmine 1.90 .90
1L13 A14 10c violet 1.50 .75
Nos. 1L11-1L13 (3) 6.40 2.40

On Postage Due Stamps Overprinted "1901 Correos"

1L14 D3 20c brn (No. 156) 4.50 1.90
1L15 D3 50c lake (No. 158)

On Surcharged Stamps of 1904-05

1L16 A16 5c on 10c (#175) 1.50 1.10
1L17 A14 5c on 10c (#178) 4.00 1.50
1L18 A16 15c on 10c vio 1.50 1.50
1L19 A17 15c on 10c vio 14.00 4.50
Nos. 1L16-1L19 (4) 21.00 8.60

On Surcharged Stamp of 1901

1L20 A14 20c on 5p blk 18.00 3.00

On Regular Issue of 1905

1906-07 *Perf. 12*
1L21 A18 1c green .30 .30
1L22 A18 2c car rose .30 .30
1L23 A18 3c violet .30 .30
1L24 A18 4c org red .45 .45
1L25 A18 5c blue .22 .22
1L26 A18 10c yel brn 3.00 1.50
1L27 A18 15c brn ol 4.50 1.75
1L28 A18 20c lake 9.00 7.50
1L29 A18 50c orange 35.00 30.00
1L30 A18 1p black 30.00 27.50
1L31 A18 2p dk grn 37.50
1L32 A18 5p violet 45.00
Nos. 1L21-1L32 (12) 165.57
Nos. 1L21-1L32 (10) 69.82

On Surcharged Stamps of 1906-08

1L33 A18 10c on 3c vio .38 .38
1L34 A18 15c on 1c grn .52 .52
1L35 A18 20c on 2c rose 3.50 3.50
1L36 A18 20c on 5c bl 1.50 1.50
1L37 A18 50c on 6c sl (R) 1.50 3.00
Nos. 1L33-1L37 (5) 7.40 8.90

B B
Dpto. Zelaya Dto. Zelaya

Stamps with the above overprints were made to fill dealers' orders but were never regularly issued or used. Stamps with similar overprints handstamped are bogus.

Surcharged Stamps of 1906 Overprinted in Red, Black or Blue

B
Dpto. Zelaya

1L38 A18 15c on 1c grn (R) 2.75 2.75
a. Red overprint inverted
1L39 A18 20c on 2c rose (Bk) 1.90 1.90
1L40 A18 20c on 5c bl (R) 3.00 3.00
1L41 A18 50c on 6c sl (Bl) 14.00 14.00
Nos. 1L38-1L41 (4) 21.65 21.65

Stamps of the 1905 issue overprinted as above No. 1L38 or similarly overprinted but with only 2¼mm space between "B" and "Dpto. Zelaya" were made to fill dealers' orders but not placed in use.

No. 205 Handstamped in Black

B
Dpto Zelaya.

Perf. 14 to 15
1L42 A18 10c yel brn 24.00 24.00

Stamps of 1907 Overprinted in Red or Black

B
Dpto Zelaya

1L43 A18 15c brn ol (R) 3.00 3.00
1L44 A18 20c lake .90 .90
a. Inverted overprint 11.00 11.00

With Additional Surcharge

5 cent.

1L45 A18 5c brn org .52 .45
a. Inverted surcharge 7.50 7.50

With Additional Surcharge

5 cent.

1L46 A18 5c on 4c brn org 12.00 12.00

On Provisional Postage Stamps of 1907-08 in Black or Blue

1L47 A18 10c on 2c rose (Bl) 4.50 4.50
1L48 A18 10c on 2c rose
1L48A A18 10c on 4c brn org
1L49 A18 10c on 20c lake 3.00 3.00
1L50 A18 10c on 50c org (Bl) 3.00 2.25

Arms Type of 1907 Overprinted in Black or Violet

"COSTA ATLANTICA"
B.

1907
1L51 A18 1c green .30 .22
1L52 A18 2c rose .30 .22
1L53 A18 3c violet .38 .38
1L54 A18 4c brn org .45 .45
1L55 A18 5c blue 4.50 2.25
1L56 A18 10c yel brn .38 .30
1L57 A18 15c brn ol .75 .38
1L58 A18 20c lake .75 .45
1L59 A18 50c orange 2.25 1.50
1L60 A18 1p blk (V) 2.25 1.50
1L61 A18 2p dk grn 2.25 1.90
1L62 A18 5p violet 3.75 2.25
Nos. 1L51-1L62 (12) 18.31 11.80

Nos. 217-225 Overprinted in Green

B
Dpto. Zelaya

1908
1L63 A19 1c on 5c yel & blk (R) .45 .38
1L64 A19 2c on 5c yel & blk (Bl) .45 .38
1L65 A19 4c on 5c yel & blk (G) .45 .38
a. Overprint reading down 11.00 11.00
b. Double overprint, reading up and down 18.00 18.00
1L66 A19 5c yel & blk .45 .45
a. "CORROE" 4.50
b. Double overprint 11.00 11.00
c. Double overprint, reading up and down 19.00 19.00
d. "CORREO 1908" double 15.00 15.00
1L67 A19 10c lt bl & blk .45 .45
a. Ovpt. reading down .52 .52
b. "CORREO 1908" triple 37.50
1L68 A19 15c on 50c ol & blk (R) .90 .90
a. "1008" 4.50
b. "8908" 4.50
1L69 A19 35c on 50c ol & blk 1.40 1.40
1L70 A19 1p yel brn & blk 1.90 1.90
a. "CORROE" 12.00 12.00
1L71 A19 2p pearl gray & blk 2.25 2.25
a. "CORROE" 15.00 15.00
Nos. 1L63-1L71 (9) 8.70 8.49

Overprinted Horizontally in Black or Green

1L72 A19 5c yel & blk 9.00 7.50
1L72A A19 2p pearl gray & blk (G)

On Nos. 1L72-1L72A, space between "B" and "Dpto. Zelaya" is 13mm.

Nos. 237-248 Overprinted in Black

B
Dpto. Zelaya

Imprint: "American Bank Note Co. NY"

1909 *Perf. 12*
1L73 A18 1c yel grn .22 .22
1L74 A18 2c vermilion .22 .22
a. Inverted overprint
1L75 A18 3c red org .22 .22
1L76 A18 4c violet .22 .22
1L77 A18 5c dp bl .30 .22
a. Inverted overprint 9.00 9.00
b. "B" inverted 7.50 7.50
c. Double overprint 12.00 12.00
1L78 A18 6c gray brn 4.50 3.00
1L79 A18 10c lake .30 .28
a. "B" inverted 9.00 9.00
1L80 A18 15c black .45 .38
a. "B" inverted 11.00 11.00
b. Inverted overprint 12.00 12.00
c. Double overprint 14.00 14.00
1L81 A18 20c brn ol .52 .52
a. "B" inverted 19.00 19.00
1L82 A18 50c dp grn 1.50 1.50
1L83 A18 1p yellow 2.25 2.25

1L84 A18 2p car rose 3.00 3.00
a. Double overprint 27.50 27.50
Nos. 1L73-1L84 (12) 13.70 12.03

One stamp in each sheet has the "o" of "Dpto." sideways.

B

Overprinted in Black

Dpto. Zelaya

1910

1L85 A18 3c red org .38 .38
1L86 A18 4c violet .38 .38
a. Inverted overprint 14.00 14.00
1L87 A18 15c black 4.50 2.25
1L88 A18 20c brn ol .22 .30
1L89 A18 50c dp grn .28 .38
1L90 A18 1p yellow .30 .45
a. Inverted overprint 7.50
1L91 A18 2p car rose .38 .75
Nos. 1L85-1L91 (7) 6.44 4.89

Z1

Black Ovpt., Green Surch., Carmine Block-outs

1910

1L92 Z1 5c on 10c lake 3.75 3.00

There are three types of the letter "B." It is stated that this stamp was used exclusively for postal purposes and not for telegrams.

No. 247 Surcharged in Black

B
Vale
5 cts.

1911

1L93 A18 5c on 1p yellow .75 .75
a. Double surcharge 14.00
1L94 A18 10c on 1p yellow 1.50 1.50
1L95 A18 15c on 1p yellow .75 .75
a. Inverted surcharge 9.00
b. Double surcharge 9.00
c. Double surcharge, one invtd. 9.00
Nos. 1L93-1L95 (3) 3.00 3.00

Revenue Stamps Surcharged in Black

B
CORREOS
05 cts.
1911

Perf. 14 to 15

1L96 A19 5c on 25c lilac .75 1.10
a. Without period 1.50 1.50
b. Inverted surcharge 9.00 9.00
1L97 A19 10c on 1p yel brn 1.10 .75
a. Without period 1.90 1.90
b. "01" for "10" 9.00 7.50
c. Inverted surcharge 13.00 13.00

Surcharged in Black

VALE
05 cts.
POSTAL B
de 1911

1L98 A19 5c on 1p yel brn 1.50 1.50
a. Without period 2.25
b. "50" for "05" 14.00 14.00
c. Inverted surcharge 15.00 15.00
1L99 A19 5c on 10p pink 1.50 1.50
a. Without period 2.25 2.25
b. "50" for "05" 11.00 11.00
1L100 A19 10c on 1p yel brn 82.50 82.50
a. Without period 95.00 95.00
1L101 A19 10c on 25p grn .75 .75
a. Without period 2.25 2.25
b. "1" for "10" 7.50

1L102 A19 10c on 50p ver 11.00 11.00
a. Without period 16.50
b. "1" for "10" 22.50
Nos. 1L98-1L102 (5) 97.25 97.25

With Additional Overprint "1904"

1L103 A19 5c on 10p pink 14.00 14.00
a. Without period 24.00 24.00
b. "50" for "05" 110.00 110.00
1L104 A19 10c on 2p gray .75 .75
a. Without period 1.90
b. "1" for "10" 7.50
1L105 A19 10c on 25p grn 92.50
a. Without period 100.00
1L106 A19 10c on 50p ver 7.50 7.50
a. Without period 14.00
b. "1" for "10" 18.00
c. Inverted surcharge

The surcharges on Nos. 1L96 to 1L106 are in settings of twenty-five. One stamp in each setting has a large square period after "cts" and another has a thick upright "c" in that word. There are two types of "1904".

No. 293C Overprinted

B
Dpto. Zelaya

1911

1L107 A21 5c on 5c on 2c bl (R) 22.50
a. "5" omitted 27.50
b. Red overprint inverted 30.00
c. As "a" and "b" 37.50

Same Overprint On Nos. 290, 291, 292 and 289D with Lines of Surcharge spaced 2½mm apart Reading Down

1L107D A21 2c on 10c on 1c red
e. Overprint reading up
1L107F A21 5c on 10c on 1c red *92.50*
1L107G A21 10c on 10c on 1c red (#292) *125.00*
1L108 A21 10c on 10c on 1c red (#289D) *120.00*

There is no evidence that Nos. 1L107D-1L108 were issued by the government.

Locomotive — Z2

1912 **Engr.** *Perf. 14*

1L109 Z2 1c yel grn .75 .50
1L110 Z2 2c vermilion .50 .25
1L111 Z2 3c org brn .75 .45
1L112 Z2 4c carmine .75 .30
1L113 Z2 5c dp bl .75 .45
1L114 Z2 6c red brn 4.00 2.50
1L115 Z2 10c slate .75 .30
1L116 Z2 15c dl lil .75 .60
1L117 Z2 20c bl vio .75 .60
1L118 Z2 25c grn & blk 1.00 .80
1L119 Z2 35c brn & blk 1.25 1.00
1L120 Z2 50c ol grn 1.25 1.00
1L121 Z2 1p orange 1.75 1.50
1L122 Z2 2p org brn 4.00 3.00
1L123 Z2 5p dk bl grn 7.00 6.50
Nos. 1L109-1L123 (15) 26.00 19.75

The stamps of this issue were for use in all places on the Atlantic Coast of Nicaragua where the currency was on a silver basis.

For surcharges see Nos. 325-337.

OFFICIAL STAMPS

Regular Issue of 1909 Overprinted in Black

Oficial
B

1909 **Unwmk.** *Perf. 12*

1LO1 A18 20c brn ol 11.00 8.00
a. Double overprint 13.00

Official Stamp of 1909 Overprinted in Black *B*

1LO2 A18 15c black 11.00 6.50

Same Overprint on Official Stamp of 1911

1911

1LO3 A18 5c on 3c red org 16.00 13.00

CABO GRACIAS A DIOS

A cape and seaport town in the extreme northeast of Nicaragua. The name was coined by Spanish explorers who had great difficulty finding a landing place along the Nicaraguan coast and when eventually locating this harbor expressed their relief by designating the point "Cape Thanks to God." Special postage stamps came into use for the same reasons as the Zelaya issues. See Zelaya.

Dangerous counterfeits exist of most of the Cabo Gracias a Dios overprints.

Regular Issues of 1900-04 Handstamped in Violet **CABO**

On Engraved Stamps of 1900

1904-05 **Unwmk.** *Perf. 12, 14*

2L1 A14 1c plum 2.25 1.10
2L2 A14 2c vermilion 4.50 1.20
2L3 A14 3c green 6.00 4.50
2L4 A14 4c ol grn 9.75 9.75
2L5 A14 15c ultra 35.00 22.50
2L6 A14 20c brown 3.00 2.25
Nos. 2L1-2L6 (6) 60.50 41.30

On Lithographed Stamps of 1902

2L7 A14 5c blue 24.00 24.00
2L8 A14 10c violet 24.00 24.00

On Surcharged Stamps of 1904

2L9 A16 5c on 10c vio 22.50 22.50
2L10 A16 15c on 10c vio

On Postage Due Stamps
Violet Handstamp

2L11 D3 20c org brn (#141) 5.00 1.25
2L12 D3 20c org brn (#156) 3.50 1.25
2L13 D3 30c dk grn (#157) 14.00 14.00
2L14 D3 50c lake (#158) 3.75 .75
Nos. 2L11-2L14 (4) 26.25 17.25

Black Handstamp

2L15 D3 30c dk grn (#157) 24.00 24.00

Stamps of 1900-05 Handstamped in Violet ***Cabo***

On Engraved Stamps of 1900

2L16 A14 1c plum 2.75 2.25
2L17 A14 2c vermilion 27.50 24.00
2L18 A14 3c green 37.50 27.50
2L19 A14 4c ol grn 40.00 37.50
2L20 A14 15c ultra 45.00 45.00
Nos. 2L16-2L20 (5) 152.75 136.25

On Lithographed Stamps of 1902

2L22 A14 5c dk bl 95.00 50.00
2L23 A14 10c violet 27.50 24.00

On Surcharged Stamp of 1904

2L24 A16 5c on 10c vio

On Postage Due Stamp

2L25 D3 20c org brn (#141)

Cabo

The editors have no evidence that stamps with this handstamp were issued. Copies were sent to the UPU and covers are known.

Stamps of 1900-08 Handstamped in Violet **CÂBO**

1905

On Stamps of 1905

2L26 A18 1c green 1.10 1.10
2L27 A18 2c car rose 1.50 1.50
2L28 A18 3c violet 1.50 1.50
2L29 A18 4c org red 3.75 3.75
2L30 A18 5c blue 1.50 1.10
2L31 A18 6c slate 3.75 3.75
2L32 A18 10c yel brn 3.00 1.90
2L33 A18 15c brn ol 4.50 4.50
2L34 A18 1p black 20.00 20.00
2L35 A18 2p dk grn 35.00 35.00
Nos. 2L26-2L35 (10) 75.60 74.10

Magenta Handstamp

2L26a A18 1c 3.75 3.00
2L27a A18 2c 3.00 2.75
2L28a A18 3c 3.75 3.00
2L30a A18 5c 7.50 6.00
2L33a A18 15c 13.50 11.00
Nos. 2L26a-2L33a (5) 31.50 25.75

On Stamps of 1900-04

2L36 A16 5c on 10c vio 14.00 14.00
2L37 A14 10c violet
2L38 A14 20c brown 12.00 12.00
2L39 A14 20c on 5p blk 95.00

On Postage Due Stamps Overprinted "Correos"

2L40 D3 20c org brn (#141) 9.00 9.00
2L41 D3 20c org brn (#156) 5.00 4.50

On Surcharged Stamps of 1906-08

2L42 A18 10c on 3c vio
2L43 A18 20c on 5c blue 9.00 9.00
2L44 A18 50c on 6c slate 24.00 24.00

On Stamps of 1907

Perf. 14 to 15

2L44A A18 2c rose
2L45 A18 10c yel brn *100.00 75.00*
2L46 A18 15c brn ol *90.00 75.00*

On Provisional Stamp of 1908 in Magenta

2L47 A19 5c yel & blk 7.50 7.50

Stamps with the above large handstamp in black instead of violet, are bogus. There are also excellent counterfeits in violet.

The foregoing overprints being handstamped are found in various positions, especially the last type.

Stamps of 1907 Type A18, Overprinted in Black or Violet

"COSTA ATLANTICA"
C.

1907

2L48 A18 1c green .30 .30
2L49 A18 2c rose .30 .30
2L50 A18 3c violet .30 .30
a. Vert. pair, imperf. btwn. 15.00
2L51 A18 4c brn org .38 .38
2L52 A18 5c blue .50 .50
2L53 A18 10c yel brn .38 .38
2L54 A18 15c brn ol .75 .75
2L55 A18 20c lake .75 .75
2L56 A18 50c orange 1.90 1.50
2L57 A18 1p blk (V) 2.25 1.90
2L58 A18 2p dk grn 3.00 2.25
2L59 A18 5p violet 4.50 3.75
Nos. 2L48-2L59 (12) 15.31 13.06

Nos. 237-248 Overprinted in Black

C
Dpto. Zelaya

Imprint: American Bank Note Co.

1909 *Perf. 12*

2L60 A18 1c yel grn .35 .38
2L61 A18 2c vermilion .35 .38
2L62 A18 3c red org .35 .38
2L63 A18 4c violet .35 .38
2L64 A18 5c dp bl .35 .60
2L65 A18 6c gray brn 6.00 6.00
2L66 A18 10c lake .60 .75
2L67 A18 15c black .90 .90
2L68 A18 20c brn ol 1.00 1.10
2L69 A18 50c dp grn 2.50 2.50
2L70 A18 1p yellow 4.00 4.00
2L71 A18 2p car rose 5.75 5.75
Nos. 2L60-2L71 (12) 22.50 23.12

No. 199 Overprinted Vertically **CABO**

2L72 A18 50c on 6c slate (R) 7.50 7.50

OFFICIAL STAMPS

Official Stamps of 1907 Overprinted in Red or Violet **CÂBO**

1907

2LO1 A18 10c on 1c green *60.00*
2LO2 A18 15c on 1c green *75.00*
2LO3 A18 20c on 1c green *100.00*
2LO4 A18 50c on 1c green *125.00*
Nos. 2LO1-2LO4 (4) *1.45*

NIGER

'nī-jər

LOCATION — Northern Africa, directly north of Nigeria
GOVT. — Republic
AREA — 458,075 sq. mi.

POP. — 6,265,000 (est. 1984)
CAPITAL — Niamey

The colony, formed in 1922, was originally a military territory. The Republic of the Niger was proclaimed December 19, 1955. In the period between issues of the colony and the republic, stamps of French West Africa were used.

100 Centimes = 1 Franc

Catalogue values for unused stamps in this country are for Never Hinged items, beginning with Scott 91 in the regular postage section, Scott B14 in the semi-postal section, Scott C14 in the airpost section, Scott J22 in the postage due section, and Scott O1 in the official section.

Watermark

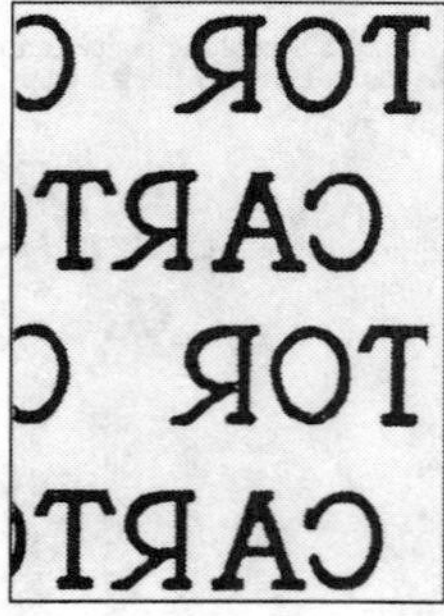

Wmk. 385

Camel and Rider — A1

Stamps of Upper Senegal and Niger Type of 1914, Overprinted

1921-26 Unwmk. Perf. 13½x14

1 A1 1c brn vio & vio .15 .15
2 A1 2c dk gray & dl vio .15 .15
3 A1 4c black & blue .15 .15
4 A1 5c ol brn & dk brn .15 .15
5 A1 10c yel grn & bl grn .65 .65
6 A1 10c mag, *bluish* ('26) .15 .15
7 A1 15c red brn & org .15 .15
8 A1 20c brn vio & blk .15 .15
9 A1 25c blk & bl grn .15 .15
10 A1 30c red org & rose .80 .80
11 A1 30c bl grn & red org ('26) .35 .35
12 A1 35c rose & violet .40 .40
13 A1 40c gray & rose .35 .35
14 A1 45c blue & ol brn .50 .50
15 A1 50c ultra & bl .40 .40
16 A1 50c dk gray & bl vio ('25) .35 .35
17 A1 60c org red ('26) .50 .50
18 A1 75c yel & ol brn .75 .75
19 A1 1fr dk brn & dl vio .75 .75
20 A1 2fr green & blue .80 .80
21 A1 5fr violet & blk 1.65 1.65
Nos. 1-21 (21) 9.45 9.45

Stamps and Type of 1921 Surcharged New Value and Bars in Black or Red

60 = 60

1922-26

22 A1 25c on 15c red brn & org ('25) .30 .30
a. Multiple surcharge 80.00
b. "25c" inverted 70.00
23 A1 25c on 2fr grn & bl (R) ('24) .35 .35
24 A1 25c on 5fr vio & blk (R) ('24) .35 .35
a. Double surcharge 80.00
25 A1 60c on 75c vio,*pnksh* .35 .35
26 A1 65c on 45c bl & ol brn ('25) 1.40 1.40
27 A1 85c on 75c yel & ol brn ('25) 1.50 1.50
28 A1 1.25fr on 1fr dp bl & lt bl (R) ('26) .25 .25
a. Surcharge omitted 140.00
Nos. 22-28 (7) 4.50 4.50

Nos. 22-24 are surcharged "25c," No. 28, "1f25." Nos. 25-27 are surcharged like illustration.

Drawing Water from Well — A2

Zinder Fortress — A4

Boat on Niger River — A3

Perf. 13x14, 13½x14, 14x13, 14x13½

1926-40 Typo.

29 A2 1c lilac rose & olive .15 .15
30 A2 2c dk gray & dl red .15 .15
31 A2 3c red vio & ol gray ('40) .15 .15
32 A2 4c amber & gray .15 .15
33 A2 5c ver & yel grn .15 .15
34 A2 10c dp bl & Prus bl .15 .15
35 A2 15c gray grn & yel grn .20 .20
36 A2 15c gray lil & lt red ('28) .15 .15
37 A3 20c Prus grn & ol brn .15 .15
38 A3 25c black & dl red .15 .15
39 A3 30c bl grn & yel grn .30 .30
40 A3 30c yel & red vio ('40) .15 .15
41 A3 35c brn org & turq bl, *bluish* .40 .40
42 A3 35c bl grn & dl grn ('38) .25 .25
43 A3 40c red brn & slate .15 .15
44 A3 45c yel & red vio .70 .70
45 A3 45c bl grn & dl grn ('40) .20 .20
46 A3 50c scar & grn,*grnsh* .15 .15
47 A3 55c dk car & brn ('38) .70 .70
48 A3 60c dk car & brn ('40) .20 .20
49 A3 65c ol grn & rose .15 .15
50 A3 70c ol grn & rose ('40) .75 .75
51 A3 75c grn & vio,*pink* .85 .75
52 A3 80c cl & ol grn ('38) .65 .65
53 A3 90c brn red & ver .65 .65
54 A3 90c brt rose & yel grn ('39) .75 .75
55 A4 1fr rose & yel grn 5.00 3.00
56 A4 1fr dk red & red org ('38) .50 .35
57 A4 1fr grn & red ('40) .30 .30
58 A4 1.10fr ol brn & grn 2.25 2.00
59 A4 1.25fr grn & red ('33) .85 .85
60 A4 1.25fr dk red & red org ('39) .25 .25
61 A4 1.40fr red vio & dk brn ('40) .25 .25
62 A4 1.50fr dp bl & pale bl .15 .15
63 A4 1.60fr ol brn & grn ('40) .65 .65
64 A4 1.75fr red vio & dk brn ('33) 1.65 1.65
65 A4 1.75fr dk bl & vio bl ('38) .50 .50
66 A4 2fr red org & ol brn .15 .15
67 A4 2.25fr dk bl & vio bl ('39) .55 .55
68 A4 2.50fr blk brn ('40) .35 .35
69 A4 3fr dl vio & blk ('27) .35 .35
70 A4 5fr vio brn & blk, *pink* .35 .35
71 A4 10fr chlky bl & mag 1.00 .90
72 A4 20fr yel grn & red org .90 .90
Nos. 29-72 (44) 24.55 21.95

For surcharges see Nos. B7-B10.

Common Design Types pictured following the introduction.

Colonial Exposition Issue
Common Design Types

1931 Typo. *Perf. 12½*
Name of Country in Black

73 CD70 40c deep green 2.25 2.25
74 CD71 50c violet 2.25 2.25
75 CD72 90c red orange 2.75 2.75
76 CD73 1.50fr dull blue 2.75 2.75
Nos. 73-76 (4) 10.00 10.00

Paris International Exposition Issue
Common Design Types

1937 *Perf. 13*

77 CD74 20c deep violet .75 .75
78 CD75 30c dark green .75 .75
79 CD76 40c carmine rose .75 .75
80 CD77 50c dark brown .75 .75
81 CD78 90c red 1.00 1.00
82 CD79 1.50fr ultra 1.00 1.00
Nos. 77-82 (6) 5.00 5.00

Colonial Arts Exhibition Issue
Souvenir Sheet
Common Design Type

1937 *Imperf.*

83 CD74 3fr magenta 3.00 3.00

Caillie Issue
Common Design Type

1939 *Perf. 12½x12*

84 CD81 90c org brn & org .50 .50
85 CD81 2fr brt violet .50 .50
86 CD81 2.25fr ultra & dk bl .50 .50
Nos. 84-86 (3) 1.50 1.50

New York World's Fair Issue
Common Design Type

1939, May 10

87 CD82 1.25fr carmine lake .50 .50
88 CD82 2.25fr ultra .50 .50

Zinder Fortress and Marshal Pétain — A5

1941 Unwmk. Engr. *Perf. 12x12½*

89 A5 1fr green .50
90 A5 2.50fr dark blue .50

Nos. 89-90 were issued by the Vichy government and were not placed on sale in the colony.

See French West Africa No. 68 for additional stamp inscribed "Niger" and "Afrique Occidentale Francaise."

Catalogue values for unused stamps in this section, from this point to the end of the section, are for Never Hinged items.

Republic of the Niger

Giraffes — A6

1fr, 2fr, Crested cranes. 5fr, 7fr, Saddle-billed storks. 15fr, 20fr, Barbary sheep. 25fr, 30fr, Giraffes. 50fr, 60fr, Ostriches. 85fr, 100fr, Lion.

1959-60 Unwmk. Engr. *Perf. 13*

91 A6 1fr multi .15 .15
92 A6 2fr multi .15 .15
93 A6 5fr blk, car & ol .15 .15
94 A6 7fr grn, blk & red .15 .15
95 A6 15fr grnsh bl & dk brn .18 .15
96 A6 20fr vio, blk & ind .20 .15
97 A6 25fr multi .22 .15
98 A6 30fr multi .28 .15
99 A6 50fr ind & org brn .50 .25
100 A6 60fr dk brn & emer .60 .35
101 A6 85fr org brn & bis .75 .40
102 A6 100fr bis & yel grn .90 .50
Nos. 91-102 (12) 4.23
Set value 2.00

Issue years: #97, 1959; others, 1960.
For surcharge see No. 103.

Imperforates

Most stamps of the republic exist imperforate in issued and trial colors, and also in small presentation sheets in issued color.

No. 102 Surcharged with New Value and: "Indépendance 3-8-60"

1960

103 A6 200fr on 100fr 4.00 4.00

Niger's independence.

C.C.T.A. Issue
Common Design Type

1960 Engr. *Perf. 13*

104 CD106 25fr buff & red brn .35 .30

Emblem of the Entente — A6a

Pres. Diori Hamani — A7

1960 Photo. *Perf. 13x13½*

105 A6a 25fr multi .35 .28

1st anniversary of the Entente (Dahomey, Ivory Coast, Niger and Upper Volta).

1960, Dec. 18 Engr. *Perf. 13*

106 A7 25fr ol bis & blk .22 .15

2nd anniversary of the proclamation of the Republic of the Niger.

Dugong — A8

1962, Jan. 29 Unwmk. *Perf. 13*

107 A8 50c grn & dk sl grn .15 .15
108 A8 10fr red brn & dk grn .15 .15
Set value .20 .15

Abidjan Games Issue
Common Design Type

25fr, Basketball & Soccer. 85fr, Track, horiz.

1962, May 26 Photo. *Perf. 12x12½*

109 CD109 15fr multi .15 .15
110 CD109 25fr multi .22 .15
111 CD109 85fr multi .65 .38
Nos. 109-111 (3) 1.02 .68

African-Malgache Union Issue
Common Design Type

1962, Sept. 8 *Perf. 12½x12*

112 CD110 30fr multi .30 .22

Pres. Diori Hamani and Map of Niger in Africa — A10

1962, Dec. 18 Photo. *Perf. 12½x12*

113 A10 25fr multi .22 .20

Woman Runner — A11

Woodworker — A12

15fr, Swimming, horiz. 45fr, Volleyball.

Unwmk.
1963, Apr. 11 Engr. *Perf. 13*

114 A11 15fr brt bl & dk brn .15 .15
115 A11 25fr dk brn & red .22 .15
116 A11 45fr grn & blk .38 .25
Nos. 114-116 (3) .75
Set value .46

Friendship Games, Dakar, Apr. 11-21.

Perf. 12x12½, 12½x12

1963, Aug. 30 **Photo.**

Designs: 10fr, Tanners, horiz. 25fr, Goldsmith. 30fr, Mat makers, horiz. 85fr, Decoy maker.

117 A12 5fr brn & multi .15 .15
118 A12 10fr dk grn & multi .15 .15
119 A12 25fr blk & multi .22 .15
120 A12 30fr vio & multi .28 .15
121 A12 85fr dk bl & multi .65 .40
Nos. 117-121,C26 (6) 2.25
Set value 1.20

Berberi (Nuba) Woman's Costume — A13

Costume Museum, Niamey — A14

Costumes: 20fr, Hausa woman. 25fr, Tuareg woman. 30fr, Tuareg man. 60fr, Djerma woman.

Perf. 12x12½, 12½x12

1963, Oct. 15 **Photo.**

122 A13 15fr multi .15 .15
123 A13 20fr blk & bl .18 .15
124 A13 25fr multi .25 .15
125 A13 30fr multi .28 .15
126 A13 60fr multi .60 .35
127 A14 85fr multi .70 .40
Nos. 122-127 (6) 2.16 1.35

Man, Globe and Scales — A15

Parkinsonia Aculeata — A16

Unwmk.

1963, Dec. 10 **Engr.** ***Perf. 13***

128 A15 25fr lt ol grn, ultra & brn org .25 .18

Issued to commemorate the 15th anniversary of the Universal Declaration of Human Rights.

1964-65 **Photo.** ***Perf. 13½x13***

Flowers: 10fr, Russelia equisetiformis. 15fr, Red sage (lantana). 20fr, Argyreia nervosa. 25fr, Luffa cylindrica. 30fr, Hibiscus rosa sinensis. 45fr, Red jasmine (frangipani). 50fr, Catharanthus roseus. 60fr, Caesalpinia pulcherrima.

129 A16 5fr dk red, grn & yel .25 .15
130 A16 10fr multi .20 .15
131 A16 15fr multi .28 .15
132 A16 20fr multi .28 .15
133 A16 25fr multi .28 .15
134 A16 30fr multi .40 .25
135 A16 45fr multi ('65) .48 .25
136 A16 50fr dk red, brt pink & grn ('65) .48 .25
137 A16 60fr multi ('65) .70 .35
Nos. 129-137 (9) 3.35 1.85

Solar Flares and IQSY Emblem — A17

1964, May 12 **Engr.** ***Perf. 13***

138 A17 30fr dp org, vio & blk .30 .22

International Quiet Sun Year, 1964-65.

Mobile Medical Unit — A18

30fr, Mobile children's clinic. 50fr, Mobile women's clinic. 60fr, Outdoor medical laboratory.

1964, May 26

139 A18 25fr bl, org & ol .25 .15
140 A18 30fr multi .28 .15
141 A18 50fr vio, org & bl .40 .18
142 A18 60fr grnsh bl, org & dk brn .48 .22
Nos. 139-142 (4) 1.41 .70

Nigerian mobile health education organization, OMNES (Organisation Médicale Mobile Nigérienne d'Education Sanitaire).

Cooperation Issue
Common Design Type

1964, Nov. 7 **Unwmk.** ***Perf. 13***

143 CD119 50fr vio, dk brn & org .40 .25

Tuareg Tent of Azawak A19

Designs: 20fr, Songhai house. 25fr, Wogo and Kourtey tents. 30fr, Djerma house. 60fr, Huts of Sorkawa fishermen. 85fr, Hausa town house.

1964-65 **Engr.**

144 A19 15fr ultra, dl grn & red brn .15 .15
145 A19 20fr multi .18 .15
146 A19 25fr Prus bl, dk brn & org brn .20 .15
147 A19 30fr multi ('65) .22 .15
148 A19 60fr red, grn & bis ('65) .40 .18
149 A19 85fr multi ('65) .60 .30
Nos. 144-149 (6) 1.75 1.08

Leprosy Examination A20

Abraham Lincoln A21

1964, Dec. 15 **Photo.** ***Perf. 13x12½***

150 A20 50fr multi .35 .28

Issued to publicize the fight against leprosy.

1965, Apr. 3 ***Perf. 13x12½***

151 A21 50fr vio bl, blk, & ocher .40 .35

Centenary of death of Abraham Lincoln.

Teaching with Radio and Pictures — A22

Designs: 25fr, Woman studying arithmetic: "A better life through knowledge." 30fr, Adult education class. 50fr, Map of Niger and 5 tribesmen, "Literacy for adults."

1965, Apr. 16 **Engr.** ***Perf. 13***

152 A22 20fr dk bl, dk brn & ocher .20 .15
153 A22 25fr sl grn, brn & ol brn .25 .15
154 A22 30fr red, sl grn & vio brn .28 .15
155 A22 50fr dp bl, brn & vio brn .45 .20
Nos. 152-155 (4) 1.18 .65

Issued to promote adult education and "a better life through knowledge."

Ader Portable Telephone A23

Runner A24

Designs: 30fr, Wheatstone telegraph interrupter. 50fr, Early telewriter.

1965, May 17 **Unwmk.** ***Perf. 13***

156 A23 25fr red brn, dk grn & ind .25 .15
157 A23 30fr lil, slate grn & red .28 .15
158 A23 50fr red, slate grn & pur .40 .25
Nos. 156-158 (3) .93 .55

International Telecommunication Union, cent.

1965, July 1 **Engr.** ***Perf. 13***

Designs: 10fr, Hurdler, horiz. 20fr, Pole vaulter, horiz. 30fr, Long jumper.

159 A24 10fr brn, ocher & blk .15 .15
160 A24 15fr gray, brn & red .18 .15
161 A24 20fr dk grn, brn & vio bl .20 .15
162 A24 30fr maroon, brn & grn .28 .15
Nos. 159-162 (4) .81
Set value .34

African Games, Brazzaville, July 18-25.

Radio Interview and Club Emblem A25

45fr, Recording folk music, vert. 50fr, Group listening to broadcast, vert. 60fr, Public debate.

1965, Oct. 1 **Engr.** ***Perf. 13***

163 A25 30fr brt vio, emer & red brn .25 .15
164 A25 45fr blk, car & buff .35 .15
165 A25 50fr dk car, bl & lt brn .38 .18
166 A25 60fr bis, ultra & brn .45 .22
Nos. 163-166 (4) 1.43 .70

Issued to promote radio clubs.

Water Cycle — A26

1966, Feb. 28 **Engr.** ***Perf. 13***

167 A26 50fr vio, ocher & bl .40 .22

Hydrological Decade, 1965-74.

Carvings, Mask and Headdresses A27

50fr, Carvings and wall decorations. 60fr, Carvings and arch. 100fr, Architecture and handicraft.

1966, Apr. 12

168 A27 30fr red brn, blk & brt grn .25 .15
169 A27 50fr brt bl, ocher & pur .40 .20
170 A27 60fr car lake, dl pur & yel brn .50 .25
171 A27 100fr brt red, bl & blk .80 .35
Nos. 168-171 (4) 1.95 .95

Intl. Negro Arts Festival, Dakar, Senegal, Apr. 1-24.

Soccer Player — A28

Color Guard — A29

50fr, Goalkeeper, horiz. 60fr, Player kicking ball.

1966, June 17 **Engr.** ***Perf. 13***

172 A28 30fr dk brn, brt bl & rose red .30 .15
173 A28 50fr bl, choc & emer .40 .15
174 A28 60fr bl, lil & brn .50 .25
Nos. 172-174 (3) 1.20 .55

8th World Soccer Cup Championship, Wembley, England, July 11-30.

Perf. 12½x13, 13x12½

1966, Aug. 23 **Photo.**

20fr, Parachutist, horiz. 45fr, Tanks, horiz.

175 A29 20fr multi .20 .15
176 A29 30fr multi .25 .15
177 A29 45fr multi .35 .22
Nos. 175-177 (3) .80 .52
Set value .44

5th anniversary of the National Armed Forces.

Cow Receiving Injection A30

1966, Sept. 26 **Litho.** ***Perf. 12½x13***

178 A30 45fr org brn, bl & blk .35 .18

Campaign against cattle plague.

UNESCO Emblem — A31

1966, Nov. 4 **Litho.** ***Perf. 13x12½***

179 A31 50fr multi .48 .18

20th anniversary of UNESCO.

Cement Works Malbaza A32

Designs: 10fr, Furnace, vert. 20fr, Electric center. 50fr, Handling of raw material.

1966, Dec. 17 **Engr.** ***Perf. 13***

180 A32 10fr ind, brn & org .15 .15
181 A32 20fr dk ol grn & dl bl .22 .15
182 A32 30fr bl, gray & red brn .28 .15
183 A32 50fr ind, bl & brn .40 .15
Nos. 180-183 (4) 1.05
Set value .36

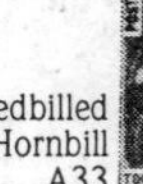

Redbilled Hornbill A33

Birds: 2fr, Pied kingfisher. 30fr, Barbary shrike. 45fr, 65fr, Little weaver and nest.

1967 Engr. *Perf. 13*

184 A33 1fr red, sl grn & dk brn .15 .15
185 A33 2fr brn, brt grn & blk .15 .15
186 A33 30fr multi .25 .15
187 A33 45fr multi .30 .15
188 A33 65fr multi ('81) .28 .18
189 A33 70fr multi .42 .30
Set value 1.30 .82

Issued: 45fr, 70fr, 11/18; others, 2/8. See #237.

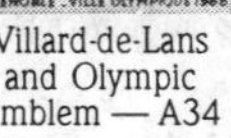

Villard-de-Lans and Olympic Emblem — A34

Lions Emblem and Family — A35

Olympic Emblem and Mountains: 45fr, Autrans and ski jump. 60fr, Saint Nizier du Moucherotte and ski jump. 90fr, Chamrousse and course for downhill and slalom races.

1967, Feb. 24

190 A34 30fr grn, ultra & brn .22 .15
191 A34 45fr grn, ultra & brn .35 .40
192 A34 60fr grn, ultra & brn .42 .22
193 A34 90fr grn, ultra & brn .65 .35
Nos. 190-193 (4) 1.64 1.12

10th Winter Olympic Games, Grenoble, 1968.

1967, Mar. 4

194 A35 50fr dk grn, brn red & ultra .40 .22

Lions International, 50th anniversary.

ITY Emblem, Views, Globe and Plane — A36

1967, Apr. 28 Engr. *Perf. 13*

195 A36 45fr vio, brt grn & red lil .35 .22

International Tourist Year, 1967.

1967 Jamboree Emblem and Scouts — A37

Red Cross Aides Carrying Sick Man — A38

Designs (Jamboree Emblem and): 45fr, Scouts gathering from all directions, horiz. 80fr, Campfire.

1967, May 25 Engr. *Perf. 13*

196 A37 30fr mar, Prus bl & ol .22 .15
197 A37 45fr org, vio bl & brn ol .32 .20
198 A37 80fr multi .60 .35
Nos. 196-198 (3) 1.14 .70

Issued to publicize the 12th Boy Scout World Jamboree, Farragut State Park, Idaho, Aug. 1-9.

1967, July 13 Engr. *Perf. 13*

Designs: 50fr, Nurse, mother and infant. 60fr, Physician examining woman.

199 A38 45fr blk, grn & car .32 .15
200 A38 50fr grn, blk & car .38 .18
201 A38 60fr blk, grn & car .42 .20
Nos. 199-201 (3) 1.12 .53

Issued for the Red Cross.

Europafrica Issue, 1967

Map of Europe and Africa — A39

1967, July 20 Photo. *Perf. 12½x12*

202 A39 50fr multi .40 .20

Women and UN Emblem — A40

1967, Oct. 21 Engr. *Perf. 13*

203 A40 50fr brn, brt bl & yel .38 .22

UN Commission on Status of Women.

Monetary Union Issue
Common Design Type

1967, Nov. 4 Engr. *Perf. 13*

204 CD125 30fr grn & dk gray .22 .15

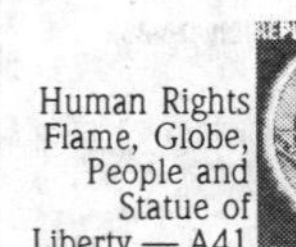

Human Rights Flame, Globe, People and Statue of Liberty — A41

1968, Feb. 19 Engr. *Perf. 13*

205 A41 50fr brn, indigo & brt bl .35 .20

International Human Rights Year.

Woman Dancing and WHO Emblem — A42

1968, Apr. 8 Engr. *Perf. 13*

206 A42 50fr brt bl, blk & red brn .35 .22

20th anniv. of WHO.

Gray Hornbill A43

Birds: 10fr, Woodland kingfisher. 15fr, Senegalese coucal. 20fr, Rose-ringed parakeets. 25fr, Abyssinian roller. 50fr, Cattle egret.

Dated "1968"

1968, Nov. 15 Photo. *Perf. 12½x13*

207 A43 5fr dk grn & multi .15 .15
208 A43 10fr grn & multi .15 .15
209 A43 15fr bl vio & multi .15 .15
210 A43 20fr pink & multi .15 .15
211 A43 25fr ol & multi .18 .15
212 A43 50fr pur & multi .30 .18
Set value .82 .55

See Nos. 233-236, 316.

ILO Emblem and "Labor Supporting the World" — A44

1969, Apr. 22 Engr. *Perf. 13*

213 A44 30fr yel grn & dk car .22 .15
214 A44 50fr dk car & yel grn .35 .22

50th anniv. of the World Labor Organization.

Red Crosses, Mother and Child — A45

Designs: 50fr, People, globe, red crosses, horiz. 70fr, Man with gift parcel and red crosses.

1969, May 5 Engr. *Perf. 13*

215 A45 45fr bl, red & brn ol .30 .18
216 A45 50fr dk grn, red & gray .35 .18
217 A45 70fr ocher, red & dk brn .42 .28
Nos. 215-217 (3) 1.07 .64

50th anniv. of the League of Red Cross Societies.

Mouth and Ear — A46

1969, May 20 Photo. *Perf. 12½x12*

218 A46 100fr multi .65 .40

First (cultural) Conference of French-speaking Community at Niamey.

National Administration College — A47

1969, July 8 Photo. *Perf. 12½x12*

219 A47 30fr emer & dp org .18 .15

Development Bank Issue
Common Design Type

1969, Sept. 10 Engr. *Perf. 13*

220 CD130 30fr pur, grn & ocher .20 .15

ASECNA Issue
Common Design Type

1969, Dec. 12 Engr. *Perf. 12*

221 CD132 100fr car rose .65 .40

Classical Pavilion, National Museum A48

Pavilions, National Museum: 45fr, Temporary exhibitions. 50fr, Audio-visual. 70fr, Nigerian musical instruments. 100fr, Craftsmanship.

1970, Feb. 23 Engr. *Perf. 13*

222 A48 30fr brt bl, sl grn & brn .20 .15
223 A48 45fr emer, Prus bl & brn .28 .15
224 A48 50fr sl grn, vio bl & brn .32 .15
225 A48 70fr brn, sl grn & lt bl .45 .25
226 A48 100fr sl grn, vio bl & brn .65 .35
Nos. 222-226 (5) 1.90 1.05

Map of Africa and Vaccination Gun — A49

1970, Mar. 31 Engr. *Perf. 13*

227 A49 50fr ultra, dp yel grn & mag .30 .18

Issued to commemorate the 100 millionth smallpox vaccination in West Africa.

Mexican Figurine and Soccer Player — A50

Designs: 70fr, Figurine, globe and soccer ball. 90fr, Figurine and 2 soccer players.

1970, Apr. 25

228 A50 40fr dk brn, red lil & emer .28 .18
229 A50 70fr red brn, bl & plum .40 .28
230 A50 90fr blk & red .60 .40
Nos. 228-230 (3) 1.28 .86

9th World Soccer Championship for the Jules Rimet Cup, Mexico City, May 29-June 21.

UPU Headquarters Issue
Common Design Type

1970, May 20 Engr. *Perf. 13*

231 CD133 30fr brn, dk gray & dk red .22 .15
232 CD133 60fr vio bl, dk car & vio .35 .18

Bird Types of 1967-68

Birds: 5fr, Gray hornbill. 10fr, Woodland kingfisher. 15fr, Senegalese coucal. 20fr, Rose-ringed parakeets. 40fr, Red bishop.

Dated "1970"

1970-71 Photo. *Perf. 13*

233 A43 5fr multi ('71) .15 .15
234 A43 10fr multi ('71) .15 .15
235 A43 15fr multi ('71) .15 .15
236 A43 20fr multi ('71) .20 .15

Engr.

237 A33 40fr multi .30 .22
Set value .75 .50

Issue dates: 40fr, Dec. 9; others Jan. 4.

World Map with Niamey in Center — A51

1971, Mar. 3 Photo. *Perf. 12½x12*

238 A51 40fr brn & multi .28 .15

First anniversary of founding of the cooperative agency of French-speaking countries.
For overprint see No. 289.

Scout Emblem, Merit Badges, Mt. Fuji, Japanese Flag — A52

Designs: 40fr, Boy Scouts and flags, vert. 45fr, Map of Japan, Boy Scouts and compass rose, vert. 50fr, Tent and "Jamboree."

1971, July 5 Engr. *Perf. 13*

239 A52 35fr rose lil, dp car & org .22 .15
240 A52 40fr dk pur, grn & mar .25 .15
241 A52 45fr ultra, cop red & grn .28 .18
242 A52 50fr multi .30 .18
Nos. 239-242 (4) 1.05 .66

13th Boy Scout World Jamboree, Asagiri Plain, Japan, Aug. 2-10.

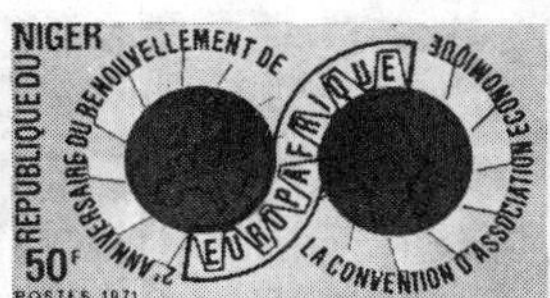
Maps of Europe and Africa — A53

1971, July 29 Photo. Perf. 13x12
243 A53 50fr lt bl & multi .35 .18

Renewal of the agreement on economic association between Europe and Africa, 2nd anniv.

Broad-tailed Whydah A54

1971, Aug. 17 Perf. 12½x12
244 A54 35fr yel grn & multi .32 .20

See No. 443.

Garaya, Haoussa — A55

UNICEF Emblem, Children of 4 Races — A56

Stringed Instruments of Niger: 25fr, Gouroumi, Haoussa. 30fr, Molo, Djerma. 40fr, Godjie, Djerma-Sonrai. 45fr, Inzad, Tuareg. 50fr, Kountigui, Sonrai.

1971-72 Engr. Perf. 13
245 A55 25fr red, emer & brn .18 .15
246 A55 30fr emer, pur & brn .20 .15
247 A55 35fr brn red, emer & ind .18 .15
248 A55 40fr emer, org & dk brn .20 .15
249 A55 45fr Prus bl, grn & bis .25 .18
250 A55 50fr blk, red & brn .32 .20
Nos. 245-250 (6) 1.33
Set value .78

Issue dates: 35fr, 40fr, 45fr, Oct. 13, 1971; others, June 16, 1972.

1971, Dec. 11 Photo. Perf. 11
251 A56 50fr multi .32 .25

25th anniversary of UNICEF.

Star with Globe, Book, UNESCO Emblem A57

Design: 40fr, Boy reading, UNESCO emblem, sailing ship, plane, mosque.

1972, Mar. 27 Engr. Perf. 13
252 A57 35fr mag & emer .22 .15
253 A57 40fr dk car & Prus bl .25 .15
Set value .24

International Book Year 1972.

Cattle Egret — A58

1972, July 31 Photo. Perf. 12½x12
254 A58 50fr tan & multi .38 .22

See No. 425.

Cattle at Salt Pond of In-Gall — A59

1972, Aug. 25 Perf. 13
255 A59 35fr shown .22 .15
256 A59 40fr Cattle wading in pond .25 .15
Set value .24

Salt cure for cattle.
For surcharge see No. 282.

Lottery Drum — A60

1972, Sept. 18
257 A60 35fr multi .22 .15

6th anniversary of the national lottery.

West African Monetary Union Issue
Common Design Type

Design: 40fr, African couple, city, village and commemorative coin.

1972, Nov. 2 Engr. Perf. 13
258 CD136 40fr brn, lil & gray .25 .15

Dromedary Race — A61

Design: 40fr, Horse race.

1972, Dec. 15 Engr. Perf. 13
259 A61 35fr brt bl, dk red & brn .22 .15
260 A61 40fr sl grn, mar & brn .28 .15

Pole Vault, Map of Africa — A62

Knight, Pawn, Chessboard — A63

Map of Africa and: 40fr, Basketball. 45fr, Boxing. 75fr, Soccer.

1973, Jan. 15 Engr. Perf. 13
261 A62 35fr claret & multi .20 .15
262 A62 40fr grn & multi .22 .15
263 A62 45fr red & multi .25 .18
264 A62 75fr dk bl & multi .38 .25
Nos. 261-264 (4) 1.05 .73

2nd African Games, Legos, Nigeria, Jan. 7-18.

1973, Feb. 16 Engr. Perf. 13
265 A63 100fr dl red, sl grn & bl .55 .35

World Chess Championship, Reykjavik, Iceland, July-Sept. 1972.

Abutilon Pannosum A64

Interpol Emblem A65

Rare African Flowers: 45fr, Crotalaria barkae. 60fr, Dichrostachys cinerea. 80fr, Caralluma decaisneana.

1973, Feb. 26 Photo. Perf. 12x12½
266 A64 30fr dk vio & multi .18 .15
267 A64 45fr red & multi .25 .15
268 A64 60fr ultra & multi .32 .22
269 A64 80fr ocher & multi .40 .25
Nos. 266-269 (4) 1.15 .77

1973, Mar. 13 Typo. Perf. 13x12½
270 A65 50fr brt grn & multi .25 .15

50th anniversary of International Criminal Police Organization (INTERPOL).

Dr. Hansen, Microscope and Petri Dish — A66

Nurse Treating Infant, UN and Red Cross Emblems — A67

1973, Mar. 29 Engr. Perf. 13
271 A66 50fr vio bl, sl grn & dk brn .28 .15

Centenary of the discovery by Dr. Armauer G. Hansen of the Hansen bacillus, the cause of leprosy.

1973, Apr. 3 Engr. Perf. 13
272 A67 50fr red, bl & brn .25 .15

25th anniversary of WHO.

Crocodile A68

Animals from W National Park: 35fr, Elephant. 40fr, Hippopotamus. 80fr, Wart hog.

1973, June 5 Typo. Perf. 12½x13
273 A68 25fr gray & blk .18 .15
274 A68 35fr blk, gold & gray .22 .15
275 A68 40fr red, lt bl & blk .25 .15
276 A68 80fr multi .40 .22
Nos. 273-276 (4) 1.05
Set value .56

Eclipse over Mountains A69

1973, June 21 Engr. Perf. 13
277 A69 40fr dk vio bl .22 .18

Solar eclipse, June 30, 1973.

Palominos — A70

Horses: 75fr, French trotters. 80fr, English thoroughbreds. 100fr, Arabian thoroughbreds.

1973, Aug. 1 Photo. Perf. 13x12½
278 A70 50fr ultra & multi .28 .15
279 A70 75fr gray & multi .38 .20
280 A70 80fr emer & multi .45 .25
281 A70 100fr ocher & multi .55 .30
Nos. 278-281 (4) 1.66 .90

No. 255 Surcharged with New Value, 2 Bars, and Overprinted in Ultramarine: "SECHERESSE/SOLIDARITE AFRICAINE"

1973, Aug. 16 Perf. 13
282 A59 100fr on 35fr multi .50 .35

African solidarity in drought emergency.

Diesel Engine and Rudolf Diesel — A71

Designs: Various Diesel locomotives.

1973, Sept. 7 Perf. 13x12½
283 A71 25fr gray, choc & Prus bl .15 .15
284 A71 50fr sl bl, gray & dk grn .25 .15
285 A71 75fr red lil, sl bl & gray .38 .28
286 A71 125fr brt grn, vio bl & car .60 .38
Nos. 283-286 (4) 1.38 .96

Rudolf Diesel (1858-1913), inventor of an internal combustion engine, later called Diesel engine.

African Postal Union Issue
Common Design Type

1973, Sept. 12 Engr. Perf. 13
287 CD137 100fr ol, dk car & sl grn .55 .35

TV Set, Map of Niger, Children A72

1973, Oct. 1 Engr. Perf. 13
288 A72 50fr car, ultra & brn .25 .18

Educational television.

Type of 1971 Overprinted

3e CONFERENCE DE LA FRANCOPHONIE
LIEGE
OCTOBRE 1973

1973, Oct. 12 Photo. Perf. 13
289 A51 40fr red & multi .25 .15

3rd Conference of French-speaking countries, Liège, Sept. 15-Oct. 14.

Apollo of Belvedère — A73

Classic Sculpture: No. 291, Venus of Milo. No. 292, Hercules. No. 293, Atlas.

1973, Oct. 15 Engr.
290 A73 50fr brn & sl grn .32 .20
291 A73 50fr rose car & pur .32 .20
292 A73 50fr red brn & dk brn .32 .20
293 A73 50fr red brn & blk .32 .20
Nos. 290-293 (4) 1.28 .80

Beehive, Bees and Globes — A74

1973, Oct. 31 Engr. Perf. 13
294 A74 40fr dl red, ocher & dl bl .22 .15

World Savings Day.

Tcherka Songhai Blanket — A75

Design: 35fr, Kounta Songhai blanket, vert.

Perf. 12½x13, 13x12½

1973, Dec. 17 **Photo.**

295 A75 35fr brn & multi .25 .15

296 A75 40fr brn & multi .25 .18

Textiles of Niger.

WPY Emblem, Infant and Globe — A76

1974, Mar. 4 **Engr.** ***Perf. 13***

297 A76 50fr multi .25 .15

World Population Year 1974.

Locomotives, 1938 and 1948 — A77

1974, May 24 **Engr.** ***Perf. 13***

298 A77 50fr shown .25 .18

299 A77 75fr Locomotive, 1893 .35 .22

300 A77 100fr Locomotives, 1866 and 1939 .48 .35

301 A77 150fr *Locomotives, 1829* .70 .55

Nos. 298-301 (4) 1.78 1.30

Map and Flags of Members A78

1974, May 29 **Photo.** ***Perf. 13x12½***

302 A78 40fr bl & multi .20 .15

15th anniversary of the Council of Accord.

Marconi Sending Radio Signals to Australia — A79

1974, July 1 **Engr.** ***Perf. 13***

303 A79 50fr pur, bl & dk brn .25 .18

Centenary of the birth of Guglielmo Marconi (1874-1937), Italian inventor and physicist.

Hand Holding Sapling — A80

Camel Saddle — A81

1974, Aug. 2 **Engr.** ***Perf. 13***

304 A80 35fr multi .18 .15

National Tree Week.

1974, Aug. 20 **Engr.** ***Perf. 13***

Design: 50fr, 3 sculptured horses, horiz.

305 A81 40fr ol brn, bl & red .20 .15

306 A81 50fr ol brn, bl & red .25 .15

Set value .22

Chopin and Polish Eagle — A82

Design: No. 308, Ludwig van Beethoven and allegory of Ninth Symphony.

1974

307 A82 100fr multi .48 .28

308 A82 100fr multi .48 .28

125th anniversary of the death of Frederic Chopin (1810-1849), composer and 150th anniversary of Beethoven's Ninth Symphony, composed 1823.

Issue dates: #307, Sept. 4; #308, Sept. 19.

Don-Don Drum — A83

1974, Nov. 12 **Engr.** ***Perf. 13***

309 A83 60fr multi .30 .18

Tenere Tree, Compass Rose and Caravan — A84

1974, Nov. 24 **Engr.** ***Perf. 13***

310 A84 50fr multi .30 .20

Tenere tree, a landmark in Sahara Desert, first death anniversary.

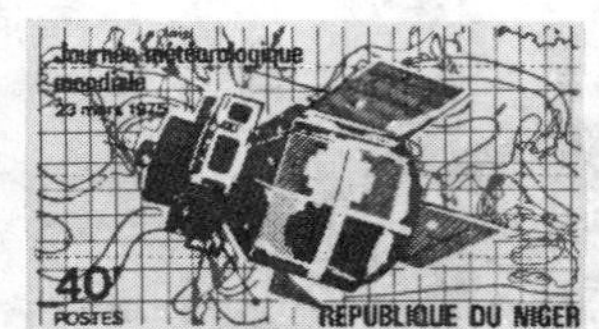

Satellite over World Weather Map — A85

1975, Mar. 23 **Litho.** ***Perf. 13***

311 A85 40fr bl, blk & red .20 .15

World Meteorological Day, Mar. 23, 1975.

"City of Truro," English, 1903 — A86

Locomotives and Flags: 75fr, "5.003," Germany, 1937. 100fr, "The General," United States, 1863. 125fr, "Electric BB 15.000," France, 1971.

1975, Apr. 24 **Typo.** ***Perf. 13***

312 A86 50fr org & multi .25 .18

313 A86 75fr yel grn & multi .35 .22

314 A86 100fr lt bl & multi .48 .32

315 A86 125fr multi .65 .40

Nos. 312-315 (4) 1.73 1.12

Bird Type of 1968 Dated "1975"

1975, Apr. **Photo.** ***Perf. 13***

316 A43 25fr ol & multi .15 .15

Zabira Leather Bag — A87

Handicrafts: 40fr, Damier tapestry. 45fr, Vase. 60fr, Gourd flask.

1975, May 28 **Litho.** ***Perf. 12½***

317 A87 35fr dp bl & multi .18 .15

318 A87 40fr dp grn & multi .20 .15

319 A87 45fr brn & multi .22 .30

320 A87 60fr dp org & multi .28 .18

Nos. 317-320 (4) .88 .78

Mother and Child, IWY Emblem — A88

1975, June 9 **Engr.** ***Perf. 13***

321 A88 50fr claret, brn & bl .25 .18

International Women's Year 1975.

Dr. Schweitzer and Lambarene Hospital — A89

1975, June 23 **Engr.** ***Perf. 13***

322 A89 100fr brn, grn & blk .42 .28

Dr. Albert Schweitzer (1875-1965), medical missionary.

Peugeot, 1892 — A90

Early Autos: 75fr, Daimler, 1895. 100fr, Fiat, 1899. 125fr, Cadillac, 1903.

1975, July 16 **Engr.** ***Perf. 13***

323 A90 50fr rose & vio bl .22 .15

324 A90 75fr bl & vio brn .21 .20

325 A90 100fr brt grn & mag .40 .28

326 A90 125fr brick red & brt grn .55 .30

Nos. 323-326 (4) 1.38 .93

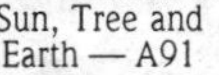

Sun, Tree and Earth — A91

Boxing — A92

1975, Aug. 2 **Engr.** ***Perf. 13***

327 A91 40fr multi .20 .15

National Tree Week.

1975, Aug. 25 **Engr.** ***Perf. 13***

Designs: 35fr, Boxing, horiz. 45fr, Wrestling, horiz. 50fr, Wrestling.

328 A92 35fr blk, org & brn .18 .15

329 A92 40fr bl grn, brn & blk .20 .15

330 A92 45fr blk, brt bl & brn .22 .15

331 A92 50fr red, brn & blk .25 .18

Nos. 328-331 (4) .85 .63

Lion's Head Tetradrachma, Leontini, 460 B.C. — A93

Greek Coins: 75fr, Owl tetradrachma, Athens, 500 B.C. 100fr, Crab diadrachma, Himera, 480 B.C. 125fr, Minotaur tetradrachma, Gela, 460 B.C.

1975, Sept. 12 **Engr.** ***Perf. 13***

332 A93 50fr red, dl bl & blk .22 .15

333 A93 75fr lil, brt bl & blk .32 .22

334 A93 100fr bl, org & blk .42 .28

335 A93 125fr grn, pur & blk .55 .32

Nos. 332-335 (4) 1.51 .97

Starving Family — A94

45fr, Animal skeletons. 60fr, Truck bringing food.

1975, Oct. 21 **Engr.** ***Perf. 13x12½***

336 A94 40fr multi .20 .18

337 A94 45fr ultra & brn .22 .15

338 A94 60fr grn, org & dk bl .28 .15

Nos. 336-338 (3) .70 .48

Fight against drought.

Niger River Crossing — A95

Designs: 45fr, Entrance to Boubon camp. 50fr, Camp building.

1975, Nov. 10 **Litho.** ***Perf. 12½***

339 A95 40fr multi .18 .15

340 A95 45fr multi .20 .15

341 A95 50fr multi .22 .15

Nos. 339-341 (3) .60 .45

Tourist publicity.

Teacher and Pupils — A96

Each stamp has different inscription in center.

1976, Jan. 12 Photo. *Perf. 13*

342 A96 25fr ol & multi .15 .15
343 A96 30fr vio bl & multi .15 .15
344 A96 40fr multi .18 .15
345 A96 50fr multi .22 .15
346 A96 60fr multi .25 .18
Nos. 342-346 (5) .95
Set value .65

Literacy campaign 1976.
For overprints see Nos. 371-375.

12th Winter Olympic Games, Innsbruck — A97

1976, Feb. 20 Litho. *Perf. 14x13½*

347 A97 40fr Ice hockey .20 .15
348 A97 50fr Luge .28 .15
349 A97 150fr Ski jump .75 .35
Nos. 347-349,C266-C267 (5) 3.73 1.70

Satellite, Telephone, ITU Emblem — A98

1976, Mar. 10 Litho. *Perf. 13*

350 A98 100fr org, bl & vio bl .42 .28

Centenary of first telephone call by Alexander Graham Bell, Mar. 10, 1876.

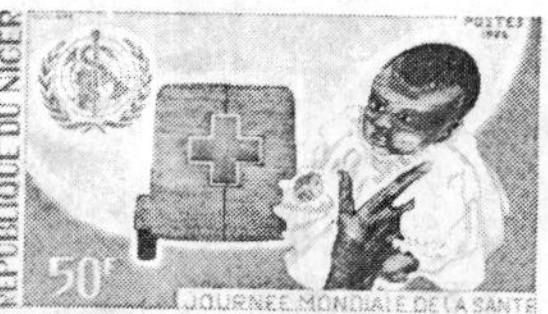

WHO Emblem, Red Cross Truck, Infant — A99

1976, Apr. 7 Engr. *Perf. 13*

351 A99 50fr multi .22 .15

World Health Day 1976.

Statue of Liberty and Washington Crossing the Delaware — A100

Design: 50fr, Statue of Liberty and call to arms.

1976, Apr. 8 Litho. *Perf. 14x13½*

352 A100 40fr multi .20 .15
353 A100 50fr multi .25 .15
Nos. 352-353,C269-C271 (5) 3.55 1.80

American Bicentennial.

The Army Helping in Development — A101

Design: 50fr, Food distribution, vert.

Perf. 12½x13, 13x12½

1976, Apr. 15 Litho.

354 A101 50fr multi .22 .15
355 A101 100fr multi .42 .28

National Armed Forces, 2nd anniv. of take-over.

Europafrica Issue 1976

Maps, Concorde, Ship and Grain — A102

1976, June 9 Litho. *Perf. 13*

356 A102 100fr multi .42 .28

Road Building A103

Design: 30fr, Rice cultivation.

1976, June 26 *Perf. 12½*

357 A103 25fr multi .15 .15
358 A103 30fr multi .15 .15
Set value .18

Community labor.

Motobecane 125, France — A104

Motorcycles: 75fr, Norton Challenge, England. 100fr, BMW 90 S, Germany. 125fr, Kawasaki 1000, Japan.

1976, July 16 Engr. *Perf. 13*

359 A104 50fr vio bl & multi .22 .15
360 A104 75fr dp grn & multi .21 .25
361 A104 100fr dk brn & multi .42 .35
362 A104 125fr slate & multi .55 .35
Nos. 359-362 (4) 1.40 1.10

Boxing A105

Designs: 50fr, Basketball. 60fr, Soccer. 80fr, Cycling, horiz. 100fr, Judo, horiz.

1976, July 17 Litho. *Perf. 14*

363 A105 40fr multi .22 .15
364 A105 50fr multi .28 .15
365 A105 60fr multi .35 .15
366 A105 80fr multi .40 .18
367 A105 100fr multi .50 .25
Nos. 363-367 (5) 1.75 .88

21st Summer Olympic games, Montreal. See No. C279.

Map of Niger, Planting Seedlings A106

Designs: 50fr, Woman watering seedling, vert. 60fr, Women planting seedlings, vert.

1976, Aug. 1 Litho. *Perf. 12½x13*

368 A106 40fr org & multi .18 .15
369 A106 50fr yel & multi .22 .18
370 A106 60fr grn & multi .28 .18
Nos. 368-370 (3) .68 .51

Reclamation of Sahel Region.

Nos. 342-346 Overprinted: "JOURNEE / INTERNATIONALE / DE L'ALPHABETISATION"

1976, Sept. 8 Photo. *Perf. 13*

371 A96 25fr ol & multi .15 .15
372 A96 30fr vio bl & multi .15 .15
373 A96 40fr multi .20 .15
374 A96 50fr multi .22 .15
375 A96 60fr multi .28 .15
Nos. 371-375 (5) 1.00
Set value .55

Literacy campaign.

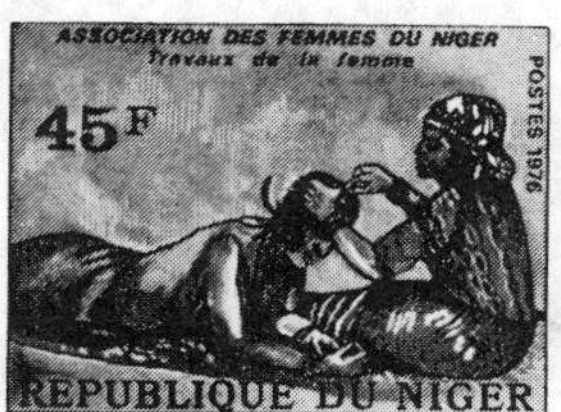

Hairdresser — A107

Designs: 40fr, Woman weaving straw, vert. 50fr, Women potters, vert.

1976, Oct. 6 *Perf. 13*

376 A107 40fr buff & multi .18 .15
377 A107 45fr bl & multi .20 .15
378 A107 50fr red & multi .22 .15
Nos. 376-378 (3) .60 .45

Niger Women's Association.

Rock Carvings A108

Archaeology: 50fr, Neolithic sculptures. 60fr, Dinosaur skeleton.

1976, Nov. 15 Photo. *Perf. 13x12½*

379 A108 40fr blk, sl & yel .18 .15
380 A108 50fr blk, red & bis .22 .15
381 A108 60fr bis, blk & brn .28 .15
Nos. 379-381 (3) .68 .45

Benin Head — A109

Weaver, Dancers and Musicians — A110

1977, Jan. 15 Engr. *Perf. 13*

382 A109 40fr dk brn .20 .15
383 A110 50fr gray bl .22 .15

2nd World Black and African Festival, Lagos, Nigeria, Jan. 15-Feb. 12.

First Aid, Student, Blackboard and Plow — A111

Midwife — A112

Designs: Inscriptions on blackboard differ on each denomination.

1977, Jan. 23 Photo. *Perf. 12½x13*

384 A111 40fr multi .18 .15
385 A111 50fr multi .22 .15
386 A111 60fr multi .28 .15
Nos. 384-386 (3) .68
Set value .38

Literacy campaign.

1977, Feb. 23 Litho. *Perf. 13*

Design: 50fr, Midwife examining newborn.

387 A112 40fr multi .18 .15
388 A112 50fr multi .22 .15
Set value .24

Village health service.

Titan Rocket Launch A113

Design: 80fr, Viking orbiter near Mars, horiz.

1977, Mar. 15 Litho. *Perf. 14*

389 A113 50fr multi .28 .15
390 A113 80fr multi .40 .20
Nos. 389-390,C283-C285 (5) 2.93 1.37

Viking Mars project.
For overprints see #497-498, C295-C297.

Marabous A114

Design: 90fr, Harnessed antelopes.

1977, Mar. 18 Engr. *Perf. 13*
391 A114 80fr multi .38 .22
392 A114 90fr multi .40 .25

Nature protection.

Weather Map, Satellite, WMO Emblem A115

1977, Mar. 23
393 A115 100fr multi .40 .28

World Meteorological Day.

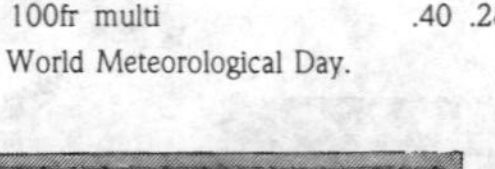

Group Gymnastics — A116

Designs: 50fr, High jump. 80fr, Folk singers.

1977, Apr. 7 Litho. *Perf. 13x12½*
394 A116 40fr dl yel & multi .20 .15
395 A116 50fr bl & multi .22 .15
396 A116 80fr org & multi .35 .18
Nos. 394-396 (3) .77 .48

2nd Tahoua Youth Festival, Apr. 7-14.

Red Cross, WHO Emblems and Children — A117

1977, Apr. 25 Engr. *Perf. 13*
397 A117 80fr lil, org & red .35 .22

World Health Day: "Immunization means protection of your children."

Eye with WHO Emblem, and Sword Killing Fly — A118

1977, May 7
398 A118 100fr multi .42 .28

Fight against onchocerciasis, a roundworm infection, transmitted by flies, causing blindness.

Guirka Tahoua Dance A119

50fr, Mailfilafili Gaya. 80fr, Naguihinayan Loga.

1977, June 7 Photo. *Perf. 13x12½*
399 A119 40fr multi .18 .15
400 A119 50fr multi .22 .15
401 A119 80fr multi .35 .20
Nos. 399-401 (3) .75 .50

Popular arts and traditions.

Cavalry — A120

Traditional chief's cavalry, different groups.

1977, July 7 Litho. *Perf. 13x12½*
402 A120 40fr multi .18 .15
403 A120 50fr multi .22 .15
404 A120 60fr multi .28 .15
Nos. 402-404 (3) .68 .45

Planting and Cultivating — A121

1977, Aug. 10
405 A121 40fr multi .18 .15

Reclamation of Sahel Region.

Albert John Luthuli Peace — A122

Designs: 80fr, Maurice Maeterlinck, literature. 100fr, Allan L. Hodgkin, medicine. 150fr, Albert Camus, literature. 200fr, Paul Ehrlich, medicine.

1977, Aug. 20 Litho. *Perf. 14*
406 A122 50fr multi .28 .15
407 A122 80fr multi .28 .18
408 A122 100fr multi .50 .20
409 A122 150fr multi .75 .28
410 A122 200fr multi 1.00 .40
Nos. 406-410 (5) 2.81 1.21

Nobel prize winners. See No. C287.

Mao Tse-tung — A123

1977, Sept. 9 Engr. *Perf. 13*
411 A123 100fr blk & red .42 .28

Argentina '78 Emblem, Soccer Players and Coach, Vittorio Pozzo, Italy — A124

Designs (Argentina '78 emblem, soccer players and coach): 50fr, Vincente Feola, Spain. 80fr, Aymore Moreira, Portugal. 100fr, Sir Alf Ramsey, England. 200fr, Helmut Schoen, Germany. 500fr, Sepp Herberger, Germany.

1977, Oct. 12 Litho. *Perf. 13½*
412 A124 40fr multi .20 .15
413 A124 50fr multi .28 .15
414 A124 80fr multi .40 .20
415 A124 100fr multi .55 .25
416 A124 200fr multi 1.10 .40
Nos. 412-416 (5) 2.53 1.15

Souvenir Sheet

417 A124 500fr multi 2.50 1.10

World Cup Soccer championship, Argentina '78. For overprints see Nos. 453-458.

Horse's Head, Parthenon and UNESCO Emblem — A125

1977, Nov. 12 Engr. *Perf. 13*
418 A125 100fr multi .42 .28

Woman Carrying Water Pots — A126

Design: 50fr, Women pounding corn.

1977, Nov. 23 Photo. *Perf. 12½x13*
419 A126 40fr multi .18 .15
420 A126 50fr red & multi .22 .15
Set value .22

Niger Women's Association.

Crocodile's Skull, 100 Million Years Old — A127

Design: 80fr, Neolithic flint tools.

1977, Dec. 14 *Perf. 13*
421 A127 50fr multi .22 .15
422 A127 80fr multi .35 .22

Raoul Follereau and Lepers A128

40fr, Raoul Follereau and woman leper, vert.

1978, Jan. 28 Engr. *Perf. 13*
423 A128 40fr multi .18 .15
424 A128 50fr multi .22 .15

25th anniversary of Leprosy Day. Follereau (1903-1977) was "Apostle to the Lepers" and educator of the blind.

Bird Type of 1972 Redrawn

1978, Feb. Photo. *Perf. 13*
425 A58 50fr tan & multi .22 .15

No. 425 is dated "1978" and has only designer's name in imprint. No. 254 has printer's name also.

Assumption, by Rubens A129

Rubens Paintings: 70fr, Rubens and Friends, horiz. 100fr, History of Marie de Medici. 150fr, Alathea Talbot and Family. 200fr, Marquise de Spinola. 500fr, Virgin and St. Ildefonso.

1978, Feb. 25 Litho. *Perf. 14*
426 A129 50fr multi .28 .15
427 A129 70fr multi .32 .18
428 A129 100fr multi .50 .22
429 A129 150fr multi .75 .35
430 A129 200fr multi 1.10 .42
Nos. 426-430 (5) 2.95 1.32

Souvenir Sheet
Perf. 13½

431 A129 500fr gold & multi 2.50 1.10

Peter Paul Rubens (1577-1640), 400th birth anniversary.

Shot Put — A130

1978, Mar. 22 Photo. *Perf. 13*
432 A130 40fr shown .18 .15
433 A130 50fr Volleyball .22 .15
434 A130 60fr Long jump .28 .15
435 A130 100fr Javelin .42 .28
Nos. 432-435 (4) 1.10 .73

Natl. University Games' Championships.

First Aid and Red Crosses A131

1978, May 13 **Litho.**
436 A131 40fr red & multi .18 .15

Niger Red Cross.

Goudel Earth Station A132

1978, May 23
437 A132 100fr multi .45 .28

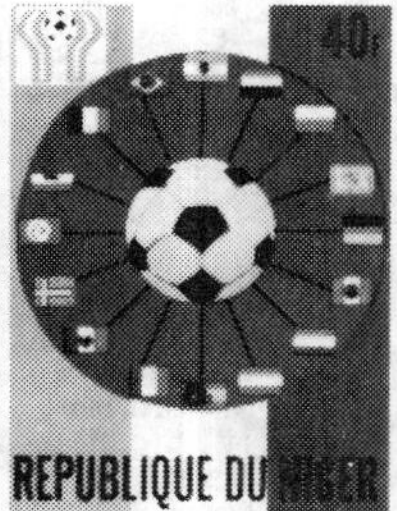

Soccer Ball, Flags of Participants A133

Argentina '78 Emblem and: 50fr, Ball in net. 100fr, Globe with South America, Soccer field. 200fr, Two players, horiz. 300fr, Player and globe.

1978, June 18 **Litho.** ***Perf. 13½***
438 A133 40fr multi .20 .15
439 A133 50fr multi .30 .18
440 A133 100fr multi .50 .35
441 A133 200fr multi 1.00 .60
Nos. 438-441 (4) 2.00 1.28

Souvenir Sheet

442 A133 300fr multi 1.60 .90

11th World Cup Soccer Championship, Argentina, June 1-25.

Bird Type of 1971 Redrawn

1978, June **Photo.** ***Perf. 13***
443 A54 35fr bl & multi .18 .15

No. 443 has no year date, nor Delrieu imprint.

Post Office, Niamey — A134

Design: 60fr, Post Office, different view.

1978, Aug. 12 **Litho.**
444 A134 40fr multi .18 .15
445 A134 60fr multi .28 .15

Goudel Water Works A135

1978, Sept. 25 **Photo.** ***Perf. 13***
446 A135 100fr multi .42 .28

Giraffe — A136

Animals and Wildlife Fund Emblem: 50fr, Ostrich. 70fr, Cheetah. 150fr, Oryx, horiz. 200fr, Addax, horiz. 300fr, Hartebeest, horiz.

1978, Nov. 20 **Litho.** ***Perf. 15***
447 A136 40fr multi .20 .15
448 A136 50fr multi .28 .15
449 A136 70fr multi .35 .20
450 A136 150fr multi .75 .40
451 A136 200fr multi 1.00 .55
452 A136 300fr multi 1.50 .80
Nos. 447-452 (6) 4.08 2.25

Endangered species.

Nos. 412-417 Overprinted in Silver
a. "EQUIPE QUATRIEME: ITALIE"
b. "EQUIPE TROISIEME: BRESIL"
c. "EQUIPE / SECONDE: / PAYS BAS"
d. "EQUIPE VAINQUEUR: ARGENTINE"
e. "ARGENTINE-PAYS BAS 3-1"

1978, Dec. 1 ***Perf. 13½***
453 A124(a) 40fr multi .18 .15
454 A124(b) 50fr multi .22 .15
455 A124(c) 80fr multi .35 .22
456 A124(d) 100fr multi .42 .28
457 A124(e) 200fr multi .85 .55
Nos. 453-457 (5) 2.02 1.35

Souvenir Sheet

458 A124(e) 500fr multi 2.25 .90

Winners, World Soccer Cup Championship, Argentina, June 1-25.

Tinguizi — A137

Musicians: No. 460, Dan Gourmou. No. 461, Chetima Ganga, horiz.

1978, Dec. 11 **Litho.** ***Perf. 13***
459 A137 100fr multi .42 .28
460 A137 100fr multi .42 .28
461 A137 100fr multi .42 .28
Nos. 459-461 (3) 1.26 .84

Virgin Mary, by Dürer — A138

50fr, The Homecoming, by Honoré Daumier (1808-79). 150fr, 200fr, 500fr, Virgin and Child, by Albrecht Dürer (1471-1528), diff.

1979, Jan. 31 **Litho.** ***Perf. 13½***
462 A138 50fr multi .30 .15
463 A138 100fr multi .50 .30
464 A138 150fr multi .75 .40
465 A138 200fr multi 1.00 .55
Nos. 462-465 (4) 2.55 1.40

Souvenir Sheet

466 A138 500fr multi 2.50 1.10

Solar Panels and Tank — A139

Design: 40fr, Tank and panels on roof, vert.

Perf. 12½x12, 12x12½
1979, Feb. 28
467 A139 40fr multi .18 .15
468 A139 50fr multi .22 .15

Hot water from solar heat.

Children with Building Blocks — A140

Children and IYC Emblem: 100fr, Reading books. 150fr, With model plane.

1979, Apr. 10 **Litho.** ***Perf. 13½***
469 A140 40fr multi .22 .15
470 A140 100fr multi .50 .28
471 A140 150fr multi .75 .40
Nos. 469-471 (3) 1.47 .83

International Year of the Child.

The Langa, Traditional Sport A141

Design: 50fr, The langa, diff.

1979, Apr. 10 **Litho.** ***Perf. 12½x12***
472 A141 40fr multi .18 .15
473 A141 50fr multi .22 .15

Rowland Hill, Mail Truck and France No. 8 — A142

Designs (Hill and): 100fr, Canoes and Austria #P4. 150fr, Air Niger plane and US #122. 200fr, Streamlined mail train and Canada type A6. 400fr, Electric train and Niger #51.

1979, June 6 **Litho.** ***Perf. 14***
474 A142 40fr multi .18 .15
475 A142 100fr multi .42 .28
476 A142 150fr multi .65 .40
477 A142 200fr multi .85 .55
Nos. 474-477 (4) 2.10 1.38

Souvenir Sheet

478 A142 400fr multi 1.90

Sir Rowland Hill (1795-1879), originator of penny postage.

Zabira Handbag and Niger No. 135 — A143

Design: 150fr, Heads with communications waves, world map, UPU emblem and satellite.

1979, June 8 **Litho.** ***Perf. 12x12½***
479 A143 50fr multi .22 .15

Engr. ***Perf. 13***
480 A143 150fr brt red & ultra .65 .80

Philexafrique II, Libreville, Gabon, June 8-17. Nos. 479, 480 each printed in sheets of 10 and 5 labels showing exhibition emblem.

Djermakoye Palace — A144

1979, Sept. 26 **Litho.** ***Perf. 13x12½***
481 A144 100fr multi .42 .28

Bororo Festive Headdress — A145

60fr, Bororo women's traditional costumes.

Perf. 13x12½, 12½x13
1979, Sept. 26
482 A145 45fr multi .20 .15
483 A145 60fr multi, vert. .25 .18

Annual Bororo Festival.

Olympic Emblem, Flame and Boxers — A146

Designs: 100fr, 150fr, 250fr, 500fr, Olympic emblem, flame and boxers, diff.

1979, Oct. 6 ***Perf. 13½***
484 A146 45fr multi .20 .15
485 A146 100fr multi .42 .28
486 A146 150fr multi .65 .40
487 A146 250fr multi 1.10 .65
Nos. 484-487 (4) 2.37 1.48

Souvenir Sheet

488 A146 500fr multi 2.50 1.50

Pre-Olympic Year.

John Alcock, Arthur Whitten Brown, Vickers-Vimy Biplane — A147

1979, Sept. 3 *Perf. 13½*
489 A147 100fr multi .45 .30

First Transatlantic flight, 60th anniversary.

Road and Traffic Safety — A148

1979, Nov. 20 Litho. *Perf. 12½*
490 A148 45fr multi .20 .15

Four-Man Bobsledding, Lake Placid '80 Emblem — A149

Lake Placid '80 Emblem and: 60fr, Downhill skiing. 100fr, Speed skating. 150fr, Two-man bobsledding. 200fr, Figure skating. 300fr, Cross-country skiing.

1979, Dec. 10 *Perf. 14½*
491 A149 40fr multi .18 .15
492 A149 60fr multi .25 .18
493 A149 100fr multi .42 .30
494 A149 150fr multi .65 .40
495 A149 200fr multi .90 .55
Nos. 491-495 (5) 2.40 1.58

Souvenir Sheet

496 A149 300fr multi 1.40 .90

13th Winter Olympic Games, Lake Placid, NY, Feb. 12-24, 1980.
For overprints see Nos. 501-506.

Nos. 389, 390 Overprinted in Silver or Black "alunissage/apollo XI/juillet 1969" and Emblem

1979, Dec. 20 Litho. *Perf. 14*
497 A113 50fr multi (S) .22 .15
498 A113 80fr multi .35 .22
Nos. 497-498,C295-C296 (4) 2.07 1.32

Apollo 11 moon landing, 10th anniv. See #C297.

Court of Sultan of Zinder A150

1980, Mar. 25 Litho. *Perf. 13x12½*
499 A150 45fr shown .20 .15
500 A150 60fr Sultan's court, diff. .25 .18

Nos. 491-496 Overprinted
a. VAINQUEUR/R.D.A.
b. VAINQUEUR/STENMARK/SUEDE
c. VAINQUEUR/HEIDEN/Etats-Unis
d. VAINQUEURS/SCHAERER-BENZ/ Suisse
e. VAINQUEUR/COUSINS/ Grande Bretagne
f. VAINQUEUR/ZIMIATOV/U.R.S.S.

1980, Mar. 31 Litho. *Perf. 14½*
501 A149 (a) 40fr multi .18 .15
502 A149 (b) 60fr multi .25 .18
503 A149 (c) 100fr multi .45 .28
504 A149 (d) 150fr multi .65 .40
505 A149 (e) 200fr multi .90 .55
Nos. 501-505 (5) 2.43 1.56

Souvenir Sheet

506 A149 (f) 300fr multi 1.25 .80

Javelin, Olympic Rings — A151

Man Smoking Cigarette, Runner — A152

1980, Apr. 17
507 A151 60fr shown .25 .18
508 A151 90fr Walking .38 .25
509 A151 100fr High jump, horiz. .42 .28
510 A151 300fr Marathon runners, horiz. 1.25 .80
Nos. 507-510 (4) 2.30 1.51

Souvenir Sheet

511 A151 500fr High jump, diff. 2.25 1.40

22nd Summer Olympic Games, Moscow, July 19-Aug. 3.
For overprints see Nos. 527-531.

1980, Apr. 7 *Perf. 13*
512 A152 100fr multi .42 .28

World Health Day; fight against cigarette smoking.

Health Year — A153

1980, May 15 Photo. *Perf. 13x12½*
513 A153 150fr multi .65 .40

Shimbashi-Yokohama Locomotive — A154

1980, June Litho. *Perf. 12½*
514 A154 45fr shown .20 .15
515 A154 60fr American type .25 .18
516 A154 90fr German Reichsbahn series 61 .40 .25
517 A154 100fr Prussian Staatsbahn P2 .42 .28
518 A154 130fr L'Aigle .55 .35
Nos. 514-518 (5) 1.82 1.21

Souvenir Sheet

519 A154 425fr Stephenson's Rocket 1.80 1.10

For overprint see No. 674.

Steve Biko, 4th Anniversary of Death — A155

1980, Sept. 12 Litho. *Perf. 13*
520 A155 150fr org & blk .65 .40

Soccer Players — A156

Designs: Various soccer scenes.

1980, Oct. 15 *Perf. 12½*
521 A156 45fr multi .20 .15
522 A156 60fr multi .25 .18
523 A156 90fr multi .38 .25
524 A156 100fr multi .42 .28
525 A156 130fr multi .55 .35
Nos. 521-525 (5) 1.80 1.21

Souvenir Sheet

526 A156 425fr multi 1.90 1.10

World Soccer Cup 1982.

Nos. 507-511 Overprinted in Gold with Winner's Name and Country

1980, Sept. 27 Litho. *Perf. 14½*
527 A151 60fr multi .25 .18
528 A151 90fr multi .38 .25
529 A151 100fr multi .45 .30
530 A151 300fr multi 1.25 .80
Nos. 527-530 (4) 2.33 1.53

Souvenir Sheet

531 A151 500fr multi 2.25 1.40

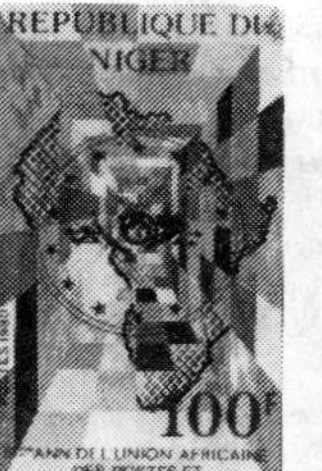

African Postal Union, 5th Anniversary A157

Terra Cotta Kareygorou Head A158

1980, Dec. 24 Photo. *Perf. 13½*
532 A157 100fr multi .45 .30

1981, Jan. 23 Litho. *Perf. 13*

Designs: Terra Cotta Kareygorou Statues, 5th-12th cent. 45fr, 150fr, horiz.

533 A158 45fr multi .20 .15
534 A158 60fr multi .25 .18
535 A158 90fr multi .40 .25
536 A158 150fr multi .65 .40
Nos. 533-536 (4) 1.50 .98

Ostrich — A159

1981, Mar. 17 Litho. *Perf. 12½*
537 A159 10fr shown .15 .15
538 A159 20fr Oryx .15 .15
539 A159 25fr Gazelle .15 .15
540 A159 30fr Great bustard .15 .15
541 A159 60fr Giraffe .25 .18
542 A159 150fr Addax .65 .40
Nos. 537-542 (6) 1.50
Set value .85

7th Anniv. of the F.A.N. — A160

1981, Apr. 14 Litho. *Perf. 13*
543 A160 100fr multi .45 .30

One-armed Archer — A161

1981, Apr. 24 Engr.
544 A161 50fr shown .22 .15
545 A161 100fr Draftsman .42 .28

Intl. Year of the Disabled.

Scene from Mahalba Ballet, 1980 Youth Festival, Dosso — A162

1981, May 17 Litho.
546 A162 100fr shown .42 .28
547 A162 100fr Ballet, diff. .42 .28

Prince Charles and Lady Diana, Coach A163

Designs: Couple and coaches.

1981, July 15 Litho. *Perf. 14½*
548 A163 150fr multi .65 .40
549 A163 200fr multi .85 .55
550 A163 300fr multi 1.25 .80
Nos. 548-550 (3) 2.75 1.75

Souvenir Sheet

551 A163 400fr multi 1.75 1.10

Royal wedding.
For overprints see Nos. 595-598.

Hegira 1500th Anniv. A164

Alexander Fleming (1881-1955) A165

1981, July 15 *Perf. 13½x13*
552 A164 100fr multi .45 .30

1981, Aug. 6 Engr. *Perf. 13*
553 A165 150fr multi .65 .40

25th Intl. Letter Writing Week, Oct. 6-12 — A167

1981, Oct. 9 **Surcharged in Black**

554 A167 65fr on 40fr multi .30 .18
555 A167 85fr on 60fr multi .35 .25

Nos. 554-555 not issued without surcharge.

World Food Day — A168

1981, Oct. 16 **Litho.**

556 A168 100fr multi .42 .30

Espana '82 World Cup Soccer A169

Designs: Various soccer players.

1981, Nov. 18 **Litho.** ***Perf. 14x13½***

557 A169 40fr multi .18 .15
558 A169 65fr multi .28 .18
559 A169 85fr multi .35 .22
560 A169 150fr multi .65 .40
561 A169 300fr multi 1.25 .80
Nos. 557-561 (5) 2.71 1.75

Souvenir Sheet

562 A169 500fr multi 2.25 1.40

For overprints see Nos. 603-608.

75th Anniv. of Grand Prix A170

Designs: Winners and their cars.

1981, Nov. 30 ***Perf. 14***

563 A170 20fr Peugeot, 1912 .15 .15
564 A170 40fr Bugatti, 1924 .18 .15
565 A170 65fr Lotus-Climax, 1962 .28 .18
566 A170 85fr Georges Boillot, 1912 .35 .22
567 A170 150fr Phil Hill, 1960 .65 .40
Nos. 563-567 (5) 1.61 1.10

Souvenir Sheet

568 A170 450fr Race 2.00 1.25

For overprint see No. 675.

Christmas 1981 — A171

Designs: Virgin and Child paintings.

1981, Dec. 24

569 A171 100fr Botticelli .42 .26
570 A171 200fr Botticini .85 .55
571 A171 300fr Botticelli, diff. 1.25 .80
Nos. 569-571 (3) 2.52 1.61

School Gardens A172

1982, Feb. 19 **Litho.** ***Perf. 13x13½***

572 A172 65fr shown .28 .18
573 A172 85fr Garden, diff. .35 .22

Fruit on a Table, by Edouard Manet (1832-1883) — A173

Anniversaries: 120fr, Arturo Toscanini (1867-1957), vert. 200fr, L'Estaque, by Georges Braque (1882-1963). 300fr, George Washington (1732-99), vert. 400fr, Goethe (1749-1832), vert. Nos. 579-580, 21st birthday of Diana, Princess of Wales (portraits), vert.

1982, Mar. 8 **Litho.** ***Perf. 13***

574 A173 120fr multi .55 .35
575 A173 140fr multi .65 .38
576 A173 200fr multi .85 .55
577 A173 300fr multi 1.25 .80
578 A173 400fr multi 1.75 1.10
579 A173 500fr multi 2.25 1.40
Nos. 574-579 (6) 7.30 4.58

Souvenir Sheet

580 A173 500fr multi 2.25 1.40

Palace of Congress — A174

1982, Mar. 17

581 A174 150fr multi .65 .40

7th Youth Festival, Agadez — A175

Reafforestation Campaign — A176

1982, Apr. 7 ***Perf. 12½***

582 A175 65fr Martial arts, horiz. .28 .18
583 A175 100fr Wrestling .42 .28

1982, Apr. 16 ***Perf. 13***

584 A176 150fr Tree planting .65 .40
585 A176 200fr Trees, Desert .85 .55

For overprints see Nos. 668-669.

Scouting Year A177

1982, May 13

586 A177 65fr Canoeing .28 .18
587 A177 85fr Scouts in rubber boat .35 .22
588 A177 130fr Canoeing, diff. .55 .35
589 A177 200fr Rafting .85 .55
Nos. 586-589 (4) 2.03 1.30

Souvenir Sheet

590 A177 400fr Beach scene 1.75 1.10

For overprint see No. 673.

13th Meeting of Islamic Countries Foreign Affairs Ministers, Niamey, Aug. 20-27 A178

1982, June 6

591 A178 100fr multi .42 .28

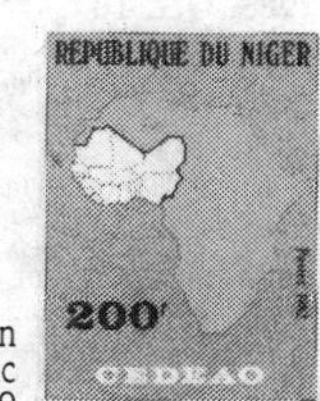

West African Economic Community — A179

1982, June 28

592 A179 200fr Map .85 .55

Fishermen in Canoe A180

1982, July 18 ***Perf. 13x12½***

593 A180 65fr shown .28 .18
594 A180 85fr Bringing in nets .35 .22

Nos. 548-551 Overprinted in Blue: "NAISSANCE ROYALE 1982"

1982, Aug. 4 ***Perf. 14½***

595 A163 150fr multi .65 .40
596 A163 200fr multi .85 .55
597 A163 300fr multi 1.25 .80
Nos. 595-597 (3) 2.75 1.75

Souvenir Sheet

598 A163 400fr multi 1.75 1.10

Flautist, by Norman Rockwell A181

1982, Sept. 10 **Litho.** ***Perf. 14***

599 A181 65fr shown .28 .18
600 A181 85fr Clerk .35 .22
601 A181 110fr Teacher and Pupil .48 .30
602 A181 150fr Girl Shopper .65 .40
Nos. 599-602 (4) 1.76 1.10

Nos. 557-562 Overprinted with Past and Present Winners in Black on Silver

1982, Sept. 28 ***Perf. 14x13½***

603 A169 40fr multi .18 .15
604 A169 65fr multi .28 .18
605 A169 85fr multi .35 .22
606 A169 150fr multi .65 .40
607 A169 300fr multi 1.25 .80
Nos. 603-607 (5) 2.71 1.75

Souvenir Sheet

608 A169 500fr multi 2.25 1.40

Italy's victory in 1982 World Cup.

ITU Plenipotentiaries Conference, Nairobi, Sept. — A182

1982, Sept. 28 ***Perf. 13***

609 A182 130fr black & blue .55 .35

Laboratory Workers A183

Various laboratory workers.

1982, Nov. 9 **Litho.** ***Perf. 13***

610 A168 65fr multi .30 .18
611 A183 115fr multi .50 .30

Self-sufficiency in Food Production A184

1983, Feb. 16 **Litho.** ***Perf. 13½x13***

612 A184 65fr Rice harvest .28 .18
613 A184 85fr Planting rice, vert. .35 .22

Grand Ducal Madonna, by Raphael A185

Raphael Paintings: 65fr, Miraculous Catch of Fishes. 100fr, Deliverance of St. Peter. 150fr, Sistine Madonna. 200fr, Christ on the Way to Calvary. 300fr, Deposition. 400fr, Transfiguration. 500fr, St. Michael Slaying the Dragon.

1983, Mar. 30 **Litho.** ***Perf. 14***

614 A185 65fr multi, vert. .28 .18
615 A185 85fr multi .35 .22
616 A185 100fr multi, vert. .42 .26
617 A185 150fr multi .65 .40
618 A185 200fr multi .85 .55
619 A185 300fr multi, vert. 1.25 .80
620 A185 400fr multi 1.75 1.10
621 A185 500fr multi 2.25 1.30
Nos. 614-621 (8) 7.80 4.81

African Economic Commission, 25th Anniv. — A186

1983, Mar. 18 *Perf. 12½x13*

622 A186 120fr multi .55 .32
623 A186 200fr multi .85 .55

Army Surveyors A187

1983, Apr. 14 *Perf. 13x12½*

624 A187 85fr shown .35 .22
625 A187 150fr Road building .65 .40

Agadez Court — A188

1983, Apr. 26 Litho. *Perf. 13x12½*

626 A188 65fr multi .28 .18

Mail Van — A189

1983, June 25 **Litho.**

627 A189 65fr Van .28 .18
628 A189 100fr Van, map .42 .25

Palestine Solidarity — A190

1983, Aug. 21 Litho. *Perf. 12½*

629 A190 65fr multi .28 .18

Intl. Literacy Year — A191

Various adult education classes. 65fr, 150fr vert.

Perf. 13½x14½, 14½x13½

1983, Sept. 8 **Litho.**

630 A191 40fr multi .15 .15
631 A191 65fr multi .15 .15
632 A191 85fr multi .18 .15
633 A191 100fr multi .22 .15
634 A191 150fr multi .32 .18
Nos. 630-634 (5) 1.02
Set value .58

7th Ballet Festival of Dosso Dept. A192

Various dancers.

1983, Oct. 7 *Perf. 14½x13½*

635 A192 65fr multi .15 .15
636 A192 85fr multi .18 .15
637 A192 120fr multi .25 .16
Nos. 635-637 (3) .58
Set value .36

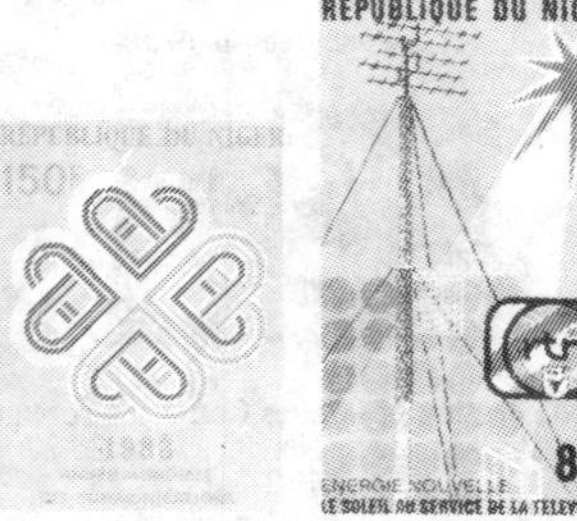

A193 A194

Perf. 13x12½, 12½x13

1983, Oct. 18

638 A193 80fr Post Office, mail van .16 .15
639 A193 120fr Sorting mail .25 .16
640 A193 150fr Emblem, vert. .32 .20
Nos. 638-640 (3) .73 .51

World Communications Year.

1983, Nov. 26 *Perf. 13*

641 A194 85fr Antenna .18 .15
642 A194 130fr Car .28 .18

Solar energy for television.

Local Butterflies — A195

1983, Dec. 9 *Perf. 12½*

643 A195 75fr Hypolimnas misippus .18 .15
644 A195 120fr Papilio demodocus .32 .16
645 A195 250fr Vanessa antiopa .70 .35
646 A195 350fr Charesex jasius .90 .45
647 A195 500fr Danaus chrisippus 1.40 .65
Nos. 643-647 (5) 3.50 1.76

SAMARIYA Natl. Development Movement — A196

1984, Jan. 18 Litho. *Perf. 13x13½*

648 A196 80fr multi .16 .15

Alestes Bouboni A197

1984, Mar. 28 Litho. *Perf. 13*

649 A197 120fr multi .32 .15

Military Pentathlon A198

1984, Apr. 10

650 A198 120fr Hurdles .32 .15
651 A198 140fr Shooting .36 .16

Radio Broadcasting Building Opening A199

1984, May 14 Litho. *Perf. 13*

652 A199 120fr multi .32 .15

25th Anniv. of Council of Unity — A200

1984, May 29 *Perf. 12½*

653 A200 65fr multi .18 .15
654 A200 85fr multi .22 .15
Set value .18

Renault, 1902 — A201

Vintage cars (#656, 658, 660, 662) & ships.

1984, June 12 *Perf. 12½*

655 A201 80fr Paris .22 .15
656 A201 100fr Gottlieb Daimler .28 .15
657 A201 120fr Three-master Jacques Coeur .32 .15
658 A201 140fr shown .36 .16
659 A201 150fr Barque Bosphorus .38 .18
660 A201 250fr Delage D8 .65 .35
661 A201 300fr Three-master Comet .80 .36
662 A201 400fr Maybach Zeppelin 1.10 .48
Nos. 655-662 (8) 4.11 1.98

1984 UPU Congress A202

1984, June 20 Engr. *Perf. 13x12½*

663 A202 300fr Ship, emblems .80 .35

Ayerou Market Place — A203

1984, July 18 Litho. *Perf. 12½*

664 A203 80fr shown .22 .15
665 A203 120fr River scene .32 .16

Vipere Echis Leucogaster — A204

1984, Aug. 16 *Perf. 13x12½*

666 A204 80fr multi .22 .15

West African Union, CEAO, 10th Anniv. A205

1984, Oct. 26 Litho. *Perf. 13½*

667 A205 80fr multi .18 .15

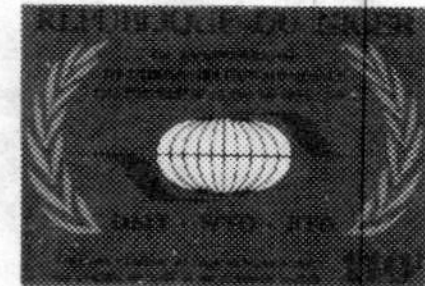

UN Disarmament Campaign, 20th Anniv. — A205a

1984, Oct. 31 *Perf. 13*

667A A205a 400fr brt grn & blk .90 .48
667B A205a 500fr brt bl & blk 1.25 .60

#584-585 Overprinted "Aide au Sahel 84"

1984 **Litho.** *Perf. 13*

668 A176 150fr multi .32 .18
669 A176 200fr multi .45 .22

World Tourism Organization, 10th Anniv. A206

1984, Jan. 2 Litho. *Perf. 12½*

670 A206 110fr WTO emblem .25 .15

Infant Survival Campaign — A207

1985, Jan. 28 Litho. *Perf. 12½*

671 A207 85fr Breastfeeding .18 .15
672 A207 110fr Weighing child, giving liquids .24 .15
Set value .24

Nos. 590, 519 and 568 Overprinted with Exhibitions in Red Souvenir Sheets

Perf. 13, 12½, 14

1985, Mar. 11 **Litho.**

673 A177 400fr MOPHILA '85 / HAMBOURG .90 .50
674 A154 425fr TSUKUBA EXPO '85 .90 .50
675 A170 450fr ROME, ITALIA '85 emblem 1.10 .55

See Nos. C356-C357.

Technical & Cultural Cooperation Agency, 15th Anniv. — A208

1985, Mar. 20 *Perf. 13*

676 A208 110fr vio, brn & car rose .24 .15

8th Niamey Festival A209

Gaya Ballet Troupe. No. 678 vert.

1985, Apr. 8 *Perf. 12½x13, 13x12½*

677 A209 85fr multi .18 .15
678 A209 110fr multi .24 .15
679 A209 150fr multi .32 .16
Nos. 677-679 (3) .74
Set value .38

Intl. Youth Year — A210

Authors and scenes from novels: 85fr, Jack London (1876-1916). 105fr, Joseph Kessel (1898-1979). 250fr, Herman Melville. 450fr, Rudyard Kipling.

1985, Apr. 29 *Perf. 13*

680 A210 85fr multi .18 .15
681 A210 105fr multi .22 .15
682 A210 250fr multi .55 .30
683 A210 450fr multi 1.10 .55
Nos. 680-683 (4) 2.05 1.15

PHILEXAFRICA '85, Lome, Togo — A211

1985, May 6 *Perf. 13x12½*

684 A211 200fr Tree planting .45 .22
685 A211 200fr Industry .45 .22
a. Pair, Nos. 684-685 .90 .60

Victor Hugo and His Son Francois, by A. de Chatillon — A212

1985, May 22 *Perf. 12½*

686 A212 500fr multi 1.10 .55

Europafrica A213

1985, June 3 *Perf. 13*

687 A213 110fr multi .24 .15

World Wildlife Fund — A214

Designs: 50fr, 60fr, Addax. 85fr, 110fr, Oryx.

1985, June 15

688 A214 50fr Head, vert. .15 .15
689 A214 60fr Grazing .15 .15
690 A214 85fr Two adults .18 .15
691 A214 110fr Head, vert. .24 .15
Nos. 688-691 (4) .72
Set value .35

Environ-destroying Species — A215

1985, July 1 *Perf. 13x12½, 12½x13*

692 A215 85fr Oedaleus sp. .18 .15
693 A215 110fr Dysdercus volkeri .24 .15
694 A215 150fr Tolyposporium ehrenbergii, Sclerospora graminicola, horiz. .32 .16
695 A215 210fr Passer luteus .45 .22
696 A215 390fr Quelea quelea .80 .40
Nos. 692-696 (5) 1.99 1.08

Official Type of 1988 and:

Cross of Agadez — A216

1985, July **Engr.** *Perf. 13*

697 A216 85fr green .18 .15
698 O2 110fr brown .24 .15
Set value .22

Natl. Independence, 25th Anniv. — A217

1985, Aug. 3 **Litho.** *Perf. 13x12½*

707 A217 110fr multi .24 .15

Protected Trees A218

Designs: 30fr, No. 711, Adansonia digitata and pod, vert. 85fr, 210fr, Acacia albida. No. 710, 390fr, Adansonia digitata, diff. Nos. 708-710 inscribed "DES ARBRES POUR LE NIGER."

1985 *Perf. 13x12½, 12½x13*

708 A218 30fr grn & multi .15 .15
709 A218 85fr brn & multi .18 .15
710 A218 110fr mag & multi .24 .15
711 A218 110fr blk & multi .24 .15
712 A218 210fr blk & multi .45 .22
713 A218 390fr blk & multi .80 .40
Nos. 708-713 (6) 2.06
Set value 1.00

Issued: #708-710, 10/1; #711-713, 8/19.

Niamey-Bamako Motorboat Race — A219

1985, Sept. 16 *Perf. 13½*

714 A219 110fr Boats on Niger River .24 .15
715 A219 150fr Helicopter, competitor .32 .16
716 A219 250fr Motorboat, map .55 .28
Nos. 714-716 (3) 1.11 .59

Mushrooms A220

1985, Oct. 3

717 A220 85fr Boletus .24 .15
718 A220 110fr Hypholoma fasciculare .32 .15
719 A220 200fr Coprinus comatus .55 .22
720 A220 300fr Agaricus arvensis .85 .32
721 A220 400fr Geastrum fimbriatum 1.25 .48
Nos. 717-721 (5) 3.21 1.32

Nos. 717-719 vert.

PHILEXAFRICA '85, Lome, Togo — A221

1985, Oct. 21 *Perf. 13x12½*

722 A221 250fr Village water pump .55 .30
723 A221 250fr Children playing dili .55 .30
a. Pair, Nos. 722-723 1.10 .75

61st World Savings Day — A222

1985, Oct. 31 *Perf. 12½x13*

724 A222 210fr multi .44 .22

European Music Year — A223

Traditional instruments.

1985, Nov. 4 *Perf. 13½*

725 A223 150fr Gouroumi, vert. .32 .16
726 A223 210fr Gassou .45 .22
727 A223 390fr Algaita, vert. .80 .40
Nos. 725-727 (3) 1.57 .78

Souvenir Sheet

Perf. 12½

728 A223 500fr Biti 1.10 .55

Civil Statutes Reform — A224

1986, Jan. 2 **Litho.** *Perf. 13x12½*

729 A224 85fr Natl. identity card .35 .18
730 A224 110fr Family services .45 .22

Traffic Safety — A225

Artists — A226

1986, Mar. 26 **Litho.** *Perf. 12½x13*

731 A225 85fr Obey signs .35 .18
732 A225 110fr Speed restriction .45 .22

1986, Apr. 11 *Perf. 12½*

60fr, Oumarou Ganda, filmmaker. 85fr, Ida Na Dadaou, entertainer. 100fr, Dan Gourmou, entertainer. 130fr, Koungoui, comedian.

733 A226 60fr multi .24 .15
734 A226 85fr multi .35 .18
735 A226 100fr multi .42 .20
736 A226 130fr multi .45 .26

Hunger Relief Campaign, Trucks of Hope — A227

1986, Aug. 27 **Litho.** *Perf. 12½*

737 A227 85fr Relief supply truck .35 .18
738 A227 110fr Mother, child, vert. .45 .22

Intl. Solidarity Day — A228

200fr, Nelson Mandela and Walter Sisulu, Robben Island prison camp. 300fr, Mandela.

1986, Oct. 8 *Perf. 13½*

739 A228 200fr multi .80 .42
740 A228 300fr multi 1.25 .60

FAO, 40th Anniv. A229

1986, Oct. 16 *Perf. 13*

741 A229 50fr Cooperative peanut farm .20 .15
742 A229 60fr Fight desert encroachment .24 .15
743 A229 85fr Irrigation management .35 .18
744 A229 100fr Breeding livestock .42 .20
745 A229 110fr Afforestation .45 .22
Nos. 741-745 (5) 1.66 .90

Improved Housing for a Healthier Niger — A230

Insects Protecting Growing Crops — A231

1987, Feb. 26 **Litho.** *Perf. 13½*

746 A230 85fr Albarka .35 .18
747 A230 110fr Mai Sauki .45 .22

1987, Mar. 26 *Perf. 13x12½*

748 A231 85fr Sphodromantis .35 .18
749 A231 110fr Delta .45 .22
750 A231 120fr Cicindela .50 .25
Nos. 748-750 (3) 1.30 .65

Liptako-Gourma Telecommunications Link Inauguration — A232

1987, Apr. 10 *Perf. 13½*

751 A232 110fr multi .45 .22

Samuel Morse — A233

1988 Seoul Summer Olympics — A234

1987, May 21 **Litho.** *Perf. 12x12½*

752 A233 120fr Telegraph key, operator, horiz. .50 .25
753 A233 200fr shown .85 .40
754 A233 350fr Receiver, horiz. 1.50 .75
Nos. 752-754 (3) 2.85 1.40

Invention of the telegraph, 150th anniv.

1987, July 15

755 A234 85fr Tennis .35 .18
756 A234 110fr Pole vault .45 .22
757 A234 250fr Soccer 1.10 .52
Nos. 755-757 (3) 1.90 .92

Souvenir Sheet

758 A234 500fr Running 2.00 1.10

1988 Winter Olympics, Calgary — A235

1987, July 28 **Litho.** *Perf. 12½*

759 A235 85fr Ice hockey .35 .18
760 A235 110fr Speed skating .45 .22
761 A235 250fr Pairs figure skating 1.10 .52
Nos. 759-761 (3) 1.90 .92

Souvenir Sheet

762 A235 500fr Downhill skiing 2.00 1.10

For overprints see Nos. 783-785.

African Games, Nairobi — A236

1987, Aug. 5 *Perf. 13*

763 A236 85fr Runners .35 .18
764 A236 110fr High jump .45 .22
765 A236 200fr Hurdles .85 .40
766 A236 400fr Javelin 1.65 .85
Nos. 763-766 (4) 3.30 1.65

Natl. Tourism Office, 10th Anniv. A237

1987, Sept. 10 *Perf. 13½*

767 A237 85fr Chief's stool, scepter, vert. .45 .22
768 A237 110fr Nomad, caravan, scepter .60 .30
769 A237 120fr Moslem village .60 .30
770 A237 200fr Bridge over Niger River 1.10 .50
Nos. 767-770 (4) 2.75 1.32

Aga Khan Architecture Prize, 1986 — A238

1987, Oct. 7 *Perf. 13*

771 A238 85fr Yaama Mosque, dawn .45 .22
772 A238 110fr At night .60 .30
773 A238 250fr In daylight 1.40 .65
Nos. 771-773 (3) 2.45 1.17

Niamey Court of Appeal A239

1987, Nov. 17 *Perf. 13x12½*

774 A239 85fr multi .45 .22
775 A239 110fr multi .60 .30
776 A239 140fr multi .75 .38
Nos. 774-776 (3) 1.80 .90

Christmas 1987 — A240

Paintings: 110fr, The Holy Family with Lamb, by Raphael. 500fr, The Adoration of the Magi, by Hans Memling (c. 1430-1494).

Perf. 12½

1987, Dec. 24 **Litho.** **Wmk. 385**

777 A240 110fr multi .60 .28

Souvenir Sheet

778 A240 500fr multi 2.50 1.40

No. 778 is airmail.

Modern Services for a Healthy Community — A241

1988, Jan. 21 *Perf. 13*

779 A241 85fr Water drainage .60 .30
780 A241 110fr Sewage .78 .40
781 A241 165fr Garbage removal 1.20 .60
Nos. 779-781 (3) 2.58 1.30

Dan-Gourmou Prize — A242

1988, Feb. 16 **Litho.** *Perf. 13½*

782 A242 85fr multi .60 .30

Natl. modern music competition.

Nos. 759-761 Ovptd. "Medaille d'or" and Name of Winner in Gold

1988, Mar. 29 *Perf. 12½*

783 A235 85fr USSR .62 .30
784 A235 110fr Gusafson, Sweden .80 .40
785 A235 250fr Gordeeva and Grinkov, USSR 1.80 .90
Nos. 783-785 (3) 3.22 1.60

New Market Building, Niamey A243

1988, Apr. 9 **Litho.** *Perf. 13x12½*

786 A243 85fr multi .60 .30

WHO 40th Anniv., Universal Immunization Campaign A244

1988, May 26 **Litho.** *Perf. 12½x13*

787 A244 85fr Mother and child .55 .28
788 A244 110fr Visiting doctor .72 .35

Organization for African Unity (OAU), 25th Anniv. — A245

1988, June 28 *Perf. 12½*

789 A245 85fr multi .55 .28

Construction of a Sand Break to Arrest Desert Encroachment — A246

1988, Sept. 27 **Litho.** *Perf. 12½x13*

790 A246 85fr multi .55 .28

Intl. Red Cross and Red Crescent Organizations, 125th Annivs. — A247

1988, Oct. 26 *Perf. 13x12½*

791 A247 85fr multi .55 .28
792 A247 110fr multi .72 .35

Niger Press Agency A248

1989, Jan. 31 **Litho.** *Perf. 12½*

793 A248 85fr blk, org & grn .55 .28

Fight Against AIDS — A249

1989, Feb. 28 *Perf. 13½*

794 A249 85fr multi .55 .28
795 A249 110fr multi .72 .35

Intl. Maritime Organization, 30th Anniv. A250

1989, Mar. 29 **Litho.** *Perf. 12½x13*

796 A250 100fr multi .65 .32
797 A250 120fr multi .78 .35

FAN Seizure of Government, 15th Anniv. — A251

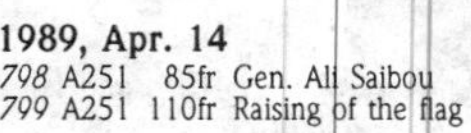

1989, Apr. 14

798 A251 85fr Gen. Ali Saibou .55 .28
799 A251 110fr Raising of the flag .72 .35

PHILEXFRANCE '89 — A252

1989, July 1 Litho. *Perf. 13*

800 A252	100fr	Eiffel Tower	.60	.30
801 A252	200fr	Simulated stamps	1.20	.60

French Revolution, Bicent. — A253

1989, July 1

802 A253	250fr	Planting a tree for liberty	1.50	.75

A254 A255

1989, Aug. 30 Litho. *Perf. 13½*

803 A254	100fr	multi	.65	.32

African Development Bank, 25th anniv.

1989, July 3 Litho. *Perf. 13½*

804 A255	85fr	multi	.55	.28

Communication and Postal Organization of West Africa (CAPTEAO), 30th anniv.

Verdant Field, Field After Locust Plague — A256

1989, Oct. 1 Litho. *Perf. 13*

805 A256	85fr	multicolored	.55	.28

Lumiere Brothers, Film Pioneers A256a

Designs: 150fr, Auguste Lumiere (1862-1954). 250fr, Louis Lumiere (1864-1948).

1989, Nov. 21 Litho. *Perf. 13½*

805A A256a	150fr	multicolored	1.05	.52
805B A256a	250fr	multicolored	1.75	.85
805C A256a	400fr	multicolored	2.75	1.38
		Nos. 805A-805C (3)	5.55	2.75

Rural Development Council, 30th Anniv. A256b

1989 Litho. *Perf. 15x14*

805D A256b	75fr	multicolored		

Flora — A257

1989, Dec. 12 Litho. *Perf. 13*

806 A257	10fr	*Russelia equisetiformis*	.15	.15
807 A257	20fr	*Argyreia nervosa*	.15	.15
808 A257	30fr	*Hibiscus rosa-sinensis*	.22	.15
809 A257	50fr	*Catharanthus roseus*	.35	.18
810 A257	100fr	*Cymothoe sangaris*, horiz.	.70	.35
		Nos. 806-810 (5)	1.57	
		Set value		.75

Caravan A257a

1989 Litho. *Perf. 15x14*

810A A257a	145fr	shown		
810B A257a	165fr	Dunes of Temet		

A258 A259

1990, Jan. 18 *Perf. 12½*

811 A258	120fr	multicolored	.85	.42

Pan-African Postal Union, 10th anniv.

1990, Feb. 27 *Perf. 13½x13*

812 A259	85fr	shown	.60	.30
813 A259	110fr	Class, diff.	.78	.40

Intl. Literacy Year.

A260 A261

1990, Mar. 15 *Perf. 13x12½*

814 A260	85fr	OCI emblem	.60	.30

Islamic Conference Organization, 20th anniv.

1990, Mar. 29 Litho. *Perf. 13½*

815 A261	300fr	multicolored	2.35	1.20
816 A261	500fr	multicolored	4.00	2.00

Mickey Leland, US Congressman, died Aug. 7, 1989 in a plane crash on a humanitarian mission.

A262 A263

1990, May 15 Litho. *Perf. 13½*

817 A262	85fr	multicolored	.60	.30

Natl. Development Society, 1st anniv.

1990, May 31 *Perf. 13x12½*

818 A263	85fr	multicolored	.60	.30

Multinational Postal School, 20th anniv.

1992 Summer Olympics, Barcelona — A263a

1990, June 4 Litho. *Perf. 13½*

818A A263a	85fr	Gymnastics	.65	.32
818B A263a	110fr	Hurdles	.85	.42
818C A263a	250fr	Running	1.95	1.00
818D A263a	400fr	Equestrian	3.10	1.55
818E A263a	500fr	Long jump	4.00	2.00
		Nos. 818A-818E (5)	10.55	5.29

Souvenir sheet

819F A263a	600fr	Cycling	4.65	2.30

Nos. 818D-818F are airmail.

Independence, 30th Anniv. A264

1990, Aug. 3 *Perf. 12½*

819 A264	85fr	gray grn & multi	.60	.30
820 A264	110fr	buff & multi	.80	.40

UN Development Program, 40th Anniv. — A265

1990, Oct. 24 Litho. *Perf. 13½*

821 A265	100fr	multicolored	.78	.40

Butterflies and Mushrooms A266 A266a

Designs: 85fr, Amanita rubescens. 110fr, Graphum pylades. 200fr, Pseudacraea hostilia. 250fr, Russula virescens. 400fr, Boletus impolitus. 500fr, Precis octavia. 600fr, Cantharellus cibarius & pseudacraea boisduvali.

1991, Jan. 15 Litho. *Perf. 13½*

822 A266	85fr	multicolored	.65	.32
823 A266	110fr	multicolored	.85	.42
824 A266	200fr	multicolored	1.55	.78
825 A266	250fr	multicolored	1.95	1.00
826 A266	400fr	multicolored	3.10	1.55
827 A266	500fr	multicolored	4.00	2.00
		Nos. 822-827 (6)	12.10	6.07

Souvenir Sheet

828 A266a	600fr	multicolored	4.65	2.30

Nos. 826-828 are airmail. No. 828 contains one 30x38mm stamp.

Palestinian Uprising — A267

1991, Mar. 30 Litho. *Perf. 12½*

829 A267	110fr	multicolored	.90	.45

Christopher Columbus (1451-1506) A268

Hypothetical portraits and: 85fr, Santa Maria. 110fr, Frigata, Portuguese caravel, 15th cent. 200fr, Four-masted caravel, 16th cent. 250fr, Estremadura, Spanish caravel, 1511. 400fr, Vija, Portuguese caravel, 1600. 500fr, Pinta. 600fr, Nina.

1991, Mar. 19 Litho. *Perf. 13½*

830 A268	85fr	multicolored	.65	.32
831 A268	110fr	multicolored	.85	.42
832 A268	200fr	multicolored	1.55	.78
833 A268	250fr	multicolored	1.95	1.00
834 A268	400fr	multicolored	3.10	1.55
835 A268	500fr	multicolored	4.00	2.00
		Nos. 830-835 (6)	12.10	6.07

Souvenir Sheet

835A A268	600fr	multicolored	4.65	2.35

Nos. 834-835A are airmail.

Timia Falls — A269

African Tourism Year — A270

Designs: 85fr, Boubon Market, horiz. 130fr, Ruins of Assode, horiz.

1991, July 10

836 A269	85fr	multicolored	.65	.32
837 A269	110fr	multicolored	.85	.42
838 A269	130fr	multicolored	1.00	.50
839 A270	200fr	multicolored	1.50	.75
		Nos. 836-839 (4)	4.00	1.99

Anniversaries and Events — A270a

200fr, Reading of Declaration of Human Rights, Honoré-Gabriel Riqueti (Comte de Mirabeau). 400fr, Charles de Gaulle and Konrad Adenauer.

1991, July 15 Litho. *Perf. 13½*

839C	A270a	200fr	multicolored	
839E	A270a	400fr	multicolored	

French Revolution, bicent. (#839C). Franco-German Cooperation Agreement, 28th anniv. (#839E). #839E is airmail & exists in a souvenir sheet of 1.

For surcharge see No. 865.

Numbers have been reserved for additional values in this set.

A271

A272

Women with various native hairstyles.

1991

840	A271	85fr multicolored	.65	.32
841	A271	110fr multicolored	.85	.42
842	A271	165fr multicolored	1.25	.62
843	A271	200fr multicolored	1.50	.75
		Nos. 840-843 (4)	4.25	2.11

1991, Dec. 17 Litho. *Perf. 12½*

844	A272	85fr multicolored	.65	.32

Natl. Conference of Niger

House Built Without Wood A273

1992, May 25 Litho. *Perf. 12½*

845	A273	85fr multicolored	.75	.38

World Population Day — A274

Designs: 85fr, Assembling world puzzle. 110fr, Globe on a kite string.

1992, July 11 Litho. *Perf. 12½*

846	A274	85fr multicolored	.75	.38
847	A274	110fr multicolored	.95	.48

Discovery of America, 500th Anniv. — A275

1992, Sept. 16 *Perf. 13*

848	A275	250fr multicolored	2.20	1.10

Hadjia Haoua Issa (1927-1990), Singer A276

1992, Sept. 23 *Perf. 12½x13*

849	A276	150fr multicolored	1.30	.65

Intl. Conference on Nutrition, Rome — A277

African School of Meteorology and Civil Aviation, 30th Anniv. — A278

1992 Litho. *Perf. 12½*

850	A277	145fr tan & multi	1.20	.60
851	A277	350fr blue & multi	2.90	1.45

1993, Feb. 7 *Perf. 13½*

852	A278	110fr blue, green & black	.88	.44

Environmental Protection — A279

1993, June 26 Litho. *Perf. 12½*

853	A279	85fr salmon & multi	.75	.38
854	A279	165fr green & multi	1.45	.75

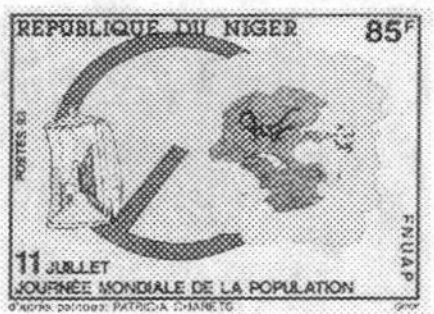

World Population Day — A280

110fr, Buildings, person with globe as head, tree.

1993, July 11 Litho. *Perf. 13½*

855	A280	85fr multicolored	.65	.32
856	A280	110fr multicolored	.85	.42

Nelson Mandela, F.W. De Klerk, Winners of 1993 Nobel Peace Prize — A282

1994, Feb. 11 Litho. *Perf. 13*

858	A282	270fr multicolored	1.10	.55

A282a

1994 Litho. *Perf. 12½x13*

858A	A282a	165fr Mountain		

Cultural Cooperation & Technique Agency, 25th Anniv. — A283

1995 Litho. *Perf. 13½x13*

859	A283	100fr multicolored	.48	.25

Animals Used for Transportation A284

1995 *Perf. 13x13½*

860	A284	500fr Donkey cart	2.25	1.10
861	A284	1000fr Man, saddled horse	4.50	2.25

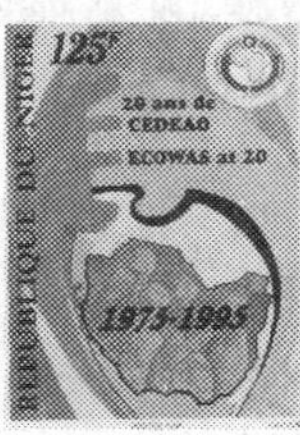

Economic Community of West African States (ECOWAS), 20th Anniv. — A285

1995 Litho. *Perf. 13½*

862	A285	125fr multicolored	.70	.35

Cattle Ranching A286

Design: 300fr, Irrigating fields.

1995 *Perf. 13½x13*

863	A286	125fr shown	.70	.35
864	A286	300fr multicolored	1.50	.75

25ème ANNIVERSAIRE DE LA MORT DU GENERAL DE GAULLE

Souvenir Sheet of No. 839E Ovptd.

1995, Nov. 8 Litho. *Perf. 13½*

865	A270a	400fr multicolored	*6.00*	*3.00*

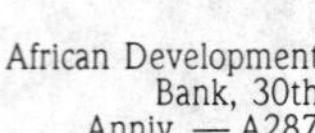
African Development Bank, 30th Anniv. — A287

1995 Litho. *Perf. 14*

866	A287	300fr green & red	1.60	.80

Boy Scouts — A288

1996 *Perf. 13½*

867	A288	350fr Robert Baden-Powell	1.50	.75
868	A288	500fr Scout saluting	2.25	1.10

Nos. 867-868 exist imperf. and in souvenir sheets of 1 both perf. and imperf.

UN, UNICEF, 50th Anniv. — A289

150fr, Child with head bandaged, UNICEF emblem. 225fr, Boy carrying bowl of food on head, dove, globes. 475fr, Woman, boy playing on artillery piece, space station Mir. 550fr, Boy, race car driver Michael Schumacker, UNICEF emblem.

1996

869	A289	150fr multicolored	.70	.35
870	A289	225fr multicolored	1.00	.50
871	A289	475fr multicolored	2.25	1.15
a.		Sheet of 2, #870-871 + label	*11.00*	*5.60*
872	A289	550fr multicolored	2.50	1.25
a.		Sheet of 2, #869, 872 + label	*11.00*	*5.60*
		Nos. 869-872 (4)	6.45	3.25

Entertainers A290

1996

873	A290	175fr Bob Marley	.80	.40
874	A290	300fr Janis Joplin	1.30	.65
875	A290	600fr Jerry Garcia	2.70	1.30
876	A290	700fr Elvis Presley	3.10	1.50
877	A290	700fr Marilyn Monroe	3.10	1.50
878	A290	750fr John Lennon	3.40	1.70
879	A290	800fr Monroe, diff.	3.60	1.80
880	A290	800fr Presley, diff.	3.60	1.80
		Nos. 873-880 (8)	21.60	10.65

Souvenir Sheets

881	A290	2000fr Presley, diff.	9.00	4.50
882	A290	2000fr Monroe, diff.	9.00	4.50

Nos. 873-882 exist imperf. and in souvenir sheets of 1 both perf. and imperf.

Butterflies A291

Boy Scout Jamboree emblem and: 150fr, Chrysiridia ripheария. 200fr, Palla ussheri. 750fr, Mylothris chloris. 800fr, Papilo dardanus.

1996 Litho. *Perf. 13½*

883 A291 150fr multicolored .70 .35
884 A291 200fr multicolored .90 .45
885 A291 750fr multicolored 3.35 1.70
886 A291 800fr multicolored 3.60 1.80
Nos. 883-886 (4) 8.55 4.30

Nos. 883-886 exist imperf. and in souvenir sheets of 1 both perf. and imperf.

Wild Animals A292

Boy Scout Jamboree emblem, Rotary emblem and: 150fr, Erythrocebus patas. 200fr, Panthera pardus. 900fr, Balearica regulorum. 1000fr, Alcelaphus buselaphus.
2000fr, Panthera leo.

1996

887 A292 150fr multicolored .70 .35
888 A292 200fr multicolored .90 .45
889 A292 900fr multicolored 4.00 2.00
890 A292 1000fr multicolored 4.50 2.25
Nos. 887-890 (4) 10.10 5.05

Souvenir Sheet

891 A292 2000fr multicolored 9.00 4.50

Nos. 887-890 exist in souvenir sheets of 1.

Rotary International A292a

Designs: 200fr, Boy holding fruits and vegetables. 700fr, Girl holding sheaves of grain.

1996 Litho. *Perf. 13½*

891A A292a 200fr multicolored 1.10 .55
891B A292a 700fr multicolored 3.75 1.90

Intl. Red Cross and Lions Intl. — A293

Designs: 250fr, Jean-Henri Dunant as young man. 300fr, Lions Intl. emblems, boy with books. 400fr, Dunant as old man. 600fr, Older boy carrying younger boy, Lions Intl. emblems.

1996 Litho. *Perf. 13½*

892 A293 250fr multicolored 1.15 .60
893 A293 300fr multicolored 1.35 .70
894 A293 400fr multicolored 1.80 .90
895 A293 600fr multicolored 2.70 1.35
Nos. 892-895 (4) 7.00 3.55

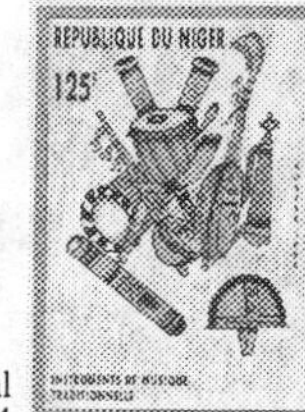

Traditional Musical Instruments — A294

1996 Litho. *Perf. 13½*

896 A294 125fr violet & multi .55 .30
897 A294 175fr pink & multi .80 .40

Sports — A295

1996

898 A295 300fr Golf 1.35 .70
899 A295 500fr Tennis 2.25 1.10
900 A295 700fr Table tennis 3.25 1.50
Nos. 898-900 (3) 6.85 3.30

Nos. 898-900 exist in souvenir sheets of one.

1996 Summer Olympic Games, Atlanta — A296

Designs: 250fr, Track & field. 350fr, Women's gymnastics, table tennis. 400fr, Tennis, swimming. 600fr, Hurdles, pole vault.
1500fr, Men's track and field.

1996 Litho. *Perf. 13½*

901 A296 250fr multicolored 1.10 .55
902 A296 350fr multicolored 1.50 .75
903 A296 400fr multicolored 1.80 .90
904 A296 600fr multicolored 2.70 1.35
Nos. 901-904 (4) 7.10 3.55

Souvenir Sheet

904A A296 1500fr multicolored 7.00 7.00

Souvenir Sheet

CHINA '96 — A297

Statues from Yunguang Grottoes, Datong, China: a, Head of Buddha. b, Side view.

1996

905 A297 140fr Sheet of 2, #a.-b. 1.25 .65

1998 Winter Olympic Games, Nagano A298

1996

906 A298 85fr Hockey .40 .20
907 A298 200fr Downhill skiing .90 .45
908 A298 400fr Slalom skiing 1.80 .90
909 A298 500fr Pairs figure skating 2.25 1.10
Nos. 906-909 (4) 5.35 2.65

Nos. 906-909 were not issued without metallic blue overprint on stamps dated 1991. Nos. 908-909 are airmail.

Nos. 906-909 exist with red metallic overprint. A 600fr souvenir sheet with red metallic overprint exists in limited quantities.

Formula I Race Car Drivers A299

Designs: 450fr, Jacques Villeneuve. 2000fr, Ayrton Senna (1960-94).

1996

910 A299 450fr multicolored 2.00 1.00

Souvenir Sheet

911 A299 2000fr multicolored 9.00 4.50

No. 910 exists in souvenir sheet of 1. No. 911 contains one 39x57mm stamp.

Tockus Nasutus A300

Coracias Abyssinica A301

Design: 35fr, Bulbucus ibis.

1996 Litho. *Perf. 13½x13*

912 A300 5fr multicolored

Perf. 13

913 A301 25fr multicolored
914 A301 35fr multicolored

1998 Winter Olympic Games, Nagano, Japan A302

1996 Litho. *Perf. 13x13½*

915 A302 125fr Ice hockey .55 .30
916 A302 175fr Slalom skiing .75 .35
917 A302 700fr Pairs figure skating 3.00 1.50
918 A302 800fr Speed skating 3.50 1.75
Nos. 915-918 (4) 7.80 3.90

Souvenir Sheet

919 A302 1500fr Downhill skiing 6.50 3.25

No. 919 contains one 57x51mm stamp.
Nos. 915-918 exist in souvenir sheets of 1.

Minerals A303

No. 920: a, Brookite. b, Elbaite indicolite. c. Elbaite rubellite verdelite. d, Olivine.
No. 921: a, Topaz. b, Autunite. c, Leucite. d, Struvite.

1996 Litho. *Perf. 13½*

920 A303 375fr Sheet of 4, #a.-d. 6.50 3.25
921 A303 500fr Sheet of 4, #a.-d. 8.75 4.50

Souvenir Sheet

922 A303 2000fr Pyrargyrite 6.50 3.25

No. 922 contains one 42x39mm stamp.

World Driving Champion Michael Schumacher A304

Schumacher: a, Grand Prix of Spain. b, In race car in pit. c, Ahead of another car. d, Behind another car.

1996 Litho. *Perf. 13½*

923 A304 375fr Sheet of 4, #a.-d. 6.50 3.25

German Soccer Team, Euro '96 Champions A305

Designs: a, Oliver Bierhoff, player jumping up. b, Bierhoff, player holding up arms. c, ChancellorHelmut Kohl, Queen Elizabeth II, Klinsmann. d, Stadium, Mathias Sammer. logos.

1996 Litho. *Perf. 13½*

924 A305 400fr Sheet of 4, #a.-d. 7.00 3.50

Dinosaurs A306

No. 925: a, Ouranosaurus. b, Spinosaurus. c, Polacanthus. d, Deinonychus.
No. 926: a, Camptosaurus. b, Allosaurus. c, Nodosaurus. d, Kritosaurus.
2000fr, Protoceratops, oviraptor, horiz.

1996

925 A306 300fr Sheet of 4, #a.-d. 5.25 2.60
926 A306 450fr Sheet of 4, #a.-d. 7.75 3.90

Souvenir Sheet

927 A306 2000fr multicolored 6.50 3.25

France '98, World Soccer Cup Championships — A307

World Cup Trophy and: 125fr, American player. 175fr, Brazilian player. 750fr, Italian player. 1000fr, German player.
1500fr, Player in action scene.

1996

928 A307 125fr multicolored .55 .25
929 A307 175fr multicolored .75 .40
930 A307 750fr multicolored 3.25 1.60
931 A307 1000fr multicolored 4.25 2.10
Nos. 928-931 (4) 8.80 4.35

Souvenir Sheet

932 A307 1500fr multicolored 6.50 3.25

No. 932 contains one 57x51mm stamp.

New Year 1997 (Year of the Ox) — A308

1997 Litho. *Perf. 13½*

933 A308 500fr shown 2.00 1.00
934 A308 500fr Riding three oxen 2.00 1.00

Nos. 933-934 exist is souvenir sheets of 1, design extending to perfs. on No. 933.

Birds A309

5fr, Tockus nasutus. 15fr, Psittacula kramer. 25fr, Coracias abyssinica. 35fr, Bulbucus ibis.

1997 Litho. *Perf. 13½*

935 A309 5fr multicolored .15 .15
936 A309 15fr multicolored .15 .15
937 A309 25fr multicolored .15 .15
938 A309 35fr multicolored .15 .15
Set value .30 .15

19th Dakar-Agades-Dakar Rally — A310

Designs: 125fr, Truck, child in traditional dress. 175fr, Ostrich, three-wheel vehicle. 300fr, Camel, heavy-duty support truck. 500fr, Motorcycles.

1997

939 A310 125fr multicolored .60 .30
940 A310 175fr multicolored .85 .40
941 A310 300fr multicolored 1.50 .75
942 A310 500fr multicolored 2.40 1.20
a. Souvenir sheet, #939-942 5.50 5.50
b. Strip of 4, #939-942 5.50 5.50

Deng Xiaoping (1904-97), Chinese Leader — A311

Designs: a, Deng, flag, eating at table, Deng as young man. b, Farming with oxen, Deng holding girl, flag. c, Flag, Deng with soldiers, camp. d, Deng bathing, ships in port, combining grain, launching space vehicle. e, Huts, heavy equipment vehicle, men working. f, Airplane, man holding up flask, operating room, Deng.
Illustration reduced.

1997

943 A311 150fr Sheet of 6, #a.-f. 3.50 1.75

Diana, Princess of Wales (1961-97) A312

#944: Various portraits performing humanitarin deeds, on world tours, with various figures.
#945: Various portraits in designer dresses.
#946: With Mother Teresa (in margin).

1997 Litho. *Perf. 13½*
Sheets of 9

944 A312 180fr #a.-i. 7.00 3.50
945 A312 180fr #a.-i. 7.00 3.50

Souvenir Sheet

946 A312 2000fr multicolored 8.75 4.40

Famous Americans A313

Various portraits: #948: a-b, John F. Kennedy. c-d, Pres. Bill Clinton.
No. 949: a, Kennedy. b, Martin Luther King (1929-68). c-d, Clinton.
2000fr, John F. Kennedy.

1997 Litho. *Perf. 13½*

948 A313 350fr Sheet of 4, #a.-d. 5.50 2.75
949 A313 400fr Sheet of 4, #a.-d. 6.25 6.25

Souvenir Sheet

950 A313 2000fr multicolored 7.75 3.90

No. 950 contains one 42x60mm stamp.

Stars of American Cinema A314

Designs: a, Eddie Murphy. b, Elizabeth Taylor. c, Bruce Willis. d, James Dean. e, Clint Eastwood. f, Elvis Presley. g, Michelle Pfeiffer. h, Marilyn Monroe. i, Robert Redford.

1997 Litho. *Perf. 13½*

951 A314 300fr Sheet of 9, #a.-i. 10.50 5.25

Communications — A315

Designs: a, 80fr, Satellite transmission, radios. b, 100fr, Computers. c, 60fr, Cellular phone transmission around world. d, 120fr, Hand holding car phone. e, 180fr, Satellite, earth. f, 50fr, Transmission tower, cellular phone.

1997

952 A315 Sheet of 6, #a.-f. 2.25 1.10

Prof. Abdou Moumouni Dioffo — A316

1997 Litho. *Perf. 13½x13*

953 A316 125fr multicolored .60 .30

Methods of Transportation — A317

Bicycles, motorcycles: No. 954: a, Jan Ullrich, 1997 Tour de France winner, Eiffel Tower. b, Diana 250, Harley Davidson. c, MK VIII motorcycle, bicycles of 1819, 1875. d, Brands Match Motorcycle Race, Great Britain.

Modern locomotives, country flags: No. 955: a, Pendolino ETR 470, Italy. b, Rame TGV 112, France. c, Eurostar, France, Belgium, UK. d, Intercity Express ICE train, Germany.

Early locomotives, country flags: No. 956: a, Trevithick, UK. b, Pacific North Chapelon, France. c, Buddicom, UK, France. d, PLM "C", France.

Trains of Switzerland: No. 957: a, Crocodile, St. Gothard. b, RE 460. c, Red Streak, RAE 2/4 1001. d, Limmat.

Classic cars, modern sports cars: No. 958: a, Mercedes 300 SL Gullwing, Mercedes E320 Cabriolet. b, Aston Martin V8, Aston Martin DBR2. c. Ferrari F50, Ferrari 250 GT Berlinette. d, Ford Thunderbird, Ford GT40.

Air flight: No. 959: a, Clement Ader's Avion 111, dirigible R101. b, Concorde jet, X36 NASA/MCDD prototype. c, Aile volante FW900, Airbus A340. d, Gaudron GIII, Montgolfier's balloon.

Space travel: No. 960: a, HII rocket, Japan, Copernicus. b, Galileo, Ariane rocket. c, Space shuttle, Neil Armstrong. d, Yuri Gagarin, orbital space station, Soyuz.

1500fr, Swiss train, RE 4/4 II 11349, vert. No. 962, Hubble Space Telescope, Concorde jet. No. 963, TGV mail train, 1958 Chevrolet Corvette.

1997 Litho. *Perf. 13½*

954 A317 300fr Sheet of 4, #a.-d. 4.70 4.70
955 A317 350fr Sheet of 4, #a.-d. 5.50 5.50
956 A317 375fr Sheet of 4, #a.-d. 6.00 6.00
957 A317 400fr Sheet of 4, #a.-d. 6.25 6.25
958 A317 450fr Sheet of 4, #a.-d. 7.00 7.00
959 A317 500fr Sheet of 4, #a.-d. 7.75 7.75
960 A317 600fr Sheet of 4, #a.-d. 9.50 9.50

Souvenir Sheets

961 A317 1500fr multicolored 5.75 5.75
962 A317 2000fr multicolored 7.75 7.75
963 A317 2000fr multicolored 7.75 7.75

Swiss Railroad, 150th anniv. (#958, #961). Nos. 961-963 each contain one 50x60mm stamp.

Diana, Princess of Wales (1961-97) A318

Various portraits.

1997 Litho. *Perf. 13½*

964 A318 250fr Sheet of 9, #a.-i. 8.75 4.40

Souvenir Sheet

965 A318 1500fr multicolored 5.75 2.90

No. 965 contains one 42x60mm stamp.

SEMI-POSTAL STAMPS

Curie Issue
Common Design Type

1938 Unwmk. Engr. *Perf. 13*

B1 CD80 1.75fr + 50c brt ultra 8.00 8.00

French Revolution Issue
Common Design Type

1939 Photo. *Perf. 13*
Name and Value Typo. in Black

B2 CD83 45c + 25c grn 3.75 3.75
B3 CD83 70c + 30c brn 3.75 3.75
B4 CD83 90c + 35c red org 3.75 3.75
B5 CD83 1.25fr + 1fr rose pink 3.75 3.75
B6 CD83 2.25fr + 2fr blue 3.75 3.75
Nos. B2-B6 (5) 18.75 18.75

Stamps of 1926-38, Surcharged in Black **SECOURS + 1 fr. NATIONAL**

1941 *Perf. 14x13½, 13½x14*

B7 A3 50c + 1fr scar & grn, *grnsh* .45 .45
B8 A3 80c + 2fr cl & ol grn 2.50 2.50
B9 A4 1.50fr + 2fr dp bl & pale bl 3.50 3.50
B10 A4 2fr + 3fr red org & ol brn 3.50 3.50
Nos. B7-B10 (4) 9.95 9.95

Common Design Type and

Colonial Cavalry — SP1

Soldiers and Tank — SP2

1941 Unwmk. Photo. *Perf. 13½*

B11 SP2 1fr + 1fr red .50
B12 CD86 1.50fr + 3fr claret .50
B13 SP1 2.50fr + 1fr blue .50
Nos. B11-B13 (3) 1.50

Nos. B11-B13 were issued by the Vichy government and were not placed on sale in the colony.
Nos. 89-90 were surcharged "OEUVRES COLONIALES" and surtax (including change of denomination of the 2.50fr to 50c). These were issued in 1944 by the Vichy government and were not placed on sale in the colony.

> **Catalogue values for unused stamps in this section, from this point to the end of the section, are for Never Hinged items.**

Republic of the Niger
Anti-Malaria Issue
Common Design Type
Perf. 12½x12

1962, Apr. 7 Engr. Unwmk.

B14 CD108 25fr + 5fr brn .38 .38

Freedom from Hunger Issue
Common Design Type

1963, Mar. 21 *Perf. 13*

B15 CD112 25fr + 5fr gray ol, red lil & brn .45 .45

Dome of the Rock — SP3

1978, Dec. 11 Litho. *Perf. 12½*
B16 SP3 40fr + 5fr multi .15 .15

Surtax was for Palestinian fighters and their families.

AIR POST STAMPS

Common Design Type

1940 Unwmk. Engr. *Perf. 12½x12*
C1 CD85 1.90fr ultra .30 .20
C2 CD85 2.90fr dk red .30 .20
C3 CD85 4.50fr dk gray grn .60 .50
C4 CD85 4.90fr yel bis .40 .35
C5 CD85 6.90fr dp org .40 .35
Nos. C1-C5 (5) 2.00 1.60

Common Design Types

1942
C6 CD88 50c car & bl .15
C7 CD88 1fr brn & blk .15
C8 CD88 2fr multi .15
C9 CD88 3fr multi .20
C10 CD88 5fr vio & brn red .20

Frame Engraved, Center Typographed
C11 CD89 10fr multi .35
C12 CD89 20fr multi .40
C13 CD89 50fr multi .75
Nos. C6-C13 (8) 2.35

There is doubt whether Nos. C6-C13 were officially placed in use. They were issued by the Vichy government.

Catalogue values for unused stamps in this section, from this point to the end of the section, are for Never Hinged items.

Republic of the Niger

Wild Animals, W National Park — AP1

1960, Apr. 11 Engr. *Perf. 13*
C14 AP1 500fr multi 6.50 3.25

For overprint see No. C112.

Nubian Carmine Bee-eater — AP2

1961, Dec. 18 Unwmk. *Perf. 13*
C15 AP2 200fr multi 1.75 1.00

UN Headquarters and Emblem, Niger Flag and Map — AP3

1961, Dec. 16
C20 AP3 25fr multi .22 .15
C21 AP3 100fr multi .80 .50

Niger's admission to the United Nations. For overprints see Nos. C28-C29.

Air Afrique Issue

Common Design Type

1962, Feb. 17 Unwmk. *Perf. 13*
C22 CD107 100fr multi .80 .48

Mosque at Agadez and UPU Emblem AP4

Designs: 85fr, Gaya Bridge. 100fr, Presidential Palace, Niamey.

1963, June 12 Photo. *Perf. 12½*
C23 AP4 50fr multi .48 .18
C24 AP4 85fr multi .70 .35
C25 AP4 100fr multi .80 .55
Nos. C23-C25 (3) 1.98 1.08

2nd anniv. of Niger's admission to the UPU.

Type of Regular Issue, 1963

Design: 100fr, Building boats (kadei), horiz.

1963, Aug. 30 *Perf. 12½x12*
Size: 47x27mm
C26 A12 100fr multi .80 .40

African Postal Union Issue

Common Design Type

1963, Sept. 8 *Perf. 12½*
C27 CD114 85fr multi .65 .35

Nos. C20-C21 Overprinted "Centenaire de la Croix-Rouge" and Cross in Red

1963, Sept. 30 Engr. *Perf. 13*
C28 AP3 25fr multi .32 .22
C29 AP3 100fr multi 1.00 .55

Centenary of International Red Cross.

White and Black before Rising Sun — AP5

1963, Oct. 25 Photo. *Perf. 12x13*
C30 AP5 50fr multi .65 .50

See note after Mauritania No. C28.

Peanut Cultivation — AP6

Designs: 45fr, Camels transporting peanuts to market. 85fr, Men closing bags. 100fr, Loading bags on truck.

1963, Nov. 5 Engr. *Perf. 13*
C31 AP6 20fr grn, bl & red brn .18 .15
C32 AP6 45fr red brn, bl & grn .35 .18
C33 AP6 85fr multi .65 .30
C34 AP6 100fr red brn, ol bis & bl .90 .40
a. Souv. sheet of 4, #C31-C34 2.25 2.25
Nos. C31-C34 (4) 2.08 1.03

To publicize Niger's peanut industry.

1963 Air Afrique Issue

Common Design Type

1963, Nov. 19 Photo. *Perf. 13x12*
C35 CD115 50fr multi .40 .28

Telstar and Capricornus and Sagittarius Constellations — AP7

100fr, Relay satellite, Leo & Virgo constellations.

1964, Feb. 11 Engr. *Perf. 13*
C36 AP7 25fr olive gray & vio .22 .15
C37 AP7 100fr grn & rose claret .70 .55

Ramses II Holding Crook and Flail, Abu Simbel — AP8

1964, Mar. 9
C38 AP8 25fr bis brn & dl bl grn .32 .25
C39 AP8 30fr dk bl & org brn .36 .28
C40 AP8 50fr dp claret & dk bl .65 .48

Issued to publicize the UNESCO world campaign to save historic monuments in Nubia.

Tiros I Weather Satellite over Globe and WMO Emblem — AP9

1964, Mar. 23 Unwmk. *Perf. 13*
C41 AP9 50fr emer, dk bl & choc .65 .40

4th World Meteorological Day, Mar. 23.

Rocket, Stars and "Stamp" — AP10

1964, June 5 Engr.
C42 AP10 50fr dk bl & magenta .55 .35

"PHILATEC," International Philatelic and Postal Techniques Exhibition, Paris, June 5-21, 1964.

Europafrica Issue, 1963

Common Design Type

Design: 50fr, European and African shaking hands, emblems of industry and agriculture.

1964, July 20 Photo. *Perf. 12x13*
C43 CD116 50fr multi .40 .22

John F. Kennedy — AP11

Discobolus and Discus Thrower — AP12

Perf. 12½
1964, Sept. 25 Unwmk. Photo.
C44 AP11 100fr multi .80 .60
a. Souvenir sheet of 4 3.25 2.75

President John F. Kennedy (1917-1963).

1964, Oct. 10 Engr. *Perf. 13*

60fr, Water polo, horiz. 85fr, Relay race, horiz. 250fr, Torch bearer & Pierre de Coubertin.

C45 AP12 60fr red brn & sl grn .40 .30
C46 AP12 85fr ultra & red brn .65 .35
C47 AP12 100fr brt grn, dk red & sl .70 .45
C48 AP12 250fr yel brn, brt grn & sl 1.65 1.10
a. Min. sheet of 4, #C45-C48 3.50 3.50
Nos. C45-C48 (4) 3.40 2.20

18th Olympic Games, Tokyo, Oct. 10-25.

Pope John XXIII (1881-1963) AP13

1965, June 3 Photo. *Perf. 12½x13*
C49 AP13 100fr multi .75 .55

Hand Crushing Crab — AP14

Sir Winston Churchill — AP15

1965, July 15 Engr. *Perf. 13*
C50 AP14 100fr yel grn, blk & brn .80 .42

Issued to publicize the fight against cancer.

Perf. 12½x13
1965, Sept. 3 Photo. Unwmk.
C51 AP15 100fr multi .80 .42

Buying Sets
It is often less expensive to purchase complete sets than individual stamps that make up the set. Set values are provided for many such sets.

Symbols of Agriculture, Industry, Education — AP16

Flags and Niamey Fair — AP17

1965, Oct. 24 **Engr.** ***Perf. 13***
C52 AP16 50fr henna brn, blk & ol .40 .22

International Cooperation Year, 1965.

1965, Dec. 10 **Photo.** ***Perf. 13x12½***
C53 AP17 100fr multi .75 .42

International Fair at Niamey.

Dr. Schweitzer, Crippled Hands and Symbols of Medicine, Religion and Music — AP18

1966, Jan. 4 **Photo.** ***Perf. 12½x13***
C54 AP18 50fr multi .40 .24

Weather Survey Frigate and WMO Emblem — AP19

1966, Mar. 23 **Engr.** ***Perf. 13***
C55 AP19 50fr brt rose lil, dl grn & dk vio bl .42 .28

6th World Meteorological Day, Mar. 23.

Edward H. White Floating in Space and Gemini IV — AP20

Design: #C57, Alexei A. Leonov & Voskhod II.

1966, Mar. 30
C56 AP20 50fr dk red brn, blk & brt grn .42 .28
C57 AP20 50fr pur, slate & org .42 .28

Issued to honor astronauts Edward H. White and Alexei A. Leonov.

A-1 Satellite and Earth — AP21

Designs: 45fr, Diamant rocket and launching pad, vert. 90fr, FR-1 satellite. 100fr, D-1 satellite.

1966, May 12 **Photo.** ***Perf. 13***
C58 AP21 45fr multi .36 .24
C59 AP21 60fr multi .48 .28
C60 AP21 90fr multi .70 .36
C61 AP21 100fr multi .85 .48
Nos. C58-C61 (4) 2.39 1.36

French achievements in space.

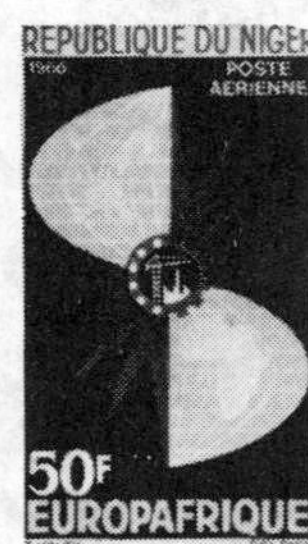

Maps of Europe and Africa and Symbols of Industry — AP22

1966, July 20 **Photo.** ***Perf. 12x13***
C62 AP22 50fr multi .40 .26

Third anniversary of economic agreement between the European Economic Community and the African and Malgache Union.

Air Afrique Issue, 1966
Common Design Type

1966, Aug. 31 **Photo.** ***Perf. 13***
C63 CD123 30fr gray, yel grn & blk .22 .15

Gemini 6 and 7 — AP23

1966, Oct. 14 **Engr.** ***Perf. 13***
C64 AP23 50fr Voskhod 1, vert. .40 .22
C65 AP23 100fr shown .80 .38

Russian & American achievements in space.

Torii and Atom Destroying Crab — AP24

1966, Dec. 2 **Photo.** ***Perf. 13***
C66 AP24 100fr dp claret, brn, vio & bl grn .75 .42

9th Intl. Anticancer Cong., Tokyo, Oct. 23-29.

New Mosque, Niamey — AP25

1967, Jan. 11 **Engr.** ***Perf. 13***
C67 AP25 100fr grn & brt bl .70 .35

Albrecht Dürer, Self-portrait AP26

Self-portraits: 100fr, Jacques Louis David. 250fr, Ferdinand Delacroix.

1967, Jan. 27 **Photo.** ***Perf. 12½***
C68 AP26 50fr multi .45 .30
C69 AP26 100fr multi .75 .60
C70 AP26 250fr multi 1.90 1.10
Nos. C68-C70 (3) 3.10 2.00

See No. C98.

Maritime Weather Station — AP27

1967, Apr. 28 **Engr.** ***Perf. 13***
C71 AP27 50fr brt bl, dk car rose & blk .65 .32

7th World Meteorological Day.

View of EXPO '67, Montreal — AP28

1967, Apr. 28 **Engr.** ***Perf. 13***
C72 AP28 100fr lil, brt bl & blk .70 .35

Issued for EXPO '67, International Exhibition, Montreal, Apr. 28-Oct. 27, 1967.

Audio-visual Center, Stylized Eye and People — AP29

1967, June 22 **Engr.** ***Perf. 13***
C73 AP29 100fr brt bl, pur & grn .70 .35

National Audio-Visual Center.

Konrad Adenauer (1876-1967), Chancellor of West Germany (1949-63) — AP30

1967, Aug. 11 **Photo.** ***Perf. 12½***
C74 AP30 100fr dk bl, gray & sepia .75 .40
a. Souv. sheet of 4 3.00 2.50

African Postal Union Issue, 1967
Common Design Type

1967, Sept. 9 **Engr.** ***Perf. 13***
C75 CD124 100fr emer, red & brt lil .70 .35

Jesus Teaching in the Temple, by Ingres — AP31

Design: 150fr, Jesus Giving the Keys to St. Peter, by Ingres, vert.

1967, Oct. 2 **Photo.** ***Perf. 12½***
C76 AP31 100fr multi 1.00 .65
C77 AP31 150fr multi 1.50 1.00

Jean Dominique Ingres (1780-1867), French painter.

Children and UNICEF Emblem — AP32

1967, Dec. 11 **Engr.** ***Perf. 13***
C78 AP32 100fr bl, brn & grn .70 .35

21st anniv. of UNICEF.

O.C.A.M. Emblem — AP33

1968, Jan. 12 **Engr.** ***Perf. 13***
C79 AP33 100fr brt bl, grn & org .70 .35

Conf. of the Organization Communitée Afrique et Malgache (OCAM), Niamey, Jan. 1968.

Vincent van Gogh, Self-portrait AP34

Self-portraits: 50fr, Jean Baptiste Camille Corot. 150fr, Francisco de Goya.

1968, Jan. 29 **Photo.** ***Perf. 12½***
C80 AP34 50fr multi .50 .22
C81 AP34 150fr multi 1.20 .55
C82 AP34 200fr multi 1.60 .80
Nos. C80-C82 (3) 3.30 1.57

See No. C98.

Breguet 27 — AP35

Planes: 80fr, Potez 25 on the ground. 100fr, Potez 25 in the air.

1968, Mar. 14 — Engr. — *Perf. 13*

C83 AP35 45fr ind, car & dk grn .34 .22
C84 AP35 80fr indigo, bl & brn .60 .28
C85 AP35 100fr sky bl, brn blk & dk grn .70 .34
Nos. C83-C85 (3) 1.64 .84

25th anniversary of air mail service between France and Niger.

Splendid Glossy Starling — AP36

Design: 100fr, Amethyst starling, vert.

1968-69 — Photo. — *Perf. 13*

C86 AP36 100fr gold & multi ('69) .65 .28

Engr.

C87 AP36 250fr mag, sl grn & brt bl 1.40 .70

See No. C255.

Dandy Horse, 1818, and Racer, 1968 — AP37

1968, May 17 — Engr. — *Perf. 13*

C88 AP37 100fr bl grn & red .65 .35

150th anniversary of the invention of the bicycle.

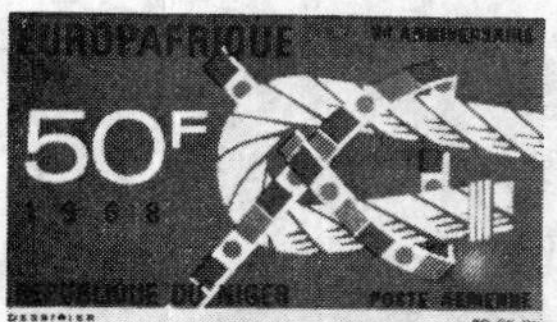

Sheet Bend Knot — AP37a

1968, July 20 — Photo. — *Perf. 13*

C89 AP37a 50fr gray, blk, red & grn .38 .22

Fifth anniversary of economic agreement between the European Economic Community and the African and Malgache Union.

Fencing — AP38

Designs: 100fr, Jackknife dive, vert. 150fr, Weight lifting, vert. 200fr, Equestrian.

1968, Sept. 10 — Engr. — *Perf. 13*

C90 AP38 50fr pur & blk .32 .18
C91 AP38 100fr choc, ultra & blk .65 .28
C92 AP38 150fr choc & org .90 .42
C93 AP38 200fr brn, emer & ind 1.25 .65
a. Min. sheet of 4, #C90-C93 3.50 3.50
Nos. C90-C93 (4) 3.12 1.53

19th Olympic Games, Mexico City, Oct. 12-27.

No. C93a is folded down the vertical gutter separating Nos. C90-C91 se-tenant at left and Nos. C92-C93 se-tenant at right.

Robert F. Kennedy — AP39

#C94, John F. Kennedy. #C95, Rev. Dr. Martin Luther King, Jr. #C96, Mahatma Gandhi.

1968, Oct. 4 — Photo. — *Perf. 12½*

C94 AP39 100fr blk & dl org .65 .30
C95 AP39 100fr blk & aqua .65 .30
C96 AP39 100fr blk & gray .65 .30
C97 AP39 100fr blk & yel .65 .30
a. Souv. sheet of 4, #C94-C97 3.00 2.50
Nos. C94-C97 (4) 2.60 1.20

Issued to honor proponents of non-violence.

PHILEXAFRIQUE Issue

Painting Type of 1968

Design: 100fr, Interior Minister Paré, by J. L. La Neuville (1748-1826).

1968, Oct. 25 — Photo. — *Perf. 12½*

C98 AP34 100fr multi .80 .80

Issued to publicize PHILEXAFRIQUE, Philatelic Exhibition in Abidjan, Feb. 14-23, 1969. Printed with alternating light blue label.

Arms and Flags of Niger AP40

1968, Dec. 17 — Litho. — *Perf. 13*

C99 AP40 100fr multi .65 .30

10th anniv. of the proclamation of the Republic.

Bonaparte as First Consul, by Ingres AP41

Paintings: 100fr, Napoleon Visiting the Plague House in Jaffa, by Antoine Jean Gros. 150fr, Napoleon on the Imperial Throne, by Jean Auguste Dominique Ingres. 200fr, Napoleon's March Through France, by Jean Louis Ernest Meissonier, horiz.

Perf. 12½x12, 12x12½

1969, Jan. 20 — Photo.

C100 AP41 50fr multi .80 .60
C101 AP41 100fr grn & multi 1.30 1.40
C102 AP41 150fr pur & multi 1.75 1.25
C103 AP41 200fr brn & multi 2.50 1.75
Nos. C100-C103 (4) 6.35 5.00

Napoleon Bonaparte (1769-1821).

2nd PHILEXAFRIQUE Issue

Common Design Type

Designs: 50fr, Niger No. 41 and giraffes.

1969, Feb. 14 — Engr. — *Perf. 13*

C104 CD128 50fr slate, brn & org .40 .34

Weather Observation Plane in Storm and Anemometer — AP42

1969, Mar. 23 — Engr. — *Perf. 13*

C105 AP42 50fr blk, brt bl & grn .35 .16

9th World Meteorological Day.

Panhard Levassor, 1900 — AP43

Early Automobiles: 45fr, De Dion Bouton 8, 1904. 50fr, Opel, 1909. 70fr, Daimler, 1910. 100fr, Vermorel 12/16, 1912.

1969, Apr. 15 — Engr. — *Perf. 13*

C106 AP43 25fr gray, lt grn & bl grn .18 .15
C107 AP43 45fr gray, bl & vio .24 .15
C108 AP43 50fr gray, yel bis & brn .40 .20
C109 AP43 70fr gray, brt pink & brt lil .55 .28
C110 AP43 100fr gray, lem & sl grn .70 .35
Nos. C106-C110 (5) 2.07 1.13

Apollo 8 Trip around Moon AP44

Embossed on Gold Foil

1969, Mar. 31 — *Die-cut Perf. 10½*

C111 AP44 1000fr gold 7.00 7.00

US Apollo 8 mission, which put the 1st men into orbit around the moon, Dec. 21-27, 1968.

No. C14 Overprinted in Red with Lunar Landing Module and: "L'HOMME / SUR LA LUNE / JUILLET 1969 / APOLLO 11"

1969, July 25 — Engr. — *Perf. 13*

C112 AP1 500fr multi 3.50 3.50

See note after Mali No. C80.

Toys — AP45

1969, Oct. 13 — Engr. — *Perf. 13*

C113 AP45 100fr bl, red brn & grn .65 .28

International Nuremberg Toy Fair.

Europafrica Issue

Links AP46

1969, Oct. 30 — Photo.

C114 AP46 50fr vio, yel & blk .35 .16

Camels and Motor Caravan Crossing Desert — AP47

100fr, Motor caravan crossing mountainous region. 150fr, Motor caravan in African village. 200fr, Map of Africa showing tour, Citroen B-2 tractor, African & European men shaking hands.

1969, Nov. 22 — Engr. — *Perf. 13*

C115 AP47 50fr lil, pink & brn .32 .15
C116 AP47 100fr dk car rose, lt bl & vio bl .65 .28
C117 AP47 150fr multi .90 .42
C118 AP47 200fr sl grn, bl & blk 1.20 .60
Nos. C115-C118 (4) 3.07 1.45

Black Tour across Africa from Colomb-Bechar, Algeria, to Mombassa, Dar es Salaam, Mozambique, Tananarive and the Cape of Good Hope.

EXPO '70 at Osaka — AP48

1970, Mar. 25 — Photo. — *Perf. 12½*

C119 AP48 100fr multi .65 .30

Issued to publicize EXPO '70 International Exhibition, Osaka, Japan, Mar. 15-Sept. 13.

Education Year Emblem and Education Symbols — AP49

1970, Apr. 6 — Engr. — *Perf. 13*

C120 AP49 100fr plum, red & gray .65 .30

Issued for International Education Year.

Rotary Emblem, Globe and Niamey Club Emblem — AP50

1970, Apr. 30 — Photo. — *Perf. 12½*

C121 AP50 100fr gold & multi .65 .30

65th anniversary of Rotary International.

Modern Plane, Clement Ader and his Flying Machine — AP51

Designs: 100fr, Joseph and Jacques Montgolfier, rocket and balloon. 150fr, Isaac Newton, planetary system and trajectories. 200fr, Galileo Galilei, spaceship and trajectories. 250fr, Leonardo da Vinci, his flying machine, and plane.

1970, May 11 Engr. *Perf. 13*

C122 AP51 50fr bl, cop red & sl .32 .15
C123 AP51 100fr cop red, bl & sl .60 .30
C124 AP51 150fr brn, grn & ocher .85 .45
C125 AP51 200fr dk car rose, dp vio & bis 1.20 .60
C126 AP51 250fr cop red, gray & pur 1.60 .80
Nos. C122-C126 (5) 4.57 2.30

Pioneers of space research.

For overprints and surcharges see Nos. C129-C130, C141-C142.

Bay of Naples, Buildings, Mt. Vesuvius and Niger No. 97 — AP52

1970, May 5 Photo. *Perf. 12½*

C127 AP52 100fr multi .65 .28

Issued to publicize the 10th Europa Philatelic Exhibition, Naples, Italy, May 2-10.

TV Tube, Books, Microscope, Globe and ITU Emblem — AP53

1970, May 16 Engr. *Perf. 13*

C128 AP53 100fr grn, brn & red .65 .28

Issued for World Telecommunications Day.

Nos. C123 and C125 Overprinted: "Solidarité Spatiale / Apollo XIII / 11-17 Avril 1970"

1970, June 6 Engr. *Perf. 13*

C129 AP51 100fr multi .65 .30
C130 AP51 200fr multi 1.10 .55

Abortive flight of Apollo 13, Apr. 11-17, 1970.

UN Emblem, Man, Woman and Doves — AP54

1970, June 26 Photo. *Perf. 12½*

C131 AP54 100fr brt bl, dk bl & org .60 .28
C132 AP54 150fr multi 1.10 .45

25th anniversary of the United Nations.

European and African Men, Globe and Fleur-de-lis — AP55

Lithographed; Embossed on Gold Foil

1970, July 22 *Perf. 12½*

C133 AP55 250fr gold & ultra 1.60 1.60

French Language Cong., Niamey, Mar. 1970.

Europafrica Issue

European and African Women — AP56

1970, July 29 Engr. *Perf. 13*

C134 AP56 50fr slate grn & dl red .32 .18

EXPO Emblem, Geisha and Torii — AP57

Design: 150fr, EXPO emblem, exhibition at night and character from Noh play.

1970, Sept. 16 Engr. *Perf. 13*

C135 AP57 100fr multi .60 .28
C136 AP57 150fr bl, dk brn & grn .85 .42

Issued to commemorate EXPO '70 International Exhibition, Osaka, Japan, Mar. 15-Sept. 13.

Gymnast on Parallel Bars — AP58

Beethoven and Piano — AP59

Sports: 100fr, Vaulting, horiz. 150fr, Flying jump, horiz. 200fr, Rings.

1970, Oct. 26 Engr. *Perf. 13*

C137 AP58 50fr brt bl .35 .20
C138 AP58 100fr brt grn .65 .35
C139 AP58 150fr brt rose lil 1.00 .50
C140 AP58 200fr red org 1.25 .65
Nos. C137-C140 (4) 3.25 1.70

17th World Gymnastics Championships, Ljubljana, Oct. 22-27.

Nos. C124 and C126 Surcharged and Overprinted: "LUNA 16 - Sept. 1970 / PREMIERS PRELEVEMENTS / AUTOMATIQUES SUR LA LUNE"

1970, Nov. 5

C141 AP51 100fr on 150fr multi .65 .30
C142 AP51 200fr on 250fr multi 1.25 .55

Unmanned moon probe of the Russian space ship Luna 16, Sept. 12-24.

1970, Nov. 18 Photo. *Perf. 12½*

Design: 150fr, Beethoven and dancers with dove, symbolic of Ode to Joy.

C143 AP59 100fr multi .65 .26
C144 AP59 150fr multi 1.25 .55

Ludwig van Beethoven (1770-1827), composer.

John F. Kennedy Bridge, Niamey — AP60

1970, Dec. 18 Photo. *Perf. 12½*

C145 AP60 100fr multi .60 .22

Proclamation of the Republic, 12th anniversary.

Gamal Abdel Nasser (1918-70), President of Egypt — AP61

Design: 200fr, Nasser with raised arm.

1971, Jan. 5 Photo. *Perf. 12½*

C146 AP61 100fr blk, org brn & grn .55 .22
C147 AP61 200fr grn, org & blk brn 1.10 .60

Charles de Gaulle AP62

Embossed on Gold Foil

1971, Jan. 22 *Die-cut Perf. 10*

C148 AP62 1000fr gold 14.00 14.00

In memory of Gen. Charles de Gaulle (1890-1970), President of France.

Olympic Rings and "Munich" — AP63

1971, Jan. 29 Engr. *Perf. 13*

C149 AP63 150fr dk bl, rose lil & grn .85 .45

1972 Summer Olympic Games, Munich.

Landing Module over Moon — AP64

Masks of Hate — AP65

1971, Feb. 5 Engr. *Perf. 13*

C150 AP64 250fr ultra, sl grn & org 1.40 .70

Apollo 14 mission, Jan. 31-Feb. 9.

1971, Mar. 20 Engr. *Perf. 13*

200fr, People & 4-leaf clover (symbol of unity).

C151 AP65 100fr red, sl & brt bl .65 .30
C152 AP65 200fr sl, red & grn 1.10 .55

Intl. Year against Racial Discrimination.

Map of Africa and Telecommunications System — AP66

1971, Apr. 6 Photo. *Perf. 12½*

C153 AP66 100fr grn & multi .60 .22

Pan-African telecommunications system.

African Mask and Japan No. 580 — AP67

Design: 100fr, Japanese actors, stamps of Niger, No. 95 on cover and No. 170.

1971, Apr. 23 Engr. *Perf. 13*

C154 AP67 50fr dk brn, emer & blk .32 .16
C155 AP67 100fr brn & multi .65 .28

Philatokyo 71, Tokyo Philatelic Exposition, Apr. 19-29.

Longwood, St. Helena, by Carle Vernet — AP68

Napoleon Bonaparte: 200fr, Napoleon's body on camp bed, by Marryat.

1971, May 5 Photo. *Perf. 13*

C156 AP68 150fr gold & multi .95 .42
C157 AP68 200fr gold & multi 1.25 .60

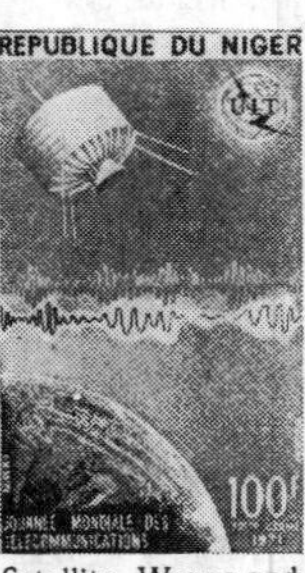

Satellite, Waves and Earth — AP69

Olympic Rings, Athletes and Torch — AP70

1971, May 17 Engr. *Perf. 13*

C158 AP69 100fr org, ultra & dk brn .60 .28

3rd World Telecommunications Day.

1971, June 10

Designs: 50fr, Pierre de Coubertin, discus throwers, horiz. 150fr, Runners, horiz.

C159 AP70 50fr red & slate .32 .15
C160 AP70 100fr sl, brn & grn .65 .22
C161 AP70 150fr plum, bl & rose lil .95 .42

75th anniv. of modern Olympic Games.

Astronauts and Landing Module on Moon — AP71

Charles de Gaulle — AP72

1971, July 26 Engr. Perf. 13

C162 AP71 150fr red brn, pur & sl .85 .40

US Apollo 15 moon mission, 7/26-8/7/71.

1971, Nov. 9 Photo. Perf. 12½x12

C163 AP72 250r multi 2.25 1.40

First anniversary of the death of Charles de Gaulle (1890-1970), president of France.

African Postal Union Issue, 1971
Common Design Type

Design: 100fr, Water carrier, cattle and UAMPT headquarters, Brazzaville, Congo.

1971, Nov. 13 Photo. Perf. 13x13½

C164 CD135 100fr blue & multi .60 .28

Al Hariri Holding Audience, Baghdad, 1237 — AP73

Designs from Mohammedan Miniatures: 150fr, Archangel Israfil, late 14th century, vert. 200fr, Horsemen, 1210.

1971, Nov. 25 Perf. 13

C165 AP73 100fr multi .55 .30
C166 AP73 150fr multi .80 .45
C167 AP73 200fr multi 1.10 .60
Nos. C165-C167 (3) 2.45 1.35

Louis Armstrong — AP74

Design: 150fr, Armstrong with trumpet.

1971, Dec. 6

C168 AP74 100fr multi .60 .28
C169 AP74 150fr multi .85 .42

Armstrong (1900-71), American jazz musician.

Adoration of the Kings, by Di Bartolo — AP75

Christmas (Paintings): 150fr, Nativity, by Domenico Ghirlandaio, vert. 200fr, Adoration of the Shepherds, by Il Perugino.

1971, Dec. 24 Photo. Perf. 13

C170 AP75 100fr blk & multi .65 .30
C171 AP75 150fr blk & multi 1.00 .45
C172 AP75 200fr blk & multi 1.25 .60
Nos. C170-C172 (3) 2.90 1.35

See Nos. C210-C212, C232-C234.

Presidents Pompidou and Diori Hamani, Flags of Niger and France — AP76

1972, Jan. 22

C173 AP76 250fr multi 2.25 1.50

Visit of President Georges Pompidou of France, Jan. 1972.

Snowflakes, Olympic Torch and Emblem — AP77

Design: 100fr, Torii made of ski poles and skis, and dwarf tree, vert.

1972, Jan. 27 Engr.

C174 AP77 100fr dk vio, grn & car .55 .25
C175 AP77 150fr dk vio, lil & red .85 .40
a. Souv. sheet of 2, #C174-C175 1.60 1.60

11th Winter Olympic Games, Sapporo, Japan, Feb. 3-13.

The Masked Ball, by Guardi — AP78

50fr, 100fr, 150fr, Details from "The Masked Ball," by Francesco Guardi (1712-93); all vert.

1972, Feb. 7 Photo.

C176 AP78 50fr gold & multi .32 .15
C177 AP78 100fr gold & multi .65 .28
C178 AP78 150fr gold & multi .95 .42
C179 AP78 200fr gold & multi 1.25 .60
Nos. C176-C179 (4) 3.17 1.45

UNESCO campaign to save Venice.
See Nos. C215-C216.

Footnotes near stamp listings often refer to other stamps of the same design.

Johannes Brahms and "Lullaby" — AP79

Scout Sign and Tents — AP80

1972, Mar. 17 Engr. Perf. 13

C180 AP79 100fr multicolored .65 .28

75th anniversary of death of Johannes Brahms (1833-1897), German composer.

1972, Mar. 22

C181 AP80 150fr pur, org & slate bl .80 .30

World Boy Scout Seminar, Cotonou, Dahomey, March 1972.

Surgical Team, Heart-shaped Globe and Emblem — AP81

1972 Engr. Perf. 13

C182 AP81 100fr dp brn & car .65 .28

"Your heart is your health," World Health Day.

Bleriot XI Crossing English Channel — AP82

Famous Aircraft: 75fr, Spirit of St. Louis crossing Atlantic. 100fr, 1st flight of Concorde supersonic jet.

1972, Apr. 24

C183 AP82 50fr multicolored .35 .18
C184 AP82 75fr multicolored .55 .30
C185 AP82 100fr multicolored .75 .45
Nos. C183-C185 (3) 1.65 .93

ITU Emblem, Satellite, Stars and Earth — AP83

1972, May 17 Engr. Perf. 13

C186 AP83 100fr pur, car & blk .60 .28

4th World Telecommunications Day.

Boxing and Opera House — AP84

100fr, Broad jump & City Hall, vert. 150fr, Soccer & Church of the Theatines, vert. 200fr, Running and Propylaeum.

1972, May 26

C187 AP84 50fr bl & grn .30 .15
C188 AP84 100fr yel grn & dk brn .55 .25
C189 AP84 150fr org red & dk brn .80 .35
C190 AP84 200fr vio & dk brn 1.10 .45
a. Min. sheet of 4, #C187-C190 3.25 2.75
Nos. C187-C190 (4) 2.75 1.20

20th Olympic Games, Munich, Aug. 26-Sept. 10.
For overprints see Nos. C196-C199.

"Alexander Graham Bell," Telephone — AP85

1972, July 7

C191 AP85 100fr car, dk pur & slate .60 .25

Alexander Graham Bell (1847-1922), inventor of the telephone. Stamp pictures Samuel F. B. Morse.

Europafrica Issue

Stylized Maps of Africa and Europe — AP86

1972, July 29 Engr. Perf. 13

C192 AP86 50fr red brn, bl & grn .30 .15

Mail Runner, UPU Emblem — AP87

Designs: 100fr, Mail truck, UPU emblem. 150fr, Mail plane, UPU emblem.

1972, Oct. 9 Engr. Perf. 13

C193 AP87 50fr multicolored .30 .18
C194 AP87 100fr multicolored .60 .30
C195 AP87 150fr multicolored .85 .45

Universal Postal Union Day.

Nos. C187-C190 Overprinted in Red or Violet Blue

a. WELTER / CORREA / MEDAILLE D'OR
b. TRIPLE SAUT / SANEEV / MEDAILLE D'OR
c. FOOTBALL / POLOGNE / MEDAILLE D'OR
d. MARATHON / SHORTER / MEDAILLE D'OR

1972, Nov. 10

C196 AP84(a) 50fr multi (R) .30 .15
C197 AP84(b) 100fr multi (R) .60 .24
C198 AP84(c) 150fr multi (VBl) .95 .38
C199 AP84(d) 200fr multi (R) 1.40 .50
Nos. C196-C199 (4) 3.25 1.27

Gold medal winners in 20th Olympic Games: Emilio Correa, Cuba, welterweight boxing; Victor Saneev, USSR, triple jump; Poland, soccer; Frank Shorter, US, marathon.

The Crow and The Fox AP88

Fables: 50fr, The Lion and the Mouse. 75fr, The Monkey and the Leopard.

1972, Nov. 23

C200 AP88 25fr emer, blk & brn	.18	.15
C201 AP88 50fr brt pink, bl grn & brn	.32	.15
C202 AP88 75fr lt brn, grn & dk brn	.48	.28
Nos. C200-C202 (3)	.98	.58

Jean de La Fontaine (1621-1695), French fabulist.

Astronauts on Moon — AP89

1972, Dec. 12 Photo. *Perf. 13*

C203 AP89 250fr multi 1.40 .65

Apollo 17 US moon mission, Dec. 7-19.

Young Athlete AP90

Design: 100fr, Head of Hermes.

1973, Feb. 7 Engr. *Perf. 13*

C204 AP90 50fr dk car	.28	.15
C205 AP90 100fr purple	.55	.25

Treasures of antiquity.

Boy Scouts and Radio Transmission — AP91

Niger Boy Scouts: 50fr, Red Cross, first aid. 100fr, Scout and gazelle. 150fr, Scouts with gazelle and bird.

1973, Mar. 21 Engr. *Perf. 13*

C206 AP91 25fr multicolored	.15	.15
C207 AP91 50fr multicolored	.28	.15
C208 AP91 100fr multicolored	.55	.28
C209 AP91 150fr multicolored	.80	.35

For overprints see Nos. C217-C218.

Christmas Type of 1971

Paintings: 50fr, Crucifixion, by Hugo van der Goes, vert. 100fr, Burial of Christ, by Cima da Conegliano. 150fr, Pietà, by Giovanni Bellini.

1973, Apr. 20 Photo. *Perf. 13*

C210 AP75 50fr gold & multi	.32	.15
C211 AP75 100fr gold & multi	.65	.32
C212 AP75 150fr gold & multi	.90	.42
Nos. C210-C212 (3)	1.87	.89

Easter 1973.

Air Afrique Plane and Mail Truck — AP92

1973, Apr. 30 Engr. *Perf. 13*

C213 AP92 100fr brt grn, choc & car .60 .28

Stamp Day 1973.

WMO Emblem, Pyramids with Weather Symbols, Satellite — AP93

1973, May 7

C214 AP93 100fr multicolored .60 .28

Cent. of intl. meteorological cooperation.

Painting Type of 1972

Paintings by Delacroix: 150fr, Prowling lioness. 200fr, Tigress and cub.

1973, May 22 Photo. *Perf. 13x12½*

C215 AP78 150fr blk & multi	.85	.40
C216 AP78 200fr blk & multi	1.20	.60

175th anniversary of the birth of Ferdinand Delacroix (1798-1863), French painter.

Nos. C208-C209 Overprinted: "24 * Conference Mondiale / du Scoutisme / NAIROBI 1973"

1973, July 19 Engr. *Perf. 13*

C217 AP91 100fr multi	.55	.28
C218 AP91 150fr multi	.80	.35

Boy Scout 24th World Jamboree, Nairobi, Kenya, July 16-21.

Head and City Hall, Brussels — AP93a

1973, Sept. 17 Engr. *Perf. 13*

C219 AP93a 100fr multicolored .60 .28

Africa Weeks, Brussels, Sept. 15-30, 1973.

Men Emptying Cornucopia, FAO Emblem, People AP94

1973, Nov. 2 Engr. *Perf. 13*

C220 AP94 50fr ultra, pur & ver .30 .15

10th anniversary of the World Food Program.

AP95

AP96

Copernicus, Sputnik 1, Heliocentric System.

1973, Nov. 12

C221 AP95 150fr mag, vio bl & brn .85 .42

1973, Nov. 22 Photo. *Perf. 12½*

C222 AP96 100fr redsh brn & multi .60 .30

Souvenir Sheet

Perf. 13

C223 AP96 200fr dp ultra & multi 1.10 1.10

10th anniv. of the death of Pres. John F. Kennedy.

Barge on Niger River AP97

Design: 75fr, Tug Baban Maza.

1974, Jan. 18 Engr. *Perf. 13*

C224 AP97 50fr mar, vio bl & grn	.24	.15
C225 AP97 75fr yel grn, bl & lil rose	.38	.20

1st anniv. of the upstream voyage of the Flotilla of Hope.

REPUBLIQUE DU NIGER Lenin — AP98

1974, Jan. 21

C226 AP98 50fr dk red brn .25 .15

Skiers AP99

1974, Feb. 8 Engr. *Perf. 11½x11*

C227 AP99 200fr bl, sepia & car 1.10 .55

50th anniversary of the first Winter Olympic Games, Chamonix, France.

Soccer and Emblem — AP100

Designs: Various views of soccer game.

1974, Apr. 8 Engr. *Perf. 13*

C228 AP100 75fr vio & blk	.30	.18
C229 AP100 150fr brn, lt & sl grn	.52	.30
C230 AP100 200fr Prus bl, grn & brn	.75	.50
Nos. C228-C230 (3)	1.57	.98

Souvenir Sheet

C231 AP100 250fr yel grn, brn & ol brn 1.10 1.10

World Soccer Championship, Munich, June 13-July 7.

For overprint see No. C239.

Christmas Type of 1971

Paintings: 50fr, Crucifixion, by Matthias Grunewald. 75fr, Avignon Pietà, attributed to Enguerrand Quarton. 125fr, Burial of Christ, by G. Isenmann.

1974, Apr. 12 Litho. *Perf. 13x12½*

C232 AP75 50fr blk & multi	.26	.15
C233 AP75 75fr blk & multi	.38	.18
C234 AP75 125r blk & multi	.65	.32
Nos. C232-C234 (3)	1.29	.65

Easter 1974.

21st Chess Olympiad, Nice, June 6-30 — AP101

1974, June 3 Engr. *Perf. 13*

C235 AP101 50fr Knights	.28	.15
C236 AP101 75fr Kings	.38	.22

Astronaut and Apollo 11 Badge AP102

1974, July 20 Engr. *Perf. 13*

C237 AP102 150fr multi .70 .40

5th anniversary of the first manned moon landing.

Europafrica Issue

The Rhinoceros, by Pietro Longhi AP103

1974, Aug. 10 Photo. *Perf. 12½x13*

C238 AP103 250fr multi 1.40 .85

No. C231 Overprinted in Red: "R.F.A. 2 / HOLLANDE 1"

1974, Sept. 27 Engr. *Perf. 13*

Souvenir Sheet

C239 AP100 250fr multi 1.40 1.40

World Cup Soccer Championship, Munich, 1974, victory of German Federal Republic. No. C239 has additional red inscription in margin: "7 JUILLET 1974 / VAINQUEUR REPUBLIQUE FEDERALE ALLEMANDE."

Caucasian Woman, Envelope, UPU Emblem and Jets — AP104

Skylab over Africa — AP105

Designs (UPU emblem, Envelope and): 100fr, Oriental woman and trains. 150fr, Indian woman and ships. 200fr, Black woman and buses.

1974, Oct. 9 Engr. *Perf. 13*

C240 AP104 50fr multi	.28	.15
C241 AP104 100fr multi	.48	.28
C242 AP104 150fr bl & multi	.70	.40
C243 AP104 200fr multi	.90	.60
Nos. C240-C243 (4)	2.36	1.43

Centenary of Universal Postal Union.

1974, Nov. 4 Engr. *Perf. 13*

C244 AP105 100fr multi .48 .28

Virgin and Child, by Correggio AP106

150fr, Virgin and Child with St. Hilary, by Filippo Lippi. 200fr, Virgin and Child, by Murillo.

1974, Dec. 24 Litho. *Perf. 12½x13*

C245 AP106 100fr multi	.55	.22
C246 AP106 150fr multi	.75	.40
C247 AP106 200fr multi	1.10	.60
Nos. C245-C247 (3)	2.40	1.22

Christmas 1974. See Nos. C252-C254, C260-C262, C280-C282.

Apollo and Emblem AP107

Designs (Emblem of Soyuz-Apollo Space Docking): 100fr, Docking in space over earth. 150fr, Soyuz in space.

1975, Jan. 31 Engr. *Perf. 13*

C248 AP107 50fr bl & multi	.25	.15
C249 AP107 100fr multi	.45	.28
C250 AP107 150fr multi	.75	.40
Nos. C248-C250 (3)	1.45	.83

Russo-American space cooperation. For overprints see Nos. C263-C265.

Europafrica Issue

European and African Women, Globe — AP108

1975, Feb. 28 Engr. *Perf. 13*

C251 AP108 250fr brn, lil & red 1.20 .70

Painting Type of 1974

Easter: 75fr, Jesus in Garden of Olives, by Delacroix, horiz. 125fr, Crucifixion, by El Greco. 150fr, Resurrection, by Leonard Limosin.

Perf. 13x12½, 12½x13

1975, Mar. 27 Litho.

C252 AP106 75fr multi	.38	.15
C253 AP106 125fr multi	.60	.32
C254 AP106 150fr multi	.75	.40
Nos. C252-C254 (3)	1.73	.87

Bird Type of 1968-69 Dated "1975"

Design: 100fr, Cinnyricinclus leucogaster, vert.

1975, Apr. Photo. *Perf. 13*

C255 AP36 100fr gold & multi .42 .25

Lt. Col. Seyni Kountche AP109

1975, Apr. 15 Litho. *Perf. 12½x13*

C256 AP109 100fr multi .42 .28

Military Government, first anniversary.

Shot Put, Maple Leaf, Montreal Olympic Emblem AP110

Design: 200fr, Gymnast on rings, Canadian flag, Montreal Olympic emblem.

1975, Oct. 6 Engr. *Perf. 13*

C257 AP110 150fr blk & red	.65	.35
C258 AP110 200fr red & blk	.85	.55

Pre-Olympic Year 1975.

UN Emblem and Dove — AP111

1975, Nov. 26 Engr. *Perf. 13*

C259 AP111 100fr grn & bl .45 .28

United Nations, 30th anniversary.

Painting Type of 1974

50fr, Virgin of Seville, by Murillo. 75fr, Adoration of the Shepherds, by Tintoretto, horiz. 125fr, Virgin with Angels, Florentine, 15th cent.

1975, Dec. 24 Litho. *Perf. 12½x13*

C260 AP106 50fr multi	.22	.15
C261 AP106 75fr multi	.32	.25
C262 AP106 125fr multi	.55	.40
Nos. C260-C262 (3)	1.09	.80

Christmas 1975.

Nos. C248-C250 Overprinted: "JONCTION / 17 Juillet 1975"

1975, Dec. 30 Engr. *Perf. 13*

C263 AP107 50fr bl & multi	.22	.15
C264 AP107 100fr multi	.45	.30
C265 AP107 150fr multi	.65	.42
Nos. C263-C265 (3)	1.32	.87

Apollo-Soyuz link-up in space, July 17, 1975.

12th Winter Olympic Games Type, 1976

Designs: 200fr, Women's figure skating. 300fr, Biathlon. 500fr, Speed skating.

1976, Feb. 20 Litho. *Perf. 14x13½*

C266 A97 200fr multi	1.10	.45
C267 A97 300fr multi	1.40	.60

Souvenir Sheet

C268 A97 500fr multi 2.50 1.10

American Bicentennial Type, 1976

Design (Statue of Liberty and): 150fr, Joseph Warren, martyr at Bunker Hill. 200fr, John Paul Jones on the bridge of the "Bonhomme Richard." 300fr, Molly Pitcher, Monmouth battle heroine. 500fr, Start of the fighting.

1976, Apr. 8

C269 A100 150fr multi	.70	.30
C270 A100 200fr multi	.90	.50
C271 A100 300fr multi	1.50	.70
Nos. C269-C271 (3)	3.10	1.50

Souvenir Sheet

C272 A100 500fr multi 2.50 1.10

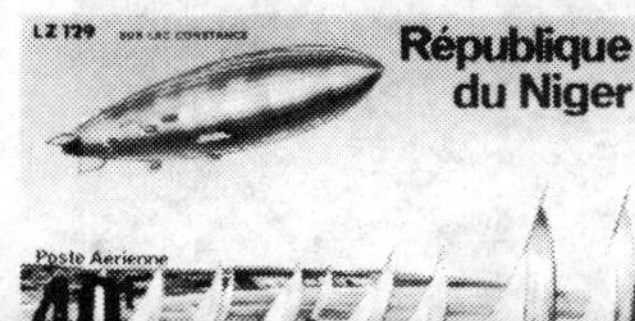

LZ-129 over Lake Constance — AP112

Designs: 50fr, LZ-3 over Würzburg. 150fr, LZ-9 over Friedrichshafen. 200fr, LZ-2 over Rothenburg, vert. 300fr, LZ-130 over Essen. 500fr, LZ-127 over the Swiss Alps.

1976, May 18 Litho. *Perf. 11*

C273 AP112 40fr multi	.20	.15
C274 AP112 50fr multi	.30	.15
C275 AP112 150fr multi	.75	.40
C276 AP112 200fr multi	1.00	.40
C277 AP112 300fr multi	1.50	.60
Nos. C273-C277 (5)	3.75	1.70

Souvenir Sheet

C278 AP112 500fr multi 2.50 1.10

75th anniversary of the Zeppelin.

Olympic Games Type, 1976
Souvenir Sheet

1976, July 17 Litho. *Perf. 14*

C279 A105 150fr Sprint .80 .38

Christmas Type of 1974

Paintings: 50fr, Nativity, by Rubens. 100fr, Virgin and Child, by Correggio. 150fr, Adoration of the Kings, by Gerard David, horiz.

1976, Dec. 24 Litho. *Perf. 12½*

C280 AP106 50fr multi	.22	.15
C281 AP106 100fr multi	.45	.28
C282 AP106 150fr multi	.65	.35
Nos. C280-C282 (3)	1.32	.78

Christmas 1976.

Viking Mars Project Type, 1977

100fr, Viking lander & nprobe, horiz. 150fr, Descent phases of Viking lander. 200fr, Titan rocket start for Mars. 400fr, Viking orbiter in flight.

1977, Mar. 15 Litho. *Perf. 14*

C283 A113 100fr multi	.50	.25
C284 A113 150fr multi	.75	.32
C285 A113 200fr multi	1.00	.45
Nos. C283-C285 (3)	2.25	1.02

Souvenir Sheet

C286 A113 400fr multi 2.25 .80

For overprints see Nos. C295-C297.

Nobel Prize Type, 1977
Souvenir Sheet

Design: 500fr, Theodore Roosevelt, peace.

1977, Aug. 20 Litho. *Perf. 14*

C287 A122 500fr multi 3.00 1.10

Games' Emblem, Wheels and Colors AP113

150fr, Rings, colors and Games' emblem.

1978, July 13 Litho. *Perf. 12½x13*

C288 AP113 40fr multi	.18	.15
C289 AP113 150fr multi	.65	.40

Third African Games, Algiers, July 13-28.

Emblem AP114

1978, Oct. 6 Litho. *Perf. 13*

C290 AP114 150fr multi .65 .40

Niger Broadcasting Company, 20th anniversary.

Philexafrique II - Essen Issue
Common Design Types

Designs: No. C291, Giraffes and Niger No. 92. No. C292, Eagle and Oldenburg No. 7.

1978, Nov. 1 Litho. *Perf. 13x12½*

C291 CD138 100fr multi	.42	.28
C292 CD139 100fr multi	.42	.28
a. Pair, #C291-C292	.85	.60

View of Campus and Laying Cornerstone — AP115

1978, Dec. 11 Litho. *Perf. 12½*

C293 AP115 100fr multi .42 .28

Islamic University of Niger.

Control Tower, Emblem, Plane, Map of Niger AP116

1979, Dec. 12 Litho. *Perf. 12½*

C294 AP116 150fr multi .65 .40

ASECNA (Air Safety Board), 20th anniversary.

Nos. C284-C286 Overprinted in Silver or Black: "alunissage / apollo XI / juillet 1969" and Emblem

1979, Dec. 20 Litho. *Perf. 14*

C295 A113 150fr multi	.65	.40
C296 A113 200fr multi (S)	.85	.55

Souvenir Sheet

C297 A113 400fr multi (S) 2.50 1.50

Apollo 11 moon landing, 10th anniversary.

Gaweye Hotel — AP117

1980, Jan. 10 Litho. *Perf. 13*

C298 AP117 100fr multi .45 .28

Self-portrait, by Rembrandt AP118

Rembrandt Portraits: 90fr, Hendrickje at the Window. 100fr, Old Man. 130fr, Maria Trip. 200fr, Self-portrait, diff. 400fr, Saskia.

1981, Feb. 12 Litho. *Perf. 12½*

C299 AP118 60fr multi	.25	.18
C300 AP118 90fr multi	.38	.25
C301 AP118 100fr multi	.42	.28
C302 AP118 130fr multi	.55	.35

C303 AP118 200fr multi .85 .55
C304 AP118 400fr multi 1.65 1.10
Nos. C299-C304 (6) 4.10 2.71

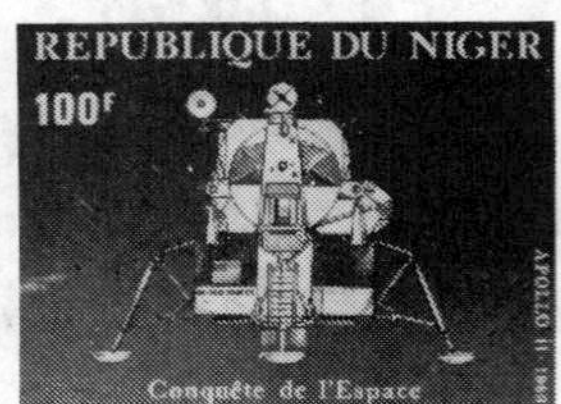

Apollo 11, 1969 — AP119

Space Conquest: Views of Columbia space shuttle, 1981.

1981, Mar. 30 Litho. *Perf. 12½*

C305 AP119 100fr multi .42 .28
C306 AP119 150fr multi .65 .40
C307 AP119 200fr multi .85 .55
C308 AP119 300fr multi 1.20 .80
Nos. C305-C308 (4) 3.12 2.03

Souvenir Sheet

C309 AP119 500fr multi 2.25 1.40

For overprint see No. C356.

Girl in a Room, by Picasso — AP120

Picasso Birth Centenary: 60fr, Olga in an Armchair. 90fr, Family of Acrobats. 120fr, Three Musicians. 200fr, Paul on a Donkey. All vert.

1981, June 25 Litho. *Perf. 12½*

C310 AP120 60fr multi .25 .18
C311 AP120 90fr multi .38 .25
C312 AP120 120fr multi .50 .32
C313 AP120 200fr multi .85 .55
C314 AP120 400fr multi 1.75 1.10
Nos. C310-C314 (5) 3.73 2.40

Christmas 1982 — AP121

Rubens Paintings.

1982, Dec. 24 Litho. *Perf. 14*

C315 AP121 200fr Adoration of the Kings .65 .42
C316 AP121 300fr Mystical Marriage of St. Catherine 1.10 .80
C317 AP121 400fr Virgin and Child 1.40 .90
Nos. C315-C317 (3) 3.15 2.12

Manned Flight Bicentenary AP122

1983, Jan. 24

C318 AP122 65fr Montgolfiere balloon, 1783, vert. .28 .18
C319 AP122 85fr Hydrogen balloon, 1783, vert. .38 .22
C320 AP122 200fr Zeppelin .85 .55
C321 AP122 250fr Farman plane 1.10 .65
C322 AP122 300fr Concorde 1.25 .80
C323 AP122 500fr Apollo 11, vert. 2.25 1.40
Nos. C318-C323 (6) 6.11 3.80

Pre-Olympic Year — AP123

1983, May 25 Litho. *Perf. 13*

C324 AP123 85fr Javelin .38 .22
C325 AP123 200fr Shot put .85 .55
C326 AP123 250fr Hammer, vert. 1.10 .70
C327 AP123 300fr Discus 1.25 .80
Nos. C324-C327 (4) 3.58 2.27

Souvenir Sheet

C328 AP123 500fr Shot put, diff. 2.25 1.40

For overprint see No. C357.

Christmas 1983 — AP124

Botticelli Paintings. 120fr, 500fr vert.

Wmk. 385 Cartor

1983 Litho. *Perf. 13*

C329 AP124 120fr Virgin and Child with Angels .25 .18
C330 AP124 350fr Adoration of the Kings .75 .45
C331 AP124 500fr Virgin of the Pomegranate 1.10 .65
Nos. C329-C331 (3) 2.10 1.28

1984 Summer Olympics — AP125

Unwmk.

1984, Feb. 22 Litho. *Perf. 13*

C332 AP125 80fr Sprint .18 .15
C333 AP125 120fr Pole vault .30 .18
C334 AP125 140fr High jump .35 .22
C335 AP125 200fr Triple jump, vert. .48 .30
C336 AP125 350fr Long jump, vert. .85 .55
Nos. C332-C336 (5) 2.16 1.40

Souvenir Sheet

C337 AP125 500fr 110-meter hurdles 1.20 .75

1984, Oct. 8 Litho.

Designs: Winners of various track events. Nos. C338-C341 vert.

C338 AP125 80fr Carl Lewis .22 .15
C339 AP125 120fr J. Cruz .32 .16
C340 AP125 140fr A. Cova .38 .18
C341 AP125 300fr Al Joyner .80 .40
Nos. C338-C341 (4) 1.72 .89

Souvenir Sheet

C342 AP125 500fr D. Mogenburg, high jump 1.40 .65

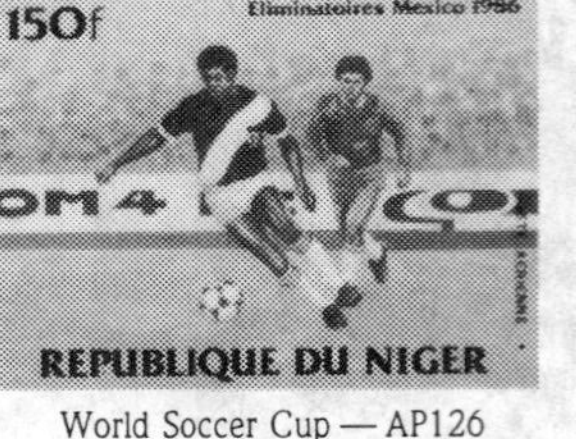

World Soccer Cup — AP126

1984, Nov. 19 Litho. *Perf. 13*

C345 AP126 150fr multi .32 .16
C346 AP126 250fr multi .55 .28
C347 AP126 450fr multi .95 .50
C348 AP126 500fr multi 1.10 .55
Nos. C345-C348 (4) 2.92 1.49

Christmas 1984 AP127

Paintings: 100fr, The Visitation, by Ghirlandajo. 200fr, Virgin and Child, by the Master of Santa Verdiana. 400fr, Virgin and Child, by J. Koning.

1984, Dec. 24 Litho. *Perf. 13*

C349 AP127 100fr multi .22 .15
C350 AP127 200fr multi .42 .22
C351 AP127 400fr multi .85 .42
Nos. C349-C351 (3) 1.49 .79

Audubon Birth Bicentennial — AP128

1985, Feb. 6 Litho. *Perf. 13*

C352 AP128 110fr Himantopus mexicanus .25 .15
C353 AP128 140fr Phoenicopterus ruber, vert. .30 .15
C354 AP128 200fr Fratercula arctica .42 .22
C355 AP128 350fr Sterna paradisaea, vert. .75 .38
Nos. C352-C355 (4) 1.72 .90

Nos. C309, C328 Ovptd. in Silver with Exhibition Emblems

1985, Mar. 11 Litho. *Perf. 12½, 13*

C356 AP119 500fr ARGENTINA '85 BUENOS AIRES 1.10 .55
C357 AP123 500fr OLYMPHILEX '85 LAUSANNE 1.10 .55

Religious Paintings by Bartolome Murillo (1617-1682) AP129

1985, Dec. 19 Litho. *Perf. 13*

C358 AP129 110fr Virgin of the Rosary .32 .16
C359 AP129 250fr The Immaculate Conception .65 .35
C360 AP129 390fr Virgin of Seville 1.10 .55
Nos. C358-C360 (3) 2.07 1.06

Christmas 1985.

Halley's Comet — AP130

1985, Dec. 26

C361 AP130 110fr Over Paris, 1910 .32 .16
C362 AP130 130fr Over New York .35 .16
C363 AP130 200fr Giotto space probe .55 .28
C364 AP130 300fr Vega probe .80 .40
C365 AP130 390fr Planet A probe 1.10 .55
Nos. C361-C365 (5) 3.12 1.55

Martin Luther King, Jr. (1929-1968), Civil Rights Activist — AP131

1986, Apr. 28 Litho. *Perf. 13½*

C366 AP131 500fr multi 2.00 1.00

1986 World Cup Soccer Championships, Mexico — AP132

Various soccer plays, stamps and labels.

1986, May 21 *Perf. 13*

C367 AP132 130fr No. 228 .45 .28
C368 AP132 210fr No. 229 .90 .42
C369 AP132 390fr No. 230 1.65 .85
C370 AP132 400fr Aztec drawing 1.65 .85
Nos. C367-C370 (4) 4.65 2.40

Souvenir Sheet

C371 AP132 500fr World Cup 2.00 1.00

Statue of Liberty, Cent. AP133

1986, June 19

C372 AP133 300fr Bartholdi, statue 1.25 .55

1988 Summer Olympics, Seoul AP134

Olympic Rings, Pierre de Coubertin and: 85fr, One-man kayak, vert. 165fr, Crew racing. 200fr, Two-man kayak. 600fr, One-man kayak, diff., vert. 750fr, One-man kayak, diff., vert.

1988, June 22 Litho. *Perf. 13*

C373	AP134	85fr multi	.58	.30
C374	AP134	165fr multi	1.10	.55
C375	AP134	200fr multi	1.35	.68
C376	AP134	600fr multi	4.00	2.00
		Nos. C373-C376 (4)	7.03	3.53

Souvenir Sheet

C377	AP134	750fr multi	5.00	5.00

REPUBLIQUE du NIGER

First Moon Landing, 20th Anniv. AP135

1989, July 27 Litho. *Perf. 13*

C378	AP135	200fr Launch	1.30	.65
C379	AP135	300fr Crew	1.90	.95
C380	AP135	350fr Lunar experiments	2.25	1.15
C381	AP135	400fr Raising flag	2.55	1.30
		Nos. C378-C381 (4)	8.00	4.05

REPUBLIQUE DU NIGER

1990 World Cup Soccer Championships, Italy — AP136

Athletes & views or symbols of Italian cities.

1990, Mar. 6 Litho. *Perf. 13*

C382	AP136	130fr Florence	.92	.45
C383	AP136	210fr Verona	1.50	.75
C384	AP136	500fr Bari	3.50	1.75
C385	AP136	600fr Rome	4.25	2.15
		Nos. C382-C385 (4)	10.17	5.10

1992 Winter Olympics, Albertville — AP138

1991, Mar. 28 Litho. *Perf. 13*

C392	AP138	110fr Speed skating	.80	.40
C393	AP138	300fr Ice hockey	2.35	1.20
C394	AP138	500fr Downhill skiing	4.00	2.00
C395	AP138	600fr Luge	4.70	2.35
		Nos. C392-C395 (4)	11.85	5.95

AIR POST SEMI-POSTAL STAMPS

Stamps of Dahomey types V1, V2, V3 and V4 inscribed "Niger" were issued in 1942 by the Vichy Government, but were not placed on sale in the colony.

POSTAGE DUE STAMPS

D1

D2

Postage Due Stamps of Upper Senegal and Niger, 1914, Overprinted

1921 Unwmk. *Perf. 14x13½*

J1	D1	5c green	.45	.45
J2	D1	10c rose	.45	.45
J3	D1	15c gray	.55	.55
J4	D1	20c brown	.55	.55
J5	D1	30c blue	.55	.55
J6	D1	50c black	.55	.55
J7	D1	60c orange	.90	.90
J8	D1	1fr violet	1.00	1.00
		Nos. J1-J8 (8)	5.00	5.00

1927 Typo.

J9	D2	2c dk bl & red	.15	.15
J10	D2	4c ver & blk	.15	.15
J11	D2	5c org & vio	.15	.15
J12	D2	10c red brn & blk vio	.20	.20
J13	D2	15c grn & org	.25	.25
J14	D2	20c cer & ol brn	.35	.35
J15	D2	25c blk & ol brn	.35	.35
J16	D2	30c dl vio & blk	.85	.85
J17	D2	50c dp red, *grnsh*	.35	.35
J18	D2	60c gray vio & org, *bluish*	.35	.35
J19	D2	1fr ind & ultra, *bluish*	.55	.55
J20	D2	2fr rose red & vio	.40	.40
J21	D2	3fr org brn & ultra	1.00	1.00
		Nos. J9-J21 (13)	5.10	5.10

Catalogue values for unused stamps in this section, from this point to the end of the section, are for Never Hinged items.

Republic of the Niger

Cross of Agadez D3

Native Metalcraft: 3fr, 5fr, 10fr, Cross of Iferouane. 15fr, 20fr, 50fr, Cross of Tahoua.

Perf. 12½

1962, July 1 Unwmk. Photo.

J22	D3	50c emerald	.15	.15
J23	D3	1fr violet	.15	.15
J24	D3	2fr slate green	.15	.15
J25	D3	3fr lilac rose	.15	.15
J26	D3	5fr green	.15	.15
J27	D3	10fr orange	.15	.15
J28	D3	15fr deep blue	.15	.15
J29	D3	20fr carmine	.15	.15
J30	D3	50fr chocolate	.28	.28
		Set value	.95	.95

1993 Litho. *Perf. 12½*

Designs as Before

Size: 50x50mm

J31	D3	5fr green	.15	.15
J32	D3	10fr orange	.15	.15
J33	D3	15fr blue	.15	.15
J34	D3	20fr red	.16	.16
J35	D3	50fr chocolate	.40	.40
		Set value	.80	.80

Imprint on Nos. J31-J35 is in black.

OFFICIAL STAMPS

Catalogue values for unused stamps in this section are for Never Hinged items.

Djerma Girl Carrying Jug
O1 O2

Perf. 14x13½

1962-71 Typo. Unwmk.

Denomination in Black

O1	O1	1fr dark purple	.15	.15
O2	O1	2fr yel grn	.15	.15
O3	O1	5fr brt blue	.15	.15
O4	O1	10fr deep red	.15	.15
O5	O1	20fr vio blue	.16	.15
O6	O1	25fr orange	.18	.15
O7	O1	30fr light blue ('65)	.22	.16
O8	O1	35fr pale grn ('71)	.28	.22
O9	O1	40fr brown ('71)	.28	.22
O10	O1	50fr black	.32	.22
O11	O1	60fr rose red	.42	.28
O12	O1	85fr blue green	.58	.28
O13	O1	100fr red lilac	.65	.28
O14	O1	200fr dark blue	1.40	.65
		Nos. O1-O14 (14)	5.09	
		Set value		2.70

1988, Nov. Typo. *Perf. 13*

O15	O2	5fr brt blue	.15	.15
O16	O2	10fr henna brn	.15	.15
O17	O2	20fr vio blue	.15	.15
O18	O2	50fr greenish blk	.25	.15

1989-96(?)

O19	O2	15fr bright yellow	.15	.15
O20	O2	45fr orange	.30	.15
O21	O2	85fr blue green		
O22	O2	100fr red lilac		
		Set value, #O15-O20	.85	.45

Issued: 15fr, 45fr, Mar. 1989; 85fr, 100fr, 1996(?).

See No. 698.

This is an expanding set. Numbers will change when complete.

NIGER COAST PROTECTORATE

'nī–jər 'kōst prə–'tek–t(ə–)rət

(Oil Rivers Protectorate)

LOCATION — West coast of Africa on Gulf of Guinea

GOVT. — British Protectorate

This territory was originally known as the Oil Rivers Protectorate, and its affairs were conducted by the British Royal Niger Company. The Company surrendered its charter to the Crown in 1899. In 1900 all of the territories formerly controlled by the Royal Niger Company were incorporated into the two protectorates of Northern and Southern Nigeria, the latter absorbing the area formerly known as Niger Coast Protectorate. In 1914 Northern and Southern Nigeria joined to form the Crown Colony of Nigeria. (See Nigeria, Northern Nigeria, Southern Nigeria and Lagos.)

12 Pence = 1 Shilling

Stamps of Great Britain, 1881-87, Overprinted in Black

BRITISH
PROTECTORATE

OIL RIVERS

1892 Wmk. 30 *Perf. 14*

1	A54	½p vermilion	6.50	3.75
2	A40	1p lilac	4.75	4.75
a.		"OIL RIVERS" at top	4,500.	
b.		Half used as ½p on cover		3,000.
3	A56	2p green & car	14.00	7.00
a.		Half used as 1p on cover		—
4	A57	2½p violet, *bl*	5.75	1.90
5	A61	5p lilac & blue	6.50	6.50
6	A65	1sh green	42.50	55.00
		Nos. 1-6 (6)	80.00	78.90

For surcharges see Nos. 7-36, 50.

No. 2 Surcharged in Red or Violet

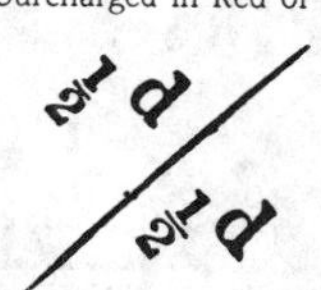

1893

7	A40	½p on half of 1p (R)	150.	140.
c.		Unsevered pair	400.	400.
d.		"½" omitted		
7A	A40	½p on half of 1p (V)	5,500.	4,750.
b.		Surcharge double	9,000.	

Nos. 3-6 Handstamp Surcharged in Violet, Red, Carmine, Bluish Black, Deep Blue, Green or Black

Half
Penny

1893 Wmk. 30 *Perf. 14*

8	A56	½p on 2p (V)	250.	250.
9	A57	½p on 2½p (V)	3,000.	
10	A57	½p on 2½p (R)	190.	130.
11	A57	½p on 2½p (C)	7,250.	6,500.
12	A57	½p on 2½p (B)	7,250.	6,500.
13	A57	½p on 2½p (G)	375.	375.

HALF
PENNY.

14	A56	½p on 2p (V)	250.	250.
15	A56	½p on 2p (Bl)	1,000.	500.
16	A57	½p on 2½p (V)	3,000.	
17	A57	½p on 2½p (R)	350.	350.
18	A57	½p on 2½p (Bl)	275.	275.
19	A57	½p on 2½p (G)	300.	300.

HALF
PENNY

20	A56	½p on 2p (V)	500.	300.
21	A57	½p on 2½p (R)	350.	350.
22	A57	½p on 2½p (C)	200.	200.
23	A57	½p on 2½p (Bl Bk)	2,500.	
24	A57	½p on 2½p (Bl)	250.	250.
25	A57	½p on 2½p (G)	250.	250.
26	A57	½p on 2½p (Bk)	2,250.	

HALF
PENNY

27	A57	½p on 2½p (R)	3,750.	
28	A57	½p on 2½p (G)	325.	325.

One
Shilling

29	A56	1sh on 2p (V)	450.	450.
30	A56	1sh on 2p (R)	375.	475.
31	A56	1sh on 2p (Bk)	5,500.	

5/–

32	A56	5sh on 2d (V)	6,250.	6,250.
33	A61	10sh on 5p (R)	6,000.	6,000.
34	A65	20sh on 1sh (V)	62,500.	
35	A65	20sh on 1sh (R)	85,000.	
36	A65	20sh on 1sh (Bk)	85,000.	

The handstamped 1893 surcharges are known inverted, vertical, etc.

Queen Victoria
A8 A9

A10 A11

A12

A13

1893 Unwmk. *Perf. 12 to 15*

No.	Design	Denomination & color	Unused	Used
37	A8	½p vermilion	3.50	3.50
38	A9	1p light blue	3.50	3.50
a.		Half used as ½p on cover		600.00
39	A10	2p green	14.00	14.00
a.		Half used as 1p on cover		*800.00*
b.		Horiz. pair, imperf. between		*4,000.*
40	A11	2½p car lake	4.75	3.00
41	A12	5p gray lilac	10.00	8.50
a.		5p lilac	10.00	12.50
42	A13	1sh black	12.50	12.00
		Nos. 37-42 (6)	48.25	44.50

For surcharge see No. 49.

A15

A16

A17

A18

A19

A20

1894 Engr.

No.	Design	Denomination & color	Unused	Used
43	A15	½p yel green	1.50	2.50
44	A16	1p vermilion	7.50	3.00
a.		1p orange vermilion	9.00	7.00
b.		Diagonal half, used as ½p on cover		600.00
45	A17	2p car lake	12.00	5.00
a.		Half used as 1p on cover		
46	A18	2½p blue	10.00	3.50
47	A19	5p dp violet	5.00	5.00
48	A20	1sh black	16.00	11.00
		Nos. 43-48 (6)	52.00	30.00

See #55-59, 61. For surcharges see #51-54.

Halves of Nos. 38, 3 and 44 Surcharged in Red, Blue, Violet or Black:

½ — No. 49 1 — No. 50 ½ — Nos. 51-53

1894

No.	Design	Denomination & color	Unused	Used
49	A9	½p on half of 1p (R)	1,100.	250.00
a.		Inverted surcharge	*5,250.*	

Perf. 14

Wmk. 30

No.	Design	Denomination & color	Unused	Used
50	A56	1p on half of 2p (R)	600.	300.
a.		Double surcharge	1,250.	1,100.
b.		Inverted surcharge		1,100.

Perf. 12 to 15

Unwmk.

No.	Design	Denomination & color	Unused	Used
51	A16	½p on half of 1p (Bl)	1,400.	250.
a.		Double surcharge		
52	A16	½p on half of 1p (V)	1,300.	400.
53	A16	½p on half of 1p (Bk)	*1,750.*	*500.*

This surcharge is found on both vertical and diagonal halves of the 1p.

No. 46 Surcharged in Black

ONE
HALF PENNY

1894

No.	Design	Denomination & color	Unused	Used
54	A18	½p on 2½p blue	300.	200.
a.		Double surcharge	1,750.	1,750.

The surcharge is found in eight types. The "OIE" variety is broken type.

A27

A28

A29

1897-98 Wmk. 2

No.	Design	Denomination & color	Unused	Used
55	A15	½p yel green	2.25	1.25
56	A16	1p vermilion	2.25	1.25
57	A17	2p car lake	1.50	1.10
58	A18	2½p blue	4.25	1.25
a.		2½p slate blue	4.00	1.65
59	A19	5p dp violet	7.50	*47.50*
60	A27	6p yel brn ('98)	6.00	5.50
61	A20	1sh black	12.00	*18.00*
62	A28	2sh6p olive bister	20.00	*60.00*
63	A29	10sh dp pur ('98)	65.00	*140.00*
a.		10sh bright purple	70.00	*140.00*
		Nos. 55-63 (9)	120.75	*275.85*

The stamps of Niger Coast Protectorate were superseded in Jan. 1900, by those of Northern and Southern Nigeria.

NIGERIA

nī-'jir-ē-ə

LOCATION — West coast of Africa, bordering on the Gulf of Guinea
GOVT. — Republic
AREA — 356,669 sq. mi.
POP. — 82,390,000 (est. 1983)
CAPITAL — Abuja

The colony and protectorate were formed in 1914 by the union of Northern and Southern Nigeria. The mandated territory of Cameroons (British) was also attached for administrative purposes. The Federation of Nigeria was formed in 1960. It became a republic in 1963. See Niger Coast Protectorate, Lagos, Northern Nigeria and Southern Nigeria.

12 Pence = 1 Shilling
20 Shillings = 1 Pound
100 Kobo = 1 Naira (1973)

Catalogue values for unused stamps in this country are for Never Hinged items, beginning with Scott 71 in the regular postage section, Scott B1 in the semi-postal section and Scott J1 in the postage due section.

Watermarks

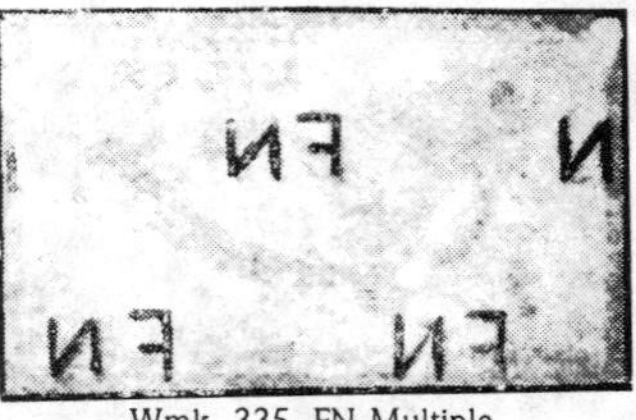
Wmk. 335- FN Multiple

Niger Coast Protectorate stamps can be mounted in the Scott British Africa album.

Wmk. 379- NIGERIA in Continuous Wavy Lines

King George V — A1

Numerals of 3p, 4p, 6p, 5sh and £1 of type A1 are in color on plain tablet.

Dies I and II are described at back of this volume.

Wmk. Multiple Crown and CA (3)

1914-27 Typo. *Perf. 14*

Die I

Ordinary Paper

No.	Design	Denomination & color	Unused	Used
1	A1	½p green	1.90	.30
a.		Booklet pane of 6		
2	A1	1p carmine	2.50	.15
a.		Booklet pane of 6		
b.		1p scarlet	3.00	.15
3	A1	2p gray	3.50	1.00
4	A1	2½p ultramarine	2.25	1.00

Chalky Paper

No.	Design	Denomination & color	Unused	Used
5	A1	3p violet, *yel*	1.10	1.50
6	A1	4p black & red, *yel*	.75	*3.00*
7	A1	6p dull vio & red vio	5.00	3.00
8	A1	1sh black, *green*	.75	*5.00*
a.		1sh black, *emerald*	.95	*8.00*
b.		1sh black, *bl grn*, ol back	13.00	15.00
c.		As "a," olive back	4.50	*18.00*
9	A1	2sh6p blk & red, *bl*	7.75	3.00
10	A1	5sh grn & red, *yel*	12.00	*22.50*
11	A1	10sh grn & red, *grn*	35.00	*85.00*
a.		10sh grn & red, *emer*	30.00	*70.00*
b.		10sh green & red, *blue grn*, olive back	650.00	*1,050.*
c.		As "a," olive back	65.00	95.00
12	A1	£1 vio & blk, *red*	125.00	*175.00*
a.		Die II ('27)	150.00	*200.00*
		Nos. 1-12 (12)	197.50	300.45

Surface-colored Paper

No.	Design	Denomination & color	Unused	Used
13	A1	3p violet, *yel*	3.25	5.00
14	A1	4p black & red, *yel*	1.25	*5.00*
15	A1	1sh black, *green*	.95	6.00
a.		1sh black, *emerald*		
16	A1	5sh grn & red, *yel*	8.50	*20.00*
17	A1	10sh grn & red, *grn*	42.50	*100.00*
		Nos. 13-17 (5)	56.45	*136.00*

1921-33 Wmk. 4

Die II

Ordinary Paper

No.	Design	Denomination & color	Unused	Used
18	A1	½p green	1.50	.75
a.		Die I	.70	.35
19	A1	1p carmine	.90	.45
a.		Booklet pane of 6	25.00	
b.		Die I	.20	.15
c.		Booklet pane of 6, Die I	25.00	
20	A1	1½p orange ('31)	2.00	.15
21	A1	2p gray	3.25	.30
a.		Die I	1.65	2.00
b.		Booklet pane of 6, Die I	50.00	
22	A1	2p red brown ('27)	2.00	.90
a.		Booklet pane of 6	50.00	
23	A1	2p dk brown ('28)	.75	.15
a.		Booklet pane of 6	25.00	
b.		Die I ('32)	4.50	.50
24	A1	2½p ultra (die I)	.75	2.25
25	A1	3p dp violet	6.00	1.25
a.		Die I ('24)	3.50	3.00
26	A1	3p ultra ('31)	2.50	2.00

Chalky Paper

No.	Design	Denomination & color	Unused	Used
27	A1	4p blk & red, *yel*	.55	.50
a.		Die I ('32)	5.00	7.00
28	A1	6p dull vio & red vio	5.00	5.00
a.		Die I	5.50	7.00
29	A1	1sh black, *emerald*	.90	.90
30	A1	2sh6p blk & red, *bl*	5.50	15.00
a.		Die I ('32)	30.00	35.00
31	A1	5sh green & red, *yel* ('26)	12.50	*45.00*
a.		Die I ('32)	45.00	*90.00*
32	A1	10sh green & red, *emer*	45.00	120.00
a.		Die I ('32)	80.00	*175.00*
		Nos. 18-32 (15)	89.10	194.60

Silver Jubilee Issue

Common Design Type

1935, May 6 Engr. *Perf. 11x12*

No.	Design	Denomination & color	Unused	Used
34	CD301	1½p black & ultra	.50	.40
35	CD301	2p indigo & green	1.25	.50
36	CD301	3p ultra & brown	2.50	*6.00*
37	CD301	1sh brown vio & ind	2.50	*12.50*
		Nos. 34-37 (4)	6.75	*19.40*

Wharf at Apapa — A2

Picking Cacao Pods — A3

Dredging for Tin — A4

Timber — A5

Fishing Village — A6

Ginning Cotton — A7

Minaret at Habe — A8

Fulani Cattle — A9

Victoria-Buea Road — A10

Oil Palms — A11

View of Niger at Jebba — A12

Nigerian Canoe — A13

1936, Feb. 1 *Perf. 11½x13*

No.	Design	Denomination & color	Unused	Used
38	A2	½p green	.40	.40
39	A3	1p rose carmine	.30	.30
40	A4	1½p brown	.30	.30
a.		Perf. 12½x13½	25.00	2.00
41	A5	2p black	.50	.50
42	A6	3p dark blue	.70	.60
a.		Perf. 12½x13½	70.00	20.00
43	A7	4p red brown	1.10	1.10
44	A8	6p dull violet	.70	.55
45	A9	1sh olive green	3.00	*12.50*

Perf. 14

No.	Design	Denomination & color	Unused	Used
46	A10	2sh6p ultra & blk	7.50	*12.50*
47	A11	5sh ol grn & blk	15.00	*17.50*
48	A12	10sh slate & blk	37.50	*50.00*
49	A13	£1 orange & blk	75.00	*110.00*
		Nos. 38-49 (12)	142.00	*206.25*

Coronation Issue
Common Design Type

1937, May 12 *Perf. 11x11½*

50 CD302 1p dark carmine .15 .15
51 CD302 1½p dark brown .55 .25
52 CD302 3p deep ultra .65 .30
Nos. 50-52 (3) 1.35 .70

George VI — A14

Victoria-Buea Road — A15

Niger at Jebba — A16

1938-51 **Wmk. 4** *Perf. 12*

53 A14 ½p deep green .15 .15
a. Perf. 11½ ('50) .15 .15
54 A14 1p dk carmine .15 .15
55 A14 1½p red brown .15 .15
a. Perf. 11½ ('50) .15 .15
56 A14 2p black .30 .15
57 A14 2½p orange ('41) .15 .20
58 A14 3p deep blue .15 .15
59 A14 4p orange 30.00 4.25
60 A14 6p brown violet .15 .15
a. Perf. 11½ ('51) .30 .15
61 A14 1sh olive green .35 .15
a. Perf. 11½ ('50) .35 .15
62 A14 1sh3p turq blue ('40) .50 .20
a. Perf. 11½ ('50) .50 .20
63 A15 2sh6p ultra & blk ('51) 4.50 2.75
a. Perf. 13½ ('42) 1.90 .70
b. Perf. 14 ('42) 1.90 .70
c. Perf. 13x11½ 40.00 6.00
64 A16 5sh org & blk, perf. 13½ ('42) 3.00 1.10
a. Perf. 12 ('49) 5.00 1.10
b. Perf. 14 ('48) 3.00 1.10
c. Perf. 13x11½ 75.00 9.00

1944, Dec. 1 *Perf. 12*

65 A14 1p red violet .15 .15
a. Perf. 11½ ('50) .15 .15
66 A14 2p deep red .15 .15
a. Perf. 11½ ('50) .15 .15
67 A14 3p black .15 .15
68 A14 4p dark blue .15 .15
Nos. 53-68 (16) 40.15 10.15

Issue date: Nos. 65a, 66a, Feb. 15.

Catalogue values for unused stamps in this section, from this point to the end of the section, are for Never Hinged items.

Peace Issue
Common Design Type

1946, Oct. 21 **Engr.** *Perf. 13½x14*

71 CD303 1½p brown .15 .15
72 CD303 4p deep blue .20 .20

Silver Wedding Issue
Common Design Types

1948, Dec. 20 **Photo.** *Perf. 14x14½*

73 CD304 1p brt red violet .20 .20

Perf. 11½x11

Engraved; Name Typographed

74 CD305 5sh brown orange 6.75 *10.00*

UPU Issue
Common Design Types

Engr.; Name Typo. on 3p, 6p

Perf. 13½, 11x11½

1949, Oct. 10 **Wmk. 4**

75 CD306 1p red violet .15 .15
76 CD307 3p indigo .25 .20
77 CD308 6p rose violet .75 .60
78 CD309 1sh olive 1.25 .95
Nos. 75-78 (4) 2.40 1.90

Coronation Issue
Common Design Type

1953, June 2 **Engr.** *Perf. 13½x13*

79 CD312 1½p brt green & black .45 .15

Manilla (Bracelet) Currency A17

Olokun Head, Ife — A18

Designs: 1p, Bornu horsemen. 1½p, Peanuts, Kano City. 2p, Mining tin. 3p, Jebba Bridge over Niger River. 4p, Cocoa industry. 1sh, Logging. 2sh6p, Victoria harbor. 5sh, Loading palm oil. 10sh, Goats and Fulani cattle. £1, Lagos waterfront, 19th and 20th centuries.

1953, Sept. 1 *Perf. 14*

Size: 35½x22½mm

80 A17 ½p red orange & blk .15 .15
a. Booklet pane of 4 ('57) .50
81 A17 1p olive gray & blk .15 .15
a. Booklet pane of 4 ('57) .50
82 A17 1½p blue green .40 .15
83 A17 2p bister & blk 3.25 .15
84 A17 3p purple & blk .45 .15
a. Booklet pane of 4 ('57)
85 A17 4p ultra & black 2.00 .15
86 A18 6p blk & org brn .25 .15
87 A17 1sh brn vio & blk .30 .15
a. Booklet pane of 4 ('57)

Size: 40½x24½mm

88 A17 2sh6p green & black 4.00 .30
89 A17 5sh ver & black 2.75 .65
90 A17 10sh red brown & blk 7.00 1.50

Size: 42x31½mm

91 A17 £1 violet & black 12.00 5.00
Nos. 80-91 (12) 32.70 8.65

See No. 93.

No. 83 Overprinted in Black **ROYAL VISIT 1956**

1956, Jan. 28 **Wmk. 4** *Perf. 13½*

92 A17 2p bister & black .15 .15

Visit of Queen Elizabeth II to Nigeria, Jan.-Feb., 1956.

Mining Tin Type of 1953

Two types:
I - Broken row of dots between "G" and miner's head.
II - Complete row of dots.

1956-57

93 A17 2p bluish gray (shades) (I) .15 .15
a. Booklet pane of 4 (I) ('57) .65
b. 2p gray (shades) (II) .15 .15

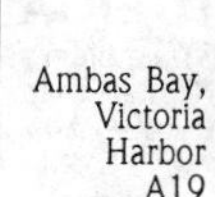

Ambas Bay, Victoria Harbor A19

Perf. 13½

1958, Dec. 1 **Wmk. 314** **Engr.**

94 A19 3p purple & black .15 .15

Cent. of the founding of Victoria, Southern Cameroons.

1959, Mar. 14

Designs: 3p, Lugard Hall, Kaduna. 1sh, Kano Mosque.

95 A19 3p purple & black .15 .15
96 A19 1sh green & black .35 .30

Attainment of self-government by the Northern Region, Mar. 15, 1959.

Federation of Nigeria

Man Paddling Canoe — A20

1p, Federal Legislature. 6p, Federal Supreme Court. 1sh3p, Map of Africa, dove and torch.

Perf. 13½

1960, Oct. 1 **Photo.** **Wmk. 335**

Size: 35x22mm

97 A20 1p carmine & black .15 .15
98 A20 3p blue & black .15 .15
99 A20 6p dk red brn & emer .15 .15

Size: 39½x23½mm

100 A20 1sh3p ultra & yellow .30 .25
Set value .55 .50

Nigeria's independence, Oct. 1, 1960.

Peanuts — A21

Central Bank, Lagos A22

Designs: 1p, Coal miner. 1½p, Adult education. 2p, Potter. 3p, Oyo carver. 4p, Weaver. 6p, Benin mask. 1sh, Yellow-casqued hornbill. 1sh3p, Camel train and map. 5sh, Nigeria museum and sculpture. 10sh, Kano airport. £1, Lagos terminal.

Perf. 14½x14

1961, Jan. 1 **Wmk. 335**

101 A21 ½p emerald .15 .15
102 A21 1p purple .15 .15
a. Booklet pane of 6 .45
103 A21 1½p rose red .15 .15
104 A21 2p ultra .15 .15
105 A21 3p dark green .15 .15
a. Booklet pane of 6 .50
106 A21 4p blue .15 .15
107 A21 6p black & yel .20 .15
a. Booklet pane of 6 1.00
b. Yellow omitted 375.00
108 A21 1sh yellow green .30 .15
109 A21 1sh3p orange .50 .15
a. Booklet pane of 6 3.25
110 A22 2sh6p yellow & blk 1.00 .20
111 A22 5sh emerald & blk 2.00 .40
112 A22 10sh dp ultra & blk 3.25 1.00
113 A22 £1 dp car & blk 5.00 3.00
Nos. 101-113 (13) 13.15
Set value 5.50

For overprint see No. 198.

Globe and Train A23

1961, July 25 **Wmk. 335**

114 A23 1p shown .15 .15
115 A23 3p Truck .15 .15
116 A23 1sh3p Plane .30 .30
117 A23 2sh6p Ship .65 .65
Nos. 114-117 (4) 1.25 1.25

Nigeria's admission to the UPU.

Coat of Arms — A24

Map and Natural Resources A25

Designs: 6p, Eagle carrying banner. 1sh3p, Flying eagles forming flag. 2sh6p, Young couple looking at flag and government building.

Perf. 14½x14, 14x14½

1961, Oct. 1 **Photo.** **Wmk. 335**

118 A24 3p multicolored .15 .15
119 A25 4p org, yel grn & dk red .20 .20
120 A25 6p emerald .20 .15
121 A25 1sh3p ultra, emer & gray .25 .20
122 A25 2sh6p blue, emer & sep .50 .50
Nos. 118-122 (5) 1.30 1.20

First anniversary of independence.

Map of Africa and Staff of Aesculapius — A26

Map of Africa and: 3p, Lyre, book and scroll. 6p, Cogwheel. 1sh, Radio beacon. 1sh3p, Hands holding globe.

1962, Jan. 25 *Perf. 14x14½*

123 A26 1p bister .15 .15
124 A26 3p deep magenta .15 .15
125 A26 6p blue green .20 .15
126 A26 1sh chestnut .30 .20
127 A26 1sh3p bright blue .40 .35
Set value 1.00 .80

Issued to honor the conference of heads of state of African and Malagasy Governments.

Malaria Eradication Emblem and Larvae — A27

Emblem and: 6p, Man with spray gun. 1sh3p, Plane spraying insecticide. 2sh6p, Microscope, retort and patient.

1962, Apr. 7 *Perf. 14½*

128 A27 3p emerald, brn & ver .15 .15
129 A27 6p lilac rose & dk blue .20 .15
130 A27 1sh3p dk blue & lil rose .25 .20
131 A27 2sh6p yel brown & blue .55 .55
Nos. 128-131 (4) 1.15
Set value .90

WHO drive to eradicate malaria.

National Monument, Lagos — A28

Ife Bronze Head and Flag — A29

Perf. 14½x14, 14x14½

1962, Oct. 1 **Wmk. 335** **Photo.**

132 A28 3p lt ultra & emerald .15 .15
a. Emerald omitted
133 A29 5sh vio, emer & org red 1.75 1.75

Second anniversary of independence.

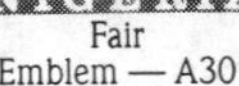

Fair Emblem — A30

Globe and Arrows — A31

Designs (horizontal): 6p, "Wheels of Industry." 1sh, Cornucopia, goods and trucks. 2sh6p, Oil derricks and tanker.

1962, Oct. 27 Wmk. 335

134 A30	1p	brown olive & org	.15	.15
135 A30	6p	crimson & blk	.15	.15
136 A30	1sh	dp orange & blk	.25	.20
137 A30	2sh6p	dk ultra, yel & blk	.55	.50
		Nos. 134-137 (4)	1.10	
		Set value		.85

Lagos Intl. Trade Fair, Oct. 27-Nov. 8.

1962, Nov. 5

4p, National Hall and Commonwealth emblem, horiz. 1sh3p, Palm tree, emblem and doves.

138 A31	2½p	sky blue	.15	.15
139 A31	4p	dp rose & slate bl	.15	.15
140 A31	1sh3p	gray & yellow	.45	.45
		Nos. 138-140 (3)	.75	
		Set value		.65

8th Commonwealth Parliamentary Conf., Lagos.

Herdsman with Cattle — A32

US Mercury Capsule over Kano Tracking Station — A33

Design: 6p, Tractor and corn, horiz.

1963, Mar. 21 Photo. ***Perf. 14½***

141 A32	3p	olive green	.15	.15
142 A32	6p	brt lilac rose	.30	.25
		Set value		.35

FAO "Freedom from Hunger" campaign.

1963, June 21 ***Perf. 14½***

Design: 1sh3p, Syncom II satellite and US tracking ship "Kingsport," Lagos harbor.

143 A33	6p	dk blue & yellow grn	.20	.15
144 A33	1sh3p	black & dp green	.40	.40

Peaceful uses of outer space.

Printed in sheets of 12 (4x3) with ornamental borders and inscriptions.

Nigerian and Greek Scouts Shaking Hands and Jamboree Emblem — A34

Design: 1sh, Scouts dancing around campfire.

1963, Aug. 1 Photo. ***Perf. 14***

145 A34	3p	gray olive & red	.15	.15
146 A34	1sh	red & black	.40	.40
a.		Souvenir sheet of 2, #145-146	1.10	1.10

11th Boy Scout Jamboree, Marathon, Greece, Aug. 1963.

Republic

First Aid — A35

Designs: 6p, Blood donors and ambulances. 1sh3p, Helping the needy.

1963, Sept. 1 Wmk. 335 ***Perf. 14½***

147 A35	3p	dk blue & red	.15	.15
148 A35	6p	dk green & red	.25	.25
149 A35	1sh3p	black & red	.65	.65
a.		Souvenir sheet of 4, #149	1.75	1.75
		Nos. 147-149 (3)	1.05	1.05

Cent. of the Intl. Red Cross.

Pres. Nnamdi Azikiwe and State House — A36

"Freedom of Worship" — A37

Designs: 1sh3p, President and Federal Supreme Court. 2sh6p, President and Parliament Building.

1963, Oct. 1 Unwmk. ***Perf. 14x13***

150 A36	3p	dull green & yel grn	.15	.15
151 A36	1sh3p	brown & bister	.25	.20
a.		Bister (head) omitted		
152 A36	2sh6p	vio bl & brt grnsh bl	.50	.50
		Nos. 150-152 (3)	.90	.85

Independence Day, Oct. 1, 1963.

1963, Dec. 10 Wmk. 335 ***Perf. 13***

3p, Charter & broken whip, horiz. 1sh3p, "Freedom from Want." 2sh6p, "Freedom of Speech."

153 A37	3p	vermilion	.15	.15
154 A37	6p	green	.15	.15
155 A37	1sh3p	deep ultra	.20	.20
156 A37	2sh6p	red lilac	.35	.35
		Set value	.65	.65

15th anniv. of the Universal Declaration of Human Rights.

Queen Nefertari — A38

1964, Mar. 8 Photo. ***Perf. 14***

157 A38	6p	shown	.20	.20
158 A38	2sh6p	Ramses II	.90	.90

UNESCO world campaign to save historic monuments in Nubia.

John F. Kennedy, US and Nigerian Flags — A39

1sh3p, Kennedy bust & laurel. 5sh, Kennedy coin (US), flags of US & Nigeria at half-mast.

1964, Aug. 20 Unwmk. ***Perf. 13x14***

159 A39	1sh3p	black & lt vio	.25	.25
160 A39	2sh6p	multicolored	.55	.55
161 A39	5sh	multicolored	1.10	1.10
a.		Souvenir sheet of 4	5.25	5.25
		Nos. 159-161 (3)	1.90	1.90

Issued in memory of President John F. Kennedy (1917-1963). No. 161a contains 4 imperf. stamps similar to No. 161 with simulated perforations.

Pres. Nnamdi Azikiwe — A40

Herbert Macaulay — A41

Design: 2sh6p, King Jaja of Opobo.

Perf. 14x13, 14

1964, Oct. 1 Photo. Unwmk.

162 A40	3p	red brown	.15	.15
163 A41	1sh3p	green	.25	.25
164 A41	2sh6p	slate green	.55	.55
		Nos. 162-164 (3)	.95	.95

First anniversary of the Republic.

Boxing Gloves and Torch — A42

Hurdling — A43

6p, High jump. 1sh3p, Woman runner, vert.

1964, Oct. ***Perf. 14½***

165 A42	3p	olive grn & sepia	.15	.15
166 A42	6p	dk blue & emer	.15	.15
167 A42	1sh3p	olive & brown	.30	.30

Perf. 14

168 A43	2sh6p	orange red & brn	.50	.50
a.		Souvenir sheet of 4	3.25	3.25
		Nos. 165-168 (4)	1.10	1.10

18th Olympic Games, Tokyo, Oct. 10-25.

No. 168a contains 4 imperf. stamps similar to No. 168 with simulated perforations.

NIGERIA

Mountain Climbing Scouts — A44

IQSY Emblem and Telstar, Map of Africa — A45

Designs: 3p, Golden Jubilee emblem. 6p, Nigeria's Scout emblem and merit badges. 1sh3p, Lord Baden-Powell and Nigerian Boy Scout.

1965, Jan. Photo. ***Perf. 14½***

169 A44	1p	brown	.15	.15
170 A44	3p	emer, blk & red	.15	.15
171 A44	6p	yel grn, red & blk	.20	.20
172 A44	1sh3p	sep, yel & dk grn	.55	.55
a.		Souvenir sheet of 4	3.00	3.00
		Nos. 169-172 (4)	1.05	1.05

Founding of the Nigerian Boy Scouts, 50th anniv.

No. 172a contains four imperf. stamps similar to No. 172 with simulated perforation.

1965, Apr. 1 Unwmk. ***Perf. 14x13***

Design: 1sh3p, Explorer XII over map of Africa.

173 A45	6p	grnsh bl & vio	.18	.18
174 A45	1sh3p	lilac & green	.42	.42

Intl. Quiet Sun Year, 1964-65. Printed in sheets of 12 (4x3) with ornamental borders and inscriptions.

ITU Emblem, Drummer, Man at Desk and Telephone A46

Cent. of the ITU: 1sh3p, ITU emblem and telecommunication tower, vert. 5sh, ITU emblem, Relay satellite and map of Africa showing Nigeria.

Perf. 11x11½, 11½x11

1965, Aug. 2 Photo. Unwmk.

175 A46	3p	ocher, red & blk	.15	.15
176 A46	1sh3p	ultra, grn & blk	.65	.65
177 A46	5sh	multicolored	2.75	2.75
		Nos. 175-177 (3)	3.55	3.55

ICY Emblem, Diesel Locomotive and Camel Caravan A47

ICY Emblem and: 1sh, Students and hospital, Lagos. 2sh6p, Kainji Dam, Niger River.

1965, Sept. 1 Wmk. 335 ***Perf. 14x15***

178 A47	3p	orange, grn & car	.22	.15
179 A47	1sh	ultra, blk & yel	.50	.35
180 A47	2sh6p	ultra, yel & grn	2.50	1.10
		Nos. 178-180 (3)	3.22	1.60

Intl. Cooperation Year and 20th anniv. of the UN.

Stone Images, Ikom — A48

Designs: 3p, Carved frieze, horiz. 5sh, Seated man, Taba bronze.

Perf. 14x15, 15x14

1965, Oct. 1 Photo. Unwmk.

181 A48	3p	ocher, black & red	.15	.15
182 A48	1sh3p	lt ultra, grn & reddish brn	.40	.40
183 A48	5sh	emer, dk brn & reddish brn	1.75	1.75
		Nos. 181-183 (3)	2.30	2.30

Second anniversary of the Republic.

Elephants A49

Designs: ½p, Lioness and cubs, vert. 1½p, Splendid sunbird. 2p, Weaverbirds. 3p, Cheetah. 4p, Leopard and cubs. 6p, Saddle-billed storks, vert. 9p, Gray parrots. 1sh, Kingfishers. 1sh3p, Crowned cranes. 2sh6p, Buffon's kobs (antelopes). 5sh, Giraffes. 10sh, Hippopotami, vert. £1, Buffalos.

"MAURICE FIEVET" below Design.*

Perf. 12x12½, 12½x12, 14x13½ (1p, 2p, 3p, 4p, 9p)

1965-66 Photo.

Size: 23x38mm, 38x23mm

184 A49	½p	multicolored	.15	.15
185 A49	1p	red & multi	.15	.15
186 A49	1½p	lt blue & multi	.16	.15
187 A49	2p	brt red & multi	.16	.15
a.		White "2d" ('70)	7.00	2.00
188 A49	3p	brt grn, yel & dl brn	1.00	.65
189 A49	4p	lilac & multi	.32	.15
a.		Perf 12½x12	.55	.15
b.		"4" 5mm wide ('71)	3.75	1.00
190 A49	6p	violet & multi	.40	.15
191 A49	9p	blue & orange	1.25	.65

Perf. 12½

Size: 45x26mm, 26x45mm

192 A49	1sh	gray & multi	.80	.15
a.		Red omitted		
193 A49	1sh3p	brt bl & multi	.85	.15
194 A49	2sh6p	dk brn, yel & ocher	1.65	.32
195 A49	5sh	brn, yel & red brown	3.25	.80

196 A49 10sh grnsh bl & multi 4.50 3.25
197 A49 £1 brt green & multi 11.00 6.50
Nos. 184-197 (14) 25.64 13.37

* The designer's name, Maurice Fievet, appears at right or left, in small or large capitals. Nos. 187a and 189b have "MAURICE FIEVET" at right, 5mm wide. No. 187a has "2d" in white instead of yellow. No. 189b has "REPUBLIC" and "4d" larger, bolder.

Issued: ½p, 1p, 11/1/65; 2p, 4/1/66; 1½p, #189a, 6p, 1sh, 1sh3p, 2sh6p, 5sh, 10sh, 1£, 5/2/66; 3p, 9p, 10/17/66; 4p, 1966.

9 values were overprinted "F. G. N./ F. G. N." (Federal Government of Nigeria) in 1969. They were not issued, but some were irregularly sold. Later the Nigerian Philatelic Service sold copies, stating they were not postally valid.

See Nos. 258-267.

No. 110 Overprinted in Red: "COMMONWEALTH / P.M. MEETING / 11. Jan. 1966"

Perf. 14½x14

1966, Jan. 11 Photo. Wmk. 335
198 A22 2sh6p yellow & black .52 .52

Conf. of British Commonwealth Prime Ministers, Lagos.

YWCA Building, Lagos — A50

Unwmk.

1966, Sept. 1 Litho. *Perf. 14*
199 A50 4p yel, green & multi .15 .15
200 A50 9p brt green & multi .32 .32

60th anniv. of the Nigerian YWCA.

Lineman and Telephone A51

Designs: 4p, Flag and letter carrying pigeon, vert. 2sh6p, Niger Bridge.

Perf. 14½x14, 14x14½

1966, Oct. 1 Photo. Wmk. 335
201 A51 4p green .15 .15
202 A51 1sh6p lilac, blk & sep .60 .60
203 A51 2sh6p multicolored 1.00 1.00
Nos. 201-203 (3) 1.75 1.75

Third anniversary of the Republic.

Book, Chemical Apparatus, Carved Head and UNESCO Emblem A52

1966, Nov. 4 *Perf. 14½x14*
204 A52 4p dl org, mar & blk .40 .15
205 A52 1sh6p bl grn, plum & black 1.25 .80
206 A52 2sh6p pink, plum & blk 2.50 2.50
Nos. 204-206 (3) 4.15 3.45

20th anniv. of UNESCO.

Surveyors and Hydrological Decade Emblem A53

Design: 2sh6p, Water depth gauge on dam and Hydrological Decade emblem, vert.

Perf. 14½x14, 14x14½

1967, Feb. 1 Photo. Wmk. 335
207 A53 4p multicolored .15 .15
208 A53 2sh6p multicolored 1.25 1.25

Hydrological Decade (UNESCO), 1965-74.

Weather Satellite Orbiting Earth — A54

Design: 1sh6p, Storm over land and sea and World Meteorological Organization emblem.

1967, Mar. 23 Photo. *Perf. 14½x14*
209 A54 4p dp ultra & brt rose .15 .15
210 A54 1sh6p ultra & yellow .75 .75

World Meteorological Day, March 23.

Eyo Masqueraders A55

1sh6p, Acrobat. 2sh6p, Stilt dancer, vert.

Perf. 11x11½, 11½x11

1967, Oct. 1 Photo. Unwmk.
211 A55 4p multicolored .15 .15
212 A55 1sh6p turq bl & multi 1.25 1.25
213 A55 2sh6p pale grn & multi 2.00 1.50
Nos. 211-213 (3) 3.40 2.90

4th anniversary of the Federal Republic.

Vaccination of Cattle — A56

1967, Dec. 1 *Perf. 14½x14*
214 A56 4p maroon & multi .16 .15
215 A56 1sh6p ultra & multi .95 .95

Campaign to eradicate cattle plague.

Anopheles Mosquito and Sick Man — A57

20th anniv. of the WHO: 4p, WHO emblem and vaccination.

1968, Apr. 7 Litho. *Perf. 14*
216 A57 4p dp lilac rose & blk .15 .15
217 A57 1sh6p orange yel & black .80 .80

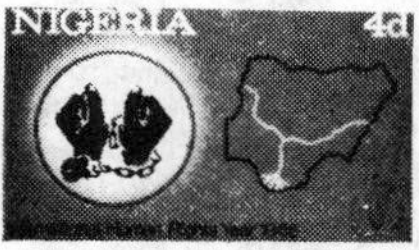

Shackled Hands, Map of Nigeria and Human Rights Flame — A58

Design: 1sh6p, Flag of Nigeria and human rights flame, vert.

1968, July 1 Photo. *Perf. 14*
218 A58 4p dp blue, yel & blk .15 .15
219 A58 1sh6p green, blk & red .55 .55

International Human Rights Year.

Hand and Doves — A59

1968, Oct. 1 Unwmk. *Perf. 14*
220 A59 4p brt blue & multi .15 .15
221 A59 1sh6p black & multi .50 .50
Set value .56

5th anniversary of the Federal Republic.

Olympic Rings, Nigerian Flag and Athletes A60

Design: 4p, Map of Nigeria and Olympic rings.

1968, Oct. 14 Photo. *Perf. 14*
222 A60 4p red, black & emer .15 .15
223 A60 1sh6p multicolored .50 .50
Set value .56

19th Olympic Games, Mexico City, Oct. 12-27.

G.P.O., Lagos — A61

1969, Apr. 11 Unwmk. *Perf. 14*
224 A61 4p emerald & black .15 .15
225 A61 1sh6p dk blue & black .48 .48
Set value .55 .54

Opening of the Nigerian Philatelic Service of the GPO, Lagos.

Gen. Yakubu Gowon and Victoria Zakari A62

Perf. 13x13½

1969, Sept. 20 Litho. Unwmk.
226 A62 4p emerald & choc .15 .15
227 A62 1sh6p emerald & black .48 .48
Set value .55 .54

Wedding of Yakubu Gowon, head of state of Nigeria, and Miss Victoria Zakari, Apr. 19, 1969.

Development Bank Emblem and "5" — A63

Design: 1sh6p, Emblem and rays.

1969, Oct. 18 Litho. *Perf. 14*
228 A63 4p dk bl, blk & org .15 .15
229 A63 1sh6p dk pur, yel & blk .55 .55

African Development Bank, 5th anniv.

ILO Emblem A64

50th anniv. of the ILO: 1sh6p, ILO emblem and world map.

1969, Nov. 15 Photo.
230 A64 4p purple & black .15 .15
231 A64 1sh6p green & black .55 .55

Tourist Year Emblem and Musicians A65

12-Spoke Wheel and Arms of Nigeria A66

Designs: 4p, Olumo Rock and Tourist Year emblem, horiz. 1sh6p, Assob Falls.

1969, Dec. 30 Photo. *Perf. 14*
232 A65 4p blue & multi .15 .15
233 A65 1sh emerald & black .36 .36
234 A65 1sh6p multicolored .55 .55
Nos. 232-234 (3) 1.06 1.06

International Year of African Tourism.

Perf. 11½x11, 11x11½

1970, May 28 Photo. Unwmk.

Designs: 4p, Map of Nigeria and tree with 12 fruits representing 12 tribes. 1sh6p, People bound by common destiny and map of Nigeria. 2sh, Torch with 12 flames and map of Africa, horiz.

235 A66 4p gold, blue & blk .15 .15
236 A66 1sh gold & multi .38 .38
237 A66 1sh6p green & black .55 .55
238 A66 2sh bl, org, gold & black .75 .75
Nos. 235-238 (4) 1.83 1.83

Establishment of a 12-state administrative structure in Nigeria.

Opening of New UPU Headquarters, Bern — A67

1970, June 29 Unwmk. *Perf. 14*
239 A67 4p purple & yellow .15 .15
240 A67 1sh6p blue & vio blue .50 .50

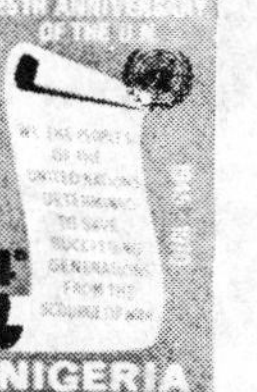

UN Emblem and Charter — A68

Student — A69

25th anniv. of the UN: 1sh6p, UN emblem and headquarters, New York.

1970, Sept. 1 Photo. *Perf. 14*
241 A68 4p brn org, buff & blk .15 .15
242 A68 1sh6p dk bl, gold & bis brn .48 .48
Set value .56 .54

1970, Sept. 30 Litho. *Perf. 14x13½*

Designs: 2p, Oil drilling platform. 6p, Durbar horsemen. 9p, Soldier and sailors raising flag. 1sh, Soccer player. 1sh6p, Parliament Building. 2sh, Kainji Dam. 2sh6p, Export products: Timber, rubber, peanuts, cocoa and palm produce.

243 A69 2p blue & multi .15 .15
244 A69 4p blue & multi .15 .15
245 A69 6p blue & multi .15 .15
246 A69 9p blue & multi .25 .25
247 A69 1sh blue & multi .35 .35
248 A69 1sh6p blue & multi .65 .65
249 A69 2sh blue & multi .85 .85
250 A69 2sh6p blue & multi 1.10 1.10
Nos. 243-250 (8) 3.65 3.65

Ten years of independence.

Black and White Men Uprooting Racism — A70

Ibibio Mask, c. 1900 — A71

Designs: 4p, Black and white school children and globe, horiz. 1sh6p, World map with black and white stripes. 2sh, Black and white men, shoulder to shoulder, horiz.

Perf. 13½x14, 14x13½

1971, Mar. 22 Photo. Unwmk.
251 A70 4p multicolored .15 .15
252 A70 1sh yellow & multi .20 .20
253 A70 1sh6p blue, yel & blk .38 .38
254 A70 2sh multicolored .60 .60
Nos. 251-254 (4) 1.33 1.33

Intl. year against racial discrimination.

1971, Sept. 30 *Perf. 13½x14*

Nigerian Antiquities: 1sh3p, Bronze mask of a King of Benin, c. 1700. 1sh9p, Bronze figure of a King of Ife.

255 A71 4p lt blue & black .15 .15
256 A71 1sh3p yellow bis & blk .44 .44
257 A71 1sh9p apple grn, dp grn & blk .60 .60
Nos. 255-257 (3) 1.19 1.19

Type of 1965-66 Redrawn
Imprint: "N.S.P. & M. Co. Ltd."
Added to "MAURICE FIEVET"

Perf. 13x13½; 14x13½ (6p)

1969-72 **Photo.**

Size: 38x23mm

258 A49 1p red & multi .15 .15
259 A49 2p brt red & multi .20 .15
260 A49 3p multi ('71) .20 .15
261 A49 4p lilac & multi .32 .15
262 A49 6p brt vio & multi ('71) .80 .24
263 A49 9p dl bl & dp org ('70) .80 .32

Size: 45x26mm

264 A49 1sh multi ('71) .90 .40
265 A49 1sh3p multi ('71) 1.25 .48
266 A49 2sh6p multi ('72) 4.75 2.00
267 A49 5sh multi ('72) 6.50 3.25
Nos. 258-267 (10) 15.87 7.29

UNICEF Emblem and Children A72

Satellite Earth Station A73

UNICEF 25th anniv.: 1sh3p, Mother and child. 1sh9p, African mother carrying child on back.

1971, Dec. 11 *Perf. 14*

270 A72 4p purple & yellow .15 .15
271 A72 1sh3p org, pur & plum .45 .45
272 A72 1sh9p blue & dk blue .65 .65
Nos. 270-272 (3) 1.25 1.25

1971, Dec. 30 **Photo.** *Perf. 14*

Designs: Various views of satellite communications earth station, Lanlate, Nigeria. All horizontal.

273 A73 4p multicolored .15 .15
274 A73 1sh3p blue, blk & grn .65 .65
275 A73 1sh9p orange & blk .95 .95
276 A73 3sh brt pink & blk 1.50 1.50
Nos. 273-276 (4) 3.25 3.25

Satellite communications earth station, Lanlate, Nigeria.

Fair Emblem — A74

Fair Emblem and: 1sh3p, Map of Africa, horiz. 1sh9p, Globe with map of Africa.

Perf. 13½x13, 13x13½

1972, Feb. 23 **Litho.**

277 A74 4p multicolored .15 .15
278 A74 1sh3p dull pur, yel & gold .48 .48
279 A74 1sh9p orange, yel & blk .70 .70
Nos. 277-279 (3) 1.33 1.33

First All-Africa Trade Fair, Nairobi, Kenya, Feb. 23-Mar. 5.

Traffic — A75

Designs: 1sh3p, Traffic flow at circle. 1sh9p, Car and truck on road. 3sh, Intersection with lights and pedestrians.

1972, June 23 **Photo.** *Perf. 13x13½*

280 A75 4p orange & blk .15 .15
281 A75 1sh3p lt blue & multi .90 .90
282 A75 1sh9p emerald & multi 1.35 1.35
283 A75 3sh yellow & multi 2.00 2.00
Nos. 280-283 (4) 4.40 4.40

Introduction of right-hand driving in Nigeria, Apr. 2, 1972.

Nok Style Terra-cotta Head, Katsina Ala — A76

Designs: 1sh3p, Roped bronze vessel, Igbo Ukwu. 1sh9p, Bone harpoon, Daima, horiz.

Perf. 13½x13, 13x13½

1972, Sept. 1 **Litho.**

284 A76 4p dk blue & multi .15 .15
285 A76 1sh3p gold & multi .65 .65
286 A76 1sh9p dp blue & multi .85 .85
Nos. 284-286 (3) 1.65 1.65

All-Nigeria Festival of the Arts, Kaduna, Dec. 9.

Games Emblem and Soccer — A77

Designs: 5k, Running. 18k, Table tennis. 25k, Stadium, vert.

1973, Jan. 8 **Litho.** *Perf. 13x13½*

287 A77 5k lilac, blue & blk .20 .20
288 A77 12k multicolored .45 .45
289 A77 18k yellow & multi .70 .70
290 A77 25k brown & multi 1.00 1.00
Nos. 287-290 (4) 2.35 2.35

2nd All-Africa Games, Lagos, Jan. 7-18.

Hides and Skins — A78

Designs: 2k, Natural gas tanks. 3k, Cement works. 5k, Cattle ranching. 7k, Lumbermill. 8k, Oil refinery. 10k, Leopards, Yankari Game Reserve. 12k, New civic building. 15k, Sugar cane harvesting. 18k, Palm oil production, vert. 20k, Vaccine production. 25k, Modern docks. 30k, Argungu Fishing Festival, vert. 35k, Textile industry. 50k, Pottery, vert. 1n, Eko Bridge. 2n, Teaching Hospital, Lagos.

Imprint at left: "N S P & M Co Ltd"
6mm on Litho. Stamps, 5¼ mm on Photo. Stamps

Litho.; Photo. (50k)

1973-74 **Unwmk.** *Perf. 14*

291 A78 1k multi, buff imprint *.22 .22*
292 A78 2k multi ('74) *.35 .32*
293 A78 3k multi ('74) *.15 .15*
294 A78 5k grn & multi ('74) *.45 .32*
295 A78 7k multicolored *.22 .16*
296 A78 8k multicolored *.25 .18*
297 A78 10k multicolored *.55 .35*
298 A78 12k multicolored *.40 .25*
299 A78 15k multicolored *.45 .35*
300 A78 18k multicolored *.60 .40*
301 A78 20k multicolored *.65 .45*
302 A78 25k multicolored *.75 .55*
303 A78 30k multicolored *.85 .65*
304 A78 35k multicolored *1.00 .70*
305 A78 50k black background *4.50 2.75*
306 A78 1n multicolored *3.00 2.25*
307 A78 2n multicolored *4.50 5.25*
Nos. 291-307 (17) 18.89 15.30

Imprint on 35k has periods.

Imprint at left: "N. S. P. & M. Co. Ltd."

1973 **Photo., Imprint 5¼mm**

291a A78 1k multi, dk grn foliage *.15 .15*
291b A78 1k multi, brt grn foliage *.15 .15*
292a A78 2k multicolored *.15 .15*
294a A78 5k multi, emer fields *.65 .45*
294b A78 5k multi, yel grn fields *.35 .22*
297a A78 10k multicolored *.45 .25*
298a A78 12k multicolored *1.10 1.00*
300a A78 18k multicolored *1.50 1.25*
301a A78 20k multicolored *2.75 2.50*
303a A78 30k multicolored *3.00 2.50*
305a A78 50k dk brn background *2.25 1.75*
306a A78 1n multicolored *9.00 8.00*
Nos. 291a-306a (12) 21.50 18.37

1975-79 **Wmk. 379**

291c A78 1k multi, dk grn foliage *.15 .15*
292b A78 2k multi ('75) *.15 .15*
293a A78 3k multi ('75) *.15 .15*
294c A78 5k emerald fields ('76) *.18 .15*
296a A78 8k multi ('76) *.22 .15*
297b A78 10k multi ('76) *.35 .18*
299a A78 15k multicolored *.35*
301b A78 20k multi, pale pink table, door, windows ('79) *.65 .45*
302a A78 25k multi, pur barges *.70 .70*
302b A78 25k multi, brn barges *.70 .70*
305b A78 50k dk brn background, grn imprint *1.50 1.25*
307a A78 2n multicolored *5.50 5.25*

OAU Headquarters A79

Designs: 18k, OAU flag, vert. 30k, Stairs leading to OAU emblem, vert.

1973, May 25 **Litho.** *Perf. 14*

308 A79 5k blue & multi .16 .16
309 A79 18k olive grn & multi .65 .65
310 A79 30k lilac & multi 1.10 1.10
Nos. 308-310 (3) 1.91 1.91

Org. for African Unity, 10th anniv.

WMO Emblem, Weather Vane — A80

1973, Sept. 4 **Litho.** *Perf. 13*

311 A80 5k multicolored .18 .18
312 A80 30k multicolored 1.40 1.40

Cent. of intl. meteorological cooperation.

View of Ibadan University A81

Designs: 12k, Campus, crest and graph showing growth, vert. 18k, Campus, students and crest. 30k, Teaching hospital.

1973, Nov. 17 *Perf. 14*

313 A81 5k lt blue & multi .20 .20
314 A81 12k lilac & multi .50 .50
315 A81 18k orange & multi .75 .75
316 A81 30k blue, org & blk 1.25 1.25
Nos. 313-316 (4) 2.70 2.70

University of Ibadan, 25th anniversary.

Growth of Mail, 1874-1974 A82

12k, Nigerian Post emblem & Northern Nigeria #18A. 18k, Postal emblem & Lagos #1. 30k, Map of Nigeria &means of transportation.

1974, June 10 **Litho.** *Perf. 14*

317 A82 5k green, black & org .20 .20
318 A82 12k green & multi .48 .48
319 A82 18k green, lilac & blk 1.25 1.25
320 A82 30k black & multi 1.65 1.65
Nos. 317-320 (4) 3.58 3.58

Centenary of first Nigerian postage stamps.

Globe and UPU Emblem A83

UPU cent.: 18k, World map and means of transportation. 30k, Letters.

1974, Oct. 9

321 A83 5k blue & multi .28 .28
322 A83 18k orange & multi 1.00 1.00
323 A83 30k brown & multi 1.65 1.65
Nos. 321-323 (3) 2.93 2.93

Hungry and Well-fed Children — A84

Designs: 12k, Chicken farm, horiz. 30k, Irrigation project.

1974, Nov. 25 **Litho.** *Perf. 14*

324 A84 5k orange, blk & grn .24 .24
325 A84 12k multicolored .55 .55
326 A84 30k multicolored 1.40 1.40
Nos. 324-326 (3) 2.19 2.19

Freedom from Hunger.

A85

Map of Nigeria with Telex Network, Teleprinter — A86

1975, July 3 **Litho.** *Perf. 14*

327 A85 5k multicolored .20 .20
328 A85 12k multicolored .50 .50
329 A86 18k multicolored .75 .75
330 A86 30k multicolored 1.25 1.25
Nos. 327-330 (4) 2.70 2.70

Inauguration of Nigeria Telex Network.

Queen Amina of Zaria (1536-1566) A87

Alexander Graham Bell A88

1975, Aug. 18 **Litho.** *Perf. 14*

331 A87 5k multicolored .25 .25
332 A87 18k multicolored .90 .90
333 A87 30k multicolored 1.50 1.50
Nos. 331-333 (3) 2.65 2.65

International Women's Year.

1976, Mar. 10 **Wmk. 379**

Designs: 18k, Hands beating gong, modern telephone operator, horiz. 25k, Telephones, 1876, 1976.

334 A88 5k pink, black & ocher .22 .22
335 A88 18k deep lilac & multi .80 .80
336 A88 25k lt bl, vio bl & blk 1.10 1.10
Nos. 334-336 (3) 2.12 2.12

Centenary of first telephone call by Alexander Graham Bell, Mar. 10, 1876.

Children Going to School — A89

Designs: 5k, Child learning to write, horiz. 25k, Classroom.

1976, Sept. 20 Litho. *Perf. 14*

337 A89 5k multicolored .22 .22
338 A89 18k multicolored .80 .80
339 A89 25k multicolored 1.10 1.10
Nos. 337-339 (3) 2.12 2.12

Launching of universal primary education in 1976.

Traditional Musical Instruments A90

5k, Carved mask (festival emblem). 10k, Natl. Arts Theater, Lagos. 12k, Nigerian & African women's hair styles. 30k, Nigerian carvings.

1976-77 Wmk. 379

340 A90 5k black, gold & grn .18 .18
341 A90 10k multicolored .35 .35
342 A90 12k multicolored .45 .45
343 A90 18k brown, ocher & blk .65 .65
344 A90 30k multicolored 1.10 1.10
Nos. 340-344 (5) 2.73 2.73

2nd World Black and African Festival of Arts and Culture, Lagos, Jan. 15-Feb. 12, 1977. Issue dates: 5k, 18k, Nov. 1, 1976; others Jan. 15, 1977.

Gen. Muhammed Broadcasting and Map of Nigeria A91

Designs: 18k, Gen. Muhammed as Commander in Chief, vert. 30k, in battle dress, vert.

1977, Feb. 13 Litho. *Perf. 14*

345 A91 5k multicolored .16 .16
346 A91 18k multicolored .60 .60
347 A91 30k multicolored 1.00 1.00
Nos. 345-347 (3) 1.76 1.76

Gen. Murtala Ramat Muhammed, Head of State and Commander in Chief, 1st death anniversary.

Scouts Clearing Street — A92

Designs: 5k, Senior and Junior Boy Scouts saluting, vert. 25k, Scouts working on farm. 30k, African Scout Jamboree emblem, map of Africa.

1977, Apr. 1 Wmk. 379

348 A92 5k multicolored .22 .22
349 A92 18k multicolored .65 .65
350 A92 25k multicolored .95 .95
351 A92 30k multicolored 1.30 1.30
Nos. 348-351 (4) 3.12 3.12

First All-Africa Boy Scout Jamboree, Sherehills, Jos, Nigeria, Apr. 2-8, 1977.

Trade Fair Emblem A93

Emblem and: 5k, View of Fair grounds. 30k, Weaver and potter.

1977, Nov. 27 Litho. *Perf. 13*

352 A93 5k multicolored .16 .16
353 A93 18k multicolored .55 .55
354 A93 30k multicolored .95 .95
Nos. 352-354 (3) 1.66 1.66

1st Lagos Intl. Trade Fair, Nov. 27-Dec. 11.

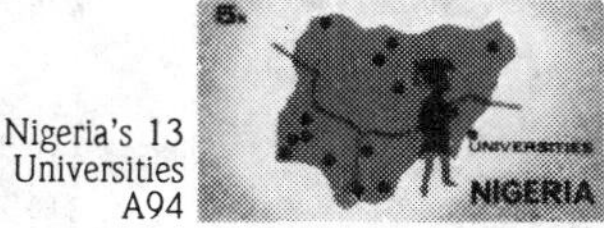

Nigeria's 13 Universities A94

Designs: 12k, Map of West African highways and telecommunications network. 18k, Training of technicians, and cogwheel. 30k, World map and map of Argentina with Buenos Aires.

1978, Apr. 28 Wmk. 379

355 A94 5k multicolored .15 .15
356 A94 12k multicolored .32 .32
357 A94 18k multicolored .48 .48
358 A94 30k multicolored .80 .80
Nos. 355-358 (4) 1.75 1.75

Global Conf. on Technical Cooperation among Developing Countries, Buenos Aires.

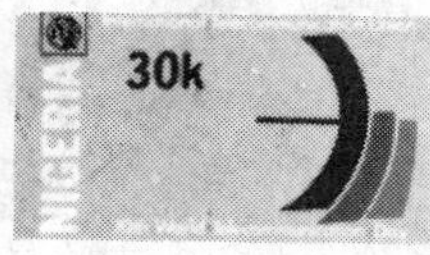

Antenna and ITU Emblem A95

1978, May 17 Litho. *Perf. 14*

359 A95 30k multicolored 1.00 1.00

10th World Telecommunications Day.

Students on Cassava Plantation A96

"Operation Feed the Nation": 18k, Woman working in backyard vegetable garden. 30k, Plantain harvest, vert.

1978, July 7 Litho. *Perf. 14*

360 A96 5k multicolored .15 .15
361 A96 18k multicolored .42 .42
362 A96 30k multicolored .65 .65
Nos. 360-362 (3) 1.22 1.22

Mother Holding Sick Child — A97

Designs: 12k, Sick boy at health station. 18k, Vaccination of children. 30k, Syringe and WHO emblem, vert.

1978, Aug. 31 Wmk. 379

363 A97 5k multicolored .15 .15
364 A97 12k multicolored .34 .34
365 A97 18k multicolored .48 .48
366 A97 30k multicolored .75 .75
Nos. 363-366 (4) 1.72 1.72

Global eradication of smallpox.

Bronze Horseman from Benin — A98

Anti-Apartheid Emblem — A99

Nigerian antiquities: 5k, Nok terracotta figure from Bwari. 12k, Bronze snail and animal from Igbo-Ukwu. 18k, Bronze statue of a king of Ife.

1978, Oct. 27 Litho. *Perf. 14*

367 A98 5k multicolored .15 .15
368 A98 12k multicolored, horiz. .32 .32
369 A98 18k multicolored .48 .48
370 A98 30k multicolored .70 .70
Nos. 367-370 (4) 1.65 1.65

1978, Dec. 10 *Perf. 14*

371 A99 18k red, yellow & black .45 .45

Anti-Apartheid Year.

Wright Brothers, Flyer A A100

18k, Nigerian Air Force fighters in formation.

1978, Dec. 28

372 A100 5k multicolored .15 .15
373 A100 18k multicolored .48 .48

75th anniversary of powered flight.

Murtala Muhammed Airport A101

1979, Mar. 15 Litho. *Perf. 14*

374 A101 5k bright blue & black .15 .15

Inauguration of Murtala Muhammed Airport.

Young Stamp Collector A102

1979, Apr. 11

375 A102 5k multicolored .15 .15

Philatelic Week; Natl. Philatelic Service, 10th anniv.

Mother Nursing Child, IYC Emblem A103

18k, Children at study. 25k, Children at play, vert.

1979, June 28 Wmk. 379 *Perf. 14*

376 A103 5k multicolored .15 .15
377 A103 18k multicolored .38 .38
378 A103 25k multicolored .48 .48
Nos. 376-378 (3) 1.01 1.01

International Year of the Child.

A104 A105

Design: 10k, Preparation of audio-visual material. 30k, Adult education class.

1979, July 25 Photo. & Engr.

379 A104 10k multicolored .18 .18
380 A104 30k multicolored .55 .55

Intl. Bureau of Education, Geneva, 50th anniv.

1979, Sept. 20 Litho. *Perf. 13½x14*

381 A105 10k Necom house, Lagos .30 .30

Intl. Radio Consultative Committee (CCIR) of the ITU, 50th anniv.

Trainees and Survey Equipment A106

1979, Dec. 12 Photo. *Perf. 14*

382 A106 10k multicolored .30 .30

Economic Commission for Africa, 21st anniv.

Soccer Cup and Ball on Map of Nigeria A107

1980, Mar. 8

383 A107 10k shown .15 .15
384 A107 30k Player, vert. .45 .45

12th African Cup of Nations Soccer Championship, Lagos and Ibadan, Mar.

Swimming, Moscow '80 Emblem A108

Litho. & Engr.

1980, July 19 *Perf. 14*

385 A108 10k Wrestling, vert. .22 .22
386 A108 20k Long jump, vert. .42 .42
387 A108 30k shown .65 .65
388 A108 45k Women's basketball, vert. 1.00 1.00
Nos. 385-388 (4) 2.29 2.29

22nd Summer Olympic Games, Moscow, July 19-Aug. 3.

Men Holding OPEC Emblem A109

1980, Sept. 15 Litho. & Engr.

389 A109 10k shown .18 .18
390 A109 45k Anniversary emblem, vert. .80 .80

OPEC, 20th anniversary.

First Steam Locomotive in Nigeria A110

1980, Oct. 2 Wmk. 379 *Perf. 14*

391 A110 10k shown .22 .22
392 A110 20k Unloading freight car .42 .42
393 A110 30k Freight train .65 .65
Nos. 391-393 (3) 1.29 1.29

Nigerian Railway Corp., 75th anniv.

Technician Performing Quality Control Test — A111

1980, Oct. 14

394 A111 10k Scale, ruler, vert. .18 .18
395 A111 30k shown .55 .55

World Standards Day.

Map of West Africa showing ECOWAS Members, Modes of Communication — A112

1980, Nov. 5 Litho. & Engr.

396 A112 10k shown .20 .20
396A A112 25k Transportation .48 .48
397 A112 30k Map, cow, cocoa .60 .60
398 A112 45k Map, industrial symbols .85 .85
Nos. 396-398 (4) 2.13 2.13

Woman with Cane Sweeping — A113

Wmk. 379

1981, June 25 Litho. *Perf. 14*

399 A113 10k shown .16 .16
400 A113 30k Amputee photographer .50 .50

Intl. Year of the Disabled.

World Food Day — A114

1981, Oct. 16 Litho. & Engr.

401 A114 10k Pres. Shenu Shagari .20 .20
402 A114 25k Produce, vert. .50 .50
403 A114 30k Tomato crop, vert. .60 .60
404 A114 45k Pig farm .90 .90
Nos. 401-404 (4) 2.20 2.20

Anti-apartheid Year — A115

1981, Dec. 10 Litho.

405 A115 30k Soweto riot .55 .55
406 A115 45k Police hitting man, vert. .80 .80

Scouting Year — A116

1982, Feb. 22 Litho. *Perf. 14*

407 A116 30k Animal first aid .50 .50
408 A116 45k Baden-Powell, scouts .75 .75

TB Bacillus Centenary A117

1982, Mar. 24 Litho. *Perf. 14*

409 A117 10k Inoculation .16 .16
410 A117 30k Research .48 .48
411 A117 45k Patient being x-rayed, vert. .70 .70
Nos. 409-411 (3) 1.34 1.34

10th Anniv. of UN Conference on Human Environment A118

1982, June 10 Litho.

412 A118 10k Keep your environment clean .15 .15
413 A118 20k Check air pollution .30 .30
414 A118 30k Preserve natural environment .48 .48
415 A118 45k Reafforestation concerns all .70 .70
Nos. 412-415 (4) 1.63 1.63

Salamis Parnassus A119

1982, Sept. 15 Litho.

416 A119 10k shown .20 .20
417 A119 20k Papilio zalmoxis .38 .38
418 A119 30k Pachylophus beckeri .60 .60
419 A119 45k Papilio hesperus .85 .85
Nos. 416-419 (4) 2.03 2.03

25th Anniv. of Natl. Museum A120

1982, Nov. 18 Wmk. 379

420 A120 10k Statuettes, vert. .16 .16
421 A120 20k Bronze leopard .30 .30
422 A120 30k Soapstone seated figure, vert. .48 .48
423 A120 45k Wooden helmet mask .70 .70
Nos. 420-423 (4) 1.64 1.64

Family Day — A121

Commonwealth Day — A122

1983, Mar. 8 Litho. *Perf. 14*

424 A121 10k Extended family, house, horiz. .25 .25
425 A121 30k Family .75 .75

1983, Mar. 14

426 A122 10k Satellite view, horiz. .22 .22
427 A122 25k Natl. Assembly buildings, horiz. .55 .55
428 A122 30k Oil exploration .70 .70
429 A122 45k Runners 1.00 1.00
Nos. 426-429 (4) 2.47 2.47

10th Anniv. of Natl. Youth Service Corps A123

1983, May 25 Litho. *Perf. 14*

430 A123 10k Construction .25 .25
431 A123 25k Climbing wall, vert. .55 .55
432 A123 30k Marching, vert. .75 .75
Nos. 430-432 (3) 1.55 1.55

World Communications Year — A124

Wmk. 379

1983, July 22 Litho. *Perf. 14*

433 A124 10k Mailman, vert. .20 .20
434 A124 25k Newspaper stand .52 .52
435 A124 30k Traditional horn messenger .65 .65
436 A124 45k TV news broadcast .95 .95
Nos. 433-436 (4) 2.32 2.32

World Fishery A125

1983, Sept. 22 Litho. Wmk. 379

437 A125 10k Pink shrimp .20 .20
438 A125 25k Long neck groaker .50 .50
439 A125 30k Barracuda .60 .60
440 A125 45k Fishing technique .90 .90
Nos. 437-440 (4) 2.20 2.20

Boys' Brigade, 75th Anniv. A126

1983, Oct. 14 *Perf. 14*

441 A126 10k Boys, emblem, vert. .22 .22
442 A126 30k Food production .55 .55
443 A126 45k Skill training 1.00 1.00
Nos. 441-443 (3) 1.77 1.77

Fight Against Polio Campaign A127

1984, Feb. 29 Litho. *Perf. 14*

444 A127 10k Crippled boy, vert. .20 .20
445 A127 25k Vaccination .50 .50
446 A127 30k Healthy child, vert. .65 .65
Nos. 444-446 (3) 1.35 1.35

Hartebeests A128

1984, May 25 Wmk. 379 *Perf. 14*

447 A128 10k Waterbuck, vert. .20 .20
448 A128 25k shown .50 .50
449 A128 30k Buffalo .65 .65
450 A128 45k African golden monkey, vert. .95 .95
Nos. 447-450 (4) 2.30 2.30

Central Bank of Nigeria, 25th Anniv. A129

1984, July 2 Wmk. 379

451 A129 10k £1 note, 1968 .22 .22
452 A129 25k Bank .55 .55
453 A129 30k £5 note, 1959 .70 .70
Nos. 451-453 (3) 1.47 1.47

1984 Summer Olympics, Los Angeles A130

African Development Bank, 20th Anniv. A131

Wmk. 379

1984, Aug. 9 Litho. *Perf. 14*

454 A130 10k Boxing .18 .18
455 A130 25k Discus .42 .42
456 A130 30k Weight lifting .50 .50
457 A130 45k Bicycling .75 .75
Nos. 454-457 (4) 1.85 1.85

1984, Sept. 10

Designs: 10k, Irrigation project, Lesotho. 25k, Bomi Hills roadway, Liberia. 30k, Education development, Seychelles. 45k, Coal mining and transportation, Niger. Nos. 459-461 horiz.

458 A131 10k multicolored .18 .18
459 A131 25k multicolored .45 .45
460 A131 30k multicolored .52 .52
461 A131 45k multicolored .80 .80
Nos. 458-461 (4) 1.95 1.95

A132

A132a

A132b

A132c

Rare bird species.

1984, Oct. 24

462 A132 10k Pin-tailed whydah .20 .20
463 A132a 25k Spur-winged plover .50 .50
464 A132b 30k Red bishop .60 .60
465 A132c 45k Francolin .90 .90
Nos. 462-465 (4) 2.20 2.20

Intl. Civil Aviation Organization, 40th Anniv. A132a

1984, Dec. 7 Litho. *Perf. 14*

465A A132a 10k shown .28 .28
465B A132a 45k Jet circling Earth 1.25 1.25

Fight Against Indiscipline A133

1985, Feb. 27

466 A133 20k Encourage punctuality .38 .38
467 A133 50k Discourage bribery .95 .95

Intl. Youth Year — A134

OPEC, 25th Anniv. — A135

1985, June 5

468 A134 20k Sports, horiz. .25 .25
469 A134 50k Nationalism .65 .65
470 A134 55k Service organizations .75 .75
Nos. 468-470 (3) 1.65 1.65

1985, Sept. 15

471 A135 20k shown .38 .38
472 A135 50k World map, horiz. .95 .95

Natl. Independence, 25th Anniv. A136

1985, Sept. 25

473 A136 20k Oil refinery .35 .35
474 A136 50k Map of states .85 .85
475 A136 55k Monument .90 .90
476 A136 60k Eleme Oil Refinery 1.00 1.00
a. Souvenir sheet of 4, #473-476 7.50
Nos. 473-476 (4) 3.10 3.10

World Tourism Day — A137

UN, 40th Anniv. — A138

1985, Sept. 27

477 A137 20k Waterfalls .24 .24
478 A137 50k Crafts, horiz. .60 .60
479 A137 55k Carved calabashes, flag .65 .65
480 A137 60k Leather goods, rug .75 .75
Nos. 477-480 (4) 2.24 2.24

1985, Oct. 7

481 A138 20k Emblem, map, flag .40 .40
482 A138 50k UN building, horiz. 1.00 1.00
483 A138 55k Emblem, horiz. 1.10 1.10
Nos. 481-483 (3) 2.50 2.50

Admission of Nigeria to UN, 25th anniv.

African Reptiles A139

1986, Apr. 15 Wmk. 379 *Perf. 14*

484 A139 10k Python .20 .20
485 A139 20k Crocodile .40 .40
486 A139 25k Gopher tortoise .50 .50
487 A139 30k Chameleon .60 .60
Nos. 484-487 (4) 1.70 1.70

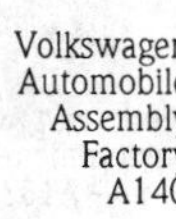

Volkswagen Automobile Assembly Factory A140

Designs: 1k, Social worker with children, vert. 5k, Modern housing development. 10k, Modern method of harvesting coconuts, vert. 15k, Port activities. 20k, Tecoma stans, flower, vert. 25k, Medical care. 30k, Birom folk dancers. 35k, Telephone operators. 40k, Nkpokiti dancers, vert. 45k, Hibiscus. 50k, Modern p.o. 1n, Stone quarry. 2n, Technical education.

1986, June 16 Wmk. 379 *Perf. 14*

488 A140 1k multicolored .15 .15
489 A140 2k multicolored .15 .15
490 A140 5k multicolored .15 .15
491 A140 10k multicolored .15 .15
492 A140 15k multicolored .15 .15
493 A140 20k multicolored .15 .15
494 A140 25k multicolored .15 .15
494A A140 30k multicolored .15 .15
495 A140 35k multicolored .18 .18
496 A140 40k multicolored .20 .20
497 A140 45k multicolored .22 .22
498 A140 50k multicolored .25 .25
499 A140 1n multicolored .50 .50
500 A140 2n multicolored 1.00 1.00
Set value 2.85 2.85

Use of some denominations began as early as 1984. Date of issue of the 30k is not definite.

Intl. Peace Year — A141

1986, June 20 Litho. *Perf. 14*

501 A141 10k Emblem .16 .16
502 A141 20k Hands touching globe .34 .34

Insects A142

1986, July 14

503 A142 10k Goliath beetle .20 .20
504 A142 20k Wasp .40 .40
505 A142 25k Cricket .50 .50
506 A142 30k Carpet beetle .60 .60
a. Souvenir sheet of 4, #503-506 1.75 1.75
Nos. 503-506 (4) 1.70 1.70

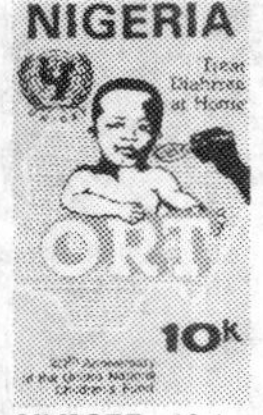

UNICEF, 40th Anniv. — A143

Institute of Intl. Affairs, 25th Anniv. — A144

1986, Nov. 11

507 A143 10k Oral rehydration .15 .15
508 A143 20k Immunization .22 .22
509 A143 25k Breast-feeding .28 .28
510 A143 30k Mother playing with child .34 .34
Nos. 507-510 (4) .99 .99

UN Child Survival Campaign.

1986, Dec. 13

511 A144 20k Intl. understanding, horiz. .15 .15
512 A144 30k shown .22 .22

Seashells A145

1987, Mar. 31

513 A145 10k Freshwater clam .15 .15
514 A145 20k Periwinkle .15 .15
515 A145 25k Bloddy cockle .16 .16
516 A145 30k Mangrove oyster .20 .20
Set value .54 .54

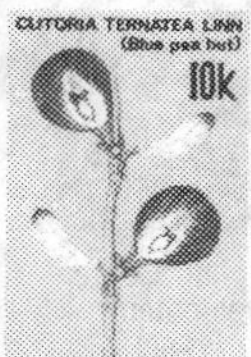

A146

A147

1987, May 28

517 A146 10k Blue pea but .15 .15
518 A146 20k Hibiscus .15 .15
519 A147 25k Acanthus montanus .18 .18
520 A147 30k Combretum racemosum .20 .20
Nos. 517-520 (4) .68 .68

Hair Styles A148

Intl. Year of Shelter for the Homeless A149

1987, Sept. 15 Wmk. 379 *Perf. 14*

521 A148 10k Doka .15 .15
522 A148 20k Eting .15 .15
523 A148 25k Agogo .15 .15
524 A148 30k Goto .15 .15
Set value .42 .42

1987, Dec. 10 Litho.

525 A149 20k Homeless family .15 .15
526 A149 30k Moving to new home .15 .15
Set value .25 .25

A150

A152

A151

1988, Feb. 17 Litho. *Perf. 14*

527 A150 20k Help the Needy .15 .15
528 A150 30k Care for the sick .15 .15
Set value .25 .25

Intl. Red Cross and Red Crescent Organizations, 125th annivs.

1988, Apr. 7 Wmk. 379 *Perf. 14*

529 A151 10k Immunization .15 .15
530 A151 20k Map, globe, emblem .15 .15
531 A151 30k Mobile hospital .15 .15
Set value .30 .30

WHO, 40th anniv.

1988, May 25

532 A152 10k shown .15 .15
533 A152 20k Emblem, map, 4 men .15 .15
Set value .25 .25

Organization of African Unity, 25th anniv.

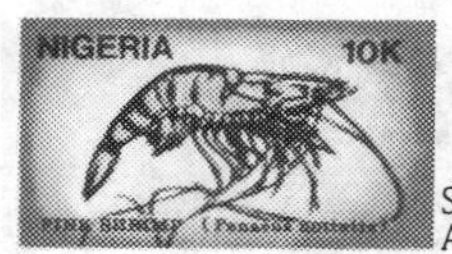

Shrimp A153

1988, June 2

534 A153 10k Pink shrimp .15 .15
535 A153 20k Tiger shrimp .15 .15
536 A153 25k Deepwater roseshrimp .15 .15
537 A153 30k Estuarine prawn .15 .15
a. Miniature sheet of 4, #534-537 .65 .65
Set value .42 .42

1988 Summer Olympics, Seoul A154

1988, Sept. 6 Wmk. 379 *Perf. 14*

538 A154 10k Weight lifting .15 .15
539 A154 20k Boxing .15 .15
540 A154 30k Running, vert. .15 .15
Set value .30 .30

A155

A156

Nigerian Security Printing and Minting Co., Ltd., 25th Anniv. A157

1988, Oct. 28

541 A155 10k Bank note production .15 .15
542 A155 20k Coin production .15 .15
543 A156 25k Products .15 .15
544 A157 30k Anniv. emblem .15 .15
Set value .42 .42

Traditional Musical Instruments A158

Wmk. 379

1989, June 29 Litho. *Perf. 14*

545 A158 10k Tambari .15 .15
546 A158 20k Kundung .15 .15
547 A158 25k Ibid .15 .15
548 A158 30k Dundun .15 .15
Set value .25 .25

African Development Bank, 25th Anniv. — A159

Nigerian Girl Guides Assoc., 70th Anniv. — A160

1989, Sept. 10

549 A159 10k Reservoir, Mali .15 .15
550 A159 20k Irrigation project, Gambia .15 .15
551 A159 25k Bank headquarters .15 .15
552 A159 30k shown .15 .15
Set value .25 .25

Nos. 549-551 horiz.

1989, Sept. 16

553 A160 10k Campfire, horiz. .15 .15
554 A160 20k shown .15 .15
Set value .15 .15

A161

A162

Traditional costumes.

1989, Oct. 26

555 A161 10k Etubom .15 .15
556 A161 20k Fulfulde .15 .15
557 A161 25k Aso-ofi .15 .15
558 A161 30k Fuska Kura .15 .15
Set value .25 .25

1990, Jan. 18

559 A162 10k shown .15 .15
560 A162 20k Map, delivery .15 .15
Set value .15 .15

Pan-African Postal Union, 10th anniv.

Ancient Wall, Kano A162a

50n, Rock Bridge.

1990, May 23 Litho. *Perf. 14*

560A A162a 20n multicolored
560B A162a 50n multicolored

Two additional stamps are known to exist with this set. The editors would like to see them.

Pottery A163

1990, May 24

561 A163 10k Oil lamp .15 .15
562 A163 20k Water pot .15 .15
563 A163 25k Musical pots .15 .15
564 A163 30k Water jug .15 .15
a. Sheet of 4 + 4 labels 2.50 2.50
Set value .26 .26

Inscriptions, including country name, denomination and descriptions vary widely in size and style.

Intl. Literacy Year — A164

1990, Aug. 8

565 A164	20k	multicolored	.15	.15
566 A164	30k	multicolored	.15	.15
		Set value	.15	.15

A165

A166 A167

1990, Sept. 14

567 A165	10k	shown	.15	.15
568 A166	20k	Flags	.15	.15
569 A165	25k	Globe	.15	.15
570 A166	30k	shown	.15	.15
		Set value	.26	.26

Organization of Petroleum Exporting Countries (OPEC), 30th anniv.

1990, Nov. 8

571 A167	20k	Grey parrot	.15	.15
572 A167	30k	Roan antelope	.15	.15
573 A167	1.50n	Grey-necked rock fowl	.38	.38
574 A167	2.50n	Mountain gorilla	.65	.65
		Nos. 571-574 (4)	1.33	1.33

Inscriptions vary widely in size and style.

A168 A170

A169

1991, Mar. 20

575 A168	10k	Eradication	.15	.15
576 A169	20k	shown	.15	.15
577 A168	30k	Prevention	.15	.15
		Set value	.15	.15

Natl. Guineaworm Eradication Day.

1991, May 26

578 A170	20k	Progress	.15	.15
579 A170	30k	Unity	.15	.15
580 A170	50k	Freedom	.15	.15
		Set value	.15	.15

OAU Heads of State Meeting, Abiya.

ECOWAS Summit, Abuja A171

1991, July 4

581 A171	20k	Flags	.15	.15
582 A171	50k	Map of West Africa	.15	.15
		Set value	.15	.15

Economic Community of West African States.

Fish — A172

1991, July 10

583 A172	10k	Electric catfish	.15	.15
584 A172	20k	Niger perch	.15	.15
585 A172	30k	Talapia	.15	.15
586 A172	50k	African catfish	.15	.15
		Set value	.18	.15

Telecom '91 — A173

1991, Oct. 7

587 A173	20k	shown	.15	.15
588 A173	50k	multi, vert.	.15	.15
		Set value	.15	.15

Sixth World Forum and Exposition on Telecommunications, Geneva, Switzerland.

1992 Summer Olympics, Barcelona A174

1992, Jan. 24 **Unwmk.**

589 A174	50k	Boxing	.15	.15
590 A174	1n	Running	.15	.15
591 A174	1.50n	Table tennis	.22	.22

Wmk. 379

592 A174	2n	Taekwondo	.28	.28
		Nos. 589-592 (4)	.80	.80

1992 Summer Olympics, Barcelona A175

World Health Day A176

Wmk. 379

1992, Apr. 3 **Litho.** ***Perf. 14***

593 A175	1.50n	multicolored	.38	.38

1992, Apr. 7 **Unwmk.**

Designs: 50k, Heart and blood pressure gauge. 1n, Globe and blood pressure guage. 1.50n, Heart in rib cage. 2n, Cross-section of heart.

594 A176	50k	multicolored	.15	.15
595 A176	1n	multicolored	.25	.25
596 A176	1.50n	multicolored	.38	.38
597 A176	2n	multicolored	.50	.50
		Nos. 594-597 (4)	1.28	1.28

Intl. Institute of Tropical Agriculture, 25th Anniv. A177

Designs: 50k, Plantain, vert. 1n, Food products. 1.50n, Harvesting cassava tubers, vert. 2n, Yam barn, vert.

1992, July 17

598 A177	50k	multicolored	.15	.15
599 A177	1n	multicolored	.25	.25
600 A177	1.50n	grn, blk & brown	.38	.38
601 A177	2n	multicolored	.50	.50
		Nos. 598-601 (4)	1.28	1.28

Olymphilex '92 — A178

1.50n, Stamp under magnifying glass.

Wmk. 379

1992, July 3 **Litho.** ***Perf. 14***

602 A178	50k	multicolored	.15	.15
603 A178	1.50n	multicolored	.18	.18
a.		Souvenir sheet of 2, #602-603 + 4 labels, unwmkd.	.24	.24
		Set value	.24	.24

Maryam Babangida, Natl. Center for Women's Development

A179 A180

A180a

Designs: 50k, Emblem of Better Life Program. 1n, Women harvesting corn. 1.50n, Natl. Center, horiz. 2n, Woman using loom.

1992, Oct. 16

604 A179	50k	multicolored	.15	.15
605 A180	1n	multicolored	.25	.25
606 A180	1.50n	multicolored	.38	.38
607 A180a	2n	multicolored	.50	.50
		Nos. 604-607 (4)	1.28	1.28

Traditional Dances — A181

Unwmk.

1992, Dec. 15 **Litho.** ***Perf. 14***

608 A181	50k	Sabada	.15	.15
609 A181	1n	Sato	.25	.25
610 A181	1.50n	Asian Ubo Ikpa	.38	.38
611 A181	2n	Dundun	.50	.50
		Nos. 608-611 (4)	1.28	1.28

Intl. Conference on Nutrition, Rome A182

1992, Dec. 1 **Litho.** ***Perf. 14***

612 A182	50k	Vegetables	.15	.15
613 A182	1n	Child eating	.25	.25
614 A182	1.50n	Fruits, vert.	.35	.35
615 A182	2n	Vegetables, diff.	.50	.50
		Nos. 612-615 (4)	1.25	1.25

Animals A182a

Leki Beach A182b

1992-93 **Litho.** ***Perf. 14***

615A A182a	1.50n	African elephant	
615B A182a	5n	Stanley crane, vert.	
615C A182b	10n	multicolored	
615D A182a	20n	Roan antelope	
615E A182a	30n	Lion	

World Environment Day — A183

Designs: 1n, Clean environment ensures good health. 1.50n, Check water polution. 5n, Preserve your environment. 10n, Environment and nature.

1993, June 4 **Litho.** ***Perf. 14***

616 A183	1n	multicolored	.15	.15
617 A183	1.50n	multicolored	.15	.15
618 A183	5n	multicolored	.40	.40
619 A183	10n	multicolored	.80	.80
		Nos. 616-619 (4)	1.50	1.50

Natl. Commission for Museums and Monuments, 50th Anniv. A184

1993, July 28 **Litho.** ***Perf. 14***

620 A184	1n	Oni figure, vert.	.15	.15
621 A184	1.50n	Queen Mother head, vert.	.15	.15
622 A184	5n	Pendant	.40	.40
623 A184	10n	Nok head, vert.	.80	.80
		Nos. 620-623 (4)	1.50	1.50

Orchids — A185

1993, Oct. 28 **Litho.** ***Perf. 14***

624 A185	1n	Bulbophyllum distans	.15	.15
625 A185	1.50n	Eulophia cristata	.15	.15
626 A185	5n	Eulophia horsfalli	.40	.40
627 A185	10n	Eulophia quartiniana	.80	.80
a.		Souv. sheet of 4, #624-627	*4.50*	*4.50*
		Nos. 624-627 (4)	1.50	1.50

No. 627a exists with perforations through either the bottom or top margins.

Intl. Year of the Family A186

Designs: 1.50n, Child abuse, classroom scene. 10n, Fending for the family, market scene.

1994, Mar. 30 **Litho.** ***Perf. 14***

628 A186	1.50n	multicolored	.15	.15
629 A186	10n	multicolored	.90	.90

Nigerian Philatelic Service, 25th Anniv. A187

1n, #224. 1.50n, Bureau building. 5n, Map made of stamps. 10n, Counter staff, customers.

1994, Apr. 11
630 A187 1n multicolored .15 .15
631 A187 1.50n multicolored .15 .15
632 A187 5n multicolored .45 .45
633 A187 10n multicolored .90 .90
Nos. 630-633 (4) 1.65 1.65

First Nigerian Postage Stamps, 120th Anniv. A188

Designs: 1n, "I love stamps." 1.50n, "I collect stamps." 5n, Methods of transporting mail. 10n, Lagos type A1 on airmail envelope.

1994, June 10 Litho. *Perf. 14*
634 A188 1n multicolored .15 .15
635 A188 1.50n multicolored .15 .15
636 A188 5n multicolored .45 .45
637 A188 10n multicolored .90 .90
Nos. 634-637 (4) 1.65 1.65

PHILAKOREA '94 — A189

1994, Aug. 16 Litho. *Perf. 14*
638 A189 30n multicolored 2.75 2.75

Crabs A190

1994, Aug. 12 Litho. *Perf. 14*
639 A190 1n Geryon quinquedens .15 .15
640 A190 1.50n Spider crab .15 .15
641 A190 5n Red spider .45 .45
642 A190 10n Geryon maritae .90 .90
Nos. 639-642 (4) 1.65 1.65

African Development Bank, 30th Anniv. — A191

1994, Sept. 16
643 A191 1.50n Water treatment plant .15 .15
644 A191 30n Emblem, field 2.75 2.75

NIPOST/NITEL, 10th Anniv. — A192

Designs: 1n, Putting letter into mailbox, vert. 1.50n, Airmail letter. 5n, NIPOST, NITEL logos. 10n, Telephones, vert.

1995, Jan. 1 Litho. *Perf. 14*
645 A192 1n multicolored .15 .15
646 A192 1.50n multicolored .15 .15
647 A192 5n multicolored .45 .45
648 A192 10n multicolored .90 .90
Nos. 645-648 (4) 1.65 1.65

Family Support Program A194

Designs: 1n, Feed the family. 1.50n, Monitoring child education. 5n, Caring for the family. 10n, Support agriculture.

1995, July 20 Litho. *Perf. 14*
653 A194 1n multicolored .15 .15
654 A194 1.50n multicolored .15 .15
655 A194 5n multicolored .45 .45
656 A194 10n multicolored .90 .90
Nos. 653-656 (4) 1.65 1.65

First Telephone in Nigeria, Cent. — A195

Designs: 1.50n, Dial telephone, c. 1919. 10n, Crank telephone, c. 1885.

1995, Oct. 9 Litho. *Perf. 14*
657 A195 1.50n multicolored .15 .15
658 A195 10n multicolored .90 .90

FAO, 50th Anniv. A196

1995, Oct. 16
659 A196 1.50n shown .15 .15
660 A196 30n Fishing boats 2.75 2.75

UN, 50th Anniv. A197

Designs: 1n, Emblem of justice, vert. 1.50n, Against illegal dumping of toxic chemicals. 5n, Tourism. 10n, Peace-keeping soldiers.

1995, Oct. 24
661 A197 1n multicolored .15 .15
662 A197 1.50n multicolored .15 .15
663 A197 5n multicolored .45 .45
664 A197 10n multicolored .90 .90
Nos. 661-664 (4) 1.65 1.65

Niger Dock, 10th Anniv. A198

5n, Overall view of dock. 10n, Boat being lifted. 20n, Boats in dock area. 30n, Boat on water.

1996, Apr. 29 Litho. *Perf. 14*
665 A198 5n multicolored .45 .45
666 A198 10n multicolored .90 .90
667 A198 20n multicolored 1.80 1.80
668 A198 30n multicolored 2.75 2.75
Nos. 665-668 (4) 5.90 5.90

Economic Community of West African States (ECOWAS), 21st Anniv. A199

Designs: 5n, Developing agriculture and scientific research. 30n, Free movement of people.

1996, May 5 Litho. *Perf. 14*
669 A199 5n multicolored .45 .45
670 A199 30n multicolored 2.75 2.75

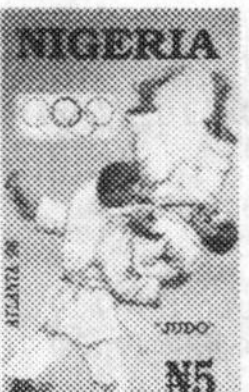

A200

A201

1996, June 28
671 A200 5n Judo .45 .45
672 A200 10n Tennis .90 .90
673 A200 20n Relay race 1.80 1.80
674 A200 30n Soccer 2.75 2.75
Nos. 671-674 (4) 5.90 5.90

1996 Summer Olympic Games, Atlanta.

1996, Oct. 10 Litho. *Perf. 14*
675 A201 30n Natl. flag, logo 2.75 2.75

Istanbul '96.

Mushrooms A202

Designs: 5n, Volvariella esculenta. 10n, Lentinus subnudus. 20n, Tricholoma lobayensis. 30n, Pleurotus tuber-regium.

1996, Nov. 19
676 A202 5n multicolored .45 .45
677 A202 10n multicolored .90 .90
678 A202 20n multicolored 1.80 1.80
679 A202 30n multicolored 2.75 2.75
Nos. 676-679 (4) 5.90 5.90

UNICEF, 50th Anniv. A203

Designs: 5n, "Child's right to play," vert. 30n, "Educate the girl child."

1996, Dec. 10
680 A203 5n multicolored .45 .45
681 A203 30n multicolored 2.75 2.75

Mass Literacy Commission, 5th Anniv. A204

Designs: 5n, "Teach one to teach one." 30n, "Education through co-operation."

1996, Dec. 30
682 A204 5n grn, blk & dk grn .45 .45
683 A204 30n grn, blk & dk grn 2.75 2.75

SEMI-POSTAL STAMPS

Catalogue values for unused stamps in this section are for Never Hinged items.

Children Drinking Milk at Orphanage SP1

Designs: 1sh6p+3p, Civilian first aid, vert. 2sh6p+3p, Military first aid.

1966, Dec. 1 Photo. *Perf. 14½x14*
B1 SP1 4p + 1p pur, blk & red .28 .28
B2 SP1 1sh6p + 3p multi 1.00 1.00
B3 SP1 2sh6p + 3p multi 1.75 1.75
Nos. B1-B3 (3) 3.03 3.03

The surtax was for the Nigerian Red Cross.

Dr. Armauer G. Hansen — SP2

1973, July 30 Litho. *Perf. 14*
B4 SP2 5k + 2k blk, brn & buff .40 .40

Centenary of the discovery of the Hansen bacillus, the cause of leprosy. The surtax was for the Nigerian Anti-Leprosy Association.

POSTAGE DUE STAMPS

Catalogue values for unused stamps in this section are for Never Hinged items.

D1

D2

Perf. 14½x14

1959, Jan. 4 Wmk. 4 Litho.
J1 D1 1p orange .15 .15
J2 D1 2p orange .15 .15
J3 D1 3p orange .15 .15
J4 D1 6p orange 1.00 *1.00*
J5 D1 1sh black 2.25 *2.25*
Nos. J1-J5 (5) 3.70 *3.70*

1961, Aug. 1 Wmk. 335
J6 D1 1p red .15 .15
J7 D1 2p blue .15 .15
J8 D1 3p emerald .18 .18
J9 D1 6p yellow .40 .40
J10 D1 1sh dark blue 1.25 *1.25*
Nos. J6-J10 (5) 2.13 *2.13*

Perf. 12½x13½

1973, May 3 Litho. Unwmk.
J11 D2 2k red .15 .15
J12 D2 3k blue .15 .15
J13 D2 5k orange .20 .20
J14 D2 10k yellow green .35 .35
Nos. J11-J14 (4) .85 .85

1987-94 *Rouletted 9*
J15 D2 2k red 1.10
J16 D2 5k yellow 2.75
J17 D2 10k green 5.75
Nos. J15-J17 (3) 9.60

NIUE

nē-'ü-(,)ā

LOCATION — Island in the south Pacific Ocean, northeast of New Zealand
GOVT. — Self-government, in free association with New Zealand
AREA — 100 sq. mi.
POP. — 3,019 (est. 1984)
CAPITAL — Alofi

Niue, also known as Savage Island, was annexed to New Zealand in 1901 with the Cook Islands. Niue achieved internal self-government in 1974.

12 Pence = 1 Shilling
20 Shillings = 1 Pound
100 Cents = 1 Dollar (1967)

Catalogue values for unused stamps in this country are for Never Hinged items, beginning with Scott 90 in the regular postage section, Scott B1 in the semi-postal section, Scott C1 in the air post section, and Scott O1 in the officials section.

Watermarks

Wmk. 61- Single-lined NZ and Star Close Together

Wmk. 253- NZ and Star

New Zealand No. 100 Handstamped in Green **NIUE**

1902 Wmk. 63 *Perf. 11*

Thick Soft Paper

1	A35	1p carmine	375.00	375.00

Stamps of New Zealand Surcharged in Carmine, Vermilion or Blue:

NIUE. ½ PENI. 1/2p — **NIUE. TAHA PENI.** 1p — **NIUE. 2½ PENI** 2 1/2p

Perf. 14

Thin Hard Paper

3	A18	½p green (C)	1.50	*3.00*
a.		Inverted surcharge	300.00	*400.00*
4	A35	1p carmine (Bl), perf. 11x14	1.25	1.10
a.		No period after "PENI"	11.00	12.50
b.		Perf. 14	8.00	10.00
c.		As "a," perf. 14	140.00	150.00

Perf. 14

Wmk. 61

6	A18	½p green (V)	.60	.85
7	A35	1p carmine (Bl)	.85	1.10
a.		No period after "PENI"	9.00	*16.00*
b.		Double surcharge	*725.00*	

Perf. 11

Unwmk.

8	A22	2½p blue (C)	4.00	4.50
a.		No period after "PENI"	45.00	47.50
9	A22	2½p blue (V)	1.75	2.00
a.		No period after "PENI"	20.00	25.00

The surcharge on the ½ & 1p stamps is printed in blocks of 60. Two stamps in each block have a space between the "U" and "E" of "NIUE" and one of the 1p stamps has a broken "E" like an "F."

Blue Surcharge on Stamps of New Zealand, Types of 1898:

NIUE. Tolu e Pene. e — **NIUE Ono e Pene.** f

NIUE. Taha e Sileni. g — **NIUE. Tahae Sileni.** h

1903 Wmk. 61 *Perf. 11*

10	A23(e)	3p yellow brown	5.00	4.50
11	A26(f)	6p rose	6.50	10.00
13	A29(g)	1sh brown red	22.50	22.50
a.		1sh scarlet	22.50	22.50
b.		1sh orange red	35.00	35.00
c.		As "b," surcharge "h" (error)	675.00	*1,100.*
		Nos. 10-13 (3)	34.00	37.00

Surcharged in Carmine or Blue on Stamps of New Zealand

NIUE. ½ PENI. j

1911-12 *Perf. 14, 14x14½*

14	A41(j)	½p yellow grn (C)	.60	.70
15	A41(f)	6p car rose (Bl)	2.50	*6.00*
16	A41(g)	1sh vermilion (Bl)	8.00	*35.00*
		Nos. 14-16 (3)	11.10	*41.70*

1915 *Perf. 14*

18	A22(d)	2½p dark blue (C)	9.00	17.50

Surcharged in Brown or Dark Blue on Stamps of New Zealand

1917 *Perf. 14x13½, 14x14½*

19	A42	1p carmine (Br)	5.00	5.50
a.		No period after "PENI"	140.00	150.00
20	A45(e)	3p violet brn (Bl)	60.00	75.00
a.		No period after "Pene"	650.00	700.00

New Zealand Stamps of 1909-19 Overprinted in Dark Blue or Red

NIUE. k

1917-20 Typo.

21	A43	½p yellow grn (R)	.40	.75
22	A42	1p carmine (Bl)	3.00	3.50
23	A47	1½p gray black (R)	.15	.90
24	A47	1½p brown org (R)	1.00	3.00
25	A43	3p chocolate (Bl)	1.60	5.25

Engr.

26	A44	2½p dull blue (R)	1.00	3.00
27	A45	3p violet brown (Bl)	1.40	1.50
28	A45	6p car rose (Bl)	4.50	15.00
29	A45	1sh vermilion (Bl)	4.50	15.00
		Nos. 21-29 (9)	17.55	47.90

Same Overprint On Postal-Fiscal Stamps of New Zealand, 1906-15

Perf. 14, 14½ and Compound

1918-23

30	PF1	2sh blue (R)	12.50	30.00
31	PF1	2sh6p brown (Bl) ('23)	14.00	40.00
32	PF1	5sh green (R)	16.00	*45.00*
33	PF1	10sh red brn (Bl) ('23)	65.00	80.00
34	PF2	£1 rose (Bl) ('23)	110.00	140.00
		Nos. 30-34 (5)	217.50	335.00

Landing of Captain Cook A16

Avarua Waterfront A17

Capt. James Cook — A18

Coconut Palm — A19

Arorangi Village — A20

Avarua Harbor — A21

Unwmk.

1920, Aug. 23 Engr. *Perf. 14*

35	A16	½p yellow grn & blk	3.00	*3.00*
36	A17	1p car & black	1.50	1.00
37	A18	1½p red & black	2.00	3.50
38	A19	3p pale blue & blk	1.00	*6.00*
39	A20	6p dp grn & red brn	1.25	*11.00*
a.		Center inverted	*500.00*	
40	A21	1sh blk brn & blk	2.50	*10.00*
		Nos. 35-40 (6)	11.25	*34.50*

See Nos. 41-42. For surcharge see No. 48.

Types of 1920 Issue and

Rarotongan Chief (Te Po) — A22

Avarua Harbor — A23

1925-27 Wmk. 61

41	A16	½p yel grn & blk ('26)	.45	.40
42	A17	1p car & black	.45	.40
43	A22	2½p dk blue & blk ('27)	4.50	5.50
44	A23	4p dull vio & blk ('27)	4.50	6.00
		Nos. 41-44 (4)	9.90	12.30

New Zealand No. 182 Overprinted Type "k" in Red

1927

47	A56	2sh blue	16.00	30.00
a.		2sh dark blue	16.00	37.50

No. 37 Surcharged **TWO PENCE**

1931 Unwmk. *Perf. 14*

48	A18	2p on 1½p red & blk	2.00	1.10

New Zealand Postal-Fiscal Stamps of 1931-32 Overprinted Type "k" in Blue or Red

1931, Nov. 12 Wmk. 61

49	PF5	2sh6p deep brown	8.00	13.00
50	PF5	5sh green (R)	17.00	27.50
51	PF5	10sh dark carmine	32.50	45.00
52	PF5	£1 pink ('32)	50.00	72.50
		Nos. 49-52 (4)	107.50	158.00

See Nos. 86-89D, 116-119.

Landing of Captain Cook — A24

Capt. James Cook — A25

Polynesian Migratory Canoe — A26

Islanders Unloading Ship — A27

View of Avarua Harbor — A28

R.M.S. Monowai — A29

King George V — A30

Perf. 13, 14 (4p, 1sh)

1932, Mar. 16 Engr. Unwmk.

53	A24	½p yel grn & blk	5.75	*7.00*
a.		Perf. 14x13	85.00	*100.00*
54	A25	1p dp red & blk	.75	.15
55	A26	2p org brn & blk	.75	*1.65*
56	A27	2½p indigo & blk	6.00	*21.00*
57	A28	4p Prus blue & blk	7.50	*17.00*
a.		Perf. 13	7.50	*17.00*
58	A29	6p dp org & blk	2.00	1.00
59	A30	1sh dull vio & blk	1.65	*2.75*
		Nos. 53-59 (7)	24.40	*50.55*

For types overprinted see Nos. 67-69.

1933-36 Wmk. 61 *Perf. 14*

60	A24	½p yel grn & blk	.40	.80
61	A25	1p deep red & blk	.40	.30
62	A26	2p brown & blk ('36)	.40	.65
63	A27	2½p indigo & blk	.40	2.00
64	A28	4p Prus blue & blk	1.10	1.10
65	A29	6p org & blk ('36)	.55	.90
66	A30	1sh dk vio & blk ('36)	5.00	12.00
		Nos. 60-66 (7)	8.25	17.75

See Nos. 77-82.

Silver Jubilee Issue

Types of 1932 Overprinted in Black or Red **SILVER JUBILEE OF KING GEORGE V. 1910 - 1935.**

1935, May 7 *Perf. 14*

67	A25	1p car & brown red	.70	1.25
68	A27	2½p indigo & bl (R)	3.00	3.00
a.		Vert. pair, imperf. horiz.	275.00	
69	A29	6p dull org & grn	3.00	5.00
		Nos. 67-69 (3)	6.70	9.25

The vertical spacing of the overprint is wider on No. 69.

No. 68a is from proof sheets.

Coronation Issue

New Zealand Stamps of 1937 Overprinted in Black **NIUE**

Perf. 13½x13

1937, May 13 Wmk. 253

70	A78	1p rose carmine	.15	.15
71	A78	2½p dark blue	.15	.15
72	A78	6p vermilion	.30	.30
		Nos. 70-72 (3)	.60	.60

George VI — A31

Village Scene — A32

Coastal Scene with Canoe — A33

Mt. Ikurangi behind Avarua — A34

1938, May 2 Wmk. 61 *Perf. 14*

73	A31	1sh dp violet & blk	4.00	2.00
74	A32	2sh dk red brown & blk	10.00	4.25
75	A33	3sh yel green & blue	15.00	7.00
		Nos. 73-75 (3)	29.00	13.25

See Nos. 83-85.

Perf. 13½x14

1940, Sept. 2 Engr. Wmk. 253

76	A34	3p on 1½p rose vio & blk	.15	.15

Examples with surcharge are from printer's archives.

Types of 1932-38

1944-46 Wmk. 253 *Perf. 14*

77	A24	½p yel grn & blk	.35	1.00
78	A25	1p dp red & blk ('45)	.35	.65
79	A26	2p org brn & blk ('46)	3.50	3.50
80	A27	2½p dk bl & blk ('45)	.45	1.00
81	A28	4p Prus blue & blk	1.25	.90
82	A29	6p dp orange & blk	.55	1.00
83	A31	1sh dp vio & blk	1.25	1.00
84	A32	2sh brn car & blk ('45)	6.50	2.75
85	A33	3sh yel grn & bl ('45)	9.00	7.00
		Nos. 77-85 (9)	23.20	18.80

New Zealand Postal-Fiscal Stamps Overprinted Type "k" (narrow "E") in Blue or Red

1941-45 Wmk. 61 *Perf. 14*

86	PF5	2sh6p brown	16.00	19.00
87	PF5	5sh green (R)	135.00	150.00
88	PF5	10sh rose	92.50	*115.00*
89	PF5	£1 pink	135.00	150.00
		Nos. 86-89 (4)	378.50	*434.00*

Wmk. 253

89A	PF5	2sh6p brown	2.75	5.00
89B	PF5	5sh green (R)	4.50	7.50
e.		5sh light yellow green, wmkd. sideways ('67)	45.00	70.00
89C	PF5	10sh rose	35.00	40.00
89D	PF5	£1 pink	30.00	35.00
		Nos. 89A-89D (4)	72.25	87.50

No. 89e exists in both line and comb perf.

Catalogue values for unused stamps in this section, from this point to the end of the section, are for Never Hinged items.

Peace Issue

New Zealand Nos. 248, 250, 254 and 255 Overprinted in Black or Blue:

NIUE p   NIUE   NIUE q   NIUE

1946, June 4 *Perf. 13x13½, 13½x13*

90 A94 (p) 1p emerald .15 .15
91 A96 (q) 2p rose violet (Bl) .15 .15
92 A100 (p) 6p org red & red brn .20 .20
93 A101 (p) 8p brn lake & blk (Bl) .25 .25
Nos. 90-93 (4) .75 .75

Map of Niue — A35

H.M.S. Resolution — A36

Designs: 2p, Alofi landing. 3p, Thatched Dwelling. 4p, Arch at Hikutavake. 6p, Alofi bay. 9p, Fisherman. 1sh, Cave at Makefu. 2sh, Gathering bananas. 3sh, Matapa Chasm.

Perf. 14x13½, 13½x14

1950, July 3 **Engr.** **Wmk. 253**

94 A35 ½p red orange & bl .15 .15
95 A36 1p green & brown .15 .15
96 A36 2p rose car & blk .15 .15
97 A36 3p blue vio & blue .25 .20
98 A36 4p brn vio & ol grn .40 .30
99 A36 6p brn org & bl grn .55 .50
100 A35 9p dk brn & brn org .85 .75
101 A36 1sh black & purple 1.00 .85
102 A35 2sh dp grn & brn org 1.35 1.20
103 A35 3sh black & dp blue 2.75 2.00
Nos. 94-103 (10) 7.60 6.25

For surcharges see Nos. 106-115.

Coronation Issue

Queen Elizabeth II — A36a

Westminster Abbey — A36b

1953, May 24 **Photo.** *Perf. 14x14½*

104 A36a 3p brown .50 .50
105 A36b 6p slate black 1.00 1.00

Nos. 94-103 Surcharged   1c

Perf. 14x13½, 13½x14

1967, July 10 **Engr.** **Wmk. 253**

106 A35 ½c on ½p red org & blue .15 .15
107 A36 1c on 1p green & brn .30 .15
108 A36 2c on 2p rose car & black .15 .15
109 A36 2½c on 3p bl vio & bl .15 .15
110 A36 3c on 4p brn vio & ol grn .15 .15
111 A36 5c on 6p brn org & green .25 .25
112 A35 8c on 9p dk brn & brn org .40 .40
113 A36 10c on 1sh blk & pur .95 .95
114 A35 20c on 2sh dp grn & brown org 1.25 1.25
115 A35 30c on 3sh blk & dp bl 1.50 1.50
Nos. 106-115 (10) 5.25 5.10

The position of the numeral varies on each denomination. The surcharge on the ½c, 2½c, 8c, 10c and 20c contains one dot only.

New Zealand Arms — A37

Wmk. 253

1967, July 10 **Typo.** *Perf. 14*

Black Surcharge

116 A37 25c yellow brown 1.10 .65
117 A37 50c green 1.65 1.25
118 A37 $1 cerise 1.25 2.50
119 A37 $2 pale pink 1.75 4.25
Nos. 116-119 (4) 5.75 8.65

1967 *Perf. 11*

116a A37 25c 8.50 13.00
117a A37 50c 9.00 15.00
118a A37 $1 12.00 15.00
119a A37 $2 16.00 20.00
Nos. 116a-119a (4) 45.50 63.00

The perf. 11 stamps were produced when a normal perforating machine broke down and 2,500 of each denomination were perforated on a treadle machine first used by the N.Z. Post Office in 1899.

Christmas Issues

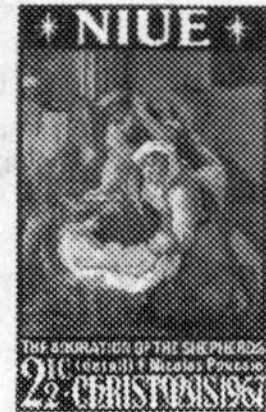

Adoration of the Shepherds, by Poussin — A37a

Nativity, by Federico Fiori — A37b

Perf. 13½x14

1967, Oct. 3 **Photo.** **Wmk. 253**

120 A37a 2½c multicolored .25 .25

1969, Oct. 1 **Photo.** **Wmk. 253**

121 A37b 2½c multicolored .25 .25

Pua — A38

Flowers (except 20c): 1c, Golden shower. 2c, Flamboyant. 2½c, Frangipani. 3c, Niue crocus. 5c, Hibiscus. 8c, Passion fruit. 10c, Kamapui. 20c, Queen Elizabeth II. 30c, Tapeu orchid.

Perf. 12½x13

1969, Nov. 27 **Litho.** **Unwmk.**

122 A38 ½c green & multi .15 .15
123 A38 1c orange & multi .15 .15
124 A38 2c gray & multi .15 .15
125 A38 2½c bister & multi .15 .15
126 A38 3c blue & multi .20 .15
127 A38 5c ver & multi .32 .22
128 A38 8c violet & multi .55 .40
129 A38 10c yellow & multi .65 .50
130 A38 20c dk blue & multi 1.10 .90
131 A38 30c olive grn & multi 1.65 1.50
Nos. 122-131 (10) 5.07 4.27

See Nos. 678.

Edible Crab — A39

Perf. 13½x12½

1969, Aug. 19 **Litho.**

132 A39 3c Kalahimu .15 .15
133 A39 5c Kalavi .22 .22
134 A39 30c Unga 1.10 1.10
Nos. 132-134 (3) 1.47 1.47

Christmas Issue

Adoration, by Correggio — A39a

1970, Oct. 1 **Litho.** *Perf. 12½*

135 A39a 2½c multicolored .20 .20

Plane over Outrigger Canoe — A40

Designs: 5c, Plane over ships in harbor. 8c, Civair plane over island.

1970, Dec. 9 **Litho.** *Perf. 13½*

136 A40 3c multicolored .15 .15
137 A40 5c multicolored .25 .25
138 A40 8c multicolored .40 .40
Nos. 136-138 (3) .80 .80

Opening of Niue Airport.

Polynesian Triller (Heahea) — A41

Birds: 10c, Crimson-crowned fruit pigeon (kulukulu). 20c, Blue-crowned lory (henga).

1971, June 23 **Litho.** *Perf. 13½x13*

139 A41 5c multicolored .25 .25
140 A41 10c multicolored .50 .50
141 A41 20c multicolored 1.00 1.00
Nos. 139-141 (3) 1.75 1.75

Christmas Issue

Holy Night, by Carlo Maratta A41a

1971, Oct. 6 **Photo.** *Perf. 13x13½*

142 A41a 3c orange & multi .20 .20

People of Niue A42

Octopus Lure and Octopus A43

1971, Nov. 17

143 A42 4c Boy .15 .15
144 A42 6c Girl .24 .24
145 A42 9c Man .32 .32
146 A42 14c Woman .55 .55
Nos. 143-146 (4) 1.26 1.26

1972, May 3 **Litho.** *Perf. 13x13½*

Designs: 5c, Warrior and weapons. 10c, Sika (spear) throwing, horiz. 25c, Vivi dance, horiz.

147 A43 3c blue & multi .15 .15
148 A43 5c rose & multi .15 .15
149 A43 10c blue & multi .25 .25
150 A43 25c yellow & multi .65 .65
Nos. 147-150 (4) 1.20 1.20

So. Pacific Festival of Arts, Fiji, May 6-20.

Alofi Wharf A44

South Pacific Commission Emblem and: 5c, Health service. 6c, School children. 18c, Cattle and dwarf palms.

1972, Sept. 6 **Litho.** *Perf. 13½x14*

151 A44 4c blue & multi .15 .15
152 A44 5c blue & multi .15 .15
153 A44 6c blue & multi .18 .18
154 A44 18c blue & multi .55 .55
Nos. 151-154 (4) 1.03 1.03

So. Pacific Commission, 25th anniv.

Christmas Issue, 1972

Madonna and Child, by Murillo — A44a

1972, Oct. 4 **Photo.** *Perf. 11½*

155 A44a 3c gray & multi .15 .15

Pempheris Oualensis A45

Designs: Various fish.

Perf. 13½x13

1973, June 27 **Litho.** **Unwmk.**

156 A45 8c shown .30 .30
157 A45 10c Cephalopholis .40 .40
158 A45 15c Variola louti .55 .55
159 A45 20c Etelis carbunculus .75 .75
Nos. 156-159 (4) 2.00 2.00

Flowers, by Jan Breughel — A46

Paintings of Flowers: 5c, by Hans Bollongier. 10c, by Rachel Ruysch.

1973, Nov. 21 **Litho.** *Perf. 13½x13*

160 A46 4c bister & multi .15 .15
161 A46 5c orange brn & multi .15 .15
162 A46 10c emerald & multi .40 .40
Nos. 160-162 (3) .70 .70

Christmas.

Capt. Cook and "Resolution" A47

Capt. Cook and: 3c, Cook's landing place and ship. 8c, Map of Niue. 20c, Administration Building and flag of 1774.

1974, June 20 **Litho.** *Perf. 13½x14*

163 A47 2c multicolored .15 .15
164 A47 3c multicolored .16 .16
165 A47 8c multicolored .40 .40
166 A47 20c multicolored 1.00 1.00
Nos. 163-166 (4) 1.71 1.71

Bicentenary of Cook's landing on Niue.

King Fataaiki — A48

Annexation Day, Oct. 19, 1900 — A49

Village Meeting A50

Design: 10c, Legislative Assembly Building.

Perf. 14x13½, 13½x14

1974, Oct. 19 **Litho.**

No.	Type	Value	Description	Unused	Used
167	A48	4c	multicolored	.15	.15
168	A49	8c	multicolored	.25	.25
169	A50	10c	multicolored	.35	.35
170	A50	20c	multicolored	.65	.65
			Nos. 167-170 (4)	1.40	1.40

Referendum for Self-government, Sept. 3, 1974.

Decorated Bicycle — A51

Christmas: 10c, Decorated motorcycle. 20c, Going to church by truck.

1974, Nov. 13 **Litho.** ***Perf. 12½***

No.	Type	Value	Description	Unused	Used
171	A51	3c	green & multi	.15	.15
172	A51	10c	dull blue & multi	.22	.22
173	A51	20c	brown & multi	.50	.50
			Nos. 171-173 (3)	.87	.87

Children Going to Church — A52

Children's Drawings: 5c, Child on bicycle trailing balloons. 10c, Balloons and gifts hanging from tree.

1975, Oct. 29 **Litho.** ***Perf. 14½***

No.	Type	Value	Description	Unused	Used
174	A52	4c	multicolored	.15	.15
175	A52	5c	multicolored	.20	.20
176	A52	10c	multicolored	.40	.40
			Nos. 174-176 (3)	.75	.75

Christmas.

Opening of Tourist Hotel — A53

Design: 20c, Hotel, building and floor plan.

1975, Nov. 19 **Litho.** ***Perf. 14x13½***

No.	Type	Value	Description	Unused	Used
177	A53	8c	multicolored	.20	.20
178	A53	20c	multicolored	.50	.50

Preparing Ground for Taro — A54

Designs: 2c, Planting taro (root vegetable). 3c, Banana harvest. 4c, Bush plantation. 5c, Shellfish gathering. 10c, Reef fishing. 20c, Luku (fern) harvest. 50c, Canoe fishing. $1, Husking coconuts. $2, Hunting uga (land crab).

1976, Mar. 3 **Litho.** ***Perf. 13½x14***

No.	Type	Value	Description	Unused	Used
179	A54	1c	multicolored	.15	.15
180	A54	2c	blue & multi	.15	.15
181	A54	3c	lilac & multi	.15	.15
182	A54	4c	red & multi	.15	.15
183	A54	5c	green & multi	.15	.15
184	A54	10c	ocher & multi	.18	.18
185	A54	20c	multicolored	.42	.42
186	A54	50c	yellow & multi	.85	.85
187	A54	$1	multicolored	1.50	1.50
188	A54	$2	multicolored	3.25	3.25
			Nos. 179-188 (10)	6.95	6.95

See #222-231. For surcharges see #203-210.

Water Tower, Girl Drawing Water — A55

15c, Teleprinter & Niue radio station. 20c, Instrument panel, generator & power station.

1976, July 7 **Litho.** ***Perf. 14x14½***

No.	Type	Value	Description	Unused	Used
189	A55	10c	multicolored	.18	.18
190	A55	15c	multicolored	.25	.25
191	A55	20c	multicolored	.35	.35
			Nos. 189-191 (3)	.78	.78

Technical achievements.

Christmas Tree (Flamboyant) and Administration Building — A56

Christmas: 15c, Avatele Church, interior.

1976, Sept. 15 **Litho.** ***Perf. 14½***

No.	Type	Value	Description	Unused	Used
192	A56	9c	orange & multi	.20	.20
193	A56	15c	orange & multi	.35	.35

Elizabeth II, Coronation Portrait, and Westminster Abbey — A57

Design: $2, Coronation regalia.

1977, June 7 **Photo.** ***Perf. 13½***

No.	Type	Value	Description	Unused	Used
194	A57	$1	multicolored	1.40	1.25
195	A57	$2	multicolored	4.25	3.75
a.			Souvenir sheet of 2, #194-195	5.75	5.75

25th anniv. of reign of Elizabeth II. Nos. 194-195 each printed in sheets of 5 stamps and label showing Niue flag and Union Jack.

For surcharge see No. 213.

Mothers and Infants — A58

Designs: 15c, Mobile school dental clinic. 20c, Elderly couple and home.

1977, June 29 **Litho.** ***Perf. 14½***

No.	Type	Value	Description	Unused	Used
196	A58	10c	multicolored	.18	.18
197	A58	15c	multicolored	.22	.22
198	A58	20c	multicolored	.30	.30
			Nos. 196-198 (3)	.70	.70

Personal (social) services.

For surcharges see Nos. 211-212.

Annunciation, by Rubens — A59

Rubens Paintings (details, Virgin and Child): 12c, Adoration of the Kings. 20c, Virgin with Garland. 35c, Holy Family.

1977, Nov. 15 **Photo.** ***Perf. 13x13½***

No.	Type	Value	Description	Unused	Used
199	A59	10c	multicolored	.15	.15
200	A59	12c	multicolored	.15	.15
201	A59	20c	multicolored	.25	.25
202	A59	35c	multicolored	.45	.45
a.			Souvenir sheet of 4, #199-202	1.25	1.25
			Nos. 199-202 (4)	1.00	1.00

Christmas and 400th birth anniversary of Peter Paul Rubens (1577-1640). Nos. 199-202 each printed in sheets of 6 stamps.

Stamps of 1976-77 Surcharged with New Value and 4 Bars in Black or Gold Printing and Perforations as Before

1977, Nov. 15

No.	Type	Value	Description	Unused	Used
203	A54	12c	on 1c (#179)	.18	.18
204	A54	16c	on 2c (#180)	.22	.22
205	A54	30c	on 3c (#181)	.40	.40
206	A54	35c	on 4c (#182)	.48	.48
207	A54	40c	on 5c (#183)	.60	.60
208	A54	60c	on 20c (#185)	.80	.80
209	A54	70c	on $1 (#187)	.90	.90
210	A54	85c	on $2 (#188)	1.25	1.25
211	A58	$1.10	on 10c (#196)	1.40	1.40
212	A58	$2.60	on 20c (#198)	3.25	3.25
213	A57	$3.20	on $2 (#195, G)	8.00	8.00
			Nos. 203-213 (11)	17.48	17.48

"An Inland View in Atooi," by John Webber A60

Scenes in Hawaii, by John Webber: 16c, A View of Karakooa in Owyhee. 20c, An Offering Before Capt. Cook in the Sandwich Islands. 30c, Tereoboo, King of Owyhee, bringing presents (boats). 35c, Masked rowers in boat.

1978, Jan. 18 **Photo.** ***Perf. 13½***

No.	Type	Value	Description	Unused	Used
214	A60	12c	gold & multi	.25	.20
215	A60	16c	gold & multi	.32	.28
216	A60	20c	gold & multi	.40	.35
217	A60	30c	gold & multi	.65	.55
218	A60	35c	gold & multi	.75	.65
a.			Souv. sheet of 5, #214-218 + label	3.00	2.50
			Nos. 214-218 (5)	2.37	2.03

Bicentenary of Capt. Cook's arrival in Hawaii. Nos. 214-218 printed in sheets of 5 stamps and one label showing flags of Hawaii and Niue.

Descent from the Cross, by Caravaggio — A61

Easter: 20c, Burial of Christ, by Bellini.

1978, Mar. 15 **Photo.** ***Perf. 13x13½***

No.	Type	Value	Description	Unused	Used
219	A61	10c	multicolored	.18	.18
220	A61	20c	multicolored	.38	.38
a.			Souv. sheet of 2, #219-220, perf. 13½	.75	.75

Nos. 219-220 issued in sheets of 8.

See Nos. B1-B2.

Souvenir Sheet

Elizabeth II — A62

1978, June 26 **Photo.** ***Perf. 13***

No.	Type	Value	Description	Unused	Used
221			Sheet of 6	8.00	8.00
a.	A62	$1.10	Niue and UK flags	1.10	1.10
b.	A62	$1.10	shown	1.10	1.10
c.	A62	$1.10	Queen's New Zealand flag	1.10	1.10
d.			Souvenir sheet of 3	5.50	5.50

25th anniv. of coronation of Elizabeth II. No. 221 contains 2 horizontal se-tenant strips of Nos. 221a-221c, separated by horizontal gutter showing coronation coach. No. 221d contains a vertical se-tenant strip of Nos. 221a-221c.

Type of 1977

12c, Preparing ground for taro. 16c, Planting taro. 30c, Banana harvest. 35c, Bush plantation. 40c, Shellfish gathering. 60c, Reef fishing. 75c, Luku (fern) harvest. $1.10, Canoe fishing. $3.20, Husking coconuts. $4.20, Hunting uga (land crab).

1978, Oct. 27 **Litho.** ***Perf. 14***

No.	Type	Value	Description	Unused	Used
222	A54	12c	silver & multi	.22	.22
223	A54	16c	silver & multi	.28	.28
224	A54	30c	silver & multi	.55	.55
225	A54	35c	silver & multi	.60	.60
226	A54	40c	silver & multi	.65	.65
227	A54	60c	silver & multi	1.00	1.00
228	A54	75c	silver & multi	1.40	1.40
229	A54	$1.10	silver & multi	2.00	2.00
230	A54	$3.20	silver & multi	4.75	4.75
231	A54	$4.20	silver & multi	5.75	5.75
			Nos. 222-231 (10)	17.20	17.20

Celebration of the Rosary, by Dürer — A63

Designs: 30c, Nativity, by Dürer. 35c, Adoration of the Kings, by Dürer.

1978, Nov. 30 **Photo.** ***Perf. 13***

No.	Type	Value	Description	Unused	Used
232	A63	20c	multicolored	.28	.28
233	A63	30c	multicolored	.45	.45
234	A63	35c	multicolored	.50	.50
a.			Souv. sheet of 3, #232-234 + label	1.50	1.50
			Nos. 232-234 (3)	1.23	1.23

Christmas and 450th death anniversary of Albrecht Dürer (1471-1528). Nos. 232-234 each printed in sheets of 5 stamps and descriptive label.

See Nos. B3-B5.

Pietà, by Gregorio Fernandez A64

Easter: 35c, Burial of Christ, by Pedro Roldan.

1979, Apr. 2

No.	Type	Value	Description	Unused	Used
235	A64	30c	multicolored	.45	.45
236	A64	35c	multicolored	.55	.55
a.			Souvenir sheet of 2, #235-236	1.10	1.10

See Nos. B6-B7.

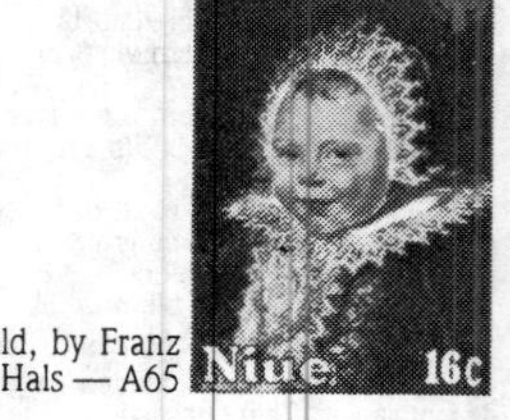

Child, by Franz Hals — A65

IYC (Emblem and Details from Paintings): 16c, Nurse and Child. 20c, Child of the Duke of Osuna, by Goya. 30c, Daughter of Robert Strozzi, by Titian. 35c, Children Eating Fruit, by Murillo.

1979, May 31 **Photo.** ***Perf. 14***

No.	Type	Value	Description	Unused	Used
237	A65	16c	multicolored	.22	.22
238	A65	20c	multicolored	.28	.28
239	A65	30c	multicolored	.42	.42
240	A65	35c	multicolored	.50	.50
a.			Souvenir sheet of 4, #237-240	1.75	1.75
			Nos. 237-240 (4)	1.42	1.42

See Nos. B8-B11.

Penny Black, Bath Mail Coach, Rowland Hill — A66

30c, Basel #3L1 & Alpine village coach. 35c, US #1 & 1st US transatlantic mail ship. 50c, France #3 & French railroad mail car, 1849. 60c, Bavaria #1 & Bavarian mail coach.

1979, July 3 Photo. *Perf. 14*

241 A66 20c pair .40 .40
242 A66 30c pair .60 .60
243 A66 35c pair .70 .70
244 A66 50c pair 1.05 1.05
245 A66 60c pair 1.25 1.25
a. Souv. sheet of 10, #241-245 + 2 labels 4.50 4.50
Nos. 241-245 (5) 4.00 4.00

Sir Rowland Hill (1795-1879), originator of penny postage.

For overprints and surcharges see Nos. 281-285, B16, B21, B26, B30, B33, B41.

Cook's Landing at Botany Bay — A68

18th Century Paintings: 30c, Cook's Men during a Landing on Erromanga. 35c, Resolution and Discovery in Queen Charlotte's Sound. 75c, Death of Capt. Cook on Hawaii, by Johann Zoffany.

1979, July 30 Photo. *Perf. 14*

251 A68 20c multicolored .28 .28
252 A68 30c multicolored .42 .42
253 A68 35c multicolored .50 .50
254 A68 75c multicolored 1.10 1.10
a. Souv. sheet of 4, #251-254, perf. 13½ 2.75 2.75
Nos. 251-254 (4) 2.30 2.30

200th death anniv. of Capt. James Cook.

For surcharges see Nos. B18, B23, B28, B36.

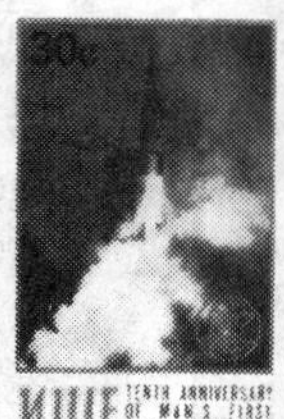

Apollo 11 Lift-off — A69

Virgin and Child, by P. Serra — A70

1979, Sept. 27 Photo. *Perf. 13½*

255 A69 30c shown .35 .35
256 A69 35c Lunar module .42 .42
257 A69 60c Splashdown .80 .80
a. Souvenir sheet of 3 2.00 2.00
Nos. 255-257 (3) 1.57 1.57

Apollo 11 moon landing, 10th anniversary. No. 257a contains Nos. 255-257 in changed colors.

For surcharges see Nos. B24, B29, B35.

1979, Nov. 29 Photo. *Perf. 13*

Virgin and Child by: 25c, R. di Mur. 30c, S. diG. Sasseta. 50c, J. Huguet.

258 A70 20c multicolored .28 .28
259 A70 25c multicolored .35 .35
260 A70 30c multicolored .42 .42
261 A70 50c multicolored .70 .70
a. Souvenir sheet of 4, #258-261 2.25 2.25
Nos. 258-261 (4) 1.75 1.75

Christmas. See Nos. B12-B15. For surcharges see Nos. B19-B20, B25, B32.

Pietà, by Giovanni Bellini — A71

Easter (Pietà, Paintings by): 30c, Botticelli. 35c, Anthony Van Dyck.

1980, Apr. 2 Photo. *Perf. 13*

262 A71 25c multicolored .25 .25
263 A71 30c multicolored .30 .30
264 A71 35c multicolored .35 .35
Nos. 262-264 (3) .90 .90

See Nos. B37-B40.

Ceremonial Stool, New Guinea — A72

1980, July 30 Photo. *Perf. 13*

265 A72 20c shown .20 .20
266 A72 20c Ku-Tagwa plaque .20 .20
267 A72 20c Suspension hook .20 .20
268 A72 20c Ancestral board .20 .20
269 A72 25c Platform post .25 .25
270 A72 25c Canoe ornament .25 .25
271 A72 25c Carved figure .25 .25
272 A72 25c Woman and child .25 .25
273 A72 30c God A'a, statue .30 .30
274 A72 30c Tangaroa, statue .30 .30
275 A72 30c Ivory pendant .30 .30
276 A72 30c Tapa cloth .30 .30
277 A72 35c Maori feather box .35 .35
a. Sheet of 4 (#265, 269, 273, 277) 1.50 1.50
278 A72 35c Hei-tiki .35 .35
a. Sheet of 4 (#266, 270, 274, 278) 1.50 1.50
279 A72 35c House post .35 .35
a. Sheet of 4 (#267, 271, 275, 279) 1.50 1.50
280 A72 35c God Ku, feather image .35 .35
a. Sheet of 4 (#268, 272, 276, 280) 1.50 1.50
Nos. 265-280 (16) 4.40 4.40

3rd South Pacific Festival of Arts, Port Moresby, Papua New Guinea, June 30-July 12. Stamps of same denomination se-tenant horizontally in sheets of 24. Souvenir sheet stamps have 2c surcharge.

For surcharges see Nos. 626-641.

Nos. 241-250, Overprinted in Black on Silver

ZEAPEX'80 AUCKLAND
NEW ZEALAND STAMP EXHIBITION

1980, Aug. 22 *Perf. 14*

281 A66 20c pair .50 .50
282 A66 30c pair .70 .70
283 A66 35c pair .80 .80
284 A66 50c pair 1.10 1.10
285 A66 60c pair 1.40 1.40
Nos. 281-285 (5) 4.50 4.50

ZEAPEX '80, New Zealand International Stamp Exhibition, Auckland, Aug. 23-31.

Queen Mother Elizabeth, 80th Birthday — A73

1980, Sept. 15 Photo. *Perf. 13x13½*

291 A73 $1.10 multicolored 1.75 1.75

Souvenir Sheet

292 A73 $3 multicolored 4.00 4.00

No. 291 issued in sheets of 5 and label showing coad of arms.

100-Meter Dash — A74

Allen Wells — A75

Designs: Nos. 295-296, 400-Meter freestyle. Nos. 297-298, Soling class yachting. Nos. 299-300, Soccer. Stamps of same denomination se-tenant in sheets of 32.

1980, Oct. 30 Photo. *Perf. 14*

293 A74 20c multicolored .28 .28
294 A75 20c multicolored .28 .28
295 A74 25c multicolored .35 .35
296 A75 25c multicolored .35 .35
297 A74 30c multicolored .40 .40
298 A75 30c multicolored .40 .40
299 A74 35c multicolored .45 .45
300 A75 35c multicolored .45 .45
Nos. 293-300 (8) 2.96 2.96

22nd Summer Olympic Games, Moscow, July 19-Aug. 3.

See No. B42.

Virgin and Child, by del Sarto — A76

Paintings of Virgin & Child, by Andrea del Sarto.

1980, Nov. 28 Photo. *Perf. 13x13½*

301 A76 20c multicolored .25 .25
302 A76 25c multicolored .30 .30
303 A76 30c multicolored .35 .35
304 A76 35c multicolored .45 .45
a. Souvenir sheet of 4, #301-304 1.65 1.65
Nos. 301-304 (4) 1.35 1.35

Christmas and 450th death anniversary of Andrea del Sarto.

See Nos. B43-B46.

Moth Orchid — A77

Golden Shower Tree — A77a

1981 Photo. *Perf. 13x13½*

305 A77 2c Phalaenopsis sp. .15 .15
306 A77 2c shown .15 .15
307 A77 5c Euphorbia pulcherrima .15 .15
308 A77 5c Poinsettia .15 .15
309 A77 10c Thunbergia alata .15 .15
310 A77 10c Black-eyed Susan .15 .15
311 A77 15c Cochlospermum hibiscoides .18 .18
312 A77 15c Buttercup tree .18 .18
313 A77 20c Begonia sp. .25 .25
314 A77 20c Begonia .25 .25
315 A77 25c Plumeria sp. .32 .32
316 A77 25c Frangipani .32 .32
317 A77 30c Sterlitzia reginae .35 .35
318 A77 30c Bird of paradise .35 .35
319 A77 35c Hibiscus syriacus .40 .40
320 A77 35c Rose of Sharon .40 .40
321 A77 40c Nymphaea sp. .45 .45
322 A77 40c Water lily .45 .45
323 A77 50c Tibouchina sp. .60 .60
324 A77 50c Princess flower .60 .60
325 A77 60c Nelumbo sp. .70 .70
326 A77 60c Lotus .70 .70
327 A77 80c Hybrid hibiscus 1.00 1.00
328 A77 80c Yellow hibiscus 1.00 1.00

Perf. 13½

329 A77a $1 shown 1.25 1.25
330 A77a $2 Orchid var. 2.50 2.50
331 A77a $3 Orchid sp. 3.50 3.50
332 A77a $4 Poinsettia 5.00 5.00
333 A77a $6 Hybrid hibiscus 7.25 7.25
334 A77a $10 Hibiscus rosa-sinensis 12.50 12.50
Nos. 305-334 (30) 41.40 41.40

Issue dates: 2c, 5c, 10c, 15c, 20c, 25c, Apr. 2, 30c, 35c, 40c, 50c, 60c, 80c, May 26. $1, $2, $3, Dec. 9, 1981; $4, $6, $10, Jan. 15, 1982.

Stamps of same denomination se-tenant.

For surcharges and overprints see Nos. 406-413, 413E, 594-595, O14, O16, O19.

Jesus Defiled, by El Greco — A78

Easter (Paintings): 50c, Pieta, by Fernando Gallego. 60c, The Supper of Emaus, by Jacopo da Pontormo.

1981, Apr. 10 *Perf. 14*

337 A78 35c multicolored .48 .48
338 A78 50c multicolored .65 .65
339 A78 60c multicolored .80 .80
Nos. 337-339 (3) 1.93 1.93

See Nos. B47-B50.

Prince Charles and Lady Diana — A79

1981, June 26 Photo. *Perf. 14*

340 A79 75c Charles .80 .80
341 A79 95c Lady Diana 1.00 1.00
342 A79 $1.20 shown 1.40 1.40
a. Souvenir sheet of 3, #340-342 4.00 4.00
Nos. 340-342 (3) 3.20 3.20

Royal Wedding. Nos. 340-342 each printed in sheets of 5 plus label showing St. Paul's Cathedral.

For overprints and surcharges see Nos. 357-359, 413A, 413C, 455, 596-598, B52-B55.

1982 World Cup Soccer A80

1981, Oct. 16 Photo. *Perf. 13*

343 Strip of 3 1.10 1.10
a. A80 30c any single .35 .35
344 Strip of 3 1.40 1.40
a. A80 35c any single .45 .45
345 Strip of 3 1.50 1.50
a. A80 40c any single .50 .50
Nos. 343-345 (3) 4.00 4.00

See No. B51.

Christmas 1981 — A81

Rembrandt Paintings: 20c, Holy Family with Angels, 1645. 35c, Presentation in the Temple, 1631. 50c, Virgin and Child in Temple, 1629. 60c, Holy Family, 1640.

1981-82 Photo. *Perf. 14x13*

346 A81 20c multicolored .25 .25
347 A81 35c multicolored .45 .45
348 A81 50c multicolored .60 .60
349 A81 60c multicolored .75 .75
a. Souvenir sheet of 4, #346-349 2.50 2.50
Nos. 346-349 (4) 2.05 2.05

Souvenir Sheets

350 A81 80c + 5c like #346 1.10 1.10
351 A81 80c + 5c like #347 1.10 1.10
352 A81 80c + 5c like #348 1.10 1.10
353 A81 80c + 5c like #349 1.10 1.10

Surtax was for school children. Issue dates: Nos. 346-349a, Dec. 11; others, Jan. 22, 1982.

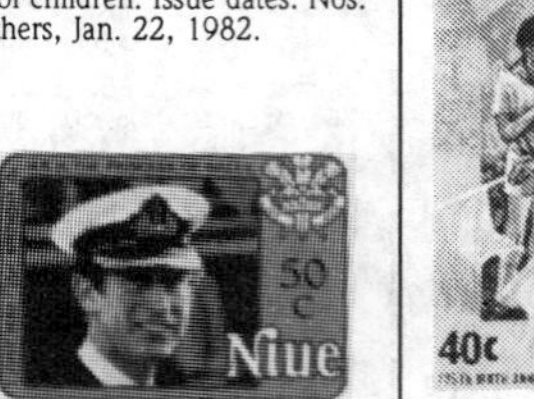
21st Birthday of Princess Diana — A82

1982, July 1 *Perf. 14*

354 A82 50c Charles .50 .50
355 A82 $1.25 Wedding 1.25 1.25
356 A82 $2.50 Diana 2.50 2.50
a. Souvenir sheet of 3, #354-356 5.25 5.25
Nos. 354-356 (3) 4.25 4.25

Nos. 354-356 each printed in sheets of 5 plus label showing wedding day picture.

For overprints and surcharges see Nos. 359B-359D, 413B, 413D, 456.

Nos. 340-342a Overprinted: "COMMEMORATING THE ROYAL BIRTH 21 JUNE 1982" or "BIRTH OF PRINCE WILLIAM OF WALES 21 JUNE 1982"

1982, July 23 *Perf. 14*

357 A79 75c multicolored 1.25 1.25
358 A79 95c multicolored 1.50 1.50
359 A79 $1.20 multicolored 2.00 2.00
a. Souvenir sheet of 3 5.00 5.00
Nos. 357-359 (3) 4.75 4.75

Birthday Type of 1982 Inscribed "COMMEMORATING THE BIRTH OF PRINCE WILLIAM OF WALES—21 JUNE 1982."

1982 Photo. *Perf. 14*

359B A82 50c like #354 .55 .55
359C A82 $1.25 like #355 1.40 1.40
359D A82 $2.50 like #356 2.75 2.75
e. Souvenir sheet of 3 4.75 4.75
Nos. 359B-359D (3) 4.70 4.70

Christmas — A83

Princess Diana Holding Prince William and Paintings of Infants by: 40c, Bronzino (1502-1572). 52c, Murillo (1617-1682). 83c, Boucher (1703-1770). Singles in No. 363a: 34x30mm, showing paintings only.

Perf. 13½x14½

1982, Dec. 3 Photo.

360 A83 40c multicolored .55 .55
361 A83 52c multicolored .65 .65
362 A83 83c multicolored 1.10 1.10
363 A83 $1.05 multicolored 1.40 1.40
a. Souvenir sheet of 4, #364-367 3.75 3.75
Nos. 360-363 (4) 3.70 3.70

Souvenir Sheets

364 A83 80c + 5c like #360 1.10 1.10
365 A83 80c + 5c like #361 1.10 1.10
366 A83 80c + 5c like #362 1.10 1.10
367 A83 80c + 5c like #363 1.10 1.10

Nos. 364-367 each contain one 30x42mm stamp showing Royal family. Surtax was for children's funds.

Commonwealth Day — A84

1983, Mar. 14 Photo. *Perf. 13*

368 A84 70c Flag, Premier Robert R. Rex .85 .85
369 A84 70c Resolution, Adventurer .85 .85
370 A84 70c Passion flower .85 .85
371 A84 70c Lime branch .85 .85
a. Block of 4, #368-371 3.40 3.40

For overprints see Nos. 484-487.

Scouting Year — A85

1983, Apr. 28 Photo. *Perf. 13*

372 A85 40c Flag signals .55 .55
373 A85 50c Tree planting .65 .65
374 A85 83c Map reading 1.20 1.20
Nos. 372-374 (3) 2.40 2.40

Souvenir Sheet

375 Sheet of 3 2.50 2.50
a. A85 40c + 3c like 40c .60 .60
b. A85 50c + 3c like 50c .65 .65
c. A85 83c + 3c like 83c 1.10 1.10

Nos. 372-375 Overprinted in Black on Silver: "XV WORLD JAMBOREE CANADA"

1983, July 14 Photo.

376 A85 40c multicolored .55 .55
377 A85 50c multicolored .65 .65
378 A85 83c multicolored 1.10 1.10
Nos. 376-378 (3) 2.30 2.30

Souvenir Sheet

379 Sheet of 3 2.50 2.50
a. A85 40c + 3c multicolored .60 .60
b. A85 50c + 3c multicolored .65 .65
c. A85 83c + 3c multicolored 1.25 1.25

Save the Whales Campaign A86

1983, Aug. 15 *Perf. 13x14*

380 A86 12c Right whale .16 .16
381 A86 25c Fin whale .35 .35
382 A86 35c Sei whale .45 .45
383 A86 40c Blue whale .55 .55
384 A86 58c Bowhead whale .80 .80
385 A86 70c Sperm whale 1.00 1.00
386 A86 83c Humpback whale 1.20 1.20
387 A86 $1.05 Lesser rorqual 1.40 1.40
388 A86 $2.50 Gray whale 3.50 3.50
Nos. 380-388 (9) 9.41 9.41

Manned Flight Bicentenary A87

1983, Oct. 14 Photo. *Perf. 14*

389 A87 25c Montgolfier, 1783 .30 .30
390 A87 40c Wright Bros. Flyer, 1903 .45 .45
391 A87 58c Graf Zeppelin, 1928 .65 .65
392 A87 70c Boeing 247, 1933 .85 .85
393 A87 83c Apollo VIII, 1968 .95 .95
394 A87 $1.05 Columbia space shuttle 1.25 1.25
a. Souvenir sheet of 6 4.50 4.50
Nos. 389-394 (6) 4.45 4.45

No. 394a contains Nos. 389-394 inscribed "AIRMAIL."

Niue stamps can be mounted in the Scott New Zealand Dependencies album.

Christmas — A87a

Paintings by Raphael (1483-1520): 30c, Garvagh Madonna, National Gallery, London. 40c, Granduca Madonna, Pitti Gallery, Florence. 58c, Goldfinch Madonna, Uffizi Gallery, Florence. 70c, Holy Family of Francis I, Louvre, Paris. 83c, Holy Family with Saints, Alte Pinakothek, Munich.

1983 Photo. *Perf. 14*

395 A87a 30c multicolored .32 .32
396 A87a 40c multicolored .40 .40
397 A87a 58c multicolored .58 .58
398 A87a 70c multicolored .70 .70
399 A87a 83c multicolored .85 .85
Nos. 395-399 (5) 2.85 2.85

Souvenir Sheets

Perf. 13½

400 Sheet of 5 3.00 3.00
a. A87a 30c + 3c like #395 .32 .32
b. A87a 40c + 3c like #396 .42 .42
c. A87a 58c + 3c like #397 .60 .60
d. A87a 70c + 3c like #398 .70 .70
e. A87a 83c + 3c like #399 .85 .85
401 A87a 85c + 5c like #395 1.00 1.00
402 A87a 85c + 5c like #396 1.00 1.00
403 A87a 85c + 5c like #397 1.00 1.00
404 A87a 85c + 5c like #398 1.00 1.00
405 A87a 85c + 5c like #399 1.00 1.00

500th birth anniv. of Raphael.
Issued: #395-400, 11/25; #401-405, 12/29.

Nos. 317-318, 323-328, 341, 355, 342, 356 and 331 Surcharged in Black or Gold with One or Two Bars

1983, Nov. 30 Photo.

406 A77 52c on 30c #317 .70 .70
407 A77 52c on 30c #318 .70 .70
408 A77 58c on 50c #323 .80 .80
409 A77 58c on 50c #324 .80 .80
410 A77 70c on 60c #325 1.00 1.00
411 A77 70c on 60c #326 1.00 1.00
412 A77 83c on 80c #327 1.25 1.25
413 A77 83c on 80c #328 1.25 1.25
413A A79 $1.10 on 95c #341 1.50 1.50
413B A82 $1.10 on $1.25 #355 (G) 1.50 1.50
413C A79 $2.60 on $1.20 #342 3.75 3.75
413D A82 $2.60 on $2.50 #356 (G) 3.75 3.75
413E A77a $3.70 on $3 #331 5.00 5.00
Nos. 406-413E (13) 23.00 23.00

World Communications Year — A88

1984, Jan. 23 Photo. *Perf. 13x13½*

414 A88 40c Telegraph sender .45 .45
415 A88 52c Early telephone .55 .55
416 A88 83c Satellite .90 .90
a. Souvenir sheet of 3, #414-416 2.00 2.00
Nos. 414-416 (3) 1.90 1.90

Moth Orchid — A89

Golden Shower Tree — A90

1984 *Perf. 13x13½*

417 A89 12c shown .18 .18
418 A89 25c Poinsettia .35 .35
419 A89 30c Buttercup tree .42 .42
420 A89 35c Begonia .50 .50
421 A89 40c Frangipani .55 .55
422 A89 52c Bird of paradise .70 .70
423 A89 58c Rose of Sharon .75 .75
424 A89 70c Princess flower .95 .95
425 A89 83c Lotus 1.10 1.10
426 A89 $1.05 Yellow hibiscus 1.50 1.50
427 A90 $1.75 shown 1.65 1.65
428 A90 $2.30 Orchid var. 2.25 2.25
429 A90 $3.90 Orchid sp. 3.50 3.50
430 A90 $5 Poinsettia, diff. 4.50 4.50
431 A90 $6.60 Hybrid hibiscus 5.75 5.75
431A A90 $8.30 Hibiscus rosasinensis 7.75 7.75
Nos. 417-431A (16) 32.40 32.40

Issued: #417-426, 2/20; #427-429, 5/10; others 6/18.

For overprints see #O1-O13, O15, O17-O18.

1984 Summer Olympics A91

Designs: Greek pottery designs, 3rd cent. BC. 30c, 70c vert.

1984, Mar. 15 Photo. *Perf. 14*

432 A91 30c Discus .40 .40
433 A91 35c Running .45 .45
434 A91 40c Equestrian .52 .52
435 A91 58c Boxing .75 .75
436 A91 70c Javelin .90 .90
Nos. 432-436 (5) 3.02 3.02

For overprints and surcharges see #446-450, 480-483.

AUSIPEX '84, Australian Animals — A92

1984 Photo. *Perf. 14*

437 A92 25c Koala .28 .28
438 A92 35c Koala, diff. .35 .35
439 A92 40c Koala, diff. .42 .42
440 A92 58c Koala, diff. .60 .60
441 A92 70c Koala, diff. .75 .75
442 A92 83c Kangaroo with joey .90 .90
443 A92 $1.05 Kangaroo with joey, diff. 1.10 1.10
444 A92 $2.50 Kangaroo, diff. 2.50 2.50
Nos. 437-444 (8) 6.90 6.90

Souvenir Sheets

445 Sheet of 2 + label 3.00 3.00
a. A92 $1.75 Wallaby 1.50 1.50
b. A92 $1.75 Koala, diff. 1.50 1.50
c. Sheet of 6, #437-441, 445b, perf. 13½ 3.50 3.50
d. Sheet of 4, #442-444, 445a, perf. 13½ 5.00 5.00

Nos. 442-444 airmail.
Issued: #437-444, Aug. 24; $445, Sept. 20.

Nos. 432-436 Ovptd. with Event, Names of Gold Medalists, Country in Gold or Red

1984, Sept. 7 *Perf. 14*

446 A91 30c Danneberg .30 .30
447 A91 35c Coe (R) .35 .35
448 A91 40c Todd .40 .40
449 A91 58c Biggs .58 .58
450 A91 70c Haerkoenen .70 .70
Nos. 446-450 (5) 2.33 2.33

10th Anniv. of Self Government — A93

1984, Oct. 19 Photo. *Perf. 13*

451 A93 40c Niue flag .40 .40
452 A93 58c Niue map .58 .58
453 A93 70c Ceremony .70 .70
a. Souvenir sheet of 3, #451-453 1.75 1.75
Nos. 451-453 (3) 1.68 1.68

Souvenir Sheet

454 A93 $2.50 like 70c 2.50 2.50

For overprints and surcharges see Nos. 655-660.

Nos. 340, 354 Surcharged: "Prince Henry / 15.9.84" and Bars and New Values in Red or Silver

1984, Oct. 22 Photo. *Perf. 14*

455 A79 $2 on 75c multi (R) 2.00 2.00
456 A82 $2 on 50c multi (S) 2.00 2.00

Nos. 455-456 issued in sheets of 5 + label.

Christmas — A94

Paintings: 40c, The Nativity, by A. Vaccaro. 58c, Virgin with Fly, anonymous. 70c, Adoration of the Shepherds, by B. Murillo. 83c, Flight into Egypt, by B. Murillo.

1984, Oct. 19 Photo. *Perf. 13x13½*

457 A94 40c multicolored .50 .50
458 A94 58c multicolored .70 .70
459 A94 70c multicolored .80 .80
460 A94 83c multicolored 1.00 1.00
Nos. 457-460 (4) 3.00 3.00

Souvenir Sheets

461 Sheet of 4 2.70 2.70
a. A94 40c + 5c Like 40c .45 .45
b. A94 58c + 5c Like 58c .58 .58
c. A94 70c + 5c Like 70c .75 .75
d. A94 83c + 5c Like 83c .82 .82

Perf. 13½

462 A94 95c + 10c Like 40c 1.05 1.05
463 A94 95c + 10c Like 58c 1.05 1.05
464 A94 95c + 10c Like 70c 1.05 1.05
465 A94 95c + 10c Like 83c 1.05 1.05

Audubon Birth Bicentenary A95

Illustrations of North American bird species by artist/naturalist John J. Audubon.

1985, Apr. 15 Photo. *Perf. 14½*

466 A95 40c House wren .32 .32
467 A95 70c Veery .55 .55
468 A95 83c Grasshopper sparrow .70 .70
469 A95 $1.05 Henslow's sparrow .85 .85
470 A95 $2.50 Vesper sparrow 2.00 2.00
Nos. 466-470 (5) 4.42 4.42

Souvenir Sheets

Perf. 14

471 A95 $1.75 like #466 1.50 1.50
472 A95 $1.75 like #467 1.50 1.50
473 A95 $1.75 like #468 1.50 1.50
474 A95 $1.75 like #469 1.50 1.50
475 A95 $1.75 like #470 1.50 1.50
Nos. 471-475 (5) 7.50 7.50

Queen Mother, 85th Birthday A96

Designs: 70c, Wearing mantle of the Order of the Garter. $1.15, With Queen Elizabeth II. $1.50, With Prince Charles. $3, Writing letter.

1985, June 14 *Perf. 13½x13*

476 A96 70c multicolored .70 .70
477 A96 $1.15 multicolored 1.15 1.15
478 A96 $1.50 multicolored 1.50 1.50
a. Souvenir sheet of 3 + label, #476-478 3.35 3.35
Nos. 476-478 (3) 3.35 3.35

Souvenir Sheet

Perf. 13½

479 A96 $3 multicolored 3.00 3.00

Nos. 476-478 issued in sheets of 5 plus label. No. 479 contains one 39x36mm stamp.
No. 478a issued Aug. 4, 1986, for 86th birthday.

Nos. 432-433, 435-436 Overprinted: "Mini South Pacific Games, Rarotonga" and Surcharged with Gold Bar and New Value in Black

1985, July 26 *Perf. 14*

480 A91 52c on 95c multi .52 .52
481 A91 83c on 58c multi .85 .85
482 A91 95c on 35c multi .95 .95
483 A91 $2 on 30c multi 2.00 2.00
Nos. 480-483 (4) 4.32 4.32

Nos. 368-371 Overprinted with Conference Emblem and: "Pacific Islands Conference, Rarotonga"

1985, July 26 *Perf. 13½x13*

484 A84 70c on #368 .70 .70
485 A84 70c on #369 .70 .70
486 A84 70c on #370 .70 .70
487 A84 70c on #371 .70 .70
a. Block of 4, #484-487 2.80 2.80

A97

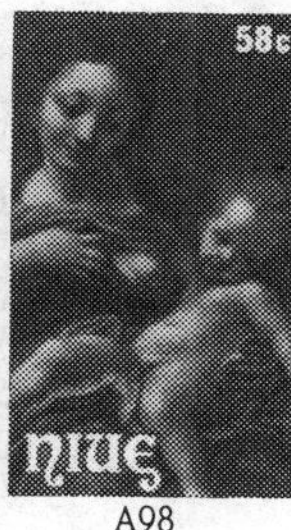

A98

Paintings of children: 38c, Portrait of R. Strozzi's Daughter, by Titian. 70c, The Fifer, by Manet. $1.15, Portrait of a Young Girl, by Renoir. $1.50, Portrait of M. Berard, by Renoir.

1985, Oct. 11 *Perf. 13*

488 A97 58c multicolored .58 .58
489 A97 70c multicolored .70 .70
490 A97 $1.15 multicolored 1.15 1.15
491 A97 $1.50 multicolored 1.50 1.50
Nos. 488-491 (4) 3.93 3.93

Souvenir Sheets

Perf. 13x13½

492 A97 $1.75 + 10c like #488 2.00 2.00
493 A97 $1.75 + 10c like #489 2.00 2.00
494 A97 $1.75 + 10c like #490 2.00 2.00
495 A97 $1.75 + 10c like #491 2.00 2.00

Intl. Youth Year.

1985, Nov. 29 Photo. *Perf. 13x13½*

Christmas, Paintings (details) by Correggio: 58c, No. 500a, Virgin and Child. 85c, No. 500b, Adoration of the Magi. $1.05, No. 500c, Virgin and Child, diff. $1.45, No. 500d, Virgin and Child with St. Catherine.

496 A98 58c multicolored .70 .70
497 A98 85c multicolored 1.05 1.05
498 A98 $1.05 multicolored 1.25 1.25
499 A98 $1.45 multicolored 1.75 1.75
Nos. 496-499 (4) 4.75 4.75

Souvenir Sheets

500 Sheet of 4 3.50 3.50
a.-d. A98 60c + 10c, any single .85 .85

Imperf

501 A98 65c like #496 .78 .78
502 A98 95c like #497 1.15 1.15
503 A98 $1.20 like #498 1.50 1.50
504 A98 $1.75 like #499 2.25 2.25
Nos. 500-504 (5) 9.18 9.18

Nos. 501-504 each contain one 61x71mm stamp.

Halley's Comet — A99

The Constellations, fresco by Giovanni De Vecchi, Farnesio Palace, Caprarola, Italy.

1986, Jan. 24 *Perf. 13½*

505 A99 60c multicolored .68 .68
506 A99 75c multicolored .85 .85
507 A99 $1.10 multicolored 1.25 1.25
508 A99 $1.50 multicolored 1.75 1.75
Nos. 505-508 (4) 4.53 4.53

Souvenir Sheet

509 Sheet of 4 4.50 4.50
a. A99 95c like #505 1.10 1.10
b. A99 95c like #506 1.10 1.10
c. A99 95c like #507 1.10 1.10
d. A99 95c like #508 1.10 1.10

Elizabeth II, 60th Birthday — A100

Designs: $1.10, No. 513a, Elizabeth and Prince Philip at Windsor Castle. $1.50, No. 513b, At Balmoral. $2, No. 513c, Elizabeth at Buckingham Palace. $3, Elizabeth seated and Prince Philip.

1986, Apr. 28 *Perf. 14½x13½*

510 A100 $1.10 multicolored 1.10 1.10
511 A100 $1.50 multicolored 1.65 1.65
512 A100 $2 multicolored 2.25 2.25
Nos. 510-512 (3) 5.00 5.00

Souvenir Sheets

513 Sheet of 3 2.75 2.75
a.-c. A100 75c, any single .90 .90
514 A100 $3 multicolored 3.50 3.50

For surcharges see Nos. 546-547.

Mt. Rushmore — A101

Statue of Liberty, Cent. — A102

1986, May 22 Photo. *Perf. 14*

515 A101 $1 Washington, US #1 1.15 1.15
516 A101 $1 Jefferson, Roosevelt, Lincoln 1.15 1.15

AMERIPEX '86. Nos. 515-516 printed se-tenant in a continuous design.

1986, July 4 *Perf. 13x13½*

Paintings: $1, Statue under construction, 1883, by Victor Dargaud. $2.50, Unveiling the Statue of Liberty, 1886, by Edmund Morand (1829-1901).

517 A102 $1 multicolored 1.15 1.15
518 A102 $2.50 multicolored 2.75 2.75

Souvenir Sheet

519 Sheet of 2 2.90 2.90
a. A102 $1.25 like #517 1.45 1.45
b. A102 $1.25 like #518 1.45 1.45

Wedding of Prince Andrew and Sarah Ferguson — A103

Designs: $2.50, Portraits, Westminster Abbey. $5, Portraits.

1986, July 23 *Perf. 13½x13*

520 A103 $2.50 multicolored 2.75 2.75

Souvenir Sheet

521 A103 $5 Portraits 5.50 5.50

No. 520 printed in sheets of 4. No. 521 contains one 45x32mm stamp.

STAMPEX '86, Adelaide, Aug. 4-10 — A104

Birds.

Perf. 13x13½, 13½x13

1986, Aug. 4 Photo.

522 A104 40c Egretta alba, vert. .45 .45
523 A104 60c Emblema picta .65 .65
524 A104 75c Aprosmictus scapularis, vert. .80 .80
525 A104 80c Malurus lamberti .88 .88
526 A104 $1 Falco peregrinus, vert. 1.10 1.10
527 A104 $1.65 Halcyon azurea 1.80 1.80
528 A104 $2.20 Melopsittacus undulatus, vert. 2.40 2.40
529 A104 $4.25 Dromaius novaehollandiae 4.60 4.60
Nos. 522-529 (8) 12.68 12.68

Christmas — A105

Paintings in the Vatican Museum: 80c, No. 534a, Virgin and Child, by Perugino (1446-1523). $1.15, No. 534b, Virgin of St. N. dei Frari, by Titian. $1.80, No. 534c, Virgin with Milk, by Lorenzo di Credi (1459-1537). $2.60, $7.50, No. 534d, Foligno Madonna, by Raphael.

1986, Nov. 14 Litho. *Perf. 14*

530 A105 80c multi .85 .85
531 A105 $1.15 multi 1.25 1.25
532 A105 $1.80 multi 1.90 1.90
533 A105 $2.60 multi 2.75 2.75
Nos. 530-533 (4) 6.75 6.75

Souvenir Sheets

Perf. 13½

534 Sheet of 4 6.40 6.40
a.-d. A105 $1.50, any single 1.60 1.60

Perf. 14½x13½

535 A105 $7.50 multi 8.00 8.00

For surcharges see Nos. B56-B61.

Souvenir Sheets

Statue of Liberty, Cent. A106

Photographs: No. 536a, Tall ship, bridge. No. 536b, Workmen, flame from torch. No. 536c, Workman, flame, diff. No. 536d, Ships, New York City. No. 536e, Tall ship, sailboat, bridge. No. 537a, Statue, front. No. 537b, Statue, left side. No. 537c, Torch dismantled. No. 537d, Statue, right side. No. 537e, Welder.

1987, May 20

536 Sheet of 5+label 4.50 4.50
a.-e. A106 75c any single .90 .90
537 Sheet of 5+label 4.50 4.50
a.-e. A106 75c any single .90 .90

Tennis Champions — A107

Olympic emblem, coin and: 80c, $1.15, $1.40, $1.80, Boris Becker. 85c, $1.05, $1.30, $1.75, Steffi Graf. Various action scenes.

1987

538 A107 80c multi 1.10 1.10
539 A107 85c multi 1.20 1.20
540 A107 $1.05 multi 1.45 1.45
541 A107 $1.15 multi 1.60 1.60
542 A107 $1.30 multi 1.80 1.80
543 A107 $1.40 multi 1.95 1.95
544 A107 $1.75 multi 2.40 2.40
545 A107 $1.80 multi 2.50 2.50
Nos. 538-545 (8) 14.00 14.00

Issue dates: 80c, $1.15, $1.40, $1.80, Sept. 25. Others, Oct. 20.

For overprints see Nos. 560-563.

Nos. 511-512 Surcharged "40th /WEDDING / ANNIV." with Denomination in Black on Gold

Perf. 14½x13½

1987, Nov. 20 **Photo.**

546 A100 $4.85 on $1.50 No. 511 6.00 6.00
547 A100 $4.85 on $2 No. 512 6.00 6.00

40th Wedding anniv. of Queen Elizabeth II and Prince Philip, Duke of Edinburgh.

Christmas — A108

Paintings (details) by Albrecht Durer (Angel with Lute on 80c, $1.05, $2.80): 80c, No. 551a, The Nativity. $1.05, No. 551b, Adoration of the Magi. $2.80, No. 551c, $7.50, Celebration of the Rosary.

1987, Dec. 4 **Photo.** *Perf. 13½*

548 A108 80c multi .90 .90
549 A108 $1.05 multi 1.25 1.25
550 A108 $2.80 multi 3.00 3.00
Nos. 548-550 (3) 5.15 5.15

Souvenir Sheets

551 Sheet of 3 4.50 4.50
a.-c. A108 $1.30 any single 1.50 1.50
552 A108 $7.50 multi 8.50 8.50

Size of Nos. 551a-551c: 49½x38½mm. No. 552 contains one 51x33mm stamp.

European Soccer Championships — A109

Highlights from Franz Beckenbauer's career: 20c, Match scene. 40c, German all-star team. 60c, Brussels, 1974. 80c, England, 1966. $1.05, Mexico, 1970. $1.30, Munich, 1974. $1.80, FC Bayern Munchen vs. Athletico Madrid.

1988, June 20 **Litho.** *Perf. 14*

553 A109 20c multi .25 .25
554 A109 40c multi .50 .50
555 A109 60c multi .75 .75
556 A109 80c multi .95 .95
557 A109 $1.05 multi 1.25 1.25
558 A109 $1.30 multi 1.65 1.65
559 A109 $1.80 multi 2.25 2.25
Nos. 553-559 (7) 7.60 7.60

Nos. 539-540, 542 and 543 Ovptd.

a. "Australia 24 Jan 88 / French Open 4 June 88"
b. "Wimbledon 2 July 88 / U S Open 10 Sept. 88"
c. "Women's Tennis Grand / Slam: 10 September 88"
d. "Seoul Olympic Games / Gold Medal Winner"

1988, Oct. 14 **Litho.** *Perf. 13½x14*

560 A107(a) 85c on No. 539 1.00 1.00
561 A107(b) $1.05 on No. 540 1.25 1.25
562 A107(c) $1.30 on No. 542 1.50 1.50
563 A107(d) $1.75 on No. 543 2.00 2.00
Nos. 560-563 (4) 5.75 5.75

Steffi Graf, 1988 Olympic gold medalist; opportunities for youth in sports.

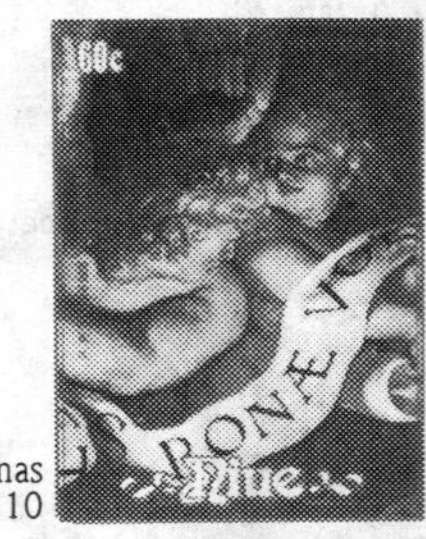

Christmas A110

Adoration of the Shepherds, by Rubens: 60c, Angels. 80c, Joseph and witness. $1.05, Madonna. $1.30, Christ child. $7.20, Entire painting.

1988, Oct. 28 **Photo.** *Perf. 13½*

564 A110 60c multi .75 .75
565 A110 80c multi 1.05 1.05
566 A110 $1.05 multi 1.35 1.35
567 A110 $1.30 multi 1.65 1.65
Nos. 564-567 (4) 4.80 4.80

Souvenir Sheet

568 A110 $7.20 multi 8.50 8.50

No. 568 contains one 40x50mm stamp.

First Moon Landing, 20th Anniv. A111

Apollo 11: No. 569, Mission emblem and astronaut. No. 570, Earth, Moon and simplified flight plan. No. 571, Olive branch, Apollo 1 mission emblem and astronaut on Moon. Printed se-tenant in a continuous design.

1989, July 20 **Photo.** *Perf. 14*

569 A111 $1.50 multi 1.75 1.75
570 A111 $1.50 multi 1.75 1.75
571 A111 $1.50 multi 1.75 1.75
Nos. 569-571 (3) 5.25 5.25

Souvenir Sheet

Perf. 13½x13

572 Sheet of 3 4.05 4.05
a.-c. A111 $1.15 like #569-571 1.35 1.35

Christmas — A112

Details of Presentation in the Temple, 1631, by Rembrandt, Royal Cabinet of Paintings, The Hague: 70c, Priests. 80c, Madonna. $1.05, Joseph. $1.30, Christ child. $7.20, Entire painting.

1989, Nov. 22 **Photo.** *Perf. 13x13½*

573 A112 70c multicolored .80 .80
574 A112 80c multicolored .90 .90
575 A112 $1.05 multicolored 1.10 1.10
576 A112 $1.30 multicolored 1.40 1.40
Nos. 573-576 (4) 4.20 4.20

Souvenir Sheet

Perf. 13½

577 A112 $7.20 multicolored 8.50 8.50

No. 577 contains one 39x50mm stamp.

Emblem of the German Natl. Soccer Team and Signatures — A113

Former team captains: 80c, Fritz Walter. $1.15, Franz Beckenbauer. $1.40, Uwe Seeler.

1990, Feb. 5 **Photo.** *Perf. 13½*

578 A113 80c multicolored .95 .95
579 A113 $1.15 multicolored 1.40 1.40
580 A113 $1.40 multicolored 1.70 1.70
581 A113 $1.80 shown 2.20 2.20
Nos. 578-581 (4) 6.25 6.25

1990 World Cup Soccer Championships, Italy.

First Postage Stamp, 150th Anniv. — A114

Paintings by Rembrandt showing letters: 80c, No. 586d, Merchant Maarten Looten (1632). $1.05, No. 586c, Rembrandt's son Titus holding pen (1655). $1.30, No. 586b, The Shipbuilder and his Wife (1633). $1.80, No. 586a, Bathsheba with King David's letter (1654).

1990, May 2 **Photo.** *Perf. 13½*

582 A114 80c multicolored .95 .95
583 A114 $1.05 multicolored 1.25 1.25
584 A114 $1.30 multicolored 1.50 1.50
585 A114 $1.80 multicolored 2.10 2.10
Nos. 582-585 (4) 5.80 5.80

Souvenir Sheet

586 Sheet of 4 7.00 7.00
a.-d. A114 $1.50 any single 1.75 1.75

A115 A116

1990, July 23 *Perf. 13x13½*

587 A115 $1.25 multicolored 1.50 1.50

Souvenir Sheet

588 A115 $7 multicolored 8.25 8.25

Queen Mother, 90th birthday.

1990, Nov. 27 **Litho.** *Perf. 14*

Christmas (Paintings): 70c, Adoration of the Magi by Bouts. 80c, Holy Family by Fra Bartolomeo. $1.05, The Nativity by Memling. $1.30, Adoration of the King by Pieter Bruegel, the Elder. $7.20, Virgin and Child Enthroned by Cosimo Tura.

589 A116 70c multicolored .85 .85
590 A116 80c multicolored 1.00 1.00
591 A116 $1.05 multicolored 1.30 1.30
592 A116 $1.30 multicolored 1.60 1.60
Nos. 589-592 (4) 4.75 4.75

Souvenir Sheet

593 A116 $7.20 multicolored 8.75 8.75

No. 334 Overprinted in Silver

1990, Dec. 5 *Perf. 13x13½*

594 A77a $10 multicolored 12.00 12.00

Birdpex '90, 20th Intl. Ornithological Congress, New Zealand.

No. 333 Overprinted "SIXTY FIFTH BIRTHDAY QUEEN ELIZABETH II"

1991, Apr. 22 **Litho.** *Perf. 13x13½*

595 A77a $6 multicolored 7.25 7.25

Nos. 340-342 Overprinted in Black or Silver

Typo. Litho.

1991, June 26 **Photo.** *Perf. 14*

596 A79 75c on #340 (S) .90 .90
a. Litho. overprint .90 .90
597 A79 95c on #341 1.15 1.15
a. Litho. overprint 1.15 1.15
598 A79 $1.20 on #342 1.45 1.45
a. Litho. overprint 1.45 1.45
Nos. 596-598 (3) 3.50 3.50
Nos. 596a-598a (3) 3.50 3.50

Nos. 596-598 issued in miniature sheets of 5 with typo. overprint. Nos. 596a-598a issued in uncut panes of 4 miniature sheets of 5. Letters of typo. overprint are taller and thinner than litho. overprint.

Christmas — A117

Birds — A118

Paintings: 20c, The Virgin and Child with Saints Jerome and Dominic, by Filippino Lippi. 50c, The Isenheim Altarpiece, The Virgin and Child, by Grunewald. $1, The Nativity, by Pittoni. $2, Adoration of the Kings, by Jan Brueghel, the Elder. $7, The Adoration of the Shepherds, by Reni.

1991, Nov. 11 **Litho.** *Perf. 14*

599 A117 20c multicolored .25 .25
600 A117 50c multicolored .60 .60
601 A117 $1 multicolored 1.20 1.20
602 A117 $2 multicolored 2.40 2.40
Nos. 599-602 (4) 4.45 4.45

Souvenir Sheet

603 A117 $7 multicolored 8.40 8.40

1992-93 **Litho.** *Perf. 14x13½*

604 A118 20c Banded rail .25 .25
605 A118 50c Red-tailed tropic-bird .60 .60
606 A118 70c Purple swamphen .85 .85
607 A118 $1 Pacific pigeon 1.20 1.20
608 A118 $1.50 White-collared kingfisher 1.80 1.80
609 A118 $2 Blue-crowned lory 2.40 2.40
610 A118 $3 Crimson-crowned fruit dove 3.60 3.60
611 A118 $5 Barn owl 5.60 5.60

Perf. 13

Size: 51x38mm

612 A118 $7 Longtailed cuckoo 7.35 7.35

Size: 49x35mm

613 A118 $10 Reef heron 10.50 10.50
614 A118 $15 Polynesian triller 16.50 16.50
Nos. 604-614 (11) 50.65 50.65

Issued $1.50, $2, 3/20; $3, 4/16; $5, 5/15; $7, 3/26/93; $10, 4/16/93; $15, 8/10/93; others, 2/92.

For overprints & surcharges see Nos. O20-O25, 676-677.

This is an expanding set. Numbers may change.

Discovery of America, 500th Anniv. — A119

$2, Queen Isabella supports Columbus. $3, Columbus' fleet. $5, Columbus landing in America.

1992 Litho. Perf. 13
621 A119 $2 multicolored 2.25 2.25
622 A119 $3 multicolored 3.40 3.40
623 A119 $5 multicolored 5.60 5.60
Nos. 621-623 (3) 11.25 11.25

1992 Summer Olympics, Barcelona — A120

#624: a, $10 coin, tennis player. b, Flags, torch. c, Gymnast, $10 coin. $5, Water polo player.

1992, July 22 Litho. Perf. 13½x13
624 A120 $2.50 Strip of 3, #a.-c. 8.50 8.50

Souvenir Sheet
625 A120 $5 multicolored 5.60 5.60

Nos. 265-280 Surcharged

$1 =

1992, Sept. 30 Photo. Perf. 13
626 A72 $1 on 20c #265 1.10 1.10
627 A72 $1 on 20c #266 1.10 1.10
628 A72 $1 on 20c #267 1.10 1.10
629 A72 $1 on 20c #268 1.10 1.10
a. Strip of 4, #626-629 4.40 4.40
630 A72 $1 on 25c #269 1.10 1.10
631 A72 $1 on 25c #270 1.10 1.10
632 A72 $1 on 25c #271 1.10 1.10
633 A72 $1 on 25c #272 1.10 1.10
a. Strip of 4, #630-633 4.40 4.40
634 A72 $1 on 30c #273 1.10 1.10
635 A72 $1 on 30c #274 1.10 1.10
636 A72 $1 on 30c #275 1.10 1.10
637 A72 $1 on 30c #276 1.10 1.10
a. Strip of 4, #634-637 4.40 4.40
638 A72 $1 on 35c #277 1.10 1.10
639 A72 $1 on 35c #278 1.10 1.10
640 A72 $1 on 35c #279 1.10 1.10
641 A72 $1 on 35c #280 1.10 1.10
a. Strip of 4, #638-641 4.40 4.40
Nos. 626-641 (16) 17.60 17.60

6th South Pacific Festival of the Arts.

Christmas A121

Design: Different details from St. Catherine's Mystic Marriage, by Hans Memling.

1992, Nov. 18 Litho. Perf. 13½
642 A121 20c multicolored .20 .20
643 A121 50c multicolored .52 .52
644 A121 $1 multicolored 1.05 1.05
645 A121 $2 multicolored 2.10 2.10
Nos. 642-645 (4) 3.87 3.87

Souvenir Sheet
646 A121 $7 like #643 7.35 7.35

No. 646 contains one 39x48mm stamp.

Queen Elizabeth II's Accession to the Throne, 40th Anniv. — A122

Various portraits of Queen Elizabeth II.

1992, Dec. 7 Perf. 14
647 A122 70c multicolored .75 .75
648 A122 $1 multicolored 1.05 1.05
649 A122 $1.50 multicolored 1.60 1.60
650 A122 $2 multicolored 2.10 2.10
Nos. 647-650 (4) 5.50 5.50

Dolphins A123

Designs: 20c, Rough-toothed dolphin. 50c, Fraser's dolphin. 75c, Pantropical spotted dolphin. $1, Risso's dolphin.

1993, Jan. 13 Litho. Perf. 14
651 A123 20c multicolored .20 .20
652 A123 50c multicolored .52 .52
653 A123 75c multicolored .80 .80
654 A123 $1 multicolored 1.05 1.05
Nos. 651-654 (4) 2.57 2.57

World Wildlife Fund.

Nos. 451-453 Ovptd. 1909 IN MEMORIAM 1992 SIR ROBERT R. REX K.B.E.

1993, Mar. 15 Photo. Perf. 13
655 A93 40c on #451 multi .42 .42
656 A93 58c on #452 multi .60 .60
657 A93 70c on #453 multi .75 .75

Nos. 655-657 Surcharged

1993, Mar. 15
658 A93 $1 on 40c #655 1.05 1.05
659 A93 $1 on 58c #656 1.05 1.05
660 A93 $1 on 70c #657 1.05 1.05
Nos. 655-660 (6) 4.92 4.92

Queen Elizabeth II, 40th Anniv. of Coronation — A124

1993, June 2 Litho. Perf. 14
661 A124 $5 multicolored 5.25 5.25

Christmas — A125

Details from Virgin of the Rosary, by Guido Reni: 20c, Infant Jesus. 70c, Cherubs. $1, Two men, one pointing upward. $1.50, Two men looking upward. $3, Madonna and child.

1993, Oct. 29 Litho. Perf. 14
662 A125 20c multicolored .22 .22
663 A125 70c multicolored .75 .75
664 A125 $1 multicolored 1.10 1.10
665 A125 $1.50 multicolored 1.65 1.65

Size: 32x47mm
Perf. 13½
666 A125 $3 multicolored 3.25 3.25
Nos. 662-666 (5) 6.97 6.97

1994 World Cup Soccer Championships, US — A126

Illustration reduced.

1994, June 17 Litho. Perf. 14
667 A126 $4 multicolored 5.25 5.25

First Manned Moon Landing, 25th Anniv. — A127

Designs: a, Flight to Moon, astronaut opening solar wind experiment lunar surface. b, Astronaut holding flag. c, Astronaut standing by lunar experiment package.

1994, July 20 Litho. Perf. 14
668 A127 $2.50 Tryptic, #a.-c. 9.00 9.00

Christmas A128

Entire paintings or details: No. 669a, The Adoration of the Kings, by Jan Gossaert. b, Madonna & Child with Saints John & Catherine, by Titian. c, The Holy Family and Shepherd, by Titian. d, Virgin & Child with Saints, by Gerard David.

No. 670: a-b, Adoration of the Shepherds, by N. Poussin. c, Madonna & Child with Saints Joseph & John, by Sebastiano. d, Adoration of the Kings, by Veronese.

1994, Nov. 28 Litho. Perf. 14
669 A128 70c Block of 4, #a.-d. 3.50 3.50
670 A128 $1 Block of 4, #a.-d. 5.00 5.00

Robert Louis Stevenson (1850-94), Writer — A129

a, Treasure Island. b, Dr. Jekyll and Mr. Hyde. c, Kidnapped. d, Stevenson, tomb, inscription.

1994, Dec. 14 Perf. 15x14
671 A129 $1.75 Block of 4, #a.-d. 8.75 8.75

Flowers — A130

1996, May 10 Litho. Perf. 14½x14
672 A130 70c Tapeu orchid 1.00 1.00
673 A130 $1 Frangipani 1.40 1.40
674 A130 $1.20 Golden shower 1.70 1.70
675 A130 $1.50 Pua 2.10 2.10
Nos. 672-675 (4) 6.20 6.20

Nos. 606, 608 Surcharged XXX 50c

1996, Feb. 19 Litho. Perf. 14x13½
676 A118 50c on 70c #606 .70 .70
677 A118 $1 on $1.50 #608 1.40 1.40

Flower Type of 1969 Redrawn

Design: 20c, Hibiscus.

1996, Aug. 22 Litho. Rouletted 7
678 A38 20c red & green .30 .30

Yachting A131

1996 Litho. Perf. 14½
679 A131 70c Jackfish 1.00 1.00
680 A131 $1 S/V Jennifer 1.40 1.40
681 A131 $1.20 Mikeva 1.70 1.70
682 A131 $2 Eye of the Wind 2.85 2.85
Nos. 679-682 (4) 6.95 6.95

Souvenir Sheet
Perf. 14
683 A131 $1.50 Desert Star 2.15 2.15

Issued: Nos. 679-682, 9/30/96. No. 683, 10/96 (Taipei '96). No. 683 contains one 30x30mm stamp.

Coral A132

Designs: 20c, Acropora gemmifera. 50c, Acropora nobilis. 70c, Goniopora lobata. $1, Stylaster. $1.20, Alveopora catalai. $1.50, Fungia scutaria. $2, Porites solida. $3, Millepora. $4, Pocillopora eydouxi. $5, Platygyra pini.

1996, Dec. 20 Litho. Perf. 14
684 A132 20c multicolored .30 .30
685 A132 50c multicolored .70 .70
686 A132 70c multicolored 1.00 1.00
687 A132 $1 multicolored 1.40 1.40
688 A132 $1.20 multicolored 1.70 1.70
689 A132 $1.50 multicolored 2.20 2.20
690 A132 $2 multicolored 2.80 2.80
691 A132 $3 multicolored 4.25 4.25
692 A132 $4 multicolored 5.70 5.70
693 A132 $5 multicolored 7.10 7.10
Nos. 684-693 (10) 27.15 27.15

Souvenir Sheet

New Year 1997 (Year of the Ox) — A133

1997, Feb. 10 Litho. Perf. 13
694 A133 $1.50 multicolored 2.00 2.00

Hong Kong '97.

Humpback Whale — A134

20c, Whale in water. 50c, Killer whale. 70c, Minke whale. $1, Adult, young whale swimming upward. $1.20, Sperm whale. $1.50, Whale breaching.

1997 Litho. Perf. 14
695 A134 20c multi .30 .30
696 A134 50c multi, vert. .70 .70
697 A134 70c multi, vert. .95 .95
698 A134 $1 multi, vert. 1.40 1.40
699 A134 $1.20 multi, vert. 1.60 1.60
700 A134 $1.50 multi, vert. 2.20 2.20
a. Souvenir sheet, #695, 698, 700 3.90 3.90
Nos. 695-700 (6) 7.15 7.15

Pacific '97 (#700a).

Island Scenes — A135

Designs: a, Steps leading over island along inlet. b, Island, vegetagion, sky. c, Coral reef, undersea vegetation. d, Reef, vegetation, diff.

1997 Litho. *Perf. 13½x14*

701 A135 $1 Block of 4, #a.-d. 5.75 5.75

Christmas — A136

Bouquets of various flowers.

1997 Litho. *Perf. 14*

702 A136 20c deep plum & multi .25 .25
703 A136 50c green & multi .65 .65
704 A136 70c blue & multi .90 .90
705 A136 $1 red & multi 1.25 1.25
Nos. 702-705 (4) 3.05 3.05

SEMI-POSTAL STAMPS

Catalogue values for unused stamps in this section are for Never Hinged items.

Easter Type of 1978
Souvenir Sheets

Designs: No. B1, Descent from the Cross, by Caravaggio. No. B2, Burial of Christ, by Bellini. Sheets show paintings from which stamp designs were taken.

1978, Mar. 15 Photo. *Perf. 13½*

B1 A61 70c + 5c multi 1.25 1.25
B2 A61 70c + 5c multi 1.25 1.25

Surtax was for school children in Niue.

Christmas Type of 1978
Souvenir Sheets

1978, Nov. 30 Photo. *Perf. 13*

B3 A63 60c + 5c like #232 1.25 1.25
B4 A63 60c + 5c like #233 1.25 1.25
B5 A63 60c + 5c like #234 1.25 1.25
Nos. B3-B5 (3) 3.75 3.75

Surtax was for school children of Niue. The sheets show paintings from which designs of stamps were taken.

Easter Type of 1979
Souvenir Sheets

1979, Apr. 2

B6 A64 70c + 5c like #235 1.50 1.50
B7 A64 70c + 5c like #236 1.50 1.50

Surtax was for school children of Niue. The sheets show altarpiece from which designs of stamps were taken.

IYC Type of 1979
Souvenir Sheets

1979, May 31 Photo. *Perf. 13*

B8 A65 70c + 5c like #237 1.25 1.25
B9 A65 70c + 5c like #238 1.25 1.25
B10 A65 70c + 5c like #239 1.25 1.25
B11 A65 70c + 5c like #240 1.25 1.25
Nos. B8-B11 (4) 5.00 5.00

Sheets show paintings from which designs of stamps were taken.

Christmas Type of 1979
Souvenir Sheets

1979, Nov. 29 Photo. *Perf. 13*

B12 A70 85c + 5c like #258 1.25 1.25
B13 A70 85c + 5c like #259 1.25 1.25
B14 A70 85c + 5c like #260 1.25 1.25
B15 A70 85c + 5c like #261 1.25 1.25
Nos. B12-B15 (4) 5.00 5.00

Multicolored margins show entire paintings.

Nos. 241-245, 251-254, 255-257, 258-261 Surcharged in Black (2 lines) or Silver (3 lines):
HURRICANE RELIEF Plus 2c

1980, Jan. 25 Photo. *Perf. 14, 13½*

B16 A66 20c + 2c pair .60 .60
B18 A68 20c + 2c multi (S) .30 .30
B19 A70 20c + 2c multi (S) .30 .30
B20 A70 25c + 2c multi (S) .40 .40
B21 A66 30c + 2c pair .90 .90
B23 A68 30c + 2c multi (S) .45 .45
B24 A69 30c + 2c multi (S) .45 .45
B25 A70 30c + 2c multi (S) .45 .45
B26 A66 35c + 2c pair 1.10 1.10
B28 A68 35c + 2c multi (S) .55 .55
B29 A69 35c + 2c multi (S) .55 .55
B30 A66 50c + 2c pair 1.40 1.40
B32 A70 50c + 2c multi (S) .70 .70
B33 A66 60c + 2c pair 1.75 1.75
B35 A69 60c + 2c multi (S) .90 .90
B36 A68 75c + 2c multi (S) 1.10 1.10
Nos. B16-B36 (16) 11.90 11.90

Easter Type of 1980
Souvenir Sheets

1980, Apr. 2 Photo. *Perf. 13*

B37 Sheet of 3 1.00 1.00
a. A71 25c + 2c like #262 .28 .28
b. A71 30c + 2c like #263 .32 .32
c. A71 35c + 2c like #264 .38 .38

1980, Apr. 2

B38 A71 85c + 5c like #262 1.10 1.10
B39 A71 85c + 5c like #263 1.10 1.10
B40 A71 85c + 5c like #264 1.10 1.10
Nos. B38-B40 (3) 3.30 3.30

Surtax was for hurricane relief.

No. 245a Overprinted Like Nos. 281-285 and Surcharged
Souvenir Sheet

1980, Aug. 22 Photo. *Perf. 14*

B41 Sheet of 10 4.50 4.50
a. A66 20c + 2c pair .45 .45
b. A66 30c + 2c pair .60 .60
c. A66 35c + 2c pair .80 .80
d. A66 50c + 2c pair 1.25 1.25
e. A66 60c + 2c pair 1.40 1.40

ZEAPEX '80, New Zealand Intl. Stamp Exhib., Auckland, Aug. 23-31.

Souvenir Sheet

1980, Oct. 30 Photo. *Perf. 14*

B42 Sheet of 8 3.75 3.75
a. A74 20c + 2c like #293 .32 .32
b. A75 20c + 2c like #294 .32 .32
c. A74 25c + 2c like #295 .42 .42
d. A75 25c + 2c like #296 .42 .42
e. A74 30c + 2c like #297 .48 .48
f. A75 30c + 2c like #298 .48 .48
g. A74 35c + 2c like #299 .55 .55
h. A75 35c + 2c like #300 .55 .55

22nd Summer Olympic Games, Moscow, July 19-Aug. 3.

Christmas Type of 1980
Souvenir Sheets

1980, Nov. 28 Photo. *Perf. 13½x13*

B43 A76 80c + 5c like #301 .90 .90
B44 A76 80c + 5c like #302 .90 .90
B45 A76 80c + 5c like #303 .90 .90
B46 A76 80c + 5c like #304 .90 .90
Nos. B43-B46 (4) 3.60 3.60

Nos. B43-B46 each contain one 31x39mm stamp.

Easter Type of 1981
Souvenir Sheets

1981, Apr. 10 Photo. *Perf. 13½*

B47 Sheet of 3 2.25 2.25
a. A78 35c + 2c like #337 .52 .52
b. A78 50c + 2c like #338 .65 .65
c. A78 60c + 2c like #339 .80 .80
B48 A78 80c + 5c like #337 1.00 1.00
B49 A78 80c + 5c like #338 1.00 1.00
B50 A78 80c + 5c like #339 1.00 1.00
Nos. B47-B50 (4) 5.25 5.25

Soccer Type of 1981

1981, Oct. 16 Photo. *Perf. 13*

B51 A80 Sheet of 9 4.50 4.50

#B51 contains #343-345 each with 3c surtax.

Royal Wedding Type of 1981
Nos. 340-342a Surcharged

1981, Nov. 3 Photo. *Perf. 14*

B52 A79 75c + 5c like #340 1.60 1.60
B53 A79 95c + 5c like #341 2.00 2.00
B54 A79 $1.20 + 5c like #342 2.50 2.50
Nos. B52-B54 (3) 6.10 6.10

Souvenir Sheet

B55 Sheet of 3 6.50 6.50
a. A79 75c + 10c like #340 1.70 1.70
b. A79 95c + 10c like #341 2.10 2.10
c. A79 $1.20 + 10c like #342 2.60 2.60

Intl. Year of the Disabled. Surtax was for disabled.

Nos. 530-535 Surcharged "CHRISTMAS VISIT TO SOUTH PACIFIC OF / POPE JOHN PAUL II, NOVEMBER 21-24 1986" in Black on Silver

1986, Nov. 21 Litho. *Perf. 14*

B56 A105 80c + 10c multi .95 .95
B57 A105 $1.15 + 10c multi 1.35 1.35
B58 A105 $1.80 + 10c multi 2.00 2.00
B59 A105 $2.60 + 10c multi 2.90 2.90
Nos. B56-B59 (4) 7.20 7.20

Souvenir Sheets

Perf. 13½

B60 Sheet of 4 6.80 6.80
a.-d. A105 $1.50 + 10c on #534a-534d 1.70 1.70

Perf. 14½x13½

B61 A105 $7.50 + 50c multi 8.50 8.50

No. B60 ovptd. "FIRST VISIT OF A POPE TO SOUTH PACIFIC" and "HIS HOLINESS POPE JOHN PAUL II" on margin. No. B61 ovptd. on margin only "Visit of Pope John Paul II, Nov 21-24 1986 / First Papal Visit to the South Pacific."

Niue $2+20c Aupex '96 Stamp Exhibition — SP1

1997 Litho. *Perf. 14x15*

B62 SP1 $2 +20c like #1 3.25 3.25

AIR POST STAMPS

Catalogue values for unused stamps in this section are for Never Hinged items.

Type of 1977

Designs: 15c, Preparing ground for taro. 20c, Banana harvest. 23c, Bush plantation. 50c, Canoe fishing. 90c, Reef fishing. $1.35, Preparing ground for taro. $2.10, Shellfish gathering. $2.60, Luku harvest.

1979 Litho. *Perf. 14*

C1 A54 15c gold & multi .16 .16
C2 A54 20c gold & multi .22 .22
C3 A54 23c gold & multi .26 .26
C4 A54 50c gold & multi .60 .60
C5 A54 90c gold & multi .90 .90
C6 A54 $1.35 gold & multi 1.40 1.40
C7 A54 $2.10 gold & multi 2.25 2.25
C8 A54 $2.60 gold & multi 2.75 2.75
C9 A54 $5.10 like #187 5.25 5.25
C10 A54 $6.35 like #188 6.75 6.75
Nos. C1-C10 (10) 20.54 20.54

Issue dates: Nos. C1-C5, Feb. 26. Nos. C6-C8, Mar. 30. C9-C10, May 28.

OFFICIAL STAMPS

Catalogue values for unused stamps in this section are for Never Hinged items.

Nos. 417-430, 332-334, 431-431A Overprinted "O.H.M.S." in Metallic Blue or Gold

Perf. 13½, 13½x13, 13x13½, 13

1985-87 Photo.

O1 A89 12c multi .15 .15
O2 A89 25c multi .18 .18
O3 A89 30c multi .22 .22
O4 A89 35c multi .25 .25
O5 A89 40c multi .30 .30
O6 A89 52c multi .40 .40
O7 A89 58c multi .48 .48
O8 A89 70c multi .55 .55
O9 A89 83c multi .65 .65
O10 A89 $1.05 multi .75 .75
O11 A90 $1.75 multi 1.40 1.40
O12 A90 $2.30 multi 2.00 2.00
O13 A90 $3.90 multi 3.75 3.75
O14 A77a $4 multi (G) 3.50 3.50
O15 A90 $5 multi 4.25 4.25
O16 A77a $6 multi ('87) (G) 9.00 9.00
O17 A90 $6.60 multi ('86) 5.50 5.50
O18 A90 $8.30 multi ('86) 7.00 7.00
O19 A77a $10 multi ('87) (G) 15.00 15.00
Nos. O1-O19 (19) 55.33 55.33

Nos. 604-613 Ovptd. "O.H.M.S." in Gold

1993-94 Litho. *Perf. 14x13½*

O20 A118 20c multicolored .22 .22
O21 A118 50c multicolored .55 .55
O22 A118 70c multicolored .80 .80
O23 A118 $1 multicolored 1.10 1.10
O24 A118 $1.50 multicolored 1.65 1.65
O25 A118 $2 multicolored 2.25 2.25
O26 A118 $3 multicolored 3.25 3.25
O27 A118 $5 multicolored 5.50 5.50
O28 A118 $7 multicolored 8.50 8.50
O29 A118 $10 multicolored 12.00 12.00
O30 A118 $15 multicolored 18.00 18.00
Nos. O20-O30 (11) 53.82 53.82

Nos. O20-O30 were not sold unused to local customers.

Issued: 20c-$2, 12/10/93; $3, $5, 4/27/94; $7, $10, 9/1/94; $15, 9/30/94.

NORFOLK ISLAND

'nȯr–fək 'ī–lənd

LOCATION — Island in the south Pacific Ocean, 900 miles east of Australia
GOVT. — Territory of Australia
AREA — 13½ sq. mi.
POP. — 1,800 (est. 1982)

12 Pence = 1 Shilling
100 Cents = 1 Dollar (1966)

Catalogue values for all unused stamps in this country are for Never Hinged items.

Watermark

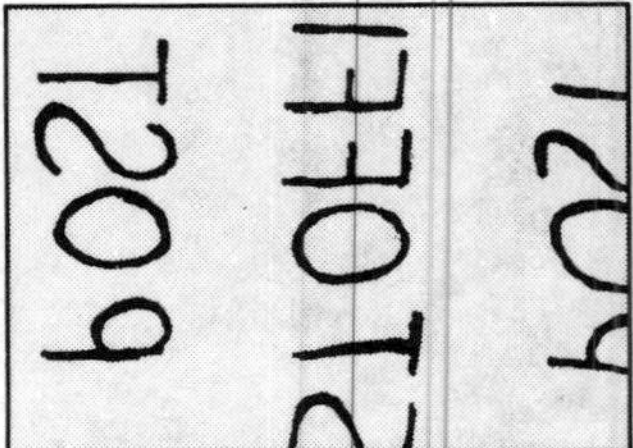

Wmk. 380- "POST OFFICE"

View of Ball Bay — A1

Unwmk.

1947, June 10 Engr. *Perf. 14*

1 A1 ½p deep orange .25 .25
2 A1 1p violet .40 .45
3 A1 1½p bright green .60 .40
4 A1 2p red violet .70 .45
5 A1 2½p red .90 .60
6 A1 3p brown orange .80 .65
7 A1 4p rose lake 1.10 .70
8 A1 5½p slate 1.25 .80
9 A1 6p sepia 1.50 1.00
10 A1 9p lilac rose 2.25 1.50
11 A1 1sh gray green 2.25 1.50
12 A1 2sh olive bister 6.00 3.25
Nos. 1-12 (12) 18.00 11.55

See Nos. 23-24.

Warder's Tower — A2

Airfield — A3

Designs: 7½p, First Governor's Residence. 8½p, Barracks entrance. 10p, Salt House. 5sh, Bloody Bridge.

1953, June 10 *Perf. 14½*

13	A2	3½p rose brown	2.00	.80
14	A3	6½p dark green	2.25	1.25
15	A3	7½p deep ultra	3.50	1.75
16	A2	8½p chocolate	5.25	2.75
17	A2	10p rose lilac	4.25	2.25
18	A3	5sh dark brown	40.00	21.00
		Nos. 13-18 (6)	57.25	29.80

See Nos. 35, 40. For surcharges see Nos. 21-22, 27. For types surcharged see Nos. 26, 28.

Original Norfolk Seal and First Settlers — A4

1956, June 8

19	A4	3p bluish green	1.00	.90
20	A4	2sh violet	4.75	*7.25*

Cent. of the landing of the Pitcairn Islanders on Norfolk Island.

Nos. 15 and 16 Surcharged with New Value and Bars

1958, July 1

21	A3	7p on 7½p dp ultra	1.90	*2.75*
22	A2	8p on 8½p choc	2.50	*3.75*

Ball Bay Type of 1947

1959, July 6 **Engr.** *Perf. 14*

23	A1	3p green	12.50	5.50
24	A1	2sh dark blue	25.00	14.00

A5

Australia #332 Surcharged in Red

1959, Dec. 7

25	A5	5p on 4p dk gray blue	1.65	1.65

No. 14 and Types of 1953 Surcharged with New Values and Bars

1960, Sept. 26 *Perf. 14½*

26	A2	1sh1p on 3½p dk bl	4.50	4.00
27	A3	2sh5p on 6½p dk grn	6.75	5.75
28	A3	2sh8p on 7½p dk brn	9.00	7.75
		Nos. 26-28 (3)	20.25	17.50

Types of 1953 and

Island Hibiscus — A6

Fairy Tern — A7

Red-Tailed Tropic Bird — A8

Designs: 2p, Lagunaria patersonii (flowers). 5p, Lantana. 8p, Red hibiscus. 9p, Cereus and Queen Elizabeth II. 10p, Salt House. 1sh1p, Fringed hibiscus. 2sh, Providence petrel, vert. 2sh5p, Passion flower. 2sh8p, Rose apple. 5sh, Bloody Bridge.

1960-62 **Unwmk.** **Engr.** *Perf. 14½*

29	A6	1p blue green	.15	.15
30	A6	2p gray grn & brt pink	.20	.15
31	A7	3p brt green ('61)	.55	.25
32	A6	5p lilac	1.10	.70
33	A6	8p vermilion	2.00	1.50
34	A6	9p ultramarine	2.00	1.50
35	A2	10p pale pur & brn ('61)	3.50	1.75
36	A6	1sh1p dark red ('61)	2.75	1.50
37	A6	2sh sepia ('61)	2.75	1.75
38	A6	2sh5p dk purple ('62)	2.75	1.75
39	A6	2sh8p green & sal ('62)	4.25	2.00
40	A3	5sh green & gray ('61)	6.50	3.00

Perf. 14½x14

41	A8	10sh green ('61)	42.50	30.00
		Nos. 29-41 (13)	71.00	46.00

See #585-586. For surcharges see #71-82.

Map of Norfolk Island — A9

1960, Oct. 24 **Engr.** *Perf. 14*

42	A9	2sh8p rose violet	20.00	20.00

Introduction of local government for Norfolk Island.

Open Bible and Candle — A9a

Page from Book of Hours, 15th Century — A9b

Madonna and Child — A9c

1960, Nov. 21 *Perf. 14½*

43	A9a	5p bright lilac rose	4.00	4.00

Christmas.

1961, Nov. 20 *Perf. 14½x14*

44	A9b	5p slate blue	1.50	1.50

Nos. 43-44 were issued to mark the beginning and the end of the 350th anniversary year of the publication of the King James translation of the Bible.

1962, Nov. 19 *Perf. 14½*

45	A9c	5p blue	1.50	1.50

Christmas.

Overlooking Kingston — A10

Dreamfish — A11

Designs: 6p, Tweed trousers (fish). 8p, Kingston scene. 9p, "The Arches." 10p, Slaughter Bay. 11p, Trumpeter fish. 1sh, Po'ov (wrasse). 1sh6p, Queensland grouper. 2sh3p, Ophie (carangidae).

Perf. 14½x14

1962-64 **Unwmk.** **Photo.**

49	A10	5p multicolored ('64)	.65	.55
50	A11	6p multicolored	.75	.75
51	A10	8p multicolored ('64)	1.00	.80
52	A10	9p multicolored ('64)	1.50	1.25
53	A10	10p multicolored ('64)	1.75	1.65
54	A11	11p multicolored ('63)	2.50	1.65
55	A11	1sh olive, bl & pink	3.00	2.50
57	A11	1sh3p bl, mar & grn ('63)	3.25	3.00
58	A11	1sh6p bl, brn & lil ('63)	3.75	3.75
60	A11	2sh3p dl bl, yel & red ('63)	4.25	4.00
		Nos. 49-60 (10)	22.40	19.90

Star of Bethlehem — A11a

Symbolic Pine Tree — A12

1963, Nov. 11 **Engr.** *Perf. 14½*

65	A11a	5p vermilion	1.40	1.40

Christmas.

1964, July 1 **Photo.** *Perf. 13½x13*

66	A12	5p orange, blk & red	.90	.60
67	A12	8p gray green, blk & red	1.50	1.50

50th anniv. of Norfolk Island as an Australian Territory.

Child Looking at Nativity Scene — A12a

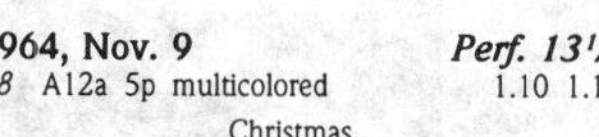
"Simpson and His Donkey" by Wallace Anderson — A12b

1964, Nov. 9 *Perf. 13½*

68	A12a	5p multicolored	1.10	1.10

Christmas.

1965, Apr. 14 **Photo.** *Perf. 13½x13*

69	A12b	5p brt green, sepia & blk	.65	.65

ANZAC issue. See note after Australia No. 387.

Nativity — A12c

1965, Oct. 25 **Unwmk.** *Perf. 13½*

70	A12c	5p gold, blk, ultra & redsh brn	.50	.50

Christmas. No. 70 is luminescent. See note after Australia No. 331.

Nos. 29-33 and 35-41 Surcharged in Black on Overprinted Metallic Rectangles

Two types of 1c on 1p:
I. Silver rectangle 4x5½mm.
II. Silver rectangle 5½x5¼mm.
Two types of $1 on 10sh:
I. Silver rectangle 7x6½mm.
II. Silver rectangle 6x4mm.

Perf. 14½, 14½x14

1966, Feb. 14 **Engr.**

71	A6	1c on 1p bl grn (I)	.15	.15
a.		Type II	.35	.35
72	A6	2c on 2p gray grn & brt pink	.15	.15
73	A7	3c on 3p brt green	.20	.20
74	A6	4c on 5p lilac	.20	.20
75	A6	5c on 8p vermilion	.25	.25
76	A2	10c on 10p pale pur & brn	.60	.60
77	A6	15c on 1sh1p dark red	.90	.90
78	A6	20c on 2sh sepia	1.10	1.10
79	A6	25c on 2sh5p dk pur	1.75	1.75
80	A6	30c on 2sh8p grn & sal	2.25	2.25
81	A3	50c on 5sh grn & gray	4.50	4.50
82	A8	$1 on 10sh green (I)	6.00	6.00
a.		Type II	6.50	6.50
		Nos. 71-82 (12)	18.05	18.05

Headstone Bridge — A13

1966, June 27 **Photo.** *Perf. 14½*

88	A13	7c shown	.30	.30
89	A13	9c Cemetary road	.50	.50

St. Barnabas Chapel — A14

Design: 4c, Interior of St. Barnabas Chapel.

Perf. 14x14½

1966, Aug. 23 **Photo.** **Unwmk.**

97	A14	4c multicolored	.15	.15
98	A14	25c multicolored	.65	.65

Centenary of the Melanesian Mission.

Star over Philip Island — A15

1966, Oct. 24 **Photo.** *Perf. 14½*

99	A15	4c violet, grn, blue & sil	.35	.35

Christmas.

H.M.S. Resolution, 1774 — A16

Ships: 2c, La Boussole and Astrolabe, 1788. 3c, Brig Supply, 1788. 4c, Sirius, 1790. 5c, The Norfolk, 1798. 7c, Survey cutter Mermaid, 1825. 9c, The Lady Franklin, 1853. 10c The Morayshire, 1856. 15c, Southern Cross, 1866. 20c, The Pitcairn, 1891. 25c, Norfolk Island whaleboat, 1895. 30c, Cable ship Iris, 1907. 50c, The Resolution, 1926. $1, S.S. Morinda, 1931.

1967-68 **Photo.** *Perf. 14x14½*

100	A16	1c multicolored	.15	.15
101	A16	2c multicolored	.15	.15
102	A16	3c multicolored	.15	.15
103	A16	4c multicolored	.15	.15
104	A16	5c multicolored	.25	.20
105	A16	7c multicolored	.30	.25
106	A16	9c multicolored	.40	.35
107	A16	10c multicolored	.50	.45
108	A16	15c multicolored	.75	.70
109	A16	20c multicolored	1.10	1.00
110	A16	25c multicolored	1.75	1.50
111	A16	30c multicolored	2.25	2.00
112	A16	50c multicolored	2.75	2.50
113	A16	$1 multicolored	4.50	4.25
		Nos. 100-113 (14)	15.15	13.80

Issued: #100-103, 4/17; #104-107, 8/19; #108-110, 3/18/68; #111-113, 6/18/68.

Lions Intl., 50th Anniv. — A16a

1967, June 7 **Photo.** *Perf. 13½*

114	A16a	4c citron, blk & blue grn	.35	.35

Printed on luminescent paper; see note after Australia No. 331.

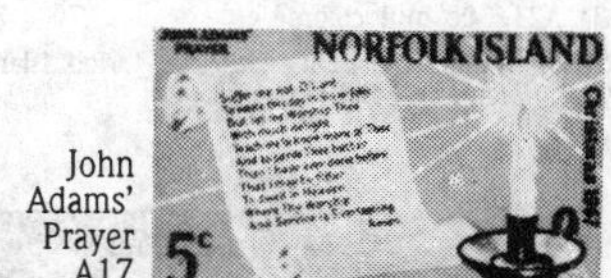
John Adams' Prayer A17

1967, Oct. 16 **Photo.** *Perf. 14x14½*

115	A17	5c brick red, black & buff	.35	.35

Christmas.

Queen Elizabeth II Type of Australia, 1966-67
Coil Stamps
Perf. 15 Horizontally

1968-71	**Photo.**	**Unwmk.**	
116 A157	3c brn org, blk & buff	.15	.15
117 A157	4c blue grn, blk & buff	.15	.15
118 A157	5c brt purple, blk & buff	.15	.15
118A A157	6c dk red, brn, blk & buff	.35	.35
	Nos. 116-118A (4)	.80	.80

Issued: 6c, Aug. 25, 1971; others, Aug. 5, 1968.

DC-4 Skymaster and Lancastrian Plane — A18

1968, Sept. 25		***Perf. 14½x14***	
119 A18	5c dk car, sky blue & indigo	.20	.20
120 A18	7c dk car, blue grn & sepia	.25	.25

21st anniv. of the Sydney to Norfolk Island air service by Qantas Airways.

Star and Hibiscus Wreath — A19

Photo.; Silver Impressed (Star)

1968, Oct. 24		***Perf. 14½x14***	
121 A19	5c sky blue & multi	.30	.30

Christmas.

Map of Pacific, Transit of Venus before Sun, Capt. Cook and Quadrant A20

1969, June 3	**Photo.**	***Perf. 14x14½***	
122 A20	10c brn, ol, pale brn & yel	.35	.35

Bicent. of the observation at Tahiti by Capt. James Cook of the transit of the planet Venus across the sun.

Map of Van Diemen's Land and Norfolk Island — A21

1969, Sept. 29		***Perf. 14x14½***	
123 A21	5c multicolored	.15	.15
124 A21	30c multicolored	.70	.70

125th anniv. of the annexation of Norfolk Island by Van Diemen's Land (Tasmania).

Nativity (Mother-of-Pearl carving) — A22

1969, Oct. 27	**Photo.**	***Perf. 14½x14***	
125 A22	5c brown & multi	.30	.30

Christmas.

Norfolk Island Flyeater A23

Birds of Norfolk Island from Book by Gregory Mathews: 1c, Robins, vert. 2c, Norfolk Island whistlers (thickheads), vert. 4c, Long-tailed cuckoos. 5c, Red-fronted parakeet, vert. 7c, Long-tailed trillers, vert. 9c, Island thrush. 10c, Owl, vert. 15c, Norfolk Island pigeon (extinct; vert.). 20c, White-breasted white-eye. 25c, Norfolk Island parrots, vert. 30c, Gray fantail. 45c, Norfolk Island starlings. 50c, Crimson rosella, vert. $1, Sacred kingfisher.

Perf. 14x14½, 14½x14

1970-71	**Photo.**	**Unwmk.**	
126 A23	1c multicolored	.15	.15
127 A23	2c multicolored	.20	.15
128 A23	3c multicolored	.25	.20
129 A23	4c multicolored	.30	.25
130 A23	5c multicolored	.35	.30
131 A23	7c multicolored	.50	.40
132 A23	9c multicolored	.70	.50
133 A23	10c multicolored	.80	.70
134 A23	15c multicolored	1.00	.70
135 A23	20c multicolored	2.00	1.00
136 A23	25c multicolored	2.00	1.25
137 A23	30c multicolored	5.00	3.00
138 A23	45c multicolored	5.50	4.25
139 A23	50c multicolored	6.75	4.75
140 A23	$1 multicolored	8.25	7.00
	Nos. 126-140 (15)	33.75	24.60

Issued: 3c, 4c, 9c, 45c, 2/25; 1c, 7c, 10c, 25c, 7/22; 2c, 2c, 5c, 15c, 50c, 2/24/71; 20c, 30c, $1, 6/16/71.

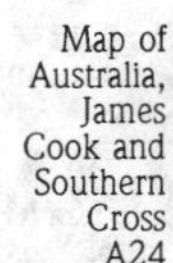

Map of Australia, James Cook and Southern Cross A24

Design: 10c, "Endeavour" entering Botany Bay, Apr. 29, 1770, and aborigine with spear. The 1776 portrait of James Cook on the 5c is by John Webber.

1970, Apr. 29	**Photo.**	***Perf. 14x14½***	
141 A24	5c multicolored	.20	.20
142 A24	10c multicolored	.45	.40

200th anniv. of Cook's discovery and exploration of the eastern coast of Australia.

First Christmas, Sydney Bay, 1788 — A25

1970, Oct. 15	**Photo.**	***Perf. 14x14½***	
143 A25	5c multicolored	.30	.30

Christmas.

Bishop Patteson, Open Bible — A26

#145, Bible opened to Acts Chap. 7, martyrdom of St. Stephen, & knotted palm fronds. #146, Bishop Patteson, rose window of Melanesian Mission Chapel on Norfolk Island. #147, Cross erected at Nukapu where Patteson died & his arms.

1971, Sept. 20			
144 A26	6c brown & multi	.20	.20
145 A26	6c brown & multi	.20	.20
a.	Pair, #144-145	.45	.45
146 A26	10c purple & multi	.40	.40
147 A26	10c purple & multi	.40	.40
a.	Pair, #146-147	.80	.80
	Nos. 144-147 (4)	1.20	1.20

Centenary of the death of Bishop John Coleridge Patteson (1827-1871), head of the Melanesian mission.

Rose Window, St. Barnabas Chapel, Norfolk Island — A27

1971, Oct. 25		***Perf. 14x13½***	
148 A27	6c dk vio blue & multi	.25	.25

Christmas.

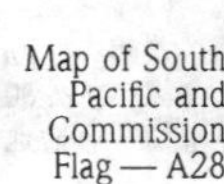

Map of South Pacific and Commission Flag — A28

1972, Feb. 6		***Perf. 14x14½***	
149 A28	7c multicolored	.40	.40

So. Pacific Commission, 25th anniv.

Stained-glass Window — A29

Cross, Church, Pines — A30

1972, Oct. 16	**Photo.**	***Perf. 14x14½***	
150 A29	7c dark olive & multi	.30	.30

Christmas. The stained-glass window by Edward Coley Burne-Jones is in All Saints Church, Norfolk Island.

1972, Nov. 20			
151 A30	12c multicolored	.40	.40

Centenary of All Saints Church, first built by Pitcairners on Norfolk Island.

"Resolution" in Antarctica — A31

1973, Jan. 17	**Photo.**	***Perf. 14½x14***	
152 A31	35c multicolored	2.75	2.75

200th anniv. of the 1st crossing of the Antarctic Circle by Cook, Jan. 17, 1773.

Sleeping Child, and Christmas Tree — A32

Christmas: 35c, Star over lagoon.

1973, Oct. 22	**Photo.**	***Perf. 14x14½***	
153 A32	7c black & multi	.25	.25
154 A32	12c black & multi	.45	.45
155 A32	35c black & multi	1.50	1.50
	Nos. 153-155 (3)	2.20	2.20

Protestant Clergyman's House A33

Designs: 2c, Royal Engineer Office. 3c, Double quarters for free overseers. 4c, Guard House. 5c, Pentagonal Gaol entrance. 7c, Pentagonal Gaol, aerial view. 8c, Convict barracks. 10c, Officers' quarters, New Military Barracks. 12c, New Military Barracks. 14c, Beach stores. 15c, Magazine. 20c, Old Military Barracks, entrance. 25c, Old Military Barracks. 30c, Old stores, Crankmill. 50c, Commissariat stores. $1, Government House.

1973-75	**Photo.**	***Perf. 14x14½***	
156 A33	1c multicolored	.15	.15
157 A33	2c multicolored	.15	.15
158 A33	3c multicolored	.15	.15
159 A33	4c multicolored	.15	.15
160 A33	5c multicolored	.20	.20
161 A33	7c multicolored	.25	.25
162 A33	8c multicolored	.30	.30
163 A33	10c multicolored	.30	.30
164 A33	12c multicolored	.35	.35
165 A33	14c multicolored	.50	.50
166 A33	15c multicolored	.55	.55
167 A33	20c multicolored	.60	.60
168 A33	25c multicolored	.70	.70
169 A33	30c multicolored	1.00	1.00
170 A33	50c multicolored	1.75	1.75
171 A33	$1 multicolored	3.00	3.00
	Nos. 156-171 (16)	10.10	10.10

Issued: 1c, 5c, 10c, 50c, 11/19/73; 2c, 7c, 12c, 30c, 5/1/74; 4c, 14c, 20c, $1, 7/12/74; 3c, 8c, 15c, 25c, 2/19/75.

Map of Norfolk Island — A34

1974, Feb. 8	**Photo.**	***Perf. 14x14½***	
172 A34	7c red lilac & multi	.35	.35
173 A34	25c dull blue & multi	1.65	1.65

Visit of Queen Elizabeth II and the Duke of Edinburgh, Feb. 11-12.

Gipsy Moth over Norfolk Island — A35

1974, Mar. 28	**Litho.**	***Perf. 14x14½***	
174 A35	14c multicolored	1.65	1.65

1st aircraft to visit Norfolk, Sir Francis Chichester's "Mme. Elijah," Mar. 28, 1931.

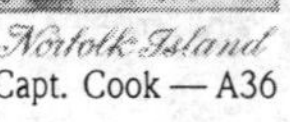

Capt. Cook — A36

Nativity — A37

Designs: 10c, "Resolution," by Henry Roberts. 14c, Norfolk Island pine, cone and seedling. 25c, Norfolk Island flax, by George Raper, 1790. Portrait of Cook on 7c by William Hodges, 1770.

1974, Oct. 8	**Litho.**	***Perf. 14***	
175 A36	7c multicolored	.60	.60
176 A36	10c multicolored	.75	.75
177 A36	14c multicolored	1.50	1.50
178 A36	25c multicolored	4.50	4.50
	Nos. 175-178 (4)	7.35	7.35

Bicentenary of the discovery of Norfolk Island by Capt. James Cook.

1974, Oct. 18	**Photo.**	***Perf. 14***	
179 A37	7c rose & multi	.30	.30
180 A37	30c violet & multi	1.50	1.50

Christmas.

Norfolk Island Pine A38

15c, Off-shore islands. 35c, Crimson rosella and sacred kingfisher. 40c, Map showing Norfolk's location. Stamps in shape of Norfolk Island.

1974, Dec. 16 Litho. *Imperf.*
Self-adhesive

181 A38	10c brown & multi	.35	.35
182 A38	15c dk blue & multi	.50	.50
183 A38	35c dk purple & multi	1.25	1.25
184 A38	40c dk blue grn & multi	1.50	2.50
a.	Souvenir sheet of 4	27.50	25.00
	Nos. 181-184 (4)	3.60	4.60

Cent. of UPU. Stamps printed on peelable paper backing. No. 184a contains 4 imperf. stamps similar to Nos. 181-184 in reduced size on a background of map of Norfolk Island. Peelable paper backing shows beach scene on Norfolk Island.

Survey Cutter "Mermaid," 1825 — A39

Design: 35c, Kingston, 1835, after painting by Thomas Seller. Stamps outlined in shape of Norfolk Island map.

1975, Aug. 18 Litho. *Imperf.*
Self-adhesive

185 A39	10c multicolored	.25	.25
186 A39	35c multicolored	1.00	1.00

Sesquicentennial of 2nd settlement of Norfolk Island. Printed on peelable paper backing with green and black design and inscription.

Star over Norfolk Island Pine and Map — A40

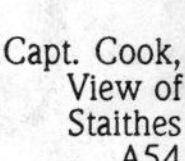

Brass Memorial Cross — A41

1975, Oct. 6 Photo. *Perf. 14½x14*

187 A40	10c lt blue & multi	.30	.30
188 A40	15c lt brown & multi	.45	.45
189 A40	35c lilac & multi	1.25	1.25
	Nos. 187-189 (3)	2.00	2.00

Christmas.

Perf. 14½x14, 14x14½
1975, Nov. 24 Photo.

Design: 60c, Laying foundation stone, 1875, and chapel, 1975, horiz.

190 A41	30c multicolored	.65	.65
191 A41	60c multicolored	1.50	1.50

St. Barnabas Chapel, centenary.

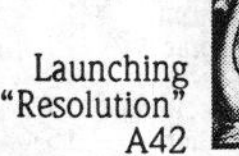

Launching "Resolution" A42

Design: 45c, "Resolution" under sail.

1975, Dec. 1 *Perf. 14x14½*

192 A42	25c multicolored	.75	.75
193 A42	45c multicolored	1.25	1.25

50th anniversary of launching of schooner "Resolution."

Bedford Flag, Charles W. Morgan Whaler — A43

Designs: 25c, Grand Union Flag, church interior. 40c, 15-stari flag, 1795, and plane over island, WWII. 45c, 13-star flag and California quail.

1976, July 5 Photo. *Perf. 14*

194 A43	18c multicolored	.40	.40
195 A43	25c multicolored	.60	.60
196 A43	40c multicolored	.80	.80
197 A43	45c multicolored	.90	.90
	Nos. 194-197 (4)	2.70	2.70

American Bicentennial.

Bird in Flight, Brilliant Sun — A44

1976, Oct. 4 Photo. *Perf. 14*

198 A44	18c blue grn & multi	.45	.45
199 A44	25c dp blue & multi	.60	.60
200 A44	45c violet & multi	1.10	1.10
	Nos. 198-200 (3)	2.15	2.15

Christmas.

Bassaris Itea — A45

Butterflies and Moths: 2c, Utetheisa pulchelloides vaga. 3c, Agathia asterias jowettorum. 4c, Cynthia kershawi. 5c, Leucania loreyimima. 10c, Hypolimnas bolina nerina. 15c, Pyrrhorachis pyrrhogona. 16c, Austrocarea iocephala millsi. 17c, Pseudocoremia christiani. 18c, Cleora idiocrossa. 19c, Simplicia caeneusalis buffetti. 20c, Austrocidaria ralstonae. 30c, Hippotion scrofa. 40c, Papilio ilioneus. 50c, Tiracola plagiata. $1, Precis villida. $2, Cepora perimale.

1976-77 Photo. *Perf. 14*

201 A45	1c multicolored	.15	.15
202 A45	2c multicolored	.15	.15
203 A45	3c multicolored	.15	.15
204 A45	4c multicolored	.15	.15
205 A45	5c multicolored	.15	.15
206 A45	10c multicolored	.15	.15
207 A45	15c multicolored	.20	.20
208 A45	16c multicolored	.25	.25
209 A45	17c multicolored	.30	.30
210 A45	18c multicolored	.30	.30
211 A45	19c multicolored	.30	.30
212 A45	20c multicolored	.35	.35
213 A45	30c multicolored	.50	.50
214 A45	40c multicolored	.60	.60
215 A45	50c multicolored	.90	.90
216 A45	$1 multicolored	1.10	1.10
217 A45	$2 multicolored	2.50	2.50
	Nos. 201-217 (17)	8.20	8.20

Issued: 1c, 5c, 10c, 16c, 18c, $1, 11/17; others, 1977.

View of Kingston A46

1977, June 10

218 A46	25c multicolored	.70	.70

25th anniv. of reign of Elizabeth II.

Hibiscus and 19th Century Whaler's Lamp — A47

Capt. Cook, by Nathaniel Dance — A48

1977, Oct. 4 Photo. *Perf. 14½*

219 A47	18c multicolored	.30	.30
220 A47	25c multicolored	.50	.50
221 A47	45c multicolored	.70	.70
	Nos. 219-221 (3)	1.50	1.50

Christmas.

1978, Jan. 18 Photo. *Perf. 14½*

Designs: 25c, Discovery of Northern Hawaiian Islands (Cook aboard ship), horiz. 80c, British flag and Island, horiz.

222 A48	18c multicolored	.30	.30
223 A48	25c multicolored	.55	.55
224 A48	80c multicolored	1.25	1.25
	Nos. 222-224 (3)	2.10	2.10

Bicentenary of Capt. Cook's arrival in Hawaiian Islands.

World Guides Flag and Globe A49

Designs: 25c, Norfolk Guides' scarf badge and trefoil. 35c, Elizabeth II and trefoil. 45c, FAO Ceres medal with portrait of Lady Olive Baden-Powell, and trefoil. Stamps outlined in shape of Norfolk Island map.

1978, Feb. 22 Litho. *Imperf.*
Self-adhesive

225 A49	18c lt ultra & multi	.25	.25
226 A49	25c yellow & multi	.30	.30
227 A49	35c lt green & multi	.55	.55
228 A49	45c yellow grn & multi	.70	.70
	Nos. 225-228 (4)	1.80	1.80

50th anniversary of Norfolk Island Girl Guides. Printed on peelable paper backing with green multiple pines and tourist publicity inscription.

St. Edward's Crown — A50

Design: 70c, Coronation regalia.

1978, June 29 Photo. *Perf. 14½*

229 A50	25c multicolored	.40	.40
230 A50	70c multicolored	1.10	1.10

25th anniv. of coronation of Elizabeth II.

Norfolk Island Boy Scouts, 50th Anniv. A51

Designs: 20c, Cliffs, Duncombe Bay, Scout Making Fire. 25c, Emily Bay, Philip and Nepean Islands from Kingston. 35c, Anson Bay, Cub and Boy Scouts. 45c, Sunset and Lord Baden-Powell. Stamps outlined in shape of Norfolk Island map.

1978, Aug. 22 Litho. *Imperf.*
Self-adhesive

231 A51	20c multicolored	.35	.35
232 A51	25c multicolored	.50	.50
233 A51	35c multicolored	.70	.70
234 A51	45c multicolored	.90	.90
	Nos. 231-234 (4)	2.45	2.45

Printed on peelable paper backing with green multiple pines and tourist publicity inscription and picture.

Map of Bering Sea and Pacific Ocean, Routes of Discovery and Resolution A52

Design: 90c, Discovery and Resolution trapped in ice, by John Webber.

1978, Aug. 29 Photo. *Perf. 14½*

235 A52	25c multicolored	.40	.40
236 A52	90c multicolored	1.65	1.65

Northernmost point of Cook's voyages.

Poinsettia and Bible — A53

Christmas: 30c, Native oak (flowers) and Bible. 55c, Hibiscus and Bible.

1978, Oct. 3 Photo. *Perf. 14½*

237 A53	20c multicolored	.30	.30
238 A53	30c multicolored	.50	.50
239 A53	55c multicolored	.80	.80
	Nos. 237-239 (3)	1.60	1.60

Capt. Cook, View of Staithes A54

80c, Capt. Cook and view of Whitby harbor.

1978, Oct. 27

240 A54	20c multicolored	.40	.40
241 A54	80c multicolored	1.65	1.65

Resolution, Map of Asia and Australia A55

Designs: No. 243, Map of Hawaii and Americas, Cook's route and statue. No. 244, Capt. Cook's death. No. 245, Ships off Hawaii.

1979, Feb. 14 Photo. *Perf. 14½*

242 A55	20c multicolored	.50	.50
243 A55	20c multicolored	.50	.50
a.	Pair, #242-243	1.00	1.00
244 A55	40c multicolored	1.00	1.00
245 A55	40c multicolored	1.00	1.00
a.	Pair, #244-245	2.00	2.00
	Nos. 242-245 (4)	3.00	3.00

Bicentenary of Capt. Cook's death.

Rowland Hill and Tasmania No. 1 A56

Rowland Hill and: 30c, Great Britain No. 8. 55c, Norfolk Island No. 2.

1979, Aug. 27 *Perf. 14x14½*
246 A56 20c multicolored .25 .25
247 A56 30c multicolored .35 .35
248 A56 55c multicolored .70 .70
a. Souvenir sheet of 1 1.40 1.40
Nos. 246-248 (3) 1.30 1.30

Sir Rowland Hill (1795-1879), originator of penny postage.

Legislative Assembly — A57

1979, Aug. **Photo.** *Perf. 14½x14*
249 A57 $1 multicolored 1.25 1.25

First session of Legislative Assembly.

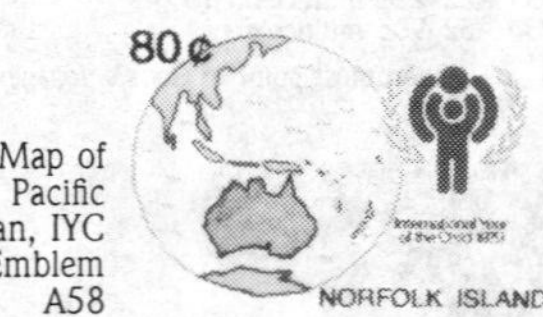

Map of Pacific Ocean, IYC Emblem A58

1979, Sept. 25 **Litho.** *Perf. 15*
250 A58 80c multicolored 1.10 1.10

International Year of the Child.

Emily Bay Beach — A59

1979, Oct. 2 **Photo.** *Perf. 12½x13*
251 A59 15c shown .25 .25
252 A59 20c Emily Bay .30 .30
253 A59 30c Salt House .55 .55
a. Souv. sheet of 3, #251-253, perf. 14x14½ 2.00 2.00
b. Strip of 3, #251-253 1.10 1.10

Christmas. #253b has continuous design.

Lions District Convention 1980 — A60

1980, Jan. 25 **Litho.** *Perf. 15*
254 A60 50c multicolored .70 .70

Rotary International, 75th Anniversary A61

1980, Feb. 21
255 A61 50c multicolored .70 .70

DH-60 "Gypsy Moth" A62

1980-81 **Litho.** *Perf. 14½*
256 A62 1c Hawker Siddeley HS-748 .15 .15
257 A62 2c shown .15 .15
258 A62 3c Curtiss P-40 Kittyhawk .15 .15
259 A62 4c Chance Vought Corsair .15 .15
260 A62 5c Grumman Avenger .15 .15
261 A62 15c Douglas Dauntless .30 .30
262 A62 20c Cessna 172 .35 .35
262A A62 25c Lockheed Hudson .45 .45
263 A62 30c Lockheed PV-1 Ventura .55 .55
264 A62 40c Avro York .70 .70
265 A62 50c DC-3 .90 .90
266 A62 60c Avro 691 Lancastrian 1.00 1.00
267 A62 80c DC-4 1.50 1.50
268 A62 $1 Beechcraft Super King Air 1.75 1.75
269 A62 $2 Fokker Friendship 2.25 2.25
270 A62 $5 Lockheed C-130 Hercules 5.75 5.75
Nos. 256-270 (16) 16.25 16.25

Issue dates: 2c, 3c, 20c, $5, Mar. 25. 4c, 5c, 15c, $2, Aug. 19. 30c, 50c, 60c, 80c, Jan. 13, 1981. 1c, 25c, 40c, $1, Mar. 3, 1981.

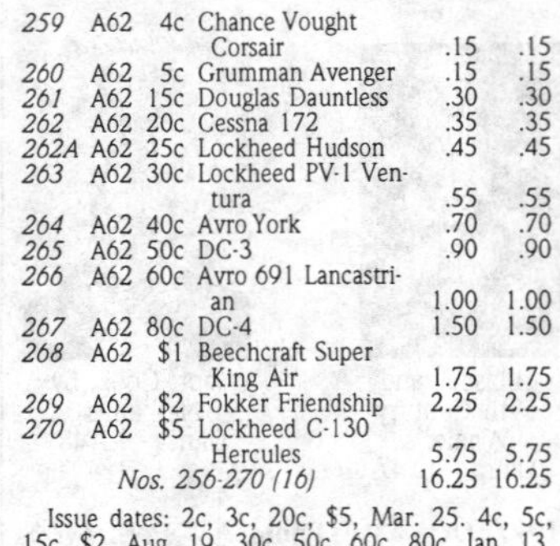

Queen Mother Elizabeth, 80th Birthday A63

1980, Aug. 4 **Litho.** *Perf. 14½*
271 A63 22c multicolored .30 .30
272 A63 60c multicolored .75 .75

Red-tailed Tropic Birds — A64

1980, Oct. 28 **Litho.** *Perf. 14x14½*
273 A64 15c shown .20 .20
274 A64 22c Fairy terns .30 .30
275 A64 35c White-capped noddys .50 .50
a. Strip of 3, #273-275 1.10 1.10
276 A64 60c Fairy terns, diff. .90 .90
Nos. 273-276 (4) 1.90 1.90

Christmas. No. 275a has continuous design.

Citizens Arriving at Norfolk Island A65

1981, June 5 **Litho.** *Perf. 14½*
277 A65 5c Departure .15 .15
278 A65 35c shown .50 .50
279 A65 60c Settlement .85 .85
a. Souvenir sheet of 3, #277-279 1.65 1.65
Nos. 277-279 (3) 1.50 1.50

Pitcairn migration to Norfolk Island, 125th anniv.

Royal Wedding Issue
Common Design Type

1981, July 22 **Litho.** *Perf. 14*
280 CD331 35c Bouquet .40 .40
281 CD331 55c Charles .65 .65
282 CD331 60c Couple .70 .70
Nos. 280-282 (3) 1.75 1.75

#280-282 each se-tenant with decorative label.

Uniting Church of Australia A66

1981, Sept. 15 **Litho.** *Perf. 14½*
283 A66 18c shown .20 .20
284 A66 24c Seventh Day Adventist Church .30 .30
285 A66 30c Church of the Sacred Heart .35 .35
286 A66 $1 St. Barnabas Church 1.25 1.25
Nos. 283-286 (4) 2.10 2.10

Christmas.

White-breasted Silvereye A67

1981, Nov. 10 **Litho.** *Perf. 14½*
287 Strip of 5 2.75 2.75
a.-e. A67 35c any single .55 .55

Philip Island A68

Views, Flora and Fauna: No. 288, Philip Isld. No. 289, Nepean Island.

1982, Jan. 12 **Litho.** *Perf. 14*
288 Strip of 5 1.50 1.50
a.-e. A68 24c any single .30 .30
289 Strip of 5 2.50 2.50
a.-e. A68 35c any single .50 .50

Sperm Whale A69

1982, Feb. 23 **Litho.** *Perf. 14½*
290 A69 24c shown .40 .40
291 A69 55c Southern right whale .90 .90
292 A69 80c Humpback whale 1.50 1.50
Nos. 290-292 (3) 2.80 2.80

Shipwrecks A70

1982 **Litho.** *Perf. 14½*
293 A70 24c Sirius, 1790 .40 .40
294 A70 27c Diocet, 1873 .45 .45
295 A70 35c Friendship, 1835 .55 .55
296 A70 40c Mary Hamilton, 1873 .65 .65
297 A70 55c Fairlie, 1840 .80 .80
298 A70 65c Warrigal, 1918 1.00 1.00
Nos. 293-298 (6) 3.85 3.85

Christmas and 40th Anniv. of Aircraft Landing A71

1982, Sept. 7 *Perf. 14*
299 A71 27c Supplies drop .35 .35
300 A71 40c Landing .60 .60
301 A71 75c Sharing supplies 1.10 1.10
Nos. 299-301 (3) 2.05 2.05

Battalion Company Officer, 50th Regiment, 1835-1842 — A72

British Army Uniforms, Second Settlement, 1839-1848: 40c, Light Company Officer, 58th Reg., 1845. 55c, Private, 80th Bat., 1838. 65c, Bat. Company Officer, 11th Reg., 1847.

1982, Nov. 9 *Perf. 14½*
302 A72 27c multicolored .35 .35
303 A72 40c multicolored .60 .60
304 A72 55c multicolored .70 .70
305 A72 65c multicolored .90 .90
Nos. 302-305 (4) 2.55 2.55

Local Mushrooms — A73

1983, Mar. 29 **Litho.** *Perf. 14x13½*
306 A73 27c Panaeolus papilonaceus .40 .40
307 A73 40c Coprinus domesticus .65 .65
308 A73 55c Marasmius niveus .80 .80
309 A73 65c Cymatoderma elegans 1.00 1.00
Nos. 306-309 (4) 2.85 2.85

Manned Flight Bicentenary A74

1983, July 12 **Litho.** *Perf. 14½x14*
310 A74 10c Beech 18, aerial mapping .20 .20
311 A74 27c Fokker F-28 .35 .35
312 A74 45c DC4 .75 .75
313 A74 75c Sikorsky helicopter 1.10 1.10
a. Souvenir sheet of 4, #310-313 2.75 2.75
Nos. 310-313 (4) 2.40 2.40

Christmas — A75

Stained-glass Windows by Edward Burne-Jones (1833-1898), St. Barnabas Chapel.

1983, Oct. 4 **Litho.** *Perf. 14*
314 A75 5c multicolored .15 .15
315 A75 24c multicolored .40 .40
316 A75 30c multicolored .45 .45
317 A75 45c multicolored .65 .65
318 A75 85c multicolored 1.25 1.25
Nos. 314-318 (5) 2.90 2.90

World Communications Year — A76

ANZCAN Cable Station: 30c, Chantik, Cable laying Ship. 45c, Shore end. 75c, Cable Ship Mercury. 85c, Map of cable route.

1983, Nov. 15 **Litho.** *Perf. 14½x14*
319 A76 30c multicolored .40 .40
320 A76 45c multicolored .60 .60
321 A76 75c multicolored 1.00 1.00
322 A76 85c multicolored 1.10 1.10
Nos. 319-322 (4) 3.10 3.10

Local Flowers — A77

1984 **Litho.** *Perf. 14*
323 A77 1c Myoporum obsurum .15 .15
324 A77 2c Ipomoea pes-caprae .15 .15
325 A77 3c Phreatia crassiuscula .15 .15
326 A77 4c Streblorrhiza speciosa .15 .15
327 A77 5c Rhopalostylis baueri .15 .15
328 A77 10c Alyxia gynopogon .15 .15
329 A77 15c Ungeria floribunda .20 .20

330 A77 20c Capparis nobilis .25 .25
331 A77 25c Lagunaria patersonia .35 .35
332 A77 30c Cordyline obtecta .45 .45
333 A77 35c Hibiscus insularis .50 .50
334 A77 40c Millettia australis .55 .55
335 A77 50c Jasminum volubile .65 .65
336 A77 $1 Passiflora aurantia 1.40 1.40
337 A77 $3 Oberonia titania 4.25 4.25
338 A77 $5 Araucaria heterophylla 7.00 7.00
Nos. 323-338 (16) 16.50 *16.50*

Issue dates: Jan. 10: 2c, 3c, 10c, 20c, 25c, 40c, 50c, $5; others Mar. 27.

Reef Fish — A78

Perf. 13¹/₂x14

1984, Apr. 17 Litho. Wmk. 373

339 A78 30c Painted morwong .50 .50
340 A78 45c Black-spot goatfish .70 .70
341 A78 75c Ring-tailed surgeon fish 1.25 1.25
342 A78 85c Three-striped butterfly fish 1.40 1.40
Nos. 339-342 (4) 3.85 3.85

Boobook Owl — A79

Designs: a, Laying eggs. b, Standing at treehole. c, Sitting on branch looking sideways. d, Looking head on. e, Flying.

Wmk. 373

1984, July 17 Litho. *Perf. 14*

343 Strip of 5 4.25 4.25
a.-e. A79 30c any single .85 .85

AUSIPEX '84 — A80

1984, Sept. 18 Litho. *Perf. 14¹/₂*

344 A80 30c Nos. 15 and 176 .55 .55
345 A80 45c First day cover .85 .85
346 A80 75c Presentation pack 1.65 1.65
a. Souvenir sheet of 3, #344-346 3.50 3.50
Nos. 344-346 (3) 3.05 3.05

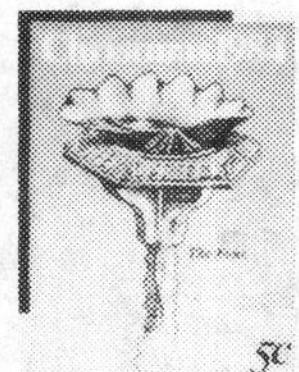

Christmas — A81

A82

1984, Oct. 9 Litho. *Perf. 13¹/₂*

347 A81 5c The Font .15 .15
348 A81 24c Church at Kingston, interior .35 .35
349 A81 30c Pastor and Mrs. Phelps .45 .45
350 A81 45c Phelps, Church of Chester .70 .70
351 A81 85c Phelps, Methodist Church, modern interior 1.40 1.40
Nos. 347-351 (5) 3.05 3.05

1984, Nov. 6 Litho. *Perf. 14x15*

352 A82 30c As teacher .45 .45
353 A82 45c As minister .65 .65
354 A82 75c As chaplain 1.10 1.10
355 A82 85c As community leader 1.40 1.40
Nos. 352-355 (4) 3.60 3.60

Rev. George Hunn Nobbs, death centenary.

Whaling Ships — A83

1985 Litho. *Perf. 13¹/₂x14*

356 A83 5c Fanny Fisher .15 .15
357 A83 15c Waterwitch .30 .30
358 A83 20c Canton .40 .40
359 A83 33c Costa Rica Packet .60 .60
360 A83 50c Splendid .90 .90
361 A83 60c Aladin 1.50 1.50
362 A83 80c California 1.75 1.75
363 A83 90c Onward 2.25 2.25
Nos. 356-363 (8) 7.85 7.85

Issued: 5c, 33c, 50c, 90c, 2/19; others 4/30.

Queen Mother 85th Birthday

Common Design Type

Perf. 14¹/₂x14

1985, June 6 Litho. Wmk. 384

364 CD336 5c Portrait, 1926 .15 .15
365 CD336 33c With Princess Anne .55 .55
366 CD336 50c Photograph by N. Parkinson .80 .80
367 CD336 90c Holding Prince Henry 1.65 1.65
Nos. 364-367 (4) 3.15 3.15

Souvenir Sheet

368 CD336 $1 With Princess Anne, Ascot Races 2.25 2.25

Intl. Youth Year — A84

Children's drawings.

1985, July 9 Litho. *Perf. 13¹/₂x14*

369 A84 33c Swimming .75 .75
370 A84 50c Nature walk 1.25 1.25

Girl, Prize-winning Cow — A85

Designs: 90c, Embroidery, jam-making, baking, animal husbandry.

1985, Sept. 10 Litho. *Perf. 13¹/₂x14*

371 A85 80c multicolored 1.10 1.10
372 A85 90c multicolored 1.25 1.25
a. Souvenir sheet of 2, #371-372 3.25 3.25

Royal Norfolk Island Agricultural & Horticultural Show, 125th anniv.

Christmas — A86

1985, Oct. 3 *Perf. 13¹/₂*

373 A86 27c Three Shepherds .45 .45
374 A86 33c Journey to Bethlehem .60 .60
375 A86 50c Three Wise Men .80 .80
376 A86 90c Nativity 1.65 1.65
Nos. 373-376 (4) 3.50 3.50

Marine Life — A87

1986, Jan. 14 *Perf. 13¹/₂x14*

377 A87 5c Long-spined sea urchin .15 .15
378 A87 33c Blue starfish .60 .60
379 A87 55c Eagle ray 1.00 1.00
380 A87 75c Moray eel 1.40 1.40
a. Souvenir sheet of 4, #377-380 3.75 3.75
Nos. 377-380 (4) 3.15 3.15

Halley's Comet — A88

Designs: a, Giotto space probe. b, Comet.

1986, Mar. 11 *Perf. 15*

381 Pair 4.00 4.00
a.-b. A88 $1 any single 2.00 2.00

Se-tenant in continuous design.

AMERIPEX '86 — A89

Designs: 33c, Isaac Robinson, US consul in Norfolk, 1887-1908, vert. 50c, Ford Model-T. 80c, Statue of Liberty.

1986, May 22 Litho. *Perf. 13¹/₂*

382 A89 33c multicolored .60 .60
383 A89 50c multicolored .90 .90
384 A89 80c multicolored 1.50 1.50
a. Souvenir sheet of #382-384 3.25 3.25
Nos. 382-384 (3) 3.00 3.00

Queen Elizabeth II, 60th Birthday — A90

Various portraits.

1986, June 12

385 A90 5c As Princess .15 .15
386 A90 33c Contemporary photograph .65 .65
387 A90 80c Opening N.I. Golf Club 1.40 1.40
388 A90 90c With Prince Philip 1.75 1.75
Nos. 385-388 (4) 3.95 3.95

Christmas A91

1986, Sept. 23 Litho. *Perf. 13¹/₂x14*

389 A91 30c multicolored .50 .50
390 A91 40c multicolored .65 .65
391 A91 $1 multicolored 1.60 1.60
Nos. 389-391 (3) 2.75 2.75

Commission of Gov. Phillip, Bicent. — A92

1986 Litho. *Perf. 14x13¹/₂*

392 A92 36c British prison, 1787 .55 .55
393 A92 55c Transportation, Court of Assize .85 .85
394 A92 90c Gov. meeting Home Society 1.40 1.40
395 A92 90c Gov. meeting Home Secretary 1.40 1.40
396 A92 $1 Gov. Phillip, 1738-1814 1.50 1.50
Nos. 392-396 (5) 5.70 5.70

No. 395 was issued because No. 394 is incorrectly inscribed.

Issued: #395, Dec. 16; others, Oct. 14.

See #417-420, 426-436.

Commission of Gov. Phillip, Bicent. — A93

1986, Dec. 16 *Perf. 13¹/₂*

397 A93 36c Maori chief .70 .70
398 A93 36c Bananas, taro .70 .70
399 A93 36c Stone tools .70 .70
400 A93 36c Polynesian outrigger .70 .70
Nos. 397-400 (4) 2.80 2.80

Pre-European occupation of the Island.

Island Scenery — A94

— A96

1987-88 Litho. *Perf. 13¹/₂*

401 A94 1c Cockpit Creek Bridge .15 .15
402 A94 2c Cemetery Bay Beach .15 .15
403 A94 3c Guesthouse .15 .15
404 A94 5c Philip Island from Point Ross .15 .15
405 A94 15c Cattle grazing .20 .20
406 A94 30c Rock fishing .40 .40
407 A94 37c Old home .50 .50
408 A94 40c Shopping center .50 .50
409 A94 50c Emily Bay .65 .65
410 A94 60c Bloody Bridge .80 .80
411 A94 80c Pitcairner-style shop 1.10 1.10
412 A94 90c Government House 1.25 1.25
413 A94 $1 Melanesian Memorial Chapel 1.40 1.40
414 A94 $2 Kingston convict settlement 2.00 2.00
415 A94 $3 Ball Bay 4.00 4.00
416 A94 $5 Northerly cliffs 10.00 10.00
Nos. 401-416 (16) 23.40 23.40

Issue dates: 5c, 50c, 90c, $1, Feb. 17. 30c, 40c, 80c, $2, Apr. 17. 15c, 37c, 60c, $3, July 27. 1c, 2c, 3c, $5, May 17, 1988.

Bicentennial Type of 1986

Designs: 5c, Loading supplies at Deptford, England, 1787. No. 418, First Fleet sailing from Spithead (buoy in water). No. 419, Sailing from Spithead (ship flying British merchant flag). $1, Convicts below deck.

1987, May 13 Litho. *Perf. 14x13¹/₂*

417 A92 5c multicolored .15 .15
418 A92 55c multicolored .70 .70
419 A92 55c multicolored .70 .70
a. Pair, #418-419 1.40 1.40
420 A92 $1 multicolored 1.50 1.50
Nos. 417-420 (4) 3.05 3.05

No. 419a has a continuous design.

1987, Sept. 16 Unwmk.

World Wildlife Fund: Green parrot.

421 Strip of 4 *6.50 6.50*
a. A96 5c Parrot facing right .25 .25
b. A96 15c Parrot, chick, egg .80 .80
c. A96 36c Parrots *1.90 1.90*
d. A96 55c Parrot facing left *3.00 3.00*

Norfolk Island stamps can be mounted in the Scott Australian Dependencies album.

Christmas
A97

Children's party: 30c, Norfolk Island pine tree, restored convicts' settlement. 42c, Santa Claus, children opening packages. 58c, Santa, children, gifts in fire engine. 63c, Meal.

Perf. 13½x14

1987, Oct. 13 Litho. Wmk. 384

422 A97 30c multicolored .45 .45
423 A97 42c multicolored .65 .65
424 A97 58c multicolored .85 .85
425 A97 63c multicolored .95 .95
Nos. 422-425 (4) 2.90 2.90

Bicentennial Type of 1986

Designs: 5c, Lt. Philip Gidley King. No. 427, La Perouse and Louis XVI of France. No. 428, Gov. Phillip sailing in ship's cutter from Botany Bay to Port Jackson. No. 429, Flag raising on Norfolk Is. 55c, Lt. King and search party exploring the island. 70c, Landfall, Sydney Bay. No. 432, L'Astrolabe and La Boussole off coast of Norfolk. No. 433, HMS Supply. No. 434, Wrecking of L'Astrolabe off the Solomon Isls. No. 435, First Fleet landing at Sydney Cove. No. 436, First settlement, Sydney Bay, 1788.

1987-88 Litho. *Perf. 14x13½*

426 A92 5c multicolored .15 .15
427 A92 37c multicolored .65 .65
428 A92 37c multicolored .65 .65
429 A92 37c multicolored .65 .65
430 A92 55c multicolored 1.00 1.00
431 A92 70c multicolored 1.25 1.25
432 A92 90c multicolored 1.50 1.50
433 A92 90c multicolored 1.50 1.50
434 A92 $1 multicolored 1.90 1.90
435 A92 $1 multicolored 1.90 1.90
436 A92 $1 multicolored 1.90 1.90
Nos. 426-436 (11) 13.05 13.05

Visit of Jean La Perouse (1741-88), French navigator, to Norfolk Is. (Nos. 427, 432, 434); arrival of the First Fleet at Sydney Cove (Nos. 428, 435); founding of Norfolk Is. (Nos. 426, 429-431, 433, 436).

Issued: #427, 432, 434, Dec. 8, 1987; #428, 435, Jan. 25, 1988; others, Mar. 4, 1988.

SYDPEX '88, July 30-Aug. 7
A98

Sydney-Norfolk transportation and communication links.

Perf. 14x13½ 13½x14

1988, July 30 Litho.

437 A98 37c Air and sea transports, vert. .75 .75
438 A98 37c shown .75 .75
439 A98 37c Telecommunications, vert. .75 .75
a. Souvenir sheet of 3, #437-439 3.50 3.50
Nos. 437-439 (3) 2.25 2.25

No. 438 exists perf. 13½ within No. 439a.

Christmas — A99

1988, Sept. 27 Litho. *Perf. 14x13½*

440 A99 30c shown .55 .55
441 A99 42c Flowers, diff. .75 .75
442 A99 58c Trees, fish 1.10 1.10
443 A99 63c Trees, sailboats 1.10 1.10
Nos. 440-443 (4) 3.50 3.50

Convict Era Georgian Architecture, c. 1825-1850
A100

Designs: 39c, Waterfront shop and boat shed. 55c, Royal Engineers' Building. 90c, Old military barracks. $1, Commissary and new barracks.

1988, Dec. 6 Litho. *Perf. 13½x14*

444 A100 39c multicolored .60 .60
445 A100 55c multicolored .85 .85
446 A100 90c multicolored 1.40 1.40
447 A100 $1 multicolored 1.65 1.65
Nos. 444-447 (4) 4.50 4.50

Indigenous Insects
A101

Perf. 13½x14

1989, Feb. 14 Litho. Unwmk.

448 A101 39c *Lamprima aenea* .70 .70
449 A101 55c *Insulascirtus nythos* 1.00 1.00
450 A101 90c *Caedicia araucariae* 1.65 1.65
451 A101 $1 *Thrincophora aridela* 1.90 1.90
Nos. 448-451 (4) 5.25 5.25

Mutiny on the Bounty
A102

Designs: 5c, *Bounty's* landfall, Adventure Bay, Tasmania. 39c, Mutineers and Polynesian maidens, c. 1790. 55c, Cumbria, Christian's home county. $1.10, Capt. Bligh and crewmen cast adrift.

Perf. 13½

1989, Apr. 28 Litho. Unwmk.

452 A102 5c multicolored .15 .15
453 A102 39c multicolored .75 .75
454 A102 55c multicolored 1.10 1.10
455 A102 $1.10 multicolored 1.90 1.90
Nos. 452-455 (4) 3.90 3.90

Souvenir Sheet

456 Sheet of 3 + label (#453, 456a-456b) 5.75 5.75
a. A102 90c Isle of Man No. 393 2.25 2.25
b. A102 $1 Pitcairn Isls. No. 321d 2.50 2.50

See Isle of Man Nos. 389-394 and Pitcairn Isls. Nos. 320-322.

A103 A104

Perf. 14x13½

1989, Aug. 10 Litho. Unwmk.

457 A103 41c Flag .65 .65
458 A103 55c Ballot box .85 .85
459 A103 $1 Norfolk Is. Act of 1979 1.50 1.50
460 A103 $1.10 Norfolk Is. crest 1.65 1.65
Nos. 457-460 (4) 4.65 4.65

Self-Government, 10th anniv.

Perf. 13½x13

1989, Sept. 25 Litho. Unwmk.

461 A104 $1 dark ultra & dark red 2.00 2.00

Natl. Red Cross, 75th anniv.

Bounty Hymns — A105

Designs: 36c, "While nature was sinking in stillness to rest, The last beams of daylight show dim in the west." 60c, "There's a land that is fairer than day, And by faith we can see it afar." 75c, "Let the lower lights be burning, Send a gleam across the wave." 80c, "Oh, have you not heard of that beautiful stream That flows through our father's lands."

1989, Oct. 9 *Perf. 13½x14*

462 A105 36c multicolored .55 .55
463 A105 60c multicolored .95 .95
464 A105 75c multicolored 1.25 1.25
465 A105 80c multicolored 1.25 1.25
Nos. 462-465 (4) 4.00 4.00

A106 A107

1989, Nov. 21 *Perf. 14x13½*

466 A106 41c Announcer John Royle .75 .75
467 A106 65c Sound waves on map 1.25 1.25
468 A106 $1.10 Jacko, the laughing kookaburra 2.00 2.00
Nos. 466-468 (3) 4.00 4.00

Radio Australia, 50th anniv.

Perf. 15x14½

1990, Jan. 23 Litho. Unwmk.

Settlement of Pitcairn (The Norfolk Islanders): 70c, The *Bounty* on fire. $1.10, Armorial ensign of Norfolk.

469 A107 70c multicolored 1.25 1.25
470 A107 $1.10 multicolored 2.00 2.00

Salvage Team at Work
A108

Designs: No. 471, HMS *Sirius* striking reef. No. 472, HMS *Supply* clearing reef. $1, Map of salvage sites, artifacts.

1990, Mar. 19 *Perf. 14x13½*

Size of Nos. 471-472: 40x27

471 A108 41c multicolored .70 .70
472 A108 41c multicolored .70 .70
a. Pair, #471-472 1.40 1.40
473 A108 65c shown 1.10 1.10
474 A108 $1 multicolored 1.65 1.65
Nos. 471-474 (4) 4.15 4.15

Wreck of HMS *Sirius*, 200th anniv. No. 472a has continuous design.

Lightering Cargo Ashore, Kingston
A109

MV Ile de Lumiere
A110

1990-91 Litho. *Perf. 14x14½*

479 A109 5c like #480 .15 .15
480 A109 10c shown .15 .15

Perf. 14½

481 A110 45c La Dunkerquoise .60 .60
482 A110 50c Dmitri Mendeleev .70 .70
483 A110 65c Pacific Rover .90 .90
484 A110 70c shown .95 .95
485 A110 75c Norfolk Trader 1.00 1.00
486 A110 80c Roseville 1.10 1.10
487 A110 90c Kalia 1.25 1.25
488 A110 $1 HMS Bounty 1.40 1.40
489 A110 $2 HMAS Success 2.75 2.75
490 A110 $5 HMAS Whyalia 7.00 7.00
Nos. 479-490 (12) 17.95 17.95

Issued: 5c, 10c, 70c, $2, 7/17/90; 45c, 50c, 65c, $5, 2/19/91; 75c, 80c, 90c, $1, 8/13/91.

Christmas — A111 A112

1990, Sept. 25 Litho. *Perf. 14½*

491 A111 38c Island home .65 .65
492 A111 43c New post office .75 .75
493 A111 65c Sydney Bay, Kingston, horiz. 1.10 1.10
494 A111 85c Officers' Quarters, 1836, horiz. 1.50 1.50
Nos. 491-494 (4) 4.00 4.00

1990, Oct. 11 Litho. *Perf. 15x14½*

Designs: 70c, William Charles Wentworth (1790-1872), Australian politician. $1.20, Thursday October Christian (1790-1831).

495 A112 70c brown 1.25 1.25
496 A112 $1.20 brown 2.00 2.00

Norfolk Island Robin
A113 A114

1990, Dec. 3 Litho. *Perf. 14½*

497 A113 65c multicolored 1.10 1.10
498 A113 $1 shown 1.65 1.65
499 A113 $1.20 multi, diff. 2.00 2.00
Nos. 497-499 (3) 4.75 4.75

Souvenir Sheet

500 Sheet of 2 4.25 4.25
a. A114 $1 shown 2.00 2.00
b. A114 $1 Two robins 2.00 2.00

Birdpex '90, 20th Intl. Ornithological Congress, New Zealand.

Ham Radio — A115

1991, Apr. 9 Litho. *Perf. 14½*

501 A115 43c Island map .75 .75
502 A115 $1 World map 1.75 1.75
503 A115 $1.20 Regional location 2.25 2.25
Nos. 501-503 (3) 4.75 4.75

Museum Displays
A116

1991, May 16 Litho. *Perf. 14½*

504 A116 43c Ship's bow, Sirius Museum, vert. .70 .70
505 A116 70c House Museum 1.25 1.25
506 A116 $1 Carronade, Sirius Museum 1.65 1.65
507 A116 $1.20 Pottery, Archaeology Museum, vert. 2.00 2.00
Nos. 504-507 (4) 5.60 5.60

Wreck of HMS Pandora, Aug. 28, 1791 — A117

Design: $1.20, HMS Pandora searching for Bounty mutineers.

1991, July 2 Litho. *Perf. 13½x14*

508 A117 $1 shown 1.65 1.65
509 A117 $1.20 multicolored 2.00 2.00

Christmas A118

1991, Sept. 23 Litho. *Perf. 14½*

510 A118 38c multicolored .60 .60
511 A118 43c multicolored .65 .65
512 A118 65c multicolored 1.00 1.00
513 A118 85c multicolored 1.40 1.40
Nos. 510-513 (4) 3.65 3.65

Start of World War II in the Pacific, 50th Anniv. A119

1991, Dec. 9 Litho. *Perf. 14½*

514 A119 43c Tank and soldier .75 .75
515 A119 70c B-17 1.10 1.10
516 A119 $1 War ships 1.65 1.65
Nos. 514-516 (3) 3.50 3.50

A120

A121

1992, Feb. 11 Litho. *Perf. 14½*

517 A120 45c Columbus' Coat of Arms .70 .70
518 A120 $1.05 Santa Maria 1.65 1.65
519 A120 $1.20 Columbus at globe 1.90 1.90
Nos. 517-519 (3) 4.25 4.25

Discovery of America, 500th anniv.

1992, May 4 Litho. *Perf. 14½*

Designs: No. 520, Map of Coral Sea Battle area. No. 521, Battle area, Midway. No. 522, HMAS Australia. No. 523, Catalina PBY5. No. 524, USS Yorktown. No. 525, Dauntless dive bomber.

520 A121 45c multicolored .65 .65
521 A121 45c multicolored .65 .65
522 A121 70c multicolored 1.10 1.10
523 A121 70c multicolored 1.10 1.10
524 A121 $1.05 multicolored 1.65 1.65
525 A121 $1.05 multicolored 1.65 1.65
Nos. 520-525 (6) 6.80 6.80

Battles of the Coral Sea and Midway, 50th anniv.

US Invasion of Guadalcanal, 50th Anniv. — A122

Designs: 45c, Troops landing on beach. 70c, Troops in battle. $1.05, Map, flags.

1992, Aug. 6 Litho. *Perf. 14½*

526 A122 45c multicolored .65 .65
527 A122 70c multicolored 1.10 1.10
528 A122 $1.05 multicolored 1.65 1.65
Nos. 526-528 (3) 3.40 3.40

Christmas — A123

Scenes of Norfolk Island: 40c, Ball Bay, looking over Point Blackbourne. 45c, Headstone Creek. 75c, Ball Bay. $1.20, Rocky Point Reserve.

1992, Oct. 29 Litho. *Perf. 15x14½*

529 A123 40c multicolored .65 .65
530 A123 45c multicolored .70 .70
531 A123 75c multicolored 1.25 1.25
532 A123 $1.20 multicolored 1.90 1.90
Nos. 529-532 (4) 4.50 4.50

Tourism A124

Tourist sites at Kingston: a, Boat shed, flaghouses. b, Old military barracks. c, All Saints Church. d, Officers quarters. e, Quality row.

1993, Feb. 23 Litho. *Perf. 14½*

533 A124 45c Strip of 5, #a.-e. 3.50 3.50

Emergency Services A125

1993, May 18 Litho. *Perf. 14½*

534 A125 45c Volunteer fire service .65 .65
535 A125 70c Rescue squad 1.00 1.00
536 A125 75c St. John ambulance 1.10 1.10
537 A125 $1.20 Police service 1.75 1.75
Nos. 534-537 (4) 4.50 4.50

Nudibranchs A126

1993, July 7 Litho. *Perf. 14½*

538 A126 45c Phyllidia ocellata .60 .60
539 A126 45c Glaucus atlanticus .60 .60
540 A126 75c Bornella sp. 1.00 1.00
541 A126 85c Glossodoris rubroannolata 1.25 1.25
542 A126 95c Halgerda willeyi 1.40 1.40
543 A126 $1.05 Chromodoris amoena 1.50 1.50
Nos. 538-543 (6) 6.35 6.35

No. 539 identified as "glauc."

A127

A128

Designs: 70c, Maori patus. $1.20, First Maori map of New Zealand on paper, 1793.

1993, Oct. 28 Litho. *Perf. 14½*

544 A127 70c tan, buff & black .90 .90
545 A127 $1.20 tan, buff & black 1.50 1.50

Cultural contact with New Zealand, bicent.

1993, Oct. 28

546 A128 40c blue & multi .50 .50
547 A128 45c red & multi .60 .60
548 A128 75c green & multi 1.00 1.00
549 A128 $1.20 black & multi 1.50 1.50
Nos. 546-549 (4) 3.60 3.60

Early Pacific Explorers A129

Explorer, ship: 5c, Vasco Nunez de Balboa, Barbara. 10c, Ferdinand Magellan, Victoria. 20c, Juan Sebastian de Elcano, Victoria. 50c, Alvaro de Saavedra, Florida. 70c, Ruy Lopez de Villalobos, San Juan. 75c, Miguel Lopez de Legaspi, San Lesmes. 80c, Sir Frances Drake, Golden Hinde. 85c, Alvaro de Mendana, Santiago. 90c, Pedro Fernandes de Quiros, San Pedro Paulo. $1, Luis Baez de Torres, San Perico. $2, Abel Tasman, Heemskerk. $5, William Dampier, Cygnet. No. 562, Golden Hinde (Francis Drake).

1994 Litho. *Perf. 14½*

550 A129 5c multicolored .15 .15
551 A129 10c multicolored .15 .15
552 A129 20c multicolored .30 .30
554 A129 50c multicolored .65 .65
556 A129 70c multicolored .90 .90
557 A129 75c multicolored 1.00 1.00
558 A129 80c multicolored 1.10 1.10
559 A129 85c multicolored 1.25 1.25
560 A129 90c multicolored 1.25 1.25
560A A129 $1 multicolored 1.40 1.40
561 A129 $2 multicolored 2.50 2.50
561A A129 $5 multicolored 6.75 6.75
Nos. 550-561A (12) 17.40 17.40

Souvenir Sheet

Perf. 13

562 A129 $1.20 multicolored 1.50 1.50

No. 562 contains one 32x52mm stamp.

Issued: 50c, 70c, 75c, $2, No. 562, 2/8/94; 5c, 10c, 20c, $5, 5/3/94. 80c, 85c, 90c, $1, 7/26/94.

This is an expanding set. Numbers may change.

A130 A131

Seabirds: a, Sooty tern. b, Red-tailed tropic bird. c, Australasian gannet. d, Wedge-tail shearwater. e, Masked booby.

1994, Aug. 17 Litho. *Perf. 14½x14*

565 A130 45c Strip of 5, #a.-e. 3.25 3.25
Booklet, 2 #565 6.50

1994, Oct. 27 Litho. *Die Cut*

Christmas: 45c, Church, flowers, words from Pitcairn anthem. 75c, Stained glass windows, "To God be the glory." $1.20, Rainbow, ship, "Ship of Fame."

Self-Adhesive

566 A131 45c multicolored .65 .65
567 A131 75c multicolored 1.10 1.10
568 A131 $1.20 multicolored 1.75 1.75
Nos. 566-568 (3) 3.50 3.50

Vintage Cars — A132

1995, Feb. 7 Litho. *Perf. 14x14½*

569 A132 45c 1926 Chevrolet .65 .65
570 A132 75c 1928 Model A Ford 1.10 1.10
571 A132 $1.05 1929 Model A A/C Ford truck 1.50 1.50
572 A132 $1.20 1930 Model A Ford 1.75 1.75
Nos. 569-572 (4) 5.00 5.00

Humpback Whales A133

Perf. 14x14½, 14½x14

1995, May 9 Litho.

573 A133 45c Tail fluke .65 .65
574 A133 75c Mother & calf 1.10 1.10
575 A133 $1.05 Breaching, vert. 1.50 1.50
Nos. 573-575 (3) 3.25 3.25

Souvenir Sheet

Perf. 14x14½

576 A133 $1.20 Bubble netting, vert. 1.75 1.75
a. Overprinted in gold & black 1.75 1.75

No. 576 contains one 30x50mm stamp and is a continuous design.

Overprint in margin of No. 576a has "Selamat Hari Merdeka" and JAKARTA '95 exhibition emblem.

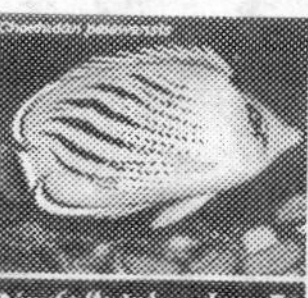

Butterfly Fish — A134

Chaetodon...: 5c, pelewensis. 45c, plebeius. $1.20, tricinctus. $1.50, auriga.

1995, June 15 Litho. *Perf. 14*

577 A134 5c multicolored .15 .15
578 A134 45c multicolored .65 .65
579 A134 $1.20 multicolored 1.75 1.75
580 A134 $1.50 multicolored 2.00 2.00
Nos. 577-580 (4) 4.55 4.55

World War II Vehicles A135

Designs: 5c, 1942 Intl. 4x4 refueler. 45c, 1942 Ford 5 passenger sedan. $1.20, 1942 Ford 3-ton tipper. $2, D8 Caterpillar with scraper.

1995, Aug. 8 Litho. *Perf. 14x15*

Black Vignettes

581 A135 5c brown & tan .15 .15
582 A135 45c blue & red lilac .65 .65
583 A135 $1.20 green & orange 1.75 1.75
584 A135 $2 red & gray 3.00 3.00
Nos. 581-584 (4) 5.55 5.55

Island Flower Type of 1960

1995, Sept. 1 Litho. *Rouletted 7*

Booklet Stamps

585 A6 5c like No. 30 .15 .15
a. Booklet pane of 18 + 3 labels 1.35
586 A6 5c like No. 33 .15 .15
a. Booklet pane of 18 + 3 labels 1.35
Complete booklet, 1 each #585a-586a 2.75

A136

Victory in the Pacific Day, 50th Anniv. — A136a

Designs: 5c, Fighter plane en route. 45c, Sgt. T.C. Derrick, VC, vert. 75c, Gen. MacArthur, vert. $1.05, Girls at victory party.

1995, Sept. 1 Litho. *Perf. 12*

587 A136 5c multicolored .15 .15
588 A136 45c multicolored .65 .65
589 A136 75c multicolored 1.10 1.10
590 A136 $1.05 multicolored 1.50 1.50
Nos. 587-590 (4) 3.40 3.40

Litho. & Embossed

591 A136a $10 Medals 15.00 15.00

Singapore '95.

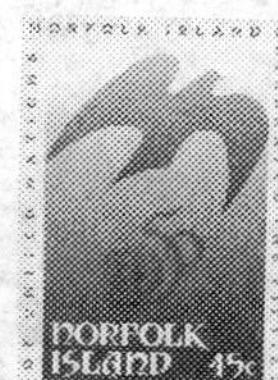

UN, 50th Anniv. — A137

1995, Nov. 7 Litho. *Perf. 14½x14*

592	A137	45c Dove	.65	.65
593	A137	75c Christmas star	1.10	1.10
594	A137	$1.05 Christmas candles	1.50	1.50
595	A137	$1.20 Olive branch	1.75	1.75
		Nos. 592-595 (4)	5.00	5.00

Christmas (#593-594).

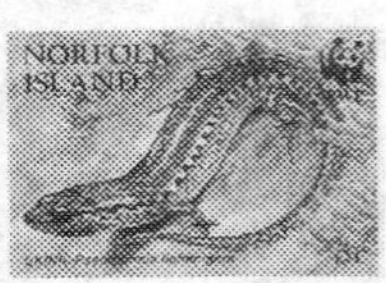

Skinks and Geckos — A138

World Wildlife Fund: a, 45c, Skink crawling left. b, 5c, Skink crawling right. c, 45c, Gecko crawling right. d, 5c, Gecko crawling left, flower.

1996, Feb. 7 Litho. *Perf. 14½x15*

596	A138	Strip of 4, #a.-d.	1.50	1.50

No. 596 was issued in sheets of 4 strips with stamps in each strip in different order.

Royal Australian Air Force, 75th Anniv. — A139

1996, Apr. 22 Litho. *Perf. 14*

597	A139	45c Sopwith pup	.75	.75
598	A139	45c Wirraway	.75	.75
599	A139	75c F-111C	1.25	1.25
600	A139	85c F/A-18 Hornet	1.40	1.40
		Nos. 597-600 (4)	4.15	4.15

Souvenir Sheet

New Year 1996 (Year of the Rat) — A140

Illustration reduced.

1996, May 17 Litho. *Perf. 12*

601	A140	$1 multicolored	1.50	1.50

Shells — A141

Designs: No. 602, Argonauta nodosa. No. 603, Janthina janthina. No. 604, Naticarius oncus. No. 605, Cypraea caputserpentis.

1996, July 2 Litho. *Perf. 14*

602	A141	45c multicolored	.75	.75
603	A141	45c multicolored	.75	.75
604	A141	45c multicolored	.75	.75
605	A141	45c multicolored	.75	.75
		Nos. 602-605 (4)	3.00	3.00

Tourism A142

1996, Sept. 17 Litho. *Perf. 13½x14*

606	A142	45c Shopping	.75	.75
607	A142	75c Bounty day	1.25	1.25
608	A142	$2.50 Horse riding	4.25	4.25
609	A142	$3.70 Working the ship	6.25	6.25
		Nos. 606-609 (4)	12.50	12.50

A143

A144

Christmas: Cow, star, Bible verse, and: No. 610, Nativity scene. No. 611, Boats, boathouses. 75c, House, trees. 85c, Flowers, fruits.

1996, Nov. 5 Litho. *Perf. 15*

610	A143	45c multicolored	.75	.75
611	A143	45c multicolored	.75	.75
612	A143	75c multicolored	1.25	1.25
613	A143	85c multicolored	1.40	1.40
		Nos. 610-613 (4)	4.15	4.15

1997, Jan. 22 Litho. *Roulette 7*

No. 614, Natl. Arms. No. 615, Natl. Seal.

614	A144	5c yellow & green	.15	.15
a.		Booklet pane of 10	.80	
615	A144	5c tan & brown	.15	.15
a.		Booklet pane of 10	.80	
		Complete booklet, 2 each #614a-615a	3.25	

Souvenir Sheet

Beef Cattle — A145

1997, Feb. 11 *Perf. 13½x13*

616	A145	$1.20 multicolored	2.00	2.00
a.		Inscribed in sheet margin	2.00	2.00

No. 616a is inscribed with Hong Kong '97 exhibition emblem.

Butterflies A146

Designs: 75c, Cepora perimale perimale. 90c, Danaus chrysippus petilia. $1, Danaus bamata bamata. $1.20, Danaus plexippus.

1997, Mar. 28 *Perf. 14½*

617	A146	75c multicolored	1.25	1.25
618	A146	90c multicolored	1.50	1.50
619	A146	$1 multicolored	1.65	1.65
620	A146	$1.20 multicolored	2.00	2.00
		Nos. 617-620 (4)	6.40	6.40

Dolphins — A147

1997, May 29 Litho. *Perf. 14*

621	A147	45c Dusky dolphin	.75	.75
622	A147	75c Common dolphin	1.25	1.25

Souvenir Sheet

623	A147	$1.05 Dolphin, diff.	1.75	1.75
a.		Inscribed in sheet margin	1.75	1.75

No. 623a is inscribed in sheet margin with PACIFIC 97 exhibition emblem.

First Norfolk Island Stamp, 50th Anniv. A148

Designs: $1, View of Ball Bay. $1.50, #4. $8, #12, view of Ball Bay.

1997, June 10 *Perf. 12*

624	A148	$1.00 multicolored	1.60	1.60
625	A148	$1.50 multicolored	2.40	2.40
a.		Pair, #624-625	4.00	4.00

Size: 90x45mm

626	A148	$8 multicolored	13.00	13.00

Queen Elizabeth II & Prince Philip, 50th Wedding Anniv. — A149

Designs: 20c, Queen. No. 628, Prince guiding 4-in-hand team. No. 629, Prince in formal suit, hat. 50c, Queen riding in royal coach.

$1.50, Younger picture of Queen, Prince riding in carriage.

1997, Aug. 12 Litho. *Perf. 14½*

627	A149	20c multicolored	.35	.35
628	A149	25c multicolored	.40	.40
a.		Pair, #627-628	.75	.75
629	A149	25c multicolored	.40	.40
630	A149	50c multicolored	.80	.80
a.		Pair, #629-630	1.20	1.20

Souvenir Sheet

631	A149	$1.50 multicolored	2.40	2.40

Souvenir Sheet

Return of Hong Kong to China — A150

1997, Sept. 16 Litho. *Perf. 14*

632	A150	45c Royal Yacht Britannia	.70	.70

Greetings Stamps — A151

1997 Litho. *Perf. 13x13½*

633	A151	45c Christmas	.70	.70
634	A151	75c New Year's Eve	1.15	1.15
635	A151	$1.20 Valentine's Day	1.80	1.80
		Nos. 633-635 (3)	3.65	3.65

Souvenir Sheet

Oriental Pearl TV Tower, Shanghai — A152

Illustration reduced.

1997, Nov. 18 *Perf. 14½*

636	A152	45c multicolored	.70	.70

Shanghai '97, Intl. Stamp & Coin Expo.

NORTH BORNEO

'nȯrth 'bȯr–nē–,ō

LOCATION — Northeast part of island of Borneo, Malay archipelago
GOVT. — British colony
AREA — 29,388 sq. mi.
POP. — 470,000 (est. 1962)
CAPITAL — Jesselton

The British North Borneo Company administered North Borneo, under a royal charter granted in 1881, until 1946 when it became a British colony. Labuan (q.v.) became part of the new colony. As "Sabah," North Borneo joined with Singapore, Sarawak and Malaya to form the Federation of Malaysia on Sept. 16, 1963.

100 Cents = 1 Dollar

Quantities of most North Borneo stamps through 1912 have been canceled to order with an oval of bars. Values given for used stamps beginning with No. 6 are for those with this form of cancellation. Stamps from No. 6 through Nos. 159 and J31 that do not exist CTO have used values in italics. Stamps with dated town cancellations sell for much higher prices.

Catalogue values for unused stamps in this country are for Never Hinged items, beginning with Scott 238.

North Borneo

Coat of Arms — A1

1883-84 Unwmk. Litho. *Perf. 12*

1	A1	2c brown	18.00	*45.00*
a.		Horiz. pair, imperf. btwn.		
2	A1	4c rose ('84)	27.50	*45.00*
3	A1	8c green ('84)	55.00	*50.00*
		Nos. 1-3 (3)	100.50	*140.00*

For surcharges see Nos. 4, 19-21.

No. 1 Surcharged in Black **EIGHT CENTS**

No.	Type	Description	Unused	Used
4	A1	8c on 2c brown	350.00	165.00
a.		Double surcharge		4,250.

Coat of Arms with Supporters
A4 A5

Perf. 14

No.	Type	Description	Unused	Used
6	A4	50c violet	80.00	12.50
7	A5	$1 red	45.00	9.00

1886 *Perf. 14*

No.	Type	Description	Unused	Used
8	A1	½c magenta	55.00	90.00
9	A1	1c orange	140.00	200.00
a.		Imperf., pair	275.00	
10	A1	2c brown	14.00	14.00
a.		Horiz. pair, imperf. between	425.00	
11	A1	4c rose	15.00	35.00
12	A1	8c green	16.00	35.00
a.		Horiz. pair, imperf. between	—	
13	A1	10c blue	17.00	35.00
a.		Imperf., pair	275.00	
		Nos. 8-13 (6)	257.00	409.00

Nos. 8, 11, 12 and 13 Surcharged or Overprinted in Black:

and Revenue
b

3 CENTS
c

3 CENTS
d

1886

No.	Type	Description	Unused	Used
14	A1 (b)	½c magenta	60.00	100.00
15	A1 (c)	3c on 4c rose	55.00	90.00
16	A1 (d)	3c on 4c rose	1,100.	
17	A1 (c)	5c on 8c green	60.00	70.00
a.		Inverted surcharge	2,250.	
18	A1 (b)	10c blue	100.00	175.00

On Nos. 2 and 3

Perf. 12

No.	Type	Description	Unused	Used
19	A1 (c)	3c on 4c rose	110.00	200.00
20	A1 (d)	3c on 4c rose	—	
a.		Double surcharge, both types of "3"		
21	A1 (c)	5c on 8c green	110.00	165.00

British North Borneo

A9

1886 Unwmk. Litho. *Perf. 12*

No.	Type	Description	Unused	Used
22	A9	½c lilac rose	100.00	250.00
23	A9	1c orange	82.50	110.00

Perf. 14

No.	Type	Description	Unused	Used
25	A9	½c rose	2.00	1.75
a.		½c lilac rose	10.00	
b.		Imperf., pair	12.00	4.00
26	A9	1c orange	1.65	1.00
a.		Imperf., pair	10.50	3.00
27	A9	2c brown	1.65	1.25
a.		Imperf., pair	5.50	3.00
b.		Horiz. pair, imperf. between	52.50	
28	A9	4c rose	1.65	.90
a.		Cliché of 1c in plate of 4c	165.00	250.00
b.		Imperf., pair	6.00	3.00
c.		As "a," imperf. in pair with #28	2,750.	
29	A9	8c green	3.25	3.50
a.		Imperf., pair	9.50	3.75
30	A9	10c blue	5.75	7.50
a.		Imperf., pair	9.50	5.75
		Nos. 25-30 (6)	15.95	15.90

For surcharges see Nos. 54-55.

A10

A11

A12

A13

No.	Type	Description	Unused	Used
31	A10	25c slate blue	85.00	7.75
a.		Imperf., pair	77.50	12.00
32	A11	50c violet	100.00	6.00
a.		Imperf., pair	70.00	8.50
33	A12	$1 red	150.00	7.25
a.		Imperf., pair	85.00	8.50
34	A13	$2 sage green	175.00	16.00
a.		Imperf., pair	100.00	15.00
		Nos. 31-34 (4)	510.00	37.00
		Nos. 22-34 (12)	708.45	412.90

See Nos. 44-47.

A14

1887-92 *Perf. 14*

No.	Type	Description	Unused	Used
35	A14	½c rose	.60	.25
a.		½c magenta	3.00	3.00
36	A14	1c orange	.80	.25
37	A14	2c red brown	1.50	.25
a.		Horiz. pair imperf. between		200.00
38	A14	3c violet	2.25	.25
39	A14	4c rose	3.00	.25
a.		Horiz. pair, imperf. vert.		
40	A14	5c slate	2.25	.25
41	A14	6c lake ('92)	5.50	.25
42	A14	8c green	8.25	.35
a.		Horiz. pair, imperf. between		
43	A14	10c blue	5.50	.35
		Nos. 35-43 (9)	29.65	2.45

Exist imperf. Value $7 each, unused, $4 used.
Forgeries exist, perf. 11½.

For surcharges see Nos. 52-53, 56-57.

Redrawn

25c. The letters of "BRITISH NORTH BORNEO" are 2mm high instead of 1½mm.

50c. The club of the native at left does not touch the frame. The 0's of "50" are flat at top and bottom instead of being oval.

$1.00. The spear of the native at right does not touch the frame. There are 14 pearls at each side of the frame instead of 13.

$2.00. "BRITISH" is 11mm long instead of 12mm. There are only six oars at the side of the dhow.

1888

No.	Type	Description	Unused	Used
44	A10	25c slate blue	21.00	.45
b.		Horiz. pair, imperf. between		
c.		Imperf., pair	80.00	2.75
45	A11	50c violet	40.00	.45
a.		Imperf., pair	85.00	3.50
46	A12	$1 red	22.50	.45
a.		Imperf., pair	85.00	3.50
47	A13	$2 sage green	70.00	1.25
a.		Imperf., pair	110.00	4.25
		Nos. 44-47 (4)	153.50	2.60

For surcharges see Nos. 50-51, 58.

A15

A16

1889

No.	Type	Description	Unused	Used
48	A15	$5 red violet	92.50	6.00
a.		Imperf., pair	140.00	12.00
49	A16	$10 brown	140.00	8.50
b.		Imperf., pair	250.00	21.00

Two Cents.
e

6 cents.
f

No. 44 Surcharged Type "e" in Red

1890

No.	Type	Description	Unused	Used
50	A10	2c on 25c slate blue	35.00	45.00
a.		Inverted surcharge	250.00	275.00
b.		With additional surcharge "2 cents" in black		
51	A10	8c on 25c slate blue	55.00	60.00

Surcharged Type "f" in Black On #42-43

1891-92

No.	Type	Description	Unused	Used
52	A14	6c on 8c green	9.00	9.00
a.		"c" of "cents" inverted	300.00	325.00
b.		"cetns"	325.00	400.00
c.		Inverted surcharge	200.00	275.00
53	A14	6c on 10c blue	85.00	9.50

On Nos. 29 and 30

No.	Type	Description	Unused	Used
54	A9	6c on 8c green	5,250.	4,500.
55	A9	6c on 10c blue	40.00	9.00
a.		Inverted surcharge	140.00	140.00
b.		Double surcharge	900.00	
c.		Triple surcharge	300.00	

Nos. 39, 40 and 44 Surcharged in Red:

1 cent.

8 Cents.

1892

No.	Type	Description	Unused	Used
56	A14	1c on 4c rose	8.00	12.00
a.		Double surcharge	325.00	
b.		Surcharged on face & back		400.00
57	A14	1c on 5c slate	3.00	4.75
58	A10	8c on 25c blue	90.00	125.00
		Nos. 56-58 (3)	101.00	141.75

North Borneo

Dyak Chief — A21

Malayan Sambar — A22

Malay Dhow — A26

Sago Palm — A23

Saltwater Crocodile — A27

Argus Pheasant — A24

Mt. Kinabalu — A28

Coat of Arms — A25

Coat of Arms with Supporters — A29

A30

A31

A32

A33

A34

NORTH BORNEO
BUYING, SELLING, APPRAISALS.
RARE AND CLASSIC STAMPS, POSTAL HISTORY, PROOFS.
For the Best Services in Classic Stamps and Postal History contact the RECOGNIZED LEADERS IN THE FIELD.
Excellent stock of classic material for most countries of the World also available.
THE CLASSIC COLLECTOR
LIANE & SERGIO SISMONDO
10035 Carousel Center Drive
Syracuse, NY 13290-0001
Ph. 315-422-2331, Fax 315-422-2956
CANADIAN OFFICE: P.O. Box 6277, Station J, Ottawa, Canada K2A 1T4. Ph. 613-722-1621, Fax: 613-728-7305

A35

Perf. 12 to 15 and Compound

1894 **Engr.** **Unwmk.**

59 A21 1c bis brown & blk 1.40 .40
a. Vert. pair, imperf. btwn.
60 A22 2c rose & black 4.00 .75
61 A23 3c vio & ol green 4.00 .55
a. Horiz. pair, imperf. btwn. 325.00
62 A24 5c org red & black 3.25 .75
a. Horiz. pair, imperf. btwn. 325.00
63 A25 6c brn ol & blk 3.00 .55
64 A26 8c lilac & black 2.50 .75
a. Vert. pair, imperf. btwn. 325.00 350.00
b. Horiz. pair, imperf. btwn. 325.00
65 A27 12c ultra & black 21.00 1.25
a. 12c blue & black 27.50 1.75
66 A28 18c green & black 15.00 1.75
67 A29 24c claret & blue 17.00 1.75

Litho. *Perf. 14*

68 A30 25c slate blue 15.00 .55
a. Imperf., pair 3.00
69 A31 50c violet 21.00 .60
a. Imperf., pair 3.00
70 A32 $1 red 9.50 .75
a. Perf. 14x11 175.00
b. Imperf., pair 6.00
71 A33 $2 gray green 18.00 .75
a. Imperf., pair 4.50
72 A34 $5 red violet 140.00 4.75
a. Imperf., pair 15.00
73 A35 $10 brown 150.00 6.00
a. Imperf., pair 15.00
Nos. 59-73 (15) 424.65 21.90

For #68-70 in other colors see Labuan #63a-65a.
For surcharges & overprints see #74-78, 91-94, 97-102, 115-119, 130-135, 115-119, 150-151, 158-159.

No. 70 Surcharged in Black

4 CENTS

1895, June

74 A32 4c on $1 red 2.75 1.25
a. Double surcharge 325.00
75 A32 10c on $1 red 6.50 .60
76 A32 20c on $1 red 21.00 .60
77 A32 30c on $1 red 14.00 .75
78 A32 40c on $1 red 15.00 .75
Nos. 74-78 (5) 59.25 3.95

See No. 99.

A37

A38

A39

A40

A41

A42

A43

"Postal Revenue"
A44 A45

Perf. 13 to 16 and Compound

1897-1900 **Engr.**

79 A37 1c bis brown & blk 5.00 .55
a. Horiz. pair, imperf. btwn. —
80 A38 2c dp rose & blk 10.00 .55
81 A38 2c green & blk ('00) 15.00 .55
82 A39 3c lilac & ol green 5.00 .55
83 A40 5c orange & black 22.50 .50
84 A41 6c ol brown & blk 15.00 .35
85 A42 8c brn lilac & blk 6.50 .50
86 A43 12c blue & black 80.00 .85
87 A44 18c green & black 12.50 .55
a. Vert. pair, imperf. btwn. 100.00
88 A45 24c claret & blue 11.00 .85
Nos. 79-88 (10) 182.50 5.80

For overprints see Nos. 105-107, 109-112. For surcharges see Nos. 124-127.

"Postage & Revenue"
A46 A47

1897

89 A46 18c green & black 50.00 .75
90 A47 24c claret & blue 40.00 .75

For surcharges & overprints see #95-96, 128-129, 113-114.

Stamps of 1894-97 Surcharged in Black

4 CENTS

1899

91 A40 4c on 5c orange & blk 18.00 14.00
92 A41 4c on 6c ol brn & blk 19.00 18.00
93 A42 4c on 8c brn lil & blk 16.00 13.00
94 A43 4c on 12c blue & blk 16.00 18.00
a. Horiz. or vert. pair, imperf. btwn. 425.00 500.00
95 A46 4c on 18c green & blk 11.00 18.00
96 A47 4c on 24c cl & blue 13.00 18.00
a. Perf. 16 42.50 50.00
97 A30 4c on 25c sl blue 6.00 14.00
98 A31 4c on 50c violet 7.00 18.00
99 A32 4c on $1 red 6.00 14.00
100 A33 4c on $2 gray grn 6.00 19.00
101 A34 4c on $5 red vio, "CENTS" 8½mm below "4" 5.50 18.00
a. Normal spacing 100.00 40.00
102 A35 4c on $10 brown, "CENTS" 8½mm below "4" 5.50 18.00
a. Normal spacing 90.00 40.00
Nos. 91-102 (12) 129.00 200.00

No. 99 differs from No. 74 in the distance between "4" and "cents" which is 4¾mm on No. 99 and 3¾mm on No. 74.

Orangutan — A48

1899-1900 **Engr.**

103 A48 4c green & black 6.25 3.25
104 A48 4c dp rose & blk ('00) 19.00 .55

For overprint see No. 108.

Stamps of 1894-1900 Overprinted in Red, Black, Green or Blue

BRITISH

m

PROTECTORATE.

1901-05

105 A37 1c bis brn & blk (R) 1.90 .25
106 A38 2c green & blk (R) 1.65 .25
107 A39 3c lilac & ol grn (Bk) 1.10 .35
108 A48 4c dp rose & blk (G) 2.25 .35
109 A40 5c org & blk (G) 2.25 .35
110 A41 6c ol brn & blk (R) 2.75 .35
111 A42 8c brown & blk (Bl) 4.00 .35
a. Vert. pair, imperf. btwn.
112 A43 12c blue & blk (R) 27.50 .65
113 A46 18c green & blk (R) 8.50 .65
114 A47 24c red & blue (Bk) 15.00 .65
115 A30 25c slate blue (R) 3.00 .45
a. Inverted overprint 425.00
116 A31 50c violet (R) 7.50 .50
117 A32 $1 red (R) 20.00 3.75
118 A32 $1 red (Bk) 10.00 2.75
a. Double overprint 325.00
119 A33 $2 gray green (R) 32.50 3.25
a. Double overprint 950.00
Nos. 105-119 (15) 139.90 14.90

Nos. 110, 111 and 122 are known without period after "PROTECTORATE."
See Nos. 122-123, 150-151.

Bruang (Sun Bear) — A49
Railroad Train — A50

1902 **Engr.**

120 A49 10c slate & dk brown 47.50 2.50
a. Vertical pair, imperf. between
121 A50 16c yel brown & grn 100.00 .90

Overprinted type "m" in Red or Black

122 A49 10c sl & dk brn (R) 21.00 .35
a. Double overprint 350.00 275.00
123 A50 16c yel brn & grn (Bk) 70.00 .45
Nos. 120-123 (4) 238.50 4.20

Stamps of 1894-97 Surcharged in Black

4 cents

1904

124 A40 4c on 5c org & blk 14.00 4.50
125 A41 4c on 6c ol brn & blk 4.25 3.00
a. Inverted surcharge 250.00
126 A42 4c on 8c brn lil & blk 9.50 3.25
a. Inverted surcharge 250.00
127 A43 4c on 12c blue & blk 14.00 3.75
128 A46 4c on 18c grn & blk 15.00 4.00
129 A47 4c on 24c cl & bl 14.00 4.00
130 A30 4c on 25c sl blue 4.50 3.75
131 A31 4c on 50c violet 4.50 3.75
132 A32 4c on $1 red 5.75 4.00
133 A33 4c on $2 gray grn 10.50 4.25
134 A34 4c on $5 red vio 11.00 4.50
135 A35 4c on $10 brown 11.00 4.50
a. Inverted surcharge 1,700.
Nos. 124-135 (12) 118.00 47.25

Malayan Tapir — A51

Traveler's Palm — A52

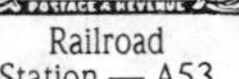
Railroad Station — A53

Meeting of the Assembly — A54

Elephant and Mahout A55

Sumatran Rhinoceros A56

Natives Plowing — A57

Wild Boar — A58

Palm Cockatoo A59

Rhinoceros Hornbill A60

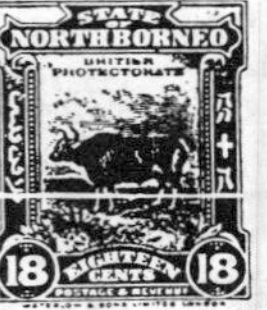
Banteng (Wild Ox)
A61 A62

Cassowary — A63

1909-22 **Unwmk.** **Engr.** *Perf. 14*

Center in Black

136 A51 1c chocolate 4.25 .15
b. Perf. 13½
c. Perf. 15 17.00 .40
137 A52 2c green .90 .15
b. Perf. 15 1.90 .20
138 A53 3c deep rose 2.25 .30
b. Perf. 15 .40
139 A53 3c green ('22) 6.50 .40
140 A54 4c dull red 1.75 .15
b. Perf. 13½ 11.00 10.50
c. Perf. 15 7.75 .40
141 A55 5c yellow brn 7.25 .30
b. Perf. 15
142 A56 6c olive green 5.50 .30
b. Perf. 15 42.50 1.00
143 A57 8c rose 2.25 .30
144 A58 10c blue 14.00 .30
b. Perf. 13½ 2.50
c. Perf. 15 32.50 6.50
145 A59 12c deep blue 20.00 .60
c. Perf. 15
146 A60 16c red brown 16.00 1.25
b. Perf. 13½ 20.00 6.50
147 A61 18c blue green 72.50 1.25
148 A62 20c on 18c bl grn (R) 5.50 .55
b. Perf. 15 150.00 75.00
149 A63 24c violet 22.50 1.50
Nos. 136-149 (14) 181.15 7.50

Issued: #139, 1922; others, July 1, 1909.
See #167-178. #136a-149a follow #162.
For surcharges and overprints see #160-162, 166, B1-B12, B14-B24, B31-B41.

Nos. 72-73 Overprinted type "m" in Red

1910

150 A34 $5 red violet 100.00 4.50
151 A35 $10 brown 92.50 6.75
a. Double overprint
b. Inverted overprint

A64

A65

1911 **Engr.** *Perf. 14*

Center in Black

152 A64 25c yellow green 4.00 1.00
a. Perf. 15 10.00
b. Imperf., pair 50.00
153 A64 50c slate blue 7.00 1.25
a. Perf. 15 24.00 8.50
b. Imperf., pair 67.50
154 A64 $1 brown 14.00 1.40
a. Perf. 15 32.50 6.75
c. Imperf., pair 67.50

155 A64 $2 dk violet 32.50 3.25
156 A65 $5 claret 57.50 20.00
a. Perf. 13½ *82.50*
b. Imperf., pair 100.00
157 A65 $10 vermilion 135.00 40.00
a. Imperf., pair 100.00
Nos. 152-157 (6) 250.00 *66.90*

See #179-184. #152c-153c follow #162.

For overprint and surcharges see Nos. B13, B25-B30, B42-B47.

Nos. 72-73 Overprinted in Red

BRITISH

PROTECTORATE

1912

158 A34 $5 red violet 800.00 9.25
159 A35 $10 brown 1,200. 9.25

Nos. 158 and 159 were prepared for use but not regularly issued.

Nos. 138, 142 and 145 Surcharged in Black or Red

2

cents

1916 **Center in Black** ***Perf. 14***

160 A53 2c on 3c dp rose 15.00 6.50
a. Inverted "S" 87.50 87.50
161 A56 4c on 6c ol grn (R) 13.00 6.50
a. Inverted "S" 100.00 100.00
162 A59 10c on 12c bl (R) 35.00 37.50
a. Inverted "S" 110.00 110.00
Nos. 160-162 (3) 63.00 50.50

Stamps and Types of 1909-11 Overprinted in Red or Blue in Three Lines: "MALAYA-BORNEO EXHIBITION 1922."

1922

Center in Black

136a A51 1c brown 5.50 *22.50*
137a A52 2c green 1.90 *13.00*
138a A53 3c deep rose (B) 4.75 *18.00*
140a A54 4c dull red (B) 2.50 *13.00*
141a A55 5c yel brown (B) 5.50 *22.50*
142a A56 6c olive green 4.75 *27.50*
143a A57 8c rose (B) 4.75 *27.50*
144a A58 10c gray blue 5.25 *35.00*
145a A59 12c deep blue 7.50 *45.00*
146a A60 16c red brown (B) 7.50 *50.00*
148a A62 20c on 18c bl grn 13.00 *57.50*
149a A63 24c violet 11.00 *55.00*
152c A64 25c yel green 11.00 *40.00*
153c A64 50c slate blue 9.50 *45.00*
Nos. 136a-153c (14) 94.40 *471.50*

Industrial fair, Singapore, Mar. 31-Apr. 15, 1922.

THREE

No. 140 Surcharged in Black

CENTS

1923

166 A54 3c on 4c dull red & blk 1.50 1.65
a. Double surcharge

Types of 1909-22 Issues

1926-28 **Engr.** ***Perf. 12½***

Center in Black

167 A51 1c chocolate .60 .50
168 A52 2c lake .40 .40
169 A53 3c green 1.25 .75
170 A54 4c dull red .40 .25
171 A55 5c yellow brown 3.50 3.50
172 A56 6c yellow green 3.75 .45
173 A57 8c rose 2.25 .30
174 A58 10c bright blue 1.90 .65
175 A59 12c deep blue 5.00 .65
176 A60 16c orange brn 12.50 *22.50*
177 A62 20c on 18c bl grn (R) 3.50 4.00
178 A63 24c dull violet 35.00 *50.00*
179 A64 25c yellow grn 5.50 5.50
180 A64 50c slate blue 8.50 *12.50*
181 A64 $1 brown 30.00 *75.00*
182 A64 $2 dark violet 50.00 *125.00*
183 A65 $5 deep rose 85.00 250.00
184 A65 $10 dull vermilion 200.00 350.00
Nos. 167-184 (18) 449.05 901.95

Murut — A66

Orangutan — A67

Dyak — A68

Mt. Kinabalu A69

Clouded Leopard A70

Arms with Supporters and Motto — A72

Coat of Arms — A71

Arms with Supporters — A73

1931, Jan. 1 **Engr.** ***Perf. 12½***

Center in Black

185 A66 3c blue green .65 *1.50*
186 A67 6c orange red 13.00 4.75
187 A68 10c carmine 2.75 6.25
188 A69 12c ultra 3.25 4.00
189 A70 25c deep violet 30.00 22.50
190 A71 $1 yellow green 18.00 30.00
191 A72 $2 red brown 40.00 37.50
192 A73 $5 red violet 110.00 *225.00*
Nos. 185-192 (8) 217.65 *331.50*

50th anniv. of the North Borneo Co.

Buffalo Transport — A74

Palm Cockatoo — A75

Murut — A76

Proboscis Monkey — A77

Bajaus — A78

Map of North Borneo and Surrounding Lands — A79

Orangutan — A80

Murut with Blowgun — A81

Dyak — A82

River Scene — A83

Proa — A84

Mt. Kinabalu — A85

Coat of Arms — A86

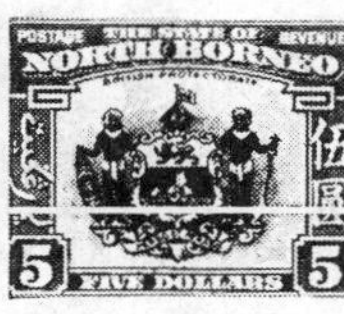

Arms with Supporters — A87

1939, Jan. 1 ***Perf. 12½***

193 A74 1c red brn & dk grn .40 .50
194 A75 2c Prus bl & red vio 2.25 .50
195 A76 3c dk grn & sl blue .90 .95
196 A77 4c rose vio & ol grn 1.25 .40
197 A78 6c dp cl & dk blue .90 1.90
198 A79 8c red 3.50 .65
199 A80 10c olive grn & vio 22.50 6.50
200 A81 12c ultra & grn 7.75 3.25
201 A82 15c bis brn & brt bl grn 9.00 3.25
202 A83 20c ind & rose vio 5.00 2.50
203 A84 25c dk brn & bl grn 6.50 4.50
204 A85 50c purple & brn 7.75 4.50
205 A86 $1 car & brown 40.00 16.00
206 A86 $2 ol grn & pur 55.00 70.00
207 A87 $5 blue & indigo 175.00 165.00
Nos. 193-207 (15) 337.70 280.40

For overprints see #208-237, N1-N15, N16-N31.

Nos. 193 to 207 Overprinted in Black

BMA

1945, Dec. 17 **Unwmk.** ***Perf. 12½***

208 A74 1c red brn & dk grn .35 .30
209 A75 2c Prus bl & red vio .40 .30
210 A76 3c dk grn & sl bl .35 .30
211 A77 4c rose vio & ol grn 14.00 8.00
212 A78 6c dp cl & dk bl .40 .35
213 A79 8c red .60 .55
214 A80 10c ol green & vio 1.75 1.00
215 A81 12c ultra & green .80 .65
216 A82 15c bis brn & brt bl grn 4.75 4.00
217 A83 20c ind & rose vio 1.40 1.10
218 A84 25c dk brn & bl grn 1.40 1.10
219 A85 50c purple & brn 2.75 2.25
220 A86 $1 carmine & brn 18.00 16.00
221 A86 $2 ol green & pur 18.00 16.00
a. Double overprint
222 A87 $5 blue & indigo 18.00 15.00
Nos. 208-222 (15) 82.95 66.90

"BMA" stands for British Military Administration.

Nos. 193 to 207 Overprinted in Black or Carmine With Bars

1947

223 A74 1c red brn & dk grn .15 .15
224 A75 2c Prus bl & red vio .30 .15
225 A76 3c dk grn & sl bl (C) .30 .15
226 A77 4c rose vio & ol grn .30 .15
227 A78 6c dp cl & dk bl (C) .30 .30
228 A79 8c red .30 .15
229 A80 10c olive grn & vio .50 .30
230 A81 12c ultra & grn .30 .30
231 A82 15c bis brn & brt bl grn .30 .30
232 A83 20c ind & rose vio .35 .35
233 A84 25c dk brn & bl grn .55 .55
234 A85 50c purple & brn .60 .60
235 A86 $1 carmine & brn .75 .75
236 A86 $2 ol green & pur 4.00 4.00
237 A87 $5 blue & ind (C) 6.75 6.75
Nos. 223-237 (15) 15.75 14.95

The bars obliterate "The State of" and "British Protectorate."

Catalogue values for unused stamps in this section, from this point to the end of the section, are for Never Hinged items.

Silver Wedding Issue

Common Design Types

Perf. 14x14½

1948, Nov. 1 **Wmk. 4** **Photo.**

238 CD304 8c scarlet .30 .20

Engraved; Name Typographed

Perf. 11½x11

239 CD305 $10 purple 13.00 *25.00*

Common Design Types pictured following the introduction.

UPU Issue

Common Design Types

Engr.; Name Typo. on 10c and 30c

1949, Oct. 10 ***Perf. 13½, 11x11½***

240 CD306 8c rose carmine .25 .20
241 CD307 10c chocolate .35 .30
242 CD308 30c deep orange 1.10 .85
243 CD309 55c blue 1.75 1.40
Nos. 240-243 (4) 3.45 2.75

Mount Kinabalu — A88

Coconut Grove — A89

Designs: 2c, Musician. 4c, Hemp drying. 5c, Cattle at Kota Belud. 8c, Map. 10c, Logging. 15c, Proa at Sandakan. 20c, Bajau Chief. 30c, Suluk Craft. 50c, Clock tower. $1, Bajau horsemen. $2, Murut with blowgun. $5, Net fishing. $10, Arms.

Perf. 13½x14½, 14½x13½

1950, July 1 **Photo.**

244 A88 1c red brown .20 .20
245 A88 2c blue .20 .20
246 A89 3c green .35 .35
247 A89 4c red violet .45 .45
248 A89 5c purple 2.25 2.25
249 A88 8c red 1.10 1.10
250 A88 10c violet brn .55 .55
251 A88 15c brt ultra .65 .65
252 A88 20c dk brown .90 .90
253 A89 30c brown 1.40 1.40
254 A89 50c cer *(Jessleton)* 1.40 1.40
255 A89 $1 red orange 2.00 2.25
256 A88 $2 dark green 5.50 6.00
257 A88 $5 emerald 14.00 14.00
258 A88 $10 gray blue 27.50 25.00
Nos. 244-258 (15) 58.45 56.70

Redrawn

1952, May 1 ***Perf. 14½x13½***

259 A89 50c cerise *(Jesselton)* .50 .50

Coronation Issue
Common Design Type

1953, June 3 Engr. *Perf. 13½x13*

260 CD312 10c carmine & black .35 .35

Types of 1950 with Portrait of Queen Elizabeth II

Perf. 13½x14½, 14½x13½

1954-57 Photo.

261 A88 1c red brown .15 .15
262 A88 2c brt blue ('56) .40 .20
263 A89 3c green ('57) .40 .20
264 A89 4c red violet ('55) .15 .15
265 A89 5c purple .25 .15
266 A88 8c red .15 .15
267 A88 10c violet brown .20 .15
268 A88 15c brt ultra ('55) .40 .15
269 A88 20c dk brown .60 .15
270 A89 30c brown .60 .20
271 A89 50c cerise ('56) .90 .30
272 A89 $1 red orange ('55) 2.25 .65
273 A88 $2 dk green ('55) 4.50 1.65
274 A88 $5 emerald ('57) 14.00 6.25
275 A88 $10 gray blue ('57) 27.50 11.00
Nos. 261-275 (15) 52.45 21.50

Issued: 10c, 3/1; 5c, 7/1; 20c, 30c, 8/3; 1c, 8c, 10/1; $1, 4/1/55; 4c, 15c, 5/16/55; $2, 10/1/55; 50c, 2/10/56; 2c, 6/1/56; 3c, $5, $10, 2/1/57.

In 1960, the 30c plate was remade, using a finer, smaller-dot (250) screen instead of the 200 screen. The background appears smoother. Value, $2.75 unused.

Borneo Railway, 1902 — A90 Comp. Arms — A91

15c, Proa (sailboat). 35c, Mount Kinabalu.

Perf. 13x13½, 13½x13

1956, Nov. 1 Engr. Wmk. 4

276 A90 10c rose car & blk .20 .20
277 A90 15c red brown & blk .30 .30
278 A90 35c green & blk .50 .50
279 A91 $1 slate & blk 1.25 1.25
Nos. 276-279 (4) 2.25 2.25

75th anniv. of the founding of the Chartered Company of North Borneo.

Malayan Sambar — A92 Orangutan — A93

Designs: 4c, Honey bear. 5c, Clouded leopard. 6c, Dusun woman with gong. 10c, Map of Borneo. 12c, Banteng (wild ox). 20c, Butterfly orchid. 25c, Rhinoceros. 30c, Murut with blowgun. 35c, Mount Kinabalu. 50c, Dusun with buffalo transport. 75c, Bajau horsemen. $2, Rhinoceros hornbill. $5, Crested wood partridge. $10, Coat of arms.

Perf. 13x12½, 12½x13

1961, Feb. 1 Wmk. 314 Engr.

280 A92 1c lt red brn & grn .15 .15
281 A92 4c orange & olive .20 .15
282 A92 5c violet & sepia .25 .15
283 A92 6c bluish grn & sl .25 .15
284 A92 10c rose red & lt grn .25 .15
285 A92 12c dull grn & brn .35 .35
286 A92 20c ultra & bl grn .50 .35
287 A92 25c rose red & gray .65 .60
288 A92 30c gray ol & sep .65 .45
289 A92 35c redsh brn & stl bl .80 .55
290 A92 50c brn org & bl grn .95 .60
291 A92 75c red vio & sl bl 1.25 .95
292 A93 $1 yel grn & brn 2.50 1.25
293 A93 $2 slate & brown 5.00 2.50
294 A93 $5 brn vio & grn 16.00 6.75
295 A93 $10 blue & car 32.50 18.00
Nos. 280-295 (16) 62.25 33.10

Freedom from Hunger Issue
Common Design Type

1963, June 4 Photo. *Perf. 14x14½*

296 CD314 12c ultramarine .90 .40

SEMI-POSTAL STAMPS

Nos. 136-138, 140-146, 148-149, 152 Overprinted in Carmine or Vermilion

1916 Unwmk. *Perf. 14*

Center in Black

B1 A51 1c chocolate 5.00 13.00
B2 A52 2c green 20.00 30.00
a. Perf. 15 27.50 37.50
B3 A53 3c deep rose 14.00 22.50
B4 A54 4c dull red 7.25 13.50
a. Perf. 15 80.00
B5 A55 5c yellow brown 30.00 26.00
B6 A56 6c olive green 22.50 32.50
a. Perf. 15
B7 A57 8c rose 14.00 26.00
B8 A58 10c brt blue 30.00 40.00
B9 A59 12c deep blue 30.00 42.50
B10 A60 16c red brown 30.00 42.50
B11 A62 20c on 18c bl grn 30.00 45.00
B12 A63 24c violet 47.50 50.00

Perf. 15

B13 A64 25c yellow green 450.00 475.00
Nos. B1-B13 (13) 730.25 858.50

All values exist with the vermilion overprint and all but the 4c with the carmine.

Of the total overprinting, a third was given to the National Philatelic War Fund Committee in London to be auctioned for the benefit of the wounded and veterans' survivors. The balance was lost en route from London to Sandakan when a submarine sank the ship. Very few were postally used.

Nos. 136-138, 140-146, 149, 152-157 Surcharged

RED CROSS
TWO CENTS

1918 *Perf. 14*

Center in Black

B14 A51 1c + 2c choc 3.25 7.00
B15 A52 2c + 2c green .70 7.00
B16 A53 3c + 2c deep rose 5.00 13.00
a. Perf. 15 25.00 60.00
B17 A54 4c + 2c dull red .50 4.00
a. Inverted surcharge 275.00
B18 A55 5c + 2c yellow brn 5.50 21.00
B19 A56 6c + 2c olive grn 4.50 15.00
a. Perf. 15 125.00
B20 A57 8c + 2c rose 4.50 6.00
B21 A58 10c + 2c brt blue 5.00 20.00
B22 A59 12c + 2c deep blue 12.50 35.00
a. Inverted surcharge 550.00
B23 A60 16c + 2c red brown 14.00 30.00
B24 A63 24c + 2c violet 15.00 30.00
B25 A64 25c + 2c yel grn 12.00 35.00
B26 A64 50c + 2c sl blue 14.00 35.00
B27 A64 $1 + 2c brown 35.00 45.00
B28 A64 $2 + 2c dk vio 50.00 85.00
B29 A65 $5 + 2c claret 240.00 325.00
B30 A65 $10 + 2c ver 240.00 325.00
Nos. B14-B30 (17) 661.45 1,038.

On Nos. B14-B24 the surcharge is 15mm high, on Nos. B25-B30 it is 19mm high.

Nos. 136-138, 140-146, 149, 152-157 Surcharged in Red

FOUR CENTS

1918

Center in Black

B31 A51 1c + 4c choc .40 4.00
B32 A52 2c + 4c green .60 6.00
B33 A53 3c + 4c dp rose .60 3.00
B34 A54 4c + 4c dull red .40 4.00
B35 A55 5c + 4c yellow brn 1.40 15.00
B36 A56 6c + 4c olive grn 1.40 10.00
a. Vert. pair, imperf. btwn. 900.00
B37 A57 8c + 4c rose 1.00 8.50
B38 A58 10c + 4c brt blue 3.25 10.00
B39 A59 12c + 4c dp blue 6.00 10.00
B40 A60 16c + 4c red brown 4.25 15.00
B41 A63 24c + 4c violet 4.25 17.50
B42 A64 25c + 4c yellow grn 5.00 40.00
B43 A64 50c + 4c sl blue 13.00 40.00
a. Perf. 15 50.00
B44 A64 $1 + 4c brown 15.00 50.00
a. Perf. 15 60.00
B45 A64 $2 + 4c dk vio 35.00 65.00
B46 A65 $5 + 4c claret 250.00 400.00
B47 A65 $10 + 4c ver 250.00 375.00
Nos. B31-B47 (17) 591.55 1,073.

POSTAGE DUE STAMPS

Regular Issues Overprinted POSTAGE DUE

Reading Up Vert. (V), or Horiz. (H)

1895, Aug. 1 Unwmk. *Perf. 14, 15*

On Nos. 60 to 67

J1 A22 2c rose & blk (V) 15.00 .95
J2 A23 3c vio & ol grn (V) 5.00 .80
J3 A24 5c org red & blk (V) 25.00 1.25
a. Period after "DUE" (V) 45.00
J4 A25 6c ol brn & blk (V) 12.00 1.50
J5 A26 8c lilac & blk (H) 32.50 2.00
a. Double ovpt. (H)
J6 A27 12c blue & blk (H) 60.00 1.50
a. Double overprint (H) 325.00
J7 A28 18c green & blk (V) 65.00 3.00
a. Ovpt. reading down 400.00 275.00
b. Overprinted horizontally 20.00 2.75
c. Same as "b" inverted 300.00 275.00
J8 A29 24c claret & bl (H) 60.00 1.65
Nos. J1-J8 (8) 274.50 12.65

On Nos. 80 and 85

1897

J9 A38 2c dp rose & blk (V) 6.00 .45
a. Overprinted horizontally 12.00 15.00
J10 A42 8c brn lil & blk (H) 40.00 40.00
a. Period after "DUE" 30.00 60.00

On Nos. 81-88 and 104
Vertically reading up

1901

J11 A38 2c green & blk 21.00 .55
a. Overprinted horizontally 27.50
J12 A39 3c lilac & ol grn 8.00 .35
a. Period after "DUE" 18.00 30.00
J13 A48 4c dp rose & blk 18.00 .45
J14 A40 5c orange & blk 21.00 .55
a. Period after "DUE" 30.00
J15 A41 6c olive brn & blk 3.50 .45
J16 A42 8c brown & blk 7.00 .45
a. Overprinted horizontally 30.00
b. Period after "DUE" (H) 60.00
J17 A43 12c blue & blk 65.00 .90
J18 A46 18c green & blk 35.00 .90
J19 A47 24c red & blue 17.50 .90
Nos. J11-J19 (9) 196.00 5.50

On Nos. 105-114, 122-123 Horizontally

1903-11 *Perf. 14*

J20 A37 1c bis brn & blk, period after "DUE" 13.00 13.00
a. Period omitted
J21 A38 2c green & blk 6.00 .25
a. Ovpt. vert., perf. 16 150.00
b. Perf 15 (ovpt. horiz.) 55.00 55.00
J22 A39 3c lilac & ol grn 6.00 .35
a. Ovpt. vert. 110.00 110.00
b. Perf. 15 (ovpt. horiz.) 95.00 17.00
J23 A48 4c dp rose & blk, perf. 15 4.50 .45
a. "Postage Due" double 110.00
b. Perf. 14 4.75 1.00
J24 A40 5c orange & blk 7.00 .45
a. Ovpt. vert., perf. 15 165.00 110.00
b. Perf. 13½ (ovpt. horiz.)
c. Perf. 15 (ovpt. horiz.) 13.00 10.00
J25 A41 6c olive brn & blk 7.25 .35
a. "Postage Due" double
b. "Postage Due" inverted 110.00
c. Perf. 16 25.00 25.00
J26 A42 8c brown & blk 14.00 .50
a. Overprint vertical 150.00 125.00
J27 A49 10c slate & brn 35.00 .90
J28 A43 12c blue & blk 10.50 .75
J29 A50 16c yel brn & grn 18.00 .90
J30 A46 18c green & blk 7.00 .60
a. "Postage Due" double 80.00
J31 A47 24c claret & blue 15.00 1.25
a. "Postage Due" double 125.00
b. Overprint vertical 85.00
Nos. J20-J31 (12) 143.25 19.75

On Nos. 137 and 139-146

1921-31 *Perf. 14, 15*

J32 A52 2c green & blk 11.00 60.00
a. Perf. 13½ 15.00 12.00
J33 A53 3c green & blk 5.25 20.00
J34 A54 4c dull red & blk 1.25 1.25
J35 A55 5c yel brn & blk 5.25 10.00
J36 A56 6c olive grn & blk 13.00 11.00
J37 A57 8c rose & blk 5.25 4.25
J38 A58 10c blue & blk 6.50 12.00
a. Perf. 15 47.50 60.00
J39 A59 12c dp vio & blk 8.50 25.00
J40 A60 16c red brn & blk 24.00 65.00
Nos. J32-J40 (9) 80.00 208.50

On Nos. 168 to 176

1926-28 *Perf. 12½*

J41 A52 2c lake & blk .45 2.00
J42 A53 3c green & blk 2.00 12.50
J43 A54 4c dull red & blk 3.25 1.00
J44 A55 5c yel brown & blk 5.75 50.00
J45 A56 6c yel green & blk 8.00 3.00
J46 A57 8c rose & black 7.00 8.50
J47 A58 10c brt blue & blk 9.00 50.00
J48 A59 12c dp blue & blk 16.00 85.00
J49 A60 16c org brn & blk 35.00 125.00
Nos. J41-J49 (9) 86.45 337.00

Crest of British North Borneo Company — D1

1939, Jan. 1 Engr. *Perf. 12½*

J50 D1 2c brown 3.75 25.00
J51 D1 4c carmine 4.75 32.50
J52 D1 6c dp rose violet 8.00 42.50
J53 D1 8c dk blue green 12.50 52.50
J54 D1 10c deep ultra 18.00 70.00
Nos. J50-J54 (5) 47.00 222.50

WAR TAX STAMPS

Nos. 193-194 Overprinted

WAR TAX
No. MR1

WAR TAX
No. MR2

1941, Feb. 24 Unwmk. *Perf. 12½*

MR1 A74 1c red brown & dk green .30 .30
MR2 A75 2c Prus blue & red violet .50 .55

For overprints see Nos. N15A-N15B.

OCCUPATION STAMPS

Issued under Japanese Occupation

Nos. 193-207 Handstamped in Violet or Black

大日本帝國政府

On Nos. N1-N15B, the violet overprint is attributed to Jesselton, the black to Sandakan. Nos. N1-N15 are generally found with violet overprint, Nos. N15A-N15B with black.

1942 Unwmk. *Perf. 12½*

N1 A74 1c 100.00 125.00
N2 A75 2c 95.00 125.00
N3 A76 3c 95.00 125.00
N4 A77 4c 50.00 95.00
N5 A78 6c 110.00 125.00
N6 A79 8c 95.00 125.00
N7 A80 10c 95.00 125.00
N8 A81 12c 120.00 190.00
N9 A82 15c 120.00 190.00
N10 A83 20c 200.00 250.00
N11 A84 25c 175.00 250.00
N12 A85 50c 275.00 300.00
N13 A86 $1 210.00 400.00
N14 A86 $2 275.00 550.00
N15 A87 $5 400.00 700.00
Nos. N1-N15 (15) 2,415. 3,670.

For overprints see Nos. N22a, N31a.

Same Overprint on Nos. MR1-MR2 in Black or Violet

1942

N15A A74 1c 575. 190.
N15B A75 2c 1,200. 250.

大日本
帝國郵便

Nos. 193 to 207 Overprinted in Black

オネルボ北

1944, Sept. 30 Unwmk. *Perf. 12½*

N16 A74 1c 3.50 6.25
N17 A75 2c 6.75 6.25
N18 A76 3c 2.50 3.50
N19 A77 4c 3.50 5.00
N20 A78 6c 3.25 3.50
N21 A79 8c 5.00 11.00
N22 A80 10c 6.00 9.00
a. On No. N7 150.00
N23 A81 12c 4.50 9.00
N24 A82 15c 3.50 9.00
N25 A83 20c 12.50 21.00
N26 A84 25c 12.50 21.00
N27 A85 50c 45.00 57.50
N28 A86 $1 72.50 95.00
Nos. N16-N28 (13) 181.00 257.00

Nos. 193 and 205 Surcharged in Black

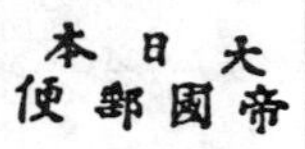

No. N30

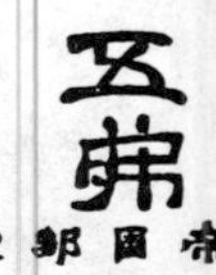

No. N31

1944, May

No.	Type	Description	Unused	Used
N30	A74	$2 on 1c	*3,750.*	*3,250.*
N31	A86	$5 on $1	3,800.	3,800.
a.		On No. N13	2,750.	2,750.

Mt. Kinabalu — OS1

Boat and Traveler's Palm — OS2

1943, Apr. 29 **Litho.**

No.	Type	Description	Unused	Used
N32	OS1	4c dull rose red	15.00	18.00
N33	OS2	8c dark blue	15.00	18.00

Aviator Saluting and Japanese Flag — A150

Miyajima Torii, Itsukushima Shrine — A96

Stamps of Japan, 1938-43, Overprinted in Black オネルボ北

1s, War factory girl. 2s, Gen. Maresuke Nogi. 3s, Power plant. 4s, Hyuga Monument and Mt. Fuji. 5s, Adm. Heihachiro Togo. 6s, Garambi Lighthouse, Formosa. 8s, Meiji Shrine, Tokyo. 10s, Palms and map of "Greater East Asia." 20s, Mt. Fuji and cherry blossoms. 25s, Horyu Temple, Nara. 50s, Golden Pavilion, Kyoto. 1y, Great Buddha, Kamakura. See Burma, Vol. 1, for illustrations of 2s, 3s, 5s, 8s, 20s and watermark. For others, see Japan.

Wmk. Curved Wavy Lines (257)

1944, Sept. 30 ***Perf. 13***

No.	Type	Description	Unused	Used
N34	A144	1s orange brown	5.25	12.00
N35	A84	2s vermilion	5.25	12.00
N36	A85	3s green	3.50	12.00
N37	A146	4s emerald	5.25	12.00
N38	A86	5s brown lake	6.25	13.00
N39	A88	6s orange	5.75	13.00
N40	A90	8s dk purple & pale vio	3.25	13.00
N41	A148	10s crim & dull rose	4.75	13.00
N42	A150	15s dull blue	4.75	13.00
N43	A94	20s ultra	100.00	200.00
N44	A95	25s brown	65.00	55.00
N45	A96	30s peacock blue	225.00	125.00
N46	A97	50s olive	70.00	55.00
N47	A98	1y lt brown	65.00	100.00
		Nos. N34-N47 (14)	569.00	648.00

The overprint translates "North Borneo."

NORTHERN NIGERIA

'nor-th̲ə(r)n nī-'jir-ē-ə

LOCATION — Western Africa
GOVT. — British Protectorate
AREA — 281,703 sq. mi.
POP. — 11,866,250
CAPITAL — Zungeru

In 1914 Northern Nigeria united with Southern Nigeria to form the Colony and Protectorate of Nigeria.

12 Pence = 1 Shilling
20 Shillings = 1 Pound

Victoria — A1

Edward VII — A2

Numerals of 5p and 6p, types A1 and A2, are in color on plain tablet.

Wmk. Crown and C A (2)

1900, Mar. **Typo.** ***Perf. 14***

No.	Type	Description	Unused	Used
1	A1	½p lilac & grn	.65	1.00
2	A1	1p lilac & rose	3.50	1.00
3	A1	2p lilac & yel	2.50	*18.00*
4	A1	2½p lilac & blue	2.50	*7.50*
5	A1	5p lilac & brn	6.75	*22.50*
6	A1	6p lilac & vio	9.75	*15.00*
7	A1	1sh green & blk	12.00	*37.50*
8	A1	2sh6p green & blue	55.00	*100.00*
9	A1	10sh green & brn	200.00	*275.00*
		Nos. 1-9 (9)	292.65	*477.50*

1902, July 1

No.	Type	Description	Unused	Used
10	A2	½p violet & green	1.00	.60
11	A2	1p violet & car rose	1.25	.25
12	A2	2p violet & org	1.25	*1.90*
13	A2	2½p violet & ultra	1.00	*4.25*
14	A2	5p violet & org brn	1.25	*4.00*
15	A2	6p violet & pur	3.00	*3.75*
16	A2	1sh green & black	2.25	*4.00*
17	A2	2sh6p green & ultra	6.50	*24.00*
18	A2	10sh green & brown	37.50	*40.00*
		Nos. 10-18 (9)	55.00	*82.75*

1904, Apr. **Wmk. 3**

No.	Type	Description	Unused	Used
18A	A2	£25 green & carmine	*27,500.*	

No. 18A was available for postage but probably was used only for fiscal purposes.

1905

No.	Type	Description	Unused	Used
19	A2	½p violet & grn	3.25	2.00
20	A2	1p violet & car rose	2.00	.20
21	A2	2p violet & org	6.50	*7.50*
22	A2	2½p violet & ultra	4.00	2.00
23	A2	5p violet & org brn	13.00	12.50
24	A2	6p violet & pur	14.00	10.50
25	A2	1sh green & black	15.00	*25.00*
26	A2	2sh6p green & ultra	24.00	22.00
		Nos. 19-26 (8)	81.75	*81.70*

All values exist on ordinary paper and all but the 2½p on chalky paper.

1910-11 **Ordinary Paper**

No.	Type	Description	Unused	Used
28	A2	½p green	1.00	.50
29	A2	1p carmine	.80	.30
30	A2	2p gray	1.25	2.00
31	A2	2½p ultra	.90	3.50

Chalky Paper

No.	Type	Description	Unused	Used
32	A2	3p violet, *yel*	2.75	.25
33	A2	5p vio & ol grn	2.50	4.25
34	A2	6p vio & red vio ('11)	1.25	4.50
a.		6p violet & deep violet	4.50	10.00
35	A2	1sh black, *green*	1.10	.55
36	A2	2sh6p blk & red, *bl*	8.00	16.00
37	A2	5sh grn & red, *yel*	17.50	47.50
38	A2	10sh grn & red, *grn*	37.50	40.00
		Nos. 28-38 (11)	74.55	119.35

George V — A3

For description of dies I and II see back of this section of the Catalogue.

Die I

1912 **Ordinary Paper**

No.	Type	Description	Unused	Used
40	A3	½p green	.55	.55
41	A3	1p carmine	.45	.15
42	A3	2p gray	1.00	1.25

Chalky Paper

No.	Type	Description	Unused	Used
43	A3	3p violet, *yel*	.75	.35
44	A3	4p blk & red, *yel*	.45	.45
45	A3	5p vio & ol grn	1.25	1.40
46	A3	6p vio & red vio	1.25	.70
47	A3	9p violet & scar	1.10	*2.50*
48	A3	1sh blk, *green*	1.75	1.00
49	A3	2sh6p blk & red, *bl*	6.50	*20.00*
50	A3	5sh grn & red, *yel*	17.50	*45.00*
51	A3	10sh grn & red, *grn*	37.50	*45.00*
52	A3	£1 vio & blk, *red*	150.00	100.00
		Nos. 40-52 (13)	220.05	*218.35*

Numerals of 3p, 4p, 5p and 6p, type A3, are in color on plain tablet.

Stamps of Northern Nigeria were replaced in 1914 by those of Nigeria.

NORTHERN RHODESIA

'nor-th̲ə(r)n rō-'dē-zh(ē-)ə

LOCATION — In southern Africa, east of Angola and separated from Southern Rhodesia by the Zambezi River.
GOVT. — British Protectorate
AREA — 287,640 sq. mi.
POP. — 2,550,000 (est. 1962)
CAPITAL — Lusaka

Prior to April 1, 1924, Northern Rhodesia was administered by the British South Africa Company. It joined the Federation of Rhodesia and Nyasaland in 1953 and used its stamps in 1954-63. It resumed issuing its own stamps in December, 1963, after the Federation was dissolved. On Oct. 24, 1964, Northern Rhodesia became the independent republic of Zambia. See Rhodesia, Southern Rhodesia, Rhodesia and Nyasaland, Zambia.

12 Pence = 1 Shilling
20 Shillings = 1 Pound

Catalogue values for unused stamps in this country are for Never Hinged items, beginning with Scott 46 in the regular postage section and Scott J5 in the postage due section.

King George V
A1 A2

1925-29 **Engr.** **Wmk. 4** ***Perf. 12½***

No.	Type	Description	Unused	Used
1	A1	½p dk green	.25	.15
2	A1	1p dk brown	.25	.15
3	A1	1½p carmine	.25	.20
4	A1	2p brown org	.60	.15
5	A1	3p ultra	.60	.50
6	A1	4p dk violet	.80	.50
7	A1	6p gray	.75	.35
8	A1	8p rose lilac	4.75	14.00
9	A1	10p olive grn	4.75	12.50
10	A2	1sh black & org	2.00	1.25
11	A2	2sh ultra & brn	8.50	10.50
12	A2	2sh6p green & blk	3.50	3.75
13	A2	3sh indigo & vio	12.00	9.00
14	A2	5sh dk vio & gray	11.00	9.50
15	A2	7sh6p blk & lil rose	80.00	*140.00*
16	A2	10sh black & green	30.00	32.50
17	A2	20sh rose lil & red	140.00	140.00
		Nos. 1-17 (17)	300.00	375.00

High values with revenue cancellations are inexpensive.

Issue dates: 3sh, 1929; others, Apr. 1.

Common Design Types pictured following the introduction.

Silver Jubilee Issue
Common Design Type

1935, May 6 ***Perf. 13½x14***

No.	Type	Description	Unused	Used
18	CD301	1p olive grn & ultra	.55	.50
19	CD301	2p indigo & grn	.95	.90
20	CD301	3p blue & brown	1.00	1.00
21	CD301	6p brt vio & indigo	4.00	4.00
		Nos. 18-21 (4)	6.50	6.40

Coronation Issue
Common Design Type

1937, May 12 ***Perf. 11x11½***

No.	Type	Description	Unused	Used
22	CD302	1½p dark carmine	.15	.15
23	CD302	2p yellow brown	.30	.30
24	CD302	3p deep ultra	.50	.50
		Nos. 22-24 (3)	.95	.95

King George VI — A3

1938-52 **Wmk. 4** ***Perf. 12½***

Size: 19x24mm

No.	Type	Description	Unused	Used
25	A3	½p green	.15	.15
26	A3	½p dk brown ('51)	.15	.40
a.		Perf. 12½x14	1.00	*2.00*
27	A3	1p dk brown	.25	.25
28	A3	1p green ('51)	.45	1.40
29	A3	1½p carmine	26.00	.25
a.		Horiz. pair, imperf. between	*12,500.*	
30	A3	1½p brown org ('41)	.25	.25
31	A3	2p brown org	40.00	1.40
32	A3	2p carmine ('41)	.25	.25
33	A3	2p rose lilac ('51)	.35	.25
34	A3	3p ultra	.25	.25
35	A3	3p red ('51)	.45	.35
36	A3	4p dk violet	.25	.35
37	A3	4½p dp blue ('52)	.35	*2.75*
38	A3	6p dark gray	.25	.25
39	A3	9p violet ('52)	.35	3.00

Size: 21½x26¾mm

No.	Type	Description	Unused	Used
40	A3	1sh blk & brn org	1.25	.40
41	A3	2sh6p green & blk	4.25	1.40
42	A3	3sh ind & dk vio	8.00	2.00
43	A3	5sh violet & gray	4.50	3.25
44	A3	10sh black & green	5.50	*11.00*
45	A3	20sh rose lil & red	20.00	*40.00*
		Nos. 25-45 (21)	113.25	*69.60*

Catalogue values for unused stamps in this section, from this point to the end of the section, are for Never Hinged items.

Peace Issue
Common Design Type

1946, Nov. 26 **Engr.** ***Perf. 13½x14***

No.	Type	Description	Unused	Used
46	CD303	1½p deep orange	.15	.15
a.		Perf. 13½	8.00	8.00
47	CD303	2p carmine	.25	.25

Silver Wedding Issue
Common Design Types

1948, Dec. 1 **Photo.** ***Perf. 14x14½***

No.	Type	Description	Unused	Used
48	CD304	1½p orange	.15	.15

Engr. ***Perf. 11½x11***

No.	Type	Description	Unused	Used
49	CD305	20sh rose brown	50.00	*57.50*

UPU Issue
Common Design Types
Engr.; Name Typo. on 3p, 6p
Perf. 13½, 11x11½

1949, Oct. 10 **Wmk. 4**

No.	Type	Description	Unused	Used
50	CD306	2p rose carmine	.25	.25
51	CD307	3p indigo	.40	.40
52	CD308	6p gray	.85	.85
53	CD309	1sh red orange	1.65	1.65
		Nos. 50-53 (4)	3.15	3.15

Victoria Falls and Railway Bridge, Cecil Rhodes and Elizabeth II — A4

1953, May 30 **Engr.** ***Perf. 12x11***

No.	Type	Description	Unused	Used
54	A4	½p brown	.15	.15
55	A4	1p green	.20	.15
56	A4	2p deep claret	.25	.15
57	A4	4½p deep blue	.75	.75
58	A4	1sh gray & orange	.95	.95
		Nos. 54-58 (5)	2.30	2.15

Cecil Rhodes (1853-1902).

Exhibition Seal — A5

1953, May 30 ***Perf. 14x13½***

No.	Type	Description	Unused	Used
59	A5	6p purple	.45	.45

Central African Rhodes Centenary Exhib.

Coronation Issue
Common Design Type

1953, June 2 ***Perf. 13½x13***

No.	Type	Description	Unused	Used
60	CD312	1½p orange & black	.35	.25

Elizabeth II A6

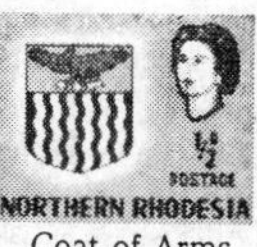

Coat of Arms A7

Perf. 12½x13½

1953, Sept. 15 **Engr.**

Size: 19x23mm

No.	Type	Description	Unused	Used
61	A6	½p dark brown	.25	.15
62	A6	1p green	.25	.15
63	A6	1½p brown orange	.25	.15
64	A6	2p rose lilac	.25	.15
65	A6	3p red	.25	.25
66	A6	4p dark violet	.35	.35
67	A6	4½p deep blue	.45	.45
68	A6	6p dark gray	.55	.55
69	A6	9p violet	.95	.95

Size: 21x27mm

No.	Type	Description	Unused	Used
70	A6	1sh black & brn org	1.10	1.10
71	A6	2sh6p green & blk	3.00	3.00
72	A6	5sh violet & gray	5.00	5.00

No.	Type	Description	Unused	Used
73	A6	10sh black & green	8.00	8.00
74	A6	20sh rose lilac & red	20.00	20.00
		Nos. 61-74 (14)	40.65	40.25

Perf. 14½

1963, Dec. 1 Unwmk. Photo.

Size: 23x19mm

Arms in Black, Blue and Orange

No.	Type	Description	Unused	Used
75	A7	½p violet & blk	.15	.15
a.		Value omitted	500.00	
76	A7	1p blue & blk	.15	.15
a.		Value omitted	11.50	
77	A7	2p brown & blk	.15	.15
78	A7	3p orange & blk	.15	.15
a.		Bklt. pane of 4	.85	
b.		Value omitted	90.00	
c.		Orange (eagle) omitted	*900.*	—
d.		Value and orange (eagle) omitted	125.00	
79	A7	4p green & blk	.15	.15
a.		Value omitted	80.00	
80	A7	6p yellow grn & blk	.15	.15
a.		Value omitted	350.00	
81	A7	9p ocher & blk	.30	.25
a.		Value omitted	300.00	
b.		Value and orange (eagle) omitted	250.00	
82	A7	1sh dk gray & blk	.25	.25
a.		Value omitted		
83	A7	1sh3p brt red lil & blk	.60	.55

Perf. 13

Size: 27x23mm

No.	Type	Description	Unused	Used
84	A7	2sh dp orange & blk	.70	.60
85	A7	2sh6p maroon & blk	.90	.90
86	A7	5sh dk car rose & blk	1.75	1.65
a.		Value omitted	*1,400.*	
87	A7	10sh brt pink & blk	3.50	3.00
88	A7	20sh dk blue & blk	8.75	8.00
a.		Value omitted	750.00	
		Nos. 75-88 (14)	17.65	16.10

Stamps of Northern Rhodesia were replaced by those of Zambia, starting Oct. 24, 1964.

POSTAGE DUE STAMPS

D1

D2

1929 Typo. Wmk. 4 *Perf. 14*

No.	Type	Description	Unused	Used
J1	D1	1p black	1.75	*3.50*
a.		Wmk. 4a (error)	110.00	
J2	D1	2p black	2.75	*6.50*
J3	D1	3p black	6.75	*22.50*
a.		Wmk. 4a (error)	150.00	
J4	D1	4p black	7.25	*25.00*
		Nos. J1-J4 (4)	18.50	*57.50*

Catalogue values for unused stamps in this section, from this point to the end of the section, are for Never Hinged items.

1964 Unwmk. Litho. *Perf. 12½*

No.	Type	Description	Unused	Used
J5	D2	1p orange	.50	*2.00*
J6	D2	2p dark blue	.80	*2.50*
J7	D2	3p rose claret	1.25	*3.00*
J8	D2	4p violet blue	1.75	*5.00*
J9	D2	6p purple	3.25	*7.50*
J10	D2	1sh emerald	4.25	*10.00*
		Nos. J5-J10 (6)	11.80	*30.00*

NORTH INGERMANLAND

'north 'iŋ-gər-mən-ˌland

LOCATION — In Northern Russia lying between the River Neva and Finland

CAPITAL — Kirjasalo

In 1920 the residents of this territory revolted from Russian rule and set up a provisional government. The new State existed only a short period as the revolution was quickly quelled by Soviet troops.

100 Pennia = 1 Markka

Arms — A1

Perf. 11½

1920, Mar. 21 Unwmk. Litho.

No.	Type	Description	Unused	Used
1	A1	5p green	2.25	2.50
2	A1	10p rose red	2.25	2.50
3	A1	25p bister	2.25	2.50
4	A1	50p dark blue	2.25	2.50
5	A1	1m car & black	35.00	40.00
6	A1	5m lilac & black	175.00	200.00
7	A1	10m brown & blk	250.00	400.00
		Nos. 1-7 (7)	469.00	650.00

Imperf., Pairs

No.	Type	Description	Unused	Used
1a	A1	5p	25.00	
2a	A1	10p	25.00	
3a	A1	25p	25.00	
4a	A1	50p	25.00	
5a	A1	1m	75.00	
6a	A1	5m	300.00	
7a	A1	10m	650.00	

Arms — A2

Peasant — A3

Plowing — A4

Milking — A5

Planting — A6

Ruins of Church — A7

Peasants Playing Zithers — A8

1920, Aug. 2

No.	Type	Description	Unused	Used
8	A2	10p gray grn & ultra	3.25	*6.00*
9	A3	30p buff & gray grn	3.25	*6.00*
10	A4	50p ultra & red brn	3.25	*6.00*
11	A5	80p claret & slate	3.25	*6.00*
12	A6	1m red & slate	22.50	*50.00*
13	A7	5m dk vio & dl rose	9.50	*20.00*
14	A8	10m brn & violet	9.50	*20.00*
a.		Center inverted	1,000.	
		Nos. 8-14 (7)	54.50	*114.00*

Counterfeits abound.

Nos. 8-14 exist imperf. Value for set in pairs, $200.

NORTH WEST PACIFIC ISLANDS

'north 'west pə-'si-fik 'ī-ləndz

LOCATION — Group of islands in the West Pacific Ocean including a part of New Guinea and adjacent islands of the Bismarck Archipelago

GOVT. — Australian military government

AREA — 96,160 sq. mi.

POP. — 636,563

Stamps of Australia were overprinted for use in the former German possessions of Nauru and German New Guinea which Australian troops had captured. Following the League of Nations' decision which placed these territories under mandate to Australia, these provisional issues were discontinued. See German New Guinea, New Britain, Nauru and New Guinea.

12 Pence = 1 Shilling

20 Shillings = 1 Pound

Stamps of Australia Overprinted

N. W. PACIFIC ISLANDS

There are two varieties of the letter "S" in the overprint: variety a, normal "S"; variety b, "S" with small head and long bottom stroke. Three combinations of these letters are found in the word "Islands": I, both are variety a; II, varieties b and a; III, both are variety b.

1915-16 Wmk. 8 *Perf. 12*

No.	Type	Description	Unused	Used
1	A1	2p gray	16.00	*30.00*
2	A1	2½p dark blue	2.50	*14.00*
3	A1	3p olive bister	16.00	*32.50*
4	A1	6p ultra	22.50	*42.50*
5	A1	9p violet	30.00	*50.00*
6	A1	1sh blue green	35.00	*50.00*
8	A1	5sh yel & gray ('16)	700.00	*850.00*
9	A1	10sh pink & gray	100.00	*140.00*
		Revenue cancel		27.50
10	A1	£1 ultra & brown	*750.00*	625.00
		Nos. 1-6,8-10 (9)	*1,672.*	*1,834.*

For surcharge see No. 39.

Wmk. Wide Crown and Narrow A (9)

Perf. 12, 14

No.	Type	Description	Unused	Used
11	A4	½p emerald	.90	*2.50*
a.		Double overprint		
12	A4	1p car (Die I)	2.00	1.50
a.		1p carmine rose (Die I)	5.00	5.00
b.		1p carmine (Die Ia)	125.00	125.00
13	A1	2p gray	10.00	*12.00*
14	A1	2½p dk bl ('16)	*7,000.*	*7,000.*
16	A4	4p orange	3.25	*9.00*
17	A4	5p org brown	1.50	*14.00*
18	A1	6p ultra	9.00	*11.00*
19	A1	9p violet	12.00	*14.00*
20	A1	1sh blue green	8.50	*21.00*
21	A1	2sh brown	70.00	90.00
22	A1	5sh yellow & gray	75.00	95.00
		Nos. 11-13,16-22 (10)	192.15	*270.00*

For description of the dies of No. 12 see Australia.

For surcharge see No. 40.

1915-19 Wmk. 10

No.	Type	Description	Unused	Used
27	A1	2p gray	4.50	*10.00*
28	A1	2½p dk bl ('19)	4.00	*14.00*
a.		"1" of fraction omitted	*5,500.*	*6,250.*
29	A1	3p ol bister	4.00	*10.00*
32	A1	6p ultra ('19)	4.75	*13.00*
33	A1	9p violet ('19)	9.50	*30.00*
34	A1	1sh bl grn ('18)	5.50	*26.00*
35	A1	2sh brown ('16)	25.00	*40.00*
36	A1	5sh yel & gray ('19)	55.00	55.00
37	A1	10sh pink & gray ('19)	150.00	175.00
38	A1	£1 ultra & brn ('16)	425.00	550.00
		Nos. 27-29,32-38 (10)	687.25	923.00

Nos. 6 and 17 Surcharged **One Penny**

1918, May 23 Wmk. 8 *Perf. 12*

No.	Type	Description	Unused	Used
39	A1	1p on 1sh bl grn	100.00	80.00

Wmk. 9 *Perf. 14*

No.	Type	Description	Unused	Used
40	A4	1p on 5p org brn	100.00	85.00

1919 Wmk. 11

No.	Type	Description	Unused	Used
41	A4	½p emerald	.65	3.00

1921-22 Wmk. 9

No.	Type	Description	Unused	Used
42	A4	1p violet ('22)	1.00	5.00
43	A4	2p orange	3.25	4.00
44	A4	2p red ('22)	5.00	7.50
45	A4	4p violet ('22)	26.00	*45.00*
46	A4	4p light ultra ('22)	10.00	45.00
		Nos. 42-46 (5)	45.25	*106.50*

North West Pacific Islands stamps were largely used in New Britain. Some were used in Nauru. They were intended to serve the Bismarck Archipelago and other places.

NORWAY

'nȯr-ˌwā

LOCATION — Western half of the Scandinavian Peninsula in northern Europe

GOVT. — Kingdom

AREA — 125,051 sq. mi.

POP. — 4,134,353 (1984)

CAPITAL — Oslo

120 Skilling = 1 Specie Daler

100 Ore = 1 Krone (1877)

Catalogue values for unused stamps in this country are for Never Hinged items, beginning with Scott 275 in the regular postage section, Scott B27 in the semi-postal section, and Scott O65 in the official section.

Watermarks

Wmk. 159- Lion

Wmk. 160- Post Horn

Coat of Arms — A1

King Oscar I — A2

1855 Typo. Wmk. 159 *Imperf.*

No.	Type	Description	Unused	Used
1	A1	4s blue	*6,000.*	125.
a.		Double foot on right hind leg of lion		2,600.

Only a few genuine unused copies of No. 1 exist. Copies often offered have had pen-markings removed. The unused catalogue value is for a copy without gum. Copies with original gum sell for much more.

No. 1 was reprinted in 1914 and 1924 unwatermarked. Lowest value reprint, $95.

Rouletted Reprints

1963: No. 1, value $25; Nos. 2-5, 15, value each $15.

1965: Nos. 57, 70a, 100, 152, J1, O1. Value each $10.

1969: Nos. 69, 92, 107, 114, 128, J12. Value each $10.

1856-57 Unwmk. *Perf. 13*

No.	Type	Description	Unused	Used
2	A2	2s yellow ('57)	500.00	150.00
3	A2	3s lilac ('57)	300.00	80.00
4	A2	4s blue	175.00	12.00
a.		Imperf.		*10,000.*
b.		Half used as 2s on cover		
5	A2	8s dull lake	1,000.	35.00
b.		Half used as 4s on cover		—

Nos. 2-5 were reprinted in 1914 and 1924, perf. 13½. Lowest valued reprint, $50 each.

No. 5b may not exist.

A3

A4

1863 Litho. *Perf. 14½x13½*

No.	Type	Description	Unused	Used
6	A3	2s yellow	700.00	190.00
7	A3	3s gray lilac	525.00	350.00
8	A3	4s blue	100.00	10.00
9	A3	8s rose	700.00	55.00
10	A3	24s brown	42.50	65.00
		Nos. 6-10 (5)	2,067.	670.00

There are four types of the 2, 3, 8 and 24 skilling and eight types of the 4 skilling. See note on used value of No. 10 following No. 21.

1867-68 Typo.

No.	Type	Description	Unused	Used
11	A4	1s black ('68)	85.00	47.50
12	A4	2s orange	25.00	22.50
b.		Vert. pair, imperf between	*1,750.*	
13	A4	3s dl lil ('68)	350.00	95.00
14	A4	4s blue	70.00	10.00

15 A4 8s car rose 350.00 45.00
a. 8s rose, clear impression 875.00 350.00
Nos. 11-15 (5) 880.00 220.00

See note on used value of #12 following #21.
For surcharges see Nos. 59-61, 149.
No. 15 was reprinted in 1914 and 1924, perf. 13½. Lowest valued reprint, $50.

Post Horn and Crown — A5

1872-75 **Wmk. 160**

16 A5 1s yel grn ('75) 9.50 10.00
a. 1s deep green ('73) 175.00 65.00
b. "E.EN" 25.00 55.00
d. Vert. pair, imperf between —
17 A5 2s ultra ('74) 13.00 22.50
a. 2s Prussian blue ('74) 11,000. 3,500.
b. 2s gray blue 10.00 200.00
18 A5 3s rose 60.00 11.00
a. 3s carmine 60.00 11.00
b. 3s carmine, *bluish* thin paper 190.00 25.00
19 A5 4s lilac ('73) 11.00 25.00
a. 4s dark violet, *bluish* thin paper 425.00 150.00
b. 4s brown violet, *bluish* thin paper ('73) 425.00 190.00
20 A5 6s org brn ('75) 425.00 50.00
21 A5 7s red brn ('73) 35.00 45.00
Nos. 16-21 (6) 553.50 163.50

In this issue there are 12 types each of Nos. 16, 17, 18 and 19; 15 types of No. 20 and 22 types of No. 21. The differences are in the words of value.
Used values of Nos. 10, 12, 16-17, 19 and 21 are for specimens canceled in later period, 1888-1908. Those canceled before 1888 are usually worth considerably more. These six stamps were used until Mar. 31, 1908.
No. 19 comes on thin and thick paper. Same value used. Unused, thick paper ten times given value.
For surcharges see Nos. 62-63.

Post Horn — A6

King Oscar II — A7

"NORGE" in Sans-serif Capitals, Ring of Post Horn Shaded

1877-78

22 A6 1o drab 6.50 6.50
23 A6 3o orange 85.00 27.50
24 A6 5o ultra 37.50 8.00
a. 5o dull blue 425.00 95.00
b. 5o bright blue 250.00 60.00
c. No period after "Postfrim" 57.50 13.00
d. Retouched plate 100.00 17.50
e. As "c," retouched plate 125.00 27.50
25 A6 10o rose 60.00 2.50
a. No period after "Postfrim" — —
b. Retouched plate 60.00 2.50
26 A6 12o lt green 90.00 15.00
27 A6 20o orange brn 275.00 12.00
28 A6 25o lilac 325.00 125.00
29 A6 35o bl grn ('78) 17.00 11.00
a. Retouched plate 250.00 110.00
30 A6 50o maroon 47.50 10.00
31 A6 60o dk bl ('78) 42.50 10.00
32 A7 1k gray grn & grn ('78) 25.00 8.50
33 A7 1.50k ultra & bl ('78) 55.00 35.00
34 A7 2k rose & mar ('78) 35.00 25.00
Nos. 22-34 (13) 1,101. 296.00

There are 6 types each of Nos. 22, 26 and 28 to 34; 12 types each of Nos. 23, 24, 25 and 27. The differences are in the numerals.
A 2nd plate of the 5o ultramarine has 100 types, the 10o, 200 types.
The retouch on 5o, 10o and 35o shows as a thin white line between crown and post horn.

Post Horn — A8

"NORGE" in Sans-serif Capitals, Ring of Horn Unshaded

1882-93 **Wmk. 160** ***Perf. 14½x13½***

35 A8 1o black brn ('86) 17.00 18.00
a. No period after "Postfrim" 60.00 60.00
b. Small "N" in "NORGE" 60.00 60.00
36 A8 1o gray ('93) 11.00 10.00
37 A8 2o brown ('90) 4.00 4.75
38 A8 3o yellow ('89) 70.00 8.00
a. 3o orange ('83) 110.00 17.50
b. Perf. 13½x12½ ('89) 2,500.
39 A8 5o bl grn ('89) 57.50 2.00
a. 5o gray green ('86) 75.00 3.00
b. 5o emerald ('88) 175.00 7.50
c. 5o yellow green ('91) 60.00 3.50
d. Perf. 13½x12½ ('92) 1,750. 950.00
40 A8 10o rose 70.00 1.25
a. 10o rose red ('86) 50.00 1.25
b. 10o carmine ('91) 55.00 1.25
c. As "b," imperf., pair 3,250.
41 A8 12o green ('84) 1,200. 350.00
42 A8 12o yellow brn ('84) 30.00 22.50
a. 12o bister brown ('83) 50.00 40.00
43 A8 20o brown 110.00 16.00
44 A8 20o blue ('86) 75.00 1.75
a. 20o ultramarine ('83) 350.00 22.50
b. No period after "Postfrim" ('85) 425.00 15.00
c. As "a," imperf., pair 3,250.
45 A8 25o dull vio ('84) 16.00 13.00

Dies vary from 20 to 21mm high. Numerous types exist due to different production methods, including separate handmade dies for value figures. Many shades exist.

No. 42 and 42a Surcharged in Black **2 Øre.**

1888 ***Perf. 14½x13½***

46 A8 2o on 12o yel brn 2.00 3.00
a. 2o on 12o bister brown 3.50 3.75

Post Horn — A10

"NORGE" in Roman instead of Sans-serif capitals

Perf. 14½x13½

1893-1908 **Wmk. 160**

Size: 16x20mm

47 A10 1o gray ('99) 3.00 1.75
48 A10 2o pale brn ('99) 3.00 1.75
49 A10 3o orange yel 2.00 .90
50 A10 5o dp green ('98) 6.25 .45
b. Booklet pane of 6
51 A10 10o car rose ('98) 12.50 .45
b. Booklet pane of 6
52 A10 15o brown ('08) 50.00 7.00
53 A10 20o dp ultra 27.50 .40
b. Booklet pane of 6
54 A10 25o red vio ('01) 55.00 3.00
55 A10 30o sl gray ('07) 50.00 3.75
56 A10 35o dk bl grn ('98) 12.50 6.50
57 A10 50o maroon ('94) 55.00 2.25
58 A10 60o dk blue ('00) 62.50 15.00
Nos. 47-58 (12) 339.25 43.20

Two dies exist of each except 2, 25 and 60o.
See Nos. 74-95, 162-166, 187-191, 193, 307-309, 325-326, 416-419, 606, 709-714, 960-968, 1141-1145.
For overprints and surcharge see Nos. 99, 207-211, 220-224, 226, 329.

1893-98 **Wmk. 160** ***Perf. 13½x12½***

47a A10 1o gray ('95) 17.50 17.50
49a A10 3o orange ('95) 40.00 7.00
50a A10 5o green 27.50 1.25
51a A10 10o carmine ('95) 25.00 1.25
c. 10o rose 50.00 1.25
53a A10 20o dull ultra ('95) 95.00 4.25
54a A10 25o red violet ('98) 82.50 25.00
56a A10 35o dark blue green ('95) 82.50 25.00
57a A10 50o maroon ('97) 165.00 17.50
Nos. 47a-57a (8) 535.00 98.75

No. 12 Surcharged in Green, Blue or Carmine **Kr. 1.00**

1905 **Unwmk.** ***Perf. 14½x13½***

59 A4 1k on 2s org (G) 40.00 20.00
60 A4 1.50k on 2s org (Bl) 65.00 42.50
61 A4 2k on 2s org (C) 67.50 37.50
Nos. 59-61 (3) 172.50 100.00

Used values are for copies canceled after 1910. Stamps used before that sell for twice as much.

Nos. 19 and 21 Surcharged in Black **30 ØRE**

1906-08 **Wmk. 160** ***Perf. 14½x13½***

62 A5 15o on 4s lilac ('08) 4.25 2.50
a. 15o on 4s violet ('08) 12.50 6.25
63 A5 30o on 7s red brown 8.00 4.50

Used values are for copies canceled after 1914. Stamps used before that sell for twice as much.

King Haakon VII — A11

Die A - Background of ruled lines. The coils at the sides are ornamented with fine cross-lines and small dots. Stamps 20¼mm high.
Die B - Background of ruled lines. The coils are ornamented with large white dots and dashes. Stamps 21¼mm high.
Die C - Solid background. The coils are without ornamental marks. Stamps 20¾mm high.

1907 **Typo.** ***Perf. 14½x13½***

Die A

64 A11 1k yellow grn 40.00 17.50
65 A11 1.50k ultra 75.00 40.00
66 A11 2k rose 125.00 62.50
Nos. 64-66 (3) 240.00 120.00

Used values are for copies canceled after 1910. Stamps used before that sell for twice as much.

1909-10

Die B

67 A11 1k green 175.00 55.00
68 A11 1.50k ultra 165.00 175.00
69 A11 2k rose 165.00 3.25
Nos. 67-69 (3) 505.00 233.25

Used values are for copies canceled after 1914. Stamps used before that sell for twice as much.

1911-18

Die C

70 A11 1k light green .70 .15
a. 1k dark green 75.00 3.00
71 A11 1.50k ultra 2.50 .15
72 A11 2k rose ('15) 3.00 .15
73 A11 5k dk violet ('18) 5.50 2.50
Nos. 70-73 (4) 11.70 2.95

See note following No. 180.

Post Horn Type Redrawn

Original Redrawn

In the redrawn stamps the white ring of the post horn is continuous instead of being broken by, a spot of color below the crown. On the 3 and 30 ore the top of the figure "3" in the oval band is rounded instead of flattened.

1910-29 ***Perf. 14½x13½***

74 A10 1o pale olive .40 .20
75 A10 2o pale brown .40 .20
76 A10 3o orange .40 .20
77 A10 5o green 3.50 .15
a. Booklet pane of 6 80.00
78 A10 5o magenta ('22) .80 .15
79 A10 7o green ('29) .80 .15
80 A10 10o car rose 4.50 .15
a. Booklet pane of 6 100.00
81 A10 10o green ('22) 6.00 .20
82 A10 12o purple ('17) .80 .50
83 A10 15o brown 5.00 .15
a. Booklet pane of 6 40.00
84 A10 15o indigo ('20) 5.00 .20
85 A10 20o deep ultra 6.50 .15
a. Booklet pane of 6 150.00
86 A10 20o ol grn ('21) 7.00 .20
87 A10 25o red lilac 30.00 .20
88 A10 25o car rose ('22) 7.00 .80
89 A10 30o slate gray 8.00 .25
90 A10 30o lt blue ('27) 10.00 3.00
91 A10 35o dk olive ('20) 10.00 .30
92 A10 40o ol grn ('17) 4.00 .30
93 A10 40o dp ultra ('22) 27.50 .30

NORWAY
STAMP BOOKLETS AND PAIRS
Now Also Available!

Excellent Stock of other
Scandinavian Stamps
Want lists welcome
... or send for our 142 page, illustrated, Wholesale Price List for only a U.S. 5 dollar bill to cover airmail charges.
• Satisfaction Guaranteed •
Rolf Gummesson AB
(Since 1939)
Kungsgatan 55
111 22 Stockholm, Sweden
We accept VISA, MasterCard. Euro Card and American Express
ASDA member since 1948.
BUY NOW AND TAKE ADVANTAGE OF THE LOW VALUE OF THE SWEDISH CURRENCY!

94 A10 50o claret 21.00 .30
95 A10 60o deep blue 27.50 .30
Nos. 74-95 (22) 186.10 8.35

Constitutional Assembly of 1814 — A12

1914, May 10 **Engr.** ***Perf. 13½***

96 A12 5o green .85 .50
97 A12 10o car rose 1.75 .50
98 A12 20o deep blue 8.50 3.50
Nos. 96-98 (3) 11.10 4.50

Norway's Constitution of May 17, 1814.

Norway
"Scandinavia exclusively since 1975"

Official Yearsets		Packets	
1994	$42.20	100 diff	$2.90
1995	47.00	400 diff	24.50
1996	45.00	600 diff	75.40
1997	45.90	800 diff	198.50

Check or VISA/MasterCard accepted plus $1.75 p&h
FREE PRICE LISTS of all Scandinavian countries... including Yearsets 1945 to date, booklets, souvenir sheets, varieties, back-of-book and rarities. Write today.
Call Toll Free 1-800-950-0058, email:northstamp@aol.com
Visit our website for monthly specials
www.northstamp.com

NORTHLAND CO. Box 34 VERONA, NJ 07044

No. 87 Surcharged **5 ØRE**

1922, Mar. 1 *Perf. 14½x13½*

99 A10 5o on 25o red lilac .40 .40

Lion Rampant A13

Polar Bear and Airplane A14

"NORGE" in Roman capitals, Line below "Ore"

1922-24 Typo. *Perf. 14½x13½*

100 A13 10o dp grn ('24) 9.00 .30
101 A13 20o dp vio 15.00 .15
102 A13 25o scarlet ('24) 30.00 .60
103 A13 45o blue ('24) 1.00 .55
Nos. 100-103 (4) 55.00 1.60

For surcharge see No. 129.

1925, Apr. 1

104 A14 2o yellow brn 2.50 2.75
105 A14 3o orange 3.50 3.50
106 A14 5o magenta 7.25 7.25
107 A14 10o yellow grn 8.00 8.00
108 A14 15o dark blue 8.00 8.00
109 A14 20o plum 16.00 16.00
110 A14 25o scarlet 3.25 3.25
Nos. 104-110 (7) 48.50 48.75
Set, never hinged 100.00

Issued to help finance Roald Amundsen's attempted flight to the North Pole.

A15

A16

1925, Aug. 19

111 A15 10o yellow green 5.00 6.00
112 A15 15o indigo 4.25 5.00
113 A15 20o plum 4.75 1.75
114 A15 45o dark blue 4.75 5.50
Nos. 111-114 (4) 18.75 18.25
Set, never hinged 62.50

Annexation of Spitsbergen (Svalbard).
For surcharge see No. 130.

"NORGE" in Sans-serif Capitals, No Line below "Ore"

1926-34 **Wmk. 160**

Size: 16x19½mm

115 A16 10o yel grn .70 .15
116 A16 14o dp org ('29) 2.25 1.50
117 A16 15o olive gray .85 .15
118 A16 20o plum 22.50 .15
119 A16 20o scar ('27) 2.00 .15
a. Booklet pane of 6 80.00
120 A16 25o red 12.00 1.75
121 A16 25o org brn ('27) 1.25 .20
122 A16 30o dull bl ('28) 1.25 .20
123 A16 35o ol brn ('27) 52.50 .20
124 A16 35o red vio ('34) 2.00 .20
125 A16 40o dull blue 3.25 .90
126 A16 40o slate ('27) 2.00 .20
127 A16 50o claret ('27) 2.00 .20
128 A16 60o Prus bl ('27) 2.00 .20
Nos. 115-128 (14) 106.55 6.15
Set, never hinged 375.00

See Nos. 167-176, 192, 194-202A. For overprints and surcharges see Nos. 131, 212-219, 225, 227-234, 237-238, 302-303.

Nos. 103 and 114 Surcharged **30 ≡**

1927, June 13

129 A13 30o on 45o blue 11.00 1.50
130 A15 30o on 45o dk blue 3.75 4.50
Set, never hinged 45.00

No. 120 Surcharged **20 ≡**

1928

131 A16 20o on 25o red 1.50 .95
Never hinged 7.00

See Nos. 302-303.

Henrik Ibsen — A17

Niels Henrik Abel — A18

1928, Mar. 20 **Litho.**

132 A17 10o yellow grn 5.75 2.50
133 A17 15o chnt brown 2.75 2.50
134 A17 20o carmine 2.75 .45
135 A17 30o dp ultra 4.00 4.00
Nos. 132-135 (4) 15.25 9.45
Set, never hinged 45.00

Ibsen (1828-1906), dramatist.

Postage Due Stamps of 1889-1923 Overprinted

Post Frimerke — a
POST — b

1929, Jan.

136 D1 (a) 1o gray .40 .30
137 D1 (a) 4o lilac rose .40 .30
138 D1 (a) 10o green 2.25 1.50
139 D1 (b) 15o brown 3.00 2.00
140 D1 (b) 20o dull vio 1.25 .50
141 D1 (b) 40o deep ultra 1.90 .50
142 D1 (b) 50o maroon 8.50 6.25
143 D1 (a) 100o orange yel 3.00 1.50
144 D1 (b) 200o dk violet 5.00 3.00
Nos. 136-144 (9) 25.70 15.85
Set, never hinged 45.00

1929, Apr. 6 Litho. *Perf. 14½x13½*

145 A18 10o green 1.75 .70
146 A18 15o red brown 1.90 1.65
147 A18 20o rose red 1.25 .35
148 A18 30o deep ultra 2.25 1.75
Nos. 145-148 (4) 7.15 4.45
Set, never hinged 25.00

Abel (1802-1829), mathematician.

No. 12 Surcharged **14 ØRE 14**

Perf. 14½x13½

1929, July 1 **Unwmk.**

149 A4 14o on 2s orange 2.25 2.25
Never hinged 5.00

Saint Olaf A19

Trondheim Cathedral A20

Death of Olaf in Battle of Stiklestad A21

Typo.; Litho. (15o)
Perf. 14½x13½

1930, Apr. 1 **Wmk. 160**

150 A19 10o yellow grn 7.50 .35
151 A20 15o brn & blk 1.00 .45
152 A19 20o scarlet 1.00 .30

Engr.
Perf. 13½

153 A21 30o deep blue 3.75 4.00
Nos. 150-153 (4) 13.25 5.10
Set, never hinged 40.00

King Olaf Haraldsson (995-1030), patron saint of Norway.

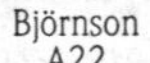

Björnson A22

Holberg A23

1932, Dec. 8 *Perf. 14½x13½*

154 A22 10o yellow grn 8.00 .40
155 A22 15o black brn 1.50 .90
156 A22 20o rose red 1.00 .30
157 A22 30o ultra 2.50 2.25
Nos. 154-157 (4) 13.00 3.85
Set, never hinged 32.50

Björnstjerne Björnson (1832-1910), novelist, poet and dramatist.

1934, Nov. 23

158 A23 10o yellow grn 1.50 .35
159 A23 15o brown .75 .60
160 A23 20o rose red 12.00 .25
161 A23 30o ultra 3.25 2.25
Nos. 158-161 (4) 17.50 3.45
Set, never hinged 50.00

Ludvig Holberg (1684-1754), Danish man of letters.

Types of 1893-1900, 1926-34
Second Redrawing
Perf. 13x13½

1937 **Wmk. 160** **Photo.**

Size: 17x21mm

162 A10 1o olive .70 .50
163 A10 2o yellow brn .70 .50
164 A10 3o deep orange 1.75 1.40
165 A10 5o rose lilac .55 .15
a. Booklet pane of 6 55.00
166 A10 7o brt green .70 .20
167 A16 10o brt green .45 .15
a. Booklet pane of 6 50.00
168 A16 14o dp orange 1.90 1.65
169 A16 15o olive bis 1.10 .15
170 A16 20o scarlet 1.10 .15
a. Booklet pane of 6 50.00
171 A16 25o dk org brn 5.50 .25
172 A16 30o ultra 2.50 .25
173 A16 35o brt vio 2.50 .25
174 A16 40o dk slate grn 3.00 .25
175 A16 50o deep claret 3.50 .40
176 A16 60o Prussian bl 1.50 .20
Nos. 162-176 (15) 27.45 6.45
Set, never hinged 90.00

Nos. 162 to 166 have a solid background inside oval. Nos. 74, 75, 76, 78, 79 have background of vertical lines.

King Haakon VII — A24

1937-38

177 A24 1k dark green .15 .15
178 A24 1.50k sapphire ('38) .65 .70
179 A24 2k rose red ('38) .65 .70
180 A24 5k dl vio ('38) 5.00 5.75
Nos. 177-180 (4) 6.45 7.30
Set, never hinged 11.00

Nos. 70-73, 177-180, 267, B19, B32-B34 and B38-B41 were demonetized from May 15, 1945 until Sept. 1, 1981. Used values are for stamps canceled after this period. Stamps with dated cancellations prior to May 15, 1945 sell for more. False cancellations exist.

Reindeer — A25

Borgund Church — A26

Jolster in Sunnfiord A27

Perf. 13x13½, 13½x13

1938, Apr. 20 **Wmk. 160**

181 A25 15o olive brn .60 .45
182 A26 20o copper red 4.00 .55
183 A27 30o brt ultra 3.75 1.65
Nos. 181-183 (3) 8.35 2.65
Set, never hinged 20.00

1939 **Unwmk.**

184 A25 15o olive brn .45 .25
185 A26 20o copper red .60 .20
186 A27 30o brt ultra .60 .35
Nos. 184-186 (3) 1.65 .80
Set, never hinged 2.75

Types of 1937
Perf. 13x13½

1940-49 **Unwmk.** **Photo.**

Size: 17x21mm

187 A10 1o olive grn ('41) .15 .15
188 A10 2o yellow brn ('41) .15 .15
189 A10 3o dp orange ('41) .15 .15
190 A10 5o rose lilac ('41) .35 .15
a. Booklet pane of 6, vert. 20.00
b. Booklet pane of 10, horiz. 8.00
191 A10 7o brt green ('41) .40 .15
192 A16 10o brt green .35 .15
a. Booklet pane of 6, vert. 24.00
b. Booklet pane of 10, horiz. 20.00
193 A10 12o brt vio .80 1.10
194 A16 14o dp org ('41) 1.00 2.00
195 A16 15o olive bister .50 .15
a. Booklet pane of 10 40.00
196 A16 20o red .45 .15
a. Booklet pane of 6, vert. 24.00
b. Booklet pane of 10, horiz. 25.00
197 A16 25o dk org brn 1.25 .15
197A A16 25o scarlet ('46) .40 .15
b. Booklet pane of 10 24.00
198 A16 30o brt ultra ('41) 1.25 .20
198A A16 30o gray ('49) 5.75 .15
199 A16 35o brt vio ('41) 1.50 .15
200 A16 40o dk sl grn ('41) 1.00 .15
200A A16 40o dp ultra ('46) 1.50 .15
201 A16 50o dp claret ('41) 1.00 .15
201A A16 55o dp org ('46) 15.00 .15
202 A16 60o Prus bl ('41) 1.00 .15
202A A16 80o dk org brn ('46) 12.50 .15
Nos. 187-202A (21) 46.45
Set, never hinged 125.00
Set value 4.90

Lion Rampant — A28

Norway
and Scandinavia
• Free Catalog • Stamps
• Postal History • Literature
• Want Lists Filled • Albums
• New Issue Service

CALL TOLL FREE
1-800-447-8267
(U.S. and CANADA)
or 336-376-9991
FAX 336-376-6750

Jay Smith
P.O. Box 650-X721
Snow Camp, NC 27349
email:info-x721@jaysmith.com

• The Scandinavia Specialist Since 1973 •

1940 Unwmk. Photo. *Perf. 13x13½*

No.	Type	Denomination / Color	Unused	Used
203	A28	1k brt green	.80	.15
204	A28	1½k deep blue	1.10	.30
205	A28	2k bright red	1.25	.90
206	A28	5k dull purple	3.00	2.50
		Nos. 203-206 (4)	6.15	3.85
		Set, never hinged	12.00	

For overprints see Nos. 235-236.

Stamps of 1937-41, Types A10, A16, A28, Overprinted "V" in Black and:

Lion Rampant with "V" — A29

1941 Wmk. 160 *Perf. 13x13½*

No.	Type	Denomination / Color	Unused	Used
207	A10	1o olive	.40	5.25
208	A10	2o yellow brn	.40	5.00
209	A10	3o orange	2.00	12.00
210	A10	5o rose lilac	.50	1.40
211	A10	7o brt green	.50	3.50
212	A16	10o brt green	7.50	30.00
213	A16	14o dp orange	1.00	11.00
214	A16	15o olive bis	.30	1.00
215	A16	30o ultra	1.00	2.75
216	A16	35o brt violet	.75	.80
217	A16	40o dk slate grn	7.50	11.00
218	A16	50o dp claret	250.00	450.00
		Never hinged	340.00	
219	A16	60o Prus blue	.75	1.75
		Nos. 207-217,219 (12)	22.60	85.45
		Set, never hinged	45.00	

Unwmk.

No.	Type	Denomination / Color	Unused	Used
220	A10	1o olive	.35	4.25
221	A10	2o yellow brn	.35	5.00
222	A10	3o deep orange	.35	4.75
223	A10	5o rose lilac	.35	.40
224	A10	7o brt green	.95	4.75
225	A16	10o brt green	.35	.25
226	A10	12o brt violet	1.10	10.00
227	A16	15o olive bis	1.90	11.00
228	A16	20o red	.35	.20
a.		Inverted overprint	925.00	1,500.
a.		Never hinged	1,300.	
229	A16	25o dk orange brn	.42	.40
230	A16	30o brt ultra	.70	1.65
231	A16	35o brt violet	.70	.70
232	A16	40o dk slate grn	.70	.55
233	A16	50o dp claret	.80	2.25
234	A16	60o Prus blue	1.90	1.25
235	A28	1k brt green	1.25	.50
236	A28	1½k dp blue	3.75	12.00
237	A16	2k bright red	10.50	37.50
238	A16	5k dull purple	19.00	72.50

Coil Stamp

No.	Type	Denomination / Color	Unused	Used
239	A29	10o brt green	1.25	10.00
		Nos. 220-239 (20)	47.02	179.90
		Set, never hinged	85.00	

Dream of Queen Ragnhild — A30

Snorri Sturluson — A32

Einar Tambarskjelve in Fight at Svolder — A31

Designs: 30o, King Olaf sailing in wedding procession to Landmerket. 50o, Syipdag's sons and followers going to Hall of Seven Kings. 60o, Before Battle of Stiklestad.

1941 *Perf. 13½x13, 13x13½*

No.	Type	Denomination / Color	Unused	Used
240	A30	10o bright green	.35	.20
241	A31	15o olive brown	.40	.55
242	A32	20o dark red	.35	.15
243	A31	30o blue	1.00	1.40
244	A31	50o dull violet	1.10	1.40
245	A31	60o Prus blue	1.10	1.40
		Nos. 240-245 (6)	4.30	5.10
		Set, never hinged	8.00	

700th anniversary of the death of Snorri Sturluson, writer and historian.

University of Oslo — A36

1941, Sept. 2 *Perf. 13x13½*

No.	Type	Denomination / Color	Unused	Used
246	A36	1k dk olive grn	32.50	40.00
		Never hinged	42.50	

Centenary of cornerstone laying of University of Oslo building.

Richard (Rikard) Nordraak (1842-66), Composer — A37

"Broad Sails Go over the North Sea" — A38

View of Coast and Lines of National Anthem A39

1942, June 12 *Perf. 13*

No.	Type	Denomination / Color	Unused	Used
247	A37	10o dp green	1.25	1.50
248	A38	15o dp brown	1.25	1.50
249	A37	20o rose red	1.25	1.50
250	A39	30o sapphire	1.25	1.50
		Nos. 247-250 (4)	5.00	6.00
		Set, never hinged	9.00	

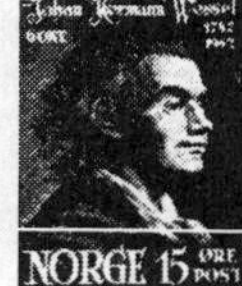

Johan Herman Wessel (1742-1785), Author — A40

1942, Oct. 6

No.	Type	Denomination / Color	Unused	Used
251	A40	15o dull brown	.20	.20
252	A40	20o henna	.20	.20
		Set, never hinged	.90	

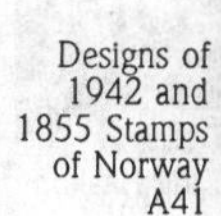

Designs of 1942 and 1855 Stamps of Norway A41

1942, Oct. 12

No.	Type	Denomination / Color	Unused	Used
253	A41	20o henna	.25	.55
254	A41	30o sapphire	.35	1.10
		Set, never hinged	.90	

European Postal Congress at Vienna, October, 1942.

Edvard Grieg (1843-1907), Composer — A42

Destroyer Sleipner — A43

1943, June 15

No.	Type	Denomination / Color	Unused	Used
255	A42	10o deep green	.25	.25
256	A42	20o henna	.25	.25
257	A42	40o grnsh black	.25	.25
258	A42	60o dk grnsh blue	.25	.25
		Nos. 255-258 (4)	1.00	1.00
		Set, never hinged	1.50	

1943-45 Unwmk. Engr. *Perf. 12½*

5o, 10o, "Sleipner." 7o, 30o, Convoy under midnight sun. 15o, Plane and pilot. 20o, "We will win." 40o, Ski troops. 60o, King Haakon VII.

No.	Type	Denomination / Color	Unused	Used
259	A43	5o rose vio ('45)	.15	.15
260	A43	7o grnsh blk ('45)	.20	.20
261	A43	10o dk blue grn	.15	.15
262	A43	15o dk olive grn	.60	.45
263	A43	20o rose red	.15	.15
264	A43	30o dp ultra	.65	.75
265	A43	40o olive black	.55	.55
266	A43	60o dark blue	.55	.55
		Nos. 259-266 (8)	3.00	2.95
		Set, never hinged	4.75	

Nos. 261-266 were used for correspondence carried on Norwegian ships until after the liberation of Norway, when they became regular postage stamps.

Nos. 261-266 exist with overprint "London 17-5-43" and serial number. Value for set, unused, $1,000; canceled $1,200.

Gran's Plane and Map of His North Sea Flight Route — A49

1944, July 30 *Perf. 13*

No.	Type	Denomination / Color	Unused	Used
267	A49	40o dk grnsh blue	.40	.20
		Never hinged	.60	

20th anniv. of the 1st flight over the North Sea, made by Tryggve Gran on July 30, 1914.

For used value see note following No. 180.

New National Arms of 1943 — A50

1945, Feb. 15 Typo. *Perf. 13*

No.	Type	Denomination / Color	Unused	Used
268	A50	1½k dark blue	.85	.40
		Never hinged	1.50	

Henrik Wergeland A51

Lion Rampant A52

1945, July 12 Photo.

No.	Type	Denomination / Color	Unused	Used
269	A51	10o dk olive green	.30	.30
270	A51	15o dark brown	.85	1.00
271	A51	20o dark red	.25	.30
		Nos. 269-271 (3)	1.40	1.60
		Set, never hinged	2.00	

Wergeland, poet & playwright, death cent.

1945, Dec. 19

No.	Type	Denomination / Color	Unused	Used
272	A52	10o dk olive green	.35	.30
273	A52	20o red	.35	.30
		Set, never hinged	1.00	

Norwegian Folklore Museum, 50th anniv.

Pilot and Mechanic — A53

King Haakon VII — A54

1946, Mar. 22 Engr. *Perf. 12*

No.	Type	Denomination / Color	Unused	Used
274	A53	15o brown rose	.40	.75
		Never hinged	.60	

Issued in honor of Little Norway, training center in Canada for Norwegian pilots.

Catalogue values for unused stamps in this section, from this point to the end of the section, are for Never Hinged items.

1946, June 7 Photo. *Perf. 13*

No.	Type	Denomination / Color	Unused	Used
275	A54	1k bright green	1.65	.15
276	A54	1½k Prus blue	4.75	.15
277	A54	2k henna brown	35.00	.15
278	A54	5k violet	21.00	.40
		Nos. 275-278 (4)	62.40	
		Set value		.60

Hannibal Sehested — A55

Designs: 10o, Letter carrier, 1700. 15o, Adm. Peter W. Tordenskjold. 25o, Christian Magnus Falsen. 30o, Cleng Peerson and "Restaurationen." 40o, Post ship "Constitution." 45o, First Norwegian locomotive. 50o, Sven Foyn and whaler. 55o, Fridtjof Nansen and Roald Amundsen. 60o, Coronation of King Haakon VII and Queen Maud, 1906. 80o, Return of King Haakon, June 7, 1945.

1947, Apr. 15 Photo. *Perf. 13*

No.	Type	Denomination / Color	Unused	Used
279	A55	5o red lilac	.15	.15
280	A55	10o green	.65	.15
281	A55	15o brown	.65	.15
282	A55	25o orange red	.65	.15
283	A55	30o gray	1.00	.15
284	A55	40o blue	1.10	.15
285	A55	45o violet	2.25	.50
286	A55	50o orange brn	2.75	.15
287	A55	55o orange	6.00	.25
288	A55	60o slate gray	4.00	.75
289	A55	80o dk brown	3.00	.25
		Nos. 279-289 (11)	22.20	
		Set value		2.30

Establishment of the Norwegian Post Office, 300th anniv.

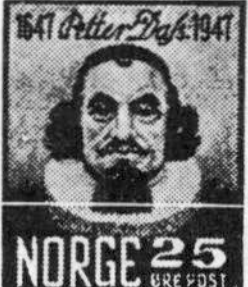

Petter Dass — A66

King Haakon VII — A67

1947, July 1 Unwmk.

No.	Type	Denomination / Color	Unused	Used
290	A66	25o bright red	.90	.55

300th birth anniv. of Petter Dass, poet.

1947, Aug. 2

No.	Type	Denomination / Color	Unused	Used
291	A67	25o orange red	.90	.55

75th birthday of King Haakon.

Axel Heiberg — A68

Alexander L. Kielland — A69

1948, June 15

No.	Type	Denomination / Color	Unused	Used
292	A68	25o deep carmine	1.10	.40
293	A68	80o dp red brown	2.25	.30

50th anniv. of the Norwegian Society of Forestry; birth cent. of Axel Heiberg, its founder.

1949, May 9

No.	Type	Denomination / Color	Unused	Used
295	A69	25o rose brown	1.65	.20
296	A69	40o greenish blue	1.65	.50
297	A69	80o orange brown	2.00	.65
		Nos. 295-297 (3)	5.30	1.35

Birth cent. of Alexander L. Kielland, author.

Symbols of UPU Members — A70

Stylized Pigeons and Globe — A71

Symbolical of the UPU — A72

1949, Oct. 9 *Perf. 13*

299 A70 10o dk green & blk .75 .60
300 A71 25o scarlet .50 .25
301 A72 40o dull blue .55 .50
Nos. 299-301 (3) 1.80 1.35

75th anniv. of the formation of the UPU.

Nos. 196 and 200A Surcharged with New Value and Bar in Black

1949 *Perf. 13x13½*

302 A16 25o on 20o red .75 .15
303 A16 45o on 40o dp ultra 2.25 .30
Set value .40

King Harald Haardraade and Oslo City Hall — A73

1950, May 15 **Photo.** *Perf. 13*

304 A73 15o green .90 1.00
305 A73 25o red .55 .35
306 A73 45o ultramarine .90 .75
Nos. 304-306 (3) 2.35 2.10

900th anniversary of Oslo.

Redrawn Post Horn Type of 1937

1950-51 **Photo.** *Perf. 13x13½*

Size: 17x21mm

307 A10 10o grnsh gray .50 .15
a. Booklet pane of 10 6.00
308 A10 15o dark green 2.00 .40
a. Booklet pane of 10 22.50
309 A10 20o chnt brn ('51) 5.00 2.25
Nos. 307-309 (3) 7.50 2.80

King Haakon VII — A74

Arne Garborg — A75

1950-51 **Photo.** *Perf. 13x13½*

310 A74 25o dk red ('50) .90 .15
a. Booklet pane of 10 40.00
311 A74 30o gray 9.00 .60
312 A74 35o red brn 19.00 .15
313 A74 45o brt blue 1.75 .85
314 A74 50o olive brn 1.75 .15
315 A74 55o orange 1.75 .85
316 A74 60o gray blue 10.00 .15
317 A74 80o chnt brn 2.75 .30
Nos. 310-317 (8) 46.90 3.20

See Nos. 322-324, 345-352. For surcharge see No. 321.

1951, Jan. 25 *Perf. 13*

318 A75 25o red .65 .25
319 A75 45o dull blue 2.25 1.50
320 A75 80o brown 3.50 1.25
Nos. 318-320 (3) 6.40 3.00

Birth cent. of Arne Garborg, poet.

No. 310 Surcharged with New Value in Black

1951 *Perf. 13x13½*

321 A74 30o on 25o dk red .60 .15

Haakon Type of 1950-51

1951-52 **Photo.**

322 A74 25o gray 22.50 .15
323 A74 30o dk red ('52) .90 .15
a. Booklet pane of 10 35.00
324 A74 55o blue ('52) 1.75 .40
Nos. 322-324 (3) 25.15
Set value .50

Redrawn Post Horn Type of 1937

1952, June 3 *Perf. 13x13½*

325 A10 15o org brn .70 .15
a. Booklet pane of 10 12.00
326 A10 20o green .70 .15
Set value .15

King Haakon VII — A76

Medieval Sculpture, Nidaros Cathedral — A77

1952, Aug. 3 **Unwmk.** *Perf. 13*

327 A76 30o red .50 .15
328 A76 55o deep blue 1.10 1.00

80th birthday of King Haakon VII.

No. 308 Surcharged with New Value

1952, Nov. 18 *Perf. 13x13½*

329 A10 20o on 15o dk grn .60 .15

1953, July 15 *Perf. 13*

330 A77 30o henna brn .60 .40

800th anniv. of the creation of the Norwegian Archbishopric of Nidaros.

Train of 1854 and Horse-drawn Sled — A78

Carsten T. Nielsen — A79

Designs: 30o, Diesel train. 55o, Engineer.

1954, Apr. 30 **Photo.**

331 A78 20o green .85 .30
332 A78 30o red .85 .20
333 A78 55o ultra 2.00 1.25
Nos. 331-333 (3) 3.70 1.75

Inauguration of the first Norwegian railway, cent.

1954, Dec. 10

Designs: 30o, Government radio towers. 55o, Lineman and telegraph poles in snow.

334 A79 20o ol grn & blk .40 .20
335 A79 30o brt red .40 .15
336 A79 55o blue 1.50 .85
Nos. 334-336 (3) 2.30 1.20

Centenary (in 1955) of the inauguration of the first Norwegian public telegraph line.

Norway No. 1 — A80

Stamp Reproductions: 30o, Post horn type A5. 55o, Lion type A13.

1955, Jan. 3 *Perf. 13*

337 A80 20o dp grn & gray bl .45 .30
338 A80 30o red & carmine .20 .15
339 A80 55o gray bl & dp bl .95 .55
Nos. 337-339 (3) 1.60 1.00

Centenary of Norway's first postage stamp.

Nos. 337-339 Overprinted in Black

1955, June 4

340 A80 20o dp grn & gray bl 12.00 10.00
341 A80 30o red & carmine 12.00 10.00
342 A80 55o gray bl & dp bl 12.00 10.00
Nos. 340-342 (3) 36.00 30.00

Norway Philatelic Exhibition, Oslo, 1955. Sold at exhibition post office for face value plus 1kr admission fee.

King Haakon VII and Queen Maud in Coronation Robes — A81

1955, Nov. 25 **Photo.** *Perf. 13*

343 A81 30o rose red .40 .20
344 A81 55o ultra .60 .50

Haakon's 50th anniv. as King of Norway.

Haakon Type of 1950-51

1955-57 **Unwmk.** *Perf. 13x13½*

345 A74 25o dk grn ('56) 1.40 .15
346 A74 35o brn red ('56) 6.00 .15
a. Booklet pane of 10 65.00
347 A74 40o pale pur 2.25 .15
a. Booklet pane of 10 60.00
348 A74 50o bister ('57) 3.25 .15
349 A74 65o ultra ('56) 1.40 .40
350 A74 70o brn ol ('56) 13.00 .15
351 A74 75o mar ('57) 2.25 .15
352 A74 90o dp org 1.40 .15
Nos. 345-352 (8) 30.95
Set value 1.00

Northern Countries Issue

Whooper Swans — A81a

1956, Oct. 30 **Engr.** *Perf. 12½*

353 A81a 35o rose red .95 .60
354 A81a 65o ultra .95 .85

Close bonds connecting the northern countries: Denmark, Finland, Iceland, Norway and Sweden.

Jan Mayen Island — A82

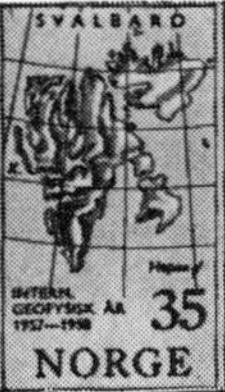

Map of Spitsbergen A83

King Haakon VII A84

Design: 65o, Map of South Pole with Queen Maud Land.

Perf. 12½x13, 13x12½

1957, July 1 **Photo.** **Unwmk.**

355 A82 25o slate green .65 .40
356 A83 35o dk red & gray .65 .15
357 A83 65o dk grn & bl .65 .50
Nos. 355-357 (3) 1.95 1.05

Intl. Geophysical Year, 1957-58.

1957, Aug. 2 *Perf. 13*

358 A84 35o dark red .35 .20
359 A84 65o ultra .85 .85

85th birthday of King Haakon VII.

King Olav V
A85 A86

1958-60 **Photo.** *Perf. 13x13½*

360 A85 25o emerald .85 .15
a. Booklet pane of 4 150.00
361 A85 30o purple ('59) 1.65 .15
361A A85 35o brown car ('60) 1.25 .15
362 A85 40o dark red 1.25 .15
a. Booklet pane of 10 85.00
363 A85 45o scarlet 1.90 .15
a. Booklet pane of 10 55.00
364 A85 50o bister ('59) 6.75 .15
365 A85 55o dk gray ('59) 2.25 .50
366 A85 65o blue 2.50 .35
367 A85 80o org brn ('60) 12.50 .20
368 A85 85o olive brn ('59) 2.25 .15
369 A85 90o orange ('59) 1.90 .15
Nos. 360-369 (11) 35.05
Set value 1.55

See Nos. 408-412.

1959, Jan. 12

370 A86 1k green .75 .15
371 A86 1.50k dark blue 3.25 .15
372 A86 2k crimson 3.75 .15
373 A86 5k lilac 45.00 .15
374 A86 10k dp orange 6.25 .25
Nos. 370-374 (5) 59.00
Set value .60

See Phosphorescence note following No. 430.

Asbjörn Kloster — A87

Agricultural Society Medal — A88

1959, Feb. 2

375 A87 45o violet brown .70 .25

Centenary of the founding of the Norwegian Temperance Movement; Asbjörn Kloster, its founder.

1959, May 26

376 A88 45o red & ocher .80 .25
377 A88 90o blue & gray 2.25 1.65

150th anniversary of the Royal Agricultural Society of Norway.

Sower — A89

Society Seal — A90

Design: 90o, Grain, vert.

1959, Oct. 1 **Photo.** *Perf. 13*

378 A89 45o ocher & blk .80 .25
379 A89 90o blue & blk 1.25 1.25

Agricultural College of Norway, cent.

1960, Feb. 26 **Unwmk.**

380 A90 45o carmine .75 .25
381 A90 90o dark blue 2.00 1.40

Bicentenary of the Royal Norwegian Society of Sciences, Trondheim.

Viking Ship — A91

Designs: 25o, Caravel and fish. 45o, Sailing ship and nautical knot. 55o, Freighter and oil derricks. 90o, Passenger ship and Statue of Liberty.

1960, Aug. 27 *Perf. 12½x13*

382 A91 20o gray & blk 1.10 .65
383 A91 25o yel grn & blk 1.10 1.00
384 A91 45o ver & blk 1.10 .20
385 A91 55o ocher & blk 2.75 2.75
386 A91 90o Prus bl & blk 3.25 1.25
Nos. 382-386 (5) 9.30 5.85

Norwegian shipping industry.

Common Design Types pictured following the introduction.

Europa Issue, 1960
Common Design Type

1960, Sept. 19 *Perf. 13*
Size: 27x21mm

387 CD3 90o blue .75 .75

DC-8 Airliner — A91a

Javelin Thrower — A92

1961, Feb. 24 **Photo.** *Perf. 13*
388 A91a 90o dark blue 1.00 .60

Scandinavian Airlines System, SAS, 10th anniv.

1961, Mar. 15
389 A92 20o shown .80 .50
390 A92 25o Skater .80 .50
391 A92 45o Ski jumper .80 .15
392 A92 90o Sailboat 1.40 1.40
Nos. 389-392 (4) 3.80 2.55

Norwegian Sports Federation centenary.

Haakonshallen A93

1961, May 25 *Perf. 12½x13*
393 A93 45o maroon & gray .70 .20
394 A93 1k gray green & gray 1.10 .25

700th anniv. of Haakonshallen, castle in Bergen.

Domus Media, Oslo University A94

1961, Sept. 2 **Photo.** *Perf. 12½x13*
395 A94 45o dark red .60 .20
396 A94 1.50k Prus blue 1.25 .25

150th anniversary of Oslo University.

Fridtjof Nansen — A95

1961, Oct. 10 *Perf. 13*
397 A95 45o orange red & gray .50 .20
398 A95 90o chlky blue & gray 1.10 .85

Birth centenary of Fridtjof Nansen, explorer.

Roald Amundsen A96

Design: 90o, Explorers and tent at Pole.

1961, Nov. 10 **Unwmk.** *Perf. 13*
399 A96 45o dl red brn & gray .90 .20
400 A96 90o dk & lt blue 1.40 .70

50th anniversary of Roald Amundsen's arrival at the South Pole.

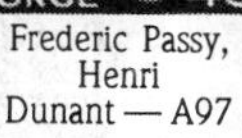

Frederic Passy, Henri Dunant — A97

Vilhelm Bjerknes — A98

1961, Dec. 9 **Photo.**
401 A97 45o henna brown .45 .20
402 A97 1k yellow green 1.25 .30

Winners of the first Nobel Peace prize. Frederic Passy, a founder of the Interparliamentary Union, and Henri Dunant, founder of the International Red Cross.

1962, Mar. 14 *Perf. 13*
403 A98 45o dk red & gray .35 .25
404 A98 1.50k dk blue & gray .90 .35

Vilhelm Bjerknes (1862-1951), physicist, mathematician, meteorologist, etc.

German Rumpler Taube over Oslo Fjord — A99

1962, June 1 **Photo.**
405 A99 1.50k dl bl & blk 1.90 .70

50th anniversary of Norwegian aviation.

Fir Branch and Cone — A100

1962, June 15
406 A100 45o salmon & blk .75 .40
407 A100 1k pale grn & blk 6.75 .30

Olav Type of 1958-60

1962 **Unwmk.** *Perf. 13x13½*
408 A85 25o slate grn 1.25 .15
a. Booklet pane of 4 150.00
b. Booklet pane of 10 30.00
409 A85 35o emerald 4.25 .15
410 A85 40o gray 4.25 .75
411 A85 50o scarlet 9.50 .15
a. Booklet pane of 10 125.00
412 A85 60o violet 4.75 .45
Nos. 408-412 (5) 24.00
Set value 1.35

Europa Issue, 1962
Common Design Type

1962, Sept. 17 **Photo.** *Perf. 13*
Size: 37x21mm

414 CD5 50o dp rose & maroon .50 .30
415 CD5 90o blue & dk blue 1.40 1.00

Post Horn Type of 1893-1908 Redrawn and

Rock Carvings A101

Boatswain's Knot A102

Designs: 30o, 55o, 85o, Rye and fish. 65o, 80o, Stave church and northern lights.

1962-63 **Engr.** *Perf. 13x13½*
416 A10 5o rose cl .15 .15
a. Booklet pane of 4, vert. 1.65
b. Booklet pane of 10, horiz. 8.00
417 A10 10o slate .15 .15
a. Booklet pane of 10 20.00
418 A10 15o orange brn .15 .15
419 A10 20o green .15 .15
a. Booklet pane of 4 8.00
420 A101 25o gray grn ('63) 1.10 .15
a. Booklet pane of 4 16.00
b. Booklet pane of 10 20.00
421 A101 30o olive brn ('63) 4.00 2.75
422 A102 35o brt green ('63) .32 .15
423 A101 40o lake ('63) 3.00 .15
424 A102 50o vermilion 4.75 .15
a. Booklet pane of 10 65.00
425 A101 55o orange brn ('63) .50 .45
426 A102 60o dk grnsh gray ('63) 8.50 .15
427 A102 65o dk blue ('63) 3.50 .15
a. Booklet pane of 10 62.50
428 A102 80o rose lake ('63) 7.25 2.00
429 A101 85o sepia ('63) .50 .22
430 A101 90o blue ('63) .32 .15
Nos. 416-430 (15) 34.34
Set value 6.00

Nos. 416-419 have been redrawn and are similar to 1910-29 issue, with vertical lines inside oval and horizontal lines in oval frame. See Nos. 462-470, 608-615.

> Phosphorescence
> Nos. 370-372, 416-419, 423, 425, 428, 430, 462, 466, O65-O68, O75, O78-O82, O83-O84 and O88 have been issued on both ordinary and phosphorescent paper.
> Nos. 463-465, 467-468, 510 to last number assigned, O86 and O89-O93 have been issued only on phosphorescent paper.

Camilla Collett (1813-1895), Author — A103

1963, Jan. 23 **Photo.** *Perf. 13*
431 A103 50o red brn & tan .40 .20
432 A103 90o slate & gray 1.50 1.10

Girl in Boat Loaded with Grain — A104

Still Life — A105

1963, Mar. 21 **Unwmk.** *Perf. 13*
433 A104 25o yellow brown .35 .25
434 A104 35o dark green .60 .45
435 A105 50o dark red .50 .35
436 A105 90o dark blue 1.50 1.10
Nos. 433-436 (4) 2.95 2.15

FAO "Freedom from Hunger" campaign.

River Boat — A106

Design: 90o, Northern sailboat.

1963, May 20 **Unwmk.** *Perf. 13*
437 A106 50o brown red 1.50 .48
438 A106 90o blue 2.25 1.50

Tercentenary of regular postal service between Northern and Southern Norway.

Ivar Aasen — A107

1963, Aug. 5 **Photo.**
439 A107 50o dk red & gray .60 .28
440 A107 90o dk blue & gray 1.25 .75

150th birth anniv. of Ivar Aasen, poet and philologist.

Europa Issue, 1963
Common Design Type

1963, Sept. 14 **Unwmk.** *Perf. 13*
Size: 27x21½mm

441 CD6 50o dull rose & org .75 .42
442 CD6 90o blue & yel grn 2.50 1.50

Patterned Fabric A108

1963, Sept. 24
443 A108 25o olive & ol grn .60 .40
444 A108 35o Prus bl & dk bl .85 .70
445 A108 50o dk car rose & plum .60 .40
Nos. 443-445 (3) 2.05 1.50

Norwegian textile industry, 150th anniv.

"Loneliness" — A109

Eilert Sundt — A110

Paintings by Edvard Munch (1863-1944): 25o, Self-portrait, vert. 35o, "Fertility." 90o, "Girls on Bridge," vert.

1963, Dec. 12 **Litho.** *Perf. 13*
446 A109 25o black .35 .22
447 A109 35o dark green .45 .35
448 A109 50o deep claret .42 .32
449 A109 90o gray bl & dk bl 1.25 1.00
Nos. 446-449 (4) 2.47 1.89

1964, Feb. 17 **Photo.**

Design: 50o, Beehive, Workers' Society emblem.

450 A110 25o dark green .40 .45
451 A110 50o dk red brown .38 .24

Centenary of the Oslo Workers' Society.

Cato M. Guldberg and Peter Waage by Stinius Fredriksen — A111

1964, Mar. 11 **Unwmk.** *Perf. 13*
452 A111 35o olive green .90 .45
453 A111 55o bister 2.00 1.75

Centenary of the presentation of the Law of Mass Action (chemistry) by Professors Cato M. Guldberg and Peter Waage in the Oslo Scientific Society.

Eidsvoll Building A112

Design: 90o, Storting (Parliament House).

1964, May 11 **Photo.**
454 A112 50o hn brn & blk .45 .30
455 A112 90o Prus bl & dk bl 1.25 1.10

150th anniv. of Norway's constitution.

Church and Ships in Harbor A113

1964, Aug. 17 *Perf. 13*
456 A113 25o dk sl grn & buff .48 .40
457 A113 90o dk bl & gray 2.00 1.65

Centenary of the Norwegian Seamen's Mission, which operates 32 stations around the world.

Europa Issue, 1964
Common Design Type

1964, Sept. 14 **Photo.** *Perf. 13*
458 CD7 90o dark blue 2.00 1.25

Herman Anker and Olaus Arvesen A114

1964, Oct. 31 **Litho.** **Unwmk.**
459 A114 50o rose .65 .30
460 A114 90o blue 2.75 1.90

Centenary of the founding of Norwegian schools of higher education (Folk High Schools).

Types of Regular Issue, 1962-63

Designs: 30o, 45o, Rye and fish. 40o, 100o, Rock carvings. 50o, 60o, 65o, 70o, Boatswain's knot.

Two types of 60o:
I - Four twists across bottom of knot.
II - Five twists.

1964-70 Engr. *Perf. 13x13½*

462 A101 30o dull green .80 .15
463 A101 40o lt bl grn ('68) .52 .15
464 A101 45o lt yel grn ('68) 1.10 .75
465 A102 50o indigo ('68) .52 .15
466 A102 60o brick red, II ('75) 2.50 .30
a. Booklet pane of 10 45.00
b. Type I 2.75 .30
467 A102 65o lake ('68) .65 .15
a. Booklet pane of 10 35.00
468 A102 70o brown ('70) .52 .15
a. Booklet pane of 10 20.00
469 A101 100o violet bl ('70) 1.10 .15
Nos. 462-469 (8) 7.71
Set value 1.60

See Phosphorescence note following #430.

Coil Stamp

1965 *Perf. 13½ Horiz.*

470 A101 30p dull green 4.25 1.25

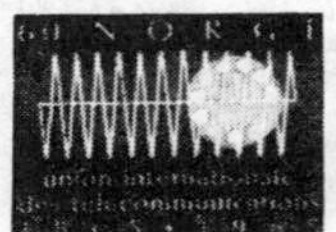

Telephone Dial and Waves — A115

Design: 90o, Television mast and antenna.

1965, Apr. 1 Engr. *Perf. 13*

471 A115 60o redsh brown .38 .15
472 A115 90o slate 1.65 1.50

ITU, centenary.

Mountain Scene A116

Design: 90o, Coastal view.

1965, June 4 Unwmk. *Perf. 13*

473 A116 60o brn blk & car .52 .35
474 A116 90o slate bl & car 3.75 3.25

Centenary of the Norwegian Red Cross.

Europa Issue, 1965
Common Design Type

1965, Sept. 25 Photo. *Perf. 13*
Size: 27x21mm

475 CD8 60o brick red .50 .24
476 CD8 90o blue 1.50 1.40

St. Sunniva and Buildings of Bergen — A117

Rondane Mountains by Harold Sohlberg — A118

90o, St. Sunniva and stylized view of Bergen.

1965, Oct. 25 *Perf. 13*

477 A117 30o dk green & blk .55 .30
478 A117 90o blue & blk, horiz. 1.65 1.25

Bicentenary of Bergen's philharmonic society "Harmonien."

1965, Nov. 29 Photo. *Perf. 13*

484 A118 1.50k dark blue 1.75 .18

Rock Carving of Skier, Rodoy Island, c. 2000 B.C. — A120

Designs: 55o, Ski jumper. 60o, Cross country skier. 90o, Holmenkollen ski jump, vert.

1966, Feb. 8 Engr. *Perf. 13*

486 A120 40o sepia .75 .70
487 A120 55o dull green 1.50 1.40
488 A120 60o dull red .60 .20
489 A120 90o blue 1.50 1.40
Nos. 486-489 (4) 4.35 3.70

World Ski Championships, Oslo, Feb. 17-27.

Open Bible and Chrismon — A121

1966, May 20 Photo. *Perf. 13*

490 A121 60o dull red .40 .15
491 A121 90o slate blue 1.40 1.00

150th anniv. of the Norwegian Bible Society.

Engine-turned Bank Note Design A122

Bank of Norway — A123

1966, June 14 Engr.

492 A122 30o green .55 .32
493 A123 60o dk carmine rose .55 .15

150th anniversary of Bank of Norway.

Johan Sverdrup A124

Nitrogen Molecule in Test Tube A125

1966, July 30 Photo. *Perf. 13*

494 A124 30o green .48 .25
495 A124 60o rose lake .48 .15
Set value .32

Johan Sverdrup (1816-92), Prime Minister of Norway (1884-89).

Canceled to Order
The Norwegian philatelic agency began in 1966 to sell commemorative and definitive issues canceled to order at face value.

Europa Issue, 1966
Common Design Type

1966, Sept. 26 Engr. *Perf. 13*
Size: 21x27mm

496 CD9 60o dark carmine .60 .25
497 CD9 90o blue gray 1.75 1.25

1966, Oct. 29 Photo. *Perf. 13x12½*

Design: 55o, Wheat and laboratory bottle.

498 A125 40o bl & dp bl 1.25 .95
499 A125 55o red, org & lil rose 2.25 1.65

Centenary of the birth of Kristian Birkeland (1867-1917), and of Sam Eyde (1866-1940), who together developed the production of nitrates.

EFTA Emblem — A126

1967, Jan. 16 Engr. *Perf. 13*

500 A126 60o rose red .52 .18
501 A126 90o dark blue 2.25 1.65

European Free Trade Association. Tariffs were abolished Dec. 31, 1966, among EFTA members: Austria, Denmark, Finland, Great Britain, Norway, Portugal, Sweden, Switzerland.

Sabers, Owl and Oak Leaves — A127

1967, Feb. 16 Engr. *Perf. 13*

502 A127 60o chocolate 1.00 .35
503 A127 90o black 3.00 2.00

Higher military training in Norway, 150th anniv.

Europa Issue, 1967
Common Design Type

1967, May 2 Photo. *Perf. 13*
Size: 21x27mm

504 CD10 60o magenta & plum .55 .20
505 CD10 90o bl & dk vio bl 1.50 1.25

Johanne Dybwad, by Per Ung — A128

1967, Aug. 2 Photo. *Perf. 13*

506 A128 40o slate blue .55 .45
507 A128 60o dk carmine rose .55 .15

Johanne Dybwad (1867-1950), actress.

Missionary L.O. Skrefsrud A129

Ebenezer Church, Benagaria, Santal A130

1967, Sept. 26 Engr. *Perf. 13*

508 A129 60o red brown .55 .15
509 A130 90o blue gray 1.25 1.10

Norwegian Santal (India) mission, cent.

Mountaineers A131

Designs: 60o, Mountain view. 90o, Glitretind mountain peak.

1968, Jan. 22 Engr. *Perf. 13*

510 A131 40o sepia .95 .60
511 A131 60o brown red .55 .20
512 A131 90o slate blue 1.25 1.10
Nos. 510-512 (3) 2.75 1.90

Centenary of the Norwegian Mountain Touring Association.

Two Smiths A132

1968, Mar. 30 Photo. *Perf. 12½x13*

513 A132 65o dk car rose & brn .45 .20
514 A132 90o blue & brown 1.10 1.10

Issued to honor Norwegian craftsmen.

A. O. Vinje — A133

Cross and Heart — A134

1968, May 21 Engr. *Perf. 13*

515 A133 50o sepia .55 .35
516 A133 65o maroon .50 .25

Aasmund Olafsson Vinje (1818-1870), poet, journalist and language reformer.

1968, Sept. 16 Photo.

517 A134 40o brt grn & brn red 3.25 1.25
518 A134 65o brn red & vio bl .45 .25

Centenary of the Norwegian Lutheran Home Mission Society.

Cathinka Guldberg — A135

1968, Oct. 31 Engr. *Perf. 13*

519 A135 50o bright blue .50 .35
520 A135 65o dull red .50 .20

Nursing profession; centenary of Deaconess House in Oslo. Cathinka Guldberg was a pioneer of Norwegian nursing and the first deaconess.

Klas P. Arnoldson and Fredrik Bajer — A136

1968, Dec. 10 Engr. *Perf. 13*

521 A136 65o red brown .45 .30
522 A136 90o dark blue 1.00 .80

60th anniv. of the awarding of the Nobel Peace prize to Klas P. Arnoldson (1844-1916), Swedish writer and statesman, and to Fredrik Bajer (1837-1922), Danish writer and statesman.

Nordic Cooperation Issue

Five Ancient Ships — A136a

1969, Feb. 28 Engr. *Perf. 13*

523 A136a 65o red .35 .30
524 A136a 90o blue 1.25 1.00

Nordic Society's 50th anniversary and centenary of postal cooperation among the northern countries: Denmark, Finland, Iceland, Norway and Sweden.

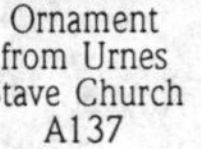

Ornament from Urnes Stave Church A137

Traena Island A138

1969 Engr. *Perf. 13*

526 A137 1.15k sepia 1.25 .50
529 A138 3.50k bluish blk 1.00 .20

Issue dates: 1.15k, Jan. 23, 3.50k, June 18.

Plane, Train, Ship and Bus — A139

Child Crossing Street A140

1969, Mar. 24 Photo. *Perf. 13*

531 A139 50o green .60 .30
532 A140 65o sl grn & dk red .42 .25

No. 531 for the centenary of the publication of "Rutebok of Norway" (Communications of Norway); No. 532 publicizes traffic safety.

Europa Issue, 1969

Common Design Type

1969, Apr. 28

Size: 37x21mm

533 CD12 65o dk red & gray .65 .25
534 CD12 90o chalky bl & gray 1.50 .85

Johan Hjort — A141

King Olav V — A142

Design: 90o, different emblem.

1969, May 30 Engr. *Perf. 13*

535 A141 40o brn & bl .90 .60
536 A141 90o bl & grn 1.50 1.50

Hjort (1869-1948), zoologist and oceanographer.

1969-83 Engr. *Perf. 13*

537 A142 1k lt ol grn ('70) .85 .15
538 A142 1.50k dk blue ('70) .85 .15
539 A142 2k dk red ('70) .85 .15
540 A142 5k vio bl ('70) 1.75 .15
541 A142 10k orange brn ('70) 3.50 .15
542 A142 20k brown 7.25 .35
543 A142 50k dk olive grn ('83) 14.00 3.00
Nos. 537-543 (7) 29.05 4.10

Man, Woman and Child, by Vigeland A143

65o, Mother and Child, by Gustav Vigeland.

1969, Sept. 8 Photo. *Perf. 13*

545 A143 65o car rose & blk .45 .35
546 A143 90o blue & black 1.10 .90

Gustav Vigeland (1869-1943), sculptor.

People A144

1969, Oct. 10

547 A144 65o Punched card .42 .35
548 A144 90o shown 1.10 .90

1st Norwegian census, 200th anniv.

Queen Maud — A145

Pulsatilla Vernalis — A146

1969, Nov. 26 Engr. *Perf. 13*

549 A145 65o dk carmine .45 .25
550 A145 90o violet blue 1.10 .90

Queen Maud (1869-1938), wife of King Haakon VII.

1970, Apr. 10 Photo. *Perf. 13*

European Nature Conservation Year: 40o, Wolf. 70o, Voringsfossen (waterfall). 100o, White-tailed sea eagle, horiz.

551 A146 40o sep & pale bl 1.25 .70
552 A146 60o lt brn & gray 1.40 1.40
553 A146 70o pale bl & brn 1.40 .60
554 A146 100o pale bl & brn 1.40 1.40
Nos. 551-554 (4) 5.45 4.10

"V" for Victory A147

"Citizens" A148

Design: 100o, Convoy, horiz.

Perf. 13x12½, 12½x13

1970, May 8 Photo.

555 A147 70o red & lilac 1.75 .45
556 A147 100o vio bl & brt grn 1.75 1.25

Norway's liberation from the Germans, 25th anniv.

1970, June 23 Engr. *Perf. 13*

Designs: 70o, "The City and the Mountains." 100o, "Ships."

557 A148 40o green 1.25 .65
558 A148 70o rose claret 2.50 .35
559 A148 100o violet blue 1.90 1.75
Nos. 557-559 (3) 5.65 2.75

City of Bergen, 900th anniversary.

Olive Wreath and Hands Upholding Globe A149

Georg Ossian Sars (1837-1927) A150

1970, Sept. 15 Engr. *Perf. 13*

560 A149 70o dk car rose 2.75 .50
561 A149 100o steel blue 1.75 1.25

25th anniversary of the United Nations.

1970, Oct. 15 Engr. *Perf. 13*

Portraits: 50o, Hans Strom (1726-1797). 70o, Johan Ernst Gunnerus (1718-1773). 100o, Michael Sars (1805-1869).

562 A150 40o brown .90 .90
563 A150 50o dull purple 1.10 .65
564 A150 70o brown red 1.10 .40
565 A150 100o bright blue 1.10 1.10
Nos. 562-565 (4) 4.20 3.05

Issued to honor Norwegian zoologists.

Leapfrog — A151

1970, Nov. 17 Photo. *Perf. 13*

566 A151 50o Ball game .55 .40
567 A151 70o shown .80 .20

Central School of Gymnastics, Oslo, cent.

Seal of Tonsberg A152

1971, Jan. 20 Photo. *Perf. 13*

568 A152 70o dark red .48 .35
569 A152 100o blue black .95 .65

City of Tonsberg, 1,100th anniversary.

Parliament A153

1971, Feb. 23

570 A153 70o red brn & lil .48 .35
571 A153 100o dk bl & sl grn .95 .65

Centenary of annual sessions of Norwegian Parliament.

Hand, Heart and Eye — A154

1971, Mar. 26 Photo. *Perf. 13*

572 A154 50o emerald & blk .55 .45
573 A154 70o scarlet & blk .55 .30

Joint northern campaign for the benefit of refugees.

"Haugianerne" by Adolph Tiedemand — A155

1971, Apr. 27 Photo. *Perf. 13*

574 A155 60o dark gray .45 .25
575 A155 70o brown .45 .25

Hans Nielsen Hauge (1771-1824), church reformer.

Worshippers Coming to Church A156

Design: 70o, Building first church, vert.

1971, May 21

576 A156 70o black & dk red .48 .35
577 A156 1k black & blue 1.90 1.25

900th anniversary of the Bishopric of Oslo.

Roald Amundsen, Antarctic Treaty Emblem A157

The Farmer and the Woman A158

1971, June 23 Engr. *Perf. 13*

578 A157 100o blue & org red 3.00 3.00

Antarctic Treaty pledging peaceful uses of and scientific cooperation in Antarctica, 10th anniv.

1971, Nov. 17 Photo. *Perf. 13*

Designs: 50o, The Preacher and the King, horiz. 70o, The Troll and the Girl. Illustrations for legends and folk tales by Erik Werenskiold.

579 A158 40o olive & blk .42 .25
580 A158 50o blue & blk .42 .25
581 A158 70o magenta & blk .85 .25
Nos. 579-581 (3) 1.69 .75

Engine Turning A159

1972, Apr. 10 Photo. *Perf. 13*

582 A159 80o red & gold .80 .35
583 A159 1.20k ultra & gold .80 .75

Norwegian Savings Bank sesquicentennial.

Norway #18 — A160

Dragon's Head, Oseberg Viking Ship — A161

1972, May 6 Engr. & Photo. *Perf. 12*

584 A160 80o shown .48 .35
585 A160 1k Norway #17 .70 .50
a. Souvenir sheet of 2, #584-585 5.00 5.50

Centenary of the post horn stamps. No. 585a sold for 2.50k.

1972, June 7 Engr. *Perf. 13*

Ancient Artifacts: 50o, Horseman from Stone of Alstad. 60o, Horseman, wood carving, stave church, Hemsedal. 1.20k, Sword hilt, found at Lodingen.

586 A161 50o yellow grn .60 .55
587 A161 60o brown 1.10 1.00
588 A161 80o dull red 1.25 .45
589 A161 1.20k ultra 1.10 1.00
Nos. 586-589 (4) 4.05 3.00

1,100th anniversary of unification.

King Haakon VII (1872-1957) A162

"Joy" A163

1972, Aug. 3 Engr. *Perf. 13*

590 A162 80o brown orange .90 .35
591 A162 1.20k Prussian bl .80 .70

1972, Aug. 15 Photo. *Perf. 13x13½*

Design: 1.20k, "Solidarity."

592 A163 80o brt magenta .70 .30
593 A163 1.20k Prussian blue .80 .70

2nd Intl. Youth Stamp Exhib., INTERJUNEX 72, Kristiansand, Aug. 25-Sept. 3.

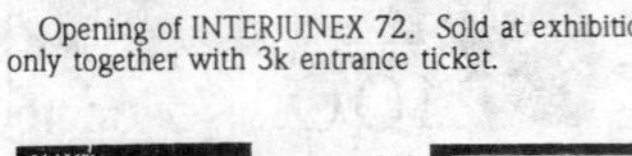

Same Overprinted "INTERJUNEX 72"

1972, Aug. 25

594 A163 80o brt magenta 3.00 2.50
595 A163 1.20k Prussian blue 3.00 2.50

Opening of INTERJUNEX 72. Sold at exhibition only together with 3k entrance ticket.

"Maud" A164 — "Little Man" A165

Polar Exploration Ships: 80o, "Fram." 1.20k, "Gjoa."

1972, Sept. 20 *Perf. 13½x13*

596 A164 60o olive & green 1.25 .70
597 A164 80o red & black 1.75 .35
598 A164 1.20k blue & red brn 1.75 1.50
Nos. 596-598 (3) 4.75 2.55

1972, Nov. 15 Litho. *Perf. 13½x13*

Illustrations for folk tales by Theodor Kittelsen (1857-1914): 60o, The Troll who wondered how old he was. 80o, The princess riding the polar bear.

599 A165 50o green & blk .45 .20
600 A165 60o blue & blk .45 .35
601 A165 80o pink & blk .45 .20
Nos. 599-601 (3) 1.35 .75

Dr. Armauer G. Hansen and Leprosy Bacillus Drawing — A166

Design: 1.40k, Dr. Hansen and leprosy bacillus, microscopic view.

1973, Feb. 28 Engr. *Perf. 13x13½*

602 A166 1k henna brn & bl .52 .35
603 A166 1.40k dk bl & dp org 1.10 1.00

Centenary of the discovery of the Hansen bacilus, the cause of leprosy.

Europa Issue 1973
Common Design Type

1973, Apr. 30 Photo. *Perf. 12½x13*
Size: 37x20mm

604 CD16 1k red, org & lil 1.65 .35
605 CD16 1.40k dk grn, grn & bl 1.10 .75

Types of 1893 and 1962-63

Designs: 75o, 85o, Rye and fish. 80o, 140o, Stave church. 100o, 110o, 120o, 125o, Rock carvings.

1972-75 Engr. *Perf. 13x13½*

606 A10 25o ultra ('74) .15 .15
a. Booklet pane of 4 3.00
608 A101 75o green ('73) .45 .15
609 A102 80o red brown .75 .15
a. Booklet pane of 10 35.00
610 A101 85o bister ('74) .60 .25
611 A101 100o red ('73) 1.10 .15
a. Booklet pane of 10 15.00
612 A101 110o rose car ('74) .75 .15
613 A101 120o gray blue .85 .50
614 A101 125o red ('75) .85 .15
a. Booklet pane of 10 12.00
615 A102 140o dk blue ('73) .95 .40
Nos. 606-615 (9) 6.45
Set value 1.55

Nordic Cooperation Issue

Nordic House, Reykjavik A167

1973, June 26 Engr. *Perf. 12½*

617 A167 1k multi 1.25 .40
618 A167 1.40k multi .65 .60

A century of postal cooperation among Denmark, Finland, Iceland, Norway and Sweden; Nordic Postal Conference, Reykjavik, Iceland.

King Olav V — A168

Jacob Aall — A169

1973, July 2 Engr. *Perf. 13*

619 A168 1k car & org brn .65 .22
620 A168 1.40k blue & org brn .70 .65

70th birthday of King Olav V.

1973, Aug. 22 Engr. *Perf. 13*

621 A169 1k deep claret .65 .20
622 A169 1.40k dk blue gray 1.00 .65

Jacob Aall (1773-1844), mill owner and industrial pioneer.

Blade Decoration A170

Viola Biflora A171

Handicraft from Lapland: 1k, Textile pattern. 1.40k, Decoration made of tin.

1973, Oct. 9 Photo. *Perf. 13x12½*

623 A170 75o blk brn & buff .40 .40
624 A170 1k dp car & buff .65 .30
625 A170 1.40k blk & dl bl .80 .50
Nos. 623-625 (3) 1.85 1.20

1973, Nov. 15 Litho. *Perf. 13*

626 A171 65o shown .48 .18
627 A171 70o Veronica Fruticans .55 .40
628 A171 1k Phyllodoce corrulea .70 .25
Nos. 626-628 (3) 1.73 .83

See Nos. 754-756, 770-771.

Surveyor in Northern Norway, 1907 — A172

1.40k, South Norway Mountains map, 1851.

1973, Dec. 14 Engr. *Perf. 13*

629 A172 1k red orange .48 .48
630 A172 1.40k slate blue .70 .70

Geographical Survey of Norway, bicent.

Lindesnes — A173

Design: 1.40k, North Cape.

1974, Apr. 25 Photo. *Perf. 13*

631 A173 1k olive .80 .50
632 A173 1.40k dark blue 1.50 1.50

Ferry in Hardanger Fjord, by A. Tidemand and H. Gude — A174

Classical Norwegian paintings: 1.40k, Stugunoset from Filefjell, by Johan Christian Dahl.

1974, May 21 Litho. *Perf. 13*

633 A174 1k multi .60 .20
634 A174 1.40k multi .80 .60

Gulating Law Manuscript, 1325 A175 — King Magnus VI Lagaböter A176

1974, June 21 Engr.

635 A175 1k red & brn .55 .20
636 A176 1.40k ultra & brn .95 .75

700th anniv. of the National Code given by King Magnus VI Lagaböter (1238-80).

Saw Blade and Pines — A177

J.H.L. Vogt — A178

Design: 1k, Cog wheel and guard.

1974, Aug. 12 Photo. *Perf. 13*

637 A177 85o grn, ol & dk grn 1.65 1.65
638 A177 1k org, plum & dk red 1.40 .60

Safe working conditions.

1974, Sept. 4 Engr. *Perf. 13*

Geologists: 85o, V. M. Goldschmidt. 1k, Theodor Kjerulf. 1.40k, Waldemar C. Brogger.

639 A178 65o olive & red brn .30 .20
640 A178 85o magenta & red brn .90 .75
641 A178 1k orange & red brn .45 .25
642 A178 1.40k blue & red brn .75 .60
Nos. 639-642 (4) 2.40 1.80

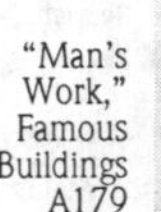

"Man's Work," Famous Buildings A179

Design: 1.40k, "Men, our brethren," people of various races.

1974, Oct. 9 Photo. *Perf. 13*

643 A179 1k green & brn .52 .20
644 A179 1.40k brn & grnsh bl .70 .60

Centenary of Universal Postal Union.

Horseback Rider A180

Flowers A181

1974, Nov. 15 Litho. *Perf. 13*

645 A180 85o multicolored .42 .35
646 A181 1k multicolored .50 .20

Norwegian folk art, rose paintings from furniture decorations.

Woman Skier, c. 1900 A182

1975, Jan. 15 Litho. *Perf. 13*

647 A182 1k shown .90 .20
648 A182 1.40k Telemark turn .90 .70

"Norway, homeland of skiing."

Women — A183

Nusfjord Fishing Harbor — A184

Design: Detail from wrought iron gates of Vigeland Park, Oslo.

1975, Mar. 7 Litho. *Perf. 13*

649 A183 1.25k brt rose lil & dk bl .65 .25
650 A183 1.40k bl & dk bl .65 .65

International Women's Year.

1975, Apr. 17 Litho. *Perf. 13*

1.25k, Street in Stavanger. 1.40k, View of Roros.

651 A184 1k yellow green .85 .40
652 A184 1.25k dull red .60 .15
653 A184 1.40k blue .70 .60

European Architectural Heritage Year.

Norwegian Krone, 1875 — A185 — Ole Jacob Broch — A186

1975, May 20 Engr. *Perf. 13*

654 A185 1.25k dark carmine .48 .70
655 A186 1.40k blue .70 .60

Centenary of Monetary Convention of Norway, Sweden and Denmark (1.25k); and of Intl. Meter Convention, Paris, 1875. Ole Jacob Broch (1818-1889) was first director of Intl. Bureau of Weights and Measures.

Scouting in Summer A187

Design: 1.40k, Scouting in winter (skiers).

1975, June 19 Litho. *Perf. 13*

656 A187 1.25k multicolored .75 .35
657 A187 1.40k multicolored .75 .75

Nordjamb 75, 14th Boy Scout Jamboree, Lillehammer, July 29-Aug. 7.

Sod Hut and Settlers A188

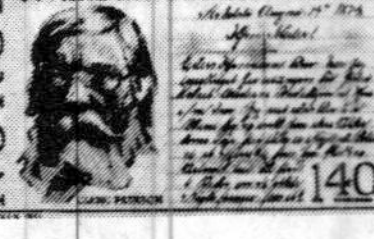

Cleng Peerson and Letter from America, 1874 A189

1975, July 4

658 A188 1.25k red brown 1.00 .15
659 A189 1.40k bluish blk .70 .65

Sesquicentennial of Norwegian emigration to America.

Templet, Tempelfjord, Spitsbergen — A190

Miners Leaving Coal Pit — A191

Design: 1.40k, Polar bear.

1975, Aug. 14 **Engr.** ***Perf. 13***

660 A190 1k olive black .80 .50
661 A191 1.25k maroon .80 .30
662 A191 1.40k Prus blue 2.25 1.75
Nos. 660-662 (3) 3.85 2.55

50th anniversary of union of Spitsbergen (Svalbard) with Norway.

Microphone with Ear Phones — A192

Radio Tower and Houses — A193

Designs after children's drawings.

1975, Oct. 9 **Litho.** ***Perf. 13***

663 A192 1.25k multi .40 .35
664 A193 1.40k multi .60 .50

50 years of broadcasting in Norway.

Annunciation A194

Nativity A195

Painted vault of stave church of Al, 13th cent: 1k, Visitation. 1.40k, Adoration of the Kings.

1975, Nov. 14

665 A194 80o red & multi .30 .20
666 A194 1k red & multi .42 .20
667 A195 1.25k red & multi .42 .20
668 A195 1.40k red & multi .70 .45
Nos. 665-668 (4) 1.84 1.05

Sigurd and Regin A196

Halling, Hallingdal Dance A197

1976, Jan. 20 **Engr.** ***Perf. 13***

669 A196 7.50k brown 2.25 .50

Norwegian folk tale, Sigurd the Dragon-killer. Design from portal of Hylestad stave church, 13th century.

1976, Feb. 25 **Litho.** ***Perf. 13***

Folk Dances: 1k, Springar, Hordaland region. 1.25k, Gangar, Setesdal.

670 A197 80o black & multi .45 .30
671 A197 1k black & multi .60 .20
672 A197 1.25k black & multi .60 .15
Nos. 670-672 (3) 1.65 .65

Silver Sugar Shaker, Stavanger, c. 1770 — A198

1.40k, Goblet, Nostetangen glass, c. 1770.

1976, Mar. 25 **Engr.** ***Perf. 13***

673 A198 1.25k multicolored .55 .42
674 A198 1.40k multicolored .70 .70

Oslo Museum of Applied Art, centenary.

Ceramic Bowl Shaped Like Bishop's Mitre A199

Europa: 1.40k, Plate and CEPT emblem. Both designs after faience works from Herrebo Potteries, c. 1760.

1976, May 3 **Litho.** ***Perf. 13***

675 A199 1.25k rose mag & brn .80 .60
676 A199 1.40k brt bl & vio bl 1.10 .95

The Pulpit, Lyse Fjord — A200

Gulleplet (Peak), Sogne Fjord — A201

Perf. 13 on 3 Sides

1976, May 20 **Litho.**

677 A200 1k multi .80 .40
a. Booklet pane of 10 5.50
678 A201 1.25k multi .80 .25
a. Booklet pane of 10 8.00

Nos. 677-678 issued only in booklets.

Graph Paper, Old and New Subjects — A202

Design: 2k, Graph of national product.

1976, July 1 **Engr.** ***Perf. 13***

679 A202 1.25k red brown .50 .20
680 A202 2k dark blue .80 .40

Central Bureau of Statistics, centenary.

Olav Duun on Dun Mountain A203

1976, Sept. 10 **Engr.** ***Perf. 13***

681 A203 1.25k multi .65 .20
682 A203 1.40k multi .70 .60

Olav Duun (1876-1939), novelist.

"Birches" by Th. Fearnley (1802-1842) A204

Design: 1.40k, "Gamle Furutraer" (trees), by L. Hertervig (1830-1902).

1976, Oct. 8 **Litho.** ***Perf. 13***

683 A204 1.25k multi .65 .25
684 A204 1.40k multi .70 .60

"April" — A205

"May" — A206

Baldishol Tapestry — A207

Design: 80o, 1k, Details from 13th century Baldishol tapestry, found in Baldishol stave church.

1976, Nov. 5 **Litho.** ***Perf. 13***

685 A205 80o multi .45 .25
686 A206 1k multi .45 .25
687 A207 1.25k multi .60 .25
Nos. 685-687 (3) 1.50 .75

Five Water Lilies — A208

Photo. & Engr.

1977, Feb. 2 ***Perf. 12½***

688 A208 1.25k multi .65 .20
689 A208 1.40k multi .65 .60

Nordic countries cooperation for protection of the environment and 25th Session of Nordic Council, Helsinki, Feb. 19.

Akershus Castle, Oslo — A209

Steinviksholm Fort, Asen Fjord — A210

Torungen Lighthouses, Arendal — A211

1977, Feb. 24 **Engr.** ***Perf. 13***

690 A209 1.25k red .45 .15
691 A210 1.30k olive brown .50 .15
692 A211 1.80k blue .65 .20
Nos. 690-692 (3) 1.60
Set value .35

See Nos. 715-724, 772-774.

Europa Issue

Hamnoy, Lofoten, Fishing Village — A212

Huldre Falls, Loen — A213

Perf. 13 on 3 Sides

1977, May 2 **Litho.**

693 A212 1.25k multi .70 .15
a. Booklet pane of 10 8.00
694 A213 1.80k multi 1.00 .60
a. Booklet pane of 10 6.00

Nos. 693-694 issued only in booklets.

Norwegian Trees — A214

1977, June 1 **Engr.** ***Perf. 13***

695 A214 1k Spruce .38 .25
696 A214 1.25k Fir .45 .25
697 A214 1.80k Birch .65 .60
Nos. 695-697 (3) 1.48 1.10

"Constitutionen," Norway's 1st Steamship, at Arendal — A215

Designs: 1.25k, "Vesteraalen" off Bodo, 1893. 1.30k, "Kong Haakon," 1904 and "Dronningen," 1893, off Stavanger. 1.80k, "Nordstjernen" and "Harald Jarl" at pier, 1970.

1977, June 22

698 A215 1k brown .55 .25
699 A215 1.25k red .65 .25
700 A215 1.30k green 1.50 1.50
701 A215 1.80k blue .75 .65
Nos. 698-701 (4) 3.45 2.65

Norwegian ships serving coastal routes.

Fishermen and Boats — A216

Fish and Fishhooks — A217

1977, Sept. 22 **Engr.** ***Perf. 13***

702 A216 1.25k buff, lt brn & dk brn .55 .20
703 A217 1.80k lt bl, bl & dk bl .75 .60

Men, by Halfdan Egedius — A218

Landscape, by August Cappelen A219

1977, Oct. 7 **Litho.** ***Perf. 13***

704 A218 1.25k multi .55 .20
705 A219 1.80k multi .75 .60

Norwegian classical painting.

David with the Bells — A220

Christmas: 1k, Singing Friars. 1.25k, Virgin and Child, horiz. Designs from Bible of Bishop Aslak Bolt, 13th century.

1977, Nov. 10 **Litho.** ***Perf. 13***

Size: 21x27mm

706 A220 80o multi .42 .20
707 A220 1k multi .42 .15

Size: 34x27mm

708 A220 1.25k multi .42 .15
Nos. 706-708 (3) 1.26 .50

Post Horn Type of 1893 and Scenic Types of 1977

Designs: 1k, Austrat Manor, 1650. 1.10k, Trondenes Chruch, early 13th Century. 1.40k, Ruins of Hamar Cathedral, 12th Century. 1.75k, Seamen's Hall, Stavern, 1926, vert. 2k, Tofte Estate, Dovre, 16-17th cent., vert. 2.25k, Oscarhall, Oslofjord, 1847, vert. 2.50k, Log house, Breiland, 1785. 2.75k, Damsgard Building, Lakesvag, 1770. 3k, Selje Monastery, 11th cent. 3.50k, Lighthouse, Lindesnes, 1655.

Perf. 13x13½, 13½x13

1978-83 **Engr.**

709 A10 40o olive .15 .15
710 A10 50o dull purple .18 .15
711 A10 60o vermilion .22 .15
712 A10 70o orange .30 .22
713 A10 80o red brown .28 .15
714 A10 90o brown .35 .22
715 A209 1k green .35 .15
716 A209 1.10k rose mag .70 .18
717 A209 1.40k dark purple .48 .18
718 A211 1.75k green ('82) .55 .18
719 A211 2k brown red ('82) .65 .18
720 A211 2.25k dp vio ('82) .80 .35
721 A209 2.50k brn red ('83) .80 .18
722 A209 2.75k dp mag ('82) 1.00 .65
723 A209 3k dk bl ('82) .90 .35
724 A209 3.50k dp vio ('83) 1.10 .45
Nos. 709-724 (16) 8.81
Set value 3.30

See Nos. 772-774.

Peer Gynt, and Reindeer by Per Krogh — A222

Henrik Ibsen, by Erik Werenskiold, 1895 — A223

1978, Mar. 10 **Litho.** ***Perf. 13***

725 A222 1.25k buff & blk .60 .28
726 A223 1.80k multicolored .70 .70

Ibsen (1828-1906), poet and dramatist.

Heddal Stave Church, c. 1250 A224

Lenangstindene and Jaegervasstindene A225

Europa: 1.80k, Borgund stave church.

1978, May 2 **Engr.** ***Perf. 13***

727 A224 1.25k dk brn & red .75 .25
728 A224 1.80k sl grn & bl .95 .70

Perf. 13 on 3 Sides

1978, June 1 **Litho.**

1.25k, Gaustatoppen, mountain, Telemark.

729 A225 1k multi .80 .40
a. Booklet pane of 10 6.50
730 A225 1.25k multi .80 .25
a. Booklet pane of 10 9.00

Nos. 729-730 issued only in booklets.

Olav V Sailing — A226

Design: 1.80k, King Olav delivering royal address in Parliament, vert.

1978, June 30 **Engr.** ***Perf. 13***

731 A226 1.25k red brown .55 .20
732 A226 1.80k violet blue .70 .60

75th birthday of King Olav V.

Norway No. 107 — A227

Stamps: b, #108. c, #109. d, #110. e, #111. f, #112. g, #113. h, #114.

Perf. 13 on 3 Sides

1978, Sept. 19 **Litho.**

733 Booklet pane of 8 8.75 9.50
a.-h. A227 1.25k, any single 1.05 1.10

NORWEX '80 Philatelic Exhibition, Oslo, June 13-22, 1980. Booklet sold for 15k; the additional 5k went for financing the exhibition.

Willow Pipe Player — A228

Musical Instruments: 1.25k, Norwegian violin. 1.80k, Norwegian zither. 7.50k, Ram's horn.

1978, Oct. 6 **Engr.** ***Perf. 13***

734 A228 1k deep green .35 .15
735 A228 1.25k dk rose car .55 .15
736 A228 1.80k dk violet blue .60 .30
737 A228 7.50k gray 2.25 .30
Nos. 734-737 (4) 3.75 .90

Wooden Doll, 1830 — A229

Ski Jump, Huseby Hill, c. 1900 — A230

Christmas: 1k, Toy town 1896-97. 1.25k, Wooden horse from Torpo in Hallingdal.

1978, Nov. 10 **Litho.**

738 A229 80o multi .45 .20
739 A229 1k multi .45 .15
740 A229 1.25k multi .45 .15
Nos. 738-740 (3) 1.35 .50

1979, Mar. 2 **Engr.** ***Perf. 13***

Designs: 1.25k, Crown Prince Olav, Holmenkollen ski jump competition, 1922. 1.80k, Cross-country race, Holmenkollen, 1976.

741 A230 1k green .42 .25
742 A230 1.25k red .52 .25
743 A230 1.80k blue .70 .60
Nos. 741-743 (3) 1.64 1.10

Huseby Hills and Holmenkollen ski competitions, centenary.

Girl, by Mathias Stoltenberg A231

Road to Briksdal Glacier A232

Portrait: 1.80k, Boy, by H. C. F. Hosenfelder.

1979, Apr. 26 **Litho.** ***Perf. 13***

744 A231 1.25k multi .52 .25
745 A231 1.80k multi .70 .60

International Year of the Child.

1979, June 13 ***Perf. 13 on 3 Sides***

1.25k, Boat on Skjernoysund, near Mandal.

746 A232 1k multi .75 .20
a. Booklet pane of 10 5.50
747 A232 1.25k multi .75 .25
a. Booklet pane of 10 7.50

Nos. 746-747 issued only in booklets.

Johan Falkberget, by Harald Dal — A233

Kylling Bridge, Verma, 1923 — A234

1.80k, "Ann-Magritt and the Hovi Bullock" (by Falkberget), monument by Kristofer Leirdal.

1979, Sept. 4 **Engr.** ***Perf. 13***

748 A233 1.25k deep claret .55 .25
749 A233 1.80k Prus blue .70 .60

Johan Falkberget (1879-1967), novelist.

1979, Oct. 5

Norwegian Engineering: 2k, Vessingsjo Dam, Nea, 1960. 10k, Stratfjord A, oil drilling platform in North Sea.

750 A234 1.25k gray brown .65 .15
751 A234 2k gray blue 1.00 .25
752 A234 10k brown olive 3.25 .65
Nos. 750-752 (3) 4.90 1.05

Souvenir Sheet

Dornier Wal over Polar Map — A235

Arctic Aviation and Polar Maps: 2k, Dirigible Norge. 2.80k, Loening air yacht amphibian. 4k, Reidar Viking DC-7C.

1979, Oct. 5 **Litho.** ***Perf. 13***

753 Sheet of 4 6.25 6.25
a. A235 1.25k multi 1.40 1.40
b. A235 2k multi 1.40 1.40
c. A235 2.80k multi 1.40 1.40
d. A235 4k multi 1.40 1.40

Norwex '80 Intl. Phil. Exhib., Oslo, June 13-22, 1980. No. 753 sold for 15k.

Mountain Flower Type of 1973

1979, Nov. 22 **Litho.** ***Perf. 13½***

754 A171 80o Ranunculus glacialis .35 .15
755 A171 1k Potentilla crantzii .55 .25
756 A171 1.25k Saxiflora oppositifolia .55 .15
Nos. 754-756 (3) 1.45 .55

Norwegian Christian Youth Assn. Centenary A237

1980, Feb. 26 **Litho.** ***Perf. 13***

757 A237 100o shown .40 .15
758 A237 180o Emblems and doves .70 .50

Oyster Catcher — A238

Perf. 13 on 3 Sides

1980, Apr. 18 **Litho.**

759 A238 100o shown .40 .15
760 A238 100o Mallard .40 .15
a. Bklt. pane, 5 #759, 5 #760 4.00
761 A238 125o Dipper .40 .15
762 A238 125o Great tit .40 .15
a. Bklt. pane, 5 #761, 5 #762 4.50
Nos. 759-762 (4) 1.60
Set value .45

Nos. 759-762 issued in booklets only.

Dish Antenna, Old Phone — A239

National Telephone Service Centenary: 1.80k, Erecting telephone pole.

1980, May 9 **Litho.** ***Perf. 13½***

763 A239 1.25k multi .48 .25
764 A239 1.80k multi .70 .52

Souvenir Sheet

Paddle Steamer "Bergen" A240

1980, June 13

765 Sheet of 4 6.00 6.00
a. A240 1.25k shown 1.40 1.40
b. A240 2k Train, 1900 1.40 1.40
c. A240 2.80k Bus, 1940 1.40 1.40
d. A240 4k Boeing 737 1.40 1.40

NORWEX '80 Stamp Exhibition, Oslo, June 13-22. Sold for 15k.

Nordic Cooperation Issue

Vulcan as an Armourer, by Henrich Bech, 1761 — A241

Henrich Bech Cast Iron Stove Ornament: 1.80k, Hercules at a Burning Altar, 1769.

1980, Sept. 9 **Engr.** ***Perf. 13***

766 A241 1.25k dk vio brn .55 .25
767 A241 1.80k dark blue .80 .50

Self-Portrait, by Christian Skredsvig (1854-1924) A242

Paintings: 1.25k, Fire, by Nikolai Astrup.

1980, Nov. 14 **Litho.** ***Perf. 13½x13***

768 A242 1.25k multi .50 .25
769 A242 1.80k multi .75 .50

Mountain Flower Type of 1973

1980, Nov. 14 ***Perf. 13***

770 A171 80o Sorbus aucuparia .48 .15
771 A171 1k Rosa canina .48 .15
Set value .24

Scenic Type of 1977

1.50k, Stavanger Cathedral, 13th cent. 1.70k, Rosenkrantz Tower, Bergen, 13th-16th cent. 2.20k, Church of Tromsdalen (Arctic Cathedral), 1965.

Perf. 13x13½, 13½x13

1981, Feb. 26 **Engr.**

772 A211 1.50k brown red .48 .15
773 A211 1.70k olive green .55 .25
774 A209 2.20k dark blue .70 .50
Nos. 772-774 (3) 1.73 .90

Lesser White-fronted Goose — A243

Nat'l Milk Producers Assn. Centenary — A244

Perf. 13 on 3 Sides

1981, Feb. 26 **Litho.**

775 A243 1.30k shown .35 .20
776 A243 1.30k Peregrine falcon .35 .20
a. Booklet pane of 10 (5 each) 3.50
777 A243 1.50k Black guillemot .42 .18
778 A243 1.50k Puffin .42 .18
a. Booklet pane of 10 (5 each) 4.25
Nos. 775-778 (4) 1.54 .76

Nos. 775-778 issued in booklets. See Nos. 800-801, 821-822.

1981, Mar. 24 **Litho.** ***Perf.* 13x13½**

779 A244 1.10k Cow .35 .20
780 A244 1.50k Goat .65 .15

A245

A246

Europa: 1.50k, The Mermaid, painted dish, Hol. 2.20k, The Proposal, painted box, Nes.

1981, May 4 **Litho.** ***Perf.* 13**

781 A245 1.50k multi .75 .25
782 A245 2.20k multi .90 .60

1981, May 4 **Engr.**

Designs: 1.30k, Weighing anchor. 1.50k, Climbing sail pole, vert. 2.20k, Training Ship Christian Radich.

783 A246 1.30k dk olive grn .48 .25
784 A246 1.50k orange red .65 .25
785 A246 2.20k dark blue .70 .60
Nos. 783-785 (3) 1.83 1.10

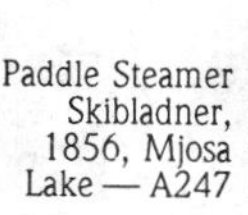

Paddle Steamer Skibladner, 1856, Mjosa Lake — A247

Lake Transportation: 1.30k, Victoria, 1882, Bandak Channel. 1.50k, Faemund II, 1905, Fermund Lake. 2.30k, Storegut, 1956, Tinnsjo Lake.

1981, June 11 **Engr.** ***Perf.* 13**

786 A247 1.10k dark brown .40 .32
787 A247 1.30k green .48 .25
788 A247 1.50k red .65 .25
789 A247 2.30k dark blue .90 .65
Nos. 786-789 (4) 2.43 1.47

Group Walking Arm in Arm — A248

1981, Aug. 25 **Engr.**

790 A248 1.50k shown .50 .25
791 A248 2.20k Group, diff. .75 .60

Intl. Year of the Disabled.

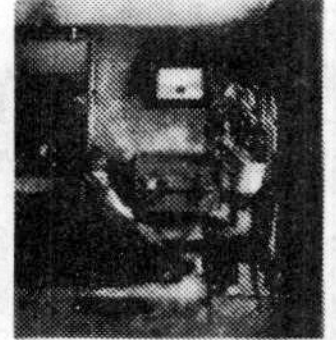

A249

A250

Paintings: 1.50k, Interior in Blue, by Harriet Backer (1845-1932). 1.70k, Peat Moor on Jaeren, by Kitty Lange Kielland (1843-1914).

1981, Oct. 9 **Litho.** ***Perf.* 13**

792 A249 1.50k multi .48 .25
793 A249 1.70k multi .65 .40

1981, Nov. 25 **Litho.** ***Perf.* 13½**

Tapestries: 1.10k, One of the Three Kings, Skjak, 1625. 1.30k, Adoration of the Infant Christ, tapestry, Skjak, 1625. 1.50k, The Marriage of Cana, Storen, 18th cent.

794 A250 1.10k multi .40 .15
795 A250 1.30k multi .40 .15

Size: 29x37mm

796 A250 1.50k multi .55 .15
Nos. 794-796 (3) 1.35
Set value .36

1921 Nobel Prize Winners Christian L. Lange (1869-1938) and Hjalmar Branting (1860-1925) A251

1981, Nov. 25 **Engr.** ***Perf.* 13**

797 A251 5k black 1.75 .40

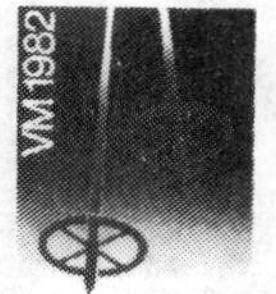

World Skiing Championship, Oslo — A252

1982, Feb. 16 ***Perf.* 13½**

798 A252 2k Poles .65 .25
799 A252 3k Skis 1.10 .60

Bird Type of 1981

Perf. 13 on 3 Sides

1982, Apr. 1 **Litho.**

800 A243 2k Blue-throat .55 .15
801 A243 2k Robin .55 .15
a. Bklt. pane of 10 (5 each) 6.00

Nos. 800-801 issued only in booklets.

Fight Against Tuberculosis — A253

1982, Apr. 1 ***Perf.* 13**

802 A253 2k Nurse .70 .20
803 A253 3k Microscope 1.10 .60

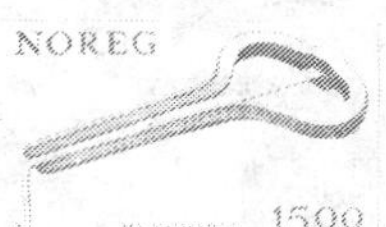

Jew's Harp — A254

1982, May 3 **Engr.** ***Perf.* 13**

804 A254 15k sepia 4.00 .65

Europa 1982 — A255

1982, May 3

805 A255 2k Haakon VII, 1905 .85 .25
806 A255 3k Prince Olav, King Haakon VII, 1945 1.40 .60

Girls from Telemark, by Erik Werenskiold (1855-1938) A256

Design: 2k, Tone Veli at the Fence, by Henrik Sorensen (1882-1962), vert.

1982, June 23 **Litho.** ***Perf.* 13**

807 A256 1.75k multi .70 .35
808 A256 2k multi .70 .20

Consecration Ceremony, Nidaros Cathedral, Trondheim — A257

Sigrid Undset (1882-1949), Writer, by A.C. Svarstad — A258

1982, Sept. 2 **Engr.** ***Perf.* 13x13½**

809 A257 3k blue 1.10 .55

Reign of King Olav, 25th anniv.

1982, Oct. 1 **Litho.** ***Perf.* 13**

Painting: 1.75k, Bjornstjerne Bjornson (1832-1910), writer, by Erik Werenskiold, horiz.

810 A258 1.75k multi .65 .30
811 A258 2k multi .75 .25

A souvenir sheet containing Nos. 810-811 was prepared by the Norwegian Philatelic Association.

Graphical Union of Norway Centenary A259

1982, Oct. 1

812 A259 2k "A" .65 .15
813 A259 3k Type 1.00 .42

Fridtjof Nansen A260

Christmas A261

1982, Nov. 15 **Engr.** ***Perf.* 13½x13**

814 A260 3k dark blue 1.10 .50

Fridtjof Nansen (1861-1930) polar explorer, 1922 Nobel Peace Prize winner.

Perf. 13 on 3 Sides

1982, Nov. 15 **Litho.**

Painting: Christmas Tradition, by Adolf Tidemand (1814-1876).

815 A261 1.75k multi .60 .32
a. Booklet pane of 10 6.00

Farm Dog — A262

1983, Feb. 16 **Litho.** ***Perf.* 13x13½**

816 A262 2k shown .60 .15
817 A262 2.50k Elk hound .80 .15
818 A262 3.50k Hunting dog 1.10 .50
Nos. 816-818 (3) 2.50 .80

Norway stamps can be mounted in the annually supplemented Scott Scandinavia and Finland album.

Nordic Cooperation Issue — A263

1983, Mar. 24 **Litho.** ***Perf.* 13**

819 A263 2.50k Mountains .90 .15
820 A263 3.50k Fjord 1.25 .65

Bird Type of 1981

1983, Apr. 14 ***Perf.* 13 on 3 Sides**

821 A243 2.50k Goose .80 .15
822 A243 2.50k Little auk .80 .15
a. Bklt. pane of 10 (5 each) 8.00

Nos. 821-822 issued only in booklets.

Europa — A264

Designs: 2.50k, Edvard Grieg (1843-1907), composer and his Piano Concerto in A-minor. 3.50k, Niels Henrik Abel (1802-1829), mathematician, by Gustav Vigeland, vert.

1983, May 3 **Engr.** ***Perf.* 13**

823 A264 2.50k red orange 1.10 .15
824 A264 3.50k dk bl & grn 1.65 .40

World Communications Year — A265

Symbolic arrow designs.

1983, May 3 **Litho.**

825 A265 2.50k multi .90 .25
826 A265 3.50k multi 1.25 .60

80th Birthday of King Olav V, July 2 — A266

1983, June 22 **Engr.** ***Perf.* 13x13½**

827 A266 5k green 1.65 .40

Jonas Lie (1833-1908), Writer — A267

Northern Ships — A268

1983, Oct. 7 **Engr.** ***Perf.* 13½x13**

828 A267 2.50k red .90 .15

1983, Oct. 7 **Litho.**

829 A268 2k Nordlandsfemboring .70 .15
830 A268 3k Nordlandsjekt 1.10 .50

Christmas 1983 — A269

Paintings: 2k, The Sleigh Ride by Axel Ender (1853-1920). 2.50k, The Guests are Arriving by Gustav Wenzel (1859-1927).

Perf. 13 on 3 sides
1983, Nov. 17 **Litho.**
831 A269 2k multi .60 .15
a. Booklet pane of 10 6.00
832 A269 2.50k multi .90 .15
a. Booklet pane of 10 9.00

Postal Services
A270

1984, Feb. 24 **Litho.** ***Perf. 13½x13***
833 A270 2k Counter service .70 .20
834 A270 2.50k Sorting .85 .15
835 A270 3.50k Delivery 1.10 .45
Nos. 833-835 (3) 2.65 .80

Freshwater Fishing
A271

Christopher Hansteen (1784-1873), Astronomer
A272

1984, Apr. 10 **Engr.** ***Perf. 13***
836 A271 2.50k shown .80 .15
837 A271 3k Salmon fishing 1.00 .45
838 A271 3.50k Ocean fishing 1.10 .45
Nos. 836-838 (3) 2.90 1.05

1984, Apr. 10
839 A272 3.50k Magnetic meridians, parallels, horiz. 1.10 .45
840 A272 5k shown 1.50 .45

Europa (1959-84) — A273

Produce, Spices — A274

1984, June 4 **Litho.** ***Perf. 13***
841 A273 2.50k multi .80 .15
842 A273 3.50k multi 1.10 .45

1984, June 4 ***Perf. 13***
843 A274 2k shown .60 .15
844 A274 2.50k Flowers .75 .15
Set value .24

Horticultural Society centenary.

A275

A276

1984, June 4
845 A275 2.50k Worker bees .80 .15
846 A275 2.50k Rooster .80 .15
Set value .24

Centenaries: Beekeeping Society (No. 845); Poultry-breeding Society (No. 846).

1984, Oct. 5 **Engr.** ***Perf. 13***
847 A276 2.50k lake .80 .15

Ludvig Holberg (1684-1754), writer, by J.M. Bernigeroth.

A277

A278

1984, Oct. 5 **Litho. & Engr.**
848 A277 2.50k Children reading .70 .15
849 A277 3.50k First edition 1.10 .45

Norwegian Weekly Press sesquicentennial.

Perf. 13½x13 on 3 sides
1984, Nov. 15 **Litho.**

Illustrations from Children's Stories by Thorbjorn Egner.

850 A278 2k Karius & Baktus .60 .15
851 A278 2k Tree Shrew .60 .15
a. Bklt. pane of 10 (5 each #850-851) 6.00
852 A278 2.50k Cardamom Rovers .75 .15
853 A278 2.50k Chief Constable Bastian .75 .15
a. Bklt. pane of 10 (5 each #852-853) 7.50
Set value .48

Nos. 850-853 issued only in booklets.

Parliament Centenary
A279

1984, Nov. 15 **Engr.** ***Perf. 13½x13***
854 A279 7.50k Sverdrup Govt. parliament, 1884 2.25 .80

Antarctic Mountains — A280

1985, Apr. 18 **Litho.** ***Perf. 13***
855 A280 2.50k The Saw Blade .70 .15
856 A280 3.50k The Chopping Block 1.10 .45

Liberation from the German Occupation Forces, 40th Anniv. — A281

1985, May 8 **Engr.** ***Perf. 13x13½***
857 A281 3.50k dk bl & red 1.00 .45

Norwegian Artillery
A282

Anniversaries: 3k, Norwegian Artillery, 300th. 4k, Artillery Officers Training School, 200th.

1985, May 22 **Litho.** ***Perf. 13½x13***
858 A282 3k multi .80 .55
859 A282 4k multi 1.10 .70

Kongsten Fort, 300th Anniv.
A283

1985, May 22
860 A283 2.50k multi .75 .25

Europa
A284

Intl. Youth Year
A285

Designs: 2.50k, Torgeir Augundsson (1801-1872), fiddler. 3.50k, Ole Bull (1810-1880), composer, violinist.

1985, June 19 **Engr.**
861 A284 2.50k brown lake .75 .15
862 A284 3.50k dark blue 1.10 .45

1985, June 19 **Litho.**

Stone and bronze sculptures: 2k, Boy and Girl, detail, Vigeland Museum, Oslo. 3.50k, Fountain, detail, Vigeland Park, Oslo.

863 A285 2k multi .60 .25
864 A285 3.50k multi 1.10 .70

Electrification of Norway, Cent. — A286

1985, Sept. 6 **Engr.** ***Perf. 13½x13***
865 A286 2.50k Glomfjord Dam penstock .75 .20
866 A286 4k Linemen 1.25 .70

Public Libraries, 200th Anniv. — A287

Designs; 2.50k, Carl Deichman (1705-1780), Public Libraries System founder. 10k, Modern library interior, horiz.

1985, Oct. 4
867 A287 2.50k hn brn & yel brn .65 .20
868 A287 10k dark green 2.50 1.00

Ship Navigation
A288

Lithographed & Engraved
1985, Nov. 14 ***Perf. 13x13½***
869 A288 2.50k Dredger Berghavn, 1980 .75 .20
870 A288 5k Sextant and chart, 1791 1.50 .70

Port Authorities, 250th anniv., Hydrographic Services, bicent.

Christmas Wreath
A289

Bullfinches
A290

Booklet Stamps
Perf. 13½ on 3 Sides
1985, Nov. 14 **Litho.**
871 A289 2k multi .60 .20
a. Booklet pane of 10 6.00
872 A290 2.50k multi .75 .20
a. Booklet pane of 10 7.50

World Biathlon Championships, Feb. 18-23 — A290a

1986, Feb. 18 ***Perf. 13x13½***
873 A290a 2.50k shown .65 .20
874 A291 3.50k Shooting upright 1.00 .70

Ornaments
A291

Fauna
A292

Mushrooms — A293

Perf. 13½x13
1986-90 **Litho. & Engr.**
875 A291 2.10k Sun .65 .22
876 A291 2.30k Fish .68 .26
877 A292 2.60k Fox .78 .28
878 A291 2.70k Flowers, wheat .78 .28
879 A292 2.90k Capercaillie .95 .35
880 A292 3k Ermine .90 .35
881 A292 3.20k Mute swan 1.00 .38
882 A292 3.80k Reindeer 1.20 .45
883 A291 4k Star 1.25 .42
883A A292 4k Squirrel 1.20 .45
883B A292 4.50k Beaver 1.40 .55
Nos. 875-883B (11) 10.79 3.99

Issued: 2.10k, #883, 2/18/86; 2.30k, 2.70k, 2/12/87; 2.90k, 3.80k, 2/18/88; 2.60k, 3k, #883A, 2/20/89; 3.20k, 4.50k, 2/23/90.
See Nos. 958-959.

Booklet Stamps
Perf. 13½x13 on 3 Sides
1987-89 **Litho.**
884 A293 2.70k Cantharellus tubaeformis .80 .60
885 A293 2.70k Rozites caperata .80 .60
a. Bklt. pane, 5 #884, 5 #885 8.00
886 A293 2.90k Lepista nuda .95 .72
887 A293 2.90k Lactarius deterrimus .95 .72
a. Bklt. pane, 5 #886, 5 #887 9.50
888 A293 3k Cantharellus cibarius .90 .68
889 A293 3k Suillus luteus .90 .68
a. Bklt. pane, 5 #888, 5 #889 9.00
Nos. 884-889 (6) 5.30 4.00

Issued: 2.70k, 5/8; 2.90k, 4/26/88; 3k, 2/20/89.

Natl. Federation of Craftsmen, Cent. — A294

1986, Apr. 11 **Engr.**
890 A294 2.50k Stone cutter .55 .25
891 A294 7k Carpenter 1.65 1.00

Europa
A295

1986, Apr. 11 **Litho.** ***Perf. 13***
892 A295 2.50k Bird, industry .55 .30
893 A295 3.50k Acid rain .80 .35

Nordic Cooperation Issue — A296

Sister towns.

1986, May 27 *Perf. 13½x13*
894 A296 2.50k Moss .55 .30
895 A296 4k Alesund .95 .50

Famous Men — A297

Designs: 2.10k, Hans Poulson Egede (1686-1758), missionary, and map of Norway and Greenland. 2.50k, Herman Wildenvey (1886-1959), poet, and poem carved in Seaman's Commemoration Hall, Stavern. 3k, Tore Orjasaeter (1886-1968), poet, and antique cupboard, Skjak. 4k, Engebret Soot, engineer, and canal lock, Orje.

Engr., Litho. & Engr. (#897)

1986, Oct. 17 *Perf. 13x13½*
896 A297 2.10k multi .48 .45
897 A297 2.50k multi .55 .52
898 A297 3k multi .65 .65
899 A297 4k multi .95 .85
Nos. 896-899 (4) 2.63 2.47

A298

NORGE 15KR
A299

Christmas (Stained glass windows by Gabriel Kielland, Nidaros Cathedral, Trondheim): 2.10k, Olav Kyrre Founding The Diocese in Nidaros. 2.50k, The King and the Peasant at Sul.

Perf. 13½ on 3 Sides

1986, Nov. 26 **Litho.**

Booklet Stamps

900 A298 2.10k multi .55 .42
a. Booklet pane of 10 5.75
901 A298 2.50k multi .65 .50
a. Booklet pane of 10 6.75

Lithographed & Engraved

1986, Nov. 26 *Perf. 13½x13*
902 A299 15k brt grn, org & lt bl 3.75 3.00

Intl. Peace Year.

A300

1987, Feb. 12 **Litho.** *Perf. 13½*
903 A300 3.50k red, yel & dk bl 1.00 .75
904 A300 4.50k bl, yel & grn 1.30 1.00

Europa A301

Modern architecture: 2.70k, Wood. 4.50k, Glass and stone.

1987, Apr. 3 **Litho.** *Perf. 13½x13*
905 A301 2.70k multi .80 .60
906 A301 4.50k multi 1.30 1.00

Odelsting (Norwegian Assembly) Voting on Law Administering Local Councils, 150th Anniv. — A302

1987, Apr. 3 **Engr.** *Perf. 13x13½*
907 A302 12k dark green 3.50 2.65

Miniature Sheet

Red Crescent-Red Cross Rehabilitation Center, Mogadishu, Somalia — A303

Illustration reduced.

1987, May 8 **Litho.** *Perf. 13½x13*
908 A303 4.50k multi 1.40 1.40

See Somalia Nos. 576-577.

Sandvig Collection, Maihaugen Open-air Museum A305

1987, June 10 **Engr.** *Perf. 13x13½*
911 A305 2.70k Bjornstad Farm, Vaga .80 .60
912 A305 3.50k Horse and Rider, by Christen E. Listad 1.05 .80

Churchyard, Inspiration for Valen's Churchyard by the Sea — A306

4.50k, Fartein Valen (1887-1952), composer.

Perf. 13x13½, 13½x13

1987, Aug. 25 **Engr.**
913 A306 2.30k emer grn & dark blue .65 .48
914 A306 4.50k dark brown 1.25 .95

Tempest at Sea, by Christian Krogh (1852-1925) A307

Painting: 5k, The Farm, by Gerhard Munthe (1849-1929).

1987, Oct. 9 **Litho.** *Perf. 13½x13*
915 A307 2.70k multi .85 .65
916 A307 5k multi 1.60 1.20

Norwegian Horse Breeds — A308

Perf. 13x13½

1987, Nov. 12 **Litho. & Engr.**
917 A308 2.30k Dales .72 .60
918 A308 2.70k Fjord .85 .65
919 A308 4.50k Nordland 1.40 1.05
Nos. 917-919 (3) 2.97 2.30

Christmas A309

Perf. 13½x13 on 3 sides

1987, Nov. 12 **Litho.**

Booklet Stamps

920 A309 2.30k Children making tree ornaments .72 .60
a. Booklet pane of 10 7.25
921 A309 2.70k Baking gingersnaps .85 .65
a. Booklet pane of 10 8.50

Salvation Army in Norway, Cent. — A310

1988, Feb. 18 *Perf. 13½*
922 A310 2.90k multi .95 .70
923 A310 4.80k multi 1.50 1.15

European North-South Solidarity Campaign A311

1988, Apr. 26 *Perf. 13x13½*
924 A311 25k multi 8.00 6.00

Defense Forces Activities — A312

Defense Forces, 300th anniv.: 2.50k, Fortress construction. 2.90k, Army Signal Corps on duty. 4.60k, Pontoon bridge under construction, Corps of Engineers.

1988, Apr. 26 **Engr.**
925 A312 2.50k dark green .80 .60
926 A312 2.90k carmine lake .95 .70
927 A312 4.60k dark blue 1.50 1.15
Nos. 925-927 (3) 3.25 2.45

Europa — A313

Transport: 2.90k, *Prinds Gustav* passing Lofoten Isls., 1st passenger steamer in northern Norway, sesquicent. 3.80k, Heroybrua Bridge, between Leinoy and Blankholm, 1976.

Perf. 13x13½

1988, July 1 **Litho. & Engr.**
928 A313 2.90k blue black & ver .95 .70
929 A313 3.80k blue black, pink & ver 1.25 .95

A souvenir sheet containing 2 No. 928 exists, though it is invalid for postage. Sold for 30k.

85th Birthday of King Olav V — A314

Reign of King Christian IV (1577-1648), 400th Anniv. — A315

Designs: No. 930, Portrait, c. 1988. No. 931a, Arrival in 1905 after Norway declared independence from Sweden. No. 931b, Olav in snowstorm at Holmenkollen.

1988, July 1 **Litho.** *Perf. 13½x13*
930 A314 2.90k multi 1.00 .75

Souvenir Sheet

931 Sheet of 3 3.00 3.00
a. A314 2.90k org red, black & ultra 1.00 1.00
b. A314 2.90k multi 1.00 1.00
c. A314 2.90k like No. 930, no date 1.00 1.00

Perf. 13½x13

1988, Oct. 7 **Litho. & Engr.**

Designs: 10k, Reverse of a rixdaler struck in Christiania (Oslo), 1628, and excerpt of a mining decree issued by Christian IV.

932 A315 2.50k black & buff .75 .60
933 A315 10k multi 3.00 2.25

Miniature Sheet

Handball A316

Ball sports: b, Soccer. c, Basketball. d, Volleyball.

1988, Oct. 7 **Litho.** *Perf. 13½x13*
934 Sheet of 4 4.50 4.50
a.-d. A316 2.90k any single 1.10 1.10

Stamp Day. No. 934 sold for 15k.

Christmas — A317

Ludvig, a cartoon character created by Kjell Aukrust: No. 935, With ski pole. No. 936, Reading letter.

Perf. 13½x13 on 3 sides

1988, Nov. 15 **Litho.**

Booklet Stamps

935 A317 2.90k multi .90 .70
936 A317 2.90k multi .90 .70
a. Bklt. pane, 5 #935, 5 #936 9.00

World Cross-Country Running Championships, Stavanger, Mar. 19 — A318

1989, Feb. 20 **Litho.** *Perf. 13x13½*
937 A318 5k multi 1.50 1.15

Port City Bicentennials A319

Nordic Cooperation Issue A320

Perf. 13½x13

1989, Apr. 20 **Litho. & Engr.**
938 A319 3k Vardo .90 .70
939 A319 4k Hammerfest 1.20 .90

1989, Apr. 20 **Litho.** *Perf. 13x13½*

Folk costumes.

940 A320 3k Setesdal (woman) .90 .70
941 A320 4k Kautokeino (man) 1.20 .90

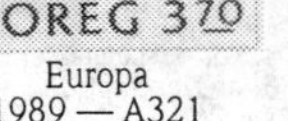
Europa 1989 — A321

Public Primary Schools, 250th Anniv. — A322

Children's games.

1989, June 7 Litho. *Perf. 13x13½*

942 A321 3.70k Building snowman 1.10 .80
943 A321 5k Cat's cradle 1.50 1.15

Perf. 13½x13

1989, June 7 Litho. & Engr.

944 A322 2.60k shown .80 .60

Engr.

945 A322 3k Child learning to write .90 .70

Souvenir Sheet

Winter Olympic Gold Medalists from Norway A323

Portraits: a, Bjoerg Eva Jensen, women's 3000-meter speed skating, 1980. b, Eirik Kvalfoss, 10k biathlon, 1984. c, Tom Sandberg, combined cross-country and ski jumping, 1984. d, Women's Nordic ski team, 20k relay, 1984.

1989, Oct. 6 Litho. *Perf. 13½x13*

946 Sheet of 4 5.50 5.50
a.-d. A323 4k any single 1.25 1.25

Sold for 20k to benefit Olympic sports promotion.
See Nos. 984, 997, 1021, 1035.

Souvenir Sheet

Impression of the Countryside, 1982, by Jakob Weidemann — A324

Illustration reduced.

1989, Oct. 6

947 A324 Sheet of 4 4.25 4.25
a.-d. 3k any single 1.00 1.00

Stamp Day. Sold for 15k to benefit philatelic promotion.

Writers A325

Portraits: 3k, Arnulf Overland (1889-1968), poet. 25k, Hanna Winsnes (1789-1872), author.

Perf. 13x13½

1989, Nov. 24 Litho. & Engr.

948 A325 3k dk red & brt bl .85 .60
949 A325 25k multicolored 7.00 5.25

Manors A326

1989, Nov. 24 Engr. *Perf. 13*

950 A326 3k Manor at Larvik .85 .60
951 A326 3k Rosendal Barony .85 .60

A327

A328

Christmas decorations.

Perf. 13 on 3 sides

1989, Nov. 24 Litho.

Booklet Stamps

952 A327 3k Star .85 .60
953 A327 3k Round ornament .85 .60
a. Bklt. pane of 10, 5 #952, 5 #953 8.50

1990, Feb. 23 Litho. *Perf. 13½*

954 A328 5k multicolored 1.55 1.15

Winter City events, Tromso.

Fauna Type of 1988 and

Scenes of Norway — A329

Designs: 4k, Cable cars. 4.50k, Goat Mountain. 5.50k, Top of the World outpost.

1991-94 Litho. *Perf. 13*

955 A329 4k multicolored 1.10 .85
956 A329 4.50k multicolored 1.25 .95
957 A329 5.50k multicolored 1.50 1.10

Litho. & Engr.

958 A292 5.50k Lynx 1.75 1.30
959 A292 6.40k Owl 2.00 1.50
Nos. 955-959 (5) 7.60 5.70

Issued: #958-959, 2/21/91; #955-957, 4/19/94.

Posthorn Type of 1893

1991-92 Engr. *Perf. 12½x13*

960 A10 1k orange & black .32 .25
961 A10 2k emerald & lake .65 .50
962 A10 3k blue & green 1.00 .75
963 A10 4k orange & henna brn 1.30 1.00
964 A10 5k green & dark blue 1.65 1.25
965 A10 6k grn & red vio 1.80 1.35
966 A10 7k red brn & bl 2.10 1.60
967 A10 8k red vio & grn 2.40 1.80
968 A10 9k ultra & red brn 2.65 2.00
Nos. 960-968 (9) 13.87 10.50

Issued: 1k-5k, 11/23/92; others, 11/22/91.

A332

A334

Orchids.

Perf. 13½x13 on 3 Sides

1990-92 Litho. Booklet Stamps

970 A332 3.20k *Dactylorhiza fuchsii* 1.00 .75
971 A332 3.20k *Epipactis atrorubens* 1.00 .75
a. Bklt. pane, 5 #970, 5 #971 10.00
972 A332 3.30k Cypripedium calceolus 1.00 .75
973 A332 3.30k Ophrys insectifera 1.00 .75
a. Bklt. pane, 5 each #972-973 10.00
Nos. 970-973 (4) 4.00 3.00

Issued: #970-971, 2/23; #972-973, 2/21/92.
This is an expanding set. Numbers will change if necessary.

1990, Apr. 9 Litho. *Perf. 13x13½*

German Invasion of Norway, 50th Anniv.: 3.20k, King Haakon VII's monogram, merchant navy, air force, Norwegian Home Guard and cannon Moses. 4k, Recapture of Narvik, May 28, 1940, by the Polish, British, Norwegian and French forces.

975 A334 3.20k shown 1.00 .75
976 A334 4k multicolored 1.25 .92

A335

A336

Souvenir Sheet

Stamps on stamps: b, Norway #1.

1990, Apr. 9 *Perf. 13½x13*

977 Sheet of 2 4.50 4.50
a.-b. A335 5k any single 2.25 2.25

Penny Black, 150th anniv. Sold for 15k.

1990, June 14 Litho. & Engr.

978 A336 3.20k Portrait 1.00 .75
979 A336 5k Coat of arms 1.50 1.15

Tordenskiold (Peter Wessel, 1690-1720), naval hero.

A337

A338

Europa: Post offices.

1990, June 14 Litho. *Perf. 13x13½*

980 A337 3.20k Trondheim 1.00 .75
981 A337 4k Longyearbyen 1.25 .92

1990, Oct. 5 Litho. & Engr. *Perf. 13*

982 A338 2.70k Svendsen .85 .62
983 A338 15k Monument by Fredriksen 4.65 3.50

Johan Severin Svendsen (1840-1911), composer.

Winter Olympic Type of 1989
Souvenir Sheet

Gold medal winners: a, Thorleif Haug, skier, 1924. b, Sonja Henie, figure skater, 1928, 1932, 1936. c, Ivar Ballangrud, speed skater, 1928, 1936. d, Hjalmar Andersen, speed skater, 1952.

1990, Oct. 5 Litho. *Perf. 13½x13*

984 Sheet of 4 6.25 6.25
a.-d. A323 4k any single 1.50 1.50

Sold for 20k to benefit Olympic sports promotion.

A339

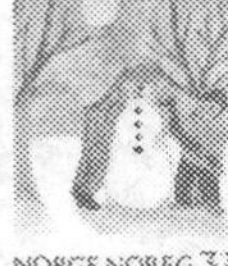
A340

1990, Nov. 23 Litho & Engr. *Perf. 13*

985 A339 30k bl, brn & car rose 10.00 7.50

Lars Olof Jonathan Soderblom (1866-1931), 1930 Nobel Peace Prize winner.

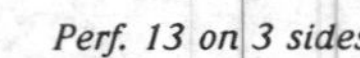

Perf. 13 on 3 sides

1990, Nov. 23 Litho.

Christmas (Children's drawings): No. 987, Church, stars, and Christmas tree.

986 A340 3.20k multicolored 1.10 .80
987 A340 3.20k multicolored 1.10 .80
a. Bklt. pane, 5 each #986-987 11.00

Ship Building Industry A341

1991, Feb. 21 Litho. *Perf. 13½x13*

988 A341 5k multicolored 1.60 1.20

Europa — A342

1991, Apr. 16 Litho. *Perf. 13*

989 A342 3.20k ERS-1 .90 .70
990 A342 4k Andoya rocket range 1.15 .85

City of Christiansand, 350th Anniv. — A343

1991, Apr. 16 Litho. & Engr. *Perf. 13*

991 A343 3.20k Early view .90 .70
992 A343 5.50k Modern view 1.55 1.15

Lifeboat Service, Cent. A344

Tourism A345

Designs: 3.20k, Rescue boat, Skomvaer III, horiz. 27k, Sailboat Colin Archer.

1991, June 7 Litho & Engr. *Perf. 13*

993 A344 3.20k multicolored .90 .70
994 A344 27k multicolored 7.50 5.65

1991, June 7 Litho. *Perf. 13½x13*

Designs: 3.20k, Fountain, Vigeland Park. 4k, Globe, North Cape.

995 A345 3.20k multicolored .90 .70
996 A345 4k multicolored 1.10 .85

Winter Olympics Type of 1989
Souvenir Sheet

Gold medal winners: a, Birger Ruud, ski jumping. b, Johan Grottumsbraten, cross country skiing. c, Knut Johannesen, speed skating. d, Magnar Solberg, biathlon.

1991, Oct. 11 Litho. *Perf. 13½x13*

997 Sheet of 4 5.60 5.60
a.-d. A323 4k any single 1.40 1.40

Sold for 20k to benefit Olympic sports promotion.

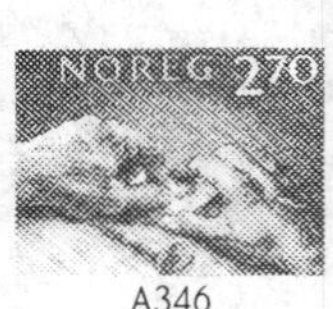
A346

A347

Natl. Stamp Day: a, Hands engraving. b, Magnifying glass above hands. c, View of hands through magnifying glass. d, Printed label being removed from plate.

1991, Oct. 11 *Perf. 13x13½*

Souvenir Sheet

998 Sheet of 4 5.60 5.60
a. A346 2.70k multicolored 1.25 1.25
b. A346 3.20k multicolored 1.00 1.00
c. A346 4k multicolored 1.40 1.40
d. A346 5k multicolored 2.00 2.00

Sold for 20k.

Perf. 13½x13 on 3 Sides

1991, Nov. 22 **Litho.**

Christmas: No. 1000, People with lantern.

Booklet Stamps

999 A347 3.20k multicolored .95 .75
1000 A347 3.20k multicolored .95 .75
a. Bklt. pane, 5 each #999-1000 9.50

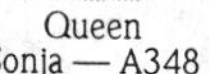

Queen Sonja — A348

King Harald — A349

A349a

Perf. 13x13½, 12½x13½ (6.50k), 13½x13 (30k)

Litho. & Engr., Engr. (6.50k)

1992-95

1004 A348 2.80k multicolored .85 .65
1005 A348 3k multicolored .90 .68
1007 A349 3.30k multicolored 1.00 .75
1008 A349 3.50k multicolored 1.05 .78
1009 A349 4.50k carmine 1.40 1.00
1011 A349 5.50k multicolored 1.70 1.25
1012 A349 5.60k multicolored 1.75 1.10
1014 A349 6.50k green 1.75 1.25
1015 A349 6.60k multicolored 2.00 1.50
1016 A349 7.50k violet 2.50 1.75
1016A A349 8.50k brown 2.75 2.00

Engr.

Perf. 13½x13

1017 A349a 10k dark green 3.50 2.65
1019 A349a 20k deep violet 7.00 3.50
1019A A349a 30k dark blue 9.00 6.75
1020 A349a 50k olive black 18.00 13.50
Nos. 1004-1020 (15) 55.15 39.11

Issued: 2.80k, 3.30k, 5.60k, 6.60k, 2/21/92; 50k, 6/12/92; 3k, 3.50k, 5.50k, 2/23/93; 10k, 20k, 6/17/93; 6.50k, 2/12/94; 30k, 11/18/94; 4.50k, 7.50k, 8.50k, 11/24/95. This is an expanding set. Numbers may change.

Winter Olympics Type of 1989
Souvenir Sheet

Gold Medal winners: a, Hallgeir Brenden, cross-country skiing. b, Arnfinn Bergmann, ski jumping. c, Stein Eriksen, giant slalom. d, Simon Slattvik, Nordic combined.

1992, Feb. 21 **Litho.** *Perf. 13½x13*

1021 Sheet of 4 6.00 6.00
a.-d. A323 4k any single 1.50 1.50

Sold for 20k to benefit Olympic sports promotion.

Expo '92, Seville A350

Designs: 3.30k, Norwegian pavilion, ship. 5.20k, Mountains, boat and fish.

1992, Apr. 20 **Litho.** *Perf. 13x13½*

1022 A350 3.30k multicolored 1.00 .75
1023 A350 5.20k multicolored 1.55 1.15

Discovery of America, 500th Anniv. — A351

Europa: 3.30k, Sailing ship Restauration at sea, 1825. 4,20k, Stavangerfjord in New York Harbor, 1918.

Perf. 13x13½

1992, Apr. 21 **Litho. & Engr.**

1024 A351 3.30k multicolored 1.00 .75
1025 A351 4.20k multicolored 1.25 .95

Kristiansund, 250th Anniv. — A352

1992, June 12 **Litho. & Engr.** *Perf. 13*

1026 A352 3.30k brn, bl & blk 1.20 .90
1027 A352 3.30k View of Molde 1.20 .90

Molde, 250th anniv. (#1027).

Souvenir Sheet

Glass — A353

Stamp Day: a, Decorated vase. b, Carafe with gold design. c, Cut glass salad bowl. d, Decorated cup.

1992, Oct. 9 **Litho.** *Perf. 13x13½*

1028 Sheet of 4 7.25 7.25
a. A353 2.80k multicolored 1.80 1.80
b. A353 3.30k multicolored 1.80 1.80
c. A353 4.20k multicolored 1.80 1.80
d. A353 5.20k multicolored 1.80 1.80

No. 1028 sold for 20k.

A354

A355

Designs: 3.30k, Flags, buildings in Lillehammer. 4.20k, Flag.

1992, Oct. 9 **Litho.** *Perf. 13x13½*

1029 A354 3.30k multicolored 1.20 .90
1030 A354 4.20k multicolored 1.50 1.10

1994 Winter Olympics, Lillehammer.
See Nos. 1047-1048, 1053-1058.

Perf. 13 on 3 Sides

1992, Nov. 23 **Litho.**

Christmas: No. 1031, Elves in front of mailbox. No. 1032, One elf holding other on shoulders to mail letters.

Booklet Stamps

1031 A355 3.30k multicolored 1.10 .80
1032 A355 3.30k multicolored 1.10 .80
b. Booklet pane, 5 each 11.00

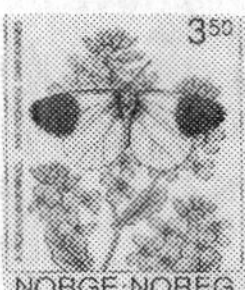

Butterflies — A356

Designs: No. 1033, Anthocharis cardamines. No. 1034, Aglais urticae.

Perf. 13½x13 on 3 Sides

1993, Feb. 23 **Litho.**

Booklet Stamps

1033 A356 3.50k multicolored 1.10 .80
1034 A356 3.50k multicolored 1.10 .80
b. Booklet pane, 5 each 11.00

Winter Olympics Type of 1989
Souvenir Sheet

1992 Gold Medal winners: a, Finn Christian Jagge, slalom. b, Bjorn Daehlie, cross-country skiing. c, Geir Karlstad, speed skating. d, Vegard Ulvang, cross-country skiing.

1993, Feb. 23 *Perf. 13½x13*

1035 Sheet of 4 6.75 6.75
a.-d. A323 4.50k any single 1.65 1.65

No. 1035 sold for 22k to benefit Olympic sports promotion.

Norden — A357

1993, Apr. 23 **Litho.** *Perf. 13½x13*

1036 A357 4k Canoe on lake 1.25 .95
1037 A357 4.50k River rafting 1.40 1.05

Edvard Grieg — A358

Perf. 13x13½

1993, Apr. 23 **Litho. & Engr.**

1038 A358 3.50k Portrait 1.10 .80
1039 A358 5.50k Landscape 1.70 1.30

1993 World Championships in Norway — A359

1993, June 17 **Litho.** *Perf. 13½x13*

1040 A359 3.50k Team handball 1.25 .95
1041 A359 5.50k Cycling 1.95 1.45

Hurtigruten Shipping Line, Cent. A360

Perf. 12½x13

1993, June 17 **Litho. & Engr.**

1042 A360 3.50k Richard With, ship 1.25 .95
1043 A360 4.50k Ship, officers 1.60 1.20

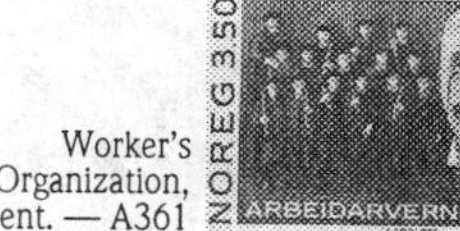

Worker's Organization, Cent. — A361

1993, Sept. 24 **Engr.** *Perf. 13x13½*

1044 A361 3.50k Johan Castberg 1.25 .90
1045 A361 12k Betzy Kjelsberg 4.00 3.00

Souvenir Sheet

Carvings A362

Stamp Day: a, Spiral leaf scroll. b, Interlocking scroll. c, "1754" surrounded by scroll. d, Face with scroll above.

1993, Sept. 24 **Litho.** *Perf. 13½x13*

1046 Sheet of 4, #a.-d. 7.00 7.00
a. A362 3k multicolored 1.75 1.75
b. A362 3.50k multicolored 1.75 1.75
c. A362 4.50k multicolored 1.75 1.75
d. A362 5.50k multicolored 1.75 1.75

No. 1046 sold for 21k.
See No. 1069.

1994 Winter Olympics Type of 1992

Designs: No. 1047, Flags, cross country skiier. No. 1048, Flags, buildings in Lillehammer.

1993, Nov. 27 **Litho.** *Perf. 13x13½*

1047 A354 3.50k multicolored 1.10 .80
1048 A354 3.50k multicolored 1.10 .80
a. Pair, #1047-1048 2.25 1.60

No. 1048a has a continuous design.

Christmas — A363

Butterflies — A364

Designs: No. 1049, Store Mangen Chapel. No. 1050, Church of Stamnes, Sandnes.

Perf. 13½x13 on 3 Sides

1993, Nov. 27

Booklet Stamps

1049 A363 3.50k shown 1.10 .80
1050 A363 3.50k multicolored 1.10 .80
b. Booklet pane, 5 each 10.50

Perf. 13½x13 on 3 Sides

1994, Feb. 12 **Litho.**

Booklet Stamps

1051 A364 3.50k Colias hecla .95 .70
1052 A364 3.50k Clossiana freija .95 .70
b. Booklet pane, 5 each 9.50

1994 Winter Olympics Type of 1992

Designs: No. 1053, Stylized Norwegian flag, Olympic rings UR. No. 1054, Stylized Norwegian flag, Olympic rings, UL. No. 1055, Olympic rings, buildings in Lillehammer. No. 1056, Olympic rings, ski jump. 4.50k, Flags of Norway, Belgium, Greece, Switzerland, Sweden, Germany, United Kingdom. 5.50k, Flags of Australia, New Zealand, Brazil, Canada, US, Japan, Mexico, South Korea.

1994, Feb. 12 *Perf. 13x13½*

1053 A354 3.50k multicolored .95 .70
1054 A354 3.50k multicolored .95 .70
1055 A354 3.50k multicolored .95 .70
1056 A354 3.50k multicolored .95 .70
a. Block of 4, #1053-1056 4.00 3.00
1057 A354 4.50k multicolored 1.25 .90
1058 A354 5.50k multicolored 1.50 1.10
Nos. 1053-1058 (6) 6.55 4.80

1994 Paralympics — A365

1994, Mar. 10 **Litho.** *Perf. 13*

1059 A365 4.50k Skier 1.25 .95
1060 A365 5.50k Skier, diff. 1.50 .45

Tromso Charter, Bicent. A366

1994, Apr. 19 Litho. & Engr. *Perf. 13*

1061 A366 3.50k Royal seal 1.00 .75
1062 A366 4.50k Cathedral 1.25 .95

Norwegian Folk Museum, Cent. A367

Designs: 3k, Log buildings, Osterdal Valley. 3.50k, Sled, 1750.

Perf. 12½x13

1994, June 14 Litho. & Engr.

1063 A367 3k multicolored .90 .70
1064 A367 3.50k multicolored 1.00 .75

Research in Norway A368

Abstract designs with various formulas, microchips, glass flasks.

1994, June 14 Litho.

1065 A368 4k multicolored 1.25 .95
1066 A368 4.50k multicolored 1.40 1.00

Electric Tram Lines, Cent. — A369

Perf. 13x13½

1994, Sept. 23 Litho. & Engr.

1067 A369 3.50k Early tram, map 1.00 .75
1068 A369 12k Modern tram, map 3.50 2.75

Stamp Day Type of 1993

Ornamental broaches: a, Gold, embossed designs. b, Silver, embossed designs. c, Silver, circular designs. d, Gold, jeweled center.

1994, Sept. 23 Litho. *Perf. 13½x13*

1069 Sheet of 4, #a.-d. 6.50 6.50
a. A362 3k multicolored 1.60 1.60
b. A362 3.50k multicolored 1.60 1.60
c. A362 4.50k multicolored 1.60 1.60
d. A362 5.50k multicolored 1.60 1.60

No. 1069 sold for 21k.

Christmas — A370

Perf. 13½x13 on 3 Sides

1994, Nov. 18 Litho.

Booklet Stamps

1070 A370 3.50k Sled 1.25 1.00
1071 A370 3.50k Kick sled 1.25 1.00
a. Booklet pane, 5 each 12.50

Berries — A371

1995-96 Litho. *Perf. 13½x13*

Booklet Stamps

1086 A371 3.50k Vaccinium vitis 1.25 1.00
1087 A371 3.50k Vaccinium myrtillus 1.25 1.00
a. Bklt. pane, 4 each #1086-1087 10.00
Complete booklet, #1087a 10.00
1088 A371 3.50k Fragaria vesca 1.10 .85
1089 A371 3.50k Rubus chamaemorus 1.10 .85
a. Bklt. pane, 4 each #1088-1089 8.80
Complete booklet, #1089a 8.80
Nos. 1086-1089 (4) 4.70 3.70

Issued: #1086-1087, 2/23/95; #1088-1089, 2/22/96.

This is an expanding set. Numbers may change.

A372 A373

Apothecary Shops, 400th Anniv.: 3.50k, Swan Pharmacy, Bergen. 25k, Apothecary's tools.

Perf. 13½x13

1995, Feb. 23 Litho. & Engr.

1090 A372 3.50k multicolored 1.10 .85
1091 A372 25k multicolored 7.75 5.75

1995, May 8 Litho. *Perf. 13½x13*

Tourism: 4k, Skudeneshavn Harbor. 4.50k, Torghatten mountain, Helgeland coastline.

Booklet Stamps

1092 A373 4k multicolored 1.40 1.00
a. Booklet pane of 8 11.50
Complete booklet, #1092a 11.50
1093 A373 4.50k multicolored 1.50 1.10
a. Booklet pane of 8 12.00
Complete booklet, #1093a 12.00

Christianity in Norway A374

Designs: 3.50k, Old Moster Church, c. 1100. 15k, Slettebakken Church, Bergen, 1970.

Perf. 13x13½

1995, May 8 Litho. & Engr.

1094 A374 3.50k multicolored 1.10 .85
1095 A374 15k multicolored 5.00 3.75

End of World War II, 50th Anniv. A375

Designs: 3.50k, German commander saluting Terje Rollem in 1945, German forces marching down Karl Johans Gate from Royal Palace, 1940. 4.50k, King Haakon VII, Crown Prince leaving Norway in 1940, King saluting upon return in 1945. 5.50k, Children waving Norwegian flags, 1945.

1995, May 8 Litho. *Perf. 13½x13*

1096 A375 3.50k multicolored 1.10 .85
1097 A375 4.50k multicolored 1.50 1.10
1098 A375 5.50k multicolored 1.75 1.40
Nos. 1096-1098 (3) 4.35 3.35

Kirsten Flagstad (1895-1962), Opera Singer — A376

Design: 5.50k, In Tristan and Isolde.

1995, June 26 Litho. *Perf. 13*

1099 A376 3.50k multicolored 1.10 .85
1100 A376 5.50k multicolored 1.75 1.40

Conciliation Boards, Bicent. A377

Designs: 7k, Three-man board between two people facing away from each other. 12k, Seated board member, two people talking to each other.

1995, June 26 *Perf. 13½*

1101 A377 7k multicolored 2.25 1.75
1102 A377 12k multicolored 3.75 2.75

UN, 50th Anniv. — A378

UN emblem and: 3.50k, Trygve Lie, Secretary General 1946-53. 5.50k, Woman drinking from clean water supply.

Litho. & Engr.

1995, Sept. 22 *Perf. 13*

1103 A378 3.50k multicolored 1.10 .85
1104 A378 5.50k multicolored 1.75 1.40

Norway Post, 350th Anniv. A379

#1105, Signature, portrait of Hannibal Sehested, letter post, 1647. #1106, Wax seal, registered letters, 1745. #1107, Christiania, etc. postmarks. #1108, Funds transfer, coins, canceled envelopes, 1883. #1109, "Norske Intelligenz-Seddeler," first newspaper, newspapers, magazines, 1660. #1110, Postmarks, label, parcel post, 1827. #1111, No. 1, Type A5, stamps, 1855. #1112, Savings book stamps, bank services, 1950.

1995, Sept. 22 Litho.

Booklet Stamps

1105 A379 3.50k multicolored 1.10 .85
1106 A379 3.50k multicolored 1.10 .85
1107 A379 3.50k multicolored 1.10 .85
1108 A379 3.50k multicolored 1.10 .85
1109 A379 3.50k multicolored 1.10 .85
1110 A379 3.50k multicolored 1.10 .85
1111 A379 3.50k multicolored 1.10 .85
a. Missing gray stamp at LR *20.00*
1112 A379 3.50k multicolored 1.10 .85
a. Booklet pane, #1105-1112 8.80
Complete booklet, #1112a 8.80
b. Booklet pane, #1105-1110, #1111a, 1112 25.00
Complete booklet, #1112b 25.00

Christmas — A380

Perf. 13 on 3 Sides

1995, Nov. 24 Litho.

Booklet Stamps

1113 A380 3.50k Knitted cap 1.10 .85
1114 A380 3.50k Knitted mitten 1.10 .85
a. Booklet pane, 4 each #1113-1114 8.80
Complete booklet, #1114a 8.80

Svalbard Islands A381

1996, Feb. 22 Litho. *Perf. 13*

1115 A381 10k Advent Bay 3.25 2.50
1116 A381 20k Polar bear 6.25 4.75

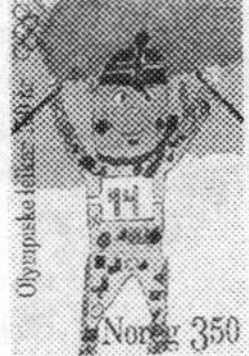

Olympic Games, Cent. A382

Tourism A383

Children's drawings: 3.50k, Cross country skier. 5.50k, Runner.

1996, Apr. 18 Litho. *Perf. 13½*

1117 A382 3.50k multicolored 1.10 .85
1118 A382 5.50k multicolored 1.70 1.30

1996, Apr. 18 *Perf. 13*

1119 A383 4k Besseggen 1.25 .90
a. Booklet pane of 8 10.00
Complete booklet, #1119a 10.00
1120 A383 4.50k Urnes Stave Church 1.40 1.00
a. Booklet pane of 8 11.25
Complete booklet, #1120a 11.25
1121 A383 5.50k Alta Rock Carvings 1.70 1.25
a. Booklet pane of 8 13.75
Complete booklet, #1121a 13.75
Nos. 1119-1121 (3) 4.35 3.15

See Nos. 1155-1157.

Railway Centennials A384

1996, June 19 Litho. & Engr. *Perf. 13*

1122 A384 3k Urskog-Holand .95 .70
1123 A384 4.50k Setesdal 1.40 1.10

The Troll Offshore Gasfield A385

3.50k, Size of Troll platform compared to Eiffel Tower. 25k, Troll platform, map of gas pipelines.

1996, June 19 Litho.

1124 A385 3.50k multicolored 1.10 .85
1125 A385 25k multicolored 7.80 5.80

Norway Post, 350th Anniv. — A386

#1126, Postal courier on skis. #1127, Fjord boat, SS "Framnaes," 1920's. #1128, Mail truck, Oslo, 1920's. #1129, Early airmail service. #1130, Unloading mail, East Railroad Station, Oslo, 1950's. #1131, Using bicycle for rural mail delivery, 1970's. #1132, Customer, mail clerk, Elverum post office. #1133, Computer, globe, E-mail service.

1996, Sept. 20 Litho. *Perf. 13*

Booklet Stamps

1126 A386 3.50k multicolored 1.10 .85
1127 A386 3.50k multicolored 1.10 .85
1128 A386 3.50k multicolored 1.10 .85
1129 A386 3.50k multicolored 1.10 .85
1130 A386 3.50k multicolored 1.10 .85
1131 A386 3.50k multicolored 1.10 .85
1132 A386 3.50k multicolored 1.10 .85
1133 A386 3.50k multicolored 1.10 .85
a. Booklet pane, #1126-1133 8.80
Complete booklet, #1133a 8.80

Motion Pictures, Cent. A387

Film strips showing: 3.50k, Leif Juster, Sean Connery, Liv Ullmann, The Olsen Gang Films, Il Temp Gigante. 5.50k, Wenche Foss, Jack Fjeldstad, Marilyn Monroe, murder, blood, shooting. 7k, Charlie Chaplin, Ottar Gladvedt, Laurel & Hardy, Marlene Dietrich.

1996, Sept. 20

1134 A387 3.50k multicolored 1.10 .85
1135 A387 5.50k multicolored 1.70 1.25
1136 A387 7k multicolored 2.20 1.70
Nos. 1134-1136 (3) 5.00 3.80

Christmas — A388

Embroidered motif from Norwegian folk costume: Denomination at UL (#1137), UR (#1138).

Perf. 13 on 3 Sides

1996, Nov. 21 **Litho.**

1137 A388 3.50k multicolored 1.10 .85
1138 A388 3.50k multicolored 1.10 .85
a. Booklet pane, 4 ea #1137-1138 9.00
Complete booklet, #1138a 9.00

Amalie Skram (1846-1905), Novelist — A389

Designs: 3.50k, Portrait. 15k, Scene from performance of Skram's "People of Hellemyr."

1996, Nov. 21 **Engr.**

1139 A389 3.50k claret 1.10 .85
1140 A389 15k claret & dk blue 4.75 2.35

Posthorn Type of 1893 Redrawn

1997, Jan. 2 **Litho.** *Perf. 13x13½*

Color of Oval

1141 A10 10o red .15 .15
1142 A10 20o blue .15 .15
1143 A10 30o orange .15 .15
1144 A10 40o gray .15 .15
1145 A10 50o green .15 .15
Set value .45 .20

Numerous design differences exist in the vertical shading lines, the size and shading of the posthorn, and in the corner wings.

Insects — A390

Flowers — A391

1997, Jan. 2 *Perf. 13 on 3 Sides*

1146 A390 3.70k Bumblebee 1.10 .85
1147 A390 3.70k Ladybug 1.10 .85
a. Booklet pane, 4 each #1146-1147 8.80
Complete booklet 8.80

See Nos. 1180-1181.

1997, Jan. 2 *Perf. 13*

1148 A391 3.20k Red clover .95 .95
1149 A391 3.70k Coltsfoot 1.10 1.10
1150 A391 4.30k Lily of the Valley 1.30 1.30
1151 A391 5k Harebell 1.50 1.50
1152 A391 6k Oxeye daisy 1.80 1.80
Nos. 1148-1152 (5) 6.65 6.65

See Nos. 1182-1187.

World Nordic Skiing Championships, Trondheim — A392

1997, Feb. 20

1153 A392 3.70k Ski jumping 1.10 1.10
1154 A392 5k Cross-country skiing 1.50 1.50

Tourism Type of 1996

Perf. 13 on 3 Sides

1997, Apr. 16 **Litho.**

Booklet Stamps

1155 A383 4.30k Roros 1.25 .95
a. Booklet pane of 8 10.00
Complete booklet, #1155a 10.00
1156 A383 5k Faerder Lighthouse 1.50 1.15
a. Booklet pane of 8 12.00
Complete booklet, #1156a 12.00
1157 A383 6k Nusfjord 1.75 1.30
a. Booklet pane of 8 14.00
Complete booklet #1157a 14.00

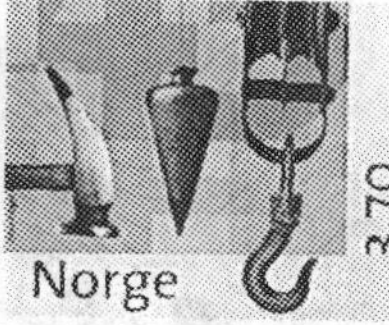

King Harald, Queen Sonja, 60th Birthdays A393

1997, Apr. 16 **Litho.** *Perf. 13*

1158 A393 3.70k shown 1.10 .85
1159 A393 3.70k King Harald, vert. 1.10 .85

Norway Post, 350th Anniv. A394

Post-World War II development: No. 1160, Tools for construction, 1945. No. 1161, Kon-Tiki Expedition, 1947. No. 1162, Environmental protection, establishing national parks, 1962. No. 1163, Welfare, help for the elderly, 1967. No. 1164, Off-shore oil drilling, 1969. No. 1165, Grete Waitz, marathon winner, 1983. No. 1166, Askoy Bridge, 1992. No. 1167, Winter Olympic Games, Lillehammer, 1994.

1997, Apr. 16

Booklet Stamps

1160 A394 3.70k multicolored 1.10 .85
1161 A394 3.70k multicolored 1.10 .85
1162 A394 3.70k multicolored 1.10 .85
1163 A394 3.70k multicolored 1.10 .85
1164 A394 3.70k multicolored 1.10 .85
1165 A394 3.70k multicolored 1.10 .85
1166 A394 3.70k multicolored 1.10 .85
1167 A394 3.70k multicolored 1.10 .85
a. Booklet pane, #1160-1167 8.80
Complete booklet, #1167a 8.80

City of Trondheim, Millenium A395

Stylized designs: 3.70k, New Trondheim. 12k, Ships entering harbor, King, early settlements in Old Nidaros.

1997, June 6 **Litho.** *Perf. 13½x13*

1168 A395 3.70k multicolored 1.00 1.00
1169 A395 12k multicolored 3.10 3.10

Einar Gerhardsen (1897-1987), Prime Minister — A396

Caricatures: 3.70k, In front on government buildings. 25k, Scenes of Norway.

1997, June 6 *Perf. 13½*

1170 A396 3.70k multicolored 1.00 1.00
1171 A396 25k multicolored 6.50 6.50

Junior Stamp Club A397

Harald Saeverud (1897-1992), Composer A398

Topics found on stamps: No. 1172, Insect, butterfly (silhouette of person's face), cartoon character, fish, flag, hand holding pen, heart, tiger, horn, boy with dog, globe. No. 1173, Flag, hand holding pen, tree, butterfly (silhouette of person's face), ladybug, cartoon character, antique postal vehicle, soccer ball, stylized bird, man on bicycle, lighthouse.

1997, Sept. 29 **Litho.** *Perf. 13*

1172 A397 3.70k multicolored 1.00 .75
1173 A397 3.70k multicolored 1.00 .75

Perf. 13½x13

1997, Sept. 19 **Litho. & Engr.**

Design: 15k, Tarjei Vesaas (1897-1970), writer.

1174 A398 10k blue 2.75 2.00
1175 A398 15k green 4.25 3.25

Petter Dass (1647-1706), Poet, Priest A399

Designs: 3.20k, Dass standing in rowboat, verse. 3.70k, Dass, church on island of Alsten.

Litho. & Engr.

1997, Nov. 26 *Perf. 13*

1176 A399 3.20k multicolored .90 .90
1177 A399 3.70k multicolored 1.00 1.00

Christmas — A400

Various designs from Norwgian calendar stick, medieval forerunner of modern day calendar.

Serpentine Die Cut 13½ on 3 Sides

1997, Nov. 26 **Litho.**

Self-Adhesive

Booklet Stamps

1178 A400 3.70k yellow & multi 1.00 1.00
1179 A400 3.70k blue & multi 1.00 1.00
a. Booklet pane, 2 each #1178-1179 4.00
Complete booklet, 2 #1179a 8.00

Insect Type of 1997

1998, Jan. 2 *Perf. 13½ on 3 Sides*

Booklet Stamps

1180 A390 3.80k Dragonfly 1.00 1.00
1181 A390 3.80k Grsshopper 1.00 1.00
a. Booklet pane, 4 each #1180-1181 8.00
Complete booklet, #1181a 8.00

Flower Type of 1997

1998, Jan. 2 **Litho.** *Perf. 13*

1182 A391 3.40k Marsh marigold .90 .90
1183 A391 3.80k Wild pansy 1.00 1.00
1184 A391 4.50k White clover 1.20 1.20
1185 A391 5.50k Hepatica 1.40 1.40
1186 A391 7.50k Pale pasqueflower 2.00 2.00
1187 A391 13k Purple saxifrage 3.40 3.40
Nos. 1182-1187 (6) 9.90 9.90

Valentine's Day — A401

1998, Feb. 9 *Die Cut Perf. 14x13*

Self-Adhesive

1188 A401 3.80k multicolored 1.00 1.00

No. 1188 was issued in sheets of 3 + 4 labels.

SEMI-POSTAL STAMPS

North Cape Issue

North Cape — SP1

Perf. 13½x14

1930, June 28 **Wmk. 160** **Photo.**

Size: 33¼x21½mm

B1 SP1 15o + 25o blk brn 2.00 2.00
B2 SP1 20o + 25o car 26.00 26.00
B3 SP1 30o + 25o ultra 75.00 75.00
Nos. B1-B3 (3) 103.00 103.00
Set, never hinged 190.00

The surtax was given to the Tourist Association. See Nos. B9-B10, B28-B30, B54-B56, B59-B61.

Radium Hospital SP2

1931, Apr. 1 *Perf. 14½x13½*

B4 SP2 20o + 10o carmine 8.50 2.75
Never hinged 35.00

The surtax aided the Norwegian Radium Hospital.

Fridtjof Nansen — SP3

Queen Maud — SP4

1935, Dec. 13 *Perf. 13½*

B5 SP3 10o + 10o green 1.25 1.50
B6 SP3 15o + 10o red brn 6.00 7.25
B7 SP3 20o + 10o crimson .95 1.20
B8 SP3 30o + 10o brt ultra 5.00 6.00
Nos. B5-B8 (4) 13.20 15.95
Set, never hinged 35.00

The surtax aided the International Nansen Office for Refugees.

North Cape Type of 1930

1938, June 20 *Perf. 13x13½*

Size: 27x21mm

B9 SP1 20o + 25o brn car 2.75 4.00
B10 SP1 30o + 25o dp ultra 11.00 13.00
Set, never hinged 25.00

Surtax given to the Tourist Assoc.

Perf. 13x13½

1939, July 24 **Photo.** **Unwmk.**

B11 SP4 10o + 5o brt grn .40 .40
B12 SP4 15o + 5o red brn .40 .40
B13 SP4 20o + 5o scarlet .40 .40
B14 SP4 30o + 5o brt ultra .40 .40
Nos. B11-B14 (4) 1.60 1.60
Set, never hinged 4.00

The surtax was used for charities.

Fridtjof Nansen — SP5

SP6

1940, Oct. 21

B15 SP5 10o + 10o dk grn 1.25 2.25
B16 SP5 15o + 10o henna brn 1.75 3.25
B17 SP5 20o + 10o dark red .50 1.10
B18 SP5 30o + 10o ultra 1.25 2.25
Nos. B15-B18 (4) 4.75 8.85
Set, never hinged 13.00

The surtax was used for war relief work.

1941, May 16

Ancient Sailing Craft off Lofoten Islands.

B19 SP6 15o + 10o deep blue .90 .60
Never hinged 3.50

Haalogaland Exposition. Surtax for relief fund for families of lost fishermen.

Nos. 70-73, 177-180, 267, B19, B32-B34 and B38-B41 were demonetized from May 15, 1945 until Sept. 1, 1981. Used values are for stamps canceled after this period. Stamps with dated cancellations prior to May 15, 1945 sell for more. False cancellations exist.

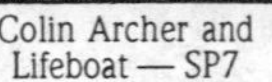

Colin Archer and Lifeboat — SP7

Lifeboat — SP8

1941, July 9 *Perf. 13x13½, 13½x13*

B20 SP7 10o + 10o yel grn .95 1.65
B21 SP7 15o + 10o dk ol brn 1.25 1.90
B22 SP8 20o + 10o brt red .45 .55
B23 SP8 30o + 10o ultra 2.50 4.00
Nos. B20-B23 (4) 5.15 8.10
Set, never hinged 10.00

Norwegian Lifeboat Society, 50th anniv.

Legionary, Norwegian and Finnish Flags SP9

Vidkun Quisling SP10

1941, Aug. 1 *Perf. 13½x13*

B24 SP9 20o + 80o scar ver 50.00 85.00
Never hinged 72.50

The surtax was for the Norwegian Legion.

1942, Feb. 1

B25 SP10 20o + 30o henna 4.00 *13.00*
Never hinged 6.00

Overprinted in Red **1–2–1942**

B26 SP10 20o + 30o henna 4.00 *13.00*
Never hinged 6.00

Inauguration of Quisling as prime minister.

Catalogue values for unused stamps in this section, from this point to the end of the section, are for Never Hinged items.

Vidkun Quisling SP11

Frontier Guardsmen Emblem SP12

1942, Sept. 26 *Perf. 13*

B27 SP11 20o + 30o henna .45 *3.00*

8th annual meeting of Nasjonal Samling, Quisling's party. The surtax aided relatives of soldiers killed in action.

North Cape Type of 1930

1943, Apr. 1

Size: 27x21mm

B28 SP1 15o + 25o olive brn 1.25 1.25
B29 SP1 20o + 25o dark car 1.75 1.75
B30 SP1 30o + 25o chalky blue 2.25 2.25
Nos. B28-B30 (3) 5.25 5.25

The surtax aided the Tourist Association.

1943, Aug. 2 **Unwmk.**

B31 SP12 20o + 30o henna .75 *3.25*

The surtax aided the Frontier Guardsmen (Norwegian Nazi Volunteers).

Fishing Village — SP13

Drying Grain — SP14

Barn in Winter — SP15

1943, Nov. 10

B32 SP13 10o + 10o gray green 1.50 .60
B33 SP14 20o + 10o henna 1.50 .60
B34 SP15 40o + 10o grnsh blk 1.50 .60
Nos. B32-B34 (3) 4.50 1.80

The surtax was for winter relief.

The Baroy Sinking — SP16

Sanct Svithun Aflame — SP17

Design: 20o+10o, "Irma" sinking.

1944, May 20

B35 SP16 10o + 10o gray grn 1.40 *3.50*
B36 SP17 15o + 10o dk olive 1.40 *3.50*
B37 SP16 20o + 10o henna 1.40 *3.50*
Nos. B35-B37 (3) 4.20 *10.50*

The surtax aided victims of wartime ship sinkings, and their families.

Spinning SP19

Plowing SP20

Tree Felling — SP21

Child Care — SP22

1944, Dec. 1

B38 SP19 5o + 10o dp mag .90 .40
B39 SP20 10o + 10o dk yel grn .90 .40
B40 SP21 15o + 10o choc .90 .40
B41 SP22 20o + 10o henna .90 .40

The surtax was for National Welfare.

Red Cross Nurse — SP23

Crown Prince Olav — SP24

1945, Sept. 22

B42 SP23 20o + 10o red 1.00 1.10

80th anniv. of the founding of the Norwegian Red Cross. The surtax was for that institution.

For surcharge see No. B47.

1946, Mar. 4 **Unwmk.**

B43 SP24 10o + 10o ol grn .45 .40
B44 SP24 15o + 10o ol brn .45 .40
B45 SP24 20o + 10o dk red .45 .40
B46 SP24 30o + 10o brt bl 2.00 1.50
Nos. B43-B46 (4) 3.35 2.70

The surtax was for war victims.

No. B42 Surcharged with New Value and Bar in Black

1948, Dec. 1

B47 SP23 25o + 5o on 20o+10o .85 .85

The surtax was for Red Cross relief work.

Child Picking Flowers — SP25

1950, Aug. 15 **Photo.** *Perf. 13*

B48 SP25 25o + 5o brt red 1.90 1.10
B49 SP25 45o + 5o dp bl 5.75 3.50

The surtax was for poliomyelitis victims.

Skater — SP26

Winter Scene SP27

Design: 30o+10o, Ski jumper.

1951, Oct. 1

B50 SP26 15o + 5o olive grn 1.50 1.25
B51 SP26 30o + 10o red 1.50 1.25
B52 SP27 55o + 20o blue 9.00 7.25
Nos. B50-B52 (3) 12.00 9.75

Olympic Winter Games, Oslo, Feb. 14-29, 1952.

Kneeling Woman — SP28

Crown Princess Martha — SP29

1953, June 1 **Photo. & Litho.**

B53 SP28 30o + 10o red & cream 2.25 2.00

The surtax was for cancer research.

North Cape Type of 1930

1953, June 15 **Photo.**

Size: 27x21mm

B54 SP1 20o + 10o green 10.50 8.50
B55 SP1 30o + 15o red 10.50 8.50
B56 SP1 55o + 25o gray blue 17.00 13.00
Nos. B54-B56 (3) 38.00 30.00

The surtax aided the Tourist Association.

1956, Mar. 28 *Perf. 13*

B57 SP29 35o + 10o dark red 1.75 1.50
B58 SP29 65o + 10o dark blue 4.25 3.50

The surtax was for the Crown Princess Martha Memorial Fund.

North Cape Type of 1930

1957, May 6

Size: 27x21mm

B59 SP1 25o + 10o green 4.75 4.00
B60 SP1 35o + 15o red 5.50 5.00
B61 SP1 65o + 25o gray blue 4.75 3.50
Nos. B59-B61 (3) 15.00 12.50

The surtax aided the Tourist Association.

White Anemone SP30

Mother, Child, WRY Emblem SP31

Design: 90o+10o, Hepatica.

1960, Jan. 12 **Litho.** *Perf. 13*

B62 SP30 45o + 10o brt red & grn 2.00 1.90
B63 SP30 90o + 10o bl, org & grn 5.75 5.50

The surtax was for anti-tuberculosis work.

1960, Apr. 7 **Photo.** **Unwmk.**

B64 SP31 45o + 25o rose & blk 5.00 3.75
B65 SP31 90o + 25o bl & blk 9.00 6.50

World Refugee Year, July 1, 1959-June 30, 1960. The surtax was for aid to refugees.

Severed Chain and Dove SP32

Design: 60o+10o, Norwegian flags.

1965, May 8 **Photo.** *Perf. 13*

B66 SP32 30o + 10o grn, blk & tan .75 .70
B67 SP32 60o + 10o red & dk bl .75 .75

20th anniversary of liberation from the Germans. The surtax was for war cripples.

Souvenir Sheet

Offshore Oil Drilling SP33

Designs: a, Ekofisk Center. b, Treasure Scout drilling rig and Odin Viking supply vessel at Tromsoflaket, 1982. c, Statfjord C oil platform, 1984. d, Men working on deck of Neptune Nordraug.

1985, Oct. 4 **Litho.** *Perf. 13½x13*

B68 Sheet of 4 2.75 3.50
a.-d. SP33 2k + 1k, any single .65 .85

Stamp Day 1985. Surtax for philatelic promotion.

Souvenir Sheet

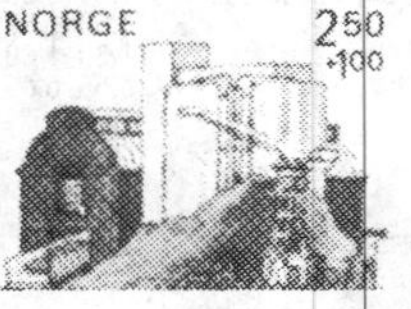

Paper Industry SP34

Paper mill: a, Wood aging containers. b, Boiling plant. c, Paper-making machine. d, Paper dryer.

1986, Oct. 17 **Litho.** *Perf. 13½*

B69 Sheet of 4 3.25 3.75
a.-d. SP34 2.50k + 1k, any single .80 .90

Surtax for philatelic promotion. Nos. B69a-B69b and B69c-B69d printed in continuous designs.

Souvenir Sheet

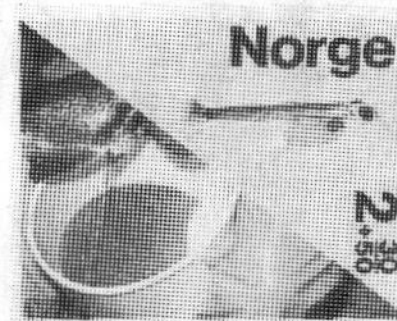

Salmon Industry SP35

Designs: a, Eggs and milt pressed out of fish by hand. b, Cultivation of eggs in tanks. c, Outdoor hatchery. d, Market.

1987, Oct. 9 Litho. *Perf. 13½x13*

B70 Sheet of 4 3.75 3.75
a. SP35 2.30k +50o multi .65 .65
b. SP35 2.70k +50o multi .75 .75
c. SP35 3.50k +50o multi .95 .95
d. SP35 4.50k +50o multi 1.25 1.25

AIR POST STAMPS

Airplane over Akershus Castle
AP1 AP2

Perf. 13½x14½

1927-34 Typo. Wmk. 160

C1 AP1 45o lt bl, strong frame line ('34) 5.25 2.00
Never hinged 20.00
a. Faint or broken frame line 20.00 4.00
Never hinged 110.00

1937, Aug. 18 Photo. *Perf. 13*

C2 AP2 45o Prussian blue 1.25 .55
Never hinged 1.75

1941, Nov. 10 Unwmk.

C3 AP2 45o indigo .40 .30
Never hinged .60

POSTAGE DUE STAMPS

Numeral of Value — D1

Perf. 14½x13½

1889-1914 Typo. Wmk. 160

Inscribed "at betale"

J1 D1 1o olive green .90 1.25
J2 D1 4o magenta 1.40 .80
J3 D1 10o carmine rose 3.50 .65
a. 10o rose red 60.00 17.00
J4 D1 15o brown ('14) 1.50 .50
J5 D1 20o ultra 2.50 .65
a. Perf. 13½x12½ 175.00 90.00
J6 D1 50o maroon 5.00 2.50
Nos. J1-J6 (6) 14.80 6.35

See #J7-J12. For overprint see #136-144.

1922-23

Inscribed "a betale"

J7 D1 4o lilac rose 6.50 6.50
Never hinged 16.00
J8 D1 10o green 2.00 2.00
Never hinged 5.00
J9 D1 20o dull violet 4.50 4.50
Never hinged 10.00
J10 D1 40o deep ultra 7.00 .50
Never hinged 16.00
J11 D1 100o orange yel 25.00 9.00
Never hinged 65.00
J12 D1 200o dark violet 60.00 20.00
Never hinged 90.00
Nos. J7-J12 (6) 105.00 42.50

OFFICIAL STAMPS

Coat of Arms
O1 O2

Perf. 14½x13½

1926 Typo. Wmk. 160

O1 O1 5o rose lilac .35 .35
O2 O1 10o yellow green .35 .15
O3 O1 15o indigo 1.40 1.40
O4 O1 20o plum .35 .15
O5 O1 30o slate 4.00 4.00
O6 O1 40o deep blue 1.25 .55
O7 O1 60o Prussian blue 4.00 4.00
Nos. O1-O7 (7) 11.70 10.60

Official Stamp of 1926 Surcharged **2 2**

1929, July 1

O8 O1 2o on 5o magenta .40 .35

Perf. 14½x13½

1933-34 Litho. Wmk. 160

Size: 35x19¼mm

O9 O2 2o ocher .60 .85
O10 O2 5o rose lilac 1.65 1.65
O11 O2 7o orange 8.00 5.00
O12 O2 10o green 16.00 .65
O13 O2 15o olive .52 .42
O14 O2 20o vermilion 16.00 .42
O15 O2 25o yellow brn .52 .42
O16 O2 30o ultra .52 .42
O18 O2 40o slate 21.00 .52
O19 O2 60o blue 6.50 .52
O20 O2 70o olive brn 1.50 1.50
O21 O2 100o violet 2.00 1.10
Nos. O9-O16,O18-O21 (12) 74.81 13.47

On the lithographed stamps, the lion's left leg is shaded.

Typo.

Size: 34x18¾mm

O10a O2 5o rose lilac .85 1.10
O11a O2 7o orange 10.00 7.25
O12a O2 10o green .70 .40
O13a O2 15o olive 10.00 12.00
O14a O2 20o vermilion .70 .25
O17 O2 35o red violet ('34) .85 .50
O18a O2 40o slate .85 .50
O19a O2 60o blue .85 .50
Nos. O10a-O14a,O17,O18a-O19a (8) 24.80 22.50

Coat of Arms — O3 Norwegian Nazi Party Emblem — O4

1937-38 Photo. *Perf. 13½x13*

O22 O3 5o rose lilac ('38) .65 .60
O23 O3 7o dp orange .65 .60
O24 O3 10o brt green .40 .25
O25 O3 15o olive bister .55 .55
O26 O3 20o carmine ('38) .55 .15
O27 O3 25o red brown ('38) 1.00 .70
O28 O3 30o ultra 1.00 .60
O29 O3 35o red vio ('38) 1.00 .60
O30 O3 40o Prus grn ('38) .85 .40
O31 O3 60o Prus bl ('38) 1.00 .60
O32 O3 100o dk vio ('38) 2.00 1.50
Nos. O22-O32 (11) 9.65 6.55
Set, never hinged 21.00

See Nos. O33-O43, O55-O56. For surcharge see No. O57.

1939-47 Unwmk.

O33 O3 5o dp red lil ('41) .40 .15
O34 O3 7o dp orange ('41) .40 .35
O35 O3 10o brt green ('41) .25 .15
O36 O3 15o olive ('45) .40 .25
O37 O3 20o carmine .25 .15
O38 O3 25o red brown 2.00 3.00
O38A O3 25o scarlet ('46) .25 .15
O39 O3 30o ultra 2.75 1.10
O39A O3 30o dk gray ('47) .65 .55
O40 O3 35o brt lilac ('41) .55 .25
O41 O3 40o grnsh blk ('41) .55 .25
O41A O3 40o dp ultra ('46) 1.25 .25
O42 O3 60o Prus blue ('41) .65 .25
O43 O3 100o dk violet ('41) .65 .25
Nos. O33-O43 (14) 11.00 7.10
Set, never hinged 18.00

1942-44

O44 O4 5o magenta .35 .85
O45 O4 7o yellow org .35 .85
O46 O4 10o emerald .15 .15
O47 O4 15o olive ('44) 2.00 5.00
O48 O4 20o bright red .15 .15
O49 O4 25o red brn ('43) 4.00 8.50
O50 O4 30o brt ultra ('44) 3.00 10.00
O51 O4 35o brt pur ('43) 3.00 7.25
O52 O4 40o grnsh blk ('43) .25 .15
O53 O4 60o indigo ('43) 2.25 5.00
O54 O4 1k blue vio ('43) 2.25 7.25
Nos. O44-O54 (11) 17.75 45.15
Set, never hinged 32.50

Type of 1937

1947, Nov. 1

O55 O3 50o deep magenta .85 .25
O56 O3 200o orange 3.25 .65
Set, never hinged 6.50

No. O37 Surcharged with New Values and Bars in Black

1949, Mar. 15

O57 O3 25o on 20o carmine .25 .35
Never hinged .35

Norway Coat of Arms
O5 O6

1951-52 Unwmk. Photo. *Perf. 13*

O58 O5 5o rose lilac .60 .15
O59 O5 10o dk gray .60 .15
O60 O5 15o dp org brn ('52) .60 .15
O61 O5 30o scarlet .60 .15
O62 O5 35o red brn ('52) .70 .45
O63 O5 60o blue gray .70 .15
O64 O5 100o vio bl ('52) 1.10 .15
Nos. O58-O64 (7) 4.90 1.35
Set, never hinged 9.00

Catalogue values for unused stamps in this section, from this point to the end of the section, are for Never Hinged items.

1955-61

O65 O6 5o rose lilac .25 .15
O66 O6 10o slate .25 .15
O67 O6 15o orange brn 1.65 1.10
O68 O6 20o bl grn ('57) .35 .15
O69 O6 25o emer ('59) .70 .15
O70 O6 30o scarlet 1.65 .65
O71 O6 35o brown red .70 .15
O72 O6 40o blue lilac 1.10 .15
O73 O6 45o scar ('58) .90 .15
O74 O6 50o gldn brn ('57) 2.50 .22
O75 O6 60o blue 2.25 .32
O76 O6 70o brn olive 3.25 1.10
O77 O6 75o maroon ('57) 8.00 6.00
O78 O6 80o org brn ('58) 3.50 .70
O79 O6 90o org ('58) 1.10 .20
O80 O6 1k vio ('57) 1.65 .15
O81 O6 2k gray grn ('60) 1.75 .15
O82 O6 5k red lil ('61) 6.25 .85
Nos. O65-O82 (18) 37.80 12.49

See Phosphorescence note after No. 430.

1962-74 Photo.

O83 O6 30o green ('64) .75 .15
O84 O6 40o ol grn ('68) .25 .15
O85 O6 50o scarlet 1.10 .25
O86 O6 50o slate ('69) .20 .15
O87 O6 60o dk red ('64) 1.10 .15
O87A O6 60o grnsh bl ('72) 3.75 .35
O88 O6 65o dk red ('68) 1.10 .15
O89 O6 70o dk red ('70) .30 .15
O90 O6 75o lt grn ('73) .75 .75
O90A O6 80o red brn ('72) .75 .75
O91 O6 85o ocher ('74) .95 .95
O92 O6 1k dp org ('73) .45 .15
O93 O6 1.10k car lake ('74) .75 .60
Nos. O83-O93 (13) 12.20 4.70

Shades exist of several values of type O6.
Nos O87A, O90A are on phosphored paper.

1975-82 Litho.

O94 O6 5o rose lil ('80) .60 .60
O95 O6 10o bluish gray ('82) .80 .80
O96 O6 15o henna brn 1.25 1.25
O97 O6 20o green ('82) .80 .80
O98 O6 25o yellow grn .40 .15
O99 O6 40o ol grn ('79) 1.00 1.00
O100 O6 50o grnsh gray ('76) .40 .15
O101 O6 60o dk grnsh bl 1.00 1.00
O102 O6 70o dk red ('82) 2.00 1.50
O103 O6 80o red brn ('76) .60 .15
O104 O6 1k vio ('80) 1.40 .35
O105 O6 1.10k red ('80) 1.25 .60
O106 O6 1.25k dull red .60 .15
O107 O6 1.30k lilac ('81) 1.00 1.00
O108 O6 1.50k red ('81) .70 .20
O109 O6 1.75k dl bl grn ('82) 1.40 1.25
O110 O6 2k dk gray grn 1.00 .20
O111 O6 2k cerise ('82) 1.40 .30
O112 O6 3k purple ('82) 2.00 .80
O113 O6 5k lt vio 15.00 2.50
O114 O6 5k blue ('77) 2.75 .80
Nos. O94-O114 (21) 37.35 15.55

In lithographed set, shield's background is dotted; on photogravure stamps it is solid color.
Official stamps invalid as of Apr. 1, 1986.

NOSSI-BE

ˌnō-sē-ˈbā

LOCATION — Island in the Indian Ocean, off the northwest coast of Madagascar
GOVT. — French Protectorate
AREA — 130 sq. mi.
POP. — 9,000 (approx. 1900)
CAPITAL — Hellville

In 1896 the island was placed under the authority of the Governor-General of Madagascar and postage stamps of Madagascar were placed in use.

100 Centimes = 1 Franc

Stamps of French Colonies Surcharged in Blue:

25 **25 c** **5 c**
a b c

On the following issues the colors of the French Colonies stamps, type A9, are: 5c, green, *greenish*; 10c, black, *lavender*; 15c, blue; 20c, red, *green*; 30c, brown, *bister*; 40c, vermilion, *straw*; 75c, carmine, *rose*; 1fr, bronze green, *straw*.

1889 Unwmk. *Imperf.*

1 A8(a) 25 on 40c red, *straw* 1,400. 500.
a. Double surcharge *1,200.*
2 A8(b) 25c on 40c red, *straw* 1,750. 1,100.

Perf. 14x13½

3 A9(b) 5c on 10c 1,750. 600.
4 A9(b) 5c on 20c 1,800. 1,000.
5 A9(c) 5c on 10c 2,000. 700.
6 A9(c) 5c on 20c 2,100. 800.
7 A9(a) 15 on 20c 1,600. 600.
a. 15 on 30c (error) *18,000.* *16,000.*
8 A9(a) 25 on 30c 1,400. 450.
9 A9(a) 25 on 40c 1,400. 425.

N S B
0 25
d

N S B
25 c.
f

g

Black Surcharge

1890

10 A9(d) 0.25 on 20c 250.00 165.00
11 A9(d) 0.25 on 75c 250.00 165.00
12 A9(d) 0.25 on 1fr 250.00 165.00
a. Without ornament
16 A9(f) 25c on 20c 250.00 165.00
17 A9(f) 25c on 75c 250.00 165.00
18 A9(f) 25c on 1fr 250.00 165.00
19 A9(g) 25 on 20c 575.00 375.00
20 A9(g) 25 on 75c 575.00 375.00
21 A9(g) 25 on 1fr 575.00 375.00

The 25c on 20c with surcharge composed of "25 c." as in "f," "N S B" as in "d," and frame as in "g" is an essay.

Surcharged or Overprinted in Black, Carmine, Vermilion or Blue:

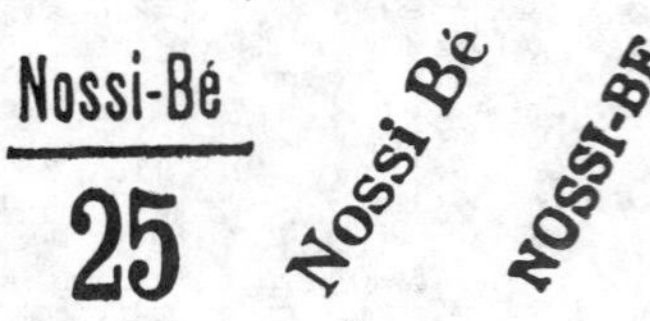

Nossi Bé

NOSSI-BE

j k m

1893

23	A9(j)	25 on 20c (Bk)	20.00	16.00
24	A9(j)	50 on 10c (Bk)	25.00	16.00
a.		Inverted surcharge	175.00	140.00
25	A9(j)	75 on 15c (Bk)	150.00	125.00
26	A9(j)	1fr on 5c (Bk)	55.00	45.00
a.		Inverted surcharge	165.00	150.00
27	A9(k)	10c (C)	8.00	7.50
a.		Inverted overprint	55.00	50.00
28	A9(k)	10c (V)	8.00	7.50
29	A9(k)	15c (Bk)	8.00	7.50
a.		Inverted overprint	55.00	50.00
30	A9(k)	20c (Bk)	325.00	35.00
a.		Double overprint		
31	A9(m)	20c (Bl)	55.00	27.50
a.		Inverted overprint	80.00	75.00

Counterfeits exist of surcharges and overprints of Nos. 1-31.

Navigation and Commerce — A14

1894 Typo. *Perf. 14x13½*

Name of Colony in Blue or Carmine

32	A14	1c	blk, *lil bl*	.65	.60
33	A14	2c	brn, *buff*	.80	.75
34	A14	4c	claret, *lav*	1.25	.75
35	A14	5c	grn, *greenish*	1.40	.95
36	A14	10c	blk, *lav*	4.00	2.25
37	A14	15c	blue, quadrille paper	4.25	2.25
38	A14	20c	red, *grn*	4.75	3.00
39	A14	25c	blk, *rose*	6.50	5.00
40	A14	30c	brn, *bister*	7.50	5.50
41	A14	40c	red, *straw*	9.00	7.00
42	A14	50c	carmine, *rose*	9.00	7.00
43	A14	75c	dp vio, *orange*	25.00	25.00
44	A14	1fr	brnz grn, *straw*	15.00	12.50
			Nos. 32-44 (13)	89.10	72.55

Perf. 13½x14 stamps are counterfeits.

POSTAGE DUE STAMPS

Stamps of French Colonies Surcharged in Black:

Nossi-Bé chiffre-taxe 0.20 A PERCEVOIR
n

Nossi-Bé chiffre-taxe 0.35 A PERCEVOIR
o

1891 Unwmk. *Perf. 14x13½*

J1	A9(n)	20 on 1c blk, *lil bl*	225.00	165.00
a.		Inverted surcharge	400.00	325.00
b.		Surcharged vertically	550.00	550.00
c.		Surcharge on back	425.00	425.00
J2	A9(n)	30 on 2c brn, *buff*	225.00	165.00
a.		Inverted surcharge	400.00	325.00
b.		Surcharge on back	425.00	425.00
J3	A9(n)	50 on 30c brn, *bister*	60.00	50.00
a.		Inverted surcharge	400.00	325.00
b.		Surcharge on back	425.00	425.00
J4	A9(o)	35 on 4c cl, *lav*	275.00	175.00
a.		Inverted surcharge	400.00	325.00
b.		Surcharge on back	425.00	425.00
c.		Pair, one without surcharge		
J5	A9(o)	35 on 20c red, *green*	275.00	175.00
a.		Inverted surcharge	400.00	325.00
J6	A9(o)	1fr on 35c vio, *orange*	150.00	100.00
a.		Inverted surcharge	400.00	325.00
b.		Surcharge on back	425.00	425.00

Nossi-Bé 5 C. A PERCEVOIR
p

Nossi-Bé 5 C. A PERCEVOIR
q

Nossi-Bé 0.10 A PERCEVOIR
r

1891

J7	A9(p)	5c on 20c	125.00	125.00
J8	A9(q)	5c on 20c	175.00	175.00
J9	A9(r)	0.10c on 5c	10.00	9.00
J10	A9(p)	10c on 15c	140.00	140.00
J11	A9(q)	10c on 15c	175.00	175.00
J12	A9(p)	15c on 10c	85.00	85.00
J13	A9(q)	15c on 10c	110.00	110.00
J14	A9(r)	0.15c on 20c	12.00	12.00
a.		25c on 20c (error)	*22,500.*	*22,500.*
J15	A9(p)	25c on 5c	85.00	85.00
J16	A9(q)	25c on 5c	125.00	125.00
J17	A9(r)	0.25c on 75c	375.00	350.00

Inverted Surcharge

J7a	A9(p)	5c on 20c	200.00	200.00
J8a	A9(q)	5c on 20c	200.00	200.00
J10a	A9(p)	10c on 15c	200.00	200.00
J11a	A9(q)	10c on 15c	200.00	200.00
J12a	A9(p)	15c on 10c	200.00	200.00
J13a	A9(q)	15c on 10c	200.00	200.00
J15a	A9(p)	25c on 5c	200.00	200.00
J16a	A9(q)	25c on 5c	200.00	200.00
J17a	A9(r)	0.25c on 75c	850.00	750.00

Stamps of Nossi-Be were superseded by those of Madagascar.

Counterfeits exist of surcharges on #J1-J17.

NYASALAND PROTECTORATE

nī-ˈa-sə-ˌland prə-ˈtek-t(ə-)rət

LOCATION — In southern Africa, bordering on Lake Nyasa
GOVT. — British Protectorate
AREA — 49,000 sq. mi.
POP. — 2,950,000 (est. 1962)
CAPITAL — Zomba

For previous issues, see British Central Africa.

Nyasaland joined the Federation of Rhodesia and Nyasaland in 1953, using its stamps until 1963. As the Federation began to dissolve in 1963, Nyasaland withdrew its postal services and issued provisional stamps. On July 6, 1964, Nyasaland became the independent state of Malawi.

12 Pence = 1 Shilling
20 Shillings = 1 Pound

Catalogue values for unused stamps in this country are for Never Hinged items, beginning with Scott 68 in the regular postage section and Scott J1 in the postage due section.

King Edward VII
A1 A2

Wmk. Crown and C A (2)

1908, July 22 Typo. *Perf. 14*

Chalky Paper

1	A1	1sh	black, *green*	2.00	*4.50*

Wmk. Multiple Crown and C A (3)

Ordinary Paper

2	A1	½p	green	.60	.40
3	A1	1p	carmine	.90	.20

Chalky Paper

4	A1	3p	violet, *yel*	1.25	2.00
5	A1	4p	scar & blk, *yel*	1.50	2.00
6	A1	6p	red vio & vio	3.25	4.75
7	A2	2sh	6p car & blk, *bl*	30.00	30.00
8	A2	4sh	black & car	55.00	*65.00*
9	A2	10sh	red & grn, *grn*	65.00	*90.00*
10	A2	£1	blk & vio, *red*	375.00	375.00
11	A2	£10	ultra & lilac	8,500.	*8,500.*
			Nos. 1-10 (10)	534.50	573.85

King George V
A3 A4

1913-18

Ordinary Paper

12	A3	½p	green	.40	.40
13	A3	1p	scarlet	.40	.25
a.			1p carmine	.65	.40
14	A3	2p	gray	1.25	.50
15	A3	2½p	ultra	.50	.60

Chalky Paper

16	A3	3p	violet, *yel*	1.50	1.50
17	A3	4p	scar & blk, *yel*	1.25	1.50
18	A3	6p	red vio & dull vio	1.50	1.75
19	A3	1sh	black, *green*	1.65	1.50
a.			1sh black, *emerald*	1.10	1.10
b.			1sh blk, *bl grn,* olive back	1.25	1.25
20	A4	2sh6p	red & blk, *bl* ('18)	12.50	16.00
21	A4	4sh	blk & red ('18)	20.00	*21.00*
22	A4	10sh	red & grn, *grn*	60.00	77.50
23	A4	£1	blk & vio, *red* ('18)	150.00	150.00
24	A4	£10	ultra & dull vio ('14)	*2,750.*	*1,750.*
			Revenue cancel		250.00
			Nos. 12-23 (12)	250.95	272.50

Stamps of Nyasaland Protectorate overprinted "N. F." are listed under German East Africa.

1921-30 Wmk. 4

Ordinary Paper

25	A3	½p	green	.35	.15
26	A3	1p	rose red	.35	.15
27	A3	1½p	orange	7.00	*10.00*
28	A3	2p	gray	.75	.30

Chalky Paper

29	A3	3p	violet, *yel*	2.25	.65
30	A3	4p	scar & blk, *yel*	1.90	1.65
31	A3	6p	red vio & dl vio	2.75	2.75
32	A3	1sh	blk, *grn* ('30)	5.50	4.00
33	A4	2sh	ultra & dl vio, *bl*	10.00	*10.00*
34	A4	2sh6p	red & blk, *bl* ('24)	14.00	11.50
35	A4	4sh	black & car	10.00	8.25
36	A4	5sh	red & grn, *yel* ('29)	30.00	27.50
37	A4	10sh	red & grn, *emer*	82.50	100.00
			Nos. 25-37 (13)	167.35	176.90

George V and Leopard — A5

1934-35 Engr. *Perf. 12½*

38	A5	½p	green	.60	.40
39	A5	1p	dark brown	.60	.35
40	A5	1½p	rose	.60	.55
41	A5	2p	gray	.75	.55
42	A5	3p	dark blue	1.50	1.50
43	A5	4p	rose lilac ('35)	2.50	2.50
44	A5	6p	dk violet	3.00	3.00
45	A5	9p	olive bis ('35)	3.75	*5.75*
46	A5	1sh	orange & blk	3.75	3.75
			Nos. 38-46 (9)	17.05	18.35

Silver Jubilee Issue

Common Design Type

1935, May 6 *Perf. 11x12*

47	CD301	1p	gray blk & ultra	.65	.65
48	CD301	2p	indigo & grn	3.75	2.25
49	CD301	3p	ultra & brn	4.50	9.00
50	CD301	1sh	brown vio & ind	14.00	17.00
			Nos. 47-50 (4)	22.90	28.90

Coronation Issue

Common Design Type

1937, May 12 *Perf. 11x11½*

51	CD302	½p	deep green	.15	.20
52	CD302	1p	dark brown	.35	.20
53	CD302	2p	gray black	.35	.35
			Nos. 51-53 (3)	.85	.75

A6

King George VI — A7

1938-44 Engr. *Perf. 12½*

54	A6	½p	green	.15	.30
54A	A6	½p	dk brown ('42)	.15	.40
55	A6	1p	dark brown	.15	.15
55A	A6	1p	green ('42)	.15	.20
56	A6	1½p	dark carmine	.65	1.90
56A	A6	1½p	gray ('42)	.15	1.25
57	A6	2p	gray	1.25	.40
57A	A6	2p	dark car ('42)	.15	.30
58	A6	3p	blue	.30	.15
59	A6	4p	rose lilac	.80	.30
60	A6	6p	dark violet	.85	.25
61	A6	9p	olive bister	1.40	1.40
62	A6	1sh	orange & blk	1.40	.55

Typo.

Perf. 14

Chalky Paper

63	A7	2sh	ultra & dl vio, *bl*	5.50	4.50
64	A7	2sh6p	red & blk, *bl*	6.50	4.50
65	A7	5sh	red & grn, *yel*	22.50	11.00
a.			5sh dk red & dp grn, *yel* ('44)	50.00	37.50
66	A7	10sh	red & grn, *grn*	32.50	14.00

Wmk. 3

67	A7	£1	blk & vio, *red*	16.00	15.00
			Nos. 54-67 (18)	90.55	56.55

Catalogue values for unused stamps in this section, from this point to the end of the section, are for Never Hinged items.

Canoe on Lake Nyasa — A8

Soldier of King's African Rifles — A9

Tea Estate, Mlanje Mountain A10

Map and Coat of Arms — A11

Fishing Village, Lake Nyasa — A12

Tobacco Estate — A13

Arms of Nyasaland and George VI A14

1945, Sept. 1 Engr. *Perf. 12*

68	A8	½p brown vio & blk	.15	.15
69	A9	1p dp green & blk	.15	.15
70	A10	1½p gray grn & blk	.30	.15
71	A11	2p scarlet & blk	.15	.15
72	A12	3p blue & blk	.40	.15
73	A13	4p rose vio & blk	.80	.50
74	A10	6p violet & blk	.80	.50
75	A8	9p ol grn & blk	1.25	1.75
76	A11	1sh myr grn & ind	.85	.50
77	A12	2sh dl red brn & grn	3.00	1.75
78	A13	2sh6p ultra & green	3.25	3.00
79	A14	5sh ultra & lt vio	4.50	3.25
80	A11	10sh green & lake	9.00	6.50
81	A14	20sh black & scar	20.00	24.00
		Nos. 68-81 (14)	44.60	42.50

Peace Issue

Common Design Type

Perf. 13½x14

1946, Dec. 16 Wmk. 4

82	CD303	1p bright green	.20	.20
83	CD303	2p red orange	.25	.25

A15

1947, Oct. 20 *Perf. 12*

84	A15	1p emerald & org brn	.25	.15

Silver Wedding Issue

Common Design Types

1948, Dec. 15 Photo. *Perf. 14x14½*

85	CD304	1p dark green	.15	.15

Engr.; Name Typo.

Perf. 11½x11

86	CD305	10sh purple	14.00	*12.00*

UPU Issue

Common Design Types

Engr.; Name Typo. on 3p, 6p

Perf. 13½, 11x11½

1949, Nov. 21 Wmk. 4

87	CD306	1p blue green	.15	.15
88	CD307	3p Prus blue	.45	.45
89	CD308	6p rose violet	1.40	.90
90	CD309	1sh violet blue	2.25	2.75
		Nos. 87-90 (4)	4.25	4.25

Arms of British Central Africa and Nyasaland Protectorate — A16

1951, May 15 Engr. *Perf. 11x12*

Arms in Black

91	A16	2p rose	.20	.20
92	A16	3p blue	.25	.25
93	A16	6p purple	.40	.80
94	A16	5sh deep blue	2.50	3.50
		Nos. 91-94 (4)	3.35	4.75

60th anniv. of the Protectorate, originally British Central Africa.

Exhibition Seal — A17

1953, May 30 *Perf. 14x13½*

95	A17	6p purple	.45	.40

Central African Rhodes Cent. Exhib.

Coronation Issue

Common Design Type

1953, June 2 *Perf. 13½x13*

96	CD312	2p orange & black	.25	.25

Types of 1945-47 with Portrait of Queen Elizabeth II and

Grading Cotton — A18

1953, Sept. 1 *Perf. 12*

97	A8	½p red brown & blk	.15	.15
a.		Booklet pane of 4	3.25	
b.		Perf. 12x12½ ('54)	.15	.15
98	A15	1p emer & org brn	.15	.15
a.		Booklet pane of 4	3.25	
99	A10	1½p gray grn & blk	.20	.20
100	A11	2p orange & blk	.15	.15
a.		Booklet pane of 4	3.25	
b.		Perf. 12x12½ ('54)	.15	.15
101	A18	2½p blk & brt grn	.15	.20
102	A13	3p scarlet & blk	.25	.25
103	A12	4½p blue & blk	.40	.40
104	A10	6p violet & blk	.45	.45
a.		Booklet pane of 4	3.00	
b.		Perf. 12x12½ ('54)	.45	.45
105	A8	9p olive & blk	.70	1.65
106	A11	1sh myr grn & ind	.85	.85
107	A12	2sh rose brn & grn	1.50	1.50
108	A13	2sh6p ultra & grn	2.00	2.00
109	A14	5sh Prus bl & rose lil	3.00	3.00
110	A11	10sh green & lake	6.75	7.75
111	A14	20sh black & scar	10.50	12.50
		Nos. 97-111 (15)	27.20	31.20

Issue date: Nos. 97b, 100b, 104b, Mar. 8.

Revenue Stamps Overprinted "POSTAGE" and Bars in Black

Arms of Nyasaland A19

Perf. 11½x12

1963, Nov. 1 Engr. Unwmk.

112	A19	½p on 1p blue	.15	.15
113	A19	1p green	.15	.15
114	A19	2p rose red	.15	.15
115	A19	3p dark blue	.25	.20
116	A19	6p rose lake	.40	.40
117	A19	9p on 1sh car rose	.50	.50
118	A19	1sh purple	.55	.55
119	A19	2sh6p black	1.00	1.00
120	A19	5sh brown	1.40	1.40
121	A19	10sh gray olive	3.50	3.50
122	A19	£1 violet	6.25	6.25
		Nos. 112-122 (11)	14.30	14.25

Nos. 112, 117 have 3 bars over old value.

Mother and Child — A20

Designs: 1p, Chambo fish. 2p, Zebu bull. 3p, Peanuts. 4p, Fishermen in boat. 6p, Harvesting tea. 1sh, Lumber and tropical pine branch. 1sh3p, Tobacco industry. 2sh6p, Cotton industry. 5sh, Monkey Bay, Lake Nyasa. 10sh, Afzelia tree (pod mahogany). £1, Nyala antelope, vert.

Perf. 14½

1964, Jan. 1 Unwmk. Photo.

Size: 23x19mm

123	A20	½p lilac	.15	.15
124	A20	1p green & blk	.15	.15
125	A20	2p red brown	.20	.15
126	A20	3p pale brn, brn red & grn	.20	.15
127	A20	4p org yel & indigo	.25	.25

Size: 41½x25mm, 25x41½mm

128	A20	6p bl pur & brt yel grn	.30	.30
129	A20	1sh yel brn & dk grn	.65	.65
130	A20	1sh3p red brn & olive	.70	.65
131	A20	2sh6p blue & brn	1.25	1.25
132	A20	5sh grn, bl, sep & yel	1.75	1.75
133	A20	10sh org brn grn & gray	3.00	3.00
134	A20	£1 yel & dk brn	6.00	6.00
		Nos. 123-134 (12)	14.60	14.45

POSTAGE DUE STAMPS

Catalogue values for unused stamps in this section are for Never Hinged items.

D1

1950, July 1 Wmk. 4 Typo. *Perf. 14*

J1	D1	1p rose red	2.50	*8.00*
J2	D1	2p ultramarine	6.00	*16.00*
J3	D1	3p green	9.00	*10.00*
J4	D1	4p claret	16.00	*35.00*
J5	D1	6p ocher	25.00	*65.00*
		Nos. J1-J5 (5)	58.50	*134.00*

NYASSA

nī-'a-sə

LOCATION — In the northern part of Mozambique in southeast Africa
AREA — 73,292 sq. mi.
POP. — 3,000,000 (estimated)
CAPITAL — Porto Amelia

The district formerly administered by the Nyassa Company is now a part of Mozambique.

1000 Reis = 1 Milreis
100 Centavos = 1 Escudo (1919)

Mozambique Nos. 24-35 Overprinted in Black

NYASSA

1898 Unwmk. *Perf. 11½, 12½*

1	A3	5r yellow	3.50	3.00
2	A3	10r redsh violet	3.50	3.00
3	A3	15r chocolate	3.50	3.00
4	A3	20r gray violet	3.50	3.00
5	A3	25r blue green	3.50	3.00
6	A3	50r light blue	3.50	3.00
a.		Inverted overprint		
b.		Perf. 12½	8.00	6.50
7	A3	75r rose	5.00	4.00
8	A3	80r yellow grn	5.00	4.00
9	A3	100r brown, *buff*	5.00	4.00
10	A3	150r car, *rose*	10.00	9.00
11	A3	200r dk blue, *blue*	8.00	7.00
12	A3	300r dk blue, *salmon*	7.50	6.00
		Nos. 1-12 (12)	61.50	52.00

Reprints of Nos. 1, 5, 8, 9, 10 and 12 have white gum and clean-cut perforation 13½. Value of No. 9, $15; others $3 each.

Same Overprint on Mozambique Issue of 1898

1898 *Perf. 11½*

13	A4	2½r gray	1.75	1.25
14	A4	5r orange	1.75	1.25
15	A4	10r light green	1.75	1.25
16	A4	15r brown	2.00	1.50
17	A4	20r gray violet	2.00	1.50
18	A4	25r sea green	3.00	1.50
19	A4	50r blue	2.00	1.50
20	A4	75r rose	3.50	1.25
21	A4	80r violet	3.50	2.00
22	A4	100r dk bl, *bl*	4.50	2.00
23	A4	150r brown, *straw*	4.50	2.00
24	A4	200r red lilac, *pnksh*	5.00	2.00
25	A4	300r dk blue, *rose*	6.00	2.00
		Nos. 13-25 (13)	41.25	21.00

Giraffe — A5 Camels — A6

1901 Engr. *Perf. 14*

26	A5	2½r blk & red brn	.75	.45
27	A5	5r blk & violet	.75	.45
28	A5	10r blk & dp grn	.75	.45
29	A5	15r blk & org brn	.75	.45
30	A5	20r blk & org red	.75	.45
31	A5	25r blk & orange	.75	.45
32	A5	50r blk & dl bl	.75	.45
33	A6	75r blk & car lake	1.00	.45
34	A6	80r blk & lilac	1.00	.45
35	A6	100r blk & brn bis	1.00	.50
36	A6	150r blk & dp org	2.00	.95
37	A6	200r blk & grnsh bl	1.50	.95
38	A6	300r blk & yel grn	1.50	1.10
		Nos. 26-38 (13)	13.25	7.55

Nos. 26 to 38 are known with inverted centers but are believed to be purely speculative and never regularly issued. Value $25 each.

Perf 13½, 14½, 15½ & compound also exist.

For overprints and surcharges see Nos. 39-50, 63-80.

Nos. 34, 36, 38 Surcharged **65 REIS**

1903

39	A6	65r on 80r	.70	.65
40	A6	115r on 150r	.70	.65
41	A6	130r on 300r	.70	.65
		Nos. 39-41 (3)	2.10	1.95

Nos. 29, 31 Overprinted **PROVISORIO**

1903

42	A5	15r black & org brn	.70	.65
43	A5	25r black & orange	.70	.65

Nos. 34, 36, 38 Surcharged **65 réis**

1903

44	A6	65r on 80r	22.50	10.00
45	A6	115r on 150r	22.50	10.00
46	A6	130r on 300r	22.50	10.00
		Nos. 44-46 (3)	67.50	30.00

Nos. 29, 31 Overprinted **PROVISORIO**

1903

47	A5	15r black & org brn	900.00	250.00
48	A5	25r black & orange	350.00	125.00

Forgeries exist of Nos. 44-48.

Nos. 26, 35 Surcharged **5 REIS PROVISORIO**

1910

49	A5	5r on 2½r	.85	.75
50	A6	50r on 100r	.85	.75
a.		"50 REIS" omitted	200.00	

Reprints of Nos. 49-50, made in 1921, have 2mm space between surcharge lines, instead of 1½mm. Value, each 25 cents.

Zebra — A7 Vasco da Gama's Flagship "San Gabriel" — A8

Red Overprint

Designs: Nos. 51-53, Camels. Nos. 57-59, Giraffe and palms.

1911

51	A7	2½r blk & dl vio	1.00	.55
52	A7	5r black	1.00	.55
53	A7	10r blk & gray grn	1.00	.55
54	A7	20r blk & car lake	1.00	.55
55	A7	25r blk & vio brn	1.00	.55
56	A7	50r blk & dp bl	1.00	.55
57	A8	75r blk & brn	1.00	.85
58	A8	100r blk & brn, *grn*	1.00	.85
59	A8	200r blk & dp grn, *sal*	1.25	1.10
60	A8	300r blk, *blue*	2.00	1.90
61	A8	400r blk & dk brn	3.00	3.00
a.		Pair, one without overprint		
62	A8	500r ol & vio brn	4.00	4.00
		Nos. 51-62 (12)	18.25	15.00

Nos. 51-62 exist without overprint but were not issued in that condition. Value $5 each.

For surcharges see Nos. 81-105.

REPUBLICA

Stamps of 1901-03 Surcharged

1½C.

1918

On Nos. 26-38

No.	Type	Description	Unused	Used
63	A5	¼c on 2½r	85.00	85.00
64	A5	½c on 5r	85.00	85.00
65	A5	1c on 10r	85.00	85.00
66	A5	1½c on 15r	5.50	5.50
67	A5	2c on 20r	4.00	4.00
68	A5	3½c on 25r	3.00	3.00
69	A5	5c on 50r	3.00	3.00
70	A6	7½c on 75r	3.00	3.00
71	A6	8c on 80r	3.00	3.00
72	A6	10c on 100r	4.50	3.00
73	A6	15c on 150r	7.50	5.00
74	A6	20c on 200r	7.50	5.00
75	A6	30c on 300r	6.50	6.50

On Nos. 39-41

No.	Type	Description	Unused	Used
76	A6	40c on 65r on 80r	30.00	30.00
77	A6	50c on 115r on 150r	8.50	8.50
78	A6	1e on 130r on 300r	8.50	6.50

On Nos. 42-43

No.	Type	Description	Unused	Used
79	A5	1½c on 15r	40.00	40.00
80	A5	3½c on 25r	10.00	10.00
		Nos. 63-80 (18)	399.50	391.00

On Nos. 70-78 there is less space between "REPUBLICA" and the new value than on the other stamps of this issue.

On Nos. 76-78 the 1903 surcharge is canceled by a bar.

The surcharge exists inverted on #64, 66-70, 72, 76, 78-80, and double on #64, 67, 69.

Nos. 51-62 Surcharged in Black or Red

7½ Centavos

1921

Lisbon Surcharges

Numerals: The "1" (large or small) is thin, sharp-pointed, and has thin serifs. The "2" is italic, with the tail thin and only slightly wavy. The "3" has a flat top. The "4" is open at the top. The "7" has thin strokes.

Centavos: The letters are shaded, i.e., they are thicker in some parts than in others. The "t" has a thin cross bar ending in a downward stroke at the right. The "s" is flat at the bottom and wider than in the next group.

No.	Type	Description	Unused	Used
81	A7	¼c on 2½r	15.00	15.00
83	A7	½c on 5r (R)	15.00	15.00
a.		½c on 2½r (R) (error)	200.00	200.00
84	A7	1c on 10r	15.00	15.00
a.		Pair, one without surcharge		
85	A8	1½c on 300r (R)	20.00	20.00
86	A7	2c on 20r	15.00	15.00
87	A7	2½c on 25r	15.00	15.00
88	A8	3c on 400r	10.00	10.00
a.		"Republica" omitted		
89	A7	5c on 50r	20.00	20.00
90	A8	7½c on 75r	11.00	11.00
91	A8	10c on 100r	20.00	20.00
92	A8	12c on 500r	10.00	10.00
93	A8	20c on 200r	14.00	14.00
		Nos. 81-93 (12)	180.00	180.00

The surcharge exists inverted on Nos. 83-85, 87-88 and 92, and double on Nos. 81, 83 and 86.

Forgeries exist of Nos. 81-93.

London Surcharges

Numerals: The "1" has the vertical stroke and serifs thicker than in the Lisbon printing. The "2" is upright and has a strong wave in the tail. The small "2" is heavily shaded. The "3" has a rounded top. The "4" is closed at the top. The "7" has thick strokes.

Centavos: The letters are heavier than in the Lisbon printing and are of even thickness throughout. The "t" has a thick cross bar with scarcely any down stroke at the end. The "s" is rounded at the bottom and narrower than in the Lisbon printing.

No.	Type	Description	Unused	Used
94	A7	¼c on 2½r	1.25	1.25
95	A7	½c on 5r (R)	1.25	1.25
96	A7	1c on 10r	1.25	1.25
97	A8	1½c on 300r (R)	1.25	1.25
98	A7	2c on 20r	1.25	1.25
99	A7	2½c on 25r	1.25	1.25
100	A8	3c on 400r	1.25	1.25
101	A7	5c on 50r	1.25	1.25
102	A8	7½c on 75r	1.25	1.25
a.		Inverted surcharge		
103	A8	10c on 100r	1.25	1.25
104	A8	12c on 500r	1.25	1.25
105	A8	20c on 200r	1.25	1.25
		Nos. 94-105 (12)	15.00	15.00

A9

Zebra and Warrior — A10

Designs: 2c-5c, Vasco da Gama. 7½c-20c, "San Gabriel." 2e-5e, Dhow and warrior.

Perf. 12½, 13½-15 & Compound

1921-23 Engr.

No.	Type	Description	Unused	Used
106	A9	¼c claret	.80	.80
107	A9	½c steel blue	.80	.80
108	A9	1c grn & blk	.80	.80
109	A9	1½c blk & ocher	.80	.80
110	A9	2c red & blk	.80	.80
111	A9	2½c blk & ol grn	.80	.80
112	A9	4c blk & org	.80	.80
113	A9	5c ultra & blk	.80	.80
114	A9	6c blk & vio	.80	.80
115	A9	7½c blk & blk brn	.80	.80
116	A9	8c blk & ol grn	.80	.80
117	A9	10c blk & red brn	.80	.80
118	A9	15c blk & carmine	.80	.80
119	A9	20c blk & pale bl	1.00	1.00
120	A10	30c blk & bister	1.00	1.00
121	A10	40c blk & gray bl	1.00	1.00
122	A10	50c blk & green	1.00	1.00
123	A10	1e blk & red brn	1.00	1.00
124	A10	2e red brn & blk ('23)	7.00	7.00
125	A10	5e ultra & red brn ('23)	6.50	6.50
		Nos. 106-125 (20)	28.90	28.90

POSTAGE DUE STAMPS

Giraffe — D1

Designs: ½c, 1c, Giraffe. 2c, 3c, Zebra. 5c, 6c, 10c, "San Gabriel." 20c, 50c, Vasco da Gama.

1924 Unwmk. Engr. *Perf. 14*

No.	Type	Description	Unused	Used
J1	D1	½c deep green	.75	.75
J2	D1	1c gray	.75	.75
J3	D1	2c red	.75	.75
J4	D1	3c red orange	.75	.75
J5	D1	5c dark brown	.75	.75
J6	D1	6c orange brown	.75	.75
J7	D1	10c brown violet	.85	.85
J8	D1	20c carmine	.85	.85
J9	D1	50c lilac gray	.85	.85
		Nos. J1-J9 (9)	7.05	7.05

NEWSPAPER STAMP

Mozambique No. P6 Overprinted Like Nos. 1-25 in Black

1898 Unwmk. *Perf. 13½*

No.	Type	Description	Unused	Used
P1	N3	2½r brown	5.00	4.00

Reprints have white gum and clean-cut perf. 13½. Value $1.

POSTAL TAX STAMPS

Pombal Issue

Mozambique Nos. RA1-RA3 Overprinted "NYASSA" in Red

1925 Unwmk. *Perf. 12½*

No.	Type	Description	Unused	Used
RA1	CD28	15c brown & blk	2.50	2.50
RA2	CD29	15c brown & blk	2.50	2.50
RA3	CD30	15c brown & blk	2.50	2.50
		Nos. RA1-RA3 (3)	7.50	7.50

POSTAL TAX DUE STAMPS

Pombal Issue

Mozambique Nos. RAJ1-RAJ3 Overprinted "NYASSA" in Red

1925 Unwmk. *Perf. 12½*

No.	Type	Description	Unused	Used
RAJ1	CD28	30c brown & blk	30.00	30.00
RAJ2	CD29	30c brown & blk	30.00	30.00
RAJ3	CD30	30c brown & blk	30.00	30.00
		Nos. RAJ1-RAJ3 (3)	90.00	90.00

OBOCK

'ō-ˌbäk

LOCATION — A seaport in eastern Africa on the Gulf of Aden, directly opposite Aden.

Obock was the point of entrance from which French Somaliland was formed. The port was acquired by the French in 1862 but was not actively occupied until 1884 when Sagallo and Tadjoura were ceded to France. In 1888 Djibouti was made into a port and the seat of government moved from Obock to the latter city. In 1902 the name Somali Coast was adopted on the postage stamps of Djibouti, these stamps superseding the individual issues of Obock.

100 Centimes = 1 Franc

Counterfeits exist of Nos. 1-31.

Stamps of French Colonies Handstamped in Black:

OBOCK — #1-11, J1-J4

OBOCK — #12-20, J5-J18

1892 Unwmk. *Perf. 14x13½*

No.	Type	Description	Unused	Used
1	A9	1c blk, *lil bl*	17.50	15.00
2	A9	2c brn, *buff*	22.50	16.00
3	A9	4c claret, *lav*	300.00	275.00
4	A9	5c grn, *grnsh*	17.50	15.00
5	A9	10c blk, *lavender*	35.00	20.00
6	A9	15c blue	35.00	30.00
7	A9	25c blk, *rose*	45.00	40.00
8	A9	35c vio, *org*	250.00	250.00
9	A9	40c red, *straw*	300.00	275.00
10	A9	75c car, *rose*	325.00	300.00
11	A9	1fr brnz grn, *straw*	300.00	300.00
		Nos. 1-11 (11)	1,647.	1,536.

No. 3 has been reprinted. On the reprints the second "O" of "OBOCK" is 4mm high instead of 3½mm. Value $7.50.

1892

No.	Type	Description	Unused	Used
12	A9	4c claret, *lav*	12.50	10.00
13	A9	5c grn, *grnsh*	15.00	10.00
14	A9	10c blk, *lavender*	14.00	12.50
15	A9	15c blue	14.00	12.50
16	A9	20c red, *grn*	27.50	12.50
17	A9	25c blk, *rose*	10.00	8.50
18	A9	40c red, *straw*	30.00	22.50
19	A9	75c car, *rose*	200.00	165.00
20	A9	1fr brnz grn, *straw*	42.50	35.00
		Nos. 12-20 (9)	365.50	288.50

Exists inverted or double on all denominations.

Nos. 14, 15, 17, 20 with Additional Surcharge Handstamped in Red, Blue or Black:

1 — Nos, 21-30

5F — No. 31

1892

No.	Type	Description	Unused	Used
21	A9	1c on 25c blk, *rose*	5.50	5.50
22	A9	2c on 10c blk, *lav*	40.00	27.50
23	A9	2c on 15c blue	7.00	7.00
24	A9	4c on 15c bl (Bk)	6.50	6.00
25	A9	4c on 25c blk, *rose* (Bk)	7.00	6.50
26	A9	5c on 25c blk, *rose*	12.50	7.50
27	A9	20c on 10c blk, *lav*	50.00	42.50
28	A9	30c on 10c blk, *lav*	65.00	55.00
29	A9	35c on 25c blk, *rose*	55.00	47.50
a.		"3" instead of "35"	450.00	450.00
30	A9	75c on 1fr brnz grn, *straw*	70.00	65.00
b.		"57" instead of "75"	*5,000.*	*5,000.*
c.		"55" instead of "75"	*5,000.*	*5,000.*
31	A9	5fr on 1fr brnz grn, *straw* (Bl)	525.00	475.00
		Nos. 21-31 (11)	843.50	745.00

Exists inverted on most denominations.

Navigation and Commerce A4

Camel and Rider A5

1892 Typo. *Perf. 14x13½*

Obock in Red (1c, 5c, 15c, 25c, 75c, 1fr) or Blue

No.	Type	Description	Unused	Used
32	A4	1c blk, *lil bl*	2.00	1.00
33	A4	2c brn, *buff*	1.00	.65
34	A4	4c claret, *lav*	2.25	1.00
35	A4	5c grn, *grnsh*	3.75	1.00
36	A4	10c blk, *lavender*	6.00	2.00
37	A4	15c bl, quadrille paper	10.00	4.00
38	A4	20c red, *grn*	20.00	12.00
39	A4	25c blk, *rose*	17.50	10.00
40	A4	30c brn, *bis*	16.00	8.00
41	A4	40c red, *straw*	16.00	7.00
42	A4	50c car, *rose*	17.50	8.00
43	A4	75c vio, *org*	22.50	8.00
a.		Name double	175.00	175.00
b.		Name inverted	*2,250.*	*2,250.*
44	A4	1fr brnz grn, *straw*	30.00	17.50
		Nos. 32-44 (13)	164.50	80.15

Perf. 13½x14 stamps are counterfeits.

1893 *Imperf.*

Quadrille Lines Printed on Paper

Size: 32mm at base

No.	Type	Description	Unused	Used
44A	A5	2fr brnz grn	32.50	30.00

Size: 45mm at base

No.	Type	Description	Unused	Used
45	A5	5fr red	75.00	70.00

Somali Warriors A7

A8

1894 *Imperf.*

Quadrille Lines Printed on Paper

No.	Type	Description	Unused	Used
46	A7	1c blk & rose	1.10	1.10
47	A7	2c vio brn & grn	1.10	1.10
48	A7	4c brn vio & org	1.10	1.10
49	A7	5c bl grn & brn	1.25	1.25
50	A7	10c blk & grn	5.50	4.50
a.		Half used as 5c on cover		90.00
51	A7	15c bl & rose	4.50	4.00
52	A7	20c brn org & mar	5.00	4.00
a.		Half used as 10c on cover		70.00
53	A7	25c blk & bl	5.00	4.00
a.		Half used on cover		60.00
54	A7	30c bis & yel grn	10.00	7.50
a.		Half used as 15c on cover		1,250.
55	A7	40c red & bl grn	7.50	5.00
56	A7	50c rose & bl	6.50	5.00
a.		Half used as 25c on cover		2,000.
57	A7	75c gray lil & org	7.50	5.00
58	A7	1fr ol grn & mar	7.50	6.00

Size: 37mm at base

No.	Type	Description	Unused	Used
60	A8	2fr vio & org	70.00	65.00

Size: 42mm at base

No.	Type	Description	Unused	Used
61	A8	5fr rose & bl	70.00	55.00

Size: 46mm at base

No.	Type	Description	Unused	Used
62	A8	10fr org & red vio	100.00	90.00
63	A8	25fr brn & bl	550.00	550.00
64	A8	50fr red vio & grn	600.00	600.00

Counterfeits exist of Nos. 63-64.

Stamps of Obock were replaced in 1901 by those of Somali Coast. The 5c on 75c, 5c on 25fr and 10c on 50fr of 1902 are listed under Somali Coast.

POSTAGE DUE STAMPS

Postage Due Stamps of French Colonies Handstamped Like #1-20

1892 Unwmk. *Imperf.*

No.	Type	Description	Unused	Used
J1	D1	5c black	*6,500.*	
J2	D1	10c black	125.00	140.00
J3	D1	30c black	200.00	250.00
J4	D1	60c black	275.00	300.00
J5	D1	1c black	25.00	25.00
J6	D1	2c black	20.00	20.00
J7	D1	3c black	20.00	20.00
J8	D1	4c black	16.00	16.00
J9	D1	5c black	6.00	6.00
J10	D1	10c black	16.00	16.00
J11	D1	15c black	10.00	10.00
J12	D1	20c black	13.00	13.00
J13	D1	30c black	16.00	16.00
J14	D1	40c black	26.00	26.00
J15	D1	60c black	40.00	40.00
J16	D1	1fr brown	125.00	125.00
J17	D1	2fr brown	125.00	125.00
J18	D1	5fr brown	300.00	300.00
		Nos. J2-J18 (17)	1,358.	1,448.

These handstamped overprints may be found double or inverted on some values. Counterfeits exist of Nos. J1-J18.

No. J1 has been reprinted. The overprint on the original measures 12½x3¾mm and on the reprint 12x3¼mm. Value, $120.

OLTRE GIUBA

ˌōl–trā–ˈjü–bə

(Italian Jubaland)

LOCATION — A strip of land, 50 to 100 miles in width, west of and parallel to the Juba River in East Africa
GOVT. — Former Italian Protectorate
AREA — 33,000 sq. mi.
POP. — 12,000
CAPITAL — Kismayu

Oltre Giuba was ceded to Italy by Great Britain in 1924 and in 1926 was incorporated with Italian Somaliland. In 1936 it became part of Italian East Africa.

100 Centesimi = 1 Lira

Watermark

Wmk. 140- Crown

Italian Stamps of 1901-26 Overprinted

OLTRE GIUBA On #1-15 — **OLTRE GIUBA** On #16-20

1925, July 29 Wmk. 140 *Perf. 14*

No.	Type	Description	Unused	Used
1	A42	1c brown	1.40	1.00
a.		Inverted overprint	65.00	
2	A43	2c yel brown	1.40	1.00
3	A48	5c green	.40	1.00
4	A48	10c claret	.40	1.00
5	A48	15c slate	.40	1.00
6	A50	20c brn orange	.40	1.00
7	A49	25c blue	.40	1.00
8	A49	30c org brown	.40	1.00
9	A49	40c brown	1.25	1.00
10	A49	50c violet	1.40	1.00
11	A49	60c carmine	1.40	1.00
12	A46	1 l brn & green	3.25	2.50
13	A46	2 l dk grn & org	24.00	14.00
14	A46	5 l blue & rose	35.00	17.00
15	A51	10 l gray grn & red	6.00	*7.25*
		Nos. 1-15 (15)	77.50	*51.75*

1925-26

No.	Type	Description	Unused	Used
16	A49	20c green	2.00	*3.00*
17	A49	30c gray	2.75	*3.00*
18	A46	75c dk red & rose	22.50	*17.00*
19	A46	1.25 l bl & ultra	24.00	*21.00*
20	A46	2.50 l dk grn & org	27.50	*27.50*
		Nos. 16-20 (5)	78.75	*71.50*

Issue years: #18-20, 1926; others 1925.

Victor Emmanuel Issue

Italian Stamps of 1925 Overprinted

OLTRE GIUBA

1925-26 Unwmk. *Perf. 11*

No.	Type	Description	Unused	Used
21	A78	60c brown car	.15	*2.00*
a.		Perf. 13½	*2,400.*	
22	A78	1 l dark blue	.20	*2.00*
a.		Perf. 13½	110.00	*500.00*
23	A78	1.25 l dk bl ('26)	.50	*6.00*
a.		Perf. 13½	.50	*7.25*
		Nos. 21-23 (3)	.85	*10.00*

Saint Francis of Assisi Issue

Italian Stamps and Type of 1926 Overprinted

Oltre Giuba

1926, Apr. 12 Wmk. 140 *Perf. 14*

No.	Type	Description	Unused	Used
24	A79	20c gray green	1.00	*3.00*
25	A80	40c dark violet	1.00	*3.00*
26	A81	60c red brown	1.00	*3.00*

Overprinted in Red **OLTRE GIUBA**

Unwmk.

No.	Type	Description	Unused	Used
27	A82	1.25 l dk bl, perf. 11	1.00	*3.00*
28	A83	5 l + 2.50 l ol grn, perf. 13½	2.00	*5.50*
		Nos. 24-28 (5)	6.00	*17.50*

Map of Oltre Giuba — A1

1926, Apr. 21 Typo. Wmk. 140

No.	Type	Description	Unused	Used
29	A1	5c yellow brown	.15	*1.65*
30	A1	20c blue green	.15	*1.65*
31	A1	25c olive brown	.15	*1.65*
32	A1	40c dull red	.15	*1.65*
33	A1	60c brown violet	.80	*1.65*
34	A1	1 l blue	.80	*1.65*
35	A1	2 l dark green	.80	*1.65*
		Nos. 29-35 (7)	3.00	*11.55*

Oltre Giuba was incorporated with Italian Somaliland on July 1, 1926, and stamps inscribed "Oltre Giuba" were discontinued.

SEMI-POSTAL STAMPS

Note preceding Italy semi-postals applies to No. 28.

Colonial Institute Issue

"Peace" Substituting Spade for Sword — SP1

Wmk. 140

1926, June 1 Typo. *Perf. 14*

No.	Type	Description	Unused	Used
B1	SP1	5c + 5c brown	.15	*1.65*
B2	SP1	10c + 5c olive green	.15	*1.65*
B3	SP1	20c + 5c blue green	.15	*1.65*
B4	SP1	40c + 5c brown red	.15	*1.65*
B5	SP1	60c + 5c orange	.15	*1.65*
B6	SP1	1 l + 5c blue	.15	*1.65*
		Nos. B1-B6 (6)	.90	*9.90*

Surtax for Italian Colonial Institute.

SPECIAL DELIVERY STAMPS

Special Delivery Stamps of Italy Overprinted

OLTRE GIUBA

1926 Wmk. 140 *Perf. 14*

No.	Type	Description	Unused	Used
E1	SD1	70c dull red	8.00	*10.00*
E2	SD2	2.50 l blue & red	18.00	*14.00*

POSTAGE DUE STAMPS

Italian Postage Due Stamps of 1870-1903 Overprinted Like Nos. E1-E2

1925, July 29 Wmk. 140 *Perf. 14*

No.	Type	Description	Unused	Used
J1	D3	5c buff & magenta	3.75	3.50
J2	D3	10c buff & magenta	3.25	3.50
J3	D3	20c buff & magenta	3.25	3.50
J4	D3	30c buff & magenta	3.25	3.50
J5	D3	40c buff & magenta	4.00	4.00
J6	D3	50c buff & magenta	8.00	5.00
J7	D3	60c buff & brown	8.00	5.00
J8	D3	1 l blue & magenta	10.00	6.00
J9	D3	2 l blue & magenta	32.50	*20.00*
J10	D3	5 l blue & magenta	32.50	*27.50*
		Nos. J1-J10 (10)	108.50	*81.50*

PARCEL POST STAMPS

These stamps were used by affixing them to the waybill so that one half remained on it following the parcel, the other half staying on the receipt given the sender. Most used halves are right halves. Complete stamps were obtainable canceled, probably to order. Both unused and used values are for complete stamps.

Italian Parcel Post Stamps of 1914-22 Overprinted

OLTRE GIUBA

1925, July 29 Wmk. 140 *Perf. 13½*

No.	Type	Description	Unused	Used
Q1	PP2	5c brown	2.50	*3.00*
Q2	PP2	10c blue	.80	*1.50*
Q3	PP2	20c black	.80	*1.50*
Q4	PP2	25c red	.80	*1.50*
Q5	PP2	50c orange	2.50	*2.50*
Q6	PP2	1 l violet	1.65	*2.50*
a.		Double overprint	65.00	
Q7	PP2	2 l green	1.65	*2.50*
Q8	PP2	3 l bister	1.65	3.00
Q9	PP2	4 l slate	4.00	4.00
Q10	PP2	10 l rose lilac	20.00	14.00
Q11	PP2	12 l red brown	52.50	50.00
Q12	PP2	15 l olive green	45.00	32.50
Q13	PP2	20 l brown violet	45.00	32.50
		Nos. Q1-Q13 (13)	178.85	151.00

Halves Used

Nos.	Value
Q1, Q10	.32
Q2-Q6	.15
Q7-Q8	.15
Q9	.15
Q11, Q13	1.00
Q12	.80

OMAN

ˈō–ˌmän

Muscat and Oman

LOCATION — Southeastern corner of the Arabian Peninsula
GOVT. — Sultanate
AREA — 105,000 sq. mi.
POP. — 1,500,000 (est. 1982)
CAPITAL — Muscat

Nos. 16-93, the stamps with 'value only' surcharges, were used not only in Muscat, but also in Dubai (Apr. 1, 1948 - Jan. 6, 1961), Qatar (Aug. 1950 - Mar. 31, 1957), and Abu Dhubi (Mar. 30, 1963 - Mar. 29, 1964). Occasionally they were also used in Bahrain and Kuwait.

The Sultanate of Muscat and Oman changed its name to Oman in 1970.

12 Pies = 1 Anna
16 Annas = 1 Rupee
100 Naye Paise = 1 Rupee (1957)
64 Baizas = 1 Rupee (1966)
1000 Baizas = 1 Rial Saidi (1970)

Catalogue values for all unused stamps in this country are for Never Hinged items.

Muscat

Stamps of India 1937-43 Overprinted in Black

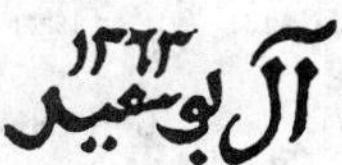

On #1-13 the overprint is smaller—13x6mm.

Wmk. Multiple Stars (196)

1944, Nov. 20 *Perf. 13½x14*

No.	Type	Description	Unused	Used
1	A83	3p slate	.15	*.15*
2	A83	½a rose violet	.15	*.15*
3	A83	9p lt green	.15	*.15*
4	A83	1a carmine rose	.15	*.15*
5	A84	1½a dark purple	.15	*.25*
a.		Double overprint	400.00	
6	A84	2a scarlet	.25	*.45*
7	A84	3a violet	.35	*.55*
8	A84	3½a ultra	.35	*.55*
9	A85	4a chocolate	.40	*.65*
10	A85	6a pck blue	.50	*.90*
11	A85	8a blue violet	.75	*1.25*
12	A85	12a car lake	.90	*1.75*
13	A81	14a rose violet	.90	*1.75*
14	A82	1r brown & slate	1.75	*3.75*
15	A82	2r dk brn & dk vio	3.00	*6.00*
		Nos. 1-15 (15)	9.90	*18.45*

200th anniv. of Al Busaid Dynasty.

Great Britain, Nos. 258 to 263, 243, 248, 249A Surcharged

Perf. 14½x14

1948, Apr. 1 Wmk. 251

No.	Type	Description	Unused	Used
16	A101	½a on ½p green	.15	*.15*
17	A101	1a on 1p vermilion	.15	*.20*
18	A101	1½a on 1½p lt red brn	.40	*.40*
19	A101	2a on 2p lt org	.45	*.55*
20	A101	2½a on 2½p ultra	.55	*.60*
21	A101	3a on 3p violet	.15	*.20*
22	A102	6a on 6p rose lilac	.45	*.25*
23	A103	1r on 1sh brown	2.00	*1.60*

Wmk. 259 *Perf. 14*

No.	Type	Description	Unused	Used
24	A104	2r on 2sh6p yel grn	16.00	*17.50*
		Nos. 16-24 (9)	20.30	*21.45*

Silver Wedding Issue

Great Britain, Nos. 267 and 268, Surcharged

Perf. 14½x14, 14x14½

1948, Apr. 26 Wmk. 251

No.	Type	Description	Unused	Used
25	A109	2½a on 2½p brt ultra	.15	.15
26	A110	15r on £1 dp chlky bl	27.50	27.50

Three bars obliterate the original denomination on No. 26.

Olympic Games Issue

Great Britain, Nos. 271-274, Surcharged

1948, July 29 *Perf. 14½x14*

No.	Type	Description	Unused	Used
27	A113	2½a on 2½p brt ultra	.25	.20
28	A114	3a on 3p dp violet	.30	.20
29	A115	6a on 6p red violet	.45	.40
30	A116	1r on 1sh dk brown	1.25	.75
a.		Double surcharge	300.00	
		Nos. 27-30 (4)	2.25	1.55

A square of dots obliterates the original denomination on Nos. 28-30.

UPU Issue

Great Britain Nos. 276 to 279 Surcharged with New Value and Square of Dots

1949, Oct. 10 Photo.

No.	Type	Description	Unused	Used
31	A117	2½a on 2½p brt ultra	.50	.30
32	A118	3a on 3p brt violet	.75	.50
33	A119	6a on 6p red violet	1.25	.85
34	A120	1r on 1sh brown	2.25	1.50
		Nos. 31-34 (4)	4.75	3.15

Great Britain Nos. 280-286 Surcharged

1951

No.	Type	Description	Unused	Used
35	A101	½a on ½p lt org	.30	.30
36	A101	1a on 1p ultra	.45	.45
37	A101	1½a on 1½p green	1.75	1.75
38	A101	2a on 2p lt red brn	.90	.90
39	A101	2½a on 2½p vermilion	1.75	1.75
40	A102	4a on 4p ultra	1.50	1.50

Wmk. 259 *Perf. 11x12*

No.	Type	Description	Unused	Used
41	A121	2r on 2sh6p green	20.00	17.50
		Nos. 35-41 (7)	26.65	24.15

Two types of surcharge on No. 41.

Stamps of Great Britain, 1952-54, Surcharged with New Value in Black and Dark Blue

1952-54 Wmk. 298 *Perf. 14½x14*

No.	Type	Description	Unused	Used
42	A126	½a on ½p red org ('53)	.15	.15
43	A126	1a on 1p ultra ('53)	.15	.15
44	A126	1½a on 1½p green ('52)	.15	.15
45	A126	2a on 2p red brn ('53)	.20	.20
46	A127	2½a on 2½p scar ('52)	.25	.25
47	A127	3a on 3p dk pur (Dk Bl)	.30	.30
48	A128	4a on 4p ultra ('53)	.45	.45

49 A129	6a on 6p lilac rose		.60	.45
50 A132	12a on 1sh3p dk grn ('53)		1.75	1.40
51 A131	1r on 1sh6p dk bl ('53)		2.00	1.60
	Nos. 42-51 (10)		6.00	5.10

Coronation Issue

Great Britain Nos. 313-316 Surcharged

1953, June 10

52 A134	2½a on 2½p scarlet	.70	.70
53 A135	4a on 4p brt ultra	1.10	1.10
54 A136	12a on 1sh3p dk green	3.50	3.50
55 A137	1r on 1sh6p dk blue	3.75	3.75
	Nos. 52-55 (4)	9.05	9.05

Squares of dots obliterate the original denominations on Nos. 54-55.

Great Britain Stamps of 1955-56 Surcharged

Perf. 14½x14

1955-57 Wmk. 308 Photo.

56 A126	1a on 1p ultra	.35	.35
56A A126	1½a on 1½p grn		*400.00*
57 A126	2a on 2p red brn	.75	.55
58 A127	2½a on 2½p scar	.85	.85
59 A127	3a on 3p dk pur	1.25	1.25
60 A128	4a on 4p ultra	5.00	1.75
61 A129	6a on 6p lilac rose	1.00	1.00
62 A131	1r on 1sh6p dk bl	3.00	1.40

Engr. ***Perf. 11x12***

63 A133	2r on 2sh6p dk brown	3.00	*8.50*
64 A133	5r on 5sh crimson	9.00	*15.00*
	Nos. 56,57-64 (9)	24.20	*30.65*

Surcharge on No. 63 exists in three types, on No. 64 in two types.

Issued: 2r, 9/23/55; 2a, 2½a, 6/8/56; 1r, 8/2/56; 4a, 12/9/56; 1½a, 1956; 3a, 2/3/57; 6a, 2/10/57; 5r, 3/1/57; 1a, 3/4/57.

Great Britain Nos. 317-325, 328, 332 Surcharged

1957, Apr. 1 ***Perf. 14½x14***

65 A129	1np on 5p lt brown	.15	.15
66 A126	3np on ½p red org	.15	.15
67 A126	6np on 1p ultra	.35	.35
68 A126	9np on 1½p green	.90	.70
69 A126	12np on 2p red brown	.50	.50
70 A127	15np on 2½p scar, I	.80	.80
a.	Type II	.60	.60
71 A127	20np on 3p dk pur	.30	.30
72 A128	25np on 4p ultra	.60	.60
73 A129	40np on 6p lilac rose	.80	.80
74 A130	50np on 9p dp ol grn	.80	.80
75 A132	75np on 1sh3p dk grn	1.25	1.25
	Nos. 65-75 (11)	6.60	6.40

The arrangement of the surcharge varies on different values; there are three bars through value on No. 74.

Jubilee Jamboree Issue

Great Britain Nos. 334-336 Surcharged with New Value and Square of Dots

Perf. 14½x14

1957, Aug. 1 Wmk. 308

76 A138	15np on 2½p scar	.35	.35
77 A138	25np on 4p ultra	.50	.50
78 A138	75np on 1sh3p dk grn	.60	.60
	Nos. 76-78 (3)	1.45	1.45

50th anniv. of the Boy Scout movement and the World Scout Jubilee Jamboree, Aug. 1-12.

Great Britain Stamps of 1958-60 Surcharged

Perf. 14½x14

1960-61 Wmk. 322 Photo.

79 A129	1np on 5p lt brown	.15	.15
80 A126	3np on ½p red org	1.00	1.00
81 A126	5np on 1p ultra	.15	.15
82 A126	6np on 1p ultra	1.75	1.75
83 A126	10np on 1½p green	.40	.25
84 A126	12np on 2p red brn	3.00	3.00
85 A127	15np on 2½p scar	.30	.30
86 A127	20np on 3p dk pur	.30	.30
87 A128	30np on 4½p hn brn	.65	.60
88 A129	40np on 6p lil rose	.55	.55
89 A130	50np on 9p dp ol grn	.80	.65
90 A132	75np on 1sh3p dk grn	1.50	1.10
91 A131	1r on 1sh6p dk blue	1.75	1.40
92 A133	2r on 2sh6p dk brn	10.00	5.00
93 A133	5r on 5sh crimson	15.00	12.00
	Nos. 79-93 (15)	37.30	28.20

Issued: 15np, 4/26; 3np, 6np, 12np, 6/21; 1np, 8/8; 20np, 40np, 9/28; 5np, 10np, 30np, 50np-5r, 4/8/61.

Muscat and Oman

Crest — A1

View of Harbor — A2

Nakhal Fort — A3

Baizas

Crest and: 50b, Samail Fort. 1r, Sohar Fort. 2r, Nizwa Fort. 5r, Matrah Fort. 10r, Mirani Fort.

Perf. 14½x14 (A1), 14x14½ (A2), 14x13½ (A3)

1966, Apr. 29 Photo. Unwmk.

94 A1	3b plum	.15	.15
95 A1	5b brown	.15	.15
96 A1	10b red brown	.15	.15
97 A2	15b black & violet	.30	.20
98 A2	20b black & ultra	.40	.25
99 A2	25b black & orange	.50	.35
100 A3	30b dk blue & lil rose	.65	.45
101 A3	50b red brn & brt grn	1.00	.60
a.	Value in "baizas" in Arabic	18.00	11.00
102 A3	1r org & dk bl	2.00	1.10
103 A3	2r grn & brn org	4.00	2.00
104 A3	5r dp car & vio	10.00	6.00
105 A3	10r dk vio & car rose	16.00	12.50
	Nos. 94-105 (12)	35.30	23.90

No. 101 has value in rupees in Arabic.

See Nos. 110-121. For overprints & surcharges see Nos. 122-133C.

Mina al Fahal Harbor A4

Designs: 25b, Oil tanks. 40b, Oil installation in the desert. 1r, View of Arabian Peninsula from Gemini IV.

Perf. 13½x13

1969, Jan. 1 Litho. Unwmk.

106 A4	20b multicolored	.80	.60
107 A4	25b multicolored	1.00	.75
108 A4	40b multicolored	1.60	1.25
109 A4	1r multicolored	4.00	3.00
	Nos. 106-109 (4)	7.40	5.60

1st oil shipment from Muscat & Oman, July, 1967.

Types of 1966

Designs: 50b, Nakhal Fort. 75b, Samail Fort. 100b, Sohar Fort. ¼r, Nizwa Fort. ½r, Matrah Fort. 1r, Mirani Fort.

Perf. 14½x14 (A1), 14x14½ (A2), 14x13½ (A3)

1970, June 27 Photo. Unwmk.

110 A1	5b plum	.15	.15
111 A1	10b brown	.15	.15
112 A1	20b red brown	.35	.15
113 A2	25b black & vio	.40	.20
114 A2	30b black & ultra	.55	.30
115 A2	40b black & org	.75	.40
116 A3	50b dk blue & lil rose	1.00	.45
117 A3	75b red brn & brt grn	1.50	.65
118 A3	100b orange & dk bl	2.00	.95
119 A3	¼r grn & brn org	6.00	2.75
120 A3	½r brn car & vio	12.50	5.50
121 A3	1r dk vio & car rose	25.00	11.00
	Nos. 110-121 (12)	50.35	22.65

Sultanate of Oman

Nos. 110-121 Overprinted

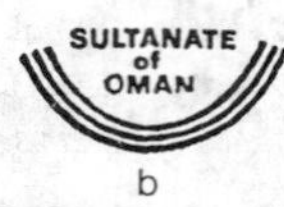

SULTANATE of OMAN

a b

سلطنة عمان

SULTANATE OF OMAN

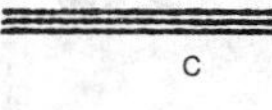

c

5b, 10b 20b:

Type 1- Lower bars 15¼mm long; letter "A" has low, thick crossbar.

Type 2- Lower bars 14¾mm; "A" crossbar high, thin.

Perf. 14½x14, 14x14½, 14x13½

1971, Jan. 16 Photo. Unwmk.

122 A1 (a)	5b plum	.15	.15
a.	Type 2	*50.00*	*35.00*
123 A1 (a)	10b brown	.15	.15
a.	Type 2	*60.00*	*40.00*
124 A1 (a)	20b red brown	.40	.20
a.	Type 2	*60.00*	*40.00*
125 A2 (b)	25b black & vio	.50	.25
126 A2 (b)	30b black & ultra	.60	.35
127 A2 (b)	40b black & org	.75	.50
128 A3 (c)	50b dk bl & lil rose	1.00	.55
129 A3 (c)	75b red brn & brt grn	1.50	1.00
130 A3 (c)	100b org & dk bl	2.25	1.25
131 A3 (c)	¼r grn & brn org	7.50	3.50
132 A3 (c)	½r brn car & vio	15.00	7.50
133 A3 (c)	1r dk vio & car rose	30.00	15.00
	Nos. 122-133 (12)	59.80	30.40

For surcharge see No. 133B.

No. 94 Surcharged Type "a," Nos. 127, 102 Surcharged

Perf. 14½x14, 14x14½, 14½x13½

1971-72

133A A1	5b on 3b	*15.00*	*4.00*
133B A2	25b on 40b	*15.00*	*5.00*
133C A3	25b on 1r	*15.00*	*6.00*
	Nos. 133A-133C (3)	*45.00*	*15.00*

No. 133C surcharge resembles type "c" with "Sultanate of Oman" omitted and bars of crisscross lines.

No. 133A exists with inverted surchagre and in pair, one with surcharge omitted. No. 133C exists with Arabic "2" or "5" omitted.

Issued: 5b, Nov; #133C, 6/6/7; #133B, 7/1/72.

Sultan Qaboos bin Said and New Buildings — A5

National Day: 40b, Sultan Qaboos and freedom symbols. 50b, Crest of Oman and health clinic. 100b, Crest of Oman, classrooms and school.

1971, July 23 Litho. ***Perf. 13½x14***

134 A5	10b multicolored	1.90	.25
135 A5	40b multicolored	1.90	.65
136 A5	50b multicolored	2.50	1.00
137 A5	100b multicolored	4.25	1.65
	Nos. 134-137 (4)	10.55	3.55

Open Book A6

1972, Jan. 3 ***Perf. 14x14½***

138 A6	25b ap grn, dk bl & dk red	7.50	2.50

International Book Year, 1972.

View of Muscat, 1809 A7

Designs: 5, 10, 20, 25b, View of Matrah, 1809. 30, 40, 50, 75b, View of Shinas, 1809.

Wmk. 314 Sideways

1972, July 23 Litho. ***Perf. 14x14½***

Size: 21x17mm

139 A7	5b tan & multi	.20	.15
140 A7	10b blue & multi	.20	.15
141 A7	20b gray green & multi	.40	.20
142 A7	25b violet & multi	.55	.25

Perf. 14½x14

Size: 25x21mm

143 A7	30b tan & multi	.75	.30
144 A7	40b gray blue & multi	1.00	.35
145 A7	50b rose brown & multi	1.25	.50
146 A7	75b olive & multi	2.00	.75

Perf. 14

Size: 41x25mm

147 A7	100b lilac & multi	2.00	.80
148 A7	¼r green & multi	4.50	1.65
149 A7	½r bister & multi	8.00	3.25
150 A7	1r dull bl grn & multi	17.50	6.25
	Nos. 139-150 (12)	38.35	14.60

Perf. 14x14½, 14½x14

1972-75 Wmk. 314 Upright

139a A7	5b tan & multi ('75)	.15	.15
140a A7	10b blue & multi ('75)	.60	.35
141a A7	20b gray grn & multi ('75)	1.10	.65
142a A7	25b violet & multi ('75)	1.50	.90
143a A7	30b tan & multi	2.00	1.20
144a A7	40b blue & multi	2.50	1.50
145a A7	50b rose brn & multi	3.00	1.75
146a A7	75b olive & multi	5.00	3.00
	Nos. 139a-146a (8)	15.85	9.50

Issue dates: Nov. 17, 1972, Sept. 11, 1975.

Perf. 14x14½, 14½x14, 14

1976-82 Wmk. 373

139b A7	5b tan & multi ('78)	.15	.15
140b A7	10b blue & multi ('78)	.25	.25
141b A7	20b gray grn & multi ('82)	.35	.25
142b A7	25b vio & multi ('78)	.40	.25
143b A7	30b tan & multi	.45	.30
144b A7	40b blue & multi	.65	.45
145b A7	50b rose brn & multi	.75	.50
146b A7	75b olive & multi	1.20	.75
147b A7	100b lilac & multi	1.65	1.10
148a A7	¼r grn & multi ('78)	4.00	2.50
149a A7	½r bister & multi	7.50	5.00
150a A7	1r dull bl grn & multi	15.00	10.00
	Nos. 139b-150a (12)	32.35	21.50

Issued: 4/12/76; 1/27/78; 3/15/82.

Ministerial Complex — A8

Litho.; Date Typo.

1973, Sept. 20 Unwmk. ***Perf. 13***

151 A8	25b emerald & multi	1.00	.50
152 A8	100b brown org & multi	3.50	1.75

Opening of ministerial complex.

Nos. 151-152 exist with date omitted and hyphen omitted.

Dhows — A9

Perf. 12½x12

1973, Nov. 18 Litho. Wmk. 314

153 A9	15b shown	.75	.35
154 A9	50b Seeb Airport	2.50	1.40
155 A9	65b Dhow and tanker	3.50	1.75
156 A9	100b Camel rider	4.50	2.50
	Nos. 153-156 (4)	11.25	6.00

National Day.

Port Qaboos — A10

1974, July 30 Litho. *Perf. 13*

157 A10 100b multicolored 7.00 3.00

Opening of Port Qaboos.

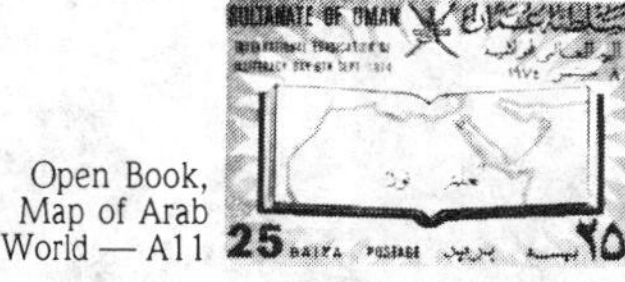

Open Book, Map of Arab World — A11

Design: 100b, Hands reaching for book, vert.

1974, Sept. 8 Wmk. 314 *Perf. 14½*

158 A11 25b multicolored 1.00 .50
159 A11 100b multicolored 3.50 1.75

International Literacy Day, Sept. 8.

Sultan Qaboos, UPU and Arab Postal Union Emblems — A12

1974, Oct. 29 Litho. *Perf. 13½*

160 A12 100b multicolored 2.50 1.25

Centenary of Universal Postal Union.

Old Man Learning to Write A13

1975, May 8 Photo. *Perf. 13x14*

161 A13 25b multicolored 5.00 3.00

Eradication of illiteracy.

New Harbor at Mina Raysoot — A14

Designs: 50b, Stadium and map of Oman. 75b, Water desalination plant. 100b, Oman color television station. 150b, Satellite earth station and map. 250b, Telephone, radar, cable and map.

Perf. 14x13½

1975, Nov. 18 Litho. Wmk. 373

162 A14 30b multicolored .35 .20
163 A14 50b multicolored .65 .30
164 A14 75b multicolored 1.00 .45
165 A14 100b multicolored 1.25 .60
166 A14 150b multicolored 2.25 .75
167 A14 250b multicolored 3.00 1.50
Nos. 162-167 (6) 8.50 3.80

National Day 1975.
For surcharges see Nos. 190A-190C.

Mother with Child, Nurse, Globe, Red Crescent, IWY Emblem — A15

Design: 150b, Hand shielding mother and children, Omani flag, IWY emblem, vert.

Perf. 13½x14, 14x13½

1975, Dec. 27 Litho.

168 A15 75b citron & multi 1.50 1.10
169 A15 150b ultra & multi 3.00 2.00

International Women's Year 1975.

Sultan Presenting Colors and Opening Seeb-Nizwa Road — A16

National Day: 40b, Paratroopers bailing out from plane and mechanized harvester. 75b, Helicopter squadron and Victory Day procession. 150b, Army building road and Salalah television station.

1976, Nov. 15 Litho. *Perf. 14½*

173 A16 25b multicolored 1.00 .25
174 A16 40b multicolored 1.50 .50
175 A16 75b multicolored 2.50 1.00
176 A16 150b multicolored 4.00 2.00
Nos. 173-176 (4) 9.00 3.75

Great Bath at Mohenjo-Daro — A17

1977, Jan. 6 Wmk. 373 *Perf. 13½*

177 A17 125b multicolored 6.00 2.00

UNESCO campaign to save Mohenjo-Daro excavations in Pakistan.

APU Emblem, Members' Flags A18

Coffeepots A19

1977, Apr. 4 Litho. *Perf. 12*

178 A18 30b emerald & multi 1.00 .60
179 A18 75b blue & multi 2.75 1.60

Arab Postal Union, 25th anniversary.

1977, Nov. 18 Litho. *Perf. 13½*

Designs: 75b, Earthenware. 100b, Stone tablet, Khor Rori, 100 B.C. 150b, Jewelry.

180 A19 40b multicolored .75 .35
181 A19 75b multicolored 1.25 .65
182 A19 100b multicolored 1.50 .80
183 A19 150b multicolored 2.50 1.25
Nos. 180-183 (4) 6.00 3.05

National Day 1977.

Forts A20

Wmk. 373

1978, Nov. 18 Litho. *Perf. 14*

184 A20 20b Jalali .40 .25
185 A20 25b Nizwa .50 .40
186 A20 40b Rostaq .90 .60
187 A20 50b Sohar 1.00 .65
188 A20 75b Bahla 1.50 1.00
189 A20 100b Jibrin 2.00 1.25
Nos. 184-189 (6) 6.30 4.15

National Day 1978.

Pilgrims, Mt. Arafat, Holy Kaaba A21

1978, Nov. 1 Litho. *Perf. 13½*

190 A21 40b multicolored 2.50 2.00

Pilgrimage to Mecca.

Nos. 166, 169 and 167 Surcharged

Perf. 14x13½

1978, July 30 Litho. Wmk. 373

190A A14 40b on 150b #166 *100.00 100.00*
190B A15 50b on 150b #169 *125.00 125.00*
190C A14 75b on 250b #167 *125.00 125.00*
Nos. 190A-190C (3) *350.00 350.00*

World Map, Book, Symbols of Learning A22

1979, Mar. 22 Litho. *Perf. 14x13½*

191 A22 40b multicolored .65 .45
192 A22 100b multicolored 1.60 1.10

Cultural achievements of the Arabs.

Girl on Swing, IYC Emblem A23

1979, Oct. 28 Litho. *Perf. 14*

193 A23 40b multicolored 2.75 1.75

International Year of the Child.

Gas Plant A24

National Day: 75b, Fisheries.

1979, Nov. 18 Photo. *Perf. 11½*

194 A24 25b multicolored 1.50 .55
195 A24 75b multicolored 2.00 1.60

Sultan on Horseback, Military Symbols — A25

Design: 100b, Soldier, parachutes, tank.

1979, Dec. 11

196 A25 40b multicolored 2.50 1.10
197 A25 100b multicolored 4.25 2.75

Armed Forces Day.

Hegira (Pilgrimage Year) — A26

1980, Nov. 9 Photo. *Perf. 11½*

198 A26 50b shown 1.00 .55
199 A26 150b Hegira emblem 3.00 1.75

Omani Women — A27

1980, Nov. 18

Granite Paper

200 A27 75b Bab Alkabir .70 .45
201 A27 100b Corniche Highway .95 .55
202 A27 250b Polo match 2.50 1.40
203 A27 500b shown 4.50 2.75
Nos. 200-203 (4) 8.65 5.15

10th National Day.
For surcharges see Nos. 212-213.

Sultan and Patrol Boat — A28

1980, Dec. 11

Granite Paper

204 A28 150b shown 3.00 1.50
205 A28 750b Sultan, mounted troops 13.00 6.50

Armed Forces Day.
For surcharges see Nos. 210-211.

Policewoman and Children Crossing Street — A29

1981, Feb. 7 Litho. *Perf. 13½x14*

206 A29 50b shown .65 .30
207 A29 100b Marching band 1.10 .55
208 A29 150b Mounted police on beach 1.75 .85
209 A29 ½r Headquarters 6.00 2.80
Nos. 206-209 (4) 9.50 4.50

First National Police Day.

Nos. 204-205, 200, 203 Surcharged in Black on Silver

1981, Apr. 8 Photo. *Perf. 11½*

210 A28 20b on 150b multi 2.00 .40
211 A28 30b on 750b multi 2.75 .60
212 A27 50b on 75b multi 5.00 .90
213 A27 100b on 500b multi 8.25 1.75
Nos. 210-213 (4) 18.00 3.65

Welfare of the Blind — A30

1981, Oct. 14 Photo. *Perf. 11½*

214 A30 10b multicolored .60 .15

World Food Day A31

1981, Oct. 16 Photo. *Perf. 12*

215 A31 50b multicolored 2.25 .75

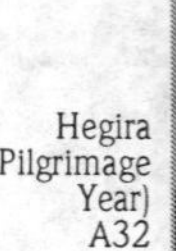

Hegira (Pilgrimage Year) A32

1981, Oct. 25 Litho. *Perf. 14½*

216 A32 50b multicolored 3.25 .75

11th Natl. Day A32a

1981, Nov. 18 Photo. *Perf. 12*

216A A32a 160b Al-Razha match (sword vs. stick) 2.00 1.00

216B A32a 300b Sultan, map, vert. 3.50 2.00

Voyage of Sinbad — A33

1981, Nov. 23 Litho. *Perf. 14½x14*

217 A33 50b Muscat Port, 1981 .75 .35

218 A33 100b Dhow Shohar 1.50 .75

219 A33 130b Map 1.75 1.00

220 A33 200b Muscat Harbor, 1650 3.00 1.50

a. Souvenir sheet of 4, #217-220 10.00 4.50

Nos. 217-220 (4) 6.75 3.60

Armed Forces Day A34

1981, Dec. 11 Photo. *Perf. 11½*

221 A34 100b Sultan, planes 2.00 1.00

222 A34 400b Patrol boats 7.00 3.50

Natl. Police Day A35

1982, Jan. 5 Litho. *Perf. 14½*

223 A35 50b Patrol launch .80 .55

224 A35 100b Band, vert. 1.60 1.10

Nerium Mascatense A36

Red-legged Partridge A37

1982, July 7 Photo. *Perf. 12½*

Granite Paper

225 A36 5b shown .25 .25

226 A36 10b Dionysia mira .25 .25

227 A36 20b Teucrium mascatense .25 .25

228 A36 25b Geranium mascatense .25 .25

229 A36 30b Cymatium boschi, horiz. .30 .30

230 A36 40b Acteon eloiseae, horiz. .45 .45

231 A36 50b Cypraea teulerei, horiz. .50 .50

232 A36 75b Cypraea pulchra, horiz. .75 .75

233 A37 100b shown 1.00 1.00

234 A37 ¼r Hoopoe 2.50 2.50

Size: 25x38mm

235 A37 ½r Tahr 5.00 5.00

236 A37 1r Arabian oryx 10.00 10.00

Nos. 225-236 (12) 21.50 21.50

2nd Municipalities Week (1981) — A38

Perf. 13½x14½

1982, Oct. 28 Litho.

237 A38 40b multicolored 2.25 .65

ITU Plenipotentiaries Conference, Nairobi, Sept. — A39

1982, Nov. 6 *Perf. 14½x13½*

238 A39 100b multicolored 3.00 .75

12th Natl. Day A40

1982, Nov. 18 *Perf. 12*

239 A40 40b State Consultative Council inaugural session 1.00 .40

240 A40 100b Oil refinery 2.25 .80

Armed Forces Day A41

1982, Dec. 11 *Perf. 13½x14*

241 A41 50b Soldiers 1.10 .45

242 A41 100b Mounted band 2.25 .90

Arab Palm Tree Day A42

Perf. 13½x14½

1982, Sept. 19 Litho.

243 A42 40b Picking coconuts 1.00 .40

244 A42 100b Dates 3.00 .90

Natl. Police Day — A43

1983, Jan. 5 Litho. *Perf. 14x13½*

245 A43 50b multicolored 2.25 .75

World Communications Year — A44

1983, May 17 *Perf. 13½x14*

246 A44 50b multicolored 2.25 .75

Beehive A45

1983, Aug. 15 Litho. *Perf. 13½*

247 Strip of 2 3.25 1.50

a.-b. A45 50b any single 1.50 .60

Hegira (Pilgrimage Year) — A46

1983, Sept. 14 Photo. *Perf. 13½*

248 A46 40b multicolored 3.00 .75

Youth Year A47

Perf. 12½x13½

1983, Nov. 15 Litho.

249 A47 50b multicolored 2.00 .65

National Day 1983 — A48

1983, Nov. 18 Litho. *Perf. 13½x14*

250 A48 50b Sohar Copper Factory 1.25 .40

251 A48 100b Sultan Qaboos University 2.25 .80

Armed Forces Day A49

1983, Dec. 11 Litho. *Perf. 13½x14*

252 A49 100b multicolored 3.00 .65

Police Day A50

1984, Jan. 5 Litho. *Perf. 13½x14*

253 A50 100b multicolored 3.00 .65

7th Arabian Gulf Soccer Tournament, Muscat, Mar. 9-26 — A51

1984, Mar. 9 Litho. *Perf. 13½*

254 A51 40b Players, cup, vert. 1.00 .25

255 A51 50b Emblem 1.25 .40

Pilgrims at Stone-Throwing Ceremony — A52

1984, Sept. 5 Litho. *Perf. 13½x14*

256 A52 50b multicolored 3.00 .50

Pilgrimage to Mecca.

National Day 1984 — A53

Perf. 13½x14, 14x13½

1984, Nov. 18 Litho.

257 A53 130b Mail sorting, new p.o. 1.90 .70

258 A53 160b Map, vert. 2.25 .80

Inauguration of the new Central P.O., development of telecommunications.

16th Arab Scout Conference, Muscat — A54

1984, Dec. 5 Litho. *Perf. 14½*

259 A54 50b Setting-up camp .75 .75
260 A54 50b Map reading .75 .75
a. Pair, #259-260 1.50 1.50
261 A54 130b Saluting natl. flag 1.75 1.75
262 A54 130b Scouts and girl guides 1.75 1.75
a. Pair, #261-262 3.50 3.50
Nos. 259-262 (4) 5.00 5.00

Armed Forces Day A55

1984, Dec. 11 *Perf. 13½x14*

263 A55 100b multicolored 3.00 .60

Police Day — A56

1985, Jan. 5 *Perf. 14x13½*

264 A56 100b multicolored 2.75 .60

Hegira (Pilgrimage Year) A57

1985, Aug. 20 Litho. *Perf. 13½x14*

265 A57 50b Al-Khaif Mosque, Mina 1.50 .50

Intl. Youth Year A58

1985, Sept. 22 Litho. *Perf. 13½x14*

266 A58 50b Emblems .70 .30
267 A58 100b Emblem, youth activities 1.40 .55

Jabrin Palace Restoration — A59

1985, Sept. 22 Litho. *Perf. 13½x14*

268 A59 100b Interior 1.25 .75
269 A59 250b Restored ceiling 3.25 1.50

Intl. Symposium on Traditional Music — A60

1985, Oct. 6 Litho. *Perf. 13½x14*

270 A60 50b multicolored 1.50 .50

UN Child Survival Campaign A61

1985, Oct. 25 Litho. *Perf. 13½x14*

271 A61 50b multicolored 1.50 .50

Flags, Map and Sultan Qaboos — A62

1985, Nov. 3 Litho. *Perf. 12½*

272 A62 40b shown .90 .30
273 A62 50b Supreme Council, vert. 1.10 .35

6th Session of Arab Gulf States Supreme Council, Muscat.

Natl. Day 1985 A63

Progress and development. 20b, Sultan Qaboos University. 50b, Date picking, plowing field. 100b, Port Qaboos Cement Factory. 200b, Post, transportation and communications. 250b, Sultan Qaboos, vert.

1985, Nov. 18

274 A63 20b multicolored .20 .15
275 A63 50b multicolored .50 .30
276 A63 100b multicolored 1.00 .60
277 A63 200b multicolored 1.90 1.25
278 A63 250b multicolored 2.50 1.50
Nos. 274-278 (5) 6.10 3.80

Armed Forces Day A64

1985, Dec. 11 *Perf. 13½x14*

279 A64 100b multicolored 1.70 .65

Fish and Crustaceans — A65

Perf. 11½x12, 12x11½

1985, Dec. 15 Photo.

280 A65 20b Chaetodon collaris .20 .15
281 A65 50b Chaetodon melapterus .65 .40
282 A65 100b Chaetodon gardineri 1.25 .75
283 A65 150b Scomberomorus commerson 1.75 1.10
284 A65 200b Panulirus homarus 2.25 1.50
Nos. 280-284 (5) 6.10 3.90

Nos. 280-282, vert.

Frankincense Trees in Oman — A66

1985, Dec. 15 Litho. *Perf. 13½x14*

285 A66 100b multicolored 1.00 .55
286 A66 3r multicolored 25.00 12.50

Police Day A67

1986, Jan. 5 Litho. *Perf. 13½x14*

287 A67 50b Camel Corps, Muscat 1.50 .30

Statue of Liberty, Cent. A68

Maps and: 50b, Sultanah, voyage from Muscat to US 1840. 100b, Statue, Shabab Oman voyage from Oman to US, 1986, and fortress.

1986, July 4 *Perf. 14½*

288 A68 50b multicolored .80 .30
289 A68 100b multicolored 1.65 .60
a. Souvenir sheet of 2, #288-289 3.75 1.50

No. 289a sold for 250b.

Pilgrimage to Mecca A69

1986, Aug. 9

290 A69 50b Holy Kaaba 1.25 .30

17th Arab Scout Camp — A70

1986, Aug. 20

291 A70 50b Erecting tent .85 .30
292 A70 100b Surveying 1.75 .60

Sultan Qaboos Sports Complex Inauguration — A71

1986, Oct. 18 Litho. *Perf. 14½*

293 A71 100b multicolored 1.50 .60

Intl. Peace Year A72

1986, Oct. 24 *Perf. 13½x13*

294 A72 130b multicolored 1.50 .80

A73

A74

Natl. Day 1986 — A75

1986, Nov. 18 *Perf. 14½*

295 A73 50b mutlicolored .45 .30
296 A74 100b multicolored .85 .60

Perf. 13½x13

297 A75 130b multicolored 2.50 .80
Nos. 295-297 (3) 3.80 1.70

Police Day A76

1987, Jan. 5 *Perf. 13½x14*

298 A76 50b multicolored 1.00 .30

Second Arab Gulf Week for Social Work, Bahrain A77

1987, Mar. 21 Litho. *Perf. 13½x13*

299 A77 50b multicolored 1.00 .25

Intl. Environment Day — A78

Perf. 13½x13, 13x13½

1987, June 5 Litho.

300 A78 50b Flamingos in flight .50 .30
301 A78 130b Irrigation canal, vert. 1.50 .70

Pilgrimage to Mecca A79

Stages of Pilgrimage (not in consecutive order): a, Pilgrims walking the tawaf, circling the Holy Kaaba 7 times. b, Tent City, Mina. c, Symbolic stoning of Satan. d, Pilgrims in Muzdalifah at dusk, picking up stones. e, Veneration of the prophet (pilgrims praying), Medina. f, Pilgrims wearing ihram, Pilgrim's Village, Jeddah.

1987, July 29 Litho. *Perf. 13½*

302 Strip of 6 5.00 2.00
a.-f. A79 50b any single .80 .30

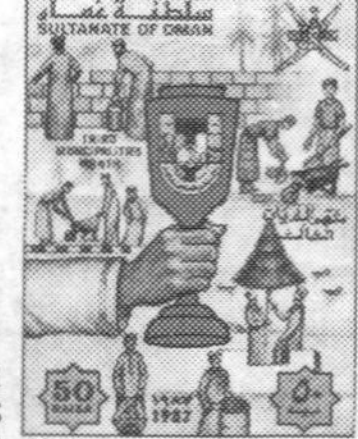

Third Municipalities Month — A80

1987, Oct. 1 *Perf. 13x13½*

303 A80 50b multicolored 1.10 .30

Natl. Day A81

Designs: 50b, Marine Biology and Fisheries Center. 130b, Royal Hospital.

1987, Nov. 18 Litho. *Perf. 13½x13*

304 A81 50b multicolored .50 .40
305 A81 130b multicolored 1.50 1.25

Royal Omani Amateur Radio Soc., 15th Anniv. — A82

1987, Dec. 23 Litho. *Perf. 13½x13*

306 A82 130b multicolored 1.10 1.10

Traditional Handicrafts A83

1988, June 1 Photo. *Perf. 12x11½*
Granite Paper

307 A83 50b Weaver .40 .40
308 A83 100b Potter .75 .75
309 A83 150b Halwa maker 1.25 1.25
310 A83 200b Silversmith 1.50 1.50
a. Souvenir sheet of 4, #307-310 5.00 5.00
Nos. 307-310 (4) 3.90 3.90

No. 310a sold for 600b.

A84 A85

1988, Sept. 17 Litho. *Perf. 14½*

311 A84 100b Equestrian .70 .70
312 A84 100b Field hockey .70 .70
313 A84 100b Soccer .70 .70
314 A84 100b Running .70 .70
315 A84 100b Swimming .70 .70
316 A84 100b Shooting .70 .70
a. Block of 6, #311-316 4.25 4.25
b. Souvenir sheet of 6, #311-316 5.25 5.25

1988 Summer Olympics, Seoul.

1988, Nov. 1 Litho. *Perf. 13½*

317 A85 100b multicolored 1.10 1.10

WHO, 40th anniv.

Natl. Day, Agriculture Year — A86

1988, Nov. 18 *Perf. 14½x13½*

318 A86 100b Tending crops 1.00 1.00
319 A86 100b Animal husbandry 1.00 1.00
a. Pair, #318-319 2.00 2.00

No. 319a has a continuous design.

Women Wearing Regional Folk Costume — A87

Designs: 200b-1r, Men wearing regional folk costumes.

Perf. 11½x12

1989 Photo. Granite Paper

320 A87 30b Dhahira .20 .20
321 A87 40b Eastern .25 .25
322 A87 50b Batinah .35 .35
323 A87 100b Interior .65 .65
324 A87 130b Southern .90 .90
325 A87 150b Muscat 1.00 1.00
a. Souvenir sheet of 6, #320-325 6.00 6.00
326 A87 200b Dhahira 1.40 1.40
327 A87 ¼r Eastern 1.65 1.65
328 A87 ½r Southern 5.00 5.00
329 A87 1r Muscat 6.75 6.75
a. Souvenir sheet of 4, #326-329 15.00 15.00
Nos. 320-329 (10) 18.15 18.15

No. 325a sold for 700b, No. 329a for 2r. Issued: 30b-150b, Aug. 26; 200b-1r, Nov. 11.

National Day, Agriculture Year — A88

1989, Nov. 18 *Perf. 12½x13*

330 A88 100b Fishing .55 .55
331 A88 100b Farming .55 .55
a. Pair, #330-331 1.10 1.10

Printed se-tenant in a continuous design.

10th Session of Supreme Council of the Cooperation Council for Arab Gulf States — A89

1989, Dec. 18 Litho. *Perf. 13x12*

332 A89 50b Flags, Omani crest .30 .30
333 A89 50b Sultan Qaboos, council emblem .30 .30
a. Pair, #332-333 .60 .60

No. 333a has a continuous design.

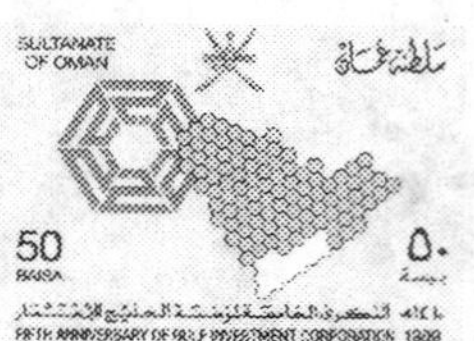

Gulf Investment Corp., 5th Anniv. (in 1989) — A90

1990, Jan. 1 Litho. *Perf. 13x12*

334 A90 50b multicolored .30 .30
335 A90 130b multicolored .70 .70

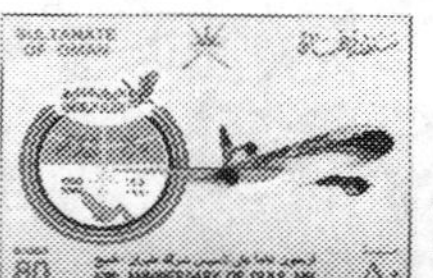

Gulf Air, 40th Anniv. A91

1990, Mar. 24 *Perf. 13x13½*

336 A91 80b multicolored .40 .40

Symposium on the Oman Ophiolite — A92

1990, Apr. 22 Photo. *Perf. 11½*
Granite Paper

337 A92 80b shown .45 .45
338 A92 150b multicolored .80 .80

First Omani Envoy to the US, 150th Anniv. — A93

1990, Apr. 30 Litho. *Perf. 13*

339 A93 200b multicolored 1.05 1.05

Sultan Qaboos Rose — A94

1990, May 5 Photo. *Perf. 11½*
Granite Paper

340 A94 200b multicolored 1.05 1.05

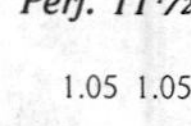

20th National Day A95

100b, Natl. Day emblem. 200b, Sultan Qaboos.

Litho. & Embossed

1990, Nov. 18 *Perf. 12x11½*
Granite Paper

341 A95 100b gold, red & green .55 .55
342 A95 200b gold, green & red 1.10 1.10
a. Souvenir sheet of 2, #341-342 2.85 2.85

No. 342a sold for 500b.

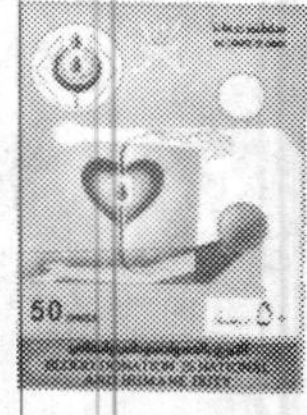

Blood Donors — A96

1991, Apr. 22 Litho. *Perf. 13½x13*

343 A96 50b multicolored .25 .25
344 A96 200b multicolored 1.10 1.10
a. Pair, #343-344 1.35 1.35

National Day — A97

1991, Nov. 18 Photo. *Perf. 13½*

345 A97 100b shown .50 .50
346 A97 200b Sultan Qaboos 1.10 1.10
a. Souvenir sheet of 2, #345-346 2.00 2.00

No. 346a sold for 400b.

Armed Forces Day A98

1991, Dec. 11 Litho. *Perf. 14½*

347 A98 100b multicolored .50 .50

A99

A100

1992, Jan. 29 Litho. *Perf. 13½x14*
348 A99 100b multicolored .50 .50
a. Sheet of 1, perf. 13x13½ 1.50 1.50

Inauguration of Omani-French Museum, Muscat. No. 348a sold for 300b.

1992, Mar. 23 Litho. *Perf. 14½*
349 A100 200b multicolored 1.00 1.00

World Meteorological Day.

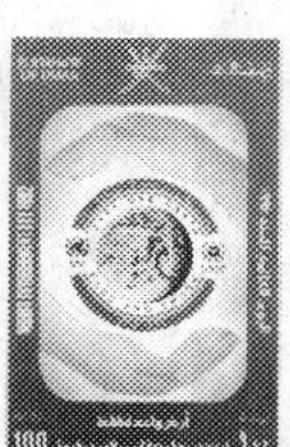

A101

A102

1992, June 5 Litho. *Perf. 13x13½*
350 A101 100b multicolored .50 .50

World Environment Day.

1992, Sept. 26 Litho. *Perf. 13½x14*
351 A102 70b multicolored .35 .35

Welfare of Handicapped Children.

Sultan Qaboos Encyclopedia of Arab Names — A103

1992, Oct. 10 *Perf. 14½*
352 A103 100b gold & multi .55 .55

National Day — A104

Sultan Qaboos and emblems of: 100b, Year of Industry. 200b, Majlis As'shura.

1992, Nov. 18 Litho. *Perf. 14x13½*
353 A104 100b multicolored .55 .55
354 A104 200b multicolored 1.05 1.05

Royal Oman Police Day A105

1993, Jan. 5 Litho. *Perf. 13½x14*
355 A105 80b multicolored .45 .45

1993 Census A106

1993, Sept. 4 Litho. *Perf. 14x13½*
356 A106 100b multicolored .55 .55

Royal Navy Day — A107

1993, Nov. 3 Litho. *Perf. 13*
357 A107 100b multicolored .55 .55

23rd National Day A108

1993, Nov. 18 Photo. *Perf. 12*
Granite Paper
358 A108 100b Year of Youth emblem .55 .55
359 A108 200b Sultan Qaboos 1.00 1.00

Scouting — A109

#360, Emblem of Scouts & Guides, Scout Headquarters. #361, Scout camp, Sultan Qaboos.

1993, Nov. 20 Litho. *Perf. 13x13½*
360 A109 100b multicolored .55 .55
361 A109 100b multicolored .55 .55
a. Pair, #360-361 1.10 1.10

Scouting movement in Oman, 61st anniv. (#360). Installation of Sultan Qaboos as chief scout, 10th anniv. (#361).

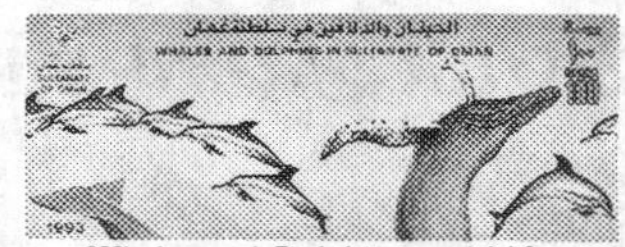

Whales and Dolphins — A110

#362, Dolphins, humpback whale. #363, Dolphins, sperm whale. Illustration reduced.

1993, Dec. 8 *Perf. 14½*
362 A110 100b multicolored .55 .55
363 A110 100b multicolored .55 .55
a. Pair, #362-363 1.10 1.10
b. Souvenir sheet of 2, #362-363 2.25 2.25

No. 363a has a continuous design. No. 363b sold for 400b and has a white border surrounding the stamps.

World Day for Water — A111

Muscat Municipality, 70th Anniv. — A112

1994, Mar. 22 Litho. *Perf. 13½*
364 A111 50b multicolored .25 .25

1994, Apr. 16
365 A112 50b multicolored .25 .25

Intl. Olympic Committee, Cent. — A113

1994, Aug. 29 Litho. *Perf. 13½*
366 A113 100b multicolored .55 .55

Al Busaid Dynasty, 250th Anniv. — A114

Natl. arms or sultan, dates: a, 1744-75. b, 1775-79. c, 1779-92. d, 1792-1804. e, 1804-7. f, Sa'id ibn Sultan, 1807-56. g, 1856-65. h, 1866-68. i, 1868-71. j, Sultan, 1871-88. k, Sultan, 1888-1913. l, Sultan Taymur ibn Faysal, 1913-32. m, Sultan Qaboos, laurel tree. n, Sultan Sa'id ibn Taymur, 1932-70. o, Sultan Qaboos, 1970-.

200b, Sultan Qaboos atop family "tree," Arabic listing of former Sultans, years in power.

Litho. & Embossed
1994, Dec. 28 *Perf. 11½*
367 A114 50b Block of 15, #a.-o. 4.50 4.50

Litho. & Typo.
Imperf
Size: 140x110mm
367A A114 200b gold & multi 1.25 1.25

Nos. 367f, 367j-367o contain portraits of sultans.

Open Parliament — A115

1995, Jan. 7 Litho. *Perf. 14*
Granite Paper
368 A115 50b silver & multi .50 .50

Arab League, 50th Anniv. — A118

1995, Mar. 22 Litho. *Perf. 13*
372 A118 100b multicolored .65 .65

UN, 50th Anniv. A119

1995, Sept. 2 *Perf. 13½*
373 A119 100b multicolored .65 .65

16th Session of Supreme Council of the Co-operative Council for Arab Gulf States A120

Designs: 100b, Emblem. 200b, Flags of Arab Gulf States, map, Sultan Qaboos.

1995, Dec. 4 *Perf. 12*
Granite Paper
374 A120 100b multicolored .65 .65
375 A120 200b multicolored 1.25 1.25

25th National Day A121

Portraits of Sultan Qaboos: 50b, In traditional attire. 100b, In military uniform.

Litho. & Embossed
1995, Nov. 18 *Perf. 11½*
Granite Paper
376 A121 50b multicolored .30 .30
377 A121 100b multicolored .65 .65
a. Souvenir sheet of 2, #376-377 1.90 1.90

No. 377a sold for 300b.

New issue listings, plus the most interesting read in the hobby, characterize the "Scott Stamp Monthly." For more information, please call 1-800-572-6885.

1996 Summer Olympic Games, Atlanta — A122

a, Shooting. b, Swimming. c, Cycling. d, Running.

1996, July 19 Litho. *Perf. 14½*

378	A122 100b Strip of 4, #a.-d.	3.00	3.00

13th Arabian Gulf Cup Soccer Tournament — A123

1996, Oct. 15 *Perf. 13½*

379	A123 100b multicolored	.75	.75

UN Decade Against Drug Abuse A124

1996, June 26 *Perf. 13½x14*

380	A124 100b multicolored	.75	.75

UNICEF, 50th Anniv. — A125

1996, Dec. 11 Litho. *Perf. 14½*

381	A125 100b multicolored	.60	.60

26th National Day — A126

Designs: No. 382, Sultan Qaboos waving, boats in harbor. No. 383, Boats in harbor, Sultan Qaboos.

1996, Nov. 26 *Perf. 13½*

382	A126 50b multicolored	.30	.30
383	A126 50b multicolored	.30	.30
a.	Pair, #382-383	.60	.60

No. 383a is a continuous design.

Tourism A128

Designs: a, Oasis fort among palm trees. b, Small waterfalls, trees. c, Highway, coastline, castle on hilltop. d, Lake, mountains. e, Ruins of ancient fort on cliff. f, Waterfall, mountain stream.

1997 Litho. *Perf. 13½x14*

393	A128 100b Block of 6, #a.-f.	3.75	3.75

SEMI-POSTAL STAMP

UNICEF Emblem, Girl with Book — SP1

Wmk. 314

1971, Dec. 25 Litho. *Perf. 14*

B1	SP1 50b + 25b multicolored	7.50	4.75

25th anniv. of UNICEF.

OFFICIAL STAMPS

Official Stamps of India 1938-43 Overprinted in Black

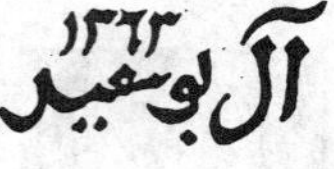

Perf. 13½x14

1944, Nov. 20 Wmk. 196

O1	O8	3p slate	.20	.15
O2	O8	½a dk rose violet	.20	.15
O3	O8	9p green	.20	.15
O4	O8	1a carmine rose	.20	.15
O5	O8	1½a dull purple	.40	.20
O6	O8	2a scarlet	.45	.20
O7	O8	2½a purple	.55	.25
O8	O8	4a dark brown	.60	.30
O9	O8	8a blue violet	1.25	.50
O10	A82	1r brown & slate	3.00	1.10
		Nos. O1-O10 (10)	7.05	3.15

Al Busaid Dynasty, 200th anniv. On Nos. O1-O9 the overprint is smaller — 13x6mm.

ORANGE RIVER COLONY

'är–inj 'ri–vər 'kä–lə–nē

(Orange Free State)

LOCATION — South Africa, north of the Cape of Good Hope between the Orange and Vaal Rivers
GOVT. — A former British Crown Colony
AREA — 49,647 sq. mi.
POP. — 528,174 (1911)
CAPITAL — Bloemfontein

Orange Free State was an independent republic, 1854-1900. Orange River Colony existed from May, 1900, to June, 1910, when it united with Cape of Good Hope, Natal and the Transvaal to form the Union of South Africa.

12 Pence = 1 Shilling

Values for unused stamps are for examples with original gum as defined in the catalogue introduction. Very fine examples of Nos. 1-60c will have perforations touching the design on one or more sides due to the narrow spacing of the stamps on the plates. Stamps with perfs clear of the design on all four sides are scarce and will command higher prices.

Een = 1
Twee = 2
Drie = 3
Vier = 4

Issues of the Republic

Orange Tree — A1

1868-1900 Unwmk. Typo. *Perf. 14*

1	A1	½p red brown ('83)	2.00	.50
2	A1	½p orange ('97)	1.00	.35
3	A1	1p brown	4.00	.40
4	A1	1p violet ('94)	1.00	.25
5	A1	2p violet ('83)	4.00	.40
6	A1	3p ultra ('83)	2.00	1.25
7	A1	4p ultra ('78)	4.00	1.25
8	A1	6p car rose ('90)	3.50	.85
a.		6p rose ('68)	15.00	4.00
b.		6p ultramarine ('00)	90.00	
10	A1	1sh orange	18.00	1.10
a.		1sh orange buff	*60.00*	*6.00*
11	A1	1sh brown ('97)	8.00	2.00
12	A1	5sh green ('78)	10.00	10.00
		Nos. 1-8,10-12 (11)	57.50	18.35

No. 8b was not placed in use without surcharge.
For surcharges see #13-53, 44j-53c, 57-60.

No. 8a Surcharged:

4 *a* **4** *b* **4** *c* **4** *d*

1877

13	(a) 4p on 6p rose	110.00	40.00
a.	Inverted surcharge	*1,000.*	500.00
b.	Double surcharge, one inverted ("a" and "c")		1,000.
14	(b) 4p on 6p rose	1,100.	225.00
a.	Inverted surcharge	*1,400.*	1,000.
b.	Double surcharge, one inverted ("b" and "d")	*1,500.*	750.00
15	(c) 4p on 6p rose	75.00	27.50
a.	Inverted surcharge	*500.00*	300.00
16	(d) 4p on 6p rose	200.00	55.00
a.	Inverted surcharge	*900.00*	400.00

No. 12 Surcharged with Bar and:

1d. *f* **1d.** *g* **1d.** *h* **1d.** *i* **1d.** *k*

1881

17	(f) 1p on 5sh green	50.00	11.00
18	(g) 1p on 5sh green	100.00	45.00
a.	Inverted surcharge	600.00	500.00
b.	Double surcharge		600.00
19	(h) 1p on 5sh green	30.00	9.00
a.	Inverted surcharge	625.00	600.00
b.	Double surcharge	625.00	600.00
20	(i) 1p on 5sh green	55.00	10.00
a.	Double surcharge	*725.00*	500.00
b.	Inverted surcharge	575.00	450.00
21	(k) 1p on 5sh green	300.00	190.00
a.	Inverted surcharge	1,250.	1,100.
b.	Double surcharge		—
	Nos. 17-21 (5)	535.00	265.00

No. 12 Surcharged: **½d**

1882

22	A1 ½p on 5sh green	4.00	4.00
a.	Double surcharge	350.00	325.00
b.	Inverted surcharge	*800.00*	*800.00*

No. 7 Surcharged with Thin Line and:

3d *m* **3d** *n* **3d** *o* **3d** *p* **3d** *q*

1882

23	(m) 3p on 4p ultra	65.00	24.00
a.	Double surcharge		625.00
24	(n) 3p on 4p ultra	50.00	19.00
a.	Double surcharge		625.00
25	(o) 3p on 4p ultra	27.50	18.00
a.	Double surcharge		625.00
26	(p) 3p on 4p ultra	150.00	60.00
a.	Double surcharge		750.00
27	(q) 3p on 4p ultra	60.00	25.00
a.	Double surcharge		625.00
	Nos. 23-27 (5)	352.50	146.00

No. 6 Surcharged **2d**

1888

28	A1 2p on 3p ultra	15.00	2.00
a.	Wide "2" at top	30.00	10.00
b.	As No. 28, invtd. surch.		350.00
c.	As No. 28a, invtd. surch.		900.00
d.	Curved base on "2"	*700.00*	*500.00*

Nos. 6 and 7 Surcharged:

1d *r* **1d** *s* **1d** *t*

1890-91

29	(r) 1p on 3p ultra ('91)	1.50	.85
a.	Double surcharge	75.00	75.00
30	(r) 1p on 4p ultra	15.00	5.00
a.	Double surcharge	120.00	100.00
31	(s) 1p on 3p ultra ('91)	10.00	3.00
a.	Double surcharge	165.00	165.00
32	(s) 1p on 4p ultra	75.00	50.00
a.	Double surcharge	275.00	250.00
b.	Triple surcharge		*1,200.*
33	(t) 1p on 4p ultra	*950.00*	*750.00*

No. 29 exists with wide space between "1" and "d."

No. 6 Surcharged **2½d.**

1892

34	A1 2½p on 3p ultra	4.00	1.00
a.	Without period	50.00	50.00

No. 6 Surcharged:

½d *v* **½d** *w* **½d** *x* **½d** *y* **½d** *z*

1896

35	(v) ½p on 3p ultra	2.50	2.50
a.	Double surcharge "v" and "y"	14.00	12.00
36	(w) ½p on 3p ultra	5.00	3.00
a.	Double surcharge "w" and "y"	15.00	15.00
37	(x) ½p on 3p ultra	5.00	3.00
38	(y) ½p on 3p ultra	2.25	2.25
a.	Double surcharge	12.50	11.00
39	(z) ½p on 3p ultra	4.50	2.75

Surcharged as "v" but "1" with Straight Serif

40	A1 ½p on 3p ultra	5.00	5.00
a.	Double surcharge, one type "y"	13.00	13.00

Surcharged as "z" but "1" with Straight Serif

41	A1 ½p on 3p ultra	4.75	5.00
a.	Double surcharge, one type "y"	12.50	11.00
	Nos. 35-41 (7)	29.00	23.50

No. 6 Surcharged **Halve Penny.**

1896

42	A1 ½p on 3p ultra	.65	.65
a.	No period after "Penny"	10.00	15.00
b.	"Peuny"	8.50	8.50
c.	Inverted surcharge	60.00	60.00
d.	Double surch., one inverted	165.00	165.00
e.	Without bar	5.00	5.00
f.	With additional surcharge as on Nos. 35-41	75.00	75.00

Nos. 42c, 42d, 42f probably were created as favors. They were not available to the public.

No. 6 Surcharged **2½**

1897

43	A1 2½p on 3p ultra	2.00	.75
a.	Roman "I" instead of "1" in "½"	150.00	90.00

Issued under British Occupation

Nos. 2-8, 8a, 10-12 Surcharged or Overprinted **V. R. I. ½d**

1900, Mar.-Apr. Unwmk. *Perf. 14*
Periods in "V.R.I." Level with Bottoms of Letters

44	A1	½p on ½p orange	1.50	1.50
a.		No period after "V"	15.00	15.00
b.		No period after "I"	170.00	170.00
c.		"I" and period after "R" omitted		
f.		"½" omitted	*175.00*	*175.00*
g.		Small "½"	45.00	45.00
h.		Double surcharge	125.00	*125.00*
i.		As "g," double surcharge	300.00	
45	A1	1p on 1p violet	1.65	.75
a.		No period after "V"	10.50	10.50
b.		"I" and period after "R" omitted	155.00	170.00
d.		"1" of "1d" omitted	165.00	175.00
e.		"d" omitted	300.00	300.00
f.		"1d" omitted, "V.R.I." at top	375.00	
45O	A1	1p on 1p brown	*600.00*	*500.00*
y.		No period after "V"	*2,250.*	

46 A1 2p on 2p violet .35 .60
a. No period after "V" 10.00 12.00
b. No period after "R" 250.00
c. No period after "I" 250.00
47 A1 '2½' on 3p ultra 4.50 4.00
a. No period after "V" 70.00 65.00
b. Roman "I" in "½" 165.00 275.00
48 A1 3p on 3p ultra 1.50 1.00
a. No period after "V" 13.00 13.00
b. Dbl. surch. one diagonal 600.00
49 A1 4p on 4p ultra 4.50 6.00
a. No period after "V" 50.00 52.50
50 A1 6p on 6p car rose 35.00 35.00
a. No period after "V" 250.00 300.00
b. "6" omitted 300.00 300.00
51 A1 6p on 6p ultra 2.75 3.25
a. No period after "V" 30.00 30.00
c. "6" omitted 65.00 65.00
52 A1 1sh on 1sh brown 3.50 3.50
a. No period after "V" 30.00 30.00
c. "1" of "1s" omitted 110.00 110.00
52G A1 1sh on 1sh org *2,250.* *2,000.*
53 A1 5sh on 5sh green 18.00 30.00
a. No period after "V" 175.00 175.00
b. "5" omitted 700.00 700.00

#47, 47c overprinted "V.R.I." on #43.

No. 45f ("1d" omitted) with "V.R.I." at bottom is a shift which sells for a fifth of the value of the listed item. Varieties such as "V.R.I." omitted, denomination omitted and pair, one without surcharge are also the result of shifts.

For surcharges see Nos. 57, 60.

1900-01

Periods in "V.R.I." Raised Above Bottoms of Letters

44j A1 ½p on ½p orange .25 .15
k. Mixed periods 1.75 1.75
l. Pair, one with level periods 8.00 13.00
m. No period after "V" 3.00 3.00
n. No period after "I" 25.00 25.00
o. "V" omitted 400.00 400.00
p. Small "½" 12.00 13.00
q. "1" for "I" in "V.R.I." 9.00 9.00
r. Thick "V" .28 .45
45i A1 1p on 1p violet .30 .15
j. Mixed periods 1.50 1.65
k. Pair, one with level periods 17.00 17.00
l. No period after "V" 6.00 6.00
m. No period after "R" 12.00 12.00
n. No period after "I" 12.00 12.00
p. Double surcharge 90.00 90.00
q. Inverted surcharge 200.00
s. Small "1" in "1d" 165.00 165.00
t. "1" for "I" in "V.R.I." 13.00 13.00
u. Thick "V" .28 .25
v. As "u," invtd. "1" for "I" in "V.R.I." 7.25 7.25
w. As "u," double surcharge 300.00 300.00
z. As "u," no period after "R" 30.00 30.00
46e A1 2p on 2p violet .50 .25
f. Mixed periods 4.50 4.50
g. Pair, one with level periods 7.25 7.25
h. Inverted surcharge 300.00 300.00
i. Thick "V" .35 .28
j. As "i," invtd. "1" for "I" in "V.R.I." 15.00 15.00
47c A1 '2½' on 3p ultramarine 190.00 165.00
d. Thick "V" 350.00 350.00
f. As "d," Roman "I" on "½"
48d A1 3p on 3p ultramarine .35 .20
e. Mixed periods 5.00 5.00
f. Pair, one with level periods 15.00 15.00
g. Double surcharge 425.00
h. Thick "V" .90 .90
i. As "h," invtd. "1" for "I" in "V.R.I." 80.00 80.00
49b A1 4p on 4p ultramarine 1.10 2.00
c. Mixed periods 7.00 7.00
d. Pair, one with level periods 15.00 18.00
50c A1 6p on 6p carmine rose 35.00 47.50
d. Mixed periods 175.00 175.00
e. Pair, one with level periods 175.00
f. Thick "V" *450.00* *450.00*
51d A1 6p on 6p ultramarine .60 .30
e. Mixed periods 6.00 6.00
f. Pair, one with level periods 15.00 15.00
g. Thick "V" 3.00 3.00
52e A1 1sh on 1sh brown 1.00 .45
f. Mixed periods 10.00 10.00
h. Pair, one with level periods 25.00 26.00
i. Thick "V" 1.75 1.50
52j A1 1sh on 1sh orange *1,050.* *1,050.*
53c A1 5sh on 5sh green 6.50 9.00
d. Mixed periods 325.00 325.00
e. Pair, one with level periods *1,600.* *2,500.*
f. "5" with short flag 60.00 60.00
g. Thick "V" 18.00 18.00

Stamps with mixed periods have one or two periods level with the bottoms of letters. One stamp in each pane had all periods level. Later settings had several stamps with thick "V." No. 52j may not have been issued. Excellent forgeries of the scarcer varieties exist.

"V.R.I." stands for Victoria Regina Imperatrix. On No. 59, "E.R.I." stands for Edward Rex Imperator.

Cape of Good Hope Stamps of 1893-98 Overprinted

ORANGE RIVER COLONY.

1900 **Wmk. 16**

54 A15 ½p green .20 .15
a. No period after "COLONY" 8.50 12.00
b. Double overprint 500.00 600.00
55 A13 2½p ultramarine .30 .30
a. No period after "COLONY" 45.00 57.50

Overprinted as in 1900

1902, May

56 A15 1p carmine rose .30 .30
a. No period after "COLONY" 10.00 15.00

Nos. 51d, 53c, Surcharged and No. 8b Surcharged like No. 51 but Reading "E.R.I."

4d

One Shilling ✳

Carmine or Vermilion and Black Surcharges

1902 **Unwmk.**

57 A1 4p on 6p on 6p ultra .60 .70
a. Thick "V" 1.75 1.25
b. As "a," inverted "1" instead of "I" 4.50 4.50
c. No period after "R" 30.00 30.00

Black Surcharge

59 A1 6p on 6p ultra 2.00 6.00
a. Double surcharge, one invtd. *600.00* *600.00*

Orange Surcharge

60 A1 1sh on 5sh on 5sh grn 5.00 6.00
a. Thick "V" 13.00 18.00
b. "5" with short flag 60.00 60.00
c. Double surcharge
Nos. 57-60 (3) 7.60 12.70

"E.R.I." stands for Edward Rex Imperator.

King Edward VII — A8

1903-04 **Wmk. 2** **Typo.**

61 A8 ½p yellow green 5.00 1.10
62 A8 1p carmine 1.50 .20
63 A8 2p chocolate 3.00 .70
64 A8 2½p ultra .90 .45
65 A8 3p violet 3.50 .80
66 A8 4p olive grn & car 18.00 2.50
67 A8 6p violet & car 5.00 1.00
68 A8 1sh bister & car 20.00 2.00
69 A8 5sh red brn & bl ('04) 62.50 18.00
Nos. 61-69 (9) 119.40 26.75

Some of the above stamps are found with the overprint "C. S. A. R." for use by the Central South African Railway.

The "IOSTAGE" variety on the 4p is the result of filled in type.

Issue dates: 1p, Feb. 3. ½p, 2p, 2½p, 3p, 4p, 6p, 1sh, July 6. 5sh, Oct. 31.

1907-08 **Wmk. 3**

70 A8 ½p yellow green 4.00 .45
71 A8 1p carmine 3.00 .20
72 A8 4p olive grn & car 4.00 1.50
73 A8 1sh bister & car 25.00 8.00
Nos. 70-73 (4) 36.00 10.15

The "IOSTAGE" variety on the 4p is the result of filled in type.

Stamps of Orange River Colony were replaced by those of Union of South Africa.

1999 Vol. 4 Catalogue Number Additions, Deletions & Changes

Number in 1998 Catalogue	Number in 1999 Catalogue
Jamaica	
new	680a, 682a
Kenya	
689-692	688-691
Korea	
new	1293a
new	1381b
1451	C45
1451a	footnoted
Laos	
new	195a
Lithuania	
573a	footnoted
Macao	
21	21a
21a	21
new	28c
170	170a
170a	170
209a	deleted
Malawi	
new	166a, 168a
new	170a, 172a
Malaya	
44	44b
44b	44
85	85a
85a	85
Malaysia	
Johore	
new	7a
Pahang	
92a, 94a, 95a	footnoted
Penang	
148a, 150a, 151a	footnoted
Perak	
new	10a, 13a
new	63a, 67a
Perlis	
49a, 51a, 52a	footnoted
Sabah	
26a, 28a, 29a	footnoted
Selangor	
130a, 132a, 133a	footnoted
Trengganu	
98a, 100a, 101a	footnoted
Mali	
905-907	902-904
902	905
908	906
903	907
909-910	908-909
904	910
new	J8a, J10a
new	J12a, J14a
new	J16a, J18a
new	J20a, J22a
new	J24a, J26a
new	J28a, J30a
Malta	
3	3c
3c	3
Marshall Islands	
new	398b
Mauritania	
new	C235a, C237a, C244a
new	J27a, J29a
new	J31a, J33a
new	J35a, J37a
new	J39a, J41a
Mauritius	
39	39a
39a	39
156	156b
156b	156
159	159d
159d	159
Mexico	
876	876a
876a	876
878	878a
878a	878
882	882b
882b	882
1112	1112c
1112c	1112
1117	1117a
1117a	1117
1123	1123c
1123c	1123
1135	1135b
1135b	1135
1168	1168a
1168a	1168
1468	1468a
1468a	1468
Monaco	
new	J39a, J40a, J41a
new	J42a, J43a, J44a
new	J45a, J46a, J47a
Montserrat	
new	614a, 616a
new	629a, 631a
Morocco	
new	192a, 296a
new	352a, 374a, 387a
new	411a, 452a
new	B11a, B12a, B13a
new	B16a, B20a, B22a
new	B27a, B30a
new	B32a, B35a
Natal	
46	46a
46a	46
Nepal	
29A	29Ab
29Ab	29A
Netherlands	
new	917a, 950a
Netherlands Antilles	
new	B266a
Nevis	
383-398	383-390
New Caledonia	
new	488b, 583b
New Zealand	
118	118a
118a	118
B157b	B158a
OY39	OY39a
OY39a	OY39
Nicaragua	
new	1029a, 1031a, 1033a
new	1035a, 1037a
new	C908a, C910a, C912a
Niger	
new	685a, 723a
Niue	
4	4b
4a	4c
4b	4
4c	4a
699-700	696-697
696	698
701	699
697	700
698	701
North Borneo	
101	101a
101a	101
102	102a
102a	102
Northern Rhodesia	
new	78c, 78d
new	81b, 86a

Dies of British Colonial Stamps Referred to in the Catalogue

DIE A

DIE B

DIE A:
1. The lines in the groundwork vary in thickness and are not uniformly straight.
2. The seventh and eighth lines from the top, in the groundwork, converge where they meet the head.
3. There is a small dash in the upper part of the second jewel in the band of the crown.
4. The vertical color line in front of the throat stops at the sixth line of shading on the neck.

DIE B:
1. The lines in the groundwork are all thin and straight.
2. All the lines of the background are parallel.
3. There is no dash in the upper part of the second jewel in the band of the crown.
4. The vertical color line in front of the throat stops at the eighth line of shading on the neck.

DIE I

DIE II

DIE I:
1. The base of the crown is well below the level of the inner white line around the vignette.
2. The labels inscribed "POSTAGE" and "REVENUE" are cut square at the top.
3. There is a white "bud" on the outer side of the main stem of the curved ornaments in each lower corner.
4. The second (thick) line below the country name has the ends next to the crown cut diagonally.

DIE Ia.
1 as die II.
2 and 3 as die I.

DIE Ib.
1 and 3 as die II.
2 as die I.

DIE II:
1. The base of the crown is aligned with the underside of the white line around the vignette.
2. The labels curve inward at the top inner corners.
3. The "bud" has been removed from the outer curve of the ornaments in each corner.
4. The second line below the country name has the ends next to the crown cut vertically.

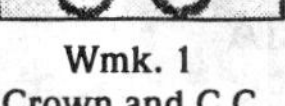
Wmk. 1
Crown and C C

Wmk. 2
Crown and C A

Wmk. 3
Multiple Crown and C A

Wmk. 4
Multiple Crown and Script C A

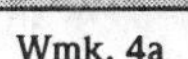
Wmk. 4a

Wmk. 314
St. Edward's Crown and C A Multiple

Wmk. 373

Wmk. 384

British Colonial and Crown Agents Watermarks

Watermarks 1 to 4, 314, 373, and 384, common to many British territories, are illustrated here to avoid duplication.

The letters "CC" of Wmk. 1 identify the paper as having been made for the use of the Crown Colonies, while the letters "CA" of the others stand for "Crown Agents." Both Wmks. 1 and 2 were used on stamps printed by De La Rue & Co.

Wmk. 3 was adopted in 1904; Wmk. 4 in 1921; Wmk. 314 in 1957; Wmk. 373 in 1974; and Wmk. 384 in 1985.

In Wmk. 4a, a non-matching crown of the general St. Edwards type (bulging on both sides at top) was substituted for one of the Wmk. 4 crowns which fell off the dandy roll. The non-matching crown occurs in 1950-52 printings in a horizontal row of crowns on certain regular stamps of Johore and Seychelles, and on various postage due stamps of Barbados, Basutoland, British Guiana, Gold Coast, Grenada, Northern Rhodesia, St. Lucia, Swaziland and Trinidad and Tobago. A variation of Wmk. 4a, with the non-matching crown in a horizontal row of crown-CA-crown, occurs on regular stamps of Bahamas, St. Kitts-Nevis and Singapore.

Wmk. 314 was intentionally used sideways, starting in 1966. When a stamp was issued with Wmk. 314 both upright and sideways, the sideways varieties usually are listed also – with minor numbers. In many of the later issues, Wmk. 314 is slightly visible.

Wmk. 373 is usually only faintly visible.

Illustrated Identifier

This section pictures stamps or parts of stamp designs that will help identify postage stamps that do not have English words on them.

Many of the symbols that identify stamps of countries are shown here as well as typical examples of their stamps.

See the Index and Identifier on the previous pages for stamps with inscriptions such as "sen," "posta," "Baja Porto," "Helvetia," "K.S.A.", etc.

Linn's Stamp Identifier is now available. The 144 pages include more 2,000 inscriptions and over 500 large stamp illustrations. Available from Linn's Stamp News, P.O. Box 29, Sidney, OH 45365-0029.

1. HEADS, PICTURES AND NUMERALS

GREAT BRITAIN

Great Britain stamps never show the country name, but, except for postage dues, show a picture of the reigning monarch.

Victoria

Edward VII George V Edward VIII

George VI

Elizabeth II

Some George VI and Elizabeth II stamps are surcharged in annas, new paisa or rupees. These are listed under Oman.

Silhouette (sometimes facing right, generally at the top of stamp)

The silhouette indicates this is a British stamp. It is not a U.S. stamp.

VICTORIA

Queen Victoria

INDIA

Other stamps of India show this portrait of Queen Victoria and the words "Service" and "Annas."

AUSTRIA

YUGOSLAVIA

(Also BOSNIA & HERZEGOVINA if imperf.)

BOSNIA & HERZEGOVINA

Denominations also appear in top corners instead of bottom corners.

HUNGARY

Another stamp has posthorn facing left

BRAZIL

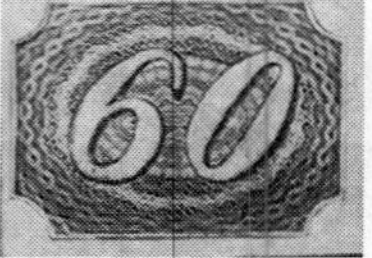

AUSTRALIA

Kangaroo and Emu

GERMANY

Mecklenburg-Vorpommern

SWITZERLAND

2. ORIENTAL INSCRIPTIONS

CHINA

Any stamp with this one character is from China (Imperial, Republic or People's Republic). This character appears in a four-character overprint on stamps of Manchukuo. These stamps are local provisionals, which are unlisted. Other overprinted Manchukuo stamps show this character, but have more than four characters in the overprints. These are listed in People's Republic of China.

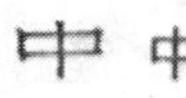

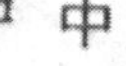

Some Chinese stamps show the Sun.

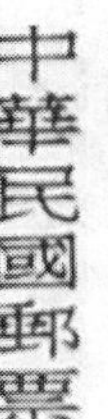

Most stamps of Republic of China show this series of characters.

Stamps with the China character and this character are from People's Republic of China. 人

中国人民邮政

Calligraphic form of People's Republic of China

Chinese stamps without China character

REPUBLIC OF CHINA

PEOPLE'S REPUBLIC OF CHINA

Mao Tse-tung

MANCHUKUO

Temple Emperor Pu-Yi

The first 3 characters are common to many Manchukuo stamps.

The last 3 characters are common to other Manchukuo stamps.

Orchid Crest

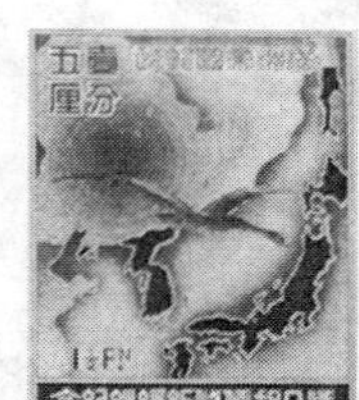

Manchukuo stamp without these elements

JAPAN

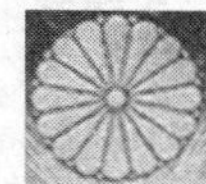

Chrysanthemum Crest Country Name

Japanese stamps without these elements

The number of characters in the center and the design of dragons on the sides will vary.

RYUKYU ISLANDS

Country Name

PHILIPPINES (Japanese Occupation)

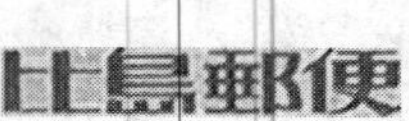

Country Name

NORTH BORNEO (Japanese Occupation)

Indicates Japanese Occupation Country Name

MALAYA (Japanese Occupation)

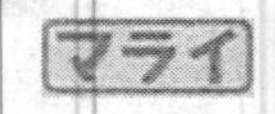

Indicates Japanese Occupation Country Name

BURMA (Japanese Occupation)

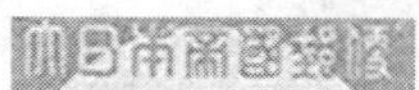
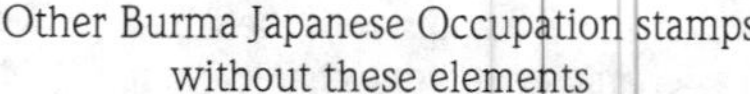

Indicates Japanese Occupation Country Name

Other Burma Japanese Occupation stamps without these elements

Burmese Script

KOREA

These two characters, in any order, are common to stamps from the Republic of Korea (South Korea) or the unlisted stamps of the People's Democratic Republic of Korea (North Korea).

This series of four characters can be found on the stamps of both Koreas.

Yin Yang appears on some stamps.

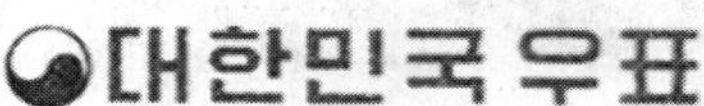

Indicates Republic of Korea (South Korea)

South Korean postage stamps issed after 1952 do not show currency expressed in Latin letters. Stamps wiith "HW," "HWAN," "WON," "WN," "W" or "W" with two lines through it, if not illustrated in listings of stamps before this date, are revenues. North Korean postage stamps do not have currency expressed in Latin letters.

THAILAND

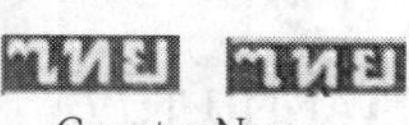

Country Name

King Chulalongkorn

King Prajadhipok and Chao P'ya Chakri

3. CENTRAL AND EASTERN ASIAN INSCRIPTIONS

INDIA - FEUDATORY STATES

Alwar

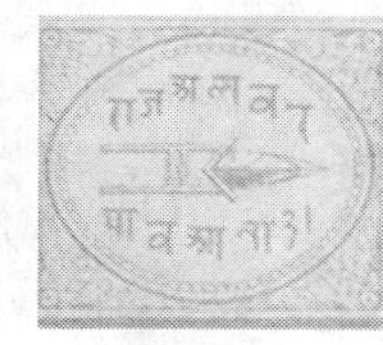

Bhor

Bundi

Similar stamps come with different designs in corners and differently drawn daggers (at center of circle).

Dhar

Faridkot

Hyderabad

Similar stamps exist with straight line frame around stamp, and also with different central design which is inscribed "Postage" or "Post & Receipt."

Indore

Jhalawar

A similar stamp has the central figure in an oval.

Nandgaon

Nowanuggur

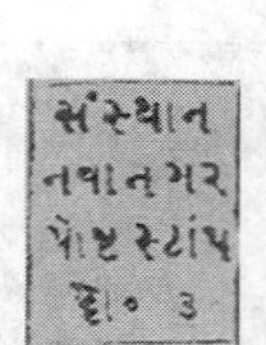

Poonch

Similar stamps exist in various sizes

Rajpeepla

Soruth

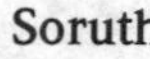

BANGLADESH

Country Name

NEPAL

Similar stamps are smaller, have squares in upper corners and have five or nine characters in central bottom panel.

TANNU TUVA

ISRAEL

GEORGIA

This inscription is found on other pictorial stamps.

Country Name

ARMENIA

The four characters are found somewhere on pictorial stamps. On some stamps only the middle two are found.

4. AFRICAN INSCRIPTIONS

ETHIOPIA

5. ARABIC INSCRIPTIONS

AFGHANISTAN

Many early Afghanistan stamps show Tiger's head, many of these have ornaments protruding from outer ring, others show inscriptions in black.

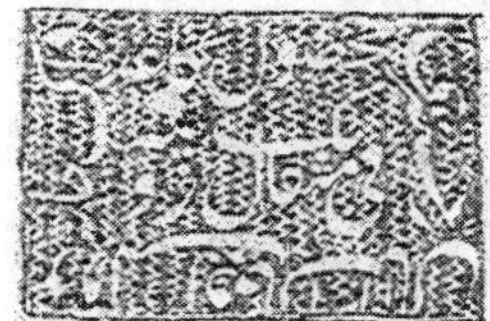

Arabic Script

Mosque Gate & Crossed Cannons
The four characters are found somewhere on pictorial stamps. On some stamps only the middle two are found.

BAHRAIN

EGYPT

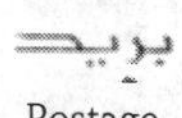

Postage

INDIA - FEUDATORY STATES

Jammu & Kashmir

Text and thickness of ovals vary. Some stamps have flower devices in corners.

India-Hyderabad

IRAN

Country Name

Royal Crown

Lion with Sword

Symbol

IRAQ

JORDAN

LEBANON

Similar types have denominations at top and slightly different design.

LIBYA

Country Name in various styles

Other Libya stamps show Eagle and Shield (head facing either direction) or Red, White and Black Shield (with or without eagle in center).

SAUDI ARABIA

Tughra (Central design)

Palm Tree and Swords

SYRIA

THRACE

YEMEN

PAKISTAN

PAKISTAN - Bahawalpur

Country Name in top panel, star and crescent

TURKEY

Star & Crescent is a device found on many Turkish stamps, but is also found on stamps from other Arabic areas (see Pakistan-Bahawalpur)

Tughra (similar tughras can be found on stamps of Turkey in Asia, Afghanistan and Saudi Arabia)

Mohammed V

Mustafa Kemal

Plane, Star and Crescent

TURKEY IN ASIA

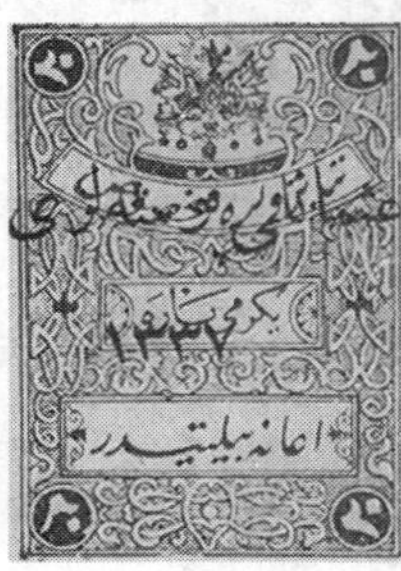

Other Turkey in Asia pictorials show star & crescent.
Other stamps show tughra shown under Turkey.

6. GREEK INSCRIPTIONS

GREECE

Country Name in various styles
(Some Crete stamps overprinted with the Greece country name are listed in Crete.)

Lepta

ΔΡΑΧΜΗ ΔΡΑΧΜΑΙ ΛΕΠΤΟΝ

Drachma Drachmas Lepton

Abbreviated Country Name ΕΛΛ

Other forms of Country Name

No country name

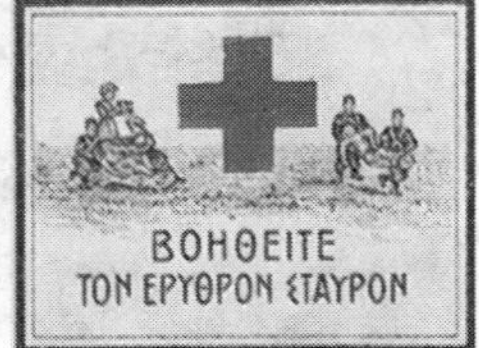

CRETE

Country Name

These words are on other stamps

Grosion

Crete stamps with a surcharge that have the year "1922" are listed under Greece.

EPIRUS

Country Name

IONIAN ISLANDS

7. CYRILLIC INSCRIPTIONS

RUSSIA

Postage Stamp

Imperial Eagle

Postage in various styles

Abbreviation for Kopeck

Abbreviation for Ruble

Russia

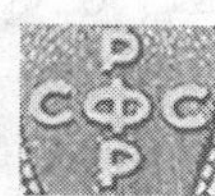

Abbreviation for Russian Soviet Federated Socialist Republic
RSFSR stamps were overprinted (see below)

Abbreviation for Union of Soviet Socialist Republics

This item is footnoted in Latvia

RUSSIA - Army of the North

"OKCA"

RUSSIA - Wenden

RUSSIAN OFFICES IN THE TURKISH EMPIRE

These letters appear on other stamps of the Russian offices.

The unoverprinted version of this stamp and a similar stamp were overprinted by various countries (see below).

ARMENIA

BELARUS

FAR EASTERN REPUBLIC

Country Name

SOUTH RUSSIA

Country Name

FINLAND

Circles and Dots on stamps similar to Imperial Russia issues

BATUM

Forms of Country Name

TRANSCAUCASIAN FEDERATED REPUBLICS

Abbreviation for Country Name

KAZAKHSTAN

Country Name

KYRGYZSTAN

КЫРГЫЗСТАН Counrty Name

ROMANIA

TADJIKISTAN

Таджик.

Counrty Name & Abbreviation

UKRAINE

Україні

Україні Україні

Country Name in various forms

The trident appears on many stamps, usually as an overprint.

Abbreviation for Ukrainian Soviet Socialist Republic

WESTERN UKRAINE

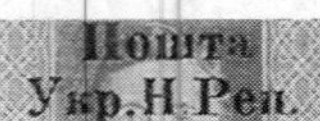

Abbreviation for Country Name

AZERBAIJAN

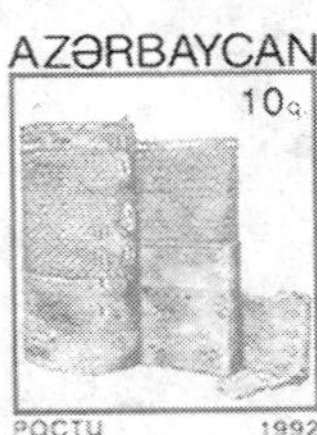

AZƏRBAYCAN

Country Name

A.C.C.P. Abbreviation for Azerbaijan Soviet Socialist Republic

MONTENEGRO

Country Name in various forms

Abbreviation for country name

No country name (A similar Montenegro stamp without country name has same vignette.)

SERBIA

Country Name in various forms

Abbreviation for country name

No country name

YUGOSLAVIA

Showing country name

No Country Name

MACEDONIA

Country Name

BULGARIA

Country Name

Postage

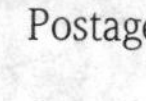

Stotinka

Stotinki (plural)

Abbreviation for Stotinki

Country Name in various forms and styles

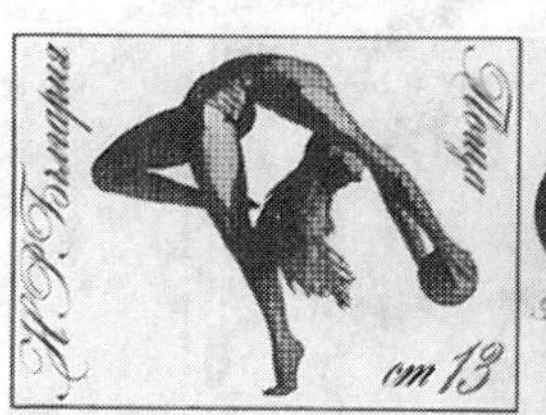

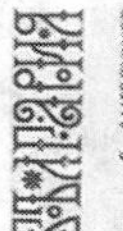

No country name

Abbreviation for Lev, leva

MONGOLIA

ШУУДАН
Country name in one word

ТӨГРӨГ
Tugrik in Cyrillic

МОНГОЛ ШУУДАН
Country name in two words

МӨНГӨ
Mung in Cyrillic

Mung in Mongolian

Tugrik in Mongolian

Arms

No Country Name

Index and Identifier

All page numbers shown are those in this Volume 4.

Postage stamps that do not have English words on them are shown in the Identifier which begins on page 994.

INDEX TO ADVERTISERS – 1999 VOLUME 4

DEALERS...TAKE ADVANTAGE OF SCOTT'S ADVERTISING OPPORTUNITIES!

SCOTT GIVES YOU THE AMERICAN MARKET...AND AN EVER INCREASING WORLD MARKET!
Present Your Buying or Selling Messages, in Your Specialty Area, to Serious Collectors by placing Your Advertisements in Scott Products!

2000 SCOTT CATALOGUES
Call now to reserve ad space and to receive advertising information. If you're interested in specific positions...call or write as soon as possible.

SCOTT STAMP MONTHLY
Whether you're buying or selling, our readership of active mail-order collectors offers you a perfect opportunity for increased sales and contacts.

SCOTT U.S. FDC CATALOGUE
The First Day Cover reference collectors of all levels have come to depend on. Call now for advertising information.

SCOTT U.S. POCKET CAT.
Now a full-color reference, this popular annual catalogue can bring you many new customers. Thousands are sold each year to active and beginning collectors.

For Information Call 1-800-895-9881, Fax 1-800-488-5349 or write SCOTT, P.O. Box 828, Sidney, OH 45365-0828 USA.

1999
VOLUME 4
DEALER DIRECTORY YELLOW PAGE LISTINGS

This section of your Scott Catalogue contains advertisements to help you conveniently find what you need, when you need it...!

Collectors:
Buying – Selling – Appraisals – The ASDA Can Help

The American Stamp Dealers Association, Inc., serving the needs of the collecting community for over 80 years, is ready to assist you.

Our members represent all segments of the philatelic marketplace.

We are the leader in establishing the highest standards of professionalism for the rest of the industry to emulate. As a collector, you are guaranteed absolute satisfaction with every transaction.

ASDA

Professionals Serving Philately Since 1914

• Integrity • Honesty •Expertise
• Dedication • Hobby Builders • Reliability

Contact Us Today For:

1.) A list of ASDA dealers in your geographic area.
2.) A list of ASDA dealers by your collecting area.
3.) The brochure, "Selling a stamp collection, - what you need to know."
4.) The brochure, "Expertizing Philatelic Materials."

Please send a #10 SASE, including 55¢ postage if ordering all of the above.

AMERICAN STAMP DEALERS ASSOCIATION, INC.
3 School St. Dept. SC, Glen Cove, NY 11542
email:asda@inx.net web:www.amerstampdlrs.com

Accessories

BROOKLYN GALLERY COIN & STAMP
8725 4th Ave.
Brooklyn, NY 11209
718-745-5701
718-745-2775 Fax

Albums & Accessories

THE KEEPING ROOM
P.O. Box 257
Trumbull, CT 06611-0257
203-372-8436

Antarctic

ANTARCTIC PHILATELIC EXCHANGE
92015-1562 Danforth Ave.
Toronto, ON M4J 5C1
Canada
416-406-2760
http://www.south-pole.com
Email:jporter@interlog.com

Appraisals

UNIQUE ESTATE APPRAISALS
1937 NE Broadway
Portland, OR 97232
503-287-4200 or
800-646-1147
Email:uea@stampsandcoins.com
http:www.stampsandcoins.com

Approvals - Personalized Worldwide & U.S.

THE KEEPING ROOM
P.O. Box 257
Trumbull, CT 06611-0257
203-372-8436

Approvals – Topicals

E. JOSEPH MCCONNELL INC.
P.O. Box 683
Monroe, NY 10950
914-496-5916
914-782-0347 Fax

S. SEREBRAKIAN, INC.
P.O. Box 448
Monroe, NY 10950
914-783-9791
914-782-0347 Fax

Approvals Worldwide

ROSS WETREICH INC.
P.O. Box 1300
Valley Stream, NY 11582-1300
516-825-8974

Approvals Worldwide - Collections

S. R. L. STAMPS
P.O. Box 296
Huguenot, NY 12746
800-369-4617 pin 3429 Phone &Fax

Asia

PACIFIC RIM PHILATELIC COMPANY
484 Lake Park Ave. #144
Oakland, CA 94610
510-835-0307 or
510-251-8001 Ext.3 Telephone & Fax
Email:pacrim@dnai.com or
Email:Pacrim484@aol

MICHAEL ROGERS, INC.
199 E. Welbourne Ave.
Winter Park, FL 32789
407-644-2290
407-645-4434 Fax
http://www.michaelrogersinc.com

SOUTHEAST STAMPS
P.O. Box 6768
Shreveport, LA 71106

Auction House

B TRADING CO.
114 Quail Street
Albany, NY 12206
518-465-3497 Telephone & Fax
Email:btradeco@wizvax.net

Auctions

CHARLES G. FIRBY AUCTIONS
6695 Highland Road Suite #107
Waterford, MI 48327-1967
248-666-5333
248-666-5020 Fax

DANIEL F. KELLEHER CO., INC.
24 Farnsworth St.
Ste. 605
Boston, MA 02210
617-443-0033
617-443-0789 Fax

LAKESIDE PHILATELIC AUCTIONS
3935 Lakeside Rd.
Penticton, BC V2A 8W1
Canada
250-493-5239
250-493-3324 Fax
http://vvv.com/~greek
Email:greek@tnet.net

JACQUES C. SCHIFF, JR., INC.
195 Main St.
Ridgefield Park, NJ 07660
201-641-5566 from NYC 662-2777
201-641-5705 Fax

JUAN N. SIMONA
Ventas Filatelicas
Casilla de Correo #40
7311 Chillar (Buenos Aires)
Argentina
54-281-97281or 54-281-97346
Phone & Fax
Email:simonafilatelia@simon-afilatelia.com.ar
http://www.simonafilatelia.com.ar

Auctions

Schiff Auctions

Buyers, Auctioneers & Appraisers of U.S. & Worldwide Stamps & Covers

We have been catering to the individual buyer and seller since 1947. Let us put our **51 years** of experience to work for you when selling your stamps, covers or your collection. Whether you prefer consigning to public auction or selling outright, call us first. Describe your material before sending. Please include your address and telephone numbers.

CATALOG SUBSCRIPTIONS	N. AMERICA	OVERSEAS
1 Year Catalogs & Prices Realized	$10.00	$18.00
1 Year Catalog Only	$7.50	$15.00
1 Catalog with Prices Realized	$1.50	$2.50
1 Catalog Only	$1.00	$1.50

JACQUES C. SCHIFF, JR., INC.

195 Main St., Ridgefield Park, NJ 07660 USA
Telephone 201-641-5566 from NYC 662-2777
FAX 201-641-5705

OFFICIAL AUCTIONEERS:
AMERIPEX 1986.
WORLD STAMP EXPO 1989.
WORLD COLUMBIAN STAMP EXPO 1992.
YEARLY: COMPEX-CHICAGO

Auctions

STAMP CENTER / DUTCH COUNTRY AUCTIONS
4115 Concord Pike
Wilmington, DE 19803
302-478-8740
302-478-8779 Fax
http://www.thestampcenter.com

THE STAMP & COIN SHOP/ AUCTIONS
725 Pike St. #6
Seattle, WA 98101
206-624-1400
206-621-8975 Fax
http://WWW.Stamp-Coin.com

Auctions - Public

ALAN BLAIR STAMPS / AUCTIONS
5520A Lakeside Avenue
Richmond, VA 23228
800-689-5602 Telephone & Fax

CONNEXUS
P.O. Box 130
Tryon, NC 28782
828-859-5882
828-859-2702 Fax
Email:Connexus1@worldnet.att.net

Austria

JOSEPH EDER
P.O. Box 5517
Hamden, CT 06518
203-281-0742
203-230-2410 Fax
Email:jeder@nai.net

Beanie Babies

M.A. STORK
651 Forest Ave.
Portland, ME 04101
800-734-7271

Booklets

PACIFIC RIM PHILATELIC COMPANY
484 Lake Park Ave. #144
Oakland, CA 94610
510-835-0307 or
510-251-8001 Ext.3 Telephone & Fax
Email:pacrim@dnai.com or
Email:Pacrim484@aol

British Colonies

EMPIRE COLLECTION
P.O. Box 19248
Encino, CA 91416
818-880-6764
818-880-6860 Fax
Email:EMPIRECOLL@AOL.COM

British Commonwealth

BRITISH COMMONWEALTH STAMP CO.
P.O. Box 10218
Wilmington, NC 28405
Email:bcstamp@stamp-mall.com
910-256-0971 Fax

DAUWALDERS OF SALISBURY
92-94 Fisherton St.
Wiltshire, SP27QY
United Kingdom
1-44-1722-412100
1-44-1722-410074 Fax
Email:DAUSTAMPS@AOL.COM

British Commonwealth

JAY'S STAMP COMPANY
Box 28484 Dept. S
Philadelphia, PA 19149
215-743-0207 Telephone & Fax
Email:JASC@Juno.com
http://jaysco.com
:jrstamps@hotmail.com

METROPOLITAN STAMP CO. of CHICAGO, INC.
P.O. Box 1133
Chicago, IL 60690-1133
815-439-0142
815-439-0143 Fax

British Commonwealth

BRITISH EMPIRE EXCLUSIVELY

Request a catalogue for our next Public Auction.
Please specify your interests.

Want lists invited from serious collectors of the BRITISH EMPIRE. References please.

Selling? Ask us about consigning *your* collection to a future sale.

Victoria Stamp Co.
Established 1962
PHOEBE A. MacGILLIVARY
P.O. BOX 745, RIDGEWOOD, NJ 07451
PHONE 201-652-7283 • FAX 201-612-0024

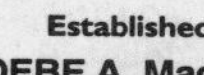

The British Empire
(A-Z 1840-1935 Mint & Used)
The Largest & Most Valuable Stock in America.

Want Lists (per Scott or S. G.) prompt expert service, 30 volumes in all price ranges, stocked individually so you can acquire exactly those you need on approval or per quotations (references appreciated).

For decades we have had the great pleasure of working closely with our clients in the formation of many fine private or international exhibition standard collections. I will be pleased to place our expertize at your disposal.

George W. Holschauer
COLONIAL STAMP CO.
5757 WILSHIRE BLVD., PH #8
LOS ANGELES, CA 90036
Ph. (213) 933-9435
Fax (213) 939-9930
CCNY, CSDA, IFSDA, INTERNATIONAL SOCIETY OF APPRAISERS

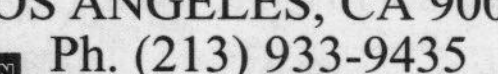

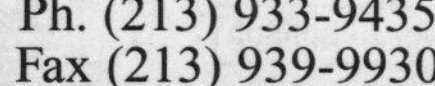

British Commonwealth

British Commonwealth Stamp Co.
Box 10218-S-3, Wilmington, NC 28405
FAX: 910-256-0971 E-mail:bcstamp@stamp-mall.com
http://www.stamp-mall.com

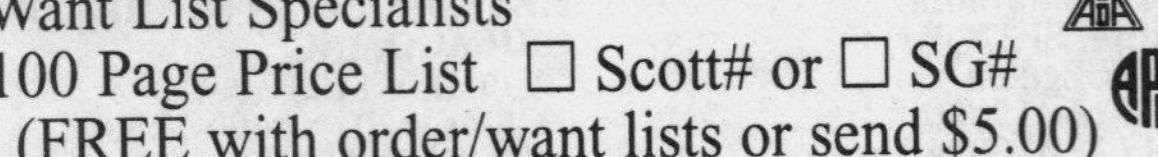

- Want List Specialists
- 100 Page Price List ☐ Scott# or ☐ SG#
  (FREE with order/want lists or send $5.00)
- Mail Auction — Rarities $150-$5,000+
- Satisfaction Guaranteed

LARGEST STOCK
of Mint/Used STAMPS TO 1952

Collections

★ ★ ★ STOP ★ ★ ★
WORLDWIDE COLLECTIONS
AT LOW, LOW PRICES!

If you spend over $25.00 per month you should subscribe to the "Money's Worth" list.
For 3 free issues, write or call:

WARREN T. WASSON
DALLAS STAMP GALLERY
1002 N. Central, Suite 501, Richardson, TX 75080
Fax: 972-669-4742
Call TOLL FREE 1-800-759-9109

British Commonwealth

PACIFIC RIM PHILATELIC COMPANY
484 Lake Park Ave. #144
Oakland, CA 94610
510-835-0307 or
510-251-8001 Ext.3 Telephone & Fax
Email:pacrim@dnai.com or
Email:Pacrim484@aol

VICTORIA STAMP COMPANY
P.O. Box 745
Ridgewood, NJ 07451
201-652-7283
201-612-0024 Fax

British Pacific

OVPT PHILATELICS
P.O. Box 36217
Los Angeles, CA 90036
818-893-4603 Telephone & Fax
Email:ovptphmc@webtv.net

Canada - Postal Bid Sales

BOW CITY PHILATELICS LTD.
P.O. Box 6444 Central P.O.
Suite 614 206 7th Ave. SW
Calgary, AB T2P 2E1
Canada
403-237-5828
403-264-5287 Fax
Email:bow.city@bbs.logicnet.com
http:www.logicnet.com/bow.city

China

MICHAEL ROGERS, INC.
199 E. Welbourne Ave.
Winter Park, FL 32789
407-644-2290
407-645-4434 Fax
http://www.michaelrogersinc.com

Collections

BOB & MARTHA FRIEDMAN STAMPS
624 Homestead Place
Joliet, IL 60434
815-725-6666
815-725-4134 Fax

DR. ROBERT FRIEDMAN & SONS
2029 West 75th St.
Woodridge, IL 60517
630-985-1515
630-985-1588 Fax

HENRY GITNER PHILATELISTS, INC.
P.O. Box 3077-S
Middletown, NY 10940
914-343-5151 or 800-947-8267
914-343-0068 Fax
Email:hgitner@hgitner.com
http://www.hgitner.com

Buying

Collections, Accumulations, Estates & Appraisals,
Dealer Stocks, Postal History, F.D.C.,Postage Lots
Send your collection for a prompt cash offer.
We carry a full-line of Albums & Accessories.
Stamps for beginner to specialists
Open Mon. thru Sat. 9 am to 5 pm

Brewart Stamps
1725A West Chapman Ave.
Orange, CA 92868
714-533-2521

All Stamps insured by Lloyds of London

Czechoslovakia

SOCIETY FOR CZECHOSLOVAK PHILATELY, INC.
Tom Cossaboom, SCP Secretary
Box 25332
Scott Air Force Base, IL 62225
USA

Disney

BROOKMAN STAMP COMPANY
P.O. Box 90
Vancouver, WA 98666
360-695-1391 or 800-545-4871
360-695-1616 Fax
Email:brookman@stampdealers.com
http:www.brookmanstamps.com

PACIFIC RIM PHILATELIC COMPANY
484 Lake Park Ave. #144
Oakland, CA 94610
510-835-0307 or
510-251-8001 Ext, 3 Telephone & Fax
Email:pacrim@dnai.com or
Email:Pacrim484@aol

Duck Stamps

MICHAEL JAFFE STAMPS, INC.
P.O. Box 61484
Vancouver, WA 98666
360-695-6161 or 800-782-6770
360-695-1616 Fax
Email:mjaffe@brookmanstamps.com
http://www.brookmanstamps.com

METROPOLITAN STAMP CO. of CHICAGO, INC.
P.O. Box 1133
Chicago, IL 60690-1133
815-439-0142
815-439-0143 Fax

PACIFIC RIM PHILATELIC COMPANY
484 Lake Park Ave. #144
Oakland, CA 94610
510-835-0307 or
510-251-8001 Ext, 3 Telephone & Fax
Email:pacrim@dnai.com or
Email:Pacrim484@aol

TRENTON STAMP & COIN CO. - THOMAS DeLUCA
Forest Glen Plaza
1804 Route 33
Hamilton Square, NJ 08690
800-446-8664
609-587-8664 Fax

Errors, Freaks & Oddities

MILL CREEK LIMITED
P.O. Box 236
Bothell, WA 98041-0236
U.S.800-495-6868 outside of U.S.
425-487-2789
Email:MillCreek@StampDealers.com
http://www.stampdealers.com/millcreek/

Exchange

ROBERT'S STAMP EXCHANGE/Robert LeFrancois
444 Summit St.
Elgin, Il 60120
847-695-6568

France

JOSEPH EDER
P.O. Box 5517
Hamden, CT 06518
203-281-0742
203-230-2410 Fax
Email:jeder@nai.net

E. JOSEPH MCCONNELL INC.
P.O. Box 683
Monroe, NY 10950
914-496-5916
914-782-0347 Fax

S. SEREBRAKIAN, INC.
P.O. Box 448
Monroe, NY 10950
914-783-9791
914-782-0347 Fax

German Areas

JOSEPH EDER
P.O. Box 5517
Hamden, CT 06518
203-281-0742
203-230-2410 Fax
Email:jeder@nai.net

Great Britain

COLONIAL STAMP COMPANY
5757 Wilshire Blvd. PH #8
Los Angeles, CA 90036
213-933-9435
213-939-9930 Fax

NOVA PHILATELIC SALES
Box 161
Lakeside, N.S. B3T 1M6
Canada
902-826-2165
902-826-1049 Fax
Email:novafil@ns.sympatico.ca

Imperial China

TREASURE -HUNTERS LIMITED
G.P.O. Box 11446
Hong Kong
852-2507-3773 or 2507-5770
852-2519-6820 Fax

Insurance

COLLECTIBLES INSURANCE AGENCY, INC.
P.O. Box 1200 SSC
Westminster, MD 21158-0299
888-837-9537 or 410-876-8833
410-876-9233 Fax
Email:collectinsure@pipeline.com

Iran - Classics

DE MOTTE STAMPS INTERNATIONAL COMPANY
2555 W. Middlefield Rd.
Ste. 212
Mountainview, CA 94043
650-968-2636
650-938-1610 Fax

Israel - New Issues

ISRAEL PHILATELIC AGENCY
535 Fifth Ave.
Suite 300
New York, NY 10017
212-818-9160 or 800-607-2799
212-818-9012 Fax

Japan

LEON FISCHER
P.O. Box 1338 Gracie Sta.
New York, NY 10028

FRANK GEIGER PHILATELISTS
Suite 2
242 West Saddle River Road
Saddle River, NJ 07458-2620
201-236-8122
201-236-8133 Fax
http://www.worldstamps.com

HENRY GITNER PHILATELISTS, INC.
P.O. Box 3077-S
Middletown, NY 10940
914-343-5151 or 800-947-8267
914-343-0068 Fax
Email:hgitner@hgitner.com
http://www.hgitner.com

JUNO STAMPS
1765 Juno Ave.
St. Paul, MN 55116
800-714-3469

THE STAMP ACT
P.O. Box 1136
Belmont, CA 94002
650-592-3315
650-508-8104 Fax
http://www.Bchang@IX.netcom.com

Jersey

FRANK GEIGER PHILATELISTS
Suite 2
242 West Saddle River Road
Saddle River, NJ 07458-2620
201-236-8122
201-236-8133 Fax
http://www.worldstamps.com

Kazakhstan

FRANK GEIGER PHILATELISTS
Suite 2
242 West Saddle River Road
Saddle River, NJ 07458-2620
201-236-8122
201-236-8133 Fax
http://www.worldstamps.com

Kenya - Uganda - Tanzania

COLONIAL STAMP COMPANY
5757 Wilshire Blvd. PH #8
Los Angeles, CA 90036
213-933-9435
213-939-9930 Fax

Kiauchau (German)

COLONIAL STAMP COMPANY
5757 Wilshire Blvd. PH #8
Los Angeles, CA 90036
213-933-9435
213-939-9930 Fax

Korea

FRANK GEIGER PHILATELISTS
Suite 2
242 West Saddle River Road
Saddle River, NJ 07458-2620
201-236-8122
201-236-8133 Fax
http://www.worldstamps.com

THE STAMP ACT
P.O. Box 1136
Belmont, CA 94002
650-592-3315
650-508-8104 Fax
http://www.Bchang@IX.netcom.com

Lagos

COLONIAL STAMP COMPANY
5757 Wilshire Blvd. PH #8
Los Angeles, CA 90036
213-933-9435
213-939-9930 Fax

Latin America

JR STAMPS
3110 Cannongate
Fort Wayne, IN 46808-4511
219-471-3746
Email:jrstamps@hotmail.com

JUAN N. SIMONA
Ventas Filatelicas
Casilla de Correo #40
7311 Chillar (Buenos Aires)
Argentina
54-281-97281or 54-281-97346
Phone & Fax
Email:simonafilatelia@simon afilatelia.com.ar
http://www.simonafilatelia.com.ar

Laos

LAOS *Official Agent*

- Stamps of Laos and other countries
- Topicals, Year Sets and Standing orders

We also buy U.S. Postage

S.E.A. International, Inc.
S.E.A. Philatelic Group
265 Hempstead Turnpike
Elmont, NY 11003
Ph. 516-626-4881 Fax 516-775-8181

Latvia

FRANK GEIGER PHILATELISTS
Suite 2
242 West Saddle River Road
Saddle River, NJ 07458-2620
201-236-8122
201-236-8133 Fax
http://www.worldstamps.com

Leeward Islands

COLONIAL STAMP COMPANY
5757 Wilshire Blvd. PH #8
Los Angeles, CA 90036
213-933-9435
213-939-9930 Fax

Liechtenstein

FRANK GEIGER PHILATELISTS
Suite 2
242 West Saddle River Road
Saddle River, NJ 07458-2620
201-236-8122
201-236-8133 Fax
http://www.worldstamps.com

HENRY GITNER PHILATELISTS, INC.
P.O. Box 3077-S
Middletown, NY 10940
914-343-5151 or 800-947-8267
914-343-0068 Fax
Email:hgitner@hgitner.com
http://www.hgitner.com

Literature

OVPT PHILATELICS
P.O. Box 36217
Los Angeles, CA 90036
818-893-4603 Telephone & Fax
Email:ovptphmc@webtv.net

Lithuania

FRANK GEIGER PHILATELISTS
Suite 2
242 West Saddle River Road
Saddle River, NJ 07458-2620
201-236-8122
201-236-8133 Fax
http://www.worldstamps.com

Lots & Collections

BOB & MARTHA FRIEDMAN STAMPS
624 Homestead Place
Joliet, IL 60434
815-725-6666
815-725-4134 Fax

DR. ROBERT FRIEDMAN & SONS
2029 West 75th St.
Woodridge, IL 60517
630-985-1515
630-985-1588 Fax

Luxembourg

FRANK GEIGER PHILATELISTS
Suite 2
242 West Saddle River Road
Saddle River, NJ 07458-2620
201-236-8122
201-236-8133 Fax
http://www.worldstamps.com

HENRY GITNER PHILATELISTS, INC.
P.O. Box 3077-S
Middletown, NY 10940
914-343-5151 or 800-947-8267
914-343-0068 Fax
Email:hgitner@hgitner.com
http://www.hgitner.com

Macedonia

FRANK GEIGER PHILATELISTS
Suite 2
242 West Saddle River Road
Saddle River, NJ 07458-2620
201-236-8122
201-236-8133 Fax
http://www.worldstamps.com

Madagascar (British Issues)

COLONIAL STAMP COMPANY
5757 Wilshire Blvd. PH #8
Los Angeles, CA 90036
213-933-9435
213-939-9930 Fax

Mail Bid Sales

JUNO STAMPS
1765 Juno Ave.
St. Paul, MN 55116
800-714-3469

Mail Order

ALMAZ CO., DEPT. VY
P.O. Box 100-812
Vanderveer Station
Brooklyn, NY 11210
718-241-6360 Telephone & Fax

SHARI'S STAMPS
104-3 Old Highway 40 #130
O'Fallon, MO 63366
800-382-3597
314-980-1552 Fax

Malaya/Malayian States

COLONIAL STAMP COMPANY
5757 Wilshire Blvd. PH #8
Los Angeles, CA 90036
213-933-9435
213-939-9930 Fax

Mariana Islands (German & Spanish)

COLONIAL STAMP COMPANY
5757 Wilshire Blvd. PH #8
Los Angeles, CA 90036
213-933-9435
213-939-9930 Fax

Marshall Islands

FRANK GEIGER PHILATELISTS
Suite 2
242 West Saddle River Road
Saddle River, NJ 07458-2620
201-236-8122
201-236-8133 Fax
http://www.worldstamps.com

Marshall Islands (British & German)

COLONIAL STAMP COMPANY
5757 Wilshire Blvd. PH #8
Los Angeles, CA 90036
213-933-9435
213-939-9930 Fax

Marshall Islands - New Issues

MARSHALL ISLAND STAMPS AND PHILATELIC CENTER
One Unicover Center
Cheyenne, WY 82008-0021
800-443-4225
800-628-3132 Fax
http:www.unicover.com

Mauritius

COLONIAL STAMP COMPANY
5757 Wilshire Blvd. PH #8
Los Angeles, CA 90036
213-933-9435
213-939-9930 Fax

Mesopotamia

COLONIAL STAMP COMPANY
5757 Wilshire Blvd. PH #8
Los Angeles, CA 90036
213-933-9435
213-939-9930 Fax

Mexico

AMEEN STAMPS
8849 Long Point Rd.
Houston, TX 77055
713-468-0644
713-468-2420 Fax

FRANK GEIGER PHILATELISTS
Suite 2
242 West Saddle River Road
Saddle River, NJ 07458-2620
201-236-8122
201-236-8133 Fax
http://www.worldstamps.com

Miconesia

FRANK GEIGER PHILATELISTS
Suite 2
242 West Saddle River Road
Saddle River, NJ 07458-2620
201-236-8122
201-236-8133 Fax
http://www.worldstamps.com

Moldova

FRANK GEIGER PHILATELISTS
Suite 2
242 West Saddle River Road
Saddle River, NJ 07458-2620
201-236-8122
201-236-8133 Fax
http://www.worldstamps.com

Monaco

FRANK GEIGER PHILATELISTS
Suite 2
242 West Saddle River Road
Saddle River, NJ 07458-2620
201-236-8122
201-236-8133 Fax
http://www.worldstamps.com

E. JOSEPH MCCONNELL INC.
P.O. Box 683
Monroe, NY 10950
914-496-5916
914-782-0347 Fax

S. SEREBRAKIAN, INC.
P.O. Box 448
Monroe, NY 10950
914-783-9791
914-782-0347 Fax

Nambia

FRANK GEIGER PHILATELISTS
Suite 2
242 West Saddle River Road
Saddle River, NJ 07458-2620
201-236-8122
201-236-8133 Fax
http://www.worldstamps.com

Natal

COLONIAL STAMP COMPANY
5757 Wilshire Blvd. PH #8
Los Angeles, CA 90036
213-933-9435
213-939-9930 Fax

Netherlands

FRANK GEIGER PHILATELISTS
Suite 2
242 West Saddle River Road
Saddle River, NJ 07458-2620
201-236-8122
201-236-8133 Fax
http://www.worldstamps.com

HENRY GITNER PHILATELISTS, INC.
P.O. Box 3077-S
Middletown, NY 10940
914-343-5151 or 800-947-8267
914-343-0068 Fax
Email:hgitner@hgitner.com
http://www.hgitner.com

Netherland Antilles

FRANK GEIGER PHILATELISTS
Suite 2
242 West Saddle River Road
Saddle River, NJ 07458-2620
201-236-8122
201-236-8133 Fax
http://www.worldstamps.com

New Britain

COLONIAL STAMP COMPANY
5757 Wilshire Blvd. PH #8
Los Angeles, CA 90036
213-933-9435
213-939-9930 Fax

OVPT PHILATELICS
P.O. Box 36217
Los Angeles, CA 90036
818-893-4603 Telephone & Fax
Email:ovptphmc@webtv.net

New Caledonia

FRANK GEIGER PHILATELISTS
Suite 2
242 West Saddle River Road
Saddle River, NJ 07458-2620
201-236-8122
201-236-8133 Fax
http://www.worldstamps.com

New Issues

DAVIDSON'S STAMP SERVICE
P.O. Box 36355
Indianapolis, IN 46236-0355
317-826-2620
Email:davidson@in.net

New Issues

FRANK GEIGER PHILATELISTS
Suite 2
242 West Saddle River Road
Saddle River, NJ 07458-2620
201-236-8122
201-236-8133 Fax
http://www.worldstamps.com

New Issues - Retail

BOMBAY PHILATELIC CO., INC.
P.O. Box 7719
Delray Beach, FL 33482-7719
561-499-7990
561-499-7553 Fax
Email:sales@bombaystamps.com
http:www.bombaystamps.com

STANLEY M. PILLER
3351 Grand Ave.
Oakland, CA 94610
510-465-8290
510-465-7121 Fax
Email:stmpdlr@aol.com

New Issues - Wholesale

BOMBAY PHILATELIC CO., INC.
P.O. Box 7719
Delray Beach, FL 33482-7719
561-499-7990
561-499-7553 Fax
Email:sales@bombaystamps.com
http:www.bombaystamps.com

PACIFIC RIM PHILATELIC COMPANY
484 Lake Park Ave. #144
Oakland, CA 94610
510-835-0307 or
510-251-8001 Ext.3 Telephone & Fax
Email:pacrim@dnai.com or
Email:Pacrim484@aol

New Zealand

COLONIAL STAMP COMPANY
5757 Wilshire Blvd. PH #8
Los Angeles, CA 90036
213-933-9435
213-939-9930 Fax

FRANK GEIGER PHILATELISTS
Suite 2
242 West Saddle River Road
Saddle River, NJ 07458-2620
201-236-8122
201-236-8133 Fax
http://www.worldstamps.com

New Issues

Extenisve Coverage - New Issues from the Entire World

NEW ISSUE SERVICE

Remember Our Specialty:
All Topicals and New Issues
Want Lists for Older Issues Serviced
Top Prices Paid for Collections & Accumulations

MONTHLY NEW ISSUE LIST WITH ILLUSTRATIONS
AVAILABLE AT www.stampcenter.com/csc/

COUNTY STAMP CENTER

CALL TOLL FREE 1-800-245-7597

FAX (410) 573-0025 email:abirman@erols.com

P.O. Box 3373, Annapolis, MD 21403

New Zealand - New Issues

NEW ZEALAND STAMP AGENCY IN NORTH AMERICA
One Unicover Center
Cheyenne, WY 82008-0014
800-443-4225
800-628-3132 Fax
http://www.unicover.com

PACIFIC RIM PHILATELIC COMPANY
484 Lake Park Ave. #144
Oakland, CA 94610
510-835-0307 or
510-251-8001 Ext.3 Telephone & Fax
Email:pacrim@dnai.com or
Email:Pacrim484@aol

Niger Coast Protectorate

COLONIAL STAMP COMPANY
5757 Wilshire Blvd. PH #8
Los Angeles, CA 90036
213-933-9435
213-939-9930 Fax

Niue

OVPT PHILATELICS
P.O. Box 36217
Los Angeles, CA 90036
818-893-4603 Telephone & Fax
Email:ovptphmc@webtv.net

Norfolk Island

FRANK GEIGER PHILATELISTS
Suite 2
242 West Saddle River Road
Saddle River, NJ 07458-2620
201-236-8122
201-236-8133 Fax
http://www.worldstamps.com

North West Pacific Islands

OVPT PHILATELICS
P.O. Box 36217
Los Angeles, CA 90036
818-893-4603 Telephone & Fax
Email:ovptphmc@webtv.net

Norway

FRANK GEIGER PHILATELISTS
Suite 2
242 West Saddle River Road
Saddle River, NJ 07458-2620
201-236-8122
201-236-8133 Fax
http://www.worldstamps.com

Orange River Colony

COLONIAL STAMP COMPANY
5757 Wilshire Blvd. PH #8
Los Angeles, CA 90036
213-933-9435
213-939-9930 Fax

PRC

GUANLUN HONG
P.O. Box 12623
Toledo, OH 43606
419-382-6096
419-382-0203 Fax
Email:guanlun@usa.net

Postage - Brokerage

PACIFIC RIM PHILATELIC COMPANY
484 Lake Park Ave. #144
Oakland, CA 94610
510-835-0307 or
510-251-8001 Ext.3 Telephone & Fax
Email:pacrim@dnai.com or
Email:Pacrim484@aol

Price Lists - Worldwide

HALL'S STAMPS
P.O. Box 8095
Spokane, WA 99203
509-838-4564
509-838-1903 Fax

Proofs & Essays

HENRY GITNER PHILATELISTS, INC.
P.O. Box 3077-S
Middletown, NY 10940
914-343-5151 or 800-947-8267
914-343-0068 Fax
Email:hgitner@hgitner.com
http://www.hgitner.com

Publications / Collector

AMERICAN PHILATELIST
Dept. TZ
P.O. Box 8000
State College, PA 16803
814-237-3803
814-237-6128 Fax
Email:flsente@stamps.org
http://www.west.net/~stamps1/aps.html

GLOBAL STAMP NEWS
P.O. Box 97
Sidney, OH 45365-0097
937-492-3183
937-492-6514 Fax
Email:global@bright.net

Scandinavia - New Issues

NORDICA
P.O. Box 284
Old Bethpage, NY 11804
516-931-3485 Telephone & Fax
Email:NordicaD@aol.com

Stamp Shows

ATLANTIC COAST EXHIBITIONS
Divison of Beach Philatelics
42 Baltimore Lane
Palm Coast, FL 32137-8850
904-445-4550
904-447-0811 Fax
Email:mrstamp2@aol.com
http://members.tripod.com/~SmitX/BeachPhilatelics.htm

STAMP STORES

Arizona

$ BUYING $

Our retail store clients require us to buy
- Quality foreign collections
- Estate holdings
- US collections & singles
- Dealer stocks & accumulations
- Coin collections - singles & sets to rarities

Call today before it's too late!

Why sell to us?
- Consignment & auction availability
- Professional service & proper prices for your collections

25 years experience
Molnar's Stamp & Coin
7118 E. Sahuaro Drive, Scottsdale, AZ 85254
602-948-9672 800-516-4850
Fax 602-948-8425 E-Mail: Molnar7118@AOL.Com

Arizona

B.J.'S STAMPS / BARBARA J. JOHNSON
6342 W. Bell Road
Glendale, AZ 85308
602-878-2080
602-412-3456 Fax

MOLNAR'S STAMP & COIN SHOP
7118 E. Sahuaro Dr.
Scottsdale, AZ 85254
602-948-9672
602-948-8425 Fax

California

ASHTREE STAMP & COIN
2410 N. Blackstone
Fresno, CA 93703
209-227-7167

BROSIUS STAMP & COIN
2105 Main Street
Santa Monica, CA 90405
310-396-7480
310-396-7455 Fax

COLONIAL STAMP COMPANY/BRITISH EMPIRE SPECIALIST
5757 Wilshire Blvd. PH #8 (appt. only)
Los Angeles, CA 90036
213-933-9435
213-939-9930 Fax

FISCHER - WOLK PHILATELICS
24771 "G" Alicia Parkway
Laguna Hills, CA 92653
714-837-2932

NATICK STAMPS & HOBBIES
405 S. Myrtle Avenue
Monrovia, CA 91016
818-305-7333
818-305-7335 Fax
http://www.natickco.com

STANLEY M. PILLER
3351 Grand Ave.
Oakland, CA 94610
510-465-8290
510-465-7121 Fax
Email:stmpdlr@aol.com

THE STAMP GALLERY
1515 Locust Street
Walnut Creek, CA 94596
925-944-9111

California

STAMPCRAFT
P.O. Box 2425
Santa Clara, CA 95055
800-245-5389
408-241-4440 Fax

Colorado

ACKLEY'S ROCKS & STAMPS
3230 N. Stone Ave.
Colorado Springs, CO 80907
719-633-1153

SHOWCASE STAMPS
3865 Wadsworth Blvd.
Wheat Ridge, CO 80033
303-425-9252
303-425-7410 Fax

Connecticut

MILLER'S STAMP SHOP
41 New London Turnpike
Uncasville, CT 06382
860-848-0468 Telephone & Fax

SILVER CITY COIN & STAMP
41 Colony Street
Meriden, CT 06451
203-235-7634

Florida

CLARK'S CORNER
4223 Bee Ridge Rd.
Sarasota, FL 34233
941-377-6909 or 800-927-3351
941-377-6604 Fax

CORBIN STAMP & COIN
115-A East Brandon Blvd.
Brandon, FL 33511
813-651-3266

HAUSER'S COIN & STAMP
3425 S. Florida Ave.
Lakeland, FL 33803
941-647-2052
941-644-5738 Fax

INTERCONTINENTAL / RICARDO DEL CAMPO
7379 Coral Way
Miami, FL 33155-1402
305-264-4983
305-262-2919 Fax

STAMP STORES

Florida

WHEN VISITING CENTRAL FLORIDA BE SURE TO STOP BY...

Send 32¢ long SASE for our MONTHLY NEWSLETTER of stamps for sale!

Michael Rogers - Alvin Hintz

WINTER PARK STAMP SHOP

199 E. Welbourne Ave., 2nd floor, Winter Park, FL 32789

Phone 407-628-1120 • FAX 407-628-0091

1-800-845-1819

Open Mon. through Fri. 10am-6pm • Sat. 10am-3pm (4 miles North of Orlando)

Florida

ROBERT LEVINE STAMPS, INC.
2219 South University Dr.
Davie, FL 33324
954-473-1303
954-473-1305 Fax

NEW ENGLAND STAMP
4987 Tamiami Trail East
Village Falls Professional Ctr.
Naples, FL 34113
941-732-8000
941-732-7701 Fax
Email:STAMPS@SPRINTMAIL.COM

JERRY SIEGEL / STAMPS FOR COLLECTORS
1920 E. Hallandale Beach Blvd.
Suite 507
Hallandale, FL 33009
954-457-0422 Telephone & Fax

THE STAMP PLACE
576 First Avenue North
St. Petersburg, FL 33701
813-894-4082

WINTER PARK STAMP SHOP
199 E. Welbourne Ave.
Suite 201
Winter Park, FL 32789
800-845-1819
407-628-0091 Fax

Georgia

STAMPS UNLIMITED OF GEORGIA
133 Carnegie Way
Room 250
Atlanta, GA 30303
404-688-9161

Illinois

DON CLARK'S STAMPS
937 1/2 W. Galena Blvd.
Aurora, IL 60506
630-896-4606

DR. ROBERT FRIEDMAN & SONS
2029 West 75th St.
Woodridge, IL 60517
630-985-1515
630-985-1588 Fax

MARSHALL FIELD'S STAMP DEPT.
111 N. State Street
Chicago, IL 60602
312-781-4237

Indiana

J & J COINS & STAMPS
7019 Calumet Avenue or
6526 Indianapolis Blvd.
Hammond, IN 46324
219-932-5818
219-845-2003 Fax

KNIGHT STAMP & COIN COMPANY
237 Main Street
Hobart, IN 46342
219-942-7529 or
800-634-2646

Kentucky

COLLECTORS STAMPS LTD.
4012 DuPont Circle #313
Louisville, KY 40207
502-897-9045
Email:csl/aye.net

TREASURE ISLAND COINS & STAMPS
232 W. Broadway
Louisville, KY 40202
502-583-1222

Maryland

BALTIMORE COIN & STAMP EXCHANGE, INC.
10194 Baltimore National Pike
Unit 104
Ellicott City, MD 21042
410-418-8282
410-418-4813 Fax

BULLDOG STAMP CO.
4641 Montgomery Ave.
Bethesda, MD 20814
301-654-1138

STAMP & COIN WORLD
511-A Delaware Avenue
Towson, MD 21286
410-828-4465 or 800-452-4560
410-828-4560 Fax

Massachusetts

FALMOUTH STAMP & COIN
11 Town Hall Square
Falmouth, MA 02540
508-548-7075 or 800-341-3701

J & N FORTIER COIN STAMPS & ANTIQUES
484 Main St.
Worcester, MA 01608
508-757-3657
508-852-8329 Fax

KAPPY'S COINS & STAMPS
534 Washington St.
Norwood, MA 02062
781-762-5552
781-762-3292 Fax

Michigan

BIRMINGHAM COIN AND JEWELRY
33802 Woodward
Birmingham, MI 48009
248-642-1234
248-642-4207 Fax

THE MOUSE AND SUCH
696 N. Mill Street
Plymouth, MI 48170
313-454-1515

Minnesota

CROSSROADS STAMP SHOP
2211 West 54th Street
Minneapolis, MN 55419-1515
612-928-0119

Nebraska

TUVA ENTERPRISES
209 So. 72nd Street
Omaha, NE 68114
402-397-9937

New Jersey

AALLSTAMPS & COLLECTABLES
38 North Main Street
P.O. Box 249
Milltown, NJ 08850
732-247-1093
732-247-1094 Fax

A.D.A STAMP CO., INC.
910 Boyd Street
Toms River, NJ 08753 or
P.O. Drawer J
Island Heights, NJ 08732
732-240-1131
732-240-2620 Fax

BERGEN STAMPS & COLLECTABLES
717 American Legion Dr.
Teaneck, NJ 07666
201-836-8987

CHARLES STAMP SHOP
47 Old Post Road
Edison, NJ 08817
732-985-1071
732-819-0549 Fax

FAIRIDGE STAMP INC.
447 Broadway
Westwood, NJ 07675
201-666-8869

RON RITZER STAMPS & COLLECTIBLES
Millburn Mall
2933 Vauxhall Road
Vauxhall, NJ 07088
908-687-0007
908-687-0795 Fax

New Jersey

TRENTON STAMP & COIN CO. - THOMAS DeLUCA
Forest Glen Plaza
1804 Route 33
Hamilton Square, NJ 08690
800-446-8664
609-587-8664 Fax

New York

CHAMPION STAMP CO.
432 West 54th Street
New York, NY 10019
212-489-8130
212-581-8130 Fax

THE FIFTH AVENUE STAMP GALLERY
535 Fifth Ave.
Suite 300
New York, NY 10017
212-818-9160 or 800-607-2799
212-818-9012 Fax

JOHN'S COINS, CARDS & STAMPS INC.
36 West 34th Street
2nd Floor
New York, NY 10001
212-244-2646

LINCOLN COIN & STAMP
33 West Tupper Street
Buffalo, NY 14202
716-856-1884

Ohio

FEDERAL COIN INC. AND ARCADE STAMP & COIN
39 The Arcade
Cleveland, OH 44114
216-861-1160
216-861-5960 Fax

HILLTOP STAMP SERVICE
P.O. Box 626
Wooster, OH 44691
330-262-8907 Telephone & Fax or
330-262-5378
Email:hilltop@bright.net

J L F STAMP STORE
3041 E. Waterloo Road
Akron, OH 44312
330-628-8343

THE LINK STAMP CO.
3461 E. Livingston Ave.
Columbus, OH 43227
614-237-4125
or 800-546-5726

NEWARK STAMP COMPANY
49 North Fourth Street
Newark, OH 43055
740-349-7900

Oregon

UNIQUE ESTATE APPRAISALS
1937 NE Broadway
Portland, OR 97232
503-287-4200
or 800-646-1147
Email:uea@stampsandcoins.com
http:www.stampsandcoins.com

STAMP STORES

Pennsylvania

DAVE ALLEGO
648 Merchant St.
Ambridge, PA 15003
724-266-4237

LARRY LEE STAMPS
322 S. Front Street
Greater Harrisburg Area
Wormleysburg, PA 17043
717-763-7605

PHILLY STAMP & COIN CO. INC.
1804 Chestnut Street
Philadelphia, PA 19103
215-563-7341
215-563-7382 Fax
Email:adelphia@uscom.com

TREASURE HUNT COLLECTABLE COINS & STAMPS
1687 Washington Road Suite 200
Pittsburgh, PA 15228
412-851-9991 or
800-259-4727

Rhode Island

PODRAT COIN EXCHANGE INC.
769 Hope Street
Providence, RI 02906
401-861-7640
401-272-3032 Fax

South Carolina

THE STAMP OUTLET
Oakbrook Center #9
4650 Ladson Road
Summerville, SC 29485
843-873-4655
843-871-6704 Fax

Tennessee

AMERICAN COIN & STAMP EXCHANGE
330 S. Gallatin Road
Madison, TN 37115
615-865-8791
615-865-4005 Fax

HERRON HILL, INC.
5007 Black Road
Suite 140
Memphis, TN 38117-4505
901-683-9644

Texas

ALAMO HEIGHTS STAMP SHOP
1201 Austin Hwy
Suite 128
San Antonio, TX 78209
800-214-9526

AUSTIN STAMP & COIN
13107 FM 969
Austin, TX 78724
512-276-7793

DALLAS STAMP GALLERY
1002 North Central Expressway
Suite 501
Richardson, TX 75080
972-669-4741
972-669-4742 Fax

Virginia

ALAN BLAIR STAMPS / AUCTIONS
5520A Lakeside Avenue
Richmond, VA 23228
800-689-5602 Telephone & Fax

KENNEDY'S STAMPS & COINS
7059 Brookfield Plaza
Springfield, VA 22150
703-569-7300
703-569-7644 Fax

LATHEROW & CO. INC.
5054 Lee Highway
Arlington, VA 22207
703-538-2727

PRINCE WILLIAM STAMP & COIN CO.
14011-H St. Germain Dr.
Centreville, VA 20121
703-830-4669

Washington

HIDDEN TREASURES INC.
328 Madison Ave.
Bainebridge Island, WA 98110
360-692-1999 or 800-322-1993
In Bainebrige 206-855-9007
206-855-9011 Fax
Email:ht@ix.netcom.com

THE STAMP & COIN PLACE
1310 Commercial
Bellingham, WA 98225
360-676-8720
360-647-6947 Fax

THE STAMP & COIN SHOP
725 Pike St. #6
Seattle, WA 98101
206-624-1400
206-621-8975 Fax
http://WWW.Stamp-Coin.com

TACOMA MALL BLVD. COIN & STAMP
5225 Tacoma Mall Blvd. E-101
Tacoma, WA 98409
253-472-9632
253-472-8948 Fax
Email:kfeldman01@sprynet.com

West Viriginia

DAVID HILL LTD.
6433 U.S. Route 60 E
Barboursville, WV 25504
304-736-4383

Wisconsin

JIM LUKES' STAMP & COIN
815 Jay Street
P.O. Box 1780
Manitowoc, WI 54221
414-682-2324

Supplies & Accessories

BEACH PHILATELICS
42 Baltimore Lane
Palm Coast, FL 32137-8850
904-445-4550
904-447-0811 Fax
Email:mrstamp2@aol.com
http://members.tripod.com/~SmitX/BeachPhilatelics.htm

Supplies - Mail Order

GOPHER SUPPLY CO.
1973 Sloan Place #20
Maplewood, MN 55117
612-771-8840 or 800-815-3868
612-771-8850 Fax
Email:gopher@pclink.com

STAMPCRAFT
P.O. Box 2425
Santa Clara, CA 95055
800-245-5389
408-241-4440 Fax

Supplies - Stamps & Coins

ECONOMICAL SUPPLY CO.
6 King Philip Road
Worcester, MA 01606
508-853-3127
508-852-8329 Fax

M.A. STORCK CO.
651 Forest Ave.
Portland, ME 04101
800-734-7271
207-774-7272 Fax

Topicals

FRANK GEIGER PHILATELISTS
Suite 2
242 West Saddle River Road
Saddle River, NJ 07458-2620
201-236-8122
201-236-8133 Fax
http://www.worldstamps.com

Topicals - Columbus

MR. COLUMBUS
Box 1492
Frankenmuth, MI 48734

Topicals - Miscellaneous

BOMBAY PHILATELIC CO., INC.
P.O. Box 7719
Delray Beach, FL 33482-7719
561-499-7990
561-499-7553 Fax
Email:sales@bombaystamps.com
http:www.bombaystamps.com

MINI - ARTS
P.O. Box 457
Estherville, IA 51334
712-362-4710

Ukraine

MR. VAL ZABIJAKA
P.O. Box 3711
Silver Spring, MD 20918
301-593-5316 Telephone & Fax
Email:BNM123@EROLS.COM

United Nations

BEACH PHILATELICS
42 Baltimore Lane
Palm Coast, FL 32137-8850
904-445-4550
904-447-0811 Fax
Email:mrstamp2@aol.com
http://members.tripod.com/~SmitX/BeachPhilatelics.htm

United States

BEACH PHILATELICS
42 Baltimore Lane
Palm Coast, FL 32137-8850
904-445-4550
904-447-0811 Fax
Email:mrstamp2@aol.com
http://members.tripod.com/~SmitX/BeachPhilatelics.htm

Topicals

TOPICALS- ALL TOPICS

For many years (first as Filatelia Pampa) we have been a leader in this field. ANY sub-topic is Not Strange for us!

VERY LARGE WORLDWIDE STOCK

... including varieties, cancels, covers, etc.

WANT LISTS WELCOME

... any Catalogue #, any main language.

ERCOLE GLORIA - Gregorio Zuskis

Piazza Pio Xi 1, 20123 Milan, ITALY
PH. +39-2-804106 • FAX +39-2-864217
email: gloria@iol.it

United States - Plate Blocks

BEACH PHILATELICS
42 Baltimore Lane
Palm Coast, FL 32137-8850
904-445-4550
904-447-0811 Fax
Email:mrstamp2@aol.com
http://members.tripod.com/~SmitX/BeachPhilatelics.htm

DR. ROBERT FRIEDMAN & SONS
2029 West 75th St.
Woodridge, IL 60517
630-985-1515
630-985-1588 Fax

United States - Price Lists

ROBERT E. BARKER
P.O. Box 888063
Dunwoody, GA 30356
770-395-1757
770-671-8918 Fax
Email:rebarker@rebarker.com

United States - Stamps

BOB & MARTHA FRIEDMAN STAMPS
624 Homestead Place
Joliet, IL 60434
815-725-6666
815-725-4134 Fax

DR. ROBERT FRIEDMAN & SONS
2029 West 75th St.
Woodridge, IL 60517
630-985-1515
630-985-1588 Fax

United States - Worldwide Mixtures

MIXTURE MART/STAMPS UNIQUE
907 Sandy Lane
Espanola, NM 87532
505-753-4078

Want Lists

BROOKMAN INTERNATIONAL
P.O. Box 450
Vancouver, WA 98666
360-695-4311 or Toll Free 888-695-4311
360-695-1616 Fax
Email:brookman@stampdealers.com

CHARLES P. SCHWARTZ
P.O. Box 165
Mora, MN 55051
320-679-4705

Want Lists - British Empire 1840-1935 German Col./Offices

COLONIAL STAMP COMPANY
5757 Wilshire Blvd. PH #8
Los Angeles, CA 90036
213-933-9435
213-939-9930 Fax

Western Europe

EDWARD J. MCKIM
1373 Isabelle
Memphis, TN 38122
901-327-8959

Wholesale

HENRY GITNER PHILATELISTS, INC.
P.O. Box 3077-S
Middletown, NY 10940
914-343-5151 or 800-947-8267
914-343-0068 Fax
Email:hgitner@hgitner.com
http://www.hgitner.com

Wholesale Collections

A.D.A STAMP CO., INC.
910 Boyd Street
Toms River, NJ 08753 or
P.O. Drawer J
Island Heights, NJ 08732
732-240-1131
732-240-2620 Fax

Wholesale Philatelic & Numismatic Accessories

CHARLES R. HEISLER INC.
500 Oak Grove Drive
Lancaster, PA 17601
800-784-6886
717-299-2366 Fax

M.A. STORCK CO.
651 Forest Ave.
Portland, ME 04101
800-734-7271
207-774-7272 Fax

Wholesale Supplies

JOHN VAN ALSTYNE STAMPS & SUPPLIES
1787 Tribute Rd. Suite J
Sacramento, CA 95815
916-565-0600
916-565-0539 Fax
Email:sherjohn@softcom.net

Worldwide

ALLKOR STAMP COMPANY
Box 1346
Port Washington, NY 11050
516-883-3296 Telephone & Fax

AMERICAN STAMP & COIN CO.
7225 N. Oracle Rd.
Suite #102
Tucson, AZ 85704
520-297-3456

EDWARD J. MCKIM
1373 Isabelle
Memphis, TN 38122

Worldwide Collections

BOB & MARTHA FRIEDMAN STAMPS
624 Homestead Place
Joliet, IL 60434
815-725-6666
815-725-4134 Fax

DR. ROBERT FRIEDMAN & SONS
2029 West 75th St.
Woodridge, IL 60517
630-985-1515
630-985-1588 Fax

Worldwide - Romania

GEORGE ARGHIR, PHILATELISTS
Detunata Str. 17-27
P.O. Box 521
RO-3400 Cluj-Napoca 9
Romania
+40-64-414036 Telephone & Fax

Worldwide - Year Sets

BOMBAY PHILATELIC CO., INC.
P.O. Box 7719
Delray Beach, FL 33482-7719
561-499-7990
561-499-7553 Fax
Email:sales@bombaystamps.com
http:www.bombaystamps.com

FRANK GEIGER PHILATELISTS
Suite 2
242 West Saddle River Road
Saddle River, NJ 07458-2620
201-236-8122
201-236-8133 Fax
http://www.worldstamps.com

HENRY GITNER PHILATELISTS, INC.
P.O. Box 3077-S
Middletown, NY 10940
914-343-5151 or 800-947-8267
914-343-0068 Fax
Email:hgitner@hgitner.com
http://www.hgitner.com

WALLACE STAMPS
Box 82
Port Washington, NY 11050
516-883-5578

ScottMounts

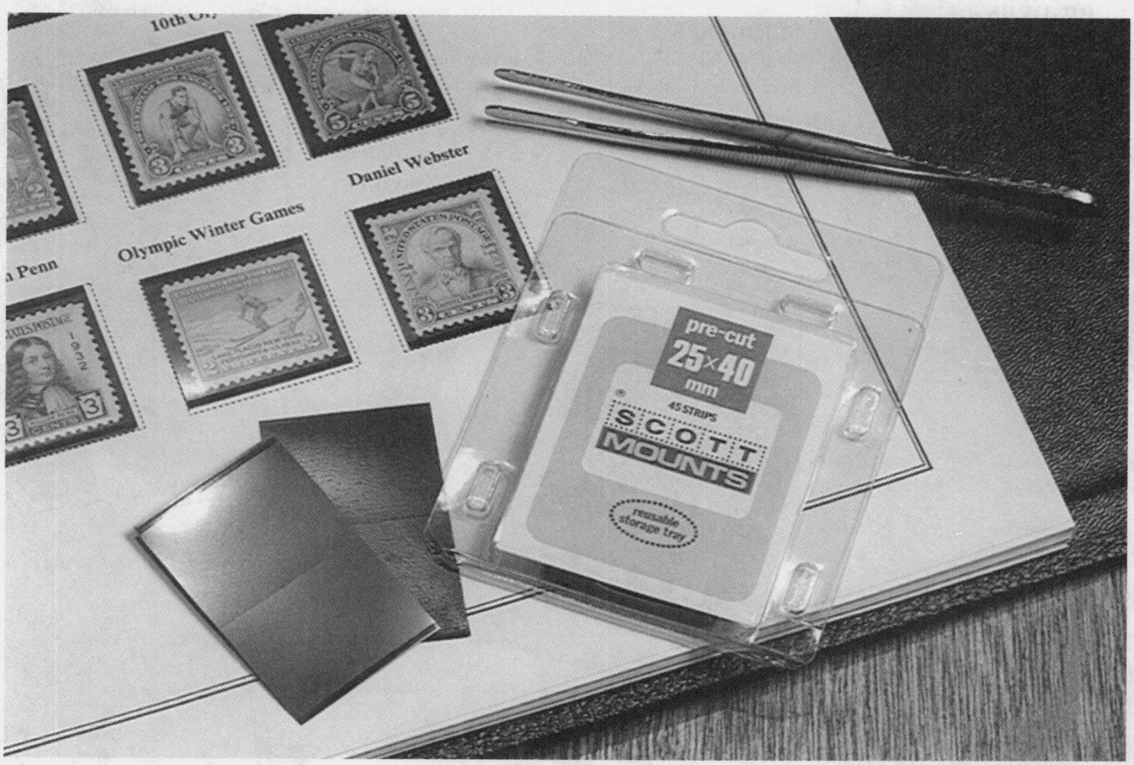

For stamp presentation unequaled in beauty and clarity, insist on ScottMounts. Made of 100% inert polystyrol foil, ScottMounts protect your stamps from the harmful effects of dust and moisture. Available in your choice of clear or black backs, ScottMounts are center-split across the back for easy insertion of stamps and feature crystal clear mount faces. Double layers of gum assure stay-put bonding on the album page. Discover the quality and value ScottMounts have to offer.
ScottMounts are available from your favorite stamp dealer or direct from:

Scott Publishing Co.
P.O. Box 828 Sidney OH 45365-0828

Discover the quality and value ScottMounts have to offer.
For a complete list of ScottMount sizes or a free sample pack call or write Scott Publishing Co.

SCOTT

1-800-572-6885

Specialty Binders & Accessories

NATIONAL AND SPECIALTY SERIES BINDERS

Binders are available for all pages in two sizes. They're covered with a tough green leatherette material that is washable and reinforced at stress points for long wear.

Large 3-Ring Binder

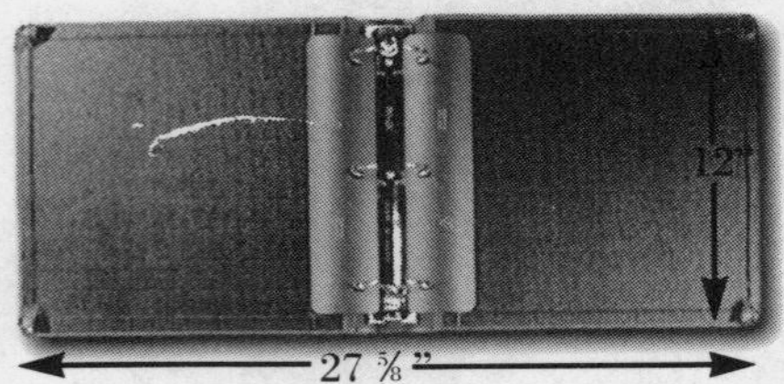

Item		Retail
ACBR01	Small 3-Ring Binder Holds up to 100 pages	**$25.00**
ACBR03	Large 3-Ring Binder Holds up to 250 pages	**$?5.00**

Large 2-Post Binder

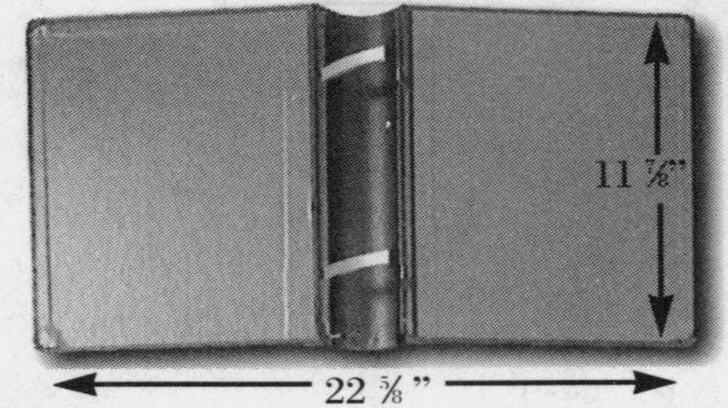

Item		Retail
ACBS0S	Small 2-Post Binder Holds up to 75 pages	**$45.00**
ACBS03	Large 2-Post Binder Holds up to 250 pages	**$45.00**

UNIVERSAL BINDER

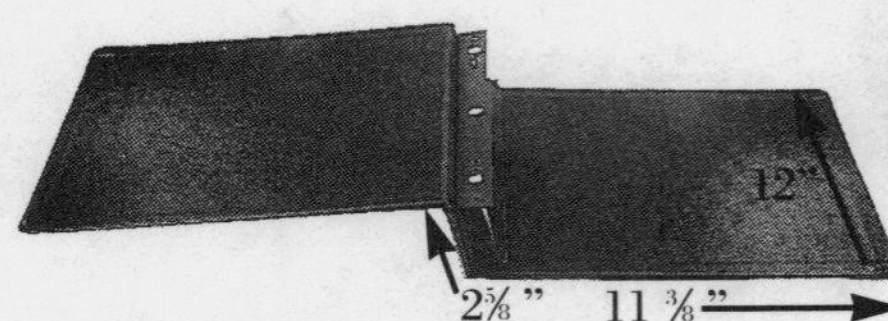

The binder features 3 adjustable screw posts to accomodate every album page sold by Scott, including the multi-ring Schaubek pages, and Platinum pages. Binder matches the traditional National/Specialty Series binder in every respect, including the handsome green leatherette covering. Use National and Specialty series labels to identify albums. Matching slipcase also available.

Item		Retail
ACBU	Universal Binder Holds up to 200 pages	**$25.00**
ACSU	Universal Slipcase	**$20.00**

SLIPCASES

Protect your binders and the album pages inside from the harmful effects of dust and dirt with slipcases. Cases available in two sizes.

Item		Retail
ACSR01	Small 3-Ring Slipcase	**$20.00**
ACSR03	Large 3-Ring Slipcase	**$20.00**
ACSS0S	Small 2-Post Slipcase	**$20.00**
ACSS03	Large 2-Post Slipcase	**$20.00**

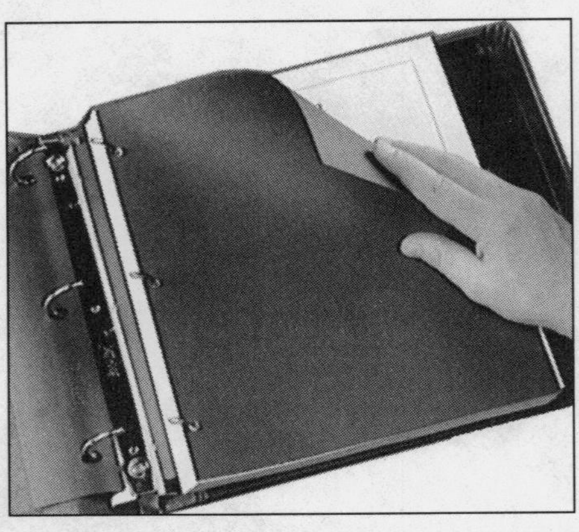

BINDER ACCESSORIES

Item		Retail
ACC101	Green Protector Fly Sheets For 2-post binders (2 per pack)	**$1.95**
ACC102	Black Protector Fly Sheets For 3-ring binders (2 per pack)	**$1.95**
ACC107	Glassine Interleaving (100 sheets per pack)	**$8.95**

SCOTT FILLER STRIPS

Use these strips every 15 to 20 pages in your 2 post albums to balance your overstuffed binders.

Item		Retail
ACC105	24 strips per package	**$3.95**

Specialty album accessories are available from your favorite dealer or direct from:
Scott Publishing Co.
P.O. Box 828
Sidney OH 45365-0828
1-800-572-6885

Pictured are the 3-ring slipcases.

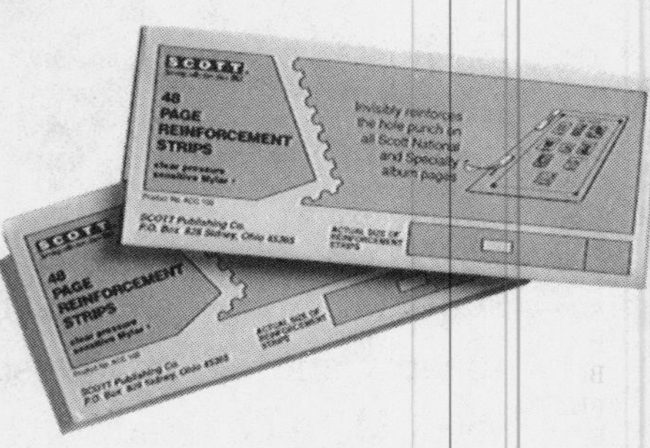

REINFORCEMENT STRIPS

Invisibly reinforce the 2-post or 3-ring holes on all album pages with clear pressure sensitive mylar.

Item		Retail
ACC100	48 Mylar strips For 2-post pages	**$3.95**
ACC103	200 Mylar rings For 3-ring pages	**$1.95**

SCOTT STAMP MONTHLY STORAGE BOX

Sturdy handsome cardboard storage box will hold 24 issues of your favorite philatelic publications including Scott Stamp Monthly and Linn's. It's a great way to keep your information organized.

Item	Retail
SSMBOX	**$8.95**

Specialty Series

Scott produces album pages for more than 160 different countries. Scott Specialty pages are renowned for their quality and detail. There are spaces for every major variety of postage stamp within each country or specialty area. Each space is identified by Scott number and many of the spaces are illustrated. Pages are printed on one side only on chemically neutral paper that will not harm your stamps.
Below is complete list of the entire line of foriegn pages produced by Scott. Albums are updated annually. For page and price breakouts see your favorite dealer or call Scott Publishing Co. direct.

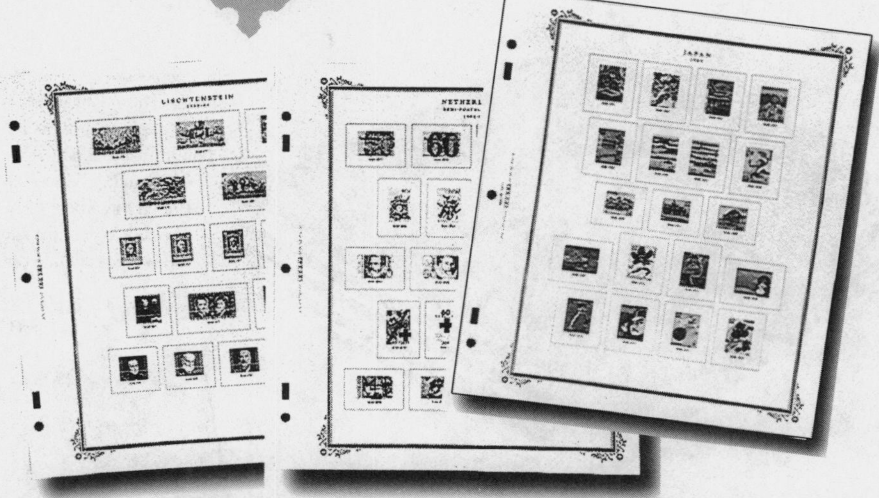

Scott Produces Album Pages for more than 160 countries.

ADEN
AFGHANISTAN
ALBANIA
ALGERIA
ANTIGUA
AUSTRALIA
AUSTRALIA DEPENDENCIES
AUSTRIA
BAHAMAS
BAHRAIN
BALTIC STATES
BANGLADESH
BARBADOS
BELGIUM
BELIZE
BERMUDA
BHUTAN
BOLIVIA
BOTSWANA
BRAZIL
BRITISH AFRICA
BRITISH ANTARCTIC TERRITORIES
BRITISH EUROPE
BRITISH HONDURAS
BRITISH ORIENT
BRITISH SOUTH ATLANTIC
BRUNEI
BULGARIA
BURKINA FASO
BURMA
BURUNDI
CANADA
CAYMAN ISLANDS
CENTRAL AFRICA
CHANNEL ISLANDS
CHILE
CHINA
COLOMBIA
COM. OF INDEPENDENT STATES
COMORO ISLANDS
CONGO
COSTA RICA
CROATIA
CZECHOSLOVAKIA
DENMARK
DOMINICA
DOMINICAN REPUBLIC
ECUADOR
EGYPT
EQUATORIAL GUINEA
ERITREA
ETHIOPIA
FALKLAND ISLANDS
FAROE ISLANDS
FIJI
FINLAND & ALAND ISLANDS
FRANCE
FRENCH OFFICES ABROAD
FRENCH POLYNESIA
FRENCH SOUTH. & ANTARCTIC TERRIT.
GABON
GAMBIA
GERMANY
EAST GERMANY
GHANA
GILBERT & ELLICE ISLANDS
GREAT BRITAIN
GREAT BRITAIN OFFICES ABROAD
GREECE
GREENLAND
GRENADA
GUATEMALA
GUINEA
GUINEA-BISSAU
HAITI
HONDURAS
HUNGARY
ICELAND
INDIA
INDONESIA
IRELAND
ISRAEL
ISRAEL TABS
ITALIAN COLONIES
ITALY
IVORY COAST
JAMAICA
JAPAN
JORDAN
KENYA
KIRIBATI
KOREA
KUWAIT
LAOS
LEBANON
LESOTHO
LIBERIA
LIECHTENSTEIN
LUXEMBOURG
MACEDONIA
MADAGASCAR
MALAWI
MALAYSIA
MALDIVE ISLANDS
MALI
MAURITIUS
MEXICO
MONACO & FRENCH ANDORRA
MONTSERRAT
MOROCCO
NAMIBIA
NAURU
NEPAL
NEW CALEDONIA
NEW HEBRIDES (BRITISH)
NEW HEBRIDES (FRENCH)
NEW ZEALAND
NEW ZEALAND DEPENDENCIES
NEVIS/ST KITTS
NICARAGUA
NIGER
NIGERIA
NORWAY
OMAN
PAKISTAN
PANAMA
PARAGUAY
PAKISTAN
PANAMA
PARAGUAY
PEOPLE'S REPUBLIC OF CHINA
PERU
PHILIPPINES
PITCAIRN ISLANDS
POLAND
PORTUGAL
PORTUGUESE COLONIES
QATAR
ROMANIA
RUSSIA
SALVADOR
SAMOA
SAN MARINO
SAUDI ARABIA
SENEGAL
SEYCHELLES
SIERRA LEONE
SLOVENIA
SOLOMON ISLANDS
SOUTH AFRICA
SPAIN & SPANISH ANDORRA
SRI LANKA
ST LUCIA
ST PIERRE & MIQUELON
ST THOMAS & PRINCE ISLANDS
ST VINCENT
SUDAN
SWAZILAND
SWEDEN
SWITZERLAND
SYRIA
TAIWAN
TANZANIA
THAILAND
TOGO
TONGA
TRINIDAD
TUNISIA
TURKEY
TURKS & CAICOS ISLANDS
TUVALU
UGANDA
UNITED ARAB EMIRATES
URUGUAY
VANUATU
VATICAN CITY
VENEZUELA
VIRGIN ISLANDS
WALLIS & FUTUNA
YEMEN
YUGOSLAVIA
ZAIRE
ZAMBIA
ZIMBABWE

SCOTT
1-800-572-6885

Value Priced Stockbooks

Stockbooks are a classic and convenient storage alternative for many collectors. These German-made stockbooks feature heavyweight archival quality paper with 9 pockets on each page. The 8½" x 11⅞" pages are bound inside a handsome leatherette grain cover and include glassine interleaving between the pages for added protection. The Value Priced Stockbooks are available in two page styles, the white page stockbooks feature glassine pockets while the black page variety includes clear acetate pockets

BLACK PAGE STOCKBOOKS ACETATE POCKETS

Item	Color	Pages	Retail
ST16RD	Red	16 pages	$9.95
ST16GR	Green	16 pages	$9.95
ST16BL	Blue	16 pages	$9.95
ST16BK	Black	16 pages	$9.95
ST32RD	Red	32 pages	$14.95
ST32GR	Green	32 pages	$14.95
ST32BL	Blue	32 pages	$14.95
ST32BK	Black	32 pages	$14.95
ST64RD	Red	64 pages	$27.95
ST64GR	Green	64 pages	$27.95
ST64BL	Blue	64 pages	$27.95
ST64BK	Black	64 pages	$27.95

WHITE PAGE STOCKBOOKS GLASSINE POCKETS

Item	Description		Retail
SW16BL	Blue	16 pages	$5.95
SW16GR	Green	16 pages	$5.95
SW16RD	Red	16 pages	$5.95

The black page stockbook is available in three sizes:
16 pages
32 pages
64 pages.

Scott Value Priced Stockbooks are available from your favorite dealer or direct from:

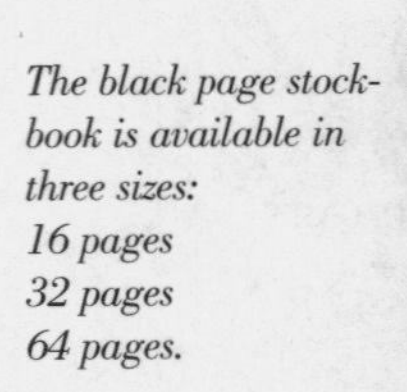

P.O. Box 828
Sidney OH 45365-0828
1-800-572-6885

Cover & Mint Sheet Storage

Cover Box

Keep your collection organized in a 7 ½" x 10 ½" x 4 ¼" cover box. Box will hold hundreds of covers. Available in classic marble styling .

Item		Retail
CVBOX	Marble Cover Box	$6.95

Cover Binders & Pages

Padded, durable, 3-ring binder will hold up to 100 covers. Features the "D" ring mechanism on the right hand side of album so you don't have to worry about creasing or wrinkling covers when opening or closing binder.

Cover pages sold separately.

Item		Retail
CBRD	Cover Binder - Red	$7.95
CBBL	Cover Binder - Blue	$7.95
CBGY	Cover Binder - Gray	$7.95
CBBK	Cover Binder - Black	$7.95
T2	Cover Pages Black (25 per pack)	$4.95
T2C	Cover Pages Clear (25 per pack)	$4.95

Mint Sheet Binders & Pages

Keep those mint sheets intact in a handsome, 3-ring binder. Just like the cover album, the Mint Sheet album features the "D" ring mechanism on the right hand side of binder so you don't have to worry about damagingyour stamps when turning the pages. Mint Sheet binder available in four colors.

Mint sheet pages sold separately.

Item		Retail
MBRD	Mint Sheet Binder - Red	$9.95
MBBL	Mint Sheet Binder - Blue	$9.95
MBGY	Mint Sheet Binder - Gray	$9.95
MBBK	Mint Sheet Binder - Black	$9.95
MS1	Mint Sheet Pages (25 per pack)	$5.95

Mint Sheet and Plate Block Storage

Item		Retail
191A000	Regular Plate Block File 24 pockets	$2.50
193A000	Mint Sheet File 24 pockets	$5.50

Available from your favorite stamp dealer direct from:

P.O. Box 828
Sidney OH 45365-0828
1-800-572-6885

Scott Stamp Monthly

Stamp collecting's most entertaining read!

12 issues $17.95

24 issues $29.95

Every month you'll get an entertaining, informative look at the world of stamp collecting from some of the hobby's most talented writers. Enjoy a wide variety of articles and regular features on U.S., foreign stamps, covers and more. In-depth stories, time-saving hints, incredible stamp discoveries plus the very latest information on the new stamp issues from around the world, you'll find it all in Scott Stamp Monthly. As a subscriber not only do you save big on all the products offered by Scott, you also get what many people consider the most original and thought-provoking read in philately today.

You get all this and more every month!

Favorite Find - Stories about stamp discoveries in some of the mostunlikely places. Learn how you too can make finds.

Catalogue Update - The #1 source for new issue news. Each month you get Scott numbers and illustrations for hundreds of stamps. The By Topic column organizes stamps by subject matter.

Amazing Stamp Stories - A new stamp story every month done in the classic-illustrated style of *Ripley's Believe It Or Not*.

Hungry Mind - A just for fun trivia quiz that tests your stamp knowledge.

Spotlight - The column zeros-in and explores a different topic every month.

Free-For-All - It's your chance to get free stamps or related collectable simply by sending in stamped addressed envelope. It's fun, It's easy, but best of all it's FREE!

Stamp Traveler - Explore some of stampdom's most famous places and the chance stamp encounter that made the trip memorable.

Catalogue Column - A behind-the-scenes look at key Scott Catalogue editorial decisions.

To Err Is Divine - A lighthearted look at stamp designs goofs and gaffes.

Stars & Stripes and Judaica - are in-depth articles covering specific areas of interest in the stamp kingdom. Each columnis written by some of the hobby's best writers.

Tip Of The Hat - Tips and techniques for the busy collector.

For subscriptions in Canada, add $8 (U.S. funds) per year.

Outside the U.S. and Canada, add $23 (U.S. funds) per year for for foreign surface mail.

SCOTT

To subscribe call 1-800-572-6885